AVMarket Place™

AV Market Place™
48th Edition

Publisher
Thomas H. Hogan

Senior Director, ITI Reference Group
Owen O'Donnell

Managing Editor
Karen Hallard

Assistant Editor
Karen DiDario

Tampa Operations:

Manager, Tampa Editorial Operations
Debra James

Project Coordinator, Tampa Editorial
Carolyn Victor

Graphics & Production:

Production Manager
Tiffany Chamenko

Production
Dana Stevenson
Jackie Crawford

AV Market Place™

2020

The Complete Business Directory of Products and Services for the Audio/Video Industry

AUDIO

FILM

VIDEO

AUDIO VISUAL

PROGRAMMING

COMPUTER SYSTEMS

 Information Today, Inc.

ISSN 1044-0445
ISBN 978-1-57387-560-8
Library of Congress Catalog Card Number 69-17201

Information Today, Inc.
143 Old Marlton Pike
Medford, NJ   08055-8750
Phone: 800-300-9868 (Customer Service)
        800-409-4929 (Editorial)
Fax: 609-654-4309
E-mail (orders): custserv@infotoday.com
Web Site: www.infotoday.com

Printed in the United States of America

US $389.50
ISBN 13: 978-1-57387-560-8

9 781573 875608

Contents

Contents

Preface

AV Market Place™, now in its 48th edition, continues to be the one-stop guide to the ever-changing AV industry. This complete business directory of audio, audio/visual, computer systems, film, video and programming covers a broad range of services and suppliers in the U.S. and Canada. *AVMP 2020* lists almost 4,300 companies that supply more than 1,250 industry-related products and services.

Contents & Indexes

AV Market Place™ includes an alphabetical listing of all products and services in the easily accessible Products & Services Index. Following is the Products, Services & Companies section which is organized into seven major categories — Audio, Audio/Visual, Computer Systems, Film, Video, Programming and Miscellaneous. Categories are further organized by state, then alphabetically by company name. For a complete description of the organization and indexes, see "How to Use *AV Market Place*™" (page ix).

The AV Product & Service Providers section provides full contact information — address, telephone, fax, e-mail & web addresses as well as personnel information. The remaining sections of *AVMP* are devoted to support services and organizations vital to the industry. The Associations section lists entries for the audio visual trade and related organizations with AV interests. The section on Film & Television Commissions includes city, county and state agencies that provide information and services to prospective filmmakers. The Awards & Festivals section lists events open to AV producers in the U.S. and Canada. Major conventions and meetings from early 2020 through 2024 are chronologically listed in the Calendar of Events section. Preceding the Calendar of Events are two indexes. The Sponsor Index is an alphabetical list of event sponsors and the events they sponsor; the Event Index is an alphabetical list of events along with the date(s) on which they are held. Trade and consumer publications, covering the audio visual field and related media, are listed in the Periodicals for the Trade section. A select list of audio/visual reference materials is included in the Reference Books for the Trade section. Finally, the Industry Indexes cover two distinct areas of data. A Company Index includes the name, address, communications information and page reference for company listings. A separate Personnel Index includes the main personnel associated with each company appearing in the Company Index as well as the page reference number.

Compilation

While we have used our best efforts to compile an accurate, comprehensive directory, in a project of this magnitude there may be errors and omissions, and we would appreciate learning of them. Updated information or suggestions for new listings can be submitted to:

AV Market Place™
Information Today, Inc.
121 Chanlon Road, Suite G-20
New Providence, NJ 07974-2195
Phone: 800-409-4929 (press 3)

Requests to have your product, service or company listed in *AVMP* should be addressed to Karen Hallard at the above address or submitted via e-mail to khallard@infotoday.com. We will then provide a listing application. Once your completed application is received, your information will be entered in our database and appear in the next possible edition of *AV Market Place*™.

The editors are grateful for the assistance and cooperation of everyone whose contributions made *AV Market Place*™ 2020 possible.

How to Use *AV Market Place*™

AV Market Place™ *(AVMP)* contains seven informational sections, the focus of which is the AV Product & Service Providers section and its Products, Services & Companies Index. The AV Product & Service Providers section lists AV product and service suppliers alphabetically and provides full listings of addresses, telecommunication information, personnel and other relevant facts. Two indexes described and illustrated below, each of which have distinctly different functions, are provided to aid the user in selecting the company that will best meet their needs.

Products & Services Index

This index alphabetically lists AV products and services that are available through the companies represented in the AV Product & Service Providers section. Here you will find over 1,250 classifications interfiled alphabetically pertaining to seven major AV categories: Audio, Audio/Visual, Computer Systems, Film, Video, Programming and Miscellaneous. Some classifications may be listed in more than one way, ensuring that the user will easily find what is required. The user must first locate the classification desired, which then refers them to a page number in the Products, Services & Companies section where they will find a list of providers of that particular product or service. This index is best suited to the user who is limiting his research to a particular segment of the industry.

This index further separates services by medium and products by company function. Where appropriate, the medium is included in parenthesis. As an example, if the user is looking for a distributor of batteries, chargers & analyzers, the classification can be found in two different locations in the index, with one of the entries being a cross reference (both found on page 3):

Analyzer (Miscellaneous) *see* Battery, Charger & ———— **classification cross reference**
  Analyzer
  —Distributors p. 646 ———————————————— **page reference to the Products, Services & Companies section**
  —Manufacturers p. 647
  —Rentals, p. 647
  —Repairs p. 648

Battery, Charger & Analyzer (Miscellaneous) ———— **classification**
  —Distributors p. 646 ———————————————— **page reference to the Products, Services & Companies section**
  —Manufacturers p. 647
  —Rentals, p. 647
  —Repairs p. 648

Products, Services & Companies

This section organizes the over 1,250 product and service classifications by seven major industry segments: Audio, Audio/Visual, Computer Systems, Film, Video, Programming and Miscellaneous. All of the major headings are included in the table of contents. Within each segment, the product and service classifications are listed alphabetically. Following each classification, arranged in state order, the user will find a list of companies that are providers of that particular product or service. A company name may be found under many classifications depending on the extent of its activities. This index may be utilized by the user who is interested in the products or services available for a particular segment of the AV industry.

The above user wants to locate a battery, charger & analyzer distributor in Washington. This would be accomplished by consulting page 646 of this section which provides a list of company names arranged by state and looking under this classification until locating companies in Washington. Page references are included with the company names.

Battery, Charger & ———————————————— **classification (begins on page 646)**
  Analyzer Distributors

WASHINGTON ————————————— **state (found on page 646)**
Alpha Technologies Inc, pg 681———————— **company**
Oppenheimer Camera Products,
  pg 847
Proforma Good Wood Marketing,
  pg 865

WISCONSIN
Alpha Source Inc, pg 681
Audio Visual of Milwaukee Inc,
  pg 694
Camera Corner Connecting Point,
  pg 715
Full Compass Systems, pg 767

AV Product & Service Providers

Having chosen Alpha Technologies Inc from the Products, Services & Companies section, the user would then refer to the AV Product & Service Providers section, page 681, to obtain more detailed information.

Alpha Technologies Inc ———————————— **company name**
Division of EnerSys ———————————————— **parent company**
3767 Alpha Way, Bellingham, WA 98226 ——————— **address**
Tel: 360-647-2360 *Toll Free Tel:* 800-322-5742 ———— **telephone & toll free telephone**
E-mail: alpha@alpha.com —————————————— **company e-mail**
Web Site: www.alpha.com —————————————— **company web site**
Key Personnel
Pres: Drew Zogby ———————————————————— **personnel**
VP, Broadband & Cable: John Hewitt
VP, Fin: Michael Perica
VP, Mktg & Prod Mgmt: Grant Clark
VP, Servs: Gary Tremblay
Founded: 1975 ———————————————————— **year founded**
Full line of power supplies, status monitoring ————— **business description**
   products, surge suppressors, batteries & enclo-
   sures for use in cable TV/broadband, industrial,
   renewable energy & FTTx industries.
Online catalog(s) available ———————————————— **catalog avilability**
Branch Office(s)
Alpha Energy, 1628 W Williams Dr, Phoenix, AZ ——— **branch office**
   85027 *Tel:* 623-251-3000 *Fax:* 623-249-7833
Alpha Industria Power Inc, 1075 Satellite Blvd
   NW, Suite 400, Suwanee, GA 30024 *Tel:* 678-
   475-3995 *Fax:* 678-584-9259
Alpha Technologies Ltd, 7700 Riverfront Gate,
   Burnaby, BC V5J 5M4, Canada *Tel:* 604-436-
   5900 *Toll Free Tel:* 800-667-8743 *Fax:* 604-
   436-1233 *E-mail:* sales@alpha.ca *Web
   Site:* www.alpha.ca
Foreign Office(s): Alpha Technologies Australia, ——— **foreign office**
   91 Phillip St, Parramatta, NSW 2150, Australia
   Tel: (02) 8599 6960 *E-mail:* ata@alpha.com
Alpha Innovations Brazil, Rua Manoel da No-
   brega, 598-CJ 88/89, 09910-720 Diadema-SP,
   Brazil *Tel:* (011) 2476 0150 *E-mail:* vendas@
   alphabrasil.net *Web Site:* www.alphabrasil.net
Alpha Tech Energy Solutions India Pvt Ltd, Vikas
   Plaza, Plot No 38/1A (4), Electronic City Phase
   2, Hosur Rd, Bangalore, Karnataka 560 100,
   India *Tel:* (080) 4123 0299; 95380 25325 (cell)
   E-mail: sales.india@alpha.com
Membership(s): SCTE ———————————————— **association membership**

In review, the user should follow these steps to locate a company offering the product or service needed:

1. Find the product or service needed in the Products & Services Index and note the page number provided.
2. Refer to that page number in the Products, Services & Companies section and select a company from the desired state and note the page number given.
3. Refer to the listing for that company in the AV Product & Service Providers section for further details.

Section Contents

AV Product & Service Providers
Entries in the AV Product & Service Providers section are arranged alphabetically by company name and generally contain address, phone and fax numbers, e-mail and web site addresses, key personnel, branch offices and catalog data. The user who is already familiar with a company, but needs contact information, should go directly to this section.

Associations
This section contains entries for AV trade-related associations. Entries contain name, address, phone, fax and contact data as well as information on upcoming events (2020-2024), the purpose of the organization, publication data (with frequency) and membership data. A chronological listing of upcoming AV-related events can be found in the Calendar of Events section.

Film & Television Commissions
Listed geographically in this section are state, county and city agencies involved with providing information and services to film, TV and commercial producers. Entries contain name, address, phone, fax and personnel data, as well as descriptions of the variety and extent of the services provided.

Awards & Festivals
Listed here are sponsoring agencies of awards & festivals open to professional, educational, student and industrial media producers. In addition to name, address, phone, fax & personnel data, entries contain information on media covered, categories and types of awards, date and location of presentation or festival, closing dates and entry fees.

Calendar of Events
This section chronologically lists AV-related meetings and conventions scheduled at press time from early 2020 through 2024. Entries — sorted by year, month and event name — contain name, address, phone, fax and personnel data as well as the date and location of the event. The calendar is preceded by two indexes. The Sponsor Index is an alphabetical list of event sponsors and a list of the events they sponsor. This index is helpful to the user who knows the name of the sponsor, but may not know the name of the event. The Event Index is an alphabetical list of events, along with the dates on which they are being held. This index should be consulted when the user knows the event name, but not the date on which the event is being held.

Periodicals for the Trade
AV-related publications are listed with the name of the publisher, address, phone, fax and contact data. Specific data such as description of content, frequency, circulation, advertising rates and close date, trim size, subscription cost and ISSN are also included.

Reference Books for the Trade
Titles related to AV topics are listed with the name of the publisher, address, phone, fax and contact data. Specific data such as author, description of content, edition, publication date and ISBN are also included.

Industry Indexes
The Industry Indexes cover two distinct areas of data. The Company Index includes the name, address, communications information and page reference for all listings in the directory with the exception of Calendar of Events, Periodicals for the Trade and Reference Books for the Trade. The Personnel Index includes the main personnel associated with each company listed in the Company Index as well as the page reference. The Personnel Index is helpful for the user who is looking to contact a specific individual for whom the company affiliation is unknown.

Comments and suggestions regarding the content and format of *AVMP* are encouraged and can be directed to *AV Market Place*™, Information Today, Inc., 121 Chanlon Road, Suite G-20, New Providence, NJ 07974-2195.

Abbreviations & Acronyms

The following is a list of acronyms & abbreviations used throughout *AVMP*.

AB – Alberta
ABA – American Booksellers Association
Acct(s) – Accounts
Acctg – Accounting
ACM SIGGRAPH – Association for Computing Machinery's Special Interest Group on Computer Graphics and Interactive Techniques
Acq(s) – Acquisition(s)
Ad – Advertising
Admin – Administrative, Administration, Administrator
AECT – Association for Educational Communications and Technology
AES – Audio Engineering Society
Aff – Affairs
AFI – American Film Institute
AICP – Association of Independent Commercial Producers
AIIM – Association for Information and Image Management
AK – Alaska
AL – Alabama
ALA – American Library Association
AMPAS – Academy of Motion Picture Arts and Sciences
appt – appointment
Apt – Apartment
AR – Arkansas
ASA – Acoustical Society of America
ASCAP – The American Society of Composers, Authors and Publishers
ASMP – American Society of Media Photographers
Assoc – Associate
Asst – Assistant
ATA – American Translators Association
ATD – Association for Talent Development
AV – Audiovisual
Ave – Avenue
AZ – Arizona

B&W – Black & White
BC – British Columbia
Bd – Board
bio – biography
Bldg – Building
Blvd – Boulevard
BMI – Broadcast Music Inc
Br – Branch
Busn – Business

CA – California
CEO – Chief Executive Officer
CFO – Chief Financial Officer

Chmn – Chairman
Chpn – Chairperson
CIO – Chief Information Officer
Circ – Circulation
CN – Canada
CO – Colorado
Co(s) – Company(-ies)
Co-edns – Co-editions
Coll(s) – College(s)
Comm – Committee
Commun(s) – Communication(s)
Comp – Compiler
Compt – Comptroller
Cont – Controller
Contrib – Contributing
COO – Chief Operating Officer
Coord – Coordinator
Corp – Corporate, Corporation
Coun – Counsel
CT – Connecticut
Ct – Court
CTO – Chief Technical / Technology Officer
Ctr – Center
Curr – Current
Cust – Customer
CZ – Canal Zone

DC – District of Columbia
DE – Delaware
Dept – Department
Devt – Development
DGA – Directors Guild of America
Dir(s) – Director(s)
Dist – Distributed, Distribution, Distributor
Div – Division
Dom – Domestic
Dr – Drive

ed – edition
Ed(s) – Editor(s)
Edit – Editorial
EDPA – Experiential Designers & Producers Association
Educ – Education, Educational
Elem – Elementary
El-hi – Elementary-High School
Ency – Encyclopedia
Eng – English
Engg – Engineering
Engr – Engineer
Equip – Equipment
ESL – English as a Second Language
Est – Established
EVP – Executive Vice President

exc – except
Exec – Executive
Expwy – Expressway
ext – extension

Fed – Federal
Fin – Finance, Financial
fl – floor
FL – Florida
Freq – Frequency
Fwy – Freeway

GA – Georgia
Gen – General
Govt – Government
GU – Guam

HD – High-definition
HDTV – High-definition television
HeSCA – Health & Science Communications Association
HI – Hawaii
HR – Human Resources
HS – High School
Hwy – Highway

IA – Iowa
IAA-VC - International Association of Audio Visual Communicators
IABC – International Association of Business Communicators
ICVM – International Christian Visual Media Association
ID – Idaho
IEEE – Institute of Electrical and Electronics Engineers Inc
IL – Illinois
Illus – Illustrator
IMCCA – Interactive Multimedia & Collaborative Communications Alliance
IN – Indiana
indiv(s) – individual(s)
Indus – Industrial, Industry
Info – Information
Instl – Institutional
Instn(s) – Institution(s)
Instrl – Instructional
Intl – International
IQ – International Quorum of Motion Picture Producers
IS&T – Society for Imaging Science and Technology
ISBN – International Standard Book Number
ISSN – International Standard Serial Number
IT – Information Technology

Jr – Junior
Jt – Joint
Juv – Juvenile

K – Kindergarten
KS – Kansas
KY – Kentucky

LA – Louisiana
Lang(s) – Language(s)
Lib(s) – Library(-ies)
Libn – Librarian
Lit – Literature

MA – Massachusetts
MB – Manitoba
MD – Maryland
Mdse – Merchandise
Mdsg – Merchandising
ME – Maine
Med – Medical
Memb(s) – Member(s)
Metro – Metropolitan
Mfg – Manufacturing
Mgmt – Management
Mgr – Manager
MI – Michigan
Mkt(s) – Market(s)
Mktg – Marketing
MN – Minnesota
Mng – Managing
MO – Missouri
mo – month
MS – Mississippi
ms(s) – manuscript(s)
MT – Montana

NAB – National Association of Broadcasters
NABET-CWA – National Association of Broadcast Employees and Technicians-Communications Workers of America
NATAS – The National Academy of Television Arts & Sciences
Natl – National
NATPE – National Association Of Television Program Executives Inc
NB – New Brunswick
NC – North Carolina
ND – North Dakota
NE – Nebraska
NH – New Hampshire
NJ – New Jersey
NL – Newfoundland and Labrador
NM – New Mexico
No – Number
NOPA – National Office Products Alliance
NS – Nova Scotia
NSCA – National Systems Contractors Association
NT – Northwest Territories

NU – Nunavut
NV – Nevada
NY – New York

Off(s) – Office(s)
Offr – Officer
OH – Ohio
OK – Oklahoma
ON – Ontario
Oper(s) – Operation(s)
OR – Oregon

PA – Pennsylvania
PE – Prince Edward Island
Perms – Permissions
Photo – Photograph
Photog – Photographer, Photography
Pkwy – Parkway
pp - pages
PPA – Professional Photographers of America
PR – Public Relations
PR – Puerto Rico
Pres – President
Proc – Processing
Prod(s) – Product(s)
Prodn – Production
Prodr – Producer
Prof – Professional, Professor
Prog(s) – Program(s)
Proj(s) – Project(s)
Promo(s) – Promotion(s)
Prop – Proprietor
Pub Aff – Public Affairs
Publg – Publishing
Publr – Publisher
Pubn(s) – Publication(s)
Purch – Purchasing

QC – Quebec

R&D – Research & Development
Rd – Road
Ref – Reference
Reg – Region
Regl – Regional
Rel – Relations
Rep(s) – Representative(s)
Res – Research
RI – Rhode Island
RIAA – The Recording Industry Association of America®
Rm – Room
RTDNA – Radio Television Digital News Association
Rte – Route
Rts – Rights

SAG-AFTRA – Screen Actors Guild - American Federation of Television and Radio Artists

SBE – Society of Broadcast Engineers Inc
SC – South Carolina
Sci – Science
SCTE – Society of Cable Telecommunications Engineers Inc
SD – South Dakota
Secy – Secretary
Serv(s) – Service(s)
SID – Society for Information Display
SK – Saskatchewan
SMPTE® – Society of Motion Picture & Television Engineers®
Soc – Social, Sociology
SPARS – Society of Professional Audio Recording Services
Spec – Special
Sq – Square
Sr – Senior
St – Street, Saint
Sta – Station
Ste – Sainte
Subn(s) – Subscription(s)
Subs – Subsidiary
Supv – Supervisor
SVP – Senior Vice President
Synd – Syndicated, Syndication

Tech – Technical
Technol – Technology
Tel – Telephone
Terr – Terrace
TN – Tennessee
Tpke – Turnpike
Treas – Treasurer
TX – Texas

UK – United Kingdom
Univ – University
USITT – United States Institute for Theatre Technology Inc
UT – Utah

V – Vice
VA – Virginia
VChmn – Vice Chairman
VI – Virgin Islands
vol(s) – volume(s)
VP – Vice President
VT – Vermont

WA – Washington
WI – Wisconsin
WV – West Virginia
WY – Wyoming

yr – year
YT – Yukon Territory

Products & Services Index

Products & Services Index

This index interfiles over 1250 classifications throughout the AV industry. Where necessary, references are specified as being audio, video or film related, etc. It provides page references to all the headings in the Products, Services & Companies index which follows. Those who are limiting their research to a certain segment of the AV industry such as Video or Film will find the Products, Services & Companies section more convenient. The "How To Use *AV Market Place*™" section is recommended to assist in understanding the indexes.

Products, Services & Companies

Products, Services & Companies

This section combines the classifications of the Products & Services Index with the company names listed in the AV Product & Service Providers section. It also serves to help those users who are focusing on only one segment of the AV industry, as the classifications are arranged under the seven major headings of Audio, Audio/Visual, Computer Systems, Film, Video, Programming and Miscellaneous. The "How To Use AVMP" section is recommended to assist in understanding the indexes.

AUDIO

Accessory, *see* Part & Accessory

Alternative Music, *see* Music Libraries— Alternative

Amplifier Distributors

ARIZONA

Allusion Studios & Pure Wave Audio, pg 681
Arizona Cine Equipment, pg 688
Coustic, pg 732
EAR Professional Audio/Video, pg 749
Metropolitan Audio-Visual Inc, pg 824
Projector SuperStore LLC, pg 865
Troxell-CDI, pg 918

CALIFORNIA

Ametron Audio/Video, pg 684
Amplifier Technologies Inc (ATI), pg 684
Apex Jr, pg 687
Associated Sound, pg 691
Assured Audio Visual, pg 691
ATV Video Center Inc, pg 692
Audio Images Corp, pg 693
AV Conferencing LLC (AVC), pg 697
Be Media, pg 702
BigFoot Mobile Systems, pg 705
BroadcastStore.com, pg 711
California Tape Products Inc, pg 714
Carvin Amps & Audio, pg 717
Christy's Editorial, pg 723
Cibola Systems, pg 723
Cinema Equipment Sales of California Inc, pg 724
Directed Electronics, pg 743
Educational Technology Services (ETS), pg 751
Empire Pro, pg 753
Gallien-Krueger, pg 768
Gluskin's Custom Audio Video, pg 771
Harman Professional Solutions, pg 776
Hosa Technology Inc, pg 781
Instructional Materials & Equipment Distributors (I-Med), pg 789
JD Audio Visual Inc, pg 793
L-Acoustics Inc, pg 802
Lloyd F McKinney Associates Inc, pg 821
Media Control Systems LLC, pg 821
MediaMation Inc, pg 822

MediaPOINTE, pg 823
OWI Inc, pg 849
Parasound Products Inc, pg 851
Pioneer Electronics (USA) Inc, pg 857
Signal Transport, pg 887
SNAP, pg 891
Sound Service Co, pg 894
Southern California Sound Image Inc, pg 895
SSL Industries Inc, pg 898
Stanislaus AV Inc, pg 899
Studio 637, pg 903
SuperVision, pg 904
TOA Electronics Inc, pg 915
Towards 2000 Inc, pg 916
VMI Inc, pg 932
Yanchar Design & Consulting Group, pg 943

COLORADO

Audio Consultant Services Inc, pg 693
Daylight Productions & Rentals, pg 739
Spectrum Audio Visual Services, pg 897
Stanco Sales LLC, pg 899

CONNECTICUT

Connecticut Audio & Theatrical Supply, pg 731
HB Communications Inc, pg 777
The Music People Inc, pg 834

DELAWARE

Actors Attic, pg 675

FLORIDA

Altel Systems Group Inc, pg 682
A2D Solutions Inc, pg 692
AVI-SPL, pg 698
Broadcasters General Store Inc, pg 711
Digital Video Systems, pg 742
Harmon's Audio-Visual Services, pg 776
Harris Corp, pg 776
Herman Pro AV, pg 779
Hi-Tech Enterprises Inc, pg 779
Hi-Tech Import Export Corp, pg 779
Intermark Industries Inc, pg 789
Lighting Sales Connection Inc, pg 808
Midtown Video Inc, pg 827
ONstage, pg 846
Recording Media & Equipment Inc (RM&E), pg 872
Stereo Sales Inc, pg 900
TAI Audio, pg 906
Technomedia Solutions, pg 909
Test Equipment Connection, pg 911

GEORGIA

Baker Audio Visual, pg 700
Clark, pg 725

Lighting & Production Equipment Inc, pg 807
Stage Front Presentation Systems, pg 899

HAWAII

The Audio Visual Co (AVCO), pg 694

ILLINOIS

Allen Visual Systems Inc, pg 680
Creative Technology (CT), pg 733
Joseph Electronics, pg 795
C V Lloyde, pg 810
Quintessence Audio Ltd, pg 868
RC Communications, pg 870
US Music Corp, pg 923
Woodside Avenue Music Productions Inc, pg 941

INDIANA

Heart Breaker Entertainment LLC, pg 778
Sensory Technologies LLC, pg 884
SHP Electronics, pg 887
Sweetwater Sound Inc, pg 905

KENTUCKY

Audio Visual Techniques Inc, pg 695
Axxis Leasing Inc, pg 700
Barney Miller's Inc, pg 827
NOR-COM Inc, pg 841

LOUISIANA

Pace Systems, pg 849
Techkno Integration & Design Services LLC, pg 908

MAINE

Headlight Audio Visual Inc, pg 777
Independent Audio Inc, pg 786

MARYLAND

Bradley Broadcast & Pro Audio, pg 709
Cardinal Sound & Video, pg 717
Human Circuit, pg 782
Kipp Visual Systems Inc, pg 799

MASSACHUSETTS

Professional Audio Design Inc, pg 865
Rule Boston Camera, pg 878

MICHIGAN

Olson Anderson Co, pg 685
City Events Group, pg 725
Digi Sign Design LLC, pg 741
On Stage Visuals, pg 846
TEL Systems LLC, pg 909

MINNESOTA

Alpha Video & Audio Inc, pg 682
Digital Audio Labs, pg 742
New Life Communications Inc, pg 839
Tierney Brothers Inc, pg 914

MISSISSIPPI

Bowie Audio Visual Enterprises Inc, pg 709

MISSOURI

Communitronics Corp, pg 729
Conference Technologies Inc, pg 730
Modern Communications Inc, pg 828
Production Support Services Inc, pg 864
Schiller's Audio-Visual, pg 881

NEBRASKA

Ballantyne Strong Inc, pg 701

NEVADA

Pignose-Gorilla, pg 856

NEW HAMPSHIRE

APS Lighting-Sound-AV, pg 688
Technet® Systems Group, pg 908

NEW JERSEY

A-V Services Inc, pg 671
Alltec Stores, a Vcom IMC Company, pg 681
AlltecPro, pg 681
Audio Visual Associates, pg 694
AV Bluebook, pg 696
Comprehensive Cable & Connectivity Co, pg 729
Diversified, pg 744
Earl Girls Inc, pg 749
Entel Systems Inc, pg 754
G&G Technologies Inc, pg 768
HamiltonBuhl, pg 775
The Music Place, pg 834
Nelson Enterprises Theatrical Supply Co, pg 838
Onkyo USA Corp, pg 846
PatchAmp, pg 852
Starlite, pg 900
SYMCO, pg 905
Total Video Products Inc, pg 916
Video Corporation of America (VCA), pg 927
Wired 4 Sound Inc, pg 940
Yorktel, pg 944

NEW MEXICO

Quickbeam Systems Inc (QSI), pg 868

AUDIO

Amplifier Distributors
(continued)

NEW YORK

ADI Global Distribution, pg 676
Albany Theatre Supply Co Inc,
 pg 679
American Video Inc, pg 684
Audio-Video Corp, pg 694
AV Workshop, pg 697
Cadence Jazz Records, pg 713
Colortone Audio Visual, pg 728
Design Audio Visual Inc, pg 741
General Audio-Visual Inc (GAVI),
 pg 769
HAVE Inc, pg 777
Hot House Professional Audio,
 pg 782
Indigo Productions, pg 787
Korg USA Inc, pg 801
KVL Audio Visual Services Inc,
 pg 802
Lee Dan® Communications Inc,
 pg 805
Long Island Video Enterprises Live
 Inc, pg 811
Mark Custom Recording Service
 Inc, pg 817
Markertek Video Supply, pg 817
Music Hall LLC, pg 834
Presentation Products Inc, pg 861
RNJ Electronics, pg 875
TecNec Distributing, pg 909
Theatrical Services & Supplies Inc,
 pg 912
Toys From The Attic, pg 916
Tri-Ed Distribution Inc, pg 918
Visual Word Systems Inc, pg 932
Whirlwind Music Distributors Inc,
 pg 937
XTA Electronics Ltd, pg 943

OHIO

Copp Integrated Systems, pg 731
ITA Audio Visual Solutions, pg 791
Luminaud Inc, pg 812
Parts Express, pg 851
Tri-State Audio Visual Co, pg 918
Tri-State Visual Products Inc,
 pg 918

OKLAHOMA

DD Audio, pg 739

OREGON

Lightspeed Technologies Inc,
 pg 808
PLUS Corp of America, pg 858
SuperDigital Ltd, pg 904

PENNSYLVANIA

Advanced AV LLC, pg 677
Audio Visions Inc, pg 694
Brodart Co, pg 711
Clair Companies, pg 725
J E Foss Co, pg 764
The Lerro Corp, pg 806
Morefield Communications Inc,
 pg 830
Sound by Fitch, pg 893
Vistacom Inc, pg 931
Visual Sound Inc, pg 931
Wespen Audio Visual Co, pg 935

RHODE ISLAND

Shanix Inc, pg 885

SOUTH CAROLINA

DaviSound, pg 739

TENNESSEE

Advanced Sound, pg 677
Allstar Audio Systems Inc, pg 681
Belew Enterprises, pg 703
Lowrance Sound Co Inc, pg 812
Mr Mark's Used Musical, Stereo &
 Studio Equipment Store, pg 828
Spectrum Sound Inc, pg 897
Technical Support Systems LLC,
 pg 908
Zion Music Group, pg 945

TEXAS

AVES Audio Visual Systems Inc,
 pg 698
Crossroads Audio Inc, pg 735
Data Projections Inc, pg 738
Digital Display Solutions Inc,
 pg 742
FitzCo Sound Inc, pg 761
Heffernan Audio Visual, pg 778
Lubbock Audio Visual Inc, pg 812
Pro Video & Film Equipment Co
 Inc, pg 863
Quality Audio Visual Service Inc,
 pg 867
RF Specialties of Texas LLC,
 pg 874
Southwest Sound Solutions, pg 896
Tarpley Media Systems, pg 907

UTAH

Performance Audio LLC, pg 854
RIA Corp, pg 874

VERMONT

Artech Electronics Ltd, pg 690
Production Advantage Inc, pg 863

VIRGINIA

Avitecture Inc, pg 699
Boitnott Visual Communications
 Corp (BVC), pg 708
Design & Production Inc, pg 740
Intellidyne LLC, pg 789
Lee Hartman & Sons Inc, pg 805
Rocktown Media, pg 876
StageSound, pg 899
The Whitlock Group, pg 937

WASHINGTON

CCI Solutions, pg 718
LOUD Technologies Inc, pg 811
Northern Lights & Pro Audio,
 pg 842
PNTA, pg 858
Proforma Good Wood Marketing,
 pg 865

WEST VIRGINIA

United Sound & Electronics, pg 921

WISCONSIN

Audio Visual of Milwaukee Inc,
 pg 694
Camera Corner Connecting Point,
 pg 715
Full Compass Systems, pg 767

PUERTO RICO

Audio Visual Concepts Inc, pg 694
Bonnin Electronics Inc, pg 708

ALBERTA

Allstar Show Industries Inc, pg 681
Infosat Communications Inc, pg 787
Matrix Video Communications Corp
 (MVCC), pg 819
Unique Communications Ltd,
 pg 921

BRITISH COLUMBIA

Commercial Electronics Ltd, pg 728

MANITOBA

Advance Pro, pg 677
Inland Audio Visual Ltd, pg 788

ONTARIO

Cinema Stage Inc, pg 724
HD Source, pg 777
Nationwide Audio Visual Co,
 pg 837
Westbury National Show Systems
 Ltd, pg 936
Yorkville Sound Inc, pg 944

QUEBEC

JAM Industries Ltd, pg 792
Panavideo Inc, pg 850
SC Media Canada, pg 881
Sennheiser (Canada) Inc, pg 884

Amplifier Manufacturers

ARIZONA

AtlasIED, pg 692
Coustic, pg 732
Fender Musical Instruments Corp,
 pg 759
MTX Audio, pg 833
Radio Design Labs (RDL), pg 869

ARKANSAS

Shaker Microphones & Promotions
 Inc, pg 885

CALIFORNIA

AB Systems Amplifiers, pg 672
ALTINEX Inc, pg 682
Amplifier Technologies Inc (ATI),
 pg 684
Audio Upgrades, pg 694
Califone International Inc, pg 714
Carvin Amps & Audio, pg 717
Digital Music Corp, pg 742
Directed Electronics, pg 743
ESE, pg 755
Extron Electronics, pg 758
FM Systems Inc, pg 763
FrontRow, pg 766
Gallien-Krueger, pg 768
Harman Professional Solutions,
 pg 776
Henry Engineering, pg 779
Hosa Technology Inc, pg 781
L-Acoustics Inc, pg 802
Laboratories Inc, pg 803
Manley Laboratories Inc, pg 816
Media Control Systems LLC,
 pg 821
Nady Systems Inc, pg 835
Opamp Labs Inc, pg 846
Orevox USA Corp, pg 847
OWI Inc, pg 849
Parasound Products Inc, pg 851
Pioneer Electronics (USA) Inc,
 pg 857
PowerPhysics Inc, pg 860
QSC Audio Products LLC, pg 867
Renkus-Heinz Inc, pg 873

Roland Corp US, pg 876
Signal Transport, pg 887
Stewart Audio, pg 901
TASCAM, pg 907
TeachLogic Inc, pg 908
TOA Electronics Inc, pg 915
Velodyne LiDAR Inc, pg 925
Wohler Technologies Inc, pg 940
Xantech LLC, pg 943

COLORADO

Liberty AV Solutions, pg 807
Video Accessory Corp, pg 927

CONNECTICUT

Sound Control Technologies Inc,
 pg 893

FLORIDA

Domo Tactical Communications
 (DTC) Ltd, pg 745
Intermark Industries Inc, pg 789
JT Communications, pg 795
Magna-Tech Electronic Co Inc,
 pg 814
Tel-Test, pg 909

ILLINOIS

AmpliVox Portable Sound Systems,
 pg 684
Dukane Corp, Audio Visual
 Products Division, pg 747
Precision Electronics Inc, pg 861
Studio Technologies Inc, pg 903
US Music Corp, pg 923

INDIANA

Auralex Acoustics Inc, pg 696

KANSAS

SoundTube Entertainment Inc,
 pg 895

MARYLAND

API, pg 687
JoLida Inc, pg 795

MINNESOTA

Atma-Sphere Music Systems Inc,
 pg 692
Bosch Security Systems Inc, pg 709
Digital Audio Labs, pg 742

MISSISSIPPI

Crest Audio Inc, pg 734
Peavey Electronics Corp, pg 852
Sherwood America Inc, pg 886

MISSOURI

Link Electronics Inc, pg 809
Lowell Manufacturing, pg 812

NEBRASKA

Ballantyne Strong Inc, pg 701
REI - Radio Engineering Industries,
 pg 873

NEVADA

Pignose-Gorilla, pg 856

NEW HAMPSHIRE

Russound, pg 879

NEW JERSEY
Apogee Sound International LLC, pg 687
ATI Audio, pg 692
Bogen Communications Inc, pg 708
Crestron Electronics Inc, pg 734
Gemini Sound, pg 769
Kramer Electronics USA Inc, pg 801
Oklahoma Sound Corp, pg 844
Onkyo USA Corp, pg 846
Radio Systems Inc, pg 869
RAMSA Professional Audio Systems, pg 870
Technics, pg 909

NEW YORK
Ashly Audio Inc, pg 691
Benchmark Media Systems Inc, pg 703
GLI Sound Systems, pg 771
Harbro Corp, pg 776
Hot House Professional Audio, pg 782
Key Digital Systems, pg 798
MultiDyne Video & Fiber Optics Systems, pg 833
Music Hall LLC, pg 834
Protech Audio Corp, pg 866
Sescom Inc, pg 884

OHIO
Luminaud Inc, pg 812

OKLAHOMA
DD Audio, pg 739

OREGON
BIAMP Systems, pg 705
Lightspeed Technologies Inc, pg 808

PENNSYLVANIA
Clair Companies, pg 725
D W Fearn, pg 759

RHODE ISLAND
Rane, pg 870

SOUTH CAROLINA
DaviSound, pg 739

TENNESSEE
Cerwin-Vega! Inc, pg 720
Remote Audio Products, pg 873

TEXAS
ETS-Lindgren, pg 756

UTAH
ClearOne Inc, pg 726
Ivie Technologies Inc, pg 792
Rolls Corp, pg 877
Spectra Sonics LLC, pg 897

WASHINGTON
AudioControl® Inc, pg 695
Conex Electro Systems Inc, pg 730
LOUD Technologies Inc, pg 811
Symetrix Inc, pg 905

BRITISH COLUMBIA
B&K AV Ltd, pg 701
Richmond Sound Design Ltd, pg 875

ONTARIO
Bryston Ltd, pg 712
Communications & Power Industries (CPI), Satcom & Medical Products Division, pg 728
Ward-Beck Systems Ltd, pg 933
Yorkville Sound Inc, pg 944

Amplifier Rentals

ALABAMA
Audio-Video Resources Inc, pg 694

ARIZONA
Arizona Cine Equipment, pg 688
Merestone, pg 823
Metropolitan Audio-Visual Inc, pg 824
Video West Inc, pg 929

CALIFORNIA
Action Audio & Visual, pg 675
AGF Media Services, pg 678
Alliant Event Services, pg 681
Ametron Audio/Video, pg 684
Artichoke Productions, pg 690
Associated Sound, pg 691
ATV Video Center Inc, pg 692
Audio Rents, pg 693
AV Guys, pg 697
Bexel, an NEP Broadcast Services Company, pg 704
Christy's Editorial, pg 723
Express Media Inc, pg 757
Hollywood Sound Systems, pg 781
Instructional Materials & Equipment Distributors (I-Med), pg 789
JD Audio Visual Inc, pg 793
LA Sound Co, pg 803
Lynch Communications, pg 813
McCune Audio-Video-Lighting, pg 821
Munday & Collins AV, pg 834
Muse Presentation Technologies, pg 834
On-Trax Inc, pg 846
Production Gear Rentals (PGR), pg 863
PSAV® Presentation Services, pg 866
Alwin Sauers Audio Productions (ASAP), pg 881
Shooting Star Video, pg 886
Sound Service Co, pg 894
Stanislaus AV Inc, pg 899
Studio 637, pg 903
Synthesizer Rental Service, pg 906
Towards 2000 Inc, pg 916
Video Resources Inc, pg 928
Westcoast Video Productions Inc, pg 936

COLORADO
Audio Consultant Services Inc, pg 693
Daylight Productions & Rentals, pg 739
Multimedia Audio Visual Inc, pg 833
Spectrum Audio Visual Services, pg 897

CONNECTICUT
A/V Davey, pg 697
Connecticut Audio & Theatrical Supply, pg 731

DELAWARE
Actors Attic, pg 675
Showorks Audio Visual Inc, pg 887
Side Door Studio Inc, pg 887

FLORIDA
AVI-SPL, pg 698
Harmon's Audio-Visual Services, pg 776
Industrial Strength Inc, pg 787
Lighting Sales Connection Inc, pg 808
ONstage, pg 846
Paradise Show & Design Inc, pg 851
Sight & Sound Productions, pg 887
TAI Audio, pg 906

GEORGIA
MAGNUM Companies Ltd, pg 815
Stage Front Presentation Systems, pg 899
Staging Directions Inc, pg 899

HAWAII
Hawaii Sound & Vision, pg 777
Sight & Sound Studios, pg 887

ILLINOIS
AV Chicago Inc, pg 696
Backstar Creative Media Inc, pg 700
Beatty TeleVisual Productions, pg 703
C V Lloyde, pg 810
Meetinghouse Event Design & Production, pg 823
OSA International Inc, pg 848
PSAV® Presentation Services (Hotel Services Division), pg 866
RC Communications, pg 870
Resolution Productions Group, pg 874
Staging Resources Inc, pg 899
Woodside Avenue Music Productions Inc, pg 941

INDIANA
Heart Breaker Entertainment LLC, pg 778

IOWA
Central Lighting & Equipment Inc (CLE), pg 719

KENTUCKY
Audio Visual Techniques Inc, pg 695
NOR-COM Inc, pg 841

LOUISIANA
Clark Services Audio Visual & Exhibit Inc, pg 725
Pace Systems, pg 849

MAINE
Headlight Audio Visual Inc, pg 777

MARYLAND
Advance Audiovisual Presentation Ltd, pg 677
Cardinal Sound & Video, pg 717
CPR MultiMedia Solutions, pg 732
dbF a Media Company, pg 739
Event Tech, pg 756
Maryland Sound International Holding Co LLC, pg 819

MASSACHUSETTS
Fastlane Productions LLC, pg 759
massAV, pg 819
Preston Productions Inc, pg 861

MICHIGAN
Olson Anderson Co, pg 685
Digi Sign Design LLC, pg 741
K&R All Media Productions LLC, pg 796
K&R's Recording Studios Inc, pg 796
On Stage Visuals, pg 846
TEL Systems LLC, pg 909

MINNESOTA
Alpha Video & Audio Inc, pg 682
New Life Communications Inc, pg 839

MISSISSIPPI
Bowie Audio Visual Enterprises Inc, pg 709

MISSOURI
Communitronics Corp, pg 729
Production Support Services Inc, pg 864
Show-Me Audio-Visual, pg 887
Switch, pg 905

MONTANA
Jereco Studios Inc, pg 793

NEBRASKA
Dog & Pony Productions Inc, pg 744

NEVADA
GES Audio Visual, pg 770
Lefco Video Services Inc, pg 806

NEW HAMPSHIRE
Apertura, pg 686
APS Lighting-Sound-AV, pg 688

NEW JERSEY
Audio Visual Associates, pg 694
Earl Girls Inc, pg 749
International Audio Visual Inc, pg 790
Moe AV LLC, pg 828
The Music Place, pg 834
Nelson Enterprises Theatrical Supply Co, pg 838
Panavid, pg 850
PLS Staging, pg 858
Soundtracks Production Services LLC, pg 895
Starlite, pg 900
Wired 4 Sound Inc, pg 940

NEW MEXICO
Quickbeam Systems Inc (QSI), pg 868

NEW YORK
Albany Theatre Supply Co Inc, pg 679
All Mobile Video Inc, pg 680
American Video Inc, pg 684
Aura Sonic Ltd (ASL), pg 695
AV Workshop, pg 697
Colortone Audio Visual, pg 728
CP Communications, pg 732
Design Audio Visual Inc, pg 741

AUDIO

Amplifier Rentals (continued)

NEW YORK (continued)
KVL Audio Visual Services Inc, pg 802
Long Island Video Enterprises Live Inc, pg 811
Posthorn Recordings, pg 859
See Factor Industry Inc, pg 883
Specialized Audio-Visual Inc, pg 896
Studio Instrument Rentals (SIR), pg 902
Visual Word Systems Inc, pg 932
WorldStage, pg 941

NORTH CAROLINA
AV Connections Inc, pg 697
AV Metro Inc, pg 697
Special Event Services, pg 896

NORTH DAKOTA
Media Productions, pg 822

OHIO
Hughie's Event Production Services, pg 782
ITA Audio Visual Solutions, pg 791
Mills James Productions, pg 828
Ohio HD Video, pg 844
Production Solutions Inc, pg 864
R&B Communications Inc, pg 870

OKLAHOMA
PDC Productions, pg 852

PENNSYLVANIA
Advanced AV LLC, pg 677
Audio Visions Inc, pg 694
Clair Companies, pg 725
FirstGeneration Audio/Visual Services, pg 761
Grise Audio Visual Center Inc, pg 774
Sound by Fitch, pg 893
Viewpoint Production Services Inc, pg 930
Vistacom Inc, pg 931
Visual Sound Inc, pg 931

SOUTH CAROLINA
Impact Technology Group LLC, pg 786
Sound & Images Inc, pg 893

TENNESSEE
Allstar Audio Systems Inc, pg 681
Brantley Sound Associates Inc, pg 709
Mr Mark's Used Musical, Stereo & Studio Equipment Store, pg 828
Technical Support Systems LLC, pg 908
Trew Audio Inc, pg 917

TEXAS
Alford Media Services, pg 680
Bright Star Productions Inc, pg 710
Crossroads Audio Inc, pg 735
FitzCo Sound Inc, pg 761
Lubbock Audio Visual Inc, pg 812
Music Lab Inc, pg 834
Onstage Systems, pg 846
Power Factory Productions, pg 860

Stage Directions, pg 898
Tropikal Productions, pg 918

UTAH
Performance Audio LLC, pg 854

VIRGINIA
American AV, pg 682
Audio Visual Actions Inc (AVA), pg 694
Lee Hartman & Sons Inc, pg 805
StageSound, pg 899
The Whitlock Group, pg 937

WASHINGTON
D A Sound, pg 737
Northern Lights & Pro Audio, pg 842
PNTA, pg 858

WEST VIRGINIA
United Sound & Electronics, pg 921

WISCONSIN
Audio Visual of Milwaukee Inc, pg 694
Camera Corner Connecting Point, pg 715
Event Essentials, pg 756
Full Compass Systems, pg 767

PUERTO RICO
Stage Crew Audiovisual Inc, pg 898

ALBERTA
Allstar Show Industries Inc, pg 681
Cine Audio Visual Sales & Service Ltd, pg 723
Evolution AV, pg 757
L R Light & Sound, pg 802
Unique Communications Ltd, pg 921

BRITISH COLUMBIA
Clark's Audio Visual Services Ltd, pg 725
Commercial Electronics Ltd, pg 728
DL Sound & Lighting Productions Ltd, pg 744
MicrophoneRentals.com, pg 826

MANITOBA
Inland Audio Visual Ltd, pg 788

ONTARIO
HD Source, pg 777
Westbury National Show Systems Ltd, pg 936
ZTV Broadcast Services Inc, pg 945

QUEBEC
Audio Visual Dynamics, pg 694
Panavideo Inc, pg 850

Amplifier Repairs

ARIZONA
Metropolitan Audio-Visual Inc, pg 824
Troxell-CDI, pg 918

CALIFORNIA
AB Systems Amplifiers, pg 672
Ametron Audio/Video, pg 684
Audio Images Corp, pg 693

BroadcastStore.com, pg 711
Christy's Editorial, pg 723
Diemer Amp & Keyboard Repair, pg 741
Gluskin's Custom Audio Video, pg 771
Instructional Materials & Equipment Distributors (I-Med), pg 789
McAlister Electronics, pg 820
Parasound Products Inc, pg 851
Sound Service Co, pg 894
Sounds Unique, pg 895
SSL Industries Inc, pg 898
TOA Electronics Inc, pg 915
Towards 2000 Inc, pg 916

CONNECTICUT
A/V Davey, pg 697
HB Communications Inc, pg 777

DELAWARE
Actors Attic, pg 675

FLORIDA
AMP Services Inc, pg 684
Digital Video Systems, pg 742
Hi-Tech Enterprises Inc, pg 779
JT Communications, pg 795
Phat Planet Recording Studios, pg 855
Stereo Sales Inc, pg 900
TAI Audio, pg 906

GEORGIA
Stage Front Presentation Systems, pg 899

ILLINOIS
Beatty TeleVisual Productions, pg 703
Dukane Corp, Audio Visual Products Division, pg 747
C V Lloyde, pg 810
RC Communications, pg 870

INDIANA
SHP Electronics, pg 887
Sweetwater Sound Inc, pg 905

KENTUCKY
Axxis Leasing Inc, pg 700
NOR-COM Inc, pg 841

MARYLAND
Cardinal Sound & Video, pg 717
Maryland Sound International Holding Co LLC, pg 819

MASSACHUSETTS
Professional Audio Design Inc, pg 865

MICHIGAN
Olson Anderson Co, pg 685
K&R's Recording Studios Inc, pg 796
TEL Systems LLC, pg 909

MISSOURI
Communitronics Corp, pg 729

NEW JERSEY
A-V Services Inc, pg 671
Audio Visual Associates, pg 694
Earl Girls Inc, pg 749
The Music Place, pg 834

Nelson Enterprises Theatrical Supply Co, pg 838
Starlite, pg 900

NEW MEXICO
Quickbeam Systems Inc (QSI), pg 868

NEW YORK
American Video Inc, pg 684
Design Audio Visual Inc, pg 741
Hot House Professional Audio, pg 782
Toys From The Attic, pg 916
Visual Word Systems Inc, pg 932
Whirlwind Music Distributors Inc, pg 937

OHIO
Copp Integrated Systems, pg 731
ITA Audio Visual Solutions, pg 791
Tri-State Audio Visual Co, pg 918

OREGON
All Service Musical Electronics Repair, pg 680

PENNSYLVANIA
Audio Visions Inc, pg 694
Clair Companies, pg 725
J E Foss Co, pg 764
Right Coast Recording Inc, pg 875
Vistacom Inc, pg 931
Wespen Audio Visual Co, pg 935

SOUTH CAROLINA
DaviSound, pg 739

TENNESSEE
Belew Enterprises, pg 703
db electronics, pg 739
Technical Support Systems LLC, pg 908
Trew Audio Inc, pg 917

TEXAS
FitzCo Sound Inc, pg 761
Lubbock Audio Visual Inc, pg 812
Quality Audio Visual Service Inc, pg 867
Southwest Sound Solutions, pg 896
Tarpley Media Systems, pg 907

VIRGINIA
Boitnott Visual Communications Corp (BVC), pg 708
Lee Hartman & Sons Inc, pg 805
The Whitlock Group, pg 937

WASHINGTON
Northern Lights & Pro Audio, pg 842
PNTA, pg 858

WEST VIRGINIA
United Sound & Electronics, pg 921

WISCONSIN
Audio Visual of Milwaukee Inc, pg 694
Full Compass Systems, pg 767

ALBERTA

Allstar Show Industries Inc, pg 681
Infosat Communications Inc, pg 787
Unique Communications Ltd,
pg 921

BRITISH COLUMBIA

Commercial Electronics Ltd, pg 728

MANITOBA

Inland Audio Visual Ltd, pg 788

ONTARIO

Communications & Power
Industries (CPI), Satcom &
Medical Products Division,
pg 728
HD Source, pg 777
Westbury National Show Systems
Ltd, pg 936
Yorkville Sound Inc, pg 944

QUEBEC

Panavideo Inc, pg 850
SC Media Canada, pg 881

Audio Editing, *see* Dubbing

Audiocassette—Blank Distributors

ARIZONA

Troxell-CDI, pg 918

CALIFORNIA

Ametron Audio/Video, pg 684
Assured Audio Visual, pg 691
Audio Images Corp, pg 693
Birns & Sawyer Inc, pg 706
California Tape Products Inc,
pg 714
Christy's Editorial, pg 723
Dan Dugan Sound Design Inc,
pg 747
El Mar Plastics Inc, pg 752
Gluskin's Custom Audio Video,
pg 771
Instructional Materials & Equipment
Distributors (I-Med), pg 789
JD Audio Visual Inc, pg 793
Lynch Communications, pg 813
Maximus Media Inc, pg 820
Media Fabricators Inc, pg 822
On-Trax Inc, pg 846
Sound Service Co, pg 894
Sounds Unique, pg 895
SSL Industries Inc, pg 898
Zack Electronics Inc, pg 945

COLORADO

Audio Consultant Services Inc,
pg 693
Daylight Productions & Rentals,
pg 739
Spectrum Audio Visual Services,
pg 897
Stanco Sales LLC, pg 899

CONNECTICUT

Connecticut Audio & Theatrical
Supply, pg 731
Rockwell Communications Inc,
pg 876
T & M Digital Services LLC,
pg 906

DELAWARE

Actors Attic, pg 675

FLORIDA

Alliance Entertainment Corp (AEC)
LLC, pg 680
AVI-SPL, pg 698
Broadcasters General Store Inc,
pg 711
Digital Video Systems, pg 742
Hi-Tech Import Export Corp,
pg 779
Industrial Strength Inc, pg 787
ONstage, pg 846
Recording Media & Equipment Inc
(RM&E), pg 872
Stereo Sales Inc, pg 900
TAI Audio, pg 906
Universal Studios Florida®
Production Group, pg 922

GEORGIA

Audio Visual Resources Inc, pg 695
Lighting & Production Equipment
Inc, pg 807
Visioneering International Inc,
pg 931

HAWAII

The Audio Visual Co (AVCO),
pg 694

ILLINOIS

Central Audio-Visual Equipment
Inc, pg 719
Creative Technology (CT), pg 733
Joseph Electronics, pg 795
Major Reproductions Equipment
Co, pg 815

INDIANA

OMNI Productions, pg 845
SHP Electronics, pg 887

KANSAS

Theatrical Services Inc, pg 912

KENTUCKY

Audio Visual Techniques Inc,
pg 695
Barney Miller's Inc, pg 827
NOR-COM Inc, pg 841

MARYLAND

Bradley Broadcast & Pro Audio,
pg 709
Kipp Visual Systems Inc, pg 799
Nicholas P Pipino Associates Inc,
pg 857
RTZ Audio Visual, pg 878

MASSACHUSETTS

Terry Hanley Audio Systems Inc,
pg 775
Hunt's Photo & Video, pg 782

MICHIGAN

City Events Group, pg 725
TEL Systems LLC, pg 909

MISSISSIPPI

Bowie Audio Visual Enterprises Inc,
pg 709
Jasper Ewing & Sons Inc, pg 757

MISSOURI

Audio-VideoGraphics Inc, pg 694
Communitronics Corp, pg 729
Conference Technologies Inc,
pg 730
Modern Communications Inc,
pg 828
Schiller's Audio-Visual, pg 881

NEBRASKA

VSA Inc, pg 933

NEW JERSEY

Alltec Stores, a Vcom IMC
Company, pg 681
AlltecPro, pg 681
Argraph Corp, pg 688
Audio Visual Dynamics®, pg 694
AV Bluebook, pg 696
Avtech Systems Inc, pg 699
Comprehensive Cable &
Connectivity Co, pg 729
G&G Technologies Inc, pg 768
Maxell Corp of America, pg 820
The Music Place, pg 834
Starlite, pg 900
Tele-Measurements Inc, pg 910
Total Media Inc, pg 916
Total Video Products Inc, pg 916
Vcom IMC, pg 925
Video Corporation of America
(VCA), pg 927
Wired 4 Sound Inc, pg 940
Yorktel, pg 944

NEW YORK

AV Workshop, pg 697
B&H Photo Video, pg 701
Burlington A/V Recording Media,
pg 712
Cadence Jazz Records, pg 713
Cine 60 Inc, pg 723
Colortone Audio Visual, pg 728
Design Audio Visual Inc, pg 741
Digital Force Ltd, pg 742
Gaylord Archival, pg 768
HAVE Inc, pg 777
Indigo Productions, pg 787
Long Island Video Enterprises Live
Inc, pg 811
Markertek Video Supply, pg 817
Saul Mineroff Electronics Inc
(SME), pg 828
Neptune Photo Inc, pg 838
Ray Supply Inc, pg 870
RNJ Electronics, pg 875
Sentry Industries Inc, pg 884
TecNec Distributing, pg 909
Tri-Ed Distribution Inc, pg 918
Visual Technologies Corp, pg 932
Visual Word Systems Inc, pg 932
WorldStage, pg 941

NORTH CAROLINA

Strategic Connections, pg 901

OHIO

Copp Integrated Systems, pg 731
Hughie's Event Production Services,
pg 782
Tri-State Audio Visual Co, pg 918

PENNSYLVANIA

Advanced AV LLC, pg 677
Bernie's Photo Center, pg 704
J E Foss Co, pg 764
Garcia Marketing Inc, pg 768
Grise Audio Visual Center Inc,
pg 774

Hite Co, pg 780
The Lerro Corp, pg 806
Morefield Communications Inc,
pg 830
Visual Sound Inc, pg 931
Wespen Audio Visual Co, pg 935

TENNESSEE

Lowrance Sound Co Inc, pg 812
Memphis Communications Corp,
pg 823
Spring Arbor Distributors Inc,
pg 898
WTSmedia, pg 942

TEXAS

CAM Audio Inc, pg 714
Heffernan Audio Visual, pg 778
JSAV, pg 795
Lubbock Audio Visual Inc, pg 812
Quality Audio Visual Service Inc,
pg 867
RF Specialties of Texas LLC,
pg 874

UTAH

Performance Audio LLC, pg 854
RIA Corp, pg 874
Webb Audio Visual, pg 935

VIRGINIA

Boitnott Visual Communications
Corp (BVC), pg 708
Lee Hartman & Sons Inc, pg 805
The Whitlock Group, pg 937

WASHINGTON

CCI Solutions, pg 718
Inland Audio Visual Co, pg 788

WISCONSIN

Camera Corner Connecting Point,
pg 715
Demco Inc, pg 740
Full Compass Systems, pg 767
School Specialty Inc, pg 882

PUERTO RICO

Bonnin Electronics Inc, pg 708

ALBERTA

Infosat Communications Inc, pg 787
McBain Camera Ltd, pg 820
Unique Communications Ltd,
pg 921

BRITISH COLUMBIA

Commercial Electronics Ltd, pg 728
Triad Communications Ltd, pg 918

MANITOBA

Advance Pro, pg 677
Inland Audio Visual Ltd, pg 788

ONTARIO

HD Source, pg 777
Nationwide Audio Visual Co,
pg 837

QUEBEC

Panavideo Inc, pg 850

AUDIO

Audiocassette—Blank Manufacturers

CALIFORNIA

ACDC Audio CD & Cassette, pg 674
Ampex Data Systems Corp, pg 684
El Mar Plastics Inc, pg 752
Sony Electronics Inc, pg 893
Sounds Unique, pg 895
United Audio Video Inc, pg 921

COLORADO

Rocky Mountain Audio/Video Productions Inc, pg 876

MASSACHUSETTS

Soundtrack Group, pg 895

MISSOURI

Audio-VideoGraphics Inc, pg 694

NEW JERSEY

AlltecPro, pg 681
CELCO, pg 719
Maxell Corp of America, pg 820

NEW YORK

Burlington A/V Recording Media, pg 712

PENNSYLVANIA

Forge Recording LLC, pg 764

TENNESSEE

WTSmedia, pg 942

TEXAS

Adams Evidence Grade Technology Inc, pg 675

WISCONSIN

Full Compass Systems, pg 767

Audiocassette Duplication, see Duplication— Audiocassettes

Audiocassette Duplicator Distributors

ARIZONA

Troxell-CDI, pg 918

CALIFORNIA

Ametron Audio/Video, pg 684
Audio Images Corp, pg 693
Instructional Materials & Equipment Distributors (I-Med), pg 789
Joseph Nicoletti Consulting-Promotion, pg 841
QRS Software Services, pg 867

COLORADO

Audio Consultant Services Inc, pg 693

CONNECTICUT

The Music People Inc, pg 834

DELAWARE

Actors Attic, pg 675

FLORIDA

Digital Video Systems, pg 742
Intermark Industries Inc, pg 789
Lighting Sales Connection Inc, pg 808
Recording Media & Equipment Inc (RM&E), pg 872
Stereo Sales Inc, pg 900

GEORGIA

Stage Front Presentation Systems, pg 899

HAWAII

The Audio Visual Co (AVCO), pg 694

ILLINOIS

Allen Visual Systems Inc, pg 680
Woodside Avenue Music Productions Inc, pg 941

INDIANA

SHP Electronics, pg 887

KENTUCKY

Audio Visual Techniques Inc, pg 695
Barney Miller's Inc, pg 827
NOR-COM Inc, pg 841

MARYLAND

Bradley Broadcast & Pro Audio, pg 709
Kipp Visual Systems Inc, pg 799

MICHIGAN

Digi Sign Design LLC, pg 741
TEL Systems LLC, pg 909

MISSOURI

Modern Communications Inc, pg 828

NEW JERSEY

Alltec Stores, a Vcom IMC Company, pg 681
AlltecPro, pg 681
AV Bluebook, pg 696
Reed Presentations Inc (RPI), pg 872
Total Video Products Inc, pg 916
Yorktel, pg 944

NEW YORK

Audio-Video Corp, pg 694
Colortone Audio Visual, pg 728
Design Audio Visual Inc, pg 741
Digital Force Ltd, pg 742
Gaylord Archival, pg 768
Markertek Video Supply, pg 817
Neptune Photo Inc, pg 838
TecNec Distributing, pg 909
Visual Word Systems Inc, pg 932

OHIO

Tri-State Audio Visual Co, pg 918

PENNSYLVANIA

Advanced AV LLC, pg 677
Bernie's Photo Center, pg 704
J E Foss Co, pg 764

Grise Audio Visual Center Inc, pg 774
The Lerro Corp, pg 806
Wespen Audio Visual Co, pg 935

TENNESSEE

Allstar Audio Systems Inc, pg 681
Lowrance Sound Co Inc, pg 812
Technical Support Systems LLC, pg 908

TEXAS

Lubbock Audio Visual Inc, pg 812
Quality Audio Visual Service Inc, pg 867
RF Specialties of Texas LLC, pg 874
Tarpley Media Systems, pg 907

UTAH

Performance Audio LLC, pg 854

VIRGINIA

Lee Hartman & Sons Inc, pg 805
The Whitlock Group, pg 937

WASHINGTON

CCI Solutions, pg 718

WISCONSIN

Full Compass Systems, pg 767

PUERTO RICO

Bonnin Electronics Inc, pg 708

ALBERTA

Matrix Video Communications Corp (MVCC), pg 819
Unique Communications Ltd, pg 921

BRITISH COLUMBIA

Commercial Electronics Ltd, pg 728

MANITOBA

Advance Pro, pg 677
Inland Audio Visual Ltd, pg 788

ONTARIO

Westbury National Show Systems Ltd, pg 936

Audiocassette Duplicator Manufacturers

CALIFORNIA

QRS Software Services, pg 867

MASSACHUSETTS

Soundtrack Group, pg 895

NEW JERSEY

Reed Presentations Inc (RPI), pg 872

NEW YORK

Chromavision Corp, pg 723
Digital Force Ltd, pg 742

BRITISH COLUMBIA

Triad Communications Ltd, pg 918

Audiocassette Duplicator Rentals

CALIFORNIA

Ametron Audio/Video, pg 684
Express Media Inc, pg 757
JD Audio Visual Inc, pg 793
Lynch Communications, pg 813

COLORADO

Audio Consultant Services Inc, pg 693
Spectrum Audio Visual Services, pg 897

CONNECTICUT

A/V Davey, pg 697

DELAWARE

Side Door Studio Inc, pg 887

FLORIDA

ONstage, pg 846

GEORGIA

Stage Front Presentation Systems, pg 899

ILLINOIS

Allen Visual Systems Inc, pg 680
OSA International Inc, pg 848
RC Communications, pg 870
Woodside Avenue Music Productions Inc, pg 941

KENTUCKY

Audio Visual Techniques Inc, pg 695

MASSACHUSETTS

massAV, pg 819

MICHIGAN

Digi Sign Design LLC, pg 741
K&R All Media Productions LLC, pg 796
K&R's Recording Studios Inc, pg 796

MISSOURI

Show-Me Audio-Visual, pg 887

NEW YORK

Design Audio Visual Inc, pg 741
Visual Word Systems Inc, pg 932

NORTH CAROLINA

AV Connections Inc, pg 697

OHIO

Hughie's Event Production Services, pg 782

PENNSYLVANIA

JPL, pg 795

TENNESSEE

Allstar Audio Systems Inc, pg 681
Mr Mark's Used Musical, Stereo & Studio Equipment Store, pg 828

TEXAS
Lubbock Audio Visual Inc, pg 812
Quality Audio Visual Service Inc,
pg 867

UTAH
Performance Audio LLC, pg 854

VIRGINIA
Lee Hartman & Sons Inc, pg 805

WISCONSIN
Audio Visual of Milwaukee Inc,
pg 694

ALBERTA
Evolution AV, pg 757
Unique Communications Ltd,
pg 921

MANITOBA
Inland Audio Visual Ltd, pg 788

ONTARIO
Westbury National Show Systems
Ltd, pg 936

Audiocassette Duplicator Repairs

CALIFORNIA
Ametron Audio/Video, pg 684
Audio Images Corp, pg 693
McAlister Electronics, pg 820

CONNECTICUT
A/V Davey, pg 697

FLORIDA
Stereo Sales Inc, pg 900

GEORGIA
Stage Front Presentation Systems,
pg 899

ILLINOIS
Allen Visual Systems Inc, pg 680

KENTUCKY
Barney Miller's Inc, pg 827
NOR-COM Inc, pg 841

NEW YORK
Visual Word Systems Inc, pg 932

OHIO
Tri-State Audio Visual Co, pg 918

OREGON
All Service Musical Electronics
Repair, pg 680

PENNSYLVANIA
J E Foss Co, pg 764
Wespen Audio Visual Co, pg 935

TEXAS
Lubbock Audio Visual Inc, pg 812
Quality Audio Visual Service Inc,
pg 867

VIRGINIA
Lee Hartman & Sons Inc, pg 805

WISCONSIN
Full Compass Systems, pg 767

ALBERTA
Unique Communications Ltd,
pg 921

MANITOBA
Inland Audio Visual Ltd, pg 788

ONTARIO
Westbury National Show Systems
Ltd, pg 936

Audiocassette Loading Equipment Distributors

CALIFORNIA
Ametron Audio/Video, pg 684

DELAWARE
Actors Attic, pg 675

FLORIDA
Digital Video Systems, pg 742
Recording Media & Equipment Inc
(RM&E), pg 872

KENTUCKY
Axxis Leasing Inc, pg 700
NOR-COM Inc, pg 841

MARYLAND
Bradley Broadcast & Pro Audio,
pg 709

NEW JERSEY
Starlite, pg 900

PENNSYLVANIA
Advanced AV LLC, pg 677
J E Foss Co, pg 764
The Lerro Corp, pg 806

TENNESSEE
Lowrance Sound Co Inc, pg 812

TEXAS
Tarpley Media Systems, pg 907

PUERTO RICO
Bonnin Electronics Inc, pg 708

MANITOBA
Advance Pro, pg 677
Inland Audio Visual Ltd, pg 788

Audiocassette Loading Equipment Rentals

CONNECTICUT
Connecticut Audio & Theatrical
Supply, pg 731

FLORIDA
Lighting Sales Connection Inc,
pg 808
ONstage, pg 846

ILLINOIS
OSA International Inc, pg 848
RC Communications, pg 870

MICHIGAN
K&R All Media Productions LLC,
pg 796

NEW JERSEY
Starlite, pg 900

MANITOBA
Inland Audio Visual Ltd, pg 788

Audiocassette Loading Equipment Repairs

CALIFORNIA
Ametron Audio/Video, pg 684
McAlister Electronics, pg 820

KENTUCKY
Axxis Leasing Inc, pg 700
NOR-COM Inc, pg 841

OREGON
All Service Musical Electronics
Repair, pg 680

MANITOBA
Inland Audio Visual Ltd, pg 788

Audiocassette Recorder & Player Distributors

ALABAMA
Curtis Company, pg 736

ARIZONA
EAR Professional Audio/Video,
pg 749
Troxell-CDI, pg 918

CALIFORNIA
Ametron Audio/Video, pg 684
Audio Images Corp, pg 693
BigFoot Mobile Systems, pg 705
Cibola Systems, pg 723
Instructional Materials & Equipment
Distributors (I-Med), pg 789
JD Audio Visual Inc, pg 793
SNAP, pg 891
Southern California Sound Image
Inc, pg 895
Towards 2000 Inc, pg 916

COLORADO
Audio Consultant Services Inc,
pg 693
Daylight Productions & Rentals,
pg 739

CONNECTICUT
Connecticut Audio & Theatrical
Supply, pg 731
The Music People Inc, pg 834

DELAWARE
Actors Attic, pg 675

FLORIDA
Alliance Entertainment Corp (AEC)
LLC, pg 680
Altel Systems Group Inc, pg 682
AVI-SPL, pg 698
Broadcasters General Store Inc,
pg 711
Digital Video Systems, pg 742
Intermark Industries Inc, pg 789
Lighting Sales Connection Inc,
pg 808
Midtown Video Inc, pg 827
Recording Media & Equipment Inc
(RM&E), pg 872
Stereo Sales Inc, pg 900
Technomedia Solutions, pg 909

GEORGIA
Lighting & Production Equipment
Inc, pg 807
Stage Front Presentation Systems,
pg 899

HAWAII
The Audio Visual Co (AVCO),
pg 694

ILLINOIS
Joseph Electronics, pg 795
Woodside Avenue Music
Productions Inc, pg 941

INDIANA
Sensory Technologies LLC, pg 884
SHP Electronics, pg 887

KENTUCKY
Audio Visual Techniques Inc,
pg 695
Axxis Leasing Inc, pg 700
NOR-COM Inc, pg 841

MARYLAND
Bradley Broadcast & Pro Audio,
pg 709
Kipp Visual Systems Inc, pg 799

MASSACHUSETTS
Professional Audio Design Inc,
pg 865

MICHIGAN
Digi Sign Design LLC, pg 741
TEL Systems LLC, pg 909

MISSOURI
Modern Communications Inc,
pg 828
Schiller's Audio-Visual, pg 881

NEW HAMPSHIRE
Technet® Systems Group, pg 908

NEW JERSEY
Alltec Stores, a Vcom IMC
Company, pg 681
AlltecPro, pg 681
AV Bluebook, pg 696
Entel Systems Inc, pg 754
Nelson Enterprises Theatrical
Supply Co, pg 838
Starlite, pg 900
Total Video Products Inc, pg 916
Yorktel, pg 944

AUDIO

Audiocassette Recorder & Player Distributors (continued)

NEW YORK

B&H Photo Video, pg 701
Cadence Jazz Records, pg 713
Colortone Audio Visual, pg 728
Design Audio Visual Inc, pg 741
Gaylord Archival, pg 768
HAVE Inc, pg 777
KVL Audio Visual Services Inc, pg 802
Markertek Video Supply, pg 817
Music Sales Corp, pg 834
Neptune Photo Inc, pg 838

OHIO

Tri-State Audio Visual Co, pg 918

OREGON

SuperDigital Ltd, pg 904

PENNSYLVANIA

Advanced AV LLC, pg 677
Bernie's Photo Center, pg 704
J E Foss Co, pg 764
Grise Audio Visual Center Inc, pg 774
The Lerro Corp, pg 806

TENNESSEE

Allstar Audio Systems Inc, pg 681
Lowrance Sound Co Inc, pg 812
Mr Mark's Used Musical, Stereo & Studio Equipment Store, pg 828
Spectrum Sound Inc, pg 897
Spring Arbor Distributors Inc, pg 898
Technical Support Systems LLC, pg 908

TEXAS

AVES Audio Visual Systems Inc, pg 698
Crossroads Audio Inc, pg 735
Lubbock Audio Visual Inc, pg 812
Quality Audio Visual Service Inc, pg 867
RF Specialties of Texas LLC, pg 874
Tarpley Media Systems, pg 907

UTAH

Performance Audio LLC, pg 854

VIRGINIA

Intellidyne LLC, pg 789
Lee Hartman & Sons Inc, pg 805
The Whitlock Group, pg 937

WASHINGTON

CCI Solutions, pg 718

WISCONSIN

Full Compass Systems, pg 767

PUERTO RICO

Bonnin Electronics Inc, pg 708

ALBERTA

Unique Communications Ltd, pg 921

BRITISH COLUMBIA

Commercial Electronics Ltd, pg 728

MANITOBA

Advance Pro, pg 677
Inland Audio Visual Ltd, pg 788

ONTARIO

Westbury National Show Systems Ltd, pg 936

Audiocassette Recorder & Player Manufacturers

MISSISSIPPI

Sherwood America Inc, pg 886

NEW JERSEY

AlltecPro, pg 681
Panasonic Corporation of North America, pg 850

NEW YORK

Sentry Industries Inc, pg 884

Audiocassette Recorder & Player Rentals

ALABAMA

Audio-Video Resources Inc, pg 694

ARIZONA

Merestone, pg 823

ARKANSAS

White Diamond Productions LLC, pg 937

CALIFORNIA

Ametron Audio/Video, pg 684
Audio Rents, pg 693
AV Guys, pg 697
Dan Dugan Sound Design Inc, pg 747
Express Media Inc, pg 757
Hollywood Sound Systems, pg 781
JD Audio Visual Inc, pg 793
Lynch Communications, pg 813
Maximus Media Inc, pg 820
Munday & Collins AV, pg 834
PSAV® Presentation Services, pg 866
Towards 2000 Inc, pg 916
Voice & Video Rentals, pg 932
Warner Bros Production Sound & Video Services, pg 934

CONNECTICUT

A/V Davey, pg 697

DELAWARE

Side Door Studio Inc, pg 887

FLORIDA

Accord Productions, pg 673
AVI-SPL, pg 698
Industrial Strength Inc, pg 787
Lighting Sales Connection Inc, pg 808
ONstage, pg 846
Universal Studios Florida® Production Group, pg 922

GEORGIA

Lighting & Production Equipment Inc, pg 807
MAGNUM Companies Ltd, pg 815
Stage Front Presentation Systems, pg 899

ILLINOIS

Allen Visual Systems Inc, pg 680
AV Chicago Inc, pg 696
OSA International Inc, pg 848
RC Communications, pg 870
Woodside Avenue Music Productions Inc, pg 941

KENTUCKY

Audio Visual Techniques Inc, pg 695

MARYLAND

CPR MultiMedia Solutions, pg 732

MASSACHUSETTS

AVFX Inc, pg 698
massAV, pg 819
Preston Productions Inc, pg 861

MICHIGAN

Digi Sign Design LLC, pg 741
K&R All Media Productions LLC, pg 796
K&R's Recording Studios Inc, pg 796

MISSOURI

Show-Me Audio-Visual, pg 887

NEVADA

GES Audio Visual, pg 770

NEW JERSEY

Moe AV LLC, pg 828
Nelson Enterprises Theatrical Supply Co, pg 838
Panavid, pg 850
Starlite, pg 900

NEW YORK

Colortone Audio Visual, pg 728
Design Audio Visual Inc, pg 741
KVL Audio Visual Services Inc, pg 802

NORTH CAROLINA

AV Connections Inc, pg 697

OHIO

Hughie's Event Production Services, pg 782
R&B Communications Inc, pg 870

PENNSYLVANIA

Grise Audio Visual Center Inc, pg 774

TENNESSEE

Allstar Audio Systems Inc, pg 681
Mr Mark's Used Musical, Stereo & Studio Equipment Store, pg 828
Technical Support Systems LLC, pg 908

TEXAS

Crossroads Audio Inc, pg 735
Lubbock Audio Visual Inc, pg 812
Quality Audio Visual Service Inc, pg 867

UTAH

Performance Audio LLC, pg 854

VIRGINIA

American AV, pg 682
Lee Hartman & Sons Inc, pg 805

WISCONSIN

Full Compass Systems, pg 767

PUERTO RICO

Stage Crew Audiovisual Inc, pg 898

ALBERTA

Evolution AV, pg 757
Unique Communications Ltd, pg 921

BRITISH COLUMBIA

Commercial Electronics Ltd, pg 728

MANITOBA

Inland Audio Visual Ltd, pg 788

ONTARIO

Westbury National Show Systems Ltd, pg 936

Audiocassette Recorder & Player Repairs

ARIZONA

Troxell-CDI, pg 918

CALIFORNIA

Ametron Audio/Video, pg 684
Audio Images Corp, pg 693
Dan Dugan Sound Design Inc, pg 747
Instructional Materials & Equipment Distributors (I-Med), pg 789
JD Audio Visual Inc, pg 793
McAlister Electronics, pg 820
Towards 2000 Inc, pg 916

CONNECTICUT

A/V Davey, pg 697

FLORIDA

Stereo Sales Inc, pg 900

GEORGIA

Lighting & Production Equipment Inc, pg 807
Stage Front Presentation Systems, pg 899

ILLINOIS

Allen Visual Systems Inc, pg 680

KENTUCKY

Axxis Leasing Inc, pg 700
NOR-COM Inc, pg 841

MASSACHUSETTS
Professional Audio Design Inc, pg 865

NEW JERSEY
Nelson Enterprises Theatrical Supply Co, pg 838
Starlite, pg 900

NEW YORK
Design Audio Visual Inc, pg 741
Visual Word Systems Inc, pg 932

OHIO
Tri-State Audio Visual Co, pg 918

OREGON
All Service Musical Electronics Repair, pg 680

PENNSYLVANIA
J E Foss Co, pg 764

TENNESSEE
Technical Support Systems LLC, pg 908

TEXAS
Lubbock Audio Visual Inc, pg 812
Quality Audio Visual Service Inc, pg 867

VIRGINIA
Lee Hartman & Sons Inc, pg 805

WISCONSIN
Full Compass Systems, pg 767

ALBERTA
Unique Communications Ltd, pg 921

BRITISH COLUMBIA
Commercial Electronics Ltd, pg 728

MANITOBA
Inland Audio Visual Ltd, pg 788

ONTARIO
Westbury National Show Systems Ltd, pg 936

Audiotape—Blank Distributors

ARIZONA
Troxell-CDI, pg 918

CALIFORNIA
Ametron Audio/Video, pg 684
Assured Audio Visual, pg 691
Birns & Sawyer Inc, pg 706
California Tape Products Inc, pg 714
Christy's Editorial, pg 723
Dan Dugan Sound Design Inc, pg 747
Gluskin's Custom Audio Video, pg 771
Instructional Materials & Equipment Distributors (I-Med), pg 789
JD Audio Visual Inc, pg 793
Lynch Communications, pg 813

Media Fabricators Inc, pg 822
MSE Media Solutions, pg 832
QRS Software Services, pg 867
Sounds Unique, pg 895
SSL Industries Inc, pg 898

COLORADO
Audio Consultant Services Inc, pg 693
Daylight Productions & Rentals, pg 739
Stanco Sales LLC, pg 899

CONNECTICUT
Connecticut Audio & Theatrical Supply, pg 731
Rockwell Communications Inc, pg 876
T & M Digital Services LLC, pg 906

FLORIDA
Alliance Entertainment Corp (AEC) LLC, pg 680
Broadcasters General Store Inc, pg 711
Digital Video Systems, pg 742
Hi-Tech Import Export Corp, pg 779
Industrial Strength Inc, pg 787
Midtown Video Inc, pg 827
ONstage, pg 846
Recording Media & Equipment Inc (RM&E), pg 872
Stereo Sales Inc, pg 900
TAI Audio, pg 906

GEORGIA
Audio Visual Resources Inc, pg 695
Visioneering International Inc, pg 931

HAWAII
The Audio Visual Co (AVCO), pg 694

ILLINOIS
Allen Visual Systems Inc, pg 680
Central Audio-Visual Equipment Inc, pg 719
Creative Technology (CT), pg 733
Major Reproductions Equipment Co, pg 815
Woodside Avenue Music Productions Inc, pg 941

INDIANA
OMNI Productions, pg 845
SHP Electronics, pg 887

KENTUCKY
American Recordable Media, pg 684
Barney Miller's Inc, pg 827
NOR-COM Inc, pg 841

MARYLAND
Nicholas P Pipino Associates Inc, pg 857
RTZ Audio Visual, pg 878

MICHIGAN
City Events Group, pg 725
TEL Systems LLC, pg 909

MINNESOTA
Cinequipt Inc, pg 724

MISSISSIPPI
Bowie Audio Visual Enterprises Inc, pg 709
Jasper Ewing & Sons Inc, pg 757

MISSOURI
Communitronics Corp, pg 729
Modern Communications Inc, pg 828
Schiller's Audio-Visual, pg 881

NEBRASKA
VSA Inc, pg 933

NEW JERSEY
Argraph Corp, pg 688
Audio Visual Dynamics®, pg 694
AV Bluebook, pg 696
G&G Technologies Inc, pg 768
Maxell Corp of America, pg 820
Starlite, pg 900
Tele-Measurements Inc, pg 910
Vcom IMC, pg 925
Video Corporation of America (VCA), pg 927
Wired 4 Sound Inc, pg 940
Yorktel, pg 944

NEW YORK
AV Workshop, pg 697
Burlington A/V Recording Media, pg 712
Cadence Jazz Records, pg 713
Cine 60 Inc, pg 723
Colortone Audio Visual, pg 728
Design Audio Visual Inc, pg 741
Digital Force Ltd, pg 742
Gaylord Archival, pg 768
HAVE Inc, pg 777
Long Island Video Enterprises Live Inc, pg 811
Markertek Video Supply, pg 817
Saul Mineroff Electronics Inc (SME), pg 828
Neptune Photo Inc, pg 838
Ray Supply Inc, pg 870
RNJ Electronics, pg 875
TecNec Distributing, pg 909
Tri-Ed Distribution Inc, pg 918
Visual Technologies Corp, pg 932
WorldStage, pg 941

NORTH CAROLINA
Duke Media Services, pg 747
Strategic Connections, pg 901

OHIO
Hughie's Event Production Services, pg 782

OREGON
SuperDigital Ltd, pg 904

PENNSYLVANIA
Advanced AV LLC, pg 677
Bernie's Photo Center, pg 704
J E Foss Co, pg 764
Morefield Communications Inc, pg 830
Visual Sound Inc, pg 931

TENNESSEE
Lowrance Sound Co Inc, pg 812
Memphis Communications Corp, pg 823

Spring Arbor Distributors Inc, pg 898
Trew Audio Inc, pg 917

TEXAS
Heffernan Audio Visual, pg 778
JSAV, pg 795
Lubbock Audio Visual Inc, pg 812
RF Specialties of Texas LLC, pg 874

UTAH
Performance Audio LLC, pg 854

VIRGINIA
Lee Hartman & Sons Inc, pg 805
The Whitlock Group, pg 937

WASHINGTON
Inland Audio Visual Co, pg 788

WISCONSIN
Camera Corner Connecting Point, pg 715
Full Compass Systems, pg 767

PUERTO RICO
Bonnin Electronics Inc, pg 708

ALBERTA
Infosat Communications Inc, pg 787
Matrix Video Communications Corp (MVCC), pg 819
McBain Camera Ltd, pg 820
Unique Communications Ltd, pg 921

BRITISH COLUMBIA
Commercial Electronics Ltd, pg 728
Triad Communications Ltd, pg 918

MANITOBA
Advance Pro, pg 677
Inland Audio Visual Ltd, pg 788

ONTARIO
HD Source, pg 777
Nationwide Audio Visual Co, pg 837

QUEBEC
Panavideo Inc, pg 850

Audiotape—Blank Manufacturers

CALIFORNIA
QRS Software Services, pg 867
Sony Electronics Inc, pg 893
Sounds Unique, pg 895

COLORADO
Rocky Mountain Audio/Video Productions Inc, pg 876

KENTUCKY
American Recordable Media, pg 684

NEW JERSEY
Maxell Corp of America, pg 820

AUDIO

Audiotape—Blank Manufacturers (continued)

NEW YORK

Sentry Industries Inc, pg 884

PENNSYLVANIA

Forge Recording LLC, pg 764

WISCONSIN

Full Compass Systems, pg 767

Audiotape Duplication, *see* Duplication—Audiotapes

Background Music, *see* Music Libraries— Background

Bass Synthesizer Distributors

COLORADO

Audio Consultant Services Inc, pg 693

FLORIDA

Recording Media & Equipment Inc (RM&E), pg 872

GEORGIA

Stage Front Presentation Systems, pg 899

ILLINOIS

Woodside Avenue Music Productions Inc, pg 941

INDIANA

Sensory Technologies LLC, pg 884
Sweetwater Sound Inc, pg 905

KENTUCKY

NOR-COM Inc, pg 841

MARYLAND

Kipp Visual Systems Inc, pg 799

MASSACHUSETTS

Professional Audio Design Inc, pg 865

NEW JERSEY

HamiltonBuhl, pg 775
Starlite, pg 900

NEW YORK

Hot House Professional Audio, pg 782
MultiDyne Video & Fiber Optics Systems, pg 833

PENNSYLVANIA

Advanced AV LLC, pg 677

TENNESSEE

Lowrance Sound Co Inc, pg 812
Mr Mark's Used Musical, Stereo & Studio Equipment Store, pg 828

TEXAS

Tarpley Media Systems, pg 907

UTAH

Performance Audio LLC, pg 854

WISCONSIN

Audio Visual of Milwaukee Inc, pg 694
Full Compass Systems, pg 767

MANITOBA

Advance Pro, pg 677

Bass Synthesizer Manufacturers

UTAH

Rolls Corp, pg 877

WASHINGTON

AudioControl® Inc, pg 695

Bass Synthesizer Rentals

ARIZONA

Merestone, pg 823

ARKANSAS

White Diamond Productions LLC, pg 937

CALIFORNIA

Lynch Communications, pg 813
Synthesizer Rental Service, pg 906

DELAWARE

Actors Attic, pg 675

GEORGIA

Stage Front Presentation Systems, pg 899

ILLINOIS

OSA International Inc, pg 848
Woodside Avenue Music Productions Inc, pg 941

MASSACHUSETTS

Preston Productions Inc, pg 861

MICHIGAN

K&R All Media Productions LLC, pg 796
K&R's Recording Studios Inc, pg 796

NEVADA

GES Audio Visual, pg 770

NEW JERSEY

Starlite, pg 900

TENNESSEE

Mr Mark's Used Musical, Stereo & Studio Equipment Store, pg 828

TEXAS

Tropikal Productions, pg 918

UTAH

Performance Audio LLC, pg 854

BRITISH COLUMBIA

MicrophoneRentals.com, pg 826

Bass Synthesizer Repairs

CALIFORNIA

Diemer Amp & Keyboard Repair, pg 741
McAlister Electronics, pg 820

DELAWARE

Actors Attic, pg 675

FLORIDA

Phat Planet Recording Studios, pg 855

GEORGIA

Stage Front Presentation Systems, pg 899

INDIANA

Sweetwater Sound Inc, pg 905

KENTUCKY

NOR-COM Inc, pg 841

MAINE

Headlight Audio Visual Inc, pg 777

MASSACHUSETTS

Professional Audio Design Inc, pg 865

NEW JERSEY

Starlite, pg 900

OREGON

All Service Musical Electronics Repair, pg 680

Blank Audiocassette, *see* Audiocassette—Blank

Blank Audiotape, *see* Audiotape—Blank

Blank Compact Disc, *see* Compact Disc—Blank

Blank Digital Audiotape, *see* Digital Audiotape— Blank

Bluegrass Music, *see* Music Libraries—Bluegrass

Blues Music, *see* Music Libraries—Blues

Bridges & Cues, *see* Music Libraries—Bridges & Cues

Broadway & Hollywood Music, *see* Music Libraries—Broadway & Hollywood

Cable Distributors

ALABAMA

Curtis Company, pg 736

ARIZONA

Allusion Studios & Pure Wave Audio, pg 681
EAR Professional Audio/Video, pg 749
Projector SuperStore LLC, pg 865

CALIFORNIA

Ametron Audio/Video, pg 684
Apex Jr, pg 687
ARS Electronics, pg 690
Associated Sound, pg 691
ATV Video Center Inc, pg 692
Audio Images Corp, pg 693
AV Conferencing LLC (AVC), pg 697
California Tape Products Inc, pg 714
Carvin Amps & Audio, pg 717
Christy's Editorial, pg 723
Cibola Systems, pg 723
Cinema Equipment Sales of California Inc, pg 724
Computer Modules Inc, pg 729
Empire Pro, pg 753
Filmtools®, pg 761
GigaSonic, pg 770
Hosa Technology Inc, pg 781
Jameco Electronics, pg 792
JD Audio Visual Inc, pg 793
The LAST Factory, pg 804
Location Sound Corp, pg 810
Marshall Electronics Inc, pg 817
MediaPOINTE, pg 823
Orvac Electronics, pg 848
Pacific Radio Electronics, pg 849
Pioneer Electronics (USA) Inc, pg 857
Promax Systems, pg 865
Signal Transport, pg 887
Sound Service Co, pg 894
Southern California Sound Image Inc, pg 895
Stanislaus AV Inc, pg 899
Towards 2000 Inc, pg 916
VMI Inc, pg 932
Zack Electronics Inc, pg 945

COLORADO

Audio Consultant Services Inc, pg 693

CONNECTICUT

Connecticut Audio & Theatrical Supply, pg 731
Lex Products Corp, pg 807
Redco Audio Inc, pg 872

DELAWARE

Actors Attic, pg 675

FLORIDA

Altel Systems Group Inc, pg 682
A2D Solutions Inc, pg 692
AudioVideoElectric, pg 695
Broadcasters General Store Inc,
  pg 711
Digital Video Systems, pg 742
Harris Corp, pg 776
Herman Pro AV, pg 779
Hi-Tech Enterprises Inc, pg 779
Intermark Industries Inc, pg 789
Midtown Video Inc, pg 827
ONstage, pg 846
Recording Media & Equipment Inc
  (RM&E), pg 872
Stereo Sales Inc, pg 900
TAI Audio, pg 906
Techni-Lux Inc, pg 908
Technomedia Solutions, pg 909

GEORGIA

Accu-Tech, pg 673
Boxlight Inc, pg 709
Lighting & Production Equipment
  Inc, pg 807
Stage Front Presentation Systems,
  pg 899

HAWAII

The Audio Visual Co (AVCO),
  pg 694

ILLINOIS

Allen Visual Systems Inc, pg 680
Anixter Inc, pg 685
Arcor Electronics Co, pg 688
Clark Wire & Cable, pg 725
Cole Wire & Cable Co Inc, pg 727
Creative Technology (CT), pg 733
Joseph Electronics, pg 795
LKG Industries Inc, pg 810
Quintessence Audio Ltd, pg 868
Waldom Electronics Corp, pg 933
Woodside Avenue Music
  Productions Inc, pg 941

INDIANA

Sensory Technologies LLC, pg 884
SHP Electronics, pg 887
Sweetwater Sound Inc, pg 905

KENTUCKY

Audio Visual Techniques Inc,
  pg 695
Axxis Leasing Inc, pg 700
General Cable, pg 769
NOR-COM Inc, pg 841

LOUISIANA

Techkno Integration & Design
  Services LLC, pg 908

MAINE

Headlight Audio Visual Inc, pg 777

MARYLAND

Bradley Broadcast & Pro Audio,
  pg 709
Cardinal Sound & Video, pg 717
Event Tech, pg 756
Human Circuit, pg 782
Noventri, pg 843

MASSACHUSETTS

Professional Audio Design Inc,
  pg 865
Rule Boston Camera, pg 878
SLR Enterprises LLC, pg 890

MICHIGAN

Olson Anderson Co, pg 685
DAWNco, pg 739
Digi Sign Design LLC, pg 741
On Stage Visuals, pg 846
TEL Systems LLC, pg 909

MINNESOTA

Tierney Brothers Inc, pg 914

MISSOURI

The RapcoHorizon Co, pg 870
Schiller's Audio-Visual, pg 881

NEW HAMPSHIRE

APS Lighting-Sound-AV, pg 688
Technet® Systems Group, pg 908

NEW JERSEY

Alltec Stores, a Vcom IMC
  Company, pg 681
AlltecPro, pg 681
Argraph Corp, pg 688
AV Bluebook, pg 696
Diversified, pg 744
Earl Girls Inc, pg 749
Entel Systems Inc, pg 754
HamiltonBuhl, pg 775
Interstate Connecting Components,
  pg 790
Nelson Enterprises Theatrical
  Supply Co, pg 838
Starlite, pg 900
Total Video Products Inc, pg 916
Varto Technologies, pg 925
Yorktel, pg 944

NEW MEXICO

Quickbeam Systems Inc (QSI),
  pg 868

NEW YORK

Albany Theatre Supply Co Inc,
  pg 679
Audio-Video Corp, pg 694
Aura Sonic Ltd (ASL), pg 695
B&H Photo Video, pg 701
Barbizon Electric Co Inc, pg 701
BMI Supply, pg 708
BTX Technologies, pg 712
Colortone Audio Visual, pg 728
Creative Stage Lighting Co Inc,
  pg 733
Crescendo Designs Inc, pg 734
Design Audio Visual Inc, pg 741
Gaylord Archival, pg 768
Gotham Sound & Communications
  Inc, pg 773
HAVE Inc, pg 777
Hot House Professional Audio,
  pg 782
KVL Audio Visual Services Inc,
  pg 802
Mark Custom Recording Service
  Inc, pg 817
Markertek Video Supply, pg 817
RNJ Electronics, pg 875
Russell Industries Inc, pg 879
TecNec Distributing, pg 909
Toys From The Attic, pg 916
Visual Word Systems Inc, pg 932
Whirlwind Music Distributors Inc,
  pg 937

NORTH CAROLINA

Verbatim Americas LLC, pg 926

OHIO

ITA Audio Visual Solutions, pg 791
Parts Express, pg 851
Tri-State Audio Visual Co, pg 918
Tri-State Visual Products Inc,
  pg 918

OKLAHOMA

Ford AV, pg 763

OREGON

SuperDigital Ltd, pg 904
TARA Labs, pg 907

PENNSYLVANIA

Advanced AV LLC, pg 677
J E Foss Co, pg 764
The Lerro Corp, pg 806
RSS Distributors, pg 878
Techni-Tool, a TestEquity LLC
  company, pg 908
Wespen Audio Visual Co, pg 935

TENNESSEE

Allstar Audio Systems Inc, pg 681
Belew Enterprises, pg 703
Lowrance Sound Co Inc, pg 812
Spectrum Sound Inc, pg 897
Technical Support Systems LLC,
  pg 908
Trew Audio Inc, pg 917

TEXAS

Crossroads Audio Inc, pg 735
Data Projections Inc, pg 738
RF Specialties of Texas LLC,
  pg 874
Tarpley Media Systems, pg 907

UTAH

Performance Audio LLC, pg 854

VERMONT

Artech Electronics Ltd, pg 690
Production Advantage Inc, pg 863

VIRGINIA

Avitecture Inc, pg 699
Intellidyne LLC, pg 789
Lee Hartman & Sons Inc, pg 805
Rocktown Media, pg 876
StageSound, pg 899

WASHINGTON

CCI Solutions, pg 718
Northern Lights & Pro Audio,
  pg 842
PNTA, pg 858

WISCONSIN

Audio Visual of Milwaukee Inc,
  pg 694
DH Satellite, pg 741
Full Compass Systems, pg 767

PUERTO RICO

Audio Visual Concepts Inc, pg 694
Bonnin Electronics Inc, pg 708

ALBERTA

Infosat Communications Inc, pg 787
Matrix Video Communications Corp
  (MVCC), pg 819
Unique Communications Ltd,
  pg 921

BRITISH COLUMBIA

BeachTek Inc, pg 702
Commercial Electronics Ltd, pg 728
Noramco Wire & Cable, pg 841

MANITOBA

Advance Pro, pg 677

ONTARIO

Cinema Stage Inc, pg 724
Henry's Camera, pg 779
Westbury National Show Systems
  Ltd, pg 936

QUEBEC

JAM Industries Ltd, pg 792
SC Media Canada, pg 881

Cable Manufacturers

ARIZONA

Covid Inc, pg 732

CALIFORNIA

ALTINEX Inc, pg 682
Ametron Audio/Video, pg 684
Apogee Electronics Corp, pg 687
Carvin Amps & Audio, pg 717
Fiber Optic Cable Shop, pg 759
Gefen, pg 769
Hosa Technology Inc, pg 781
Marshall Electronics Inc, pg 817
Monster Cable Products Inc, pg 829
Pioneer Electronics (USA) Inc,
  pg 857
RF Industries, pg 874
Signal Transport, pg 887
Taperwire, pg 907
TASCAM, pg 907
Towards 2000 Inc, pg 916

COLORADO

Liberty AV Solutions, pg 807

CONNECTICUT

Lex Products Corp, pg 807
The Music People Inc, pg 834
Redco Audio Inc, pg 872

FLORIDA

Intermark Industries Inc, pg 789
Nemal Electronics International Inc,
  pg 838

ILLINOIS

Arcor Electronics Co, pg 688
Clark Wire & Cable, pg 725
Joseph Electronics, pg 795
Magnetic Shield Corp, pg 815
Tripp Lite, pg 918
Woodside Avenue Music
  Productions Inc, pg 941

INDIANA

Belden Inc, pg 703

KENTUCKY

General Cable, pg 769

MAINE

Dielectric, pg 741

AUDIO

Cable Manufacturers (continued)

MARYLAND

Event Tech, pg 756
RCI Custom Products, pg 871

MASSACHUSETTS

Mohawk, pg 829
Quabbin Wire & Cable Co Inc, pg 867

MINNESOTA

Intercon 1, pg 789

MISSISSIPPI

Peavey Electronics Corp, pg 852

MISSOURI

The RapcoHorizon Co, pg 870

NEW JERSEY

Alltec Stores, a Vcom IMC Company, pg 681
AlltecPro, pg 681
Alpha Wire Co, pg 682
Brim Electronics, pg 710
Crestron Electronics Inc, pg 734
Daburn Electronics & Cable Corp, pg 737
FSR Inc, pg 766
JSC Wire & Cable, pg 795
Kramer Electronics USA Inc, pg 801
Starlite, pg 900
Wireworks Corp, pg 940

NEW YORK

Creative Stage Lighting Co Inc, pg 733
Hannay Reels Inc, pg 775
HAVE Inc, pg 777
Hot House Professional Audio, pg 782
Key Digital Systems, pg 798
Laird Digital Cinema, pg 803
MultiDyne Video & Fiber Optics Systems, pg 833
Servoreeler Systems, pg 884
TecNec Distributing, pg 909

NORTH CAROLINA

CommScope Inc, pg 728
Verbatim Americas LLC, pg 926

OHIO

Audio-Technica US Inc, pg 694

OREGON

TARA Labs, pg 907

PENNSYLVANIA

West Penn Wire, pg 935

RHODE ISLAND

APC by Schneider Electric, pg 686

TENNESSEE

Remote Audio Products, pg 873
Trew Audio Inc, pg 917

WASHINGTON

D A Sound, pg 737

ONTARIO

Bryston Ltd, pg 712
Westbury National Show Systems Ltd, pg 936

Cable Repairs

CALIFORNIA

Ametron Audio/Video, pg 684
Diemer Amp & Keyboard Repair, pg 741

FLORIDA

Hi-Tech Enterprises Inc, pg 779

ILLINOIS

Joseph Electronics, pg 795

KENTUCKY

NOR-COM Inc, pg 841

MASSACHUSETTS

Professional Audio Design Inc, pg 865

MICHIGAN

On Stage Visuals, pg 846
TEL Systems LLC, pg 909

NEW JERSEY

Starlite, pg 900

OREGON

All Service Musical Electronics Repair, pg 680

PENNSYLVANIA

Right Coast Recording Inc, pg 875

TENNESSEE

Technical Support Systems LLC, pg 908

TEXAS

Tarpley Media Systems, pg 907

WASHINGTON

D A Sound, pg 737

Children's Music, *see* Music Libraries—Children's

Choral Music, *see* Music Libraries—Choral

Classical Music, *see* Music Libraries—Classical

Commercial Jingles, *see* Music Libraries—Commercial Jingles

Compact Disc—Blank Distributors

ARIZONA

EAR Professional Audio/Video, pg 749
Troxell-CDI, pg 918

CALIFORNIA

Ametron Audio/Video, pg 684
California Tape Products Inc, pg 714
El Mar Plastics Inc, pg 752
Filmtools®, pg 761
JD Audio Visual Inc, pg 793
MSE Media Solutions, pg 832
New Cyberian Systems Inc, pg 839
Joseph Nicoletti Consulting-Promotion, pg 841
Polyline LLC, pg 859
QRS Software Services, pg 867
Reel Picture, pg 872
Sound Service Co, pg 894
Sounds Unique, pg 895

COLORADO

Audio Consultant Services Inc, pg 693
Mike's Camera, pg 827

CONNECTICUT

Sennheiser Electronic Corp, pg 884
T & M Digital Services LLC, pg 906

FLORIDA

Alliance Entertainment Corp (AEC) LLC, pg 680
Digital Video Systems, pg 742
ONstage, pg 846
Recording Media & Equipment Inc (RM&E), pg 872
Technomedia Solutions, pg 909

ILLINOIS

Major Media Inc, pg 815
Major Reproductions Equipment Co, pg 815

INDIANA

SHP Electronics, pg 887
Sweetwater Sound Inc, pg 905

KENTUCKY

Audio Visual Techniques Inc, pg 695
NOR-COM Inc, pg 841

MAINE

Headlight Audio Visual Inc, pg 777

MARYLAND

Absolute Hollywood, pg 672

MASSACHUSETTS

Terry Hanley Audio Systems Inc, pg 775
Hunt's Photo & Video, pg 782
Professional Audio Design Inc, pg 865

MISSISSIPPI

Bowie Audio Visual Enterprises Inc, pg 709

NEW JERSEY

AlltecPro, pg 681
Starlite, pg 900
Total Media Inc, pg 916

NEW YORK

Aura Sonic Ltd (ASL), pg 695
Design Audio Visual Inc, pg 741
Light Impressions, pg 807
Mark Custom Recording Service Inc, pg 817

NORTH CAROLINA

Verbatim Americas LLC, pg 926

OHIO

Central Ohio Audio Video, pg 719
Midwest Photo Exchange, pg 827
Tri-State Audio Visual Co, pg 918

OREGON

SuperDigital Ltd, pg 904

PENNSYLVANIA

Advanced AV LLC, pg 677
Brodart Co, pg 711
J E Foss Co, pg 764
The Lerro Corp, pg 806
Wespen Audio Visual Co, pg 935

TENNESSEE

Lowrance Sound Co Inc, pg 812
NTS ProMedia, pg 843

TEXAS

CAM Audio Inc, pg 714
TWIST Integration Solutions Technology, pg 920

VIRGINIA

Furnace MFG, pg 767
Lee Hartman & Sons Inc, pg 805
National Media Services Inc, pg 836

WASHINGTON

CCI Solutions, pg 718

WISCONSIN

Audio Visual of Milwaukee Inc, pg 694

ALBERTA

Matrix Video Communications Corp (MVCC), pg 819

BRITISH COLUMBIA

Triad Communications Ltd, pg 918

MANITOBA

Advance Pro, pg 677
Inland Audio Visual Ltd, pg 788

ONTARIO

Westbury National Show Systems Ltd, pg 936

Compact Disc—Blank Manufacturers

ARIZONA

Tempe Tape & Disc, pg 911

CALIFORNIA

QRS Software Services, pg 867
SF Global Sourcing, pg 885
Sony Electronics Inc, pg 893

FLORIDA

Jordan Klein Film & Video (JKFV), pg 795
Pandisc Music Corp, pg 851

MARYLAND

Absolute Hollywood, pg 672

MISSOURI

Audio-VideoGraphics Inc, pg 694

NEW JERSEY

Disc Makers, pg 743
Panasonic Consumer Electronics Co, pg 850
Panasonic Corporation of North America, pg 850
Reed Presentations Inc (RPI), pg 872
Synergem, pg 905

NEW YORK

Digital Force Ltd, pg 742
Entertainment One US, pg 754
HAVE Inc, pg 777

NORTH CAROLINA

Verbatim Americas LLC, pg 926

OHIO

QCA, pg 867

PENNSYLVANIA

Forge Recording LLC, pg 764

TEXAS

Adams Evidence Grade Technology Inc, pg 675
Crystal Clear Media Group, pg 735

UTAH

One Stop CD Shop LLC, pg 846

WISCONSIN

Excel Duplication Services, pg 757

Compact Disc Duplication, *see* Duplication— Compact Discs

Compact Disc Recorder & Player Distributors

ALABAMA

Curtis Company, pg 736

ARIZONA

Arizona Cine Equipment, pg 688
EAR Professional Audio/Video, pg 749
Troxell-CDI, pg 918

CALIFORNIA

Advanced Systems Group LLC, pg 677
Ametron Audio/Video, pg 684

Associated Sound, pg 691
Audio Images Corp, pg 693
Be Media, pg 702
Christy's Editorial, pg 723
Cibola Systems, pg 723
Computer Modules Inc, pg 729
Gluskin's Custom Audio Video, pg 771
Instructional Materials & Equipment Distributors (I-Med), pg 789
Jaguar Distribution Corp, pg 792
JD Audio Visual Inc, pg 793
MediaPOINTE, pg 823
Pioneer Electronics (USA) Inc, pg 857
SNAP, pg 891
Sound Service Co, pg 894
Sounds Unique, pg 895
Southern California Sound Image Inc, pg 895
SSL Industries Inc, pg 898
SuperVision, pg 904
TASCAM, pg 907
Towards 2000 Inc, pg 916
VMI Inc, pg 932
VTP Inc, pg 933

COLORADO

Audio Consultant Services Inc, pg 693
Daylight Productions & Rentals, pg 739

CONNECTICUT

Connecticut Audio & Theatrical Supply, pg 731
HB Communications Inc, pg 777
MAVCO, pg 820
The Music People Inc, pg 834
Sennheiser Electronic Corp, pg 884

DELAWARE

Actors Attic, pg 675

FLORIDA

Access Media Group, pg 673
Alliance Entertainment Corp (AEC) LLC, pg 680
Altel Systems Group Inc, pg 682
Broadcasters General Store Inc, pg 711
Digital Video Systems, pg 742
Harris Corp, pg 776
Hi-Tech Import Export Corp, pg 779
Intermark Industries Inc, pg 789
Lighting Sales Connection Inc, pg 808
Midtown Video Inc, pg 827
ONstage, pg 846
Recording Media & Equipment Inc (RM&E), pg 872
Stereo Sales Inc, pg 900
TAI Audio, pg 906
Technomedia Solutions, pg 909

GEORGIA

Baker Audio Visual, pg 700
Clark, pg 725
Lighting & Production Equipment Inc, pg 807
Stage Front Presentation Systems, pg 899

HAWAII

The Audio Visual Co (AVCO), pg 694

ILLINOIS

Esoteric Sound, pg 755
Quintessence Audio Ltd, pg 868
Woodside Avenue Music Productions Inc, pg 941

INDIANA

Sensory Technologies LLC, pg 884
SHP Electronics, pg 887
Sweetwater Sound Inc, pg 905

KENTUCKY

Barney Miller's Inc, pg 827
NOR-COM Inc, pg 841

MAINE

Headlight Audio Visual Inc, pg 777

MARYLAND

Bradley Broadcast & Pro Audio, pg 709
Cardinal Sound & Video, pg 717
Human Circuit, pg 782
Kipp Visual Systems Inc, pg 799
RTZ Audio Visual, pg 878

MASSACHUSETTS

Terry Hanley Audio Systems Inc, pg 775
Hunt's Photo & Video, pg 782
Professional Audio Design Inc, pg 865
Rule Boston Camera, pg 878

MICHIGAN

Olson Anderson Co, pg 685
City Events Group, pg 725
TEL Systems LLC, pg 909

MINNESOTA

Microboards Technology LLC, pg 826
Tierney Brothers Inc, pg 914

MISSOURI

Communitronics Corp, pg 729
Conference Technologies Inc, pg 730
Modern Communications Inc, pg 828
Schiller's Audio-Visual, pg 881

NEVADA

GES Audio Visual, pg 770

NEW HAMPSHIRE

Technet® Systems Group, pg 908

NEW JERSEY

A-V Services Inc, pg 671
Alltec Stores, a Vcom IMC Company, pg 681
AlltecPro, pg 681
Audio Visual Associates, pg 694
Diversified, pg 744
Earl Girls Inc, pg 749
G&G Technologies Inc, pg 768
HamiltonBuhl, pg 775
The Music Place, pg 834
Onkyo USA Corp, pg 846
SDI Technologies Inc, pg 883
Starlite, pg 900
SYMCO Inc, pg 905
Total Video Products Inc, pg 916
Vcom IMC, pg 925

Video Corporation of America (VCA), pg 927
Wired 4 Sound Inc, pg 940
Yorktel, pg 944

NEW MEXICO

Quickbeam Systems Inc (QSI), pg 868

NEW YORK

Aura Sonic Ltd (ASL), pg 695
AV Workshop, pg 697
Burlington A/V Recording Media, pg 712
Cadence Jazz Records, pg 713
Colortone Audio Visual, pg 728
Gaylord Archival, pg 768
Hot House Professional Audio, pg 782
Indigo Productions, pg 787
KVL Audio Visual Services Inc, pg 802
Long Island Video Enterprises Live Inc, pg 811
Mark Custom Recording Service Inc, pg 817
Markertek Video Supply, pg 817
Music Hall LLC, pg 834
Music Sales Corp, pg 834
RNJ Electronics, pg 875
TecNec Distributing, pg 909
Toys From The Attic, pg 916

NORTH CAROLINA

Micro Technology Unlimited Inc, pg 826

OHIO

Copp Integrated Systems, pg 731
ITA Audio Visual Solutions, pg 791
Tri-State Audio Visual Co, pg 918

OREGON

SuperDigital Ltd, pg 904

PENNSYLVANIA

Advanced AV LLC, pg 677
Audio Visions Inc, pg 694
Brodart Co, pg 711
J E Foss Co, pg 764
Garcia Marketing Inc, pg 768
Grise Audio Visual Center Inc, pg 774
The Lerro Corp, pg 806
Morefield Communications Inc, pg 830
Vistacom Inc, pg 931
Wespen Audio Visual Co, pg 935

TENNESSEE

Advanced Sound, pg 677
Allstar Audio Systems Inc, pg 681
Lowrance Sound Co Inc, pg 812
National School Products, pg 836
Spectrum Sound Inc, pg 897
Spring Arbor Distributors Inc, pg 898
Technical Support Systems LLC, pg 908
Zion Music Group, pg 945

TEXAS

AVES Audio Visual Systems Inc, pg 698
CAM Audio Inc, pg 714
Crossroads Audio Inc, pg 735
Data Projections Inc, pg 738
FitzCo Sound Inc, pg 761

AUDIO

Compact Disc Recorder & Player Distributors (continued)

TEXAS (continued)

Heffernan Audio Visual, pg 778
Lubbock Audio Visual Inc, pg 812
Quality Audio Visual Service Inc, pg 867
RF Specialties of Texas LLC, pg 874
Southwest Sound Solutions, pg 896
Stage Directions, pg 898
Tarpley Media Systems, pg 907

UTAH

Performance Audio LLC, pg 854

VERMONT

Artech Electronics Ltd, pg 690

VIRGINIA

Lee Hartman & Sons Inc, pg 805
The Whitlock Group, pg 937

WASHINGTON

CCI Solutions, pg 718
Northern Lights & Pro Audio, pg 842
Proforma Good Wood Marketing, pg 865

WEST VIRGINIA

United Sound & Electronics, pg 921

WISCONSIN

Audio Visual of Milwaukee Inc, pg 694
Camera Corner Connecting Point, pg 715
Demco Inc, pg 740
Full Compass Systems, pg 767

PUERTO RICO

Bonnin Electronics Inc, pg 708

ALBERTA

Unique Communications Ltd, pg 921

BRITISH COLUMBIA

Commercial Electronics Ltd, pg 728
Richmond Sound Design Ltd, pg 875

MANITOBA

Advance Pro, pg 677
Inland Audio Visual Ltd, pg 788

ONTARIO

HD Source, pg 777
Nationwide Audio Visual Co, pg 837
Westbury National Show Systems Ltd, pg 936

Compact Disc Recorder & Player Manufacturers

CALIFORNIA

Califone International Inc, pg 714
Citizens Systems America Corp, pg 725
Laboratories Inc, pg 803
Pioneer Electronics (USA) Inc, pg 857
Sony Electronics Inc, pg 893
TASCAM, pg 907
TEAC America Inc, pg 908

ILLINOIS

Superscope LLC, pg 904

MISSISSIPPI

Sherwood America Inc, pg 886

NEW JERSEY

Bogen Communications Inc, pg 708
Emerson Radio Corp, pg 753
Onkyo USA Corp, pg 846
Panasonic Consumer Electronics Co, pg 850
SDI Technologies Inc, pg 883
Technics, pg 909

NEW YORK

Harbro Corp, pg 776
Music Hall LLC, pg 834

RHODE ISLAND

Numark Industries LP, pg 843

TENNESSEE

Adtec Digital Inc, pg 677

VIRGINIA

Lee Hartman & Sons Inc, pg 805

ONTARIO

Bryston Ltd, pg 712

Compact Disc Recorder & Player Rentals

ALABAMA

Audio-Video Resources Inc, pg 694

ARIZONA

Arizona Cine Equipment, pg 688
Merestone, pg 823
Metropolitan Audio-Visual Inc, pg 824
Video West Inc, pg 929

ARKANSAS

White Diamond Productions LLC, pg 937

CALIFORNIA

Acey Decy Lighting, pg 674
Advanced Media LLC, pg 677
AGF Media Services, pg 678
Alliant Event Services, pg 681
Ametron Audio/Video, pg 684
Associated Sound, pg 691
Audio Rents, pg 693
AV Guys, pg 697
Bexel, an NEP Broadcast Services Company, pg 704
Express Media Inc, pg 757

Gold Standard Productions, pg 772
Hollywood Sound Systems, pg 781
JD Audio Visual Inc, pg 793
Lynch Communications, pg 813
Maximus Media Inc, pg 820
McCune Audio-Video-Lighting, pg 821
Munday & Collins AV, pg 834
Muse Presentation Technologies, pg 834
On-Trax Inc, pg 846
PSAV® Presentation Services, pg 866
Sound Service Co, pg 894
Synthesizer Rental Service, pg 906
Towards 2000 Inc, pg 916
VMI Inc, pg 932
Voice & Video Rentals, pg 932
Warner Bros Production Sound & Video Services, pg 934

COLORADO

Daylight Productions & Rentals, pg 739
Spectrum Audio Visual Services, pg 897

CONNECTICUT

A/V Davey, pg 697

DELAWARE

Showorks Audio Visual Inc, pg 887
Side Door Studio Inc, pg 887

FLORIDA

Accord Productions, pg 673
Industrial Strength Inc, pg 787
Lighting Sales Connection Inc, pg 808
ONstage, pg 846
Paradise Show & Design Inc, pg 851
Photosound of Orlando Inc, pg 856
TAI Audio, pg 906
Universal Studios Florida® Production Group, pg 922

GEORGIA

Lighting & Production Equipment Inc, pg 807
Stage Front Presentation Systems, pg 899
Staging Directions Inc, pg 899

HAWAII

Sight & Sound Studios, pg 887

ILLINOIS

AV Chicago Inc, pg 696
Backstar Creative Media Inc, pg 700
Creative Technology (CT), pg 733
OSA International Inc, pg 848
PSAV® Presentation Services (Hotel Services Division), pg 866
RC Communications, pg 870
Resolution Productions Group, pg 874
Staging Resources Inc, pg 899
Woodside Avenue Music Productions Inc, pg 941

KENTUCKY

Audio Visual Techniques Inc, pg 695

LOUISIANA

Clark Services Audio Visual & Exhibit Inc, pg 725

MARYLAND

Advance Audiovisual Presentation Ltd, pg 677
CPR MultiMedia Solutions, pg 732
Event Tech, pg 756
Maryland Sound International Holding Co LLC, pg 819

MASSACHUSETTS

AVFX Inc, pg 698
Terry Hanley Audio Systems Inc, pg 775
massAV, pg 819
Preston Productions Inc, pg 861

MICHIGAN

City Events Group, pg 725
K&R All Media Productions LLC, pg 796
K&R's Recording Studios Inc, pg 796

MISSISSIPPI

Bowie Audio Visual Enterprises Inc, pg 709

MISSOURI

Show-Me Audio-Visual, pg 887

MONTANA

Jereco Studios Inc, pg 793

NEVADA

GES Audio Visual, pg 770
Lefco Video Services Inc, pg 806

NEW JERSEY

Audio Visual Associates, pg 694
Audio Visual Dynamics®, pg 694
Earl Girls Inc, pg 749
Panavid, pg 850
PLS Staging, pg 858
Starlite, pg 900
Wired 4 Sound Inc, pg 940

NEW MEXICO

Quickbeam Systems Inc (QSI), pg 868

NEW YORK

Aura Sonic Ltd (ASL), pg 695
AV Workshop, pg 697
Colortone Audio Visual, pg 728
CP Communications, pg 732
KVL Audio Visual Services Inc, pg 802
Long Island Video Enterprises Live Inc, pg 811
Posthorn Recordings, pg 859
Specialized Audio-Visual Inc, pg 896
WorldStage, pg 941

NORTH CAROLINA

AV Connections Inc, pg 697
AV Metro Inc, pg 697
Special Event Services, pg 896

NORTH DAKOTA

Media Productions, pg 822

OHIO

Hughie's Event Production Services, pg 782
Lyon Video Inc, pg 813
R&B Communications Inc, pg 870

OREGON

Northwest Film Center, pg 842
Rose City Sound, pg 877

PENNSYLVANIA

Advanced AV LLC, pg 677
Audio Visions Inc, pg 694
FMP Media Solutions Inc, pg 763
Grise Audio Visual Center Inc, pg 774
Visual Sound Inc, pg 931

TENNESSEE

Allstar Audio Systems Inc, pg 681
Brantley Sound Associates Inc, pg 709
Love Shack Recording Studios, pg 811
Technical Support Systems LLC, pg 908

TEXAS

Alford Media Services, pg 680
Bright Star Productions Inc, pg 710
Crossroads Audio Inc, pg 735
Lubbock Audio Visual Inc, pg 812
Music Lab Inc, pg 834
Onstage Systems, pg 846
Quality Audio Visual Service Inc, pg 867
Stage Directions, pg 898

UTAH

Performance Audio LLC, pg 854

VIRGINIA

American AV, pg 682
Audio Visual Actions Inc (AVA), pg 694
Lee Hartman & Sons Inc, pg 805
StageSound, pg 899

WASHINGTON

Northern Lights & Pro Audio, pg 842

WEST VIRGINIA

United Sound & Electronics, pg 921

WISCONSIN

Camera Corner Connecting Point, pg 715
Full Compass Systems, pg 767

WYOMING

Bridger Productions Inc, pg 710

PUERTO RICO

Stage Crew Audiovisual Inc, pg 898

ALBERTA

Evolution AV, pg 757
L R Light & Sound, pg 802
Unique Communications Ltd, pg 921

BRITISH COLUMBIA

Clark's Audio Visual Services Ltd, pg 725
Commercial Electronics Ltd, pg 728

MANITOBA

Inland Audio Visual Ltd, pg 788

ONTARIO

HD Source, pg 777
Westbury National Show Systems Ltd, pg 936

QUEBEC

Audio Visual Dynamics, pg 694

Compact Disc Recorder & Player Repairs

CALIFORNIA

Advanced Media LLC, pg 677
Ametron Audio/Video, pg 684
Audio Images Corp, pg 693
Gluskin's Custom Audio Video, pg 771
McAlister Electronics, pg 820
Sound Service Co, pg 894
SSL Industries Inc, pg 898
Towards 2000 Inc, pg 916

CONNECTICUT

A/V Davey, pg 697
Sennheiser Electronic Corp, pg 884

FLORIDA

Digital Video Systems, pg 742
Hi-Tech Enterprises Inc, pg 779
JT Communications, pg 795
Stereo Sales Inc, pg 900
TAI Audio, pg 906

GEORGIA

Lighting & Production Equipment Inc, pg 807
Stage Front Presentation Systems, pg 899

ILLINOIS

Beatty TeleVisual Productions, pg 703
Midwest Digital Corp, pg 827

INDIANA

Sweetwater Sound Inc, pg 905

KENTUCKY

Barney Miller's Inc, pg 827
NOR-COM Inc, pg 841

MASSACHUSETTS

Professional Audio Design Inc, pg 865

MICHIGAN

City Events Group, pg 725
K&R's Recording Studios Inc, pg 796
TEL Systems LLC, pg 909

MINNESOTA

Microboards Technology LLC, pg 826

NEW JERSEY

A-V Services Inc, pg 671
Audio Visual Associates, pg 694
Earl Girls Inc, pg 749
Starlite, pg 900

NEW MEXICO

Quickbeam Systems Inc (QSI), pg 868

NEW YORK

Toys From The Attic, pg 916

OHIO

Copp Integrated Systems, pg 731
ITA Audio Visual Solutions, pg 791
Tri-State Audio Visual Co, pg 918

OREGON

All Service Musical Electronics Repair, pg 680

PENNSYLVANIA

J E Foss Co, pg 764

TENNESSEE

Technical Support Systems LLC, pg 908

TEXAS

Lubbock Audio Visual Inc, pg 812
Quality Audio Visual Service Inc, pg 867
Southwest Sound Solutions, pg 896

VIRGINIA

Lee Hartman & Sons Inc, pg 805
The Whitlock Group, pg 937

WASHINGTON

Northern Lights & Pro Audio, pg 842

WEST VIRGINIA

United Sound & Electronics, pg 921

WISCONSIN

Full Compass Systems, pg 767

ALBERTA

Unique Communications Ltd, pg 921

BRITISH COLUMBIA

Commercial Electronics Ltd, pg 728

MANITOBA

Inland Audio Visual Ltd, pg 788

ONTARIO

HD Source, pg 777
Westbury National Show Systems Ltd, pg 936

Compression & Decompression Equipment Distributors

ARIZONA

Allusion Studios & Pure Wave Audio, pg 681
EAR Professional Audio/Video, pg 749
Troxell-CDI, pg 918

CALIFORNIA

Ametron Audio/Video, pg 684
Associated Sound, pg 691
Audio Images Corp, pg 693
Computer Modules Inc, pg 729
Empire Pro, pg 753
Harman Professional Solutions, pg 776
MediaMation Inc, pg 822
MediaPOINTE, pg 823
SNAP, pg 891
Sound Service Co, pg 894
Towards 2000 Inc, pg 916
VMI Inc, pg 932
VTP Inc, pg 933

COLORADO

Audio Consultant Services Inc, pg 693

CONNECTICUT

Connecticut Audio & Theatrical Supply, pg 731
HB Communications Inc, pg 777
The Music People Inc, pg 834

FLORIDA

Access Media Group, pg 673
Broadcasters General Store Inc, pg 711
CD ROM™ Inc, pg 718
Digital Video Systems, pg 742
Harris Corp, pg 776
Intermark Industries Inc, pg 789
Midtown Video Inc, pg 827
ONstage, pg 846
Recording Media & Equipment Inc (RM&E), pg 872
Stereo Sales Inc, pg 900
TAI Audio, pg 906
Technomedia Solutions, pg 909

GEORGIA

Clark, pg 725
Lighting & Production Equipment Inc, pg 807
Stage Front Presentation Systems, pg 899

HAWAII

The Audio Visual Co (AVCO), pg 694

ILLINOIS

Joseph Electronics, pg 795

INDIANA

Sensory Technologies LLC, pg 884
SHP Electronics, pg 887

KENTUCKY

NOR-COM Inc, pg 841

MAINE

Headlight Audio Visual Inc, pg 777

AUDIO

Compression & Decompression Equipment Distributors (continued)

MARYLAND

Bradley Broadcast & Pro Audio, pg 709
Cardinal Sound & Video, pg 717

NEW HAMPSHIRE

Technet® Systems Group, pg 908

NEW JERSEY

Earl Girls Inc, pg 749
Starlite, pg 900
Wired 4 Sound Inc, pg 940
Yorktel, pg 944

NEW MEXICO

Quickbeam Systems Inc (QSI), pg 868

NEW YORK

ADI Global Distribution, pg 676
Audio-Video Corp, pg 694
B&H Photo Video, pg 701
Group One Ltd, pg 774
Markertek Video Supply, pg 817
XTA Electronics Ltd, pg 943

OHIO

ITA Audio Visual Solutions, pg 791

OREGON

SuperDigital Ltd, pg 904

PENNSYLVANIA

Advanced AV LLC, pg 677
Clair Companies, pg 725

SOUTH CAROLINA

DaviSound, pg 739

TENNESSEE

Allstar Audio Systems Inc, pg 681
Lowrance Sound Co Inc, pg 812
Mr Mark's Used Musical, Stereo & Studio Equipment Store, pg 828
Technical Support Systems LLC, pg 908
Zion Music Group, pg 945

TEXAS

Crossroads Audio Inc, pg 735
Lubbock Audio Visual Inc, pg 812
RF Specialties of Texas LLC, pg 874
Southwest Sound Solutions, pg 896
Tarpley Media Systems, pg 907

UTAH

Performance Audio LLC, pg 854

VIRGINIA

Intellidyne LLC, pg 789
Rocktown Media, pg 876

WASHINGTON

CCI Solutions, pg 718
Northern Lights & Pro Audio, pg 842

WISCONSIN

Audio Visual of Milwaukee Inc, pg 694
Camera Corner Connecting Point, pg 715
Full Compass Systems, pg 767

PUERTO RICO

Bonnin Electronics Inc, pg 708

ALBERTA

Unique Communications Ltd, pg 921

MANITOBA

Advance Pro, pg 677

QUEBEC

JAM Industries Ltd, pg 792
SC Media Canada, pg 881

Compression & Decompression Equipment Manufacturers

ARIZONA

Applied Integration Corp, pg 687
Radio Design Labs (RDL), pg 869

CALIFORNIA

Harman Professional Solutions, pg 776
Linkabit, pg 809
Manley Laboratories Inc, pg 816
Millennia Media, FPC, pg 827
Physical Optics Corp (POC), pg 856
Summit Audio Inc, pg 903
Telestream Inc, pg 910

FLORIDA

CD ROM™ Inc, pg 718

MARYLAND

API, pg 687

MASSACHUSETTS

Comrex Corp, pg 730

MINNESOTA

Bosch Security Systems Inc, pg 709

NEW JERSEY

ATI Audio, pg 692
Orban, pg 847

NEW YORK

Ashly Audio Inc, pg 691
Laird Digital Cinema, pg 803
Solid State Logic Inc, pg 892

NORTH CAROLINA

Micro Technology Unlimited Inc, pg 826

SOUTH CAROLINA

DaviSound, pg 739

TENNESSEE

Adtec Digital Inc, pg 677

Compression & Decompression Equipment Rentals

ARIZONA

Merestone, pg 823
Video West Inc, pg 929

CALIFORNIA

Ametron Audio/Video, pg 684
Associated Sound, pg 691
Audio Rents, pg 693
Express Media Inc, pg 757
Lynch Communications, pg 813
McCune Audio-Video-Lighting, pg 821
On-Trax Inc, pg 846
Sound Service Co, pg 894
Synthesizer Rental Service, pg 906
Total Creative, pg 916
Towards 2000 Inc, pg 916
Westcoast Video Productions Inc, pg 936

COLORADO

Audio Consultant Services Inc, pg 693
Spectrum Audio Visual Services, pg 897

DELAWARE

Actors Attic, pg 675
Side Door Studio Inc, pg 887

FLORIDA

Access Media Group, pg 673
ONstage, pg 846
TAI Audio, pg 906
Universal Studios Florida® Production Group, pg 922

GEORGIA

Lighting & Production Equipment Inc, pg 807
Stage Front Presentation Systems, pg 899

HAWAII

Sight & Sound Studios, pg 887

ILLINOIS

OSA International Inc, pg 848
Staging Resources Inc, pg 899

KENTUCKY

Audio Visual Techniques Inc, pg 695
NOR-COM Inc, pg 841

MARYLAND

CPR MultiMedia Solutions, pg 732
Event Tech, pg 756

MASSACHUSETTS

massAV, pg 819
Preston Productions Inc, pg 861

MICHIGAN

K&R All Media Productions LLC, pg 796
K&R's Recording Studios Inc, pg 796

MISSOURI

Show-Me Audio-Visual, pg 887

NEW JERSEY

Earl Girls Inc, pg 749
Moe AV LLC, pg 828
Panavid, pg 850
PLS Staging, pg 858
Starlite, pg 900
Wired 4 Sound Inc, pg 940

NEW MEXICO

Quickbeam Systems Inc (QSI), pg 868

NEW YORK

Aura Sonic Ltd (ASL), pg 695
CP Communications, pg 732
HB-Content, pg 777
See Factor Industry Inc, pg 883

NORTH CAROLINA

Special Event Services, pg 896

OHIO

ITA Audio Visual Solutions, pg 791
Lyon Video Inc, pg 813
R&B Communications Inc, pg 870

OKLAHOMA

PDC Productions, pg 852

PENNSYLVANIA

Advanced AV LLC, pg 677

TENNESSEE

Allstar Audio Systems Inc, pg 681
Mr Mark's Used Musical, Stereo & Studio Equipment Store, pg 828
Technical Support Systems LLC, pg 908

TEXAS

Bright Star Productions Inc, pg 710
Crossroads Audio Inc, pg 735
Lubbock Audio Visual Inc, pg 812
Music Lab Inc, pg 834
Onstage Systems, pg 846

UTAH

Performance Audio LLC, pg 854

VIRGINIA

American AV, pg 682

WASHINGTON

Northern Lights & Pro Audio, pg 842

WISCONSIN

Full Compass Systems, pg 767

PUERTO RICO

Stage Crew Audiovisual Inc, pg 898

Compression & Decompression Equipment Repairs

CALIFORNIA

Ametron Audio/Video, pg 684
Audio Images Corp, pg 693
McAlister Electronics, pg 820

Sound Service Co, pg 894
Towards 2000 Inc, pg 916

CONNECTICUT

HB Communications Inc, pg 777

FLORIDA

JT Communications, pg 795
Phat Planet Recording Studios,
  pg 855
Stereo Sales Inc, pg 900
TAI Audio, pg 906

GEORGIA

Lighting & Production Equipment
  Inc, pg 807
Stage Front Presentation Systems,
  pg 899

ILLINOIS

Midwest Digital Corp, pg 827

KENTUCKY

NOR-COM Inc, pg 841

MICHIGAN

K&R's Recording Studios Inc,
  pg 796
TEL Systems LLC, pg 909

NEW JERSEY

Earl Girls Inc, pg 749
Starlite, pg 900

NEW MEXICO

Quickbeam Systems Inc (QSI),
  pg 868

OHIO

ITA Audio Visual Solutions, pg 791

OREGON

All Service Musical Electronics
  Repair, pg 680

SOUTH CAROLINA

DaviSound, pg 739

TENNESSEE

Technical Support Systems LLC,
  pg 908

TEXAS

Lubbock Audio Visual Inc, pg 812

VIRGINIA

Intellidyne LLC, pg 789

WASHINGTON

Northern Lights & Pro Audio,
  pg 842

WISCONSIN

Full Compass Systems, pg 767

QUEBEC

SC Media Canada, pg 881

Consulting

ALABAMA

Sound of Birmingham Productions,
  pg 894

ARIZONA

Aardvark Productions LLC, pg 671
Allusion Studios & Pure Wave
  Audio, pg 681
Creative Backstage, pg 733
Fire Power Music LLC, pg 761
Merestone, pg 823
Metropolitan Audio-Visual Inc,
  pg 824
SPEAK HOUSE Audio™, pg 896
Teaberry, pg 908

CALIFORNIA

AB Audio Visual Entertainment Inc,
  pg 672
ACDC Audio CD & Cassette,
  pg 674
Ahead Stereo Inc, pg 678
AlphaDogs Inc, pg 682
Ametron Audio/Video, pg 684
Artichoke Productions, pg 690
Associated Sound, pg 691
Audio Upgrades, pg 694
Audio Visual Consultants, pg 694
AV Conferencing LLC (AVC),
  pg 697
Berkeley Sound Artists Inc, pg 704
Richard W Burden Associates,
  pg 712
Chace Audio by Deluxe, pg 720
Charles M Salter Associates Inc,
  pg 721
Creative Technology, pg 733
Crystal Pyramid Productions™,
  pg 735
Custom Video Productions Inc,
  pg 736
John J Davis & Associates
  Consulting Engineers, pg 739
Design Media, pg 741
Diamond Dreams Music
  Productions, pg 741
DL Acoustics, pg 744
Dolphin MultiMedia Inc, pg 745
Earwax Productions Inc, pg 749
ECONEWS (Environmental
  Television Series) &
  (Environmental Directions Radio
  Series), pg 750
Express Media Inc, pg 757
Eye & I Productions, pg 758
Film TV Sound, pg 760
Goal Productions, pg 772
Gold Standard Productions, pg 772
Gordon Productions Inc, pg 772
Steven Halpern's Inner Peace
  Music, pg 775
Havas Edge, pg 777
Increase Video/Silver Mine Video,
  pg 786
Jaguar Distribution Corp, pg 792
JD Audio Visual Inc, pg 793
JDS Video & Media Productions
  Inc, pg 793
Kaleidosound, pg 796
K2B2 Records, pg 802
KVIE-Channel 6, pg 802
Ludlow Media, pg 812
Lynch Communications, pg 813
Main Street Media Inc, pg 815
McCune Audio-Video-Lighting,
  pg 821
McKay Conant Hoover Inc, pg 821
The Media Staff, pg 822
Media Systems Design Group,
  pg 822

MediaMation Inc, pg 822
Joseph Nicoletti Consulting-
  Promotion, pg 841
On-Trax Inc, pg 846
Oral Tradition Sound & Music,
  pg 847
OTR Studios, pg 848
piXvfm Inc, pg 857
PM Productions, pg 858
Point of View Productions, pg 858
Private Island Audio Inc, pg 862
Producers Group Ltd, pg 863
Promax Systems, pg 865
PSI Inc, pg 866
Pyramind Studios, pg 867
Pyro Spectaculars Inc, pg 867
QRS Software Services, pg 867
Redwood Audiobooks, pg 872
RetinaVision Productions, pg 874
Russ InVision Co/AbridgeClub.com,
  pg 879
Sahara Records & Filmworks
  Entertainment Co, pg 879
Saturn Studios, pg 881
Alwin Sauers Audio Productions
  (ASAP), pg 881
Steve Shapiro Music, pg 885
SonicPool, pg 892
Sound Service Co, pg 894
Still N' Motion, pg 901
Studio 132, pg 902
Sunburst Recording, pg 904
Synthesizer Rental Service, pg 906
Tam Communications, pg 906
Technical Services, pg 908
Thorburn Associates (TA), pg 913
Total Creative, pg 916
Trac Recording Studio, pg 916
Twisted Media Inc, pg 920
Z-Ville Productions, pg 944

COLORADO

D L Adams Associates Inc, pg 675
Audio Consultant Services Inc,
  pg 693
Ceavco Audio Visual Company Inc,
  pg 719
Tim Cissell Music, pg 725
Daylight Productions & Rentals,
  pg 739
Flashback Media Productions,
  pg 762
Open Media Foundation, pg 846
Rocky Mountain Audio/Video
  Productions Inc, pg 876
Starwest Productions, pg 900
Wind River Broadcast Center,
  pg 939

CONNECTICUT

Antenna International, pg 686
A/V Davey, pg 697
Boyce Nemec Designs, pg 709
BRB Audiovisual Productions,
  pg 709
Gold Line/TEF, pg 772
Guymark Studios LLC, pg 775
Ironik Design & Post, pg 791
JaffeHolden, pg 792
MAVCO, pg 820
New London Media, pg 839
Save the Children Federation Inc,
  pg 881

DELAWARE

Side Door Studio Inc, pg 887

DISTRICT OF COLUMBIA

Hillmann & Carr Inc, pg 780
Northeastern Digital Recording Inc,
  pg 842

O'Keefe Communications Inc,
  pg 844
Smithsonian National Museum of
  the American Indian, pg 891

FLORIDA

CD ROM™ Inc, pg 718
Steven Cohen Motion Picture
  Production, pg 727
Communications Concepts Inc
  (CCI), pg 729
JT Communications, pg 795
The Kitchen, pg 799
LHV Audio Services, pg 807
Lighting Sales Connection Inc,
  pg 808
ONstage, pg 846
Phat Planet Recording Studios,
  pg 855
Stage America LLC, pg 898
Stereo Sales Inc, pg 900
Sunfire Communications Inc,
  pg 904
TAI Audio, pg 906
Universal Studios Florida®
  Production Group, pg 922

GEORGIA

Guerrilla Productions LLC, pg 774
Hottrax Records, pg 782
Lighting & Production Equipment
  Inc, pg 807
Merck & Hill Consultants Inc,
  pg 823
Malcolm Neal Productions, pg 837
Omega Media Group Inc, pg 845
Stage Front Presentation Systems,
  pg 899
Visioneering International Inc,
  pg 931

HAWAII

D L Adams Associates Ltd, pg 675
Media Bridge Gamekids, pg 821

ILLINOIS

ABS Enterprises, pg 672
Accenture, pg 672
Audiobook Department, pg 695
Beatty TeleVisual Productions,
  pg 703
CCore Media Inc, pg 718
Creative Technology (CT), pg 733
Major Media Inc, pg 815
Multimedia Marketing Group,
  pg 833
On Site Video, pg 846
Jim Passin Productions, pg 852
Sound/Video Impressions Inc,
  pg 894
Sparkfactor, pg 896
20/20 Communications Inc, pg 920
Woodside Avenue Music
  Productions Inc, pg 941

INDIANA

A-V-A Video Productions, pg 671
Bright Ideas Creative Services,
  pg 710
Gaither Studios LLC, pg 767
Alan Johnson Recording, pg 794
OMNI Productions, pg 845
Sweetwater Sound Inc, pg 905

IOWA

Educational Technology & Media
  Services, pg 751
Hedquist Productions Inc, pg 778

AUDIO

Consulting (continued)

KENTUCKY

Axxis Leasing Inc, pg 700
Broadway Digital, pg 711
Hammond Communications Group Inc, pg 775
NOR-COM Inc, pg 841

LOUISIANA

Louisiana State University Division of Strategic Communications, pg 811
Moxie Media, pg 832

MAINE

Slim Goodbody Corp, pg 890

MARYLAND

CPR MultiMedia Solutions, pg 732
The Cutting Corporation, GraphicAudio® & Archival Sound Lab, pg 736
dbF a Media Company, pg 739
Kramer Communications Video Production, pg 801
Omega Recording Studios, pg 845
Pro Cuts Editing Services, pg 862
Smolian Sound Studios, pg 891

MASSACHUSETTS

Capron Lighting & Sound Co Inc, pg 716
Cavanaugh Tocci Associates Inc, pg 717
CommCreative, pg 728
Communications Design Associates, pg 729
Continental Recordings Inc, pg 731
Cramer, pg 732
Green Mountain Post Films (GMP), pg 774
Terry Hanley Audio Systems Inc, pg 775
Labrecque Creative Sound, pg 803
M Works Mastering Studio, pg 813
Monadnock Media Inc, pg 829
Northern Light Productions (NLP), pg 842
Penfield Productions Ltd, pg 853
PixMix Video Services, pg 857
Preston Productions Inc, pg 861
Professional Audio Design Inc, pg 865
Soundtrack Group, pg 895
TR Productions, pg 916
TVN-The Video Network, pg 919
Yellow Moon Press, pg 944

MICHIGAN

Audio Graphic Services, pg 693
Brilliance Audio, pg 710
Digi Sign Design LLC, pg 741
GMP Music, pg 772
K&R's Recording Studios Inc, pg 796
MessageMakers, pg 824
Michigan Recording Arts Institute & Technologies, pg 825
On Stage Visuals, pg 846

MINNESOTA

Alpha Video & Audio Inc, pg 682
Big Event Productions LLC, pg 705
Digital Audio Labs, pg 742
Media Loft Inc, pg 822

MISSOURI

Communitronics Corp, pg 729
Show-Me Audio-Visual, pg 887
Switch, pg 905
Visionworks Design Services Inc, pg 931

NEVADA

Aardvark Video & Media Productions, pg 671
Encore Event Technologies LLC, pg 754
Lefco Video Services Inc, pg 806
MeshTel, pg 824
Ron Roy Productions/Moodtapes, pg 878
Tanglewood Productions, pg 907

NEW HAMPSHIRE

Apertura, pg 686
Captain Fiddle Music & Publications, pg 716
Chip Taylor Communications LLC, pg 907

NEW JERSEY

AJS Events, pg 679
Audio Vistas LLC, pg 694
Audio Visual Dynamics®, pg 694
CFP Video Productions Inc, pg 720
Color Leasing Studios, pg 727
Diversified, pg 744
Euro-Pacific Film & Video Productions Inc, pg 756
Jeep Jazz Media Solutions, pg 793
Laurel Video Productions, pg 804
Mia Mind Music, pg 825
MiB MediaWorks, pg 825
Milgrom Productions, pg 827
Moe AV LLC, pg 828
Optisonics Productions, pg 847
Outside The Box Interactive LLC, pg 849
PatchAmp, pg 852
PeopleVisionFX, pg 854
PLS Staging, pg 858
Reed Presentations Inc (RPI), pg 872
Starlite, pg 900
Suede Interactive, pg 903
Telemanagement Resources International Inc (TRI), pg 910
Varto Technologies, pg 925
VCSvideo, pg 925
Wired 4 Sound Inc, pg 940

NEW MEXICO

Production Outfitters, pg 864
Quickbeam Systems Inc (QSI), pg 868

NEW YORK

Aura Sonic Ltd (ASL), pg 695
Aural Gratification Inc, pg 695
aurora productions, pg 696
Big Fish Production US, pg 705
The Big House Group, pg 705
Buffalo Video Production, pg 712
BZ/Rights & Permissions Inc, pg 713
Chromavision Corp, pg 723
Cohn Creative Group LLC, pg 727
CP Communications, pg 732
Custom Computer Specialists Inc, pg 736
De Nonno Productions Inc (DPI), pg 739
Foothill Digital Inc, pg 763
4-D Creative Media, pg 764
A Gentle Wind, pg 770

GHO Group LLC, pg 770
HB-Content, pg 777
Heavy Melody, pg 778
Hello World Communications, pg 778
IAI Records & Video, pg 783
Lylofilm Productions, pg 813
Manhattan Center Studios Inc, pg 816
Mark Custom Recording Service Inc, pg 817
Mother West, pg 831
The Palmer Group, pg 850
Posthorn Recordings, pg 859
David Rapkin Audio Production, pg 870
Round Hill Music LLC, pg 878
Shen Milsom & Wilke LLC, pg 885
Synaptic Digital, pg 905
VIEW Inc (Video International Entertainment World Inc), pg 930
Visual Technologies Corp, pg 932
Zelman Studios Ltd, pg 945

NORTH CAROLINA

Pat Appleson Studios Inc, pg 687
Audio Art, pg 693
AV Connections Inc, pg 697
Lawrence Behr Associates Inc, pg 703
Camcor Inc, pg 715
The Communications Group Inc, pg 729
Digital Rain LLC, pg 742
Duke Media Services, pg 747
Horizon Video Productions Inc, pg 781
Pamela Johnston Voice Talent, pg 794
On Location North Carolina, pg 846
Special Event Services, pg 896
Studio B Mastering, pg 902

NORTH DAKOTA

Media Productions, pg 822

OHIO

Advent Media Inc, pg 677
Challenge Productions/Challenge Aerial Imaging, pg 720
GatesAir, pg 768
Icom Multimedia, pg 783
Lyon Video Inc, pg 813
R&B Communications Inc, pg 870
Tri-State Audio Visual Co, pg 918
Vista Color Imaging Inc, pg 931

OKLAHOMA

Academic Media & Digital Services, pg 672
DD Audio, pg 739
PDC Productions, pg 852
Piper Media Services Inc, pg 857

OREGON

ASC-Tube Trap, pg 690
Consolidated Communications Consultants, pg 731

PENNSYLVANIA

American Artist Studio, pg 682
Berry & Homer, pg 704
Clair Companies, pg 725
Dreambox Media Inc, pg 746
Filmaker Technology, pg 760
JPL, pg 795
Metropolitan Acoustics LLC, pg 824
Right Coast Recording Inc, pg 875

The Videohouse Inc, pg 929
WQED-Multimedia, pg 942

RHODE ISLAND

Sound-FX-Design, pg 894

SOUTH CAROLINA

DaviSound, pg 739

TENNESSEE

Allstar Audio Systems Inc, pg 681
American Blackguard Inc, pg 683
Analog Man Recording Studio, pg 685
Ardent Studios Inc, pg 688
Continental Film, pg 731
Fricon Entertainment Co Inc, pg 766
Love Shack Recording Studios, pg 811
Memphis Communications Corp, pg 823
Mr Mark's Used Musical, Stereo & Studio Equipment Store, pg 828
Motion Picture Services, pg 831
Spectrum Sound Inc, pg 897
Stage Post, pg 899
Technical Support Systems LLC, pg 908
Zion Music Group, pg 945

TEXAS

Anaphora Literary Press, pg 685
AVES Audio Visual Systems Inc, pg 698
Biway Media, pg 706
Bright Star Productions Inc, pg 710
Castleview Productions, pg 717
Communication Arts Multimedia Inc, pg 728
Crossroads Audio Inc, pg 735
The Editing Co, pg 750
Emergency Film Group, pg 753
James Loupas Associates Inc, pg 811
The Music Bakery, pg 834
Julye Newlin Productions Inc, pg 840
Onstage Systems, pg 846
Out of the BLUE Media, pg 849
Phillips Media Source, pg 855
Planet Dallas Recording Studios, pg 857
The Samuels Co, pg 879
The Sound Lab Inc, pg 894
Sound Works, pg 894
Stage Directions, pg 898
Tarpley Media Systems, pg 907
Texas Heart Institute Visual Communication Services, pg 911
TopCat Records LLC, pg 915
Tropikal Productions, pg 918
The Yesterday USA Radio Networks, pg 944

UTAH

ELS Productions Inc, pg 753
ImageWorks Communications, pg 785
Performance Audio LLC, pg 854
Spectrum Engineers, pg 897

VERMONT

University of Vermont, Instructional Television Dept, pg 923

VIRGINIA

Advance Concepts Inc, pg 677
Allied Media Corp, pg 681

American AV, pg 682
AudioImage Recording, pg 695
CACI Integrated Communications, pg 713
CDR Communications Inc, pg 719
Design & Production Inc, pg 740
Mark Sonder Productions & Entertainment Agency, pg 817
Metro Productions, pg 824
National Media Services Inc, pg 836
Studio Center Corp, pg 902

WASHINGTON

Adams Creative & Production Services, pg 675
D A Sound, pg 737
Inland Audio Visual Co, pg 788
Kostov Productions, pg 801
Laser Fantasy/HECK Industries/Photon Manufacturing, pg 804
Media Elite Productions, pg 822
Northern Lights & Pro Audio, pg 842
PNTA, pg 858
Quiet Planet LLC, pg 868
Sound Sound, pg 894

WISCONSIN

Audio Visual of Milwaukee Inc, pg 694
Concept Productions Inc, pg 730
Full Compass Systems, pg 767
Learning Technology Services, pg 805
Meridian Studios, pg 824
University of Wisconsin-Oshkosh Radio-TV-Film Dept, pg 923
USAV Group Inc, pg 923
Video Wisconsin Inc, pg 929
Watts Communications Inc, pg 934
Wisconsin Public Television, pg 940

WYOMING

Bridger Productions Inc, pg 710

PUERTO RICO

Stage Crew Audiovisual Inc, pg 898

ALBERTA

Unique Communications Ltd, pg 921

BRITISH COLUMBIA

DWD Theatre Design & Consulting, pg 748
MicrophoneRentals.com, pg 826
Pinewood Sound, pg 857

MANITOBA

DACAPO Productions Inc, pg 737

ONTARIO

ADS Media, pg 677
AMPLUS Productions, pg 684
Artaflex Inc, pg 690
Cinema Stage Inc, pg 724
DebsVoice, pg 739
GAPC (General Assembly Production Centre), pg 768
JFB Communications, pg 794
MCS Recording Studios, pg 821
MVI - MultiVision Inc, pg 835
Sonic IT Communications, pg 892
State of the Art Acoustik Inc, pg 900
Video Excellence Productions, pg 927

Wanted! Sound + Picture, pg 933
Westbury National Show Systems Ltd, pg 936

QUEBEC

Group PVP, pg 774
Sceno Plus, pg 881
20k, pg 920

Continuous Recorder & Player Distributors

ARIZONA

Arizona Cine Equipment, pg 688
Coustic, pg 732
Troxell-CDI, pg 918

CALIFORNIA

Advanced Systems Group LLC, pg 677
Ametron Audio/Video, pg 684
Be Media, pg 702
Cibola Systems, pg 723
Empire Pro, pg 753
Lloyd F McKinney Associates Inc, pg 821
MediaPOINTE, pg 823
Sound Service Co, pg 894
Southern California Sound Image Inc, pg 895
SSL Industries Inc, pg 898

COLORADO

Audio Consultant Services Inc, pg 693

CONNECTICUT

MAVCO, pg 820
USI Inc, pg 924
Vista Group International Inc, pg 931

DELAWARE

Actors Attic, pg 675

FLORIDA

Digital Video Systems, pg 742
Harris Corp, pg 776
Hi-Tech Import Export Corp, pg 779
ONstage, pg 846
Recording Media & Equipment Inc (RM&E), pg 872
Stereo Sales Inc, pg 900
TAI Audio, pg 906
Technomedia Solutions, pg 909

GEORGIA

Baker Audio Visual, pg 700
Clark, pg 725
Lighting & Production Equipment Inc, pg 807
Stage Front Presentation Systems, pg 899

ILLINOIS

Quintessence Audio Ltd, pg 868

INDIANA

Sensory Technologies LLC, pg 884
SHP Electronics, pg 887
Sweetwater Sound Inc, pg 905

KENTUCKY

NOR-COM Inc, pg 841

MAINE

Headlight Audio Visual Inc, pg 777

MARYLAND

Bradley Broadcast & Pro Audio, pg 709
Human Circuit, pg 782
Kipp Visual Systems Inc, pg 799
RTZ Audio Visual, pg 878

MICHIGAN

City Events Group, pg 725

MISSOURI

Communitronics Corp, pg 729
Conference Technologies Inc, pg 730

NEW JERSEY

Alltec Stores, a Vcom IMC Company, pg 681
Audio Visual Associates, pg 694
HamiltonBuhl, pg 775
Onkyo USA Corp, pg 846
Starlite, pg 900
Video Corporation of America (VCA), pg 927
Wired 4 Sound Inc, pg 940

NEW YORK

AV Workshop, pg 697
Cadence Jazz Records, pg 713
Design Audio Visual Inc, pg 741
Indigo Productions, pg 787
KVL Audio Visual Services Inc, pg 802

OHIO

ITA Audio Visual Solutions, pg 791

PENNSYLVANIA

Advanced AV LLC, pg 677
The Lerro Corp, pg 806
Morefield Communications Inc, pg 830

TENNESSEE

Allstar Audio Systems Inc, pg 681
Lowrance Sound Co Inc, pg 812

TEXAS

AVES Audio Visual Systems Inc, pg 698
Crossroads Audio Inc, pg 735
Heffernan Audio Visual, pg 778
Lubbock Audio Visual Inc, pg 812
Tarpley Media Systems, pg 907

UTAH

Performance Audio LLC, pg 854

VIRGINIA

Intellidyne LLC, pg 789
Lee Hartman & Sons Inc, pg 805
The Whitlock Group, pg 937

WISCONSIN

Audio Visual of Milwaukee Inc, pg 694
Full Compass Systems, pg 767

PUERTO RICO

Bonnin Electronics Inc, pg 708

ALBERTA

Unique Communications Ltd, pg 921

BRITISH COLUMBIA

Commercial Electronics Ltd, pg 728

MANITOBA

Advance Pro, pg 677
Inland Audio Visual Ltd, pg 788

ONTARIO

Nationwide Audio Visual Co, pg 837
Technovision® Interactive Inc, pg 909

Continuous Recorder & Player Manufacturers

ARIZONA

Applied Integration Corp, pg 687
Coustic, pg 732

CALIFORNIA

Gilderfluke & Co Inc, pg 771
Mackenzie Laboratories Inc, pg 814
TASCAM, pg 907

CONNECTICUT

Alarmco Intelligent Message Repeaters, pg 679

GEORGIA

Register Data Systems, pg 873

MINNESOTA

Digital Audio Labs, pg 742

NEW JERSEY

Onkyo USA Corp, pg 846
Panasonic Consumer Electronics Co, pg 850

NEW YORK

RCS Enterprises, pg 871

TENNESSEE

Adtec Digital Inc, pg 677

BRITISH COLUMBIA

Creation Technologies Inc, pg 733
Richmond Sound Design Ltd, pg 875

Continuous Recorder & Player Rentals

ARIZONA

Arizona Cine Equipment, pg 688
Merestone, pg 823
Metropolitan Audio-Visual Inc, pg 824

CALIFORNIA

Alliant Event Services, pg 681
Ametron Audio/Video, pg 684
Artichoke Productions, pg 690
Express Media Inc, pg 757
Lynch Communications, pg 813
McCune Audio-Video-Lighting, pg 821

AUDIO

Continuous Recorder & Player Rentals (continued)

CALIFORNIA (continued)
Munday & Collins AV, pg 834
PSAV® Presentation Services, pg 866

COLORADO
Daylight Productions & Rentals, pg 739

DELAWARE
Showorks Audio Visual Inc, pg 887

FLORIDA
ONstage, pg 846
TAI Audio, pg 906

GEORGIA
Lighting & Production Equipment Inc, pg 807
Stage Front Presentation Systems, pg 899
Staging Directions Inc, pg 899

ILLINOIS
Backstar Creative Media Inc, pg 700
Beatty TeleVisual Productions, pg 703
OSA International Inc, pg 848
RC Communications, pg 870

MARYLAND
CPR MultiMedia Solutions, pg 732
Event Tech, pg 756

MASSACHUSETTS
AVFX Inc, pg 698
massAV, pg 819
Preston Productions Inc, pg 861

MICHIGAN
City Events Group, pg 725
K&R All Media Productions LLC, pg 796
K&R's Recording Studios Inc, pg 796

MISSOURI
Show-Me Audio-Visual, pg 887

NEVADA
GES Audio Visual, pg 770

NEW JERSEY
Audio Visual Associates, pg 694
Panavid, pg 850
Starlite, pg 900

NEW YORK
AV Workshop, pg 697
Design Audio Visual Inc, pg 741
KVL Audio Visual Services Inc, pg 802
WorldStage, pg 941

NORTH DAKOTA
Media Productions, pg 822

PENNSYLVANIA
Advanced AV LLC, pg 677

TENNESSEE
Allstar Audio Systems Inc, pg 681
Love Shack Recording Studios, pg 811

TEXAS
Crossroads Audio Inc, pg 735
Lubbock Audio Visual Inc, pg 812

UTAH
Performance Audio LLC, pg 854

VIRGINIA
American AV, pg 682

WYOMING
Bridger Productions Inc, pg 710

ALBERTA
Unique Communications Ltd, pg 921

BRITISH COLUMBIA
Commercial Electronics Ltd, pg 728
Triad Communications Ltd, pg 918

MANITOBA
Inland Audio Visual Ltd, pg 788

Continuous Recorder & Player Repairs

CALIFORNIA
Ametron Audio/Video, pg 684
Audio Images Corp, pg 693
McAlister Electronics, pg 820
SSL Industries Inc, pg 898

FLORIDA
Digital Video Systems, pg 742
Hi-Tech Enterprises Inc, pg 779
Phat Planet Recording Studios, pg 855
Stereo Sales Inc, pg 900
TAI Audio, pg 906

GEORGIA
Lighting & Production Equipment Inc, pg 807
Stage Front Presentation Systems, pg 899

ILLINOIS
Beatty TeleVisual Productions, pg 703
Midwest Digital Corp, pg 827

INDIANA
Sweetwater Sound Inc, pg 905

KENTUCKY
NOR-COM Inc, pg 841

MICHIGAN
City Events Group, pg 725
K&R's Recording Studios Inc, pg 796
TEL Systems LLC, pg 909

NEW JERSEY
Audio Visual Associates, pg 694
Starlite, pg 900

OREGON
All Service Musical Electronics Repair, pg 680

TEXAS
Lubbock Audio Visual Inc, pg 812

VIRGINIA
The Whitlock Group, pg 937

WISCONSIN
Full Compass Systems, pg 767

BRITISH COLUMBIA
Commercial Electronics Ltd, pg 728

MANITOBA
Inland Audio Visual Ltd, pg 788

ONTARIO
Technovision® Interactive Inc, pg 909

Control System & Equipment Distributors

ARIZONA
EAR Professional Audio/Video, pg 749
Troxell-CDI, pg 918

ARKANSAS
Jay S Stanley & Associates Inc, pg 899

CALIFORNIA
Ametron Audio/Video, pg 684
Associated Sound, pg 691
Be Media, pg 702
Cibola Systems, pg 723
Empire Pro, pg 753
GigaSonic, pg 770
Hi-Tech Audio Systems Inc, pg 779
Instructional Materials & Equipment Distributors (I-Med), pg 789
JD Audio Visual Inc, pg 793
Kontron America, pg 801
Media Fabricators Inc, pg 822
Media Vision USA, pg 822
MediaMation Inc, pg 822
MediaPOINTE, pg 823
Pristine Systems Inc, pg 862
Sanako Inc, pg 880
Sound Service Co, pg 894
Southern California Sound Image Inc, pg 895
Stanislaus AV Inc, pg 899
Towards 2000 Inc, pg 916
Videobotics, pg 929
VMI Inc, pg 932
VTP Inc, pg 933

COLORADO
Audio Consultant Services Inc, pg 693
Daylight Productions & Rentals, pg 739

CONNECTICUT
HB Communications Inc, pg 777
The Music People Inc, pg 834
Vista Group International Inc, pg 931

DELAWARE
Actors Attic, pg 675

FLORIDA
Access Media Group, pg 673
Alcorn McBride Inc, pg 679
Altel Systems Group Inc, pg 682
Digital Video Systems, pg 742
Harris Corp, pg 776
Hi-Tech Enterprises Inc, pg 779
Midtown Video Inc, pg 827
ONstage, pg 846
Recording Media & Equipment Inc (RM&E), pg 872
Stereo Sales Inc, pg 900
Technomedia Solutions, pg 909

GEORGIA
Lighting & Production Equipment Inc, pg 807
Stage Front Presentation Systems, pg 899

HAWAII
The Audio Visual Co (AVCO), pg 694

ILLINOIS
Quintessence Audio Ltd, pg 868
Woodside Avenue Music Productions Inc, pg 941

INDIANA
Sensory Technologies LLC, pg 884
SHP Electronics, pg 887
Sweetwater Sound Inc, pg 905

KENTUCKY
Axxis Leasing Inc, pg 700
NOR-COM Inc, pg 841

MAINE
Headlight Audio Visual Inc, pg 777

MARYLAND
Bradley Broadcast & Pro Audio, pg 709
Human Circuit, pg 782
Kipp Visual Systems Inc, pg 799

MASSACHUSETTS
Burk Technology Inc, pg 712

MICHIGAN
TEL Systems LLC, pg 909

MINNESOTA
Tierney Brothers Inc, pg 914

NEW HAMPSHIRE
Technet® Systems Group, pg 908

NEW JERSEY
Alltec Stores, a Vcom IMC Company, pg 681
AlltecPro, pg 681
Audio Visual Associates, pg 694
AV Bluebook, pg 696

Earl Girls Inc, pg 749
Starlite, pg 900
Total Video Products Inc, pg 916
Wired 4 Sound Inc, pg 940
Yorktel, pg 944

NEW YORK

BMI Supply, pg 708
Colortone Audio Visual, pg 728
Group One Ltd, pg 774
Presentation Products Inc, pg 861
Visual Word Systems Inc, pg 932

OHIO

ITA Audio Visual Solutions, pg 791
Tri-State Audio Visual Co, pg 918

OKLAHOMA

Ford AV, pg 763

PENNSYLVANIA

Advanced AV LLC, pg 677
The Lerro Corp, pg 806
Vistacom Inc, pg 931

RHODE ISLAND

Shanix Inc, pg 885

TENNESSEE

Advanced Sound, pg 677
Lowrance Sound Co Inc, pg 812
Technical Support Systems LLC,
    pg 908

TEXAS

Crossroads Audio Inc, pg 735
Data Projections Inc, pg 738
Lubbock Audio Visual Inc, pg 812
MusicMaster Inc, pg 835
Southwest Sound Solutions, pg 896
Tarpley Media Systems, pg 907

UTAH

Performance Audio LLC, pg 854

VIRGINIA

Avitecture Inc, pg 699
Intellidyne LLC, pg 789
The Whitlock Group, pg 937

WASHINGTON

D A Sound, pg 737
Northern Lights & Pro Audio,
    pg 842
Telect Inc, pg 910

WISCONSIN

Audio Visual of Milwaukee Inc,
    pg 694
Full Compass Systems, pg 767
Safe Harbor Computers, pg 879

PUERTO RICO

Bonnin Electronics Inc, pg 708

ALBERTA

Infosat Communications Inc, pg 787
Matrix Video Communications Corp
    (MVCC), pg 819
Unique Communications Ltd,
    pg 921

BRITISH COLUMBIA

Commercial Electronics Ltd, pg 728

MANITOBA

Advance Pro, pg 677
Inland Audio Visual Ltd, pg 788

ONTARIO

Cinema Stage Inc, pg 724
Soundmaster Group, pg 894
Westbury National Show Systems
    Ltd, pg 936

QUEBEC

SC Media Canada, pg 881

Control System & Equipment Manufacturers

CALIFORNIA

ALTINEX Inc, pg 682
Gefen, pg 769
Kontron America, pg 801
Mackenzie Laboratories Inc, pg 814
Media Control Systems LLC,
    pg 821
QSC Audio Products LLC, pg 867
Renkus-Heinz Inc, pg 873
Simon - Kaloi Engineering Ltd,
    pg 888
TV Pro Gear, pg 919
Videobotics, pg 929
Xantech LLC, pg 943
Yanchar Design & Consulting
    Group, pg 943

COLORADO

Arrakis Systems, pg 689

FLORIDA

Alcorn McBride Inc, pg 679
Compuvideo Sales USA Ltd,
    pg 729
CTGaudio, pg 735
Z-Systems Audio Engineering,
    pg 944

GEORGIA

Register Data Systems, pg 873

IDAHO

Marketron Broadcast Solutions,
    pg 817

MASSACHUSETTS

Burk Technology Inc, pg 712

MISSISSIPPI

Crest Audio Inc, pg 734

NEW HAMPSHIRE

Russound, pg 879

NEW JERSEY

AlltecPro, pg 681
Crestron Electronics Inc, pg 734
FSR Inc, pg 766
Starlite, pg 900

NEW YORK

acouStaCorp, pg 674
Harry Joseph & Associates Inc,
    pg 795
Monroe Electronics Inc, pg 829
Protech Audio Corp, pg 866

OREGON

BIAMP Systems, pg 705

RHODE ISLAND

Numark Industries LP, pg 843

TENNESSEE

Adtec Digital Inc, pg 677
Remote Audio Products, pg 873

TEXAS

MusicMaster Inc, pg 835

UTAH

Vantage Controls, a Legrand AV Inc
    brand, pg 924

VIRGINIA

Avitecture Inc, pg 699

WASHINGTON

AudioControl® Inc, pg 695
Conex Electro Systems Inc, pg 730
Telect Inc, pg 910

BRITISH COLUMBIA

Commercial Electronics Ltd, pg 728
Richmond Sound Design Ltd,
    pg 875

ONTARIO

Soundmaster Group, pg 894

Control System & Equipment Rentals

ARIZONA

Merestone, pg 823
Video West Inc, pg 929

CALIFORNIA

Ametron Audio/Video, pg 684
Associated Sound, pg 691
Express Media Inc, pg 757
Hi-Tech Audio Systems Inc, pg 779
JD Audio Visual Inc, pg 793
Lynch Communications, pg 813
McCune Audio-Video-Lighting,
    pg 821
Media Fabricators Inc, pg 822
Muse Presentation Technologies,
    pg 834
Sound Service Co, pg 894
Towards 2000 Inc, pg 916

DELAWARE

Actors Attic, pg 675

FLORIDA

ONstage, pg 846

GEORGIA

Lighting & Production Equipment
    Inc, pg 807
Stage Front Presentation Systems,
    pg 899

ILLINOIS

OSA International Inc, pg 848
RC Communications, pg 870

Resolution Productions Group,
    pg 874
Woodside Avenue Music
    Productions Inc, pg 941

KENTUCKY

Audio Visual Techniques Inc,
    pg 695
NOR-COM Inc, pg 841

MARYLAND

CPR MultiMedia Solutions, pg 732

MASSACHUSETTS

AVFX Inc, pg 698
massAV, pg 819
Preston Productions Inc, pg 861

MICHIGAN

K&R All Media Productions LLC,
    pg 796

MISSOURI

Show-Me Audio-Visual, pg 887

NEVADA

GES Audio Visual, pg 770

NEW JERSEY

Earl Girls Inc, pg 749
PLS Staging, pg 858
Starlite, pg 900

NEW YORK

See Factor Industry Inc, pg 883

NORTH CAROLINA

AV Metro Inc, pg 697

OHIO

ITA Audio Visual Solutions, pg 791
Lyon Video Inc, pg 813

TENNESSEE

Technical Support Systems LLC,
    pg 908

TEXAS

Crossroads Audio Inc, pg 735
Lubbock Audio Visual Inc, pg 812

UTAH

Performance Audio LLC, pg 854

VIRGINIA

American AV, pg 682

WASHINGTON

D A Sound, pg 737
Northern Lights & Pro Audio,
    pg 842

WISCONSIN

Full Compass Systems, pg 767

ALBERTA

Unique Communications Ltd,
    pg 921

BRITISH COLUMBIA

Commercial Electronics Ltd, pg 728

AUDIO

Control System & Equipment Rentals (continued)

MANITOBA

Inland Audio Visual Ltd, pg 788

ONTARIO

Westbury National Show Systems Ltd, pg 936

Control System & Equipment Repairs

CALIFORNIA

Ametron Audio/Video, pg 684
Audio Images Corp, pg 693
Diemer Amp & Keyboard Repair, pg 741
McAlister Electronics, pg 820
Sound Service Co, pg 894
Towards 2000 Inc, pg 916

CONNECTICUT

HB Communications Inc, pg 777

FLORIDA

Hi-Tech Enterprises Inc, pg 779
Midtown Video Inc, pg 827
Phat Planet Recording Studios, pg 855
Stereo Sales Inc, pg 900

GEORGIA

Lighting & Production Equipment Inc, pg 807
Stage Front Presentation Systems, pg 899

ILLINOIS

Midwest Digital Corp, pg 827

INDIANA

Sweetwater Sound Inc, pg 905

KENTUCKY

Axxis Leasing Inc, pg 700
NOR-COM Inc, pg 841

MICHIGAN

TEL Systems LLC, pg 909

NEVADA

MUSIC Group Services Nevada, pg 834

NEW JERSEY

Audio Visual Associates, pg 694
Earl Girls Inc, pg 749
Starlite, pg 900

OHIO

ITA Audio Visual Solutions, pg 791
Tri-State Audio Visual Co, pg 918

TENNESSEE

Technical Support Systems LLC, pg 908

TEXAS

Lubbock Audio Visual Inc, pg 812
Southwest Sound Solutions, pg 896

VIRGINIA

Avitecture Inc, pg 699
Intellidyne LLC, pg 789
The Whitlock Group, pg 937

WASHINGTON

Northern Lights & Pro Audio, pg 842

WISCONSIN

Full Compass Systems, pg 767

ALBERTA

Infosat Communications Inc, pg 787
Unique Communications Ltd, pg 921

BRITISH COLUMBIA

Commercial Electronics Ltd, pg 728

MANITOBA

Inland Audio Visual Ltd, pg 788

ONTARIO

Westbury National Show Systems Ltd, pg 936

QUEBEC

SC Media Canada, pg 881

Co-Production Services

ARIZONA

Allusion Studios & Pure Wave Audio, pg 681
Merestone, pg 823
Teaberry, pg 908

CALIFORNIA

AB Audio Visual Entertainment Inc, pg 672
ACDC Audio CD & Cassette, pg 674
Aliso Creek Productions Inc, pg 680
Artichoke Productions, pg 690
Automated Entertainment, pg 696
Creative Media Recording, pg 733
Crystal Pyramid Productions™, pg 735
Deja View Video, pg 740
Design Media, pg 741
Diamond Dreams Music Productions, pg 741
Earwax Productions Inc, pg 749
ECONEWS (Environmental Television Series) & (Environmental Directions Radio Series), pg 750
Eye & I Productions, pg 758
Full Moon & High Tide Productions & Studios, pg 767
Steven Halpern's Inner Peace Music, pg 775
Havas Edge, pg 777
IFM World Releasing Inc, pg 784
Jaguar Distribution Corp, pg 792
JDS Video & Media Productions Inc, pg 793
KVIE-Channel 6, pg 802
Lynch Communications, pg 813
Main Street Media Inc, pg 815
Maximus Media Inc, pg 820

McCune Audio-Video-Lighting, pg 821
MediaMation Inc, pg 822
Joseph Nicoletti Consulting-Promotion, pg 841
Oral Tradition Sound & Music, pg 847
OTR Studios, pg 848
piXvfm Inc, pg 857
PM Productions, pg 858
Point of View Productions, pg 858
PSI Inc, pg 866
Pyramind Studios, pg 867
QRS Software Services, pg 867
Redwood Audiobooks, pg 872
Regent Press Publishers & Printers, pg 873
Russ InVision Co/AbridgeClub.com, pg 879
Sahara Records & Filmworks Entertainment Co, pg 879
Saturn Studios, pg 881
Steve Shapiro Music, pg 885
Sonora Recorders, pg 893
Still N' Motion, pg 901
Studio Circle Recordings, pg 902
Studio 132, pg 902
Sunburst Recording, pg 904
Tam Communications Inc, pg 906
Timeless Productions, pg 914
Total Creative, pg 916
Z-Ville Productions, pg 944

COLORADO

Apogee Communications Group, pg 687
Audio Consultant Services Inc, pg 693
Centre Communications Inc, pg 720
Tim Cissell Music, pg 725
Daylight Productions & Rentals, pg 739
Flashback Media Productions, pg 762
Open Media Foundation, pg 846
Rocky Mountain Audio/Video Productions Inc, pg 876
Shambhala Publications, pg 885

CONNECTICUT

Antenna International, pg 686
Guymark Studios LLC, pg 775
Ironik Design & Post, pg 791
MAVCO, pg 820
Save the Children Federation Inc, pg 881

DELAWARE

Side Door Studio Inc, pg 887

DISTRICT OF COLUMBIA

Hillmann & Carr Inc, pg 780

FLORIDA

Steven Cohen Motion Picture Production, pg 727
Communications Concepts Inc (CCI), pg 729
JT Communications, pg 795
The Kitchen, pg 799
LHV Audio Services, pg 807
Phat Planet Recording Studios, pg 855
Stage America LLC, pg 898
Sunfire Communications Inc, pg 904
Times-Square Fantasy Theatre, pg 914
Universal Studios Florida® Production Group, pg 922

GEORGIA

Hottrax Records, pg 782
MAGNUM Companies Ltd, pg 815
Stage Front Presentation Systems, pg 899
White Dog Studios, pg 937

HAWAII

Media Bridge Gamekids, pg 821

IDAHO

KTVB-TV, pg 802

ILLINOIS

ABS Enterprises, pg 672
CCore Media Inc, pg 718
Cresta Creative, pg 734
Jim Passin Productions, pg 852
Pepper Group, pg 854
Steven Samler Music & Sound, pg 879
SCI Television & Creative Media LLC, pg 882
Solid Sound Recording Studio, pg 892
Sound/Video Impressions Inc, pg 894
20/20 Communications Inc, pg 920
Woodside Avenue Music Productions Inc, pg 941

INDIANA

A-V-A Video Productions, pg 671
Bright Ideas Creative Services, pg 710
Alan Johnson Recording, pg 794
OMNI Productions, pg 845
Sweetwater Sound Inc, pg 905

IOWA

Educational Technology & Media Services, pg 751

KENTUCKY

Broadway Digital, pg 711
Hammond Communications Group Inc, pg 775

LOUISIANA

Louisiana State University Division of Strategic Communications, pg 811

MARYLAND

CPR MultiMedia Solutions, pg 732
The Cutting Corporation, GraphicAudio® & Archival Sound Lab, pg 736
dbF a Media Company, pg 739
Kramer Communications Video Production, pg 801
Milner-Fenwick Inc, pg 828
Omega Recording Studios, pg 845

MASSACHUSETTS

Capron Lighting & Sound Co Inc, pg 716
Green Mountain Post Films (GMP), pg 774
Labrecque Creative Sound, pg 803
M Works Mastering Studio, pg 813
Monadnock Media Inc, pg 829
PixMix Video Services, pg 857
Professional Audio Design Inc, pg 865
Soundtrack Group, pg 895

MICHIGAN

Audio Graphic Services, pg 693
Brilliance Audio, pg 710
Digi Sign Design LLC, pg 741
GMP Music, pg 772
K&R's Recording Studios Inc,
  pg 796
MessageMakers, pg 824
Michigan Recording Arts Institute
  & Technologies, pg 825
On Stage Visuals, pg 846

MINNESOTA

Winterland Studios, pg 940

MISSOURI

Communitronics Corp, pg 729
Hardcastle Films & Video, pg 776
Visionworks Design Services Inc,
  pg 931

NEVADA

Encore Event Technologies LLC,
  pg 754
Lefco Video Services Inc, pg 806
Ron Roy Productions/Moodtapes,
  pg 878

NEW HAMPSHIRE

Apertura, pg 686
Captain Fiddle Music &
  Publications, pg 716
Chip Taylor Communications LLC,
  pg 907

NEW JERSEY

Allegro Productions Inc, pg 680
CFP Video Productions Inc, pg 720
Color Leasing Studios, pg 727
Euro-Pacific Film & Video
  Productions Inc, pg 756
Hogpenny Studios, pg 780
Jeep Jazz Media Solutions, pg 793
Laurel Video Productions, pg 804
Milgrom Productions, pg 827
Optisonics Productions, pg 847
Outside The Box Interactive LLC,
  pg 849
Starlite, pg 900
Suede Interactive, pg 903
VCSvideo, pg 925

NEW MEXICO

Production Outfitters, pg 864
Quickbeam Systems Inc (QSI),
  pg 868

NEW YORK

A&E Home Video, pg 671
Aura Sonic Ltd (ASL), pg 695
Aural Gratification Inc, pg 695
aurora productions, pg 696
The Big House Group, pg 705
Buffalo Video Production, pg 712
De Nonno Productions Inc (DPI),
  pg 739
4-D Creative Media, pg 764
A Gentle Wind, pg 770
HB-Content, pg 777
Heavy Melody, pg 778
Hello World Communications,
  pg 778
IAI Records & Video, pg 783
Icontent, pg 783
Lylofilm Productions, pg 813
Manhattan Center Studios Inc,
  pg 816
Mother West, pg 831

SISU Home Entertainment Inc,
  pg 889
Synaptic Digital, pg 905
Tiki Recording Studios Inc, pg 914
Visual Technologies Corp, pg 932
Zelman Studios Ltd, pg 945

NORTH CAROLINA

Pat Appleson Studios Inc, pg 687
The Communications Group Inc,
  pg 729
Digital Rain LLC, pg 742
Duke Media Services, pg 747
Horizon Video Productions Inc,
  pg 781
Image Associates Inc, pg 784
On Location North Carolina, pg 846
Special Event Services, pg 896

NORTH DAKOTA

Media Productions, pg 822

OHIO

Challenge Productions/Challenge
  Aerial Imaging, pg 720
Cuyahoga Community College
  Student Production Office (SPO),
  pg 736
Icom Multimedia, pg 783
Mills James Productions, pg 828
Musicol Recording, pg 835
R&B Communications Inc, pg 870
Vista Color Imaging Inc, pg 931

OKLAHOMA

Academic Media & Digital
  Services, pg 672
PDC Productions, pg 852

OREGON

KVAL, pg 802
REX, pg 874

PENNSYLVANIA

American Artist Studio, pg 682
Ivory Productions, pg 792
JPL, pg 795
Production Masters Inc (PMI),
  pg 864
The Videohouse Inc, pg 929
WQED-Multimedia, pg 942

RHODE ISLAND

Sound-FX-Design, pg 894

SOUTH CAROLINA

DaviSound, pg 739
Venture Media, pg 925

TENNESSEE

Allstar Audio Systems Inc, pg 681
American Blackguard Inc, pg 683
Analog Man Recording Studio,
  pg 685
Ardent Studios Inc, pg 688
Fricon Entertainment Co Inc,
  pg 766
Love Shack Recording Studios,
  pg 811
Memphis Communications Corp,
  pg 823
Mr Mark's Used Musical, Stereo &
  Studio Equipment Store, pg 828
Motion Picture Services, pg 831
Stage Post, pg 899
Zion Music Group, pg 945

TEXAS

AMA Nystrom Printing/Finishing,
  pg 682
Anaphora Literary Press, pg 685
Audiomoxie®, pg 695
Biway Media, pg 706
Bright Star Productions Inc, pg 710
Castleview Productions, pg 717
Crossroads Audio Inc, pg 735
Dykeman Associates Inc, pg 748
The Editing Co, pg 750
Emergency Film Group, pg 753
The Music Bakery, pg 834
Julye Newlin Productions Inc,
  pg 840
Out of the BLUE Media, pg 849
Romar Learning Solutions LLC,
  pg 877
The Samuels Co, pg 879
The Sound Lab Inc, pg 894
Sound Works, pg 894
Stage Directions, pg 898
Texas Heart Institute Visual
  Communication Services, pg 911
TopCat Records LLC, pg 915
Tropikal Productions, pg 918
The Yesterday USA Radio
  Networks, pg 944

UTAH

Performance Audio LLC, pg 854

VERMONT

University of Vermont, Instructional
  Television Dept, pg 923

VIRGINIA

Advance Concepts Inc, pg 677
AudioImage Recording, pg 695
CACI Integrated Communications,
  pg 713
CDR Communications Inc, pg 719
Metro Productions, pg 824
National Media Services Inc,
  pg 836

WASHINGTON

Adams Creative & Production
  Services, pg 675
Inland Audio Visual Co, pg 788
North-by-Northwest - A Digital
  Studio, pg 842
Sound Sound, pg 894

WEST VIRGINIA

Sweetsong Productions, pg 905

WISCONSIN

Audio Visual of Milwaukee Inc,
  pg 694
Concept Productions Inc, pg 730
5th Floor Recording Co, pg 760
Learning Technology Services,
  pg 805
Meridian Studios, pg 824
University of Wisconsin-Oshkosh
  Radio-TV-Film Dept, pg 923
USAV Group Inc, pg 923
Video Wisconsin Inc, pg 929
Watts Communications Inc, pg 934
Wisconsin Public Television, pg 940

WYOMING

Bridger Productions Inc, pg 710

MANITOBA

DACAPO Productions Inc, pg 737

ONTARIO

ADS Media, pg 677
AMPLUS Productions, pg 684
DebsVoice, pg 739
GAPC (General Assembly
  Production Centre), pg 768
JFB Communications, pg 794
MCS Recording Studios, pg 821
Trebas Institute, pg 917
Westbury National Show Systems
  Ltd, pg 936

QUEBEC

Trebas Institute, pg 917

Country Music, *see* Music Libraries—Country

Digital Audiotape—Blank Distributors

ARIZONA

Troxell-CDI, pg 918

CALIFORNIA

Ametron Audio/Video, pg 684
Assured Audio Visual, pg 691
Audio Images Corp, pg 693
California Tape Products Inc,
  pg 714
Dan Dugan Sound Design Inc,
  pg 747
JD Audio Visual Inc, pg 793
Lynch Communications, pg 813
MSE Media Solutions, pg 832
On-Trax Inc, pg 846
Polyline LLC, pg 859
QRS Software Services, pg 867
Sound Service Co, pg 894

COLORADO

Audio Consultant Services Inc,
  pg 693

CONNECTICUT

Sennheiser Electronic Corp, pg 884

FLORIDA

Broadcasters General Store Inc,
  pg 711
Digital Video Systems, pg 742
Harris Corp, pg 776
ONstage, pg 846
Recording Media & Equipment Inc
  (RM&E), pg 872
Stereo Sales Inc, pg 900
TAI Audio, pg 906

GEORGIA

Lighting & Production Equipment
  Inc, pg 807
Stage Front Presentation Systems,
  pg 899

HAWAII

The Audio Visual Co (AVCO),
  pg 694

ILLINOIS

Major Media Inc, pg 815
Major Reproductions Equipment
  Co, pg 815
Woodside Avenue Music
  Productions Inc, pg 941

AUDIO

Digital Audiotape—Blank Distributors (continued)

INDIANA

SHP Electronics, pg 887

KENTUCKY

American Recordable Media, pg 684
Barney Miller's Inc, pg 827
NOR-COM Inc, pg 841

MARYLAND

Bradley Broadcast & Pro Audio, pg 709
Human Circuit, pg 782
Kipp Visual Systems Inc, pg 799
RTZ Audio Visual, pg 878

MASSACHUSETTS

Terry Hanley Audio Systems Inc, pg 775
Professional Audio Design Inc, pg 865

MICHIGAN

TEL Systems LLC, pg 909

MISSOURI

Audio-VideoGraphics Inc, pg 694
Modern Communications Inc, pg 828

NEBRASKA

VSA Inc, pg 933

NEVADA

JCS Video Productions, pg 793

NEW JERSEY

AlltecPro, pg 681
Argraph Corp, pg 688
AV Bluebook, pg 696
Diversified, pg 744
HamiltonBuhl, pg 775
Onkyo USA Corp, pg 846
Panasonic Consumer Electronics Co, pg 850
Starlite, pg 900
Total Media Inc, pg 916
Yorktel, pg 944

NEW YORK

Aura Sonic Ltd (ASL), pg 695
B&H Photo Video, pg 701
Burlington A/V Recording Media, pg 712
Colortone Audio Visual, pg 728
Design Audio Visual Inc, pg 741
HAVE Inc, pg 777
Markertek Video Supply, pg 817
RNJ Electronics, pg 875
TecNec Distributing, pg 909

NORTH CAROLINA

Duke Media Services, pg 747

OHIO

ITA Audio Visual Solutions, pg 791
Lyon Video Inc, pg 813

OREGON

SuperDigital Ltd, pg 904

PENNSYLVANIA

Advanced AV LLC, pg 677
Grise Audio Visual Center Inc, pg 774
The Lerro Corp, pg 806

TENNESSEE

Lowrance Sound Co Inc, pg 812
Trew Audio Inc, pg 917

TEXAS

Heffernan Audio Visual, pg 778
Lubbock Audio Visual Inc, pg 812
RF Specialties of Texas LLC, pg 874

UTAH

Performance Audio LLC, pg 854

VIRGINIA

Lee Hartman & Sons Inc, pg 805
The Whitlock Group, pg 937

WISCONSIN

Camera Corner Connecting Point, pg 715
Full Compass Systems, pg 767

PUERTO RICO

Bonnin Electronics Inc, pg 708

BRITISH COLUMBIA

Commercial Electronics Ltd, pg 728
Triad Communications Ltd, pg 918

MANITOBA

Advance Pro, pg 677
Inland Audio Visual Ltd, pg 788

ONTARIO

Westbury National Show Systems Ltd, pg 936

Digital Audiotape—Blank Manufacturers

CALIFORNIA

QRS Software Services, pg 867

ILLINOIS

Woodside Avenue Music Productions Inc, pg 941

KENTUCKY

American Recordable Media, pg 684

NEW JERSEY

Onkyo USA Corp, pg 846

Digital Disc Recorder & Player Distributors

ARIZONA

Allusion Studios & Pure Wave Audio, pg 681
EAR Professional Audio/Video, pg 749
Troxell-CDI, pg 918

CALIFORNIA

Ametron Audio/Video, pg 684
Associated Sound, pg 691
Audio Images Corp, pg 693
Be Media, pg 702
Cibola Systems, pg 723
Educational Technology Services (ETS), pg 751
Empire Pro, pg 753
Instructional Materials & Equipment Distributors (I-Med), pg 789
JD Audio Visual Inc, pg 793
MediaPOINTE, pg 823
SNAP, pg 891
Sound Service Co, pg 894
Southern California Sound Image Inc, pg 895
Stanislaus AV Inc, pg 899
SuperVision, pg 904
Towards 2000 Inc, pg 916
VMI Inc, pg 932
VTP Inc, pg 933

COLORADO

Audio Consultant Services Inc, pg 693

CONNECTICUT

Connecticut Audio & Theatrical Supply, pg 731
HB Communications Inc, pg 777
The Music People Inc, pg 834
Vista Group International Inc, pg 931

DELAWARE

Actors Attic, pg 675

FLORIDA

Access Media Group, pg 673
Broadcasters General Store Inc, pg 711
CD ROM™ Inc, pg 718
Digital Video Systems, pg 742
Harris Corp, pg 776
Hi-Tech Enterprises Inc, pg 779
Midtown Video Inc, pg 827
ONstage, pg 846
Recording Media & Equipment Inc (RM&E), pg 872
Stereo Sales Inc, pg 900
TAI Audio, pg 906
Technomedia Solutions, pg 909

GEORGIA

Clark, pg 725
Lighting & Production Equipment Inc, pg 807
Stage Front Presentation Systems, pg 899

ILLINOIS

Joseph Electronics, pg 795
Woodside Avenue Music Productions Inc, pg 941

INDIANA

Sensory Technologies LLC, pg 884
SHP Electronics, pg 887
Sweetwater Sound Inc, pg 905

KENTUCKY

Axxis Leasing Inc, pg 700
Barney Miller's Inc, pg 827
NOR-COM Inc, pg 841

MARYLAND

Bradley Broadcast & Pro Audio, pg 709
Cardinal Sound & Video, pg 717
Kipp Visual Systems Inc, pg 799

MASSACHUSETTS

Avid Technology Inc, pg 698
Hunt's Photo & Video, pg 782
Professional Audio Design Inc, pg 865
Rule Boston Camera, pg 878

MICHIGAN

TEL Systems LLC, pg 909

MINNESOTA

Alpha Video & Audio Inc, pg 682

MISSISSIPPI

Bowie Audio Visual Enterprises Inc, pg 709

MISSOURI

Conference Technologies Inc, pg 730
Modern Communications Inc, pg 828
Schiller's Audio-Visual, pg 881

NEVADA

JCS Video Productions, pg 793

NEW HAMPSHIRE

APS Lighting-Sound-AV, pg 688
Technet® Systems Group, pg 908

NEW JERSEY

AlltecPro, pg 681
Diversified, pg 744
Earl Girls Inc, pg 749
HamiltonBuhl, pg 775
Onkyo USA Corp, pg 846
Starlite, pg 900
SYMCO Inc, pg 905
Yorktel, pg 944

NEW YORK

Cadence Jazz Records, pg 713
Colortone Audio Visual, pg 728
Design Audio Visual Inc, pg 741
HAVE Inc, pg 777
Hot House Professional Audio, pg 782
Korg USA Inc, pg 801
KVL Audio Visual Services Inc, pg 802
TecNec Distributing, pg 909
Toys From The Attic, pg 916

OHIO

ITA Audio Visual Solutions, pg 791
Tri-State Audio Visual Co, pg 918

OREGON

SuperDigital Ltd, pg 904

PENNSYLVANIA

Advanced AV LLC, pg 677
Bernie's Photo Center, pg 704
J E Foss Co, pg 764
The Lerro Corp, pg 806

RHODE ISLAND

Akai Professional, pg 679

TENNESSEE

Advanced Sound, pg 677
Lowrance Sound Co Inc, pg 812
Technical Support Systems LLC,
pg 908
Trew Audio Inc, pg 917
Zion Music Group, pg 945

TEXAS

Crossroads Audio Inc, pg 735
Data Projections Inc, pg 738
Lubbock Audio Visual Inc, pg 812
Replicopy Digital Media Center,
pg 873
RF Specialties of Texas LLC,
pg 874
Tarpley Media Systems, pg 907

UTAH

Performance Audio LLC, pg 854

VIRGINIA

Intellidyne LLC, pg 789
Lee Hartman & Sons Inc, pg 805
The Whitlock Group, pg 937

WISCONSIN

Audio Visual of Milwaukee Inc,
pg 694
Full Compass Systems, pg 767

PUERTO RICO

Bonnin Electronics Inc, pg 708

ALBERTA

Matrix Video Communications Corp
(MVCC), pg 819

BRITISH COLUMBIA

Commercial Electronics Ltd, pg 728

MANITOBA

Advance Pro, pg 677
Inland Audio Visual Ltd, pg 788

ONTARIO

Westbury National Show Systems
Ltd, pg 936

Digital Disc Recorder & Player Manufacturers

ARIZONA

Applied Integration Corp, pg 687

CALIFORNIA

Mackenzie Laboratories Inc, pg 814
TASCAM, pg 907
360 Systems, pg 913

COLORADO

Arrakis Systems, pg 689

FLORIDA

Alcorn McBride Inc, pg 679
CD ROM™ Inc, pg 718

ILLINOIS

Superscope LLC, pg 904

MASSACHUSETTS

Avid Technology Inc, pg 698

MICHIGAN

ENCO Systems Inc, pg 754

NEW JERSEY

Onkyo USA Corp, pg 846

NEW YORK

Laird Digital Cinema, pg 803

RHODE ISLAND

Akai Professional, pg 679
M-Audio, pg 813

TENNESSEE

Adtec Digital Inc, pg 677

BRITISH COLUMBIA

Creation Technologies Inc, pg 733

Digital Disc Recorder & Player Rentals

ARIZONA

Merestone, pg 823
Video West Inc, pg 929

CALIFORNIA

Advanced Media LLC, pg 677
Alliant Event Services, pg 681
Ametron Audio/Video, pg 684
Associated Sound, pg 691
ATV Video Center Inc, pg 692
Audio Rents, pg 693
AV Guys, pg 697
Express Media Inc, pg 757
Hollywood Sound Systems, pg 781
JD Audio Visual Inc, pg 793
Lynch Communications, pg 813
Maximus Media Inc, pg 820
McCune Audio-Video-Lighting,
pg 821
PSAV® Presentation Services,
pg 866
Alwin Sauers Audio Productions
(ASAP), pg 881
Sound Service Co, pg 894
Synthesizer Rental Service, pg 906
Towards 2000 Inc, pg 916
VMI Inc, pg 932

COLORADO

Audio Consultant Services Inc,
pg 693
Spectrum Audio Visual Services,
pg 897

CONNECTICUT

A/V Davey, pg 697

FLORIDA

Accord Productions, pg 673
ONstage, pg 846
Phat Planet Recording Studios,
pg 855
TAI Audio, pg 906
Universal Studios Florida®
Production Group, pg 922

GEORGIA

Lighting & Production Equipment
Inc, pg 807
Stage Front Presentation Systems,
pg 899

ILLINOIS

Backstar Creative Media Inc,
pg 700
Creative Technology (CT), pg 733
OSA International Inc, pg 848
RC Communications, pg 870
Resolution Productions Group,
pg 874
Woodside Avenue Music
Productions Inc, pg 941

KENTUCKY

Audio Visual Techniques Inc,
pg 695

MARYLAND

CPR MultiMedia Solutions, pg 732
Event Tech, pg 756
Maryland Sound International
Holding Co LLC, pg 819

MASSACHUSETTS

Preston Productions Inc, pg 861

MICHIGAN

K&R All Media Productions LLC,
pg 796

MINNESOTA

Alpha Video & Audio Inc, pg 682

MISSISSIPPI

Bowie Audio Visual Enterprises Inc,
pg 709

MISSOURI

Show-Me Audio-Visual, pg 887

NEVADA

GES Audio Visual, pg 770

NEW HAMPSHIRE

APS Lighting-Sound-AV, pg 688

NEW JERSEY

Earl Girls Inc, pg 749
Moe AV LLC, pg 828
PLS Staging, pg 858
Starlite, pg 900

NEW YORK

CP Communications, pg 732
Design Audio Visual Inc, pg 741
KVL Audio Visual Services Inc,
pg 802

NORTH CAROLINA

Take One Productions Ltd, pg 906

OHIO

Lyon Video Inc, pg 813
R&B Communications Inc, pg 870

PENNSYLVANIA

FMP Media Solutions Inc, pg 763
JPL, pg 795

TENNESSEE

Love Shack Recording Studios,
pg 811
Technical Support Systems LLC,
pg 908

TEXAS

Alford Media Services, pg 680
Crossroads Audio Inc, pg 735
Stage Directions, pg 898

UTAH

Performance Audio LLC, pg 854

VIRGINIA

Audio Visual Actions Inc (AVA),
pg 694

WISCONSIN

Full Compass Systems, pg 767

PUERTO RICO

Stage Crew Audiovisual Inc, pg 898

MANITOBA

Inland Audio Visual Ltd, pg 788

ONTARIO

Westbury National Show Systems
Ltd, pg 936

Digital Disc Recorder & Player Repairs

CALIFORNIA

Advanced Media LLC, pg 677
Ametron Audio/Video, pg 684
Audio Images Corp, pg 693
McAlister Electronics, pg 820
Sound Service Co, pg 894
Towards 2000 Inc, pg 916

CONNECTICUT

A/V Davey, pg 697

FLORIDA

Digital Video Systems, pg 742
Hi-Tech Enterprises Inc, pg 779
Stereo Sales Inc, pg 900
TAI Audio, pg 906

GEORGIA

Lighting & Production Equipment
Inc, pg 807
Stage Front Presentation Systems,
pg 899

ILLINOIS

Midwest Digital Corp, pg 827

INDIANA

Sweetwater Sound Inc, pg 905

KENTUCKY

Axxis Leasing Inc, pg 700
Barney Miller's Inc, pg 827
NOR-COM Inc, pg 841

MASSACHUSETTS

Professional Audio Design Inc,
pg 865

MICHIGAN

K&R's Recording Studios Inc,
pg 796
TEL Systems LLC, pg 909

AUDIO

Digital Disc Recorder & Player Repairs (continued)

NEW JERSEY

Earl Girls Inc, pg 749
Starlite, pg 900

NEW YORK

Toys From The Attic, pg 916

OHIO

Tri-State Audio Visual Co, pg 918

OREGON

All Service Musical Electronics
    Repair, pg 680

TENNESSEE

Technical Support Systems LLC,
    pg 908

WISCONSIN

Full Compass Systems, pg 767

MANITOBA

Inland Audio Visual Ltd, pg 788

ONTARIO

Westbury National Show Systems
    Ltd, pg 936

Digital Editor Distributors

ARIZONA

EAR Professional Audio/Video,
    pg 749
Troxell-CDI, pg 918

CALIFORNIA

Ametron Audio/Video, pg 684
Audio Images Corp, pg 693
Bitcentral Inc, pg 706
MediaPOINTE, pg 823
Pristine Systems Inc, pg 862
Sanako Inc, pg 880
Southern California Sound Image
    Inc, pg 895
VMI Inc, pg 932
VTP Inc, pg 933

COLORADO

Audio Consultant Services Inc,
    pg 693
Spectrum Audio Visual Services,
    pg 897

CONNECTICUT

HB Communications Inc, pg 777

DELAWARE

Actors Attic, pg 675

FLORIDA

Access Media Group, pg 673
AVI-SPL, pg 698
Digital Video Systems, pg 742
Harris Corp, pg 776
Hi-Tech Enterprises Inc, pg 779
ONstage, pg 846

Recording Media & Equipment Inc
    (RM&E), pg 872
TAI Audio, pg 906

GEORGIA

Clark, pg 725
Stage Front Presentation Systems,
    pg 899

ILLINOIS

Woodside Avenue Music
    Productions Inc, pg 941

INDIANA

Heart Breaker Entertainment LLC,
    pg 778
Sensory Technologies LLC, pg 884
Sweetwater Sound Inc, pg 905

KENTUCKY

Axxis Leasing Inc, pg 700
NOR-COM Inc, pg 841

MAINE

Headlight Audio Visual Inc, pg 777
Independent Audio Inc, pg 786

MARYLAND

Bradley Broadcast & Pro Audio,
    pg 709
Human Circuit, pg 782
Noventri, pg 843

MASSACHUSETTS

Avid Technology Inc, pg 698
Rule Boston Camera, pg 878

MICHIGAN

Digi Sign Design LLC, pg 741
TEL Systems LLC, pg 909

MINNESOTA

Alpha Video & Audio Inc, pg 682
Microboards Technology LLC,
    pg 826

NEVADA

JCS Video Productions, pg 793

NEW JERSEY

Diversified, pg 744
HamiltonBuhl, pg 775
SADiE Inc, pg 879
Starlite, pg 900
Total Video Products Inc, pg 916
Yorktel, pg 944

OHIO

ITA Audio Visual Solutions, pg 791

OREGON

SuperDigital Ltd, pg 904

PENNSYLVANIA

Advanced AV LLC, pg 677
The Lerro Corp, pg 806
Vistacom Inc, pg 931

RHODE ISLAND

Akai Professional, pg 679

TENNESSEE

Lowrance Sound Co Inc, pg 812
Zion Music Group, pg 945

TEXAS

Lubbock Audio Visual Inc, pg 812
Pro Video & Film Equipment Co
    Inc, pg 863
RF Specialties of Texas LLC,
    pg 874
Tarpley Media Systems, pg 907

UTAH

Performance Audio LLC, pg 854

VIRGINIA

Avitecture Inc, pg 699
Lee Hartman & Sons Inc, pg 805
Rocktown Media, pg 876
The Whitlock Group, pg 937

WASHINGTON

CCI Solutions, pg 718

WISCONSIN

Audio Visual of Milwaukee Inc,
    pg 694
Full Compass Systems, pg 767
Safe Harbor Computers, pg 879

PUERTO RICO

Bonnin Electronics Inc, pg 708

BRITISH COLUMBIA

Commercial Electronics Ltd, pg 728

MANITOBA

Advance Pro, pg 677
Inland Audio Visual Ltd, pg 788

ONTARIO

Soundmaster Group, pg 894

QUEBEC

JAM Industries Ltd, pg 792

Digital Editor Manufacturers

CALIFORNIA

Grande Vitesse Systems Inc (GVS),
    pg 773
360 Systems, pg 913

COLORADO

Arrakis Systems, pg 689

MASSACHUSETTS

Avid Technology Inc, pg 698

MISSOURI

GlobalStreams™ Corp, pg 771

NEW JERSEY

SADiE Inc, pg 879

NEW YORK

Dalet Digital Media Systems,
    pg 737
Laird Digital Cinema, pg 803

RHODE ISLAND

Akai Professional, pg 679

TENNESSEE

Adtec Digital Inc, pg 677

BRITISH COLUMBIA

Creation Technologies Inc, pg 733

ONTARIO

Soundmaster Group, pg 894

Digital Editor Rentals

ARIZONA

Merestone, pg 823

CALIFORNIA

Ametron Audio/Video, pg 684
Artichoke Productions, pg 690
Audio Rents, pg 693
Bexel, an NEP Broadcast Services
    Company, pg 704
Express Media Inc, pg 757
Lynch Communications, pg 813
On-Trax Inc, pg 846
Reality Check Systems, pg 871
Synthesizer Rental Service, pg 906
VMI Inc, pg 932

COLORADO

Audio Consultant Services Inc,
    pg 693

DELAWARE

Side Door Studio Inc, pg 887

FLORIDA

ONstage, pg 846
Universal Studios Florida®
    Production Group, pg 922

GEORGIA

Stage Front Presentation Systems,
    pg 899

ILLINOIS

OSA International Inc, pg 848
Resolution Productions Group,
    pg 874
Woodside Avenue Music
    Productions Inc, pg 941

INDIANA

Heart Breaker Entertainment LLC,
    pg 778

MARYLAND

Kramer Communications Video
    Production, pg 801
Maryland Sound International
    Holding Co LLC, pg 819

MASSACHUSETTS

Preston Productions Inc, pg 861

MICHIGAN

Digi Sign Design LLC, pg 741
K&R All Media Productions LLC,
    pg 796

MISSOURI

Show-Me Audio-Visual, pg 887

MONTANA

Jereco Studios Inc, pg 793

NEW JERSEY
CFP Video Productions Inc, pg 720
Jeep Jazz Media Solutions, pg 793
Starlite, pg 900

NEW YORK
HB-Content, pg 777

NORTH DAKOTA
Media Productions, pg 822

OHIO
R&B Communications Inc, pg 870

PENNSYLVANIA
The Videohouse Inc, pg 929

SOUTH CAROLINA
Genesis Creative, pg 769

TENNESSEE
Love Shack Recording Studios, pg 811

TEXAS
Onstage Systems, pg 846
Stage Directions, pg 898

UTAH
Performance Audio LLC, pg 854

WASHINGTON
Victory Studios, pg 927

WISCONSIN
Full Compass Systems, pg 767

BRITISH COLUMBIA
Video Out Distribution, pg 928

MANITOBA
Inland Audio Visual Ltd, pg 788

Digital Editor Repairs

CALIFORNIA
Ametron Audio/Video, pg 684
Audio Images Corp, pg 693
Diemer Amp & Keyboard Repair, pg 741
McAlister Electronics, pg 820

CONNECTICUT
HB Communications Inc, pg 777

FLORIDA
Hi-Tech Enterprises Inc, pg 779

GEORGIA
Stage Front Presentation Systems, pg 899

ILLINOIS
Midwest Digital Corp, pg 827

INDIANA
Sweetwater Sound Inc, pg 905

KENTUCKY
Axxis Leasing Inc, pg 700
NOR-COM Inc, pg 841

MICHIGAN
K&R's Recording Studios Inc, pg 796
TEL Systems LLC, pg 909

MINNESOTA
Microboards Technology LLC, pg 826

NEW JERSEY
Starlite, pg 900

TEXAS
Pro Video & Film Equipment Co Inc, pg 863

WISCONSIN
Full Compass Systems, pg 767

MANITOBA
Inland Audio Visual Ltd, pg 788

Digital Mixer Distributors

ARIZONA
EAR Professional Audio/Video, pg 749
Troxell-CDI, pg 918

CALIFORNIA
Ametron Audio/Video, pg 684
Associated Sound, pg 691
Audio Images Corp, pg 693
Empire Pro, pg 753
Hi-Tech Audio Systems Inc, pg 779
Location Sound Corp, pg 810
MediaPOINTE, pg 823
Promax Systems, pg 865
SNAP, pg 891
Sound Service Co, pg 894
Southern California Sound Image Inc, pg 895
TOA Electronics Inc, pg 915
Videobotics, pg 929
VMI Inc, pg 932
VTP Inc, pg 933

COLORADO
Audio Consultant Services Inc, pg 693
Spectrum Audio Visual Services, pg 897

CONNECTICUT
Connecticut Audio & Theatrical Supply, pg 731
HB Communications Inc, pg 777
The Music People Inc, pg 834

DELAWARE
Actors Attic, pg 675

FLORIDA
Access Media Group, pg 673
Altel Systems Group Inc, pg 682
AVI-SPL, pg 698
Digital Video Systems, pg 742
Harris Corp, pg 776
Hi-Tech Enterprises Inc, pg 779
Lighting Sales Connection Inc, pg 808
ONstage, pg 846
Recording Media & Equipment Inc (RM&E), pg 872
TAI Audio, pg 906

GEORGIA
Clark, pg 725
Lighting & Production Equipment Inc, pg 807
Stage Front Presentation Systems, pg 899

ILLINOIS
Quintessence Audio Ltd, pg 868

INDIANA
Heart Breaker Entertainment LLC, pg 778
Sensory Technologies LLC, pg 884
SHP Electronics, pg 887
Sweetwater Sound Inc, pg 905

KENTUCKY
Axxis Leasing Inc, pg 700
NOR-COM Inc, pg 841

LOUISIANA
Techkno Integration & Design Services LLC, pg 908

MAINE
Headlight Audio Visual Inc, pg 777
Independent Audio Inc, pg 786

MARYLAND
Bradley Broadcast & Pro Audio, pg 709
Human Circuit, pg 782
Kipp Visual Systems Inc, pg 799
Noventri, pg 843

MASSACHUSETTS
Professional Audio Design Inc, pg 865
Rule Boston Camera, pg 878

MICHIGAN
Digi Sign Design LLC, pg 741
TEL Systems LLC, pg 909

MINNESOTA
Alpha Video & Audio Inc, pg 682

MISSOURI
Modern Communications Inc, pg 828
Schiller's Audio-Visual, pg 881

NEBRASKA
VSA Inc, pg 933

NEW HAMPSHIRE
Technet® Systems Group, pg 908

NEW JERSEY
Alltec Stores, a Vcom IMC Company, pg 681
Audio Visual Associates, pg 694
Diversified, pg 744
HamiltonBuhl, pg 775
Starlite, pg 900
Total Video Products Inc, pg 916
Yorktel, pg 944

NEW YORK
Albany Theatre Supply Co Inc, pg 679
Aura Sonic Ltd (ASL), pg 695
Design Audio Visual Inc, pg 741

HAVE Inc, pg 777
Hot House Professional Audio, pg 782
Indigo Productions, pg 787
Posthorn Recordings, pg 859
TecNec Distributing, pg 909

OHIO
ITA Audio Visual Solutions, pg 791
Parts Express, pg 851
The Telos Alliance, pg 910

OREGON
SuperDigital Ltd, pg 904

PENNSYLVANIA
Advanced AV LLC, pg 677
The Lerro Corp, pg 806
Vistacom Inc, pg 931

RHODE ISLAND
Shanix Inc, pg 885

TENNESSEE
Allstar Audio Systems Inc, pg 681
Lowrance Sound Co Inc, pg 812
Mr Mark's Used Musical, Stereo & Studio Equipment Store, pg 828
Technical Support Systems LLC, pg 908
Trew Audio Inc, pg 917
Zion Music Group, pg 945

TEXAS
Crossroads Audio Inc, pg 735
Lubbock Audio Visual Inc, pg 812
Pro Video & Film Equipment Co Inc, pg 863
RF Specialties of Texas LLC, pg 874
Tarpley Media Systems, pg 907

UTAH
Performance Audio LLC, pg 854

VIRGINIA
Avitecture Inc, pg 699
Intellidyne LLC, pg 789
Lee Hartman & Sons Inc, pg 805
Rocktown Media, pg 876
The Whitlock Group, pg 937

WASHINGTON
CCI Solutions, pg 718
PNTA, pg 858

WISCONSIN
Audio Visual of Milwaukee Inc, pg 694
Full Compass Systems, pg 767
Safe Harbor Computers, pg 879

PUERTO RICO
Bonnin Electronics Inc, pg 708

ALBERTA
Allstar Show Industries Inc, pg 681

BRITISH COLUMBIA
Commercial Electronics Ltd, pg 728

MANITOBA
Advance Pro, pg 677
Inland Audio Visual Ltd, pg 788

AUDIO

Digital Mixer Distributors (continued)

ONTARIO

Cinema Stage Inc, pg 724
HD Source, pg 777
Westbury National Show Systems
Ltd, pg 936

QUEBEC

JAM Industries Ltd, pg 792
SC Media Canada, pg 881

Digital Mixer Manufacturers

CALIFORNIA

Opticomm-EMCORE, pg 847
Roland Corp US, pg 876
Soundcraft, pg 894
TASCAM, pg 907
TOA Electronics Inc, pg 915

CONNECTICUT

Sound Control Technologies Inc,
pg 893

NEW JERSEY

Bogen Communications Inc, pg 708
Sony Pro Audio, pg 893

NEW YORK

Harbro Corp, pg 776

NORTH CAROLINA

Audioarts Engineering, pg 695
Wheatstone Corp, pg 937

OHIO

Omnia Audio, pg 845
The Telos Alliance, pg 910

PENNSYLVANIA

Aviom Inc, pg 699

TENNESSEE

Harrison Consoles, pg 776

TEXAS

Logitek Electronic Systems Inc,
pg 811

BRITISH COLUMBIA

Richmond Sound Design Ltd,
pg 875

Digital Mixer Rentals

ALABAMA

Audio-Video Resources Inc, pg 694

ARIZONA

Merestone, pg 823
Video West Inc, pg 929

CALIFORNIA

AGF Media Services, pg 678
Ametron Audio/Video, pg 684
Artichoke Productions, pg 690
Associated Sound, pg 691

Audio Rents, pg 693
Bexel, an NEP Broadcast Services
Company, pg 704
Express Media Inc, pg 757
Hi-Tech Audio Systems Inc, pg 779
Lynch Communications, pg 813
McCune Audio-Video-Lighting,
pg 821
Muse Presentation Technologies,
pg 834
On-Trax Inc, pg 846
VER, pg 926
Westcoast Video Productions Inc,
pg 936

COLORADO

Audio Consultant Services Inc,
pg 693
Multimedia Audio Visual Inc,
pg 833
Open Media Foundation, pg 846
Spectrum Audio Visual Services,
pg 897

FLORIDA

Lighting Sales Connection Inc,
pg 808
ONstage, pg 846
Sight & Sound Productions, pg 887
TAI Audio, pg 906
Universal Studios Florida®
Production Group, pg 922

GEORGIA

ECG Productions, pg 750
Lighting & Production Equipment
Inc, pg 807
Stage Front Presentation Systems,
pg 899

ILLINOIS

OSA International Inc, pg 848
RC Communications, pg 870
Resolution Productions Group,
pg 874
SCI Television & Creative Media
LLC, pg 882

INDIANA

Heart Breaker Entertainment LLC,
pg 778

KENTUCKY

Audio Visual Techniques Inc,
pg 695

MARYLAND

CPR MultiMedia Solutions, pg 732
Event Tech, pg 756
Maryland Sound International
Holding Co LLC, pg 819

MASSACHUSETTS

Preston Productions Inc, pg 861

MICHIGAN

Digi Sign Design LLC, pg 741
K&R All Media Productions LLC,
pg 796

MISSOURI

Show-Me Audio-Visual, pg 887

MONTANA

Jereco Studios Inc, pg 793

NEW JERSEY

Audio Visual Associates, pg 694
Starlite, pg 900

NEW YORK

Aura Sonic Ltd (ASL), pg 695
CP Communications, pg 732
HB-Content, pg 777
Posthorn Recordings, pg 859

NORTH DAKOTA

Media Productions, pg 822

OHIO

Production Solutions Inc, pg 864

OKLAHOMA

PDC Productions, pg 852

OREGON

Picture This Production Services,
pg 856

PENNSYLVANIA

Advanced AV LLC, pg 677
The Videohouse Inc, pg 929

TENNESSEE

Allstar Audio Systems Inc, pg 681
Love Shack Recording Studios,
pg 811
Mr Mark's Used Musical, Stereo &
Studio Equipment Store, pg 828
Technical Support Systems LLC,
pg 908

TEXAS

Alford Media Services, pg 680
Bright Star Productions Inc, pg 710
Crossroads Audio Inc, pg 735
Lubbock Audio Visual Inc, pg 812
Music Lab Inc, pg 834
Stage Directions, pg 898

UTAH

Performance Audio LLC, pg 854

VIRGINIA

American AV, pg 682

WASHINGTON

D A Sound, pg 737
Victory Studios, pg 927

ALBERTA

Allstar Show Industries Inc, pg 681

BRITISH COLUMBIA

Video Out Distribution, pg 928

MANITOBA

Inland Audio Visual Ltd, pg 788

ONTARIO

HD Source, pg 777
Westbury National Show Systems
Ltd, pg 936

Digital Mixer Repairs

CALIFORNIA

Ametron Audio/Video, pg 684
Audio Images Corp, pg 693

Diemer Amp & Keyboard Repair,
pg 741
McAlister Electronics, pg 820
TOA Electronics Inc, pg 915

CONNECTICUT

HB Communications Inc, pg 777

FLORIDA

Hi-Tech Enterprises Inc, pg 779
TAI Audio, pg 906

GEORGIA

Lighting & Production Equipment
Inc, pg 807
Stage Front Presentation Systems,
pg 899

ILLINOIS

Midwest Digital Corp, pg 827

INDIANA

Sweetwater Sound Inc, pg 905

KENTUCKY

Axxis Leasing Inc, pg 700
NOR-COM Inc, pg 841

MASSACHUSETTS

Professional Audio Design Inc,
pg 865

MICHIGAN

K&R's Recording Studios Inc,
pg 796
TEL Systems LLC, pg 909

NEW JERSEY

Starlite, pg 900

OHIO

ITA Audio Visual Solutions, pg 791

OREGON

All Service Musical Electronics
Repair, pg 680

TENNESSEE

Technical Support Systems LLC,
pg 908

TEXAS

Lubbock Audio Visual Inc, pg 812
Pro Video & Film Equipment Co
Inc, pg 863

WASHINGTON

PNTA, pg 858

WISCONSIN

Full Compass Systems, pg 767

MANITOBA

Inland Audio Visual Ltd, pg 788

ONTARIO

Westbury National Show Systems
Ltd, pg 936

QUEBEC

SC Media Canada, pg 881

Digital Tape Recorder & Player Distributors

ALABAMA
Dogwood Productions Inc, pg 745

ARIZONA
Arizona Cine Equipment, pg 688
EAR Professional Audio/Video, pg 749
Troxell-CDI, pg 918

CALIFORNIA
Advanced Systems Group LLC, pg 677
Ametron Audio/Video, pg 684
Audio Images Corp, pg 693
Audio/Video Supply Inc, pg 694
BigFoot Mobile Systems, pg 705
Electronic Design Solutions Inc, pg 752
Gluskin's Custom Audio Video, pg 771
Instructional Materials & Equipment Distributors (I-Med), pg 789
JD Audio Visual Inc, pg 793
MediaPOINTE, pg 823
SNAP, pg 891
Southern California Sound Image Inc, pg 895
SSL Industries Inc, pg 898
Stanislaus AV Inc, pg 899
TASCAM, pg 907
Towards 2000 Inc, pg 916
Videobotics, pg 929
VMI Inc, pg 932
VTP Inc, pg 933

COLORADO
Audio Consultant Services Inc, pg 693
Spectrum Audio Visual Services, pg 897

CONNECTICUT
Connecticut Audio & Theatrical Supply, pg 731
HB Communications Inc, pg 777
The Music People Inc, pg 834

DELAWARE
Actors Attic, pg 675

FLORIDA
Access Media Group, pg 673
Alcorn McBride Inc, pg 679
Altel Systems Group Inc, pg 682
Broadcasters General Store Inc, pg 711
Digital Video Systems, pg 742
Harris Corp, pg 776
Hi-Tech Enterprises Inc, pg 779
Hi-Tech Import Export Corp, pg 779
Intermark Industries Inc, pg 789
Lighting Sales Connection Inc, pg 808
Midtown Video, pg 827
ONstage, pg 846
Recording Media & Equipment Inc (RM&E), pg 872
Stereo Sales Inc, pg 900
TAI Audio, pg 906

GEORGIA
Clark, pg 725
Lighting & Production Equipment Inc, pg 807

LT Sound Inc, pg 812
Stage Front Presentation Systems, pg 899

HAWAII
The Audio Visual Co (AVCO), pg 694

ILLINOIS
Allen Visual Systems Inc, pg 680
C V Lloyde, pg 810
RC Communications, pg 870

INDIANA
Sensory Technologies LLC, pg 884
SHP Electronics, pg 887
Sweetwater Sound Inc, pg 905

KENTUCKY
Barney Miller's Inc, pg 827
NOR-COM Inc, pg 841

MAINE
Headlight Audio Visual Inc, pg 777
Independent Audio Inc, pg 786

MARYLAND
Bradley Broadcast & Pro Audio, pg 709
Human Circuit, pg 782
Kipp Visual Systems Inc, pg 799
RTZ Audio Visual, pg 878

MASSACHUSETTS
Avid Technology Inc, pg 698
Professional Audio Design Inc, pg 865

MICHIGAN
TEL Systems LLC, pg 909

MINNESOTA
Alpha Video & Audio Inc, pg 682

MISSOURI
Communitronics Corp, pg 729
Modern Communications Inc, pg 828
Schiller's Audio-Visual, pg 881

NEBRASKA
VSA Inc, pg 933

NEW HAMPSHIRE
APS Lighting-Sound-AV, pg 688
Technet® Systems Group, pg 908

NEW JERSEY
A-V Services Inc, pg 671
Alltec Stores, a Vcom IMC Company, pg 681
AlltecPro, pg 681
Diversified, pg 744
G&G Technologies Inc, pg 768
HamiltonBuhl, pg 775
The Music Place, pg 834
Onkyo USA Corp, pg 846
Starlite, pg 900
Video Corporation of America (VCA), pg 927
Wired 4 Sound Inc, pg 940
Yorktel, pg 944

NEW YORK
American Video Inc, pg 684
Aura Sonic Ltd (ASL), pg 695
AV Workshop, pg 697
Cadence Jazz Records, pg 713
Colortone Audio Visual, pg 728
Design Audio Visual Inc, pg 741
HAVE Inc, pg 777
Hot House Professional Audio, pg 782
Long Island Video Enterprises Live Inc, pg 811
Mark Custom Recording Service Inc, pg 817
Posthorn Recordings, pg 859
RNJ Electronics, pg 875
TecNec Distributing, pg 909

OHIO
ITA Audio Visual Solutions, pg 791

OREGON
SuperDigital Ltd, pg 904

PENNSYLVANIA
Advanced AV LLC, pg 677
The Lerro Corp, pg 806
Morefield Communications Inc, pg 830
Vistacom Inc, pg 931

TENNESSEE
Allstar Audio Systems Inc, pg 681
Lowrance Sound Co Inc, pg 812
Mr Mark's Used Musical, Stereo & Studio Equipment Store, pg 828
Technical Support Systems LLC, pg 908
Trew Audio Inc, pg 917

TEXAS
AVES Audio Visual Systems Inc, pg 698
Crossroads Audio Inc, pg 735
FitzCo Sound Inc, pg 761
Heffernan Audio Visual, pg 778
Lubbock Audio Visual Inc, pg 812
Pro Video & Film Equipment Co Inc, pg 863
RF Specialties of Texas LLC, pg 874
Tarpley Media Systems, pg 907

UTAH
Performance Audio LLC, pg 854
RIA Corp, pg 874

VIRGINIA
Avitecture Inc, pg 699
Intellidyne LLC, pg 789
Lee Hartman & Sons Inc, pg 805
The Whitlock Group, pg 937

WISCONSIN
Audio Visual of Milwaukee Inc, pg 694
Camera Corner Connecting Point, pg 715
Full Compass Systems, pg 767

PUERTO RICO
Bonnin Electronics Inc, pg 708

BRITISH COLUMBIA
Commercial Electronics Ltd, pg 728

MANITOBA
Advance Pro, pg 677
Inland Audio Visual Ltd, pg 788

ONTARIO
HD Source, pg 777
Nationwide Audio Visual Co, pg 837
Westbury National Show Systems Ltd, pg 936

QUEBEC
Panavideo Inc, pg 850

Digital Tape Recorder & Player Manufacturers

ARIZONA
Applied Integration Corp, pg 687

CALIFORNIA
Gilderfluke & Co Inc, pg 771
Grande Vitesse Systems Inc (GVS), pg 773
Sony Electronics Inc, pg 893
TASCAM, pg 907

MASSACHUSETTS
Avid Technology Inc, pg 698

NEW JERSEY
Onkyo USA Corp, pg 846
Panasonic Consumer Electronics Co, pg 850
RAMSA Professional Audio Systems, pg 870
Technics, pg 909

TENNESSEE
Adtec Digital Inc, pg 677

BRITISH COLUMBIA
Richmond Sound Design Ltd, pg 875

Digital Tape Recorder & Player Rentals

ARIZONA
Arizona Cine Equipment, pg 688
Merestone, pg 823
Metropolitan Audio-Visual Inc, pg 824

ARKANSAS
White Diamond Productions LLC, pg 937

CALIFORNIA
Advanced Media LLC, pg 677
AGF Media Services, pg 678
Ametron Audio/Video, pg 684
Artichoke Productions, pg 690
Audio Rents, pg 693
AV Guys, pg 697
Bexel, an NEP Broadcast Services Company, pg 704
Express Media Inc, pg 757
Hollywood Sound Systems, pg 781
JD Audio Visual Inc, pg 793
Lynch Communications, pg 813
Maximus Media Inc, pg 820
McCune Audio-Video-Lighting, pg 821

AUDIO

Digital Tape Recorder & Player Rentals (continued)

CALIFORNIA (continued)
Munday & Collins AV, pg 834
On-Trax Inc, pg 846
PSAV® Presentation Services, pg 866
Pyramind Studios, pg 867
Total Creative, pg 916
Towards 2000 Inc, pg 916
VER, pg 926
Video Resources Inc, pg 928
VMI Inc, pg 932
Warner Bros Production Sound & Video Services, pg 934

COLORADO
Audio Consultant Services Inc, pg 693
Daylight Productions & Rentals, pg 739
Multimedia Audio Visual Inc, pg 833

CONNECTICUT
A/V Davey, pg 697

DELAWARE
Side Door Studio Inc, pg 887

FLORIDA
Accord Productions, pg 673
Lighting Sales Connection Inc, pg 808
ONstage, pg 846
TAI Audio, pg 906
Universal Studios Florida® Production Group, pg 922

GEORGIA
Lighting & Production Equipment Inc, pg 807
Stage Front Presentation Systems, pg 899
Staging Directions Inc, pg 899

HAWAII
Sight & Sound Studios, pg 887

ILLINOIS
Allen Visual Systems Inc, pg 680
AV Chicago Inc, pg 696
Backstar Creative Media Inc, pg 700
Beatty TeleVisual Productions, pg 703
OSA International Inc, pg 848
RBR Productions, pg 870
RC Communications, pg 870
Resolution Productions Group, pg 874
Woodside Avenue Music Productions Inc, pg 941

KENTUCKY
Audio Visual Techniques Inc, pg 695

MARYLAND
Advance Audiovisual Presentation Ltd, pg 677
CPR MultiMedia Solutions, pg 732
Event Tech, pg 756

MASSACHUSETTS
massAV, pg 819
Preston Productions Inc, pg 861

MICHIGAN
K&R All Media Productions LLC, pg 796

MINNESOTA
Alpha Video & Audio Inc, pg 682

MISSOURI
Show-Me Audio-Visual, pg 887

MONTANA
Jereco Studios Inc, pg 793

NEVADA
GES Audio Visual, pg 770

NEW HAMPSHIRE
APS Lighting-Sound-AV, pg 688

NEW JERSEY
Jeep Jazz Media Solutions, pg 793
Moe AV LLC, pg 828
Panavid, pg 850
Starlite, pg 900
Wired 4 Sound Inc, pg 940

NEW MEXICO
Production Outfitters, pg 864

NEW YORK
American Video Inc, pg 684
Aura Sonic Ltd (ASL), pg 695
AV Workshop, pg 697
CP Communications, pg 732
Design Audio Visual Inc, pg 741
Hello World Communications, pg 778
Manhattan Center Studios Inc, pg 816
Posthorn Recordings, pg 859
WorldStage, pg 941

NORTH CAROLINA
Duke Media Services, pg 747
Special Event Services, pg 896
Take One Productions Ltd, pg 906

NORTH DAKOTA
Media Productions, pg 822

OHIO
ITA Audio Visual Solutions, pg 791
Lyon Video Inc, pg 813

OREGON
Northwest Film Center, pg 842

PENNSYLVANIA
Advanced AV LLC, pg 677
Right Coast Recording Inc, pg 875

TENNESSEE
Allstar Audio Systems Inc, pg 681
Love Shack Recording Studios, pg 811
Mr Mark's Used Musical, Stereo & Studio Equipment Store, pg 828
Technical Support Systems LLC, pg 908

TEXAS
Alford Media Services, pg 680
FitzCo Sound Inc, pg 761
Lubbock Audio Visual Inc, pg 812
Music Lab Inc, pg 834
Onstage Systems, pg 846

UTAH
Performance Audio LLC, pg 854

VIRGINIA
American AV, pg 682

WASHINGTON
Victory Studios, pg 927

WISCONSIN
Full Compass Systems, pg 767

BRITISH COLUMBIA
Commercial Electronics Ltd, pg 728

MANITOBA
Inland Audio Visual Ltd, pg 788

ONTARIO
HD Source, pg 777
Westbury National Show Systems Ltd, pg 936

QUEBEC
Panavideo Inc, pg 850

Digital Tape Recorder & Player Repairs

CALIFORNIA
Advanced Media LLC, pg 677
Ametron Audio/Video, pg 684
Audio Images Corp, pg 693
Gluskin's Custom Audio Video, pg 771
Instructional Materials & Equipment Distributors (I-Med), pg 789
McAlister Electronics, pg 820
SSL Industries Inc, pg 898
Towards 2000 Inc, pg 916

FLORIDA
AMP Services Inc, pg 684
Hi-Tech Enterprises Inc, pg 779
Stereo Sales Inc, pg 900
TAI Audio, pg 906

GEORGIA
Lighting & Production Equipment Inc, pg 807
Stage Front Presentation Systems, pg 899

ILLINOIS
Allen Visual Systems Inc, pg 680
Beatty TeleVisual Productions, pg 703

C V Lloyde, pg 810
Midwest Digital Corp, pg 827

INDIANA
Sweetwater Sound Inc, pg 905

KENTUCKY
Barney Miller's Inc, pg 827
NOR-COM Inc, pg 841

MASSACHUSETTS
Professional Audio Design Inc, pg 865

MICHIGAN
K&R's Recording Studios Inc, pg 796
TEL Systems LLC, pg 909

NEW JERSEY
A-V Services Inc, pg 671
Starlite, pg 900

OHIO
ITA Audio Visual Solutions, pg 791

OREGON
All Service Musical Electronics Repair, pg 680

PENNSYLVANIA
Right Coast Recording Inc, pg 875

TENNESSEE
Technical Support Systems LLC, pg 908

TEXAS
Lubbock Audio Visual Inc, pg 812
Pro Video & Film Equipment Co Inc, pg 863

WISCONSIN
Full Compass Systems, pg 767

BRITISH COLUMBIA
Commercial Electronics Ltd, pg 728

MANITOBA
Inland Audio Visual Ltd, pg 788

ONTARIO
Westbury National Show Systems Ltd, pg 936

QUEBEC
Panavideo Inc, pg 850

Dubbing

ARIZONA
Merestone, pg 823
On-Site Video, pg 846
SPEAK HOUSE Audio™, pg 896
Star Video Duplicating, pg 900

ARKANSAS
Live'N'Loud, pg 810

CALIFORNIA

AB Audio Visual Entertainment Inc, pg 672
Access Video in Berkeley, pg 673
ACDC Audio CD & Cassette, pg 674
AlphaDogs Inc, pg 682
Artichoke Productions, pg 690
Chace Audio by Deluxe, pg 720
Custom Video Productions Inc, pg 736
Express Media Inc, pg 757
International Contact Inc, pg 790
Juice Studios, pg 795
Lynch Communications, pg 813
Maximus Media Inc, pg 820
Penrose Productions, pg 854
PM Productions, pg 858
Point.360, pg 858
Private Island Audio Inc, pg 862
QRS Software Services, pg 867
Roundabout Entertainment Inc, pg 878
Sahara Records & Filmworks Entertainment Co, pg 879
Saturn Studios, pg 881
SonicPool, pg 892
Still N' Motion, pg 901
Studio 132, pg 902
Total Creative, pg 916

COLORADO

Colorado Sound Recording Ltd, pg 728
Flashback Media Productions, pg 762
Open Media Foundation, pg 846
Rocky Mountain Audio/Video Productions Inc, pg 876

CONNECTICUT

A/V Davey, pg 697
Ironik Design & Post, pg 791
T & M Digital Services LLC, pg 906

FLORIDA

Access Media Group, pg 673
Comtel Inc, pg 730
JT Communications, pg 795
The Kitchen, pg 799
Phat Planet Recording Studios, pg 855
Video Techniques Inc, pg 928

GEORGIA

Crawford Media Services Inc, pg 733
Digital Projection, pg 742
Guerrilla Productions LLC, pg 774
Hottrax Records, pg 782
Lighting & Production Equipment Inc, pg 807
ON Services, a GES Company, pg 846
Stage Front Presentation Systems, pg 899

HAWAII

Media Bridge Gamekids, pg 821

ILLINOIS

CCore Media Inc, pg 718
Esoteric Sound, pg 755
IV Media Resources, pg 792
Multimedia Marketing Group, pg 833
Solid Sound Recording Studio, pg 892

Sound/Video Impressions Inc, pg 894
20/20 Communications Inc, pg 920
Woodside Avenue Music Productions Inc, pg 941

INDIANA

Sweetwater Sound Inc, pg 905

IOWA

Duplication Media, pg 748

KENTUCKY

Audio Visual Techniques Inc, pg 695
Hammond Communications Group Inc, pg 775

LOUISIANA

Louisiana State University Division of Strategic Communications, pg 811

MARYLAND

CPR MultiMedia Solutions, pg 732
dbF a Media Company, pg 739
Omega Recording Studios, pg 845
Smolian Sound Studios, pg 891
Welocalize, pg 935

MASSACHUSETTS

Continental Recordings Inc, pg 731
Cramer, pg 732
Linguistic Systems Inc, pg 809
Monadnock Media Inc, pg 829
Soundtrack Group, pg 895

MICHIGAN

Audio Graphic Services, pg 693
Brilliance Audio, pg 710
The Brookwood Studio Inc, pg 711
Digi Sign Design LLC, pg 741
K&R's Recording Studios Inc, pg 796

MINNESOTA

The ADS Group, pg 676
Winterland Studios, pg 940

MISSOURI

Avatar Studios, pg 697
Hardcastle Films & Video, pg 776
Show-Me Audio-Visual, pg 887

NEVADA

Encore Event Technologies LLC, pg 754

NEW HAMPSHIRE

Chip Taylor Communications LLC, pg 907

NEW JERSEY

AJS Events, pg 679
Allegro Productions Inc, pg 680
CFP Video Productions Inc, pg 720
Color Leasing Studios, pg 727
Laurel Video Productions, pg 804
Midnight Media Group Inc, pg 827
Milgrom Productions, pg 827
Optisonics Productions, pg 847
Suede Interactive, pg 903
VCSvideo, pg 925

NEW MEXICO

Production Outfitters, pg 864

NEW YORK

Ace Video, pg 674
Aural Gratification Inc, pg 695
The Big House Group, pg 705
Burlington A/V Recording Media, pg 712
Chromavision Corp, pg 723
DuArt Media Services, pg 747
Duplication Depot Inc, pg 748
Fingerpaint, pg 761
Foothill Digital Inc, pg 763
HB-Content, pg 777
Heavy Melody, pg 778
InterNation Inc, pg 789
International Digital Centre, pg 790
iProbe Multilingual Solutions Inc, pg 791
Manhattan Center Studios Inc, pg 816
Mark Custom Recording Service Inc, pg 817
Mood Creations Ltd, pg 829
Tiki Recording Studios Inc, pg 914
Visual Technologies Corp, pg 932

NORTH CAROLINA

Pat Appleson Studios Inc, pg 687
Duke Media Services, pg 747
Horizon Video Productions Inc, pg 781
Take One Productions Ltd, pg 906

NORTH DAKOTA

Media Productions, pg 822

OHIO

Curtis Inc, pg 736
Lyon Video Inc, pg 813
Mills James Productions, pg 828
Musicol Recording, pg 835

OKLAHOMA

PDC Productions, pg 852

PENNSYLVANIA

American Artist Studio, pg 682
Audio Visual Communications Inc, pg 694
Forge Recording LLC, pg 764
Laser Video Corp, pg 804
Production Masters Inc (PMI), pg 864
The Videohouse Inc, pg 929

RHODE ISLAND

Sound-FX-Design, pg 894

SOUTH CAROLINA

DaviSound, pg 739
Genesis Creative, pg 769

TENNESSEE

Analog Man Recording Studio, pg 685
Anode Inc, pg 686
Ardent Studios Inc, pg 688
Love Shack Recording Studios, pg 811
Motion Picture Services, pg 831
Stage Post, pg 899
Technical Support Systems LLC, pg 908

TEXAS

Anaphora Literary Press, pg 685
Castleview Productions, pg 717
Crystal Clear Media Group, pg 735

Dub King, pg 747
The Editing Co, pg 750
Julye Newlin Productions Inc, pg 840
Omni Intercommunications Inc, pg 845
Replicopy Digital Media Center, pg 873
The Samuels Co, pg 879
The Sound Lab Inc, pg 894
Sound Works, pg 894
Stage Directions, pg 898
Texas Heart Institute Visual Communication Services, pg 911
Tropikal Productions, pg 918
World Beat Studio, pg 941
The Yesterday USA Radio Networks, pg 944

UTAH

ImageWorks Communications, pg 785

VIRGINIA

American AV, pg 682
AudioImage Recording, pg 695
CDR Communications Inc, pg 719
Wally Cleaver's Recording Service, pg 726
Studio Center Corp, pg 902

WASHINGTON

Victory Studios, pg 927

WISCONSIN

Audio Visual of Milwaukee Inc, pg 694
5th Floor Recording Co, pg 760
Meridian Studios, pg 824
Video Wisconsin Inc, pg 929
Watts Communications Inc, pg 934

PUERTO RICO

Stage Crew Audiovisual Inc, pg 898

BRITISH COLUMBIA

Pinewood Sound, pg 857
Triad Communications Ltd, pg 918

ONTARIO

GAPC (General Assembly Production Centre), pg 768
Silver Creek Media Inc, pg 888
Video Excellence Productions, pg 927
Wanted! Sound + Picture, pg 933

Duplication— Audiocassettes

ARIZONA

Merestone, pg 823
Metropolitan Audio-Visual Inc, pg 824
SPEAK HOUSE Audio™, pg 896
Star Video Duplicating, pg 900

ARKANSAS

White Diamond Productions LLC, pg 937

CALIFORNIA

AB Audio Visual Entertainment Inc, pg 672
ACDC Audio CD & Cassette, pg 674

AUDIO

Duplication—
Audiocassettes
(continued)

CALIFORNIA (continued)

ALOM Technologies Corp, pg 681
AlphaDogs Inc, pg 682
Ametron Audio/Video, pg 684
Creative Media Recording, pg 733
Crystal Pyramid Productions™, pg 735
Custom Video Productions Inc, pg 736
KVIE-Channel 6, pg 802
Lynch Communications, pg 813
Maximus Media Inc, pg 820
M2 Communications, pg 833
On-Trax Inc, pg 846
PM Productions, pg 858
Point.360, pg 858
PSI Inc, pg 866
QRS Software Services, pg 867
Reel Picture, pg 872
Roundabout Entertainment Inc, pg 878
Sahara Records & Filmworks Entertainment Co, pg 879
Saturn Studios, pg 881
SonicPool, pg 892
Sounds Unique, pg 895
Trac Recording Studio, pg 916

COLORADO

Daylight Productions & Rentals, pg 739

CONNECTICUT

A/V Davey, pg 697
MAVCO, pg 820
Rockwell Communications Inc, pg 876

DELAWARE

Ken-Del Productions Inc, pg 797
Side Door Studio Inc, pg 887

DISTRICT OF COLUMBIA

Library of Congress, Motion Picture, Broadcasting & Recorded Sound Division, pg 807

FLORIDA

Access Media Group, pg 673
Accord Productions, pg 673
Communications Concepts Inc (CCI), pg 729
Easy Edit Video Inc, pg 750
Jordan Klein Film & Video (JKFV), pg 795
Mach 1 Productions, pg 813
Video Techniques Inc, pg 928

GEORGIA

Audio Visual Resources Inc, pg 695
Lighting & Production Equipment Inc, pg 807
Omega Media Group Inc, pg 845
Playback Now Inc, pg 858

ILLINOIS

ABS Enterprises, pg 672
Backstar Creative Media Inc, pg 700
CCore Media Inc, pg 718
Helix Camera & Video, pg 778
IV Media Resources, pg 792

Major Media Inc, pg 815
Major Media Productions Inc, pg 815
RBR Productions, pg 870
Sound/Video Impressions Inc, pg 894
Southern Illinois University, pg 895
Woodside Avenue Music Productions Inc, pg 941

INDIANA

OMNI Productions, pg 845
Sweetwater Sound Inc, pg 905

IOWA

Duplication Media, pg 748
Educational Technology & Media Services, pg 751
Iowa State University-Information Technology Services, pg 791

KENTUCKY

Audio Visual Techniques Inc, pg 695
Barney Miller's Inc, pg 827

LOUISIANA

Louisiana State University Division of Strategic Communications, pg 811

MAINE

Headlight Audio Visual Inc, pg 777

MARYLAND

Absolute Hollywood, pg 672
CPR MultiMedia Solutions, pg 732
The Cutting Corporation, GraphicAudio® & Archival Sound Lab, pg 736
dbF a Media Company, pg 739
Omega Recording Studios, pg 845
Sign Media Inc, pg 887
Soundtrax Inc, pg 895

MASSACHUSETTS

Capron Lighting & Sound Co Inc, pg 716
Continental Recordings Inc, pg 731
Soundtrack Group, pg 895
Video Express, pg 928

MICHIGAN

Brilliance Audio, pg 710
Digi Sign Design LLC, pg 741
K&R's Recording Studios Inc, pg 796
The Transfer Zone®, pg 917

MINNESOTA

GMI Productions, pg 771

MISSISSIPPI

Bowie Audio Visual Enterprises Inc, pg 709
Jasper Ewing & Sons Inc, pg 757

MISSOURI

Audio-VideoGraphics Inc, pg 694
Hardcastle Films & Video, pg 776
Show-Me Audio-Visual, pg 887
Visionworks Design Services Inc, pg 931

NEVADA

JCS Video Productions, pg 793

NEW HAMPSHIRE

Academic & Campus Technology Services, pg 672
Apertura, pg 686
Captain Fiddle Music & Publications, pg 716
Chip Taylor Communications LLC, pg 907

NEW JERSEY

AJS Events, pg 679
Audio Visual Dynamics®, pg 694
CFP Video Productions Inc, pg 720
Laurel Video Productions, pg 804
Milgrom Productions, pg 827
NFL Films Music Library, pg 841
Starlite, pg 900
Suede Interactive, pg 903
Video Corporation of America (VCA), pg 927

NEW YORK

The Big House Group, pg 705
Burlington A/V Recording Media, pg 712
Chromavision Corp, pg 723
CMI Communications, pg 727
Colortone Audio Visual, pg 728
Thomas Craven Film Corp, pg 733
Design Audio Visual Inc, pg 741
Digital Force Ltd, pg 742
DuArt Media Services, pg 747
Duplication Depot Inc, pg 748
Duplication Specialists Inc, pg 748
HAVE Inc, pg 777
HB-Content, pg 777
HOThead, pg 782
Icontent, pg 783
International Digital Centre, pg 790
Long Island Video Enterprises Live Inc, pg 811
Manhattan Center Studios Inc, pg 816
Mood Creations Ltd, pg 829
New York Audio Productions, pg 840
Sony Music Entertainment, pg 893
Specialized Audio-Visual Inc, pg 896
Teatown Communications Group, pg 908
TeleTime Productions, pg 910
Tiki Recording Studios Inc, pg 914
USA Studios, pg 923
Visual Technologies Corp, pg 932

NORTH CAROLINA

Pat Appleson Studios Inc, pg 687
AV Connections Inc, pg 697
Duke Media Services, pg 747
Take One Productions Ltd, pg 906
Trailblazer Studios®, pg 917

NORTH DAKOTA

Media Productions, pg 822

OHIO

Cuyahoga Community College Student Production Office (SPO), pg 736
Mills James Productions, pg 828
Musicol Recording, pg 835
SoundSpace Inc, pg 895
Thread Marketing Group, pg 913
Vista Color Imaging Inc, pg 931

OKLAHOMA

Academic Media & Digital Services, pg 672
Garman Productions LLC, pg 768

OREGON

REX, pg 874

PENNSYLVANIA

American Artist Studio, pg 682
FMP Media Solutions Inc, pg 763
Forge Recording LLC, pg 764
Production Masters Inc (PMI), pg 864
The Videohouse Inc, pg 929
Visual Sound Inc, pg 931

RHODE ISLAND

Sound-FX-Design, pg 894

SOUTH CAROLINA

DaviSound, pg 739

TENNESSEE

Ardent Studios Inc, pg 688
Memphis Communications Corp, pg 823
Stage Post, pg 899

TEXAS

Dub King, pg 747
JSAV, pg 795
Sound Works, pg 894
Texas Heart Institute Visual Communication Services, pg 911
The Yesterday USA Radio Networks, pg 944

VERMONT

University of Vermont, Instructional Television Dept, pg 923

VIRGINIA

American AV, pg 682
AudioImage Recording, pg 695
BES Studios, pg 704
CDR Communications Inc, pg 719
Wally Cleaver's Recording Service, pg 726
Lee Hartman & Sons Inc, pg 805
The Whitlock Group, pg 937

WASHINGTON

Inland Audio Visual Co, pg 788
Kostov Productions, pg 801
Pacific Multimedia Inc, pg 849
Victory Studios, pg 927

WISCONSIN

Audio Visual of Milwaukee Inc, pg 694
5th Floor Recording Co, pg 760
USAV Group Inc, pg 923

WYOMING

Bridger Productions Inc, pg 710

PUERTO RICO

Stage Crew Audiovisual Inc, pg 898

ALBERTA

Cine Audio Visual Sales & Service Ltd, pg 723
Unique Communications Ltd, pg 921

BRITISH COLUMBIA

Commercial Electronics Ltd, pg 728
Triad Communications Ltd, pg 918

ONTARIO

Silver Creek Media Inc, pg 888
Wanted! Sound + Picture, pg 933

Duplication—Audiotapes

ARIZONA

Merestone, pg 823
Star Video Duplicating, pg 900

ARKANSAS

White Diamond Productions LLC,
   pg 937

CALIFORNIA

AB Audio Visual Entertainment Inc,
   pg 672
ACDC Audio CD & Cassette,
   pg 674
ALOM Technologies Corp, pg 681
AlphaDogs Inc, pg 682
Ametron Audio/Video, pg 684
Creative Media Recording, pg 733
Creative Support Services/CSS
   Music, pg 733
Crystal Pyramid Productions™,
   pg 735
Custom Video Productions Inc,
   pg 736
Lynch Communications, pg 813
Maximus Media Inc, pg 820
M2 Communications, pg 833
On-Trax Inc, pg 846
Point.360, pg 858
PSI Inc, pg 866
QRS Software Services, pg 867
Sahara Records & Filmworks
   Entertainment Co, pg 879
Saturn Studios, pg 881
SonicPool, pg 892
Sounds Unique, pg 895
United Audio Video Inc, pg 921

COLORADO

Daylight Productions & Rentals,
   pg 739

CONNECTICUT

A/V Davey, pg 697
MAVCO, pg 820
Rockwell Communications Inc,
   pg 876

DELAWARE

Ken-Del Productions Inc, pg 797
Ken-Del Studios, pg 797

DISTRICT OF COLUMBIA

Library of Congress, Motion
   Picture, Broadcasting & Recorded
   Sound Division, pg 807

FLORIDA

Access Media Group, pg 673
Communications Concepts Inc
   (CCI), pg 729
Mach 1 Productions, pg 813
Video Techniques Inc, pg 928

GEORGIA

Audio Visual Resources Inc, pg 695
Beast Atlanta, pg 703

Lighting & Production Equipment
   Inc, pg 807
White Dog Studios, pg 937

ILLINOIS

ABS Enterprises, pg 672
CCore Media Inc, pg 718
IV Media Resources, pg 792
Major Media Inc, pg 815
Major Media Productions Inc,
   pg 815
RBR Productions, pg 870
Woodside Avenue Music
   Productions Inc, pg 941

INDIANA

OMNI Productions, pg 845
Sweetwater Sound Inc, pg 905

IOWA

Duplication Media, pg 748
Educational Technology & Media
   Services, pg 751

LOUISIANA

Louisiana State University Division
   of Strategic Communications,
   pg 811

MAINE

Headlight Audio Visual Inc, pg 777

MARYLAND

Absolute Hollywood, pg 672
The Cutting Corporation,
   GraphicAudio® & Archival
   Sound Lab, pg 736
dbF a Media Company, pg 739
Omega Recording Studios, pg 845
Soundtrax Inc, pg 895

MASSACHUSETTS

CommCreative, pg 728
Continental Recordings Inc, pg 731
Cramer, pg 732
Soundtrack Group, pg 895
Video Express, pg 928

MICHIGAN

Brilliance Audio, pg 710
Digi Sign Design LLC, pg 741
K&R's Recording Studios Inc,
   pg 796
MessageMakers, pg 824

MINNESOTA

GMI Productions, pg 771

MISSISSIPPI

Jasper Ewing & Sons Inc, pg 757

MISSOURI

Audio-VideoGraphics Inc, pg 694
Hardcastle Films & Video, pg 776
Show-Me Audio-Visual, pg 887

NEW HAMPSHIRE

Academic & Campus Technology
   Services, pg 672
Apertura, pg 686
Chip Taylor Communications LLC,
   pg 907

NEW JERSEY

AJS Events, pg 679
NFL Films Music Library, pg 841

Reed Presentations Inc (RPI),
   pg 872
Starlite, pg 900
Suede Interactive, pg 903
Video Corporation of America
   (VCA), pg 927

NEW YORK

The Big House Group, pg 705
Burlington A/V Recording Media,
   pg 712
Chromavision Corp, pg 723
CMI Communications, pg 727
Digital Force Ltd, pg 742
DuArt Media Services, pg 747
Duplication Depot Inc, pg 748
Duplication Specialists Inc, pg 748
HAVE Inc, pg 777
HB-Content, pg 777
HOThead, pg 782
Magno Sound Inc, pg 815
Manhattan Center Studios Inc,
   pg 816
Mood Creations Ltd, pg 829
New York Audio Productions,
   pg 840
Elliot Sokolov Music, pg 892
Sony Music Entertainment, pg 893
Specialized Audio-Visual Inc,
   pg 896
Teatown Communications Group,
   pg 908
USA Studios, pg 923
Visual Technologies Corp, pg 932
Zelman Studios Ltd, pg 945

NORTH CAROLINA

Pat Appleson Studios Inc, pg 687
Duke Media Services, pg 747
Take One Productions Ltd, pg 906
Trailblazer Studios®, pg 917

OHIO

Cuyahoga Community College
   Student Production Office (SPO),
   pg 736
Mills James Productions, pg 828
Musicol Recording, pg 835
SoundSpace Inc, pg 895

OKLAHOMA

Academic Media & Digital
   Services, pg 672
Garman Productions LLC, pg 768

OREGON

REX, pg 874

PENNSYLVANIA

American Artist Studio, pg 682
Craig Recording Studios, pg 732
FMP Media Solutions Inc, pg 763
Forge Recording LLC, pg 764
JPL, pg 795
Production Masters Inc (PMI),
   pg 864
The Videohouse Inc, pg 929

RHODE ISLAND

Sound-FX-Design, pg 894

SOUTH CAROLINA

DaviSound, pg 739

TENNESSEE

Ardent Studios Inc, pg 688
Memphis Communications Corp,
   pg 823
Stage Post, pg 899

TEXAS

Dub King, pg 747
Sound Works, pg 894
Stage Directions, pg 898
Texas Heart Institute Visual
   Communication Services, pg 911
U-Edit Video, pg 920

VERMONT

University of Vermont, Instructional
   Television Dept, pg 923

VIRGINIA

BES Studios, pg 704
Lee Hartman & Sons Inc, pg 805
The Whitlock Group, pg 937

WASHINGTON

Inland Audio Visual Co, pg 788
Kostov Productions, pg 801
Pacific Multimedia Inc, pg 849
Victory Studios, pg 927

WISCONSIN

Audio Visual of Milwaukee Inc,
   pg 694
5th Floor Recording Co, pg 760
USAV Group Inc, pg 923

PUERTO RICO

Stage Crew Audiovisual Inc, pg 898

BRITISH COLUMBIA

Triad Communications Ltd, pg 918

ONTARIO

Wanted! Sound + Picture, pg 933

Duplication—Compact Discs

ALABAMA

Sound of Birmingham Productions,
   pg 894

ARIZONA

Allusion Studios & Pure Wave
   Audio, pg 681
Film Creations Ltd, pg 760
Fire Power Music LLC, pg 761
Merestone, pg 823
On-Site Video, pg 846
SPEAK HOUSE Audio™, pg 896
Star Video Duplicating, pg 900
Tempe Tape & Disc, pg 911

ARKANSAS

Michael Mueller Video Productions,
   pg 833
White Diamond Productions LLC,
   pg 937

CALIFORNIA

AB Audio Visual Entertainment Inc,
   pg 672
ACDC Audio CD & Cassette,
   pg 674
Action Video, pg 675

AUDIO

Duplication—Compact Discs (continued)

CALIFORNIA (continued)

AGF Media Services, pg 678
AlphaDogs Inc, pg 682
Assured Audio Visual, pg 691
Audio Rents, pg 693
Bay Records, pg 702
California Tape Products Inc, pg 714
Creative Media Recording, pg 733
Creative Sound Corp, pg 733
Custom Video Productions Inc, pg 736
DiskFaktory, pg 743
FJ Productions Inc, pg 762
JD Audio Visual Inc, pg 793
JDS Video & Media Productions Inc, pg 793
Lightning Media, pg 808
Maximus Media Inc, pg 820
M2 Communications, pg 833
New Cyberian Systems Inc, pg 839
PME Audio/Video, pg 858
QRS Software Services, pg 867
Quality Clones, pg 867
Reel Picture, pg 872
RJ Video Productions, pg 875
Roundabout Entertainment Inc, pg 878
SF Global Sourcing, pg 885
SonicPool, pg 892
Sounds Unique, pg 895
Staylor-Made Communications Inc, pg 900
Sunburst Recording, pg 904
Total Creative, pg 916
Trac Recording Studio, pg 916
United Audio Video Inc, pg 921
Video Movie Magic, pg 928
Visions Plus, pg 931

COLORADO

Audio Consultant Services Inc, pg 693
Flashback Media Productions, pg 762
Mike's Camera, pg 827
Rocky Mountain Audio/Video Productions Inc, pg 876
Rose Packaging & Design Inc, pg 877
Side 3 Studios, pg 887

CONNECTICUT

A/V Davey, pg 697
Cine-Med Inc, pg 723
CMI Media Management, pg 727
New London Media, pg 839
T & M Digital Services LLC, pg 906
Video Production Associates Inc, pg 928

DELAWARE

Ken-Del Productions Inc, pg 797
Ken-Del Studios, pg 797
Side Door Studio Inc, pg 887

FLORIDA

Access Media Group, pg 673
Accord Productions, pg 673
Civins Productions Inc, pg 725
Easy Edit Video Inc, pg 750
MAC Production Group, pg 813
Mach 1 Productions, pg 813

ONstage, pg 846
Sunrise Studios, pg 904
Video Techniques Inc, pg 928

GEORGIA

Beast Atlanta, pg 703
ECG Productions, pg 750
Hottrax Records, pg 782
Omega Media Group Inc, pg 845
ON Services, a GES Company, pg 846
Playback Now Inc, pg 858
Video Copy Services Inc, pg 927

ILLINOIS

Advanced Audio Technology, pg 677
IV Media Resources, pg 792
Kelmscott Communications, pg 797
Major Media Inc, pg 815
Major Media Productions Inc, pg 815
Midwest Digital Corp, pg 827
RADMAR Inc, pg 869
RBR Productions, pg 870
Sound/Video Impressions Inc, pg 894
20/20 Communications Inc, pg 920

INDIANA

Advanced Media Integration, pg 677
Sweetwater Sound Inc, pg 905

IOWA

Duplication Media, pg 748

KENTUCKY

American Recordable Media, pg 684
Audio Visual Techniques Inc, pg 695

MAINE

Headlight Audio Visual Inc, pg 777

MARYLAND

Absolute Hollywood, pg 672
Carpel Video Inc, pg 717
CPR MultiMedia Solutions, pg 732
dbF a Media Company, pg 739
Lion & Fox Recording Studios, pg 809
Saah Video, pg 879
Satellite Media Production, pg 881

MASSACHUSETTS

Continental Recordings Inc, pg 731
M Works Mastering Studio, pg 813
Soundtrack Group, pg 895
Rik Tinory Productions, pg 914
Video Express, pg 928

MICHIGAN

Brilliance Audio, pg 710
Digi Sign Design LLC, pg 741
GMP Music, pg 772
TGA Recording Co, pg 911
The Transfer Zone®, pg 917

MINNESOTA

The ADS Group, pg 676
Rum Jungle Media, pg 878

MISSISSIPPI

Bowie Audio Visual Enterprises Inc, pg 709

MISSOURI

Allied Photocolor Co, pg 681
Show-Me Audio-Visual, pg 887
Studio Worx Inc, pg 903
VSG Digital Media Solutions, pg 933

MONTANA

Jereco Studios Inc, pg 793

NEBRASKA

Three Pillars Media, pg 913

NEVADA

Aardvark Video & Media Productions, pg 671

NEW HAMPSHIRE

Captain Fiddle Music & Publications, pg 716

NEW JERSEY

AJS Events, pg 679
Allegro Productions Inc, pg 680
Audio Visual Dynamics®, pg 694
Color Leasing Studios, pg 727
Disc Makers, pg 743
Euro-Pacific Film & Video Productions Inc, pg 756
International Audio Visual Inc, pg 790
Midnight Media Group Inc, pg 827
Milgrom Productions, pg 827
Oasis Disc Manufacturing, pg 844
Starlite, pg 900
Synergem, pg 905

NEW MEXICO

Production Outfitters, pg 864
Rainbow Media Taos, pg 869

NEW YORK

Adwar Video, pg 678
Bellin Productions, pg 703
The Big House Group, pg 705
Cornell Laboratory of Ornithology, pg 731
Design Audio Visual Inc, pg 741
Digital Art Video Inc, pg 741
Duplication Depot Inc, pg 748
Foothill Digital Inc, pg 763
HB-Content, pg 777
HOThead, pg 782
International Digital Centre, pg 790
J&D Laboratories Inc, pg 793
Mark Custom Recording Service Inc, pg 817
Mood Creations Ltd, pg 829
Teatown Communications Group, pg 908
Visual Technologies Corp, pg 932

NORTH CAROLINA

Pat Appleson Studios Inc, pg 687
Camcor Inc, pg 715
Take One Productions Ltd, pg 906

NORTH DAKOTA

Media Productions, pg 822

OHIO

Central Ohio Audio Video, pg 719
Curtis Inc, pg 736
Musicol Recording, pg 835
QCA, pg 867

OKLAHOMA

Piper Media Services Inc, pg 857

OREGON

KTVA Productions, pg 802
REX, pg 874

PENNSYLVANIA

American Artist Studio, pg 682
Audio Visual Communications Inc, pg 694
Craig Recording Studios, pg 732
Innovision Media Group, pg 788
Laser Video Corp, pg 804
The Videohouse Inc, pg 929

RHODE ISLAND

Sound-FX-Design, pg 894

SOUTH CAROLINA

Genesis Creative, pg 769

TENNESSEE

Anode Inc, pg 686
Ardent Studios Inc, pg 688
CRT Custom Products Inc, pg 735
International Marketing Group, pg 790
JamSync, pg 793
Motion Picture Services, pg 831
NTS ProMedia, pg 843
Stage Post, pg 899
WTSmedia, pg 942

TEXAS

Arcube Multimedia Inc, pg 688
Crystal Clear Media Group, pg 735
The Editing Co, pg 750
Great Recordings LLC, pg 773
Matson Multi-Media, pg 820
Omega Broadcast Group, pg 845
Replicopy Digital Media Center, pg 873
The Samuels Co, pg 879
The Sound Lab Inc, pg 894
Tropikal Productions, pg 918
U-Edit Video, pg 920
World Media Group Inc, pg 941
The Yesterday USA Radio Networks, pg 944

UTAH

ELS Productions Inc, pg 753
ImageWorks Communications, pg 785
One Stop CD Shop LLC, pg 846

VIRGINIA

American AV, pg 682
AudioImage Recording, pg 695
CDR Communications Inc, pg 719
Furnace MFG, pg 767
Lee Hartman & Sons Inc, pg 805
National Media Services Inc, pg 836

WASHINGTON

CCI Solutions, pg 718
Pacific Multimedia Inc, pg 849

WEST VIRGINIA

Blackwater Video Productions, pg 707

WISCONSIN

Audio Visual of Milwaukee Inc, pg 694
Concept Productions Inc, pg 730
Excel Duplication Services, pg 757
5th Floor Recording Co, pg 760
Sound Strations Audio Productions Inc, pg 894
Watts Communications Inc, pg 934

PUERTO RICO

Stage Crew Audiovisual Inc, pg 898

BRITISH COLUMBIA

Triad Communications Ltd, pg 918

MANITOBA

Ironstone Technologies Inc, pg 791

ONTARIO

ADS Media, pg 677
Silver Creek Media Inc, pg 888
Video Excellence Productions, pg 927
Wanted! Sound + Picture, pg 933

Duplicator, *see* Tape Duplicator

Easy Listening Music, *see* Music Libraries—Easy Listening

Editing

ALABAMA

Dogwood Productions Inc, pg 745

ARIZONA

Aardvark Productions LLC, pg 671
Allusion Studios & Pure Wave Audio, pg 681
Fire Power Music LLC, pg 761
Forensic Video Deposition Service, pg 764
Merestone, pg 823
Metropolitan Audio-Visual Inc, pg 824
SPEAK HOUSE Audio™, pg 896
Star Video Duplicating, pg 900

ARKANSAS

Live'N'Loud, pg 810
Michael Mueller Video Productions, pg 833
White Diamond Productions LLC, pg 937

CALIFORNIA

AB Audio Visual Entertainment Inc, pg 672
ACDC Audio CD & Cassette, pg 674
Action Video, pg 675
Aliso Creek Productions Inc, pg 680
AlphaDogs Inc, pg 682
Artichoke Productions, pg 690
Audio Upgrades, pg 694
The Banquet Sound Studios, pg 701
Berkeley Sound Artists Inc, pg 704
Blue Lotus Temple Studio, pg 707
Chace Audio by Deluxe, pg 720
Creative Media Recording, pg 733

Custom Video Productions Inc, pg 736
Different Fur Recording Ltd, pg 741
Digital Jungle, pg 742
DV Post, pg 748
Earwax Productions Inc, pg 749
ECONEWS (Environmental Television Series) & (Environmental Directions Radio Series), pg 750
Express Media Inc, pg 757
Eye & I Productions, pg 758
5 Alarm Music, pg 762
FJ Productions Inc, pg 762
48 Windows, pg 764
Full Moon & High Tide Productions & Studios, pg 767
Gold Standard Productions, pg 772
Gordon Productions Inc, pg 772
Havas Edge, pg 777
iCorpTv, pg 783
Illuminate Post/Digital Finishing, pg 784
JDS Video & Media Productions Inc, pg 793
Juice Studios, pg 795
Kris Stevens Enterprises, pg 801
K2B2 Records, pg 802
KVIE-Channel 6, pg 802
Ludlow Media, pg 812
Lynch Communications, pg 813
Main Street Media Inc, pg 815
Maximus Media Inc, pg 820
McCune Audio-Video-Lighting, pg 821
Media Magic, pg 822
The Media Staff Inc, pg 822
On-Trax Inc, pg 846
Oral Tradition Sound & Music, pg 847
OTR Studios, pg 848
Palardo Productions, pg 850
Penrose Productions, pg 854
piXvfm Inc, pg 857
PM Productions, pg 858
PME Audio/Video, pg 858
Point.360, pg 858
Polarity Post Production, pg 858
Private Island Audio Inc, pg 862
Pyramind Studios, pg 867
QRS Software Services, pg 867
Reality Check Systems, pg 871
Regent Press Publishers & Printers, pg 873
Roundabout Entertainment Inc, pg 878
Saturn Studios, pg 881
Shapeshifter, pg 885
Steve Shapiro Music, pg 885
SonicPool, pg 892
Sounds Unique, pg 895
Staylor-Made Communications Inc, pg 900
Still N' Motion, pg 901
Studio Circle Recordings, pg 902
Studio 132, pg 902
Studio 637, pg 903
Tam Communications Inc, pg 906
Total Creative, pg 916
Trac Recording Studio, pg 916
United Audio Video Inc, pg 921
Universal Studios, pg 922
Z-Ville Productions, pg 944

COLORADO

Audio Consultant Services Inc, pg 693
Ceavco Audio Visual Company Inc, pg 719
Tim Cissell Music, pg 725
Conly Productions, pg 730
Daylight Productions & Rentals, pg 739

Flashback Media Productions, pg 762
Mike's Camera, pg 827
Open Media Foundation, pg 846
Rocky Mountain Audio/Video Productions Inc, pg 876

CONNECTICUT

Antenna International, pg 686
A/V Davey, pg 697
BRB Audiovisual Productions, pg 709
Cine-Med Inc, pg 723
The Gary-Paul Agency, pg 768
Guymark Studios LLC, pg 775
Ironik Design & Post, pg 791
New London Media, pg 839
Palace Production Center, pg 850
P&P Studios Inc, pg 851
Powerstation Events, pg 860
T & M Digital Services LLC, pg 906

DELAWARE

Ken-Del Studios, pg 797
Side Door Studio Inc, pg 887

DISTRICT OF COLUMBIA

Hillmann & Carr Inc, pg 780
Interface Media Group, pg 789
Northeastern Digital Recording Inc, pg 842

FLORIDA

A Cut Above Video Productions Inc, pg 671
Access Media Group, pg 673
Accord Productions, pg 673
Adrenaline Films, pg 676
Audacity Recording Studios, pg 693
CD ROM™ Inc, pg 718
Communications Concepts Inc (CCI), pg 729
Comtel Inc, pg 730
The Kitchen, pg 799
LHV Audio Services, pg 807
Morrisound Recording, pg 830
Phat Planet Recording Studios, pg 855
Photosound of Orlando Inc, pg 856
Shooting Stars Post Inc, pg 886
Stage America LLC, pg 898
Sunfire Communications Inc, pg 904
Sunrise Studios, pg 904
Universal Studios Florida® Production Group, pg 922
WKMG-TV News 6, pg 940

GEORGIA

Beast Atlanta, pg 703
Crawford Media Services Inc, pg 733
ECG Productions, pg 750
Encyclomedia, pg 754
Guerrilla Productions LLC, pg 774
Hottrax Records, pg 782
Lighting & Production Equipment Inc, pg 807
Stage Front Presentation Systems, pg 899
White Dog Studios, pg 937

HAWAII

Hyperspective Studios Inc, pg 783
Media Bridge Gamekids, pg 821

ILLINOIS

ABS Enterprises, pg 672
Advanced Audio Technology, pg 677
AnswersMedia, pg 686
Big Shoulders Digital Video Productions, pg 705
CCore Media Inc, pg 718
Esoteric Media, pg 755
IV Media Resources, pg 792
Major Media Inc, pg 815
Multimedia Marketing Group, pg 833
Optimus, pg 847
Pepper Group, pg 854
PSAV® Presentation Services (Hotel Services Division), pg 866
Steven Samler Music & Sound, pg 879
Solid Sound Recording Studio, pg 892
Sound/Video Impressions Inc, pg 894
20/20 Communications Inc, pg 920
WEEK TV, pg 935
Woodside Avenue Music Productions Inc, pg 941

INDIANA

A-V-A Video Productions, pg 671
Bright Ideas Creative Services, pg 710
Communication Ministries, pg 728
Alan Johnson Recording, pg 794
OMNI Productions, pg 845
Sweetwater Sound Inc, pg 905

IOWA

Educational Technology & Media Services, pg 751
Hedquist Productions Inc, pg 778
Iowa State University-Information Technology Services, pg 791

KENTUCKY

Audio Visual Techniques Inc, pg 695
Broadway Digital, pg 711
Hammond Communications Group Inc, pg 775
Barney Miller's Inc, pg 827

LOUISIANA

Launch Media, pg 804
Louisiana State University Division of Strategic Communications, pg 811
Vidox Motion Imagery, pg 930

MAINE

Headlight Audio Visual Inc, pg 777
WGME-TV, pg 936

MARYLAND

CPR MultiMedia Solutions, pg 732
The Cutting Corporation, GraphicAudio® & Archival Sound Lab, pg 736
dbF a Media Company, pg 739
The Image Generators, pg 785
Kramer Communications Video Production, pg 801
Lion & Fox Recording Studios, pg 809
Omega Recording Studios, pg 845
Satellite Media Production, pg 881
Sheffield Audio/Video Productions, pg 885
Smolian Sound Studios, pg 891

AUDIO

Editing (continued)

MARYLAND (continued)

Speakeasy™ Productions Inc, pg 896
Welocalize, pg 935

MASSACHUSETTS

CommCreative, pg 728
Continental Recordings Inc, pg 731
Extreme Reach Inc, pg 757
Labrecque Creative Sound, pg 803
M Works Mastering Studio, pg 813
Monadnock Media Inc, pg 829
Northern Light Productions (NLP), pg 842
Penfield Productions Ltd, pg 853
Soundtrack Group, pg 895
Rik Tinory Productions, pg 914
TR Productions, pg 916
WGBH Production Group, pg 936

MICHIGAN

Audio Graphic Services, pg 693
Brilliance Audio, pg 710
The Brookwood Studio Inc, pg 711
Digi Sign Design LLC, pg 741
Digital Image Studios LLC, pg 742
GMP Music, pg 772
K&R's Recording Studios Inc, pg 796
MessageMakers, pg 824
Michigan Recording Arts Institute & Technologies, pg 825
RingSide Creative, pg 875
TGA Recording Co, pg 911

MINNESOTA

The ADS Group, pg 676
Alpha Video & Audio Inc, pg 682
Badiyan Inc, pg 700
BeyerSound & Essay Audio, pg 705
GMI Productions, pg 771
Media Loft Inc, pg 822
Winterland Studios, pg 940

MISSOURI

Avatar Studios, pg 697
Hardcastle Films & Video, pg 776
Show-Me Audio-Visual, pg 887
Studio Worx Inc, pg 903

MONTANA

Jereco Studios Inc, pg 793
KUSM TV, pg 802
ooLite Media LLC, pg 846

NEBRASKA

JoeAudio, pg 794
Three Pillars Media, pg 913

NEVADA

JCS Video Productions, pg 793
Tanglewood Productions, pg 907
VirtualMix, pg 930

NEW HAMPSHIRE

Apertura, pg 686
Captain Fiddle Music & Publications, pg 716
Chip Taylor Communications LLC, pg 907

NEW JERSEY

AJS Events, pg 679
Allegro Productions Inc, pg 680
The Audio Department Inc, pg 693
CFP Video Productions Inc, pg 720
Color Leasing Studios, pg 727
Euro-Pacific Film & Video Productions Inc, pg 756
Laurel Video Productions, pg 804
MiB MediaWorks, pg 825
Midnight Media Group Inc, pg 827
Milgrom Productions, pg 827
NFL Films Inc, pg 841
NFL Films Music Library, pg 841
Optisonics Productions, pg 847
SADiE Inc, pg 879
Starlite, pg 900
Suede Interactive, pg 903
VCSvideo, pg 925

NEW MEXICO

Production Outfitters, pg 864

NEW YORK

A-List Quality Videographer, pg 671
Aural Gratification Inc, pg 695
Bellin Productions, pg 703
The Big House Group, pg 705
Buffalo Video Production, pg 712
Chromavision Corp, pg 723
Design Audio Visual Inc, pg 741
Digital Art Video Inc, pg 741
Digital Arts NY, pg 742
Digital Force Ltd, pg 742
DuArt Media Services, pg 747
Duplication Depot Inc, pg 748
Fingerpaint, pg 761
Foothill Digital Inc, pg 763
4-D Creative Media, pg 764
HB-Content, pg 777
HBO Studio Productions, pg 777
Headroom Digital Audio, pg 777
Heavy Melody, pg 778
Hello World Communications, pg 778
HOThead, pg 782
InterNation Inc, pg 789
Jupiter Moon Productions, pg 795
KAS Music & Sound, pg 796
L A Bruell Inc, pg 802
La Paloma Films, pg 803
Manhattan Center Studios Inc, pg 816
Mark Custom Recording Service Inc, pg 817
Masterdisk Corp, pg 819
Mood Creations Ltd, pg 829
Mother West, pg 831
New York Audio Productions, pg 840
The Palmer Group, pg 850
Posthorn Recordings, pg 859
RadioArt/Bob & Ray CDs & MP3 Files, pg 869
David Rapkin Audio Production, pg 870
Sear Sound, pg 883
Elliot Sokolov Music, pg 892
Sony Music Entertainment, pg 893
SoundByte Productions Inc, pg 894
Synaptic Digital, pg 905
Teatown Communications Group, pg 908
TeleTime Productions, pg 910
Tiki Recording Studios Inc, pg 914
USA Studios, pg 923
Visual Technologies Corp, pg 932
Zelman Studios Ltd, pg 945

NORTH CAROLINA

Pat Appleson Studios Inc, pg 687
Audio Art, pg 693
The Communications Group Inc, pg 729
Digital Rain LLC, pg 742
Duke Media Services, pg 747
Franklin Video Inc, pg 765
Horizon Video Productions Inc, pg 781
On Location North Carolina, pg 846
Studio B Mastering, pg 902
Take One Productions Ltd, pg 906
Trailblazer Studios®, pg 917
2BruceStudio, pg 920

NORTH DAKOTA

Media Productions, pg 822

OHIO

Alegra House Publishers, pg 679
Bartha, pg 702
Cinecraft Productions Inc, pg 723
Curtis Inc, pg 736
Cuyahoga Community College Student Production Office (SPO), pg 736
Lyon Video Inc, pg 813
Mills James Productions, pg 828
Musicol Recording, pg 835
R&B Communications Inc, pg 870
SoundSpace Inc, pg 895
The Telos Alliance, pg 910
Vista Color Imaging Inc, pg 931

OKLAHOMA

Academic Media & Digital Services, pg 672
Garman Productions LLC, pg 768
PDC Productions, pg 852

OREGON

Future Disc LLC, pg 767
KTVA Productions, pg 802
Odyssey Productions Inc, pg 844
REX, pg 874

PENNSYLVANIA

American Artist Studio, pg 682
Audio Visual Communications Inc, pg 694
Craig Recording Studios, pg 732
Filmaker Technology, pg 760
FMP Media Solutions Inc, pg 763
Forge Recording LLC, pg 764
Innovision Media Group, pg 788
Ivory Productions, pg 792
JPL, pg 795
Laser Video Corp, pg 804
Panta Rhei Media Inc, pg 851
Production Masters Inc (PMI), pg 864
Right Coast Recording Inc, pg 875
The Videohouse Inc, pg 929
Visual Sound Inc, pg 931
WHYY Inc, pg 938

RHODE ISLAND

Sound-FX-Design, pg 894

SOUTH CAROLINA

DaviSound, pg 739
Genesis Creative, pg 769
Venture Media, pg 925

TENNESSEE

American Blackguard Inc, pg 683
Analog Man Recording Studio, pg 685
Anode Inc, pg 686
Ardent Music LLC, pg 688
Ardent Studios Inc, pg 688
Brantley Sound Associates Inc, pg 709
Continental Film, pg 731
JamSync, pg 793
Kingswood Productions, pg 799
Love Shack Recording Studios, pg 811
Memphis Communications Corp, pg 823
Mr Mark's Used Musical, Stereo & Studio Equipment Store, pg 828
Motion Picture Services, pg 831
Scripps Networks, pg 882
Stage Post, pg 899
Technical Support Systems LLC, pg 908
Zion Music Group, pg 945

TEXAS

AMA Nystrom Printing/Finishing, pg 682
AMS Pictures, pg 684
Anaphora Literary Press, pg 685
Audiomoxie®, pg 695
Biway Media, pg 706
Castleview Productions, pg 717
Cerutti Productions Inc, pg 720
Communication Arts Multimedia Inc, pg 728
The Editing Co, pg 750
Fire Station Studios, pg 761
Freeman, pg 765
Great Recordings LLC, pg 773
Horizon Film + Video Productions, pg 781
Marx InDigital, pg 818
Matson Multi-Media, pg 820
Maverick Video Productions, pg 820
Julye Newlin Productions Inc, pg 840
Out of the BLUE Media, pg 849
Phillips Media Source, pg 855
Planet Dallas Recording Studios, pg 857
Real to Reel Studios Inc, pg 871
Romar Learning Solutions LLC, pg 877
The Samuels Co, pg 879
The Sound Lab Inc, pg 894
Sound Works, pg 894
South Coast Film & Video, pg 895
Stage Directions, pg 898
Texas Heart Institute Visual Communication Services, pg 911
TopCat Records LLC, pg 915
Tropikal Productions, pg 918
World Media Group Inc, pg 941

UTAH

ELS Productions Inc, pg 753
ImageWorks Communications, pg 785
Performance Audio LLC, pg 854
Soularium Recording Studios, pg 893

VERMONT

University of Vermont, Instructional Television Dept, pg 923

VIRGINIA

AudioImage Recording, pg 695
Bias Studios, pg 705

CACI Integrated Communications, pg 713
CDR Communications Inc, pg 719
Wally Cleaver's Recording Service, pg 726
Metro Productions, pg 824
National Media Services Inc, pg 836
Studio Center Corp, pg 902
The Whitlock Group, pg 937

WASHINGTON

Inland Audio Visual Co, pg 788
Kostov Productions, pg 801
North-by-Northwest - A Digital Studio, pg 842
Pacific Multimedia Inc, pg 849
Sound Sound, pg 894
Victory Studios, pg 927

WEST VIRGINIA

Sweetsong Productions, pg 905

WISCONSIN

Audio Visual of Milwaukee Inc, pg 694
Concept Productions Inc, pg 730
5th Floor Recording Co, pg 760
Learning Technology Services, pg 805
Meridian Studios, pg 824
Sound Strations Audio Productions Inc, pg 894
TBC Studios, pg 907
University of Wisconsin-Oshkosh Radio-TV-Film Dept, pg 923
USAV Group Inc, pg 923
Video Wisconsin Inc, pg 929
Watts Communications Inc, pg 934
Wisconsin Public Television, pg 940

PUERTO RICO

Stage Crew Audiovisual Inc, pg 898

ALBERTA

Global TV, pg 771

BRITISH COLUMBIA

Pinewood Sound, pg 857
Triad Communications Ltd, pg 918

MANITOBA

DACAPO Productions Inc, pg 737

ONTARIO

ADS Media, pg 677
AMPLUS Productions, pg 684
DebsVoice, pg 739
Eggplant Pictures & Sound, pg 751
GAPC (General Assembly Production Centre), pg 768
JFB Communications, pg 794
JL Recording Studios, pg 794
MCS Recording Studios, pg 821
Metalworks Recording Studios Inc, pg 824
Nightingale Music Productions Inc, pg 841
Silver Creek Media Inc, pg 888
Spence-Thomas Audio Post, pg 897
Trebas Institute, pg 917
Video Excellence Productions, pg 927
VO2 Mix Audio Post, pg 932
Wanted! Sound + Picture, pg 933

QUEBEC

Group PVP, pg 774
Trebas Institute, pg 917

Electronic Music, *see* Music Libraries—Electronic

Equalizer Distributors

ARIZONA

Allusion Studios & Pure Wave Audio, pg 681
EAR Professional Audio/Video, pg 749
Radio Design Labs (RDL), pg 869
Troxell-CDI, pg 918

CALIFORNIA

Ametron Audio/Video, pg 684
Associated Sound, pg 691
Audio Images Corp, pg 693
BigFoot Mobile Systems, pg 705
Cibola Systems, pg 723
Empire Pro, pg 753
Harman Professional Solutions, pg 776
JD Audio Visual Inc, pg 793
MediaMation Inc, pg 822
MediaPOINTE, pg 823
SNAP, pg 891
Sound Service Co, pg 894
Sounds Unique, pg 895
Southern California Sound Image Inc, pg 895
Stanislaus AV Inc, pg 899
TOA Electronics Inc, pg 915
Towards 2000 Inc, pg 916
VMI Inc, pg 932

COLORADO

Audio Consultant Services Inc, pg 693

CONNECTICUT

Connecticut Audio & Theatrical Supply, pg 731
HB Communications Inc, pg 777
The Music People Inc, pg 834

DELAWARE

Actors Attic, pg 675

FLORIDA

Access Media Group, pg 673
Altel Systems Group Inc, pg 682
AVI-SPL, pg 698
Broadcasters General Store Inc, pg 711
Digital Video Systems, pg 742
Harris Corp, pg 776
Hi-Tech Enterprises Inc, pg 779
Industrial Strength Inc, pg 787
Intermark Industries Inc, pg 789
Lighting Sales Connection Inc, pg 808
ONstage, pg 846
Recording Media & Equipment Inc (RM&E), pg 872
Stereo Sales Inc, pg 900
TAI Audio, pg 906
Technomedia Solutions, pg 909

GEORGIA

Clark, pg 725
Lighting & Production Equipment Inc, pg 807
Stage Front Presentation Systems, pg 899

ILLINOIS

Allen Visual Systems Inc, pg 680
Woodside Avenue Music Productions Inc, pg 941

INDIANA

Heart Breaker Entertainment LLC, pg 778
Sensory Technologies LLC, pg 884
SHP Electronics, pg 887
Sweetwater Sound Inc, pg 905

KENTUCKY

Axxis Leasing Inc, pg 700
Barney Miller's Inc, pg 827
NOR-COM Inc, pg 841

MAINE

Headlight Audio Visual Inc, pg 777
Independent Audio Inc, pg 786

MARYLAND

Bradley Broadcast & Pro Audio, pg 709
Cardinal Sound & Video, pg 717
Kipp Visual Systems Inc, pg 799

MASSACHUSETTS

Terry Hanley Audio Systems Inc, pg 775
Professional Audio Design Inc, pg 865
Rule Boston Camera, pg 878

MICHIGAN

Digi Sign Design LLC, pg 741
On Stage Visuals, pg 846
TEL Systems LLC, pg 909

MISSOURI

Production Support Services Inc, pg 864
Schiller's Audio-Visual, pg 881

NEW HAMPSHIRE

APS Lighting-Sound-AV, pg 688
Technet® Systems Group, pg 908

NEW JERSEY

Alltec Stores, a Vcom IMC Company, pg 681
AlltecPro, pg 681
Audio Visual Associates, pg 694
AV Bluebook, pg 696
Diversified, pg 744
Earl Girls Inc, pg 749
HamiltonBuhl, pg 775
Nelson Enterprises Theatrical Supply Co, pg 838
Starlite, pg 900
Wired 4 Sound Inc, pg 940
Yorktel, pg 944

NEW MEXICO

Quickbeam Systems Inc (QSI), pg 868

NEW YORK

ADI Global Distribution, pg 676
Aura Sonic Ltd (ASL), pg 695
Cadence Jazz Records, pg 713
Colortone Audio Visual, pg 728
Design Audio Visual Inc, pg 741
Group One Ltd, pg 774
HAVE Inc, pg 777
Hot House Professional Audio, pg 782
KVL Audio Visual Services Inc, pg 802
Markertek Video Supply, pg 817
MultiDyne Video & Fiber Optics Systems, pg 833
Posthorn Recordings, pg 859
TecNec Distributing, pg 909
Toys From The Attic, pg 916
Visual Word Systems Inc, pg 932
XTA Electronics Ltd, pg 943

OHIO

ITA Audio Visual Solutions, pg 791
Parts Express, pg 851
The Telos Alliance, pg 910
Tri-State Audio Visual Co, pg 918

OREGON

SuperDigital Ltd, pg 904

PENNSYLVANIA

Advanced AV LLC, pg 677
Clair Companies, pg 725
Vistacom Inc, pg 931

RHODE ISLAND

Shanix Inc, pg 885

SOUTH CAROLINA

DaviSound, pg 739

TENNESSEE

Allstar Audio Systems Inc, pg 681
Belew Enterprises, pg 703
Lowrance Sound Co Inc, pg 812
Mr Mark's Used Musical, Stereo & Studio Equipment Store, pg 828
Spectrum Sound Inc, pg 897
Technical Support Systems LLC, pg 908
Zion Music Group, pg 945

TEXAS

AVES Audio Visual Systems Inc, pg 698
CAM Audio Inc, pg 714
Crossroads Audio Inc, pg 735
Data Projections Inc, pg 738
Lubbock Audio Visual Inc, pg 812
Pro Video & Film Equipment Co Inc, pg 863
Quality Audio Visual Service Inc, pg 867
RF Specialties of Texas LLC, pg 874
Southwest Sound Solutions, pg 896
Tarpley Media Systems, pg 907

UTAH

Performance Audio LLC, pg 854

VERMONT

Production Advantage Inc, pg 863

VIRGINIA

Avitecture Inc, pg 699
Design & Production Inc, pg 740

AUDIO

Equalizer Distributors (continued)

VIRGINIA (continued)

Intellidyne LLC, pg 789
Lee Hartman & Sons Inc, pg 805
Rocktown Media, pg 876
The Whitlock Group, pg 937

WASHINGTON

CCI Solutions, pg 718
D A Sound, pg 737
Northern Lights & Pro Audio, pg 842

WISCONSIN

Audio Visual of Milwaukee Inc, pg 694
Full Compass Systems, pg 767

PUERTO RICO

Audio Visual Concepts Inc, pg 694
Bonnin Electronics Inc, pg 708

ALBERTA

Infosat Communications Inc, pg 787
Unique Communications Ltd, pg 921

BRITISH COLUMBIA

Commercial Electronics Ltd, pg 728

MANITOBA

Advance Pro, pg 677
Inland Audio Visual Ltd, pg 788

ONTARIO

Cinema Stage Inc, pg 724
Westbury National Show Systems Ltd, pg 936
Yorkville Sound Inc, pg 944

QUEBEC

JAM Industries Ltd, pg 792
SC Media Canada, pg 881

Equalizer Manufacturers

ARIZONA

Radio Design Labs (RDL), pg 869

CALIFORNIA

Furman®, pg 767
Harman Professional Solutions, pg 776
Manley Laboratories Inc, pg 816
Martinsound Inc, pg 818
Meyer Sound Laboratories Inc, pg 824
Millennia Media, FPC, pg 827
Nady Systems Inc, pg 835
Summit Audio Inc, pg 903
TOA Electronics Inc, pg 915

COLORADO

Video Accessory Corp, pg 927

CONNECTICUT

Sound Control Technologies Inc, pg 893

FLORIDA

JT Communications, pg 795

ILLINOIS

Esoteric Sound, pg 755
Precision Electronics Inc, pg 861

MARYLAND

API, pg 687

MINNESOTA

Bosch Security Systems Inc, pg 709
Digital Audio Labs, pg 742
Great River Electronics, pg 773

MISSISSIPPI

Peavey Electronics Corp, pg 852
Sherwood America Inc, pg 886

NEW JERSEY

Apogee Sound International LLC, pg 687

NEW MEXICO

Lectrosonics Inc, pg 805

NEW YORK

Ashly Audio Inc, pg 691
GLI Sound Systems, pg 771
Harbro Corp, pg 776
Hot House Professional Audio, pg 782
MultiDyne Video & Fiber Optics Systems, pg 833

NORTH CAROLINA

Audioarts Engineering, pg 695
Micro Technology Unlimited Inc, pg 826
Wheatstone Corp, pg 937

OHIO

Omnia Audio, pg 845
The Telos Alliance, pg 910

OREGON

BIAMP Systems, pg 705

RHODE ISLAND

M-Audio, pg 813
Numark Industries LP, pg 843
Rane, pg 870

SOUTH CAROLINA

DaviSound, pg 739

UTAH

Rolls Corp, pg 877

WASHINGTON

AudioControl® Inc, pg 695

BRITISH COLUMBIA

Richmond Sound Design Ltd, pg 875

ONTARIO

Yorkville Sound Inc, pg 944

Equalizer Rentals

ARIZONA

Merestone, pg 823
Video West Inc, pg 929

CALIFORNIA

AGF Media Services, pg 678
Alliant Event Services, pg 681
Ametron Audio/Video, pg 684
Associated Sound, pg 691
Audio Rents, pg 693
AV Guys, pg 697
Express Media Inc, pg 757
JD Audio Visual Inc, pg 793
Lynch Communications, pg 813
McCune Audio-Video-Lighting, pg 821
Muse Presentation Technologies, pg 834
On-Trax Inc, pg 846
Sound Service Co, pg 894
Stanislaus AV Inc, pg 899
Synthesizer Rental Service, pg 906
Total Creative, pg 916
Towards 2000 Inc, pg 916
Video Resources Inc, pg 928
VMI Inc, pg 932

COLORADO

Audio Consultant Services Inc, pg 693
Multimedia Audio Visual Inc, pg 833
Spectrum Audio Visual Services, pg 897

CONNECTICUT

A/V Davey, pg 697
Connecticut Audio & Theatrical Supply, pg 731

DELAWARE

Side Door Studio Inc, pg 887

FLORIDA

AVI-SPL, pg 698
Industrial Strength Inc, pg 787
Lighting Sales Connection Inc, pg 808
ONstage, pg 846
TAI Audio, pg 906
Universal Studios Florida® Production Group, pg 922

GEORGIA

Lighting & Production Equipment Inc, pg 807
MAGNUM Companies Ltd, pg 815
Stage Front Presentation Systems, pg 899

HAWAII

Sight & Sound Studios, pg 887

ILLINOIS

AV Chicago Inc, pg 696
OSA International Inc, pg 848
RC Communications, pg 870
Resolution Productions Group, pg 874
Staging Resources Inc, pg 899
Woodside Avenue Music Productions Inc, pg 941

IOWA

Central Lighting & Equipment Inc (CLE), pg 719

KENTUCKY

Audio Visual Techniques Inc, pg 695

MARYLAND

Advance Audiovisual Presentation Ltd, pg 677
Cardinal Sound & Video, pg 717
CPR MultiMedia Solutions, pg 732
Event Tech, pg 756
Maryland Sound International Holding Co LLC, pg 819

MASSACHUSETTS

AVFX Inc, pg 698
Terry Hanley Audio Systems Inc, pg 775
massAV, pg 819
Preston Productions Inc, pg 861

MICHIGAN

Digi Sign Design LLC, pg 741
K&R All Media Productions LLC, pg 796
K&R's Recording Studios Inc, pg 796
On Stage Visuals, pg 846

MISSOURI

Production Support Services Inc, pg 864
Show-Me Audio-Visual, pg 887

MONTANA

Jereco Studios Inc, pg 793

NEVADA

GES Audio Visual, pg 770

NEW HAMPSHIRE

APS Lighting-Sound-AV, pg 688

NEW JERSEY

Audio Visual Associates, pg 694
Audio Visual Dynamics®, pg 694
CFP Video Productions Inc, pg 720
Earl Girls Inc, pg 749
Jeep Jazz Media Solutions, pg 793
Moe AV LLC, pg 828
Nelson Enterprises Theatrical Supply Co, pg 838
Panavid, pg 850
PLS Staging, pg 858
Starlite, pg 900
Wired 4 Sound Inc, pg 940

NEW MEXICO

Quickbeam Systems Inc (QSI), pg 868

NEW YORK

Aura Sonic Ltd (ASL), pg 695
Colortone Audio Visual, pg 728
CP Communications, pg 732
Design Audio Visual Inc, pg 741
KVL Audio Visual Services Inc, pg 802
Posthorn Recordings, pg 859
Visual Word Systems Inc, pg 932

NORTH CAROLINA
AV Connections Inc, pg 697
AV Metro Inc, pg 697

OHIO
ITA Audio Visual Solutions, pg 791
Lyon Video Inc, pg 813
Mills James Productions, pg 828
Production Solutions Inc, pg 864
R&B Communications Inc, pg 870

OKLAHOMA
PDC Productions, pg 852

OREGON
Rose City Sound, pg 877

PENNSYLVANIA
Advanced AV LLC, pg 677
FMP Media Solutions Inc, pg 763
Right Coast Recording Inc, pg 875

TENNESSEE
Allstar Audio Systems Inc, pg 681
Mr Mark's Used Musical, Stereo &
   Studio Equipment Store, pg 828
Technical Support Systems LLC,
   pg 908

TEXAS
Alford Media Services, pg 680
Bright Star Productions Inc, pg 710
Crossroads Audio Inc, pg 735
Lubbock Audio Visual Inc, pg 812
Music Lab Inc, pg 834
Onstage Systems, pg 846
Stage Directions, pg 898

UTAH
Performance Audio LLC, pg 854

VERMONT
Dark Star Lighting & Production,
   pg 737
Edgewood Studios, pg 750

VIRGINIA
American AV, pg 682

WASHINGTON
D A Sound, pg 737
Northern Lights & Pro Audio,
   pg 842
PNTA, pg 858

WISCONSIN
Full Compass Systems, pg 767

PUERTO RICO
Stage Crew Audiovisual Inc, pg 898

ALBERTA
Evolution AV, pg 757
Unique Communications Ltd,
   pg 921

BRITISH COLUMBIA
Commercial Electronics Ltd, pg 728
DL Sound & Lighting Productions
   Ltd, pg 744

MANITOBA
Inland Audio Visual Ltd, pg 788

ONTARIO
RB Productions, pg 870
Westbury National Show Systems
   Ltd, pg 936

Equalizer Repairs

CALIFORNIA
Ametron Audio/Video, pg 684
Audio Images Corp, pg 693
Audio Upgrades, pg 694
Diemer Amp & Keyboard Repair,
   pg 741
McAlister Electronics, pg 820
Sound Service Co, pg 894
TOA Electronics Inc, pg 915
Towards 2000 Inc, pg 916

CONNECTICUT
HB Communications Inc, pg 777

FLORIDA
Hi-Tech Enterprises Inc, pg 779
JT Communications, pg 795
Phat Planet Recording Studios,
   pg 855
Stereo Sales Inc, pg 900
TAI Audio, pg 906

GEORGIA
Lighting & Production Equipment
   Inc, pg 807
Stage Front Presentation Systems,
   pg 899

ILLINOIS
Midwest Digital Corp, pg 827

INDIANA
SHP Electronics, pg 887
Sweetwater Sound Inc, pg 905

KENTUCKY
Axxis Leasing Inc, pg 700
Barney Miller's Inc, pg 827
NOR-COM Inc, pg 841

MASSACHUSETTS
Professional Audio Design Inc,
   pg 865

MICHIGAN
TEL Systems LLC, pg 909

NEW JERSEY
Earl Girls Inc, pg 749
Nelson Enterprises Theatrical
   Supply Co, pg 838
Starlite, pg 900

NEW MEXICO
Quickbeam Systems Inc (QSI),
   pg 868

NEW YORK
Design Audio Visual Inc, pg 741
Hot House Professional Audio,
   pg 782
Toys From The Attic, pg 916

OHIO
ITA Audio Visual Solutions, pg 791
Tri-State Audio Visual Co, pg 918

OREGON
All Service Musical Electronics
   Repair, pg 680

PENNSYLVANIA
Right Coast Recording Inc, pg 875

SOUTH CAROLINA
DaviSound, pg 739

TENNESSEE
Belew Enterprises, pg 703
Technical Support Systems LLC,
   pg 908

TEXAS
Lubbock Audio Visual Inc, pg 812
Quality Audio Visual Service Inc,
   pg 867

VIRGINIA
Avitecture Inc, pg 699

WASHINGTON
Northern Lights & Pro Audio,
   pg 842
PNTA, pg 858

WISCONSIN
Full Compass Systems, pg 767

ALBERTA
Infosat Communications Inc, pg 787
Unique Communications Ltd,
   pg 921

BRITISH COLUMBIA
Commercial Electronics Ltd, pg 728

MANITOBA
Inland Audio Visual Ltd, pg 788

ONTARIO
Westbury National Show Systems
   Ltd, pg 936

QUEBEC
SC Media Canada, pg 881

Ethnic Music, *see* Music Libraries—Ethnic & International

Fiber Optic Cable Distributors

ARIZONA
EAR Professional Audio/Video,
   pg 749
Troxell-CDI, pg 918

ARKANSAS
Jay S Stanley & Associates Inc,
   pg 899

CALIFORNIA
Ametron Audio/Video, pg 684
Audio Images Corp, pg 693
Hosa Technology Inc, pg 781
Southern California Sound Image
   Inc, pg 895

SSL Industries Inc, pg 898
SuperVision, pg 904
Towards 2000 Inc, pg 916
Zack Electronics Inc, pg 945

COLORADO
Audio Consultant Services Inc,
   pg 693

CONNECTICUT
Connecticut Audio & Theatrical
   Supply, pg 731
HB Communications Inc, pg 777
Redco Audio Inc, pg 872

DELAWARE
Actors Attic, pg 675

FLORIDA
Access Media Group, pg 673
Digital Video Systems, pg 742
Herman Pro AV, pg 779
Martin Professional Inc, pg 818
ONstage, pg 846
Stereo Sales Inc, pg 900

GEORGIA
Accu-Tech, pg 673
Stage Front Presentation Systems,
   pg 899

ILLINOIS
Allen Visual Systems Inc, pg 680
Arcor Electronics Co, pg 688
Clark Wire & Cable, pg 725
Cole Wire & Cable Co Inc, pg 727
Joseph Electronics, pg 795
Quintessence Audio Ltd, pg 868

INDIANA
Sensory Technologies LLC, pg 884
SHP Electronics, pg 887
Sweetwater Sound Inc, pg 905

KENTUCKY
Axxis Leasing Inc, pg 700
General Cable, pg 769
NOR-COM Inc, pg 841

MARYLAND
Bradley Broadcast & Pro Audio,
   pg 709
Kipp Visual Systems Inc, pg 799
Siqura Inc, pg 889

MASSACHUSETTS
Professional Audio Design Inc,
   pg 865
SLR Enterprises LLC, pg 890

MICHIGAN
DAWNco, pg 739
TEL Systems LLC, pg 909

MISSOURI
The RapcoHorizon Co, pg 870

NEVADA
MeshTel, pg 824

NEW JERSEY
Alltec Stores, a Vcom IMC
   Company, pg 681
Argraph Corp, pg 688

AUDIO

Fiber Optic Cable Distributors (continued)

NEW JERSEY (continued)

Canare Corporation of America, pg 716
Diversified, pg 744
Fiber Optic Systems Inc (FOSI), pg 759
Interstate Connecting Components, pg 790
Onkyo USA Corp, pg 846
Starlite, pg 900
Yorktel, pg 944

NEW YORK

Albany Theatre Supply Co Inc, pg 679
BTX Technologies, pg 712
HAVE Inc, pg 777
Markertek Video Supply, pg 817
MultiDyne Video & Fiber Optics Systems, pg 833
TecNec Distributing, pg 909

OREGON

TARA Labs, pg 907

PENNSYLVANIA

Advanced AV LLC, pg 677
The Lerro Corp, pg 806
Techni-Tool, a TestEquity LLC company, pg 908

TENNESSEE

Lowrance Sound Co Inc, pg 812

TEXAS

Lubbock Audio Visual Inc, pg 812
Sundance Systems, Fibox Products Division, pg 904

UTAH

Performance Audio LLC, pg 854

VERMONT

Power & Telephone Supply Co, pg 860

VIRGINIA

Avitecture Inc, pg 699
The Whitlock Group, pg 937

WASHINGTON

Telect Inc, pg 910

WISCONSIN

Audio Visual of Milwaukee Inc, pg 694
Full Compass Systems, pg 767

PUERTO RICO

Bonnin Electronics Inc, pg 708

ALBERTA

Infosat Communications Inc, pg 787

MANITOBA

Advance Pro, pg 677

ONTARIO

Cinema Stage Inc, pg 724

Fiber Optic Cable Manufacturers

ARIZONA

Covid Inc, pg 732

CALIFORNIA

Fiber Optic Cable Shop, pg 759
Gefen, pg 769
Hosa Technology Inc, pg 781
Monster Cable Products Inc, pg 829
Opticomm-EMCORE, pg 847
Physical Optics Corp (POC), pg 856

ILLINOIS

Joseph Electronics, pg 795

INDIANA

Belden Inc, pg 703

MARYLAND

RCI Custom Products, pg 871

MASSACHUSETTS

Mohawk, pg 829

MISSOURI

The RapcoHorizon Co, pg 870

NEVADA

MeshTel, pg 824

NEW JERSEY

Brim Electronics, pg 710
Canare Corporation of America, pg 716
Crestron Electronics Inc, pg 734
Onkyo USA Corp, pg 846

NEW YORK

MultiDyne Video & Fiber Optics Systems, pg 833

NORTH CAROLINA

CommScope Inc, pg 728

OREGON

TARA Labs, pg 907

PENNSYLVANIA

West Penn Wire, pg 935

WASHINGTON

Telect Inc, pg 910

Fiber Optic Cable Repairs

CALIFORNIA

Audio Images Corp, pg 693
McAlister Electronics, pg 820
SSL Industries Inc, pg 898
Towards 2000 Inc, pg 916

ILLINOIS

Allen Visual Systems Inc, pg 680
Joseph Electronics, pg 795

KENTUCKY

Axxis Leasing Inc, pg 700
NOR-COM Inc, pg 841

MICHIGAN

K&R's Recording Studios Inc, pg 796
TEL Systems LLC, pg 909

ALBERTA

Infosat Communications Inc, pg 787

Folk Music, see Music Libraries—Folk

Headset & Headphone Distributors

ALABAMA

Curtis Company, pg 736

ARIZONA

Arizona Cine Equipment, pg 688
EAR Professional Audio/Video, pg 749
Metropolitan Audio-Visual Inc, pg 824
Projector SuperStore LLC, pg 865
Tempe Camera, pg 910
Troxell-CDI, pg 918

CALIFORNIA

AKG Acoustics US, pg 679
Ametron Audio/Video, pg 684
Arkon Resources Inc, pg 689
Associated Sound, pg 691
Assured Audio Visual, pg 691
Audio Images Corp, pg 693
Band Pro Film & Digital Inc, pg 701
Be Media, pg 702
California Tape Products Inc, pg 714
Christy's Editorial, pg 723
Cibola Systems, pg 723
Clear-Com® LLC, pg 726
Electronic Design Solutions Inc, pg 752
Empire Pro, pg 753
Filmtools®, pg 761
GigaSonic, pg 770
Gluskin's Custom Audio Video, pg 771
Gravity Media, pg 773
Harman Professional Solutions, pg 776
Instructional Materials & Equipment Distributors (I-Med), pg 789
JD Audio Visual Inc, pg 793
Logitech, pg 811
Lloyd F McKinney Associates Inc, pg 821
Media Fabricators Inc, pg 822
MediaPOINTE, pg 823
Pacific Radio Electronics, pg 849
Pioneer Electronics (USA) Inc, pg 857
PMP Marketing Inc, pg 858
Premier Lighting & Production Co, pg 861
Professional Sound Corp, pg 865
Promax Systems, pg 865
Sanako Inc, pg 880
Sound Service Co, pg 894
Sounds Unique, pg 895
Southern California Sound Image Inc, pg 895

SSL Industries Inc, pg 898

SuperVision, pg 904
Towards 2000 Inc, pg 916
VMI Inc, pg 932
VTP Inc, pg 933
Zack Electronics Inc, pg 945

COLORADO

Audio Consultant Services Inc, pg 693
Mike's Camera, pg 827
Spectrum Audio Visual Services, pg 897

CONNECTICUT

Connecticut Audio & Theatrical Supply, pg 731
HB Communications Inc, pg 777
MAVCO, pg 820
The Music People Inc, pg 834
Sennheiser Electronic Corp, pg 884

DELAWARE

Actors Attic, pg 675

FLORIDA

Access Media Group, pg 673
Alliance Entertainment Corp (AEC) LLC, pg 680
Broadcasters General Store Inc, pg 711
Digital Video Systems, pg 742
Harris Corp, pg 776
Herman Pro AV, pg 779
Hi-Tech Enterprises Inc, pg 779
Hi-Tech Import Export Corp, pg 779
Industrial Strength Inc, pg 787
Intermark Industries Inc, pg 789
Lighting Sales Connection Inc, pg 808
Midtown Video Inc, pg 827
ONstage, pg 846
Recording Media & Equipment Inc (RM&E), pg 872
Stereo Sales Inc, pg 900
TAI Audio, pg 906
Technomedia Solutions, pg 909

GEORGIA

Baker Audio Visual, pg 700
Innocinema, pg 788
Lighting & Production Equipment Inc, pg 807
LT Sound Inc, pg 812
Stage Front Presentation Systems, pg 899
Visioneering International Inc, pg 931

HAWAII

The Audio Visual Co (AVCO), pg 694

ILLINOIS

Allen Visual Systems Inc, pg 680
Central Audio-Visual Equipment Inc, pg 719
Joseph Electronics, pg 795
LKG Industries Inc, pg 810
C V Lloyde, pg 810
Quintessence Audio Ltd, pg 868
RC Communications, pg 870
Waldom Electronics Corp, pg 933
Woodside Avenue Music Productions Inc, pg 941

INDIANA

Sensory Technologies LLC, pg 884
SHP Electronics, pg 887
Sweetwater Sound Inc, pg 905

KENTUCKY

Axxis Leasing Inc, pg 700
Barney Miller's Inc, pg 827
NOR-COM Inc, pg 841

LOUISIANA

Pace Systems, pg 849
Techkno Integration & Design
  Services LLC, pg 908

MAINE

Headlight Audio Visual Inc, pg 777

MARYLAND

Bradley Broadcast & Pro Audio,
  pg 709
Cardinal Sound & Video, pg 717
Human Circuit, pg 782
Kipp Visual Systems Inc, pg 799
Noventri, pg 843

MASSACHUSETTS

Terry Hanley Audio Systems Inc,
  pg 775
Hunt's Photo & Video, pg 782
Professional Audio Design Inc,
  pg 865
Rule Boston Camera, pg 878
University Products Inc, pg 923

MICHIGAN

Olson Anderson Co, pg 685
City Events Group, pg 725
Digi Sign Design LLC, pg 741
TEL Systems LLC, pg 909

MINNESOTA

Harris Communications Inc, pg 776
New Life Communications Inc,
  pg 839

MISSISSIPPI

Bowie Audio Visual Enterprises Inc,
  pg 709

MISSOURI

Communitronics Corp, pg 729
Conference Technologies Inc,
  pg 730
ITC, pg 791
Modern Communications Inc,
  pg 828
Schiller's Audio-Visual, pg 881

NEW HAMPSHIRE

APS Lighting-Sound-AV, pg 688
Technet® Systems Group, pg 908

NEW JERSEY

Alltec Stores, a Vcom IMC
  Company, pg 681
AlltecPro, pg 681
Argraph Corp, pg 688
Audio Visual Associates, pg 694
Audio Visual Dynamics®, pg 694
AV Bluebook, pg 696
Comprehensive Cable &
  Connectivity Co, pg 729
Earl Girls Inc, pg 749
Entel Systems Inc, pg 754
HamiltonBuhl, pg 775

The Music Place, pg 834
Nelson Enterprises Theatrical
  Supply Co Inc, pg 838
Onkyo USA Corp, pg 846
PatchAmp, pg 852
SDI Technologies Inc, pg 883
Starlite, pg 900
Video Corporation of America
  (VCA), pg 927
Wired 4 Sound Inc, pg 940
Yorktel, pg 944

NEW YORK

Albany Theatre Supply Co Inc,
  pg 679
American Video Inc, pg 684
Audio-Video Corp, pg 694
Aura Sonic Ltd (ASL), pg 695
AV Workshop, pg 697
beyerdynamic Inc, pg 704
BMI Supply, pg 708
Cadence Jazz Records, pg 713
Colortone Audio Visual, pg 728
Creative Stage Lighting Co Inc,
  pg 733
Design Audio Visual Inc, pg 741
Gaylord Archival, pg 768
Gotham Sound & Communications
  Inc, pg 773
HAVE Inc, pg 777
Hot House Professional Audio,
  pg 782
Indigo Productions, pg 787
KVL Audio Visual Services Inc,
  pg 802
Long Island Video Enterprises Live
  Inc, pg 811
Markertek Video Supply, pg 817
Neptune Photo Inc, pg 838
RNJ Electronics, pg 875
Russell Industries Inc, pg 879
Sentry Industries Inc, pg 884
Stampede Presentation Products Inc,
  pg 899
Syracuse Scenery & Stage Lighting
  Co Inc, pg 906
TecNec Distributing, pg 909
Theatrical Services & Supplies Inc,
  pg 912
Tri-Ed Distribution Inc, pg 918
Visual Word Systems Inc, pg 932
Voyetra Turtle Beach, pg 933
Willoughby's® Camera, pg 939

NORTH CAROLINA

Camcor Inc, pg 715
Strategic Connections, pg 901

OHIO

Copp Integrated Systems, pg 731
ITA Audio Visual Solutions, pg 791
Midwest Photo Exchange, pg 827
Parts Express, pg 851
Tri-State Audio Visual Co, pg 918
Tri-State Visual Products Inc,
  pg 918

OKLAHOMA

Ford AV, pg 763

OREGON

Lightspeed Technologies Inc,
  pg 808
SuperDigital Ltd, pg 904

PENNSYLVANIA

Advanced AV LLC, pg 677
Audio Visions Inc, pg 694
Brodart Co, pg 711
J E Foss Co, pg 764

Grise Audio Visual Center Inc,
  pg 774
The Lerro Corp, pg 806
Morefield Communications Inc,
  pg 830
Visual Sound Inc, pg 931
Wespen Audio Visual Co, pg 935
Wire X 17 LLC, pg 940

TENNESSEE

Allstar Audio Systems Inc, pg 681
Lowrance Sound Co Inc, pg 812
National School Products, pg 836
Spectrum Sound Inc, pg 897
Technical Support Systems LLC,
  pg 908
Trew Audio Inc, pg 917
Zion Music Group, pg 945

TEXAS

Audio Visual Technologies Group
  (AVTG), pg 695
AVES Audio Visual Systems Inc,
  pg 698
CAM Audio Inc, pg 714
Crossroads Audio Inc, pg 735
FitzCo Sound Inc, pg 761
Heffernan Audio Visual, pg 778
Lubbock Audio Visual Inc, pg 812
Precision Camera & Video, pg 861
Pro Video & Film Equipment Co
  Inc, pg 863
Quality Audio Visual Service Inc,
  pg 867
RF Specialties of Texas LLC,
  pg 874
Southwest Sound Solutions, pg 896
Tarpley Media Systems, pg 907

UTAH

Performance Audio LLC, pg 854
RIA Corp, pg 874

VIRGINIA

Avitecture Inc, pg 699
Boitnott Visual Communications
  Corp (BVC), pg 708
Design & Production Inc, pg 740
Lee Hartman & Sons Inc, pg 805
StageSound, pg 899
The Whitlock Group, pg 937

WASHINGTON

Broadcast Supply World Wide,
  pg 711
CCI Solutions, pg 718
Northern Lights & Pro Audio,
  pg 842
PNTA, pg 858
Proforma Good Wood Marketing,
  pg 865

WISCONSIN

Audio Visual of Milwaukee Inc,
  pg 694
Camera Corner Connecting Point,
  pg 715
Demco Inc, pg 740
Full Compass Systems, pg 767

PUERTO RICO

Bonnin Electronics Inc, pg 708

ALBERTA

McBain Camera Ltd, pg 820
Unique Communications Ltd,
  pg 921

BRITISH COLUMBIA

Commercial Electronics Ltd, pg 728

MANITOBA

Advance Pro, pg 677
Inland Audio Visual Ltd, pg 788

ONTARIO

Carr McLean Ltd, pg 717
HD Source, pg 777
Henry's Camera, pg 779
Nationwide Audio Visual Co,
  pg 837
Westbury National Show Systems
  Ltd, pg 936

QUEBEC

JAM Industries Ltd, pg 792
SC Media Canada, pg 881
Sennheiser (Canada) Inc, pg 884

Headset & Headphone Manufacturers

CALIFORNIA

AKG Acoustics US, pg 679
Anchor Audio Inc, pg 685
Arkon Resources Inc, pg 689
Califone International Inc, pg 714
Calrad Electronics, pg 714
Clear-Com® LLC, pg 726
Harman Professional Solutions,
  pg 776
HM Electronics Inc (HME), pg 780
Hosa Technology Inc, pg 781
Logitech, pg 811
Nady Systems Inc, pg 835
Pioneer Electronics (USA) Inc,
  pg 857
Point Source Audio, pg 858
Poly, pg 859
Simon - Kaloi Engineering Ltd,
  pg 888
Sony Electronics Inc, pg 893
Sounds Unique, pg 895
TEAC America Inc, pg 908
TeachLogic Inc, pg 908

CONNECTICUT

Redco Audio Inc, pg 872
Vista Group International Inc,
  pg 931

FLORIDA

Domo Tactical Communications
  (DTC) Ltd, pg 745
Intermark Industries Inc, pg 789

ILLINOIS

AmpliVox Portable Sound Systems,
  pg 684
Central Audio-Visual Equipment
  Inc, pg 719
Shure Inc, pg 887
Technical Exhibits Corp, pg 908

INDIANA

Klipsch Group Inc, pg 799

MASSACHUSETTS

Bose Corp, pg 709
David Clark Co Inc, pg 738

MINNESOTA

Bosch Security Systems Inc, pg 709

AUDIO

Headset & Headphone Manufacturers (continued)

NEW JERSEY

AlltecPro, pg 681
Onkyo USA Corp, pg 846
Panasonic Consumer Electronics Co, pg 850
SDI Technologies Inc, pg 883
Sony Pro Audio, pg 893

NEW YORK

Benchmark Media Systems Inc, pg 703
beyerdynamic Inc, pg 704
Sentry Industries Inc, pg 884
Television Equipment Associates Inc (TEA), pg 910
Voyetra Turtle Beach, pg 933

OHIO

Audio-Technica US Inc, pg 694

OREGON

Lightspeed Technologies Inc, pg 808

PENNSYLVANIA

Wire X 17 LLC, pg 940

RHODE ISLAND

Numark Industries LP, pg 843

TENNESSEE

KRK Systems, pg 802
Remote Audio Products, pg 873
Stanton Magnetics, pg 900

TEXAS

Setcom Corp™, pg 884

WISCONSIN

Koss Corp, pg 801

Headset & Headphone Rentals

ALABAMA

Audio-Video Resources Inc, pg 694

ARIZONA

Arizona Cine Equipment, pg 688
Merestone, pg 823
Metropolitan Audio-Visual Inc, pg 824
Video West Inc, pg 929

ARKANSAS

White Diamond Productions LLC, pg 937

CALIFORNIA

Alliant Event Services, pg 681
Alternative Rentals, pg 682
Ametron Audio/Video, pg 684
Artichoke Productions, pg 690
Associated Sound, pg 691
Audio Rents, pg 693
AV Guys, pg 697
Express Media Inc, pg 757

Express Video Supply Inc, pg 757
Golden Gate Studios, pg 772
Hollywood Sound Systems, pg 781
Imagecraft Productions, pg 785
JD Audio Visual Inc, pg 793
Lynch Communications, pg 813
McCune Audio-Video-Lighting, pg 821
Media Fabricators Inc, pg 822
Munday & Collins AV, pg 834
Muse Presentation Technologies, pg 834
Old School Cameras, pg 844
On-Trax Inc, pg 846
Premier Lighting & Production Co, pg 861
Pro HD Rentals, pg 863
Production Gear Rentals (PGR), pg 863
PSAV® Presentation Services, pg 866
Radiant Images, pg 869
Shooting Star Video, pg 886
Sound Service Co, pg 894
The Studios at Paramount, pg 903
Synthesizer Rental Service, pg 906
Total Creative, pg 916
Towards 2000 Inc, pg 916
VER, pg 926
Video Resources Inc, pg 928
Voice & Video Rentals, pg 932
Warner Bros Production Sound & Video Services, pg 934
Westcoast Video Productions Inc, pg 936

COLORADO

Audio Consultant Services Inc, pg 693
Daylight Productions & Rentals, pg 739
Multimedia Audio Visual Inc, pg 833
Spectrum Audio Visual Services, pg 897

CONNECTICUT

A/V Davey, pg 697
Connecticut Audio & Theatrical Supply, pg 731

DELAWARE

Actors Attic, pg 675
Side Door Studio Inc, pg 887

FLORIDA

Budget Video Rentals, pg 712
Hi-Tech Enterprises Inc, pg 779
Industrial Strength Inc, pg 787
Jordan Klein Film & Video (JKFV), pg 795
Knowles Video Inc (KVI), pg 800
Lighting Sales Connection Inc, pg 808
ONstage, pg 846
TAI Audio, pg 906

GEORGIA

ECG Productions, pg 750
Lighting & Production Equipment Inc, pg 807
MAGNUM Companies Ltd, pg 815
Stage Front Presentation Systems, pg 899
Staging Directions Inc, pg 899

HAWAII

Sight & Sound Studios, pg 887

ILLINOIS

AV Chicago Inc, pg 696
Backstar Creative Media Inc, pg 700
Beatty TeleVisual Productions, pg 703
Central Audio-Visual Equipment Inc, pg 719
Firehouse Studios, pg 761
On Site Video, pg 846
OSA International Inc, pg 848
RC Communications, pg 870
Woodside Avenue Music Productions Inc, pg 941
Zacuto, pg 945

INDIANA

Advanced Media Integration, pg 677

IOWA

Pro Video, pg 863

KANSAS

Lights On, pg 808

KENTUCKY

Audio Visual Techniques Inc, pg 695

LOUISIANA

Pace Systems, pg 849

MARYLAND

Advance Audiovisual Presentation Ltd, pg 677
CPR MultiMedia Solutions, pg 732
Event Tech, pg 756
Maryland Sound International Holding Co LLC, pg 819
Soundtrax Inc, pg 895

MASSACHUSETTS

Terry Hanley Audio Systems Inc, pg 775
massAV, pg 819
Preston Productions Inc, pg 861

MICHIGAN

City Events Group, pg 725
Digi Sign Design LLC, pg 741
K&R All Media Productions LLC, pg 796
K&R's Recording Studios Inc, pg 796
Lowing Light & Grip Inc, pg 812

MISSISSIPPI

Bowie Audio Visual Enterprises Inc, pg 709

MISSOURI

ITC, pg 791
Show-Me Audio-Visual, pg 887

NEVADA

GES Audio Visual, pg 770

NEW HAMPSHIRE

Apertura, pg 686
APS Lighting-Sound-AV, pg 688

NEW JERSEY

Audio Visual Associates, pg 694
Audio Visual Dynamics®, pg 694
Earl Girls Inc, pg 749

Moe AV LLC, pg 828
Nelson Enterprises Theatrical Supply Co, pg 838
PLS Staging, pg 858
Starlite, pg 900
Wired 4 Sound Inc, pg 940

NEW MEXICO

Production Outfitters, pg 864

NEW YORK

Adorama Rental Co, pg 676
American Video Inc, pg 684
Aura Sonic Ltd (ASL), pg 695
AV Workshop, pg 697
Bond Street Studio, pg 708
CP Communications, pg 732
Design Audio Visual Inc, pg 741
Gotham Sound & Communications Inc, pg 773
Hello World Communications, pg 778
KVL Audio Visual Services Inc, pg 802
LightHouse Films, pg 807
Long Island Video Enterprises Live Inc, pg 811
Manhattan Center Studios Inc, pg 816
Specialized Audio-Visual Inc, pg 896
Syracuse Scenery & Stage Lighting Co Inc, pg 906
Theatrical Services & Supplies Inc, pg 912
Visual Word Systems Inc, pg 932
WorldStage, pg 941
Xtech Systems Inc, pg 943

NORTH CAROLINA

AV Metro Inc, pg 697
Special Event Services, pg 896

NORTH DAKOTA

Media Productions, pg 822

OHIO

Hughie's Event Production Services, pg 782
Lyon Video Inc, pg 813
Mills James Productions, pg 828
Ohio HD Video, pg 844

OKLAHOMA

PDC Productions, pg 852

OREGON

Northwest Film Center, pg 842
Rose City Sound, pg 877

PENNSYLVANIA

Advanced AV LLC, pg 677
Audio Visions Inc, pg 694
Grise Audio Visual Center Inc, pg 774
Right Coast Recording Inc, pg 875
The Videohouse Inc, pg 929
Viewpoint Production Services Inc, pg 930
Visual Sound Inc, pg 931

TENNESSEE

Allstar Audio Systems Inc, pg 681
Brantley Sound Associates Inc, pg 709
Mr Mark's Used Musical, Stereo & Studio Equipment Store, pg 828

Nashville Production Rentals
(NPR), pg 836
Technical Support Systems LLC,
pg 908
Trew Audio Inc, pg 917

TEXAS

Alford Media Services, pg 680
Audio Visual Technologies Group
(AVTG), pg 695
Crossroads Audio Inc, pg 735
Lubbock Audio Visual Inc, pg 812
Music Lab Inc, pg 834
Onstage Systems, pg 846
Stage Directions, pg 898
Texcam Inc, pg 911

UTAH

Performance Audio LLC, pg 854
Redman Movies & Stories, pg 872

VERMONT

Dark Star Lighting & Production,
pg 737
Edgewood Studios, pg 750

VIRGINIA

American AV, pg 682
Boitnott Visual Communications
Corp (BVC), pg 708
StageSound, pg 899

WASHINGTON

D A Sound, pg 737
Northern Lights & Pro Audio,
pg 842
Victory Studios, pg 927

WISCONSIN

Event Essentials, pg 756
Full Compass Systems, pg 767
MKE Production Rental, pg 828

PUERTO RICO

Stage Crew Audiovisual Inc, pg 898

ALBERTA

McBain Camera Ltd, pg 820
Unique Communications Ltd,
pg 921

BRITISH COLUMBIA

Clark's Audio Visual Services Ltd,
pg 725
Commercial Electronics Ltd, pg 728
Inspired Image Picture Co (IIPC),
pg 788
MicrophoneRentals.com, pg 826
Video Out Distribution, pg 928

MANITOBA

Inland Audio Visual Ltd, pg 788

ONTARIO

HD Source, pg 777
SIM Digital, pg 888
Westbury National Show Systems
Ltd, pg 936

Headset & Headphone
Repairs

CALIFORNIA

Ametron Audio/Video, pg 684
Audio Images Corp, pg 693

McAlister Electronics, pg 820
Poly, pg 859
Sound Service Co, pg 894
Towards 2000 Inc, pg 916

CONNECTICUT

HB Communications Inc, pg 777
Sennheiser Electronic Corp, pg 884

DELAWARE

Actors Attic, pg 675

FLORIDA

Hi-Tech Enterprises Inc, pg 779
Midtown Video Inc, pg 827
Stereo Sales Inc, pg 900
TAI Audio, pg 906

GEORGIA

Lighting & Production Equipment
Inc, pg 807
Stage Front Presentation Systems,
pg 899

ILLINOIS

Beatty TeleVisual Productions,
pg 703
On Site Video, pg 846
RC Communications, pg 870

INDIANA

Sweetwater Sound Inc, pg 905

KENTUCKY

Axxis Leasing Inc, pg 700
NOR-COM Inc, pg 841

MARYLAND

Cardinal Sound & Video, pg 717

MICHIGAN

City Events Group, pg 725
K&R's Recording Studios Inc,
pg 796
TEL Systems LLC, pg 909

MISSOURI

Cintrex Audio Visual, pg 725

NEW JERSEY

Earl Girls Inc, pg 749
Nelson Enterprises Theatrical
Supply Co, pg 838
Starlite, pg 900

NEW YORK

beyerdynamic Inc, pg 704
Xtech Systems Inc, pg 943

NORTH CAROLINA

Camcor Inc, pg 715

OHIO

Copp Integrated Systems, pg 731

OREGON

All Service Musical Electronics
Repair, pg 680

PENNSYLVANIA

J E Foss Co, pg 764
Right Coast Recording Inc, pg 875

TENNESSEE

Technical Support Systems LLC,
pg 908
Trew Audio Inc, pg 917

TEXAS

Audio Visual Technologies Group
(AVTG), pg 695
Lubbock Audio Visual Inc, pg 812
Quality Audio Visual Service Inc,
pg 867
Southwest Sound Solutions, pg 896

VIRGINIA

Boitnott Visual Communications
Corp (BVC), pg 708
The Whitlock Group, pg 937

WASHINGTON

Northern Lights & Pro Audio,
pg 842

WISCONSIN

Full Compass Systems, pg 767

BRITISH COLUMBIA

Commercial Electronics Ltd, pg 728

MANITOBA

Inland Audio Visual Ltd, pg 788

ONTARIO

HD Source, pg 777
Westbury National Show Systems
Ltd, pg 936

QUEBEC

SC Media Canada, pg 881

Hearing Assistance System
Distributors

ARIZONA

EAR Professional Audio/Video,
pg 749
Troxell-CDI, pg 918
David Wexler & Co, pg 936

ARKANSAS

Jay S Stanley & Associates Inc,
pg 899

CALIFORNIA

Ametron Audio/Video, pg 684
Associated Sound, pg 691
Richard W Burden Associates,
pg 712
Cibola Systems, pg 723
Cinema Equipment Sales of
California Inc, pg 724
Instructional Materials & Equipment
Distributors (I-Med), pg 789
JD Audio Visual Inc, pg 793
Media Vision USA, pg 822
Sound Service Co, pg 894
Southern California Sound Image
Inc, pg 895
Stanislaus AV Inc, pg 899

COLORADO

Audio Consultant Services Inc,
pg 693
Daylight Productions & Rentals,
pg 739
Oval Window Audio, pg 849

CONNECTICUT

Connecticut Audio & Theatrical
Supply, pg 731
Sennheiser Electronic Corp, pg 884

DELAWARE

Actors Attic, pg 675

FLORIDA

Cinema Equipment & Supplies Inc,
pg 724
Harris Corp, pg 776
Hi-Tech Import Export Corp,
pg 779
Intermark Industries Inc, pg 789
ONstage, pg 846
Technomedia Solutions, pg 909

GEORGIA

Lighting & Production Equipment
Inc, pg 807
Stage Front Presentation Systems,
pg 899

HAWAII

The Audio Visual Co (AVCO),
pg 694

ILLINOIS

Allen Visual Systems Inc, pg 680

INDIANA

Sensory Technologies LLC, pg 884
SHP Electronics, pg 887
Sweetwater Sound Inc, pg 905

KENTUCKY

Axxis Leasing Inc, pg 700
NOR-COM Inc, pg 841

MAINE

Headlight Audio Visual Inc, pg 777

MARYLAND

Cardinal Sound & Video, pg 717

MASSACHUSETTS

Terry Hanley Audio Systems Inc,
pg 775

MICHIGAN

Olson Anderson Co, pg 685

MINNESOTA

Harris Communications Inc, pg 776

MISSOURI

Schiller's Audio-Visual, pg 881

NEW HAMPSHIRE

APS Lighting-Sound-AV, pg 688

NEW JERSEY

Alltec Stores, a Vcom IMC
Company, pg 681
AlltecPro, pg 681
AV Bluebook, pg 696
Starlite, pg 900
Wired 4 Sound Inc, pg 940
Yorktel, pg 944

AUDIO

Hearing Assistance System Distributors (continued)

NEW YORK

Albany Theatre Supply Co Inc, pg 679
BMI Supply, pg 708
Colortone Audio Visual, pg 728
Design Audio Visual Inc, pg 741
iProbe Multilingual Solutions Inc, pg 791
RNJ Electronics, pg 875
Sound Associates Inc, pg 893

OHIO

ITA Audio Visual Solutions, pg 791
Tri-State Audio Visual Co, pg 918

OREGON

Lightspeed Technologies Inc, pg 808

PENNSYLVANIA

Advanced AV LLC, pg 677
J E Foss Co, pg 764
Vistacom Inc, pg 931

TENNESSEE

Allstar Audio Systems Inc, pg 681
Belew Enterprises, pg 703
Lowrance Sound Co Inc, pg 812
Spectrum Sound Inc, pg 897
Trew Audio Inc, pg 917
Zion Music Group, pg 945

TEXAS

CAM Audio Inc, pg 714
Tarpley Media Systems, pg 907

UTAH

Comtek Communications Technology Inc, pg 730

VIRGINIA

Intellidyne LLC, pg 789
Lee Hartman & Sons Inc, pg 805

WASHINGTON

CCI Solutions, pg 718
PNTA, pg 858

WISCONSIN

Audio Visual of Milwaukee Inc, pg 694
Full Compass Systems, pg 767

PUERTO RICO

Bonnin Electronics Inc, pg 708

ALBERTA

Infosat Communications Inc, pg 787
Matrix Video Communications Corp (MVCC), pg 819

MANITOBA

Advance Pro, pg 677
Inland Audio Visual Ltd, pg 788

ONTARIO

Cinema Stage Inc, pg 724
Westbury National Show Systems Ltd, pg 936

Hearing Assistance System Manufacturers

CALIFORNIA

Anchor Audio Inc, pg 685
Calrad Electronics, pg 714
FrontRow, pg 766
Nady Systems Inc, pg 835

COLORADO

Oval Window Audio, pg 849

CONNECTICUT

Sennheiser Electronic Corp, pg 884
Vista Group International Inc, pg 931

ILLINOIS

AmpliVox Portable Sound Systems, pg 684

MINNESOTA

Bosch Security Systems Inc, pg 709
Williams AV LLC, pg 939

NEW JERSEY

Bogen Communications Inc, pg 708
Crestron Electronics Inc, pg 734

NEW YORK

Sound Associates Inc, pg 893

OREGON

Lightspeed Technologies Inc, pg 808

UTAH

Comtek Communications Technology Inc, pg 730
Listen Technologies Corp, pg 810

Hearing Assistance System Rentals

CALIFORNIA

Alliant Event Services, pg 681
Ametron Audio/Video, pg 684
Associated Sound, pg 691
AV Guys, pg 697
JD Audio Visual Inc, pg 793
Lynch Communications, pg 813
McCune Audio-Video-Lighting, pg 821
Sound Service Co, pg 894
Stanislaus AV Inc, pg 899

CONNECTICUT

A/V Davey, pg 697

FLORIDA

ONstage, pg 846

GEORGIA

Stage Front Presentation Systems, pg 899

ILLINOIS

AV Chicago Inc, pg 696
OSA International Inc, pg 848

KENTUCKY

Audio Visual Techniques Inc, pg 695

MARYLAND

Cardinal Sound & Video, pg 717

MASSACHUSETTS

Terry Hanley Audio Systems Inc, pg 775

MICHIGAN

K&R All Media Productions LLC, pg 796

MISSOURI

Show-Me Audio-Visual, pg 887

NEW HAMPSHIRE

APS Lighting-Sound-AV, pg 688

NEW JERSEY

Starlite, pg 900
Wired 4 Sound Inc, pg 940

NEW YORK

Colortone Audio Visual, pg 728
CP Communications, pg 732
Design Audio Visual Inc, pg 741
iProbe Multilingual Solutions Inc, pg 791
Sound Associates Inc, pg 893

OREGON

Rose City Sound, pg 877

TENNESSEE

Allstar Audio Systems Inc, pg 681

UTAH

Listen Technologies Corp, pg 810

VIRGINIA

American AV, pg 682

WISCONSIN

Full Compass Systems, pg 767

MANITOBA

Inland Audio Visual Ltd, pg 788

Hearing Assistance System Repairs

CALIFORNIA

Ametron Audio/Video, pg 684
McAlister Electronics, pg 820
Sound Service Co, pg 894

CONNECTICUT

HB Communications Inc, pg 777
Sennheiser Electronic Corp, pg 884

GEORGIA

Stage Front Presentation Systems, pg 899

ILLINOIS

Allen Visual Systems Inc, pg 680

KENTUCKY

Axxis Leasing Inc, pg 700
NOR-COM Inc, pg 841

MARYLAND

Cardinal Sound & Video, pg 717

MICHIGAN

TEL Systems LLC, pg 909

NEW JERSEY

Starlite, pg 900

NEW YORK

Sound Associates Inc, pg 893

OHIO

Tri-State Audio Visual Co, pg 918

OREGON

All Service Musical Electronics Repair, pg 680

TENNESSEE

Belew Enterprises, pg 703

UTAH

Comtek Communications Technology Inc, pg 730

WASHINGTON

PNTA, pg 858

WISCONSIN

Full Compass Systems, pg 767

ALBERTA

Infosat Communications Inc, pg 787

MANITOBA

Inland Audio Visual Ltd, pg 788

ONTARIO

Westbury National Show Systems Ltd, pg 936

Holiday Music, see Music Libraries—Holiday

Hollywood Music, see Music Libraries—Broadway & Hollywood

Instrumental Music, see Music Libraries—Instrumental

International Music, see Music Libraries—Ethnic & International

Jazz Music, see Music Libraries—Jazz

Language Lab Carrell & Equipment Distributors

ALABAMA

Curtis Company, pg 736

ARIZONA

Troxell-CDI, pg 918

CALIFORNIA

Ametron Audio/Video, pg 684
Assured Audio Visual, pg 691
California Tape Products Inc,
  pg 714
Instructional Materials & Equipment
  Distributors (I-Med), pg 789
Lloyd F McKinney Associates Inc,
  pg 821
Media Fabricators Inc, pg 822
Sanako Inc, pg 880
SSL Industries Inc, pg 898

CONNECTICUT

MAVCO, pg 820
Rockwell Communications Inc,
  pg 876

FLORIDA

Harris Corp, pg 776
Intermark Industries Inc, pg 789

GEORGIA

Visioneering International Inc,
  pg 931

HAWAII

The Audio Visual Co (AVCO),
  pg 694

INDIANA

Sensory Technologies LLC, pg 884

KENTUCKY

NOR-COM Inc, pg 841

MAINE

Headlight Audio Visual Inc, pg 777

MARYLAND

Nicholas P Pipino Associates Inc,
  pg 857

MICHIGAN

Olson Anderson Co, pg 685
City Events Group, pg 725

MISSOURI

Communitronics Corp, pg 729
Conference Technologies Inc,
  pg 730

NEW JERSEY

HamiltonBuhl, pg 775
Starlite, pg 900
Tele-Measurements Inc, pg 910
Total Video Products Inc, pg 916
Video Corporation of America
  (VCA), pg 927
Yorktel, pg 944

NEW YORK

Indigo Productions, pg 787
Langie Audio Visual Systems,
  pg 803
RNJ Electronics, pg 875
Visual Technologies Corp, pg 932

OHIO

Tri-State Visual Products Inc,
  pg 918

PENNSYLVANIA

Advanced AV LLC, pg 677
Morefield Communications Inc,
  pg 830
Visual Sound Inc, pg 931

TEXAS

Audio Visual Technologies Group
  (AVTG), pg 695
Heffernan Audio Visual, pg 778

UTAH

Listen Technologies Corp, pg 810
Webb Audio Visual, pg 935

VIRGINIA

Lee Hartman & Sons Inc, pg 805
The Whitlock Group, pg 937

WASHINGTON

Inland Audio Visual Co, pg 788

WISCONSIN

Audio Visual of Milwaukee Inc,
  pg 694
Demco Inc, pg 740
School Specialty Inc, pg 882
Spectrum Industries Inc, pg 897

PUERTO RICO

Audio Visual Concepts Inc, pg 694
Bonnin Electronics Inc, pg 708

ALBERTA

Matrix Video Communications Corp
  (MVCC), pg 819
McBain Camera Ltd, pg 820

MANITOBA

Advance Pro, pg 677
Inland Audio Visual Ltd, pg 788

ONTARIO

Westbury National Show Systems
  Ltd, pg 936

QUEBEC

Panavideo Inc, pg 850

Language Lab Carrell & Equipment Manufacturers

ALABAMA

Omni International Inc, pg 845

CALIFORNIA

Califone International Inc, pg 714

ILLINOIS

Marshall Furniture Inc, pg 817

WISCONSIN

Spectrum Industries Inc, pg 897

Language Lab Carrell & Equipment Rentals

CALIFORNIA

Ametron Audio/Video, pg 684
Lynch Communications, pg 813

GEORGIA

Staging Directions Inc, pg 899

ILLINOIS

OSA International Inc, pg 848

MASSACHUSETTS

Preston Productions Inc, pg 861

UTAH

Webb Audio Visual, pg 935

VIRGINIA

American AV, pg 682

MANITOBA

Inland Audio Visual Ltd, pg 788

Language Lab Carrell & Equipment Repairs

CALIFORNIA

Ametron Audio/Video, pg 684
McAlister Electronics, pg 820
SSL Industries Inc, pg 898

CONNECTICUT

HB Communications Inc, pg 777

KENTUCKY

NOR-COM Inc, pg 841

MICHIGAN

City Events Group, pg 725
K&R's Recording Studios Inc,
  pg 796
TEL Systems LLC, pg 909

MINNESOTA

AVI Systems, pg 698

NEW YORK

Langie Audio Visual Systems,
  pg 803
Visual Technologies Corp, pg 932

OHIO

Tri-State Audio Visual Co, pg 918

OREGON

All Service Musical Electronics
  Repair, pg 680

TEXAS

Audio Visual Technologies Group
  (AVTG), pg 695

VIRGINIA

Lee Hartman & Sons Inc, pg 805
The Whitlock Group, pg 937

WASHINGTON

Inland Audio Visual Co, pg 788

WEST VIRGINIA

United Sound & Electronics, pg 921

MANITOBA

Inland Audio Visual Ltd, pg 788

ONTARIO

Westbury National Show Systems
  Ltd, pg 936

Magnetic Recording Equipment Distributors

ARIZONA

Arizona Cine Equipment, pg 688
Troxell-CDI, pg 918

ARKANSAS

Jay S Stanley & Associates Inc,
  pg 899
White Diamond Productions LLC,
  pg 937

CALIFORNIA

Ametron Audio/Video, pg 684
Assured Audio Visual, pg 691
Audio Images Corp, pg 693
Audio/Video Supply Inc, pg 694
BigFoot Mobile Systems, pg 705
Birns & Sawyer Inc, pg 706
California Tape Products Inc,
  pg 714
Educational Technology Services
  (ETS), pg 751
Gluskin's Custom Audio Video,
  pg 771
Alan Gordon Enterprises Inc,
  pg 772
Instructional Materials & Equipment
  Distributors (I-Med), pg 789
JD Audio Visual Inc, pg 793
Martel Electronics Sales Inc, pg 818
Media Fabricators Inc, pg 822
MediaMation Inc, pg 822
MediaPOINTE, pg 823
Sound Service Co, pg 894
SSL Industries Inc, pg 898
SuperVision, pg 904
VTP Inc, pg 933
Yamaha Electronics Corp, pg 943

COLORADO

Audio Consultant Services Inc,
  pg 693
Ceavco Audio Visual Company Inc,
  pg 719
Spectrum Audio Visual Services,
  pg 897

CONNECTICUT

HB Communications Inc, pg 777
MAVCO, pg 820
Rockwell Communications Inc,
  pg 876

DELAWARE

Actors Attic, pg 675

FLORIDA

Broadcasters General Store Inc,
  pg 711
CD ROM™ Inc, pg 718
Harris Corp, pg 776
Hi-Tech Import Export Corp,
  pg 779
Industrial Strength Inc, pg 787
ONstage, pg 846
Recording Media & Equipment Inc
  (RM&E), pg 872
Stereo Sales Inc, pg 900
TAI Audio, pg 906

AUDIO

Magnetic Recording Equipment Distributors (continued)

GEORGIA

Baker Audio Visual, pg 700
Convergent Media Systems, pg 731
Lighting & Production Equipment Inc, pg 807
Stage Front Presentation Systems, pg 899
Visioneering International Inc, pg 931

ILLINOIS

Creative Technology (CT), pg 733
International Electro-Magnetics Inc, pg 790
Major Reproductions Equipment Co, pg 815
Woodside Avenue Music Productions Inc, pg 941

INDIANA

Sensory Technologies LLC, pg 884

KENTUCKY

Axxis Leasing Inc, pg 700
Barney Miller's Inc, pg 827
NOR-COM Inc, pg 841

MAINE

Headlight Audio Visual Inc, pg 777
Independent Audio Inc, pg 786

MARYLAND

Bradley Broadcast & Pro Audio, pg 709
Cardinal Sound & Video, pg 717
Kipp Visual Systems Inc, pg 799
Nicholas P Pipino Associates Inc, pg 857
RTZ Audio Visual, pg 878

MASSACHUSETTS

Professional Audio Design Inc, pg 865

MICHIGAN

City Events Group, pg 725
TEL Systems LLC, pg 909

MINNESOTA

AVI Systems, pg 698
Cinequipt Inc, pg 724
New Life Communications Inc, pg 839

MISSISSIPPI

Jasper Ewing & Sons Inc, pg 757

MISSOURI

Communitronics Corp, pg 729
Conference Technologies Inc, pg 730
ITC, pg 791
Modern Communications Inc, pg 828

NEW JERSEY

AlltecPro, pg 681
Audio Visual Dynamics®, pg 694
AV Bluebook, pg 696

Comprehensive Cable & Connectivity Co, pg 729
FlagHouse, pg 762
G&G Technologies Inc, pg 768
HamiltonBuhl, pg 775
JRF Magnetic Sciences Inc, pg 795
Onkyo USA Corp, pg 846
Starlite, pg 900
Tele-Measurements Inc, pg 910
Vcom IMC, pg 925
Video Corporation of America (VCA), pg 927
Yorktel, pg 944

NEW YORK

American Video Inc, pg 684
AV Workshop, pg 697
Flash Electronics Inc, pg 762
HAVE Inc, pg 777
Hot House Professional Audio, pg 782
Indigo Productions, pg 787
Langie Audio Visual Systems, pg 803
Long Island Video Enterprises Live Inc, pg 811
Markertek Video Supply, pg 817
Posthorn Recordings, pg 859
Tri-Ed Distribution Inc, pg 918

NORTH CAROLINA

Camcor Inc, pg 715
Strategic Connections, pg 901

OHIO

Copp Integrated Systems, pg 731

OREGON

SuperDigital Ltd, pg 904

PENNSYLVANIA

Advanced AV LLC, pg 677
Audio Visual Communications Inc, pg 694
Brodart Co, pg 711
J E Foss Co, pg 764
Grise Audio Visual Center Inc, pg 774
The Lerro Corp, pg 806
Morefield Communications Inc, pg 830
Visual Sound Inc, pg 931

TENNESSEE

Allstar Audio Systems Inc, pg 681
Lowrance Sound Co Inc, pg 812
Technical Support Systems LLC, pg 908
Zion Music Group, pg 945

TEXAS

Audio Visual Technologies Group (AVTG), pg 695
Crossroads Audio Inc, pg 735
FitzCo Sound Inc, pg 761
JSAV, pg 795
Lubbock Audio Visual Inc, pg 812
Pro Video & Film Equipment Co Inc, pg 863
Quality Audio Visual Service Inc, pg 867
RF Specialties of Texas LLC, pg 874
Stage Directions, pg 898
Tarpley Media Systems, pg 907

UTAH

Performance Audio LLC, pg 854
RIA Corp, pg 874
Webb Audio Visual, pg 935

VIRGINIA

Lee Hartman & Sons Inc, pg 805
The Whitlock Group, pg 937

WASHINGTON

Inland Audio Visual Co, pg 788

WISCONSIN

Full Compass Systems, pg 767
School Specialty Inc, pg 882

PUERTO RICO

Audio Visual Concepts Inc, pg 694
Bonnin Electronics Inc, pg 708

ALBERTA

Unique Communications Ltd, pg 921

MANITOBA

Advance Pro, pg 677
Inland Audio Visual Ltd, pg 788

ONTARIO

Nationwide Audio Visual Co, pg 837

Magnetic Recording Equipment Manufacturers

CALIFORNIA

Ametron Audio/Video, pg 684
Sony Electronics Inc, pg 893
TASCAM, pg 907
360 Systems, pg 913
Yamaha Electronics Corp, pg 943

FLORIDA

Magna-Tech Electronic Co Inc, pg 814

ILLINOIS

International Electro-Magnetics Inc, pg 790

NEW JERSEY

Onkyo USA Corp, pg 846
RAMSA Professional Audio Systems, pg 870

NEW YORK

Posthorn Recordings, pg 859

PENNSYLVANIA

The Martin Guitar Co, pg 818

Magnetic Recording Equipment Rentals

ARIZONA

Arizona Cine Equipment, pg 688
Video West Inc, pg 929

ARKANSAS

White Diamond Productions LLC, pg 937

CALIFORNIA

Advanced Media LLC, pg 677
Ametron Audio/Video, pg 684
Artichoke Productions, pg 690
Audio Rents, pg 693
Birns & Sawyer Inc, pg 706
Express Media Inc, pg 757
Gold Standard Productions, pg 772
Alan Gordon Enterprises Inc, pg 772
JD Audio Visual Inc, pg 793
Lynch Communications, pg 813
Maximus Media Inc, pg 820
Media Fabricators Inc, pg 822
Munday & Collins AV, pg 834
On-Trax Inc, pg 846
PSAV® Presentation Services, pg 866
Sound Service Co, pg 894
VER, pg 926
Video Resources Inc, pg 928

COLORADO

Audio Consultant Services Inc, pg 693
Ceavco Audio Visual Company Inc, pg 719
Daylight Productions & Rentals, pg 739

CONNECTICUT

A/V Davey, pg 697
Rockwell Communications Inc, pg 876

DELAWARE

Side Door Studio Inc, pg 887

FLORIDA

Industrial Strength Inc, pg 787
Jordan Klein Film & Video (JKFV), pg 795
ONstage, pg 846
Paradise Show & Design Inc, pg 851
Photosound of Orlando Inc, pg 856
TAI Audio, pg 906
Universal Studios Florida® Production Group, pg 922

GEORGIA

Convergent Media Systems, pg 731
Lighting & Production Equipment Inc, pg 807
Stage Front Presentation Systems, pg 899
Staging Directions Inc, pg 899

ILLINOIS

Central Audio-Visual Equipment Inc, pg 719
Creative Technology (CT), pg 733
Helix Camera & Video, pg 778
OSA International Inc, pg 848
PSAV® Presentation Services (Hotel Services Division), pg 866
Resolution Productions Group, pg 874
Woodside Avenue Music Productions Inc, pg 941

INDIANA

Gaither Studios LLC, pg 767
OMNI Productions, pg 845

MAINE

Headlight Audio Visual Inc, pg 777

MARYLAND

Cardinal Sound & Video, pg 717
CPR MultiMedia Solutions, pg 732
Hargrove Inc, pg 776
RTZ Audio Visual, pg 878
Soundtrax Inc, pg 895

MASSACHUSETTS

Capron Lighting & Sound Co Inc,
   pg 716
massAV, pg 819
Preston Productions Inc, pg 861

MICHIGAN

City Events Group, pg 725
K&R All Media Productions LLC,
   pg 796
K&R's Recording Studios Inc,
   pg 796
TEL Systems LLC, pg 909

MINNESOTA

AVI Systems, pg 698

MISSISSIPPI

Jasper Ewing & Sons Inc, pg 757

MISSOURI

Show-Me Audio-Visual, pg 887

NEVADA

Lefco Video Services Inc, pg 806

NEW HAMPSHIRE

Apertura, pg 686

NEW JERSEY

Audio Visual Dynamics®, pg 694
JRF Magnetic Sciences Inc, pg 795
PLS Staging, pg 858

NEW YORK

Ace Video, pg 674
American Video Inc, pg 684
AV Workshop, pg 697
Hello World Communications,
   pg 778
Langie Audio Visual Systems,
   pg 803
Long Island Video Enterprises Live
   Inc, pg 811
Manhattan Center Studios Inc,
   pg 816
Posthorn Recordings, pg 859
Specialized Audio-Visual Inc,
   pg 896
WorldStage, pg 941

NORTH CAROLINA

AV Metro Inc, pg 697
Duke Media Services, pg 747
Special Event Services, pg 896
Strategic Connections, pg 901

OHIO

Icom Multimedia, pg 783
Mills James Productions, pg 828
R&B Communications Inc, pg 870

OREGON

Northwest Film Center, pg 842

PENNSYLVANIA

Audio Visions Inc, pg 694
Audio Visual Communications Inc,
   pg 694
Grise Audio Visual Center Inc,
   pg 774
JPL, pg 795
Visual Sound Inc, pg 931

TENNESSEE

Allstar Audio Systems Inc, pg 681
Brantley Sound Associates Inc,
   pg 709
Love Shack Recording Studios,
   pg 811
Technical Support Systems LLC,
   pg 908

TEXAS

Audio Visual Technologies Group
   (AVTG), pg 695
Crossroads Audio Inc, pg 735
JSAV, pg 795
Lubbock Audio Visual Inc, pg 812
Omega Productions, pg 845
South Coast Film & Video, pg 895
Stage Directions, pg 898

UTAH

Performance Audio LLC, pg 854
Webb Audio Visual, pg 935

VIRGINIA

American AV, pg 682
Lee Hartman & Sons Inc, pg 805
Projection, pg 865
The Whitlock Group, pg 937

WASHINGTON

Inland Audio Visual Co, pg 788
PNTA, pg 858

WISCONSIN

Event Essentials, pg 756
Full Compass Systems, pg 767
University of Wisconsin-Oshkosh
   Radio-TV-Film Dept, pg 923
USAV Group Inc, pg 923
Wisconsin Public Television, pg 940

WYOMING

Bridger Productions Inc, pg 710

PUERTO RICO

Stage Crew Audiovisual Inc, pg 898

ALBERTA

McBain Camera Ltd, pg 820
Unique Communications Ltd,
   pg 921

MANITOBA

Inland Audio Visual Ltd, pg 788

QUEBEC

Freeman Audio Visual, pg 765
Group PVP, pg 774

Magnetic Recording Equipment Repairs

CALIFORNIA

Advanced Media LLC, pg 677
Ametron Audio/Video, pg 684

Audio Images Corp, pg 693
Dan Dugan Sound Design Inc,
   pg 747
Gluskin's Custom Audio Video,
   pg 771
McAlister Electronics, pg 820
Sound Service Co, pg 894
SSL Industries Inc, pg 898
Yamaha Electronics Corp, pg 943

CONNECTICUT

HB Communications Inc, pg 777
Rockwell Communications Inc,
   pg 876

FLORIDA

Phat Planet Recording Studios,
   pg 855
Stereo Sales Inc, pg 900
TAI Audio, pg 906

GEORGIA

Lighting & Production Equipment
   Inc, pg 807
Stage Front Presentation Systems,
   pg 899

ILLINOIS

Midwest Digital Corp, pg 827
On Site Video, pg 846

KENTUCKY

Axxis Leasing Inc, pg 700
Barney Miller's Inc, pg 827
NOR-COM Inc, pg 841

MAINE

Headlight Audio Visual Inc, pg 777

MARYLAND

RTZ Audio Visual, pg 878

MASSACHUSETTS

Capron Lighting & Sound Co Inc,
   pg 716
Professional Audio Design Inc,
   pg 865

MICHIGAN

City Events Group, pg 725
K&R's Recording Studios Inc,
   pg 796
TEL Systems LLC, pg 909

MINNESOTA

AVI Systems, pg 698

NEW JERSEY

JRF Magnetic Sciences Inc, pg 795
Starlite, pg 900

NEW YORK

Colortone Audio Visual, pg 728
Langie Audio Visual Systems,
   pg 803

NORTH CAROLINA

Strategic Connections, pg 901

OHIO

Copp Integrated Systems, pg 731

OREGON

All Service Musical Electronics
   Repair, pg 680

PENNSYLVANIA

Audio Visual Communications Inc,
   pg 694
J E Foss Co, pg 764

TENNESSEE

Technical Support Systems LLC,
   pg 908

TEXAS

Audio Visual Technologies Group
   (AVTG), pg 695
FitzCo Sound Inc, pg 761
Lubbock Audio Visual Inc, pg 812
Pro Video & Film Equipment Co
   Inc, pg 863

VIRGINIA

Lee Hartman & Sons Inc, pg 805

WASHINGTON

Inland Audio Visual Co, pg 788

WISCONSIN

Full Compass Systems, pg 767

ALBERTA

Unique Communications Ltd,
   pg 921

BRITISH COLUMBIA

Commercial Electronics Ltd, pg 728

MANITOBA

Inland Audio Visual Ltd, pg 788

Magnetic Sound Recording, *see* Sound Recording—Magnetic

Microphone Distributors

ALABAMA

Curtis Company, pg 736

ARIZONA

Allusion Studios & Pure Wave
   Audio, pg 681
Arizona Cine Equipment, pg 688
EAR Professional Audio/Video,
   pg 749
Metropolitan Audio-Visual Inc,
   pg 824
Projector SuperStore LLC, pg 865
Tempe Camera, pg 910
Troxell-CDI, pg 918

ARKANSAS

White Diamond Productions LLC,
   pg 937

CALIFORNIA

Advanced Systems Group LLC,
   pg 677
AKG Acoustics US, pg 679
Ametron Audio/Video, pg 684
ARS Electronics, pg 690
Associated Sound, pg 691

AUDIO

Microphone Distributors (continued)

CALIFORNIA (continued)

Assured Audio Visual, pg 691
ATV Video Center Inc, pg 692
Audio Images Corp, pg 693
Audio/Video Supply Inc, pg 694
AV Conferencing LLC (AVC), pg 697
Band Pro Film & Digital Inc, pg 701
Be Media, pg 702
Birns & Sawyer Inc, pg 706
BroadcastStore.com, pg 711
California Tape Products Inc, pg 714
Carvin Amps & Audio, pg 717
Cibola Systems, pg 723
Educational Technology Services (ETS), pg 751
Electronic Design Solutions Inc, pg 752
Empire Pro, pg 753
Filmtools®, pg 761
GigaSonic, pg 770
Gluskin's Custom Audio Video, pg 771
Alan Gordon Enterprises Inc, pg 772
Gravity Media, pg 773
Hosa Technology Inc, pg 781
IAMP Professional Audio, pg 783
Instructional Materials & Equipment Distributors (I-Med), pg 789
JD Audio Visual Inc, pg 793
Location Sound Corp, pg 810
Logitech, pg 811
Marshall Electronics Inc, pg 817
Martel Electronics Sales Inc, pg 818
Lloyd F McKinney Associates Inc, pg 821
Media Fabricators Inc, pg 822
Media Vision USA, pg 822
MediaPOINTE, pg 823
Mole-Richardson Co, pg 829
Pacific Radio Electronics, pg 849
Professional Sound Corp, pg 865
Promax Systems, pg 865
SNAP, pg 891
Sound Service Co, pg 894
Southern California Sound Image Inc, pg 895
SSL Industries Inc, pg 898
Stanislaus AV Inc, pg 899
TOA Electronics Inc, pg 915
Towards 2000 Inc, pg 916
VMI Inc, pg 932
VTP Inc, pg 933
Zack Electronics Inc, pg 945

COLORADO

Audio Consultant Services Inc, pg 693
Daylight Productions & Rentals, pg 739
Mike's Camera, pg 827
Spectrum Audio Visual Services, pg 897

CONNECTICUT

Connecticut Audio & Theatrical Supply, pg 731
Gold Line/TEF, pg 772
HB Communications Inc, pg 777
MAVCO, pg 820
The Music People Inc, pg 834
Neumann USA, pg 838
Sennheiser Electronic Corp, pg 884

DELAWARE

Actors Attic, pg 675

FLORIDA

Access Media Group, pg 673
Alliance Entertainment Corp (AEC) LLC, pg 680
Altel Systems Group Inc, pg 682
A2D Solutions Inc, pg 692
AVI-SPL, pg 698
Broadcasters General Store Inc, pg 711
Digital Video Systems, pg 742
Enhanced View Services Inc, pg 754
Harmon's Audio-Visual Services, pg 776
Harris Corp, pg 776
Herman Pro AV, pg 779
Hi-Tech Enterprises Inc, pg 779
Hi-Tech Import Export Corp, pg 779
Hollywood Theatre Equipment Inc, pg 781
Industrial Strength Inc, pg 787
Intermark Industries Inc, pg 789
Lighting Sales Connection Inc, pg 808
Midtown Video Inc, pg 827
ONstage, pg 846
Photosound of Orlando Inc, pg 856
Recording Media & Equipment Inc (RM&E), pg 872
The Singing Machine Co Inc, pg 889
Stereo Sales Inc, pg 900
TAI Audio, pg 906
Tallahassee Audio Visual, pg 906
Technomedia Solutions, pg 909

GEORGIA

Baker Audio Visual, pg 700
Clark, pg 725
Convergent Media Systems, pg 731
Innocinema, pg 788
Lighting & Production Equipment Inc, pg 807
LT Sound Inc, pg 812
Stage Front Presentation Systems, pg 899
Visioneering International Inc, pg 931

HAWAII

The Audio Visual Co (AVCO), pg 694

ILLINOIS

Allen Visual Systems Inc, pg 680
Central Audio-Visual Equipment Inc, pg 719
Joseph Electronics, pg 795
LKG Industries Inc, pg 810
C V Lloyde, pg 810
Major Media Inc, pg 815
Precision Electronics Inc, pg 861
Quintessence Audio Ltd, pg 868
RC Communications, pg 870
Waldom Electronics Corp, pg 933

INDIANA

Heart Breaker Entertainment LLC, pg 778
Jack's Camera Shop, pg 792
Sensory Technologies LLC, pg 884
SHP Electronics, pg 887
Sweetwater Sound Inc, pg 905

KENTUCKY

Audio Visual Techniques Inc, pg 695
Axxis Leasing Inc, pg 700
Barney Miller's Inc, pg 827
NOR-COM Inc, pg 841

LOUISIANA

Pace Systems, pg 849
Techkno Integration & Design Services LLC, pg 908

MAINE

Headlight Audio Visual Inc, pg 777
Independent Audio Inc, pg 786

MARYLAND

Advance Audiovisual Presentation Ltd, pg 677
Bradley Broadcast & Pro Audio, pg 709
Cardinal Sound & Video, pg 717
Human Circuit, pg 782
Kipp Visual Systems Inc, pg 799
Noventri, pg 843
RTZ Audio Visual, pg 878

MASSACHUSETTS

Terry Hanley Audio Systems Inc, pg 775
Hunt's Photo & Video, pg 782
Professional Audio Design Inc, pg 865
Rule Boston Camera, pg 878

MICHIGAN

Olson Anderson Co, pg 685
City Events Group, pg 725
On Stage Visuals, pg 846
TEL Systems LLC, pg 909

MINNESOTA

AVI Systems, pg 698
Cinequipt Inc, pg 724
New Life Communications Inc, pg 839
Tierney Brothers Inc, pg 914

MISSISSIPPI

Bowie Audio Visual Enterprises Inc, pg 709
Jasper Ewing & Sons Inc, pg 757

MISSOURI

Communitronics Corp, pg 729
Conference Technologies Inc, pg 730
ITC, pg 791
Modern Communications Inc, pg 828
Production Support Services Inc, pg 864
Schiller's Audio-Visual, pg 881

NEBRASKA

VSA Inc, pg 933

NEVADA

Pignose-Gorilla, pg 856

NEW HAMPSHIRE

APS Lighting-Sound-AV, pg 688
Technet® Systems Group, pg 908

NEW JERSEY

A-V Services Inc, pg 671
Alltec Stores, a Vcom IMC Company, pg 681
AlltecPro, pg 681
Audio Visual Associates, pg 694
Audio Visual Dynamics®, pg 694
AV Bluebook, pg 696
C-Ducer/C T Audio, pg 713
Comprehensive Cable & Connectivity Co, pg 729
Diversified, pg 744
Earl Girls Inc, pg 749
Euro-Pacific Film & Video Productions Inc, pg 756
FlagHouse, pg 762
G&G Technologies Inc, pg 768
HamiltonBuhl, pg 775
The Music Place, pg 834
Nelson Enterprises Theatrical Supply Co, pg 838
PatchAmp, pg 852
Ritz Camera & Image, pg 875
Starlite, pg 900
Tele-Measurements Inc, pg 910
Total Video Products Inc, pg 916
Turner Engineering Inc, pg 919
Vcom IMC, pg 925
Video Corporation of America (VCA), pg 927
Wired 4 Sound Inc, pg 940
Yorktel, pg 944

NEW MEXICO

Quickbeam Systems Inc (QSI), pg 868

NEW YORK

ADI Global Distribution, pg 676
Albany Theatre Supply Co Inc, pg 679
American Video Inc, pg 684
Aura Sonic Ltd (ASL), pg 695
AV Workshop, pg 697
beyerdynamic Inc, pg 704
BMI Supply, pg 708
BTX Technologies, pg 712
Cadence Jazz Records, pg 713
Colortone Audio Visual, pg 728
Design Audio Visual Inc, pg 741
Gaylord Archival, pg 768
Gotham Sound & Communications Inc, pg 773
HAVE Inc, pg 777
Hot House Professional Audio, pg 782
Indigo Productions, pg 787
KVL Audio Visual Services Inc, pg 802
Lee Dan® Communications Inc, pg 805
Long Island Video Enterprises Live Inc, pg 811
Mark Custom Recording Service Inc, pg 817
Markertek Video Supply, pg 817
Saul Mineroff Electronics Inc (SME), pg 828
Neptune Photo Inc, pg 838
Posthorn Recordings, pg 859
Ray Supply Inc, pg 870
RNJ Electronics, pg 875
Stampede Presentation Products Inc, pg 899
TecNec Distributing, pg 909
Theatrical Services & Supplies Inc, pg 912
Toys From The Attic, pg 916
Tri-Ed Distribution Inc, pg 918
Videoguys, pg 929
Visual Technologies Corp, pg 932

Visual Word Systems Inc, pg 932
Voyetra Turtle Beach, pg 933

NORTH CAROLINA

Camcor Inc, pg 715
Strategic Connections, pg 901

OHIO

Copp Integrated Systems, pg 731
Hughie's Event Production Services, pg 782
ITA Audio Visual Solutions, pg 791
Midwest Photo Exchange, pg 827
Parts Express, pg 851
Tri-State Audio Visual Co, pg 918
Tri-State Visual Products Inc, pg 918
Visual Products Inc, pg 931

OKLAHOMA

Ford AV, pg 763

OREGON

Audix Microphones, pg 695
PLUS Corp of America, pg 858
SuperDigital Ltd, pg 904

PENNSYLVANIA

Advanced AV LLC, pg 677
Audio Visions Inc, pg 694
Clair Companies, pg 725
J E Foss Co, pg 764
Garcia Marketing Inc, pg 768
Grise Audio Visual Center Inc, pg 774
The Lerro Corp, pg 806
Morefield Communications Inc, pg 830
RSS Distributors, pg 878
Sound by Fitch, pg 893
Vistacom Inc, pg 931
Visual Sound Inc, pg 931
Wespen Audio Visual Co, pg 935

RHODE ISLAND

Shanix Inc, pg 885

SOUTH CAROLINA

DaviSound, pg 739
Impact Technology Group LLC, pg 786

TENNESSEE

Allstar Audio Systems Inc, pg 681
Belew Enterprises, pg 703
Lowrance Sound Co Inc, pg 812
Memphis Communications Corp, pg 823
Mr Mark's Used Musical, Stereo & Studio Equipment Store, pg 828
Spectrum Sound Inc, pg 897
Technical Support Systems LLC, pg 908
Trew Audio Inc, pg 917
Zion Music Group, pg 945

TEXAS

Audio Visual Technologies Group (AVTG), pg 695
AVES Audio Visual Systems Inc, pg 698
CAM Audio Inc, pg 714
Cinema Antiques, pg 723
Crossroads Audio Inc, pg 735
Data Projections Inc, pg 738
Digital Display Solutions Inc, pg 742
FitzCo Sound Inc, pg 761

Heffernan Audio Visual, pg 778
JSAV, pg 795
Lubbock Audio Visual Inc, pg 812
Precision Camera & Video, pg 861
Pro Video & Film Equipment Co Inc, pg 863
Quality Audio Visual Service Inc, pg 867
RF Specialties of Texas LLC, pg 874
Sound Works, pg 894
Southwest Sound Solutions, pg 896
Stage Directions, pg 898
Tarpley Media Systems, pg 907

UTAH

Performance Audio LLC, pg 854
RIA Corp, pg 874
Webb Audio Visual, pg 935

VERMONT

Dark Star Lighting & Production, pg 737
Production Advantage Inc, pg 863

VIRGINIA

Avitecture Inc, pg 699
Boitnott Visual Communications Corp (BVC), pg 708
Intellidyne LLC, pg 789
Lee Hartman & Sons Inc, pg 805
Rocktown Media, pg 876
StageSound, pg 899
The Whitlock Group, pg 937

WASHINGTON

Broadcast Supply World Wide, pg 711
CCI Solutions, pg 718
D A Sound, pg 737
Northern Lights & Pro Audio, pg 842
PNTA, pg 858

WISCONSIN

Audio Visual of Milwaukee Inc, pg 694
Camera Corner Connecting Point, pg 715
Demco Inc, pg 740
Full Compass Systems, pg 767

PUERTO RICO

Audio Visual Concepts Inc, pg 694
Bonnin Electronics Inc, pg 708

ALBERTA

Allstar Show Industries Inc, pg 681
Evolution AV, pg 757
Infosat Communications Inc, pg 787
Matrix Video Communications Corp (MVCC), pg 819
McBain Camera Ltd, pg 820
Unique Communications Ltd, pg 921

BRITISH COLUMBIA

Commercial Electronics Ltd, pg 728

MANITOBA

Advance Pro, pg 677
Inland Audio Visual Ltd, pg 788

ONTARIO

Cinema Stage Inc, pg 724
HD Source, pg 777
Henry's Camera, pg 779

The Hollywood Edge, pg 780
Nationwide Audio Visual Co, pg 837
Westbury National Show Systems Ltd, pg 936
Yorkville Sound Inc, pg 944

QUEBEC

JAM Industries Ltd, pg 792
Panavideo Inc, pg 850
SC Media Canada, pg 881
Sennheiser (Canada) Inc, pg 884

Microphone Manufacturers

ARIZONA

AtlasIED, pg 692
Fender Musical Instruments Corp, pg 759
David Wexler & Co, pg 936

CALIFORNIA

ACO Pacific Inc, pg 674
AKG Acoustics US, pg 679
Anchor Audio Inc, pg 685
Califone International Inc, pg 714
Calrad Electronics, pg 714
Carvin Amps & Audio, pg 717
Countryman Associates Inc, pg 732
Filmtools®, pg 761
Hosa Technology Inc, pg 781
Josephson Engineering Inc, pg 795
Logitech, pg 811
Manley Laboratories Inc, pg 816
Marshall Electronics Inc, pg 817
Millennia Media, FPC, pg 827
Nady Systems Inc, pg 835
Point Source Audio, pg 858
Professional Sound Corp, pg 865
Sony Electronics Inc, pg 893
TEAC America Inc, pg 908
TeachLogic Inc, pg 908
TOA Electronics Inc, pg 915
Wohler Technologies Inc, pg 940

CONNECTICUT

Gold Line/TEF, pg 772
The Music People Inc, pg 834
Neumann USA, pg 838
Sennheiser Electronic Corp, pg 884
Sound Control Technologies Inc, pg 893

FLORIDA

CTGaudio, pg 735
Intermark Industries Inc, pg 789
TAI Audio, pg 906

ILLINOIS

AmpliVox Portable Sound Systems, pg 684
Shure Inc, pg 887

MINNESOTA

Bosch Security Systems Inc, pg 709

MISSISSIPPI

Peavey Electronics Corp, pg 852

NEVADA

Pignose-Gorilla, pg 856

NEW HAMPSHIRE

Earthworks Inc, pg 749

NEW JERSEY

AlltecPro, pg 681
Bogen Communications Inc, pg 708
Oklahoma Sound Corp, pg 844
Panasonic Consumer Electronics Co, pg 850
RAMSA Professional Audio Systems, pg 870
Sony Pro Audio, pg 893

NEW YORK

beyerdynamic Inc, pg 704
GLI Sound Systems, pg 771
Harbro Corp, pg 776
Posthorn Recordings, pg 859
Servoreeler Systems, pg 884
Television Equipment Associates Inc (TEA), pg 910
Voyetra Turtle Beach, pg 933

OHIO

Audio-Technica US Inc, pg 694
CAD Audio, pg 713

OREGON

Audix Microphones, pg 695

PENNSYLVANIA

Ac-cetera Inc, pg 672

SOUTH CAROLINA

DaviSound, pg 739

UTAH

ClearOne Inc, pg 726

WASHINGTON

AudioControl® Inc, pg 695

Microphone Rentals

ALABAMA

Audio-Video Resources Inc, pg 694

ALASKA

Connections Film & Video Inc, pg 731

ARIZONA

Arizona Cine Equipment, pg 688
AV Concepts Inc, pg 696
Broadcast Rentals, pg 711
Merestone, pg 823
Metropolitan Audio-Visual Inc, pg 824
Tempe Camera, pg 910
Ultimate Presentation Systems Inc, pg 920
Video West Inc, pg 929

ARKANSAS

White Diamond Productions LLC, pg 937

CALIFORNIA

Absolute Rentals, pg 672
Acey Decy Lighting, pg 674
Action Audio & Visual, pg 675
AGF Media Services, pg 678
Alliant Event Services, pg 681
Alternative Rentals, pg 682
Ametron Audio/Video, pg 684
Artichoke Productions, pg 690
Associated Sound, pg 691
Assured Audio Visual, pg 691

AUDIO

Microphone Rentals (continued)

CALIFORNIA (continued)

ATV Video Center Inc, pg 692
AV Conferencing LLC (AVC), pg 697
AV Guys, pg 697
Bexel, an NEP Broadcast Services Company, pg 704
Chater Camera Inc, pg 721
Cherry Multimedia, pg 721
Cinema Camera Rentals, pg 723
Electronic Design Solutions Inc, pg 752
Express Media Inc, pg 757
Express Video Supply Inc, pg 757
First Camera, pg 761
Flip 2 Media Inc, pg 762
Full Moon & High Tide Productions & Studios, pg 767
Gear Monkey, pg 769
Gold Standard Productions, pg 772
Golden Gate Studios, pg 772
Alan Gordon Enterprises Inc, pg 772
Gravity Media, pg 773
HDrental.com, pg 777
Hollywood Sound Systems, pg 781
IAMP Professional Audio, pg 783
Imagecraft Productions, pg 785
Instructional Materials & Equipment Distributors (I-Med), pg 789
JD Audio Visual Inc, pg 793
JFA Studio, pg 794
LA Sound Co, pg 803
Lynch Communications, pg 813
Maximus Media Inc, pg 820
McCune Audio-Video-Lighting, pg 821
Media Fabricators Inc, pg 822
Media Vision USA, pg 822
Munday & Collins AV, pg 834
Muse Presentation Technologies, pg 834
New Circuit Films LLC, pg 839
North County Media Center, pg 842
Old School Cameras, pg 844
On-Trax Inc, pg 846
Photo Film Stage, pg 856
Prime Cut Productions, pg 862
Pro HD Rentals, pg 863
Production Gear Rentals (PGR), pg 863
PSAV® Presentation Services, pg 866
Pyxis Industries Inc, pg 867
Radiant Images, pg 869
Alwin Sauers Audio Productions (ASAP), pg 881
Shooting Star Video, pg 886
Shoulder High Productions, pg 886
SNAP, pg 891
Sound Service Co, pg 894
Stanislaus AV Inc, pg 899
Stray Angel Films, pg 902
Studio Circle Recordings, pg 902
Studio 637, pg 903
The Studios at Paramount, pg 903
Synthesizer Rental Service, pg 906
T-stop Inc, pg 906
Third Ear Sound Co, pg 912
Total Creative, pg 916
Towards 2000 Inc, pg 916
VER, pg 926
Video Resources Inc, pg 928
VMI Inc, pg 932
Voice & Video Rentals, pg 932
Warner Bros Production Sound & Video Services, pg 934

Westcoast Video Productions Inc, pg 936
Westlake Recording Studios, pg 936

COLORADO

Audio Consultant Services Inc, pg 693
Daylight Productions & Rentals, pg 739
Mike's Camera, pg 827
Multimedia Audio Visual Inc, pg 833
Open Media Foundation, pg 846
Spectrum Audio Visual Services, pg 897

CONNECTICUT

A/V Davey, pg 697
Connecticut Audio & Theatrical Supply, pg 731

DELAWARE

Actors Attic, pg 675
Showorks Audio Visual Inc, pg 887
Side Door Studio Inc, pg 887

DISTRICT OF COLUMBIA

Metro Teleproductions Inc (MTI), pg 824

FLORIDA

Access Media Group, pg 673
Accord Productions, pg 673
All Comm Rentals Inc (ALLCOMM), pg 680
AVI-SPL, pg 698
Blackburst Entertainment LLC, pg 706
Budget Video Rentals, pg 712
Digital Zoetrope Productions, pg 742
Harmon's Audio-Visual Services, pg 776
Hi-Tech Enterprises Inc, pg 779
Industrial Strength Inc, pg 787
Jordan Klein Film & Video (JKFV), pg 795
Knowles Video Inc (KVI), pg 800
Lighting Sales Connection Inc, pg 808
ONstage, pg 846
Paradise Show & Design Inc, pg 851
Phat Planet Recording Studios, pg 855
Photosound of Orlando Inc, pg 856
Sight & Sound Productions, pg 887
TAI Audio, pg 906
Technomedia Solutions, pg 909
Universal Studios Florida® Production Group, pg 922
Zebedee Productions, pg 945

GEORGIA

Convergent Media Systems, pg 731
ECG Productions, pg 750
Lighting & Production Equipment Inc, pg 807
MAGNUM Companies Ltd, pg 815
See Production Services, pg 883
Stage Front Presentation Systems, pg 899
Staging Directions Inc, pg 899
Studio Space Atlanta, pg 903

HAWAII

Hawaii Sound & Vision, pg 777
Sight & Sound Studios, pg 887

ILLINOIS

Allen Visual Systems Inc, pg 680
AV Chicago Inc, pg 696
Backstar Creative Media Inc, pg 700
Beatty TeleVisual Productions, pg 703
Central Audio-Visual Equipment Inc, pg 719
Firehouse Studios, pg 761
C V Lloyde, pg 810
Magnanimous Media, pg 814
Meetinghouse Event Design & Production, pg 823
On Site Video, pg 846
OSA International Inc, pg 848
Pepper Group, pg 854
Product Productions, pg 863
PSAV® Presentation Services (Hotel Services Division), pg 866
RC Communications, pg 870
Resolution Productions Group, pg 874
SCI Television & Creative Media LLC, pg 882
Staging Resources Inc, pg 899
Woodside Avenue Music Productions Inc, pg 941
Zacuto, pg 945

INDIANA

Advanced Media Integration, pg 677
Gaither Studios LLC, pg 767
Heart Breaker Entertainment LLC, pg 778

IOWA

Central Lighting & Equipment Inc (CLE), pg 719
Pro Video, pg 863

KANSAS

Lights On, pg 808

KENTUCKY

Audio Visual Techniques Inc, pg 695

LOUISIANA

Clark Services Audio Visual & Exhibit Inc, pg 725
Pace Systems, pg 849

MAINE

Headlight Audio Visual Inc, pg 777
University of Maine Media Services, pg 922

MARYLAND

Advance Audiovisual Presentation Ltd, pg 677
Archai Media, pg 688
Cardinal Sound & Video, pg 717
CPR MultiMedia Solutions, pg 732
Event Tech, pg 756
Hargrove Inc, pg 776
Maryland Sound International Holding Co LLC, pg 819
Nelson White Systems Inc, pg 838
RTZ Audio Visual, pg 878
Soundtrax Inc, pg 895

MASSACHUSETTS

AVFX Inc, pg 698
Capron Lighting & Sound Co Inc, pg 716
Fastlane Productions LLC, pg 759

Terry Hanley Audio Systems Inc, pg 775
massAV, pg 819
Preston Productions Inc, pg 861

MICHIGAN

City Events Group, pg 725
K&R All Media Productions LLC, pg 796
K&R's Recording Studios Inc, pg 796
On Stage Visuals, pg 846
TEL Systems LLC, pg 909

MINNESOTA

Alpha Video & Audio Inc, pg 682
AVI Systems, pg 698
Pro Media Productions, pg 863

MISSISSIPPI

Bowie Audio Visual Enterprises Inc, pg 709
Jasper Ewing & Sons Inc, pg 757

MISSOURI

Communitronics Corp, pg 729
Production Support Services Inc, pg 864
Schiller's Audio-Visual, pg 881
Show-Me Audio-Visual, pg 887

MONTANA

High Plains Films, pg 779
Jereco Studios Inc, pg 793

NEBRASKA

Dog & Pony Productions Inc, pg 744

NEVADA

GES Audio Visual, pg 770

NEW HAMPSHIRE

Apertura, pg 686
APS Lighting-Sound-AV, pg 688

NEW JERSEY

Audio Visual Associates, pg 694
Audio Visual Dynamics®, pg 694
CFP Video Productions Inc, pg 720
Earl Girls Inc, pg 749
Euro-Pacific Film & Video Productions Inc, pg 756
International Audio Visual Inc, pg 790
Moe AV LLC, pg 828
The Music Place, pg 834
Nelson Enterprises Theatrical Supply Co, pg 838
Panavid, pg 850
PLS Staging, pg 858
Soundtracks Production Services LLC, pg 895
Starlite, pg 900
Wired 4 Sound Inc, pg 940

NEW MEXICO

Production Outfitters, pg 864
Quickbeam Systems Inc (QSI), pg 868

NEW YORK

Ace Video, pg 674
Adorama Rental Co, pg 676
All Mobile Video Inc, pg 680
American Video Inc, pg 684
Aura Sonic Ltd (ASL), pg 695

Microphone Repairs

AUDIO

Microphone Repairs
(continued)

NEW MEXICO

Quickbeam Systems Inc (QSI),
  pg 868

NEW YORK

beyerdynamic Inc, pg 704
Design Audio Visual Inc, pg 741
Toys From The Attic, pg 916
Visual Technologies Corp, pg 932

NORTH CAROLINA

Camcor Inc, pg 715
Strategic Connections, pg 901

OHIO

Copp Integrated Systems, pg 731
Hughie's Event Production Services,
  pg 782
ITA Audio Visual Solutions, pg 791
Tri-State Audio Visual Co, pg 918

OREGON

All Service Musical Electronics
  Repair, pg 680

PENNSYLVANIA

J E Foss Co, pg 764
Right Coast Recording Inc, pg 875
Vistacom Inc, pg 931

SOUTH CAROLINA

DaviSound, pg 739

TENNESSEE

Belew Enterprises, pg 703
Memphis Communications Corp,
  pg 823
Technical Support Systems LLC,
  pg 908

TEXAS

Audio Visual Technologies Group
  (AVTG), pg 695
Lubbock Audio Visual Inc, pg 812
Pro Video & Film Equipment Co
  Inc, pg 863
Quality Audio Visual Service Inc,
  pg 867
Southwest Sound Solutions, pg 896
Tarpley Media Systems, pg 907

VIRGINIA

Boitnott Visual Communications
  Corp (BVC), pg 708

WASHINGTON

Northern Lights & Pro Audio,
  pg 842
PNTA, pg 858

WEST VIRGINIA

United Sound & Electronics, pg 921

WISCONSIN

Full Compass Systems, pg 767

ALBERTA

Allstar Show Industries Inc, pg 681
Evolution AV, pg 757

Infosat Communications Inc, pg 787
Unique Communications Ltd,
  pg 921

BRITISH COLUMBIA

Commercial Electronics Ltd, pg 728

MANITOBA

Inland Audio Visual Ltd, pg 788

ONTARIO

HD Source, pg 777
Westbury National Show Systems
  Ltd, pg 936

QUEBEC

Panavideo Inc, pg 850
SC Media Canada, pg 881

Microphone Stand, Boom
& Accessory Distributors

ALABAMA

Curtis Company, pg 736

ARIZONA

Allusion Studios & Pure Wave
  Audio, pg 681
Arizona Cine Equipment, pg 688
EAR Professional Audio/Video,
  pg 749
Metropolitan Audio-Visual Inc,
  pg 824
Olsen Audio Group Inc, pg 845
Troxell-CDI, pg 918
WindTech™ Microphone
  Windscreens & Accessories,
  pg 939

ARKANSAS

White Diamond Productions LLC,
  pg 937

CALIFORNIA

AKG Acoustics US, pg 679
Ametron Audio/Video, pg 684
Associated Sound, pg 691
Assured Audio Visual, pg 691
ATV Video Center Inc, pg 692
Audio Images Corp, pg 693
Band Pro Film & Digital Inc,
  pg 701
BroadcastStore.com, pg 711
California Tape Products Inc,
  pg 714
Cibola Systems, pg 723
Empire Pro, pg 753
Filmtools®, pg 761
Alan Gordon Enterprises Inc,
  pg 772
IAMP Professional Audio, pg 783
Instructional Materials & Equipment
  Distributors (I-Med), pg 789
JD Audio Visual Inc, pg 793
Location Sound Corp, pg 810
LTM Corp of America, pg 812
Martel Electronics Sales Inc, pg 818
Lloyd F McKinney Associates Inc,
  pg 821
MediaPOINTE, pg 823
Mole-Richardson Co, pg 829
Pacific Radio Electronics, pg 849
Professional Sound Corp, pg 865
Sound Service Co, pg 894
Southern California Sound Image
  Inc, pg 895
SSL Industries Inc, pg 898

Stanislaus AV Inc, pg 899
Towards 2000 Inc, pg 916
VMI Inc, pg 932
VTP Inc, pg 933

COLORADO

Audio Consultant Services Inc,
  pg 693
Daylight Productions & Rentals,
  pg 739
Mike's Camera, pg 827
Spectrum Audio Visual Services,
  pg 897

CONNECTICUT

Connecticut Audio & Theatrical
  Supply, pg 731
HB Communications Inc, pg 777
The Music People Inc, pg 834
Neumann USA, pg 838
Redco Audio Inc, pg 872
Sennheiser Electronic Corp, pg 884

DELAWARE

Actors Attic, pg 675

FLORIDA

Access Media Group, pg 673
Altel Systems Group Inc, pg 682
AVI-SPL, pg 698
Broadcasters General Store Inc,
  pg 711
Digital Video Systems, pg 742
Enhanced View Services Inc,
  pg 754
Harris Corp, pg 776
Herman Pro AV, pg 779
Hi-Tech Enterprises Inc, pg 779
Hi-Tech Import Export Corp,
  pg 779
Industrial Strength Inc, pg 787
Intermark Industries Inc, pg 789
Lighting Sales Connection Inc,
  pg 808
Midtown Video Inc, pg 827
ONstage, pg 846
Recording Media & Equipment Inc
  (RM&E), pg 872
Stereo Sales Inc, pg 900
TAI Audio, pg 906
Technomedia Solutions, pg 909

GEORGIA

Baker Audio Visual, pg 700
Clark, pg 725
Lighting & Production Equipment
  Inc, pg 807
Stage Front Presentation Systems,
  pg 899

HAWAII

The Audio Visual Co (AVCO),
  pg 694

ILLINOIS

Allen Visual Systems Inc, pg 680
Central Audio-Visual Equipment
  Inc, pg 719
Joseph Electronics, pg 795
LKG Industries Inc, pg 810
C V Lloyde, pg 810
Major Media Inc, pg 815
Quintessence Audio Ltd, pg 868
Woodside Avenue Music
  Productions Inc, pg 941

INDIANA

Heart Breaker Entertainment LLC,
  pg 778
Jack's Camera Shop, pg 792
Sensory Technologies LLC, pg 884
SHP Electronics, pg 887
Sweetwater Sound Inc, pg 905

KANSAS

Lights On, pg 808

KENTUCKY

Audio Visual Techniques Inc,
  pg 695
Axxis Leasing Inc, pg 700
Barney Miller's Inc, pg 827
NOR-COM Inc, pg 841

LOUISIANA

Techkno Integration & Design
  Services LLC, pg 908

MAINE

Headlight Audio Visual Inc, pg 777

MARYLAND

Advance Audiovisual Presentation
  Ltd, pg 677
Bradley Broadcast & Pro Audio,
  pg 709
Cardinal Sound & Video, pg 717
Human Circuit, pg 782
Noventri, pg 843

MASSACHUSETTS

Terry Hanley Audio Systems Inc,
  pg 775
Hunt's Photo & Video, pg 782
Professional Audio Design Inc,
  pg 865
Rule Boston Camera, pg 878

MICHIGAN

Olson Anderson Co, pg 685
City Events Group, pg 725
On Stage Visuals, pg 846
Stedman Corp, pg 900
TEL Systems LLC, pg 909

MINNESOTA

New Life Communications Inc,
  pg 839
Tierney Brothers Inc, pg 914

MISSISSIPPI

Bowie Audio Visual Enterprises Inc,
  pg 709

MISSOURI

Communitronics Corp, pg 729
Conference Technologies Inc,
  pg 730
Modern Communications Inc,
  pg 828
Production Support Services Inc,
  pg 864
The RapcoHorizon Co, pg 870
Schiller's Audio-Visual, pg 881

NEW HAMPSHIRE

APS Lighting-Sound-AV, pg 688
Technet® Systems Group, pg 908

NEW JERSEY
A-V Services Inc, pg 671
Alltec Stores, a Vcom IMC
　Company, pg 681
AlltecPro, pg 681
AV Bluebook, pg 696
Comprehensive Cable &
　Connectivity Co, pg 729
Diversified, pg 744
Earl Girls Inc, pg 749
Euro-Pacific Film & Video
　Productions Inc, pg 756
G&G Technologies Inc, pg 768
HamiltonBuhl, pg 775
Manfrotto Distribution Inc, pg 816
The Music Place, pg 834
Nelson Enterprises Theatrical
　Supply Co, pg 838
Ritz Camera & Image, pg 875
Starlite, pg 900
Total Video Products Inc, pg 916
Vcom IMC, pg 925
Video Corporation of America
　(VCA), pg 927
Wired 4 Sound Inc, pg 940
Yorktel, pg 944

NEW MEXICO
Quickbeam Systems Inc (QSI),
　pg 868

NEW YORK
Albany Theatre Supply Co Inc,
　pg 679
American Video Inc, pg 684
Audio-Video Corp, pg 694
Aura Sonic Ltd (ASL), pg 695
AV Workshop, pg 697
Barbizon Electric Co Inc, pg 701
beyerdynamic Inc, pg 704
BTX Technologies, pg 712
Colortone Audio Visual, pg 728
Design Audio Visual Inc, pg 741
Gaylord Archival, pg 768
Gotham Sound & Communications
　Inc, pg 773
HAVE Inc, pg 777
Hot House Professional Audio,
　pg 782
Indigo Productions, pg 787
KVL Audio Visual Services Inc,
　pg 802
Long Island Video Enterprises Live
　Inc, pg 811
Mark Custom Recording Service
　Inc, pg 817
Markertek Video Supply, pg 817
Neptune Photo Inc, pg 838
Posthorn Recordings, pg 859
Presentation Products Inc, pg 861
RNJ Electronics, pg 875
TecNec Distributing, pg 909
Theatrical Services & Supplies Inc,
　pg 912
Toys From The Attic, pg 916
Tri-Ed Distribution Inc, pg 918
Visual Technologies Corp, pg 932
Visual Word Systems Inc, pg 932

OHIO
Copp Integrated Systems, pg 731
Hughie's Event Production Services,
　pg 782
ITA Audio Visual Solutions, pg 791
Parts Express, pg 851
Tri-State Audio Visual Co, pg 918
Tri-State Visual Products Inc,
　pg 918

OKLAHOMA
Ford AV, pg 763

OREGON
SuperDigital Ltd, pg 904

PENNSYLVANIA
Advanced AV LLC, pg 677
Audio Visions Inc, pg 694
Clair Companies, pg 725
J E Foss Co, pg 764
Grise Audio Visual Center Inc,
　pg 774
The Lerro Corp, pg 806
Morefield Communications Inc,
　pg 830
RSS Distributors, pg 878
Sound by Fitch, pg 893
Vistacom Inc, pg 931
Visual Sound Inc, pg 931
Wespen Audio Visual Co, pg 935

SOUTH CAROLINA
Impact Technology Group LLC,
　pg 786

TENNESSEE
Allstar Audio Systems Inc, pg 681
Lowrance Sound Co Inc, pg 812
Mr Mark's Used Musical, Stereo &
　Studio Equipment Store, pg 828
Spectrum Sound Inc, pg 897
Technical Support Systems LLC,
　pg 908
Trew Audio Inc, pg 917
Zion Music Group, pg 945

TEXAS
CAM Audio Inc, pg 714
Crossroads Audio Inc, pg 735
Data Projections Inc, pg 738
FitzCo Sound Inc, pg 761
Heffernan Audio Visual, pg 778
Lubbock Audio Visual Inc, pg 812
Pro Video & Film Equipment Co
　Inc, pg 863
Quality Audio Visual Service Inc,
　pg 867
RF Specialties of Texas LLC,
　pg 874
Sound Works, pg 894
Southwest Sound Solutions, pg 896
Stage Directions, pg 898
Tarpley Media Systems, pg 907

UTAH
Performance Audio LLC, pg 854
RIA Corp, pg 874
Spectra Sonics LLC, pg 897

VERMONT
Production Advantage Inc, pg 863

VIRGINIA
Avitecture Inc, pg 699
Boitnott Visual Communications
　Corp (BVC), pg 708
Intellidyne LLC, pg 789
Lee Hartman & Sons Inc, pg 805
Rocktown Media, pg 876
StageSound, pg 899
The Whitlock Group, pg 937

WASHINGTON
CCI Solutions, pg 718
D A Sound, pg 737
Northern Lights & Pro Audio,
　pg 842
PNTA, pg 858

WEST VIRGINIA
United Sound & Electronics, pg 921

WISCONSIN
Audio Visual of Milwaukee Inc,
　pg 694
Camera Corner Connecting Point,
　pg 715
Full Compass Systems, pg 767

PUERTO RICO
Audio Visual Concepts Inc, pg 694
Bonnin Electronics Inc, pg 708

ALBERTA
Allstar Show Industries Inc, pg 681
Infosat Communications Inc, pg 787
Matrix Video Communications Corp
　(MVCC), pg 819
McBain Camera Ltd, pg 820
Unique Communications Ltd,
　pg 921

BRITISH COLUMBIA
Commercial Electronics Ltd, pg 728

MANITOBA
Advance Pro, pg 677
Inland Audio Visual Ltd, pg 788

ONTARIO
Cinema Stage Inc, pg 724
HD Source, pg 777
Henry's Camera, pg 779
Nationwide Audio Visual Co,
　pg 837
Westbury National Show Systems
　Ltd, pg 936
Yorkville Sound Inc, pg 944

QUEBEC
JAM Industries Ltd, pg 792
SC Media Canada, pg 881
Sennheiser (Canada) Inc, pg 884

Microphone Stand, Boom & Accessory Manufacturers

ARIZONA
AtlasIED, pg 692
Olsen Audio Group Inc, pg 845
WindTech™ Microphone
　Windscreens & Accessories,
　pg 939

CALIFORNIA
AKG Acoustics US, pg 679
Ametron Audio/Video, pg 684
Anchor Audio Inc, pg 685
Califone International Inc, pg 714
Calrad Electronics, pg 714
Filmtools®, pg 761
Alan Gordon Enterprises Inc,
　pg 772
Hosa Technology Inc, pg 781
Josephson Engineering Inc, pg 795
LTM Corp of America, pg 812
Manley Laboratories Inc, pg 816
Nady Systems Inc, pg 835
TeachLogic Inc, pg 908

COLORADO
Display Devices Inc, pg 743
Ultimate Support Systems Inc,
　pg 920

CONNECTICUT
The Music People Inc, pg 834
Neumann USA, pg 838
Sennheiser Electronic Corp, pg 884

FLORIDA
Intermark Industries Inc, pg 789

ILLINOIS
AmpliVox Portable Sound Systems,
　pg 684
Shure Inc, pg 887
Switchcraft® Inc, pg 905

MARYLAND
RCI Custom Products, pg 871

MICHIGAN
Stedman Corp, pg 900

MISSISSIPPI
Peavey Electronics Corp, pg 852

MISSOURI
The RapcoHorizon Co, pg 870

NEW JERSEY
AlltecPro, pg 681
Bogen Communications Inc, pg 708
FSR Inc, pg 766

NEW YORK
beyerdynamic Inc, pg 704
Harry Joseph & Associates Inc,
　pg 795
Posthorn Recordings, pg 859

OHIO
Audio-Technica US Inc, pg 694

PENNSYLVANIA
Ac-cetera Inc, pg 672

Microphone Stand, Boom & Accessory Rentals

ALABAMA
Audio-Video Resources Inc, pg 694

ALASKA
Connections Film & Video Inc,
　pg 731

ARIZONA
Arizona Cine Equipment, pg 688
Broadcast Rentals, pg 711
Merestone, pg 823
Metropolitan Audio-Visual Inc,
　pg 824
Tempe Camera, pg 910
Video West Inc, pg 929

ARKANSAS
White Diamond Productions LLC,
　pg 937

CALIFORNIA
Absolute Rentals, pg 672
Acey Decy Lighting, pg 674
AGF Media Services, pg 678
Alliant Event Services, pg 681

AUDIO

Microphone Stand, Boom & Accessory Rentals (continued)

CALIFORNIA (continued)
Ametron Audio/Video, pg 684
Artichoke Productions, pg 690
Associated Sound, pg 691
Assured Audio Visual, pg 691
ATV Video Center Inc, pg 692
Audio Rents, pg 693
AV Guys, pg 697
Bexel, an NEP Broadcast Services Company, pg 704
Chater Camera Inc, pg 721
Cherry Multimedia, pg 721
Cinema Camera Rentals, pg 723
Dan Dugan Sound Design Inc, pg 747
Express Media Inc, pg 757
Express Video Supply Inc, pg 757
First Camera, pg 761
Flip 2 Media Inc, pg 762
Full Moon & High Tide Productions & Studios, pg 767
Golden Gate Studios, pg 772
Alan Gordon Enterprises Inc, pg 772
Hollywood Sound Systems, pg 781
IAMP Professional Audio, pg 783
Imagecraft Productions, pg 785
JD Audio Visual Inc, pg 793
Lynch Communications, pg 813
Maximus Media Inc, pg 820
McCune Audio-Video-Lighting, pg 821
Munday & Collins AV, pg 834
Muse Presentation Technologies, pg 834
Old School Cameras, pg 844
On-Trax Inc, pg 846
Prime Cut Productions, pg 862
Pro HD Rentals, pg 863
Production Gear Rentals (PGR), pg 863
PSAV® Presentation Services, pg 866
Pyxis Industries Inc, pg 867
Radiant Images, pg 869
Alwin Sauers Audio Productions (ASAP), pg 881
Shooting Star Video, pg 886
Sound Service Co, pg 894
Stanislaus AV Inc, pg 899
The Studios at Paramount, pg 903
Synthesizer Rental Service, pg 906
Third Ear Sound Co, pg 912
Total Creative, pg 916
Towards 2000 Inc, pg 916
VER, pg 926
Video Resources Inc, pg 928
VMI Inc, pg 932
Voice & Video Rentals, pg 932
Warner Bros Production Sound & Video Services, pg 934
Westcoast Video Productions Inc, pg 936

COLORADO
Audio Consultant Services Inc, pg 693
Daylight Productions & Rentals, pg 739
Multimedia Audio Visual Inc, pg 833
Open Media Foundation, pg 846
Spectrum Audio Visual Services, pg 897

CONNECTICUT
A/V Davey, pg 697
Connecticut Audio & Theatrical Supply, pg 731

DELAWARE
Actors Attic, pg 675
Showorks Audio Visual Inc, pg 887
Side Door Studio Inc, pg 887

FLORIDA
AVI-SPL, pg 698
Blackburst Entertainment LLC, pg 706
Budget Video Rentals, pg 712
Hi-Tech Enterprises Inc, pg 779
Industrial Strength Inc, pg 787
Knowles Video Inc (KVI), pg 800
Lighting Sales Connection Inc, pg 808
Miami Daylight Studios, pg 825
ONstage, pg 846
Paradise Show & Design Inc, pg 851
Phat Planet Recording Studios, pg 855
PRI Productions, pg 862
Sight & Sound Productions, pg 887
TAI Audio, pg 906
Technomedia Solutions, pg 909
Universal Studios Florida® Production Group, pg 922

GEORGIA
ECG Productions, pg 750
Lighting & Production Equipment Inc, pg 807
MAGNUM Companies Ltd, pg 815
See Production Services, pg 883
Stage Front Presentation Systems, pg 899
Staging Directions Inc, pg 899
Studio Space Atlanta, pg 903

HAWAII
Sight & Sound Studios, pg 887

ILLINOIS
Allen Visual Systems Inc, pg 680
AV Chicago Inc, pg 696
Beatty TeleVisual Productions, pg 703
Central Audio-Visual Equipment Inc, pg 719
Firehouse Studios, pg 761
C V Lloyde, pg 810
Meetinghouse Event Design & Production, pg 823
OSA International Inc, pg 848
Product Productions, pg 863
RC Communications, pg 870
Resolution Productions Group, pg 874
SCI Television & Creative Media LLC, pg 882
Woodside Avenue Music Productions Inc, pg 941
Zacuto, pg 945

INDIANA
Gaither Studios LLC, pg 767
Heart Breaker Entertainment LLC, pg 778

IOWA
Central Lighting & Equipment Inc (CLE), pg 719
Pro Video, pg 863

KANSAS
Lights On, pg 808

KENTUCKY
Audio Visual Techniques Inc, pg 695
Idle Minds Productions Inc, pg 784

LOUISIANA
Clark Services Audio Visual & Exhibit Inc, pg 725

MARYLAND
Advance Audiovisual Presentation Ltd, pg 677
Archai Media, pg 688
Cardinal Sound & Video, pg 717
CPR MultiMedia Solutions, pg 732
Event Tech, pg 756
Maryland Sound International Holding Co LLC, pg 819
Soundtrax Inc, pg 895

MASSACHUSETTS
AVFX Inc, pg 698
Terry Hanley Audio Systems Inc, pg 775
massAV, pg 819
Preston Productions Inc, pg 861

MICHIGAN
Olson Anderson Co, pg 685
City Events Group, pg 725
K&R All Media Productions LLC, pg 796
K&R's Recording Studios Inc, pg 796
On Stage Visuals, pg 846
Stedman Corp, pg 900
TEL Systems LLC, pg 909

MINNESOTA
Alpha Video & Audio Inc, pg 682

MISSISSIPPI
Bowie Audio Visual Enterprises Inc, pg 709

MISSOURI
Communitronics Corp, pg 729
Production Support Services Inc, pg 864
Schiller's Audio-Visual, pg 881
Show-Me Audio-Visual, pg 887
Switch, pg 905

MONTANA
Jereco Studios Inc, pg 793

NEBRASKA
Dog & Pony Productions Inc, pg 744

NEVADA
GES Audio Visual, pg 770
MG Studio, pg 825

NEW HAMPSHIRE
Apertura, pg 686
APS Lighting-Sound-AV, pg 688

NEW JERSEY
CFP Video Productions Inc, pg 720
Earl Girls Inc, pg 749

Euro-Pacific Film & Video Productions Inc, pg 756
International Audio Visual Inc, pg 790
MiB MediaWorks, pg 825
Moe AV LLC, pg 828
The Music Place, pg 834
Nelson Enterprises Theatrical Supply Co, pg 838
Panavid, pg 850
PLS Staging, pg 858
Starlite, pg 900
Video Corporation of America (VCA), pg 927
Wired 4 Sound Inc, pg 940

NEW MEXICO
Production Outfitters, pg 864
Quickbeam Systems Inc (QSI), pg 868

NEW YORK
Ace Video, pg 674
American Video Inc, pg 684
Aura Sonic Ltd (ASL), pg 695
AV Workshop, pg 697
Big Foot Productions Inc, pg 705
Bond Street Studio, pg 708
Camart, pg 714
Colortone Audio Visual, pg 728
CP Communications, pg 732
CSI Rentals, pg 735
Design Audio Visual Inc, pg 741
Gearhead Rentals, pg 769
Gotham Sound & Communications Inc, pg 773
Hello World Communications, pg 778
KVL Audio Visual Services Inc, pg 802
Long Island Video Enterprises Live Inc, pg 811
Posthorn Recordings, pg 859
See Factor Industry Inc, pg 883
Specialized Audio-Visual Inc, pg 896
Studio Instrument Rentals (SIR), pg 902
Theatrical Services & Supplies Inc, pg 912
Tri-Ed Distribution Inc, pg 918
Visual Technologies Corp, pg 932
Visual Word Systems Inc, pg 932
WorldStage, pg 941

NORTH CAROLINA
AV Connections Inc, pg 697
AV Metro Inc, pg 697
Duke Media Services, pg 747
Special Event Services, pg 896
Take One Productions Ltd, pg 906

NORTH DAKOTA
Media Productions, pg 822

OHIO
Hughie's Event Production Services, pg 782
Lyon Video Inc, pg 813
Mills James Productions, pg 828
Production Solutions Inc, pg 864
R&B Communications Inc, pg 870

OKLAHOMA
PDC Productions, pg 852

OREGON

Northwest Film Center, pg 842
Picture This Production Services,
   pg 856
Rose City Sound, pg 877

PENNSYLVANIA

Advanced AV LLC, pg 677
Argentine Productions Inc, pg 688
Audio Visions Inc, pg 694
Audio Visual Communications Inc,
   pg 694
FirstGeneration Audio/Visual
   Services, pg 761
FMP Media Solutions Inc, pg 763
Grise Audio Visual Center Inc,
   pg 774
New York Camera & Video, pg 840
Right Coast Recording Inc, pg 875
Sound by Fitch, pg 893
Upstage Video, pg 923
The Videohouse Inc, pg 929
Viewpoint Production Services Inc,
   pg 930
Vistacom Inc, pg 931
Visual Sound Inc, pg 931

SOUTH CAROLINA

Impact Technology Group LLC,
   pg 786
Sound & Images Inc, pg 893

TENNESSEE

Allstar Audio Systems Inc, pg 681
Brantley Sound Associates Inc,
   pg 709
Love Shack Recording Studios,
   pg 811
Mr Mark's Used Musical, Stereo &
   Studio Equipment Store, pg 828
Technical Support Systems LLC,
   pg 908
Trew Audio Inc, pg 917

TEXAS

Alford Media Services, pg 680
Bright Star Productions Inc, pg 710
Crossroads Audio Inc, pg 735
FitzCo Sound Inc, pg 761
GEAR Cameras & Lighting, pg 769
Lubbock Audio Visual Inc, pg 812
Music Lab Inc, pg 834
Onstage Systems, pg 846
Quality Audio Visual Service Inc,
   pg 867
South Coast Film & Video, pg 895
Stage Directions, pg 898
Texcam Inc, pg 911
Video Perspective, pg 928

UTAH

Performance Audio LLC, pg 854
Redman Movies & Stories, pg 872

VERMONT

Dark Star Lighting & Production,
   pg 737
Edgewood Studios, pg 750

VIRGINIA

American AV, pg 682
Boitnott Visual Communications
   Corp (BVC), pg 708
Lee Hartman & Sons Inc, pg 805
StageSound, pg 899

WASHINGTON

D A Sound, pg 737
Northern Lights & Pro Audio,
   pg 842
Oppenheimer Camera Products,
   pg 847
PNTA, pg 858
Victory Studios, pg 927

WEST VIRGINIA

United Sound & Electronics, pg 921

WISCONSIN

Camera Corner Connecting Point,
   pg 715
Event Essentials, pg 756
Full Compass Systems, pg 767

WYOMING

Bridger Productions Inc, pg 710

PUERTO RICO

Stage Crew Audiovisual Inc, pg 898

ALBERTA

Allstar Show Industries Inc, pg 681
Evolution AV, pg 757
L R Light & Sound, pg 802
McBain Camera Ltd, pg 820
Unique Communications Ltd,
   pg 921

BRITISH COLUMBIA

Clark's Audio Visual Services Ltd,
   pg 725
Commercial Electronics Ltd, pg 728
DL Sound & Lighting Productions
   Ltd, pg 744
Inspired Image Picture Co (IIPC),
   pg 788
MicrophoneRentals.com, pg 826
Video Out Distribution, pg 928

MANITOBA

Inland Audio Visual Ltd, pg 788

ONTARIO

HD Source, pg 777
RB Productions, pg 870
Westbury National Show Systems
   Ltd, pg 936

QUEBEC

Audio Visual Dynamics, pg 694
Group PVP, pg 774

Microphone Stand, Boom & Accessory Repairs

CALIFORNIA

Ametron Audio/Video, pg 684
Audio Images Corp, pg 693
Alan Gordon Enterprises Inc,
   pg 772
LTM Corp of America, pg 812
McAlister Electronics, pg 820
Professional Sound Corp, pg 865
Sound Service Co, pg 894
Towards 2000 Inc, pg 916

CONNECTICUT

HB Communications Inc, pg 777
Sennheiser Electronic Corp, pg 884

FLORIDA

Hi-Tech Enterprises Inc, pg 779
Phat Planet Recording Studios,
   pg 855
Stereo Sales Inc, pg 900
TAI Audio, pg 906

GEORGIA

Lighting & Production Equipment
   Inc, pg 807
Stage Front Presentation Systems,
   pg 899

ILLINOIS

Allen Visual Systems Inc, pg 680

INDIANA

Sweetwater Sound Inc, pg 905

KENTUCKY

Axxis Leasing Inc, pg 700
NOR-COM Inc, pg 841

MARYLAND

Cardinal Sound & Video, pg 717

MICHIGAN

City Events Group, pg 725
K&R's Recording Studios Inc,
   pg 796
On Stage Visuals, pg 846
Stedman Corp, pg 900
TEL Systems LLC, pg 909

NEW JERSEY

A-V Services Inc, pg 671
Earl Girls Inc, pg 749
Nelson Enterprises Theatrical
   Supply Co, pg 838
Starlite, pg 900

NEW MEXICO

Quickbeam Systems Inc (QSI),
   pg 868

NEW YORK

beyerdynamic Inc, pg 704
Toys From The Attic, pg 916
Visual Technologies Corp, pg 932

OHIO

Hughie's Event Production Services,
   pg 782
ITA Audio Visual Solutions, pg 791

PENNSYLVANIA

Audio Visions Inc, pg 694
Vistacom Inc, pg 931

TENNESSEE

Technical Support Systems LLC,
   pg 908

TEXAS

Lubbock Audio Visual Inc, pg 812
Southwest Sound Solutions, pg 896
Tarpley Media Systems, pg 907

VIRGINIA

Boitnott Visual Communications
   Corp (BVC), pg 708

WASHINGTON

Northern Lights & Pro Audio,
   pg 842

WEST VIRGINIA

United Sound & Electronics, pg 921

ALBERTA

Allstar Show Industries Inc, pg 681
Infosat Communications Inc, pg 787
Unique Communications Ltd,
   pg 921

BRITISH COLUMBIA

Commercial Electronics Ltd, pg 728

MANITOBA

Inland Audio Visual Ltd, pg 788

ONTARIO

Westbury National Show Systems
   Ltd, pg 936

Microphone—Wireless Distributors

ARIZONA

Allusion Studios & Pure Wave
   Audio, pg 681
Arizona Cine Equipment, pg 688
EAR Professional Audio/Video,
   pg 749
Metropolitan Audio-Visual Inc,
   pg 824
Projector SuperStore LLC, pg 865
Tempe Camera, pg 910
Troxell-CDI, pg 918
Ultimate Presentation Systems Inc,
   pg 920

ARKANSAS

Sound-Craft Systems Inc, pg 894
Jay S Stanley & Associates Inc,
   pg 899
White Diamond Productions LLC,
   pg 937

CALIFORNIA

AKG Acoustics US, pg 679
Ametron Audio/Video, pg 684
ARS Electronics, pg 690
Associated Sound, pg 691
Assured Audio Visual, pg 691
ATV Video Center Inc, pg 692
Audio Images Corp, pg 693
AV Conferencing LLC (AVC),
   pg 697
Band Pro Film & Digital Inc,
   pg 701
Be Media, pg 702
BroadcastStore.com, pg 711
California Tape Products Inc,
   pg 714
Calrad Electronics, pg 714
Carvin Amps & Audio, pg 717
Cibola Systems, pg 723
Empire Pro, pg 753
Filmtools®, pg 761
GigaSonic, pg 770
Gluskin's Custom Audio Video,
   pg 771
Alan Gordon Enterprises Inc,
   pg 772
Gravity Media, pg 773
IAMP Professional Audio, pg 783
Instructional Materials & Equipment
   Distributors (I-Med), pg 789

AUDIO

Microphone—Wireless Distributors (continued)

CALIFORNIA (continued)

JD Audio Visual Inc, pg 793
Location Sound Corp, pg 810
Martel Electronics Sales Inc, pg 818
Lloyd F McKinney Associates Inc, pg 821
Media Vision USA, pg 822
MediaPOINTE, pg 823
Mole-Richardson Co, pg 829
Premier Lighting & Production Co, pg 861
Promax Systems, pg 865
Sound Service Co, pg 894
Southern California Sound Image Inc, pg 895
SSL Industries Inc, pg 898
Stanislaus AV Inc, pg 899
TOA Electronics Inc, pg 915
Towards 2000 Inc, pg 916
VMI Inc, pg 932
VTP Inc, pg 933
Zack Electronics Inc, pg 945

COLORADO

Audio Consultant Services Inc, pg 693
Daylight Productions & Rentals, pg 739
Mike's Camera, pg 827
Spectrum Audio Visual Services, pg 897

CONNECTICUT

Connecticut Audio & Theatrical Supply, pg 731
HB Communications Inc, pg 777
The Music People Inc, pg 834
Sennheiser Electronic Corp, pg 884

DELAWARE

Actors Attic, pg 675

FLORIDA

Access Media Group, pg 673
Altel Systems Group Inc, pg 682
AVI-SPL, pg 698
Broadcasters General Store Inc, pg 711
Digital Video Systems, pg 742
Harmon's Audio-Visual Services, pg 776
Harris Corp, pg 776
Herman Pro AV, pg 779
Hi-Tech Enterprises Inc, pg 779
Hi-Tech Import Export Corp, pg 779
Industrial Strength Inc, pg 787
Intermark Industries Inc, pg 789
Lighting Sales Connection Inc, pg 808
Midtown Video Inc, pg 827
ONstage, pg 846
Recording Media & Equipment Inc (RM&E), pg 872
The Singing Machine Co Inc, pg 889
Stereo Sales Inc, pg 900
TAI Audio, pg 906
Technomedia Solutions, pg 909

GEORGIA

Baker Audio Visual, pg 700
Clark, pg 725
Innocinema, pg 788

Lighting & Production Equipment Inc, pg 807
Stage Front Presentation Systems, pg 899

HAWAII

The Audio Visual Co (AVCO), pg 694

ILLINOIS

Allen Visual Systems Inc, pg 680
Central Audio-Visual Equipment Inc, pg 719
Dukane Corp, Audio Visual Products Division, pg 747
Joseph Electronics, pg 795
C V Lloyde, pg 810
Major Media Inc, pg 815
Quintessence Audio Ltd, pg 868
RC Communications, pg 870
Woodside Avenue Music Productions Inc, pg 941

INDIANA

Heart Breaker Entertainment LLC, pg 778
Sensory Technologies LLC, pg 884
SHP Electronics, pg 887
Sweetwater Sound Inc, pg 905

KENTUCKY

Audio Visual Techniques Inc, pg 695
Axxis Leasing Inc, pg 700
Barney Miller's Inc, pg 827
NOR-COM Inc, pg 841

LOUISIANA

Pace Systems, pg 849
Techkno Integration & Design Services LLC, pg 908

MAINE

Headlight Audio Visual Inc, pg 777

MARYLAND

Advance Audiovisual Presentation Ltd, pg 677
Bradley Broadcast & Pro Audio, pg 709
Cardinal Sound & Video, pg 717
Human Circuit, pg 782
Noventri, pg 843

MASSACHUSETTS

Terry Hanley Audio Systems Inc, pg 775
Hunt's Photo & Video, pg 782
Professional Audio Design Inc, pg 865
Rule Boston Camera, pg 878

MICHIGAN

Olson Anderson Co, pg 685
City Events Group, pg 725
Digi Sign Design LLC, pg 741
On Stage Visuals, pg 846
TEL Systems LLC, pg 909

MINNESOTA

New Life Communications Inc, pg 839
Tierney Brothers Inc, pg 914

MISSISSIPPI

Bowie Audio Visual Enterprises Inc, pg 709

MISSOURI

Communitronics Corp, pg 729
Conference Technologies Inc, pg 730
Modern Communications Inc, pg 828
Production Support Services Inc, pg 864
Schiller's Audio-Visual, pg 881

NEW HAMPSHIRE

APS Lighting-Sound-AV, pg 688
Technet® Systems Group, pg 908

NEW JERSEY

A-V Services Inc, pg 671
Alltec Stores, a Vcom IMC Company, pg 681
AlltecPro, pg 681
Audio Visual Associates, pg 694
AV Bluebook, pg 696
Comprehensive Cable & Connectivity Co, pg 729
Diversified, pg 744
Earl Girls Inc, pg 749
Euro-Pacific Film & Video Productions Inc, pg 756
G&G Technologies Inc, pg 768
HamiltonBuhl, pg 775
The Music Place, pg 834
Nelson Enterprises Theatrical Supply Co, pg 838
PatchAmp, pg 852
Starlite, pg 900
Total Video Products Inc, pg 916
Vcom IMC, pg 925
Video Corporation of America (VCA), pg 927
Wired 4 Sound Inc, pg 940
Yorktel, pg 944

NEW MEXICO

Quickbeam Systems Inc (QSI), pg 868

NEW YORK

ADI Global Distribution, pg 676
Albany Theatre Supply Co Inc, pg 679
American Video Inc, pg 684
Audio-Video Corp, pg 694
Aura Sonic Ltd (ASL), pg 695
AV Workshop, pg 697
beyerdynamic Inc, pg 704
BMI Supply, pg 708
BTX Technologies, pg 712
Colortone Audio Visual, pg 728
Design Audio Visual Inc, pg 741
Gaylord Archival, pg 768
Gotham Sound & Communications Inc, pg 773
HAVE Inc, pg 777
Hot House Professional Audio, pg 782
Indigo Productions, pg 787
iProbe Multilingual Solutions Inc, pg 791
KVL Audio Visual Services Inc, pg 802
Long Island Video Enterprises Live Inc, pg 811
Markertek Video Supply, pg 817
Neptune Photo Inc, pg 838
Posthorn Recordings, pg 859
Presentation Products Inc, pg 861
RNJ Electronics, pg 875
Samson Technologies Corp, pg 879
TecNec Distributing, pg 909
Theatrical Services & Supplies Inc, pg 912

Toys From The Attic, pg 916
Tri-Ed Distribution Inc, pg 918
Visual Technologies Corp, pg 932
Visual Word Systems Inc, pg 932

NORTH CAROLINA

Camcor Inc, pg 715

OHIO

Copp Integrated Systems, pg 731
Hughie's Event Production Services, pg 782
ITA Audio Visual Solutions, pg 791
Luminaud Inc, pg 812
Midwest Photo Exchange, pg 827
Parts Express, pg 851
Tri-State Audio Visual Co, pg 918
Tri-State Visual Products Inc, pg 918

OREGON

Audix Microphones, pg 695
Lightspeed Technologies Inc, pg 808
PLUS Corp of America, pg 858
SuperDigital Ltd, pg 904

PENNSYLVANIA

Advanced AV LLC, pg 677
Audio Visions Inc, pg 694
Bernie's Photo Center, pg 704
Clair Companies, pg 725
J E Foss Co, pg 764
Garcia Marketing Inc, pg 768
Grise Audio Visual Center Inc, pg 774
The Lerro Corp, pg 806
Morefield Communications Inc, pg 830
RSS Distributors, pg 878
Sound by Fitch, pg 893
Vistacom Inc, pg 931
Visual Sound Inc, pg 931
Wespen Audio Visual Co, pg 935

RHODE ISLAND

Shanix Inc, pg 885

SOUTH CAROLINA

Impact Technology Group LLC, pg 786

TENNESSEE

Allstar Audio Systems Inc, pg 681
Belew Enterprises, pg 703
Lowrance Sound Co Inc, pg 812
National School Products, pg 836
Spectrum Sound Inc, pg 897
Technical Support Systems LLC, pg 908
Trew Audio Inc, pg 917
Zion Music Group, pg 945

TEXAS

Audio Visual Technologies Group (AVTG), pg 695
AVES Audio Visual Systems Inc, pg 698
CAM Audio Inc, pg 714
Crossroads Audio Inc, pg 735
Data Projections Inc, pg 738
Digital Display Solutions Inc, pg 742
FitzCo Sound Inc, pg 761
Heffernan Audio Visual, pg 778
Lubbock Audio Visual Inc, pg 812
Precision Camera & Video, pg 861

Pro Video & Film Equipment Co Inc, pg 863
Quality Audio Visual Service Inc, pg 867
RF Specialties of Texas LLC, pg 874
Sound Works, pg 894
Southwest Sound Solutions, pg 896
Stage Directions, pg 898
Tarpley Media Systems, pg 907
TWIST Integration Solutions Technology, pg 920

UTAH

Comtek Communications Technology Inc, pg 730
Performance Audio LLC, pg 854
RIA Corp, pg 874
Spectra Sonics LLC, pg 897

VERMONT

Production Advantage Inc, pg 863

VIRGINIA

Avitecture Inc, pg 699
Boitnott Visual Communications Corp (BVC), pg 708
Intellidyne LLC, pg 789
Lee Hartman & Sons Inc, pg 805
Rocktown Media, pg 876
StageSound, pg 899
The Whitlock Group, pg 937

WASHINGTON

CCI Solutions, pg 718
D A Sound, pg 737
Northern Lights & Pro Audio, pg 842
PNTA, pg 858

WEST VIRGINIA

United Sound & Electronics, pg 921

WISCONSIN

Audio Visual of Milwaukee Inc, pg 694
Camera Corner Connecting Point, pg 715
Demco Inc, pg 740
Full Compass Systems, pg 767

PUERTO RICO

Audio Visual Concepts Inc, pg 694
Bonnin Electronics Inc, pg 708

ALBERTA

Allstar Show Industries Inc, pg 681
Infosat Communications Inc, pg 787
Matrix Video Communications Corp (MVCC), pg 819
McBain Camera Ltd, pg 820
Unique Communications Ltd, pg 921

BRITISH COLUMBIA

Commercial Electronics Ltd, pg 728

MANITOBA

Advance Pro, pg 677
Inland Audio Visual Ltd, pg 788

ONTARIO

Cinema Stage Inc, pg 724
HD Source, pg 777
Henry's Camera, pg 779

Nationwide Audio Visual Co, pg 837
Westbury National Show Systems Ltd, pg 936

QUEBEC

JAM Industries Ltd, pg 792
Panavideo Inc, pg 850
SC Media Canada, pg 881

Microphone—Wireless Manufacturers

CALIFORNIA

AKG Acoustics US, pg 679
Anchor Audio Inc, pg 685
Califone International Inc, pg 714
Calrad Electronics, pg 714
Carvin Amps & Audio, pg 717
Countryman Associates Inc, pg 732
FrontRow, pg 766
Nady Systems Inc, pg 835
Point Source Audio, pg 858
TeachLogic Inc, pg 908
TOA Electronics Inc, pg 915
Wohler Technologies Inc, pg 940

CONNECTICUT

Sennheiser Electronic Corp, pg 884

ILLINOIS

AmpliVox Portable Sound Systems, pg 684
Dukane Corp, Audio Visual Products Division, pg 747
Shure Inc, pg 887

MINNESOTA

Bosch Security Systems Inc, pg 709

MISSISSIPPI

Peavey Electronics Corp, pg 852

NEVADA

Pignose-Gorilla, pg 856

NEW JERSEY

Bogen Communications Inc, pg 708
Gemini Sound, pg 769
Oklahoma Sound Corp, pg 844
Sony Pro Audio, pg 893

NEW MEXICO

Lectrosonics Inc, pg 805

NEW YORK

beyerdynamic Inc, pg 704
MG Electronics, pg 825
Samson Technologies Corp, pg 879

OHIO

Audio-Technica US Inc, pg 694
CAD Audio, pg 713

OREGON

Audix Microphones, pg 695
Lightspeed Technologies Inc, pg 808

RHODE ISLAND

Numark Industries LP, pg 843

UTAH

ClearOne Inc, pg 726
Comtek Communications Technology Inc, pg 730

Microphone—Wireless Rentals

ALABAMA

Audio-Video Resources Inc, pg 694

ALASKA

Connections Film & Video Inc, pg 731

ARIZONA

Arizona Cine Equipment, pg 688
AV Concepts Inc, pg 696
Broadcast Rentals, pg 711
Glendale Media Center, pg 771
Merestone, pg 823
Metropolitan Audio-Visual Inc, pg 824
Ultimate Presentation Systems Inc, pg 920
Video West Inc, pg 929

ARKANSAS

White Diamond Productions LLC, pg 937

CALIFORNIA

Absolute Rentals, pg 672
AGF Media Services, pg 678
Alliant Event Services, pg 681
Ametron Audio/Video, pg 684
Artichoke Productions, pg 690
Associated Sound, pg 691
Assured Audio Visual, pg 691
ATV Video Center Inc, pg 692
Audio Rents, pg 693
AV Conferencing LLC (AVC), pg 697
AV Guys, pg 697
Bexel, an NEP Broadcast Services Company, pg 704
Cherry Multimedia, pg 721
Express Media Inc, pg 757
First Camera, pg 761
Flip 2 Media Inc, pg 762
Full Moon & High Tide Productions & Studios, pg 767
Gold Standard Productions, pg 772
Golden Gate Studios, pg 772
Alan Gordon Enterprises Inc, pg 772
Gravity Media, pg 773
IAMP Professional Audio, pg 783
Imagecraft Productions, pg 785
Images in Motion Media Inc, pg 785
Instructional Materials & Equipment Distributors (I-Med), pg 789
JD Audio Visual Inc, pg 793
Lynch Communications, pg 813
Maximus Media Inc, pg 820
McCune Audio-Video-Lighting, pg 821
Media Vision USA, pg 822
Munday & Collins AV, pg 834
Muse Presentation Technologies, pg 834
New Circuit Films LLC, pg 839
Next Arts, pg 841
North County Media Center, pg 842
Old School Cameras, pg 844
On-Trax Inc, pg 846
Prime Cut Productions, pg 862
Pro HD Rentals, pg 863

Production Gear Rentals (PGR), pg 863
PSAV® Presentation Services, pg 866
Pyxis Industries Inc, pg 867
Shooting Star Video, pg 886
Shoulder High Productions, pg 886
SNAP, pg 891
Sound Service Co, pg 894
Stanislaus AV Inc, pg 899
Stray Angel Films, pg 902
Studio 637, pg 903
The Studios at Paramount, pg 903
Third Ear Sound Co, pg 912
Total Creative, pg 916
Towards 2000 Inc, pg 916
VER, pg 926
Video Resources Inc, pg 928
Vitruvian Entertainment, pg 932
VMI Inc, pg 932
Voice & Video Rentals, pg 932
Warner Bros Entertainment Inc, pg 934
Warner Bros Production Sound & Video Services, pg 934
Westcoast Video Productions Inc, pg 936

COLORADO

Audio Consultant Services Inc, pg 693
Daylight Productions & Rentals, pg 739
Denver Media Center, pg 740
Multimedia Audio Visual Inc, pg 833
Open Media Foundation, pg 846
Spectrum Audio Visual Services, pg 897

CONNECTICUT

A/V Davey, pg 697
Connecticut Audio & Theatrical Supply, pg 731
Digital Video Productions, pg 742

DELAWARE

Actors Attic, pg 675
Showorks Audio Visual Inc, pg 887

DISTRICT OF COLUMBIA

Metro Teleproductions Inc (MTI), pg 824

FLORIDA

Access Media Group, pg 673
Accord Productions, pg 673
AVI-SPL, pg 698
Blackburst Entertainment LLC, pg 706
Budget Video Rentals, pg 712
Harmon's Audio-Visual Services, pg 776
Hi-Tech Enterprises Inc, pg 779
Industrial Strength Inc, pg 787
Knowles Video Inc (KVI), pg 800
Lighting Sales Connection Inc, pg 808
ONstage, pg 846
Paradise Show & Design Inc, pg 851
Sight & Sound Productions, pg 887
TAI Audio, pg 906
Technomedia Solutions, pg 909
Universal Studios Florida® Production Group, pg 922

AUDIO

Microphone—Wireless Rentals (continued)

GEORGIA

ECG Productions, pg 750
Lighting & Production Equipment Inc, pg 807
MAGNUM Companies Ltd, pg 815
See Production Services, pg 883
Stage Front Presentation Systems, pg 899
Staging Directions Inc, pg 899
Studio Space Atlanta, pg 903

HAWAII

Sight & Sound Studios, pg 887

ILLINOIS

Allen Visual Systems Inc, pg 680
AV Chicago Inc, pg 696
Backstar Creative Media Inc, pg 700
Beatty TeleVisual Productions, pg 703
Central Audio-Visual Equipment Inc, pg 719
Creative Technology (CT), pg 733
Firehouse Studios, pg 761
C V Lloyde, pg 810
Magnanimous Media, pg 814
Meetinghouse Event Design & Production, pg 823
OSA International Inc, pg 848
Product Productions, pg 863
RC Communications, pg 870
Resolution Productions Group, pg 874
SCI Television & Creative Media LLC, pg 882
Staging Resources Inc, pg 899
Winter Productions, pg 939
Woodside Avenue Music Productions Inc, pg 941
Zacuto, pg 945

INDIANA

Heart Breaker Entertainment LLC, pg 778

IOWA

Central Lighting & Equipment Inc (CLE), pg 719
Pro Video, pg 863

KANSAS

Lights On, pg 808

KENTUCKY

Audio Visual Techniques Inc, pg 695
Idle Minds Productions Inc, pg 784
Kentucky Grip & Lighting, pg 798
Barney Miller's Inc, pg 827

LOUISIANA

Clark Services Audio Visual & Exhibit Inc, pg 725
Pace Systems, pg 849

MAINE

Headlight Audio Visual Inc, pg 777

MARYLAND

Advance Audiovisual Presentation Ltd, pg 677
Cardinal Sound & Video, pg 717
CPR MultiMedia Solutions, pg 732
Event Tech, pg 756
Hargrove Inc, pg 776
Kramer Communications Video Production, pg 801
Maryland Sound International Holding Co LLC, pg 819
Soundtrax Inc, pg 895

MASSACHUSETTS

AVFX Inc, pg 698
Fastlane Productions LLC, pg 759
Terry Hanley Audio Systems Inc, pg 775
massAV, pg 819
Preston Productions Inc, pg 861

MICHIGAN

Olson Anderson Co, pg 685
City Events Group, pg 725
Digi Sign Design LLC, pg 741
K&R All Media Productions LLC, pg 796
K&R's Recording Studios Inc, pg 796
On Stage Visuals, pg 846
TEL Systems LLC, pg 909

MINNESOTA

Alpha Video & Audio Inc, pg 682
Big Event Productions LLC, pg 705
New Life Communications Inc, pg 839
Pro Media Productions, pg 863

MISSISSIPPI

Bowie Audio Visual Enterprises Inc, pg 709

MISSOURI

Communitronics Corp, pg 729
Production Support Services Inc, pg 864
Schiller's Audio-Visual, pg 881
Show-Me Audio-Visual, pg 887
Switch, pg 905
Wise Audio Video, pg 940

MONTANA

High Plains Films, pg 779
Jereco Studios Inc, pg 793

NEBRASKA

Dog & Pony Productions Inc, pg 744

NEVADA

GES Audio Visual, pg 770
MG Studio, pg 825

NEW HAMPSHIRE

Apertura, pg 686
APS Lighting-Sound-AV, pg 688

NEW JERSEY

Audio Visual Associates, pg 694
CFP Video Productions Inc, pg 720
Earl Girls Inc, pg 749
Euro-Pacific Film & Video Productions Inc, pg 756
International Audio Visual Inc, pg 790
MiB MediaWorks, pg 825

Moe AV LLC, pg 828
The Music Place, pg 834
Nelson Enterprises Theatrical Supply Co, pg 838
Panavid, pg 850
PLS Staging, pg 858
Soundtracks Production Services LLC, pg 895
Starlite, pg 900
Video Corporation of America (VCA), pg 927
Wired 4 Sound Inc, pg 940

NEW MEXICO

Production Outfitters, pg 864
Quickbeam Systems Inc (QSI), pg 868

NEW YORK

Ace Video, pg 674
All Mobile Video Inc, pg 680
American Video Inc, pg 684
Aura Sonic Ltd (ASL), pg 695
AV Workshop, pg 697
Big Foot Productions Inc, pg 705
Bond Street Studio, pg 708
Colortone Audio Visual, pg 728
CP Communications, pg 732
CSI Rentals, pg 735
Design Audio Visual Inc, pg 741
Gearhead Rentals, pg 769
Gotham Sound & Communications Inc, pg 773
Hello World Communications, pg 778
iProbe Multilingual Solutions Inc, pg 791
KVL Audio Visual Services Inc, pg 802
LightHouse Films, pg 807
Long Island Video Enterprises Live Inc, pg 811
Posthorn Recordings, pg 859
See Factor Industry Inc, pg 883
SmartSource Computer & AV Rentals, pg 891
Specialized Audio-Visual Inc, pg 896
Studio Instrument Rentals (SIR), pg 902
Theatrical Services & Supplies Inc, pg 912
Visual Technologies Corp, pg 932
Visual Word Systems Inc, pg 932
WorldStage, pg 941

NORTH CAROLINA

All Pro Media Inc, pg 680
Audio & Light, pg 693
AV Connections Inc, pg 697
AV Metro Inc, pg 697
Duke Media Services, pg 747
Special Event Services, pg 896
Take One Productions Ltd, pg 906

NORTH DAKOTA

Media Productions, pg 822

OHIO

Hughie's Event Production Services, pg 782
ITA Audio Visual Solutions, pg 791
Lyon Video Inc, pg 813
Mills James Productions, pg 828
Production Solutions Inc, pg 864
R&B Communications Inc, pg 870

OKLAHOMA

PDC Productions, pg 852

OREGON

Picture This Production Services, pg 856
Rose City Sound, pg 877

PENNSYLVANIA

Advanced AV LLC, pg 677
Argentine Productions Inc, pg 688
Audio Visions Inc, pg 694
Audio Visual Communications Inc, pg 694
FirstGeneration Audio/Visual Services, pg 761
FMP Media Solutions Inc, pg 763
Grise Audio Visual Center Inc, pg 774
JPL, pg 795
Muderick Media, pg 833
New York Camera & Video, pg 840
Raven Rental, pg 870
Sound by Fitch, pg 893
Upstage Video, pg 923
The Videohouse Inc, pg 929
Vistacom Inc, pg 931
Visual Sound Inc, pg 931

SOUTH CAROLINA

Impact Technology Group LLC, pg 786
Sound & Images Inc, pg 893

TENNESSEE

Allstar Audio Systems Inc, pg 681
Nashville Production Rentals (NPR), pg 836
RentACamera.com, pg 873
Technical Support Systems LLC, pg 908
Trew Audio Inc, pg 917

TEXAS

Alford Media Services, pg 680
Audio Visual Technologies Group (AVTG), pg 695
Bright Star Productions Inc, pg 710
Crossroads Audio Inc, pg 735
FitzCo Sound Inc, pg 761
GEAR Cameras & Lighting, pg 769
Lubbock Audio Visual Inc, pg 812
Music Lab Inc, pg 834
Onstage Systems, pg 846
Quality Audio Visual Service Inc, pg 867
South Coast Film & Video, pg 895
Stage Directions, pg 898
Texcam Inc, pg 911
Video Perspective, pg 928

UTAH

Performance Audio LLC, pg 854

VERMONT

Dark Star Lighting & Production, pg 737
Edgewood Studios, pg 750

VIRGINIA

American AV, pg 682
Audio Visual Actions Inc (AVA), pg 694
Boitnott Visual Communications Corp (BVC), pg 708
Lee Hartman & Sons Inc, pg 805
StageSound, pg 899

WASHINGTON

D A Sound, pg 737
Northern Lights & Pro Audio,
pg 842
Oppenheimer Camera Products,
pg 847
PNTA, pg 858
Victory Studios, pg 927

WEST VIRGINIA

United Sound & Electronics, pg 921

WISCONSIN

Camera Corner Connecting Point,
pg 715
Event Essentials, pg 756
Full Compass Systems, pg 767
MKE Production Rental, pg 828

WYOMING

Bridger Productions Inc, pg 710

PUERTO RICO

Stage Crew Audiovisual Inc, pg 898

ALBERTA

Allstar Show Industries Inc, pg 681
Evolution AV, pg 757
L R Light & Sound, pg 802
McBain Camera Ltd, pg 820
Unique Communications Ltd,
pg 921

BRITISH COLUMBIA

Clark's Audio Visual Services Ltd,
pg 725
Commercial Electronics Ltd, pg 728
DL Sound & Lighting Productions
Ltd, pg 744
Inspired Image Picture Co (IIPC),
pg 788

MANITOBA

Inland Audio Visual Ltd, pg 788
MidCanada Production Services Inc
(MidCan), pg 826

ONTARIO

HD Source, pg 777
JIB Shots Equipment Inc, pg 794
Metalworks Recording Studios Inc,
pg 824
RB Productions, pg 870
Westbury National Show Systems
Ltd, pg 936
ZTV Broadcast Services Inc, pg 945

QUEBEC

Audio Visual Dynamics, pg 694
Group PVP, pg 774
Panavideo Inc, pg 850

Microphone—Wireless
   Repairs

ARIZONA

Metropolitan Audio-Visual Inc,
pg 824

CALIFORNIA

Ametron Audio/Video, pg 684
Audio Images Corp, pg 693
McAlister Electronics, pg 820
Sound Service Co, pg 894
SSL Industries Inc, pg 898

TOA Electronics Inc, pg 915
Towards 2000 Inc, pg 916

CONNECTICUT

HB Communications Inc, pg 777
Sennheiser Electronic Corp, pg 884

FLORIDA

Hi-Tech Enterprises Inc, pg 779
Midtown Video Inc, pg 827
Stereo Sales Inc, pg 900
TAI Audio, pg 906

GEORGIA

Lighting & Production Equipment
Inc, pg 807
Stage Front Presentation Systems,
pg 899

ILLINOIS

Allen Visual Systems Inc, pg 680
Beatty TeleVisual Productions,
pg 703
C V Lloyde, pg 810
RC Communications, pg 870

INDIANA

Sweetwater Sound Inc, pg 905

KENTUCKY

Axxis Leasing Inc, pg 700
Barney Miller's Inc, pg 827
NOR-COM Inc, pg 841

MAINE

Headlight Audio Visual Inc, pg 777

MARYLAND

Cardinal Sound & Video, pg 717

MICHIGAN

City Events Group, pg 725
K&R's Recording Studios Inc,
pg 796
On Stage Visuals, pg 846
TEL Systems LLC, pg 909

NEW JERSEY

A-V Services Inc, pg 671
Earl Girls Inc, pg 749
The Music Place, pg 834
Nelson Enterprises Theatrical
Supply Co, pg 838
Starlite, pg 900

NEW MEXICO

Quickbeam Systems Inc (QSI),
pg 868

NEW YORK

American Video Inc, pg 684
beyerdynamic, pg 704
Toys From The Attic, pg 916
Visual Technologies Corp, pg 932

NORTH CAROLINA

Camcor Inc, pg 715

OHIO

Copp Integrated Systems, pg 731
Hughie's Event Production Services,
pg 782
Tri-State Audio Visual Co, pg 918

OREGON

All Service Musical Electronics
Repair, pg 680

PENNSYLVANIA

Audio Visions Inc, pg 694
J E Foss Co, pg 764
Vistacom Inc, pg 931

TENNESSEE

Belew Enterprises, pg 703
Technical Support Systems LLC,
pg 908
Trew Audio Inc, pg 917

TEXAS

Lubbock Audio Visual Inc, pg 812
Quality Audio Visual Service Inc,
pg 867
Southwest Sound Solutions, pg 896
Tarpley Media Systems, pg 907

UTAH

Comtek Communications
Technology Inc, pg 730

VIRGINIA

Boitnott Visual Communications
Corp (BVC), pg 708

WASHINGTON

Northern Lights & Pro Audio,
pg 842
PNTA, pg 858

WEST VIRGINIA

United Sound & Electronics, pg 921

WISCONSIN

Full Compass Systems, pg 767

ALBERTA

Allstar Show Industries Inc, pg 681
Infosat Communications Inc, pg 787
Unique Communications Ltd,
pg 921

BRITISH COLUMBIA

Commercial Electronics Ltd, pg 728

MANITOBA

Inland Audio Visual Ltd, pg 788

ONTARIO

HD Source, pg 777
Westbury National Show Systems
Ltd, pg 936

QUEBEC

Panavideo Inc, pg 850
SC Media Canada, pg 881

Mixer Distributors

ARIZONA

Arizona Cine Equipment, pg 688
EAR Professional Audio/Video,
pg 749
Metropolitan Audio-Visual Inc,
pg 824
Projector SuperStore LLC, pg 865
Troxell-CDI, pg 918

ARKANSAS

White Diamond Productions LLC,
pg 937

CALIFORNIA

American Music & Sound (AM&S),
pg 684
Ametron Audio/Video, pg 684
ARS Electronics, pg 690
Associated Sound, pg 691
Assured Audio Visual, pg 691
ATV Video Center Inc, pg 692
Audio Images Corp, pg 693
AV Conferencing LLC (AVC),
pg 697
Be Media, pg 702
Bext Inc, pg 704
BigFoot Mobile Systems, pg 705
BroadcastStore.com, pg 711
California Tape Products Inc,
pg 714
Carvin Amps & Audio, pg 717
Christy's Editorial, pg 723
Cibola Systems, pg 723
Computer Modules Inc, pg 729
DigiTech, pg 742
Educational Technology Services
(ETS), pg 751
Electronic Design Solutions Inc,
pg 752
Empire Pro, pg 753
GigaSonic, pg 770
Gravity Media, pg 773
Hi-Tech Audio Systems Inc, pg 779
Hosa Technology Inc, pg 781
IAMP Professional Audio, pg 783
Instructional Materials & Equipment
Distributors (I-Med), pg 789
JD Audio Visual Inc, pg 793
Location Sound Corp, pg 810
Martel Electronics Sales Inc, pg 818
Lloyd F McKinney Associates Inc,
pg 821
Media Fabricators Inc, pg 822
MediaPOINTE, pg 823
Orvac Electronics, pg 848
Pioneer Electronics (USA) Inc,
pg 857
Professional Sound Corp, pg 865
Promax Systems, pg 865
SNAP, pg 891
Sound Service Co, pg 894
Soundcraft, pg 894
Southern California Sound Image
Inc, pg 895
SSL Industries Inc, pg 898
Stanislaus AV Inc, pg 899
TASCAM, pg 907
TOA Electronics Inc, pg 915
Towards 2000 Inc, pg 916
VMI Inc, pg 932
VTP Inc, pg 933

COLORADO

Audio Consultant Services Inc,
pg 693
Daylight Productions & Rentals,
pg 739
Spectrum Audio Visual Services,
pg 897

CONNECTICUT

Connecticut Audio & Theatrical
Supply, pg 731
HB Communications Inc, pg 777
MAVCO, pg 820
The Music People Inc, pg 834

DELAWARE

Actors Attic, pg 675

AUDIO

Mixer Distributors
(continued)

FLORIDA
Access Media Group, pg 673
Altel Systems Group Inc, pg 682
A2D Solutions Inc, pg 692
AVI-SPL, pg 698
Broadcasters General Store Inc,
pg 711
Digital Video Systems, pg 742
Enhanced View Services Inc,
pg 754
Harris Corp, pg 776
Herman Pro AV, pg 779
Hi-Tech Enterprises Inc, pg 779
Hi-Tech Import Export Corp,
pg 779
Industrial Strength Inc, pg 787
Intermark Industries Inc, pg 789
Lighting Sales Connection Inc,
pg 808
Midtown Video Inc, pg 827
ONstage, pg 846
Recording Media & Equipment Inc
(RM&E), pg 872
Stereo Sales Inc, pg 900
TAI Audio, pg 906
Technomedia Solutions, pg 909

GEORGIA
Baker Audio Visual, pg 700
Clark, pg 725
Innocinema, pg 788
Lighting & Production Equipment
Inc, pg 807
LT Sound Inc, pg 812
Stage Front Presentation Systems,
pg 899
Visioneering International Inc,
pg 931

HAWAII
The Audio Visual Co (AVCO),
pg 694

ILLINOIS
Allen Visual Systems Inc, pg 680
Central Audio-Visual Equipment
Inc, pg 719
Joseph Electronics, pg 795
C V Lloyde, pg 810
Manning Productions, pg 816
Quintessence Audio Ltd, pg 868
RC Communications, pg 870
Woodside Avenue Music
Productions Inc, pg 941

INDIANA
Heart Breaker Entertainment LLC,
pg 778
Sensory Technologies LLC, pg 884
SHP Electronics, pg 887
Sweetwater Sound Inc, pg 905

KENTUCKY
Audio Visual Techniques Inc,
pg 695
Axxis Leasing Inc, pg 700
Barney Miller's Inc, pg 827
NOR-COM Inc, pg 841

LOUISIANA
Pace Systems, pg 849
Techkno Integration & Design
Services LLC, pg 908

MAINE
Headlight Audio Visual Inc, pg 777
Independent Audio Inc, pg 786

MARYLAND
Advance Audiovisual Presentation
Ltd, pg 677
Bradley Broadcast & Pro Audio,
pg 709
Cardinal Sound & Video, pg 717
Human Circuit, pg 782
Noventri, pg 843

MASSACHUSETTS
Terry Hanley Audio Systems Inc,
pg 775
Professional Audio Design Inc,
pg 865
Rule Boston Camera, pg 878

MICHIGAN
Olson Anderson Co, pg 685
City Events Group, pg 725
On Stage Visuals, pg 846
TEL Systems LLC, pg 909

MINNESOTA
Alpha Video & Audio Inc, pg 682
New Life Communications Inc,
pg 839

MISSISSIPPI
Bowie Audio Visual Enterprises Inc,
pg 709

MISSOURI
Communitronics Corp, pg 729
Conference Technologies Inc,
pg 730
ITC, pg 791
Modern Communications Inc,
pg 828
Schiller's Audio-Visual, pg 881

NEBRASKA
VSA Inc, pg 933

NEW HAMPSHIRE
APS Lighting-Sound-AV, pg 688
Technet® Systems Group, pg 908

NEW JERSEY
A-V Services Inc, pg 671
Alltec Stores, a Vcom IMC
Company, pg 681
AlltecPro, pg 681
Audio Visual Associates, pg 694
Audio Visual Dynamics®, pg 694
AV Bluebook, pg 696
Comprehensive Cable &
Connectivity Co, pg 729
Diversified, pg 744
Earl Girls Inc, pg 749
Euro-Pacific Film & Video
Productions Inc, pg 756
G&G Technologies Inc, pg 768
HamiltonBuhl, pg 775
MCCOM Inc, pg 820
The Music Place, pg 834
Nelson Enterprises Theatrical
Supply Co, pg 838
PatchAmp, pg 852
Starlite, pg 900
Total Video Products Inc, pg 916
Video Corporation of America
(VCA), pg 927

NEW YORK
ADI Global Distribution, pg 676
Albany Theatre Supply Co Inc,
pg 679
American Video Inc, pg 684
Audio-Video Corp, pg 694
Aura Sonic Ltd (ASL), pg 695
AV Workshop, pg 697
BTX Technologies, pg 712
Colortone Audio Visual, pg 728
Design Audio Visual Inc, pg 741
Gotham Sound & Communications
Inc, pg 773
Group One Ltd, pg 774
HAVE Inc, pg 777
Hot House Professional Audio,
pg 782
Indigo Productions, pg 787
KVL Audio Visual Services Inc,
pg 802
Lee Dan® Communications Inc,
pg 805
Long Island Video Enterprises Live
Inc, pg 811
Markertek Video Supply, pg 817
Neptune Photo Inc, pg 838
Posthorn Recordings, pg 859
RNJ Electronics, pg 875
Solid State Logic Inc, pg 892
TecNec Distributing, pg 909
Theatrical Services & Supplies Inc,
pg 912
Toys From The Attic, pg 916
Tri-Ed Distribution Inc, pg 918
Visual Word Systems Inc, pg 932
Whirlwind Music Distributors Inc,
pg 937

Wired 4 Sound Inc, pg 940
Yorktel, pg 944

NEW MEXICO
Quickbeam Systems Inc (QSI),
pg 868

NORTH CAROLINA
Strategic Connections, pg 901

OHIO
Copp Integrated Systems, pg 731
Hughie's Event Production Services,
pg 782
ITA Audio Visual Solutions, pg 791
Midwest Photo Exchange, pg 827
Parts Express, pg 851
The Telos Alliance, pg 910
Tri-State Audio Visual Co, pg 918
Visual Products Inc, pg 931

OREGON
SuperDigital Ltd, pg 904

PENNSYLVANIA
Advanced AV LLC, pg 677
Audio Visions Inc, pg 694
Clair Companies, pg 725
J E Foss Co, pg 764
Grise Audio Visual Center Inc,
pg 774
The Lerro Corp, pg 806
Morefield Communications Inc,
pg 830
Sound by Fitch, pg 893
Vistacom Inc, pg 931
Visual Sound Inc, pg 931
Wespen Audio Visual Co, pg 935

RHODE ISLAND
Shanix Inc, pg 885

SOUTH CAROLINA
DaviSound, pg 739
Impact Technology Group LLC,
pg 786

TENNESSEE
Allstar Audio Systems Inc, pg 681
Belew Enterprises, pg 703
Lowrance Sound Co Inc, pg 812
Mr Mark's Used Musical, Stereo &
Studio Equipment Store, pg 828
Spectrum Sound Inc, pg 897
Technical Support Systems LLC,
pg 908
Trew Audio Inc, pg 917
WhisperRoom™ Inc, pg 937
Zion Music Group, pg 945

TEXAS
Audio Visual Technologies Group
(AVTG), pg 695
AVES Audio Visual Systems Inc,
pg 698
CAM Audio Inc, pg 714
Crossroads Audio Inc, pg 735
Data Projections Inc, pg 738
FitzCo Sound Inc, pg 761
Heffernan Audio Visual, pg 778
Lubbock Audio Visual Inc, pg 812
Pro Video & Film Equipment Co
Inc, pg 863
RF Specialties of Texas LLC,
pg 874
Southwest Sound Solutions, pg 896
Stage Directions, pg 898
Tarpley Media Systems, pg 907

UTAH
Performance Audio LLC, pg 854
RIA Corp, pg 874

VERMONT
Production Advantage Inc, pg 863

VIRGINIA
Avitecture Inc, pg 699
Boitnott Visual Communications
Corp (BVC), pg 708
Intellidyne LLC, pg 789
Lee Hartman & Sons Inc, pg 805
Rocktown Media, pg 876
StageSound, pg 899
The Whitlock Group, pg 937

WASHINGTON
Broadcast Supply World Wide,
pg 711
CCI Solutions, pg 718
D A Sound, pg 737
LOUD Technologies Inc, pg 811
Northern Lights & Pro Audio,
pg 842
PNTA, pg 858

WEST VIRGINIA
United Sound & Electronics, pg 921

WISCONSIN
Audio Visual of Milwaukee Inc,
pg 694
Camera Corner Connecting Point,
pg 715
Full Compass Systems, pg 767
Safe Harbor Computers, pg 879

PUERTO RICO
Audio Visual Concepts Inc, pg 694
Bonnin Electronics Inc, pg 708

ALBERTA
Allstar Show Industries Inc, pg 681
Infosat Communications Inc, pg 787
Matrix Video Communications Corp (MVCC), pg 819
McBain Camera Ltd, pg 820
Unique Communications Ltd, pg 921

BRITISH COLUMBIA
Commercial Electronics Ltd, pg 728

MANITOBA
Advance Pro, pg 677
Inland Audio Visual Ltd, pg 788

ONTARIO
Cinema Stage Inc, pg 724
HD Source, pg 777
Henry's Camera, pg 779
Nationwide Audio Visual Co, pg 837
Westbury National Show Systems Ltd, pg 936
Yorkville Sound Inc, pg 944

QUEBEC
JAM Industries Ltd, pg 792
Panavideo Inc, pg 850
SC Media Canada, pg 881

Mixer Manufacturers

ARIZONA
AtlasIED, pg 692
Fender Musical Instruments Corp, pg 759
MTX Audio, pg 833
Radio Design Labs (RDL), pg 869

ARKANSAS
Autogram/CRL, pg 696

CALIFORNIA
American Music & Sound (AM&S), pg 684
Califone International Inc, pg 714
Carvin Amps & Audio, pg 717
DigiTech, pg 742
Ensemble Designs Inc, pg 754
For-A Corp of America, pg 763
Henry Engineering, pg 779
Hosa Technology Inc, pg 781
Martinsound Inc, pg 818
Millennia Media, FPC, pg 827
Nady Systems Inc, pg 835
Pioneer Electronics (USA) Inc, pg 857
Professional Sound Corp, pg 865
Roland Corp US, pg 876
Sony Electronics Inc, pg 893
Sound Service Co, pg 894
Soundcraft, pg 894
Summit Audio Inc, pg 903
TASCAM, pg 907
TEAC America Inc, pg 908
TOA Electronics Inc, pg 915

COLORADO
Arrakis Systems, pg 689
Liberty AV Solutions, pg 807

CONNECTICUT
Sound Control Technologies Inc, pg 893

FLORIDA
CircuitWerkes Inc, pg 725
Intermark Industries Inc, pg 789

ILLINOIS
AmpliVox Portable Sound Systems, pg 684
J K Audio Inc, pg 792
Precision Electronics Inc, pg 861
Shure Inc, pg 887
Studio Technologies Inc, pg 903

MARYLAND
API, pg 687

MINNESOTA
Bosch Security Systems Inc, pg 709

MISSISSIPPI
Crest Audio Inc, pg 734
Peavey Electronics Corp, pg 852

MISSOURI
Lowell Manufacturing, pg 812

NEW JERSEY
ATI Audio, pg 692
Bogen Communications Inc, pg 708
Gemini Sound, pg 769
Kramer Electronics USA Inc, pg 801
Radio Systems Inc, pg 869
RAMSA Professional Audio Systems, pg 870

NEW MEXICO
Lectrosonics Inc, pg 805

NEW YORK
Ashly Audio Inc, pg 691
Broadcast Devices Inc, pg 710
GLI Sound Systems, pg 771
Harbro Corp, pg 776
Protech Audio Corp, pg 866
Sescom Inc, pg 884
Solid State Logic Inc, pg 892
TecNec Distributing, pg 909

NORTH CAROLINA
Audioarts Engineering, pg 695
Wheatstone Corp, pg 937

OHIO
Audio-Technica US Inc, pg 694
Omnia Audio, pg 845
The Telos Alliance, pg 910

OREGON
BIAMP Systems, pg 705

PENNSYLVANIA
Right Coast Recording Inc, pg 875

RHODE ISLAND
M-Audio, pg 813
Numark Industries LP, pg 843
Rane, pg 870

SOUTH CAROLINA
DaviSound, pg 739

TENNESSEE
Harrison Consoles, pg 776
WhisperRoom™ Inc, pg 937

UTAH
ClearOne Inc, pg 726
Ivie Technologies Inc, pg 792
Rolls Corp, pg 877
Spectra Sonics LLC, pg 897

WASHINGTON
LOUD Technologies Inc, pg 811

ONTARIO
Yorkville Sound Inc, pg 944

Mixer Rentals

ALABAMA
Audio-Video Resources Inc, pg 694

ALASKA
Connections Film & Video Inc, pg 731

ARIZONA
Arizona Cine Equipment, pg 688
Broadcast Rentals, pg 711
Glendale Media Center, pg 771
Merestone, pg 823
Metropolitan Audio-Visual Inc, pg 824
Video West Inc, pg 929

ARKANSAS
White Diamond Productions LLC, pg 937

CALIFORNIA
Acey Decy Lighting, pg 674
Action Audio & Visual, pg 675
AGF Media Services, pg 678
Alliant Event Services, pg 681
Ametron Audio/Video, pg 684
Artichoke Productions, pg 690
Associated Sound, pg 691
Assured Audio Visual, pg 691
ATV Video Center Inc, pg 692
Audio Rents, pg 693
AV Guys, pg 697
Bexel, an NEP Broadcast Services Company, pg 704
Chater Camera Inc, pg 721
Cherry Multimedia, pg 721
Express Media Inc, pg 757
Express Video Supply Inc, pg 757
First Camera, pg 761
Flip 2 Media Inc, pg 762
Gear Monkey, pg 769
Gold Standard Productions, pg 772
Golden Gate Studios, pg 772
HDrental.com, pg 777
Hi-Tech Audio Systems Inc, pg 779
Hollywood Sound Systems, pg 781
IAMP Professional Audio, pg 783
Imagecraft Productions, pg 785
JD Audio Visual Inc, pg 793
Maximus Media Inc, pg 820
McCune Audio-Video-Lighting, pg 821
Media Fabricators Inc, pg 822
Munday & Collins AV, pg 834
Muse Presentation Technologies, pg 834
Next Arts, pg 841
Old School Cameras, pg 844
On-Trax Inc, pg 846
Prime Cut Productions, pg 862
PSAV® Presentation Services, pg 866
Pyxis Industries Inc, pg 867

Alwin Sauers Audio Productions (ASAP), pg 881
Shooting Star Video, pg 886
Shoulder High Productions, pg 886
SNAP, pg 891
Sound Service Co, pg 894
Stanislaus AV Inc, pg 899
Stray Angel Films, pg 902
Synthesizer Rental Service, pg 906
T-stop Inc, pg 906
Third Ear Sound Co, pg 912
Total Creative, pg 916
Towards 2000 Inc, pg 916
VER, pg 926
Video Resources Inc, pg 928
VMI Inc, pg 932
Voice & Video Rentals, pg 932
Warner Bros Production Sound & Video Services, pg 934
Westcoast Video Productions Inc, pg 936

COLORADO
Audio Consultant Services Inc, pg 693
Daylight Productions & Rentals, pg 739
Denver Media Center, pg 740
Multimedia Audio Visual Inc, pg 833
Open Media Foundation, pg 846
Spectrum Audio Visual Services, pg 897

CONNECTICUT
A/V Davey, pg 697
Connecticut Audio & Theatrical Supply, pg 731
Digital Video Productions, pg 742

DELAWARE
Actors Attic, pg 675
Showorks Audio Visual Inc, pg 887
Side Door Studio Inc, pg 887

DISTRICT OF COLUMBIA
Metro Teleproductions Inc (MTI), pg 824

FLORIDA
Access Media Group, pg 673
All Comm Rentals Inc (ALLCOMM), pg 680
AVI-SPL, pg 698
Blackburst Entertainment LLC, pg 706
Budget Video Rentals, pg 712
Industrial Strength Inc, pg 787
Jordan Klein Film & Video (JKFV), pg 795
Knowles Video Inc (KVI), pg 800
Lighting Sales Connection Inc, pg 808
ONstage, pg 846
Paradise Show & Design Inc, pg 851
Phat Planet Recording Studios, pg 855
Sight & Sound Productions, pg 887
TAI Audio, pg 906
Technomedia Solutions, pg 909
Universal Studios Florida® Production Group, pg 922
Zebedee Productions, pg 945

GEORGIA
ECG Productions, pg 750
Lighting & Production Equipment Inc, pg 807
MAGNUM Companies Ltd, pg 815

AUDIO

Mixer Rentals (continued)

GEORGIA (continued)

See Production Services, pg 883
Stage Front Presentation Systems, pg 899
Staging Directions Inc, pg 899
Studio Space Atlanta, pg 903

HAWAII

Hawaii Sound & Vision, pg 777
Sight & Sound Studios, pg 887

ILLINOIS

Allen Visual Systems Inc, pg 680
AV Chicago Inc, pg 696
Backstar Creative Media Inc, pg 700
Beatty TeleVisual Productions, pg 703
Central Audio-Visual Equipment Inc, pg 719
Firehouse Studios, pg 761
C V Lloyde, pg 810
Meetinghouse Event Design & Production, pg 823
On Site Video, pg 846
OSA International Inc, pg 848
RC Communications, pg 870
Resolution Productions Group, pg 874
Staging Resources Inc, pg 899
Woodside Avenue Music Productions Inc, pg 941
Zacuto, pg 945

INDIANA

Advanced Media Integration, pg 677
Gaither Studios LLC, pg 767
Heart Breaker Entertainment LLC, pg 778

IOWA

Central Lighting & Equipment Inc (CLE), pg 719

KANSAS

Lights On, pg 808

KENTUCKY

Audio Visual Techniques Inc, pg 695
Kentucky Grip & Lighting, pg 798

LOUISIANA

Clark Services Audio Visual & Exhibit Inc, pg 725
Pace Systems, pg 849

MAINE

Headlight Audio Visual Inc, pg 777

MARYLAND

Advance Audiovisual Presentation Ltd, pg 677
Cardinal Sound & Video, pg 717
CPR MultiMedia Solutions, pg 732
Event Tech, pg 756
Hargrove Inc, pg 776
Kramer Communications Video Production, pg 801
Maryland Sound International Holding Co LLC, pg 819
Soundtrax Inc, pg 895

MASSACHUSETTS

AVFX Inc, pg 698
Capron Lighting & Sound Co Inc, pg 716
Terry Hanley Audio Systems Inc, pg 775
massAV, pg 819
Preston Productions Inc, pg 861

MICHIGAN

Olson Anderson Co, pg 685
City Events Group, pg 725
K&R All Media Productions LLC, pg 796
K&R's Recording Studios Inc, pg 796
On Stage Visuals, pg 846
TEL Systems LLC, pg 909

MINNESOTA

Alpha Video & Audio Inc, pg 682
Big Event Productions LLC, pg 705
New Life Communications Inc, pg 839

MISSISSIPPI

Bowie Audio Visual Enterprises Inc, pg 709

MISSOURI

Show-Me Audio-Visual, pg 887
Switch, pg 905
Wise Audio Video, pg 940

MONTANA

Jereco Studios Inc, pg 793

NEBRASKA

Dog & Pony Productions Inc, pg 744

NEVADA

GES Audio Visual, pg 770
MG Studio, pg 825

NEW HAMPSHIRE

Apertura, pg 686
APS Lighting-Sound-AV, pg 688

NEW JERSEY

Audio Visual Associates, pg 694
Audio Visual Dynamics®, pg 694
CFP Video Productions Inc, pg 720
Earl Girls Inc, pg 749
Euro-Pacific Film & Video Productions Inc, pg 756
International Audio Visual Inc, pg 790
Moe AV LLC, pg 828
The Music Place, pg 834
Nelson Enterprises Theatrical Supply Co, pg 838
Panavid, pg 850
PLS Staging, pg 858
Starlite, pg 900
Video Corporation of America (VCA), pg 927
Wired 4 Sound Inc, pg 940

NEW MEXICO

Production Outfitters, pg 864
Quickbeam Systems Inc (QSI), pg 868

NEW YORK

Adorama Rental Co, pg 676
All Mobile Video Inc, pg 680
American Video Inc, pg 684
Aura Sonic Ltd (ASL), pg 695
AV Workshop, pg 697
Big Foot Productions Inc, pg 705
Colortone Audio Visual, pg 728
CP Communications, pg 732
Design Audio Visual Inc, pg 741
Gearhead Rentals, pg 769
Gotham Sound & Communications Inc, pg 773
Hello World Communications, pg 778
KVL Audio Visual Services Inc, pg 802
LightHouse Films, pg 807
Long Island Video Enterprises Live Inc, pg 811
Posthorn Recordings, pg 859
Production Central, pg 863
See Factor Industry Inc, pg 883
Specialized Audio-Visual Inc, pg 896
Studio Instrument Rentals (SIR), pg 902
Theatrical Services & Supplies Inc, pg 912
Visual Word Systems Inc, pg 932
WorldStage, pg 941

NORTH CAROLINA

All Pro Media Inc, pg 680
AV Connections Inc, pg 697
AV Metro Inc, pg 697
Duke Media Services, pg 747
Special Event Services, pg 896
Strategic Connections, pg 901
Take One Productions Ltd, pg 906

NORTH DAKOTA

Media Productions, pg 822

OHIO

Hughie's Event Production Services, pg 782
ITA Audio Visual Solutions, pg 791
Lyon Video Inc, pg 813
Mills James Productions, pg 828
Ohio HD Video, pg 844
Production Solutions Inc, pg 864
R&B Communications Inc, pg 870

OKLAHOMA

PDC Productions, pg 852

OREGON

Northwest Film Center, pg 842
Picture This Production Services, pg 856
Rose City Sound, pg 877

PENNSYLVANIA

Advanced AV LLC, pg 677
Audio Visions Inc, pg 694
Audio Visual Communications Inc, pg 694
FirstGeneration Audio/Visual Services, pg 761
FMP Media Solutions Inc, pg 763
Grise Audio Visual Center Inc, pg 774
JPL, pg 795
Muderick Media, pg 833
New York Camera & Video, pg 840
Right Coast Recording Inc, pg 875
Sound by Fitch, pg 893
Upstage Video, pg 923

The Videohouse Inc, pg 929
Viewpoint Production Services Inc, pg 930
Vistacom Inc, pg 931
Visual Sound Inc, pg 931

SOUTH CAROLINA

Impact Technology Group LLC, pg 786
Sound & Images Inc, pg 893

TENNESSEE

Allstar Audio Systems Inc, pg 681
Brantley Sound Associates Inc, pg 709
Love Shack Recording Studios, pg 811
Mr Mark's Used Musical, Stereo & Studio Equipment Store, pg 828
RentACamera.com, pg 873
Technical Support Systems LLC, pg 908
Trew Audio Inc, pg 917

TEXAS

Alford Media Services, pg 680
Audio Visual Technologies Group (AVTG), pg 695
Big House Sound Inc, pg 705
Bright Star Productions Inc, pg 710
Crossroads Audio Inc, pg 735
FitzCo Sound Inc, pg 761
GEAR Cameras & Lighting, pg 769
Lubbock Audio Visual Inc, pg 812
Music Lab Inc, pg 834
Omega Productions, pg 845
Onstage Systems, pg 846
Power Factory Productions, pg 860
South Coast Film & Video, pg 895
Stage Directions, pg 898
Tropikal Productions, pg 918
Video Perspective, pg 928

UTAH

Ron Hill Imagery, pg 780
Performance Audio LLC, pg 854
Redman Movies & Stories, pg 872

VERMONT

Dark Star Lighting & Production, pg 737
Edgewood Studios, pg 750

VIRGINIA

American AV, pg 682
Audio Visual Actions Inc (AVA), pg 694
Boitnott Visual Communications Corp (BVC), pg 708
Lee Hartman & Sons Inc, pg 805
StageSound, pg 899

WASHINGTON

D A Sound, pg 737
Northern Lights & Pro Audio, pg 842
Oppenheimer Camera Products, pg 847
PNTA, pg 858
Victory Studios, pg 927

WEST VIRGINIA

United Sound & Electronics, pg 921

WISCONSIN

Camera Corner Connecting Point, pg 715
Event Essentials, pg 756
Full Compass Systems, pg 767

WYOMING

Bridger Productions Inc, pg 710

PUERTO RICO

Stage Crew Audiovisual Inc, pg 898

ALBERTA

Allstar Show Industries Inc, pg 681
Cine Audio Visual Sales & Service Ltd, pg 723
Evolution AV, pg 757
L R Light & Sound, pg 802
McBain Camera Ltd, pg 820
Unique Communications Ltd, pg 921

BRITISH COLUMBIA

Clark's Audio Visual Services Ltd, pg 725
Commercial Electronics Ltd, pg 728
DL Sound & Lighting Productions Ltd, pg 744
MicrophoneRentals.com, pg 826
Video Out Distribution, pg 928

MANITOBA

Inland Audio Visual Ltd, pg 788
MidCanada Production Services Inc (MidCan), pg 826

ONTARIO

HD Source, pg 777
JIB Shots Equipment Inc, pg 794
RB Productions, pg 870
SIM Digital, pg 888
Westbury National Show Systems Ltd, pg 936
ZTV Broadcast Services Inc, pg 945

QUEBEC

Audio Visual Dynamics, pg 694
Group PVP, pg 774
Panavideo Inc, pg 850

Mixer Repairs

CALIFORNIA

Ametron Audio/Video, pg 684
Audio Images Corp, pg 693
Audio Upgrades, pg 694
Diemer Amp & Keyboard Repair, pg 741
Digitron Electronics, pg 743
McAlister Electronics, pg 820
Professional Sound Corp, pg 865
Sound Service Co, pg 894
SSL Industries Inc, pg 898
TOA Electronics Inc, pg 915
Towards 2000 Inc, pg 916
VMI Inc, pg 932

CONNECTICUT

HB Communications Inc, pg 777

FLORIDA

Digital Video Systems, pg 742
Hi-Tech Enterprises Inc, pg 779
JT Communications, pg 795
Midtown Video Inc, pg 827

Phat Planet Recording Studios, pg 855
Stereo Sales Inc, pg 900
TAI Audio, pg 906
Tel-Test, pg 909

GEORGIA

Lighting & Production Equipment Inc, pg 807
Stage Front Presentation Systems, pg 899

ILLINOIS

Allen Visual Systems Inc, pg 680
Beatty TeleVisual Productions, pg 703
C V Lloyde, pg 810
Midwest Digital Corp, pg 827
On Site Video, pg 846
RC Communications, pg 870

INDIANA

SHP Electronics, pg 887
Sweetwater Sound Inc, pg 905

KENTUCKY

Axxis Leasing Inc, pg 700
NOR-COM Inc, pg 841

MAINE

Headlight Audio Visual Inc, pg 777

MARYLAND

Cardinal Sound & Video, pg 717

MASSACHUSETTS

Capron Lighting & Sound Co Inc, pg 716
Professional Audio Design Inc, pg 865

MICHIGAN

City Events Group, pg 725
K&R's Recording Studios Inc, pg 796
On Stage Visuals, pg 846
TEL Systems LLC, pg 909

NEVADA

MUSIC Group Services Nevada, pg 834

NEW JERSEY

A-V Services Inc, pg 671
Earl Girls Inc, pg 749
The Music Place, pg 834
Nelson Enterprises Theatrical Supply Co, pg 838
Starlite, pg 900

NEW MEXICO

Quickbeam Systems Inc (QSI), pg 868

NEW YORK

American Video Inc, pg 684
Toys From The Attic, pg 916
Whirlwind Music Distributors Inc, pg 937

NORTH CAROLINA

Strategic Connections, pg 901

OHIO

Copp Integrated Systems, pg 731
Hughie's Event Production Services, pg 782
ITA Audio Visual Solutions, pg 791
Tri-State Audio Visual Co, pg 918

OREGON

All Service Musical Electronics Repair, pg 680

PENNSYLVANIA

Audio Visions Inc, pg 694
Vistacom Inc, pg 931

SOUTH CAROLINA

DaviSound, pg 739

TENNESSEE

Belew Enterprises, pg 703
Technical Support Systems LLC, pg 908
Trew Audio Inc, pg 917

TEXAS

Audio Visual Technologies Group (AVTG), pg 695
Lubbock Audio Visual Inc, pg 812
Music Lab Inc, pg 834
Southwest Sound Solutions, pg 896
Tarpley Media Systems, pg 907

VIRGINIA

Boitnott Visual Communications Corp (BVC), pg 708
The Whitlock Group, pg 937

WASHINGTON

Northern Lights & Pro Audio, pg 842
PNTA, pg 858

WEST VIRGINIA

United Sound & Electronics, pg 921

WISCONSIN

Full Compass Systems, pg 767

ALBERTA

Allstar Show Industries Inc, pg 681
Infosat Communications Inc, pg 787
Unique Communications Ltd, pg 921

BRITISH COLUMBIA

Commercial Electronics Ltd, pg 728

MANITOBA

Inland Audio Visual Ltd, pg 788

ONTARIO

HD Source, pg 777
Westbury National Show Systems Ltd, pg 936
Yorkville Sound Inc, pg 944

QUEBEC

SC Media Canada, pg 881

Mixing—Stereo or Dolby Stereo

ALABAMA

Dogwood Productions Inc, pg 745
Sound of Birmingham Productions, pg 894

ARIZONA

Aardvark Productions LLC, pg 671
Allusion Studios & Pure Wave Audio, pg 681
Fire Power Music LLC, pg 761
Merestone, pg 823
Metropolitan Audio-Visual Inc, pg 824

ARKANSAS

White Diamond Productions LLC, pg 937

CALIFORNIA

AB Audio Visual Entertainment Inc, pg 672
ACDC Audio CD & Cassette, pg 674
AlphaDogs Inc, pg 682
Artichoke Productions, pg 690
Audio Mechanics, pg 693
Audio Upgrades, pg 694
Bay Records, pg 702
Creative Media Recording, pg 733
Creative Technology, pg 733
Custom Video Productions Inc, pg 736
Different Fur Recording Ltd, pg 741
Digital Jungle, pg 742
Earwax Productions Inc, pg 749
5 Alarm Music, pg 762
48 Windows, pg 764
iCorpTv, pg 783
Juice Studios, pg 795
Kris Stevens Enterprises, pg 801
Ludlow Media, pg 812
Lynch Communications, pg 813
Main Street Media Inc, pg 815
Martinsound, pg 818
Maximus Media Inc, pg 820
McCune Audio-Video-Lighting, pg 821
On-Trax Inc, pg 846
PM Productions, pg 858
Private Island Audio Inc, pg 862
Pyramind Studios, pg 867
QRS Software Services, pg 867
Roundabout Entertainment Inc, pg 878
Saturn Studios, pg 881
Shapeshifter, pg 885
Steve Shapiro Music, pg 885
SonicPool, pg 892
Still N' Motion, pg 901
Tam Communications Inc, pg 906
Timeless Productions, pg 914
Total Creative, pg 916
Universal Studios, pg 922

COLORADO

Tim Cissell Music, pg 725
Conly Productions, pg 730
Daylight Productions & Rentals, pg 739
Flashback Media Productions, pg 762
Rocky Mountain Audio/Video Productions Inc, pg 876

AUDIO

Mixing—Stereo or Dolby Stereo (continued)

CONNECTICUT

BRB Audiovisual Productions, pg 709
Ironik Design & Post, pg 791
Palace Production Center, pg 850

DELAWARE

Side Door Studio Inc, pg 887

DISTRICT OF COLUMBIA

Interface Media Group, pg 789

FLORIDA

Access Media Group, pg 673
The Kitchen, pg 799
LHV Audio Services, pg 807
Morrisound Recording, pg 830
Phat Planet Recording Studios, pg 855
Stereo Sales Inc, pg 900
Sunfire Communications Inc, pg 904
Universal Studios Florida® Production Group, pg 922

GEORGIA

Beast Atlanta, pg 703
Crawford Media Services Inc, pg 733
Guerrilla Productions LLC, pg 774
Hottrax Records, pg 782
Lighting & Production Equipment Inc, pg 807
Stage Front Presentation Systems, pg 899

HAWAII

Media Bridge Gamekids, pg 821

ILLINOIS

CCore Media Inc, pg 718
IV Media Resources, pg 792
Solid Sound Recording Studio, pg 892
Sound/Video Impressions Inc, pg 894
20/20 Communications Inc, pg 920
Woodside Avenue Music Productions Inc, pg 941

INDIANA

A-V-A Video Productions, pg 671
Bright Ideas Creative Services, pg 710
Alan Johnson Recording, pg 794
Sweetwater Sound Inc, pg 905

KENTUCKY

Broadway Digital, pg 711

LOUISIANA

WVLA-TV, pg 942

MARYLAND

CPR MultiMedia Solutions, pg 732
dbF a Media Company, pg 739
Lion & Fox Recording Studios, pg 809
Omega Recording Studios, pg 845
Sheffield Audio/Video Productions, pg 885

Smolian Sound Studios, pg 891
Welocalize, pg 935

MASSACHUSETTS

Continental Recordings Inc, pg 731
Cramer, pg 732
Labrecque Creative Sound, pg 803
Northern Light Productions (NLP), pg 842
Penfield Productions Ltd, pg 853
Soundtrack Group, pg 895

MICHIGAN

Audio Graphic Services, pg 693
Brilliance Audio, pg 710
Digi Sign Design LLC, pg 741
Digital Image Studios LLC, pg 742
GMP Music, pg 772
K&R's Recording Studios Inc, pg 796
Michigan Recording Arts Institute & Technologies, pg 825
TGA Recording Co, pg 911

MINNESOTA

The ADS Group, pg 676
Rum Jungle Media, pg 878
Winterland Studios, pg 940

MISSOURI

Audio-VideoGraphics Inc, pg 694
Avatar Studios, pg 697
Show-Me Audio-Visual, pg 887

MONTANA

Jereco Studios Inc, pg 793

NEBRASKA

JoeAudio, pg 794
Three Pillars Media, pg 913

NEVADA

JCS Video Productions, pg 793
Tanglewood Productions, pg 907

NEW JERSEY

Allegro Productions Inc, pg 680
CFP Video Productions Inc, pg 720
Jeep Jazz Media Solutions, pg 793
Laurel Video Productions, pg 804
MiB MediaWorks, pg 825
Midnight Media Group Inc, pg 827
Milgrom Productions, pg 827
Optisonics Productions, pg 847
Starlite, pg 900
Suede Interactive, pg 903
VCSvideo, pg 925
Video Ideas Productions, pg 928

NEW MEXICO

Production Outfitters, pg 864

NEW YORK

Aura Sonic Ltd (ASL), pg 695
Aural Gratification Inc, pg 695
Big Fish Production US, pg 705
The Big House Group, pg 705
Chromavision Corp, pg 723
Digital Art Video Inc, pg 741
Digital Force Ltd, pg 742
DuArt Media Services, pg 747
Fingerpaint, pg 761
HB-Content, pg 777
Headroom Digital Audio, pg 777
Manhattan Center Studios Inc, pg 816

Mark Custom Recording Service Inc, pg 817
Mood Creations Ltd, pg 829
RadioArt/Bob & Ray CDs & MP3 Files, pg 869
Sear Sound, pg 883
Visual Technologies Corp, pg 932

NORTH CAROLINA

Pat Appleson Studios Inc, pg 687
The Communications Group Inc, pg 729
Duke Media Services, pg 747
Franklin Video Inc, pg 765
Horizon Video Productions Inc, pg 781
Take One Productions Ltd, pg 906
2BruceStudio, pg 920

NORTH DAKOTA

Media Productions, pg 822

OHIO

Advent Media Inc, pg 677
Curtis Inc, pg 736
Lyon Video Inc, pg 813
Mills James Productions, pg 828
Musicol Recording, pg 835
R&B Communications Inc, pg 870
SoundSpace Inc, pg 895
The Telos Alliance, pg 910

OKLAHOMA

PDC Productions, pg 852

OREGON

REX, pg 874

PENNSYLVANIA

AccuWeather Inc, pg 674
American Artist Studio, pg 682
Audio Visual Communications Inc, pg 694
Craig Recording Studios, pg 732
FMP Media Solutions Inc, pg 763
Forge Recording LLC, pg 764
Innovision Media Group, pg 788
Ivory Productions, pg 792
Laser Video Corp, pg 804
Panta Rhei Media Inc, pg 851
Right Coast Recording Inc, pg 875
The Videohouse Inc, pg 929
WHYY Inc, pg 938

RHODE ISLAND

Sound-FX-Design, pg 894

SOUTH CAROLINA

DaviSound, pg 739
Genesis Creative, pg 769

TENNESSEE

Allstar Audio Systems Inc, pg 681
American Blackguard Inc, pg 683
Analog Man Recording Studio, pg 685
Ardent Studios Inc, pg 688
JamSync, pg 793
Love Shack Recording Studios, pg 811
Motion Picture Services, pg 831
Scripps Networks, pg 882
Stage Post, pg 899
Technical Support Systems LLC, pg 908
Zion Music Group, pg 945

TEXAS

Anaphora Literary Press, pg 685
Audiomoxie®, pg 695
Crossroads Audio Inc, pg 735
The Editing Co, pg 750
Fire Station Studios, pg 761
Julye Newlin Productions Inc, pg 840
Out of the BLUE Media, pg 849
Phillips Media Source, pg 855
Real to Reel Studios Inc, pg 871
The Samuels Co, pg 879
The Sound Lab Inc, pg 894
South Coast Film & Video, pg 895
Stage Directions, pg 898
TopCat Records LLC, pg 915
Tropikal Productions, pg 918

UTAH

Performance Audio LLC, pg 854
Soularium Recording Studios, pg 893

VERMONT

Edgewood Studios, pg 750

VIRGINIA

AudioImage Recording, pg 695
Bias Studios, pg 705
CDR Communications Inc, pg 719
Wally Cleaver's Recording Service, pg 726
Henninger Media Services, pg 779
Metro Productions, pg 824
Studio Center Corp, pg 902

WASHINGTON

D A Sound, pg 737
Hamilton Studio, pg 775
North-by-Northwest - A Digital Studio, pg 842
Sound Sound, pg 894
Victory Studios, pg 927

WISCONSIN

Audio Visual of Milwaukee Inc, pg 694
Concept Productions Inc, pg 730
5th Floor Recording Co, pg 760
Video Wisconsin Inc, pg 929

BRITISH COLUMBIA

Pinewood Sound, pg 857
Triad Communications Ltd, pg 918

MANITOBA

DACAPO Productions Inc, pg 737

ONTARIO

ADS Media, pg 677
AMPLUS Productions, pg 684
DebsVoice, pg 739
Eggplant Pictures & Sound, pg 751
JL Recording Studios, pg 794
MCS Recording Studios, pg 821
Metalworks Recording Studios Inc, pg 824
Phase One Studios, pg 855
Silver Creek Media Inc, pg 888
Spence-Thomas Audio Post, pg 897
Trebas Institute, pg 917
Video Excellence Productions, pg 927
VO2 Mix Audio Post, pg 932
Wanted! Sound + Picture, pg 933

QUEBEC

Group PVP, pg 774
Trebas Institute, pg 917

Mixing—Stereo Surround or Dolby Surround

ALABAMA

Sound of Birmingham Productions, pg 894

ARIZONA

Allusion Studios & Pure Wave Audio, pg 681
Fire Power Music LLC, pg 761
Merestone, pg 823

ARKANSAS

White Diamond Productions LLC, pg 937

CALIFORNIA

ACDC Audio CD & Cassette, pg 674
AlphaDogs Inc, pg 682
Berkeley Sound Artists Inc, pg 704
Creative Technology, pg 733
Digital Jungle, pg 742
Earwax Productions Inc, pg 749
Express Media Inc, pg 757
48 Windows, pg 764
iCorpTv, pg 783
Illuminate Post/Digital Finishing, pg 784
Juice Studios, pg 795
Lynch Communications, pg 813
Martinsound Inc, pg 818
Maximus Media Inc, pg 820
McCune Audio-Video-Lighting, pg 821
Playback Recording Studio, pg 858
Private Island Audio Inc, pg 862
QRS Software Services, pg 867
Roundabout Entertainment Inc, pg 878
Shapeshifter, pg 885
SonicPool, pg 892
Still N' Motion, pg 901
Studio Circle Recordings, pg 902
Total Creative, pg 916
Universal Studios, pg 922

COLORADO

Tim Cissell Music, pg 725
Rocky Mountain Audio/Video Productions Inc, pg 876

CONNECTICUT

Palace Production Center, pg 850
Sonalysts Media, pg 892

DISTRICT OF COLUMBIA

Interface Media Group, pg 789

FLORIDA

Access Media Group, pg 673
Audacity Recording Studios, pg 693
Florida Film & Tape, pg 763
The Kitchen, pg 799
LHV Audio Services, pg 807
Morrisound Recording, pg 830
Phat Planet Recording Studios, pg 855
Sunfire Communications Inc, pg 904

GEORGIA

Beast Atlanta, pg 703
Crawford Media Services Inc, pg 733
Guerrilla Productions LLC, pg 774
Magick Lantern, pg 814
Stage Front Presentation Systems, pg 899

HAWAII

Media Bridge Gamekids, pg 821

ILLINOIS

Optimus, pg 847
Solid Sound Recording Studio, pg 892

INDIANA

Bright Ideas Creative Services, pg 710
Sweetwater Sound Inc, pg 905

MARYLAND

CPR MultiMedia Solutions, pg 732
dbF a Media Company, pg 739
Omega Recording Studios, pg 845
Sheffield Audio/Video Productions, pg 885

MASSACHUSETTS

Cramer, pg 732
Northern Light Productions (NLP), pg 842
Soundtrack Group, pg 895
Rik Tinory Productions, pg 914
WGBH Production Group, pg 936

MICHIGAN

Audio Graphic Services, pg 693
Brilliance Audio, pg 710
Digi Sign Design LLC, pg 741
Digital Image Studios LLC, pg 742
GMP Music, pg 772
K&R's Recording Studios Inc, pg 796
Michigan Recording Arts Institute & Technologies, pg 825
TGA Recording Co, pg 911

MINNESOTA

The ADS Group, pg 676

MISSOURI

Show-Me Audio-Visual, pg 887

MONTANA

Jereco Studios Inc, pg 793

NEW JERSEY

Allegro Productions Inc, pg 680
CFP Video Productions Inc, pg 720
Creative Video, pg 734
Milgrom Productions, pg 827
NFL Films Inc, pg 841
Starlite, pg 900
Suede Interactive, pg 903

NEW MEXICO

Production Outfitters, pg 864

NEW YORK

Aura Sonic Ltd (ASL), pg 695
Big Fish Production US, pg 705
The Big House Group, pg 705
Chromavision Corp, pg 723

Digital Art Video Inc, pg 741
Digital Arts NY, pg 742
HB-Content, pg 777
HBO Studio Productions, pg 777

NORTH CAROLINA

Pat Appleson Studios Inc, pg 687
Horizon Video Productions Inc, pg 781

OHIO

Curtis Inc, pg 736
Mills James Productions, pg 828
The Telos Alliance, pg 910

OKLAHOMA

PDC Productions, pg 852

OREGON

Future Disc LLC, pg 767
REX, pg 874

PENNSYLVANIA

Audio Visual Communications Inc, pg 694
Forge Recording LLC, pg 764
Innovision Media Group, pg 788
Ivory Productions, pg 792
Laser Video Corp, pg 804
Production Masters Inc (PMI), pg 864
Right Coast Recording Inc, pg 875
The Videohouse Inc, pg 929

RHODE ISLAND

Sound-FX-Design, pg 894

SOUTH CAROLINA

DaviSound, pg 739
Genesis Creative, pg 769

TENNESSEE

American Blackguard Inc, pg 683
Ardent Music LLC, pg 688
Ardent Studios Inc, pg 688
JamSync, pg 793
Love Shack Recording Studios, pg 811
Motion Picture Services, pg 831
Scripps Networks, pg 882
Stage Post, pg 899

TEXAS

Anaphora Literary Press, pg 685
The Samuels Co, pg 879
South Coast Film & Video, pg 895

UTAH

One Stop CD Shop LLC, pg 846
Soularium Recording Studios, pg 893

VIRGINIA

Wally Cleaver's Recording Service, pg 726
Metro Productions, pg 824
Studio Center Corp, pg 902

WASHINGTON

North-by-Northwest - A Digital Studio, pg 842
Victory Studios, pg 927

WISCONSIN

5th Floor Recording Co, pg 760
Sound Strations Audio Productions Inc, pg 894
TBC Studios, pg 907
Video Wisconsin Inc, pg 929

BRITISH COLUMBIA

Pinewood Sound, pg 857

MANITOBA

DACAPO Productions Inc, pg 737

ONTARIO

ADS Media, pg 677
DebsVoice, pg 739
GAPC (General Assembly Production Centre), pg 768
Metalworks Recording Studios Inc, pg 824
Phase One Studios, pg 855
Spence-Thomas Audio Post, pg 897
VO2 Mix Audio Post, pg 932
Wanted! Sound + Picture, pg 933

Music Libraries— Alternative

ALABAMA

Sound of Birmingham Productions, pg 894

ARIZONA

Direct Current Video Productions, pg 743
Film Creations Ltd, pg 760
Merestone, pg 823

ARKANSAS

White Diamond Productions LLC, pg 937

CALIFORNIA

Artichoke Productions, pg 690
Berkeley Sound Artists Inc, pg 704
Creative Support Services/CSS Music, pg 733
Creative Technology, pg 733
Diamond Dreams Music Productions, pg 741
Eye & I Productions, pg 758
5 Alarm Music, pg 762
Kaleidosound, pg 796
Killer Tracks, pg 798
Lynch Communications, pg 813
Megatrax, pg 823
The Music Kitchen Inc, pg 834
OGM Production Music, pg 844
Reality Check Systems, pg 871
Regent Press Publishers & Printers, pg 873
Saturn Studios, pg 881
Steve Shapiro Music, pg 885
Sonoton Music Library, pg 893
Still N' Motion, pg 901
Total Creative, pg 916
Twisted Media Inc, pg 920
Visions Plus, pg 931

COLORADO

Tim Cissell Music, pg 725
Flashback Media Productions, pg 762
Los Angeles Post Music Inc, pg 811

DELAWARE

Ken-Del Productions Inc, pg 797

AUDIO

Music Libraries—
Alternative (continued)

FLORIDA

Alliance Entertainment Corp (AEC) LLC, pg 680
LHV Audio Services, pg 807
Universal Studios Florida® Production Group, pg 922

GEORGIA

ECG Productions, pg 750
Guerrilla Productions LLC, pg 774
Hottrax Records, pg 782

ILLINOIS

Convenience, pg 731

KANSAS

KAKE-TV, pg 796

MARYLAND

Adelphi Records Inc, pg 676
CPR MultiMedia Solutions, pg 732

MASSACHUSETTS

Soundtrack Group, pg 895

MICHIGAN

GMP Music, pg 772

MISSOURI

Show-Me Audio-Visual, pg 887

MONTANA

Jereco Studios Inc, pg 793

NEBRASKA

JoeAudio, pg 794

NEVADA

JCS Video Productions, pg 793
Tanglewood Productions, pg 907

NEW JERSEY

Milgrom Productions, pg 827
TRF Production Music Libraries, pg 917
VCSvideo, pg 925

NEW MEXICO

Production Outfitters, pg 864

NEW YORK

A-List Quality Videographer, pg 671
Audio Network US Inc, pg 693
Beekman Books Inc, pg 703
Getty Images Music, pg 770
Heavy Melody, pg 778
Mother West, pg 831
TecNec Distributing, pg 909

NORTH CAROLINA

Pat Appleson Studios Inc, pg 687
Ladyslipper Music, pg 803
Take One Productions Ltd, pg 906

NORTH DAKOTA

Media Productions, pg 822

OHIO

Aztec Video Productions, pg 700
Mills James Productions, pg 828
R&B Communications Inc, pg 870
Take 1 Media Services, pg 906

OKLAHOMA

PDC Productions, pg 852

PENNSYLVANIA

Monster Tracks, pg 829
The Videohouse Inc, pg 929

RHODE ISLAND

Sound-FX-Design, pg 894

SOUTH CAROLINA

Genesis Creative, pg 769
Stages Video Productions, pg 899

TENNESSEE

Anode Inc, pg 686
Film House Inc, pg 760
Fricon Entertainment Co Inc, pg 766

TEXAS

The Editing Co, pg 750
FirstCom Music, pg 761
Mediaforce Productions, pg 822
The Music Bakery, pg 834
Julye Newlin Productions Inc, pg 840
Production Garden Music, pg 863
The Sound Lab Inc, pg 894
South Coast Film & Video, pg 895

VERMONT

Inner Traditions International, pg 788

WISCONSIN

5th Floor Recording Co, pg 760

ONTARIO

Canamedia Inc, pg 715
DebsVoice, pg 739
Entertainment One Distribution, pg 754
GAPC (General Assembly Production Centre), pg 768
Kool Music, pg 801
MCS Recording Studios, pg 821
Metalworks Recording Studios Inc, pg 824
Nightingale Music Productions Inc, pg 841
Sound Ideas, pg 894
StockMusic.com, pg 901
Video Excellence Productions, pg 927
Wanted! Sound + Picture, pg 933
Westar Music, pg 936

Music Libraries—
Background

ARIZONA

Direct Current Video Productions, pg 743
Film Creations Ltd, pg 760
Fire Power Music LLC, pg 761
Merestone, pg 823
SPEAK HOUSE Audio™, pg 896

ARKANSAS

White Diamond Productions LLC, pg 937

CALIFORNIA

Aliso Creek Productions Inc, pg 680
Associated Production Music LLC, pg 691
Berkeley Sound Artists Inc, pg 704
CCI Digital, a DVS Company, pg 718
Creative Support Services/CSS Music, pg 733
Diamond Dreams Music Productions, pg 741
Eye & I Productions, pg 758
5 Alarm Music, pg 762
Jaguar Distribution Corp, pg 792
Kaleidosound, pg 796
Killer Tracks, pg 798
K2B2 Records, pg 802
Lynch Communications, pg 813
Manchester Music Library Inc, pg 816
Megatrax, pg 823
The Music Kitchen Inc, pg 834
Joseph Nicoletti Consulting-Promotion, pg 841
OGM Production Music, pg 844
OTR Studios, pg 848
Polarity Post Production, pg 858
Pyramind Studios, pg 867
Reality Check Systems, pg 871
RJ Video Productions, pg 875
Saturn Studios, pg 881
Steve Shapiro Music, pg 885
Sonoton Music Library, pg 893
Still N' Motion, pg 901
Timeless Productions, pg 914
Total Creative, pg 916
Twisted Media Inc, pg 920
Visions Plus, pg 931

COLORADO

Tim Cissell Music, pg 725
Conly Productions, pg 730
Flashback Media Productions, pg 762
Los Angeles Post Music Inc, pg 811
Transtar Entertainment Co Inc, pg 917

CONNECTICUT

Ironik Design & Post, pg 791
P&P Studios Inc, pg 851

DELAWARE

Ken-Del Productions Inc, pg 797

DISTRICT OF COLUMBIA

Smithsonian Folkways Recordings, pg 891

FLORIDA

Alliance Entertainment Corp (AEC) LLC, pg 680
Applebox Studio, pg 687
Kat Epple Music Productions, pg 755
Hard Hat Radio Music Service, pg 776
Jordan Klein Film & Video (JKFV), pg 795
LHV Audio Services, pg 807
Pandisc Music Corp, pg 851
Universal Studios Florida® Production Group, pg 922

GEORGIA

Beachwood Productions, pg 702
ECG Productions, pg 750
Guerrilla Productions LLC, pg 774
Hottrax Records, pg 782
LT Sound Inc, pg 812
On-Line Productions, pg 845

ILLINOIS

Jim Passin Productions, pg 852
WEEK TV, pg 935
Woodside Avenue Music Productions Inc, pg 941

INDIANA

A-V-A Video Productions, pg 671

KANSAS

KAKE-TV, pg 796

MAINE

Serendipity Recordings, pg 884

MARYLAND

CAS Video Productions, pg 717
CPR MultiMedia Solutions, pg 732
The Cutting Corporation, GraphicAudio® & Archival Sound Lab, pg 736

MASSACHUSETTS

CommCreative, pg 728
Soundtrack Group, pg 895
TR Productions, pg 916
The Well-Tempered Music Library, pg 935

MICHIGAN

American Music Environments Inc (AME), pg 684
GMP Music, pg 772

MINNESOTA

Media Loft Inc, pg 822

MISSOURI

Show-Me Audio-Visual, pg 887

MONTANA

Jereco Studios Inc, pg 793

NEBRASKA

JoeAudio, pg 794

NEVADA

DVDs4Less, pg 748
JCS Video Productions, pg 793
Tanglewood Productions, pg 907

NEW HAMPSHIRE

Channell One Video, pg 720
The Troupe, pg 918

NEW JERSEY

The Audio Department Inc, pg 693
CFP Video Productions Inc, pg 720
Milbrodt/Music & Sound Design, pg 827
Milgrom Productions, pg 827
NFL Films Music Library, pg 841
Richard Reiter Productions Inc, pg 873

TRF Production Music Libraries, pg 917
VCSvideo, pg 925

NEW MEXICO

Production Outfitters, pg 864
Uncharted Country Publishing, pg 921

NEW YORK

A-List Quality Videographer, pg 671
Big Fish Production US, pg 705
Cornell Laboratory of Ornithology, pg 731
de Wolfe Music USA, pg 739
Getty Images Music, pg 770
Heavy Melody, pg 778
HOThead, pg 782
Manhattan Production Music Inc, pg 816
The Palmer Group, pg 850
David Rapkin Audio Production, pg 870
Sony Music Commercial Music Group, pg 893
Sony Music Entertainment, pg 893
TecNec Distributing, pg 909
WNET/New York Public Media, pg 940

NORTH CAROLINA

Pat Appleson Studios Inc, pg 687
Duke Media Services, pg 747
Franklin Video Inc, pg 765
NASCAR Productions LLC, pg 835
Take One Productions Ltd, pg 906

NORTH DAKOTA

Media Productions, pg 822

OHIO

Aztec Video Productions, pg 700
Bartha, pg 702
Mills James Productions, pg 828
R&B Communications Inc, pg 870
Take 1 Media Services, pg 906
Vista Color Imaging Inc, pg 931

OKLAHOMA

Academic Media & Digital Services, pg 672
PDC Productions, pg 852

OREGON

Instant Music Now, pg 788

PENNSYLVANIA

Audio Visual Communications Inc, pg 694
Craig Recording Studios, pg 732
Monster Tracks, pg 829
The Videohouse Inc, pg 929

RHODE ISLAND

Sound-FX-Design, pg 894

SOUTH CAROLINA

DaviSound, pg 739
Genesis Creative, pg 769
Stages Video Productions, pg 899

TENNESSEE

Anode Inc, pg 686
Film House Inc, pg 760
Fricon Entertainment Co Inc, pg 766

Memphis Communications Corp, pg 823
Word Label Group, pg 941

TEXAS

Audiomoxie®, pg 695
The Editing Co, pg 750
FirstCom Music, pg 761
Horizon Film + Video Productions, pg 781
Mediaforce Productions, pg 822
The Music Bakery, pg 834
Julye Newlin Productions Inc, pg 840
Production Garden Music, pg 863
Real to Reel Studios Inc, pg 871
The Sound Lab Inc, pg 894
Sound Works, pg 894
South Coast Film & Video, pg 895
Stage Directions, pg 898
Texas Heart Institute Visual Communication Services, pg 911
TM Studios Inc, pg 915
Tropikal Productions, pg 918

WASHINGTON

Avast! Recording Co, pg 697

WEST VIRGINIA

Sweetsong Productions, pg 905

WISCONSIN

5th Floor Recording Co, pg 760
Mirror 34 Productions, pg 828
USAV Group Inc, pg 923
Video Wisconsin Inc, pg 929
Wisconsin Public Television, pg 940

ONTARIO

Canamedia Inc, pg 715
DebsVoice, pg 739
Entertainment One Distribution, pg 754
GAPC (General Assembly Production Centre), pg 768
The Hollywood Edge, pg 780
MCS Recording Studios, pg 821
Metalworks Recording Studios Inc, pg 824
Morning Music Ltd, pg 830
Nightingale Music Productions Inc, pg 841
Sound Ideas, pg 894
StockMusic.com, pg 901
Video Excellence Productions, pg 927
Wanted! Sound + Picture, pg 933
Westar Music, pg 936

QUEBEC

Muse Entertainment Enterprises, pg 834

Music Libraries— Bluegrass

ALABAMA

Sound of Birmingham Productions, pg 894

ARIZONA

Direct Current Video Productions, pg 743
Film Creations Ltd, pg 760
Merestone, pg 823

ARKANSAS

White Diamond Productions LLC, pg 937

CALIFORNIA

Associated Production Music LLC, pg 691
Creative Support Services/CSS Music, pg 733
5 Alarm Music, pg 762
Bruce Goldberg Inc, pg 772
Increase Video/Silver Mine Video, pg 786
Jaguar Distribution Corp, pg 792
Kaleidosound, pg 796
Killer Tracks, pg 798
K2B2 Records, pg 802
Lynch Communications, pg 813
Megatrax, pg 823
The Music Kitchen Inc, pg 834
Joseph Nicoletti Consulting-Promotion, pg 841
OGM Production Music, pg 844
OTR Studios, pg 848
Polarity Post Production, pg 858
Steve Shapiro Music, pg 885
Sonoton Music Library, pg 893
Still N' Motion, pg 901
Total Creative, pg 916
Welk Music Group, pg 935

COLORADO

Tim Cissell Music, pg 725
Flashback Media Productions, pg 762
Transtar Entertainment Co Inc, pg 917

CONNECTICUT

American Melody, pg 683

DELAWARE

Ken-Del Productions Inc, pg 797

FLORIDA

Alliance Entertainment Corp (AEC) LLC, pg 680
Applebox Studio, pg 687
LHV Audio Services, pg 807
Universal Studios Florida® Production Group, pg 922

GEORGIA

Beachwood Productions, pg 702
Guerrilla Productions LLC, pg 774

ILLINOIS

WEEK TV, pg 935
Woodside Avenue Music Productions Inc, pg 941

MASSACHUSETTS

Ben Rudnick and Friends, pg 878
Soundtrack Group, pg 895

MICHIGAN

GMP Music, pg 772

MISSOURI

Show-Me Audio-Visual, pg 887

MONTANA

Jereco Studios Inc, pg 793

NEBRASKA

JoeAudio, pg 794

NEVADA

JCS Video Productions, pg 793
Tanglewood Productions, pg 907

NEW JERSEY

Milbrodt/Music & Sound Design, pg 827
Milgrom Productions, pg 827
Richard Reiter Productions Inc, pg 873
Shanachie Entertainment Corp, pg 885
TRF Production Music Libraries, pg 917
VCSvideo, pg 925

NEW MEXICO

Production Outfitters, pg 864

NEW YORK

A-List Quality Videographer, pg 671
Audio Network US Inc, pg 693
Beekman Books Inc, pg 703
Getty Images Music, pg 770
Historic Films, pg 780
Manhattan Production Music Inc, pg 816
Sony Music Entertainment, pg 893
TecNec Distributing, pg 909

NORTH CAROLINA

Pat Appleson Studios Inc, pg 687
Take One Productions Ltd, pg 906

NORTH DAKOTA

Media Productions, pg 822

OHIO

Aztec Video Productions, pg 700
Mills James Productions, pg 828
R&B Communications Inc, pg 870
Take 1 Media Services, pg 906
WOUB Public Media, pg 942

OKLAHOMA

PDC Productions, pg 852

OREGON

Instant Music Now, pg 788

PENNSYLVANIA

The Videohouse Inc, pg 929

RHODE ISLAND

Sound-FX-Design, pg 894

SOUTH CAROLINA

Genesis Creative, pg 769
Stages Video Productions, pg 899

TENNESSEE

Anode Inc, pg 686
Film House Inc, pg 760
Fricon Entertainment Co Inc, pg 766
Sun Entertainment Corp, pg 903

TEXAS

The Editing Co, pg 750
FirstCom Music, pg 761
Mediaforce Productions, pg 822
The Music Bakery, pg 834
Julye Newlin Productions Inc, pg 840

AUDIO

Music Libraries— Bluegrass (continued)

TEXAS (continued)
The Sound Lab Inc, pg 894
Sound Works, pg 894
South Coast Film & Video, pg 895
The Yesterday USA Radio
  Networks, pg 944

VERMONT
Multicultural Media Inc, pg 833

WASHINGTON
Avast! Recording Co, pg 697

WISCONSIN
5th Floor Recording Co, pg 760
Mirror 34 Productions, pg 828
USAV Group Inc, pg 923

ONTARIO
Canamedia Inc, pg 715
DebsVoice, pg 739
Entertainment One Distribution,
  pg 754
MCS Recording Studios, pg 821
Metalworks Recording Studios Inc,
  pg 824
Nightingale Music Productions Inc,
  pg 841
Sound Ideas, pg 894
StockMusic.com, pg 901
Wanted! Sound + Picture, pg 933
Westar Music, pg 936

Music Libraries—Blues

ALABAMA
Sound of Birmingham Productions,
  pg 894

ARIZONA
Direct Current Video Productions,
  pg 743
Film Creations Ltd, pg 760
Merestone, pg 823

ARKANSAS
White Diamond Productions LLC,
  pg 937

CALIFORNIA
Aliso Creek Productions Inc, pg 680
Creative Support Services/CSS
  Music, pg 733
Diamond Dreams Music
  Productions, pg 741
5 Alarm Music, pg 762
Bruce Goldberg Inc, pg 772
Increase Video/Silver Mine Video,
  pg 786
Kaleidosound, pg 796
Killer Tracks, pg 798
K2B2 Records, pg 802
Lynch Communications, pg 813
Manchester Music Library Inc,
  pg 816
Megatrax, pg 823
The Music Kitchen Inc, pg 834
Joseph Nicoletti Consulting-
  Promotion, pg 841
OGM Production Music, pg 844
Polarity Post Production, pg 858
Pyramind Studios, pg 867

Steve Shapiro Music, pg 885
Sonoton Music Library, pg 893
Still N' Motion, pg 901
Total Creative, pg 916
Welk Music Group, pg 935

COLORADO
Tim Cissell Music, pg 725
Flashback Media Productions,
  pg 762
Los Angeles Post Music Inc, pg 811
Transtar Entertainment Co Inc,
  pg 917

DELAWARE
Ken-Del Productions Inc, pg 797

FLORIDA
Alliance Entertainment Corp (AEC)
  LLC, pg 680
Applebox Studio, pg 687
Jordan Klein Film & Video (JKFV),
  pg 795
LHV Audio Services, pg 807
Universal Studios Florida®
  Production Group, pg 922

GEORGIA
Beachwood Productions, pg 702
ECG Productions, pg 750
Guerrilla Productions LLC, pg 774
Hottrax Records, pg 782

ILLINOIS
Alligator Records & Artist
  Management Inc, pg 681
Delmark Records, pg 740
Earwig Music Co Inc, pg 749
WEEK TV, pg 935
Woodside Avenue Music
  Productions Inc, pg 941

MAINE
WGME-TV, pg 936

MARYLAND
Adelphi Records Inc, pg 676

MASSACHUSETTS
Soundtrack Group, pg 895

MICHIGAN
GMP Music, pg 772

MISSOURI
Show-Me Audio-Visual, pg 887

MONTANA
Jereco Studios Inc, pg 793

NEBRASKA
JoeAudio, pg 794

NEVADA
JCS Video Productions, pg 793
Tanglewood Productions, pg 907

NEW JERSEY
Milbrodt/Music & Sound Design,
  pg 827
Milgrom Productions, pg 827
Richard Reiter Productions Inc,
  pg 873
Shanachie Entertainment Corp,
  pg 885

TRF Production Music Libraries,
  pg 917
VCSvideo, pg 925

NEW MEXICO
Production Outfitters, pg 864

NEW YORK
A-List Quality Videographer,
  pg 671
Beekman Books Inc, pg 703
Cadence Jazz Records, pg 713
Getty Images Music, pg 770
Heavy Melody, pg 778
Historic Films, pg 780
Manhattan Production Music Inc,
  pg 816
Sony Music Entertainment, pg 893
TecNec Distributing, pg 909
Yessian, pg 944

NORTH CAROLINA
Pat Appleson Studios Inc, pg 687
The Communications Group Inc,
  pg 729
Ladyslipper Music, pg 803
Take One Productions Ltd, pg 906

NORTH DAKOTA
Media Productions, pg 822

OHIO
Aztec Video Productions, pg 700
Mills James Productions, pg 828
R&B Communications Inc, pg 870
Take 1 Media Services, pg 906

OKLAHOMA
PDC Productions, pg 852

PENNSYLVANIA
The Videohouse Inc, pg 929

RHODE ISLAND
Sound-FX-Design, pg 894

SOUTH CAROLINA
Genesis Creative, pg 769
Stages Video Productions, pg 899

TENNESSEE
Anode Inc, pg 686
Center for Southern Folklore Inc,
  pg 719
Film House Inc, pg 760
Fricon Entertainment Co Inc,
  pg 766

TEXAS
The Editing Co, pg 750
FirstCom Music, pg 761
Mediaforce Productions, pg 822
The Music Bakery, pg 834
Julye Newlin Productions Inc,
  pg 840
Production Garden Music, pg 863
The Sound Lab Inc, pg 894
Sound Works, pg 894
South Coast Film & Video, pg 895
TopCat Records LLC, pg 915
The Yesterday USA Radio
  Networks, pg 944

WASHINGTON
Avast! Recording Co, pg 697

WISCONSIN
5th Floor Recording Co, pg 760
Mirror 34 Productions, pg 828
USAV Group Inc, pg 923

ONTARIO
Canamedia Inc, pg 715
DebsVoice, pg 739
Entertainment One Distribution,
  pg 754
Kool Music, pg 801
MCS Recording Studios, pg 821
Metalworks Recording Studios Inc,
  pg 824
Nightingale Music Productions Inc,
  pg 841
Sound Ideas, pg 894
StockMusic.com, pg 901
Wanted! Sound + Picture, pg 933
Westar Music, pg 936

Music Libraries—Bridges & Cues

ALABAMA
Sound of Birmingham Productions,
  pg 894

ARIZONA
Direct Current Video Productions,
  pg 743
Film Creations Ltd, pg 760
Merestone, pg 823
SPEAK HOUSE Audio™, pg 896

ARKANSAS
White Diamond Productions LLC,
  pg 937

CALIFORNIA
Associated Production Music LLC,
  pg 691
CCI Digital, a DVS Company,
  pg 718
Creative Support Services/CSS
  Music, pg 733
Creative Technology, pg 733
Diamond Dreams Music
  Productions, pg 741
5 Alarm Music, pg 762
Kaleidosound, pg 796
Killer Tracks, pg 798
Lynch Communications, pg 813
Manchester Music Library Inc,
  pg 816
Megatrax, pg 823
The Music Kitchen Inc, pg 834
Joseph Nicoletti Consulting-
  Promotion, pg 841
OGM Production Music, pg 844
Polarity Post Production, pg 858
Reality Check Systems, pg 871
Steve Shapiro Music, pg 885
Sonoton Music Library, pg 893
Still N' Motion, pg 901
Total Creative, pg 916
Twisted Media Inc, pg 920

COLORADO
Tim Cissell Music, pg 725
Flashback Media Productions,
  pg 762

CONNECTICUT
P&P Studios Inc, pg 851

DELAWARE
Ken-Del Productions Inc, pg 797

FLORIDA
Alliance Entertainment Corp (AEC) LLC, pg 680
Applebox Studio, pg 687
Jordan Klein Film & Video (JKFV), pg 795
LHV Audio Services, pg 807
Universal Studios Florida® Production Group, pg 922

GEORGIA
Beachwood Productions, pg 702
ECG Productions, pg 750
Guerrilla Productions LLC, pg 774

ILLINOIS
Jim Passin Productions, pg 852
WEEK TV, pg 935

KANSAS
KAKE-TV, pg 796

MARYLAND
CPR MultiMedia Solutions, pg 732
The Cutting Corporation, GraphicAudio® & Archival Sound Lab, pg 736

MASSACHUSETTS
CommCreative, pg 728
Soundtrack Group, pg 895
TR Productions, pg 916

MICHIGAN
GMP Music, pg 772

MINNESOTA
Media Loft Inc, pg 822

MISSOURI
Show-Me Audio-Visual, pg 887

NEBRASKA
JoeAudio, pg 794

NEVADA
DVDs4Less, pg 748
Tanglewood Productions, pg 907

NEW JERSEY
Milbrodt/Music & Sound Design, pg 827
Milgrom Productions, pg 827
NFL Films Music Library, pg 841
Richard Reiter Productions Inc, pg 873
TRF Production Music Libraries, pg 917
VCSvideo, pg 925

NEW MEXICO
Production Outfitters, pg 864

NEW YORK
A-List Quality Videographer, pg 671
de Wolfe Music USA, pg 739
Heavy Melody, pg 778
HOThead, pg 782
Manhattan Production Music Inc, pg 816

The Palmer Group, pg 850
David Rapkin Audio Production, pg 870
Sony Music Entertainment, pg 893
TecNec Distributing, pg 909

NORTH CAROLINA
Pat Appleson Studios Inc, pg 687
Duke Media Services, pg 747
Take One Productions Ltd, pg 906

NORTH DAKOTA
Media Productions, pg 822

OHIO
Aztec Video Productions, pg 700
R&B Communications Inc, pg 870
Take 1 Media Services, pg 906
Vista Color Imaging Inc, pg 931

OKLAHOMA
PDC Productions, pg 852

PENNSYLVANIA
Audio Visual Communications Inc, pg 694
Craig Recording Studios, pg 732
Monster Tracks, pg 829
The Videohouse Inc, pg 929

SOUTH CAROLINA
Genesis Creative, pg 769
Stages Video Productions, pg 899

TENNESSEE
Anode Inc, pg 686
Film House Inc, pg 760
Fricon Entertainment Co Inc, pg 766
Memphis Communications Corp, pg 823

TEXAS
The Editing Co, pg 750
FirstCom Music, pg 761
Horizon Film + Video Productions, pg 781
Mediaforce Productions, pg 822
The Music Bakery, pg 834
Production Garden Music, pg 863
The Sound Lab Inc, pg 894
Sound Works, pg 894
South Coast Film & Video, pg 895
Texas Heart Institute Visual Communication Services, pg 911
TM Studios Inc, pg 915

WISCONSIN
5th Floor Recording Co, pg 760
Mirror 34 Productions, pg 828
USAV Group Inc, pg 923

ONTARIO
Canamedia Inc, pg 715
Entertainment One Distribution, pg 754
GAPC (General Assembly Production Centre), pg 768
MCS Recording Studios, pg 821
Metalworks Recording Studios Inc, pg 824
Morning Music Ltd, pg 830
Nightingale Music Productions Inc, pg 841
Sound Ideas, pg 894
StockMusic.com, pg 901

Wanted! Sound + Picture, pg 933
Westar Music, pg 936

Music Libraries— Broadway & Hollywood

ALABAMA
Sound of Birmingham Productions, pg 894

ARIZONA
Direct Current Video Productions, pg 743
Film Creations Ltd, pg 760
Merestone, pg 823

ARKANSAS
White Diamond Productions LLC, pg 937

CALIFORNIA
Aliso Creek Productions Inc, pg 680
Associated Production Music LLC, pg 691
CCI Digital, a DVS Company, pg 718
Creative Support Services/CSS Music, pg 733
Creative Technology, pg 733
Diamond Dreams Music Productions, pg 741
5 Alarm Music, pg 762
Increase Video/Silver Mine Video, pg 786
Kaleidosound, pg 796
Killer Tracks, pg 798
Lynch Communications, pg 813
Megatrax, pg 823
The Music Kitchen Inc, pg 834
Joseph Nicoletti Consulting-Promotion, pg 841
OGM Production Music, pg 844
Reality Check Systems, pg 871
Steve Shapiro Music, pg 885
Sonoton Music Library, pg 893
Still N' Motion, pg 901
Total Creative, pg 916

COLORADO
Tim Cissell Music, pg 725
Flashback Media Productions, pg 762
Transtar Entertainment Co Inc, pg 917

CONNECTICUT
Original Cast Records, pg 848

DELAWARE
Ken-Del Productions Inc, pg 797

FLORIDA
Alliance Entertainment Corp (AEC) LLC, pg 680
Applebox Studio, pg 687
Hard Hat Radio Music Service, pg 776
LHV Audio Services, pg 807
Times-Square Fantasy Theatre, pg 914
Universal Studios Florida® Production Group, pg 922

ILLINOIS
WEEK TV, pg 935

MAINE
Serendipity Recordings, pg 884

MARYLAND
CPR MultiMedia Solutions, pg 732
The Cutting Corporation, GraphicAudio® & Archival Sound Lab, pg 736

MASSACHUSETTS
Soundtrack Group, pg 895

MICHIGAN
GMP Music, pg 772

MISSOURI
Show-Me Audio-Visual, pg 887

NEBRASKA
JoeAudio, pg 794

NEVADA
Tanglewood Productions, pg 907

NEW JERSEY
CFP Video Productions Inc, pg 720
Milgrom Productions, pg 827
TRF Production Music Libraries, pg 917
VCSvideo, pg 925

NEW MEXICO
Production Outfitters, pg 864

NEW YORK
A-List Quality Videographer, pg 671
Beekman Books Inc, pg 703
Historic Films, pg 780
HOThead, pg 782
Manhattan Production Music Inc, pg 816
New World Records, pg 840
The Palmer Group, pg 850
Sony Music Entertainment, pg 893
TecNec Distributing, pg 909
WNET/New York Public Media, pg 940

NORTH CAROLINA
Pat Appleson Studios Inc, pg 687
Ladyslipper Music, pg 803
Take One Productions Ltd, pg 906

NORTH DAKOTA
Media Productions, pg 822

OHIO
Aztec Video Productions, pg 700
Mills James Productions, pg 828
R&B Communications Inc, pg 870
Take 1 Media Services, pg 906

OKLAHOMA
PDC Productions, pg 852

PENNSYLVANIA
Audio Visual Communications Inc, pg 694
Craig Recording Studios, pg 732
The Videohouse Inc, pg 929

AUDIO

Music Libraries—
Broadway & Hollywood (continued)

SOUTH CAROLINA

Genesis Creative, pg 769
Stages Video Productions, pg 899

TENNESSEE

Anode Inc, pg 686
Film House Inc, pg 760
Fricon Entertainment Co Inc, pg 766
Memphis Communications Corp, pg 823

TEXAS

The Editing Co, pg 750
FirstCom Music, pg 761
Horizon Film + Video Productions, pg 781
Mediaforce Productions, pg 822
The Music Bakery, pg 834
The Sound Lab Inc, pg 894
Sound Works, pg 894
South Coast Film & Video, pg 895
Stage Directions, pg 898
TM Studios Inc, pg 915

WISCONSIN

5th Floor Recording Co, pg 760
Mirror 34 Productions, pg 828
USAV Group Inc, pg 923

ONTARIO

Canamedia Inc, pg 715
Entertainment One Distribution, pg 754
GAPC (General Assembly Production Centre), pg 768
MCS Recording Studios, pg 821
Metalworks Recording Studios Inc, pg 824
Morning Music Ltd, pg 830
Nightingale Music Productions Inc, pg 841
Sound Ideas, pg 894
StockMusic.com, pg 901
Wanted! Sound + Picture, pg 933
Westar Music, pg 936

Music Libraries—
Children's

ALABAMA

Sound of Birmingham Productions, pg 894

ARIZONA

Direct Current Video Productions, pg 743
Film Creations Ltd, pg 760

ARKANSAS

White Diamond Productions LLC, pg 937

CALIFORNIA

Aliso Creek Productions Inc, pg 680
Associated Production Music LLC, pg 691
Berkeley Sound Artists Inc, pg 704
Creative Support Services/CSS Music, pg 733

5 Alarm Music, pg 762
Bruce Goldberg Inc, pg 772
Kaleidosound, pg 796
Killer Tracks, pg 798
K2B2 Records, pg 802
Lynch Communications, pg 813
Megatrax, pg 823
Moose School Productions, pg 830
Joseph Nicoletti Consulting-Promotion, pg 841
OGM Production Music, pg 844
OTR Studios, pg 848
Rhythms Productions (Tom Thumb Music), pg 874
Russ InVision Co/AbridgeClub.com, pg 879
Steve Shapiro Music, pg 885
Sonoton Music Library, pg 893
Still N' Motion, pg 901
Total Creative, pg 916

COLORADO

Tim Cissell Music, pg 725
Conly Productions, pg 730
Flashback Media Productions, pg 762
Los Angeles Post Music Inc, pg 811

DELAWARE

Ken-Del Productions Inc, pg 797

FLORIDA

Alliance Entertainment Corp (AEC) LLC, pg 680
LHV Audio Services, pg 807
Universal Studios Florida® Production Group, pg 922

ILLINOIS

Earwig Music Co Inc, pg 749
WEEK TV, pg 935
Woodside Avenue Music Productions Inc, pg 941

MAINE

WGME-TV, pg 936

MARYLAND

The Cutting Corporation, GraphicAudio® & Archival Sound Lab, pg 736

MASSACHUSETTS

Ben Rudnick and Friends, pg 878
Soundtrack Group, pg 895

MICHIGAN

AirBrands Event & Marketing Group, pg 679
GMP Music, pg 772
HighScope Press, pg 780

MISSOURI

Show-Me Audio-Visual, pg 887

NEBRASKA

JoeAudio, pg 794

NEVADA

JCS Video Productions, pg 793
Tanglewood Productions, pg 907

NEW JERSEY

CFP Video Productions Inc, pg 720
Milbrodt/Music & Sound Design, pg 827

Milgrom Productions, pg 827
TRF Production Music Libraries, pg 917
VCSvideo, pg 925

NEW MEXICO

Production Outfitters, pg 864
SouthWest Organizing Project (SWOP), pg 896

NEW YORK

A-List Quality Videographer, pg 671
Audio Network US Inc, pg 693
Getty Images Music, pg 770
HOThead, pg 782
Manhattan Center Studios Inc, pg 816
Manhattan Production Music Inc, pg 816
The Palmer Group, pg 850
Sony Music Entertainment, pg 893
TecNec Distributing, pg 909

NORTH CAROLINA

Pat Appleson Studios Inc, pg 687
Ladyslipper Music, pg 803
Take One Productions Ltd, pg 906

NORTH DAKOTA

Media Productions, pg 822

OHIO

Aztec Video Productions, pg 700
Mills James Productions, pg 828
R&B Communications Inc, pg 870
Take 1 Media Services, pg 906
Twin Sisters® Digital Media™, pg 920

OKLAHOMA

PDC Productions, pg 852

OREGON

Instant Music Now, pg 788

PENNSYLVANIA

Craig Recording Studios, pg 732
The Videohouse Inc, pg 929

RHODE ISLAND

Sound-FX-Design, pg 894

SOUTH CAROLINA

Stages Video Productions, pg 899

TENNESSEE

Anode Inc, pg 686
Film House Inc, pg 760
Fricon Entertainment Co Inc, pg 766
Spring Arbor Distributors Inc, pg 898
Word Label Group, pg 941

TEXAS

The Editing Co, pg 750
FirstCom Music, pg 761
Horizon Film + Video Productions, pg 781
The Music Bakery, pg 834
Production Garden Music, pg 863
Real to Reel Studios Inc, pg 871
The Sound Lab Inc, pg 894
Sound Works, pg 894
South Coast Film & Video, pg 895

VERMONT

Multicultural Media Inc, pg 833

VIRGINIA

Allied Media Corp, pg 681

WISCONSIN

5th Floor Recording Co, pg 760
USAV Group Inc, pg 923

ONTARIO

Canamedia Inc, pg 715
DebsVoice, pg 739
Entertainment One Distribution, pg 754
GAPC (General Assembly Production Centre), pg 768
MCS Recording Studios, pg 821
Metalworks Recording Studios Inc, pg 824
Morning Music Ltd, pg 830
Nightingale Music Productions Inc, pg 841
Sound Ideas, pg 894
StockMusic.com, pg 901
Wanted! Sound + Picture, pg 933
Westar Music, pg 936

Music Libraries—Choral

ALABAMA

Sound of Birmingham Productions, pg 894

ARIZONA

Direct Current Video Productions, pg 743
Film Creations Ltd, pg 760
Merestone, pg 823

ARKANSAS

White Diamond Productions LLC, pg 937

CALIFORNIA

Associated Production Music LLC, pg 691
Creative Support Services/CSS Music, pg 733
5 Alarm Music, pg 762
Kaleidosound, pg 796
Killer Tracks, pg 798
Lynch Communications, pg 813
Megatrax, pg 823
Joseph Nicoletti Consulting-Promotion, pg 841
OGM Production Music, pg 844
OTR Studios, pg 848
Steve Shapiro Music, pg 885
Sonoton Music Library, pg 893
Still N' Motion, pg 901
Total Creative, pg 916

COLORADO

Tim Cissell Music, pg 725
Flashback Media Productions, pg 762

DELAWARE

Ken-Del Productions Inc, pg 797

FLORIDA

Alliance Entertainment Corp (AEC) LLC, pg 680
Catholic Books & Tapes, pg 717
Children of Mary, pg 722

Hard Hat Radio Music Service, pg 776
LHV Audio Services, pg 807
Universal Studios Florida®
  Production Group, pg 922

ILLINOIS

Bolchazy - Carducci Publishers Inc, pg 708
WEEK TV, pg 935

MAINE

Serendipity Recordings, pg 884

MARYLAND

CPR MultiMedia Solutions, pg 732

MASSACHUSETTS

Soundtrack Group, pg 895

MISSOURI

Show-Me Audio-Visual, pg 887

NEBRASKA

JoeAudio, pg 794

NEVADA

Tanglewood Productions, pg 907

NEW JERSEY

CFP Video Productions Inc, pg 720
Milgrom Productions, pg 827
TRF Production Music Libraries, pg 917
VCSvideo, pg 925

NEW MEXICO

Production Outfitters, pg 864

NEW YORK

A-List Quality Videographer, pg 671
Manhattan Production Music Inc, pg 816
Mark Custom Recording Service Inc, pg 817
Sony Music Entertainment, pg 893
TecNec Distributing, pg 909

NORTH CAROLINA

Pat Appleson Studios Inc, pg 687
Ladyslipper Music, pg 803
Take One Productions Ltd, pg 906

NORTH DAKOTA

Media Productions, pg 822

OHIO

Aztec Video Productions, pg 700
Mills James Productions, pg 828
R&B Communications Inc, pg 870
Take 1 Media Services, pg 906

OKLAHOMA

PDC Productions, pg 852

TENNESSEE

Anode Inc, pg 686
Film House Inc, pg 760
Fricon Entertainment Co Inc, pg 766
Spring Arbor Distributors Inc, pg 898
Word Label Group, pg 941

TEXAS

FirstCom Music, pg 761
Mediaforce Productions, pg 822
The Music Bakery, pg 834
Real to Reel Studios Inc, pg 871
The Sound Lab Inc, pg 894
Sound Works, pg 894
South Coast Film & Video, pg 895

WISCONSIN

5th Floor Recording Co, pg 760
USAV Group Inc, pg 923

ONTARIO

Canamedia Inc, pg 715
Entertainment One Distribution, pg 754
MCS Recording Studios, pg 821
Metalworks Recording Studios Inc, pg 824
Nightingale Music Productions Inc, pg 841
StockMusic.com, pg 901
Wanted! Sound + Picture, pg 933
Westar Music, pg 936

QUEBEC

Muse Entertainment Enterprises, pg 834

Music Libraries—Classical

ALABAMA

Sound of Birmingham Productions, pg 894

ARIZONA

Direct Current Video Productions, pg 743
Film Creations Ltd, pg 760
Fire Power Music LLC, pg 761
Merestone, pg 823
SPEAK HOUSE Audio™, pg 896

ARKANSAS

White Diamond Productions LLC, pg 937

CALIFORNIA

Associated Production Music LLC, pg 691
Berkeley Sound Artists Inc, pg 704
CCI Digital, a DVS Company, pg 718
Creative Support Services/CSS Music, pg 733
Creative Technology, pg 733
5 Alarm Music, pg 762
Kaleidosound, pg 796
Killer Tracks, pg 798
K2B2 Records, pg 802
Lynch Communications, pg 813
Manchester Music Library Inc, pg 816
Megatrax, pg 823
The Music Kitchen Inc, pg 834
Joseph Nicoletti Consulting-Promotion, pg 841
OGM Production Music, pg 844
OTR Studios, pg 848
Polarity Post Production, pg 858
Rhythms Productions (Tom Thumb Music), pg 874
Steve Shapiro Music, pg 885
Sonoton Music Library, pg 893
Still N' Motion, pg 901
Telarc International Corp, pg 909
Total Creative, pg 916

Twisted Media Inc, pg 920
Visions Plus, pg 931

COLORADO

Tim Cissell Music, pg 725
Daylight Productions & Rentals, pg 739
Flashback Media Productions, pg 762
Transtar Entertainment Co Inc, pg 917

CONNECTICUT

Ironik Design & Post, pg 791
P&P Studios Inc, pg 851

DELAWARE

Ken-Del Productions Inc, pg 797

DISTRICT OF COLUMBIA

Smithsonian Folkways Recordings, pg 891

FLORIDA

Alliance Entertainment Corp (AEC) LLC, pg 680
Applebox Studio, pg 687
Kat Epple Music Productions, pg 755
LHV Audio Services, pg 807
Universal Studios Florida®
  Production Group, pg 922

GEORGIA

ECG Productions, pg 750
Guerrilla Productions LLC, pg 774

ILLINOIS

Bolchazy - Carducci Publishers Inc, pg 708
WEEK TV, pg 935
Woodside Avenue Music Productions Inc, pg 941

INDIANA

Indiana University Press, pg 786

KANSAS

KAKE-TV, pg 796

LOUISIANA

Centaur Records Inc, pg 719

MAINE

Serendipity Recordings, pg 884

MARYLAND

CPR MultiMedia Solutions, pg 732
The Cutting Corporation,
  GraphicAudio® & Archival
  Sound Lab, pg 736

MASSACHUSETTS

CommCreative, pg 728
Soundtrack Group, pg 895
TR Productions, pg 916
The Well-Tempered Music Library, pg 935

MICHIGAN

GMP Music, pg 772

MISSOURI

Show-Me Audio-Visual, pg 887

MONTANA

Jereco Studios Inc, pg 793

NEBRASKA

JoeAudio, pg 794

NEVADA

DVDs4Less, pg 748
JCS Video Productions, pg 793
Tanglewood Productions, pg 907

NEW JERSEY

CFP Video Productions Inc, pg 720
Milbrodt/Music & Sound Design, pg 827
Milgrom Productions, pg 827
NFL Films Music Library, pg 841
Richard Reiter Productions Inc, pg 873
TRF Production Music Libraries, pg 917
VCSvideo, pg 925

NEW MEXICO

Production Outfitters, pg 864

NEW YORK

A-List Quality Videographer, pg 671
Audio Network US Inc, pg 693
Beekman Books Inc, pg 703
de Wolfe Music USA, pg 739
Getty Images Music, pg 770
HOThead, pg 782
Manhattan Center Studios Inc, pg 816
Manhattan Production Music Inc, pg 816
Mark Custom Recording Service Inc, pg 817
New World Records, pg 840
The Palmer Group, pg 850
David Rapkin Audio Production, pg 870
Sony Music Commercial Music Group, pg 893
Sony Music Entertainment, pg 893
TecNec Distributing, pg 909
WNET/New York Public Media, pg 940
Yessian, pg 944

NORTH CAROLINA

Pat Appleson Studios Inc, pg 687
Duke Media Services, pg 747
Ladyslipper Music, pg 803
NASCAR Productions LLC, pg 835
Take One Productions Ltd, pg 906

NORTH DAKOTA

Media Productions, pg 822

OHIO

Aztec Video Productions, pg 700
Mills James Productions, pg 828
R&B Communications Inc, pg 870
Take 1 Media Services, pg 906
Twin Sisters® Digital Media™, pg 920

OKLAHOMA

Academic Media & Digital Services, pg 672
PDC Productions, pg 852

AUDIO

Music Libraries—Classical (continued)

OREGON

Instant Music Now, pg 788

PENNSYLVANIA

Craig Recording Studios, pg 732
The Videohouse Inc, pg 929

RHODE ISLAND

Sound-FX-Design, pg 894

SOUTH CAROLINA

Genesis Creative, pg 769
Stages Video Productions, pg 899

TENNESSEE

Anode Inc, pg 686
Film House Inc, pg 760
Fricon Entertainment Co Inc,
  pg 766
Memphis Communications Corp,
  pg 823

TEXAS

The Editing Co, pg 750
FirstCom Music, pg 761
Horizon Film + Video Productions,
  pg 781
Mediaforce Productions, pg 822
The Music Bakery, pg 834
Julye Newlin Productions Inc,
  pg 840
Pro Video & Film Equipment Co
  Inc, pg 863
Production Garden Music, pg 863
Real to Reel Studios Inc, pg 871
The Sound Lab Inc, pg 894
Sound Works, pg 894
South Coast Film & Video, pg 895

VERMONT

Multicultural Media Inc, pg 833

VIRGINIA

Allied Media Corp, pg 681

WASHINGTON

Crystal Records Inc, pg 735

WISCONSIN

5th Floor Recording Co, pg 760
Koss Corp, pg 801
Mirror 34 Productions, pg 828
USAV Group Inc, pg 923

ONTARIO

Canamedia Inc, pg 715
DebsVoice, pg 739
Entertainment One Distribution,
  pg 754
GAPC (General Assembly
  Production Centre), pg 768
Kool Music, pg 801
MCS Recording Studios, pg 821
Metalworks Recording Studios Inc,
  pg 824
Nightingale Music Productions Inc,
  pg 841
Sound Ideas, pg 894
StockMusic.com, pg 901
Wanted! Sound + Picture, pg 933
Westar Music, pg 936

Music Libraries— Commercial Jingles

ALABAMA

Sound of Birmingham Productions,
  pg 894

ARIZONA

Direct Current Video Productions,
  pg 743
Film Creations Ltd, pg 760
Merestone, pg 823

ARKANSAS

White Diamond Productions LLC,
  pg 937

CALIFORNIA

Aliso Creek Productions Inc, pg 680
Associated Production Music LLC,
  pg 691
Creative Media Recording, pg 733
Creative Support Services/CSS
  Music, pg 733
Diamond Dreams Music
  Productions, pg 741
Eye & I Productions, pg 758
5 Alarm Music, pg 762
Kaleidosound, pg 796
Killer Tracks, pg 798
Lynch Communications, pg 813
Manchester Music Library Inc,
  pg 816
Megatrax, pg 823
The Music Kitchen Inc, pg 834
Joseph Nicoletti Consulting-
  Promotion, pg 841
OTR Studios, pg 848
Polarity Post Production, pg 858
Pyramind Studios, pg 867
Reality Check Systems, pg 871
Steve Shapiro Music, pg 885
Sonoton Music Library, pg 893
Still N' Motion, pg 901
Total Creative, pg 916
Twisted Media Inc, pg 920

COLORADO

Tim Cissell Music, pg 725
Flashback Media Productions,
  pg 762
Los Angeles Post Music Inc, pg 811
Transtar Entertainment Co Inc,
  pg 917

DELAWARE

Ken-Del Productions Inc, pg 797

FLORIDA

Kat Epple Music Productions,
  pg 755
Jordan Klein Film & Video (JKFV),
  pg 795
LHV Audio Services, pg 807
Universal Studios Florida®
  Production Group, pg 922

GEORGIA

Beachwood Productions, pg 702
ECG Productions, pg 750
Guerrilla Productions LLC, pg 774

ILLINOIS

WEEK TV, pg 935
Woodside Avenue Music
  Productions Inc, pg 941

LOUISIANA

Disk Productions Inc, pg 743

MAINE

Serendipity Recordings, pg 884

MARYLAND

The Cutting Corporation,
  GraphicAudio® & Archival
  Sound Lab, pg 736

MASSACHUSETTS

Soundtrack Group, pg 895
The Well-Tempered Music Library,
  pg 935

MISSOURI

Show-Me Audio-Visual, pg 887

MONTANA

Jereco Studios Inc, pg 793

NEVADA

JCS Video Productions, pg 793
Tanglewood Productions, pg 907

NEW HAMPSHIRE

Channell One Video, pg 720

NEW JERSEY

CFP Video Productions Inc, pg 720
Milgrom Productions, pg 827
Richard Reiter Productions Inc,
  pg 873
TRF Production Music Libraries,
  pg 917
VCSvideo, pg 925

NEW MEXICO

Production Outfitters, pg 864

NEW YORK

A-List Quality Videographer,
  pg 671
Big Fish Production US, pg 705
Heavy Melody, pg 778
HOThead, pg 782
Manhattan Center Studios Inc,
  pg 816
The Palmer Group, pg 850
Sony Music Entertainment, pg 893
TecNec Distributing, pg 909
WNET/New York Public Media,
  pg 940

NORTH CAROLINA

Pat Appleson Studios Inc, pg 687
Duke Media Services, pg 747
Franklin Video Inc, pg 765
NASCAR Productions LLC, pg 835
Take One Productions Ltd, pg 906

NORTH DAKOTA

Media Productions, pg 822

OHIO

Aztec Video Productions, pg 700
Mills James Productions, pg 828
R&B Communications Inc, pg 870
Take 1 Media Services, pg 906

OKLAHOMA

PDC Productions, pg 852

OREGON

Instant Music Now, pg 788

PENNSYLVANIA

Monster Tracks, pg 829

RHODE ISLAND

Sound-FX-Design, pg 894

SOUTH CAROLINA

Genesis Creative, pg 769

TENNESSEE

Anode Inc, pg 686
Film House Inc, pg 760
Fricon Entertainment Co Inc,
  pg 766
Memphis Communications Corp,
  pg 823

TEXAS

Audiomoxie®, pg 695
The Editing Co, pg 750
FirstCom Music, pg 761
Mediaforce Productions, pg 822
The Music Bakery, pg 834
Julye Newlin Productions Inc,
  pg 840
The Sound Lab Inc, pg 894
Sound Works, pg 894
South Coast Film & Video, pg 895
Stage Directions, pg 898
Texas Heart Institute Visual
  Communication Services, pg 911
TM Studios Inc, pg 915
Tropikal Productions, pg 918

WEST VIRGINIA

Sweetsong Productions, pg 905

WISCONSIN

5th Floor Recording Co, pg 760
Mirror 34 Productions, pg 828
USAV Group Inc, pg 923
Video Wisconsin Inc, pg 929

MANITOBA

DACAPO Productions Inc, pg 737

ONTARIO

Canamedia Inc, pg 715
DebsVoice, pg 739
Entertainment One Distribution,
  pg 754
MCS Recording Studios, pg 821
Metalworks Recording Studios Inc,
  pg 824
Morning Music Ltd, pg 830
Nightingale Music Productions Inc,
  pg 841
Sound Ideas, pg 894
StockMusic.com, pg 901
Wanted! Sound + Picture, pg 933
Westar Music, pg 936

Music Libraries—Country

ALABAMA

Sound of Birmingham Productions,
  pg 894

ARIZONA

Direct Current Video Productions,
  pg 743
Film Creations Ltd, pg 760

Fire Power Music LLC, pg 761
Merestone, pg 823

ARKANSAS

White Diamond Productions LLC,
pg 937

CALIFORNIA

Aliso Creek Productions Inc, pg 680
Associated Production Music LLC,
pg 691
CCI Digital, a DVS Company,
pg 718
Creative Support Services/CSS
Music, pg 733
5 Alarm Music, pg 762
Bruce Goldberg Inc, pg 772
Kaleidosound, pg 796
Killer Tracks, pg 798
Lynch Communications, pg 813
Megatrax, pg 823
The Music Kitchen Inc, pg 834
Joseph Nicoletti Consulting-
Promotion, pg 841
OGM Production Music, pg 844
OTR Studios, pg 848
Polarity Post Production, pg 858
Pyramind Studios, pg 867
Steve Shapiro Music, pg 885
Sonoton Music Library, pg 893
Still N' Motion, pg 901
Total Creative, pg 916
Visions Plus, pg 931

COLORADO

Tim Cissell Music, pg 725
Flashback Media Productions,
pg 762
Los Angeles Post Music Inc, pg 811
Transtar Entertainment Co Inc,
pg 917

CONNECTICUT

P&P Studios Inc, pg 851

DELAWARE

Ken-Del Productions Inc, pg 797

DISTRICT OF COLUMBIA

Library of Congress, Motion
Picture, Broadcasting & Recorded
Sound Division, pg 807

FLORIDA

Alliance Entertainment Corp (AEC)
LLC, pg 680
Applebox Studio, pg 687
Hard Hat Radio Music Service,
pg 776
LHV Audio Services, pg 807
Universal Studios Florida®
Production Group, pg 922

GEORGIA

Beachwood Productions, pg 702

ILLINOIS

WEEK TV, pg 935
Woodside Avenue Music
Productions Inc, pg 941

LOUISIANA

Flat Town Music Co, pg 762

MARYLAND

Adelphi Records Inc, pg 676
The Cutting Corporation,
GraphicAudio® & Archival
Sound Lab, pg 736

MASSACHUSETTS

Soundtrack Group, pg 895

MICHIGAN

GMP Music, pg 772

MISSOURI

Show-Me Audio-Visual, pg 887

NEBRASKA

JoeAudio, pg 794

NEVADA

DVDs4Less, pg 748
JCS Video Productions, pg 793
Tanglewood Productions, pg 907

NEW JERSEY

Milbrodt/Music & Sound Design,
pg 827
Milgrom Productions, pg 827
NFL Films Music Library, pg 841
Richard Reiter Productions Inc,
pg 873
TRF Production Music Libraries,
pg 917
VCSvideo, pg 925

NEW MEXICO

Production Outfitters, pg 864

NEW YORK

A-List Quality Videographer,
pg 671
Audio Network US Inc, pg 693
Beekman Books Inc, pg 703
de Wolfe Music USA, pg 739
Getty Images Music, pg 770
Historic Films, pg 780
HOThead, pg 782
Manhattan Production Music Inc,
pg 816
Mother West, pg 831
New World Records, pg 840
The Palmer Group, pg 850
David Rapkin Audio Production,
pg 870
Sony Music Commercial Music
Group, pg 893
Sony Music Entertainment, pg 893
TecNec Distributing, pg 909
Yessian, pg 944

NORTH CAROLINA

Pat Appleson Studios Inc, pg 687
Ladyslipper Music, pg 803
Take One Productions Ltd, pg 906

NORTH DAKOTA

Media Productions, pg 822

OHIO

Aztec Video Productions, pg 700
Mills James Productions, pg 828
R&B Communications Inc, pg 870
Take 1 Media Services, pg 906

OKLAHOMA

PDC Productions, pg 852

OREGON

Instant Music Now, pg 788

PENNSYLVANIA

Craig Recording Studios, pg 732
Monster Tracks, pg 829
The Videohouse Inc, pg 929

RHODE ISLAND

Sound-FX-Design, pg 894

SOUTH CAROLINA

Genesis Creative, pg 769
Stages Video Productions, pg 899

TENNESSEE

Anode Inc, pg 686
Film House Inc, pg 760
Fricon Entertainment Co Inc,
pg 766
Sun Entertainment Corp, pg 903
Word Label Group, pg 941

TEXAS

Audiomoxie®, pg 695
The Editing Co, pg 750
FirstCom Music, pg 761
Mediaforce Productions, pg 822
The Music Bakery, pg 834
Julye Newlin Productions Inc,
pg 840
Production Garden Music, pg 863
Real to Reel Studios Inc, pg 871
The Samuels Co, pg 879
The Sound Lab Inc, pg 894
Sound Works, pg 894
South Coast Film & Video, pg 895
TM Studios Inc, pg 915
TopCat Records LLC, pg 915
The Yesterday USA Radio
Networks, pg 944

VIRGINIA

Allied Media Corp, pg 681

WASHINGTON

Avast! Recording Co, pg 697

WISCONSIN

5th Floor Recording Co, pg 760
Mirror 34 Productions, pg 828
USAV Group Inc, pg 923

ONTARIO

Canamedia Inc, pg 715
DebsVoice, pg 739
Entertainment One Distribution,
pg 754
The Hollywood Edge, pg 780
Kool Music, pg 801
MCS Recording Studios, pg 821
Metalworks Recording Studios Inc,
pg 824
Morning Music Ltd, pg 830
Nightingale Music Productions Inc,
pg 841
Sound Ideas, pg 894
StockMusic.com, pg 901
Wanted! Sound + Picture, pg 933
Westar Music, pg 936

Music Libraries—Easy Listening

ALABAMA

Sound of Birmingham Productions,
pg 894

ARIZONA

Direct Current Video Productions,
pg 743
Film Creations Ltd, pg 760
Fire Power Music LLC, pg 761
Merestone, pg 823

ARKANSAS

White Diamond Productions LLC,
pg 937

CALIFORNIA

Aliso Creek Productions Inc, pg 680
Associated Production Music LLC,
pg 691
Berkeley Sound Artists Inc, pg 704
Creative Support Services/CSS
Music, pg 733
Creative Technology, pg 733
Diamond Dreams Music
Productions, pg 741
5 Alarm Music, pg 762
Bruce Goldberg Inc, pg 772
Increase Video/Silver Mine Video,
pg 786
Kaleidosound, pg 796
Killer Tracks, pg 798
Lynch Communications, pg 813
Megatrax, pg 823
The Music Kitchen Inc, pg 834
Joseph Nicoletti Consulting-
Promotion, pg 841
OGM Production Music, pg 844
Polarity Post Production, pg 858
Pyramind Studios, pg 867
Saturn Studios, pg 881
Steve Shapiro Music, pg 885
Sonoton Music Library, pg 893
Still N' Motion, pg 901
Timeless Productions, pg 914
Total Creative, pg 916
Visions Plus, pg 931
Welk Music Group, pg 935

COLORADO

Tim Cissell Music, pg 725
Conly Productions, pg 730
Daylight Productions & Rentals,
pg 739
Flashback Media Productions,
pg 762
Los Angeles Post Music Inc, pg 811
Transtar Entertainment Co Inc,
pg 917

CONNECTICUT

Ironik Design & Post, pg 791

DELAWARE

Ken-Del Productions Inc, pg 797

FLORIDA

Alliance Entertainment Corp (AEC)
LLC, pg 680
Kat Epple Music Productions,
pg 755
Hard Hat Radio Music Service,
pg 776
LHV Audio Services, pg 807

AUDIO

Music Libraries—Easy Listening (continued)

FLORIDA (continued)

Times-Square Fantasy Theatre, pg 914
Universal Studios Florida® Production Group, pg 922

GEORGIA

Beachwood Productions, pg 702
ECG Productions, pg 750

ILLINOIS

Creative Technology (CT), pg 733
WEEK TV, pg 935

LOUISIANA

Flat Town Music Co, pg 762

MAINE

Serendipity Recordings, pg 884

MASSACHUSETTS

Soundtrack Group, pg 895
The Well-Tempered Music Library, pg 935

MICHIGAN

GMP Music, pg 772

MISSOURI

Show-Me Audio-Visual, pg 887

MONTANA

Jereco Studios Inc, pg 793

NEBRASKA

JoeAudio, pg 794

NEVADA

JCS Video Productions, pg 793
Tanglewood Productions, pg 907

NEW JERSEY

CFP Video Productions Inc, pg 720
Milgrom Productions, pg 827
Richard Reiter Productions Inc, pg 873
TRF Production Music Libraries, pg 917
VCSvideo, pg 925

NEW MEXICO

Production Outfitters, pg 864

NEW YORK

A-List Quality Videographer, pg 671
Audio Network US Inc, pg 693
Getty Images Music, pg 770
Heavy Melody, pg 778
Manhattan Production Music Inc, pg 816
Sony Music Entertainment, pg 893
TecNec Distributing, pg 909

NORTH CAROLINA

Pat Appleson Studios Inc, pg 687
NASCAR Productions LLC, pg 835
Take One Productions Ltd, pg 906

NORTH DAKOTA

Media Productions, pg 822

OHIO

Aztec Video Productions, pg 700
Mills James Productions, pg 828
R&B Communications Inc, pg 870
Take 1 Media Services, pg 906
Twin Sisters® Digital Media™, pg 920

OKLAHOMA

Academic Media & Digital Services, pg 672
PDC Productions, pg 852

OREGON

Instant Music Now, pg 788

PENNSYLVANIA

Craig Recording Studios, pg 732
The Videohouse Inc, pg 929

RHODE ISLAND

Sound-FX-Design, pg 894

SOUTH CAROLINA

Genesis Creative, pg 769
Stages Video Productions, pg 899

TENNESSEE

Anode Inc, pg 686
Film House Inc, pg 760
Fricon Entertainment Co Inc, pg 766

TEXAS

The Editing Co, pg 750
FirstCom Music, pg 761
Horizon Film + Video Productions, pg 781
Mediaforce Productions, pg 822
The Music Bakery, pg 834
Julye Newlin Productions Inc, pg 840
Production Garden Music, pg 863
Real to Reel Studios Inc, pg 871
The Sound Lab Inc, pg 894
Sound Works, pg 894
South Coast Film & Video, pg 895
TM Studios Inc, pg 915

VIRGINIA

Allied Media Corp, pg 681

WASHINGTON

Avast! Recording Co, pg 697

WEST VIRGINIA

Sweetsong Productions, pg 905

WISCONSIN

5th Floor Recording Co, pg 760
Mirror 34 Productions, pg 828
USAV Group Inc, pg 923

ONTARIO

Canamedia Inc, pg 715
DebsVoice, pg 739
Entertainment One Distribution, pg 754
GAPC (General Assembly Production Centre), pg 768
Kool Music, pg 801
MCS Recording Studios, pg 821

Metalworks Recording Studios Inc, pg 824
Morning Music Ltd, pg 830
Nightingale Music Productions Inc, pg 841
Sound Ideas, pg 894
StockMusic.com, pg 901
Video Excellence Productions, pg 927
Wanted! Sound + Picture, pg 933
Westar Music, pg 936

Music Libraries— Electronic

ALABAMA

Sound of Birmingham Productions, pg 894

ARIZONA

Direct Current Video Productions, pg 743
Film Creations Ltd, pg 760
Fire Power Music LLC, pg 761
Merestone, pg 823
SPEAK HOUSE Audio™, pg 896

ARKANSAS

White Diamond Productions LLC, pg 937

CALIFORNIA

Aliso Creek Productions Inc, pg 680
Artichoke Productions, pg 690
Associated Production Music LLC, pg 691
Berkeley Sound Artists Inc, pg 704
CCI Digital, a DVS Company, pg 718
Creative Support Services/CSS Music, pg 733
Creative Technology, pg 733
Diamond Dreams Music Productions, pg 741
Eye & I Productions, pg 758
5 Alarm Music, pg 762
Kaleidosound, pg 796
Killer Tracks, pg 798
Lynch Communications, pg 813
Manchester Music Library Inc, pg 816
Megatrax, pg 823
The Music Kitchen Inc, pg 834
Joseph Nicoletti Consulting-Promotion, pg 841
OGM Production Music, pg 844
OTR Studios, pg 848
Pyramind Studios, pg 867
Reality Check Systems, pg 871
Rhythms Productions (Tom Thumb Music), pg 874
Saturn Studios, pg 881
Steve Shapiro Music, pg 885
Sonoton Music Library, pg 893
Still N' Motion, pg 901
Timeless Productions, pg 914
Total Creative, pg 916
Twisted Media Inc, pg 920

COLORADO

Tim Cissell Music, pg 725
Conly Productions, pg 730
Daylight Productions & Rentals, pg 739
Flashback Media Productions, pg 762
Los Angeles Post Music Inc, pg 811
Transtar Entertainment Co Inc, pg 917

CONNECTICUT

Ironik Design & Post, pg 791
P&P Studios Inc, pg 851

DELAWARE

Ken-Del Productions Inc, pg 797

FLORIDA

Alliance Entertainment Corp (AEC) LLC, pg 680
Applebox Studio, pg 687
Kat Epple Music Productions, pg 755
LHV Audio Services, pg 807
Universal Studios Florida® Production Group, pg 922

GEORGIA

Beachwood Productions, pg 702
ECG Productions, pg 750
Guerrilla Productions LLC, pg 774

ILLINOIS

Convenience, pg 731
Jim Passin Productions, pg 852
Video Impressions, pg 928
WEEK TV, pg 935
Woodside Avenue Music Productions Inc, pg 941

LOUISIANA

Centaur Records Inc, pg 719

MAINE

WGME-TV, pg 936

MARYLAND

CPR MultiMedia Solutions, pg 732
The Cutting Corporation, GraphicAudio® & Archival Sound Lab, pg 736

MASSACHUSETTS

CommCreative, pg 728
Soundtrack Group, pg 895
TR Productions, pg 916
The Well-Tempered Music Library, pg 935

MICHIGAN

GMP Music, pg 772

MISSOURI

Show-Me Audio-Visual, pg 887

MONTANA

Jereco Studios Inc, pg 793

NEBRASKA

JoeAudio, pg 794

NEVADA

DVDs4Less, pg 748
Tanglewood Productions, pg 907

NEW HAMPSHIRE

Channell One Video, pg 720

NEW JERSEY

CFP Video Productions Inc, pg 720
Milbrodt/Music & Sound Design, pg 827
Milgrom Productions, pg 827

NFL Films Music Library, pg 841
Richard Reiter Productions Inc,
  pg 873
TRF Production Music Libraries,
  pg 917
VCSvideo, pg 925

NEW MEXICO

Production Outfitters, pg 864

NEW YORK

A-List Quality Videographer,
  pg 671
Audio Network US Inc, pg 693
Aural Gratification Inc, pg 695
de Wolfe Music USA, pg 739
Getty Images Music, pg 770
Heavy Melody, pg 778
HOThead, pg 782
IAI Records & Video, pg 783
Manhattan Production Music Inc,
  pg 816
Mother West, pg 831
New World Records, pg 840
The Palmer Group, pg 850
David Rapkin Audio Production,
  pg 870
Sear Sound, pg 883
Sony Music Commercial Music
  Group, pg 893
Sony Music Entertainment, pg 893
TecNec Distributing, pg 909
Yessian, pg 944

NORTH CAROLINA

Pat Appleson Studios Inc, pg 687
The Communications Group Inc,
  pg 729
Franklin Video Inc, pg 765
NASCAR Productions LLC, pg 835
Take One Productions Ltd, pg 906

NORTH DAKOTA

Media Productions, pg 822

OHIO

Aztec Video Productions, pg 700
Mills James Productions, pg 828
R&B Communications Inc, pg 870
Take 1 Media Services, pg 906

OKLAHOMA

Academic Media & Digital
  Services, pg 672
PDC Productions, pg 852

OREGON

Instant Music Now, pg 788

PENNSYLVANIA

Audio Visual Communications Inc,
  pg 694
Monster Tracks, pg 829
The Videohouse Inc, pg 929

RHODE ISLAND

Sound-FX-Design, pg 894

SOUTH CAROLINA

DaviSound, pg 739
Genesis Creative, pg 769
Stages Video Productions, pg 899

TENNESSEE

Anode Inc, pg 686
Film House Inc, pg 760

Fricon Entertainment Co Inc,
  pg 766
Memphis Communications Corp,
  pg 823

TEXAS

Audiomoxie®, pg 695
The Editing Co, pg 750
FirstCom Music, pg 761
The Music Bakery, pg 834
Julye Newlin Productions Inc,
  pg 840
Production Garden Music, pg 863
Real to Reel Studios Inc, pg 871
The Sound Lab Inc, pg 894
Sound Works, pg 894
South Coast Film & Video, pg 895
Stage Directions, pg 898
Texas Heart Institute Visual
  Communication Services, pg 911
TM Studios Inc, pg 915

WASHINGTON

Avast! Recording Co, pg 697

WISCONSIN

5th Floor Recording Co, pg 760
Mirror 34 Productions, pg 828
USAV Group Inc, pg 923

ONTARIO

Canamedia Inc, pg 715
DebsVoice, pg 739
Entertainment One Distribution,
  pg 754
GAPC (General Assembly
  Production Centre), pg 768
Kool Music, pg 801
MCS Recording Studios, pg 821
Metalworks Recording Studios Inc,
  pg 824
Morning Music Ltd, pg 830
Nightingale Music Productions Inc,
  pg 841
Sound Ideas, pg 894
StockMusic.com, pg 901
Video Excellence Productions,
  pg 927
Wanted! Sound + Picture, pg 933
Westar Music, pg 936

Music Libraries—Ethnic & International

ALABAMA

Sound of Birmingham Productions,
  pg 894

ARIZONA

Direct Current Video Productions,
  pg 743
Drumbeat Indian Arts Inc, pg 747
Film Creations Ltd, pg 760
Merestone, pg 823

ARKANSAS

White Diamond Productions LLC,
  pg 937

CALIFORNIA

Ancient Future, pg 685
Associated Production Music LLC,
  pg 691
CCI Digital, a DVS Company,
  pg 718
Creative Support Services/CSS
  Music, pg 733

Diamond Dreams Music
  Productions, pg 741
Eye & I Productions, pg 758
5 Alarm Music, pg 762
Kaleidosound, pg 796
Killer Tracks, pg 798
Lynch Communications, pg 813
Megatrax, pg 823
The Music Kitchen Inc, pg 834
Joseph Nicoletti Consulting-
  Promotion, pg 841
OGM Production Music, pg 844
Osho Viha Information Center &
  Book Distributors, pg 848
OTR Studios, pg 848
Steve Shapiro Music, pg 885
Sonoton Music Library, pg 893
Still N' Motion, pg 901
Total Creative, pg 916
Twisted Media Inc, pg 920
Visions Plus, pg 931

COLORADO

Tim Cissell Music, pg 725
Daylight Productions & Rentals,
  pg 739
Flashback Media Productions,
  pg 762
Los Angeles Post Music Inc, pg 811

CONNECTICUT

Ironik Design & Post, pg 791

DELAWARE

Ken-Del Productions Inc, pg 797

DISTRICT OF COLUMBIA

Sano Videos, pg 880

FLORIDA

Alliance Entertainment Corp (AEC)
  LLC, pg 680
Applebox Studio, pg 687
Kat Epple Music Productions,
  pg 755
LHV Audio Services, pg 807
Universal Studios Florida®
  Production Group, pg 922

GEORGIA

Beachwood Productions, pg 702
Hottrax Records, pg 782

ILLINOIS

Bolchazy - Carducci Publishers Inc,
  pg 708
Video Impressions, pg 928
WEEK TV, pg 935

MARYLAND

Adelphi Records Inc, pg 676
The Cutting Corporation,
  GraphicAudio® & Archival
  Sound Lab, pg 736

MASSACHUSETTS

Revels Records, pg 874
Soundtrack Group, pg 895

MICHIGAN

GMP Music, pg 772
Rebirth Inc, pg 871

MISSOURI

Show-Me Audio-Visual, pg 887

MONTANA

Jereco Studios Inc, pg 793

NEBRASKA

JoeAudio, pg 794

NEVADA

JCS Video Productions, pg 793
Tanglewood Productions, pg 907

NEW HAMPSHIRE

French American Music Enterprises,
  pg 765

NEW JERSEY

Milbrodt/Music & Sound Design,
  pg 827
Milgrom Productions, pg 827
Shanachie Entertainment Corp,
  pg 885
TRF Production Music Libraries,
  pg 917
VCSvideo, pg 925

NEW MEXICO

Production Outfitters, pg 864

NEW YORK

A-List Quality Videographer,
  pg 671
Beekman Books Inc, pg 703
Getty Images Music, pg 770
Heavy Melody, pg 778
HOThead, pg 782
Manhattan Production Music Inc,
  pg 816
Mother West, pg 831
The Palmer Group, pg 850
Sony Music Entertainment, pg 893
TecNec Distributing, pg 909
VIEW Inc (Video International
  Entertainment World Inc), pg 930
Yessian, pg 944

NORTH CAROLINA

Pat Appleson Studios Inc, pg 687
Ladyslipper Music, pg 803
Take One Productions Ltd, pg 906

NORTH DAKOTA

Media Productions, pg 822

OHIO

Aztec Video Productions, pg 700
Mills James Productions, pg 828
R&B Communications Inc, pg 870
Take 1 Media Services, pg 906

OKLAHOMA

PDC Productions, pg 852

PENNSYLVANIA

Monster Tracks, pg 829
The Videohouse Inc, pg 929

RHODE ISLAND

Sound-FX-Design, pg 894

SOUTH CAROLINA

Genesis Creative, pg 769
Stages Video Productions, pg 899

AUDIO

Music Libraries—Ethnic & International (continued)

TENNESSEE

Anode Inc, pg 686
Film House Inc, pg 760
Fricon Entertainment Co Inc, pg 766
Word Label Group, pg 941

TEXAS

Audiomoxie®, pg 695
The Editing Co, pg 750
FirstCom Music, pg 761
Horizon Film + Video Productions, pg 781
Mediaforce Productions, pg 822
The Music Bakery, pg 834
Julye Newlin Productions Inc, pg 840
Production Garden Music, pg 863
Real to Reel Studios Inc, pg 871
The Sound Lab Inc, pg 894
Sound Works, pg 894
South Coast Film & Video, pg 895
TM Studios Inc, pg 915
Tropikal Productions, pg 918

VERMONT

Inner Traditions International, pg 788
Multicultural Media Inc, pg 833

VIRGINIA

Allied Media Corp, pg 681

WISCONSIN

5th Floor Recording Co, pg 760
USAV Group Inc, pg 923

ONTARIO

Canamedia Inc, pg 715
DebsVoice, pg 739
Entertainment One Distribution, pg 754
GAPC (General Assembly Production Centre), pg 768
Kool Music, pg 801
MCS Recording Studios, pg 821
Metalworks Recording Studios Inc, pg 824
Morning Music Ltd, pg 830
Nightingale Music Productions Inc, pg 841
Sound Ideas, pg 894
StockMusic.com, pg 901
Wanted! Sound + Picture, pg 933
Westar Music, pg 936

Music Libraries—Folk

ALABAMA

Sound of Birmingham Productions, pg 894

ARIZONA

Direct Current Video Productions, pg 743
Film Creations Ltd, pg 760
Fire Power Music LLC, pg 761
Merestone, pg 823

ARKANSAS

White Diamond Productions LLC, pg 937

CALIFORNIA

Aliso Creek Productions Inc, pg 680
Associated Production Music LLC, pg 691
Creative Support Services/CSS Music, pg 733
Diamond Dreams Music Productions, pg 741
5 Alarm Music, pg 762
Bruce Goldberg Inc, pg 772
Kaleidosound, pg 796
Killer Tracks, pg 798
Lynch Communications, pg 813
Megatrax, pg 823
The Music Kitchen Inc, pg 834
Joseph Nicoletti Consulting-Promotion, pg 841
OGM Production Music, pg 844
OTR Studios, pg 848
Steve Shapiro Music, pg 885
Sonoton Music Library, pg 893
Still N' Motion, pg 901
Total Creative, pg 916
Welk Music Group, pg 935

COLORADO

Tim Cissell Music, pg 725
Conly Productions, pg 730
Flashback Media Productions, pg 762
Los Angeles Post Music Inc, pg 811
Transtar Entertainment Co Inc, pg 917

CONNECTICUT

American Melody, pg 683
Ironik Design & Post, pg 791

DELAWARE

Ken-Del Productions Inc, pg 797

FLORIDA

Alliance Entertainment Corp (AEC) LLC, pg 680
Applebox Studio, pg 687
Kat Epple Music Productions, pg 755
LHV Audio Services, pg 807
Universal Studios Florida® Production Group, pg 922

GEORGIA

Beachwood Productions, pg 702

ILLINOIS

Video Impressions, pg 928
WEEK TV, pg 935
Woodside Avenue Music Productions Inc, pg 941

MAINE

Serendipity Recordings, pg 884

MARYLAND

Adelphi Records Inc, pg 676

MASSACHUSETTS

Revels Records, pg 874
Ben Rudnick and Friends, pg 878
Soundtrack Group, pg 895
The Well-Tempered Music Library, pg 935

MICHIGAN

GMP Music, pg 772
HighScope Press, pg 780

MISSOURI

Show-Me Audio-Visual, pg 887

MONTANA

Jereco Studios Inc, pg 793

NEBRASKA

JoeAudio, pg 794

NEVADA

JCS Video Productions, pg 793
Tanglewood Productions, pg 907

NEW HAMPSHIRE

French American Music Enterprises, pg 765

NEW JERSEY

Milgrom Productions, pg 827
TRF Production Music Libraries, pg 917
VCSvideo, pg 925

NEW MEXICO

Production Outfitters, pg 864

NEW YORK

A-List Quality Videographer, pg 671
Audio Network US Inc, pg 693
Beekman Books Inc, pg 703
Dyer-Bennet Records, pg 748
Getty Images Music, pg 770
Heavy Melody, pg 778
Manhattan Production Music Inc, pg 816
Mother West, pg 831
Sony Music Entertainment, pg 893
TecNec Distributing, pg 909
Yessian, pg 944

NORTH CAROLINA

Pat Appleson Studios Inc, pg 687
Duke Media Services, pg 747
Ladyslipper Music, pg 803
Take One Productions Ltd, pg 906

NORTH DAKOTA

Media Productions, pg 822

OHIO

Aztec Video Productions, pg 700
Mills James Productions, pg 828
R&B Communications Inc, pg 870
Take 1 Media Services, pg 906

OKLAHOMA

PDC Productions, pg 852

PENNSYLVANIA

Monster Tracks, pg 829
The Videohouse Inc, pg 929

RHODE ISLAND

Sound-FX-Design, pg 894

SOUTH CAROLINA

Genesis Creative, pg 769
Stages Video Productions, pg 899

TENNESSEE

Anode Inc, pg 686
Center for Southern Folklore Inc, pg 719

MISSOURI

Film House Inc, pg 760
Fricon Entertainment Co Inc, pg 766

TEXAS

The Editing Co, pg 750
FirstCom Music, pg 761
The Music Bakery, pg 834
Julye Newlin Productions Inc, pg 840
Production Garden Music, pg 863
The Sound Lab Inc, pg 894
South Coast Film & Video, pg 895

VERMONT

Multicultural Media Inc, pg 833

VIRGINIA

Allied Media Corp, pg 681

WASHINGTON

Avast! Recording Co, pg 697

WISCONSIN

5th Floor Recording Co, pg 760
USAV Group Inc, pg 923

ONTARIO

Canamedia Inc, pg 715
DebsVoice, pg 739
Entertainment One Distribution, pg 754
Kool Music, pg 801
MCS Recording Studios, pg 821
Metalworks Recording Studios Inc, pg 824
Morning Music Ltd, pg 830
Nightingale Music Productions Inc, pg 841
Sound Ideas, pg 894
StockMusic.com, pg 901
Wanted! Sound + Picture, pg 933
Westar Music, pg 936

Music Libraries—Holiday

ALABAMA

Sound of Birmingham Productions, pg 894

ARIZONA

Direct Current Video Productions, pg 743
Film Creations Ltd, pg 760
Fire Power Music LLC, pg 761
Merestone, pg 823

ARKANSAS

White Diamond Productions LLC, pg 937

CALIFORNIA

Aliso Creek Productions Inc, pg 680
Associated Production Music LLC, pg 691
Creative Support Services/CSS Music, pg 733
5 Alarm Music, pg 762
Bruce Goldberg Inc, pg 772
Kaleidosound, pg 796
Killer Tracks, pg 798
Lynch Communications, pg 813
Megatrax, pg 823
The Music Kitchen Inc, pg 834

Joseph Nicoletti Consulting-
Promotion, pg 841
OGM Production Music, pg 844
Steve Shapiro Music, pg 885
Sonoton Music Library, pg 893
Still N' Motion, pg 901
Welk Music Group, pg 935

COLORADO

Tim Cissell Music, pg 725
Daylight Productions & Rentals,
pg 739
Flashback Media Productions,
pg 762
Los Angeles Post Music Inc, pg 811
Transtar Entertainment Co Inc,
pg 917

DELAWARE

Ken-Del Productions Inc, pg 797

FLORIDA

Alliance Entertainment Corp (AEC)
LLC, pg 680
Applebox Studio, pg 687
Catholic Books & Tapes, pg 717
Kat Epple Music Productions,
pg 755
LHV Audio Services, pg 807
Universal Studios Florida®
Production Group, pg 922

GEORGIA

Beachwood Productions, pg 702
ECG Productions, pg 750
Guerrilla Productions LLC, pg 774

ILLINOIS

Video Impressions, pg 928
WEEK TV, pg 935

LOUISIANA

Flat Town Music Co, pg 762

MAINE

Serendipity Recordings, pg 884

MARYLAND

Adelphi Records Inc, pg 676

MASSACHUSETTS

Revels Records, pg 874
Soundtrack Group, pg 895

MICHIGAN

GMP Music, pg 772

MISSOURI

Show-Me Audio-Visual, pg 887

NEBRASKA

JoeAudio, pg 794

NEVADA

JCS Video Productions, pg 793
Tanglewood Productions, pg 907

NEW HAMPSHIRE

French American Music Enterprises,
pg 765

NEW JERSEY

CFP Video Productions Inc, pg 720
Milgrom Productions, pg 827

TRF Production Music Libraries,
pg 917
VCSvideo, pg 925

NEW MEXICO

Production Outfitters, pg 864

NEW YORK

A-List Quality Videographer,
pg 671
Audio Network US Inc, pg 693
Beekman Books Inc, pg 703
Getty Images Music, pg 770
Manhattan Production Music Inc,
pg 816
Mark Custom Recording Service
Inc, pg 817
Mother West, pg 831
Sony Music Entertainment, pg 893
TecNec Distributing, pg 909
Yessian, pg 944

NORTH CAROLINA

Pat Appleson Studios Inc, pg 687
Duke Media Services, pg 747
Franklin Video Inc, pg 765
Ladyslipper Music, pg 803
NASCAR Productions LLC, pg 835
Take One Productions Ltd, pg 906

NORTH DAKOTA

Media Productions, pg 822

OHIO

Aztec Video Productions, pg 700
Mills James Productions, pg 828
R&B Communications Inc, pg 870
Take 1 Media Services, pg 906

OKLAHOMA

PDC Productions, pg 852

OREGON

Instant Music Now, pg 788

PENNSYLVANIA

Craig Recording Studios, pg 732
The Videohouse Inc, pg 929

RHODE ISLAND

Sound-FX-Design, pg 894

SOUTH CAROLINA

Genesis Creative, pg 769
Stages Video Productions, pg 899

TENNESSEE

Anode Inc, pg 686
Film House Inc, pg 760
Fricon Entertainment Co Inc,
pg 766
Word Label Group, pg 941

TEXAS

The Editing Co, pg 750
FirstCom Music, pg 761
Mediaforce Productions, pg 822
The Music Bakery, pg 834
Julye Newlin Productions Inc,
pg 840
Production Garden Music, pg 863
Real to Reel Studios Inc, pg 871
The Sound Lab Inc, pg 894
Sound Works, pg 894
South Coast Film & Video, pg 895
TM Studios Inc, pg 915

VERMONT

Multicultural Media Inc, pg 833

VIRGINIA

Allied Media Corp, pg 681

WEST VIRGINIA

Sweetsong Productions, pg 905

WISCONSIN

5th Floor Recording Co, pg 760
USAV Group Inc, pg 923

ONTARIO

Canamedia Inc, pg 715
DebsVoice, pg 739
Entertainment One Distribution,
pg 754
MCS Recording Studios, pg 821
Metalworks Recording Studios Inc,
pg 824
Morning Music Ltd, pg 830
Nightingale Music Productions Inc,
pg 841
Sound Ideas, pg 894
StockMusic.com, pg 901
Wanted! Sound + Picture, pg 933
Westar Music, pg 936

Music Libraries— Instrumental

ALABAMA

Sound of Birmingham Productions,
pg 894

ARIZONA

Direct Current Video Productions,
pg 743
Film Creations Ltd, pg 760
Fire Power Music LLC, pg 761
Merestone, pg 823
SPEAK HOUSE Audio™, pg 896

ARKANSAS

White Diamond Productions LLC,
pg 937

CALIFORNIA

Aliso Creek Productions Inc, pg 680
Ancient Future, pg 685
Associated Production Music LLC,
pg 691
Berkeley Sound Artists Inc, pg 704
Creative Support Services/CSS
Music, pg 733
Creative Technology, pg 733
Diamond Dreams Music
Productions, pg 741
Eye & I Productions, pg 758
5 Alarm Music, pg 762
Bruce Goldberg Inc, pg 772
Increase Video/Silver Mine Video,
pg 786
Kaleidosound, pg 796
Killer Tracks, pg 798
K2B2 Records, pg 802
Lynch Communications, pg 813
Manchester Music Library Inc,
pg 816
Megatrax, pg 823
The Music Kitchen Inc, pg 834
Joseph Nicoletti Consulting-
Promotion, pg 841
OGM Production Music, pg 844
Osho Viha Information Center &
Book Distributors, pg 848

OTR Studios, pg 848
Polarity Post Production, pg 858
Pyramind Studios, pg 867
Reality Check Systems, pg 871
Regent Press Publishers & Printers,
pg 873
Saturn Studios, pg 881
Steve Shapiro Music, pg 885
Sonoton Music Library, pg 893
Still N' Motion, pg 901
Timeless Productions, pg 914
Total Creative, pg 916
Twisted Media Inc, pg 920
Visions Plus, pg 931

COLORADO

Tim Cissell Music, pg 725
Conly Productions, pg 730
Daylight Productions & Rentals,
pg 739
Flashback Media Productions,
pg 762
Los Angeles Post Music Inc, pg 811
Transtar Entertainment Co Inc,
pg 917

CONNECTICUT

Ironik Design & Post, pg 791

DELAWARE

Ken-Del Productions Inc, pg 797

FLORIDA

Alliance Entertainment Corp (AEC)
LLC, pg 680
Applebox Studio, pg 687
Kat Epple Music Productions,
pg 755
Hard Hat Radio Music Service,
pg 776
LHV Audio Services, pg 807
Universal Studios Florida®
Production Group, pg 922

GEORGIA

Beachwood Productions, pg 702
ECG Productions, pg 750
Guerrilla Productions LLC, pg 774
Hottrax Records, pg 782

ILLINOIS

Convenience, pg 731
Creative Technology (CT), pg 733
Video Impressions, pg 928
WEEK TV, pg 935
Woodside Avenue Music
Productions Inc, pg 941

INDIANA

Indiana University Press, pg 786

KANSAS

KAKE-TV, pg 796

MAINE

Serendipity Recordings, pg 884

MARYLAND

Adelphi Records Inc, pg 676
CPR MultiMedia Solutions, pg 732

MASSACHUSETTS

Soundtrack Group, pg 895

MICHIGAN

GMP Music, pg 772

AUDIO

Music Libraries—
Instrumental (continued)

MISSOURI

Show-Me Audio-Visual, pg 887

MONTANA

Jereco Studios Inc, pg 793

NEBRASKA

JoeAudio, pg 794

NEVADA

JCS Video Productions, pg 793
Ron Roy Productions/Moodtapes,
  pg 878
Tanglewood Productions, pg 907

NEW HAMPSHIRE

Channell One Video, pg 720

NEW JERSEY

CFP Video Productions Inc, pg 720
Milgrom Productions, pg 827
Richard Reiter Productions Inc,
  pg 873
Shanachie Entertainment Corp,
  pg 885
TRF Production Music Libraries,
  pg 917
VCSvideo, pg 925

NEW MEXICO

Production Outfitters, pg 864
Uncharted Country Publishing,
  pg 921

NEW YORK

A-List Quality Videographer,
  pg 671
Beekman Books Inc, pg 703
Big Fish Production US, pg 705
Getty Images Music, pg 770
Heavy Melody, pg 778
IAI Records & Video, pg 783
Manhattan Production Music Inc,
  pg 816
Mark Custom Recording Service
  Inc, pg 817
Mother West, pg 831
Sony Music Entertainment, pg 893
TecNec Distributing, pg 909

NORTH CAROLINA

Pat Appleson Studios Inc, pg 687
Duke Media Services, pg 747
Franklin Video Inc, pg 765
Ladyslipper Music, pg 803
NASCAR Productions LLC, pg 835
Take One Productions Ltd, pg 906

NORTH DAKOTA

Media Productions, pg 822

OHIO

Aztec Video Productions, pg 700
Mills James Productions, pg 828
R&B Communications Inc, pg 870
Take 1 Media Services, pg 906
Twin Sisters® Digital Media™,
  pg 920
Vista Color Imaging Inc, pg 931

OKLAHOMA

Academic Media & Digital
  Services, pg 672
PDC Productions, pg 852

OREGON

Instant Music Now, pg 788

PENNSYLVANIA

Craig Recording Studios, pg 732
Monster Tracks, pg 829
The Videohouse Inc, pg 929

RHODE ISLAND

Sound-FX-Design, pg 894

SOUTH CAROLINA

DaviSound, pg 739
Genesis Creative, pg 769
Stages Video Productions, pg 899

TENNESSEE

Anode Inc, pg 686
Film House Inc, pg 760
Fricon Entertainment Co Inc,
  pg 766
Word Label Group, pg 941

TEXAS

Audiomoxie®, pg 695
The Editing Co, pg 750
FirstCom Music, pg 761
The Music Bakery, pg 834
Julye Newlin Productions Inc,
  pg 840
Production Garden Music, pg 863
Real to Reel Studios Inc, pg 871
The Sound Lab Inc, pg 894
Sound Works, pg 894
South Coast Film & Video, pg 895
Stage Directions, pg 898
TM Studios Inc, pg 915
Tropikal Productions, pg 918

VIRGINIA

Allied Media Corp, pg 681
CVW Event Productions, pg 736

WASHINGTON

Avast! Recording Co, pg 697

WEST VIRGINIA

Sweetsong Productions, pg 905

WISCONSIN

5th Floor Recording Co, pg 760
Mirror 34 Productions, pg 828
USAV Group Inc, pg 923

ONTARIO

Broughton's Church Supplies,
  Religious Books & Gifts, pg 711
Canamedia Inc, pg 715
DebsVoice, pg 739
Entertainment One Distribution,
  pg 754
Kool Music, pg 801
MCS Recording Studios, pg 821
Metalworks Recording Studios Inc,
  pg 824
Morning Music Ltd, pg 830
Nightingale Music Productions Inc,
  pg 841
Sound Ideas, pg 894
StockMusic.com, pg 901

Video Excellence Productions,
  pg 927
Wanted! Sound + Picture, pg 933
Westar Music, pg 936

QUEBEC

Muse Entertainment Enterprises,
  pg 834

Music Libraries—Jazz

ALABAMA

Sound of Birmingham Productions,
  pg 894

ARIZONA

Direct Current Video Productions,
  pg 743
Film Creations Ltd, pg 760
Fire Power Music LLC, pg 761
Merestone, pg 823

ARKANSAS

White Diamond Productions LLC,
  pg 937

CALIFORNIA

Aliso Creek Productions Inc, pg 680
Ancient Future, pg 685
Associated Production Music LLC,
  pg 691
CCI Digital, a DVS Company,
  pg 718
Concord Records, pg 730
Creative Support Services/CSS
  Music, pg 733
Diamond Dreams Music
  Productions, pg 741
Eye & I Productions, pg 758
5 Alarm Music, pg 762
Bruce Goldberg Inc, pg 772
Increase Video/Silver Mine Video,
  pg 786
Kaleidosound, pg 796
Killer Tracks, pg 798
K2B2 Records, pg 802
Lynch Communications, pg 813
Manchester Music Library Inc,
  pg 816
Megatrax, pg 823
The Music Kitchen Inc, pg 834
Joseph Nicoletti Consulting-
  Promotion, pg 841
OGM Production Music, pg 844
OTR Studios, pg 848
Polarity Post Production, pg 858
Saturn Studios, pg 881
Steve Shapiro Music, pg 885
Sonoton Music Library, pg 893
Still N' Motion, pg 901
Total Creative, pg 916
Visions Plus, pg 931

COLORADO

Tim Cissell Music, pg 725
Flashback Media Productions,
  pg 762
Los Angeles Post Music Inc, pg 811
Transtar Entertainment Co Inc,
  pg 917

CONNECTICUT

Ironik Design & Post, pg 791
P&P Studios Inc, pg 851

DELAWARE

Ken-Del Productions Inc, pg 797

DISTRICT OF COLUMBIA

Library of Congress, Motion
  Picture, Broadcasting & Recorded
  Sound Division, pg 807
Smithsonian Folkways Recordings,
  pg 891

FLORIDA

Alliance Entertainment Corp (AEC)
  LLC, pg 680
Applebox Studio, pg 687
Kat Epple Music Productions,
  pg 755
LHV Audio Services, pg 807
Universal Studios Florida®
  Production Group, pg 922

GEORGIA

Beachwood Productions, pg 702
ECG Productions, pg 750
Guerrilla Productions LLC, pg 774
Hottrax Records, pg 782

ILLINOIS

Convenience, pg 731
Delmark Records, pg 740
Jim Passin Productions, pg 852
Video Impressions, pg 928
WEEK TV, pg 935
Woodside Avenue Music
  Productions Inc, pg 941

INDIANA

Indiana University Press, pg 786

LOUISIANA

Centaur Records Inc, pg 719
Great Chefs/Leisure Jazz Video,
  pg 773
Leisure Video, pg 806

MAINE

Serendipity Recordings, pg 884

MARYLAND

Adelphi Records Inc, pg 676
CPR MultiMedia Solutions, pg 732
The Cutting Corporation,
  GraphicAudio® & Archival
  Sound Lab, pg 736

MASSACHUSETTS

CommCreative, pg 728
Soundtrack Group, pg 895
TR Productions, pg 916
The Well-Tempered Music Library,
  pg 935

MICHIGAN

AirBrands Event & Marketing
  Group, pg 679
GMP Music, pg 772
Rebirth Inc, pg 871

MISSOURI

Show-Me Audio-Visual, pg 887

MONTANA

Jereco Studios Inc, pg 793

NEBRASKA

JoeAudio, pg 794

NEVADA

Tanglewood Productions, pg 907

AUDIO

Music Libraries—New Age (continued)

TEXAS (continued)

The Music Bakery, pg 834
Julye Newlin Productions Inc, pg 840
Production Garden Music, pg 863
Real to Reel Studios Inc, pg 871
The Sound Lab Inc, pg 894
South Coast Film & Video, pg 895
Tropikal Productions, pg 918

VIRGINIA

Allied Media Corp, pg 681

WISCONSIN

5th Floor Recording Co, pg 760

ONTARIO

Canamedia Inc, pg 715
DebsVoice, pg 739
Entertainment One Distribution, pg 754
GAPC (General Assembly Production Centre), pg 768
MCS Recording Studios, pg 821
Metalworks Recording Studios Inc, pg 824
Nightingale Music Productions Inc, pg 841
Sound Ideas, pg 894
StockMusic.com, pg 901
Video Excellence Productions, pg 927
Wanted! Sound + Picture, pg 933
Westar Music, pg 936

Music Libraries—Popular

ALABAMA

Sound of Birmingham Productions, pg 894

ARIZONA

Direct Current Video Productions, pg 743
Film Creations Ltd, pg 760
Fire Power Music LLC, pg 761
Merestone, pg 823

ARKANSAS

White Diamond Productions LLC, pg 937

CALIFORNIA

Aliso Creek Productions Inc, pg 680
Associated Production Music LLC, pg 691
Berkeley Sound Artists Inc, pg 704
CCI Digital, a DVS Company, pg 718
Creative Support Services/CSS Music, pg 733
Creative Technology, pg 733
Diamond Dreams Music Productions, pg 741
5 Alarm Music, pg 762
Bruce Goldberg Inc, pg 772
Increase Video/Silver Mine Video, pg 786
Kaleidosound, pg 796
Killer Tracks, pg 798
Lynch Communications, pg 813

Manchester Music Library Inc, pg 816
Megatrax, pg 823
The Music Kitchen Inc, pg 834
Joseph Nicoletti Consulting-Promotion, pg 841
OGM Production Music, pg 844
OTR Studios, pg 848
Polarity Post Production, pg 858
Pyramind Studios, pg 867
Reality Check Systems, pg 871
Reprise Records, pg 873
Saturn Studios, pg 881
Steve Shapiro Music, pg 885
Sonoton Music Library, pg 893
Still N' Motion, pg 901
Total Creative, pg 916
Twisted Media Inc, pg 920
Visions Plus, pg 931
Welk Music Group, pg 935

COLORADO

Tim Cissell Music, pg 725
Flashback Media Productions, pg 762
Los Angeles Post Music Inc, pg 811
Transtar Entertainment Co Inc, pg 917

CONNECTICUT

P&P Studios Inc, pg 851

DELAWARE

Ken-Del Productions Inc, pg 797

FLORIDA

Alliance Entertainment Corp (AEC) LLC, pg 680
Applebox Studio, pg 687
Hard Hat Radio Music Service, pg 776
LHV Audio Services, pg 807
Times-Square Fantasy Theatre, pg 914
Universal Studios Florida® Production Group, pg 922

GEORGIA

Beachwood Productions, pg 702
ECG Productions, pg 750
Guerrilla Productions LLC, pg 774

ILLINOIS

Video Impressions, pg 928
WEEK TV, pg 935
Woodside Avenue Music Productions Inc, pg 941

LOUISIANA

Flat Town Music Co, pg 762

MAINE

Serendipity Recordings, pg 884
WGME-TV, pg 936

MARYLAND

CPR MultiMedia Solutions, pg 732
The Cutting Corporation, GraphicAudio® & Archival Sound Lab, pg 736

MASSACHUSETTS

CommCreative, pg 728
Soundtrack Group, pg 895
TR Productions, pg 916

MICHIGAN

AirBrands Event & Marketing Group, pg 679
GMP Music, pg 772

MISSOURI

Show-Me Audio-Visual, pg 887

MONTANA

Jereco Studios Inc, pg 793

NEBRASKA

JoeAudio, pg 794

NEVADA

DVDs4Less, pg 748
Tanglewood Productions, pg 907

NEW JERSEY

CFP Video Productions Inc, pg 720
Milbrodt/Music & Sound Design, pg 827
Milgrom Productions, pg 827
NFL Films Music Library, pg 841
Richard Reiter Productions Inc, pg 873
TRF Production Music Libraries, pg 917
VCSvideo, pg 925

NEW MEXICO

Production Outfitters, pg 864

NEW YORK

A-List Quality Videographer, pg 671
Audio Network US Inc, pg 693
Beekman Books Inc, pg 703
de Wolfe Music USA, pg 739
Getty Images Music, pg 770
Heavy Melody, pg 778
Historic Films, pg 780
HOThead, pg 782
Manhattan Center Studios Inc, pg 816
Manhattan Production Music Inc, pg 816
Mother West, pg 831
The Palmer Group, pg 850
Pennebaker Hegedus Films Inc, pg 854
Sony Music Commercial Music Group, pg 893
Sony Music Entertainment, pg 893
TecNec Distributing, pg 909
Yessian, pg 944

NORTH CAROLINA

Pat Appleson Studios Inc, pg 687
Duke Media Services, pg 747
Ladyslipper Music, pg 803
NASCAR Productions LLC, pg 835
Take One Productions Ltd, pg 906

NORTH DAKOTA

Media Productions, pg 822

OHIO

Aztec Video Productions, pg 700
Mills James Productions, pg 828
R&B Communications Inc, pg 870
Take 1 Media Services, pg 906

OKLAHOMA

PDC Productions, pg 852

PENNSYLVANIA

Craig Recording Studios, pg 732
Monster Tracks, pg 829
The Videohouse Inc, pg 929

RHODE ISLAND

Sound-FX-Design, pg 894

SOUTH CAROLINA

Genesis Creative, pg 769
Stages Video Productions, pg 899

TENNESSEE

Anode Inc, pg 686
Film House Inc, pg 760
Fricon Entertainment Co Inc, pg 766
Memphis Communications Corp, pg 823
Word Label Group, pg 941

TEXAS

Audiomoxie®, pg 695
The Editing Co, pg 750
FirstCom Music, pg 761
Horizon Film + Video Productions, pg 781
Mediaforce Productions, pg 822
The Music Bakery, pg 834
Julye Newlin Productions Inc, pg 840
Production Garden Music, pg 863
Real to Reel Studios Inc, pg 871
The Samuels Co, pg 879
The Sound Lab Inc, pg 894
Sound Works, pg 894
South Coast Film & Video, pg 895
Stage Directions, pg 898
TM Studios Inc, pg 915

WASHINGTON

Avast! Recording Co, pg 697

WEST VIRGINIA

Sweetsong Productions, pg 905

WISCONSIN

5th Floor Recording Co, pg 760
Mirror 34 Productions, pg 828
USAV Group Inc, pg 923

ONTARIO

Canamedia Inc, pg 715
DebsVoice, pg 739
Entertainment One Distribution, pg 754
GAPC (General Assembly Production Centre), pg 768
Kool Music, pg 801
MCS Recording Studios, pg 821
Metalworks Recording Studios Inc, pg 824
Morning Music Ltd, pg 830
Nightingale Music Productions Inc, pg 841
Sound Ideas, pg 894
StockMusic.com, pg 901
Wanted! Sound + Picture, pg 933
Westar Music, pg 936

Music Libraries—Rap

ALABAMA

Sound of Birmingham Productions, pg 894

ARIZONA
Direct Current Video Productions, pg 743
Film Creations Ltd, pg 760
Merestone, pg 823

ARKANSAS
White Diamond Productions LLC, pg 937

CALIFORNIA
Aliso Creek Productions Inc, pg 680
Creative Support Services/CSS Music, pg 733
Diamond Dreams Music Productions, pg 741
Eye & I Productions, pg 758
5 Alarm Music, pg 762
Kaleidosound, pg 796
Killer Tracks, pg 798
Lynch Communications, pg 813
Megatrax, pg 823
The Music Kitchen Inc, pg 834
OGM Production Music, pg 844
Reality Check Systems, pg 871
Steve Shapiro Music, pg 885
Sonoton Music Library, pg 893
Still N' Motion, pg 901
Total Creative, pg 916
Twisted Media Inc, pg 920

COLORADO
Tim Cissell Music, pg 725
Flashback Media Productions, pg 762
Los Angeles Post Music Inc, pg 811

DELAWARE
Ken-Del Productions Inc, pg 797

FLORIDA
Alliance Entertainment Corp (AEC) LLC, pg 680
Applebox Studio, pg 687
LHV Audio Services, pg 807
Universal Studios Florida® Production Group, pg 922

GEORGIA
ECG Productions, pg 750

ILLINOIS
Video Impressions, pg 928

MASSACHUSETTS
Soundtrack Group, pg 895

MICHIGAN
GMP Music, pg 772

MISSOURI
Show-Me Audio-Visual, pg 887

MONTANA
Jereco Studios Inc, pg 793

NEBRASKA
JoeAudio, pg 794

NEVADA
Tanglewood Productions, pg 907

NEW JERSEY
Milgrom Productions, pg 827
VCSvideo, pg 925

NEW MEXICO
Production Outfitters, pg 864

NEW YORK
A-List Quality Videographer, pg 671
Audio Network US Inc, pg 693
Beekman Books Inc, pg 703
Big Fish Production US, pg 705
Heavy Melody, pg 778
Mother West, pg 831
TecNec Distributing, pg 909

NORTH CAROLINA
Take One Productions Ltd, pg 906

NORTH DAKOTA
Media Productions, pg 822

OHIO
Aztec Video Productions, pg 700
Mills James Productions, pg 828
R&B Communications Inc, pg 870
Take 1 Media Services, pg 906

OKLAHOMA
PDC Productions, pg 852

PENNSYLVANIA
The Videohouse Inc, pg 929

RHODE ISLAND
Sound-FX-Design, pg 894

SOUTH CAROLINA
Stages Video Productions, pg 899

TENNESSEE
Anode Inc, pg 686
Film House Inc, pg 760
Fricon Entertainment Co Inc, pg 766

TEXAS
The Editing Co, pg 750
FirstCom Music, pg 761
Horizon Film + Video Productions, pg 781
Mediaforce Productions, pg 822
The Music Bakery, pg 834
Julye Newlin Productions Inc, pg 840
Production Garden Music, pg 863
The Sound Lab Inc, pg 894
South Coast Film & Video, pg 895
TM Studios Inc, pg 915
Tropikal Productions, pg 918

WISCONSIN
5th Floor Recording Co, pg 760

ONTARIO
Canamedia Inc, pg 715
DebsVoice, pg 739
Entertainment One Distribution, pg 754
Kool Music, pg 801
MCS Recording Studios, pg 821
Metalworks Recording Studios Inc, pg 824

Nightingale Music Productions Inc, pg 841
Sound Ideas, pg 894
StockMusic.com, pg 901
Wanted! Sound + Picture, pg 933
Westar Music, pg 936

Music Libraries—Rhythm & Blues

ALABAMA
Sound of Birmingham Productions, pg 894

ARIZONA
Direct Current Video Productions, pg 743
Film Creations Ltd, pg 760
Merestone, pg 823

ARKANSAS
White Diamond Productions LLC, pg 937

CALIFORNIA
Aliso Creek Productions Inc, pg 680
Creative Support Services/CSS Music, pg 733
Diamond Dreams Music Productions, pg 741
5 Alarm Music, pg 762
Kaleidosound, pg 796
Killer Tracks, pg 798
Lynch Communications, pg 813
Megatrax, pg 823
The Music Kitchen Inc, pg 834
OGM Production Music, pg 844
Reality Check Systems, pg 871
Steve Shapiro Music, pg 885
Sonoton Music Library, pg 893
Still N' Motion, pg 901
Total Creative, pg 916
Visions Plus, pg 931

COLORADO
Tim Cissell Music, pg 725
Flashback Media Productions, pg 762
Los Angeles Post Music Inc, pg 811

CONNECTICUT
Ironik Design & Post, pg 791

DELAWARE
Ken-Del Productions Inc, pg 797

FLORIDA
Alliance Entertainment Corp (AEC) LLC, pg 680
Applebox Studio, pg 687
LHV Audio Services, pg 807
Universal Studios Florida® Production Group, pg 922

GEORGIA
ECG Productions, pg 750
Guerrilla Productions LLC, pg 774

ILLINOIS
Video Impressions, pg 928

LOUISIANA
Flat Town Music Co, pg 762

MAINE
WGME-TV, pg 936

MARYLAND
Adelphi Records Inc, pg 676
CPR MultiMedia Solutions, pg 732

MASSACHUSETTS
Soundtrack Group, pg 895

MICHIGAN
GMP Music, pg 772

MISSOURI
Show-Me Audio-Visual, pg 887

MONTANA
Jereco Studios Inc, pg 793

NEBRASKA
JoeAudio, pg 794

NEVADA
JCS Video Productions, pg 793
Tanglewood Productions, pg 907

NEW JERSEY
Milbrodt/Music & Sound Design, pg 827
Milgrom Productions, pg 827
TRF Production Music Libraries, pg 917
VCSvideo, pg 925

NEW MEXICO
Production Outfitters, pg 864

NEW YORK
A-List Quality Videographer, pg 671
Audio Network US Inc, pg 693
Beekman Books Inc, pg 703
Big Fish Production US, pg 705
Getty Images Music, pg 770
Heavy Melody, pg 778
Historic Films, pg 780
TecNec Distributing, pg 909

NORTH CAROLINA
Pat Appleson Studios Inc, pg 687
The Communications Group Inc, pg 729
Ladyslipper Music, pg 803
Take One Productions Ltd, pg 906

NORTH DAKOTA
Media Productions, pg 822

OHIO
Aztec Video Productions, pg 700
Mills James Productions, pg 828
R&B Communications Inc, pg 870
Take 1 Media Services, pg 906

OKLAHOMA
PDC Productions, pg 852

PENNSYLVANIA
Monster Tracks, pg 829
The Videohouse Inc, pg 929

RHODE ISLAND
Sound-FX-Design, pg 894

AUDIO

Music Libraries—Rhythm & Blues (continued)

SOUTH CAROLINA

Genesis Creative, pg 769
Stages Video Productions, pg 899

TENNESSEE

Anode Inc, pg 686
Film House Inc, pg 760
Fricon Entertainment Co Inc, pg 766

TEXAS

The Editing Co, pg 750
FirstCom Music, pg 761
Horizon Film + Video Productions, pg 781
The Music Bakery, pg 834
Julye Newlin Productions Inc, pg 840
Production Garden Music, pg 863
The Sound Lab Inc, pg 894
South Coast Film & Video, pg 895
Tropikal Productions, pg 918

WISCONSIN

5th Floor Recording Co, pg 760

ONTARIO

Canamedia Inc, pg 715
DebsVoice, pg 739
Entertainment One Distribution, pg 754
MCS Recording Studios, pg 821
Metalworks Recording Studios Inc, pg 824
Nightingale Music Productions Inc, pg 841
Sound Ideas, pg 894
StockMusic.com, pg 901
Wanted! Sound + Picture, pg 933
Westar Music, pg 936

Music Libraries—Rock

ALABAMA

Sound of Birmingham Productions, pg 894

ARIZONA

Direct Current Video Productions, pg 743
Film Creations Ltd, pg 760
Fire Power Music LLC, pg 761
Merestone, pg 823

ARKANSAS

White Diamond Productions LLC, pg 937

CALIFORNIA

Aliso Creek Productions Inc, pg 680
Associated Production Music LLC, pg 691
Berkeley Sound Artists Inc, pg 704
CCI Digital, a DVS Company, pg 718
Creative Support Services/CSS Music, pg 733
Creative Technology, pg 733
Diamond Dreams Music Productions, pg 741
Eye & I Productions, pg 758
5 Alarm Music, pg 762

Kaleidosound, pg 796
Killer Tracks, pg 798
Lynch Communications, pg 813
Manchester Music Library Inc, pg 816
Megatrax, pg 823
The Music Kitchen Inc, pg 834
Joseph Nicoletti Consulting-Promotion, pg 841
OGM Production Music, pg 844
OTR Studios, pg 848
Polarity Post Production, pg 858
Pyramind Studios, pg 867
Reality Check Systems, pg 871
Reprise Records, pg 873
Saturn Studios, pg 881
Steve Shapiro Music, pg 885
Sonoton Music Library, pg 893
Still N' Motion, pg 901
Total Creative, pg 916
Twisted Media Inc, pg 920
Visions Plus, pg 931
Welk Music Group, pg 935

COLORADO

Tim Cissell Music, pg 725
Conly Productions, pg 730
Daylight Productions & Rentals, pg 739
Flashback Media Productions, pg 762
Los Angeles Post Music Inc, pg 811
Transtar Entertainment Co Inc, pg 917

CONNECTICUT

Ironik Design & Post, pg 791
P&P Studios Inc, pg 851

DELAWARE

Ken-Del Productions Inc, pg 797

FLORIDA

Alliance Entertainment Corp (AEC) LLC, pg 680
Applebox Studio, pg 687
Hard Hat Radio Music Service, pg 776
Jordan Klein Film & Video (JKFV), pg 795
LHV Audio Services, pg 807
Universal Studios Florida® Production Group, pg 922

GEORGIA

Beachwood Productions, pg 702
ECG Productions, pg 750
Guerrilla Productions LLC, pg 774
Hottrax Records, pg 782

ILLINOIS

Convenience, pg 731
Video Impressions, pg 928
WEEK TV, pg 935
Woodside Avenue Music Productions Inc, pg 941

LOUISIANA

Flat Town Music Co, pg 762

MARYLAND

Adelphi Records Inc, pg 676
CPR MultiMedia Solutions, pg 732
The Cutting Corporation, GraphicAudio® & Archival Sound Lab, pg 736

MASSACHUSETTS

CommCreative, pg 728
Soundtrack Group, pg 895
TR Productions, pg 916
The Well-Tempered Music Library, pg 935

MICHIGAN

AirBrands Event & Marketing Group, pg 679
GMP Music, pg 772

MISSOURI

Show-Me Audio-Visual, pg 887

MONTANA

Jereco Studios Inc, pg 793

NEBRASKA

JoeAudio, pg 794

NEVADA

JCS Video Productions, pg 793
Tanglewood Productions, pg 907

NEW HAMPSHIRE

Channell One Video, pg 720

NEW JERSEY

CFP Video Productions Inc, pg 720
Milbrodt/Music & Sound Design, pg 827
Milgrom Productions, pg 827
Richard Reiter Productions Inc, pg 873
TRF Production Music Libraries, pg 917
VCSvideo, pg 925

NEW MEXICO

Production Outfitters, pg 864

NEW YORK

A-List Quality Videographer, pg 671
Beekman Books Inc, pg 703
Big Fish Production US, pg 705
de Wolfe Music USA, pg 739
Getty Images Music, pg 770
Heavy Melody, pg 778
Historic Films, pg 780
HOThead, pg 782
Manhattan Center Studios Inc, pg 816
Manhattan Production Music Inc, pg 816
Mother West, pg 831
New York Sound Inc, pg 840
The Palmer Group, pg 850
Pennebaker Hegedus Films Inc, pg 854
David Rapkin Audio Production, pg 870
Sony Music Commercial Music Group, pg 893
Sony Music Entertainment, pg 893
TecNec Distributing, pg 909
Yessian, pg 944

NORTH CAROLINA

Pat Appleson Studios Inc, pg 687
Duke Media Services, pg 747
Ladyslipper Music, pg 803
NASCAR Productions LLC, pg 835
Take One Productions Ltd, pg 906

NORTH DAKOTA

Media Productions, pg 822

OHIO

Aztec Video Productions, pg 700
Mills James Productions, pg 828
R&B Communications Inc, pg 870
Take 1 Media Services, pg 906

OKLAHOMA

PDC Productions, pg 852

OREGON

Instant Music Now, pg 788

PENNSYLVANIA

Craig Recording Studios, pg 732
Monster Tracks, pg 829
The Videohouse Inc, pg 929

RHODE ISLAND

Sound-FX-Design, pg 894

SOUTH CAROLINA

Genesis Creative, pg 769
Stages Video Productions, pg 899

TENNESSEE

Anode Inc, pg 686
Film House Inc, pg 760
Fricon Entertainment Co Inc, pg 766
Sun Entertainment Corp, pg 903
Word Label Group, pg 941

TEXAS

The Editing Co, pg 750
FirstCom Music, pg 761
Horizon Film + Video Productions, pg 781
Mediaforce Productions, pg 822
The Music Bakery, pg 834
Julye Newlin Productions Inc, pg 840
Production Garden Music, pg 863
Real to Reel Studios Inc, pg 871
The Sound Lab Inc, pg 894
Sound Works, pg 894
South Coast Film & Video, pg 895
TM Studios Inc, pg 915
Tropikal Productions, pg 918

VIRGINIA

Allied Media Corp, pg 681

WASHINGTON

Avast! Recording Co, pg 697

WISCONSIN

5th Floor Recording Co, pg 760
Mirror 34 Productions, pg 828
USAV Group Inc, pg 923

ONTARIO

Canamedia Inc, pg 715
DebsVoice, pg 739
Entertainment One Distribution, pg 754
The Hollywood Edge, pg 780
Kool Music, pg 801
MCS Recording Studios, pg 821
Metalworks Recording Studios Inc, pg 824
Nightingale Music Productions Inc, pg 841

98

Sound Ideas, pg 894
StockMusic.com, pg 901
Wanted! Sound + Picture, pg 933
Westar Music, pg 936

Music Libraries—Spiritual

ALABAMA

Sound of Birmingham Productions,
pg 894

ARIZONA

Direct Current Video Productions,
pg 743
Film Creations Ltd, pg 760
Fire Power Music LLC, pg 761
Merestone, pg 823
Valley of the Sun Publishing Co,
pg 924

ARKANSAS

White Diamond Productions LLC,
pg 937

CALIFORNIA

Aliso Creek Productions Inc, pg 680
Associated Production Music LLC,
pg 691
Christian Media Network, pg 722
Creative Support Services/CSS
Music, pg 733
Diamond Dreams Music
Productions, pg 741
Eye & I Productions, pg 758
5 Alarm Music, pg 762
Kaleidosound, pg 796
Killer Tracks, pg 798
Lynch Communications, pg 813
Megatrax, pg 823
The Music Kitchen Inc, pg 834
Joseph Nicoletti Consulting-
Promotion, pg 841
OGM Production Music, pg 844
Osho Viha Information Center &
Book Distributors, pg 848
Steve Shapiro Music, pg 885
Sonoton Music Library, pg 893
Still N' Motion, pg 901
Timeless Productions, pg 914
Total Creative, pg 916
Welk Music Group, pg 935

COLORADO

Tim Cissell Music, pg 725
Flashback Media Productions,
pg 762
Los Angeles Post Music Inc, pg 811

DELAWARE

Ken-Del Productions Inc, pg 797

DISTRICT OF COLUMBIA

Library of Congress, Motion
Picture, Broadcasting & Recorded
Sound Division, pg 807

FLORIDA

Alliance Entertainment Corp (AEC)
LLC, pg 680
Applebox Studio, pg 687
Children of Mary, pg 722
Jordan Klein Film & Video (JKFV),
pg 795
LHV Audio Services, pg 807
Sound*Light, pg 894
Universal Studios Florida®
Production Group, pg 922

GEORGIA

Beachwood Productions, pg 702
Guerrilla Productions LLC, pg 774

ILLINOIS

Video Impressions, pg 928
WEEK TV, pg 935
Woodside Avenue Music
Productions Inc, pg 941

LOUISIANA

Flat Town Music Co, pg 762

MARYLAND

Adelphi Records Inc, pg 676
The Cutting Corporation,
GraphicAudio® & Archival
Sound Lab, pg 736

MASSACHUSETTS

Soundtrack Group, pg 895

MICHIGAN

AirBrands Event & Marketing
Group, pg 679
GMP Music, pg 772

MISSOURI

Show-Me Audio-Visual, pg 887

MONTANA

Jereco Studios Inc, pg 793

NEBRASKA

JoeAudio, pg 794

NEVADA

JCS Video Productions, pg 793
Tanglewood Productions, pg 907

NEW JERSEY

CFP Video Productions Inc, pg 720
Milgrom Productions, pg 827
TRF Production Music Libraries,
pg 917
VCSvideo, pg 925

NEW MEXICO

Production Outfitters, pg 864

NEW YORK

A-List Quality Videographer,
pg 671
Audio Network US Inc, pg 693
Beekman Books Inc, pg 703
Big Fish Production US, pg 705
de Wolfe Music USA, pg 739
Historic Films, pg 780
Manhattan Production Music Inc,
pg 816
The Palmer Group, pg 850
Sony Music Commercial Music
Group, pg 893
Sony Music Entertainment, pg 893
TecNec Distributing, pg 909

NORTH CAROLINA

Pat Appleson Studios Inc, pg 687
Ladyslipper Music, pg 803
Take One Productions Ltd, pg 906

NORTH DAKOTA

Media Productions, pg 822

OHIO

Aztec Video Productions, pg 700
Mills James Productions, pg 828
R&B Communications Inc, pg 870
Take 1 Media Services, pg 906
Twin Sisters® Digital Media™,
pg 920

OKLAHOMA

PDC Productions, pg 852

OREGON

Instant Music Now, pg 788

PENNSYLVANIA

Monster Tracks, pg 829
The Videohouse Inc, pg 929

SOUTH CAROLINA

Genesis Creative, pg 769
Stages Video Productions, pg 899

TENNESSEE

Anode Inc, pg 686
Center for Southern Folklore Inc,
pg 719
Film House Inc, pg 760
Fricon Entertainment Co Inc,
pg 766
Provident Distribution, pg 866
Spring Arbor Distributors Inc,
pg 898
Word Label Group, pg 941

TEXAS

The Editing Co, pg 750
FirstCom Music, pg 761
Mediaforce Productions, pg 822
The Music Bakery, pg 834
The Sound Lab Inc, pg 894
Sound Works, pg 894
South Coast Film & Video, pg 895
TM Studios Inc, pg 915
Tropikal Productions, pg 918

VERMONT

Multicultural Media Inc, pg 833

WISCONSIN

5th Floor Recording Co, pg 760
USAV Group Inc, pg 923

ONTARIO

Broughton's Church Supplies,
Religious Books & Gifts, pg 711
Canamedia Inc, pg 715
DebsVoice, pg 739
Entertainment One Distribution,
pg 754
MCS Recording Studios, pg 821
Metalworks Recording Studios Inc,
pg 824
Nightingale Music Productions Inc,
pg 841
Novalis, pg 843
Sound Ideas, pg 894
StockMusic.com, pg 901
Wanted! Sound + Picture, pg 933
Westar Music, pg 936

Music—Original

ALABAMA

Dogwood Productions Inc, pg 745
Sound of Birmingham Productions,
pg 894

ARIZONA

Fire Power Music LLC, pg 761
Merestone, pg 823

ARKANSAS

Live'N'Loud, pg 810

CALIFORNIA

AB Audio Visual Entertainment Inc,
pg 672
Aliso Creek Productions Inc, pg 680
Artichoke Productions, pg 690
Audio Upgrades, pg 694
Automated Entertainment, pg 696
Backstage Pass Entertainment Inc,
pg 700
Berkeley Sound Artists Inc, pg 704
Christian Media Network, pg 722
Creative Support Services/CSS
Music, pg 733
Creative Technology, pg 733
Crystal Pyramid Productions™,
pg 735
Diamond Dreams Music
Productions, pg 741
Earwax Productions Inc, pg 749
5 Alarm Music, pg 762
48 Windows, pg 764
4th Street Recording, pg 764
Bruce Goldberg Inc, pg 772
GrooveWorx, pg 774
Steven Halpern's Inner Peace
Music, pg 775
iCorpTv, pg 783
Increase Video/Silver Mine Video,
pg 786
JDS Video & Media Productions
Inc, pg 793
Kaleidosound, pg 796
Lynch Communications, pg 813
Manchester Music Library Inc,
pg 816
Martinsound Inc, pg 818
Maximus Media Inc, pg 820
MediaMation Inc, pg 822
Megatrax, pg 823
The Music Kitchen Inc, pg 834
Musikvergnuegen, pg 835
New & Unique Videos™, pg 839
Joseph Nicoletti Consulting-
Promotion, pg 841
On-Trax Inc, pg 846
OTR Studios, pg 848
Palardo Productions, pg 850
piXvfm Inc, pg 857
PM Productions, pg 858
Polarity Post Production, pg 858
Pyramind Studios, pg 867
QRS Software Services, pg 867
Reality Check Systems, pg 871
Sahara Records & Filmworks
Entertainment Co, pg 879
Saturn Studios, pg 881
Steve Shapiro Music, pg 885
Sonic Gravy, pg 892
SonicPool, pg 892
Sound Feelings Records, pg 894
Still N' Motion, pg 901
Studio 132, pg 902
Timeless Productions, pg 914
Total Creative, pg 916
Twisted Media Inc, pg 920
West Coast Projections Inc, pg 935
Z-Ville Productions, pg 944

COLORADO

Tim Cissell Music, pg 725
Conly Productions, pg 730
Full Spectrum Arts & Services,
pg 767

AUDIO

Music—Original
(continued)

COLORADO (continued)
Los Angeles Post Music Inc, pg 811
Shambhala Publications, pg 885

CONNECTICUT
Antenna International, pg 686
New London Media, pg 839
Palace Production Center, pg 850
P&P Studios Inc, pg 851

DISTRICT OF COLUMBIA
Interface Media Group, pg 789
Sano Videos, pg 880

FLORIDA
Audacity Recording Studios, pg 693
Civins Productions Inc, pg 725
Hard Hat Radio Music Service,
   pg 776
JT Communications, pg 795
The Kitchen, pg 799
LHV Audio Services, pg 807
Mach 1 Productions, pg 813
Morrisound Recording, pg 830
Pandisc Music Corp, pg 851
Phat Planet Recording Studios,
   pg 855
Sunfire Communications Inc,
   pg 904
Times-Square Fantasy Theatre,
   pg 914
Mike Vasilinda Productions Inc,
   pg 925

GEORGIA
Beast Atlanta, pg 703
Crawford Media Services Inc,
   pg 733
Hottrax Records, pg 782
Stage Front Presentation Systems,
   pg 899
White Dog Studios, pg 937

HAWAII
Hyperspective Studios Inc, pg 783
Media Bridge Gamekids, pg 821

ILLINOIS
CCore Media Inc, pg 718
Mightybytes Inc, pg 827
Jim Passin Productions, pg 852
Pepper Group, pg 854
RBR Productions, pg 870
Steven Samler Music & Sound,
   pg 879
Solid Sound Recording Studio,
   pg 892
Woodside Avenue Music
   Productions Inc, pg 941

INDIANA
A-V-A Video Productions, pg 671
Gaither Studios LLC, pg 767
Alan Johnson Recording, pg 794

IOWA
Hedquist Productions Inc, pg 778

KENTUCKY
Broadway Digital, pg 711
The Media Collaboratory, pg 821

LOUISIANA
Disk Productions Inc, pg 743
Vidox Motion Imagery, pg 930

MAINE
Slim Goodbody Corp, pg 890

MARYLAND
Bethesda Softworks LLC, pg 704
CPR MultiMedia Solutions, pg 732
The Cutting Corporation,
   GraphicAudio® & Archival
   Sound Lab, pg 736
dbF a Media Company, pg 739
Omega Recording Studios, pg 845

MASSACHUSETTS
ARF! ARF!, pg 688
Continental Recordings Inc, pg 731
Green Mountain Post Films (GMP),
   pg 774
Professional Audio Design Inc,
   pg 865
Ben Rudnick and Friends, pg 878
Sounds Interesting Studio, pg 894
Soundtrack Group, pg 895
Rik Tinory Productions, pg 914
TR Productions, pg 916

MICHIGAN
Audio Graphic Services, pg 693
Digi Sign Design LLC, pg 741
Digital Image Studios LLC, pg 742
GMP Music, pg 772
K&R's Recording Studios Inc,
   pg 796
MessageMakers, pg 824
Michigan Recording Arts Institute
   & Technologies, pg 825
Rebirth Inc, pg 871
RingSide Creative, pg 875

MINNESOTA
The ADS Group, pg 676
BeyerSound & Essay Audio, pg 705
Media Loft Inc, pg 822
Winterland Studios, pg 940

MISSOURI
Avatar Studios, pg 697

MONTANA
Jereco Studios Inc, pg 793
KCFW Television, pg 797

NEVADA
Tanglewood Productions, pg 907

NEW HAMPSHIRE
Apertura, pg 686
Captain Fiddle Music &
   Publications, pg 716
Chip Taylor Communications LLC,
   pg 907

NEW JERSEY
Allegro Productions Inc, pg 680
CFP Video Productions Inc, pg 720
Jeep Jazz Media Solutions, pg 793
Mia Mind Music, pg 825
Milbrodt/Music & Sound Design,
   pg 827
Milgrom Productions, pg 827
NFL Films Inc, pg 841
Presence Records, pg 861
Richard Reiter Productions Inc,
   pg 873

Starlite, pg 900
Suede Interactive, pg 903
TRF Production Music Libraries,
   pg 917
VCSvideo, pg 925

NEW MEXICO
Uncharted Country Publishing,
   pg 921

NEW YORK
Aural Gratification Inc, pg 695
aurora productions, pg 696
Big Fish Production US, pg 705
The Big House Group, pg 705
Chromavision Corp, pg 723
Fingerpaint, pg 761
A Gentle Wind, pg 770
HB-Content, pg 777
Headroom Digital Audio, pg 777
Heavy Melody, pg 778
IAI Records & Video, pg 783
Icontent, pg 783
Jupiter Moon Productions, pg 795
KAS Music & Sound, pg 796
Magnetic Music Publishing Co,
   pg 814
Manhattan Center Studios Inc,
   pg 816
Manhattan Production Music Inc,
   pg 816
Mark Custom Recording Service
   Inc, pg 817
Jack Morton Worldwide, pg 830
The Palmer Group, pg 850
Propeller Music & Sound Design
   Inc, pg 865
Elliot Sokolov Music, pg 892
Sony Music Entertainment, pg 893
TeleTime Productions, pg 910
Tiki Recording Studios Inc, pg 914
Yessian, pg 944

NORTH CAROLINA
Pat Appleson Studios Inc, pg 687
Audio Art, pg 693
Davenport Music Library, pg 738
Franklin Video Inc, pg 765
Howard Hanger, pg 775
Horizon Video Productions Inc,
   pg 781
Trailblazer Studios®, pg 917
2BruceStudio, pg 920

NORTH DAKOTA
Media Productions, pg 822

OHIO
Bartha, pg 702
Challenge Productions/Challenge
   Aerial Imaging, pg 720
Mills James Productions, pg 828
SoundSpace Inc, pg 895
Twin Sisters® Digital Media™,
   pg 920

OKLAHOMA
PDC Productions, pg 852

OREGON
REX, pg 874

PENNSYLVANIA
American Artist Studio, pg 682
Dreambox Media Inc, pg 746
Filmaker Technology, pg 760
Innovision Media Group, pg 788
Ivory Productions, pg 792

JPL, pg 795
Monster Tracks, pg 829
Production Masters Inc (PMI),
   pg 864
Right Coast Recording Inc, pg 875
The Videohouse Inc, pg 929

RHODE ISLAND
Sound-FX-Design, pg 894
StarTrak Studios Inc, pg 900

TENNESSEE
American Blackguard Inc, pg 683
Analog Man Recording Studio,
   pg 685
Ardent Music LLC, pg 688
Compass Records, pg 729
Fricon Entertainment Co Inc,
   pg 766
JamSync, pg 793
Mr Mark's Used Musical, Stereo &
   Studio Equipment Store, pg 828
Motion Picture Services, pg 831
Scripps Networks, pg 882
Stage Post, pg 899
Zion Music Group, pg 945

TEXAS
AMS Pictures, pg 684
Audiomoxie®, pg 695
Biway Media, pg 706
Communication Arts Multimedia
   Inc, pg 728
The Editing Co, pg 750
FirstCom Music, pg 761
Mediaforce Productions, pg 822
The Music Bakery, pg 834
Out of the BLUE Media, pg 849
Planet Dallas Recording Studios,
   pg 857
The Samuels Co, pg 879
Sound Arts Recording Studio,
   pg 893
The Sound Lab Inc, pg 894
Stage Directions, pg 898
TM Studios Inc, pg 915
TopCat Records LLC, pg 915
Tropikal Productions, pg 918
World Beat Studio, pg 941

UTAH
Soularium Recording Studios,
   pg 893

VERMONT
University of Vermont, Instructional
   Television Dept, pg 923

VIRGINIA
AudioImage Recording, pg 695
BES Studios, pg 704
Wally Cleaver's Recording Service,
   pg 726
Henninger Media Services, pg 779
Mark Sonder Productions &
   Entertainment Agency, pg 817
Metro Productions, pg 824
Studio Center Corp, pg 902

WASHINGTON
D A Sound, pg 737
Hamilton Studio, pg 775
Inland Audio Visual Co, pg 788
Kostov Productions, pg 801
North-by-Northwest - A Digital
   Studio, pg 842
Sound Sound, pg 894

WEST VIRGINIA

Sweetsong Productions, pg 905

WISCONSIN

Concept Productions Inc, pg 730
5th Floor Recording Co, pg 760
USAV Group Inc, pg 923
Wisconsin Public Television, pg 940

WYOMING

Bridger Productions Inc, pg 710

BRITISH COLUMBIA

Pinewood Sound, pg 857

MANITOBA

DACAPO Productions Inc, pg 737

ONTARIO

ADS Media, pg 677
AMPLUS Productions, pg 684
GAPC (General Assembly
   Production Centre), pg 768
JL Recording Studios, pg 794
Morning Music Ltd, pg 830
Nightingale Music Productions Inc,
   pg 841
Silver Creek Media Inc, pg 888
Sound Ideas, pg 894
StockMusic.com, pg 901
Wanted! Sound + Picture, pg 933
Westbury National Show Systems
   Ltd, pg 936

Music Scoring

ALABAMA

Dogwood Productions Inc, pg 745
Sound of Birmingham Productions,
   pg 894

ARIZONA

Creative Backstage, pg 733
Merestone, pg 823

CALIFORNIA

AB Audio Visual Entertainment Inc,
   pg 672
Aliso Creek Productions Inc, pg 680
Backstage Pass Entertainment Inc,
   pg 700
Berkeley Sound Artists Inc, pg 704
Creative Media Recording, pg 733
Creative Support Services/CSS
   Music, pg 733
Creative Technology, pg 733
Crystal Pyramid Productions™,
   pg 735
Diamond Dreams Music
   Productions, pg 741
Earwax Productions Inc, pg 749
48 Windows, pg 764
4th Street Recording, pg 764
Bruce Goldberg Inc, pg 772
GrooveWorx, pg 774
iCorpTv, pg 783
Increase Video/Silver Mine Video,
   pg 786
JDS Video & Media Productions
   Inc, pg 793
Kaleidosound, pg 796
K2B2 Records, pg 802
Lynch Communications, pg 813
Manchester Music Library Inc,
   pg 816
Martinsound Inc, pg 818
Maximus Media Inc, pg 820

The Media Staff Inc, pg 822
MediaMation Inc, pg 822
Megatrax, pg 823
The Music Kitchen Inc, pg 834
Musikvergnuegen, pg 835
Joseph Nicoletti Consulting-
   Promotion, pg 841
OTR Studios, pg 848
Palardo Productions, pg 850
PM Productions, pg 858
Polarity Post Production, pg 858
Private Island Audio Inc, pg 862
Pyramind Studios, pg 867
QRS Software Services, pg 867
Reality Check Systems, pg 871
Russ InVision Co/AbridgeClub.com,
   pg 879
Sahara Records & Filmworks
   Entertainment Co, pg 879
Saturn Studios, pg 881
Steve Shapiro Music, pg 885
Sonic Gravy, pg 892
SonicPool, pg 892
Sonora Recorders, pg 893
Still N' Motion, pg 901
Studio Circle Recordings, pg 902
Studio 132, pg 902
Timeless Productions, pg 914
Total Creative, pg 916

COLORADO

Tim Cissell Music, pg 725
Colorado Sound Recording Ltd,
   pg 728
Conly Productions, pg 730
Los Angeles Post Music Inc, pg 811

CONNECTICUT

Guymark Studios LLC, pg 775
Palace Production Center, pg 850
P&P Studios Inc, pg 851

DELAWARE

Side Door Studio Inc, pg 887

DISTRICT OF COLUMBIA

Interface Media Group, pg 789

FLORIDA

Audacity Recording Studios, pg 693
Kat Epple Music Productions,
   pg 755
JT Communications, pg 795
The Kitchen, pg 799
LHV Audio Services, pg 807
Mach 1 Productions, pg 813
Phat Planet Recording Studios,
   pg 855
Sunfire Communications Inc,
   pg 904
Mike Vasilinda Productions Inc,
   pg 925

GEORGIA

Crawford Media Services Inc,
   pg 733
Stage Front Presentation Systems,
   pg 899
White Dog Studios, pg 937

HAWAII

Media Bridge Gamekids, pg 821

ILLINOIS

ABS Enterprises, pg 672
Mightybytes Inc, pg 827
Jim Passin Productions, pg 852
Pepper Group, pg 854

RBR Productions, pg 870
Steven Samler Music & Sound,
   pg 879
Sound/Video Impressions Inc,
   pg 894
WEEK TV, pg 935
Woodside Avenue Music
   Productions Inc, pg 941

INDIANA

Gaither Studios LLC, pg 767
Alan Johnson Recording, pg 794

IOWA

Hedquist Productions Inc, pg 778

LOUISIANA

Disk Productions Inc, pg 743
Vidox Motion Imagery, pg 930

MARYLAND

CPR MultiMedia Solutions, pg 732
dbF a Media Company, pg 739
Kramer Communications Video
   Production, pg 801
Lion & Fox Recording Studios,
   pg 809
Omega Recording Studios, pg 845
Satellite Media Production, pg 881

MASSACHUSETTS

Continental Recordings Inc, pg 731
Green Mountain Post Films (GMP),
   pg 774
Penfield Productions Ltd, pg 853
Professional Audio Design Inc,
   pg 865
Sounds Interesting Studio, pg 894
Soundtrack Group, pg 895
Rik Tinory Productions, pg 914
TR Productions, pg 916

MICHIGAN

Audio Graphic Services, pg 693
Digi Sign Design LLC, pg 741
Digital Image Studios LLC, pg 742
GMP Music, pg 772
K&R's Recording Studios Inc,
   pg 796
MessageMakers, pg 824
Rebirth Inc, pg 871
RingSide Creative, pg 875

MINNESOTA

The ADS Group, pg 676
BeyerSound & Essay Audio, pg 705

MONTANA

Jereco Studios Inc, pg 793

NEVADA

Tanglewood Productions, pg 907

NEW HAMPSHIRE

Captain Fiddle Music &
   Publications, pg 716
Chip Taylor Communications LLC,
   pg 907

NEW JERSEY

Allegro Productions Inc, pg 680
CFP Video Productions Inc, pg 720
Composer Louis Anthony deLise,
   pg 729
Jeep Jazz Media Solutions, pg 793
Mia Mind Music, pg 825

Milbrodt/Music & Sound Design,
   pg 827
Milgrom Productions, pg 827
NFL Films Inc, pg 841
NFL Films Music Library, pg 841
Richard Reiter Productions Inc,
   pg 873
Suede Interactive, pg 903
TRF Production Music Libraries,
   pg 917

NEW YORK

Air Sea Land Productions Inc
   (ASL), pg 678
Aural Gratification Inc, pg 695
Big Fish Production US, pg 705
The Big House Group, pg 705
Chromavision Corp, pg 723
Fingerpaint, pg 761
HB-Content, pg 777
Headroom Digital Audio, pg 777
Heavy Melody, pg 778
IAI Records & Video, pg 783
Icontent, pg 783
KAS Music & Sound, pg 796
Manhattan Production Music Inc,
   pg 816
Jack Morton Worldwide, pg 830
New York Audio Productions,
   pg 840
The Palmer Group, pg 850
Propeller Music & Sound Design
   Inc, pg 865
David Rapkin Audio Production,
   pg 870
Round Hill Music LLC, pg 878
Elliot Sokolov Music, pg 892
Sony Music Entertainment, pg 893
Tiki Recording Studios Inc, pg 914
Zelman Studios Ltd, pg 945

NORTH CAROLINA

Audio Art, pg 693
Franklin Video Inc, pg 765
Horizon Video Productions Inc,
   pg 781
Trailblazer Studios®, pg 917
2BruceStudio, pg 920

NORTH DAKOTA

Media Productions, pg 822

OHIO

Challenge Productions/Challenge
   Aerial Imaging, pg 720
Mills James Productions, pg 828

OKLAHOMA

Garman Productions LLC, pg 768

OREGON

Odyssey Productions Inc, pg 844
REX, pg 874

PENNSYLVANIA

Dreambox Media Inc, pg 746
Filmaker Technology, pg 760
Monster Tracks, pg 829
Production Masters Inc (PMI),
   pg 864

RHODE ISLAND

Sound-FX-Design, pg 894
StarTrak Studios Inc, pg 900

AUDIO

Music Scoring (continued)

TENNESSEE

American Blackguard Inc, pg 683
Analog Man Recording Studio, pg 685
Compass Records, pg 729
Motion Picture Services, pg 831
Stage Post, pg 899
Zion Music Group, pg 945

TEXAS

AMS Pictures, pg 684
Audiomoxie®, pg 695
Biway Media, pg 706
Communication Arts Multimedia Inc, pg 728
Mediaforce Productions, pg 822
The Music Bakery, pg 834
Reelsound Recording Co, pg 872
The Samuels Co, pg 879
The Sound Lab Inc, pg 894
Stage Directions, pg 898
TM Studios Inc, pg 915
Tropikal Productions, pg 918

UTAH

Soularium Recording Studios, pg 893

VERMONT

University of Vermont, Instructional Television Dept, pg 923

VIRGINIA

AudioImage Recording, pg 695
BES Studios, pg 704
Wally Cleaver's Recording Service, pg 726
Studio Center Corp, pg 902

WASHINGTON

Hamilton Studio, pg 775
Inland Audio Visual Co, pg 788
Kostov Productions, pg 801
North-by-Northwest - A Digital Studio, pg 842
Sound Sound, pg 894

WISCONSIN

5th Floor Recording Co, pg 760
USAV Group Inc, pg 923

WYOMING

Bridger Productions Inc, pg 710

BRITISH COLUMBIA

Pinewood Sound, pg 857

MANITOBA

DACAPO Productions Inc, pg 737

ONTARIO

ADS Media, pg 677
GAPC (General Assembly Production Centre), pg 768
Nightingale Music Productions Inc, pg 841

New Age Music, *see* Music Libraries—New Age

Noise Reducer Distributors

ARIZONA

EAR Professional Audio/Video, pg 749
Troxell-CDI, pg 918
David Wexler & Co, pg 936

CALIFORNIA

Ametron Audio/Video, pg 684
ARS Electronics, pg 690
Associated Sound, pg 691
Audio Images Corp, pg 693
Be Media, pg 702
Location Sound Corp, pg 810
MediaPOINTE, pg 823
Sound Service Co, pg 894
Towards 2000 Inc, pg 916
VMI Inc, pg 932

COLORADO

Audio Consultant Services Inc, pg 693

DELAWARE

Actors Attic, pg 675

FLORIDA

Access Media Group, pg 673
Altel Systems Group Inc, pg 682
Broadcasters General Store Inc, pg 711
Digital Video Systems, pg 742
Hi-Tech Enterprises Inc, pg 779
Lighting Sales Connection Inc, pg 808
ONstage, pg 846
Recording Media & Equipment Inc (RM&E), pg 872
Stereo Sales Inc, pg 900
TAI Audio, pg 906
Technomedia Solutions, pg 909

GEORGIA

Clark, pg 725
Lighting & Production Equipment Inc, pg 807
Stage Front Presentation Systems, pg 899

HAWAII

The Audio Visual Co (AVCO), pg 694

ILLINOIS

Allen Visual Systems Inc, pg 680
Quintessence Audio Ltd, pg 868
Woodside Avenue Music Productions Inc, pg 941

INDIANA

Sensory Technologies LLC, pg 884
SHP Electronics, pg 887
Sweetwater Sound Inc, pg 905

KENTUCKY

Audio Visual Techniques Inc, pg 695
Axxis Leasing Inc, pg 700
NOR-COM Inc, pg 841

MAINE

Headlight Audio Visual Inc, pg 777
Independent Audio Inc, pg 786

MARYLAND

Bradley Broadcast & Pro Audio, pg 709

MASSACHUSETTS

Professional Audio Design Inc, pg 865
Rule Boston Camera, pg 878
Silent Source, pg 888

MICHIGAN

Olson Anderson Co, pg 685
Digi Sign Design LLC, pg 741
TEL Systems LLC, pg 909

MINNESOTA

NetWell Noise Control, pg 838

NEW HAMPSHIRE

Technet® Systems Group, pg 908

NEW JERSEY

Alltec Stores, a Vcom IMC Company, pg 681
Panasonic Industrial Devices Sales Company of America, pg 850
Starlite, pg 900
Wired 4 Sound Inc, pg 940
Yorktel, pg 944

NEW YORK

Audio-Video Corp, pg 694
BTX Technologies, pg 712
Colortone Audio Visual, pg 728
Design Audio Visual Inc, pg 741
DSan Corp, pg 747
HAVE Inc, pg 777
Toys From The Attic, pg 916

OHIO

ITA Audio Visual Solutions, pg 791

OKLAHOMA

Ford AV, pg 763

OREGON

ASC-Tube Trap, pg 690
TARA Labs, pg 907

PENNSYLVANIA

Advanced AV LLC, pg 677
Grise Audio Visual Center Inc, pg 774
Vistacom Inc, pg 931

TENNESSEE

Allstar Audio Systems Inc, pg 681
Lowrance Sound Co Inc, pg 812
Mr Mark's Used Musical, Stereo & Studio Equipment Store, pg 828
Spectrum Sound Inc, pg 897
Technical Support Systems LLC, pg 908
WhisperRoom™ Inc, pg 937

TEXAS

AVES Audio Visual Systems Inc, pg 698
Lubbock Audio Visual Inc, pg 812
Pro Video & Film Equipment Co Inc, pg 863
RF Specialties of Texas LLC, pg 874
Southwest Sound Solutions, pg 896
Tarpley Media Systems, pg 907

UTAH

Performance Audio LLC, pg 854

VIRGINIA

Avitecture Inc, pg 699
Intellidyne LLC, pg 789
Rocktown Media, pg 876

WASHINGTON

CCI Solutions, pg 718
Northern Lights & Pro Audio, pg 842
PNTA, pg 858

WISCONSIN

Audio Visual of Milwaukee Inc, pg 694
Full Compass Systems, pg 767

PUERTO RICO

Audio Visual Concepts Inc, pg 694
Bonnin Electronics Inc, pg 708

ALBERTA

Evolution AV, pg 757
Infosat Communications Inc, pg 787
Matrix Video Communications Corp (MVCC), pg 819

BRITISH COLUMBIA

Commercial Electronics Ltd, pg 728

MANITOBA

Advance Pro, pg 677
Inland Audio Visual Ltd, pg 788

ONTARIO

Cinema Stage Inc, pg 724
Westbury National Show Systems Ltd, pg 936

QUEBEC

SC Media Canada, pg 881

Noise Reducer Manufacturers

CALIFORNIA

FM Systems Inc, pg 763
Furman®, pg 767
Mackenzie Laboratories Inc, pg 814

FLORIDA

Compuvideo Sales USA Ltd, pg 729

ILLINOIS

Esoteric Sound, pg 755
J K Audio Inc, pg 792

MINNESOTA

NetWell Noise Control, pg 838

NEW JERSEY

Panasonic Industrial Devices Sales Company of America, pg 850

NEW YORK

acouStaCorp, pg 674
Allen Avionics Inc, pg 680
Broadcast Devices Inc, pg 710
DSan Corp, pg 747

NORTH CAROLINA

Micro Technology Unlimited Inc, pg 826

OHIO

Omnia Audio, pg 845

OREGON

ASC-Tube Trap, pg 690
TARA Labs, pg 907

TENNESSEE

WhisperRoom™ Inc, pg 937

TEXAS

ETA Systems, pg 756
ETS-Lindgren, pg 756
International Cellulose Corp, pg 790

VIRGINIA

Acoustical Solutions LLC, pg 674

BRITISH COLUMBIA

Primacoustic, pg 862

Noise Reducer Rentals

ALABAMA

Audio-Video Resources Inc, pg 694

ARIZONA

Merestone, pg 823
Video West Inc, pg 929

CALIFORNIA

Alliant Event Services, pg 681
Ametron Audio/Video, pg 684
Associated Sound, pg 691
Audio Rents, pg 693
Express Media Inc, pg 757
McCune Audio-Video-Lighting, pg 821
Munday & Collins AV, pg 834
On-Trax Inc, pg 846
Towards 2000 Inc, pg 916
VER, pg 926

COLORADO

Audio Consultant Services Inc, pg 693

CONNECTICUT

A/V Davey, pg 697

DELAWARE

Actors Attic, pg 675

FLORIDA

Lighting Sales Connection Inc, pg 808
ONstage, pg 846
TAI Audio, pg 906

GEORGIA

Lighting & Production Equipment Inc, pg 807
Stage Front Presentation Systems, pg 899

HAWAII

Sight & Sound Studios, pg 887

ILLINOIS

OSA International Inc, pg 848
Resolution Productions Group, pg 874
Woodside Avenue Music Productions Inc, pg 941

KENTUCKY

Audio Visual Techniques Inc, pg 695

MARYLAND

CPR MultiMedia Solutions, pg 732
Maryland Sound International Holding Co LLC, pg 819

MASSACHUSETTS

AVFX Inc, pg 698
Preston Productions Inc, pg 861

MICHIGAN

Digi Sign Design LLC, pg 741
K&R All Media Productions LLC, pg 796
K&R's Recording Studios Inc, pg 796

MINNESOTA

Big Event Productions LLC, pg 705

MISSOURI

Show-Me Audio-Visual, pg 887

NEVADA

GES Audio Visual, pg 770

NEW JERSEY

Audio Visual Dynamics®, pg 694
CFP Video Productions Inc, pg 720
PLS Staging, pg 858
Starlite, pg 900
Wired 4 Sound Inc, pg 940

NEW YORK

All Mobile Video Inc, pg 680
Colortone Audio Visual, pg 728
CP Communications, pg 732
Design Audio Visual Inc, pg 741
Manhattan Center Studios Inc, pg 816

PENNSYLVANIA

Advanced AV LLC, pg 677
Grise Audio Visual Center Inc, pg 774

TENNESSEE

Allstar Audio Systems Inc, pg 681
Mr Mark's Used Musical, Stereo & Studio Equipment Store, pg 828
Technical Support Systems LLC, pg 908

TEXAS

Lubbock Audio Visual Inc, pg 812
Onstage Systems, pg 846
Stage Directions, pg 898

UTAH

Performance Audio LLC, pg 854

VIRGINIA

American AV, pg 682

WASHINGTON

PNTA, pg 858

WISCONSIN

Full Compass Systems, pg 767

PUERTO RICO

Stage Crew Audiovisual Inc, pg 898

BRITISH COLUMBIA

Commercial Electronics Ltd, pg 728

MANITOBA

Inland Audio Visual Ltd, pg 788

ONTARIO

RB Productions, pg 870
Westbury National Show Systems Ltd, pg 936

Noise Reducer Repairs

CALIFORNIA

Ametron Audio/Video, pg 684
Audio Images Corp, pg 693
McAlister Electronics, pg 820
Towards 2000 Inc, pg 916

CONNECTICUT

HB Communications Inc, pg 777

FLORIDA

Hi-Tech Enterprises Inc, pg 779
Phat Planet Recording Studios, pg 855
Stereo Sales Inc, pg 900
TAI Audio, pg 906

GEORGIA

Lighting & Production Equipment Inc, pg 807
Stage Front Presentation Systems, pg 899

INDIANA

Sweetwater Sound Inc, pg 905

KENTUCKY

Axxis Leasing Inc, pg 700
NOR-COM Inc, pg 841

MASSACHUSETTS

Professional Audio Design Inc, pg 865

MICHIGAN

K&R's Recording Studios Inc, pg 796
TEL Systems LLC, pg 909

NEW JERSEY

Starlite, pg 900

NEW YORK

Toys From The Attic, pg 916

NORTH CAROLINA

Micro Technology Unlimited Inc, pg 826

OREGON

All Service Musical Electronics Repair, pg 680

TENNESSEE

Technical Support Systems LLC, pg 908

TEXAS

Southwest Sound Solutions, pg 896
Tarpley Media Systems, pg 907

VIRGINIA

Avitecture Inc, pg 699

WASHINGTON

PNTA, pg 858

WISCONSIN

Full Compass Systems, pg 767

ALBERTA

Infosat Communications Inc, pg 787

BRITISH COLUMBIA

Commercial Electronics Ltd, pg 728

MANITOBA

Inland Audio Visual Ltd, pg 788

ONTARIO

Westbury National Show Systems Ltd, pg 936

QUEBEC

SC Media Canada, pg 881

Optical Sound Recording, *see* Sound Recording— Optical

Original Music, *see* Music—Original

Part & Accessory Distributors

ARIZONA

Arizona Cine Equipment, pg 688
Troxell-CDI, pg 918
WindTech™ Microphone Windscreens & Accessories, pg 939

ARKANSAS

Jay S Stanley & Associates Inc, pg 899

CALIFORNIA

Adaptive Technologies Group Inc, pg 675
Advanced Systems Group LLC, pg 677
Ametron Audio/Video, pg 684
Apex Jr, pg 687
ARS Electronics, pg 690
Associated Sound, pg 691
Audio Images Corp, pg 693
Be Media, pg 702
BroadcastStore.com, pg 711

AUDIO

Part & Accessory Distributors (continued)

CALIFORNIA (continued)

California Tape Products Inc, pg 714
Carvin Amps & Audio, pg 717
Christy's Editorial, pg 723
DigiTech, pg 742
El Mar Plastics Inc, pg 752
Electronic Design Solutions Inc, pg 752
Empire Pro, pg 753
Hosa Technology Inc, pg 781
IAMP Professional Audio, pg 783
Instructional Materials & Equipment Distributors (I-Med), pg 789
Jameco Electronics, pg 792
JD Audio Visual Inc, pg 793
The LAST Factory, pg 804
Magnet Sales & Manufacturing Inc, pg 814
Lloyd F McKinney Associates Inc, pg 821
Media Fabricators Inc, pg 822
MediaPOINTE, pg 823
Orevox USA Corp, pg 847
Professional Sound Corp, pg 865
Signal Transport, pg 887
Sound Service Co, pg 894
Southern California Sound Image Inc, pg 895
SSL Industries Inc, pg 898
TOA Electronics Inc, pg 915
Towards 2000 Inc, pg 916
Yamaha Electronics Corp, pg 943
Zack Electronics Inc, pg 945

COLORADO

Audio Consultant Services Inc, pg 693
Case Logic Inc, pg 717
Ceavco Audio Visual Company Inc, pg 719

CONNECTICUT

Connecticut Audio & Theatrical Supply, pg 731
HB Communications Inc, pg 777
MAVCO, pg 820
The Music People Inc, pg 834
Rockwell Communications Inc, pg 876
Sennheiser Electronic Corp, pg 884

DELAWARE

Actors Attic, pg 675

FLORIDA

AMP Services Inc, pg 684
Broadcasters General Store Inc, pg 711
Digital Video Systems, pg 742
Hi-Tech Import Export Corp, pg 779
Intermark Industries Inc, pg 789
Midtown Video Inc, pg 827
ONstage, pg 846
Recording Media & Equipment Inc (RM&E), pg 872
Stereo Sales Inc, pg 900
Straight Wire Inc, pg 901
TAI Audio, pg 906
Tallahassee Audio Visual, pg 906
Technomedia Solutions, pg 909

GEORGIA

Audio Visual Resources Inc, pg 695
Baker Audio Visual, pg 700
Convergent Media Systems, pg 731
Lighting & Production Equipment Inc, pg 807
Stage Front Presentation Systems, pg 899
Visioneering International Inc, pg 931

HAWAII

The Audio Visual Co (AVCO), pg 694

ILLINOIS

Allen Visual Systems Inc, pg 680
Clark Wire & Cable, pg 725
Joseph Electronics, pg 795
C V Lloyde, pg 810
On Site Video, pg 846
Quintessence Audio Ltd, pg 868
Rauland-Borg Corp, pg 870
US Music Corp, pg 923
Woodside Avenue Music Productions Inc, pg 941

INDIANA

Sensory Technologies LLC, pg 884
SHP Electronics, pg 887
Sweetwater Sound Inc, pg 905

KENTUCKY

Audio Visual Techniques Inc, pg 695
Axxis Leasing Inc, pg 700
General Cable, pg 769
Barney Miller's Inc, pg 827
NOR-COM Inc, pg 841

LOUISIANA

Techkno Integration & Design Services LLC, pg 908

MAINE

Independent Audio Inc, pg 786

MARYLAND

Bradley Broadcast & Pro Audio, pg 709
Cardinal Sound & Video, pg 717
Noventri, pg 843
Nicholas P Pipino Associates Inc, pg 857
RTZ Audio Visual, pg 878

MASSACHUSETTS

Professional Audio Design Inc, pg 865

MICHIGAN

Olson Anderson Co, pg 685
City Events Group, pg 725
Digi Sign Design LLC, pg 741
Lowing Light & Grip Inc, pg 812
On Stage Visuals, pg 846
Stedman Corp, pg 900
TEL Systems LLC, pg 909

MINNESOTA

Alpha Video & Audio Inc, pg 682
AVI Systems, pg 698
Cinequipt Inc, pg 724
New Life Communications Inc, pg 839

MISSISSIPPI

Jasper Ewing & Sons Inc, pg 757

MISSOURI

Communitronics Corp, pg 729
Modern Communications Inc, pg 828
The RapcoHorizon Co, pg 870

NEVADA

Selco Products Co, pg 883

NEW HAMPSHIRE

Audio Accessories Inc, pg 693

NEW JERSEY

Alltec Stores, a Vcom IMC Company, pg 681
AlltecPro, pg 681
AV Bluebook, pg 696
Canare Corporation of America, pg 716
Earl Girls Inc, pg 749
FlagHouse, pg 762
HamiltonBuhl, pg 775
Interstate Connecting Components, pg 790
JRF Magnetic Sciences Inc, pg 795
PatchAmp, pg 852
Starlite, pg 900
Tele-Measurements Inc, pg 910
Turner Engineering Inc, pg 919
Vcom IMC, pg 925
Video Corporation of America (VCA), pg 927
Yorktel, pg 944

NEW MEXICO

Quickbeam Systems Inc (QSI), pg 868

NEW YORK

Audio-Video Corp, pg 694
Aura Sonic Ltd (ASL), pg 695
AV Workshop, pg 697
beyerdynamic Inc, pg 704
BTX Technologies, pg 712
Cine 60 Inc, pg 723
Colortone Audio Visual, pg 728
Gaylord Archival, pg 768
HAVE Inc, pg 777
Indigo Productions, pg 787
Langie Audio Visual Systems, pg 803
Long Island Video Enterprises Live Inc, pg 811
Saul Mineroff Electronics Inc (SME), pg 828
Posthorn Recordings, pg 859
Ray Supply Inc, pg 870
RNJ Electronics, pg 875
Russell Industries Inc, pg 879
Sentry Industries Inc, pg 884
Visual Technologies Corp, pg 932
Whirlwind Music Distributors Inc, pg 937

NORTH CAROLINA

Camcor Inc, pg 715
Strategic Connections, pg 901

OHIO

Copp Integrated Systems, pg 731
ITA Audio Visual Solutions, pg 791
Parts Express, pg 851

OREGON

ASC-Tube Trap, pg 690
TARA Labs, pg 907

PENNSYLVANIA

Advanced AV LLC, pg 677
Audio Visions Inc, pg 694
Brodart Co, pg 711
Clair Companies, pg 725
J E Foss Co, pg 764
Grise Audio Visual Center Inc, pg 774
The Lerro Corp, pg 806
Morefield Communications Inc, pg 830
Wire X 17 LLC, pg 940

TENNESSEE

Advanced Sound, pg 677
Allstar Audio Systems Inc, pg 681
Brantley Sound Associates Inc, pg 709
Green Dot Audio Electronics, pg 774
Lowrance Sound Co Inc, pg 812
Memphis Communications Corp, pg 823
Mr Mark's Used Musical, Stereo & Studio Equipment Store, pg 828
Spectrum Sound Inc, pg 897
Technical Support Systems LLC, pg 908
Trew Audio Inc, pg 917

TEXAS

Audio Visual Technologies Group (AVTG), pg 695
Crossroads Audio Inc, pg 735
Data Projections Inc, pg 738
FitzCo Sound Inc, pg 761
Heffernan Audio Visual, pg 778
JSAV, pg 795
Lubbock Audio Visual Inc, pg 812
Precision Camera & Video, pg 861
Quality Audio Visual Service Inc, pg 867
Southwest Sound Solutions, pg 896
Sundance Systems, Fibox Products Division, pg 904
Tarpley Media Systems, pg 907

UTAH

Performance Audio LLC, pg 854
RIA Corp, pg 874

VERMONT

Artech Electronics Ltd, pg 690

VIRGINIA

Acoustics First Corp, pg 674
Avitecture Inc, pg 699
Boitnott Visual Communications Corp (BVC), pg 708
Intellidyne LLC, pg 789
Lee Hartman & Sons Inc, pg 805
Rocktown Media, pg 876
The Whitlock Group, pg 937

WASHINGTON

CCI Solutions, pg 718
D A Sound, pg 737
Daily Electronics Corp, pg 737
Inland Audio Visual Co, pg 788
LOUD Technologies Inc, pg 811

WEST VIRGINIA

United Sound & Electronics, pg 921

WISCONSIN

Audio Visual of Milwaukee Inc, pg 694
Brady Corp, pg 709
Demco Inc, pg 740
Full Compass Systems, pg 767
Safe Harbor Computers, pg 879
School Specialty Inc, pg 882

PUERTO RICO

Audio Visual Concepts Inc, pg 694
Bonnin Electronics Inc, pg 708

ALBERTA

Evolution AV, pg 757
Infosat Communications Inc, pg 787
McBain Camera Ltd, pg 820
Unique Communications Ltd, pg 921

BRITISH COLUMBIA

BeachTek Inc, pg 702
Commercial Electronics Ltd, pg 728

MANITOBA

Advance Pro, pg 677
Inland Audio Visual Ltd, pg 788

ONTARIO

Cinema Stage Inc, pg 724
HD Source, pg 777
KDM Electronics Inc, pg 797
Nationwide Audio Visual Co, pg 837
Westbury National Show Systems Ltd, pg 936
Yorkville Sound Inc, pg 944

QUEBEC

Panavideo Inc, pg 850
SC Media Canada, pg 881
Sennheiser (Canada) Inc, pg 884

Part & Accessory Manufacturers

ARIZONA

AtlasIED, pg 692
NKK Switches of America Inc, pg 841
OmniMount Systems, pg 845
David Wexler & Co, pg 936
WindTech™ Microphone Windscreens & Accessories, pg 939

ARKANSAS

Autogram/CRL, pg 696

CALIFORNIA

Adaptive Technologies Group Inc, pg 675
Ametron Audio/Video, pg 684
AMX® by Harman, pg 685
Aphex, pg 687
Auton Motorized Systems, pg 696
Calrad Electronics, pg 714
Carvin Amps & Audio, pg 717
Digital Music Corp, pg 742
DigiTech, pg 742
Dorrough Electronics Inc, pg 746
El Mar Plastics Inc, pg 752
For-A Corp of America, pg 763
Henry Engineering, pg 779
Hosa Technology Inc, pg 781
Jensen Transformers Inc, pg 793

The LAST Factory, pg 804
LEMO USA Inc, pg 806
Magnet Sales & Manufacturing Inc, pg 814
Opamp Labs Inc, pg 846
Penn Elcom Inc, pg 853
Professional Sound Corp, pg 865
Renkus-Heinz Inc, pg 873
RF Industries, pg 874
The Rip-Tie Co, pg 875
Roland Corp US, pg 876
Signal Transport, pg 887
TeachLogic Inc, pg 908
Thermodyne Cases, pg 912
TOA Electronics Inc, pg 915
Xantech LLC, pg 943
Yamaha Electronics Corp, pg 943
Young Chang America, pg 944

COLORADO

ProLine Digital, pg 865
Rose Packaging & Design Inc, pg 877

CONNECTICUT

The Music People Inc, pg 834
Redco Audio Inc, pg 872
Sennheiser Electronic Corp, pg 884
Vista Group International Inc, pg 931
Winchester Electronics Corp, pg 939

FLORIDA

Imtronics Industries Inc, pg 786
Intermark Industries Inc, pg 789
JT Communications, pg 795
Magna-Tech Electronic Co Inc, pg 814
Straight Wire Inc, pg 901

IDAHO

LEA International, pg 804

ILLINOIS

AmpliVox Portable Sound Systems, pg 684
Bag End Loudspeakers, pg 700
International Electro-Magnetics Inc, pg 790
Rauland-Borg Corp, pg 870
Shure Inc, pg 887
SOTA Sales & Service Center, pg 893
Switchcraft® Inc, pg 905
US Music Corp, pg 923
Waldom Electronics Corp, pg 933

INDIANA

R B Annis Instruments Inc, pg 686
Auralex Acoustics Inc, pg 696
Star Case Manufacturing Co Inc, pg 900

MARYLAND

RCI Custom Products, pg 871
Video Mount Products (VMP), pg 928

MASSACHUSETTS

David Clark Co Inc, pg 738
Eastern Acoustic Works Inc (EAW), pg 749

MICHIGAN

Littlite LLC, pg 810
Stedman Corp, pg 900

MISSISSIPPI

Peavey Electronics Corp, pg 852
Sherwood America Inc, pg 886

MISSOURI

The RapcoHorizon Co, pg 870

NEBRASKA

REI - Radio Engineering Industries, pg 873

NEW HAMPSHIRE

Audio Accessories Inc, pg 693

NEW JERSEY

AlltecPro, pg 681
Astrodyne TDI, pg 691
Canare Corporation of America, pg 716
Comprehensive Cable & Connectivity Co, pg 729
Daburn Electronics & Cable Corp, pg 737
FSR Inc, pg 766
Orban, pg 847
Panasonic Consumer Electronics Co, pg 850
Pro-Tape & Specialities Inc, pg 863
RAMSA Professional Audio Systems, pg 870
Starlite, pg 900
Techflex Inc, pg 908
Turner Engineering Inc, pg 919
Wireworks Corp, pg 940

NEW YORK

ART (Applied Research & Technology Inc), pg 690
beyerdynamic Inc, pg 704
Broadcast Devices Inc, pg 710
BTX Technologies, pg 712
Microwave Filter Co Inc, pg 826
Saul Mineroff Electronics Inc (SME), pg 828
Posthorn Recordings, pg 859
Russell Industries Inc, pg 879
Sescom Inc, pg 884

NORTH CAROLINA

Neutrik® USA Inc, pg 838

OREGON

ASC-Tube Trap, pg 690
TARA Labs, pg 907

PENNSYLVANIA

The Martin Guitar Co, pg 818
Wire X 17 LLC, pg 940

TENNESSEE

Mystery Electronics LLC, pg 835

UTAH

Spectra Sonics LLC, pg 897

VIRGINIA

Acoustics First Corp, pg 674

WASHINGTON

LOUD Technologies Inc, pg 811
Tecplot Inc, pg 909

WISCONSIN

Brady Corp, pg 709
Koss Corp, pg 801

ONTARIO

DW Electrochemicals Ltd, pg 748
KDM Electronics Inc, pg 797
Ward-Beck Systems Ltd, pg 933

Part & Accessory Rentals

ARIZONA

Arizona Cine Equipment, pg 688
Merestone, pg 823

CALIFORNIA

Ametron Audio/Video, pg 684
Associated Sound, pg 691
Express Media Inc, pg 757
Gold Standard Productions, pg 772
Alan Gordon Enterprises Inc, pg 772
IAMP Professional Audio, pg 783
McCune Audio-Video-Lighting, pg 821
Media Fabricators Inc, pg 822
PSAV® Presentation Services, pg 866
Sound Service Co, pg 894
Total Creative, pg 916
Towards 2000 Inc, pg 916

COLORADO

Audio Consultant Services Inc, pg 693

CONNECTICUT

A/V Davey, pg 697
Rockwell Communications Inc, pg 876
Videofilm Systems Inc, pg 929

FLORIDA

Steven Cohen Motion Picture Production, pg 727
ONstage, pg 846
Paradise Show & Design Inc, pg 851
PRI Productions, pg 862
Technomedia Solutions, pg 909

GEORGIA

Convergent Media Systems, pg 731
First Cut Communications LLC, pg 761
Lighting & Production Equipment Inc, pg 807
MAGNUM Companies Ltd, pg 815
Stage Front Presentation Systems, pg 899
Staging Directions Inc, pg 899

ILLINOIS

Allen Visual Systems Inc, pg 680
Helix Camera & Video, pg 778
OSA International Inc, pg 848
Resolution Productions Group, pg 874
Woodside Avenue Music Productions Inc, pg 941

KENTUCKY

Audio Visual Techniques Inc, pg 695

MARYLAND

CPR MultiMedia Solutions, pg 732
Event Tech, pg 756
Maryland Sound International Holding Co LLC, pg 819
RTZ Audio Visual, pg 878

AUDIO

Part & Accessory Rentals
(continued)

MASSACHUSETTS

Capron Lighting & Sound Co Inc, pg 716
massAV, pg 819
Preston Productions Inc, pg 861

MICHIGAN

City Events Group, pg 725
Digi Sign Design LLC, pg 741
K&R All Media Productions LLC, pg 796
K&R's Recording Studios Inc, pg 796
Lowing Light & Grip Inc, pg 812
On Stage Visuals, pg 846
Stedman Corp, pg 900
TEL Systems LLC, pg 909

MINNESOTA

Alpha Video & Audio Inc, pg 682

MISSOURI

ITC, pg 791
Show-Me Audio-Visual, pg 887

NEW HAMPSHIRE

Apertura, pg 686

NEW JERSEY

Audio Visual Dynamics®, pg 694
Earl Girls Inc, pg 749
JRF Magnetic Sciences Inc, pg 795
PLS Staging, pg 858
Starlite, pg 900
Video Corporation of America (VCA), pg 927

NEW MEXICO

Production Outfitters, pg 864

NEW YORK

AV Workshop, pg 697
CP Communications, pg 732
Langie Audio Visual Systems, pg 803
Long Island Video Enterprises Live Inc, pg 811
Posthorn Recordings, pg 859
Specialized Audio-Visual Inc, pg 896
Visual Technologies Corp, pg 932
WorldStage, pg 941

NORTH CAROLINA

AV Metro Inc, pg 697
Special Event Services, pg 896
Strategic Connections, pg 901
Take One Productions Ltd, pg 906

OREGON

Rose City Sound, pg 877

PENNSYLVANIA

Advanced AV LLC, pg 677
Audio Visual Communications Inc, pg 694
Grise Audio Visual Center Inc, pg 774
Visual Sound Inc, pg 931

TENNESSEE

Allstar Audio Systems Inc, pg 681
Brantley Sound Associates Inc, pg 709
Mr Mark's Used Musical, Stereo & Studio Equipment Store, pg 828
Technical Support Systems LLC, pg 908

TEXAS

FitzCo Sound Inc, pg 761
JSAV, pg 795
Music Lab Inc, pg 834

UTAH

Performance Audio LLC, pg 854

VIRGINIA

American AV, pg 682
Boitnott Visual Communications Corp (BVC), pg 708
Lee Hartman & Sons Inc, pg 805
Projection, pg 865

WASHINGTON

D A Sound, pg 737
Inland Audio Visual Co, pg 788
PNTA, pg 858

WEST VIRGINIA

United Sound & Electronics, pg 921

WISCONSIN

Event Essentials, pg 756
Full Compass Systems, pg 767
Wisconsin Public Television, pg 940

WYOMING

Bridger Productions Inc, pg 710

PUERTO RICO

Stage Crew Audiovisual Inc, pg 898

BRITISH COLUMBIA

Clark's Audio Visual Services Ltd, pg 725
Commercial Electronics Ltd, pg 728
DL Sound & Lighting Productions Ltd, pg 744

MANITOBA

Inland Audio Visual Ltd, pg 788

ONTARIO

Westbury National Show Systems Ltd, pg 936

QUEBEC

Panavideo Inc, pg 850

Part & Accessory Repairs

CALIFORNIA

Ametron Audio/Video, pg 684
Audio Images Corp, pg 693
Alan Gordon Enterprises Inc, pg 772
McAlister Electronics, pg 820
Sound Service Co, pg 894
TOA Electronics Inc, pg 915
Towards 2000 Inc, pg 916

CONNECTICUT

HB Communications Inc, pg 777
Rockwell Communications Inc, pg 876
Sennheiser Electronic Corp, pg 884

FLORIDA

AMP Services Inc, pg 684
JT Communications, pg 795
Stereo Sales Inc, pg 900

GEORGIA

Audio Visual Resources Inc, pg 695
Lighting & Production Equipment Inc, pg 807
Stage Front Presentation Systems, pg 899

ILLINOIS

Allen Visual Systems Inc, pg 680
Midwest Digital Corp, pg 827

KENTUCKY

NOR-COM Inc, pg 841

MAINE

Headlight Audio Visual Inc, pg 777

MARYLAND

RTZ Audio Visual, pg 878

MICHIGAN

K&R's Recording Studios Inc, pg 796
Stedman Corp, pg 900
TEL Systems LLC, pg 909

MINNESOTA

AVI Systems, pg 698

NEW JERSEY

Earl Girls Inc, pg 749
Starlite, pg 900

NEW YORK

beyerdynamic Inc, pg 704
Colortone Audio Visual, pg 728
Langie Audio Visual Systems, pg 803
Visual Technologies Corp, pg 932

NORTH CAROLINA

Camcor Inc, pg 715
Strategic Connections, pg 901

OHIO

Icom Multimedia, pg 783

TENNESSEE

db electronics, pg 739
Memphis Communications Corp, pg 823
Technical Support Systems LLC, pg 908

TEXAS

Southwest Sound Solutions, pg 896

VIRGINIA

Avitecture Inc, pg 699

WASHINGTON

D A Sound, pg 737

WISCONSIN

Full Compass Systems, pg 767

ALBERTA

Infosat Communications Inc, pg 787

BRITISH COLUMBIA

Commercial Electronics Ltd, pg 728

MANITOBA

Inland Audio Visual Ltd, pg 788

ONTARIO

Westbury National Show Systems Ltd, pg 936

Phonograph Equipment & Supply Distributors

ALABAMA

Curtis Company, pg 736

ARIZONA

Troxell-CDI, pg 918

CALIFORNIA

Ametron Audio/Video, pg 684
Assured Audio Visual, pg 691
Audio Images Corp, pg 693
Instructional Materials & Equipment Distributors (I-Med), pg 789
The LAST Factory, pg 804
Parasound Products Inc, pg 851
Pioneer Electronics (USA) Inc, pg 857
Sound Service Co, pg 894
Sounds Unique, pg 895
Sumiko Inc, pg 903
Towards 2000 Inc, pg 916

COLORADO

Audio Consultant Services Inc, pg 693

CONNECTICUT

HB Communications Inc, pg 777
MAVCO, pg 820
The Music People Inc, pg 834

DELAWARE

Actors Attic, pg 675

FLORIDA

Alliance Entertainment Corp (AEC) LLC, pg 680
Broadcasters General Store Inc, pg 711
Harris Corp, pg 776
Hi-Tech Import Export Corp, pg 779
ONstage, pg 846
Recording Media & Equipment Inc (RM&E), pg 872
Stereo Sales Inc, pg 900
Tallahassee Audio Visual, pg 906

GEORGIA

Audio Visual Resources Inc, pg 695
Lighting & Production Equipment Inc, pg 807

HAWAII

The Audio Visual Co (AVCO), pg 694

ILLINOIS

Central Audio-Visual Equipment Inc, pg 719
Esoteric Sound, pg 755
Joseph Electronics, pg 795
LKG Industries Inc, pg 810
Quintessence Audio Ltd, pg 868

KANSAS

KK Office Solutions Inc, pg 799

KENTUCKY

NOR-COM Inc, pg 841

MAINE

Headlight Audio Visual Inc, pg 777

MARYLAND

Bradley Broadcast & Pro Audio, pg 709
Cardinal Sound & Video, pg 717
Nicholas P Pipino Associates Inc, pg 857
RTZ Audio Visual, pg 878

MICHIGAN

City Events Group, pg 725

MINNESOTA

Magnepan Inc, pg 814

MISSISSIPPI

Bowie Audio Visual Enterprises Inc, pg 709

MISSOURI

Conference Technologies Inc, pg 730
ITC, pg 791
Schiller's Audio-Visual, pg 881

NEW HAMPSHIRE

Technet® Systems Group, pg 908

NEW JERSEY

Alltec Stores, a Vcom IMC Company, pg 681
AlltecPro, pg 681
AV Bluebook, pg 696
FlagHouse, pg 762
G&G Technologies Inc, pg 768
HamiltonBuhl, pg 775
Starlite, pg 900
Vcom IMC, pg 925
Wired 4 Sound Inc, pg 940
Yorktel, pg 944

NEW YORK

AV Workshop, pg 697
Colortone Audio Visual, pg 728
Gaylord Archival, pg 768
Hot House Professional Audio, pg 782
Indigo Productions, pg 787
Langie Audio Visual Systems, pg 803
Music Hall LLC, pg 834
RNJ Electronics, pg 875
Russell Industries Inc, pg 879
Sound by Singer Ltd, pg 893
Toys From The Attic, pg 916
Visual Technologies Corp, pg 932

NORTH CAROLINA

Camcor Inc, pg 715

OHIO

Audio Visual Media, pg 694

PENNSYLVANIA

Advanced AV LLC, pg 677
Audio Visions Inc, pg 694
Brodart Co, pg 711
J E Foss Co, pg 764
Grise Audio Visual Center Inc, pg 774
The Lerro Corp, pg 806
Morefield Communications Inc, pg 830
Visual Sound Inc, pg 931

TENNESSEE

Mr Mark's Used Musical, Stereo & Studio Equipment Store, pg 828
Technical Support Systems LLC, pg 908

TEXAS

Audio Visual Technologies Group (AVTG), pg 695
Cinema Antiques, pg 723
Crossroads Audio Inc, pg 735
JSAV, pg 795
Lubbock Audio Visual Inc, pg 812
Tarpley Media Systems, pg 907

UTAH

Performance Audio LLC, pg 854
Webb Audio Visual, pg 935

VERMONT

Artech Electronics Ltd, pg 690

VIRGINIA

Boitnott Visual Communications Corp (BVC), pg 708
Lee Hartman & Sons Inc, pg 805
The Whitlock Group, pg 937

WASHINGTON

Inland Audio Visual Co, pg 788

WISCONSIN

Audio Visual of Milwaukee Inc, pg 694
Camera Corner Connecting Point, pg 715
Full Compass Systems, pg 767
School Specialty Inc, pg 882

PUERTO RICO

Bonnin Electronics Inc, pg 708

ALBERTA

McBain Camera Ltd, pg 820

BRITISH COLUMBIA

Commercial Electronics Ltd, pg 728

MANITOBA

Advance Pro, pg 677
Inland Audio Visual Ltd, pg 788

ONTARIO

Nationwide Audio Visual Co, pg 837
Westbury National Show Systems Ltd, pg 936

QUEBEC

JAM Industries Ltd, pg 792

Phonograph Equipment & Supply Manufacturers

ARIZONA

Radio Design Labs (RDL), pg 869

CALIFORNIA

Califone International Inc, pg 714
The LAST Factory, pg 804
Nady Systems Inc, pg 835
Parasound Products Inc, pg 851
Pioneer Electronics (USA) Inc, pg 857
Sumiko Inc, pg 903

IDAHO

Transtector Systems Inc, pg 917

ILLINOIS

Esoteric Sound, pg 755
LKG Industries Inc, pg 810
Shure Inc, pg 887
SOTA Sales & Service Center, pg 893

INDIANA

Klipsch Group Inc, pg 799

NEW JERSEY

AlltecPro, pg 681
Pro-Tape & Specialities Inc, pg 863
Technics, pg 909

NEW YORK

GLI Sound Systems, pg 771
Harbro Corp, pg 776
Music Hall LLC, pg 834
Russell Industries Inc, pg 879

OHIO

Audio-Technica US Inc, pg 694

TENNESSEE

Stanton Magnetics, pg 900

UTAH

Rolls Corp, pg 877

Phonograph Equipment & Supply Rentals

ARIZONA

Merestone, pg 823

CALIFORNIA

Ametron Audio/Video, pg 684
Audio Rents, pg 693
Instructional Materials & Equipment Distributors (I-Med), pg 789
McCune Audio-Video-Lighting, pg 821
Media Fabricators Inc, pg 822
Muse Presentation Technologies, pg 834
Sound Service Co, pg 894
Towards 2000 Inc, pg 916

COLORADO

Audio Consultant Services Inc, pg 693

CONNECTICUT

A/V Davey, pg 697
Videofilm Systems Inc, pg 929

DELAWARE

Actors Attic, pg 675

FLORIDA

ONstage, pg 846

GEORGIA

Audio Visual Resources Inc, pg 695
Lighting & Production Equipment Inc, pg 807
Staging Directions Inc, pg 899

ILLINOIS

AV Chicago Inc, pg 696
Central Audio-Visual Equipment Inc, pg 719
OSA International Inc, pg 848

KENTUCKY

Audio Visual Techniques Inc, pg 695

LOUISIANA

Pace Systems, pg 849

MARYLAND

Event Tech, pg 756
Nicholas P Pipino Associates Inc, pg 857
RTZ Audio Visual, pg 878

MASSACHUSETTS

AVFX Inc, pg 698
massAV, pg 819
Preston Productions Inc, pg 861

MICHIGAN

City Events Group, pg 725
K&R All Media Productions LLC, pg 796
K&R's Recording Studios Inc, pg 796

MISSISSIPPI

Bowie Audio Visual Enterprises Inc, pg 709

MISSOURI

ITC, pg 791
Show-Me Audio-Visual, pg 887

NEW JERSEY

Starlite, pg 900
Video Corporation of America (VCA), pg 927

NEW YORK

AV Workshop, pg 697
Langie Audio Visual Systems, pg 803
Long Island Video Enterprises Live Inc, pg 811
Visual Technologies Corp, pg 932

NORTH CAROLINA

Special Event Services, pg 896

OHIO

Audio Visual Media, pg 694

AUDIO

Phonograph Equipment & Supply Rentals (continued)

PENNSYLVANIA

Audio Visions Inc, pg 694
Grise Audio Visual Center Inc, pg 774

TENNESSEE

Mr Mark's Used Musical, Stereo & Studio Equipment Store, pg 828
Technical Support Systems LLC, pg 908

TEXAS

Audio Visual Technologies Group (AVTG), pg 695
Crossroads Audio Inc, pg 735
JSAV, pg 795
Lubbock Audio Visual Inc, pg 812
Stage Directions, pg 898

UTAH

Performance Audio LLC, pg 854
Webb Audio Visual, pg 935

VIRGINIA

American AV, pg 682
Lee Hartman & Sons Inc, pg 805

WASHINGTON

Inland Audio Visual Co, pg 788

WEST VIRGINIA

United Sound & Electronics, pg 921

WISCONSIN

Event Essentials, pg 756
Full Compass Systems, pg 767

BRITISH COLUMBIA

Commercial Electronics Ltd, pg 728

MANITOBA

Inland Audio Visual Ltd, pg 788

ONTARIO

Westbury National Show Systems Ltd, pg 936

Phonograph Equipment & Supply Repairs

CALIFORNIA

Ametron Audio/Video, pg 684
Audio Images Corp, pg 693
Instructional Materials & Equipment Distributors (I-Med), pg 789
McAlister Electronics, pg 820
Sound Service Co, pg 894
Towards 2000 Inc, pg 916
Yamaha Electronics Corp, pg 943

CONNECTICUT

HB Communications Inc, pg 777

FLORIDA

JT Communications, pg 795
Stereo Sales Inc, pg 900

GEORGIA

Audio Visual Resources Inc, pg 695
Lighting & Production Equipment Inc, pg 807

KANSAS

KK Office Solutions Inc, pg 799

KENTUCKY

Barney Miller's Inc, pg 827
NOR-COM Inc, pg 841

MARYLAND

Nicholas P Pipino Associates Inc, pg 857
RTZ Audio Visual, pg 878

MICHIGAN

City Events Group, pg 725
K&R's Recording Studios Inc, pg 796
TEL Systems LLC, pg 909

MISSISSIPPI

Bowie Audio Visual Enterprises Inc, pg 709

NEW JERSEY

Starlite, pg 900

NEW YORK

Colortone Audio Visual, pg 728
Langie Audio Visual Systems, pg 803
Toys From The Attic, pg 916
Visual Technologies Corp, pg 932

NORTH CAROLINA

Camcor Inc, pg 715

OHIO

Audio Visual Media, pg 694

OREGON

All Service Musical Electronics Repair, pg 680

PENNSYLVANIA

J E Foss Co, pg 764
Visual Sound Inc, pg 931
Wespen Audio Visual Co, pg 935

TENNESSEE

Technical Support Systems LLC, pg 908

TEXAS

Audio Visual Technologies Group (AVTG), pg 695
Lubbock Audio Visual Inc, pg 812

VIRGINIA

Boitnott Visual Communications Corp (BVC), pg 708
Lee Hartman & Sons Inc, pg 805
The Whitlock Group, pg 937

WASHINGTON

Inland Audio Visual Co, pg 788

WEST VIRGINIA

United Sound & Electronics, pg 921

WISCONSIN

Full Compass Systems, pg 767
School Specialty Inc, pg 882

BRITISH COLUMBIA

Commercial Electronics Ltd, pg 728

MANITOBA

Inland Audio Visual Ltd, pg 788

ONTARIO

Westbury National Show Systems Ltd, pg 936

Player & Recorder Distributors

ALABAMA

Curtis Company, pg 736

ARIZONA

EAR Professional Audio/Video, pg 749
Projector SuperStore LLC, pg 865
Troxell-CDI, pg 918

ARKANSAS

Jay S Stanley & Associates Inc, pg 899
White Diamond Productions LLC, pg 937

CALIFORNIA

Ametron Audio/Video, pg 684
Associated Sound, pg 691
Assured Audio Visual, pg 691
Audio Images Corp, pg 693
Audio/Video Supply Inc, pg 694
BigFoot Mobile Systems, pg 705
Electronic Design Solutions Inc, pg 752
Empire Pro, pg 753
Filmtools®, pg 761
GigaSonic, pg 770
Instructional Materials & Equipment Distributors (I-Med), pg 789
Location Sound Corp, pg 810
Martel Electronics Sales Inc, pg 818
Media Fabricators Inc, pg 822
MediaPOINTE, pg 823
Promax Systems, pg 865
Sound Service Co, pg 894
Sounds Unique, pg 895
Southern California Sound Image Inc, pg 895
SSL Industries Inc, pg 898
Towards 2000 Inc, pg 916
VTP Inc, pg 933
Yamaha Electronics Corp, pg 943

COLORADO

Audio Consultant Services Inc, pg 693
Ceavco Audio Visual Company Inc, pg 719
Spectrum Audio Visual Services, pg 897
Stanco Sales LLC, pg 899

CONNECTICUT

HB Communications Inc, pg 777
MAVCO, pg 820
Rockwell Communications Inc, pg 876

DELAWARE

Actors Attic, pg 675

FLORIDA

Access Media Group, pg 673
Broadcasters General Store Inc, pg 711
Harris Corp, pg 776
Hi-Tech Enterprises Inc, pg 779
Hi-Tech Import Export Corp, pg 779
ONstage, pg 846
Photosound of Orlando Inc, pg 856
Recording Media & Equipment Inc (RM&E), pg 872
Stereo Sales Inc, pg 900
TAI Audio, pg 906
Tallahassee Audio Visual, pg 906

GEORGIA

Audio Visual Resources Inc, pg 695
Baker Audio Visual, pg 700
Convergent Media Systems, pg 731
Lighting & Production Equipment Inc, pg 807
Stage Front Presentation Systems, pg 899

HAWAII

The Audio Visual Co (AVCO), pg 694

ILLINOIS

Allen Visual Systems Inc, pg 680
Central Audio-Visual Equipment Inc, pg 719
Creative Technology (CT), pg 733
Joseph Electronics, pg 795
On Site Video, pg 846
Woodside Avenue Music Productions Inc, pg 941

INDIANA

Sensory Technologies LLC, pg 884
Sweetwater Sound Inc, pg 905

KANSAS

KK Office Solutions Inc, pg 799

KENTUCKY

NOR-COM Inc, pg 841

MAINE

Headlight Audio Visual Inc, pg 777
Independent Audio Inc, pg 786

MARYLAND

Bradley Broadcast & Pro Audio, pg 709
Cardinal Sound & Video, pg 717
Human Circuit, pg 782
Kipp Visual Systems Inc, pg 799
Nicholas P Pipino Associates Inc, pg 857
RTZ Audio Visual, pg 878

MASSACHUSETTS

Professional Audio Design Inc, pg 865

WISCONSIN (column 3, top)

Full Compass Systems, pg 767
School Specialty Inc, pg 882

Sennheiser Electronic Corp, pg 884

Vista Group International Inc, pg 931

MICHIGAN
City Events Group, pg 725
On Stage Visuals, pg 846
TEL Systems LLC, pg 909

MINNESOTA
Alpha Video & Audio Inc, pg 682
AVI Systems, pg 698

MISSISSIPPI
Bowie Audio Visual Enterprises Inc, pg 709

MISSOURI
Communitronics Corp, pg 729
Conference Technologies Inc, pg 730
Production Support Services Inc, pg 864
Schiller's Audio-Visual, pg 881

NEW HAMPSHIRE
APS Lighting-Sound-AV, pg 688
Technet® Systems Group, pg 908

NEW JERSEY
AlltecPro, pg 681
Audio Visual Associates, pg 694
Audio Visual Dynamics®, pg 694
AV Bluebook, pg 696
Entel Systems Inc, pg 754
FlagHouse, pg 762
G&G Technologies Inc, pg 768
HamiltonBuhl, pg 775
Learning Ally, pg 805
PatchAmp, pg 852
Starlite, pg 900
Tele-Measurements Inc, pg 910
Vcom IMC, pg 925
Video Corporation of America (VCA), pg 927
Wired 4 Sound Inc, pg 940
Yorktel, pg 944

NEW YORK
American Video Inc, pg 684
Aura Sonic Ltd (ASL), pg 695
AV Workshop, pg 697
Colortone Audio Visual, pg 728
Flash Electronics Inc, pg 762
Gaylord Archival, pg 768
Indigo Productions, pg 787
KVL Audio Visual Services Inc, pg 802
Long Island Video Enterprises Live Inc, pg 811
Saul Mineroff Electronics Inc (SME), pg 828
Ray Supply Inc, pg 870
RNJ Electronics, pg 875
Visual Technologies Corp, pg 932

NORTH CAROLINA
Camcor Inc, pg 715
Strategic Connections, pg 901

OHIO
Audio Visual Media, pg 694
Copp Integrated Systems, pg 731
Icom Multimedia, pg 783
ITA Audio Visual Solutions, pg 791

PENNSYLVANIA
Advanced AV LLC, pg 677
Brodart Co, pg 711
Clair Companies, pg 725
J E Foss Co, pg 764

Garcia Marketing Inc, pg 768
Grise Audio Visual Center Inc, pg 774
The Lerro Corp, pg 806
Morefield Communications Inc, pg 830
Visual Sound Inc, pg 931
Wespen Audio Visual Co, pg 935

TENNESSEE
Allstar Audio Systems Inc, pg 681
Continental Film, pg 731
Lowrance Sound Co Inc, pg 812
Memphis Communications Corp, pg 823
Mr Mark's Used Musical, Stereo & Studio Equipment Store, pg 828
Technical Support Systems LLC, pg 908
Zion Music Group, pg 945

TEXAS
Audio Visual Technologies Group (AVTG), pg 695
AVES Audio Visual Systems Inc, pg 698
CAM Audio Inc, pg 714
Crossroads Audio Inc, pg 735
Data Projections Inc, pg 738
Heffernan Audio Visual, pg 778
JSAV, pg 795
Lubbock Audio Visual Inc, pg 812
Pro Video & Film Equipment Co Inc, pg 863
Stage Directions, pg 898
Tarpley Media Systems, pg 907

UTAH
Performance Audio LLC, pg 854
RIA Corp, pg 874
Webb Audio Visual, pg 935

VIRGINIA
Boitnott Visual Communications Corp (BVC), pg 708
Intellidyne LLC, pg 789
Lee Hartman & Sons Inc, pg 805
The Whitlock Group, pg 937

WASHINGTON
CCI Solutions, pg 718
Inland Audio Visual Co, pg 788

WEST VIRGINIA
United Sound & Electronics, pg 921

WISCONSIN
Audio Visual of Milwaukee Inc, pg 694
Camera Corner Connecting Point, pg 715
Demco Inc, pg 740
Full Compass Systems, pg 767
School Specialty Inc, pg 882

PUERTO RICO
Bonnin Electronics Inc, pg 708

ALBERTA
Evolution AV, pg 757
McBain Camera Ltd, pg 820
Unique Communications Ltd, pg 921

MANITOBA
Advance Pro, pg 677
Inland Audio Visual Ltd, pg 788

ONTARIO
HD Source, pg 777
Nationwide Audio Visual Co, pg 837
Technovision® Interactive Inc, pg 909
Westbury National Show Systems Ltd, pg 936

QUEBEC
JAM Industries Ltd, pg 792

Player & Recorder Manufacturers

CALIFORNIA
Califone International Inc, pg 714
Gilderfluke & Co Inc, pg 771
Laboratories Inc, pg 803
Mackenzie Laboratories Inc, pg 814
Roland Corp US, pg 876
360 Systems, pg 913
Yamaha Electronics Corp, pg 943
Young Chang America, pg 944

COLORADO
Arrakis Systems, pg 689

CONNECTICUT
Alarmco Intelligent Message Repeaters, pg 679
Vista Group International Inc, pg 931

FLORIDA
Magna-Tech Electronic Co Inc, pg 814

ILLINOIS
AmpliVox Portable Sound Systems, pg 684

MICHIGAN
TEL Systems LLC, pg 909

MISSISSIPPI
Peavey Electronics Corp, pg 852

NEW JERSEY
AlltecPro, pg 681
Emerson Radio Corp, pg 753
Panasonic Consumer Electronics Co, pg 850
Panasonic Corporation of North America, pg 850
RAMSA Professional Audio Systems, pg 870

NEW YORK
RCS Enterprises, pg 871
Recordex USA Inc, pg 872

RHODE ISLAND
Numark Industries LP, pg 843

TENNESSEE
Adtec Digital Inc, pg 677

Player & Recorder Rentals

ALABAMA
Audio-Video Resources Inc, pg 694

ARIZONA
Arizona Cine Equipment, pg 688
Merestone, pg 823
Metropolitan Audio-Visual Inc, pg 824
Video West Inc, pg 929

ARKANSAS
White Diamond Productions LLC, pg 937

CALIFORNIA
Absolute Rentals, pg 672
Alliant Event Services, pg 681
Ametron Audio/Video, pg 684
Artichoke Productions, pg 690
Associated Sound, pg 691
Audio Rents, pg 693
BigFoot Mobile Systems, pg 705
Cherry Multimedia, pg 721
Electronic Design Solutions Inc, pg 752
Express Media Inc, pg 757
Gold Standard Productions, pg 772
Golden Gate Studios, pg 772
Hollywood Sound Systems, pg 781
Instructional Materials & Equipment Distributors (I-Med), pg 789
LA Sound Co, pg 803
McCune Audio-Video-Lighting, pg 821
Media Fabricators Inc, pg 822
Munday & Collins AV, pg 834
PSAV® Presentation Services, pg 866
Pyxis Industries Inc, pg 867
Alwin Sauers Audio Productions (ASAP), pg 881
Sound Service Co, pg 894
Towards 2000 Inc, pg 916
VER, pg 926
Warner Bros Production Sound & Video Services, pg 934

COLORADO
Audio Consultant Services Inc, pg 693
Ceavco Audio Visual Company Inc, pg 719
Daylight Productions & Rentals, pg 739
Multimedia Audio Visual Inc, pg 833
Open Media Foundation, pg 846
Spectrum Audio Visual Services, pg 897

CONNECTICUT
A/V Davey, pg 697
Rockwell Communications Inc, pg 876
Videofilm Systems Inc, pg 929

DELAWARE
Showorks Audio Visual Inc, pg 887
Side Door Studio Inc, pg 887

FLORIDA
Access Media Group, pg 673
Accord Productions, pg 673
Steven Cohen Motion Picture Production, pg 727
Miami Daylight Studios, pg 825
ONstage, pg 846
Photosound of Orlando Inc, pg 856
Sight & Sound Productions, pg 887
TAI Audio, pg 906

AUDIO

Player & Recorder Rentals (continued)

FLORIDA (continued)

Tallahassee Audio Visual, pg 906
Universal Studios Florida® Production Group, pg 922

GEORGIA

Audio Visual Resources Inc, pg 695
Convergent Media Systems, pg 731
ECG Productions, pg 750
First Cut Communications LLC, pg 761
Lighting & Production Equipment Inc, pg 807
Stage Front Presentation Systems, pg 899
Staging Directions Inc, pg 899

HAWAII

Hawaii Sound & Vision, pg 777

ILLINOIS

Allen Visual Systems Inc, pg 680
AV Chicago Inc, pg 696
Central Audio-Visual Equipment Inc, pg 719
Creative Technology (CT), pg 733
Helix Camera & Video, pg 778
On Site Video, pg 846
OSA International Inc, pg 848
PSAV® Presentation Services (Hotel Services Division), pg 866
RC Communications, pg 870
SCI Television & Creative Media LLC, pg 882
Woodside Avenue Music Productions Inc, pg 941

INDIANA

Advanced Media Integration, pg 677
Gaither Studios LLC, pg 767
OMNI Productions, pg 845

KENTUCKY

Audio Visual Techniques Inc, pg 695

MAINE

Headlight Audio Visual Inc, pg 777
University of Maine Media Services, pg 922

MARYLAND

Cardinal Sound & Video, pg 717
CPR MultiMedia Solutions, pg 732
Event Tech, pg 756
Hargrove Inc, pg 776
Maryland Sound International Holding Co LLC, pg 819

MASSACHUSETTS

AVFX Inc, pg 698
Capron Lighting & Sound Co Inc, pg 716
Integrated Solutions Group, pg 789
massAV, pg 819
Preston Productions Inc, pg 861
TR Productions, pg 916

MICHIGAN

City Events Group, pg 725
K&R All Media Productions LLC, pg 796

K&R's Recording Studios Inc, pg 796
Madonna University Information Technology, pg 814
On Stage Visuals, pg 846

MINNESOTA

Alpha Video & Audio Inc, pg 682
AVI Systems, pg 698

MISSISSIPPI

Bowie Audio Visual Enterprises Inc, pg 709

MISSOURI

Production Support Services Inc, pg 864
Show-Me Audio-Visual, pg 887

MONTANA

Jereco Studios Inc, pg 793

NEVADA

GES Audio Visual, pg 770
Lefco Video Services Inc, pg 806
MG Studio, pg 825

NEW HAMPSHIRE

Academic & Campus Technology Services, pg 672
APS Lighting-Sound-AV, pg 688

NEW JERSEY

Audio Visual Associates, pg 694
Audio Visual Dynamics®, pg 694
International Audio Visual Inc, pg 790
Panavid, pg 850
PLS Staging, pg 858
Starlite, pg 900

NEW YORK

Adwar Video, pg 678
All Mobile Video Inc, pg 680
American Video Inc, pg 684
Aura Sonic Ltd (ASL), pg 695
AV Workshop, pg 697
Bond Street Studio, pg 708
CMI Communications, pg 727
Colortone Audio Visual, pg 728
CP Communications, pg 732
Hello World Communications, pg 778
KVL Audio Visual Services Inc, pg 802
Langie Audio Visual Systems, pg 803
Long Island Video Enterprises Live Inc, pg 811
Manhattan Center Studios Inc, pg 816
Ray Supply Inc, pg 870
See Factor Industry Inc, pg 883
Specialized Audio-Visual Inc, pg 896
Visual Technologies Corp, pg 932
WorldStage, pg 941

NORTH CAROLINA

AV Metro Inc, pg 697
Special Event Services, pg 896
Strategic Connections, pg 901
Take One Productions Ltd, pg 906

NORTH DAKOTA

Media Productions, pg 822

OHIO

Audio Visual Media, pg 694
Icom Multimedia, pg 783
Vista Color Imaging Inc, pg 931

OREGON

Picture This Production Services, pg 856

PENNSYLVANIA

Advanced AV LLC, pg 677
Audio Visions Inc, pg 694
Audio Visual Communications Inc, pg 694
FMP Media Solutions Inc, pg 763
Grise Audio Visual Center Inc, pg 774
Visual Sound Inc, pg 931

TENNESSEE

Allstar Audio Systems Inc, pg 681
Memphis Communications Corp, pg 823
Mr Mark's Used Musical, Stereo & Studio Equipment Store, pg 828
Technical Support Systems LLC, pg 908

TEXAS

Alford Media Services, pg 680
Audio Visual Technologies Group (AVTG), pg 695
Crossroads Audio Inc, pg 735
Heffernan Audio Visual, pg 778
JSAV, pg 795
Lubbock Audio Visual Inc, pg 812
Omega Productions, pg 845
Stage Directions, pg 898

UTAH

Performance Audio LLC, pg 854
Webb Audio Visual, pg 935

VIRGINIA

American AV, pg 682
Boitnott Visual Communications Corp (BVC), pg 708
Lee Hartman & Sons Inc, pg 805
Projection, pg 865
The Whitlock Group, pg 937

WASHINGTON

Inland Audio Visual Co, pg 788
PNTA, pg 858
Victory Studios, pg 927

WEST VIRGINIA

United Sound & Electronics, pg 921

WISCONSIN

Camera Corner Connecting Point, pg 715
Event Essentials, pg 756
Full Compass Systems, pg 767
School Specialty Inc, pg 882
University of Wisconsin-Oshkosh Radio-TV-Film Dept, pg 923
USAV Group Inc, pg 923
Wisconsin Public Television, pg 940

WYOMING

Bridger Productions Inc, pg 710

PUERTO RICO

Stage Crew Audiovisual Inc, pg 898

ALBERTA

McBain Camera Ltd, pg 820
Unique Communications Ltd, pg 921

BRITISH COLUMBIA

Clark's Audio Visual Services Ltd, pg 725
Commercial Electronics Ltd, pg 728
DL Sound & Lighting Productions Ltd, pg 744
MicrophoneRentals.com, pg 826
Video Out Distribution, pg 928

MANITOBA

Inland Audio Visual Ltd, pg 788

ONTARIO

HD Source, pg 777
SIM Digital, pg 888
Westbury National Show Systems Ltd, pg 936

QUEBEC

Audio Visual Dynamics, pg 694
Freeman Audio Visual, pg 765
Group PVP, pg 774

Player & Recorder Repairs

ARKANSAS

Jay S Stanley & Associates Inc, pg 899

CALIFORNIA

Ametron Audio/Video, pg 684
Audio Images Corp, pg 693
Audio Upgrades, pg 694
Instructional Materials & Equipment Distributors (I-Med), pg 789
Martel Electronics Sales Inc, pg 818
McAlister Electronics, pg 820
Lloyd F McKinney Associates Inc, pg 821
Sound Service Co, pg 894
SSL Industries Inc, pg 898
Towards 2000 Inc, pg 916
Yamaha Electronics Corp, pg 943

COLORADO

Ceavco Audio Visual Company Inc, pg 719

CONNECTICUT

HB Communications Inc, pg 777
Rockwell Communications Inc, pg 876
Sennheiser Electronic Corp, pg 884

FLORIDA

AMP Services Inc, pg 684
Hi-Tech Enterprises Inc, pg 779
JT Communications, pg 795
Phat Planet Recording Studios, pg 855
Stereo Sales Inc, pg 900
TAI Audio, pg 906
Tallahassee Audio Visual, pg 906

GEORGIA

Audio Visual Resources Inc, pg 695
Lighting & Production Equipment Inc, pg 807
Stage Front Presentation Systems, pg 899

ILLINOIS
Allen Visual Systems Inc, pg 680
Central Audio-Visual Equipment
  Inc, pg 719
Midwest Digital Corp, pg 827

INDIANA
Sweetwater Sound Inc, pg 905

KANSAS
KK Office Solutions Inc, pg 799

KENTUCKY
NOR-COM Inc, pg 841

MAINE
Headlight Audio Visual Inc, pg 777

MARYLAND
Cardinal Sound & Video, pg 717
RTZ Audio Visual, pg 878

MASSACHUSETTS
Capron Lighting & Sound Co Inc,
  pg 716
Integrated Solutions Group, pg 789
Professional Audio Design Inc,
  pg 865

MICHIGAN
City Events Group, pg 725
K&R's Recording Studios Inc,
  pg 796
TEL Systems LLC, pg 909

MINNESOTA
AVI Systems, pg 698

MISSISSIPPI
Bowie Audio Visual Enterprises Inc,
  pg 709

MISSOURI
Communitronics Corp, pg 729

NEW JERSEY
Starlite, pg 900

NEW YORK
Adwar Video, pg 678
American Video Inc, pg 684
Colortone Audio Visual, pg 728
Langie Audio Visual Systems,
  pg 803
Ray Supply Inc, pg 870
Visual Technologies Corp, pg 932

NORTH CAROLINA
Camcor Inc, pg 715
Strategic Connections, pg 901

OHIO
Audio Visual Media, pg 694
Copp Integrated Systems, pg 731
Icom Multimedia, pg 783

OREGON
All Service Musical Electronics
  Repair, pg 680

PENNSYLVANIA
J E Foss Co, pg 764
Visual Sound Inc, pg 931
Wespen Audio Visual Co, pg 935

TENNESSEE
Memphis Communications Corp,
  pg 823
Technical Support Systems LLC,
  pg 908

TEXAS
Audio Visual Technologies Group
  (AVTG), pg 695
Heffernan Audio Visual, pg 778
Lubbock Audio Visual Inc, pg 812

VIRGINIA
Avitecture Inc, pg 699
Boitnott Visual Communications
  Corp (BVC), pg 708
Lee Hartman & Sons Inc, pg 805
The Whitlock Group, pg 937

WASHINGTON
Inland Audio Visual Co, pg 788

WEST VIRGINIA
United Sound & Electronics, pg 921

WISCONSIN
Camera Corner Connecting Point,
  pg 715
Full Compass Systems, pg 767
School Specialty Inc, pg 882

ALBERTA
Evolution AV, pg 757
Unique Communications Ltd,
  pg 921

BRITISH COLUMBIA
Commercial Electronics Ltd, pg 728

MANITOBA
Inland Audio Visual Ltd, pg 788

ONTARIO
Technovision® Interactive Inc,
  pg 909
Westbury National Show Systems
  Ltd, pg 936

Popular Music, *see* Music Libraries—Popular

Portable Sound System, *see* Sound System—Portable

Public Address System Distributors

ALABAMA
Curtis Company, pg 736

ARIZONA
Arizona Cine Equipment, pg 688
EAR Professional Audio/Video,
  pg 749
Metropolitan Audio-Visual Inc,
  pg 824

Projector SuperStore LLC, pg 865
Troxell-CDI, pg 918
Ultimate Presentation Systems Inc,
  pg 920

ARKANSAS
Jay S Stanley & Associates Inc,
  pg 899

CALIFORNIA
Ametron Audio/Video, pg 684
Associated Sound, pg 691
Assured Audio Visual, pg 691
ATV Video Center Inc, pg 692
Audio Images Corp, pg 693
Be Media, pg 702
California Tape Products Inc,
  pg 714
Empire Pro, pg 753
Hosa Technology Inc, pg 781
IAMP Professional Audio, pg 783
Instructional Materials & Equipment
  Distributors (I-Med), pg 789
Jaguar Distribution Corp, pg 792
JD Audio Visual Inc, pg 793
L-Acoustics Inc, pg 802
Location Sound Corp, pg 810
Lloyd F McKinney Associates Inc,
  pg 821
MediaPOINTE, pg 823
QSC Audio Products LLC, pg 867
Sonance, pg 892
Sound Service Co, pg 894
Sounds Unique, pg 895
SSL Industries Inc, pg 898
Stanislaus AV Inc, pg 899
TOA Electronics Inc, pg 915
Towards 2000 Inc, pg 916
VMI Inc, pg 932

COLORADO
Audio Consultant Services Inc,
  pg 693
Spectrum Audio Visual Services,
  pg 897

CONNECTICUT
Connecticut Audio & Theatrical
  Supply, pg 731
HB Communications Inc, pg 777

DELAWARE
Actors Attic, pg 675

FLORIDA
Broadcasters General Store Inc,
  pg 711
Digital Video Systems, pg 742
Harmon's Audio-Visual Services,
  pg 776
Harris Corp, pg 776
Hi-Tech Import Export Corp,
  pg 779
Lighting Sales Connection Inc,
  pg 808
ONstage, pg 846
Recording Media & Equipment Inc
  (RM&E), pg 872
Stereo Sales Inc, pg 900
TAI Audio, pg 906
Technomedia Solutions, pg 909

GEORGIA
Baker Audio Visual, pg 700
Lighting & Production Equipment
  Inc, pg 807
Stage Front Presentation Systems,
  pg 899

HAWAII
The Audio Visual Co (AVCO),
  pg 694

ILLINOIS
Allen Visual Systems Inc, pg 680
Central Audio-Visual Equipment
  Inc, pg 719
Joseph Electronics, pg 795
C V Lloyde, pg 810
G T Luscombe Co Inc, pg 812
RC Communications, pg 870

INDIANA
Sensory Technologies LLC, pg 884
SHP Electronics, pg 887
Sweetwater Sound Inc, pg 905

KENTUCKY
Axxis Leasing Inc, pg 700
Barney Miller's Inc, pg 827
NOR-COM Inc, pg 841

MAINE
Headlight Audio Visual Inc, pg 777

MARYLAND
Bradley Broadcast & Pro Audio,
  pg 709
Cardinal Sound & Video, pg 717

MASSACHUSETTS
AirCraft Production Libraries,
  pg 679
Terry Hanley Audio Systems Inc,
  pg 775
Pro AV Systems, pg 862
Professional Audio Design Inc,
  pg 865

MICHIGAN
Olson Anderson Co, pg 685
City Events Group, pg 725
Digi Sign Design LLC, pg 741
On Stage Visuals, pg 846
TEL Systems LLC, pg 909

MINNESOTA
New Life Communications Inc,
  pg 839

MISSISSIPPI
Bowie Audio Visual Enterprises Inc,
  pg 709

MISSOURI
Communitronics Corp, pg 729
Conference Technologies Inc,
  pg 730
Production Support Services Inc,
  pg 864
Schiller's Audio-Visual, pg 881

NEVADA
Pignose-Gorilla, pg 856

NEW HAMPSHIRE
APS Lighting-Sound-AV, pg 688

NEW JERSEY
A-V Services Inc, pg 671
Alltec Stores, a Vcom IMC
  Company, pg 681
AlltecPro, pg 681
Audio Visual Associates, pg 694

AUDIO

Public Address System Distributors (continued)

NEW JERSEY (continued)

AV Bluebook, pg 696
Comprehensive Cable & Connectivity Co, pg 729
Earl Girls Inc, pg 749
HamiltonBuhl, pg 775
Nelson Enterprises Theatrical Supply Co, pg 838
Starlite, pg 900
Total Video Products Inc, pg 916
Video Corporation of America (VCA), pg 927
Wired 4 Sound Inc, pg 940
Yorktel, pg 944

NEW MEXICO

Quickbeam Systems Inc (QSI), pg 868

NEW YORK

ADI Global Distribution, pg 676
Albany Theatre Supply Co Inc, pg 679
Audio-Video Corp, pg 694
AV Workshop, pg 697
Colortone Audio Visual, pg 728
Design Audio Visual Inc, pg 741
Gaylord Archival, pg 768
Hot House Professional Audio, pg 782
Indigo Productions, pg 787
iProbe Multilingual Solutions Inc, pg 791
Korg USA Inc, pg 801
KVL Audio Visual Services Inc, pg 802
Lee Dan® Communications Inc, pg 805
Long Island Video Enterprises Live Inc, pg 811
Markertek Video Supply, pg 817
Neptune Photo Inc, pg 838
RNJ Electronics, pg 875
Theatrical Services & Supplies Inc, pg 912
Visual Word Systems Inc, pg 932

OHIO

Copp Integrated Systems, pg 731
ITA Audio Visual Solutions, pg 791
Luminaud Inc, pg 812
Parts Express, pg 851
Tri-State Audio Visual Co, pg 918

OKLAHOMA

Ford AV, pg 763

OREGON

Lightspeed Technologies Inc, pg 808
PLUS Corp of America, pg 858
SuperDigital Ltd, pg 904

PENNSYLVANIA

Advanced AV LLC, pg 677
Audio Visions Inc, pg 694
Bernie's Photo Center, pg 704
J E Foss Co, pg 764
Grise Audio Visual Center Inc, pg 774
The Lerro Corp, pg 806
Morefield Communications Inc, pg 830

RSS Distributors, pg 878
Sound by Fitch, pg 893
Vistacom Inc, pg 931
Visual Sound Inc, pg 931
Wespen Audio Visual Co, pg 935

TENNESSEE

Allstar Audio Systems Inc, pg 681
Belew Enterprises, pg 703
Lowrance Sound Co Inc, pg 812
Mr Mark's Used Musical, Stereo & Studio Equipment Store, pg 828
Spectrum Sound Inc, pg 897
Technical Support Systems LLC, pg 908
Zion Music Group, pg 945

TEXAS

AVES Audio Visual Systems Inc, pg 698
CAM Audio Inc, pg 714
Crossroads Audio Inc, pg 735
FitzCo Sound Inc, pg 761
Heffernan Audio Visual, pg 778
Lubbock Audio Visual Inc, pg 812
Quality Audio Visual Service Inc, pg 867
Southwest Sound Solutions, pg 896
Stage Directions, pg 898
Tarpley Media Systems, pg 907

UTAH

Performance Audio LLC, pg 854

VIRGINIA

Acoustics First Corp, pg 674
Aviteture Inc, pg 699
Boitnott Visual Communications Corp (BVC), pg 708
Lee Hartman & Sons Inc, pg 805
Rocktown Media, pg 876
The Whitlock Group, pg 937

WASHINGTON

CCI Solutions, pg 718
D A Sound, pg 737
LOUD Technologies Inc, pg 811
Northern Lights & Pro Audio, pg 842
PNTA, pg 858

WEST VIRGINIA

United Sound & Electronics, pg 921

WISCONSIN

Audio Visual of Milwaukee Inc, pg 694
Camera Corner Connecting Point, pg 715
Demco Inc, pg 740
Full Compass Systems, pg 767

PUERTO RICO

Bonnin Electronics Inc, pg 708

ALBERTA

Evolution AV, pg 757
Genesis Integration, pg 769
Infosat Communications Inc, pg 787
McBain Camera Ltd, pg 820
Unique Communications Ltd, pg 921

BRITISH COLUMBIA

Commercial Electronics Ltd, pg 728

MANITOBA

Advance Pro, pg 677
Inland Audio Visual Ltd, pg 788

ONTARIO

Cinema Stage Inc, pg 724
HD Source, pg 777
KDM Electronics Inc, pg 797
Music Group Commercial Ltd, pg 834
Nationwide Audio Visual Co, pg 837
Westbury National Show Systems Ltd, pg 936

QUEBEC

JAM Industries Ltd, pg 792

Public Address System Manufacturers

ARIZONA

AtlasIED, pg 692
Fender Musical Instruments Corp, pg 759
MTX Audio, pg 833
Radio Design Labs (RDL), pg 869

ARKANSAS

Sound-Craft Systems Inc, pg 894

CALIFORNIA

Anchor Audio Inc, pg 685
Aphex, pg 687
Califone International Inc, pg 714
Calrad Electronics, pg 714
FrontRow, pg 766
Gilderfluke & Co Inc, pg 771
Hosa Technology Inc, pg 781
L-Acoustics Inc, pg 802
Mackenzie Laboratories Inc, pg 814
Nady Systems Inc, pg 835
QSC Audio Products LLC, pg 867
Renkus-Heinz Inc, pg 873
Sonance, pg 892
TeachLogic Inc, pg 908
TOA Electronics Inc, pg 915

CONNECTICUT

Alarmco Intelligent Message Repeaters, pg 679

ILLINOIS

ACCO Brands Corp, pg 673
AmpliVox Portable Sound Systems, pg 684
Bag End Loudspeakers, pg 700
C V Lloyde, pg 810
Precision Electronics Inc, pg 861
Shure Inc, pg 887

KANSAS

Galaxy Audio, pg 767
Tributestone, pg 918

MASSACHUSETTS

Bose Corp, pg 709
Technomad™ Inc, pg 909

MINNESOTA

Bosch Security Systems Inc, pg 709
Digital Audio Labs, pg 742

MISSISSIPPI

Peavey Electronics Corp, pg 852

NEBRASKA

REI - Radio Engineering Industries, pg 873

NEVADA

Pignose-Gorilla, pg 856

NEW JERSEY

Apogee Sound International LLC, pg 687
Bogen Communications Inc, pg 708
Oklahoma Sound Corp, pg 844
Starlite, pg 900

NEW MEXICO

Lectrosonics Inc, pg 805

NEW YORK

Protech Audio Corp, pg 866

OREGON

BIAMP Systems, pg 705

PENNSYLVANIA

Community Professional Loudspeakers, pg 729

TENNESSEE

Brantley Sound Associates Inc, pg 709
Cerwin-Vega! Inc, pg 720

VIRGINIA

Acoustics First Corp, pg 674

WASHINGTON

Aiphone Corp, pg 678
LOUD Technologies Inc, pg 811

ONTARIO

KDM Electronics Inc, pg 797
Music Group Commercial Ltd, pg 834

Public Address System Rentals

ALABAMA

Audio-Video Resources Inc, pg 694

ARIZONA

Arizona Cine Equipment, pg 688
Fire Power Music LLC, pg 761
Merestone, pg 823
Metropolitan Audio-Visual Inc, pg 824
Ultimate Presentation Systems Inc, pg 920
Video West Inc, pg 929

CALIFORNIA

Alliant Event Services, pg 681
Ametron Audio/Video, pg 684
Associated Sound, pg 691
Assured Audio Visual, pg 691
ATV Video Center Inc, pg 692
Audio Rents, pg 693
AV Guys, pg 697
Dan Dugan Sound Design Inc, pg 747
Express Media Inc, pg 757
Fuller Street Productions, pg 767
IAMP Professional Audio, pg 783

Instructional Materials & Equipment Distributors (I-Med), pg 789
JD Audio Visual Inc, pg 793
Lynch Communications, pg 813
Maximus Media Inc, pg 820
McCune Audio-Video-Lighting, pg 821
Munday & Collins AV, pg 834
Muse Presentation Technologies, pg 834
On-Trax Inc, pg 846
PSAV® Presentation Services, pg 866
Alwin Sauers Audio Productions (ASAP), pg 881
Sound Service Co, pg 894
Stanislaus AV Inc, pg 899
The Studios at Paramount, pg 903
Synthesizer Rental Service, pg 906
Third Ear Sound Co, pg 912
Towards 2000 Inc, pg 916
Video Resources Inc, pg 928
VMI Inc, pg 932
Voice & Video Rentals, pg 932
Westcoast Video Productions Inc, pg 936

COLORADO

Audio Consultant Services Inc, pg 693
Daylight Productions & Rentals, pg 739
Multimedia Audio Visual Inc, pg 833
Spectrum Audio Visual Services, pg 897

CONNECTICUT

A/V Davey, pg 697
Connecticut Audio & Theatrical Supply, pg 731

DELAWARE

Actors Attic, pg 675
Showorks Audio Visual Inc, pg 887
Side Door Studio Inc, pg 887

FLORIDA

AVI-SPL, pg 698
Harmon's Audio-Visual Services, pg 776
Industrial Strength Inc, pg 787
Lighting Sales Connection Inc, pg 808
ONstage, pg 846
Paradise Show & Design Inc, pg 851
Sight & Sound Productions, pg 887
TAI Audio, pg 906
Technomedia Solutions, pg 909
Universal Studios Florida® Production Group, pg 922

GEORGIA

Lighting & Production Equipment Inc, pg 807
MAGNUM Companies Ltd, pg 815
Stage Front Presentation Systems, pg 899
Staging Directions Inc, pg 899

HAWAII

Hawaii Sound & Vision, pg 777

ILLINOIS

Allen Visual Systems Inc, pg 680
AV Chicago Inc, pg 696
Beatty TeleVisual Productions, pg 703

Central Audio-Visual Equipment Inc, pg 719
Creative Technology (CT), pg 733
C V Lloyde, pg 810
OSA International Inc, pg 848
RC Communications, pg 870
Resolution Productions Group, pg 874
SCI Television & Creative Media LLC, pg 882

KENTUCKY

Audio Visual Techniques Inc, pg 695
Barney Miller's Inc, pg 827

LOUISIANA

Clark Services Audio Visual & Exhibit Inc, pg 725
Pace Systems, pg 849

MARYLAND

Advance Audiovisual Presentation Ltd, pg 677
Cardinal Sound & Video, pg 717
CPR MultiMedia Solutions, pg 732
Event Tech, pg 756
Hargrove Inc, pg 776

MASSACHUSETTS

AVFX Inc, pg 698
Terry Hanley Audio Systems Inc, pg 775
massAV, pg 819
Preston Productions Inc, pg 861

MICHIGAN

Olson Anderson Co, pg 685
City Events Group, pg 725
Digi Sign Design LLC, pg 741
K&R All Media Productions LLC, pg 796
K&R's Recording Studios Inc, pg 796
On Stage Visuals, pg 846
TEL Systems LLC, pg 909

MINNESOTA

Big Event Productions LLC, pg 705
New Life Communications Inc, pg 839

MISSISSIPPI

Bowie Audio Visual Enterprises Inc, pg 709

MISSOURI

Communitronics Corp, pg 729
Production Support Services Inc, pg 864
Schiller's Audio-Visual, pg 881
Show-Me Audio-Visual, pg 887
Switch, pg 905

NEBRASKA

Dog & Pony Productions Inc, pg 744

NEW HAMPSHIRE

APS Lighting-Sound-AV, pg 688

NEW JERSEY

Audio Visual Associates, pg 694
Audio Visual Dynamics®, pg 694
Earl Girls Inc, pg 749
International Audio Visual Inc, pg 790

Moe AV LLC, pg 828
Nelson Enterprises Theatrical Supply Co, pg 838
Panavid, pg 850
PLS Staging, pg 858
Starlite, pg 900
Video Corporation of America (VCA), pg 927
Wired 4 Sound Inc, pg 940

NEW MEXICO

Quickbeam Systems Inc (QSI), pg 868

NEW YORK

Ace Video, pg 674
AV Workshop, pg 697
Colortone Audio Visual, pg 728
CP Communications, pg 732
Design Audio Visual Inc, pg 741
Hello World Communications, pg 778
iProbe Multilingual Solutions Inc, pg 791
KVL Audio Visual Services Inc, pg 802
Long Island Video Enterprises Live Inc, pg 811
Manhattan Center Studios Inc, pg 816
See Factor Industry Inc, pg 883
Specialized Audio-Visual Inc, pg 896
Studio Instrument Rentals (SIR), pg 902
Theatrical Services & Supplies Inc, pg 912
Visual Word Systems Inc, pg 932

NORTH CAROLINA

AV Connections Inc, pg 697
AV Metro Inc, pg 697
Special Event Services, pg 896

NORTH DAKOTA

Media Productions, pg 822

OHIO

Bartha, pg 702
Hughie's Event Production Services, pg 782
ITA Audio Visual Solutions, pg 791
Mills James Productions, pg 828
Ohio HD Video, pg 844
Production Solutions Inc, pg 864
R&B Communications Inc, pg 870

OKLAHOMA

PDC Productions, pg 852

OREGON

Rose City Sound, pg 877

PENNSYLVANIA

Advanced AV LLC, pg 677
Audio Visions Inc, pg 694
Audio Visual Communications Inc, pg 694
FMP Media Solutions Inc, pg 763
Grise Audio Visual Center Inc, pg 774
Sound by Fitch, pg 893
Vistacom Inc, pg 931
Visual Sound Inc, pg 931

SOUTH CAROLINA

Impact Technology Group LLC, pg 786

TENNESSEE

Allstar Audio Systems Inc, pg 681
Belew Enterprises, pg 703
Brantley Sound Associates Inc, pg 709
Mr Mark's Used Musical, Stereo & Studio Equipment Store, pg 828
Technical Support Systems LLC, pg 908

TEXAS

Alford Media Services, pg 680
Crossroads Audio Inc, pg 735
FitzCo Sound Inc, pg 761
Heffernan Audio Visual, pg 778
Lubbock Audio Visual Inc, pg 812
Music Lab Inc, pg 834
Onstage Systems, pg 846
Power Factory Productions, pg 860
Quality Audio Visual Service Inc, pg 867
Stage Directions, pg 898
Tropikal Productions, pg 918

UTAH

Performance Audio LLC, pg 854

VIRGINIA

American AV, pg 682
Boitnott Visual Communications Corp (BVC), pg 708
Lee Hartman & Sons Inc, pg 805
The Whitlock Group, pg 937

WASHINGTON

D A Sound, pg 737
Northern Lights & Pro Audio, pg 842
PNTA, pg 858

WEST VIRGINIA

Blackwater Video Productions, pg 707
United Sound & Electronics, pg 921

WISCONSIN

Camera Corner Connecting Point, pg 715
Event Essentials, pg 756
Full Compass Systems, pg 767

PUERTO RICO

Stage Crew Audiovisual Inc, pg 898

ALBERTA

Allstar Show Industries Inc, pg 681
Evolution AV, pg 757
L R Light & Sound, pg 802
McBain Camera Ltd, pg 820
Unique Communications Ltd, pg 921

BRITISH COLUMBIA

Clark's Audio Visual Services Ltd, pg 725
Commercial Electronics Ltd, pg 728
DL Sound & Lighting Productions Ltd, pg 744
MicrophoneRentals.com, pg 826

MANITOBA

Inland Audio Visual Ltd, pg 788

AUDIO

Public Address System Rentals (continued)

ONTARIO

HD Source, pg 777
Metalworks Recording Studios Inc, pg 824
Westbury National Show Systems Ltd, pg 936

QUEBEC

Audio Visual Dynamics, pg 694

Public Address System Repairs

CALIFORNIA

Ametron Audio/Video, pg 684
Audio Images Corp, pg 693
Diemer Amp & Keyboard Repair, pg 741
IAMP Professional Audio, pg 783
JD Audio Visual Inc, pg 793
McAlister Electronics, pg 820
QSC Audio Products LLC, pg 867
Sonance, pg 892
Sound Service Co, pg 894
SSL Industries Inc, pg 898
Third Ear Sound Co, pg 912
TOA Electronics Inc, pg 915
Towards 2000 Inc, pg 916

CONNECTICUT

HB Communications Inc, pg 777

FLORIDA

JT Communications, pg 795
Stereo Sales Inc, pg 900
TAI Audio, pg 906

GEORGIA

Lighting & Production Equipment Inc, pg 807
Stage Front Presentation Systems, pg 899

ILLINOIS

Allen Visual Systems Inc, pg 680
Beatty TeleVisual Productions, pg 703
C V Lloyde, pg 810

INDIANA

SHP Electronics, pg 887
Sweetwater Sound Inc, pg 905

KENTUCKY

Axxis Leasing Inc, pg 700
Barney Miller's Inc, pg 827
NOR-COM Inc, pg 841

MARYLAND

Cardinal Sound & Video, pg 717

MASSACHUSETTS

Professional Audio Design Inc, pg 865

MICHIGAN

City Events Group, pg 725
K&R's Recording Studios Inc, pg 796

On Stage Visuals, pg 846
TEL Systems LLC, pg 909

MISSISSIPPI

Bowie Audio Visual Enterprises Inc, pg 709

MISSOURI

Communitronics Corp, pg 729

NEW JERSEY

A-V Services Inc, pg 671
Earl Girls Inc, pg 749
Nelson Enterprises Theatrical Supply Co, pg 838
Starlite, pg 900

NEW MEXICO

Quickbeam Systems Inc (QSI), pg 868

NEW YORK

Design Audio Visual Inc, pg 741

OHIO

Copp Integrated Systems, pg 731
ITA Audio Visual Solutions, pg 791
Tri-State Audio Visual Co, pg 918

OREGON

All Service Musical Electronics Repair, pg 680

PENNSYLVANIA

Sound by Fitch, pg 893
Tri-State Loudspeaker, pg 918
Vistacom Inc, pg 931
Visual Sound Inc, pg 931

TENNESSEE

Belew Enterprises, pg 703
Brantley Sound Associates Inc, pg 709
Technical Support Systems LLC, pg 908

TEXAS

Lubbock Audio Visual Inc, pg 812
Quality Audio Visual Service Inc, pg 867

VIRGINIA

Boitnott Visual Communications Corp (BVC), pg 708
Lee Hartman & Sons Inc, pg 805
The Whitlock Group, pg 937

WASHINGTON

Aiphone Corp, pg 678
D A Sound, pg 737
Northern Lights & Pro Audio, pg 842
PNTA, pg 858

WEST VIRGINIA

United Sound & Electronics, pg 921

WISCONSIN

Camera Corner Connecting Point, pg 715
Full Compass Systems, pg 767

ALBERTA

Allstar Show Industries Inc, pg 681
Infosat Communications Inc, pg 787
Unique Communications Ltd, pg 921

BRITISH COLUMBIA

Commercial Electronics Ltd, pg 728

MANITOBA

Inland Audio Visual Ltd, pg 788

ONTARIO

Westbury National Show Systems Ltd, pg 936

Radio & Accessory Equipment Distributors

ARIZONA

Coustic, pg 732
Troxell-CDI, pg 918
WindTech™ Microphone Windscreens & Accessories, pg 939

ARKANSAS

White Diamond Productions LLC, pg 937

CALIFORNIA

Ametron Audio/Video, pg 684
Audio Images Corp, pg 693
Educational Technology Services (ETS), pg 751
Jaguar Distribution Corp, pg 792
Location Sound Corp, pg 810
MediaPOINTE, pg 823
Sound Service Co, pg 894
Southern California Sound Image Inc, pg 895
Towards 2000 Inc, pg 916

COLORADO

Audio Consultant Services Inc, pg 693
Stanco Sales LLC, pg 899

CONNECTICUT

Sennheiser Electronic Corp, pg 884

DELAWARE

Actors Attic, pg 675

FLORIDA

Broadcasters General Store Inc, pg 711
Harris Corp, pg 776
Hi-Tech Import Export Corp, pg 779
Recording Media & Equipment Inc (RM&E), pg 872
Stereo Sales Inc, pg 900
TAI Audio, pg 906

GEORGIA

Lighting & Production Equipment Inc, pg 807
Stage Front Presentation Systems, pg 899

ILLINOIS

Joseph Electronics, pg 795
RC Communications, pg 870

INDIANA

Sensory Technologies LLC, pg 884

KENTUCKY

Axxis Leasing Inc, pg 700
Barney Miller's Inc, pg 827
NOR-COM Inc, pg 841

MAINE

Independent Audio Inc, pg 786

MARYLAND

Bradley Broadcast & Pro Audio, pg 709
Cardinal Sound & Video, pg 717
RTZ Audio Visual, pg 878

MISSOURI

ITC, pg 791

NEW HAMPSHIRE

Technet® Systems Group, pg 908

NEW JERSEY

Alltec Stores, a Vcom IMC Company, pg 681
AlltecPro, pg 681
AV Bluebook, pg 696
FlagHouse, pg 762
SDI Technologies Inc, pg 883
Starlite, pg 900
Tele-Measurements Inc, pg 910
Turner Engineering Inc, pg 919
Video Corporation of America (VCA), pg 927
Wired 4 Sound Inc, pg 940

NEW YORK

Audiovox®, pg 695
Indigo Productions, pg 787
Langie Audio Visual Systems, pg 803
Ray Supply Inc, pg 870
RNJ Electronics, pg 875
Visual Technologies Corp, pg 932

NORTH CAROLINA

Camcor Inc, pg 715
Strategic Connections, pg 901

OHIO

Universal Radio Inc, pg 922

OREGON

Frontier Communications Corp, pg 766

PENNSYLVANIA

Advanced AV LLC, pg 677
The Lerro Corp, pg 806
Morefield Communications Inc, pg 830

TENNESSEE

Allstar Audio Systems Inc, pg 681
Lowrance Sound Co Inc, pg 812
Technical Support Systems LLC, pg 908

TEXAS

Cinema Antiques, pg 723
Crossroads Audio Inc, pg 735
Lubbock Audio Visual Inc, pg 812

RF Specialties of Texas LLC, pg 874
Sundance Systems, Fibox Products Division, pg 904

UTAH

Performance Audio LLC, pg 854
Webb Audio Visual, pg 935

VIRGINIA

Lee Hartman & Sons Inc, pg 805

WASHINGTON

Proforma Good Wood Marketing, pg 865

WEST VIRGINIA

United Sound & Electronics, pg 921

WISCONSIN

Audio Visual of Milwaukee Inc, pg 694
Camera Corner Connecting Point, pg 715
Full Compass Systems, pg 767

PUERTO RICO

Bonnin Electronics Inc, pg 708

ALBERTA

Infosat Communications Inc, pg 787

MANITOBA

Advance Pro, pg 677
Inland Audio Visual Ltd, pg 788

ONTARIO

Applied Electronics Ltd, pg 687
Nationwide Audio Visual Co, pg 837
Westbury National Show Systems Ltd, pg 936

Radio & Accessory Equipment Manufacturers

ARIZONA

East Arizona Good Luck Enterprises Inc, pg 749
WindTech™ Microphone Windscreens & Accessories, pg 939

ARKANSAS

Autogram/CRL, pg 696

CALIFORNIA

Aphex, pg 687
Magnum Towers Inc, pg 815
Nady Systems Inc, pg 835
TeachLogic Inc, pg 908

CONNECTICUT

Harman International Industries Inc, pg 776
Sennheiser Electronic Corp, pg 884

FLORIDA

CircuitWerkes Inc, pg 725
JT Communications, pg 795
Sonar Radio Corp, pg 892

IDAHO

Marketron Broadcast Solutions, pg 817
Transtector Systems Inc, pg 917

ILLINOIS

Broadcast Electronics, pg 710
J K Audio Inc, pg 792
Kart-A-Bag Manufacturing Inc, pg 796
Switchcraft® Inc, pg 905

INDIANA

Auralex Acoustics Inc, pg 696
Star Case Manufacturing Co Inc, pg 900

MAINE

Dielectric, pg 741

MASSACHUSETTS

David Clark Co Inc, pg 738

NEBRASKA

REI - Radio Engineering Industries, pg 873

NEW JERSEY

ATI Audio, pg 692
Panasonic Consumer Electronics Co, pg 850
Pioneer Research Inc, pg 857
RAMSA Professional Audio Systems, pg 870
SDI Technologies Inc, pg 883
Techflex Inc, pg 908
Technics, pg 909
Turner Engineering Inc, pg 919

NEW YORK

RCS Enterprises, pg 871

NORTH CAROLINA

LBA Technology Inc, pg 804

PENNSYLVANIA

Belar Electronics Laboratory Inc, pg 703
Wire X 17 LLC, pg 940

TEXAS

Setcom Corp™, pg 884
Sundance Systems, Fibox Products Division, pg 904

UTAH

Rolls Corp, pg 877

ONTARIO

DW Electrochemicals Ltd, pg 748

Radio & Accessory Equipment Rentals

ARIZONA

Arizona Cine Equipment, pg 688
Merestone, pg 823
Metropolitan Audio-Visual Inc, pg 824

ARKANSAS

White Diamond Productions LLC, pg 937

CALIFORNIA

Alliant Event Services, pg 681
Ametron Audio/Video, pg 684
Audio Rents, pg 693
AV Guys, pg 697
Golden Gate Studios, pg 772
Munday & Collins AV, pg 834
Protocol Telecommunications Inc, pg 866
PSAV® Presentation Services, pg 866
Sound Service Co, pg 894
Towards 2000 Inc, pg 916

COLORADO

Audio Consultant Services Inc, pg 693

CONNECTICUT

A/V Davey, pg 697
Videofilm Systems Inc, pg 929

FLORIDA

Sight & Sound Productions, pg 887
TAI Audio, pg 906

GEORGIA

Lighting & Production Equipment Inc, pg 807
Stage Front Presentation Systems, pg 899
Staging Directions Inc, pg 899

ILLINOIS

AV Chicago Inc, pg 696
OSA International Inc, pg 848
RC Communications, pg 870
Resolution Productions Group, pg 874

KENTUCKY

Audio Visual Techniques Inc, pg 695

MARYLAND

Event Tech, pg 756
RTZ Audio Visual, pg 878

MASSACHUSETTS

Capron Lighting & Sound Co Inc, pg 716
massAV, pg 819
Preston Productions Inc, pg 861

MICHIGAN

K&R All Media Productions LLC, pg 796
K&R's Recording Studios Inc, pg 796
Lowing Light & Grip Inc, pg 812

MISSOURI

ITC, pg 791
Show-Me Audio-Visual, pg 887

NEW JERSEY

Audio Visual Dynamics®, pg 694
PLS Staging, pg 858
Starlite, pg 900

NEW YORK

Ace Video, pg 674
Big Foot Productions Inc, pg 705
CP Communications, pg 732

Hello World Communications, pg 778
Specialized Audio-Visual Inc, pg 896
Visual Technologies Corp, pg 932
Xtech Systems Inc, pg 943

NORTH CAROLINA

Special Event Services, pg 896
Strategic Connections, pg 901

NORTH DAKOTA

Media Productions, pg 822

PENNSYLVANIA

Advanced AV LLC, pg 677

TENNESSEE

Allstar Audio Systems Inc, pg 681
Technical Support Systems LLC, pg 908

TEXAS

Crossroads Audio Inc, pg 735
GEAR Cameras & Lighting, pg 769
Lubbock Audio Visual Inc, pg 812

UTAH

Performance Audio LLC, pg 854

VIRGINIA

American AV, pg 682
Lee Hartman & Sons Inc, pg 805
Projection, pg 865

WEST VIRGINIA

United Sound & Electronics, pg 921

WISCONSIN

Event Essentials, pg 756

BRITISH COLUMBIA

Clark's Audio Visual Services Ltd, pg 725
MicrophoneRentals.com, pg 826

MANITOBA

Inland Audio Visual Ltd, pg 788

ONTARIO

Westbury National Show Systems Ltd, pg 936

Radio & Accessory Equipment Repairs

CALIFORNIA

Ametron Audio/Video, pg 684
Audio Images Corp, pg 693
McAlister Electronics, pg 820
Protocol Telecommunications Inc, pg 866
Sound Service Co, pg 894
Towards 2000 Inc, pg 916

CONNECTICUT

HB Communications Inc, pg 777
Videofilm Systems Inc, pg 929

FLORIDA

JT Communications, pg 795
Stereo Sales Inc, pg 900
TAI Audio, pg 906

AUDIO

Radio & Accessory Equipment Repairs (continued)

GEORGIA

Audio Visual Resources Inc, pg 695
Lighting & Production Equipment Inc, pg 807
Stage Front Presentation Systems, pg 899

ILLINOIS

Midwest Digital Corp, pg 827

KENTUCKY

Axxis Leasing Inc, pg 700
Barney Miller's Inc, pg 827
NOR-COM Inc, pg 841

MARYLAND

RTZ Audio Visual, pg 878

MICHIGAN

K&R's Recording Studios Inc, pg 796
TEL Systems LLC, pg 909

NEW JERSEY

Starlite, pg 900

NEW YORK

Langie Audio Visual Systems, pg 803
Visual Technologies Corp, pg 932
Xtech Systems Inc, pg 943

NORTH CAROLINA

Camcor Inc, pg 715
Strategic Connections, pg 901

OREGON

All Service Musical Electronics Repair, pg 680
Frontier Communications Corp, pg 766

TENNESSEE

Technical Support Systems LLC, pg 908

TEXAS

Audio Visual Technologies Group (AVTG), pg 695
Lubbock Audio Visual Inc, pg 812

VIRGINIA

Lee Hartman & Sons Inc, pg 805

WEST VIRGINIA

United Sound & Electronics, pg 921

WISCONSIN

Full Compass Systems, pg 767

ALBERTA

Infosat Communications Inc, pg 787

MANITOBA

Inland Audio Visual Ltd, pg 788

ONTARIO

Westbury National Show Systems Ltd, pg 936

Rap Music, see Music Libraries—Rap

Record Mastering

ARIZONA

Allusion Studios & Pure Wave Audio, pg 681
Fire Power Music LLC, pg 761
Merestone, pg 823

CALIFORNIA

AB Audio Visual Entertainment Inc, pg 672
ACDC Audio CD & Cassette, pg 674
Audio Mechanics, pg 693
Audio Upgrades, pg 694
The Banquet Sound Studios, pg 701
Berkeley Sound Artists Inc, pg 704
Capitol Records, pg 716
Christian Media Network, pg 722
Custom Video Productions Inc, pg 736
Different Fur Recording Ltd, pg 741
Digital Jungle, pg 742
DiskFaktory, pg 743
5 Alarm Music, pg 762
JDS Video & Media Productions Inc, pg 793
K2B2 Records, pg 802
KVIE-Channel 6, pg 802
Lynch Communications, pg 813
On-Trax Inc, pg 846
Private Island Audio Inc, pg 862
Pyramind Studios, pg 867
QRS Software Services, pg 867
Reference Recordings, pg 872
Saturn Studios, pg 881
SonicPool, pg 892
Studio Circle Recordings, pg 902
Studio 132, pg 902
Timeless Productions, pg 914
Todd-AO Studios, pg 915
Total Creative, pg 916
Trac Recording Studio, pg 916

COLORADO

Tim Cissell Music, pg 725
Colorado Sound Recording Ltd, pg 728
Daylight Productions & Rentals, pg 739
Side 3 Studios, pg 887

CONNECTICUT

American Melody, pg 683
BRB Audiovisual Productions, pg 709
Ironik Design & Post, pg 791

DISTRICT OF COLUMBIA

Northeastern Digital Recording Inc, pg 842

FLORIDA

Morrisound Recording, pg 830
Phat Planet Recording Studios, pg 855
Sunfire Communications Inc, pg 904

GEORGIA

Hottrax Records, pg 782
Stage Front Presentation Systems, pg 899

HAWAII

Media Bridge Gamekids, pg 821

ILLINOIS

RBR Productions, pg 870
Sound/Video Impressions Inc, pg 894
Southern Illinois University, pg 895
Woodside Avenue Music Productions Inc, pg 941

INDIANA

A-V-A Video Productions, pg 671
Bright Ideas Creative Services, pg 710
Alan Johnson Recording, pg 794
Sweetwater Sound Inc, pg 905

MARYLAND

The Cutting Corporation, GraphicAudio® & Archival Sound Lab, pg 736
dbF a Media Company, pg 739
Omega Recording Studios, pg 845
Pro Cuts Editing Services, pg 862
Smolian Sound Studios, pg 891

MASSACHUSETTS

M Works Mastering Studio, pg 813
Soundtrack Group, pg 895
TR Productions, pg 916

MICHIGAN

Brilliance Audio, pg 710
The Brookwood Studio Inc, pg 711
Digi Sign Design LLC, pg 741
K&R's Recording Studios Inc, pg 796

MINNESOTA

The ADS Group, pg 676
BeyerSound & Essay Audio, pg 705
Winterland Studios, pg 940

MISSOURI

Show-Me Audio-Visual, pg 887
Studio Worx Inc, pg 903

MONTANA

Jereco Studios Inc, pg 793

NEW JERSEY

CFP Video Productions Inc, pg 720
Disc Makers, pg 743
Milgrom Productions, pg 827
Oasis Disc Manufacturing, pg 844
Suede Interactive, pg 903

NEW YORK

Aura Sonic Ltd (ASL), pg 695
Big Fish Production US, pg 705
The Big House Group, pg 705
Digital Force Ltd, pg 742
Fingerpaint, pg 761
Foothill Digital Inc, pg 763
HB-Content, pg 777
Masterdisk Corp, pg 819
Posthorn Recordings, pg 859
Sony Music Entertainment, pg 893

NORTH CAROLINA

Pat Appleson Studios Inc, pg 687
Duke Media Services, pg 747
Studio B Mastering, pg 902

NORTH DAKOTA

Media Productions, pg 822

OHIO

Lyon Video Inc, pg 813
Mills James Productions, pg 828
Musicol Recording, pg 835
The Telos Alliance, pg 910

PENNSYLVANIA

American Artist Studio, pg 682
Audio Visual Communications Inc, pg 694
Ivory Productions, pg 792
JPL, pg 795
Right Coast Recording Inc, pg 875

RHODE ISLAND

Sound-FX-Design, pg 894

TENNESSEE

American Blackguard Inc, pg 683
Analog Man Recording Studio, pg 685
Ardent Music LLC, pg 688
Ardent Studios Inc, pg 688
Green Dot Audio Electronics, pg 774
JamSync, pg 793
Love Shack Recording Studios, pg 811
Motion Picture Services, pg 831
Stage Post, pg 899
Zion Music Group, pg 945

TEXAS

Anaphora Literary Press, pg 685
Audiomoxie®, pg 695
Digital Services Recording Studios, pg 742
Fire Station Studios, pg 761
Phillips Media Source, pg 855
Planet Dallas Recording Studios, pg 857
The Samuels Co, pg 879
The Sound Lab Inc, pg 894
Stage Directions, pg 898
TopCat Records LLC, pg 915
World Beat Studio, pg 941

UTAH

ELS Productions Inc, pg 753

VIRGINIA

Furnace MFG, pg 767
Metro Productions, pg 824

WASHINGTON

Sound Sound, pg 894

WISCONSIN

Concept Productions Inc, pg 730
5th Floor Recording Co, pg 760
Sound Strations Audio Productions Inc, pg 894
Video Wisconsin Inc, pg 929

BRITISH COLUMBIA

Triad Communications Ltd, pg 918

MANITOBA

DACAPO Productions Inc, pg 737

ONTARIO

ADS Media, pg 677
GAPC (General Assembly
   Production Centre), pg 768
JL Recording Studios, pg 794
Legendary Entertainment, pg 806
MCS Recording Studios, pg 821
Metalworks Recording Studios Inc,
   pg 824
Phase One Studios, pg 855
Westbury National Show Systems
   Ltd, pg 936

Record Pressing

ARIZONA

Merestone, pg 823

CALIFORNIA

Audio Upgrades, pg 694
Christian Media Network, pg 722
Lynch Communications, pg 813
QRS Software Services, pg 867
Saturn Studios, pg 881

FLORIDA

Sunfire Communications Inc,
   pg 904

HAWAII

Media Bridge Gamekids, pg 821

INDIANA

Sweetwater Sound Inc, pg 905

MASSACHUSETTS

M Works Mastering Studio, pg 813

MICHIGAN

Brilliance Audio, pg 710
Digi Sign Design LLC, pg 741
GMP Music, pg 772
K&R's Recording Studios Inc,
   pg 796

MINNESOTA

The ADS Group, pg 676

NEW JERSEY

Suede Interactive, pg 903

NEW YORK

Sony Music Entertainment, pg 893

OHIO

Musicol Recording, pg 835

PENNSYLVANIA

American Artist Studio, pg 682

TENNESSEE

Stage Post, pg 899

TEXAS

The Samuels Co, pg 879
TopCat Records LLC, pg 915
World Media Group Inc, pg 941

Recorder & Player, *see* Player & Recorder

Recording, *see* Sound Recording

Recording Equipment Distributors

ARIZONA

Allusion Studios & Pure Wave
   Audio, pg 681
Arizona Cine Equipment, pg 688
ATCi (Antenna Technology
   Communication Solutions Inc),
   pg 692
EAR Professional Audio/Video,
   pg 749
Metropolitan Audio-Visual Inc,
   pg 824
Troxell-CDI, pg 918

ARKANSAS

White Diamond Productions LLC,
   pg 937

CALIFORNIA

Advanced Systems Group LLC,
   pg 677
American Music & Sound (AM&S),
   pg 684
Ametron Audio/Video, pg 684
Audio Images Corp, pg 693
DigiTech, pg 742
Empire Pro, pg 753
GigaSonic, pg 770
Instructional Materials & Equipment
   Distributors (I-Med), pg 789
JD Audio Visual Inc, pg 793
Location Sound Corp, pg 810
Media Fabricators Inc, pg 822
MediaPOINTE, pg 823
Professional Sound Corp, pg 865
Sanako Inc, pg 880
SNAP, pg 891
Sound Service Co, pg 894
Soundcraft, pg 894
Southern California Sound Image
   Inc, pg 895
SSL Industries Inc, pg 898
TASCAM, pg 907
Towards 2000 Inc, pg 916
VTP Inc, pg 933

COLORADO

Audio Consultant Services Inc,
   pg 693
Spectrum Audio Visual Services,
   pg 897
Stanco Sales LLC, pg 899

CONNECTICUT

Connecticut Audio & Theatrical
   Supply, pg 731
HB Communications Inc, pg 777
MAVCO, pg 820
The Music People Inc, pg 834
Sennheiser Electronic Corp, pg 884

FLORIDA

A2D Solutions Inc, pg 692
Broadcasters General Store Inc,
   pg 711
Digital Video Systems, pg 742
Harris Corp, pg 776
Hi-Tech Enterprises Inc, pg 779

Hi-Tech Import Export Corp,
   pg 779
Industrial Strength Inc, pg 787
Midtown Video Inc, pg 827
ONstage, pg 846
Photosound of Orlando Inc, pg 856
Recording Media & Equipment Inc
   (RM&E), pg 872
Stereo Sales Inc, pg 900
TAI Audio, pg 906
Tallahassee Audio Visual, pg 906
Technomedia Solutions, pg 909

GEORGIA

Baker Audio Visual, pg 700
Convergent Media Systems, pg 731
Lighting & Production Equipment
   Inc, pg 807
LT Sound Inc, pg 812
Stage Front Presentation Systems,
   pg 899

HAWAII

The Audio Visual Co (AVCO),
   pg 694

ILLINOIS

Allen Visual Systems Inc, pg 680
Central Audio-Visual Equipment
   Inc, pg 719
C V Lloyde, pg 810
Woodside Avenue Music
   Productions Inc, pg 941

INDIANA

Sensory Technologies LLC, pg 884
SHP Electronics, pg 887
Sweetwater Sound Inc, pg 905

KENTUCKY

Axxis Leasing Inc, pg 700
Barney Miller's Inc, pg 827
NOR-COM Inc, pg 841

MAINE

Independent Audio Inc, pg 786

MARYLAND

Bradley Broadcast & Pro Audio,
   pg 709
RTZ Audio Visual, pg 878

MASSACHUSETTS

Avid Technology Inc, pg 698
Terry Hanley Audio Systems Inc,
   pg 775
Professional Audio Design Inc,
   pg 865

MICHIGAN

City Events Group, pg 725
Digi Sign Design LLC, pg 741
On Stage Visuals, pg 846
TEL Systems LLC, pg 909

MINNESOTA

Alpha Video & Audio Inc, pg 682
AVI Systems, pg 698
Digital Audio Labs, pg 742

MISSISSIPPI

Bowie Audio Visual Enterprises Inc,
   pg 709

MISSOURI

Conference Technologies Inc,
   pg 730

NEW HAMPSHIRE

APS Lighting-Sound-AV, pg 688
Technet® Systems Group, pg 908

NEW JERSEY

Alltec Stores, a Vcom IMC
   Company, pg 681
AlltecPro, pg 681
Audio Visual Associates, pg 694
Audio Visual Dynamics®, pg 694
AV Bluebook, pg 696
Comprehensive Cable &
   Connectivity Co, pg 729
Diversified, pg 744
Entel Systems Inc, pg 754
FlagHouse, pg 762
G&G Technologies Inc, pg 768
HamiltonBuhl, pg 775
The Music Place, pg 834
PatchAmp, pg 852
Starlite, pg 900
Wired 4 Sound Inc, pg 940
Yorktel, pg 944

NEW YORK

ADI Global Distribution, pg 676
Aura Sonic Ltd (ASL), pg 695
AV Workshop, pg 697
B&H Photo Video, pg 701
Colortone Audio Visual, pg 728
Design Audio Visual Inc, pg 741
Flash Electronics Inc, pg 762
Hot House Professional Audio,
   pg 782
Indigo Productions, pg 787
Korg USA Inc, pg 801
Long Island Video Enterprises Live
   Inc, pg 811
Mark Custom Recording Service
   Inc, pg 817
Markertek Video Supply, pg 817
Saul Mineroff Electronics Inc
   (SME), pg 828
Posthorn Recordings, pg 859
RNJ Electronics, pg 875
Tri-Ed Distribution Inc, pg 918
Visual Technologies Corp, pg 932
Visual Word Systems Inc, pg 932

NORTH CAROLINA

Camcor Inc, pg 715
Strategic Connections, pg 901

OHIO

Copp Integrated Systems, pg 731
ITA Audio Visual Solutions, pg 791
Tri-State Audio Visual Co, pg 918

OREGON

ASC-Tube Trap, pg 690
SuperDigital Ltd, pg 904

PENNSYLVANIA

Advanced AV LLC, pg 677
Audio Visions Inc, pg 694
Innovision Media Group, pg 788
Morefield Communications Inc,
   pg 830
Vistacom Inc, pg 931
Visual Sound Inc, pg 931

RHODE ISLAND

Akai Professional, pg 679
M-Audio, pg 813

AUDIO

Recording Equipment Distributors (continued)

SOUTH CAROLINA

DaviSound, pg 739

TENNESSEE

Allstar Audio Systems Inc, pg 681
Lowrance Sound Co Inc, pg 812
Mr Mark's Used Musical, Stereo & Studio Equipment Store, pg 828
Technical Support Systems LLC, pg 908
Trew Audio Inc, pg 917
WhisperRoom™ Inc, pg 937
Zion Music Group, pg 945

TEXAS

Audio Visual Technologies Group (AVTG), pg 695
AVES Audio Visual Systems Inc, pg 698
CAM Audio Inc, pg 714
Crossroads Audio Inc, pg 735
FitzCo Sound Inc, pg 761
Heffernan Audio Visual, pg 778
JSAV, pg 795
Lubbock Audio Visual Inc, pg 812
Precision Camera & Video, pg 861
Pro Video & Film Equipment Co Inc, pg 863
Stage Directions, pg 898
Sundance Systems, Fibox Products Division, pg 904
Tarpley Media Systems, pg 907
TWIST Integration Solutions Technology, pg 920

UTAH

Performance Audio LLC, pg 854
RIA Corp, pg 874
Webb Audio Visual, pg 935

VIRGINIA

Avitecture Inc, pg 699
Boitnott Visual Communications Corp (BVC), pg 708
Intellidyne LLC, pg 789
Lee Hartman & Sons Inc, pg 805
The Whitlock Group, pg 937

WASHINGTON

Broadcast Supply World Wide, pg 711
CCI Solutions, pg 718
Northern Lights & Pro Audio, pg 842

WEST VIRGINIA

United Sound & Electronics, pg 921

WISCONSIN

Audio Visual of Milwaukee Inc, pg 694
Camera Corner Connecting Point, pg 715
Full Compass Systems, pg 767
Safe Harbor Computers, pg 879

PUERTO RICO

Bonnin Electronics Inc, pg 708

ALBERTA

Infosat Communications Inc, pg 787
McBain Camera Ltd, pg 820
Unique Communications Ltd, pg 921

BRITISH COLUMBIA

Commercial Electronics Ltd, pg 728
Radial Engineering Ltd, pg 868

MANITOBA

Advance Pro, pg 677
Inland Audio Visual Ltd, pg 788

ONTARIO

HD Source, pg 777
Henry's Camera, pg 779
Nationwide Audio Visual Co, pg 837
SVAT Electronics, pg 905
Westbury National Show Systems Ltd, pg 936

QUEBEC

JAM Industries Ltd, pg 792

Recording Equipment Manufacturers

CALIFORNIA

American Music & Sound (AM&S), pg 684
Aphex, pg 687
Audio Upgrades, pg 694
DigiTech, pg 742
Dolby Laboratories Inc, pg 745
Dorrough Electronics Inc, pg 746
Furman®, pg 767
Henry Engineering, pg 779
Jensen Transformers Inc, pg 793
Lynx Studio Technology Inc, pg 813
Mackenzie Laboratories Inc, pg 814
Manley Laboratories Inc, pg 816
Martinsound Inc, pg 818
Opamp Labs Inc, pg 846
Roland Corp US, pg 876
Simon - Kaloi Engineering Ltd, pg 888
Sony Electronics Inc, pg 893
Soundcraft, pg 894
TASCAM, pg 907
360 Systems, pg 913

COLORADO

Arrakis Systems, pg 689

CONNECTICUT

Sennheiser Electronic Corp, pg 884

FLORIDA

Magna-Tech Electronic Co Inc, pg 814

GEORGIA

LT Sound Inc, pg 812
Register Data Systems, pg 873

ILLINOIS

Bag End Loudspeakers, pg 700
Superscope LLC, pg 904

INDIANA

Auralex Acoustics Inc, pg 696

MASSACHUSETTS

Avid Technology Inc, pg 698

MINNESOTA

Bosch Security Systems Inc, pg 709
Digital Audio Labs, pg 742
Great River Electronics, pg 773

MISSISSIPPI

Peavey Electronics Corp, pg 852

NEW JERSEY

AlltecPro, pg 681
Orban, pg 847
Wireworks Corp, pg 940

NEW YORK

ART (Applied Research & Technology Inc), pg 690
Ashly Audio Inc, pg 691
MultiDyne Video & Fiber Optics Systems, pg 833
Posthorn Recordings, pg 859
RCS Enterprises, pg 871

OREGON

ASC-Tube Trap, pg 690

PENNSYLVANIA

D W Fearn, pg 759
Right Coast Recording Inc, pg 875

RHODE ISLAND

Akai Professional, pg 679
M-Audio, pg 813

SOUTH CAROLINA

DaviSound, pg 739

TENNESSEE

Audio Media Productions, pg 693
KRK Systems, pg 802
WhisperRoom™ Inc, pg 937

TEXAS

Sundance Systems, Fibox Products Division, pg 904

UTAH

Spectra Sonics LLC, pg 897

WASHINGTON

Conex Electro Systems Inc, pg 730

BRITISH COLUMBIA

Creation Technologies Inc, pg 733
Radial Engineering Ltd, pg 868

ONTARIO

SVAT Electronics, pg 905

Recording Equipment Rentals

ALABAMA

Airwave Recording Studio, pg 679
Audio-Video Resources Inc, pg 694

ARIZONA

Arizona Cine Equipment, pg 688
Broadcast Rentals, pg 711

Merestone, pg 823
Metropolitan Audio-Visual Inc, pg 824

ARKANSAS

White Diamond Productions LLC, pg 937

CALIFORNIA

Absolute Rentals, pg 672
Advanced Media LLC, pg 677
AGF Media Services, pg 678
Ametron Audio/Video, pg 684
Artichoke Productions, pg 690
ATV Video Center Inc, pg 692
Audio Rents, pg 693
Chater Camera Inc, pg 721
Express Media Inc, pg 757
Express Video Supply Inc, pg 757
FJ Productions Inc, pg 762
Gold Standard Productions, pg 772
Golden Gate Studios, pg 772
Imagecraft Productions, pg 785
JD Audio Visual Inc, pg 793
Location Sound Corp, pg 810
Maximus Media Inc, pg 820
McCune Audio-Video-Lighting, pg 821
Media Fabricators Inc, pg 822
Munday & Collins AV, pg 834
On-Trax Inc, pg 846
Production Gear Rentals (PGR), pg 863
PSAV® Presentation Services, pg 866
Roundabout Entertainment Inc, pg 878
Alwin Sauers Audio Productions (ASAP), pg 881
Shoulder High Productions, pg 886
Sound Service Co, pg 894
Stray Angel Films, pg 902
Studio Circle Recordings, pg 902
Synthesizer Rental Service, pg 906
Total Creative, pg 916
Towards 2000 Inc, pg 916
Video Resources Inc, pg 928
Voice & Video Rentals, pg 932

COLORADO

Audio Consultant Services Inc, pg 693
Daylight Productions & Rentals, pg 739
Multimedia Audio Visual Inc, pg 833
Spectrum Audio Visual Services, pg 897

CONNECTICUT

A/V Davey, pg 697
SoNo Studios, pg 892
Videofilm Systems Inc, pg 929

DELAWARE

Showorks Audio Visual Inc, pg 887
Side Door Studio Inc, pg 887

FLORIDA

Accord Productions, pg 673
Budget Video Rentals, pg 712
CineVideotech Inc, pg 725
Industrial Strength Inc, pg 787
ONstage, pg 846
Paradise Show & Design Inc, pg 851
Phat Planet Recording Studios, pg 855
Photosound of Orlando Inc, pg 856
Sight & Sound Productions, pg 887

South Florida Rehearsal Studios, pg 895
TAI Audio, pg 906
Tallahassee Audio Visual, pg 906
Universal Studios Florida®
Production Group, pg 922
Mike Vasilinda Productions Inc, pg 925

GEORGIA

Convergent Media Systems, pg 731
Lighting & Production Equipment Inc, pg 807
See Production Services, pg 883
Stage Front Presentation Systems, pg 899
Staging Directions Inc, pg 899

HAWAII

Sight & Sound Studios, pg 887

ILLINOIS

Allen Visual Systems Inc, pg 680
AV Chicago Inc, pg 696
Beatty TeleVisual Productions, pg 703
Central Audio-Visual Equipment Inc, pg 719
On Site Video, pg 846
OSA International Inc, pg 848
PSAV® Presentation Services (Hotel Services Division), pg 866
RC Communications, pg 870
Resolution Productions Group, pg 874
SCI Television & Creative Media LLC, pg 882
Winter Productions, pg 939
Woodside Avenue Music Productions Inc, pg 941
Zacuto, pg 945

INDIANA

Advanced Media Integration, pg 677
Gaither Studios LLC, pg 767

KENTUCKY

Audio Visual Techniques Inc, pg 695

MAINE

Headlight Audio Visual Inc, pg 777

MARYLAND

Advance Audiovisual Presentation Ltd, pg 677
CPR MultiMedia Solutions, pg 732
Maryland Sound International Holding Co LLC, pg 819
RTZ Audio Visual, pg 878
Soundtrax Inc, pg 895

MASSACHUSETTS

Capron Lighting & Sound Co Inc, pg 716
Terry Hanley Audio Systems Inc, pg 775
massAV, pg 819
Preston Productions Inc, pg 861

MICHIGAN

City Events Group, pg 725
Digi Sign Design LLC, pg 741
K&R All Media Productions LLC, pg 796
K&R's Recording Studios Inc, pg 796

On Stage Visuals, pg 846
TEL Systems LLC, pg 909

MINNESOTA

Alpha Video & Audio Inc, pg 682
AVI Systems, pg 698

MISSISSIPPI

Bowie Audio Visual Enterprises Inc, pg 709
Jasper Ewing & Sons Inc, pg 757

MISSOURI

Avatar Studios, pg 697
Show-Me Audio-Visual, pg 887

MONTANA

Jereco Studios Inc, pg 793

NEBRASKA

Dog & Pony Productions Inc, pg 744

NEVADA

Lefco Video Services Inc, pg 806

NEW HAMPSHIRE

Academic & Campus Technology Services, pg 672
Apertura, pg 686
APS Lighting-Sound-AV, pg 688

NEW JERSEY

Audio Visual Associates, pg 694
Audio Visual Dynamics®, pg 694
CFP Video Productions Inc, pg 720
Jeep Jazz Media Solutions, pg 793
MiB MediaWorks, pg 825
Moe AV LLC, pg 828
Panavid, pg 850
PLS Staging, pg 858
Starlite, pg 900

NEW MEXICO

Production Outfitters, pg 864

NEW YORK

Adorama Rental Co, pg 676
Aura Sonic Ltd (ASL), pg 695
AV Workshop, pg 697
Colortone Audio Visual, pg 728
Design Audio Visual Inc, pg 741
HB-Content, pg 777
Hello World Communications, pg 778
LightHouse Films, pg 807
Long Island Video Enterprises Live Inc, pg 811
Manhattan Center Studios Inc, pg 816
Posthorn Recordings, pg 859
RadioArt/Bob & Ray CDs & MP3 Files, pg 869
Specialized Audio-Visual Inc, pg 896
Tiki Recording Studios Inc, pg 914
Visual Technologies Corp, pg 932
Visual Word Systems Inc, pg 932
WorldStage, pg 941

NORTH CAROLINA

AV Connections Inc, pg 697
AV Metro Inc, pg 697
Duke Media Services, pg 747
Special Event Services, pg 896
Take One Productions Ltd, pg 906

NORTH DAKOTA

Media Productions, pg 822

OHIO

Lyon Video Inc, pg 813
R&B Communications Inc, pg 870
Vista Color Imaging Inc, pg 931

OREGON

Northwest Film Center, pg 842

PENNSYLVANIA

Audio Visions Inc, pg 694
Audio Visual Communications Inc, pg 694
Dreambox Media Inc, pg 746
FirstGeneration Audio/Visual Services, pg 761
FMP Media Solutions Inc, pg 763
Grise Audio Visual Center Inc, pg 774
Innovision Media Group, pg 788
Ivory Productions, pg 792
New York Camera & Video, pg 840
Right Coast Recording Inc, pg 875
Viewpoint Production Services Inc, pg 930
Visual Sound Inc, pg 931

SOUTH CAROLINA

Genesis Creative, pg 769

TENNESSEE

Allstar Audio Systems Inc, pg 681
Brantley Sound Associates Inc, pg 709
Love Shack Recording Studios, pg 811
Mr Mark's Used Musical, Stereo & Studio Equipment Store, pg 828
OMNISound Recording Studio, pg 845
RentACamera.com, pg 873
Technical Support Systems LLC, pg 908
Trew Audio Inc, pg 917

TEXAS

Alford Media Services, pg 680
Audio Visual Technologies Group (AVTG), pg 695
Crossroads Audio Inc, pg 735
Digital Services Recording Studios, pg 742
FitzCo Sound Inc, pg 761
JSAV, pg 795
Lubbock Audio Visual Inc, pg 812
Music Lab Inc, pg 834
Omega Productions, pg 845
Phillips Media Source, pg 855
Stage Directions, pg 898
Tropikal Productions, pg 918

UTAH

Ron Hill Imagery, pg 780
Performance Audio LLC, pg 854
Webb Audio Visual, pg 935

VERMONT

Edgewood Studios, pg 750

VIRGINIA

American AV, pg 682
Audio Visual Actions Inc (AVA), pg 694
Boitnott Visual Communications Corp (BVC), pg 708

Projection, pg 865
The Whitlock Group, pg 937

WASHINGTON

Northern Lights & Pro Audio, pg 842
Victory Studios, pg 927

WEST VIRGINIA

United Sound & Electronics, pg 921

WISCONSIN

Audio Visual of Milwaukee Inc, pg 694
Event Essentials, pg 756
Full Compass Systems, pg 767
University of Wisconsin-Oshkosh Radio-TV-Film Dept, pg 923
USAV Group Inc, pg 923
Wisconsin Public Television, pg 940

WYOMING

Bridger Productions Inc, pg 710

PUERTO RICO

Stage Crew Audiovisual Inc, pg 898

ALBERTA

Allstar Show Industries Inc, pg 681
McBain Camera Ltd, pg 820
Unique Communications Ltd, pg 921

BRITISH COLUMBIA

Clark's Audio Visual Services Ltd, pg 725
Commercial Electronics Ltd, pg 728
MicrophoneRentals.com, pg 826

MANITOBA

Inland Audio Visual Ltd, pg 788

ONTARIO

GAPC (General Assembly Production Centre), pg 768
HD Source, pg 777
Phase One Studios, pg 855
RB Productions, pg 870
Westbury National Show Systems Ltd, pg 936

QUEBEC

Audio Visual Dynamics, pg 694
Freeman Audio Visual, pg 765
Group PVP, pg 774

Recording Equipment Repairs

CALIFORNIA

Advanced Media LLC, pg 677
Audio Images Corp, pg 693
Audio Upgrades, pg 694
Diemer Amp & Keyboard Repair, pg 741
McAlister Electronics, pg 820
Sound Service Co, pg 894
SSL Industries Inc, pg 898
Towards 2000 Inc, pg 916

CONNECTICUT

HB Communications Inc, pg 777
Sennheiser Electronic Corp, pg 884

AUDIO

Recording Equipment Repairs (continued)

FLORIDA

AMP Services Inc, pg 684
Digital Video Systems, pg 742
Hi-Tech Enterprises Inc, pg 779
JT Communications, pg 795
Midtown Video Inc, pg 827
Phat Planet Recording Studios, pg 855
Stereo Sales Inc, pg 900
TAI Audio, pg 906
Tallahassee Audio Visual, pg 906

GEORGIA

Lighting & Production Equipment Inc, pg 807
Stage Front Presentation Systems, pg 899

ILLINOIS

Allen Visual Systems Inc, pg 680
Beatty TeleVisual Productions, pg 703
C V Lloyde, pg 810
Midwest Digital Corp, pg 827
On Site Video, pg 846

INDIANA

SHP Electronics, pg 887

KENTUCKY

Axxis Leasing Inc, pg 700
Barney Miller's Inc, pg 827
NOR-COM Inc, pg 841

MARYLAND

RTZ Audio Visual, pg 878

MASSACHUSETTS

Capron Lighting & Sound Co Inc, pg 716
Professional Audio Design Inc, pg 865

MICHIGAN

City Events Group, pg 725
K&R's Recording Studios Inc, pg 796
On Stage Visuals, pg 846
TEL Systems LLC, pg 909

MINNESOTA

AVI Systems, pg 698

NEVADA

MUSIC Group Services Nevada, pg 834

NEW JERSEY

JRF Magnetic Sciences Inc, pg 795
The Music Place, pg 834
Starlite, pg 900

NEW YORK

Design Audio Visual Inc, pg 741
Visual Technologies Corp, pg 932

NORTH CAROLINA

Camcor Inc, pg 715

OHIO

Copp Integrated Systems, pg 731
Tri-State Audio Visual Co, pg 918

OREGON

All Service Musical Electronics Repair, pg 680

PENNSYLVANIA

Right Coast Recording Inc, pg 875
Vistacom Inc, pg 931

SOUTH CAROLINA

DaviSound, pg 739

TENNESSEE

Technical Support Systems LLC, pg 908
Trew Audio Inc, pg 917

TEXAS

Lubbock Audio Visual Inc, pg 812
Pro Video & Film Equipment Co Inc, pg 863
Tarpley Media Systems, pg 907

UTAH

Spectra Sonics LLC, pg 897

VIRGINIA

Boitnott Visual Communications Corp (BVC), pg 708
Intellidyne LLC, pg 789
The Whitlock Group, pg 937

WASHINGTON

Northern Lights & Pro Audio, pg 842

WEST VIRGINIA

United Sound & Electronics, pg 921

WISCONSIN

Audio Visual of Milwaukee Inc, pg 694
Camera Corner Connecting Point, pg 715
Full Compass Systems, pg 767

ALBERTA

Allstar Show Industries Inc, pg 681
Infosat Communications Inc, pg 787
Unique Communications Ltd, pg 921

BRITISH COLUMBIA

Commercial Electronics Ltd, pg 728

MANITOBA

Inland Audio Visual Ltd, pg 788

ONTARIO

Westbury National Show Systems Ltd, pg 936

Recording Equipment— Magnetic, see Magnetic Recording Equipment

Recording Facility Manufacturers

CALIFORNIA

Ametron Audio/Video, pg 684
The Banquet Sound Studios, pg 701
Martinsound Inc, pg 818
QRS Software Services, pg 867
Westlake Recording Studios, pg 936
Yanchar Design & Consulting Group, pg 943

COLORADO

Arrakis Systems, pg 689

ILLINOIS

Delmark Records, pg 740
IAC Acoustics, pg 783

MICHIGAN

Studio Consulting & Construction Inc, pg 902

NEW JERSEY

Diversified, pg 744
Radio Visions, pg 869

NEW YORK

CP Communications, pg 732

PENNSYLVANIA

Forge Recording LLC, pg 764
Right Coast Recording Inc, pg 875

TENNESSEE

Carl Tatz Design, pg 907
WhisperRoom™ Inc, pg 937

TEXAS

ETS-Lindgren, pg 756
Planet Dallas Recording Studios, pg 857

UTAH

Spectra Sonics LLC, pg 897

VIRGINIA

Acoustics First Corp, pg 674

Recording Facility Rentals

ALABAMA

Airwave Recording Studio, pg 679

ARIZONA

Arizona Cine Equipment, pg 688
Merestone, pg 823
Sky City Audio, pg 890

ARKANSAS

Live'N'Loud, pg 810
White Diamond Productions LLC, pg 937

CALIFORNIA

Advanced Digital Design, pg 677
Aliso Creek Productions Inc, pg 680
AlphaDogs Inc, pg 682
Artichoke Productions, pg 690
Audio Upgrades, pg 694
Berke Creative Inc, pg 704
Berkeley Sound Artists Inc, pg 704
Big Door, pg 705

Blue Lotus Temple Studio, pg 707
Cantrax Recorders, pg 716
Creative Media Recording, pg 733
Different Fur Recording Ltd, pg 741
Express Media Inc, pg 757
FJ Productions Inc, pg 762
4th Street Recording, pg 764
Full Moon & High Tide Productions & Studios, pg 767
Golden Gate Studios, pg 772
Greenery Studios, pg 774
Hybrid Studios, pg 783
The Jim Henson Co, pg 794
Juice Studios, pg 795
Kris Stevens Enterprises, pg 801
KTVU-Retail Services, pg 802
Larrabee Sound Studio, pg 803
Lynch Communications, pg 813
Maximus Media Inc, pg 820
McCune Audio-Video-Lighting, pg 821
North County Media Center, pg 842
On-Trax Inc, pg 846
Playback Recording Studio, pg 858
Pyramind Studios, pg 867
Roundabout Entertainment Inc, pg 878
SNAP, pg 891
Sonora Recorders, pg 893
Still N' Motion, pg 901
Studio Circle Recordings, pg 902
Studio 132, pg 902
Studio 637, pg 903
Todd-AO Studios, pg 915
Total Creative, pg 916
Video Resources Inc, pg 928
Warner Bros Entertainment Inc, pg 934
Westlake Recording Studios, pg 936

COLORADO

Audio Consultant Services Inc, pg 693
Colorado Sound Recording Ltd, pg 728
Conly Productions, pg 730
Daylight Productions & Rentals, pg 739
Denver Media Center, pg 740
Side 3 Studios, pg 887

CONNECTICUT

Presence Studios, pg 861
Sonalysts Media, pg 892
SoNo Studios, pg 892

DELAWARE

Cornerstone Media Productions Inc, pg 731
Side Door Studio Inc, pg 887

DISTRICT OF COLUMBIA

The American University, pg 684
NPR Distribution Services, pg 843

FLORIDA

Accord Productions, pg 673
Audacity Recording Studios, pg 693
Blackburst Entertainment LLC, pg 706
Comtel Inc, pg 730
Jordan Klein Film & Video (JKFV), pg 795
The Kitchen, pg 799
LHV Audio Services, pg 807
National Teleproductions Inc, pg 837
Phat Planet Recording Studios, pg 855

South Florida Rehearsal Studios, pg 895
Universal Studios Florida® Production Group, pg 922
Mike Vasilinda Productions Inc, pg 925
Venice Media Group, pg 925

GEORGIA

ECG Productions, pg 750
Encyclomedia, pg 754
Lighting & Production Equipment Inc, pg 807
Magick Lantern, pg 814
Stage Front Presentation Systems, pg 899
Staging Directions Inc, pg 899
White Dog Studios, pg 937

HAWAII

Media Bridge Gamekids, pg 821

ILLINOIS

Beatty TeleVisual Productions, pg 703
CCore Media Inc, pg 718
Major Media Inc, pg 815
On Site Video, pg 846
OSA International Inc, pg 848
Pepper Group, pg 854
PSAV® Presentation Services (Hotel Services Division), pg 866
RBR Productions, pg 870
Resolution Productions Group, pg 874
ShiftFocus Productions, pg 886
Tone Zone Recording, pg 915
Woodside Avenue Music Productions Inc, pg 941

INDIANA

Advanced Media Integration, pg 677
Gaither Studios LLC, pg 767
OMNI Productions, pg 845
Sweetwater Sound Inc, pg 905

MARYLAND

CPR MultiMedia Solutions, pg 732
dbF a Media Company, pg 739
Omega Recording Studios, pg 845

MASSACHUSETTS

Preston Productions Inc, pg 861
Sounds Interesting Studio, pg 894
Soundtrack Group, pg 895
TR Productions, pg 916
WGBH Production Group, pg 936

MICHIGAN

Audio Graphic Services, pg 693
Brilliance Audio, pg 710
The Brookwood Studio Inc, pg 711
City Events Group, pg 725
Digi Sign Design LLC, pg 741
K&R All Media Productions LLC, pg 796
K&R's Recording Studios Inc, pg 796
Madonna University Information Technology, pg 814
MessageMakers, pg 824
RingSide Creative, pg 875

MINNESOTA

The ADS Group, pg 676
Winterland Studios, pg 940

MISSOURI

Avatar Studios, pg 697
Show-Me Audio-Visual, pg 887
Studio Worx Inc, pg 903

MONTANA

Jereco Studios Inc, pg 793

NEVADA

MG Studio, pg 825
Tanglewood Productions, pg 907

NEW HAMPSHIRE

Apertura, pg 686
Rocking Horse Studio, pg 876

NEW JERSEY

The Audio Department Inc, pg 693
Color Leasing Studios, pg 727
IMP Digital Studios, A PharmaSphere Company, pg 786
Jeep Jazz Media Solutions, pg 793
Laurel Video Productions, pg 804
MiB MediaWorks, pg 825
Milgrom Productions, pg 827
Record Plant Remote, pg 871
Richard Reiter Productions Inc, pg 873

NEW MEXICO

Production Outfitters, pg 864

NEW YORK

Acme Recording Studios Inc, pg 674
All Mobile Video Inc, pg 680
Aura Sonic Ltd (ASL), pg 695
Design Audio Visual Inc, pg 741
Electric Lady Studios, pg 752
Fingerpaint, pg 761
HB-Content, pg 777
Headroom Digital Audio, pg 777
Heavy Melody, pg 778
InterNation Inc, pg 789
KAS Music & Sound, pg 796
Long Island Video Enterprises Live Inc, pg 811
Manhattan Center Studios Inc, pg 816
Mark Custom Recording Service Inc, pg 817
MetroSonic Recording Studio, pg 824
NBC Production Facilities, pg 837
New York Audio Productions, pg 840
The Palmer Group, pg 850
RadioArt/Bob & Ray CDs & MP3 Files, pg 869
Sony Music Entertainment, pg 893
Tiki Recording Studios Inc, pg 914
Zelman Studios Ltd, pg 945

NORTH CAROLINA

Duke Media Services, pg 747
Evolve Inc, pg 757
Media-Comm, pg 821
Take One Productions Ltd, pg 906

NORTH DAKOTA

Media Productions, pg 822

OHIO

Icom Multimedia, pg 783
Lyon Video Inc, pg 813
Mills James Productions, pg 828

OSV Studios, pg 848
Vista Color Imaging Inc, pg 931

OKLAHOMA

PDC Productions, pg 852

PENNSYLVANIA

American Artist Studio, pg 682
Audio Visual Communications Inc, pg 694
Canadian American Records, pg 715
Dreambox Media Inc, pg 746
Filmaker Technology, pg 760
Innovision Media Group, pg 788
Ivory Productions, pg 792
JPL, pg 795
Raven Rental, pg 870
Right Coast Recording Inc, pg 875
Visual Sound Inc, pg 931
WHYY Inc, pg 938
WQED-Multimedia, pg 942

SOUTH CAROLINA

DaviSound, pg 739

TENNESSEE

Ardent Music LLC, pg 688
Brantley Sound Associates Inc, pg 709
Continental Film, pg 731
Love Shack Recording Studios, pg 811
Mr Mark's Used Musical, Stereo & Studio Equipment Store, pg 828
OMNISound Recording Studio, pg 845
Technical Support Systems LLC, pg 908
University of Memphis, Music Industry Division, pg 922
Zion Music Group, pg 945

TEXAS

Bismeaux Studios, pg 706
Digital Services Recording Studios, pg 742
Fire Station Studios, pg 761
Music Lab Inc, pg 834
Omega Productions, pg 845
Out of the BLUE Media, pg 849
Phillips Media Source, pg 855
Real to Reel Studios Inc, pg 871
Reelsound Recording Co, pg 872
Replicopy Digital Media Center, pg 873
The Sound Lab Inc, pg 894
Stage Directions, pg 898
TM Studios Inc, pg 915
Trinity Recording Studio, pg 918
Tropikal Productions, pg 918

UTAH

ELS Productions Inc, pg 753
Ron Hill Imagery, pg 780
Performance Audio LLC, pg 854

VERMONT

Edgewood Studios, pg 750

VIRGINIA

Advance Concepts Inc, pg 677
Video Solutions, pg 928

WASHINGTON

Avast! Recording Co, pg 697
Inland Audio Visual Co, pg 788
Victory Studios, pg 927

WISCONSIN

Audio Visual of Milwaukee Inc, pg 694
5th Floor Recording Co, pg 760
Sound Strations Audio Productions Inc, pg 894
TBC Studios, pg 907
University of Wisconsin-Oshkosh Radio-TV-Film Dept, pg 923
USAV Group Inc, pg 923
Wisconsin Public Television, pg 940

WYOMING

Bridger Productions Inc, pg 710

ALBERTA

Black Media Works, pg 706
Global TV, pg 771

BRITISH COLUMBIA

The Vocal Point/Profile Communications Ltd, pg 932

ONTARIO

ADS Media, pg 677
GAPC (General Assembly Production Centre), pg 768
Phase One Studios, pg 855
Silver Creek Media Inc, pg 888

Recording Facility Repairs

CALIFORNIA

Audio Images Corp, pg 693
Audio Upgrades, pg 694
McAlister Electronics, pg 820
SSL Industries Inc, pg 898

CONNECTICUT

HB Communications Inc, pg 777

FLORIDA

Phat Planet Recording Studios, pg 855
Stereo Sales Inc, pg 900

GEORGIA

Stage Front Presentation Systems, pg 899

ILLINOIS

Midwest Digital Corp, pg 827

KENTUCKY

NOR-COM Inc, pg 841

MASSACHUSETTS

Professional Audio Design Inc, pg 865

MICHIGAN

City Events Group, pg 725
K&R's Recording Studios Inc, pg 796
Studio Consulting & Construction Inc, pg 902
TEL Systems LLC, pg 909

NEW JERSEY

Radio Visions, pg 869
Starlite, pg 900

AUDIO

Recording Facility Repairs (continued)

PENNSYLVANIA

Audio Visual Communications Inc, pg 694
Right Coast Recording Inc, pg 875

TEXAS

Pro Video & Film Equipment Co Inc, pg 863
The Sound Lab Inc, pg 894

WISCONSIN

Audio Visual of Milwaukee Inc, pg 694
Full Compass Systems, pg 767

Rehearsal Studio Manufacturers

CALIFORNIA

Ametron Audio/Video, pg 684
Yanchar Design & Consulting Group, pg 943

ILLINOIS

IAC Acoustics, pg 783

NEW YORK

CP Communications, pg 732

OHIO

Soundfold Inc, pg 894

TENNESSEE

WhisperRoom™ Inc, pg 937

TEXAS

L'AIR International, pg 802

VIRGINIA

Acoustics First Corp, pg 674

Rehearsal Studio Rentals

ALABAMA

Airwave Recording Studio, pg 679

ARIZONA

Merestone, pg 823

CALIFORNIA

Ametron Audio/Video, pg 684
Chapman/Leonard Studio Equipment Inc, pg 720
Full Moon & High Tide Productions & Studios, pg 767
Golden Gate Studios, pg 772
Lynch Communications, pg 813
Still N' Motion, pg 901
Studio 637, pg 903
Total Creative, pg 916
Towards 2000 Inc, pg 916

COLORADO

Daylight Productions & Rentals, pg 739

DELAWARE

Side Door Studio Inc, pg 887

FLORIDA

CopShopMiami.com, pg 731
Jordan Klein Film & Video (JKFV), pg 795
National Teleproductions Inc, pg 837
Phat Planet Recording Studios, pg 855
South Florida Rehearsal Studios, pg 895
Mike Vasilinda Productions Inc, pg 925

GEORGIA

Convergent Media Systems, pg 731
Lighting & Production Equipment Inc, pg 807
Stage Front Presentation Systems, pg 899
Staging Directions Inc, pg 899

ILLINOIS

Atomic Imaging Inc/Golan Studios, pg 692
OSA International Inc, pg 848
Resolution Productions Group, pg 874
Woodside Avenue Music Productions Inc, pg 941

INDIANA

Sweetwater Sound Inc, pg 905

MARYLAND

CPR MultiMedia Solutions, pg 732
Sheffield Audio/Video Productions, pg 885

MASSACHUSETTS

Preston Productions Inc, pg 861

MICHIGAN

Brilliance Audio, pg 710
City Events Group, pg 725
Digi Sign Design LLC, pg 741
K&R All Media Productions LLC, pg 796
K&R's Recording Studios Inc, pg 796

MISSOURI

Show-Me Audio-Visual, pg 887

NEW JERSEY

Audio Visual Dynamics®, pg 694
Color Leasing Studios, pg 727
MiB MediaWorks, pg 825

NEW YORK

Big Foot Productions Inc, pg 705
Manhattan Center Studios Inc, pg 816
The Palmer Group, pg 850
Sony Music Entertainment, pg 893
Studio Instrument Rentals (SIR), pg 902
Videograf, pg 929

NORTH CAROLINA

Duke Media Services, pg 747
Take One Productions Ltd, pg 906

NORTH DAKOTA

Media Productions, pg 822

OHIO

Bartha, pg 702
Vista Color Imaging Inc, pg 931

PENNSYLVANIA

Innovision Media Group, pg 788
WHYY Inc, pg 938

SOUTH CAROLINA

DaviSound, pg 739

TENNESSEE

Ardent Music LLC, pg 688
Mr Mark's Used Musical, Stereo & Studio Equipment Store, pg 828
Technical Support Systems LLC, pg 908

TEXAS

Fire Station Studios, pg 761
Music Lab Inc, pg 834
South Coast Film & Video, pg 895
Stage Directions, pg 898

UTAH

Performance Audio LLC, pg 854

VERMONT

Edgewood Studios, pg 750

WASHINGTON

Victory Studios, pg 927

WISCONSIN

TBC Studios, pg 907
USAV Group Inc, pg 923
Wisconsin Public Television, pg 940

WYOMING

Bridger Productions Inc, pg 710

ALBERTA

Global TV, pg 771

BRITISH COLUMBIA

Video Out Distribution, pg 928

ONTARIO

Silver Creek Media Inc, pg 888

Rehearsal Studio Repairs

CALIFORNIA

Audio Images Corp, pg 693
McAlister Electronics, pg 820

CONNECTICUT

HB Communications Inc, pg 777

FLORIDA

Stereo Sales Inc, pg 900

GEORGIA

Stage Front Presentation Systems, pg 899

ILLINOIS

Midwest Digital Corp, pg 827

KENTUCKY

NOR-COM Inc, pg 841

MICHIGAN

K&R's Recording Studios Inc, pg 796
TEL Systems LLC, pg 909

NEW JERSEY

Starlite, pg 900

TEXAS

Pro Video & Film Equipment Co Inc, pg 863

Repetitive Tape Equipment Distributors

ARIZONA

Arizona Cine Equipment, pg 688

ARKANSAS

Jay S Stanley & Associates Inc, pg 899

CALIFORNIA

Ametron Audio/Video, pg 684
Media Fabricators Inc, pg 822
MediaPOINTE, pg 823

CONNECTICUT

MAVCO, pg 820

DELAWARE

Actors Attic, pg 675

FLORIDA

Hi-Tech Import Export Corp, pg 779
Recording Media & Equipment Inc (RM&E), pg 872
Stereo Sales Inc, pg 900
TAI Audio, pg 906

GEORGIA

Baker Audio Visual, pg 700
Stage Front Presentation Systems, pg 899
Visioneering International Inc, pg 931

ILLINOIS

Major Reproductions Equipment Co, pg 815

INDIANA

Sensory Technologies LLC, pg 884

KENTUCKY

NOR-COM Inc, pg 841

MARYLAND

Bradley Broadcast & Pro Audio, pg 709

MICHIGAN

City Events Group, pg 725
TEL Systems LLC, pg 909

MISSISSIPPI

Jasper Ewing & Sons Inc, pg 757

NEW JERSEY

Audio Visual Dynamics®, pg 694
G&G Technologies Inc, pg 768
HamiltonBuhl, pg 775
Starlite, pg 900

NEW YORK

Design Audio Visual Inc, pg 741
Indigo Productions, pg 787
Visual Technologies Corp, pg 932

NORTH CAROLINA

Strategic Connections, pg 901

PENNSYLVANIA

Advanced AV LLC, pg 677
Morefield Communications Inc,
    pg 830

TENNESSEE

Continental Film, pg 731
Lowrance Sound Co Inc, pg 812

TEXAS

Audio Visual Technologies Group
    (AVTG), pg 695
Heffernan Audio Visual, pg 778
JSAV, pg 795
Lubbock Audio Visual Inc, pg 812

UTAH

Performance Audio LLC, pg 854

WISCONSIN

Audio Visual of Milwaukee Inc,
    pg 694
Demco Inc, pg 740
Full Compass Systems, pg 767

PUERTO RICO

Bonnin Electronics Inc, pg 708

MANITOBA

Advance Pro, pg 677
Inland Audio Visual Ltd, pg 788

ONTARIO

Nationwide Audio Visual Co,
    pg 837

Repetitive Tape Equipment Manufacturers

CALIFORNIA

Mackenzie Laboratories Inc, pg 814

NEW YORK

Clever Devices Ltd, pg 726
MultiDyne Video & Fiber Optics
    Systems, pg 833

Repetitive Tape Equipment Rentals

ARIZONA

Arizona Cine Equipment, pg 688
Metropolitan Audio-Visual Inc,
    pg 824

CALIFORNIA

Ametron Audio/Video, pg 684
Lynch Communications, pg 813
Media Fabricators Inc, pg 822

GEORGIA

Stage Front Presentation Systems,
    pg 899
Staging Directions Inc, pg 899

ILLINOIS

OSA International Inc, pg 848

KENTUCKY

Audio Visual Techniques Inc,
    pg 695

MASSACHUSETTS

massAV, pg 819
Preston Productions Inc, pg 861

MICHIGAN

City Events Group, pg 725
K&R All Media Productions LLC,
    pg 796
K&R's Recording Studios Inc,
    pg 796

NEW JERSEY

Audio Visual Dynamics®, pg 694
Starlite, pg 900

NEW YORK

Design Audio Visual Inc, pg 741
Visual Technologies Corp, pg 932

NORTH CAROLINA

Strategic Connections, pg 901

TEXAS

JSAV, pg 795
Lubbock Audio Visual Inc, pg 812

UTAH

Performance Audio LLC, pg 854

VIRGINIA

American AV, pg 682
Projection, pg 865

WISCONSIN

Audio Visual of Milwaukee Inc,
    pg 694

BRITISH COLUMBIA

Clark's Audio Visual Services Ltd,
    pg 725

MANITOBA

Inland Audio Visual Ltd, pg 788

Repetitive Tape Equipment Repairs

CALIFORNIA

Ametron Audio/Video, pg 684
Audio Images Corp, pg 693
Audio Upgrades, pg 694
McAlister Electronics, pg 820

CONNECTICUT

HB Communications Inc, pg 777

FLORIDA

Stereo Sales Inc, pg 900

GEORGIA

Stage Front Presentation Systems,
    pg 899

KENTUCKY

NOR-COM Inc, pg 841

MICHIGAN

City Events Group, pg 725
K&R's Recording Studios Inc,
    pg 796
TEL Systems LLC, pg 909

NEW JERSEY

Starlite, pg 900

NEW YORK

Visual Technologies Corp, pg 932

OREGON

All Service Musical Electronics
    Repair, pg 680

TEXAS

Audio Visual Technologies Group
    (AVTG), pg 695
Lubbock Audio Visual Inc, pg 812

WISCONSIN

Audio Visual of Milwaukee Inc,
    pg 694
Full Compass Systems, pg 767

MANITOBA

Inland Audio Visual Ltd, pg 788

Rhythm & Blues Music, *see* Music Libraries— Rhythm & Blues

Rock Music, *see* Music Libraries—Rock

Sampling

ALABAMA

Dogwood Productions Inc, pg 745

ARIZONA

Merestone, pg 823

CALIFORNIA

Aliso Creek Productions Inc, pg 680
Artichoke Productions, pg 690
Creative Technology, pg 733
Diamond Dreams Music
    Productions, pg 741
Earwax Productions Inc, pg 749
Eye & I Productions, pg 758
ILIO Enterprises LLC, pg 784
Lynch Communications, pg 813
Maximus Media Inc, pg 820
Pyramind Studios, pg 867
QRS Software Services, pg 867
Reality Check Systems, pg 871
Saturn Studios, pg 881
Steve Shapiro Music, pg 885
Studio 132, pg 902

Timeless Productions, pg 914
Total Creative, pg 916

COLORADO

Tim Cissell Music, pg 725
Colorado Sound Recording Ltd,
    pg 728
Conly Productions, pg 730

DELAWARE

Side Door Studio Inc, pg 887

FLORIDA

LHV Audio Services, pg 807
Phat Planet Recording Studios,
    pg 855
Sunfire Communications Inc,
    pg 904

HAWAII

Hyperspective Studios Inc, pg 783
Media Bridge Gamekids, pg 821

ILLINOIS

Solid Sound Recording Studio,
    pg 892
Woodside Avenue Music
    Productions Inc, pg 941

INDIANA

Sweetwater Sound Inc, pg 905

MARYLAND

CPR MultiMedia Solutions, pg 732
dbF a Media Company, pg 739
Omega Recording Studios, pg 845

MASSACHUSETTS

Cramer, pg 732
Professional Audio Design Inc,
    pg 865
Soundtrack Group, pg 895
Rik Tinory Productions, pg 914

MICHIGAN

Digi Sign Design LLC, pg 741
GMP Music, pg 772
K&R's Recording Studios Inc,
    pg 796

MINNESOTA

The ADS Group, pg 676

MISSOURI

Avatar Studios, pg 697

MONTANA

Jereco Studios Inc, pg 793

NEW JERSEY

Jeep Jazz Media Solutions, pg 793
Suede Interactive, pg 903

NEW YORK

Aural Gratification Inc, pg 695
The Big House Group, pg 705
Manhattan Center Studios Inc,
    pg 816

NORTH CAROLINA

Pat Appleson Studios Inc, pg 687
2BruceStudio, pg 920

AUDIO

Sampling (continued)

OHIO

Mills James Productions, pg 828
SoundSpace Inc, pg 895
The Telos Alliance, pg 910

PENNSYLVANIA

Forge Recording LLC, pg 764
Ivory Productions, pg 792
Right Coast Recording Inc, pg 875

RHODE ISLAND

Sound-FX-Design, pg 894

TENNESSEE

American Blackguard Inc, pg 683
Analog Man Recording Studio,
    pg 685
Mr Mark's Used Musical, Stereo &
    Studio Equipment Store, pg 828
Stage Post, pg 899

TEXAS

Anaphora Literary Press, pg 685
Audiomoxie®, pg 695
Biway Media, pg 706
Fire Station Studios, pg 761
Stage Directions, pg 898
Tropikal Productions, pg 918
World Beat Studio, pg 941

VIRGINIA

CDR Communications Inc, pg 719
Wally Cleaver's Recording Service,
    pg 726

WASHINGTON

Sound Sound, pg 894

WISCONSIN

5th Floor Recording Co, pg 760

MANITOBA

DACAPO Productions Inc, pg 737

ONTARIO

DebsVoice, pg 739
JL Recording Studios, pg 794

Script Writing

ALABAMA

Dogwood Productions Inc, pg 745

ALASKA

Aurora Films, pg 696

ARIZONA

Film Creations Ltd, pg 760
Fire Power Music LLC, pg 761
Merestone, pg 823
Metropolitan Audio-Visual Inc,
    pg 824
On-Site Video, pg 846
Teaberry, pg 908

ARKANSAS

Live'N'Loud, pg 810
White Diamond Productions LLC,
    pg 937

CALIFORNIA

Action Video, pg 675
Audio Visual Consultants, pg 694
Concrete Images, pg 730
Creative Technology, pg 733
Crystal Pyramid Productions™,
    pg 735
Custom Video Productions Inc,
    pg 736
Design Media, pg 741
Direct Cinema Ltd Inc, pg 743
Goal Productions, pg 772
Gold Standard Productions, pg 772
Havas Edge, pg 777
iCorpTv, pg 783
Increase Video/Silver Mine Video,
    pg 786
Kris Stevens Enterprises, pg 801
KTVU-Retail Services, pg 802
KVIE-Channel 6, pg 802
Lynch Communications, pg 813
Maximus Media Inc, pg 820
Media Magic, pg 822
The Media Staff Inc, pg 822
Palardo Productions, pg 850
Penrose Productions, pg 854
piXvfm Inc, pg 857
PM Productions, pg 858
Point of View Productions, pg 858
Prime Cut Productions, pg 862
PSI Inc, pg 866
QRS Software Services, pg 867
Sahara Records & Filmworks
    Entertainment Co, pg 879
Staylor-Made Communications Inc,
    pg 900
Still N' Motion, pg 901
Tam Communications Inc, pg 906
Total Creative, pg 916
West Coast Projections Inc, pg 935
WMS Media Inc, pg 940

COLORADO

Conly Productions, pg 730
Daylight Productions & Rentals,
    pg 739
Shambhala Publications, pg 885
Starwest Productions, pg 900

CONNECTICUT

Antenna International, pg 686
Cine-Med Inc, pg 723
The Gary-Paul Agency, pg 768
Guymark Studios LLC, pg 775
Ironik Design & Post, pg 791
New London Media, pg 839
P&P Studios Inc, pg 851
Powerstation Events, pg 860
Save the Children Federation Inc,
    pg 881
Vista Group International Inc,
    pg 931

DISTRICT OF COLUMBIA

Hillmann & Carr Inc, pg 780

FLORIDA

Communications Concepts Inc
    (CCI), pg 729
LHV Audio Services, pg 807
The Newhouse Media Group,
    pg 840
Sunfire Communications Inc,
    pg 904
Sunrise Studios, pg 904

GEORGIA

Guerrilla Productions LLC, pg 774
Myriad Productions, pg 835
Malcolm Neal Productions, pg 837

On-Line Productions, pg 845
Visioneering International Inc,
    pg 931

HAWAII

Media Bridge Gamekids, pg 821

IDAHO

KTVB-TV, pg 802
Wide Eye Productions, pg 938

ILLINOIS

ABS Enterprises, pg 672
Airways Digital Media, pg 679
Audiobook Department, pg 695
Beatty TeleVisual Productions,
    pg 703
CCore Media Inc, pg 718
Extraordinary Demos/Videos,
    pg 757
Major Media Productions Inc,
    pg 815
Manning Productions, pg 816
Mightybytes Inc, pg 827
Multimedia Marketing Group,
    pg 833
Jim Passin Productions, pg 852
Pepper Group, pg 854
PSAV® Presentation Services
    (Hotel Services Division), pg 866
Sound/Video Impressions Inc,
    pg 894
Sparkfactor, pg 896
20/20 Communications Inc, pg 920
WEEK TV, pg 935
Woodside Avenue Music
    Productions Inc, pg 941

INDIANA

A-V-A Video Productions, pg 671
Bright Ideas Creative Services,
    pg 710
Communication Ministries, pg 728
OMNI Productions, pg 845

IOWA

Educational Technology & Media
    Services, pg 751
Hedquist Productions, pg 778

KENTUCKY

Broadway Digital, pg 711

LOUISIANA

Launch Media, pg 804
Louisiana State University Division
    of Strategic Communications,
    pg 811
Moxie Media, pg 832
Vidox Motion Imagery, pg 930

MAINE

Serendipity Recordings, pg 884
Slim Goodbody Corp, pg 890

MARYLAND

CPR MultiMedia Solutions, pg 732
The Cutting Corporation,
    GraphicAudio® & Archival
    Sound Lab, pg 736
dbF a Media Company, pg 739
The Image Generators, pg 785
Kramer Communications Video
    Production, pg 801
Milner-Fenwick Inc, pg 828
Pro Cuts Editing Services, pg 862

MASSACHUSETTS

CommCreative, pg 728
Cramer, pg 732
Labrecque Creative Sound, pg 803
Monadnock Media Inc, pg 829
Northern Light Productions (NLP),
    pg 842
Penfield Productions Ltd, pg 853
Preston Productions Inc, pg 861
Sound & Vision Media, pg 893
TR Productions, pg 916

MICHIGAN

Brilliance Audio, pg 710
Digi Sign Design LLC, pg 741
Digital Image Studios LLC, pg 742
K&R's Recording Studios Inc,
    pg 796
Madonna University Information
    Technology, pg 814
MessageMakers, pg 824

MINNESOTA

The ADS Group, pg 676
Badiyan Inc, pg 700
Media Loft Inc, pg 822

MISSOURI

Show-Me Audio-Visual, pg 887
Switch, pg 905

MONTANA

KCFW Television, pg 797
KUSM TV, pg 802

NEBRASKA

JoeAudio, pg 794

NEVADA

DVDs4Less, pg 748
JCS Video Productions, pg 793
Tanglewood Productions, pg 907

NEW HAMPSHIRE

Apertura, pg 686
Chip Taylor Communications LLC,
    pg 907
The Troupe, pg 918

NEW JERSEY

AJS Events, pg 679
Allegro Productions Inc, pg 680
Audio Vistas LLC, pg 694
CFP Video Productions Inc, pg 720
Color Leasing Studios, pg 727
Euro-Pacific Film & Video
    Productions Inc, pg 756
Laurel Video Productions, pg 804
MediaNow Inc, pg 822
MiB MediaWorks, pg 825
Milgrom Productions, pg 827
Optisonics Productions, pg 847
Reed Presentations Inc (RPI),
    pg 872
Suede Interactive, pg 903
VCSvideo, pg 925

NEW MEXICO

Production Outfitters, pg 864

NEW YORK

aurora productions, pg 696
Big Fish Production US, pg 705
The Big House Group, pg 705
Broadstreet Productions LLC,
    pg 711
Buffalo Video Production, pg 712

Chromavision Corp, pg 723
Cohn Creative Group LLC, pg 727
Thomas Craven Film Corp, pg 733
De Nonno Productions Inc (DPI),
 pg 739
The Food & Beverage Institute,
 pg 763
4-D Creative Media, pg 764
HB-Content, pg 777
Icontent, pg 783
La Paloma Films, pg 803
Manhattan Center Studios Inc,
 pg 816
Mood Creations Ltd, pg 829
Jack Morton Worldwide, pg 830
MRM//McCANN, pg 832
MRY, pg 832
News Broadcast Network Inc,
 pg 840
Northeast Video Productions Inc,
 pg 842
The Palmer Group, pg 850
Peckham Productions Inc, pg 852
Split Image Productions, pg 898
Synaptic Digital, pg 905
Zelman Studios Ltd, pg 945

NORTH CAROLINA

Pat Appleson Studios Inc, pg 687
The Communications Group Inc,
 pg 729
Digital Rain LLC, pg 742
Duke Media Services, pg 747

NORTH DAKOTA

Media Productions, pg 822

OHIO

Advent Media Inc, pg 677
Challenge Productions/Challenge
 Aerial Imaging, pg 720
Curtis Inc, pg 736
Cuyahoga Community College
 Student Production Office (SPO),
 pg 736
Icom Multimedia, pg 783
MainSail Production Services Inc,
 pg 815
Mills James Productions, pg 828
R&B Communications Inc, pg 870
Treehaus Communications Inc,
 pg 917
Vista Color Imaging Inc, pg 931

OKLAHOMA

Academic Media & Digital
 Services, pg 672
Garman Productions LLC, pg 768
PDC Productions, pg 852

OREGON

KTVA Productions, pg 802
Odyssey Productions Inc, pg 844

PENNSYLVANIA

Audio Visual Communications Inc,
 pg 694
Filmaker Technology, pg 760
Innovision Media Group, pg 788
JPL, pg 795
Panta Rhei Media Inc, pg 851
Production Masters Inc (PMI),
 pg 864
The Videohouse Inc, pg 929
WPHL-TV, pg 942
WQED-Multimedia, pg 942

RHODE ISLAND

Sound-FX-Design, pg 894
StarTrak Studios Inc, pg 900

SOUTH CAROLINA

DaviSound, pg 739
Genesis Creative, pg 769
Venture Media, pg 925

TENNESSEE

American Blackguard Inc, pg 683
Continental Film, pg 731
Memphis Communications Corp,
 pg 823
Motion Picture Services, pg 831
Scripps Networks, pg 882
Stage Post, pg 899

TEXAS

Anaphora Literary Press, pg 685
Best Film & Video, pg 704
Biway Media, pg 706
The Black Academy of Arts &
 Letters Inc, pg 706
Castleview Productions, pg 717
Cerutti Productions Inc, pg 720
Communication Arts Multimedia
 Inc, pg 728
Dykeman Associates Inc, pg 748
The Editing Co, pg 750
Emergency Film Group, pg 753
Epic Software Group Inc, pg 755
Phillips Media Source, pg 855
Romar Learning Solutions LLC,
 pg 877
The Samuels Co, pg 879
Stage Directions, pg 898
Texas Heart Institute Visual
 Communication Services, pg 911
The Yesterday USA Radio
 Networks, pg 944

UTAH

ImageWorks Communications,
 pg 785

VERMONT

University of Vermont, Instructional
 Television Dept, pg 923
Wilson McLeran Inc, pg 939

VIRGINIA

Advance Concepts Inc, pg 677
Blair Inc, pg 707
CACI Integrated Communications,
 pg 713
CDR Communications Inc, pg 719
Wally Cleaver's Recording Service,
 pg 726
Studio Center Corp, pg 902

WASHINGTON

Adams Creative & Production
 Services, pg 675
Inland Audio Visual Co, pg 788
Kostov Productions, pg 801
Laser Fantasy/HECK
 Industries/Photon Manufacturing,
 pg 804
North-by-Northwest - A Digital
 Studio, pg 842
Sound Sound, pg 894
Victory Studios, pg 927

WISCONSIN

Audio Visual of Milwaukee Inc,
 pg 694
Learning Technology Services,
 pg 805
Meridian Studios, pg 824
Sound Strations Audio Productions
 Inc, pg 894
USAV Group Inc, pg 923
Video Wisconsin Inc, pg 929
Watts Communications Inc, pg 934
Wisconsin Public Television, pg 940

WYOMING

Bridger Productions Inc, pg 710

ALBERTA

Global TV, pg 771

BRITISH COLUMBIA

Triad Communications Ltd, pg 918

ONTARIO

DebsVoice, pg 739
GAPC (General Assembly
 Production Centre), pg 768
JFB Communications, pg 794
Silver Creek Media Inc, pg 888
Wanted! Sound + Picture, pg 933

**Signal Compression
Equipment,** *see*
**Compression &
Decompression
Equipment**

**Signal Processing
Equipment Distributors**

ALABAMA

PESA, pg 855

ARIZONA

Allusion Studios & Pure Wave
 Audio, pg 681
EAR Professional Audio/Video,
 pg 749
Troxell-CDI, pg 918

CALIFORNIA

Ametron Audio/Video, pg 684
Associated Sound, pg 691
Audio Images Corp, pg 693
Be Media, pg 702
Empire Pro, pg 753
GigaSonic, pg 770
Harman Professional Solutions,
 pg 776
Hi-Tech Audio Systems Inc, pg 779
JD Audio Visual Inc, pg 793
Media Control Systems LLC,
 pg 821
MediaMation Inc, pg 822
MediaPOINTE, pg 823
Nortek Security & Control LLC,
 pg 842
Parasound Products Inc, pg 851
QSC Audio Products LLC, pg 867
Signal Transport, pg 887
Sound Service Co, pg 894
Southern California Sound Image
 Inc, pg 895
TOA Electronics Inc, pg 915
Towards 2000 Inc, pg 916

COLORADO

Audio Consultant Services Inc,
 pg 693

CONNECTICUT

Gold Line/TEF, pg 772
HB Communications Inc, pg 777
The Music People Inc, pg 834
Sennheiser Electronic Corp, pg 884

DELAWARE

Actors Attic, pg 675

FLORIDA

Access Media Group, pg 673
Altel Systems Group Inc, pg 682
Broadcasters General Store Inc,
 pg 711
Digital Video Systems, pg 742
Harris Corp, pg 776
Hi-Tech Enterprises Inc, pg 779
Intermark Industries Inc, pg 789
L3Harris Technologies Inc, pg 812
Midtown Video Inc, pg 827
Recording Media & Equipment Inc
 (RM&E), pg 872
Stereo Sales Inc, pg 900
TAI Audio, pg 906
Technomedia Solutions, pg 909

GEORGIA

Lighting & Production Equipment
 Inc, pg 807
Stage Front Presentation Systems,
 pg 899

INDIANA

Sensory Technologies LLC, pg 884
SHP Electronics, pg 887
Sweetwater Sound Inc, pg 905

KENTUCKY

NOR-COM Inc, pg 841

MAINE

Independent Audio Inc, pg 786

MARYLAND

Bradley Broadcast & Pro Audio,
 pg 709
Cardinal Sound & Video, pg 717
Human Circuit, pg 782

MASSACHUSETTS

Terry Hanley Audio Systems Inc,
 pg 775
Professional Audio Design Inc,
 pg 865

MICHIGAN

On Stage Visuals, pg 846
TEL Systems LLC, pg 909

NEW HAMPSHIRE

APS Lighting-Sound-AV, pg 688
Technet® Systems Group, pg 908

NEW JERSEY

Alltec Stores, a Vcom IMC
 Company, pg 681
Diversified, pg 744
Earl Girls Inc, pg 749
JRF Magnetic Sciences Inc, pg 795
Onkyo USA Corp, pg 846
PatchAmp, pg 852

AUDIO

Signal Processing Equipment Distributors (continued)

NEW JERSEY (continued)

Starlite, pg 900
Wired 4 Sound Inc, pg 940
Yorktel, pg 944

NEW YORK

ADI Global Distribution, pg 676
Aura Sonic Ltd (ASL), pg 695
BTX Technologies, pg 712
Design Audio Visual Inc, pg 741
Group One Ltd, pg 774
Hot House Professional Audio, pg 782
Korg USA Inc, pg 801
Mark Custom Recording Service Inc, pg 817
Markertek Video Supply, pg 817
Posthorn Recordings, pg 859
XTA Electronics Ltd, pg 943

NORTH CAROLINA

Moog Music Inc, pg 830

OHIO

GatesAir, pg 768
ITA Audio Visual Solutions, pg 791
The Telos Alliance, pg 910

OREGON

SuperDigital Ltd, pg 904

PENNSYLVANIA

Advanced AV LLC, pg 677
Clair Companies, pg 725
Vistacom Inc, pg 931

SOUTH CAROLINA

DaviSound, pg 739

SOUTH DAKOTA

Sencore Inc, pg 883

TENNESSEE

Allstar Audio Systems Inc, pg 681
Lowrance Sound Co Inc, pg 812
Spectrum Sound Inc, pg 897
Technical Support Systems LLC, pg 908
Zion Music Group, pg 945

TEXAS

Crossroads Audio Inc, pg 735
Data Projections Inc, pg 738
Lubbock Audio Visual Inc, pg 812
Pro Video & Film Equipment Co Inc, pg 863
RF Specialties of Texas LLC, pg 874
Southwest Sound Solutions, pg 896
Tarpley Media Systems, pg 907

UTAH

Performance Audio LLC, pg 854

VERMONT

Production Advantage Inc, pg 863

VIRGINIA

Avitecture Inc, pg 699
Intellidyne LLC, pg 789

WASHINGTON

CCI Solutions, pg 718
D A Sound, pg 737
Northern Lights & Pro Audio, pg 842

WISCONSIN

Audio Visual of Milwaukee Inc, pg 694
Camera Corner Connecting Point, pg 715
Full Compass Systems, pg 767

ALBERTA

Infosat Communications Inc, pg 787
Matrix Video Communications Corp (MVCC), pg 819
Unique Communications Ltd, pg 921

BRITISH COLUMBIA

Radial Engineering Ltd, pg 868

MANITOBA

Advance Pro, pg 677
Inland Audio Visual Ltd, pg 788

ONTARIO

Cinema Stage Inc, pg 724
Westbury National Show Systems Ltd, pg 936
Yorkville Sound Inc, pg 944

QUEBEC

JAM Industries Ltd, pg 792
SC Media Canada, pg 881

Signal Processing Equipment Manufacturers

ALABAMA

PESA, pg 855

ARIZONA

AtlasIED, pg 692
MTX Audio, pg 833
Radio Design Labs (RDL), pg 869

ARKANSAS

Autogram/CRL, pg 696

CALIFORNIA

AB Systems Amplifiers, pg 672
ALTINEX Inc, pg 682
Aphex, pg 687
BBE Sound Inc, pg 702
Digital Music Corp, pg 742
DigiTech, pg 742
Dorrough Electronics Inc, pg 746
Dan Dugan Sound Design Inc, pg 747
Ensemble Designs Inc, pg 754
ESE, pg 755
FM Systems Inc, pg 763
Furman®, pg 767
Linkabit, pg 809
Lynx Studio Technology Inc, pg 813
Manley Laboratories Inc, pg 816
Martinsound Inc, pg 818

Media Control Systems LLC, pg 821
Millennia Media, FPC, pg 827
Nady Systems Inc, pg 835
Nortek Security & Control LLC, pg 842
Parasound Products Inc, pg 851
Physical Optics Corp (POC), pg 856
PowerPhysics Inc, pg 860
Renkus-Heinz Inc, pg 873
Signal Transport, pg 887
Simon - Kaloi Engineering Ltd, pg 888
Soundcraft, pg 894
Summit Audio Inc, pg 903
TOA Electronics Inc, pg 915
Xantech LLC, pg 943

COLORADO

Liberty AV Solutions, pg 807

CONNECTICUT

Gold Line/TEF, pg 772
Sound Control Technologies Inc, pg 893
Titus Technological Laboratories (TTL), pg 914

FLORIDA

Compuvideo Sales USA Ltd, pg 729
JT Communications, pg 795
Tel-Test, pg 909
Z-Systems Audio Engineering, pg 944

ILLINOIS

Bag End Loudspeakers, pg 700
Esoteric Sound, pg 755
Studio Technologies Inc, pg 903
Symbolic Sound Corp, pg 905

MAINE

Dielectric, pg 741

MARYLAND

API, pg 687
RCI Custom Products, pg 871

MASSACHUSETTS

Eastern Acoustic Works Inc (EAW), pg 749

MICHIGAN

ASC Systems, pg 690

MINNESOTA

Bosch Security Systems Inc, pg 709
Digital Audio Labs, pg 742
Great River Electronics, pg 773

MISSISSIPPI

Peavey Electronics Corp, pg 852

NEW JERSEY

ATI Audio, pg 692
Bogen Communications Inc, pg 708
Crestron Electronics Inc, pg 734
Eventide Inc, pg 756
FSR Inc, pg 766
Kramer Electronics USA Inc, pg 801
Onkyo USA Corp, pg 846
Tech 21 USA Inc, pg 908

NEW MEXICO

Lectrosonics Inc, pg 805

NEW YORK

Ashly Audio Inc, pg 691
Broadcast Devices Inc, pg 710
ChyronHego Corp, pg 723
GLI Sound Systems, pg 771
Hot House Professional Audio, pg 782
Key Digital Systems, pg 798
Laird Digital Cinema, pg 803
MultiDyne Video & Fiber Optics Systems, pg 833
Sescom Inc, pg 884
Solid State Logic Inc, pg 892

NORTH CAROLINA

Audioarts Engineering, pg 695
Moog Music Inc, pg 830
Wheatstone Corp, pg 937

OHIO

GatesAir, pg 768
Omnia Audio, pg 845
The Telos Alliance, pg 910
TV One Multimedia Solutions, pg 919

OREGON

BIAMP Systems, pg 705

PENNSYLVANIA

D W Fearn, pg 759

RHODE ISLAND

Rane, pg 870

SOUTH CAROLINA

DaviSound, pg 739

SOUTH DAKOTA

Sencore Inc, pg 883
Tepco Corp, pg 911

UTAH

ClearOne Inc, pg 726
Ivie Technologies Inc, pg 792
Rolls Corp, pg 877

WASHINGTON

AudioControl® Inc, pg 695

BRITISH COLUMBIA

Radial Engineering Ltd, pg 868

ONTARIO

Artaflex Inc, pg 690
Ward-Beck Systems Ltd, pg 933
Yorkville Sound Inc, pg 944

Signal Processing Equipment Rentals

ARIZONA

Video West Inc, pg 929

ARKANSAS

White Diamond Productions LLC, pg 937

CALIFORNIA
Action Audio & Visual, pg 675
Ametron Audio/Video, pg 684
Artichoke Productions, pg 690
Associated Sound, pg 691
Audio Rents, pg 693
Dan Dugan Sound Design Inc,
   pg 747
Express Media Inc, pg 757
Golden Gate Studios, pg 772
JD Audio Visual Inc, pg 793
Maximus Media Inc, pg 820
Munday & Collins AV, pg 834
Muse Presentation Technologies,
   pg 834
PSAV® Presentation Services,
   pg 866
Alwin Sauers Audio Productions
   (ASAP), pg 881
Sound Service Co, pg 894
VER, pg 926
Video Resources Inc, pg 928

COLORADO
Audio Consultant Services Inc,
   pg 693

DELAWARE
Side Door Studio Inc, pg 887

FLORIDA
Access Media Group, pg 673
Hi-Tech Enterprises Inc, pg 779
Universal Studios Florida®
   Production Group, pg 922

GEORGIA
Stage Front Presentation Systems,
   pg 899

ILLINOIS
AV Chicago Inc, pg 696
Meetinghouse Event Design &
   Production, pg 823
Resolution Productions Group,
   pg 874

KENTUCKY
Audio Visual Techniques Inc,
   pg 695

MARYLAND
CPR MultiMedia Solutions, pg 732
Event Tech, pg 756

MASSACHUSETTS
Terry Hanley Audio Systems Inc,
   pg 775
Preston Productions Inc, pg 861

MICHIGAN
K&R All Media Productions LLC,
   pg 796
On Stage Visuals, pg 846

MISSOURI
Show-Me Audio-Visual, pg 887

NEW HAMPSHIRE
APS Lighting-Sound-AV, pg 688

NEW JERSEY
Audio Visual Dynamics®, pg 694
Earl Girls Inc, pg 749

Soundtracks Production Services
   LLC, pg 895
Starlite, pg 900
Wired 4 Sound Inc, pg 940

NEW YORK
Aura Sonic Ltd (ASL), pg 695
CP Communications, pg 732
Design Audio Visual Inc, pg 741

NORTH CAROLINA
Take One Productions Ltd, pg 906

NORTH DAKOTA
Media Productions, pg 822

OHIO
Production Solutions Inc, pg 864

PENNSYLVANIA
Right Coast Recording Inc, pg 875

TENNESSEE
Allstar Audio Systems Inc, pg 681
Love Shack Recording Studios,
   pg 811
Mr Mark's Used Musical, Stereo &
   Studio Equipment Store, pg 828
Technical Support Systems LLC,
   pg 908

TEXAS
Alford Media Services, pg 680
Bright Star Productions Inc, pg 710
Crossroads Audio Inc, pg 735
Music Lab Inc, pg 834
Tropikal Productions, pg 918

VIRGINIA
Audio Visual Actions Inc (AVA),
   pg 694

WASHINGTON
D A Sound, pg 737

PUERTO RICO
Stage Crew Audiovisual Inc, pg 898

MANITOBA
Inland Audio Visual Ltd, pg 788

ONTARIO
Westbury National Show Systems
   Ltd, pg 936

Signal Processing Equipment Repairs

CALIFORNIA
AB Systems Amplifiers, pg 672
Ametron Audio/Video, pg 684
Audio Images Corp, pg 693
Audio Upgrades, pg 694
Diemer Amp & Keyboard Repair,
   pg 741
McAlister Electronics, pg 820
QSC Audio Products LLC, pg 867
Sound Service Co, pg 894
TOA Electronics Inc, pg 915
Towards 2000 Inc, pg 916

CONNECTICUT
HB Communications Inc, pg 777
Sennheiser Electronic Corp, pg 884

FLORIDA
Hi-Tech Enterprises Inc, pg 779
JT Communications, pg 795
Phat Planet Recording Studios,
   pg 855
Stereo Sales Inc, pg 900
TAI Audio, pg 906
Tel-Test, pg 909

GEORGIA
Lighting & Production Equipment
   Inc, pg 807
Stage Front Presentation Systems,
   pg 899

INDIANA
SHP Electronics, pg 887
Sweetwater Sound Inc, pg 905

KENTUCKY
NOR-COM Inc, pg 841

MASSACHUSETTS
Professional Audio Design Inc,
   pg 865

MICHIGAN
K&R's Recording Studios Inc,
   pg 796
On Stage Visuals, pg 846
TEL Systems LLC, pg 909

NEVADA
MUSIC Group Services Nevada,
   pg 834

NEW JERSEY
Earl Girls Inc, pg 749
Starlite, pg 900

NEW YORK
Hot House Professional Audio,
   pg 782

OHIO
GatesAir, pg 768
ITA Audio Visual Solutions, pg 791

OREGON
All Service Musical Electronics
   Repair, pg 680

PENNSYLVANIA
Right Coast Recording Inc, pg 875

SOUTH CAROLINA
DaviSound, pg 739

TENNESSEE
Technical Support Systems LLC,
   pg 908

TEXAS
Lubbock Audio Visual Inc, pg 812
Southwest Sound Solutions, pg 896

WASHINGTON
Northern Lights & Pro Audio,
   pg 842

WISCONSIN
Full Compass Systems, pg 767

ALBERTA
Infosat Communications Inc, pg 787
Unique Communications Ltd,
   pg 921

MANITOBA
Inland Audio Visual Ltd, pg 788

ONTARIO
Westbury National Show Systems
   Ltd, pg 936

QUEBEC
SC Media Canada, pg 881

Sound Booths

ALABAMA
Sound of Birmingham Productions,
   pg 894

ARIZONA
Allusion Studios & Pure Wave
   Audio, pg 681
Cox Creative Studios, pg 732
Film Creations Ltd, pg 760
Fire Power Music LLC, pg 761
Merestone, pg 823
Metropolitan Audio-Visual Inc,
   pg 824

ARKANSAS
Live'N'Loud, pg 810

CALIFORNIA
AlphaDogs Inc, pg 682
Artichoke Productions, pg 690
Blue Lotus Temple Studio, pg 707
CCI Digital, a DVS Company,
   pg 718
Chace Audio by Deluxe, pg 720
Creative Media Recording, pg 733
Creative Technology, pg 733
Digital Jungle, pg 742
48 Windows, pg 764
iCorpTv, pg 783
Juice Studios, pg 795
KTVU-Retail Services, pg 802
KVIE-Channel 6, pg 802
Ludlow Media, pg 812
Lynch Communications, pg 813
Maximus Media Inc, pg 820
The Media Staff Inc, pg 822
On-Trax Inc, pg 846
Palardo Productions, pg 850
Playback Recording Studio, pg 858
Polarity Post Production, pg 858
Private Island Audio Inc, pg 862
PSI Inc, pg 866
Pyramind Studios, pg 867
QRS Software Services, pg 867
Roundabout Entertainment Inc,
   pg 878
Steve Shapiro Music, pg 885
SonicPool, pg 892
Still N' Motion, pg 901
Total Creative, pg 916
Twin Peaks Creative, pg 920
Visions Plus, pg 931

COLORADO
Conly Productions, pg 730
Daylight Productions & Rentals,
   pg 739
Flashback Media Productions,
   pg 762
Rocky Mountain Audio/Video
   Productions Inc, pg 876

AUDIO

Sound Booths (continued)

CONNECTICUT

BRB Audiovisual Productions, pg 709
Guymark Studios LLC, pg 775
Palace Production Center, pg 850
P&P Studios Inc, pg 851

DISTRICT OF COLUMBIA

Interface Media Group, pg 789

FLORIDA

A Cut Above Video Productions Inc, pg 671
Accord Productions, pg 673
Audacity Recording Studios, pg 693
Civins Productions Inc, pg 725
Communications Concepts Inc (CCI), pg 729
Comtel Inc, pg 730
Easy Edit Video Inc, pg 750
The Kitchen, pg 799
LHV Audio Services, pg 807
Mach 1 Productions, pg 813
Morrisound Recording, pg 830
Shooting Stars Post Inc, pg 886
Sunfire Communications Inc, pg 904
Sunrise Studios, pg 904
Universal Studios Florida® Production Group, pg 922
Mike Vasilinda Productions Inc, pg 925

GEORGIA

Beachwood Productions, pg 702
Beast Atlanta, pg 703
Crawford Media Services Inc, pg 733
Guerrilla Productions LLC, pg 774
Omega Media Group Inc, pg 845

ILLINOIS

ABSA Films, pg 672
Beatty TeleVisual Productions, pg 703
Big Shoulders Digital Video Productions, pg 705
Mightybytes Inc, pg 827
Multimedia Marketing Group, pg 833
Sound/Video Impressions Inc, pg 894
20/20 Communications Inc, pg 920
WEEK TV, pg 935
Woodside Avenue Music Productions Inc, pg 941

INDIANA

A-V-A Video Productions, pg 671
Alan Johnson Recording, pg 794
OMNI Productions, pg 845

IOWA

Hedquist Productions Inc, pg 778

KENTUCKY

Broadway Digital, pg 711
The Media Collaboratory, pg 821

LOUISIANA

Launch Media, pg 804
Moxie Media, pg 832

Vidox Motion Imagery, pg 930
WVLA-TV, pg 942

MARYLAND

Bethesda Softworks LLC, pg 704
CPR MultiMedia Solutions, pg 732
The Cutting Corporation, GraphicAudio® & Archival Sound Lab, pg 736
dbF a Media Company, pg 739
Lion & Fox Recording Studios, pg 809
Pro Cuts Editing Services, pg 862

MASSACHUSETTS

Continental Recordings Inc, pg 731
Cramer, pg 732
Monadnock Media Inc, pg 829
Penfield Productions Ltd, pg 853
Silent Source, pg 888
Soundtrack Group, pg 895
Rik Tinory Productions, pg 914
TR Productions, pg 916

MICHIGAN

Audio Graphic Services, pg 693
Brilliance Audio, pg 710
Digi Sign Design LLC, pg 741
Digital Image Studios LLC, pg 742
K&R's Recording Studios Inc, pg 796
MessageMakers, pg 824
RingSide Creative, pg 875

MINNESOTA

The ADS Group, pg 676
Badiyan Inc, pg 700
GMI Productions, pg 771
NetWell Noise Control, pg 838
pinta acoustic inc, pg 857

MISSOURI

Avatar Studios, pg 697
Show-Me Audio-Visual, pg 887

MONTANA

Jereco Studios Inc, pg 793
KCFW Television, pg 797

NEBRASKA

JoeAudio, pg 794

NEVADA

Tanglewood Productions, pg 907

NEW HAMPSHIRE

Apertura, pg 686

NEW JERSEY

Allegro Productions Inc, pg 680
Euro-Pacific Film & Video Productions Inc, pg 756
Laurel Video Productions, pg 804
Midnight Media Group Inc, pg 827
Milgrom Productions, pg 827
NFL Films Inc, pg 841
NFL Films Music Library, pg 841
Optisonics Productions, pg 847
Shamrock Communications, pg 885
Suede Interactive, pg 903
VCSvideo, pg 925

NEW MEXICO

Production Outfitters, pg 864

NEW YORK

The Big House Group, pg 705
Chromavision Corp, pg 723
Cornell Laboratory of Ornithology, pg 731
CP Communications, pg 732
de Wolfe Music USA, pg 739
DuArt Media Services, pg 747
HB-Content, pg 777
Headroom Digital Audio, pg 777
Heavy Melody, pg 778
Mood Creations Ltd, pg 829
MRM//McCANN, pg 832
The Palmer Group, pg 850
RadioArt/Bob & Ray CDs & MP3 Files, pg 869
Sony Music Entertainment, pg 893
TeleTime Productions, pg 910
WNET/New York Public Media, pg 940
Zelman Studios Ltd, pg 945

NORTH CAROLINA

Pat Appleson Studios Inc, pg 687
The Communications Group Inc, pg 729
Duke Media Services, pg 747
Franklin Video Inc, pg 765
Horizon Video Productions Inc, pg 781
Take One Productions Ltd, pg 906
Trailblazer Studios®, pg 917

NORTH DAKOTA

Media Productions, pg 822

OHIO

Curtis Inc, pg 736
Cuyahoga Community College Student Production Office (SPO), pg 736
Lyon Video Inc, pg 813
Mills James Productions, pg 828
Vista Color Imaging Inc, pg 931

OKLAHOMA

Academic Media & Digital Services, pg 672
Garman Productions LLC, pg 768
PDC Productions, pg 852

OREGON

KTVA Productions, pg 802
REX, pg 874

PENNSYLVANIA

Audio Visual Communications Inc, pg 694
FMP Media Solutions Inc, pg 763
Forge Recording LLC, pg 764
Innovision Media Group, pg 788
JPL, pg 795
Panta Rhei Media Inc, pg 851
Production Masters Inc (PMI), pg 864
The Videohouse Inc, pg 929
Visual Sound Inc, pg 931
WHYY Inc, pg 938
WPHL-TV, pg 942

RHODE ISLAND

Sound-FX-Design, pg 894

SOUTH CAROLINA

DaviSound, pg 739
Genesis Creative, pg 769
Venture Media, pg 925

TENNESSEE

Anode Inc, pg 686
Continental Film, pg 731
Love Shack Recording Studios, pg 811
Memphis Communications Corp, pg 823
Scripps Networks, pg 882
Stage Post, pg 899
Technical Support Systems LLC, pg 908
United Methodist Productions, pg 921
Zion Music Group, pg 945

TEXAS

Audiomoxie®, pg 695
The Editing Co, pg 750
ETS-Lindgren, pg 756
Fire Station Studios, pg 761
Marx InDigital, pg 818
Matson Multi-Media, pg 820
Maverick Video Productions, pg 820
Out of the BLUE Media, pg 849
Phillips Media Source, pg 855
Romar Learning Solutions LLC, pg 877
The Samuels Co, pg 879
The Sound Lab Inc, pg 894
Sound Works, pg 894
South Coast Film & Video, pg 895
Stage Directions, pg 898
Texas Heart Institute Visual Communication Services, pg 911
TM Studios Inc, pg 915
The Yesterday USA Radio Networks, pg 944

UTAH

Performance Audio LLC, pg 854
Soularium Recording Studios, pg 893

VERMONT

University of Vermont, Instructional Television Dept, pg 923

VIRGINIA

Acoustical Solutions LLC, pg 674
AudioImage Recording, pg 695
BES Studios, pg 704
CACI Integrated Communications, pg 713
CDR Communications Inc, pg 719
Wally Cleaver's Recording Service, pg 726
CVW Event Productions, pg 736
Metro Productions, pg 824
Studio Center Corp, pg 902
Video Solutions, pg 928

WASHINGTON

Avast! Recording Co, pg 697
Hamilton Studio, pg 775
Inland Audio Visual Co, pg 788
North-by-Northwest - A Digital Studio, pg 842
Sound Sound, pg 894
Victory Studios, pg 927

WISCONSIN

Audio Visual of Milwaukee Inc, pg 694
Concept Productions Inc, pg 730
5th Floor Recording Co, pg 760
Logan Productions Inc, pg 811
USAV Group Inc, pg 923
Video Wisconsin Inc, pg 929
Wisconsin Public Television, pg 940

BRITISH COLUMBIA

Pinewood Sound, pg 857
Triad Communications Ltd, pg 918

MANITOBA

DACAPO Productions Inc, pg 737

ONTARIO

ADS Media, pg 677
AMPLUS Productions, pg 684
DebsVoice, pg 739
GAPC (General Assembly
    Production Centre), pg 768
JL Recording Studios, pg 794
MCS Recording Studios, pg 821
Metalworks Recording Studios Inc,
    pg 824
Silver Creek Media Inc, pg 888
Spence-Thomas Audio Post, pg 897
Wanted! Sound + Picture, pg 933

Sound Effect Libraries

ALABAMA

Airwave Recording Studio, pg 679
Dogwood Productions Inc, pg 745

ARIZONA

Direct Current Video Productions,
    pg 743
Film Creations Ltd, pg 760
Merestone, pg 823
SPEAK HOUSE Audio™, pg 896

ARKANSAS

White Diamond Productions LLC,
    pg 937

CALIFORNIA

Artichoke Productions, pg 690
Associated Production Music LLC,
    pg 691
The Banquet Sound Studios, pg 701
Berkeley Sound Artists Inc, pg 704
CCI Digital, a DVS Company,
    pg 718
Creative Media Recording, pg 733
Creative Support Services/CSS
    Music, pg 733
Earwax Productions Inc, pg 749
Eye & I Productions, pg 758
Gilderfluke & Co Inc, pg 771
ILIO Enterprises LLC, pg 784
ITV Productions, pg 792
Jaguar Distribution Corp, pg 792
JDS Video & Media Productions
    Inc, pg 793
Juice Studios, pg 795
Kaleidosound, pg 796
Killer Tracks, pg 798
Maximus Media Inc, pg 820
Megatrax, pg 823
Polarity Post Production, pg 858
Pyramind Studios, pg 867
Reality Check Systems, pg 871
Saturn Studios, pg 881
Steve Shapiro Music, pg 885
SonicPool, pg 892
Sonoton Music Library, pg 893
Still N' Motion, pg 901
Total Creative, pg 916
Universal Studios, pg 922
Visions Plus, pg 931

COLORADO

Conly Productions, pg 730
Daylight Productions & Rentals,
    pg 739
Flashback Media Productions,
    pg 762

CONNECTICUT

P&P Studios Inc, pg 851

DELAWARE

Ken-Del Productions Inc, pg 797
Ken-Del Studios, pg 797

DISTRICT OF COLUMBIA

Interface Media Group, pg 789
Smithsonian Folkways Recordings,
    pg 891

FLORIDA

Jordan Klein Film & Video (JKFV),
    pg 795
LHV Audio Services, pg 807
Paradise Show & Design Inc,
    pg 851
Universal Studios Florida®
    Production Group, pg 922

GEORGIA

Beachwood Productions, pg 702
ECG Productions, pg 750
Guerrilla Productions LLC, pg 774

IDAHO

Brad Shaw Productions Inc, pg 885

ILLINOIS

AnswersMedia, pg 686
Creative Technology (CT), pg 733
Esoteric Sound, pg 755
Jim Passin Productions, pg 852
Pepper Group, pg 854
RBR Productions, pg 870
WEEK TV, pg 935
Woodside Avenue Music
    Productions Inc, pg 941

INDIANA

A-V-A Video Productions, pg 671
OMNI Productions, pg 845

KANSAS

KAKE-TV, pg 796
Walterscheid Productions, pg 933

KENTUCKY

Hammond Communications Group
    Inc, pg 775
Prosper Media Group Inc, pg 866

MARYLAND

Adventure Productions LLC, pg 678
Bethesda Softworks LLC, pg 704
CAS Video Productions, pg 717
CPR MultiMedia Solutions, pg 732
The Cutting Corporation,
    GraphicAudio® & Archival
    Sound Lab, pg 736
Pro Cuts Editing Services, pg 862
Satellite Media Production, pg 881

MASSACHUSETTS

CommCreative, pg 728
Labrecque Creative Sound, pg 803

MICHIGAN

Soundtrack Group, pg 895
TR Productions, pg 916

Audio Graphic Services, pg 693
GMP Music, pg 772
K&R's Recording Studios Inc,
    pg 796
MessageMakers, pg 824

MINNESOTA

The ADS Group, pg 676
Media Loft Inc, pg 822

MISSOURI

Show-Me Audio-Visual, pg 887

MONTANA

Jereco Studios Inc, pg 793

NEBRASKA

JoeAudio, pg 794

NEVADA

JCS Video Productions, pg 793
Tanglewood Productions, pg 907

NEW HAMPSHIRE

Apertura, pg 686
The Troupe, pg 918

NEW JERSEY

The Audio Department Inc, pg 693
Megavideo LLC, pg 823
Midnight Media Group Inc, pg 827
Milbrodt/Music & Sound Design,
    pg 827
Milgrom Productions, pg 827
Richard Reiter Productions Inc,
    pg 873
TRF Production Music Libraries,
    pg 917
VCSvideo, pg 925

NEW MEXICO

Production Outfitters, pg 864

NEW YORK

A-List Quality Videographer,
    pg 671
Cornell Laboratory of Ornithology,
    pg 731
de Wolfe Music USA, pg 739
Fingerpaint, pg 761
Getty Images Music, pg 770
Heavy Melody, pg 778
HOThead, pg 782
Korg USA Inc, pg 801
Madison Square Garden, pg 814
Manhattan Production Music Inc,
    pg 816
New York Sound Inc, pg 840
The Palmer Group, pg 850
David Rapkin Audio Production,
    pg 870
Robbins Media Inc, pg 876
Sear Sound, pg 883
Sony Music Commercial Music
    Group, pg 893
Sony Music Entertainment, pg 893
TecNec Distributing, pg 909
Tiki Recording Studios Inc, pg 914
Zelman Studios Ltd, pg 945

NORTH CAROLINA

Pat Appleson Studios Inc, pg 687
Franklin Video Inc, pg 765

NASCAR Productions LLC, pg 835
2BruceStudio, pg 920

OHIO

Bartha, pg 702
Lyon Video Inc, pg 813
Mills James Productions, pg 828
Take 1 Media Services, pg 906
Vista Color Imaging Inc, pg 931

OKLAHOMA

PDC Productions, pg 852

PENNSYLVANIA

John E Allen Inc, pg 680
Audio Visual Communications Inc,
    pg 694
Craig Recording Studios, pg 732
FMP Media Solutions Inc, pg 763
JPL, pg 795
Panta Rhei Media Inc, pg 851

SOUTH CAROLINA

Genesis Creative, pg 769

TENNESSEE

Film House Inc, pg 760
Memphis Communications Corp,
    pg 823

TEXAS

The Editing Co, pg 750
FirstCom Music, pg 761
Mediaforce Productions, pg 822
The Music Bakery, pg 834
Julye Newlin Productions Inc,
    pg 840
Planet Dallas Recording Studios,
    pg 857
Pro Video & Film Equipment Co
    Inc, pg 863
Real to Reel Studios Inc, pg 871
South Coast Film & Video, pg 895
Stage Directions, pg 898
Texas Heart Institute Visual
    Communication Services, pg 911
TM Studios Inc, pg 915
The Yesterday USA Radio
    Networks, pg 944

UTAH

Soularium Recording Studios,
    pg 893

VERMONT

Production Advantage Inc, pg 863

VIRGINIA

AudioImage Recording, pg 695
Wally Cleaver's Recording Service,
    pg 726
Henninger Media Services, pg 779
National Media Services Inc,
    pg 836
Rocktown Media, pg 876

WASHINGTON

Avast! Recording Co, pg 697
Kostov Productions, pg 801
Laser Fantasy/HECK
    Industries/Photon Manufacturing,
    pg 804
Quiet Planet LLC, pg 868
Victory Studios, pg 927

AUDIO

Sound Effect Libraries (continued)

WISCONSIN

5th Floor Recording Co, pg 760
Mirror 34 Productions, pg 828
USAV Group Inc, pg 923
Video Wisconsin Inc, pg 929
Wisconsin Public Television, pg 940

WYOMING

Bridger Productions Inc, pg 710

MANITOBA

DACAPO Productions Inc, pg 737

ONTARIO

The Hollywood Edge, pg 780
JL Recording Studios, pg 794
MCS Recording Studios, pg 821
Metalworks Recording Studios Inc, pg 824
Nightingale Music Productions Inc, pg 841
Sonic IT Communications, pg 892
Sound Ideas, pg 894
StockMusic.com, pg 901
Video Excellence Productions, pg 927

QUEBEC

Group PVP, pg 774

Sound Effect Production Services

ALABAMA

Sound of Birmingham Productions, pg 894

ARIZONA

Fire Power Music LLC, pg 761
Merestone, pg 823

ARKANSAS

Live'N'Loud, pg 810

CALIFORNIA

AB Audio Visual Entertainment Inc, pg 672
AlphaDogs Inc, pg 682
Artichoke Productions, pg 690
Berkeley Sound Artists Inc, pg 704
CCI Digital, a DVS Company, pg 718
Chace Audio by Deluxe, pg 720
Creative Media Recording, pg 733
Creative Support Services/CSS Music, pg 733
Creative Technology, pg 733
Crystal Pyramid Productions™, pg 735
Custom Video Productions Inc, pg 736
Diamond Dreams Music Productions, pg 741
Digital Jungle, pg 742
Earwax Productions Inc, pg 749
Eye & I Productions, pg 758
48 Windows, pg 764
iCorpTv, pg 783
ITV Productions, pg 792
Kaleidosound, pg 796
Kris Stevens Enterprises, pg 801

KTVU-Retail Services, pg 802
KVIE-Channel 6, pg 802
Maximus Media Inc, pg 820
McCune Audio-Video-Lighting, pg 821
The Media Staff Inc, pg 822
MediaMation Inc, pg 822
On-Trax Inc, pg 846
Palardo Productions, pg 850
piXvfm Inc, pg 857
Polarity Post Production, pg 858
Private Island Audio Inc, pg 862
PSI Inc, pg 866
Pyramind Studios, pg 867
QRS Software Services, pg 867
Reality Check Systems, pg 871
Roundabout Entertainment Inc, pg 878
Sahara Records & Filmworks Entertainment Co, pg 879
Saturn Studios, pg 881
Steve Shapiro Music, pg 885
SonicPool, pg 892
Still N' Motion, pg 901
Studio Circle Recordings, pg 902
Studio 132, pg 902
Total Creative, pg 916
Universal Studios, pg 922
West Coast Projections Inc, pg 935

COLORADO

Tim Cissell Music, pg 725
Conly Productions, pg 730
Daylight Productions & Rentals, pg 739
Flashback Media Productions, pg 762
Open Media Foundation, pg 846
Starwest Productions, pg 900

CONNECTICUT

Antenna International, pg 686
BRB Audiovisual Productions, pg 709
The Gary-Paul Agency, pg 768
Guymark Studios LLC, pg 775
Ironik Design & Post, pg 791
Palace Production Center, pg 850
P&P Studios Inc, pg 851
Sonalysts Media, pg 892

DISTRICT OF COLUMBIA

Interface Media Group, pg 789

FLORIDA

Access Media Group, pg 673
Audacity Recording Studios, pg 693
Audio Visual Imagineering Inc, pg 694
Communications Concepts Inc (CCI), pg 729
The Kitchen, pg 799
LHV Audio Services, pg 807
Mach 1 Productions, pg 813
Morrisound Recording, pg 830
Phat Planet Recording Studios, pg 855
Sunfire Communications Inc, pg 904
Universal Studios Florida® Production Group, pg 922

GEORGIA

Crawford Media Services Inc, pg 733
Guerrilla Productions LLC, pg 774
Magick Lantern, pg 814
White Dog Studios, pg 937

HAWAII

Hyperspective Studios Inc, pg 783
Media Bridge Gamekids, pg 821

ILLINOIS

ABS Enterprises, pg 672
Beatty TeleVisual Productions, pg 703
CCore Media Inc, pg 718
Esoteric Sound, pg 755
Major Media Inc, pg 815
Mightybytes Inc, pg 827
Jim Passin Productions, pg 852
RBR Productions, pg 870
Steven Samler Music & Sound, pg 879
Sound/Video Impressions Inc, pg 894
Sparkfactor, pg 896
WEEK TV, pg 935
Woodside Avenue Music Productions Inc, pg 941

INDIANA

A-V-A Video Productions, pg 671
Alan Johnson Recording, pg 794
OMNI Productions, pg 845
Sweetwater Sound Inc, pg 905

IOWA

Hedquist Productions Inc, pg 778

LOUISIANA

Disk Productions Inc, pg 743
Vidox Motion Imagery, pg 930

MARYLAND

Bethesda Softworks LLC, pg 704
CPR MultiMedia Solutions, pg 732
The Cutting Corporation, GraphicAudio® & Archival Sound Lab, pg 736
dbF a Media Company, pg 739
Kramer Communications Video Production, pg 801
Lion & Fox Recording Studios, pg 809
Omega Recording Studios, pg 845

MASSACHUSETTS

CommCreative, pg 728
Continental Recordings Inc, pg 731
Cramer, pg 732
Green Mountain Post Films (GMP), pg 774
Penfield Productions Ltd, pg 853
Soundtrack Group, pg 895
TR Productions, pg 916

MICHIGAN

Audio Graphic Services, pg 693
Digi Sign Design LLC, pg 741
Digital Image Studios LLC, pg 742
GMP Music, pg 772
K&R's Recording Studios Inc, pg 796

MINNESOTA

The ADS Group, pg 676
Badiyan Inc, pg 700
Media Loft Inc, pg 822

MISSOURI

Avatar Studios, pg 697
Ozam Productions Inc, pg 849
Show-Me Audio-Visual, pg 887

MONTANA

Jereco Studios Inc, pg 793

NEBRASKA

JoeAudio, pg 794

NEVADA

DVDs4Less, pg 748
Tanglewood Productions, pg 907
VirtualMix, pg 930

NEW HAMPSHIRE

Apertura, pg 686

NEW JERSEY

Allegro Productions Inc, pg 680
Jeep Jazz Media Solutions, pg 793
Laurel Video Productions, pg 804
Megavideo LLC, pg 823
Midnight Media Group Inc, pg 827
Milgrom Productions, pg 827
NFL Films Inc, pg 841
NFL Films Music Library, pg 841
Optisonics Productions, pg 847
Suede Interactive, pg 903
TRF Production Music Libraries, pg 917
VCSvideo, pg 925

NEW MEXICO

Production Outfitters, pg 864

NEW YORK

Aural Gratification Inc, pg 695
Big Fish Production US, pg 705
The Big House Group, pg 705
Chromavision Corp, pg 723
de Wolfe Music USA, pg 739
Donnelly Sound Inc, pg 745
Headroom Digital Audio, pg 777
Heavy Melody, pg 778
KAS Music & Sound, pg 796
Magno Sound Inc, pg 815
Mood Creations Ltd, pg 829
MRM//McCANN, pg 832
Mutual Hardware, pg 835
New York Audio Productions, pg 840
The Palmer Group, pg 850
David Rapkin Audio Production, pg 870
Elliot Sokolov Music, pg 892
TeleTime Productions, pg 910
Tiki Recording Studios Inc, pg 914
Visual Technologies Corp, pg 932
Zelman Studios Ltd, pg 945

NORTH CAROLINA

Pat Appleson Studios Inc, pg 687
Audio Art, pg 693
Franklin Video Inc, pg 765
Horizon Video Productions Inc, pg 781
Take One Productions Ltd, pg 906
Trailblazer Studios®, pg 917
2BruceStudio, pg 920

NORTH DAKOTA

Media Productions, pg 822

OHIO

Curtis Inc, pg 736
Lyon Video Inc, pg 813
Mills James Productions, pg 828
R&B Communications Inc, pg 870
Vista Color Imaging Inc, pg 931

OKLAHOMA

Academic Media & Digital
  Services, pg 672
Garman Productions LLC, pg 768
PDC Productions, pg 852

OREGON

KPDX-TV Production Center,
  pg 801
REX, pg 874

PENNSYLVANIA

American Artist Studio, pg 682
Audio Visual Communications Inc,
  pg 694
Dreambox Media Inc, pg 746
Filmaker Technology, pg 760
Forge Recording LLC, pg 764
Production Masters Inc (PMI),
  pg 864
The Videohouse Inc, pg 929
WPHL-TV, pg 942

RHODE ISLAND

Sound-FX-Design, pg 894

SOUTH CAROLINA

DaviSound, pg 739
Genesis Creative, pg 769

TENNESSEE

Analog Man Recording Studio,
  pg 685
Anode Inc, pg 686
Brantley Sound Associates Inc,
  pg 709
Continental Film, pg 731
Memphis Communications Corp,
  pg 823
Mr Mark's Used Musical, Stereo &
  Studio Equipment Store, pg 828
Motion Picture Services, pg 831
Scripps Networks, pg 882
Stage Post, pg 899
Technical Support Systems LLC,
  pg 908

TEXAS

Anaphora Literary Press, pg 685
Audiomoxie®, pg 695
Biway Media, pg 706
FirstCom Music, pg 761
Marx InDigital, pg 818
Matson Multi-Media, pg 820
Phillips Media Source, pg 855
The Samuels Co, pg 879
The Sound Lab Inc, pg 894
Sound Works, pg 894
South Coast Film & Video, pg 895
Stage Directions, pg 898
Texas Heart Institute Visual
  Communication Services, pg 911
TM Studios Inc, pg 915
Tropikal Productions, pg 918

UTAH

Soularium Recording Studios,
  pg 893
Spectra Sonics LLC, pg 897

VERMONT

University of Vermont, Instructional
  Television Dept, pg 923

VIRGINIA

AudioImage Recording, pg 695
BES Studios, pg 704

CACI Integrated Communications,
  pg 713
Wally Cleaver's Recording Service,
  pg 726
Metro Productions, pg 824
Studio Center Corp, pg 902

WASHINGTON

Avast! Recording Co, pg 697
D A Sound, pg 737
Inland Audio Visual Co, pg 788
Kostov Productions, pg 801
North-by-Northwest - A Digital
  Studio, pg 842
Pacific Multimedia Inc, pg 849
Quiet Planet LLC, pg 868
Victory Studios, pg 927

WISCONSIN

Audio Visual of Milwaukee Inc,
  pg 694
Concept Productions Inc, pg 730
5th Floor Recording Co, pg 760
USAV Group Inc, pg 923
Video Wisconsin Inc, pg 929
Wisconsin Public Television, pg 940

WYOMING

Bridger Productions Inc, pg 710

BRITISH COLUMBIA

Pinewood Sound, pg 857
Triad Communications Ltd, pg 918

MANITOBA

DACAPO Productions Inc, pg 737

ONTARIO

ADS Media, pg 677
AMPLUS Productions, pg 684
DebsVoice, pg 739
GAPC (General Assembly
  Production Centre), pg 768
The Hollywood Edge, pg 780
JL Recording Studios, pg 794
MCS Recording Studios, pg 821
Metalworks Recording Studios Inc,
  pg 824
Nightingale Music Productions Inc,
  pg 841
Sonic IT Communications, pg 892
Spence-Thomas Audio Post, pg 897
VO2 Mix Audio Post, pg 932
Wanted! Sound + Picture, pg 933

Sound Recording

ALABAMA

Dogwood Productions Inc, pg 745
Sound of Birmingham Productions,
  pg 894

ARIZONA

Aardvark Productions LLC, pg 671
Allusion Studios & Pure Wave
  Audio, pg 681
Cox Creative Studios, pg 732
Film Creations Ltd, pg 760
Fire Power Music LLC, pg 761
Merestone, pg 823
Metropolitan Audio-Visual Inc,
  pg 824
SPEAK HOUSE Audio™, pg 896

ARKANSAS

Live'N'Loud, pg 810

CALIFORNIA

AB Audio Visual Entertainment Inc,
  pg 672
Aliso Creek Productions Inc, pg 680
AlphaDogs Inc, pg 682
Artichoke Productions, pg 690
Audio Upgrades, pg 694
Automated Entertainment, pg 696
Bay Records, pg 702
Berkeley Sound Artists Inc, pg 704
Blue Lotus Temple Studio, pg 707
CCI Digital, a DVS Company,
  pg 718
Chace Audio by Deluxe, pg 720
Creative Media Recording, pg 733
Creative Technology, pg 733
Crystal Pyramid Productions™,
  pg 735
Custom Video Productions Inc,
  pg 736
Diamond Dreams Music
  Productions, pg 741
Different Fur Recording Ltd, pg 741
Digital Jungle, pg 742
DV Post, pg 748
Earwax Productions Inc, pg 749
Express Media Inc, pg 757
5 Alarm Music, pg 762
48 Windows, pg 764
Goal Productions, pg 772
Gold Standard Productions, pg 772
iCorpTv, pg 783
Kris Stevens Enterprises, pg 801
KTVU-Retail Services, pg 802
Ludlow Media, pg 812
Lynch Communications, pg 813
Main Street Media Inc, pg 815
Martinsound Inc, pg 818
Maximus Media Inc, pg 820
McCune Audio-Video-Lighting,
  pg 821
The Media Staff Inc, pg 822
Nandar Entertainment Pictures,
  pg 835
On-Trax Inc, pg 846
Oral Tradition Sound & Music,
  pg 847
OTR Studios, pg 848
Palardo Productions, pg 850
Penrose Productions, pg 854
piXvfm Inc, pg 857
Playback Recording Studio, pg 858
PM Productions, pg 858
Polarity Post Production, pg 858
Private Island Audio Inc, pg 862
PSI Inc, pg 866
Pyramid Studios, pg 867
QRS Software Services, pg 867
Reality Check Systems, pg 871
Reference Recordings, pg 872
Roundabout Entertainment Inc,
  pg 878
Sahara Records & Filmworks
  Entertainment Co, pg 879
Saturn Studios, pg 881
Alwin Sauers Audio Productions
  (ASAP), pg 881
Shapeshifter, pg 885
Steve Shapiro Music, pg 885
SonicPool, pg 892
Staylor-Made Communications Inc,
  pg 900
Still N' Motion, pg 901
Studio Circle Recordings, pg 902
Studio 637, pg 903
Timeless Productions, pg 914
Todd-AO Studios, pg 915
Total Creative, pg 916
Trac Recording Studio, pg 916
TSR/Baja/Damabi Records, pg 919
Twin Peaks Creative, pg 920
United Audio Video Inc, pg 921
West Coast Projections Inc, pg 935

COLORADO

Audio Consultant Services Inc,
  pg 693
Ceavco Audio Visual Company Inc,
  pg 719
Tim Cissell Music, pg 725
Colorado Sound Recording Ltd,
  pg 728
Conly Productions, pg 730
Daylight Productions & Rentals,
  pg 739
Denver Media Center, pg 740
Flashback Media Productions,
  pg 762
Full Spectrum Arts & Services,
  pg 767
Rocky Mountain Audio/Video
  Productions Inc, pg 876
Side 3 Studios, pg 887
Starwest Productions, pg 900

CONNECTICUT

Antenna International, pg 686
A/V Davey, pg 697
Digital Video Productions, pg 742
The Gary-Paul Agency, pg 768
Guymark Studios LLC, pg 775
MAVCO, pg 820
Palace Production Center, pg 850
P&P Studios Inc, pg 851
UConn Health Multimedia Services,
  pg 920
Vista Group International Inc,
  pg 931

DELAWARE

Ken-Del Studios, pg 797
Side Door Studio Inc, pg 887

DISTRICT OF COLUMBIA

Interface Media Group, pg 789
Northeastern Digital Recording Inc,
  pg 842

FLORIDA

A Cut Above Video Productions
  Inc, pg 671
Accord Productions, pg 673
Audio Visual Imagineering Inc,
  pg 694
Steven Cohen Motion Picture
  Production, pg 727
Communications Concepts Inc
  (CCI), pg 729
Kat Epple Music Productions,
  pg 755
Florida Film & Tape, pg 763
Jordan Klein Film & Video (JKFV),
  pg 795
The Kitchen, pg 799
LHV Audio Services, pg 807
Mach 1 Productions, pg 813
Morrisound Recording, pg 830
Phat Planet Recording Studios,
  pg 855
Shooting Stars Post Inc, pg 886
Stereo Sales Inc, pg 900
Sunfire Communications Inc,
  pg 904
Sunrise Studios, pg 904
Tel-Air Interests Inc, pg 909
Times-Square Fantasy Theatre,
  pg 914
Universal Studios Florida®
  Production Group, pg 922

GEORGIA

Beachwood Productions, pg 702
Beast Atlanta, pg 703

AUDIO

Sound Recording (continued)

GEORGIA (continued)
Crawford Media Services Inc, pg 733
ECG Productions, pg 750
Guerrilla Productions LLC, pg 774
Hottrax Records, pg 782
Lighting & Production Equipment Inc, pg 807
Omega Media Group Inc, pg 845
White Dog Studios, pg 937

HAWAII
Media Bridge Gamekids, pg 821

IDAHO
Rex Morris Productions, pg 830

ILLINOIS
ABS Enterprises, pg 672
AnswersMedia, pg 686
Audiobook Department, pg 695
Beatty TeleVisual Productions, pg 703
CCore Media Inc, pg 718
Edit House Chicago, pg 750
Major Media Inc, pg 815
Mightybytes Inc, pg 827
Multimedia Marketing Group, pg 833
Jim Passin Productions, pg 852
PSAV® Presentation Services (Hotel Services Division), pg 866
RBR Productions, pg 870
Solid Sound Recording Studio, pg 892
Sound/Video Impressions Inc, pg 894
WEEK TV, pg 935
Woodside Avenue Music Productions Inc, pg 941

INDIANA
A-V-A Video Productions, pg 671
Advanced Media Integration, pg 677
Bright Ideas Creative Services, pg 710
Gaither Studios LLC, pg 767
Alan Johnson Recording, pg 794
OMNI Productions, pg 845
Sweetwater Sound Inc, pg 905

IOWA
Educational Technology & Media Services, pg 751
Hedquist Productions Inc, pg 778

KENTUCKY
Broadway Digital, pg 711
Hammond Communications Group Inc, pg 775
Idle Minds Productions Inc, pg 784
The PPS Group, pg 860

LOUISIANA
Disk Productions Inc, pg 743
Moxie Media, pg 832
Vidox Motion Imagery, pg 930

MAINE
Headlight Audio Visual Inc, pg 777

MARYLAND
Bella Faccia Inc, pg 703
Bethesda Softworks LLC, pg 704
CPR MultiMedia Solutions, pg 732
The Cutting Corporation, GraphicAudio® & Archival Sound Lab, pg 736
dbF a Media Company, pg 739
The Image Generators, pg 785
Lion & Fox Recording Studios, pg 809
Milner-Fenwick Inc, pg 828
Omega Recording Studios, pg 845
Pro Cuts Editing Services, pg 862
Satellite Media Production, pg 881
Sheffield Audio/Video Productions, pg 885
Soundtrax Inc, pg 895
Speakeasy™ Productions Inc, pg 896

MASSACHUSETTS
Continental Recordings Inc, pg 731
Cramer, pg 732
Green Mountain Post Films (GMP), pg 774
Labrecque Creative Sound, pg 803
M Works Mastering Studio, pg 813
Penfield Productions Ltd, pg 853
Preston Productions Inc, pg 861
Professional Audio Design Inc, pg 865
Revels Records, pg 874
Ben Rudnick and Friends, pg 878
Sound & Vision Media, pg 893
Sounds Interesting Studio, pg 894
Soundtrack Group, pg 895
Rik Tinory Productions, pg 914

MICHIGAN
Audio Graphic Services, pg 693
Brilliance Audio, pg 710
The Brookwood Studio Inc, pg 711
Digi Sign Design LLC, pg 741
GMP Music, pg 772
K&R's Recording Studios Inc, pg 796
MessageMakers, pg 824
Michigan Recording Arts Institute & Technologies, pg 825
Rebirth Inc, pg 871
TGA Recording Co, pg 911

MINNESOTA
The ADS Group, pg 676
Badiyan Inc, pg 700
BeyerSound & Essay Audio, pg 705
GMI Productions, pg 771
Media Loft Inc, pg 822
Rum Jungle Media, pg 878
Winterland Studios, pg 940

MISSOURI
Avatar Studios, pg 697
Hardcastle Films & Video, pg 776
Ozam Productions Inc, pg 849
Show-Me Audio-Visual, pg 887
Studio Worx Inc, pg 903

MONTANA
Jereco Studios Inc, pg 793
KCFW Television, pg 797
KUSM TV, pg 802
ooLite Media LLC, pg 846

NEBRASKA
JoeAudio, pg 794
Three Pillars Media, pg 913

NEVADA
DVDs4Less, pg 748
JCS Video Productions, pg 793
Tanglewood Productions, pg 907
VirtualMix, pg 930

NEW HAMPSHIRE
Apertura, pg 686
Captain Fiddle Music & Publications, pg 716

NEW JERSEY
AJS Events, pg 679
Allegro Productions Inc, pg 680
The Audio Department Inc, pg 693
Audio Visual Dynamics®, pg 694
Color Leasing Studios, pg 727
Euro-Pacific Film & Video Productions Inc, pg 756
Image Up Studio, pg 785
Jeep Jazz Media Solutions, pg 793
Kimbo Educational, pg 799
Laurel Video Productions, pg 804
Mia Mind Music, pg 825
MiB MediaWorks, pg 825
Midnight Media Group Inc, pg 827
Milbrodt/Music & Sound Design, pg 827
Milgrom Productions, pg 827
Moe AV LLC, pg 828
NFL Films Inc, pg 841
NFL Films Music Library, pg 841
Optisonics Productions, pg 847
Shanachie Entertainment Corp, pg 885
Starlite, pg 900
Suede Interactive, pg 903
VCSvideo, pg 925
Video Ideas Productions, pg 928

NEW MEXICO
Production Outfitters, pg 864

NEW YORK
Acme Recording Studios Inc, pg 674
Aura Sonic Ltd (ASL), pg 695
Aural Gratification Inc, pg 695
aurora productions, pg 696
Big Fish Production US, pg 705
The Big House Group, pg 705
Bridge Records Inc, pg 710
Buffalo Video Production, pg 712
Chromavision Corp, pg 723
Electric Lady Studios, pg 752
Fingerpaint, pg 761
HB-Content, pg 777
Headroom Digital Audio, pg 777
Heavy Melody, pg 778
Hello World Communications, pg 778
InterNation Inc, pg 789
KAS Music & Sound, pg 796
L A Bruell Inc, pg 802
Magno Sound Inc, pg 815
Manhattan Center Studios Inc, pg 816
Mark Custom Recording Service Inc, pg 817
Jack Morton Worldwide, pg 830
Mother West, pg 831
MRM//McCANN, pg 832
New York Audio Productions, pg 840
The Palmer Group, pg 850
Posthorn Recordings, pg 859
RadioArt/Bob & Ray CDs & MP3 Files, pg 869
David Rapkin Audio Production, pg 870

Sear Sound, pg 883
Elliot Sokolov Music, pg 892
Sony Music Entertainment, pg 893
Tiki Recording Studios Inc, pg 914
Visual Technologies Corp, pg 932
Zelman Studios Ltd, pg 945

NORTH CAROLINA
Pat Appleson Studios Inc, pg 687
Audio Art, pg 693
The Communications Group Inc, pg 729
Duke Media Services, pg 747
Horizon Video Productions Inc, pg 781
Image Associates Inc, pg 784
On Location North Carolina, pg 846
Special Event Services, pg 896
Take One Productions Ltd, pg 906
Trailblazer Studios®, pg 917
2BruceStudio, pg 920

NORTH DAKOTA
Media Productions, pg 822

OHIO
Advent Media Inc, pg 677
Bartha, pg 702
Cinecraft Productions Inc, pg 723
Curtis Inc, pg 736
Cuyahoga Community College Student Production Office (SPO), pg 736
Lyon Video Inc, pg 813
Mills James Productions, pg 828
Musicol Recording, pg 835
SoundSpace Inc, pg 895
The Telos Alliance, pg 910
Vista Color Imaging Inc, pg 931

OKLAHOMA
Academic Media & Digital Services, pg 672
Garman Productions LLC, pg 768
PDC Productions, pg 852

OREGON
KTVA Productions, pg 802
REX, pg 874

PENNSYLVANIA
American Artist Studio, pg 682
Audio Visual Communications Inc, pg 694
Craig Recording Studios, pg 732
Dreambox Media Inc, pg 746
Filmaker Technology, pg 760
FMP Media Solutions Inc, pg 763
Forge Recording LLC, pg 764
Ivory Productions, pg 792
JPL, pg 795
Production Masters Inc (PMI), pg 864
Right Coast Recording Inc, pg 875
The Videohouse Inc, pg 929
WHYY Inc, pg 938

RHODE ISLAND
Sound-FX-Design, pg 894
StarTrak Studios Inc, pg 900

SOUTH CAROLINA
Assignment Desk, pg 691
DaviSound, pg 739
Genesis Creative, pg 769

TENNESSEE

American Blackguard Inc, pg 683
Analog Man Recording Studio, pg 685
Anode Inc, pg 686
Ardent Studios Inc, pg 688
Audio Media Productions, pg 693
Brantley Sound Associates Inc, pg 709
Continental Film, pg 731
High Water Records, pg 779
JamSync, pg 793
Love Shack Recording Studios, pg 811
Memphis Communications Corp, pg 823
Mr Mark's Used Musical, Stereo & Studio Equipment Store, pg 828
Motion Picture Services, pg 831
Scripps Networks, pg 882
Stage Post, pg 899
Technical Support Systems LLC, pg 908
United Methodist Productions, pg 921
Zion Music Group, pg 945

TEXAS

Audiomoxie®, pg 695
Crossroads Audio Inc, pg 735
The Editing Co, pg 750
Emergency Film Group, pg 753
Fire Station Studios, pg 761
Great Recordings LLC, pg 773
Horizon Film + Video Productions, pg 781
Marx InDigital, pg 818
Matson Multi-Media, pg 820
Phillips Media Source, pg 855
Planet Dallas Recording Studios, pg 857
Real to Reel Studios Inc, pg 871
Reelsound Recording Co, pg 872
Romar Learning Solutions LLC, pg 877
The Samuels Co, pg 879
Sound Arts Recording Studio, pg 893
The Sound Lab Inc, pg 894
Sound Works, pg 894
South Coast Film & Video, pg 895
Stage Directions, pg 898
Texas Heart Institute Visual Communication Services, pg 911
Tropikal Productions, pg 918
World Beat Studio, pg 941

UTAH

Soularium Recording Studios, pg 893

VERMONT

Edgewood Studios, pg 750
University of Vermont, Instructional Television Dept, pg 923

VIRGINIA

American AV, pg 682
AudioImage Recording, pg 695
BES Studios, pg 704
Bias Studios, pg 705
CACI Integrated Communications, pg 713
Wally Cleaver's Recording Service, pg 726
Goose Creek Music & Entertainment, pg 772
Metro Productions, pg 824
National Media Services Inc, pg 836
Studio Center Corp, pg 902

WASHINGTON

Avast! Recording Co, pg 697
D A Sound, pg 737
Hamilton Studio, pg 775
Inland Audio Visual Co, pg 788
Kostov Productions, pg 801
North-by-Northwest - A Digital Studio, pg 842
Pacific Multimedia Inc, pg 849
Quiet Planet LLC, pg 868
Sound Sound, pg 894
Victory Studios, pg 927

WEST VIRGINIA

Blackwater Video Productions, pg 707
Sweetsong Productions, pg 905

WISCONSIN

Audio Visual of Milwaukee Inc, pg 694
Concept Productions Inc, pg 730
Learning Technology Services, pg 805
Logan Productions Inc, pg 811
Sound Strations Audio Productions Inc, pg 894
TBC Studios, pg 907
USAV Group Inc, pg 923
Video Wisconsin Inc, pg 929
Wisconsin Public Television, pg 940

WYOMING

Bridger Productions Inc, pg 710

ALBERTA

Allstar Show Industries Inc, pg 681

BRITISH COLUMBIA

Creation Technologies Inc, pg 733
Pinewood Sound, pg 857
Triad Communications Ltd, pg 918
The Vocal Point/Profile Communications Ltd, pg 932

MANITOBA

DACAPO Productions Inc, pg 737

ONTARIO

ADS Media, pg 677
AMPLUS Productions, pg 684
DebsVoice, pg 739
GAPC (General Assembly Production Centre), pg 768
JL Recording Studios, pg 794
MCS Recording Studios, pg 821
Metalworks Recording Studios Inc, pg 824
Phase One Studios, pg 855
Silver Creek Media Inc, pg 888
Spence-Thomas Audio Post, pg 897
Trebas Institute, pg 917
Video Excellence Productions, pg 927
Wanted! Sound + Picture, pg 933
Westar Music, pg 936
Westbury National Show Systems Ltd, pg 936

QUEBEC

Trebas Institute, pg 917

Sound Recording— Magnetic

ALABAMA

Dogwood Productions Inc, pg 745

ARIZONA

Merestone, pg 823
Metropolitan Audio-Visual Inc, pg 824

CALIFORNIA

Artichoke Productions, pg 690
CCI Digital, a DVS Company, pg 718
Chace Audio by Deluxe, pg 720
Creative Technology, pg 733
Custom Video Productions Inc, pg 736
Earwax Productions Inc, pg 749
Express Media Inc, pg 757
4th Street Recording, pg 764
Lynch Communications, pg 813
Main Street Media Inc, pg 815
Maximus Media Inc, pg 820
The Media Staff Inc, pg 822
On-Trax Inc, pg 846
OTR Studios, pg 848
Palardo Productions, pg 850
Penrose Productions, pg 854
piXvfm Inc, pg 857
PM Productions, pg 858
Polarity Post Production, pg 858
QRS Software Services, pg 867
Saturn Studios, pg 881
SonicPool, pg 892
Still N' Motion, pg 901
Todd-AO Studios, pg 915
Total Creative, pg 916
United Audio Video Inc, pg 921

CONNECTICUT

A/V Davey, pg 697
Guymark Studios LLC, pg 775
MAVCO, pg 820

DELAWARE

Side Door Studio Inc, pg 887

DISTRICT OF COLUMBIA

Library of Congress, Motion Picture, Broadcasting & Recorded Sound Division, pg 807

FLORIDA

Communications Concepts Inc (CCI), pg 729
LHV Audio Services, pg 807
Mach 1 Productions, pg 813
Morrisound Recording, pg 830
Phat Planet Recording Studios, pg 855
Universal Studios Florida® Production Group, pg 922
Mike Vasilinda Productions Inc, pg 925

GEORGIA

Beachwood Productions, pg 702
Hottrax Records, pg 782
Stage Front Presentation Systems, pg 899

HAWAII

Media Bridge Gamekids, pg 821

ILLINOIS

CCore Media Inc, pg 718
Delmark Records, pg 740
Multimedia Marketing Group, pg 833
On Site Video, pg 846
RBR Productions, pg 870

ARIZONA (right col)

WEEK TV, pg 935
Woodside Avenue Music Productions Inc, pg 941

INDIANA

Communication Ministries, pg 728
OMNI Productions, pg 845

IOWA

Educational Technology & Media Services, pg 751

LOUISIANA

Moxie Media, pg 832

MARYLAND

Bethesda Softworks LLC, pg 704
CPR MultiMedia Solutions, pg 732
The Cutting Corporation, GraphicAudio® & Archival Sound Lab, pg 736
dbF a Media Company, pg 739
Omega Recording Studios, pg 845
Satellite Media Production, pg 881
Sheffield Audio/Video Productions, pg 885

MASSACHUSETTS

CommCreative, pg 728
Continental Recordings Inc, pg 731
Green Mountain Post Films (GMP), pg 774
Monadnock Media Inc, pg 829
Professional Audio Design Inc, pg 865
Soundtrack Group, pg 895

MICHIGAN

Audio Graphic Services, pg 693
Brilliance Audio, pg 710
The Brookwood Studio Inc, pg 711
Digi Sign Design LLC, pg 741
GMP Music, pg 772
K&R's Recording Studios Inc, pg 796
MessageMakers, pg 824
Michigan Recording Arts Institute & Technologies, pg 825

MINNESOTA

The ADS Group, pg 676
Badiyan Inc, pg 700
GMI Productions, pg 771

MISSOURI

Avatar Studios, pg 697
Show-Me Audio-Visual, pg 887

MONTANA

Jereco Studios Inc, pg 793
KCFW Television, pg 797
KUSM TV, pg 802

NEVADA

DVDs4Less, pg 748

NEW HAMPSHIRE

Apertura, pg 686
Captain Fiddle Music & Publications, pg 716

NEW JERSEY

AJS Events, pg 679
Allegro Productions Inc, pg 680

AUDIO

Sound Recording— Magnetic (continued)

NEW JERSEY (continued)
Audio Visual Dynamics®, pg 694
Midnight Media Group Inc, pg 827
NFL Films Music Library, pg 841
Optisonics Productions, pg 847
Shanachie Entertainment Corp, pg 885
Suede Interactive, pg 903
VCSvideo, pg 925

NEW MEXICO
Production Outfitters, pg 864

NEW YORK
aurora productions, pg 696
The Big House Group, pg 705
Chromavision Corp, pg 723
DuArt Media Services, pg 747
Heavy Melody, pg 778
KAS Music & Sound, pg 796
Magno Sound Inc, pg 815
MRM//McCANN, pg 832
New York Audio Productions, pg 840
The Palmer Group, pg 850
Posthorn Recordings, pg 859
David Rapkin Audio Production, pg 870
Sony Music Entertainment, pg 893
Zelman Studios Ltd, pg 945

NORTH CAROLINA
Pat Appleson Studios Inc, pg 687
Duke Media Services, pg 747
Franklin Video Inc, pg 765
Horizon Video Productions Inc, pg 781
Special Event Services, pg 896
Trailblazer Studios®, pg 917
2BruceStudio, pg 920

OHIO
Russ Beckner Pictures, pg 703
Cuyahoga Community College Student Production Office (SPO), pg 736
Lyon Video Inc, pg 813
Mills James Productions, pg 828
Musicol Recording, pg 835
SoundSpace Inc, pg 895
The Telos Alliance, pg 910
Vista Color Imaging Inc, pg 931

PENNSYLVANIA
Audio Visual Communications Inc, pg 694
Craig Recording Studios, pg 732
FMP Media Solutions Inc, pg 763
Forge Recording LLC, pg 764
Ivory Productions, pg 792
Production Masters Inc (PMI), pg 864
Right Coast Recording Inc, pg 875

RHODE ISLAND
Sound-FX-Design, pg 894

SOUTH CAROLINA
DaviSound, pg 739
Venture Media, pg 925

TENNESSEE
Analog Man Recording Studio, pg 685
Ardent Studios Inc, pg 688
Continental Film, pg 731
Love Shack Recording Studios, pg 811
Memphis Communications Corp, pg 823
Mr Mark's Used Musical, Stereo & Studio Equipment Store, pg 828
Motion Picture Services, pg 831
Scripps Networks, pg 882
Stage Post, pg 899
Technical Support Systems LLC, pg 908
Zion Music Group, pg 945

TEXAS
Audiomoxie®, pg 695
Fire Station Studios, pg 761
Marx InDigital, pg 818
The Samuels Co, pg 879
Sound Works, pg 894
South Coast Film & Video, pg 895
Texas Heart Institute Visual Communication Services, pg 911
Tropikal Productions, pg 918

VIRGINIA
American AV, pg 682
AudioImage Recording, pg 695
BES Studios, pg 704
Bias Studios, pg 705
CACI Integrated Communications, pg 713
Wally Cleaver's Recording Service, pg 726

WASHINGTON
Inland Audio Visual Co, pg 788
Pacific Multimedia Inc, pg 849
Victory Studios, pg 927

WISCONSIN
Audio Visual of Milwaukee Inc, pg 694
USAV Group Inc, pg 923
Wisconsin Public Television, pg 940

WYOMING
Bridger Productions Inc, pg 710

BRITISH COLUMBIA
Pinewood Sound, pg 857

ONTARIO
MCS Recording Studios, pg 821
Metalworks Recording Studios Inc, pg 824
Spence-Thomas Audio Post, pg 897
Westbury National Show Systems Ltd, pg 936

Sound Recording—Optical

ARIZONA
Allusion Studios & Pure Wave Audio, pg 681
Merestone, pg 823

CALIFORNIA
AB Audio Visual Entertainment Inc, pg 672
Chace Audio by Deluxe, pg 720
Diamond Dreams Music Productions, pg 741

Earwax Productions Inc, pg 749
Lynch Communications, pg 813
Main Street Media Inc, pg 815
OTR Studios, pg 848
QRS Software Services, pg 867
Saturn Studios, pg 881
SonicPool, pg 892
Todd-AO Studios, pg 915
Total Creative, pg 916

FLORIDA
CD ROM™ Inc, pg 718
LHV Audio Services, pg 807
Phat Planet Recording Studios, pg 855

GEORGIA
Hottrax Records, pg 782
Stage Front Presentation Systems, pg 899

HAWAII
Media Bridge Gamekids, pg 821

ILLINOIS
RBR Productions, pg 870
Sparrow Sound Design, pg 896
Woodside Avenue Music Productions Inc, pg 941

INDIANA
Alan Johnson Recording, pg 794

LOUISIANA
Disk Productions Inc, pg 743

MARYLAND
Bethesda Softworks LLC, pg 704
Omega Recording Studios, pg 845
Sheffield Audio/Video Productions, pg 885
Soundtrax Inc, pg 895

MASSACHUSETTS
CommCreative, pg 728
Professional Audio Design Inc, pg 865
Soundtrack Group, pg 895
WVP Boston, pg 942

MICHIGAN
Brilliance Audio, pg 710
Digi Sign Design LLC, pg 741
GMP Music, pg 772
K&R's Recording Studios Inc, pg 796
Michigan Recording Arts Institute & Technologies, pg 825

MISSOURI
Avatar Studios, pg 697
Show-Me Audio-Visual, pg 887

MONTANA
Jereco Studios Inc, pg 793

NEW HAMPSHIRE
Apertura, pg 686

NEW JERSEY
Allegro Productions Inc, pg 680
CFP Video Productions Inc, pg 720
Midnight Media Group Inc, pg 827
Milgrom Productions, pg 827

NFL Films Music Library, pg 841
Suede Interactive, pg 903

NEW YORK
DuArt Media Services, pg 747
Heavy Melody, pg 778
Magno Sound Inc, pg 815
The Palmer Group, pg 850

NORTH CAROLINA
Pat Appleson Studios Inc, pg 687

OHIO
Advent Media Inc, pg 677
The Telos Alliance, pg 910

PENNSYLVANIA
Craig Recording Studios, pg 732

RHODE ISLAND
Sound-FX-Design, pg 894

TENNESSEE
American Blackguard Inc, pg 683
Analog Man Recording Studio, pg 685
Ardent Studios Inc, pg 688
Memphis Communications Corp, pg 823
Motion Picture Services, pg 831
Stage Post, pg 899

TEXAS
The Sound Lab Inc, pg 894
Tropikal Productions, pg 918

VIRGINIA
AudioImage Recording, pg 695

WASHINGTON
Quiet Planet LLC, pg 868

WISCONSIN
Audio Visual of Milwaukee Inc, pg 694

ONTARIO
Metalworks Recording Studios Inc, pg 824

Sound Stripping

ARIZONA
Merestone, pg 823

CALIFORNIA
Lynch Communications, pg 813
PM Productions, pg 858
Polarity Post Production, pg 858
QRS Software Services, pg 867

FLORIDA
Phat Planet Recording Studios, pg 855

ILLINOIS
Woodside Avenue Music Productions Inc, pg 941

MARYLAND
Bethesda Softworks LLC, pg 704
CPR MultiMedia Solutions, pg 732

MASSACHUSETTS

Soundtrack Group, pg 895

MICHIGAN

Digi Sign Design LLC, pg 741
K&R's Recording Studios Inc,
pg 796
Michigan Recording Arts Institute
& Technologies, pg 825

NEW JERSEY

CFP Video Productions Inc, pg 720
Suede Interactive, pg 903

NEW YORK

The Big House Group, pg 705
Heavy Melody, pg 778
Hello World Communications,
pg 778
KAS Music & Sound, pg 796
The Palmer Group, pg 850

NORTH CAROLINA

Pat Appleson Studios Inc, pg 687

TENNESSEE

Love Shack Recording Studios,
pg 811
Motion Picture Services, pg 831
Stage Post, pg 899

TEXAS

Sound Works, pg 894

WASHINGTON

Hamilton Studio, pg 775

WISCONSIN

Audio Visual of Milwaukee Inc,
pg 694
Wisconsin Public Television, pg 940

MANITOBA

DACAPO Productions Inc, pg 737

ONTARIO

Spence-Thomas Audio Post, pg 897

Sound System—Portable Distributors

ALABAMA

Curtis Company, pg 736

ARIZONA

Arizona Cine Equipment, pg 688
EAR Professional Audio/Video,
pg 749
Metropolitan Audio-Visual Inc,
pg 824
Projector SuperStore LLC, pg 865
Troxell-CDI, pg 918
Ultimate Presentation Systems Inc,
pg 920

ARKANSAS

White Diamond Productions LLC,
pg 937

CALIFORNIA

Ametron Audio/Video, pg 684
Associated Sound, pg 691
Assured Audio Visual, pg 691

ATV Video Center Inc, pg 692
Audio Images Corp, pg 693
Be Media, pg 702
California Tape Products Inc,
pg 714
Carvin Amps & Audio, pg 717
Empire Pro, pg 753
Gallien-Krueger, pg 768
Hosa Technology Inc, pg 781
IAMP Professional Audio, pg 783
Instructional Materials & Equipment
Distributors (I-Med), pg 789
JD Audio Visual Inc, pg 793
L-Acoustics Inc, pg 802
Location Sound Corp, pg 810
Lloyd F McKinney Associates Inc,
pg 821
MediaPOINTE, pg 823
Professional Sound Corp, pg 865
QSC Audio Products LLC, pg 867
Radian Audio Engineering Inc,
pg 869
Sonance, pg 892
Sound Service Co, pg 894
Southern California Sound Image
Inc, pg 895
SSL Industries Inc, pg 898
Stanislaus AV Inc, pg 899
TOA Electronics Inc, pg 915
Towards 2000 Inc, pg 916
VMI Inc, pg 932

COLORADO

Audio Consultant Services Inc,
pg 693
Daylight Productions & Rentals,
pg 739
Spectrum Audio Visual Services,
pg 897

CONNECTICUT

Connecticut Audio & Theatrical
Supply, pg 731
HB Communications Inc, pg 777
Sennheiser Electronic Corp, pg 884

DELAWARE

Actors Attic, pg 675

FLORIDA

Altel Systems Group Inc, pg 682
AVI-SPL, pg 698
Broadcasters General Store Inc,
pg 711
Digital Video Systems, pg 742
Harmon's Audio-Visual Services,
pg 776
Harris Corp, pg 776
Hi-Tech Import Export Corp,
pg 779
Industrial Strength Inc, pg 787
Lighting Sales Connection Inc,
pg 808
Midtown Video Inc, pg 827
ONstage, pg 846
Recording Media & Equipment Inc
(RM&E), pg 872
Stereo Sales Inc, pg 900
TAI Audio, pg 906
Technomedia Solutions, pg 909

GEORGIA

Lighting & Production Equipment
Inc, pg 807
LT Sound Inc, pg 812
Stage Front Presentation Systems,
pg 899

HAWAII

The Audio Visual Co (AVCO),
pg 694

ILLINOIS

Allen Visual Systems Inc, pg 680
Central Audio-Visual Equipment
Inc, pg 719
Joseph Electronics, pg 795
G T Luscombe Co Inc, pg 812

INDIANA

Heart Breaker Entertainment LLC,
pg 778
Sensory Technologies LLC, pg 884
SHP Electronics, pg 887
Sweetwater Sound Inc, pg 905

KENTUCKY

Audio Visual Techniques Inc,
pg 695
Axxis Leasing Inc, pg 700
Barney Miller's Inc, pg 827
NOR-COM Inc, pg 841

LOUISIANA

Pace Systems, pg 849
Techkno Integration & Design
Services LLC, pg 908

MAINE

Headlight Audio Visual Inc, pg 777

MARYLAND

Advance Audiovisual Presentation
Ltd, pg 677
Bradley Broadcast & Pro Audio,
pg 709
Cardinal Sound & Video, pg 717
Kipp Visual Systems Inc, pg 799

MASSACHUSETTS

Terry Hanley Audio Systems Inc,
pg 775
Rule Boston Camera, pg 878

MICHIGAN

Olson Anderson Co, pg 685
City Events Group, pg 725
Digi Sign Design LLC, pg 741
On Stage Visuals, pg 846
TEL Systems LLC, pg 909

MINNESOTA

Alpha Video & Audio Inc, pg 682
Harris Communications Inc, pg 776
New Life Communications Inc,
pg 839

MISSISSIPPI

Bowie Audio Visual Enterprises Inc,
pg 709

MISSOURI

Communitronics Corp, pg 729
Conference Technologies Inc,
pg 730
Schiller's Audio-Visual, pg 881

NEVADA

Pignose-Gorilla, pg 856

NEW HAMPSHIRE

APS Lighting-Sound-AV, pg 688

NEW JERSEY

Alltec Stores, a Vcom IMC
Company, pg 681
AlltecPro, pg 681
Audio Visual Associates, pg 694
AV Bluebook, pg 696
Comprehensive Cable &
Connectivity Co, pg 729
Earl Girls Inc, pg 749
G&G Technologies Inc, pg 768
HamiltonBuhl, pg 775
The Music Place, pg 834
Nelson Enterprises Theatrical
Supply Co, pg 838
Onkyo USA Corp, pg 846
SDI Technologies Inc, pg 883
Starlite, pg 900
Total Video Products Inc, pg 916
Video Corporation of America
(VCA), pg 927
Wired 4 Sound Inc, pg 940
Yorktel, pg 944

NEW MEXICO

Quickbeam Systems Inc (QSI),
pg 868

NEW YORK

Ace Video, pg 674
ADI Global Distribution, pg 676
Albany Theatre Supply Co Inc,
pg 679
Audio-Video Corp, pg 694
Aura Sonic Ltd (ASL), pg 695
AV Workshop, pg 697
Colortone Audio Visual, pg 728
Design Audio Visual Inc, pg 741
Gaylord Archival, pg 768
Hot House Professional Audio,
pg 782
Indigo Productions, pg 787
iProbe Multilingual Solutions Inc,
pg 791
KVL Audio Visual Services Inc,
pg 802
Lee Dan® Communications Inc,
pg 805
Long Island Video Enterprises Live
Inc, pg 811
Markertek Video Supply, pg 817
RNJ Electronics, pg 875
Theatrical Services & Supplies Inc,
pg 912
Visual Word Systems Inc, pg 932

OHIO

Copp Integrated Systems, pg 731
ITA Audio Visual Solutions, pg 791
Lubell Labs Inc, pg 812
Luminaud Inc, pg 812
Parts Express, pg 851
Tri-State Audio Visual Co, pg 918

OREGON

Lightspeed Technologies Inc,
pg 808
SuperDigital Ltd, pg 904

PENNSYLVANIA

Advanced AV LLC, pg 677
Audio Visions Inc, pg 694
Audio Visual Communications Inc,
pg 694
Bernie's Photo Center, pg 704
Clair Companies, pg 725
J E Foss Co, pg 764
Garcia Marketing Inc, pg 768
Grise Audio Visual Center Inc,
pg 774

AUDIO

Sound System—Portable Distributors (continued)

PENNSYLVANIA (continued)

Morefield Communications Inc, pg 830
RSS Distributors, pg 878
Sound by Fitch, pg 893
Vistacom Inc, pg 931
Visual Sound Inc, pg 931

SOUTH CAROLINA

DaviSound, pg 739

TENNESSEE

Allstar Audio Systems Inc, pg 681
Belew Enterprises, pg 703
Lowrance Sound Co Inc, pg 812
Mr Mark's Used Musical, Stereo & Studio Equipment Store, pg 828
Spectrum Sound Inc, pg 897
Technical Support Systems LLC, pg 908
Trew Audio Inc, pg 917
Zion Music Group, pg 945

TEXAS

AVES Audio Visual Systems Inc, pg 698
CAM Audio Inc, pg 714
Crossroads Audio Inc, pg 735
Data Projections Inc, pg 738
Digital Display Solutions Inc, pg 742
FitzCo Sound Inc, pg 761
Heffernan Audio Visual, pg 778
Lubbock Audio Visual Inc, pg 812
Pro Video & Film Equipment Co Inc, pg 863
Quality Audio Visual Service Inc, pg 867
Southwest Sound Solutions, pg 896
Stage Directions, pg 898
Tarpley Media Systems, pg 907

UTAH

Performance Audio LLC, pg 854

VIRGINIA

Acoustics First Corp, pg 674
Avitecture Inc, pg 699
Boitnott Visual Communications Corp (BVC), pg 708
Lee Hartman & Sons Inc, pg 805
Rocktown Media, pg 876
The Whitlock Group, pg 937

WASHINGTON

CCI Solutions, pg 718
D A Sound, pg 737
Northern Lights & Pro Audio, pg 842
PNTA, pg 858

WEST VIRGINIA

United Sound & Electronics, pg 921

WISCONSIN

Audio Visual of Milwaukee Inc, pg 694
Camera Corner Connecting Point, pg 715
Full Compass Systems, pg 767

PUERTO RICO

Audio Visual Concepts Inc, pg 694
Bonnin Electronics Inc, pg 708

ALBERTA

Evolution AV, pg 757
Infosat Communications Inc, pg 787
Matrix Video Communications Corp (MVCC), pg 819
McBain Camera Ltd, pg 820
Unique Communications Ltd, pg 921

BRITISH COLUMBIA

Commercial Electronics Ltd, pg 728

MANITOBA

Advance Pro, pg 677
Inland Audio Visual Ltd, pg 788

ONTARIO

Cinema Stage Inc, pg 724
HD Source, pg 777
Nationwide Audio Visual Co, pg 837
Westbury National Show Systems Ltd, pg 936
Yorkville Sound Inc, pg 944

QUEBEC

JAM Industries Ltd, pg 792
SC Media Canada, pg 881

Sound System—Portable Manufacturers

ARIZONA

Fender Musical Instruments Corp, pg 759
MTX Audio, pg 833

ARKANSAS

Sound-Craft Systems Inc, pg 894

CALIFORNIA

Anchor Audio Inc, pg 685
Califone International Inc, pg 714
Carvin Amps & Audio, pg 717
Directed Electronics, pg 743
FrontRow, pg 766
Gallien-Krueger, pg 768
Hosa Technology Inc, pg 781
L-Acoustics Inc, pg 802
Laboratories Inc, pg 803
Orevox USA Corp, pg 847
Professional Sound Corp, pg 865
Radian Audio Engineering Inc, pg 869
Renkus-Heinz Inc, pg 873
Sonance, pg 892
TeachLogic Inc, pg 908
TOA Electronics Inc, pg 915

FLORIDA

Magna-Tech Electronic Co Inc, pg 814

ILLINOIS

ACCO Brands Corp, pg 673
AmpliVox Portable Sound Systems, pg 684
Bag End Loudspeakers, pg 700

KANSAS

Galaxy Audio, pg 767

MARYLAND

RCI Custom Products, pg 871

MASSACHUSETTS

Bose Corp, pg 709
Eastern Acoustic Works Inc (EAW), pg 749
Technomad™ Inc, pg 909

MINNESOTA

Bosch Security Systems Inc, pg 709

MISSISSIPPI

Peavey Electronics Corp, pg 852

NEVADA

Pignose-Gorilla, pg 856

NEW JERSEY

AlltecPro, pg 681
Oklahoma Sound Corp, pg 844
Onkyo USA Corp, pg 846
Panasonic Corporation of North America, pg 850
RAMSA Professional Audio Systems, pg 870
SDI Technologies Inc, pg 883

NEW MEXICO

Lectrosonics Inc, pg 805

NEW YORK

Ashly Audio Inc, pg 691
MG Electronics, pg 825

OHIO

Luminaud Inc, pg 812

OKLAHOMA

DD Audio, pg 739

OREGON

BIAMP Systems, pg 705
Lightspeed Technologies Inc, pg 808

PENNSYLVANIA

Clair Companies, pg 725
Community Professional Loudspeakers, pg 729

RHODE ISLAND

Numark Industries LP, pg 843

SOUTH CAROLINA

DaviSound, pg 739

TENNESSEE

Brantley Sound Associates Inc, pg 709
Cerwin-Vega! Inc, pg 720

UTAH

Listen Technologies Corp, pg 810
Spectra Sonics LLC, pg 897

VIRGINIA

Acoustics First Corp, pg 674

WEST VIRGINIA

United Sound & Electronics, pg 921

ONTARIO

Music Group Commercial Ltd, pg 834
Yorkville Sound Inc, pg 944

Sound System—Portable Rentals

ALABAMA

Audio-Video Resources Inc, pg 694

ARIZONA

Arizona Cine Equipment, pg 688
AV Concepts Inc, pg 696
Merestone, pg 823
Metropolitan Audio-Visual Inc, pg 824
Ultimate Presentation Systems Inc, pg 920
Video West Inc, pg 929

ARKANSAS

White Diamond Productions LLC, pg 937

CALIFORNIA

AGF Media Services, pg 678
Alliant Event Services, pg 681
Ametron Audio/Video, pg 684
Associated Sound, pg 691
Assured Audio Visual, pg 691
ATV Video Center Inc, pg 692
Audio Rents, pg 693
AV Guys, pg 697
Express Media Inc, pg 757
IAMP Professional Audio, pg 783
Instructional Materials & Equipment Distributors (I-Med), pg 789
JD Audio Visual Inc, pg 793
Location Sound Corp, pg 810
Lynch Communications, pg 813
Maximus Media Inc, pg 820
McCune Audio-Video-Lighting, pg 821
Munday & Collins AV, pg 834
Muse Presentation Technologies, pg 834
On-Trax Inc, pg 846
PSAV® Presentation Services, pg 866
Alwin Sauers Audio Productions (ASAP), pg 881
Sonance, pg 892
Sound Service Co, pg 894
Stanislaus AV Inc, pg 899
Towards 2000 Inc, pg 916
VER, pg 926
Video Resources Inc, pg 928
VMI Inc, pg 932
Voice & Video Rentals, pg 932

COLORADO

Audio Consultant Services Inc, pg 693
Daylight Productions & Rentals, pg 739
Maniac Productions, pg 816
Multimedia Audio Visual Inc, pg 833
Spectrum Audio Visual Services, pg 897

CONNECTICUT

A/V Davey, pg 697
Connecticut Audio & Theatrical Supply, pg 731
Videofilm Systems Inc, pg 929

DELAWARE

Actors Attic, pg 675
Showorks Audio Visual Inc, pg 887
Side Door Studio Inc, pg 887

FLORIDA

AVI-SPL, pg 698
Harmon's Audio-Visual Services, pg 776
Hi-Tech Enterprises Inc, pg 779
Industrial Strength Inc, pg 787
Lighting Sales Connection Inc, pg 808
ONstage, pg 846
Paradise Show & Design Inc, pg 851
Sight & Sound Productions, pg 887
TAI Audio, pg 906
Technomedia Solutions, pg 909
Universal Studios Florida® Production Group, pg 922

GEORGIA

Lighting & Production Equipment Inc, pg 807
MAGNUM Companies Ltd, pg 815
Stage Front Presentation Systems, pg 899
Staging Directions Inc, pg 899

HAWAII

Sight & Sound Studios, pg 887

ILLINOIS

Allen Visual Systems Inc, pg 680
AV Chicago Inc, pg 696
Backstar Creative Media Inc, pg 700
Beatty TeleVisual Productions, pg 703
Central Audio-Visual Equipment Inc, pg 719
Creative Technology (CT), pg 733
Meetinghouse Event Design & Production, pg 823
OSA International Inc, pg 848
RC Communications, pg 870
Resolution Productions Group, pg 874

INDIANA

Heart Breaker Entertainment LLC, pg 778

IOWA

Central Lighting & Equipment Inc (CLE), pg 719

KENTUCKY

Audio Visual Techniques Inc, pg 695
Barney Miller's Inc, pg 827

LOUISIANA

Clark Services Audio Visual & Exhibit Inc, pg 725
Pace Systems, pg 849

MAINE

Headlight Audio Visual Inc, pg 777

MARYLAND

Advance Audiovisual Presentation Ltd, pg 677
Cardinal Sound & Video, pg 717
CPR MultiMedia Solutions, pg 732

Event Tech, pg 756
Hargrove Inc, pg 776

MASSACHUSETTS

AVFX Inc, pg 698
Terry Hanley Audio Systems Inc, pg 775
massAV, pg 819
Preston Productions Inc, pg 861

MICHIGAN

City Events Group, pg 725
Digi Sign Design LLC, pg 741
K&R All Media Productions LLC, pg 796
K&R's Recording Studios Inc, pg 796
On Stage Visuals, pg 846
TEL Systems LLC, pg 909

MINNESOTA

Alpha Video & Audio Inc, pg 682
Big Event Productions LLC, pg 705
New Life Communications Inc, pg 839

MISSISSIPPI

Bowie Audio Visual Enterprises Inc, pg 709

MISSOURI

Show-Me Audio-Visual, pg 887
Switch, pg 905

MONTANA

Jereco Studios Inc, pg 793

NEBRASKA

Dog & Pony Productions Inc, pg 744

NEVADA

GES Audio Visual, pg 770
Lefco Video Services Inc, pg 806

NEW HAMPSHIRE

APS Lighting-Sound-AV, pg 688

NEW JERSEY

Audio Visual Associates, pg 694
Audio Visual Dynamics®, pg 694
Earl Girls Inc, pg 749
International Audio Visual Inc, pg 790
MiB MediaWorks, pg 825
Moe AV LLC, pg 828
The Music Place, pg 834
Nelson Enterprises Theatrical Supply Co, pg 838
Panavid, pg 850
PLS Staging, pg 858
Starlite, pg 900
Wired 4 Sound Inc, pg 940

NEW MEXICO

Production Outfitters, pg 864
Quickbeam Systems Inc (QSI), pg 868

NEW YORK

Ace Video, pg 674
Albany Theatre Supply Co Inc, pg 679
Aura Sonic Ltd (ASL), pg 695
AV Workshop, pg 697
Colortone Audio Visual, pg 728

CP Communications, pg 732
Design Audio Visual Inc, pg 741
Hello World Communications, pg 778
iProbe Multilingual Solutions Inc, pg 791
KVL Audio Visual Services Inc, pg 802
Long Island Video Enterprises Live Inc, pg 811
Posthorn Recordings, pg 859
See Factor Industry Inc, pg 883
SmartSource Computer & AV Rentals, pg 891
Specialized Audio-Visual Inc, pg 896
Studio Instrument Rentals (SIR), pg 902
Theatrical Services & Supplies Inc, pg 912
Visual Word Systems Inc, pg 932
WorldStage, pg 941

NORTH CAROLINA

All Pro Media Inc, pg 680
Audio & Light, pg 693
AV Connections Inc, pg 697
AV Metro Inc, pg 697
Special Event Services, pg 896

NORTH DAKOTA

Media Productions, pg 822

OHIO

Hughie's Event Production Services, pg 782
ITA Audio Visual Solutions, pg 791
Mills James Productions, pg 828
Production Solutions Inc, pg 864
R&B Communications Inc, pg 870

OKLAHOMA

PDC Productions, pg 852

OREGON

Rose City Sound, pg 877

PENNSYLVANIA

Advanced AV LLC, pg 677
Audio Visions Inc, pg 694
Audio Visual Communications Inc, pg 694
Clair Companies, pg 725
FMP Media Solutions Inc, pg 763
Grise Audio Visual Center Inc, pg 774
North Star Satellite Communications Inc, pg 842
Raven Rental, pg 870
Sound by Fitch, pg 893
Vistacom Inc, pg 931
Visual Sound Inc, pg 931

SOUTH CAROLINA

DaviSound, pg 739

TENNESSEE

Allstar Audio Systems Inc, pg 681
Belew Enterprises, pg 703
Brantley Sound Associates Inc, pg 709
Love Shack Recording Studios, pg 811
Mr Mark's Used Musical, Stereo & Studio Equipment Store, pg 828
Technical Support Systems LLC, pg 908
Trew Audio Inc, pg 917

TEXAS

Alford Media Services, pg 680
Bright Star Productions Inc, pg 710
Crossroads Audio Inc, pg 735
Data Projections Inc, pg 738
FitzCo Sound Inc, pg 761
Lubbock Audio Visual Inc, pg 812
Music Lab Inc, pg 834
Onstage Systems, pg 846
Power Factory Productions, pg 860
Quality Audio Visual Service Inc, pg 867
Tropikal Productions, pg 918

UTAH

Listen Technologies Corp, pg 810
Performance Audio LLC, pg 854

VIRGINIA

Advance Concepts Inc, pg 677
American AV, pg 682
Avitecture Inc, pg 699
Boitnott Visual Communications Corp (BVC), pg 708
Lee Hartman & Sons Inc, pg 805
The Whitlock Group, pg 937

WASHINGTON

D A Sound, pg 737
Northern Lights & Pro Audio, pg 842
PNTA, pg 858

WEST VIRGINIA

Blackwater Video Productions, pg 707
United Sound & Electronics, pg 921

WISCONSIN

Camera Corner Connecting Point, pg 715
Event Essentials, pg 756
Full Compass Systems, pg 767

WYOMING

Bridger Productions Inc, pg 710

PUERTO RICO

Stage Crew Audiovisual Inc, pg 898

ALBERTA

Allstar Show Industries Inc, pg 681
Cine Audio Visual Sales & Service Ltd, pg 723
Evolution AV, pg 757
L R Light & Sound, pg 802
McBain Camera Ltd, pg 820
Unique Communications Ltd, pg 921

BRITISH COLUMBIA

Clark's Audio Visual Services Ltd, pg 725
DL Sound & Lighting Productions Ltd, pg 744

MANITOBA

Inland Audio Visual Ltd, pg 788

ONTARIO

HD Source, pg 777
Westbury National Show Systems Ltd, pg 936

QUEBEC

Audio Visual Dynamics, pg 694

AUDIO

Sound System—Portable Repairs

ARIZONA

Metropolitan Audio-Visual Inc, pg 824

CALIFORNIA

Ametron Audio/Video, pg 684
Audio Images Corp, pg 693
Diemer Amp & Keyboard Repair, pg 741
Instructional Materials & Equipment Distributors (I-Med), pg 789
McAlister Electronics, pg 820
Professional Sound Corp, pg 865
QSC Audio Products LLC, pg 867
Radian Audio Engineering Inc, pg 869
Sonance, pg 892
Sound Service Co, pg 894
SSL Industries Inc, pg 898
TOA Electronics Inc, pg 915
Towards 2000 Inc, pg 916

CONNECTICUT

HB Communications Inc, pg 777
Sennheiser Electronic Corp, pg 884

DELAWARE

Actors Attic, pg 675

FLORIDA

JT Communications, pg 795
Stereo Sales Inc, pg 900
TAI Audio, pg 906

GEORGIA

Lighting & Production Equipment Inc, pg 807
Stage Front Presentation Systems, pg 899

ILLINOIS

Allen Visual Systems Inc, pg 680
Beatty TeleVisual Productions, pg 703

INDIANA

SHP Electronics, pg 887
Sweetwater Sound Inc, pg 905

KENTUCKY

Axxis Leasing Inc, pg 700
Barney Miller's Inc, pg 827
NOR-COM Inc, pg 841

MAINE

Headlight Audio Visual Inc, pg 777

MARYLAND

Cardinal Sound & Video, pg 717

MICHIGAN

City Events Group, pg 725
K&R's Recording Studios Inc, pg 796
On Stage Visuals, pg 846
TEL Systems LLC, pg 909

MISSISSIPPI

Bowie Audio Visual Enterprises Inc, pg 709

NEW JERSEY

Audio Visual Associates, pg 694
Earl Girls Inc, pg 749
Nelson Enterprises Theatrical Supply Co, pg 838
Starlite, pg 900

NEW MEXICO

Quickbeam Systems Inc (QSI), pg 868

NEW YORK

Visual Word Systems Inc, pg 932

OHIO

Copp Integrated Systems, pg 731
ITA Audio Visual Solutions, pg 791
Tri-State Audio Visual Co, pg 918

OREGON

All Service Musical Electronics Repair, pg 680

PENNSYLVANIA

Audio Visions Inc, pg 694
Clair Companies, pg 725
J E Foss Co, pg 764
Sound by Fitch, pg 893
Vistacom Inc, pg 931
Visual Sound Inc, pg 931

SOUTH CAROLINA

DaviSound, pg 739

TENNESSEE

Belew Enterprises, pg 703
Brantley Sound Associates Inc, pg 709
Technical Support Systems LLC, pg 908

TEXAS

Lubbock Audio Visual Inc, pg 812
Quality Audio Visual Service Inc, pg 867
Southwest Sound Solutions, pg 896

VIRGINIA

Boitnott Visual Communications Corp (BVC), pg 708
The Whitlock Group, pg 937

WASHINGTON

D A Sound, pg 737
Northern Lights & Pro Audio, pg 842
PNTA, pg 858

WEST VIRGINIA

United Sound & Electronics, pg 921

WISCONSIN

Full Compass Systems, pg 767

ALBERTA

Allstar Show Industries Inc, pg 681
Infosat Communications Inc, pg 787
Unique Communications Ltd, pg 921

MANITOBA

Inland Audio Visual Ltd, pg 788

ONTARIO

Westbury National Show Systems Ltd, pg 936

QUEBEC

SC Media Canada, pg 881

Sound Transfer

ALABAMA

Sound of Birmingham Productions, pg 894

ARIZONA

Allusion Studios & Pure Wave Audio, pg 681
Merestone, pg 823

ARKANSAS

White Diamond Productions LLC, pg 937

CALIFORNIA

AB Audio Visual Entertainment Inc, pg 672
ACDC Audio CD & Cassette, pg 674
Audio Mechanics, pg 693
Berkeley Sound Artists Inc, pg 704
Chace Audio by Deluxe, pg 720
Custom Video Productions Inc, pg 736
Digital Jungle, pg 742
Eye & I Productions, pg 758
48 Windows, pg 764
Goal Productions, pg 772
JD Audio Visual Inc, pg 793
Lynch Communications, pg 813
Maximus Media Inc, pg 820
Polarity Post Production, pg 858
Private Island Audio Inc, pg 862
QRS Software Services, pg 867
Roundabout Entertainment Inc, pg 878
SonicPool, pg 892
Studio 132, pg 902
Total Creative, pg 916
Trac Recording Studio, pg 916
Universal Studios, pg 922

COLORADO

Tim Cissell Music, pg 725
CSI Film & Video LLC, pg 735
Daylight Productions & Rentals, pg 739
Mike's Camera, pg 827
Rocky Mountain Audio/Video Productions Inc, pg 876

CONNECTICUT

Guymark Studios LLC, pg 775
MAVCO, pg 820

FLORIDA

LHV Audio Services, pg 807
Mach 1 Productions, pg 813
Phat Planet Recording Studios, pg 855
Sunfire Communications Inc, pg 904

GEORGIA

Guerrilla Productions LLC, pg 774
Hottrax Records, pg 782
White Dog Studios, pg 937

ILLINOIS

Esoteric Sound, pg 755
Midwest Digital Corp, pg 827
RBR Productions, pg 870
Sound/Video Impressions Inc, pg 894
Woodside Avenue Music Productions Inc, pg 941

MARYLAND

Bethesda Softworks LLC, pg 704
CPR MultiMedia Solutions, pg 732
The Cutting Corporation, GraphicAudio® & Archival Sound Lab, pg 736
dbF a Media Company, pg 739
Lion & Fox Recording Studios, pg 809
Omega Recording Studios, pg 845
Pro Cuts Editing Services, pg 862
Satellite Media Production, pg 881
Smolian Sound Studios, pg 891
Soundtrax Inc, pg 895

MASSACHUSETTS

Continental Recordings Inc, pg 731
M Works Mastering Studio, pg 813
Penfield Productions Ltd, pg 853
Soundtrack Group, pg 895

MICHIGAN

Audio Graphic Services, pg 693
Digi Sign Design LLC, pg 741
K&R's Recording Studios Inc, pg 796
Michigan Recording Arts Institute & Technologies, pg 825
RingSide Creative, pg 875

MINNESOTA

The ADS Group, pg 676
Winterland Studios, pg 940

MISSOURI

Show-Me Audio-Visual, pg 887

MONTANA

Jereco Studios Inc, pg 793

NEBRASKA

Three Pillars Media, pg 913

NEW HAMPSHIRE

Apertura, pg 686

NEW JERSEY

AJS Events, pg 679
CFP Video Productions Inc, pg 720
Image Up Studio, pg 785
Midnight Media Group Inc, pg 827
NFL Films Inc, pg 841
NFL Films Music Library, pg 841
SADiE Inc, pg 879
Suede Interactive, pg 903
TRF Production Music Libraries, pg 917

NEW YORK

Ace Video, pg 674
aurora productions, pg 696
The Big House Group, pg 705

Chromavision Corp, pg 723
de Wolfe Music USA, pg 739
Digital Force Ltd, pg 742
Heavy Melody, pg 778
KAS Music & Sound, pg 796
Magno Sound Inc, pg 815
Masterdisk Corp, pg 819
The Palmer Group, pg 850
Peckham Productions Inc, pg 852
Posthorn Recordings, pg 859
Sear Sound, pg 883
Elliot Sokolov Music, pg 892
Zelman Studios Ltd, pg 945

NORTH CAROLINA

Pat Appleson Studios Inc, pg 687
Duke Media Services, pg 747
Trailblazer Studios®, pg 917

OHIO

Cuyahoga Community College
  Student Production Office (SPO),
  pg 736
Lyon Video Inc, pg 813
Musicol Recording, pg 835
The Telos Alliance, pg 910
Vista Color Imaging Inc, pg 931

OREGON

Lightspeed Technologies Inc,
  pg 808

PENNSYLVANIA

American Artist Studio, pg 682
New York Camera & Video, pg 840

RHODE ISLAND

Sound-FX-Design, pg 894

TENNESSEE

Continental Film, pg 731
Love Shack Recording Studios,
  pg 811
Mr Mark's Used Musical, Stereo &
  Studio Equipment Store, pg 828
Motion Picture Services, pg 831
Stage Post, pg 899
United Methodist Productions,
  pg 921

TEXAS

Audiomoxie®, pg 695
The Editing Co, pg 750
Out of the BLUE Media, pg 849
The Samuels Co, pg 879
Texas Heart Institute Visual
  Communication Services, pg 911
Tropikal Productions, pg 918

VERMONT

University of Vermont, Instructional
  Television Dept, pg 923

WASHINGTON

Hamilton Studio, pg 775

WISCONSIN

Audio Visual of Milwaukee Inc,
  pg 694
Concept Productions Inc, pg 730
5th Floor Recording Co, pg 760
USAV Group Inc, pg 923
Wisconsin Public Television, pg 940

WYOMING

Bridger Productions Inc, pg 710

PUERTO RICO

Stage Crew Audiovisual Inc, pg 898

BRITISH COLUMBIA

Pinewood Sound, pg 857

MANITOBA

DACAPO Productions Inc, pg 737

ONTARIO

GAPC (General Assembly
  Production Centre), pg 768
JL Recording Studios, pg 794
Spence-Thomas Audio Post, pg 897
Wanted! Sound + Picture, pg 933

Speaker Distributors

ALABAMA

Curtis Company, pg 736

ARIZONA

Allusion Studios & Pure Wave
  Audio, pg 681
Arizona Cine Equipment, pg 688
Coustic, pg 732
EAR Professional Audio/Video,
  pg 749
Metropolitan Audio-Visual Inc,
  pg 824
Projector SuperStore LLC, pg 865
Troxell-CDI, pg 918

ARKANSAS

White Diamond Productions LLC,
  pg 937

CALIFORNIA

Ametron Audio/Video, pg 684
Apex Jr, pg 687
ARS Electronics, pg 690
Associated Sound, pg 691
Assured Audio Visual, pg 691
ATV Video Center Inc, pg 692
Audio Images Corp, pg 693
AV Conferencing LLC (AVC),
  pg 697
Be Media, pg 702
Carvin Amps & Audio, pg 717
Christy's Editorial, pg 723
Cibola Systems, pg 723
Cinema Equipment Sales of
  California Inc, pg 724
Directed Electronics, pg 743
Educational Technology Services
  (ETS), pg 751
Empire Pro, pg 753
Gallien-Krueger, pg 768
Gluskin's Custom Audio Video,
  pg 771
Harman Professional Solutions,
  pg 776
Hosa Technology Inc, pg 781
IAMP Professional Audio, pg 783
Instructional Materials & Equipment
  Distributors (I-Med), pg 789
Jameco Electronics, pg 792
JD Audio Visual Inc, pg 793
L-Acoustics Inc, pg 802
Location Sound Corp, pg 810
Media Fabricators Inc, pg 822
MediaMation Inc, pg 822
MediaPOINTE, pg 823
Orvac Electronics, pg 848
OWI Inc, pg 849
Parasound Products Inc, pg 851
Pioneer Electronics (USA) Inc,
  pg 857

Promax Systems, pg 865
QSC Audio Products LLC, pg 867
Radian Audio Engineering Inc,
  pg 869
SNAP, pg 891
Sonance, pg 892
Sound Service Co, pg 894
Sounds Unique, pg 895
Southern California Sound Image
  Inc, pg 895
SSL Industries Inc, pg 898
Stanislaus AV Inc, pg 899
SuperVision, pg 904
TOA Electronics Inc, pg 915
Towards 2000 Inc, pg 916
VMI Inc, pg 932
VTP Inc, pg 933
Waterworks Acoustics Design Inc,
  pg 934
Yamaha Electronics Corp, pg 943
Yanchar Design & Consulting
  Group, pg 943

COLORADO

Audio Consultant Services Inc,
  pg 693
Daylight Productions & Rentals,
  pg 739

CONNECTICUT

Connecticut Audio & Theatrical
  Supply, pg 731
HB Communications Inc, pg 777
MAVCO, pg 820
The Music People Inc, pg 834
Sennheiser Electronic Corp, pg 884

DELAWARE

Actors Attic, pg 675

FLORIDA

Access Media Group, pg 673
Alliance Entertainment Corp (AEC)
  LLC, pg 680
Altel Systems Group Inc, pg 682
A2D Solutions Inc, pg 692
AVI-SPL, pg 698
Broadcasters General Store Inc,
  pg 711
Cinema Equipment & Supplies Inc,
  pg 724
D A S Audio of America Inc,
  pg 737
Digital Video Systems, pg 742
Harmon's Audio-Visual Services,
  pg 776
Harris Corp, pg 776
Herman Pro AV, pg 779
Hi-Tech Enterprises Inc, pg 779
Hi-Tech Import Export Corp,
  pg 779
Industrial Strength Inc, pg 787
Intermark Industries Inc, pg 789
Midtown Video Inc, pg 827
ONstage, pg 846
Recording Media & Equipment Inc
  (RM&E), pg 872
The Singing Machine Co Inc,
  pg 889
Stereo Sales Inc, pg 900
TAI Audio, pg 906
Technomedia Solutions, pg 909

GEORGIA

Baker Audio Visual, pg 700
Lighting & Production Equipment
  Inc, pg 807
Stage Front Presentation Systems,
  pg 899
Visioneering International Inc,
  pg 931

HAWAII

The Audio Visual Co (AVCO),
  pg 694

ILLINOIS

Allen Visual Systems Inc, pg 680
Joseph Electronics, pg 795
C V Lloyde, pg 810
Quintessence Audio Ltd, pg 868
Waldom Electronics Corp, pg 933
Woodside Avenue Music
  Productions Inc, pg 941

INDIANA

Heart Breaker Entertainment LLC,
  pg 778
Sensory Technologies LLC, pg 884
SHP Electronics, pg 887
Sweetwater Sound Inc, pg 905

KENTUCKY

Audio Visual Techniques Inc,
  pg 695
Axxis Leasing Inc, pg 700
Barney Miller's Inc, pg 827
NOR-COM Inc, pg 841

LOUISIANA

Pace Systems, pg 849
Techkno Integration & Design
  Services LLC, pg 908

MAINE

Headlight Audio Visual Inc, pg 777

MARYLAND

Bradley Broadcast & Pro Audio,
  pg 709
Cardinal Sound & Video, pg 717
Human Circuit, pg 782
Kipp Visual Systems Inc, pg 799

MASSACHUSETTS

Terry Hanley Audio Systems Inc,
  pg 775
Pro AV Systems, pg 862
Professional Audio Design Inc,
  pg 865
Rule Boston Camera, pg 878
Technomad™ Inc, pg 909

MICHIGAN

Olson Anderson Co, pg 685
City Events Group, pg 725
On Stage Visuals, pg 846
TEL Systems LLC, pg 909

MINNESOTA

Alpha Video & Audio Inc, pg 682
New Life Communications Inc,
  pg 839

MISSISSIPPI

Bowie Audio Visual Enterprises Inc,
  pg 709

MISSOURI

Communitronics Corp, pg 729
Conference Technologies Inc,
  pg 730
ITC, pg 791
Production Support Services Inc,
  pg 864
Schiller's Audio-Visual, pg 881

AUDIO

Speaker Distributors (continued)

NEBRASKA

Ballantyne Strong Inc, pg 701

NEVADA

Pignose-Gorilla, pg 856

NEW HAMPSHIRE

APS Lighting-Sound-AV, pg 688
Technet® Systems Group, pg 908

NEW JERSEY

Alltec Stores, a Vcom IMC Company, pg 681
AlltecPro, pg 681
Audio Visual Associates, pg 694
Audio Visual Dynamics®, pg 694
Comprehensive Cable & Connectivity Co, pg 729
Diversified, pg 744
Earl Girls Inc, pg 749
Entel Systems Inc, pg 754
FlagHouse, pg 762
G&G Technologies Inc, pg 768
HamiltonBuhl, pg 775
The Music Place, pg 834
Nelson Enterprises Theatrical Supply Co, pg 838
Onkyo USA Corp, pg 846
SDI Technologies Inc, pg 883
Starlite, pg 900
SYMCO Inc, pg 905
Total Video Products Inc, pg 916
Video Corporation of America (VCA), pg 927
Wired 4 Sound Inc, pg 940
Yorktel, pg 944

NEW MEXICO

Quickbeam Systems Inc (QSI), pg 868

NEW YORK

ADI Global Distribution, pg 676
Albany Theatre Supply Co Inc, pg 679
American Video Inc, pg 684
Audio-Video Corp, pg 694
Audiovox®, pg 695
Aura Sonic Ltd (ASL), pg 695
AV Workshop, pg 697
Colortone Audio Visual, pg 728
Crescendo Designs Inc, pg 734
Design Audio Visual Inc, pg 741
Gaylord Archival, pg 768
General Audio-Visual Inc (GAVI), pg 769
Gotham Sound & Communications Inc, pg 773
Group One Ltd, pg 774
Hot House Professional Audio, pg 782
Indigo Productions, pg 787
KVL Audio Visual Services Inc, pg 802
Lee Dan® Communications Inc, pg 805
Long Island Video Enterprises Live Inc, pg 811
Markertek Video Supply, pg 817
Posthorn Recordings, pg 859
Presentation Products Inc, pg 861
RNJ Electronics, pg 875
Theatrical Services & Supplies Inc, pg 912

Toys From The Attic, pg 916
Tri-Ed Distribution Inc, pg 918
Visual Word Systems Inc, pg 932
Willoughby's® Camera, pg 939

NORTH CAROLINA

Strategic Connections, pg 901
Verbatim Americas LLC, pg 926

OHIO

Copp Integrated Systems, pg 731
ITA Audio Visual Solutions, pg 791
Lubell Labs Inc, pg 812
Parts Express, pg 851
Tri-State Audio Visual Co, pg 918

OKLAHOMA

DD Audio, pg 739
Ford AV, pg 763

OREGON

Audix Microphones, pg 695
SuperDigital Ltd, pg 904

PENNSYLVANIA

Advanced AV LLC, pg 677
Audio Visions Inc, pg 694
J E Foss Co, pg 764
Grise Audio Visual Center Inc, pg 774
Innovision Media Group, pg 788
The Lerro Corp, pg 806
Morefield Communications Inc, pg 830
Sound by Fitch, pg 893
Tri-State Loudspeaker, pg 918
Vistacom Inc, pg 931
Visual Sound Inc, pg 931
Wespen Audio Visual Co, pg 935
Wire X 17 LLC, pg 940

RHODE ISLAND

M-Audio, pg 813
Shanix Inc, pg 885

SOUTH CAROLINA

DaviSound, pg 739

TENNESSEE

Advanced Sound, pg 677
Allstar Audio Systems Inc, pg 681
Belew Enterprises, pg 703
Lowrance Sound Co Inc, pg 812
Mr Mark's Used Musical, Stereo & Studio Equipment Store, pg 828
Spectrum Sound Inc, pg 897
Technical Support Systems LLC, pg 908
Trew Audio Inc, pg 917
Zion Music Group, pg 945

TEXAS

Audio Visual Technologies Group (AVTG), pg 695
AVES Audio Visual Systems Inc, pg 698
CAM Audio Inc, pg 714
Crossroads Audio Inc, pg 735
Data Projections Inc, pg 738
Digital Display Solutions Inc, pg 742
FitzCo Sound Inc, pg 761
Heffernan Audio Visual, pg 778
Lubbock Audio Visual Inc, pg 812
Pro Video & Film Equipment Co Inc, pg 863
Quality Audio Visual Service Inc, pg 867

RF Specialties of Texas LLC, pg 874
Southwest Sound Solutions, pg 896
Stage Directions, pg 898
Tarpley Media Systems, pg 907

UTAH

ClearOne Inc, pg 726
Performance Audio LLC, pg 854

VERMONT

Artech Electronics Ltd, pg 690
Production Advantage Inc, pg 863

VIRGINIA

Avitecture Inc, pg 699
Boitnott Visual Communications Corp (BVC), pg 708
Intellidyne LLC, pg 789
Lee Hartman & Sons Inc, pg 805
StageSound, pg 899
The Whitlock Group, pg 937

WASHINGTON

CCI Solutions, pg 718
D A Sound, pg 737
LOUD Technologies Inc, pg 811
Northern Lights & Pro Audio, pg 842
PNTA, pg 858
Proforma Good Wood Marketing, pg 865

WEST VIRGINIA

United Sound & Electronics, pg 921

WISCONSIN

Audio Visual of Milwaukee Inc, pg 694
Camera Corner Connecting Point, pg 715
Full Compass Systems, pg 767
Madisound Speaker Components Inc, pg 814
Safe Harbor Computers, pg 879

PUERTO RICO

Audio Visual Concepts Inc, pg 694
Bonnin Electronics Inc, pg 708

ALBERTA

Allstar Show Industries Inc, pg 681
Evolution AV, pg 757
Infosat Communications Inc, pg 787
Matrix Video Communications Corp (MVCC), pg 819
Unique Communications Ltd, pg 921

BRITISH COLUMBIA

Commercial Electronics Ltd, pg 728

MANITOBA

Advance Pro, pg 677
Inland Audio Visual Ltd, pg 788

ONTARIO

Cinema Stage Inc, pg 724
HD Source, pg 777
KDM Electronics Inc, pg 797
Music Group Commercial Ltd, pg 834
Nationwide Audio Visual Co, pg 837
PSB Speakers International, pg 866

Westbury National Show Systems Ltd, pg 936
Yorkville Sound Inc, pg 944

QUEBEC

JAM Industries Ltd, pg 792
Panavideo Inc, pg 850
SC Media Canada, pg 881

Speaker Manufacturers

ARIZONA

AtlasIED, pg 692
Coustic, pg 732
Fender Musical Instruments Corp, pg 759
David Wexler & Co, pg 936

CALIFORNIA

Boston Acoustics, pg 709
Califone International Inc, pg 714
Calrad Electronics, pg 714
Carvin Amps & Audio, pg 717
Clear-Com® LLC, pg 726
Definitive Technology LLP, pg 740
Directed Electronics, pg 743
Extron Electronics, pg 758
FrontRow, pg 766
Gallien-Krueger, pg 768
Harman Professional Solutions, pg 776
Hosa Technology Inc, pg 781
JBL Professional, pg 793
L-Acoustics Inc, pg 802
Laboratories Inc, pg 803
Meyer Sound Laboratories Inc, pg 824
Nady Systems Inc, pg 835
Orevox USA Corp, pg 847
OWI Inc, pg 849
Parasound Products Inc, pg 851
Penn Elcom Inc, pg 853
Pioneer Electronics (USA) Inc, pg 857
Radian Audio Engineering Inc, pg 869
Recortec Inc, pg 872
Renkus-Heinz Inc, pg 873
Roland Corp US, pg 876
Sonance, pg 892
Sony Electronics Inc, pg 893
TeachLogic Inc, pg 908
TOA Electronics Inc, pg 915
Velodyne LiDAR Inc, pg 925
Waterworks Acoustics Design Inc, pg 934
Wohler Technologies Inc, pg 940
Xantech LLC, pg 943
Yamaha Electronics Corp, pg 943
Yanchar Design & Consulting Group, pg 943

COLORADO

Avalon Acoustics, pg 697

CONNECTICUT

Soundsphere, pg 895

FLORIDA

CTGaudio, pg 735
Intermark Industries Inc, pg 789
Phase Technology, pg 855

GEORGIA

OAP Audio Products, pg 844

ILLINOIS

AmpliVox Portable Sound Systems, pg 684
Bag End Loudspeakers, pg 700
Dukane Corp, Audio Visual Products Division, pg 747

INDIANA

Auralex Acoustics Inc, pg 696
Klipsch Group Inc, pg 799

KANSAS

Galaxy Audio, pg 767
SoundTube Entertainment Inc, pg 895

MASSACHUSETTS

Bose Corp, pg 709
Eastern Acoustic Works Inc (EAW), pg 749
Technomad™ Inc, pg 909

MINNESOTA

Bosch Security Systems Inc, pg 709
Magnepan Inc, pg 814
MISCO, pg 828

MISSISSIPPI

Peavey Electronics Corp, pg 852
Sherwood America Inc, pg 886

MISSOURI

Lowell Manufacturing, pg 812

NEBRASKA

Ballantyne Strong Inc, pg 701
REI - Radio Engineering Industries, pg 873

NEVADA

Pignose-Gorilla, pg 856

NEW HAMPSHIRE

Russound, pg 879

NEW JERSEY

Apogee Sound International LLC, pg 687
Bogen Communications Inc, pg 708
Crestron Electronics Inc, pg 734
Gemini Sound, pg 769
Onkyo USA Corp, pg 846
Panasonic Consumer Electronics Co, pg 850
Panasonic Corporation of North America, pg 850
RAMSA Professional Audio Systems, pg 870
SDI Technologies Inc, pg 883
Technics, pg 909

NEW YORK

GLI Sound Systems, pg 771
Harbro Corp, pg 776
Hot House Professional Audio, pg 782
MG Electronics, pg 825
Sentry Industries Inc, pg 884

NORTH CAROLINA

Verbatim Americas LLC, pg 926

OHIO

Lubell Labs Inc, pg 812

OKLAHOMA

DD Audio, pg 739

OREGON

Audix Microphones, pg 695

PENNSYLVANIA

Community Professional Loudspeakers, pg 729
Right Coast Recording Inc, pg 875
Tri-State Loudspeaker, pg 918
Wire X 17 LLC, pg 940

RHODE ISLAND

M-Audio, pg 813
Numark Industries LP, pg 843

SOUTH CAROLINA

DaviSound, pg 739

TENNESSEE

Advanced Sound, pg 677
Cerwin-Vega! Inc, pg 720
KRK Systems, pg 802
Remote Audio Products, pg 873

TEXAS

Mitchell Acoustics Research, pg 828

UTAH

Spectra Sonics LLC, pg 897

WASHINGTON

D A Sound, pg 737
LOUD Technologies Inc, pg 811

WISCONSIN

Madisound Speaker Components Inc, pg 814

BRITISH COLUMBIA

B&K AV Ltd, pg 701

ONTARIO

Bryston Ltd, pg 712
KDM Electronics Inc, pg 797
Music Group Commercial Ltd, pg 834
PSB Speakers International, pg 866
Yorkville Sound Inc, pg 944

Speaker Rentals

ALABAMA

Audio-Video Resources Inc, pg 694

ARIZONA

Arizona Cine Equipment, pg 688
AV Concepts Inc, pg 696
Merestone, pg 823
Metropolitan Audio-Visual Inc, pg 824
Reel Men Rentals Inc, pg 872
Video West Inc, pg 929

ARKANSAS

White Diamond Productions LLC, pg 937

CALIFORNIA

Action Audio & Visual, pg 675
AGF Media Services, pg 678
Alliant Event Services, pg 681
Ametron Audio/Video, pg 684
Associated Sound, pg 691
ATV Video Center Inc, pg 692
Audio Rents, pg 693
AV Guys, pg 697
Dan Dugan Sound Design Inc, pg 747
Express Media Inc, pg 757
Hollywood Sound Systems, pg 781
IAMP Professional Audio, pg 783
Imagecraft Productions, pg 785
JD Audio Visual Inc, pg 793
LA Sound Co, pg 803
Location Sound Corp, pg 810
Lynch Communications, pg 813
Maximus Media Inc, pg 820
McCune Audio-Video-Lighting, pg 821
Media Fabricators Inc, pg 822
Munday & Collins AV, pg 834
Muse Presentation Technologies, pg 834
Next Arts, pg 841
Old School Cameras, pg 844
On-Trax Inc, pg 846
PSAV® Presentation Services, pg 866
Pyxis Industries Inc, pg 867
Alwin Sauers Audio Productions (ASAP), pg 881
Sound Service Co, pg 894
Stanislaus AV Inc, pg 899
The Studios at Paramount, pg 903
Synthesizer Rental Service, pg 906
Third Ear Sound Co, pg 912
Towards 2000 Inc, pg 916
VER, pg 926
Video Resources Inc, pg 928
VMI Inc, pg 932
Voice & Video Rentals, pg 932
Warner Bros Production Sound & Video Services, pg 934
Westcoast Video Productions Inc, pg 936

COLORADO

Audio Consultant Services Inc, pg 693
Daylight Productions & Rentals, pg 739
Multimedia Audio Visual Inc, pg 833
Spectrum Audio Visual Services, pg 897

CONNECTICUT

A/V Davey, pg 697
Connecticut Audio & Theatrical Supply, pg 731
Videofilm Systems Inc, pg 929

DELAWARE

Actors Attic, pg 675
Showorks Audio Visual Inc, pg 887
Side Door Studio Inc, pg 887

FLORIDA

All Comm Rentals Inc (ALLCOMM), pg 680
AVI-SPL, pg 698
Budget Video Rentals, pg 712
Harmon's Audio-Visual Services, pg 776
Industrial Strength Inc, pg 787
Jordan Klein Film & Video (JKFV), pg 795
ONstage, pg 846
PRI Productions, pg 862
Sight & Sound Productions, pg 887
TAI Audio, pg 906

Universal Studios Florida® Production Group, pg 922
Zebedee Productions, pg 945

GEORGIA

Lighting & Production Equipment Inc, pg 807
MAGNUM Companies Ltd, pg 815
Stage Front Presentation Systems, pg 899
Staging Directions Inc, pg 899

HAWAII

Hawaii Sound & Vision, pg 777

ILLINOIS

Allen Visual Systems Inc, pg 680
AV Chicago Inc, pg 696
Beatty TeleVisual Productions, pg 703
Meetinghouse Event Design & Production, pg 823
On Site Video, pg 846
OSA International Inc, pg 848
PSAV® Presentation Services (Hotel Services Division), pg 866
RC Communications, pg 870
Resolution Productions Group, pg 874
Staging Resources Inc, pg 899
Woodside Avenue Music Productions Inc, pg 941

INDIANA

Advanced Media Integration, pg 677
Heart Breaker Entertainment LLC, pg 778

IOWA

Central Lighting & Equipment Inc (CLE), pg 719

KENTUCKY

Audio Visual Techniques Inc, pg 695

LOUISIANA

Clark Services Audio Visual & Exhibit Inc, pg 725
Pace Systems, pg 849

MAINE

Headlight Audio Visual Inc, pg 777

MARYLAND

Advance Audiovisual Presentation Ltd, pg 677
Cardinal Sound & Video, pg 717
CPR MultiMedia Solutions, pg 732
dbF a Media Company, pg 739
Event Tech, pg 756
Maryland Sound International Holding Co LLC, pg 819

MASSACHUSETTS

AVFX Inc, pg 698
Capron Lighting & Sound Co Inc, pg 716
Terry Hanley Audio Systems Inc, pg 775
massAV, pg 819
Preston Productions Inc, pg 861

MICHIGAN

City Events Group, pg 725
K&R All Media Productions LLC, pg 796

AUDIO

Speaker Rentals
(continued)

MICHIGAN (continued)
K&R's Recording Studios Inc, pg 796
On Stage Visuals, pg 846
TEL Systems LLC, pg 909

MINNESOTA
Alpha Video & Audio Inc, pg 682

MISSISSIPPI
Bowie Audio Visual Enterprises Inc, pg 709

MISSOURI
Communitronics Corp, pg 729
Production Support Services Inc, pg 864
Show-Me Audio-Visual, pg 887
Wise Audio Video, pg 940

MONTANA
Jereco Studios Inc, pg 793

NEBRASKA
Dog & Pony Productions Inc, pg 744

NEVADA
GES Audio Visual, pg 770

NEW HAMPSHIRE
APS Lighting-Sound-AV, pg 688

NEW JERSEY
Audio Visual Associates, pg 694
Audio Visual Dynamics®, pg 694
Earl Girls Inc, pg 749
International Audio Visual Inc, pg 790
Moe AV LLC, pg 828
The Music Place, pg 834
Nelson Enterprises Theatrical Supply Co, pg 838
Panavid, pg 850
PLS Staging, pg 858
Soundtracks Production Services LLC, pg 895
Starlite, pg 900
Wired 4 Sound Inc, pg 940

NEW MEXICO
Production Outfitters, pg 864
Quickbeam Systems Inc (QSI), pg 868

NEW YORK
Albany Theatre Supply Co Inc, pg 679
All Mobile Video Inc, pg 680
American Video Inc, pg 684
Aura Sonic Ltd (ASL), pg 695
AV Workshop, pg 697
Colortone Audio Visual, pg 728
CP Communications, pg 732
Design Audio Visual Inc, pg 741
Digital Arts NY, pg 742
Gotham Sound & Communications Inc, pg 773
Hello World Communications, pg 778

KVL Audio Visual Services Inc, pg 802
Long Island Video Enterprises Live Inc, pg 811
Posthorn Recordings, pg 859
See Factor Industry Inc, pg 883
Studio Instrument Rentals (SIR), pg 902
Theatrical Services & Supplies Inc, pg 912
Visual Word Systems Inc, pg 932
WorldStage, pg 941

NORTH CAROLINA
All Pro Media Inc, pg 680
AV Connections Inc, pg 697
AV Metro Inc, pg 697
Special Event Services, pg 896

NORTH DAKOTA
Media Productions, pg 822

OHIO
Hughie's Event Production Services, pg 782
ITA Audio Visual Solutions, pg 791
Lyon Video Inc, pg 813
Mills James Productions, pg 828
Production Solutions Inc, pg 864
R&B Communications Inc, pg 870

OKLAHOMA
PDC Productions, pg 852

OREGON
Rose City Sound, pg 877

PENNSYLVANIA
Advanced AV LLC, pg 677
Audio Visions Inc, pg 694
Audio Visual Communications Inc, pg 694
FirstGeneration Audio/Visual Services, pg 761
FMP Media Solutions Inc, pg 763
Grise Audio Visual Center Inc, pg 774
Innovision Media Group, pg 788
New York Camera & Video, pg 840
Right Coast Recording Inc, pg 875
Sound by Fitch, pg 893
Upstage Video, pg 923
Viewpoint Production Services Inc, pg 930
Visual Sound Inc, pg 931

SOUTH CAROLINA
DaviSound, pg 739
Impact Technology Group LLC, pg 786
Sound & Images Inc, pg 893

TENNESSEE
Allstar Audio Systems Inc, pg 681
Belew Enterprises, pg 703
Brantley Sound Associates Inc, pg 709
Love Shack Recording Studios, pg 811
Mr Mark's Used Musical, Stereo & Studio Equipment Store, pg 828
Technical Support Systems LLC, pg 908
Trew Audio Inc, pg 917

TEXAS
Alford Media Services, pg 680
Big House Sound Inc, pg 705

Bright Star Productions Inc, pg 710
Crossroads Audio Inc, pg 735
Lubbock Audio Visual Inc, pg 812
Music Lab Inc, pg 834
Onstage Systems, pg 846
Power Factory Productions, pg 860
Stage Directions, pg 898
Tropikal Productions, pg 918

UTAH
Performance Audio LLC, pg 854

VERMONT
Dark Star Lighting & Production, pg 737

VIRGINIA
Advance Concepts Inc, pg 677
American AV, pg 682
Boitnott Visual Communications Corp (BVC), pg 708
Lee Hartman & Sons Inc, pg 805
StageSound, pg 899

WASHINGTON
D A Sound, pg 737
Northern Lights & Pro Audio, pg 842
PNTA, pg 858

WISCONSIN
Camera Corner Connecting Point, pg 715
Event Essentials, pg 756
Full Compass Systems, pg 767

WYOMING
Bridger Productions Inc, pg 710

PUERTO RICO
Stage Crew Audiovisual Inc, pg 898

ALBERTA
Allstar Show Industries Inc, pg 681
Evolution AV, pg 757
L R Light & Sound, pg 802
McBain Camera Ltd, pg 820
Unique Communications Ltd, pg 921

BRITISH COLUMBIA
Clark's Audio Visual Services Ltd, pg 725
Commercial Electronics Ltd, pg 728
DL Sound & Lighting Productions Ltd, pg 744
Inspired Image Picture Co (IIPC), pg 788
MicrophoneRentals.com, pg 826

MANITOBA
Inland Audio Visual Ltd, pg 788

ONTARIO
HD Source, pg 777
RB Productions, pg 870
Westbury National Show Systems Ltd, pg 936
ZTV Broadcast Services Inc, pg 945

QUEBEC
Audio Visual Dynamics, pg 694
Panavideo Inc, pg 850

Speaker Repairs

ARIZONA
Metropolitan Audio-Visual Inc, pg 824

CALIFORNIA
Ametron Audio/Video, pg 684
Audio Images Corp, pg 693
Digitron Electronics, pg 743
Gluskin's Custom Audio Video, pg 771
IAMP Professional Audio, pg 783
Instructional Materials & Equipment Distributors (I-Med), pg 789
McAlister Electronics, pg 820
Parasound Products Inc, pg 851
QSC Audio Products LLC, pg 867
Radian Audio Engineering Inc, pg 869
Sonance, pg 892
Sound Service Co, pg 894
SSL Industries Inc, pg 898
Third Ear Sound Co, pg 912
TOA Electronics Inc, pg 915
Towards 2000 Inc, pg 916
Yamaha Electronics Corp, pg 943

CONNECTICUT
HB Communications Inc, pg 777
Sennheiser Electronic Corp, pg 884
Soundsphere, pg 895

DELAWARE
Actors Attic, pg 675

FLORIDA
AMP Services Inc, pg 684
Hi-Tech Enterprises Inc, pg 779
TAI Audio, pg 906

GEORGIA
Lighting & Production Equipment Inc, pg 807
Stage Front Presentation Systems, pg 899

ILLINOIS
Allen Visual Systems Inc, pg 680
Beatty TeleVisual Productions, pg 703
C V Lloyde, pg 810
On Site Video, pg 846

INDIANA
SHP Electronics, pg 887
Sweetwater Sound Inc, pg 905

KENTUCKY
Axxis Leasing Inc, pg 700
Barney Miller's Inc, pg 827
NOR-COM Inc, pg 841

MARYLAND
Cardinal Sound & Video, pg 717

MASSACHUSETTS
Capron Lighting & Sound Co Inc, pg 716
Professional Audio Design Inc, pg 865

MICHIGAN
City Events Group, pg 725
K&R's Recording Studios Inc, pg 796

On Stage Visuals, pg 846
TEL Systems LLC, pg 909

MISSOURI

Communitronics Corp, pg 729

NEW JERSEY

Audio Visual Associates, pg 694
Earl Girls Inc, pg 749
The Music Place, pg 834
Nelson Enterprises Theatrical
   Supply Co, pg 838
Starlite, pg 900

NEW MEXICO

Quickbeam Systems Inc (QSI),
   pg 868

NEW YORK

Hot House Professional Audio,
   pg 782
Toys From The Attic, pg 916

OHIO

Copp Integrated Systems, pg 731
ITA Audio Visual Solutions, pg 791

OREGON

All Service Musical Electronics
   Repair, pg 680

PENNSYLVANIA

Right Coast Recording Inc, pg 875
Tri-State Loudspeaker, pg 918

SOUTH CAROLINA

DaviSound, pg 739

TENNESSEE

Belew Enterprises, pg 703
Technical Support Systems LLC,
   pg 908

TEXAS

Audio Visual Technologies Group
   (AVTG), pg 695
Music Lab Inc, pg 834
Quality Audio Visual Service Inc,
   pg 867

VIRGINIA

Boitnott Visual Communications
   Corp (BVC), pg 708
Intellidyne LLC, pg 789

WASHINGTON

D A Sound, pg 737
Northern Lights & Pro Audio,
   pg 842
PNTA, pg 858

WEST VIRGINIA

United Sound & Electronics, pg 921

WISCONSIN

Full Compass Systems, pg 767
Madisound Speaker Components
   Inc, pg 814

ALBERTA

Allstar Show Industries Inc, pg 681
Infosat Communications Inc, pg 787
Unique Communications Ltd,
   pg 921

MANITOBA

Inland Audio Visual Ltd, pg 788

ONTARIO

HD Source, pg 777
Westbury National Show Systems
   Ltd, pg 936

QUEBEC

Panavideo Inc, pg 850
SC Media Canada, pg 881

Spiritual, *see* Music Libraries—Spiritual

Surround Sound Device Distributors

ARIZONA

EAR Professional Audio/Video,
   pg 749
Troxell-CDI, pg 918

CALIFORNIA

Ametron Audio/Video, pg 684
Associated Sound, pg 691
Audio Images Corp, pg 693
Be Media, pg 702
Cinema Equipment Sales of
   California Inc, pg 724
MediaPOINTE, pg 823
Nortek Security & Control LLC,
   pg 842
Parasound Products Inc, pg 851
Sound Service Co, pg 894
Southern California Sound Image
   Inc, pg 895
SuperVision, pg 904
Towards 2000 Inc, pg 916
Universal Audio Inc, pg 922

COLORADO

Audio Consultant Services Inc,
   pg 693

DELAWARE

Actors Attic, pg 675

FLORIDA

Altel Systems Group Inc, pg 682
Broadcasters General Store Inc,
   pg 711
Digital Video Systems, pg 742
ONstage, pg 846
Recording Media & Equipment Inc
   (RM&E), pg 872
Stereo Sales Inc, pg 900
TAI Audio, pg 906
Technomedia Solutions, pg 909

GEORGIA

Lighting & Production Equipment
   Inc, pg 807
Stage Front Presentation Systems,
   pg 899

HAWAII

The Audio Visual Co (AVCO),
   pg 694

ILLINOIS

Allen Visual Systems Inc, pg 680
Quintessence Audio Ltd, pg 868

INDIANA

Sensory Technologies LLC, pg 884
SHP Electronics, pg 887
Sweetwater Sound Inc, pg 905

KENTUCKY

Axxis Leasing Inc, pg 700
Barney Miller's Inc, pg 827
NOR-COM Inc, pg 841

MAINE

Independent Audio Inc, pg 786

MARYLAND

Bradley Broadcast & Pro Audio,
   pg 709
Kipp Visual Systems Inc, pg 799

MICHIGAN

Olson Anderson Co, pg 685
On Stage Visuals, pg 846
TEL Systems LLC, pg 909

NEW JERSEY

AlltecPro, pg 681
Diversified, pg 744
Onkyo USA Corp, pg 846
Starlite, pg 900
SYMCO Inc, pg 905
Wired 4 Sound Inc, pg 940
Yorktel, pg 944

NEW YORK

Audio-Video Corp, pg 694
Aura Sonic Ltd (ASL), pg 695
beyerdynamic Inc, pg 704
Design Audio Visual Inc, pg 741
General Audio-Visual Inc (GAVI),
   pg 769
Group One Ltd, pg 774
Posthorn Recordings, pg 859
Presentation Products Inc, pg 861
RNJ Electronics, pg 875
Toys From The Attic, pg 916

OHIO

ITA Audio Visual Solutions, pg 791
Parts Express, pg 851
The Telos Alliance, pg 910

OREGON

Lightspeed Technologies Inc,
   pg 808

PENNSYLVANIA

Advanced AV LLC, pg 677
J E Foss Co, pg 764

RHODE ISLAND

Shanix Inc, pg 885

TENNESSEE

Advanced Sound, pg 677
Allstar Audio Systems Inc, pg 681
Lowrance Sound Co Inc, pg 812
Technical Support Systems LLC,
   pg 908
Zion Music Group, pg 945

TEXAS

Audio Visual Technologies Group
   (AVTG), pg 695
Crossroads Audio Inc, pg 735
Data Projections Inc, pg 738

Lubbock Audio Visual Inc, pg 812
Tarpley Media Systems, pg 907

UTAH

Performance Audio LLC, pg 854

VIRGINIA

Avitecture Inc, pg 699
Intellidyne LLC, pg 789
Lee Hartman & Sons Inc, pg 805
The Whitlock Group, pg 937

WASHINGTON

Northern Lights & Pro Audio,
   pg 842

WISCONSIN

Audio Visual of Milwaukee Inc,
   pg 694
Full Compass Systems, pg 767

PUERTO RICO

Bonnin Electronics Inc, pg 708

ALBERTA

Infosat Communications Inc, pg 787

BRITISH COLUMBIA

Commercial Electronics Ltd, pg 728

MANITOBA

Advance Pro, pg 677
Inland Audio Visual Ltd, pg 788

ONTARIO

Cinema Stage Inc, pg 724
Westbury National Show Systems
   Ltd, pg 936

Surround Sound Device Manufacturers

ARIZONA

MTX Audio, pg 833
OmniMount Systems, pg 845

CALIFORNIA

AB Systems Amplifiers, pg 672
Dorrough Electronics Inc, pg 746
Lynx Studio Technology Inc,
   pg 813
Martinsound Inc, pg 818
Nortek Security & Control LLC,
   pg 842
Orevox USA Corp, pg 847
OWI Inc, pg 849
Parasound Products Inc, pg 851
TeachLogic Inc, pg 908
Wohler Technologies Inc, pg 940

ILLINOIS

AmpliVox Portable Sound Systems,
   pg 684
Bag End Loudspeakers, pg 700

MINNESOTA

Digital Audio Labs, pg 742

MISSISSIPPI

Sherwood America Inc, pg 886

AUDIO

Surround Sound Device Manufacturers (continued)

NEW JERSEY
Crestron Electronics Inc, pg 734
Onkyo USA Corp, pg 846

NEW YORK
beyerdynamic Inc, pg 704
Posthorn Recordings, pg 859

OHIO
Omnia Audio, pg 845
The Telos Alliance, pg 910

PENNSYLVANIA
Community Professional Loudspeakers, pg 729

RHODE ISLAND
Rane, pg 870

TENNESSEE
Advanced Sound, pg 677
Harrison Consoles, pg 776

WASHINGTON
AudioControl® Inc, pg 695

BRITISH COLUMBIA
B&K AV Ltd, pg 701
Richmond Sound Design Ltd, pg 875

ONTARIO
Music Group Commercial Ltd, pg 834
Ward-Beck Systems Ltd, pg 933

Surround Sound Device Rentals

ARIZONA
Merestone, pg 823
Video West Inc, pg 929

CALIFORNIA
Alliant Event Services, pg 681
Ametron Audio/Video, pg 684
Associated Sound, pg 691
Audio Rents, pg 693
AV Guys, pg 697
Hollywood Sound Systems, pg 781
Lynch Communications, pg 813
McCune Audio-Video-Lighting, pg 821
Muse Presentation Technologies, pg 834
Sound Service Co, pg 894
Total Creative, pg 916
Towards 2000 Inc, pg 916
VER, pg 926

COLORADO
Audio Consultant Services Inc, pg 693

FLORIDA
ONstage, pg 846
Phat Planet Recording Studios, pg 855

GEORGIA
Lighting & Production Equipment Inc, pg 807
Stage Front Presentation Systems, pg 899

ILLINOIS
Allen Visual Systems Inc, pg 680
OSA International Inc, pg 848
RC Communications, pg 870

KENTUCKY
Audio Visual Techniques Inc, pg 695

MARYLAND
CPR MultiMedia Solutions, pg 732
Event Tech, pg 756

MASSACHUSETTS
AVFX Inc, pg 698
massAV, pg 819
Preston Productions Inc, pg 861

MICHIGAN
K&R All Media Productions LLC, pg 796
On Stage Visuals, pg 846

MISSOURI
Show-Me Audio-Visual, pg 887

MONTANA
Jereco Studios Inc, pg 793

NEW JERSEY
PLS Staging, pg 858
Starlite, pg 900
Wired 4 Sound Inc, pg 940

NEW YORK
Aura Sonic Ltd (ASL), pg 695
CP Communications, pg 732
Posthorn Recordings, pg 859

OKLAHOMA
PDC Productions, pg 852

PENNSYLVANIA
Advanced AV LLC, pg 677

TENNESSEE
Allstar Audio Systems Inc, pg 681
Love Shack Recording Studios, pg 811
Technical Support Systems LLC, pg 908

TEXAS
Alford Media Services, pg 680

UTAH
Performance Audio LLC, pg 854

VIRGINIA
Lee Hartman & Sons Inc, pg 805

WASHINGTON
Northern Lights & Pro Audio, pg 842

MANITOBA
Inland Audio Visual Ltd, pg 788

Surround Sound Device Repairs

CALIFORNIA
AB Systems Amplifiers, pg 672
Ametron Audio/Video, pg 684
Audio Images Corp, pg 693
McAlister Electronics, pg 820
Sound Service Co, pg 894
Towards 2000 Inc, pg 916

CONNECTICUT
HB Communications Inc, pg 777

FLORIDA
JT Communications, pg 795
Phat Planet Recording Studios, pg 855
Stereo Sales Inc, pg 900
TAI Audio, pg 906

GEORGIA
Lighting & Production Equipment Inc, pg 807
Stage Front Presentation Systems, pg 899

ILLINOIS
Allen Visual Systems Inc, pg 680

INDIANA
Sweetwater Sound Inc, pg 905

KENTUCKY
Axxis Leasing Inc, pg 700
Barney Miller's Inc, pg 827
NOR-COM Inc, pg 841

MICHIGAN
K&R's Recording Studios Inc, pg 796
TEL Systems LLC, pg 909

NEW JERSEY
Starlite, pg 900

NEW YORK
Toys From The Attic, pg 916

OREGON
All Service Musical Electronics Repair, pg 680

TENNESSEE
Technical Support Systems LLC, pg 908

WASHINGTON
Northern Lights & Pro Audio, pg 842

WISCONSIN
Full Compass Systems, pg 767

ALBERTA
Infosat Communications Inc, pg 787

MANITOBA
Inland Audio Visual Ltd, pg 788

ONTARIO
Westbury National Show Systems Ltd, pg 936

Switcher & Matrix— Analog & Digital Distributors

ALABAMA
PESA, pg 855

ARIZONA
EAR Professional Audio/Video, pg 749
Troxell-CDI, pg 918

ARKANSAS
White Diamond Productions LLC, pg 937

CALIFORNIA
Ametron Audio/Video, pg 684
Associated Sound, pg 691
ATV Video Center Inc, pg 692
Audio Images Corp, pg 693
Be Media, pg 702
Cibola Systems, pg 723
Empire Pro, pg 753
JD Audio Visual Inc, pg 793
MediaPOINTE, pg 823
Southern California Sound Image Inc, pg 895
Stanislaus AV Inc, pg 899
TOA Electronics Inc, pg 915
Towards 2000 Inc, pg 916
Videobotics, pg 929
VMI Inc, pg 932
VTP Inc, pg 933
Zack Electronics Inc, pg 945

COLORADO
Audio Consultant Services Inc, pg 693

CONNECTICUT
HB Communications Inc, pg 777

DELAWARE
Actors Attic, pg 675

FLORIDA
Access Media Group, pg 673
Altel Systems Group Inc, pg 682
Digital Video Systems, pg 742
Harris Corp, pg 776
Hi-Tech Enterprises Inc, pg 779
Midtown Video Inc, pg 827
Recording Media & Equipment Inc (RM&E), pg 872
Stereo Sales Inc, pg 900
Technomedia Solutions, pg 909

GEORGIA
Stage Front Presentation Systems, pg 899

HAWAII
The Audio Visual Co (AVCO), pg 694

ILLINOIS
Allen Visual Systems Inc, pg 680
Joseph Electronics, pg 795
Quintessence Audio Ltd, pg 868

INDIANA

Sensory Technologies LLC, pg 884
SHP Electronics, pg 887

KENTUCKY

Audio Visual Techniques Inc,
   pg 695
Axxis Leasing Inc, pg 700
NOR-COM Inc, pg 841

LOUISIANA

Techkno Integration & Design
   Services LLC, pg 908

MAINE

Headlight Audio Visual Inc, pg 777
Independent Audio Inc, pg 786

MARYLAND

Bradley Broadcast & Pro Audio,
   pg 709
Cardinal Sound & Video, pg 717
Human Circuit, pg 782
Kipp Visual Systems Inc, pg 799

MASSACHUSETTS

Professional Audio Design Inc,
   pg 865

MICHIGAN

On Stage Visuals, pg 846
TEL Systems LLC, pg 909

MINNESOTA

Alpha Video & Audio Inc, pg 682

MISSISSIPPI

Bowie Audio Visual Enterprises Inc,
   pg 709

NEW JERSEY

Alltec Stores, a Vcom IMC
   Company, pg 681
AlltecPro, pg 681
Audio Visual Associates, pg 694
AV Bluebook, pg 696
Diversified, pg 744
PatchAmp, pg 852
Starlite, pg 900
SYMCO Inc, pg 905
Total Video Products Inc, pg 916
Wired 4 Sound Inc, pg 940
Yorktel, pg 944

NEW YORK

Audio-Video Corp, pg 694
Design Audio Visual Inc, pg 741
Markertek Video Supply, pg 817
Presentation Products Inc, pg 861
Toys From The Attic, pg 916
Visual Word Systems Inc, pg 932

OHIO

ITA Audio Visual Solutions, pg 791
The Telos Alliance, pg 910
Tri-State Audio Visual Co, pg 918

OKLAHOMA

Ford AV, pg 763

PENNSYLVANIA

Advanced AV LLC, pg 677
Innovision Media Group, pg 788
The Lerro Corp, pg 806
Vistacom Inc, pg 931

RHODE ISLAND

Shanix Inc, pg 885

TENNESSEE

Allstar Audio Systems Inc, pg 681
Lowrance Sound Co Inc, pg 812
Spectrum Sound Inc, pg 897
Technical Support Systems LLC,
   pg 908

TEXAS

Audio Visual Technologies Group
   (AVTG), pg 695
Data Projections Inc, pg 738
Digital Display Solutions Inc,
   pg 742
Lubbock Audio Visual Inc, pg 812
Pro Video & Film Equipment Co
   Inc, pg 863
Southwest Sound Solutions, pg 896
Stage Directions, pg 898
Sundance Systems, Fibox Products
   Division, pg 904
Tarpley Media Systems, pg 907

UTAH

Performance Audio LLC, pg 854

VIRGINIA

Avitecture Inc, pg 699
Intellidyne LLC, pg 789
Lee Hartman & Sons Inc, pg 805

WASHINGTON

CCI Solutions, pg 718
Telect Inc, pg 910

WISCONSIN

Audio Visual of Milwaukee Inc,
   pg 694
Full Compass Systems, pg 767
Safe Harbor Computers, pg 879

PUERTO RICO

Bonnin Electronics Inc, pg 708

ALBERTA

Infosat Communications Inc, pg 787

BRITISH COLUMBIA

Commercial Electronics Ltd, pg 728
Dav Tronics Ltd, pg 738

MANITOBA

Advance Pro, pg 677
Inland Audio Visual Ltd, pg 788

ONTARIO

Cinema Stage Inc, pg 724
Westbury National Show Systems
   Ltd, pg 936

Switcher & Matrix— Analog & Digital Manufacturers

ALABAMA

PESA, pg 855

ARIZONA

Radio Design Labs (RDL), pg 869

CALIFORNIA

ALTINEX Inc, pg 682
Digital Music Corp, pg 742
Extron Electronics, pg 758
Gefen, pg 769
Henry Engineering, pg 779
Opamp Labs Inc, pg 846
Opticomm-EMCORE, pg 847
Sierra Automated Systems, pg 887
Sprocket Digital, pg 898
TOA Electronics Inc, pg 915

COLORADO

Liberty AV Solutions, pg 807

CONNECTICUT

Sound Control Technologies Inc,
   pg 893
Titus Technological Laboratories
   (TTL), pg 914

FLORIDA

Compuvideo Sales USA Ltd,
   pg 729
Tel-Test, pg 909
Z-Systems Audio Engineering,
   pg 944

GEORGIA

Analog Way Inc, pg 685

INDIANA

JFW Industries Inc, pg 794

KANSAS

SoundTube Entertainment Inc,
   pg 895

MISSOURI

Link Electronics Inc, pg 809

NEW JERSEY

Crestron Electronics Inc, pg 734
FSR Inc, pg 766
Kramer Electronics USA Inc,
   pg 801
Sony Pro Audio, pg 893

NEW MEXICO

Burst Electronics Inc, pg 713

NEW YORK

Benchmark Media Systems Inc,
   pg 703
Broadcast Devices Inc, pg 710
Key Digital Systems, pg 798
Laird Digital Cinema, pg 803
MultiDyne Video & Fiber Optics
   Systems, pg 833
Protech Audio Corp, pg 866
Sescom Inc, pg 884

NORTH CAROLINA

Audioarts Engineering, pg 695
Wheatstone Corp, pg 937

OHIO

Omnia Audio, pg 845
The Telos Alliance, pg 910
TV One Multimedia Solutions,
   pg 919

OREGON

BIAMP Systems, pg 705

PENNSYLVANIA

Aviom Inc, pg 699

TEXAS

Logitek Electronic Systems Inc,
   pg 811
Sundance Systems, Fibox Products
   Division, pg 904

UTAH

Ivie Technologies Inc, pg 792
Utah Scientific Inc, pg 924

WASHINGTON

AudioControl® Inc, pg 695
Conex Electro Systems Inc, pg 730
Telect Inc, pg 910

BRITISH COLUMBIA

Dav Tronics Ltd, pg 738
Richmond Sound Design Ltd,
   pg 875

Switcher & Matrix— Analog & Digital Rentals

ALABAMA

Audio-Video Resources Inc, pg 694

ARIZONA

AV Concepts Inc, pg 696
Merestone, pg 823
Video West Inc, pg 929

ARKANSAS

White Diamond Productions LLC,
   pg 937

CALIFORNIA

AGF Media Services, pg 678
Ametron Audio/Video, pg 684
Associated Sound, pg 691
ATV Video Center Inc, pg 692
Audio Rents, pg 693
Express Media Inc, pg 757
Golden Gate Studios, pg 772
JD Audio Visual Inc, pg 793
Muse Presentation Technologies,
   pg 834
PSAV® Presentation Services,
   pg 866
VER, pg 926
Voice & Video Rentals, pg 932

COLORADO

Audio Consultant Services Inc,
   pg 693

CONNECTICUT

Videofilm Systems Inc, pg 929

FLORIDA

Access Media Group, pg 673
Sight & Sound Productions, pg 887
Universal Studios Florida®
   Production Group, pg 922

GEORGIA

Stage Front Presentation Systems,
   pg 899

AUDIO

Switcher & Matrix—Analog & Digital Rentals (continued)

ILLINOIS
RC Communications, pg 870
Resolution Productions Group, pg 874

KENTUCKY
Audio Visual Techniques Inc, pg 695

MAINE
Headlight Audio Visual Inc, pg 777

MARYLAND
CPR MultiMedia Solutions, pg 732
Event Tech, pg 756
Kramer Communications Video Production, pg 801

MASSACHUSETTS
Preston Productions Inc, pg 861

MICHIGAN
K&R All Media Productions LLC, pg 796
On Stage Visuals, pg 846

MISSISSIPPI
Bowie Audio Visual Enterprises Inc, pg 709

MISSOURI
Show-Me Audio-Visual, pg 887

NEW JERSEY
Audio Visual Associates, pg 694
MiB MediaWorks, pg 825
Starlite, pg 900
Wired 4 Sound Inc, pg 940

NEW YORK
CP Communications, pg 732
Design Audio Visual Inc, pg 741
Visual Word Systems Inc, pg 932

NORTH CAROLINA
Take One Productions Ltd, pg 906

PENNSYLVANIA
Innovision Media Group, pg 788

TENNESSEE
Allstar Audio Systems Inc, pg 681
Technical Support Systems LLC, pg 908

TEXAS
Alford Media Services, pg 680
Stage Directions, pg 898

VIRGINIA
Lee Hartman & Sons Inc, pg 805

BRITISH COLUMBIA
DL Sound & Lighting Productions Ltd, pg 744

MANITOBA
Inland Audio Visual Ltd, pg 788

Switcher & Matrix—Analog & Digital Repairs

CALIFORNIA
Ametron Audio/Video, pg 684
TOA Electronics Inc, pg 915

FLORIDA
Hi-Tech Enterprises Inc, pg 779

GEORGIA
Analog Way Inc, pg 685
Stage Front Presentation Systems, pg 899

KENTUCKY
NOR-COM Inc, pg 841

MASSACHUSETTS
Professional Audio Design Inc, pg 865

MICHIGAN
TEL Systems LLC, pg 909

NEW JERSEY
Audio Visual Associates, pg 694
Starlite, pg 900

NEW YORK
Toys From The Attic, pg 916

OHIO
Tri-State Audio Visual Co, pg 918

OREGON
All Service Musical Electronics Repair, pg 680

TENNESSEE
Technical Support Systems LLC, pg 908

ALBERTA
Infosat Communications Inc, pg 787

MANITOBA
Inland Audio Visual Ltd, pg 788

ONTARIO
Westbury National Show Systems Ltd, pg 936

Switcher & Matrix—Mechanical & Electronic Distributors

ARIZONA
EAR Professional Audio/Video, pg 749
Troxell-CDI, pg 918

CALIFORNIA
Ametron Audio/Video, pg 684
Audio Images Corp, pg 693
Be Media, pg 702

Cibola Systems, pg 723
Media Control Systems LLC, pg 821
MediaPOINTE, pg 823
Southern California Sound Image Inc, pg 895
Stanislaus AV Inc, pg 899
Towards 2000 Inc, pg 916
Videobotics, pg 929
VMI Inc, pg 932

CONNECTICUT
HB Communications Inc, pg 777

DELAWARE
Actors Attic, pg 675

FLORIDA
Access Media Group, pg 673
Altel Systems Group Inc, pg 682
Harris Corp, pg 776
Hi-Tech Enterprises Inc, pg 779
Midtown Video Inc, pg 827
Recording Media & Equipment Inc (RM&E), pg 872
Stereo Sales Inc, pg 900
Technomedia Solutions, pg 909

GEORGIA
Stage Front Presentation Systems, pg 899

HAWAII
The Audio Visual Co (AVCO), pg 694

ILLINOIS
Allen Visual Systems Inc, pg 680
Joseph Electronics, pg 795
Quintessence Audio Ltd, pg 868

INDIANA
Sensory Technologies LLC, pg 884
SHP Electronics, pg 887

KENTUCKY
Audio Visual Techniques Inc, pg 695
Axxis Leasing Inc, pg 700
NOR-COM Inc, pg 841

LOUISIANA
Techkno Integration & Design Services LLC, pg 908

MAINE
Headlight Audio Visual Inc, pg 777

MARYLAND
Bradley Broadcast & Pro Audio, pg 709
Kipp Visual Systems Inc, pg 799

MICHIGAN
On Stage Visuals, pg 846
TEL Systems LLC, pg 909

NEW HAMPSHIRE
Technet® Systems Group, pg 908

NEW JERSEY
AlltecPro, pg 681
Audio Visual Associates, pg 694
Diversified, pg 744
PatchAmp, pg 852

Starlite, pg 900
SYMCO Inc, pg 905
Total Video Products Inc, pg 916
Wired 4 Sound Inc, pg 940
Yorktel, pg 944

NEW YORK
Audio-Video Corp, pg 694
Design Audio Visual Inc, pg 741
Markertek Video Supply, pg 817
Presentation Products Inc, pg 861
TecNec Distributing, pg 909
Toys From The Attic, pg 916

OHIO
Tri-State Audio Visual Co, pg 918

PENNSYLVANIA
Advanced AV LLC, pg 677
Vistacom Inc, pg 931

TENNESSEE
Allstar Audio Systems Inc, pg 681
Lowrance Sound Co Inc, pg 812
Technical Support Systems LLC, pg 908

TEXAS
Data Projections Inc, pg 738
Digital Display Solutions Inc, pg 742
Lubbock Audio Visual Inc, pg 812
Pro Video & Film Equipment Co Inc, pg 863
Tarpley Media Systems, pg 907

UTAH
Performance Audio LLC, pg 854

VIRGINIA
Avitecture Inc, pg 699
Lee Hartman & Sons Inc, pg 805

WASHINGTON
Telect Inc, pg 910

WISCONSIN
Audio Visual of Milwaukee Inc, pg 694
Full Compass Systems, pg 767
Safe Harbor Computers, pg 879

PUERTO RICO
Bonnin Electronics Inc, pg 708

ALBERTA
Infosat Communications Inc, pg 787

BRITISH COLUMBIA
Commercial Electronics Ltd, pg 728
Dav Tronics Ltd, pg 738

MANITOBA
Advance Pro, pg 677
Inland Audio Visual Ltd, pg 788

ONTARIO
Cinema Stage Inc, pg 724

Switcher & Matrix— Mechanical & Electronic Manufacturers

CALIFORNIA

ALTINEX Inc, pg 682
Henry Engineering, pg 779
Opticomm-EMCORE, pg 847
Wohler Technologies Inc, pg 940

FLORIDA

Compuvideo Sales USA Ltd, pg 729
Tel-Test, pg 909

GEORGIA

Analog Way Inc, pg 685

ILLINOIS

Esoteric Sound, pg 755

INDIANA

JFW Industries Inc, pg 794

NEW JERSEY

FSR Inc, pg 766
Kramer Electronics USA Inc, pg 801

NEW YORK

MultiDyne Video & Fiber Optics Systems, pg 833
Protech Audio Corp, pg 866
Sescom Inc, pg 884
TecNec Distributing, pg 909

OREGON

BIAMP Systems, pg 705

TEXAS

Logitek Electronic Systems Inc, pg 811

UTAH

ClearOne Inc, pg 726

WASHINGTON

Conex Electro Systems Inc, pg 730
Telect Inc, pg 910

BRITISH COLUMBIA

Dav Tronics Ltd, pg 738

Switcher & Matrix— Mechanical & Electronic Rentals

ARIZONA

Merestone, pg 823

CALIFORNIA

Ametron Audio/Video, pg 684
Golden Gate Studios, pg 772
VER, pg 926

FLORIDA

Access Media Group, pg 673
Universal Studios Florida® Production Group, pg 922

GEORGIA

Stage Front Presentation Systems, pg 899

ILLINOIS

RC Communications, pg 870

KENTUCKY

Audio Visual Techniques Inc, pg 695

MARYLAND

CPR MultiMedia Solutions, pg 732
Event Tech, pg 756

MASSACHUSETTS

Preston Productions Inc, pg 861

MICHIGAN

K&R All Media Productions LLC, pg 796
On Stage Visuals, pg 846

MISSOURI

Show-Me Audio-Visual, pg 887

NEW JERSEY

Audio Visual Associates, pg 694
Starlite, pg 900
Wired 4 Sound Inc, pg 940

NEW YORK

CP Communications, pg 732
Design Audio Visual Inc, pg 741

NORTH CAROLINA

Take One Productions Ltd, pg 906

TENNESSEE

Allstar Audio Systems Inc, pg 681
Technical Support Systems LLC, pg 908

VIRGINIA

Lee Hartman & Sons Inc, pg 805

BRITISH COLUMBIA

DL Sound & Lighting Productions Ltd, pg 744

MANITOBA

Inland Audio Visual Ltd, pg 788

Switcher & Matrix— Mechanical & Electronic Repairs

CALIFORNIA

Ametron Audio/Video, pg 684

FLORIDA

Hi-Tech Enterprises Inc, pg 779

GEORGIA

Analog Way Inc, pg 685
Stage Front Presentation Systems, pg 899

ILLINOIS

Midwest Digital Corp, pg 827

GEORGIA

Stage Front Presentation Systems, pg 899

ILLINOIS

RC Communications, pg 870

KENTUCKY

Audio Visual Techniques Inc, pg 695

MARYLAND

CPR MultiMedia Solutions, pg 732
Event Tech, pg 756

MASSACHUSETTS

Preston Productions Inc, pg 861

MICHIGAN

K&R All Media Productions LLC, pg 796
On Stage Visuals, pg 846

MISSOURI

Show-Me Audio-Visual, pg 887

NEW JERSEY

Audio Visual Associates, pg 694
Starlite, pg 900
Wired 4 Sound Inc, pg 940

NEW YORK

CP Communications, pg 732
Design Audio Visual Inc, pg 741

NORTH CAROLINA

Take One Productions Ltd, pg 906

TENNESSEE

Allstar Audio Systems Inc, pg 681
Technical Support Systems LLC, pg 908

VIRGINIA

Lee Hartman & Sons Inc, pg 805

BRITISH COLUMBIA

DL Sound & Lighting Productions Ltd, pg 744

MANITOBA

Inland Audio Visual Ltd, pg 788

KENTUCKY

NOR-COM Inc, pg 841

MICHIGAN

TEL Systems LLC, pg 909

NEW JERSEY

Audio Visual Associates, pg 694
Starlite, pg 900

NEW YORK

Toys From The Attic, pg 916

OHIO

Tri-State Audio Visual Co, pg 918

OREGON

All Service Musical Electronics Repair, pg 680

TENNESSEE

Technical Support Systems LLC, pg 908

ALBERTA

Infosat Communications Inc, pg 787

MANITOBA

Inland Audio Visual Ltd, pg 788

Synchronizer Distributors

ARIZONA

Arizona Cine Equipment, pg 688
EAR Professional Audio/Video, pg 749

CALIFORNIA

Ametron Audio/Video, pg 684
Audio Images Corp, pg 693
Be Media, pg 702
BroadcastStore.com, pg 711
Christy's Editorial, pg 723
MediaPOINTE, pg 823
TASCAM, pg 907
VTP Inc, pg 933

COLORADO

Audio Consultant Services Inc, pg 693
Spectrum Audio Visual Services, pg 897

CONNECTICUT

HB Communications Inc, pg 777
Sennheiser Electronic Corp, pg 884

FLORIDA

Access Media Group, pg 673
Digital Video Systems, pg 742
Hi-Tech Enterprises Inc, pg 779
Hi-Tech Import Export Corp, pg 779
Recording Media & Equipment Inc (RM&E), pg 872
Stereo Sales Inc, pg 900
TAI Audio, pg 906

GEORGIA

Stage Front Presentation Systems, pg 899

ILLINOIS

Allen Visual Systems Inc, pg 680
Joseph Electronics, pg 795
Woodside Avenue Music Productions Inc, pg 941

INDIANA

Sensory Technologies LLC, pg 884
Sweetwater Sound Inc, pg 905

KENTUCKY

Axxis Leasing Inc, pg 700
NOR-COM Inc, pg 841

MAINE

Independent Audio Inc, pg 786

MARYLAND

Bradley Broadcast & Pro Audio, pg 709
Kipp Visual Systems Inc, pg 799

MASSACHUSETTS

Professional Audio Design Inc, pg 865

MICHIGAN

Olson Anderson Co, pg 685
City Events Group, pg 725
TEL Systems LLC, pg 909

NEW JERSEY

AlltecPro, pg 681
Diversified, pg 744
HamiltonBuhl, pg 775
JRF Magnetic Sciences Inc, pg 795
PatchAmp, pg 852
Starlite, pg 900
Wired 4 Sound Inc, pg 940
Yorktel, pg 944

NEW YORK

Audio-Video Corp, pg 694
AV Workshop, pg 697
Design Audio Visual Inc, pg 741
Tri-Ed Distribution Inc, pg 918

OHIO

ITA Audio Visual Solutions, pg 791

PENNSYLVANIA

Advanced AV LLC, pg 677
The Lerro Corp, pg 806
Morefield Communications Inc, pg 830

TENNESSEE

Allstar Audio Systems Inc, pg 681
Lowrance Sound Co Inc, pg 812
Technical Support Systems LLC, pg 908

TEXAS

Lubbock Audio Visual Inc, pg 812
Pro Video & Film Equipment Co Inc, pg 863
Stage Directions, pg 898
Tarpley Media Systems, pg 907

UTAH

Performance Audio LLC, pg 854

AUDIO

Synchronizer Distributors (continued)

VIRGINIA

Avitecture Inc, pg 699
Boitnott Visual Communications Corp (BVC), pg 708
Intellidyne LLC, pg 789

WISCONSIN

Audio Visual of Milwaukee Inc, pg 694
Full Compass Systems, pg 767

PUERTO RICO

Bonnin Electronics Inc, pg 708

BRITISH COLUMBIA

Commercial Electronics Ltd, pg 728

MANITOBA

Advance Pro, pg 677
Inland Audio Visual Ltd, pg 788

ONTARIO

Nationwide Audio Visual Co, pg 837
Soundmaster Group, pg 894

Synchronizer Manufacturers

CALIFORNIA

ESE, pg 755
FutureVideo, pg 767
Roland Corp US, pg 876
TASCAM, pg 907

RHODE ISLAND

M-Audio, pg 813

TENNESSEE

Adtec Digital Inc, pg 677

ONTARIO

Soundmaster Group, pg 894

Synchronizer Rentals

ALABAMA

Audio-Video Resources Inc, pg 694

ARIZONA

Arizona Cine Equipment, pg 688
Merestone, pg 823

CALIFORNIA

Ametron Audio/Video, pg 684
Audio Rents, pg 693
Bexel, an NEP Broadcast Services Company, pg 704
Christy's Editorial, pg 723
Lynch Communications, pg 813
McCune Audio-Video-Lighting, pg 821
Munday & Collins AV, pg 834
PSAV® Presentation Services, pg 866
Synthesizer Rental Service, pg 906
VER, pg 926

COLORADO

Audio Consultant Services Inc, pg 693
Daylight Productions & Rentals, pg 739
Spectrum Audio Visual Services, pg 897

FLORIDA

Access Media Group, pg 673
TAI Audio, pg 906

GEORGIA

Stage Front Presentation Systems, pg 899
Staging Directions Inc, pg 899

ILLINOIS

Allen Visual Systems Inc, pg 680
OSA International Inc, pg 848
Resolution Productions Group, pg 874
Woodside Avenue Music Productions Inc, pg 941

MARYLAND

Maryland Sound International Holding Co LLC, pg 819

MASSACHUSETTS

Preston Productions Inc, pg 861

MICHIGAN

City Events Group, pg 725
K&R All Media Productions LLC, pg 796

MISSOURI

Show-Me Audio-Visual, pg 887

NEW HAMPSHIRE

Apertura, pg 686

NEW JERSEY

Starlite, pg 900
Video Corporation of America (VCA), pg 927

NEW YORK

AV Workshop, pg 697
Design Audio Visual Inc, pg 741
Manhattan Center Studios Inc, pg 816
WorldStage, pg 941

OREGON

Northwest Film Center, pg 842

PENNSYLVANIA

Advanced AV LLC, pg 677

TENNESSEE

Allstar Audio Systems Inc, pg 681
Technical Support Systems LLC, pg 908

TEXAS

Lubbock Audio Visual Inc, pg 812
Stage Directions, pg 898

UTAH

Performance Audio LLC, pg 854

VIRGINIA

American AV, pg 682
Boitnott Visual Communications Corp (BVC), pg 708

WISCONSIN

Event Essentials, pg 756

BRITISH COLUMBIA

Commercial Electronics Ltd, pg 728

MANITOBA

Inland Audio Visual Ltd, pg 788

QUEBEC

Audio Visual Dynamics, pg 694

Synchronizer Repairs

CALIFORNIA

Ametron Audio/Video, pg 684
Audio Images Corp, pg 693
Christy's Editorial, pg 723
McAlister Electronics, pg 820

CONNECTICUT

Sennheiser Electronic Corp, pg 884

FLORIDA

Hi-Tech Enterprises Inc, pg 779
Stereo Sales Inc, pg 900
TAI Audio, pg 906

GEORGIA

Stage Front Presentation Systems, pg 899

ILLINOIS

Allen Visual Systems Inc, pg 680

KENTUCKY

NOR-COM Inc, pg 841

MICHIGAN

City Events Group, pg 725
K&R's Recording Studios Inc, pg 796
TEL Systems LLC, pg 909

NEW JERSEY

Starlite, pg 900

OREGON

All Service Musical Electronics Repair, pg 680

TENNESSEE

Technical Support Systems LLC, pg 908

VIRGINIA

Boitnott Visual Communications Corp (BVC), pg 708

WISCONSIN

Full Compass Systems, pg 767

MANITOBA

Inland Audio Visual Ltd, pg 788

Synthesizer—Bass, see Bass Synthesizer

Tape Duplicator Distributors

ARIZONA

Arizona Cine Equipment, pg 688
Metropolitan Audio-Visual Inc, pg 824
Troxell-CDI, pg 918

ARKANSAS

Jay S Stanley & Associates Inc, pg 899
White Diamond Productions LLC, pg 937

CALIFORNIA

Ametron Audio/Video, pg 684
Assured Audio Visual, pg 691
Audio Images Corp, pg 693
Audio/Video Supply Inc, pg 694
BroadcastStore.com, pg 711
California Tape Products Inc, pg 714
Instructional Materials & Equipment Distributors (I-Med), pg 789
JD Audio Visual Inc, pg 793
Media Fabricators Inc, pg 822
MediaPOINTE, pg 823
SSL Industries Inc, pg 898

COLORADO

Audio Consultant Services Inc, pg 693
Ceavco Audio Visual Company Inc, pg 719
Spectrum Audio Visual Services, pg 897

CONNECTICUT

HB Communications Inc, pg 777
MAVCO, pg 820
Rockwell Communications Inc, pg 876

DELAWARE

Actors Attic, pg 675

FLORIDA

Access Media Group, pg 673
Digital Video Systems, pg 742
Harris Corp, pg 776
Hi-Tech Import Export Corp, pg 779
Intermark Industries Inc, pg 789
Photosound of Orlando Inc, pg 856
Recording Media & Equipment Inc (RM&E), pg 872
Stereo Sales Inc, pg 900
TAI Audio, pg 906
Tallahassee Audio Visual, pg 906

GEORGIA

Audio Visual Resources Inc, pg 695
Stage Front Presentation Systems, pg 899
Visioneering International Inc, pg 931

HAWAII

The Audio Visual Co (AVCO), pg 694

INDIANA
Sensory Technologies LLC, pg 884
SHP Electronics, pg 887

KANSAS
KK Office Solutions Inc, pg 799

KENTUCKY
Axxis Leasing Inc, pg 700
Barney Miller's Inc, pg 827
NOR-COM Inc, pg 841

MAINE
Headlight Audio Visual Inc, pg 777
Independent Audio Inc, pg 786

MARYLAND
Bradley Broadcast & Pro Audio,
  pg 709
Cardinal Sound & Video, pg 717
Kipp Visual Systems Inc, pg 799
Nicholas P Pipino Associates Inc,
  pg 857
RTZ Audio Visual, pg 878

MICHIGAN
Olson Anderson Co, pg 685
City Events Group, pg 725
Digi Sign Design LLC, pg 741
TEL Systems LLC, pg 909

MINNESOTA
New Life Communications Inc,
  pg 839

MISSISSIPPI
Bowie Audio Visual Enterprises Inc,
  pg 709
Jasper Ewing & Sons Inc, pg 757

MISSOURI
Communitronics Corp, pg 729
Conference Technologies Inc,
  pg 730
ITC, pg 791
Modern Communications Inc,
  pg 828
Schiller's Audio-Visual, pg 881

NEW JERSEY
Alltec Stores, a Vcom IMC
  Company, pg 681
AlltecPro, pg 681
Audio Visual Associates, pg 694
Audio Visual Dynamics®, pg 694
AV Bluebook, pg 696
Diversified, pg 744
G&G Technologies Inc, pg 768
HamiltonBuhl, pg 775
PatchAmp, pg 852
Starlite, pg 900
Turner Engineering Inc, pg 919
Vcom IMC, pg 925
Wired 4 Sound Inc, pg 940
Yorktel, pg 944

NEW YORK
AV Workshop, pg 697
Burlington A/V Recording Media,
  pg 712
Design Audio Visual Inc, pg 741
Gaylord Archival, pg 768
Indigo Productions, pg 787
Long Island Video Enterprises Live
  Inc, pg 811
Neptune Photo Inc, pg 838
Ray Supply Inc, pg 870

RNJ Electronics, pg 875
Visual Technologies Corp, pg 932

NORTH CAROLINA
Camcor Inc, pg 715
Strategic Connections, pg 901

OHIO
Audio Visual Media, pg 694
Copp Integrated Systems, pg 731
ITA Audio Visual Solutions, pg 791
Tri-State Audio Visual Co, pg 918

OKLAHOMA
Piper Media Services Inc, pg 857

PENNSYLVANIA
Advanced AV LLC, pg 677
Audio Visual Communications Inc,
  pg 694
Brodart Co, pg 711
FMP Media Solutions Inc, pg 763
J E Foss Co, pg 764
Garcia Marketing Inc, pg 768
Grise Audio Visual Center Inc,
  pg 774
The Lerro Corp, pg 806
Morefield Communications Inc,
  pg 830
Visual Sound Inc, pg 931
Wespen Audio Visual Co, pg 935

TENNESSEE
Allstar Audio Systems Inc, pg 681
Continental Film, pg 731
Lowrance Sound Co Inc, pg 812
Memphis Communications Corp,
  pg 823
Mr Mark's Used Musical, Stereo &
  Studio Equipment Store, pg 828
Technical Support Systems LLC,
  pg 908
Zion Music Group, pg 945

TEXAS
Audio Visual Technologies Group
  (AVTG), pg 695
Crossroads Audio Inc, pg 735
Heffernan Audio Visual, pg 778
JSAV, pg 795
Lubbock Audio Visual Inc, pg 812
Pro Video & Film Equipment Co
  Inc, pg 863
RF Specialties of Texas LLC,
  pg 874
Tarpley Media Systems, pg 907

UTAH
Performance Audio LLC, pg 854
RIA Corp, pg 874

VIRGINIA
Boitnott Visual Communications
  Corp (BVC), pg 708
Lee Hartman & Sons Inc, pg 805
The Whitlock Group, pg 937

WASHINGTON
CCI Solutions, pg 718
Inland Audio Visual Co, pg 788

WEST VIRGINIA
United Sound & Electronics, pg 921

WISCONSIN
Audio Visual of Milwaukee Inc,
  pg 694
Camera Corner Connecting Point,
  pg 715
Full Compass Systems, pg 767
School Specialty Inc, pg 882

PUERTO RICO
Bonnin Electronics Inc, pg 708

ALBERTA
Matrix Video Communications Corp
  (MVCC), pg 819
McBain Camera Ltd, pg 820
Unique Communications Ltd,
  pg 921

BRITISH COLUMBIA
Commercial Electronics Ltd, pg 728

MANITOBA
Advance Pro, pg 677
Inland Audio Visual Ltd, pg 788

ONTARIO
Nationwide Audio Visual Co,
  pg 837
Westbury National Show Systems
  Ltd, pg 936

Tape Duplicator Manufacturers

CALIFORNIA
SF Global Sourcing, pg 885
Sony Electronics Inc, pg 893

NEW YORK
Recordex USA Inc, pg 872

PENNSYLVANIA
FMP Media Solutions Inc, pg 763

TEXAS
Crystal Clear Media Group, pg 735

Tape Duplicator Rentals

ALABAMA
Audio-Video Resources Inc, pg 694

ARIZONA
Arizona Cine Equipment, pg 688
Merestone, pg 823
Metropolitan Audio-Visual Inc,
  pg 824

ARKANSAS
White Diamond Productions LLC,
  pg 937

CALIFORNIA
Alliant Event Services, pg 681
Ametron Audio/Video, pg 684
Express Media Inc, pg 757
Golden Gate Studios, pg 772
Instructional Materials & Equipment
  Distributors (I-Med), pg 789
JD Audio Visual Inc, pg 793
Lynch Communications, pg 813

Munday & Collins AV, pg 834
Roundabout Entertainment Inc,
  pg 878

COLORADO
Audio Consultant Services Inc,
  pg 693
Daylight Productions & Rentals,
  pg 739
Spectrum Audio Visual Services,
  pg 897

CONNECTICUT
A/V Davey, pg 697
Rockwell Communications Inc,
  pg 876

DELAWARE
Side Door Studio Inc, pg 887

FLORIDA
Access Media Group, pg 673
ONstage, pg 846
Photosound of Orlando Inc, pg 856

GEORGIA
Stage Front Presentation Systems,
  pg 899
Staging Directions Inc, pg 899

ILLINOIS
Central Audio-Visual Equipment
  Inc, pg 719
Helix Camera & Video, pg 778
OSA International Inc, pg 848
Pepper Group, pg 854

INDIANA
Advanced Media Integration, pg 677

MAINE
Headlight Audio Visual Inc, pg 777

MARYLAND
Advance Audiovisual Presentation
  Ltd, pg 677
RTZ Audio Visual, pg 878

MASSACHUSETTS
massAV, pg 819
Preston Productions Inc, pg 861

MICHIGAN
Olson Anderson Co, pg 685
City Events Group, pg 725
Digi Sign Design LLC, pg 741
K&R All Media Productions LLC,
  pg 796
K&R's Recording Studios Inc,
  pg 796

MINNESOTA
AVI Systems, pg 698

MISSISSIPPI
Bowie Audio Visual Enterprises Inc,
  pg 709

MISSOURI
Schiller's Audio-Visual, pg 881
Show-Me Audio-Visual, pg 887

AUDIO

Tape Duplicator Rentals (continued)

NEW JERSEY

Audio Visual Dynamics®, pg 694
Starlite, pg 900
Wired 4 Sound Inc, pg 940

NEW YORK

AV Workshop, pg 697
CMI Communications, pg 727
Design Audio Visual Inc, pg 741
Long Island Video Enterprises Live Inc, pg 811
Manhattan Center Studios Inc, pg 816
Specialized Audio-Visual Inc, pg 896
Visual Technologies Corp, pg 932
Visual Word Systems Inc, pg 932

NORTH CAROLINA

AV Connections Inc, pg 697
Special Event Services, pg 896
Strategic Connections, pg 901

OHIO

Audio Visual Media, pg 694
Hughie's Event Production Services, pg 782

PENNSYLVANIA

American Artist Studio, pg 682
Audio Visual Communications Inc, pg 694
Forge Recording LLC, pg 764
Grise Audio Visual Center Inc, pg 774
Visual Sound Inc, pg 931

TENNESSEE

Allstar Audio Systems Inc, pg 681
Brantley Sound Associates Inc, pg 709
Memphis Communications Corp, pg 823
Mr Mark's Used Musical, Stereo & Studio Equipment Store, pg 828
Technical Support Systems LLC, pg 908

TEXAS

Audio Visual Technologies Group (AVTG), pg 695
JSAV, pg 795
Lubbock Audio Visual Inc, pg 812
Omega Productions, pg 845

VIRGINIA

Boitnott Visual Communications Corp (BVC), pg 708
Lee Hartman & Sons Inc, pg 805
Projection, pg 865

WASHINGTON

Inland Audio Visual Co, pg 788
Victory Studios, pg 927

WISCONSIN

Event Essentials, pg 756
School Specialty Inc, pg 882

WYOMING

Bridger Productions Inc, pg 710

ALBERTA

McBain Camera Ltd, pg 820
Unique Communications Ltd, pg 921

BRITISH COLUMBIA

Clark's Audio Visual Services Ltd, pg 725
Commercial Electronics Ltd, pg 728

MANITOBA

Inland Audio Visual Ltd, pg 788

QUEBEC

Audio Visual Dynamics, pg 694
Freeman Audio Visual, pg 765

Tape Duplicator Repairs

CALIFORNIA

Ametron Audio/Video, pg 684
Audio Images Corp, pg 693
Instructional Materials & Equipment Distributors (I-Med), pg 789
McAlister Electronics, pg 820
Lloyd F McKinney Associates Inc, pg 821
SSL Industries Inc, pg 898

CONNECTICUT

HB Communications Inc, pg 777
Rockwell Communications Inc, pg 876

FLORIDA

Hi-Tech Enterprises Inc, pg 779
JT Communications, pg 795
Stereo Sales Inc, pg 900
Tallahassee Audio Visual, pg 906

GEORGIA

Audio Visual Resources Inc, pg 695
Stage Front Presentation Systems, pg 899

ILLINOIS

Central Audio-Visual Equipment Inc, pg 719
Midwest Digital Corp, pg 827

KANSAS

KK Office Solutions Inc, pg 799

KENTUCKY

Barney Miller's Inc, pg 827
NOR-COM Inc, pg 841

MAINE

Headlight Audio Visual Inc, pg 777

MARYLAND

Cardinal Sound & Video, pg 717
RTZ Audio Visual, pg 878

MICHIGAN

Olson Anderson Co, pg 685
City Events Group, pg 725
K&R's Recording Studios Inc, pg 796
TEL Systems LLC, pg 909

MINNESOTA

AVI Systems, pg 698

MISSISSIPPI

Bowie Audio Visual Enterprises Inc, pg 709

NEW JERSEY

Starlite, pg 900

NEW YORK

Colortone Audio Visual, pg 728
Visual Technologies Corp, pg 932

NORTH CAROLINA

Camcor Inc, pg 715
Strategic Connections, pg 901

OHIO

Audio Visual Media, pg 694
Copp Integrated Systems, pg 731
Tri-State Audio Visual Co, pg 918

OREGON

All Service Musical Electronics Repair, pg 680

PENNSYLVANIA

Audio Visions Inc, pg 694
J E Foss Co, pg 764
Visual Sound Inc, pg 931
Wespen Audio Visual Co, pg 935

TENNESSEE

Memphis Communications Corp, pg 823
Technical Support Systems LLC, pg 908

TEXAS

Audio Visual Technologies Group (AVTG), pg 695
Lubbock Audio Visual Inc, pg 812

VIRGINIA

Boitnott Visual Communications Corp (BVC), pg 708
Lee Hartman & Sons Inc, pg 805
The Whitlock Group, pg 937

WASHINGTON

Inland Audio Visual Co, pg 788

WEST VIRGINIA

United Sound & Electronics, pg 921

WISCONSIN

Camera Corner Connecting Point, pg 715
Full Compass Systems, pg 767
School Specialty Inc, pg 882

ALBERTA

Unique Communications Ltd, pg 921

BRITISH COLUMBIA

Commercial Electronics Ltd, pg 728

MANITOBA

Inland Audio Visual Ltd, pg 788

Tape Equipment, *see* Repetitive Tape Equipment

Tape Eraser Distributors

ARIZONA

Troxell-CDI, pg 918

ARKANSAS

White Diamond Productions LLC, pg 937

CALIFORNIA

Ametron Audio/Video, pg 684
Audio Images Corp, pg 693
California Tape Products Inc, pg 714
Christy's Editorial, pg 723
Instructional Materials & Equipment Distributors (I-Med), pg 789
JD Audio Visual Inc, pg 793
MediaPOINTE, pg 823
SNAP, pg 891

CONNECTICUT

HB Communications Inc, pg 777

FLORIDA

Access Media Group, pg 673
Broadcasters General Store Inc, pg 711
Digital Video Systems, pg 742
Harris Corp, pg 776
Midtown Video Inc, pg 827
Recording Media & Equipment Inc (RM&E), pg 872
Stereo Sales Inc, pg 900

GEORGIA

Stage Front Presentation Systems, pg 899

HAWAII

The Audio Visual Co (AVCO), pg 694

INDIANA

R B Annis Instruments Inc, pg 686
Sensory Technologies LLC, pg 884

KENTUCKY

Barney Miller's Inc, pg 827
NOR-COM Inc, pg 841

MAINE

Headlight Audio Visual Inc, pg 777

MARYLAND

Bradley Broadcast & Pro Audio, pg 709
Kipp Visual Systems Inc, pg 799

MASSACHUSETTS

Rule Boston Camera, pg 878

MICHIGAN

TEL Systems LLC, pg 909

MISSOURI

Schiller's Audio-Visual, pg 881

NEW HAMPSHIRE

Technet® Systems Group, pg 908

NEW JERSEY
AlltecPro, pg 681
AV Bluebook, pg 696
HamiltonBuhl, pg 775
Starlite, pg 900
Vcom IMC, pg 925
Yorktel, pg 944

NEW YORK
B&H Photo Video, pg 701
Design Audio Visual Inc, pg 741

OHIO
Tri-State Audio Visual Co, pg 918

PENNSYLVANIA
Advanced AV LLC, pg 677
Brodart Co, pg 711
J E Foss Co, pg 764
The Lerro Corp, pg 806
Wespen Audio Visual Co, pg 935

TENNESSEE
Lowrance Sound Co Inc, pg 812

TEXAS
Lubbock Audio Visual Inc, pg 812
Pro Video & Film Equipment Co
 Inc, pg 863
RF Specialties of Texas LLC,
 pg 874
Tarpley Media Systems, pg 907

UTAH
Performance Audio LLC, pg 854

VIRGINIA
Lee Hartman & Sons Inc, pg 805

WASHINGTON
CCI Solutions, pg 718
Northern Lights & Pro Audio,
 pg 842

WISCONSIN
Audio Visual of Milwaukee Inc,
 pg 694
Full Compass Systems, pg 767

PUERTO RICO
Bonnin Electronics Inc, pg 708

ALBERTA
Matrix Video Communications Corp
 (MVCC), pg 819

BRITISH COLUMBIA
Commercial Electronics Ltd, pg 728

MANITOBA
Advance Pro, pg 677
Inland Audio Visual Ltd, pg 788

Tape Eraser Manufacturers

CALIFORNIA
Garner Products Inc, pg 768

FLORIDA
Sonar Radio Corp, pg 892

INDIANA
R B Annis Instruments Inc, pg 686

NEBRASKA
Data Security Inc, pg 738

Tape Eraser Rentals

ARIZONA
Merestone, pg 823

ARKANSAS
White Diamond Productions LLC,
 pg 937

CALIFORNIA
Ametron Audio/Video, pg 684
Artichoke Productions, pg 690
Garner Products Inc, pg 768
Golden Gate Studios, pg 772

CONNECTICUT
A/V Davey, pg 697

GEORGIA
Stage Front Presentation Systems,
 pg 899

MASSACHUSETTS
Preston Productions Inc, pg 861

MICHIGAN
Digi Sign Design LLC, pg 741
K&R All Media Productions LLC,
 pg 796

NEW JERSEY
Starlite, pg 900

MANITOBA
Inland Audio Visual Ltd, pg 788

Tape Eraser Repairs

CALIFORNIA
Ametron Audio/Video, pg 684
Garner Products Inc, pg 768

GEORGIA
Stage Front Presentation Systems,
 pg 899

KENTUCKY
NOR-COM Inc, pg 841

MICHIGAN
TEL Systems LLC, pg 909

NEW JERSEY
Starlite, pg 900

OREGON
All Service Musical Electronics
 Repair, pg 680

MANITOBA
Inland Audio Visual Ltd, pg 788

Tape Loading Equipment Distributors

ARIZONA
Troxell-CDI, pg 918

CALIFORNIA
Ametron Audio/Video, pg 684
VTP Inc, pg 933

FLORIDA
Digital Video Systems, pg 742
Recording Media & Equipment Inc
 (RM&E), pg 872

INDIANA
Sensory Technologies LLC, pg 884

KENTUCKY
NOR-COM Inc, pg 841

MARYLAND
Bradley Broadcast & Pro Audio,
 pg 709

NEW JERSEY
HamiltonBuhl, pg 775
Starlite, pg 900
Yorktel, pg 944

PENNSYLVANIA
Advanced AV LLC, pg 677
The Lerro Corp, pg 806

TEXAS
Tarpley Media Systems, pg 907

WISCONSIN
Audio Visual of Milwaukee Inc,
 pg 694

PUERTO RICO
Bonnin Electronics Inc, pg 708

MANITOBA
Advance Pro, pg 677
Inland Audio Visual Ltd, pg 788

Tape Loading Equipment Manufacturers

CALIFORNIA
Opticomm-EMCORE, pg 847

Tape Loading Equipment Rentals

ARIZONA
Merestone, pg 823

CALIFORNIA
Ametron Audio/Video, pg 684
Roundabout Entertainment Inc,
 pg 878

ILLINOIS
OSA International Inc, pg 848

MASSACHUSETTS
Preston Productions Inc, pg 861

MICHIGAN
K&R All Media Productions LLC,
 pg 796

MANITOBA
Inland Audio Visual Ltd, pg 788

Tape Loading Equipment Repairs

CALIFORNIA
Ametron Audio/Video, pg 684
McAlister Electronics, pg 820

ILLINOIS
Midwest Digital Corp, pg 827

KENTUCKY
NOR-COM Inc, pg 841

MICHIGAN
TEL Systems LLC, pg 909

NEW JERSEY
Starlite, pg 900

WISCONSIN
Full Compass Systems, pg 767

MANITOBA
Inland Audio Visual Ltd, pg 788

Teleconferencing

ARIZONA
Merestone, pg 823
Metropolitan Audio-Visual Inc,
 pg 824

ARKANSAS
White Diamond Productions LLC,
 pg 937

CALIFORNIA
AGF Media Services, pg 678
Associated Sound, pg 691
AV Conferencing LLC (AVC),
 pg 697
Avaya Inc, pg 697
Cibola Systems, pg 723
Earwax Productions Inc, pg 749
Havas Edge, pg 777
JDS Video & Media Productions
 Inc, pg 793
Lynch Communications, pg 813
McCune Audio-Video-Lighting,
 pg 821
Opticomm-EMCORE, pg 847
Palardo Productions, pg 850
Producers Group Ltd, pg 863
PSSI Global Services LLC, pg 866
QRS Software Services, pg 867
Thorburn Associates (TA), pg 913
Total Creative, pg 916

COLORADO
Ceavco Audio Visual Company Inc,
 pg 719
Level 3 Communications Inc,
 pg 806
Spectrum Audio Visual Services,
 pg 897

AUDIO

Teleconferencing (continued)

CONNECTICUT
A/V Davey, pg 697
Guymark Studios LLC, pg 775

DISTRICT OF COLUMBIA
Interface Media Group, pg 789

FLORIDA
Communications Concepts Inc (CCI), pg 729
Comtel Inc, pg 730
Stage America LLC, pg 898
Universal Studios Florida® Production Group, pg 922

GEORGIA
Convergent Media Systems, pg 731
Lighting & Production Equipment Inc, pg 807
PGi, pg 855
Stage Front Presentation Systems, pg 899
Staging Directions Inc, pg 899

ILLINOIS
ABS Enterprises, pg 672
Cresta Creative, pg 734
OSA International Inc, pg 848
PSAV® Presentation Services (Hotel Services Division), pg 866

INDIANA
OMNI Productions, pg 845

IOWA
Educational Technology & Media Services, pg 751
Iowa State University-Information Technology Services, pg 791

KENTUCKY
Audio Visual Techniques Inc, pg 695
Axxis Leasing Inc, pg 700
Broadway Digital, pg 711
Hammond Communications Group Inc, pg 775
The Learning House Inc, pg 805
NOR-COM Inc, pg 841

LOUISIANA
Louisiana State University Division of Strategic Communications, pg 811
Moxie Media, pg 832

MAINE
Headlight Audio Visual Inc, pg 777

MARYLAND
CPR MultiMedia Solutions, pg 732
Omega Recording Studios, pg 845

MASSACHUSETTS
Terry Hanley Audio Systems Inc, pg 775

MICHIGAN
Digi Sign Design LLC, pg 741
K&R's Recording Studios Inc, pg 796
RingSide Creative, pg 875
TEL Systems LLC, pg 909

MINNESOTA
Alpha Video & Audio Inc, pg 682

MISSOURI
Avatar Studios, pg 697
Communitronics Corp, pg 729
Ozam Productions Inc, pg 849
Show-Me Audio-Visual, pg 887

MONTANA
Jereco Studios Inc, pg 793
KUSM TV, pg 802

NEBRASKA
Three Pillars Media, pg 913

NEVADA
Encore Event Technologies LLC, pg 754
Lefco Video Services Inc, pg 806

NEW JERSEY
Avtech Systems Inc, pg 699
Diversified, pg 744
International Audio Visual Inc, pg 790
Laurel Video Productions, pg 804
Midnight Media Group Inc, pg 827
NFL Films Inc, pg 841
Starlite, pg 900
Suede Interactive, pg 903
Tele-Measurements Inc, pg 910
Telemanagement Resources International Inc (TRI), pg 910
Total Video Products Inc, pg 916
Wired 4 Sound Inc, pg 940

NEW YORK
The Big House Group, pg 705
Broadstreet Productions LLC, pg 711
Colortone Audio Visual, pg 728
Design Audio Visual Inc, pg 741
Jack Morton Worldwide, pg 830
NBC Production Facilities, pg 837
The Palmer Group, pg 850
RadioArt/Bob & Ray CDs & MP3 Files, pg 869
Servoreeler Systems, pg 884
Synaptic Digital, pg 905
Visual Technologies Corp, pg 932

NORTH CAROLINA
Pat Appleson Studios Inc, pg 687

OHIO
Copp Integrated Systems, pg 731
Cuyahoga Community College Student Production Office (SPO), pg 736
Mills James Productions, pg 828
The Telos Alliance, pg 910
WOUB Public Media, pg 942

OKLAHOMA
Academic Media & Digital Services, pg 672

PENNSYLVANIA
Production Masters Inc (PMI), pg 864
Visual Sound Inc, pg 931
WHYY Inc, pg 938
WPHL-TV, pg 942
WQED-Multimedia, pg 942

RHODE ISLAND
Sound-FX-Design, pg 894

TENNESSEE
Continental Film, pg 731
Love Shack Recording Studios, pg 811
Stage Post, pg 899
Technical Support Systems LLC, pg 908

TEXAS
JSAV, pg 795
Earl Miller Productions Inc, pg 827
Romar Learning Solutions LLC, pg 877
The Sound Lab Inc, pg 894
Stage Directions, pg 898
Tarpley Media Systems, pg 907
Texas Heart Institute Visual Communication Services, pg 911

UTAH
ClearOne Inc, pg 726
ImageWorks Communications, pg 785
Performance Audio LLC, pg 854

VERMONT
University of Vermont, Instructional Television Dept, pg 923

VIRGINIA
American AV, pg 682

WISCONSIN
Audio Visual of Milwaukee Inc, pg 694
Camera Corner Connecting Point, pg 715
University of Wisconsin-Oshkosh Radio-TV-Film Dept, pg 923
USAV Group Inc, pg 923
Video Wisconsin Inc, pg 929
Wisconsin Public Television, pg 940

ALBERTA
Global TV, pg 771

BRITISH COLUMBIA
Commercial Electronics Ltd, pg 728

ONTARIO
Cinema Stage Inc, pg 724
DebsVoice, pg 739
Westbury National Show Systems Ltd, pg 936

Teleconferencing Equipment Distributors

ARIZONA
EAR Professional Audio/Video, pg 749
Projector SuperStore LLC, pg 865
Troxell-CDI, pg 918

ARKANSAS
Jay S Stanley & Associates Inc, pg 899
White Diamond Productions LLC, pg 937

CALIFORNIA
Ametron Audio/Video, pg 684
Associated Sound, pg 691
AV Conferencing LLC (AVC), pg 697
Avaya Inc, pg 697
Cibola Systems, pg 723
Computer Modules Inc, pg 729
Empire Pro, pg 753
Southern California Sound Image Inc, pg 895
Stanislaus AV Inc, pg 899
VMI Inc, pg 932
VTP Inc, pg 933

COLORADO
Daylight Productions & Rentals, pg 739
Spectrum Audio Visual Services, pg 897

CONNECTICUT
HB Communications Inc, pg 777

DELAWARE
Actors Attic, pg 675

FLORIDA
Access Media Group, pg 673
Altel Systems Group Inc, pg 682
AVI-SPL, pg 698
Digital Video Systems, pg 742
Harmon's Audio-Visual Services, pg 776
Harris Corp, pg 776
Hi-Tech Enterprises Inc, pg 779
Hi-Tech Import Export Corp, pg 779
L3Harris Technologies Inc, pg 812
Recording Media & Equipment Inc (RM&E), pg 872
Technomedia Solutions, pg 909

GEORGIA
Lighting & Production Equipment Inc, pg 807
Stage Front Presentation Systems, pg 899

HAWAII
The Audio Visual Co (AVCO), pg 694

ILLINOIS
Allen Visual Systems Inc, pg 680
Quintessence Audio Ltd, pg 868

INDIANA
Sensory Technologies LLC, pg 884

KANSAS
SKC Communication Products Inc, pg 890

KENTUCKY
Audio Visual Techniques Inc, pg 695
Axxis Leasing Inc, pg 700
NOR-COM Inc, pg 841

MAINE
Headlight Audio Visual Inc, pg 777

MARYLAND
Bradley Broadcast & Pro Audio, pg 709
Cardinal Sound & Video, pg 717
Human Circuit, pg 782

MASSACHUSETTS
Terry Hanley Audio Systems Inc, pg 775

MINNESOTA
Alpha Video & Audio Inc, pg 682

MISSOURI
Schiller's Audio-Visual, pg 881

NEW JERSEY
AlltecPro, pg 681
Audio Visual Associates, pg 694
Diversified, pg 744
Entel Systems Inc, pg 754
Starlite, pg 900
Total Video Products Inc, pg 916
Wired 4 Sound Inc, pg 940
Yorktel, pg 944

NEW YORK
Audio-Video Corp, pg 694
Colortone Audio Visual, pg 728
Design Audio Visual Inc, pg 741
KVL Audio Visual Services Inc, pg 802
Theatrical Services & Supplies Inc, pg 912
Toys From The Attic, pg 916
Visual Technologies Corp, pg 932

OHIO
ITA Audio Visual Solutions, pg 791
The Telos Alliance, pg 910
Tri-State Audio Visual Co, pg 918

OKLAHOMA
Ford AV, pg 763

PENNSYLVANIA
Advanced AV LLC, pg 677
Grise Audio Visual Center Inc, pg 774
The Lerro Corp, pg 806

RHODE ISLAND
Shanix Inc, pg 885

TENNESSEE
Continental Film, pg 731
Lowrance Sound Co Inc, pg 812
Technical Support Systems LLC, pg 908

TEXAS
Audio Visual Technologies Group (AVTG), pg 695
Data Projections Inc, pg 738
Tarpley Media Systems, pg 907

VIRGINIA
Avitecture Inc, pg 699
Intellidyne LLC, pg 789
Lee Hartman & Sons Inc, pg 805

WASHINGTON
PNTA, pg 858

WISCONSIN
Audio Visual of Milwaukee Inc, pg 694
Full Compass Systems, pg 767

PUERTO RICO
Audio Visual Concepts Inc, pg 694
Bonnin Electronics Inc, pg 708

ALBERTA
Evolution AV, pg 757
Infosat Communications Inc, pg 787
Matrix Video Communications Corp (MVCC), pg 819

BRITISH COLUMBIA
Commercial Electronics Ltd, pg 728

MANITOBA
Advance Pro, pg 677
Inland Audio Visual Ltd, pg 788

ONTARIO
Cinema Stage Inc, pg 724
Westbury National Show Systems Ltd, pg 936

QUEBEC
Sennheiser (Canada) Inc, pg 884

Teleconferencing Equipment Manufacturers

ARIZONA
AtlasIED, pg 692
Covid Inc, pg 732

CALIFORNIA
ALTINEX Inc, pg 682
Avaya Inc, pg 697
Computer Modules Inc, pg 729

COLORADO
Display Devices Inc, pg 743
Image Audiovisuals, pg 784

CONNECTICUT
Collective Systems LLC, pg 727
Sound Control Technologies Inc, pg 893
Titus Technological Laboratories (TTL), pg 914

FLORIDA
CircuitWerkes Inc, pg 725

ILLINOIS
J K Audio Inc, pg 792
Marshall Furniture Inc, pg 817

MASSACHUSETTS
Comrex Corp, pg 730

MICHIGAN
ASC Systems, pg 690

MINNESOTA
Bosch Security Systems Inc, pg 709
Winsted Corp, pg 939

NEW JERSEY
Bogen Communications Inc, pg 708
Crestron Electronics Inc, pg 734

NEW MEXICO
Lectrosonics Inc, pg 805

NEW YORK
Harry Joseph & Associates Inc, pg 795
MultiDyne Video & Fiber Optics Systems, pg 833

OHIO
Omnia Audio, pg 845
The Telos Alliance, pg 910

OREGON
BIAMP Systems, pg 705

TENNESSEE
Adtec Digital Inc, pg 677

UTAH
ClearOne Inc, pg 726

WASHINGTON
Avidex Inc, pg 699

Teleconferencing Equipment Rentals

ARIZONA
Merestone, pg 823
Video West Inc, pg 929

ARKANSAS
White Diamond Productions LLC, pg 937

CALIFORNIA
AGF Media Services, pg 678
Ametron Audio/Video, pg 684
Associated Sound, pg 691
AV Conferencing LLC (AVC), pg 697
AV Guys, pg 697
Lynch Communications, pg 813
McCune Audio-Video-Lighting, pg 821
Stanislaus AV Inc, pg 899
VER, pg 926
VMI Inc, pg 932

COLORADO
Spectrum Audio Visual Services, pg 897

CONNECTICUT
A/V Davey, pg 697
Videofilm Systems Inc, pg 929

DELAWARE
Actors Attic, pg 675

FLORIDA
Digital Video Systems, pg 742
Harmon's Audio-Visual Services, pg 776
ONstage, pg 846

GEORGIA
Stage Front Presentation Systems, pg 899

ILLINOIS
Allen Visual Systems Inc, pg 680
OSA International Inc, pg 848
RC Communications, pg 870

KENTUCKY
Audio Visual Techniques Inc, pg 695

MARYLAND
Advance Audiovisual Presentation Ltd, pg 677
CPR MultiMedia Solutions, pg 732

MASSACHUSETTS
Terry Hanley Audio Systems Inc, pg 775
Preston Productions Inc, pg 861

MICHIGAN
K&R All Media Productions LLC, pg 796

MINNESOTA
Alpha Video & Audio Inc, pg 682

MISSOURI
Show-Me Audio-Visual, pg 887

NEBRASKA
Dog & Pony Productions Inc, pg 744

NEW JERSEY
Audio Visual Associates, pg 694
MiB MediaWorks, pg 825
Starlite, pg 900
Wired 4 Sound Inc, pg 940

NEW YORK
Colortone Audio Visual, pg 728
Design Audio Visual Inc, pg 741
KVL Audio Visual Services Inc, pg 802
Visual Technologies Corp, pg 932

OHIO
ITA Audio Visual Solutions, pg 791
Mills James Productions, pg 828

PENNSYLVANIA
Grise Audio Visual Center Inc, pg 774

TENNESSEE
Love Shack Recording Studios, pg 811
Technical Support Systems LLC, pg 908

TEXAS
Audio Visual Technologies Group (AVTG), pg 695

AUDIO

Teleconferencing Equipment Rentals (continued)

VIRGINIA

American AV, pg 682
Audio Visual Actions Inc (AVA), pg 694
Intellidyne LLC, pg 789
Lee Hartman & Sons Inc, pg 805

PUERTO RICO

Stage Crew Audiovisual Inc, pg 898

BRITISH COLUMBIA

Commercial Electronics Ltd, pg 728

MANITOBA

Inland Audio Visual Ltd, pg 788

ONTARIO

Westbury National Show Systems Ltd, pg 936

Teleconferencing Equipment Repairs

CALIFORNIA

Ametron Audio/Video, pg 684
McAlister Electronics, pg 820

CONNECTICUT

HB Communications Inc, pg 777

DELAWARE

Actors Attic, pg 675

FLORIDA

Hi-Tech Enterprises Inc, pg 779

GEORGIA

Lighting & Production Equipment Inc, pg 807
Stage Front Presentation Systems, pg 899

ILLINOIS

Allen Visual Systems Inc, pg 680

KENTUCKY

NOR-COM Inc, pg 841

MICHIGAN

TEL Systems LLC, pg 909

NEW JERSEY

Audio Visual Associates, pg 694
Starlite, pg 900

NEW YORK

Toys From The Attic, pg 916
Visual Technologies Corp, pg 932

OHIO

ITA Audio Visual Solutions, pg 791
Tri-State Audio Visual Co, pg 918

TENNESSEE

Technical Support Systems LLC, pg 908

VIRGINIA

Avitecture Inc, pg 699
Intellidyne LLC, pg 789

WASHINGTON

PNTA, pg 858

WISCONSIN

Full Compass Systems, pg 767

ALBERTA

Infosat Communications Inc, pg 787

BRITISH COLUMBIA

Commercial Electronics Ltd, pg 728

MANITOBA

Inland Audio Visual Ltd, pg 788

ONTARIO

Westbury National Show Systems Ltd, pg 936

Test Equipment Distributors

ARIZONA

Arizona Cine Equipment, pg 688
ATCi (Antenna Technology Communication Solutions Inc), pg 692
Troxell-CDI, pg 918

ARKANSAS

White Diamond Productions LLC, pg 937

CALIFORNIA

Ametron Audio/Video, pg 684
Apex Jr, pg 687
Assured Audio Visual, pg 691
Audio Images Corp, pg 693
BigFoot Mobile Systems, pg 705
BroadcastStore.com, pg 711
DigiTech, pg 742
Gravity Media, pg 773
Jameco Electronics, pg 792
Leader Instruments Corp, pg 805
Magnetic Reference Laboratory Inc, pg 815
MediaPOINTE, pg 823
Southern California Sound Image Inc, pg 895
SSL Industries Inc, pg 898
Stanford Research Systems Inc, pg 899
VMI Inc, pg 932
VTP Inc, pg 933
Zack Electronics Inc, pg 945

COLORADO

Spectrum Audio Visual Services, pg 897

CONNECTICUT

Gold Line/TEF, pg 772
HB Communications Inc, pg 777

FLORIDA

Access Media Group, pg 673
Broadcasters General Store Inc, pg 711
Digital Video Systems, pg 742
Harris Corp, pg 776
Hi-Tech Enterprises Inc, pg 779
Hi-Tech Import Export Corp, pg 779
Intermark Industries Inc, pg 789
Midtown Video Inc, pg 827
ONstage, pg 846
Recording Media & Equipment Inc (RM&E), pg 872
Stereo Sales Inc, pg 900
Technomedia Solutions, pg 909

GEORGIA

Convergent Media Systems, pg 731

HAWAII

The Audio Visual Co (AVCO), pg 694

ILLINOIS

Allen Visual Systems Inc, pg 680
Joseph Electronics, pg 795
Research Technology International (RTI), pg 873

INDIANA

Sensory Technologies LLC, pg 884

KENTUCKY

Axxis Leasing Inc, pg 700
NOR-COM Inc, pg 841

MARYLAND

Bradley Broadcast & Pro Audio, pg 709
Human Circuit, pg 782
Kipp Visual Systems Inc, pg 799
Rohde & Schwarz USA Inc, pg 876

MASSACHUSETTS

Capron Lighting & Sound Co Inc, pg 716
JENSEN Tools + Supply, pg 793

MICHIGAN

TEL Systems LLC, pg 909

MINNESOTA

AVI Systems, pg 698
Digital Audio Labs, pg 742

MISSOURI

Modern Communications Inc, pg 828

NEW JERSEY

Alltec Stores, a Vcom IMC Company, pg 681
AlltecPro, pg 681
Comprehensive Cable & Connectivity Co, pg 729
Diversified, pg 744
Electro Impulse Laboratory Inc, pg 752
JRF Magnetic Sciences Inc, pg 795
PatchAmp, pg 852
Starlite, pg 900
SYMCO Inc, pg 905
Wired 4 Sound Inc, pg 940
Yorktel, pg 944

NEW YORK

Audio-Video Corp, pg 694
AV Workshop, pg 697
BTX Technologies, pg 712
Design Audio Visual Inc, pg 741
Group One Ltd, pg 774
Hot House Professional Audio, pg 782
Indigo Productions, pg 787
Long Island Video Enterprises Live Inc, pg 811
Posthorn Recordings, pg 859
Ray Supply Inc, pg 870
RNJ Electronics, pg 875
Russell Industries Inc, pg 879
Tri-Ed Distribution Inc, pg 918
Unitron Ltd, pg 921

NORTH CAROLINA

Camcor Inc, pg 715

OHIO

Parts Express, pg 851

OREGON

Audio Precision, pg 693
NTi Audio Inc, pg 843

PENNSYLVANIA

Advanced AV LLC, pg 677
The Lerro Corp, pg 806
Techni-Tool, a TestEquity LLC company, pg 908

SOUTH DAKOTA

Sencore Inc, pg 883

TENNESSEE

Allstar Audio Systems Inc, pg 681
Green Dot Audio Electronics, pg 774
Lowrance Sound Co Inc, pg 812
Memphis Communications Corp, pg 823
True Audio, pg 919

TEXAS

Lubbock Audio Visual Inc, pg 812
Pro Video & Film Equipment Co Inc, pg 863
Specialized Products Co, pg 896
Tarpley Media Systems, pg 907

UTAH

Performance Audio LLC, pg 854
RIA Corp, pg 874

VIRGINIA

Intellidyne LLC, pg 789
Lee Hartman & Sons Inc, pg 805

WASHINGTON

CCI Solutions, pg 718
Northern Lights & Pro Audio, pg 842

WEST VIRGINIA

United Sound & Electronics, pg 921

WISCONSIN

Audio Visual of Milwaukee Inc, pg 694
Full Compass Systems, pg 767

PUERTO RICO
Bonnin Electronics Inc, pg 708

ALBERTA
Matrix Video Communications Corp (MVCC), pg 819

MANITOBA
Advance Pro, pg 677

ONTARIO
The Hollywood Edge, pg 780
Nationwide Audio Visual Co, pg 837

QUEBEC
Panavideo Inc, pg 850

Test Equipment Manufacturers

CALIFORNIA
ACO Pacific Inc, pg 674
Ametek Programmable Power Inc, pg 684
Calrad Electronics, pg 714
DigiTech, pg 742
Dorrough Electronics Inc, pg 746
Ensemble Designs Inc, pg 754
ESE, pg 755
FM Systems Inc, pg 763
Horita Co Inc, pg 781
Leader Instruments Corp, pg 805
Magnetic Reference Laboratory Inc, pg 815
Stanford Research Systems Inc, pg 899

CONNECTICUT
Gold Line/TEF, pg 772

FLORIDA
Compuvideo Sales USA Ltd, pg 729
Imtronics Industries Inc, pg 786
JT Communications, pg 795

ILLINOIS
Magnetic Shield Corp, pg 815
Quantum Data Inc, pg 868
Research Technology International (RTI), pg 873

INDIANA
R B Annis Instruments Inc, pg 686

KANSAS
Galaxy Audio, pg 767

MARYLAND
Potomac Instruments Inc, pg 860

MASSACHUSETTS
AEMC Instruments, pg 678
Capron Lighting & Sound Co Inc, pg 716
Eastern Acoustic Works Inc (EAW), pg 749
Prior Scientific Inc, pg 862

MINNESOTA
Digital Audio Labs, pg 742
Tremetrics Inc Industrial Instruments Division, pg 917

NEW HAMPSHIRE
Earthworks Inc, pg 749

NEW JERSEY
ATI Audio, pg 692
Boonton Electronics, pg 709
Wireworks Corp, pg 940

NEW YORK
Entertainment One US, pg 754
Laird Digital Cinema, pg 803
MultiDyne Video & Fiber Optics Systems, pg 833
Sescom Inc, pg 884

OREGON
Audio Precision, pg 693
NTi Audio Inc, pg 843

PENNSYLVANIA
Belar Electronics Laboratory Inc, pg 703

SOUTH DAKOTA
Sencore Inc, pg 883

TENNESSEE
Remote Audio Products, pg 873
True Audio, pg 919

TEXAS
Logitek Electronic Systems Inc, pg 811
National Instruments Corp, pg 836

UTAH
Ivie Technologies Inc, pg 792
Rolls Corp, pg 877

VIRGINIA
Delta Electronics Inc, pg 740

WASHINGTON
AudioControl® Inc, pg 695
Conex Electro Systems Inc, pg 730
Fluke Corp, pg 763

WISCONSIN
Magnetek Inc, pg 814
Simpson Electric Co, pg 889

ONTARIO
The Hollywood Edge, pg 780
Ward-Beck Systems Ltd, pg 933

Test Equipment Rentals

ARIZONA
Arizona Cine Equipment, pg 688
Merestone, pg 823

ARKANSAS
White Diamond Productions LLC, pg 937

CALIFORNIA
Audio Rents, pg 693
Bexel, an NEP Broadcast Services Company, pg 704
Express Media Inc, pg 757
Golden Gate Studios, pg 772
McCune Audio-Video-Lighting, pg 821

Stanford Research Systems Inc, pg 899
VER, pg 926

COLORADO
Spectrum Audio Visual Services, pg 897

CONNECTICUT
Videofilm Systems Inc, pg 929

FLORIDA
Access Media Group, pg 673
ONstage, pg 846
Phat Planet Recording Studios, pg 855

GEORGIA
Convergent Media Systems, pg 731
Staging Directions Inc, pg 899

ILLINOIS
Allen Visual Systems Inc, pg 680
OSA International Inc, pg 848
RC Communications, pg 870

MASSACHUSETTS
Capron Lighting & Sound Co Inc, pg 716
Preston Productions Inc, pg 861

MICHIGAN
K&R All Media Productions LLC, pg 796
K&R's Recording Studios Inc, pg 796

MINNESOTA
AVI Systems, pg 698

NEVADA
GES Audio Visual, pg 770

NEW HAMPSHIRE
Apertura, pg 686

NEW JERSEY
Moe AV LLC, pg 828
Starlite, pg 900
Video Corporation of America (VCA), pg 927
Wired 4 Sound Inc, pg 940

NEW YORK
All Mobile Video Inc, pg 680
AV Workshop, pg 697
Design Audio Visual Inc, pg 741
Long Island Video Enterprises Live Inc, pg 811
Manhattan Center Studios Inc, pg 816
Posthorn Recordings, pg 859
Specialized Audio-Visual Inc, pg 896

NORTH CAROLINA
Take One Productions Ltd, pg 906

OREGON
NTi Audio Inc, pg 843

PENNSYLVANIA
Audio Visions Inc, pg 694
Right Coast Recording Inc, pg 875

TENNESSEE
Allstar Audio Systems Inc, pg 681
Brantley Sound Associates Inc, pg 709

TEXAS
Lubbock Audio Visual Inc, pg 812

WASHINGTON
D A Sound, pg 737
Northern Lights & Pro Audio, pg 842

WISCONSIN
Full Compass Systems, pg 767

ALBERTA
L R Light & Sound, pg 802

Test Equipment Repairs

CALIFORNIA
Ametron Audio/Video, pg 684
Audio Images Corp, pg 693
McAlister Electronics, pg 820
SSL Industries Inc, pg 898

CONNECTICUT
HB Communications Inc, pg 777

FLORIDA
Hi-Tech Enterprises Inc, pg 779
Phat Planet Recording Studios, pg 855
Stereo Sales Inc, pg 900

ILLINOIS
Allen Visual Systems Inc, pg 680

KENTUCKY
NOR-COM Inc, pg 841

MASSACHUSETTS
Capron Lighting & Sound Co Inc, pg 716

MICHIGAN
TEL Systems LLC, pg 909

MINNESOTA
AVI Systems, pg 698

NEW JERSEY
Starlite, pg 900

NORTH CAROLINA
Camcor Inc, pg 715

OREGON
NTi Audio Inc, pg 843

PENNSYLVANIA
Right Coast Recording Inc, pg 875

VIRGINIA
Boitnott Visual Communications Corp (BVC), pg 708

WASHINGTON
Northern Lights & Pro Audio, pg 842

AUDIO

Test Equipment Repairs
(continued)

Wireless Microphone, *see*
Microphone—Wireless

AUDIO/VISUAL

Animation System Distributors

ARIZONA

Troxell-CDI, pg 918

CALIFORNIA

Audio Images Corp, pg 693
Audio/Video Supply Inc, pg 694
California Tape Products Inc,
 pg 714
Diaquest, pg 741
Educational Technology Services
 (ETS), pg 751
Kris Stevens Enterprises, pg 801
MAXON Computer Inc, pg 820
Videobotics, pg 929
VMI Inc, pg 932

COLORADO

Spectrum Audio Visual Services,
 pg 897

CONNECTICUT

HB Communications Inc, pg 777

FLORIDA

Digital Video Systems, pg 742
Hi-Tech Enterprises Inc, pg 779

GEORGIA

Stage Front Presentation Systems,
 pg 899

LOUISIANA

Digital FX Inc, pg 742

MASSACHUSETTS

Integrated Solutions Group, pg 789
Psychsoft Inc, pg 866
The Weather Company, An IBM
 Business, pg 935

MICHIGAN

ASC Systems, pg 690
TEL Systems LLC, pg 909

MISSOURI

Conference Technologies Inc,
 pg 730

NEW JERSEY

Yorktel, pg 944

NEW YORK

Audio-Video Corp, pg 694
B&H Photo Video, pg 701
Indigo Productions, pg 787
Tri-Ed Distribution Inc, pg 918

OHIO

Audio Visual Media, pg 694
Copp Integrated Systems, pg 731

PENNSYLVANIA

AccuWeather Inc, pg 674
Advanced AV LLC, pg 677
The Lerro Corp, pg 806

TEXAS

Lubbock Audio Visual Inc, pg 812
Pro Video & Film Equipment Co
 Inc, pg 863
Videotex Systems Inc, pg 930

UTAH

RIA Corp, pg 874

WISCONSIN

Audio Visual of Milwaukee Inc,
 pg 694
Camera Corner Connecting Point,
 pg 715
Full Compass Systems, pg 767
Safe Harbor Computers, pg 879

PUERTO RICO

Bonnin Electronics Inc, pg 708

MANITOBA

Inland Audio Visual Ltd, pg 788

ONTARIO

HD Source, pg 777
Nationwide Audio Visual Co,
 pg 837

Animation System Manufacturers

CALIFORNIA

Apple Inc, pg 687
Diaquest, pg 741
Fax Animation Co, pg 759
Gilderfluke & Co Inc, pg 771
Alan Gordon Enterprises Inc,
 pg 772
Linker Systems Inc, pg 809
MAXON Computer Inc, pg 820

ILLINOIS

EPIX Inc, pg 755

MASSACHUSETTS

Psychsoft Inc, pg 866
The Weather Company, An IBM
 Business, pg 935

NEW JERSEY

Fiber Optic Systems Inc (FOSI),
 pg 759
PeopleVisionFX, pg 854

NEW YORK

Gagne Inc, pg 767

PENNSYLVANIA

AccuWeather Inc, pg 674

WASHINGTON

Laser Fantasy/HECK
 Industries/Photon Manufacturing,
 pg 804

WISCONSIN

Safe Harbor Computers, pg 879

BRITISH COLUMBIA

Triad Communications Ltd, pg 918

ONTARIO

Corel Corp, pg 731

Animation System Rentals

ARIZONA

Merestone, pg 823

CALIFORNIA

Artichoke Productions, pg 690
Fax Animation Co, pg 759
Alan Gordon Enterprises Inc,
 pg 772
McCune Audio-Video-Lighting,
 pg 821
Total Creative, pg 916

COLORADO

Daylight Productions & Rentals,
 pg 739

GEORGIA

Stage Front Presentation Systems,
 pg 899
Staging Directions Inc, pg 899

LOUISIANA

Digital FX Inc, pg 742

MASSACHUSETTS

Preston Productions Inc, pg 861

MICHIGAN

K&R All Media Productions LLC,
 pg 796

NEW JERSEY

MediaMix Inc, pg 822
PLS Staging, pg 858

NEW YORK

AV Workshop, pg 697
HB-Content, pg 777
Manhattan Center Studios Inc,
 pg 816

NORTH CAROLINA

Take One Productions Ltd, pg 906

OREGON

Northwest Film Center, pg 842

PENNSYLVANIA

FMP Media Solutions Inc, pg 763

TEXAS

Phillips Media Source, pg 855
Stage Directions, pg 898

WASHINGTON

Laser Fantasy/HECK
 Industries/Photon Manufacturing,
 pg 804

WYOMING

Bridger Productions Inc, pg 710

MANITOBA

Inland Audio Visual Ltd, pg 788

Animation System Repairs

CALIFORNIA

Fax Animation Co, pg 759
Alan Gordon Enterprises Inc,
 pg 772
McAlister Electronics, pg 820
Technical Services, pg 908

FLORIDA

Hi-Tech Enterprises Inc, pg 779

GEORGIA

Stage Front Presentation Systems,
 pg 899

MICHIGAN

TEL Systems LLC, pg 909

OHIO

Copp Integrated Systems, pg 731

WASHINGTON

Laser Fantasy/HECK
 Industries/Photon Manufacturing,
 pg 804

WISCONSIN

Full Compass Systems, pg 767

MANITOBA

Inland Audio Visual Ltd, pg 788

Artwork & Titling Services

ALASKA

Alaska Media Pros LLC, pg 679

ARIZONA

Merestone, pg 823

ARKANSAS

Live'N'Loud, pg 810
White Diamond Productions LLC,
 pg 937

CALIFORNIA

Action Video, pg 675
Blind™, pg 707
Christopher Gray Post Production,
 pg 722
Coloredge Inc, pg 728
Creative Technology, pg 733
Custom Video Productions Inc,
 pg 736
Diamond Dreams Music
 Productions, pg 741
Digital Jungle, pg 742
First Person Inc, pg 761
Gold Standard Productions, pg 772
Gordon Productions Inc, pg 772
Havas Edge, pg 777
iCorpTv, pg 783
JDS Video & Media Productions
 Inc, pg 793
K2B2 Records, pg 802
Lumeni Productions Inc, pg 812
Maximus Media Inc, pg 820
The Media Staff Inc, pg 822
Medical Visual Creations (MVC),
 pg 823
Moving Art by Louie Schwartzberg,
 pg 831
Nineteen87, pg 841
piXvfm Inc, pg 857

AUDIO/VISUAL

Artwork & Titling Services (continued)

CALIFORNIA (continued)

PM Productions, pg 858
PSI Inc, pg 866
QRS Software Services, pg 867
Reality Check Systems, pg 871
Shapeshifter, pg 885
SonicPool, pg 892
Still N' Motion, pg 901
TIMECODE Post Production, pg 914
Total Creative, pg 916
Universal Studios, pg 922
West Coast Projections Inc, pg 935

COLORADO

CSI Film & Video LLC, pg 735
Flashback Media Productions, pg 762
Full Spectrum Arts & Services, pg 767
Starwest Productions, pg 900

CONNECTICUT

Guymark Studios LLC, pg 775
Ironik Design & Post, pg 791
New London Media, pg 839

DISTRICT OF COLUMBIA

O'Keefe Communications Inc, pg 844

FLORIDA

Civins Productions Inc, pg 725
Communications Concepts Inc (CCI), pg 729
Jordan Klein Film & Video (JKFV), pg 795
The Kitchen, pg 799
Photosound of Orlando Inc, pg 856
Sunrise Studios, pg 904
Video Techniques Inc, pg 928
Vistamax Productions, pg 931

GEORGIA

Beachwood Productions, pg 702
Beast Atlanta, pg 703
ECG Productions, pg 750
Guerrilla Productions LLC, pg 774
Imagers, pg 785

HAWAII

Hyperspective Studios Inc, pg 783

ILLINOIS

ABS Enterprises, pg 672
ABSA Films, pg 672
Airways Digital Media, pg 679
Backstar Creative Media Inc, pg 700
Breeze Productions Inc, pg 710
CCore Media Inc, pg 718
IV Media Resources, pg 792
Mightybytes Inc, pg 827
Multimedia Marketing Group, pg 833
Jim Passin Productions, pg 852
Pepper Group, pg 854
Southern Illinois University, pg 895
Sparkfactor, pg 896
20/20 Communications Inc, pg 920
WEEK TV, pg 935

INDIANA

A-V-A Video Productions, pg 671
Bright Ideas Creative Services, pg 710
OMNI Productions, pg 845

IOWA

Educational Technology & Media Services, pg 751

LOUISIANA

Digital FX Inc, pg 742
Louisiana State University Division of Strategic Communications, pg 811
Vidox Motion Imagery, pg 930

MARYLAND

Adventure Productions LLC, pg 678
CPR MultiMedia Solutions, pg 732
dbF a Media Company, pg 739
Kramer Communications Video Production, pg 801
Pro Cuts Editing Services, pg 862

MASSACHUSETTS

CommCreative, pg 728
MotionArt Studios, pg 831
Northern Light Productions (NLP), pg 842
Penfield Productions Ltd, pg 853
Gabriel Polonsky Studio, pg 859
Preston Productions Inc, pg 861
TR Productions, pg 916

MICHIGAN

Arbor Oakland Group, pg 688
Audio Graphic Services, pg 693
Blue Mouse Studio, pg 707
Digi Sign Design LLC, pg 741
Digital Image Studios LLC, pg 742
K&R's Recording Studios Inc, pg 796
Progressive AE, pg 865
RingSide Creative, pg 875
Tectonics Industries LLC, pg 909

MINNESOTA

BeyerSound & Essay Audio, pg 705
Media Loft Inc, pg 822

MISSOURI

Allied Photocolor Co, pg 681
Visionworks Design Services Inc, pg 931

NEBRASKA

Three Pillars Media, pg 913

NEVADA

Aardvark Video & Media Productions, pg 671
Encore Event Technologies LLC, pg 754
JCS Video Productions, pg 793
Tanglewood Productions, pg 907

NEW HAMPSHIRE

Apertura, pg 686
Chip Taylor Communications LLC, pg 907

NEW JERSEY

Allegro Productions Inc, pg 680
CELCO, pg 719
CFP Video Productions Inc, pg 720

Laurel Video Productions, pg 804
NFL Films Music Library, pg 841
Optisonics Productions, pg 847
Outside The Box Interactive LLC, pg 849
Video Ideas Productions, pg 928

NEW YORK

Animotion Inc, pg 685
Big Film Design, pg 705
The Big House Group, pg 705
Buffalo Video Production, pg 712
Digital Art Video Inc, pg 741
Duggal Visual Solutions Inc, pg 747
4-D Creative Media, pg 764
HB-Content, pg 777
Icontent, pg 783
InterNation Inc, pg 789
Lylofilm Productions, pg 813
Manhattan Center Studios Inc, pg 816
Jack Morton Worldwide, pg 830
Polestar Films & Associated Arts Ltd, pg 859
Joseph Struhl Company Inc, pg 902
Tiki Recording Studios Inc, pg 914
Zelman Studios Ltd, pg 945

NORTH CAROLINA

Pat Appleson Studios Inc, pg 687
Image Associates Inc, pg 784
Moving Pictures, pg 832
Studio South, pg 903
Take One Productions Ltd, pg 906

NORTH DAKOTA

Media Productions, pg 822

OHIO

Aztec Video Productions, pg 700
Cuyahoga Community College Student Production Office (SPO), pg 736
Mills James Productions, pg 828
Take 1 Media Services, pg 906
Vista Color Imaging Inc, pg 931

OKLAHOMA

Comm-Arts Inc, pg 728
Garman Productions LLC, pg 768
PDC Productions, pg 852

OREGON

REX, pg 874

PENNSYLVANIA

Bang! Pictures Inc, pg 701
Innovision Media Group, pg 788
JPL, pg 795
Main Point Productions, pg 815
The Videohouse Inc, pg 929
WPHL-TV, pg 942

RHODE ISLAND

Sound-FX-Design, pg 894

SOUTH CAROLINA

Genesis Creative, pg 769

TENNESSEE

American Blackguard Inc, pg 683
Continental Film, pg 731
Paradigm Marketing & Creative, pg 851
Scripps Networks, pg 882
Stage Post, pg 899

TEXAS

Anaphora Literary Press, pg 685
Biway Media, pg 706
Hurst Digital, pg 782
Romar Learning Solutions LLC, pg 877
The Samuels Co, pg 879
South Coast Film & Video, pg 895
Stage Directions, pg 898
Texas Heart Institute Visual Communication Services, pg 911

VERMONT

University of Vermont, Instructional Television Dept, pg 923

VIRGINIA

Allied Media Corp, pg 681
Blair Inc, pg 707
Rocktown Media, pg 876

WASHINGTON

Adams Creative & Production Services, pg 675
Inland Audio Visual Co, pg 788
Victory Studios, pg 927

WISCONSIN

Audio Visual of Milwaukee Inc, pg 694
Meridian Studios, pg 824
Midland Video Productions Inc, pg 827
USAV Group Inc, pg 923
Video Wisconsin Inc, pg 929
Watts Communications Inc, pg 934

WYOMING

Bridger Productions Inc, pg 710

ONTARIO

ADS Media, pg 677
Image Video Services & Productions, pg 785
Silver Creek Media Inc, pg 888
Video Excellence Productions, pg 927
Westbury National Show Systems Ltd, pg 936

AV Pulsing, see Pulsing—AV

AV System Design & Installation, see System Design & Installation

Color Correction Services

ARIZONA

Film Creations Ltd, pg 760
Merestone, pg 823

ARKANSAS

White Diamond Productions LLC, pg 937

CALIFORNIA

Action Video, pg 675
Angstrom Lighting, pg 685
Christopher Gray Post Production, pg 722
Coloredge Inc, pg 728
Creative Technology, pg 733

Custom Video Productions Inc, pg 736
Digital Jungle, pg 742
First Person Inc, pg 761
Havas Edge, pg 777
iCorpTv, pg 783
JDS Video & Media Productions Inc, pg 793
Main Street Media Inc, pg 815
McCune Audio-Video-Lighting, pg 821
Nineteen87, pg 841
PM Productions, pg 858
Pro8mm, pg 862
QRS Software Services, pg 867
Reality Check Systems, pg 871
Shapeshifter, pg 885
SonicPool, pg 892
Still N' Motion, pg 901
TIMECODE Post Production, pg 914
Total Creative, pg 916
Twin Peaks Creative, pg 920
Two Door Productions LLC, pg 920
Universal Studios, pg 922

COLORADO

Rocky Mountain Audio/Video Productions Inc, pg 876

CONNECTICUT

Digital Video Productions, pg 742
Guymark Studios LLC, pg 775
Ironik Design & Post, pg 791
MAVCO, pg 820

DISTRICT OF COLUMBIA

Interface Media Group, pg 789

FLORIDA

Access Media Group, pg 673
Civins Productions Inc, pg 725
Communications Concepts Inc (CCI), pg 729
Sunrise Studios, pg 904
Video Techniques Inc, pg 928
Vistamax Productions, pg 931

GEORGIA

ECG Productions, pg 750
Guerrilla Productions LLC, pg 774
Imagers, pg 785
Stage Front Presentation Systems, pg 899
Staging Directions Inc, pg 899
Visioneering International Inc, pg 931

HAWAII

Hyperspective Studios Inc, pg 783

ILLINOIS

Breeze Productions Inc, pg 710
CCore Media Inc, pg 718
Chicago Spotlight Inc, pg 721
Mightybytes Inc, pg 827
Sparkfactor, pg 896
20/20 Communications Inc, pg 920

INDIANA

OMNI Productions, pg 845

KANSAS

Custom Color Corp, pg 736

MARYLAND

CPR MultiMedia Solutions, pg 732
dbF a Media Company, pg 739

Kramer Communications Video Production, pg 801
Pro Cuts Editing Services, pg 862

MASSACHUSETTS

Monotype Imaging Inc, pg 829
Northern Light Productions (NLP), pg 842
TR Productions, pg 916

MICHIGAN

Arbor Oakland Group, pg 688
Audio Graphic Services, pg 693
Digi Sign Design LLC, pg 741
K&R's Recording Studios Inc, pg 796
Tectonics Industries LLC, pg 909

MINNESOTA

AVI Systems, pg 698

MISSOURI

Allied Photocolor Co, pg 681

NEBRASKA

Three Pillars Media, pg 913

NEVADA

Aardvark Video & Media Productions, pg 671
Encore Event Technologies LLC, pg 754
JCS Video Productions, pg 793
Lefco Video Services Inc, pg 806
Wells-Gardner Technologies Inc, pg 935

NEW JERSEY

CELCO, pg 719
CFP Video Productions Inc, pg 720
NFL Films Music Library, pg 841

NEW YORK

Air Sea Land Productions Inc (ASL), pg 678
Albany Theatre Supply Co Inc, pg 679
aurora productions, pg 696
The Big House Group, pg 705
BMI Supply, pg 708
Digital Art Video Inc, pg 741
Duggal Visual Solutions Inc, pg 747
4-D Creative Media, pg 764
HB-Content, pg 777
Hello World Communications, pg 778
International Digital Centre, pg 790
Modernage Photographic Services Inc, pg 828
Jack Morton Worldwide, pg 830
Mutual Hardware, pg 835
Sima Products Corp, pg 888
USA Studios, pg 923

NORTH CAROLINA

Pat Appleson Studios Inc, pg 687
Take One Productions Ltd, pg 906

OHIO

Aztec Video Productions, pg 700
Mills James Productions, pg 828

OKLAHOMA

Garman Productions LLC, pg 768
PDC Productions, pg 852

OREGON

REX, pg 874

PENNSYLVANIA

Berry & Homer, pg 704
FMP Media Solutions Inc, pg 763
Panta Rhei Media Inc, pg 851
The Videohouse Inc, pg 929
WPHL-TV, pg 942

RHODE ISLAND

Sound-FX-Design, pg 894

SOUTH CAROLINA

Genesis Creative, pg 769

TENNESSEE

Stage Post, pg 899

TEXAS

Anaphora Literary Press, pg 685
Biway Media, pg 706
Epic Software Group Inc, pg 755
Freeman, pg 765
Hurst Digital, pg 782
Julye Newlin Productions Inc, pg 840
South Coast Film & Video, pg 895
Thomas Printworks, pg 912

VERMONT

University of Vermont, Instructional Television Dept, pg 923

VIRGINIA

Allied Media Corp, pg 681
The Whitlock Group, pg 937

WASHINGTON

Bennett-Watt HD Productions Inc, pg 703
Victory Studios, pg 927

WISCONSIN

Audio Visual of Milwaukee Inc, pg 694
Meridian Studios, pg 824
Mirror 34 Productions, pg 828
USAV Group Inc, pg 923
Video Wisconsin Inc, pg 929
Watts Communications Inc, pg 934

ONTARIO

ADS Media, pg 677
Video Excellence Productions, pg 927

Color Media Distributors

CALIFORNIA

Angstrom Lighting, pg 685
Penn Elcom Inc, pg 853
Sacramento Theatrical Lighting Ltd (STL), pg 879
Towards 2000 Inc, pg 916

FLORIDA

Bay Stage Lighting Co Inc, pg 702

GEORGIA

Lighting & Production Equipment Inc, pg 807
Stage Front Presentation Systems, pg 899

ILLINOIS

Chicago Spotlight Inc, pg 721

INDIANA

Apollo Design Technology Inc, pg 687

KANSAS

Theatrical Services Inc, pg 912

LOUISIANA

Techkno Integration & Design Services LLC, pg 908

MASSACHUSETTS

Advanced Lighting & Production Services Inc (ALPS), pg 677
Limelight Production® Inc, pg 809
Lineco, pg 809

MICHIGAN

On Stage Visuals, pg 846

MINNESOTA

Tierney Brothers Inc, pg 914

NEW HAMPSHIRE

APS Lighting-Sound-AV, pg 688

NEW JERSEY

Earl Girls Inc, pg 749
Starlite, pg 900

NEW YORK

BMI Supply, pg 708
Creative Stage Lighting Co Inc, pg 733
PASCO, pg 851
Syracuse Scenery & Stage Lighting Co Inc, pg 906
Theatrical Services & Supplies Inc, pg 912

OREGON

Hollywood Lights Inc, pg 780

PENNSYLVANIA

Advanced AV LLC, pg 677
The Lerro Corp, pg 806

TENNESSEE

Zion Music Group, pg 945

TEXAS

Crossroads Audio Inc, pg 735

VERMONT

Production Advantage Inc, pg 863

WISCONSIN

Audio Visual of Milwaukee Inc, pg 694

MANITOBA

Inland Audio Visual Ltd, pg 788

Color Media Manufacturers

COLORADO

Colorado Time Systems LLC, pg 728

AUDIO/VISUAL

Color Media Manufacturers (continued)

NEW YORK

Century Business Solutions, pg 720
TRUMATCH Inc, pg 919

Color Media Rentals

ARIZONA

Merestone, pg 823

CALIFORNIA

Aztek Inc, pg 700

GEORGIA

Stage Front Presentation Systems, pg 899

MICHIGAN

K&R All Media Productions LLC, pg 796
On Stage Visuals, pg 846

NEW JERSEY

Starlite, pg 900

NEW YORK

Creative Stage Lighting Co Inc, pg 733

MANITOBA

Inland Audio Visual Ltd, pg 788

Color Media Repairs

CALIFORNIA

VMI Inc, pg 932

GEORGIA

Stage Front Presentation Systems, pg 899

MICHIGAN

TEL Systems LLC, pg 909

MANITOBA

Inland Audio Visual Ltd, pg 788

Color Photostats

ARIZONA

Merestone, pg 823

CALIFORNIA

ARC Document Solutions, pg 688
Canyon Cinema Inc, pg 716
Coloredge Inc, pg 728
JDS Video & Media Productions Inc, pg 793
QRS Software Services, pg 867

CONNECTICUT

Guymark Studios LLC, pg 775

FLORIDA

Communications Concepts Inc (CCI), pg 729
SuperStock Inc, pg 904

GEORGIA

Guerrilla Productions LLC, pg 774

ILLINOIS

Gamma Imaging, pg 768

IOWA

Educational Technology & Media Services, pg 751

KANSAS

Custom Color Corp, pg 736

LOUISIANA

Louisiana State University Division of Strategic Communications, pg 811

MARYLAND

Kramer Communications Video Production, pg 801

MASSACHUSETTS

Colortek of Boston, pg 728

MICHIGAN

Digi Sign Design LLC, pg 741
K&R's Recording Studios Inc, pg 796
Tectonics Industries LLC, pg 909

MINNESOTA

Linhoff Photo & Digital Imaging, pg 809
Media Loft Inc, pg 822
Pointward, pg 858

MISSOURI

Avatar Studios, pg 697
Visionworks Design Services Inc, pg 931

NEVADA

Aardvark Video & Media Productions, pg 671
Encore Event Technologies LLC, pg 754

NEW HAMPSHIRE

The Troupe, pg 918

NEW JERSEY

Broadcast Center Studios, pg 710
C2 Imaging, pg 735

NEW YORK

Duggal Visual Solutions Inc, pg 747
Long Island University Media Arts Dept, pg 811
Jack Morton Worldwide, pg 830
R/GA, pg 868
SMP Digital Graphics, pg 891
Tisch School of the Arts, pg 914
Videograf, pg 929

NORTH DAKOTA

UND Television Center, pg 921

OHIO

Aztec Video Productions, pg 700
WOUB Public Media, pg 942

PENNSYLVANIA

Audio Visual Communications Inc, pg 694
Berry & Homer, pg 704
Main Point Productions, pg 815

RHODE ISLAND

Sound-FX-Design, pg 894

TENNESSEE

Stage Post, pg 899

TEXAS

Hurst Digital, pg 782
Thomas Printworks, pg 912

UTAH

Signs.com, pg 888

VIRGINIA

Blair Inc, pg 707

WISCONSIN

Audio Visual of Milwaukee Inc, pg 694
USAV Group Inc, pg 923

BRITISH COLUMBIA

Triad Communications Ltd, pg 918

Computer Graphics

ARIZONA

Merestone, pg 823
On-Site Video, pg 846
Professional Marketing Services Inc, pg 865

ARKANSAS

White Diamond Productions LLC, pg 937

CALIFORNIA

Action Video, pg 675
Aztek Inc, pg 700
Buttercup Pictures, pg 713
Classic Images Stock Footage LLC, pg 726
Coloredge Inc, pg 728
Creative Technology, pg 733
Crystal Pyramid Productions™, pg 735
Custom Video Productions Inc, pg 736
Diamond Dreams Music Productions, pg 741
Diaquest, pg 741
Digital Jungle, pg 742
Dolphin MultiMedia Inc, pg 745
Express Media Inc, pg 757
First Person Inc, pg 761
Gold Standard Productions, pg 772
Havas Edge, pg 777
iCorpTv, pg 783
JDS Video & Media Productions Inc, pg 793
KO Creative, pg 800
K2B2 Records, pg 802
Lumeni Productions Inc, pg 812
Maximus Media Inc, pg 820

McCune Audio-Video-Lighting, pg 821
Media Fabricators Inc, pg 822
Media Magic, pg 822
The Media Staff Inc, pg 822
Medical Visual Creations (MVC), pg 823
New Wave Entertainment, pg 839
Nineteen87, pg 841
On-Trax Inc, pg 846
piXvfm Inc, pg 857
PM Productions, pg 858
PSI Inc, pg 866
QRS Software Services, pg 867
Reality Check Systems, pg 871
RetinaVision Productions, pg 874
Shapeshifter, pg 885
SonicPool, pg 892
Staylor-Made Communications Inc, pg 900
Still N' Motion, pg 901
Tam Communications Inc, pg 906
TIMECODE Post Production, pg 914
Total Creative, pg 916
Towards 2000 Inc, pg 916
Twin Peaks Creative, pg 920
Twisted Media Inc, pg 920
Two Door Productions LLC, pg 920
Universal Studios, pg 922
Videografix LLC, pg 929
Wavemaker Media Design, pg 934
West Coast Projections Inc, pg 935

COLORADO

CSI Film & Video LLC, pg 735
Daylight Productions & Rentals, pg 739
Flashback Media Productions, pg 762
Full Spectrum Arts & Services, pg 767

CONNECTICUT

Cine-Med Inc, pg 723
The Gary-Paul Agency, pg 768
Guymark Studios LLC, pg 775
Musivision Inc, pg 835
New London Media, pg 839

DELAWARE

Side Door Studio Inc, pg 887

DISTRICT OF COLUMBIA

Interface Media Group, pg 789
O'Keefe Communications Inc, pg 844

FLORIDA

Access Media Group, pg 673
AVI-SPL, pg 698
CD ROM™ Inc, pg 718
Civins Productions Inc, pg 725
Communications Concepts Inc (CCI), pg 729
Digimation, pg 741
The Kitchen, pg 799
Sunfire Communications Inc, pg 904
Sunrise Studios, pg 904
Teach America Corp, pg 908
Universal Studios Florida® Production Group, pg 922
Vistamax Productions, pg 931

GEORGIA

Beachwood Productions, pg 702
Beast Atlanta, pg 703
ECG Productions, pg 750
Guerrilla Productions LLC, pg 774

AUDIO/VISUAL

Computer Three-D Effects on Slide

ALABAMA
Diamond Studios, pg 741

ARIZONA
Merestone, pg 823

CALIFORNIA
Custom Video Productions Inc, pg 736
Diaquest, pg 741
Dolphin MultiMedia Inc, pg 745
First Person Inc, pg 761
JDS Video & Media Productions Inc, pg 793
Lumeni Productions Inc, pg 812
The Media Staff Inc, pg 822
PSI Inc, pg 866
QRS Software Services, pg 867
Reality Check Systems, pg 871
SonicPool, pg 892
Total Creative, pg 916

DISTRICT OF COLUMBIA
Interface Media Group, pg 789
O'Keefe Communications Inc, pg 844

FLORIDA
Access Media Group, pg 673
AVI-SPL, pg 698
Digimation, pg 741
Tricycle Studios, pg 918

GEORGIA
Beachwood Productions, pg 702
Guerrilla Productions LLC, pg 774
Imagers, pg 785
Stage Front Presentation Systems, pg 899
Staging Directions Inc, pg 899
Visioneering International Inc, pg 931

HAWAII
Hyperspective Studios Inc, pg 783

ILLINOIS
CCore Media Inc, pg 718
Extraordinary Demos/Videos, pg 757
Mightybytes Inc, pg 827
Jim Passin Productions, pg 852
Pepper Group, pg 854
Southern Illinois University, pg 895

MARYLAND
Sign Media Inc, pg 887

MICHIGAN
ASC Systems, pg 690
Digi Sign Design LLC, pg 741
Digital Image Studios LLC, pg 742
K&R's Recording Studios Inc, pg 796
On Stage Visuals, pg 846
Tectonics Industries LLC, pg 909

MISSOURI
Avatar Studios, pg 697
Show-Me Audio-Visual, pg 887
Switch, pg 905

NEVADA
Encore Event Technologies LLC, pg 754
JCS Video Productions, pg 793

NEW JERSEY
Broadcast Center Studios, pg 710
CELCO, pg 719
Laurel Video Productions, pg 804
Suede Interactive, pg 903

NEW YORK
Digital Art Video Inc, pg 741
4-D Creative Media, pg 764
Manhattan Center Studios Inc, pg 816
Jack Morton Worldwide, pg 830
R/GA, pg 868

NORTH CAROLINA
Horizon Video Productions Inc, pg 781
Image Associates Inc, pg 784

NORTH DAKOTA
Media Productions, pg 822

OHIO
Aztec Video Productions, pg 700

PENNSYLVANIA
Audio Visual Communications Inc, pg 694
FMP Media Solutions Inc, pg 763
Innovision Media Group, pg 788
Main Point Productions, pg 815

RHODE ISLAND
Sound-FX-Design, pg 894

SOUTH CAROLINA
Genesis Creative, pg 769

TENNESSEE
Stage Post, pg 899

TEXAS
Epic Software Group Inc, pg 755
Hurst Digital, pg 782
South Coast Film & Video, pg 895
Stage Directions, pg 898
Texas Heart Institute Visual Communication Services, pg 911

VIRGINIA
Advance Concepts Inc, pg 677
Allied Media Corp, pg 681

WISCONSIN
Audio Visual of Milwaukee Inc, pg 694
AVS Group, pg 699
USAV Group Inc, pg 923
Watts Communications Inc, pg 934

Computerized Animation Production Services, see Animation System

Consulting

ALASKA
Aurora Films, pg 696

ARIZONA
Covid Inc, pg 732
Creative Backstage, pg 733
Merestone, pg 823
Metropolitan Audio-Visual Inc, pg 824
Teaberry, pg 908

CALIFORNIA
AGF Media Services, pg 678
Associated Sound, pg 691
AV Conferencing LLC (AVC), pg 697
Charles M Salter Associates Inc, pg 721
Cibola Systems, pg 723
Coloredge Inc, pg 728
Creative Technology, pg 733
Crystal Pyramid Productions™, pg 735
Custom Video Productions Inc, pg 736
Design Media, pg 741
Dolphin MultiMedia Inc, pg 745
Electrosonic Inc, pg 752
Em Gee Film Library, pg 753
Express Media Inc, pg 757
First Person Inc, pg 761
Goal Productions, pg 772
Gold Standard Productions, pg 772
Havas Edge, pg 777
Jaguar Distribution Corp, pg 792
JDS Video & Media Productions Inc, pg 793
KVIE-Channel 6, pg 802
Lumeni Productions Inc, pg 812
Lynch Communications, pg 813
Maximus Media Inc, pg 820
McCune Audio-Video-Lighting, pg 821
McKay Conant Hoover Inc, pg 821
Media Fabricators Inc, pg 822
Media Systems Design Group, pg 822
New & Unique Videos™, pg 839
New Wave Entertainment, pg 839
Joseph Nicoletti Consulting-Promotion, pg 841
piXvfm Inc, pg 857
PM Productions, pg 858
Prime Cut Productions, pg 862
PSI Inc, pg 866
Pyro Spectaculars Inc, pg 867
QRS Software Services, pg 867
Regent Press Publishers & Printers, pg 873
RetinaVision Productions, pg 874
Russ InVision Co/AbridgeClub.com, pg 879
Sahara Records & Filmworks Entertainment Co, pg 879
The Sextant Group Inc, pg 885
SNAP, pg 891
SonicPool, pg 892
Still N' Motion, pg 901
Tam Communications Inc, pg 906
Thorburn Associates (TA), pg 913
Total Creative, pg 916
WARPed Pictures, pg 934
Wavemaker Media Design, pg 934
West Coast Projections Inc, pg 935

COLORADO
D L Adams Associates Inc, pg 675
Audio Consultant Services Inc, pg 693

(continued, next column)
CSI Film & Video LLC, pg 735
Daylight Productions & Rentals, pg 739
Flashback Media Productions, pg 762
Maniac Productions, pg 816
MVP International Inc, pg 835
Spectrum Audio Visual Services, pg 897

CONNECTICUT
Boyce Nemec Designs, pg 709
Guymark Studios LLC, pg 775
MAVCO, pg 820
New London Media, pg 839
P&P Studios Inc, pg 851
Skyviews Survey Inc, pg 890

DELAWARE
So Smart Productions, pg 891

DISTRICT OF COLUMBIA
Hillmann & Carr Inc, pg 780
Susan Hormuth, Visual Resource Consultant, pg 781
O'Keefe Communications Inc, pg 844

FLORIDA
Access Media Group, pg 673
AVI-SPL, pg 698
CD ROM™ Inc, pg 718
Communications Concepts Inc (CCI), pg 729
Digital Video Systems, pg 742
The Kitchen, pg 799
National Teleproductions Inc, pg 837
ONstage, pg 846
Stereo Sales Inc, pg 900
Sunfire Communications Inc, pg 904
Teach America Corp, pg 908
Tricycle Studios, pg 918
Universal Studios Florida® Production Group, pg 922
Vistamax Productions, pg 931

GEORGIA
Guerrilla Productions LLC, pg 774
Lighting & Production Equipment Inc, pg 807
Merck & Hill Consultants Inc, pg 823
Stage Front Presentation Systems, pg 899
Staging Directions Inc, pg 899
Visioneering International Inc, pg 931

HAWAII
D L Adams Associates Ltd, pg 675
Hyperspective Studios Inc, pg 783
Media Bridge Gamekids, pg 821

IDAHO
KTVB-TV, pg 802

ILLINOIS
ABSA Films, pg 672
Accenture, pg 672
Airways Digital Media, pg 679
Beatty TeleVisual Productions, pg 703
CCore Media Inc, pg 718
Cresta Creative, pg 734
Extraordinary Demos/Videos, pg 757

Film Police, pg 760
Multimedia Marketing Group, pg 833
Jim Passin Productions, pg 852
Pepper Group, pg 854
PSAV® Presentation Services (Hotel Services Division), pg 866
Southern Illinois University, pg 895
Sparkfactor, pg 896
20/20 Communications Inc, pg 920
Woodside Avenue Music Productions Inc, pg 941

INDIANA

Bright Ideas Creative Services, pg 710

IOWA

Educational Technology & Media Services, pg 751

KENTUCKY

Axxis Leasing Inc, pg 700
Broadway Digital, pg 711
Idle Minds Productions Inc, pg 784
NOR-COM Inc, pg 841
Prosper Media Group Inc, pg 866

LOUISIANA

Louisiana State University Division of Strategic Communications, pg 811
Moxie Media, pg 832

MAINE

Headlight Audio Visual Inc, pg 777

MARYLAND

CPR MultiMedia Solutions, pg 732
The Cutting Corporation, GraphicAudio® & Archival Sound Lab, pg 736
dbF a Media Company, pg 739
Kramer Communications Video Production, pg 801
Media Dimensions LLC, pg 821
Welocalize, pg 935

MASSACHUSETTS

Capron Lighting & Sound Co Inc, pg 716
Cavanaugh Tocci Associates Inc, pg 717
CommCreative, pg 728
Communications Design Associates, pg 729
Continental Recordings Inc, pg 731
High Output Inc, pg 779
Monadnock Media Inc, pg 829
MotionArt Studios, pg 831
Northern Light Productions (NLP), pg 842
Preston Productions Inc, pg 861
TR Productions, pg 916
TVN-The Video Network, pg 919

MICHIGAN

ASC Systems, pg 690
Audio Graphic Services, pg 693
Digi Sign Design LLC, pg 741
K&R's Recording Studios Inc, pg 796
Michigan Recording Arts Institute & Technologies, pg 825
On Stage Visuals, pg 846
The Program Source International, pg 865

MINNESOTA

Alpha Video & Audio Inc, pg 682
BeyerSound & Essay Audio, pg 705
Media Loft Inc, pg 822

MISSOURI

Communitronics Corp, pg 729
Switch, pg 905

MONTANA

KCFW Television, pg 797

NEVADA

Aardvark Video & Media Productions, pg 671
Encore Event Technologies LLC, pg 754
Lefco Video Services Inc, pg 806
Ron Roy Productions/Moodtapes, pg 878

NEW HAMPSHIRE

Apertura, pg 686
Chip Taylor Communications LLC, pg 907

NEW JERSEY

Audio Visual Dynamics®, pg 694
Broadcast Center Studios, pg 710
CELCO, pg 719
CFP Video Productions Inc, pg 720
Diversified, pg 744
Euro-Pacific Film & Video Productions Inc, pg 756
Laurel Video Productions, pg 804
Megavideo LLC, pg 823
MiB MediaWorks, pg 825
Optisonics Productions, pg 847
Outside The Box Interactive LLC, pg 849
PatchAmp, pg 852
Telemanagement Resources International Inc (TRI), pg 910
Total Video Products Inc, pg 916
Varto Technologies, pg 925
Video Corporation of America (VCA), pg 927
Wired 4 Sound Inc, pg 940

NEW YORK

Animotion Inc, pg 685
aurora productions, pg 696
The Big House Group, pg 705
Buffalo Video Production, pg 712
BZ/Rights & Permissions Inc, pg 713
Chromavision Corp, pg 723
Custom Computer Specialists Inc, pg 736
Digital Art Video Inc, pg 741
Duggal Visual Solutions Inc, pg 747
4-D Creative Media, pg 764
GHO Group LLC, pg 770
Ketchum Inc, pg 798
Modernage Photographic Services Inc, pg 828
Jack Morton Worldwide, pg 830
MRY, pg 832
Judson Rosebush Co Inc, pg 877
Shen Milsom & Wilke LLC, pg 885
SMP Digital Graphics, pg 891
Tritech Communications, pg 918
VIEW Inc (Video International Entertainment World Inc), pg 930
Visual Word Systems Inc, pg 932
Zelman Studios Ltd, pg 945

NORTH CAROLINA

Pat Appleson Studios Inc, pg 687
Lawrence Behr Associates Inc, pg 703
Camcor Inc, pg 715
The Communications Group Inc, pg 729
Digital Rain LLC, pg 742
Image Associates Inc, pg 784
On Location North Carolina, pg 846
Special Event Services, pg 896
Take One Productions Ltd, pg 906

NORTH DAKOTA

Media Productions, pg 822

OHIO

Advent Media Inc, pg 677
Aztec Video Productions, pg 700
Copp Integrated Systems, pg 731
Mills James Productions, pg 828
Take 1 Media Services, pg 906
Thread Marketing Group, pg 913
Treehaus Communications Inc, pg 917
Vista Color Imaging Inc, pg 931

OKLAHOMA

Academic Media & Digital Services, pg 672
DD Audio, pg 739
Ford AV, pg 763
PDC Productions, pg 852

OREGON

InterVision Media, pg 791

PENNSYLVANIA

Bang! Pictures Inc, pg 701
Beholder Productions Inc, pg 703
Innovision Media Group, pg 788
JPL, pg 795
Main Point Productions, pg 815
Metropolitan Acoustics LLC, pg 824
Panta Rhei Media Inc, pg 851
The Videohouse Inc, pg 929
WPHL-TV, pg 942

RHODE ISLAND

Sound-FX-Design, pg 894

TENNESSEE

American Blackguard Inc, pg 683
Fricon Entertainment Co Inc, pg 766
Paradigm Marketing & Creative, pg 851
Scripps Networks, pg 882
Stage Post, pg 899
Russ Sturgeon Productions/RSVP, pg 903
Take One Film & Video, pg 906
Zion Music Group, pg 945

TEXAS

Audio Visual Technologies Group (AVTG), pg 695
AVES Audio Visual Systems Inc, pg 698
Biway Media, pg 706
Cerutti Productions Inc, pg 720
Hurst Digital, pg 782
James Loupas Associates Inc, pg 811
Lubbock Audio Visual Inc, pg 812
Mediaforce Productions, pg 822
Earl Miller Productions Inc, pg 827

Julye Newlin Productions Inc, pg 840
Stage Directions, pg 898
Technical Services, pg 908
Texas Heart Institute Visual Communication Services, pg 911

UTAH

ImageWorks Communications, pg 785
Spectrum Engineers, pg 897

VIRGINIA

Advance Concepts Inc, pg 677
Allied Media Corp, pg 681
Altruist Media LLC, pg 682
American AV, pg 682
CACI Integrated Communications, pg 713
CDR Communications Inc, pg 719
Quince Imaging Inc, pg 868
Rocktown Media, pg 876

WASHINGTON

Adams Creative & Production Services, pg 675
Bennett-Watt HD Productions Inc, pg 703
Kostov Productions, pg 801
Laser Fantasy/HECK Industries/Photon Manufacturing, pg 804
Media Elite Productions, pg 822
Medical Media Systems, pg 823
North-by-Northwest - A Digital Studio, pg 842
Northern Lights & Pro Audio, pg 842
Victory Studios, pg 927

WISCONSIN

Audio Visual of Milwaukee Inc, pg 694
Meridian Studios, pg 824
Midland Video Productions Inc, pg 827
University of Wisconsin-Oshkosh Radio-TV-Film Dept, pg 923
USAV Group Inc, pg 923
Video Wisconsin Inc, pg 929
Watts Communications Inc, pg 934
Wisconsin Public Television, pg 940

WYOMING

Bridger Productions Inc, pg 710

PUERTO RICO

Stage Crew Audiovisual Inc, pg 898

ALBERTA

Unique Communications Ltd, pg 921

BRITISH COLUMBIA

Triad Communications Ltd, pg 918

NORTHWEST TERRITORIES

Yellowknife Films Inc, pg 944

ONTARIO

ADS Media, pg 677
Artaflex Inc, pg 690
Cinema Stage Inc, pg 724
DebsVoice, pg 739
GestureTek, pg 770
Image Video Services & Productions, pg 785

AUDIO/VISUAL

Consulting (continued)

ONTARIO (continued)

MVI - MultiVision Inc, pg 835
State of the Art Acoustik Inc,
  pg 900
Technovision® Interactive Inc,
  pg 909
Video Excellence Productions,
  pg 927

QUEBEC

Audio Visual Dynamics, pg 694
Sceno Plus, pg 881
20k, pg 920

SASKATCHEWAN

Thomega Entertainment Inc, pg 913

Co-Production Services

ARIZONA

Aardvark Productions LLC, pg 671
Merestone, pg 823
Teaberry, pg 908

CALIFORNIA

Bridge Publications Inc, pg 710
Concrete Images, pg 730
Crystal Pyramid Productions™,
  pg 735
Custom Video Productions Inc,
  pg 736
Deja View Video, pg 740
Design Media, pg 741
Dolphin MultiMedia Inc, pg 745
ECONEWS (Environmental
  Television Series) &
  (Environmental Directions Radio
  Series), pg 750
Express Media Inc, pg 757
First Person Inc, pg 761
Havas Edge, pg 777
iCorpTv, pg 783
Jaguar Distribution Corp, pg 792
JDS Video & Media Productions
  Inc, pg 793
KVIE-Channel 6, pg 802
Lynch Communications, pg 813
Maximus Media Inc, pg 820
McCune Audio-Video-Lighting,
  pg 821
New & Unique Videos™, pg 839
Nineteen87, pg 841
piXvfm Inc, pg 857
PM Productions, pg 858
PSI Inc, pg 866
Pyramid Studios, pg 867
QRS Software Services, pg 867
Regent Press Publishers & Printers,
  pg 873
Russ InVision Co/AbridgeClub.com,
  pg 879
Sahara Records & Filmworks
  Entertainment Co, pg 879
Sports Cinematography Group,
  pg 898
Still N' Motion, pg 901
Tam Communications Inc, pg 906
Total Creative, pg 916
WARPed Pictures, pg 934
Wavemaker Media Design, pg 934
Z-Ville Productions, pg 944

COLORADO

Daylight Productions & Rentals,
  pg 739
Flashback Media Productions,
  pg 762
Spectrum Audio Visual Services,
  pg 897

CONNECTICUT

Guymark Studios LLC, pg 775
Ironik Design & Post, pg 791
MAVCO, pg 820
New London Media, pg 839
Skyviews Survey Inc, pg 890

DELAWARE

So Smart Productions, pg 891

DISTRICT OF COLUMBIA

Hillmann & Carr Inc, pg 780
O'Keefe Communications Inc,
  pg 844

FLORIDA

Audio Visual Imagineering Inc,
  pg 694
Communications Concepts Inc
  (CCI), pg 729
The Kitchen, pg 799
National Teleproductions Inc,
  pg 837
Sunfire Communications Inc,
  pg 904
Teach America Corp, pg 908
Tricycle Studios, pg 918

GEORGIA

Beast Atlanta, pg 703
Guerrilla Productions LLC, pg 774
Myriad Productions, pg 835
Stage Front Presentation Systems,
  pg 899
Staging Directions Inc, pg 899
Visioneering International Inc,
  pg 931

HAWAII

Hyperspective Studios Inc, pg 783
Media Bridge Gamekids, pg 821

IDAHO

KTVB-TV, pg 802

ILLINOIS

ABSA Films, pg 672
Airways Digital Media, pg 679
CCore Media Inc, pg 718
Cresta Creative, pg 734
Explore, pg 757
Extraordinary Demos/Videos,
  pg 757
Film Police, pg 760
Multimedia Marketing Group,
  pg 833
Pepper Group, pg 854
PSAV® Presentation Services
  (Hotel Services Division), pg 866
Steven Samler Music & Sound,
  pg 879
Sound/Video Impressions Inc,
  pg 894
20/20 Communications Inc, pg 920
Woodside Avenue Music
  Productions Inc, pg 941

INDIANA

Bright Ideas Creative Services,
  pg 710
PentaVision Communications Inc,
  pg 854

IOWA

Educational Technology & Media
  Services, pg 751

KENTUCKY

Broadway Digital, pg 711
Idle Minds Productions Inc, pg 784
Prosper Media Group Inc, pg 866

LOUISIANA

Louisiana State University Division
  of Strategic Communications,
  pg 811

MAINE

Headlight Audio Visual Inc, pg 777

MARYLAND

CPR MultiMedia Solutions, pg 732
The Cutting Corporation,
  GraphicAudio® & Archival
  Sound Lab, pg 736
dbF a Media Company, pg 739
Kramer Communications Video
  Production, pg 801

MASSACHUSETTS

Capron Lighting & Sound Co Inc,
  pg 716
Monadnock Media Inc, pg 829
MotionArt Studios, pg 831
Preston Productions Inc, pg 861
TR Productions, pg 916

MICHIGAN

ASC Systems, pg 690
Digi Sign Design LLC, pg 741
K&R's Recording Studios Inc,
  pg 796
On Stage Visuals, pg 846

MISSOURI

Visionworks Design Services Inc,
  pg 931

MONTANA

KCFW Television, pg 797

NEVADA

Aardvark Video & Media
  Productions, pg 671
Encore Event Technologies LLC,
  pg 754
JCS Video Productions, pg 793
Lefco Video Services Inc, pg 806
Ron Roy Productions/Moodtapes,
  pg 878

NEW HAMPSHIRE

Apertura, pg 686
Chip Taylor Communications LLC,
  pg 907

NEW JERSEY

CELCO, pg 719
CFP Video Productions Inc, pg 671
Euro-Pacific Film & Video
  Productions Inc, pg 756
Laurel Video Productions, pg 804

INDIANA (right col continued)

MiB MediaWorks, pg 825
Optisonics Productions, pg 847
Outside The Box Interactive LLC,
  pg 849

NEW YORK

A&E Home Video, pg 671
aurora productions, pg 696
BC Studio, pg 702
The Big House Group, pg 705
Chromavision Corp, pg 723
Duggal Visual Solutions Inc, pg 747
4-D Creative Media, pg 764
HAVE Inc, pg 777
HB-Content, pg 777
Hello World Communications,
  pg 778
Icontent, pg 783
Long Island Video Enterprises Live
  Inc, pg 811
Jack Morton Worldwide, pg 830
VIEW Inc (Video International
  Entertainment World Inc), pg 930
Zelman Studios Ltd, pg 945

NORTH CAROLINA

Pat Appleson Studios Inc, pg 687
The Communications Group Inc,
  pg 729
Digital Rain LLC, pg 742
Special Event Services, pg 896
Take One Productions Ltd, pg 906

NORTH DAKOTA

Media Productions, pg 822

OHIO

Advent Media Inc, pg 677
Aztec Video Productions, pg 700
Cuyahoga Community College
  Student Production Office (SPO),
  pg 736
Take 1 Media Services, pg 906
Treehaus Communications Inc,
  pg 917
Vista Color Imaging Inc, pg 931

OKLAHOMA

Academic Media & Digital
  Services, pg 672
PDC Productions, pg 852

OREGON

REX, pg 874

PENNSYLVANIA

Audio Visions Inc, pg 694
Bang! Pictures Inc, pg 701
Innovision Media Group, pg 788
JPL, pg 795
Main Point Productions, pg 815
The Videohouse Inc, pg 929
Visual Sound Inc, pg 931

RHODE ISLAND

Sound-FX-Design, pg 894

SOUTH CAROLINA

Impact Technology Group LLC,
  pg 786

TENNESSEE

American Blackguard Inc, pg 683
Fricon Entertainment Co Inc,
  pg 766
Scripps Networks, pg 882
Stage Post, pg 899

TEXAS

Anaphora Literary Press, pg 685
Biway Media, pg 706
Cerutti Productions Inc, pg 720
Dykeman Associates Inc, pg 748
Hurst Digital, pg 782
Mediaforce Productions, pg 822
Earl Miller Productions Inc, pg 827
Julye Newlin Productions Inc, pg 840
Texas Heart Institute Visual Communication Services, pg 911
Tropikal Productions, pg 918

VIRGINIA

Advance Concepts Inc, pg 677
Altruist Media LLC, pg 682
CACI Integrated Communications, pg 713
CDR Communications Inc, pg 719
Quince Imaging Inc, pg 868

WASHINGTON

Adams Creative & Production Services, pg 675
Bennett-Watt HD Productions Inc, pg 703
Laser Fantasy/HECK Industries/Photon Manufacturing, pg 804
North-by-Northwest - A Digital Studio, pg 842

WISCONSIN

Audio Visual of Milwaukee Inc, pg 694
Meridian Studios, pg 824
University of Wisconsin-Oshkosh Radio-TV-Film Dept, pg 923
USAV Group Inc, pg 923
Video Wisconsin Inc, pg 929
Watts Communications Inc, pg 934
Wisconsin Public Television, pg 940

WYOMING

Bridger Productions Inc, pg 710

PUERTO RICO

Stage Crew Audiovisual Inc, pg 898

NORTHWEST TERRITORIES

Yellowknife Films Inc, pg 944

ONTARIO

ADS Media, pg 677
Canamedia Inc, pg 715
DebsVoice, pg 739
GAPC (General Assembly Production Centre), pg 768
GestureTek, pg 770
Image Video Services & Productions, pg 785

SASKATCHEWAN

Thomega Entertainment Inc, pg 913

Display Equipment, Easel & Accessory Distributors

ALABAMA

Curtis Company, pg 736

ARIZONA

Arizona Cine Equipment, pg 688
Metropolitan Audio-Visual Inc, pg 824
Troxell-CDI, pg 918

ARKANSAS

Jay S Stanley & Associates Inc, pg 899
White Diamond Productions LLC, pg 937

CALIFORNIA

Advanced Systems Group LLC, pg 677
Ametron Audio/Video, pg 684
Associated Sound, pg 691
ATV Video Center Inc, pg 692
Audio Images Corp, pg 693
Auton Motorized Systems, pg 696
AV Conferencing LLC (AVC), pg 697
Boland Communications Inc, pg 708
California Tape Products Inc, pg 714
Christy's Editorial, pg 723
Cinema Equipment Sales of California Inc, pg 724
Instructional Materials & Equipment Distributors (I-Med), pg 789
JD Audio Visual Inc, pg 793
Media Fabricators Inc, pg 822
MediaPOINTE, pg 823
Pacific Video Products Inc, pg 849
Pioneer Electronics (USA) Inc, pg 857
PMP Marketing Inc, pg 858
Stanislaus AV Inc, pg 899
VMI Inc, pg 932

COLORADO

American Educational Products LLC, pg 683
Ceavco Audio Visual Company Inc, pg 719
Daylight Productions & Rentals, pg 739
Spectrum Audio Visual Services, pg 897

CONNECTICUT

HB Communications Inc, pg 777
MAVCO, pg 820
USI Inc, pg 924

FLORIDA

AVI-SPL, pg 698
Digital Video Systems, pg 742
Harmon's Audio-Visual Services, pg 776
Industrial Strength Inc, pg 787
Lighting Sales Connection Inc, pg 808
ONstage, pg 846
Photosound of Orlando Inc, pg 856
The Singing Machine Co Inc, pg 889
Tallahassee Audio Visual, pg 906
Techni-Lux Inc, pg 908

GEORGIA

Audio Visual Resources Inc, pg 695
Baker Audio Visual, pg 700
Convergent Media Systems, pg 731
Lighting & Production Equipment Inc, pg 807
PolyVision Corporation, pg 859

Stage Front Presentation Systems, pg 899
Visioneering International Inc, pg 931

HAWAII

The Audio Visual Co (AVCO), pg 694

ILLINOIS

Allen Visual Systems Inc, pg 680
Central Audio-Visual Equipment Inc, pg 719
Creative Technology (CT), pg 733
Joseph Electronics, pg 795
G T Luscombe Co Inc, pg 812
National Safety Council (NSC), pg 836
Quintessence Audio Ltd, pg 868

INDIANA

Sensory Technologies LLC, pg 884
SHP Electronics, pg 887

KENTUCKY

Audio Visual Techniques Inc, pg 695
Axxis Leasing Inc, pg 700
NOR-COM Inc, pg 841

LOUISIANA

Techkno Integration & Design Services LLC, pg 908

MAINE

Headlight Audio Visual Inc, pg 777

MARYLAND

Absolute Hollywood, pg 672
Cardinal Sound & Video, pg 717
Human Circuit, pg 782
Theatre Service & Supply Corp, pg 912

MASSACHUSETTS

Chartpak Inc, pg 721
Hannecke Display Systems Inc, pg 775
University Products Inc, pg 923

MICHIGAN

Olson Anderson Co, pg 685
City Events Group, pg 725
Michigan Office Solutions (MOS), A Xerox Company, pg 825
TEL Systems LLC, pg 909

MINNESOTA

AVI Systems, pg 698
Tierney Brothers Inc, pg 914

MISSISSIPPI

Bowie Audio Visual Enterprises Inc, pg 709
Jasper Ewing & Sons Inc, pg 757

MISSOURI

Communitronics Corp, pg 729
Conference Technologies Inc, pg 730
ITC, pg 791
Schiller's Audio-Visual, pg 881

NEW JERSEY

AlltecPro, pg 681
Argraph Corp, pg 688

Audio Visual Associates, pg 694
Audio Visual Dynamics®, pg 694
AV Bluebook, pg 696
Earl Girls Inc, pg 749
FlagHouse, pg 762
HamiltonBuhl, pg 775
Starlite, pg 900
SYMCO Inc, pg 905
Tele-Measurements Inc, pg 910
Total Video Products Inc, pg 916
Wired 4 Sound Inc, pg 940
Yorktel, pg 944

NEW YORK

AV Workshop, pg 697
B&H Photo Video, pg 701
BMI Supply, pg 708
BTX Technologies, pg 712
Bulbtronics Inc, pg 712
Canon USA Inc, pg 716
Century Business Solutions, pg 720
Colortone Audio Visual, pg 728
Design Audio Visual Inc, pg 741
eMagin Corp, pg 753
Indigo Productions, pg 787
KVL Audio Visual Services Inc, pg 802
Langie Audio Visual Systems, pg 803
Light Impressions, pg 807
Long Island Video Enterprises Live Inc, pg 811
PASCO, pg 851
Presentation Products Inc, pg 861
Ray Supply Inc, pg 870
RNJ Electronics, pg 875
Joseph Struhl Company Inc, pg 902
Topbulb, a Semmer Lighting Company, pg 915
Tri-Ed Distribution Inc, pg 918
Visual Technologies Corp, pg 932

NORTH CAROLINA

Camcor Inc, pg 715
Harrison Brothers, pg 776
Strategic Connections, pg 901

OHIO

Audio Visual Media, pg 694
Copp Integrated Systems, pg 731
Hughie's Event Production Services, pg 782
ITA Audio Visual Solutions, pg 791
Tri-State Audio Visual Co, pg 918
Tri-State Visual Products Inc, pg 918

PENNSYLVANIA

Advanced AV LLC, pg 677
Audio Visions Inc, pg 694
Aydin Displays, a Sparton Company, pg 700
Bernie's Photo Center, pg 704
Brodart Co, pg 711
Clair Companies, pg 725
J E Foss Co, pg 764
The Lerro Corp, pg 806
RSS Distributors, pg 878
Visual Sound Inc, pg 931
Wespen Audio Visual Co, pg 935

TENNESSEE

Continental Film, pg 731
Memphis Communications Corp, pg 823
Spring Arbor Distributors Inc, pg 898
Technical Support Systems LLC, pg 908
Zion Music Group, pg 945

AUDIO/VISUAL

Display Equipment, Easel & Accessory Distributors (continued)

TEXAS

Audio Visual Technologies Group (AVTG), pg 695
AVES Audio Visual Systems Inc, pg 698
Heffernan Audio Visual, pg 778
Lubbock Audio Visual Inc, pg 812
Radius® Display Products Inc, pg 869
Videotex Systems Inc, pg 930

UTAH

KAE Corp, pg 796
Webb Audio Visual, pg 935

VIRGINIA

Avitecture Inc, pg 699
Boitnott Visual Communications Corp (BVC), pg 708
Intellidyne LLC, pg 789
Lee Hartman & Sons Inc, pg 805
Metropolitan Audio Visual Co LLC, pg 824
Quince Imaging Inc, pg 868
The Whitlock Group, pg 937

WASHINGTON

Inland Audio Visual Co, pg 788

WISCONSIN

Audio Visual of Milwaukee Inc, pg 694
Camera Corner Connecting Point, pg 715
Demco Inc, pg 740
Full Compass Systems, pg 767
Safe Harbor Computers, pg 879
School Specialty Inc, pg 882

ALBERTA

Infosat Communications Inc, pg 787
McBain Camera Ltd, pg 820
SMART Technologies ULC, pg 891
Unique Communications Ltd, pg 921

BRITISH COLUMBIA

Commercial Electronics Ltd, pg 728

MANITOBA

Inland Audio Visual Ltd, pg 788

ONTARIO

Carr McLean Ltd, pg 717
CBM Ltd, pg 718
MVI - MultiVision Inc, pg 835
Westbury National Show Systems Ltd, pg 936

Display Equipment, Easel & Accessory Manufacturers

ARIZONA

OmniMount Systems, pg 845

CALIFORNIA

ALTINEX Inc, pg 682
Auton Motorized Systems, pg 696
Boland Communications Inc, pg 708
Extron Electronics, pg 758
Hoodman Corp, pg 781
Omnirax Furniture Co, pg 845
Penn Elcom Inc, pg 853
Pioneer Electronics (USA) Inc, pg 857
Silvestri California, pg 888
Tasman Group Pacific Rim, pg 907
Wohler Technologies Inc, pg 940

COLORADO

American Educational Products LLC, pg 683
Colorado Time Systems LLC, pg 728
Display Devices Inc, pg 743

CONNECTICUT

KOH Design Inc, pg 801

FLORIDA

The Great Southern Studios, pg 773
Vutec Corp, pg 933

GEORGIA

PolyVision Corporation, pg 859

ILLINOIS

Bretford Manufacturing Inc, pg 710
Kart-A-Bag Manufacturing Inc, pg 796
Luxor, pg 812
Peerless Industries, pg 853
Windel International/Weyel, pg 939

INDIANA

Da-Lite, a Legrand AV Inc brand, pg 737
Draper Inc, pg 746

MARYLAND

Absolute Hollywood, pg 672
Video Mount Products (VMP), pg 928

MASSACHUSETTS

Hannecke Display Systems Inc, pg 775
International Display & Exhibit Corp (IDEC), pg 790
Lineco, pg 809
University Products Inc, pg 923

MINNESOTA

Chief, a Legrand AV Inc brand, pg 722

MISSOURI

Magna Visual Inc, pg 814

NEW JERSEY

AlltecPro, pg 681
PeopleVisionFX, pg 854
Pro-Tape & Specialities Inc, pg 863
Sharp Electronics Corp, Professional Display Division, pg 885
Tally Display Corp, pg 906
Techflex Inc, pg 908

NEW YORK

Canon USA Inc, pg 716
Century Business Solutions, pg 720
ELMO USA Corp, pg 753
eMagin Corp, pg 753
General Audio-Visual Inc (GAVI), pg 769
Light Impressions, pg 807
Swivelier, pg 905
TecNec Distributing, pg 909

OHIO

Ghent Manufacturing, pg 770
Hilferty & Associates Inc, pg 780

PENNSYLVANIA

Automatic Devices Co (ADC), pg 696
Aydin Displays, a Sparton Company, pg 700

TEXAS

MooreCo Inc, pg 830
Radius® Display Products Inc, pg 869

UTAH

KAE Corp, pg 796

VIRGINIA

Avitecture Inc, pg 699
Drytac Corp, pg 747
Optikinetics Ltd - The Americas, pg 847

ALBERTA

SMART Technologies ULC, pg 891

ONTARIO

CBM Ltd, pg 718
Egan Visual Inc/Egan TeamBoard Inc, pg 751

Display Equipment, Easel & Accessory Rentals

ALABAMA

Audio-Video Resources Inc, pg 694

ALASKA

Imig Audio/Video Inc, pg 786

ARIZONA

Arizona Cine Equipment, pg 688
Merestone, pg 823
Metropolitan Audio-Visual Inc, pg 824

ARKANSAS

White Diamond Productions LLC, pg 937

CALIFORNIA

Ametron Audio/Video, pg 684
Associated Sound, pg 691
ATV Video Center Inc, pg 692
AV Guys, pg 697
Instructional Materials & Equipment Distributors (I-Med), pg 789
JD Audio Visual Inc, pg 793
Lynch Communications, pg 813
McCune Audio-Video-Lighting, pg 821
Media Fabricators Inc, pg 822

NEW YORK (continued)

MSI Production Services, pg 832
Munday & Collins AV, pg 834
PSAV® Presentation Services, pg 866
Stanislaus AV Inc, pg 899
Total Creative, pg 916
VER, pg 926

COLORADO

Daylight Productions & Rentals, pg 739

CONNECTICUT

A/V Davey, pg 697

FLORIDA

AVI-SPL, pg 698
The Great Southern Studios, pg 773
Harmon's Audio-Visual Services, pg 776
Industrial Strength Inc, pg 787
Jordan Klein Film & Video (JKFV), pg 795
Lighting Sales Connection Inc, pg 808
ONstage, pg 846
Photosound of Orlando Inc, pg 856
Sight & Sound Productions, pg 887
Tallahassee Audio Visual, pg 906

GEORGIA

Convergent Media Systems, pg 731
Lighting & Production Equipment Inc, pg 807
ON Services, a GES Company, pg 846
Stage Front Presentation Systems, pg 899
Staging Directions Inc, pg 899

ILLINOIS

Allen Visual Systems Inc, pg 680
Backstar Creative Media Inc, pg 700
Beatty TeleVisual Productions, pg 703
Central Audio-Visual Equipment Inc, pg 719
Helix Camera & Video, pg 778
PSAV® Presentation Services (Hotel Services Division), pg 866
Resolution Productions Group, pg 874

INDIANA

OMNI Productions, pg 845

KENTUCKY

Audio Visual Techniques Inc, pg 695

LOUISIANA

Clark Services Audio Visual & Exhibit Inc, pg 725

MARYLAND

Absolute Hollywood, pg 672
Advance Audiovisual Presentation Ltd, pg 677

MASSACHUSETTS

Capron Lighting & Sound Co Inc, pg 716
massAV, pg 819
Preston Productions Inc, pg 861

MICHIGAN

Olson Anderson Co, pg 685
City Events Group, pg 725
K&R All Media Productions LLC, pg 796
TEL Systems LLC, pg 909

MINNESOTA

AVI Systems, pg 698

MISSISSIPPI

Bowie Audio Visual Enterprises Inc, pg 709

MISSOURI

Communitronics Corp, pg 729
Schiller's Audio-Visual, pg 881
Show-Me Audio-Visual, pg 887

NEW HAMPSHIRE

Academic & Campus Technology Services, pg 672

NEW JERSEY

Audio Visual Associates, pg 694
Audio Visual Dynamics®, pg 694
Earl Girls Inc, pg 749
International Audio Visual Inc, pg 790
PLS Staging, pg 858
Starlite, pg 900

NEW YORK

AV Workshop, pg 697
Colortone Audio Visual, pg 728
Design Audio Visual Inc, pg 741
KVL Audio Visual Services Inc, pg 802
Langie Audio Visual Systems, pg 803
Long Island Video Enterprises Live Inc, pg 811
Manhattan Center Studios Inc, pg 816
Specialized Audio-Visual Inc, pg 896
Visual Technologies Corp, pg 932
Visual Word Systems Inc, pg 932
Zelman Studios Ltd, pg 945

NORTH CAROLINA

AV Metro Inc, pg 697

OHIO

Audio Visual Media, pg 694
Hughie's Event Production Services, pg 782
ITA Audio Visual Solutions, pg 791
Mills James Productions, pg 828

PENNSYLVANIA

Advanced AV LLC, pg 677
Audio Visions Inc, pg 694
FirstGeneration Audio/Visual Services, pg 761
FMP Media Solutions Inc, pg 763
Visual Sound Inc, pg 931

SOUTH CAROLINA

Sound & Images Inc, pg 893

TENNESSEE

Memphis Communications Corp, pg 823
Technical Support Systems LLC, pg 908

TEXAS

Audio Visual Technologies Group (AVTG), pg 695
Lubbock Audio Visual Inc, pg 812
Stage Directions, pg 898

UTAH

Webb Audio Visual, pg 935

VIRGINIA

American AV, pg 682
Boitnott Visual Communications Corp (BVC), pg 708
Lee Hartman & Sons Inc, pg 805
Projection, pg 865
Quince Imaging Inc, pg 868

WASHINGTON

Inland Audio Visual Co, pg 788

WISCONSIN

Event Essentials, pg 756
Full Compass Systems, pg 767

PUERTO RICO

Bonnin Electronics Inc, pg 708
Stage Crew Audiovisual Inc, pg 898

ALBERTA

Allstar Show Industries Inc, pg 681
Cine Audio Visual Sales & Service Ltd, pg 723
Evolution AV, pg 757
McBain Camera Ltd, pg 820
Unique Communications Ltd, pg 921

BRITISH COLUMBIA

Triad Communications Ltd, pg 918
Video Out Distribution, pg 928

MANITOBA

Inland Audio Visual Ltd, pg 788

ONTARIO

HD Source, pg 777
MVI - MultiVision Inc, pg 835
Westbury National Show Systems Ltd, pg 936

Display Equipment, Easel & Accessory Repairs

CALIFORNIA

Ametron Audio/Video, pg 684
McAlister Electronics, pg 820
Lloyd F McKinney Associates Inc, pg 821

COLORADO

Colorado Time Systems LLC, pg 728

FLORIDA

AVI-SPL, pg 698

GEORGIA

Lighting & Production Equipment Inc, pg 807
Stage Front Presentation Systems, pg 899

ILLINOIS

Allen Visual Systems Inc, pg 680

KENTUCKY

Axxis Leasing Inc, pg 700
NOR-COM Inc, pg 841

MARYLAND

Absolute Hollywood, pg 672

MICHIGAN

City Events Group, pg 725
TEL Systems LLC, pg 909

MINNESOTA

AVI Systems, pg 698

NEW JERSEY

Audio Visual Associates, pg 694

NEW YORK

Colortone Audio Visual, pg 728
Visual Technologies Corp, pg 932

NORTH CAROLINA

Camcor Inc, pg 715

OHIO

Audio Visual Media, pg 694
ITA Audio Visual Solutions, pg 791

PENNSYLVANIA

Advanced AV LLC, pg 677
Audio Visions Inc, pg 694

TENNESSEE

Memphis Communications Corp, pg 823
Technical Support Systems LLC, pg 908

TEXAS

Audio Visual Technologies Group (AVTG), pg 695
Lubbock Audio Visual Inc, pg 812

VIRGINIA

Avitecture Inc, pg 699

WASHINGTON

Inland Audio Visual Co, pg 788

WISCONSIN

Full Compass Systems, pg 767

ALBERTA

Infosat Communications Inc, pg 787

MANITOBA

Inland Audio Visual Ltd, pg 788

ONTARIO

MVI - MultiVision Inc, pg 835

Dry Mounting & Laminating Equipment & Supply Distributors

ALABAMA

Curtis Company, pg 736

ARIZONA

Professional Marketing Services Inc, pg 865
Troxell-CDI, pg 918

CALIFORNIA

Assured Audio Visual, pg 691
Educational Technology Services (ETS), pg 751
Gluskin's Custom Audio Video, pg 771
Hooper Camera & Imaging, pg 781
Instructional Materials & Equipment Distributors (I-Med), pg 789
Media Fabricators Inc, pg 822

COLORADO

Ceavco Audio Visual Company Inc, pg 719

CONNECTICUT

HB Communications Inc, pg 777
MAVCO, pg 820
Rockwell Communications Inc, pg 876
USI Inc, pg 924

FLORIDA

Hi-Tech Import Export Corp, pg 779
Tallahassee Audio Visual, pg 906

GEORGIA

Audio Visual Resources Inc, pg 695

ILLINOIS

Central Audio-Visual Equipment Inc, pg 719

IOWA

Sitler's Supplies Inc, pg 890

KANSAS

KK Office Solutions Inc, pg 799
Nazdar®, pg 837

LOUISIANA

Techkno Integration & Design Services LLC, pg 908

MAINE

Headlight Audio Visual Inc, pg 777

MARYLAND

Nelson White Systems Inc, pg 838
Nicholas P Pipino Associates Inc, pg 857
RTZ Audio Visual, pg 878

MASSACHUSETTS

Hunt's Photo & Video, pg 782
Lineco, pg 809
University Products Inc, pg 923

MICHIGAN

Olson Anderson Co, pg 685
City Events Group, pg 725
Michigan Office Solutions (MOS), A Xerox Company, pg 825

MINNESOTA

Tierney Brothers Inc, pg 914

AUDIO/VISUAL

Dry Mounting & Laminating Equipment & Supply Distributors (continued)

MISSISSIPPI

Bowie Audio Visual Enterprises Inc, pg 709
Jasper Ewing & Sons Inc, pg 757

MISSOURI

Conference Technologies Inc, pg 730
ITC, pg 791

NEW JERSEY

AlltecPro, pg 681
Argraph Corp, pg 688
AV Bluebook, pg 696
Falcon Safety Products Inc, pg 758
HamiltonBuhl, pg 775
Vcom IMC, pg 925

NEW YORK

Affton Graphics Inc, pg 678
Gaylord Archival, pg 768
Indigo Productions, pg 787
Langie Audio Visual Systems, pg 803
Light Impressions, pg 807
Markertek Video Supply, pg 817
Neptune Photo Inc, pg 838
PASCO, pg 851
Ray Supply Inc, pg 870

NORTH CAROLINA

Camcor Inc, pg 715

OHIO

Audio Visual Media, pg 694
Graphic Laminating LLC, pg 773
Tri-State Audio Visual Co, pg 918
Tri-State Visual Products Inc, pg 918

PENNSYLVANIA

Advanced AV LLC, pg 677
Bernie's Photo Center, pg 704
Brodart Co, pg 711
J E Foss Co, pg 764
Garcia Marketing Inc, pg 768
Grise Audio Visual Center Inc, pg 774
IDenticard Systems Inc, pg 784
Visual Sound Inc, pg 931
Wespen Audio Visual Co, pg 935

TEXAS

AVES Audio Visual Systems Inc, pg 698
Heffernan Audio Visual, pg 778
JSAV, pg 795
Lubbock Audio Visual Inc, pg 812

VIRGINIA

Drytac Corp, pg 747
Lee Hartman & Sons Inc, pg 805
Metropolitan Audio Visual Co LLC, pg 824
The Whitlock Group, pg 937

WASHINGTON

Inland Audio Visual Co, pg 788

WISCONSIN

Audio Visual of Milwaukee Inc, pg 694
Camera Corner Connecting Point, pg 715
Demco Inc, pg 740
School Specialty Inc, pg 882

PUERTO RICO

Audio Visual Concepts Inc, pg 694
Bonnin Electronics Inc, pg 708

ALBERTA

McBain Camera Ltd, pg 820

Dry Mounting & Laminating Equipment & Supply Manufacturers

ARIZONA

Savage Universal Corp, pg 881

CONNECTICUT

USI Inc, pg 924

FLORIDA

Kinetronics Corp, pg 799

ILLINOIS

ACCO Brands Corp, pg 673
GBC Document Finishing, pg 768
Pres-On Corp, pg 861
Sprayway Inc, pg 898

MASSACHUSETTS

University Products Inc, pg 923

MISSOURI

Southwest Binding & Laminating, pg 896

NEW JERSEY

Falcon Safety Products Inc, pg 758

NEW YORK

TecNec Distributing, pg 909

OKLAHOMA

Marvel Photo Inc, pg 818

PENNSYLVANIA

IDenticard Systems Inc, pg 784

TEXAS

MooreCo Inc, pg 830

VIRGINIA

Drytac Corp, pg 747

Dry Mounting & Laminating Equipment & Supply Rentals

ARIZONA

Merestone, pg 823

CALIFORNIA

Media Fabricators Inc, pg 822
VER, pg 926

GEORGIA

Staging Directions Inc, pg 899

ILLINOIS

Central Audio-Visual Equipment Inc, pg 719
Helix Camera & Video, pg 778

MINNESOTA

AVI Systems, pg 698

MISSISSIPPI

Bowie Audio Visual Enterprises Inc, pg 709
Jasper Ewing & Sons Inc, pg 757

MISSOURI

ITC, pg 791

NEW HAMPSHIRE

Apertura, pg 686

NEW JERSEY

Video Corporation of America (VCA), pg 927

NEW YORK

Ray Supply Inc, pg 870

OHIO

Audio Visual Media, pg 694
Vista Color Imaging Inc, pg 931

PENNSYLVANIA

Grise Audio Visual Center Inc, pg 774

VIRGINIA

Lee Hartman & Sons Inc, pg 805
Projection, pg 865

WASHINGTON

Inland Audio Visual Co, pg 788

Dry Mounting & Laminating Equipment & Supply Repairs

CALIFORNIA

McAlister Electronics, pg 820

CONNECTICUT

HB Communications Inc, pg 777

KANSAS

KK Office Solutions Inc, pg 799

MAINE

Headlight Audio Visual Inc, pg 777

MARYLAND

Nelson White Systems Inc, pg 838

MICHIGAN

City Events Group, pg 725
TEL Systems LLC, pg 909

MINNESOTA

AVI Systems, pg 698

MISSISSIPPI

Bowie Audio Visual Enterprises Inc, pg 709

NEW YORK

Colortone Audio Visual, pg 728
Langie Audio Visual Systems, pg 803
Ray Supply Inc, pg 870

OHIO

Audio Visual Media, pg 694
Tri-State Audio Visual Co, pg 918

PENNSYLVANIA

J E Foss Co, pg 764
IDenticard Systems Inc, pg 784

TEXAS

Audio Visual Technologies Group (AVTG), pg 695
Lubbock Audio Visual Inc, pg 812

VIRGINIA

Boitnott Visual Communications Corp (BVC), pg 708
Drytac Corp, pg 747
Metropolitan Audio Visual Co LLC, pg 824
The Whitlock Group, pg 937

WASHINGTON

Inland Audio Visual Co, pg 788

WISCONSIN

School Specialty Inc, pg 882

Duplication—Filmstrips

CALIFORNIA

Allied Artists International Inc, pg 681
Coloredge Inc, pg 728
Lynch Communications, pg 813
QRS Software Services, pg 867

COLORADO

Maniac Productions, pg 816

FLORIDA

Jordan Klein Film & Video (JKFV), pg 795

GEORGIA

Imagers, pg 785
Visioneering International Inc, pg 931

MASSACHUSETTS

Colortek of Boston, pg 728
CommCreative, pg 728
TR Productions, pg 916

MISSOURI

Show-Me Audio-Visual, pg 887

NEW HAMPSHIRE

Apertura, pg 686

NEW JERSEY

Broadcast Center Studios, pg 710
CELCO, pg 719
Reed Presentations Inc (RPI),
pg 872

NEW YORK

Duggal Visual Solutions Inc, pg 747
Duplication Specialists Inc, pg 748
Ketchum Inc, pg 798
Modernage Photographic Services
Inc, pg 828
Visual Technologies Corp, pg 932
Visual Word Systems Inc, pg 932
Zelman Studios Ltd, pg 945

OHIO

Aztec Video Productions, pg 700

PENNSYLVANIA

Audio Visual Communications Inc,
pg 694
Berry & Homer, pg 704

TENNESSEE

Memphis Communications Corp,
pg 823
Stage Post, pg 899

TEXAS

Hurst Digital, pg 782
Stage Directions, pg 898

VIRGINIA

Blair Inc, pg 707

WISCONSIN

Audio Visual of Milwaukee Inc,
pg 694
USAV Group Inc, pg 923

ONTARIO

McNabb & Connolly, pg 821

Duplication—Slides

ARIZONA

Image Craft LLC, pg 784

CALIFORNIA

Action Photo Digital Graphics,
pg 675
CCI Digital, a DVS Company,
pg 718
Coloredge Inc, pg 728
Gluskin's Custom Audio Video,
pg 771
Joan Kramer & Associates Inc,
pg 801
Lynch Communications, pg 813
PSI Inc, pg 866
QRS Software Services, pg 867
Shokus Video, pg 886

FLORIDA

Cheuvront Studios, pg 721
Communications Concepts Inc
(CCI), pg 729

GEORGIA

Imagers, pg 785
Visioneering International Inc,
pg 931

ILLINOIS

CCore Media Inc, pg 718
Gamma Imaging, pg 768
Helix Camera & Video, pg 778
JMC Photo & Digital Services Inc,
pg 794
Major Media Inc, pg 815
Southern Illinois University, pg 895

INDIANA

OMNI Productions, pg 845

IOWA

Educational Technology & Media
Services, pg 751

LOUISIANA

Louisiana State University Division
of Strategic Communications,
pg 811

MASSACHUSETTS

Colortek of Boston, pg 728
CommCreative, pg 728
DGI-Invisuals LLC, pg 741
Integrated Solutions Group, pg 789
TR Productions, pg 916

MICHIGAN

Arbor Oakland Group, pg 688
K&R's Recording Studios Inc,
pg 796
Michigan Office Solutions (MOS),
A Xerox Company, pg 825

MINNESOTA

Linhoff Photo & Digital Imaging,
pg 809
Pointward, pg 858

MISSISSIPPI

Jasper Ewing & Sons Inc, pg 757

MISSOURI

Allied Photocolor Co, pg 681
Show-Me Audio-Visual, pg 887
Visionworks Design Services Inc,
pg 931

MONTANA

KUSM TV, pg 802

NEVADA

Aardvark Video & Media
Productions, pg 671

NEW HAMPSHIRE

Apertura, pg 686

NEW JERSEY

Broadcast Center Studios, pg 710
CELCO, pg 719
Laurel Video Productions, pg 804
Reed Presentations Inc (RPI),
pg 872
Suede Interactive, pg 903
Video Corporation of America
(VCA), pg 927

NEW YORK

Duggal Visual Solutions Inc, pg 747
Duplication Specialists Inc, pg 748
Modernage Photographic Services
Inc, pg 828
Jack Morton Worldwide, pg 830

SMP Digital Graphics, pg 891
Visual Technologies Corp, pg 932
Visual Word Systems Inc, pg 932
Zelman Studios Ltd, pg 945

NORTH CAROLINA

Camcor Inc, pg 715
Image Associates Inc, pg 784

OHIO

Aztec Video Productions, pg 700
Cuyahoga Community College
Student Production Office (SPO),
pg 736
Thread Marketing Group, pg 913
Vista Color Imaging Inc, pg 931

PENNSYLVANIA

Audio Visual Communications Inc,
pg 694
Bernie's Photo Center, pg 704
Berry & Homer, pg 704
FMP Media Solutions Inc, pg 763
Main Point Productions, pg 815

TENNESSEE

Memphis Communications Corp,
pg 823
Stage Post, pg 899

TEXAS

Hurst Digital, pg 782
IntegraColor, pg 789
Stage Directions, pg 898
Texas Heart Institute Visual
Communication Services, pg 911
Thomas Printworks, pg 912

VERMONT

University of Vermont, Instructional
Television Dept, pg 923

VIRGINIA

Blair Inc, pg 707

WASHINGTON

Kostov Productions, pg 801

WISCONSIN

Audio Visual of Milwaukee Inc,
pg 694
USAV Group Inc, pg 923

ALBERTA

Cine Audio Visual Sales & Service
Ltd, pg 723

ONTARIO

Silver Creek Media Inc, pg 888

Duplication—
Transparencies

ARIZONA

Image Craft LLC, pg 784

CALIFORNIA

Action Photo Digital Graphics,
pg 675
Coloredge Inc, pg 728
Gluskin's Custom Audio Video,
pg 771
Lynch Communications, pg 813
McCune Audio-Video-Lighting,
pg 821

QRS Software Services, pg 867
Total Creative, pg 916

CONNECTICUT

MAVCO, pg 820
USI Inc, pg 924

FLORIDA

Cheuvront Studios, pg 721
Jordan Klein Film & Video (JKFV),
pg 795

GEORGIA

Imagers, pg 785
Visioneering International Inc,
pg 931

ILLINOIS

Gamma Imaging, pg 768
JMC Photo & Digital Services Inc,
pg 794
Southern Illinois University, pg 895

INDIANA

OMNI Productions, pg 845

IOWA

Educational Technology & Media
Services, pg 751

MARYLAND

Satellite Media Production, pg 881

MASSACHUSETTS

Capron Lighting & Sound Co Inc,
pg 716
Colortek of Boston, pg 728
CommCreative, pg 728
DGI-Invisuals LLC, pg 741
TR Productions, pg 916

MICHIGAN

K&R's Recording Studios Inc,
pg 796
Michigan Office Solutions (MOS),
A Xerox Company, pg 825

MISSISSIPPI

Jasper Ewing & Sons Inc, pg 757

MISSOURI

Allied Photocolor Co, pg 681
Visionworks Design Services Inc,
pg 931
VSG Digital Media Solutions,
pg 933

NEW HAMPSHIRE

Apertura, pg 686
Chip Taylor Communications LLC,
pg 907

NEW JERSEY

Broadcast Center Studios, pg 710
CELCO, pg 719
C2 Imaging, pg 735
NFL Films Music Library, pg 841
Reed Presentations Inc (RPI),
pg 872
Video Corporation of America
(VCA), pg 927

AUDIO/VISUAL

Duplication—Transparencies (continued)

NEW YORK

Duggal Visual Solutions Inc, pg 747
Long Island Video Enterprises Live Inc, pg 811
Modernage Photographic Services Inc, pg 828
Jack Morton Worldwide, pg 830
Neptune Photo Inc, pg 838
SMP Digital Graphics, pg 891
Visual Technologies Corp, pg 932
Zelman Studios Ltd, pg 945

NORTH CAROLINA

Image Associates Inc, pg 784

OHIO

Aztec Video Productions, pg 700
Thread Marketing Group, pg 913
Vista Color Imaging Inc, pg 931

PENNSYLVANIA

Audio Visual Communications Inc, pg 694
Berry & Homer, pg 704

TENNESSEE

Memphis Communications Corp, pg 823
Stage Post, pg 899

TEXAS

Hurst Digital, pg 782
Stage Directions, pg 898
Thomas Printworks, pg 912

VIRGINIA

Blair Inc, pg 707
The Whitlock Group, pg 937

WISCONSIN

Audio Visual of Milwaukee Inc, pg 694
USAV Group Inc, pg 923

Easels, see Display Equipment, Easel & Accessory

Electronic Chalkboard Distributors

ARIZONA

Troxell-CDI, pg 918
Ultimate Presentation Systems Inc, pg 920

ARKANSAS

Jay S Stanley & Associates Inc, pg 899
White Diamond Productions LLC, pg 937

CALIFORNIA

Ametron Audio/Video, pg 684
Beta Electronics Inc, pg 704
Christy's Editorial, pg 723
Cibola Systems, pg 723

MediaPOINTE, pg 823
Stanislaus AV Inc, pg 899

COLORADO

Daylight Productions & Rentals, pg 739

CONNECTICUT

HB Communications Inc, pg 777

FLORIDA

Altel Systems Group Inc, pg 682
AVI-SPL, pg 698
Harris Corp, pg 776
ONstage, pg 846

GEORGIA

PolyVision Corporation, pg 859
Stage Front Presentation Systems, pg 899

HAWAII

The Audio Visual Co (AVCO), pg 694

ILLINOIS

Allen Visual Systems Inc, pg 680
Quintessence Audio Ltd, pg 868
The Screen Works®, pg 882

INDIANA

Sensory Technologies LLC, pg 884

KENTUCKY

NOR-COM Inc, pg 841

LOUISIANA

Techkno Integration & Design Services LLC, pg 908

MAINE

Headlight Audio Visual Inc, pg 777

MARYLAND

Cardinal Sound & Video, pg 717

MASSACHUSETTS

Pro AV Systems, pg 862
Rule Boston Camera, pg 878

MICHIGAN

Michigan Office Solutions (MOS), A Xerox Company, pg 825
TEL Systems LLC, pg 909

MINNESOTA

Tierney Brothers Inc, pg 914

MISSOURI

Schiller's Audio-Visual, pg 881

NEW JERSEY

AlltecPro, pg 681
Audio Visual Associates, pg 694
AV Bluebook, pg 696
HamiltonBuhl, pg 775
Total Video Products Inc, pg 916
Wired 4 Sound Inc, pg 940
Yorktel, pg 944

NEW YORK

Audio-Video Corp, pg 694
Colortone Audio Visual, pg 728

Design Audio Visual Inc, pg 741
General Audio-Visual Inc (GAVI), pg 769
Markertek Video Supply, pg 817
Presentation Products Inc, pg 861
Stampede Presentation Products Inc, pg 899

OHIO

Tri-State Audio Visual Co, pg 918
Tri-State Visual Products Inc, pg 918

PENNSYLVANIA

Advanced AV LLC, pg 677
J E Foss Co, pg 764
Grise Audio Visual Center Inc, pg 774
Wespen Audio Visual Co, pg 935

RHODE ISLAND

Shanix Inc, pg 885

TENNESSEE

Spring Arbor Distributors Inc, pg 898
Technical Support Systems LLC, pg 908

TEXAS

Audio Visual Technologies Group (AVTG), pg 695
AVES Audio Visual Systems Inc, pg 698
Data Projections Inc, pg 738
Lubbock Audio Visual Inc, pg 812
Tarpley Media Systems, pg 907

VIRGINIA

Avitecture Inc, pg 699
Design & Production Inc, pg 740
Intellidyne LLC, pg 789
Lee Hartman & Sons Inc, pg 805

WISCONSIN

Audio Visual of Milwaukee Inc, pg 694
Full Compass Systems, pg 767
Safe Harbor Computers, pg 879

PUERTO RICO

Audio Visual Concepts Inc, pg 694

ALBERTA

Infosat Communications Inc, pg 787
Matrix Video Communications Corp (MVCC), pg 819
SMART Technologies ULC, pg 891

BRITISH COLUMBIA

Commercial Electronics Ltd, pg 728

MANITOBA

Inland Audio Visual Ltd, pg 788

ONTARIO

Cinema Stage Inc, pg 724
Westbury National Show Systems Ltd, pg 936

Electronic Chalkboard Manufacturers

CALIFORNIA

Beta Electronics Inc, pg 704

GEORGIA

PolyVision Corporation, pg 859

NEW JERSEY

Tally Display Corp, pg 906

NEW YORK

TecNec Distributing, pg 909

OHIO

Turning Technologies LLC, pg 919

OREGON

PLUS Corp of America, pg 858

ALBERTA

SMART Technologies ULC, pg 891

Electronic Chalkboard Rentals

ARIZONA

Merestone, pg 823
Ultimate Presentation Systems Inc, pg 920

ARKANSAS

White Diamond Productions LLC, pg 937

CALIFORNIA

Alliant Event Services, pg 681
Ametron Audio/Video, pg 684
Lynch Communications, pg 813
VER, pg 926
Video Resources Inc, pg 928

CONNECTICUT

A/V Davey, pg 697

FLORIDA

AVI-SPL, pg 698
ONstage, pg 846

GEORGIA

ON Services, a GES Company, pg 846
Stage Front Presentation Systems, pg 899

ILLINOIS

Allen Visual Systems Inc, pg 680

MASSACHUSETTS

Preston Productions Inc, pg 861

NEW JERSEY

Wired 4 Sound Inc, pg 940

NEW YORK

Colortone Audio Visual, pg 728

TENNESSEE

Technical Support Systems LLC, pg 908

VIRGINIA

Lee Hartman & Sons Inc, pg 805

WISCONSIN
Full Compass Systems, pg 767

MANITOBA
Inland Audio Visual Ltd, pg 788

ONTARIO
Westbury National Show Systems
Ltd, pg 936

Electronic Chalkboard Repairs

CALIFORNIA
Ametron Audio/Video, pg 684
McAlister Electronics, pg 820

GEORGIA
Stage Front Presentation Systems,
pg 899

ILLINOIS
Allen Visual Systems Inc, pg 680

KENTUCKY
NOR-COM Inc, pg 841

MAINE
Headlight Audio Visual Inc, pg 777

MICHIGAN
TEL Systems LLC, pg 909

MISSOURI
Schiller's Audio-Visual, pg 881

OHIO
ITA Audio Visual Solutions, pg 791

TENNESSEE
Technical Support Systems LLC,
pg 908

TEXAS
Audio Visual Technologies Group
(AVTG), pg 695
Tarpley Media Systems, pg 907

VIRGINIA
Avitecture Inc, pg 699

WISCONSIN
Full Compass Systems, pg 767

ALBERTA
Infosat Communications Inc, pg 787

MANITOBA
Inland Audio Visual Ltd, pg 788

Enlargement— Transparencies

ARIZONA
Image Craft LLC, pg 784
Merestone, pg 823

CALIFORNIA
Action Photo Digital Graphics,
pg 675
Bay Photo Lab, pg 702
Coloredge Inc, pg 728
Lynch Communications, pg 813
QRS Software Services, pg 867

COLORADO
Stanco Sales LLC, pg 899

CONNECTICUT
New London Media, pg 839

GEORGIA
Imagers, pg 785
Staging Directions Inc, pg 899

ILLINOIS
Gamma Imaging, pg 768
Helix Camera & Video, pg 778
JMC Photo & Digital Services Inc,
pg 794
Southern Illinois University, pg 895

IOWA
American Color Imaging (ACI),
pg 683
Educational Technology & Media
Services, pg 751

KENTUCKY
Kinetic Corp, pg 799

LOUISIANA
Louisiana State University Division
of Strategic Communications,
pg 811

MASSACHUSETTS
Colortek of Boston, pg 728
DGI-Invisuals LLC, pg 741

MICHIGAN
Arbor Oakland Group, pg 688
K&R's Recording Studios Inc,
pg 796
Michigan Office Solutions (MOS),
A Xerox Company, pg 825
Tectonics Industries LLC, pg 909

MISSISSIPPI
Jasper Ewing & Sons Inc, pg 757

MISSOURI
Allied Photocolor Co, pg 681
Visionworks Design Services Inc,
pg 931

NEW JERSEY
C2 Imaging, pg 735

NEW YORK
Duggal Visual Solutions Inc, pg 747
Modernage Photographic Services
Inc, pg 828
Neptune Photo Inc, pg 838
Zelman Studios Ltd, pg 945

NORTH CAROLINA
Image Associates Inc, pg 784

OHIO
Aztec Video Productions, pg 700
Thread Marketing Group, pg 913
Vista Color Imaging Inc, pg 931

PENNSYLVANIA
Berry & Homer, pg 704

TENNESSEE
Stage Post, pg 899

TEXAS
IntegraColor, pg 789
Thomas Printworks, pg 912

VIRGINIA
Blair Inc, pg 707

WISCONSIN
USAV Group Inc, pg 923

BRITISH COLUMBIA
Triad Communications Ltd, pg 918

Filmstrip Duplication, *see* Duplication—Filmstrips

Filmstrip Printing, *see* Processing & Printing— Filmstrips

Filmstrip Printing, *see* Volume Printing— Filmstrips

Filmstrip Processing & Printing, *see* Processing & Printing—Filmstrips

Filmstrip Projector, Viewer & Equipment Distributors

ALABAMA
Curtis Company, pg 736

ARIZONA
Arizona Cine Equipment, pg 688
Professional Marketing Services Inc,
pg 865
Troxell-CDI, pg 918

ARKANSAS
White Diamond Productions LLC,
pg 937

CALIFORNIA
Ametron Audio/Video, pg 684
Assured Audio Visual, pg 691
California Tape Products Inc,
pg 714
Christy's Editorial, pg 723
Gluskin's Custom Audio Video,
pg 771
Instructional Materials & Equipment
Distributors (I-Med), pg 789
Media Fabricators Inc, pg 822

COLORADO
American Educational Products
LLC, pg 683
Stanco Sales LLC, pg 899

CONNECTICUT
HB Communications Inc, pg 777
MAVCO, pg 820
Rockwell Communications Inc,
pg 876
USI Inc, pg 924

FLORIDA
Hi-Tech Import Export Corp,
pg 779
ONstage, pg 846
Tallahassee Audio Visual, pg 906

GEORGIA
Audio Visual Resources Inc, pg 695
Stage Front Presentation Systems,
pg 899
Visioneering International Inc,
pg 931

HAWAII
The Audio Visual Co (AVCO),
pg 694

ILLINOIS
Allen Visual Systems Inc, pg 680
Central Audio-Visual Equipment
Inc, pg 719
Major Reproductions Equipment
Co, pg 815

KENTUCKY
NOR-COM Inc, pg 841

LOUISIANA
Techkno Integration & Design
Services LLC, pg 908

MARYLAND
Cardinal Sound & Video, pg 717

MASSACHUSETTS
University Products Inc, pg 923

MICHIGAN
City Events Group, pg 725
Michigan Office Solutions (MOS),
A Xerox Company, pg 825

MISSISSIPPI
Bowie Audio Visual Enterprises Inc,
pg 709

MISSOURI
Communitronics Corp, pg 729
Conference Technologies Inc,
pg 730
ITC, pg 791
Schiller's Audio-Visual, pg 881

NEW JERSEY
AlltecPro, pg 681
Audio Visual Associates, pg 694
Audio Visual Dynamics®, pg 694
AV Bluebook, pg 696
HamiltonBuhl, pg 775
SYMCO Inc, pg 905
Vcom IMC, pg 925
Video Corporation of America
(VCA), pg 927

AUDIO/VISUAL

Filmstrip Projector, Viewer & Equipment Distributors (continued)

NEW JERSEY (continued)

Wired 4 Sound Inc, pg 940
Yorktel, pg 944

NEW YORK

Audio-Video Corp, pg 694
AV Workshop, pg 697
Gaylord Archival, pg 768
Indigo Productions, pg 787
Langie Audio Visual Systems, pg 803
Long Island Video Enterprises Live Inc, pg 811
Markertek Video Supply, pg 817
Neptune Photo Inc, pg 838
Ray Supply Inc, pg 870
Topbulb, a Semmer Lighting Company, pg 915
Visual Technologies Corp, pg 932

NORTH CAROLINA

Camcor Inc, pg 715

OHIO

Audio Visual Media, pg 694
Tri-State Visual Products Inc, pg 918

PENNSYLVANIA

Advanced AV LLC, pg 677
Audio Visions Inc, pg 694
Audio Visual Communications Inc, pg 694
Bernie's Photo Center, pg 704
Brodart Co, pg 711
J E Foss Co, pg 764
Grise Audio Visual Center Inc, pg 774
Visual Sound Inc, pg 931
Wespen Audio Visual Co, pg 935

TENNESSEE

Memphis Communications Corp, pg 823

TEXAS

Audio Visual Technologies Group (AVTG), pg 695
JSAV, pg 795
Lubbock Audio Visual Inc, pg 812
Quality Audio Visual Service Inc, pg 867

VIRGINIA

Lee Hartman & Sons Inc, pg 805
Metropolitan Audio Visual Co LLC, pg 824
The Whitlock Group, pg 937

WASHINGTON

Inland Audio Visual Co, pg 788

WISCONSIN

Audio Visual of Milwaukee Inc, pg 694
Camera Corner Connecting Point, pg 715
Demco Inc, pg 740
School Specialty Inc, pg 882

ALBERTA

McBain Camera Ltd, pg 820

MANITOBA

Inland Audio Visual Ltd, pg 788

ONTARIO

Nationwide Audio Visual Co, pg 837

Filmstrip Projector, Viewer & Equipment Manufacturers

CALIFORNIA

Auton Motorized Systems, pg 696

COLORADO

American Educational Products LLC, pg 683

INDIANA

Star Case Manufacturing Co Inc, pg 900

NEW YORK

General Audio-Visual Inc (GAVI), pg 769
TecNec Distributing, pg 909

Filmstrip Projector, Viewer & Equipment Rentals

ARIZONA

Arizona Cine Equipment, pg 688
Merestone, pg 823
Metropolitan Audio-Visual Inc, pg 824

ARKANSAS

White Diamond Productions LLC, pg 937

CALIFORNIA

Ametron Audio/Video, pg 684
Artichoke Productions, pg 690
Gluskin's Custom Audio Video, pg 771
Instructional Materials & Equipment Distributors (I-Med), pg 789
Lynch Communications, pg 813
McCune Audio-Video-Lighting, pg 821
Media Fabricators Inc, pg 822
Munday & Collins AV, pg 834
VER, pg 926

COLORADO

Multimedia Audio Visual Inc, pg 833

CONNECTICUT

A/V Davey, pg 697
Rockwell Communications Inc, pg 876

FLORIDA

Jordan Klein Film & Video (JKFV), pg 795
ONstage, pg 846
Sight & Sound Productions, pg 887
Tallahassee Audio Visual, pg 906

GEORGIA

Audio Visual Resources Inc, pg 695
ON Services, a GES Company, pg 846
Stage Front Presentation Systems, pg 899
Staging Directions Inc, pg 899

ILLINOIS

Allen Visual Systems Inc, pg 680
Central Audio-Visual Equipment Inc, pg 719
Helix Camera & Video, pg 778
Pepper Group, pg 854
PSAV® Presentation Services (Hotel Services Division), pg 866
RC Communications, pg 870

INDIANA

Advanced Media Integration, pg 677
Gary Camera & Digital, pg 768
OMNI Productions, pg 845

KENTUCKY

Audio Visual Techniques Inc, pg 695

MARYLAND

dbF a Media Company, pg 739
Nelson White Systems Inc, pg 838

MASSACHUSETTS

massAV, pg 819

MICHIGAN

City Events Group, pg 725

MINNESOTA

AVI Systems, pg 698

MISSISSIPPI

Bowie Audio Visual Enterprises Inc, pg 709
Jasper Ewing & Sons Inc, pg 757

MISSOURI

Communitronics Corp, pg 729
Show-Me Audio-Visual, pg 887

NEW JERSEY

Audio Visual Dynamics®, pg 694
International Audio Visual Inc, pg 790

NEW YORK

Ace Video, pg 674
AV Workshop, pg 697
CMI Communications, pg 727
Langie Audio Visual Systems, pg 803
Long Island Video Enterprises Live Inc, pg 811
Neptune Photo Inc, pg 838
Ray Supply Inc, pg 870
Visual Technologies Corp, pg 932

OHIO

Audio Visual Media, pg 694

PENNSYLVANIA

Advanced AV LLC, pg 677
Audio Visions Inc, pg 694
Audio Visual Communications Inc, pg 694

GEORGIA

Grise Audio Visual Center Inc, pg 774
Visual Sound Inc, pg 931

TENNESSEE

Memphis Communications Corp, pg 823

TEXAS

Audio Visual Technologies Group (AVTG), pg 695
JSAV, pg 795
Lubbock Audio Visual Inc, pg 812

VIRGINIA

Lee Hartman & Sons Inc, pg 805
Metropolitan Audio Visual Co LLC, pg 824
Projection, pg 865
The Whitlock Group, pg 937

WASHINGTON

Inland Audio Visual Co, pg 788

WISCONSIN

Camera Corner Connecting Point, pg 715
Event Essentials, pg 756
School Specialty Inc, pg 882

PUERTO RICO

Stage Crew Audiovisual Inc, pg 898

ALBERTA

Global TV, pg 771
Unique Communications Ltd, pg 921

BRITISH COLUMBIA

Clark's Audio Visual Services Ltd, pg 725
Triad Communications Ltd, pg 918

MANITOBA

Inland Audio Visual Ltd, pg 788

QUEBEC

Group PVP, pg 774

Filmstrip Projector, Viewer & Equipment Repairs

CALIFORNIA

Ametron Audio/Video, pg 684
Instructional Materials & Equipment Distributors (I-Med), pg 789
McAlister Electronics, pg 820
Lloyd F McKinney Associates Inc, pg 821
Pro Camera Repair, pg 862

CONNECTICUT

HB Communications Inc, pg 777
Rockwell Communications Inc, pg 876

FLORIDA

Tallahassee Audio Visual, pg 906

GEORGIA

Audio Visual Resources Inc, pg 695
Stage Front Presentation Systems, pg 899

ILLINOIS

Allen Visual Systems Inc, pg 680
Central Audio-Visual Equipment Inc, pg 719

INDIANA

Gary Camera & Digital, pg 768

KENTUCKY

NOR-COM Inc, pg 841

MICHIGAN

City Events Group, pg 725
TEL Systems LLC, pg 909

MINNESOTA

AVI Systems, pg 698

MISSISSIPPI

Bowie Audio Visual Enterprises Inc, pg 709

MISSOURI

Cintrex Audio Visual, pg 725
Communitronics Corp, pg 729
Schiller's Audio-Visual, pg 881

NEW JERSEY

Audio Visual Associates, pg 694

NEW YORK

Colortone Audio Visual, pg 728
Langie Audio Visual Systems, pg 803
Ray Supply Inc, pg 870
Visual Technologies Corp, pg 932

NORTH CAROLINA

Camcor Inc, pg 715

OHIO

Audio Visual Media, pg 694
Tri-State Audio Visual Co, pg 918
Tri-State Visual Products Inc, pg 918

PENNSYLVANIA

Audio Visions Inc, pg 694
J E Foss Co, pg 764
Wespen Audio Visual Co, pg 935

TENNESSEE

Memphis Communications Corp, pg 823

TEXAS

Audio Visual Technologies Group (AVTG), pg 695
Lubbock Audio Visual Inc, pg 812
Quality Audio Visual Service Inc, pg 867

VIRGINIA

Boitnott Visual Communications Corp (BVC), pg 708
Lee Hartman & Sons Inc, pg 805
Metropolitan Audio Visual Co LLC, pg 824
The Whitlock Group, pg 937

WASHINGTON

Inland Audio Visual Co, pg 788

WISCONSIN

Camera Corner Connecting Point, pg 715
School Specialty Inc, pg 882

ALBERTA

Infosat Communications Inc, pg 787

MANITOBA

Inland Audio Visual Ltd, pg 788

Filmstrip Pulsing, *see* Pulsing—Filmstrip

Filmstrip Retouching, *see* Retouching—Filmstrips

Filmstrip to Slide Transfers, *see* Transfers—Filmstrip to Slide

Filmstrip Viewer, *see* Filmstrip Projector, Viewer & Equipment

Intercom System Distributors

ALABAMA

Curtis Company, pg 736

ARIZONA

Arizona Cine Equipment, pg 688
EAR Professional Audio/Video, pg 749
Metropolitan Audio-Visual Inc, pg 824
Projector SuperStore LLC, pg 865
Troxell-CDI, pg 918

ARKANSAS

White Diamond Productions LLC, pg 937

CALIFORNIA

Advanced Systems Group LLC, pg 677
Ametron Audio/Video, pg 684
Associated Sound, pg 691
Audio Images Corp, pg 693
Clear-Com® LLC, pg 726
Electronic Design Solutions Inc, pg 752
Empire Pro, pg 753
JD Audio Visual Inc, pg 793
Location Sound Corp, pg 810
Lloyd F McKinney Associates Inc, pg 821
Media Fabricators Inc, pg 822
MediaPOINTE, pg 823
Orvac Electronics, pg 848
Sanako Inc, pg 880
Southern California Sound Image Inc, pg 895
SSL Industries Inc, pg 898
TOA Electronics Inc, pg 915
VMI Inc, pg 932

COLORADO

Ceavco Audio Visual Company Inc, pg 719

CONNECTICUT

Connecticut Audio & Theatrical Supply, pg 731
HB Communications Inc, pg 777
Sennheiser Electronic Corp, pg 884

FLORIDA

Access Media Group, pg 673
Altel Systems Group Inc, pg 682
Broadcasters General Store Inc, pg 711
Digital Video Systems, pg 742
Harris Corp, pg 776
Hi-Tech Import Export Corp, pg 779
Intermark Industries Inc, pg 789
Lighting Sales Connection Inc, pg 808
ONstage, pg 846
Stereo Sales Inc, pg 900
TAI Audio, pg 906

GEORGIA

Lighting & Production Equipment Inc, pg 807
Stage Front Presentation Systems, pg 899

HAWAII

The Audio Visual Co (AVCO), pg 694

ILLINOIS

Allen Visual Systems Inc, pg 680
Chicago Spotlight Inc, pg 721
Joseph Electronics, pg 795
Quintessence Audio Ltd, pg 868
Rauland-Borg Corp, pg 870
Tele-Time Systems, pg 910

INDIANA

Sensory Technologies LLC, pg 884
SHP Electronics, pg 887

KENTUCKY

Axxis Leasing Inc, pg 700
NOR-COM Inc, pg 841

LOUISIANA

Pace Systems, pg 849

MAINE

Headlight Audio Visual Inc, pg 777

MARYLAND

Cardinal Sound & Video, pg 717
Theatre Service & Supply Corp, pg 912

MASSACHUSETTS

Advanced Lighting & Production Services Inc (ALPS), pg 677
Antronics Inc, pg 686

MICHIGAN

Olson Anderson Co, pg 685
City Events Group, pg 725
On Stage Visuals, pg 846
TEL Systems LLC, pg 909
Tobins Lake Sales, pg 915

MINNESOTA

AVI Systems, pg 698
New Life Communications Inc, pg 839

MISSOURI

A to Z Theatrical Supply & Service, pg 671
Production Support Services Inc, pg 864
Southwest Audio-Visual Inc, pg 895

NEW HAMPSHIRE

APS Lighting-Sound-AV, pg 688

NEW JERSEY

A-V Services Inc, pg 671
Alltec Stores, a Vcom IMC Company, pg 681
Audio Visual Dynamics®, pg 694
Comprehensive Cable & Connectivity Co, pg 729
Earl Girls Inc, pg 749
HamiltonBuhl, pg 775
Starlite, pg 900
Vcom IMC, pg 925
Video Corporation of America (VCA), pg 927
Wired 4 Sound Inc, pg 940
Yorktel, pg 944

NEW YORK

Audio-Video Corp, pg 694
AV Workshop, pg 697
BMI Supply, pg 708
Creative Stage Lighting Co Inc, pg 733
Design Audio Visual Inc, pg 741
Goddard Design Co, pg 772
Indigo Productions, pg 787
Langie Audio Visual Systems, pg 803
Lee Dan® Communications Inc, pg 805
Long Island Video Enterprises Live Inc, pg 811
Markertek Video Supply, pg 817
Ray Supply Inc, pg 870
RNJ Electronics, pg 875
Syracuse Scenery & Stage Lighting Co Inc, pg 906
Theatrical Services & Supplies Inc, pg 912
Tri-Ed Distribution Inc, pg 918

NORTH CAROLINA

Camcor Inc, pg 715
Strategic Connections, pg 901

OHIO

Copp Integrated Systems, pg 731
ITA Audio Visual Solutions, pg 791
Tri-State Visual Products Inc, pg 918

PENNSYLVANIA

Advanced AV LLC, pg 677
Audio Visions Inc, pg 694
Hite Co, pg 780
The Lerro Corp, pg 806
Morefield Communications Inc, pg 830
Vistacom Inc, pg 931
Visual Sound Inc, pg 931

RHODE ISLAND

Shanix Inc, pg 885

173

AUDIO/VISUAL

Intercom System Distributors (continued)

SOUTH CAROLINA

DaviSound, pg 739

TENNESSEE

Advanced Sound, pg 677
Allstar Audio Systems Inc, pg 681
Belew Enterprises, pg 703
Lowrance Sound Co Inc, pg 812
Memphis Communications Corp, pg 823
Technical Support Systems LLC, pg 908
Zion Music Group, pg 945

TEXAS

Audio Visual Technologies Group (AVTG), pg 695
Crossroads Audio Inc, pg 735
Lubbock Audio Visual Inc, pg 812
Pro Video & Film Equipment Co Inc, pg 863
Southwest Sound Solutions, pg 896
Tarpley Media Systems, pg 907

UTAH

RIA Corp, pg 874
Webb Audio Visual, pg 935

VERMONT

Production Advantage Inc, pg 863

VIRGINIA

Avitecture Inc, pg 699
Boitnott Visual Communications Corp (BVC), pg 708
Lee Hartman & Sons Inc, pg 805

WASHINGTON

CCI Solutions, pg 718
Northern Lights & Pro Audio, pg 842
PNTA, pg 858

WEST VIRGINIA

United Sound & Electronics, pg 921

WISCONSIN

Audio Visual of Milwaukee Inc, pg 694
Camera Corner Connecting Point, pg 715
Full Compass Systems, pg 767
Safe Harbor Computers, pg 879

PUERTO RICO

Bonnin Electronics Inc, pg 708

ALBERTA

Allstar Show Industries Inc, pg 681
Infosat Communications Inc, pg 787
Matrix Video Communications Corp (MVCC), pg 819
Unique Communications Ltd, pg 921

BRITISH COLUMBIA

Commercial Electronics Ltd, pg 728

MANITOBA

Inland Audio Visual Ltd, pg 788

ONTARIO

Cinema Stage Inc, pg 724
Nationwide Audio Visual Co, pg 837
Westbury National Show Systems Ltd, pg 936

Intercom System Manufacturers

ARIZONA

AtlasIED, pg 692

CALIFORNIA

ALTINEX Inc, pg 682
Anchor Audio Inc, pg 685
Clear-Com® LLC, pg 726
HM Electronics Inc (HME), pg 780
Mackenzie Laboratories Inc, pg 814
TOA Electronics Inc, pg 915

CONNECTICUT

Sennheiser Electronic Corp, pg 884

ILLINOIS

Jeron Electronic Systems Inc, pg 794
Rauland-Borg Corp, pg 870
Studio Technologies Inc, pg 903
Talk-A-Phone Co, pg 906

MASSACHUSETTS

David Clark Co Inc, pg 738

MINNESOTA

Bosch Security Systems Inc, pg 709
Digital Audio Labs, pg 742

MISSISSIPPI

Peavey Electronics Corp, pg 852

NEW JERSEY

Bogen Communications Inc, pg 708

NEW YORK

Goddard Design Co, pg 772
Lee Dan® Communications Inc, pg 805
Protech Audio Corp, pg 866
TecNec Distributing, pg 909
Television Equipment Associates Inc (TEA), pg 910

NORTH CAROLINA

Strategic Connections, pg 901

SOUTH CAROLINA

DaviSound, pg 739

TEXAS

Setcom Corp™, pg 884

WASHINGTON

Aiphone Corp, pg 678

WEST VIRGINIA

United Sound & Electronics, pg 921

Intercom System Rentals

ARIZONA

Arizona Cine Equipment, pg 688
Glendale Media Center, pg 771
Merestone, pg 823
Metropolitan Audio-Visual Inc, pg 824

ARKANSAS

White Diamond Productions LLC, pg 937

CALIFORNIA

Absolute Rentals, pg 672
Acey Decy Lighting, pg 674
AGF Media Services, pg 678
Alliant Event Services, pg 681
Ametron Audio/Video, pg 684
Associated Sound, pg 691
AV Guys, pg 697
Electronic Design Solutions Inc, pg 752
Express Media Inc, pg 757
Golden Gate Studios, pg 772
JD Audio Visual Inc, pg 793
Location Sound Corp, pg 810
Lynch Communications, pg 813
McCune Audio-Video-Lighting, pg 821
Media Fabricators Inc, pg 822
MSI Production Services, pg 832
Munday & Collins AV, pg 834
PSAV® Presentation Services, pg 866
Video Resources Inc, pg 928
VMI Inc, pg 932
Voice & Video Rentals, pg 932
Warner Bros Entertainment Inc, pg 934
Warner Bros Production Sound & Video Services, pg 934

COLORADO

Ceavco Audio Visual Company Inc, pg 719
Daylight Productions & Rentals, pg 739
Multimedia Audio Visual Inc, pg 833

CONNECTICUT

Connecticut Audio & Theatrical Supply, pg 731

DELAWARE

Ken-Del Productions Inc, pg 797
Showorks Audio Visual Inc, pg 887

FLORIDA

Access Media Group, pg 673
Jordan Klein Film & Video (JKFV), pg 795
Lighting Sales Connection Inc, pg 808
ONstage, pg 846
Paradise Show & Design Inc, pg 851
TAI Audio, pg 906
Universal Studios Florida® Production Group, pg 922

GEORGIA

Lighting & Production Equipment Inc, pg 807
Stage Front Presentation Systems, pg 899
Staging Directions Inc, pg 899

HAWAII

Sight & Sound Studios, pg 887

ILLINOIS

Allen Visual Systems Inc, pg 680
AV Chicago Inc, pg 696
Backstar Creative Media Inc, pg 700
Beatty TeleVisual Productions, pg 703
Chicago Spotlight Inc, pg 721
Creative Technology (CT), pg 733
Helix Camera & Video, pg 778
PSAV® Presentation Services (Hotel Services Division), pg 866
RC Communications, pg 870
Resolution Productions Group, pg 874

INDIANA

Gary Camera & Digital, pg 768

IOWA

Central Lighting & Equipment Inc (CLE), pg 719

LOUISIANA

Pace Systems, pg 849

MARYLAND

CPR MultiMedia Solutions, pg 732
Event Tech, pg 756
Hargrove Inc, pg 776

MASSACHUSETTS

Advanced Lighting & Production Services Inc (ALPS), pg 677
AVFX Inc, pg 698
Capron Lighting & Sound Co Inc, pg 716
massAV, pg 819
Preston Productions Inc, pg 861

MICHIGAN

Olson Anderson Co, pg 685
City Events Group, pg 725
On Stage Visuals, pg 846

MINNESOTA

AVI Systems, pg 698

MISSOURI

A to Z Theatrical Supply & Service, pg 671
Production Support Services Inc, pg 864
Show-Me Audio-Visual, pg 887
Southwest Audio-Visual Inc, pg 895
Switch, pg 905

NEW HAMPSHIRE

APS Lighting-Sound-AV, pg 688

NEW JERSEY

Audio Visual Dynamics®, pg 694
Earl Girls Inc, pg 749
Moe AV LLC, pg 828
Panavid, pg 850
PLS Staging, pg 858
Starlite, pg 900
Video Corporation of America (VCA), pg 927
Wired 4 Sound Inc, pg 940

NEW YORK

AV Workshop, pg 697
Big Foot Productions Inc, pg 705
CMI Communications, pg 727
CP Communications, pg 732
Creative Stage Lighting Co Inc, pg 733
Langie Audio Visual Systems, pg 803
Long Island Video Enterprises Live Inc, pg 811
Specialized Audio-Visual Inc, pg 896
Syracuse Scenery & Stage Lighting Co Inc, pg 906
Theatrical Services & Supplies Inc, pg 912
WorldStage, pg 941

NORTH CAROLINA

AV Connections Inc, pg 697
Special Event Services, pg 896
Strategic Connections, pg 901

NORTH DAKOTA

Media Productions, pg 822

OHIO

Bartha, pg 702
Hughie's Event Production Services, pg 782
Lyon Video Inc, pg 813
Mills James Productions, pg 828

OKLAHOMA

PDC Productions, pg 852

OREGON

Picture This Production Services, pg 856

PENNSYLVANIA

JPL, pg 795
Visual Sound Inc, pg 931

SOUTH CAROLINA

Sound & Images Inc, pg 893

TENNESSEE

Allstar Audio Systems Inc, pg 681
Memphis Communications Corp, pg 823
Technical Support Systems LLC, pg 908

TEXAS

Alford Media Services, pg 680
GEAR Cameras & Lighting, pg 769
JSAV, pg 795
Lubbock Audio Visual Inc, pg 812

VIRGINIA

American AV, pg 682
Boitnott Visual Communications Corp (BVC), pg 708
Lee Hartman & Sons Inc, pg 805

WASHINGTON

D A Sound, pg 737
Northern Lights & Pro Audio, pg 842
PNTA, pg 858

WEST VIRGINIA

United Sound & Electronics, pg 921

WISCONSIN

Event Essentials, pg 756

PUERTO RICO

Stage Crew Audiovisual Inc, pg 898

ALBERTA

Allstar Show Industries Inc, pg 681
Global TV, pg 771
Unique Communications Ltd, pg 921

ONTARIO

HD Source, pg 777
JIB Shots Equipment Inc, pg 794
SIM Digital, pg 888
Westbury National Show Systems Ltd, pg 936

QUEBEC

Audio Visual Dynamics, pg 694

Intercom System Repairs

CALIFORNIA

Ametron Audio/Video, pg 684
Electronic Design Solutions Inc, pg 752
HM Electronics Inc (HME), pg 780
McAlister Electronics, pg 820
Lloyd F McKinney Associates Inc, pg 821
SSL Industries Inc, pg 898
Technical Services, pg 908
TOA Electronics Inc, pg 915

COLORADO

Ceavco Audio Visual Company Inc, pg 719

CONNECTICUT

HB Communications Inc, pg 777
Sennheiser Electronic Corp, pg 884

FLORIDA

Stereo Sales Inc, pg 900
TAI Audio, pg 906

GEORGIA

Lighting & Production Equipment Inc, pg 807
Stage Front Presentation Systems, pg 899

ILLINOIS

Allen Visual Systems Inc, pg 680
Beatty TeleVisual Productions, pg 703
Chicago Spotlight Inc, pg 721

INDIANA

Gary Camera & Digital, pg 768

KENTUCKY

Axxis Leasing Inc, pg 700
NOR-COM Inc, pg 841

MARYLAND

Cardinal Sound & Video, pg 717

MASSACHUSETTS

Capron Lighting & Sound Co Inc, pg 716

MICHIGAN

Olson Anderson Co, pg 685
City Events Group, pg 725
On Stage Visuals, pg 846
TEL Systems LLC, pg 909

MINNESOTA

AVI Systems, pg 698

MISSOURI

A to Z Theatrical Supply & Service, pg 671
Cintrex Audio Visual, pg 725

NEW JERSEY

Earl Girls Inc, pg 749
Starlite, pg 900

NEW YORK

Langie Audio Visual Systems, pg 803

NORTH CAROLINA

Camcor Inc, pg 715
Strategic Connections, pg 901

OHIO

Copp Integrated Systems, pg 731
ITA Audio Visual Solutions, pg 791
Tri-State Audio Visual Co, pg 918

PENNSYLVANIA

Audio Visions Inc, pg 694
Vistacom Inc, pg 931

SOUTH CAROLINA

DaviSound, pg 739

TENNESSEE

Belew Enterprises, pg 703
Memphis Communications Corp, pg 823
Technical Support Systems LLC, pg 908

TEXAS

Crossroads Audio Inc, pg 735
Lubbock Audio Visual Inc, pg 812
Southwest Sound Solutions, pg 896

VIRGINIA

Aviteture Inc, pg 699
Boitnott Visual Communications Corp (BVC), pg 708
Lee Hartman & Sons Inc, pg 805
The Whitlock Group, pg 937

WASHINGTON

Aiphone Corp, pg 678
Northern Lights & Pro Audio, pg 842
PNTA, pg 858

WEST VIRGINIA

United Sound & Electronics, pg 921

WISCONSIN

Full Compass Systems, pg 767

ALBERTA

Infosat Communications Inc, pg 787
Unique Communications Ltd, pg 921

MANITOBA

Inland Audio Visual Ltd, pg 788

ONTARIO

Westbury National Show Systems Ltd, pg 936

Laminating Equipment, *see* Dry Mounting & Laminating Equipment & Supply

Laser Pointer & Laser Projection Equipment Distributors

ALABAMA

Curtis Company, pg 736

ARIZONA

Arizona Cine Equipment, pg 688
Metropolitan Audio-Visual Inc, pg 824
Professional Marketing Services Inc, pg 865
Troxell-CDI, pg 918

ARKANSAS

Jay S Stanley & Associates Inc, pg 899
White Diamond Productions LLC, pg 937

CALIFORNIA

Ametron Audio/Video, pg 684
Assured Audio Visual, pg 691
Audio/Video Supply Inc, pg 694
Beta Electronics Inc, pg 704
California Tape Products Inc, pg 714
Christy's Editorial, pg 723
Cibola Systems, pg 723
Educational Technology Services (ETS), pg 751
Gluskin's Custom Audio Video, pg 771
Hooper Camera & Imaging, pg 781
Instructional Materials & Equipment Distributors (I-Med), pg 789
Jaguar Distribution Corp, pg 792
Jameco Electronics, pg 792
JD Audio Visual Inc, pg 793
Laser Magic Productions, pg 804
Lloyd F McKinney Associates Inc, pg 821
Media Fabricators Inc, pg 822
MediaPOINTE, pg 823
Precision Projection Systems Inc, pg 861
Sound Service Co, pg 894
Stanislaus AV Inc, pg 899
Towards 2000 Inc, pg 916
VMI Inc, pg 932

COLORADO

Daylight Productions & Rentals, pg 739
Spectrum Audio Visual Services, pg 897

CONNECTICUT

HB Communications Inc, pg 777
MAVCO, pg 820
USI Inc, pg 924

AUDIO/VISUAL

Laser Pointer & Laser Projection Equipment Distributors (continued)

FLORIDA

Audio Visual Imagineering Inc, pg 694
AVI-SPL, pg 698
Digital Video Systems, pg 742
Hi-Tech Import Export Corp, pg 779
Industrial Strength Inc, pg 787
ONstage, pg 846
Photosound of Orlando Inc, pg 856
Recording Media & Equipment Inc (RM&E), pg 872
Tallahassee Audio Visual, pg 906
Techni-Lux Inc, pg 908

GEORGIA

Convergent Media Systems, pg 731
Stage Front Presentation Systems, pg 899
Visioneering International Inc, pg 931

HAWAII

The Audio Visual Co (AVCO), pg 694

ILLINOIS

Allen Visual Systems Inc, pg 680
Central Audio-Visual Equipment Inc, pg 719
RC Communications, pg 870

INDIANA

Da-Lite, a Legrand AV Inc brand, pg 737
Sensory Technologies LLC, pg 884

KENTUCKY

Audio Visual Techniques Inc, pg 695
Axxis Leasing Inc, pg 700
Barney Miller's Inc, pg 827
NOR-COM Inc, pg 841
Theatre Effects, pg 911

LOUISIANA

Techkno Integration & Design Services LLC, pg 908

MAINE

Headlight Audio Visual Inc, pg 777

MARYLAND

Advance Audiovisual Presentation Ltd, pg 677
Cardinal Sound & Video, pg 717
Nelson White Systems Inc, pg 838
RTZ Audio Visual, pg 878

MASSACHUSETTS

Limelight Production® Inc, pg 809

MICHIGAN

Olson Anderson Co, pg 685
City Events Group, pg 725
Michigan Office Solutions (MOS), A Xerox Company, pg 825
TEL Systems LLC, pg 909

MINNESOTA

AVI Systems, pg 698
Tierney Brothers Inc, pg 914

MISSISSIPPI

Bowie Audio Visual Enterprises Inc, pg 709
Jasper Ewing & Sons Inc, pg 757

MISSOURI

Communitronics Corp, pg 729
Conference Technologies Inc, pg 730
ITC, pg 791
Modern Communications Inc, pg 828
Schiller's Audio-Visual, pg 881

NEVADA

MeshTel, pg 824

NEW JERSEY

A-V Services Inc, pg 671
AlltecPro, pg 681
Audio Visual Associates, pg 694
Audio Visual Dynamics®, pg 694
AV Bluebook, pg 696
Earl Girls Inc, pg 749
HamiltonBuhl, pg 775
Starlite, pg 900
Total Video Products Inc, pg 916
Vcom IMC, pg 925
Video Corporation of America (VCA), pg 927
Wired 4 Sound Inc, pg 940
Yorktel, pg 944

NEW YORK

American Video Inc, pg 684
Audio-Video Corp, pg 694
AV Workshop, pg 697
Bulbtronics Inc, pg 712
Design Audio Visual Inc, pg 741
DSan Corp, pg 747
Gaylord Archival, pg 768
Indigo Productions, pg 787
KVL Audio Visual Services Inc, pg 802
Long Island Video Enterprises Live Inc, pg 811
Markertek Video Supply, pg 817
Neptune Photo Inc, pg 838
Presentation Products Inc, pg 861
Scientifics Direct Inc, pg 882
Theatrical Services & Supplies Inc, pg 912
Tri-Ed Distribution Inc, pg 918

NORTH CAROLINA

Camcor Inc, pg 715
Strategic Connections, pg 901

OHIO

Copp Integrated Systems, pg 731
ITA Audio Visual Solutions, pg 791
Tri-State Audio Visual Co, pg 918
Tri-State Visual Products Inc, pg 918

OREGON

Laserium®, pg 804

PENNSYLVANIA

Advanced AV LLC, pg 677
Audio Visions Inc, pg 694
Audio Visual Communications Inc, pg 694

Bernie's Photo Center, pg 704
J E Foss Co, pg 764
Garcia Marketing Inc, pg 768
Grise Audio Visual Center Inc, pg 774
The Lerro Corp, pg 806
Vistacom Inc, pg 931
Visual Sound Inc, pg 931

SOUTH CAROLINA

Impact Technology Group LLC, pg 786

TENNESSEE

Lowrance Sound Co Inc, pg 812

TEXAS

Audio Visual Technologies Group (AVTG), pg 695
AVES Audio Visual Systems Inc, pg 698
Data Projections Inc, pg 738
FitzCo Sound Inc, pg 761
Heffernan Audio Visual, pg 778
JSAV, pg 795
Laser Spectacles Inc, pg 804
Lubbock Audio Visual Inc, pg 812
Quality Audio Visual Service Inc, pg 867
Southwest Sound Solutions, pg 896
Stage Directions, pg 898

UTAH

Webb Audio Visual, pg 935

VIRGINIA

Boitnott Visual Communications Corp (BVC), pg 708
Intellidyne LLC, pg 789
Lee Hartman & Sons Inc, pg 805
Metropolitan Audio Visual Co LLC, pg 824
The Whitlock Group, pg 937

WISCONSIN

Audio Visual of Milwaukee Inc, pg 694
Camera Corner Connecting Point, pg 715
Full Compass Systems, pg 767

PUERTO RICO

Bonnin Electronics Inc, pg 708

ALBERTA

Infosat Communications Inc, pg 787
McBain Camera Ltd, pg 820
Unique Communications Ltd, pg 921

BRITISH COLUMBIA

Commercial Electronics Ltd, pg 728

MANITOBA

Inland Audio Visual Ltd, pg 788

ONTARIO

Nationwide Audio Visual Co, pg 837

QUEBEC

Panavideo Inc, pg 850

Laser Pointer & Laser Projection Equipment Manufacturers

CALIFORNIA

Alpec®, pg 681
Beta Electronics Inc, pg 704
Laser Magic Productions, pg 804
Precision Projection Systems Inc, pg 861

FLORIDA

Audio Visual Imagineering Inc, pg 694
Pangolin Laser Systems Inc, pg 851
Vutec Corp, pg 933

ILLINOIS

ACCO Brands Corp, pg 673

INDIANA

Da-Lite, a Legrand AV Inc brand, pg 737

NEVADA

MeshTel, pg 824

NEW HAMPSHIRE

ProPhotonix Ltd, pg 865

NEW JERSEY

AlltecPro, pg 681

NEW YORK

DSan Corp, pg 747
TecNec Distributing, pg 909

OREGON

Laserium®, pg 804
Lumalaser, pg 812
PLUS Corp of America, pg 858

TEXAS

Laser Spectacles Inc, pg 804

WASHINGTON

Laser Fantasy/HECK Industries/Photon Manufacturing, pg 804

Laser Pointer & Laser Projection Equipment Rentals

ALABAMA

Audio-Video Resources Inc, pg 694

ARIZONA

Arizona Cine Equipment, pg 688
Merestone, pg 823
Metropolitan Audio-Visual Inc, pg 824
Video West Inc, pg 929

ARKANSAS

White Diamond Productions LLC, pg 937

CALIFORNIA

AGF Media Services, pg 678
Alliant Event Services, pg 681
Ametron Audio/Video, pg 684

Automated Entertainment, pg 696
AV Guys, pg 697
Gluskin's Custom Audio Video, pg 771
Gold Standard Productions, pg 772
JD Audio Visual Inc, pg 793
Laser Magic Productions, pg 804
Lynch Communications, pg 813
McCune Audio-Video-Lighting, pg 821
Media Fabricators Inc, pg 822
Munday & Collins AV, pg 834
Precision Projection Systems Inc, pg 861
PSAV® Presentation Services, pg 866
Sound Service Co, pg 894
Stanislaus AV Inc, pg 899
VER, pg 926
Video Resources Inc, pg 928
Voice & Video Rentals, pg 932

COLORADO

Daylight Productions & Rentals, pg 739
Spectrum Audio Visual Services, pg 897

CONNECTICUT

A/V Davey, pg 697

DELAWARE

Ken-Del Productions Inc, pg 797
Showorks Audio Visual Inc, pg 887

FLORIDA

Audio Visual Imagineering Inc, pg 694
AVI-SPL, pg 698
Industrial Strength Inc, pg 787
ONstage, pg 846
Sight & Sound Productions, pg 887

GEORGIA

Convergent Media Systems, pg 731
ON Services, a GES Company, pg 846
Stage Front Presentation Systems, pg 899
Staging Directions Inc, pg 899

ILLINOIS

Allen Visual Systems Inc, pg 680
AV Chicago Inc, pg 696
Backstar Creative Media Inc, pg 700
Beatty TeleVisual Productions, pg 703
Central Audio-Visual Equipment Inc, pg 719
Pepper Group, pg 854

KENTUCKY

Audio Visual Techniques Inc, pg 695

LOUISIANA

Pace Systems, pg 849

MAINE

Headlight Audio Visual Inc, pg 777

MARYLAND

Absolute Hollywood, pg 672
Advance Audiovisual Presentation Ltd, pg 677

Nelson White Systems Inc, pg 838
RTZ Audio Visual, pg 878

MASSACHUSETTS

Capron Lighting & Sound Co Inc, pg 716
Limelight Production® Inc, pg 809
massAV, pg 819
Preston Productions Inc, pg 861

MICHIGAN

Olson Anderson Co, pg 685
City Events Group, pg 725

MINNESOTA

AVI Systems, pg 698

MISSISSIPPI

Bowie Audio Visual Enterprises Inc, pg 709

MISSOURI

Communitronics Corp, pg 729
Schiller's Audio-Visual, pg 881
Show-Me Audio-Visual, pg 887

NEVADA

GES Audio Visual, pg 770

NEW JERSEY

Audio Visual Associates, pg 694
Audio Visual Dynamics®, pg 694
Earl Girls Inc, pg 749
Moe AV LLC, pg 828
Panavid, pg 850
PLS Staging, pg 858
Starlite, pg 900
Video Corporation of America (VCA), pg 927
Wired 4 Sound Inc, pg 940

NEW YORK

Ace Video, pg 674
American Video Inc, pg 684
AV Workshop, pg 697
CMI Communications, pg 727
KVL Audio Visual Services Inc, pg 802
Long Island Video Enterprises Live Inc, pg 811
SmartSource Computer & AV Rentals, pg 891
Visual Word Systems Inc, pg 932
WorldStage, pg 941

NORTH CAROLINA

AV Connections Inc, pg 697
AV Metro Inc, pg 697
Special Event Services, pg 896

NORTH DAKOTA

Media Productions, pg 822

OHIO

Mills James Productions, pg 828

OREGON

Laserium®, pg 804

PENNSYLVANIA

Advanced AV LLC, pg 677
Audio Visions Inc, pg 694
Audio Visual Communications Inc, pg 694

FirstGeneration Audio/Visual Services, pg 761
Grise Audio Visual Center Inc, pg 774
Visual Sound Inc, pg 931

SOUTH CAROLINA

Impact Technology Group LLC, pg 786
Sound & Images Inc, pg 893

TENNESSEE

Memphis Communications Corp, pg 823

TEXAS

Alford Media Services, pg 680
Audio Visual Technologies Group (AVTG), pg 695
FitzCo Sound Inc, pg 761
JSAV, pg 795
Laser Spectacles Inc, pg 804
Lubbock Audio Visual Inc, pg 812
Quality Audio Visual Service Inc, pg 867
Stage Directions, pg 898

UTAH

Webb Audio Visual, pg 935

VIRGINIA

American AV, pg 682
Boitnott Visual Communications Corp (BVC), pg 708
Lee Hartman & Sons Inc, pg 805
The Whitlock Group, pg 937

WASHINGTON

Laser Fantasy/HECK Industries/Photon Manufacturing, pg 804

WISCONSIN

Audio Visual of Milwaukee Inc, pg 694
Camera Corner Connecting Point, pg 715
Event Essentials, pg 756

PUERTO RICO

Stage Crew Audiovisual Inc, pg 898

ALBERTA

Evolution AV, pg 757
McBain Camera Ltd, pg 820
Unique Communications Ltd, pg 921

BRITISH COLUMBIA

Clark's Audio Visual Services Ltd, pg 725
Commercial Electronics Ltd, pg 728

MANITOBA

Inland Audio Visual Ltd, pg 788

ONTARIO

HD Source, pg 777

QUEBEC

Audio Visual Dynamics, pg 694
Panavideo Inc, pg 850

Laser Pointer & Laser Projection Equipment Repairs

CALIFORNIA

Ametron Audio/Video, pg 684
Beta Electronics Inc, pg 704
McAlister Electronics, pg 820
Lloyd F McKinney Associates Inc, pg 821
Towards 2000 Inc, pg 916

CONNECTICUT

HB Communications Inc, pg 777

GEORGIA

Stage Front Presentation Systems, pg 899

ILLINOIS

Allen Visual Systems Inc, pg 680
RC Communications, pg 870

KENTUCKY

Axxis Leasing Inc, pg 700
NOR-COM Inc, pg 841

MARYLAND

RTZ Audio Visual, pg 878

MICHIGAN

City Events Group, pg 725
TEL Systems LLC, pg 909

MINNESOTA

AVI Systems, pg 698

MISSISSIPPI

Bowie Audio Visual Enterprises Inc, pg 709

MISSOURI

Communitronics Corp, pg 729

NEW JERSEY

Earl Girls Inc, pg 749

NORTH CAROLINA

Camcor Inc, pg 715

OHIO

ITA Audio Visual Solutions, pg 791

PENNSYLVANIA

Audio Visions Inc, pg 694

TENNESSEE

Memphis Communications Corp, pg 823

TEXAS

Audio Visual Technologies Group (AVTG), pg 695
Lubbock Audio Visual Inc, pg 812

VIRGINIA

Boitnott Visual Communications Corp (BVC), pg 708
The Whitlock Group, pg 937

AUDIO/VISUAL

Laser Pointer & Laser Projection Equipment Repairs (continued)

WASHINGTON

Laser Fantasy/HECK Industries/Photon Manufacturing, pg 804

ALBERTA

Infosat Communications Inc, pg 787

MANITOBA

Inland Audio Visual Ltd, pg 788

Lectern Distributors

ALABAMA

Curtis Company, pg 736

ARIZONA

Arizona Cine Equipment, pg 688
Metropolitan Audio-Visual Inc, pg 824
Troxell-CDI, pg 918

ARKANSAS

Jay S Stanley & Associates Inc, pg 899
White Diamond Productions LLC, pg 937

CALIFORNIA

Ametron Audio/Video, pg 684
Associated Sound, pg 691
Assured Audio Visual, pg 691
Audio Images Corp, pg 693
Auton Motorized Systems, pg 696
AV Conferencing LLC (AVC), pg 697
BigFoot Mobile Systems, pg 705
California Tape Products Inc, pg 714
Christy's Editorial, pg 723
Electronic Design Solutions Inc, pg 752
Gluskin's Custom Audio Video, pg 771
Instructional Materials & Equipment Distributors (I-Med), pg 789
JD Audio Visual Inc, pg 793
Lloyd F McKinney Associates Inc, pg 821
Media Fabricators Inc, pg 822
MediaPOINTE, pg 823
Sound Service Co, pg 894
Southern California Sound Image Inc, pg 895
SSL Industries Inc, pg 898
Stanislaus AV Inc, pg 899
Towards 2000 Inc, pg 916

COLORADO

Ceavco Audio Visual Company Inc, pg 719
Spectrum Audio Visual Services, pg 897

CONNECTICUT

Connecticut Audio & Theatrical Supply, pg 731
HB Communications Inc, pg 777

MAVCO, pg 820
Rockwell Communications Inc, pg 876

FLORIDA

Altel Systems Group Inc, pg 682
AVI-SPL, pg 698
Broadcasters General Store Inc, pg 711
Digital Video Systems, pg 742
Harmon's Audio-Visual Services, pg 776
Hi-Tech Import Export Corp, pg 779
Hollywood Theatre Equipment Inc, pg 781
Industrial Strength Inc, pg 787
ONstage, pg 846
Photosound of Orlando Inc, pg 856
Recording Media & Equipment Inc (RM&E), pg 872
Stereo Sales Inc, pg 900
TAI Audio, pg 906
Tallahassee Audio Visual, pg 906

GEORGIA

Audio Visual Resources Inc, pg 695
Baker Audio Visual, pg 700
Convergent Media Systems, pg 731
PolyVision Corporation, pg 859
Stage Front Presentation Systems, pg 899
Visioneering International Inc, pg 931

HAWAII

The Audio Visual Co (AVCO), pg 694

ILLINOIS

Allen Visual Systems Inc, pg 680
AmpliVox Portable Sound Systems, pg 684
Central Audio-Visual Equipment Inc, pg 719
Joseph Electronics, pg 795
G T Luscombe Co Inc, pg 812
Quintessence Audio Ltd, pg 868

INDIANA

Heart Breaker Entertainment LLC, pg 778
Sensory Technologies LLC, pg 884
SHP Electronics, pg 887

KANSAS

KK Office Solutions Inc, pg 799

KENTUCKY

Audio Visual Techniques Inc, pg 695
Axxis Leasing Inc, pg 700
Barney Miller's Inc, pg 827
NOR-COM Inc, pg 841

LOUISIANA

Techkno Integration & Design Services LLC, pg 908

MAINE

Headlight Audio Visual Inc, pg 777

MARYLAND

Advance Audiovisual Presentation Ltd, pg 677
Cardinal Sound & Video, pg 717
Nelson White Systems Inc, pg 838

Nicholas P Pipino Associates Inc, pg 857
RTZ Audio Visual, pg 878

MASSACHUSETTS

Antronics Inc, pg 686
International Display & Exhibit Corp (IDEC), pg 790
Rule Boston Camera, pg 878
University Products Inc, pg 923

MICHIGAN

Olson Anderson Co, pg 685
City Events Group, pg 725
Michigan Office Solutions (MOS), A Xerox Company, pg 825
On Stage Visuals, pg 846
TEL Systems LLC, pg 909

MINNESOTA

AVI Systems, pg 698

MISSISSIPPI

Bowie Audio Visual Enterprises Inc, pg 709
Jasper Ewing & Sons Inc, pg 757

MISSOURI

Communitronics Corp, pg 729
Conference Technologies Inc, pg 730
ITC, pg 791
Schiller's Audio-Visual, pg 881
Southwest Audio-Visual Inc, pg 895

NEW HAMPSHIRE

APS Lighting-Sound-AV, pg 688

NEW JERSEY

A-V Services Inc, pg 671
Alltec Stores, a Vcom IMC Company, pg 681
AlltecPro, pg 681
Audio Visual Associates, pg 694
Audio Visual Dynamics®, pg 694
AV Bluebook, pg 696
Comprehensive Cable & Connectivity Co, pg 729
Earl Girls Inc, pg 749
FlagHouse, pg 762
HamiltonBuhl, pg 775
Starlite, pg 900
Tele-Measurements Inc, pg 910
Total Video Products Inc, pg 916
Vcom IMC, pg 925
Video Corporation of America (VCA), pg 927
Wired 4 Sound Inc, pg 940
Yorktel, pg 944

NEW YORK

Albany Theatre Supply Co Inc, pg 679
Audio-Video Corp, pg 694
AV Workshop, pg 697
BMI Supply, pg 708
Colortone Audio Visual, pg 728
Design Audio Visual Inc, pg 741
Gaylord Archival, pg 768
Indigo Productions, pg 787
KVL Audio Visual Services Inc, pg 802
Langie Audio Visual Systems, pg 803
Lee Dan® Communications Inc, pg 805
Long Island Video Enterprises Live Inc, pg 811

Markertek Video Supply, pg 817
Presentation Products Inc, pg 861
Ray Supply Inc, pg 870
RNJ Electronics, pg 875
Talas, pg 906
Theatrical Services & Supplies Inc, pg 912
Tri-Ed Distribution Inc, pg 918
Visual Technologies Corp, pg 932

NORTH CAROLINA

Camcor Inc, pg 715
Strategic Connections, pg 901

OHIO

Audio Visual Media, pg 694
Copp Integrated Systems, pg 731
Hughie's Event Production Services, pg 782
ITA Audio Visual Solutions, pg 791
Tri-State Audio Visual Co, pg 918
Tri-State Visual Products Inc, pg 918

PENNSYLVANIA

Advanced AV LLC, pg 677
Audio Visions Inc, pg 694
Bernie's Photo Center, pg 704
Brodart Co, pg 711
J E Foss Co, pg 764
Garcia Marketing Inc, pg 768
Hite Co, pg 780
The Lerro Corp, pg 806
RSS Distributors, pg 878
Vistacom Inc, pg 931
Visual Sound Inc, pg 931
Wespen Audio Visual Co, pg 935

RHODE ISLAND

Shanix Inc, pg 885

SOUTH CAROLINA

Impact Technology Group LLC, pg 786

TENNESSEE

Allstar Audio Systems Inc, pg 681
Continental Film, pg 731
Lowrance Sound Co Inc, pg 812
Memphis Communications Corp, pg 823
Technical Support Systems LLC, pg 908
Zion Music Group, pg 945

TEXAS

Audio Visual Technologies Group (AVTG), pg 695
AVES Audio Visual Systems Inc, pg 698
Data Projections Inc, pg 738
Heffernan Audio Visual, pg 778
JSAV, pg 795
Lubbock Audio Visual Inc, pg 812
Quality Audio Visual Service Inc, pg 867
Southwest Sound Solutions, pg 896
Tarpley Media Systems, pg 907

UTAH

Performance Audio LLC, pg 854
Webb Audio Visual, pg 935

VIRGINIA

Avitecture Inc, pg 699
Boitnott Visual Communications Corp (BVC), pg 708
Design & Production Inc, pg 740

Intellidyne LLC, pg 789
Lee Hartman & Sons Inc, pg 805
Metropolitan Audio Visual Co LLC, pg 824
The Whitlock Group, pg 937

WASHINGTON

Inland Audio Visual Co, pg 788
PNTA, pg 858

WISCONSIN

Audio Visual of Milwaukee Inc, pg 694
Camera Corner Connecting Point, pg 715
Demco Inc, pg 740
Full Compass Systems, pg 767
School Specialty Inc, pg 882
Spectrum Industries Inc, pg 897

PUERTO RICO

Audio Visual Concepts Inc, pg 694
Bonnin Electronics Inc, pg 708

ALBERTA

Infosat Communications Inc, pg 787
Matrix Video Communications Corp (MVCC), pg 819
McBain Camera Ltd, pg 820

BRITISH COLUMBIA

Commercial Electronics Ltd, pg 728

MANITOBA

Inland Audio Visual Ltd, pg 788

ONTARIO

Carr McLean Ltd, pg 717
Cinema Stage Inc, pg 724
Nationwide Audio Visual Co, pg 837
Westbury National Show Systems Ltd, pg 936

Lectern Manufacturers

ALABAMA

Marco Inc, pg 816
Omni International Inc, pg 845

ARIZONA

Merestone, pg 823

ARKANSAS

Sound-Craft Systems Inc, pg 894

CALIFORNIA

Anchor Audio Inc, pg 685
Auton Motorized Systems, pg 696
Califone International Inc, pg 714
MediaPOINTE, pg 823

GEORGIA

PolyVision Corporation, pg 859

ILLINOIS

ACCO Brands Corp, pg 673
AmpliVox Portable Sound Systems, pg 684
Bretford Manufacturing Inc, pg 710
Luxor, pg 812
Marshall Furniture Inc, pg 817
Windel International/Weyel, pg 939

INDIANA

Da-Lite, a Legrand AV Inc brand, pg 737
HSA Inc, pg 782

MISSOURI

Shure Manufacturing Corp, pg 887

NEW JERSEY

AlltecPro, pg 681
Oklahoma Sound Corp, pg 844

NEW YORK

TecNec Distributing, pg 909
Theatrical Services & Supplies Inc, pg 912

PENNSYLVANIA

A/S Custom Furniture, pg 671

TEXAS

MooreCo Inc, pg 830

UTAH

Spectra Sonics LLC, pg 897

VIRGINIA

Optikinetics Ltd - The Americas, pg 847

WASHINGTON

D A Sound, pg 737

WISCONSIN

Spectrum Industries Inc, pg 897

ONTARIO

Egan Visual Inc/Egan TeamBoard Inc, pg 751

Lectern Rentals

ALABAMA

Audio-Video Resources Inc, pg 694

ARIZONA

Arizona Cine Equipment, pg 688
Merestone, pg 823
Metropolitan Audio-Visual Inc, pg 824
Ultimate Presentation Systems Inc, pg 920

ARKANSAS

White Diamond Productions LLC, pg 937

CALIFORNIA

AGF Media Services, pg 678
Alliant Event Services, pg 681
Ametron Audio/Video, pg 684
Associated Sound, pg 691
Assured Audio Visual, pg 691
AV Guys, pg 697
Gluskin's Custom Audio Video, pg 771
Instructional Materials & Equipment Distributors (I-Med), pg 789
JD Audio Visual Inc, pg 793
Lynch Communications, pg 813
McCune Audio-Video-Lighting, pg 821
Media Fabricators Inc, pg 822
Munday & Collins AV, pg 834

PSAV® Presentation Services, pg 866

Sound Service Co, pg 894
Stanislaus AV Inc, pg 899
Towards 2000 Inc, pg 916
Video Resources Inc, pg 928
Voice & Video Rentals, pg 932

COLORADO

Ceavco Audio Visual Company Inc, pg 719
Daylight Productions & Rentals, pg 739
Spectrum Audio Visual Services, pg 897

CONNECTICUT

A/V Davey, pg 697
Rockwell Communications Inc, pg 876

DELAWARE

Actors Attic, pg 675
Ken-Del Productions Inc, pg 797
Showorks Audio Visual Inc, pg 887

FLORIDA

AVI-SPL, pg 698
Harmon's Audio-Visual Services, pg 776
Industrial Strength Inc, pg 787
National Teleproductions Inc, pg 837
ONstage, pg 846
Paradise Show & Design Inc, pg 851
Photosound of Orlando Inc, pg 856
TAI Audio, pg 906
Tallahassee Audio Visual, pg 906

GEORGIA

Audio Visual Resources Inc, pg 695
Convergent Media Systems, pg 731
Lighting & Production Equipment Inc, pg 807
ON Services, a GES Company, pg 846
Stage Front Presentation Systems, pg 899
Staging Directions Inc, pg 899

ILLINOIS

Allen Visual Systems Inc, pg 680
AV Chicago Inc, pg 696
Backstar Creative Media Inc, pg 700
Beatty TeleVisual Productions, pg 703
Central Audio-Visual Equipment Inc, pg 719
Creative Technology (CT), pg 733
Helix Camera & Video, pg 778
RC Communications, pg 870
Resolution Productions Group, pg 874

INDIANA

Heart Breaker Entertainment LLC, pg 778

IOWA

Central Lighting & Equipment Inc (CLE), pg 719

KENTUCKY

Audio Visual Techniques Inc, pg 695

LOUISIANA

Clark Services Audio Visual & Exhibit Inc, pg 725
Pace Systems, pg 849

MAINE

Headlight Audio Visual Inc, pg 777

MARYLAND

Absolute Hollywood, pg 672
Advance Audiovisual Presentation Ltd, pg 677
Cardinal Sound & Video, pg 717
CPR MultiMedia Solutions, pg 732
Hargrove Inc, pg 776
Nelson White Systems Inc, pg 838
RTZ Audio Visual, pg 878

MASSACHUSETTS

massAV, pg 819
Preston Productions Inc, pg 861

MICHIGAN

Olson Anderson Co, pg 685
City Events Group, pg 725
K&R All Media Productions LLC, pg 796
K&R's Recording Studios Inc, pg 796
On Stage Visuals, pg 846

MINNESOTA

AVI Systems, pg 698

MISSISSIPPI

Bowie Audio Visual Enterprises Inc, pg 709
Jasper Ewing & Sons Inc, pg 757

MISSOURI

Communitronics Corp, pg 729
EZ Scenic, pg 758
Schiller's Audio-Visual, pg 881
Show-Me Audio-Visual, pg 887
Southwest Audio-Visual Inc, pg 895
Switch, pg 905

NEVADA

GES Audio Visual, pg 770

NEW HAMPSHIRE

APS Lighting-Sound-AV, pg 688

NEW JERSEY

Audio Visual Associates, pg 694
Audio Visual Dynamics®, pg 694
Earl Girls Inc, pg 749
International Audio Visual Inc, pg 790
Panavid, pg 850
Starlite, pg 900
Video Corporation of America (VCA), pg 927
Wired 4 Sound Inc, pg 940

NEW YORK

Ace Video, pg 674
AV Workshop, pg 697
Colortone Audio Visual, pg 728
Design Audio Visual Inc, pg 741
KVL Audio Visual Services Inc, pg 802
Langie Audio Visual Systems, pg 803
Long Island Video Enterprises Live Inc, pg 811

AUDIO/VISUAL

Lectern Rentals (continued)

NEW YORK (continued)

Ray Supply Inc, pg 870
Visual Technologies Corp, pg 932
Visual Word Systems Inc, pg 932

NORTH CAROLINA

AV Connections Inc, pg 697
AV Metro Inc, pg 697
Special Event Services, pg 896
Strategic Connections, pg 901

NORTH DAKOTA

Media Productions, pg 822

OHIO

Audio Visual Media, pg 694
Hughie's Event Production Services, pg 782
ITA Audio Visual Solutions, pg 791

OKLAHOMA

PDC Productions, pg 852

OREGON

Rose City Sound, pg 877

PENNSYLVANIA

Advanced AV LLC, pg 677
Audio Visions Inc, pg 694
Audio Visual Communications Inc, pg 694
Visual Sound Inc, pg 931

SOUTH CAROLINA

Sound & Images Inc, pg 893

TENNESSEE

Allstar Audio Systems Inc, pg 681
Brantley Sound Associates Inc, pg 709
Memphis Communications Corp, pg 823
Technical Support Systems LLC, pg 908

TEXAS

Alford Media Services, pg 680
Audio Visual Technologies Group (AVTG), pg 695
Heffernan Audio Visual, pg 778
JSAV, pg 795
Lubbock Audio Visual Inc, pg 812

UTAH

Performance Audio LLC, pg 854
Webb Audio Visual, pg 935

VIRGINIA

American AV, pg 682
Audio Visual Actions Inc (AVA), pg 694
Boitnott Visual Communications Corp (BVC), pg 708
Lee Hartman & Sons Inc, pg 805
Metropolitan Audio Visual Co LLC, pg 824
Projection, pg 865

WASHINGTON

D A Sound, pg 737
Inland Audio Visual Co, pg 788
PNTA, pg 858

WISCONSIN

Audio Visual of Milwaukee Inc, pg 694
Camera Corner Connecting Point, pg 715
Event Essentials, pg 756
Full Compass Systems, pg 767

PUERTO RICO

Stage Crew Audiovisual Inc, pg 898

ALBERTA

Evolution AV, pg 757
McBain Camera Ltd, pg 820
Unique Communications Ltd, pg 921

BRITISH COLUMBIA

Clark's Audio Visual Services Ltd, pg 725

MANITOBA

Inland Audio Visual Ltd, pg 788

ONTARIO

HD Source, pg 777
Westbury National Show Systems Ltd, pg 936

QUEBEC

Audio Visual Dynamics, pg 694

Lectern Repairs

ARKANSAS

Jay S Stanley & Associates Inc, pg 899

CALIFORNIA

Ametron Audio/Video, pg 684
Instructional Materials & Equipment Distributors (I-Med), pg 789
McAlister Electronics, pg 820
Lloyd F McKinney Associates Inc, pg 821
SSL Industries Inc, pg 898
Towards 2000 Inc, pg 916

COLORADO

Ceavco Audio Visual Company Inc, pg 719

CONNECTICUT

HB Communications Inc, pg 777
Rockwell Communications Inc, pg 876

FLORIDA

Stereo Sales Inc, pg 900
TAI Audio, pg 906

GEORGIA

Audio Visual Resources Inc, pg 695
Lighting & Production Equipment Inc, pg 807
Stage Front Presentation Systems, pg 899

ILLINOIS

Allen Visual Systems Inc, pg 680

KENTUCKY

Axxis Leasing Inc, pg 700
NOR-COM Inc, pg 841

MAINE

Headlight Audio Visual Inc, pg 777

MARYLAND

Cardinal Sound & Video, pg 717
RTZ Audio Visual, pg 878

MICHIGAN

Olson Anderson Co, pg 685
City Events Group, pg 725
TEL Systems LLC, pg 909

MINNESOTA

AVI Systems, pg 698

MISSISSIPPI

Bowie Audio Visual Enterprises Inc, pg 709

MISSOURI

Schiller's Audio-Visual, pg 881

NEW JERSEY

Earl Girls Inc, pg 749

NEW YORK

Langie Audio Visual Systems, pg 803
Ray Supply Inc, pg 870
Visual Technologies Corp, pg 932

NORTH CAROLINA

Camcor Inc, pg 715

OHIO

Audio Visual Media, pg 694
ITA Audio Visual Solutions, pg 791

OREGON

All Service Musical Electronics Repair, pg 680

PENNSYLVANIA

Audio Visions Inc, pg 694

TENNESSEE

Memphis Communications Corp, pg 823
Technical Support Systems LLC, pg 908

TEXAS

Audio Visual Technologies Group (AVTG), pg 695
Heffernan Audio Visual, pg 778
Lubbock Audio Visual Inc, pg 812
Quality Audio Visual Service Inc, pg 867
Southwest Sound Solutions, pg 896
Tarpley Media Systems, pg 907

VIRGINIA

Avitecture Inc, pg 699
Boitnott Visual Communications Corp (BVC), pg 708
Lee Hartman & Sons Inc, pg 805

Metropolitan Audio Visual Co LLC, pg 824
The Whitlock Group, pg 937

WASHINGTON

D A Sound, pg 737
Inland Audio Visual Co, pg 788

WISCONSIN

Full Compass Systems, pg 767

ALBERTA

Infosat Communications Inc, pg 787

MANITOBA

Inland Audio Visual Ltd, pg 788

Manual Slide Presentation System, *see* Slide Presentation System— Programmable & Manual

Megaphone—Power Distributors

ARIZONA

Arizona Cine Equipment, pg 688
Troxell-CDI, pg 918

ARKANSAS

Sound-Craft Systems Inc, pg 894

CALIFORNIA

Ametron Audio/Video, pg 684
Associated Sound, pg 691
Assured Audio Visual, pg 691
California Tape Products Inc, pg 714
Electronic Design Solutions Inc, pg 752
Instructional Materials & Equipment Distributors (I-Med), pg 789
JD Audio Visual Inc, pg 793
Location Sound Corp, pg 810
Lloyd F McKinney Associates Inc, pg 821
Media Fabricators Inc, pg 822
SSL Industries Inc, pg 898
Stanislaus AV Inc, pg 899
TOA Electronics Inc, pg 915
Towards 2000 Inc, pg 916

COLORADO

Ceavco Audio Visual Company Inc, pg 719
Daylight Productions & Rentals, pg 739

CONNECTICUT

HB Communications Inc, pg 777
MAVCO, pg 820

DELAWARE

Actors Attic, pg 675

FLORIDA

Broadcasters General Store Inc, pg 711
Hi-Tech Import Export Corp, pg 779
Hollywood Theatre Equipment Inc, pg 781

ONstage, pg 846
Photosound of Orlando Inc, pg 856
Stereo Sales Inc, pg 900
TAI Audio, pg 906

GEORGIA

Stage Front Presentation Systems, pg 899
Visioneering International Inc, pg 931

HAWAII

The Audio Visual Co (AVCO), pg 694

ILLINOIS

Allen Visual Systems Inc, pg 680
Joseph Electronics, pg 795

INDIANA

SHP Electronics, pg 887

KANSAS

KK Office Solutions Inc, pg 799

KENTUCKY

Audio Visual Techniques Inc, pg 695
NOR-COM Inc, pg 841

MAINE

Headlight Audio Visual Inc, pg 777

MARYLAND

Cardinal Sound & Video, pg 717
RTZ Audio Visual, pg 878

MASSACHUSETTS

Rule Boston Camera, pg 878

MICHIGAN

Olson Anderson Co, pg 685
City Events Group, pg 725
TEL Systems LLC, pg 909

MINNESOTA

AVI Systems, pg 698
New Life Communications Inc, pg 839

MISSISSIPPI

Jasper Ewing & Sons Inc, pg 757

MISSOURI

Communitronics Corp, pg 729
ITC, pg 791
Schiller's Audio-Visual, pg 881

NEW HAMPSHIRE

APS Lighting-Sound-AV, pg 688

NEW JERSEY

Alltec Stores, a Vcom IMC Company, pg 681
AlltecPro, pg 681
Audio Visual Associates, pg 694
Audio Visual Dynamics®, pg 694
AV Bluebook, pg 696
Earl Girls Inc, pg 749
FlagHouse, pg 762
HamiltonBuhl, pg 775
Starlite, pg 900
Total Video Products Inc, pg 916

Vcom IMC, pg 925
Wired 4 Sound Inc, pg 940

NEW YORK

Audio-Video Corp, pg 694
AV Workshop, pg 697
Design Audio Visual Inc, pg 741
Indigo Productions, pg 787
Langie Audio Visual Systems, pg 803
Lee Dan® Communications Inc, pg 805
Long Island Video Enterprises Live Inc, pg 811
Markertek Video Supply, pg 817
Neptune Photo Inc, pg 838
Presentation Products Inc, pg 861
Ray Supply Inc, pg 870
RNJ Electronics, pg 875
Visual Technologies Corp, pg 932

NORTH CAROLINA

Camcor Inc, pg 715
Strategic Connections, pg 901

OHIO

Copp Integrated Systems, pg 731
ITA Audio Visual Solutions, pg 791
Tri-State Audio Visual Co, pg 918
Tri-State Visual Products Inc, pg 918

PENNSYLVANIA

Advanced AV LLC, pg 677
Audio Visions Inc, pg 694
Brodart Co, pg 711
J E Foss Co, pg 764
Garcia Marketing Inc, pg 768
Grise Audio Visual Center Inc, pg 774
Morefield Communications Inc, pg 830
RSS Distributors, pg 878
Vistacom Inc, pg 931
Visual Sound Inc, pg 931
Wespen Audio Visual Co, pg 935

TENNESSEE

Allstar Audio Systems Inc, pg 681
Lowrance Sound Co Inc, pg 812
Memphis Communications Corp, pg 823
Technical Support Systems LLC, pg 908

TEXAS

Audio Visual Technologies Group (AVTG), pg 695
AVES Audio Visual Systems Inc, pg 698
Crossroads Audio Inc, pg 735
Heffernan Audio Visual, pg 778
JSAV, pg 795
Lubbock Audio Visual Inc, pg 812
Quality Audio Visual Service Inc, pg 867
Southwest Sound Solutions, pg 896
Tarpley Media Systems, pg 907

UTAH

Performance Audio LLC, pg 854
Webb Audio Visual, pg 935

VIRGINIA

Avitecture Inc, pg 699
Boitnott Visual Communications Corp (BVC), pg 708
Lee Hartman & Sons Inc, pg 805
The Whitlock Group, pg 937

WASHINGTON

CCI Solutions, pg 718
Inland Audio Visual Co, pg 788
PNTA, pg 858

WEST VIRGINIA

United Sound & Electronics, pg 921

WISCONSIN

Audio Visual of Milwaukee Inc, pg 694
Camera Corner Connecting Point, pg 715
Full Compass Systems, pg 767

PUERTO RICO

Audio Visual Concepts Inc, pg 694
Bonnin Electronics Inc, pg 708

ALBERTA

Infosat Communications Inc, pg 787
McBain Camera Ltd, pg 820

BRITISH COLUMBIA

Commercial Electronics Ltd, pg 728

MANITOBA

Inland Audio Visual Ltd, pg 788

ONTARIO

Cinema Stage Inc, pg 724
Nationwide Audio Visual Co, pg 837
Westbury National Show Systems Ltd, pg 936

Megaphone—Power Manufacturers

ARIZONA

David Wexler & Co, pg 936

CALIFORNIA

Anchor Audio Inc, pg 685
Califone International Inc, pg 714
TOA Electronics Inc, pg 915

ILLINOIS

AmpliVox Portable Sound Systems, pg 684

NEVADA

Pignose-Gorilla, pg 856

NEW JERSEY

AlltecPro, pg 681

NEW YORK

MG Electronics, pg 825
TecNec Distributing, pg 909

Megaphone—Power Rentals

ALABAMA

Audio-Video Resources Inc, pg 694

ARIZONA

Arizona Cine Equipment, pg 688
Merestone, pg 823
Metropolitan Audio-Visual Inc, pg 824

CALIFORNIA

AGF Media Services, pg 678
Alliant Event Services, pg 681
Ametron Audio/Video, pg 684
Artichoke Productions, pg 690
Associated Sound, pg 691
Assured Audio Visual, pg 691
Audio Rents, pg 693
Electronic Design Solutions Inc, pg 752
Instructional Materials & Equipment Distributors (I-Med), pg 789
JD Audio Visual Inc, pg 793
Location Sound Corp, pg 810
Lynch Communications, pg 813
McCune Audio-Video-Lighting, pg 821
Media Fabricators Inc, pg 822
Munday & Collins AV, pg 834
Stanislaus AV Inc, pg 899
Towards 2000 Inc, pg 916
Voice & Video Rentals, pg 932

COLORADO

Multimedia Audio Visual Inc, pg 833

CONNECTICUT

A/V Davey, pg 697

DELAWARE

Actors Attic, pg 675

FLORIDA

AVI-SPL, pg 698
ONstage, pg 846
Paradise Show & Design Inc, pg 851
Photosound of Orlando Inc, pg 856
TAI Audio, pg 906

GEORGIA

Stage Front Presentation Systems, pg 899
Staging Directions Inc, pg 899

ILLINOIS

Allen Visual Systems Inc, pg 680
AV Chicago Inc, pg 696
Central Audio-Visual Equipment Inc, pg 719
Helix Camera & Video, pg 778
RC Communications, pg 870

INDIANA

OMNI Productions, pg 845

KENTUCKY

Audio Visual Techniques Inc, pg 695

MARYLAND

Advance Audiovisual Presentation Ltd, pg 677
Cardinal Sound & Video, pg 717
Event Tech, pg 756
RTZ Audio Visual, pg 878

MASSACHUSETTS

Preston Productions Inc, pg 861

MICHIGAN

Olson Anderson Co, pg 685
City Events Group, pg 725
K&R All Media Productions LLC, pg 796

AUDIO/VISUAL

Megaphone—Power Rentals (continued)

MINNESOTA

AVI Systems, pg 698

MISSOURI

Communitronics Corp, pg 729
Show-Me Audio-Visual, pg 887

NEVADA

GES Audio Visual, pg 770

NEW HAMPSHIRE

APS Lighting-Sound-AV, pg 688

NEW JERSEY

Audio Visual Associates, pg 694
Earl Girls Inc, pg 749
Video Corporation of America (VCA), pg 927

NEW YORK

Ace Video, pg 674
AV Workshop, pg 697
Design Audio Visual Inc, pg 741
Hello World Communications, pg 778
Langie Audio Visual Systems, pg 803
Production Resource Group LLC (PRG), pg 864
Visual Technologies Corp, pg 932

NORTH CAROLINA

Special Event Services, pg 896
Strategic Connections, pg 901

OHIO

ITA Audio Visual Solutions, pg 791

OREGON

Rose City Sound, pg 877

PENNSYLVANIA

Advanced AV LLC, pg 677
Audio Visions Inc, pg 694
Grise Audio Visual Center Inc, pg 774

TENNESSEE

Allstar Audio Systems Inc, pg 681
Brantley Sound Associates Inc, pg 709
Memphis Communications Corp, pg 823
Technical Support Systems LLC, pg 908

TEXAS

Audio Visual Technologies Group (AVTG), pg 695
GEAR Cameras & Lighting, pg 769
JSAV, pg 795
Lubbock Audio Visual Inc, pg 812
Quality Audio Visual Service Inc, pg 867

UTAH

Performance Audio LLC, pg 854
Redman Movies & Stories, pg 872
Webb Audio Visual, pg 935

VIRGINIA

American AV, pg 682
Boitnott Visual Communications Corp (BVC), pg 708
Lee Hartman & Sons Inc, pg 805
Projection, pg 865

WASHINGTON

Inland Audio Visual Co, pg 788
Oppenheimer Camera Products, pg 847
PNTA, pg 858

WEST VIRGINIA

United Sound & Electronics, pg 921

WISCONSIN

Audio Visual of Milwaukee Inc, pg 694
Event Essentials, pg 756

ALBERTA

Evolution AV, pg 757
McBain Camera Ltd, pg 820
Unique Communications Ltd, pg 921

BRITISH COLUMBIA

Clark's Audio Visual Services Ltd, pg 725
Commercial Electronics Ltd, pg 728

MANITOBA

Inland Audio Visual Ltd, pg 788

ONTARIO

Westbury National Show Systems Ltd, pg 936

QUEBEC

Audio Visual Dynamics, pg 694

Megaphone—Power Repairs

CALIFORNIA

Ametron Audio/Video, pg 684
Instructional Materials & Equipment Distributors (I-Med), pg 789
McAlister Electronics, pg 820
Lloyd F McKinney Associates Inc, pg 821
SSL Industries Inc, pg 898
TOA Electronics Inc, pg 915
Towards 2000 Inc, pg 916

CONNECTICUT

HB Communications Inc, pg 777

FLORIDA

Stereo Sales Inc, pg 900
TAI Audio, pg 906

GEORGIA

Stage Front Presentation Systems, pg 899

ILLINOIS

Allen Visual Systems Inc, pg 680
Central Audio-Visual Equipment Inc, pg 719

KENTUCKY

NOR-COM Inc, pg 841

MARYLAND

Cardinal Sound & Video, pg 717
RTZ Audio Visual, pg 878

MICHIGAN

Olson Anderson Co, pg 685
City Events Group, pg 725
TEL Systems LLC, pg 909

MINNESOTA

AVI Systems, pg 698

NEW JERSEY

Earl Girls Inc, pg 749

NEW YORK

Colortone Audio Visual, pg 728
Langie Audio Visual Systems, pg 803

OHIO

ITA Audio Visual Solutions, pg 791
Tri-State Audio Visual Co, pg 918

OREGON

All Service Musical Electronics Repair, pg 680

PENNSYLVANIA

Audio Visions Inc, pg 694
J E Foss Co, pg 764

TENNESSEE

Memphis Communications Corp, pg 823
Technical Support Systems LLC, pg 908

TEXAS

Audio Visual Technologies Group (AVTG), pg 695
Lubbock Audio Visual Inc, pg 812
Quality Audio Visual Service Inc, pg 867
Southwest Sound Solutions, pg 896
Tarpley Media Systems, pg 907

VIRGINIA

Boitnott Visual Communications Corp (BVC), pg 708

WASHINGTON

Inland Audio Visual Co, pg 788
PNTA, pg 858

WEST VIRGINIA

United Sound & Electronics, pg 921

WISCONSIN

Full Compass Systems, pg 767

ALBERTA

Infosat Communications Inc, pg 787

BRITISH COLUMBIA

Commercial Electronics Ltd, pg 728

MANITOBA

Inland Audio Visual Ltd, pg 788

Microcomputer Distributors

ARIZONA

Arizona Cine Equipment, pg 688
Troxell-CDI, pg 918

CALIFORNIA

Ametron Audio/Video, pg 684
Audio Images Corp, pg 693
CADint, pg 713
California Tape Products Inc, pg 714
Instructional Materials & Equipment Distributors (I-Med), pg 789
Kontron America, pg 801
Media Fabricators Inc, pg 822
Photodyne Technologies, pg 856
Promax Systems, pg 865
VMI Inc, pg 932

FLORIDA

Hi-Tech Import Export Corp, pg 779
ONstage, pg 846

GEORGIA

Lighting & Production Equipment Inc, pg 807
Stage Front Presentation Systems, pg 899
Visioneering International Inc, pg 931

ILLINOIS

Creative Technology (CT), pg 733
Major Reproductions Equipment Co, pg 815
Woodside Avenue Music Productions Inc, pg 941

KENTUCKY

NOR-COM Inc, pg 841

MAINE

Headlight Audio Visual Inc, pg 777

MARYLAND

Kipp Visual Systems Inc, pg 799

MASSACHUSETTS

Professional Audio Design Inc, pg 865
Psychsoft Inc, pg 866

MICHIGAN

Digi Sign Design LLC, pg 741
TEL Systems LLC, pg 909

MINNESOTA

AVI Systems, pg 698

MISSISSIPPI

Jasper Ewing & Sons Inc, pg 757

MISSOURI

Schiller's Audio-Visual, pg 881

NEW JERSEY

Audio Visual Dynamics®, pg 694
AV Bluebook, pg 696
HamiltonBuhl, pg 775
Starlite, pg 900
Yorktel, pg 944

NEW YORK
Langie Audio Visual Systems, pg 803
Presentation Products Inc, pg 861

NORTH CAROLINA
Camcor Inc, pg 715

OHIO
Tri-State Audio Visual Co, pg 918

PENNSYLVANIA
Advanced AV LLC, pg 677
Garcia Marketing Inc, pg 768
Visual Sound Inc, pg 931

TENNESSEE
Memphis Communications Corp, pg 823
Spring Arbor Distributors Inc, pg 898

TEXAS
Lubbock Audio Visual Inc, pg 812
Tarpley Media Systems, pg 907
Videotex Systems Inc, pg 930

VIRGINIA
The Whitlock Group, pg 937

WISCONSIN
Audio Visual of Milwaukee Inc, pg 694
Camera Corner Connecting Point, pg 715
Comprompter Inc, pg 729
Full Compass Systems, pg 767

Microcomputer Manufacturers

CALIFORNIA
CADint, pg 713
Kontron America, pg 801
Micro Express, pg 825
Recortec Inc, pg 872

MASSACHUSETTS
Psychsoft Inc, pg 866

MICHIGAN
ASC Systems, pg 690

ONTARIO
Technovision® Interactive Inc, pg 909

Microcomputer Rentals

ARIZONA
Arizona Cine Equipment, pg 688
Merestone, pg 823

CALIFORNIA
Ametron Audio/Video, pg 684
AV Guys, pg 697
CADint, pg 713
McCune Audio-Video-Lighting, pg 821
Media Fabricators Inc, pg 822
Munday & Collins AV, pg 834

Muse Presentation Technologies, pg 834
PSAV® Presentation Services, pg 866

CONNECTICUT
A/V Davey, pg 697

FLORIDA
Industrial Strength Inc, pg 787
ONstage, pg 846
Paradise Show & Design Inc, pg 851

GEORGIA
Lighting & Production Equipment Inc, pg 807
Stage Front Presentation Systems, pg 899
Staging Directions Inc, pg 899

ILLINOIS
Creative Technology (CT), pg 733
Resolution Productions Group, pg 874
Woodside Avenue Music Productions Inc, pg 941

LOUISIANA
Pace Systems, pg 849

MASSACHUSETTS
Preston Productions Inc, pg 861

MICHIGAN
Digi Sign Design LLC, pg 741
K&R All Media Productions LLC, pg 796
K&R's Recording Studios Inc, pg 796

MINNESOTA
AVI Systems, pg 698

MISSISSIPPI
Bowie Audio Visual Enterprises Inc, pg 709

MISSOURI
Show-Me Audio-Visual, pg 887

NEW HAMPSHIRE
Academic & Campus Technology Services, pg 672

NEW JERSEY
Audio Visual Dynamics®, pg 694
PLS Staging, pg 858
Starlite, pg 900

NEW YORK
Ace Video, pg 674
Design Audio Visual Inc, pg 741
Langie Audio Visual Systems, pg 803
Long Island Video Enterprises Live Inc, pg 811

NORTH CAROLINA
AV Connections Inc, pg 697
Special Event Services, pg 896
Strategic Connections, pg 901

OHIO
Icom Multimedia, pg 783
Mills James Productions, pg 828

OKLAHOMA
PDC Productions, pg 852

PENNSYLVANIA
Visual Sound Inc, pg 931

TENNESSEE
Memphis Communications Corp, pg 823

TEXAS
Lubbock Audio Visual Inc, pg 812

VIRGINIA
American AV, pg 682
Projection, pg 865
Quince Imaging Inc, pg 868

WEST VIRGINIA
United Sound & Electronics, pg 921

WISCONSIN
Audio Visual of Milwaukee Inc, pg 694
Camera Corner Connecting Point, pg 715

BRITISH COLUMBIA
Clark's Audio Visual Services Ltd, pg 725

Microcomputer Repairs

CALIFORNIA
Ametron Audio/Video, pg 684
McAlister Electronics, pg 820

FLORIDA
Hi-Tech Enterprises Inc, pg 779
Tel-Test, pg 909

GEORGIA
Lighting & Production Equipment Inc, pg 807

KENTUCKY
NOR-COM Inc, pg 841

MARYLAND
RTZ Audio Visual, pg 878

MICHIGAN
TEL Systems LLC, pg 909

MINNESOTA
AVI Systems, pg 698

NEW YORK
Langie Audio Visual Systems, pg 803

NORTH CAROLINA
Camcor Inc, pg 715

OHIO
Tri-State Audio Visual Co, pg 918

PENNSYLVANIA
Visual Sound Inc, pg 931

TENNESSEE
Memphis Communications Corp, pg 823

TEXAS
Lubbock Audio Visual Inc, pg 812

VIRGINIA
Quince Imaging Inc, pg 868
The Whitlock Group, pg 937

WEST VIRGINIA
United Sound & Electronics, pg 921

WISCONSIN
Camera Corner Connecting Point, pg 715
Full Compass Systems, pg 767

Multi-Image Device & Presentation Accessory Distributors

ARIZONA
Arizona Cine Equipment, pg 688
Metropolitan Audio-Visual Inc, pg 824
Troxell-CDI, pg 918
Ultimate Presentation Systems Inc, pg 920

ARKANSAS
Jay S Stanley & Associates Inc, pg 899
White Diamond Productions LLC, pg 937

CALIFORNIA
Ametron Audio/Video, pg 684
Associated Sound, pg 691
Assured Audio Visual, pg 691
AVerMedia Technologies Inc, pg 697
BigFoot Mobile Systems, pg 705
California Tape Products Inc, pg 714
Christy's Editorial, pg 723
Cibola Systems, pg 723
Electrosonic Inc, pg 752
Gluskin's Custom Audio Video, pg 771
JD Audio Visual Inc, pg 793
Laser Magic Productions, pg 804
Lloyd F McKinney Associates Inc, pg 821
Media Fabricators Inc, pg 822
MediaPOINTE, pg 823
PMP Marketing Inc, pg 858
Southern California Sound Image Inc, pg 895
Stanislaus AV Inc, pg 899

COLORADO
American Educational Products LLC, pg 683
Ceavco Audio Visual Company Inc, pg 719
Daylight Productions & Rentals, pg 739

CONNECTICUT
HB Communications Inc, pg 777
MAVCO, pg 820

AUDIO/VISUAL

Multi-Image Device & Presentation Accessory Distributors (continued)

CONNECTICUT (continued)

Rockwell Communications Inc, pg 876
USI Inc, pg 924
The Video Messenger Co, pg 928

FLORIDA

AVI-SPL, pg 698
Digital Video Systems, pg 742
Harmon's Audio-Visual Services, pg 776
Harris Corp, pg 776
Industrial Strength Inc, pg 787
ONstage, pg 846
Photosound of Orlando Inc, pg 856
The Singing Machine Co Inc, pg 889
Tallahassee Audio Visual, pg 906

GEORGIA

Audio Visual Resources Inc, pg 695
Baker Audio Visual, pg 700
Convergent Media Systems, pg 731
PolyVision Corporation, pg 859
Stage Front Presentation Systems, pg 899
Visioneering International Inc, pg 931

HAWAII

The Audio Visual Co (AVCO), pg 694

ILLINOIS

Creative Technology (CT), pg 733
Dukane Corp, Audio Visual Products Division, pg 747
Quintessence Audio Ltd, pg 868
RC Communications, pg 870

INDIANA

Sensory Technologies LLC, pg 884
SHP Electronics, pg 887

KENTUCKY

Audio Visual Techniques Inc, pg 695
Axxis Leasing Inc, pg 700
NOR-COM Inc, pg 841

LOUISIANA

Techkno Integration & Design Services LLC, pg 908

MAINE

Headlight Audio Visual Inc, pg 777

MARYLAND

Absolute Hollywood, pg 672
Hargrove Inc, pg 776
Image Logic Corp, pg 785
Kipp Visual Systems Inc, pg 799
Nelson White Systems Inc, pg 838
Nicholas P Pipino Associates Inc, pg 857
RTZ Audio Visual, pg 878

MASSACHUSETTS

Lineco, pg 809
Pro AV Systems, pg 862

MICHIGAN

ASC Systems, pg 690
City Events Group, pg 725
Digi Sign Design LLC, pg 741
Michigan Office Solutions (MOS), A Xerox Company, pg 825
TEL Systems LLC, pg 909

MINNESOTA

AVI Systems, pg 698
Media Loft Inc, pg 822

MISSISSIPPI

Bowie Audio Visual Enterprises Inc, pg 709
Jasper Ewing & Sons Inc, pg 757

MISSOURI

Communitronics Corp, pg 729
Conference Technologies Inc, pg 730
ITC, pg 791
Schiller's Audio-Visual, pg 881

NEW JERSEY

A-V Services Inc, pg 671
AlltecPro, pg 681
Audio Visual Associates, pg 694
Audio Visual Dynamics®, pg 694
AV Bluebook, pg 696
Color Leasing Studios, pg 727
Earl Girls Inc, pg 749
HamiltonBuhl, pg 775
Reed Presentations Inc (RPI), pg 872
Starlite, pg 900
SYMCO Inc, pg 905
Video Corporation of America (VCA), pg 927
Wired 4 Sound Inc, pg 940
Yorktel, pg 944

NEW YORK

AV Workshop, pg 697
Design Audio Visual Inc, pg 741
DSan Corp, pg 747
General Audio-Visual Inc (GAVI), pg 769
Indigo Productions, pg 787
Langie Audio Visual Systems, pg 803
Long Island Video Enterprises Live Inc, pg 811
Markertek Video Supply, pg 817
Neptune Photo Inc, pg 838
Presentation Products Inc, pg 861
Ray Supply Inc, pg 870
RNJ Electronics, pg 875
Tri-Ed Distribution Inc, pg 918
Visual Technologies Corp, pg 932
Willoughby's® Camera, pg 939

NORTH CAROLINA

Camcor Inc, pg 715
Strategic Connections, pg 901

OHIO

Audio Visual Media, pg 694
Copp Integrated Systems, pg 731
Icom Multimedia, pg 783
Tri-State Audio Visual Co, pg 918
Tri-State Visual Products Inc, pg 918

OKLAHOMA

Ford AV, pg 763

PENNSYLVANIA

Advanced AV LLC, pg 677
Audio Visions Inc, pg 694
Audio Visual Communications Inc, pg 694
Bernie's Photo Center, pg 704
Brodart Co, pg 711
J E Foss Co, pg 764
Vistacom Inc, pg 931
Visual Sound Inc, pg 931
Wespen Audio Visual Co, pg 935

RHODE ISLAND

Shanix Inc, pg 885

TENNESSEE

Continental Film, pg 731
Lowrance Sound Co Inc, pg 812
Memphis Communications Corp, pg 823
Technical Support Systems LLC, pg 908

TEXAS

Audio Visual Technologies Group (AVTG), pg 695
Heffernan Audio Visual, pg 778
High End Systems Inc, pg 779
JSAV, pg 795
Lubbock Audio Visual Inc, pg 812
Quality Audio Visual Service Inc, pg 867
Stage Directions, pg 898
Tarpley Media Systems, pg 907
Videotex Systems Inc, pg 930

UTAH

Webb Audio Visual, pg 935

VIRGINIA

Boitnott Visual Communications Corp (BVC), pg 708
Design & Production Inc, pg 740
Intellidyne LLC, pg 789
Quince Imaging Inc, pg 868
The Whitlock Group, pg 937

WASHINGTON

Inland Audio Visual Co, pg 788

WISCONSIN

Audio Visual of Milwaukee Inc, pg 694
Camera Corner Connecting Point, pg 715
Full Compass Systems, pg 767
School Specialty Inc, pg 882
USAV Group Inc, pg 923

PUERTO RICO

Audio Visual Concepts Inc, pg 694

ALBERTA

Evolution AV, pg 757
Infosat Communications Inc, pg 787
McBain Camera Ltd, pg 820
SMART Technologies ULC, pg 891
Unique Communications Ltd, pg 921

BRITISH COLUMBIA

Commercial Electronics Ltd, pg 728

MANITOBA

Inland Audio Visual Ltd, pg 788

ONTARIO

GestureTek, pg 770
Image Video, pg 785
Westbury National Show Systems Ltd, pg 936

Multi-Image Device & Presentation Accessory Manufacturers

ARIZONA

Boeckeler Instruments Inc, pg 708

CALIFORNIA

AITech International, pg 679
AMX® by Harman, pg 685
AVerMedia Technologies Inc, pg 697
Extron Electronics, pg 758
Laser Magic Productions, pg 804
MediaPOINTE, pg 823
RGB Spectrum, pg 874
Xantech LLC, pg 943

COLORADO

American Educational Products LLC, pg 683

CONNECTICUT

The Video Messenger Co, pg 928

FLORIDA

Vutec Corp, pg 933

GEORGIA

Analog Way Inc, pg 685
PolyVision Corporation, pg 859

ILLINOIS

Bretford Manufacturing Inc, pg 710
Dukane Corp, Audio Visual Products Division, pg 747

INDIANA

Da-Lite, a Legrand AV Inc brand, pg 737
Draper Inc, pg 746
Star Case Manufacturing Co Inc, pg 900

MARYLAND

Absolute Hollywood, pg 672
Image Logic Corp, pg 785

MICHIGAN

Leightronix Inc, pg 806

MINNESOTA

Chief, a Legrand AV Inc brand, pg 722

NEVADA

N&N Productions Ltd, pg 835

NEW JERSEY

AlltecPro, pg 681
Crestron Electronics Inc, pg 734
FSR Inc, pg 766
Reed Presentations Inc (RPI), pg 872

NEW YORK

DSan Corp, pg 747
Eastman Kodak Co, pg 750
ELMO USA Corp, pg 753
General Audio-Visual Inc (GAVI), pg 769
Judson Rosebush Co Inc, pg 877

OHIO

Turning Technologies LLC, pg 919
TV One Multimedia Solutions, pg 919

PENNSYLVANIA

Scala Inc, pg 881

TEXAS

High End Systems Inc, pg 779

VIRGINIA

Quince Imaging Inc, pg 868

ALBERTA

SMART Technologies ULC, pg 891

ONTARIO

GestureTek, pg 770
Image Video, pg 785
Technovision® Interactive Inc, pg 909

QUEBEC

Matrox Video Products Group, pg 819

Multi-Image Device & Presentation Accessory Rentals

ARIZONA

Arizona Cine Equipment, pg 688
Merestone, pg 823
Metropolitan Audio-Visual Inc, pg 824
Ultimate Presentation Systems Inc, pg 920

ARKANSAS

White Diamond Productions LLC, pg 937

CALIFORNIA

Ametron Audio/Video, pg 684
Associated Sound, pg 691
Assured Audio Visual, pg 691
AV Guys, pg 697
California Teleprompter, pg 714
Gold Standard Productions, pg 772
JD Audio Visual Inc, pg 793
Lynch Communications, pg 813
McCune Audio-Video-Lighting, pg 821
Media Fabricators Inc, pg 822
Munday & Collins AV, pg 834
Muse Presentation Technologies, pg 834
PSAV® Presentation Services, pg 866
Stanislaus AV Inc, pg 899
Towards 2000 Inc, pg 916
VER, pg 926
Video Resources Inc, pg 928

COLORADO

Ceavco Audio Visual Company Inc, pg 719
Daylight Productions & Rentals, pg 739
Multimedia Audio Visual Inc, pg 833
Spectrum Audio Visual Services, pg 897

CONNECTICUT

A/V Davey, pg 697
Videofilm Systems Inc, pg 929

DELAWARE

Showorks Audio Visual Inc, pg 887

FLORIDA

AVI-SPL, pg 698
Harmon's Audio-Visual Services, pg 776
Industrial Strength Inc, pg 787
Jordan Klein Film & Video (JKFV), pg 795
ONstage, pg 846
Photosound of Orlando Inc, pg 856
Sight & Sound Productions, pg 887
Tallahassee Audio Visual, pg 906

GEORGIA

Convergent Media Systems, pg 731
Stage Front Presentation Systems, pg 899
Staging Directions Inc, pg 899

ILLINOIS

Airways Digital Media, pg 679
Beatty TeleVisual Productions, pg 703
Creative Technology (CT), pg 733
Helix Camera & Video, pg 778
Pepper Group, pg 854
PSAV® Presentation Services (Hotel Services Division), pg 866
RC Communications, pg 870
Resolution Productions Group, pg 874
SCI Television & Creative Media LLC, pg 882

INDIANA

Advanced Media Integration, pg 677
OMNI Productions, pg 845

KENTUCKY

Audio Visual Techniques Inc, pg 695

LOUISIANA

Clark Services Audio Visual & Exhibit Inc, pg 725
Pace Systems, pg 849

MARYLAND

Absolute Hollywood, pg 672
Advance Audiovisual Presentation Ltd, pg 677
dbF a Media Company, pg 739
Hargrove Inc, pg 776
Nelson White Systems Inc, pg 838
RTZ Audio Visual, pg 878

MASSACHUSETTS

AVFX Inc, pg 698
Capron Lighting & Sound Co Inc, pg 716
massAV, pg 819

Preston Productions Inc, pg 861
TR Productions, pg 916

MICHIGAN

City Events Group, pg 725
Digi Sign Design LLC, pg 741
K&R All Media Productions LLC, pg 796
K&R's Recording Studios Inc, pg 796

MINNESOTA

AVI Systems, pg 698
Media Loft Inc, pg 822

MISSISSIPPI

Bowie Audio Visual Enterprises Inc, pg 709
Jasper Ewing & Sons Inc, pg 757

MISSOURI

Communitronics Corp, pg 729
Show-Me Audio-Visual, pg 887
Switch, pg 905

NEVADA

GES Audio Visual, pg 770

NEW HAMPSHIRE

Academic & Campus Technology Services, pg 672
Apertura, pg 686

NEW JERSEY

Audio Visual Associates, pg 694
Audio Visual Dynamics®, pg 694
Color Leasing Studios, pg 727
Earl Girls Inc, pg 749
International Audio Visual Inc, pg 796
Moe AV LLC, pg 828
PLS Staging, pg 858
Starlite, pg 900
Wired 4 Sound Inc, pg 940

NEW YORK

AV Workshop, pg 697
CMI Communications, pg 727
CP Communications, pg 732
Design Audio Visual Inc, pg 741
General Audio-Visual Inc (GAVI), pg 769
Langie Audio Visual Systems, pg 803
Long Island Video Enterprises Live Inc, pg 811
SmartSource Computer & AV Rentals, pg 891
Tri-Ed Distribution Inc, pg 918
Visual Technologies Corp, pg 932
Visual Word Systems Inc, pg 932
WorldStage, pg 941

NORTH CAROLINA

AV Connections Inc, pg 697
AV Metro Inc, pg 697
Special Event Services, pg 896
Strategic Connections, pg 901

NORTH DAKOTA

Media Productions, pg 822

OHIO

Audio Visual Media, pg 694
Icom Multimedia, pg 783
Thread Marketing Group, pg 913
Vista Color Imaging Inc, pg 931

PENNSYLVANIA

Advanced AV LLC, pg 677
Audio Visions Inc, pg 694
Audio Visual Communications Inc, pg 694
FMP Media Solutions Inc, pg 763
Grise Audio Visual Center Inc, pg 774
Visual Sound Inc, pg 931

SOUTH CAROLINA

Sound & Images Inc, pg 893

TENNESSEE

Memphis Communications Corp, pg 823
Russ Sturgeon Productions/RSVP, pg 903
Technical Support Systems LLC, pg 908

TEXAS

Audio Visual Technologies Group (AVTG), pg 695
Freeman, pg 765
JSAV, pg 795
Lubbock Audio Visual Inc, pg 812
Stage Directions, pg 898

UTAH

Webb Audio Visual, pg 935

VIRGINIA

American AV, pg 682
Boitnott Visual Communications Corp (BVC), pg 708
Projection, pg 865
Quince Imaging Inc, pg 868

WASHINGTON

D A Sound, pg 737
Inland Audio Visual Co, pg 788
Kostov Productions, pg 801

WISCONSIN

Audio Visual of Milwaukee Inc, pg 694
Camera Corner Connecting Point, pg 715
Event Essentials, pg 756
Full Compass Systems, pg 767

WYOMING

Bridger Productions Inc, pg 710

PUERTO RICO

Stage Crew Audiovisual Inc, pg 898

ALBERTA

Cine Audio Visual Sales & Service Ltd, pg 723
Evolution AV, pg 757
McBain Camera Ltd, pg 820
Unique Communications Ltd, pg 921

BRITISH COLUMBIA

Clark's Audio Visual Services Ltd, pg 725
Commercial Electronics Ltd, pg 728

MANITOBA

Inland Audio Visual Ltd, pg 788

AUDIO/VISUAL

Multi-Image Device & Presentation Accessory Rentals (continued)

ONTARIO

GestureTek, pg 770
HD Source, pg 777
MVI - MultiVision Inc, pg 835
Westbury National Show Systems
Ltd, pg 936

QUEBEC

Audio Visual Dynamics, pg 694
Freeman Audio Visual, pg 765

Multi-Image Device & Presentation Accessory Repairs

ARKANSAS

Jay S Stanley & Associates Inc,
pg 899

CALIFORNIA

Ametron Audio/Video, pg 684
AVerMedia Technologies Inc,
pg 697
Electrosonic Inc, pg 752
Instructional Materials & Equipment
Distributors (I-Med), pg 789
McAlister Electronics, pg 820
Lloyd F McKinney Associates Inc,
pg 821
Pro Camera Repair, pg 862
Towards 2000 Inc, pg 916

COLORADO

Ceavco Audio Visual Company Inc,
pg 719

CONNECTICUT

HB Communications Inc, pg 777

FLORIDA

Tallahassee Audio Visual, pg 906

GEORGIA

Analog Way Inc, pg 685
Audio Visual Resources Inc, pg 695
Stage Front Presentation Systems,
pg 899

ILLINOIS

RC Communications, pg 870

KENTUCKY

Axxis Leasing Inc, pg 700
NOR-COM Inc, pg 841

MARYLAND

Nelson White Systems Inc, pg 838
RTZ Audio Visual, pg 878

MICHIGAN

City Events Group, pg 725
TEL Systems LLC, pg 909

MINNESOTA

AVI Systems, pg 698

MISSISSIPPI

Bowie Audio Visual Enterprises Inc,
pg 709

MISSOURI

Communitronics Corp, pg 729

NEW JERSEY

Earl Girls Inc, pg 749
Starlite, pg 900

NEW YORK

Colortone Audio Visual, pg 728
ELMO USA Corp, pg 753
Langie Audio Visual Systems,
pg 803
Visual Technologies Corp, pg 932

NORTH CAROLINA

Camcor Inc, pg 715
Strategic Connections, pg 901

OHIO

Audio Visual Media, pg 694
Icom Multimedia, pg 783
Tri-State Audio Visual Co, pg 918

PENNSYLVANIA

Audio Visions Inc, pg 694

TENNESSEE

Memphis Communications Corp,
pg 823
Technical Support Systems LLC,
pg 908

TEXAS

Audio Visual Technologies Group
(AVTG), pg 695
Heffernan Audio Visual, pg 778
Lubbock Audio Visual Inc, pg 812

VIRGINIA

Boitnott Visual Communications
Corp (BVC), pg 708
Lee Hartman & Sons Inc, pg 805
Quince Imaging Inc, pg 868
The Whitlock Group, pg 937

WASHINGTON

Inland Audio Visual Co, pg 788

WISCONSIN

Full Compass Systems, pg 767

ALBERTA

Evolution AV, pg 757
Infosat Communications Inc, pg 787
Unique Communications Ltd,
pg 921

MANITOBA

Inland Audio Visual Ltd, pg 788

ONTARIO

MVI - MultiVision Inc, pg 835
Technovision® Interactive Inc,
pg 909
Westbury National Show Systems
Ltd, pg 936

Music Scoring

ALABAMA

Sound of Birmingham Productions,
pg 894

ARIZONA

Creative Backstage, pg 733
Merestone, pg 823

ARKANSAS

Live'N'Loud, pg 810

CALIFORNIA

AB Audio Visual Entertainment Inc,
pg 672
Aliso Creek Productions Inc, pg 680
Berkeley Sound Artists Inc, pg 704
CCI Digital, a DVS Company,
pg 718
Creative Media Recording, pg 733
Creative Support Services/CSS
Music, pg 733
Crystal Pyramid Productions™,
pg 735
Diamond Dreams Music
Productions, pg 741
Earwax Productions Inc, pg 749
GrooveWorx, pg 774
iCorpTv, pg 783
JDS Video & Media Productions
Inc, pg 793
Kaleidosound, pg 796
K2B2 Records, pg 802
Lynch Communications, pg 813
Maximus Media Inc, pg 820
The Media Staff Inc, pg 822
Joseph Nicoletti Consulting-
Promotion, pg 841
OTR Studios, pg 848
piXvfm Inc, pg 857
PM Productions, pg 858
Polarity Post Production, pg 858
Pyramind Studios, pg 867
QRS Software Services, pg 867
Reality Check Systems, pg 871
Russ InVision Co/AbridgeClub.com,
pg 879
Sahara Records & Filmworks
Entertainment Co, pg 879
Sonic Gravy, pg 892
SonicPool, pg 892
Still N' Motion, pg 901
Studio 132, pg 902
Total Creative, pg 916
Twisted Media Inc, pg 920
West Coast Projections Inc, pg 935

COLORADO

Tim Cissell Music, pg 725
Conly Productions, pg 730
Flashback Media Productions,
pg 762
Los Angeles Post Music Inc, pg 811

CONNECTICUT

Guymark Studios LLC, pg 775
MAVCO, pg 820
P&P Studios Inc, pg 851

DELAWARE

Side Door Studio Inc, pg 887

DISTRICT OF COLUMBIA

Interface Media Group, pg 789

FLORIDA

Audacity Recording Studios, pg 693
Kat Epple Music Productions,
pg 755
The Kitchen, pg 799
Mach 1 Productions, pg 813
Sunfire Communications Inc,
pg 904

GEORGIA

Crawford Media Services Inc,
pg 733
Visioneering International Inc,
pg 931
White Dog Studios, pg 937

HAWAII

Media Bridge Gamekids, pg 821

ILLINOIS

ABS Enterprises, pg 672
Mightybytes Inc, pg 827
Jim Passin Productions, pg 852
Pepper Group, pg 854
Steven Samler Music & Sound,
pg 879
Solid Sound Recording Studio,
pg 892
Woodside Avenue Music
Productions Inc, pg 941

INDIANA

OMNI Productions, pg 845

KENTUCKY

Broadway Digital, pg 711
The Media Collaboratory, pg 821

LOUISIANA

Disk Productions Inc, pg 743

MARYLAND

dbF a Media Company, pg 739

MASSACHUSETTS

Continental Recordings Inc, pg 731
Northern Light Productions (NLP),
pg 842
Penfield Productions Ltd, pg 853
Preston Productions Inc, pg 861
Soundtrack Group, pg 895
TR Productions, pg 916

MICHIGAN

Audio Graphic Services, pg 693
Digi Sign Design LLC, pg 741
GMP Music, pg 772
K&R's Recording Studios Inc,
pg 796
Michigan Recording Arts Institute
& Technologies, pg 825

MINNESOTA

The ADS Group, pg 676
BeyerSound & Essay Audio, pg 705
Media Loft Inc, pg 822

NEVADA

Tanglewood Productions, pg 907

NEW HAMPSHIRE

Chip Taylor Communications LLC,
pg 907

NEW JERSEY

Allegro Productions Inc, pg 680
CFP Video Productions Inc, pg 720
Color Leasing Studios, pg 727
Milbrodt/Music & Sound Design, pg 827
Milgrom Productions, pg 827
NFL Films Music Library, pg 841
Richard Reiter Productions Inc, pg 873
Suede Interactive, pg 903
TRF Production Music Libraries, pg 917
VCSvideo, pg 925

NEW YORK

Air Sea Land Productions Inc (ASL), pg 678
Big Fish Production US, pg 705
The Big House Group, pg 705
Duggal Visual Solutions Inc, pg 747
Fingerpaint, pg 761
HB-Content, pg 777
Headroom Digital Audio, pg 777
Heavy Melody, pg 778
Icontent, pg 783
KAS Music & Sound, pg 796
Manhattan Production Music Inc, pg 816
Jack Morton Worldwide, pg 830
New York Audio Productions, pg 840
The Palmer Group, pg 850
David Rapkin Audio Production, pg 870
Score Productions Inc, pg 882
Elliot Sokolov Music, pg 892
Sony Music Entertainment, pg 893
Tiki Recording Studios Inc, pg 914
USA Studios, pg 923
Zelman Studios Ltd, pg 945

NORTH CAROLINA

Audio Art, pg 693
Davenport Music Library, pg 738
Trailblazer Studios®, pg 917
2BruceStudio, pg 920

NORTH DAKOTA

Media Productions, pg 822

OHIO

Aztec Video Productions, pg 700
Mills James Productions, pg 828

OKLAHOMA

Garman Productions LLC, pg 768

OREGON

REX, pg 874

PENNSYLVANIA

Audio Visual Communications Inc, pg 694
Dreambox Media Inc, pg 746
Monster Tracks, pg 829
Panta Rhei Media Inc, pg 851
Production Masters Inc (PMI), pg 864

RHODE ISLAND

Sound-FX-Design, pg 894
StarTrak Studios Inc, pg 900

TENNESSEE

American Blackguard Inc, pg 683
Continental Film, pg 731

Fricon Entertainment Co Inc, pg 766
Motion Picture Services, pg 831
Scripps Networks, pg 882
Stage Post, pg 899
Zion Music Group, pg 945

TEXAS

Audio Visual Technologies Group (AVTG), pg 695
Audiomoxie®, pg 695
Communication Arts Multimedia Inc, pg 728
Mediaforce Productions, pg 822
The Sound Lab Inc, pg 894
Sound Works, pg 894
Stage Directions, pg 898
TM Studios Inc, pg 915
Tropikal Productions, pg 918

VERMONT

University of Vermont, Instructional Television Dept, pg 923

VIRGINIA

Studio Center Corp, pg 902

WASHINGTON

Hamilton Studio, pg 775
Inland Audio Visual Co, pg 788
Kostov Productions, pg 801
North-by-Northwest - A Digital Studio, pg 842
Sound Sound, pg 894

WISCONSIN

5th Floor Recording Co, pg 760
USAV Group Inc, pg 923

WYOMING

Bridger Productions Inc, pg 710

BRITISH COLUMBIA

Pinewood Sound, pg 857

ONTARIO

ADS Media, pg 677
GAPC (General Assembly Production Centre), pg 768
Metalworks Recording Studios Inc, pg 824
Nightingale Music Productions Inc, pg 841

Opaque & Overhead Projector Distributors

ALABAMA

Curtis Company, pg 736

ARIZONA

Arizona Cine Equipment, pg 688
Metropolitan Audio-Visual Inc, pg 824
Professional Marketing Services Inc, pg 865
Troxell-CDI, pg 918

ARKANSAS

Carlton-Bates Co, pg 717
Jay S Stanley & Associates Inc, pg 899
White Diamond Productions LLC, pg 937

CALIFORNIA

Ametron Audio/Video, pg 684
Associated Sound, pg 691
Assured Audio Visual, pg 691
Audio/Video Supply Inc, pg 694
California Tape Products Inc, pg 714
Christy's Editorial, pg 723
Gluskin's Custom Audio Video, pg 771
Hooper Camera & Imaging, pg 781
Instructional Materials & Equipment Distributors (I-Med), pg 789
JD Audio Visual Inc, pg 793
Media Fabricators Inc, pg 822
MediaMation Inc, pg 822
MediaPOINTE, pg 823
PMP Marketing Inc, pg 858
Southern California Sound Image Inc, pg 895
Towards 2000 Inc, pg 916

COLORADO

Ceavco Audio Visual Company Inc, pg 719
Daylight Productions & Rentals, pg 739
Spectrum Audio Visual Services, pg 897
Stanco Sales LLC, pg 899

CONNECTICUT

HB Communications Inc, pg 777
MAVCO, pg 820
Rockwell Communications Inc, pg 876
USI Inc, pg 924

FLORIDA

Altel Systems Group Inc, pg 682
AVI-SPL, pg 698
Digital Video Systems, pg 742
Harmon's Audio-Visual Services, pg 776
Hi-Tech Import Export Corp, pg 779
Industrial Strength Inc, pg 787
ONstage, pg 846
Photosound of Orlando Inc, pg 856
Tallahassee Audio Visual, pg 906

GEORGIA

Audio Visual Resources Inc, pg 695
Baker Audio Visual, pg 700
Stage Front Presentation Systems, pg 899
Visioneering International Inc, pg 931

HAWAII

The Audio Visual Co (AVCO), pg 694

ILLINOIS

Allen Visual Systems Inc, pg 680
Central Audio-Visual Equipment Inc, pg 719
RC Communications, pg 870

INDIANA

SHP Electronics, pg 887

KANSAS

KK Office Solutions Inc, pg 799

KENTUCKY

Audio Visual Techniques Inc, pg 695
Axxis Leasing Inc, pg 700
NOR-COM Inc, pg 841

LOUISIANA

Techkno Integration & Design Services LLC, pg 908

MAINE

Headlight Audio Visual Inc, pg 777

MARYLAND

Cardinal Sound & Video, pg 717
Kipp Visual Systems Inc, pg 799
Nelson White Systems Inc, pg 838
Nicholas P Pipino Associates Inc, pg 857
RTZ Audio Visual, pg 878

MASSACHUSETTS

Hunt's Photo & Video, pg 782
Integrated Solutions Group, pg 789
Rule Boston Camera, pg 878
University Products Inc, pg 923

MICHIGAN

Olson Anderson Co, pg 685
City Events Group, pg 725
Digi Sign Design LLC, pg 741
Michigan Office Solutions (MOS), A Xerox Company, pg 825
TEL Systems LLC, pg 909

MINNESOTA

AVI Systems, pg 698
Tierney Brothers Inc, pg 914

MISSISSIPPI

Bowie Audio Visual Enterprises Inc, pg 709
Jasper Ewing & Sons Inc, pg 757

MISSOURI

Communitronics Corp, pg 729
Conference Technologies Inc, pg 730
ITC, pg 791
Schiller's Audio-Visual, pg 881

NEW JERSEY

A-V Services Inc, pg 671
AlltecPro, pg 681
Argraph Corp, pg 688
Audio Visual Associates, pg 694
Audio Visual Dynamics®, pg 694
AV Bluebook, pg 696
HamiltonBuhl, pg 775
Ritz Camera & Image, pg 875
Starlite, pg 900
SYMCO Inc, pg 905
Total Video Products Inc, pg 916
Vcom IMC, pg 925
Video Corporation of America (VCA), pg 927
Wired 4 Sound Inc, pg 940
Yorktel, pg 944

NEW YORK

AV Workshop, pg 697
Colortone Audio Visual, pg 728
Design Audio Visual Inc, pg 741
Gaylord Archival, pg 768
Indigo Productions, pg 787
Langie Audio Visual Systems, pg 803

AUDIO/VISUAL

Opaque & Overhead Projector Distributors (continued)

NEW YORK (continued)

Long Island Video Enterprises Live Inc, pg 811
Markertek Video Supply, pg 817
Neptune Photo Inc, pg 838
Ray Supply Inc, pg 870
RNJ Electronics, pg 875
Topbulb, a Semmer Lighting Company, pg 915
Tri-Ed Distribution Inc, pg 918
Visual Technologies Corp, pg 932

NORTH CAROLINA

Camcor Inc, pg 715
Strategic Connections, pg 901

OHIO

Audio Visual Media, pg 694
Copp Integrated Systems, pg 731
Tri-State Audio Visual Co, pg 918
Tri-State Visual Products Inc, pg 918

OREGON

PLUS Corp of America, pg 858

PENNSYLVANIA

Advanced AV LLC, pg 677
Audio Visions Inc, pg 694
Audio Visual Communications Inc, pg 694
Bernie's Photo Center, pg 704
Brodart Co, pg 711
J E Foss Co, pg 764
Garcia Marketing Inc, pg 768
Grise Audio Visual Center Inc, pg 774
TRC Interactive Inc, pg 917
Vistacom Inc, pg 931
Visual Sound Inc, pg 931
Wespen Audio Visual Co, pg 935

TENNESSEE

Lowrance Sound Co Inc, pg 812
Memphis Communications Corp, pg 823
Spring Arbor Distributors Inc, pg 898

TEXAS

Audio Visual Technologies Group (AVTG), pg 695
AVES Audio Visual Systems Inc, pg 698
Data Projections Inc, pg 738
FitzCo Sound Inc, pg 761
JSAV, pg 795
Lubbock Audio Visual Inc, pg 812
Quality Audio Visual Service Inc, pg 866
Videotex Systems Inc, pg 930

UTAH

Webb Audio Visual, pg 935

VIRGINIA

Boitnott Visual Communications Corp (BVC), pg 708
Intellidyne LLC, pg 789
Lee Hartman & Sons Inc, pg 805

Metropolitan Audio Visual Co LLC, pg 824
The Whitlock Group, pg 937

WASHINGTON

CCI Solutions, pg 718
Inland Audio Visual Co, pg 788
PNTA, pg 858

WISCONSIN

Camera Corner Connecting Point, pg 715
Demco Inc, pg 740
Full Compass Systems, pg 767
School Specialty Inc, pg 882

PUERTO RICO

Bonnin Electronics Inc, pg 708

ALBERTA

Infosat Communications Inc, pg 787
McBain Camera Ltd, pg 820
Unique Communications Ltd, pg 921

BRITISH COLUMBIA

Commercial Electronics Ltd, pg 728

MANITOBA

Inland Audio Visual Ltd, pg 788

ONTARIO

Carr McLean Ltd, pg 717
Nationwide Audio Visual Co, pg 837
Westbury National Show Systems Ltd, pg 936

QUEBEC

Panavideo Inc, pg 850

Opaque & Overhead Projector Manufacturers

ILLINOIS

ACCO Brands Corp, pg 673
Dukane Corp, Audio Visual Products Division, pg 747

MINNESOTA

Artograph Inc, pg 690

NEW JERSEY

AlltecPro, pg 681

NEW YORK

ELMO USA Corp, pg 753
Gagne Inc, pg 767
TecNec Distributing, pg 909

Opaque & Overhead Projector Rentals

ALABAMA

Audio-Video Resources Inc, pg 694

ARIZONA

Arizona Cine Equipment, pg 688
Merestone, pg 823
Metropolitan Audio-Visual Inc, pg 824

ARKANSAS

Carlton-Bates Co, pg 717
White Diamond Productions LLC, pg 937

CALIFORNIA

AGF Media Services, pg 678
Alliant Event Services, pg 681
Ametron Audio/Video, pg 684
Associated Sound, pg 691
Assured Audio Visual, pg 691
AV Guys, pg 697
Hooper Camera & Imaging, pg 781
Instructional Materials & Equipment Distributors (I-Med), pg 789
JD Audio Visual Inc, pg 793
Lynch Communications, pg 813
Media Fabricators Inc, pg 822
Munday & Collins AV, pg 834
PSAV® Presentation Services, pg 866
Stanislaus AV Inc, pg 899
Towards 2000 Inc, pg 916
VER, pg 926
Voice & Video Rentals, pg 932

COLORADO

Ceavco Audio Visual Company Inc, pg 719
Daylight Productions & Rentals, pg 739
Multimedia Audio Visual Inc, pg 833
Spectrum Audio Visual Services, pg 897

CONNECTICUT

A/V Davey, pg 697
Rockwell Communications Inc, pg 876
Videofilm Systems Inc, pg 929

FLORIDA

AVI-SPL, pg 698
Harmon's Audio-Visual Services, pg 776
Industrial Strength Inc, pg 787
ONstage, pg 846
Photosound of Orlando Inc, pg 856
Sight & Sound Productions, pg 887
Tallahassee Audio Visual, pg 906
Universal Studios Florida® Production Group, pg 922

GEORGIA

Audio Visual Resources Inc, pg 695
MAGNUM Companies Ltd, pg 815
ON Services, a GES Company, pg 846
Stage Front Presentation Systems, pg 899
Staging Directions Inc, pg 899

ILLINOIS

Allen Visual Systems Inc, pg 680
AV Chicago Inc, pg 696
Backstar Creative Media Inc, pg 700
Beatty TeleVisual Productions, pg 703
Central Audio-Visual Equipment Inc, pg 719
Helix Camera & Video, pg 778
PSAV® Presentation Services (Hotel Services Division), pg 866
RC Communications, pg 870

INDIANA

Gary Camera & Digital, pg 768

KENTUCKY

Audio Visual Techniques Inc, pg 695

LOUISIANA

Clark Services Audio Visual & Exhibit Inc, pg 725

MAINE

Headlight Audio Visual Inc, pg 777

MARYLAND

Advance Audiovisual Presentation Ltd, pg 677
CPR MultiMedia Solutions, pg 732
dbF a Media Company, pg 739
Nelson White Systems Inc, pg 838
Nicholas P Pipino Associates Inc, pg 857
RTZ Audio Visual, pg 878

MASSACHUSETTS

Capron Lighting & Sound Co Inc, pg 716
Integrated Solutions Group, pg 789
massAV, pg 819
Preston Productions Inc, pg 861

MICHIGAN

Olson Anderson Co, pg 685
City Events Group, pg 725
Digi Sign Design LLC, pg 741
K&R All Media Productions LLC, pg 796

MINNESOTA

AVI Systems, pg 698

MISSISSIPPI

Bowie Audio Visual Enterprises Inc, pg 709
Jasper Ewing & Sons Inc, pg 757

MISSOURI

Communitronics Corp, pg 729
Schiller's Audio-Visual, pg 881
Show-Me Audio-Visual, pg 887

NEVADA

GES Audio Visual, pg 770

NEW HAMPSHIRE

Academic & Campus Technology Services, pg 672

NEW JERSEY

Audio Visual Associates, pg 694
Audio Visual Dynamics®, pg 694
International Audio Visual Inc, pg 790
Moe AV LLC, pg 828
Starlite, pg 900
Video Corporation of America (VCA), pg 927
Wired 4 Sound Inc, pg 940

NEW YORK

Ace Video, pg 674
AV Workshop, pg 697
Colortone Audio Visual, pg 728
Design Audio Visual Inc, pg 741
Langie Audio Visual Systems, pg 803
Long Island Video Enterprises Live Inc, pg 811
Neptune Photo Inc, pg 838

Specialized Audio-Visual Inc, pg 896
Visual Technologies Corp, pg 932
Visual Word Systems Inc, pg 932
WorldStage, pg 941

NORTH CAROLINA

AV Connections Inc, pg 697
Special Event Services, pg 896

OHIO

Audio Visual Media, pg 694
Hughie's Event Production Services, pg 782

PENNSYLVANIA

Advanced AV LLC, pg 677
Audio Visions Inc, pg 694
Audio Visual Communications Inc, pg 694
Grise Audio Visual Center Inc, pg 774
Visual Sound Inc, pg 931

SOUTH CAROLINA

Impact Technology Group LLC, pg 786
Sound & Images Inc, pg 893

TENNESSEE

Memphis Communications Corp, pg 823

TEXAS

Audio Visual Technologies Group (AVTG), pg 695
FitzCo Sound Inc, pg 761
JSAV, pg 795
Lubbock Audio Visual Inc, pg 812
Quality Audio Visual Service Inc, pg 867

UTAH

Webb Audio Visual, pg 935

VIRGINIA

American AV, pg 682
Boitnott Visual Communications Corp (BVC), pg 708
Lee Hartman & Sons Inc, pg 805
Metropolitan Audio Visual Co LLC, pg 824
Projection, pg 865
The Whitlock Group, pg 937

WASHINGTON

D A Sound, pg 737
Inland Audio Visual Co, pg 788
PNTA, pg 858

WISCONSIN

Camera Corner Connecting Point, pg 715
Event Essentials, pg 756
Full Compass Systems, pg 767
School Specialty Inc, pg 882

PUERTO RICO

Stage Crew Audiovisual Inc, pg 898

ALBERTA

Allstar Show Industries Inc, pg 681
Evolution AV, pg 757
McBain Camera Ltd, pg 820
Unique Communications Ltd, pg 921

BRITISH COLUMBIA

Clark's Audio Visual Services Ltd, pg 725
Commercial Electronics Ltd, pg 728
Triad Communications Ltd, pg 918

MANITOBA

Inland Audio Visual Ltd, pg 788

ONTARIO

HD Source, pg 777
Westbury National Show Systems Ltd, pg 936

QUEBEC

Audio Visual Dynamics, pg 694
Freeman Audio Visual, pg 765
Panavideo Inc, pg 850

Opaque & Overhead Projector Repairs

ARKANSAS

Carlton-Bates Co, pg 717
Jay S Stanley & Associates Inc, pg 899

CALIFORNIA

Ametron Audio/Video, pg 684
Gluskin's Custom Audio Video, pg 771
Hooper Camera & Imaging, pg 781
Instructional Materials & Equipment Distributors (I-Med), pg 789
McAlister Electronics, pg 820
Lloyd F McKinney Associates Inc, pg 821
Pro Camera Repair, pg 862
Towards 2000 Inc, pg 916

COLORADO

Ceavco Audio Visual Company Inc, pg 719

CONNECTICUT

HB Communications Inc, pg 777
Rockwell Communications Inc, pg 876

FLORIDA

Tallahassee Audio Visual, pg 906

GEORGIA

Audio Visual Resources Inc, pg 695
Stage Front Presentation Systems, pg 899

ILLINOIS

Allen Visual Systems Inc, pg 680
RC Communications, pg 870

INDIANA

Gary Camera & Digital, pg 768

KANSAS

KK Office Solutions Inc, pg 799

KENTUCKY

Axxis Leasing Inc, pg 700
NOR-COM Inc, pg 841

MAINE

Headlight Audio Visual Inc, pg 777

MARYLAND

Nelson White Systems Inc, pg 838
Nicholas P Pipino Associates Inc, pg 857
RTZ Audio Visual, pg 878

MASSACHUSETTS

Integrated Solutions Group, pg 789

MICHIGAN

City Events Group, pg 725
TEL Systems LLC, pg 909

MINNESOTA

AVI Systems, pg 698

MISSISSIPPI

Bowie Audio Visual Enterprises Inc, pg 709

MISSOURI

Cintrex Audio Visual, pg 725
Communitronics Corp, pg 729
Schiller's Audio-Visual, pg 881

NEW JERSEY

Audio Visual Associates, pg 694

NEW YORK

Colortone Audio Visual, pg 728
ELMO USA Corp, pg 753
Langie Audio Visual Systems, pg 803
Ray Supply Inc, pg 870
Visual Technologies Corp, pg 932

NORTH CAROLINA

Camcor Inc, pg 715

OHIO

Audio Visual Media, pg 694
Copp Integrated Systems, pg 731
Tri-State Audio Visual Co, pg 918

PENNSYLVANIA

Audio Visions Inc, pg 694
J E Foss Co, pg 764
Wespen Audio Visual Co, pg 935

TENNESSEE

Memphis Communications Corp, pg 823

TEXAS

Audio Visual Technologies Group (AVTG), pg 695
Lubbock Audio Visual Inc, pg 812
Quality Audio Visual Service Inc, pg 867

VIRGINIA

Boitnott Visual Communications Corp (BVC), pg 708
Lee Hartman & Sons Inc, pg 805
Metropolitan Audio Visual Co LLC, pg 824
The Whitlock Group, pg 937

WASHINGTON

Inland Audio Visual Co, pg 788
PNTA, pg 858

WISCONSIN

Full Compass Systems, pg 767
School Specialty Inc, pg 882

ALBERTA

Infosat Communications Inc, pg 787

MANITOBA

Inland Audio Visual Ltd, pg 788

ONTARIO

Westbury National Show Systems Ltd, pg 936

QUEBEC

Panavideo Inc, pg 850

Opaque & Overhead Supply & Accessory Distributors

ALABAMA

Curtis Company, pg 736

ARIZONA

Arizona Cine Equipment, pg 688
Docter Optics Inc, pg 744
Metropolitan Audio-Visual Inc, pg 824
Troxell-CDI, pg 918

ARKANSAS

Carlton-Bates Co, pg 717
Jay S Stanley & Associates Inc, pg 899
White Diamond Productions LLC, pg 937

CALIFORNIA

Ametron Audio/Video, pg 684
Assured Audio Visual, pg 691
California Tape Products Inc, pg 714
Christy's Editorial, pg 723
Educational Technology Services (ETS), pg 751
Hooper Camera & Imaging, pg 781
Instructional Materials & Equipment Distributors (I-Med), pg 789
JD Audio Visual Inc, pg 793
Media Fabricators Inc, pg 822
MediaPOINTE, pg 823
PMP Marketing Inc, pg 858
Southern California Sound Image Inc, pg 895

COLORADO

Ceavco Audio Visual Company Inc, pg 719
Daylight Productions & Rentals, pg 739
Spectrum Audio Visual Services, pg 897

CONNECTICUT

HB Communications Inc, pg 777
MAVCO, pg 820
Rockwell Communications Inc, pg 876
USI Inc, pg 924

FLORIDA

AVI-SPL, pg 698
Digital Video Systems, pg 742

AUDIO/VISUAL

Opaque & Overhead Supply & Accessory Distributors (continued)

FLORIDA (continued)

Hi-Tech Import Export Corp, pg 779
Industrial Strength Inc, pg 787
ONstage, pg 846
Photosound of Orlando Inc, pg 856
Tallahassee Audio Visual, pg 906

GEORGIA

Audio Visual Resources Inc, pg 695
Convergent Media Systems, pg 731
Stage Front Presentation Systems, pg 899
Visioneering International Inc, pg 931

HAWAII

The Audio Visual Co (AVCO), pg 694

ILLINOIS

Allen Visual Systems Inc, pg 680
Central Audio-Visual Equipment Inc, pg 719
G T Luscombe Co Inc, pg 812

KANSAS

KK Office Solutions Inc, pg 799

KENTUCKY

Audio Visual Techniques Inc, pg 695
NOR-COM Inc, pg 841

LOUISIANA

Techkno Integration & Design Services LLC, pg 908

MAINE

Headlight Audio Visual Inc, pg 777

MARYLAND

Nelson White Systems Inc, pg 838
Nicholas P Pipino Associates Inc, pg 857
RTZ Audio Visual, pg 878

MASSACHUSETTS

Integrated Solutions Group, pg 789
University Products Inc, pg 923

MICHIGAN

City Events Group, pg 725
Digi Sign Design LLC, pg 741
Michigan Office Solutions (MOS), A Xerox Company, pg 825
TEL Systems LLC, pg 909

MINNESOTA

AVI Systems, pg 698
Tierney Brothers Inc, pg 914

MISSISSIPPI

Bowie Audio Visual Enterprises Inc, pg 709
Jasper Ewing & Sons Inc, pg 757

MISSOURI

Communitronics Corp, pg 729
Conference Technologies Inc, pg 730
ITC, pg 791
Schiller's Audio-Visual, pg 881

NEVADA

Bulbman Inc, pg 712

NEW JERSEY

AlltecPro, pg 681
Argraph Corp, pg 688
Audio Visual Associates, pg 694
Audio Visual Dynamics®, pg 694
AV Bluebook, pg 696
HamiltonBuhl, pg 775
Starlite, pg 900
SYMCO Inc, pg 905
Tele-Measurements Inc, pg 910
Total Video Products Inc, pg 916
Vcom IMC, pg 925
Video Corporation of America (VCA), pg 927
Wired 4 Sound Inc, pg 940
Yorktel, pg 944

NEW YORK

AV Workshop, pg 697
Bulbtronics Inc, pg 712
Colortone Audio Visual, pg 728
Gaylord Archival, pg 768
Indigo Productions, pg 787
Langie Audio Visual Systems, pg 803
Long Island Video Enterprises Live Inc, pg 811
Markertek Video Supply, pg 817
Neptune Photo Inc, pg 838
Ray Supply Inc, pg 870
Scientifics Direct Inc, pg 882
Topbulb, a Semmer Lighting Company, pg 915
Tri-Ed Distribution Inc, pg 918
Visual Technologies Corp, pg 932

NORTH CAROLINA

Camcor Inc, pg 715
Strategic Connections, pg 901

OHIO

Audio Visual Media, pg 694
Copp Integrated Systems, pg 731
Hughie's Event Production Services, pg 782
Tri-State Audio Visual Co, pg 918
Tri-State Visual Products Inc, pg 918

PENNSYLVANIA

Advanced AV LLC, pg 677
Audio Visions Inc, pg 694
Audio Visual Communications Inc, pg 694
Bernie's Photo Center, pg 704
Brodart Co, pg 711
J E Foss Co, pg 764
Grise Audio Visual Center Inc, pg 774
Visual Sound Inc, pg 931
Wespen Audio Visual Co, pg 935

TENNESSEE

Lowrance Sound Co Inc, pg 812
Memphis Communications Corp, pg 823
Spring Arbor Distributors Inc, pg 898

TEXAS

Audio Visual Technologies Group (AVTG), pg 695
AVES Audio Visual Systems Inc, pg 698
Data Projections Inc, pg 738
JSAV, pg 795
Lubbock Audio Visual Inc, pg 812
Quality Audio Visual Service Inc, pg 867
Stage Directions, pg 898

VIRGINIA

Boitnott Visual Communications Corp (BVC), pg 708
Intellidyne LLC, pg 789
Lee Hartman & Sons Inc, pg 805
Metropolitan Audio Visual Co LLC, pg 824
The Whitlock Group, pg 937

WASHINGTON

Inland Audio Visual Co, pg 788

WISCONSIN

Camera Corner Connecting Point, pg 715
Demco Inc, pg 740
Full Compass Systems, pg 767
School Specialty Inc, pg 882

PUERTO RICO

Bonnin Electronics Inc, pg 708

ALBERTA

Infosat Communications Inc, pg 787
McBain Camera Ltd, pg 820
Unique Communications Ltd, pg 921

BRITISH COLUMBIA

Commercial Electronics Ltd, pg 728
Specialty Bulb Products Inc, pg 896

MANITOBA

Inland Audio Visual Ltd, pg 788

ONTARIO

Carr McLean Ltd, pg 717
Nationwide Audio Visual Co, pg 837
Westbury National Show Systems Ltd, pg 936

QUEBEC

Panavideo Inc, pg 850

Opaque & Overhead Supply & Accessory Manufacturers

ILLINOIS

ACCO Brands Corp, pg 673
Dukane Corp, Audio Visual Products Division, pg 747
Kart-A-Bag Manufacturing Inc, pg 796

MASSACHUSETTS

University Products Inc, pg 923

MINNESOTA

Artograph Inc, pg 690

NEW JERSEY

AlltecPro, pg 681
Pro-Tape & Specialities Inc, pg 863

NEW YORK

Eastman Kodak Co, pg 750
ELMO USA Corp, pg 753
Gagne Inc, pg 767
TecNec Distributing, pg 909

ONTARIO

Staedtler-Mars Ltd, pg 898

Opaque & Overhead Supply & Accessory Rentals

ARIZONA

Arizona Cine Equipment, pg 688
Merestone, pg 823

ARKANSAS

Carlton-Bates Co, pg 717
White Diamond Productions LLC, pg 937

CALIFORNIA

Ametron Audio/Video, pg 684
AV Guys, pg 697
Hooper Camera & Imaging, pg 781
JD Audio Visual Inc, pg 793
Lynch Communications, pg 813
Media Fabricators Inc, pg 822
Munday & Collins AV, pg 834
PSAV® Presentation Services, pg 866
Towards 2000 Inc, pg 916
VER, pg 926
Voice & Video Rentals, pg 932

COLORADO

Ceavco Audio Visual Company Inc, pg 719
Daylight Productions & Rentals, pg 739

CONNECTICUT

A/V Davey, pg 697
Rockwell Communications Inc, pg 876

FLORIDA

Industrial Strength Inc, pg 787
ONstage, pg 846
Photosound of Orlando Inc, pg 856
Tallahassee Audio Visual, pg 906

GEORGIA

Audio Visual Resources Inc, pg 695
Convergent Media Systems, pg 731
MAGNUM Companies Ltd, pg 815
ON Services, a GES Company, pg 846
Stage Front Presentation Systems, pg 899
Staging Directions Inc, pg 899

ILLINOIS

Allen Visual Systems Inc, pg 680
Beatty TeleVisual Productions, pg 703
Creative Technology (CT), pg 733
Helix Camera & Video, pg 778
Jim Passin Productions, pg 852
PSAV® Presentation Services (Hotel Services Division), pg 866

Overhead Projector, *see* Opaque & Overhead Projector

Overhead Supply and Accessory, *see* Opaque & Overhead Supply & Accessory

Overhead Transparency Printing, *see* Volume Printing—Overhead Transparencies

Phonograph Distributors

AUDIO/VISUAL

Phonograph Distributors (continued)

ARIZONA

Arizona Cine Equipment, pg 688
Troxell-CDI, pg 918

CALIFORNIA

Ametron Audio/Video, pg 684
Assured Audio Visual, pg 691
Empire Pro, pg 753
Instructional Materials & Equipment Distributors (I-Med), pg 789
Media Fabricators Inc, pg 822
Sounds Unique, pg 895
Towards 2000 Inc, pg 916

CONNECTICUT

MAVCO, pg 820
Rockwell Communications Inc, pg 876

FLORIDA

Alliance Entertainment Corp (AEC) LLC, pg 680
Hi-Tech Import Export Corp, pg 779
ONstage, pg 846
Stereo Sales Inc, pg 900

GEORGIA

Audio Visual Resources Inc, pg 695

HAWAII

The Audio Visual Co (AVCO), pg 694

ILLINOIS

Central Audio-Visual Equipment Inc, pg 719
Esoteric Sound, pg 755
LKG Industries Inc, pg 810
Quintessence Audio Ltd, pg 868

KANSAS

KK Office Solutions Inc, pg 799

KENTUCKY

Barney Miller's Inc, pg 827
NOR-COM Inc, pg 841

MAINE

Headlight Audio Visual Inc, pg 777

MARYLAND

Nicholas P Pipino Associates Inc, pg 857

MICHIGAN

City Events Group, pg 725

MISSOURI

Conference Technologies Inc, pg 730
Schiller's Audio-Visual, pg 881

NEW JERSEY

Alltec Stores, a Vcom IMC Company, pg 681
AlltecPro, pg 681
AV Bluebook, pg 696
FlagHouse, pg 762

HamiltonBuhl, pg 775
Onkyo USA Corp, pg 846
Starlite, pg 900
Vcom IMC, pg 925
Video Corporation of America (VCA), pg 927
Wired 4 Sound Inc, pg 940

NEW YORK

AV Workshop, pg 697
Cadence Jazz Records, pg 713
Gaylord Archival, pg 768
Indigo Productions, pg 787
Langie Audio Visual Systems, pg 803
RNJ Electronics, pg 875
Toys From The Attic, pg 916

NORTH CAROLINA

Camcor Inc, pg 715

OHIO

Audio Visual Media, pg 694

PENNSYLVANIA

Advanced AV LLC, pg 677
Brodart Co, pg 711
J E Foss Co, pg 764
Grise Audio Visual Center Inc, pg 774
Visual Sound Inc, pg 931
Wespen Audio Visual Co, pg 935

TENNESSEE

Lowrance Sound Co Inc, pg 812
Technical Support Systems LLC, pg 908

TEXAS

Audio Visual Technologies Group (AVTG), pg 695
Crossroads Audio Inc, pg 735
JSAV, pg 795
Lubbock Audio Visual Inc, pg 812
Quality Audio Visual Service Inc, pg 867

UTAH

Webb Audio Visual, pg 935

VIRGINIA

Boitnott Visual Communications Corp (BVC), pg 708
Lee Hartman & Sons Inc, pg 805
Metropolitan Audio Visual Co LLC, pg 824
The Whitlock Group, pg 937

WASHINGTON

D A Sound, pg 737
Inland Audio Visual Co, pg 788

WISCONSIN

Camera Corner Connecting Point, pg 715
Demco Inc, pg 740
Full Compass Systems, pg 767
School Specialty Inc, pg 882

BRITISH COLUMBIA

Commercial Electronics Ltd, pg 728

MANITOBA

Inland Audio Visual Ltd, pg 788

ONTARIO

Nationwide Audio Visual Co, pg 837
Westbury National Show Systems Ltd, pg 936

Phonograph Manufacturers

CALIFORNIA

Califone International Inc, pg 714

ILLINOIS

Esoteric Sound, pg 755

NEW JERSEY

HamiltonBuhl, pg 775
Onkyo USA Corp, pg 846
Panasonic Corporation of North America, pg 850

Phonograph Rentals

ARIZONA

Arizona Cine Equipment, pg 688
Merestone, pg 823

CALIFORNIA

Ametron Audio/Video, pg 684
Audio Rents, pg 693
Instructional Materials & Equipment Distributors (I-Med), pg 789
JD Audio Visual Inc, pg 793
Lynch Communications, pg 813
McCune Audio-Video-Lighting, pg 821
Media Fabricators Inc, pg 822
Munday & Collins AV, pg 834
Towards 2000 Inc, pg 916

CONNECTICUT

A/V Davey, pg 697
Rockwell Communications Inc, pg 876

FLORIDA

ONstage, pg 846

GEORGIA

Audio Visual Resources Inc, pg 695
Staging Directions Inc, pg 899

ILLINOIS

AV Chicago Inc, pg 696
Central Audio-Visual Equipment Inc, pg 719

INDIANA

OMNI Productions, pg 845

MARYLAND

Event Tech, pg 756

MASSACHUSETTS

Preston Productions Inc, pg 861

MICHIGAN

City Events Group, pg 725
K&R All Media Productions LLC, pg 796
K&R's Recording Studios Inc, pg 796
On Stage Visuals, pg 846

MISSISSIPPI

Bowie Audio Visual Enterprises Inc, pg 709
Jasper Ewing & Sons Inc, pg 757

MISSOURI

Show-Me Audio-Visual, pg 887
Southwest Audio-Visual Inc, pg 895

NEW HAMPSHIRE

Academic & Campus Technology Services, pg 672

NEW JERSEY

Starlite, pg 900

NEW YORK

AV Workshop, pg 697
Langie Audio Visual Systems, pg 803
Long Island Video Enterprises Live Inc, pg 811

NORTH CAROLINA

Special Event Services, pg 896
Strategic Connections, pg 901

OHIO

Audio Visual Media, pg 694

PENNSYLVANIA

Grise Audio Visual Center Inc, pg 774

TENNESSEE

Technical Support Systems LLC, pg 908

TEXAS

Audio Visual Technologies Group (AVTG), pg 695
Lubbock Audio Visual Inc, pg 812
Stage Directions, pg 898
The Yesterday USA Radio Networks, pg 944

UTAH

Webb Audio Visual, pg 935

VIRGINIA

American AV, pg 682
Lee Hartman & Sons Inc, pg 805
The Whitlock Group, pg 937

WASHINGTON

D A Sound, pg 737
Inland Audio Visual Co, pg 788

WISCONSIN

Event Essentials, pg 756
Full Compass Systems, pg 767
School Specialty Inc, pg 882

WYOMING

Bridger Productions Inc, pg 710

BRITISH COLUMBIA

Commercial Electronics Ltd, pg 728
MicrophoneRentals.com, pg 826

MANITOBA

Inland Audio Visual Ltd, pg 788

ONTARIO

Westbury National Show Systems Ltd, pg 936

Phonograph Repairs

CALIFORNIA

Ametron Audio/Video, pg 684
Instructional Materials & Equipment Distributors (I-Med), pg 789
McAlister Electronics, pg 820
Towards 2000 Inc, pg 916

CONNECTICUT

HB Communications Inc, pg 777
Rockwell Communications Inc, pg 876

FLORIDA

JT Communications, pg 795
Stereo Sales Inc, pg 900

GEORGIA

Audio Visual Resources Inc, pg 695

ILLINOIS

Central Audio-Visual Equipment Inc, pg 719

KANSAS

KK Office Solutions Inc, pg 799

KENTUCKY

Barney Miller's Inc, pg 827
NOR-COM Inc, pg 841

MICHIGAN

City Events Group, pg 725
TEL Systems LLC, pg 909

MISSISSIPPI

Bowie Audio Visual Enterprises Inc, pg 709

MISSOURI

Schiller's Audio-Visual, pg 881

NEW JERSEY

Starlite, pg 900

NEW YORK

Colortone Audio Visual, pg 728
Langie Audio Visual Systems, pg 803
Toys From The Attic, pg 916

OHIO

Audio Visual Media, pg 694
Tri-State Audio Visual Co, pg 918

OREGON

All Service Musical Electronics Repair, pg 680

PENNSYLVANIA

J E Foss Co, pg 764
Wespen Audio Visual Co, pg 935

TENNESSEE

Technical Support Systems LLC, pg 908

TEXAS

Audio Visual Technologies Group (AVTG), pg 695
Crossroads Audio Inc, pg 735
Lubbock Audio Visual Inc, pg 812
Quality Audio Visual Service Inc, pg 867
The Yesterday USA Radio Networks, pg 944

VIRGINIA

Lee Hartman & Sons Inc, pg 805
Metropolitan Audio Visual Co LLC, pg 824
The Whitlock Group, pg 937

WASHINGTON

Inland Audio Visual Co, pg 788

WISCONSIN

Audio Visual of Milwaukee Inc, pg 694
Full Compass Systems, pg 767
School Specialty Inc, pg 882

BRITISH COLUMBIA

Commercial Electronics Ltd, pg 728

MANITOBA

Inland Audio Visual Ltd, pg 788

ONTARIO

Westbury National Show Systems Ltd, pg 936

Photograph Printing, *see* Processing & Printing—Photographs

Photograph Processing, *see* Processing & Printing—Photographs

Photographs from Slides, *see* Prints from Slides

Photostats, *see* Color Photostats

Planetarium Distributors

ARIZONA

Arizona Cine Equipment, pg 688

CALIFORNIA

Cinema Xenon International Inc, pg 724

FLORIDA

Audio Visual Imagineering Inc, pg 694
Hi-Tech Import Export Corp, pg 779
Science First/STARLAB™, pg 882

GEORGIA

Visioneering International Inc, pg 931

MARYLAND

Nicholas P Pipino Associates Inc, pg 857

NEW JERSEY

Starlite, pg 900

NEW YORK

Langie Audio Visual Systems, pg 803
Scientifics Direct Inc, pg 882

PENNSYLVANIA

Advanced AV LLC, pg 677

TEXAS

Lubbock Audio Visual Inc, pg 812

WASHINGTON

Laser Fantasy/HECK Industries/Photon Manufacturing, pg 804

WISCONSIN

Audio Visual of Milwaukee Inc, pg 694
Demco Inc, pg 740

MANITOBA

Inland Audio Visual Ltd, pg 788

Planetarium Manufacturers

CALIFORNIA

Cinema Xenon International Inc, pg 724

FLORIDA

Audio Visual Imagineering Inc, pg 694
Science First/STARLAB™, pg 882

MARYLAND

Absolute Hollywood, pg 672
MMI Marketing, pg 828

NEW JERSEY

Konica Minolta Business Solutions, pg 801
Starlite, pg 900

Planetarium Rentals

ARIZONA

Arizona Cine Equipment, pg 688

FLORIDA

Audio Visual Imagineering Inc, pg 694

GEORGIA

Staging Directions Inc, pg 899

MARYLAND

Absolute Hollywood, pg 672

WASHINGTON

Laser Fantasy/HECK Industries/Photon Manufacturing, pg 804

ALBERTA

McBain Camera Ltd, pg 820

MANITOBA

Inland Audio Visual Ltd, pg 788

Planetarium Repairs

CALIFORNIA

McAlister Electronics, pg 820

MICHIGAN

TEL Systems LLC, pg 909

NEW JERSEY

Konica Minolta Business Solutions, pg 801
Starlite, pg 900

TENNESSEE

Memphis Communications Corp, pg 823

TEXAS

Lubbock Audio Visual Inc, pg 812

MANITOBA

Inland Audio Visual Ltd, pg 788

Power Megaphone, *see* Megaphone—Power

Presentation Board & Supply Distributors

ALABAMA

Curtis Company, pg 736

ARIZONA

Arizona Cine Equipment, pg 688
Metropolitan Audio-Visual Inc, pg 824
Troxell-CDI, pg 918
Ultimate Presentation Systems Inc, pg 920

ARKANSAS

Jay S Stanley & Associates Inc, pg 899
White Diamond Productions LLC, pg 937

CALIFORNIA

Advanced Systems Group LLC, pg 677
Ametron Audio/Video, pg 684
Assured Audio Visual, pg 691
California Tape Products Inc, pg 714
Christy's Editorial, pg 723
Educational Technology Services (ETS), pg 751
Instructional Materials & Equipment Distributors (I-Med), pg 789
JD Audio Visual Inc, pg 793
Media Fabricators Inc, pg 822
MediaPOINTE, pg 823
Stanislaus AV Inc, pg 899

AUDIO/VISUAL

Presentation Board & Supply Distributors (continued)

COLORADO

American Educational Products LLC, pg 683
Ceavco Audio Visual Company Inc, pg 719
Daylight Productions & Rentals, pg 739
Spectrum Audio Visual Services, pg 897
Stanco Sales LLC, pg 899

CONNECTICUT

HB Communications Inc, pg 777
MAVCO, pg 820

FLORIDA

Altel Systems Group Inc, pg 682
AVI-SPL, pg 698
Digital Video Systems, pg 742
Harris Corp, pg 776
Hi-Tech Import Export Corp, pg 779
Industrial Strength Inc, pg 787
ONstage, pg 846

GEORGIA

Audio Visual Resources Inc, pg 695
PolyVision Corporation, pg 859
Stage Front Presentation Systems, pg 899

HAWAII

The Audio Visual Co (AVCO), pg 694

ILLINOIS

Allen Visual Systems Inc, pg 680
Central Audio-Visual Equipment Inc, pg 719
Dukane Corp, Audio Visual Products Division, pg 747
G T Luscombe Co Inc, pg 812

INDIANA

Heart Breaker Entertainment LLC, pg 778
Sensory Technologies LLC, pg 884

KANSAS

KK Office Solutions Inc, pg 799

KENTUCKY

Axxis Leasing Inc, pg 700
NOR-COM Inc, pg 841

LOUISIANA

Techkno Integration & Design Services LLC, pg 908

MAINE

Headlight Audio Visual Inc, pg 777

MARYLAND

Cardinal Sound & Video, pg 717
Kipp Visual Systems Inc, pg 799
RTZ Audio Visual, pg 878

MASSACHUSETTS

Lineco, pg 809
Pro AV Systems, pg 862
University Products Inc, pg 923

MICHIGAN

City Events Group, pg 725
Digi Sign Design LLC, pg 741
Michigan Office Solutions (MOS), A Xerox Company, pg 825
TEL Systems LLC, pg 909

MINNESOTA

AVI Systems, pg 698
Tierney Brothers Inc, pg 914

MISSISSIPPI

Bowie Audio Visual Enterprises Inc, pg 709
Jasper Ewing & Sons Inc, pg 757

MISSOURI

Communitronics Corp, pg 729
Conference Technologies Inc, pg 730
ITC, pg 791
Schiller's Audio-Visual, pg 881

NEW JERSEY

AlltecPro, pg 681
Argraph Corp, pg 688
Audio Visual Associates, pg 694
AV Bluebook, pg 696
Callen Photo Mount Corp, pg 714
FlagHouse, pg 762
HamiltonBuhl, pg 775
Starlite, pg 900
Tele-Measurements Inc, pg 910
Total Video Products Inc, pg 916
Vcom IMC, pg 925
Video Corporation of America (VCA), pg 927
Wired 4 Sound Inc, pg 940

NEW YORK

Audio-Video Corp, pg 694
AV Workshop, pg 697
Design Audio Visual Inc, pg 741
Gaylord Archival, pg 768
Indigo Productions, pg 787
KVL Audio Visual Services Inc, pg 802
Langie Audio Visual Systems, pg 803
Light Impressions, pg 807
Long Island Video Enterprises Live Inc, pg 811
Markertek Video Supply, pg 817
Presentation Products Inc, pg 861
Raven Screen Corp, pg 870
RNJ Electronics, pg 875
Sargent Welch, pg 880
Visual Technologies Corp, pg 932

NORTH CAROLINA

Camcor Inc, pg 715
Strategic Connections, pg 901

OHIO

Audio Visual Media, pg 694
Copp Integrated Systems, pg 731
ITA Audio Visual Solutions, pg 791
Tri-State Audio Visual Co, pg 918
Tri-State Visual Products Inc, pg 918
Walltalkers, pg 933

OKLAHOMA

Ford AV, pg 763

PENNSYLVANIA

Advanced AV LLC, pg 677
Audio Visions Inc, pg 694
Brodart Co, pg 711
J E Foss Co, pg 764
Grise Audio Visual Center Inc, pg 774
The Lerro Corp, pg 806
Visual Sound Inc, pg 931
Wespen Audio Visual Co, pg 935

RHODE ISLAND

Shanix Inc, pg 885

TENNESSEE

Lowrance Sound Co Inc, pg 812
Memphis Communications Corp, pg 823
Spring Arbor Distributors Inc, pg 898
Technical Support Systems LLC, pg 908

TEXAS

Audio Visual Technologies Group (AVTG), pg 695
AVES Audio Visual Systems Inc, pg 698
Heffernan Audio Visual, pg 778
JSAV, pg 795
Lubbock Audio Visual Inc, pg 812

VIRGINIA

Avitecture Inc, pg 699
Boitnott Visual Communications Corp (BVC), pg 708
Intellidyne LLC, pg 789
Lee Hartman & Sons Inc, pg 805
Metropolitan Audio Visual Co LLC, pg 824
The Whitlock Group, pg 937

WASHINGTON

Inland Audio Visual Co, pg 788

WISCONSIN

Audio Visual of Milwaukee Inc, pg 694
Camera Corner Connecting Point, pg 715
Demco Inc, pg 740
Safe Harbor Computers, pg 879
School Specialty Inc, pg 882

PUERTO RICO

Audio Visual Concepts Inc, pg 694

ALBERTA

Evolution AV, pg 757
Infosat Communications Inc, pg 787
McBain Camera Ltd, pg 820
SMART Technologies ULC, pg 891

BRITISH COLUMBIA

Commercial Electronics Ltd, pg 728

MANITOBA

Inland Audio Visual Ltd, pg 788

ONTARIO

Carr McLean Ltd, pg 717
Cinema Stage Inc, pg 724

Egan Visual Inc/Egan TeamBoard Inc, pg 751
Westbury National Show Systems Ltd, pg 936

Presentation Board & Supply Manufacturers

ARIZONA

Applied Integration Corp, pg 687
The BD Co, pg 702
Savage Universal Corp, pg 881

CALIFORNIA

AITech International, pg 679
Penn Elcom Inc, pg 853

COLORADO

American Educational Products LLC, pg 683

CONNECTICUT

KOH Design Inc, pg 801

GEORGIA

PolyVision Corporation, pg 859

ILLINOIS

AmpliVox Portable Sound Systems, pg 684
Bretford Manufacturing Inc, pg 710
GBC Document Finishing, pg 768
Marshall Furniture Inc, pg 817
Pres-On Corp, pg 861
Windel International/Weyel, pg 939

INDIANA

Da-Lite, a Legrand AV Inc brand, pg 737
Draper Inc, pg 746

MASSACHUSETTS

International Display & Exhibit Corp (IDEC), pg 790
Lineco, pg 809
University Products Inc, pg 923

MINNESOTA

Chief, a Legrand AV Inc brand, pg 722

MISSOURI

Magna Visual Inc, pg 814

NEW JERSEY

AlltecPro, pg 681
Callen Photo Mount Corp, pg 714

NEW YORK

Light Impressions, pg 807
TecNec Distributing, pg 909

OHIO

Ghent Manufacturing, pg 770
Turning Technologies LLC, pg 919
Walltalkers, pg 933

PENNSYLVANIA

Interactive Products, pg 789

TEXAS

MooreCo Inc, pg 830

VIRGINIA
Drytac Corp, pg 747

WISCONSIN
Bardes Products Inc, pg 702
USAV Group Inc, pg 923

ALBERTA
SMART Technologies ULC, pg 891

ONTARIO
Egan Visual Inc/Egan TeamBoard
Inc, pg 751

Presentation Board & Supply Rentals

ARIZONA
Arizona Cine Equipment, pg 688
Merestone, pg 823
Metropolitan Audio-Visual Inc,
pg 824
Ultimate Presentation Systems Inc,
pg 920

ARKANSAS
White Diamond Productions LLC,
pg 937

CALIFORNIA
Alliant Event Services, pg 681
Ametron Audio/Video, pg 684
Assured Audio Visual, pg 691
AV Guys, pg 697
Bexel, an NEP Broadcast Services
Company, pg 704
Golden Gate Studios, pg 772
Lynch Communications, pg 813
McCune Audio-Video-Lighting,
pg 821
Media Fabricators Inc, pg 822
Munday & Collins AV, pg 834
PSAV® Presentation Services,
pg 866
Stanislaus AV Inc, pg 899
VER, pg 926
Video Resources Inc, pg 928
Voice & Video Rentals, pg 932

COLORADO
Ceavco Audio Visual Company Inc,
pg 719
Spectrum Audio Visual Services,
pg 897

CONNECTICUT
A/V Davey, pg 697

DELAWARE
Ken-Del Productions Inc, pg 797

FLORIDA
Industrial Strength Inc, pg 787
ONstage, pg 846
Photosound of Orlando Inc, pg 856
Sight & Sound Productions, pg 887

GEORGIA
Stage Front Presentation Systems,
pg 899
Staging Directions Inc, pg 899

ILLINOIS
Allen Visual Systems Inc, pg 680
AV Chicago Inc, pg 696
PSAV® Presentation Services
(Hotel Services Division), pg 866

INDIANA
Heart Breaker Entertainment LLC,
pg 778

MARYLAND
Advance Audiovisual Presentation
Ltd, pg 677
RTZ Audio Visual, pg 878

MASSACHUSETTS
massAV, pg 819
Preston Productions Inc, pg 861

MICHIGAN
City Events Group, pg 725
Digi Sign Design LLC, pg 741
K&R All Media Productions LLC,
pg 796

MINNESOTA
AVI Systems, pg 698

MISSISSIPPI
Bowie Audio Visual Enterprises Inc,
pg 709
Jasper Ewing & Sons Inc, pg 757

MISSOURI
Show-Me Audio-Visual, pg 887

NEVADA
GES Audio Visual, pg 770

NEW JERSEY
Audio Visual Associates, pg 694
Panavid, pg 850
Tele-Measurements Inc, pg 910
Wired 4 Sound Inc, pg 940

NEW YORK
AV Workshop, pg 697
KVL Audio Visual Services Inc,
pg 802
Langie Audio Visual Systems,
pg 803
Long Island Video Enterprises Live
Inc, pg 811
Visual Technologies Corp, pg 932
Visual Word Systems Inc, pg 932

NORTH CAROLINA
AV Connections Inc, pg 697
Strategic Connections, pg 901

OHIO
Audio Visual Media, pg 694
Mills James Productions, pg 828
Vista Color Imaging Inc, pg 931

PENNSYLVANIA
Audio Visions Inc, pg 694
FirstGeneration Audio/Visual
Services, pg 761
FMP Media Solutions Inc, pg 763
Visual Sound Inc, pg 931

TENNESSEE
Memphis Communications Corp,
pg 823
Technical Support Systems LLC,
pg 908

TEXAS
Audio Visual Technologies Group
(AVTG), pg 695
Lubbock Audio Visual Inc, pg 812

VIRGINIA
American AV, pg 682
Lee Hartman & Sons Inc, pg 805
Projection, pg 865
The Whitlock Group, pg 937

WASHINGTON
Inland Audio Visual Co, pg 788

WISCONSIN
Audio Visual of Milwaukee Inc,
pg 694
Camera Corner Connecting Point,
pg 715
USAV Group Inc, pg 923

PUERTO RICO
Stage Crew Audiovisual Inc, pg 898

ALBERTA
Evolution AV, pg 757
McBain Camera Ltd, pg 820

BRITISH COLUMBIA
Clark's Audio Visual Services Ltd,
pg 725

MANITOBA
Inland Audio Visual Ltd, pg 788

ONTARIO
HD Source, pg 777
Westbury National Show Systems
Ltd, pg 936

Presentation Board & Supply Repairs

CALIFORNIA
Ametron Audio/Video, pg 684
McAlister Electronics, pg 820
Lloyd F McKinney Associates Inc,
pg 821

COLORADO
Ceavco Audio Visual Company Inc,
pg 719

GEORGIA
Stage Front Presentation Systems,
pg 899

ILLINOIS
Allen Visual Systems Inc, pg 680

KENTUCKY
Axxis Leasing Inc, pg 700
NOR-COM Inc, pg 841

MARYLAND
RTZ Audio Visual, pg 878

MICHIGAN
City Events Group, pg 725
TEL Systems LLC, pg 909

MINNESOTA
AVI Systems, pg 698

NEW YORK
Colortone Audio Visual, pg 728
Langie Audio Visual Systems,
pg 803
Visual Technologies Corp, pg 932

OHIO
Audio Visual Media, pg 694
ITA Audio Visual Solutions, pg 791
Tri-State Audio Visual Co, pg 918

PENNSYLVANIA
Audio Visions Inc, pg 694

TENNESSEE
Memphis Communications Corp,
pg 823
Technical Support Systems LLC,
pg 908

TEXAS
Audio Visual Technologies Group
(AVTG), pg 695

VIRGINIA
Avitecture Inc, pg 699

ALBERTA
Infosat Communications Inc, pg 787

MANITOBA
Inland Audio Visual Ltd, pg 788

ONTARIO
Westbury National Show Systems
Ltd, pg 936

Prints from Slides

ARIZONA
Image Craft LLC, pg 784

ARKANSAS
White Diamond Productions LLC,
pg 937

CALIFORNIA
Action Photo Digital Graphics,
pg 675
Coloredge Inc, pg 728
Custom Video Productions Inc,
pg 736
Lynch Communications, pg 813
QRS Software Services, pg 867
Total Creative, pg 916

CONNECTICUT
Guymark Studios LLC, pg 775

FLORIDA
Jordan Klein Film & Video (JKFV),
pg 795

GEORGIA
Imagers, pg 785

AUDIO/VISUAL

Prints from Slides
(continued)

ILLINOIS

CCore Media Inc, pg 718
Gamma Imaging, pg 768
Helix Camera & Video, pg 778
JMC Photo & Digital Services Inc,
 pg 794
Pepper Group, pg 854

INDIANA

OMNI Productions, pg 845

IOWA

American Color Imaging (ACI),
 pg 683

KENTUCKY

Kinetic Corp, pg 799

LOUISIANA

Louisiana State University Division
 of Strategic Communications,
 pg 811

MASSACHUSETTS

Colortek of Boston, pg 728
CommCreative, pg 728
Graphx Inc, pg 773
Integrated Solutions Group, pg 789

MICHIGAN

Arbor Oakland Group, pg 688
Digi Sign Design LLC, pg 741
K&R's Recording Studios Inc,
 pg 796
Michigan Office Solutions (MOS),
 A Xerox Company, pg 825
Tectonics Industries LLC, pg 909

MINNESOTA

Linhoff Photo & Digital Imaging,
 pg 809

MISSISSIPPI

Jasper Ewing & Sons Inc, pg 757

MISSOURI

Allied Photocolor Co, pg 681
Communitronics Corp, pg 729
Visionworks Design Services Inc,
 pg 931

MONTANA

KUSM TV, pg 802

NEVADA

Encore Event Technologies LLC,
 pg 754

NEW HAMPSHIRE

Apertura, pg 686

NEW JERSEY

AJS Events, pg 679
C2 Imaging, pg 735
Video Corporation of America
 (VCA), pg 927

NEW YORK

Broadstreet Productions LLC,
 pg 711
Duggal Visual Solutions Inc, pg 747
Duplication Depot Inc, pg 748
Modernage Photographic Services
 Inc, pg 828
Neptune Photo Inc, pg 838
SMP Digital Graphics, pg 891
Zelman Studios Ltd, pg 945

NORTH CAROLINA

Image Associates Inc, pg 784

OHIO

Advent Media Inc, pg 677
Aztec Video Productions, pg 700
Thread Marketing Group, pg 913
Vista Color Imaging Inc, pg 931

OKLAHOMA

Garman Productions LLC, pg 768

PENNSYLVANIA

Audio Visual Communications Inc,
 pg 694
Bernie's Photo Center, pg 704
Berry & Homer, pg 704
Main Point Productions, pg 815
Visual Sound Inc, pg 931

TENNESSEE

Mid-South Color Labs Inc, pg 826
Stage Post, pg 899

TEXAS

Audio Visual Technologies Group
 (AVTG), pg 695
IntegraColor, pg 789
The Samuels Co, pg 879
Thomas Printworks, pg 912

VERMONT

University of Vermont, Instructional
 Television Dept, pg 923

VIRGINIA

Blair Inc, pg 707

WISCONSIN

Audio Visual of Milwaukee Inc,
 pg 694
USAV Group Inc, pg 923

BRITISH COLUMBIA

Triad Communications Ltd, pg 918

Processing & Printing—
   Filmstrips

CALIFORNIA

Coloredge Inc, pg 728
Lynch Communications, pg 813
Pro8mm, pg 862
QRS Software Services, pg 867

MASSACHUSETTS

Colortek of Boston, pg 728
DGI-Invisuals LLC, pg 741
TR Productions, pg 916

MICHIGAN

Tectonics Industries LLC, pg 909

MISSOURI

Allied Photocolor Co, pg 681

NEW JERSEY

AJS Events, pg 679

NEW YORK

Duggal Visual Solutions Inc, pg 747
Modernage Photographic Services
 Inc, pg 828
SMP Digital Graphics, pg 891

NORTH CAROLINA

Camcor Inc, pg 715

OHIO

Aztec Video Productions, pg 700

PENNSYLVANIA

Berry & Homer, pg 704
Visual Sound Inc, pg 931

TENNESSEE

Memphis Communications Corp,
 pg 823
Stage Post, pg 899

TEXAS

McNee Productions Inc, pg 821
The Samuels Co, pg 879
Stage Directions, pg 898

VIRGINIA

Blair Inc, pg 707

WISCONSIN

Pechman Imaging, pg 852
USAV Group Inc, pg 923

Processing & Printing—
   Photographs

ARIZONA

Professional Marketing Services Inc,
 pg 865

CALIFORNIA

Action Photo Digital Graphics,
 pg 675
Lynch Communications, pg 813
QRS Software Services, pg 867

CONNECTICUT

New London Media, pg 839
Skyviews Survey Inc, pg 890

FLORIDA

Cheuvront Studios, pg 721

GEORGIA

Imagers, pg 785

ILLINOIS

Beatty TeleVisual Productions,
 pg 703

IOWA

American Color Imaging (ACI),
 pg 683
Educational Technology & Media
 Services, pg 751

LOUISIANA

Louisiana State University Division
 of Strategic Communications,
 pg 811

MASSACHUSETTS

Dorian Color, pg 745

MICHIGAN

Arbor Oakland Group, pg 688
K&R's Recording Studios Inc,
 pg 796

NEW JERSEY

AJS Events, pg 679
Ritz Camera & Image, pg 875

NEW YORK

Modernage Photographic Services
 Inc, pg 828
Neptune Photo Inc, pg 838

NORTH CAROLINA

Image Associates Inc, pg 784

OHIO

Aztec Video Productions, pg 700
Thread Marketing Group, pg 913
Vista Color Imaging Inc, pg 931

PENNSYLVANIA

Bernie's Photo Center, pg 704
Main Point Productions, pg 815
Visual Sound Inc, pg 931

TENNESSEE

Mid-South Color Labs Inc, pg 826
Stage Post, pg 899

TEXAS

Fugro, pg 766
Institute of Texan Cultures, pg 788
Pounds Photographic Labs Inc,
 pg 860
The Samuels Co, pg 879
Texas Heart Institute Visual
 Communication Services, pg 911

UTAH

Signs.com, pg 888

WISCONSIN

USAV Group Inc, pg 923

Processing & Printing—
   Slides

ARIZONA

Image Craft LLC, pg 784
Professional Marketing Services Inc,
 pg 865

CALIFORNIA

Action Photo Digital Graphics,
 pg 675
Coloredge Inc, pg 728
Lynch Communications, pg 813
QRS Software Services, pg 867

DISTRICT OF COLUMBIA

O'Keefe Communications Inc,
 pg 844

FLORIDA
Cheuvront Studios, pg 721
Communications Concepts Inc (CCI), pg 729

GEORGIA
Imagers, pg 785

ILLINOIS
CCore Media Inc, pg 718
Gamma Imaging, pg 768
Helix Camera & Video, pg 778
JMC Photo & Digital Services Inc, pg 794
Pepper Group, pg 854

INDIANA
OMNI Productions, pg 845

IOWA
American Color Imaging (ACI), pg 683
Educational Technology & Media Services, pg 751

LOUISIANA
Louisiana State University Division of Strategic Communications, pg 811

MASSACHUSETTS
Colortek of Boston, pg 728
CommCreative, pg 728
DGI-Invisuals LLC, pg 741
Graphx Inc, pg 773
ICL Imaging Inc, pg 783
Integrated Solutions Group, pg 789
TR Productions, pg 916

MICHIGAN
Arbor Oakland Group, pg 688
K&R's Recording Studios Inc, pg 796
Tectonics Industries LLC, pg 909

MINNESOTA
Linhoff Photo & Digital Imaging, pg 809
Pointward, pg 858

MISSISSIPPI
Jasper Ewing & Sons Inc, pg 757

MISSOURI
Allied Photocolor Co, pg 681

NEW HAMPSHIRE
Academic & Campus Technology Services, pg 672

NEW JERSEY
AJS Events, pg 679
C2 Imaging, pg 735

NEW YORK
Duggal Visual Solutions Inc, pg 747
Modernage Photographic Services Inc, pg 828
Jack Morton Worldwide, pg 830
Neptune Photo Inc, pg 838
SMP Digital Graphics, pg 891

NORTH CAROLINA
Image Associates Inc, pg 784

OHIO
Aztec Video Productions, pg 700
Cuyahoga Community College Student Production Office (SPO), pg 736
Thread Marketing Group, pg 913
Vista Color Imaging Inc, pg 931

PENNSYLVANIA
Audio Visual Communications Inc, pg 694
Bernie's Photo Center, pg 704
Berry & Homer, pg 704
FMP Media Solutions Inc, pg 763
Main Point Productions, pg 815
Visual Sound Inc, pg 931

TENNESSEE
Memphis Communications Corp, pg 823
Stage Post, pg 899

TEXAS
IntegraColor, pg 789
The Samuels Co, pg 879
Texas Heart Institute Visual Communication Services, pg 911

VERMONT
University of Vermont, Instructional Television Dept, pg 923

VIRGINIA
Advance Concepts Inc, pg 677
Blair Inc, pg 707

WISCONSIN
Audio Visual of Milwaukee Inc, pg 694
Pechman Imaging, pg 852
USAV Group Inc, pg 923

ONTARIO
Silver Creek Media Inc, pg 888

Production Workshops

ARIZONA
Creative Backstage, pg 733
Teaberry, pg 908

CALIFORNIA
Crystal Pyramid Productions™, pg 735
Film TV Sound, pg 760
JDS Video & Media Productions Inc, pg 793
QRS Software Services, pg 867
Russ InVision Co/AbridgeClub.com, pg 879

DISTRICT OF COLUMBIA
Theatrical Technicians Inc (TTI), pg 912

FLORIDA
Communications Concepts Inc (CCI), pg 729

GEORGIA
Lighting & Production Equipment Inc, pg 807

IDAHO
Wide Eye Productions, pg 938

ILLINOIS
ABS Enterprises, pg 672
CCore Media Inc, pg 718
Gamma Imaging, pg 768
Jim Passin Productions, pg 852
Pepper Group, pg 854
PSAV® Presentation Services (Hotel Services Division), pg 866
Southern Illinois University, pg 895

INDIANA
Communication Ministries, pg 728
OMNI Productions, pg 845

IOWA
Educational Technology & Media Services, pg 751

LOUISIANA
Moxie Media, pg 832

MARYLAND
The Image Generators, pg 785

MASSACHUSETTS
Limelight Production® Inc, pg 809
MotionArt Studios, pg 831
TR Productions, pg 916

MICHIGAN
Digi Sign Design LLC, pg 741
K&R's Recording Studios Inc, pg 796
Michigan Recording Arts Institute & Technologies, pg 825

NEW JERSEY
Euro-Pacific Film & Video Productions Inc, pg 756

NEW YORK
De Nonno Productions Inc (DPI), pg 739
SMP Digital Graphics, pg 891
Zelman Studios Ltd, pg 945

NORTH CAROLINA
Camcor Inc, pg 715
Duke Media Services, pg 747

NORTH DAKOTA
Media Productions, pg 822

OHIO
Aztec Video Productions, pg 700
Thread Marketing Group, pg 913
Vista Color Imaging Inc, pg 931

RHODE ISLAND
Sound-FX-Design, pg 894

TENNESSEE
Memphis Communications Corp, pg 823
Stage Post, pg 899

TEXAS
Julye Newlin Productions Inc, pg 840
Pounds Photographic Labs Inc, pg 860
Stage Directions, pg 898

VERMONT
Edgewood Studios, pg 750
University of Vermont, Instructional Television Dept, pg 923

VIRGINIA
Rocktown Media, pg 876

WASHINGTON
Inland Audio Visual Co, pg 788

WISCONSIN
Audio Visual of Milwaukee Inc, pg 694
USAV Group Inc, pg 923
Wisconsin Public Television, pg 940

BRITISH COLUMBIA
Video Out Distribution, pg 928

ONTARIO
GAPC (General Assembly Production Centre), pg 768
Trebas Institute, pg 917

QUEBEC
Trebas Institute, pg 917

Programmable Slide Presentation System, *see* **Slide Presentation System—Programmable & Manual**

Projection Equipment & Accessory Distributors

ALABAMA
Curtis Company, pg 736

ARIZONA
Arizona Cine Equipment, pg 688
Docter Optics Inc, pg 744
EAR Professional Audio/Video, pg 749
Metropolitan Audio-Visual Inc, pg 824
Professional Marketing Services Inc, pg 865
Projector SuperStore LLC, pg 865
Troxell-CDI, pg 918
Ultimate Presentation Systems Inc, pg 920

ARKANSAS
Jay S Stanley & Associates Inc, pg 899
White Diamond Productions LLC, pg 937

CALIFORNIA
Advanced Systems Group LLC, pg 677
Ametron Audio/Video, pg 684
Associated Sound, pg 691

AUDIO/VISUAL

Projection Equipment & Accessory Distributors (continued)

CALIFORNIA (continued)

Assured Audio Visual, pg 691
ATV Video Center Inc, pg 692
Audio/Video Supply Inc, pg 694
Auton Motorized Systems, pg 696
AV Conferencing LLC (AVC), pg 697
AVerMedia Technologies Inc, pg 697
Barber Tech Video Products, pg 701
Be Media, pg 702
Birns & Sawyer Inc, pg 706
California Tape Products Inc, pg 714
Christie Digital Systems USA Inc, pg 722
Christy's Editorial, pg 723
Cinema Equipment Sales of California Inc, pg 724
Cinema Xenon International Inc, pg 724
Derksen (USA) Inc, pg 740
Educational Technology Services (ETS), pg 751
Electronic Design Solutions Inc, pg 752
Electrosonic Inc, pg 752
Gluskin's Custom Audio Video, pg 771
Hi-Tech Lamps Inc, pg 779
Hooper Camera & Imaging, pg 781
Instructional Materials & Equipment Distributors (I-Med), pg 789
JD Audio Visual Inc, pg 793
Laser Magic Productions, pg 804
Lloyd F McKinney Associates Inc, pg 821
Media Fabricators Inc, pg 822
MediaMation Inc, pg 822
OWI Inc, pg 849
PMP Marketing Inc, pg 858
Promax Systems, pg 865
SNAP, pg 891
Sound Service Co, pg 894
Southern California Sound Image Inc, pg 895
Stanislaus AV Inc, pg 899
SuperVision, pg 904
Towards 2000 Inc, pg 916
VMI Inc, pg 932
VTP Inc, pg 933
Zack Electronics Inc, pg 945

COLORADO

Ceavco Audio Visual Company Inc, pg 719
Daylight Productions & Rentals, pg 739
Goldberg Brothers Inc, pg 772
Stanco Sales LLC, pg 899

CONNECTICUT

HB Communications Inc, pg 777
MAVCO, pg 820
Rockwell Communications Inc, pg 876
USI Inc, pg 924

FLORIDA

Altel Systems Group Inc, pg 682
AVI-SPL, pg 698
Cinema Equipment & Supplies Inc, pg 724
Digital Video Systems, pg 742

Harmon's Audio-Visual Services, pg 776
Harris Corp, pg 776
Hi-Tech Import Export Corp, pg 779
Hollywood Theatre Equipment Inc, pg 781
Industrial Strength Inc, pg 787
Intermark Industries Inc, pg 789
Lighting Sales Connection Inc, pg 808
ONstage, pg 846
Photosound of Orlando Inc, pg 856
Tallahassee Audio Visual, pg 906

GEORGIA

Audio Visual Resources Inc, pg 695
Baker Audio Visual, pg 700
Boxlight Inc, pg 709
Convergent Media Systems, pg 731
Digital Projection, pg 742
Lighting & Production Equipment Inc, pg 807
Stage Front Presentation Systems, pg 899
Visioneering International Inc, pg 931

HAWAII

The Audio Visual Co (AVCO), pg 694

ILLINOIS

Allen Visual Systems Inc, pg 680
Central Audio-Visual Equipment Inc, pg 719
Chicago Spotlight Inc, pg 721
Creative Technology (CT), pg 733
Dukane Corp, Audio Visual Products Division, pg 747
G T Luscombe Co Inc, pg 812
Major Reproductions Equipment Co, pg 815
Quintessence Audio Ltd, pg 868
RC Communications, pg 870
The Screen Works®, pg 882
Tele-Time Systems, pg 910

INDIANA

Heart Breaker Entertainment LLC, pg 778
Sensory Technologies LLC, pg 884
SHP Electronics, pg 887

IOWA

Sitler's Supplies Inc, pg 890

KANSAS

KK Office Solutions Inc, pg 799
SKC Communication Products Inc, pg 890

KENTUCKY

Audio Visual Techniques Inc, pg 695
Axxis Leasing Inc, pg 700
Barney Miller's Inc, pg 827
NOR-COM Inc, pg 841

LOUISIANA

Techkno Integration & Design Services LLC, pg 908

MAINE

Headlight Audio Visual Inc, pg 777

MARYLAND

Absolute Hollywood, pg 672
Advance Audiovisual Presentation Ltd, pg 677
Baron Stage Curtain & Equipment Co Inc, pg 702
Cardinal Sound & Video, pg 717
CPR MultiMedia Solutions, pg 732
DSR Computer Technology Specialists Inc, pg 747
Kipp Visual Systems Inc, pg 799
Nelson White Systems Inc, pg 838
Nicholas P Pipino Associates Inc, pg 857
RTZ Audio Visual, pg 878
Theatre Service & Supply Corp, pg 912

MASSACHUSETTS

Antronics Inc, pg 686
Elite Video Inc, pg 753
Hunt's Photo & Video, pg 782
Integrated Solutions Group, pg 789
Limelight Production® Inc, pg 809
Rule Boston Camera, pg 878
University Products Inc, pg 923

MICHIGAN

Olson Anderson Co, pg 685
ASC Systems, pg 690
City Events Group, pg 725
Digi Sign Design LLC, pg 741
Michigan Office Solutions (MOS), A Xerox Company, pg 825
On Stage Visuals, pg 846
TEL Systems LLC, pg 909

MINNESOTA

Alpha Video & Audio Inc, pg 682
AVI Systems, pg 698
Media Loft Inc, pg 822
Tierney Brothers Inc, pg 914

MISSISSIPPI

Bowie Audio Visual Enterprises Inc, pg 709
Jasper Ewing & Sons Inc, pg 757

MISSOURI

A to Z Theatrical Supply & Service, pg 671
Communitronics Corp, pg 729
Conference Technologies Inc, pg 730
ITC, pg 791
Modern Communications Inc, pg 828
Schiller's Audio-Visual, pg 881
Southwest Audio-Visual Inc, pg 895

NEBRASKA

ATV Research Inc, pg 692
Ballantyne Strong Inc, pg 701

NEVADA

Bulbman Inc, pg 712

NEW JERSEY

A-V Services Inc, pg 671
AlltecPro, pg 681
Argraph Corp, pg 688
Audio Visual Dynamics®, pg 694
AV Bluebook, pg 696
Color Leasing Studios, pg 727
Diversified, pg 744
Earl Girls Inc, pg 749
G&G Technologies Inc, pg 768
HamiltonBuhl, pg 775

MARYLAND

JVC Professional Products Co, pg 796
Leica Camera Inc, pg 806
Sharp Electronics Corp, Professional Display Division, pg 885
Starlite, pg 900
SYMCO Inc, pg 905
Tele-Measurements Inc, pg 910
Total Video Products Inc, pg 916
Vcom IMC, pg 925
Video Corporation of America (VCA), pg 927
Wired 4 Sound Inc, pg 940
Yorktel, pg 944

NEW MEXICO

Quickbeam Systems Inc (QSI), pg 868

NEW YORK

Ace Video, pg 674
American Video Inc, pg 684
Audio-Video Corp, pg 694
AV Workshop, pg 697
BTX Technologies, pg 712
Bulbtronics Inc, pg 712
Colortone Audio Visual, pg 728
Creative Stage Lighting Co Inc, pg 733
Design Audio Visual Inc, pg 741
DSan Corp, pg 747
Gaylord Archival, pg 768
Indigo Productions, pg 787
Just Bulbs - The Light Bulb Store, pg 795
KVL Audio Visual Services Inc, pg 802
Langie Audio Visual Systems, pg 803
Levy NYC Design & Production, pg 806
Long Island Video Enterprises Live Inc, pg 811
Markertek Video Supply, pg 817
Motion Picture Enterprises Inc, pg 831
Neptune Photo Inc, pg 838
Presentation Products Inc, pg 861
Raven Screen Corp, pg 870
Ray Supply Inc, pg 870
RNJ Electronics, pg 875
Sargent Welch, pg 880
Stampede Presentation Products Inc, pg 899
Theatrical Services & Supplies Inc, pg 912
Topbulb, a Semmer Lighting Company, pg 915
Toys From The Attic, pg 916
Tri-Ed Distribution Inc, pg 918
Video Technology Services Inc, pg 929
Visual Technologies Corp, pg 932

NORTH CAROLINA

Camcor Inc, pg 715
Strategic Connections, pg 901

OHIO

Audio Visual Media, pg 694
Copp Integrated Systems, pg 731
Hughie's Event Production Services, pg 782
Icom Multimedia, pg 783
ITA Audio Visual Solutions, pg 791
Tri-State Audio Visual Co, pg 918
Tri-State Visual Products Inc, pg 918

OKLAHOMA

Ford AV, pg 763

OREGON

PLUS Corp of America, pg 858

PENNSYLVANIA

Advanced AV LLC, pg 677
Audio Visions Inc, pg 694
Audio Visual Communications Inc, pg 694
Bernie's Photo Center, pg 704
Brodart Co, pg 711
Clair Companies, pg 725
J E Foss Co, pg 764
Garcia Marketing Inc, pg 768
Grise Audio Visual Center Inc, pg 774
Innovision Media Group, pg 788
The Lerro Corp, pg 806
RSS Distributors, pg 878
Vistacom Inc, pg 931
Visual Sound Inc, pg 931
Wespen Audio Visual Co, pg 935

RHODE ISLAND

Shanix Inc, pg 885

TENNESSEE

Continental Film, pg 731
Lowrance Sound Co Inc, pg 812
Memphis Communications Corp, pg 823
Technical Support Systems LLC, pg 908
Zion Music Group, pg 945

TEXAS

Audio Visual Technologies Group (AVTG), pg 695
AVES Audio Visual Systems Inc, pg 698
CAM Audio Inc, pg 714
Crossroads Audio Inc, pg 735
Data Projections Inc, pg 738
Digital Display Solutions Inc, pg 742
FitzCo Sound Inc, pg 761
Heffernan Audio Visual, pg 778
JSAV, pg 795
Lubbock Audio Visual Inc, pg 812
Quality Audio Visual Service Inc, pg 867
Southwest Sound Solutions, pg 896
Stage Directions, pg 898
Tarpley Media Systems, pg 907

UTAH

Webb Audio Visual, pg 935

VIRGINIA

Avitecture Inc, pg 699
Boitnott Visual Communications Corp (BVC), pg 708
Design & Production Inc, pg 740
Intellidyne LLC, pg 789
Lee Hartman & Sons Inc, pg 805
Metropolitan Audio Visual Co LLC, pg 824
Quince Imaging Inc, pg 868
Rocktown Media, pg 876
The Whitlock Group, pg 937

WASHINGTON

CCI Solutions, pg 718
Inland Audio Visual Co, pg 788

WISCONSIN

Alpha Source Inc, pg 681
Audio Visual of Milwaukee Inc, pg 694

Camera Corner Connecting Point, pg 715
Demco Inc, pg 740
Full Compass Systems, pg 767
Safe Harbor Computers, pg 879
School Specialty Inc, pg 882

PUERTO RICO

Audio Visual Concepts Inc, pg 694

ALBERTA

Allstar Show Industries Inc, pg 681
Evolution AV, pg 757
Genesis Integration, pg 769
Infosat Communications Inc, pg 787
Matrix Video Communications Corp (MVCC), pg 819
McBain Camera Ltd, pg 820
SMART Technologies ULC, pg 891
Unique Communications Ltd, pg 921

BRITISH COLUMBIA

Commercial Electronics Ltd, pg 728
Specialty Bulb Products Inc, pg 896

MANITOBA

Advance Pro, pg 677
Inland Audio Visual Ltd, pg 788

ONTARIO

Carr McLean Ltd, pg 717
CBM Ltd, pg 718
Cinema Stage Inc, pg 724
HD Source, pg 777
MVI - MultiVision Inc, pg 835
Nationwide Audio Visual Co, pg 837
Technovision® Interactive Inc, pg 909
Westbury National Show Systems Ltd, pg 936

QUEBEC

Panavideo Inc, pg 850
Strong Screen Systems, pg 902

Projection Equipment & Accessory Manufacturers

CALIFORNIA

ALTINEX Inc, pg 682
AVerMedia Technologies Inc, pg 697
Christie Digital Systems USA Inc, pg 722
Cinema Xenon International Inc, pg 724
Citizens Systems America Corp, pg 725
Eiki International Inc, pg 751
Extron Electronics, pg 758
Laser Magic Productions, pg 804
Lasergraphics Inc, pg 804
MediaPOINTE, pg 823
Precision Projection Systems Inc, pg 861
Stewart Filmscreen Corp, pg 901
Xantech LLC, pg 943

COLORADO

Display Devices Inc, pg 743
Goldberg Brothers Inc, pg 772

CONNECTICUT

KOH Design Inc, pg 801

FLORIDA

Magna-Tech Electronic Co Inc, pg 814
SVS Inc, pg 905
Vutec Corp, pg 933

GEORGIA

Analog Way Inc, pg 685
Digital Projection, pg 742

ILLINOIS

ACCO Brands Corp, pg 673
AmpliVox Portable Sound Systems, pg 684
Bretford Manufacturing Inc, pg 710
Dukane Corp, Audio Visual Products Division, pg 747
Luxor, pg 812
NEC Display Solutions of America, pg 837
The Screen Works®, pg 882
La Vezzi Precision Inc, pg 926

INDIANA

Da-Lite, a Legrand AV Inc brand, pg 737
Draper Inc, pg 746
Star Case Manufacturing Co Inc, pg 900

KANSAS

Tributestone, pg 918

MARYLAND

Absolute Hollywood, pg 672
Video Mount Products (VMP), pg 928

MASSACHUSETTS

Chartpak Inc, pg 721
Elite Video Inc, pg 753

MINNESOTA

Chief, a Legrand AV Inc brand, pg 722
Winsted Corp, pg 939

MISSOURI

Ken-A-Vision Manufacturing Co Inc, pg 797

NEBRASKA

Ballantyne Strong Inc, pg 701
Strong Cinema Products, pg 902

NEVADA

Keystone View, pg 798

NEW JERSEY

AlltecPro, pg 681
Casio America Inc, pg 717
Crestron Electronics Inc, pg 734
Gerriets International, pg 770
JVC Professional Products Co, pg 796
Leica Camera Inc, pg 806
PeopleVisionFX, pg 854
Pro-Tape & Specialities Inc, pg 863
RAMSA Professional Audio Systems, pg 870
Sharp Electronics Corp, Professional Display Division, pg 885
Techflex Inc, pg 908

NEW YORK

American Video Inc, pg 684
DSan Corp, pg 747
Eastman Kodak Co, pg 750
ELMO USA Corp, pg 753
General Audio-Visual Inc (GAVI), pg 769
Levy NYC Design & Production, pg 806
Navitar Inc, pg 837
Raven Screen Corp, pg 870
TecNec Distributing, pg 909
Video Technology Services Inc, pg 929

OREGON

InFocus Corp, pg 787

TENNESSEE

Adtec Digital Inc, pg 677

VIRGINIA

Optikinetics Ltd - The Americas, pg 847
Quince Imaging Inc, pg 868

WASHINGTON

Laser Fantasy/HECK Industries/Photon Manufacturing, pg 804

ALBERTA

SMART Technologies ULC, pg 891

ONTARIO

CBM Ltd, pg 718
DW Electrochemicals Ltd, pg 748
Evertz Microsystems Ltd, pg 757

QUEBEC

Strong Screen Systems, pg 902

Projection Equipment & Accessory Rentals

ALABAMA

Audio-Video Resources Inc, pg 694

ALASKA

Imig Audio/Video Inc, pg 786

ARIZONA

Arizona Cine Equipment, pg 688
AV Concepts Inc, pg 696
Broadcast Rentals, pg 711
Creative Backstage, pg 733
Merestone, pg 823
Metropolitan Audio-Visual Inc, pg 824
Ultimate Presentation Systems Inc, pg 920
Video West Inc, pg 929

ARKANSAS

White Diamond Productions LLC, pg 937

CALIFORNIA

Action Audio & Visual, pg 675
Ametron Audio/Video, pg 684
Angstrom Lighting, pg 685
Artichoke Productions, pg 690
Associated Sound, pg 691
Assured Audio Visual, pg 691

AUDIO/VISUAL

Projection Equipment & Accessory Rentals (continued)

CALIFORNIA (continued)

ATV Video Center Inc, pg 692
AV Conferencing LLC (AVC), pg 697
AV Guys, pg 697
Bexel, an NEP Broadcast Services Company, pg 704
Birns & Sawyer Inc, pg 706
California Teleprompter, pg 714
First Camera, pg 761
Gold Standard Productions, pg 772
Alan Gordon Enterprises Inc, pg 772
Hooper Camera & Imaging, pg 781
Instructional Materials & Equipment Distributors (I-Med), pg 789
JD Audio Visual Inc, pg 793
Lynch Communications, pg 813
McCune Audio-Video-Lighting, pg 821
Media Fabricators Inc, pg 822
MSI Production Services, pg 832
Munday & Collins AV, pg 834
Muse Presentation Technologies, pg 834
On-Trax Inc, pg 846
PSAV® Presentation Services, pg 866
Sound Service Co, pg 894
Stanislaus AV Inc, pg 899
Towards 2000 Inc, pg 916
VER, pg 926
Video Resources Inc, pg 928
Voice & Video Rentals, pg 932

COLORADO

Ceavco Audio Visual Company Inc, pg 719
Daylight Productions & Rentals, pg 739
Multimedia Audio Visual Inc, pg 833

CONNECTICUT

A/V Davey, pg 697
Rockwell Communications Inc, pg 876
Videofilm Systems Inc, pg 929

DELAWARE

Showorks Audio Visual Inc, pg 887

FLORIDA

All Comm Rentals Inc (ALLCOMM), pg 680
AVI-SPL, pg 698
Harmon's Audio-Visual Services, pg 776
Industrial Strength Inc, pg 787
Jordan Klein Film & Video (JKFV), pg 795
Lighting Sales Connection Inc, pg 808
Multivision Video & Film, pg 833
ONstage, pg 846
Paradise Show & Design Inc, pg 851
Photosound of Orlando Inc, pg 856
PRI Productions, pg 862
Sight & Sound Productions, pg 887
Sound*Light, pg 894

Tallahassee Audio Visual, pg 906
Universal Studios Florida® Production Group, pg 922

GEORGIA

Audio Visual Resources Inc, pg 695
Cinevision Corp, pg 725
Convergent Media Systems, pg 731
Lighting & Production Equipment Inc, pg 807
MAGNUM Companies Ltd, pg 815
ON Services, a GES Company, pg 846
Stage Front Presentation Systems, pg 899
Staging Directions Inc, pg 899

ILLINOIS

Allen Visual Systems Inc, pg 680
AV Chicago Inc, pg 696
Backstar Creative Media Inc, pg 700
Beatty TeleVisual Productions, pg 703
Central Audio-Visual Equipment Inc, pg 719
Chicago Spotlight Inc, pg 721
Creative Technology (CT), pg 733
Helix Camera & Video, pg 778
Meetinghouse Event Design & Production, pg 823
Pepper Group, pg 854
PSAV® Presentation Services (Hotel Services Division), pg 866
RC Communications, pg 870
Resolution Productions Group, pg 874
SCI Television & Creative Media LLC, pg 882
The Screen Works®, pg 882

INDIANA

Advanced Media Integration, pg 677
Gary Camera & Digital, pg 768
Heart Breaker Entertainment LLC, pg 778
OMNI Productions, pg 845

IOWA

Central Lighting & Equipment Inc (CLE), pg 719

KENTUCKY

Audio Visual Techniques Inc, pg 695
Barney Miller's Inc, pg 827

LOUISIANA

Clark Services Audio Visual & Exhibit Inc, pg 725
Pace Systems, pg 849
Techkno Integration & Design Services LLC, pg 908

MAINE

University of Maine Media Services, pg 922

MARYLAND

Absolute Hollywood, pg 672
Advance Audiovisual Presentation Ltd, pg 677
CPR MultiMedia Solutions, pg 732
Event Tech, pg 756
Hargrove Inc, pg 776
Nelson White Systems Inc, pg 838
RTZ Audio Visual, pg 878

MASSACHUSETTS

A/V Presentations Inc, pg 697
AVFX Inc, pg 698
Capron Lighting & Sound Co Inc, pg 716
Cramer, pg 732
Elite Video Inc, pg 753
Integrated Solutions Group, pg 789
massAV, pg 819
Preston Productions Inc, pg 861
TR Productions, pg 916

MICHIGAN

Olson Anderson Co, pg 685
City Events Group, pg 725
Digi Sign Design LLC, pg 741
K&R All Media Productions LLC, pg 796
On Stage Visuals, pg 846
TEL Systems LLC, pg 909

MINNESOTA

Alpha Video & Audio Inc, pg 682
AVI Systems, pg 698
Big Event Productions LLC, pg 705
Media Loft Inc, pg 822

MISSISSIPPI

Bowie Audio Visual Enterprises Inc, pg 709
Jasper Ewing & Sons Inc, pg 757

MISSOURI

Communitronics Corp, pg 729
Show-Me Audio-Visual, pg 887
Southwest Audio-Visual Inc, pg 895

NEBRASKA

Dog & Pony Productions Inc, pg 744

NEVADA

GES Audio Visual, pg 770
Lefco Video Services Inc, pg 806

NEW HAMPSHIRE

Academic & Campus Technology Services, pg 672
Apertura, pg 686

NEW JERSEY

Audio Visual Dynamics®, pg 694
Color Leasing Studios, pg 727
Earl Girls Inc, pg 749
Gerriets International, pg 770
International Audio Visual Inc, pg 790
MiB MediaWorks, pg 825
Panavid, pg 850
Starlite, pg 900
Tele-Measurements Inc, pg 910
Video Corporation of America (VCA), pg 927
Wired 4 Sound Inc, pg 940

NEW MEXICO

Quickbeam Systems Inc (QSI), pg 868

NEW YORK

Ace Video, pg 674
American Video Inc, pg 684
AV Workshop, pg 697
CMI Communications, pg 727
Colortone Audio Visual, pg 728
Creative Stage Lighting Co Inc, pg 733

Design Audio Visual Inc, pg 741
Hello World Communications, pg 778
KVL Audio Visual Services Inc, pg 802
Langie Audio Visual Systems, pg 803
Long Island Video Enterprises Live Inc, pg 811
Manhattan Center Studios Inc, pg 816
Motion Picture Enterprises Inc, pg 831
See Factor Industry Inc, pg 883
SmartSource Computer & AV Rentals, pg 891
Specialized Audio-Visual Inc, pg 896
Theatrical Services & Supplies Inc, pg 912
Visual Technologies Corp, pg 932
WorldStage, pg 941

NORTH CAROLINA

Audio & Light, pg 693
AV Connections Inc, pg 697
AV Metro Inc, pg 697
Special Event Services, pg 896
Strategic Connections, pg 901

NORTH DAKOTA

Media Productions, pg 822

OHIO

Audio Visual Media, pg 694
Bartha, pg 702
Hughie's Event Production Services, pg 782
Icom Multimedia, pg 783
ITA Audio Visual Solutions, pg 791
Lyon Video Inc, pg 813
Mills James Productions, pg 828
Thread Marketing Group, pg 913
Tri-State Visual Products Inc, pg 918
Vista Color Imaging Inc, pg 931

OKLAHOMA

PDC Productions, pg 852

OREGON

Northwest Film Center, pg 842
Rose City Sound, pg 877

PENNSYLVANIA

Advanced AV LLC, pg 677
Audio Visions Inc, pg 694
Audio Visual Communications Inc, pg 694
Bernie's Photo Center, pg 704
FMP Media Solutions Inc, pg 763
Grise Audio Visual Center Inc, pg 774
Innovision Media Group, pg 788
Upstage Video, pg 923
Vistacom Inc, pg 931
Visual Sound Inc, pg 931

SOUTH CAROLINA

Encore Video Productions, pg 754
Sound & Images Inc, pg 893

TENNESSEE

Memphis Communications Corp, pg 823
Russ Sturgeon Productions/RSVP, pg 903
Technical Support Systems LLC, pg 908

TEXAS

Alford Media Services, pg 680
Audio Visual Technologies Group (AVTG), pg 695
AVES Audio Visual Systems Inc, pg 698
Bright Star Productions Inc, pg 710
Data Projections Inc, pg 738
FitzCo Sound Inc, pg 761
GEAR Cameras & Lighting, pg 769
Heffernan Audio Visual, pg 778
JSAV, pg 795
Lubbock Audio Visual Inc, pg 812
Quality Audio Visual Service Inc, pg 867
Stage Directions, pg 898

UTAH

Webb Audio Visual, pg 935

VIRGINIA

Advance Concepts Inc, pg 677
American AV, pg 682
Audio Visual Actions Inc (AVA), pg 694
Boitnott Visual Communications Corp (BVC), pg 708
Lee Hartman & Sons Inc, pg 805
Projection, pg 865
Quince Imaging Inc, pg 868
The Whitlock Group, pg 937

WASHINGTON

CCI Solutions, pg 718
D A Sound, pg 737
Inland Audio Visual Co, pg 788
Kostov Productions, pg 801
Laser Fantasy/HECK Industries/Photon Manufacturing, pg 804
PNTA, pg 858

WEST VIRGINIA

Blackwater Video Productions, pg 707

WISCONSIN

Audio Visual of Milwaukee Inc, pg 694
Camera Corner Connecting Point, pg 715
Event Essentials, pg 756
Full Compass Systems, pg 767
Logan Productions Inc, pg 811

PUERTO RICO

Stage Crew Audiovisual Inc, pg 898

ALBERTA

Allstar Show Industries Inc, pg 681
Cine Audio Visual Sales & Service Ltd, pg 723
Evolution AV, pg 757
L R Light & Sound, pg 802
Unique Communications Ltd, pg 921

BRITISH COLUMBIA

Clark's Audio Visual Services Ltd, pg 725
Commercial Electronics Ltd, pg 728
DL Sound & Lighting Productions Ltd, pg 744
Triad Communications Ltd, pg 918

MANITOBA

Advance Pro, pg 677
Inland Audio Visual Ltd, pg 788

ONTARIO

HD Source, pg 777
Metalworks Recording Studios Inc, pg 824
MVI - MultiVision Inc, pg 835
Technovision® Interactive Inc, pg 909
Westbury National Show Systems Ltd, pg 936

QUEBEC

Audio Visual Dynamics, pg 694
Freeman Audio Visual, pg 765
Panavideo Inc, pg 850

Projection Equipment & Accessory Repairs

ARKANSAS

Jay S Stanley & Associates Inc, pg 899

CALIFORNIA

Ametron Audio/Video, pg 684
Assured Audio Visual, pg 691
AVerMedia Technologies Inc, pg 697
Christie Digital Systems USA Inc, pg 722
Electrosonic Inc, pg 752
Gluskin's Custom Audio Video, pg 771
Hooper Camera & Imaging, pg 781
Instructional Materials & Equipment Distributors (I-Med), pg 789
McAlister Electronics, pg 820
Lloyd F McKinney Associates Inc, pg 821
Pro Camera Repair, pg 862
Sound Service Co, pg 894
VMI Inc, pg 932

COLORADO

Ceavco Audio Visual Company Inc, pg 719

CONNECTICUT

A/V Davey, pg 697
HB Communications Inc, pg 777
Precision Camera & Video Repair Inc, pg 861
Rockwell Communications Inc, pg 876

FLORIDA

AVI-SPL, pg 698
Digital Video Systems, pg 742
ELC Sales & Service Inc, pg 752
Hi-Tech Enterprises Inc, pg 779
Hollywood Theatre Equipment Inc, pg 781
Tallahassee Audio Visual, pg 906

GEORGIA

Analog Way Inc, pg 685
Audio Visual Resources Inc, pg 695
Boxlight Inc, pg 709
Lighting & Production Equipment Inc, pg 807
Stage Front Presentation Systems, pg 899

ILLINOIS

Allen Visual Systems Inc, pg 680
Chicago Spotlight Inc, pg 721
RC Communications, pg 870
The Screen Works®, pg 882

INDIANA

Gary Camera & Digital, pg 768

KANSAS

KK Office Solutions Inc, pg 799

KENTUCKY

Axxis Leasing Inc, pg 700
Barney Miller's Inc, pg 827
NOR-COM Inc, pg 841

MARYLAND

DSR Computer Technology Specialists Inc, pg 747
RTZ Audio Visual, pg 878

MASSACHUSETTS

Capron Lighting & Sound Co Inc, pg 716
Elite Video Inc, pg 753
Integrated Solutions Group, pg 789

MICHIGAN

Olson Anderson Co, pg 685
City Events Group, pg 725
TEL Systems LLC, pg 909

MINNESOTA

Alpha Video & Audio Inc, pg 682
AVI Systems, pg 698

MISSISSIPPI

Bowie Audio Visual Enterprises Inc, pg 709

MISSOURI

Cintrex Audio Visual, pg 725
Communitronics Corp, pg 729
Schiller's Audio-Visual, pg 881

NEW JERSEY

Earl Girls Inc, pg 749
Leica Camera Inc, pg 806
Starlite, pg 900

NEW MEXICO

Quickbeam Systems Inc (QSI), pg 868

NEW YORK

American Video Inc, pg 684
Colortone Audio Visual, pg 728
ELMO USA Corp, pg 753
Langie Audio Visual Systems, pg 803
Motion Picture Enterprises, pg 831
Raven Screen Corp, pg 870
Toys From The Attic, pg 916
Video Technology Services Inc, pg 929
Visual Technologies Corp, pg 932

NORTH CAROLINA

Camcor Inc, pg 715
Strategic Connections, pg 901

OHIO

Audio Visual Media, pg 694
Icom Multimedia, pg 783
ITA Audio Visual Solutions, pg 791
Tri-State Audio Visual Co, pg 918
Tri-State Visual Products Inc, pg 918

PENNSYLVANIA

Advanced AV LLC, pg 677
Audio Visions Inc, pg 694
Bernie's Photo Center, pg 704
Vistacom Inc, pg 931
Visual Sound Inc, pg 931

TENNESSEE

Memphis Communications Corp, pg 823
Technical Support Systems LLC, pg 908

TEXAS

Audio Visual Technologies Group (AVTG), pg 695
Data Projections Inc, pg 738
Lubbock Audio Visual Inc, pg 812
Quality Audio Visual Service Inc, pg 867
Tarpley Media Systems, pg 907

VIRGINIA

Avitecture Inc, pg 699
Boitnott Visual Communications Corp (BVC), pg 708
Quince Imaging Inc, pg 868
The Whitlock Group, pg 937

WASHINGTON

Inland Audio Visual Co, pg 788
Laser Fantasy/HECK Industries/Photon Manufacturing, pg 804

WISCONSIN

Audio Visual of Milwaukee Inc, pg 694
Full Compass Systems, pg 767

ALBERTA

Evolution AV, pg 757
Infosat Communications Inc, pg 787
Unique Communications Ltd, pg 921

BRITISH COLUMBIA

Commercial Electronics Ltd, pg 728

MANITOBA

Inland Audio Visual Ltd, pg 788

ONTARIO

MVI - MultiVision Inc, pg 835
Technovision® Interactive Inc, pg 909
Westbury National Show Systems Ltd, pg 936

QUEBEC

Panavideo Inc, pg 850

Projection Panel Distributors

ARIZONA

EAR Professional Audio/Video, pg 749
Professional Marketing Services Inc, pg 865
Troxell-CDI, pg 918

AUDIO/VISUAL

Projection Panel Distributors (continued)

ARKANSAS

White Diamond Productions LLC, pg 937

CALIFORNIA

Ametron Audio/Video, pg 684
Associated Sound, pg 691
California Tape Products Inc, pg 714
Cibola Systems, pg 723
Computer Modules Inc, pg 729
Electrosonic Inc, pg 752
MediaPOINTE, pg 823
Sound Service Co, pg 894
Southern California Sound Image Inc, pg 895
Towards 2000 Inc, pg 916
VTP Inc, pg 933

COLORADO

Daylight Productions & Rentals, pg 739

CONNECTICUT

HB Communications Inc, pg 777

FLORIDA

Digital Video Systems, pg 742
Hi-Tech Import Export Corp, pg 779
Industrial Strength Inc, pg 787
Lighting Sales Connection Inc, pg 808
ONstage, pg 846
Techni-Lux Inc, pg 908

GEORGIA

Boxlight Inc, pg 709
Stage Front Presentation Systems, pg 899

HAWAII

The Audio Visual Co (AVCO), pg 694

ILLINOIS

Allen Visual Systems Inc, pg 680
Dukane Corp, Audio Visual Products Division, pg 747
Joseph Electronics, pg 795
Quintessence Audio Ltd, pg 868

INDIANA

Sensory Technologies LLC, pg 884
SHP Electronics, pg 887

KENTUCKY

NOR-COM Inc, pg 841

LOUISIANA

Techkno Integration & Design Services LLC, pg 908

MARYLAND

Absolute Hollywood, pg 672
DSR Computer Technology Specialists Inc, pg 747
Kipp Visual Systems Inc, pg 799

MICHIGAN

Digi Sign Design LLC, pg 741
Michigan Office Solutions (MOS), A Xerox Company, pg 825
TEL Systems LLC, pg 909

MINNESOTA

Alpha Video & Audio Inc, pg 682
Tierney Brothers Inc, pg 914

MISSOURI

Modern Communications Inc, pg 828
Schiller's Audio-Visual, pg 881

NEBRASKA

Strong Cinema Products, pg 902

NEW JERSEY

AV Bluebook, pg 696
Diversified, pg 744
Earl Girls Inc, pg 749
HamiltonBuhl, pg 775
Starlite, pg 900
Total Video Products Inc, pg 916
Wired 4 Sound Inc, pg 940
Yorktel, pg 944

NEW YORK

Audio-Video Corp, pg 694
Colortone Audio Visual, pg 728
Gaylord Archival, pg 768
KVL Audio Visual Services Inc, pg 802
Markertek Video Supply, pg 817
Neptune Photo Inc, pg 838
Presentation Products Inc, pg 861
Video Technology Services Inc, pg 929
Visual Technologies Corp, pg 932

OHIO

Tri-State Audio Visual Co, pg 918
Walltalkers, pg 933

OKLAHOMA

Ford AV, pg 763

PENNSYLVANIA

Advanced AV LLC, pg 677
Bernie's Photo Center, pg 704
Clair Companies, pg 725
J E Foss Co, pg 764
Grise Audio Visual Center Inc, pg 774
The Lerro Corp, pg 806
Vistacom Inc, pg 931
Visual Sound Inc, pg 931

TENNESSEE

Lowrance Sound Co Inc, pg 812
Spring Arbor Distributors Inc, pg 898
Technical Support Systems LLC, pg 908
Zion Music Group, pg 945

TEXAS

Lubbock Audio Visual Inc, pg 812
Quality Audio Visual Service Inc, pg 867
Tarpley Media Systems, pg 907
Videotex Systems Inc, pg 930

VIRGINIA

Avitecture Inc, pg 699
Intellidyne LLC, pg 789
Lee Hartman & Sons Inc, pg 805
Quince Imaging Inc, pg 868

WASHINGTON

CCI Solutions, pg 718

WISCONSIN

Audio Visual of Milwaukee Inc, pg 694
Full Compass Systems, pg 767

PUERTO RICO

Audio Visual Concepts Inc, pg 694

ALBERTA

Evolution AV, pg 757
Genesis Integration, pg 769

BRITISH COLUMBIA

Commercial Electronics Ltd, pg 728

MANITOBA

Inland Audio Visual Ltd, pg 788

ONTARIO

MVI - MultiVision Inc, pg 835
Westbury National Show Systems Ltd, pg 936

Projection Panel Manufacturers

FLORIDA

Vutec Corp, pg 933

ILLINOIS

ACCO Brands Corp, pg 673
GBC Document Finishing, pg 768

INDIANA

Da-Lite, a Legrand AV Inc brand, pg 737

MARYLAND

Absolute Hollywood, pg 672

NEW JERSEY

Sharp Electronics Corp, Professional Display Division, pg 885

NEW YORK

TecNec Distributing, pg 909
Video Technology Services Inc, pg 929

OHIO

Walltalkers, pg 933

TEXAS

MooreCo Inc, pg 830

VIRGINIA

Optikinetics Ltd - The Americas, pg 847
Quince Imaging Inc, pg 868

ONTARIO

Evertz Microsystems Ltd, pg 757

Projection Panel Rentals

ARIZONA

Broadcast Rentals, pg 711
Merestone, pg 823

CALIFORNIA

Alliant Event Services, pg 681
Ametron Audio/Video, pg 684
Associated Sound, pg 691
Lynch Communications, pg 813
McCune Audio-Video-Lighting, pg 821
Munday & Collins AV, pg 834
Muse Presentation Technologies, pg 834
Sound Service Co, pg 894
Towards 2000 Inc, pg 916
VER, pg 926
Video Resources Inc, pg 928

COLORADO

Multimedia Audio Visual Inc, pg 833

CONNECTICUT

Digital Video Productions, pg 742

FLORIDA

AVI-SPL, pg 698
Industrial Strength Inc, pg 787
Lighting Sales Connection Inc, pg 808
ONstage, pg 846
PRI Productions, pg 862

GEORGIA

ON Services, a GES Company, pg 846
Stage Front Presentation Systems, pg 899

ILLINOIS

Allen Visual Systems Inc, pg 680
Backstar Creative Media Inc, pg 700
RC Communications, pg 870
SCI Television & Creative Media LLC, pg 882

KENTUCKY

Audio Visual Techniques Inc, pg 695

MARYLAND

Absolute Hollywood, pg 672
CPR MultiMedia Solutions, pg 732
Event Tech, pg 756

MASSACHUSETTS

massAV, pg 819
Preston Productions Inc, pg 861

MICHIGAN

Digi Sign Design LLC, pg 741
K&R All Media Productions LLC, pg 796

MINNESOTA

Alpha Video & Audio Inc, pg 682

MISSOURI

Schiller's Audio-Visual, pg 881
Show-Me Audio-Visual, pg 887

NEVADA
GES Audio Visual, pg 770

NEW JERSEY
Earl Girls Inc, pg 749
Moe AV LLC, pg 828
PLS Staging, pg 858
Starlite, pg 900
Wired 4 Sound Inc, pg 940

NEW YORK
Colortone Audio Visual, pg 728
KVL Audio Visual Services Inc,
pg 802
Visual Technologies Corp, pg 932

NORTH CAROLINA
Audio & Light, pg 693
AV Connections Inc, pg 697
Special Event Services, pg 896

OHIO
Hughie's Event Production Services,
pg 782
Mills James Productions, pg 828

PENNSYLVANIA
Advanced AV LLC, pg 677
FirstGeneration Audio/Visual
Services, pg 761
Grise Audio Visual Center Inc,
pg 774
Visual Sound Inc, pg 931

TENNESSEE
Technical Support Systems LLC,
pg 908

TEXAS
Alford Media Services, pg 680
Lubbock Audio Visual Inc, pg 812
Quality Audio Visual Service Inc,
pg 867

VIRGINIA
American AV, pg 682
Audio Visual Actions Inc (AVA),
pg 694
Quince Imaging Inc, pg 868

WISCONSIN
Audio Visual of Milwaukee Inc,
pg 694
Full Compass Systems, pg 767

ALBERTA
L R Light & Sound, pg 802

BRITISH COLUMBIA
Commercial Electronics Ltd, pg 728
DL Sound & Lighting Productions
Ltd, pg 744

MANITOBA
Inland Audio Visual Ltd, pg 788

ONTARIO
Metalworks Recording Studios Inc,
pg 824
MVI - MultiVision Inc, pg 835
Westbury National Show Systems
Ltd, pg 936

Projection Panel Repairs

CALIFORNIA
Ametron Audio/Video, pg 684
Electrosonic Inc, pg 752
McAlister Electronics, pg 820
Towards 2000 Inc, pg 916

CONNECTICUT
HB Communications Inc, pg 777

FLORIDA
AVI-SPL, pg 698
ELC Sales & Service Inc, pg 752

GEORGIA
Boxlight Inc, pg 709
Stage Front Presentation Systems,
pg 899

ILLINOIS
Allen Visual Systems Inc, pg 680

KENTUCKY
Axxis Leasing Inc, pg 700
NOR-COM Inc, pg 841

MICHIGAN
TEL Systems LLC, pg 909

MINNESOTA
Alpha Video & Audio Inc, pg 682

NEW JERSEY
Earl Girls Inc, pg 749
Starlite, pg 900

NEW YORK
Visual Technologies Corp, pg 932

OHIO
Tri-State Audio Visual Co, pg 918

PENNSYLVANIA
J E Foss Co, pg 764

TENNESSEE
Technical Support Systems LLC,
pg 908

TEXAS
Lubbock Audio Visual Inc, pg 812
Quality Audio Visual Service Inc,
pg 867
Tarpley Media Systems, pg 907

VIRGINIA
Avitecture Inc, pg 699
Quince Imaging Inc, pg 868

WISCONSIN
Audio Visual of Milwaukee Inc,
pg 694
Full Compass Systems, pg 767

MANITOBA
Inland Audio Visual Ltd, pg 788

ONTARIO
MVI - MultiVision Inc, pg 835
Westbury National Show Systems
Ltd, pg 936

Projection Part Distributors

ARIZONA
Metropolitan Audio-Visual Inc,
pg 824
Troxell-CDI, pg 918

ARKANSAS
White Diamond Productions LLC,
pg 937

CALIFORNIA
Ametron Audio/Video, pg 684
Barber Tech Video Products, pg 701
California Tape Products Inc,
pg 714
Cinema Equipment Sales of
California Inc, pg 724
Educational Technology Services
(ETS), pg 751
Alan Gordon Enterprises Inc,
pg 772
Instructional Materials & Equipment
Distributors (I-Med), pg 789
J & R Film Co, pg 792
Media Fabricators Inc, pg 822
MediaPOINTE, pg 823
PMP Marketing Inc, pg 858
Sound Service Co, pg 894
Southern California Sound Image
Inc, pg 895
VTP Inc, pg 933

COLORADO
Ceavco Audio Visual Company Inc,
pg 719
Goldberg Brothers Inc, pg 772
Stanco Sales LLC, pg 899

CONNECTICUT
HB Communications Inc, pg 777
MAVCO, pg 820
Rockwell Communications Inc,
pg 876

FLORIDA
AVI-SPL, pg 698
Cinema Equipment & Supplies Inc,
pg 724
Digital Video Systems, pg 742
Hi-Tech Import Export Corp,
pg 779
ONstage, pg 846
Tallahassee Audio Visual, pg 906
Techni-Lux Inc, pg 908
Technomedia Solutions, pg 909

GEORGIA
Audio Visual Resources Inc, pg 695
Convergent Media Systems, pg 731
Stage Front Presentation Systems,
pg 899
Visioneering International Inc,
pg 931

HAWAII
The Audio Visual Co (AVCO),
pg 694

ILLINOIS
Joseph Electronics, pg 795

INDIANA
Sensory Technologies LLC, pg 884
SHP Electronics, pg 887

KENTUCKY
Audio Visual Techniques Inc,
pg 695
Axxis Leasing Inc, pg 700
NOR-COM Inc, pg 841

LOUISIANA
Techkno Integration & Design
Services LLC, pg 908

MARYLAND
Nicholas P Pipino Associates Inc,
pg 857

MASSACHUSETTS
Elite Video Inc, pg 753

MICHIGAN
City Events Group, pg 725
Digi Sign Design LLC, pg 741

MINNESOTA
Alpha Video & Audio Inc, pg 682
AVI Systems, pg 698
Tierney Brothers Inc, pg 914

MISSISSIPPI
Bowie Audio Visual Enterprises Inc,
pg 709
Jasper Ewing & Sons Inc, pg 757

MISSOURI
Communitronics Corp, pg 729
Conference Technologies Inc,
pg 730
Modern Communications Inc,
pg 828
Schiller's Audio-Visual, pg 881
Southwest Audio-Visual Inc, pg 895

NEBRASKA
Ballantyne Strong Inc, pg 701

NEW JERSEY
Earl Girls Inc, pg 749
HamiltonBuhl, pg 775
Starlite, pg 900
Total Video Products Inc, pg 916
Vcom IMC, pg 925
Video Corporation of America
(VCA), pg 927
Wired 4 Sound Inc, pg 940
Yorktel, pg 944

NEW YORK
American Video Inc, pg 684
Audio-Video Corp, pg 694
AV Workshop, pg 697
Bulbtronics Inc, pg 712
General Audio-Visual Inc (GAVI),
pg 769
Indigo Productions, pg 787
Langie Audio Visual Systems,
pg 803
Long Island Video Enterprises Live
Inc, pg 811
Ray Supply Inc, pg 870
Russell Industries Inc, pg 879
Theatrical Services & Supplies Inc,
pg 912
Topbulb, a Semmer Lighting
Company, pg 915
Video Technology Services Inc,
pg 929
Visual Technologies Corp, pg 932

AUDIO/VISUAL

Projection Part Distributors (continued)

NORTH CAROLINA

Camcor Inc, pg 715
Strategic Connections, pg 901

OHIO

Audio Visual Media, pg 694
Hughie's Event Production Services, pg 782
ITA Audio Visual Solutions, pg 791
Tri-State Visual Products Inc, pg 918

OKLAHOMA

Ford AV, pg 763

PENNSYLVANIA

Advanced AV LLC, pg 677
Audio Visions Inc, pg 694
Clair Companies, pg 725
J E Foss Co, pg 764
Grise Audio Visual Center Inc, pg 774
The Lerro Corp, pg 806
Wespen Audio Visual Co, pg 935

TENNESSEE

Lowrance Sound Co Inc, pg 812
Memphis Communications Corp, pg 823
Technical Support Systems LLC, pg 908

TEXAS

Audio Visual Technologies Group (AVTG), pg 695
AVES Audio Visual Systems Inc, pg 698
Lubbock Audio Visual Inc, pg 812
Tarpley Media Systems, pg 907

VIRGINIA

Avitecture Inc, pg 699
Boitnott Visual Communications Corp (BVC), pg 708
Intellidyne LLC, pg 789
Lee Hartman & Sons Inc, pg 805
Metropolitan Audio Visual Co LLC, pg 824
Quince Imaging Inc, pg 868
The Whitlock Group, pg 937

WASHINGTON

CCI Solutions, pg 718
Inland Audio Visual Co, pg 788

WISCONSIN

Alpha Source Inc, pg 681
Audio Visual of Milwaukee Inc, pg 694
Camera Corner Connecting Point, pg 715
Full Compass Systems, pg 767

ALBERTA

Evolution AV, pg 757
McBain Camera Ltd, pg 820

BRITISH COLUMBIA

Specialty Bulb Products Inc, pg 896

MANITOBA

Inland Audio Visual Ltd, pg 788

ONTARIO

Nationwide Audio Visual Co, pg 837
Westbury National Show Systems Ltd, pg 936

QUEBEC

Panavideo Inc, pg 850
Strong Screen Systems, pg 902

Projection Part Manufacturers

ARIZONA

NKK Switches of America Inc, pg 841

CALIFORNIA

Alan Gordon Enterprises Inc, pg 772
J & R Film Co, pg 792

FLORIDA

Vutec Corp, pg 933

ILLINOIS

Dukane Corp, Audio Visual Products Division, pg 747
La Vezzi Precision Inc, pg 926

INDIANA

Da-Lite, a Legrand AV Inc brand, pg 737

KANSAS

Tributestone, pg 918

MASSACHUSETTS

Elite Video Inc, pg 753
General Electric Co, pg 769

NEBRASKA

Ballantyne Strong Inc, pg 701
Strong Cinema Products, pg 902

NEW YORK

American Video Inc, pg 684
General Audio-Visual Inc (GAVI), pg 769
Russell Industries Inc, pg 879

VIRGINIA

Optikinetics Ltd - The Americas, pg 847
Quince Imaging Inc, pg 868

ONTARIO

Evertz Microsystems Ltd, pg 757

QUEBEC

Strong Screen Systems, pg 902

Projection Part Rentals

ARIZONA

Merestone, pg 823
Metropolitan Audio-Visual Inc, pg 824

CALIFORNIA

Ametron Audio/Video, pg 684
Lynch Communications, pg 813
McCune Audio-Video-Lighting, pg 821
Media Fabricators Inc, pg 822
Sound Service Co, pg 894

COLORADO

Ceavco Audio Visual Company Inc, pg 719

FLORIDA

ONstage, pg 846

GEORGIA

Stage Front Presentation Systems, pg 899
Staging Directions Inc, pg 899

ILLINOIS

SCI Television & Creative Media LLC, pg 882

KENTUCKY

Audio Visual Techniques Inc, pg 695

LOUISIANA

Pace Systems, pg 849

MARYLAND

CPR MultiMedia Solutions, pg 732
RTZ Audio Visual, pg 878

MICHIGAN

Digi Sign Design LLC, pg 741
K&R All Media Productions LLC, pg 796

MINNESOTA

AVI Systems, pg 698

MISSOURI

Schiller's Audio-Visual, pg 881
Show-Me Audio-Visual, pg 887
Southwest Audio-Visual Inc, pg 895

NEW HAMPSHIRE

Apertura, pg 686

NEW JERSEY

Earl Girls Inc, pg 749
Moe AV LLC, pg 828
Video Corporation of America (VCA), pg 927

NEW YORK

American Video Inc, pg 684
AV Workshop, pg 697
Langie Audio Visual Systems, pg 803
Long Island Video Enterprises Live Inc, pg 811
Specialized Audio-Visual Inc, pg 896

NORTH CAROLINA

AV Metro Inc, pg 697
Special Event Services, pg 896

OHIO

Audio Visual Media, pg 694
Icom Multimedia, pg 783

PENNSYLVANIA

Advanced AV LLC, pg 677
Grise Audio Visual Center Inc, pg 774

TENNESSEE

Memphis Communications Corp, pg 823
Technical Support Systems LLC, pg 908

VIRGINIA

American AV, pg 682
Quince Imaging Inc, pg 868

WISCONSIN

Audio Visual of Milwaukee Inc, pg 694

PUERTO RICO

Stage Crew Audiovisual Inc, pg 898

ALBERTA

McBain Camera Ltd, pg 820
Unique Communications Ltd, pg 921

BRITISH COLUMBIA

DL Sound & Lighting Productions Ltd, pg 744

ONTARIO

Metalworks Recording Studios Inc, pg 824
Westbury National Show Systems Ltd, pg 936

QUEBEC

Audio Visual Dynamics, pg 694

Projection Part Repairs

CALIFORNIA

Ametron Audio/Video, pg 684
McAlister Electronics, pg 820
Lloyd F McKinney Associates Inc, pg 821
Pro Camera Repair, pg 862

COLORADO

Ceavco Audio Visual Company Inc, pg 719

CONNECTICUT

HB Communications Inc, pg 777
Rockwell Communications Inc, pg 876

DISTRICT OF COLUMBIA

Future View Inc, pg 767

FLORIDA

ELC Sales & Service Inc, pg 752

GEORGIA

Audio Visual Resources Inc, pg 695
Stage Front Presentation Systems, pg 899

KENTUCKY

Axxis Leasing Inc, pg 700
NOR-COM Inc, pg 841

MARYLAND

RTZ Audio Visual, pg 878

MASSACHUSETTS

Elite Video Inc, pg 753

MICHIGAN

TEL Systems LLC, pg 909

MINNESOTA

AVI Systems, pg 698

NEW JERSEY

Earl Girls Inc, pg 749

NEW YORK

American Video Inc, pg 684
Colortone Audio Visual, pg 728
Langie Audio Visual Systems,
 pg 803
Visual Technologies Corp, pg 932

NORTH CAROLINA

Camcor Inc, pg 715

OHIO

Audio Visual Media, pg 694
Icom Multimedia, pg 783

TENNESSEE

Memphis Communications Corp,
 pg 823
Technical Support Systems LLC,
 pg 908

TEXAS

Audio Visual Technologies Group
 (AVTG), pg 695
Tarpley Media Systems, pg 907

VIRGINIA

Avitecture Inc, pg 699
Quince Imaging Inc, pg 868

WISCONSIN

Audio Visual of Milwaukee Inc,
 pg 694
Full Compass Systems, pg 767

ONTARIO

HD Source, pg 777
Westbury National Show Systems
 Ltd, pg 936

Public Address System Distributors

ALABAMA

Curtis Company, pg 736

ARIZONA

Arizona Cine Equipment, pg 688
EAR Professional Audio/Video,
 pg 749
Metropolitan Audio-Visual Inc,
 pg 824
Troxell-CDI, pg 918

ARKANSAS

Carlton-Bates Co, pg 717

CALIFORNIA

Ametron Audio/Video, pg 684
Associated Sound, pg 691
Assured Audio Visual, pg 691
ATV Video Center Inc, pg 692
Audio Images Corp, pg 693
AV Conferencing LLC (AVC),
 pg 697
Be Media, pg 702
California Tape Products Inc,
 pg 714
Electronic Design Solutions Inc,
 pg 752
Empire Pro, pg 753
Instructional Materials & Equipment
 Distributors (I-Med), pg 789
JD Audio Visual Inc, pg 793
L-Acoustics Inc, pg 802
Marshall Electronics Inc, pg 817
Lloyd F McKinney Associates Inc,
 pg 821
Media Fabricators Inc, pg 822
MediaMation Inc, pg 822
MediaPOINTE, pg 823
Sound Service Co, pg 894
SSL Industries Inc, pg 898
Stanislaus AV Inc, pg 899
Third Ear Sound Co, pg 912
TOA Electronics Inc, pg 915
Towards 2000 Inc, pg 916
VMI Inc, pg 932
VTP Inc, pg 933

COLORADO

Audio Consultant Services Inc,
 pg 693
Ceavco Audio Visual Company Inc,
 pg 719

CONNECTICUT

Connecticut Audio & Theatrical
 Supply, pg 731
MAVCO, pg 820
Sennheiser Electronic Corp, pg 884

DELAWARE

Actors Attic, pg 675

FLORIDA

Altel Systems Group Inc, pg 682
Broadcasters General Store Inc,
 pg 711
Digital Video Systems, pg 742
Harmon's Audio-Visual Services,
 pg 776
Harris Corp, pg 776
Hi-Tech Import Export Corp,
 pg 779
Hollywood Theatre Equipment Inc,
 pg 781
Lighting Sales Connection Inc,
 pg 808
ONstage, pg 846
Photosound of Orlando Inc, pg 856
Stereo Sales Inc, pg 900
TAI Audio, pg 906

GEORGIA

Baker Audio Visual, pg 700
Lighting & Production Equipment
 Inc, pg 807
Stage Front Presentation Systems,
 pg 899
Visioneering International Inc,
 pg 931

HAWAII

The Audio Visual Co (AVCO),
 pg 694

ILLINOIS

Allen Visual Systems Inc, pg 680
Central Audio-Visual Equipment
 Inc, pg 719
Creative Technology (CT), pg 733
Joseph Electronics, pg 795
G T Luscombe Co Inc, pg 812
Quintessence Audio Ltd, pg 868

INDIANA

Sensory Technologies LLC, pg 884
SHP Electronics, pg 887

KENTUCKY

Audio Visual Techniques Inc,
 pg 695
Barney Miller's Inc, pg 827
NOR-COM Inc, pg 841

MAINE

Headlight Audio Visual Inc, pg 777

MARYLAND

Cardinal Sound & Video, pg 717
Nicholas P Pipino Associates Inc,
 pg 857
RTZ Audio Visual, pg 878

MASSACHUSETTS

Antronics Inc, pg 686
Terry Hanley Audio Systems Inc,
 pg 775
Pro AV Systems, pg 862
Professional Audio Design Inc,
 pg 865

MICHIGAN

Olson Anderson Co, pg 685
City Events Group, pg 725
Digi Sign Design LLC, pg 741
On Stage Visuals, pg 846
TEL Systems LLC, pg 909

MINNESOTA

AVI Systems, pg 698
New Life Communications Inc,
 pg 839

MISSISSIPPI

Bowie Audio Visual Enterprises Inc,
 pg 709
Jasper Ewing & Sons Inc, pg 757

MISSOURI

Communitronics Corp, pg 729
Conference Technologies Inc,
 pg 730
ITC, pg 791
Modern Communications Inc,
 pg 828
Schiller's Audio-Visual, pg 881
Southwest Audio-Visual Inc, pg 895

NEW HAMPSHIRE

APS Lighting-Sound-AV, pg 688

NEW JERSEY

A-V Services Inc, pg 671
Alltec Stores, a Vcom IMC
 Company, pg 681
AlltecPro, pg 681
Audio Visual Associates, pg 694
Audio Visual Dynamics®, pg 694
AV Bluebook, pg 696
Comprehensive Cable &
 Connectivity Co, pg 729

Earl Girls Inc, pg 749
FlagHouse, pg 762
HamiltonBuhl, pg 775
Starlite, pg 900
Total Video Products Inc, pg 916
Wired 4 Sound Inc, pg 940
Yorktel, pg 944

NEW MEXICO

Quickbeam Systems Inc (QSI),
 pg 868

NEW YORK

Albany Theatre Supply Co Inc,
 pg 679
Audio-Video Corp, pg 694
AV Workshop, pg 697
Colortone Audio Visual, pg 728
Design Audio Visual Inc, pg 741
Gaylord Archival, pg 768
Indigo Productions, pg 787
iProbe Multilingual Solutions Inc,
 pg 791
Langie Audio Visual Systems,
 pg 803
Lee Dan® Communications Inc,
 pg 805
Long Island Video Enterprises Live
 Inc, pg 811
Markertek Video Supply, pg 817
Neptune Photo Inc, pg 838
Ray Supply Inc, pg 870
RNJ Electronics, pg 875
Theatrical Services & Supplies Inc,
 pg 912
Visual Technologies Corp, pg 932
Whirlwind Music Distributors Inc,
 pg 937

NORTH CAROLINA

Camcor Inc, pg 715
Strategic Connections, pg 901

OHIO

Audio Visual Media, pg 694
Copp Integrated Systems, pg 731
ITA Audio Visual Solutions, pg 791
Luminaud Inc, pg 812
Tri-State Audio Visual Co, pg 918
Tri-State Visual Products Inc,
 pg 918

OKLAHOMA

Ford AV, pg 763

OREGON

Lightspeed Technologies Inc,
 pg 808
PLUS Corp of America, pg 858

PENNSYLVANIA

Advanced AV LLC, pg 677
Audio Visions Inc, pg 694
Bernie's Photo Center, pg 704
Brodart Co, pg 711
Clair Companies, pg 725
J E Foss Co, pg 764
Garcia Marketing Inc, pg 768
Grise Audio Visual Center Inc,
 pg 774
Hite Co, pg 780
The Lerro Corp, pg 806
Morefield Communications Inc,
 pg 830
RSS Distributors, pg 878
Vistacom Inc, pg 931
Visual Sound Inc, pg 931
Wespen Audio Visual Co, pg 935

AUDIO/VISUAL

Public Address System Distributors (continued)

SOUTH CAROLINA

DaviSound, pg 739

TENNESSEE

Allstar Audio Systems Inc, pg 681
Belew Enterprises, pg 703
Continental Film, pg 731
Lowrance Sound Co Inc, pg 812
Memphis Communications Corp, pg 823
Technical Support Systems LLC, pg 908
Zion Music Group, pg 945

TEXAS

Audio Visual Technologies Group (AVTG), pg 695
AVES Audio Visual Systems Inc, pg 698
CAM Audio Inc, pg 714
Crossroads Audio Inc, pg 735
Digital Display Solutions Inc, pg 742
FitzCo Sound Inc, pg 761
Heffernan Audio Visual, pg 778
JSAV, pg 795
Lubbock Audio Visual Inc, pg 812
Quality Audio Visual Service Inc, pg 867
Southwest Sound Solutions, pg 896
Tarpley Media Systems, pg 907

UTAH

Performance Audio LLC, pg 854
Webb Audio Visual, pg 935

VERMONT

Production Advantage Inc, pg 863

VIRGINIA

Acoustics First Corp, pg 674
Avitecture Inc, pg 699
Boitnott Visual Communications Corp (BVC), pg 708
Lee Hartman & Sons Inc, pg 805
Rocktown Media, pg 876
The Whitlock Group, pg 937

WASHINGTON

CCI Solutions, pg 718
D A Sound, pg 737
Inland Audio Visual Co, pg 788
Northern Lights & Pro Audio, pg 842
PNTA, pg 858

WEST VIRGINIA

United Sound & Electronics, pg 921

WISCONSIN

Audio Visual of Milwaukee Inc, pg 694
Camera Corner Connecting Point, pg 715
Demco Inc, pg 740
Full Compass Systems, pg 767

PUERTO RICO

Bonnin Electronics Inc, pg 708

ALBERTA

Evolution AV, pg 757
Infosat Communications Inc, pg 787
McBain Camera Ltd, pg 820
Unique Communications Ltd, pg 921

BRITISH COLUMBIA

Commercial Electronics Ltd, pg 728

MANITOBA

Advance Pro, pg 677
Inland Audio Visual Ltd, pg 788

ONTARIO

Cinema Stage Inc, pg 724
HD Source, pg 777
Nationwide Audio Visual Co, pg 837
Westbury National Show Systems Ltd, pg 936

Public Address System Manufacturers

ARIZONA

AtlasIED, pg 692
Fender Musical Instruments Corp, pg 759

ARKANSAS

Sound-Craft Systems Inc, pg 894

CALIFORNIA

Anchor Audio Inc, pg 685
Califone International Inc, pg 714
Gilderfluke & Co Inc, pg 771
JBL Professional, pg 793
L-Acoustics Inc, pg 802
Mackenzie Laboratories Inc, pg 814
QSC Audio Products LLC, pg 867
Renkus-Heinz Inc, pg 873
TOA Electronics Inc, pg 915

COLORADO

Colorado Time Systems LLC, pg 728

ILLINOIS

ACCO Brands Corp, pg 673
AmpliVox Portable Sound Systems, pg 684
Bag End Loudspeakers, pg 700
Shure Inc, pg 887

KANSAS

Galaxy Audio, pg 767
Tributestone, pg 918

MASSACHUSETTS

Bose Corp, pg 709

MINNESOTA

Bosch Security Systems Inc, pg 709
Digital Audio Labs, pg 742

MISSISSIPPI

Peavey Electronics Corp, pg 852

NEW JERSEY

AlltecPro, pg 681
Bogen Communications Inc, pg 708
RAMSA Professional Audio Systems, pg 870

NEW MEXICO

Lectrosonics Inc, pg 805

NEW YORK

Protech Audio Corp, pg 866
RCS Enterprises, pg 871

OREGON

BIAMP Systems, pg 705
Lightspeed Technologies Inc, pg 808

PENNSYLVANIA

Community Professional Loudspeakers, pg 729

SOUTH CAROLINA

DaviSound, pg 739

UTAH

Spectra Sonics LLC, pg 897

VIRGINIA

Acoustics First Corp, pg 674

WASHINGTON

Aiphone Corp, pg 678

WEST VIRGINIA

United Sound & Electronics, pg 921

ONTARIO

Music Group Commercial Ltd, pg 834

Public Address System Rentals

ALABAMA

Audio-Video Resources Inc, pg 694

ARIZONA

Arizona Cine Equipment, pg 688
Broadcast Rentals, pg 711
Merestone, pg 823
Metropolitan Audio-Visual Inc, pg 824
Video West Inc, pg 929

CALIFORNIA

AGF Media Services, pg 678
Alliant Event Services, pg 681
Ametron Audio/Video, pg 684
Associated Sound, pg 691
Assured Audio Visual, pg 691
ATV Video Center Inc, pg 692
Audio Rents, pg 693
AV Conferencing LLC (AVC), pg 697
AV Guys, pg 697
Bexel, an NEP Broadcast Services Company, pg 704
Electronic Design Solutions Inc, pg 752
Gold Standard Productions, pg 772
Instructional Materials & Equipment Distributors (I-Med), pg 789
JD Audio Visual Inc, pg 793
Lynch Communications, pg 813
Maximus Media Inc, pg 820
McCune Audio-Video-Lighting, pg 821
Media Fabricators Inc, pg 822
MSI Production Services, pg 832
Munday & Collins AV, pg 834
On-Trax Inc, pg 846
Sound Service Co, pg 894
Stanislaus AV Inc, pg 899
Synthesizer Rental Service, pg 906
Third Ear Sound Co, pg 912
Towards 2000 Inc, pg 916
Video Resources Inc, pg 928
VMI Inc, pg 932
Voice & Video Rentals, pg 932

COLORADO

Audio Consultant Services Inc, pg 693
Ceavco Audio Visual Company Inc, pg 719
Daylight Productions & Rentals, pg 739
Maniac Productions, pg 816
Multimedia Audio Visual Inc, pg 833
Spectrum Audio Visual Services, pg 897

CONNECTICUT

A/V Davey, pg 697
Connecticut Audio & Theatrical Supply, pg 731
Rockwell Communications Inc, pg 876

DELAWARE

Actors Attic, pg 675
Ken-Del Productions Inc, pg 797
Showorks Audio Visual Inc, pg 887
Side Door Studio Inc, pg 887

FLORIDA

AVI-SPL, pg 698
Harmon's Audio-Visual Services, pg 776
Industrial Strength Inc, pg 787
Jordan Klein Film & Video (JKFV), pg 795
Lighting Sales Connection Inc, pg 808
National Teleproductions Inc, pg 837
ONstage, pg 846
Photosound of Orlando Inc, pg 856
Sight & Sound Productions, pg 887
TAI Audio, pg 906
Universal Studios Florida® Production Group, pg 922

GEORGIA

Audio Visual Resources Inc, pg 695
Lighting & Production Equipment Inc, pg 807
MAGNUM Companies Ltd, pg 815
ON Services, a GES Company, pg 846
Stage Front Presentation Systems, pg 899
Staging Directions Inc, pg 899

ILLINOIS

Allen Visual Systems Inc, pg 680
AV Chicago Inc, pg 696
Beatty TeleVisual Productions, pg 703
Central Audio-Visual Equipment Inc, pg 719
Creative Technology (CT), pg 733
Helix Camera & Video, pg 778
Meetinghouse Event Design & Production, pg 823
PSAV® Presentation Services (Hotel Services Division), pg 866

RC Communications, pg 870
Resolution Productions Group,
   pg 874

INDIANA

Advanced Media Integration, pg 677
OMNI Productions, pg 845

KENTUCKY

Audio Visual Techniques Inc,
   pg 695
Barney Miller's Inc, pg 827

LOUISIANA

Clark Services Audio Visual &
   Exhibit Inc, pg 725
Pace Systems, pg 849

MAINE

Headlight Audio Visual Inc, pg 777
University of Maine Media
   Services, pg 922

MARYLAND

Cardinal Sound & Video, pg 717
CPR MultiMedia Solutions, pg 732
Event Tech, pg 756
Hargrove Inc, pg 776
Nelson White Systems Inc, pg 838
RTZ Audio Visual, pg 878

MASSACHUSETTS

AVFX Inc, pg 698
Capron Lighting & Sound Co Inc,
   pg 716
Terry Hanley Audio Systems Inc,
   pg 775
massAV, pg 819
Preston Productions Inc, pg 861

MICHIGAN

Olson Anderson Co, pg 685
City Events Group, pg 725
Digi Sign Design LLC, pg 741
K&R All Media Productions LLC,
   pg 796
On Stage Visuals, pg 846
TEL Systems LLC, pg 909

MINNESOTA

AVI Systems, pg 698
New Life Communications Inc,
   pg 839

MISSISSIPPI

Bowie Audio Visual Enterprises Inc,
   pg 709
Jasper Ewing & Sons Inc, pg 757

MISSOURI

Communitronics Corp, pg 729
Schiller's Audio-Visual, pg 881
Show-Me Audio-Visual, pg 887
Southwest Audio-Visual Inc, pg 895

NEBRASKA

Dog & Pony Productions Inc,
   pg 744

NEVADA

GES Audio Visual, pg 770

NEW HAMPSHIRE

Academic & Campus Technology
   Services, pg 672
APS Lighting-Sound-AV, pg 688

NEW JERSEY

Audio Visual Associates, pg 694
Audio Visual Dynamics®, pg 694
Earl Girls Inc, pg 749
International Audio Visual Inc,
   pg 790
MiB MediaWorks, pg 825
Moe AV LLC, pg 828
Panavid, pg 850
Starlite, pg 900
Wired 4 Sound Inc, pg 940

NEW MEXICO

Quickbeam Systems Inc (QSI),
   pg 868

NEW YORK

Ace Video, pg 674
AV Workshop, pg 697
CMI Communications, pg 727
Colortone Audio Visual, pg 728
CP Communications, pg 732
Design Audio Visual Inc, pg 741
Hello World Communications,
   pg 778
iProbe Multilingual Solutions Inc,
   pg 791
Langie Audio Visual Systems,
   pg 803
Long Island Video Enterprises Live
   Inc, pg 811
Manhattan Center Studios Inc,
   pg 816
Ray Supply Inc, pg 870
Specialized Audio-Visual Inc,
   pg 896
Visual Technologies Corp, pg 932
Visual Word Systems Inc, pg 932
WorldStage, pg 941

NORTH CAROLINA

AV Connections Inc, pg 697
AV Metro Inc, pg 697
Special Event Services, pg 896
Strategic Connections, pg 901

NORTH DAKOTA

Media Productions, pg 822

OHIO

Audio Visual Media, pg 694
Bartha, pg 702
Hughie's Event Production Services,
   pg 782
ITA Audio Visual Solutions, pg 791
Mills James Productions, pg 828
OSV Studios, pg 848

OKLAHOMA

PDC Productions, pg 852

OREGON

Rose City Sound, pg 877

PENNSYLVANIA

Advanced AV LLC, pg 677
Audio Visions Inc, pg 694
Audio Visual Communications Inc,
   pg 694
Grise Audio Visual Center Inc,
   pg 774
Vistacom Inc, pg 931
Visual Sound Inc, pg 931

SOUTH CAROLINA

Impact Technology Group LLC,
   pg 786
Sound & Images Inc, pg 893

TENNESSEE

Allstar Audio Systems Inc, pg 681
Brantley Sound Associates Inc,
   pg 709
Memphis Communications Corp,
   pg 823
Russ Sturgeon Productions/RSVP,
   pg 903
Technical Support Systems LLC,
   pg 908

TEXAS

Audio Visual Technologies Group
   (AVTG), pg 695
FitzCo Sound Inc, pg 761
JSAV, pg 795
Lubbock Audio Visual Inc, pg 812
Music Lab Inc, pg 834
Quality Audio Visual Service Inc,
   pg 867
Southwest Sound Solutions, pg 896
Stage Directions, pg 898

UTAH

Performance Audio LLC, pg 854
Webb Audio Visual, pg 935

VIRGINIA

American AV, pg 682
Avitecture Inc, pg 699
Boitnott Visual Communications
   Corp (BVC), pg 708
Lee Hartman & Sons Inc, pg 805
Projection, pg 865
The Whitlock Group, pg 937

WASHINGTON

CCI Solutions, pg 718
D A Sound, pg 737
Inland Audio Visual Co, pg 788
Northern Lights & Pro Audio,
   pg 842
PNTA, pg 858

WEST VIRGINIA

Blackwater Video Productions,
   pg 707
United Sound & Electronics, pg 921

WISCONSIN

Audio Visual of Milwaukee Inc,
   pg 694
Camera Corner Connecting Point,
   pg 715
Event Essentials, pg 756
Full Compass Systems, pg 767
USAV Group Inc, pg 923

PUERTO RICO

Stage Crew Audiovisual Inc, pg 898

ALBERTA

Allstar Show Industries Inc, pg 681
Cine Audio Visual Sales & Service
   Ltd, pg 723
Evolution AV, pg 757
L R Light & Sound, pg 802
McBain Camera Ltd, pg 820
Unique Communications Ltd,
   pg 921

BRITISH COLUMBIA

Clark's Audio Visual Services Ltd,
   pg 725
Commercial Electronics Ltd, pg 728
DL Sound & Lighting Productions
   Ltd, pg 744

MANITOBA

Advance Pro, pg 677
Inland Audio Visual Ltd, pg 788

ONTARIO

HD Source, pg 777
Metalworks Recording Studios Inc,
   pg 824
Westbury National Show Systems
   Ltd, pg 936

QUEBEC

Audio Visual Dynamics, pg 694

Public Address System Repairs

ARKANSAS

Carlton-Bates Co, pg 717

CALIFORNIA

Ametron Audio/Video, pg 684
Diemer Amp & Keyboard Repair,
   pg 741
Electronic Design Solutions Inc,
   pg 752
Instructional Materials & Equipment
   Distributors (I-Med), pg 789
McAlister Electronics, pg 820
Lloyd F McKinney Associates Inc,
   pg 821
Sound Service Co, pg 894
SSL Industries Inc, pg 898
Third Ear Sound Co, pg 912
TOA Electronics Inc, pg 915
Towards 2000 Inc, pg 916

COLORADO

Ceavco Audio Visual Company Inc,
   pg 719

CONNECTICUT

A/V Davey, pg 697
HB Communications Inc, pg 777
Rockwell Communications Inc,
   pg 876
Sennheiser Electronic Corp, pg 884

DELAWARE

Actors Attic, pg 675

FLORIDA

JT Communications, pg 795
Stereo Sales Inc, pg 900
TAI Audio, pg 906

GEORGIA

Audio Visual Resources Inc, pg 695
Lighting & Production Equipment
   Inc, pg 807
Stage Front Presentation Systems,
   pg 899

ILLINOIS

Allen Visual Systems Inc, pg 680
Central Audio-Visual Equipment
   Inc, pg 719

INDIANA

SHP Electronics, pg 887

AUDIO/VISUAL

Public Address System Repairs (continued)

KENTUCKY

Axxis Leasing Inc, pg 700
Barney Miller's Inc, pg 827
NOR-COM Inc, pg 841

MAINE

Headlight Audio Visual Inc, pg 777

MARYLAND

Cardinal Sound & Video, pg 717
RTZ Audio Visual, pg 878

MASSACHUSETTS

Capron Lighting & Sound Co Inc,
   pg 716
Professional Audio Design Inc,
   pg 865

MICHIGAN

Olson Anderson Co, pg 685
City Events Group, pg 725
On Stage Visuals, pg 846
TEL Systems LLC, pg 909

MINNESOTA

AVI Systems, pg 698

MISSOURI

Communitronics Corp, pg 729

NEW JERSEY

Audio Visual Associates, pg 694
Earl Girls Inc, pg 749
Starlite, pg 900

NEW MEXICO

Quickbeam Systems Inc (QSI),
   pg 868

NEW YORK

Colortone Audio Visual, pg 728
Langie Audio Visual Systems,
   pg 803
Ray Supply Inc, pg 870
Visual Technologies Corp, pg 932

NORTH CAROLINA

Camcor Inc, pg 715
Strategic Connections, pg 901

OHIO

Audio Visual Media, pg 694
Copp Integrated Systems, pg 731
ITA Audio Visual Solutions, pg 791
Tri-State Audio Visual Co, pg 918

OREGON

All Service Musical Electronics
   Repair, pg 680

PENNSYLVANIA

Audio Visions Inc, pg 694
Vistacom Inc, pg 931

SOUTH CAROLINA

DaviSound, pg 739

TENNESSEE

Belew Enterprises, pg 703
Memphis Communications Corp,
   pg 823
Technical Support Systems LLC,
   pg 908

TEXAS

Audio Visual Technologies Group
   (AVTG), pg 695
Crossroads Audio Inc, pg 735
Lubbock Audio Visual Inc, pg 812
Quality Audio Visual Service Inc,
   pg 867
Southwest Sound Solutions, pg 896
Tarpley Media Systems, pg 907

VIRGINIA

Avitecture Inc, pg 699
Boitnott Visual Communications
   Corp (BVC), pg 708
Lee Hartman & Sons Inc, pg 805
The Whitlock Group, pg 937

WASHINGTON

Aiphone Corp, pg 678
D A Sound, pg 737
Inland Audio Visual Co, pg 788
Northern Lights & Pro Audio,
   pg 842
PNTA, pg 858

WEST VIRGINIA

United Sound & Electronics, pg 921

WISCONSIN

Audio Visual of Milwaukee Inc,
   pg 694
Full Compass Systems, pg 767

ALBERTA

Evolution AV, pg 757
Infosat Communications Inc, pg 787
Unique Communications Ltd,
   pg 921

MANITOBA

Inland Audio Visual Ltd, pg 788

ONTARIO

Westbury National Show Systems
   Ltd, pg 936

Pulsing—AV

ARIZONA

Metropolitan Audio-Visual Inc,
   pg 824

CALIFORNIA

Assured Audio Visual, pg 691
CCI Digital, a DVS Company,
   pg 718
Creative Media Recording, pg 733
Lynch Communications, pg 813
McCune Audio-Video-Lighting,
   pg 821
The Media Staff Inc, pg 822
PSI Inc, pg 866
QRS Software Services, pg 867

COLORADO

Ceavco Audio Visual Company Inc,
   pg 719
Daylight Productions & Rentals,
   pg 739

DISTRICT OF COLUMBIA

Hillmann & Carr Inc, pg 780

FLORIDA

Communications Concepts Inc
   (CCI), pg 729

GEORGIA

Audio Visual Resources Inc, pg 695
Visioneering International Inc,
   pg 931

ILLINOIS

ABS Enterprises, pg 672
Creative Technology (CT), pg 733
Major Media Productions Inc,
   pg 815
PSAV® Presentation Services
   (Hotel Services Division), pg 866

INDIANA

OMNI Productions, pg 845

IOWA

Educational Technology & Media
   Services, pg 751

LOUISIANA

Digital FX Inc, pg 742

MARYLAND

The Cutting Corporation,
   GraphicAudio® & Archival
   Sound Lab, pg 736
Spectrum Productions, pg 897

MASSACHUSETTS

CommCreative, pg 728
Continental Recordings Inc, pg 731
Preston Productions Inc, pg 861
TR Productions, pg 916

MICHIGAN

K&R's Recording Studios Inc,
   pg 796

MINNESOTA

GMI Productions, pg 771
Media Loft Inc, pg 822

MISSISSIPPI

Jasper Ewing & Sons Inc, pg 757

NEVADA

Encore Event Technologies LLC,
   pg 754

NEW HAMPSHIRE

Apertura, pg 686

NEW JERSEY

Audio Visual Dynamics®, pg 694
Laurel Video Productions, pg 804
Optisonics Productions, pg 847
VCSvideo, pg 925

NEW YORK

Buffalo Video Production, pg 712
Jack Morton Worldwide, pg 830
Visual Technologies Corp, pg 932
Zelman Studios Ltd, pg 945

NORTH CAROLINA

Pat Appleson Studios Inc, pg 687
Camcor Inc, pg 715
Trailblazer Studios®, pg 917

NORTH DAKOTA

Media Productions, pg 822

OHIO

Aztec Video Productions, pg 700
Cuyahoga Community College
   Student Production Office (SPO),
   pg 736
Take 1 Media Services, pg 906
Vista Color Imaging Inc, pg 931

PENNSYLVANIA

Audio Visual Communications Inc,
   pg 694
FMP Media Solutions Inc, pg 763
Innovision Media Group, pg 788
Main Point Productions, pg 815
Visual Sound Inc, pg 931

TENNESSEE

Memphis Communications Corp,
   pg 823
Stage Post, pg 899
Russ Sturgeon Productions/RSVP,
   pg 903

TEXAS

Matson Multi-Media, pg 820
Stage Directions, pg 898

VIRGINIA

American AV, pg 682
AudioImage Recording, pg 695

WASHINGTON

Inland Audio Visual Co, pg 788
Kostov Productions, pg 801

WISCONSIN

AVS Group, pg 699
Concept Productions Inc, pg 730
USAV Group Inc, pg 923

ALBERTA

Unique Communications Ltd,
   pg 921

Pulsing—Filmstrip

CALIFORNIA

Creative Media Recording, pg 733
Lynch Communications, pg 813
QRS Software Services, pg 867

GEORGIA

Staging Directions Inc, pg 899

ILLINOIS

CCore Media Inc, pg 718
Pepper Group, pg 854
PSAV® Presentation Services
   (Hotel Services Division), pg 866

INDIANA

OMNI Productions, pg 845

MASSACHUSETTS

CommCreative, pg 728
TR Productions, pg 916

MONTANA
KUSM TV, pg 802

NEVADA
Encore Event Technologies LLC, pg 754

NEW JERSEY
Optisonics Productions, pg 847

NEW YORK
De Nonno Productions Inc (DPI), pg 739
The Palmer Group, pg 850
David Rapkin Audio Production, pg 870
Visual Technologies Corp, pg 932
Zelman Studios Ltd, pg 945

NORTH CAROLINA
Camcor Inc, pg 715

NORTH DAKOTA
Media Productions, pg 822

OHIO
Aztec Video Productions, pg 700

OREGON
REX, pg 874

PENNSYLVANIA
Visual Sound Inc, pg 931

TENNESSEE
Memphis Communications Corp, pg 823
Stage Post, pg 899

TEXAS
Matson Multi-Media, pg 820

WASHINGTON
Inland Audio Visual Co, pg 788

WISCONSIN
USAV Group Inc, pg 923

Record Player, *see* **Phonograph**

Retouching—Filmstrips

ARKANSAS
White Diamond Productions LLC, pg 937

CALIFORNIA
Pro8mm, pg 862
QRS Software Services, pg 867

MASSACHUSETTS
TR Productions, pg 916

NEW JERSEY
AJS Events, pg 679

NEW YORK
Duggal Visual Solutions Inc, pg 747
Modernage Photographic Services Inc, pg 828

OHIO
Aztec Video Productions, pg 700

PENNSYLVANIA
Berry & Homer, pg 704

TENNESSEE
Stage Post, pg 899

VIRGINIA
Blair Inc, pg 707

Retouching—Slides

ARIZONA
Professional Marketing Services Inc, pg 865

ARKANSAS
White Diamond Productions LLC, pg 937

CALIFORNIA
Action Photo Digital Graphics, pg 675
QRS Software Services, pg 867

ILLINOIS
Gamma Imaging, pg 768
Pepper Group, pg 854

INDIANA
OMNI Productions, pg 845

KENTUCKY
Kinetic Corp, pg 799

MASSACHUSETTS
TR Productions, pg 916

MICHIGAN
Tectonics Industries LLC, pg 909

NEW JERSEY
AJS Events, pg 679
C2 Imaging, pg 735

NEW YORK
Duggal Visual Solutions Inc, pg 747
Modernage Photographic Services Inc, pg 828

NORTH CAROLINA
Image Associates Inc, pg 784

OHIO
Aztec Video Productions, pg 700
Thread Marketing Group, pg 913
Vista Color Imaging Inc, pg 931

PENNSYLVANIA
Bernie's Photo Center, pg 704
Berry & Homer, pg 704

TENNESSEE
Stage Post, pg 899

TEXAS
Texas Heart Institute Visual Communication Services, pg 911
Thomas Printworks, pg 912

VIRGINIA
Advance Concepts Inc, pg 677
Blair Inc, pg 707

WISCONSIN
USAV Group Inc, pg 923

Script Writing

ALASKA
Aurora Films, pg 696

ARIZONA
Merestone, pg 823
Metropolitan Audio-Visual Inc, pg 824
On-Site Video, pg 846
Teaberry, pg 908

ARKANSAS
Live'N'Loud, pg 810
White Diamond Productions LLC, pg 937

CALIFORNIA
Action Video, pg 675
Coastline Productions, pg 727
Crystal Pyramid Productions™, pg 735
Custom Video Productions Inc, pg 736
Deja View Video, pg 740
Design Media, pg 741
Dolphin MultiMedia Inc, pg 745
Final Draft, A Cast & Crew Company, pg 761
Gold Standard Productions, pg 772
iCorpTv, pg 783
Increase Video/Silver Mine Video, pg 786
KVIE-Channel 6, pg 802
Lynch Communications, pg 813
Main Street Media Inc, pg 815
Maximus Media Inc, pg 820
Media Magic, pg 822
The Media Staff Inc, pg 822
Joseph Nicoletti Consulting-Promotion, pg 841
piXvfm Inc, pg 857
PM Productions, pg 858
PSI Inc, pg 866
QRS Software Services, pg 867
Regent Press Publishers & Printers, pg 873
Sahara Records & Filmworks Entertainment Co, pg 879
Staylor-Made Communications Inc, pg 900
Still N' Motion, pg 901
Tam Communications Inc, pg 906
Total Creative, pg 916
West Coast Projections Inc, pg 935
WMS Media Inc, pg 940

COLORADO
Daylight Productions & Rentals, pg 739
Flashback Media Productions, pg 762
Tatum Video, pg 907

CONNECTICUT
Cine-Med Inc, pg 723
The Gary-Paul Agency, pg 768
New London Media, pg 839
P&P Studios Inc, pg 851

DELAWARE
So Smart Productions, pg 891

DISTRICT OF COLUMBIA
Hillmann & Carr Inc, pg 780
O'Keefe Communications Inc, pg 844

FLORIDA
AVI-SPL, pg 698
Civins Productions Inc, pg 725
Communications Concepts Inc (CCI), pg 729
National Teleproductions Inc, pg 837
The Newhouse Media Group, pg 840
Video Techniques Inc, pg 928

GEORGIA
ECG Productions, pg 750
Myriad Productions, pg 835
On-Line Productions, pg 845
Visioneering International Inc, pg 931

HAWAII
FilmWorks Pacific, pg 761
Hyperspective Studios Inc, pg 783

IDAHO
KTVB-TV, pg 802
Wide Eye Productions, pg 938

ILLINOIS
ABSA Films, pg 672
Airways Digital Media, pg 679
CCore Media Inc, pg 718
Film Police, pg 760
Major Media Productions Inc, pg 815
Manning Productions, pg 816
Mightybytes Inc, pg 827
Pepper Group, pg 854
PSAV® Presentation Services (Hotel Services Division), pg 866
SCI Television & Creative Media LLC, pg 882
Sound/Video Impressions Inc, pg 894
Sparkfactor, pg 896
20/20 Communications Inc, pg 920
WEEK TV, pg 935

INDIANA
Bright Ideas Creative Services, pg 710

IOWA
Educational Technology & Media Services, pg 751

KENTUCKY
Broadway Digital, pg 711
Prosper Media Group Inc, pg 866

AUDIO/VISUAL

Script Writing (continued)

Slide & Transparency Equipment & Supply Distributors

LOUISIANA

Techkno Integration & Design
Services LLC, pg 908

MAINE

Headlight Audio Visual Inc, pg 777

MARYLAND

RTZ Audio Visual, pg 878

MASSACHUSETTS

Hunt's Photo & Video, pg 782
University Products Inc, pg 923

MICHIGAN

City Events Group, pg 725
Michigan Office Solutions (MOS),
A Xerox Company, pg 825

MISSISSIPPI

Bowie Audio Visual Enterprises Inc,
pg 709
Jasper Ewing & Sons Inc, pg 757

MISSOURI

Conference Technologies Inc,
pg 730
ITC, pg 791
Modern Communications Inc,
pg 828
Schiller's Audio-Visual, pg 881

NEBRASKA

Images II Inc, pg 785

NEVADA

Bulbman Inc, pg 712

NEW JERSEY

AlltecPro, pg 681
Argraph Corp, pg 688
AV Bluebook, pg 696
HamiltonBuhl, pg 775
Leica Camera Inc, pg 806
Starlite, pg 900
SYMCO Inc, pg 905
Total Video Products Inc, pg 916
Transparent Office Products LLC,
pg 917
Wired 4 Sound Inc, pg 940
Yorktel, pg 944

NEW YORK

AV Workshop, pg 697
Bulbtronics Inc, pg 712
Gaylord Archival, pg 768
Get Smart Products, pg 770
Langie Audio Visual Systems,
pg 803
Light Impressions, pg 807
Long Island Video Enterprises Live
Inc, pg 811
Markertek Video Supply, pg 817
Motion Picture Enterprises Inc,
pg 831
Neptune Photo Inc, pg 838
Olden Camera & Lens Co Inc,
pg 845
Ray Supply Inc, pg 870
Visual Technologies Corp, pg 932

NORTH CAROLINA

Camcor Inc, pg 715

OHIO

Audio Visual Media, pg 694
Copp Integrated Systems, pg 731
Icom Multimedia, pg 783
Tri-State Visual Products Inc,
pg 918

PENNSYLVANIA

Advanced AV LLC, pg 677
Audio Visions Inc, pg 694
Audio Visual Communications Inc,
pg 694
Bernie's Photo Center, pg 704
Brodart Co, pg 711
Charles Beseler Co, pg 721
Electron Microscopy Sciences
(EMS), pg 752
J E Foss Co, pg 764
Grise Audio Visual Center Inc,
pg 774
Vistacom Inc, pg 931

TENNESSEE

Continental Film, pg 731
Lowrance Sound Co Inc, pg 812
Memphis Communications Corp,
pg 823

TEXAS

Audio Visual Technologies Group
(AVTG), pg 695
JSAV, pg 795
Lubbock Audio Visual Inc, pg 812
Quality Audio Visual Service Inc,
pg 867
Stage Directions, pg 898
Videotex Systems Inc, pg 930

VIRGINIA

Boitnott Visual Communications
Corp (BVC), pg 708
Intellidyne LLC, pg 789
Lee Hartman & Sons Inc, pg 805
Metropolitan Audio Visual Co LLC,
pg 824
The Whitlock Group, pg 937

WASHINGTON

Inland Audio Visual Co, pg 788

WISCONSIN

Audio Visual of Milwaukee Inc,
pg 694
Camera Corner Connecting Point,
pg 715
Demco Inc, pg 740
Full Compass Systems, pg 767
School Specialty Inc, pg 882

ALBERTA

Infosat Communications Inc, pg 787
Unique Communications Ltd,
pg 921

BRITISH COLUMBIA

Commercial Electronics Ltd, pg 728
Specialty Bulb Products Inc, pg 896

MANITOBA

Inland Audio Visual Ltd, pg 788

ONTARIO

Carr McLean Ltd, pg 717
CBM Ltd, pg 718

QUEBEC

Panavideo Inc, pg 850

Slide & Transparency Equipment & Supply Manufacturers

ARIZONA

The BD Co, pg 702

CALIFORNIA

Hall Productions, pg 775
Lasergraphics Inc, pg 804

COLORADO

American Educational Products
LLC, pg 683

FLORIDA

Cinema Equipment & Supplies Inc,
pg 724
Print File Inc, pg 862

ILLINOIS

ACCO Brands Corp, pg 673
Bretford Manufacturing Inc, pg 710
Luxor, pg 812
Smith-Victor Corp, pg 891

INDIANA

Star Case Manufacturing Co Inc,
pg 900

MASSACHUSETTS

University Products Inc, pg 923

NEW JERSEY

CELCO, pg 719
Leica Camera Inc, pg 806
Pro-Tape & Specialities Inc, pg 863
Transparent Office Products LLC,
pg 917

NEW YORK

Century Business Solutions, pg 720
Eastman Kodak Co, pg 750
Gagne Inc, pg 767
GTI (Graphic Technology Inc),
pg 774
Light Impressions, pg 807
TecNec Distributing, pg 909

PENNSYLVANIA

Charles Beseler Co, pg 721
Electron Microscopy Sciences
(EMS), pg 752

WISCONSIN

Bardes Products Inc, pg 702

ONTARIO

CBM Ltd, pg 718

Slide & Transparency Equipment & Supply Rentals

ALABAMA

Audio-Video Resources Inc, pg 694

ARIZONA

Arizona Cine Equipment, pg 688
Metropolitan Audio-Visual Inc,
pg 824

CALIFORNIA

Ametron Audio/Video, pg 684
AV Guys, pg 697
Gold Standard Productions, pg 772
Hooper Camera & Imaging, pg 781
Instructional Materials & Equipment
Distributors (I-Med), pg 789
Lynch Communications, pg 813
McCune Audio-Video-Lighting,
pg 821
Media Fabricators Inc, pg 822
MSI Production Services, pg 832
Munday & Collins AV, pg 834
Samy's Camera, pg 879
Video Resources Inc, pg 928
Voice & Video Rentals, pg 932

COLORADO

Ceavco Audio Visual Company Inc,
pg 719

CONNECTICUT

A/V Davey, pg 697

FLORIDA

ONstage, pg 846
Photosound of Orlando Inc, pg 856

GEORGIA

ON Services, a GES Company,
pg 846
Staging Directions Inc, pg 899

ILLINOIS

Allen Visual Systems Inc, pg 680
AV Chicago Inc, pg 696
Helix Camera & Video, pg 778
PSAV® Presentation Services
(Hotel Services Division), pg 866

INDIANA

Gary Camera & Digital, pg 768
OMNI Productions, pg 845

KENTUCKY

Audio Visual Techniques Inc,
pg 695

MAINE

Headlight Audio Visual Inc, pg 777

MARYLAND

RTZ Audio Visual, pg 878

MASSACHUSETTS

AVFX Inc, pg 698
massAV, pg 819
TR Productions, pg 916

MICHIGAN

Digi Sign Design LLC, pg 741
K&R All Media Productions LLC,
pg 796

MINNESOTA

AVI Systems, pg 698

AUDIO/VISUAL

Slide & Transparency Equipment & Supply Rentals (continued)

MISSISSIPPI

Bowie Audio Visual Enterprises Inc, pg 709
Jasper Ewing & Sons Inc, pg 757

MISSOURI

Schiller's Audio-Visual, pg 881
Show-Me Audio-Visual, pg 887

NEVADA

GES Audio Visual, pg 770

NEW HAMPSHIRE

Academic & Campus Technology Services, pg 672
Apertura, pg 686

NEW JERSEY

Audio Visual Dynamics®, pg 694
Moe AV LLC, pg 828
PLS Staging, pg 858
Video Corporation of America (VCA), pg 927

NEW YORK

AV Workshop, pg 697
CMI Communications, pg 727
Long Island Video Enterprises Live Inc, pg 811
Visual Technologies Corp, pg 932
WorldStage, pg 941

NORTH CAROLINA

Special Event Services, pg 896

NORTH DAKOTA

Media Productions, pg 822

OHIO

Audio Visual Media, pg 694
Icom Multimedia, pg 783
Mills James Productions, pg 828
Vista Color Imaging Inc, pg 931

PENNSYLVANIA

Advanced AV LLC, pg 677
Audio Visions Inc, pg 694
Audio Visual Communications Inc, pg 694
Bernie's Photo Center, pg 704
FMP Media Solutions Inc, pg 763
Grise Audio Visual Center Inc, pg 774
Visual Sound Inc, pg 931

TENNESSEE

Memphis Communications Corp, pg 823

TEXAS

Audio Visual Technologies Group (AVTG), pg 695
Lubbock Audio Visual Inc, pg 812
Quality Audio Visual Service Inc, pg 867
Stage Directions, pg 898

VIRGINIA

American AV, pg 682
Projection, pg 865

WISCONSIN

Audio Visual of Milwaukee Inc, pg 694
Event Essentials, pg 756
Full Compass Systems, pg 767

PUERTO RICO

Stage Crew Audiovisual Inc, pg 898

ALBERTA

Unique Communications Ltd, pg 921

BRITISH COLUMBIA

Clark's Audio Visual Services Ltd, pg 725

QUEBEC

Freeman Audio Visual, pg 765
Panavideo Inc, pg 850

Slide & Transparency Equipment & Supply Repairs

CALIFORNIA

Ametron Audio/Video, pg 684
Gluskin's Custom Audio Video, pg 771
Hooper Camera & Imaging, pg 781
Instructional Materials & Equipment Distributors (I-Med), pg 789
McAlister Electronics, pg 820
Lloyd F McKinney Associates Inc, pg 821
Pro Camera Repair, pg 862

COLORADO

Ceavco Audio Visual Company Inc, pg 719

CONNECTICUT

A/V Davey, pg 697
HB Communications Inc, pg 777

ILLINOIS

Allen Visual Systems Inc, pg 680

INDIANA

Gary Camera & Digital, pg 768

KENTUCKY

Axxis Leasing Inc, pg 700
NOR-COM Inc, pg 841

MAINE

Headlight Audio Visual Inc, pg 777

MARYLAND

RTZ Audio Visual, pg 878

MICHIGAN

City Events Group, pg 725
TEL Systems LLC, pg 909

MINNESOTA

AVI Systems, pg 698

MISSISSIPPI

Bowie Audio Visual Enterprises Inc, pg 709

MISSOURI

Cintrex Audio Visual, pg 725
Communitronics Corp, pg 729
Schiller's Audio-Visual, pg 881

NEW JERSEY

Leica Camera Inc, pg 806

NEW YORK

Langie Audio Visual Systems, pg 803
Ray Supply Inc, pg 870
Visual Technologies Corp, pg 932

OHIO

Audio Visual Media, pg 694
Icom Multimedia, pg 783
Tri-State Audio Visual Co, pg 918

PENNSYLVANIA

Audio Visions Inc, pg 694
Bernie's Photo Center, pg 704

TENNESSEE

Memphis Communications Corp, pg 823

TEXAS

Audio Visual Technologies Group (AVTG), pg 695
Lubbock Audio Visual Inc, pg 812
Quality Audio Visual Service Inc, pg 867

VIRGINIA

Metropolitan Audio Visual Co LLC, pg 824
The Whitlock Group, pg 937

WISCONSIN

Audio Visual of Milwaukee Inc, pg 694
Full Compass Systems, pg 767

QUEBEC

Panavideo Inc, pg 850

Slide Binding & Mounting Equipment & Supply Distributors

ARIZONA

Troxell-CDI, pg 918

CALIFORNIA

Ametron Audio/Video, pg 684
California Tape Products Inc, pg 714
Media Fabricators Inc, pg 822

CONNECTICUT

MAVCO, pg 820
USI Inc, pg 924

FLORIDA

AVI-SPL, pg 698
ONstage, pg 846
Tallahassee Audio Visual, pg 906

GEORGIA

Visioneering International Inc, pg 931

KENTUCKY

K&R PhotoDigital, pg 796
NOR-COM Inc, pg 841

MASSACHUSETTS

University Products Inc, pg 923

MICHIGAN

Michigan Office Solutions (MOS), A Xerox Company, pg 825

MISSISSIPPI

Jasper Ewing & Sons Inc, pg 757

MISSOURI

Schiller's Audio-Visual, pg 881

NEW JERSEY

AlltecPro, pg 681
Argraph Corp, pg 688
AV Bluebook, pg 696
Callen Photo Mount Corp, pg 714
HamiltonBuhl, pg 775
Vcom IMC, pg 925
Wired 4 Sound Inc, pg 940
Yorktel, pg 944

NEW YORK

AV Workshop, pg 697
Gaylord Archival, pg 768
Get Smart Products, pg 770
Langie Audio Visual Systems, pg 803
Light Impressions, pg 807
Markertek Video Supply, pg 817
Ray Supply Inc, pg 870
Visual Technologies Corp, pg 932

NORTH CAROLINA

Camcor Inc, pg 715

OHIO

Icom Multimedia, pg 783

PENNSYLVANIA

Advanced AV LLC, pg 677
Audio Visions Inc, pg 694
Bernie's Photo Center, pg 704
J E Foss Co, pg 764
Wespen Audio Visual Co, pg 935

TENNESSEE

Memphis Communications Corp, pg 823

TEXAS

Lubbock Audio Visual Inc, pg 812

VIRGINIA

Intellidyne LLC, pg 789
Lee Hartman & Sons Inc, pg 805

WISCONSIN

Audio Visual of Milwaukee Inc, pg 694

ALBERTA

McBain Camera Ltd, pg 820

Slide Binding & Mounting Equipment & Supply Manufacturers

ARIZONA

Savage Universal Corp, pg 881

NEW JERSEY

Leica Camera Inc, pg 806
Pro-Tape & Specialities Inc, pg 863

NEW YORK

Light Impressions, pg 807

WISCONSIN

Bardes Products Inc, pg 702

Slide Binding & Mounting Equipment & Supply Rentals

ARIZONA

Arizona Cine Equipment, pg 688

CALIFORNIA

Ametron Audio/Video, pg 684
Media Fabricators Inc, pg 822
Samy's Camera, pg 879

FLORIDA

ONstage, pg 846

GEORGIA

Staging Directions Inc, pg 899

MICHIGAN

Digi Sign Design LLC, pg 741
K&R All Media Productions LLC,
   pg 796

MINNESOTA

AVI Systems, pg 698

NEW HAMPSHIRE

Apertura, pg 686

NEW YORK

AV Workshop, pg 697

OHIO

Icom Multimedia, pg 783
Vista Color Imaging Inc, pg 931

TENNESSEE

Memphis Communications Corp,
   pg 823

WISCONSIN

Audio Visual of Milwaukee Inc,
   pg 694

ALBERTA

McBain Camera Ltd, pg 820

Slide Binding & Mounting Equipment & Supply Repairs

CALIFORNIA

Ametron Audio/Video, pg 684
McAlister Electronics, pg 820

CONNECTICUT

HB Communications Inc, pg 777

KENTUCKY

NOR-COM Inc, pg 841

MICHIGAN

TEL Systems LLC, pg 909

MINNESOTA

AVI Systems, pg 698

MISSOURI

Schiller's Audio-Visual, pg 881

OHIO

Icom Multimedia, pg 783

TENNESSEE

Memphis Communications Corp,
   pg 823

WISCONSIN

Audio Visual of Milwaukee Inc,
   pg 694

Slide Duplication, *see* Duplication—Slides

Slide Mounting Equipment & Supply, *see* Slide Binding & Mounting Equipment & Supply

Slide Presentation System—Programmable & Manual Distributors

ARIZONA

Arizona Cine Equipment, pg 688
Metropolitan Audio-Visual Inc,
   pg 824
Professional Marketing Services Inc,
   pg 865
Troxell-CDI, pg 918

ARKANSAS

Jay S Stanley & Associates Inc,
   pg 899

CALIFORNIA

Ametron Audio/Video, pg 684
Assured Audio Visual, pg 691
California Tape Products Inc,
   pg 714
Educational Technology Services
   (ETS), pg 751
Lloyd F McKinney Associates Inc,
   pg 821
Media Fabricators Inc, pg 822
MediaPOINTE, pg 823

PMP Marketing Inc, pg 858
Southern California Sound Image
   Inc, pg 895

COLORADO

Spectrum Audio Visual Services,
   pg 897

CONNECTICUT

HB Communications Inc, pg 777
MAVCO, pg 820
Rockwell Communications Inc,
   pg 876

FLORIDA

AVI-SPL, pg 698
Cinema Equipment & Supplies Inc,
   pg 724
Lighting Sales Connection Inc,
   pg 808
ONstage, pg 846
Techni-Lux Inc, pg 908

GEORGIA

Audio Visual Resources Inc, pg 695
Baker Audio Visual, pg 700
Convergent Media Systems, pg 731
Imagers, pg 785
Stage Front Presentation Systems,
   pg 899
Visioneering International Inc,
   pg 931

HAWAII

The Audio Visual Co (AVCO),
   pg 694

KENTUCKY

Audio Visual Techniques Inc,
   pg 695
Axxis Leasing Inc, pg 700
NOR-COM Inc, pg 841

MARYLAND

RTZ Audio Visual, pg 878

MASSACHUSETTS

Graphx Inc, pg 773
University Products Inc, pg 923

MICHIGAN

City Events Group, pg 725
Michigan Office Solutions (MOS),
   A Xerox Company, pg 825

MINNESOTA

AVI Systems, pg 698

MISSISSIPPI

Bowie Audio Visual Enterprises Inc,
   pg 709
Jasper Ewing & Sons Inc, pg 757

MISSOURI

Communitronics Corp, pg 729
Conference Technologies Inc,
   pg 730
ITC, pg 791
Modern Communications Inc,
   pg 828
Schiller's Audio-Visual, pg 881

NEW JERSEY

AlltecPro, pg 681
Argraph Corp, pg 688

AV Bluebook, pg 696
HamiltonBuhl, pg 775
Leica Camera Inc, pg 806
Reed Presentations Inc (RPI),
   pg 872
Starlite, pg 900
Total Video Products Inc, pg 916
Transparent Office Products LLC,
   pg 917
Video Corporation of America
   (VCA), pg 927
Wired 4 Sound Inc, pg 940
Yorktel, pg 944

NEW YORK

AV Workshop, pg 697
Design Audio Visual Inc, pg 741
DSan Corp, pg 747
Gaylord Archival, pg 768
Indigo Productions, pg 787
Long Island Video Enterprises Live
   Inc, pg 811
Neptune Photo Inc, pg 838
Ray Supply Inc, pg 870
Visual Technologies Corp, pg 932

NORTH CAROLINA

Camcor Inc, pg 715

OHIO

Audio Visual Media, pg 694
Icom Multimedia, pg 783

PENNSYLVANIA

Advanced AV LLC, pg 677
Audio Visions Inc, pg 694
Audio Visual Communications Inc,
   pg 694
Bernie's Photo Center, pg 704
J E Foss Co, pg 764
Grise Audio Visual Center Inc,
   pg 774
The Lerro Corp, pg 806

TENNESSEE

Memphis Communications Corp,
   pg 823
Technical Support Systems LLC,
   pg 908

TEXAS

Audio Visual Technologies Group
   (AVTG), pg 695
JSAV, pg 795
Lubbock Audio Visual Inc, pg 812
Videotex Systems Inc, pg 930

VIRGINIA

Boitnott Visual Communications
   Corp (BVC), pg 708
Intellidyne LLC, pg 789
Lee Hartman & Sons Inc, pg 805
Quince Imaging Inc, pg 868

WASHINGTON

Inland Audio Visual Co, pg 788
PNTA, pg 858

WISCONSIN

Audio Visual of Milwaukee Inc,
   pg 694
Camera Corner Connecting Point,
   pg 715
Full Compass Systems, pg 767
School Specialty Inc, pg 882

AUDIO/VISUAL

Slide Presentation System—Programmable & Manual Distributors (continued)

ALBERTA

McBain Camera Ltd, pg 820
SMART Technologies ULC, pg 891
Unique Communications Ltd, pg 921

BRITISH COLUMBIA

Commercial Electronics Ltd, pg 728

MANITOBA

Inland Audio Visual Ltd, pg 788

ONTARIO

Nationwide Audio Visual Co, pg 837

QUEBEC

Panavideo Inc, pg 850

Slide Presentation System—Programmable & Manual Manufacturers

CALIFORNIA

AMX® by Harman, pg 685

MASSACHUSETTS

Graphx Inc, pg 773

NEW JERSEY

Crestron Electronics Inc, pg 734
Leica Camera Inc, pg 806
Transparent Office Products LLC, pg 917

NEW YORK

DSan Corp, pg 747
ELMO USA Corp, pg 753

PENNSYLVANIA

Scala Inc, pg 881

VIRGINIA

Quince Imaging Inc, pg 868

WISCONSIN

Bardes Products Inc, pg 702

ALBERTA

SMART Technologies ULC, pg 891

Slide Presentation System—Programmable & Manual Rentals

ARIZONA

Arizona Cine Equipment, pg 688
Metropolitan Audio-Visual Inc, pg 824

CALIFORNIA

Alliant Event Services, pg 681
Ametron Audio/Video, pg 684
Assured Audio Visual, pg 691
Gold Standard Productions, pg 772
Media Fabricators Inc, pg 822
Samy's Camera, pg 879

COLORADO

Daylight Productions & Rentals, pg 739
Spectrum Audio Visual Services, pg 897

CONNECTICUT

A/V Davey, pg 697

DELAWARE

Ken-Del Productions Inc, pg 797
Showorks Audio Visual Inc, pg 887

FLORIDA

Lighting Sales Connection Inc, pg 808
ONstage, pg 846
Photosound of Orlando Inc, pg 856
Universal Studios Florida® Production Group, pg 922

GEORGIA

Convergent Media Systems, pg 731
MAGNUM Companies Ltd, pg 815
ON Services, a GES Company, pg 846
Stage Front Presentation Systems, pg 899
Staging Directions Inc, pg 899

ILLINOIS

Backstar Creative Media Inc, pg 700
PSAV® Presentation Services (Hotel Services Division), pg 866
Resolution Productions Group, pg 874

KENTUCKY

Audio Visual Techniques Inc, pg 695

LOUISIANA

Pace Systems, pg 849

MARYLAND

dbF a Media Company, pg 739
RTZ Audio Visual, pg 878

MASSACHUSETTS

AVFX Inc, pg 698
massAV, pg 819
Preston Productions Inc, pg 861

MICHIGAN

City Events Group, pg 725
Digi Sign Design LLC, pg 741
K&R All Media Productions LLC, pg 796
K&R's Recording Studios Inc, pg 796

MINNESOTA

AVI Systems, pg 698

MISSISSIPPI

Bowie Audio Visual Enterprises Inc, pg 709

MISSOURI

Communitronics Corp, pg 729
Schiller's Audio-Visual, pg 881
Southwest Audio-Visual Inc, pg 895

NEVADA

GES Audio Visual, pg 770

NEW HAMPSHIRE

Academic & Campus Technology Services, pg 672
Apertura, pg 686

NEW JERSEY

PLS Staging, pg 858

NEW YORK

AV Workshop, pg 697
Design Audio Visual Inc, pg 741
Langie Audio Visual Systems, pg 803
Long Island Video Enterprises Live Inc, pg 811
Manhattan Center Studios Inc, pg 816
Specialized Audio-Visual Inc, pg 896
Visual Technologies Corp, pg 932
Visual Word Systems Inc, pg 932

NORTH CAROLINA

AV Connections Inc, pg 697
Special Event Services, pg 896

NORTH DAKOTA

Media Productions, pg 822

OHIO

Audio Visual Media, pg 694
Hughie's Event Production Services, pg 782
Icom Multimedia, pg 783
Mills James Productions, pg 828
Vista Color Imaging Inc, pg 931

PENNSYLVANIA

Advanced AV LLC, pg 677
Audio Visions Inc, pg 694
Audio Visual Communications Inc, pg 694
Bernie's Photo Center, pg 704
Grise Audio Visual Center Inc, pg 774

TENNESSEE

Memphis Communications Corp, pg 823
Russ Sturgeon Productions/RSVP, pg 903
Technical Support Systems LLC, pg 908

TEXAS

Audio Visual Technologies Group (AVTG), pg 695
JSAV, pg 795
Lubbock Audio Visual Inc, pg 812
Stage Directions, pg 898

VIRGINIA

American AV, pg 682
Boitnott Visual Communications Corp (BVC), pg 708
Lee Hartman & Sons Inc, pg 805
Projection, pg 865
Quince Imaging Inc, pg 868

WASHINGTON

Inland Audio Visual Co, pg 788
PNTA, pg 858

WISCONSIN

Audio Visual of Milwaukee Inc, pg 694
Camera Corner Connecting Point, pg 715
Event Essentials, pg 756
Full Compass Systems, pg 767

PUERTO RICO

Stage Crew Audiovisual Inc, pg 898

ALBERTA

Allstar Show Industries Inc, pg 681
Evolution AV, pg 757
McBain Camera Ltd, pg 820
Unique Communications Ltd, pg 921

BRITISH COLUMBIA

Triad Communications Ltd, pg 918

MANITOBA

Inland Audio Visual Ltd, pg 788

QUEBEC

Freeman Audio Visual, pg 765
Panavideo Inc, pg 850

Slide Presentation System—Programmable & Manual Repairs

CALIFORNIA

Ametron Audio/Video, pg 684
McAlister Electronics, pg 820
Lloyd F McKinney Associates Inc, pg 821
Pro Camera Repair, pg 862

CONNECTICUT

A/V Davey, pg 697
HB Communications Inc, pg 777
Precision Camera & Video Repair Inc, pg 861

GEORGIA

Stage Front Presentation Systems, pg 899

KENTUCKY

Axxis Leasing Inc, pg 700
NOR-COM Inc, pg 841

MAINE

Headlight Audio Visual Inc, pg 777

MARYLAND

RTZ Audio Visual, pg 878

MICHIGAN
City Events Group, pg 725
TEL Systems LLC, pg 909

MINNESOTA
AVI Systems, pg 698

MISSISSIPPI
Bowie Audio Visual Enterprises Inc, pg 709

MISSOURI
Schiller's Audio-Visual, pg 881

NEW JERSEY
Leica Camera Inc, pg 806

NEW YORK
ELMO USA Corp, pg 753
Langie Audio Visual Systems, pg 803
Visual Technologies Corp, pg 932

OHIO
Audio Visual Media, pg 694
Icom Multimedia, pg 783

PENNSYLVANIA
Audio Visions Inc, pg 694
Bernie's Photo Center, pg 704

TENNESSEE
Memphis Communications Corp, pg 823
Technical Support Systems LLC, pg 908

TEXAS
Audio Visual Technologies Group (AVTG), pg 695
Lubbock Audio Visual Inc, pg 812

VIRGINIA
Boitnott Visual Communications Corp (BVC), pg 708
Quince Imaging Inc, pg 868

WASHINGTON
Inland Audio Visual Co, pg 788
PNTA, pg 858

WISCONSIN
Audio Visual of Milwaukee Inc, pg 694
Full Compass Systems, pg 767

ALBERTA
Infosat Communications Inc, pg 787
Unique Communications Ltd, pg 921

MANITOBA
Inland Audio Visual Ltd, pg 788

QUEBEC
Panavideo Inc, pg 850

Slide Printing, *see* Processing & Printing— Slides

Slide Printing, *see* **Volume Printing—Slides**

Slide Processing, *see* **Processing & Printing— Slides**

Slide Projector Distributors

ALABAMA
Curtis Company, pg 736

ARIZONA
Arizona Cine Equipment, pg 688
Troxell-CDI, pg 918
Ultimate Presentation Systems Inc, pg 920

ARKANSAS
Carlton-Bates Co, pg 717
Jay S Stanley & Associates Inc, pg 899
White Diamond Productions LLC, pg 937

CALIFORNIA
Ametron Audio/Video, pg 684
Audio/Video Supply Inc, pg 694
California Tape Products Inc, pg 714
Gluskin's Custom Audio Video, pg 771
Hooper Camera & Imaging, pg 781
Instructional Materials & Equipment Distributors (I-Med), pg 789
Lloyd F McKinney Associates Inc, pg 821
Media Fabricators Inc, pg 822
MediaMation Inc, pg 822
MediaPOINTE Inc, pg 823
PMP Marketing Inc, pg 858
Southern California Sound Image Inc, pg 895
Stanislaus AV Inc, pg 899

COLORADO
Ceavco Audio Visual Company Inc, pg 719
Spectrum Audio Visual Services, pg 897

CONNECTICUT
HB Communications Inc, pg 777
MAVCO, pg 820
Rockwell Communications Inc, pg 876

FLORIDA
AVI-SPL, pg 698
Cinema Equipment & Supplies Inc, pg 724
Digital Video Systems, pg 742
Harmon's Audio-Visual Services, pg 776
Hi-Tech Import Export Corp, pg 779
Industrial Strength Inc, pg 787
Intermark Industries Inc, pg 789
Lighting Sales Connection Inc, pg 808
ONstage, pg 846
Tallahassee Audio Visual, pg 906
Techni-Lux Inc, pg 908

GEORGIA
Audio Visual Resources Inc, pg 695
Baker Audio Visual, pg 700
Convergent Media Systems, pg 731
Imagers, pg 785
Lighting & Production Equipment Inc, pg 807
Stage Front Presentation Systems, pg 899
Visioneering International Inc, pg 931

HAWAII
The Audio Visual Co (AVCO), pg 694

ILLINOIS
Allen Visual Systems Inc, pg 680
Central Audio-Visual Equipment Inc, pg 719
Creative Technology (CT), pg 733
FUJIFILM Graphic Systems Division, pg 766
RC Communications, pg 870

KENTUCKY
Axxis Leasing Inc, pg 700
NOR-COM Inc, pg 841

LOUISIANA
Techkno Integration & Design Services LLC, pg 908

MAINE
Headlight Audio Visual Inc, pg 777

MARYLAND
Cardinal Sound & Video, pg 717
Nelson White Systems Inc, pg 838
RTZ Audio Visual, pg 878

MASSACHUSETTS
Integrated Solutions Group, pg 789
Rule Boston Camera, pg 878
University Products Inc, pg 923

MICHIGAN
Olson Anderson Co, pg 685
City Events Group, pg 725
Michigan Office Solutions (MOS), A Xerox Company, pg 825
TEL Systems LLC, pg 909

MINNESOTA
AVI Systems, pg 698
Media Loft Inc, pg 822

MISSISSIPPI
Bowie Audio Visual Enterprises Inc, pg 709
Jasper Ewing & Sons Inc, pg 757

MISSOURI
Communitronics Corp, pg 729
Conference Technologies Inc, pg 730
ITC, pg 791
Modern Communications Inc, pg 828
Schiller's Audio-Visual, pg 881
Southwest Audio-Visual Inc, pg 895

NEW JERSEY
A-V Services Inc, pg 671
AlltecPro, pg 681

Argraph Corp, pg 688
Audio Visual Dynamics®, pg 694
AV Bluebook, pg 696
HamiltonBuhl, pg 775
Hasselblad Bron Inc, pg 776
Leica Camera Inc, pg 806
Ritz Camera & Image, pg 875
Starlite, pg 900
SYMCO Inc, pg 905
Total Video Products Inc, pg 916
Vcom IMC, pg 925
Video Corporation of America (VCA), pg 927
Wired 4 Sound Inc, pg 940
Yorktel, pg 944

NEW YORK
Audio Visual Sales & Service Inc, pg 695
AV Workshop, pg 697
Design Audio Visual Inc, pg 741
Eastman Kodak Co, pg 750
Gaylord Archival, pg 768
General Audio-Visual Inc (GAVI), pg 769
Indigo Productions, pg 787
Long Island Video Enterprises Live Inc, pg 811
Markertek Video Supply, pg 817
Motion Picture Enterprises Inc, pg 831
Neptune Photo Inc, pg 838
Presentation Products Inc, pg 861
Topbulb, a Semmer Lighting Company, pg 915
Visual Technologies Corp, pg 932

NORTH CAROLINA
Camcor Inc, pg 715
Strategic Connections, pg 901

OHIO
Audio Visual Media, pg 694
Copp Integrated Systems, pg 731
Icom Multimedia, pg 783
Tri-State Visual Products Inc, pg 918

PENNSYLVANIA
Advanced AV LLC, pg 677
Audio Visions Inc, pg 694
Audio Visual Communications Inc, pg 694
Bernie's Photo Center, pg 704
Brodart Co, pg 711
J E Foss Co, pg 764
Garcia Marketing Inc, pg 768
Grise Audio Visual Center Inc, pg 774
Vistacom Inc, pg 931
Wespen Audio Visual Co, pg 935

TENNESSEE
Continental Film, pg 731
Lowrance Sound Co Inc, pg 812
Memphis Communications Corp, pg 823
Technical Support Systems LLC, pg 908

TEXAS
Audio Visual Technologies Group (AVTG), pg 695
Digital Display Solutions Inc, pg 742
FitzCo Sound Inc, pg 761
JSAV, pg 795
Lubbock Audio Visual Inc, pg 812
Quality Audio Visual Service Inc, pg 867

AUDIO/VISUAL

Slide Projector Distributors (continued)

VIRGINIA

Boitnott Visual Communications Corp (BVC), pg 708
Intellidyne LLC, pg 789
Lee Hartman & Sons Inc, pg 805
Metropolitan Audio Visual Co LLC, pg 824
The Whitlock Group, pg 937

WASHINGTON

Inland Audio Visual Co, pg 788
Northern Lights & Pro Audio, pg 842
PNTA, pg 858

WISCONSIN

Audio Visual of Milwaukee Inc, pg 694
Demco Inc, pg 740
Full Compass Systems, pg 767
School Specialty Inc, pg 882

PUERTO RICO

Bonnin Electronics Inc, pg 708

ALBERTA

Infosat Communications Inc, pg 787
Unique Communications Ltd, pg 921

BRITISH COLUMBIA

Commercial Electronics Ltd, pg 728

MANITOBA

Inland Audio Visual Ltd, pg 788

ONTARIO

Carr McLean Ltd, pg 717
Nationwide Audio Visual Co, pg 837

QUEBEC

Panavideo Inc, pg 850

Slide Projector Manufacturers

CALIFORNIA

Lasergraphics Inc, pg 804

ILLINOIS

ACCO Brands Corp, pg 673

NEVADA

Keystone View, pg 798

NEW JERSEY

Crestron Electronics Inc, pg 734
Leica Camera Inc, pg 806

NEW YORK

American Video Inc, pg 684
Eastman Kodak Co, pg 750
ELMO USA Corp, pg 753
General Audio-Visual Inc (GAVI), pg 769
Navitar Inc, pg 837
TecNec Distributing, pg 909

Slide Projector Rentals

ALABAMA

Audio-Video Resources Inc, pg 694

ARIZONA

Arizona Cine Equipment, pg 688
Merestone, pg 823
Metropolitan Audio-Visual Inc, pg 824
Ultimate Presentation Systems Inc, pg 920

ARKANSAS

Carlton-Bates Co, pg 717
White Diamond Productions LLC, pg 937

CALIFORNIA

AGF Media Services, pg 678
Alliant Event Services, pg 681
Ametron Audio/Video, pg 684
Artichoke Productions, pg 690
Assured Audio Visual, pg 691
AV Guys, pg 697
Gluskin's Custom Audio Video, pg 771
Gold Standard Productions, pg 772
Hooper Camera & Imaging, pg 781
Instructional Materials & Equipment Distributors (I-Med), pg 789
JD Audio Visual Inc, pg 793
McCune Audio-Video-Lighting, pg 821
Media Fabricators Inc, pg 822
Munday & Collins AV, pg 834
On-Trax Inc, pg 846
PSAV® Presentation Services, pg 866
Samy's Camera, pg 879
Sound Service Co, pg 894
Stanislaus AV Inc, pg 899
VER, pg 926
Voice & Video Rentals, pg 932

COLORADO

Ceavco Audio Visual Company Inc, pg 719
Daylight Productions & Rentals, pg 739
Multimedia Audio Visual Inc, pg 833
Spectrum Audio Visual Services, pg 897

CONNECTICUT

A/V Davey, pg 697
Rockwell Communications Inc, pg 876

DELAWARE

Ken-Del Productions Inc, pg 797

FLORIDA

AVI-SPL, pg 698
Harmon's Audio-Visual Services, pg 776
Industrial Strength Inc, pg 787
Lighting Sales Connection Inc, pg 808
ONstage, pg 846
Photosound of Orlando Inc, pg 856
Tallahassee Audio Visual, pg 906
Universal Studios Florida® Production Group, pg 922

GEORGIA

Audio Visual Resources Inc, pg 695
Convergent Media Systems, pg 731
Lighting & Production Equipment Inc, pg 807
MAGNUM Companies Ltd, pg 815
ON Services, a GES Company, pg 846
Stage Front Presentation Systems, pg 899
Staging Directions Inc, pg 899

ILLINOIS

Allen Visual Systems Inc, pg 680
AV Chicago Inc, pg 696
Backstar Creative Media Inc, pg 700
Beatty TeleVisual Productions, pg 703
Central Audio-Visual Equipment Inc, pg 719
Creative Technology (CT), pg 733
Helix Camera & Video, pg 778
Pepper Group, pg 854
PSAV® Presentation Services (Hotel Services Division), pg 866
RC Communications, pg 870
Resolution Productions Group, pg 874

INDIANA

Advanced Media Integration, pg 677
Gary Camera & Digital, pg 768

KENTUCKY

Audio Visual Techniques Inc, pg 695
Barney Miller's Inc, pg 827

LOUISIANA

Clark Services Audio Visual & Exhibit Inc, pg 725
Pace Systems, pg 849

MAINE

Headlight Audio Visual Inc, pg 777

MARYLAND

Advance Audiovisual Presentation Ltd, pg 677
dbF a Media Company, pg 739
Hargrove Inc, pg 776
Nelson White Systems Inc, pg 838
RTZ Audio Visual, pg 878

MASSACHUSETTS

AVFX Inc, pg 698
Capron Lighting & Sound Co Inc, pg 716
Integrated Solutions Group, pg 789
massAV, pg 819
Preston Productions Inc, pg 861
TR Productions, pg 916

MICHIGAN

Olson Anderson Co, pg 685
Digi Sign Design LLC, pg 741
K&R All Media Productions LLC, pg 796
K&R's Recording Studios Inc, pg 796
TEL Systems LLC, pg 909

MINNESOTA

AVI Systems, pg 698
Media Loft Inc, pg 822

MISSISSIPPI

Bowie Audio Visual Enterprises Inc, pg 709
Jasper Ewing & Sons Inc, pg 757

MISSOURI

Communitronics Corp, pg 729
Schiller's Audio-Visual, pg 881
Show-Me Audio-Visual, pg 887
Southwest Audio-Visual Inc, pg 895

NEVADA

GES Audio Visual, pg 770

NEW HAMPSHIRE

Apertura, pg 686

NEW JERSEY

Audio Visual Dynamics®, pg 694
International Audio Visual Inc, pg 790
Moe AV LLC, pg 828
Panavid, pg 850
PLS Staging, pg 858
Starlite, pg 900
Wired 4 Sound Inc, pg 940

NEW YORK

Ace Video, pg 674
Adwar Video, pg 678
American Video Inc, pg 684
AV Workshop, pg 697
CMI Communications, pg 727
Design Audio Visual Inc, pg 741
Langie Audio Visual Systems, pg 803
Long Island Video Enterprises Live Inc, pg 811
Manhattan Center Studios Inc, pg 816
Neptune Photo Inc, pg 838
Specialized Audio-Visual Inc, pg 896
Visual Technologies Corp, pg 932
Visual Word Systems Inc, pg 932
WorldStage, pg 941

NORTH CAROLINA

AV Connections Inc, pg 697
Special Event Services, pg 896
Strategic Connections, pg 901

NORTH DAKOTA

Media Productions, pg 822

OHIO

Audio Visual Media, pg 694
Hughie's Event Production Services, pg 782
Icom Multimedia, pg 783
ITA Audio Visual Solutions, pg 791
Mills James Productions, pg 828
Thread Marketing Group, pg 913
Vista Color Imaging Inc, pg 931

OREGON

Rose City Sound, pg 877

PENNSYLVANIA

Advanced AV LLC, pg 677
Audio Visions Inc, pg 694
Audio Visual Communications Inc, pg 694
Grise Audio Visual Center Inc, pg 774
Visual Sound Inc, pg 931

SOUTH CAROLINA

Impact Technology Group LLC, pg 786
Sound & Images Inc, pg 893

TENNESSEE

Memphis Communications Corp, pg 823
Russ Sturgeon Productions/RSVP, pg 903
Technical Support Systems LLC, pg 908

TEXAS

Audio Visual Technologies Group (AVTG), pg 695
Bright Star Productions Inc, pg 710
FitzCo Sound Inc, pg 761
JSAV, pg 795
Lubbock Audio Visual Inc, pg 812
Quality Audio Visual Service Inc, pg 867
Stage Directions, pg 898

VIRGINIA

American AV, pg 682
Boitnott Visual Communications Corp (BVC), pg 708
Lee Hartman & Sons Inc, pg 805
Metropolitan Audio Visual Co LLC, pg 824
Projection, pg 865
The Whitlock Group, pg 937

WASHINGTON

Inland Audio Visual Co, pg 788
Kostov Productions, pg 801
PNTA, pg 858

WISCONSIN

Audio Visual of Milwaukee Inc, pg 694
Camera Corner Connecting Point, pg 715
Event Essentials, pg 756
Full Compass Systems, pg 767
School Specialty Inc, pg 882

PUERTO RICO

Stage Crew Audiovisual Inc, pg 898

ALBERTA

Allstar Show Industries Inc, pg 681
Cine Audio Visual Sales & Service Ltd, pg 723
Evolution AV, pg 757
McBain Camera Ltd, pg 820
Unique Communications Ltd, pg 921

BRITISH COLUMBIA

Clark's Audio Visual Services Ltd, pg 725
Commercial Electronics Ltd, pg 728
Triad Communications Ltd, pg 918

MANITOBA

Inland Audio Visual Ltd, pg 788

ONTARIO

HD Source, pg 777

QUEBEC

Audio Visual Dynamics, pg 694
Freeman Audio Visual, pg 765
Panavideo Inc, pg 850

Slide Projector Repairs

ARKANSAS

Carlton-Bates Co, pg 717

CALIFORNIA

Ametron Audio/Video, pg 684
Gluskin's Custom Audio Video, pg 771
Hooper Camera & Imaging, pg 781
Instructional Materials & Equipment Distributors (I-Med), pg 789
McAlister Electronics, pg 820
Lloyd F McKinney Associates Inc, pg 821
Pro Camera Repair, pg 862

COLORADO

Ceavco Audio Visual Company Inc, pg 719

CONNECTICUT

A/V Davey, pg 697
HB Communications Inc, pg 777
Precision Camera & Video Repair Inc, pg 861
Rockwell Communications Inc, pg 876

FLORIDA

Tallahassee Audio Visual, pg 906

GEORGIA

Audio Visual Resources Inc, pg 695
Lighting & Production Equipment Inc, pg 807
Stage Front Presentation Systems, pg 899

ILLINOIS

Allen Visual Systems Inc, pg 680
Beatty TeleVisual Productions, pg 703
Central Audio-Visual Equipment Inc, pg 719
RC Communications, pg 870

INDIANA

Gary Camera & Digital, pg 768

KENTUCKY

Axxis Leasing Inc, pg 700
NOR-COM Inc, pg 841

MAINE

Headlight Audio Visual Inc, pg 777

MARYLAND

Nelson White Systems Inc, pg 838
RTZ Audio Visual, pg 878

MASSACHUSETTS

Capron Lighting & Sound Co Inc, pg 716
Integrated Solutions Group, pg 789

MICHIGAN

Olson Anderson Co, pg 685
City Events Group, pg 725
TEL Systems LLC, pg 909

MINNESOTA

AVI Systems, pg 698

MISSISSIPPI

Bowie Audio Visual Enterprises Inc, pg 709

MISSOURI

Cintrex Audio Visual, pg 725
Communitronics Corp, pg 729
Schiller's Audio-Visual, pg 881

NEW JERSEY

Hasselblad Bron Inc, pg 776
Leica Camera Inc, pg 806

NEW YORK

Colortone Audio Visual, pg 728
ELMO USA Corp, pg 753
Langie Audio Visual Systems, pg 803
Visual Technologies Corp, pg 932

NORTH CAROLINA

Camcor Inc, pg 715
Strategic Connections, pg 901

OHIO

Audio Visual Media, pg 694
Copp Integrated Systems, pg 731
Icom Multimedia, pg 783
Tri-State Audio Visual Co, pg 918

PENNSYLVANIA

Audio Visions Inc, pg 694
J E Foss Co, pg 764
Wespen Audio Visual Co, pg 935

TENNESSEE

Memphis Communications Corp, pg 823
Technical Support Systems LLC, pg 908

TEXAS

Audio Visual Technologies Group (AVTG), pg 695
Lubbock Audio Visual Inc, pg 812
Quality Audio Visual Service Inc, pg 867

VIRGINIA

Avitecture Inc, pg 699
Boitnott Visual Communications Corp (BVC), pg 708
Lee Hartman & Sons Inc, pg 805
Metropolitan Audio Visual Co LLC, pg 824
The Whitlock Group, pg 937

WASHINGTON

Inland Audio Visual Co, pg 788
PNTA, pg 858

WISCONSIN

Audio Visual of Milwaukee Inc, pg 694
Camera Corner Connecting Point, pg 715
Full Compass Systems, pg 767
School Specialty Inc, pg 882

ALBERTA

Infosat Communications Inc, pg 787
Unique Communications Ltd, pg 921

BRITISH COLUMBIA

Commercial Electronics Ltd, pg 728

MANITOBA

Inland Audio Visual Ltd, pg 788

QUEBEC

Panavideo Inc, pg 850

Slide Retouching, *see* Retouching—Slides

Slide to Film Transfers, *see* Transfers—Slide to Film

Slide to Filmstrip Transfers, *see* Transfers—Slide to Filmstrip

Slide to Video Transfers, *see* Transfers—Slide to Video

Slides from Artwork

ARIZONA

Image Craft LLC, pg 784
Merestone, pg 823
Professional Marketing Services Inc, pg 865

ARKANSAS

White Diamond Productions LLC, pg 937

CALIFORNIA

Action Photo Digital Graphics, pg 675
Coloredge Inc, pg 728
Lynch Communications, pg 813
The Media Staff Inc, pg 822
Point of View Productions, pg 858
PSI Inc, pg 866
QRS Software Services, pg 867
Regent Press Publishers & Printers, pg 873
Dick Reizner Film & Video, pg 873

DISTRICT OF COLUMBIA

O'Keefe Communications Inc, pg 844

FLORIDA

Communications Concepts Inc (CCI), pg 729
Jordan Klein Film & Video (JKFV), pg 795

GEORGIA

Imagers, pg 785
Visioneering International Inc, pg 931

ILLINOIS

CCore Media Inc, pg 718
Gamma Imaging, pg 768
Helix Camera & Video, pg 778
JMC Photo & Digital Services Inc, pg 794

AUDIO/VISUAL

Slides from Artwork (continued)

ILLINOIS (continued)

Major Media Inc, pg 815
Pepper Group, pg 854
PSAV® Presentation Services
    (Hotel Services Division), pg 866
Southern Illinois University, pg 895

INDIANA

Communication Ministries, pg 728
OMNI Productions, pg 845

IOWA

Educational Technology & Media
    Services, pg 751

LOUISIANA

Louisiana State University Division
    of Strategic Communications,
    pg 811

MASSACHUSETTS

Colortek of Boston, pg 728
CommCreative, pg 728
DGI-Invisuals LLC, pg 741
Preston Productions Inc, pg 861
TR Productions, pg 916

MICHIGAN

Arbor Oakland Group, pg 688
Blue Mouse Studio, pg 707
Digi Sign Design LLC, pg 741
K&R's Recording Studios Inc,
    pg 796
MessageMakers, pg 824
Michigan Office Solutions (MOS),
    A Xerox Company, pg 825
On Stage Visuals, pg 846
Tectonics Industries LLC, pg 909

MINNESOTA

Linhoff Photo & Digital Imaging,
    pg 809
Media Loft Inc, pg 822
Pointward, pg 858

MISSISSIPPI

Jasper Ewing & Sons Inc, pg 757

MISSOURI

Allied Photocolor Co, pg 681
Communitronics Corp, pg 729
Visionworks Design Services Inc,
    pg 931

MONTANA

Clarkson Studio, pg 726
KUSM TV, pg 802

NEVADA

Encore Event Technologies LLC,
    pg 754

NEW HAMPSHIRE

Academic & Campus Technology
    Services, pg 672
Apertura, pg 686

NEW JERSEY

AJS Events, pg 679
CELCO, pg 719

C2 Imaging, pg 735
Laurel Video Productions, pg 804
Reed Presentations Inc (RPI),
    pg 872

NEW YORK

Broadstreet Productions LLC,
    pg 711
Duggal Visual Solutions Inc, pg 747
Gage-Line Technology Inc, pg 767
Ketchum Inc, pg 798
Modernage Photographic Services
    Inc, pg 828
Jack Morton Worldwide, pg 830
SMP Digital Graphics, pg 891
Zelman Studios Ltd, pg 945

NORTH CAROLINA

Image Associates Inc, pg 784

NORTH DAKOTA

Media Productions, pg 822

OHIO

Aztec Video Productions, pg 700
Cuyahoga Community College
    Student Production Office (SPO),
    pg 736
Thread Marketing Group, pg 913
Treehaus Communications Inc,
    pg 917
Vista Color Imaging Inc, pg 931

PENNSYLVANIA

Audio Visual Communications Inc,
    pg 694
Bernie's Photo Center, pg 704
Berry & Homer, pg 704
Kensington Falls Animation, pg 797
Main Point Productions, pg 815

TENNESSEE

Memphis Communications Corp,
    pg 823
Stage Post, pg 899

TEXAS

Emergency Film Group, pg 753
Houston Photo Imaging, pg 782
IntegraColor, pg 789
Matson Multi-Media, pg 820
Romar Learning Solutions LLC,
    pg 877
Stage Directions, pg 898
Texas Heart Institute Visual
    Communication Services, pg 911
Thomas Printworks, pg 912

VERMONT

University of Vermont, Instructional
    Television Dept, pg 923

VIRGINIA

Blair Inc, pg 707

WASHINGTON

Inland Audio Visual Co, pg 788

WISCONSIN

AVS Group, pg 699
USAV Group Inc, pg 923

WYOMING

Bridger Productions Inc, pg 710

ONTARIO

Silver Creek Media Inc, pg 888

Slides from Color Negatives

ARIZONA

Image Craft LLC, pg 784
Professional Marketing Services Inc,
    pg 865

CALIFORNIA

Action Photo Digital Graphics,
    pg 675
Coloredge Inc, pg 728
Lynch Communications, pg 813
QRS Software Services, pg 867

FLORIDA

Jordan Klein Film & Video (JKFV),
    pg 795

GEORGIA

Visioneering International Inc,
    pg 931

ILLINOIS

Gamma Imaging, pg 768
Helix Camera & Video, pg 778

INDIANA

OMNI Productions, pg 845

KANSAS

Custom Color Corp, pg 736

LOUISIANA

Louisiana State University Division
    of Strategic Communications,
    pg 811

MASSACHUSETTS

Colortek of Boston, pg 728
CommCreative, pg 728
Preston Productions Inc, pg 861
TR Productions, pg 916

MICHIGAN

Arbor Oakland Group, pg 688
K&R's Recording Studios Inc,
    pg 796
Tectonics Industries LLC, pg 909

MINNESOTA

Linhoff Photo & Digital Imaging,
    pg 809
Media Loft Inc, pg 822

MISSISSIPPI

Jasper Ewing & Sons Inc, pg 757

MISSOURI

Allied Photocolor Co, pg 681
Communitronics Corp, pg 729

MONTANA

KUSM TV, pg 802

NEVADA

Encore Event Technologies LLC,
    pg 754

NEW JERSEY

AJS Events, pg 679
CELCO, pg 719
Reed Presentations Inc (RPI),
    pg 872

NEW YORK

Broadstreet Productions LLC,
    pg 711
Duggal Visual Solutions Inc, pg 747
Ketchum Inc, pg 798
Modernage Photographic Services
    Inc, pg 828
Jack Morton Worldwide, pg 830
SMP Digital Graphics, pg 891
Zelman Studios Ltd, pg 945

OHIO

Aztec Video Productions, pg 700
Thread Marketing Group, pg 913
Vista Color Imaging Inc, pg 931

PENNSYLVANIA

Audio Visual Communications Inc,
    pg 694
Bernie's Photo Center, pg 704
Berry & Homer, pg 704
Main Point Productions, pg 815
Visual Sound Inc, pg 931

TENNESSEE

Memphis Communications Corp,
    pg 823
Stage Post, pg 899

TEXAS

Houston Photo Imaging, pg 782
Pounds Photographic Labs Inc,
    pg 860
Texas Heart Institute Visual
    Communication Services, pg 911
Thomas Printworks, pg 912

VERMONT

University of Vermont, Instructional
    Television Dept, pg 923

VIRGINIA

Blair Inc, pg 707

WISCONSIN

USAV Group Inc, pg 923

Slides from Other Media

ARIZONA

Professional Marketing Services Inc,
    pg 865

CALIFORNIA

Action Photo Digital Graphics,
    pg 675
Coloredge Inc, pg 728
Jaguar Distribution Corp, pg 792
Lynch Communications, pg 813
Media Fabricators Inc, pg 822
PSI Inc, pg 866
QRS Software Services, pg 867
Total Creative, pg 916

FLORIDA

Communications Concepts Inc
    (CCI), pg 729

AUDIO/VISUAL

System Design & Installation (continued)

OKLAHOMA

DD Audio, pg 739

PENNSYLVANIA

Clair Companies, pg 725
Visual Sound Inc, pg 931

RHODE ISLAND

Sound-FX-Design, pg 894

TENNESSEE

Continental Film, pg 731
Memphis Communications Corp, pg 823
Stage Post, pg 899
Technical Support Systems LLC, pg 908

TEXAS

Audio Visual Technologies Group (AVTG), pg 695
AVES Audio Visual Systems Inc, pg 698
Lubbock Audio Visual Inc, pg 812
Stage Directions, pg 898
Tarpley Media Systems, pg 907

VERMONT

University of Vermont, Instructional Television Dept, pg 923

VIRGINIA

Acoustics First Corp, pg 674
American AV, pg 682
Design & Production Inc, pg 740
Opterna, a Belden brand, pg 847

WASHINGTON

Inland Audio Visual Co, pg 788
Kostov Productions, pg 801
Laser Fantasy/HECK Industries/Photon Manufacturing, pg 804

WEST VIRGINIA

United Sound & Electronics, pg 921

WISCONSIN

Full Compass Systems, pg 767
USAV Group Inc, pg 923
Video Wisconsin Inc, pg 929
Wisconsin Public Television, pg 940

WYOMING

Bridger Productions Inc, pg 710

ALBERTA

Unique Communications Ltd, pg 921

BRITISH COLUMBIA

DL Sound & Lighting Productions Ltd, pg 744

ONTARIO

Cinema Stage Inc, pg 724
MVI - MultiVision Inc, pg 835
State of the Art Acoustik Inc, pg 900

Technovision® Interactive Inc, pg 909
Trebas Institute, pg 917
Westbury National Show Systems Ltd, pg 936

QUEBEC

Sceno Plus, pg 881
Trebas Institute, pg 917

Tape Recorder & Player Distributors

ALABAMA

Curtis Company, pg 736

ARIZONA

Arizona Cine Equipment, pg 688
EAR Professional Audio/Video, pg 749
Troxell-CDI, pg 918

ARKANSAS

White Diamond Productions LLC, pg 937

CALIFORNIA

Ametron Audio/Video, pg 684
Associated Sound, pg 691
Assured Audio Visual, pg 691
ATV Video Center Inc, pg 692
Audio Images Corp, pg 693
BigFoot Mobile Systems, pg 705
Birns & Sawyer Inc, pg 706
California Tape Products Inc, pg 714
Electronic Design Solutions Inc, pg 752
Empire Pro, pg 753
Gluskin's Custom Audio Video, pg 771
Instructional Materials & Equipment Distributors (I-Med), pg 789
Jaguar Distribution Corp, pg 792
Martel Electronics Sales Inc, pg 818
Media Fabricators Inc, pg 822
MediaPOINTE, pg 823
Sanako Inc, pg 880
SNAP, pg 891
Southern California Sound Image Inc, pg 895
SSL Industries Inc, pg 898
SuperVision, pg 904
Towards 2000 Inc, pg 916
VMI Inc, pg 932

COLORADO

Spectrum Audio Visual Services, pg 897
Stanco Sales LLC, pg 899

CONNECTICUT

Connecticut Audio & Theatrical Supply, pg 731
HB Communications Inc, pg 777
MAVCO, pg 820

DELAWARE

Actors Attic, pg 675

FLORIDA

Altel Systems Group Inc, pg 682
AVI-SPL, pg 698
Broadcasters General Store Inc, pg 711
Digital Video Systems, pg 742

Harmon's Audio-Visual Services, pg 776
Harris Corp, pg 776
Hi-Tech Enterprises Inc, pg 779
Hi-Tech Import Export Corp, pg 779
Industrial Strength Inc, pg 787
Intermark Industries Inc, pg 789
ONstage, pg 846
Photosound of Orlando Inc, pg 856
Recording Media & Equipment Inc (RM&E), pg 872
Stereo Sales Inc, pg 900
TAI Audio, pg 906

GEORGIA

Baker Audio Visual, pg 700
Convergent Media Systems, pg 731
Lighting & Production Equipment Inc, pg 807
Stage Front Presentation Systems, pg 899
Visioneering International Inc, pg 931

HAWAII

The Audio Visual Co (AVCO), pg 694

ILLINOIS

Allen Visual Systems Inc, pg 680
Central Audio-Visual Equipment Inc, pg 719
Joseph Electronics, pg 795
Quintessence Audio Ltd, pg 868
RC Communications, pg 870

INDIANA

Sensory Technologies LLC, pg 884
SHP Electronics, pg 887

KANSAS

KK Office Solutions Inc, pg 799

KENTUCKY

Axxis Leasing Inc, pg 700
Barney Miller's Inc, pg 827
NOR-COM Inc, pg 841

MARYLAND

Cardinal Sound & Video, pg 717
RTZ Audio Visual, pg 878

MASSACHUSETTS

Professional Audio Design Inc, pg 865
University Products Inc, pg 923

MICHIGAN

City Events Group, pg 725
On Stage Visuals, pg 846

MINNESOTA

Alpha Video & Audio Inc, pg 682
AVI Systems, pg 698

MISSISSIPPI

Bowie Audio Visual Enterprises Inc, pg 709

MISSOURI

Communitronics Corp, pg 729
Conference Technologies Inc, pg 730
ITC, pg 791

Modern Communications Inc, pg 828
Schiller's Audio-Visual, pg 881

NEW HAMPSHIRE

APS Lighting-Sound-AV, pg 688

NEW JERSEY

A-V Services Inc, pg 671
Alltec Stores, a Vcom IMC Company, pg 681
AlltecPro, pg 681
Audio Visual Dynamics®, pg 694
AV Bluebook, pg 696
Earl Girls Inc, pg 749
FlagHouse, pg 762
G&G Technologies Inc, pg 768
HamiltonBuhl, pg 775
Starlite, pg 900
SYMCO Inc, pg 905
Total Video Products Inc, pg 916
Video Corporation of America (VCA), pg 927
Wired 4 Sound Inc, pg 940
Yorktel, pg 944

NEW YORK

American Video Inc, pg 684
AV Workshop, pg 697
Design Audio Visual Inc, pg 741
Flash Electronics Inc, pg 762
Gaylord Archival, pg 768
Indigo Productions, pg 787
Long Island Video Enterprises Live Inc, pg 811
Markertek Video Supply, pg 817
Neptune Photo Inc, pg 838
Ray Supply Inc, pg 870
RNJ Electronics, pg 875
Tri-Ed Distribution Inc, pg 918
Video Technology Services Inc, pg 929

NORTH CAROLINA

Camcor Inc, pg 715
Strategic Connections, pg 901

OHIO

Copp Integrated Systems, pg 731

PENNSYLVANIA

Advanced AV LLC, pg 677
Audio Visions Inc, pg 694
Audio Visual Communications Inc, pg 694
Bernie's Photo Center, pg 704
Brodart Co, pg 711
J E Foss Co, pg 764
Grise Audio Visual Center Inc, pg 774
The Lerro Corp, pg 806
Morefield Communications Inc, pg 830
Vistacom Inc, pg 931
Wespen Audio Visual Co, pg 935

TENNESSEE

Allstar Audio Systems Inc, pg 681
Lowrance Sound Co Inc, pg 812
Spring Arbor Distributors Inc, pg 898
Technical Support Systems LLC, pg 908
Zion Music Group, pg 945

TEXAS

Audio Visual Technologies Group
 (AVTG), pg 695
AVES Audio Visual Systems Inc,
 pg 698
Crossroads Audio Inc, pg 735
JSAV, pg 795
Lubbock Audio Visual Inc, pg 812
Pro Video & Film Equipment Co
 Inc, pg 863
Quality Audio Visual Service Inc,
 pg 867
Tarpley Media Systems, pg 907

UTAH

Performance Audio LLC, pg 854
RIA Corp, pg 874

VIRGINIA

Boitnott Visual Communications
 Corp (BVC), pg 708
Cybernetics, pg 736
Intellidyne LLC, pg 789
Lee Hartman & Sons Inc, pg 805
Metropolitan Audio Visual Co LLC,
 pg 824
The Whitlock Group, pg 937

WASHINGTON

CCI Solutions, pg 718
Northern Lights & Pro Audio,
 pg 842
PNTA, pg 858

WEST VIRGINIA

United Sound & Electronics, pg 921

WISCONSIN

Audio Visual of Milwaukee Inc,
 pg 694
Demco Inc, pg 740
Full Compass Systems, pg 767

PUERTO RICO

Bonnin Electronics Inc, pg 708

ALBERTA

McBain Camera Ltd, pg 820
Unique Communications Ltd,
 pg 921

BRITISH COLUMBIA

Commercial Electronics Ltd, pg 728

MANITOBA

Inland Audio Visual Ltd, pg 788

ONTARIO

HD Source, pg 777
Nationwide Audio Visual Co,
 pg 837
Westbury National Show Systems
 Ltd, pg 936

QUEBEC

Panavideo Inc, pg 850

Tape Recorder & Player Manufacturers

CALIFORNIA

Califone International Inc, pg 714
TEAC America Inc, pg 908

NEW JERSEY

AlltecPro, pg 681
HamiltonBuhl, pg 775
Panasonic Corporation of North
 America, pg 850
RAMSA Professional Audio
 Systems, pg 870

NEW YORK

TecNec Distributing, pg 909
Video Technology Services Inc,
 pg 929

Tape Recorder & Player Rentals

ALABAMA

Audio-Video Resources Inc, pg 694

ARIZONA

Arizona Cine Equipment, pg 688
Merestone, pg 823
Metropolitan Audio-Visual Inc,
 pg 824
Video West Inc, pg 929

ARKANSAS

White Diamond Productions LLC,
 pg 937

CALIFORNIA

Advanced Media LLC, pg 677
AGF Media Services, pg 678
Ametron Audio/Video, pg 684
Artichoke Productions, pg 690
Associated Sound, pg 691
Assured Audio Visual, pg 691
ATV Video Center Inc, pg 692
Audio Rents, pg 693
AV Guys, pg 697
BigFoot Mobile Systems, pg 705
Electronic Design Solutions Inc,
 pg 752
Express Media Inc, pg 757
Gold Standard Productions, pg 772
Golden Gate Studios, pg 772
Instructional Materials & Equipment
 Distributors (I-Med), pg 789
JD Audio Visual Inc, pg 793
Lynch Communications, pg 813
Maximus Media Inc, pg 820
Media Fabricators Inc, pg 822
Munday & Collins AV, pg 834
On-Trax Inc, pg 846
PSAV® Presentation Services,
 pg 866
QRS Software Services, pg 867
SNAP, pg 891
Technical Services, pg 908
Third Ear Sound Co, pg 912
Towards 2000 Inc, pg 916
VER, pg 926
Video Resources Inc, pg 928
VMI Inc, pg 932
Voice & Video Rentals, pg 932

COLORADO

Daylight Productions & Rentals,
 pg 739
Spectrum Audio Visual Services,
 pg 897

CONNECTICUT

A/V Davey, pg 697
Connecticut Audio & Theatrical
 Supply, pg 731

DELAWARE

Actors Attic, pg 675
Ken-Del Productions Inc, pg 797

FLORIDA

Accord Productions, pg 673
AVI-SPL, pg 698
Harmon's Audio-Visual Services,
 pg 776
Industrial Strength Inc, pg 787
Jordan Klein Film & Video (JKFV),
 pg 795
ONstage, pg 846
Photosound of Orlando Inc, pg 856
TAI Audio, pg 906
Universal Studios Florida®
 Production Group, pg 922

GEORGIA

Convergent Media Systems, pg 731
Lighting & Production Equipment
 Inc, pg 807
MAGNUM Companies Ltd, pg 815
ON Services, a GES Company,
 pg 846
Stage Front Presentation Systems,
 pg 899

ILLINOIS

Allen Visual Systems Inc, pg 680
AV Chicago Inc, pg 696
Backstar Creative Media Inc,
 pg 700
Beatty TeleVisual Productions,
 pg 703
Central Audio-Visual Equipment
 Inc, pg 719
On Site Video, pg 846
PSAV® Presentation Services
 (Hotel Services Division), pg 866
RC Communications, pg 870
Resolution Productions Group,
 pg 874
SCI Television & Creative Media
 LLC, pg 882

INDIANA

Advanced Media Integration, pg 677

KENTUCKY

Barney Miller's Inc, pg 827

LOUISIANA

Clark Services Audio Visual &
 Exhibit Inc, pg 725
Pace Systems, pg 849

MARYLAND

Advance Audiovisual Presentation
 Ltd, pg 677
CPR MultiMedia Solutions, pg 732
dbF a Media Company, pg 739
Hargrove Inc, pg 776
Maryland Sound International
 Holding Co LLC, pg 819
RTZ Audio Visual, pg 878

MASSACHUSETTS

AVFX Inc, pg 698
Capron Lighting & Sound Co Inc,
 pg 716
massAV, pg 819
Preston Productions Inc, pg 861

MICHIGAN

City Events Group, pg 725
Digi Sign Design LLC, pg 741

K&R All Media Productions LLC,
 pg 796
K&R's Recording Studios Inc,
 pg 796
On Stage Visuals, pg 846

MINNESOTA

Alpha Video & Audio Inc, pg 682
AVI Systems, pg 698

MISSISSIPPI

Bowie Audio Visual Enterprises Inc,
 pg 709

MISSOURI

Communitronics Corp, pg 729
Schiller's Audio-Visual, pg 881
Show-Me Audio-Visual, pg 887

MONTANA

Jereco Studios Inc, pg 793

NEVADA

GES Audio Visual, pg 770
Lefco Video Services Inc, pg 806

NEW HAMPSHIRE

Academic & Campus Technology
 Services, pg 672
Apertura, pg 686
APS Lighting-Sound-AV, pg 688

NEW JERSEY

Audio Visual Dynamics®, pg 694
Earl Girls Inc, pg 749
International Audio Visual Inc,
 pg 790
MiB MediaWorks, pg 825
Moe AV LLC, pg 828
Panavid, pg 850
PLS Staging, pg 858
Starlite, pg 900
Wired 4 Sound Inc, pg 940

NEW YORK

Ace Video, pg 674
Adwar Video, pg 678
American Video Inc, pg 684
AV Workshop, pg 697
CMI Communications, pg 727
CP Communications, pg 732
Design Audio Visual Inc, pg 741
Hello World Communications,
 pg 778
Long Island Video Enterprises Live
 Inc, pg 811
Manhattan Center Studios Inc,
 pg 816
Ray Supply Inc, pg 870
Specialized Audio-Visual Inc,
 pg 896
Visual Word Systems Inc, pg 932
WorldStage, pg 941

NORTH CAROLINA

AV Connections Inc, pg 697
AV Metro Inc, pg 697
Special Event Services, pg 896
Take One Productions Ltd, pg 906

NORTH DAKOTA

Media Productions, pg 822

AUDIO/VISUAL

Tape Recorder & Player Rentals (continued)

OHIO

Hughie's Event Production Services, pg 782
Mills James Productions, pg 828
Vista Color Imaging Inc, pg 931

OREGON

Northwest Film Center, pg 842

PENNSYLVANIA

Advanced AV LLC, pg 677
Audio Visions Inc, pg 694
Audio Visual Communications Inc, pg 694
FMP Media Solutions Inc, pg 763
Grise Audio Visual Center Inc, pg 774
North Star Satellite Communications Inc, pg 842
Vistacom Inc, pg 931
Visual Sound Inc, pg 931

TENNESSEE

Allstar Audio Systems Inc, pg 681
Brantley Sound Associates Inc, pg 709
Love Shack Recording Studios, pg 811
Memphis Communications Corp, pg 823
Russ Sturgeon Productions/RSVP, pg 903
Technical Support Systems LLC, pg 908

TEXAS

Audio Visual Technologies Group (AVTG), pg 695
JSAV, pg 795
Lubbock Audio Visual Inc, pg 812
Music Lab Inc, pg 834
Quality Audio Visual Service Inc, pg 867
Video Perspective, pg 928

UTAH

Performance Audio LLC, pg 854

VIRGINIA

American AV, pg 682
Boitnott Visual Communications Corp (BVC), pg 708
Metropolitan Audio Visual Co LLC, pg 824
The Whitlock Group, pg 937

WASHINGTON

Kostov Productions, pg 801
Northern Lights & Pro Audio, pg 842
PNTA, pg 858

WEST VIRGINIA

United Sound & Electronics, pg 921

WISCONSIN

Audio Visual of Milwaukee Inc, pg 694
Event Essentials, pg 756
Full Compass Systems, pg 767

University of Wisconsin-Oshkosh Radio-TV-Film Dept, pg 923
USAV Group Inc, pg 923

WYOMING

Bridger Productions Inc, pg 710

PUERTO RICO

Stage Crew Audiovisual Inc, pg 898

ALBERTA

Allstar Show Industries Inc, pg 681
Evolution AV, pg 757
McBain Camera Ltd, pg 820
Unique Communications Ltd, pg 921

BRITISH COLUMBIA

Clark's Audio Visual Services Ltd, pg 725
MicrophoneRentals.com, pg 826
Triad Communications Ltd, pg 918
Video Out Distribution, pg 928

MANITOBA

Inland Audio Visual Ltd, pg 788

ONTARIO

HD Source, pg 777
Metalworks Recording Studios Inc, pg 824
Westbury National Show Systems Ltd, pg 936

QUEBEC

Freeman Audio Visual, pg 765
Group PVP, pg 774
Panavideo Inc, pg 850

Tape Recorder & Player Repairs

CALIFORNIA

Advanced Media LLC, pg 677
Ametron Audio/Video, pg 684
BigFoot Mobile Systems, pg 705
Gluskin's Custom Audio Video, pg 771
Instructional Materials & Equipment Distributors (I-Med), pg 789
McAlister Electronics, pg 820
Lloyd F McKinney Associates Inc, pg 821
SSL Industries Inc, pg 898
Technical Services, pg 908
Towards 2000 Inc, pg 916
VMI Inc, pg 932

CONNECTICUT

A/V Davey, pg 697
HB Communications Inc, pg 777

FLORIDA

Hi-Tech Enterprises Inc, pg 779
JT Communications, pg 795
Stereo Sales Inc, pg 900
TAI Audio, pg 906

GEORGIA

Lighting & Production Equipment Inc, pg 807
Stage Front Presentation Systems, pg 899

ILLINOIS

Allen Visual Systems Inc, pg 680
Beatty TeleVisual Productions, pg 703
Central Audio-Visual Equipment Inc, pg 719
Midwest Digital Corp, pg 827
On Site Video, pg 846

KANSAS

KK Office Solutions Inc, pg 799

KENTUCKY

Axxis Leasing Inc, pg 700
Barney Miller's Inc, pg 827
NOR-COM Inc, pg 841

MARYLAND

Nelson White Systems Inc, pg 838
RTZ Audio Visual, pg 878

MASSACHUSETTS

Capron Lighting & Sound Co Inc, pg 716
Professional Audio Design Inc, pg 865

MICHIGAN

City Events Group, pg 725
TEL Systems LLC, pg 909

MINNESOTA

Alpha Video & Audio Inc, pg 682
AVI Systems, pg 698

MISSISSIPPI

Bowie Audio Visual Enterprises Inc, pg 709

MISSOURI

Cintrex Audio Visual, pg 725
Communitronics Corp, pg 729
Schiller's Audio-Visual, pg 881

NEW JERSEY

Earl Girls Inc, pg 749
Starlite, pg 900

NEW YORK

Adwar Video, pg 678
American Video Inc, pg 684
Ray Supply Inc, pg 870
Video Technology Services Inc, pg 929

NORTH CAROLINA

Camcor Inc, pg 715
Strategic Connections, pg 901

OHIO

Copp Integrated Systems, pg 731
Tri-State Audio Visual Co, pg 918

PENNSYLVANIA

Audio Visions Inc, pg 694
Bernie's Photo Center, pg 704
J E Foss Co, pg 764
Vistacom Inc, pg 931

TENNESSEE

Memphis Communications Corp, pg 823
Technical Support Systems LLC, pg 908

TEXAS

Audio Visual Technologies Group (AVTG), pg 695
Crossroads Audio Inc, pg 735
Lubbock Audio Visual Inc, pg 812
Music Lab Inc, pg 834
Quality Audio Visual Service Inc, pg 867
Tarpley Media Systems, pg 907

VIRGINIA

Boitnott Visual Communications Corp (BVC), pg 708
Metropolitan Audio Visual Co LLC, pg 824
The Whitlock Group, pg 937

WASHINGTON

Northern Lights & Pro Audio, pg 842
PNTA, pg 858

WEST VIRGINIA

United Sound & Electronics, pg 921

WISCONSIN

Audio Visual of Milwaukee Inc, pg 694
Full Compass Systems, pg 767

ALBERTA

Evolution AV, pg 757
Unique Communications Ltd, pg 921

MANITOBA

Inland Audio Visual Ltd, pg 788

ONTARIO

HD Source, pg 777
Westbury National Show Systems Ltd, pg 936

QUEBEC

Panavideo Inc, pg 850

Three-D Effects, see Computer Three-D Effects on Slide

Titling & Artwork Services, see Artwork & Titling Services

Transfers—Filmstrip to Slide

ARIZONA

Professional Marketing Services Inc, pg 865

CALIFORNIA

Action Photo Digital Graphics, pg 675
Coloredge Inc, pg 728
iCorpTv, pg 783
Lynch Communications, pg 813
QRS Software Services, pg 867

GEORGIA

Staging Directions Inc, pg 899

ILLINOIS

Gamma Imaging, pg 768

MASSACHUSETTS

CommCreative, pg 728
TR Productions, pg 916

MICHIGAN

K&R's Recording Studios Inc,
pg 796

MISSOURI

Allied Photocolor Co, pg 681

NEVADA

JCS Video Productions, pg 793

NEW JERSEY

AJS Events, pg 679
CELCO, pg 719
Reed Presentations Inc (RPI),
pg 872

NEW YORK

Duggal Visual Solutions Inc, pg 747
Jack Morton Worldwide, pg 830
The Palmer Group, pg 850
Zelman Studios Ltd, pg 945

OHIO

Aztec Video Productions, pg 700
Vista Color Imaging Inc, pg 931

PENNSYLVANIA

Audio Visual Communications Inc,
pg 694
Berry & Homer, pg 704
FMP Media Solutions Inc, pg 763

TENNESSEE

Memphis Communications Corp,
pg 823
Stage Post, pg 899

TEXAS

Stage Directions, pg 898

VIRGINIA

Blair Inc, pg 707

WISCONSIN

USAV Group Inc, pg 923

Transfers—Slide to Film

ARIZONA

Professional Marketing Services Inc,
pg 865
Star Video Duplicating, pg 900

CALIFORNIA

iCorpTv, pg 783
Lynch Communications, pg 813
QRS Software Services, pg 867

FLORIDA

Communications Concepts Inc
(CCI), pg 729

GEORGIA

Staging Directions Inc, pg 899
Visioneering International Inc,
pg 931

MAINE

Headlight Audio Visual Inc, pg 777

MASSACHUSETTS

CommCreative, pg 728
Integrated Solutions Group, pg 789
TR Productions, pg 916

MICHIGAN

K&R's Recording Studios Inc,
pg 796

MISSOURI

Allied Photocolor Co, pg 681

NEVADA

JCS Video Productions, pg 793

NEW HAMPSHIRE

Apertura, pg 686

NEW JERSEY

AJS Events, pg 679
CELCO, pg 719

NEW YORK

Thomas Craven Film Corp, pg 733
Modernage Photographic Services
Inc, pg 828
Jack Morton Worldwide, pg 830
The Palmer Group, pg 850
Zelman Studios Ltd, pg 945

OHIO

Aztec Video Productions, pg 700

PENNSYLVANIA

John E Allen Inc, pg 680
Audio Visual Communications Inc,
pg 694
FMP Media Solutions Inc, pg 763

TENNESSEE

Memphis Communications Corp,
pg 823
Stage Post, pg 899

TEXAS

Hurst Digital, pg 782
The Samuels Co, pg 879
Stage Directions, pg 898

VIRGINIA

Blair Inc, pg 707

WISCONSIN

Audio Visual of Milwaukee Inc,
pg 694
USAV Group Inc, pg 923

Transfers—Slide to Filmstrip

ARIZONA

Professional Marketing Services Inc,
pg 865

CALIFORNIA

Coloredge Inc, pg 728
iCorpTv, pg 783
Lynch Communications, pg 813
QRS Software Services, pg 867

GEORGIA

Staging Directions Inc, pg 899
Visioneering International Inc,
pg 931

ILLINOIS

Southern Illinois University, pg 895

MASSACHUSETTS

CommCreative, pg 728
TR Productions, pg 916

MICHIGAN

K&R's Recording Studios Inc,
pg 796

MISSOURI

Allied Photocolor Co, pg 681

NEVADA

JCS Video Productions, pg 793

NEW JERSEY

AJS Events, pg 679
CELCO, pg 719

NEW YORK

Duggal Visual Solutions Inc, pg 747
Jack Morton Worldwide, pg 830
The Palmer Group, pg 850
Zelman Studios Ltd, pg 945

OHIO

Aztec Video Productions, pg 700

PENNSYLVANIA

Audio Visual Communications Inc,
pg 694
FMP Media Solutions Inc, pg 763
Innovision Media Group, pg 788

TENNESSEE

Memphis Communications Corp,
pg 823
Stage Post, pg 899

TEXAS

Hurst Digital, pg 782
McNee Productions Inc, pg 821
Stage Directions, pg 898

VIRGINIA

Blair Inc, pg 707

WISCONSIN

Audio Visual of Milwaukee Inc,
pg 694
USAV Group Inc, pg 923

Transfers—Slide to Video

ARIZONA

Metropolitan Audio-Visual Inc,
pg 824
On-Site Video, pg 846
Star Video Duplicating, pg 900

ARKANSAS

White Diamond Productions LLC,
pg 937

CALIFORNIA

Access Video in Berkeley, pg 673
Action Photo Digital Graphics,
pg 675
CCI Digital, a DVS Company,
pg 718
Steve Chandler, pg 720
Custom Video Productions Inc,
pg 736
Gold Standard Productions, pg 772
iCorpTv, pg 783
Lynch Communications, pg 813
PM Productions, pg 858
PSI Inc, pg 866
QRS Software Services, pg 867
RJ Video Productions, pg 875
Shokus Video, pg 886
SonicPool, pg 892
Wavemaker Media Design, pg 934
WMS Media Inc, pg 940

COLORADO

Ceavco Audio Visual Company Inc,
pg 719
CSI Film & Video LLC, pg 735
Daylight Productions & Rentals,
pg 739
Mike's Camera, pg 827
Rocky Mountain Audio/Video
Productions Inc, pg 876
Spectrum Audio Visual Services,
pg 897

CONNECTICUT

Digital Video Productions, pg 742
Guymark Studios LLC, pg 775
Rockwell Communications Inc,
pg 876

DISTRICT OF COLUMBIA

Interface Media Group, pg 789
O'Keefe Communications Inc,
pg 844

FLORIDA

Access Media Group, pg 673
Communications Concepts Inc
(CCI), pg 729
Sunrise Studios, pg 904
Video Techniques Inc, pg 928

GEORGIA

Beachwood Productions, pg 702
Staging Directions Inc, pg 899
Visioneering International Inc,
pg 931

ILLINOIS

Beatty TeleVisual Productions,
pg 703
CCore Media Inc, pg 718
Major Media Inc, pg 815
Major Media Productions Inc,
pg 815
PSAV® Presentation Services
(Hotel Services Division), pg 866
20/20 Communications Inc, pg 920
WEEK TV, pg 935

INDIANA

OMNI Productions, pg 845

IOWA

Educational Technology & Media
Services, pg 751

AUDIO/VISUAL

Transfers—Slide to Video (continued)

KENTUCKY

Audio Visual Techniques Inc, pg 695
Barney Miller's Inc, pg 827

LOUISIANA

Louisiana State University Division of Strategic Communications, pg 811
Moxie Media, pg 832
Vidox Motion Imagery, pg 930

MAINE

Headlight Audio Visual Inc, pg 777

MARYLAND

Pro Cuts Editing Services, pg 862
Satellite Media Production, pg 881
Spectrum Productions, pg 897

MASSACHUSETTS

Capron Lighting & Sound Co Inc, pg 716
CommCreative, pg 728
Integrated Solutions Group, pg 789
TR Productions, pg 916

MICHIGAN

K&R's Recording Studios Inc, pg 796
MessageMakers, pg 824
The Program Source International, pg 865
RingSide Creative, pg 875
The Transfer Zone®, pg 917

MINNESOTA

Badiyan Inc, pg 700
Media Loft Inc, pg 822
Rum Jungle Media, pg 878

MISSISSIPPI

Jasper Ewing & Sons Inc, pg 757

MISSOURI

Communitronics Corp, pg 729
Show-Me Audio-Visual, pg 887

NEVADA

JCS Video Productions, pg 793
Peterson's Video Transfer Services, pg 855

NEW HAMPSHIRE

Academic & Campus Technology Services, pg 672
Apertura, pg 686

NEW JERSEY

AJS Events, pg 679
CELCO, pg 719
Laurel Video Productions, pg 804
VCSvideo, pg 925
Video Corporation of America (VCA), pg 927

NEW YORK

aurora productions, pg 696
Buffalo Video Production, pg 712
Colortone Audio Visual, pg 728
Thomas Craven Film Corp, pg 733
Duggal Visual Solutions Inc, pg 747
Duplication Depot Inc, pg 748
Duplication Specialists Inc, pg 748
Long Island Video Enterprises Live Inc, pg 811
Jack Morton Worldwide, pg 830
Neptune Photo Inc, pg 838
The Palmer Group, pg 850
Teatown Communications Group, pg 908
TeleTime Productions, pg 910
Visual Technologies Corp, pg 932
Zelman Studios Ltd, pg 945

NORTH CAROLINA

Camcor Inc, pg 715
Duke Media Services, pg 747
Image Associates Inc, pg 784

NORTH DAKOTA

Media Productions, pg 822

OHIO

Advent Media Inc, pg 677
Aztec Video Productions, pg 700
Curtis Inc, pg 736
Take 1 Media Services, pg 906
Ungar Video & Film, pg 921
Vista Color Imaging Inc, pg 931

OKLAHOMA

Garman Productions LLC, pg 768

OREGON

KTVA Productions, pg 802
REX, pg 874

PENNSYLVANIA

John E Allen Inc, pg 680
Audio Visions Inc, pg 694
Audio Visual Communications Inc, pg 694
Bernie's Photo Center, pg 704
Center City Film & Video Inc, pg 719
FMP Media Solutions Inc, pg 763
Innovision Media Group, pg 788
Panta Rhei Media Inc, pg 851
Production Masters Inc (PMI), pg 864
The Videohouse Inc, pg 929
Visual Sound Inc, pg 931
WPHL-TV, pg 942

TENNESSEE

Memphis Communications Corp, pg 823
Stage Post, pg 899

TEXAS

Dub King, pg 747
Hurst Digital, pg 782
Replicopy Digital Media Center, pg 873
Romar Learning Solutions LLC, pg 877
South Coast Film & Video, pg 895
Stage Directions, pg 898
Texas Heart Institute Visual Communication Services, pg 911

VERMONT

University of Vermont, Instructional Television Dept, pg 923

VIRGINIA

Advance Concepts Inc, pg 677

WASHINGTON

Inland Audio Visual Co, pg 788

WISCONSIN

Audio Visual of Milwaukee Inc, pg 694
AVS Group, pg 699
University of Wisconsin-Oshkosh Radio-TV-Film Dept, pg 923
USAV Group Inc, pg 923
Video Wisconsin Inc, pg 929
Wisconsin Public Television, pg 940

PUERTO RICO

Stage Crew Audiovisual Inc, pg 898

BRITISH COLUMBIA

Commercial Electronics Ltd, pg 728
Triad Communications Ltd, pg 918
24 Frames Film & Video, pg 920

ONTARIO

Silver Creek Media Inc, pg 888
Video Excellence Productions, pg 927

Transparency & Slide Equipment & Supply, *see* Slide & Transparency Equipment & Supply

Transparency Duplication, *see* Duplication—Transparencies

Transparency Enlargement, *see* Enlargement—Transparencies

Transparency Printing, *see* Volume Printing—Overhead Transparencies

Volume Printing—Filmstrips

CALIFORNIA

Coloredge Inc, pg 728
QRS Software Services, pg 867

GEORGIA

Staging Directions Inc, pg 899

ILLINOIS

Gamma Imaging, pg 768

MICHIGAN

K&R's Recording Studios Inc, pg 796

NEW YORK

Duggal Visual Solutions Inc, pg 747
Zelman Studios Ltd, pg 945

OHIO

Aztec Video Productions, pg 700

PENNSYLVANIA

Audio Visual Communications Inc, pg 694
Berry & Homer, pg 704

TENNESSEE

Stage Post, pg 899

TEXAS

Hurst Digital, pg 782

VIRGINIA

Blair Inc, pg 707

WISCONSIN

Audio Visual of Milwaukee Inc, pg 694

Volume Printing—Overhead Transparencies

ARIZONA

Professional Marketing Services Inc, pg 865

CALIFORNIA

Action Photo Digital Graphics, pg 675
Lynch Communications, pg 813
QRS Software Services, pg 867

GEORGIA

Staging Directions Inc, pg 899

ILLINOIS

Gamma Imaging, pg 768

KENTUCKY

NIMCO Inc, pg 841

MICHIGAN

K&R's Recording Studios Inc, pg 796

NEW JERSEY

Reed Presentations Inc (RPI), pg 872

NEW YORK

Modernage Photographic Services Inc, pg 828
SMP Digital Graphics, pg 891

OHIO

Aztec Video Productions, pg 700
Thread Marketing Group, pg 913

PENNSYLVANIA

Audio Visual Communications Inc, pg 694

TENNESSEE

Stage Post, pg 899

TEXAS

Thomas Printworks, pg 912

WISCONSIN

USAV Group Inc, pg 923

Volume Printing—Slides

ARIZONA

Professional Marketing Services Inc, pg 865

CALIFORNIA

Action Photo Digital Graphics, pg 675
Coloredge Inc, pg 728
Lynch Communications, pg 813
QRS Software Services, pg 867

GEORGIA

Imagers, pg 785
Staging Directions Inc, pg 899

ILLINOIS

Gamma Imaging, pg 768
Pepper Group, pg 854

MASSACHUSETTS

Colortek of Boston, pg 728
CommCreative, pg 728
DGI-Invisuals LLC, pg 741
Graphx Inc, pg 773

MICHIGAN

K&R's Recording Studios Inc, pg 796
Tectonics Industries LLC, pg 909

MINNESOTA

Linhoff Photo & Digital Imaging, pg 809
Pointward, pg 858

MISSOURI

Allied Photocolor Co, pg 681

NEW YORK

Duggal Visual Solutions Inc, pg 747
Modernage Photographic Services Inc, pg 828
Jack Morton Worldwide, pg 830
Zelman Studios Ltd, pg 945

NORTH CAROLINA

Image Associates Inc, pg 784

OHIO

Aztec Video Productions, pg 700
Vista Color Imaging Inc, pg 931

PENNSYLVANIA

Audio Visual Communications Inc, pg 694
Bernie's Photo Center, pg 704
Berry & Homer, pg 704

TENNESSEE

Memphis Communications Corp, pg 823
Stage Post, pg 899

TEXAS

IntegraColor, pg 789
Thomas Printworks, pg 912

VIRGINIA

Blair Inc, pg 707

WISCONSIN

USAV Group Inc, pg 923

ONTARIO

Silver Creek Media Inc, pg 888

Workshops, *see* Production Workshops

COMPUTER SYSTEMS

Animation System Distributors

CALIFORNIA

Audio Images Corp, pg 693
California Tape Products Inc, pg 714
Computer Modules Inc, pg 729
Diaquest, pg 741
MediaPOINTE, pg 823
Promax Systems, pg 865
Videobotics, pg 929
VMI Inc, pg 932

COLORADO

Aspen Systems Inc, pg 691
G W Hannaway & Associates, pg 775

CONNECTICUT

HB Communications Inc, pg 777

FLORIDA

Access Media Group, pg 673
Digital Video Systems, pg 742
Hi-Tech Enterprises Inc, pg 779

MARYLAND

Kipp Visual Systems Inc, pg 799

MASSACHUSETTS

Avid Technology Inc, pg 698
Psychsoft Inc, pg 866
Rule Boston Camera, pg 878
The Weather Company, An IBM Business, pg 935

MICHIGAN

ASC Systems, pg 690
Digi Sign Design LLC, pg 741
On Stage Visuals, pg 846
TEL Systems LLC, pg 909

MISSOURI

Conference Technologies Inc, pg 730
Modern Communications Inc, pg 828

NEW JERSEY

Yorktel, pg 944

OHIO

AutoDesSys Inc, pg 696

PENNSYLVANIA

AccuWeather Inc, pg 674
Advanced AV LLC, pg 677
The Lerro Corp, pg 806

TEXAS

Biway Media, pg 706
Epic Software Group Inc, pg 755
Videotex Systems Inc, pg 930

VIRGINIA

The Whitlock Group, pg 937

WISCONSIN

Audio Visual of Milwaukee Inc, pg 694
Full Compass Systems, pg 767
Safe Harbor Computers, pg 879

BRITISH COLUMBIA

Credo Interactive Inc, pg 734

MANITOBA

Advance Pro, pg 677

ONTARIO

GestureTek, pg 770

Animation System Manufacturers

CALIFORNIA

Diaquest, pg 741
Gilderfluke & Co Inc, pg 771
Grande Vitesse Systems Inc (GVS), pg 773
Linker Systems Inc, pg 809

COLORADO

Aspen Systems Inc, pg 691

FLORIDA

Midtown Video Inc, pg 827

MASSACHUSETTS

Avid Technology Inc, pg 698
Psychsoft Inc, pg 866
The Weather Company, An IBM Business, pg 935

NEW JERSEY

CELCO, pg 719

OHIO

AutoDesSys Inc, pg 696

PENNSYLVANIA

AccuWeather Inc, pg 674

TEXAS

Biway Media, pg 706

VERMONT

Polhemus, pg 859

WISCONSIN

Safe Harbor Computers, pg 879

BRITISH COLUMBIA

Credo Interactive Inc, pg 734
Richmond Sound Design Ltd, pg 875
Triad Communications Ltd, pg 918

ONTARIO

GestureTek, pg 770

Animation System Rentals

ARIZONA

Merestone, pg 823

CALIFORNIA

Artichoke Productions, pg 690
Muse Presentation Technologies, pg 834

FLORIDA

Access Media Group, pg 673

MARYLAND

Kramer Communications Video Production, pg 801

MASSACHUSETTS

Preston Productions Inc, pg 861

MICHIGAN

Digi Sign Design LLC, pg 741
K&R All Media Productions LLC, pg 796
On Stage Visuals, pg 846

NEW MEXICO

Production Outfitters, pg 864

NEW YORK

HB-Content, pg 777

NORTH CAROLINA

Take One Productions Ltd, pg 906

PENNSYLVANIA

The Videohouse Inc, pg 929

TEXAS

Stage Directions, pg 898

ONTARIO

RB Productions, pg 870

Animation System Repairs

FLORIDA

Hi-Tech Enterprises Inc, pg 779

TEXAS

Biway Media, pg 706

WISCONSIN

Full Compass Systems, pg 767

Audience Response System Distributors

ARIZONA

Troxell-CDI, pg 918

ARKANSAS

Jay S Stanley & Associates Inc, pg 899

CALIFORNIA

Ametron Audio/Video, pg 684
California Tape Products Inc, pg 714
Media Fabricators Inc, pg 822
MediaPOINTE, pg 823
One Touch Systems Inc, pg 846

CONNECTICUT

HB Communications Inc, pg 777

FLORIDA

Access Media Group, pg 673
Alcorn McBride Inc, pg 679
AVI-SPL, pg 698

INDIANA

Audience Response Systems Inc, pg 693

KENTUCKY

NOR-COM Inc, pg 841

MICHIGAN

TEL Systems LLC, pg 909

NEW JERSEY

Audio Visual Associates, pg 694

NEW YORK

General Audio-Visual Inc (GAVI), pg 769

PENNSYLVANIA

Advanced AV LLC, pg 677
Meridia ARS, pg 823

WISCONSIN

Audio Visual of Milwaukee Inc, pg 694

MANITOBA

Advance Pro, pg 677
Inland Audio Visual Ltd, pg 788

Audience Response System Manufacturers

CALIFORNIA

One Touch Systems Inc, pg 846

FLORIDA

Alcorn McBride Inc, pg 679

MICHIGAN

ENCO Systems Inc, pg 754

OHIO

Turning Technologies LLC, pg 919

PENNSYLVANIA

Meridia ARS, pg 823

BRITISH COLUMBIA

Commercial Electronics Ltd, pg 728

Audience Response System Rentals

ARIZONA

Merestone, pg 823

CALIFORNIA

Ametron Audio/Video, pg 684
AV Guys, pg 697
Lynch Communications, pg 813
Muse Presentation Technologies, pg 834
Video Resources Inc, pg 928

COLORADO

Multimedia Audio Visual Inc, pg 833
Spectrum Audio Visual Services, pg 897

FLORIDA

Access Media Group, pg 673
ONstage, pg 846

GEORGIA

Stage Front Presentation Systems, pg 899

ILLINOIS

Meetinghouse Event Design & Production, pg 823

INDIANA

Audience Response Systems Inc, pg 693

KENTUCKY

Audio Visual Techniques Inc, pg 695

MASSACHUSETTS

Preston Productions Inc, pg 861

MICHIGAN

K&R All Media Productions LLC, pg 796
TEL Systems LLC, pg 909

NEW JERSEY

Audio Visual Associates, pg 694

NEW YORK

Design Audio Visual Inc, pg 741
SmartSource Computer & AV Rentals, pg 891
Visual Word Systems Inc, pg 932

OKLAHOMA

PDC Productions, pg 852

PENNSYLVANIA

Meridia ARS, pg 823

TEXAS

Stage Directions, pg 898

PUERTO RICO

Stage Crew Audiovisual Inc, pg 898

MANITOBA

Inland Audio Visual Ltd, pg 788

QUEBEC

Audio Visual Dynamics, pg 694
Freeman Audio Visual, pg 765

Audience Response System Repairs

CALIFORNIA

Ametron Audio/Video, pg 684

INDIANA

Audience Response Systems Inc, pg 693

KENTUCKY

NOR-COM Inc, pg 841

MANITOBA

Inland Audio Visual Ltd, pg 788

CD-ROM Equipment Distributors

ARIZONA

EAR Professional Audio/Video, pg 749
Professional Marketing Services Inc, pg 865
Troxell-CDI, pg 918

ARKANSAS

White Diamond Productions LLC, pg 937

CALIFORNIA

Ametron Audio/Video, pg 684
Audio Images Corp, pg 693
CADint, pg 713
California Tape Products Inc, pg 714
Computer Modules Inc, pg 729
Ingram Micro, pg 788
Jameco Electronics, pg 792
Kontron America, pg 801
Media Fabricators Inc, pg 822
MediaPOINTE, pg 823
New Cyberian Systems Inc, pg 839
Photodyne Technologies, pg 856
Videobotics, pg 929
VMI Inc, pg 932

COLORADO

G W Hannaway & Associates, pg 775

CONNECTICUT

HB Communications Inc, pg 777

FLORIDA

Access Media Group, pg 673
CD ROM™ Inc, pg 718
Communications Concepts Inc (CCI), pg 729
Hi-Tech Import Export Corp, pg 779
Recording Media & Equipment Inc (RM&E), pg 872

GEORGIA

Stage Front Presentation Systems, pg 899
TAPPI, pg 907

HAWAII

The Audio Visual Co (AVCO), pg 694

ILLINOIS

Woodside Avenue Music Productions Inc, pg 941

MARYLAND

Kipp Visual Systems Inc, pg 799

MASSACHUSETTS

PrimeArray Systems Inc, pg 862
Professional Audio Design Inc, pg 865

MICHIGAN

ASC Systems, pg 690
TEL Systems LLC, pg 909

MINNESOTA

Microboards Technology LLC, pg 826

MISSOURI

Conference Technologies Inc, pg 730
Modern Communications Inc, pg 828
Schiller's Audio-Visual, pg 881

NEW JERSEY

Starlite, pg 900
SYMCO Inc, pg 905
Total Video Products Inc, pg 916
Vcom IMC, pg 925
Yorktel, pg 944

NEW YORK

Design Audio Visual Inc, pg 741
Duplication Depot Inc, pg 748
Gaylord Archival, pg 768
Guidance Associates Inc Center for Humanities, pg 774
Neptune Photo Inc, pg 838

PENNSYLVANIA

Advanced AV LLC, pg 677
Brodart Co, pg 711
The Lerro Corp, pg 806

SOUTH CAROLINA

Keymark Inc, pg 798

TENNESSEE

Spring Arbor Distributors Inc, pg 898

TEXAS

Audio Visual Technologies Group (AVTG), pg 695
Biway Media, pg 706
Replicopy Digital Media Center, pg 873
Tarpley Media Systems, pg 907
Videotex Systems Inc, pg 930

UTAH

Performance Audio LLC, pg 854

VIRGINIA

Lee Hartman & Sons Inc, pg 805
The Whitlock Group, pg 937

WISCONSIN

Audio Visual of Milwaukee Inc, pg 694
Full Compass Systems, pg 767
Indus International Inc, pg 787

WYOMING

Bridger Productions Inc, pg 710

BRITISH COLUMBIA

Richmond Sound Design Ltd, pg 875

MANITOBA

Advance Pro, pg 677
Inland Audio Visual Ltd, pg 788

ONTARIO

HD Source, pg 777

CD-ROM Equipment Manufacturers

CALIFORNIA

New Cyberian Systems Inc, pg 839
Pioneer Electronics (USA) Inc, pg 857
QRS Software Services, pg 867
Tasman Group Pacific Rim, pg 907

COLORADO

ProLine Digital, pg 865

FLORIDA

CD ROM™ Inc, pg 718
Midtown Video Inc, pg 827

ILLINOIS

Woodside Avenue Music Productions Inc, pg 941

MASSACHUSETTS

PrimeArray Systems Inc, pg 862

NORTH CAROLINA

Micro Technology Unlimited Inc, pg 826

TEXAS

Biway Media, pg 706

WISCONSIN

Bardes Products Inc, pg 702

BRITISH COLUMBIA

Triad Communications Ltd, pg 918

CD-ROM Equipment Repairs

CALIFORNIA

Ametron Audio/Video, pg 684

CONNECTICUT

HB Communications Inc, pg 777

GEORGIA

Stage Front Presentation Systems, pg 899

MASSACHUSETTS

PrimeArray Systems Inc, pg 862

MINNESOTA

Microboards Technology LLC, pg 826

NEW JERSEY

Starlite, pg 900

OHIO

Tri-State Audio Visual Co, pg 918

TEXAS

Biway Media, pg 706

COMPUTER SYSTEMS

CD-ROM Equipment Repairs (continued)

WISCONSIN

Full Compass Systems, pg 767

MANITOBA

Inland Audio Visual Ltd, pg 788

Character Generator Distributors

ARIZONA

EAR Professional Audio/Video, pg 749
Troxell-CDI, pg 918

ARKANSAS

Jay S Stanley & Associates Inc, pg 899
White Diamond Productions LLC, pg 937

CALIFORNIA

Ametron Audio/Video, pg 684
California Tape Products Inc, pg 714
Diaquest, pg 741
Media Control Systems LLC, pg 821
MediaPOINTE, pg 823
SNAP, pg 891
VMI Inc, pg 932

COLORADO

Spectrum Audio Visual Services, pg 897

CONNECTICUT

HB Communications Inc, pg 777

FLORIDA

Access Media Group, pg 673
Communications Concepts Inc (CCI), pg 729
Digital Video Systems, pg 742
Hi-Tech Enterprises Inc, pg 779
Hi-Tech Import Export Corp, pg 779
Midtown Video Inc, pg 827

GEORGIA

Lighting & Production Equipment Inc, pg 807
Stage Front Presentation Systems, pg 899

HAWAII

The Audio Visual Co (AVCO), pg 694

INDIANA

Sensory Technologies LLC, pg 884

KENTUCKY

NOR-COM Inc, pg 841

MARYLAND

Human Circuit, pg 782
Image Logic Corp, pg 785
Kipp Visual Systems Inc, pg 799

MASSACHUSETTS

Duxbury Systems Inc, pg 748
Rule Boston Camera, pg 878

MICHIGAN

DAWNco, pg 739
On Stage Visuals, pg 846
TEL Systems LLC, pg 909

MISSOURI

Conference Technologies Inc, pg 730
Modern Communications Inc, pg 828
Schiller's Audio-Visual, pg 881

NEW JERSEY

AlltecPro, pg 681
Diversified, pg 744
Starlite, pg 900
SYMCO Inc, pg 905
Total Video Products Inc, pg 916
Wired 4 Sound Inc, pg 940
Yorktel, pg 944

NEW YORK

Audio-Video Corp, pg 694
Design Audio Visual Inc, pg 741

NORTH CAROLINA

Crispin Corp, pg 734

PENNSYLVANIA

Advanced AV LLC, pg 677
The Lerro Corp, pg 806

TENNESSEE

Lowrance Sound Co Inc, pg 812
Zion Music Group, pg 945

TEXAS

Videotex Systems Inc, pg 930

VIRGINIA

Quince Imaging Inc, pg 868
The Whitlock Group, pg 937

WASHINGTON

Linguist's Software Inc, pg 809

WISCONSIN

Audio Visual of Milwaukee Inc, pg 694
Camera Corner Connecting Point, pg 715
Full Compass Systems, pg 767

ALBERTA

Infosat Communications Inc, pg 787
Matrix Video Communications Corp (MVCC), pg 819

BRITISH COLUMBIA

Commercial Electronics Ltd, pg 728
Credo Interactive Inc, pg 734

MANITOBA

Advance Pro, pg 677
Inland Audio Visual Ltd, pg 788

ONTARIO

HD Source, pg 777

SASKATCHEWAN

Display Systems International, pg 743

Character Generator Manufacturers

CALIFORNIA

AJA Video Systems Inc, pg 679

CONNECTICUT

The Video Messenger Co, pg 928

GEORGIA

Visix™ Inc, pg 931

KANSAS

Keywest Technology Inc, pg 798

LOUISIANA

Outland Technology Inc, pg 849

MASSACHUSETTS

Duxbury Systems Inc, pg 748
INTER-Media Electronics, pg 789

NEW JERSEY

CELCO, pg 719

NEW MEXICO

Burst Electronics Inc, pg 713

NEW YORK

ChyronHego Corp, pg 723
MultiDyne Video & Fiber Optics Systems, pg 833

NORTH CAROLINA

Micro Technology Unlimited Inc, pg 826

PENNSYLVANIA

Scala Inc, pg 881

TENNESSEE

Adtec Digital Inc, pg 677

WASHINGTON

Linguist's Software Inc, pg 809

BRITISH COLUMBIA

Credo Interactive Inc, pg 734
Triad Communications Ltd, pg 918

SASKATCHEWAN

Display Systems International, pg 743

Character Generator Rentals

ARIZONA

Merestone, pg 823
Video West Inc, pg 929

CALIFORNIA

Artichoke Productions, pg 690
Express Media Inc, pg 757
Golden Gate Studios, pg 772
VER, pg 926
Video Resources Inc, pg 928

CONNECTICUT

Videofilm Systems Inc, pg 929

FLORIDA

Access Media Group, pg 673

GEORGIA

Stage Front Presentation Systems, pg 899

ILLINOIS

Resolution Productions Group, pg 874

KENTUCKY

Audio Visual Techniques Inc, pg 695

MARYLAND

CPR MultiMedia Solutions, pg 732

MASSACHUSETTS

Preston Productions Inc, pg 861

MICHIGAN

K&R All Media Productions LLC, pg 796
On Stage Visuals, pg 846

MISSOURI

Show-Me Audio-Visual, pg 887

NEBRASKA

Dog & Pony Productions Inc, pg 744

NEW JERSEY

Wired 4 Sound Inc, pg 940

NEW MEXICO

Production Outfitters, pg 864

NEW YORK

All Mobile Video Inc, pg 680
Design Audio Visual Inc, pg 741
HB-Content, pg 777

OKLAHOMA

PDC Productions, pg 852

PENNSYLVANIA

Upstage Video, pg 923
The Videohouse Inc, pg 929

TEXAS

Stage Directions, pg 898

VIRGINIA

Quince Imaging Inc, pg 868

MANITOBA

Inland Audio Visual Ltd, pg 788

QUEBEC
Group PVP, pg 774

Character Generator Repairs

CALIFORNIA
Ametron Audio/Video, pg 684
VMI Inc, pg 932

FLORIDA
Hi-Tech Enterprises Inc, pg 779

GEORGIA
Stage Front Presentation Systems,
   pg 899

KENTUCKY
NOR-COM Inc, pg 841

WISCONSIN
Camera Corner Connecting Point,
   pg 715
Full Compass Systems, pg 767

ALBERTA
Infosat Communications Inc, pg 787

MANITOBA
Inland Audio Visual Ltd, pg 788

Computer Interfacing Device Distributors

ARIZONA
Arizona Cine Equipment, pg 688
Troxell-CDI, pg 918
Ultimate Presentation Systems Inc,
   pg 920

ARKANSAS
Jay S Stanley & Associates Inc,
   pg 899

CALIFORNIA
Advanced Systems Group LLC,
   pg 677
Ametron Audio/Video, pg 684
Audio/Video Supply Inc, pg 694
AV Conferencing LLC (AVC),
   pg 697
CADint, pg 713
California Tape Products Inc,
   pg 714
Educational Technology Services
   (ETS), pg 751
Electrosonic Inc, pg 752
Elo TouchSystems, pg 753
Ingram Micro, pg 788
Jaguar Distribution Corp, pg 792
JD Audio Visual Inc, pg 793
Kontron America, pg 801
Lloyd F McKinney Associates Inc,
   pg 821
MediaPOINTE, pg 823
Orevox USA Corp, pg 847
Photodyne Technologies, pg 856
PMP Marketing Inc, pg 858
Promax Systems, pg 865
Seagate Technology LLC, pg 883
Skjonberg Controls Inc, pg 890
Videobotics, pg 929
VMI Inc, pg 932

COLORADO
Daylight Productions & Rentals,
   pg 739

CONNECTICUT
HB Communications Inc, pg 777

FLORIDA
Access Media Group, pg 673
Hi-Tech Enterprises Inc, pg 779
Industrial Strength Inc, pg 787
ITEC Entertainment Corp, pg 791
L3Harris Technologies Inc, pg 812
Midtown Video Inc, pg 827
ONstage, pg 846

GEORGIA
PolyVision Corporation, pg 859
Stage Front Presentation Systems,
   pg 899

HAWAII
The Audio Visual Co (AVCO),
   pg 694

ILLINOIS
RC Communications, pg 870
Woodside Avenue Music
   Productions Inc, pg 941

INDIANA
Sensory Technologies LLC, pg 884

KENTUCKY
NOR-COM Inc, pg 841

MARYLAND
Image Logic Corp, pg 785
Kipp Visual Systems Inc, pg 799
OmegaBrandess Distribution,
   pg 845

MASSACHUSETTS
Data Translation, pg 738
Graphx Inc, pg 773
Professional Audio Design Inc,
   pg 865

MICHIGAN
ASC Systems, pg 690
City Events Group, pg 725
Digi Sign Design LLC, pg 741
On Stage Visuals, pg 846

MINNESOTA
3M Touch Systems, pg 913

MISSOURI
Communitronics Corp, pg 729
Conference Technologies Inc,
   pg 730
Modern Communications Inc,
   pg 828
Schiller's Audio-Visual, pg 881

NEW JERSEY
A-V Services Inc, pg 671
Audio Visual Associates, pg 694
Earl Girls Inc, pg 749
Starlite, pg 900
SYMCO Inc, pg 905
Total Video Products Inc, pg 916
Video Corporation of America
   (VCA), pg 927
Yorktel, pg 944

NEW YORK
American Video Inc, pg 684
Design Audio Visual Inc, pg 741
General Audio-Visual Inc (GAVI),
   pg 769
KVL Audio Visual Services Inc,
   pg 802
Long Island Video Enterprises Live
   Inc, pg 811
Tri-Ed Distribution Inc, pg 918
Visual Technologies Corp, pg 932
Visual Word Systems Inc, pg 932

NORTH CAROLINA
Crispin Corp, pg 734

OHIO
Copp Integrated Systems, pg 731
ITA Audio Visual Solutions, pg 791
iVideo Technologies, pg 792

OKLAHOMA
Ford AV, pg 763

PENNSYLVANIA
Advanced AV LLC, pg 677
Garcia Marketing Inc, pg 768
The Lerro Corp, pg 806
Visual Sound Inc, pg 931

SOUTH CAROLINA
Impact Technology Group LLC,
   pg 786

TENNESSEE
Lowrance Sound Co Inc, pg 812
Technical Support Systems LLC,
   pg 908
Zion Music Group, pg 945

TEXAS
AVES Audio Visual Systems Inc,
   pg 698
Biway Media, pg 706
Heffernan Audio Visual, pg 778
JSAV, pg 795
Quality Audio Visual Service Inc,
   pg 867
Stage Directions, pg 898
Tarpley Media Systems, pg 907
Video Associates Labs Inc, pg 927
Videotex Systems Inc, pg 930

UTAH
NVerzion Inc, pg 843
Performance Audio LLC, pg 854
RIA Corp, pg 874

VIRGINIA
Avitecture Inc, pg 699
Cybernetics, pg 736
Quince Imaging Inc, pg 868
The Whitlock Group, pg 937

WISCONSIN
Audio Visual of Milwaukee Inc,
   pg 694
Camera Corner Connecting Point,
   pg 715
DNASTAR Inc, pg 744
Full Compass Systems, pg 767

ALBERTA
McBain Camera Ltd, pg 820

MANITOBA
Advance Pro, pg 677
Inland Audio Visual Ltd, pg 788

ONTARIO
GestureTek, pg 770
HD Source, pg 777
Technovision® Interactive Inc,
   pg 909

QUEBEC
Freeman Audio Visual, pg 765

Computer Interfacing Device Manufacturers

ARIZONA
Covid Inc, pg 732

CALIFORNIA
Advanced Systems Group LLC,
   pg 677
AITech International, pg 679
ALTINEX Inc, pg 682
DASAN Zhone Solutions (DZS)
   Inc, pg 737
Diaquest, pg 741
Extron Electronics, pg 758
FutureVideo, pg 767
Gefen, pg 769
Hewlett-Packard Co, pg 779
Kontron America, pg 801
Nexsan Inc, pg 840
Opticomm-EMCORE, pg 847
Photodyne Technologies, pg 856
RetinaVision Productions, pg 874
RGB Spectrum, pg 874
Roland Corp US, pg 876
Skjonberg Controls Inc, pg 890
Videobotics, pg 929
VITEC Multimedia, pg 932
Western Digital Corp, pg 936

COLORADO
Arrakis Systems, pg 689

FLORIDA
Tel-Test, pg 909

GEORGIA
PolyVision Corporation, pg 859

ILLINOIS
B+B SmartWorx, pg 701
NEC Display Solutions of America,
   pg 837
Woodside Avenue Music
   Productions Inc, pg 941

INDIANA
General Devices Co Inc, pg 769

MARYLAND
Image Logic Corp, pg 785

MASSACHUSETTS
Data Translation, pg 738
Graphx Inc, pg 773
INTER-Media Electronics, pg 789
Monotype Imaging Inc, pg 829
New England Keyboard Inc, pg 839

MICHIGAN
ASC Systems, pg 690
Leightronix Inc, pg 806

COMPUTER SYSTEMS

Computer Interfacing Device Manufacturers (continued)

MINNESOTA

Digital Audio Labs, pg 742
3M Touch Systems, pg 913

MISSOURI

Link Electronics Inc, pg 809

NEW JERSEY

CELCO, pg 719
FSR Inc, pg 766

NEW MEXICO

Adrienne Electronics Corp (AEC), pg 676

NEW YORK

American Video Inc, pg 684
ATTO Technology Inc, pg 692
Judson Rosebush Co Inc, pg 877

NORTH CAROLINA

Eaton Corp, pg 750
Micro Technology Unlimited Inc, pg 826

OHIO

Network Technologies Inc, pg 838
Turning Technologies LLC, pg 919

OKLAHOMA

Versatech Industries Inc, pg 926

PENNSYLVANIA

DecisionOne Corp, pg 740
Scala Inc, pg 881

RHODE ISLAND

M-Audio, pg 813

TEXAS

National Instruments Corp, pg 836

UTAH

Ivie Technologies Inc, pg 792
NVerzion Inc, pg 843

VIRGINIA

Opterna, a Belden brand, pg 847
Quince Imaging Inc, pg 868

WISCONSIN

Comprompter Inc, pg 729

BRITISH COLUMBIA

Triad Communications Ltd, pg 918

ONTARIO

GestureTek, pg 770
Technovision® Interactive Inc, pg 909

QUEBEC

Matrox Video Products Group, pg 819

Computer Interfacing Device Rentals

ALABAMA

Audio-Video Resources Inc, pg 694

ARIZONA

Merestone, pg 823
Ultimate Presentation Systems Inc, pg 920

CALIFORNIA

AV Guys, pg 697
Express Media Inc, pg 757
JD Audio Visual Inc, pg 793
Muse Presentation Technologies, pg 834
RetinaVision Productions, pg 874
VER, pg 926
VMI Inc, pg 932

FLORIDA

Universal Studios Florida®
Production Group, pg 922

GEORGIA

Stage Front Presentation Systems, pg 899

KENTUCKY

Audio Visual Techniques Inc, pg 695

MARYLAND

CPR MultiMedia Solutions, pg 732

MASSACHUSETTS

Preston Productions Inc, pg 861

MICHIGAN

Digi Sign Design LLC, pg 741
K&R All Media Productions LLC, pg 796
On Stage Visuals, pg 846

MISSOURI

Show-Me Audio-Visual, pg 887

NEBRASKA

Dog & Pony Productions Inc, pg 744

NEW JERSEY

Audio Visual Associates, pg 694
Earl Girls Inc, pg 749
Starlite, pg 900

NEW YORK

Design Audio Visual Inc, pg 741
KVL Audio Visual Services Inc, pg 802
Visual Word Systems Inc, pg 932

NORTH CAROLINA

Take One Productions Ltd, pg 906

OKLAHOMA

PDC Productions, pg 852

SOUTH CAROLINA

Encore Video Productions, pg 754

TENNESSEE

Technical Support Systems LLC, pg 908

TEXAS

Stage Directions, pg 898

VIRGINIA

Quince Imaging Inc, pg 868

PUERTO RICO

Stage Crew Audiovisual Inc, pg 898

MANITOBA

Inland Audio Visual Ltd, pg 788

QUEBEC

Group PVP, pg 774

Computer Interfacing Device Repairs

CALIFORNIA

Ametron Audio/Video, pg 684
Electrosonic Inc, pg 752

FLORIDA

Hi-Tech Enterprises Inc, pg 779
Tel-Test, pg 909

GEORGIA

Stage Front Presentation Systems, pg 899

KENTUCKY

NOR-COM Inc, pg 841

MASSACHUSETTS

BitFlow Inc, pg 706

NEW JERSEY

Earl Girls Inc, pg 749
Starlite, pg 900

NEW YORK

American Video Inc, pg 684
Visual Technologies Corp, pg 932

OHIO

ITA Audio Visual Solutions, pg 791
Tri-State Audio Visual Co, pg 918

TENNESSEE

Technical Support Systems LLC, pg 908

VIRGINIA

The Whitlock Group, pg 937

WISCONSIN

Camera Corner Connecting Point, pg 715
Full Compass Systems, pg 767

MANITOBA

Inland Audio Visual Ltd, pg 788

Control System & Equipment Distributors

ARIZONA

EAR Professional Audio/Video, pg 749
Troxell-CDI, pg 918

ARKANSAS

Jay S Stanley & Associates Inc, pg 899

CALIFORNIA

Ametron Audio/Video, pg 684
Associated Sound, pg 691
Auton Motorized Systems, pg 696
AV Conferencing LLC (AVC), pg 697
Be Media, pg 702
California Tape Products Inc, pg 714
Diaquest, pg 741
Electrosonic Inc, pg 752
HM Electronics Inc (HME), pg 780
JD Audio Visual Inc, pg 793
JLCooper Electronics, pg 794
Kontron America, pg 801
Media Control Systems LLC, pg 821
MediaMation Inc, pg 822
MediaPOINTE, pg 823
Photodyne Technologies, pg 856
Pristine Systems Inc, pg 862
Promax Systems, pg 865
Skjonberg Controls Inc, pg 890
Stanislaus AV Inc, pg 899
Unique Business Systems, pg 921
Videobotics, pg 929

CONNECTICUT

HB Communications Inc, pg 777
Vista Group International Inc, pg 931

FLORIDA

Access Media Group, pg 673
Alcorn McBride Inc, pg 679
Digital Video Systems, pg 742
Harris Corp, pg 776
Hi-Tech Enterprises Inc, pg 779
ITEC Entertainment Corp, pg 791
Midtown Video Inc, pg 827
ONstage, pg 846

GEORGIA

Stage Front Presentation Systems, pg 899

HAWAII

The Audio Visual Co (AVCO), pg 694

INDIANA

Sensory Technologies LLC, pg 884

KENTUCKY

NOR-COM Inc, pg 841

MARYLAND

Image Logic Corp, pg 785
Wiltronix Inc, pg 939

MASSACHUSETTS

Professional Audio Design Inc, pg 865

MICHIGAN

ASC Systems, pg 690

MISSOURI

Modern Communications Inc,
pg 828
Schiller's Audio-Visual, pg 881

NEW JERSEY

Earl Girls Inc, pg 749
Starlite, pg 900
Total Video Products Inc, pg 916
Wired 4 Sound Inc, pg 940
Yorktel, pg 944

NEW YORK

beyerdynamic Inc, pg 704
Colortone Audio Visual, pg 728
Design Audio Visual Inc, pg 741
DSan Corp, pg 747
Monroe Electronics Inc, pg 829
Visual Word Systems Inc, pg 932

NORTH CAROLINA

Crispin Corp, pg 734

OHIO

ITA Audio Visual Solutions, pg 791

OKLAHOMA

Ford AV, pg 763

PENNSYLVANIA

Advanced AV LLC, pg 677
The Lerro Corp, pg 806
Sensaphone, pg 884
Vistacom Inc, pg 931

TENNESSEE

Lowrance Sound Co Inc, pg 812
Navigator Systems Ltd, pg 837
Technical Support Systems LLC,
pg 908

TEXAS

Biway Media, pg 706
Data Projections Inc, pg 738
Graftek Imaging Inc, pg 773
MusicMaster Inc, pg 835
Tarpley Media Systems, pg 907

UTAH

NVerzion Inc, pg 843
Performance Audio LLC, pg 854
SirsiDynix, pg 889

VIRGINIA

Avitecture Inc, pg 699
Design & Production Inc, pg 740
Intellidyne LLC, pg 789

WASHINGTON

Asentria Corp, pg 690

WISCONSIN

Audio Visual of Milwaukee Inc,
pg 694
Camera Corner Connecting Point,
pg 715
Full Compass Systems, pg 767
Safe Harbor Computers, pg 879

ALBERTA

Infosat Communications Inc, pg 787
Matrix Video Communications Corp
(MVCC), pg 819

MANITOBA

Advance Pro, pg 677
Inland Audio Visual Ltd, pg 788

ONTARIO

Broadview Software Inc, pg 711
Cinema Stage Inc, pg 724
HD Source, pg 777
MVI - MultiVision Inc, pg 835
Soundmaster Group, pg 894
Westbury National Show Systems
Ltd, pg 936

Control System & Equipment Manufacturers

ARIZONA

AtlasIED, pg 692
Covid Inc, pg 732

CALIFORNIA

ALTINEX Inc, pg 682
Diaquest, pg 741
Extron Electronics, pg 758
FM Systems Inc, pg 763
FrontRow, pg 766
FutureVideo, pg 767
JLCooper Electronics, pg 794
Kontron America, pg 801
Media Control Systems LLC,
pg 821
Nexsan Inc, pg 840
Photodyne Technologies, pg 856
QSC Audio Products LLC, pg 867
RetinaVision Productions, pg 874
RGB Spectrum, pg 874
Skjonberg Controls Inc, pg 890
Unique Business Systems, pg 921

FLORIDA

Alcorn McBride Inc, pg 679
Harris Corp, pg 776

GEORGIA

Register Data Systems, pg 873
Visix™ Inc, pg 931

ILLINOIS

B+B SmartWorx, pg 701
Dukane Corp, Audio Visual
Products Division, pg 747

INDIANA

General Devices Co Inc, pg 769

LOUISIANA

Outland Technology Inc, pg 849

MARYLAND

Image Logic Corp, pg 785

MASSACHUSETTS

AVFX Inc, pg 698
INTER-Media Electronics, pg 789

MICHIGAN

ASC Systems, pg 690

NEW JERSEY

Crestron Electronics Inc, pg 734
FSR Inc, pg 766
Starlite, pg 900

NEW MEXICO

Adrienne Electronics Corp (AEC),
pg 676

NEW YORK

ATTO Technology Inc, pg 692
beyerdynamic Inc, pg 704
ChyronHego Corp, pg 723
DSan Corp, pg 747
Monroe Electronics Inc, pg 829

NORTH CAROLINA

Eaton Corp, pg 750
Micro Technology Unlimited Inc,
pg 826

PENNSYLVANIA

Scala Inc, pg 881
Sensaphone, pg 884

RHODE ISLAND

APC by Schneider Electric, pg 686

TEXAS

Contemporary Research, pg 731
Graftek Imaging Inc, pg 773
MusicMaster Inc, pg 835
National Instruments Corp, pg 836

UTAH

NVerzion Inc, pg 843
SirsiDynix, pg 889

VIRGINIA

Opterna, a Belden brand, pg 847

ALBERTA

Johnson Systems Inc (JSI), pg 794

BRITISH COLUMBIA

Commercial Electronics Ltd, pg 728
Richmond Sound Design Ltd,
pg 875

ONTARIO

Broadview Software Inc, pg 711
Soundmaster Group, pg 894
Technovision® Interactive Inc,
pg 909

Control System & Equipment Rentals

ARIZONA

Merestone, pg 823

CALIFORNIA

Ametron Audio/Video, pg 684
Express Media Inc, pg 757
JD Audio Visual Inc, pg 793
Lynch Communications, pg 813
Muse Presentation Technologies,
pg 834
RetinaVision Productions, pg 874
Skjonberg Controls Inc, pg 890
VER, pg 926
Video Resources Inc, pg 928

CONNECTICUT

A/V Davey, pg 697

FLORIDA

ONstage, pg 846
Universal Studios Florida®
Production Group, pg 922

GEORGIA

Stage Front Presentation Systems,
pg 899

KENTUCKY

Audio Visual Techniques Inc,
pg 695

MARYLAND

CPR MultiMedia Solutions, pg 732

MASSACHUSETTS

AVFX Inc, pg 698
Preston Productions Inc, pg 861

MICHIGAN

K&R All Media Productions LLC,
pg 796

MISSOURI

Schiller's Audio-Visual, pg 881
Show-Me Audio-Visual, pg 887

NEBRASKA

Dog & Pony Productions Inc,
pg 744

NEW JERSEY

Earl Girls Inc, pg 749
PLS Staging, pg 858
Starlite, pg 900
Wired 4 Sound Inc, pg 940

NEW YORK

Visual Word Systems Inc, pg 932

OHIO

ITA Audio Visual Solutions, pg 791

SOUTH CAROLINA

Encore Video Productions, pg 754

TENNESSEE

Technical Support Systems LLC,
pg 908

UTAH

Performance Audio LLC, pg 854

VIRGINIA

American AV, pg 682
Quince Imaging Inc, pg 868

WISCONSIN

Full Compass Systems, pg 767

MANITOBA

Inland Audio Visual Ltd, pg 788

ONTARIO

HD Source, pg 777
MVI - MultiVision Inc, pg 835
Westbury National Show Systems
Ltd, pg 936

COMPUTER SYSTEMS

Control System & Equipment Repairs

CALIFORNIA

Ametron Audio/Video, pg 684
Electrosonic Inc, pg 752
HM Electronics Inc (HME), pg 780
Skjonberg Controls Inc, pg 890

CONNECTICUT

A/V Davey, pg 697
HB Communications Inc, pg 777

KENTUCKY

NOR-COM Inc, pg 841

NEW JERSEY

Earl Girls Inc, pg 749
Starlite, pg 900

OHIO

ITA Audio Visual Solutions, pg 791
Tri-State Audio Visual Co, pg 918

TENNESSEE

Technical Support Systems LLC,
    pg 908

TEXAS

Tarpley Media Systems, pg 907

VIRGINIA

Intellidyne LLC, pg 789

WISCONSIN

Camera Corner Connecting Point,
    pg 715
Full Compass Systems, pg 767

ALBERTA

Infosat Communications Inc, pg 787

MANITOBA

Inland Audio Visual Ltd, pg 788

ONTARIO

HD Source, pg 777
MVI - MultiVision Inc, pg 835
Westbury National Show Systems
    Ltd, pg 936

Digital Multimedia Distributors

ALABAMA

CMEinfo™, pg 727

ARIZONA

EAR Professional Audio/Video,
    pg 749
Professional Marketing Services Inc,
    pg 865
Troxell-CDI, pg 918

CALIFORNIA

Ametron Audio/Video, pg 684
Audio Images Corp, pg 693
BigFoot Mobile Systems, pg 705

CADint, pg 713
California Tape Products Inc,
    pg 714
Computer Modules Inc, pg 729
Diaquest, pg 741
HM Electronics Inc (HME), pg 780
Ingram Micro, pg 788
Kontron America, pg 801
Media Fabricators Inc, pg 822
Photodyne Technologies, pg 856
Promax Systems, pg 865
QRS Software Services, pg 867
Sanako Inc, pg 880
Total Creative, pg 916
Videobotics, pg 929
VMI Inc, pg 932

COLORADO

American Educational Products
    LLC, pg 683
G W Hannaway & Associates,
    pg 775

CONNECTICUT

HB Communications Inc, pg 777
The Video Messenger Co, pg 928

FLORIDA

Access Media Group, pg 673
Accusoft, pg 674
CD ROM™ Inc, pg 718
Communications Concepts Inc
    (CCI), pg 729
Digital Video Systems, pg 742
Harris Corp, pg 776
Midtown Video Inc, pg 827
ONstage, pg 846

GEORGIA

Ligos Corporation, pg 808
PolyVision Corporation, pg 859
Stage Front Presentation Systems,
    pg 899

HAWAII

The Audio Visual Co (AVCO),
    pg 694

INDIANA

Sensory Technologies LLC, pg 884

IOWA

Prositions Inc, pg 865

KENTUCKY

NOR-COM Inc, pg 841

LOUISIANA

Techkno Integration & Design
    Services LLC, pg 908

MARYLAND

dbF a Media Company, pg 739
Human Circuit, pg 782

MASSACHUSETTS

Avid Technology Inc, pg 698
Psychsoft Inc, pg 866
Rule Boston Camera, pg 878
SeaChange International Inc, pg 883

MICHIGAN

ASC Systems, pg 690
Digi Sign Design LLC, pg 741
On Stage Visuals, pg 846

MINNESOTA

BeyerSound & Essay Audio, pg 705
Microboards Technology LLC,
    pg 826

MISSOURI

Schiller's Audio-Visual, pg 881

NEW JERSEY

AlltecPro, pg 681
Diversified, pg 744
MiB MediaWorks, pg 825
SDI Technologies Inc, pg 883
Starlite, pg 900
Total Media Inc, pg 916
Total Video Products Inc, pg 916
Yorktel, pg 944

NEW YORK

Audio-Video Corp, pg 694
Videoguys, pg 929

NORTH CAROLINA

Alien Skin Software LLC, pg 680

PENNSYLVANIA

AccuWeather Inc, pg 674
Advanced AV LLC, pg 677
Bernie's Photo Center, pg 704
Brodart Co, pg 711
The Lerro Corp, pg 806
Vistacom Inc, pg 931
Visual Sound Inc, pg 931
Wespen Audio Visual Co, pg 935

RHODE ISLAND

M-Audio, pg 813

TENNESSEE

Lowrance Sound Co Inc, pg 812
Technical Support Systems LLC,
    pg 908

TEXAS

Audio Visual Technologies Group
    (AVTG), pg 695
Biway Media, pg 706
Epic Software Group Inc, pg 755
Videotex Systems Inc, pg 930

UTAH

Performance Audio LLC, pg 854

VIRGINIA

Avitecture Inc, pg 699
Design & Production Inc, pg 740
Rocktown Media, pg 876
The Whitlock Group, pg 937

WISCONSIN

Audio Visual of Milwaukee Inc,
    pg 694
Full Compass Systems, pg 767
Safe Harbor Computers, pg 879

ALBERTA

Evolution AV, pg 757
Matrix Video Communications Corp
    (MVCC), pg 819

BRITISH COLUMBIA

Kodak Graphic Communications
    Canada Co, pg 800

MANITOBA

Advance Pro, pg 677
Inland Audio Visual Ltd, pg 788
Tek Gear, pg 909

ONTARIO

Cinema Stage Inc, pg 724
GestureTek, pg 770
HD Source, pg 777

SASKATCHEWAN

Display Systems International,
    pg 743

Digital Multimedia Manufacturers

ARIZONA

Applied Integration Corp, pg 687

CALIFORNIA

AITech International, pg 679
The Banquet Sound Studios, pg 701
Diaquest, pg 741
Gefen, pg 769
Photodyne Technologies, pg 856
QRS Software Services, pg 867
RGB Spectrum, pg 874
VITEC Multimedia, pg 932

COLORADO

American Educational Products
    LLC, pg 683

CONNECTICUT

The Video Messenger Co, pg 928

FLORIDA

CD ROM™ Inc, pg 718

GEORGIA

Ligos Corporation, pg 808
PolyVision Corporation, pg 859

ILLINOIS

Symbolic Sound Corp, pg 905

MARYLAND

dbF a Media Company, pg 739
Media Cybernetics Inc, pg 821

MASSACHUSETTS

Avid Technology Inc, pg 698
Psychsoft Inc, pg 866
SeaChange International Inc, pg 883
Small Planet Communications Inc,
    pg 890

MICHIGAN

ENCO Systems Inc, pg 754

NEVADA

Wells-Gardner Technologies Inc,
    pg 935

NEW JERSEY

CELCO, pg 719
Map Resources, pg 816
SDI Technologies Inc, pg 883

NEW YORK

RCS Enterprises, pg 871

NORTH CAROLINA
Alien Skin Software LLC, pg 680
Computer Dynamics, pg 729
SAS Institute Inc, pg 880

OHIO
Tosoh USA Inc, pg 916

OREGON
NeoSoft Corp, pg 838

PENNSYLVANIA
AccuWeather Inc, pg 674
Prime Image Inc, pg 862
Scala Inc, pg 881

RHODE ISLAND
M-Audio, pg 813

WASHINGTON
Victory Studios, pg 927

BRITISH COLUMBIA
Kodak Graphic Communications
  Canada Co, pg 800
Richmond Sound Design Ltd,
  pg 875
Triad Communications Ltd, pg 918

ONTARIO
GestureTek, pg 770
PixeLINK, pg 857

SASKATCHEWAN
Display Systems International,
  pg 743

Digital Multimedia Rentals

ARIZONA
Merestone, pg 823

CALIFORNIA
Advanced Media LLC, pg 677
Express Media Inc, pg 757
Golden Gate Studios, pg 772
Muse Presentation Technologies,
  pg 834
PSAV® Presentation Services,
  pg 866
RetinaVision Productions, pg 874

FLORIDA
Access Media Group, pg 673
Universal Studios Florida®
  Production Group, pg 922

GEORGIA
Stage Front Presentation Systems,
  pg 899

ILLINOIS
Resolution Productions Group,
  pg 874

MARYLAND
dbF a Media Company, pg 739
Kramer Communications Video
  Production, pg 801

MASSACHUSETTS
Preston Productions Inc, pg 861

MICHIGAN
Digi Sign Design LLC, pg 741
K&R All Media Productions LLC,
  pg 796
On Stage Visuals, pg 846

MISSOURI
Show-Me Audio-Visual, pg 887

NEBRASKA
Dog & Pony Productions Inc,
  pg 744

NEW JERSEY
Audio Visual Dynamics®, pg 694
MiB MediaWorks, pg 825
Milgrom Productions, pg 827
Starlite, pg 900

NEW MEXICO
Production Outfitters, pg 864

OHIO
Bartha, pg 702

OKLAHOMA
PDC Productions, pg 852

OREGON
Hollywood Lights Inc, pg 780

PENNSYLVANIA
Argentine Productions Inc, pg 688
FMP Media Solutions Inc, pg 763

SOUTH CAROLINA
Encore Video Productions, pg 754

TENNESSEE
Love Shack Recording Studios,
  pg 811
Technical Support Systems LLC,
  pg 908

TEXAS
Stage Directions, pg 898

VIRGINIA
Advance Concepts Inc, pg 677
Quince Imaging Inc, pg 868

MANITOBA
Inland Audio Visual Ltd, pg 788

QUEBEC
Group PVP, pg 774

SASKATCHEWAN
plan9films, pg 857

Digital Multimedia Repairs

CALIFORNIA
Advanced Media LLC, pg 677
Ametron Audio/Video, pg 684
HM Electronics Inc (HME), pg 780
Technical Services, pg 908

CONNECTICUT
HB Communications Inc, pg 777

GEORGIA
Stage Front Presentation Systems,
  pg 899

KENTUCKY
NOR-COM Inc, pg 841

MINNESOTA
Microboards Technology LLC,
  pg 826

TENNESSEE
Technical Support Systems LLC,
  pg 908

WISCONSIN
Full Compass Systems, pg 767

ALBERTA
Evolution AV, pg 757

MANITOBA
Inland Audio Visual Ltd, pg 788

Digitizing Input System Distributors

ARIZONA
Arizona Cine Equipment, pg 688
EAR Professional Audio/Video,
  pg 749

ARKANSAS
Jay S Stanley & Associates Inc,
  pg 899

CALIFORNIA
Ametron Audio/Video, pg 684
Audio Images Corp, pg 693
Audio/Video Supply Inc, pg 694
California Tape Products Inc,
  pg 714
Diaquest, pg 741
Ingram Micro, pg 788
Jaguar Distribution Corp, pg 792
Media Control Systems LLC,
  pg 821
Media Fabricators Inc, pg 822
MediaPOINTE, pg 823
Photodyne Technologies, pg 856
Promax Systems, pg 865
Total Creative, pg 916

CONNECTICUT
HB Communications Inc, pg 777

FLORIDA
Access Media Group, pg 673
Accusoft, pg 674
Midtown Video Inc, pg 827
ONstage, pg 846

GEORGIA
PolyVision Corporation, pg 859
Stage Front Presentation Systems,
  pg 899

HAWAII
The Audio Visual Co (AVCO),
  pg 694

ILLINOIS
Manning Productions, pg 816
Woodside Avenue Music
  Productions Inc, pg 941

KENTUCKY
NOR-COM Inc, pg 841

MARYLAND
Kipp Visual Systems Inc, pg 799
Wiltronix Inc, pg 939

MASSACHUSETTS
Avid Technology Inc, pg 698
Data Translation, pg 738
Monotype Imaging Inc, pg 829
Psychsoft Inc, pg 866
Rule Boston Camera, pg 878
SeaChange International Inc, pg 883

MICHIGAN
ASC Systems, pg 690

MINNESOTA
3M Touch Systems, pg 913

MISSOURI
Communitronics Corp, pg 729
Modern Communications Inc,
  pg 828
Schiller's Audio-Visual, pg 881

NEW JERSEY
Advanced Imaging Concepts Inc,
  pg 677
MiB MediaWorks, pg 825
Starlite, pg 900
SYMCO Inc, pg 905
Video Corporation of America
  (VCA), pg 927

NEW YORK
Audio-Video Corp, pg 694
Neptune Photo Inc, pg 838

NORTH CAROLINA
DNP Imagingcomm America Corp
  (DNP IAM), pg 744

OHIO
iVideo Technologies, pg 792

OREGON
Wacom Technology Corp, pg 933

PENNSYLVANIA
Advanced AV LLC, pg 677
Visual Sound Inc, pg 931

SOUTH CAROLINA
Keymark Inc, pg 798

TEXAS
Audio Visual Technologies Group
  (AVTG), pg 695
Biway Media, pg 706
Stage Directions, pg 898
Videotex Systems Inc, pg 930

UTAH
NVerzion Inc, pg 843

COMPUTER SYSTEMS

Digitizing Input System Distributors (continued)

VIRGINIA
The Whitlock Group, pg 937

WASHINGTON
Linguist's Software Inc, pg 809
Macrosystem US Inc, pg 814

WISCONSIN
Audio Visual of Milwaukee Inc, pg 694
Camera Corner Connecting Point, pg 715
DNASTAR Inc, pg 744
Full Compass Systems, pg 767
Indus International Inc, pg 787

MANITOBA
Advance Pro, pg 677
Inland Audio Visual Ltd, pg 788

Digitizing Input System Manufacturers

ARIZONA
Mutoh America Inc, pg 835

CALIFORNIA
AJA Video Systems Inc, pg 679
Aztek Inc, pg 700
Diaquest, pg 741
Opticomm-EMCORE, pg 847
Photodyne Technologies, pg 856

COLORADO
Vexcel Corp, pg 926

GEORGIA
PolyVision Corporation, pg 859

ILLINOIS
EPIX Inc, pg 755
Woodside Avenue Music Productions Inc, pg 941

MASSACHUSETTS
Avid Technology Inc, pg 698
Data Translation, pg 738
Monotype Imaging Inc, pg 829
Psychsoft Inc, pg 866
SeaChange International Inc, pg 883

MICHIGAN
ASC Systems, pg 690

MINNESOTA
3M Touch Systems, pg 913

NEW JERSEY
CELCO, pg 719

NEW YORK
Laird Digital Cinema, pg 803
Judson Rosebush Co Inc, pg 877

NORTH CAROLINA
DNP Imagingcomm America Corp (DNP IAM), pg 744

OHIO
Turning Technologies LLC, pg 919

PENNSYLVANIA
Interactive Products, pg 789

TENNESSEE
Adtec Digital Inc, pg 677

TEXAS
Biway Media, pg 706

UTAH
NVerzion Inc, pg 843

VERMONT
Polhemus, pg 859

WASHINGTON
Linguist's Software Inc, pg 809
Macrosystem US Inc, pg 814

WISCONSIN
DNASTAR Inc, pg 744

BRITISH COLUMBIA
Kodak Graphic Communications Canada Co, pg 800
Triad Communications Ltd, pg 918

ONTARIO
PixeLINK, pg 857

QUEBEC
Matrox Video Products Group, pg 819

Digitizing Input System Rentals

ARIZONA
Arizona Cine Equipment, pg 688
Merestone, pg 823

CALIFORNIA
Ametron Audio/Video, pg 684
Artichoke Productions, pg 690
Aztek Inc, pg 700
Deck Hand Inc, pg 740
Express Media Inc, pg 757
Golden Gate Studios, pg 772
Lynch Communications, pg 813
Media Fabricators Inc, pg 822
PSAV® Presentation Services, pg 866
RetinaVision Productions, pg 874
Total Creative, pg 916

COLORADO
Open Media Foundation, pg 846

CONNECTICUT
A/V Davey, pg 697

FLORIDA
ONstage, pg 846
Universal Studios Florida® Production Group, pg 922

GEORGIA
Stage Front Presentation Systems, pg 899
Staging Directions Inc, pg 899

ILLINOIS
Resolution Productions Group, pg 874

LOUISIANA
Pace Systems, pg 849

MASSACHUSETTS
massAV, pg 819
Preston Productions Inc, pg 861

MICHIGAN
K&R All Media Productions LLC, pg 796

MISSOURI
Show-Me Audio-Visual, pg 887

MONTANA
High Plains Films, pg 779

NEW JERSEY
MiB MediaWorks, pg 825
PLS Staging, pg 858

NEW MEXICO
Production Outfitters, pg 864

NEW YORK
HB-Content, pg 777
Manhattan Center Studios Inc, pg 816

NORTH CAROLINA
Take One Productions Ltd, pg 906

OREGON
Northwest Film Center, pg 842

PENNSYLVANIA
FMP Media Solutions Inc, pg 763
Rahlic Publishing Co, pg 869

TEXAS
JSAV, pg 795

VIRGINIA
Quince Imaging Inc, pg 868

WISCONSIN
Full Compass Systems, pg 767

WYOMING
Bridger Productions Inc, pg 710

BRITISH COLUMBIA
Video Out Distribution, pg 928

MANITOBA
Inland Audio Visual Ltd, pg 788

QUEBEC
Group PVP, pg 774

SASKATCHEWAN
plan9films, pg 857

Digitizing Input System Repairs

CALIFORNIA
Ametron Audio/Video, pg 684
Technical Services, pg 908

CONNECTICUT
HB Communications Inc, pg 777

GEORGIA
Stage Front Presentation Systems, pg 899

KENTUCKY
NOR-COM Inc, pg 841

MASSACHUSETTS
BitFlow Inc, pg 706
Monotype Imaging Inc, pg 829

TEXAS
Biway Media, pg 706

WASHINGTON
Macrosystem US Inc, pg 814

WISCONSIN
Camera Corner Connecting Point, pg 715
Full Compass Systems, pg 767

MANITOBA
Inland Audio Visual Ltd, pg 788

DVD Equipment Distributors

ARIZONA
EAR Professional Audio/Video, pg 749
Troxell-CDI, pg 918

ARKANSAS
White Diamond Productions LLC, pg 937

CALIFORNIA
Be Media, pg 702
Computer Modules Inc, pg 729
Educational Technology Services (ETS), pg 751
JD Audio Visual Inc, pg 793
MSE Media Solutions, pg 832
New Cyberian Systems Inc, pg 839
Promax Systems, pg 865
Sound Service Co, pg 894
Stanislaus AV Inc, pg 899

FLORIDA
Access Media Group, pg 673
Communications Concepts Inc (CCI), pg 729
Digital Video Systems, pg 742
Recording Media & Equipment Inc (RM&E), pg 872

GEORGIA
Stage Front Presentation Systems, pg 899

ILLINOIS

Dukane Corp, Audio Visual
Products Division, pg 747
Quintessence Audio Ltd, pg 868

INDIANA

Sensory Technologies LLC, pg 884

KENTUCKY

NOR-COM Inc, pg 841

LOUISIANA

Techkno Integration & Design
Services LLC, pg 908

MARYLAND

Human Circuit, pg 782

MASSACHUSETTS

Rule Boston Camera, pg 878

MICHIGAN

Digi Sign Design LLC, pg 741
On Stage Visuals, pg 846

MINNESOTA

Alpha Video & Audio Inc, pg 682

MISSISSIPPI

Bowie Audio Visual Enterprises Inc,
pg 709

NEBRASKA

Strong Cinema Products, pg 902

NEW HAMPSHIRE

APS Lighting-Sound-AV, pg 688

NEW JERSEY

Audio Visual Associates, pg 694
Earl Girls Inc, pg 749
MiB MediaWorks, pg 825
Starlite, pg 900
Total Video Products Inc, pg 916
Wired 4 Sound Inc, pg 940

NEW YORK

Colortone Audio Visual, pg 728
Design Audio Visual Inc, pg 741
Duplication Depot Inc, pg 748
KVL Audio Visual Services Inc,
pg 802

NORTH CAROLINA

DNP Imagingcomm America Corp
(DNP IAM), pg 744

OHIO

Tri-State Audio Visual Co, pg 918

PENNSYLVANIA

Advanced AV LLC, pg 677
Audio Visions Inc, pg 694
Brodart Co, pg 711
J E Foss Co, pg 764
Innovision Media Group, pg 788
Vistacom Inc, pg 931
Wespen Audio Visual Co, pg 935

TENNESSEE

Lowrance Sound Co Inc, pg 812
Technical Support Systems LLC,
pg 908
Zion Music Group, pg 945

TEXAS

AVES Audio Visual Systems Inc,
pg 698
Biway Media, pg 706
Data Projections Inc, pg 738
Digital Display Solutions Inc,
pg 742
Replicopy Digital Media Center,
pg 873

VIRGINIA

Avitecture Inc, pg 699
Design & Production Inc, pg 740
Intellidyne LLC, pg 789
Lee Hartman & Sons Inc, pg 805

WASHINGTON

Macrosystem US Inc, pg 814

WISCONSIN

Audio Visual of Milwaukee Inc,
pg 694
Camera Corner Connecting Point,
pg 715
Safe Harbor Computers, pg 879

WYOMING

Bridger Productions Inc, pg 710

ALBERTA

Infosat Communications Inc, pg 787
Matrix Video Communications Corp
(MVCC), pg 819

MANITOBA

Advance Pro, pg 677
Inland Audio Visual Ltd, pg 788

ONTARIO

Westbury National Show Systems
Ltd, pg 936

DVD Equipment Manufacturers

CALIFORNIA

Grande Vitesse Systems Inc (GVS),
pg 773
New Cyberian Systems Inc, pg 839

FLORIDA

CD ROM™ Inc, pg 718

NORTH CAROLINA

DNP Imagingcomm America Corp
(DNP IAM), pg 744

OKLAHOMA

BCD Associates Inc, pg 702

TENNESSEE

Adtec Digital Inc, pg 677

TEXAS

Adams Evidence Grade Technology
Inc, pg 675
Biway Media, pg 706

WASHINGTON

Macrosystem US Inc, pg 814

BRITISH COLUMBIA

Triad Communications Ltd, pg 918

DVD Equipment Rentals

ARIZONA

Merestone, pg 823
Video West Inc, pg 929

ARKANSAS

White Diamond Productions LLC,
pg 937

CALIFORNIA

Absolute Rentals, pg 672
Advanced Media LLC, pg 677
AGF Media Services, pg 678
Artichoke Productions, pg 690
Audio Rents, pg 693
AV Guys, pg 697
Express Media Inc, pg 757
JD Audio Visual Inc, pg 793
Maximus Media Inc, pg 820
Muse Presentation Technologies,
pg 834
PSAV® Presentation Services,
pg 866
RetinaVision Productions, pg 874
Sound Service Co, pg 894
Stanislaus AV Inc, pg 899
Total Creative, pg 916
VER, pg 926
Video Resources Inc, pg 928
VMI Inc, pg 932
Voice & Video Rentals, pg 932

COLORADO

Open Media Foundation, pg 846

CONNECTICUT

A/V Davey, pg 697

FLORIDA

Accord Productions, pg 673

GEORGIA

Stage Front Presentation Systems,
pg 899

ILLINOIS

RC Communications, pg 870
Resolution Productions Group,
pg 874

IOWA

Central Lighting & Equipment Inc
(CLE), pg 719

KENTUCKY

Audio Visual Techniques Inc,
pg 695

MARYLAND

CPR MultiMedia Solutions, pg 732
dbF a Media Company, pg 739
Event Tech, pg 756

MASSACHUSETTS

Preston Productions Inc, pg 861

MICHIGAN

Digi Sign Design LLC, pg 741
K&R All Media Productions LLC,
pg 796
On Stage Visuals, pg 846

MINNESOTA

Alpha Video & Audio Inc, pg 682

MISSISSIPPI

Bowie Audio Visual Enterprises Inc,
pg 709

MISSOURI

Show-Me Audio-Visual, pg 887

NEBRASKA

Dog & Pony Productions Inc,
pg 744

NEW HAMPSHIRE

APS Lighting-Sound-AV, pg 688

NEW JERSEY

Audio Visual Associates, pg 694
Audio Visual Dynamics®, pg 694
Earl Girls Inc, pg 749
MiB MediaWorks, pg 825
Starlite, pg 900
Wired 4 Sound Inc, pg 940

NEW MEXICO

Production Outfitters, pg 864

NEW YORK

Colortone Audio Visual, pg 728
Design Audio Visual Inc, pg 741
HB-Content, pg 777
KVL Audio Visual Services Inc,
pg 802

NORTH CAROLINA

Take One Productions Ltd, pg 906

OKLAHOMA

PDC Productions, pg 852

PENNSYLVANIA

Audio Visual Communications Inc,
pg 694
FMP Media Solutions Inc, pg 763
Innovision Media Group, pg 788

SOUTH CAROLINA

Encore Video Productions, pg 754

TENNESSEE

Love Shack Recording Studios,
pg 811
Technical Support Systems LLC,
pg 908

TEXAS

Stage Directions, pg 898

VIRGINIA

Advance Concepts Inc, pg 677
Lee Hartman & Sons Inc, pg 805
Quince Imaging Inc, pg 868

PUERTO RICO

Stage Crew Audiovisual Inc, pg 898

COMPUTER SYSTEMS

DVD Equipment Rentals (continued)

MANITOBA
Inland Audio Visual Ltd, pg 788

ONTARIO
RB Productions, pg 870
Westbury National Show Systems Ltd, pg 936

QUEBEC
Group PVP, pg 774

SASKATCHEWAN
plan9films, pg 857

DVD Equipment Repairs

CALIFORNIA
Advanced Media LLC, pg 677
Sound Service Co, pg 894

CONNECTICUT
A/V Davey, pg 697

FLORIDA
Hi-Tech Enterprises Inc, pg 779

GEORGIA
Stage Front Presentation Systems, pg 899

ILLINOIS
Midwest Digital Corp, pg 827

KENTUCKY
NOR-COM Inc, pg 841

NEW JERSEY
Earl Girls Inc, pg 749
Starlite, pg 900

OHIO
Tri-State Audio Visual Co, pg 918

TENNESSEE
Technical Support Systems LLC, pg 908

TEXAS
Biway Media, pg 706

WASHINGTON
Macrosystem US Inc, pg 814

WISCONSIN
Camera Corner Connecting Point, pg 715

ALBERTA
Infosat Communications Inc, pg 787

MANITOBA
Inland Audio Visual Ltd, pg 788

ONTARIO
Westbury National Show Systems Ltd, pg 936

Frame Grabber Distributors

ARIZONA
EAR Professional Audio/Video, pg 749
Troxell-CDI, pg 918

CALIFORNIA
Audio Images Corp, pg 693
California Tape Products Inc, pg 714
Computer Modules Inc, pg 729
Diaquest, pg 741
Ingram Micro, pg 788
Kappa optronics Inc, pg 796
Kontron America, pg 801
MediaPOINTE, pg 823
VMI Inc, pg 932

COLORADO
Aspen Systems Inc, pg 691

CONNECTICUT
HB Communications Inc, pg 777

FLORIDA
Access Media Group, pg 673
Accusoft, pg 674
Digital Video Systems, pg 742
Hi-Tech Enterprises Inc, pg 779
Midtown Video Inc, pg 827
ONstage, pg 846

GEORGIA
Stage Front Presentation Systems, pg 899

HAWAII
The Audio Visual Co (AVCO), pg 694

MARYLAND
Kipp Visual Systems Inc, pg 799
Wiltronix Inc, pg 939

MICHIGAN
TEL Systems LLC, pg 909

MISSOURI
Modern Communications Inc, pg 828
Schiller's Audio-Visual, pg 881

NEW JERSEY
Advanced Imaging Concepts Inc, pg 677
SYMCO Inc, pg 905

NEW YORK
Audio-Video Corp, pg 694
Design Audio Visual Inc, pg 741
Langie Audio Visual Systems, pg 803
Neptune Photo Inc, pg 838
Vision Identics Systems Inc, pg 930

PENNSYLVANIA
Advanced AV LLC, pg 677
Innovision Media Group, pg 788

TEXAS
Graftek Imaging Inc, pg 773
Videotex Systems Inc, pg 930

VIRGINIA
The Whitlock Group, pg 937

WISCONSIN
Audio Visual of Milwaukee Inc, pg 694
Camera Corner Connecting Point, pg 715
Full Compass Systems, pg 767

ALBERTA
Infosat Communications Inc, pg 787

BRITISH COLUMBIA
Commercial Electronics Ltd, pg 728

MANITOBA
Advance Pro, pg 677

ONTARIO
HD Source, pg 777

Frame Grabber Manufacturers

ARIZONA
Applied Integration Corp, pg 687

CALIFORNIA
Linkabit, pg 809

COLORADO
Colorado Video Inc, pg 728

ILLINOIS
EPIX Inc, pg 755

MARYLAND
Media Cybernetics Inc, pg 821

MASSACHUSETTS
BitFlow Inc, pg 706
Foresight Imaging, pg 764

MINNESOTA
CyberOptics Corp, pg 736

MISSOURI
GlobalStreams™ Corp, pg 771
Ken-A-Vision Manufacturing Co Inc, pg 797

TEXAS
National Instruments Corp, pg 836

Frame Grabber Rentals

ARIZONA
Merestone, pg 823

CALIFORNIA
AV Guys, pg 697
Express Media Inc, pg 757
RetinaVision Productions, pg 874

GEORGIA
Stage Front Presentation Systems, pg 899

ILLINOIS
Resolution Productions Group, pg 874

MARYLAND
CPR MultiMedia Solutions, pg 732

MASSACHUSETTS
Preston Productions Inc, pg 861

MICHIGAN
K&R All Media Productions LLC, pg 796

NEW MEXICO
Production Outfitters, pg 864

NEW YORK
Design Audio Visual Inc, pg 741

NORTH DAKOTA
Media Productions, pg 822

PENNSYLVANIA
Innovision Media Group, pg 788

TEXAS
Stage Directions, pg 898

VIRGINIA
Quince Imaging Inc, pg 868

SASKATCHEWAN
plan9films, pg 857

Frame Grabber Repairs

CONNECTICUT
HB Communications Inc, pg 777

FLORIDA
Hi-Tech Enterprises Inc, pg 779

GEORGIA
Stage Front Presentation Systems, pg 899

MASSACHUSETTS
BitFlow Inc, pg 706

WISCONSIN
Camera Corner Connecting Point, pg 715
Full Compass Systems, pg 767

Graphic Card Distributors

ARIZONA
EAR Professional Audio/Video, pg 749
Troxell-CDI, pg 918

CALIFORNIA
Audio Images Corp, pg 693
Audio/Video Supply Inc, pg 694
Be Media, pg 702
CADint, pg 713

California Tape Products Inc,
  pg 714
Diaquest, pg 741
Ingram Micro, pg 788
Jameco Electronics, pg 792
Kontron America, pg 801
Media Fabricators Inc, pg 822
MediaPOINTE, pg 823
Promax Systems, pg 865
Total Creative, pg 916
VMI Inc, pg 932

COLORADO

Aspen Systems Inc, pg 691
Stanco Sales LLC, pg 899

CONNECTICUT

HB Communications Inc, pg 777

FLORIDA

Access Media Group, pg 673
Digital Video Systems, pg 742
Hi-Tech Enterprises Inc, pg 779
Hi-Tech Import Export Corp,
  pg 779

GEORGIA

Stage Front Presentation Systems,
  pg 899

MARYLAND

Human Circuit, pg 782

MASSACHUSETTS

Psychsoft Inc, pg 866

MICHIGAN

TEL Systems LLC, pg 909

MISSOURI

Communitronics Corp, pg 729
Schiller's Audio-Visual, pg 881

NEW JERSEY

Argraph Corp, pg 688
SYMCO Inc, pg 905
Video Corporation of America
  (VCA), pg 927

NEW YORK

Audio-Video Corp, pg 694

OHIO

iVideo Technologies, pg 792

PENNSYLVANIA

Advanced AV LLC, pg 677
The Lerro Corp, pg 806
Visual Sound Inc, pg 931

TENNESSEE

Lowrance Sound Co Inc, pg 812
Spring Arbor Distributors Inc,
  pg 898

TEXAS

Biway Media, pg 706
Videotex Systems Inc, pg 930

VIRGINIA

Lee Hartman & Sons Inc, pg 805
The Whitlock Group, pg 937

WISCONSIN

Audio Visual of Milwaukee Inc,
  pg 694
Camera Corner Connecting Point,
  pg 715
Full Compass Systems, pg 767
Safe Harbor Computers, pg 879

ALBERTA

Infosat Communications Inc, pg 787

BRITISH COLUMBIA

Commercial Electronics Ltd, pg 728

MANITOBA

Advance Pro, pg 677

Graphic Card Manufacturers

CALIFORNIA

AJA Video Systems Inc, pg 679
Apple Inc, pg 687
Diaquest, pg 741
Hewlett-Packard Co, pg 779
Linkabit, pg 809

MASSACHUSETTS

Foresight Imaging, pg 764

BRITISH COLUMBIA

Triad Communications Ltd, pg 918

Graphic System Distributors

ARIZONA

EAR Professional Audio/Video,
  pg 749
Professional Marketing Services Inc,
  pg 865

ARKANSAS

White Diamond Productions LLC,
  pg 937

CALIFORNIA

Audio Images Corp, pg 693
Be Media, pg 702
California Tape Products Inc,
  pg 714
Diaquest, pg 741
Media Fabricators Inc, pg 822
MediaPOINTE, pg 823
Promax Systems, pg 865
Total Creative, pg 916
VMI Inc, pg 932

COLORADO

Aspen Systems Inc, pg 691

CONNECTICUT

HB Communications Inc, pg 777

FLORIDA

Access Media Group, pg 673
Digital Video Systems, pg 742
Hi-Tech Enterprises Inc, pg 779
ITEC Entertainment Corp, pg 791
ONstage, pg 846

GEORGIA

Stage Front Presentation Systems,
  pg 899

INDIANA

Advanced Designs Corp, pg 677

MASSACHUSETTS

Psychsoft Inc, pg 866
The Weather Company, An IBM
  Business, pg 935

MICHIGAN

Michigan Office Solutions (MOS),
  A Xerox Company, pg 825

MINNESOTA

Varitronics LLC, pg 925

MISSOURI

Schiller's Audio-Visual, pg 881

NEW JERSEY

Argraph Corp, pg 688

NEW YORK

Affton Graphics Inc, pg 678
Audio-Video Corp, pg 694

OHIO

AutoDesSys Inc, pg 696

PENNSYLVANIA

AccuWeather Inc, pg 674
Advanced AV LLC, pg 677
The Lerro Corp, pg 806

TENNESSEE

Lowrance Sound Co Inc, pg 812

TEXAS

Biway Media, pg 706
Videotex Systems Inc, pg 930

VIRGINIA

Rocktown Media, pg 876

WISCONSIN

Audio Visual of Milwaukee Inc,
  pg 694
Camera Corner Connecting Point,
  pg 715
Full Compass Systems, pg 767

MANITOBA

Advance Pro, pg 677

Graphic System Manufacturers

CALIFORNIA

Aztek Inc, pg 700
Diaquest, pg 741
Grande Vitesse Systems Inc (GVS),
  pg 773

COLORADO

Aspen Systems Inc, pg 691
Vexcel Corp, pg 926

ILLINOIS

IBM SPSS, pg 783

KANSAS

Keywest Technology Inc, pg 798

MASSACHUSETTS

Psychsoft Inc, pg 866
The Weather Company, An IBM
  Business, pg 935

NEW JERSEY

CELCO, pg 719

NEW YORK

ChyronHego Corp, pg 723

NORTH CAROLINA

Computer Dynamics, pg 729

OHIO

AutoDesSys Inc, pg 696

PENNSYLVANIA

AccuWeather Inc, pg 674

TEXAS

Biway Media, pg 706

WISCONSIN

Safe Harbor Computers, pg 879

BRITISH COLUMBIA

Triad Communications Ltd, pg 918

ONTARIO

Corel Corp, pg 731

QUEBEC

Grass Valley, pg 773

Graphic System Rentals

ARIZONA

Merestone, pg 823
Video West Inc, pg 929

ARKANSAS

White Diamond Productions LLC,
  pg 937

CALIFORNIA

Artichoke Productions, pg 690
Bexel, an NEP Broadcast Services
  Company, pg 704
Express Media Inc, pg 757
Golden Gate Studios, pg 772
Lynch Communications, pg 813
Media Fabricators Inc, pg 822
Total Creative, pg 916

CONNECTICUT

Videofilm Systems Inc, pg 929

FLORIDA

Accord Productions, pg 673
ONstage, pg 846
Universal Studios Florida®
  Production Group, pg 922

COMPUTER SYSTEMS

Graphic System Rentals (continued)

GEORGIA

Stage Front Presentation Systems, pg 899

ILLINOIS

Airways Digital Media, pg 679
Resolution Productions Group, pg 874

MARYLAND

CPR MultiMedia Solutions, pg 732

MASSACHUSETTS

Preston Productions Inc, pg 861

MISSOURI

Show-Me Audio-Visual, pg 887

NEW MEXICO

Production Outfitters, pg 864

NEW YORK

HB-Content, pg 777
Manhattan Center Studios Inc, pg 816

NORTH CAROLINA

AV Metro Inc, pg 697
Take One Productions Ltd, pg 906

OHIO

Lyon Video Inc, pg 813

OKLAHOMA

PDC Productions, pg 852

PENNSYLVANIA

FMP Media Solutions Inc, pg 763
The Videohouse Inc, pg 929

TEXAS

Phillips Media Source, pg 855

VIRGINIA

Quince Imaging Inc, pg 868

ONTARIO

RB Productions, pg 870
Westbury National Show Systems Ltd, pg 936

QUEBEC

Group PVP, pg 774

SASKATCHEWAN

plan9films, pg 857

Graphic System Repairs

FLORIDA

Hi-Tech Enterprises Inc, pg 779

GEORGIA

Stage Front Presentation Systems, pg 899

TEXAS

Biway Media, pg 706

WISCONSIN

Camera Corner Connecting Point, pg 715
Full Compass Systems, pg 767

ONTARIO

Westbury National Show Systems Ltd, pg 936

Graphic Tablet Distributors

ARIZONA

EAR Professional Audio/Video, pg 749
Troxell-CDI, pg 918

ARKANSAS

Jay S Stanley & Associates Inc, pg 899

CALIFORNIA

Advanced Systems Group LLC, pg 677
CADint, pg 713
Diaquest, pg 741
Ingram Micro, pg 788
Media Fabricators Inc, pg 822
MediaPOINTE, pg 823
Promax Systems, pg 865
VMI Inc, pg 932

COLORADO

Stanco Sales LLC, pg 899

CONNECTICUT

HB Communications Inc, pg 777

FLORIDA

Digital Video Systems, pg 742
Hi-Tech Import Export Corp, pg 779

GEORGIA

PolyVision Corporation, pg 859
Stage Front Presentation Systems, pg 899

MASSACHUSETTS

Psychsoft Inc, pg 866

MINNESOTA

3M Touch Systems, pg 913

MISSOURI

Communitronics Corp, pg 729
Schiller's Audio-Visual, pg 881

NEW JERSEY

Argraph Corp, pg 688
Video Corporation of America (VCA), pg 927

NEW YORK

Audio-Video Corp, pg 694
Design Audio Visual Inc, pg 741

OHIO

iVideo Technologies, pg 792

PENNSYLVANIA

Advanced AV LLC, pg 677
Visual Sound Inc, pg 931

TENNESSEE

Lowrance Sound Co Inc, pg 812

TEXAS

Videotex Systems Inc, pg 930

VIRGINIA

Lee Hartman & Sons Inc, pg 805
The Whitlock Group, pg 937

WISCONSIN

Audio Visual of Milwaukee Inc, pg 694
Camera Corner Connecting Point, pg 715
Safe Harbor Computers, pg 879

ALBERTA

Infosat Communications Inc, pg 787

MANITOBA

Advance Pro, pg 677

ONTARIO

Westbury National Show Systems Ltd, pg 936

Graphic Tablet Manufacturers

CALIFORNIA

Apple Inc, pg 687
Hewlett-Packard Co, pg 779

GEORGIA

PolyVision Corporation, pg 859

MINNESOTA

3M Touch Systems, pg 913

OHIO

Turning Technologies LLC, pg 919

PENNSYLVANIA

Interactive Products, pg 789

Image Capture Equipment Distributors

ARIZONA

Troxell-CDI, pg 918

ARKANSAS

Jay S Stanley & Associates Inc, pg 899
White Diamond Productions LLC, pg 937

CALIFORNIA

Audio Images Corp, pg 693
California Tape Products Inc, pg 714
Computer Modules Inc, pg 729
Diaquest, pg 741
Educational Technology Services (ETS), pg 751
Electrosonic Inc, pg 752
Hooper Camera & Imaging, pg 781

Ingram Micro, pg 788
Kappa optronics Inc, pg 796
Media Fabricators Inc, pg 822
MediaPOINTE, pg 823
Videobotics, pg 929
VMI Inc, pg 932

COLORADO

G W Hannaway & Associates, pg 775

CONNECTICUT

HB Communications Inc, pg 777

FLORIDA

Access Media Group, pg 673
Digital Video Systems, pg 742
Hi-Tech Enterprises Inc, pg 779

GEORGIA

PolyVision Corporation, pg 859
Stage Front Presentation Systems, pg 899

KENTUCKY

NOR-COM Inc, pg 841

MARYLAND

Wiltronix Inc, pg 939

MASSACHUSETTS

Rule Boston Camera, pg 878
SeaChange International Inc, pg 883

MICHIGAN

ASC Systems, pg 690
On Stage Visuals, pg 846
TEL Systems LLC, pg 909

MINNESOTA

3M Touch Systems, pg 913

MISSOURI

Ken-A-Vision Manufacturing Co Inc, pg 797
Schiller's Audio-Visual, pg 881

NEW JERSEY

Advanced Imaging Concepts Inc, pg 677
Alltec Stores, a Vcom IMC Company, pg 681
AlltecPro, pg 681
Argraph Corp, pg 688
Hasselblad Bron Inc, pg 776
Starlite, pg 900
SYMCO Inc, pg 905

NEW YORK

Audio-Video Corp, pg 694
Design Audio Visual Inc, pg 741
DocuWare Corp, pg 744
Image Management Systems Inc, pg 785
Neptune Photo Inc, pg 838
Vision Identics Systems Inc, pg 930

PENNSYLVANIA

Advanced AV LLC, pg 677
Bernie's Photo Center, pg 704

SOUTH CAROLINA

Keymark Inc, pg 798

TENNESSEE
Lowrance Sound Co Inc, pg 812
Zion Music Group, pg 945

TEXAS
Biway Media, pg 706
Graftek Imaging Inc, pg 773
Tarpley Media Systems, pg 907
Videotex Systems Inc, pg 930

VIRGINIA
Avitecture Inc, pg 699
The Whitlock Group, pg 937

WASHINGTON
Proforma Good Wood Marketing, pg 865

WISCONSIN
Audio Visual of Milwaukee Inc, pg 694
Camera Corner Connecting Point, pg 715
Full Compass Systems, pg 767
Indus International Inc, pg 787
Safe Harbor Computers, pg 879

ALBERTA
Infosat Communications Inc, pg 787

BRITISH COLUMBIA
Commercial Electronics Ltd, pg 728

MANITOBA
Advance Pro, pg 677
Inland Audio Visual Ltd, pg 788

Image Capture Equipment Manufacturers

ARIZONA
Applied Integration Corp, pg 687

CALIFORNIA
Aztek Inc, pg 700
Diaquest, pg 741
Grande Vitesse Systems Inc (GVS), pg 773
Hoodman Corp, pg 781
Kappa optronics Inc, pg 796
Kofax Inc, pg 800
Linkabit, pg 809

COLORADO
Vexcel Corp, pg 926

GEORGIA
PolyVision Corporation, pg 859

ILLINOIS
EPIX Inc, pg 755

MARYLAND
Media Cybernetics Inc, pg 821

MASSACHUSETTS
BitFlow Inc, pg 706
Foresight Imaging, pg 764
INTER-Media Electronics, pg 789
MorphoTrust USA, A Safran Company, pg 830
SeaChange International Inc, pg 883

MICHIGAN
ASC Systems, pg 690

MISSOURI
Ken-A-Vision Manufacturing Co Inc, pg 797

NEW JERSEY
AlltecPro, pg 681
CELCO, pg 719

NEW YORK
DocuWare Corp, pg 744
Judson Rosebush Co Inc, pg 877

TEXAS
Biway Media, pg 706
Graftek Imaging Inc, pg 773
National Instruments Corp, pg 836

BRITISH COLUMBIA
Kodak Graphic Communications Canada Co, pg 800
Triad Communications Ltd, pg 918

ONTARIO
PixeLINK, pg 857

QUEBEC
Matrox Video Products Group, pg 819

Image Capture Equipment Rentals

ARIZONA
Merestone, pg 823

ARKANSAS
White Diamond Productions LLC, pg 937

CALIFORNIA
Artichoke Productions, pg 690
Express Media Inc, pg 757
Golden Gate Studios, pg 772
Muse Presentation Technologies, pg 834
RetinaVision Productions, pg 874

CONNECTICUT
Videofilm Systems Inc, pg 929

GEORGIA
Stage Front Presentation Systems, pg 899

KENTUCKY
Audio Visual Techniques Inc, pg 695

MARYLAND
CPR MultiMedia Solutions, pg 732
Kramer Communications Video Production, pg 801

MASSACHUSETTS
Preston Productions Inc, pg 861

MICHIGAN
K&R All Media Productions LLC, pg 796
On Stage Visuals, pg 846

NEW JERSEY
Starlite, pg 900

NEW YORK
Design Audio Visual Inc, pg 741
HB-Content, pg 777

NORTH DAKOTA
Media Productions, pg 822

OKLAHOMA
PDC Productions, pg 852

TEXAS
Stage Directions, pg 898

PUERTO RICO
Stage Crew Audiovisual Inc, pg 898

MANITOBA
Inland Audio Visual Ltd, pg 788

ONTARIO
RB Productions, pg 870

QUEBEC
Group PVP, pg 774

SASKATCHEWAN
plan9films, pg 857

Image Capture Equipment Repairs

CALIFORNIA
Electrosonic Inc, pg 752

FLORIDA
Hi-Tech Enterprises Inc, pg 779

GEORGIA
Stage Front Presentation Systems, pg 899

KENTUCKY
NOR-COM Inc, pg 841

MASSACHUSETTS
BitFlow Inc, pg 706

TEXAS
Biway Media, pg 706
Tarpley Media Systems, pg 907

WISCONSIN
Camera Corner Connecting Point, pg 715
Full Compass Systems, pg 767

MANITOBA
Inland Audio Visual Ltd, pg 788

Interactive System Distributors

ARKANSAS
Jay S Stanley & Associates Inc, pg 899

CALIFORNIA
Audio Images Corp, pg 693
Beta Electronics Inc, pg 704
California Tape Products Inc, pg 714
JD Audio Visual Inc, pg 793
MediaPOINTE, pg 823
Promax Systems, pg 865
Sanako Inc, pg 880
VMI Inc, pg 932

COLORADO
MakeMusic® Inc, pg 815

FLORIDA
Access Media Group, pg 673
Alcorn McBride Inc, pg 679
Digital Video Systems, pg 742
Hi-Tech Enterprises Inc, pg 779
Technomedia Solutions, pg 909

GEORGIA
PolyVision Corporation, pg 859
Stage Front Presentation Systems, pg 899

INDIANA
Sensory Technologies LLC, pg 884

KENTUCKY
Axxis Leasing Inc, pg 700
NOR-COM Inc, pg 841

MASSACHUSETTS
Psychsoft Inc, pg 866

MICHIGAN
Mastery Technologies Inc, pg 819
TEL Systems LLC, pg 909

NEW JERSEY
AlltecPro, pg 681
MiB MediaWorks, pg 825
Starlite, pg 900

NEW YORK
Neptune Photo Inc, pg 838

OHIO
ITA Audio Visual Solutions, pg 791
Tri-State Audio Visual Co, pg 918

OKLAHOMA
Ford AV, pg 763

OREGON
NeoSoft Corp, pg 838

PENNSYLVANIA
Advanced AV LLC, pg 677
Innovision Media Group, pg 788
Meridia ARS, pg 823

COMPUTER SYSTEMS

Interactive System Distributors (continued)

TEXAS

Epic Software Group Inc, pg 755
Tarpley Media Systems, pg 907
Videotex Systems Inc, pg 930

VIRGINIA

Avitecture Inc, pg 699
Design & Production Inc, pg 740
Lee Hartman & Sons Inc, pg 805

WISCONSIN

Audio Visual of Milwaukee Inc, pg 694
Full Compass Systems, pg 767

ALBERTA

Genesis Integration, pg 769
SMART Technologies ULC, pg 891

MANITOBA

Advance Pro, pg 677
Inland Audio Visual Ltd, pg 788
Tek Gear, pg 909

ONTARIO

Cinema Stage Inc, pg 724
GestureTek, pg 770
Technovision® Interactive Inc, pg 909
Westbury National Show Systems Ltd, pg 936

QUEBEC

Presagis, pg 861

Interactive System Manufacturers

CALIFORNIA

Beta Electronics Inc, pg 704
FrontRow, pg 766
One Touch Systems Inc, pg 846

CONNECTICUT

Vista Group International Inc, pg 931

FLORIDA

Alcorn McBride Inc, pg 679
Pangolin Laser Systems Inc, pg 851

GEORGIA

PolyVision Corporation, pg 859

KANSAS

Keywest Technology Inc, pg 798

MASSACHUSETTS

INTER-Media Electronics, pg 789
MorphoTrust USA, A Safran Company, pg 830
Psychsoft Inc, pg 866

MICHIGAN

ASC Systems, pg 690
Mastery Technologies Inc, pg 819

NEW JERSEY

AlltecPro, pg 681

NORTH CAROLINA

Computer Dynamics, pg 729

OHIO

Turning Technologies LLC, pg 919

OREGON

NeoSoft Corp, pg 838

PENNSYLVANIA

Meridia ARS, pg 823

BRITISH COLUMBIA

Commercial Electronics Ltd, pg 728
Richmond Sound Design Ltd, pg 875
Triad Communications Ltd, pg 918

MANITOBA

Tek Gear, pg 909

ONTARIO

GestureTek, pg 770
Technovision® Interactive Inc, pg 909

QUEBEC

Freeman Audio Visual, pg 765
Presagis, pg 861

Interactive System Rentals

ARIZONA

Merestone, pg 823

CALIFORNIA

Express Media Inc, pg 757
JD Audio Visual Inc, pg 793
Lynch Communications, pg 813
Muse Presentation Technologies, pg 834
RetinaVision Productions, pg 874
Total Creative, pg 916

GEORGIA

Stage Front Presentation Systems, pg 899

ILLINOIS

Airways Digital Media, pg 679
Resolution Productions Group, pg 874

MASSACHUSETTS

Preston Productions Inc, pg 861

MICHIGAN

K&R All Media Productions LLC, pg 796

NEW JERSEY

PLS Staging, pg 858
Starlite, pg 900

NEW YORK

SmartSource Computer & AV Rentals, pg 891

PENNSYLVANIA

FMP Media Solutions Inc, pg 763
Innovision Media Group, pg 788
Meridia ARS, pg 823

TEXAS

Stage Directions, pg 898

VIRGINIA

American AV, pg 682

MANITOBA

Inland Audio Visual Ltd, pg 788
Tek Gear, pg 909

ONTARIO

GestureTek, pg 770
RB Productions, pg 870
Westbury National Show Systems Ltd, pg 936

QUEBEC

Freeman Audio Visual, pg 765

Interactive System Repairs

FLORIDA

Hi-Tech Enterprises Inc, pg 779

GEORGIA

Stage Front Presentation Systems, pg 899

KENTUCKY

Axxis Leasing Inc, pg 700
NOR-COM Inc, pg 841

NEW JERSEY

Starlite, pg 900

OHIO

Tri-State Audio Visual Co, pg 918

TEXAS

Tarpley Media Systems, pg 907

WISCONSIN

Full Compass Systems, pg 767

MANITOBA

Inland Audio Visual Ltd, pg 788

ONTARIO

Westbury National Show Systems Ltd, pg 936

LCD Panel Distributors

ARIZONA

EAR Professional Audio/Video, pg 749
Professional Marketing Services Inc, pg 865
Troxell-CDI, pg 918
Ultimate Presentation Systems Inc, pg 920

ARKANSAS

Jay S Stanley & Associates Inc, pg 899
White Diamond Productions LLC, pg 937

CALIFORNIA

Ametron Audio/Video, pg 684
Associated Sound, pg 691
Be Media, pg 702
BigFoot Mobile Systems, pg 705
Boland Communications Inc, pg 708
CADint, pg 713
California Tape Products Inc, pg 714
Educational Insights, pg 750
Hooper Camera & Imaging, pg 781
Kappa optronics Inc, pg 796
Marshall Electronics Inc, pg 817
Media Fabricators Inc, pg 822
MediaPOINTE, pg 823
Promax Systems, pg 865
TEK Media Group, pg 909
Transvideo International, pg 917
VMI Inc, pg 932
Zack Electronics Inc, pg 945

COLORADO

Aspen Systems Inc, pg 691
Daylight Productions & Rentals, pg 739
ProLine Digital, pg 865
Spectrum Audio Visual Services, pg 897

CONNECTICUT

The Video Messenger Co, pg 928

FLORIDA

Access Media Group, pg 673
Altel Systems Group Inc, pg 682
AVI-SPL, pg 698
Digital Video Systems, pg 742
Hi-Tech Enterprises Inc, pg 779
Hi-Tech Import Export Corp, pg 779
Industrial Strength Inc, pg 787
ONstage, pg 846
Technomedia Solutions, pg 909

GEORGIA

Boxlight Inc, pg 709
Clark, pg 725
Stage Front Presentation Systems, pg 899

HAWAII

The Audio Visual Co (AVCO), pg 694

ILLINOIS

Allen Visual Systems Inc, pg 680
Dukane Corp, Audio Visual Products Division, pg 747
Joseph Electronics, pg 795
Quintessence Audio Ltd, pg 868

INDIANA

Sensory Technologies LLC, pg 884

KENTUCKY

Creative Realities Inc (CRI), pg 733
NOR-COM Inc, pg 841

LOUISIANA

Techkno Integration & Design Services LLC, pg 908

MARYLAND

Cardinal Sound & Video, pg 717
DSR Computer Technology Specialists Inc, pg 747

Human Circuit, pg 782
Nelson White Systems Inc, pg 838
Noventri, pg 843

MASSACHUSETTS

Professional Audio Design Inc,
    pg 865
Psychsoft Inc, pg 866
Rule Boston Camera, pg 878

MICHIGAN

Olson Anderson Co, pg 685
ASC Systems, pg 690
Michigan Office Solutions (MOS),
    A Xerox Company, pg 825

MINNESOTA

Alpha Video & Audio Inc, pg 682

MISSISSIPPI

Bowie Audio Visual Enterprises Inc,
    pg 709

MISSOURI

Modern Communications Inc,
    pg 828
Schiller's Audio-Visual, pg 881

NEW JERSEY

Argraph Corp, pg 688
Audio Visual Associates, pg 694
AV Bluebook, pg 696
Diversified, pg 744
MiB MediaWorks, pg 825
Starlite, pg 900
Total Video Products Inc, pg 916
Wired 4 Sound Inc, pg 940

NEW YORK

Audio-Video Corp, pg 694
BTX Technologies, pg 712
Colortone Audio Visual, pg 728
Gaylord Archival, pg 768
KVL Audio Visual Services Inc,
    pg 802
Langie Audio Visual Systems,
    pg 803
Neptune Photo Inc, pg 838
Stampede Presentation Products Inc,
    pg 899
Video Technology Services Inc,
    pg 929
Vision Identics Systems Inc, pg 930
Visual Technologies Corp, pg 932
Visual Word Systems Inc, pg 932

NORTH CAROLINA

Crest Electronics Inc, pg 734
Crispin Corp, pg 734

OHIO

ITA Audio Visual Solutions, pg 791
Tri-State Audio Visual Co, pg 918

OKLAHOMA

Ford AV, pg 763

PENNSYLVANIA

Advanced AV LLC, pg 677
Aydin Displays, a Sparton
    Company, pg 700
Bernie's Photo Center, pg 704
Brodart Co, pg 711
J E Foss Co, pg 764
Interactive Products, pg 789
The Lerro Corp, pg 806

TENNESSEE

Continental Film, pg 731
Lowrance Sound Co Inc, pg 812
Technical Support Systems LLC,
    pg 908
Zion Music Group, pg 945

TEXAS

Audio Visual Technologies Group
    (AVTG), pg 695
AVES Audio Visual Systems Inc,
    pg 698
Biway Media, pg 706
Tarpley Media Systems, pg 907
Videotex Systems Inc, pg 930

VIRGINIA

Avitecture Inc, pg 699
Design & Production Inc, pg 740
Intellidyne LLC, pg 789
Lee Hartman & Sons Inc, pg 805
Quince Imaging Inc, pg 868
Rocktown Media, pg 876

WISCONSIN

Audio Visual of Milwaukee Inc,
    pg 694
Camera Corner Connecting Point,
    pg 715
Full Compass Systems, pg 767
Safe Harbor Computers, pg 879

BRITISH COLUMBIA

Commercial Electronics Ltd, pg 728
Richmond Sound Design Ltd,
    pg 875

MANITOBA

Advance Pro, pg 677
Inland Audio Visual Ltd, pg 788

ONTARIO

Cinema Stage Inc, pg 724
Image Video, pg 785
MVI - MultiVision Inc, pg 835
Westbury National Show Systems
    Ltd, pg 936

LCD Panel Manufacturers

CALIFORNIA

Auton Motorized Systems, pg 696
Boland Communications Inc,
    pg 708
Grande Vitesse Systems Inc (GVS),
    pg 773
Hoodman Corp, pg 781
Marshall Electronics Inc, pg 817
NDS Surgical Imaging LLC, pg 837
Tatung Co of America Inc, pg 907
Transvideo International, pg 917

ILLINOIS

ACCO Brands Corp, pg 673
Canvys™, pg 716
Dukane Corp, Audio Visual
    Products Division, pg 747

NEVADA

Wells-Gardner Technologies Inc,
    pg 935

NEW JERSEY

Sharp Electronics Corp, Professional
    Display Division, pg 885
Tally Display Corp, pg 906

NEW YORK

Video Technology Services Inc,
    pg 929

NORTH CAROLINA

Computer Dynamics, pg 729

OHIO

Turning Technologies LLC, pg 919
TV One Multimedia Solutions,
    pg 919

VIRGINIA

Quince Imaging Inc, pg 868

BRITISH COLUMBIA

Triad Communications Ltd, pg 918

ONTARIO

Image Video, pg 785

LCD Panel Rentals

ALABAMA

Audio-Video Resources Inc, pg 694

ARIZONA

Merestone, pg 823
Ultimate Presentation Systems Inc,
    pg 920
Video West Inc, pg 929

ARKANSAS

White Diamond Productions LLC,
    pg 937

CALIFORNIA

Advanced Media LLC, pg 677
AGF Media Services, pg 678
Alliant Event Services, pg 681
Ametron Audio/Video, pg 684
AV Conferencing LLC (AVC),
    pg 697
AV Guys, pg 697
Express Media Inc, pg 757
Hooper Camera & Imaging, pg 781
Lynch Communications, pg 813
McCune Audio-Video-Lighting,
    pg 821
Media Fabricators Inc, pg 822
Muse Presentation Technologies,
    pg 834
PSAV® Presentation Services,
    pg 866
RetinaVision Productions, pg 874
Sound Service Co, pg 894
VER, pg 926
Voice & Video Rentals, pg 932
Warner Bros Entertainment Inc,
    pg 934
Warner Bros Production Sound &
    Video Services, pg 934

COLORADO

Multimedia Audio Visual Inc,
    pg 833
Spectrum Audio Visual Services,
    pg 897

CONNECTICUT

A/V Davey, pg 697

FLORIDA

Access Media Group, pg 673
Hi-Tech Enterprises Inc, pg 779

Industrial Strength Inc, pg 787
ONstage, pg 846

GEORGIA

Stage Front Presentation Systems,
    pg 899

ILLINOIS

Allen Visual Systems Inc, pg 680
Backstar Creative Media Inc,
    pg 700
RC Communications, pg 870
Resolution Productions Group,
    pg 874

IOWA

Central Lighting & Equipment Inc
    (CLE), pg 719

MAINE

Headlight Audio Visual Inc, pg 777

MARYLAND

CPR MultiMedia Solutions, pg 732
Event Tech, pg 756
Kramer Communications Video
    Production, pg 801
Nelson White Systems Inc, pg 838

MASSACHUSETTS

Cramer, pg 732
massAV, pg 819
Preston Productions Inc, pg 861

MICHIGAN

K&R All Media Productions LLC,
    pg 796
TEL Systems LLC, pg 909

MINNESOTA

Alpha Video & Audio Inc, pg 682

MISSISSIPPI

Bowie Audio Visual Enterprises Inc,
    pg 709

MISSOURI

Schiller's Audio-Visual, pg 881
Show-Me Audio-Visual, pg 887

NEVADA

GES Audio Visual, pg 770

NEW JERSEY

Audio Visual Dynamics®, pg 694
International Audio Visual Inc,
    pg 790
PLS Staging, pg 858
Starlite, pg 900
Wired 4 Sound Inc, pg 940

NEW MEXICO

Production Outfitters, pg 864

NEW YORK

Colortone Audio Visual, pg 728
KVL Audio Visual Services Inc,
    pg 802
Langie Audio Visual Systems,
    pg 803
SmartSource Computer & AV
    Rentals, pg 891
Visual Technologies Corp, pg 932
Visual Word Systems Inc, pg 932

COMPUTER SYSTEMS

LCD Panel Rentals (continued)

NORTH CAROLINA
AV Connections Inc, pg 697
AV Metro Inc, pg 697

NORTH DAKOTA
Media Productions, pg 822

OHIO
Hughie's Event Production Services, pg 782

PENNSYLVANIA
Audio Visual Communications Inc, pg 694
FMP Media Solutions Inc, pg 763

TENNESSEE
Technical Support Systems LLC, pg 908

TEXAS
Alford Media Services, pg 680
Audio Visual Technologies Group (AVTG), pg 695
Stage Directions, pg 898

VIRGINIA
American AV, pg 682
Quince Imaging Inc, pg 868

WASHINGTON
Osum Event Rentals, pg 848

WISCONSIN
Audio Visual of Milwaukee Inc, pg 694
Full Compass Systems, pg 767

PUERTO RICO
Stage Crew Audiovisual Inc, pg 898

BRITISH COLUMBIA
Commercial Electronics Ltd, pg 728

MANITOBA
Inland Audio Visual Ltd, pg 788

ONTARIO
MVI - MultiVision Inc, pg 835
RB Productions, pg 870
Westbury National Show Systems Ltd, pg 936

LCD Panel Repairs

CALIFORNIA
Advanced Media LLC, pg 677
Ametron Audio/Video, pg 684
McAlister Electronics, pg 820
Transvideo International, pg 917

CONNECTICUT
HB Communications Inc, pg 777

FLORIDA
Hi-Tech Enterprises Inc, pg 779

GEORGIA
Stage Front Presentation Systems, pg 899

ILLINOIS
Allen Visual Systems Inc, pg 680

KENTUCKY
NOR-COM Inc, pg 841

MAINE
Headlight Audio Visual Inc, pg 777

MARYLAND
Nelson White Systems Inc, pg 838

MICHIGAN
TEL Systems LLC, pg 909

NEW YORK
Langie Audio Visual Systems, pg 803
Video Technology Services Inc, pg 929
Visual Technologies Corp, pg 932

OHIO
ITA Audio Visual Solutions, pg 791
Tri-State Audio Visual Co, pg 918

PENNSYLVANIA
J E Foss Co, pg 764

TENNESSEE
Technical Support Systems LLC, pg 908

TEXAS
Tarpley Media Systems, pg 907

VIRGINIA
Avitecture Inc, pg 699

WISCONSIN
Camera Corner Connecting Point, pg 715
Full Compass Systems, pg 767

MANITOBA
Inland Audio Visual Ltd, pg 788

ONTARIO
Westbury National Show Systems Ltd, pg 936

Monitor Distributors

ARIZONA
EAR Professional Audio/Video, pg 749
Troxell-CDI, pg 918

ARKANSAS
White Diamond Productions LLC, pg 937

CALIFORNIA
Ametron Audio/Video, pg 684
Associated Sound, pg 691
Audio Images Corp, pg 693
Be Media, pg 702
BigFoot Mobile Systems, pg 705
Boland Communications Inc, pg 708
CADint, pg 713
California Tape Products Inc, pg 714
Jameco Electronics, pg 792
Kappa optronics Inc, pg 796
Kontron America, pg 801
Media Fabricators Inc, pg 822
MediaPOINTE, pg 823
Photodyne Technologies, pg 856
Promax Systems, pg 865
SNAP, pg 891
Stanislaus AV Inc, pg 899
Transvideo International, pg 917
VMI Inc, pg 932

COLORADO
Aspen Systems Inc, pg 691
Daylight Productions & Rentals, pg 739
Spectrum Audio Visual Services, pg 897

FLORIDA
Access Media Group, pg 673
Altel Systems Group Inc, pg 682
AVI-SPL, pg 698
Digital Video Systems, pg 742
Harris Corp, pg 776
Hi-Tech Enterprises Inc, pg 779
Hi-Tech Import Export Corp, pg 779
Midtown Video Inc, pg 827
ONstage, pg 846
The Singing Machine Co Inc, pg 889

GEORGIA
Clark, pg 725
Stage Front Presentation Systems, pg 899
TAPPI, pg 907

HAWAII
The Audio Visual Co (AVCO), pg 694

ILLINOIS
Allen Visual Systems Inc, pg 680
Dukane Corp, Audio Visual Products Division, pg 747
Joseph Electronics, pg 795
Quintessence Audio Ltd, pg 868
Woodside Avenue Music Productions Inc, pg 941

INDIANA
Sensory Technologies LLC, pg 884

KENTUCKY
NOR-COM Inc, pg 841

LOUISIANA
Techkno Integration & Design Services LLC, pg 908

MAINE
Headlight Audio Visual Inc, pg 777

MARYLAND
DSR Computer Technology Specialists Inc, pg 747
Human Circuit, pg 782
Noventri, pg 843

MASSACHUSETTS
Professional Audio Design Inc, pg 865
Psychsoft Inc, pg 866
Rule Boston Camera, pg 878

MICHIGAN
Olson Anderson Co, pg 685
Digi Sign Design LLC, pg 741
Michigan Office Solutions (MOS), A Xerox Company, pg 825
On Stage Visuals, pg 846

MINNESOTA
Alpha Video & Audio Inc, pg 682

MISSOURI
Modern Communications Inc, pg 828
Schiller's Audio-Visual, pg 881

NEW JERSEY
Argraph Corp, pg 688
Audio Visual Associates, pg 694
Diversified, pg 744
Earl Girls Inc, pg 749
Starlite, pg 900
Total Video Products Inc, pg 916
Wired 4 Sound Inc, pg 940

NEW YORK
All Mobile Video Inc, pg 680
Audio-Video Corp, pg 694
Colortone Audio Visual, pg 728
Design Audio Visual Inc, pg 741
eMagin Corp, pg 753
Guidance Associates Inc Center for Humanities, pg 774
KVL Audio Visual Services Inc, pg 802
Langie Audio Visual Systems, pg 803
Video Technology Services Inc, pg 929
Videoguys, pg 929
Vision Identics Systems Inc, pg 930
Visual Word Systems Inc, pg 932

NORTH CAROLINA
Crest Electronics Inc, pg 734
Crispin Corp, pg 734

OHIO
ITA Audio Visual Solutions, pg 791
Midwest Photo Exchange, pg 827
Tri-State Audio Visual Co, pg 918

PENNSYLVANIA
Advanced AV LLC, pg 677
Aydin Displays, a Sparton Company, pg 700
J E Foss Co, pg 764
Innovision Media Group, pg 788
The Lerro Corp, pg 806

TENNESSEE
Lowrance Sound Co Inc, pg 812
Spring Arbor Distributors Inc, pg 898
Technical Support Systems LLC, pg 908
Zion Music Group, pg 945

TEXAS
AVES Audio Visual Systems Inc, pg 698
Biway Media, pg 706

242

CAM Audio Inc, pg 714
Data Projections Inc, pg 738
Digital Display Solutions Inc,
    pg 742
Supercircuits, pg 904
Tarpley Media Systems, pg 907
Videotex Systems Inc, pg 930

VIRGINIA

Avitecture Inc, pg 699
Design & Production Inc, pg 740
Intellidyne LLC, pg 789
Lee Hartman & Sons Inc, pg 805
Quince Imaging Inc, pg 868
Rocktown Media, pg 876

WASHINGTON

ToteVision, pg 916

WISCONSIN

Audio Visual of Milwaukee Inc,
    pg 694
Camera Corner Connecting Point,
    pg 715
Full Compass Systems, pg 767
Safe Harbor Computers, pg 879

ALBERTA

Allstar Show Industries Inc, pg 681
Evolution AV, pg 757
Infosat Communications Inc, pg 787
Matrix Video Communications Corp
    (MVCC), pg 819

BRITISH COLUMBIA

Commercial Electronics Ltd, pg 728

MANITOBA

Advance Pro, pg 677
Inland Audio Visual Ltd, pg 788

ONTARIO

Cinema Stage Inc, pg 724

Monitor Manufacturers

CALIFORNIA

Aztek Inc, pg 700
Boland Communications Inc,
    pg 708
GVISION USA Inc, pg 775
Hoodman Corp, pg 781
Recortec Inc, pg 872
Tatung Co of America Inc, pg 907
Transvideo International, pg 917
ViewSonic, pg 930

ILLINOIS

Canvys™, pg 716

NEW JERSEY

Sharp Electronics Corp, Professional
    Display Division, pg 885

NEW YORK

eMagin Corp, pg 753
Video Technology Services Inc,
    pg 929

NORTH CAROLINA

Computer Dynamics, pg 729

PENNSYLVANIA

Aydin Displays, a Sparton
    Company, pg 700

VIRGINIA

Quince Imaging Inc, pg 868

WASHINGTON

ToteVision, pg 916

BRITISH COLUMBIA

Triad Communications Ltd, pg 918

Monitor Rentals

ALABAMA

Audio-Video Resources Inc, pg 694

ALASKA

Imig Audio/Video Inc, pg 786

ARIZONA

Merestone, pg 823
Video West Inc, pg 929

ARKANSAS

White Diamond Productions LLC,
    pg 937

CALIFORNIA

Absolute Rentals, pg 672
Advanced Media LLC, pg 677
AGF Media Services, pg 678
Alliant Event Services, pg 681
Ametron Audio/Video, pg 684
Artichoke Productions, pg 690
Associated Sound, pg 691
Audio Rents, pg 693
AV Guys, pg 697
Bexel, an NEP Broadcast Services
    Company, pg 704
Cherry Multimedia, pg 721
Deck Hand Inc, pg 740
Express Media Inc, pg 757
Golden Gate Studios, pg 772
Lynch Communications, pg 813
McCune Audio-Video-Lighting,
    pg 821
Media Fabricators Inc, pg 822
Munday & Collins AV, pg 834
Muse Presentation Technologies,
    pg 834
Production Gear Rentals (PGR),
    pg 863
PSAV® Presentation Services,
    pg 866
Radiant Images, pg 869
RetinaVision Productions, pg 874
Sound Service Co, pg 894
Stanislaus AV Inc, pg 899
Synthesizer Rental Service, pg 906
Total Creative, pg 916
VER, pg 926
VMI Inc, pg 932
Voice & Video Rentals, pg 932
Warner Bros Production Sound &
    Video Services, pg 934

COLORADO

Multimedia Audio Visual Inc,
    pg 833
Open Media Foundation, pg 846
Spectrum Audio Visual Services,
    pg 897

CONNECTICUT

A/V Davey, pg 697
Videofilm Systems Inc, pg 929

FLORIDA

Access Media Group, pg 673
Accord Productions, pg 673
AVI-SPL, pg 698
Hi-Tech Enterprises Inc, pg 779
Industrial Strength Inc, pg 787
MAPS Production House, pg 816
ONstage, pg 846
Sight & Sound Productions, pg 887

GEORGIA

Lighting & Production Equipment
    Inc, pg 807
Stage Front Presentation Systems,
    pg 899

HAWAII

FOTON Hawaii, pg 764

ILLINOIS

Allen Visual Systems Inc, pg 680
AV Chicago Inc, pg 696
Backstar Creative Media Inc,
    pg 700
Product Productions, pg 863
RC Communications, pg 870
Resolution Productions Group,
    pg 874
Woodside Avenue Music
    Productions Inc, pg 941

KENTUCKY

Audio Visual Techniques Inc,
    pg 695

MAINE

Headlight Audio Visual Inc, pg 777

MARYLAND

Advance Audiovisual Presentation
    Ltd, pg 677
CPR MultiMedia Solutions, pg 732
Event Tech, pg 756

MASSACHUSETTS

AVFX Inc, pg 698
Cramer, pg 732
massAV, pg 819
Preston Productions Inc, pg 861

MICHIGAN

Digi Sign Design LLC, pg 741
K&R All Media Productions LLC,
    pg 796
On Stage Visuals, pg 846

MINNESOTA

Alpha Video & Audio Inc, pg 682

MISSOURI

Schiller's Audio-Visual, pg 881
Show-Me Audio-Visual, pg 887

NEBRASKA

Dog & Pony Productions Inc,
    pg 744

NEVADA

GES Audio Visual, pg 770

NEW JERSEY

Audio Visual Dynamics®, pg 694
Earl Girls Inc, pg 749
Panavid, pg 850
PLS Staging, pg 858

Starlite, pg 900
Wired 4 Sound Inc, pg 940

NEW MEXICO

Production Outfitters, pg 864

NEW YORK

All Mobile Video Inc, pg 680
Colortone Audio Visual, pg 728
Design Audio Visual Inc, pg 741
Hello World Communications,
    pg 778
KVL Audio Visual Services Inc,
    pg 802
Langie Audio Visual Systems,
    pg 803
Manhattan Center Studios Inc,
    pg 816
SmartSource Computer & AV
    Rentals, pg 891
Visual Word Systems Inc, pg 932

NORTH CAROLINA

AV Connections Inc, pg 697
AV Metro Inc, pg 697

NORTH DAKOTA

Media Productions, pg 822

OHIO

Hughie's Event Production Services,
    pg 782

OKLAHOMA

PDC Productions, pg 852

PENNSYLVANIA

Advanced AV LLC, pg 677
Argentine Productions Inc, pg 688
FMP Media Solutions Inc, pg 763
Innovision Media Group, pg 788
The Videohouse Inc, pg 929

TENNESSEE

RentACamera.com, pg 873
Technical Support Systems LLC,
    pg 908

TEXAS

Alford Media Services, pg 680
Stage Directions, pg 898

VIRGINIA

American AV, pg 682
Quince Imaging Inc, pg 868

WASHINGTON

The House Studios, pg 782

WISCONSIN

Audio Visual of Milwaukee Inc,
    pg 694
Full Compass Systems, pg 767

PUERTO RICO

Stage Crew Audiovisual Inc, pg 898

ALBERTA

Evolution AV, pg 757

BRITISH COLUMBIA

Commercial Electronics Ltd, pg 728
Inspired Image Picture Co (IIPC),
    pg 788

COMPUTER SYSTEMS

Monitor Rentals (continued)

MANITOBA

Inland Audio Visual Ltd, pg 788

ONTARIO

RB Productions, pg 870

QUEBEC

Audio Visual Dynamics, pg 694

Monitor Repairs

CALIFORNIA

Advanced Media LLC, pg 677
Ametron Audio/Video, pg 684
McAlister Electronics, pg 820
Transvideo International, pg 917
TV Pro Gear, pg 919
VMI Inc, pg 932

CONNECTICUT

HB Communications Inc, pg 777

FLORIDA

Digital Video Systems, pg 742
Hi-Tech Enterprises Inc, pg 779

GEORGIA

Stage Front Presentation Systems, pg 899

ILLINOIS

Allen Visual Systems Inc, pg 680
Midwest Digital Corp, pg 827

KENTUCKY

NOR-COM Inc, pg 841

MAINE

Headlight Audio Visual Inc, pg 777

MICHIGAN

TEL Systems LLC, pg 909

NEW JERSEY

Earl Girls Inc, pg 749

NEW YORK

Langie Audio Visual Systems, pg 803
Video Technology Services Inc, pg 929

OHIO

ITA Audio Visual Solutions, pg 791
Tri-State Audio Visual Co, pg 918

PENNSYLVANIA

J E Foss Co, pg 764

TENNESSEE

Technical Support Systems LLC, pg 908

VIRGINIA

Avitecture Inc, pg 699

WASHINGTON

ToteVision, pg 916

WISCONSIN

Camera Corner Connecting Point, pg 715
Full Compass Systems, pg 767

ALBERTA

Evolution AV, pg 757
Infosat Communications Inc, pg 787

BRITISH COLUMBIA

Commercial Electronics Ltd, pg 728

MANITOBA

Inland Audio Visual Ltd, pg 788

Mouse System Distributors

CALIFORNIA

Ametron Audio/Video, pg 684
Assured Audio Visual, pg 691
Audio Images Corp, pg 693
California Tape Products Inc, pg 714
Gyration, pg 775
Jameco Electronics, pg 792
Kontron America, pg 801
MediaPOINTE, pg 823
Photodyne Technologies, pg 856
Promax Systems, pg 865

COLORADO

Spectrum Audio Visual Services, pg 897

FLORIDA

Access Media Group, pg 673
Altel Systems Group Inc, pg 682
Hi-Tech Import Export Corp, pg 779
ONstage, pg 846

GEORGIA

Stage Front Presentation Systems, pg 899

ILLINOIS

Manning Productions, pg 816
Woodside Avenue Music Productions Inc, pg 941

KENTUCKY

NOR-COM Inc, pg 841

MARYLAND

DSR Computer Technology Specialists Inc, pg 747

MASSACHUSETTS

Psychsoft Inc, pg 866

MICHIGAN

Olson Anderson Co, pg 685

MISSOURI

Schiller's Audio-Visual, pg 881

NEW JERSEY

Argraph Corp, pg 688
Starlite, pg 900

NEW YORK

Audio-Video Corp, pg 694
Design Audio Visual Inc, pg 741
Guidance Associates Inc Center for Humanities, pg 774

NORTH CAROLINA

Crispin Corp, pg 734
Verbatim Americas LLC, pg 926

PENNSYLVANIA

Advanced AV LLC, pg 677
The Lerro Corp, pg 806

TENNESSEE

Lowrance Sound Co Inc, pg 812
Technical Support Systems LLC, pg 908

TEXAS

Videotex Systems Inc, pg 930

VIRGINIA

Intellidyne LLC, pg 789
Lee Hartman & Sons Inc, pg 805

WISCONSIN

Audio Visual of Milwaukee Inc, pg 694
Camera Corner Connecting Point, pg 715
Full Compass Systems, pg 767

ALBERTA

Infosat Communications Inc, pg 787

MANITOBA

Advance Pro, pg 677
Inland Audio Visual Ltd, pg 788

Mouse System Manufacturers

ARIZONA

Covid Inc, pg 732

CALIFORNIA

Gyration, pg 775
Kensington Technology Group, pg 797
Kontron America, pg 801

NORTH CAROLINA

Verbatim Americas LLC, pg 926

TEXAS

Origin Instruments Corp, pg 848

Multimedia System Distributors

ARIZONA

EAR Professional Audio/Video, pg 749

ARKANSAS

Jay S Stanley & Associates Inc, pg 899
White Diamond Productions LLC, pg 937

CALIFORNIA

Ametron Audio/Video, pg 684
Associated Sound, pg 691
Audio Images Corp, pg 693
Be Media, pg 702
BigFoot Mobile Systems, pg 705
California Tape Products Inc, pg 714
Computer Modules Inc, pg 729
Diaquest, pg 741
Electrosonic Inc, pg 752
Jameco Electronics, pg 792
JD Audio Visual Inc, pg 793
Kontron America, pg 801
Media Fabricators Inc, pg 822
MediaMation Inc, pg 822
MediaPOINTE, pg 823
Photodyne Technologies, pg 856
Promax Systems, pg 865
Sanako Inc, pg 880
Stanislaus AV Inc, pg 899
Total Creative, pg 916
Videobotics, pg 929
VMI Inc, pg 932

COLORADO

Aspen Systems Inc, pg 691
G W Hannaway & Associates, pg 775

FLORIDA

Access Media Group, pg 673
Digital Video Systems, pg 742
Harmon's Audio-Visual Services, pg 776
Harris Corp, pg 776
Hi-Tech Enterprises Inc, pg 779
Hi-Tech Import Export Corp, pg 779
ITEC Entertainment Corp, pg 791
Technomedia Solutions, pg 909

GEORGIA

Clark, pg 725
PolyVision Corporation, pg 859
Stage Front Presentation Systems, pg 899
TAPPI, pg 907

HAWAII

The Audio Visual Co (AVCO), pg 694

INDIANA

Sensory Technologies LLC, pg 884

KENTUCKY

NOR-COM Inc, pg 841

LOUISIANA

Techkno Integration & Design Services LLC, pg 908

MARYLAND

DSR Computer Technology Specialists Inc, pg 747
Human Circuit, pg 782
Image Logic Corp, pg 785
Nelson White Systems Inc, pg 838

MASSACHUSETTS

Avid Technology Inc, pg 698
Professional Audio Design Inc, pg 865
Psychsoft Inc, pg 866
Rule Boston Camera, pg 878

MICHIGAN

Olson Anderson Co, pg 685
Digi Sign Design LLC, pg 741
Michigan Office Solutions (MOS),
A Xerox Company, pg 825

MINNESOTA

Alpha Video & Audio Inc, pg 682
BeyerSound & Essay Audio, pg 705

MISSISSIPPI

Bowie Audio Visual Enterprises Inc,
pg 709

MISSOURI

Schiller's Audio-Visual, pg 881

NEBRASKA

Strong Cinema Products, pg 902

NEW JERSEY

AlltecPro, pg 681
Diversified, pg 744
Earl Girls Inc, pg 749
Entel Systems Inc, pg 754
MiB MediaWorks, pg 825
Starlite, pg 900
Total Video Products Inc, pg 916

NEW YORK

Audio-Video Corp, pg 694
Colortone Audio Visual, pg 728
Guidance Associates Inc Center for
Humanities, pg 774
Sargent Welch, pg 880
Visual Technologies Corp, pg 932

OHIO

Tri-State Audio Visual Co, pg 918

OREGON

NeoSoft Corp, pg 838

PENNSYLVANIA

AccuWeather Inc, pg 674
Advanced AV LLC, pg 677
J E Foss Co, pg 764
Innovision Media Group, pg 788
The Lerro Corp, pg 806
Wespen Audio Visual Co, pg 935

TENNESSEE

Lowrance Sound Co Inc, pg 812
Spring Arbor Distributors Inc,
pg 898
Technical Support Systems LLC,
pg 908
Zion Music Group, pg 945

TEXAS

Audio Visual Technologies Group
(AVTG), pg 695
Biway Media, pg 706
Data Projections Inc, pg 738
Epic Software Group Inc, pg 755
Tarpley Media Systems, pg 907
Videotex Systems Inc, pg 930

VIRGINIA

Design & Production Inc, pg 740
Intellidyne LLC, pg 789
Lee Hartman & Sons Inc, pg 805
RGB Technology Inc, pg 874
Rocktown Media, pg 876

WISCONSIN

Audio Visual of Milwaukee Inc,
pg 694
Camera Corner Connecting Point,
pg 715
Full Compass Systems, pg 767
Safe Harbor Computers, pg 879

WYOMING

Bridger Productions Inc, pg 710

ALBERTA

Infosat Communications Inc, pg 787
Matrix Video Communications Corp
(MVCC), pg 819
SMART Technologies ULC, pg 891

MANITOBA

Advance Pro, pg 677
Inland Audio Visual Ltd, pg 788
Tek Gear, pg 909

ONTARIO

Cinema Stage Inc, pg 724
GestureTek, pg 770
Westbury National Show Systems
Ltd, pg 936

Multimedia System Manufacturers

ARIZONA

Applied Integration Corp, pg 687

CALIFORNIA

AITech International, pg 679
Computer Modules Inc, pg 729
Diaquest, pg 741
FutureVideo, pg 767
Grande Vitesse Systems Inc (GVS),
pg 773
Micro Express, pg 825
QRS Software Services, pg 867
Toshiba America Information
Systems Inc, pg 916
VITEC Multimedia, pg 932

COLORADO

Aspen Systems Inc, pg 691

FLORIDA

CD ROM™ Inc, pg 718

GEORGIA

PolyVision Corporation, pg 859

ILLINOIS

AmpliVox Portable Sound Systems,
pg 684

KANSAS

Keywest Technology Inc, pg 798

MARYLAND

Image Logic Corp, pg 785

MASSACHUSETTS

Avid Technology Inc, pg 698
MorphoTrust USA, A Safran
Company, pg 830
Psychsoft Inc, pg 866

MICHIGAN

ASC Systems, pg 690

NEW JERSEY

CELCO, pg 719
Crestron Electronics Inc, pg 734
FSR Inc, pg 766
PeopleVisionFX, pg 854

NEW YORK

Laird Digital Cinema, pg 803
RCS Enterprises, pg 871

NORTH CAROLINA

Micro Technology Unlimited Inc,
pg 826

OHIO

Interlink Technologies, pg 789
Omnia Audio, pg 845

OREGON

NeoSoft Corp, pg 838

PENNSYLVANIA

AccuWeather Inc, pg 674
Scala Inc, pg 881

TENNESSEE

Adtec Digital Inc, pg 677

TEXAS

Biway Media, pg 706

VIRGINIA

Intellidyne LLC, pg 789
RGB Technology Inc, pg 874

ALBERTA

SMART Technologies ULC, pg 891

BRITISH COLUMBIA

Triad Communications Ltd, pg 918

MANITOBA

Tek Gear, pg 909

ONTARIO

GestureTek, pg 770

Multimedia System Rentals

ALABAMA

Audio-Video Resources Inc, pg 694

ARIZONA

Merestone, pg 823

ARKANSAS

White Diamond Productions LLC,
pg 937

CALIFORNIA

Ametron Audio/Video, pg 684
Associated Sound, pg 691
Express Media Inc, pg 757
Golden Gate Studios, pg 772
Hooper Camera & Imaging, pg 781
JD Audio Visual Inc, pg 793
Lynch Communications, pg 813
Muse Presentation Technologies,
pg 834

RetinaVision Productions, pg 874
Total Creative, pg 916

CONNECTICUT

A/V Davey, pg 697
Videofilm Systems Inc, pg 929

FLORIDA

Access Media Group, pg 673
Harmon's Audio-Visual Services,
pg 776
Industrial Strength Inc, pg 787
Universal Studios Florida®
Production Group, pg 922

GEORGIA

Stage Front Presentation Systems,
pg 899

ILLINOIS

Airways Digital Media, pg 679
Creative Technology (CT), pg 733
RC Communications, pg 870
Resolution Productions Group,
pg 874

KENTUCKY

Audio Visual Techniques Inc,
pg 695

MARYLAND

Advance Audiovisual Presentation
Ltd, pg 677
Kramer Communications Video
Production, pg 801
Nelson White Systems Inc, pg 838

MASSACHUSETTS

Preston Productions Inc, pg 861

MICHIGAN

Digi Sign Design LLC, pg 741
K&R All Media Productions LLC,
pg 796

MISSISSIPPI

Bowie Audio Visual Enterprises Inc,
pg 709

MISSOURI

Show-Me Audio-Visual, pg 887

NEW JERSEY

Earl Girls Inc, pg 749
PLS Staging, pg 858

NEW YORK

Manhattan Center Studios Inc,
pg 816
Visual Technologies Corp, pg 932

NORTH DAKOTA

Media Productions, pg 822

OHIO

Bartha, pg 702

OKLAHOMA

PDC Productions, pg 852

PENNSYLVANIA

FMP Media Solutions Inc, pg 763
Innovision Media Group, pg 788

COMPUTER SYSTEMS

Multimedia System Rentals (continued)

TENNESSEE

Love Shack Recording Studios, pg 811
Technical Support Systems LLC, pg 908

TEXAS

Stage Directions, pg 898

VIRGINIA

Advance Concepts Inc, pg 677
American AV, pg 682

WISCONSIN

Full Compass Systems, pg 767

PUERTO RICO

Stage Crew Audiovisual Inc, pg 898

MANITOBA

Inland Audio Visual Ltd, pg 788
Tek Gear, pg 909

ONTARIO

RB Productions, pg 870
Westbury National Show Systems Ltd, pg 936

QUEBEC

Group PVP, pg 774

Multimedia System Repairs

CALIFORNIA

Ametron Audio/Video, pg 684
Technical Services, pg 908

COLORADO

Aspen Systems Inc, pg 691

CONNECTICUT

HB Communications Inc, pg 777

FLORIDA

Hi-Tech Enterprises Inc, pg 779

GEORGIA

Stage Front Presentation Systems, pg 899

KENTUCKY

NOR-COM Inc, pg 841

MARYLAND

DSR Computer Technology Specialists Inc, pg 747
Nelson White Systems Inc, pg 838

NEW JERSEY

Earl Girls Inc, pg 749

NEW YORK

Visual Technologies Corp, pg 932

OHIO

Tri-State Audio Visual Co, pg 918

TENNESSEE

Technical Support Systems LLC, pg 908

TEXAS

Biway Media, pg 706

VIRGINIA

Intellidyne LLC, pg 789

WISCONSIN

Camera Corner Connecting Point, pg 715
Full Compass Systems, pg 767

ALBERTA

Infosat Communications Inc, pg 787

MANITOBA

Inland Audio Visual Ltd, pg 788

ONTARIO

Westbury National Show Systems Ltd, pg 936

Multimedia Workstation Distributors

ARIZONA

EAR Professional Audio/Video, pg 749

CALIFORNIA

Ametron Audio/Video, pg 684
Audio Images Corp, pg 693
Be Media, pg 702
BigFoot Mobile Systems, pg 705
CADint, pg 713
California Tape Products Inc, pg 714
Computer Modules Inc, pg 729
Diaquest, pg 741
Electrosonic Inc, pg 752
Media Fabricators Inc, pg 822
MediaPOINTE, pg 823
Photodyne Technologies, pg 856
Promax Systems, pg 865
Sanako Inc, pg 880
Total Creative, pg 916
Videobotics, pg 929
VMI Inc, pg 932
Zack Electronics Inc, pg 945

COLORADO

Aspen Systems Inc, pg 691
G W Hannaway & Associates, pg 775

FLORIDA

Access Media Group, pg 673
CD ROM™ Inc, pg 718
Digital Video Systems, pg 742
Harris Corp, pg 776
Hi-Tech Enterprises Inc, pg 779
Hi-Tech Import Export Corp, pg 779

GEORGIA

Stage Front Presentation Systems, pg 899

HAWAII

The Audio Visual Co (AVCO), pg 694

ILLINOIS

Luxor, pg 812
Manning Productions, pg 816

KENTUCKY

NOR-COM Inc, pg 841

LOUISIANA

Techkno Integration & Design Services LLC, pg 908

MARYLAND

Bradley Broadcast & Pro Audio, pg 709
DSR Computer Technology Specialists Inc, pg 747
Human Circuit, pg 782
Image Logic Corp, pg 785

MASSACHUSETTS

Avid Technology Inc, pg 698
Psychsoft Inc, pg 866
Rule Boston Camera, pg 878

MICHIGAN

Olson Anderson Co, pg 685
Digi Sign Design LLC, pg 741

MISSOURI

Schiller's Audio-Visual, pg 881

NEW JERSEY

Diversified, pg 744
MiB MediaWorks, pg 825

NEW YORK

Audio-Video Corp, pg 694
Korg USA Inc, pg 801
KVL Audio Visual Services Inc, pg 802
Videoguys, pg 929

OHIO

Tri-State Audio Visual Co, pg 918

PENNSYLVANIA

AccuWeather Inc, pg 674
Advanced AV LLC, pg 677
J E Foss Co, pg 764
The Lerro Corp, pg 806

TENNESSEE

Technical Support Systems LLC, pg 908

TEXAS

Biway Media, pg 706
Tarpley Media Systems, pg 907
Videotex Systems Inc, pg 930

VIRGINIA

Lee Hartman & Sons Inc, pg 805
RGB Technology Inc, pg 874

WISCONSIN

Audio Visual of Milwaukee Inc, pg 694
Camera Corner Connecting Point, pg 715
Full Compass Systems, pg 767

Safe Harbor Computers, pg 879
Spectrum Industries Inc, pg 897

ALBERTA

Genesis Integration, pg 769
Matrix Video Communications Corp (MVCC), pg 819

MANITOBA

Advance Pro, pg 677
Inland Audio Visual Ltd, pg 788

Multimedia Workstation Manufacturers

ALABAMA

Marco Inc, pg 816

ARKANSAS

Sound-Craft Systems Inc, pg 894

CALIFORNIA

Diaquest, pg 741
Grande Vitesse Systems Inc (GVS), pg 773
Kontron America, pg 801
Micro Express, pg 825
VITEC Multimedia, pg 932

COLORADO

Aspen Systems Inc, pg 691

FLORIDA

CD ROM™ Inc, pg 718
Hi-Tech Enterprises Inc, pg 779

ILLINOIS

Bretford Manufacturing Inc, pg 710
Dukane Corp, Audio Visual Products Division, pg 747
Luxor, pg 812
Marshall Furniture Inc, pg 817

INDIANA

Da-Lite, a Legrand AV Inc brand, pg 737

MARYLAND

Image Logic Corp, pg 785

MASSACHUSETTS

Avid Technology Inc, pg 698
Psychsoft Inc, pg 866

MICHIGAN

ASC Systems, pg 690

MINNESOTA

Emcor Enclosures-Crenlo, pg 753
Winsted Corp, pg 939

NEW JERSEY

Sony Pro Audio, pg 893

NEW YORK

Laird Digital Cinema, pg 803

NORTH CAROLINA

Computer Dynamics, pg 729
Micro Technology Unlimited Inc, pg 826

TENNESSEE

Adtec Digital Inc, pg 677

TEXAS

Biway Media, pg 706
MooreCo Inc, pg 830

VIRGINIA

RGB Technology Inc, pg 874

WASHINGTON

Watson Desking, pg 934

WISCONSIN

Safe Harbor Computers, pg 879
Spectrum Industries Inc, pg 897

BRITISH COLUMBIA

Richmond Sound Design Ltd,
pg 875

ONTARIO

Corel Corp, pg 731

Multimedia Workstation Rentals

ARIZONA

Merestone, pg 823

CALIFORNIA

Absolute Rentals, pg 672
Express Media Inc, pg 757
Golden Gate Studios, pg 772
Lynch Communications, pg 813
Maximus Media Inc, pg 820
Media Fabricators Inc, pg 822
Muse Presentation Technologies,
pg 834
Porter Productions, pg 859
Total Creative, pg 916
VER, pg 926
Warner Bros Production Sound &
Video Services, pg 934

DELAWARE

Side Door Studio Inc, pg 887

FLORIDA

Access Media Group, pg 673
Universal Studios Florida®
Production Group, pg 922

GEORGIA

Stage Front Presentation Systems,
pg 899

ILLINOIS

Airways Digital Media, pg 679
RC Communications, pg 870

MARYLAND

Kramer Communications Video
Production, pg 801

MASSACHUSETTS

Preston Productions Inc, pg 861

MICHIGAN

Digi Sign Design LLC, pg 741
K&R All Media Productions LLC,
pg 796

MISSOURI

Schiller's Audio-Visual, pg 881

NEW JERSEY

PLS Staging, pg 858

NEW YORK

KVL Audio Visual Services Inc,
pg 802
SmartSource Computer & AV
Rentals, pg 891

OHIO

Hughie's Event Production Services,
pg 782

OKLAHOMA

PDC Productions, pg 852

PENNSYLVANIA

FMP Media Solutions Inc, pg 763

TENNESSEE

Love Shack Recording Studios,
pg 811
Technical Support Systems LLC,
pg 908

VIRGINIA

Advance Concepts Inc, pg 677

PUERTO RICO

Stage Crew Audiovisual Inc, pg 898

MANITOBA

Inland Audio Visual Ltd, pg 788

ONTARIO

RB Productions, pg 870

QUEBEC

Group PVP, pg 774

Multimedia Workstation Repairs

CALIFORNIA

Ametron Audio/Video, pg 684

CONNECTICUT

HB Communications Inc, pg 777

FLORIDA

Hi-Tech Enterprises Inc, pg 779

GEORGIA

Stage Front Presentation Systems,
pg 899

KENTUCKY

NOR-COM Inc, pg 841

MARYLAND

DSR Computer Technology
Specialists Inc, pg 747

OHIO

Tri-State Audio Visual Co, pg 918

TENNESSEE

Technical Support Systems LLC,
pg 908

TEXAS

Biway Media, pg 706

WISCONSIN

Camera Corner Connecting Point,
pg 715
Full Compass Systems, pg 767

MANITOBA

Inland Audio Visual Ltd, pg 788

Networking System Distributors

ARIZONA

EAR Professional Audio/Video,
pg 749

CALIFORNIA

Advanced Systems Group LLC,
pg 677
Audio Images Corp, pg 693
CADint, pg 713
California Tape Products Inc,
pg 714
DataDirect Networks, pg 738
Electrosonic Inc, pg 752
Ingram Micro, pg 788
Jameco Electronics, pg 792
Kontron America, pg 801
Media Fabricators Inc, pg 822
MediaPOINTE, pg 823
Joseph Nicoletti Consulting-
Promotion, pg 841
Photodyne Technologies, pg 856
Promax Systems, pg 865
Sanako Inc, pg 880
Seagate Technology LLC, pg 883
TOA Electronics Inc, pg 915

COLORADO

Aspen Systems Inc, pg 691

CONNECTICUT

The Video Messenger Co, pg 928

FLORIDA

Access Media Group, pg 673
Digital Video Systems, pg 742
Harris Corp, pg 776
Hi-Tech Import Export Corp,
pg 779

GEORGIA

Accu-Tech, pg 673
Stage Front Presentation Systems,
pg 899

ILLINOIS

Anixter Inc, pg 685

KENTUCKY

NOR-COM Inc, pg 841

MARYLAND

DSR Computer Technology
Specialists Inc, pg 747
Human Circuit, pg 782

MASSACHUSETTS

Artel Video Systems, pg 690
Avid Technology Inc, pg 698
Psychsoft Inc, pg 866

MICHIGAN

ASC Systems, pg 690
Digi Sign Design LLC, pg 741

MINNESOTA

Alpha Video & Audio Inc, pg 682

NEW JERSEY

Diversified, pg 744
Nesbit Systems Inc, pg 838
Starlite, pg 900

NORTH CAROLINA

Crispin Corp, pg 734

OHIO

iVideo Technologies, pg 792
Tri-State Audio Visual Co, pg 918

PENNSYLVANIA

Advanced AV LLC, pg 677
The Lerro Corp, pg 806
Visual Sound Inc, pg 931

SOUTH CAROLINA

Keymark Inc, pg 798

TEXAS

Biway Media, pg 706

UTAH

SirsiDynix, pg 889

VIRGINIA

Intellidyne LLC, pg 789
Lee Hartman & Sons Inc, pg 805
The Whitlock Group, pg 937

WISCONSIN

Audio Visual of Milwaukee Inc,
pg 694
Camera Corner Connecting Point,
pg 715
Comprompter Inc, pg 729
Full Compass Systems, pg 767

ALBERTA

Infosat Communications Inc, pg 787

MANITOBA

Advance Pro, pg 677
Inland Audio Visual Ltd, pg 788

ONTARIO

Technovision® Interactive Inc,
pg 909
Westbury National Show Systems
Ltd, pg 936

QUEBEC

Presagis, pg 861

COMPUTER SYSTEMS

Networking System Manufacturers

CALIFORNIA

DataDirect Networks, pg 738
Grande Vitesse Systems Inc (GVS), pg 773
Hewlett-Packard Co, pg 779
Kontron America, pg 801
Nexsan Inc, pg 840
Opticomm-EMCORE, pg 847
QSC Audio Products LLC, pg 867
RF Industries, pg 874
TOA Electronics Inc, pg 915
VITEC Multimedia, pg 932
Western Digital Corp, pg 936

COLORADO

Aspen Systems Inc, pg 691

CONNECTICUT

The Video Messenger Co, pg 928

GEORGIA

Visix™ Inc, pg 931

ILLINOIS

Broadcast Electronics, pg 710

MASSACHUSETTS

Artel Video Systems, pg 690
Avid Technology Inc, pg 698
CSPI, pg 735
Psychsoft Inc, pg 866

MICHIGAN

ASC Systems, pg 690

NEW JERSEY

Nesbit Systems Inc, pg 838
Starlite, pg 900

NEW YORK

ATTO Technology Inc, pg 692
MultiDyne Video & Fiber Optics Systems, pg 833

OHIO

Network Technologies Inc, pg 838
Omnia Audio, pg 845

PENNSYLVANIA

Mastech Digital, pg 819
Scala Inc, pg 881

TEXAS

Biway Media, pg 706

BRITISH COLUMBIA

Richmond Sound Design Ltd, pg 875

ONTARIO

Technovision® Interactive Inc, pg 909

QUEBEC

Presagis, pg 861

Networking System Rentals

ARIZONA

Merestone, pg 823

CALIFORNIA

Muse Presentation Technologies, pg 834
PSAV® Presentation Services, pg 866

GEORGIA

Stage Front Presentation Systems, pg 899

KENTUCKY

Audio Visual Techniques Inc, pg 695

MASSACHUSETTS

Preston Productions Inc, pg 861

MICHIGAN

Digi Sign Design LLC, pg 741
K&R All Media Productions LLC, pg 796

MISSOURI

Show-Me Audio-Visual, pg 887

NEW JERSEY

Audio Visual Dynamics®, pg 694

NEW YORK

SmartSource Computer & AV Rentals, pg 891

OHIO

Hughie's Event Production Services, pg 782

MANITOBA

Inland Audio Visual Ltd, pg 788

Networking System Repairs

CALIFORNIA

Aztek Inc, pg 700
TOA Electronics Inc, pg 915

COLORADO

Aspen Systems Inc, pg 691

CONNECTICUT

HB Communications Inc, pg 777

KENTUCKY

NOR-COM Inc, pg 841

MARYLAND

DSR Computer Technology Specialists Inc, pg 747

OHIO

Tri-State Audio Visual Co, pg 918

TEXAS

Biway Media, pg 706

VIRGINIA

The Whitlock Group, pg 937

WISCONSIN

Camera Corner Connecting Point, pg 715
Full Compass Systems, pg 767

ALBERTA

Infosat Communications Inc, pg 787

MANITOBA

Inland Audio Visual Ltd, pg 788

Optical Disc Recorder Distributors

ARIZONA

EAR Professional Audio/Video, pg 749

CALIFORNIA

Ametron Audio/Video, pg 684
California Tape Products Inc, pg 714
Computer Modules Inc, pg 729
Media Fabricators Inc, pg 822
MediaPOINTE, pg 823
VMI Inc, pg 932

COLORADO

Aspen Systems Inc, pg 691

FLORIDA

Access Media Group, pg 673
CD ROM™ Inc, pg 718
Digital Video Systems, pg 742
Harris Corp, pg 776
Hi-Tech Import Export Corp, pg 779
ONstage, pg 846
Recording Media & Equipment Inc (RM&E), pg 872
TAI Audio, pg 906

GEORGIA

Stage Front Presentation Systems, pg 899

KENTUCKY

NOR-COM Inc, pg 841

MARYLAND

DSR Computer Technology Specialists Inc, pg 747

MASSACHUSETTS

Psychsoft Inc, pg 866

MICHIGAN

Digi Sign Design LLC, pg 741
Michigan Office Solutions (MOS), A Xerox Company, pg 825

MINNESOTA

Microboards Technology LLC, pg 826

MISSOURI

Modern Communications Inc, pg 828
Schiller's Audio-Visual, pg 881

NEW JERSEY

Starlite, pg 900
Total Video Products Inc, pg 916

NEW YORK

Audio-Video Corp, pg 694

NORTH CAROLINA

Crispin Corp, pg 734

PENNSYLVANIA

Advanced AV LLC, pg 677

TEXAS

Biway Media, pg 706
Replicopy Digital Media Center, pg 873
Tarpley Media Systems, pg 907
Videotex Systems Inc, pg 930

UTAH

Performance Audio LLC, pg 854

VIRGINIA

Avitecture Inc, pg 699
Cybernetics, pg 736

WISCONSIN

Audio Visual of Milwaukee Inc, pg 694
Full Compass Systems, pg 767
Indus International Inc, pg 787

ALBERTA

Matrix Video Communications Corp (MVCC), pg 819

MANITOBA

Advance Pro, pg 677
Inland Audio Visual Ltd, pg 788

Optical Disc Recorder Manufacturers

CALIFORNIA

Grande Vitesse Systems Inc (GVS), pg 773
Nexsan Inc, pg 840

FLORIDA

CD ROM™ Inc, pg 718

OHIO

Tosoh USA Inc, pg 916

Optical Disc Recorder Rentals

ARIZONA

Merestone, pg 823

CALIFORNIA

Ametron Audio/Video, pg 684
Muse Presentation Technologies, pg 834
VER, pg 926

FLORIDA

ONstage, pg 846

GEORGIA
Stage Front Presentation Systems, pg 899

MASSACHUSETTS
Preston Productions Inc, pg 861

MICHIGAN
Digi Sign Design LLC, pg 741
K&R All Media Productions LLC, pg 796
K&R's Recording Studios Inc, pg 796
TEL Systems LLC, pg 909

WISCONSIN
Full Compass Systems, pg 767

PUERTO RICO
Stage Crew Audiovisual Inc, pg 898

MANITOBA
Inland Audio Visual Ltd, pg 788

ONTARIO
Technovision® Interactive Inc, pg 909

QUEBEC
Group PVP, pg 774

Optical Disc Recorder Repairs

CALIFORNIA
Ametron Audio/Video, pg 684
McAlister Electronics, pg 820

CONNECTICUT
HB Communications Inc, pg 777

KENTUCKY
NOR-COM Inc, pg 841

MINNESOTA
Microboards Technology LLC, pg 826

WISCONSIN
Full Compass Systems, pg 767

MANITOBA
Inland Audio Visual Ltd, pg 788

Plotter Distributors

ARIZONA
Mutoh America Inc, pg 835
Professional Marketing Services Inc, pg 865

CALIFORNIA
Aztek Inc, pg 700
CADint, pg 713
Ingram Micro, pg 788
MediaPOINTE, pg 823

COLORADO
Aspen Systems Inc, pg 691
Stanco Sales LLC, pg 899

FLORIDA
Hi-Tech Import Export Corp, pg 779

GEORGIA
Stage Front Presentation Systems, pg 899

KENTUCKY
NOR-COM Inc, pg 841

MARYLAND
DSR Computer Technology Specialists Inc, pg 747

MASSACHUSETTS
Psychsoft Inc, pg 866

MICHIGAN
ASC Systems, pg 690
Michigan Office Solutions (MOS), A Xerox Company, pg 825

MINNESOTA
Tierney Brothers Inc, pg 914

MISSOURI
Communitronics Corp, pg 729

NEW JERSEY
Argraph Corp, pg 688
Starlite, pg 900
Video Corporation of America (VCA), pg 927

OHIO
iVideo Technologies, pg 792

PENNSYLVANIA
Advanced AV LLC, pg 677
Visual Sound Inc, pg 931

VIRGINIA
Lee Hartman & Sons Inc, pg 805
The Whitlock Group, pg 937

WISCONSIN
Audio Visual of Milwaukee Inc, pg 694
Camera Corner Connecting Point, pg 715

MANITOBA
Advance Pro, pg 677

Plotter Manufacturers

ARIZONA
Mutoh America Inc, pg 835

CALIFORNIA
Hewlett-Packard Co, pg 779

Plotter Rentals

ARIZONA
Merestone, pg 823

CALIFORNIA
Artichoke Productions, pg 690
Express Media Inc, pg 757

MISSOURI
Show-Me Audio-Visual, pg 887

Plotter Repairs

CONNECTICUT
HB Communications Inc, pg 777

GEORGIA
Stage Front Presentation Systems, pg 899

KENTUCKY
NOR-COM Inc, pg 841

WISCONSIN
Camera Corner Connecting Point, pg 715

Presentation System Distributors

ARIZONA
EAR Professional Audio/Video, pg 749

ARKANSAS
White Diamond Productions LLC, pg 937

CALIFORNIA
AITech International, pg 679
Ametron Audio/Video, pg 684
Associated Sound, pg 691
ATV Video Center Inc, pg 692
Be Media, pg 702
BigFoot Mobile Systems, pg 705
California Tape Products Inc, pg 714
Computer Modules Inc, pg 729
Electrosonic Inc, pg 752
Hooper Camera & Imaging, pg 781
JD Audio Visual Inc, pg 793
Laser Magic Productions, pg 804
Media Fabricators Inc, pg 822
MediaPOINTE, pg 823
Promax Systems, pg 865
Stanislaus AV Inc, pg 899
Total Creative, pg 916

COLORADO
Aspen Systems Inc, pg 691
Daylight Productions & Rentals, pg 739
ProLine Digital, pg 865

CONNECTICUT
The Video Messenger Co, pg 928

FLORIDA
AVI-SPL, pg 698
Digital Video Systems, pg 742
ONstage, pg 846

GEORGIA
PolyVision Corporation, pg 859
Stage Front Presentation Systems, pg 899

HAWAII
The Audio Visual Co (AVCO), pg 694

ILLINOIS
Dukane Corp, Audio Visual Products Division, pg 747
G T Luscombe Co Inc, pg 812

KENTUCKY
NOR-COM Inc, pg 841

LOUISIANA
Techkno Integration & Design Services LLC, pg 908

MARYLAND
DSR Computer Technology Specialists Inc, pg 747
Human Circuit, pg 782
Image Logic Corp, pg 785
Nelson White Systems Inc, pg 838

MASSACHUSETTS
Graphx Inc, pg 773
Monotype Imaging Inc, pg 829
Psychsoft Inc, pg 866
Rule Boston Camera, pg 878
The Weather Company, An IBM Business, pg 935

MICHIGAN
ASC Systems, pg 690
Digi Sign Design LLC, pg 741
Michigan Office Solutions (MOS), A Xerox Company, pg 825
On Stage Visuals, pg 846

MINNESOTA
Alpha Video & Audio Inc, pg 682
Tierney Brothers Inc, pg 914
Varitronics LLC, pg 925

MISSOURI
Modern Communications Inc, pg 828
Schiller's Audio-Visual, pg 881

NEW HAMPSHIRE
Optics 1 Inc, pg 847

NEW JERSEY
Audio Visual Associates, pg 694
Diversified, pg 744
Starlite, pg 900
Total Video Products Inc, pg 916
Wired 4 Sound Inc, pg 940

NEW YORK
Audio-Video Corp, pg 694
Design Audio Visual Inc, pg 741
DSan Corp, pg 747
eMagin Corp, pg 753
KVL Audio Visual Services Inc, pg 802
Visual Technologies Corp, pg 932

OHIO
ITA Audio Visual Solutions, pg 791
Midwest Photo Exchange, pg 827
Tri-State Audio Visual Co, pg 918

OREGON
NeoSoft Corp, pg 838

PENNSYLVANIA
AccuWeather Inc, pg 674
Advanced AV LLC, pg 677
Bernie's Photo Center, pg 704

COMPUTER SYSTEMS

Presentation System Distributors (continued)

PENNSYLVANIA (continued)

Grise Audio Visual Center Inc, pg 774
Innovision Media Group, pg 788
The Lerro Corp, pg 806
Meridia ARS, pg 823
Wespen Audio Visual Co, pg 935

TENNESSEE

Lowrance Sound Co Inc, pg 812
Technical Support Systems LLC, pg 908
Zion Music Group, pg 945

TEXAS

Audio Visual Technologies Group (AVTG), pg 695
AVES Audio Visual Systems Inc, pg 698
Data Projections Inc, pg 738
Epic Software Group Inc, pg 755
Stage Directions, pg 898
Videotex Systems Inc, pg 930

VIRGINIA

Avitecture Inc, pg 699
Intellidyne LLC, pg 789
Lee Hartman & Sons Inc, pg 805
Quince Imaging Inc, pg 868

WISCONSIN

Audio Visual of Milwaukee Inc, pg 694
Camera Corner Connecting Point, pg 715
Full Compass Systems, pg 767
Safe Harbor Computers, pg 879

ALBERTA

Infosat Communications Inc, pg 787
Matrix Video Communications Corp (MVCC), pg 819
SMART Technologies ULC, pg 891

BRITISH COLUMBIA

Commercial Electronics Ltd, pg 728

MANITOBA

Advance Pro, pg 677
Inland Audio Visual Ltd, pg 788

ONTARIO

Cinema Stage Inc, pg 724
GestureTek, pg 770
Image Video, pg 785
Westbury National Show Systems Ltd, pg 936

Presentation System Manufacturers

ARIZONA

Boeckeler Instruments Inc, pg 708
Covid Inc, pg 732

CALIFORNIA

AITech International, pg 679
Extron Electronics, pg 758

Gefen, pg 769
Grande Vitesse Systems Inc (GVS), pg 773
Laser Magic Productions, pg 804
Micro Express, pg 825
VITEC Multimedia, pg 932

CONNECTICUT

The Video Messenger Co, pg 928

GEORGIA

PolyVision Corporation, pg 859
Visix™ Inc, pg 931

ILLINOIS

Bretford Manufacturing Inc, pg 710
Dukane Corp, Audio Visual Products Division, pg 747
Kart-A-Bag Manufacturing Inc, pg 796

MARYLAND

Image Logic Corp, pg 785

MASSACHUSETTS

Graphx Inc, pg 773
Monotype Imaging Inc, pg 829
Psychsoft Inc, pg 866
The Weather Company, An IBM Business, pg 935

MISSOURI

Ken-A-Vision Manufacturing Co Inc, pg 797
Magna Visual Inc, pg 814

NEW HAMPSHIRE

Optics 1 Inc, pg 847

NEW JERSEY

Crestron Electronics Inc, pg 734
FSR Inc, pg 766

NEW YORK

DSan Corp, pg 747
eMagin Corp, pg 753

OHIO

Turning Technologies LLC, pg 919

OREGON

NeoSoft Corp, pg 838

PENNSYLVANIA

AccuWeather Inc, pg 674
Interactive Products, pg 789
Meridia ARS, pg 823
Scala Inc, pg 881

TENNESSEE

Adtec Digital Inc, pg 677

TEXAS

MooreCo Inc, pg 830

VIRGINIA

Avitecture Inc, pg 699
Quince Imaging Inc, pg 868

WISCONSIN

Bardes Products Inc, pg 702

ALBERTA

SMART Technologies ULC, pg 891

BRITISH COLUMBIA

Richmond Sound Design Ltd, pg 875

ONTARIO

GestureTek, pg 770
Image Video, pg 785

Presentation System Rentals

ALABAMA

Audio-Video Resources Inc, pg 694

ARIZONA

Merestone, pg 823
Video West Inc, pg 929

ARKANSAS

White Diamond Productions LLC, pg 937

CALIFORNIA

Alliant Event Services, pg 681
Ametron Audio/Video, pg 684
Associated Sound, pg 691
ATV Video Center Inc, pg 692
Express Media Inc, pg 757
Hooper Camera & Imaging, pg 781
JD Audio Visual Inc, pg 793
Lynch Communications, pg 813
Media Fabricators Inc, pg 822
Muse Presentation Technologies, pg 834
VER, pg 926

COLORADO

Multimedia Audio Visual Inc, pg 833

CONNECTICUT

A/V Davey, pg 697

FLORIDA

Industrial Strength Inc, pg 787
ONstage, pg 846

GEORGIA

Stage Front Presentation Systems, pg 899

ILLINOIS

Airways Digital Media, pg 679
Backstar Creative Media Inc, pg 700
RC Communications, pg 870
Resolution Productions Group, pg 874

KENTUCKY

Audio Visual Techniques Inc, pg 695

MARYLAND

Advance Audiovisual Presentation Ltd, pg 677
CPR MultiMedia Solutions, pg 732
Nelson White Systems Inc, pg 838

MASSACHUSETTS

AVFX Inc, pg 698
massAV, pg 819

MICHIGAN

Digi Sign Design LLC, pg 741
K&R All Media Productions LLC, pg 796
On Stage Visuals, pg 846

MINNESOTA

Alpha Video & Audio Inc, pg 682

MISSOURI

Schiller's Audio-Visual, pg 881
Show-Me Audio-Visual, pg 887

NEW JERSEY

Audio Visual Dynamics®, pg 694
PLS Staging, pg 858
Starlite, pg 900
Wired 4 Sound Inc, pg 940

NEW YORK

Design Audio Visual Inc, pg 741
KVL Audio Visual Services Inc, pg 802
SmartSource Computer & AV Rentals, pg 891
Visual Technologies Corp, pg 932

NORTH CAROLINA

AV Metro Inc, pg 697

NORTH DAKOTA

Media Productions, pg 822

OHIO

Bartha, pg 702

OKLAHOMA

PDC Productions, pg 852

PENNSYLVANIA

Advanced AV LLC, pg 677
Grise Audio Visual Center Inc, pg 774
Innovision Media Group, pg 788
Meridia ARS, pg 823

TENNESSEE

Technical Support Systems LLC, pg 908

TEXAS

Freeman, pg 765
Stage Directions, pg 898

VIRGINIA

Advance Concepts Inc, pg 677
Quince Imaging Inc, pg 868

WISCONSIN

Audio Visual of Milwaukee Inc, pg 694
Full Compass Systems, pg 767

PUERTO RICO

Stage Crew Audiovisual Inc, pg 898

BRITISH COLUMBIA

Commercial Electronics Ltd, pg 728

MANITOBA

Inland Audio Visual Ltd, pg 788

ONTARIO

Metalworks Recording Studios Inc, pg 824
Westbury National Show Systems Ltd, pg 936

QUEBEC

Audio Visual Dynamics, pg 694

Presentation System Repairs

CONNECTICUT

HB Communications Inc, pg 777

GEORGIA

Stage Front Presentation Systems, pg 899

KENTUCKY

NOR-COM Inc, pg 841

MARYLAND

Nelson White Systems Inc, pg 838

MASSACHUSETTS

Monotype Imaging Inc, pg 829

NEW JERSEY

Starlite, pg 900

NEW YORK

Visual Technologies Corp, pg 932

OHIO

ITA Audio Visual Solutions, pg 791
Tri-State Audio Visual Co, pg 918

TENNESSEE

Technical Support Systems LLC, pg 908

VIRGINIA

Avitecture Inc, pg 699

WISCONSIN

Camera Corner Connecting Point, pg 715
Full Compass Systems, pg 767

ALBERTA

Infosat Communications Inc, pg 787

MANITOBA

Inland Audio Visual Ltd, pg 788

ONTARIO

Westbury National Show Systems Ltd, pg 936

Projection Panel Distributors

ARIZONA

EAR Professional Audio/Video, pg 749
Professional Marketing Services Inc, pg 865

Troxell-CDI, pg 918
Ultimate Presentation Systems Inc, pg 920

CALIFORNIA

Ametron Audio/Video, pg 684
Barber Tech Video Products, pg 701
Be Media, pg 702
California Tape Products Inc, pg 714
Cibola Systems, pg 723
Electrosonic Inc, pg 752
Media Fabricators Inc, pg 822
MediaPOINTE, pg 823
VMI Inc, pg 932

COLORADO

Daylight Productions & Rentals, pg 739

FLORIDA

Altel Systems Group Inc, pg 682
AVI-SPL, pg 698
Digital Video Systems, pg 742
Harmon's Audio-Visual Services, pg 776
Industrial Strength Inc, pg 787
ONstage, pg 846

GEORGIA

Boxlight Inc, pg 709
Clark, pg 725
Stage Front Presentation Systems, pg 899

HAWAII

The Audio Visual Co (AVCO), pg 694

ILLINOIS

Joseph Electronics, pg 795

INDIANA

Lee Co Inc, pg 805
Sensory Technologies LLC, pg 884

KENTUCKY

Axxis Leasing Inc, pg 700
NOR-COM Inc, pg 841

LOUISIANA

Techkno Integration & Design Services LLC, pg 908

MARYLAND

Cardinal Sound & Video, pg 717
dbF a Media Company, pg 739
DSR Computer Technology Specialists Inc, pg 747

MASSACHUSETTS

Integrated Solutions Group, pg 789

MICHIGAN

Digi Sign Design LLC, pg 741
Michigan Office Solutions (MOS), A Xerox Company, pg 825

MINNESOTA

Alpha Video & Audio Inc, pg 682

MISSOURI

Modern Communications Inc, pg 828
Schiller's Audio-Visual, pg 881

NEBRASKA

Strong Cinema Products, pg 902

NEVADA

Aardvark Video & Media Productions, pg 671

NEW JERSEY

AV Bluebook, pg 696
Diversified, pg 744
Earl Girls Inc, pg 749
Starlite, pg 900
Total Video Products Inc, pg 916
Wired 4 Sound Inc, pg 940

NEW YORK

Audio-Video Corp, pg 694
Crescendo Designs Inc, pg 734
Gaylord Archival, pg 768
Langie Audio Visual Systems, pg 803
Neptune Photo Inc, pg 838
TecNec Distributing, pg 909
Video Technology Services Inc, pg 929
Visual Technologies Corp, pg 932

OHIO

ITA Audio Visual Solutions, pg 791
Midwest Photo Exchange, pg 827
Tri-State Audio Visual Co, pg 918

PENNSYLVANIA

Advanced AV LLC, pg 677
Bernie's Photo Center, pg 704
Clair Companies, pg 725
J E Foss Co, pg 764
The Lerro Corp, pg 806
Vistacom Inc, pg 931

TENNESSEE

Lowrance Sound Co Inc, pg 812
Technical Support Systems LLC, pg 908

TEXAS

Audio Visual Technologies Group (AVTG), pg 695
Tarpley Media Systems, pg 907
Videotex Systems Inc, pg 930

VIRGINIA

Lee Hartman & Sons Inc, pg 805

WASHINGTON

CCI Solutions, pg 718

WISCONSIN

Camera Corner Connecting Point, pg 715
Full Compass Systems, pg 767

ALBERTA

Genesis Integration, pg 769
SMART Technologies ULC, pg 891

BRITISH COLUMBIA

Commercial Electronics Ltd, pg 728

MANITOBA

Inland Audio Visual Ltd, pg 788

ONTARIO

Westbury National Show Systems Ltd, pg 936

Projection Panel Manufacturers

FLORIDA

Vutec Corp, pg 933

ILLINOIS

ACCO Brands Corp, pg 673

NEW JERSEY

Sharp Electronics Corp, Professional Display Division, pg 885

TEXAS

MooreCo Inc, pg 830

VIRGINIA

Optikinetics Ltd - The Americas, pg 847
Quince Imaging Inc, pg 868

ALBERTA

SMART Technologies ULC, pg 891

ONTARIO

Evertz Microsystems Ltd, pg 757

Projection Panel Rentals

ARIZONA

Merestone, pg 823
Ultimate Presentation Systems Inc, pg 920

CALIFORNIA

Alliant Event Services, pg 681
Ametron Audio/Video, pg 684
Barber Tech Video Products, pg 701
Media Fabricators Inc, pg 822
Munday & Collins AV, pg 834
Muse Presentation Technologies, pg 834
PSAV® Presentation Services, pg 866
Voice & Video Rentals, pg 932

COLORADO

Daylight Productions & Rentals, pg 739
Multimedia Audio Visual Inc, pg 833

FLORIDA

AVI-SPL, pg 698
Harmon's Audio-Visual Services, pg 776
Industrial Strength Inc, pg 787
ONstage, pg 846

GEORGIA

Stage Front Presentation Systems, pg 899

ILLINOIS

Backstar Creative Media Inc, pg 700
RC Communications, pg 870

COMPUTER SYSTEMS

Projection Panel Rentals (continued)

KENTUCKY

Audio Visual Techniques Inc, pg 695

MARYLAND

CPR MultiMedia Solutions, pg 732
dbF a Media Company, pg 739
Event Tech, pg 756

MASSACHUSETTS

Cramer, pg 732
massAV, pg 819
Preston Productions Inc, pg 861

MICHIGAN

Digi Sign Design LLC, pg 741
K&R All Media Productions LLC, pg 796
TEL Systems LLC, pg 909

MINNESOTA

Alpha Video & Audio Inc, pg 682

MISSOURI

Schiller's Audio-Visual, pg 881
Show-Me Audio-Visual, pg 887

NEVADA

GES Audio Visual, pg 770

NEW JERSEY

Audio Visual Dynamics®, pg 694
Earl Girls Inc, pg 749
Starlite, pg 900
Wired 4 Sound Inc, pg 940

NEW YORK

Langie Audio Visual Systems, pg 803
Visual Technologies Corp, pg 932

NORTH CAROLINA

AV Metro Inc, pg 697

PENNSYLVANIA

Advanced AV LLC, pg 677
FMP Media Solutions Inc, pg 763

TENNESSEE

Technical Support Systems LLC, pg 908

TEXAS

Stage Directions, pg 898

ALBERTA

L R Light & Sound, pg 802

BRITISH COLUMBIA

Commercial Electronics Ltd, pg 728

MANITOBA

Inland Audio Visual Ltd, pg 788

ONTARIO

Metalworks Recording Studios Inc, pg 824
Westbury National Show Systems Ltd, pg 936

Projection Panel Repairs

CALIFORNIA

Ametron Audio/Video, pg 684
Electrosonic Inc, pg 752
VMI Inc, pg 932

CONNECTICUT

HB Communications Inc, pg 777

GEORGIA

Stage Front Presentation Systems, pg 899

KENTUCKY

Axxis Leasing Inc, pg 700
NOR-COM Inc, pg 841

MISSOURI

Schiller's Audio-Visual, pg 881

NEW JERSEY

Earl Girls Inc, pg 749
Starlite, pg 900

NEW YORK

Langie Audio Visual Systems, pg 803
Visual Technologies Corp, pg 932

OHIO

ITA Audio Visual Solutions, pg 791
Tri-State Audio Visual Co, pg 918

PENNSYLVANIA

J E Foss Co, pg 764

TENNESSEE

Technical Support Systems LLC, pg 908

WISCONSIN

Camera Corner Connecting Point, pg 715
Full Compass Systems, pg 767

MANITOBA

Inland Audio Visual Ltd, pg 788

ONTARIO

Westbury National Show Systems Ltd, pg 936

RGB/NTSC Converter Distributors

ALABAMA

PESA, pg 855

ARIZONA

EAR Professional Audio/Video, pg 749
Troxell-CDI, pg 918
Ultimate Presentation Systems Inc, pg 920

ARKANSAS

Jay S Stanley & Associates Inc, pg 899
White Diamond Productions LLC, pg 937

CALIFORNIA

Advanced Systems Group LLC, pg 677
AITech International, pg 679
Ametron Audio/Video, pg 684
Audio Images Corp, pg 693
Audio/Video Supply Inc, pg 694
Be Media, pg 702
California Tape Products Inc, pg 714
Ingram Micro, pg 788
MediaPOINTE, pg 823
Total Creative, pg 916
Videobotics, pg 929
VMI Inc, pg 932
Zack Electronics Inc, pg 945

FLORIDA

Access Media Group, pg 673
Altel Systems Group Inc, pg 682
Digital Video Systems, pg 742
Hi-Tech Enterprises Inc, pg 779
Hi-Tech Import Export Corp, pg 779
Industrial Strength Inc, pg 787
Midtown Video Inc, pg 827
ONstage, pg 846

GEORGIA

Baker Audio Visual, pg 700
Barco Inc, pg 701
Stage Front Presentation Systems, pg 899

HAWAII

The Audio Visual Co (AVCO), pg 694

ILLINOIS

Allen Visual Systems Inc, pg 680
Joseph Electronics, pg 795

INDIANA

Sensory Technologies LLC, pg 884

KENTUCKY

Audio Visual Techniques Inc, pg 695
NOR-COM Inc, pg 841

MAINE

Headlight Audio Visual Inc, pg 777

MARYLAND

Cardinal Sound & Video, pg 717

MASSACHUSETTS

Data Translation, pg 738
Integrated Solutions Group, pg 789

MICHIGAN

ASC Systems, pg 690
City Events Group, pg 725
Digi Sign Design LLC, pg 741
On Stage Visuals, pg 846

MISSOURI

Communitronics Corp, pg 729
Modern Communications Inc, pg 828
Schiller's Audio-Visual, pg 881

NEVADA

Aardvark Video & Media Productions, pg 671

NEW JERSEY

A-V Services Inc, pg 671
Audio Visual Associates, pg 694
Comprehensive Cable & Connectivity Co, pg 729
Diversified, pg 744
Earl Girls Inc, pg 749
PatchAmp, pg 852
PLS Staging, pg 858
Starlite, pg 900
SYMCO Inc, pg 905
Total Video Products Inc, pg 916
Video Corporation of America (VCA), pg 927
Wired 4 Sound Inc, pg 940

NEW YORK

Audio-Video Corp, pg 694
AV Workshop, pg 697
BTX Technologies, pg 712
General Audio-Visual Inc (GAVI), pg 769
Indigo Productions, pg 787
Langie Audio Visual Systems, pg 803
TecNec Distributing, pg 909
Tri-Ed Distribution Inc, pg 918
Visual Technologies Corp, pg 932
Visual Word Systems Inc, pg 932

NORTH CAROLINA

Crest Electronics Inc, pg 734

OHIO

Copp Integrated Systems, pg 731
ITA Audio Visual Solutions, pg 791
iVideo Technologies, pg 792
Tri-State Audio Visual Co, pg 918
Tri-State Visual Products Inc, pg 918

PENNSYLVANIA

Advanced AV LLC, pg 677
Aydin Displays, a Sparton Company, pg 700
Clair Companies, pg 725
The Lerro Corp, pg 806
Vistacom Inc, pg 931
Visual Sound Inc, pg 931

TENNESSEE

Lowrance Sound Co Inc, pg 812
Technical Support Systems LLC, pg 908

TEXAS

Audio Visual Technologies Group (AVTG), pg 695
AVES Audio Visual Systems Inc, pg 698
Biway Media, pg 706
Stage Directions, pg 898
Tarpley Media Systems, pg 907
Videotex Systems Inc, pg 930

UTAH

RIA Corp, pg 874

VIRGINIA

Quince Imaging Inc, pg 868
The Whitlock Group, pg 937

WISCONSIN

Audio Visual of Milwaukee Inc,
  pg 694
Camera Corner Connecting Point,
  pg 715
Full Compass Systems, pg 767
Safe Harbor Computers, pg 879

ALBERTA

Infosat Communications Inc, pg 787
Matrix Video Communications Corp
  (MVCC), pg 819

BRITISH COLUMBIA

Commercial Electronics Ltd, pg 728

MANITOBA

Tek Gear, pg 909

ONTARIO

Westbury National Show Systems
  Ltd, pg 936

RGB/NTSC Converter Manufacturers

ALABAMA

PESA, pg 855

ARIZONA

Covid Inc, pg 732

CALIFORNIA

AITech International, pg 679
ALTINEX Inc, pg 682
Extron Electronics, pg 758
For-A Corp of America, pg 763
Grande Vitesse Systems Inc (GVS),
  pg 773
Opticomm-EMCORE, pg 847
QRS Software Services, pg 867
RGB Spectrum, pg 874

GEORGIA

Barco Inc, pg 701

ILLINOIS

NEC Display Solutions of America,
  pg 837

MASSACHUSETTS

Data Translation, pg 738

MISSOURI

Link Electronics Inc, pg 809

NEW JERSEY

FSR Inc, pg 766

NEW YORK

MultiDyne Video & Fiber Optics
  Systems, pg 833
Judson Rosebush Co Inc, pg 877

VIRGINIA

Quince Imaging Inc, pg 868

BRITISH COLUMBIA

Triad Communications Ltd, pg 918

QUEBEC

Matrox Video Products Group,
  pg 819

RGB/NTSC Converter Rentals

ARIZONA

Video West Inc, pg 929

ARKANSAS

White Diamond Productions LLC,
  pg 937

CALIFORNIA

Ametron Audio/Video, pg 684
AV Guys, pg 697
Express Media Inc, pg 757
Munday & Collins AV, pg 834
Muse Presentation Technologies,
  pg 834
RetinaVision Productions, pg 874
VMI Inc, pg 932
Voice & Video Rentals, pg 932

FLORIDA

Access Media Group, pg 673
Accord Productions, pg 673
Universal Studios Florida®
  Production Group, pg 922

GEORGIA

Stage Front Presentation Systems,
  pg 899

ILLINOIS

Resolution Productions Group,
  pg 874

KENTUCKY

Audio Visual Techniques Inc,
  pg 695

MAINE

Headlight Audio Visual Inc, pg 777

MARYLAND

CPR MultiMedia Solutions, pg 732
Event Tech, pg 756

MASSACHUSETTS

Preston Productions Inc, pg 861

MICHIGAN

Digi Sign Design LLC, pg 741
K&R All Media Productions LLC,
  pg 796
On Stage Visuals, pg 846

MISSOURI

Show-Me Audio-Visual, pg 887

NEW JERSEY

Audio Visual Associates, pg 694
Audio Visual Dynamics®, pg 694
Earl Girls Inc, pg 749
Panavid, pg 850
Starlite, pg 900
Wired 4 Sound Inc, pg 940

NEW YORK

Visual Word Systems Inc, pg 932

NORTH CAROLINA

Take One Productions Ltd, pg 906

NORTH DAKOTA

Media Productions, pg 822

OKLAHOMA

PDC Productions, pg 852

PENNSYLVANIA

FMP Media Solutions Inc, pg 763
Visual Sound Inc, pg 931

TENNESSEE

Technical Support Systems LLC,
  pg 908

TEXAS

Stage Directions, pg 898

VIRGINIA

Quince Imaging Inc, pg 868

WISCONSIN

Audio Visual of Milwaukee Inc,
  pg 694

PUERTO RICO

Stage Crew Audiovisual Inc, pg 898

ONTARIO

Westbury National Show Systems
  Ltd, pg 936

RGB/NTSC Converter Repairs

CALIFORNIA

Ametron Audio/Video, pg 684

FLORIDA

Hi-Tech Enterprises Inc, pg 779
JT Communications, pg 795

GEORGIA

Stage Front Presentation Systems,
  pg 899

ILLINOIS

Allen Visual Systems Inc, pg 680
Midwest Digital Corp, pg 827

KENTUCKY

NOR-COM Inc, pg 841

NEW JERSEY

Audio Visual Associates, pg 694

NEW YORK

Visual Technologies Corp, pg 932

OHIO

Tri-State Audio Visual Co, pg 918

TENNESSEE

Technical Support Systems LLC,
  pg 908

TEXAS

Tarpley Media Systems, pg 907

VIRGINIA

Quince Imaging Inc, pg 868

WISCONSIN

Audio Visual of Milwaukee Inc,
  pg 694
Camera Corner Connecting Point,
  pg 715
Full Compass Systems, pg 767

ALBERTA

Infosat Communications Inc, pg 787

ONTARIO

Westbury National Show Systems
  Ltd, pg 936

Sound Card Distributors

ARIZONA

Allusion Studios & Pure Wave
  Audio, pg 681
EAR Professional Audio/Video,
  pg 749
Troxell-CDI, pg 918

CALIFORNIA

Ametron Audio/Video, pg 684
Audio Images Corp, pg 693
Be Media, pg 702
California Tape Products Inc,
  pg 714
Empire Pro, pg 753
Eye & I Productions, pg 758
Media Fabricators Inc, pg 822
MediaPOINTE, pg 823
Promax Systems, pg 865
Total Creative, pg 916
VMI Inc, pg 932

FLORIDA

Access Media Group, pg 673
Digital Video Systems, pg 742
Harris Corp, pg 776
Hi-Tech Enterprises Inc, pg 779
TAI Audio, pg 906

GEORGIA

Stage Front Presentation Systems,
  pg 899

HAWAII

The Audio Visual Co (AVCO),
  pg 694

INDIANA

Lee Co Inc, pg 805

KENTUCKY

NOR-COM Inc, pg 841

MARYLAND

DSR Computer Technology
  Specialists Inc, pg 747

MASSACHUSETTS

Integrated Solutions Group, pg 789
Professional Audio Design Inc,
  pg 865

COMPUTER SYSTEMS

Sound Card Distributors (continued)

MICHIGAN
Digi Sign Design LLC, pg 741

MINNESOTA
Digital Audio Labs, pg 742

MISSOURI
Modern Communications Inc, pg 828
Schiller's Audio-Visual, pg 881

NEVADA
Aardvark Video & Media Productions, pg 671

NEW JERSEY
Argraph Corp, pg 688

NEW YORK
Audio-Video Corp, pg 694

PENNSYLVANIA
Advanced AV LLC, pg 677
Clair Companies, pg 725
The Lerro Corp, pg 806

RHODE ISLAND
M-Audio, pg 813

TENNESSEE
Lowrance Sound Co Inc, pg 812

TEXAS
Biway Media, pg 706
Tarpley Media Systems, pg 907
Videotex Systems Inc, pg 930

VIRGINIA
Lee Hartman & Sons Inc, pg 805

WASHINGTON
CCI Solutions, pg 718

WISCONSIN
Audio Visual of Milwaukee Inc, pg 694
Camera Corner Connecting Point, pg 715
Full Compass Systems, pg 767
Safe Harbor Computers, pg 879

BRITISH COLUMBIA
Richmond Sound Design Ltd, pg 875

MANITOBA
Inland Audio Visual Ltd, pg 788

ONTARIO
Westbury National Show Systems Ltd, pg 936

Sound Card Manufacturers

CALIFORNIA
Eye & I Productions, pg 758
Lynx Studio Technology Inc, pg 813
QRS Software Services, pg 867

ILLINOIS
Symbolic Sound Corp, pg 905

MINNESOTA
Digital Audio Labs, pg 742

RHODE ISLAND
M-Audio, pg 813

BRITISH COLUMBIA
Triad Communications Ltd, pg 918

Sound Card Rentals

CALIFORNIA
Ametron Audio/Video, pg 684
Synthesizer Rental Service, pg 906
Total Creative, pg 916

PENNSYLVANIA
Advanced AV LLC, pg 677
FMP Media Solutions Inc, pg 763

Sound Card Repairs

CALIFORNIA
Ametron Audio/Video, pg 684

CONNECTICUT
HB Communications Inc, pg 777

WISCONSIN
Full Compass Systems, pg 767

Touch Panel Distributors

ARIZONA
Troxell-CDI, pg 918

ARKANSAS
Jay S Stanley & Associates Inc, pg 899

CALIFORNIA
Ametron Audio/Video, pg 684
Associated Sound, pg 691
AV Conferencing LLC (AVC), pg 697
Be Media, pg 702
Boland Communications Inc, pg 708
California Tape Products Inc, pg 714
Electrosonic Inc, pg 752
Elo TouchSystems, pg 753
JD Audio Visual Inc, pg 793
MediaMation Inc, pg 822
MediaPOINTE, pg 823
Sound Service Co, pg 894
Stanislaus AV Inc, pg 899

COLORADO
Daylight Productions & Rentals, pg 739

FLORIDA
Altel Systems Group Inc, pg 682
AVI-SPL, pg 698
Digital Video Systems, pg 742
Hi-Tech Enterprises Inc, pg 779
ONstage, pg 846

GEORGIA
Lighting & Production Equipment Inc, pg 807
Stage Front Presentation Systems, pg 899

HAWAII
The Audio Visual Co (AVCO), pg 694

ILLINOIS
Allen Visual Systems Inc, pg 680
Quintessence Audio Ltd, pg 868

INDIANA
Lee Co Inc, pg 805
Sensory Technologies LLC, pg 884

KENTUCKY
Axxis Leasing Inc, pg 700
NOR-COM Inc, pg 841

LOUISIANA
Techkno Integration & Design Services LLC, pg 908

MAINE
Headlight Audio Visual Inc, pg 777

MARYLAND
Human Circuit, pg 782
Nelson White Systems Inc, pg 838

MICHIGAN
Digi Sign Design LLC, pg 741

MINNESOTA
Tierney Brothers Inc, pg 914

NEVADA
Wells-Gardner Technologies Inc, pg 935

NEW JERSEY
AlltecPro, pg 681
Argraph Corp, pg 688
Audio Visual Associates, pg 694
Starlite, pg 900
Total Video Products Inc, pg 916

NEW YORK
Audio-Video Corp, pg 694
General Audio-Visual Inc (GAVI), pg 769
Langie Audio Visual Systems, pg 803

OHIO
ITA Audio Visual Solutions, pg 791
Tri-State Audio Visual Co, pg 918

PENNSYLVANIA
Advanced AV LLC, pg 677
Aydin Displays, a Sparton Company, pg 700
Clair Companies, pg 725
The Lerro Corp, pg 806

Vistacom Inc, pg 931
Wespen Audio Visual Co, pg 935

TENNESSEE
Lowrance Sound Co Inc, pg 812
Spring Arbor Distributors Inc, pg 898
Technical Support Systems LLC, pg 908

TEXAS
Data Projections Inc, pg 738
Tarpley Media Systems, pg 907
Videotex Systems Inc, pg 930

VIRGINIA
Intellidyne LLC, pg 789
Lee Hartman & Sons Inc, pg 805

WISCONSIN
Audio Visual of Milwaukee Inc, pg 694
Camera Corner Connecting Point, pg 715
Full Compass Systems, pg 767

PUERTO RICO
Audio Visual Concepts Inc, pg 694

ALBERTA
SMART Technologies ULC, pg 891

BRITISH COLUMBIA
Richmond Sound Design Ltd, pg 875

MANITOBA
Inland Audio Visual Ltd, pg 788

ONTARIO
Cinema Stage Inc, pg 724
GestureTek, pg 770
Westbury National Show Systems Ltd, pg 936

Touch Panel Manufacturers

CALIFORNIA
AMX® by Harman, pg 685
Boland Communications Inc, pg 708

ILLINOIS
Windel International/Weyel, pg 939

MICHIGAN
ASC Systems, pg 690

NEW JERSEY
AlltecPro, pg 681
Crestron Electronics Inc, pg 734
FSR Inc, pg 766

OHIO
Turning Technologies LLC, pg 919

PENNSYLVANIA
Aydin Displays, a Sparton Company, pg 700

TENNESSEE
Spring Arbor Distributors Inc, pg 898

UTAH
Vantage Controls, a Legrand AV Inc brand, pg 924

ALBERTA
SMART Technologies ULC, pg 891

ONTARIO
GestureTek, pg 770

Touch Panel Rentals

ARIZONA
Merestone, pg 823

CALIFORNIA
Alliant Event Services, pg 681
Ametron Audio/Video, pg 684
Associated Sound, pg 691
Bexel, an NEP Broadcast Services Company, pg 704
McCune Audio-Video-Lighting, pg 821
Muse Presentation Technologies, pg 834
VER, pg 926

FLORIDA
ONstage, pg 846

GEORGIA
Stage Front Presentation Systems, pg 899

ILLINOIS
Allen Visual Systems Inc, pg 680

MARYLAND
CPR MultiMedia Solutions, pg 732

MICHIGAN
Digi Sign Design LLC, pg 741

MISSOURI
Show-Me Audio-Visual, pg 887

PENNSYLVANIA
FMP Media Solutions Inc, pg 763

TENNESSEE
Technical Support Systems LLC, pg 908

MANITOBA
Inland Audio Visual Ltd, pg 788

ONTARIO
Westbury National Show Systems Ltd, pg 936

Touch Panel Repairs

CALIFORNIA
Ametron Audio/Video, pg 684

GEORGIA
Lighting & Production Equipment Inc, pg 807
Stage Front Presentation Systems, pg 899

ILLINOIS
Allen Visual Systems Inc, pg 680

KENTUCKY
Axxis Leasing Inc, pg 700
NOR-COM Inc, pg 841

MAINE
Headlight Audio Visual Inc, pg 777

OHIO
ITA Audio Visual Solutions, pg 791
Tri-State Audio Visual Co, pg 918

TENNESSEE
Technical Support Systems LLC, pg 908

TEXAS
Tarpley Media Systems, pg 907

VIRGINIA
Avitecture Inc, pg 699

WISCONSIN
Camera Corner Connecting Point, pg 715
Full Compass Systems, pg 767

MANITOBA
Inland Audio Visual Ltd, pg 788

ONTARIO
Westbury National Show Systems Ltd, pg 936

Touch Screen Monitor Distributors

ARIZONA
Troxell-CDI, pg 918

ARKANSAS
Jay S Stanley & Associates Inc, pg 899

CALIFORNIA
Ametron Audio/Video, pg 684
Associated Sound, pg 691
Be Media, pg 702
California Tape Products Inc, pg 714
Elo TouchSystems, pg 753
MediaMation Inc, pg 822
MediaPOINTE, pg 823
Sound Service Co, pg 894
Stanislaus AV Inc, pg 899
Total Creative, pg 916

FLORIDA
Altel Systems Group Inc, pg 682
AVI-SPL, pg 698
Digital Video Systems, pg 742
Harris Corp, pg 776
Hi-Tech Enterprises Inc, pg 779
ONstage, pg 846

GEORGIA
PolyVision Corporation, pg 859
Stage Front Presentation Systems, pg 899

HAWAII
The Audio Visual Co (AVCO), pg 694

ILLINOIS
Allen Visual Systems Inc, pg 680
Quintessence Audio Ltd, pg 868

INDIANA
Lee Co Inc, pg 805
Sensory Technologies LLC, pg 884

KANSAS
Keywest Technology Inc, pg 798

KENTUCKY
NOR-COM Inc, pg 841

LOUISIANA
Techkno Integration & Design Services LLC, pg 908

MAINE
Headlight Audio Visual Inc, pg 777

MARYLAND
DSR Computer Technology Specialists Inc, pg 747
Human Circuit, pg 782
Nelson White Systems Inc, pg 838

MASSACHUSETTS
Graphx Inc, pg 773

MICHIGAN
ASC Systems, pg 690
Digi Sign Design LLC, pg 741

MINNESOTA
Tierney Brothers Inc, pg 914

NEW JERSEY
AlltecPro, pg 681
Argraph Corp, pg 688
Diversified, pg 744
Starlite, pg 900
SYMCO Inc, pg 905
Total Video Products Inc, pg 916

NEW YORK
General Audio-Visual Inc (GAVI), pg 769
Langie Audio Visual Systems, pg 803

OHIO
ITA Audio Visual Solutions, pg 791
Tri-State Audio Visual Co, pg 918

PENNSYLVANIA
Advanced AV LLC, pg 677
Clair Companies, pg 725
Innovision Media Group, pg 788
The Lerro Corp, pg 806
Vistacom Inc, pg 931

TENNESSEE
Lowrance Sound Co Inc, pg 812
Spring Arbor Distributors Inc, pg 898
Technical Support Systems LLC, pg 908

TEXAS
Audio Visual Technologies Group (AVTG), pg 695
Data Projections Inc, pg 738
Tarpley Media Systems, pg 907

VIRGINIA
Avitecture Inc, pg 699
Design & Production Inc, pg 740
Intellidyne LLC, pg 789
Lee Hartman & Sons Inc, pg 805

WASHINGTON
ToteVision, pg 916

WISCONSIN
Audio Visual of Milwaukee Inc, pg 694
Camera Corner Connecting Point, pg 715
Full Compass Systems, pg 767

ALBERTA
Infosat Communications Inc, pg 787

MANITOBA
Inland Audio Visual Ltd, pg 788

ONTARIO
Cinema Stage Inc, pg 724
Egan Visual Inc/Egan TeamBoard Inc, pg 751
GestureTek, pg 770
Westbury National Show Systems Ltd, pg 936

Touch Screen Monitor Manufacturers

CALIFORNIA
Boland Communications Inc, pg 708
GVISION USA Inc, pg 775

GEORGIA
PolyVision Corporation, pg 859

MICHIGAN
ASC Systems, pg 690

MINNESOTA
3M Touch Systems, pg 913

NEVADA
Wells-Gardner Technologies Inc, pg 935

NEW JERSEY
AlltecPro, pg 681
Crestron Electronics Inc, pg 734

NORTH CAROLINA
Computer Dynamics, pg 729

WASHINGTON
ToteVision, pg 916

COMPUTER SYSTEMS

Touch Screen Monitor Manufacturers (continued)

ONTARIO
GestureTek, pg 770

Touch Screen Monitor Rentals

ARIZONA
Merestone, pg 823

CALIFORNIA
Ametron Audio/Video, pg 684
Munday & Collins AV, pg 834
Muse Presentation Technologies, pg 834
VER, pg 926
Video Resources Inc, pg 928

GEORGIA
Stage Front Presentation Systems, pg 899

ILLINOIS
RC Communications, pg 870

MARYLAND
CPR MultiMedia Solutions, pg 732

MICHIGAN
Digi Sign Design LLC, pg 741

MISSOURI
Show-Me Audio-Visual, pg 887

NEW YORK
SmartSource Computer & AV Rentals, pg 891

PENNSYLVANIA
Innovision Media Group, pg 788
Upstage Video, pg 923

TENNESSEE
Technical Support Systems LLC, pg 908

TEXAS
Bright Star Productions Inc, pg 710

UTAH
Redman Movies & Stories, pg 872

MANITOBA
Inland Audio Visual Ltd, pg 788

ONTARIO
Westbury National Show Systems Ltd, pg 936

Touch Screen Monitor Repairs

CALIFORNIA
Ametron Audio/Video, pg 684

FLORIDA
Hi-Tech Enterprises Inc, pg 779

GEORGIA
Stage Front Presentation Systems, pg 899

ILLINOIS
Allen Visual Systems Inc, pg 680

KENTUCKY
Axxis Leasing Inc, pg 700
NOR-COM Inc, pg 841

MINNESOTA
3M Touch Systems, pg 913

OHIO
ITA Audio Visual Solutions, pg 791
Tri-State Audio Visual Co, pg 918

TENNESSEE
Technical Support Systems LLC, pg 908

TEXAS
Tarpley Media Systems, pg 907

VIRGINIA
Avitecture Inc, pg 699

WASHINGTON
ToteVision, pg 916

WISCONSIN
Camera Corner Connecting Point, pg 715
Full Compass Systems, pg 767

ALBERTA
Infosat Communications Inc, pg 787

MANITOBA
Inland Audio Visual Ltd, pg 788

ONTARIO
Westbury National Show Systems Ltd, pg 936

Virtual Reality Force Feedback Device Distributors

GEORGIA
Stage Front Presentation Systems, pg 899

INDIANA
Sensory Technologies LLC, pg 884

KENTUCKY
NOR-COM Inc, pg 841

PENNSYLVANIA
AccuWeather Inc, pg 674
Advanced AV LLC, pg 677

VIRGINIA
Avitecture Inc, pg 699

WISCONSIN
Audio Visual of Milwaukee Inc, pg 694

Virtual Reality Force Feedback Device Manufacturers

CALIFORNIA
Immersion Corp, pg 786

Virtual Reality Force Feedback Device Repairs

KENTUCKY
NOR-COM Inc, pg 841

Virtual Reality Imaging Device Distributors

CALIFORNIA
Ametron Audio/Video, pg 684
California Tape Products Inc, pg 714
Laser Magic Productions, pg 804
Total Creative, pg 916
Videobotics, pg 929

GEORGIA
Stage Front Presentation Systems, pg 899

INDIANA
Sensory Technologies LLC, pg 884

KENTUCKY
NOR-COM Inc, pg 841

LOUISIANA
Techkno Integration & Design Services LLC, pg 908

NEW HAMPSHIRE
Optics 1 Inc, pg 847

NEW YORK
eMagin Corp, pg 753

PENNSYLVANIA
AccuWeather Inc, pg 674
Advanced AV LLC, pg 677

TEXAS
Supercircuits, pg 904

VIRGINIA
Avitecture Inc, pg 699
Quince Imaging Inc, pg 868

WISCONSIN
Audio Visual of Milwaukee Inc, pg 694

MANITOBA
Inland Audio Visual Ltd, pg 788
Tek Gear, pg 909

ONTARIO
GestureTek, pg 770

QUEBEC
Presagis, pg 861

Virtual Reality Imaging Device Manufacturers

CALIFORNIA
For-A Corp of America, pg 763
Immersion Corp, pg 786
Laser Magic Productions, pg 804

MARYLAND
Absolute Hollywood, pg 672

NEW HAMPSHIRE
Optics 1 Inc, pg 847

NEW JERSEY
CELCO, pg 719

NEW YORK
eMagin Corp, pg 753

VIRGINIA
Quince Imaging Inc, pg 868

MANITOBA
Tek Gear, pg 909

ONTARIO
GestureTek, pg 770

QUEBEC
Presagis, pg 861

Virtual Reality Imaging Device Rentals

CALIFORNIA
Ametron Audio/Video, pg 684

GEORGIA
Stage Front Presentation Systems, pg 899

MARYLAND
Absolute Hollywood, pg 672

VIRGINIA
Quince Imaging Inc, pg 868

MANITOBA
Inland Audio Visual Ltd, pg 788
Tek Gear, pg 909

Virtual Reality Imaging Device Repairs

CALIFORNIA
Ametron Audio/Video, pg 684

KENTUCKY
NOR-COM Inc, pg 841

VIRGINIA
Quince Imaging Inc, pg 868

FILM

Accessory, *see* Equipment & Accessory

Aerial Photography, *see* Photography—Aerial

Animation Production Services

ARIZONA

Merestone, pg 823

CALIFORNIA

Artichoke Productions, pg 690
Classic Images Stock Footage LLC, pg 726
Creative Technology, pg 733
Crystal Pyramid Productions™, pg 735
Diaquest, pg 741
First Person Inc, pg 761
Goal Productions, pg 772
Hydrogen Whiskey Studios, pg 783
iCorpTv, pg 783
Industrial Light & Magic (ILM), pg 787
JDS Video & Media Productions Inc, pg 793
Laser Magic Productions, pg 804
Lumeni Productions Inc, pg 812
Moving Art by Louie Schwartzberg, pg 831
New & Unique Videos™, pg 839
Palardo Productions, pg 850
piXvfm Inc, pg 857
QRS Software Services, pg 867
Timestream Video, pg 914
Two Door Productions LLC, pg 920
Warner Bros Animation, pg 934
Warner Bros Entertainment Inc, pg 934
Wavemaker Media Design, pg 934

COLORADO

CSI Film & Video LLC, pg 735
Flashback Media Productions, pg 762
Full Spectrum Arts & Services, pg 767

CONNECTICUT

New London Media, pg 839

DISTRICT OF COLUMBIA

Hillmann & Carr Inc, pg 780

FLORIDA

Communications Concepts Inc (CCI), pg 729
Universal Studios Florida® Production Group, pg 922

GEORGIA

First Cut Communications LLC, pg 761
Guerrilla Productions LLC, pg 774

HAWAII

Hyperspective Studios Inc, pg 783

ILLINOIS

ABS Enterprises, pg 672
Richter Studios, pg 875

INDIANA

OMNI Productions, pg 845
Perennial Pictures Film Corp, pg 854

IOWA

Educational Technology & Media Services, pg 751
Hellman Associates Inc, pg 778

KENTUCKY

Hammond Communications Group Inc, pg 775

LOUISIANA

Digital FX Inc, pg 742

MARYLAND

Kramer Communications Video Production, pg 801
Milner-Fenwick Inc, pg 828

MASSACHUSETTS

CommCreative, pg 728
Extreme Reach Inc, pg 757
MotionArt Studios, pg 831
Northern Light Productions (NLP), pg 842
Gabriel Polonsky Studio, pg 859
Preston Productions Inc, pg 861
TR Productions, pg 916
The Weather Company, An IBM Business, pg 935

MICHIGAN

Blue Mouse Studio, pg 707
Digi Sign Design LLC, pg 741

NEW HAMPSHIRE

Apertura, pg 686
Chip Taylor Communications LLC, pg 907

NEW JERSEY

MediaNow Inc, pg 822
NFL Films Music Library, pg 841
PeopleVisionFX, pg 854
Telequest Inc, pg 910
Two Animators LLP, pg 920

NEW MEXICO

Little Big Bang Design Inc, pg 810
Stevens Design & Animation LLC, pg 900

NEW YORK

American Artists Representatives Inc, pg 682
Animotion Inc, pg 685
Big Fish Production US, pg 705
Buzzco Associates Inc, pg 713
Digital Art Video Inc, pg 741
DuArt Media Services, pg 747
Lylofilm Productions, pg 813
Polestar Films & Associated Arts Ltd, pg 859
R/GA, pg 868

NORTH CAROLINA

NASCAR Productions LLC, pg 835
Trailblazer Studios®, pg 917

OREGON

Artbeats, pg 690
Wallace Creative LLC, pg 933

PENNSYLVANIA

Innovision Media Group, pg 788
JPL, pg 795
Kensington Falls Animation, pg 797
WPHL-TV, pg 942

RHODE ISLAND

Sound-FX-Design, pg 894

TENNESSEE

Motion Picture Services, pg 831
Paradigm Marketing & Creative, pg 851
Stage Post, pg 899

TEXAS

Alexander Media Productions, pg 679
Anaphora Literary Press, pg 685
Epic Software Group Inc, pg 755
Horizon Film + Video Productions, pg 781
Hurst Digital, pg 782
Stage Directions, pg 898
Texas Heart Institute Visual Communication Services, pg 911

VERMONT

University of Vermont, Instructional Television Dept, pg 923

VIRGINIA

Blair Inc, pg 707
Eagle Films, pg 749
Metro Productions, pg 824

WISCONSIN

USAV Group Inc, pg 923

WYOMING

Bridger Productions Inc, pg 710

BRITISH COLUMBIA

Credo Interactive Inc, pg 734

ONTARIO

Loopmedia Inc, pg 811
Silver Creek Media Inc, pg 888

QUEBEC

National Film Board of Canada/Office National du Film du Canada, pg 836

Animation Production Services—Computerized

ARIZONA

Merestone, pg 823

CALIFORNIA

Artichoke Productions, pg 690
Blind™, pg 707
Classic Images Stock Footage LLC, pg 726
Creative Technology, pg 733
Crystal Pyramid Productions™, pg 735
Diaquest, pg 741
Dolphin MultiMedia Inc, pg 745

Elektrashock, pg 753

First Person Inc, pg 761
Havas Edge, pg 777
House of Moves, pg 782
Hydrogen Whiskey Studios, pg 783
iCorpTv, pg 783
Industrial Light & Magic (ILM), pg 787
JDS Video & Media Productions Inc, pg 793
Laser Magic Productions, pg 804
Lumeni Productions Inc, pg 812
Moving Art by Louie Schwartzberg, pg 831
New & Unique Videos™, pg 839
Pixar Animation Studios, pg 857
QRS Software Services, pg 867
Reality Check Systems, pg 871
Renegade Animation Inc, pg 873
Rhythm & Hues Studios Inc, pg 874
Two Door Productions LLC, pg 920
Universal Studios, pg 922
Wavemaker Media Design, pg 934

COLORADO

CSI Film & Video LLC, pg 735
Flashback Media Productions, pg 762
Full Spectrum Arts & Services, pg 767

CONNECTICUT

New London Media, pg 839

DISTRICT OF COLUMBIA

Hillmann & Carr Inc, pg 780

FLORIDA

Audio Visual Imagineering Inc, pg 694
CD ROM™ Inc, pg 718
Communications Concepts Inc (CCI), pg 729
Comtel Inc, pg 730
Digimation, pg 741
Universal Studios Florida® Production Group, pg 922

GEORGIA

Cinema Concepts, pg 724
Guerrilla Productions LLC, pg 774

HAWAII

Hyperspective Studios Inc, pg 783

ILLINOIS

ABS Enterprises, pg 672
Mightybytes Inc, pg 827
Richter Studios, pg 875

INDIANA

A-V-A Video Productions, pg 671
Bright Ideas Creative Services, pg 710
OMNI Productions, pg 845

LOUISIANA

Digital FX Inc, pg 742

MASSACHUSETTS

CommCreative, pg 728
Northern Light Productions (NLP), pg 842
The Weather Company, An IBM Business, pg 935

MICHIGAN

ASC Systems, pg 690
Digi Sign Design LLC, pg 741
Digital Image Studios LLC, pg 742

MINNESOTA

BeyerSound & Essay Audio, pg 705

MISSOURI

Avatar Studios, pg 697

NEW HAMPSHIRE

Chip Taylor Communications LLC,
pg 907

NEW JERSEY

CELCO, pg 719
Early Films, pg 749
NFL Films Inc, pg 841
NFL Films Music Library, pg 841
Outside The Box Interactive LLC,
pg 849
Suede Interactive, pg 903
Two Animators LLP, pg 920

NEW MEXICO

Stevens Design & Animation LLC,
pg 900

NEW YORK

American Artists Representatives
Inc, pg 682
Animotion Inc, pg 685
Big Film Design, pg 705
Buzzco Associates Inc, pg 713
Digital Art Video Inc, pg 741
DuArt Media Services, pg 747
4-D Creative Media, pg 764
HB-Content, pg 777
Lylofilm Productions, pg 813
R/GA, pg 868
Judson Rosebush Co Inc, pg 877

NORTH CAROLINA

The Communications Group Inc,
pg 729
Image Associates Inc, pg 784
NASCAR Productions LLC, pg 835

OHIO

Lyon Video Inc, pg 813
Mills James Productions, pg 828

OREGON

Artbeats, pg 690
Wallace Creative LLC, pg 933

PENNSYLVANIA

AccuWeather Inc, pg 674
Bang! Pictures Inc, pg 701
Innovision Media Group, pg 788
JPL, pg 795
NEP Group Inc, pg 838
The Videohouse Inc, pg 929
WPHL-TV, pg 942

RHODE ISLAND

Sound-FX-Design, pg 894

SOUTH CAROLINA

Genesis Creative, pg 769

TENNESSEE

Motion Picture Services, pg 831
Paradigm Marketing & Creative,
pg 851
Stage Post, pg 899

TEXAS

Anaphora Literary Press, pg 685
Castleview Productions, pg 717
Epic Software Group Inc, pg 755
Horizon Film + Video Productions,
pg 781
Hurst Digital, pg 782
Maverick Video Productions, pg 820

UTAH

Strata™, pg 901

VIRGINIA

Eagle Films, pg 749
Maniglia Media LLC, pg 816
Metro Productions, pg 824

WASHINGTON

North-by-Northwest - A Digital
Studio, pg 842

WISCONSIN

USAV Group Inc, pg 923
Watts Communications Inc, pg 934

BRITISH COLUMBIA

Credo Interactive Inc, pg 734

ONTARIO

GAPC (General Assembly
Production Centre), pg 768

Artwork & Titling Services

ARIZONA

Merestone, pg 823

CALIFORNIA

Blind™, pg 707
Creative Technology, pg 733
First Person Inc, pg 761
Goal Productions, pg 772
Havas Edge, pg 777
Hydrogen Whiskey Studios, pg 783
iCorpTv, pg 783
JDS Video & Media Productions
Inc, pg 793
Laser Magic Productions, pg 804
Lumeni Productions Inc, pg 812
Moving Art by Louie Schwartzberg,
pg 831
New & Unique Videos™, pg 839
Nineteen87, pg 841
Palardo Productions, pg 850
QRS Software Services, pg 867
Reality Check Systems, pg 871
Shapeshifter, pg 885
SonicPool, pg 892
TIMECODE Post Production,
pg 914
Total Creative, pg 916
Universal Studios, pg 922
Wavemaker Media Design, pg 934

COLORADO

CSI Film & Video LLC, pg 735
Flashback Media Productions,
pg 762
Full Spectrum Arts & Services,
pg 767

CONNECTICUT

Cine-Med Inc, pg 723
New London Media, pg 839

FLORIDA

Communications Concepts Inc
(CCI), pg 729
Jordan Klein Film & Video (JKFV),
pg 795

GEORGIA

Guerrilla Productions LLC, pg 774

HAWAII

Hyperspective Studios Inc, pg 783

ILLINOIS

ABSA Films, pg 672
Mightybytes Inc, pg 827
RADMAR Inc, pg 869

INDIANA

A-V-A Video Productions, pg 671
Bright Ideas Creative Services,
pg 710

IOWA

Educational Technology & Media
Services, pg 751

LOUISIANA

Digital FX Inc, pg 742

MASSACHUSETTS

CommCreative, pg 728
MotionArt Studios, pg 831
Northern Light Productions (NLP),
pg 842
Gabriel Polonsky Studio, pg 859

MICHIGAN

Blue Mouse Studio, pg 707
Digi Sign Design LLC, pg 741
Michigan Recording Arts Institute
& Technologies, pg 825
Progressive AE, pg 865

NEW HAMPSHIRE

Apertura, pg 686
Chip Taylor Communications LLC,
pg 907

NEW JERSEY

CELCO, pg 719
Early Films, pg 749
Outside The Box Interactive LLC,
pg 849
Two Animators LLP, pg 920

NEW YORK

Animotion Inc, pg 685
aurora productions, pg 696
Big Film Design, pg 705
Digital Art Video Inc, pg 741
4-D Creative Media, pg 764
Gage-Line Technology Inc, pg 767
HB-Content, pg 777
Lylofilm Productions, pg 813
Polestar Films & Associated Arts
Ltd, pg 859
R/GA, pg 868
VDO Lab Inc, pg 925

OHIO

Lyon Video Inc, pg 813

PENNSYLVANIA

Bang! Pictures Inc, pg 701
JPL, pg 795
Kensington Falls Animation, pg 797
The Videohouse Inc, pg 929

RHODE ISLAND

Sound-FX-Design, pg 894

TENNESSEE

Motion Picture Services, pg 831
Paradigm Marketing & Creative,
pg 851
Stage Post, pg 899

TEXAS

Anaphora Literary Press, pg 685
Epic Software Group Inc, pg 755
Hurst Digital, pg 782

VIRGINIA

Eagle Films, pg 749

WISCONSIN

USAV Group Inc, pg 923
Watts Communications Inc, pg 934

ALBERTA

Global TV, pg 771

ONTARIO

ADS Media, pg 677

Audio Editing, *see* Dubbing

Camera, *see* Movie & Still Camera

Can, *see* Reel & Can

Chain & Multiplexer Equipment Distributors

CALIFORNIA

Media Fabricators Inc, pg 822
MediaPOINTE, pg 823

COLORADO

Ceavco Audio Visual Company Inc,
pg 719
Spectrum Audio Visual Services,
pg 897

CONNECTICUT

Rockwell Communications Inc,
pg 876

GEORGIA

Visioneering International Inc,
pg 931

ILLINOIS

Urbanski Film, pg 923

INDIANA

Lee Co Inc, pg 805

KENTUCKY

NOR-COM Inc, pg 841

FILM

Chain & Multiplexer Equipment Distributors (continued)

MICHIGAN
City Events Group, pg 725
TEL Systems LLC, pg 909

MINNESOTA
AVI Systems, pg 698

MISSISSIPPI
Jasper Ewing & Sons Inc, pg 757

MISSOURI
Communitronics Corp, pg 729

NEVADA
Peterson's Video Transfer Services, pg 855

NEW JERSEY
Audio Visual Dynamics®, pg 694
Tele-Measurements Inc, pg 910
Video Corporation of America (VCA), pg 927

NEW YORK
Colortone Audio Visual, pg 728
Langie Audio Visual Systems, pg 803
Visual Technologies Corp, pg 932

NORTH CAROLINA
Camcor Inc, pg 715
Strategic Connections, pg 901

OHIO
Copp Integrated Systems, pg 731

PENNSYLVANIA
J E Foss Co, pg 764
Hite Co, pg 780
Visual Sound Inc, pg 931

TENNESSEE
Memphis Communications Corp, pg 823

TEXAS
Pro Video & Film Equipment Co Inc, pg 863

UTAH
RIA Corp, pg 874

VIRGINIA
Lee Hartman & Sons Inc, pg 805

ALBERTA
McBain Camera Ltd, pg 820

Chain & Multiplexer Equipment Manufacturers

CALIFORNIA
FM Systems Inc, pg 763

FLORIDA
Magna-Tech Electronic Co Inc, pg 814

Chain & Multiplexer Equipment Rentals

ARIZONA
Arizona Cine Equipment, pg 688

CALIFORNIA
Artichoke Productions, pg 690

CONNECTICUT
Rockwell Communications Inc, pg 876

MICHIGAN
TEL Systems LLC, pg 909

MINNESOTA
AVI Systems, pg 698

NEW JERSEY
Video Corporation of America (VCA), pg 927

NEW YORK
Adwar Video, pg 678
CMI Communications, pg 727

NORTH CAROLINA
Duke Media Services, pg 747

OHIO
Vista Color Imaging Inc, pg 931

TENNESSEE
Russ Sturgeon Productions/RSVP, pg 903

VIRGINIA
Projection, pg 865

WISCONSIN
University of Wisconsin-Oshkosh Radio-TV-Film Dept, pg 923

Chain & Multiplexer Equipment Repairs

KENTUCKY
NOR-COM Inc, pg 841

MINNESOTA
AVI Systems, pg 698

NEW YORK
Langie Audio Visual Systems, pg 803
Visual Technologies Corp, pg 932

VIRGINIA
Lee Hartman & Sons Inc, pg 805

Cleaning Equipment, see Film Cleaning & Inspection Equipment

Computerized Animation Production Services, see Animation Production Services—Computerized

Computerized Editing, see Editing—Computerized

Consulting

ALABAMA
Diamond Studios, pg 741

ALASKA
Alaska Media Pros LLC, pg 679
Aurora Films, pg 696

ARIZONA
Merestone, pg 823
Metropolitan Audio-Visual Inc, pg 824
Teaberry, pg 908

CALIFORNIA
Air Philosophy Inc, pg 678
Artichoke Productions, pg 690
Automated Entertainment, pg 696
Blind™, pg 707
CinemaGear.com, pg 724
Creative Artists Agency LLC, pg 733
Creative Technology, pg 733
Crystal Pyramid Productions™, pg 735
Design Media, pg 741
Dolphin MultiMedia Inc, pg 745
Durrin Productions Inc, pg 748
Film Marketing Services Inc, pg 760
Film TV Sound, pg 760
First Person Inc, pg 761
Goal Productions, pg 772
Gold Standard Productions, pg 772
Havas Edge, pg 777
iCorpTv, pg 783
imageReal Pictures LLC, pg 785
Industrial Light & Magic (ILM), pg 787
Ishtar Films, pg 791
ITV Productions, pg 792
Jaguar Distribution Corp, pg 792
JDS Video & Media Productions Inc, pg 793
Lumeni Productions Inc, pg 812
Main Street Media Inc, pg 815
McKay Conant Hoover Inc, pg 821
Media Systems Design Group, pg 822
Moving Art by Louie Schwartzberg, pg 831
New & Unique Videos™, pg 839
Joseph Nicoletti Consulting-Promotion, pg 841
Nineteen87, pg 841
PK Productions, pg 857
Prime Cut Productions, pg 862
Pro8mm, pg 862
QRS Software Services, pg 867
RetinaVision Productions, pg 874
Russ InVision Co/AbridgeClub.com, pg 879
Sahara Records & Filmworks Entertainment Co, pg 879
Sea Studios Foundation, pg 883
Signature Entertainment, pg 888
SNAP, pg 891
SonicPool, pg 892

Stunt Wings Adventure Sports Talent & Equipment, pg 903
Tam Communications Inc, pg 906
Total Creative, pg 916
WARPed Pictures, pg 934
Z-Ville Productions, pg 944

COLORADO
Blue River Productions, pg 708
CSI Film & Video LLC, pg 735
Flashback Media Productions, pg 762
G W Hannaway & Associates, pg 775
7seas Productions, pg 885
Transtar Entertainment Co Inc, pg 917

CONNECTICUT
Boyce Nemec Designs, pg 709
The Gary-Paul Agency, pg 768
New London Media, pg 839
P&P Studios Inc, pg 851

DISTRICT OF COLUMBIA
Hillmann & Carr Inc, pg 780
Susan Hormuth, Visual Resource Consultant, pg 781
O'Keefe Communications Inc, pg 844

FLORIDA
CD ROM™ Inc, pg 718
Civins Productions Inc, pg 725
Communications Concepts Inc (CCI), pg 729
ONstage, pg 846
Universal Studios Florida® Production Group, pg 922

GEORGIA
Burst Video/Film Inc, pg 713
Guerrilla Productions LLC, pg 774
Lighting & Production Equipment Inc, pg 807

HAWAII
Hyperspective Studios Inc, pg 783
Media Bridge Gamekids, pg 821
1013 Integrated, pg 911

IDAHO
Brad Shaw Productions Inc, pg 885

ILLINOIS
Accenture, pg 672
Atomic Imaging Inc/Golan Studios, pg 692
Cresta Creative, pg 734
Film Police, pg 760
Pepper Group, pg 854
SCI Television & Creative Media LLC, pg 882
Terra Nova Films Inc, pg 911
WEEK TV, pg 935

INDIANA
A-V-A Video Productions, pg 671
Bright Ideas Creative Services, pg 710

IOWA
Educational Technology & Media Services, pg 751

KENTUCKY
Idle Minds Productions Inc, pg 784

LOUISIANA

Digital FX Inc, pg 742
Louisiana State University Division
  of Strategic Communications,
  pg 811
Moxie Media, pg 832

MARYLAND

The Image Generators, pg 785
Image Logic Corp, pg 785
James Agee Film Project, pg 792

MASSACHUSETTS

Capron Lighting & Sound Co Inc,
  pg 716
CommCreative, pg 728
Communications Design Associates,
  pg 729
Documentary Educational Resources
  Inc, pg 744
Green Mountain Post Films (GMP),
  pg 774
Heliotrope Studios, pg 778
High Output Inc, pg 779
MotionArt Studios, pg 831
Northern Light Productions (NLP),
  pg 842
Preston Productions Inc, pg 861

MICHIGAN

ASC Systems, pg 690
Digi Sign Design LLC, pg 741
The Program Source International,
  pg 865

MINNESOTA

House of Cinemagraphics, pg 782
Media Loft Inc, pg 822

MISSOURI

Switch, pg 905
Visionworks Design Services Inc,
  pg 931

MONTANA

KCFW Television, pg 797

NEVADA

DVDs4Less, pg 748
Encore Event Technologies LLC,
  pg 754
Ron Roy Productions/Moodtapes,
  pg 878

NEW HAMPSHIRE

Apertura, pg 686
Chip Taylor Communications LLC,
  pg 907

NEW JERSEY

CELCO, pg 719
Euro-Pacific Film & Video
  Productions Inc, pg 756
Outside The Box Interactive LLC,
  pg 849
PatchAmp, pg 852

NEW MEXICO

Mountainair Films Inc, pg 831

NEW YORK

Animotion Inc, pg 685
aurora productions, pg 696
BZ/Rights & Permissions Inc,
  pg 713
Duggal Visual Solutions Inc, pg 747

Four Corners Productions, pg 764
4-D Creative Media, pg 764
GHO Group LLC, pg 770
Icontent, pg 783
International Robotics Inc, pg 790
Richard Kaplan Productions, pg 796
Ketchum Inc, pg 798
Kinetic Arts, pg 799
Lylofilm Productions, pg 813
Jack Morton Worldwide, pg 830
R/GA, pg 868
S&P Global Marketing Intelligence,
  pg 880
Shen Milsom & Wilke LLC, pg 885
Third World Newsreel/Camera
  News Inc, pg 912
Timed Exposures Films, pg 914
VIEW Inc (Video International
  Entertainment World Inc), pg 930
Zelman Studios Ltd, pg 945

NORTH CAROLINA

Camcor Inc, pg 715
The Communications Group Inc,
  pg 729
Sinclair Institute, pg 889

NORTH DAKOTA

Media Productions, pg 822

OHIO

Challenge Productions/Challenge
  Aerial Imaging, pg 720
Griesinger Films LLC, pg 774
Lyon Video Inc, pg 813
Take 1 Media Services, pg 906
Vista Color Imaging Inc, pg 931

OKLAHOMA

Academic Media & Digital
  Services, pg 672

PENNSYLVANIA

Argentine Productions Inc, pg 688
Berry & Homer, pg 704
JPL, pg 795
Kensington Falls Animation, pg 797
Main Point Productions, pg 815

RHODE ISLAND

Sound-FX-Design, pg 894

SOUTH CAROLINA

Genesis Creative, pg 769

TENNESSEE

American Blackguard Inc, pg 683
Fricon Entertainment Co Inc,
  pg 766
Motion Picture Services, pg 831
Paradigm Marketing & Creative,
  pg 851
Stage Post, pg 899
United Methodist Productions,
  pg 921

TEXAS

Anaphora Literary Press, pg 685
Castleview Productions, pg 717
Cerutti Productions Inc, pg 720
Epic Software Group Inc, pg 755
Horizon Film + Video Productions,
  pg 781
Hurst Digital, pg 782
Earl Miller Productions Inc, pg 827
The Music Bakery, pg 834

Julye Newlin Productions Inc,
  pg 840
Texas Heart Institute Visual
  Communication Services, pg 911

VIRGINIA

Altruist Media LLC, pg 682
CACI Integrated Communications,
  pg 713
CDR Communications Inc, pg 719
Eagle Films, pg 749

WASHINGTON

Adams Creative & Production
  Services, pg 675
Media Elite Productions, pg 822
North-by-Northwest - A Digital
  Studio, pg 842
Pal Productions Inc, pg 850

WISCONSIN

University of Wisconsin-Oshkosh
  Radio-TV-Film Dept, pg 923
USAV Group Inc, pg 923
Wisconsin Public Television, pg 940

WYOMING

Bridger Productions Inc, pg 710

ALBERTA

Black Media Works, pg 706
Global TV, pg 771

BRITISH COLUMBIA

MicrophoneRentals.com, pg 826
Network Entertainment Inc, pg 838
West Eagle Films Inc, pg 935

NORTHWEST TERRITORIES

Yellowknife Films Inc, pg 944

ONTARIO

ADS Media, pg 677
Artaflex Inc, pg 690

QUEBEC

Sceno Plus, pg 881

SASKATCHEWAN

Thomega Entertainment Inc, pg 913

Continuous Still Projector Distributors

ARIZONA

Troxell-CDI, pg 918

ARKANSAS

Jay S Stanley & Associates Inc,
  pg 899

CALIFORNIA

Jaguar Distribution Corp, pg 792
Media Fabricators Inc, pg 822
MediaPOINTE, pg 823

COLORADO

American Educational Products
  LLC, pg 683
Ceavco Audio Visual Company Inc,
  pg 719

FLORIDA

Tallahassee Audio Visual, pg 906

GEORGIA

Visioneering International Inc,
  pg 931

ILLINOIS

Major Reproductions Equipment
  Co, pg 815

INDIANA

Lee Co Inc, pg 805

KENTUCKY

NOR-COM Inc, pg 841

MARYLAND

RTZ Audio Visual, pg 878

MICHIGAN

City Events Group, pg 725

MINNESOTA

AVI Systems, pg 698

MISSISSIPPI

Jasper Ewing & Sons Inc, pg 757

MISSOURI

Communitronics Corp, pg 729
Schiller's Audio-Visual, pg 881

NEW JERSEY

Audio Visual Dynamics®, pg 694
Leica Camera Inc, pg 806

NEW YORK

AV Workshop, pg 697
Colortone Audio Visual, pg 728
Langie Audio Visual Systems,
  pg 803
Visual Technologies Corp, pg 932

NORTH CAROLINA

Strategic Connections, pg 901

OHIO

Audio Visual Media, pg 694
Copp Integrated Systems, pg 731
Icom Multimedia, pg 783

TENNESSEE

Memphis Communications Corp,
  pg 823

TEXAS

Audio Visual Technologies Group
  (AVTG), pg 695

VIRGINIA

Lee Hartman & Sons Inc, pg 805
The Whitlock Group, pg 937

WASHINGTON

Inland Audio Visual Co, pg 788

ALBERTA

McBain Camera Ltd, pg 820

FILM

Continuous Still Projector Manufacturers

COLORADO
American Educational Products LLC, pg 683

MISSOURI
Schiller's Audio-Visual, pg 881

NEW JERSEY
Leica Camera Inc, pg 806

NEW YORK
ELMO USA Corp, pg 753

Continuous Still Projector Rentals

ALABAMA
Audio-Video Resources Inc, pg 694

ARIZONA
Merestone, pg 823

CALIFORNIA
JD Audio Visual Inc, pg 793
McCune Audio-Video-Lighting, pg 821
Media Fabricators Inc, pg 822

COLORADO
Ceavco Audio Visual Company Inc, pg 719

ILLINOIS
Helix Camera & Video, pg 778
RC Communications, pg 870

MARYLAND
RTZ Audio Visual, pg 878

MICHIGAN
City Events Group, pg 725

MINNESOTA
AVI Systems, pg 698

MISSISSIPPI
Jasper Ewing & Sons Inc, pg 757

NEW JERSEY
Audio Visual Dynamics®, pg 694
PLS Staging, pg 858

NEW YORK
AV Workshop, pg 697
Colortone Audio Visual, pg 728
Langie Audio Visual Systems, pg 803
Visual Technologies Corp, pg 932

NORTH CAROLINA
Strategic Connections, pg 901

OHIO
Audio Visual Media, pg 694
Icom Multimedia, pg 783

TENNESSEE
Memphis Communications Corp, pg 823

VIRGINIA
Lee Hartman & Sons Inc, pg 805
Projection, pg 865

WASHINGTON
Inland Audio Visual Co, pg 788

Continuous Still Projector Repairs

ARKANSAS
Jay S Stanley & Associates Inc, pg 899

CALIFORNIA
Pro Camera Repair, pg 862

COLORADO
Ceavco Audio Visual Company Inc, pg 719

CONNECTICUT
Precision Camera & Video Repair Inc, pg 861

FLORIDA
Hi-Tech Enterprises Inc, pg 779

KENTUCKY
NOR-COM Inc, pg 841

MARYLAND
RTZ Audio Visual, pg 878

MINNESOTA
AVI Systems, pg 698

MISSOURI
Schiller's Audio-Visual, pg 881

NEW YORK
Colortone Audio Visual, pg 728
ELMO USA Corp, pg 753
Langie Audio Visual Systems, pg 803
Visual Technologies Corp, pg 932

NORTH CAROLINA
Strategic Connections, pg 901

OHIO
Audio Visual Media, pg 694
Icom Multimedia, pg 783

TENNESSEE
Memphis Communications Corp, pg 823

VIRGINIA
Lee Hartman & Sons Inc, pg 805
The Whitlock Group, pg 937

WASHINGTON
Inland Audio Visual Co, pg 788

Co-Production Services

ALABAMA
Diamond Studios, pg 741

ALASKA
Alaska Media Pros LLC, pg 679
Aurora Films, pg 696
Connections Film & Video Inc, pg 731

ARIZONA
Creative Backstage, pg 733
Merestone, pg 823
Metropolitan Audio-Visual Inc, pg 824
Teaberry, pg 908

CALIFORNIA
Artichoke Productions, pg 690
Automated Entertainment, pg 696
Backstage Pass Entertainment Inc, pg 700
Bridge Publications Inc, pg 710
Concrete Images, pg 730
Creative Technology, pg 733
Crystal Pyramid Productions™, pg 735
Custom Video Productions Inc, pg 736
deKramer Productions Inc, pg 740
Design Media, pg 741
Durrin Productions Inc, pg 748
First Person Inc, pg 761
Havas Edge, pg 777
iCorpTv, pg 783
Ishtar Films, pg 791
Jaguar Distribution Corp, pg 792
JDS Video & Media Productions Inc, pg 793
Main Street Media Inc, pg 815
New & Unique Videos™, pg 839
New Circuit Films LLC, pg 839
Joseph Nicoletti Consulting-Promotion, pg 841
Nineteen87, pg 841
Point of View Productions, pg 858
QRS Software Services, pg 867
Russ InVision Co/AbridgeClub.com, pg 879
Sahara Records & Filmworks Entertainment Co, pg 879
Sea Studios Foundation, pg 883
Signature Entertainment, pg 888
Sports Cinematography Group, pg 898
Tam Communications Inc, pg 906
Total Creative, pg 916
Via Verde Productions, pg 926
Visual Communications - Southern California Asian American Studies Central Inc, pg 931
WARPed Pictures, pg 934
Wavemaker Media Design, pg 934
Z-Ville Productions, pg 944

COLORADO
Conly Productions, pg 730
Flashback Media Productions, pg 762
Tatum Video, pg 907
Transtar Entertainment Co Inc, pg 917

CONNECTICUT
The Gary-Paul Agency, pg 768
New London Media, pg 839

DISTRICT OF COLUMBIA
Hillmann & Carr Inc, pg 780

FLORIDA
C&I An Idea Agency, pg 716
Chatterbox Productions Inc, pg 721
Civins Productions Inc, pg 725
Communications Concepts Inc (CCI), pg 729
The Kitchen, pg 799
Universal Studios Florida® Production Group, pg 922

GEORGIA
Guerrilla Productions LLC, pg 774
MAGNUM Companies Ltd, pg 815
Myriad Productions, pg 835
Malcolm Neal Productions, pg 837

HAWAII
FilmWorks Pacific, pg 761
Hyperspective Studios Inc, pg 783
Media Bridge Gamekids, pg 821
1013 Integrated, pg 911

ILLINOIS
Cresta Creative, pg 734
Film Police, pg 760
Pepper Group, pg 854
SCI Television & Creative Media LLC, pg 882
WEEK TV, pg 935

INDIANA
A-V-A Video Productions, pg 671
Bright Ideas Creative Services, pg 710
Perennial Pictures Film Corp, pg 854

IOWA
Educational Technology & Media Services, pg 751

KENTUCKY
Idle Minds Productions Inc, pg 784

LOUISIANA
Digital FX Inc, pg 742
Louisiana State University Division of Strategic Communications, pg 811
Moxie Media, pg 832

MARYLAND
DBM Communications Inc, pg 739
DSR Computer Technology Specialists Inc, pg 747
James Agee Film Project, pg 792

MASSACHUSETTS
Documentary Educational Resources Inc, pg 744
Green Mountain Post Films (GMP), pg 774
Heliotrope Studios, pg 778
MotionArt Studios, pg 831
Northern Light Productions (NLP), pg 842
Gabriel Polonsky Studio, pg 859

MICHIGAN
Digi Sign Design LLC, pg 741

MINNESOTA
House of Cinemagraphics, pg 782

MISSOURI

Visionworks Design Services Inc, pg 931

MONTANA

KCFW Television, pg 797

NEVADA

DVDs4Less, pg 748
Encore Event Technologies LLC, pg 754
Lefco Video Services Inc, pg 806
Ron Roy Productions/Moodtapes, pg 878

NEW HAMPSHIRE

Apertura, pg 686
Chip Taylor Communications LLC, pg 907

NEW JERSEY

CELCO, pg 719
Euro-Pacific Film & Video Productions Inc, pg 756
Outside The Box Interactive LLC, pg 849
VCSvideo, pg 925

NEW YORK

American Artists Representatives Inc, pg 682
aurora productions, pg 696
De Nonno Productions Inc (DPI), pg 739
4-D Creative Media, pg 764
HB-Content, pg 777
Icontent, pg 783
The Independent Production Fund, pg 786
Richard Kaplan Productions, pg 796
Kinetic Arts, pg 799
Lylofilm Productions, pg 813
Mastervision, pg 819
Jack Morton Worldwide, pg 830
Timed Exposures Films, pg 914
VIEW Inc (Video International Entertainment World Inc), pg 930
Zelman Studios Ltd, pg 945

NORTH CAROLINA

The Communications Group Inc, pg 729
Moving Pictures, pg 832

NORTH DAKOTA

Media Productions, pg 822

OHIO

Challenge Productions/Challenge Aerial Imaging, pg 720
Take 1 Media Services, pg 906
Vista Color Imaging Inc, pg 931

PENNSYLVANIA

Innovision Media Group, pg 788
JPL, pg 795
Kensington Falls Animation, pg 797
Main Point Productions, pg 815

RHODE ISLAND

Sound-FX-Design, pg 894

TENNESSEE

American Blackguard Inc, pg 683
Fricon Entertainment Co Inc, pg 766

Motion Picture Services, pg 831
Paradigm Marketing & Creative, pg 851
Scripps Networks, pg 882
Stage Post, pg 899

TEXAS

Anaphora Literary Press, pg 685
Castleview Productions, pg 717
Cerutti Productions Inc, pg 720
Emergency Film Group, pg 753
Epic Software Group Inc, pg 755
Hurst Digital, pg 782
Earl Miller Productions Inc, pg 827
Julye Newlin Productions Inc, pg 840
RuffHouse LLC, pg 878
Texas Heart Institute Visual Communication Services, pg 911

VERMONT

Edgewood Studios, pg 750
Dorothy Tod Films, pg 915

VIRGINIA

Altruist Media LLC, pg 682
CACI Integrated Communications, pg 713
CDR Communications Inc, pg 719
Eagle Films, pg 749

WASHINGTON

Adams Creative & Production Services, pg 675
North-by-Northwest - A Digital Studio, pg 842
Pal Productions Inc, pg 850

WISCONSIN

Meridian Studios, pg 824
University of Wisconsin-Oshkosh Radio-TV-Film Dept, pg 923
Wisconsin Public Television, pg 940

WYOMING

Bridger Productions Inc, pg 710

ALBERTA

Black Media Works, pg 706
Global TV, pg 771

BRITISH COLUMBIA

Network Entertainment Inc, pg 838

NORTHWEST TERRITORIES

Yellowknife Films Inc, pg 944

ONTARIO

ADS Media, pg 677
Canamedia Inc, pg 715
DebsVoice, pg 739
GAPC (General Assembly Production Centre), pg 768

QUEBEC

Muse Entertainment Enterprises, pg 834

SASKATCHEWAN

Thomega Entertainment Inc, pg 913

Dubbing

ARIZONA

Merestone, pg 823

CALIFORNIA

Artichoke Productions, pg 690
Creative Technology, pg 733
Crystal Pyramid Productions™, pg 735
Havas Edge, pg 777
iCorpTv, pg 783
International Contact Inc, pg 790
JDS Video & Media Productions Inc, pg 793
Maximus Media Inc, pg 820
McCune Audio-Video-Lighting, pg 821
Polarity Post Production, pg 858
QRS Software Services, pg 867
Roundabout Entertainment Inc, pg 878
SonicPool, pg 892
Total Creative, pg 916
Universal Studios, pg 922

CONNECTICUT

The Gary-Paul Agency, pg 768

FLORIDA

Communications Concepts Inc (CCI), pg 729
The Kitchen, pg 799

GEORGIA

Guerrilla Productions LLC, pg 774

HAWAII

Media Bridge Gamekids, pg 821

ILLINOIS

WEEK TV, pg 935

KENTUCKY

Idle Minds Productions Inc, pg 784

LOUISIANA

Digital FX Inc, pg 742

MARYLAND

DSR Computer Technology Specialists Inc, pg 747
Milner-Fenwick Inc, pg 828
Pro Cuts Editing Services, pg 862

MASSACHUSETTS

Labrecque Creative Sound, pg 803
Linguistic Systems Inc, pg 809
TR Productions, pg 916

MICHIGAN

Digi Sign Design LLC, pg 741

MONTANA

KUSM TV, pg 802

NEVADA

DVDs4Less, pg 748

NEW HAMPSHIRE

Apertura, pg 686

NEW JERSEY

Allegro Productions Inc, pg 680
NFL Films Music Library, pg 841
Suede Interactive, pg 903

NEW YORK

HB-Content, pg 777
iProbe Multilingual Solutions Inc, pg 791
Magno Sound Inc, pg 815
The Palmer Group, pg 850
Visual Technologies Corp, pg 932
Zelman Studios Ltd, pg 945

PENNSYLVANIA

WPHL-TV, pg 942

SOUTH CAROLINA

Genesis Creative, pg 769

TENNESSEE

Continental Film, pg 731
Motion Picture Services, pg 831
Stage Post, pg 899

TEXAS

Anaphora Literary Press, pg 685
Castleview Productions, pg 717
Horizon Film + Video Productions, pg 781
Hurst Digital, pg 782

VERMONT

University of Vermont, Instructional Television Dept, pg 923

VIRGINIA

CACI Integrated Communications, pg 713

WASHINGTON

Hamilton Studio, pg 775

WISCONSIN

Wisconsin Public Television, pg 940

ALBERTA

Cine Audio Visual Sales & Service Ltd, pg 723
Global TV, pg 771

QUEBEC

Muse Entertainment Enterprises, pg 834

SASKATCHEWAN

Thomega Entertainment Inc, pg 913

Edge Numbering

ARIZONA

Merestone, pg 823

CALIFORNIA

Creative Technology, pg 733
Goal Productions, pg 772
QRS Software Services, pg 867

NEW JERSEY

NFL Films Music Library, pg 841
Reed Presentations Inc (RPI), pg 872

NEW YORK

DuArt Media Services, pg 747

FILM

Edge Numbering (continued)

OHIO
Cuyahoga Community College Student Production Office (SPO), pg 736

TENNESSEE
Stage Post, pg 899

TEXAS
Hurst Digital, pg 782

ALBERTA
Global TV, pg 771

Editing

ALASKA
Alaska Media Pros LLC, pg 679
Aurora Films, pg 696
Connections Film & Video Inc, pg 731

ARIZONA
Merestone, pg 823

CALIFORNIA
Artichoke Productions, pg 690
Creative Technology, pg 733
The Dreaming Tree, pg 746
Goal Productions, pg 772
Gordon Productions Inc, pg 772
Havas Edge, pg 777
iCorpTv, pg 783
JDS Video & Media Productions Inc, pg 793
KO Creative, pg 800
Main Street Media Inc, pg 815
Nandar Entertainment Pictures, pg 835
New & Unique Videos™, pg 839
New Circuit Films LLC, pg 839
Nineteen87, pg 841
Pacific Video Products Inc, pg 849
Palardo Productions, pg 850
Point of View Productions, pg 858
QRS Software Services, pg 867
Reality Check Systems, pg 871
RetinaVision Productions, pg 874
Roundabout Entertainment Inc, pg 878
Shapeshifter, pg 885
SonicPool, pg 892
TIMECODE Post Production, pg 914
Total Creative, pg 916
Universal Studios, pg 922
Via Verde Productions, pg 926
VidCan Media Solutions, pg 927
Z-Ville Productions, pg 944

COLORADO
Colorado Studios, pg 728
CSI Film & Video LLC, pg 735
G W Hannaway & Associates, pg 775
Transtar Entertainment Co Inc, pg 917

CONNECTICUT
Cine-Med Inc, pg 723
Essex Television Group Inc, pg 755

DISTRICT OF COLUMBIA
Hillmann & Carr Inc, pg 780
Interface Media Group, pg 789

FLORIDA
ACT Productions, pg 675
Communications Concepts Inc (CCI), pg 729
Comtel Inc, pg 730
Jordan Klein Film & Video (JKFV), pg 795
Tel-Air Interests Inc, pg 909
Universal Studios Florida® Production Group, pg 922

GEORGIA
Guerrilla Productions LLC, pg 774

HAWAII
Hyperspective Studios Inc, pg 783

IDAHO
Brad Shaw Productions Inc, pg 885

ILLINOIS
ABS Enterprises, pg 672
Mightybytes Inc, pg 827
Optimus, pg 847
Richter Studios, pg 875
WEEK TV, pg 935

INDIANA
A-V-A Video Productions, pg 671
OMNI Productions, pg 845

IOWA
Educational Technology & Media Services, pg 751

KENTUCKY
Horizon Films & Media LLC, pg 781

LOUISIANA
Digital FX Inc, pg 742
Moxie Media, pg 832

MAINE
Films by Huey, pg 760

MARYLAND
DBM Communications Inc, pg 739
James Agee Film Project, pg 792
Kramer Communications Video Production, pg 801
Milner-Fenwick Inc, pg 828
Pro Cuts Editing Services, pg 862
Satellite Media Production, pg 881

MASSACHUSETTS
CommCreative, pg 728
Documentary Educational Resources Inc, pg 744
Extreme Reach Inc, pg 757
Green Mountain Post Films (GMP), pg 774
Penfield Productions Ltd, pg 853
Preston Productions Inc, pg 861
WGBH Production Group, pg 936

MINNESOTA
Badiyan Inc, pg 700
House of Cinemagraphics, pg 782

MONTANA
KCFW Television, pg 797
KUSM TV, pg 802

NEW HAMPSHIRE
Apertura, pg 686
Chip Taylor Communications LLC, pg 907

NEW JERSEY
Allegro Productions Inc, pg 680
Early Films, pg 749
Image Up Studio, pg 785
NFL Films Inc, pg 841
NFL Films Music Library, pg 841
Reed Presentations Inc (RPI), pg 872
Suede Interactive, pg 903
Telequest Inc, pg 910

NEW YORK
aurora productions, pg 696
Big Apple Films, pg 705
Buffalo Video Production, pg 712
Thomas Craven Film Corp, pg 733
DuArt Media Services, pg 747
William Greaves Productions Inc, pg 774
HB-Content, pg 777
Long Island University Media Arts Dept, pg 811
Magno Sound Inc, pg 815
Jack Morton Worldwide, pg 830
Mother West, pg 831
Peckham Productions Inc, pg 852
Pennebaker Hegedus Films Inc, pg 854
R/GA, pg 868
Richter Productions Inc, pg 875
Split Image Productions, pg 898
Third World Newsreel/Camera News Inc, pg 912
Videography Productions, pg 929
Visual Technologies Corp, pg 932
Zelman Studios Ltd, pg 945

NORTH CAROLINA
The Communications Group Inc, pg 729
Trailblazer Studios®, pg 917

OHIO
Challenge Productions/Challenge Aerial Imaging, pg 720
Griesinger Films LLC, pg 774
Mills James Productions, pg 828
Ungar Video & Film, pg 921

OREGON
Odyssey Productions Inc, pg 844

RHODE ISLAND
Sound-FX-Design, pg 894

SOUTH CAROLINA
Genesis Creative, pg 769
Studio Charleston, pg 902

TENNESSEE
Anode Inc, pg 686
Continental Film, pg 731
Motion Picture Services, pg 831
Paradigm Marketing & Creative, pg 851
Stage Post, pg 899

TEXAS
Alexander Media Productions, pg 679
Anaphora Literary Press, pg 685
Castleview Productions, pg 717
Cerutti Productions Inc, pg 720
Emergency Film Group, pg 753
Horizon Film + Video Productions, pg 781
Hurst Digital, pg 782
Julye Newlin Productions Inc, pg 840
Romar Learning Solutions LLC, pg 877
Stage Directions, pg 898
Texas Heart Institute Visual Communication Services, pg 911

VERMONT
Edgewood Studios, pg 750
University of Vermont, Instructional Television Dept, pg 923

VIRGINIA
CACI Integrated Communications, pg 713
Eagle Films, pg 749
Metro Productions, pg 824
The Whitlock Group, pg 937

WASHINGTON
Hamilton Studio, pg 775
Pal Productions Inc, pg 850

WISCONSIN
University of Wisconsin-Oshkosh Radio-TV-Film Dept, pg 923
Wisconsin Public Television, pg 940

ALBERTA
Global TV, pg 771

BRITISH COLUMBIA
Network Entertainment Inc, pg 838

ONTARIO
ADS Media, pg 677
Silver Creek Media Inc, pg 888
Trebas Institute, pg 917

QUEBEC
Muse Entertainment Enterprises, pg 834
Trebas Institute, pg 917

SASKATCHEWAN
Thomega Entertainment Inc, pg 913

Editing—Computerized

ALASKA
Alaska Media Pros LLC, pg 679

ARIZONA
Merestone, pg 823
Metropolitan Audio-Visual Inc, pg 824
Teaberry, pg 908

CALIFORNIA
Artichoke Productions, pg 690
Creative Technology, pg 733
Crystal Pyramid Productions™, pg 735

Editing Equipment Distributors

FILM

Editing Equipment
Distributors (continued)

PENNSYLVANIA

Hite Co, pg 780
The Lerro Corp, pg 806
Wespen Audio Visual Co, pg 935

SOUTH CAROLINA

Keymark Inc, pg 798

TENNESSEE

Memphis Communications Corp,
   pg 823

TEXAS

Pro Video & Film Equipment Co
   Inc, pg 863

UTAH

Webb Audio Visual, pg 935

VIRGINIA

Cybernetics, pg 736
Lee Hartman & Sons Inc, pg 805
The Whitlock Group, pg 937

WISCONSIN

Full Compass Systems, pg 767
Safe Harbor Computers, pg 879

Editing Equipment
Manufacturers

CALIFORNIA

Christy's Editorial, pg 723
J & R Film Co, pg 792
Moviola, pg 832
Sprocket Digital, pg 898
TV Pro Gear, pg 919

FLORIDA

Tel-Test, pg 909

ILLINOIS

Lipsner-Smith Co, pg 809
Research Technology International
   (RTI), pg 873

MASSACHUSETTS

Avid Technology Inc, pg 698
The Boston Connection Inc, pg 709

NEW JERSEY

CELCO, pg 719

NEW YORK

GTI (Graphic Technology Inc),
   pg 774

SOUTH CAROLINA

Keymark Inc, pg 798

Editing Equipment Rentals

ARIZONA

Arizona Cine Equipment, pg 688
Merestone, pg 823

ARKANSAS

White Diamond Productions LLC,
   pg 937

CALIFORNIA

Artichoke Productions, pg 690
Big Door, pg 705
Birns & Sawyer Inc, pg 706
Christy's Editorial, pg 723
Direct Cinema Ltd Inc, pg 743
Alan Gordon Enterprises Inc,
   pg 772
J & R Film Co, pg 792
Main Street Media Inc, pg 815
Moviola, pg 832
Reality Check Systems, pg 871
The Studios at Paramount, pg 903
Total Creative, pg 916
Universal Studios, pg 922

COLORADO

Centre Communications Inc, pg 720

FLORIDA

Jordan Klein Film & Video (JKFV),
   pg 795

ILLINOIS

Helix Camera & Video, pg 778

LOUISIANA

Digital FX Inc, pg 742

MARYLAND

Kramer Communications Video
   Production, pg 801
RTZ Audio Visual, pg 878

MASSACHUSETTS

The Boston Connection Inc, pg 709
Capron Lighting & Sound Co Inc,
   pg 716
Green Mountain Post Films (GMP),
   pg 774

MICHIGAN

City Events Group, pg 725
TEL Systems LLC, pg 909

MINNESOTA

AVI Systems, pg 698
Cinequipt Inc, pg 724
House of Cinemagraphics, pg 782

MISSOURI

Show-Me Audio-Visual, pg 887

NEW HAMPSHIRE

Apertura, pg 686

NEW JERSEY

Audio Visual Dynamics®, pg 694

NEW YORK

Adwar Video, pg 678
Buffalo Video Production, pg 712
CMI Communications, pg 727
Colortone Audio Visual, pg 728
HB-Content, pg 777
Langie Audio Visual Systems,
   pg 803
Motion Picture Enterprises Inc,
   pg 831

Richter Productions Inc, pg 875
The Visual Studies Workshop
   (VSW), pg 931

PENNSYLVANIA

FMP Media Solutions Inc, pg 763
Videosmith Inc, pg 930

SOUTH CAROLINA

Keymark Inc, pg 798

UTAH

Webb Audio Visual, pg 935

VERMONT

Marlboro Productions, pg 817

WASHINGTON

Inland Audio Visual Co, pg 788

WISCONSIN

University of Wisconsin-Oshkosh
   Radio-TV-Film Dept, pg 923
Wisconsin Public Television, pg 940

ALBERTA

Global TV, pg 771

BRITISH COLUMBIA

24 Frames Film & Video, pg 920
Video Out Distribution, pg 928

Editing Equipment Repairs

ARKANSAS

Carlton-Bates Co, pg 717

CALIFORNIA

Birns & Sawyer Inc, pg 706
Christy's Editorial, pg 723
Alan Gordon Enterprises Inc,
   pg 772
J & R Film Co, pg 792
Moviola, pg 832
Pro Camera Repair, pg 862

CONNECTICUT

HB Communications Inc, pg 777

FLORIDA

Hi-Tech Enterprises Inc, pg 779
Tel-Test, pg 909

KENTUCKY

NOR-COM Inc, pg 841

MARYLAND

RTZ Audio Visual, pg 878

MASSACHUSETTS

The Boston Connection Inc, pg 709

MICHIGAN

City Events Group, pg 725

MINNESOTA

AVI Systems, pg 698

MISSOURI

Communitronics Corp, pg 729

NEW YORK

Adwar Video, pg 678
Langie Audio Visual Systems,
   pg 803
Motion Picture Enterprises Inc,
   pg 831

SOUTH CAROLINA

Keymark Inc, pg 798

VIRGINIA

The Whitlock Group, pg 937

WISCONSIN

Full Compass Systems, pg 767

Eight mm Projector &
Equipment, *see* Projector
& Equipment—8mm

Equipment & Accessory
Distributors

ARIZONA

Arizona Cine Equipment, pg 688
Troxell-CDI, pg 918

ARKANSAS

Jay S Stanley & Associates Inc,
   pg 899

CALIFORNIA

Ametron Audio/Video, pg 684
ARRI Inc, pg 689
Band Pro Film & Digital Inc,
   pg 701
Birns & Sawyer Inc, pg 706
Camera Essentials, pg 715
Christy's Editorial, pg 723
Cinema Equipment Sales of
   California Inc, pg 724
Cinematography Electronics Inc,
   pg 724
Filmtools®, pg 761
Alan Gordon Enterprises Inc,
   pg 772
IDX System Technology Inc,
   pg 784
J & R Film Co, pg 792
Manios Digital & Film, pg 816
MediaPOINTE, pg 823
Mole-Richardson Co, pg 829
Moviola, pg 832
Nalpak Inc, pg 835
Steeldeck® Inc, pg 900
Thermodyne Cases, pg 912
Transvideo International, pg 917
Visual Systems, pg 931

COLORADO

Ceavco Audio Visual Company Inc,
   pg 719
Goldberg Brothers Inc, pg 772
Mike's Camera, pg 827
Stanco Sales LLC, pg 899

CONNECTICUT

Rockwell Communications Inc,
   pg 876
Vitec Videocom Inc, pg 932

FLORIDA

AVI-SPL, pg 698
Cinema Equipment & Supplies Inc,
   pg 724

GEORGIA
Audio Visual Resources Inc, pg 695
PC&E, pg 852
Visioneering International Inc,
  pg 931

ILLINOIS
Creative Technology (CT), pg 733
Joseph Electronics, pg 795
Research Technology International
  (RTI), pg 873
Urbanski Film, pg 923
Zacuto, pg 945

INDIANA
Lee Co Inc, pg 805

KENTUCKY
NOR-COM Inc, pg 841

MARYLAND
RTZ Audio Visual, pg 878

MASSACHUSETTS
The Boston Connection Inc, pg 709
High Output Inc, pg 779
Hunt's Photo & Video, pg 782
University Products Inc, pg 923

MINNESOTA
Alpha Video & Audio Inc, pg 682
AVI Systems, pg 698
Cinequipt Inc, pg 724

MISSISSIPPI
Jasper Ewing & Sons Inc, pg 757

MISSOURI
Communitronics Corp, pg 729
ITC, pg 791

NEVADA
Aardvark Video & Media
  Productions, pg 671

NEW HAMPSHIRE
APS Lighting-Sound-AV, pg 688

NEW JERSEY
Agfa Graphics, pg 678
AlltecPro, pg 681
Argraph Corp, pg 688
AV Bluebook, pg 696
Caprock Developments Inc, pg 716
Comprehensive Cable &
  Connectivity Co, pg 729
Rose Brand, pg 877
Transparent Office Products LLC,
  pg 917
Vcom IMC, pg 925

NEW YORK
AZ Spectrum, pg 700
Bulbtronics Inc, pg 712
Cine 60 Inc, pg 723
Colortone Audio Visual, pg 728
Gaylord Archival, pg 768
Get Smart Products, pg 770
Just Bulbs - The Light Bulb Store,
  pg 795
Langie Audio Visual Systems,
  pg 803
MAC Group, pg 813
Motion Picture Enterprises Inc,
  pg 831

Rafik, pg 869
Visual Technologies Corp, pg 932
Willoughby's® Camera, pg 939

NORTH CAROLINA
Strategic Connections, pg 901

OHIO
Graphic Laminating LLC, pg 773
Visual Products Inc, pg 931

PENNSYLVANIA
Charles Beseler Co, pg 721
Garcia Marketing Inc, pg 768
Hite Co, pg 780

TENNESSEE
Memphis Communications Corp,
  pg 823

TEXAS
Audio Visual Technologies Group
  (AVTG), pg 695
Pro Video & Film Equipment Co
  Inc, pg 863
Stage Directions, pg 898

UTAH
Redman Movies & Stories, pg 872

VIRGINIA
Design & Production Inc, pg 740
Lee Hartman & Sons Inc, pg 805
The Whitlock Group, pg 937

WASHINGTON
Inland Audio Visual Co, pg 788
Oppenheimer Camera Products,
  pg 847

WISCONSIN
Demco Inc, pg 740
Full Compass Systems, pg 767
Safe Harbor Computers, pg 879

BRITISH COLUMBIA
Specialty Bulb Products Inc, pg 896

ONTARIO
VFGadgets Inc, pg 926

Equipment & Accessory Manufacturers

CALIFORNIA
ARRI Inc, pg 689
Backstage Equipment Inc, pg 700
Birns & Sawyer Inc, pg 706
Camera Essentials, pg 715
CineBags Inc, pg 723
Cinematography Electronics Inc,
  pg 724
DataDirect Networks, pg 738
Filmtools®, pg 761
General Production Services, pg 769
Alan Gordon Enterprises Inc,
  pg 772
IDX System Technology Inc,
  pg 784
J & R Film Co, pg 792
Lasergraphics Inc, pg 804
Mole-Richardson Co, pg 829
Moviola, pg 832
O'Connor Engineering Labs, pg 844
The Rip-Tie Co, pg 875

Sprocket Digital, pg 898
Steeldeck® Inc, pg 900
Thermodyne Cases, pg 912
Transvideo International, pg 917
TV Pro Gear, pg 919

COLORADO
Goldberg Brothers Inc, pg 772

CONNECTICUT
Vitec Videocom Inc, pg 932

FLORIDA
Magna-Tech Electronic Co Inc,
  pg 814
Techni-Lux Inc, pg 908
Tel-Test, pg 909

GEORGIA
Lighting & Production Equipment
  Inc, pg 807

ILLINOIS
Kart-A-Bag Manufacturing Inc,
  pg 796
Lipsner-Smith Co, pg 809
March Manufacturing Inc, pg 816
PolyScience, pg 859
Research Technology International
  (RTI), pg 873
Sprayway Inc, pg 898
La Vezzi Precision Inc, pg 926

INDIANA
General Devices Co Inc, pg 769
Star Case Manufacturing Co Inc,
  pg 900
Stouffer Graphic Arts, pg 901

MASSACHUSETTS
The Boston Connection Inc, pg 709
Glidecam Industries Inc, pg 771

NEVADA
Calculated Industries Inc, pg 714

NEW JERSEY
AlltecPro, pg 681
CELCO, pg 719
Falcon Safety Products Inc, pg 758
Pro-Tape & Specialities Inc, pg 863

NEW YORK
MultiDyne Video & Fiber Optics
  Systems, pg 833
Precision Microproducts of
  America, pg 861
Joseph Struhl Company Inc, pg 902

PENNSYLVANIA
Charles Beseler Co, pg 721

WASHINGTON
Oppenheimer Camera Products,
  pg 847

WISCONSIN
ETC, pg 756

ONTARIO
DW Electrochemicals Ltd, pg 748

Equipment & Accessory Rentals

ARIZONA
Arizona Cine Equipment, pg 688
Creative Backstage, pg 733
Merestone, pg 823
Reel Men Rentals Inc, pg 872

CALIFORNIA
Alternative Rentals, pg 682
Ametron Audio/Video, pg 684
Big Door, pg 705
Birns & Sawyer Inc, pg 706
CamTec Motion Picture Cameras,
  pg 715
Chapman/Leonard Studio
  Equipment Inc, pg 720
Christy's Editorial, pg 723
Cinema Camera Rentals, pg 723
Cinema Rentals Inc, pg 724
DTC Lighting & Grip, pg 747
Alan Gordon Enterprises Inc,
  pg 772
Greenery Studios, pg 774
Imagecraft Productions, pg 785
J & R Film Co, pg 792
The Lot (Skye Partners), pg 811
Main Street Media Inc, pg 815
Mole-Richardson Co, pg 829
Motion Picture Marine, pg 831
Moviola, pg 832
Otto Nemenz International Inc,
  pg 838
North County Media Center, pg 842
Panavision, pg 850
Pro HD Rentals, pg 863
Radiant Images, pg 869
RED Studios Hollywood, pg 872
SpaceCam, pg 896
Steeldeck® Inc, pg 900
Stray Angel Films, pg 902
The Studios at Paramount, pg 903
T-stop Inc, pg 906
Total Creative, pg 916
Tyler Camera Systems, pg 920
VER, pg 926
Videofax, pg 929
Z-Ville Productions, pg 944

COLORADO
Ceavco Audio Visual Company Inc,
  pg 719
Mike's Camera, pg 827
Tatum Video, pg 907

CONNECTICUT
Rockwell Communications Inc,
  pg 876

FLORIDA
Jordan Klein Film & Video (JKFV),
  pg 795
MAPS Production House, pg 816
Moving Picture, pg 831
Photosound of Orlando Inc, pg 856

GEORGIA
Audio Visual Resources Inc, pg 695
PC&E, pg 852
Studio Space Atlanta, pg 903

ILLINOIS
Creative Technology (CT), pg 733
Helix Camera & Video, pg 778
LITE-IT Grip Truck Rentals, pg 810
Magnanimous Media, pg 814
Product Productions, pg 863

FILM

Equipment & Accessory Rentals (continued)

ILLINOIS (continued)

PSAV® Presentation Services (Hotel Services Division), pg 866
Zacuto, pg 945

MARYLAND

Kramer Communications Video Production, pg 801
RTZ Audio Visual, pg 878

MASSACHUSETTS

The Boston Connection Inc, pg 709
Green Mountain Post Films (GMP), pg 774
High Output Inc, pg 779

MICHIGAN

Magnicon Media/Image d'Or, pg 815

MINNESOTA

AVI Systems, pg 698
Cinequipt Inc, pg 724
House of Cinemagraphics, pg 782

MISSISSIPPI

Jasper Ewing & Sons Inc, pg 757

MISSOURI

Show-Me Audio-Visual, pg 887

MONTANA

Filmlites Montana, pg 760

NEVADA

MG Studio, pg 825

NEW HAMPSHIRE

Apertura, pg 686
APS Lighting-Sound-AV, pg 688

NEW JERSEY

Butter Tree Studios, pg 713
Ironbound Film & Television Studios LLC, pg 791
PLS Staging, pg 858

NEW YORK

Adorama Rental Co, pg 676
Adwar Video, pg 678
Available Light, pg 697
Big Apple Films, pg 705
Bond Street Studio, pg 708
Bravo Studios, pg 709
Brooklyn Studios, pg 711
Cine 60 Inc, pg 723
Colortone Audio Visual, pg 728
Hand Held Films, pg 775
Langie Audio Visual Systems, pg 803
LightHouse Films, pg 807
LightSpace Studios, pg 808
Motion Picture Enterprises Inc, pg 831
Scheimpflug Digital, pg 881
See Factor Industry Inc, pg 883
The Visual Studies Workshop (VSW), pg 931
Visual Technologies Corp, pg 932

NORTH CAROLINA

K2 Productions, pg 802
Strategic Connections, pg 901

OHIO

Production Partners Media, pg 864

OREGON

Koerner Camera Systems, pg 800
Northwest Film Center, pg 842
Pacific Grip & Lighting Inc, pg 849
Picture This Production Services, pg 856

PENNSYLVANIA

Videosmith Inc, pg 930

SOUTH CAROLINA

Studio Charleston, pg 902

TENNESSEE

Memphis Communications Corp, pg 823

TEXAS

Earl Miller Productions Inc, pg 827
Muller Entertainment LLC, pg 833

UTAH

Ron Hill Imagery, pg 780
Redman Movies & Stories, pg 872

VIRGINIA

Projection, pg 865

WASHINGTON

Inland Audio Visual Co, pg 788
Oppenheimer Camera Products, pg 847

WISCONSIN

University of Wisconsin-Oshkosh Radio-TV-Film Dept, pg 923
Wisconsin Public Television, pg 940

WYOMING

Bridger Productions Inc, pg 710

ALBERTA

Global TV, pg 771

MANITOBA

MidCanada Production Services Inc (MidCan), pg 826

ONTARIO

JIB Shots Equipment Inc, pg 794
SIM Digital, pg 888
Wallace Film Studios, pg 933
William F White International Inc, pg 937

Equipment & Accessory Repairs

ARIZONA

PROCAM, pg 863

ARKANSAS

Jay S Stanley & Associates Inc, pg 899

CALIFORNIA

ARRI Inc, pg 689
Birns & Sawyer Inc, pg 706
Christy's Editorial, pg 723
Alan Gordon Enterprises Inc, pg 772
J & R Film Co, pg 792
Moviola, pg 832
Pro Camera Repair, pg 862
Transvideo International, pg 917

COLORADO

Ceavco Audio Visual Company Inc, pg 719

CONNECTICUT

Precision Camera & Video Repair Inc, pg 861
Rockwell Communications Inc, pg 876
Vitec Videocom Inc, pg 932

FLORIDA

Hi-Tech Enterprises Inc, pg 779
Tel-Test, pg 909

GEORGIA

Audio Visual Resources Inc, pg 695

KENTUCKY

NOR-COM Inc, pg 841

MARYLAND

RTZ Audio Visual, pg 878

MASSACHUSETTS

The Boston Connection Inc, pg 709
High Output Inc, pg 779

MINNESOTA

AVI Systems, pg 698

NEW YORK

AZ Spectrum, pg 700
Colortone Audio Visual, pg 728
Langie Audio Visual Systems, pg 803
MAC Group, pg 813
Motion Picture Enterprises Inc, pg 831
Precision Microproducts of America, pg 861
Visual Technologies Corp, pg 932

TENNESSEE

Memphis Communications Corp, pg 823

UTAH

Redman Movies & Stories, pg 872

VIRGINIA

The Whitlock Group, pg 937

WASHINGTON

Oppenheimer Camera Products, pg 847

WISCONSIN

Full Compass Systems, pg 767

Film Cleaning & Inspection Equipment Distributors

ARIZONA

Arizona Cine Equipment, pg 688

CALIFORNIA

Christy's Editorial, pg 723
Samy's Camera, pg 879

COLORADO

Stanco Sales LLC, pg 899

FLORIDA

Cinema Equipment & Supplies Inc, pg 724
Photosol Inc, pg 856

ILLINOIS

Facets Multi-Media Inc, pg 758
Lipsner-Smith Co, pg 809
Research Technology International (RTI), pg 873
Urbanski Film, pg 923

KENTUCKY

K&R PhotoDigital, pg 796

MISSOURI

Communitronics Corp, pg 729

NEVADA

Aardvark Video & Media Productions, pg 671
Peterson's Video Transfer Services, pg 855

NEW JERSEY

Argraph Corp, pg 688

NEW YORK

Barbizon Electric Co Inc, pg 701
Get Smart Products, pg 770
NRD Static Control LLC, pg 843

PENNSYLVANIA

Bernie's Photo Center, pg 704

SOUTH CAROLINA

Keymark Inc, pg 798

TEXAS

Pro Video & Film Equipment Co Inc, pg 863

VIRGINIA

The Whitlock Group, pg 937

ALBERTA

McBain Camera Ltd, pg 820

Film Cleaning & Inspection Equipment Manufacturers

FLORIDA

Kinetronics Corp, pg 799
Photosol Inc, pg 856

ILLINOIS
Lipsner-Smith Co, pg 809
Research Technology International (RTI), pg 873
Sprayway Inc, pg 898
Urbanski Film, pg 923

NEW JERSEY
Falcon Safety Products Inc, pg 758

NEW YORK
NRD Static Control LLC, pg 843
Precision Microproducts of America, pg 861

Film Cleaning & Inspection Equipment Rentals

ARIZONA
Arizona Cine Equipment, pg 688

CALIFORNIA
Christy's Editorial, pg 723

FLORIDA
Jordan Klein Film & Video (JKFV), pg 795

MISSOURI
Show-Me Audio-Visual, pg 887

Film Cleaning & Inspection Equipment Repairs

CALIFORNIA
Christy's Editorial, pg 723
Mole-Richardson Co, pg 829

NEW YORK
Precision Microproducts of America, pg 861

SOUTH CAROLINA
Keymark Inc, pg 798

Film Libraries, *see* Libraries—Film or Stock-Shot

Film to Videotape Transfers, *see* Transfers—Film to Videotape

Grip Equipment Distributors

ARIZONA
Arizona Cine Equipment, pg 688
CamMate Systems, pg 715
Troxell-CDI, pg 918

CALIFORNIA
Birns & Sawyer Inc, pg 706
Christy's Editorial, pg 723
Cinemills Corp, pg 724

DTC Lighting & Grip, pg 747
Filmtools®, pg 761
Alan Gordon Enterprises Inc, pg 772
Innovision Optics, pg 788
LEE Filters, pg 805
Manios Digital & Film, pg 816
Matthews Studio Equipment Inc, pg 820
Mole-Richardson Co, pg 829
Nalpak Inc, pg 835
The Rosenthal Group, pg 877
Sacramento Theatrical Lighting Ltd (STL), pg 879
San Diego Stage & Lighting Supply Inc, pg 879
SNAP, pg 891
Steeldeck® Inc, pg 900
Thermodyne Cases, pg 912
Ver Sales Inc, pg 926

COLORADO
Ceavco Audio Visual Company Inc, pg 719

CONNECTICUT
Lex Products Corp, pg 807
Vitec Videocom Inc, pg 932

FLORIDA
EZ FX Inc, pg 758
Hi-Tech Enterprises Inc, pg 779

GEORGIA
Lighting & Production Equipment Inc, pg 807
MAGNUM Companies Ltd, pg 815

ILLINOIS
Cool-Lux, pg 731
Facets Multi-Media Inc, pg 758
Grand Stage Co Inc, pg 773
Photoflex Inc, pg 856

LOUISIANA
Available Lighting & Motion Picture Services Inc, pg 697

MASSACHUSETTS
High Output Inc, pg 779
Limelight Production® Inc, pg 809

MICHIGAN
Lowing Light & Grip Inc, pg 812

MINNESOTA
AVI Systems, pg 698
Cinequipt Inc, pg 724

MISSOURI
Communitronics Corp, pg 729
Schiller's Audio-Visual, pg 881

NEVADA
Aardvark Video & Media Productions, pg 671

NEW HAMPSHIRE
APS Lighting-Sound-AV, pg 688

NEW JERSEY
Comprehensive Cable & Connectivity Co, pg 729
Manfrotto Distribution Inc, pg 816
Rose Brand, pg 877

NEW MEXICO
Quickbeam Systems Inc (QSI), pg 868

NEW YORK
BMI Supply, pg 708
Bulbtronics Inc, pg 712
Cine 60 Inc, pg 723
MAC Group, pg 813
Production Resource Group LLC (PRG), pg 864
TecNec Distributing, pg 909

OHIO
Future Light Inc, pg 767
Vincent Lighting Systems, pg 930
Visual Products Inc, pg 931

OREGON
Pacific Grip & Lighting Inc, pg 849

PENNSYLVANIA
Innovision Media Group, pg 788
The Lerro Corp, pg 806

TEXAS
GEAR Cameras & Lighting, pg 769
Olden Lighting, pg 845
Pro Video & Film Equipment Co Inc, pg 863
Stage Directions, pg 898

UTAH
Redman Movies & Stories, pg 872
RIA Corp, pg 874

VERMONT
Production Advantage Inc, pg 863

WASHINGTON
Oppenheimer Camera Products, pg 847

WISCONSIN
Egripment USA, pg 751
Full Compass Systems, pg 767
Safe Harbor Computers, pg 879

MANITOBA
Lank/Beach Productions Inc, pg 803

ONTARIO
VFGadgets Inc, pg 926

Grip Equipment Manufacturers

ARIZONA
CamMate Systems, pg 715

CALIFORNIA
Birns & Sawyer Inc, pg 706
CineBags Inc, pg 723
Filmtools®, pg 761
Alan Gordon Enterprises Inc, pg 772
Innovision Optics, pg 788
LEE Filters, pg 805
Matthews Studio Equipment Inc, pg 820
Microdolly Hollywood, pg 826
Mole-Richardson Co, pg 829
Nalpak Inc, pg 835
Porta-Jib, pg 859

Spectra Cine Inc, pg 897
Steeldeck® Inc, pg 900
Thermodyne Cases, pg 912
Ver Sales Inc, pg 926

CONNECTICUT
Lex Products Corp, pg 807

FLORIDA
Techni-Lux Inc, pg 908

GEORGIA
Lighting & Production Equipment Inc, pg 807

ILLINOIS
Photoflex Inc, pg 856

INDIANA
Star Case Manufacturing Co Inc, pg 900

MASSACHUSETTS
Glidecam Industries Inc, pg 771

MICHIGAN
Lowing Light & Grip Inc, pg 812

MISSOURI
Schiller's Audio-Visual, pg 881

NEBRASKA
Strong Cinema Products, pg 902

NEW JERSEY
Pro-Tape & Specialities Inc, pg 863
Unilux Inc, pg 921

WISCONSIN
Egripment USA, pg 751

Grip Equipment Rentals

ALASKA
Connections Film & Video Inc, pg 731

ARIZONA
Arizona Cine Equipment, pg 688
Creative Backstage, pg 733
Merestone, pg 823
Metropolitan Audio-Visual Inc, pg 824
Reel Men Rentals Inc, pg 872

ARKANSAS
White Diamond Productions LLC, pg 937

CALIFORNIA
Artichoke Productions, pg 690
Available Light, pg 697
Big Door, pg 705
Birns & Sawyer Inc, pg 706
Chapman/Leonard Studio Equipment Inc, pg 720
Cinema Camera Rentals, pg 723
The Dreaming Tree, pg 746
DTC Lighting & Grip, pg 747
Gold Standard Productions, pg 772
Golden Gate Studios, pg 772
Alan Gordon Enterprises Inc, pg 772
Greenery Studios, pg 774

FILM

Grip Equipment Rentals (continued)

CALIFORNIA (continued)
Imagecraft Productions, pg 785
Innovision Optics, pg 788
KTVU-Retail Services, pg 802
The Lot (Skye Partners), pg 811
Mole-Richardson Co, pg 829
North County Media Center, pg 842
Panavision, pg 850
Pro HD Rentals, pg 863
Radiant Images, pg 869
RED Studios Hollywood, pg 872
The Rosenthal Group, pg 877
Samy's Camera, pg 879
Santa Clarita Studios, pg 880
SNAP, pg 891
Steeldeck® Inc, pg 900
Still N' Motion, pg 901
Straight Shoot'r Cranes Inc, pg 901
Stray Angel Films, pg 902
The Studios at Paramount, pg 903
T-stop Inc, pg 906
Total Creative, pg 916
Universal Studios, pg 922
Valencia Studios, pg 924
Warner Bros Entertainment Inc, pg 934
Z-Ville Productions, pg 944

COLORADO
Ceavco Audio Visual Company Inc, pg 719
Daylight Productions & Rentals, pg 739
Maniac Productions, pg 816

CONNECTICUT
KJfilms LLC, pg 799

FLORIDA
CineVideotech Inc, pg 725
Jordan Klein Film & Video (JKFV), pg 795
MAPS Production House, pg 816
National Teleproductions Inc, pg 837

GEORGIA
Lighting & Production Equipment Inc, pg 807
MAGNUM Companies Ltd, pg 815
Studio Space Atlanta, pg 903

ILLINOIS
Helix Camera & Video, pg 778
LITE-IT Grip Truck Rentals, pg 810
Product Productions, pg 863
PSAV® Presentation Services (Hotel Services Division), pg 866

IOWA
Musco Lighting, pg 834

KENTUCKY
Idle Minds Productions Inc, pg 784
Kentucky Grip & Lighting, pg 798

LOUISIANA
Available Lighting & Motion Picture Services Inc, pg 697
Digital FX Inc, pg 742
Moxie Media, pg 832
Second Line Stages, pg 883

MARYLAND
Event Tech, pg 756
Kramer Communications Video Production, pg 801

MASSACHUSETTS
Capron Lighting & Sound Co Inc, pg 716
Green Mountain Post Films (GMP), pg 774
High Output Inc, pg 779
Limelight Production® Inc, pg 809

MICHIGAN
Lowing Light & Grip Inc, pg 812

MINNESOTA
AVI Systems, pg 698
Cinequipt Inc, pg 724
House of Cinemagraphics, pg 782

MISSOURI
Show-Me Audio-Visual, pg 887
Sight & Sound Production Services Inc, pg 887

MONTANA
Filmlites Montana, pg 760

NEVADA
MG Studio, pg 825

NEW HAMPSHIRE
Apertura, pg 686
APS Lighting-Sound-AV, pg 688

NEW JERSEY
Ironbound Film & Television Studios LLC, pg 791
Unilux Inc, pg 921

NEW MEXICO
Quickbeam Systems Inc (QSI), pg 868

NEW YORK
Available Light, pg 697
BC Studio, pg 702
Bond Street Studio, pg 708
Bravo Studios, pg 709
Brooklyn Fire Proof, pg 711
Brooklyn Studios, pg 711
Cine 60 Inc, pg 723
Digital Arts NY, pg 742
Eastern Effects Inc, pg 749
LightSpace Studios, pg 808
Production Resource Group LLC (PRG), pg 864
Scheimpflug Digital, pg 881
See Factor Industry Inc, pg 883
Steiner Studios, pg 900
Umbra of Newburgh LLC, pg 921

NORTH CAROLINA
The Communications Group Inc, pg 729
Duke Media Services, pg 747
Take One Productions Ltd, pg 906

NORTH DAKOTA
Media Productions, pg 822

OHIO
Lyon Video Inc, pg 813
Vincent Lighting Systems, pg 930

OREGON
Pacific Grip & Lighting Inc, pg 849
Picture This Production Services, pg 856

PENNSYLVANIA
Innovision Media Group, pg 788
The Videohouse Inc, pg 929
Videosmith Inc, pg 930

TENNESSEE
DR&A Inc, pg 746
RentACamera.com, pg 873

TEXAS
GEAR Cameras & Lighting, pg 769
Earl Miller Productions Inc, pg 827
Muller Entertainment LLC, pg 833
Olden Lighting, pg 845
Phillips Media Source, pg 855
Stage Directions, pg 898
Studio Thirteen11, pg 903
Texcam Inc, pg 911

UTAH
Redman Movies & Stories, pg 872

WASHINGTON
Oppenheimer Camera Products, pg 847
Victory Studios, pg 927

WEST VIRGINIA
Blackwater Video Productions, pg 707

WYOMING
Bridger Productions Inc, pg 710

ALBERTA
Global TV, pg 771

ONTARIO
JIB Shots Equipment Inc, pg 794
SIM Digital, pg 888
Wallace Film Studios, pg 933
William F White International Inc, pg 937

Grip Equipment Repairs

CALIFORNIA
Cinemills Corp, pg 724
DTC Lighting & Grip, pg 747
Matthews Studio Equipment Inc, pg 820
Mole-Richardson Co, pg 829
Spectra Cine Inc, pg 897

COLORADO
Ceavco Audio Visual Company Inc, pg 719

CONNECTICUT
Vitec Videocom Inc, pg 932

FLORIDA
Hi-Tech Enterprises Inc, pg 779

GEORGIA
Lighting & Production Equipment Inc, pg 807
MAGNUM Companies Ltd, pg 815

MARYLAND
RTZ Audio Visual, pg 878

MASSACHUSETTS
Capron Lighting & Sound Co Inc, pg 716
High Output Inc, pg 779
Limelight Production® Inc, pg 809

MICHIGAN
Lowing Light & Grip Inc, pg 812

MINNESOTA
AVI Systems, pg 698

NEW MEXICO
Quickbeam Systems Inc (QSI), pg 868

NEW YORK
MAC Group, pg 813
Production Resource Group LLC (PRG), pg 864

OHIO
Future Light Inc, pg 767
Vincent Lighting Systems, pg 930

TEXAS
GEAR Cameras & Lighting, pg 769
Olden Lighting, pg 845

UTAH
Redman Movies & Stories, pg 872

WISCONSIN
Full Compass Systems, pg 767

Inspection Equipment, see Film Cleaning & Inspection Equipment

Lens Distributors

ARIZONA
Arizona Cine Equipment, pg 688
Docter Optics Inc, pg 744
EAR Professional Audio/Video, pg 749
PROCAM, pg 863
Troxell-CDI, pg 918

ARKANSAS
Carlton-Bates Co, pg 717
Jay S Stanley & Associates Inc, pg 899

CALIFORNIA
ARRI Inc, pg 689
Assured Audio Visual, pg 691
Band Pro Film & Digital Inc, pg 701
Birns & Sawyer Inc, pg 706
Cibola Systems, pg 723
Cinema Equipment Sales of California Inc, pg 724
CinemaGear.com, pg 724
Cinemills Corp, pg 724
DTC Lighting & Grip, pg 747
Express Video Supply Inc, pg 757
Filmtools®, pg 761

Gluskin's Custom Audio Video,
pg 771
Alan Gordon Enterprises Inc,
pg 772
Hooper Camera & Imaging, pg 781
Innovision Optics, pg 788
Instructional Materials & Equipment
Distributors (I-Med), pg 789
Jaguar Distribution Corp, pg 792
Kenko Tokina USA, pg 797
Lloyd F McKinney Associates Inc,
pg 821
Media Fabricators Inc, pg 822
MediaPOINTE, pg 823
Otto Nemenz International Inc,
pg 838
Promax Systems, pg 865
Qioptiq, An Excelitas Technologies
Company, pg 867
Visual Instrumentation Corp, pg 931

COLORADO

Ceavco Audio Visual Company Inc,
pg 719
Mike's Camera, pg 827

CONNECTICUT

Rockwell Communications Inc,
pg 876

FLORIDA

Access Media Group, pg 673
AVI-SPL, pg 698
Cinema Equipment & Supplies Inc,
pg 724
Hollywood Theatre Equipment Inc,
pg 781
Tallahassee Audio Visual, pg 906

GEORGIA

Audio Visual Resources Inc, pg 695
Visioneering International Inc,
pg 931

ILLINOIS

Creative Technology (CT), pg 733
Facets Multi-Media Inc, pg 758
Major Reproductions Equipment
Co, pg 815
Urbanski Film, pg 923

KENTUCKY

NOR-COM Inc, pg 841

MARYLAND

OmegaBrandess Distribution,
pg 845
Nicholas P Pipino Associates Inc,
pg 857
RTZ Audio Visual, pg 878

MASSACHUSETTS

Hunt's Photo & Video, pg 782

MICHIGAN

Olson Anderson Co, pg 685
City Events Group, pg 725
Michigan Office Solutions (MOS),
A Xerox Company, pg 825
TEL Systems LLC, pg 909

MINNESOTA

AVI Systems, pg 698
Cinequipt Inc, pg 724

MISSISSIPPI

Bowie Audio Visual Enterprises Inc,
pg 709
Jasper Ewing & Sons Inc, pg 757

MISSOURI

Communitronics Corp, pg 729
Conference Technologies Inc,
pg 730
ITC, pg 791

NEVADA

Aardvark Video & Media
Productions, pg 671
MeshTel, pg 824

NEW JERSEY

AlltecPro, pg 681
Angenieux, pg 685
Audio Visual Dynamics®, pg 694
AV Bluebook, pg 696
Avtech Systems Inc, pg 699
Comprehensive Cable &
Connectivity Co, pg 729
Leica Camera Inc, pg 806
Starlite, pg 900
SYMCO Inc, pg 905
Tele-Measurements Inc, pg 910
Vcom IMC, pg 925
ZGC Inc, pg 945

NEW YORK

AV Workshop, pg 697
Canon USA Inc, pg 716
Colortone Audio Visual, pg 728
Langie Audio Visual Systems,
pg 803
Mamiya, pg 815
Neptune Photo Inc, pg 838
Nikon Inc, pg 841
Olden Camera & Lens Co Inc,
pg 845
Ray Supply Inc, pg 870
Schneider Optics Inc, pg 881
Sigma Corp of America, pg 887
Visual Technologies Corp, pg 932
Willoughby's® Camera, pg 939

NORTH CAROLINA

Strategic Connections, pg 901

OHIO

Audio Visual Media, pg 694
Copp Integrated Systems, pg 731
Icom Multimedia, pg 783
Tri-State Audio Visual Co, pg 918
Visual Products Inc, pg 931

PENNSYLVANIA

Audio Visions Inc, pg 694
Bernie's Photo Center, pg 704
Brodart Co, pg 711
Charles Beseler Co, pg 721
Garcia Marketing Inc, pg 768
Grise Audio Visual Center Inc,
pg 774
Innovision Media Group, pg 788
The Lerro Corp, pg 806
Wespen Audio Visual Co, pg 935

TENNESSEE

Continental Film, pg 731
Memphis Communications Corp,
pg 823

TEXAS

Audio Visual Technologies Group
(AVTG), pg 695
AVES Audio Visual Systems Inc,
pg 698
Pro Video & Film Equipment Co
Inc, pg 863
Stage Directions, pg 898

UTAH

RIA Corp, pg 874

VIRGINIA

Lee Hartman & Sons Inc, pg 805
The Whitlock Group, pg 937

WASHINGTON

Inland Audio Visual Co, pg 788
Oppenheimer Camera Products,
pg 847

WISCONSIN

Camera Corner Connecting Point,
pg 715

ALBERTA

McBain Camera Ltd, pg 820

ONTARIO

Kingsway Motion Picture Inc,
pg 799
Nationwide Audio Visual Co,
pg 837

Lens Manufacturers

CALIFORNIA

Alan Gordon Enterprises Inc,
pg 772
Innovision Optics, pg 788
Preston Cinema Systems, pg 861
Qioptiq, An Excelitas Technologies
Company, pg 867

NEBRASKA

Strong Cinema Products, pg 902

NEVADA

MeshTel, pg 824

NEW JERSEY

AlltecPro, pg 681
Angenieux, pg 685
CELCO, pg 719
FUJIFILM Optical Devices
Division, pg 766
Konica Minolta Business Solutions,
pg 801
Leica Camera Inc, pg 806
Pioneer Research Inc, pg 857
Sofradir EC, pg 892
ZGC Inc, pg 945

NEW YORK

Canon USA Inc, pg 716
ELMO USA Corp, pg 753
Navitar Inc, pg 837
Nikon Inc, pg 841
Schneider Optics Inc, pg 881
Sigma Corp of America, pg 887
Tamron USA Inc, pg 906

PENNSYLVANIA

Charles Beseler Co, pg 721
Kopp Glass, pg 801

WASHINGTON

Oppenheimer Camera Products,
pg 847

Lens Rentals

ALABAMA

Audio-Video Resources Inc, pg 694

ALASKA

Connections Film & Video Inc,
pg 731

ARIZONA

Arizona Cine Equipment, pg 688
Merestone, pg 823
Reel Men Rentals Inc, pg 872

CALIFORNIA

Alternative Rentals, pg 682
Artichoke Productions, pg 690
Assured Audio Visual, pg 691
Big Door, pg 705
Birns & Sawyer Inc, pg 706
CamTec Motion Picture Cameras,
pg 715
Chater Camera Inc, pg 721
Cinema Camera Rentals, pg 723
DTC Lighting & Grip, pg 747
Gluskin's Custom Audio Video,
pg 771
Gold Standard Productions, pg 772
Alan Gordon Enterprises Inc,
pg 772
Greenery Studios, pg 774
Imagecraft Productions, pg 785
Innovision Optics, pg 788
JD Audio Visual Inc, pg 793
McCune Audio-Video-Lighting,
pg 821
Media Fabricators Inc, pg 822
Otto Nemenz International Inc,
pg 838
New Circuit Films LLC, pg 839
Old School Cameras, pg 844
Photographic Rental Service Inc
(PRS), pg 856
Pro HD Rentals, pg 863
Radiant Images, pg 869
Samy's Camera, pg 879
Shoulder High Productions, pg 886
Stray Angel Films, pg 902
The Studios at Paramount, pg 903
T-stop Inc, pg 906
Total Creative, pg 916
Visual Instrumentation Corp, pg 931

COLORADO

Ceavco Audio Visual Company Inc,
pg 719
Mike's Camera, pg 827

DELAWARE

Showorks Audio Visual Inc, pg 887

FLORIDA

Steven Cohen Motion Picture
Production, pg 727
Jordan Klein Film & Video (JKFV),
pg 795
Photosound of Orlando Inc, pg 856

GEORGIA

Audio Visual Resources Inc, pg 695
PC&E, pg 852
Staging Directions Inc, pg 899

FILM

Lens Rentals (continued)

ILLINOIS
Creative Technology (CT), pg 733
Helix Camera & Video, pg 778
Resolution Productions Group,
  pg 874

INDIANA
Gary Camera & Digital, pg 768
OMNI Productions, pg 845

MARYLAND
Kramer Communications Video
  Production, pg 801
RTZ Audio Visual, pg 878

MASSACHUSETTS
Capron Lighting & Sound Co Inc,
  pg 716
Green Mountain Post Films (GMP),
  pg 774

MICHIGAN
Olson Anderson Co, pg 685
City Events Group, pg 725

MINNESOTA
AVI Systems, pg 698
House of Cinemagraphics, pg 782

MISSISSIPPI
Bowie Audio Visual Enterprises Inc,
  pg 709

MISSOURI
Show-Me Audio-Visual, pg 887

NEVADA
MG Studio, pg 825

NEW HAMPSHIRE
Apertura, pg 686

NEW JERSEY
Audio Visual Dynamics®, pg 694
PLS Staging, pg 858

NEW YORK
Adorama Rental Co, pg 676
AV Workshop, pg 697
Big Apple Films, pg 705
Bond Street Studio, pg 708
Cine 60 Inc, pg 723
Cinema-Vision, pg 724
CMI Communications, pg 727
Colortone Audio Visual, pg 728
CPT Rental Inc, pg 732
Hand Held Films, pg 775
Langie Audio Visual Systems,
  pg 803
LightHouse Films, pg 807
LightSpace Studios, pg 808
Olden Camera & Lens Co Inc,
  pg 845
Scheimpflug Digital, pg 881
Visual Technologies Corp, pg 932

NORTH CAROLINA
JDC Wilmington Camera Services,
  pg 793
Strategic Connections, pg 901
Take One Productions Ltd, pg 906

NORTH DAKOTA
Media Productions, pg 822

OHIO
Audio Visual Media, pg 694
Icom Multimedia, pg 783
Thread Marketing Group, pg 913

OREGON
Koerner Camera Systems, pg 800
Northwest Film Center, pg 842
Picture This Production Services,
  pg 856

PENNSYLVANIA
Audio Visions Inc, pg 694
Bernie's Photo Center, pg 704
Grise Audio Visual Center Inc,
  pg 774
Innovision Media Group, pg 788
Location Camera Ltd, pg 810
Videosmith Inc, pg 930
Visual Sound Inc, pg 931

TENNESSEE
RentACamera.com, pg 873
Russ Sturgeon Productions/RSVP,
  pg 903

TEXAS
Audio Visual Technologies Group
  (AVTG), pg 695
Bright Star Productions Inc, pg 710
GEAR Cameras & Lighting, pg 769
Stage Directions, pg 898
Studio Thirteen11, pg 903
Texcam Inc, pg 911

UTAH
Ron Hill Imagery, pg 780
Redman Movies & Stories, pg 872

VIRGINIA
Lee Hartman & Sons Inc, pg 805
Projection, pg 865

WASHINGTON
Inland Audio Visual Co, pg 788
Oppenheimer Camera Products,
  pg 847

WISCONSIN
Camera Corner Connecting Point,
  pg 715
Event Essentials, pg 756
Wisconsin Public Television, pg 940

ALBERTA
Global TV, pg 771
McBain Camera Ltd, pg 820

ONTARIO
JIB Shots Equipment Inc, pg 794
Kingsway Motion Picture Inc,
  pg 799
SIM Digital, pg 888
William F White International Inc,
  pg 937

Lens Repairs

ARIZONA
PROCAM, pg 863

CALIFORNIA
ARRI Inc, pg 689
Birns & Sawyer Inc, pg 706
CinemaGear.com, pg 724
Alan Gordon Enterprises Inc,
  pg 772
Pro Camera Repair, pg 862
Visual Instrumentation Corp, pg 931

COLORADO
Ceavco Audio Visual Company Inc,
  pg 719

CONNECTICUT
Precision Camera & Video Repair
  Inc, pg 861

FLORIDA
Hi-Tech Enterprises Inc, pg 779

INDIANA
Gary Camera & Digital, pg 768

KENTUCKY
NOR-COM Inc, pg 841

MARYLAND
RTZ Audio Visual, pg 878

MINNESOTA
AVI Systems, pg 698

NEW JERSEY
Angenieux, pg 685
FUJIFILM Optical Devices
  Division, pg 766
Konica Minolta Business Solutions,
  pg 801
Leica Camera Inc, pg 806
ZGC Inc, pg 945

NEW YORK
Colortone Audio Visual, pg 728
CPT Rental Inc, pg 732
Langie Audio Visual Systems,
  pg 803
Mamiya, pg 815
Schneider Optics Inc, pg 881
Sigma Corp of America, pg 887
Visual Technologies Corp, pg 932

OHIO
Audio Visual Media, pg 694

PENNSYLVANIA
Audio Visions Inc, pg 694
Bernie's Photo Center, pg 704

WASHINGTON
Oppenheimer Camera Products,
  pg 847

ONTARIO
Kingsway Motion Picture Inc,
  pg 799

Libraries—Film or
Stock-Shot

ALASKA
Alaska Media Pros LLC, pg 679

ARIZONA
The Source Stock Footage Library
  Inc, pg 895

CALIFORNIA
Action Sports/All Stock, pg 675
AM Stock-Cameo Film Library,
  pg 682
American Playback Images, pg 684
Carl Barth Images, pg 702
Birds & Animals Unlimited, pg 706
Budget Films Stock Footage Inc,
  pg 712
Burrud Productions Inc, pg 713
Classic Images Stock Footage LLC,
  pg 726
Creative Technology, pg 733
Crystal Pyramid Productions™,
  pg 735
eFootage LLC, pg 751
Em Gee Film Library, pg 753
Fish Films Footage World, pg 761
FootageBank HD, pg 763
Gold Standard Productions, pg 772
Havas Edge, pg 777
iCorpTv, pg 783
JDS Video & Media Productions
  Inc, pg 793
MacGillivray Freeman Films Inc,
  pg 813
Moving Art by Louie Schwartzberg,
  pg 831
Nineteen87, pg 841
Oddball Films Inc, pg 844
Palardo Productions, pg 850
piXvfm Inc, pg 857
Prelinger Archives, pg 861
Producers Library, pg 863
Pyramid Media, pg 867
QRS Software Services, pg 867
Sports Cinematography Group,
  pg 898
The Studios at Paramount, pg 903
Total Creative, pg 916

COLORADO
Apogee Communications Group,
  pg 687
CSI Film & Video LLC, pg 735
Flashback Media Productions,
  pg 762
Freewheelin' Films, pg 765
Greg Hensley Productions, pg 779
Mammoth HD, pg 815
Tatum Video, pg 907

CONNECTICUT
Cine-Med Inc, pg 723
Skyviews Survey Inc, pg 890

DISTRICT OF COLUMBIA
Susan Hormuth, Visual Resource
  Consultant, pg 781
Smithsonian National Museum of
  the American Indian, pg 891

FLORIDA
Bill Bachmann Studios, pg 705
NatureVision Stock Footage Library,
  pg 837
SuperStock Inc, pg 904

GEORGIA
Guerrilla Productions LLC, pg 774

ILLINOIS
Moviecraft Inc, pg 831
WPA Film Library, pg 942

INDIANA

OMNI Productions, pg 845

KENTUCKY

Horizon Films & Media LLC, pg 781

LOUISIANA

Digital FX Inc, pg 742

MARYLAND

Easy Street Productions LLC, pg 750
James Agee Film Project, pg 792
Special Archives Division, Motion Picture Branch, pg 896

MASSACHUSETTS

CommCreative, pg 728
Documentary Educational Resources Inc, pg 744
Green Mountain Post Films (GMP), pg 774
WGBH Production Group, pg 936
WGBH Stock Sales, pg 936

MINNESOTA

Pro Media Productions, pg 863

NEVADA

DVDs4Less, pg 748
Globe Photos LLC, pg 771

NEW HAMPSHIRE

Apertura, pg 686
Chip Taylor Communications LLC, pg 907

NEW JERSEY

CELCO, pg 719
Global ImageWorks LLC, pg 771
NFL Films Inc, pg 841
NFL Films Music Library, pg 841
TimeSteps Productions Inc, pg 914

NEW YORK

AP Images, pg 686
Art Resource, pg 690
aurora productions, pg 696
Black Star Publishing Co Inc, pg 706
Broadstreet Productions LLC, pg 711
Debbie Regan Locations Ltd, pg 739
FILM Archives Inc, pg 760
Framepool, pg 765
GRANGER - Historical Picture Archive, pg 773
Historic Films, pg 780
The Independent Production Fund, pg 786
Jalbert Productions International, pg 792
Museum of the City of New York, pg 834
NBC News Archives, pg 837
The New York Historical Society, pg 840
The New York Times Photo Archive, pg 840
Pennebaker Hegedus Films Inc, pg 854
Richter Productions Inc, pg 875
Sovfoto/Eastfoto Inc, pg 896

United Nations Department of Public Information-News & Media Division, pg 921
Zelman Studios Ltd, pg 945

NORTH CAROLINA

The Communications Group Inc, pg 729
Crystal Pictures Inc, pg 735

OHIO

Treehaus Communications Inc, pg 917

OREGON

Artbeats, pg 690
Odyssey Productions Inc, pg 844

PENNSYLVANIA

John E Allen Inc, pg 680
ClassicStock.com/Robertstock.com, pg 726
Grant Heilman Photography Inc, pg 778

TENNESSEE

Motion Picture Services, pg 831
Stage Post, pg 899

TEXAS

Castleview Productions, pg 717
Emergency Film Group, pg 753
Hurst Digital, pg 782
McNee Productions Inc, pg 821
Prairie Pictures Film & Video, pg 860
The Samuels Co, pg 879
Ron Scott, pg 882
Stockyard Photos/Jim Olive Photography, pg 901

UTAH

Stockfootage.com, pg 901
USDA/FSA Aerial Photography Field Office, pg 924

VERMONT

University of Vermont, Instructional Television Dept, pg 923

VIRGINIA

Stuart Finley Films, pg 761
Maniglia Media LLC, pg 816
Lynda Richardson Photography, pg 875

WASHINGTON

Getty Images, pg 770
White Rain Films Ltd, pg 937

WISCONSIN

Fotosearch Stock Photography, pg 764
USAV Group Inc, pg 923
Wisconsin Public Television, pg 940

WYOMING

Bridger Productions Inc, pg 710

NORTHWEST TERRITORIES

Yellowknife Films Inc, pg 944

ONTARIO

Spence-Thomas Audio Post, pg 897

QUEBEC

Les Productions Via Le Monde (Daniel Bertolino) Inc, pg 864

SASKATCHEWAN

Thomega Entertainment Inc, pg 913

Location Equipment & Facility Distributors

CALIFORNIA

Audio Images Corp, pg 693
DTC Lighting & Grip, pg 747
International E-Z UP Inc, pg 790
Mole-Richardson Co, pg 829

COLORADO

Ceavco Audio Visual Company Inc, pg 719
Chimera®, pg 722

GEORGIA

Lighting & Production Equipment Inc, pg 807

ILLINOIS

Cool-Lux, pg 731
Facets Multi-Media Inc, pg 758
Photoflex Inc, pg 856

MINNESOTA

AVI Systems, pg 698
Cinequipt Inc, pg 724

MISSOURI

Conference Technologies Inc, pg 730

NEVADA

Aardvark Video & Media Productions, pg 671

NEW JERSEY

Audio Visual Dynamics®, pg 694
Comprehensive Cable & Connectivity Co, pg 729

NEW YORK

Barbizon Electric Co Inc, pg 701
Cine 60 Inc, pg 723
Production Resource Group LLC (PRG), pg 864

PENNSYLVANIA

Innovision Media Group, pg 788

TEXAS

Pro Video & Film Equipment Co Inc, pg 863
Stage Directions, pg 898

UTAH

Webb Audio Visual, pg 935

VERMONT

Production Advantage Inc, pg 863

Location Equipment & Facility Manufacturers

CALIFORNIA

ALTINEX Inc, pg 682
Clear-Com® LLC, pg 726
DASAN Zhone Solutions (DZS) Inc, pg 737
International E-Z UP Inc, pg 790
Microdolly Hollywood, pg 826
Mole-Richardson Co, pg 829
Synergy Group Inc, pg 906
TV Pro Gear, pg 919

COLORADO

Chimera®, pg 722

FLORIDA

Magna-Tech Electronic Co Inc, pg 814

GEORGIA

Lighting & Production Equipment Inc, pg 807

ILLINOIS

Cool-Lux, pg 731
Kart-A-Bag Manufacturing Inc, pg 796
Photoflex Inc, pg 856

MICHIGAN

Studio Consulting & Construction Inc, pg 902

OHIO

Future Light Inc, pg 767

PENNSYLVANIA

Aztech Productions LLC, pg 700

Location Equipment & Facility Rentals

ALASKA

Connections Film & Video Inc, pg 731

ARIZONA

Arizona Cine Equipment, pg 688

ARKANSAS

White Diamond Productions LLC, pg 937

CALIFORNIA

Antelope Valley Locations & Production Services, pg 686
Big Door, pg 705
Chapman/Leonard Studio Equipment Inc, pg 720
DTC Lighting & Grip, pg 747
Golden Gate Studios, pg 772
Innovision Optics, pg 788
KTVU-Retail Services, pg 802
The Location Connection Inc, pg 810
Mole-Richardson Co, pg 829
Panavision, pg 850
Samy's Camera, pg 879
Santa Clarita Studios, pg 880
SOS Film Works (Space Ordnance Systems), pg 893
The Studios at Paramount, pg 903

FILM

Location Equipment & Facility Rentals (continued)

CALIFORNIA (continued)

Sunset Bronson Studios, pg 904
Total Creative, pg 916
Warner Bros Entertainment Inc, pg 934
Z-Ville Productions, pg 944

COLORADO

Apogee Communications Group, pg 687
Ceavco Audio Visual Company Inc, pg 719
Chimera®, pg 722
Tatum Video, pg 907

FLORIDA

Steven Cohen Motion Picture Production, pg 727
CopShopMiami.com, pg 731
Jordan Klein Film & Video (JKFV), pg 795
Universal Studios Florida® Production Group, pg 922

GEORGIA

Lighting & Production Equipment Inc, pg 807

ILLINOIS

Beatty TeleVisual Productions, pg 703
LITE-IT Grip Truck Rentals, pg 810
On Site Video, pg 846
Product Productions, pg 863
PSAV® Presentation Services (Hotel Services Division), pg 866

INDIANA

OMNI Productions, pg 845

IOWA

Musco Lighting, pg 834

KENTUCKY

Idle Minds Productions Inc, pg 784

LOUISIANA

Digital FX Inc, pg 742
Moxie Media, pg 832

MARYLAND

Producers Video, pg 863

MASSACHUSETTS

The Boston Connection Inc, pg 709
Green Mountain Post Films (GMP), pg 774
High Output Inc, pg 779

MICHIGAN

City Events Group, pg 725

MINNESOTA

AVI Systems, pg 698
Cinequipt Inc, pg 724

MISSOURI

Show-Me Audio-Visual, pg 887

MONTANA

Jereco Studios Inc, pg 793

NEW HAMPSHIRE

Apertura, pg 686

NEW JERSEY

Audio Visual Dynamics®, pg 694

NEW YORK

Available Light, pg 697
Cine 60 Inc, pg 723
CMI Communications, pg 727
Manhattan Center Studios Inc, pg 816
Production Resource Group LLC (PRG), pg 864

NORTH CAROLINA

The Communications Group Inc, pg 729
Take One Productions Ltd, pg 906

NORTH DAKOTA

Media Productions, pg 822

OHIO

Lyon Video Inc, pg 813
Mills James Productions, pg 828
Thread Marketing Group, pg 913

OREGON

Pacific Grip & Lighting Inc, pg 849

PENNSYLVANIA

Innovision Media Group, pg 788
Videosmith Inc, pg 930

TENNESSEE

Russ Sturgeon Productions/RSVP, pg 903
United Methodist Productions, pg 921

TEXAS

Earl Miller Productions Inc, pg 827
Muller Entertainment LLC, pg 833
Omega Productions, pg 845
Phillips Media Source, pg 855
Stage Directions, pg 898
Texcam Inc, pg 911

UTAH

Redman Movies & Stories, pg 872
Webb Audio Visual, pg 935

VERMONT

Marlboro Productions, pg 817

WISCONSIN

Logan Productions Inc, pg 811
University of Wisconsin-Oshkosh Radio-TV-Film Dept, pg 923
Wisconsin Public Television, pg 940

WYOMING

Bridger Productions Inc, pg 710

ALBERTA

Global TV, pg 771

BRITISH COLUMBIA

Video Out Distribution, pg 928

ONTARIO

JIB Shots Equipment Inc, pg 794

Location Equipment & Facility Repairs

CALIFORNIA

Mole-Richardson Co, pg 829

COLORADO

Ceavco Audio Visual Company Inc, pg 719

GEORGIA

Lighting & Production Equipment Inc, pg 807

ILLINOIS

On Site Video, pg 846

MASSACHUSETTS

The Boston Connection Inc, pg 709

MICHIGAN

Studio Consulting & Construction Inc, pg 902

MINNESOTA

AVI Systems, pg 698

NEW YORK

Production Resource Group LLC (PRG), pg 864

Location Photography, see Photography—Location

Magnetic Recording Equipment Distributors

ARIZONA

Troxell-CDI, pg 918

CALIFORNIA

Assured Audio Visual, pg 691
Audio Images Corp, pg 693
Birns & Sawyer Inc, pg 706
Christy's Editorial, pg 723
Media Fabricators Inc, pg 822
MediaPOINTE, pg 823

GEORGIA

Lighting & Production Equipment Inc, pg 807

KENTUCKY

NOR-COM Inc, pg 841

MINNESOTA

AVI Systems, pg 698
Cinequipt Inc, pg 724

NEW JERSEY

AlltecPro, pg 681
Comprehensive Cable & Connectivity Co, pg 729
JRF Magnetic Sciences Inc, pg 795

NEW YORK

Motion Picture Enterprises Inc, pg 831
Solid State Logic Inc, pg 892
Tri-Ed Distribution Inc, pg 918

OHIO

Tri-State Audio Visual Co, pg 918

PENNSYLVANIA

Audio Visions Inc, pg 694

TEXAS

Pro Video & Film Equipment Co Inc, pg 863

ONTARIO

Nationwide Audio Visual Co, pg 837

Magnetic Recording Equipment Manufacturers

FLORIDA

Magna-Tech Electronic Co Inc, pg 814

Magnetic Recording Equipment Rentals

ARIZONA

Arizona Cine Equipment, pg 688
Metropolitan Audio-Visual Inc, pg 824

ARKANSAS

White Diamond Productions LLC, pg 937

CALIFORNIA

Artichoke Productions, pg 690
Birns & Sawyer Inc, pg 706
Dan Dugan Sound Design Inc, pg 747
Golden Gate Studios, pg 772
Maximus Media Inc, pg 820
Media Fabricators Inc, pg 822
Total Creative, pg 916

FLORIDA

Jordan Klein Film & Video (JKFV), pg 795

GEORGIA

Lighting & Production Equipment Inc, pg 807

ILLINOIS

Beatty TeleVisual Productions, pg 703

MARYLAND

RTZ Audio Visual, pg 878
Soundtrax Inc, pg 895

MASSACHUSETTS

The Boston Connection Inc, pg 709
Green Mountain Post Films (GMP), pg 774

FILM

Mixing—Stereo or Dolby Stereo (continued)

DELAWARE

Side Door Studio Inc, pg 887

DISTRICT OF COLUMBIA

Interface Media Group, pg 789

FLORIDA

Audio Visual Imagineering Inc, pg 694
Communications Concepts Inc (CCI), pg 729
Morrisound Recording, pg 830

GEORGIA

First Cut Communications LLC, pg 761
Guerrilla Productions LLC, pg 774

HAWAII

Media Bridge Gamekids, pg 821

ILLINOIS

ABSA Films, pg 672
Steven Samler Music & Sound, pg 879

INDIANA

A-V-A Video Productions, pg 671

KENTUCKY

Horizon Films & Media LLC, pg 781

MARYLAND

Bethesda Softworks LLC, pg 704
dbF a Media Company, pg 739
Pro Cuts Editing Services, pg 862

MASSACHUSETTS

CommCreative, pg 728
Labrecque Creative Sound, pg 803
Northern Light Productions (NLP), pg 842
Preston Productions Inc, pg 861
WGBH Production Group, pg 936

MICHIGAN

Digi Sign Design LLC, pg 741
Digital Image Studios LLC, pg 742
GMP Music, pg 772
Michigan Recording Arts Institute & Technologies, pg 825

MONTANA

Jereco Studios Inc, pg 793

NEW JERSEY

Milgrom Productions, pg 827
NFL Films Inc, pg 841

NEW YORK

Aura Sonic Ltd (ASL), pg 695
DuArt Media Services, pg 747
Fingerpaint, pg 761
HB-Content, pg 777
KAS Music & Sound, pg 796
Magno Sound Inc, pg 815
The Palmer Group, pg 850

NORTH CAROLINA

Horizon Video Productions Inc, pg 781
2BruceStudio, pg 920

OHIO

The Telos Alliance, pg 910

PENNSYLVANIA

Right Coast Recording Inc, pg 875

RHODE ISLAND

Sound-FX-Design, pg 894

SOUTH CAROLINA

Venture Media, pg 925

TENNESSEE

American Blackguard Inc, pg 683
JamSync, pg 793
Love Shack Recording Studios, pg 811
Motion Picture Services, pg 831
Stage Post, pg 899
Zion Music Group, pg 945

TEXAS

Anaphora Literary Press, pg 685
Julye Newlin Productions Inc, pg 840
The Samuels Co, pg 879
The Sound Lab Inc, pg 894
Sound Works, pg 894

UTAH

Soularium Recording Studios, pg 893

WASHINGTON

North-by-Northwest - A Digital Studio, pg 842
Sound Sound, pg 894
Victory Studios, pg 927

WISCONSIN

5th Floor Recording Co, pg 760
USAV Group Inc, pg 923

ALBERTA

Global TV, pg 771

BRITISH COLUMBIA

Pinewood Sound, pg 857

MANITOBA

DACAPO Productions Inc, pg 737

ONTARIO

ADS Media, pg 677
Metalworks Recording Studios Inc, pg 824
Phase One Studios, pg 855
Wanted! Sound + Picture, pg 933

QUEBEC

Muse Entertainment Enterprises, pg 834

Mixing—Stereo Surround or Dolby Surround

CALIFORNIA

Audio Mechanics, pg 693
Berkeley Sound Artists Inc, pg 704
Chace Audio by Deluxe, pg 720
Creative Technology, pg 733
Earwax Productions Inc, pg 749
iCorpTv, pg 783
Maximus Media Inc, pg 820
OTR Studios, pg 848
Palardo Productions, pg 850
piXvfm Inc, pg 857
Polarity Post Production, pg 858
Private Island Audio Inc, pg 862
QRS Software Services, pg 867
Roundabout Entertainment Inc, pg 878
Shapeshifter, pg 885
SonicPool, pg 892
Total Creative, pg 916
Universal Studios, pg 922

COLORADO

Tim Cissell Music, pg 725

DISTRICT OF COLUMBIA

Interface Media Group, pg 789

FLORIDA

Communications Concepts Inc (CCI), pg 729
Morrisound Recording, pg 830
WKMG-TV News 6, pg 940

GEORGIA

Guerrilla Productions LLC, pg 774

HAWAII

Media Bridge Gamekids, pg 821

INDIANA

OMNI Productions, pg 845

MARYLAND

dbF a Media Company, pg 739

MASSACHUSETTS

Northern Light Productions (NLP), pg 842
Preston Productions Inc, pg 861
WGBH Production Group, pg 936

MICHIGAN

Digi Sign Design LLC, pg 741
Digital Image Studios LLC, pg 742
GMP Music, pg 772
Michigan Recording Arts Institute & Technologies, pg 825

MONTANA

Jereco Studios Inc, pg 793

NEW JERSEY

Milgrom Productions, pg 827
NFL Films Inc, pg 841

NEW YORK

Aura Sonic Ltd (ASL), pg 695
Big Fish Production US, pg 705
Magno Sound Inc, pg 815
The Palmer Group, pg 850
Zelman Studios Ltd, pg 945

NORTH CAROLINA

Horizon Video Productions Inc, pg 781

OHIO

The Telos Alliance, pg 910

OREGON

REX, pg 874

PENNSYLVANIA

Right Coast Recording Inc, pg 875

RHODE ISLAND

Sound-FX-Design, pg 894

TENNESSEE

American Blackguard Inc, pg 683
JamSync, pg 793
Love Shack Recording Studios, pg 811
Motion Picture Services, pg 831
Stage Post, pg 899

TEXAS

Anaphora Literary Press, pg 685
Media Event Concepts Inc, pg 822
The Samuels Co, pg 879

UTAH

Soularium Recording Studios, pg 893

WASHINGTON

North-by-Northwest - A Digital Studio, pg 842
Victory Studios, pg 927

WISCONSIN

5th Floor Recording Co, pg 760

ALBERTA

Global TV, pg 771

BRITISH COLUMBIA

Pinewood Sound, pg 857

MANITOBA

DACAPO Productions Inc, pg 737

ONTARIO

ADS Media, pg 677
Metalworks Recording Studios Inc, pg 824
Phase One Studios, pg 855
Wanted! Sound + Picture, pg 933

QUEBEC

Muse Entertainment Enterprises, pg 834

Mobile Production Vehicle Distributors

MICHIGAN

TEL Systems LLC, pg 909

NEW JERSEY

Tele-Measurements Inc, pg 910

PENNSYLVANIA

Innovision Media Group, pg 788
The Lerro Corp, pg 806

TEXAS

Pro Video & Film Equipment Co
Inc, pg 863
Shook Mobile Technology LP,
pg 886

UTAH

RIA Corp, pg 874

VIRGINIA

Acoustics First Corp, pg 674

Mobile Production Vehicle Manufacturers

CALIFORNIA

Technical Services, pg 908

TEXAS

Shook Mobile Technology LP,
pg 886

VIRGINIA

Acoustics First Corp, pg 674

Mobile Production Vehicle Rentals

ALASKA

Connections Film & Video Inc,
pg 731

CALIFORNIA

DTC Lighting & Grip, pg 747
The Rosenthal Group, pg 877
Santa Clarita Studios, pg 880
SNAP, pg 891
Stray Angel Films, pg 902
Total Creative, pg 916
Z-Ville Productions, pg 944

FLORIDA

ACT Productions, pg 675
CopShopMiami.com, pg 731
Jordan Klein Film & Video (JKFV),
pg 795

ILLINOIS

Product Productions, pg 863
PSAV® Presentation Services
(Hotel Services Division), pg 866

LOUISIANA

Digital FX Inc, pg 742
Moxie Media, pg 832

MARYLAND

Producers Video, pg 863

MASSACHUSETTS

Green Mountain Post Films (GMP),
pg 774

MISSOURI

Show-Me Audio-Visual, pg 887

NEW HAMPSHIRE

Apertura, pg 686

NEW YORK

CP Communications, pg 732

OHIO

Lyon Video Inc, pg 813

OREGON

Pacific Grip & Lighting Inc, pg 849

PENNSYLVANIA

Innovision Media Group, pg 788
Location Lighting Ltd, pg 810
WPHL-TV, pg 942

TENNESSEE

DR&A Inc, pg 746

TEXAS

Muller Entertainment LLC, pg 833
Omega Productions, pg 845
Phillips Media Source, pg 855
Reelsound Recording Co, pg 872
Texcam Inc, pg 911

WISCONSIN

Logan Productions Inc, pg 811
Wisconsin Public Television, pg 940

ALBERTA

Global TV, pg 771

ONTARIO

JIB Shots Equipment Inc, pg 794

Mobile Production Vehicle Repairs

CALIFORNIA

Technical Services, pg 908

TEXAS

Shook Mobile Technology LP,
pg 886

Mobile Unit Distributors

COLORADO

Ceavco Audio Visual Company Inc,
pg 719

MARYLAND

Nicholas P Pipino Associates Inc,
pg 857

MINNESOTA

Alpha Video & Audio Inc, pg 682

MISSOURI

Conference Technologies Inc,
pg 730

NEW YORK

Ray Supply Inc, pg 870
Visual Technologies Corp, pg 932

PENNSYLVANIA

Innovision Media Group, pg 788
The Lerro Corp, pg 806

TEXAS

Pro Video & Film Equipment Co
Inc, pg 863
Shook Mobile Technology LP,
pg 886

Mobile Unit Manufacturers

CALIFORNIA

Technical Services, pg 908
TV Pro Gear, pg 919

COLORADO

Display Devices Inc, pg 743

MARYLAND

Absolute Hollywood, pg 672

TEXAS

Shook Mobile Technology LP,
pg 886

Mobile Unit Rentals

CALIFORNIA

RetinaVision Productions, pg 874
SNAP, pg 891
Z-Ville Productions, pg 944

COLORADO

Ceavco Audio Visual Company Inc,
pg 719
Maniac Productions, pg 816

FLORIDA

CineVideotech Inc, pg 725
Jordan Klein Film & Video (JKFV),
pg 795

GEORGIA

Studio Space Atlanta, pg 903

ILLINOIS

On Site Video, pg 846
PSAV® Presentation Services
(Hotel Services Division), pg 866

LOUISIANA

Digital FX Inc, pg 742

MARYLAND

Absolute Hollywood, pg 672

MICHIGAN

Lowing Light & Grip Inc, pg 812

NEW HAMPSHIRE

Apertura, pg 686

NEW JERSEY

Ironbound Film & Television
Studios LLC, pg 791

NEW YORK

Scheimpflug Digital, pg 881
Visual Technologies Corp, pg 932

OHIO

Lyon Video Inc, pg 813

OREGON

Pacific Grip & Lighting Inc, pg 849

PENNSYLVANIA

Innovision Media Group, pg 788

TEXAS

Muller Entertainment LLC, pg 833
Omega Productions, pg 845

WISCONSIN

Logan Productions Inc, pg 811
Wisconsin Public Television, pg 940

ALBERTA

Global TV, pg 771

MANITOBA

MidCanada Production Services Inc
(MidCan), pg 826

Mobile Unit Repairs

CALIFORNIA

Technical Services, pg 908

COLORADO

Ceavco Audio Visual Company Inc,
pg 719

NEW YORK

Visual Technologies Corp, pg 932

Movie & Still Camera Distributors

ARIZONA

EAR Professional Audio/Video,
pg 749
Troxell-CDI, pg 918

CALIFORNIA

ARRI Inc, pg 689
Birns & Sawyer Inc, pg 706
Express Video Supply Inc, pg 757
Filmtools®, pg 761
Alan Gordon Enterprises Inc,
pg 772
Hooper Camera & Imaging, pg 781
MediaPOINTE, pg 823
Otto Nemenz International Inc,
pg 838
Point of View Productions, pg 858
Pro8mm, pg 862
Yale Film & Video, pg 943

COLORADO

Mike's Camera, pg 827

FLORIDA

AVI-SPL, pg 698
Hi-Tech Enterprises Inc, pg 779

ILLINOIS

Urbanski Film, pg 923

MARYLAND

RTZ Audio Visual, pg 878

MASSACHUSETTS

Hunt's Photo & Video, pg 782

FILM

Movie & Still Camera Distributors (continued)

MINNESOTA

AVI Systems, pg 698
Cinequipt Inc, pg 724

MISSISSIPPI

Jasper Ewing & Sons Inc, pg 757

NEW JERSEY

AlltecPro, pg 681
Leica Camera Inc, pg 806

NEW YORK

AZ Spectrum, pg 700
Canon USA Inc, pg 716
Colortone Audio Visual, pg 728
Langie Audio Visual Systems, pg 803
Mamiya, pg 815
Motion Picture Enterprises Inc, pg 831
Neptune Photo Inc, pg 838
Olden Camera & Lens Co Inc, pg 845
Ray Supply Inc, pg 870
Sigma Corp of America, pg 887
Visual Technologies Corp, pg 932
Willoughby's® Camera, pg 939

NORTH CAROLINA

Camcor Inc, pg 715

OHIO

Midwest Photo Exchange, pg 827

PENNSYLVANIA

Audio Visions Inc, pg 694
Bernie's Photo Center, pg 704
Brodart Co, pg 711
The Lerro Corp, pg 806

TENNESSEE

Memphis Communications Corp, pg 823

TEXAS

AVES Audio Visual Systems Inc, pg 698
Cinema Antiques, pg 723
Pro Video & Film Equipment Co Inc, pg 863

VIRGINIA

Lee Hartman & Sons Inc, pg 805

WASHINGTON

Inland Audio Visual Co, pg 788
Oppenheimer Camera Products, pg 847

WISCONSIN

Camera Corner Connecting Point, pg 715

Movie & Still Camera Manufacturers

CALIFORNIA

ARRI Inc, pg 689
Birns & Sawyer Inc, pg 706

Alan Gordon Enterprises Inc, pg 772
Preston Cinema Systems, pg 861
Pro8mm, pg 862

NEW JERSEY

CELCO, pg 719
Leica Camera Inc, pg 806

NEW YORK

Canon USA Inc, pg 716
ELMO USA Corp, pg 753
Sigma Corp of America, pg 887

ONTARIO

IMAX Corp, pg 786

Movie & Still Camera Rentals

ALASKA

Connections Film & Video Inc, pg 731

ARIZONA

Arizona Cine Equipment, pg 688
Merestone, pg 823
Reel Men Rentals Inc, pg 872

CALIFORNIA

Alternative Rentals, pg 682
Artichoke Productions, pg 690
Birns & Sawyer Inc, pg 706
Blue Lotus Temple Studio, pg 707
CamTec Motion Picture Cameras, pg 715
Chater Camera Inc, pg 721
Cinema Camera Rentals, pg 723
Express Video Supply Inc, pg 757
Gear Monkey, pg 769
Gold Standard Productions, pg 772
Alan Gordon Enterprises Inc, pg 772
Greenery Studios, pg 774
Illuminate Studios, pg 784
Imagecraft Productions, pg 785
Main Street Media Inc, pg 815
Otto Nemenz International Inc, pg 838
Old School Cameras, pg 844
Panavision, pg 850
Porter Productions, pg 859
Pro8mm, pg 862
Pro HD Rentals, pg 863
Shoulder High Productions, pg 886
Stray Angel Films, pg 902
The Studios at Paramount, pg 903
T-stop Inc, pg 906

COLORADO

Mike's Camera, pg 827

FLORIDA

AVI-SPL, pg 698
CineVideotech Inc, pg 725
Steven Cohen Motion Picture Production, pg 727
CopShopMiami.com, pg 731
Jordan Klein Film & Video (JKFV), pg 795

ILLINOIS

Helix Camera & Video, pg 778
Magnanimous Media, pg 814
RC Communications, pg 870
2nd Cine Inc, pg 883

INDIANA

Gary Camera & Digital, pg 768
OMNI Productions, pg 845

KENTUCKY

Idle Minds Productions Inc, pg 784

LOUISIANA

Digital FX Inc, pg 742
Moxie Media, pg 832

MARYLAND

Kramer Communications Video Production, pg 801
RTZ Audio Visual, pg 878

MASSACHUSETTS

Green Mountain Post Films (GMP), pg 774

MINNESOTA

AVI Systems, pg 698
Cinequipt Inc, pg 724
House of Cinemagraphics, pg 782

MISSISSIPPI

Jasper Ewing & Sons Inc, pg 757

MISSOURI

Show-Me Audio-Visual, pg 887

NEVADA

MG Studio, pg 825

NEW HAMPSHIRE

Apertura, pg 686

NEW JERSEY

Audio Visual Dynamics®, pg 694

NEW YORK

Adorama Rental Co, pg 676
Big Apple Films, pg 705
Bond Street Studio, pg 708
Cinema-Vision, pg 724
Colortone Audio Visual, pg 728
CPT Rental Inc, pg 732
Digital Arts NY, pg 742
Gearhead Rentals, pg 769
Hand Held Films, pg 775
Langie Audio Visual Systems, pg 803
LightHouse Films, pg 807
LightSpace Studios, pg 808
Manhattan Center Studios Inc, pg 816
Motion Picture Enterprises Inc, pg 831
Olden Camera & Lens Co Inc, pg 845
Visual Technologies Corp, pg 932

NORTH CAROLINA

JDC Wilmington Camera Services, pg 793

NORTH DAKOTA

Media Productions, pg 822

OHIO

Ohio HD Video, pg 844

OREGON

Koerner Camera Systems, pg 800
Northwest Film Center, pg 842
Picture This Production Services, pg 856

PENNSYLVANIA

Audio Visions Inc, pg 694
Bernie's Photo Center, pg 704
Location Camera Ltd, pg 810
Location Lighting Ltd, pg 810
Videosmith Inc, pg 930

TENNESSEE

Memphis Communications Corp, pg 823
RentACamera.com, pg 873

TEXAS

Earl Miller Productions Inc, pg 827
Phillips Media Source, pg 855
Texcam Inc, pg 911

UTAH

Ron Hill Imagery, pg 780
Redman Movies & Stories, pg 872

VERMONT

Marlboro Productions, pg 817

VIRGINIA

Projection, pg 865

WASHINGTON

Oppenheimer Camera Products, pg 847

WISCONSIN

University of Wisconsin-Oshkosh Radio-TV-Film Dept, pg 923
Wisconsin Public Television, pg 940

WYOMING

Bridger Productions Inc, pg 710

ALBERTA

Global TV, pg 771
McBain Camera Ltd, pg 820

MANITOBA

MidCanada Production Services Inc (MidCan), pg 826

ONTARIO

IMAX Corp, pg 786
JIB Shots Equipment Inc, pg 794
Kingsway Motion Picture Inc, pg 799
SIM Digital, pg 888
William F White International Inc, pg 937

Movie & Still Camera Repairs

CALIFORNIA

ARRI Inc, pg 689
Birns & Sawyer Inc, pg 706
Alan Gordon Enterprises Inc, pg 772
McAlister Electronics, pg 820
Pro Camera Repair, pg 862
Pro8mm, pg 862
Visual Instrumentation Corp, pg 931

COLORADO

Mike's Camera, pg 827

CONNECTICUT

Precision Camera & Video Repair Inc, pg 861

INDIANA

Gary Camera & Digital, pg 768

MARYLAND

RTZ Audio Visual, pg 878

MINNESOTA

AVI Systems, pg 698

NEW YORK

AZ Spectrum, pg 700
Colortone Audio Visual, pg 728
CPT Rental Inc, pg 732
ELMO USA Corp, pg 753
Langie Audio Visual Systems, pg 803
Mamiya, pg 815
Motion Picture Enterprises Inc, pg 831
Sigma Corp of America, pg 887

PENNSYLVANIA

Bernie's Photo Center, pg 704

TENNESSEE

Memphis Communications Corp, pg 823

WASHINGTON

Oppenheimer Camera Products, pg 847

WISCONSIN

Camera Corner Connecting Point, pg 715

Multiplexer Equipment, *see* Chain & Multiplexer Equipment

Music Scoring

ALABAMA

Airwave Recording Studio, pg 679
Sound of Birmingham Productions, pg 894

ARIZONA

Creative Backstage, pg 733
Merestone, pg 823

ARKANSAS

Live'N'Loud, pg 810

CALIFORNIA

AB Audio Visual Entertainment Inc, pg 672
Aliso Creek Productions Inc, pg 680
Berkeley Sound Artists Inc, pg 704
Creative Media Recording, pg 733
Creative Support Services/CSS Music, pg 733
Creative Technology, pg 733
Crystal Pyramid Productions™, pg 735

Diamond Dreams Music Productions, pg 741
Earwax Productions Inc, pg 749
4th Street Recording, pg 764
GrooveWorx, pg 774
Havas Edge, pg 777
iCorpTv, pg 783
Kaleidosound, pg 796
Lynch Communications, pg 813
Maximus Media Inc, pg 820
The Media Staff Inc, pg 822
Megatrax, pg 823
New & Unique Videos™, pg 839
OTR Studios, pg 848
Palardo Productions, pg 850
Polarity Post Production, pg 858
Private Island Audio Inc, pg 862
Pyramid Studios, pg 867
QRS Software Services, pg 867
Regent Press Publishers & Printers, pg 873
Russ InVision Co/AbridgeClub.com, pg 879
Sahara Records & Filmworks Entertainment Co, pg 879
Sonic Gravy, pg 892
SonicPool, pg 892
Studio 132, pg 902
Timeless Productions, pg 914
Total Creative, pg 916
West Coast Projections Inc, pg 935

COLORADO

Tim Cissell Music, pg 725
Conly Productions, pg 730
Flashback Media Productions, pg 762

DELAWARE

Side Door Studio Inc, pg 887

DISTRICT OF COLUMBIA

Interface Media Group, pg 789

FLORIDA

Kat Epple Music Productions, pg 755
Mach 1 Productions, pg 813
Sunfire Communications Inc, pg 904

GEORGIA

First Cut Communications LLC, pg 761
White Dog Studios, pg 937

HAWAII

Media Bridge Gamekids, pg 821

ILLINOIS

ABS Enterprises, pg 672
Mightybytes Inc, pg 827
Jim Passin Productions, pg 852
Pepper Group, pg 854
Steven Samler Music & Sound, pg 879

INDIANA

OMNI Productions, pg 845

KENTUCKY

Horizon Films & Media LLC, pg 781
The Media Collaboratory, pg 821

LOUISIANA

Disk Productions Inc, pg 743

MARYLAND

dbF a Media Company, pg 739
Kramer Communications Video Production, pg 801
Satellite Media Production, pg 881

MASSACHUSETTS

Green Mountain Post Films (GMP), pg 774
Northern Light Productions (NLP), pg 842
Penfield Productions Ltd, pg 853
Soundtrack Group, pg 895
TR Productions, pg 916

MICHIGAN

Digi Sign Design LLC, pg 741
GMP Music, pg 772
K&R's Recording Studios Inc, pg 796
Michigan Recording Arts Institute & Technologies, pg 825

MONTANA

Jereco Studios Inc, pg 793

NEVADA

Tanglewood Productions, pg 907

NEW JERSEY

Milbrodt/Music & Sound Design, pg 827
Milgrom Productions, pg 827
NFL Films Music Library, pg 841
Richard Reiter Productions Inc, pg 873
Suede Interactive, pg 903
TRF Production Music Libraries, pg 917

NEW YORK

Air Sea Land Productions Inc (ASL), pg 678
aurora productions, pg 696
Big Fish Production US, pg 705
Fingerpaint, pg 761
HB-Content, pg 777
Headroom Digital Audio, pg 777
Heavy Melody, pg 778
Icontent, pg 783
KAS Music & Sound, pg 796
Manhattan Production Music Inc, pg 816
Jack Morton Worldwide, pg 830
Mother West, pg 831
New York Audio Productions, pg 840
The Palmer Group, pg 850
Peckham Productions Inc, pg 852
David Rapkin Audio Production, pg 870
Elliot Sokolov Music, pg 892
Sony Music Entertainment, pg 893
Tiki Recording Studios Inc, pg 914
Zelman Studios Ltd, pg 945

NORTH CAROLINA

Audio Art, pg 693
Horizon Video Productions Inc, pg 781
Trailblazer Studios®, pg 917
2BruceStudio, pg 920

OHIO

Challenge Productions/Challenge Aerial Imaging, pg 720
Mills James Productions, pg 828

OREGON

Odyssey Productions Inc, pg 844

PENNSYLVANIA

Dreambox Media Inc, pg 746
Monster Tracks, pg 829
WPHL-TV, pg 942

RHODE ISLAND

Sound-FX-Design, pg 894

TENNESSEE

American Blackguard Inc, pg 683
Continental Film, pg 731
Fricon Entertainment Co Inc, pg 766
Motion Picture Services, pg 831
Stage Post, pg 899
Zion Music Group, pg 945

TEXAS

Anaphora Literary Press, pg 685
Audiomoxie®, pg 695
Communication Arts Multimedia Inc, pg 728
The Sound Lab Inc, pg 894
Sound Works, pg 894
Stage Directions, pg 898
TM Studios Inc, pg 915
Tropikal Productions, pg 918

UTAH

Soularium Recording Studios, pg 893

VERMONT

University of Vermont, Instructional Television Dept, pg 923

VIRGINIA

BES Studios, pg 704
Mark Sonder Productions & Entertainment Agency, pg 817

WASHINGTON

Hamilton Studio, pg 775
Inland Audio Visual Co, pg 788
Kostov Productions, pg 801
North-by-Northwest - A Digital Studio, pg 842
Sound Sound, pg 894

WEST VIRGINIA

Sweetsong Productions, pg 905

WISCONSIN

5th Floor Recording Co, pg 760
USAV Group Inc, pg 923

WYOMING

Bridger Productions Inc, pg 710

BRITISH COLUMBIA

Pinewood Sound, pg 857

MANITOBA

DACAPO Productions Inc, pg 737

ONTARIO

ADS Media, pg 677
Metalworks Recording Studios Inc, pg 824

FILM

Music Scoring (continued)

QUEBEC

Muse Entertainment Enterprises, pg 834

Optical Effects, *see* Special Effects

Optical Printing

CALIFORNIA

Crystal Pyramid Productions™, pg 735
Goal Productions, pg 772
iCorpTv, pg 783
Palardo Productions, pg 850
piXvfm Inc, pg 857
QRS Software Services, pg 867
SonicPool, pg 892

NEW HAMPSHIRE

Apertura, pg 686

NEW JERSEY

CELCO, pg 719

NEW YORK

Black Star Publishing Co Inc, pg 706
Gage-Line Technology Inc, pg 767
Ketchum Inc, pg 798
R/GA, pg 868

OHIO

Vista Color Imaging Inc, pg 931

PENNSYLVANIA

John E Allen Inc, pg 680

TENNESSEE

Motion Picture Services, pg 831
Stage Post, pg 899

TEXAS

Stage Directions, pg 898

WASHINGTON

Inland Audio Visual Co, pg 788

WISCONSIN

USAV Group Inc, pg 923

BRITISH COLUMBIA

Pinewood Sound, pg 857

Photographic Equipment & Supply Distributors

ARIZONA

Docter Optics Inc, pg 744
Professional Marketing Services Inc, pg 865
Troxell-CDI, pg 918

ARKANSAS

Carlton-Bates Co, pg 717

CALIFORNIA

Backdrop Outlet, pg 700
Birns & Sawyer Inc, pg 706
Camera Essentials, pg 715
CinemaGear, pg 724
DTC Lighting & Grip, pg 747
Filmtools®, pg 761
Freestyle Photographic Supplies, pg 765
Gluskin's Custom Audio Video, pg 771
Alan Gordon Enterprises Inc, pg 772
Hooper Camera & Imaging, pg 781
J & R Film Co, pg 792
Kenko Tokina USA, pg 797
LEE Filters, pg 805
Matthews Studio Equipment Inc, pg 820
Mole-Richardson Co, pg 829
Noritsu America Corp, pg 842
Promax Systems, pg 865
Qioptiq, An Excelitas Technologies Company, pg 867
The Rip-Tie Co, pg 875
Thermodyne Cases, pg 912

COLORADO

Goldberg Brothers Inc, pg 772
Stanco Sales LLC, pg 899

CONNECTICUT

Connecticut Audio & Theatrical Supply, pg 731
Kenyon Laboratories LLC, pg 798

FLORIDA

Harmon's Audio-Visual Services, pg 776
Lumedyne Inc, pg 812
Photosol Inc, pg 856
Tallahassee Audio Visual, pg 906
Techni-Lux Inc, pg 908

GEORGIA

Audio Visual Resources Inc, pg 695

IDAHO

Idaho Camera Inc, pg 784

ILLINOIS

Facets Multi-Media Inc, pg 758
FUJIFILM Graphic Systems Division, pg 766
Leedal Inc, pg 805
Lipsner-Smith Co, pg 809
Photoflex Inc, pg 856
Smith-Victor Corp, pg 891
Speedotron Corp, pg 897
Urbanski Film, pg 923

LOUISIANA

Available Lighting & Motion Picture Services Inc, pg 697

MARYLAND

OmegaBrandess Distribution, pg 845
RTZ Audio Visual, pg 878

MASSACHUSETTS

Hunt's Photo & Video, pg 782
Lineco, pg 809
Visual Departures Ltd, pg 931

MICHIGAN

Lacquer-Mat Inc, pg 803
Lowing Light & Grip Inc, pg 812

MINNESOTA

Alpha Video & Audio Inc, pg 682
AVI Systems, pg 698
Cinequipt Inc, pg 724

MISSISSIPPI

Jasper Ewing & Sons Inc, pg 757

MISSOURI

Schiller's Audio-Visual, pg 881

MONTANA

Photographers' Formulary Inc, pg 856

NEBRASKA

Images II Inc, pg 785

NEVADA

Aardvark Video & Media Productions, pg 671
Bulbman Inc, pg 712

NEW JERSEY

Agfa Graphics, pg 678
AlltecPro, pg 681
Argraph Corp, pg 688
AV Bluebook, pg 696
Caprock Developments Inc, pg 716
Hasselblad Bron Inc, pg 776
Leica Camera Inc, pg 806
Manfrotto Distribution Inc, pg 816
Pioneer Research Inc, pg 857
Ritz Camera & Image, pg 875
ToCad America Inc, pg 915

NEW YORK

Barbizon Electric Co Inc, pg 701
Bulbtronics Inc, pg 712
Century Business Solutions, pg 720
Colortone Audio Visual, pg 728
Eastman Kodak Co, pg 750
Gage-Line Technology Inc, pg 767
Get Smart Products, pg 770
Just Bulbs - The Light Bulb Store, pg 795
Langie Audio Visual Systems, pg 803
Light Impressions, pg 807
MAC Group, pg 813
Motion Picture Enterprises Inc, pg 831
Neptune Photo Inc, pg 838
Nikon Inc, pg 841
Olden Camera & Lens Co Inc, pg 845
PASCO, pg 851
Precision Microproducts of America, pg 861
Production Resource Group LLC (PRG), pg 864
Ray Supply Inc, pg 870
RTS Inc, pg 878
Schneider Optics Inc, pg 881
Scientifics Direct Inc, pg 882
Sigma Corp of America, pg 887
The Tiffen Co LLC, pg 914
Tri-Ed Distribution Inc, pg 918
Vincent Associates, pg 930
Visual Technologies Corp, pg 932
Willoughby's® Camera, pg 939

NORTH CAROLINA

Camcor Inc, pg 715

OREGON

Pacific Grip & Lighting Inc, pg 849

PENNSYLVANIA

Audio Visions Inc, pg 694
Bernie's Photo Center, pg 704
Charles Beseler Co, pg 721
Electron Microscopy Sciences (EMS), pg 752
Garcia Marketing Inc, pg 768
Innovision Media Group, pg 788
The Lerro Corp, pg 806
Visual Sound Inc, pg 931
VWR International LLC, pg 933

TENNESSEE

Memphis Communications Corp, pg 823

TEXAS

Audio Visual Technologies Group (AVTG), pg 695
Olden Lighting, pg 845
Video Associates Labs Inc, pg 927

UTAH

Redman Movies & Stories, pg 872
Webb Audio Visual, pg 935

VIRGINIA

Lee Hartman & Sons Inc, pg 805

WASHINGTON

Inland Audio Visual Co, pg 788
Oppenheimer Camera Products, pg 847
Proforma Good Wood Marketing, pg 865

WISCONSIN

Alpha Source Inc, pg 681
Camera Corner Connecting Point, pg 715
Indus International Inc, pg 787
Regal Photo Products Inc/Arkay Corp, pg 873
Safe Harbor Computers, pg 879

BRITISH COLUMBIA

Specialty Bulb Products Inc, pg 896

ONTARIO

Henry's Camera, pg 779

Photographic Equipment & Supply Manufacturers

CALIFORNIA

Backdrop Outlet, pg 700
California Stainless Manufacturing Inc, pg 714
Camera Essentials, pg 715
Cinema Xenon International Inc, pg 724
CinemaGear.com, pg 724
Filmtools®, pg 761
Alan Gordon Enterprises Inc, pg 772
Hooper Camera & Imaging, pg 781
LEE Filters, pg 805
Matthews Studio Equipment Inc, pg 820
Mole-Richardson Co, pg 829
Noritsu America Corp, pg 842
O'Connor Engineering Labs, pg 844

Qioptiq, An Excelitas Technologies
Company, pg 867
The Rip-Tie Co, pg 875
Stewart Filmscreen Corp, pg 901
Thermodyne Cases, pg 912

COLORADO

Goldberg Brothers Inc, pg 772

CONNECTICUT

Kenyon Laboratories LLC, pg 798

FLORIDA

Kinetronics Corp, pg 799
Lumedyne Inc, pg 812
Magna-Tech Electronic Co Inc,
pg 814
Photosol Inc, pg 856
Print File Inc, pg 862

GEORGIA

Lighting & Production Equipment
Inc, pg 807

ILLINOIS

Kart-A-Bag Manufacturing Inc,
pg 796
Leedal Inc, pg 805
Photoflex Inc, pg 856
Quantum Instruments Inc, pg 868
Smith-Victor Corp, pg 891
Speedotron Corp, pg 897

INDIANA

Star Case Manufacturing Co Inc,
pg 900
Stouffer Graphic Arts, pg 901

MARYLAND

OmegaBrandess Distribution,
pg 845

MASSACHUSETTS

Lineco, pg 809
Solutek Corp, pg 892
Visual Departures Ltd, pg 931

MICHIGAN

X-Rite, pg 942

NEVADA

Lensless Camera Manufacturing Co,
pg 806

NEW JERSEY

Konica Minolta Business Solutions,
pg 801
Leica Camera Inc, pg 806
Pioneer Research Inc, pg 857
Pro-Tape & Specialities Inc, pg 863
Sofradir EC, pg 892
ToCad America Inc, pg 915
Unilux Inc, pg 921

NEW YORK

Century Business Solutions, pg 720
Gage-Line Technology Inc, pg 767
Gagne Inc, pg 767
Nikon Inc, pg 841
Precision Microproducts of
America, pg 861
Schneider Optics Inc, pg 881
Sigma Corp of America, pg 887
Sima Products Corp, pg 888
Tamron USA Inc, pg 906

The Tiffen Co LLC, pg 914
Vincent Associates, pg 930

OKLAHOMA

Dunning Photo Equipment Inc,
pg 747
ESECO Speedmaster, pg 755

OREGON

Rockland Colloid LLC, pg 876

PENNSYLVANIA

Beseler Photo, pg 704
Charles Beseler Co, pg 721
Electron Microscopy Sciences
(EMS), pg 752
IDenticard Systems Inc, pg 784
Tobias Associates Inc, pg 915

RHODE ISLAND

Sihl Inc, pg 888

WISCONSIN

Bardes Products Inc, pg 702
Indus International Inc, pg 787
Photo Tech Inc, pg 856
Regal Photo Products Inc/Arkay
Corp, pg 873

ONTARIO

DW Electrochemicals Ltd, pg 748
FUJIFILM Canada Inc, pg 766
Osram Sylvania Ltd/Ltee, pg 848

Photographic Equipment & Supply Rentals

ARIZONA

Reel Men Rentals Inc, pg 872

CALIFORNIA

Artichoke Productions, pg 690
Backdrop Outlet, pg 700
Birns & Sawyer Inc, pg 706
Gluskin's Custom Audio Video,
pg 771
Hooper Camera & Imaging, pg 781
Main Street Media Inc, pg 815
Mole-Richardson Co, pg 829
Photographic Rental Service Inc
(PRS), pg 856
Samy's Camera, pg 879
Straight Shoot'r Cranes Inc, pg 901
Total Creative, pg 916

CONNECTICUT

Kenyon Laboratories LLC, pg 798

FLORIDA

Jordan Klein Film & Video (JKFV),
pg 795
Tallahassee Audio Visual, pg 906

ILLINOIS

Helix Camera & Video, pg 778

INDIANA

Gary Camera & Digital, pg 768
Jack's Camera Shop, pg 792
OMNI Productions, pg 845

KENTUCKY

Idle Minds Productions Inc, pg 784

LOUISIANA

Available Lighting & Motion
Picture Services Inc, pg 697

MARYLAND

RTZ Audio Visual, pg 878

MASSACHUSETTS

The Boston Connection Inc, pg 709

MICHIGAN

Lowing Light & Grip Inc, pg 812

MINNESOTA

AVI Systems, pg 698

MISSISSIPPI

Jasper Ewing & Sons Inc, pg 757

MISSOURI

Schiller's Audio-Visual, pg 881
Show-Me Audio-Visual, pg 887

NEW HAMPSHIRE

Apertura, pg 686

NEW JERSEY

Unilux Inc, pg 921

NEW YORK

Available Light, pg 697
Colortone Audio Visual, pg 728
Langie Audio Visual Systems,
pg 803
Manhattan Center Studios Inc,
pg 816
Motion Picture Enterprises Inc,
pg 831
Production Resource Group LLC
(PRG), pg 864

NORTH DAKOTA

Media Productions, pg 822

OHIO

Vista Color Imaging Inc, pg 931

OREGON

Pacific Grip & Lighting Inc, pg 849

PENNSYLVANIA

Audio Visions Inc, pg 694
Bernie's Photo Center, pg 704
Innovision Media Group, pg 788

TENNESSEE

Memphis Communications Corp,
pg 823

TEXAS

Olden Lighting, pg 845
Studio Thirteen11, pg 903
Texcam Inc, pg 911

UTAH

Redman Movies & Stories, pg 872
Webb Audio Visual, pg 935

VIRGINIA

Lee Hartman & Sons Inc, pg 805

WASHINGTON

Inland Audio Visual Co, pg 788
Oppenheimer Camera Products,
pg 847

ALBERTA

Global TV, pg 771
McBain Camera Ltd, pg 820

Photographic Equipment & Supply Repairs

ARIZONA

PROCAM, pg 863

CALIFORNIA

Gluskin's Custom Audio Video,
pg 771
Hooper Camera & Imaging, pg 781
Matthews Studio Equipment Inc,
pg 820
Mole-Richardson Co, pg 829
Photographic Rental Service Inc
(PRS), pg 856
Pro Camera Repair, pg 862

CONNECTICUT

Precision Camera & Video Repair
Inc, pg 861

FLORIDA

Tallahassee Audio Visual, pg 906

INDIANA

Gary Camera & Digital, pg 768

MARYLAND

OmegaBrandess Distribution,
pg 845
RTZ Audio Visual, pg 878

MASSACHUSETTS

The Boston Connection Inc, pg 709

MICHIGAN

Lowing Light & Grip Inc, pg 812

MINNESOTA

AVI Systems, pg 698

MISSOURI

Schiller's Audio-Visual, pg 881

NEW JERSEY

Hasselblad Bron Inc, pg 776
Konica Minolta Business Solutions,
pg 801
Leica Camera Inc, pg 806
ToCad America Inc, pg 915

NEW YORK

Colortone Audio Visual, pg 728
Langie Audio Visual Systems,
pg 803
MAC Group, pg 813
Nikon Inc, pg 841
Precision Microproducts of
America, pg 861
Production Resource Group LLC
(PRG), pg 864
Schneider Optics Inc, pg 881
Sigma Corp of America, pg 887

FILM

Photographic Equipment & Supply Repairs (continued)

NORTH CAROLINA

Camcor Inc, pg 715

PENNSYLVANIA

Bernie's Photo Center, pg 704
IDenticard Systems Inc, pg 784

TENNESSEE

Memphis Communications Corp, pg 823

VIRGINIA

Lee Hartman & Sons Inc, pg 805

WASHINGTON

Oppenheimer Camera Products, pg 847

WISCONSIN

Camera Corner Connecting Point, pg 715

Photography—Aerial

ALABAMA

Diamond Studios, pg 741

ALASKA

Connections Film & Video Inc, pg 731

ARIZONA

Aardvark Productions LLC, pg 671

CALIFORNIA

Action Sports/All Stock, pg 675
Classic Images Stock Footage LLC, pg 726
Concrete Images, pg 730
Creative Technology, pg 733
Crystal Pyramid Productions™, pg 735
Custom Video Productions Inc, pg 736
Dolphin MultiMedia Inc, pg 745
Goal Productions, pg 772
Gold Standard Productions, pg 772
iCorpTv, pg 783
Indie Aerials, pg 787
Joan Kramer & Associates Inc, pg 801
KTVU-Retail Services, pg 802
MacGillivray Freeman Films Inc, pg 813
Moving Art by Louie Schwartzberg, pg 831
Nineteen87, pg 841
Palardo Productions, pg 850
PK Productions, pg 857
Point of View Productions, pg 858
QRS Software Services, pg 867
Dick Reizner Film & Video, pg 873
RetinaVision Productions, pg 874
SpaceCam, pg 896
Stunt Wings Adventure Sports Talent & Equipment, pg 903
Total Creative, pg 916
Two Door Productions LLC, pg 920
Tyler Camera Systems, pg 920
WARPed Pictures, pg 934

COLORADO

Flashback Media Productions, pg 762
Greg Hensley Productions, pg 779
Tatum Video, pg 907
Transtar Entertainment Co Inc, pg 917

CONNECTICUT

Digital Video Productions, pg 742
MAVCO, pg 820
Skyviews Survey Inc, pg 890

FLORIDA

America By Air LLC, pg 682
Bill Bachmann Studios, pg 705
Civins Productions Inc, pg 725
Steven Cohen Motion Picture Production, pg 727
Communications Concepts Inc (CCI), pg 729
Jordan Klein Film & Video (JKFV), pg 795
Norman Kent Productions, pg 798
Paradise Video & Film, pg 851
Roger Scruggs Films, pg 883
Shooting Stars Post Inc, pg 886
Sunrise Studios, pg 904
SuperStock Inc, pg 904

GEORGIA

Guerrilla Productions LLC, pg 774
Visioneering International Inc, pg 931

HAWAII

1013 Integrated, pg 911

IDAHO

Rex Morris Productions, pg 830

ILLINOIS

ABS Enterprises, pg 672
WEEK TV, pg 935

INDIANA

OMNI Productions, pg 845

IOWA

Educational Technology & Media Services, pg 751

KENTUCKY

Idle Minds Productions Inc, pg 784

LOUISIANA

Digital FX Inc, pg 742
Moxie Media, pg 832

MARYLAND

Richard Chisolm Cinematography, pg 722
Kramer Communications Video Production, pg 801

MASSACHUSETTS

Cramer, pg 732
Green Mountain Post Films (GMP), pg 774
Heliotrope Studios, pg 778
Northern Light Productions (NLP), pg 842
Penfield Productions Ltd, pg 853
Frank Siteman Photography, pg 889

MICHIGAN

Digi Sign Design LLC, pg 741

MINNESOTA

Badiyan Inc, pg 700
House of Cinemagraphics, pg 782

MISSOURI

Visionworks Design Services Inc, pg 931

NEVADA

DVDs4Less, pg 748

NEW HAMPSHIRE

Apertura, pg 686

NEW JERSEY

Allegro Productions Inc, pg 680

NEW YORK

aurora productions, pg 696
Broadstreet Productions LLC, pg 711
Buffalo Video Production, pg 712
Hover-Views Unlimited, pg 782
La Paloma Films, pg 803
Jack Morton Worldwide, pg 830
Museum of the City of New York, pg 834
The Old Rhinebeck Aerodome®, pg 844
Peckham Productions Inc, pg 852
R/GA, pg 868
Split Image Productions, pg 898
Zelman Studios Ltd, pg 945

NORTH CAROLINA

The Communications Group Inc, pg 729
Horizon Video Productions Inc, pg 781
K2 Productions, pg 802
On Location North Carolina, pg 846
Take One Productions Ltd, pg 906

NORTH DAKOTA

Media Productions, pg 822

OHIO

Challenge Productions/Challenge Aerial Imaging, pg 720
Lyon Video Inc, pg 813
Mills James Productions, pg 828
Thread Marketing Group, pg 913
Vista Color Imaging Inc, pg 931

OKLAHOMA

Academic Media & Digital Services, pg 672

OREGON

Odyssey Productions Inc, pg 844

PENNSYLVANIA

Argentine Productions Inc, pg 688
Berry & Homer, pg 704
Innovision Media Group, pg 788
JPL, pg 795
Production Masters Inc (PMI), pg 864

SOUTH CAROLINA

Genesis Creative, pg 769
Venture Media, pg 925

TENNESSEE

Continental Film, pg 731
Motion Picture Services, pg 831
Phoenix Aerial Photography Inc, pg 855
Scripps Networks, pg 882
Stage Post, pg 899

TEXAS

Alexander Media Productions, pg 679
AMS Pictures, pg 684
Castleview Productions, pg 717
Communication Arts Multimedia Inc, pg 728
Fugro, pg 766
Horizon Film + Video Productions, pg 781
Inferno Films, pg 787
McNee Productions Inc, pg 821
Earl Miller Productions Inc, pg 827
Julye Newlin Productions Inc, pg 840
Phillips Media Source, pg 855
The Samuels Co, pg 879
South Coast Film & Video, pg 895
Stage Directions, pg 898
Stockyard Photos/Jim Olive Photography, pg 901

VERMONT

University of Vermont, Instructional Television Dept, pg 923

VIRGINIA

Advance Concepts Inc, pg 677
CACI Integrated Communications, pg 713
HeloAir Inc, pg 778
Metro Productions, pg 824
Lynda Richardson Photography, pg 875

WASHINGTON

North-by-Northwest - A Digital Studio, pg 842
Oppenheimer Camera Products, pg 847
White Rain Films Ltd, pg 937

WISCONSIN

Audio Visual of Milwaukee Inc, pg 694
USAV Group Inc, pg 923
Wisconsin Public Television, pg 940

WYOMING

Bridger Productions Inc, pg 710

ALBERTA

Black Media Works, pg 706

NORTHWEST TERRITORIES

Yellowknife Films Inc, pg 944

ONTARIO

GAPC (General Assembly Production Centre), pg 768
L-3 WESCAM, pg 802

Photography—Location

ALABAMA

Diamond Studios, pg 741

FILM

Photography—Location (continued)

TEXAS (continued)
Stockyard Photos/Jim Olive Photography, pg 901
Texas Heart Institute Visual Communication Services, pg 911

VERMONT
Marlboro Productions, pg 817

VIRGINIA
Advance Concepts Inc, pg 677
BES Studios, pg 704
CACI Integrated Communications, pg 713
Metro Productions, pg 824
Lynda Richardson Photography, pg 875

WASHINGTON
Hamilton Studio, pg 775
North-by-Northwest - A Digital Studio, pg 842
Oppenheimer Camera Products, pg 847
Pal Productions Inc, pg 850
White Rain Films Ltd, pg 937

WEST VIRGINIA
MotionMasters, pg 831

WISCONSIN
Audio Visual of Milwaukee Inc, pg 694
Logan Productions Inc, pg 811
Meridian Studios, pg 824
University of Wisconsin-Oshkosh Radio-TV-Film Dept, pg 923
USAV Group Inc, pg 923
Video Wisconsin Inc, pg 929
Watts Communications Inc, pg 934
Wisconsin Public Television, pg 940

WYOMING
Bridger Productions Inc, pg 710

ALBERTA
Black Media Works, pg 706
Global TV, pg 771

NORTHWEST TERRITORIES
Yellowknife Films Inc, pg 944

ONTARIO
ADS Media, pg 677
Doomsday Studios Limited, pg 745
GAPC (General Assembly Production Centre), pg 768

QUEBEC
Muse Entertainment Enterprises, pg 834

Photography—Slow Motion

ALABAMA
Diamond Studios, pg 741

ALASKA
Connections Film & Video Inc, pg 731

ARIZONA
Metropolitan Audio-Visual Inc, pg 824

CALIFORNIA
A Go Go Films, pg 671
Action Sports/All Stock, pg 675
CinemaGear.com, pg 724
Classic Images Stock Footage LLC, pg 726
Concrete Images, pg 730
Creative Technology, pg 733
Crystal Pyramid Productions™, pg 735
Goal Productions, pg 772
Havas Edge, pg 777
iCorpTv, pg 783
Jaguar Distribution Corp, pg 792
Keslow Camera Inc, pg 798
Moving Art by Louie Schwartzberg, pg 831
New Circuit Films LLC, pg 839
Nineteen87, pg 841
Palardo Productions, pg 850
Photo-Sonics Inc, pg 856
QRS Software Services, pg 867
Dick Reizner Film & Video, pg 873
RetinaVision Productions, pg 874
Still N' Motion, pg 901
Total Creative, pg 916
Visual Instrumentation Corp, pg 931
WARPed Pictures, pg 934

COLORADO
Flashback Media Productions, pg 762
Greg Hensley Productions, pg 779
Tatum Video, pg 907

FLORIDA
Civins Productions Inc, pg 725
Steven Cohen Motion Picture Production, pg 727
Communications Concepts Inc (CCI), pg 729
CopShopMiami.com, pg 731
Jordan Klein Film & Video (JKFV), pg 795

GEORGIA
Guerrilla Productions LLC, pg 774

ILLINOIS
WEEK TV, pg 935

INDIANA
A-V-A Video Productions, pg 671

IOWA
Educational Technology & Media Services, pg 751

LOUISIANA
Digital FX Inc, pg 742
Moxie Media, pg 832

MARYLAND
Richard Chisolm Cinematography, pg 722
Kramer Communications Video Production, pg 801

MASSACHUSETTS
Green Mountain Post Films (GMP), pg 774
Heliotrope Studios, pg 778
Northern Light Productions (NLP), pg 842

MICHIGAN
Digi Sign Design LLC, pg 741

MINNESOTA
Badiyan Inc, pg 700
House of Cinemagraphics, pg 782

MISSOURI
Avatar Studios, pg 697

NEVADA
DVDs4Less, pg 748

NEW HAMPSHIRE
Apertura, pg 686

NEW YORK
Broadstreet Productions LLC, pg 711
Buffalo Video Production, pg 712
Jack Morton Worldwide, pg 830
R/GA, pg 868

NORTH CAROLINA
Horizon Video Productions Inc, pg 781
Take One Productions Ltd, pg 906
Trailblazer Studios®, pg 917

NORTH DAKOTA
Media Productions, pg 822

OHIO
Challenge Productions/Challenge Aerial Imaging, pg 720

OKLAHOMA
Academic Media & Digital Services, pg 672

OREGON
Odyssey Productions Inc, pg 844

PENNSYLVANIA
Argentine Productions Inc, pg 688
Center City Film & Video Inc, pg 719
Innovision Media Group, pg 788
Production Masters Inc (PMI), pg 864

SOUTH CAROLINA
Venture Media, pg 925

TENNESSEE
Motion Picture Services, pg 831
Scripps Networks, pg 882
Stage Post, pg 899

TEXAS
Castleview Productions, pg 717
Horizon Film + Video Productions, pg 781
Inferno Films, pg 787
The Samuels Co, pg 879
Stage Directions, pg 898

VIRGINIA
BES Studios, pg 704
CACI Integrated Communications, pg 713
Metro Productions, pg 824

WASHINGTON
North-by-Northwest - A Digital Studio, pg 842
Oppenheimer Camera Products, pg 847
White Rain Films Ltd, pg 937

WISCONSIN
Video Wisconsin Inc, pg 929
Wisconsin Public Television, pg 940

WYOMING
Bridger Productions Inc, pg 710

ALBERTA
Global TV, pg 771

NORTHWEST TERRITORIES
Yellowknife Films Inc, pg 944

Photography—Studio

ALABAMA
Diamond Studios, pg 741

ALASKA
Connections Film & Video Inc, pg 731

ARIZONA
Aardvark Productions LLC, pg 671
Metropolitan Audio-Visual Inc, pg 824
Professional Marketing Services Inc, pg 865

CALIFORNIA
Artichoke Productions, pg 690
Concrete Images, pg 730
Creative Technology, pg 733
Crystal Pyramid Productions™, pg 735
deKramer Productions Inc, pg 740
Design Media, pg 741
Goal Productions, pg 772
Havas Edge, pg 777
iCorpTv, pg 783
Kavich Reynolds Productions Inc, pg 797
Keslow Camera Inc, pg 798
Joan Kramer & Associates Inc, pg 801
KTVU-Retail Services, pg 802
KVIE-Channel 6, pg 802
Main Street Media Inc, pg 815
The Media Staff Inc, pg 822
Moving Art by Louie Schwartzberg, pg 831
New Circuit Films LLC, pg 839
Nineteen87, pg 841
Opulen Studios, pg 847
Palardo Productions, pg 850
Point of View Productions, pg 858
James Porter Photography, pg 859
PSI Inc, pg 866
QRS Software Services, pg 867
Dick Reizner Film & Video, pg 873
RetinaVision Productions, pg 874
The Mack Sennett Studios, pg 883
Still N' Motion, pg 901
Stray Angel Films, pg 902

The Studio of David Inocencio, pg 911
Total Creative, pg 916
Warner Bros Entertainment Inc, pg 934
WARPed Pictures, pg 934
Wavemaker Media Design, pg 934

COLORADO

CSI Film & Video LLC, pg 735
Flashback Media Productions, pg 762
Greg Hensley Productions, pg 779

CONNECTICUT

MAVCO, pg 820
New London Media, pg 839

FLORIDA

Bill Bachmann Studios, pg 705
Civins Productions Inc, pg 725
Steven Cohen Motion Picture Production, pg 727
Communications Concepts Inc (CCI), pg 729
CopShopMiami.com, pg 731
The Great Southern Studios, pg 773
Jordan Klein Film & Video (JKFV), pg 795
Paradise Video & Film, pg 851
Shooting Stars Post Inc, pg 886
Sound*Light, pg 894
Sunrise Studios, pg 904
SuperStock Inc, pg 904
Tallahassee Photo & Frame, pg 906
Mike Vasilinda Productions Inc, pg 925

GEORGIA

Guerrilla Productions LLC, pg 774
Malcolm Neal Productions, pg 837

HAWAII

1013 Integrated, pg 911

ILLINOIS

Film Police, pg 760
Mightybytes Inc, pg 827
SCI Television & Creative Media LLC, pg 882
WEEK TV, pg 935

INDIANA

A-V-A Video Productions, pg 671

IOWA

Educational Technology & Media Services, pg 751

LOUISIANA

Digital FX Inc, pg 742
Moxie Media, pg 832

MARYLAND

DBM Communications Inc, pg 739
Kramer Communications Video Production, pg 801

MASSACHUSETTS

Cramer, pg 732
Heliotrope Studios, pg 778
National Boston, pg 836
Northern Light Productions (NLP), pg 842

MICHIGAN

Digi Sign Design LLC, pg 741
K&R's Recording Studios Inc, pg 796

MINNESOTA

Badiyan Inc, pg 700
House of Cinemagraphics, pg 782
Media Loft Inc, pg 822

MISSOURI

Avatar Studios, pg 697

MONTANA

Clarkson Studio, pg 726
KCFW Television, pg 797

NEVADA

DVDs4Less, pg 748

NEW HAMPSHIRE

Apertura, pg 686
Chip Taylor Communications LLC, pg 907

NEW JERSEY

C2 Imaging, pg 735
18 Label Studios, pg 751
Euro-Pacific Film & Video Productions Inc, pg 756
NFL Films Inc, pg 841
Allan Reider Photography & Video Productions, pg 873
Set To Go Studios, pg 884

NEW YORK

Bevilacqua Studios, pg 704
Big Film Design, pg 705
Black Star Publishing Co Inc, pg 706
Brian Film Productions LLC, pg 710
Broadstreet Productions LLC, pg 711
Buffalo Video Production, pg 712
HB-Content, pg 777
La Paloma Films, pg 803
MHS-TV, pg 825
Jack Morton Worldwide, pg 830
Museum of the City of New York, pg 834
New Horizon Studios, pg 839
Peckham Productions Inc, pg 852
R/GA, pg 868
Zelman Studios Ltd, pg 945

NORTH CAROLINA

The Communications Group Inc, pg 729
Horizon Video Productions Inc, pg 781
Image Associates Inc, pg 784
On Location North Carolina, pg 846
Take One Productions Ltd, pg 906
Trailblazer Studios®, pg 917

NORTH DAKOTA

Media Productions, pg 822

OHIO

Challenge Productions/Challenge Aerial Imaging, pg 720
Lyon Video Inc, pg 813
Mills James Productions, pg 828
Thread Marketing Group, pg 913

MICHIGAN

Treehaus Communications Inc, pg 917
Vista Color Imaging Inc, pg 931

OKLAHOMA

Academic Media & Digital Services, pg 672

OREGON

KTVA Productions, pg 802
Odyssey Productions Inc, pg 844

PENNSYLVANIA

Argentine Productions Inc, pg 688
Berry & Homer, pg 704
Center City Film & Video Inc, pg 719
Innovision Media Group, pg 788
JPL, pg 795
Production Masters Inc (PMI), pg 864

SOUTH CAROLINA

Genesis Creative, pg 769
Venture Media, pg 925

TENNESSEE

Motion Picture Services, pg 831
Scripps Networks, pg 882
Stage Post, pg 899
United Methodist Productions, pg 921

TEXAS

AMS Pictures, pg 684
Best Film & Video, pg 704
Castleview Productions, pg 717
Cerutti Productions Inc, pg 720
Communication Arts Multimedia Inc, pg 728
Emergency Film Group, pg 753
Horizon Film + Video Productions, pg 781
Inferno Films, pg 787
Maverick Video Productions, pg 820
Prairie Pictures Film & Video, pg 860
The Samuels Co, pg 879
South Coast Film & Video, pg 895
South Trunk Studios, pg 895
Stage Directions, pg 898
Stockyard Photos/Jim Olive Photography, pg 901
Texcam Inc, pg 911

VIRGINIA

Advance Concepts Inc, pg 677
BES Studios, pg 704
CACI Integrated Communications, pg 713
Maniglia Media LLC, pg 816
Lynda Richardson Photography, pg 875

WASHINGTON

Hamilton Studio, pg 775
North-by-Northwest - A Digital Studio, pg 842
Oppenheimer Camera Products, pg 847
White Rain Films Ltd, pg 937

WEST VIRGINIA

MotionMasters, pg 831

WISCONSIN

Logan Productions Inc, pg 811
Meridian Studios, pg 824

University of Wisconsin-Oshkosh Radio-TV-Film Dept, pg 923
USAV Group Inc, pg 923
Video Wisconsin Inc, pg 929
Watts Communications Inc, pg 934
Wisconsin Public Television, pg 940

WYOMING

Bridger Productions Inc, pg 710

ALBERTA

Global TV, pg 771

ONTARIO

ADS Media, pg 677
GAPC (General Assembly Production Centre), pg 768
Silver Creek Media Inc, pg 888

QUEBEC

Muse Entertainment Enterprises, pg 834

Photography—Underwater

ALASKA

Connections Film & Video Inc, pg 731

CALIFORNIA

Action Sports/All Stock, pg 675
Classic Images Stock Footage LLC, pg 726
Concrete Images, pg 730
Goal Productions, pg 772
iCorpTv, pg 783
MacGillivray Freeman Films Inc, pg 813
Motion Picture Marine, pg 831
Moving Art by Louie Schwartzberg, pg 831
New Circuit Films LLC, pg 839
Nineteen87, pg 841
QRS Software Services, pg 867
Dick Reizner Film & Video, pg 873
Sea Studios Foundation, pg 883
Utopia Films, pg 924
WARPed Pictures, pg 934

COLORADO

CSI Film & Video LLC, pg 735
Flashback Media Productions, pg 762
Greg Hensley Productions, pg 779

CONNECTICUT

Skyviews Survey Inc, pg 890

FLORIDA

Steven Cohen Motion Picture Production, pg 727
Communications Concepts Inc (CCI), pg 729
Courter Films LLC, pg 732
Jordan Klein Film & Video (JKFV), pg 795
SuperStock Inc, pg 904

GEORGIA

Guerrilla Productions LLC, pg 774

ILLINOIS

ABS Enterprises, pg 672
Film Police, pg 760

FILM

Photography—Underwater (continued)

ILLINOIS (continued)

Helix Camera & Video, pg 778
Major Media Productions Inc,
pg 815

LOUISIANA

Digital FX Inc, pg 742

MARYLAND

Kramer Communications Video
Production, pg 801

MASSACHUSETTS

CommCreative, pg 728
In the Wild Productions, pg 786
Northern Light Productions (NLP),
pg 842

MINNESOTA

House of Cinemagraphics, pg 782
Media Loft Inc, pg 822

MONTANA

Clarkson Studio, pg 726

NEW JERSEY

Allegro Productions Inc, pg 680
Pioneer Research Inc, pg 857

NEW YORK

Black Star Publishing Co Inc,
pg 706
Broadstreet Productions LLC,
pg 711
Buffalo Video Production, pg 712
Ketchum Inc, pg 798
La Paloma Films, pg 803
Jack Morton Worldwide, pg 830
R/GA, pg 868
Split Image Productions, pg 898

NORTH DAKOTA

Media Productions, pg 822

OHIO

Challenge Productions/Challenge
Aerial Imaging, pg 720

OREGON

Odyssey Productions Inc, pg 844

PENNSYLVANIA

Argentine Productions Inc, pg 688
Innovision Media Group, pg 788

SOUTH CAROLINA

Venture Media, pg 925

TENNESSEE

Motion Picture Services, pg 831
Scripps Networks, pg 882
Stage Post, pg 899

TEXAS

Alexander Media Productions,
pg 679
Horizon Film + Video Productions,
pg 781

Julye Newlin Productions Inc,
pg 840
South Coast Film & Video, pg 895

VIRGINIA

CACI Integrated Communications,
pg 713
Lynda Richardson Photography,
pg 875

WISCONSIN

USAV Group Inc, pg 923
Video Wisconsin Inc, pg 929
Wisconsin Public Television, pg 940

ALBERTA

Global TV, pg 771

Post-Production Services

ALABAMA

Motion & Graphic Image Corp Inc
(MAGIC), pg 831

ALASKA

Aurora Films, pg 696
Connections Film & Video Inc,
pg 731

ARIZONA

Candee Productions Inc, pg 716
Merestone, pg 823
Metropolitan Audio-Visual Inc,
pg 824

CALIFORNIA

A&I - Fine Art & Photography,
pg 671
AB Audio Visual Entertainment Inc,
pg 672
Access Video in Berkeley, pg 673
Allied Artists International Inc,
pg 681
ARC Document Solutions, pg 688
Artichoke Productions, pg 690
Audio Mechanics, pg 693
Audio Visual Consultants, pg 694
Berkeley Sound Artists Inc, pg 704
Creative Technology, pg 733
Crystal Pyramid Productions™,
pg 735
Custom Video Productions Inc,
pg 736
deKramer Productions Inc, pg 740
The Dreaming Tree, pg 746
DV Post, pg 748
Earwax Productions Inc, pg 749
First Person Inc, pg 761
4th Street Recording, pg 764
Goal Productions, pg 772
Gold Standard Productions, pg 772
Gordon Productions Inc, pg 772
Havas Edge, pg 777
Hollywood Vaults Inc, pg 781
iCorpTv, pg 783
Illuminate Post/Digital Finishing,
pg 784
imageReal Pictures LLC, pg 785
Jaguar Distribution Corp, pg 792
Kavich Reynolds Productions Inc,
pg 797
KO Creative, pg 800
KTVU-Retail Services, pg 802
Main Street Media Inc, pg 815
Maximus Media Inc, pg 820
Method Studios, pg 824
Nandar Entertainment Pictures,
pg 835

New & Unique Videos™, pg 839
New Deal Studios, pg 839
Nineteen87, pg 841
Palardo Productions, pg 850
piXvfm Inc, pg 857
PK Productions, pg 857
Point of View Productions, pg 858
Pro8mm, pg 862
PSI Inc, pg 866
Pyramind Studios, pg 867
QRS Software Services, pg 867
Reality Check Systems, pg 871
Renegade Animation Inc, pg 873
RetinaVision Productions, pg 874
Roundabout Entertainment Inc,
pg 878
Russ InVision Co/AbridgeClub.com,
pg 879
Sahara Records & Filmworks
Entertainment Co, pg 879
Sea Studios Foundation, pg 883
Shapeshifter, pg 885
Shoulder High Productions, pg 886
SonicPool, pg 892
Studio 132, pg 902
The Studios at Paramount, pg 903
Tam Communications Inc, pg 906
TIMECODE Post Production,
pg 914
Todd-AO Studios, pg 915
Total Creative, pg 916
Two Door Productions LLC, pg 920
Universal Studios, pg 922
Via Verde Productions, pg 926
VidCan Media Solutions, pg 927
Warner Bros Entertainment Inc,
pg 934
WARPed Pictures, pg 934
WMS Media Inc, pg 940

COLORADO

Flashback Media Productions,
pg 762
Open Media Foundation, pg 846
Rocky Mountain Audio/Video
Productions Inc, pg 876
Tatum Video, pg 907

CONNECTICUT

Essex Television Group Inc, pg 755
The Gary-Paul Agency, pg 768
Moving Pictures, pg 832
Musivision Inc, pg 835
New London Media, pg 839

DISTRICT OF COLUMBIA

Hillmann & Carr Inc, pg 780
Interface Media Group, pg 789

FLORIDA

Audacity Recording Studios, pg 693
Bill Bachmann Studios, pg 705
Civins Productions Inc, pg 725
Communications Concepts Inc
(CCI), pg 729
Comtel Inc, pg 730
Courter Films LLC, pg 732
Kat Epple Music Productions,
pg 755
Glanz Technologies Inc, pg 771
Jordan Klein Film & Video (JKFV),
pg 795
Norman Kent Productions, pg 798
Sunfire Communications Inc,
pg 904
Universal Studios Florida®
Production Group, pg 922
WKMG-TV News 6, pg 940

GEORGIA

Cinema Concepts, pg 724
Guerrilla Productions LLC, pg 774
Malcolm Neal Productions, pg 837
On-Line Productions, pg 845

HAWAII

Dot C Software Inc, pg 746
Hyperspective Studios Inc, pg 783

IDAHO

Brad Shaw Productions Inc, pg 885

ILLINOIS

ABS Enterprises, pg 672
ABSA Films, pg 672
AnswersMedia, pg 686
Atomic Imaging Inc/Golan Studios,
pg 692
Beatty TeleVisual Productions,
pg 703
Mightybytes Inc, pg 827
Optimus, pg 847
Pepper Group, pg 854
RADMAR Inc, pg 869
Richter Studios, pg 875

INDIANA

A-V-A Video Productions, pg 671
Communication Ministries, pg 728
OMNI Productions, pg 845

IOWA

Educational Technology & Media
Services, pg 751

KENTUCKY

Broadway Digital, pg 711
Hammond Communications Group
Inc, pg 775
Idle Minds Productions Inc, pg 784
The PPS Group, pg 860

LOUISIANA

Digital FX Inc, pg 742
Moxie Media, pg 832
Vidox Motion Imagery, pg 930

MARYLAND

Adventure Productions LLC, pg 678
dbF a Media Company, pg 739
DBM Communications Inc, pg 739
Kramer Communications Video
Production, pg 801
Milner-Fenwick Inc, pg 828

MASSACHUSETTS

CommCreative, pg 728
Cramer, pg 732
Green Mountain Post Films (GMP),
pg 774
Heliotrope Studios, pg 778
Labrecque Creative Sound, pg 803
MotionArt Studios, pg 831
Northern Light Productions (NLP),
pg 842
Penfield Productions Ltd, pg 853
Gabriel Polonsky Studio, pg 859
TR Productions, pg 916
WGBH Production Group, pg 936

MICHIGAN

Digi Sign Design LLC, pg 741
MessageMakers, pg 824
WGVU TV, pg 936

MINNESOTA

Badiyan Inc, pg 700
House of Cinemagraphics, pg 782

MISSOURI

Avatar Studios, pg 697

MONTANA

Jereco Studios Inc, pg 793
KUSM TV, pg 802

NEVADA

DVDs4Less, pg 748
Peterson's Video Transfer Services, pg 855
VirtualMix, pg 930

NEW HAMPSHIRE

Apertura, pg 686

NEW JERSEY

Audio Vistas LLC, pg 694
CELCO, pg 719
Euro-Pacific Film & Video Productions Inc, pg 756
Hogpenny Studios, pg 780
Image Up Studio, pg 785
Milbrodt/Music & Sound Design, pg 827
NFL Films Inc, pg 841
NFL Films Music Library, pg 841
PeopleVisionFX, pg 854
Set To Go Studios, pg 884
Suede Interactive, pg 903
Telequest Inc, pg 910
VCSvideo, pg 925

NEW MEXICO

I-25 Studios, pg 783
Little Big Bang Design Inc, pg 810
Mountainair Films Inc, pg 831

NEW YORK

American Montage Inc, pg 683
aurora productions, pg 696
Bevilacqua Studios, pg 704
Big Film Design, pg 705
Broadstreet Productions LLC, pg 711
Brooklyn College Television Center, pg 711
Thomas Craven Film Corp, pg 733
DuArt Media Services, pg 747
East of Hollywood NY, pg 749
Four Corners Productions, pg 764
HB-Content, pg 777
Hello World Communications, pg 778
KAS Music & Sound, pg 796
La Paloma Films, pg 803
Long Island University Media Arts Dept, pg 811
Magno Sound Inc, pg 815
Jack Morton Worldwide, pg 830
NBC Production Facilities, pg 837
New York Sound Inc, pg 840
Peckham Productions Inc, pg 852
R/GA, pg 868
David Rapkin Audio Production, pg 870
TeleTime Productions, pg 910
Third World Newsreel/Camera News Inc, pg 912
Videography Productions, pg 929
Zelman Studios Ltd, pg 945

NORTH CAROLINA

Pat Appleson Studios Inc, pg 687
The Communications Group Inc, pg 729
Horizon Video Productions Inc, pg 781
Image Associates Inc, pg 784
Kino Mountain Productions LLC, pg 799
K2 Productions, pg 802
Trailblazer Studios®, pg 917
2BruceStudio, pg 920

NORTH DAKOTA

Media Productions, pg 822

OHIO

Challenge Productions/Challenge Aerial Imaging, pg 720
Mills James Productions, pg 828
The Telos Alliance, pg 910
Thread Marketing Group, pg 913
Vista Color Imaging Inc, pg 931

OREGON

Artbeats, pg 690
CMD Agency, pg 726
KVAL, pg 802
Odyssey Productions Inc, pg 844

PENNSYLVANIA

Argentine Productions Inc, pg 688
Berry & Homer, pg 704
Center City Film & Video Inc, pg 719
Innovision Media Group, pg 788
JPL, pg 795
NEP Group Inc, pg 838
Rahlic Publishing Co, pg 869
WPGH-TV, pg 942
WQED-Multimedia, pg 942

RHODE ISLAND

Sound-FX-Design, pg 894

TENNESSEE

Continental Film, pg 731
Fricon Entertainment Co Inc, pg 766
Love Shack Recording Studios, pg 811
Motion Picture Services, pg 831
Scripps Networks, pg 882
Stage Post, pg 899
Zion Music Group, pg 945

TEXAS

Alexander Media Productions, pg 679
Anaphora Literary Press, pg 685
Biway Media, pg 706
Castleview Productions, pg 717
Cerutti Productions Inc, pg 720
Emergency Film Group, pg 753
Horizon Film + Video Productions, pg 781
Inferno Films, pg 787
Julye Newlin Productions Inc, pg 840
Phillips Media Source, pg 855
Romar Learning Solutions LLC, pg 877
RuffHouse LLC, pg 878
The Samuels Co, pg 879
The Sound Lab Inc, pg 894
Stage Directions, pg 898
Texas Heart Institute Visual Communication Services, pg 911
3008, pg 913

UTAH

Soularium Recording Studios, pg 893

VERMONT

Marlboro Productions, pg 817
University of Vermont, Instructional Television Dept, pg 923

VIRGINIA

CACI Integrated Communications, pg 713
Henninger Media Services, pg 779
Maniglia Media LLC, pg 816
Metro Productions, pg 824
United Way Worldwide, pg 921

WASHINGTON

Hamilton Studio, pg 775
Inland Audio Visual Co, pg 788
Sound Sound, pg 894
Victory Studios, pg 927

WEST VIRGINIA

Blackwater Video Productions, pg 707

WISCONSIN

5th Floor Recording Co, pg 760
Logan Productions Inc, pg 811
Meridian Studios, pg 824
University of Wisconsin-Oshkosh Radio-TV-Film Dept, pg 923
USAV Group Inc, pg 923
Watts Communications Inc, pg 934
WFRV-TV 5 CBS, pg 936
Wisconsin Public Television, pg 940

WYOMING

Bridger Productions Inc, pg 710

ALBERTA

Black Media Works, pg 706
Global TV, pg 771

BRITISH COLUMBIA

Pinewood Sound, pg 857
24 Frames Film & Video, pg 920
Video Out Distribution, pg 928
West Eagle Films Inc, pg 935

MANITOBA

Lank/Beach Productions Inc, pg 803

NORTHWEST TERRITORIES

Yellowknife Films Inc, pg 944

ONTARIO

ADS Media, pg 677
GAPC (General Assembly Production Centre), pg 768
Silver Creek Media Inc, pg 888
Trebas Institute, pg 917
Video Advantage, pg 927
Wanted! Sound + Picture, pg 933

QUEBEC

Muse Entertainment Enterprises, pg 834
Trebas Institute, pg 917

Preservation & Rejuvenation

CALIFORNIA

Audio Mechanics, pg 693
Chace Audio by Deluxe, pg 720
Hollywood Vaults Inc, pg 781
Jaguar Distribution Corp, pg 792
Pro8mm, pg 862
QRS Software Services, pg 867
SonicPool, pg 892
Universal Studios, pg 922

CONNECTICUT

The Gary-Paul Agency, pg 768

GEORGIA

Guerrilla Productions LLC, pg 774

ILLINOIS

Beatty TeleVisual Productions, pg 703
Major Media Productions Inc, pg 815

LOUISIANA

Digital FX Inc, pg 742

MARYLAND

dbF a Media Company, pg 739

MINNESOTA

House of Cinemagraphics, pg 782

MONTANA

Clarkson Studio, pg 726

NEW HAMPSHIRE

Apertura, pg 686

NEW JERSEY

CELCO, pg 719
C2 Imaging, pg 735

NEW YORK

Broadstreet Productions LLC, pg 711

OHIO

Thread Marketing Group, pg 913

PENNSYLVANIA

John E Allen Inc, pg 680
Innovision Media Group, pg 788

TENNESSEE

Continental Film, pg 731
Stage Post, pg 899

TEXAS

Fugro, pg 766
Matson Multi-Media, pg 820

Printing, see Processing & Printing

Printing, see Release Printing

FILM

Processing & Printing

CALIFORNIA

A&I - Fine Art & Photography, pg 671
Action Photo Digital Graphics, pg 675
Hooper Camera & Imaging, pg 781
Pro8mm, pg 862
QRS Software Services, pg 867
SonicPool, pg 892

CONNECTICUT

New London Media, pg 839
Skyviews Survey Inc, pg 890

FLORIDA

Tallahassee Photo & Frame, pg 906

GEORGIA

Guerrilla Productions LLC, pg 774

INDIANA

OMNI Productions, pg 845

IOWA

American Color Imaging (ACI), pg 683

KENTUCKY

Kinetic Corp, pg 799

MASSACHUSETTS

Colortek of Boston, pg 728
DGI-Invisuals LLC, pg 741
ICL Imaging Inc, pg 783
Integrated Solutions Group, pg 789

MICHIGAN

Arbor Oakland Group, pg 688

MISSISSIPPI

Jasper Ewing & Sons Inc, pg 757

MISSOURI

Allied Photocolor Co, pg 681
Schiller's Audio-Visual, pg 881

NEW JERSEY

NFL Films Inc, pg 841

NEW YORK

DuArt Media Services, pg 747
Duggal Visual Solutions Inc, pg 747
Gage-Line Technology Inc, pg 767
PASCO, pg 851

NORTH CAROLINA

Camcor Inc, pg 715
Image Associates Inc, pg 784

OHIO

Vista Color Imaging Inc, pg 931

PENNSYLVANIA

John E Allen Inc, pg 680
Audio Visual Communications Inc, pg 694
Bernie's Photo Center, pg 704
Berry & Homer, pg 704
Visual Sound Inc, pg 931

TENNESSEE

Continental Film, pg 731
Motion Picture Services, pg 831
Phoenix Aerial Photography Inc, pg 855
Stage Post, pg 899

TEXAS

Fugro, pg 766
IntegraColor, pg 789

UTAH

Signs.com, pg 888

VERMONT

University of Vermont, Instructional Television Dept, pg 923

VIRGINIA

Blair Inc, pg 707

WISCONSIN

Pechman Imaging, pg 852
USAV Group Inc, pg 923

Production Workshops

ARIZONA

Teaberry, pg 908

CALIFORNIA

Opticomm-EMCORE, pg 847
Palardo Productions, pg 850
Pro8mm, pg 862
QRS Software Services, pg 867
Dick Reizner Film & Video, pg 873
Russ InVision Co/AbridgeClub.com, pg 879

COLORADO

Open Media Foundation, pg 846

CONNECTICUT

The Gary-Paul Agency, pg 768

FLORIDA

Audacity Recording Studios, pg 693
Communications Concepts Inc (CCI), pg 729
Glanz Technologies Inc, pg 771

GEORGIA

Guerrilla Productions LLC, pg 774
Lighting & Production Equipment Inc, pg 807
On-Line Productions, pg 845

IOWA

Educational Technology & Media Services, pg 751

LOUISIANA

Moxie Media, pg 832

MASSACHUSETTS

DGI-Invisuals LLC, pg 741
MotionArt Studios, pg 831

MICHIGAN

Digi Sign Design LLC, pg 741
Michigan Recording Arts Institute & Technologies, pg 825

MINNESOTA

House of Cinemagraphics, pg 782

NEW YORK

De Nonno Productions Inc (DPI), pg 739
Richard Kaplan Productions, pg 796
Third World Newsreel/Camera News Inc, pg 912
Zelman Studios Ltd, pg 945

OHIO

Challenge Productions/Challenge Aerial Imaging, pg 720
Thread Marketing Group, pg 913

PENNSYLVANIA

Kensington Falls Animation, pg 797
Video/Film Associates, pg 928

TENNESSEE

Stage Post, pg 899

TEXAS

Julye Newlin Productions Inc, pg 840

WISCONSIN

Wisconsin Public Television, pg 940

ONTARIO

GAPC (General Assembly Production Centre), pg 768
Trebas Institute, pg 917

QUEBEC

Trebas Institute, pg 917

Projection Equipment & Accessory Distributors

ARIZONA

Docter Optics Inc, pg 744
EAR Professional Audio/Video, pg 749
Troxell-CDI, pg 918

ARKANSAS

White Diamond Productions LLC, pg 937

CALIFORNIA

Ametron Audio/Video, pg 684
Be Media, pg 702
Christie Digital Systems USA Inc, pg 722
Christy's Editorial, pg 723
Cibola Systems, pg 723
Cinema Equipment Sales of California Inc, pg 724
Cinema Xenon International Inc, pg 724
Derksen (USA) Inc, pg 740
Hi-Tech Lamps Inc, pg 779
Hooper Camera & Imaging, pg 781
Instructional Materials & Equipment Distributors (I-Med), pg 789
JD Audio Visual Inc, pg 793
Lloyd F McKinney Associates Inc, pg 821
Media Fabricators Inc, pg 822
MediaPOINTE, pg 823
PMP Marketing Inc, pg 858
Stanislaus AV Inc, pg 899
SuperVision, pg 904

COLORADO

Goldberg Brothers Inc, pg 772
Stanco Sales LLC, pg 899

CONNECTICUT

MAVCO, pg 820
USI Inc, pg 924

FLORIDA

AVI-SPL, pg 698
Cinema Equipment & Supplies Inc, pg 724
Harmon's Audio-Visual Services, pg 776
Hi-Tech Enterprises Inc, pg 779
Hollywood Theatre Equipment Inc, pg 781
Tallahassee Audio Visual, pg 906
Techni-Lux Inc, pg 908

GEORGIA

Baker Audio Visual, pg 700
Digital Projection, pg 742
Lighting & Production Equipment Inc, pg 807

ILLINOIS

Chicago Spotlight Inc, pg 721
Facets Multi-Media Inc, pg 758
FUJIFILM Graphic Systems Division, pg 766
Urbanski Film, pg 923

KENTUCKY

NOR-COM Inc, pg 841

LOUISIANA

Techkno Integration & Design Services LLC, pg 908

MARYLAND

Cardinal Sound & Video, pg 717
Nelson White Systems Inc, pg 838
RTZ Audio Visual, pg 878

MASSACHUSETTS

Hunt's Photo & Video, pg 782

MICHIGAN

Michigan Office Solutions (MOS), A Xerox Company, pg 825

MINNESOTA

Alpha Video & Audio Inc, pg 682
AVI Systems, pg 698

MISSISSIPPI

Bowie Audio Visual Enterprises Inc, pg 709
Jasper Ewing & Sons Inc, pg 757

MISSOURI

ITC, pg 791
Schiller's Audio-Visual, pg 881

NEBRASKA

Ballantyne Strong Inc, pg 701

NEVADA

Aardvark Video & Media Productions, pg 671

NEW HAMPSHIRE
APS Lighting-Sound-AV, pg 688

NEW JERSEY
AlltecPro, pg 681
Argraph Corp, pg 688
Audio Visual Associates, pg 694
AV Bluebook, pg 696
SYMCO Inc, pg 905
Video Corporation of America
   (VCA), pg 927

NEW YORK
Albany Theatre Supply Co Inc,
   pg 679
AV Workshop, pg 697
Barbizon Electric Co Inc, pg 701
Gaylord Archival, pg 768
Motion Picture Enterprises Inc,
   pg 831
Neptune Photo Inc, pg 838
Ray Supply Inc, pg 870
Tri-Ed Distribution Inc, pg 918

NORTH CAROLINA
Camcor Inc, pg 715

PENNSYLVANIA
Audio Visions Inc, pg 694
Bernie's Photo Center, pg 704
Garcia Marketing Inc, pg 768
Grise Audio Visual Center Inc,
   pg 774
The Lerro Corp, pg 806
Vistacom Inc, pg 931
Visual Sound Inc, pg 931

TEXAS
Audio Visual Technologies Group
   (AVTG), pg 695
Pro Video & Film Equipment Co
   Inc, pg 863

UTAH
Webb Audio Visual, pg 935

VIRGINIA
Boitnott Visual Communications
   Corp (BVC), pg 708
Quince Imaging Inc, pg 868
The Whitlock Group, pg 937

WISCONSIN
Camera Corner Connecting Point,
   pg 715
Demco Inc, pg 740

PUERTO RICO
Audio Visual Concepts Inc, pg 694

ALBERTA
Unique Communications Ltd,
   pg 921

BRITISH COLUMBIA
Specialty Bulb Products Inc, pg 896

ONTARIO
Cinema Stage Inc, pg 724
Nationwide Audio Visual Co,
   pg 837
Westbury National Show Systems
   Ltd, pg 936

QUEBEC
Strong Screen Systems, pg 902

Projection Equipment & Accessory Manufacturers

CALIFORNIA
ALTINEX Inc, pg 682
AMX® by Harman, pg 685
Christie Digital Systems USA Inc,
   pg 722
Stewart Filmscreen Corp, pg 901

COLORADO
Goldberg Brothers Inc, pg 772

FLORIDA
Magna-Tech Electronic Co Inc,
   pg 814

GEORGIA
Digital Projection, pg 742

ILLINOIS
Bretford Manufacturing Inc, pg 710
La Vezzi Precision Inc, pg 926

INDIANA
Da-Lite, a Legrand AV Inc brand,
   pg 737
Draper Inc, pg 746
Star Case Manufacturing Co Inc,
   pg 900

NEBRASKA
Ballantyne Strong Inc, pg 701

NEW JERSEY
CELCO, pg 719
Gerriets International, pg 770

NEW YORK
ELMO USA Corp, pg 753
Navitar Inc, pg 837

VIRGINIA
Optikinetics Ltd - The Americas,
   pg 847
Quince Imaging Inc, pg 868

WISCONSIN
ETC, pg 756

ONTARIO
DW Electrochemicals Ltd, pg 748

QUEBEC
Strong Screen Systems, pg 902

Projection Equipment & Accessory Rentals

ARIZONA
Arizona Cine Equipment, pg 688

ARKANSAS
White Diamond Productions LLC,
   pg 937

CALIFORNIA
Ametron Audio/Video, pg 684
Artichoke Productions, pg 690
Hooper Camera & Imaging, pg 781
Instructional Materials & Equipment
   Distributors (I-Med), pg 789
JD Audio Visual Inc, pg 793
Main Street Media Inc, pg 815
Media Fabricators Inc, pg 822
PSAV® Presentation Services,
   pg 866
Samy's Camera, pg 879
Stanislaus AV Inc, pg 899

DELAWARE
Ken-Del Productions Inc, pg 797

FLORIDA
AVI-SPL, pg 698
Jordan Klein Film & Video (JKFV),
   pg 795
Tallahassee Audio Visual, pg 906

GEORGIA
Lighting & Production Equipment
   Inc, pg 807

ILLINOIS
Beatty TeleVisual Productions,
   pg 703
Chicago Spotlight Inc, pg 721
PSAV® Presentation Services
   (Hotel Services Division), pg 866
Resolution Productions Group,
   pg 874

INDIANA
Advanced Media Integration, pg 677
Jack's Camera Shop, pg 792

MARYLAND
Absolute Hollywood, pg 672
Advance Audiovisual Presentation
   Ltd, pg 677
Nelson White Systems Inc, pg 838
RTZ Audio Visual, pg 878

MASSACHUSETTS
The Boston Connection Inc, pg 709
Capron Lighting & Sound Co Inc,
   pg 716
massAV, pg 819

MICHIGAN
City Events Group, pg 725

MINNESOTA
AVI Systems, pg 698

MISSISSIPPI
Bowie Audio Visual Enterprises Inc,
   pg 709
Jasper Ewing & Sons Inc, pg 757

MISSOURI
Schiller's Audio-Visual, pg 881
Show-Me Audio-Visual, pg 887

NEW HAMPSHIRE
Apertura, pg 686
APS Lighting-Sound-AV, pg 688

NEW JERSEY
Audio Visual Associates, pg 694
Gerriets International, pg 770

NEW YORK
Albany Theatre Supply Co Inc,
   pg 679
AV Workshop, pg 697
CMI Communications, pg 727
Motion Picture Enterprises Inc,
   pg 831
Specialized Audio-Visual Inc,
   pg 896

NORTH DAKOTA
Media Productions, pg 822

OHIO
Mills James Productions, pg 828
Thread Marketing Group, pg 913

OREGON
Northwest Film Center, pg 842

PENNSYLVANIA
Audio Visions Inc, pg 694
Bernie's Photo Center, pg 704
Grise Audio Visual Center Inc,
   pg 774
Vistacom Inc, pg 931
Visual Sound Inc, pg 931

TENNESSEE
Memphis Communications Corp,
   pg 823

UTAH
Webb Audio Visual, pg 935

VERMONT
Marlboro Productions, pg 817

VIRGINIA
Boitnott Visual Communications
   Corp (BVC), pg 708
Projection, pg 865
Quince Imaging Inc, pg 868
The Whitlock Group, pg 937

WASHINGTON
Kostov Productions, pg 801

ALBERTA
Global TV, pg 771
McBain Camera Ltd, pg 820
Unique Communications Ltd,
   pg 921

BRITISH COLUMBIA
Clark's Audio Visual Services Ltd,
   pg 725

ONTARIO
SIM Digital, pg 888
Westbury National Show Systems
   Ltd, pg 936

QUEBEC
Audio Visual Dynamics, pg 694

Projection Equipment & Accessory Repairs

CALIFORNIA
Christie Digital Systems USA Inc,
   pg 722
Hooper Camera & Imaging, pg 781

FILM

Projection Equipment & Accessory Repairs (continued)

CALIFORNIA (continued)

Instructional Materials & Equipment Distributors (I-Med), pg 789
Lloyd F McKinney Associates Inc, pg 821

CONNECTICUT

Precision Camera & Video Repair Inc, pg 861

FLORIDA

Hi-Tech Enterprises Inc, pg 779
Hollywood Theatre Equipment Inc, pg 781
Tallahassee Audio Visual, pg 906
Tallahassee Photo & Frame, pg 906

GEORGIA

Lighting & Production Equipment Inc, pg 807

ILLINOIS

Beatty TeleVisual Productions, pg 703
Chicago Spotlight Inc, pg 721

KENTUCKY

NOR-COM Inc, pg 841

MARYLAND

RTZ Audio Visual, pg 878

MASSACHUSETTS

The Boston Connection Inc, pg 709
Capron Lighting & Sound Co Inc, pg 716

MINNESOTA

AVI Systems, pg 698

MISSISSIPPI

Bowie Audio Visual Enterprises Inc, pg 709

MISSOURI

Cintrex Audio Visual, pg 725
Schiller's Audio-Visual, pg 881

NEW JERSEY

Audio Visual Associates, pg 694

NEW YORK

ELMO USA Corp, pg 753
Motion Picture Enterprises Inc, pg 831

NORTH CAROLINA

Camcor Inc, pg 715

PENNSYLVANIA

Audio Visions Inc, pg 694
Bernie's Photo Center, pg 704
Vistacom Inc, pg 931

VIRGINIA

Boitnott Visual Communications Corp (BVC), pg 708
Quince Imaging Inc, pg 868

WISCONSIN

Camera Corner Connecting Point, pg 715

ONTARIO

Westbury National Show Systems Ltd, pg 936

Projection Part Distributors

ARIZONA

Troxell-CDI, pg 918

CALIFORNIA

Be Media, pg 702
Christy's Editorial, pg 723
Cinema Equipment Sales of California Inc, pg 724
Hooper Camera & Imaging, pg 781
JD Audio Visual Inc, pg 793
Media Fabricators Inc, pg 822

COLORADO

Stanco Sales LLC, pg 899

FLORIDA

AVI-SPL, pg 698
Cinema Equipment & Supplies Inc, pg 724
Hollywood Theatre Equipment Inc, pg 781

ILLINOIS

Joseph Electronics, pg 795
Urbanski Film, pg 923

KENTUCKY

NOR-COM Inc, pg 841

LOUISIANA

Techkno Integration & Design Services LLC, pg 908

MINNESOTA

AVI Systems, pg 698

MISSISSIPPI

Bowie Audio Visual Enterprises Inc, pg 709

MISSOURI

Schiller's Audio-Visual, pg 881

NEBRASKA

Ballantyne Strong Inc, pg 701

NEW JERSEY

AlltecPro, pg 681
Audio Visual Associates, pg 694
Video Corporation of America (VCA), pg 927

NEW YORK

AV Workshop, pg 697
Bulbtronics Inc, pg 712
DSan Corp, pg 747

Ray Supply Inc, pg 870
Russell Industries Inc, pg 879

NORTH CAROLINA

Camcor Inc, pg 715

OHIO

Tri-State Audio Visual Co, pg 918

PENNSYLVANIA

Audio Visions Inc, pg 694
J E Foss Co, pg 764
Grise Audio Visual Center Inc, pg 774
The Lerro Corp, pg 806

TENNESSEE

Memphis Communications Corp, pg 823

TEXAS

Audio Visual Technologies Group (AVTG), pg 695

VIRGINIA

Boitnott Visual Communications Corp (BVC), pg 708
Lee Hartman & Sons Inc, pg 805
The Whitlock Group, pg 937

WISCONSIN

Alpha Source Inc, pg 681

ONTARIO

Nationwide Audio Visual Co, pg 837
Westbury National Show Systems Ltd, pg 936

QUEBEC

Strong Screen Systems, pg 902

Projection Part Manufacturers

ILLINOIS

Dukane Corp, Audio Visual Products Division, pg 747
La Vezzi Precision Inc, pg 926

NEBRASKA

Strong Cinema Products, pg 902

NEW YORK

Russell Industries Inc, pg 879

TEXAS

Crystal Clear Media Group, pg 735

VIRGINIA

Optikinetics Ltd - The Americas, pg 847

Projection Part Rentals

CALIFORNIA

Hooper Camera & Imaging, pg 781
JD Audio Visual Inc, pg 793
Media Fabricators Inc, pg 822

DELAWARE

Ken-Del Productions Inc, pg 797

FLORIDA

Jordan Klein Film & Video (JKFV), pg 795

MARYLAND

RTZ Audio Visual, pg 878

MINNESOTA

AVI Systems, pg 698

MISSISSIPPI

Bowie Audio Visual Enterprises Inc, pg 709

MISSOURI

Show-Me Audio-Visual, pg 887

NEW HAMPSHIRE

Apertura, pg 686

NEW YORK

AV Workshop, pg 697

PENNSYLVANIA

Audio Visions Inc, pg 694
Grise Audio Visual Center Inc, pg 774

BRITISH COLUMBIA

Clark's Audio Visual Services Ltd, pg 725

Projection Part Repairs

CALIFORNIA

Hooper Camera & Imaging, pg 781
Lloyd F McKinney Associates Inc, pg 821

CONNECTICUT

MAVCO, pg 820

KENTUCKY

NOR-COM Inc, pg 841

MARYLAND

RTZ Audio Visual, pg 878

MINNESOTA

AVI Systems, pg 698

MISSOURI

Cintrex Audio Visual, pg 725

NORTH CAROLINA

Camcor Inc, pg 715

PENNSYLVANIA

Audio Visions Inc, pg 694

Projector & Equipment— 8mm Distributors

ARIZONA

Troxell-CDI, pg 918

CALIFORNIA

Ametron Audio/Video, pg 684
Be Media, pg 702

Jaguar Distribution Corp, pg 792
Pro8mm, pg 862

COLORADO
Ceavco Audio Visual Company Inc, pg 719
Stanco Sales LLC, pg 899

CONNECTICUT
MAVCO, pg 820
Rockwell Communications Inc, pg 876

FLORIDA
AVI-SPL, pg 698

GEORGIA
Visioneering International Inc, pg 931

ILLINOIS
Urbanski Film, pg 923

LOUISIANA
Techkno Integration & Design Services LLC, pg 908

MINNESOTA
AVI Systems, pg 698

MISSISSIPPI
Jasper Ewing & Sons Inc, pg 757

MISSOURI
ITC, pg 791

NEW JERSEY
Audio Visual Associates, pg 694
Audio Visual Dynamics®, pg 694
Video Corporation of America (VCA), pg 927

NEW YORK
AV Workshop, pg 697
Colortone Audio Visual, pg 728
Langie Audio Visual Systems, pg 803
Motion Picture Enterprises Inc, pg 831

NORTH CAROLINA
Camcor Inc, pg 715
Strategic Connections, pg 901

OHIO
Audio Visual Media, pg 694

PENNSYLVANIA
Audio Visions Inc, pg 694
Bernie's Photo Center, pg 704
The Lerro Corp, pg 806

TEXAS
Cinema Antiques, pg 723
Pro Video & Film Equipment Co Inc, pg 863

UTAH
Webb Audio Visual, pg 935

Projector & Equipment— 8mm Manufacturers

CALIFORNIA
Pro8mm, pg 862

NEW YORK
General Audio-Visual Inc (GAVI), pg 769

BRITISH COLUMBIA
Triad Communications Ltd, pg 918

Projector & Equipment— 8mm Rentals

ARIZONA
Arizona Cine Equipment, pg 688

ARKANSAS
White Diamond Productions LLC, pg 937

CALIFORNIA
Ametron Audio/Video, pg 684
Gold Standard Productions, pg 772
Pro8mm, pg 862
PSAV® Presentation Services, pg 866

COLORADO
Ceavco Audio Visual Company Inc, pg 719

CONNECTICUT
A/V Davey, pg 697
Rockwell Communications Inc, pg 876

DELAWARE
Ken-Del Productions Inc, pg 797

FLORIDA
Jordan Klein Film & Video (JKFV), pg 795

ILLINOIS
Beatty TeleVisual Productions, pg 703
Helix Camera & Video, pg 778
PSAV® Presentation Services (Hotel Services Division), pg 866

INDIANA
Gary Camera & Digital, pg 768
OMNI Productions, pg 845

KENTUCKY
Audio Visual Techniques Inc, pg 695

LOUISIANA
Pace Systems, pg 849

MARYLAND
Advance Audiovisual Presentation Ltd, pg 677
RTZ Audio Visual, pg 878

MINNESOTA
AVI Systems, pg 698
House of Cinemagraphics, pg 782

MISSISSIPPI
Jasper Ewing & Sons Inc, pg 757

MISSOURI
ITC, pg 791
Show-Me Audio-Visual, pg 887

NEW HAMPSHIRE
Academic & Campus Technology Services, pg 672
Apertura, pg 686

NEW JERSEY
Audio Visual Dynamics®, pg 694

NEW YORK
AV Workshop, pg 697
CMI Communications, pg 727
Colortone Audio Visual, pg 728
Langie Audio Visual Systems, pg 803
Motion Picture Enterprises Inc, pg 831

NORTH CAROLINA
Strategic Connections, pg 901

OHIO
Audio Visual Media, pg 694
Hughie's Event Production Services, pg 782

OREGON
Northwest Film Center, pg 842

PENNSYLVANIA
Audio Visions Inc, pg 694
Bernie's Photo Center, pg 704
Grise Audio Visual Center Inc, pg 774
Visual Sound Inc, pg 931

TENNESSEE
Belew Enterprises, pg 703
Memphis Communications Corp, pg 823
Russ Sturgeon Productions/RSVP, pg 903

UTAH
Webb Audio Visual, pg 935

VIRGINIA
Boitnott Visual Communications Corp (BVC), pg 708
Projection, pg 865

WASHINGTON
Inland Audio Visual Co, pg 788

WISCONSIN
Event Essentials, pg 756
USAV Group Inc, pg 923

WYOMING
Bridger Productions Inc, pg 710

ALBERTA
Unique Communications Ltd, pg 921

BRITISH COLUMBIA
MicrophoneRentals.com, pg 826

Projector & Equipment— 8mm Repairs

CALIFORNIA
Pro Camera Repair, pg 862
Pro8mm, pg 862

COLORADO
Ceavco Audio Visual Company Inc, pg 719

CONNECTICUT
A/V Davey, pg 697
Precision Camera & Video Repair Inc, pg 861
Rockwell Communications Inc, pg 876

GEORGIA
Audio Visual Resources Inc, pg 695

INDIANA
Gary Camera & Digital, pg 768

MARYLAND
RTZ Audio Visual, pg 878

MINNESOTA
AVI Systems, pg 698

NEW JERSEY
Konica Minolta Business Solutions, pg 801

NEW YORK
Colortone Audio Visual, pg 728
Langie Audio Visual Systems, pg 803
Motion Picture Enterprises Inc, pg 831

NORTH CAROLINA
Camcor Inc, pg 715
Strategic Connections, pg 901

OHIO
Audio Visual Media, pg 694

PENNSYLVANIA
Audio Visions Inc, pg 694
Bernie's Photo Center, pg 704

TENNESSEE
Memphis Communications Corp, pg 823

TEXAS
Audio Visual Technologies Group (AVTG), pg 695

WASHINGTON
Inland Audio Visual Co, pg 788

WISCONSIN
Audio Visual of Milwaukee Inc, pg 694

FILM

Projector & Equipment—16mm Distributors

ALABAMA

Curtis Company, pg 736

ARIZONA

Troxell-CDI, pg 918

ARKANSAS

Carlton-Bates Co, pg 717
Jay S Stanley & Associates Inc,
pg 899

CALIFORNIA

Ametron Audio/Video, pg 684
Assured Audio Visual, pg 691
Be Media, pg 702
Birns & Sawyer Inc, pg 706
Christy's Editorial, pg 723
Cinema Equipment Sales of
California Inc, pg 724
Glenn Photo Supply, pg 771
Alan Gordon Enterprises Inc,
pg 772
Instructional Materials & Equipment
Distributors (I-Med), pg 789
Jaguar Distribution Corp, pg 792
JD Audio Visual Inc, pg 793
Lloyd F McKinney Associates Inc,
pg 821
Media Fabricators Inc, pg 822
MediaPOINTE, pg 823
PMP Marketing Inc, pg 858
Pro8mm, pg 862

COLORADO

Ceavco Audio Visual Company Inc,
pg 719
Stanco Sales LLC, pg 899

CONNECTICUT

MAVCO, pg 820
Rockwell Communications Inc,
pg 876

FLORIDA

AVI-SPL, pg 698
Cinema Equipment & Supplies Inc,
pg 724
Hi-Tech Enterprises Inc, pg 779

GEORGIA

Audio Visual Resources Inc, pg 695
Baker Audio Visual, pg 700

HAWAII

The Audio Visual Co (AVCO),
pg 694

ILLINOIS

Creative Technology (CT), pg 733
Urbanski Film, pg 923

INDIANA

Lee Co Inc, pg 805

LOUISIANA

Techkno Integration & Design
Services LLC, pg 908

MARYLAND

Cardinal Sound & Video, pg 717
Nelson White Systems Inc, pg 838
Nicholas P Pipino Associates Inc,
pg 857
RTZ Audio Visual, pg 878

MICHIGAN

Michigan Office Solutions (MOS),
A Xerox Company, pg 825

MINNESOTA

AVI Systems, pg 698

MISSISSIPPI

Bowie Audio Visual Enterprises Inc,
pg 709
Jasper Ewing & Sons Inc, pg 757

MISSOURI

Conference Technologies Inc,
pg 730
ITC, pg 791

NEW JERSEY

AlltecPro, pg 681
Audio Visual Associates, pg 694
Audio Visual Dynamics®, pg 694
AV Bluebook, pg 696
Leica Camera Inc, pg 806
Total Video Products Inc, pg 916
Video Corporation of America
(VCA), pg 927

NEW YORK

AV Workshop, pg 697
Colortone Audio Visual, pg 728
Eastman Kodak Co, pg 750
Gaylord Archival, pg 768
Indigo Productions, pg 787
Langie Audio Visual Systems,
pg 803
Long Island Video Enterprises Live
Inc, pg 811
Motion Picture Enterprises Inc,
pg 831
Neptune Photo Inc, pg 838

NORTH CAROLINA

Camcor Inc, pg 715
Strategic Connections, pg 901

OHIO

Audio Visual Media, pg 694
Copp Integrated Systems, pg 731
Tri-State Audio Visual Co, pg 918
Visual Products Inc, pg 931

PENNSYLVANIA

Audio Visions Inc, pg 694
Bernie's Photo Center, pg 704
J E Foss Co, pg 764
Grise Audio Visual Center Inc,
pg 774
The Lerro Corp, pg 806
Vistacom Inc, pg 931
Visual Sound Inc, pg 931

TENNESSEE

Memphis Communications Corp,
pg 823

TEXAS

Audio Visual Technologies Group
(AVTG), pg 695
Cinema Antiques, pg 723
Pro Video & Film Equipment Co
Inc, pg 863

UTAH

Webb Audio Visual, pg 935

VIRGINIA

Lee Hartman & Sons Inc, pg 805
The Whitlock Group, pg 937

WASHINGTON

Inland Audio Visual Co, pg 788

WISCONSIN

Demco Inc, pg 740
School Specialty Inc, pg 882

ALBERTA

Unique Communications Ltd,
pg 921

MANITOBA

Inland Audio Visual Ltd, pg 788
Lank/Beach Productions Inc, pg 803

ONTARIO

Nationwide Audio Visual Co,
pg 837

Projector & Equipment—16mm Manufacturers

CALIFORNIA

Alan Gordon Enterprises Inc,
pg 772
Pro8mm, pg 862
Visual Instrumentation Corp, pg 931

FLORIDA

Magna-Tech Electronic Co Inc,
pg 814

ILLINOIS

Lipsner-Smith Co, pg 809

NEW YORK

Eastman Kodak Co, pg 750
ELMO USA Corp, pg 753

WISCONSIN

Indus International Inc, pg 787

BRITISH COLUMBIA

Triad Communications Ltd, pg 918

Projector & Equipment—16mm Rentals

ALABAMA

Audio-Video Resources Inc, pg 694

ARKANSAS

White Diamond Productions LLC,
pg 937

CALIFORNIA

Ametron Audio/Video, pg 684
Artichoke Productions, pg 690
Birns & Sawyer Inc, pg 706
Alan Gordon Enterprises Inc,
pg 772
Instructional Materials & Equipment
Distributors (I-Med), pg 789
JD Audio Visual Inc, pg 793
Media Fabricators Inc, pg 822
Munday & Collins AV, pg 834
Pro8mm, pg 862
PSAV® Presentation Services,
pg 866

COLORADO

Ceavco Audio Visual Company Inc,
pg 719
Daylight Productions & Rentals,
pg 739

CONNECTICUT

A/V Davey, pg 697
Rockwell Communications Inc,
pg 876

DELAWARE

Ken-Del Productions Inc, pg 797

FLORIDA

Jordan Klein Film & Video (JKFV),
pg 795
Photosound of Orlando Inc, pg 856

GEORGIA

Audio Visual Resources Inc, pg 695

ILLINOIS

Beatty TeleVisual Productions,
pg 703
Creative Technology (CT), pg 733
Helix Camera & Video, pg 778
PSAV® Presentation Services
(Hotel Services Division), pg 866
Resolution Productions Group,
pg 874

INDIANA

Advanced Media Integration, pg 677
Gary Camera & Digital, pg 768
OMNI Productions, pg 845

KENTUCKY

Audio Visual Techniques Inc,
pg 695

MARYLAND

Advance Audiovisual Presentation
Ltd, pg 677
Nelson White Systems Inc, pg 838
RTZ Audio Visual, pg 878

MASSACHUSETTS

Capron Lighting & Sound Co Inc,
pg 716
massAV, pg 819
Preston Productions Inc, pg 861

MICHIGAN

City Events Group, pg 725

MINNESOTA

AVI Systems, pg 698
House of Cinemagraphics, pg 782

MISSISSIPPI

Bowie Audio Visual Enterprises Inc, pg 709
Jasper Ewing & Sons Inc, pg 757

MISSOURI

Show-Me Audio-Visual, pg 887

NEVADA

GES Audio Visual, pg 770

NEW HAMPSHIRE

Academic & Campus Technology Services, pg 672
Apertura, pg 686

NEW JERSEY

Audio Visual Associates, pg 694
Audio Visual Dynamics®, pg 694
PLS Staging, pg 858

NEW YORK

AV Workshop, pg 697
CMI Communications, pg 727
Colortone Audio Visual, pg 728
Langie Audio Visual Systems, pg 803
Long Island Video Enterprises Live Inc, pg 811
Motion Picture Enterprises Inc, pg 831

NORTH CAROLINA

AV Connections Inc, pg 697
Strategic Connections, pg 901

OHIO

Audio Visual Media, pg 694
Hughie's Event Production Services, pg 782

OREGON

Northwest Film Center, pg 842

PENNSYLVANIA

Audio Visions Inc, pg 694
Bernie's Photo Center, pg 704
Grise Audio Visual Center Inc, pg 774
Visual Sound Inc, pg 931

TENNESSEE

Belew Enterprises, pg 703
Memphis Communications Corp, pg 823
Russ Sturgeon Productions/RSVP, pg 903

TEXAS

Audio Visual Technologies Group (AVTG), pg 695

UTAH

Webb Audio Visual, pg 935

VERMONT

Marlboro Productions, pg 817

VIRGINIA

Boitnott Visual Communications Corp (BVC), pg 708
Lee Hartman & Sons Inc, pg 805
Projection, pg 865
The Whitlock Group, pg 937

WASHINGTON

Inland Audio Visual Co, pg 788

WISCONSIN

Event Essentials, pg 756
School Specialty Inc, pg 882
USAV Group Inc, pg 923

ALBERTA

Global TV, pg 771
Unique Communications Ltd, pg 921

BRITISH COLUMBIA

Clark's Audio Visual Services Ltd, pg 725

MANITOBA

Inland Audio Visual Ltd, pg 788

QUEBEC

Audio Visual Dynamics, pg 694
Freeman Audio Visual, pg 765

Projector & Equipment— 16mm Repairs

ARKANSAS

Carlton-Bates Co, pg 717

CALIFORNIA

Alan Gordon Enterprises Inc, pg 772
Instructional Materials & Equipment Distributors (I-Med), pg 789
Lloyd F McKinney Associates Inc, pg 821
Pro Camera Repair, pg 862
Pro8mm, pg 862
Visual Instrumentation Corp, pg 931

COLORADO

Ceavco Audio Visual Company Inc, pg 719

CONNECTICUT

A/V Davey, pg 697
Precision Camera & Video Repair Inc, pg 861
Rockwell Communications Inc, pg 876

GEORGIA

Audio Visual Resources Inc, pg 695

ILLINOIS

Beatty TeleVisual Productions, pg 703

INDIANA

Gary Camera & Digital, pg 768

MARYLAND

Nelson White Systems Inc, pg 838
RTZ Audio Visual, pg 878

MASSACHUSETTS

Capron Lighting & Sound Co Inc, pg 716

MINNESOTA

AVI Systems, pg 698

MISSISSIPPI

Bowie Audio Visual Enterprises Inc, pg 709

MISSOURI

Cintrex Audio Visual, pg 725

NEW JERSEY

Audio Visual Associates, pg 694

NEW YORK

Colortone Audio Visual, pg 728
ELMO USA Corp, pg 753
Langie Audio Visual Systems, pg 803
Motion Picture Enterprises Inc, pg 831

NORTH CAROLINA

Camcor Inc, pg 715
Strategic Connections, pg 901

OHIO

Audio Visual Media, pg 694
Tri-State Audio Visual Co, pg 918

PENNSYLVANIA

Audio Visions Inc, pg 694
Bernie's Photo Center, pg 704
J E Foss Co, pg 764
Visual Sound Inc, pg 931
Wespen Audio Visual Co, pg 935

TENNESSEE

Memphis Communications Corp, pg 823

TEXAS

Audio Visual Technologies Group (AVTG), pg 695

VIRGINIA

Boitnott Visual Communications Corp (BVC), pg 708
Lee Hartman & Sons Inc, pg 805
The Whitlock Group, pg 937

WASHINGTON

Inland Audio Visual Co, pg 788

WISCONSIN

Audio Visual of Milwaukee Inc, pg 694
Camera Corner Connecting Point, pg 715
School Specialty Inc, pg 882

MANITOBA

Inland Audio Visual Ltd, pg 788

Projector & Equipment— 35mm Distributors

ALABAMA

Curtis Company, pg 736

ARIZONA

Troxell-CDI, pg 918

ARKANSAS

Carlton-Bates Co, pg 717

CALIFORNIA

Ametron Audio/Video, pg 684
Be Media, pg 702
Christie Digital Systems USA Inc, pg 722
Cinema Equipment Sales of California Inc, pg 724
Alan Gordon Enterprises Inc, pg 772
Instructional Materials & Equipment Distributors (I-Med), pg 789
Jaguar Distribution Corp, pg 792
Lloyd F McKinney Associates Inc, pg 821
Media Fabricators Inc, pg 822

COLORADO

American Educational Products LLC, pg 683
Stanco Sales LLC, pg 899

FLORIDA

Altel Systems Group Inc, pg 682
AVI-SPL, pg 698
Cinema Equipment & Supplies Inc, pg 724
Hollywood Theatre Equipment Inc, pg 781

GEORGIA

Cinevision Corp, pg 725

ILLINOIS

Creative Technology (CT), pg 733
Urbanski Film, pg 923

INDIANA

Lee Co Inc, pg 805

LOUISIANA

Techkno Integration & Design Services LLC, pg 908

MARYLAND

Nicholas P Pipino Associates Inc, pg 857

MASSACHUSETTS

Boston Light & Sound Inc, pg 709

MINNESOTA

Cinequipt Inc, pg 724

MISSISSIPPI

Jasper Ewing & Sons Inc, pg 757

NEBRASKA

Ballantyne Strong Inc, pg 701

NEW JERSEY

Argraph Corp, pg 688
Audio Visual Associates, pg 694

NEW YORK

Colortone Audio Visual, pg 728
Motion Picture Enterprises Inc, pg 831
Neptune Photo Inc, pg 838
Rafik, pg 869

OHIO

Audio Visual Media, pg 694
Visual Products Inc, pg 931

FILM

Projector & Equipment—
35mm Distributors
(continued)

PENNSYLVANIA

Audio Visions Inc, pg 694
Bernie's Photo Center, pg 704
J E Foss Co, pg 764
The Lerro Corp, pg 806
Wespen Audio Visual Co, pg 935

TENNESSEE

Memphis Communications Corp,
pg 823

TEXAS

Audio Visual Technologies Group
(AVTG), pg 695
Cinema Antiques, pg 723
Pro Video & Film Equipment Co
Inc, pg 863

VIRGINIA

The Whitlock Group, pg 937

WISCONSIN

School Specialty Inc, pg 882

MANITOBA

Inland Audio Visual Ltd, pg 788
Lank/Beach Productions Inc, pg 803

ONTARIO

Cinema Stage Inc, pg 724

QUEBEC

Strong Screen Systems, pg 902

Projector & Equipment—
35mm Manufacturers

CALIFORNIA

Christie Digital Systems USA Inc,
pg 722
Alan Gordon Enterprises Inc,
pg 772
Lasergraphics Inc, pg 804

COLORADO

American Educational Products
LLC, pg 683

FLORIDA

Magna-Tech Electronic Co Inc,
pg 814

ILLINOIS

Lipsner-Smith Co, pg 809

NEBRASKA

Ballantyne Strong Inc, pg 701
Strong Cinema Products, pg 902

WISCONSIN

Indus International Inc, pg 787

QUEBEC

Strong Screen Systems, pg 902

Projector & Equipment—
35mm Rentals

ARIZONA

Arizona Cine Equipment, pg 688

ARKANSAS

Carlton-Bates Co, pg 717

CALIFORNIA

Ametron Audio/Video, pg 684
Artichoke Productions, pg 690
Alan Gordon Enterprises Inc,
pg 772
Instructional Materials & Equipment
Distributors (I-Med), pg 789
Media Fabricators Inc, pg 822
PSAV® Presentation Services,
pg 866

DELAWARE

Ken-Del Productions Inc, pg 797

FLORIDA

Jordan Klein Film & Video (JKFV),
pg 795

ILLINOIS

Creative Technology (CT), pg 733

MASSACHUSETTS

Boston Light & Sound Inc, pg 709

MICHIGAN

City Events Group, pg 725
K&R All Media Productions LLC,
pg 796

MINNESOTA

House of Cinemagraphics, pg 782

MISSISSIPPI

Jasper Ewing & Sons Inc, pg 757

NEW HAMPSHIRE

Academic & Campus Technology
Services, pg 672

NEW JERSEY

Audio Visual Associates, pg 694

NEW YORK

Colortone Audio Visual, pg 728
Motion Picture Enterprises Inc,
pg 831

NORTH DAKOTA

Media Productions, pg 822

OHIO

Audio Visual Media, pg 694
Thread Marketing Group, pg 913

PENNSYLVANIA

Audio Visions Inc, pg 694
Bernie's Photo Center, pg 704

TENNESSEE

Memphis Communications Corp,
pg 823
Russ Sturgeon Productions/RSVP,
pg 903

TEXAS

Audio Visual Technologies Group
(AVTG), pg 695
Bright Star Productions Inc, pg 710

VIRGINIA

Projection, pg 865
The Whitlock Group, pg 937

WISCONSIN

School Specialty Inc, pg 882

ALBERTA

Global TV, pg 771

MANITOBA

Inland Audio Visual Ltd, pg 788

Projector & Equipment—
35mm Repairs

ARKANSAS

Carlton-Bates Co, pg 717

CALIFORNIA

Alan Gordon Enterprises Inc,
pg 772
Instructional Materials & Equipment
Distributors (I-Med), pg 789
Pro Camera Repair, pg 862

FLORIDA

Hollywood Theatre Equipment Inc,
pg 781

MASSACHUSETTS

Boston Light & Sound Inc, pg 709

NEW JERSEY

Audio Visual Associates, pg 694

NEW YORK

Colortone Audio Visual, pg 728
Motion Picture Enterprises Inc,
pg 831

NORTH CAROLINA

Strategic Connections, pg 901

OHIO

Audio Visual Media, pg 694

PENNSYLVANIA

Audio Visions Inc, pg 694
Bernie's Photo Center, pg 704
Wespen Audio Visual Co, pg 935

TENNESSEE

Memphis Communications Corp,
pg 823

TEXAS

Audio Visual Technologies Group
(AVTG), pg 695

VIRGINIA

The Whitlock Group, pg 937

WISCONSIN

School Specialty Inc, pg 882

MANITOBA

Inland Audio Visual Ltd, pg 788

Property Agencies, see
Talent & Property
Agencies

Raw Stock Distributors

CALIFORNIA

Christy's Editorial, pg 723
Express Video Supply Inc, pg 757
Media Distributors, pg 822
Total Creative, pg 916
Yale Film & Video, pg 943

FLORIDA

CineVideotech Inc, pg 725
Jordan Klein Film & Video (JKFV),
pg 795

ILLINOIS

Creative Technology (CT), pg 733

NEW JERSEY

Tele-Measurements Inc, pg 910

NEW YORK

Film Emporium, pg 760

OREGON

Wilderness Video, pg 938

PENNSYLVANIA

FMP Media Solutions Inc, pg 763

TEXAS

Texcam Inc, pg 911

WASHINGTON

Inland Audio Visual Co, pg 788

WISCONSIN

USAV Group Inc, pg 923

Raw Stock Manufacturers

CALIFORNIA

Media Distributors, pg 822

NEW YORK

Eastman Kodak Co, pg 750

OREGON

Wilderness Video, pg 938

BRITISH COLUMBIA

Kodak Graphic Communications
Canada Co, pg 800

ONTARIO

FUJIFILM Canada Inc, pg 766

Recording Equipment—
Magnetic, see Magnetic
Recording Equipment

Recording Facility Manufacturers

CALIFORNIA

Yanchar Design & Consulting Group, pg 943

ILLINOIS

IAC Acoustics, pg 783

TEXAS

Stage Directions, pg 898

Recording Facility Rentals

ARIZONA

Arizona Studios, pg 688
Glendale Media Center, pg 771
Loft 19, pg 811

CALIFORNIA

Ametron Audio/Video, pg 684
AMG Studios (Los Angeles), pg 684
Blue Lotus Temple Studio, pg 707
Cutting Edge Productions, pg 736
Different Fur Recording Ltd, pg 741
Golden Gate Studios, pg 772
Greenery Studios, pg 774
LA Castle Studios, pg 803
Los Angeles Center Studios, pg 811
Maximus Media Inc, pg 820
North County Media Center, pg 842
Opulen Studios, pg 847
Polarity Post Production, pg 858
Pro HD Rentals, pg 863
The Producer's Loft, pg 863
RED Studios Hollywood, pg 872
Roundabout Entertainment Inc, pg 878
Santa Clarita Studios, pg 880
ShowBiz Studios, pg 887
Sonora Recorders, pg 893
Stray Angel Films, pg 902
Studio 1444, pg 902
The Studios at Paramount, pg 903
Sunset Bronson Studios, pg 904
Sunset Las Palmas Studios, pg 904
Total Creative, pg 916
Valencia Studios, pg 924

FLORIDA

C&I An Idea Agency, pg 716
Comtel Inc, pg 730
Jordan Klein Film & Video (JKFV), pg 795
LHV Audio Services, pg 807
MAPS Production House, pg 816
Phat Planet Recording Studios, pg 855
South Florida Rehearsal Studios, pg 895
Universal Studios Florida® Production Group, pg 922

GEORGIA

Atlanta Filmworks, pg 692
Mailing Avenue Stageworks, pg 815
Studio Space Atlanta, pg 903

ILLINOIS

Beatty TeleVisual Productions, pg 703
Magnanimous Media, pg 814
PSAV® Presentation Services (Hotel Services Division), pg 866
RBR Productions, pg 870

LOUISIANA

Second Line Stages, pg 883
WVLA-TV, pg 942

MARYLAND

Cre-a-tv Studios, pg 734
The Cutting Corporation, GraphicAudio® & Archival Sound Lab, pg 736
Soundtrax Inc, pg 895

MICHIGAN

City Events Group, pg 725
K&R All Media Productions LLC, pg 796

MISSOURI

Show-Me Audio-Visual, pg 887

MONTANA

Jereco Studios Inc, pg 793

NEW HAMPSHIRE

Apertura, pg 686

NEW JERSEY

Butter Tree Studios, pg 713
18 Label Studios, pg 751
Ironbound Film & Television Studios LLC, pg 791

NEW MEXICO

I-25 Studios, pg 783

NEW YORK

BC Studio, pg 702
Bond Street Studio, pg 708
Bravo Studios, pg 709
Brooklyn Fire Proof, pg 711
Brooklyn Studios, pg 711
KAS Music & Sound, pg 796
LightBox-NY, pg 807
LightSpace Studios, pg 808
Location 05 Studios, pg 811
Manhattan Center Studios Inc, pg 816
The Palmer Group, pg 850
Steiner Studios, pg 900
Umbra of Newburgh LLC, pg 921

NORTH CAROLINA

Duke Media Services, pg 747
K2 Productions, pg 802

NORTH DAKOTA

Media Productions, pg 822

OHIO

Vista Color Imaging Inc, pg 931

PENNSYLVANIA

31st Street Studios, pg 912

SOUTH CAROLINA

Studio Charleston, pg 902

TENNESSEE

DR&A Inc, pg 746
Memphis Communications Corp, pg 823

TEXAS

Maverick Video Productions, pg 820
Omega Productions, pg 845

Phillips Media Source, pg 855
Real to Reel Studios Inc, pg 871
Reelsound Recording Co, pg 872
Saint Elmo Soundstage, pg 879
Stage Directions, pg 898
Texcam Inc, pg 911

WASHINGTON

Kostov Productions, pg 801

WISCONSIN

University of Wisconsin-Oshkosh Radio-TV-Film Dept, pg 923
Wisconsin Public Television, pg 940

WYOMING

Bridger Productions Inc, pg 710

ALBERTA

Global TV, pg 771

BRITISH COLUMBIA

Vancouver Film Studios Ltd, pg 924

MANITOBA

MidCanada Production Services Inc (MidCan), pg 826

ONTARIO

Wallace Film Studios, pg 933

Recording Facility Repairs

CALIFORNIA

Technical Services, pg 908

Reel & Can Distributors

ALABAMA

Curtis Company, pg 736

ARIZONA

Troxell-CDI, pg 918

ARKANSAS

Carlton-Bates Co, pg 717

CALIFORNIA

Birns & Sawyer Inc, pg 706
Christy's Editorial, pg 723
Cinema Equipment Sales of California Inc, pg 724
El Mar Plastics Inc, pg 752
Alan Gordon Enterprises Inc, pg 772
Instructional Materials & Equipment Distributors (I-Med), pg 789
J & R Film Co, pg 792
Jaguar Distribution Corp, pg 792
Media Fabricators Inc, pg 822
Pro8mm, pg 862
Yale Film & Video, pg 943

COLORADO

Goldberg Brothers Inc, pg 772
Stanco Sales LLC, pg 899

CONNECTICUT

MAVCO, pg 820
Rockwell Communications Inc, pg 876

FLORIDA

Cinema Equipment & Supplies Inc, pg 724
Hollywood Theatre Equipment Inc, pg 781
Tallahassee Audio Visual, pg 906

GEORGIA

Audio Visual Resources Inc, pg 695
Cinevision Corp, pg 725

ILLINOIS

Research Technology International (RTI), pg 873
Urbanski Film, pg 923

INDIANA

Lee Co Inc, pg 805

KENTUCKY

Audio Visual Techniques Inc, pg 695

MARYLAND

Nicholas P Pipino Associates Inc, pg 857

MASSACHUSETTS

Hunt's Photo & Video, pg 782
University Products Inc, pg 923

MINNESOTA

AVI Systems, pg 698

MISSISSIPPI

Bowie Audio Visual Enterprises Inc, pg 709
Jasper Ewing & Sons Inc, pg 757

NEW YORK

Colortone Audio Visual, pg 728
Film Emporium, pg 760
Motion Picture Enterprises Inc, pg 831
Neptune Photo Inc, pg 838
Rafik, pg 869

NORTH CAROLINA

Camcor Inc, pg 715

OHIO

Tri-State Audio Visual Co, pg 918

PENNSYLVANIA

Audio Visions Inc, pg 694
Brodart Co, pg 711
Visual Sound Inc, pg 931
Wespen Audio Visual Co, pg 935

TENNESSEE

Memphis Communications Corp, pg 823

TEXAS

Audio Visual Technologies Group (AVTG), pg 695
Cinema Antiques, pg 723
Pro Video & Film Equipment Co Inc, pg 863

UTAH

Redman Movies & Stories, pg 872

FILM

Reel & Can Distributors (continued)

VIRGINIA
Lee Hartman & Sons Inc, pg 805
The Whitlock Group, pg 937

WASHINGTON
Inland Audio Visual Co, pg 788

MANITOBA
Inland Audio Visual Ltd, pg 788

ONTARIO
Carr McLean Ltd, pg 717

Reel & Can Manufacturers

CALIFORNIA
J & R Film Co, pg 792

COLORADO
Goldberg Brothers Inc, pg 772

ILLINOIS
Research Technology International (RTI), pg 873
Urbanski Film, pg 923

NEBRASKA
Strong Cinema Products, pg 902

NEW YORK
Motion Picture Enterprises Inc, pg 831

WISCONSIN
Regal Photo Products Inc/Arkay Corp, pg 873

Reel & Can Rentals

ARIZONA
Arizona Cine Equipment, pg 688

CALIFORNIA
Ametron Audio/Video, pg 684
Christy's Editorial, pg 723

FLORIDA
Jordan Klein Film & Video (JKFV), pg 795

ILLINOIS
Helix Camera & Video, pg 778

MISSISSIPPI
Bowie Audio Visual Enterprises Inc, pg 709
Jasper Ewing & Sons Inc, pg 757

NEW HAMPSHIRE
Apertura, pg 686

NEW YORK
Motion Picture Enterprises Inc, pg 831

PENNSYLVANIA
Audio Visions Inc, pg 694

TENNESSEE
Memphis Communications Corp, pg 823

UTAH
Redman Movies & Stories, pg 872

ALBERTA
Global TV, pg 771

Rehearsal Studio Manufacturers

CALIFORNIA
Yanchar Design & Consulting Group, pg 943

GEORGIA
Lighting & Production Equipment Inc, pg 807

MICHIGAN
Studio Consulting & Construction Inc, pg 902

TENNESSEE
WhisperRoom™ Inc, pg 937

Rehearsal Studio Rentals

ARIZONA
Arizona Cine Equipment, pg 688

CALIFORNIA
Big Door, pg 705
Chapman/Leonard Studio Equipment Inc, pg 720
Golden Gate Studios, pg 772
ShowBiz Studios, pg 887

FLORIDA
CopShopMiami.com, pg 731
Jordan Klein Film & Video (JKFV), pg 795
Phat Planet Recording Studios, pg 855
South Florida Rehearsal Studios, pg 895

GEORGIA
Lighting & Production Equipment Inc, pg 807

LOUISIANA
WVLA-TV, pg 942

MASSACHUSETTS
National Boston, pg 836

MICHIGAN
City Events Group, pg 725
K&R All Media Productions LLC, pg 796

MISSOURI
Show-Me Audio-Visual, pg 887

NEW JERSEY
Audio Visual Dynamics®, pg 694

NEW YORK
Manhattan Center Studios Inc, pg 816
Studio Instrument Rentals (SIR), pg 902

NORTH CAROLINA
Take One Productions Ltd, pg 906

OHIO
Mills James Productions, pg 828
Vista Color Imaging Inc, pg 931

OREGON
Pacific Grip & Lighting Inc, pg 849

PENNSYLVANIA
WHYY Inc, pg 938

TEXAS
Maverick Video Productions, pg 820
Muller Entertainment LLC, pg 833
Stage Directions, pg 898

WASHINGTON
Victory Studios, pg 927

WISCONSIN
Wisconsin Public Television, pg 940

WYOMING
Bridger Productions Inc, pg 710

ALBERTA
Global TV, pg 771

ONTARIO
JIB Shots Equipment Inc, pg 794

Rehearsal Studio Repairs

MICHIGAN
Studio Consulting & Construction Inc, pg 902

Rejuvenation, see Preservation & Rejuvenation

Release Printing

CALIFORNIA
Point of View Productions, pg 858
QRS Software Services, pg 867

CONNECTICUT
Century Color Labs Inc, pg 720

FLORIDA
Roger Scruggs Films, pg 883

MASSACHUSETTS
Extreme Reach Inc, pg 757

MINNESOTA
Badiyan Inc, pg 700

NEW HAMPSHIRE
Apertura, pg 686
Chip Taylor Communications LLC, pg 907

NEW YORK
De Nonno Productions Inc (DPI), pg 739

PENNSYLVANIA
John E Allen Inc, pg 680

TENNESSEE
Motion Picture Services, pg 831
Stage Post, pg 899

WISCONSIN
USAV Group Inc, pg 923

Script Writing

ALABAMA
Diamond Studios, pg 741

ALASKA
Alaska Media Pros LLC, pg 679
Aurora Films, pg 696

ARIZONA
Merestone, pg 823
Metropolitan Audio-Visual Inc, pg 824
Teaberry, pg 908

ARKANSAS
Live'N'Loud, pg 810

CALIFORNIA
Concrete Images, pg 730
Creative Technology, pg 733
Crystal Pyramid Productions™, pg 735
Custom Video Productions Inc, pg 736
Design Media, pg 741
Goal Productions, pg 772
Gold Standard Productions, pg 772
Havas Edge, pg 777
iCorpTv, pg 783
Increase Video/Silver Mine Video, pg 786
ITV Productions, pg 792
Joyce Media Inc, pg 795
Kavich Reynolds Productions Inc, pg 797
KO Creative, pg 800
KTVU-Retail Services, pg 802
The Media Staff Inc, pg 822
Nandar Entertainment Pictures, pg 835
New & Unique Videos™, pg 839
Palardo Productions, pg 850
PSI Inc, pg 866
QRS Software Services, pg 867
Regent Press Publishers & Printers, pg 873
Signature Entertainment, pg 888
Tam Communications Inc, pg 906
Total Creative, pg 916
WMS Media Inc, pg 940

COLORADO
Flashback Media Productions, pg 762
Open Media Foundation, pg 846

Tatum Video, pg 907
Transtar Entertainment Co Inc,
 pg 917

CONNECTICUT

ACM Productions Ltd, pg 674
Essex Television Group Inc, pg 755
New London Media, pg 839

DISTRICT OF COLUMBIA

Hillmann & Carr Inc, pg 780
O'Keefe Communications Inc,
 pg 844

FLORIDA

ACT Productions, pg 675
Chatterbox Productions Inc, pg 721
Civins Productions Inc, pg 725
Communications Concepts Inc
 (CCI), pg 729
CopShopMiami.com, pg 731
Courter Films LLC, pg 732
Jordan Klein Film & Video (JKFV),
 pg 795
Multivision Video & Film, pg 833
Universal Studios Florida®
 Production Group, pg 922

GEORGIA

Burst Video/Film Inc, pg 713
Guerrilla Productions LLC, pg 774
Myriad Productions, pg 835
Malcolm Neal Productions, pg 837
On-Line Productions, pg 845
Visioneering International Inc,
 pg 931

HAWAII

Media Bridge Gamekids, pg 821
1013 Integrated, pg 911

IDAHO

Brad Shaw Productions Inc, pg 885

ILLINOIS

ABSA Films, pg 672
Atomic Imaging Inc/Golan Studios,
 pg 692
Film Police, pg 760
Major Media Productions Inc,
 pg 815
Mightybytes Inc, pg 827
PSAV® Presentation Services
 (Hotel Services Division), pg 866
SCI Television & Creative Media
 LLC, pg 882
WEEK TV, pg 935

INDIANA

A-V-A Video Productions, pg 671
Perennial Pictures Film Corp,
 pg 854

IOWA

Educational Technology & Media
 Services, pg 751

KENTUCKY

Hammond Communications Group
 Inc, pg 775
Horizon Films & Media LLC,
 pg 781

LOUISIANA

Digital FX Inc, pg 742
Louisiana State University Division
 of Strategic Communications,
 pg 811
Moxie Media, pg 832
Vidox Motion Imagery, pg 930

MAINE

Slim Goodbody Corp, pg 890

MARYLAND

Adventure Productions LLC, pg 678
dbF a Media Company, pg 739
James Agee Film Project, pg 792
Kramer Communications Video
 Production, pg 801

MASSACHUSETTS

CommCreative, pg 728
Cramer, pg 732
Green Mountain Post Films (GMP),
 pg 774
Northern Light Productions (NLP),
 pg 842
Gabriel Polonsky Studio, pg 859
Preston Productions Inc, pg 861

MICHIGAN

Digi Sign Design LLC, pg 741
Michigan Recording Arts Institute
 & Technologies, pg 825

MINNESOTA

Badiyan Inc, pg 700

MISSOURI

Switch, pg 905

MONTANA

KCFW Television, pg 797

NEBRASKA

JoeAudio, pg 794

NEW HAMPSHIRE

Apertura, pg 686
Chip Taylor Communications LLC,
 pg 907

NEW JERSEY

Euro-Pacific Film & Video
 Productions Inc, pg 756
PeopleVisionFX, pg 854
Telequest Inc, pg 910
TimeSteps Productions Inc, pg 914

NEW YORK

American Montage Inc, pg 683
aurora productions, pg 696
Bevilacqua Studios, pg 704
Big Fish Production US, pg 705
Broadstreet Productions LLC,
 pg 711
Buffalo Video Production, pg 712
De Nonno Productions Inc (DPI),
 pg 739
Four Corners Productions, pg 764
4-D Creative Media, pg 764
Icontent, pg 783
Richard Kaplan Productions, pg 796
La Paloma Films, pg 803
Jack Morton Worldwide, pg 830
MRM//McCANN, pg 832
The Palmer Group, pg 850
Peckham Productions Inc, pg 852

Richter Productions Inc, pg 875
Vanguard Documentaries, pg 924
Zelman Studios Ltd, pg 945

NORTH CAROLINA

The Communications Group Inc,
 pg 729
Horizon Video Productions Inc,
 pg 781
Kino Mountain Productions LLC,
 pg 799
Moving Pictures, pg 832
Take One Productions Ltd, pg 906

NORTH DAKOTA

Media Productions, pg 822

OHIO

Challenge Productions/Challenge
 Aerial Imaging, pg 720
MainSail Production Services Inc,
 pg 815
Mills James Productions, pg 828
Take 1 Media Services, pg 906
Treehaus Communications Inc,
 pg 917

OKLAHOMA

Academic Media & Digital
 Services, pg 672

OREGON

Ideascape Inc, pg 784
Odyssey Productions Inc, pg 844

PENNSYLVANIA

Argentine Productions Inc, pg 688
Audio Visual Communications Inc,
 pg 694
Center City Film & Video Inc,
 pg 719
FMP Media Solutions Inc, pg 763
Innovision Media Group, pg 788
JPL, pg 795
Kensington Falls Animation, pg 797
Production Masters Inc (PMI),
 pg 864
Video/Film Associates, pg 928

RHODE ISLAND

Sound-FX-Design, pg 894

SOUTH CAROLINA

Genesis Creative, pg 769
Venture Media, pg 925

TENNESSEE

American Blackguard Inc, pg 683
Anode Inc, pg 686
Motion Picture Services, pg 831
Paradigm Marketing & Creative,
 pg 851
Scripps Networks, pg 882
Stage Post, pg 899

TEXAS

Alexander Media Productions,
 pg 679
Anaphora Literary Press, pg 685
Best Film & Video, pg 704
Biway Media, pg 706
Cerutti Productions Inc, pg 720
Chalk Dust Co, pg 720
Dykeman Associates Inc, pg 748
Emergency Film Group, pg 753
Horizon Film + Video Productions,
 pg 781

Prairie Pictures Film & Video,
 pg 860
Romar Learning Solutions LLC,
 pg 877
RuffHouse LLC, pg 878
The Samuels Co, pg 879
Stage Directions, pg 898
Texas Heart Institute Visual
 Communication Services, pg 911

VIRGINIA

Altruist Media LLC, pg 682
BES Studios, pg 704
CACI Integrated Communications,
 pg 713
CDR Communications Inc, pg 719
Metro Productions, pg 824

WASHINGTON

Adams Creative & Production
 Services, pg 675
North-by-Northwest - A Digital
 Studio, pg 842

WISCONSIN

Audio Visual of Milwaukee Inc,
 pg 694
Meridian Studios, pg 824
Video Wisconsin Inc, pg 929
Wisconsin Public Television, pg 940

WYOMING

Bridger Productions Inc, pg 710

ALBERTA

Black Media Works, pg 706
Global TV, pg 771

BRITISH COLUMBIA

West Eagle Films Inc, pg 935

MANITOBA

Lank/Beach Productions Inc, pg 803

NORTHWEST TERRITORIES

Yellowknife Films Inc, pg 944

ONTARIO

ADS Media, pg 677
Doomsday Studios Limited, pg 745
GAPC (General Assembly
 Production Centre), pg 768
RB Productions, pg 870

QUEBEC

Muse Entertainment Enterprises,
 pg 834

**Sixteen mm Projector and
 Equipment,** *see* **Projector
 & Equipment—16mm**

Slide to Film Transfers, *see*
 Transfers—Slide to Film

Slow Motion Photography,
 see **Photography—Slow
 Motion**

FILM

Special Effects

ARIZONA

Creative Backstage, pg 733
Merestone, pg 823

CALIFORNIA

Artichoke Productions, pg 690
Calbor Enterprises Two Inc, pg 713
CinemaGear.com, pg 724
Coloredge Inc, pg 728
Creative Technology, pg 733
Crystal Pyramid Productions™, pg 735
First Person Inc, pg 761
Full Scale Effects, pg 767
iCorpTv, pg 783
Industrial Light & Magic (ILM), pg 787
Jaguar Distribution Corp, pg 792
Laser Magic Productions, pg 804
Lumeni Productions Inc, pg 812
New Deal Studios, pg 839
Palardo Productions, pg 850
piXvfm Inc, pg 857
QRS Software Services, pg 867
Reality Check Systems, pg 871
RetinaVision Productions, pg 874
Shapeshifter, pg 885
SonicPool, pg 892
Special Effects Unlimited Inc, pg 896
Total Creative, pg 916
Two Door Productions LLC, pg 920
VidCan Media Solutions, pg 927
Wavemaker Media Design, pg 934
Mark Woollen & Associates, pg 941

COLORADO

Full Spectrum Arts & Services, pg 767
Maniac Productions, pg 816

CONNECTICUT

Think 3-D.com, pg 912

DISTRICT OF COLUMBIA

Interface Media Group, pg 789

FLORIDA

Audio Visual Imagineering Inc, pg 694
Multivision Video & Film, pg 833
Orlando Special Effects, pg 848
Universal Studios Florida® Production Group, pg 922

GEORGIA

First Cut Communications LLC, pg 761
Guerrilla Productions LLC, pg 774
WaveGuide Studios, pg 934

HAWAII

Dot C Software Inc, pg 746
Hyperspective Studios Inc, pg 783

ILLINOIS

ABSA Films, pg 672
Chicago Spotlight Inc, pg 721
Consolidated Display Co Inc, pg 731
Mightybytes Inc, pg 827
Multimedia Marketing Group, pg 833
Pepper Group, pg 854

INDIANA

A-V-A Video Productions, pg 671

KENTUCKY

Theatre Effects, pg 911

LOUISIANA

Story Teller Effects Group LLC, pg 901
Vidox Motion Imagery, pg 930

MARYLAND

Kramer Communications Video Production, pg 801

MASSACHUSETTS

CommCreative, pg 728
MotionArt Studios, pg 831
Northern Light Productions (NLP), pg 842
Preston Productions Inc, pg 861
TR Productions, pg 916

MICHIGAN

Digi Sign Design LLC, pg 741
Tectonics Industries LLC, pg 909

MINNESOTA

House of Cinemagraphics, pg 782
Media Loft Inc, pg 822
Pointward, pg 858

MISSOURI

Fantasy Creations FX, pg 759

MONTANA

Filmlites Montana, pg 760

NEVADA

DVDs4Less, pg 748
GES Audio Visual, pg 770
Ron Roy Productions/Moodtapes, pg 878

NEW HAMPSHIRE

Apertura, pg 686

NEW JERSEY

CELCO, pg 719
Early Films, pg 749
NFL Films Inc, pg 841
NFL Films Music Library, pg 841
Starlite, pg 900

NEW YORK

Big Film Design, pg 705
Big Fish Production US, pg 705
Broadstreet Productions LLC, pg 711
Chromavision Corp, pg 723
La Paloma Films, pg 803
The Palmer Group, pg 850
R/GA, pg 868
Judson Rosebush Co Inc, pg 877

NORTH CAROLINA

The Communications Group Inc, pg 729
Image Associates Inc, pg 784

OHIO

Mills James Productions, pg 828
Thread Marketing Group, pg 913

OREGON

Artbeats, pg 690

PENNSYLVANIA

Innovision Media Group, pg 788
Shore Manufacturing Co, pg 886
31st Street Studios, pg 912

RHODE ISLAND

Sound-FX-Design, pg 894

SOUTH CAROLINA

Genesis Creative, pg 769

TENNESSEE

High-Tech Special Effects Inc, pg 779
Motion Picture Services, pg 831
Paradigm Marketing & Creative, pg 851
Stage Post, pg 899

TEXAS

Anaphora Literary Press, pg 685
Biway Media, pg 706
The Samuels Co, pg 879
Stage Directions, pg 898

UTAH

Strata™, pg 901

VIRGINIA

Blair Inc, pg 707

WASHINGTON

Inland Audio Visual Co, pg 788
Laser Fantasy/HECK Industries/Photon Manufacturing, pg 804

WISCONSIN

5th Floor Recording Co, pg 760
USAV Group Inc, pg 923

WYOMING

Bridger Productions Inc, pg 710

ALBERTA

Global TV, pg 771

ONTARIO

ADS Media, pg 677
The Fluorescent Co Inc, pg 763
GestureTek, pg 770
Pyrotek Special Effects Inc, pg 867

Still Camera, *see* Movie & Still Camera

Still Projector, *see* Continuous Still Projector

Stock-Shot Libraries, *see* Libraries—Film or Stock-Shot

Stock Transfer

CALIFORNIA

Audio Mechanics, pg 693
Chace Audio by Deluxe, pg 720
Goal Productions, pg 772
iCorpTv, pg 783
Polarity Post Production, pg 858
QRS Software Services, pg 867
SonicPool, pg 892

KENTUCKY

Broadway Digital, pg 711

MARYLAND

Bethesda Softworks LLC, pg 704
dbF a Media Company, pg 739
Soundtrax Inc, pg 895

MASSACHUSETTS

Green Mountain Post Films (GMP), pg 774
Soundtrack Group, pg 895

MICHIGAN

Digi Sign Design LLC, pg 741

NEW HAMPSHIRE

Apertura, pg 686

NEW JERSEY

CELCO, pg 719
NFL Films Music Library, pg 841

NEW YORK

KAS Music & Sound, pg 796
The Palmer Group, pg 850

TENNESSEE

Motion Picture Services, pg 831
Stage Post, pg 899

WISCONSIN

Video Wisconsin Inc, pg 929

QUEBEC

Muse Entertainment Enterprises, pg 834

Storage Vault Rentals

CALIFORNIA

Total Creative, pg 916

NORTH CAROLINA

Take One Productions Ltd, pg 906

Studio Photography, *see* Photography—Studio

Synchronizer Distributors

ARIZONA

EAR Professional Audio/Video, pg 749

CALIFORNIA

Christy's Editorial, pg 723
Cinema Equipment Sales of California Inc, pg 724

Alan Gordon Enterprises Inc, pg 772
J & R Film Co, pg 792
JLCooper Electronics, pg 794

COLORADO

Ceavco Audio Visual Company Inc, pg 719
Stanco Sales LLC, pg 899

CONNECTICUT

Rockwell Communications Inc, pg 876

FLORIDA

Recording Media & Equipment Inc (RM&E), pg 872

KENTUCKY

NOR-COM Inc, pg 841

MARYLAND

RTZ Audio Visual, pg 878

MICHIGAN

TEL Systems LLC, pg 909

MINNESOTA

AVI Systems, pg 698

MISSISSIPPI

Jasper Ewing & Sons Inc, pg 757

NEW JERSEY

Audio Visual Dynamics®, pg 694
JRF Magnetic Sciences Inc, pg 795
SYMCO Inc, pg 905

NEW YORK

Colortone Audio Visual, pg 728
Motion Picture Enterprises Inc, pg 831
Tri-Ed Distribution Inc, pg 918

OHIO

Audio Visual Media, pg 694
Icom Multimedia, pg 783

PENNSYLVANIA

J E Foss Co, pg 764
Hite Co, pg 780
Wespen Audio Visual Co, pg 935

TENNESSEE

Memphis Communications Corp, pg 823

TEXAS

Audio Visual Technologies Group (AVTG), pg 695
Pro Video & Film Equipment Co Inc, pg 863

UTAH

Performance Audio LLC, pg 854
RIA Corp, pg 874

VIRGINIA

Lee Hartman & Sons Inc, pg 805

WASHINGTON

Inland Audio Visual Co, pg 788

ONTARIO

Nationwide Audio Visual Co, pg 837

Synchronizer Manufacturers

CALIFORNIA

J & R Film Co, pg 792
JLCooper Electronics, pg 794

FLORIDA

Magna-Tech Electronic Co Inc, pg 814

RHODE ISLAND

M-Audio, pg 813

Synchronizer Rentals

CALIFORNIA

Artichoke Productions, pg 690
Christy's Editorial, pg 723
Alan Gordon Enterprises Inc, pg 772
J & R Film Co, pg 792
Synthesizer Rental Service, pg 906

COLORADO

Ceavco Audio Visual Company Inc, pg 719

CONNECTICUT

Rockwell Communications Inc, pg 876

ILLINOIS

Helix Camera & Video, pg 778

INDIANA

OMNI Productions, pg 845

MARYLAND

RTZ Audio Visual, pg 878

MASSACHUSETTS

Green Mountain Post Films (GMP), pg 774

MICHIGAN

City Events Group, pg 725
K&R All Media Productions LLC, pg 796

MINNESOTA

AVI Systems, pg 698

MISSISSIPPI

Jasper Ewing & Sons Inc, pg 757

NEW HAMPSHIRE

Apertura, pg 686

NEW JERSEY

Audio Visual Dynamics®, pg 694

NEW YORK

Langie Audio Visual Systems, pg 803
Motion Picture Enterprises Inc, pg 831

OHIO

Audio Visual Media, pg 694
Icom Multimedia, pg 783

OREGON

Northwest Film Center, pg 842

TENNESSEE

Memphis Communications Corp, pg 823

TEXAS

Omega Productions, pg 845

VIRGINIA

Projection, pg 865

WASHINGTON

Inland Audio Visual Co, pg 788

ALBERTA

Global TV, pg 771

Synchronizer Repairs

CALIFORNIA

Christy's Editorial, pg 723
Alan Gordon Enterprises Inc, pg 772
J & R Film Co, pg 792

COLORADO

Ceavco Audio Visual Company Inc, pg 719

CONNECTICUT

Rockwell Communications Inc, pg 876

FLORIDA

Hi-Tech Enterprises Inc, pg 779

KENTUCKY

NOR-COM Inc, pg 841

MARYLAND

RTZ Audio Visual, pg 878

MINNESOTA

AVI Systems, pg 698

NEW YORK

Langie Audio Visual Systems, pg 803
Motion Picture Enterprises Inc, pg 831

OHIO

Audio Visual Media, pg 694
Icom Multimedia, pg 783

PENNSYLVANIA

Wespen Audio Visual Co, pg 935

TENNESSEE

Memphis Communications Corp, pg 823

VIRGINIA

Lee Hartman & Sons Inc, pg 805

WASHINGTON

Inland Audio Visual Co, pg 788

Syndication

CALIFORNIA

Custom Video Productions Inc, pg 736
Point of View Productions, pg 858
QRS Software Services, pg 867

FLORIDA

Multivision Video & Film, pg 833

GEORGIA

Guerrilla Productions LLC, pg 774

ILLINOIS

Moviecraft Inc, pg 831

INDIANA

Perennial Pictures Film Corp, pg 854

MASSACHUSETTS

Extreme Reach Inc, pg 757

NEW YORK

Jalbert Productions International, pg 792
The Palmer Group, pg 850
VIEW Inc (Video International Entertainment World Inc), pg 930

NORTH CAROLINA

Crystal Pictures Inc, pg 735

TENNESSEE

Continental Film, pg 731
Motion Picture Services, pg 831
Stage Post, pg 899

VIRGINIA

CACI Integrated Communications, pg 713

WISCONSIN

Wisconsin Public Television, pg 940

WYOMING

Bridger Productions Inc, pg 710

ALBERTA

Global TV, pg 771

Talent & Property Agencies

ALABAMA

Sound of Birmingham Productions, pg 894

ALASKA

Alaska Media Pros LLC, pg 679

CALIFORNIA

Creative Artists Agency LLC, pg 733
Havas Edge, pg 777
International Contact Inc, pg 790

FILM

Talent & Property Agencies (continued)

CALIFORNIA (continued)

The Location Connection Inc, pg 810
Palardo Productions, pg 850
QRS Software Services, pg 867
Sahara Records & Filmworks Entertainment Co, pg 879
Santa Barbara Location Services, pg 880
Signature Entertainment, pg 888
SonicPool, pg 892
WARPed Pictures, pg 934

FLORIDA

CopShopMiami.com, pg 731

HAWAII

Media Bridge Gamekids, pg 821

MARYLAND

The Image Generators, pg 785

MASSACHUSETTS

Preston Productions Inc, pg 861

MICHIGAN

Digi Sign Design LLC, pg 741

MINNESOTA

Moore Creative Talent Inc, pg 830

NEW HAMPSHIRE

Chip Taylor Communications LLC, pg 907

NEW JERSEY

Suede Interactive, pg 903

NEW YORK

InterNation Inc, pg 789

RHODE ISLAND

Sound-FX-Design, pg 894

TENNESSEE

Motion Picture Services, pg 831
Stage Post, pg 899

TEXAS

The Campbell Agency, pg 715

VIRGINIA

CACI Integrated Communications, pg 713

WYOMING

Bridger Productions Inc, pg 710

BRITISH COLUMBIA

MicrophoneRentals.com, pg 826

Thirty-Five mm Projector & Equipment, see Projector & Equipment—35mm

Titling & Artwork Services, see Artwork & Titling Services

Transfer & Conversion Equipment Distributors

ARIZONA

Professional Marketing Services Inc, pg 865
Troxell-CDI, pg 918

ARKANSAS

White Diamond Productions LLC, pg 937

CALIFORNIA

MediaPOINTE, pg 823
Yale Film & Video, pg 943

FLORIDA

ONstage, pg 846

ILLINOIS

Lipsner-Smith Co, pg 809
Urbanski Film, pg 923

INDIANA

Lee Co Inc, pg 805

KENTUCKY

Barney Miller's Inc, pg 827
NOR-COM Inc, pg 841

MISSOURI

Cintrex Audio Visual, pg 725
Schiller's Audio-Visual, pg 881

NEW JERSEY

SADiE Inc, pg 879

NEW YORK

Neptune Photo Inc, pg 838

PENNSYLVANIA

J E Foss Co, pg 764

TEXAS

Pro Video & Film Equipment Co Inc, pg 863

WISCONSIN

Safe Harbor Computers, pg 879

BRITISH COLUMBIA

Commercial Electronics Ltd, pg 728

Transfer & Conversion Equipment Manufacturers

NEW JERSEY

CELCO, pg 719
SADiE Inc, pg 879

NEW YORK

ELMO USA Corp, pg 753

BRITISH COLUMBIA

Triad Communications Ltd, pg 918

Transfer & Conversion Equipment Rentals

ARKANSAS

White Diamond Productions LLC, pg 937

CALIFORNIA

Roundabout Entertainment Inc, pg 878

FLORIDA

ONstage, pg 846

MISSOURI

Schiller's Audio-Visual, pg 881
Show-Me Audio-Visual, pg 887

NEW YORK

Posthorn Recordings, pg 859

NORTH CAROLINA

Duke Media Services, pg 747

PENNSYLVANIA

FMP Media Solutions Inc, pg 763

Transfer & Conversion Equipment Repairs

KENTUCKY

NOR-COM Inc, pg 841

MISSOURI

Cintrex Audio Visual, pg 725

NEW YORK

ELMO USA Corp, pg 753

Transfers—Film to Videotape

ARIZONA

On-Site Video, pg 846

CALIFORNIA

Access Video in Berkeley, pg 673
Action Photo Digital Graphics, pg 675
Action Video, pg 675
Artichoke Productions, pg 690
Creative Technology, pg 733
Custom Video Productions Inc, pg 736
Digital Jungle, pg 742
Em Gee Film Library, pg 753
Havas Edge, pg 777
Hooper Camera & Imaging, pg 781
iCorpTv, pg 783
Method Studios, pg 824
Pacific Video Products Inc, pg 849
Point.360, pg 858
Pro8mm, pg 862
QRS Software Services, pg 867
RetinaVision Productions, pg 874
SonicPool, pg 892
Wavemaker Media Design, pg 934
Yale Film & Video, pg 943

COLORADO

Ceavco Audio Visual Company Inc, pg 719
Rocky Mountain Audio/Video Productions Inc, pg 876

CONNECTICUT

Digital Video Productions, pg 742
The Gary-Paul Agency, pg 768
Rockwell Communications Inc, pg 876

DELAWARE

Ken-Del Productions Inc, pg 797
Ken-Del Studios, pg 797

DISTRICT OF COLUMBIA

Interface Media Group, pg 789
Library of Congress, Motion Picture, Broadcasting & Recorded Sound Division, pg 807

FLORIDA

Accord Productions, pg 673
Civins Productions Inc, pg 725
Communications Concepts Inc (CCI), pg 729
Multivision Video & Film, pg 833
Photosound of Orlando Inc, pg 856
Sunrise Studios, pg 904

GEORGIA

Audio Visual Resources Inc, pg 695

ILLINOIS

Beatty TeleVisual Productions, pg 703
Major Media Inc, pg 815
Major Media Productions Inc, pg 815
Midwest Digital Corp, pg 827
Moviecraft Inc, pg 831
Optimus, pg 847
Pepper Group, pg 854
Sound/Video Impressions Inc, pg 894
WEEK TV, pg 935

INDIANA

OMNI Productions, pg 845

IOWA

Duplication Media, pg 748
Educational Technology & Media Services, pg 751

KENTUCKY

Audio Visual Techniques Inc, pg 695
Barney Miller's Inc, pg 827
The PPS Group, pg 860

LOUISIANA

Moxie Media, pg 832

MARYLAND

Kramer Communications Video Production, pg 801
Milner-Fenwick Inc, pg 828

MASSACHUSETTS

Capron Lighting & Sound Co Inc, pg 716
CommCreative, pg 728
Integrated Solutions Group, pg 789
National Boston, pg 836

MICHIGAN

K&R's Recording Studios Inc,
  pg 796
RingSide Creative, pg 875
The Transfer Zone®, pg 917

MINNESOTA

Badiyan Inc, pg 700
Rum Jungle Media, pg 878

MISSISSIPPI

Jasper Ewing & Sons Inc, pg 757

MISSOURI

Schiller's Audio-Visual, pg 881

MONTANA

KUSM TV, pg 802

NEVADA

Peterson's Video Transfer Services,
  pg 855

NEW HAMPSHIRE

Academic & Campus Technology
  Services, pg 672
Apertura, pg 686

NEW JERSEY

CELCO, pg 719
NFL Films Inc, pg 841
NFL Films Music Library, pg 841
Video Corporation of America
  (VCA), pg 927

NEW YORK

aurora productions, pg 696
Colortone Audio Visual, pg 728
Thomas Craven Film Corp, pg 733
DuArt Media Services, pg 747
Duplication Specialists Inc, pg 748
International Digital Centre, pg 790
Magno Sound Inc, pg 815
The Palmer Group, pg 850
PostWorks, pg 860
TeleTime Productions, pg 910
USA Studios, pg 923
Zelman Studios Ltd, pg 945

NORTH CAROLINA

Camcor Inc, pg 715
Duke Media Services, pg 747

OHIO

Advent Media Inc, pg 677
Russ Beckner Pictures, pg 703
Vista Color Imaging Inc, pg 931

PENNSYLVANIA

John E Allen Inc, pg 680
Audio Visions Inc, pg 694
Audio Visual Communications Inc,
  pg 694
Bernie's Photo Center, pg 704
Center City Film & Video Inc,
  pg 719

Muderick Media, pg 833
Visual Sound Inc, pg 931
WPHL-TV, pg 942

TENNESSEE

Motion Picture Services, pg 831
Stage Post, pg 899

TEXAS

Dub King, pg 747
Matson Multi-Media, pg 820
McNee Productions Inc, pg 821
Julye Newlin Productions Inc,
  pg 840
Replicopy Digital Media Center,
  pg 873
Texas Heart Institute Visual
  Communication Services, pg 911

VERMONT

University of Vermont, Instructional
  Television Dept, pg 923

VIRGINIA

BES Studios, pg 704
CDR Communications Inc, pg 719
Henninger Media Services, pg 779

WASHINGTON

Victory Studios, pg 927

WISCONSIN

Audio Visual of Milwaukee Inc,
  pg 694
University of Wisconsin-Oshkosh
  Radio-TV-Film Dept, pg 923
Wisconsin Public Television, pg 940

WYOMING

Bridger Productions Inc, pg 710

BRITISH COLUMBIA

Commercial Electronics Ltd, pg 728
Triad Communications Ltd, pg 918

QUEBEC

Muse Entertainment Enterprises,
  pg 834

Transfers—Slide to Film

ARIZONA

Professional Marketing Services Inc,
  pg 865

CALIFORNIA

Artichoke Productions, pg 690
iCorpTv, pg 783
QRS Software Services, pg 867
RetinaVision Productions, pg 874

FLORIDA

Sunrise Studios, pg 904

GEORGIA

Visioneering International Inc,
  pg 931

LOUISIANA

Moxie Media, pg 832

MICHIGAN

K&R's Recording Studios Inc,
  pg 796

MISSOURI

Schiller's Audio-Visual, pg 881

NEW HAMPSHIRE

Apertura, pg 686

NEW JERSEY

CELCO, pg 719

NEW YORK

Buffalo Video Production, pg 712
Jack Morton Worldwide, pg 830
The Palmer Group, pg 850
Zelman Studios Ltd, pg 945

PENNSYLVANIA

John E Allen Inc, pg 680
Audio Visual Communications Inc,
  pg 694
Bernie's Photo Center, pg 704

TENNESSEE

Motion Picture Services, pg 831
Stage Post, pg 899

TEXAS

Stage Directions, pg 898

WISCONSIN

Audio Visual of Milwaukee Inc,
  pg 694

ALBERTA

Global TV, pg 771

Transfers—Videotape to Film

CALIFORNIA

Artichoke Productions, pg 690
Havas Edge, pg 777
iCorpTv, pg 783
Opticomm-EMCORE, pg 847
QRS Software Services, pg 867
RetinaVision Productions, pg 874
SonicPool, pg 892

GEORGIA

Cinema Concepts, pg 724

MARYLAND

Kramer Communications Video
  Production, pg 801

MASSACHUSETTS

CommCreative, pg 728

MICHIGAN

K&R's Recording Studios Inc,
  pg 796
The Transfer Zone®, pg 917

NEW HAMPSHIRE

Apertura, pg 686

NEW JERSEY

CELCO, pg 719
Video Corporation of America
  (VCA), pg 927

NEW YORK

aurora productions, pg 696
Thomas Craven Film Corp, pg 733
DuArt Media Services, pg 747
Jack Morton Worldwide, pg 830
The Palmer Group, pg 850
Zelman Studios Ltd, pg 945

PENNSYLVANIA

Audio Visual Communications Inc,
  pg 694
Bernie's Photo Center, pg 704

TENNESSEE

Motion Picture Services, pg 831
Stage Post, pg 899

TEXAS

McNee Productions Inc, pg 821

WISCONSIN

Audio Visual of Milwaukee Inc,
  pg 694
Video Wisconsin Inc, pg 929

ALBERTA

Global TV, pg 771

QUEBEC

Muse Entertainment Enterprises,
  pg 834

Underwater Photography, *see* Photography—Underwater

Videotape to Film Transfers, *see* Transfers—Videotape to Film

Workshops, *see* Production Workshops

VIDEO

Accessory, *see* Equipment & Accessory

Aerial Photography, *see* Photography—Aerial

Animation Production Services

ALABAMA

Diamond Studios, pg 741

ARIZONA

Merestone, pg 823

ARKANSAS

White Diamond Productions LLC, pg 937

CALIFORNIA

Access Video in Berkeley, pg 673
Advanced Systems Group LLC, pg 677
Artichoke Productions, pg 690
Blind™, pg 707
Buttercup Pictures, pg 713
CCI Digital, a DVS Company, pg 718
Classic Images Stock Footage LLC, pg 726
Creative Technology, pg 733
Crystal Pyramid Productions™, pg 735
Custom Video Productions Inc, pg 736
Diaquest, pg 741
digital OutPost, pg 742
Direct Images Interactive Inc, pg 743
First Person Inc, pg 761
Goal Productions, pg 772
Havas Edge, pg 777
Hydrogen Whiskey Studios, pg 783
iCorpTv, pg 783
Images in Motion Media Inc, pg 785
Imageworks, pg 785
JDS Video & Media Productions Inc, pg 793
Laser Magic Productions, pg 804
Lumeni Productions Inc, pg 812
Lynch Communications, pg 813
Maximus Media Inc, pg 820
The Media Staff Inc, pg 822
Medical Visual Creations (MVC), pg 823
New & Unique Videos™, pg 839
Nolte Media, pg 841
QRS Software Services, pg 867
Regent Press Publishers & Printers, pg 873
Saturn Studios, pg 881
Staylor-Made Communications Inc, pg 900
Still N' Motion, pg 901
Tam Communications Inc, pg 906
Timestream Video, pg 914
Total Creative, pg 916
Twin Peaks Creative, pg 920
Two Door Productions LLC, pg 920
Uniconn Productions, pg 921
Universal Studios, pg 922
VidCan Media Solutions, pg 927

Videobotics, pg 929
Warner Bros Entertainment Inc, pg 934
Wavemaker Media Design, pg 934
WMS Media Inc, pg 940

COLORADO

CSI Film & Video LLC, pg 735
Flashback Media Productions, pg 762
Full Spectrum Arts & Services, pg 767
Spectrum Audio Visual Services, pg 897

CONNECTICUT

BRB Audiovisual Productions, pg 709
Geomatrix Productions, pg 770
Musivision Inc, pg 835
New London Media, pg 839
Palace Production Center, pg 850
Bret Stern Productions, pg 900

DELAWARE

So Smart Productions, pg 891

DISTRICT OF COLUMBIA

Hillmann & Carr Inc, pg 780
Interface Media Group, pg 789
O'Keefe Communications Inc, pg 844

FLORIDA

Access Media Group, pg 673
Accord Productions, pg 673
Applebox Studio, pg 687
Audio Visual Imagineering Inc, pg 694
Civins Productions Inc, pg 725
Communications Concepts Inc (CCI), pg 729
Hi-Tech Enterprises Inc, pg 779
Sunfire Communications Inc, pg 904
Tricycle Studios, pg 918
Mike Vasilinda Productions Inc, pg 925
Video Techniques Inc, pg 928
Vistamax Productions, pg 931

GEORGIA

Beachwood Productions, pg 702
Beast Atlanta, pg 703
The DVI Group, pg 748
ECG Productions, pg 750
First Cut Communications LLC, pg 761
Guerrilla Productions LLC, pg 774
Staging Directions Inc, pg 899

HAWAII

Hyperspective Studios Inc, pg 783
Media Bridge Gamekids, pg 821

ILLINOIS

Airways Digital Media, pg 679
Manning Productions, pg 816
Optimus, pg 847
Pepper Group, pg 854
Richter Studios, pg 875
SCI Television & Creative Media LLC, pg 882
Sparkfactor, pg 896
Tele-Time Systems, pg 910
Video Impressions, pg 928
WEEK TV, pg 935

INDIANA

A-V-A Video Productions, pg 671
OMNI Productions, pg 845

KENTUCKY

Broadway Digital, pg 711
Hammond Communications Group Inc, pg 775
The PPS Group, pg 860

LOUISIANA

Digital FX Inc, pg 742
Louisiana State University Division of Strategic Communications, pg 811
Vidox Motion Imagery, pg 930
WVLA-TV, pg 942

MARYLAND

Adventure Productions LLC, pg 678
CPR MultiMedia Solutions, pg 732
dbF a Media Company, pg 739
Kramer Communications Video Production, pg 801
Media Dimensions LLC, pg 821
Pro Cuts Editing Services, pg 862
Producers Video, pg 863

MASSACHUSETTS

CommCreative, pg 728
Cramer, pg 732
Extreme Reach Inc, pg 757
Monadnock Media Inc, pg 829
MotionArt Studios, pg 831
Northern Light Productions (NLP), pg 842
Penfield Productions Ltd, pg 853
Gabriel Polonsky Studio, pg 859
Preston Productions Inc, pg 861
Real Cool Productions, pg 871
The Weather Company, An IBM Business, pg 935

MICHIGAN

Blue Mouse Studio, pg 707
Digi Sign Design LLC, pg 741
Digital Image Studios LLC, pg 742
K&R's Recording Studios Inc, pg 796
Michigan Recording Arts Institute & Technologies, pg 825

MINNESOTA

The ADS Group, pg 676

MISSOURI

Avatar Studios, pg 697
Conference Technologies Inc, pg 730
Show-Me Audio-Visual, pg 887
StoryTrack, pg 901

NEVADA

Aardvark Video & Media Productions, pg 671
Encore Event Technologies LLC, pg 754
JCS Video Productions, pg 793
21st Century Video Productions, pg 919

NEW HAMPSHIRE

Apertura, pg 686
Chip Taylor Communications LLC, pg 907

NEW JERSEY

A-V Services Inc, pg 671
Allegro Productions Inc, pg 680
Broadcast Center Studios, pg 710
CD Meyer Inc, pg 718
Diversified, pg 744
MediaMix Inc, pg 822
MediaNow Inc, pg 822
MiB MediaWorks, pg 825
NFL Films Inc, pg 841
PeopleVisionFX, pg 854
PLS Staging, pg 858
Two Animators LLP, pg 920
VCSvideo, pg 925

NEW MEXICO

Little Big Bang Design Inc, pg 810
Production Outfitters, pg 864

NEW YORK

American Artists Representatives Inc, pg 682
Animotion Inc, pg 685
The Big House Group, pg 705
Buzzco Associates Inc, pg 713
Chromavision Corp, pg 723
Cohn Creative Group LLC, pg 727
CP Digital, pg 732
Digital Art Video Inc, pg 741
DuArt Media Services, pg 747
4-D Creative Media, pg 764
IAI Records & Video, pg 783
Lylofilm Productions, pg 813
Manhattan Center Studios Inc, pg 816
Mood Creations Ltd, pg 829
MRY, pg 832
Polestar Films & Associated Arts Ltd, pg 859
PostWorks, pg 860
PrimeLight Productions Inc, pg 862
Synaptic Digital, pg 905
Teatown Communications Group, pg 908
Alan Weiss Productions, pg 935

NORTH CAROLINA

The Communications Group Inc, pg 729
Franklin Video Inc, pg 765
Horizon Video Productions Inc, pg 781
L A Management Co LLC, pg 802
Moving Pictures, pg 832
On Location North Carolina, pg 846
Take One Productions Ltd, pg 906

OHIO

Advent Media Inc, pg 677
Aztec Video Productions, pg 700
Bartha, pg 702
Lyon Video Inc, pg 813
Mills James Productions, pg 828
Vista Color Imaging Inc, pg 931

OKLAHOMA

PDC Productions, pg 852

OREGON

Artbeats, pg 690
InterVision Media, pg 791
Wallace Creative LLC, pg 933

PENNSYLVANIA

AccuWeather Inc, pg 674
FMP Media Solutions Inc, pg 763
Innovision Media Group, pg 788
JPL, pg 795

Main Point Productions, pg 815
Muderick Media, pg 833
Production Masters Inc (PMI),
  pg 864
Scala Inc, pg 881
WPHL-TV, pg 942

RHODE ISLAND

Sound-FX-Design, pg 894

SOUTH CAROLINA

American Production Services LLC,
  pg 684
Genesis Creative, pg 769

TENNESSEE

Motion Picture Services, pg 831
Paradigm Marketing & Creative,
  pg 851
Running Pony Productions LLC,
  pg 878
Scripps Networks, pg 882
Stage Post, pg 899
Russ Sturgeon Productions/RSVP,
  pg 903

TEXAS

AMS Pictures, pg 684
Anaphora Literary Press, pg 685
Biway Media, pg 706
Chalk Dust Co, pg 720
Epic Software Group Inc, pg 755
Horizon Film + Video Productions,
  pg 781
Hurst Digital, pg 782
McNee Productions Inc, pg 821
Julye Newlin Productions Inc,
  pg 840
Phillips Media Source, pg 855
South Coast Film & Video, pg 895
Texas Heart Institute Visual
  Communication Services, pg 911

UTAH

ImageWorks Communications,
  pg 785

VIRGINIA

Allied Media Corp, pg 681
Altruist Media LLC, pg 682
BES Studios, pg 704
CACI Integrated Communications,
  pg 713
Eagle Films, pg 749
EFX Media, pg 751
Henninger Media Services, pg 779
Metro Productions, pg 824

WASHINGTON

North-by-Northwest - A Digital
  Studio, pg 842
Sparkworks Media, pg 896
Victory Studios, pg 927

WISCONSIN

Learning Technology Services,
  pg 805
Logan Productions Inc, pg 811
Meridian Studios, pg 824
Mirror 34 Productions, pg 828
USAV Group Inc, pg 923
Video Wisconsin Inc, pg 929

WYOMING

Bridger Productions Inc, pg 710

ALBERTA

Black Media Works, pg 706
Global TV, pg 771

BRITISH COLUMBIA

Credo Interactive Inc, pg 734
Triad Communications Ltd, pg 918
24 Frames Film & Video, pg 920

NEWFOUNDLAND AND LABRADOR

Vidcraft Productions Ltd, pg 927

ONTARIO

ADS Media, pg 677
RB Productions, pg 870
Silver Creek Media Inc, pg 888
Video Excellence Productions,
  pg 927

QUEBEC

Group PVP, pg 774
National Film Board of
  Canada/Office National du Film
  du Canada, pg 836

Animation Production Services—Computerized

ALABAMA

Diamond Studios, pg 741
Motion & Graphic Image Corp Inc
  (MAGIC), pg 831

ARIZONA

Arizona Studios, pg 688
Fox 10 Productions (KSAZ-TV),
  pg 765
Merestone, pg 823

ARKANSAS

Live'N'Loud, pg 810
White Diamond Productions LLC,
  pg 937

CALIFORNIA

Access Video in Berkeley, pg 673
Advanced Systems Group LLC,
  pg 677
AlphaDogs Inc, pg 682
Artichoke Productions, pg 690
Audio Visual Consultants, pg 694
Blind™, pg 707
Buttercup Pictures, pg 713
Steve Chandler, pg 720
Classic Images Stock Footage LLC,
  pg 726
Creative Technology, pg 733
Crystal Pyramid Productions™,
  pg 735
Custom Video Productions Inc,
  pg 736
Diaquest, pg 741
digital OutPost, pg 742
Direct Images Interactive Inc,
  pg 743
Dolphin MultiMedia Inc, pg 745
Elektrashock, pg 753
Ferrari Productions, pg 759
First Person Inc, pg 761
Havas Edge, pg 777
House of Moves, pg 782
Hydrogen Whiskey Studios, pg 783
iCorpTv, pg 783
Imageworks, pg 785
Joyce Media Inc, pg 795
KTVU-Retail Services, pg 802

Ludlow Media, pg 812
Lumeni Productions Inc, pg 812
Lynch Communications, pg 813
Maximus Media Inc, pg 820
The Media Staff Inc, pg 822
Medical Visual Creations (MVC),
  pg 823
New & Unique Videos™, pg 839
Nolte Media, pg 841
On-Trax Inc, pg 846
Palardo Productions, pg 850
Pixar Animation Studios, pg 857
QRS Software Services, pg 867
Reality Check Systems, pg 871
Renegade Animation Inc, pg 873
Saturn Studios, pg 881
Starburns Industries, pg 900
Staylor-Made Communications Inc,
  pg 900
Still N' Motion, pg 901
Tam Communications Inc, pg 906
Total Creative, pg 916
Towards 2000 Inc, pg 916
Two Door Productions LLC, pg 920
Uniconn Productions, pg 921
Universal Studios, pg 922
VidCan Media Solutions, pg 927
Videobotics, pg 929
Videografix LLC, pg 929
Wavemaker Media Design, pg 934
WMS Media Inc, pg 940

COLORADO

Colorado Studios, pg 728
CSI Film & Video LLC, pg 735
Daylight Productions & Rentals,
  pg 739
Flashback Media Productions,
  pg 762
Full Spectrum Arts & Services,
  pg 767
People Productions, pg 854
Side 3 Studios, pg 887
Z-Axis Corp, pg 944

CONNECTICUT

BRB Audiovisual Productions,
  pg 709
Guymark Studios LLC, pg 775
Musivision Inc, pg 835
New London Media, pg 839
Palace Production Center, pg 850
Palace Productions MediaVision,
  pg 850
Sonalysts Media, pg 892
Bret Stern Productions, pg 900

DELAWARE

So Smart Productions, pg 891

DISTRICT OF COLUMBIA

Hillmann & Carr Inc, pg 780
Interface Media Group, pg 789

FLORIDA

Access Media Group, pg 673
Accord Productions, pg 673
Audio Visual Imagineering Inc,
  pg 694
Civins Productions Inc, pg 725
Communications Concepts Inc
  (CCI), pg 729
Comtel Inc, pg 730
Digimation, pg 741
Gemstone Media Inc, pg 769
Hi-Tech Enterprises Inc, pg 779
JungleTV, pg 795
Shooting Stars Post Inc, pg 886
Sound & Vision Communications
  Inc, pg 893

Sunfire Communications Inc,
  pg 904
Tricycle Studios, pg 918
Mike Vasilinda Productions Inc,
  pg 925
Video Techniques Inc, pg 928
Vistamax Productions, pg 931

GEORGIA

Beachwood Productions, pg 702
Beast Atlanta, pg 703
Cinema Concepts, pg 724
The DVI Group, pg 748
ECG Productions, pg 750
Guerrilla Productions LLC, pg 774
Staging Directions Inc, pg 899

HAWAII

Hyperspective Studios Inc, pg 783
Media Bridge Gamekids, pg 821

ILLINOIS

ABSA Films, pg 672
Airways Digital Media, pg 679
Atomic Imaging Inc/Golan Studios,
  pg 692
CCore Media Inc, pg 718
Edit House Chicago, pg 750
Explore, pg 757
Extraordinary Demos/Videos,
  pg 757
IV Media Resources, pg 792
Manning Productions, pg 816
Mightybytes Inc, pg 827
Optimus, pg 847
Jim Passin Productions, pg 852
Pepper Group, pg 854
PSAV® Presentation Services
  (Hotel Services Division), pg 866
Richter Studios, pg 875
SCI Television & Creative Media
  LLC, pg 882
Sound/Video Impressions Inc,
  pg 894
Southern Illinois University, pg 895
Sparkfactor, pg 896
Tele-Time Systems, pg 910
20/20 Communications Inc, pg 920
Video Impressions, pg 928

INDIANA

A-V-A Video Productions, pg 671
Bright Ideas Creative Services,
  pg 710
OMNI Productions, pg 845

IOWA

Iowa State University-Information
  Technology Services, pg 791

KENTUCKY

Broadway Digital, pg 711
The PPS Group, pg 860

LOUISIANA

Digital FX Inc, pg 742
Launch Media, pg 804
Louisiana State University Division
  of Strategic Communications,
  pg 811
Moxie Media, pg 832
Pace Systems, pg 849
Vidox Motion Imagery, pg 930
WVLA-TV, pg 942

MARYLAND

Adventure Productions LLC, pg 678
CPR MultiMedia Solutions, pg 732

VIDEO

Animation Production Services—Computerized (continued)

Animation System Distributors

ARIZONA
Troxell-CDI, pg 918

CALIFORNIA
Advanced Systems Group LLC, pg 677
Ametron Audio/Video, pg 684
Audio Images Corp, pg 693
Audio/Video Supply Inc, pg 694
California Tape Products Inc, pg 714
Computer Modules Inc, pg 729
Diaquest, pg 741
Jaguar Distribution Corp, pg 792
MediaPOINTE, pg 823
PMP Marketing Inc, pg 858
Videobotics, pg 929
VMI Inc, pg 932

FLORIDA
Access Media Group, pg 673
Digital Video Systems, pg 742
Hi-Tech Enterprises Inc, pg 779
ONstage, pg 846

GEORGIA
Stage Front Presentation Systems, pg 899

MAINE
Headlight Audio Visual Inc, pg 777

MARYLAND
Kipp Visual Systems Inc, pg 799

MASSACHUSETTS
Integrated Solutions Group, pg 789
Psychsoft Inc, pg 866

MICHIGAN
ASC Systems, pg 690
Digi Sign Design LLC, pg 741
On Stage Visuals, pg 846

MINNESOTA
Alpha Video & Audio Inc, pg 682

MISSOURI
Communitronics Corp, pg 729
Modern Communications Inc, pg 828
Southwest Audio-Visual Inc, pg 895

NEVADA
Aardvark Video & Media Productions, pg 671

NEW JERSEY
Color Leasing Studios, pg 727
PatchAmp, pg 852
PLS Staging, pg 858
Total Video Products Inc, pg 916

NEW YORK
Audio-Video Corp, pg 694
Creative Stage Lighting Co Inc, pg 733
Indigo Productions, pg 787
Tri-Ed Distribution Inc, pg 918

PENNSYLVANIA
AccuWeather Inc, pg 674
Advanced AV LLC, pg 677
The Lerro Corp, pg 806
Morefield Communications Inc, pg 830
Visual Sound Inc, pg 931

TEXAS
Biway Media, pg 706
Epic Software Group Inc, pg 755
Pro Video & Film Equipment Co Inc, pg 863

UTAH
RIA Corp, pg 874

VIRGINIA
Lee Hartman & Sons Inc, pg 805
The Whitlock Group, pg 937

WISCONSIN
Camera Corner Connecting Point, pg 715
Full Compass Systems, pg 767
Safe Harbor Computers, pg 879

ALBERTA
Matrix Video Communications Corp (MVCC), pg 819

QUEBEC
Panavideo Inc, pg 850

SASKATCHEWAN
Display Systems International, pg 743

Animation System Manufacturers

CALIFORNIA
Advanced Systems Group LLC, pg 677
Diaquest, pg 741
Grande Vitesse Systems Inc (GVS), pg 773
Linker Systems Inc, pg 809
Rough House, pg 878
Simon - Kaloi Engineering Ltd, pg 888

ILLINOIS
EPIX Inc, pg 755

MASSACHUSETTS
Psychsoft Inc, pg 866

MICHIGAN
ASC Systems, pg 690

MISSOURI
GlobalStreams™ Corp, pg 771

NEW JERSEY
CELCO, pg 719
PeopleVisionFX, pg 854

PENNSYLVANIA
AccuWeather Inc, pg 674

TEXAS
Biway Media, pg 706

VERMONT
Polhemus, pg 859

WISCONSIN
Safe Harbor Computers, pg 879

BRITISH COLUMBIA
Triad Communications Ltd, pg 918

SASKATCHEWAN
Display Systems International, pg 743

Animation System Rentals

ARIZONA
Merestone, pg 823

CALIFORNIA
Artichoke Productions, pg 690

CONNECTICUT
Videofilm Systems Inc, pg 929

FLORIDA
Access Media Group, pg 673
Accord Productions, pg 673

GEORGIA
Stage Front Presentation Systems, pg 899

MARYLAND
Kramer Communications Video Production, pg 801

MASSACHUSETTS
Preston Productions Inc, pg 861

MICHIGAN
Digi Sign Design LLC, pg 741
K&R All Media Productions LLC, pg 796
On Stage Visuals, pg 846

NEW YORK
Creative Stage Lighting Co Inc, pg 733
HB-Content, pg 777

NORTH CAROLINA
Take One Productions Ltd, pg 906

OKLAHOMA
PDC Productions, pg 852

PENNSYLVANIA
JPL, pg 795
The Videohouse Inc, pg 929

VIRGINIA
Quince Imaging Inc, pg 868

Animation System Repairs

CALIFORNIA
Ametron Audio/Video, pg 684

FLORIDA
Hi-Tech Enterprises Inc, pg 779

GEORGIA
Stage Front Presentation Systems, pg 899

MICHIGAN
TEL Systems LLC, pg 909

MINNESOTA
Alpha Video & Audio Inc, pg 682

TEXAS
Biway Media, pg 706

UTAH
RIA Corp, pg 874

WISCONSIN
Full Compass Systems, pg 767

Artwork & Titling Services

ALASKA
Alaska Media Pros LLC, pg 679

ARIZONA
Fox 10 Productions (KSAZ-TV), pg 765
Merestone, pg 823

ARKANSAS
Live'N'Loud, pg 810
White Diamond Productions LLC, pg 937

CALIFORNIA
Aberdeen Broadcast Services, pg 672
Access Video in Berkeley, pg 673
All Video Productions, pg 680
AlphaDogs Inc, pg 682
Artichoke Productions, pg 690
Steve Chandler, pg 720
Creative Technology, pg 733
Crystal Pyramid Productions™, pg 735
Custom Video Productions Inc, pg 736
Digital Jungle, pg 742
digital OutPost, pg 742
Direct Images Interactive Inc, pg 743
First Person Inc, pg 761
Goal Productions, pg 772
Gold Standard Productions, pg 772
Havas Edge, pg 777
Hydrogen Whiskey Studios, pg 783
iCorpTv, pg 783
ITV Productions, pg 792
JDS Video & Media Productions Inc, pg 793
KPBS Public Broadcasting, pg 801
KTVU-Retail Services, pg 802
Laser Magic Productions, pg 804
Ludlow Media, pg 812
Lumeni Productions Inc, pg 812
Maximus Media Inc, pg 820
Media Magic, pg 822
The Media Staff Inc, pg 822
Medical Visual Creations (MVC), pg 823
Moving Art by Louie Schwartzberg, pg 831
New & Unique Videos™, pg 839
Nolte Media, pg 841
Palardo Productions, pg 850
PM Productions, pg 858
Point.360, pg 858

VIDEO

Artwork & Titling Services (continued)

CALIFORNIA (continued)

PSI Inc, pg 866
QRS Software Services, pg 867
Reality Check Systems, pg 871
Saturn Studios, pg 881
Shapeshifter, pg 885
Shokus Video, pg 886
SonicPool, pg 892
Staylor-Made Communications Inc, pg 900
Still N' Motion, pg 901
Tam Communications Inc, pg 906
TIMECODE Post Production, pg 914
Total Creative, pg 916
Universal Studios, pg 922
Via Verde Productions, pg 926
Videografix LLC, pg 929
Visions Plus, pg 931
Wavemaker Media Design, pg 934
West Coast Projections Inc, pg 935

COLORADO

CSI Film & Video LLC, pg 735
Daylight Productions & Rentals, pg 739
Flashback Media Productions, pg 762
Full Spectrum Arts & Services, pg 767

CONNECTICUT

BRB Audiovisual Productions, pg 709
Cine-Med Inc, pg 723
Guymark Studios LLC, pg 775
Ironik Design & Post, pg 791
Musivision Inc, pg 835
New London Media, pg 839
Palace Production Center, pg 850
Powerstation Events, pg 860
Video Production Associates Inc, pg 928

DISTRICT OF COLUMBIA

Interface Media Group, pg 789

FLORIDA

Access Media Group, pg 673
Applebox Studio, pg 687
Civins Productions Inc, pg 725
Communications Concepts Inc (CCI), pg 729
Comtel Inc, pg 730
Courter Films LLC, pg 732
Hi-Tech Enterprises Inc, pg 779
Jordan Klein Film & Video (JKFV), pg 795
Photosound of Orlando Inc, pg 856
Shooting Stars Post Inc, pg 886
Sound & Vision Communications Inc, pg 893
Sunfire Communications Inc, pg 904
Sunrise Studios, pg 904
Tricycle Studios, pg 918
Universal Studios Florida® Production Group, pg 922
Mike Vasilinda Productions Inc, pg 925
Video Techniques Inc, pg 928
Vistamax Productions, pg 931

GEORGIA

Beachwood Productions, pg 702
Beast Atlanta, pg 703
The DVI Group, pg 748
ECG Productions, pg 750
Guerrilla Productions LLC, pg 774
Imagers, pg 785
Staging Directions Inc, pg 899

HAWAII

Hyperspective Studios Inc, pg 783
Media Bridge Gamekids, pg 821
1013 Integrated, pg 911

ILLINOIS

ABSA Films, pg 672
Airways Digital Media, pg 679
Beatty TeleVisual Productions, pg 703
Breeze Productions Inc, pg 710
CCore Media Inc, pg 718
IV Media Resources, pg 792
Manning Productions, pg 816
Mightybytes Inc, pg 827
Optimus, pg 847
Jim Passin Productions, pg 852
Pepper Group, pg 854
Richter Studios, pg 875
SCI Television & Creative Media LLC, pg 882
Sound/Video Impressions Inc, pg 894
Southern Illinois University, pg 895
Sparkfactor, pg 896
Tele-Time Systems, pg 910
20/20 Communications Inc, pg 920
Video Impressions, pg 928
WEEK TV, pg 935

INDIANA

A-V-A Video Productions, pg 671
Bright Ideas Creative Services, pg 710

IOWA

Educational Technology & Media Services, pg 751

KANSAS

KAKE-TV, pg 796

KENTUCKY

WKYT-TV, pg 940

LOUISIANA

Digital FX Inc, pg 742
Louisiana State University Division of Strategic Communications, pg 811
Pace Systems, pg 849
Vidox Motion Imagery, pg 930
YES Productions, pg 944

MARYLAND

Adventure Productions LLC, pg 678
CPR MultiMedia Solutions, pg 732
CSPMedia.com, pg 735
DBM Communications Inc, pg 739
Kramer Communications Video Production, pg 801
Media Dimensions LLC, pg 821
Pro Cuts Editing Services, pg 862
Quality Film & Video, pg 868

MASSACHUSETTS

Boston Productions Inc (BPI), pg 709
CommCreative, pg 728

MotionArt Studios, pg 831
Northern Light Productions (NLP), pg 842
Penfield Productions Ltd, pg 853
Gabriel Polonsky Studio, pg 859
Preston Productions Inc, pg 861
TR Productions, pg 916
TVN-The Video Network, pg 919

MICHIGAN

Digi Sign Design LLC, pg 741
K&R's Recording Studios Inc, pg 796
Michigan Recording Arts Institute & Technologies, pg 825
Progressive AE, pg 865

MINNESOTA

The ADS Group, pg 676
MastCom, pg 819
Worthwhile Films, pg 941

MISSOURI

Communitronics Corp, pg 729
Conference Technologies Inc, pg 730
Show-Me Audio-Visual, pg 887

MONTANA

ooLite Media LLC, pg 846

NEBRASKA

B & B Video Productions Inc, pg 700

NEVADA

Aardvark Video & Media Productions, pg 671
Encore Event Technologies LLC, pg 754
JCS Video Productions, pg 793
Tanglewood Productions, pg 907
21st Century Video Productions, pg 919

NEW HAMPSHIRE

Apertura, pg 686
Channell One Video, pg 720
Chip Taylor Communications LLC, pg 907

NEW JERSEY

Allegro Productions Inc, pg 680
Broadcast Center Studios, pg 710
CD Meyer Inc, pg 718
CFP Video Productions Inc, pg 720
Diversified, pg 744
Early Films, pg 749
Laurel Video Productions, pg 804
MediaMix Inc, pg 822
MediaNow Inc, pg 822
Megavideo LLC, pg 823
MiB MediaWorks, pg 825
Midnight Media Group Inc, pg 827
Outside The Box Interactive LLC, pg 849
Suede Interactive, pg 903
Two Animators LLP, pg 920
VCSvideo, pg 925
Video Ideas Productions, pg 928

NEW MEXICO

Production Outfitters, pg 864
30 Second Street Ltd, pg 912

NEW YORK

Animotion Inc, pg 685
aurora productions, pg 696

Big Film Design, pg 705
The Big House Group, pg 705
Buffalo Video Production, pg 712
Chromavision Corp, pg 723
Designomotion, pg 741
Digital Art Video Inc, pg 741
Downtown Community Television Center (DCTV), pg 746
4-D Creative Media, pg 764
HAVE Inc, pg 777
IAI Records & Video, pg 783
InterNation Inc, pg 789
Lylofilm Productions, pg 813
MRY, pg 832
Polestar Films & Associated Arts Ltd, pg 859
R/GA, pg 868
Rafik, pg 869
Synaptic Digital, pg 905
Teatown Communications Group, pg 908
TeleTime Productions, pg 910

NORTH CAROLINA

Pat Appleson Studios Inc, pg 687
Horizon Video Productions Inc, pg 781
Kino Mountain Productions LLC, pg 799
Moving Pictures, pg 832
Take One Productions Ltd, pg 906

OHIO

Advent Media Inc, pg 677
Aztec Video Productions, pg 700
Russ Beckner Pictures, pg 703
Cinecraft Productions Inc, pg 723
Cuyahoga Community College Student Production Office (SPO), pg 736
Lyon Video Inc, pg 813
MainSail Production Services Inc, pg 815
Mills James Productions, pg 828
R&B Communications Inc, pg 870
Take 1 Media Services, pg 906
Vista Color Imaging Inc, pg 931

OKLAHOMA

Institute for Teaching & Learning Excellence (ITLE), pg 788
PDC Productions, pg 852

OREGON

BingoLewis, pg 706
InterVision Media, pg 791
KVAL, pg 802
Production West, pg 864
REX, pg 874

PENNSYLVANIA

Bang! Pictures Inc, pg 701
FMP Media Solutions Inc, pg 763
Innovision Media Group, pg 788
JPL, pg 795
Laser Video Corp, pg 804
Main Point Productions, pg 815
The Videohouse Inc, pg 929
WPHL-TV, pg 942

RHODE ISLAND

Sound-FX-Design, pg 894

SOUTH CAROLINA

Encore Video Productions, pg 754
Genesis Creative, pg 769
Stages Video Productions, pg 899
Venture Media, pg 925

TENNESSEE

Motion Picture Services, pg 831
Paradigm Marketing & Creative, pg 851
Running Pony Productions LLC, pg 878
Scripps Networks, pg 882
Stage Post, pg 899
Russ Sturgeon Productions/RSVP, pg 903

TEXAS

Anaphora Literary Press, pg 685
Biway Media, pg 706
Chalk Dust Co, pg 720
The Editing Co, pg 750
Epic Software Group Inc, pg 755
Hurst Digital, pg 782
McNee Productions Inc, pg 821
Julye Newlin Productions Inc, pg 840
Out of the BLUE Media, pg 849
South Coast Film & Video, pg 895
Texas Heart Institute Visual Communication Services, pg 911

UTAH

ImageWorks Communications, pg 785

VIRGINIA

Advance Concepts Inc, pg 677
Allied Media Corp, pg 681
CACI Integrated Communications, pg 713
Eagle Films, pg 749
Limelight Communications Inc, pg 808
Maniglia Media LLC, pg 816
Metro Productions, pg 824
Rocktown Media, pg 876
Video Solutions, pg 928

WASHINGTON

Bennett-Watt HD Productions Inc, pg 703
North-by-Northwest - A Digital Studio, pg 842
Victory Studios, pg 927

WEST VIRGINIA

WSAZ-TV NewsChannel 3, pg 942

WISCONSIN

Audio Visual of Milwaukee Inc, pg 694
Meridian Studios, pg 824
Mirror 34 Productions, pg 828
USAV Group Inc, pg 923
Video Wisconsin Inc, pg 929
Watts Communications Inc, pg 934

WYOMING

Bridger Productions Inc, pg 710

PUERTO RICO

Stage Crew Audiovisual Inc, pg 898

ALBERTA

Global TV, pg 771

NEWFOUNDLAND AND LABRADOR

Vidcraft Productions Ltd, pg 927

ONTARIO

ADS Media, pg 677
GAPC (General Assembly Production Centre), pg 768
Image Video Services & Productions, pg 785
RB Productions, pg 870
Silver Creek Media Inc, pg 888
Video Excellence Productions, pg 927
Westbury National Show Systems Ltd, pg 936

Audio Editing, *see* Dubbing

Blank DVD, *see* DVD— Blank

Blank Videocassette, *see* Videocassette—Blank

Blank Videodisc, *see* Videodisc—Blank

Blank Videotape, *see* Videotape—Blank

Cable Distributors

ARIZONA

EAR Professional Audio/Video, pg 749

CALIFORNIA

Ametron Audio/Video, pg 684
ARS Electronics, pg 690
Associated Sound, pg 691
Audio Images Corp, pg 693
AV Conferencing LLC (AVC), pg 697
Band Pro Film & Digital Inc, pg 701
California Tape Products Inc, pg 714
Christy's Editorial, pg 723
Cibola Systems, pg 723
Diaquest, pg 741
Hosa Technology Inc, pg 781
Jameco Electronics, pg 792
JD Audio Visual Inc, pg 793
Kappa optronics Inc, pg 796
Marshall Electronics Inc, pg 817
Orvac Electronics, pg 848
Photodyne Technologies, pg 856
Sound Service Co, pg 894
Southern California Sound Image Inc, pg 895
Stanislaus AV Inc, pg 899
VMI Inc, pg 932
Zack Electronics Inc, pg 945

COLORADO

Daylight Productions & Rentals, pg 739

FLORIDA

Access Media Group, pg 673
Altel Systems Group Inc, pg 682
A2D Solutions Inc, pg 692
AudioVideoElectric, pg 695
Digital Video Systems, pg 742
Harris Corp, pg 776
Herman Pro AV, pg 779

Hi-Tech Enterprises Inc, pg 779
Midtown Video Inc, pg 827
Multicom Inc, pg 833
TAI Audio, pg 906

GEORGIA

Accu-Tech, pg 673
Stage Front Presentation Systems, pg 899

HAWAII

The Audio Visual Co (AVCO), pg 694

ILLINOIS

Arcor Electronics Co, pg 688
Clark Wire & Cable, pg 725
Cole Wire & Cable Co Inc, pg 727
Joseph Electronics, pg 795
LKG Industries Inc, pg 810
Quintessence Audio Ltd, pg 868
Waldom Electronics Corp, pg 933

INDIANA

Sensory Technologies LLC, pg 884
SHP Electronics, pg 887

KENTUCKY

Axxis Leasing Inc, pg 700
General Cable, pg 769
NOR-COM Inc, pg 841

LOUISIANA

Techkno Integration & Design Services LLC, pg 908

MAINE

Headlight Audio Visual Inc, pg 777

MARYLAND

Noventri, pg 843

MASSACHUSETTS

Antronics Inc, pg 686
Integrated Solutions Group, pg 789
Rule Boston Camera, pg 878
SLR Enterprises LLC, pg 890

MICHIGAN

DAWNco, pg 739
On Stage Visuals, pg 846

MINNESOTA

Alpha Video & Audio Inc, pg 682

MISSOURI

Modern Communications Inc, pg 828
The RapcoHorizon Co, pg 870
Southwest Audio-Visual Inc, pg 895

NEW JERSEY

Alltec Stores, a Vcom IMC Company, pg 681
AlltecPro, pg 681
Argraph Corp, pg 688
AV Bluebook, pg 696
Avtech Systems Inc, pg 699
Diversified, pg 744
Earl Girls Inc, pg 749
MCCOM Inc, pg 820
MiB MediaWorks, pg 825
Starlite, pg 900
Tele-Measurements Inc, pg 910
Total Video Products Inc, pg 916

Vcom IMC, pg 925
Wired 4 Sound Inc, pg 940

NEW YORK

Audio-Video Corp, pg 694
BMI Supply, pg 708
BTX Technologies, pg 712
Design Audio Visual Inc, pg 741
Gaylord Archival, pg 768
Gotham Sound & Communications Inc, pg 773
HAVE Inc, pg 777
KVL Audio Visual Services Inc, pg 802
Markertek Video Supply, pg 817
Neptune Photo Inc, pg 838
RNJ Electronics, pg 875
Russell Industries Inc, pg 879
TecNec Distributing, pg 909
Whirlwind Music Distributors Inc, pg 937

OHIO

ITA Audio Visual Solutions, pg 791
Parts Express, pg 851
Tri-State Audio Visual Co, pg 918

OKLAHOMA

Ford AV, pg 763

OREGON

TARA Labs, pg 907

PENNSYLVANIA

Advanced AV LLC, pg 677
The Lerro Corp, pg 806
West Penn Wire, pg 935

TENNESSEE

Lowrance Sound Co Inc, pg 812
Technical Support Systems LLC, pg 908

TEXAS

Data Projections Inc, pg 738
Digital Display Solutions Inc, pg 742
Precision Camera & Video, pg 861
Pro Video & Film Equipment Co Inc, pg 863

UTAH

Performance Audio LLC, pg 854

VERMONT

Power & Telephone Supply Co, pg 860

VIRGINIA

Avitecture Inc, pg 699
Lee Hartman & Sons Inc, pg 805

WASHINGTON

CCI Solutions, pg 718
PNTA, pg 858
Telect Inc, pg 910

WISCONSIN

Full Compass Systems, pg 767
Safe Harbor Computers, pg 879

ALBERTA

Matrix Video Communications Corp (MVCC), pg 819

VIDEO

Cable Distributors (continued)

BRITISH COLUMBIA

BeachTek Inc, pg 702
Commercial Electronics Ltd, pg 728
Noramco Wire & Cable, pg 841

ONTARIO

Cinema Stage Inc, pg 724
Westbury National Show Systems Ltd, pg 936

Cable Manufacturers

ARIZONA

Covid Inc, pg 732

CALIFORNIA

AITech International, pg 679
ALTINEX Inc, pg 682
Calrad Electronics, pg 714
Extron Electronics, pg 758
Fiber Optic Cable Shop, pg 759
Hosa Technology Inc, pg 781
Marshall Electronics Inc, pg 817
Monster Cable Products Inc, pg 829
Taperwire, pg 907

COLORADO

Liberty AV Solutions, pg 807

FLORIDA

Multicom Inc, pg 833
Nemal Electronics International Inc, pg 838

ILLINOIS

Arcor Electronics Co, pg 688
Clark Wire & Cable, pg 725
Joseph Electronics, pg 795
Tripp Lite, pg 918

INDIANA

Belden Inc, pg 703

KENTUCKY

General Cable, pg 769

MARYLAND

RCI Custom Products, pg 871

MASSACHUSETTS

Mohawk, pg 829

MINNESOTA

Bel Fuse Inc, pg 703
Intercon 1, pg 789
Vaddio, pg 924

MISSOURI

The RapcoHorizon Co, pg 870

NEW JERSEY

Alltec Stores, a Vcom IMC Company, pg 681
AlltecPro, pg 681
Alpha Wire Co, pg 682
Brim Electronics, pg 710
Comprehensive Cable & Connectivity Co, pg 729

Crestron Electronics Inc, pg 734
Daburn Electronics & Cable Corp, pg 737
FSR Inc, pg 766
JSC Wire & Cable, pg 795
Kramer Electronics USA Inc, pg 801

NEW YORK

Hannay Reels Inc, pg 775
HAVE Inc, pg 777
Laird Digital Cinema, pg 803
Markertek Video Supply, pg 817
MultiDyne Video & Fiber Optics Systems, pg 833

NORTH CAROLINA

CommScope Inc, pg 728

OHIO

Network Technologies Inc, pg 838

OREGON

TARA Labs, pg 907

PENNSYLVANIA

MicroImage Video Systems, pg 826
West Penn Wire, pg 935

WASHINGTON

Telect Inc, pg 910

BRITISH COLUMBIA

Triad Communications Ltd, pg 918

ONTARIO

Westbury National Show Systems Ltd, pg 936

Cable Repairs

FLORIDA

ELC Sales & Service Inc, pg 752
Hi-Tech Enterprises Inc, pg 779

GEORGIA

Stage Front Presentation Systems, pg 899

ILLINOIS

Joseph Electronics, pg 795

KENTUCKY

NOR-COM Inc, pg 841

MICHIGAN

TEL Systems LLC, pg 909

NEW JERSEY

Starlite, pg 900

OHIO

Tri-State Audio Visual Co, pg 918

OREGON

All Service Musical Electronics Repair, pg 680

TENNESSEE

Technical Support Systems LLC, pg 908

Camcorder Distributors

ALABAMA

Curtis Company, pg 736

ARIZONA

EAR Professional Audio/Video, pg 749
Troxell-CDI, pg 918

ARKANSAS

White Diamond Productions LLC, pg 937

CALIFORNIA

Advanced Systems Group LLC, pg 677
Ametron Audio/Video, pg 684
Assured Audio Visual, pg 691
Audio/Video Supply Inc, pg 694
Band Pro Film & Digital Inc, pg 701
Barber Tech Video Products, pg 701
Be Media, pg 702
BigFoot Mobile Systems, pg 705
BroadcastStore.com, pg 711
Christy's Editorial, pg 723
Computer Modules Inc, pg 729
Diaquest, pg 741
Express Video Supply Inc, pg 757
Filmtools®, pg 761
Gluskin's Custom Audio Video, pg 771
Alan Gordon Enterprises Inc, pg 772
Gravity Media, pg 773
Hooper Camera & Imaging, pg 781
JD Audio Visual Inc, pg 793
MediaPOINTE, pg 823
Photodyne Technologies, pg 856
Point of View Productions, pg 858
Promax Systems, pg 865
SNAP, pg 891
Southern California Sound Image Inc, pg 895
SSL Industries Inc, pg 898
VMI Inc, pg 932
VTP Inc, pg 933

COLORADO

Daylight Productions & Rentals, pg 739
Mike's Camera, pg 827
Spectrum Audio Visual Services, pg 897
Stanco Sales LLC, pg 899

FLORIDA

Access Media Group, pg 673
Altel Systems Group Inc, pg 682
A2D Solutions Inc, pg 692
AVI-SPL, pg 698
Digital Video Systems, pg 742
Encore Broadcast Solutions, pg 754
Enhanced View Services Inc, pg 754
Harmon's Audio-Visual Services, pg 776
Harris Corp, pg 776
Hi-Tech Enterprises Inc, pg 779
Hi-Tech Import Export Corp, pg 779
Midtown Video Inc, pg 827
ONstage, pg 846
Recording Media & Equipment Inc (RM&E), pg 872
Reef Photo & Video, pg 872

GEORGIA

Baker Audio Visual, pg 700
Stage Front Presentation Systems, pg 899

HAWAII

The Audio Visual Co (AVCO), pg 694

ILLINOIS

Allen Visual Systems Inc, pg 680
RC Communications, pg 870

INDIANA

Jack's Camera Shop, pg 792
Lee Co Inc, pg 805
Sensory Technologies LLC, pg 884
SHP Electronics, pg 887

KENTUCKY

Audio Visual Techniques Inc, pg 695
Axxis Leasing Inc, pg 700
Barney Miller's Inc, pg 827
NOR-COM Inc, pg 841

MAINE

Headlight Audio Visual Inc, pg 777

MARYLAND

Noventri, pg 843

MASSACHUSETTS

Hunt's Photo & Video, pg 782
Integrated Solutions Group, pg 789
Rule Boston Camera, pg 878

MICHIGAN

TEL Systems LLC, pg 909

MINNESOTA

Alpha Video & Audio Inc, pg 682
Vaddio, pg 924

MISSISSIPPI

Bowie Audio Visual Enterprises Inc, pg 709

MISSOURI

Communitronics Corp, pg 729
Conference Technologies Inc, pg 730
Modern Communications Inc, pg 828
Schiller's Audio-Visual, pg 881
Southwest Audio-Visual Inc, pg 895

NEBRASKA

VSA Inc, pg 933

NEVADA

Aardvark Video & Media Productions, pg 671

NEW JERSEY

A-V Services Inc, pg 671
Alltec Stores, a Vcom IMC Company, pg 681
AlltecPro, pg 681
AV Bluebook, pg 696
Diversified, pg 744
Earl Girls Inc, pg 749
Euro-Pacific Film & Video Productions Inc, pg 756

G&G Technologies Inc, pg 768
HamiltonBuhl, pg 775
MCCOM Inc, pg 820
MiB MediaWorks, pg 825
PatchAmp, pg 852
Ritz Camera & Image, pg 875
Starlite, pg 900
SYMCO Inc, pg 905
Tele-Measurements Inc, pg 910
Total Video Products Inc, pg 916
Video Corporation of America
  (VCA), pg 927

NEW YORK

Audio-Video Corp, pg 694
AV Workshop, pg 697
Canon USA Inc, pg 716
Colortone Audio Visual, pg 728
Design Audio Visual Inc, pg 741
Indigo Productions, pg 787
KVL Audio Visual Services Inc,
  pg 802
Long Island Video Enterprises Live
  Inc, pg 811
Markertek Video Supply, pg 817
Neptune Photo Inc, pg 838
Nikon Inc, pg 841
Ray Supply Inc, pg 870
RNJ Electronics, pg 875
Tri-Ed Distribution Inc, pg 918
Visual Technologies Corp, pg 932
Visual Word Systems Inc, pg 932
Willoughby's® Camera, pg 939

OHIO

Copp Integrated Systems, pg 731
ITA Audio Visual Solutions, pg 791
Midwest Photo Exchange, pg 827
Tri-State Audio Visual Co, pg 918
Tri-State Visual Products Inc,
  pg 918

PENNSYLVANIA

Advanced AV LLC, pg 677
Audio Visions Inc, pg 694
Bernie's Photo Center, pg 704
Brodart Co, pg 711
Clair Companies, pg 725
J E Foss Co, pg 764
Garcia Marketing Inc, pg 768
Grise Audio Visual Center Inc,
  pg 774
Innovision Media Group, pg 788
The Lerro Corp, pg 806
Morefield Communications Inc,
  pg 830
New York Camera & Video, pg 840
Visual Sound Inc, pg 931

TENNESSEE

Lowrance Sound Co Inc, pg 812
Technical Support Systems LLC,
  pg 908
Zion Music Group, pg 945

TEXAS

Audio Visual Technologies Group
  (AVTG), pg 695
AVES Audio Visual Systems Inc,
  pg 698
Biway Media, pg 706
CAM Audio Inc, pg 714
Data Projections Inc, pg 738
Digital Display Solutions Inc,
  pg 742
Heffernan Audio Visual, pg 778
Omega Broadcast Group, pg 845
Precision Camera & Video, pg 861
Pro Video & Film Equipment Co
  Inc, pg 863

Quality Audio Visual Service Inc,
  pg 867
Tarpley Media Systems, pg 907
TWIST Integration Solutions
  Technology, pg 920
Videotex Systems Inc, pg 930

UTAH

RIA Corp, pg 874
TV Specialists Inc, pg 919

VIRGINIA

Avitecture Inc, pg 699
Boitnott Visual Communications
  Corp (BVC), pg 708
Lee Hartman & Sons Inc, pg 805
Metropolitan Audio Visual Co LLC,
  pg 824
The Whitlock Group, pg 937

WASHINGTON

CCI Solutions, pg 718
Oppenheimer Camera Products,
  pg 847

WISCONSIN

Camera Corner Connecting Point,
  pg 715
Full Compass Systems, pg 767
Safe Harbor Computers, pg 879

ALBERTA

Infosat Communications Inc, pg 787
Matrix Video Communications Corp
  (MVCC), pg 819

BRITISH COLUMBIA

Commercial Electronics Ltd, pg 728

ONTARIO

Cinema Stage Inc, pg 724
FUJIFILM Canada Inc, pg 766
HD Source, pg 777
Henry's Camera, pg 779
Majortech Inc, pg 815
Nationwide Audio Visual Co,
  pg 837

QUEBEC

Panavideo Inc, pg 850

Camcorder Manufacturers

CALIFORNIA

Sony Electronics Inc, pg 893

NEW JERSEY

Ikegami Electronics (USA) Inc,
  pg 784
JVC Professional Products Co,
  pg 796
Panasonic Corporation of North
  America, pg 850

NEW YORK

Canon USA Inc, pg 716
Nikon Inc, pg 841

BRITISH COLUMBIA

Triad Communications Ltd, pg 918

ONTARIO

FUJIFILM Canada Inc, pg 766

Camcorder Rentals

ALASKA

Connections Film & Video Inc,
  pg 731

ARIZONA

Creative Backstage, pg 733
Merestone, pg 823
Metropolitan Audio-Visual Inc,
  pg 824
Ultimate Presentation Systems Inc,
  pg 920

ARKANSAS

White Diamond Productions LLC,
  pg 937

CALIFORNIA

Absolute Rentals, pg 672
Action Audio & Visual, pg 675
Advanced Media LLC, pg 677
Aerial Video Systems, pg 678
Alliant Event Services, pg 681
Alternative Rentals, pg 682
Ametron Audio/Video, pg 684
Artichoke Productions, pg 690
Assured Audio Visual, pg 691
AV Guys, pg 697
Barber Tech Video Products, pg 701
Bexel, an NEP Broadcast Services
  Company, pg 704
Big Door, pg 705
BroadcastStore.com, pg 711
The Camera Division, pg 715
Cherry Multimedia, pg 721
Clean Slate Video, pg 726
Crystal Pyramid Productions™,
  pg 735
Deck Hand Inc, pg 740
The Dreaming Tree, pg 746
Express Media Inc, pg 757
Express Video Supply Inc, pg 757
First Camera, pg 761
Flip 2 Media Inc, pg 762
Full Moon & High Tide Productions
  & Studios, pg 767
Gear Monkey, pg 769
Glendale Production Center, pg 771
Gluskin's Custom Audio Video,
  pg 771
Goal Productions, pg 772
Gold Standard Productions, pg 772
Alan Gordon Enterprises Inc,
  pg 772
Gravity Media, pg 773
iCorpTv, pg 783
Image Integration, pg 785
Images in Motion Media Inc,
  pg 785
JD Audio Visual Inc, pg 793
Lynch Communications, pg 813
Main Street Media Inc, pg 815
Maximus Media Inc, pg 820
McCune Audio-Video-Lighting,
  pg 821
Munday & Collins AV, pg 834
New Circuit Films LLC, pg 839
North County Media Center, pg 842
On-Trax Inc, pg 846
Prime Cut Productions, pg 862
PSAV® Presentation Services,
  pg 866
PSSI Global Services LLC, pg 866
RetinaVision Productions, pg 874
SNAP, pg 891
Sound Service Co, pg 894
Studio 637, pg 903
Total Video, pg 916
Twin Peaks Creative, pg 920
VER, pg 926

VMI Inc, pg 932
Voice & Video Rentals, pg 932
Warner Bros Production Sound &
  Video Services, pg 934
Westcoast Video Productions Inc,
  pg 936

COLORADO

Daylight Productions & Rentals,
  pg 739
Mike's Camera, pg 827
Multimedia Audio Visual Inc,
  pg 833
Open Media Foundation, pg 846
Spectrum Audio Visual Services,
  pg 897
Tatum Video, pg 907

CONNECTICUT

A/V Davey, pg 697
Videofilm Systems Inc, pg 929

DELAWARE

Ken-Del Productions Inc, pg 797
Showorks Audio Visual Inc, pg 887

DISTRICT OF COLUMBIA

Metro Teleproductions Inc (MTI),
  pg 824

FLORIDA

Access Media Group, pg 673
Accord Productions, pg 673
AVI-SPL, pg 698
Budget Video Rentals, pg 712
CopShopMiami.com, pg 731
Digital Zoetrope Productions,
  pg 742
Harmon's Audio-Visual Services,
  pg 776
Industrial Strength Inc, pg 787
JungleTV, pg 795
Knowles Video Inc (KVI), pg 800
Midtown Video Inc, pg 827
Moving Picture, pg 831
ONstage, pg 846
Universal Studios Florida®
  Production Group, pg 922

GEORGIA

ECG Productions, pg 750
MAGNUM Companies Ltd, pg 815
ON Services, a GES Company,
  pg 846
Stage Front Presentation Systems,
  pg 899

HAWAII

Sight & Sound Studios, pg 887

ILLINOIS

Allen Visual Systems Inc, pg 680
AV Chicago Inc, pg 696
Backstar Creative Media Inc,
  pg 700
Beatty TeleVisual Productions,
  pg 703
Central Audio-Visual Equipment
  Inc, pg 719
Creative Technology (CT), pg 733
RC Communications, pg 870
Resolution Productions Group,
  pg 874
SCI Television & Creative Media
  LLC, pg 882
Staging Resources Inc, pg 899
Tele-Time Systems, pg 910
Winter Productions, pg 939

VIDEO

Camcorder Rentals
(continued)

KENTUCKY

Audio Visual Techniques Inc,
pg 695
Idle Minds Productions Inc, pg 784
Kentucky Grip & Lighting, pg 798

LOUISIANA

Clark Services Audio Visual &
Exhibit Inc, pg 725
Digital FX Inc, pg 742
Pace Systems, pg 849
YES Productions, pg 944

MAINE

Headlight Audio Visual Inc, pg 777
University of Maine Media
Services, pg 922

MARYLAND

Advance Audiovisual Presentation
Ltd, pg 677
Archai Media, pg 688
CPR MultiMedia Solutions, pg 732
Event Tech, pg 756
Kramer Communications Video
Production, pg 801

MASSACHUSETTS

AVFX Inc, pg 698
Green Mountain Post Films (GMP),
pg 774
Integrated Solutions Group, pg 789
massAV, pg 819
Preston Productions Inc, pg 861
Small Planet Communications Inc,
pg 890

MICHIGAN

City Events Group, pg 725
Digi Sign Design LLC, pg 741
K&R All Media Productions LLC,
pg 796
K&R's Recording Studios Inc,
pg 796
TEL Systems LLC, pg 909

MINNESOTA

Alpha Video & Audio Inc, pg 682
House of Cinemagraphics, pg 782

MISSISSIPPI

Bowie Audio Visual Enterprises Inc,
pg 709

MISSOURI

Schiller's Audio-Visual, pg 881
Show-Me Audio-Visual, pg 887
Southwest Audio-Visual Inc, pg 895

NEBRASKA

Dog & Pony Productions Inc,
pg 744

NEVADA

GES Audio Visual, pg 770
Tanglewood Productions, pg 907

NEW JERSEY

Audio Visual Dynamics®, pg 694
CFP Video Productions Inc, pg 720

Earl Girls Inc, pg 749
Euro-Pacific Film & Video
Productions Inc, pg 756
G&G Technologies Inc, pg 768
International Audio Visual Inc,
pg 790
MediaMix Inc, pg 822
MiB MediaWorks, pg 825
PLS Staging, pg 858
Starlite, pg 900
Tele-Measurements Inc, pg 910
Video Corporation of America
(VCA), pg 927

NEW MEXICO

Production Outfitters, pg 864

NEW YORK

Ace Video, pg 674
Adorama Rental Co, pg 676
Air Sea Land Productions Inc
(ASL), pg 678
AV Workshop, pg 697
Big Foot Productions Inc, pg 705
Bond Street Studio, pg 708
Cinema-Vision, pg 724
Colortone Audio Visual, pg 728
CP Communications, pg 732
CSI Rentals, pg 735
Design Audio Visual Inc, pg 741
Gearhead Rentals, pg 769
Hello World Communications,
pg 778
KVL Audio Visual Services Inc,
pg 802
LightSpace Studios, pg 808
Long Island Video Enterprises Live
Inc, pg 811
Manhattan Center Studios Inc,
pg 816
PrimaLux Video Inc, pg 862
Production Central, pg 863
Ray Supply Inc, pg 870
Tri-Ed Distribution Inc, pg 918
The Visual Studies Workshop
(VSW), pg 931
Visual Technologies Corp, pg 932
Visual Word Systems Inc, pg 932
WNET/New York Public Media,
pg 940

NORTH CAROLINA

AV Connections Inc, pg 697
AV Metro Inc, pg 697
The Communications Group Inc,
pg 729
Digital Rain LLC, pg 742
Duke Media Services, pg 747
On Location North Carolina, pg 846
Special Event Services, pg 896
Take One Productions Ltd, pg 906

NORTH DAKOTA

Media Productions, pg 822

OHIO

Hughie's Event Production Services,
pg 782
ITA Audio Visual Solutions, pg 791
Lyon Video Inc, pg 813
Mills James Productions, pg 828
Ohio HD Video, pg 844
OSV Studios, pg 848
R&B Communications Inc, pg 870

OKLAHOMA

PDC Productions, pg 852

OREGON

Northwest Film Center, pg 842
Picture This Production Services,
pg 856

PENNSYLVANIA

Argentine Productions Inc, pg 688
Audio Visions Inc, pg 694
Bang! Pictures Inc, pg 701
Bernie's Photo Center, pg 704
FMP Media Solutions Inc, pg 763
Grise Audio Visual Center Inc,
pg 774
Innovision Media Group, pg 788
JPL, pg 795
Muderick Media, pg 833
New York Camera & Video, pg 840
The Videohouse Inc, pg 929
Viewpoint Production Services Inc,
pg 930
Visual Sound Inc, pg 931

SOUTH CAROLINA

Genesis Creative, pg 769
Impact Technology Group LLC,
pg 786

TENNESSEE

Nashville Production Rentals
(NPR), pg 836
NuMynd Studios, pg 843
RentACamera.com, pg 873
Russ Sturgeon Productions/RSVP,
pg 903
Technical Support Systems LLC,
pg 908

TEXAS

Audio Visual Technologies Group
(AVTG), pg 695
FitzCo Sound Inc, pg 761
GEAR Cameras & Lighting, pg 769
Mediaforce Productions, pg 822
Muller Entertainment LLC, pg 833
Omega Broadcast Group, pg 845
Precision Camera & Video, pg 861
Quality Audio Visual Service Inc,
pg 867
South Coast Film & Video, pg 895
Stage Directions, pg 898
Texcam Inc, pg 911
Video Perspective, pg 928

UTAH

TV Specialists Inc, pg 919

VIRGINIA

Boitnott Visual Communications
Corp (BVC), pg 708
CVW Event Productions, pg 736
Lee Hartman & Sons Inc, pg 805
Quince Imaging Inc, pg 868
StageSound, pg 899
The Whitlock Group, pg 937

WASHINGTON

D A Sound, pg 737
The House Studios, pg 782
Kostov Productions, pg 801
Oppenheimer Camera Products,
pg 847
Victory Studios, pg 927

WEST VIRGINIA

Blackwater Video Productions,
pg 707

WISCONSIN

Camera Corner Connecting Point,
pg 715
Event Essentials, pg 756
Full Compass Systems, pg 767
Logan Productions Inc, pg 811
MKE Production Rental, pg 828

WYOMING

Bridger Productions Inc, pg 710

PUERTO RICO

Stage Crew Audiovisual Inc, pg 898

ALBERTA

Cine Audio Visual Sales & Service
Ltd, pg 723
Evolution AV, pg 757
Matrix Video Communications Corp
(MVCC), pg 819
Unique Communications Ltd,
pg 921

BRITISH COLUMBIA

Commercial Electronics Ltd, pg 728

ONTARIO

GAPC (General Assembly
Production Centre), pg 768
HD Source, pg 777
JIB Shots Equipment Inc, pg 794
ZTV Broadcast Services Inc, pg 945

QUEBEC

Audio Visual Dynamics, pg 694
Group PVP, pg 774
Kerrigan Productions Inc, pg 798
Panavideo Inc, pg 850

Camcorder Repairs

CALIFORNIA

Advanced Media LLC, pg 677
Ametron Audio/Video, pg 684
Band Pro Film & Digital Inc,
pg 701
BroadcastStore.com, pg 711
Digitron Electronics, pg 743
Gluskin's Custom Audio Video,
pg 771
McAlister Electronics, pg 820
Pro Camera Repair, pg 862
SSL Industries Inc, pg 898
Technical Services, pg 908
TEK Media Group, pg 909
TV Pro Gear, pg 919
VMI Inc, pg 932

COLORADO

Mike's Camera, pg 827

CONNECTICUT

A/V Davey, pg 697
Precision Camera & Video Repair
Inc, pg 861

FLORIDA

Access Media Group, pg 673
Digital Video Systems, pg 742
ELC Sales & Service Inc, pg 752
Hi-Tech Enterprises Inc, pg 779
Midtown Video Inc, pg 827
Tallahassee Photo & Frame, pg 906

GEORGIA

Stage Front Presentation Systems,
pg 899

ILLINOIS

Allen Visual Systems Inc, pg 680
Beatty TeleVisual Productions,
pg 703
Midwest Digital Corp, pg 827

KENTUCKY

Axxis Leasing Inc, pg 700
Barney Miller's Inc, pg 827
NOR-COM Inc, pg 841

MAINE

Headlight Audio Visual Inc, pg 777

MICHIGAN

TEL Systems LLC, pg 909

MINNESOTA

Alpha Video & Audio Inc, pg 682

MISSISSIPPI

Bowie Audio Visual Enterprises Inc,
pg 709

MISSOURI

Schiller's Audio-Visual, pg 881
Southwest Audio-Visual Inc, pg 895

NEW JERSEY

Starlite, pg 900

NEW YORK

Nikon Inc, pg 841
Ray Supply Inc, pg 870
Tri-Ed Distribution Inc, pg 918
Visual Technologies Corp, pg 932

OHIO

Copp Integrated Systems, pg 731
ITA Audio Visual Solutions, pg 791
Tri-State Audio Visual Co, pg 918
Tri-State Visual Products Inc,
pg 918

PENNSYLVANIA

Audio Visions Inc, pg 694
Bernie's Photo Center, pg 704
J E Foss Co, pg 764
Visual Sound Inc, pg 931

TENNESSEE

Technical Support Systems LLC,
pg 908

TEXAS

Quality Audio Visual Service Inc,
pg 867
Tarpley Media Systems, pg 907

UTAH

RIA Corp, pg 874
TV Specialists Inc, pg 919

VIRGINIA

Boitnott Visual Communications
Corp (BVC), pg 708
Lee Hartman & Sons Inc, pg 805
The Whitlock Group, pg 937

WISCONSIN

Camera Corner Connecting Point,
pg 715
Full Compass Systems, pg 767

ALBERTA

Infosat Communications Inc, pg 787
Matrix Video Communications Corp
(MVCC), pg 819

BRITISH COLUMBIA

Commercial Electronics Ltd, pg 728

ONTARIO

HD Source, pg 777

QUEBEC

Panavideo Inc, pg 850

Camera, *see* Video Camera

Camera Tripod Distributors

ALABAMA

Curtis Company, pg 736

ARIZONA

EAR Professional Audio/Video,
pg 749
Troxell-CDI, pg 918

ARKANSAS

White Diamond Productions LLC,
pg 937

CALIFORNIA

AbelCine, pg 672
Advanced Systems Group LLC,
pg 677
Ametron Audio/Video, pg 684
Assured Audio Visual, pg 691
Audio/Video Supply Inc, pg 694
Band Pro Film & Digital Inc,
pg 701
Barber Tech Video Products, pg 701
BigFoot Mobile Systems, pg 705
BroadcastStore.com, pg 711
Christy's Editorial, pg 723
Cibola Systems, pg 723
Diaquest, pg 741
Gluskin's Custom Audio Video,
pg 771
Alan Gordon Enterprises Inc,
pg 772
Gravity Media, pg 773
Hooper Camera & Imaging, pg 781
JD Audio Visual Inc, pg 793
Manios Digital & Film, pg 816
Media Fabricators Inc, pg 822
MediaPOINTE, pg 823
Photodyne Technologies, pg 856
SNAP, pg 891
Southern California Sound Image
Inc, pg 895
SSL Industries Inc, pg 898
VMI Inc, pg 932
VTP Inc, pg 933

COLORADO

Daylight Productions & Rentals,
pg 739
Mike's Camera, pg 827

Spectrum Audio Visual Services,
pg 897
Stanco Sales LLC, pg 899

CONNECTICUT

Connecticut Audio & Theatrical
Supply, pg 731
Vitec Videocom Inc, pg 932

FLORIDA

Access Media Group, pg 673
Altel Systems Group Inc, pg 682
A2D Solutions Inc, pg 692
AVI-SPL, pg 698
Digital Video Systems, pg 742
Enhanced View Services Inc,
pg 754
EZ FX Inc, pg 758
Harris Corp, pg 776
Hi-Tech Enterprises Inc, pg 779
Hi-Tech Import Export Corp,
pg 779
Midtown Video Inc, pg 827
ONstage, pg 846

GEORGIA

Baker Audio Visual, pg 700
Innocinema, pg 788
Stage Front Presentation Systems,
pg 899

HAWAII

The Audio Visual Co (AVCO),
pg 694

ILLINOIS

Allen Visual Systems Inc, pg 680
RC Communications, pg 870
Smith-Victor Corp, pg 891

INDIANA

Lee Co Inc, pg 805
Sensory Technologies LLC, pg 884
SHP Electronics, pg 887

KENTUCKY

Audio Visual Techniques Inc,
pg 695
Axxis Leasing Inc, pg 700
Barney Miller's Inc, pg 827
NOR-COM Inc, pg 841

MAINE

Headlight Audio Visual Inc, pg 777

MARYLAND

Noventri, pg 843

MASSACHUSETTS

Hunt's Photo & Video, pg 782
Integrated Solutions Group, pg 789
Rule Boston Camera, pg 878

MICHIGAN

Digi Sign Design LLC, pg 741
Lowing Light & Grip Inc, pg 812
On Stage Visuals, pg 846
TEL Systems LLC, pg 909

MINNESOTA

Alpha Video & Audio Inc, pg 682
Vaddio, pg 924

MISSISSIPPI

Bowie Audio Visual Enterprises Inc,
pg 709

MISSOURI

Communitronics Corp, pg 729
Conference Technologies Inc,
pg 730
Modern Communications Inc,
pg 828
Schiller's Audio-Visual, pg 881
Southwest Audio-Visual Inc, pg 895

NEBRASKA

VSA Inc, pg 933

NEVADA

Aardvark Video & Media
Productions, pg 671

NEW JERSEY

A-V Services Inc, pg 671
Alltec Stores, a Vcom IMC
Company, pg 681
AlltecPro, pg 681
Argraph Corp, pg 688
AV Bluebook, pg 696
Comprehensive Cable &
Connectivity Co, pg 729
Diversified, pg 744
Earl Girls Inc, pg 749
Euro-Pacific Film & Video
Productions Inc, pg 756
G&G Technologies Inc, pg 768
HamiltonBuhl, pg 775
Manfrotto Distribution Inc, pg 816
MCCOM Inc, pg 820
MiB MediaWorks, pg 825
Miller Camera Support LLC,
pg 827
PatchAmp, pg 852
Ritz Camera & Image, pg 875
Starlite, pg 900
SYMCO Inc, pg 905
Tele-Measurements Inc, pg 910
ToCad America Inc, pg 915
Total Video Products Inc, pg 916
Video Corporation of America
(VCA), pg 927

NEW YORK

Audio-Video Corp, pg 694
AV Workshop, pg 697
Benro, pg 704
Colortone Audio Visual, pg 728
Design Audio Visual Inc, pg 741
HAVE Inc, pg 777
Indigo Productions, pg 787
Induro, pg 787
KVL Audio Visual Services Inc,
pg 802
Long Island Video Enterprises Live
Inc, pg 811
MAC Group, pg 813
Markertek Video Supply, pg 817
Neptune Photo Inc, pg 838
RNJ Electronics, pg 875
Sargent Welch, pg 880
Scientifics Direct Inc, pg 882
TecNec Distributing, pg 909
Tri-Ed Distribution Inc, pg 918
Visual Technologies Corp, pg 932
Visual Word Systems Inc, pg 932

OHIO

Copp Integrated Systems, pg 731
ITA Audio Visual Solutions, pg 791
Midwest Photo Exchange, pg 827
Tri-State Audio Visual Co, pg 918
Tri-State Visual Products Inc,
pg 918
Visual Products Inc, pg 931

VIDEO

Camera Tripod Distributors (continued)

PENNSYLVANIA

Advanced AV LLC, pg 677
Audio Visions Inc, pg 694
Bernie's Photo Center, pg 704
Brodart Co, pg 711
Clair Companies, pg 725
J E Foss Co, pg 764
Garcia Marketing Inc, pg 768
Grise Audio Visual Center Inc, pg 774
The Lerro Corp, pg 806
Morefield Communications Inc, pg 830
New York Camera & Video, pg 840
Visual Sound Inc, pg 931

TENNESSEE

Allstar Audio Systems Inc, pg 681
Lowrance Sound Co Inc, pg 812
Technical Support Systems LLC, pg 908
Zion Music Group, pg 945

TEXAS

Audio Visual Technologies Group (AVTG), pg 695
AVES Audio Visual Systems Inc, pg 698
Biway Media, pg 706
CAM Audio Inc, pg 714
Data Projections Inc, pg 738
Heffernan Audio Visual, pg 778
Omega Broadcast Group, pg 845
Precision Camera & Video, pg 861
Pro Video & Film Equipment Co Inc, pg 863
Quality Audio Visual Service Inc, pg 867
Stage Directions, pg 898
Tarpley Media Systems, pg 907

UTAH

Redman Movies & Stories, pg 872
RIA Corp, pg 874

VIRGINIA

Avitecture Inc, pg 699
Boitnott Visual Communications Corp (BVC), pg 708
Lee Hartman & Sons Inc, pg 805
The Whitlock Group, pg 937

WASHINGTON

CCI Solutions, pg 718
Oppenheimer Camera Products, pg 847

WISCONSIN

Camera Corner Connecting Point, pg 715
Demco Inc, pg 740
Full Compass Systems, pg 767
Safe Harbor Computers, pg 879

ALBERTA

Infosat Communications Inc, pg 787
Matrix Video Communications Corp (MVCC), pg 819

BRITISH COLUMBIA

Commercial Electronics Ltd, pg 728

ONTARIO

FUJIFILM Canada Inc, pg 766
HD Source, pg 777
Henry's Camera, pg 779
Nationwide Audio Visual Co, pg 837
Westbury National Show Systems Ltd, pg 936

QUEBEC

Panavideo Inc, pg 850

Camera Tripod Manufacturers

CALIFORNIA

Microdolly Hollywood, pg 826
O'Connor Engineering Labs, pg 844

CONNECTICUT

Skyviews Survey Inc, pg 890

ILLINOIS

ACCO Brands Corp, pg 673
Smith-Victor Corp, pg 891

NEW JERSEY

AlltecPro, pg 681

NEW YORK

Induro, pg 787
Sima Products Corp, pg 888

VIRGINIA

Spider Support Systems, pg 897

WISCONSIN

Regal Photo Products Inc/Arkay Corp, pg 873

BRITISH COLUMBIA

Triad Communications Ltd, pg 918

Camera Tripod Rentals

ALASKA

Connections Film & Video Inc, pg 731

ARIZONA

AV Concepts Inc, pg 696
Broadcast Rentals, pg 711
Merestone, pg 823
Metropolitan Audio-Visual Inc, pg 824
Video West Inc, pg 929

ARKANSAS

White Diamond Productions LLC, pg 937

CALIFORNIA

AbelCine, pg 672
Absolute Rentals, pg 672
Action Video, pg 675
Advanced Media LLC, pg 677
Alliant Event Services, pg 681
Alternative Rentals, pg 682
Ametron Audio/Video, pg 684
Artichoke Productions, pg 690
Assured Audio Visual, pg 691
AV Guys, pg 697
Barber Tech Video Products, pg 701

Bexel, an NEP Broadcast Services Company, pg 704
Big Door, pg 705
Chater Camera Inc, pg 721
Cherry Multimedia, pg 721
Clean Slate Video, pg 726
Crystal Pyramid Productions™, pg 735
Deck Hand Inc, pg 740
The Dreaming Tree, pg 746
Dystopian Studios, pg 748
Express Media Inc, pg 757
First Camera, pg 761
Full Moon & High Tide Productions & Studios, pg 767
Gear Monkey, pg 769
Gluskin's Custom Audio Video, pg 771
Gold Standard Productions, pg 772
Golden Gate Studios, pg 772
Alan Gordon Enterprises Inc, pg 772
Gravity Media, pg 773
HD Cinema, pg 777
HDrental.com, pg 777
Hollywood Sound Systems, pg 781
iCorpTv, pg 783
Image Integration, pg 785
Imagecraft Productions, pg 785
Images in Motion Media Inc, pg 785
JD Audio Visual Inc, pg 793
JFA Studio, pg 794
Loyal Studios, pg 812
Lynch Communications, pg 813
Main Street Media Inc, pg 815
Maximus Media Inc, pg 820
McCune Audio-Video-Lighting, pg 821
Media Fabricators Inc, pg 822
Motion Picture Marine, pg 831
Munday & Collins AV, pg 834
Otto Nemenz International Inc, pg 838
New Circuit Films LLC, pg 839
Next Arts, pg 841
On-Trax Inc, pg 846
Pollution Studios, pg 859
Pro HD Rentals, pg 863
PSAV® Presentation Services, pg 866
PSSI Global Services LLC, pg 866
RetinaVision Productions, pg 874
Samy's Camera, pg 879
Shooting Star Video, pg 886
Shoulder High Productions, pg 886
SNAP, pg 891
Sound Service Co, pg 894
Stray Angel Films, pg 902
T-stop Inc, pg 906
Total Creative, pg 916
Twin Peaks Creative, pg 920
VER, pg 926
Videofax, pg 929
VMI Inc, pg 932
Voice & Video Rentals, pg 932
Westcoast Video Productions Inc, pg 936

COLORADO

Daylight Productions & Rentals, pg 739
Mike's Camera, pg 827
Multimedia Audio Visual Inc, pg 833
Open Media Foundation, pg 846

CONNECTICUT

A/V Davey, pg 697
Videofilm Systems Inc, pg 929

DELAWARE

Ken-Del Productions Inc, pg 797
Showorks Audio Visual Inc, pg 887

DISTRICT OF COLUMBIA

Metro Teleproductions Inc (MTI), pg 824

FLORIDA

Access Media Group, pg 673
AVI-SPL, pg 698
Budget Video Rentals, pg 712
CopShopMiami.com, pg 731
Digital Zoetrope Productions, pg 742
Facet Media, pg 758
Industrial Strength Inc, pg 787
Knowles Video Inc (KVI), pg 800
Midtown Video Inc, pg 827
Moving Picture, pg 831
National Teleproductions Inc, pg 837
ONstage, pg 846
Paradise Show & Design Inc, pg 851
Universal Studios Florida® Production Group, pg 922

GEORGIA

ECG Productions, pg 750
MAGNUM Companies Ltd, pg 815
ON Services, a GES Company, pg 846
See Production Services, pg 883
Stage Front Presentation Systems, pg 899
Studio Space Atlanta, pg 903

HAWAII

FOTON Hawaii, pg 764
Sight & Sound Studios, pg 887

ILLINOIS

Allen Visual Systems Inc, pg 680
AV Chicago Inc, pg 696
Backstar Creative Media Inc, pg 700
Beatty TeleVisual Productions, pg 703
Central Audio-Visual Equipment Inc, pg 719
Creative Technology (CT), pg 733
Firehouse Studios, pg 761
Magnanimous Media, pg 814
RC Communications, pg 870
Resolution Productions Group, pg 874
SCI Television & Creative Media LLC, pg 882
Tele-Time Systems, pg 910
Winter Productions, pg 939

INDIANA

Jack's Camera Shop, pg 792

KANSAS

Lights On, pg 808

KENTUCKY

Audio Visual Techniques Inc, pg 695
Idle Minds Productions Inc, pg 784
Kentucky Grip & Lighting, pg 798

LOUISIANA

Clark Services Audio Visual & Exhibit Inc, pg 725
Digital FX Inc, pg 742

Moxie Media, pg 832
Pace Systems, pg 849

MAINE

University of Maine Media
Services, pg 922

MARYLAND

Advance Audiovisual Presentation
Ltd, pg 677
Archai Media, pg 688
CPR MultiMedia Solutions, pg 732
Event Tech, pg 756
Kramer Communications Video
Production, pg 801

MASSACHUSETTS

AVFX Inc, pg 698
Green Mountain Post Films (GMP),
pg 774
Integrated Solutions Group, pg 789
massAV, pg 819
Preston Productions Inc, pg 861
Small Planet Communications Inc,
pg 890

MICHIGAN

City Events Group, pg 725
Digi Sign Design LLC, pg 741
K&R All Media Productions LLC,
pg 796
K&R's Recording Studios Inc,
pg 796
Lowing Light & Grip Inc, pg 812
On Stage Visuals, pg 846
TEL Systems LLC, pg 909

MINNESOTA

Alpha Video & Audio Inc, pg 682
House of Cinemagraphics, pg 782
Pro Media Productions, pg 863

MISSISSIPPI

Bowie Audio Visual Enterprises Inc,
pg 709

MISSOURI

Communitronics Corp, pg 729
Schiller's Audio-Visual, pg 881
Show-Me Audio-Visual, pg 887
Southwest Audio-Visual Inc, pg 895
Switch, pg 905

MONTANA

Filmlites Montana, pg 760

NEBRASKA

Dog & Pony Productions Inc,
pg 744

NEVADA

GES Audio Visual, pg 770
MG Studio, pg 825

NEW JERSEY

Audio Visual Dynamics®, pg 694
CFP Video Productions Inc, pg 720
Color Leasing Studios, pg 727
Earl Girls Inc, pg 749
Euro-Pacific Film & Video
Productions Inc, pg 756
G&G Technologies Inc, pg 768
International Audio Visual Inc,
pg 790
MediaMix Inc, pg 822
MiB MediaWorks, pg 825
Panavid, pg 850

PLS Staging, pg 858
Starlite, pg 900
Tele-Measurements Inc, pg 910
Video Corporation of America
(VCA), pg 927

NEW MEXICO

Production Outfitters, pg 864

NEW YORK

Ace Video, pg 674
Air Sea Land Productions Inc
(ASL), pg 678
AV Workshop, pg 697
Big Apple Films, pg 705
Big Foot Productions Inc, pg 705
Bond Street Studio, pg 708
Camart, pg 714
Cinema-Vision, pg 724
Colortone Audio Visual, pg 728
CP Communications, pg 732
CSI Rentals, pg 735
Design Audio Visual Inc, pg 741
Downtown Community Television
Center (DCTV), pg 746
The Food & Beverage Institute,
pg 763
Gearhead Rentals, pg 769
Hand Held Films, pg 775
Hello World Communications,
pg 778
KVL Audio Visual Services Inc,
pg 802
Long Island Video Enterprises Live
Inc, pg 811
Manhattan Center Studios Inc,
pg 816
PrimaLux Video Inc, pg 862
Production Central, pg 863
Scheimpflug Digital, pg 881
Tri-Ed Distribution Inc, pg 918
Visual Technologies Corp, pg 932
Visual Word Systems Inc, pg 932

NORTH CAROLINA

All Pro Media Inc, pg 680
AV Connections Inc, pg 697
AV Metro Inc, pg 697
The Communications Group Inc,
pg 729
Duke Media Services, pg 747
Moving Pictures, pg 832
On Location North Carolina, pg 846
Special Event Services, pg 896
Take One Productions Ltd, pg 906

NORTH DAKOTA

Media Productions, pg 822

OHIO

Hughie's Event Production Services,
pg 782
ITA Audio Visual Solutions, pg 791
Lyon Video Inc, pg 813
Mills James Productions, pg 828
Ohio HD Video, pg 844
R&B Communications Inc, pg 870

OKLAHOMA

PDC Productions, pg 852

OREGON

Koerner Camera Systems, pg 800
Northwest Film Center, pg 842
Picture This Production Services,
pg 856

PENNSYLVANIA

Argentine Productions Inc, pg 688
Audio Visions Inc, pg 694
Bernie's Photo Center, pg 704
FirstGeneration Audio/Visual
Services, pg 761
FMP Media Solutions Inc, pg 763
Grise Audio Visual Center Inc,
pg 774
Innovision Media Group, pg 788
JPL, pg 795
Muderick Media, pg 833
New York Camera & Video, pg 840
Upstage Video, pg 923
The Videohouse Inc, pg 929
Visual Sound Inc, pg 931

SOUTH CAROLINA

Genesis Creative, pg 769
Impact Technology Group LLC,
pg 786

TENNESSEE

Allstar Audio Systems Inc, pg 681
Nashville Production Rentals
(NPR), pg 836
RentACamera.com, pg 873
Russ Sturgeon Productions/RSVP,
pg 903
Technical Support Systems LLC,
pg 908

TEXAS

Audio Visual Technologies Group
(AVTG), pg 695
FitzCo Sound Inc, pg 761
GEAR Cameras & Lighting, pg 769
Media Event Concepts Inc, pg 822
Mediaforce Productions, pg 822
Muller Entertainment LLC, pg 833
Omega Broadcast Group, pg 845
Precision Camera & Video, pg 861
Quality Audio Visual Service Inc,
pg 867
South Coast Film & Video, pg 895
Stage Directions, pg 898
Texcam Inc, pg 911
Video Perspective, pg 928

UTAH

Ron Hill Imagery, pg 780
Redman Movies & Stories, pg 872

VIRGINIA

Audio Visual Actions Inc (AVA),
pg 694
Boitnott Visual Communications
Corp (BVC), pg 708
CVW Event Productions, pg 736
Lee Hartman & Sons Inc, pg 805
Quince Imaging Inc, pg 868
StageSound, pg 899
The Whitlock Group, pg 937

WASHINGTON

D A Sound, pg 737
The House Studios, pg 782
Kostov Productions, pg 801
Oppenheimer Camera Products,
pg 847
Victory Studios, pg 927

WEST VIRGINIA

Blackwater Video Productions,
pg 707

WISCONSIN

Camera Corner Connecting Point,
pg 715
Event Essentials, pg 756
Full Compass Systems, pg 767
MKE Production Rental, pg 828

WYOMING

Bridger Productions Inc, pg 710

PUERTO RICO

Stage Crew Audiovisual Inc, pg 898

ALBERTA

Evolution AV, pg 757
Matrix Video Communications Corp
(MVCC), pg 819
Unique Communications Ltd,
pg 921

BRITISH COLUMBIA

Commercial Electronics Ltd, pg 728
Inspired Image Picture Co (IIPC),
pg 788
Video Out Distribution, pg 928

MANITOBA

MidCanada Production Services Inc
(MidCan), pg 826

ONTARIO

GAPC (General Assembly
Production Centre), pg 768
HD Source, pg 777
JIB Shots Equipment Inc, pg 794
RB Productions, pg 870
SIM Digital, pg 888
Westbury National Show Systems
Ltd, pg 936
ZTV Broadcast Services Inc, pg 945

QUEBEC

Audio Visual Dynamics, pg 694
Group PVP, pg 774
Kerrigan Productions Inc, pg 798
Panavideo Inc, pg 850

Camera Tripod Repairs

CALIFORNIA

Ametron Audio/Video, pg 684
BroadcastStore.com, pg 711
Gluskin's Custom Audio Video,
pg 771
Alan Gordon Enterprises Inc,
pg 772
Matthews Studio Equipment Inc,
pg 820
VMI Inc, pg 932

CONNECTICUT

Precision Camera & Video Repair
Inc, pg 861

FLORIDA

Hi-Tech Enterprises Inc, pg 779
Midtown Video Inc, pg 827

GEORGIA

Stage Front Presentation Systems,
pg 899

VIDEO

Camera Tripod Repairs (continued)

ILLINOIS

Allen Visual Systems Inc, pg 680
Beatty TeleVisual Productions, pg 703

KENTUCKY

Axxis Leasing Inc, pg 700
NOR-COM Inc, pg 841

MICHIGAN

Lowing Light & Grip Inc, pg 812
TEL Systems LLC, pg 909

MINNESOTA

Alpha Video & Audio Inc, pg 682

MISSISSIPPI

Bowie Audio Visual Enterprises Inc, pg 709

MISSOURI

Schiller's Audio-Visual, pg 881
Southwest Audio-Visual Inc, pg 895

NEW JERSEY

Miller Camera Support LLC, pg 827
ToCad America Inc, pg 915

NEW YORK

Benro, pg 704
Induro, pg 787
MAC Group, pg 813
The Tiffen Co LLC, pg 914
Visual Technologies Corp, pg 932

OHIO

ITA Audio Visual Solutions, pg 791

PENNSYLVANIA

Audio Visions Inc, pg 694
Bernie's Photo Center, pg 704

TENNESSEE

Technical Support Systems LLC, pg 908

TEXAS

Quality Audio Visual Service Inc, pg 867
Tarpley Media Systems, pg 907

UTAH

RIA Corp, pg 874

VIRGINIA

Boitnott Visual Communications Corp (BVC), pg 708
Lee Hartman & Sons Inc, pg 805
The Whitlock Group, pg 937

WASHINGTON

Oppenheimer Camera Products, pg 847

WISCONSIN

Camera Corner Connecting Point, pg 715
Full Compass Systems, pg 767

ALBERTA

Infosat Communications Inc, pg 787

BRITISH COLUMBIA

Commercial Electronics Ltd, pg 728

ONTARIO

HD Source, pg 777

QUEBEC

Panavideo Inc, pg 850

Can, *see* Reel & Can

CD-ROM Interactive Production Services

ARIZONA

Merestone, pg 823
Teaberry, pg 908

CALIFORNIA

All Video Productions, pg 680
Steve Chandler, pg 720
Christian Media Network, pg 722
Coloredge Inc, pg 728
Creative Technology, pg 733
Custom Video Productions Inc, pg 736
digital OutPost, pg 742
Direct Images Interactive Inc, pg 743
DV Post, pg 748
First Person Inc, pg 761
Havas Edge, pg 777
iCorpTv, pg 783
Imageworks, pg 785
JDS Video & Media Productions Inc, pg 793
Ludlow Media, pg 812
Lumeni Productions Inc, pg 812
Lynch Communications, pg 813
Maximus Media Inc, pg 820
Media Magic, pg 822
Medical Visual Creations (MVC), pg 823
New Cyberian Systems Inc, pg 839
Nineteen87, pg 841
Nolte Media, pg 841
QRS Software Services, pg 867
RetinaVision Productions, pg 874
SonicPool, pg 892
Staylor-Made Communications Inc, pg 900
Still N' Motion, pg 901
Tam Communications Inc, pg 906
TIMECODE Post Production, pg 914
TiVo Corp, pg 914
Total Creative, pg 916
Towards 2000 Inc, pg 916
Twin Peaks Creative, pg 920
Via Verde Productions, pg 926
Video Movie Magic, pg 928
Wavemaker Media Design, pg 934
WMS Media Inc, pg 940

COLORADO

Daylight Productions & Rentals, pg 739
Flashback Media Productions, pg 762

CONNECTICUT

BRB Audiovisual Productions, pg 709
Geomatrix Productions, pg 770
Ironik Design & Post, pg 791
New London Media, pg 839
Palace Production Center, pg 850
T & M Digital Services LLC, pg 906
Video Production Associates Inc, pg 928

DELAWARE

So Smart Productions, pg 891

DISTRICT OF COLUMBIA

Interface Media Group, pg 789
O'Keefe Communications Inc, pg 844

FLORIDA

Access Media Group, pg 673
Applebox Studio, pg 687
Civins Productions Inc, pg 725
Florida Digital Studios, pg 762
Hi-Tech Enterprises Inc, pg 779
Shooting Stars Post Inc, pg 886
Sound & Vision Communications Inc, pg 893
Sunfire Communications Inc, pg 904
Sunrise Studios, pg 904
Tricycle Studios, pg 918
Video Techniques Inc, pg 928

GEORGIA

The DVI Group, pg 748
ECG Productions, pg 750
Guerrilla Productions LLC, pg 774
Imagers, pg 785
Omega Media Group Inc, pg 845

HAWAII

Hyperspective Studios Inc, pg 783
1013 Integrated, pg 911

ILLINOIS

ABSA Films, pg 672
Advanced Audio Technology, pg 677
Airways Digital Media, pg 679
CCore Media Inc, pg 718
Extraordinary Demos/Videos, pg 757
IV Media Resources, pg 792
Kelmscott Communications, pg 797
Major Media Inc, pg 815
Manning Productions, pg 816
Mightybytes Inc, pg 827
Pepper Group, pg 854
RADMAR Inc, pg 869
Richter Studios, pg 875
Sparkfactor, pg 896
20/20 Communications Inc, pg 920
Video I-D Teleproductions Inc, pg 928
Video Impressions, pg 928

INDIANA

Bright Ideas Creative Services, pg 710
PentaVision Communications Inc, pg 854

IOWA

Iowa State University-Information Technology Services, pg 791

KENTUCKY

Prosper Media Group Inc, pg 866

LOUISIANA

Louisiana State University Division of Strategic Communications, pg 811
Vidox Motion Imagery, pg 930

MARYLAND

CPR MultiMedia Solutions, pg 732
dbF a Media Company, pg 739
DBM Communications Inc, pg 739
Kramer Communications Video Production, pg 801
Media Dimensions LLC, pg 821
Saah Video, pg 879

MASSACHUSETTS

Boston Productions Inc (BPI), pg 709
Cramer, pg 732
Northern Light Productions (NLP), pg 842
Penfield Productions Ltd, pg 853
TR Productions, pg 916

MICHIGAN

ASC Systems, pg 690
Digi Sign Design LLC, pg 741
Digital Image Studios LLC, pg 742
K&R's Recording Studios Inc, pg 796
TGA Recording Co, pg 911

MINNESOTA

The ADS Group, pg 676
BeyerSound & Essay Audio, pg 705
MastCom, pg 819
Worthwhile Films, pg 941

MISSOURI

Avatar Studios, pg 697
Show-Me Audio-Visual, pg 887

MONTANA

ooLite Media LLC, pg 846

NEBRASKA

B & B Video Productions Inc, pg 700
Rainbow Video Productions Inc, pg 869
Three Pillars Media, pg 913

NEVADA

Aardvark Video & Media Productions, pg 671
JCS Video Productions, pg 793

NEW HAMPSHIRE

Heinemann, pg 778
Chip Taylor Communications LLC, pg 907

NEW JERSEY

AJS Events, pg 679
Allegro Productions Inc, pg 680
CD Meyer Inc, pg 718
CFP Video Productions Inc, pg 720
Diversified, pg 744
Megavideo LLC, pg 823
MiB MediaWorks, pg 825
Midnight Media Group Inc, pg 827
Outside The Box Interactive LLC, pg 849

Reed Presentations Inc (RPI), pg 872
Suede Interactive, pg 903
Two Animators LLP, pg 920
VCSvideo, pg 925

NEW YORK

American Artists Representatives Inc, pg 682
Animotion Inc, pg 685
Bellin Productions, pg 703
The Big House Group, pg 705
Chromavision Corp, pg 723
Thomas Craven Film Corp, pg 733
Digital Force Ltd, pg 742
Duplication Depot Inc, pg 748
Duplication Specialists Inc, pg 748
4-D Creative Media, pg 764
Guidance Associates Inc Center for Humanities, pg 774
HAVE Inc, pg 777
HB-Content, pg 777
International Digital Centre, pg 790
L A Bruell Inc, pg 802
New York Audio Productions, pg 840
Teatown Communications Group, pg 908

NORTH CAROLINA

Pat Appleson Studios Inc, pg 687
The Communications Group Inc, pg 729
Horizon Video Productions Inc, pg 781
Moving Pictures, pg 832
NASCAR Productions LLC, pg 835
On Location North Carolina, pg 846
Take One Productions Ltd, pg 906
2BruceStudio, pg 920

OHIO

Advent Media Inc, pg 677
Aztec Video Productions, pg 700
Cinecraft Productions Inc, pg 723
Curtis Inc, pg 736
Lyon Video Inc, pg 813
Mills James Productions, pg 828
Take 1 Media Services, pg 906

OREGON

InterVision Media, pg 791
Odyssey Productions Inc, pg 844
Production West, pg 864
REX, pg 874
Wallace Creative LLC, pg 933
Wilderness Video, pg 938

PENNSYLVANIA

Beholder Productions Inc, pg 703
FMP Media Solutions Inc, pg 763
Innovision Media Group, pg 788
JPL, pg 795
Production Masters Inc (PMI), pg 864

RHODE ISLAND

Sound-FX-Design, pg 894

SOUTH CAROLINA

Genesis Creative, pg 769

TENNESSEE

Motion Picture Services, pg 831
Paradigm Marketing & Creative, pg 851
Running Pony Productions LLC, pg 878
Stage Post, pg 899

TEXAS

Biway Media, pg 706
Communication Arts Multimedia Inc, pg 728
The Editing Co, pg 750
Epic Software Group Inc, pg 755
Fire Station Studios, pg 761
Horizon Film + Video Productions, pg 781
Hurst Digital, pg 782
Mediaforce Productions, pg 822
Julye Newlin Productions Inc, pg 840
Out of the BLUE Media, pg 849
Replicopy Digital Media Center, pg 873
South Coast Film & Video, pg 895
Stage Directions, pg 898
Texas Heart Institute Visual Communication Services, pg 911
TopCat Records LLC, pg 915

UTAH

ImageWorks Communications, pg 785

VIRGINIA

Advance Concepts Inc, pg 677
Allied Media Corp, pg 681
Altruist Media LLC, pg 682
Metro Productions, pg 824

WASHINGTON

Evia, pg 757
North-by-Northwest - A Digital Studio, pg 842
Victory Studios, pg 927

WISCONSIN

Logan Productions Inc, pg 811
Video Wisconsin Inc, pg 929
Win Media Inc, pg 939

PUERTO RICO

Stage Crew Audiovisual Inc, pg 898

BRITISH COLUMBIA

Credo Interactive Inc, pg 734
Triad Communications Ltd, pg 918
24 Frames Film & Video, pg 920

NEWFOUNDLAND AND LABRADOR

Vidcraft Productions Ltd, pg 927

ONTARIO

ADS Media, pg 677
GestureTek, pg 770
Image Video Services & Productions, pg 785
JFB Communications, pg 794
Marblemedia, pg 816
RB Productions, pg 870
Silver Creek Media Inc, pg 888
Video Excellence Productions, pg 927

QUEBEC

Group PVP, pg 774

Character Generator Distributors

ARIZONA

ATCi (Antenna Technology Communication Solutions Inc), pg 692
EAR Professional Audio/Video, pg 749
Troxell-CDI, pg 918

ARKANSAS

Jay S Stanley & Associates Inc, pg 899
White Diamond Productions LLC, pg 937

CALIFORNIA

Advanced Systems Group LLC, pg 677
Ametron Audio/Video, pg 684
Audio/Video Supply Inc, pg 694
BroadcastStore.com, pg 711
Cibola Systems, pg 723
Diaquest, pg 741
Gluskin's Custom Audio Video, pg 771
Media Control Systems LLC, pg 821
Media Fabricators Inc, pg 822
MediaPOINTE, pg 823
Metro Video Systems Inc, pg 824
Nortek Security & Control LLC, pg 842
SNAP, pg 891
VMI Inc, pg 932
VTP Inc, pg 933

COLORADO

Spectrum Audio Visual Services, pg 897

CONNECTICUT

MAVCO, pg 820
The Video Messenger Co, pg 928

FLORIDA

Access Media Group, pg 673
Altel Systems Group Inc, pg 682
AVI-SPL, pg 698
Digital Video Systems, pg 742
Harris Corp, pg 776
Hi-Tech Enterprises Inc, pg 779
Hi-Tech Import Export Corp, pg 779
Industrial Strength Inc, pg 787
Midtown Video Inc, pg 827
Multicom Inc, pg 833
ONstage, pg 846
Tallahassee Audio Visual, pg 906

GEORGIA

Convergent Media Systems, pg 731
Stage Front Presentation Systems, pg 899

HAWAII

The Audio Visual Co (AVCO), pg 694

ILLINOIS

Allen Visual Systems Inc, pg 680
Joseph Electronics, pg 795
Tele-Time Systems, pg 910

INDIANA

Sensory Technologies LLC, pg 884

KENTUCKY

Barney Miller's Inc, pg 827
NOR-COM Inc, pg 841

LOUISIANA

Digital FX Inc, pg 742

MAINE

Headlight Audio Visual Inc, pg 777

MARYLAND

Image Logic Corp, pg 785
RTZ Audio Visual, pg 878

MASSACHUSETTS

Integrated Solutions Group, pg 789
Rule Boston Camera, pg 878

MICHIGAN

ASC Systems, pg 690
City Events Group, pg 725
DAWNco, pg 739
Digi Sign Design LLC, pg 741
Michigan Office Solutions (MOS), A Xerox Company, pg 825
On Stage Visuals, pg 846
TEL Systems LLC, pg 909

MINNESOTA

Alpha Video & Audio Inc, pg 682
AVI Systems, pg 698

MISSISSIPPI

MFJ Enterprises Inc, pg 825

MISSOURI

Communitronics Corp, pg 729
Conference Technologies Inc, pg 730
Modern Communications Inc, pg 828
Schiller's Audio-Visual, pg 881
Southwest Audio-Visual Inc, pg 895

NEVADA

Aardvark Video & Media Productions, pg 671

NEW JERSEY

A-V Services Inc, pg 671
Alltec Stores, a Vcom IMC Company, pg 681
AlltecPro, pg 681
Audio Visual Dynamics®, pg 694
AV Bluebook, pg 696
Comprehensive Cable & Connectivity Co, pg 729
Diversified, pg 744
G&G Technologies Inc, pg 768
HamiltonBuhl, pg 775
MCCOM Inc, pg 820
Starlite, pg 900
SYMCO Inc, pg 905
Tele-Measurements Inc, pg 910
Video Corporation of America (VCA), pg 927
Wired 4 Sound Inc, pg 940

NEW YORK

Audio-Video Corp, pg 694
AV Workshop, pg 697
ChyronHego Corp, pg 723
Creative Stage Lighting Co Inc, pg 733
Design Audio Visual Inc, pg 741
Gaylord Archival, pg 768

VIDEO

Character Generator Distributors (continued)

NEW YORK (continued)

Indigo Productions, pg 787
Long Island Video Enterprises Live Inc, pg 811
Markertek Video Supply, pg 817
Neptune Photo Inc, pg 838
RNJ Electronics, pg 875
TecNec Distributing, pg 909
Tri-Ed Distribution Inc, pg 918
Visual Word Systems Inc, pg 932
Willoughby's® Camera, pg 939

NORTH CAROLINA

Camcor Inc, pg 715
Crispin Corp, pg 734
Strategic Connections, pg 901

OHIO

Copp Integrated Systems, pg 731
ITA Audio Visual Solutions, pg 791
Tri-State Audio Visual Co, pg 918

PENNSYLVANIA

Clair Companies, pg 725
J E Foss Co, pg 764
Grise Audio Visual Center Inc, pg 774
The Lerro Corp, pg 806
Morefield Communications Inc, pg 830
Visual Sound Inc, pg 931

TENNESSEE

Lowrance Sound Co Inc, pg 812
Memphis Communications Corp, pg 823
Technical Support Systems LLC, pg 908
Zion Music Group, pg 945

TEXAS

AVES Audio Visual Systems Inc, pg 698
Pro Video & Film Equipment Co Inc, pg 863
Stage Directions, pg 898
Tarpley Media Systems, pg 907
Videotex Systems Inc, pg 930

VIRGINIA

Boitnott Visual Communications Corp (BVC), pg 708
Lee Hartman & Sons Inc, pg 805
RGB Technology Inc, pg 874
The Whitlock Group, pg 937

WISCONSIN

Camera Corner Connecting Point, pg 715
Full Compass Systems, pg 767

ALBERTA

Infosat Communications Inc, pg 787
Matrix Video Communications Corp (MVCC), pg 819
McBain Camera Ltd, pg 820

BRITISH COLUMBIA

Commercial Electronics Ltd, pg 728

ONTARIO

HD Source, pg 777
Nationwide Audio Visual Co, pg 837

SASKATCHEWAN

Display Systems International, pg 743

Character Generator Manufacturers

CALIFORNIA

AJA Video Systems Inc, pg 679
Horita Co Inc, pg 781
Nortek Security & Control LLC, pg 842
TV Pro Gear, pg 919

CONNECTICUT

The Video Messenger Co, pg 928

FLORIDA

Compuvideo Sales USA Ltd, pg 729

KANSAS

Keywest Technology Inc, pg 798

MARYLAND

Image Logic Corp, pg 785

MISSISSIPPI

MFJ Enterprises Inc, pg 825

MISSOURI

GlobalStreams™ Corp, pg 771

NEW JERSEY

CELCO, pg 719

NEW MEXICO

Burst Electronics Inc, pg 713

NEW YORK

ChyronHego Corp, pg 723
EEG Enterprises Inc, pg 751
Markertek Video Supply, pg 817
MultiDyne Video & Fiber Optics Systems, pg 833

PENNSYLVANIA

MicroImage Video Systems, pg 826
Scala Inc, pg 881

RHODE ISLAND

M-Audio, pg 813

TENNESSEE

Adtec Digital Inc, pg 677

VIRGINIA

RGB Technology Inc, pg 874

BRITISH COLUMBIA

Triad Communications Ltd, pg 918

SASKATCHEWAN

Display Systems International, pg 743

Character Generator Rentals

ARIZONA

Merestone, pg 823
Metropolitan Audio-Visual Inc, pg 824

ARKANSAS

White Diamond Productions LLC, pg 937

CALIFORNIA

Ametron Audio/Video, pg 684
Artichoke Productions, pg 690
Bexel, an NEP Broadcast Services Company, pg 704
Express Media Inc, pg 757
Full Moon & High Tide Productions & Studios, pg 767
Golden Gate Studios, pg 772
Lynch Communications, pg 813
McCune Audio-Video-Lighting, pg 821
Media Fabricators Inc, pg 822
Munday & Collins AV, pg 834
On-Trax Inc, pg 846
PSAV® Presentation Services, pg 866
PSSI Global Services LLC, pg 866
Technical Services, pg 908
Total Creative, pg 916
Twin Peaks Creative, pg 920
VER, pg 926
VMI Inc, pg 932
Voice & Video Rentals, pg 932
Westcoast Video Productions Inc, pg 936

COLORADO

Daylight Productions & Rentals, pg 739
Multimedia Audio Visual Inc, pg 833
Spectrum Audio Visual Services, pg 897

CONNECTICUT

Videofilm Systems Inc, pg 929

FLORIDA

Access Media Group, pg 673
Budget Video Rentals, pg 712
Industrial Strength Inc, pg 787
Jordan Klein Film & Video (JKFV), pg 795
Midtown Video Inc, pg 827
ONstage, pg 846
Paradise Show & Design Inc, pg 851

GEORGIA

Convergent Media Systems, pg 731
ON Services, a GES Company, pg 846
Stage Front Presentation Systems, pg 899
Staging Directions Inc, pg 899

ILLINOIS

Allen Visual Systems Inc, pg 680
Backstar Creative Media Inc, pg 700
On Site Video, pg 846
Resolution Productions Group, pg 874
Tele-Time Systems, pg 910

KENTUCKY

Audio Visual Techniques Inc, pg 695

LOUISIANA

Digital FX Inc, pg 742
Pace Systems, pg 849

MARYLAND

CPR MultiMedia Solutions, pg 732

MASSACHUSETTS

Integrated Solutions Group, pg 789
Preston Productions Inc, pg 861

MICHIGAN

Digi Sign Design LLC, pg 741
K&R All Media Productions LLC, pg 796
K&R's Recording Studios Inc, pg 796
On Stage Visuals, pg 846
TEL Systems LLC, pg 909

MINNESOTA

Alpha Video & Audio Inc, pg 682
AVI Systems, pg 698
Cinequipt Inc, pg 724

MISSOURI

Schiller's Audio-Visual, pg 881
Show-Me Audio-Visual, pg 887
Southwest Audio-Visual Inc, pg 895

NEBRASKA

Dog & Pony Productions Inc, pg 744

NEVADA

GES Audio Visual, pg 770
Lefco Video Services Inc, pg 806

NEW HAMPSHIRE

Academic & Campus Technology Services, pg 672

NEW JERSEY

MediaMix Inc, pg 822
PLS Staging, pg 858
Starlite, pg 900
Wired 4 Sound Inc, pg 940

NEW MEXICO

Production Outfitters, pg 864

NEW YORK

Adwar Video, pg 678
AV Workshop, pg 697
CMI Communications, pg 727
Creative Stage Lighting Co Inc, pg 733
Design Audio Visual Inc, pg 741
Long Island Video Enterprises Live Inc, pg 811
Manhattan Center Studios Inc, pg 816
PrimaLux Video Inc, pg 862
Visual Word Systems Inc, pg 932

NORTH CAROLINA

AV Connections Inc, pg 697
The Communications Group Inc, pg 729
Duke Media Services, pg 747

OHIO

Lyon Video Inc, pg 813
R&B Communications Inc, pg 870
Vista Color Imaging Inc, pg 931

OKLAHOMA

PDC Productions, pg 852

PENNSYLVANIA

FMP Media Solutions Inc, pg 763
Grise Audio Visual Center Inc,
  pg 774
Innovision Media Group, pg 788
Muderick Media, pg 833
Producers Management Television
  (PMTV), pg 863
Upstage Video, pg 923
The Videohouse Inc, pg 929

TENNESSEE

Memphis Communications Corp,
  pg 823
Russ Sturgeon Productions/RSVP,
  pg 903
Technical Support Systems LLC,
  pg 908

TEXAS

JSAV, pg 795
Media Event Concepts Inc, pg 822
Phillips Media Source, pg 855
Stage Directions, pg 898

VIRGINIA

Boitnott Visual Communications
  Corp (BVC), pg 708
CVW Event Productions, pg 736
Lee Hartman & Sons Inc, pg 805
Quince Imaging Inc, pg 868

WISCONSIN

Camera Corner Connecting Point,
  pg 715
Full Compass Systems, pg 767
University of Wisconsin-Oshkosh
  Radio-TV-Film Dept, pg 923
Wisconsin Public Television, pg 940

PUERTO RICO

Stage Crew Audiovisual Inc, pg 898

ALBERTA

Global TV, pg 771
Matrix Video Communications Corp
  (MVCC), pg 819

BRITISH COLUMBIA

Commercial Electronics Ltd, pg 728
Video Out Distribution, pg 928

ONTARIO

HD Source, pg 777
RB Productions, pg 870

Character Generator Repairs

CALIFORNIA

Ametron Audio/Video, pg 684
Metro Video Systems Inc, pg 824
Technical Services, pg 908
VMI Inc, pg 932

FLORIDA

ELC Sales & Service Inc, pg 752
Hi-Tech Enterprises Inc, pg 779
Midtown Video Inc, pg 827

GEORGIA

Stage Front Presentation Systems,
  pg 899

ILLINOIS

Allen Visual Systems Inc, pg 680
On Site Video, pg 846

KENTUCKY

Barney Miller's Inc, pg 827
NOR-COM Inc, pg 841

MICHIGAN

City Events Group, pg 725
TEL Systems LLC, pg 909

MINNESOTA

Alpha Video & Audio Inc, pg 682
AVI Systems, pg 698

MISSOURI

Southwest Audio-Visual Inc, pg 895

NEW YORK

Ace Video, pg 674

NORTH CAROLINA

Camcor Inc, pg 715

OHIO

Copp Integrated Systems, pg 731
ITA Audio Visual Solutions, pg 791

TENNESSEE

Memphis Communications Corp,
  pg 823
Technical Support Systems LLC,
  pg 908

TEXAS

Tarpley Media Systems, pg 907

VIRGINIA

Boitnott Visual Communications
  Corp (BVC), pg 708
The Whitlock Group, pg 937

WISCONSIN

Full Compass Systems, pg 767

ALBERTA

Infosat Communications Inc, pg 787

BRITISH COLUMBIA

Commercial Electronics Ltd, pg 728

Character Generator Production Services

ALABAMA

Diamond Studios, pg 741

ARIZONA

Direct Current Video Productions,
  pg 743
Fox 10 Productions (KSAZ-TV),
  pg 765

Merestone, pg 823
Metropolitan Audio-Visual Inc,
  pg 824
On-Site Video, pg 846
Star Video Duplicating, pg 900

ARKANSAS

White Diamond Productions LLC,
  pg 937

CALIFORNIA

Access Video in Berkeley, pg 673
Action Video, pg 675
AlphaDogs Inc, pg 682
Artichoke Productions, pg 690
Steve Chandler, pg 720
Creative Technology, pg 733
Crystal Pyramid Productions™,
  pg 735
Custom Video Productions Inc,
  pg 736
Digital Jungle, pg 742
DV Post, pg 748
Express Media Inc, pg 757
First Person Inc, pg 761
Full Moon & High Tide Productions
  & Studios, pg 767
Golden Gate Studios, pg 772
Hydrogen Whiskey Studios, pg 783
iCorpTv, pg 783
JDS Video & Media Productions
  Inc, pg 793
Lumeni Productions Inc, pg 812
Lynch Communications, pg 813
Maximus Media Inc, pg 820
McCune Audio-Video-Lighting,
  pg 821
Medical Visual Creations (MVC),
  pg 823
Nolte Media, pg 841
PM Productions, pg 858
Point.360, pg 858
QRS Software Services, pg 867
Reality Check Systems, pg 871
Saturn Studios, pg 881
Shapeshifter, pg 885
SonicPool, pg 892
Tam Communications Inc, pg 906
Total Creative, pg 916
Twin Peaks Creative, pg 920
Universal Studios, pg 922
Videografix LLC, pg 929
Visions Plus, pg 931
Wavemaker Media Design, pg 934

COLORADO

CSI Film & Video LLC, pg 735
Daylight Productions & Rentals,
  pg 739
Flashback Media Productions,
  pg 762
Rocky Mountain Audio/Video
  Productions Inc, pg 876
Spectrum Audio Visual Services,
  pg 897

CONNECTICUT

BRB Audiovisual Productions,
  pg 709
Guymark Studios LLC, pg 775
Ironik Design & Post, pg 791
MAVCO, pg 820
New London Media, pg 839
Palace Production Center, pg 850
The Video Messenger Co, pg 928

DISTRICT OF COLUMBIA

Interface Media Group, pg 789

FLORIDA

Access Media Group, pg 673
Applebox Studio, pg 687
Civins Productions Inc, pg 725
Communications Concepts Inc
  (CCI), pg 729
Comtel Inc, pg 730
Easy Edit Video Inc, pg 750
Jordan Klein Film & Video (JKFV),
  pg 795
Knowles Video Inc (KVI), pg 800
ONstage, pg 846
Shooting Stars Post Inc, pg 886
Sunfire Communications Inc,
  pg 904
Sunrise Studios, pg 904
Tricycle Studios, pg 918
Universal Studios Florida®
  Production Group, pg 922
Mike Vasilinda Productions Inc,
  pg 925
Video Techniques Inc, pg 928
Vistamax Productions, pg 931

GEORGIA

Beachwood Productions, pg 702
Beast Atlanta, pg 703
The DVI Group, pg 748
Guerrilla Productions LLC, pg 774
On-Line Productions, pg 845
Staging Directions Inc, pg 899

IDAHO

KTVB-TV, pg 802

ILLINOIS

ABSA Films, pg 672
Atomic Imaging Inc/Golan Studios,
  pg 692
Backstar Creative Media Inc,
  pg 700
Breeze Productions Inc, pg 710
CCore Media Inc, pg 718
IV Media Resources, pg 792
Multimedia Marketing Group,
  pg 833
SCI Television & Creative Media
  LLC, pg 882
Sound/Video Impressions Inc,
  pg 894
Sparkfactor, pg 896
20/20 Communications Inc, pg 920
Video Impressions, pg 928
WEEK TV, pg 935

INDIANA

A-V-A Video Productions, pg 671
Bright Ideas Creative Services,
  pg 710

IOWA

Iowa State University-Information
  Technology Services, pg 791

KANSAS

KAKE-TV, pg 796

KENTUCKY

Hammond Communications Group
  Inc, pg 775
Barney Miller's Inc, pg 827
WKYT-TV, pg 940

LOUISIANA

Louisiana State University Division
  of Strategic Communications,
  pg 811
Moxie Media, pg 832

VIDEO

Character Generator Production Services (continued)

LOUISIANA (continued)

Vidox Motion Imagery, pg 930
WVLA-TV, pg 942

MAINE

WGME-TV, pg 936

MARYLAND

CPR MultiMedia Solutions, pg 732
dbF a Media Company, pg 739
DBM Communications Inc, pg 739
Image Logic Corp, pg 785
Kramer Communications Video Production, pg 801
Media Dimensions LLC, pg 821
Saah Video, pg 879
Sheffield Audio/Video Productions, pg 885
Spectrum Productions, pg 897
Welocalize, pg 935

MASSACHUSETTS

Award Productions Inc, pg 699
Penfield Productions Ltd, pg 853

MICHIGAN

Digi Sign Design LLC, pg 741
Digital Image Studios LLC, pg 742
K&R's Recording Studios Inc, pg 796
On Stage Visuals, pg 846
RingSide Creative, pg 875

MINNESOTA

The ADS Group, pg 676
AVI Systems, pg 698
Worthwhile Films, pg 941

MISSOURI

Avatar Studios, pg 697
Communitronics Corp, pg 729
Show-Me Audio-Visual, pg 887

MONTANA

KCFW Television, pg 797

NEBRASKA

Three Pillars Media, pg 913

NEVADA

Aardvark Video & Media Productions, pg 671
DVDs4Less, pg 748
Encore Event Technologies LLC, pg 754
JCS Video Productions, pg 793
Peterson's Video Transfer Services, pg 855
21st Century Video Productions, pg 919

NEW HAMPSHIRE

Apertura, pg 686
Channell One Video, pg 720
Chip Taylor Communications LLC, pg 907

NEW JERSEY

AJS Events, pg 679
Allegro Productions Inc, pg 680
Broadcast Center Studios, pg 710
CFP Video Productions Inc, pg 720
Diversified, pg 744
Laurel Video Productions, pg 804
MediaMix Inc, pg 822
MiB MediaWorks, pg 825
Midnight Media Group Inc, pg 827
NFL Films Inc, pg 841
PLS Staging, pg 858
Suede Interactive, pg 903
Total Video Products Inc, pg 916
VCSvideo, pg 925
Video Ideas Productions, pg 928

NEW MEXICO

Production Outfitters, pg 864

NEW YORK

American Artists Representatives Inc, pg 682
aurora productions, pg 696
The Big House Group, pg 705
Chromavision Corp, pg 723
Cohn Creative Group LLC, pg 727
Design Audio Visual Inc, pg 741
Digital Art Video Inc, pg 741
Downtown Community Television Center (DCTV), pg 746
4-D Creative Media, pg 764
HAVE Inc, pg 777
HB-Content, pg 777
Heavy Melody, pg 778
InterNation Inc, pg 789
Lylofilm Productions, pg 813
Mood Creations Ltd, pg 829
Jack Morton Worldwide, pg 830
PostWorks, pg 860
Rafik, pg 869
Teatown Communications Group, pg 908
TeleTime Productions, pg 910
Video Caption Corp, pg 927
Visual Technologies Corp, pg 932
WTL Productions, pg 942

NORTH CAROLINA

Pat Appleson Studios Inc, pg 687
Camcor Inc, pg 715
The Communications Group Inc, pg 729
Duke Media Services, pg 747
Horizon Video Productions Inc, pg 781
Moving Pictures, pg 832
NASCAR Productions LLC, pg 835
On Location North Carolina, pg 846
Take One Productions Ltd, pg 906

NORTH DAKOTA

UND Television Center, pg 921

OHIO

Aztec Video Productions, pg 700
Bartha, pg 702
Cuyahoga Community College Student Production Office (SPO), pg 736
Lyon Video Inc, pg 813
Mills James Productions, pg 828
R&B Communications Inc, pg 870
Take 1 Media Services, pg 906
Vista Color Imaging Inc, pg 931

OKLAHOMA

Garman Productions LLC, pg 768
PDC Productions, pg 852

OREGON

KTVA Productions, pg 802
Production West, pg 864

PENNSYLVANIA

FMP Media Solutions Inc, pg 763
Innovision Media Group, pg 788
JPL, pg 795
The Videohouse Inc, pg 929
WPHL-TV, pg 942

RHODE ISLAND

Sound-FX-Design, pg 894

SOUTH CAROLINA

American Production Services LLC, pg 684
Encore Video Productions, pg 754
Genesis Creative, pg 769
Stages Video Productions, pg 899

TENNESSEE

Memphis Communications Corp, pg 823
Motion Picture Services, pg 831
Running Pony Productions LLC, pg 878
Scripps Networks, pg 882
Stage Post, pg 899

TEXAS

CEV Multimedia Ltd, pg 720
Communication Arts Multimedia Inc, pg 728
Contemporary Research, pg 731
Dub King, pg 747
The Editing Co, pg 750
Epic Software Group Inc, pg 755
Horizon Film + Video Productions, pg 781
Hurst Digital, pg 782
JSAV, pg 795
Mediaforce Productions, pg 822
Earl Miller Productions Inc, pg 827
Julye Newlin Productions Inc, pg 840
Phillips Media Source, pg 855
The Samuels Co, pg 879
South Coast Film & Video, pg 895
Stage Directions, pg 898

UTAH

ImageWorks Communications, pg 785

VIRGINIA

American AV, pg 682
CDR Communications Inc, pg 719
CVW Event Productions, pg 736
Eagle Films, pg 749
Henninger Media Services, pg 779
Maniglia Media LLC, pg 816
Metro Productions, pg 824
Rocktown Media, pg 876
The Whitlock Group, pg 937

WASHINGTON

Bennett-Watt HD Productions Inc, pg 703
Linguist's Software Inc, pg 809
North-by-Northwest - A Digital Studio, pg 842
Victory Studios, pg 927

WISCONSIN

Audio Visual of Milwaukee Inc, pg 694
Meridian Studios, pg 824

Mirror 34 Productions, pg 828
University of Wisconsin-Oshkosh Radio-TV-Film Dept, pg 923
Video Wisconsin Inc, pg 929
Watts Communications Inc, pg 934
Wisconsin Public Television, pg 940

WYOMING

Bridger Productions Inc, pg 710

PUERTO RICO

Stage Crew Audiovisual Inc, pg 898

BRITISH COLUMBIA

Triad Communications Ltd, pg 918

NEWFOUNDLAND AND LABRADOR

Vidcraft Productions Ltd, pg 927

ONTARIO

ADS Media, pg 677
Image Video Services & Productions, pg 785
JFB Communications, pg 794
Video Excellence Productions, pg 927

QUEBEC

Group PVP, pg 774

Closed Captioning Production Services

ARIZONA

Merestone, pg 823
Star Video Duplicating, pg 900

CALIFORNIA

Aberdeen Broadcast Services, pg 672
Express Media Inc, pg 757
Full Moon & High Tide Productions & Studios, pg 767
Havas Edge, pg 777
iCorpTv, pg 783
JDS Video & Media Productions Inc, pg 793
Lightning Media, pg 808
Ludlow Media, pg 812
Lumeni Productions Inc, pg 812
Lynch Communications, pg 813
Point.360, pg 858
QRS Software Services, pg 867
Roundabout Entertainment Inc, pg 878
Shapeshifter, pg 885
SonicPool, pg 892
Staylor-Made Communications Inc, pg 900
Studio 637, pg 903
Total Creative, pg 916

COLORADO

Flashback Media Productions, pg 762
VITAC, pg 932

CONNECTICUT

Ironik Design & Post, pg 791
Bret Stern Productions, pg 900

DISTRICT OF COLUMBIA

Interface Media Group, pg 789

FLORIDA

Access Media Group, pg 673
Accord Productions, pg 673
Easy Edit Video Inc, pg 750
Florida Digital Studios, pg 762
Gemstone Media Inc, pg 769
The Kitchen, pg 799
Sunfire Communications Inc,
   pg 904
Tricycle Studios, pg 918
Video Techniques Inc, pg 928

GEORGIA

Guerrilla Productions LLC, pg 774

ILLINOIS

Atomic Imaging Inc/Golan Studios,
   pg 692
Captions & Subtitle Services Ltd,
   pg 716
Joseph Electronics, pg 795
Richter Studios, pg 875
SCI Television & Creative Media
   LLC, pg 882
Video Impressions, pg 928

INDIANA

A-V-A Video Productions, pg 671

KANSAS

KAKE-TV, pg 796

KENTUCKY

Broadway Digital, pg 711
Prosper Media Group Inc, pg 866

MAINE

WGME-TV, pg 936

MARYLAND

Adventure Productions LLC, pg 678
CPR MultiMedia Solutions, pg 732
Image Logic Corp, pg 785
Kramer Communications Video
   Production, pg 801
Pro Cuts Editing Services, pg 862

MASSACHUSETTS

Award Productions Inc, pg 699
Extreme Reach Inc, pg 757
Video Express, pg 928
WGBH Production Group, pg 936

MICHIGAN

Digi Sign Design LLC, pg 741
K&R's Recording Studios Inc,
   pg 796

MINNESOTA

The ADS Group, pg 676
CaptionMax, pg 716

MISSOURI

Show-Me Audio-Visual, pg 887

MONTANA

ooLite Media LLC, pg 846

NEW HAMPSHIRE

Chip Taylor Communications LLC,
   pg 907

NEW JERSEY

Allegro Productions Inc, pg 680
Color Leasing Studios, pg 727
Diversified, pg 744
Laurel Video Productions, pg 804
MiB MediaWorks, pg 825
Suede Interactive, pg 903

NEW MEXICO

Production Outfitters, pg 864

NEW YORK

All Mobile Video Inc, pg 680
Chromavision Corp, pg 723
Digital Arts NY, pg 742
Giant Interactive, pg 770
HAVE Inc, pg 777
International Digital Centre, pg 790
iProbe Multilingual Solutions Inc,
   pg 791
Magno Sound Inc, pg 815
Mood Creations Ltd, pg 829
PostWorks, pg 860
Teatown Communications Group,
   pg 908
USA Studios, pg 923
Video Caption Corp, pg 927
Visual Technologies Corp, pg 932

NORTH CAROLINA

Pat Appleson Studios Inc, pg 687

OHIO

Advent Media Inc, pg 677
Aztec Video Productions, pg 700
Bartha, pg 702
Curtis Inc, pg 736
Mills James Productions, pg 828
Production Partners Media, pg 864
Take 1 Media Services, pg 906

OKLAHOMA

Garman Productions LLC, pg 768

OREGON

Odyssey Productions Inc, pg 844
Production West, pg 864

PENNSYLVANIA

FMP Media Solutions Inc, pg 763
Innovision Media Group, pg 788
JPL, pg 795
Laser Video Corp, pg 804
Panta Rhei Media Inc, pg 851
Production Masters Inc (PMI),
   pg 864

SOUTH CAROLINA

American Production Services LLC,
   pg 684

TENNESSEE

Motion Picture Services, pg 831
Running Pony Productions LLC,
   pg 878
Stage Post, pg 899

TEXAS

Anaphora Literary Press, pg 685
Contemporary Research, pg 731
The Editing Co, pg 750
Horizon Film + Video Productions,
   pg 781
Hurst Digital, pg 782
Mediaforce Productions, pg 822
Replicopy Digital Media Center,
   pg 873

UTAH

ImageWorks Communications,
   pg 785

VIRGINIA

Henninger Media Services, pg 779
Metro Productions, pg 824

WASHINGTON

Victory Studios, pg 927

BRITISH COLUMBIA

24 Frames Film & Video, pg 920

ONTARIO

GAPC (General Assembly
   Production Centre), pg 768

Color Correction Services

ALASKA

Connections Film & Video Inc,
   pg 731

ARIZONA

Film Creations Ltd, pg 760
Merestone, pg 823
Metropolitan Audio-Visual Inc,
   pg 824

CALIFORNIA

Access Video in Berkeley, pg 673
Action Video, pg 675
Advanced Digital Design, pg 677
Advanced Media LLC, pg 677
All Video Productions, pg 680
AlphaDogs Inc, pg 682
Angstrom Lighting, pg 685
Artichoke Productions, pg 690
Audio Visual Consultants, pg 694
CCI Digital, a DVS Company,
   pg 718
Christopher Gray Post Production,
   pg 722
Creative Technology, pg 733
Custom Video Productions Inc,
   pg 736
Deja View Video, pg 740
Deluxe Entertainment Services
   Group Inc, pg 740
Digital Jungle, pg 742
First Person Inc, pg 761
For-A Corp of America, pg 763
Full Moon & High Tide Productions
   & Studios, pg 767
Glix Entertainment Inc, pg 771
Golden Gate Studios, pg 772
Havas Edge, pg 777
iCorpTv, pg 783
Illuminate Post/Digital Finishing,
   pg 784
JDS Video & Media Productions
   Inc, pg 793
KTVU-Retail Services, pg 802
Lightning Media, pg 808
Ludlow Media, pg 812
Lynch Communications, pg 813
Maximus Media Inc, pg 820
Method Studios, pg 824
Nandar Entertainment Pictures,
   pg 835
Nineteen87, pg 841
PM Productions, pg 858
Point.360, pg 858
Pro8mm, pg 862
QRS Software Services, pg 867
Reality Check Systems, pg 871

Roundabout Entertainment Inc,
   pg 878
Saturn Studios, pg 881
Shapeshifter, pg 885
SonicPool, pg 892
Still N' Motion, pg 901
Studio 637, pg 903
TIMECODE Post Production,
   pg 914
Total Creative, pg 916
Twin Peaks Creative, pg 920
Two Door Productions LLC, pg 920
Universal Studios, pg 922
VidCan Media Solutions, pg 927
Videografix LLC, pg 929
Visions Plus, pg 931
Vitruvian Entertainment, pg 932

COLORADO

Colorado Sound Recording Ltd,
   pg 728
Daylight Productions & Rentals,
   pg 739
Rocky Mountain Audio/Video
   Productions Inc, pg 876

CONNECTICUT

Digital Video Productions, pg 742
Guymark Studios LLC, pg 775
Ironik Design & Post, pg 791
Palace Production Center, pg 850
Sonalysts Media, pg 892
T & M Digital Services LLC,
   pg 906

DISTRICT OF COLUMBIA

Interface Media Group, pg 789

FLORIDA

Access Media Group, pg 673
ACT Productions, pg 675
Adrenaline Films, pg 676
Applebox Studio, pg 687
Civins Productions Inc, pg 725
Communications Concepts Inc
   (CCI), pg 729
Courter Films LLC, pg 732
JungleTV, pg 795
ONstage, pg 846
Shooting Stars Post Inc, pg 886
Sunfire Communications Inc,
   pg 904
Sunrise Studios, pg 904
Tricycle Studios, pg 918
Universal Studios Florida®
   Production Group, pg 922
Video Techniques Inc, pg 928
Vistamax Productions, pg 931

GEORGIA

The DVI Group, pg 748
ECG Productions, pg 750
Guerrilla Productions LLC, pg 774
Staging Directions Inc, pg 899

HAWAII

Hyperspective Studios Inc, pg 783

ILLINOIS

Airways Digital Media, pg 679
Atomic Imaging Inc/Golan Studios,
   pg 692
Beatty TeleVisual Productions,
   pg 703
Breeze Productions Inc, pg 710
Chicago Spotlight Inc, pg 721
IV Media Resources, pg 792
Optimus, pg 847

VIDEO

Color Correction Services (continued)

ILLINOIS (continued)

SCI Television & Creative Media LLC, pg 882
Southern Illinois University, pg 895
Sparkfactor, pg 896
Tele-Time Systems, pg 910
20/20 Communications Inc, pg 920

INDIANA

A-V-A Video Productions, pg 671

KANSAS

KAKE-TV, pg 796

KENTUCKY

The PPS Group, pg 860
Prosper Media Group Inc, pg 866

LOUISIANA

Digital FX Inc, pg 742
Moxie Media, pg 832
Pace Systems, pg 849
Vidox Motion Imagery, pg 930

MARYLAND

Adventure Productions LLC, pg 678
CPR MultiMedia Solutions, pg 732
dbF a Media Company, pg 739
Kramer Communications Video Production, pg 801
Producers Video, pg 863
Spectrum Productions, pg 897

MASSACHUSETTS

Award Productions Inc, pg 699
HOME Inc, pg 781
TVN-The Video Network, pg 919

MICHIGAN

Digi Sign Design LLC, pg 741
K&R's Recording Studios Inc, pg 796
Michigan Recording Arts Institute & Technologies, pg 825
The Program Source International, pg 865
RingSide Creative, pg 875
The Transfer Zone®, pg 917

MINNESOTA

The ADS Group, pg 676
MastCom, pg 819
Norcostco Inc, pg 842
Worthwhile Films, pg 941

MISSOURI

Show-Me Audio-Visual, pg 887

NEBRASKA

Three Pillars Media, pg 913

NEVADA

Aardvark Video & Media Productions, pg 671
Encore Event Technologies LLC, pg 754
JCS Video Productions, pg 793
Lefco Video Services Inc, pg 806

Peterson's Video Transfer Services, pg 855
Wells-Gardner Technologies Inc, pg 935

NEW HAMPSHIRE

Chip Taylor Communications LLC, pg 907
The Troupe, pg 918

NEW JERSEY

AJS Events, pg 679
Allegro Productions Inc, pg 680
CFP Video Productions Inc, pg 720
Creative Video, pg 734
Diversified, pg 744
MediaMix Inc, pg 822
MediaNow Inc, pg 822
MiB MediaWorks, pg 825
NFL Films Inc, pg 841
Starlite, pg 900
Suede Interactive, pg 903
VCSvideo, pg 925

NEW MEXICO

Production Outfitters, pg 864

NEW YORK

Adwar Video, pg 678
Air Sea Land Productions Inc (ASL), pg 678
aurora productions, pg 696
Big Apple Films, pg 705
The Big House Group, pg 705
Buffalo Video Production, pg 712
Design Audio Visual Inc, pg 741
Digital Art Video Inc, pg 741
Digital Arts NY, pg 742
Downtown Community Television Center (DCTV), pg 746
DuArt Media Services, pg 747
4-D Creative Media, pg 764
HAVE Inc, pg 777
HB-Content, pg 777
Hello World Communications, pg 778
PostWorks, pg 860
Sima Products Corp, pg 888
Teatown Communications Group, pg 908
USA Studios, pg 923

NORTH CAROLINA

Pat Appleson Studios Inc, pg 687
Horizon Video Productions Inc, pg 781
Kino Mountain Productions LLC, pg 799
Moving Pictures, pg 832
On Location North Carolina, pg 846
Take One Productions Ltd, pg 906

OHIO

Advent Media Inc, pg 677
Aztec Video Productions, pg 700
iVideo Technologies, pg 792
Lyon Video Inc, pg 813
Mills James Productions, pg 828
R&B Communications Inc, pg 870

OKLAHOMA

Garman Productions LLC, pg 768

OREGON

BingoLewis, pg 706
KTVA Productions, pg 802
Production West, pg 864

PENNSYLVANIA

Center City Film & Video Inc, pg 719
FMP Media Solutions Inc, pg 763
Production Masters Inc (PMI), pg 864
The Videohouse Inc, pg 929
WPHL-TV, pg 942

RHODE ISLAND

Sound-FX-Design, pg 894

SOUTH CAROLINA

Genesis Creative, pg 769
Venture Media, pg 925

TENNESSEE

Motion Picture Services, pg 831
Running Pony Productions LLC, pg 878
Scripps Networks, pg 882
Stage Post, pg 899

TEXAS

Biway Media, pg 706
Dub King, pg 747
The Editing Co, pg 750
Freeman, pg 765
Horizon Film + Video Productions, pg 781
Hurst Digital, pg 782
Julye Newlin Productions Inc, pg 840
The Samuels Co, pg 879
South Coast Film & Video, pg 895
Stage Directions, pg 898

UTAH

Ron Hill Imagery, pg 780
ImageWorks Communications, pg 785

VIRGINIA

CACI Integrated Communications, pg 713
Henninger Media Services, pg 779
Limelight Communications Inc, pg 808
Maniglia Media LLC, pg 816
Metro Productions, pg 824
Rocktown Media, pg 876

WASHINGTON

North-by-Northwest - A Digital Studio, pg 842
Victory Studios, pg 927

WISCONSIN

Meridian Studios, pg 824
Video Wisconsin Inc, pg 929
Watts Communications Inc, pg 934

WYOMING

Bridger Productions Inc, pg 710

PUERTO RICO

Stage Crew Audiovisual Inc, pg 898

ALBERTA

Global TV, pg 771

BRITISH COLUMBIA

24 Frames Film & Video, pg 920

MANITOBA

Spectra Video Productions Ltd, pg 897

ONTARIO

ADS Media, pg 677
Eggplant Pictures & Sound, pg 751
GAPC (General Assembly Production Centre), pg 768
Video Excellence Productions, pg 927

QUEBEC

Grass Valley, pg 773

Compact Disc Recorder & Player Distributors

ARIZONA

EAR Professional Audio/Video, pg 749

ARKANSAS

White Diamond Productions LLC, pg 937

CALIFORNIA

Ametron Audio/Video, pg 684
Be Media, pg 702
Cibola Systems, pg 723
Empire Pro, pg 753
Gluskin's Custom Audio Video, pg 771
JD Audio Visual Inc, pg 793
Media Control Systems LLC, pg 821
Photodyne Technologies, pg 856
Sound Service Co, pg 894
Southern California Sound Image Inc, pg 895
Videobotics, pg 929
VMI Inc, pg 932
VTP Inc, pg 933

COLORADO

Daylight Productions & Rentals, pg 739
Spectrum Audio Visual Services, pg 897

CONNECTICUT

Connecticut Audio & Theatrical Supply, pg 731
Sennheiser Electronic Corp, pg 884

FLORIDA

Access Media Group, pg 673
Alcorn McBride Inc, pg 679
Alliance Entertainment Corp (AEC) LLC, pg 680
Altel Systems Group Inc, pg 682
CD ROM™ Inc, pg 718
Digital Video Systems, pg 742
Harris Corp, pg 776
ONstage, pg 846
Recording Media & Equipment Inc (RM&E), pg 872

GEORGIA

Clark, pg 725
Stage Front Presentation Systems, pg 899

HAWAII

The Audio Visual Co (AVCO), pg 694

ILLINOIS

Allen Visual Systems Inc, pg 680
Joseph Electronics, pg 795
Quintessence Audio Ltd, pg 868

INDIANA

Lee Co Inc, pg 805
Sensory Technologies LLC, pg 884
SHP Electronics, pg 887

KENTUCKY

Axxis Leasing Inc, pg 700
NOR-COM Inc, pg 841

MAINE

Headlight Audio Visual Inc, pg 777

MARYLAND

Cardinal Sound & Video, pg 717

MASSACHUSETTS

Rule Boston Camera, pg 878

MICHIGAN

Digi Sign Design LLC, pg 741
On Stage Visuals, pg 846

MISSISSIPPI

Bowie Audio Visual Enterprises Inc, pg 709

NEVADA

Aardvark Video & Media Productions, pg 671

NEW JERSEY

Alltec Stores, a Vcom IMC Company, pg 681
AlltecPro, pg 681
Audio Visual Associates, pg 694
AV Bluebook, pg 696
Diversified, pg 744
Earl Girls Inc, pg 749
HamiltonBuhl, pg 775
Starlite, pg 900
Total Video Products Inc, pg 916
Wired 4 Sound Inc, pg 940

NEW YORK

Audio-Video Corp, pg 694
Design Audio Visual Inc, pg 741
HAVE Inc, pg 777
Image Management Systems Inc, pg 785
KVL Audio Visual Services Inc, pg 802
RNJ Electronics, pg 875
TecNec Distributing, pg 909

OHIO

Tri-State Audio Visual Co, pg 918

PENNSYLVANIA

Advanced AV LLC, pg 677
Clair Companies, pg 725
J E Foss Co, pg 764
Grise Audio Visual Center Inc, pg 774
The Lerro Corp, pg 806

TENNESSEE

Lowrance Sound Co Inc, pg 812
Technical Support Systems LLC, pg 908
Zion Music Group, pg 945

TEXAS

Audio Visual Technologies Group (AVTG), pg 695
AVES Audio Visual Systems Inc, pg 698
Biway Media, pg 706
CAM Audio Inc, pg 714
Data Projections Inc, pg 738
Pro Video & Film Equipment Co Inc, pg 863
Replicopy Digital Media Center, pg 873
Tarpley Media Systems, pg 907

UTAH

Performance Audio LLC, pg 854

VIRGINIA

Avitecture Inc, pg 699
Lee Hartman & Sons Inc, pg 805

WASHINGTON

CCI Solutions, pg 718

WISCONSIN

Audio Visual of Milwaukee Inc, pg 694
Full Compass Systems, pg 767

ALBERTA

Infosat Communications Inc, pg 787

MANITOBA

Inland Audio Visual Ltd, pg 788

ONTARIO

Westbury National Show Systems Ltd, pg 936

Compact Disc Recorder & Player Manufacturers

FLORIDA

Alcorn McBride Inc, pg 679

TENNESSEE

Adtec Digital Inc, pg 677

Compact Disc Recorder & Player Rentals

ARIZONA

Merestone, pg 823
Video West Inc, pg 929

ARKANSAS

White Diamond Productions LLC, pg 937

CALIFORNIA

Absolute Rentals, pg 672
Advanced Media LLC, pg 677
AGF Media Services, pg 678
Ametron Audio/Video, pg 684
Artichoke Productions, pg 690
Audio Rents, pg 693
AV Guys, pg 697
Express Media Inc, pg 757
JD Audio Visual Inc, pg 793
Lynch Communications, pg 813
Maximus Media Inc, pg 820
McCune Audio-Video-Lighting, pg 821

Munday & Collins AV, pg 834
Muse Presentation Technologies, pg 834
PSAV® Presentation Services, pg 866
RetinaVision Productions, pg 874
Roundabout Entertainment Inc, pg 878
SNAP, pg 891
Sound Service Co, pg 894
Total Creative, pg 916
Twin Peaks Creative, pg 920
VER, pg 926
VMI Inc, pg 932
Voice & Video Rentals, pg 932

COLORADO

Spectrum Audio Visual Services, pg 897

CONNECTICUT

A/V Davey, pg 697

FLORIDA

Accord Productions, pg 673
ONstage, pg 846
Paradise Show & Design Inc, pg 851
Universal Studios Florida® Production Group, pg 922

GEORGIA

Stage Front Presentation Systems, pg 899

ILLINOIS

Allen Visual Systems Inc, pg 680
AV Chicago Inc, pg 696
Backstar Creative Media Inc, pg 700
RC Communications, pg 870
Resolution Productions Group, pg 874

KENTUCKY

Audio Visual Techniques Inc, pg 695

MARYLAND

CPR MultiMedia Solutions, pg 732
Event Tech, pg 756

MASSACHUSETTS

massAV, pg 819
Preston Productions Inc, pg 861

MICHIGAN

Digi Sign Design LLC, pg 741
K&R All Media Productions LLC, pg 796
K&R's Recording Studios Inc, pg 796
On Stage Visuals, pg 846

MISSISSIPPI

Bowie Audio Visual Enterprises Inc, pg 709

MISSOURI

Show-Me Audio-Visual, pg 887

NEBRASKA

Dog & Pony Productions Inc, pg 744

NEVADA

GES Audio Visual, pg 770
JCS Video Productions, pg 793

NEW JERSEY

Audio Visual Associates, pg 694
Audio Visual Dynamics®, pg 694
CFP Video Productions Inc, pg 720
Earl Girls Inc, pg 749
Panavid, pg 850
Starlite, pg 900
Wired 4 Sound Inc, pg 940

NEW MEXICO

Production Outfitters, pg 864

NEW YORK

CP Communications, pg 732
Design Audio Visual Inc, pg 741
Hello World Communications, pg 778
KVL Audio Visual Services Inc, pg 802

NORTH CAROLINA

The Communications Group Inc, pg 729
Digital Rain LLC, pg 742
Take One Productions Ltd, pg 906

OHIO

Hughie's Event Production Services, pg 782
Lyon Video Inc, pg 813
Mills James Productions, pg 828

OREGON

Northwest Film Center, pg 842
Rose City Sound, pg 877

PENNSYLVANIA

Advanced AV LLC, pg 677
Audio Visual Communications Inc, pg 694
FMP Media Solutions Inc, pg 763
Grise Audio Visual Center Inc, pg 774

TENNESSEE

Love Shack Recording Studios, pg 811
Technical Support Systems LLC, pg 908

TEXAS

Alford Media Services, pg 680
Stage Directions, pg 898

VIRGINIA

Lee Hartman & Sons Inc, pg 805
Quince Imaging Inc, pg 868

WASHINGTON

Victory Studios, pg 927

WISCONSIN

Full Compass Systems, pg 767

PUERTO RICO

Stage Crew Audiovisual Inc, pg 898

MANITOBA

Inland Audio Visual Ltd, pg 788

VIDEO

Compact Disc Recorder & Player Rentals (continued)

ONTARIO

Wanted! Sound + Picture, pg 933
Westbury National Show Systems Ltd, pg 936

QUEBEC

Group PVP, pg 774

Compact Disc Recorder & Player Repairs

CALIFORNIA

Advanced Media LLC, pg 677
Ametron Audio/Video, pg 684
McAlister Electronics, pg 820
Pro Camera Repair, pg 862
Towards 2000 Inc, pg 916
VMI Inc, pg 932

FLORIDA

Digital Video Systems, pg 742
ELC Sales & Service Inc, pg 752
Hi-Tech Enterprises Inc, pg 779

GEORGIA

Stage Front Presentation Systems, pg 899

ILLINOIS

Allen Visual Systems Inc, pg 680
Midwest Digital Corp, pg 827

KENTUCKY

Axxis Leasing Inc, pg 700
NOR-COM Inc, pg 841

MICHIGAN

TEL Systems LLC, pg 909

NEW JERSEY

Audio Visual Associates, pg 694
Earl Girls Inc, pg 749
Starlite, pg 900

OHIO

Tri-State Audio Visual Co, pg 918

OREGON

All Service Musical Electronics Repair, pg 680

PENNSYLVANIA

J E Foss Co, pg 764

TENNESSEE

Technical Support Systems LLC, pg 908

TEXAS

Pro Video & Film Equipment Co Inc, pg 863
Tarpley Media Systems, pg 907

WISCONSIN

Full Compass Systems, pg 767

ALBERTA

Infosat Communications Inc, pg 787

MANITOBA

Inland Audio Visual Ltd, pg 788

ONTARIO

Westbury National Show Systems Ltd, pg 936

Compression & Decompression Equipment Distributors

ARIZONA

EAR Professional Audio/Video, pg 749

ARKANSAS

Jay S Stanley & Associates Inc, pg 899

CALIFORNIA

Ametron Audio/Video, pg 684
Computer Modules Inc, pg 729
Diaquest, pg 741
Electrosonic Inc, pg 752
Media Control Systems LLC, pg 821
MediaPOINTE, pg 823
Promax Systems, pg 865
Videobotics, pg 929
VMI Inc, pg 932
VTP Inc, pg 933

FLORIDA

Access Media Group, pg 673
Digital Video Systems, pg 742
Harris Corp, pg 776
ONstage, pg 846
Recording Media & Equipment Inc (RM&E), pg 872
Vela Research, pg 925

GEORGIA

Ligos Corporation, pg 808
Stage Front Presentation Systems, pg 899

HAWAII

The Audio Visual Co (AVCO), pg 694

ILLINOIS

Joseph Electronics, pg 795
Toko America Inc, pg 915

INDIANA

Sensory Technologies LLC, pg 884
SHP Electronics, pg 887

KENTUCKY

NOR-COM Inc, pg 841

MAINE

Headlight Audio Visual Inc, pg 777

MARYLAND

Siqura Inc, pg 889

MASSACHUSETTS

Rule Boston Camera, pg 878
SeaChange International Inc, pg 883

MICHIGAN

ASC Systems, pg 690
Digi Sign Design LLC, pg 741

MINNESOTA

Alpha Video & Audio Inc, pg 682

MISSOURI

Modern Communications Inc, pg 828
Schiller's Audio-Visual, pg 881
Southwest Audio-Visual Inc, pg 895

NEW JERSEY

Diversified, pg 744
Starlite, pg 900
SYMCO Inc, pg 905
Tele-Measurements Inc, pg 910
Total Video Products Inc, pg 916
Wired 4 Sound Inc, pg 940

NEW YORK

Audio-Video Corp, pg 694
TecNec Distributing, pg 909

OHIO

Tri-State Audio Visual Co, pg 918

PENNSYLVANIA

AccuWeather Inc, pg 674
Advanced AV LLC, pg 677
Innovision Media Group, pg 788
The Lerro Corp, pg 806

SOUTH DAKOTA

Sencore Inc, pg 883

TENNESSEE

Lowrance Sound Co Inc, pg 812
Technical Support Systems LLC, pg 908
Zion Music Group, pg 945

TEXAS

Biway Media, pg 706
Pro Video & Film Equipment Co Inc, pg 863
Tarpley Media Systems, pg 907
Videotex Systems Inc, pg 930

WISCONSIN

Audio Visual of Milwaukee Inc, pg 694
Full Compass Systems, pg 767
Safe Harbor Computers, pg 879

MANITOBA

Inland Audio Visual Ltd, pg 788

ONTARIO

ATX Networks, pg 692

Compression & Decompression Equipment Manufacturers

ARIZONA

Applied Integration Corp, pg 687

CALIFORNIA

Computer Modules Inc, pg 729
Linkabit, pg 809

Opticomm-EMCORE, pg 847
Telestream Inc, pg 910
VITEC Multimedia, pg 932

FLORIDA

CD ROM™ Inc, pg 718
Compuvideo Sales USA Ltd, pg 729
Vela Research, pg 925

GEORGIA

Ligos Corporation, pg 808
Wegener Communications Inc, pg 935

ILLINOIS

Toko America Inc, pg 915

MARYLAND

Siqura Inc, pg 889

MASSACHUSETTS

SeaChange International Inc, pg 883

MINNESOTA

Vaddio, pg 924

NEW JERSEY

Ikegami Electronics (USA) Inc, pg 784

NEW YORK

Laird Digital Cinema, pg 803
Judson Rosebush Co Inc, pg 877

SOUTH DAKOTA

Sencore Inc, pg 883

TENNESSEE

Adtec Digital Inc, pg 677

QUEBEC

Grass Valley, pg 773
Matrox Video Products Group, pg 819

Compression & Decompression Equipment Rentals

ARIZONA

Merestone, pg 823
Video West Inc, pg 929

CALIFORNIA

Ametron Audio/Video, pg 684
Audio Rents, pg 693
Express Media Inc, pg 757
Golden Gate Studios, pg 772
Image Integration, pg 785
Lynch Communications, pg 813
Main Street Media Inc, pg 815
McCune Audio-Video-Lighting, pg 821
Muse Presentation Technologies, pg 834
PSSI Global Services LLC, pg 866
Total Creative, pg 916
Twin Peaks Creative, pg 920

COLORADO

Spectrum Audio Visual Services, pg 897

FLORIDA

Access Media Group, pg 673
ONstage, pg 846
Universal Studios Florida®
Production Group, pg 922

GEORGIA

Stage Front Presentation Systems,
pg 899

ILLINOIS

Resolution Productions Group,
pg 874

MARYLAND

CPR MultiMedia Solutions, pg 732
Event Tech, pg 756

MASSACHUSETTS

Preston Productions Inc, pg 861

MICHIGAN

Digi Sign Design LLC, pg 741
K&R All Media Productions LLC,
pg 796

MINNESOTA

Alpha Video & Audio Inc, pg 682

MISSOURI

Show-Me Audio-Visual, pg 887
Southwest Audio-Visual Inc, pg 895

NEVADA

JCS Video Productions, pg 793

NEW JERSEY

Audio Visual Dynamics®, pg 694
Starlite, pg 900
Tele-Measurements Inc, pg 910
Wired 4 Sound Inc, pg 940

NEW YORK

CP Communications, pg 732
Manhattan Center Studios Inc,
pg 816

NORTH CAROLINA

The Communications Group Inc,
pg 729
Take One Productions Ltd, pg 906

OHIO

Lyon Video Inc, pg 813
Mills James Productions, pg 828

PENNSYLVANIA

Advanced AV LLC, pg 677
FMP Media Solutions Inc, pg 763
Innovision Media Group, pg 788

TENNESSEE

Technical Support Systems LLC,
pg 908

VIRGINIA

Quince Imaging Inc, pg 868

WISCONSIN

Full Compass Systems, pg 767

MANITOBA

Inland Audio Visual Ltd, pg 788

ONTARIO

Wanted! Sound + Picture, pg 933

QUEBEC

Group PVP, pg 774

Compression & Decompression Equipment Repairs

CALIFORNIA

Ametron Audio/Video, pg 684
Electrosonic Inc, pg 752

FLORIDA

ELC Sales & Service Inc, pg 752
Vela Research, pg 925

GEORGIA

Stage Front Presentation Systems,
pg 899

ILLINOIS

Midwest Digital Corp, pg 827

KENTUCKY

NOR-COM Inc, pg 841

MICHIGAN

TEL Systems LLC, pg 909

MINNESOTA

Alpha Video & Audio Inc, pg 682

MISSOURI

Southwest Audio-Visual Inc, pg 895

NEW JERSEY

Starlite, pg 900

OREGON

All Service Musical Electronics
Repair, pg 680

TENNESSEE

Technical Support Systems LLC,
pg 908

TEXAS

Pro Video & Film Equipment Co
Inc, pg 863
Tarpley Media Systems, pg 907

WISCONSIN

Full Compass Systems, pg 767

MANITOBA

Inland Audio Visual Ltd, pg 788

Computer Graphics

ALABAMA

Diamond Studios, pg 741

ALASKA

Imig Audio/Video Inc, pg 786

ARIZONA

Film Creations Ltd, pg 760
Fox 10 Productions (KSAZ-TV),
pg 765
Merestone, pg 823
Metropolitan Audio-Visual Inc,
pg 824
On-Site Video, pg 846
Video West Inc, pg 929

ARKANSAS

Live'N'Loud, pg 810
White Diamond Productions LLC,
pg 937

CALIFORNIA

Access Video in Berkeley, pg 673
Action Video, pg 675
Advanced Media LLC, pg 677
Advanced Systems Group LLC,
pg 677
All Video Productions, pg 680
AlphaDogs Inc, pg 682
Artichoke Productions, pg 690
Audio Visual Consultants, pg 694
Blind™, pg 707
Buttercup Pictures, pg 713
CCI Digital, a DVS Company,
pg 718
Steve Chandler, pg 720
Christopher Gray Post Production,
pg 722
Classic Images Stock Footage LLC,
pg 726
Creative Technology, pg 733
Custom Video Productions Inc,
pg 736
Diaquest, pg 741
Digital Jungle, pg 742
digital OutPost, pg 742
Direct Images Interactive Inc,
pg 743
Dolphin MultiMedia Inc, pg 745
DV Post, pg 748
Elektrashock, pg 753
Express Media Inc, pg 757
Ferrari Productions, pg 759
First Camera, pg 761
First Person Inc, pg 761
Glix Entertainment Inc, pg 771
Gold Standard Productions, pg 772
Golden Gate Studios, pg 772
Havas Edge, pg 777
Hydrogen Whiskey Studios, pg 783
iCorpTv, pg 783
Industrial Light & Magic (ILM),
pg 787
JDS Video & Media Productions
Inc, pg 793
KO Creative, pg 800
KPBS Public Broadcasting, pg 801
KVIE-Channel 6, pg 802
Laser Magic Productions, pg 804
Lumeni Productions Inc, pg 812
Maximus Media Inc, pg 820
McCune Audio-Video-Lighting,
pg 821
Media Magic, pg 822
The Media Staff Inc, pg 822
Medical Visual Creations (MVC),
pg 823
Method Studios, pg 824
New & Unique Videos™, pg 839
Nineteen87, pg 841
Nolte Media, pg 841
On-Trax Inc, pg 846
Pacific Video Image, pg 849
Penrose Productions, pg 854
Pixar Animation Studios, pg 857
piXvfm Inc, pg 857
PM Productions, pg 858

PME Audio/Video, pg 858
Point.360, pg 858
PSI Inc, pg 866
QRS Software Services, pg 867
Reality Check Systems, pg 871
Rough House, pg 878
Roundabout Entertainment Inc,
pg 878
Saturn Studios, pg 881
Shapeshifter, pg 885
SonicPool, pg 892
Staylor-Made Communications Inc,
pg 900
Still N' Motion, pg 901
Tam Communications Inc, pg 906
Three D Graphics Inc, pg 913
TIMECODE Post Production,
pg 914
Total Creative, pg 916
Towards 2000 Inc, pg 916
Twin Peaks Creative, pg 920
Two Door Productions LLC, pg 920
Universal Studios, pg 922
Videobotics, pg 929
Videografix LLC, pg 929
Visions Plus, pg 931
Wavemaker Media Design, pg 934
WMS Media Inc, pg 940
Mark Woollen & Associates, pg 941

COLORADO

CSI Film & Video LLC, pg 735
Daylight Productions & Rentals,
pg 739
Flashback Media Productions,
pg 762
Full Spectrum Arts & Services,
pg 767
Rocky Mountain Audio/Video
Productions Inc, pg 876
Spectrum Audio Visual Services,
pg 897
Z-Axis Corp, pg 944

CONNECTICUT

BRB Audiovisual Productions,
pg 709
Cine-Med Inc, pg 723
The Gary-Paul Agency, pg 768
Guymark Studios LLC, pg 775
Ironik Design & Post, pg 791
Moving Pictures, pg 832
Musivision Inc, pg 835
New London Media, pg 839
Palace Production Center, pg 850
Palace Productions MediaVision,
pg 850
P&P Studios Inc, pg 851
T & M Digital Services LLC,
pg 906
Video Production Associates Inc,
pg 928

DISTRICT OF COLUMBIA

Interface Media Group, pg 789
Yellow Cat Productions Inc, pg 944

FLORIDA

A Cut Above Video Productions
Inc, pg 671
Access Media Group, pg 673
Applebox Studio, pg 687
Audio Visual Imagineering Inc,
pg 694
Civins Productions Inc, pg 725
Communications Concepts Inc
(CCI), pg 729
Comtel Inc, pg 730
Courter Films LLC, pg 732
Digimation, pg 741
Easy Edit Video Inc, pg 750

VIDEO

Computer Graphics (continued)

FLORIDA (continued)

Everlast Productions, pg 757
JungleTV, pg 795
The Kitchen, pg 799
PRI Productions, pg 862
Shooting Stars Post Inc, pg 886
Sound & Vision Communications Inc, pg 893
Sunfire Communications Inc, pg 904
Sunrise Studios, pg 904
Tricycle Studios, pg 918
Universal Studios Florida® Production Group, pg 922
Mike Vasilinda Productions Inc, pg 925
Video Techniques Inc, pg 928
Vistamax Productions, pg 931

GEORGIA

Beachwood Productions, pg 702
Beast Atlanta, pg 703
The DVI Group, pg 748
ECG Productions, pg 750
Guerrilla Productions LLC, pg 774
Imagers, pg 785
Myriad Productions, pg 835
Staging Directions Inc, pg 899

HAWAII

Dot C Software Inc, pg 746
Hyperspective Studios Inc, pg 783
1013 Integrated, pg 911

ILLINOIS

ABSA Films, pg 672
Airways Digital Media, pg 679
AnswersMedia, pg 686
Atomic Imaging Inc/Golan Studios, pg 692
Beatty TeleVisual Productions, pg 703
Breeze Productions Inc, pg 710
CCore Media Inc, pg 718
Cresta Creative, pg 734
Explore, pg 757
Freeman Pictures Inc, pg 765
IV Media Resources, pg 792
Optimus, pg 847
Jim Passin Productions, pg 852
Pepper Group, pg 854
Richter Studios, pg 875
SCI Television & Creative Media LLC, pg 882
Sound/Video Impressions Inc, pg 894
Southern Illinois University, pg 895
Sparkfactor, pg 896
Tele-Time Systems, pg 910
20/20 Communications Inc, pg 920
Video I-D Teleproductions Inc, pg 928
Video Impressions, pg 928

INDIANA

A-V-A Video Productions, pg 671
Bright Ideas Creative Services, pg 710
OMNI Productions, pg 845

IOWA

Iowa State University-Information Technology Services, pg 791

KANSAS

KAKE-TV, pg 796

KENTUCKY

Hammond Communications Group Inc, pg 775
The PPS Group, pg 860

LOUISIANA

Digital FX Inc, pg 742
Launch Media, pg 804
Louisiana State University Division of Strategic Communications, pg 811
Moxie Media, pg 832
Vidox Motion Imagery, pg 930
WVLA-TV, pg 942
YES Productions, pg 944

MARYLAND

Adventure Productions LLC, pg 678
CAS Video Productions, pg 717
CPR MultiMedia Solutions, pg 732
dbF a Media Company, pg 739
DBM Communications Inc, pg 739
Kramer Communications Video Production, pg 801
Media Dimensions LLC, pg 821
Mobile-Video Productions Inc, pg 828
Pro Cuts Editing Services, pg 862
Producers Video, pg 863
Quality Film & Video, pg 868
Sheffield Audio/Video Productions, pg 885
Sign Media Inc, pg 887
Welocalize, pg 935

MASSACHUSETTS

Award Productions Inc, pg 699
Boston Productions Inc (BPI), pg 709
CommCreative, pg 728
Cramer, pg 732
HOME Inc, pg 781
Penfield Productions Ltd, pg 853
Preston Productions Inc, pg 861
TR Productions, pg 916
TVN-The Video Network, pg 919
The Weather Company, An IBM Business, pg 935

MICHIGAN

ASC Systems, pg 690
Blue Mouse Studio, pg 707
Digi Sign Design LLC, pg 741
Digital Image Studios LLC, pg 742
K&R's Recording Studios Inc, pg 796
On Stage Visuals, pg 846
Progressive AE, pg 865
RingSide Creative, pg 875

MINNESOTA

The ADS Group, pg 676
MastCom, pg 819
Babe Winkelman Productions Inc, pg 939
Worthwhile Films, pg 941

MISSOURI

Avatar Studios, pg 697
Communitronics Corp, pg 729
Show-Me Audio-Visual, pg 887
Switch, pg 905

MONTANA

ooLite Media LLC, pg 846

NEBRASKA

B & B Video Productions Inc, pg 700
Dog & Pony Productions Inc, pg 744
Rainbow Video Productions Inc, pg 869
Three Pillars Media, pg 913

NEVADA

Aardvark Video & Media Productions, pg 671
Encore Event Technologies LLC, pg 754
JCS Video Productions, pg 793

NEW HAMPSHIRE

Academic & Campus Technology Services, pg 672
Channell One Video, pg 720
Chip Taylor Communications LLC, pg 907
The Troupe, pg 918

NEW JERSEY

A-V Services Inc, pg 671
AJS Events, pg 679
Allegro Productions Inc, pg 680
Audio Visual Dynamics®, pg 694
CD Meyer Inc, pg 718
CFP Video Productions Inc, pg 720
Creative Video, pg 734
Diversified, pg 744
Early Films, pg 749
Euro-Pacific Film & Video Productions Inc, pg 756
Laurel Video Productions, pg 804
MediaMix Inc, pg 822
MediaNow Inc, pg 822
Megavideo LLC, pg 823
MiB MediaWorks, pg 825
Midnight Media Group Inc, pg 827
NFL Films Inc, pg 841
NFL Films Music Library, pg 841
Outside The Box Interactive LLC, pg 849
PLS Staging, pg 858
Shamrock Communications, pg 885
Suede Interactive, pg 903
VCSvideo, pg 925
Video Ideas Productions, pg 928

NEW MEXICO

Production Outfitters, pg 864

NEW YORK

Air Sea Land Productions Inc (ASL), pg 678
American Artists Representatives Inc, pg 682
Animotion Inc, pg 685
aurora productions, pg 696
Big Film Design, pg 705
The Big House Group, pg 705
Buffalo Video Production, pg 712
Chromavision Corp, pg 723
Cohn Creative Group LLC, pg 727
CP Digital, pg 732
Designomotion, pg 741
Digital Art Video Inc, pg 741
Downtown Community Television Center (DCTV), pg 746
4-D Creative Media, pg 764
Hallel Communications, pg 775
HAVE Inc, pg 777
HB-Content, pg 777
Heavy Melody, pg 778
Hello World Communications, pg 778
IAI Records & Video, pg 783

L A Bruell Inc, pg 802
Lylofilm Productions, pg 813
Magnetic Post Production, pg 815
Magno Sound Inc, pg 815
Manhattan Center Studios Inc, pg 816
Meltzer Media Productions, pg 823
Mood Creations Ltd, pg 829
Jack Morton Worldwide, pg 830
MRY, pg 832
PostWorks, pg 860
PrimeLight Productions Inc, pg 862
R/GA, pg 868
Judson Rosebush Co Inc, pg 877
Teatown Communications Group, pg 908
TeleTime Productions, pg 910
USA Studios, pg 923
Visual Technologies Corp, pg 932
WNET/New York Public Media, pg 940

NORTH CAROLINA

Pat Appleson Studios Inc, pg 687
The Communications Group Inc, pg 729
Horizon Video Productions Inc, pg 781
L A Management Co LLC, pg 802
Moving Pictures, pg 832
NASCAR Productions LLC, pg 835
On Location North Carolina, pg 846
Take One Productions Ltd, pg 906

NORTH DAKOTA

Media Productions, pg 822

OHIO

Advent Media Inc, pg 677
Aztec Video Productions, pg 700
Bartha, pg 702
Russ Beckner Pictures, pg 703
Cinecraft Productions Inc, pg 723
Clear Choice Creative Corp, pg 726
Cuyahoga Community College Student Production Office (SPO), pg 736
Image Video Teleproductions Inc, pg 785
iVideo Technologies, pg 792
Lyon Video Inc, pg 813
Mills James Productions, pg 828
R&B Communications Inc, pg 870
Shelburne Films, pg 885
Take 1 Media Services, pg 906
Vista Color Imaging Inc, pg 931

OKLAHOMA

Garman Productions LLC, pg 768
Institute for Teaching & Learning Excellence (ITLE), pg 788
PDC Productions, pg 852

OREGON

Artbeats, pg 690
InterVision Media, pg 791
KTVA Productions, pg 802
KVAL, pg 802
Limbo Films, pg 808
Production West, pg 864
REX, pg 874
Wallace Creative LLC, pg 933

PENNSYLVANIA

AccuWeather Inc, pg 674
Bang! Pictures Inc, pg 701
Beholder Productions Inc, pg 703
Center City Film & Video Inc, pg 719

FMP Media Solutions Inc, pg 763
Innovision Media Group, pg 788
JPL, pg 795
Main Point Productions, pg 815
NEP Group Inc, pg 838
Panta Rhei Media Inc, pg 851
Production Masters Inc (PMI),
pg 864
Scala Inc, pg 881
The Videohouse Inc, pg 929
Visual Sound Inc, pg 931
WHYY Inc, pg 938

RHODE ISLAND

Sound-FX-Design, pg 894

SOUTH CAROLINA

American Production Services LLC,
pg 684
Genesis Creative, pg 769
Stages Video Productions, pg 899
Venture Media, pg 925

TENNESSEE

American Blackguard Inc, pg 683
Kingswood Productions, pg 799
Memphis Communications Corp,
pg 823
Motion Picture Services, pg 831
Paradigm Marketing & Creative,
pg 851
Running Pony Productions LLC,
pg 878
Scripps Networks, pg 882
Stage Post, pg 899
Russ Sturgeon Productions/RSVP,
pg 903
United Methodist Productions,
pg 921

TEXAS

AMS Pictures, pg 684
Anaphora Literary Press, pg 685
Aries Productions Inc, pg 688
Biway Media, pg 706
Cerutti Productions Inc, pg 720
CEV Multimedia Ltd, pg 720
Chalk Dust Co, pg 720
Communication Arts Multimedia
Inc, pg 728
The Editing Co, pg 750
Epic Software Group Inc, pg 755
Freeman, pg 765
Horizon Film + Video Productions,
pg 781
Horizon Worldwide, pg 781
Hurst Digital, pg 782
Maverick Video Productions, pg 820
McNee Productions Inc, pg 821
Media Event Concepts Inc, pg 822
Mediaforce Productions, pg 822
Julye Newlin Productions Inc,
pg 840
Out of the BLUE Media, pg 849
Phillips Media Source, pg 855
Romar Learning Solutions LLC,
pg 877
The Samuels Co, pg 879
South Coast Film & Video, pg 895
Stage Directions, pg 898
Texas Heart Institute Visual
Communication Services, pg 911
Video Perspective, pg 928

UTAH

ImageWorks Communications,
pg 785
Strata™, pg 901
Zygote Media Group Inc, pg 945

VIRGINIA

Advance Concepts Inc, pg 677
Allied Media Corp, pg 681
Altruist Media LLC, pg 682
BES Studios, pg 704
CACI Integrated Communications,
pg 713
CVW Event Productions, pg 736
Eagle Films, pg 749
EFX Media, pg 751
Maniglia Media LLC, pg 816
Metro Productions, pg 824
Quince Imaging Inc, pg 868
Rocktown Media, pg 876
WETA Production Center, pg 936

WASHINGTON

Adams Creative & Production
Services, pg 675
Bennett-Watt HD Productions Inc,
pg 703
Hamilton Studio, pg 775
Linguist's Software Inc, pg 809
Medical Media Systems, pg 823
North-by-Northwest - A Digital
Studio, pg 842
Victory Studios, pg 927

WEST VIRGINIA

MotionMasters, pg 831
WSAZ-TV NewsChannel 3, pg 942

WISCONSIN

Audio Visual of Milwaukee Inc,
pg 694
Logan Productions Inc, pg 811
Meridian Studios, pg 824
Midland Video Productions Inc,
pg 827
Mirror 34 Productions, pg 828
USAV Group Inc, pg 923
Video Wisconsin Inc, pg 929
Watts Communications Inc, pg 934
Win Media Inc, pg 939

WYOMING

Bridger Productions Inc, pg 710

PUERTO RICO

Stage Crew Audiovisual Inc, pg 898

ALBERTA

Black Media Works, pg 706
Global TV, pg 771

BRITISH COLUMBIA

Triad Communications Ltd, pg 918
24 Frames Film & Video, pg 920

MANITOBA

Lank/Beach Productions Inc, pg 803
Spectra Video Productions Ltd,
pg 897
Tek Gear, pg 909

NEWFOUNDLAND AND
LABRADOR

Vidcraft Productions Ltd, pg 927

ONTARIO

ADS Media, pg 677
Eggplant Pictures & Sound, pg 751
GAPC (General Assembly
Production Centre), pg 768
GestureTek, pg 770
JFB Communications, pg 794

Marblemedia, pg 816
RB Productions, pg 870
Silver Creek Media Inc, pg 888
Video Excellence Productions,
pg 927

QUEBEC

Group PVP, pg 774
Presagis, pg 861

Computerized Animation Production Services, *see* Animation Production Services—Computerized

Computerized Editing, *see* Editing—Computerized

Consulting

ALABAMA

AVS Media Group, pg 699
Diamond Studios, pg 741

ALASKA

Alaska Media Pros LLC, pg 679
Aurora Films, pg 696

ARIZONA

Creative Backstage, pg 733
Direct Current Video Productions,
pg 743
Film Creations Ltd, pg 760
Fox 10 Productions (KSAZ-TV),
pg 765
Merestone, pg 823
Metropolitan Audio-Visual Inc,
pg 824
On-Site Video, pg 846
Rodeo Video Inc, pg 876
Teaberry, pg 908

ARKANSAS

Live'N'Loud, pg 810
White Diamond Productions LLC,
pg 937

CALIFORNIA

Access Video in Berkeley, pg 673
Air Philosophy Inc, pg 678
AlphaDogs Inc, pg 682
Artichoke Productions, pg 690
Audio Visual Consultants, pg 694
Automated Entertainment, pg 696
Barber Tech Video Products, pg 701
Blind™, pg 707
Steve Chandler, pg 720
Christopher Gray Post Production,
pg 722
Coastline Productions, pg 727
Coloredge Inc, pg 728
Creative Technology, pg 733
Crystal Pyramid Productions™,
pg 735
Custom Video Productions Inc,
pg 736
deKramer Productions Inc, pg 740
Design Media, pg 741
Digital Jungle, pg 742
Direct Images Interactive Inc,
pg 743
Dolphin MultiMedia Inc, pg 745
Durrin Productions Inc, pg 748

ECONEWS (Environmental
Television Series) &
(Environmental Directions Radio
Series), pg 750
Express Media Inc, pg 757
Far West Media Services Inc,
pg 759
Film TV Sound, pg 760
First Person Inc, pg 761
Goal Productions, pg 772
Gold Standard Productions, pg 772
Havas Edge, pg 777
iCorpTv, pg 783
imageReal Pictures LLC, pg 785
Imageworks, pg 785
ITV Productions, pg 792
Jaguar Distribution Corp, pg 792
JDS Video & Media Productions
Inc, pg 793
KPBS Public Broadcasting, pg 801
KVIE-Channel 6, pg 802
Ludlow Media, pg 812
Lumeni Productions Inc, pg 812
Main Street Media Inc, pg 815
Maximus Media Inc, pg 820
McKay Conant Hoover Inc, pg 821
Media Magic, pg 822
Media Systems Design Group,
pg 822
Moving Art by Louie Schwartzberg,
pg 831
New & Unique Videos™, pg 839
Nineteen87, pg 841
Nolte Media, pg 841
Penrose Productions, pg 854
piXvfm Inc, pg 857
PK Productions, pg 857
PM Productions, pg 858
Point of View Productions, pg 858
Prime Cut Productions, pg 862
Promax Systems, pg 865
PSI Inc, pg 866
PSSI Global Services LLC, pg 866
QRS Software Systems, pg 867
Regent Press Publishers & Printers,
pg 873
RetinaVision Productions, pg 874
Rough House, pg 878
Russ InVision Co/AbridgeClub.com,
pg 879
Sahara Records & Filmworks
Entertainment Co, pg 879
Screen Door Entertainment Inc,
pg 882
Sea Studios Foundation, pg 883
Semiconductor Services, pg 883
SNAP, pg 891
SonicPool, pg 892
Staylor-Made Communications Inc,
pg 900
Still N' Motion, pg 901
Stunt Wings Adventure Sports
Talent & Equipment, pg 903
Tam Communications Inc, pg 906
Technical Services, pg 908
Thorburn Associates (TA), pg 913
Total Creative, pg 916
Twin Peaks Creative, pg 920
Via Verde Productions, pg 926
Videobotics, pg 929
Visions Plus, pg 931
VMI Inc, pg 932
WARPed Pictures, pg 934
Wavemaker Media Design, pg 934
West Coast Projections Inc, pg 935
Z-Ville Productions, pg 944

COLORADO

D L Adams Associates Inc, pg 675
Blue River Productions, pg 708
Conly Productions, pg 730
Daylight Productions & Rentals,
pg 739

VIDEO

Consulting (continued)

COLORADO (continued)

Flashback Media Productions, pg 762

G W Hannaway & Associates, pg 775

Maniac Productions, pg 816

Old Army Press (OAP), pg 844

Spectrum Audio Visual Services, pg 897

Transtar Entertainment Co Inc, pg 917

Z-Axis Corp, pg 944

CONNECTICUT

ACM Productions Ltd, pg 674

Antenna International, pg 686

Boyce Nemec Designs, pg 709

BRB Audiovisual Productions, pg 709

The Gary-Paul Agency, pg 768

Geomatrix Productions, pg 770

Guymark Studios LLC, pg 775

Ironik Design & Post, pg 791

MAVCO, pg 820

Moving Pictures, pg 832

New London Media, pg 839

Palace Production Center, pg 850

P&P Studios Inc, pg 851

Video Production Associates Inc, pg 928

DELAWARE

So Smart Productions, pg 891

DISTRICT OF COLUMBIA

Hillmann & Carr Inc, pg 780

Susan Hormuth, Visual Resource Consultant, pg 781

Interface Media Group, pg 789

Metro Teleproductions Inc (MTI), pg 824

O'Keefe Communications Inc, pg 844

Yellow Cat Productions Inc, pg 944

FLORIDA

Access Media Group, pg 673

America By Air LLC, pg 682

Applebox Studio, pg 687

Civins Productions Inc, pg 725

Communications Concepts Inc (CCI), pg 729

Courter Films LLC, pg 732

Digital Video Systems, pg 742

Florida Digital Studios, pg 762

Hi-Tech Enterprises Inc, pg 779

The Kitchen, pg 799

National Teleproductions Inc, pg 837

ONstage, pg 846

Roger Scruggs Films, pg 883

Shooting Stars Post Inc, pg 886

Sound & Vision Communications Inc, pg 893

Sunfire Communications Inc, pg 904

Sunrise Studios, pg 904

Tricycle Studios, pg 918

Universal Studios Florida® Production Group, pg 922

Mike Vasilinda Productions Inc, pg 925

Video Techniques Inc, pg 928

Vistamax Productions, pg 931

GEORGIA

Beast Atlanta, pg 703

Burst Video/Film Inc, pg 713

ECG Productions, pg 750

Guerrilla Productions LLC, pg 774

Lighting & Production Equipment Inc, pg 807

Myriad Productions, pg 835

Malcolm Neal Productions, pg 837

On-Line Productions, pg 845

Staging Directions Inc, pg 899

HAWAII

D L Adams Associates Ltd, pg 675

Hyperspective Studios Inc, pg 783

Media Bridge Gamekids, pg 821

1013 Integrated, pg 911

IDAHO

KTVB-TV, pg 802

Brad Shaw Productions Inc, pg 885

Wide Eye Productions, pg 938

ILLINOIS

ABSA Films, pg 672

Accenture, pg 672

Airways Digital Media, pg 679

AnswersMedia, pg 686

Atomic Imaging Inc/Golan Studios, pg 692

Beatty TeleVisual Productions, pg 703

Breeze Productions Inc, pg 710

CCore Media Inc, pg 718

Creative Technology (CT), pg 733

Cresta Creative, pg 734

Explore, pg 757

Extraordinary Demos/Videos, pg 757

Film Police, pg 760

IV Media Resources, pg 792

The Market Place, pg 817

Mimi Productions, pg 828

Multimedia Marketing Group, pg 833

On Site Video, pg 846

Jim Passin Productions, pg 852

Pepper Group, pg 854

PSAV® Presentation Services (Hotel Services Division), pg 866

Richter Studios, pg 875

SCI Television & Creative Media LLC, pg 882

Sound/Video Impressions Inc, pg 894

Southern Illinois University, pg 895

Sparkfactor, pg 896

Terra Nova Films Inc, pg 911

20/20 Communications Inc, pg 920

Video I-D Teleproductions Inc, pg 928

Video Impressions, pg 928

WEEK TV, pg 935

INDIANA

A-V-A Video Productions, pg 671

Bright Ideas Creative Services, pg 710

PentaVision Communications Inc, pg 854

IOWA

Educational Technology & Media Services, pg 751

Iowa State University-Information Technology Services, pg 791

KANSAS

KAKE-TV, pg 796

KENTUCKY

Axxis Leasing Inc, pg 700

Broadway Digital, pg 711

Hammond Communications Group Inc, pg 775

Idle Minds Productions Inc, pg 784

NOR-COM Inc, pg 841

Prosper Media Group Inc, pg 866

WKYT-TV, pg 940

LOUISIANA

Digital FX Inc, pg 742

Louisiana State University Division of Strategic Communications, pg 811

Moxie Media, pg 832

Vidox Motion Imagery, pg 930

WVLA-TV, pg 942

MAINE

Slim Goodbody Corp, pg 890

MARYLAND

CPR MultiMedia Solutions, pg 732

dbF a Media Company, pg 739

DBM Communications Inc, pg 739

The Image Generators, pg 785

James Agee Film Project, pg 792

Kramer Communications Video Production, pg 801

Media Dimensions LLC, pg 821

Mobile-Video Productions Inc, pg 828

Producers Video, pg 863

Spectrum Productions, pg 897

Welocalize, pg 935

MASSACHUSETTS

Award Productions Inc, pg 699

Capron Lighting & Sound Co Inc, pg 716

Cavanaugh Tocci Associates Inc, pg 717

CommCreative, pg 728

Communications Design Associates, pg 729

Cramer, pg 732

Documentary Educational Resources Inc, pg 744

Green Mountain Post Films (GMP), pg 774

HOME Inc, pg 781

Monadnock Media Inc, pg 829

MotionArt Studios, pg 831

Northern Light Productions (NLP), pg 842

Penfield Productions Ltd, pg 853

PixMix Video Services, pg 857

Gabriel Polonsky Studio, pg 859

Preston Productions Inc, pg 861

TVN-The Video Network, pg 919

WVP Boston, pg 942

MICHIGAN

ASC Systems, pg 690

Digi Sign Design LLC, pg 741

K&R's Recording Studios Inc, pg 796

Madonna University Information Technology, pg 814

Michigan Recording Arts Institute & Technologies, pg 825

On Stage Visuals, pg 846

The Program Source International, pg 865

MINNESOTA

The ADS Group, pg 676

BeyerSound & Essay Audio, pg 705

Big Event Productions LLC, pg 705

House of Cinemagraphics, pg 782

MastCom, pg 819

Media Loft Inc, pg 822

Worthwhile Films, pg 941

MISSOURI

Avatar Studios, pg 697

Communitronics Corp, pg 729

Schiller's Audio-Visual, pg 881

Show-Me Audio-Visual, pg 887

Switch, pg 905

Visionworks Design Services Inc, pg 931

MONTANA

KCFW Television, pg 797

NEBRASKA

Rainbow Video Productions Inc, pg 869

Three Pillars Media, pg 913

NEVADA

Aardvark Video & Media Productions, pg 671

DVDs4Less, pg 748

Encore Event Technologies LLC, pg 754

JCS Video Productions, pg 793

Lefco Video Services Inc, pg 806

Ron Roy Productions/Moodtapes, pg 878

NEW HAMPSHIRE

Academic & Campus Technology Services, pg 672

Apertura, pg 686

Channell One Video, pg 720

Chip Taylor Communications LLC, pg 907

The Troupe, pg 918

NEW JERSEY

A-V Services Inc, pg 671

AJS Events, pg 679

Allegro Productions Inc, pg 680

Audio Visual Dynamics®, pg 694

Broadcast Center Studios, pg 710

CD Meyer Inc, pg 718

CFP Video Productions Inc, pg 720

Diversified, pg 744

Euro-Pacific Film & Video Productions Inc, pg 756

Laurel Video Productions, pg 804

MediaNow Inc, pg 822

Megavideo LLC, pg 823

MiB MediaWorks, pg 825

Midnight Media Group Inc, pg 827

Ray Mueller Productions, pg 833

NFL Films Inc, pg 841

Outside The Box Interactive LLC, pg 849

PatchAmp, pg 852

PLS Staging, pg 858

Reed Presentations Inc (RPI), pg 872

Starlite, pg 900

Suede Interactive, pg 903

Telemanagement Resources International Inc (TRI), pg 910

Varto Technologies, pg 925

VCSvideo, pg 925

Video Ideas Productions, pg 928

Wired 4 Sound Inc, pg 940

Yorktel, pg 944

NEW MEXICO

Mountainair Films Inc, pg 831
Production Outfitters, pg 864

NEW YORK

Air Sea Land Productions Inc (ASL), pg 678
Animotion Inc, pg 685
aurora productions, pg 696
Bellin Productions, pg 703
Bevilacqua Studios, pg 704
The Big House Group, pg 705
Buffalo Video Production, pg 712
BZ/Rights & Permissions Inc, pg 713
Chromavision Corp, pg 723
Cohn Creative Group LLC, pg 727
Custom Computer Specialists Inc, pg 736
Designomotion, pg 741
Digital Art Video Inc, pg 741
Downtown Community Television Center (DCTV), pg 746
Four Corners Productions, pg 764
4-D Creative Media, pg 764
GHO Group LLC, pg 770
Hallel Communications, pg 775
HAVE Inc, pg 777
HB-Content, pg 777
Hello World Communications, pg 778
IAI Records & Video, pg 783
Icontent, pg 783
International Robotics Inc, pg 790
Richard Kaplan Productions, pg 796
Kinetic Arts, pg 799
L A Bruell Inc, pg 802
Lylofilm Productions, pg 813
Mood Creations Ltd, pg 829
Jack Morton Worldwide, pg 830
MRY, pg 832
News Broadcast Network Inc, pg 840
Pat Kogan Productions Inc, pg 852
PostWorks, pg 860
PrimaLux Video Inc, pg 862
Judson Rosebush Co Inc, pg 877
Shen Milsom & Wilke LLC, pg 885
D S Simon Productions, pg 888
Synaptic Digital, pg 905
Teatown Communications Group, pg 908
Third World Newsreel/Camera News Inc, pg 912
VIEW Inc (Video International Entertainment World Inc), pg 930
Visual Technologies Corp, pg 932
Visual Word Systems Inc, pg 932
Willow Mixed Media Inc, pg 939
WNET/New York Public Media, pg 940
Zelman Studios Ltd, pg 945

NORTH CAROLINA

Pat Appleson Studios Inc, pg 687
Bill Barnes Video Productions LLC, pg 702
Lawrence Behr Associates Inc, pg 703
Camcor Inc, pg 715
The Communications Group Inc, pg 729
Digital Rain LLC, pg 742
Duke Media Services, pg 747
Franklin Video Inc, pg 765
Horizon Video Productions Inc, pg 781
Moving Pictures, pg 832
NASCAR Productions LLC, pg 835
On Location North Carolina, pg 846
Sinclair Institute, pg 889
Special Event Services, pg 896

Take One Productions Ltd, pg 906
Videowerks, pg 930

NORTH DAKOTA

UND Television Center, pg 921

OHIO

Advent Media Inc, pg 677
Aztec Video Productions, pg 700
Bartha, pg 702
Russ Beckner Pictures, pg 703
CET, pg 720
Challenge Productions/Challenge Aerial Imaging, pg 720
Copp Integrated Systems, pg 731
Griesinger Films LLC, pg 774
iVideo Technologies, pg 792
Lyon Video Inc, pg 813
MainSail Production Services Inc, pg 815
Mills James Productions, pg 828
Production Partners Media, pg 864
R&B Communications Inc, pg 870
Take 1 Media Services, pg 906
Treehaus Communications Inc, pg 917
Vista Color Imaging Inc, pg 931

OKLAHOMA

Academic Media & Digital Services, pg 672
Ford AV, pg 763
Garman Productions LLC, pg 768
PDC Productions, pg 852

OREGON

InterVision Media, pg 791
KTVA Productions, pg 802
MediaFX, pg 822
Production West, pg 864
Spirit Media, pg 897
Sugar Mountain PR, pg 903

PENNSYLVANIA

Argentine Productions Inc, pg 688
Bang! Pictures Inc, pg 701
Beholder Productions Inc, pg 703
FMP Media Solutions Inc, pg 763
Innovision Media Group, pg 788
JPL, pg 795
Main Point Productions, pg 815
Panta Rhei Media Inc, pg 851
Producers Management Television (PMTV), pg 863
Production Masters Inc (PMI), pg 864
Scala Inc, pg 881
The Videohouse Inc, pg 929
The Whale Video Co, pg 936
WPHL-TV, pg 942

RHODE ISLAND

Sound-FX-Design, pg 894

SOUTH CAROLINA

American Production Services LLC, pg 684
Genesis Creative, pg 769
Stages Video Productions, pg 899

TENNESSEE

American Blackguard Inc, pg 683
Fricon Entertainment Co Inc, pg 766
Memphis Communications Corp, pg 823
Motion Picture Services, pg 831
Paradigm Marketing & Creative, pg 851

Running Pony Productions LLC, pg 878
Scripps Networks, pg 882
Stage Post, pg 899
Russ Sturgeon Productions/RSVP, pg 903
Take One Film & Video, pg 906
United Methodist Productions, pg 921
Zion Music Group, pg 945

TEXAS

AMS Pictures, pg 684
AVES Audio Visual Systems Inc, pg 698
Biway Media, pg 706
Castleview Productions, pg 717
Cerutti Productions Inc, pg 720
Communication Arts Multimedia Inc, pg 728
Dykeman Associates Inc, pg 748
The Editing Co, pg 750
Epic Software Group Inc, pg 755
Horizon Film + Video Productions, pg 781
Hurst Digital, pg 782
Imagine Communications Corp, pg 786
Matson Multi-Media, pg 820
Mediaforce Productions, pg 822
Earl Miller Productions Inc, pg 827
Julye Newlin Productions Inc, pg 840
Out of the BLUE Media, pg 849
Phillips Media Source, pg 855
Romar Learning Solutions LLC, pg 877
The Samuels Co, pg 879
South Coast Film & Video, pg 895
Texas Heart Institute Visual Communication Services, pg 911

UTAH

ImageWorks Communications, pg 785
Redman Movies & Stories, pg 872
Spectrum Engineers, pg 897

VIRGINIA

Advance Concepts Inc, pg 677
Allied Media Corp, pg 681
BES Studios, pg 704
CACI Integrated Communications, pg 713
CDR Communications Inc, pg 719
DXC Technology Co, pg 748
Eagle Films, pg 749
EFX Media, pg 751
Limelight Communications Inc, pg 808
Metro Productions, pg 824
Quince Imaging Inc, pg 868
Rocktown Media, pg 876
Video Solutions, pg 928

WASHINGTON

Adams Creative & Production Services, pg 675
Bennett-Watt HD Productions Inc, pg 703
Kostov Productions, pg 801
Laser Fantasy/HECK Industries/Photon Manufacturing, pg 804
Media Elite Productions, pg 822
Medical Media Systems, pg 823
North-by-Northwest - A Digital Studio, pg 842
Pal Productions Inc, pg 850
Victory Studios, pg 927

WEST VIRGINIA

Focus on Animals, pg 763

WISCONSIN

Audio Visual of Milwaukee Inc, pg 694
Full Compass Systems, pg 767
Learning Technology Services, pg 805
Meridian Studios, pg 824
Mirror 34 Productions, pg 828
University of Wisconsin-Oshkosh Radio-TV-Film Dept, pg 923
USAV Group Inc, pg 923
Video Wisconsin Inc, pg 929
Watts Communications Inc, pg 934
Wisconsin Public Television, pg 940

WYOMING

Bridger Productions Inc, pg 710

PUERTO RICO

Stage Crew Audiovisual Inc, pg 898

ALBERTA

Black Media Works, pg 706
Global TV, pg 771

BRITISH COLUMBIA

DWD Theatre Design & Consulting, pg 748
Triad Communications Ltd, pg 918

MANITOBA

Spectra Video Productions Ltd, pg 897
Tek Gear, pg 909

NEWFOUNDLAND AND LABRADOR

Vidcraft Productions Ltd, pg 927

ONTARIO

ADS Media, pg 677
Artaflex Inc, pg 690
Cinema Stage Inc, pg 724
GAPC (General Assembly Production Centre), pg 768
GestureTek, pg 770
JFB Communications, pg 794
Marblemedia, pg 816
Silver Creek Media Inc, pg 888
State of the Art Acoustik Inc, pg 900
Technovision® Interactive Inc, pg 909
Video Excellence Productions, pg 927

QUEBEC

Group PVP, pg 774
Sceno Plus, pg 881
20k, pg 920

Control System & Equipment Distributors

ALABAMA

PESA, pg 855

ARIZONA

EAR Professional Audio/Video, pg 749

VIDEO

Control System & Equipment Distributors (continued)

ARKANSAS

Jay S Stanley & Associates Inc, pg 899

CALIFORNIA

Ametron Audio/Video, pg 684
Be Media, pg 702
Cibola Systems, pg 723
Diaquest, pg 741
Electrosonic Inc, pg 752
Innovision Optics, pg 788
JD Audio Visual Inc, pg 793
Media Control Systems LLC, pg 821
MediaPOINTE, pg 823
Photodyne Technologies, pg 856
Southern California Sound Image Inc, pg 895
Videobotics, pg 929
VTP Inc, pg 933

FLORIDA

Access Media Group, pg 673
Alcorn McBride Inc, pg 679
AVI-SPL, pg 698
Digital Video Systems, pg 742
Harris Corp, pg 776
Hi-Tech Enterprises Inc, pg 779
Midtown Video Inc, pg 827
ONstage, pg 846

GEORGIA

Clark, pg 725
Stage Front Presentation Systems, pg 899

HAWAII

The Audio Visual Co (AVCO), pg 694

ILLINOIS

Allen Visual Systems Inc, pg 680
Joseph Electronics, pg 795
Quintessence Audio Ltd, pg 868

INDIANA

Lee Co Inc, pg 805
Sensory Technologies LLC, pg 884
SHP Electronics, pg 887

KENTUCKY

Axxis Leasing Inc, pg 700
NOR-COM Inc, pg 841

MARYLAND

Image Logic Corp, pg 785
Noventri, pg 843

MASSACHUSETTS

Antronics Inc, pg 686
Rule Boston Camera, pg 878

MICHIGAN

On Stage Visuals, pg 846

MINNESOTA

Alpha Video & Audio Inc, pg 682

MISSOURI

Modern Communications Inc, pg 828
Schiller's Audio-Visual, pg 881
Southwest Audio-Visual Inc, pg 895

NEW JERSEY

Alltec Stores, a Vcom IMC Company, pg 681
AlltecPro, pg 681
Audio Visual Associates, pg 694
AV Bluebook, pg 696
Diversified, pg 744
Earl Girls Inc, pg 749
HamiltonBuhl, pg 775
MCCOM Inc, pg 820
Starlite, pg 900
Tele-Measurements Inc, pg 910
Total Video Products Inc, pg 916
Wired 4 Sound Inc, pg 940

NEW YORK

Audio-Video Corp, pg 694
Creative Stage Lighting Co Inc, pg 733
Design Audio Visual Inc, pg 741
General Audio-Visual Inc (GAVI), pg 769
Presentation Products Inc, pg 861

NORTH CAROLINA

Crispin Corp, pg 734

OHIO

Tri-State Audio Visual Co, pg 918
Vincent Lighting Systems, pg 930

OKLAHOMA

Ford AV, pg 763

PENNSYLVANIA

Advanced AV LLC, pg 677
Clair Companies, pg 725
The Lerro Corp, pg 806
Vistacom Inc, pg 931

RHODE ISLAND

Shanix Inc, pg 885

TENNESSEE

Lowrance Sound Co Inc, pg 812
Technical Support Systems LLC, pg 908

TEXAS

Audio Visual Technologies Group (AVTG), pg 695
Biway Media, pg 706
Data Projections Inc, pg 738
Digital Display Solutions Inc, pg 742
Graftek Imaging Inc, pg 773
Omega Broadcast Group, pg 845
Pro Video & Film Equipment Co Inc, pg 863
Tarpley Media Systems, pg 907

UTAH

SirsiDynix, pg 889

VIRGINIA

Avitecture Inc, pg 699
Intellidyne LLC, pg 789

WISCONSIN

Audio Visual of Milwaukee Inc, pg 694
Full Compass Systems, pg 767
Safe Harbor Computers, pg 879

ALBERTA

Infosat Communications Inc, pg 787

BRITISH COLUMBIA

Norsat International Inc, pg 842

MANITOBA

Inland Audio Visual Ltd, pg 788

ONTARIO

Cinema Stage Inc, pg 724
Soundmaster Group, pg 894
Technovision® Interactive Inc, pg 909
Westbury National Show Systems Ltd, pg 936

Control System & Equipment Manufacturers

ALABAMA

PESA, pg 855

CALIFORNIA

ALTINEX Inc, pg 682
CohuHD Costar LLC, pg 727
Diaquest, pg 741
FM Systems Inc, pg 763
FutureVideo, pg 767
Innovision Optics, pg 788
Jupiter Systems, pg 795
Media Control Systems LLC, pg 821
Photodyne Technologies, pg 856
RetinaVision Productions, pg 874
Simon - Kaloi Engineering Ltd, pg 888
TV Pro Gear, pg 919
Videobotics, pg 929
Xantech LLC, pg 943

FLORIDA

Alcorn McBride Inc, pg 679
Compuvideo Sales USA Ltd, pg 729
Harris Corp, pg 776

GEORGIA

Barco Inc, pg 701
Wegener Communications Inc, pg 935

MARYLAND

Image Logic Corp, pg 785

MICHIGAN

Leightronix Inc, pg 806

MINNESOTA

Vaddio, pg 924

NEW JERSEY

Crestron Electronics Inc, pg 734
FSR Inc, pg 766
Starlite, pg 900
Telemetrics Inc, pg 910

NEW YORK

Monroe Electronics Inc, pg 829
Vicon Industries Inc, pg 926

OHIO

R L Drake Co, pg 746

PENNSYLVANIA

Scala Inc, pg 881

TENNESSEE

Adtec Digital Inc, pg 677

TEXAS

Contemporary Research, pg 731

UTAH

SirsiDynix, pg 889

BRITISH COLUMBIA

Norsat International Inc, pg 842
Richmond Sound Design Ltd, pg 875

ONTARIO

Soundmaster Group, pg 894
Technovision® Interactive Inc, pg 909

Control System & Equipment Rentals

ARIZONA

Merestone, pg 823
Video West Inc, pg 929

CALIFORNIA

Ametron Audio/Video, pg 684
Bexel, an NEP Broadcast Services Company, pg 704
Express Media Inc, pg 757
Innovision Optics, pg 788
JD Audio Visual Inc, pg 793
Lynch Communications, pg 813
McCune Audio-Video-Lighting, pg 821
Munday & Collins AV, pg 834
Muse Presentation Technologies, pg 834
RetinaVision Productions, pg 874
Total Creative, pg 916
Twin Peaks Creative, pg 920

COLORADO

Spectrum Audio Visual Services, pg 897

CONNECTICUT

Videofilm Systems Inc, pg 929

FLORIDA

Midtown Video Inc, pg 827
ONstage, pg 846
Paradise Show & Design Inc, pg 851

GEORGIA

Stage Front Presentation Systems, pg 899

ILLINOIS

Allen Visual Systems Inc, pg 680
Backstar Creative Media Inc,
pg 700
Creative Technology (CT), pg 733
RC Communications, pg 870
Resolution Productions Group,
pg 874

KENTUCKY

Audio Visual Techniques Inc,
pg 695

MARYLAND

CPR MultiMedia Solutions, pg 732

MASSACHUSETTS

AVFX Inc, pg 698
Preston Productions Inc, pg 861

MICHIGAN

K&R's Recording Studios Inc,
pg 796
On Stage Visuals, pg 846

MINNESOTA

Alpha Video & Audio Inc, pg 682

MISSOURI

Show-Me Audio-Visual, pg 887
Southwest Audio-Visual Inc, pg 895

NEW JERSEY

Earl Girls Inc, pg 749
PLS Staging, pg 858
Starlite, pg 900
Tele-Measurements Inc, pg 910
Wired 4 Sound Inc, pg 940

NEW MEXICO

Production Outfitters, pg 864

NEW YORK

CP Communications, pg 732
Creative Stage Lighting Co Inc,
pg 733
Manhattan Center Studios Inc,
pg 816

OHIO

Lyon Video Inc, pg 813
Vincent Lighting Systems, pg 930

PENNSYLVANIA

Advanced AV LLC, pg 677
FMP Media Solutions Inc, pg 763
Upstage Video, pg 923

TENNESSEE

Technical Support Systems LLC,
pg 908

TEXAS

Alford Media Services, pg 680
Omega Broadcast Group, pg 845

VIRGINIA

Quince Imaging Inc, pg 868

WISCONSIN

Full Compass Systems, pg 767

MANITOBA

Inland Audio Visual Ltd, pg 788

ONTARIO

Wanted! Sound + Picture, pg 933
Westbury National Show Systems
Ltd, pg 936

Control System & Equipment Repairs

CALIFORNIA

Ametron Audio/Video, pg 684
Electrosonic Inc, pg 752
Media Control Systems LLC,
pg 821

FLORIDA

ELC Sales & Service Inc, pg 752
Hi-Tech Enterprises Inc, pg 779
Midtown Video Inc, pg 827

GEORGIA

Stage Front Presentation Systems,
pg 899

ILLINOIS

Allen Visual Systems Inc, pg 680

KENTUCKY

Axxis Leasing Inc, pg 700
NOR-COM Inc, pg 841

MICHIGAN

TEL Systems LLC, pg 909

MINNESOTA

Alpha Video & Audio Inc, pg 682

MISSOURI

Southwest Audio-Visual Inc, pg 895

NEW JERSEY

Audio Visual Associates, pg 694
Earl Girls Inc, pg 749
Starlite, pg 900

OHIO

Vincent Lighting Systems, pg 930

OREGON

All Service Musical Electronics
Repair, pg 680

TENNESSEE

Technical Support Systems LLC,
pg 908

TEXAS

Pro Video & Film Equipment Co
Inc, pg 863
Tarpley Media Systems, pg 907

VIRGINIA

Intellidyne LLC, pg 789

WISCONSIN

Full Compass Systems, pg 767

ALBERTA

Infosat Communications Inc, pg 787

MANITOBA

Inland Audio Visual Ltd, pg 788

ONTARIO

Westbury National Show Systems
Ltd, pg 936

Co-Production Services

ALABAMA

Diamond Studios, pg 741
Dogwood Productions Inc, pg 745

ALASKA

Alaska Media Pros LLC, pg 679
Aurora Films, pg 696

ARIZONA

Creative Backstage, pg 733
Direct Current Video Productions,
pg 743
Film Creations Ltd, pg 760
Fox 10 Productions (KSAZ-TV),
pg 765
Merestone, pg 823
On-Site Video, pg 846
Rodeo Video Inc, pg 876
Teaberry, pg 908

ARKANSAS

Live'N'Loud, pg 810

CALIFORNIA

Access Video in Berkeley, pg 673
All Video Productions, pg 680
Artichoke Productions, pg 690
Automated Entertainment, pg 696
Backstage Pass Entertainment Inc,
pg 700
Blind™, pg 707
Bridge Publications Inc, pg 710
Coastline Productions, pg 727
Concrete Images, pg 730
Creative Technology, pg 733
Crystal Pyramid Productions™,
pg 735
Custom Video Productions Inc,
pg 736
deKramer Productions Inc, pg 740
Design Media, pg 741
Direct Images Interactive Inc,
pg 743
Dolphin MultiMedia Inc, pg 745
Durrin Productions Inc, pg 748
ECONEWS (Environmental
Television Series) &
(Environmental Directions Radio
Series), pg 750
Express Media Inc, pg 757
First Camera, pg 761
First Person Inc, pg 761
FJ Productions Inc, pg 762
Full Moon & High Tide Productions
& Studios, pg 767
Geddes Productions LLC, pg 769
Goal Productions, pg 772
Havas Edge, pg 777
iCorpTv, pg 783
imageReal Pictures LLC, pg 785
Imageworks, pg 785
Ishtar Films, pg 791
ITV Productions, pg 792
Jaguar Distribution Corp, pg 792
JDS Video & Media Productions
Inc, pg 793
JFA Studio, pg 794
Kantola Productions LLC, pg 796
Kavich Reynolds Productions Inc,
pg 797

KPBS Public Broadcasting, pg 801
K2B2 Records, pg 802
KVIE-Channel 6, pg 802
Ludlow Media, pg 812
Main Street Media Inc, pg 815
Maximus Media Inc, pg 820
McCune Audio-Video-Lighting,
pg 821
Media Magic, pg 822
New & Unique Videos™, pg 839
New Circuit Films LLC, pg 839
Nineteen87, pg 841
Nolte Media, pg 841
Penrose Productions, pg 854
piXvfm Inc, pg 857
PM Productions, pg 858
Point of View Productions, pg 858
Point.360, pg 858
Prime Cut Productions, pg 862
PSI Inc, pg 866
PSSI Global Services LLC, pg 866
QRS Software Services, pg 867
Regent Press Publishers & Printers,
pg 873
Rough House, pg 878
Russ InVision Co/AbridgeClub.com,
pg 879
Sahara Records & Filmworks
Entertainment Co, pg 879
Screen Door Entertainment Inc,
pg 882
Sea Studios Foundation, pg 883
SNAP, pg 891
Staylor-Made Communications Inc,
pg 900
Still N' Motion, pg 901
Tam Communications Inc, pg 906
Total Creative, pg 916
Twin Peaks Creative, pg 920
Via Verde Productions, pg 926
Visions Plus, pg 931
Visual Communications - Southern
California Asian American
Studies Central Inc, pg 931
WARPed Pictures, pg 934
Wavemaker Media Design, pg 934
West Coast Projections Inc, pg 935
Z-Ville Productions, pg 944

COLORADO

Centre Communications Inc, pg 720
Conly Productions, pg 730
Daylight Productions & Rentals,
pg 739
Flashback Media Productions,
pg 762
Maniac Productions, pg 816
Old Army Press (OAP), pg 844
Spectrum Audio Visual Services,
pg 897
Tatum Video, pg 907
Transtar Entertainment Co Inc,
pg 917

CONNECTICUT

Antenna International, pg 686
BRB Audiovisual Productions,
pg 709
The Gary-Paul Agency, pg 768
Guymark Studios LLC, pg 775
Ironik Design & Post, pg 791
MAVCO, pg 820
Moving Pictures, pg 832
New London Media, pg 839
Video Production Associates Inc,
pg 928

DELAWARE

So Smart Productions, pg 891

VIDEO

Co-Production Services (continued)

DISTRICT OF COLUMBIA

Hillmann & Carr Inc, pg 780
Interface Media Group, pg 789
Metro Teleproductions Inc (MTI), pg 824
O'Keefe Communications Inc, pg 844
Yellow Cat Productions Inc, pg 944

FLORIDA

Access Media Group, pg 673
Applebox Studio, pg 687
C&I An Idea Agency, pg 716
Chatterbox Productions Inc, pg 721
Civins Productions Inc, pg 725
Communications Concepts Inc (CCI), pg 729
Florida Digital Studios, pg 762
Florida Film & Tape, pg 763
Hi-Tech Enterprises Inc, pg 779
JungleTV, pg 795
The Kitchen, pg 799
Knowles Video Inc (KVI), pg 800
National Teleproductions Inc, pg 837
Paradise Video & Film, pg 851
Roger Scruggs Films, pg 883
Sound & Vision Communications Inc, pg 893
Sunfire Communications Inc, pg 904
Tricycle Studios, pg 918
Universal Studios Florida® Production Group, pg 922
Mike Vasilinda Productions Inc, pg 925
Video Techniques Inc, pg 928
Vistamax Productions, pg 931

GEORGIA

Beachwood Productions, pg 702
Beast Atlanta, pg 703
Guerrilla Productions LLC, pg 774
Myriad Productions, pg 835
On-Line Productions, pg 845
Staging Directions Inc, pg 899

HAWAII

FilmWorks Pacific, pg 761
Hyperspective Studios Inc, pg 783
Media Bridge Gamekids, pg 821
Sight & Sound Studios, pg 887
1013 Integrated, pg 911

IDAHO

KTVB-TV, pg 802
Wide Eye Productions, pg 938

ILLINOIS

ABSA Films, pg 672
Airways Digital Media, pg 679
CCore Media Inc, pg 718
The Chicago Production Center, pg 721
Cresta Creative, pg 734
Extraordinary Demos/Videos, pg 757
Film Police, pg 760
IV Media Resources, pg 792
Mimi Productions, pg 828
PSAV® Presentation Services (Hotel Services Division), pg 866
Questar Entertainment Inc, pg 868

SCI Television & Creative Media LLC, pg 882
Sound/Video Impressions Inc, pg 894
Southern Illinois University, pg 895
Sparkfactor, pg 896
20/20 Communications Inc, pg 920
Video I-D Teleproductions Inc, pg 928
Video Impressions, pg 928
WEEK TV, pg 935

INDIANA

A-V-A Video Productions, pg 671
Bright Ideas Creative Services, pg 710
Educational Video Group Inc, pg 751
PentaVision Communications Inc, pg 854

IOWA

Educational Technology & Media Services, pg 751
Iowa State University-Information Technology Services, pg 791
Kuhn Productions LLC, pg 802

KANSAS

KAKE-TV, pg 796

KENTUCKY

Broadway Digital, pg 711
Hammond Communications Group Inc, pg 775
Horizon Films & Media LLC, pg 781
Idle Minds Productions Inc, pg 784
Prosper Media Group Inc, pg 866
WKYT-TV, pg 940

LOUISIANA

Louisiana State University Division of Strategic Communications, pg 811
Moxie Media, pg 832
Vidox Motion Imagery, pg 930
WVLA-TV, pg 942

MAINE

WGME-TV, pg 936

MARYLAND

Adventure Productions LLC, pg 678
CPR MultiMedia Solutions, pg 732
dbF a Media Company, pg 739
DBM Communications Inc, pg 739
DSR Computer Technology Specialists Inc, pg 747
James Agee Film Project, pg 792
Kramer Communications Video Production, pg 801
Quality Film & Video, pg 868
Sign Media Inc, pg 887
Spectrum Productions, pg 897

MASSACHUSETTS

Award Productions Inc, pg 699
Capron Lighting & Sound Co Inc, pg 716
Documentary Educational Resources Inc, pg 744
Green Mountain Post Films (GMP), pg 774
Heliotrope Studios, pg 778
HOME Inc, pg 781
Monadnock Media Inc, pg 829
MotionArt Studios, pg 831

Northern Light Productions (NLP), pg 842
Penfield Productions Ltd, pg 853
PixMix Video Services, pg 857
Preston Productions Inc, pg 861
TVN-The Video Network, pg 919

MICHIGAN

ASC Systems, pg 690
Digi Sign Design LLC, pg 741
Digital Image Studios LLC, pg 742
K&R's Recording Studios Inc, pg 796
Michigan Recording Arts Institute & Technologies, pg 825
On Stage Visuals, pg 846
WTVS, Detroit Public Television, pg 942

MINNESOTA

BeyerSound & Essay Audio, pg 705
House of Cinemagraphics, pg 782
MastCom, pg 819
Worthwhile Films, pg 941

MISSOURI

Communitronics Corp, pg 729
Conference Technologies Inc, pg 730
Show-Me Audio-Visual, pg 887
Visionworks Design Services Inc, pg 931

MONTANA

KCFW Television, pg 797

NEVADA

Aardvark Video & Media Productions, pg 671
DVDs4Less, pg 748
Encore Event Technologies LLC, pg 754
JCS Video Productions, pg 793
Lefco Video Services Inc, pg 806
Ron Roy Productions/Moodtapes, pg 878

NEW HAMPSHIRE

Apertura, pg 686
Channell One Video, pg 720
Chip Taylor Communications LLC, pg 907
The Troupe, pg 918

NEW JERSEY

AJS Events, pg 679
Allegro Productions Inc, pg 680
CFP Video Productions Inc, pg 720
Diversified, pg 744
E Video Productions LLC, pg 749
Euro-Pacific Film & Video Productions Inc, pg 756
Hogpenny Studios, pg 780
Laurel Video Productions, pg 804
Megavideo LLC, pg 823
MiB MediaWorks, pg 825
Optisonics Productions, pg 847
Outside The Box Interactive LLC, pg 849
PLS Staging, pg 858
Suede Interactive, pg 903
VCSvideo, pg 925
Video Ideas Productions, pg 928
Yorktel, pg 944

NEW MEXICO

Production Outfitters, pg 864
30 Second Street Ltd, pg 912

NEW YORK

Air Sea Land Productions Inc (ASL), pg 678
Associated Press Television News, pg 691
aurora productions, pg 696
BC Studio, pg 702
Bellin Productions, pg 703
The Big House Group, pg 705
Bravo Studios, pg 709
Buffalo Video Production, pg 712
Chromavision Corp, pg 723
Digital Art Video Inc, pg 741
Downtown Community Television Center (DCTV), pg 746
4-D Creative Media, pg 764
Hallel Communications, pg 775
HAVE Inc, pg 777
Hayden 5 Media LLC, pg 777
HB-Content, pg 777
Heavy Melody, pg 778
Hello World Communications, pg 778
IAI Records & Video, pg 783
Icontent, pg 783
The Independent Production Fund, pg 786
Richard Kaplan Productions, pg 796
Ketchum Inc, pg 798
Kinetic Arts, pg 799
L A Bruell Inc, pg 802
Long Island Video Enterprises Live Inc, pg 811
Lylofilm Productions, pg 813
Manhattan Center Studios Inc, pg 816
Mastervision Inc, pg 819
Mood Creations Ltd, pg 829
Jack Morton Worldwide, pg 830
News Broadcast Network Inc, pg 840
PostWorks, pg 860
PrimaLux Video Inc, pg 862
PrimeLight Productions Inc, pg 862
Rollin Studios, pg 877
SISU Home Entertainment Inc, pg 889
Synaptic Digital, pg 905
Teatown Communications Group, pg 908
United Nations Multimedia Resources Unit, pg 921
VIEW Inc (Video International Entertainment World Inc), pg 930
Visual Technologies Corp, pg 932
Willow Mixed Media Inc, pg 939
WNET/New York Public Media, pg 940
Worldview Entertainment Holdings Inc, pg 941
Zelman Studios Ltd, pg 945

NORTH CAROLINA

Pat Appleson Studios Inc, pg 687
Bill Barnes Video Productions LLC, pg 702
The Communications Group Inc, pg 729
Digital Rain LLC, pg 742
Duke Media Services, pg 747
Horizon Video Productions Inc, pg 781
Image Associates Inc, pg 784
Kino Mountain Productions LLC, pg 799
K2 Productions, pg 802
Moving Pictures, pg 832
NASCAR Productions LLC, pg 835
On Location North Carolina, pg 846
Special Event Services, pg 896
Take One Productions Ltd, pg 906
Videowerks, pg 930

NORTH DAKOTA

UND Television Center, pg 921

OHIO

Advent Media Inc, pg 677
Aztec Video Productions, pg 700
Bartha, pg 702
Russ Beckner Pictures, pg 703
CET, pg 720
Challenge Productions/Challenge
    Aerial Imaging, pg 720
Cuyahoga Community College
    Student Production Office (SPO),
    pg 736
iVideo Technologies, pg 792
Lyon Video Inc, pg 813
MainSail Production Services Inc,
    pg 815
Mills James Productions, pg 828
R&B Communications Inc, pg 870
Take 1 Media Services, pg 906
Treehaus Communications Inc,
    pg 917
Vista Color Imaging Inc, pg 931

OKLAHOMA

Academic Media & Digital
    Services, pg 672
Garman Productions LLC, pg 768
PDC Productions, pg 852

OREGON

KPDX-TV Production Center,
    pg 801
KTVA Productions, pg 802
Production West, pg 864
REX, pg 874
Spirit Media, pg 897

PENNSYLVANIA

Audio Visions Inc, pg 694
Bang! Pictures Inc, pg 701
Beholder Productions Inc, pg 703
FMP Media Solutions Inc, pg 763
Innovision Media Group, pg 788
JPL, pg 795
Main Point Productions, pg 815
Muderick Media, pg 833
Production Masters Inc (PMI),
    pg 864
The Videohouse Inc, pg 929
Visual Sound Inc, pg 931

RHODE ISLAND

Sound-FX-Design, pg 894

SOUTH CAROLINA

American Production Services LLC,
    pg 684
Stages Video Productions, pg 899
Venture Media, pg 925

TENNESSEE

American Blackguard Inc, pg 683
Fricon Entertainment Co Inc,
    pg 766
Memphis Communications Corp,
    pg 823
Motion Picture Services, pg 831
Paradigm Marketing & Creative,
    pg 851
Running Pony Productions LLC,
    pg 878
Scripps Networks, pg 882
ST Productions, pg 898
Stage Post, pg 899
Zion Music Group, pg 945

TEXAS

AMS Pictures, pg 684
Biway Media, pg 706
Castleview Productions, pg 717
Cerutti Productions Inc, pg 720
Countdown Productions Inc, pg 732
Eyecon Video Productions, pg 758
Hurst Digital, pg 782
Mediaforce Productions, pg 822
Earl Miller Productions Inc, pg 827
Julye Newlin Productions Inc,
    pg 840
Out of the BLUE Media, pg 849
Phillips Media Source, pg 855
Romar Learning Solutions LLC,
    pg 877
RuffHouse LLC, pg 878
The Samuels Co, pg 879
South Coast Film & Video, pg 895
Stage Directions, pg 898
Texas Heart Institute Visual
    Communication Services, pg 911

UTAH

ImageWorks Communications,
    pg 785

VERMONT

Dorothy Tod Films, pg 915

VIRGINIA

Advance Concepts Inc, pg 677
Altruist Media LLC, pg 682
BES Studios, pg 704
CACI Integrated Communications,
    pg 713
CDR Communications Inc, pg 719
DXC Technology Co, pg 748
Eagle Films, pg 749
EFX Media, pg 751
Henninger Media Services, pg 779
Metro Productions, pg 824
Quince Imaging Inc, pg 868
Video Solutions, pg 928

WASHINGTON

Adams Creative & Production
    Services, pg 675
Bennett-Watt HD Productions Inc,
    pg 703
Hamilton Studio, pg 775
The House Studios, pg 782
North-by-Northwest - A Digital
    Studio, pg 842
Pal Productions, pg 850
Small World Productions Inc,
    pg 890
Victory Studios, pg 927

WEST VIRGINIA

Sweetsong Productions, pg 905
WSAZ-TV NewsChannel 3, pg 942

WISCONSIN

Audio Visual of Milwaukee Inc,
    pg 694
Learning Technology Services,
    pg 805
Meridian Studios, pg 824
Midland Video Productions Inc,
    pg 827
University of Wisconsin-Oshkosh
    Radio-TV-Film Dept, pg 923
USAV Group Inc, pg 923
Video Wisconsin Inc, pg 929
Watts Communications Inc, pg 934
Wisconsin Public Television, pg 940

WYOMING

Bridger Productions Inc, pg 710

PUERTO RICO

Stage Crew Audiovisual Inc, pg 898

ALBERTA

Black Media Works, pg 706
Global TV, pg 771
HDTV Productions Inc, pg 777

BRITISH COLUMBIA

Inspired Image Picture Co (IIPC),
    pg 788
Video Out Distribution, pg 928

MANITOBA

Spectra Video Productions Ltd,
    pg 897

*NEWFOUNDLAND AND
    LABRADOR*

Vidcraft Productions Ltd, pg 927

NORTHWEST TERRITORIES

Yellowknife Films Inc, pg 944

ONTARIO

ADS Media, pg 677
DebsVoice, pg 739
GAPC (General Assembly
    Production Centre), pg 768
Image Video Services &
    Productions, pg 785
JFB Communications, pg 794
Marblemedia, pg 816
Silver Creek Media Inc, pg 888
Video Excellence Productions,
    pg 927

QUEBEC

Group PVP, pg 774

SASKATCHEWAN

Thomega Entertainment Inc, pg 913

Cueing System, *see* Teleprompting & Cueing System

Digital Special Effect Generator Distributors

ARIZONA

EAR Professional Audio/Video,
    pg 749

CALIFORNIA

Ametron Audio/Video, pg 684
BroadcastStore.com, pg 711
Diaquest, pg 741
MediaPOINTE, pg 823
Photodyne Technologies, pg 856
SNAP, pg 891
Videobotics, pg 929
VMI Inc, pg 932
VTP Inc, pg 933

COLORADO

Spectrum Audio Visual Services,
    pg 897

FLORIDA

Access Media Group, pg 673
Digital Video Systems, pg 742
Harris Corp, pg 776
Hi-Tech Enterprises Inc, pg 779
Midtown Video Inc, pg 827
ONstage, pg 846

GEORGIA

Stage Front Presentation Systems,
    pg 899

HAWAII

The Audio Visual Co (AVCO),
    pg 694

ILLINOIS

Joseph Electronics, pg 795

INDIANA

Sensory Technologies LLC, pg 884

KENTUCKY

Barney Miller's Inc, pg 827
NOR-COM Inc, pg 841

MASSACHUSETTS

Rule Boston Camera, pg 878

MICHIGAN

ASC Systems, pg 690
Digi Sign Design LLC, pg 741

MINNESOTA

Alpha Video & Audio Inc, pg 682

MISSOURI

Conference Technologies Inc,
    pg 730
Modern Communications Inc,
    pg 828
Schiller's Audio-Visual, pg 881
Southwest Audio-Visual Inc, pg 895

NEVADA

Aardvark Video & Media
    Productions, pg 671

NEW JERSEY

Alltec Stores, a Vcom IMC
    Company, pg 681
Diversified, pg 744
HamiltonBuhl, pg 775
MCCOM Inc, pg 820
PatchAmp, pg 852
SYMCO Inc, pg 905
Tele-Measurements Inc, pg 910
Total Video Products Inc, pg 916

NEW YORK

Audio-Video Corp, pg 694
BMI Supply, pg 708
Creative Stage Lighting Co Inc,
    pg 733
Indigo Productions, pg 787

NORTH CAROLINA

Alien Skin Software LLC, pg 680

PENNSYLVANIA

AccuWeather Inc, pg 674
Advanced AV LLC, pg 677
Clair Companies, pg 725
J E Foss Co, pg 764

VIDEO

Digital Special Effect Generator Distributors (continued)

PENNSYLVANIA (continued)

Innovision Media Group, pg 788
The Lerro Corp, pg 806

TENNESSEE

Lowrance Sound Co Inc, pg 812
Technical Support Systems LLC, pg 908
Zion Music Group, pg 945

TEXAS

AVES Audio Visual Systems Inc, pg 698
Biway Media, pg 706
High End Systems Inc, pg 779
Pro Video & Film Equipment Co Inc, pg 863
Videotex Systems Inc, pg 930

UTAH

Strata™, pg 901

VIRGINIA

Lee Hartman & Sons Inc, pg 805
The Whitlock Group, pg 937

WASHINGTON

CCI Solutions, pg 718

WISCONSIN

Audio Visual of Milwaukee Inc, pg 694
Camera Corner Connecting Point, pg 715
Full Compass Systems, pg 767

ALBERTA

Matrix Video Communications Corp (MVCC), pg 819

MANITOBA

Inland Audio Visual Ltd, pg 788

ONTARIO

Corel Corp, pg 731

Digital Special Effect Generator Manufacturers

CALIFORNIA

Blackmagic Design Pty Ltd, pg 707
Diaquest, pg 741
For-A Corp of America, pg 763
Grande Vitesse Systems Inc (GVS), pg 773
Linker Systems Inc, pg 809

FLORIDA

Compuvideo Sales USA Ltd, pg 729

MISSOURI

GlobalStreams™ Corp, pg 771

NEW JERSEY

CELCO, pg 719

NORTH CAROLINA

Alien Skin Software LLC, pg 680

PENNSYLVANIA

AccuWeather Inc, pg 674

TEXAS

High End Systems Inc, pg 779

UTAH

Strata™, pg 901

BRITISH COLUMBIA

Triad Communications Ltd, pg 918

ONTARIO

Corel Corp, pg 731

Digital Special Effect Generator Rentals

ARIZONA

Merestone, pg 823
Video West Inc, pg 929

CALIFORNIA

Artichoke Productions, pg 690
Express Media Inc, pg 757
Maximus Media Inc, pg 820
McCune Audio-Video-Lighting, pg 821
Reality Check Systems, pg 871
RetinaVision Productions, pg 874
Twin Peaks Creative, pg 920

CONNECTICUT

Videofilm Systems Inc, pg 929

FLORIDA

Access Media Group, pg 673
ONstage, pg 846
Paradise Show & Design Inc, pg 851

GEORGIA

Stage Front Presentation Systems, pg 899

ILLINOIS

RC Communications, pg 870
Resolution Productions Group, pg 874

MARYLAND

CPR MultiMedia Solutions, pg 732

MASSACHUSETTS

massAV, pg 819
Preston Productions Inc, pg 861

MICHIGAN

Digi Sign Design LLC, pg 741
K&R All Media Productions LLC, pg 796

MISSOURI

Show-Me Audio-Visual, pg 887

NEW JERSEY

CFP Video Productions Inc, pg 720
Tele-Measurements Inc, pg 910

NEW YORK

Creative Stage Lighting Co Inc, pg 733

NORTH DAKOTA

Media Productions, pg 822

OHIO

Lyon Video Inc, pg 813
Mills James Productions, pg 828

PENNSYLVANIA

Advanced AV LLC, pg 677
Innovision Media Group, pg 788
Producers Management Television (PMTV), pg 863
The Videohouse Inc, pg 929

TENNESSEE

Technical Support Systems LLC, pg 908

TEXAS

Alford Media Services, pg 680
Stage Directions, pg 898

VIRGINIA

Quince Imaging Inc, pg 868

MANITOBA

Inland Audio Visual Ltd, pg 788

SASKATCHEWAN

plan9films, pg 857

Digital Special Effect Generator Repairs

CALIFORNIA

Ametron Audio/Video, pg 684
Effective Engineering Inc, pg 751
VMI Inc, pg 932

FLORIDA

ELC Sales & Service Inc, pg 752
Hi-Tech Enterprises Inc, pg 779
Midtown Video Inc, pg 827

GEORGIA

Stage Front Presentation Systems, pg 899

KENTUCKY

Barney Miller's Inc, pg 827
NOR-COM Inc, pg 841

MICHIGAN

TEL Systems LLC, pg 909

MINNESOTA

Alpha Video & Audio Inc, pg 682

MISSOURI

Southwest Audio-Visual Inc, pg 895

TENNESSEE

Technical Support Systems LLC, pg 908

TEXAS

Pro Video & Film Equipment Co Inc, pg 863

WISCONSIN

Full Compass Systems, pg 767

MANITOBA

Inland Audio Visual Ltd, pg 788

Digital Video Workstation Distributors

ARIZONA

EAR Professional Audio/Video, pg 749

ARKANSAS

White Diamond Productions LLC, pg 937

CALIFORNIA

Ametron Audio/Video, pg 684
Audio Images Corp, pg 693
California Tape Products Inc, pg 714
Computer Modules Inc, pg 729
Diaquest, pg 741
MediaPOINTE, pg 823
Photodyne Technologies, pg 856
Point of View Productions, pg 858
Promax Systems, pg 865
SNAP, pg 891
Southern California Sound Image Inc, pg 895
Videobotics, pg 929
VMI Inc, pg 932
VTP Inc, pg 933

FLORIDA

Access Media Group, pg 673
Digital Video Systems, pg 742
Harris Corp, pg 776
Hi-Tech Enterprises Inc, pg 779
Midtown Video Inc, pg 827
ONstage, pg 846
Recording Media & Equipment Inc (RM&E), pg 872

GEORGIA

Stage Front Presentation Systems, pg 899

HAWAII

The Audio Visual Co (AVCO), pg 694

INDIANA

Lee Co Inc, pg 805
Sensory Technologies LLC, pg 884

KENTUCKY

Barney Miller's Inc, pg 827
NOR-COM Inc, pg 841

MARYLAND

Image Logic Corp, pg 785
Kipp Visual Systems Inc, pg 799
Wiltronix Inc, pg 939

MASSACHUSETTS

Avid Technology Inc, pg 698
Psychsoft Inc, pg 866
Rule Boston Camera, pg 878

MICHIGAN
Digi Sign Design LLC, pg 741
TEL Systems LLC, pg 909

MINNESOTA
Alpha Video & Audio Inc, pg 682

MISSOURI
Modern Communications Inc,
  pg 828
Schiller's Audio-Visual, pg 881
Southwest Audio-Visual Inc, pg 895

NEVADA
Aardvark Video & Media
  Productions, pg 671

NEW JERSEY
Diversified, pg 744
HamiltonBuhl, pg 775
MCCOM Inc, pg 820
Total Video Products Inc, pg 916

NEW YORK
Audio-Video Corp, pg 694
Image Management Systems Inc,
  pg 785

PENNSYLVANIA
AccuWeather Inc, pg 674
Advanced AV LLC, pg 677
The Lerro Corp, pg 806

TENNESSEE
Lowrance Sound Co Inc, pg 812
Technical Support Systems LLC,
  pg 908
Zion Music Group, pg 945

TEXAS
Biway Media, pg 706
Digital Display Solutions Inc,
  pg 742
Pro Video & Film Equipment Co
  Inc, pg 863
Videotex Systems Inc, pg 930

WASHINGTON
CCI Solutions, pg 718
Macrosystem US Inc, pg 814

WISCONSIN
Audio Visual of Milwaukee Inc,
  pg 694
Full Compass Systems, pg 767
Safe Harbor Computers, pg 879
Spectrum Industries Inc, pg 897

ALBERTA
Matrix Video Communications Corp
  (MVCC), pg 819

MANITOBA
Inland Audio Visual Ltd, pg 788

ONTARIO
Drastic Technologies Ltd, pg 746
HD Source, pg 777

Digital Video Workstation Manufacturers

ARIZONA
Applied Integration Corp, pg 687

CALIFORNIA
Computer Modules Inc, pg 729
Diaquest, pg 741
FutureVideo, pg 767
Grande Vitesse Systems Inc (GVS),
  pg 773
Ipitek Inc, pg 791
Opticomm-EMCORE, pg 847
Photodyne Technologies, pg 856
VITEC Multimedia, pg 932

FLORIDA
Hi-Tech Enterprises Inc, pg 779

MARYLAND
Image Logic Corp, pg 785

MASSACHUSETTS
Avid Technology Inc, pg 698
Psychsoft Inc, pg 866

NEW YORK
Laird Digital Cinema, pg 803
Sima Products Corp, pg 888
Vicon Industries Inc, pg 926

PENNSYLVANIA
AccuWeather Inc, pg 674
Aztech Productions LLC, pg 700

TENNESSEE
Adtec Digital Inc, pg 677

TEXAS
Biway Media, pg 706

WASHINGTON
Macrosystem US Inc, pg 814
Watson Desking, pg 934

WISCONSIN
Safe Harbor Computers, pg 879
Spectrum Industries Inc, pg 897

ONTARIO
Corel Corp, pg 731
Drastic Technologies Ltd, pg 746
Evertz Microsystems Ltd, pg 757

Digital Video Workstation Rentals

ARIZONA
Merestone, pg 823

ARKANSAS
White Diamond Productions LLC,
  pg 937

CALIFORNIA
Absolute Rentals, pg 672
Advanced Media LLC, pg 677
Ametron Audio/Video, pg 684
Artichoke Productions, pg 690
Express Media Inc, pg 757
Image Integration, pg 785

Lynch Communications, pg 813
Main Street Media Inc, pg 815
McCune Audio-Video-Lighting,
  pg 821
RetinaVision Productions, pg 874
Roundabout Entertainment Inc,
  pg 878
Total Creative, pg 916
Twin Peaks Creative, pg 920
Universal Studios, pg 922

COLORADO
Open Media Foundation, pg 846

FLORIDA
Access Media Group, pg 673
Accord Productions, pg 673
ONstage, pg 846
Universal Studios Florida®
  Production Group, pg 922

GEORGIA
ECG Productions, pg 750
Stage Front Presentation Systems,
  pg 899

ILLINOIS
Airways Digital Media, pg 679
Resolution Productions Group,
  pg 874

MARYLAND
CPR MultiMedia Solutions, pg 732

MASSACHUSETTS
massAV, pg 819
Preston Productions Inc, pg 861

MICHIGAN
Digi Sign Design LLC, pg 741
K&R All Media Productions LLC,
  pg 796
TEL Systems LLC, pg 909

MINNESOTA
Alpha Video & Audio Inc, pg 682

MISSOURI
Schiller's Audio-Visual, pg 881
Show-Me Audio-Visual, pg 887
Southwest Audio-Visual Inc, pg 895

NEVADA
JCS Video Productions, pg 793

NEW JERSEY
CFP Video Productions Inc, pg 720
MiB MediaWorks, pg 825
PLS Staging, pg 858

NEW MEXICO
Production Outfitters, pg 864

NEW YORK
Buffalo Video Production, pg 712
HB-Content, pg 777
Manhattan Center Studios Inc,
  pg 816

NORTH CAROLINA
The Communications Group Inc,
  pg 729
Duke Media Services, pg 747
Moving Pictures, pg 832

On Location North Carolina, pg 846
Take One Productions Ltd, pg 906

OHIO
Lyon Video Inc, pg 813
Mills James Productions, pg 828

OKLAHOMA
PDC Productions, pg 852

OREGON
Northwest Film Center, pg 842

PENNSYLVANIA
Argentine Productions Inc, pg 688
FMP Media Solutions Inc, pg 763
Innovision Media Group, pg 788
Rahlic Publishing Co, pg 869
The Videohouse Inc, pg 929

SOUTH CAROLINA
Genesis Creative, pg 769

TENNESSEE
Technical Support Systems LLC,
  pg 908

TEXAS
Countdown Productions Inc, pg 732
South Coast Film & Video, pg 895
Stage Directions, pg 898
Video Perspective, pg 928

VIRGINIA
CVW Event Productions, pg 736

WISCONSIN
Full Compass Systems, pg 767

PUERTO RICO
Stage Crew Audiovisual Inc, pg 898

BRITISH COLUMBIA
Video Out Distribution, pg 928

MANITOBA
Inland Audio Visual Ltd, pg 788

QUEBEC
Group PVP, pg 774
Whalley-Abbey Media Holdings
  Inc, pg 937

SASKATCHEWAN
plan9films, pg 857

Digital Video Workstation Repairs

CALIFORNIA
Advanced Media LLC, pg 677
Ametron Audio/Video, pg 684
VMI Inc, pg 932

FLORIDA
ELC Sales & Service Inc, pg 752
Hi-Tech Enterprises Inc, pg 779

GEORGIA
Stage Front Presentation Systems,
  pg 899

VIDEO

Digital Video Workstation Repairs (continued)

KENTUCKY
Barney Miller's Inc, pg 827
NOR-COM Inc, pg 841

MICHIGAN
TEL Systems LLC, pg 909

MINNESOTA
Alpha Video & Audio Inc, pg 682

MISSOURI
Schiller's Audio-Visual, pg 881
Southwest Audio-Visual Inc, pg 895

TENNESSEE
Technical Support Systems LLC, pg 908

TEXAS
Biway Media, pg 706
Pro Video & Film Equipment Co Inc, pg 863

WASHINGTON
Macrosystem US Inc, pg 814

WISCONSIN
Full Compass Systems, pg 767

MANITOBA
Inland Audio Visual Ltd, pg 788

Digitizer Distributors

ARIZONA
EAR Professional Audio/Video, pg 749

CALIFORNIA
Ametron Audio/Video, pg 684
Media Control Systems LLC, pg 821
QRS Software Services, pg 867
VMI Inc, pg 932
VTP Inc, pg 933

FLORIDA
Access Media Group, pg 673
Altel Systems Group Inc, pg 682
Digital Video Systems, pg 742
Hi-Tech Enterprises Inc, pg 779

GEORGIA
Stage Front Presentation Systems, pg 899

HAWAII
The Audio Visual Co (AVCO), pg 694

ILLINOIS
Joseph Electronics, pg 795

INDIANA
Sensory Technologies LLC, pg 884

KENTUCKY
NOR-COM Inc, pg 841

MASSACHUSETTS
Avid Technology Inc, pg 698
Rule Boston Camera, pg 878

MICHIGAN
Digi Sign Design LLC, pg 741

MISSOURI
Ken-A-Vision Manufacturing Co Inc, pg 797
Schiller's Audio-Visual, pg 881

NEVADA
Aardvark Video & Media Productions, pg 671

NEW JERSEY
Diversified, pg 744

NEW YORK
Audio-Video Corp, pg 694
B&H Photo Video, pg 701
Gaylord Archival, pg 768
Vision Identics Systems Inc, pg 930

PENNSYLVANIA
Advanced AV LLC, pg 677

TENNESSEE
Lowrance Sound Co Inc, pg 812

TEXAS
AVES Audio Visual Systems Inc, pg 698
Digital Display Solutions Inc, pg 742
Pro Video & Film Equipment Co Inc, pg 863

VIRGINIA
The Whitlock Group, pg 937

WISCONSIN
Audio Visual of Milwaukee Inc, pg 694
Full Compass Systems, pg 767

MANITOBA
Inland Audio Visual Ltd, pg 788

Digitizer Manufacturers

CALIFORNIA
AJA Video Systems Inc, pg 679
Grande Vitesse Systems Inc (GVS), pg 773
QRS Software Services, pg 867

CONNECTICUT
Xintekvideo Inc, pg 943

MASSACHUSETTS
Avid Technology Inc, pg 698

MICHIGAN
Leightronix Inc, pg 806

MISSOURI
Ken-A-Vision Manufacturing Co Inc, pg 797

NEW JERSEY
CELCO, pg 719

OHIO
Turning Technologies LLC, pg 919

TENNESSEE
Adtec Digital Inc, pg 677

ONTARIO
PixeLINK, pg 857

Digitizer Rentals

ARIZONA
Merestone, pg 823

CALIFORNIA
Absolute Rentals, pg 672
Artichoke Productions, pg 690
Express Media Inc, pg 757
RetinaVision Productions, pg 874
Twin Peaks Creative, pg 920

FLORIDA
Access Media Group, pg 673
Universal Studios Florida® Production Group, pg 922

GEORGIA
Stage Front Presentation Systems, pg 899

ILLINOIS
RC Communications, pg 870
Resolution Productions Group, pg 874

MARYLAND
CPR MultiMedia Solutions, pg 732

MASSACHUSETTS
Preston Productions Inc, pg 861

MICHIGAN
Digi Sign Design LLC, pg 741
K&R All Media Productions LLC, pg 796

MISSOURI
Show-Me Audio-Visual, pg 887

NEW YORK
HB-Content, pg 777

NORTH CAROLINA
On Location North Carolina, pg 846
Take One Productions Ltd, pg 906

PENNSYLVANIA
Argentine Productions Inc, pg 688
Innovision Media Group, pg 788
The Videohouse Inc, pg 929

TEXAS
Stage Directions, pg 898

VIRGINIA
Quince Imaging Inc, pg 868

PUERTO RICO
Stage Crew Audiovisual Inc, pg 898

MANITOBA
Inland Audio Visual Ltd, pg 788

SASKATCHEWAN
plan9films, pg 857

Digitizer Repairs

CALIFORNIA
Ametron Audio/Video, pg 684

FLORIDA
ELC Sales & Service Inc, pg 752
Hi-Tech Enterprises Inc, pg 779

GEORGIA
Stage Front Presentation Systems, pg 899

KENTUCKY
NOR-COM Inc, pg 841

MICHIGAN
TEL Systems LLC, pg 909

MINNESOTA
Alpha Video & Audio Inc, pg 682

MISSOURI
Southwest Audio-Visual Inc, pg 895

TEXAS
Pro Video & Film Equipment Co Inc, pg 863

WISCONSIN
Full Compass Systems, pg 767

MANITOBA
Inland Audio Visual Ltd, pg 788

Dubbing

ALABAMA
Diamond Studios, pg 741

ARIZONA
Film Creations Ltd, pg 760
Merestone, pg 823
Metropolitan Audio-Visual Inc, pg 824
On-Site Video, pg 846
Rodeo Video Inc, pg 876
Star Video Duplicating, pg 900

ARKANSAS
Live'N'Loud, pg 810
White Diamond Productions LLC, pg 937

CALIFORNIA
AB Audio Visual Entertainment Inc, pg 672
Aberdeen Broadcast Services, pg 672

VIDEO

Dubbing (continued)

NEW YORK (continued)

PrimaLux Video Inc, pg 862
Rafik, pg 869
Synaptic Digital, pg 905
Teatown Communications Group, pg 908
TeleTime Productions, pg 910
USA Studios, pg 923
Visual Technologies Corp, pg 932
Zelman Studios Ltd, pg 945

NORTH CAROLINA

All Pro Media Inc, pg 680
Pat Appleson Studios Inc, pg 687
Camcor Inc, pg 715
Duke Media Services, pg 747
Franklin Video Inc, pg 765
Horizon Video Productions Inc, pg 781
Moving Pictures, pg 832
Take One Productions Ltd, pg 906

OHIO

Aztec Video Productions, pg 700
Russ Beckner Pictures, pg 703
Central Ohio Audio Video, pg 719
CET, pg 720
Cinecraft Productions Inc, pg 723
Curtis Inc, pg 736
Cuyahoga Community College Student Production Office (SPO), pg 736
Image Video Teleproductions Inc, pg 785
iVideo Technologies, pg 792
Lyon Video Inc, pg 813
MainSail Production Services Inc, pg 815
Mills James Productions, pg 828
Musicol Recording, pg 835
R&B Communications Inc, pg 870
Take 1 Media Services, pg 906
Vista Color Imaging Inc, pg 931

OKLAHOMA

Academic Media & Digital Services, pg 672
Garman Productions LLC, pg 768
Piper Media Services Inc, pg 857

OREGON

KPDX-TV Production Center, pg 801
KTVA Productions, pg 802
Production West, pg 864
REX, pg 874

PENNSYLVANIA

Argentine Productions Inc, pg 688
Audio Visions Inc, pg 694
Audio Visual Communications Inc, pg 694
Center City Film & Video Inc, pg 719
FMP Media Solutions Inc, pg 763
Innovision Media Group, pg 788
JPL, pg 795
Laser Video Corp, pg 804
Production Masters Inc (PMI), pg 864
The Videohouse Inc, pg 929
WPHL-TV, pg 942

SOUTH CAROLINA

American Production Services LLC, pg 684
Genesis Creative, pg 769
Sound & Images Inc, pg 893
Stages Video Productions, pg 899
Venture Media, pg 925

TENNESSEE

Continental Film, pg 731
Motion Picture Services, pg 831
Running Pony Productions LLC, pg 878
Scripps Networks, pg 882
Stage Post, pg 899
Russ Sturgeon Productions/RSVP, pg 903
United Methodist Productions, pg 921

TEXAS

Biway Media, pg 706
Castleview Productions, pg 717
Dub King, pg 747
The Editing Co, pg 750
Horizon Film + Video Productions, pg 781
Matson Multi-Media, pg 820
Maverick Video Productions, pg 820
McNee Productions Inc, pg 821
Mediaforce Productions, pg 822
Earl Miller Productions Inc, pg 827
Julye Newlin Productions Inc, pg 840
Replicopy Digital Media Center, pg 873
Romar Learning Solutions LLC, pg 877
The Samuels Co, pg 879
South Coast Film & Video, pg 895
Texas Heart Institute Visual Communication Services, pg 911

UTAH

ImageWorks Communications, pg 785

VERMONT

University of Vermont, Instructional Television Dept, pg 923

VIRGINIA

American AV, pg 682
BES Studios, pg 704
CACI Integrated Communications, pg 713
CDR Communications Inc, pg 719
CVW Event Productions, pg 736
Henninger Media Services, pg 779
Limelight Communications Inc, pg 808
Video Solutions, pg 928

WASHINGTON

Bennett-Watt HD Productions Inc, pg 703
Inland Audio Visual Co, pg 788
North-by-Northwest - A Digital Studio, pg 842
Victory Studios, pg 927

WISCONSIN

Audio Visual of Milwaukee Inc, pg 694
Learning Technology Services, pg 805
Meridian Studios, pg 824
Mirror 34 Productions, pg 828

USAV Group Inc, pg 923
Video Wisconsin Inc, pg 929
Watts Communications Inc, pg 934
Wisconsin Public Television, pg 940

WYOMING

Bridger Productions Inc, pg 710

PUERTO RICO

Stage Crew Audiovisual Inc, pg 898

ALBERTA

Cine Audio Visual Sales & Service Ltd, pg 723
Global TV, pg 771

BRITISH COLUMBIA

Triad Communications Ltd, pg 918
24 Frames Film & Video, pg 920
Video Out Distribution, pg 928

NEWFOUNDLAND AND LABRADOR

Vidcraft Productions Ltd, pg 927

ONTARIO

GAPC (General Assembly Production Centre), pg 768
Image Video Services & Productions, pg 785
Silver Creek Media Inc, pg 888
Video Excellence Productions, pg 927

QUEBEC

Group PVP, pg 774

SASKATCHEWAN

Thomega Entertainment Inc, pg 913

Duplication—DVDs

ALABAMA

AVS Media Group, pg 699
Sound of Birmingham Productions, pg 894

ARIZONA

Creative Backstage, pg 733
Film Creations Ltd, pg 760
Forensic Video Deposition Service, pg 764
Merestone, pg 823
Metropolitan Audio-Visual Inc, pg 824
On-Site Video, pg 846
Star Video Duplicating, pg 900
Tempe Tape & Disc, pg 911

ARKANSAS

Michael Mueller Video Productions, pg 833
White Diamond Productions LLC, pg 937

CALIFORNIA

AB Audio Visual Entertainment Inc, pg 672
ACDC Audio CD & Cassette, pg 674
Action Video, pg 675
Advanced Digital Design, pg 677
Advanced Media LLC, pg 677
AGF Media Services, pg 678
All Video Productions, pg 680

Assured Audio Visual, pg 691
Audio Rents, pg 693
Audio Visual Consultants, pg 694
AVerMedia Technologies Inc, pg 697
California Tape Products Inc, pg 714
Steve Chandler, pg 720
Christopher Gray Post Production, pg 722
Coloredge Inc, pg 728
Creative Sound Corp, pg 733
Crystal Pyramid Productions™, pg 735
Custom Video Productions Inc, pg 736
Digital Jungle, pg 742
digital OutPost, pg 742
DiskFaktory, pg 743
Express Media Inc, pg 757
FJ Productions Inc, pg 762
Gluskin's Custom Audio Video, pg 771
Havas Edge, pg 777
iCorpTv, pg 783
Imageworks, pg 785
JD Audio Visual Inc, pg 793
JDS Video & Media Productions Inc, pg 793
Lightning Media, pg 808
Ludlow Media, pg 812
Maximus Media Inc, pg 820
Media Magic, pg 822
New & Unique Videos™, pg 839
New Cyberian Systems Inc, pg 839
On-Trax Inc, pg 846
Pacific Video Image, pg 849
Penrose Productions, pg 854
PM Productions, pg 858
PME Audio/Video, pg 858
Pro8mm, pg 862
QRS Software Services, pg 867
Quality Clones, pg 867
Reel Picture, pg 872
RJ Video Productions, pg 875
Rough House, pg 878
Roundabout Entertainment Inc, pg 878
Saturn Studios, pg 881
SF Global Sourcing, pg 885
Shapeshifter, pg 885
Shokus Video, pg 886
SonicPool, pg 892
Staylor-Made Communications Inc, pg 900
Still N' Motion, pg 901
Studio 637, pg 903
TIMECODE Post Production, pg 914
Total Creative, pg 916
Twin Peaks Creative, pg 920
United Audio Video Inc, pg 921
Universal Studios, pg 922
VidCan Media Solutions, pg 927
Video Movie Magic, pg 928
Visions Plus, pg 931
VMI Inc, pg 932

COLORADO

Flashback Media Productions, pg 762
Jeppesen, pg 793
Mike's Camera, pg 827
Rocky Mountain Audio/Video Productions Inc, pg 876
Rose Packaging & Design Inc, pg 877
Side 3 Studios, pg 887

CONNECTICUT

A/V Davey, pg 697
BRB Audiovisual Productions, pg 709

Cine-Med Inc, pg 723
CMI Media Management, pg 727
Digital Video Productions, pg 742
Guymark Studios LLC, pg 775
Ironik Design & Post, pg 791
New London Media, pg 839
Rockwell Communications Inc, pg 876
T & M Digital Services LLC, pg 906
Video Production Associates Inc, pg 928

DELAWARE

Ken-Del Productions Inc, pg 797
Ken-Del Studios, pg 797

DISTRICT OF COLUMBIA

Interface Media Group, pg 789

FLORIDA

Access Media Group, pg 673
Accord Productions, pg 673
Applebox Studio, pg 687
CD ROM™ Inc, pg 718
Civins Productions Inc, pg 725
Comtel Inc, pg 730
Easy Edit Video Inc, pg 750
Florida Digital Studios, pg 762
Gemstone Media Inc, pg 769
Harmon's Audio-Visual Services, pg 776
Hi-Tech Enterprises Inc, pg 779
MAC Production Group, pg 813
Mach 1 Productions, pg 813
The Newhouse Media Group, pg 840
ONstage, pg 846
Photosound of Orlando Inc, pg 856
Sound & Vision Communications Inc, pg 893
Sunrise Studios, pg 904
Tallahassee Photo & Frame, pg 906
Tricycle Studios, pg 918
Mike Vasilinda Productions Inc, pg 925
Venice Media Group, pg 925
Video Techniques Inc, pg 928

GEORGIA

Beast Atlanta, pg 703
Cinema Concepts, pg 724
ECG Productions, pg 750
Guerrilla Productions LLC, pg 774
Omega Media Group Inc, pg 845
On-Line Productions, pg 845
ON Services, a GES Company, pg 846

ILLINOIS

ABSA Films, pg 672
Advanced Audio Technology, pg 677
Airways Digital Media, pg 679
AnswersMedia, pg 686
Atomic Imaging Inc/Golan Studios, pg 692
Backstar Creative Media Inc, pg 700
Big Shoulders Digital Video Productions, pg 705
International Historic Films Inc, pg 790
Intervideo Duplication Services, pg 791
IV Media Resources, pg 792
Kelmscott Communications, pg 797
Major Media Inc, pg 815
Midwest Digital Corp, pg 827
RADMAR Inc, pg 869

RBR Productions, pg 870
SCI Television & Creative Media LLC, pg 882
Sound/Video Impressions Inc, pg 894
20/20 Communications Inc, pg 920
Video I-D Teleproductions Inc, pg 928
Video Impressions, pg 928

INDIANA

A-V-A Video Productions, pg 671
Advanced Media Integration, pg 677
Educational Video Group Inc, pg 751

IOWA

Duplication Media, pg 748
Pro Video, pg 863

KENTUCKY

American Recordable Media, pg 684
Audio Visual Techniques Inc, pg 695
The PPS Group, pg 860
Prosper Media Group Inc, pg 866

LOUISIANA

Louisiana State University Division of Strategic Communications, pg 811
Moxie Media, pg 832
Vidox Motion Imagery, pg 930

MAINE

Headlight Audio Visual Inc, pg 777

MARYLAND

Adventure Productions LLC, pg 678
Carpel Video Inc, pg 717
CPR MultiMedia Solutions, pg 732
dbF a Media Company, pg 739
DBM Communications Inc, pg 739
Kramer Communications Video Production, pg 801
Lion & Fox Recording Studios, pg 809
Media Dimensions LLC, pg 821
Milner-Fenwick Inc, pg 828
Pro Cuts Editing Services, pg 862
Quality Film & Video, pg 868
RTZ Audio Visual, pg 878
Saah Video, pg 879
Satellite Media Production, pg 881

MASSACHUSETTS

Continental Recordings Inc, pg 731
Documentary Educational Resources Inc, pg 744
In the Wild Productions, pg 786
TR Productions, pg 916
Video Express, pg 928

MICHIGAN

Digi Sign Design LLC, pg 741
The Program Source International, pg 865
TGA Recording Co, pg 911
The Transfer Zone®, pg 917

MINNESOTA

The ADS Group, pg 676
C Vision Productions, pg 713
Linhoff Photo & Digital Imaging, pg 809
Pro Media Productions, pg 863
Rum Jungle Media, pg 878

MISSISSIPPI

Bowie Audio Visual Enterprises Inc, pg 709

MISSOURI

Allied Photocolor Co, pg 681
Show-Me Audio-Visual, pg 887
Studio Worx Inc, pg 903
VSG Digital Media Solutions, pg 933

MONTANA

Jereco Studios Inc, pg 793

NEBRASKA

Three Pillars Media, pg 913

NEVADA

Aardvark Video & Media Productions, pg 671
JCS Video Productions, pg 793
Peterson's Video Transfer Services, pg 855

NEW HAMPSHIRE

Channell One Video, pg 720
Chip Taylor Communications LLC, pg 907

NEW JERSEY

AJS Events, pg 679
Allegro Productions Inc, pg 680
Audio Visual Associates, pg 694
Color Leasing Studios, pg 727
Creative Video, pg 734
Disc Makers, pg 743
Diversified, pg 744
Euro-Pacific Film & Video Productions Inc, pg 756
International Audio Visual Inc, pg 790
Megavideo LLC, pg 823
MiB MediaWorks, pg 825
Midnight Media Group Inc, pg 827
Oasis Disc Manufacturing, pg 844
Starlite, pg 900
Synergem, pg 905
VCSvideo, pg 925
Video Ideas Productions, pg 928

NEW MEXICO

Production Outfitters, pg 864

NEW YORK

Adwar Video, pg 678
Bellin Productions, pg 703
Big Foot Productions Inc, pg 705
The Big House Group, pg 705
Chromavision Corp, pg 723
Design Audio Visual Inc, pg 741
Digital Art Video Inc, pg 741
Downtown Community Television Center (DCTV), pg 746
DuArt Media Services, pg 747
Duplication Depot Inc, pg 748
Foothill Digital Inc, pg 763
4-D Creative Media, pg 764
HB-Content, pg 777
Heavy Melody, pg 778
Hello World Communications, pg 778
International Digital Centre, pg 790
iProbe Multilingual Solutions Inc, pg 791
J&D Laboratories Inc, pg 793
Mark Custom Recording Service Inc, pg 817
Mood Creations Ltd, pg 829

Motion Picture Enterprises Inc, pg 831
Production Central, pg 863
Teatown Communications Group, pg 908
Video Caption Corp, pg 927
Visual Technologies Corp, pg 932
Visual Word Systems Inc, pg 932
WTL Productions, pg 942

NORTH CAROLINA

All Pro Media Inc, pg 680
Pat Appleson Studios Inc, pg 687
AV Connections Inc, pg 697
Camcor Inc, pg 715
Franklin Video Inc, pg 765
Horizon Video Productions Inc, pg 781
Ladyslipper Music, pg 803
Moving Pictures, pg 832
Take One Productions Ltd, pg 906

OHIO

Central Ohio Audio Video, pg 719
Curtis Inc, pg 736
Musicol Recording, pg 835
Production Partners Media, pg 864
QCA, pg 867
R&B Communications Inc, pg 870
Ungar Video & Film, pg 921
Vista Color Imaging Inc, pg 931

OKLAHOMA

Garman Productions LLC, pg 768
Piper Media Services Inc, pg 857

OREGON

KTVA Productions, pg 802
MediaFX, pg 822
REX, pg 874

PENNSYLVANIA

John E Allen Inc, pg 680
Argentine Productions Inc, pg 688
Audio Visions Inc, pg 694
Audio Visual Communications Inc, pg 694
Beholder Productions Inc, pg 703
Bernie's Photo Center, pg 704
FMP Media Solutions Inc, pg 763
Innovision Media Group, pg 788
Laser Video Corp, pg 804
New York Camera & Video, pg 840
Panta Rhei Media Inc, pg 851
The Videohouse Inc, pg 929

SOUTH CAROLINA

American Production Services LLC, pg 684
Genesis Creative, pg 769
Stages Video Productions, pg 899
Venture Media, pg 925

TENNESSEE

Anode Inc, pg 686
CRT Custom Products Inc, pg 735
JamSync, pg 793
Kingswood Productions, pg 799
Motion Picture Services, pg 831
NTS ProMedia, pg 843
Running Pony Productions LLC, pg 878
Stage Post, pg 899
WTSmedia, pg 942

TEXAS

Arcube Multimedia Inc, pg 688
Biway Media, pg 706

VIDEO

Duplication—DVDs (continued)

TEXAS (continued)

CEV Multimedia Ltd, pg 720
Chalk Dust Co, pg 720
Communication Arts Multimedia Inc, pg 728
Crystal Clear Media Group, pg 735
The Editing Co, pg 750
Horizon Film + Video Productions, pg 781
Matson Multi-Media, pg 820
Mediaforce Productions, pg 822
Julye Newlin Productions Inc, pg 840
Omega Broadcast Group, pg 845
Replicopy Digital Media Center, pg 873
The Samuels Co, pg 879
Stage Directions, pg 898
U-Edit Video, pg 920

UTAH

ELS Productions Inc, pg 753
ImageWorks Communications, pg 785
One Stop CD Shop LLC, pg 846

VIRGINIA

American AV, pg 682
CDR Communications Inc, pg 719
Furnace MFG, pg 767
Lee Hartman & Sons Inc, pg 805
Limelight Communications Inc, pg 808
National Media Services Inc, pg 836
Rocktown Media, pg 876

WASHINGTON

Bennett-Watt HD Productions Inc, pg 703
CCI Solutions, pg 718
Robert McConnell Productions, pg 820
Pacific Multimedia Inc, pg 849
Proforma Good Wood Marketing, pg 865
Victory Studios, pg 927
Washington State University College of Nursing, pg 934

WEST VIRGINIA

Blackwater Video Productions, pg 707
MotionMasters, pg 831

WISCONSIN

Audio Visual of Milwaukee Inc, pg 694
AVS Group, pg 699
Concept Productions Inc, pg 730
Excel Duplication Services, pg 757
NEWIST/CESA 7, pg 840
Sound Strations Audio Productions Inc, pg 894
USAV Group Inc, pg 923
Watts Communications Inc, pg 934
Win Media Inc, pg 939

WYOMING

Bridger Productions Inc, pg 710

PUERTO RICO

Stage Crew Audiovisual Inc, pg 898

BRITISH COLUMBIA

Triad Communications Ltd, pg 918
24 Frames Film & Video, pg 920

MANITOBA

Ironstone Technologies Inc, pg 791

NEWFOUNDLAND AND LABRADOR

Vidcraft Productions Ltd, pg 927

ONTARIO

ADS Media, pg 677
GAPC (General Assembly Production Centre), pg 768
Image Video Services & Productions, pg 785
Silver Creek Media Inc, pg 888
Video Excellence Productions, pg 927

QUEBEC

Group PVP, pg 774
Muse Entertainment Enterprises, pg 834

SASKATCHEWAN

Thomega Entertainment Inc, pg 913

Duplication— Videocassettes

ALABAMA

AVS Media Group, pg 699

ARIZONA

Allusion Studios & Pure Wave Audio, pg 681
Film Creations Ltd, pg 760
Merestone, pg 823
Metropolitan Audio-Visual Inc, pg 824
Star Video Duplicating, pg 900

ARKANSAS

White Diamond Productions LLC, pg 937

CALIFORNIA

Aberdeen Broadcast Services, pg 672
ACDC Audio CD & Cassette, pg 674
Action Video, pg 675
Advanced Media LLC, pg 677
All Video Productions, pg 680
ALOM Technologies Corp, pg 681
AlphaDogs Inc, pg 682
Audio Visual Consultants, pg 694
California Tape Products Inc, pg 714
CCI Digital, a DVS Company, pg 718
Christopher Gray Post Production, pg 722
Creative Media Recording, pg 733
Crystal Pyramid Productions™, pg 735
Custom Video Productions Inc, pg 736
Digital Jungle, pg 742
digital OutPost, pg 742
DVS InteleStream, pg 748
Express Media Inc, pg 757
Far West Media Services Inc, pg 759

Gluskin's Custom Audio Video, pg 771
Gold Standard Productions, pg 772
Golden Gate Studios, pg 772
Gordon Productions Inc, pg 772
Havas Edge, pg 777
iCorpTv, pg 783
Imageworks, pg 785
JD Audio Visual Inc, pg 793
KTVU-Retail Services, pg 802
Ludlow Media, pg 812
Lynch Communications, pg 813
Maximus Media Inc, pg 820
Media Magic, pg 822
Method Studios, pg 824
New & Unique Videos™, pg 839
Joseph Nicoletti Consulting-Promotion, pg 841
Nolte Media, pg 841
On-Trax Inc, pg 846
piXvfm Inc, pg 857
PM Productions, pg 858
Point.360, pg 858
Pro8mm, pg 862
PSI Inc, pg 866
QRS Software Services, pg 867
Reel Picture, pg 872
RJ Video Productions, pg 875
Rough House, pg 878
Roundabout Entertainment Inc, pg 878
Saturn Studios, pg 881
Shapeshifter, pg 885
Shokus Video, pg 886
SonicPool, pg 892
Staylor-Made Communications Inc, pg 900
Still N' Motion, pg 901
Technicolor USA Inc, pg 908
TiVo Corp, pg 914
Total Creative, pg 916
TVA Media Group, pg 919
Twin Peaks Creative, pg 920
United Audio Video Inc, pg 921
Universal Studios, pg 922
VidCan Media Solutions, pg 927
Video Movie Magic, pg 928
VMI Inc, pg 932

COLORADO

Daylight Productions & Rentals, pg 739
Flashback Media Productions, pg 762
Rocky Mountain Audio/Video Productions Inc, pg 876
Spectrum Audio Visual Services, pg 897

CONNECTICUT

A/V Davey, pg 697
BRB Audiovisual Productions, pg 709
Cine-Med Inc, pg 723
CMI Media Management, pg 727
Digital Video Productions, pg 742
Ironik Design & Post, pg 791
MAVCO, pg 820
Rockwell Communications Inc, pg 876
T & M Digital Services LLC, pg 906
Video Production Associates Inc, pg 928

DELAWARE

Ken-Del Productions Inc, pg 797

DISTRICT OF COLUMBIA

Interface Media Group, pg 789
Library of Congress, Motion Picture, Broadcasting & Recorded Sound Division, pg 807

FLORIDA

Access Media Group, pg 673
Accord Productions, pg 673
Civins Productions Inc, pg 725
Communications Concepts Inc (CCI), pg 729
Easy Edit Video Inc, pg 750
Hi-Tech Enterprises Inc, pg 779
Mach 1 Productions, pg 813
Mike Vasilinda Productions Inc, pg 925
Video Techniques Inc, pg 928

GEORGIA

Audio Visual Resources Inc, pg 695
Beachwood Productions, pg 702
Beast Atlanta, pg 703
Guerrilla Productions LLC, pg 774
Omega Media Group Inc, pg 845
Staging Directions Inc, pg 899
Video Copy Services Inc, pg 927
WaveGuide Studios, pg 934

HAWAII

1013 Integrated, pg 911

IDAHO

KTVB-TV, pg 802

ILLINOIS

AnswersMedia, pg 686
Atomic Imaging Inc/Golan Studios, pg 692
Backstar Creative Media Inc, pg 700
Beatty TeleVisual Productions, pg 703
Big Shoulders Digital Video Productions, pg 705
CCore Media Inc, pg 718
International Historic Films Inc, pg 790
Major Media Inc, pg 815
Moviecraft Inc, pg 831
Pepper Group, pg 854
PSAV® Presentation Services (Hotel Services Division), pg 866
SCI Television & Creative Media LLC, pg 882
Sound/Video Impressions Inc, pg 894
Southern Illinois University, pg 895
Tele-Time Systems, pg 910
Video I-D Teleproductions Inc, pg 928
Video Impressions, pg 928
WEEK TV, pg 935

INDIANA

Advanced Media Integration, pg 677
PentaVision Communications Inc, pg 854

IOWA

Duplication Media, pg 748
Educational Technology & Media Services, pg 751
Iowa State University-Information Technology Services, pg 791

VIDEO

Duplication— Videocassettes (continued)

QUEBEC

Group PVP, pg 774

SASKATCHEWAN

Thomega Entertainment Inc, pg 913

Duplication—Videodiscs

ARIZONA

Film Creations Ltd, pg 760
Merestone, pg 823

CALIFORNIA

Advanced Media LLC, pg 677
All Video Productions, pg 680
Custom Video Productions Inc, pg 736
iCorpTv, pg 783
ITV Productions, pg 792
Lynch Communications, pg 813
Maximus Media Inc, pg 820
PM Productions, pg 858
QRS Software Services, pg 867
Roundabout Entertainment Inc, pg 878
Shapeshifter, pg 885
SNAP, pg 891
SonicPool, pg 892
Still N' Motion, pg 901
Universal Studios, pg 922

COLORADO

Flashback Media Productions, pg 762
Spectrum Audio Visual Services, pg 897

CONNECTICUT

Cine-Med Inc, pg 723
Ironik Design & Post, pg 791

DELAWARE

Ken-Del Productions Inc, pg 797

FLORIDA

Civins Productions Inc, pg 725

GEORGIA

Guerrilla Productions LLC, pg 774
Omega Media Group Inc, pg 845
Staging Directions Inc, pg 899

ILLINOIS

Big Shoulders Digital Video Productions, pg 705
Major Media Inc, pg 815
SCI Television & Creative Media LLC, pg 882
Tele-Time Systems, pg 910

LOUISIANA

Digital FX Inc, pg 742
Louisiana State University Division of Strategic Communications, pg 811

MAINE

Headlight Audio Visual Inc, pg 777

MARYLAND

dbF a Media Company, pg 739
Pro Cuts Editing Services, pg 862
Saah Video, pg 879

MICHIGAN

Digi Sign Design LLC, pg 741
K&R's Recording Studios Inc, pg 796

NEVADA

Encore Event Technologies LLC, pg 754

NEW HAMPSHIRE

Apertura, pg 686

NEW JERSEY

Broadcast Center Studios, pg 710
Diversified, pg 744
MiB MediaWorks, pg 825
Reed Presentations Inc (RPI), pg 872
SES SA, pg 884
Suede Interactive, pg 903

NEW YORK

Burlington A/V Recording Media, pg 712
Design Audio Visual Inc, pg 741
Duplication Specialists Inc, pg 748
General Audio-Visual Inc (GAVI), pg 769
HAVE Inc, pg 777
International Digital Centre, pg 790
Mood Creations Ltd, pg 829
PostWorks, pg 860
PrimaLux Video Inc, pg 862
Teatown Communications Group, pg 908
Visual Technologies Corp, pg 932

NORTH CAROLINA

Pat Appleson Studios Inc, pg 687

OHIO

Aztec Video Productions, pg 700

PENNSYLVANIA

Innovision Media Group, pg 788
Laser Video Corp, pg 804

SOUTH CAROLINA

American Production Services LLC, pg 684

TENNESSEE

Stage Post, pg 899

TEXAS

The Editing Co, pg 750
Horizon Film + Video Productions, pg 781
Mediaforce Productions, pg 822
Stage Directions, pg 898

VIRGINIA

Lee Hartman & Sons Inc, pg 805

WASHINGTON

Victory Studios, pg 927

WISCONSIN

Audio Visual of Milwaukee Inc, pg 694
NEWIST/CESA 7, pg 840

BRITISH COLUMBIA

Triad Communications Ltd, pg 918
24 Frames Film & Video, pg 920

ONTARIO

Silver Creek Media Inc, pg 888

Duplication—Videotapes

ARIZONA

Film Creations Ltd, pg 760
Merestone, pg 823
Metropolitan Audio-Visual Inc, pg 824
Star Video Duplicating, pg 900

ARKANSAS

White Diamond Productions LLC, pg 937

CALIFORNIA

Action Video, pg 675
Advanced Media LLC, pg 677
All Video Productions, pg 680
ALOM Technologies Corp, pg 681
AlphaDogs Inc, pg 682
California Tape Products Inc, pg 714
CCI Digital, a DVS Company, pg 718
Steve Chandler, pg 720
Christopher Gray Post Production, pg 722
Creative Media Recording, pg 733
Crystal Pyramid Productions™, pg 735
Custom Video Productions Inc, pg 736
Digital Jungle, pg 742
digital OutPost, pg 742
DVS InteleStream, pg 748
Express Media Inc, pg 757
First Person Inc, pg 761
Fox Television Center, pg 765
Gluskin's Custom Audio Video, pg 771
Golden Gate Studios, pg 772
Gordon Productions Inc, pg 772
Havas Edge, pg 777
iCorpTv, pg 783
JD Audio Visual Inc, pg 793
KTVU-Retail Services, pg 802
KVIE-Channel 6, pg 802
Ludlow Media, pg 812
Lynch Communications, pg 813
Maximus Media Inc, pg 820
Media Magic, pg 822
Method Studios, pg 824
Joseph Nicoletti Consulting-Promotion, pg 841
Nolte Media, pg 841
On-Trax Inc, pg 846
Pacific Video Image, pg 849
piXvfm Inc, pg 857
PM Productions, pg 858
Point.360, pg 858
Prime Cut Productions, pg 862
Pro8mm, pg 864
PSI Inc, pg 866
QRS Software Services, pg 867
Reel Picture, pg 872
Rough House, pg 878
Roundabout Entertainment Inc, pg 878

Shapeshifter, pg 885
SonicPool, pg 892
Still N' Motion, pg 901
Technicolor USA Inc, pg 908
TiVo Corp, pg 914
Total Creative, pg 916
TVA Media Group, pg 919
Twin Peaks Creative, pg 920
Universal Studios, pg 922
VidCan Media Solutions, pg 927
Video Movie Magic, pg 928
VMI Inc, pg 932
WMS Media Inc, pg 940

COLORADO

Daylight Productions & Rentals, pg 739
Flashback Media Productions, pg 762
Rocky Mountain Audio/Video Productions Inc, pg 876

CONNECTICUT

A/V Davey, pg 697
BRB Audiovisual Productions, pg 709
Cine-Med Inc, pg 723
CMI Media Management, pg 727
Digital Video Productions, pg 742
Ironik Design & Post, pg 791
MAVCO, pg 820
Palace Production Center, pg 850
Rockwell Communications Inc, pg 876

DELAWARE

Ken-Del Productions Inc, pg 797
Ken-Del Studios, pg 797

DISTRICT OF COLUMBIA

Interface Media Group, pg 789
Library of Congress, Motion Picture, Broadcasting & Recorded Sound Division, pg 807

FLORIDA

Access Media Group, pg 673
Accord Productions, pg 673
Applebox Studio, pg 687
Civins Productions Inc, pg 725
Steven Cohen Motion Picture Production, pg 727
Communications Concepts Inc (CCI), pg 729
Comtel Inc, pg 730
Easy Edit Video Inc, pg 750
Hi-Tech Enterprises Inc, pg 779
Jordan Klein Film & Video (JKFV), pg 795
Knowles Video Inc (KVI), pg 800
Paradise Video & Film, pg 851
Mike Vasilinda Productions Inc, pg 925
Video Techniques Inc, pg 928

GEORGIA

Audio Visual Resources Inc, pg 695
Beachwood Productions, pg 702
Beast Atlanta, pg 703
ECG Productions, pg 750
First Cut Communications LLC, pg 761
Guerrilla Productions LLC, pg 774
Omega Media Group Inc, pg 845
Staging Directions Inc, pg 899
Video Copy Services Inc, pg 927
WaveGuide Studios, pg 934

VIDEO

Duplication—Videotapes (continued)

ALBERTA

Cine Audio Visual Sales & Service Ltd, pg 723

BRITISH COLUMBIA

Triad Communications Ltd, pg 918
24 Frames Film & Video, pg 920
Video Out Distribution, pg 928

ONTARIO

Silver Creek Media Inc, pg 888
Video Excellence Productions, pg 927

QUEBEC

Group PVP, pg 774

Duplicator, *see* Tape Duplicator

DVD Authoring

ALABAMA

AVS Media Group, pg 699

ARIZONA

Allusion Studios & Pure Wave Audio, pg 681
Arizona Studios, pg 688
Creative Backstage, pg 733
Film Creations Ltd, pg 760
Merestone, pg 823
Star Video Duplicating, pg 900

ARKANSAS

Michael Mueller Video Productions, pg 833
White Diamond Productions LLC, pg 937

CALIFORNIA

AB Audio Visual Entertainment Inc, pg 672
Access Video in Berkeley, pg 673
Action Video, pg 675
Advanced Digital Design, pg 677
Advanced Media LLC, pg 677
All Video Productions, pg 680
AlphaDogs Inc, pg 682
Artichoke Productions, pg 690
Audio Visual Consultants, pg 694
AVerMedia Technologies Inc, pg 697
CCI Digital, a DVS Company, pg 718
Christopher Gray Post Production, pg 722
Coloredge Inc, pg 728
Crystal Pyramid Productions™, pg 735
Custom Video Productions Inc, pg 736
Digital Jungle, pg 742
digital OutPost, pg 742
Direct Images Interactive Inc, pg 743
DiskFaktory, pg 743
DV Post, pg 748
Express Media Inc, pg 757
First Person Inc, pg 761

Glix Entertainment Inc, pg 771
Gold Standard Productions, pg 772
Havas Edge, pg 777
iCorpTv, pg 783
Imageworks, pg 785
JDS Video & Media Productions Inc, pg 793
Joyce Media Inc, pg 795
K2B2 Records, pg 802
Lightning Media, pg 808
Ludlow Media, pg 812
Main Street Media Inc, pg 815
Maximus Media Inc, pg 820
Media Magic, pg 822
New & Unique Videos™, pg 839
New Cyberian Systems Inc, pg 839
Nineteen87, pg 841
On-Trax Inc, pg 846
Pacific Video Image, pg 849
Penrose Productions, pg 854
QRS Software Services, pg 867
Quality Clones, pg 867
Reality Check Systems, pg 871
Reel Picture, pg 872
RetinaVision Productions, pg 874
Roundabout Entertainment Inc, pg 878
Saturn Studios, pg 881
SF Global Sourcing, pg 885
Shapeshifter, pg 885
Shokus Video, pg 886
SonicPool, pg 892
Staylor-Made Communications Inc, pg 900
Still N' Motion, pg 901
Studio 637, pg 903
Tam Communications Inc, pg 906
TIMECODE Post Production, pg 914
Total Creative, pg 916
Twin Peaks Creative, pg 920
United Audio Video Inc, pg 921
Via Verde Productions, pg 926
VidCan Media Solutions, pg 927
Visions Plus, pg 931
Wavemaker Media Design, pg 934

COLORADO

Flashback Media Productions, pg 762
Full Spectrum Arts & Services, pg 767
Rocky Mountain Audio/Video Productions Inc, pg 876
Tatum Video, pg 907

CONNECTICUT

BRB Audiovisual Productions, pg 709
Cine-Med Inc, pg 723
CMI Media Management, pg 727
Digital Video Productions, pg 742
Geomatrix Productions, pg 770
Ironik Design & Post, pg 791
New London Media, pg 839
Powerstation Events, pg 860

DISTRICT OF COLUMBIA

Metro Teleproductions Inc (MTI), pg 824

FLORIDA

A Cut Above Video Productions Inc, pg 671
Access Media Group, pg 673
Accord Productions, pg 673
Applebox Studio, pg 687
Astoria Communications Inc, pg 691
Audacity Recording Studios, pg 693
CD ROM™ Inc, pg 718

Civins Productions Inc, pg 725
Courter Films LLC, pg 732
Easy Edit Video Inc, pg 750
Florida Digital Studios, pg 762
Hi-Tech Enterprises Inc, pg 779
The Newhouse Media Group, pg 840
ONstage, pg 846
Shooting Stars Post Inc, pg 886
Sound & Vision Communications Inc, pg 893
Sunfire Communications Inc, pg 904
Sunrise Studios, pg 904
Teach America Corp, pg 908
Tricycle Studios, pg 918
Universal Studios Florida® Production Group, pg 922
Mike Vasilinda Productions Inc, pg 925
Video Techniques Inc, pg 928
Vistamax Productions, pg 931

GEORGIA

Cinema Concepts, pg 724
The DVI Group, pg 748
ECG Productions, pg 750
Guerrilla Productions LLC, pg 774
Omega Media Group Inc, pg 845
On-Line Productions, pg 845

HAWAII

Hyperspective Studios Inc, pg 783

ILLINOIS

ABSA Films, pg 672
Advanced Audio Technology, pg 677
Airways Digital Media, pg 679
Atomic Imaging Inc/Golan Studios, pg 692
Backstar Creative Media Inc, pg 700
Breeze Productions Inc, pg 710
Captions & Subtitle Services Ltd, pg 716
Edit House Chicago, pg 750
Explore, pg 757
Extraordinary Demos/Videos, pg 757
IV Media Resources, pg 792
Manning Productions, pg 816
Mightybytes Inc, pg 827
Multimedia Marketing Group, pg 833
RADMAR Inc, pg 869
RBR Productions, pg 870
Richter Studios, pg 875
SCI Television & Creative Media LLC, pg 882
Sparkfactor, pg 896
20/20 Communications Inc, pg 920
Video Impressions, pg 928

INDIANA

Advanced Media Integration, pg 677
Bright Ideas Creative Services, pg 710
Lighthouse Photo & Video Productions, pg 807
PentaVision Communications Inc, pg 854

KENTUCKY

Audio Visual Techniques Inc, pg 695
The PPS Group, pg 860
Prosper Media Group Inc, pg 866

LOUISIANA

Launch Media, pg 804
Louisiana State University Division of Strategic Communications, pg 811
Vidox Motion Imagery, pg 930

MAINE

Headlight Audio Visual Inc, pg 777

MARYLAND

Adventure Productions LLC, pg 678
CAS Video Productions, pg 717
CPR MultiMedia Solutions, pg 732
dbF a Media Company, pg 739
DBM Communications Inc, pg 739
Kramer Communications Video Production, pg 801
Media Dimensions LLC, pg 821
Milner-Fenwick Inc, pg 828
Pro Cuts Editing Services, pg 862
Saah Video, pg 879

MASSACHUSETTS

In the Wild Productions, pg 786
Preston Productions Inc, pg 861

MICHIGAN

Blue Mouse Studio, pg 707
Digi Sign Design LLC, pg 741
Digital Image Studios LLC, pg 742
Michigan Recording Arts Institute & Technologies, pg 825
The Program Source International, pg 865
TGA Recording Co, pg 911

MINNESOTA

The ADS Group, pg 676
C Vision Productions, pg 713
House of Cinemagraphics, pg 782
MastCom, pg 819
Pro Media Productions, pg 863
Rum Jungle Media, pg 878
Worthwhile Films, pg 941

MISSOURI

Avatar Studios, pg 697
Show-Me Audio-Visual, pg 887
Studio Worx Inc, pg 903
VSG Digital Media Solutions, pg 933

MONTANA

ooLite Media LLC, pg 846

NEBRASKA

Rainbow Video Productions Inc, pg 869
Three Pillars Media, pg 913

NEVADA

Aardvark Video & Media Productions, pg 671
JCS Video Productions, pg 793
Peterson's Video Transfer Services, pg 855

NEW HAMPSHIRE

Captain Fiddle Music & Publications, pg 716
Chip Taylor Communications LLC, pg 907

DVD—Blank Distributors

VIDEO

DVD—Blank Distributors (continued)

NEW YORK

Design Audio Visual Inc, pg 741
Digital Force Ltd, pg 742
Duplication Depot Inc, pg 748
Janson Media Inc, pg 793
Mark Custom Recording Service Inc, pg 817
Women Make Movies Inc, pg 941

NORTH CAROLINA

Verbatim Americas LLC, pg 926

OHIO

Central Ohio Audio Video, pg 719
Midwest Photo Exchange, pg 827
Tri-State Audio Visual Co, pg 918

PENNSYLVANIA

Advanced AV LLC, pg 677
Bernie's Photo Center, pg 704
J E Foss Co, pg 764
Innovision Media Group, pg 788

TENNESSEE

Lowrance Sound Co Inc, pg 812
NTS ProMedia, pg 843
WTSmedia, pg 942

TEXAS

Biway Media, pg 706
CAM Audio Inc, pg 714
Replicopy Digital Media Center, pg 873
TWIST Integration Solutions Technology, pg 920

VIRGINIA

Furnace MFG, pg 767
Lee Hartman & Sons Inc, pg 805

WASHINGTON

CCI Solutions, pg 718

WISCONSIN

Audio Visual of Milwaukee Inc, pg 694

ALBERTA

Matrix Video Communications Corp (MVCC), pg 819

MANITOBA

Inland Audio Visual Ltd, pg 788

DVD—Blank Manufacturers

KENTUCKY

American Recordable Media, pg 684

NEW JERSEY

Disc Makers, pg 743
Synergem, pg 905

NEW YORK

Digital Force Ltd, pg 742

NORTH CAROLINA

Verbatim Americas LLC, pg 926

TENNESSEE

WTSmedia, pg 942

TEXAS

Adams Evidence Grade Technology Inc, pg 675

UTAH

One Stop CD Shop LLC, pg 846

DVD Duplication, *see* Duplication—DVDs

DVD Recorder & Player Distributors

ARIZONA

EAR Professional Audio/Video, pg 749

ARKANSAS

White Diamond Productions LLC, pg 937

CALIFORNIA

Ametron Audio/Video, pg 684
Associated Sound, pg 691
Be Media, pg 702
Empire Pro, pg 753
Gluskin's Custom Audio Video, pg 771
Instructional Materials & Equipment Distributors (I-Med), pg 789
JD Audio Visual Inc, pg 793
Photodyne Technologies, pg 856
Pioneer Electronics (USA) Inc, pg 857
SNAP, pg 891
Southern California Sound Image Inc, pg 895
Stanislaus AV Inc, pg 899
VMI Inc, pg 932

CONNECTICUT

Rockwell Communications Inc, pg 876

FLORIDA

Access Media Group, pg 673
Alliance Entertainment Corp (AEC) LLC, pg 680
Altel Systems Group Inc, pg 682
CD ROM™ Inc, pg 718
Digital Video Systems, pg 742
Recording Media & Equipment Inc (RM&E), pg 872

GEORGIA

Clark, pg 725
Stage Front Presentation Systems, pg 899

ILLINOIS

Dukane Corp, Audio Visual Products Division, pg 747
Quintessence Audio Ltd, pg 868
Zenith Electronics LLC, pg 945

INDIANA

Lee Co Inc, pg 805
Sensory Technologies LLC, pg 884
SHP Electronics, pg 887

KENTUCKY

NOR-COM Inc, pg 841

LOUISIANA

Techkno Integration & Design Services LLC, pg 908

MAINE

Headlight Audio Visual Inc, pg 777

MARYLAND

DSR Computer Technology Specialists Inc, pg 747
RTZ Audio Visual, pg 878

MASSACHUSETTS

Hunt's Photo & Video, pg 782
Rule Boston Camera, pg 878

MICHIGAN

Digi Sign Design LLC, pg 741
On Stage Visuals, pg 846

MINNESOTA

Alpha Video & Audio Inc, pg 682

MISSISSIPPI

Bowie Audio Visual Enterprises Inc, pg 709

MISSOURI

Modern Communications Inc, pg 828
Schiller's Audio-Visual, pg 881

NEBRASKA

ATV Research Inc, pg 692
Strong Cinema Products, pg 902

NEVADA

Aardvark Video & Media Productions, pg 671

NEW JERSEY

Alltec Stores, a Vcom IMC Company, pg 681
Samsung Electronics America, pg 879
Starlite, pg 900
Total Video Products Inc, pg 916
Wired 4 Sound Inc, pg 940

NEW YORK

Audiovox®, pg 695
Colortone Audio Visual, pg 728
Crescendo Designs Inc, pg 734
Design Audio Visual Inc, pg 741
Duplication Depot Inc, pg 748
Gaylord Archival, pg 768
General Audio-Visual Inc (GAVI), pg 769
Image Management Systems Inc, pg 785
KVL Audio Visual Services Inc, pg 802
Presentation Products Inc, pg 861
Visual Technologies Corp, pg 932
Visual Word Systems Inc, pg 932

OHIO

ITA Audio Visual Solutions, pg 791
Tri-State Audio Visual Co, pg 918
Tri-State Visual Products Inc, pg 918

PENNSYLVANIA

Advanced AV LLC, pg 677
Bernie's Photo Center, pg 704
J E Foss Co, pg 764
Vistacom Inc, pg 931

RHODE ISLAND

Shanix Inc, pg 885

TENNESSEE

Lowrance Sound Co Inc, pg 812
Technical Support Systems LLC, pg 908
Zion Music Group, pg 945

TEXAS

AVES Audio Visual Systems Inc, pg 698
Biway Media, pg 706
CAM Audio Inc, pg 714
Data Projections Inc, pg 738
Digital Display Solutions Inc, pg 742
Heffernan Audio Visual, pg 778
Replicopy Digital Media Center, pg 873
Tarpley Media Systems, pg 907

UTAH

Performance Audio LLC, pg 854

VIRGINIA

Lee Hartman & Sons Inc, pg 805

WASHINGTON

CCI Solutions, pg 718
ToteVision, pg 916

WISCONSIN

Audio Visual of Milwaukee Inc, pg 694
Safe Harbor Computers, pg 879

ALBERTA

Infosat Communications Inc, pg 787
Matrix Video Communications Corp (MVCC), pg 819
Unique Communications Ltd, pg 921

BRITISH COLUMBIA

DL Sound & Lighting Productions Ltd, pg 744

MANITOBA

Advance Pro, pg 677
Inland Audio Visual Ltd, pg 788

ONTARIO

HD Source, pg 777
SVAT Electronics, pg 905
Westbury National Show Systems Ltd, pg 936

DVD Recorder & Player Manufacturers

ARIZONA
Applied Integration Corp, pg 687

CALIFORNIA
Grande Vitesse Systems Inc (GVS), pg 773
Pioneer Electronics (USA) Inc, pg 857
TEAC America Inc, pg 908

NEW JERSEY
Emerson Radio Corp, pg 753
Samsung Electronics America, pg 879

NEW YORK
Video Technology Services Inc, pg 929

OKLAHOMA
BCD Associates Inc, pg 702

TENNESSEE
Adtec Digital Inc, pg 677

BRITISH COLUMBIA
Triad Communications Ltd, pg 918

ONTARIO
SVAT Electronics, pg 905

DVD Recorder & Player Rentals

ARIZONA
Merestone, pg 823
Video West Inc, pg 929

ARKANSAS
White Diamond Productions LLC, pg 937

CALIFORNIA
Absolute Rentals, pg 672
AGF Media Services, pg 678
Ametron Audio/Video, pg 684
Artichoke Productions, pg 690
Associated Sound, pg 691
Audio Rents, pg 693
AV Guys, pg 697
Express Media Inc, pg 757
Gluskin's Custom Audio Video, pg 771
Gold Standard Productions, pg 772
Hollywood Sound Systems, pg 781
Image Integration, pg 785
Instructional Materials & Equipment Distributors (I-Med), pg 789
JD Audio Visual Inc, pg 793
Maximus Media Inc, pg 820
Media Fabricators Inc, pg 822
Munday & Collins AV, pg 834
PSAV® Presentation Services, pg 866
Pyxis Industries Inc, pg 867
RetinaVision Productions, pg 874
Stanislaus AV Inc, pg 899
Total Creative, pg 916
Twin Peaks Creative, pg 920
VMI Inc, pg 932

Voice & Video Rentals, pg 932
Warner Bros Production Sound & Video Services, pg 934

COLORADO
Multimedia Audio Visual Inc, pg 833
Open Media Foundation, pg 846

CONNECTICUT
A/V Davey, pg 697
Videofilm Systems Inc, pg 929

FLORIDA
Accord Productions, pg 673
Paradise Show & Design Inc, pg 851
Photosound of Orlando Inc, pg 856
Universal Studios Florida® Production Group, pg 922

GEORGIA
Stage Front Presentation Systems, pg 899

HAWAII
Hawaii Sound & Vision, pg 777

ILLINOIS
AV Chicago Inc, pg 696
Backstar Creative Media Inc, pg 700
Meetinghouse Event Design & Production, pg 823
RC Communications, pg 870
Resolution Productions Group, pg 874

IOWA
Central Lighting & Equipment Inc (CLE), pg 719
Pro Video, pg 863

KENTUCKY
Audio Visual Techniques Inc, pg 695

MARYLAND
Advance Audiovisual Presentation Ltd, pg 677
CPR MultiMedia Solutions, pg 732
Event Tech, pg 756
RTZ Audio Visual, pg 878

MASSACHUSETTS
Preston Productions Inc, pg 861

MICHIGAN
Digi Sign Design LLC, pg 741
K&R All Media Productions LLC, pg 796
On Stage Visuals, pg 846

MINNESOTA
Alpha Video & Audio Inc, pg 682

MISSISSIPPI
Bowie Audio Visual Enterprises Inc, pg 709

MISSOURI
Schiller's Audio-Visual, pg 881
Show-Me Audio-Visual, pg 887

NEBRASKA
Dog & Pony Productions Inc, pg 744

NEVADA
JCS Video Productions, pg 793

NEW JERSEY
Audio Visual Dynamics®, pg 694
Color Leasing Studios, pg 727
Euro-Pacific Film & Video Productions Inc, pg 756
International Audio Visual Inc, pg 790
Starlite, pg 900
Tele-Measurements Inc, pg 910
Wired 4 Sound Inc, pg 940

NEW MEXICO
Production Outfitters, pg 864

NEW YORK
Colortone Audio Visual, pg 728
Design Audio Visual Inc, pg 741
HB-Content, pg 777
Hello World Communications, pg 778
KVL Audio Visual Services Inc, pg 802
PrimaLux Video Inc, pg 862
Production Central, pg 863
Visual Technologies Corp, pg 932
Visual Word Systems Inc, pg 932

NORTH CAROLINA
AV Connections Inc, pg 697
Digital Rain LLC, pg 742
On Location North Carolina, pg 846
Take One Productions Ltd, pg 906

NORTH DAKOTA
Media Productions, pg 822

OHIO
Vista Color Imaging Inc, pg 931

OKLAHOMA
PDC Productions, pg 852

OREGON
Rose City Sound, pg 877

PENNSYLVANIA
Audio Visual Communications Inc, pg 694
FirstGeneration Audio/Visual Services, pg 761
FMP Media Solutions Inc, pg 763
Innovision Media Group, pg 788
The Videohouse Inc, pg 929

TENNESSEE
Love Shack Recording Studios, pg 811
Technical Support Systems LLC, pg 908

TEXAS
Alford Media Services, pg 680
Bright Star Productions Inc, pg 710
Heffernan Audio Visual, pg 778
Stage Directions, pg 898

VERMONT
Dark Star Lighting & Production, pg 737

VIRGINIA
Lee Hartman & Sons Inc, pg 805
Quince Imaging Inc, pg 868
StageSound, pg 899

WISCONSIN
Audio Visual of Milwaukee Inc, pg 694
USAV Group Inc, pg 923

PUERTO RICO
Stage Crew Audiovisual Inc, pg 898

ALBERTA
Allstar Show Industries Inc, pg 681
Unique Communications Ltd, pg 921

BRITISH COLUMBIA
DL Sound & Lighting Productions Ltd, pg 744

MANITOBA
Inland Audio Visual Ltd, pg 788

ONTARIO
HD Source, pg 777
Wanted! Sound + Picture, pg 933
Westbury National Show Systems Ltd, pg 936

QUEBEC
Group PVP, pg 774

SASKATCHEWAN
plan9films, pg 857

DVD Recorder & Player Repairs

CALIFORNIA
Gluskin's Custom Audio Video, pg 771
VMI Inc, pg 932

CONNECTICUT
A/V Davey, pg 697

FLORIDA
ELC Sales & Service Inc, pg 752
Hi-Tech Enterprises Inc, pg 779

GEORGIA
Stage Front Presentation Systems, pg 899

ILLINOIS
Midwest Digital Corp, pg 827

KENTUCKY
NOR-COM Inc, pg 841

MICHIGAN
TEL Systems LLC, pg 909

MISSOURI
Schiller's Audio-Visual, pg 881

VIDEO

DVD Recorder & Player Repairs (continued)

NEW JERSEY

Starlite, pg 900

NEW YORK

Video Technology Services Inc, pg 929
Visual Technologies Corp, pg 932

OHIO

Tri-State Audio Visual Co, pg 918

OREGON

All Service Musical Electronics Repair, pg 680

TENNESSEE

Technical Support Systems LLC, pg 908

TEXAS

Tarpley Media Systems, pg 907

ALBERTA

Infosat Communications Inc, pg 787

MANITOBA

Inland Audio Visual Ltd, pg 788

ONTARIO

HD Source, pg 777
Westbury National Show Systems Ltd, pg 936

Edit Controller Distributors

ARIZONA

EAR Professional Audio/Video, pg 749

CALIFORNIA

Ametron Audio/Video, pg 684
BigFoot Mobile Systems, pg 705
BroadcastStore.com, pg 711
Christy's Editorial, pg 723
Diaquest, pg 741
JLCooper Electronics, pg 794
MediaPOINTE, pg 823
SNAP, pg 891
VMI Inc, pg 932
VTP Inc, pg 933

COLORADO

Spectrum Audio Visual Services, pg 897

FLORIDA

Access Media Group, pg 673
Digital Video Systems, pg 742
Harris Corp, pg 776
Hi-Tech Enterprises Inc, pg 779
Midtown Video Inc, pg 827
ONstage, pg 846
Recording Media & Equipment Inc (RM&E), pg 872

GEORGIA

Stage Front Presentation Systems, pg 899

HAWAII

The Audio Visual Co (AVCO), pg 694

ILLINOIS

Allen Visual Systems Inc, pg 680
Quintessence Audio Ltd, pg 868

INDIANA

Sensory Technologies LLC, pg 884

KENTUCKY

Barney Miller's Inc, pg 827
NOR-COM Inc, pg 841

MAINE

Headlight Audio Visual Inc, pg 777

MARYLAND

Noventri, pg 843

MASSACHUSETTS

Rule Boston Camera, pg 878

MICHIGAN

Digi Sign Design LLC, pg 741
TEL Systems LLC, pg 909

MINNESOTA

Alpha Video & Audio Inc, pg 682

MISSOURI

Modern Communications Inc, pg 828
Schiller's Audio-Visual, pg 881
Southwest Audio-Visual Inc, pg 895

NEBRASKA

VSA Inc, pg 933

NEVADA

Aardvark Video & Media Productions, pg 671

NEW JERSEY

AV Bluebook, pg 696
Diversified, pg 744
HamiltonBuhl, pg 775
MCCOM Inc, pg 820
Starlite, pg 900
Tele-Measurements Inc, pg 910
Total Video Products Inc, pg 916
Wired 4 Sound Inc, pg 940

NEW YORK

Audio-Video Corp, pg 694
B&H Photo Video, pg 701
Markertek Video Supply, pg 817
Neptune Photo Inc, pg 838
Visual Technologies Corp, pg 932
Visual Word Systems Inc, pg 932

OHIO

ITA Audio Visual Solutions, pg 791
Tri-State Audio Visual Co, pg 918

PENNSYLVANIA

Advanced AV LLC, pg 677
Clair Companies, pg 725

J E Foss Co, pg 764
Innovision Media Group, pg 788
The Lerro Corp, pg 806
Vistacom Inc, pg 931

TENNESSEE

Lowrance Sound Co Inc, pg 812
Technical Support Systems LLC, pg 908
Zion Music Group, pg 945

TEXAS

AVES Audio Visual Systems Inc, pg 698
Biway Media, pg 706
Pro Video & Film Equipment Co Inc, pg 863
Videotex Systems Inc, pg 930

VIRGINIA

Lee Hartman & Sons Inc, pg 805

WISCONSIN

Audio Visual of Milwaukee Inc, pg 694
Full Compass Systems, pg 767
Safe Harbor Computers, pg 879

ALBERTA

Infosat Communications Inc, pg 787
Matrix Video Communications Corp (MVCC), pg 819

BRITISH COLUMBIA

Commercial Electronics Ltd, pg 728

ONTARIO

Soundmaster Group, pg 894

Edit Controller Manufacturers

CALIFORNIA

BUF Technology, pg 712
Diaquest, pg 741
FutureVideo, pg 767
JLCooper Electronics, pg 794
QRS Software Services, pg 867
TV Pro Gear, pg 919

FLORIDA

Florical Systems Inc, pg 762

MINNESOTA

Vaddio, pg 924

MISSOURI

GlobalStreams™ Corp, pg 771

BRITISH COLUMBIA

Triad Communications Ltd, pg 918

ONTARIO

Soundmaster Group, pg 894

Edit Controller Rentals

ARIZONA

Merestone, pg 823
Video West Inc, pg 929

CALIFORNIA

Ametron Audio/Video, pg 684
Artichoke Productions, pg 690
Bexel, an NEP Broadcast Services Company, pg 704
BUF Technology, pg 712
Express Media Inc, pg 757
Lynch Communications, pg 813
McCune Audio-Video-Lighting, pg 821
Munday & Collins AV, pg 834
RetinaVision Productions, pg 874
SNAP, pg 891
Total Creative, pg 916
Twin Peaks Creative, pg 920
VMI Inc, pg 932

COLORADO

Spectrum Audio Visual Services, pg 897

FLORIDA

Access Media Group, pg 673
Budget Video Rentals, pg 712
Midtown Video Inc, pg 827
ONstage, pg 846

GEORGIA

ON Services, a GES Company, pg 846
Stage Front Presentation Systems, pg 899

ILLINOIS

Airways Digital Media, pg 679
Allen Visual Systems Inc, pg 680
Backstar Creative Media Inc, pg 700
Resolution Productions Group, pg 874

KENTUCKY

Audio Visual Techniques Inc, pg 695

MARYLAND

CPR MultiMedia Solutions, pg 732

MASSACHUSETTS

Preston Productions Inc, pg 861
Small Planet Communications Inc, pg 890

MICHIGAN

Digi Sign Design LLC, pg 741
K&R All Media Productions LLC, pg 796
TEL Systems LLC, pg 909

MINNESOTA

Alpha Video & Audio Inc, pg 682

MISSOURI

Show-Me Audio-Visual, pg 887
Southwest Audio-Visual Inc, pg 895

NEVADA

JCS Video Productions, pg 793

NEW JERSEY

PLS Staging, pg 858
Starlite, pg 900
Tele-Measurements Inc, pg 910
Wired 4 Sound Inc, pg 940

VIDEO

Editing—Computerized (continued)

CONNECTICUT (continued)

Powerstation Events, pg 860
Presence Studios, pg 861
Bret Stern Productions, pg 900
UConn Health Multimedia Services, pg 920
The Video Messenger Co, pg 928

DISTRICT OF COLUMBIA

Hillmann & Carr Inc, pg 780
Interface Media Group, pg 789
Metro Teleproductions Inc (MTI), pg 824
Yellow Cat Productions Inc, pg 944

FLORIDA

A Cut Above Video Productions Inc, pg 671
Access Media Group, pg 673
Accord Productions, pg 673
ACT Productions, pg 675
Adrenaline Films, pg 676
Applebox Studio, pg 687
Audacity Recording Studios, pg 693
AVI-SPL, pg 698
CD ROM™ Inc, pg 718
Civins Productions Inc, pg 725
Communications Concepts Inc (CCI), pg 729
Courter Films LLC, pg 732
DME Studios, pg 744
Easy Edit Video Inc, pg 750
Florida Digital Studios, pg 762
Gemstone Media Inc, pg 769
Glanz Technologies Inc, pg 771
Harmon's Audio-Visual Services, pg 776
Hi-Tech Enterprises Inc, pg 779
Knowles Video Inc (KVI), pg 800
The Newhouse Media Group, pg 840
ONstage, pg 846
Photosound of Orlando Inc, pg 856
Shooting Stars Post Inc, pg 886
Sound & Vision Communications Inc, pg 893
Sunfire Communications Inc, pg 904
Sunrise Studios, pg 904
Tricycle Studios, pg 918
Universal Studios Florida® Production Group, pg 922
Mike Vasilinda Productions Inc, pg 925
Video Techniques Inc, pg 928
Vistamax Productions, pg 931

GEORGIA

Beachwood Productions, pg 702
Beast Atlanta, pg 703
The DVI Group, pg 748
ECG Productions, pg 750
First Cut Communications LLC, pg 761
Guerrilla Productions LLC, pg 774
Malcolm Neal Productions, pg 837
Omega Media Group Inc, pg 845
On-Line Productions, pg 845
Staging Directions Inc, pg 899
Video Copy Services Inc, pg 927
WATL-TV Inc, pg 934

HAWAII

FilmWorks Pacific, pg 761
Hyperspective Studios Inc, pg 783

1013 Integrated, pg 911
Tropical Visions Video Inc, pg 918

IDAHO

KTVB-TV, pg 802
Brad Shaw Productions Inc, pg 885
Wide Eye Productions, pg 938

ILLINOIS

Abacus Group of Saint Louis LLC, pg 672
ABSA Films, pg 672
Airways Digital Media, pg 679
AnswersMedia, pg 686
Atomic Imaging Inc/Golan Studios, pg 692
Backstar Creative Media Inc, pg 700
Beatty TeleVisual Productions, pg 703
Big Shoulders Digital Video Productions, pg 705
Breeze Productions Inc, pg 710
Edit House Chicago, pg 750
Explore, pg 757
Freeman Pictures Inc, pg 765
IV Media Resources, pg 792
Manning Productions, pg 816
Mightybytes Inc, pg 827
Mimi Productions, pg 828
Optimus, pg 847
Rob Orr Productions Ltd, pg 848
Pepper Group, pg 854
PSAV® Presentation Services (Hotel Services Division), pg 866
RADMAR Inc, pg 869
Richter Studios, pg 875
SCI Television & Creative Media LLC, pg 882
Sound/Video Impressions Inc, pg 894
Sparkfactor, pg 896
Tele-Time Systems, pg 910
20/20 Communications Inc, pg 920
Video I-D Teleproductions Inc, pg 928
Video Impressions, pg 928
WEEK TV, pg 935
WIFR-TV, pg 938

INDIANA

A-V-A Video Productions, pg 671
Advanced Media Integration, pg 677
Bright Ideas Creative Services, pg 710
Educational Video Group Inc, pg 751
Lakeshore Public Media, pg 803
Lighthouse Photo & Video Productions, pg 807
PentaVision Communications Inc, pg 854

IOWA

Educational Technology & Media Services, pg 751
Iowa State University-Information Technology Services, pg 791
Kuhn Productions LLC, pg 802

KANSAS

KAKE-TV, pg 796

KENTUCKY

Audio Visual Techniques Inc, pg 695
Horizon Films & Media LLC, pg 781
Idle Minds Productions Inc, pg 784
The Media Collaboratory, pg 821

The PPS Group, pg 860
Prosper Media Group Inc, pg 866
WKYT-TV, pg 940

LOUISIANA

Digital FX Inc, pg 742
Launch Media, pg 804
Louisiana State University Division of Strategic Communications, pg 811
Moxie Media, pg 832
Vidox Motion Imagery, pg 930
WVLA-TV, pg 942
YES Productions, pg 944

MAINE

Films by Huey, pg 760
Headlight Audio Visual Inc, pg 777
WGME-TV, pg 936

MARYLAND

Adventure Productions LLC, pg 678
Carpel Video Inc, pg 717
CAS Video Productions, pg 717
CPR MultiMedia Solutions, pg 732
CSPMedia.com, pg 735
dbF a Media Company, pg 739
DBM Communications Inc, pg 739
Kramer Communications Video Production, pg 801
Media Dimensions LLC, pg 821
Mobile-Video Productions Inc, pg 828
Pro Cuts Editing Services, pg 862
Producers Video, pg 863
Quality Film & Video, pg 868
Sheffield Audio/Video Productions, pg 885
Sign Media Inc, pg 887

MASSACHUSETTS

Award Productions Inc, pg 699
Boston Productions Inc (BPI), pg 709
Capron Lighting & Sound Co Inc, pg 716
CommCreative, pg 728
Cramer, pg 732
Documentary Educational Resources Inc, pg 744
Extreme Reach Inc, pg 757
HOME Inc, pg 781
In the Wild Productions, pg 786
Monadnock Media Inc, pg 829
Northern Light Productions (NLP), pg 842
Penfield Productions Ltd, pg 853
Preston Productions Inc, pg 861
Real Cool Productions, pg 871
Small Planet Communications Inc, pg 890
TR Productions, pg 916
VideoLink Inc, an AVI-SPL company, pg 929

MICHIGAN

Digi Sign Design LLC, pg 741
Digital Image Studios LLC, pg 742
K&R's Recording Studios Inc, pg 796
Lawrence Productions Inc, pg 804
Michigan Recording Arts Institute & Technologies, pg 825
On Stage Visuals, pg 846
The Program Source International, pg 865
RingSide Creative, pg 875
TGA Recording Co, pg 911
The Transfer Zone®, pg 917
WGVU TV, pg 936

MINNESOTA

The ADS Group, pg 676
Badiyan Inc, pg 700
BeyerSound & Essay Audio, pg 705
Big Event Productions LLC, pg 705
Blue Earth Pictures, pg 707
GMI Productions, pg 771
House of Cinemagraphics, pg 782
MastCom, pg 819
Media Loft Inc, pg 822
Rum Jungle Media, pg 878
Worthwhile Films, pg 941

MISSOURI

Avatar Studios, pg 697
Communitronics Corp, pg 729
Conference Technologies Inc, pg 730
KPLR-TV, pg 801
Show-Me Audio-Visual, pg 887
StoryTrack, pg 901
Studio Worx Inc, pg 903

MONTANA

High Plains Films, pg 779
ooLite Media LLC, pg 846

NEBRASKA

B & B Video Productions Inc, pg 700
Rainbow Video Productions Inc, pg 869
Three Pillars Media, pg 913

NEVADA

Aardvark Video & Media Productions, pg 671
DVDs4Less, pg 748
Encore Event Technologies LLC, pg 754
JCS Video Productions, pg 793
Lefco Video Services Inc, pg 806
Peterson's Video Transfer Services, pg 855

NEW HAMPSHIRE

Apertura, pg 686
Chip Taylor Communications LLC, pg 907
The Troupe, pg 918

NEW JERSEY

AJS Events, pg 679
Allegro Productions Inc, pg 680
Audio Visual Associates, pg 694
Broadcast Center Studios, pg 710
CD Meyer Inc, pg 718
CFP Video Productions Inc, pg 720
Color Leasing Studios, pg 727
Creative Video, pg 734
Diversified, pg 744
Early Films, pg 749
Euro-Pacific Film & Video Productions Inc, pg 756
Laurel Video Productions, pg 804
MediaMix Inc, pg 822
Megavideo LLC, pg 823
MiB MediaWorks, pg 825
Midnight Media Group Inc, pg 827
Ray Mueller Productions, pg 833
Optisonics Productions, pg 847
Suede Interactive, pg 903
Tele-Measurements Inc, pg 910
Telequest Inc, pg 910
VCSvideo, pg 925
Video Corporation of America (VCA), pg 927
Video Ideas Productions, pg 928

VIDEO

Editing—Computerized (continued)

MANITOBA

Lank/Beach Productions Inc, pg 803
Spectra Video Productions Ltd, pg 897

NEWFOUNDLAND AND LABRADOR

Vidcraft Productions Ltd, pg 927

NORTHWEST TERRITORIES

Yellowknife Films Inc, pg 944

ONTARIO

ADS Media, pg 677
Canamedia Inc, pg 715
GAPC (General Assembly Production Centre), pg 768
Image Video Services & Productions, pg 785
JFB Communications, pg 794
Marblemedia, pg 816
Metalworks Recording Studios Inc, pg 824
RB Productions, pg 870
Silver Creek Media Inc, pg 888
Video Excellence Productions, pg 927
VO2 Mix Audio Post, pg 932
Westbury National Show Systems Ltd, pg 936

QUEBEC

Group PVP, pg 774

Editing Equipment Distributors

ARIZONA

EAR Professional Audio/Video, pg 749
Troxell-CDI, pg 918

ARKANSAS

White Diamond Productions LLC, pg 937

CALIFORNIA

Advanced Systems Group LLC, pg 677
Ametron Audio/Video, pg 684
Audio/Video Supply Inc, pg 694
Band Pro Film & Digital Inc, pg 701
BigFoot Mobile Systems, pg 705
BroadcastStore.com, pg 711
Christy's Editorial, pg 723
Diaquest, pg 741
Gluskin's Custom Audio Video, pg 771
Media Fabricators Inc, pg 822
MediaPOINTE, pg 823
Point of View Productions, pg 858
Promax Systems, pg 865
SNAP, pg 891
SSL Industries Inc, pg 898
Stanislaus AV Inc, pg 899
VMI Inc, pg 932
VTP Inc, pg 933

COLORADO

G W Hannaway & Associates, pg 775
Spectrum Audio Visual Services, pg 897
Stanco Sales LLC, pg 899

CONNECTICUT

MAVCO, pg 820

FLORIDA

Access Media Group, pg 673
AVI-SPL, pg 698
Digital Video Systems, pg 742
Enhanced View Services Inc, pg 754
Harris Corp, pg 776
Hi-Tech Enterprises Inc, pg 779
Midtown Video Inc, pg 827
ONstage, pg 846
Recording Media & Equipment Inc (RM&E), pg 872
Tallahassee Audio Visual, pg 906

GEORGIA

Convergent Media Systems, pg 731
Stage Front Presentation Systems, pg 899

HAWAII

The Audio Visual Co (AVCO), pg 694

ILLINOIS

Allen Visual Systems Inc, pg 680
Joseph Electronics, pg 795
Photoflex Inc, pg 856
Quintessence Audio Ltd, pg 868
RC Communications, pg 870
Research Technology International (RTI), pg 873
Tele-Time Systems, pg 910

INDIANA

Lee Co Inc, pg 805
Sensory Technologies LLC, pg 884

KENTUCKY

Axxis Leasing Inc, pg 700
Barney Miller's Inc, pg 827
NOR-COM Inc, pg 841

MAINE

Headlight Audio Visual Inc, pg 777

MARYLAND

Noventri, pg 843
RTZ Audio Visual, pg 878

MASSACHUSETTS

Avid Technology Inc, pg 698
Integrated Solutions Group, pg 789
Psychsoft Inc, pg 866
Rule Boston Camera, pg 878

MICHIGAN

ASC Systems, pg 690
Digi Sign Design LLC, pg 741
TEL Systems LLC, pg 909

MINNESOTA

Alpha Video & Audio Inc, pg 682
AVI Systems, pg 698
Cinequipt Inc, pg 724

MISSISSIPPI

Bowie Audio Visual Enterprises Inc, pg 709
Jasper Ewing & Sons Inc, pg 757
MFJ Enterprises Inc, pg 825

MISSOURI

Communitronics Corp, pg 729
Conference Technologies Inc, pg 730
ITC, pg 791
Modern Communications Inc, pg 828
Schiller's Audio-Visual, pg 881
Southwest Audio-Visual Inc, pg 895

NEBRASKA

VSA Inc, pg 933

NEVADA

Aardvark Video & Media Productions, pg 671

NEW JERSEY

AlltecPro, pg 681
Audio Visual Dynamics®, pg 694
AV Bluebook, pg 696
Comprehensive Cable & Connectivity Co, pg 729
Diversified, pg 744
Euro-Pacific Film & Video Productions Inc, pg 756
G&G Technologies Inc, pg 768
HamiltonBuhl, pg 775
MCCOM Inc, pg 820
MiB MediaWorks, pg 825
PatchAmp, pg 852
Starlite, pg 900
SYMCO Inc, pg 905
Tele-Measurements Inc, pg 910
Total Video Products Inc, pg 916
Video Corporation of America (VCA), pg 927
Wired 4 Sound Inc, pg 940

NEW YORK

Adwar Video, pg 678
Audio-Video Corp, pg 694
AV Workshop, pg 697
B&H Photo Video, pg 701
Gaylord Archival, pg 768
Indigo Productions, pg 787
Long Island Video Enterprises Live Inc, pg 811
Markertek Video Supply, pg 817
Neptune Photo Inc, pg 838
TecNec Distributing, pg 909
Tri-Ed Distribution Inc, pg 918
Visual Technologies Corp, pg 932

NORTH CAROLINA

Camcor Inc, pg 715
Crispin Corp, pg 734
Strategic Connections, pg 901

OHIO

ITA Audio Visual Solutions, pg 791
iVideo Technologies, pg 792
Tri-State Audio Visual Co, pg 918
Visual Products Inc, pg 931

PENNSYLVANIA

Advanced AV LLC, pg 677
Audio Visions Inc, pg 694
Bernie's Photo Center, pg 704
Clair Companies, pg 725
J E Foss Co, pg 764
Innovision Media Group, pg 788

The Lerro Corp, pg 806
Morefield Communications Inc, pg 830
Vistacom Inc, pg 931
Visual Sound Inc, pg 931

TENNESSEE

Lowrance Sound Co Inc, pg 812
Technical Support Systems LLC, pg 908
Zion Music Group, pg 945

TEXAS

Audio Visual Technologies Group (AVTG), pg 695
AVES Audio Visual Systems Inc, pg 698
Biway Media, pg 706
Pro Video & Film Equipment Co Inc, pg 863
Videotex Systems Inc, pg 930

UTAH

RIA Corp, pg 874
TV Specialists Inc, pg 919
Webb Audio Visual, pg 935

VIRGINIA

Boitnott Visual Communications Corp (BVC), pg 708
Cybernetics, pg 736
Lee Hartman & Sons Inc, pg 805
The Whitlock Group, pg 937

WASHINGTON

Macrosystem US Inc, pg 814

WISCONSIN

Audio Visual of Milwaukee Inc, pg 694
Camera Corner Connecting Point, pg 715
Demco Inc, pg 740
Full Compass Systems, pg 767
Safe Harbor Computers, pg 879

ALBERTA

Matrix Video Communications Corp (MVCC), pg 819

BRITISH COLUMBIA

Commercial Electronics Ltd, pg 728

ONTARIO

HD Source, pg 777
Majortech Inc, pg 815
Nationwide Audio Visual Co, pg 837
Soundmaster Group, pg 894

QUEBEC

Panavideo Inc, pg 850

Editing Equipment Manufacturers

CALIFORNIA

BUF Technology, pg 712
Diaquest, pg 741
FutureVideo, pg 767
Horita Co Inc, pg 781
Hotronic Inc, pg 782
Sony Electronics Inc, pg 893
TimeLogic Corp, pg 914
TV Pro Gear, pg 919
VITEC Multimedia, pg 932

FLORIDA

Hi-Tech Enterprises Inc, pg 779

MASSACHUSETTS

Avid Technology Inc, pg 698
Psychsoft Inc, pg 866

MISSISSIPPI

MFJ Enterprises Inc, pg 825

MISSOURI

GlobalStreams™ Corp, pg 771

NEW JERSEY

CELCO, pg 719
Pro-Tape & Specialities Inc, pg 863

NEW MEXICO

Burst Electronics Inc, pg 713

NEW YORK

Laird Digital Cinema, pg 803
Judson Rosebush Co Inc, pg 877
Sima Products Corp, pg 888
TBC Consoles Inc, pg 907

PENNSYLVANIA

Prime Image Inc, pg 862

TEXAS

Biway Media, pg 706

WASHINGTON

Macrosystem US Inc, pg 814

BRITISH COLUMBIA

Triad Communications Ltd, pg 918

ONTARIO

Corel Corp, pg 731
Soundmaster Group, pg 894

QUEBEC

Matrox Video Products Group,
  pg 819
Skotel Corp, pg 890

Editing Equipment Rentals

ALASKA

Connections Film & Video Inc,
  pg 731

ARIZONA

Arizona Cine Equipment, pg 688
Merestone, pg 823
Metropolitan Audio-Visual Inc,
  pg 824
Rodeo Video Inc, pg 876

ARKANSAS

White Diamond Productions LLC,
  pg 937

CALIFORNIA

Absolute Rentals, pg 672
Access Video in Berkeley, pg 673
Advanced Media LLC, pg 677
Alliant Event Services, pg 681
AlphaDogs Inc, pg 682
Ametron Audio/Video, pg 684
Artichoke Productions, pg 690

Bexel, an NEP Broadcast Services
  Company, pg 704
Big Door, pg 705
Blue Lotus Temple Studio, pg 707
BUF Technology, pg 712
Christy's Editorial, pg 723
Deck Hand Inc, pg 740
The Dreaming Tree, pg 746
Express Media Inc, pg 757
First Camera, pg 761
FJ Productions Inc, pg 762
Flip 2 Media Inc, pg 762
Goal Productions, pg 772
Kaboom Productions, pg 796
Lynch Communications, pg 813
Main Street Media Inc, pg 815
Maximus Media Inc, pg 820
McCune Audio-Video-Lighting,
  pg 821
Media Fabricators Inc, pg 822
Munday & Collins AV, pg 834
New Circuit Films LLC, pg 839
Prime Cut Productions, pg 862
Reality Check Systems, pg 871
RetinaVision Productions, pg 874
Screen Door Entertainment Inc,
  pg 882
SNAP, pg 891
Synthesizer Rental Service, pg 906
Timestream Video, pg 914
Total Creative, pg 916
Twin Peaks Creative, pg 920
Universal Studios, pg 922
VMI Inc, pg 932
Voice & Video Rentals, pg 932

COLORADO

Daylight Productions & Rentals,
  pg 739
Multimedia Audio Visual Inc,
  pg 833
Open Media Foundation, pg 846
Spectrum Audio Visual Services,
  pg 897

CONNECTICUT

Videofilm Systems Inc, pg 929

FLORIDA

Access Media Group, pg 673
Glanz Technologies Inc, pg 771
Industrial Strength Inc, pg 787
Jordan Klein Film & Video (JKFV),
  pg 795
Midtown Video Inc, pg 827
National Teleproductions Inc,
  pg 837
ONstage, pg 846
Paradise Show & Design Inc,
  pg 851
Photosound of Orlando Inc, pg 856

GEORGIA

Convergent Media Systems, pg 731
ECG Productions, pg 750
ON Services, a GES Company,
  pg 846
Stage Front Presentation Systems,
  pg 899

HAWAII

Sight & Sound Studios, pg 887

ILLINOIS

Airways Digital Media, pg 679
Allen Visual Systems Inc, pg 680
Atomic Imaging Inc/Golan Studios,
  pg 692
Backstar Creative Media Inc,
  pg 700

Beatty TeleVisual Productions,
  pg 703
PSAV® Presentation Services
  (Hotel Services Division), pg 866
Resolution Productions Group,
  pg 874
SCI Television & Creative Media
  LLC, pg 882
Tele-Time Systems, pg 910

INDIANA

Advanced Media Integration, pg 677

KENTUCKY

Audio Visual Techniques Inc,
  pg 695
The PPS Group, pg 860

LOUISIANA

Digital FX Inc, pg 742
Moxie Media, pg 832
Pace Systems, pg 849

MARYLAND

CPR MultiMedia Solutions, pg 732
Kramer Communications Video
  Production, pg 801
Producers Video, pg 863
Quality Film & Video, pg 868
RTZ Audio Visual, pg 878

MASSACHUSETTS

Capron Lighting & Sound Co Inc,
  pg 716
Green Mountain Post Films (GMP),
  pg 774
HOME Inc, pg 781
massAV, pg 819
Preston Productions Inc, pg 861
Small Planet Communications Inc,
  pg 890

MICHIGAN

City Events Group, pg 725
Digi Sign Design LLC, pg 741
K&R All Media Productions LLC,
  pg 796
K&R's Recording Studios Inc,
  pg 796
Madonna University Information
  Technology, pg 814
TEL Systems LLC, pg 909

MINNESOTA

Alpha Video & Audio Inc, pg 682
AVI Systems, pg 698
Cinequipt Inc, pg 724
House of Cinemagraphics, pg 782

MISSISSIPPI

Bowie Audio Visual Enterprises Inc,
  pg 709

MISSOURI

Schiller's Audio-Visual, pg 881
Show-Me Audio-Visual, pg 887
Southwest Audio-Visual Inc, pg 895
Switch, pg 905

NEVADA

GES Audio Visual, pg 770
JCS Video Productions, pg 793
Lefco Video Services Inc, pg 806
Tanglewood Productions, pg 907

NEW HAMPSHIRE

Apertura, pg 686

NEW JERSEY

Audio Visual Dynamics®, pg 694
CFP Video Productions Inc, pg 720
Euro-Pacific Film & Video
  Productions Inc, pg 756
MediaMix Inc, pg 822
MiB MediaWorks, pg 825
PLS Staging, pg 858
Starlite, pg 900
Suede Interactive, pg 903
Video Corporation of America
  (VCA), pg 927
Wired 4 Sound Inc, pg 940

NEW MEXICO

Production Outfitters, pg 864

NEW YORK

Ace Video, pg 674
Adwar Video, pg 678
All Mobile Video Inc, pg 680
AV Workshop, pg 697
Big Foot Productions Inc, pg 705
CMI Communications, pg 727
Design Audio Visual Inc, pg 741
Downtown Community Television
  Center (DCTV), pg 746
HB-Content, pg 777
Hello World Communications,
  pg 778
Manhattan Center Studios Inc,
  pg 816
PrimaLux Video Inc, pg 862
Rafik, pg 869
Tri-Ed Distribution Inc, pg 918
The Visual Studies Workshop
  (VSW), pg 931
Visual Technologies Corp, pg 932

NORTH CAROLINA

The Communications Group Inc,
  pg 729
Duke Media Services, pg 747
Moving Pictures, pg 832
On Location North Carolina, pg 846
Special Event Services, pg 896
Strategic Connections, pg 901
Take One Productions Ltd, pg 906

NORTH DAKOTA

Media Productions, pg 822

OHIO

CET, pg 720
iVideo Technologies, pg 792
Lyon Video Inc, pg 813
Mills James Productions, pg 828
R&B Communications Inc, pg 870
Vista Color Imaging Inc, pg 931

OREGON

Northwest Film Center, pg 842

PENNSYLVANIA

Argentine Productions Inc, pg 688
FMP Media Solutions Inc, pg 763
Innovision Media Group, pg 788
Muderick Media, pg 833
Producers Management Television
  (PMTV), pg 863
Rahlic Publishing Co, pg 869
The Videohouse Inc, pg 929
Visual Sound Inc, pg 931

SOUTH CAROLINA

Genesis Creative, pg 769
Sound & Images Inc, pg 893

VIDEO

Editing Equipment Rentals (continued)

TENNESSEE

Memphis Communications Corp, pg 823
Russ Sturgeon Productions/RSVP, pg 903
Technical Support Systems LLC, pg 908

TEXAS

JSAV, pg 795
Earl Miller Productions Inc, pg 827
Phillips Media Source, pg 855
South Coast Film & Video, pg 895
Stage Directions, pg 898
Texcam Inc, pg 911
Video Perspective, pg 928

UTAH

TV Specialists Inc, pg 919
Webb Audio Visual, pg 935

VERMONT

Marlboro Productions, pg 817

VIRGINIA

Boitnott Visual Communications Corp (BVC), pg 708
CVW Event Productions, pg 736
Lee Hartman & Sons Inc, pg 805
The Whitlock Group, pg 937

WASHINGTON

Kostov Productions, pg 801
Victory Studios, pg 927

WEST VIRGINIA

Blackwater Video Productions, pg 707

WISCONSIN

Camera Corner Connecting Point, pg 715
Full Compass Systems, pg 767
University of Wisconsin-Oshkosh Radio-TV-Film Dept, pg 923
USAV Group Inc, pg 923
Wisconsin Public Television, pg 940

WYOMING

Bridger Productions Inc, pg 710

PUERTO RICO

Stage Crew Audiovisual Inc, pg 898

ALBERTA

Cine Audio Visual Sales & Service Ltd, pg 723
Global TV, pg 771
Matrix Video Communications Corp (MVCC), pg 819

BRITISH COLUMBIA

Commercial Electronics Ltd, pg 728
Video Out Distribution, pg 928

ONTARIO

GAPC (General Assembly Production Centre), pg 768
HD Source, pg 777

JIB Shots Equipment Inc, pg 794
RB Productions, pg 870

QUEBEC

Group PVP, pg 774
Kerrigan Productions Inc, pg 798
Panavideo Inc, pg 850

SASKATCHEWAN

plan9films, pg 857

Editing Equipment Repairs

CALIFORNIA

Advanced Media LLC, pg 677
Advanced Systems Group LLC, pg 677
Ametron Audio/Video, pg 684
BigFoot Mobile Systems, pg 705
BroadcastStore.com, pg 711
Christy's Editorial, pg 723
Effective Engineering Inc, pg 751
Gluskin's Custom Audio Video, pg 771
SSL Industries Inc, pg 898
Technical Services, pg 908
VMI Inc, pg 932

FLORIDA

ELC Sales & Service Inc, pg 752
Glanz Technologies Inc, pg 771
Hi-Tech Enterprises Inc, pg 779
Midtown Video Inc, pg 827

GEORGIA

Stage Front Presentation Systems, pg 899

ILLINOIS

Allen Visual Systems Inc, pg 680
Beatty TeleVisual Productions, pg 703
Midwest Digital Corp, pg 827
On Site Video, pg 846
RC Communications, pg 870
Tele-Time Systems, pg 910

KENTUCKY

Axxis Leasing Inc, pg 700
NOR-COM Inc, pg 841

MARYLAND

Noventri, pg 843
RTZ Audio Visual, pg 878

MASSACHUSETTS

Capron Lighting & Sound Co Inc, pg 716
Integrated Solutions Group, pg 789

MICHIGAN

TEL Systems LLC, pg 909

MINNESOTA

Alpha Video & Audio Inc, pg 682
AVI Systems, pg 698

MISSOURI

Southwest Audio-Visual Inc, pg 895

NEW YORK

Ace Video, pg 674
Adwar Video, pg 678
Tri-Ed Distribution Inc, pg 918
Visual Technologies Corp, pg 932

NORTH CAROLINA

Camcor Inc, pg 715
Strategic Connections, pg 901

OHIO

ITA Audio Visual Solutions, pg 791
iVideo Technologies, pg 792

PENNSYLVANIA

Audio Visions Inc, pg 694

TENNESSEE

Memphis Communications Corp, pg 823
Technical Support Systems LLC, pg 908

TEXAS

Biway Media, pg 706
Pro Video & Film Equipment Co Inc, pg 863

UTAH

RIA Corp, pg 874
TV Specialists Inc, pg 919

VIRGINIA

Boitnott Visual Communications Corp (BVC), pg 708
The Whitlock Group, pg 937

WASHINGTON

Macrosystem US Inc, pg 814

WISCONSIN

Camera Corner Connecting Point, pg 715
Full Compass Systems, pg 767

ALBERTA

Matrix Video Communications Corp (MVCC), pg 819

BRITISH COLUMBIA

Commercial Electronics Ltd, pg 728

ONTARIO

HD Source, pg 777

QUEBEC

Panavideo Inc, pg 850

Editing—Videocassettes

ALASKA

Aurora Films, pg 696

ARIZONA

Film Creations Ltd, pg 760
Merestone, pg 823
Metropolitan Audio-Visual Inc, pg 824
Rodeo Video Inc, pg 876
Star Video Duplicating, pg 900

ARKANSAS

Live'N'Loud, pg 810
White Diamond Productions LLC, pg 937

CALIFORNIA

Action Video, pg 675
Advanced Media LLC, pg 677

All Video Productions, pg 680
AlphaDogs Inc, pg 682
Artichoke Productions, pg 690
Audio Visual Consultants, pg 694
CCI Digital, a DVS Company, pg 718
Steve Chandler, pg 720
Crystal Pyramid Productions™, pg 735
Custom Video Productions Inc, pg 736
Deja View Video, pg 740
digital OutPost, pg 742
The Dreaming Tree, pg 746
DVS InteleStream, pg 748
Express Media Inc, pg 757
First Camera, pg 761
First Person Inc, pg 761
Full Moon & High Tide Productions & Studios, pg 767
Goal Productions, pg 772
Gold Standard Productions, pg 772
Gordon Productions Inc, pg 772
Havas Edge, pg 777
iCorpTv, pg 783
Imageworks, pg 785
ITV Productions, pg 792
JDS Video & Media Productions Inc, pg 793
Joyce Media Inc, pg 795
KPBS Public Broadcasting, pg 801
K2B2 Records, pg 802
KVIE-Channel 6, pg 802
Ludlow Media, pg 812
Lynch Communications, pg 813
Main Street Media Inc, pg 815
Maximus Media Inc, pg 820
McCune Audio-Video-Lighting, pg 821
Media Magic, pg 822
New & Unique Videos™, pg 839
Nineteen87, pg 841
Nolte Media, pg 841
On-Trax Inc, pg 846
Palardo Productions, pg 850
piXvfm Inc, pg 857
PM Productions, pg 858
Point of View Productions, pg 858
Point.360, pg 858
Prime Cut Productions, pg 862
PSI Inc, pg 866
QRS Software Services, pg 867
Dick Reizner Film & Video, pg 873
RetinaVision Productions, pg 874
Rough House, pg 878
Roundabout Entertainment Inc, pg 878
Saturn Studios, pg 881
Shapeshifter, pg 885
Shokus Video, pg 886
SNAP, pg 891
SonicPool, pg 892
Still N' Motion, pg 901
Tam Communications Inc, pg 906
Total Creative, pg 916
Twin Peaks Creative, pg 920
Universal Studios, pg 922
Via Verde Productions, pg 926
VidCan Media Solutions, pg 927
Video Movie Magic, pg 928
Visions Plus, pg 931
Wavemaker Media Design, pg 934
West Coast Projections Inc, pg 935
WMS Media Inc, pg 940

COLORADO

Daylight Productions & Rentals, pg 739
Flashback Media Productions, pg 762
Rocky Mountain Audio/Video Productions Inc, pg 876

Spectrum Audio Visual Services, pg 897
Transtar Entertainment Co Inc, pg 917
Z-Axis Corp, pg 944

CONNECTICUT

A/V Davey, pg 697
BRB Audiovisual Productions, pg 709
Cine-Med Inc, pg 723
Ironik Design & Post, pg 791
MAVCO, pg 820
Palace Production Center, pg 850
Rockwell Communications Inc, pg 876
Video Production Associates Inc, pg 928

DISTRICT OF COLUMBIA

Hillmann & Carr Inc, pg 780
Interface Media Group, pg 789

FLORIDA

Access Media Group, pg 673
Accord Productions, pg 673
AVI-SPL, pg 698
Civins Productions Inc, pg 725
Communications Concepts Inc (CCI), pg 729
Courter Films LLC, pg 732
Easy Edit Video Inc, pg 750
Hi-Tech Enterprises Inc, pg 779
Jordan Klein Film & Video (JKFV), pg 795
Knowles Video Inc (KVI), pg 800
National Teleproductions Inc, pg 837
Shooting Stars Post Inc, pg 886
Sound & Vision Communications Inc, pg 893
Stage America LLC, pg 898
Sunfire Communications Inc, pg 904
Universal Studios Florida® Production Group, pg 922
Video Techniques Inc, pg 928
Vistamax Productions, pg 931

GEORGIA

Beachwood Productions, pg 702
ECG Productions, pg 750
First Cut Communications LLC, pg 761
Guerrilla Productions LLC, pg 774
Omega Media Group Inc, pg 845
Staging Directions Inc, pg 899
Video Copy Services Inc, pg 927
WaveGuide Studios, pg 934

HAWAII

Hyperspective Studios Inc, pg 783
Sight & Sound Studios, pg 887
1013 Integrated, pg 911

IDAHO

KTVB-TV, pg 802
Brad Shaw Productions Inc, pg 885
Wide Eye Productions, pg 938

ILLINOIS

AnswersMedia, pg 686
Backstar Creative Media Inc, pg 700
Beatty TeleVisual Productions, pg 703
Breeze Productions Inc, pg 710
Major Media Inc, pg 815
Manning Productions, pg 816

Optimus, pg 847
Pepper Group, pg 854
PSAV® Presentation Services (Hotel Services Division), pg 866
RBR Productions, pg 870
SCI Television & Creative Media LLC, pg 882
Southern Illinois University, pg 895
20/20 Communications Inc, pg 920
Video I-D Teleproductions Inc, pg 928
Video Impressions, pg 928
WEEK TV, pg 935

INDIANA

A-V-A Video Productions, pg 671
Communication Ministries, pg 728
OMNI Productions, pg 845

IOWA

Educational Technology & Media Services, pg 751

KENTUCKY

The Media Collaboratory, pg 821
Barney Miller's Inc, pg 827

LOUISIANA

Digital FX Inc, pg 742
Louisiana State University Division of Strategic Communications, pg 811
Moxie Media, pg 832
Vidox Motion Imagery, pg 930

MAINE

Headlight Audio Visual Inc, pg 777
WGME-TV, pg 936

MARYLAND

Carpel Video Inc, pg 717
CPR MultiMedia Solutions, pg 732
dbF a Media Company, pg 739
Media Dimensions LLC, pg 821
Milner-Fenwick Inc, pg 828
Mobile-Video Productions, pg 828
Pro Cuts Editing Services, pg 862
Quality Film & Video, pg 868
Sheffield Audio/Video Productions, pg 885
Sign Media Inc, pg 887
Spectrum Productions, pg 897

MASSACHUSETTS

Award Productions Inc, pg 699
Boston Productions Inc (BPI), pg 709
Green Mountain Post Films (GMP), pg 774
HOME Inc, pg 781
In the Wild Productions, pg 786
Integrated Solutions Group, pg 789
Preston Productions Inc, pg 861
Small Planet Communications Inc, pg 890
TVN-The Video Network, pg 919

MICHIGAN

Digi Sign Design LLC, pg 741
K&R's Recording Studios Inc, pg 796
MessageMakers, pg 824
RingSide Creative, pg 875
The Transfer Zone®, pg 917

MINNESOTA

GMI Productions, pg 771
House of Cinemagraphics, pg 782
MastCom, pg 819
Media Loft Inc, pg 822
Worthwhile Films, pg 941

MISSOURI

Avatar Studios, pg 697
Communitronics Corp, pg 729
Conference Technologies Inc, pg 730
KPLR-TV, pg 801
Show-Me Audio-Visual, pg 887
Visionworks Design Services Inc, pg 931

MONTANA

KCFW Television, pg 797
KUSM TV, pg 802

NEBRASKA

Rainbow Video Productions Inc, pg 869

NEVADA

Aardvark Video & Media Productions, pg 671
DVDs4Less, pg 748
Encore Event Technologies LLC, pg 754
JCS Video Productions, pg 793
Lefco Video Services Inc, pg 806

NEW HAMPSHIRE

Academic & Campus Technology Services, pg 672
Apertura, pg 686
Channell One Video, pg 720
Chip Taylor Communications LLC, pg 907

NEW JERSEY

AJS Events, pg 679
Audio Visual Associates, pg 694
Broadcast Center Studios, pg 710
CFP Video Productions Inc, pg 720
Color Leasing Studios, pg 727
Diversified, pg 744
Hogpenny Studios, pg 780
Laurel Video Productions, pg 804
Megavideo LLC, pg 823
MiB MediaWorks, pg 825
NFL Films Music Library, pg 841
Optisonics Productions, pg 847
Suede Interactive, pg 903
Tele-Measurements Inc, pg 910
Telequest Inc, pg 910
VCSvideo, pg 925
Video Corporation of America (VCA), pg 927
Video Ideas Productions, pg 928

NEW MEXICO

30 Second Street Ltd, pg 912

NEW YORK

Adwar Video, pg 678
The Big House Group, pg 705
Broadstreet Productions LLC, pg 711
Chromavision Corp, pg 723
CMI Communications, pg 727
Thomas Craven Film Corp, pg 733
Design Audio Visual Inc, pg 741
Downtown Community Television Center (DCTV), pg 746
DuArt Media Services, pg 747

Duplication Depot Inc, pg 748
General Audio-Visual Inc (GAVI), pg 769
William Greaves Productions Inc, pg 774
HAVE Inc, pg 777
International Digital Centre, pg 790
J&D Laboratories Inc, pg 793
Ketchum Inc, pg 798
Magno Sound Inc, pg 815
Mood Creations Ltd, pg 829
Jack Morton Worldwide, pg 830
NBC Production Facilities, pg 837
PostWorks, pg 860
PrimaLux Video Inc, pg 862
Rafik, pg 869
Richter Productions Inc, pg 875
Split Image Productions, pg 898
Synaptic Digital, pg 905
Teatown Communications Group, pg 908
TeleTime Productions, pg 910
Third World Newsreel/Camera News Inc, pg 912
USA Studios, pg 923
VDO Lab Inc, pg 925
Visual Technologies Corp, pg 932
Alan Weiss Productions, pg 935
WNET/New York Public Media, pg 940
Zelman Studios Ltd, pg 945

NORTH CAROLINA

Pat Appleson Studios Inc, pg 687
Bill Barnes Video Productions LLC, pg 702
The Communications Group Inc, pg 729
Digital Rain LLC, pg 742
Duke Media Services, pg 747
Horizon Video Productions Inc, pg 781
Moving Pictures, pg 832
NASCAR Productions LLC, pg 835
On Location North Carolina, pg 846
Take One Productions Ltd, pg 906
Trailblazer Studios®, pg 917

NORTH DAKOTA

Media Productions, pg 822
UND Television Center, pg 921

OHIO

Aztec Video Productions, pg 700
Russ Beckner Pictures, pg 703
Curtis Inc, pg 736
Cuyahoga Community College Student Production Office (SPO), pg 736
Image Video Teleproductions Inc, pg 785
Lyon Video Inc, pg 813
MainSail Production Services Inc, pg 815
Mills James Productions, pg 828
Musicol Recording, pg 835
R&B Communications Inc, pg 870
Shelburne Films, pg 885
Take 1 Media Services, pg 906
Vista Color Imaging Inc, pg 931

OKLAHOMA

Academic Media & Digital Services, pg 672
Institute for Teaching & Learning Excellence (ITLE), pg 788

OREGON

InterVision Media, pg 791
KPDX-TV Production Center, pg 801

VIDEO

Editing—Videocassettes (continued)

OREGON (continued)

KTVA Productions, pg 802
Odyssey Productions Inc, pg 844
Production West, pg 864
REX, pg 874

PENNSYLVANIA

Audio Visions Inc, pg 694
Audio Visual Communications Inc, pg 694
Center City Film & Video Inc, pg 719
FMP Media Solutions Inc, pg 763
Innovision Media Group, pg 788
JPL, pg 795
Muderick Media, pg 833
Production Masters Inc (PMI), pg 864
Rahlic Publishing Co, pg 869
The Videohouse Inc, pg 929
Visual Sound Inc, pg 931
WPHL-TV, pg 942

SOUTH CAROLINA

American Production Services LLC, pg 684
Genesis Creative, pg 769
Venture Media, pg 925

TENNESSEE

Memphis Communications Corp, pg 823
Motion Picture Services, pg 831
Running Pony Productions LLC, pg 878
Scripps Networks, pg 882
ST Productions, pg 898
Stage Post, pg 899
Russ Sturgeon Productions/RSVP, pg 903
Technical Support Systems LLC, pg 908

TEXAS

Cerutti Productions Inc, pg 720
Communication Arts Multimedia Inc, pg 728
Dub King, pg 747
The Editing Co, pg 750
Emergency Film Group, pg 753
Horizon Film + Video Productions, pg 781
JSAV, pg 795
McNee Productions Inc, pg 821
Mediaforce Productions, pg 822
Earl Miller Productions Inc, pg 827
Phillips Media Source, pg 855
Romar Learning Solutions LLC, pg 877
The Samuels Co, pg 879
South Coast Film & Video, pg 895
Texas Heart Institute Visual Communication Services, pg 911

UTAH

ImageWorks Communications, pg 785

VERMONT

University of Vermont, Instructional Television Dept, pg 923

VIRGINIA

CACI Integrated Communications, pg 713
CVW Event Productions, pg 736
EFX Media, pg 751
The Whitlock Group, pg 937

WASHINGTON

Bennett-Watt HD Productions Inc, pg 703
Inland Audio Visual Co, pg 788
Robert McConnell Productions, pg 820
Victory Studios, pg 927

WEST VIRGINIA

Blackwater Video Productions, pg 707
WSAZ-TV NewsChannel 3, pg 942

WISCONSIN

Audio Visual of Milwaukee Inc, pg 694
Meridian Studios, pg 824
Mirror 34 Productions, pg 828
University of Wisconsin-Oshkosh Radio-TV-Film Dept, pg 923
USAV Group Inc, pg 923
Video Wisconsin Inc, pg 929
Watts Communications Inc, pg 934
Wisconsin Public Television, pg 940

WYOMING

Bridger Productions Inc, pg 710

PUERTO RICO

Stage Crew Audiovisual Inc, pg 898

ALBERTA

Black Media Works, pg 706
Global TV, pg 771

BRITISH COLUMBIA

Triad Communications Ltd, pg 918
Video Out Distribution, pg 928

MANITOBA

Spectra Video Productions Ltd, pg 897

ONTARIO

Marblemedia, pg 816
RB Productions, pg 870
Silver Creek Media Inc, pg 888
Video Excellence Productions, pg 927

Editing—Videotapes

ALASKA

Aurora Films, pg 696

ARIZONA

Direct Current Video Productions, pg 743
Film Creations Ltd, pg 760
Fox 10 Productions (KSAZ-TV), pg 765
Merestone, pg 823
Metropolitan Audio-Visual Inc, pg 824
Rodeo Video Inc, pg 876
Star Video Duplicating, pg 900

ARKANSAS

Live'N'Loud, pg 810
White Diamond Productions LLC, pg 937

CALIFORNIA

Action Video, pg 675
Advanced Media LLC, pg 677
All Video Productions, pg 680
AlphaDogs Inc, pg 682
CCI Digital, a DVS Company, pg 718
Steve Chandler, pg 720
Creative Technology, pg 733
Crystal Pyramid Productions™, pg 735
Custom Video Productions Inc, pg 736
Deja View Video, pg 740
digital OutPost, pg 742
The Dreaming Tree, pg 746
DVS InteleStream, pg 748
Express Media Inc, pg 757
First Camera, pg 761
First Person Inc, pg 761
Fox Television Center, pg 765
Gold Standard Productions, pg 772
Golden Gate Studios, pg 772
Gordon Productions Inc, pg 772
Havas Edge, pg 777
iCorpTv, pg 783
ITV Productions, pg 792
JDS Video & Media Productions Inc, pg 793
Joyce Media Inc, pg 795
Kavich Reynolds Productions Inc, pg 797
KPBS Public Broadcasting, pg 801
K2B2 Records, pg 802
KVIE-Channel 6, pg 802
Lieberman Productions, pg 807
Ludlow Media, pg 812
Lynch Communications, pg 813
Main Street Media Inc, pg 815
Maximus Media Inc, pg 820
McCune Audio-Video-Lighting, pg 821
Media Magic, pg 822
Medical Visual Creations (MVC), pg 823
Method Studios, pg 824
New & Unique Videos™, pg 839
New Cyberian Systems Inc, pg 839
Nineteen87, pg 841
Nolte Media, pg 841
On-Trax Inc, pg 846
Palardo Productions, pg 850
piXvfm Inc, pg 857
PM Productions, pg 858
Point of View Productions, pg 858
Point.360, pg 858
Prime Cut Productions, pg 862
PSI Inc, pg 866
QRS Software Services, pg 867
Rough House, pg 878
Roundabout Entertainment Inc, pg 878
Shapeshifter, pg 885
Shokus Video, pg 886
SNAP, pg 891
SonicPool, pg 892
Still N' Motion, pg 901
Tam Communications Inc, pg 906
Total Creative, pg 916
Twin Peaks Creative, pg 920
Universal Studios, pg 922
VidCan Media Solutions, pg 927
Video Movie Magic, pg 928
Visions Plus, pg 931
Wavemaker Media Design, pg 934
WMS Media Inc, pg 940

COLORADO

CSI Film & Video LLC, pg 735
Daylight Productions & Rentals, pg 739
Flashback Media Productions, pg 762
Open Media Foundation, pg 846
Rocky Mountain Audio/Video Productions Inc, pg 876

CONNECTICUT

A/V Davey, pg 697
BRB Audiovisual Productions, pg 709
Cine-Med Inc, pg 723
Essex Television Group Inc, pg 755
Geomatrix Productions, pg 770
Ironik Design & Post, pg 791
MAVCO, pg 820
Palace Production Center, pg 850

DISTRICT OF COLUMBIA

Hillmann & Carr Inc, pg 780
Interface Media Group, pg 789
O'Keefe Communications Inc, pg 844

FLORIDA

Access Media Group, pg 673
Accord Productions, pg 673
Applebox Studio, pg 687
AVI-SPL, pg 698
Civins Productions Inc, pg 725
Communications Concepts Inc (CCI), pg 729
Courter Films LLC, pg 732
Easy Edit Video Inc, pg 750
Hi-Tech Enterprises Inc, pg 779
Jordan Klein Film & Video (JKFV), pg 795
Knowles Video Inc (KVI), pg 800
National Teleproductions Inc, pg 837
Shooting Stars Post Inc, pg 886
Sound & Vision Communications Inc, pg 893
Stage America LLC, pg 898
Sunfire Communications Inc, pg 904
Universal Studios Florida® Production Group, pg 922
University of Florida, Warrington College of Business Information Technology Support Programs, pg 922
Mike Vasilinda Productions Inc, pg 925
Video Techniques Inc, pg 928
Vistamax Productions, pg 931

GEORGIA

Beachwood Productions, pg 702
ECG Productions, pg 750
First Cut Communications LLC, pg 761
Guerrilla Productions LLC, pg 774
Omega Media Group Inc, pg 845
Staging Directions Inc, pg 899
Video Copy Services Inc, pg 927
WaveGuide Studios, pg 934

HAWAII

Hyperspective Studios Inc, pg 783
Sight & Sound Studios, pg 887
1013 Integrated, pg 911

IDAHO

KTVB-TV, pg 802
Brad Shaw Productions Inc, pg 885
Wide Eye Productions, pg 938

ILLINOIS

Airways Digital Media, pg 679
AnswersMedia, pg 686
Backstar Creative Media Inc,
  pg 700
Beatty TeleVisual Productions,
  pg 703
Extraordinary Demos/Videos,
  pg 757
Major Media Inc, pg 815
Manning Productions, pg 816
Multimedia Marketing Group,
  pg 833
Optimus, pg 847
Rob Orr Productions Ltd, pg 848
Pepper Group, pg 854
PSAV® Presentation Services
  (Hotel Services Division), pg 866
RBR Productions, pg 870
SCI Television & Creative Media
  LLC, pg 882
Sound/Video Impressions Inc,
  pg 894
Southern Illinois University, pg 895
Sparkfactor, pg 896
Tele-Time Systems, pg 910
20/20 Communications Inc, pg 920
Video I-D Teleproductions Inc,
  pg 928
Video Impressions, pg 928
WEEK TV, pg 935

INDIANA

A-V-A Video Productions, pg 671
Communication Ministries, pg 728
PentaVision Communications Inc,
  pg 854

IOWA

Educational Technology & Media
  Services, pg 751

KENTUCKY

Audio Visual Techniques Inc,
  pg 695
EKU Media, pg 752
The Media Collaboratory, pg 821
Barney Miller's Inc, pg 827
The PPS Group, pg 860
WKYT-TV, pg 940

LOUISIANA

Digital FX Inc, pg 742
Louisiana State University Division
  of Strategic Communications,
  pg 811
Moxie Media, pg 832
Vidox Motion Imagery, pg 930
YES Productions, pg 944

MAINE

Headlight Audio Visual Inc, pg 777
WGME-TV, pg 936

MARYLAND

Adventure Productions LLC, pg 678
Carpel Video Inc, pg 717
CPR MultiMedia Solutions, pg 732
dbF a Media Company, pg 739
Media Dimensions LLC, pg 821
Milner-Fenwick Inc, pg 828
Mobile-Video Productions Inc,
  pg 828

Pro Cuts Editing Services, pg 862
Producers Video, pg 863
Satellite Media Production, pg 881
Sheffield Audio/Video Productions,
  pg 885
Sign Media Inc, pg 887
Welocalize, pg 935

MASSACHUSETTS

Award Productions Inc, pg 699
Boston Productions Inc (BPI),
  pg 709
Capron Lighting & Sound Co Inc,
  pg 716
CommCreative, pg 728
Documentary Educational Resources
  Inc, pg 744
HOME Inc, pg 781
In the Wild Productions, pg 786
Preston Productions Inc, pg 861
Small Planet Communications Inc,
  pg 890
TR Productions, pg 916

MICHIGAN

Digi Sign Design LLC, pg 741
K&R's Recording Studios Inc,
  pg 796
MessageMakers, pg 824
Michigan Recording Arts Institute
  & Technologies, pg 825
RingSide Creative, pg 875
The Transfer Zone®, pg 917
WGVU TV, pg 936
WTVS, Detroit Public Television,
  pg 942

MINNESOTA

The ADS Group, pg 676
Badiyan Inc, pg 700
GMI Productions, pg 771
House of Cinemagraphics, pg 782
MastCom, pg 819
Media Loft Inc, pg 822
Rum Jungle Media, pg 878
Worthwhile Films, pg 941

MISSOURI

Avatar Studios, pg 697
Conference Technologies Inc,
  pg 730
Hardcastle Films & Video, pg 776
KPLR-TV, pg 801
Show-Me Audio-Visual, pg 887
Switch, pg 905
Visionworks Design Services Inc,
  pg 931

MONTANA

KCFW Television, pg 797
KUSM TV, pg 802

NEBRASKA

Rainbow Video Productions Inc,
  pg 869

NEVADA

Aardvark Video & Media
  Productions, pg 671
Encore Event Technologies LLC,
  pg 754
JCS Video Productions, pg 793
Lefco Video Services Inc, pg 806
21st Century Video Productions,
  pg 919

NEW HAMPSHIRE

Apertura, pg 686
Channel One Video, pg 720

Chip Taylor Communications LLC,
  pg 907
The Troupe, pg 918

NEW JERSEY

AJS Events, pg 679
Broadcast Center Studios, pg 710
CFP Video Productions Inc, pg 720
Color Leasing Studios, pg 727
Diversified, pg 744
Hogpenny Studios, pg 780
Laurel Video Productions, pg 804
MiB MediaWorks, pg 825
NFL Films Inc, pg 841
NFL Films Music Library, pg 841
Optisonics Productions, pg 847
Reed Presentations Inc (RPI),
  pg 872
Suede Interactive, pg 903
Tele-Measurements Inc, pg 910
Telequest Inc, pg 910
VCSvideo, pg 925
Video Corporation of America
  (VCA), pg 927

NEW MEXICO

Production Outfitters, pg 864
30 Second Street Ltd, pg 912

NEW YORK

A-List Quality Videographer,
  pg 671
Ace Video, pg 674
Adwar Video, pg 678
aurora productions, pg 696
BC Studio, pg 702
Bevilacqua Studios, pg 704
The Big House Group, pg 705
Broadstreet Productions LLC,
  pg 711
Chromavision Corp, pg 723
Thomas Craven Film Corp, pg 733
Design Audio Visual Inc, pg 741
Downtown Community Television
  Center (DCTV), pg 746
DuArt Media Services, pg 747
Duplication Depot Inc, pg 748
Fingerpaint, pg 761
General Audio-Visual Inc (GAVI),
  pg 769
William Greaves Productions Inc,
  pg 774
HAVE Inc, pg 777
HB-Content, pg 777
Hello World Communications,
  pg 778
International Digital Centre, pg 790
J&D Laboratories Inc, pg 793
Ketchum Inc, pg 798
Magnetic Post Production, pg 815
Magno Sound Inc, pg 815
Manhattan Center Studios Inc,
  pg 816
Mood Creations Ltd, pg 829
MRM//McCANN, pg 832
NBC Production Facilities, pg 837
New Horizon Studios, pg 839
New York Audio Productions,
  pg 840
News Broadcast Network Inc,
  pg 840
PostWorks, pg 860
PrimaLux Video Inc, pg 862
Richter Productions Inc, pg 875
SoundByte Productions Inc, pg 894
Split Image Productions, pg 898
Synaptic Digital, pg 905
Teatown Communications Group,
  pg 908
TeleTime Productions, pg 910
USA Studios, pg 923

VDO Lab Inc, pg 925
Videograf, pg 929
Visual Technologies Corp, pg 932
Willow Mixed Media Inc, pg 939
WNET/New York Public Media,
  pg 940
Zelman Studios Ltd, pg 945

NORTH CAROLINA

Pat Appleson Studios Inc, pg 687
AV Connections Inc, pg 697
The Communications Group Inc,
  pg 729
Duke Media Services, pg 747
Franklin Video Inc, pg 765
Horizon Video Productions Inc,
  pg 781
Moving Pictures, pg 832
NASCAR Productions LLC, pg 835
On Location North Carolina, pg 846
PACE Worldwide, pg 849
Take One Productions Ltd, pg 906
Trailblazer Studios®, pg 917
Videowerks, pg 930

NORTH DAKOTA

Media Productions, pg 822

OHIO

Alegra House Publishers, pg 679
Aztec Video Productions, pg 700
Russ Beckner Pictures, pg 703
Curtis Inc, pg 736
Cuyahoga Community College
  Student Production Office (SPO),
  pg 736
Image Video Teleproductions Inc,
  pg 785
Lyon Video Inc, pg 813
MainSail Production Services Inc,
  pg 815
Mills James Productions, pg 828
R&B Communications Inc, pg 870
Shelburne Films, pg 885
Take 1 Media Services, pg 906
Treehaus Communications Inc,
  pg 917
Vista Color Imaging Inc, pg 931

OKLAHOMA

Academic Media & Digital
  Services, pg 672

OREGON

InterVision Media, pg 791
KPDX-TV Production Center,
  pg 801
KTVA Productions, pg 802
Odyssey Productions Inc, pg 844
Production West, pg 864
REX, pg 874

PENNSYLVANIA

Audio Visual Communications Inc,
  pg 694
Beholder Productions Inc, pg 703
Center City Film & Video Inc,
  pg 719
FMP Media Solutions Inc, pg 763
Innovision Media Group, pg 788
JPL, pg 795
Laser Video Corp, pg 804
Muderick Media, pg 833
Production Masters Inc (PMI),
  pg 864
Rahlic Publishing Co, pg 869
The Videohouse Inc, pg 929
Visual Sound Inc, pg 931
WHYY Inc, pg 938
WPHL-TV, pg 942

VIDEO

Editing—Videotapes (continued)

SOUTH CAROLINA

American Production Services LLC, pg 684
Genesis Creative, pg 769
Sound & Images Inc, pg 893
Stages Video Productions, pg 899
Venture Media, pg 925

TENNESSEE

Memphis Communications Corp, pg 823
Motion Picture Services, pg 831
Running Pony Productions LLC, pg 878
Scripps Networks, pg 882
ST Productions, pg 898
Stage Post, pg 899
Russ Sturgeon Productions/RSVP, pg 903
Technical Support Systems LLC, pg 908

TEXAS

Castleview Productions, pg 717
Cerutti Productions Inc, pg 720
Communication Arts Multimedia Inc, pg 728
Dub King, pg 747
The Editing Co, pg 750
Emergency Film Group, pg 753
Horizon Film + Video Productions, pg 781
Marx InDigital, pg 818
McNee Productions Inc, pg 821
Media Event Concepts Inc, pg 822
Mediaforce Productions, pg 822
Earl Miller Productions Inc, pg 827
Phillips Media Source, pg 855
The Samuels Co, pg 879
South Coast Film & Video, pg 895
Texas Heart Institute Visual Communication Services, pg 911

UTAH

ImageWorks Communications, pg 785

VERMONT

Marlboro Productions, pg 817
University of Vermont, Instructional Television Dept, pg 923

VIRGINIA

Allied Media Corp, pg 681
BES Studios, pg 704
CACI Integrated Communications, pg 713
CVW Event Productions, pg 736
EFX Media, pg 751
The Whitlock Group, pg 937

WASHINGTON

Bennett-Watt HD Productions Inc, pg 703
Pal Productions Inc, pg 850
Victory Studios, pg 927

WEST VIRGINIA

Blackwater Video Productions, pg 707
WSAZ-TV NewsChannel 3, pg 942

WISCONSIN

Audio Visual of Milwaukee Inc, pg 694
Learning Technology Services, pg 805
Logan Productions Inc, pg 811
Meridian Studios, pg 824
Mirror 34 Productions, pg 828
University of Wisconsin-Oshkosh Radio-TV-Film Dept, pg 923
USAV Group Inc, pg 923
Video Wisconsin Inc, pg 929
Watts Communications Inc, pg 934
Wisconsin Public Television, pg 940

WYOMING

Bridger Productions Inc, pg 710

PUERTO RICO

Stage Crew Audiovisual Inc, pg 898

ALBERTA

Black Media Works, pg 706
Cine Audio Visual Sales & Service Ltd, pg 723
Global TV, pg 771

BRITISH COLUMBIA

Triad Communications Ltd, pg 918
Video Out Distribution, pg 928

MANITOBA

Spectra Video Productions Ltd, pg 897

ONTARIO

RB Productions, pg 870
Silver Creek Media Inc, pg 888
Video Excellence Productions, pg 927

QUEBEC

Group PVP, pg 774
Muse Entertainment Enterprises, pg 834

Equipment & Accessory Distributors

ARIZONA

EAR Professional Audio/Video, pg 749
On-Site Video, pg 846
Troxell-CDI, pg 918

ARKANSAS

Carlton-Bates Co, pg 717
Jay S Stanley & Associates Inc, pg 899
White Diamond Productions LLC, pg 937

CALIFORNIA

Advanced Systems Group LLC, pg 677
Ametron Audio/Video, pg 684
Audio/Video Supply Inc, pg 694
AVerMedia Technologies Inc, pg 697
Band Pro Film & Digital Inc, pg 701
Be Media, pg 702
BigFoot Mobile Systems, pg 705
Birns & Sawyer Inc, pg 706
Boland Communications, pg 708

BroadcastStore.com, pg 711
Christy's Editorial, pg 723
Cibola Systems, pg 723
Cinema Xenon International Inc, pg 724
DTC Lighting & Grip, pg 747
Eiki International Inc, pg 751
Electronic Design Solutions Inc, pg 752
IDX System Technology Inc, pg 784
Innovision Optics, pg 788
Jameco Electronics, pg 792
JD Audio Visual Inc, pg 793
Leader Instruments Corp, pg 805
Marshall Electronics Inc, pg 817
Matthews Studio Equipment Inc, pg 820
Media Control Systems LLC, pg 821
Media Fabricators Inc, pg 822
MediaPOINTE, pg 823
Metro Video Systems Inc, pg 824
Nalpak Inc, pg 835
Promax Systems, pg 865
The Rip-Tie Co, pg 875
16 x 9 Inc, pg 890
Southern California Sound Image Inc, pg 895
SSL Industries Inc, pg 898
Stanislaus AV Inc, pg 899
Steeldeck® Inc, pg 900
Thermodyne Cases, pg 912
Transvideo International, pg 917
The Video Store Shopper, pg 928
Visual Systems, pg 931
VMI Inc, pg 932
VTP Inc, pg 933
Xantech LLC, pg 943
Zack Electronics Inc, pg 945

COLORADO

Ceavco Audio Visual Company Inc, pg 719
Goldberg Brothers Inc, pg 772
Mike's Camera, pg 827
ProLine Digital, pg 865
Spectrum Audio Visual Services, pg 897
Stanco Sales LLC, pg 899

CONNECTICUT

MAVCO, pg 820
Rockwell Communications Inc, pg 876
Vitec Videocom Inc, pg 932

FLORIDA

Access Media Group, pg 673
A2D Solutions Inc, pg 692
Digital Video Systems, pg 742
Encore Broadcast Solutions, pg 754
Enhanced View Services Inc, pg 754
EZ FX Inc, pg 758
Glanz Technologies Inc, pg 771
Harris Corp, pg 776
Hi-Tech Enterprises Inc, pg 779
Hi-Tech Import Export Corp, pg 779
Hollywood Theatre Equipment Inc, pg 781
Midtown Video Inc, pg 827
Multicom Inc, pg 833
Nemal Electronics International Inc, pg 838
ONstage, pg 846
Photosound of Orlando Inc, pg 856
Recording Media & Equipment Inc (RM&E), pg 872
Reef Photo & Video, pg 872

Summit Electronics Corp, pg 903
Tallahassee Audio Visual, pg 906
Test Equipment Connection, pg 911

GEORGIA

Audio Visual Resources Inc, pg 695
Convergent Media Systems, pg 731
Stage Front Presentation Systems, pg 899

HAWAII

The Audio Visual Co (AVCO), pg 694

ILLINOIS

Joseph Electronics, pg 795
LKG Industries Inc, pg 810
Quintessence Audio Ltd, pg 868
Research Technology International (RTI), pg 873
Tele-Time Systems, pg 910
Toko America Inc, pg 915
Zacuto, pg 945

INDIANA

Jack's Camera Shop, pg 792
Lee Co Inc, pg 805
Sensory Technologies LLC, pg 884
SHP Electronics, pg 887

KENTUCKY

General Cable, pg 769
Barney Miller's Inc, pg 827
NOR-COM Inc, pg 841

LOUISIANA

Techkno Integration & Design Services LLC, pg 908

MARYLAND

Image Logic Corp, pg 785
Noventri, pg 843
Nicholas P Pipino Associates Inc, pg 857
Rohde & Schwarz USA Inc, pg 876
RTZ Audio Visual, pg 878
Siqura Inc, pg 889
Wiltronix Inc, pg 939

MASSACHUSETTS

Hannecke Display Systems Inc, pg 775
Hunt's Photo & Video, pg 782
Rule Boston Camera, pg 878
Visual Departures Ltd, pg 931

MICHIGAN

Olson Anderson Co, pg 685
Lowing Light & Grip Inc, pg 812
On Stage Visuals, pg 846
TEL Systems LLC, pg 909

MINNESOTA

Alpha Video & Audio Inc, pg 682
AVI Systems, pg 698
Cinequipt Inc, pg 724

MISSISSIPPI

Jasper Ewing & Sons Inc, pg 757
MFJ Enterprises Inc, pg 825

MISSOURI

Communitronics Corp, pg 729
Conference Technologies Inc, pg 730
ITC, pg 791

Modern Communications Inc, pg 828
Production Support Services Inc, pg 864
Schiller's Audio-Visual, pg 881
Southwest Audio-Visual Inc, pg 895

NEBRASKA

VSA Inc, pg 933

NEVADA

Bulbman Inc, pg 712
DVDs4Less, pg 748

NEW HAMPSHIRE

APS Lighting-Sound-AV, pg 688

NEW JERSEY

AlltecPro, pg 681
Audio Visual Dynamics®, pg 694
AV Bluebook, pg 696
Avtech Systems Inc, pg 699
Canare Corporation of America, pg 716
Color Leasing Studios, pg 727
Diversified, pg 744
Earl Girls Inc, pg 749
Euro-Pacific Film & Video Productions Inc, pg 756
G&G Technologies Inc, pg 768
HamiltonBuhl, pg 775
MCCOM Inc, pg 820
PatchAmp, pg 852
Radio Visions, pg 869
Starlite, pg 900
SYMCO Inc, pg 905
Tele-Measurements Inc, pg 910
ToCad America Inc, pg 915
Total Video Products Inc, pg 916
Vcom IMC, pg 925

NEW YORK

Adwar Video, pg 678
Allen Avionics Inc, pg 680
Audio-Video Corp, pg 694
Audio Visual Sales & Service Inc, pg 695
Audiovox®, pg 695
AV Workshop, pg 697
B&H Photo Video, pg 701
BTX Technologies, pg 712
Bulbtronics Inc, pg 712
Canon USA Inc, pg 716
Design Audio Visual Inc, pg 741
Flash Electronics Inc, pg 762
General Audio-Visual Inc (GAVI), pg 769
HAVE Inc, pg 777
Indigo Productions, pg 787
KVL Audio Visual Services Inc, pg 802
Langie Audio Visual Systems, pg 803
Long Island Video Enterprises Live Inc, pg 811
MAC Group, pg 813
Markertek Video Supply, pg 817
Russell Industries Inc, pg 879
TecNec Distributing, pg 909
The Tiffen Co LLC, pg 914
Topbulb, a Semmer Lighting Company, pg 915
Tri-Ed Distribution Inc, pg 918
Visual Technologies Corp, pg 932
Visual Word Systems Inc, pg 932
Willoughby's® Camera, pg 939

NORTH CAROLINA

Camcor Inc, pg 715
Carolina Biological Supply Co, pg 717
Strategic Connections, pg 901

OHIO

Audio Visual Media, pg 694
Central Ohio Audio Video, pg 719
ITA Audio Visual Solutions, pg 791
iVideo Technologies, pg 792
Midwest Photo Exchange, pg 827
Parts Express, pg 851
Tri-State Audio Visual Co, pg 918
Visual Products Inc, pg 931

OKLAHOMA

Ford AV, pg 763

PENNSYLVANIA

Advanced AV LLC, pg 677
Bernie's Photo Center, pg 704
Clair Companies, pg 725
J E Foss Co, pg 764
Garcia Marketing Inc, pg 768
Hite Co, pg 780
Innovision Media Group, pg 788
The Lerro Corp, pg 806
Morefield Communications Inc, pg 830
Visual Sound Inc, pg 931
Wespen Audio Visual Co, pg 935

TENNESSEE

Continental Film, pg 731
Lowrance Sound Co Inc, pg 812
Memphis Communications Corp, pg 823
Technical Support Systems LLC, pg 908

TEXAS

Audio Visual Technologies Group (AVTG), pg 695
AVES Audio Visual Systems Inc, pg 698
Biway Media, pg 706
Digital Display Solutions Inc, pg 742
Heffernan Audio Visual, pg 778
JSAV, pg 795
Pro Video & Film Equipment Co Inc, pg 863
Specialized Products Co, pg 896
TWIST Integration Solutions Technology, pg 920

UTAH

Performance Audio LLC, pg 854
RIA Corp, pg 874
TV Specialists Inc, pg 919

VIRGINIA

Boitnott Visual Communications Corp (BVC), pg 708
Design & Production Inc, pg 740
Lee Hartman & Sons Inc, pg 805
Quince Imaging Inc, pg 868
StageSound, pg 899
The Whitlock Group, pg 937

WASHINGTON

Inland Audio Visual Co, pg 788
Oppenheimer Camera Products, pg 847

WISCONSIN

Audio Visual of Milwaukee Inc, pg 694
Brady Corp, pg 709
Camera Corner Connecting Point, pg 715
Demco Inc, pg 740
Full Compass Systems, pg 767
Safe Harbor Computers, pg 879

PUERTO RICO

Bonnin Electronics Inc, pg 708

ALBERTA

Allstar Show Industries Inc, pg 681
Evolution AV, pg 757
Matrix Video Communications Corp (MVCC), pg 819

BRITISH COLUMBIA

BeachTek Inc, pg 702
Commercial Electronics Ltd, pg 728
DL Sound & Lighting Productions Ltd, pg 744
Specialty Bulb Products Inc, pg 896

ONTARIO

Applied Electronics Ltd, pg 687
CBM Ltd, pg 718
Cinema Stage Inc, pg 724
HD Source, pg 777
Teledyne DALSA Inc, pg 910
VFGadgets Inc, pg 926

Equipment & Accessory Manufacturers

ALABAMA

Marco Inc, pg 816

ARIZONA

Covid Inc, pg 732
OmniMount Systems, pg 845

CALIFORNIA

AheadTeK, pg 678
ALTINEX Inc, pg 682
Ampex Data Systems Corp, pg 684
Auton Motorized Systems, pg 696
AVerMedia Technologies Inc, pg 697
Blackmagic Design Pty Ltd, pg 707
Boland Communications Inc, pg 708
California Stainless Manufacturing Inc, pg 714
Calrad Electronics, pg 714
CineBags Inc, pg 723
CohuHD Costar LLC, pg 727
DataDirect Networks, pg 738
Deerfield Laboratory Inc, pg 740
Dow-Key Microwave Corp, pg 746
Eiki International Inc, pg 751
ESE, pg 755
Extron Electronics, pg 758
FM Systems Inc, pg 763
For-A Corp of America, pg 763
Jerry Hill Steadicam Products, pg 780
Hoodman Corp, pg 781
Horita Co Inc, pg 781
IDX System Technology Inc, pg 784
Innovision Optics, pg 788
Jensen Transformers Inc, pg 793
LEMO USA Inc, pg 806
Marshall Electronics Inc, pg 817

Matthews Studio Equipment Inc, pg 820
Media Control Systems LLC, pg 821
Nalpak Inc, pg 835
Nevion USA Inc, pg 838
O'Connor Engineering Labs, pg 844
Opticomm-EMCORE, pg 847
Sony Electronics Inc, pg 893
Sprocket Digital, pg 898
Steeldeck® Inc, pg 900
Tasman Group Pacific Rim, pg 907
Thermodyne Cases, pg 912
Transvideo International, pg 917
TV Pro Gear, pg 919
VITEC Multimedia, pg 932
Xantech LLC, pg 943

COLORADO

Colorado Video Inc, pg 728
Goldberg Brothers Inc, pg 772
ProLine Digital, pg 865
Rose Packaging & Design Inc, pg 877
Video Accessory Corp, pg 927
Videomagnetics, pg 929

CONNECTICUT

Anton/Bauer®, pg 686
Sound Control Technologies Inc, pg 893
Xintekvideo Inc, pg 943

FLORIDA

Compuvideo Sales USA Ltd, pg 729
Electriduct Inc, pg 752
Straight Wire Inc, pg 901
Techni-Lux Inc, pg 908
Union Connector Co Inc, pg 921
Vutec Corp, pg 933

GEORGIA

ARRIS Group Inc, pg 689
Lighting & Production Equipment Inc, pg 807

ILLINOIS

Bretford Manufacturing Inc, pg 710
Cool-Lux, pg 731
FJW Optical Systems Inc, pg 762
Kart-A-Bag Manufacturing Inc, pg 796
Luxor, pg 812
Peerless Industries, pg 853
Photoflex Inc, pg 856
Quantum Instruments Inc, pg 868
Research Technology International (RTI), pg 873
Switchcraft® Inc, pg 905
Toko America Inc, pg 915
Waldom Electronics Corp, pg 933

INDIANA

R B Annis Instruments Inc, pg 686
Auralex Acoustics Inc, pg 696
Dage-MTI, pg 737
General Devices Co Inc, pg 769
Star Case Manufacturing Co Inc, pg 900

IOWA

Winegard Co, pg 939

KANSAS

Desktop Video Systems, pg 741

357

VIDEO

Equipment & Accessory Manufacturers (continued)

MARYLAND

Image Logic Corp, pg 785
Siqura Inc, pg 889
Video Mount Products (VMP), pg 928

MASSACHUSETTS

David Clark Co Inc, pg 738
Dedotec USA Inc, pg 740
Glidecam Industries Inc, pg 771
Hannecke Display Systems Inc, pg 775
Visual Departures Ltd, pg 931

MICHIGAN

Leightronix Inc, pg 806
TEL Systems LLC, pg 909

MINNESOTA

Bel Fuse Inc, pg 703
Bosch Security Systems Inc, pg 709
Vaddio, pg 924
Winsted Corp, pg 939

MISSISSIPPI

MFJ Enterprises Inc, pg 825

MISSOURI

Link Electronics Inc, pg 809

NEBRASKA

Data Security Inc, pg 738

NEVADA

Calculated Industries Inc, pg 714

NEW HAMPSHIRE

ProPhotonix Ltd, pg 865

NEW JERSEY

AlltecPro, pg 681
Alpha Wire Co, pg 682
ATI Audio, pg 692
Canare Corporation of America, pg 716
Daburn Electronics & Cable Corp, pg 737
Konica Minolta Business Solutions, pg 801
Kramer Electronics USA Inc, pg 801
Middle Atlantic Products, a Legrand AV Inc brand, pg 826
Pioneer Research Inc, pg 857
Pro-Tape & Specialities Inc, pg 863
Radio Visions, pg 869
Sofradir EC, pg 892
Sony Pro Audio, pg 893
Techflex Inc, pg 908
Telemetrics Inc, pg 910
Turner Engineering Inc, pg 919
Wireworks Corp, pg 940

NEW MEXICO

Burst Electronics Inc, pg 713

NEW YORK

Allen Avionics Inc, pg 680
BTX Technologies, pg 712

Canon USA Inc, pg 716
ChyronHego Corp, pg 723
Key Digital Systems, pg 798
Microwave Filter Co Inc, pg 826
Sima Products Corp, pg 888
Joseph Struhl Company Inc, pg 902
TBC Consoles Inc, pg 907
Television Equipment Associates Inc (TEA), pg 910
The Tiffen Co LLC, pg 914

NORTH CAROLINA

Crest Electronics Inc, pg 734

PENNSYLVANIA

Ac-cetera Inc, pg 672
MicroImage Video Systems, pg 826
Prime Image Inc, pg 862
Sandusky Lee Corp, pg 880

TEXAS

Biway Media, pg 706

UTAH

Tamrac® Inc, pg 906

VIRGINIA

Quince Imaging Inc, pg 868

WASHINGTON

Oppenheimer Camera Products, pg 847

WISCONSIN

Brady Corp, pg 709
DH Satellite, pg 741

BRITISH COLUMBIA

Cavision Enterprises Ltd, pg 717
Triad Communications Ltd, pg 918

ONTARIO

CBM Ltd, pg 718
DW Electrochemicals Ltd, pg 748
Ross Video Ltd, pg 877
Ward-Beck Systems Ltd, pg 933

QUEBEC

Skotel Corp, pg 890

Equipment & Accessory Rentals

ARIZONA

Arizona Cine Equipment, pg 688
Broadcast Rentals, pg 711
Cox Creative Studios, pg 732
Creative Backstage, pg 733
Crew West Inc, pg 734
Merestone, pg 823
Metropolitan Audio-Visual Inc, pg 824
Reel Men Rentals Inc, pg 872
Rodeo Video Inc, pg 876
Video West Inc, pg 929

ARKANSAS

White Diamond Productions LLC, pg 937

CALIFORNIA

Action Audio & Visual, pg 675
Advanced Media LLC, pg 677
Ametron Audio/Video, pg 684

Artichoke Productions, pg 690
Bexel, an NEP Broadcast Services Company, pg 704
Big Door, pg 705
Birns & Sawyer Inc, pg 706
The Camera Division, pg 715
CenterStaging LLC, pg 719
Chapman/Leonard Studio Equipment Inc, pg 720
Chater Camera Inc, pg 721
Cherry Multimedia, pg 721
Christy's Editorial, pg 723
Cinema Camera Rentals, pg 723
Cinema Rentals Inc, pg 724
Crystal Pyramid Productions™, pg 735
Dadco, pg 737
DTC Lighting & Grip, pg 747
Express Media Inc, pg 757
Express Video Supply Inc, pg 757
First Camera, pg 761
Gear Monkey, pg 769
Goal Productions, pg 772
Gold Standard Productions, pg 772
Golden Gate Studios, pg 772
Alan Gordon Enterprises Inc, pg 772
Greenery Studios, pg 774
Illuminate Studios, pg 784
Imagecraft Productions, pg 785
Images in Motion Media Inc, pg 785
Innovision Optics, pg 788
JD Audio Visual Inc, pg 793
JFA Studio, pg 794
Laurel Canyon Stages, pg 804
Lynch Communications, pg 813
Main Street Media Inc, pg 815
Maximus Media Inc, pg 820
McCune Audio-Video-Lighting, pg 821
Media Fabricators Inc, pg 822
Motion Picture Marine, pg 831
Munday & Collins AV, pg 834
New Circuit Films LLC, pg 839
North County Media Center, pg 842
Old School Cameras, pg 844
Pro HD Rentals, pg 863
Production Gear Rentals (PGR), pg 863
RetinaVision Productions, pg 874
Shooting Star Video, pg 886
Shoulder High Productions, pg 886
SNAP, pg 891
Source Film Studio, pg 895
Steeldeck® Inc, pg 900
Straight Shoot'r Cranes Inc, pg 901
Stray Angel Films, pg 902
Sunset Las Palmas Studios, pg 904
Synthesizer Rental Service, pg 906
T-stop Inc, pg 906
Timestream Video, pg 914
Total Creative, pg 916
Twin Peaks Creative, pg 920
VER, pg 926
Videofax, pg 929
Vitruvian Entertainment, pg 932
VMI Inc, pg 932
Voice & Video Rentals, pg 932
Warner Bros Entertainment Inc, pg 934
Z-Ville Productions, pg 944

COLORADO

Apogee Communications Group, pg 687
Ceavco Audio Visual Company Inc, pg 719
Daylight Productions & Rentals, pg 739
Spectrum Audio Visual Services, pg 897
Tatum Video, pg 907

CONNECTICUT

Rockwell Communications Inc, pg 876
Videofilm Systems Inc, pg 929

DISTRICT OF COLUMBIA

Future View Inc, pg 767

FLORIDA

Access Media Group, pg 673
Budget Video Rentals, pg 712
C&I An Idea Agency, pg 716
Facet Media, pg 758
F&F Productions LLC, pg 759
Glanz Technologies Inc, pg 771
The Great Southern Studios, pg 773
Jordan Klein Film & Video (JKFV), pg 795
JungleTV, pg 795
MAPS Production House, pg 816
Midtown Video Inc, pg 827
Moving Picture, pg 831
National Teleproductions Inc, pg 837
ONstage, pg 846
Photosound of Orlando Inc, pg 856
Tallahassee Audio Visual, pg 906
Trendy Studio LLC, pg 917
Universal Studios Florida® Production Group, pg 922

GEORGIA

Audio Visual Resources Inc, pg 695
Convergent Media Systems, pg 731
First Cut Communications LLC, pg 761
Stage Front Presentation Systems, pg 899
Studio Space Atlanta, pg 903

HAWAII

Sight & Sound Studios, pg 887

ILLINOIS

Atomic Imaging Inc/Golan Studios, pg 692
AV Chicago Inc, pg 696
Backstar Creative Media Inc, pg 700
Helix Camera & Video, pg 778
Magnanimous Media, pg 814
On Site Video, pg 846
Product Productions, pg 863
PSAV® Presentation Services (Hotel Services Division), pg 866
Resolution Productions Group, pg 874
2nd Cine Inc, pg 883
Tele-Time Systems, pg 910
Zacuto, pg 945

INDIANA

Gary Camera & Digital, pg 768
OMNI Productions, pg 845

IOWA

Central Lighting & Equipment Inc (CLE), pg 719
Pro Video, pg 863

KENTUCKY

Audio Visual Techniques Inc, pg 695

LOUISIANA

Digital FX Inc, pg 742
Moxie Media, pg 832
Pace Systems, pg 849

MARYLAND

Archai Media, pg 688
Kramer Communications Video
    Production, pg 801
Milner-Fenwick Inc, pg 828
Quality Film & Video, pg 868
RTZ Audio Visual, pg 878

MASSACHUSETTS

Capron Lighting & Sound Co Inc,
    pg 716
Green Mountain Post Films (GMP),
    pg 774
High Output Inc, pg 779
HOME Inc, pg 781
massAV, pg 819
Preston Productions Inc, pg 861
Small Planet Communications Inc,
    pg 890

MICHIGAN

Olson Anderson Co, pg 685
City Events Group, pg 725
K&R All Media Productions LLC,
    pg 796
Lowing Light & Grip Inc, pg 812
Madonna University Information
    Technology, pg 814
Magnicon Media/Image d'Or,
    pg 815
On Stage Visuals, pg 846
TEL Systems LLC, pg 909

MINNESOTA

Alpha Video & Audio Inc, pg 682
AVI Systems, pg 698
Cinequipt Inc, pg 724
House of Cinemagraphics, pg 782

MISSISSIPPI

Jasper Ewing & Sons Inc, pg 757

MISSOURI

Production Support Services Inc,
    pg 864
Schiller's Audio-Visual, pg 881
Show-Me Audio-Visual, pg 887
Southwest Audio-Visual Inc, pg 895
Switch, pg 905

NEVADA

MG Studio, pg 825

NEW HAMPSHIRE

Apertura, pg 686
APS Lighting-Sound-AV, pg 688

NEW JERSEY

Audio Visual Dynamics®, pg 694
Butter Tree Studios, pg 713
CFP Video Productions Inc, pg 720
Color Leasing Studios, pg 727
Earl Girls Inc, pg 749
Euro-Pacific Film & Video
    Productions Inc, pg 756
Ironbound Film & Television
    Studios LLC, pg 791
MediaMix Inc, pg 822
PLS Staging, pg 858
Starlite, pg 900
Telemetrics Inc, pg 910
Video Corporation of America
    (VCA), pg 927

NEW MEXICO

Production Outfitters, pg 864

NEW YORK

Ace Video, pg 674
Adorama Rental Co, pg 676
Adwar Video, pg 678
Air Sea Land Productions Inc
    (ASL), pg 678
All Mobile Video Inc, pg 680
AV Workshop, pg 697
Big Apple Films, pg 705
Big Foot Productions Inc, pg 705
Bond Street Studio, pg 708
Bravo Studios, pg 709
Brooklyn Studios, pg 711
Cine 60 Inc, pg 723
Cinema-Vision, pg 724
CP Communications, pg 732
CPT Rental Inc, pg 732
Design Audio Visual Inc, pg 741
Gearhead Rentals, pg 769
Hand Held Films, pg 775
HB-Content, pg 777
KVL Audio Visual Services Inc,
    pg 802
Langie Audio Visual Systems,
    pg 803
LightHouse Films, pg 807
LightSpace Studios, pg 808
Long Island Video Enterprises Live
    Inc, pg 811
Manhattan Center Studios Inc,
    pg 816
PrimaLux Video Inc, pg 862
Rollin Studios, pg 877
Scheimpflug Digital, pg 881
Specialized Audio-Visual Inc,
    pg 896
Tri-Ed Distribution Inc, pg 918
Visual Technologies Corp, pg 932
Visual Word Systems Inc, pg 932

NORTH CAROLINA

The Communications Group Inc,
    pg 729
Digital Rain LLC, pg 742
K2 Productions, pg 802
Moving Pictures, pg 832
On Location North Carolina, pg 846
Special Event Services, pg 896
Strategic Connections, pg 901
Take One Productions Ltd, pg 906
Trailblazer Studios®, pg 917

NORTH DAKOTA

Media Productions, pg 822

OHIO

Audio Visual Media, pg 694
ITA Audio Visual Solutions, pg 791
iVideo Technologies, pg 792
Lyon Video Inc, pg 813
Mills James Productions, pg 828
Production Partners Media, pg 864
R&B Communications Inc, pg 870
Vista Color Imaging Inc, pg 931

OKLAHOMA

PDC Productions, pg 852

OREGON

Koerner Camera Systems, pg 800
Northwest Film Center, pg 842
Pacific Grip & Lighting Inc, pg 849
Picture This Production Services,
    pg 856

PENNSYLVANIA

Argentine Productions Inc, pg 688
Bernie's Photo Center, pg 704

FirstGeneration Audio/Visual
    Services, pg 761
FMP Media Solutions Inc, pg 763
Innovision Media Group, pg 788
Muderick Media, pg 833
New York Camera & Video, pg 840
Videosmith Inc, pg 930
Viewpoint Production Services Inc,
    pg 930
Visual Sound Inc, pg 931

SOUTH CAROLINA

Studio Charleston, pg 902

TENNESSEE

Memphis Communications Corp,
    pg 823
RentACamera.com, pg 873
Russ Sturgeon Productions/RSVP,
    pg 903
Technical Support Systems LLC,
    pg 908

TEXAS

Audio Visual Technologies Group
    (AVTG), pg 695
GEAR Cameras & Lighting, pg 769
JSAV, pg 795
Earl Miller Productions Inc, pg 827
Muller Entertainment LLC, pg 833
Phillips Media Source, pg 855
South Coast Film & Video, pg 895
Stage Directions, pg 898
Texcam Inc, pg 911

UTAH

Ron Hill Imagery, pg 780
TV Specialists Inc, pg 919

VERMONT

Dark Star Lighting & Production,
    pg 737
Marlboro Productions, pg 817

VIRGINIA

Audio Visual Actions Inc (AVA),
    pg 694
Boitnott Visual Communications
    Corp (BVC), pg 708
CVW Event Productions, pg 736
Lee Hartman & Sons Inc, pg 805
Projection, pg 865
Quince Imaging Inc, pg 868
StageSound, pg 899

WASHINGTON

The House Studios, pg 782
Inland Audio Visual Co, pg 788
Kostov Productions, pg 801
Oppenheimer Camera Products,
    pg 847

WISCONSIN

Audio Visual of Milwaukee Inc,
    pg 694
Camera Corner Connecting Point,
    pg 715
Event Essentials, pg 756
Full Compass Systems, pg 767
USAV Group Inc, pg 923
Wisconsin Public Television, pg 940

WYOMING

Bridger Productions Inc, pg 710

PUERTO RICO

Stage Crew Audiovisual Inc, pg 898

ALBERTA

Allstar Show Industries Inc, pg 681
Global TV, pg 771

BRITISH COLUMBIA

Commercial Electronics Ltd, pg 728
DL Sound & Lighting Productions
    Ltd, pg 744
Video Out Distribution, pg 928

MANITOBA

MidCanada Production Services Inc
    (MidCan), pg 826

ONTARIO

GAPC (General Assembly
    Production Centre), pg 768
HD Source, pg 777
RB Productions, pg 870
SIM Digital, pg 888
ZTV Broadcast Services Inc, pg 945

QUEBEC

Freeman Audio Visual, pg 765
Group PVP, pg 774
Kerrigan Productions Inc, pg 798

Equipment & Accessory Repairs

CALIFORNIA

Advanced Media LLC, pg 677
Advanced Systems Group LLC,
    pg 677
Ametron Audio/Video, pg 684
AVerMedia Technologies Inc,
    pg 697
Christy's Editorial, pg 723
Matthews Studio Equipment Inc,
    pg 820
Metro Video Systems Inc, pg 824
Pro Camera Repair, pg 862
SSL Industries Inc, pg 898
Steeldeck® Inc, pg 900
Technical Services, pg 908
Transvideo International, pg 917
VMI Inc, pg 932

COLORADO

Ceavco Audio Visual Company Inc,
    pg 719
Videomagnetics, pg 929

CONNECTICUT

Precision Camera & Video Repair
    Inc, pg 861
Rockwell Communications Inc,
    pg 876
Vitec Videocom Inc, pg 932

FLORIDA

ELC Sales & Service Inc, pg 752
Encore Broadcast Solutions, pg 754
Glanz Technologies Inc, pg 771
Midtown Video Inc, pg 827
Tallahassee Audio Visual, pg 906

GEORGIA

Audio Visual Resources Inc, pg 695
Stage Front Presentation Systems,
    pg 899

VIDEO

Equipment & Accessory Repairs (continued)

ILLINOIS

Beatty TeleVisual Productions, pg 703
On Site Video, pg 846
Tele-Time Systems, pg 910

INDIANA

Gary Camera & Digital, pg 768

KENTUCKY

NOR-COM Inc, pg 841

MARYLAND

RTZ Audio Visual, pg 878

MICHIGAN

Olson Anderson Co, pg 685
Lowing Light & Grip Inc, pg 812
TEL Systems LLC, pg 909

MINNESOTA

Alpha Video & Audio Inc, pg 682
AVI Systems, pg 698

MISSOURI

Southwest Audio-Visual Inc, pg 895

NEW JERSEY

Earl Girls Inc, pg 749
Konica Minolta Business Solutions, pg 801
Starlite, pg 900
Turner Engineering Inc, pg 919

NEW YORK

Adwar Video, pg 678
Colortone Audio Visual, pg 728
Langie Audio Visual Systems, pg 803
MAC Group, pg 813
Tri-Ed Distribution Inc, pg 918
Visual Technologies Corp, pg 932

NORTH CAROLINA

Camcor Inc, pg 715
Strategic Connections, pg 901

OHIO

Audio Visual Media, pg 694
ITA Audio Visual Solutions, pg 791
iVideo Technologies, pg 792

PENNSYLVANIA

Bernie's Photo Center, pg 704
Wespen Audio Visual Co, pg 935

TENNESSEE

Memphis Communications Corp, pg 823
Technical Support Systems LLC, pg 908

TEXAS

Audio Visual Technologies Group (AVTG), pg 695
Pro Video & Film Equipment Co Inc, pg 863

UTAH

RIA Corp, pg 874
TV Specialists Inc, pg 919

VIRGINIA

Avitecture Inc, pg 699
Lee Hartman & Sons Inc, pg 805

WASHINGTON

Inland Audio Visual Co, pg 788
Oppenheimer Camera Products, pg 847

WISCONSIN

Camera Corner Connecting Point, pg 715
Full Compass Systems, pg 767

ALBERTA

Evolution AV, pg 757

BRITISH COLUMBIA

Commercial Electronics Ltd, pg 728

ONTARIO

HD Source, pg 777

Fiber Optic Cable Distributors

ARIZONA

EAR Professional Audio/Video, pg 749

ARKANSAS

Jay S Stanley & Associates Inc, pg 899

CALIFORNIA

Ametron Audio/Video, pg 684
Hosa Technology Inc, pg 781
MediaPOINTE, pg 823
Orvac Electronics, pg 848
Southern California Sound Image Inc, pg 895
SSL Industries Inc, pg 898
VMI Inc, pg 932
VTP Inc, pg 933
Westlake Recording Studios, pg 936
Zack Electronics Inc, pg 945

FLORIDA

Digital Video Systems, pg 742
Herman Pro AV, pg 779
Multicom Inc, pg 833

GEORGIA

Accu-Tech, pg 673
Stage Front Presentation Systems, pg 899

HAWAII

The Audio Visual Co (AVCO), pg 694

ILLINOIS

Arcor Electronics Co, pg 688
Clark Wire & Cable, pg 725
Cole Wire & Cable Co Inc, pg 727
Joseph Electronics, pg 795
Quintessence Audio Ltd, pg 868

INDIANA

Sensory Technologies LLC, pg 884
SHP Electronics, pg 887

KENTUCKY

Axxis Leasing Inc, pg 700
General Cable, pg 769
NOR-COM Inc, pg 841

MARYLAND

Siqura Inc, pg 889

MASSACHUSETTS

Antronics Inc, pg 686
Rule Boston Camera, pg 878
SLR Enterprises LLC, pg 890

MICHIGAN

DAWNco, pg 739

MINNESOTA

Alpha Video & Audio Inc, pg 682

MISSOURI

Modern Communications Inc, pg 828
The RapcoHorizon Co, pg 870
Southwest Audio-Visual Inc, pg 895

NEVADA

MeshTel, pg 824

NEW JERSEY

Alltec Stores, a Vcom IMC Company, pg 681
American Fibertek Inc, pg 683
Avtech Systems Inc, pg 699
Canare Corporation of America, pg 716
Diversified, pg 744
Fiber Optic Systems Inc (FOSI), pg 759
Tele-Measurements Inc, pg 910

NEW YORK

BTX Technologies, pg 712
CP Communications, pg 732
HAVE Inc, pg 777
Markertek Video Supply, pg 817
MultiDyne Video & Fiber Optics Systems, pg 833
TecNec Distributing, pg 909

PENNSYLVANIA

Advanced AV LLC, pg 677
Clair Companies, pg 725
West Penn Wire, pg 935

TENNESSEE

Lowrance Sound Co Inc, pg 812

TEXAS

AVES Audio Visual Systems Inc, pg 698
Digital Display Solutions Inc, pg 742
Sundance Systems, Fibox Products Division, pg 904

VIRGINIA

Avitecture Inc, pg 699
The Whitlock Group, pg 937

WASHINGTON

Telect Inc, pg 910

WISCONSIN

Audio Visual of Milwaukee Inc, pg 694
Full Compass Systems, pg 767

ALBERTA

Infosat Communications Inc, pg 787

ONTARIO

Westbury National Show Systems Ltd, pg 936

Fiber Optic Cable Manufacturers

ARIZONA

Covid Inc, pg 732

CALIFORNIA

Fiber Optic Cable Shop, pg 759
Gefen, pg 769
Hosa Technology Inc, pg 781
Monster Cable Products Inc, pg 829
Physical Optics Corp (POC), pg 856

FLORIDA

Nemal Electronics International Inc, pg 838

ILLINOIS

Joseph Electronics, pg 795

INDIANA

Belden Inc, pg 703

KENTUCKY

General Cable, pg 769

MARYLAND

RCI Custom Products, pg 871
Siqura Inc, pg 889

MASSACHUSETTS

Mohawk, pg 829

MISSOURI

The RapcoHorizon Co, pg 870

NEVADA

MeshTel, pg 824

NEW JERSEY

Canare Corporation of America, pg 716
Crestron Electronics Inc, pg 734

NEW YORK

CP Communications, pg 732
MultiDyne Video & Fiber Optics Systems, pg 833

PENNSYLVANIA

West Penn Wire, pg 935

WASHINGTON

Telect Inc, pg 910

VIDEO
Filter Rentals (continued)

NORTH DAKOTA
Media Productions, pg 822

OHIO
Lyon Video Inc, pg 813
Mills James Productions, pg 828
R&B Communications Inc, pg 870

OREGON
Koerner Camera Systems, pg 800
Northwest Film Center, pg 842
Picture This Production Services,
    pg 856

PENNSYLVANIA
Argentine Productions Inc, pg 688
FMP Media Solutions Inc, pg 763
Location Camera Ltd, pg 810
New York Camera & Video, pg 840
The Videohouse Inc, pg 929
Viewpoint Production Services Inc,
    pg 930

TEXAS
GEAR Cameras & Lighting, pg 769
Texcam Inc, pg 911

WASHINGTON
Oppenheimer Camera Products,
    pg 847

WISCONSIN
MKE Production Rental, pg 828

MANITOBA
MidCanada Production Services Inc
    (MidCan), pg 826

ONTARIO
JIB Shots Equipment Inc, pg 794
RB Productions, pg 870
William F White International Inc,
    pg 937

Filter Repairs

GEORGIA
Stage Front Presentation Systems,
    pg 899

KENTUCKY
NOR-COM Inc, pg 841

MICHIGAN
TEL Systems LLC, pg 909

NEW YORK
MAC Group, pg 813

Frame Storage Device, *see*
Still Frame Storage
Device

Grip Equipment
Distributors

ARIZONA
CamMate Systems, pg 715
Troxell-CDI, pg 918

ARKANSAS
White Diamond Productions LLC,
    pg 937

CALIFORNIA
Ametron Audio/Video, pg 684
BroadcastStore.com, pg 711
Christy's Editorial, pg 723
Filmtools®, pg 761
Alan Gordon Enterprises Inc,
    pg 772
LEE Filters, pg 805
Manios Digital & Film, pg 816
Matthews Studio Equipment Inc,
    pg 820
Mole-Richardson Co, pg 829
Nalpak Inc, pg 835
Premier Lighting & Production Co,
    pg 861
The Rosenthal Group, pg 877
Sacramento Theatrical Lighting Ltd
    (STL), pg 879
San Diego Stage & Lighting Supply
    Inc, pg 879
SNAP, pg 891
Steeldeck® Inc, pg 900
VMI Inc, pg 932

CONNECTICUT
Connecticut Audio & Theatrical
    Supply, pg 731
Vitec Videocom Inc, pg 932

FLORIDA
Access Media Group, pg 673
Digital Video Systems, pg 742
EZ FX Inc, pg 758
Hi-Tech Enterprises Inc, pg 779
Hi-Tech Import Export Corp,
    pg 779
ONstage, pg 846
Techni-Lux Inc, pg 908

GEORGIA
Innocinema, pg 788
Lighting & Production Equipment
    Inc, pg 807
MAGNUM Companies Ltd, pg 815
Stage Front Presentation Systems,
    pg 899

HAWAII
The Audio Visual Co (AVCO),
    pg 694

ILLINOIS
Grand Stage Co Inc, pg 773
Photoflex Inc, pg 856

INDIANA
Sensory Technologies LLC, pg 884

KANSAS
Lights On, pg 808

LOUISIANA
Available Lighting & Motion
    Picture Services Inc, pg 697

MARYLAND
Noventri, pg 843
Theatre Service & Supply Corp,
    pg 912

MASSACHUSETTS
Hunt's Photo & Video, pg 782
Limelight Production® Inc, pg 809
Rule Boston Camera, pg 878
Visual Departures Ltd, pg 931

MICHIGAN
Lowing Light & Grip Inc, pg 812

MINNESOTA
Alpha Video & Audio Inc, pg 682
Cinequipt Inc, pg 724

MISSOURI
Modern Communications Inc,
    pg 828
Schiller's Audio-Visual, pg 881
Southwest Audio-Visual Inc, pg 895

NEVADA
Aardvark Video & Media
    Productions, pg 671

NEW HAMPSHIRE
APS Lighting-Sound-AV, pg 688

NEW JERSEY
AV Bluebook, pg 696
Comprehensive Cable &
    Connectivity Co, pg 729
Earl Girls Inc, pg 749
Euro-Pacific Film & Video
    Productions Inc, pg 756
Manfrotto Distribution Inc, pg 816
Rose Brand, pg 877
Video Corporation of America
    (VCA), pg 927

NEW MEXICO
Quickbeam Systems Inc (QSI),
    pg 868

NEW YORK
Audio-Video Corp, pg 694
AV Workshop, pg 697
B&H Photo Video, pg 701
Barbizon Electric Co Inc, pg 701
BMI Supply, pg 708
Creative Stage Lighting Co Inc,
    pg 733
Gotham Sound & Communications
    Inc, pg 773
HAVE Inc, pg 777
Long Island Video Enterprises Live
    Inc, pg 811
MAC Group, pg 813
Markertek Video Supply, pg 817
Production Resource Group LLC
    (PRG), pg 864
TecNec Distributing, pg 909
Tri-Ed Distribution Inc, pg 918

NORTH CAROLINA
Camcor Inc, pg 715
Harrison Brothers, pg 776
Strategic Connections, pg 901

OHIO
Future Light Inc, pg 767
Vincent Lighting Systems, pg 930
Visual Products Inc, pg 931

OREGON
Pacific Grip & Lighting Inc, pg 849

PENNSYLVANIA
Advanced AV LLC, pg 677
Innovision Media Group, pg 788
The Lerro Corp, pg 806
Morefield Communications Inc,
    pg 830

TENNESSEE
Lowrance Sound Co Inc, pg 812

TEXAS
GEAR Cameras & Lighting, pg 769
Olden Lighting, pg 845
Omega Broadcast Group, pg 845
Precision Camera & Video, pg 861
Pro Video & Film Equipment Co
    Inc, pg 863

UTAH
Redman Movies & Stories, pg 872
RIA Corp, pg 874

VERMONT
Production Advantage Inc, pg 863

VIRGINIA
Lee Hartman & Sons Inc, pg 805

WASHINGTON
Oppenheimer Camera Products,
    pg 847

WEST VIRGINIA
Blackwater Video Productions,
    pg 707

WISCONSIN
Audio Visual of Milwaukee Inc,
    pg 694
Camera Corner Connecting Point,
    pg 715
Egripment USA, pg 751
Full Compass Systems, pg 767
Safe Harbor Computers, pg 879

ALBERTA
Matrix Video Communications Corp
    (MVCC), pg 819

MANITOBA
Lank/Beach Productions Inc, pg 803

ONTARIO
HD Source, pg 777
VFGadgets Inc, pg 926

Grip Equipment
Manufacturers

ARIZONA
CamMate Systems, pg 715
Zippertubing® Co, pg 945

CALIFORNIA
CineBags Inc, pg 723
Filmtools®, pg 761
LEE Filters, pg 805
Matthews Studio Equipment Inc,
    pg 820
Microdolly Hollywood, pg 826

Mole-Richardson Co, pg 829
Nalpak Inc, pg 835
Porta-Jib, pg 859
Steeldeck® Inc, pg 900

COLORADO

Checkers Safety Group, pg 721

FLORIDA

Union Connector Co Inc, pg 921

GEORGIA

Lighting & Production Equipment Inc, pg 807

ILLINOIS

Photoflex Inc, pg 856

INDIANA

Star Case Manufacturing Co Inc, pg 900

MARYLAND

Theatre Service & Supply Corp, pg 912

MASSACHUSETTS

Glidecam Industries Inc, pg 771
Visual Departures Ltd, pg 931

MICHIGAN

Lowing Light & Grip Inc, pg 812

NEW JERSEY

Hasselblad Bron Inc, pg 776
Unilux Inc, pg 921

OHIO

Future Light Inc, pg 767

WASHINGTON

RAM® Mounts, pg 869

WISCONSIN

Egriment USA, pg 751

Grip Equipment Rentals

ALASKA

Connections Film & Video Inc, pg 731

ARIZONA

Arizona Cine Equipment, pg 688
Merestone, pg 823
Metropolitan Audio-Visual Inc, pg 824
Reel Men Rentals Inc, pg 872

ARKANSAS

White Diamond Productions LLC, pg 937

CALIFORNIA

Acey Decy Lighting, pg 674
Action Audio & Visual, pg 675
Action Video, pg 675
Ametron Audio/Video, pg 684
Artichoke Productions, pg 690
Big Door, pg 705
The Camera Division, pg 715
Chapman/Leonard Studio Equipment Inc, pg 720

Chater Camera Inc, pg 721
Cherry Multimedia, pg 721
Cinema Camera Rentals, pg 723
Clean Slate Video, pg 726
Crash Video Productions, pg 733
Digital Film Studios LLC, pg 742
The Dreaming Tree, pg 746
DTC Lighting & Grip, pg 747
Express Media Inc, pg 757
First Camera, pg 761
Full Moon & High Tide Productions & Studios, pg 767
Gear Monkey, pg 769
Glix Entertainment Inc, pg 771
Gold Standard Productions, pg 772
Golden Gate Studios, pg 772
Alan Gordon Enterprises Inc, pg 772
Greenery Studios, pg 774
HDrental.com, pg 777
iCorpTv, pg 783
Illuminate Studios, pg 784
Imagecraft Productions, pg 785
Images in Motion Media Inc, pg 785
Laurel Canyon Stages, pg 804
Loyal Studios, pg 812
Lynch Communications, pg 813
Mole-Richardson Co, pg 829
New Circuit Films LLC, pg 839
North County Media Center, pg 842
Pollution Studios, pg 859
Porter Productions, pg 859
Power & Light, pg 860
Premier Lighting & Production Co, pg 861
Prime Cut Productions, pg 862
Pro HD Rentals, pg 863
The Producer's Loft, pg 863
Production Gear Rentals (PGR), pg 863
RED Studios Hollywood, pg 872
The Rosenthal Group, pg 877
Samy's Camera, pg 879
Santa Clarita Studios, pg 880
SNAP, pg 891
Source Film Studio, pg 895
Steeldeck® Inc, pg 900
Still N' Motion, pg 901
Straight Shoot'r Cranes Inc, pg 901
Stray Angel Films, pg 902
The Studios at Paramount, pg 903
Sunset Las Palmas Studios, pg 904
T-stop Inc, pg 906
Total Creative, pg 916
Twin Peaks Creative, pg 920
Universal Studios, pg 922
Valencia Studios, pg 924
Vitruvian Entertainment, pg 932
Voice & Video Rentals, pg 932
Warner Bros Entertainment Inc, pg 934
Westcoast Video Productions Inc, pg 936
Z-Ville Productions, pg 944

COLORADO

Daylight Productions & Rentals, pg 739
Maniac Productions, pg 816
Westworks Studios, pg 936
Zelo Productions Inc, pg 945

CONNECTICUT

KJfilms LLC, pg 799
Videofilm Systems Inc, pg 929
Vitec Videocom Inc, pg 932

DISTRICT OF COLUMBIA

Interface Media Group, pg 789

FLORIDA

Access Media Group, pg 673
Accord Productions, pg 673
Adrenaline Films, pg 676
Aperture Studios Miami, pg 687
Budget Video Rentals, pg 712
C&I An Idea Agency, pg 716
CopShopMiami.com, pg 731
Digital Zoetrope Productions, pg 742
Facet Media, pg 758
Fiddler Films, pg 759
The Great Southern Studios, pg 773
HD House, pg 777
Hi-Tech Enterprises Inc, pg 779
Jordan Klein Film & Video (JKFV), pg 795
JungleTV, pg 795
Knowles Video Inc (KVI), pg 800
MAPS Production House, pg 816
Miami Daylight Studios, pg 825
Moving Picture, pg 831
National Teleproductions Inc, pg 837
ONstage, pg 846
Universal Studios Florida® Production Group, pg 922
Mike Vasilinda Productions Inc, pg 925

GEORGIA

Lighting & Production Equipment Inc, pg 807
Magick Lantern, pg 814
MAGNUM Companies Ltd, pg 815
Stage Front Presentation Systems, pg 899
Studio Space Atlanta, pg 903

HAWAII

FOTON Hawaii, pg 764
Sight & Sound Studios, pg 887

ILLINOIS

Backstar Creative Media Inc, pg 700
LITE-IT Grip Truck Rentals, pg 810
Magnanimous Media, pg 814
Product Productions, pg 863
PSAV® Presentation Services (Hotel Services Division), pg 866
Resolution Productions Group, pg 874
2nd Cine Inc, pg 883
Zacuto, pg 945

IOWA

Musco Lighting, pg 834

KANSAS

Lights On, pg 808

KENTUCKY

Idle Minds Productions Inc, pg 784
Kentucky Grip & Lighting, pg 798

LOUISIANA

Available Lighting & Motion Picture Services Inc, pg 697
Digital FX Inc, pg 742
Moxie Media, pg 832
Pace Systems, pg 849
Second Line Stages, pg 883

MARYLAND

Archai Media, pg 688
CPR MultiMedia Solutions, pg 732
Event Tech, pg 756

Kramer Communications Video Production, pg 801
RTZ Audio Visual, pg 878

MASSACHUSETTS

Capron Lighting & Sound Co Inc, pg 716
Green Mountain Post Films (GMP), pg 774
High Output Inc, pg 779
Limelight Production® Inc, pg 809
Red Sky Studios, pg 872

MICHIGAN

City Events Group, pg 725
K&R All Media Productions LLC, pg 796
K&R's Recording Studios Inc, pg 796
Lowing Light & Grip Inc, pg 812

MINNESOTA

Alpha Video & Audio Inc, pg 682
Cinequipt Inc, pg 724
House of Cinemagraphics, pg 782

MISSOURI

Schiller's Audio-Visual, pg 881
Show-Me Audio-Visual, pg 887
Sight & Sound Production Services Inc, pg 887
Southwest Audio-Visual Inc, pg 895

MONTANA

Filmlites Montana, pg 760

NEBRASKA

Lights On Nebraska, pg 808

NEVADA

JCS Video Productions, pg 793
MG Studio, pg 825

NEW HAMPSHIRE

Apertura, pg 686
APS Lighting-Sound-AV, pg 688

NEW JERSEY

Butter Tree Studios, pg 713
CFP Video Productions Inc, pg 720
Earl Girls Inc, pg 749
Euro-Pacific Film & Video Productions Inc, pg 756
Ironbound Film & Television Studios LLC, pg 791
MediaMix, pg 822
MiB MediaWorks, pg 825
Unilux Inc, pg 921
Video Corporation of America (VCA), pg 927

NEW MEXICO

Production Outfitters, pg 864
Quickbeam Systems Inc (QSI), pg 868

NEW YORK

Ace Video, pg 674
Adorama Rental Co, pg 676
AV Workshop, pg 697
Available Light, pg 697
BC Studio, pg 702
Big Foot Productions Inc, pg 705
Bond Street Studio, pg 708
Bravo Studios, pg 709
Brooklyn Fire Proof, pg 711
Brooklyn Studios, pg 711

VIDEO

Grip Equipment Rentals (continued)

NEW YORK (continued)

Creative Stage Lighting Co Inc, pg 733
CSI Rentals, pg 735
Digital Arts NY, pg 742
Gearhead Rentals, pg 769
Gotham Sound & Communications Inc, pg 773
Hand Held Films, pg 775
Hello World Communications, pg 778
LightHouse Films, pg 807
LightSpace Studios, pg 808
Long Island Video Enterprises Live Inc, pg 811
Manhattan Center Studios Inc, pg 816
PrimaLux Video Inc, pg 862
Production Central, pg 863
Production Resource Group LLC (PRG), pg 864
Rollin Studios, pg 877
Scheimpflug Digital, pg 881
Steiner Studios, pg 900

NORTH CAROLINA

All Pro Media Inc, pg 680
The Communications Group Inc, pg 729
Duke Media Services, pg 747
Moving Pictures, pg 832
On Location North Carolina, pg 846
Special Event Services, pg 896
Take One Productions Ltd, pg 906

NORTH DAKOTA

Media Productions, pg 822

OHIO

Lyon Video Inc, pg 813
Mills James Productions, pg 828
Ohio HD Video, pg 844
OSV Studios, pg 848
R&B Communications Inc, pg 870
Vincent Lighting Systems, pg 930
Vista Color Imaging Inc, pg 931

OREGON

Pacific Grip & Lighting Inc, pg 849
Picture This Production Services, pg 856

PENNSYLVANIA

FMP Media Solutions Inc, pg 763
Innovision Media Group, pg 788
JPL, pg 795
Location Camera Ltd, pg 810
Location Lighting Ltd, pg 810
New York Camera & Video, pg 840
The Videohouse Inc, pg 929
Viewpoint Production Services Inc, pg 930

SOUTH CAROLINA

Assignment Desk, pg 691
Studio Charleston, pg 902

TENNESSEE

DR&A Inc, pg 746
NuMynd Studios, pg 843
Russ Sturgeon Productions/RSVP, pg 903

TEXAS

GEAR Cameras & Lighting, pg 769
Earl Miller Productions Inc, pg 827
Muller Entertainment LLC, pg 833
Olden Lighting, pg 845
Omega Broadcast Group, pg 845
Phillips Media Source, pg 855
Photogroup Studios, pg 856
South Coast Film & Video, pg 895
Stage Directions, pg 898
Texcam Inc, pg 911
Video Perspective, pg 928

UTAH

Ron Hill Imagery, pg 780
Redman Movies & Stories, pg 872

WASHINGTON

The House Studios, pg 782
Intermedia Inc, pg 789
Oppenheimer Camera Products, pg 847
Victory Studios, pg 927

WEST VIRGINIA

Blackwater Video Productions, pg 707

WISCONSIN

Audio Visual of Milwaukee Inc, pg 694
MKE Production Rental, pg 828

WYOMING

Bridger Productions Inc, pg 710

ALBERTA

Global TV, pg 771
Matrix Video Communications Corp (MVCC), pg 819

BRITISH COLUMBIA

Inspired Image Picture Co (IIPC), pg 788

MANITOBA

MidCanada Production Services Inc (MidCan), pg 826

ONTARIO

GAPC (General Assembly Production Centre), pg 768
HD Source, pg 777
JIB Shots Equipment Inc, pg 794
RB Productions, pg 870
SIM Digital, pg 888
William F White International Inc, pg 937
ZTV Broadcast Services Inc, pg 945

QUEBEC

Group PVP, pg 774
Kerrigan Productions Inc, pg 798

Grip Equipment Repairs

CALIFORNIA

Ametron Audio/Video, pg 684
Chapman/Leonard Studio Equipment Inc, pg 720
Matthews Studio Equipment Inc, pg 820
Mole-Richardson Co, pg 829
Steeldeck® Inc, pg 900

CONNECTICUT

Vitec Videocom Inc, pg 932

FLORIDA

Hi-Tech Enterprises Inc, pg 779

GEORGIA

Lighting & Production Equipment Inc, pg 807
MAGNUM Companies Ltd, pg 815
Stage Front Presentation Systems, pg 899

MICHIGAN

Lowing Light & Grip Inc, pg 812
TEL Systems LLC, pg 909

MINNESOTA

Alpha Video & Audio Inc, pg 682

MISSOURI

Schiller's Audio-Visual, pg 881
Southwest Audio-Visual Inc, pg 895

NEW JERSEY

Earl Girls Inc, pg 749

NEW MEXICO

Quickbeam Systems Inc (QSI), pg 868

NEW YORK

MAC Group, pg 813
Production Resource Group LLC (PRG), pg 864

NORTH CAROLINA

Camcor Inc, pg 715

TEXAS

GEAR Cameras & Lighting, pg 769
Olden Lighting, pg 845

UTAH

Redman Movies & Stories, pg 872
RIA Corp, pg 874

WISCONSIN

Full Compass Systems, pg 767

Head Distributors

ARIZONA

EAR Professional Audio/Video, pg 749

CALIFORNIA

Ametron Audio/Video, pg 684
BigFoot Mobile Systems, pg 705
Christy's Editorial, pg 723
Cibola Systems, pg 723
Manios Digital & Film, pg 816
SNAP, pg 891

CONNECTICUT

Connecticut Audio & Theatrical Supply, pg 731

FLORIDA

Digital Video Systems, pg 742
Enhanced View Services Inc, pg 754

HAWAII

The Audio Visual Co (AVCO), pg 694

ILLINOIS

International Electro-Magnetics Inc, pg 790
Joseph Electronics, pg 795

INDIANA

Sensory Technologies LLC, pg 884

MARYLAND

Noventri, pg 843

MASSACHUSETTS

Hunt's Photo & Video, pg 782
Rule Boston Camera, pg 878

MINNESOTA

Alpha Video & Audio Inc, pg 682

MISSOURI

Modern Communications Inc, pg 828
Schiller's Audio-Visual, pg 881
Southwest Audio-Visual Inc, pg 895

NEW JERSEY

AV Bluebook, pg 696
JRF Magnetic Sciences Inc, pg 795
Manfrotto Distribution Inc, pg 816
MCCOM Inc, pg 820
Total Video Products Inc, pg 916

NEW YORK

Audio-Video Corp, pg 694
Benro, pg 704
Induro, pg 787
RNJ Electronics, pg 875
Russell Industries Inc, pg 879

PENNSYLVANIA

Advanced AV LLC, pg 677
The Lerro Corp, pg 806

TENNESSEE

Lowrance Sound Co Inc, pg 812

TEXAS

Pro Video & Film Equipment Co Inc, pg 863

WASHINGTON

Oppenheimer Camera Products, pg 847

WISCONSIN

Audio Visual of Milwaukee Inc, pg 694
Egripment USA, pg 751
Full Compass Systems, pg 767

BRITISH COLUMBIA

Commercial Electronics Ltd, pg 728

MANITOBA

Lank/Beach Productions Inc, pg 803

Head Manufacturers

CALIFORNIA

Microdolly Hollywood, pg 826

COLORADO

Videomagnetics, pg 929

MASSACHUSETTS

Glidecam Industries Inc, pg 771

NEW YORK

Induro, pg 787

WISCONSIN

Egripment USA, pg 751

Interactive TV Hardware Distributors

ARKANSAS

Jay S Stanley & Associates Inc, pg 899

CALIFORNIA

VMI Inc, pg 932

FLORIDA

Access Media Group, pg 673
Digital Video Systems, pg 742
Hi-Tech Enterprises Inc, pg 779
ONstage, pg 846

GEORGIA

PolyVision Corporation, pg 859
Stage Front Presentation Systems, pg 899

HAWAII

The Audio Visual Co (AVCO), pg 694

INDIANA

Sensory Technologies LLC, pg 884

KENTUCKY

Axxis Leasing Inc, pg 700
NOR-COM Inc, pg 841

NEVADA

Aardvark Video & Media Productions, pg 671

NEW JERSEY

Alltec Stores, a Vcom IMC Company, pg 681
Tele-Measurements Inc, pg 910

NEW YORK

Audio-Video Corp, pg 694

PENNSYLVANIA

Advanced AV LLC, pg 677

TENNESSEE

Lowrance Sound Co Inc, pg 812

VIRGINIA

Lee Hartman & Sons Inc, pg 805

WISCONSIN

Full Compass Systems, pg 767

ALBERTA

SMART Technologies ULC, pg 891

MANITOBA

Inland Audio Visual Ltd, pg 788
Tek Gear, pg 909

ONTARIO

GestureTek, pg 770
Westbury National Show Systems Ltd, pg 936

Interactive TV Hardware Manufacturers

ARIZONA

Boeckeler Instruments Inc, pg 708

FLORIDA

Vutec Corp, pg 933

GEORGIA

PolyVision Corporation, pg 859

MICHIGAN

ASC Systems, pg 690

NEVADA

MeshTel, pg 824

NEW YORK

ChyronHego Corp, pg 723
Key Digital Systems, pg 798

TENNESSEE

Adtec Digital Inc, pg 677

ALBERTA

SMART Technologies ULC, pg 891

MANITOBA

Tek Gear, pg 909

ONTARIO

GestureTek, pg 770

Interactive TV Hardware Rentals

ARIZONA

Merestone, pg 823

CALIFORNIA

Big Door, pg 705
Munday & Collins AV, pg 834
RetinaVision Productions, pg 874

FLORIDA

Access Media Group, pg 673
ONstage, pg 846

GEORGIA

Stage Front Presentation Systems, pg 899

PENNSYLVANIA

FMP Media Solutions Inc, pg 763
Innovision Media Group, pg 788

TEXAS

GEAR Cameras & Lighting, pg 769

MANITOBA

Inland Audio Visual Ltd, pg 788

ONTARIO

Westbury National Show Systems Ltd, pg 936

Interactive TV Hardware Repairs

FLORIDA

ELC Sales & Service Inc, pg 752
Hi-Tech Enterprises Inc, pg 779

GEORGIA

Stage Front Presentation Systems, pg 899

KENTUCKY

Axxis Leasing Inc, pg 700
NOR-COM Inc, pg 841

MICHIGAN

TEL Systems LLC, pg 909

WISCONSIN

Full Compass Systems, pg 767

MANITOBA

Inland Audio Visual Ltd, pg 788
Tek Gear, pg 909

ONTARIO

Westbury National Show Systems Ltd, pg 936

Lens Distributors

ARIZONA

EAR Professional Audio/Video, pg 749
Image Marketing Corp, pg 785
Projector SuperStore LLC, pg 865
Tempe Camera, pg 910
Troxell-CDI, pg 918

ARKANSAS

Jay S Stanley & Associates Inc, pg 899

CALIFORNIA

AbelCine, pg 672
Advanced Systems Group LLC, pg 677
Ametron Audio/Video, pg 684
Audio/Video Supply Inc, pg 694
Band Pro Film & Digital Inc, pg 701
Birns & Sawyer Inc, pg 706
BroadcastStore.com, pg 711
Cibola Systems, pg 723
CohuHD Costar LLC, pg 727
DTC Lighting & Grip, pg 747
Eiki International Inc, pg 751
Express Video Supply Inc, pg 757
Gravity Media, pg 773
Hooper Camera & Imaging, pg 781
Innovision Optics, pg 788
Jai Inc, pg 792
Kappa optronics Inc, pg 796
Kenko Tokina USA, pg 797
Marshall Electronics Inc, pg 817
MediaPOINTE, pg 823
Photo-Sonics Inc, pg 856

PMP Marketing Inc, pg 858
Promax Systems, pg 865
Qioptiq, An Excelitas Technologies Company, pg 867
16 x 9 Inc, pg 890
SNAP, pg 891
Southern California Sound Image Inc, pg 895
SSL Industries Inc, pg 898
Visual Instrumentation Corp, pg 931
VMI Inc, pg 932
VTP Inc, pg 933

COLORADO

Mike's Camera, pg 827

CONNECTICUT

MAVCO, pg 820

FLORIDA

Access Media Group, pg 673
Cinema Equipment & Supplies Inc, pg 724
Digital Video Systems, pg 742
Glanz Technologies Inc, pg 771
Midtown Video Inc, pg 827
ONstage, pg 846
Reef Photo & Video, pg 872
Tallahassee Audio Visual, pg 906

GEORGIA

Convergent Media Systems, pg 731
Innocinema, pg 788
Stage Front Presentation Systems, pg 899
WolfVision Inc, pg 940

HAWAII

The Audio Visual Co (AVCO), pg 694

ILLINOIS

Tele-Time Systems, pg 910

INDIANA

Sensory Technologies LLC, pg 884

KENTUCKY

Barney Miller's Inc, pg 827
NOR-COM Inc, pg 841

LOUISIANA

Techkno Integration & Design Services LLC, pg 908

MARYLAND

Noventri, pg 843
RTZ Audio Visual, pg 878

MASSACHUSETTS

Antronics Inc, pg 686
Integrated Solutions Group, pg 789
Rule Boston Camera, pg 878

MINNESOTA

Alpha Video & Audio Inc, pg 682
AVI Systems, pg 698
Cinequipt Inc, pg 724

MISSISSIPPI

Bowie Audio Visual Enterprises Inc, pg 709
Jasper Ewing & Sons Inc, pg 757

VIDEO

Lens Distributors
(continued)

MISSOURI

Communitronics Corp, pg 729
Conference Technologies Inc, pg 730
Modern Communications Inc, pg 828
Schiller's Audio-Visual, pg 881
Southwest Audio-Visual Inc, pg 895

NEBRASKA

ATV Research Inc, pg 692
VSA Inc, pg 933

NEVADA

Aardvark Video & Media Productions, pg 671
MeshTel, pg 824

NEW JERSEY

Alltec Stores, a Vcom IMC Company, pg 681
Angenieux, pg 685
Audio Visual Dynamics®, pg 694
Avtech Systems Inc, pg 699
Comprehensive Cable & Connectivity Co, pg 729
Diversified, pg 744
DSI RF Systems Inc, pg 747
FUJIFILM Optical Devices Division, pg 766
G&G Technologies Inc, pg 768
HamiltonBuhl, pg 775
MCCOM Inc, pg 820
PatchAmp, pg 852
Starlite, pg 900
SYMCO Inc, pg 905
ToCad America Inc, pg 915
Total Video Products Inc, pg 916
Turner Engineering Inc, pg 919
Video Corporation of America (VCA), pg 927

NEW YORK

Audio-Video Corp, pg 694
AV Workshop, pg 697
B&H Photo Video, pg 701
Barbizon Electric Co Inc, pg 701
BTX Technologies, pg 712
Gage-Line Technology Inc, pg 767
Indigo Productions, pg 787
KVL Audio Visual Services Inc, pg 802
Long Island Video Enterprises Live Inc, pg 811
Mamiya, pg 815
Markertek Video Supply, pg 817
RNJ Electronics, pg 875
Sargent Welch, pg 880
Schneider Optics Inc, pg 881
Tri-Ed Distribution Inc, pg 918
Universe Kogaku America Inc, pg 922
Vision Identics Systems Inc, pg 930
Willoughby's® Camera, pg 939

NORTH CAROLINA

Alpine Optics Inc, pg 682
Camcor Inc, pg 715

OHIO

Copp Integrated Systems, pg 731
iVideo Technologies, pg 792
Visual Products Inc, pg 931

OKLAHOMA

Ford AV, pg 763

OREGON

PLUS Corp of America, pg 858

PENNSYLVANIA

Advanced AV LLC, pg 677
Audio Visions Inc, pg 694
Bernie's Photo Center, pg 704
J E Foss Co, pg 764
Grise Audio Visual Center Inc, pg 774
The Lerro Corp, pg 806
Morefield Communications Inc, pg 830
New York Camera & Video, pg 840
Questar Corp, pg 868
Visual Sound Inc, pg 931

TENNESSEE

Lowrance Sound Co Inc, pg 812
Memphis Communications Corp, pg 823
Technical Support Systems LLC, pg 908

TEXAS

Audio Visual Technologies Group (AVTG), pg 695
AVES Audio Visual Systems Inc, pg 698
Biway Media, pg 706
Heffernan Audio Visual, pg 778
IVS Imaging, pg 792
Omega Broadcast Group, pg 845
Precision Camera & Video, pg 861
Pro Video & Film Equipment Co Inc, pg 863
Supercircuits, pg 904

UTAH

RIA Corp, pg 874
Webb Audio Visual, pg 935

VIRGINIA

Avitecture Inc, pg 699
Boitnott Visual Communications Corp (BVC), pg 708
Lee Hartman & Sons Inc, pg 805
The Whitlock Group, pg 937

WASHINGTON

Oppenheimer Camera Products, pg 847

WISCONSIN

Camera Corner Connecting Point, pg 715
Full Compass Systems, pg 767

ALBERTA

Allstar Show Industries Inc, pg 681
Infosat Communications Inc, pg 787
Matrix Video Communications Corp (MVCC), pg 819

MANITOBA

Inland Audio Visual Ltd, pg 788

ONTARIO

HD Source, pg 777
Henry's Camera, pg 779
Majortech Inc, pg 815
Nationwide Audio Visual Co, pg 837

Lens Manufacturers

CALIFORNIA

Innovision Optics, pg 788
Marshall Electronics Inc, pg 817
Photo-Sonics Inc, pg 856
Physical Optics Corp (POC), pg 856
Qioptiq, An Excelitas Technologies Company, pg 867

GEORGIA

WolfVision Inc, pg 940

MINNESOTA

Vaddio, pg 924

NEBRASKA

Strong Cinema Products, pg 902

NEW JERSEY

Angenieux, pg 685
CELCO, pg 719
FUJIFILM Optical Devices Division, pg 766
Sofradir EC, pg 892

NEW YORK

Canon USA Inc, pg 716
Gage-Line Technology Inc, pg 767
Navitar Inc, pg 837
Schneider Optics Inc, pg 881
Scientifics Direct Inc, pg 882
Tamron USA Inc, pg 906
Universe Kogaku America Inc, pg 922
Vicon Industries Inc, pg 926

NORTH CAROLINA

Crest Electronics Inc, pg 734

PENNSYLVANIA

Kopp Glass, pg 801
Questar Corp, pg 868

TEXAS

IVS Imaging, pg 792

BRITISH COLUMBIA

Cavision Enterprises Ltd, pg 717
Triad Communications Ltd, pg 918

Lens Rentals

ALABAMA

Audio-Video Resources Inc, pg 694

ALASKA

Connections Film & Video Inc, pg 731

ARIZONA

Arizona Cine Equipment, pg 688
AV Concepts Inc, pg 696
Broadcast Rentals, pg 711
Merestone, pg 823
Metropolitan Audio-Visual Inc, pg 824
Reel Men Rentals Inc, pg 872
Video West Inc, pg 929

CALIFORNIA

AbelCine, pg 672
Action Audio & Visual, pg 675
Aerial Video Systems, pg 678
Alternative Rentals, pg 682
Ametron Audio/Video, pg 684
Artichoke Productions, pg 690
Bexel, an NEP Broadcast Services Company, pg 704
Big Door, pg 705
The Camera Division, pg 715
Chater Camera Inc, pg 721
Cherry Multimedia, pg 721
Cinema Camera Rentals, pg 723
Clean Slate Video, pg 726
Digital Film Studios LLC, pg 742
Dystopian Studios, pg 748
Express Media Inc, pg 757
Express Video Supply Inc, pg 757
First Camera, pg 761
Gear Monkey, pg 769
Glendale Production Center, pg 771
Golden Gate Studios, pg 772
Gravity Media, pg 773
HD Cinema, pg 777
HDrental.com, pg 777
Image Integration, pg 785
Imagecraft Productions, pg 785
Innovision Optics, pg 788
Lynch Communications, pg 813
McCune Audio-Video-Lighting, pg 821
Munday & Collins AV, pg 834
New Circuit Films LLC, pg 839
North County Media Center, pg 842
Old School Cameras, pg 844
Pollution Studios, pg 859
Pro HD Rentals, pg 863
Production Gear Rentals (PGR), pg 863
Samy's Camera, pg 879
Shooting Star Video, pg 886
Shoulder High Productions, pg 886
SNAP, pg 891
Stray Angel Films, pg 902
The Studios at Paramount, pg 903
T-stop Inc, pg 906
Total Creative, pg 916
Twin Peaks Creative, pg 920
VER, pg 926
Videofax, pg 929
Vitruvian Entertainment, pg 932
VMI Inc, pg 932
Voice & Video Rentals, pg 932
Westcoast Video Productions Inc, pg 936

COLORADO

Spectrum Audio Visual Services, pg 897

CONNECTICUT

A/V Davey, pg 697
Videofilm Systems Inc, pg 929

DELAWARE

Ken-Del Productions Inc, pg 797

FLORIDA

Access Media Group, pg 673
Budget Video Rentals, pg 712
C&I An Idea Agency, pg 716
Facet Media, pg 758
HD House, pg 777
Jordan Klein Film & Video (JKFV), pg 795
Midtown Video Inc, pg 827
Moving Picture, pg 831
ONstage, pg 846
Universal Studios Florida® Production Group, pg 922

GEORGIA

Convergent Media Systems, pg 731
ON Services, a GES Company, pg 846
See Production Services, pg 883
Stage Front Presentation Systems, pg 899

HAWAII

Sight & Sound Studios, pg 887

ILLINOIS

Backstar Creative Media Inc, pg 700
Magnanimous Media, pg 814
PSAV® Presentation Services (Hotel Services Division), pg 866
Resolution Productions Group, pg 874
2nd Cine Inc, pg 883
Zacuto, pg 945

KANSAS

Lights On, pg 808

KENTUCKY

Audio Visual Techniques Inc, pg 695

LOUISIANA

Digital FX Inc, pg 742
Pace Systems, pg 849

MARYLAND

Archai Media, pg 688
CPR MultiMedia Solutions, pg 732
Event Tech, pg 756
Kramer Communications Video Production, pg 801
RTZ Audio Visual, pg 878

MASSACHUSETTS

Integrated Solutions Group, pg 789
massAV, pg 819
Preston Productions Inc, pg 861

MICHIGAN

City Events Group, pg 725
K&R's Recording Studios Inc, pg 796

MINNESOTA

Alpha Video & Audio Inc, pg 682
AVI Systems, pg 698
Cinequipt Inc, pg 724
House of Cinemagraphics, pg 782
Pro Media Productions, pg 863

MISSISSIPPI

Bowie Audio Visual Enterprises Inc, pg 709

MISSOURI

Show-Me Audio-Visual, pg 887
Southwest Audio-Visual Inc, pg 895

NEBRASKA

Dog & Pony Productions Inc, pg 744
Lights On Nebraska, pg 808

NEVADA

MG Studio, pg 825

NEW JERSEY

Audio Visual Dynamics®, pg 694
CFP Video Productions Inc, pg 720
DSI RF Systems Inc, pg 747
MediaMix Inc, pg 822
PLS Staging, pg 858
Starlite, pg 900

NEW MEXICO

Production Outfitters, pg 864

NEW YORK

Adorama Rental Co, pg 676
All Mobile Video Inc, pg 680
AV Workshop, pg 697
Big Apple Films, pg 705
Bond Street Studio, pg 708
Cinema-Vision, pg 724
CMI Communications, pg 727
CP Communications, pg 732
CSI Rentals, pg 735
Gearhead Rentals, pg 769
Hand Held Films, pg 775
KVL Audio Visual Services Inc, pg 802
LightHouse Films, pg 807
LightSpace Studios, pg 808
Long Island Video Enterprises Live Inc, pg 811
Manhattan Center Studios Inc, pg 816
Scheimpflug Digital, pg 881
Tri-Ed Distribution Inc, pg 918

NORTH CAROLINA

All Pro Media Inc, pg 680
The Communications Group Inc, pg 729
Moving Pictures, pg 832
On Location North Carolina, pg 846
Strategic Connections, pg 901
Take One Productions Ltd, pg 906

OHIO

Lyon Video Inc, pg 813
Mills James Productions, pg 828
Ohio HD Video, pg 844
R&B Communications Inc, pg 870
Vista Color Imaging Inc, pg 931

OKLAHOMA

PDC Productions, pg 852

OREGON

Koerner Camera Systems, pg 800
Picture This Production Services, pg 856

PENNSYLVANIA

Argentine Productions Inc, pg 688
Audio Visions Inc, pg 694
Bernie's Photo Center, pg 704
FMP Media Solutions Inc, pg 763
Grise Audio Visual Center Inc, pg 774
Innovision Media Group, pg 788
JPL, pg 795
Location Camera Ltd, pg 810
Muderick Media, pg 833
New York Camera & Video, pg 840
Producers Management Television (PMTV), pg 863
The Videohouse Inc, pg 929
Videosmith, pg 930
Viewpoint Production Services Inc, pg 930

TENNESSEE

Memphis Communications Corp, pg 823
Nashville Production Rentals (NPR), pg 836
RentACamera.com, pg 873
Russ Sturgeon Productions/RSVP, pg 903
Technical Support Systems LLC, pg 908

TEXAS

Alford Media Services, pg 680
Omega Broadcast Group, pg 845
Precision Camera & Video, pg 861
Stage Directions, pg 898
Texcam Inc, pg 911

UTAH

Ron Hill Imagery, pg 780
Webb Audio Visual, pg 935

VIRGINIA

Boitnott Visual Communications Corp (BVC), pg 708
Quince Imaging Inc, pg 868
StageSound, pg 899

WASHINGTON

The House Studios, pg 782
Oppenheimer Camera Products, pg 847
Victory Studios, pg 927

WISCONSIN

Audio Visual of Milwaukee Inc, pg 694
Full Compass Systems, pg 767
Logan Productions Inc, pg 811
MKE Production Rental, pg 828

WYOMING

Bridger Productions Inc, pg 710

ALBERTA

Allstar Show Industries Inc, pg 681
Global TV, pg 771
Matrix Video Communications Corp (MVCC), pg 819

BRITISH COLUMBIA

Inspired Image Picture Co (IIPC), pg 788

MANITOBA

Inland Audio Visual Ltd, pg 788
MidCanada Production Services Inc (MidCan), pg 826

ONTARIO

HD Source, pg 777
JIB Shots Equipment Inc, pg 794
RB Productions, pg 870
SIM Digital, pg 888
William F White International Inc, pg 937
ZTV Broadcast Services Inc, pg 945

QUEBEC

Freeman Audio Visual, pg 765
Group PVP, pg 774
Kerrigan Productions Inc, pg 798

Lens Repairs

CALIFORNIA

Ametron Audio/Video, pg 684
Lloyd F McKinney Associates Inc, pg 821
Pro Camera Repair, pg 862
TEK Media Group, pg 909
VMI Inc, pg 932

CONNECTICUT

Precision Camera & Video Repair Inc, pg 861

FLORIDA

Midtown Video Inc, pg 827

KENTUCKY

NOR-COM Inc, pg 841

MARYLAND

Noventri, pg 843
RTZ Audio Visual, pg 878

MICHIGAN

TEL Systems LLC, pg 909

MINNESOTA

Alpha Video & Audio Inc, pg 682
AVI Systems, pg 698

MISSOURI

Southwest Audio-Visual Inc, pg 895

NEW JERSEY

Angenieux, pg 685
FUJIFILM Optical Devices Division, pg 766

NEW YORK

Mamiya, pg 815

NORTH CAROLINA

Alpine Optics Inc, pg 682
Camcor Inc, pg 715

PENNSYLVANIA

Bernie's Photo Center, pg 704
Questar Corp, pg 868

TENNESSEE

Memphis Communications Corp, pg 823
Technical Support Systems LLC, pg 908

TEXAS

Pro Video & Film Equipment Co Inc, pg 863

UTAH

RIA Corp, pg 874

WISCONSIN

Full Compass Systems, pg 767

ALBERTA

Infosat Communications Inc, pg 787
Matrix Video Communications Corp (MVCC), pg 819

VIDEO

Lens Repairs (continued)

MANITOBA
Inland Audio Visual Ltd, pg 788

ONTARIO
HD Source, pg 777

Libraries—Film or Stock-Shot

ALASKA
Alaska Media Pros LLC, pg 679

ARIZONA
Fox 10 Productions (KSAZ-TV), pg 765
Merestone, pg 823
The Source Stock Footage Library Inc, pg 895
Wild Visions Inc, pg 938

ARKANSAS
White Diamond Productions LLC, pg 937

CALIFORNIA
Action Sports/All Stock, pg 675
American Playback Images, pg 684
Artichoke Productions, pg 690
Carl Barth Images, pg 702
Birds & Animals Unlimited, pg 706
Budget Films Stock Footage Inc, pg 712
Steve Chandler, pg 720
Classic Images Stock Footage LLC, pg 726
Crystal Pyramid Productions™, pg 735
ECONEWS (Environmental Television Series) & (Environmental Directions Radio Series), pg 750
Em Gee Film Library, pg 753
First Camera, pg 761
Fish Films Footage World, pg 761
FJ Productions Inc, pg 762
Geddes Productions LLC, pg 769
Gold Standard Productions, pg 772
Howard Hall Productions, pg 775
iCorpTv, pg 783
JDS Video & Media Productions Inc, pg 793
KTVU-Retail Services, pg 802
Lieberman Productions, pg 807
Media Magic, pg 822
Moving Art by Louie Schwartzberg, pg 831
New & Unique Videos™, pg 839
Nineteen87, pg 841
Palardo Productions, pg 850
PM Productions, pg 858
Prelinger Archives, pg 861
Producers Library, pg 863
Pyramid Media, pg 867
QRS Software Services, pg 867
Regent Press Publishers & Printers, pg 873
RJ Video Productions, pg 875
The Studios at Paramount, pg 903
Total Creative, pg 916
Twin Peaks Creative, pg 920
Universal Studios, pg 922
Via Verde Productions, pg 926
Vineyard Video & Photography, pg 930
Visions Plus, pg 931

COLORADO
Apogee Communications Group, pg 687
CSI Film & Video LLC, pg 735
Flashback Media Productions, pg 762
Greg Hensley Productions, pg 779
Tatum Video, pg 907
Transtar Entertainment Co Inc, pg 917

CONNECTICUT
Cine-Med Inc, pg 723
Ironik Design & Post, pg 791
Mystic Seaport (Film & Video Archives), pg 835

DISTRICT OF COLUMBIA
Susan Hormuth, Visual Resource Consultant, pg 781
Interface Media Group, pg 789

FLORIDA
Accord Productions, pg 673
America By Air LLC, pg 682
Bill Bachmann Studios, pg 705
Communications Concepts Inc (CCI), pg 729
Florida Digital Studios, pg 762
Jordan Klein Film & Video (JKFV), pg 795
NatureVision Stock Footage Library, pg 837
The Newhouse Media Group, pg 840
Roger Scruggs Films, pg 883
Sunfire Communications Inc, pg 904
Sunrise Studios, pg 904
Universal Studios Florida® Production Group, pg 922
Mike Vasilinda Productions Inc, pg 925
Video Techniques Inc, pg 928
Vistamax Productions, pg 931

GEORGIA
Beachwood Productions, pg 702
Guerrilla Productions LLC, pg 774
On-Line Productions, pg 845
Staging Directions Inc, pg 899
Video Copy Services Inc, pg 927

HAWAII
FilmWorks Pacific, pg 761
Ka Io Productions Inc, pg 796
Tropical Visions Video Inc, pg 918

ILLINOIS
International Historic Films Inc, pg 790
Moviecraft Inc, pg 831
PSAV® Presentation Services (Hotel Services Division), pg 866
Sound/Video Impressions Inc, pg 894
Southern Illinois University, pg 895
Video I-D Teleproductions Inc, pg 928
WEEK TV, pg 935
WPA Film Library, pg 942

INDIANA
A-V-A Video Productions, pg 671

IOWA
Iowa State University-Information Technology Services, pg 791

KENTUCKY
Horizon Films & Media LLC, pg 781

LOUISIANA
Digital FX Inc, pg 742
Vidox Motion Imagery, pg 930

MARYLAND
dbF a Media Company, pg 739

MASSACHUSETTS
Documentary Educational Resources Inc, pg 744
Green Mountain Post Films (GMP), pg 774
HOME Inc, pg 781
In the Wild Productions, pg 786
WGBH Stock Sales, pg 936

MICHIGAN
Digi Sign Design LLC, pg 741
K&R's Recording Studios Inc, pg 796
The Program Source International, pg 865

MISSOURI
Show-Me Audio-Visual, pg 887

MONTANA
ooLite Media LLC, pg 846

NEVADA
DVDs4Less, pg 748
JCS Video Productions, pg 793

NEW HAMPSHIRE
Apertura, pg 686
Chip Taylor Communications LLC, pg 907

NEW JERSEY
Allegro Productions Inc, pg 680
Broadcast Center Studios, pg 710
Diversified, pg 744
Global ImageWorks LLC, pg 771
MiB MediaWorks, pg 825
Ray Mueller Productions, pg 833
Suede Interactive, pg 903
TimeSteps Productions Inc, pg 914

NEW MEXICO
Blue Sky Stock Footage, pg 708
Production Outfitters, pg 864

NEW YORK
Air Sea Land Productions Inc (ASL), pg 678
AP Images, pg 686
aurora productions, pg 696
BBC Worldwide Learning, pg 702
BC Studio, pg 702
Broadstreet Productions LLC, pg 711
Debbie Regan Locations Ltd, pg 739
Digital Art Video Inc, pg 741
Downtown Community Television Center (DCTV), pg 746
Framepool, pg 765
Icontent, pg 783
The Independent Production Fund, pg 786
Jalbert Productions International, pg 792

NBC News Archives, pg 837
PostWorks, pg 860
Richter Productions Inc, pg 875
TeleTime Productions, pg 910
United Nations Department of Public Information-News & Media Division, pg 921
Video Catalogue Co Inc, pg 927

NORTH CAROLINA
Pat Appleson Studios Inc, pg 687
The Communications Group Inc, pg 729
Crystal Pictures Inc, pg 735
Horizon Video Productions Inc, pg 781
NASCAR Productions LLC, pg 835
On Location North Carolina, pg 846

OHIO
Aztec Video Productions, pg 700
Bartha, pg 702
R&B Communications Inc, pg 870
Take 1 Media Services, pg 906
Treehaus Communications Inc, pg 917

OKLAHOMA
PDC Productions, pg 852

OREGON
Artbeats, pg 690
Encounter Video Inc, pg 754
Odyssey Productions Inc, pg 844
Wilderness Video, pg 938

PENNSYLVANIA
John E Allen Inc, pg 680
Corinth Films Inc, pg 731
FMP Media Solutions Inc, pg 763
Production Masters Inc (PMI), pg 864
The Whale Video Co, pg 936
WPHL-TV, pg 942

SOUTH CAROLINA
Stages Video Productions, pg 899
Venture Media, pg 925

TENNESSEE
Anode Inc, pg 686
Motion Picture Services, pg 831
Scripps Networks, pg 882
Stage Post, pg 899

TEXAS
CEV Multimedia Ltd, pg 720
Horizon Film + Video Productions, pg 781
McNee Productions Inc, pg 821
Mediaforce Productions, pg 822
Julye Newlin Productions Inc, pg 840
Phillips Media Source, pg 855
Prairie Pictures Film & Video, pg 860
The Samuels Co, pg 879
South Coast Film & Video, pg 895

UTAH
Stockfootage.com, pg 901

VIRGINIA
CVW Event Productions, pg 736
Limelight Communications Inc, pg 808

Maniglia Media LLC, pg 816
Rocktown Media, pg 876

WASHINGTON

Bennett-Watt HD Productions Inc,
pg 703
Getty Images, pg 770
North-by-Northwest - A Digital
Studio, pg 842
Victory Studios, pg 927
White Rain Films Ltd, pg 937

WEST VIRGINIA

Focus on Animals, pg 763
WSAZ-TV NewsChannel 3, pg 942

WISCONSIN

Audio Visual of Milwaukee Inc,
pg 694
USAV Group Inc, pg 923
Video Wisconsin Inc, pg 929
Wisconsin Public Television, pg 940

WYOMING

Bridger Productions Inc, pg 710

PUERTO RICO

Stage Crew Audiovisual Inc, pg 898

MANITOBA

Spectra Video Productions Ltd,
pg 897

NEWFOUNDLAND AND
LABRADOR

Vidcraft Productions Ltd, pg 927

NORTHWEST TERRITORIES

Yellowknife Films Inc, pg 944

ONTARIO

Canamedia Inc, pg 715
GAPC (General Assembly
Production Centre), pg 768
Silver Creek Media Inc, pg 888

QUEBEC

Les Productions Via Le Monde
(Daniel Bertolino) Inc, pg 864

SASKATCHEWAN

Thomega Entertainment Inc, pg 913

Location Equipment &
Facility Distributors

ARKANSAS

White Diamond Productions LLC,
pg 937

CALIFORNIA

Advanced Systems Group LLC,
pg 677
Ametron Audio/Video, pg 684
DTC Lighting & Grip, pg 747
Mole-Richardson Co, pg 829
Satellite Digital Teleproductions
(SDTV), pg 881
VMI Inc, pg 932

COLORADO

Chimera®, pg 722

FLORIDA

Access Media Group, pg 673
Midtown Video Inc, pg 827
ONstage, pg 846

GEORGIA

Convergent Media Systems, pg 731
Lighting & Production Equipment
Inc, pg 807
Stage Front Presentation Systems,
pg 899

HAWAII

The Audio Visual Co (AVCO),
pg 694

ILLINOIS

Cool-Lux, pg 731
Photoflex Inc, pg 856

INDIANA

Sensory Technologies LLC, pg 884

MARYLAND

Theatre Service & Supply Corp,
pg 912

MASSACHUSETTS

Rule Boston Camera, pg 878

MINNESOTA

Alpha Video & Audio Inc, pg 682
AVI Systems, pg 698

MISSOURI

Communitronics Corp, pg 729
Conference Technologies Inc,
pg 730
Modern Communications Inc,
pg 828
Southwest Audio-Visual Inc, pg 895

NEW JERSEY

Comprehensive Cable &
Connectivity Co, pg 729
Earl Girls Inc, pg 749

NEW YORK

Audio-Video Corp, pg 694
Barbizon Electric Co Inc, pg 701
Long Island Video Enterprises Live
Inc, pg 811
Xtech Systems Inc, pg 943

NORTH CAROLINA

Camcor Inc, pg 715
Strategic Connections, pg 901

PENNSYLVANIA

Advanced AV LLC, pg 677
Morefield Communications Inc,
pg 830

TENNESSEE

Memphis Communications Corp,
pg 823
Technical Support Systems LLC,
pg 908
TOMCAT USA Inc, pg 915

TEXAS

Pro Video & Film Equipment Co
Inc, pg 863
Shook Mobile Technology LP,
pg 886

UTAH

RIA Corp, pg 874

VERMONT

Production Advantage Inc, pg 863

VIRGINIA

Avitecture Inc, pg 699

WISCONSIN

Audio Visual of Milwaukee Inc,
pg 694
Full Compass Systems, pg 767

ONTARIO

HD Source, pg 777

Location Equipment &
Facility Manufacturers

ALABAMA

Marco Inc, pg 816

CALIFORNIA

ALTINEX Inc, pg 682
Clear-Com® LLC, pg 726
Microdolly Hollywood, pg 826
Mole-Richardson Co, pg 829
Synergy Group Inc, pg 906

COLORADO

Chimera®, pg 722

FLORIDA

Union Connector Co Inc, pg 921

ILLINOIS

Kart-A-Bag Manufacturing Inc,
pg 796
Photoflex Inc, pg 856

INDIANA

Star Case Manufacturing Co Inc,
pg 900

MARYLAND

Theatre Service & Supply Corp,
pg 912

MASSACHUSETTS

Dedotec USA Inc, pg 740

MICHIGAN

Studio Consulting & Construction
Inc, pg 902

PENNSYLVANIA

Aztech Productions LLC, pg 700

TENNESSEE

TOMCAT USA Inc, pg 915

TEXAS

Shook Mobile Technology LP,
pg 886

Location Equipment &
Facility Rentals

ALABAMA

AVS Media Group, pg 699

ALASKA

Connections Film & Video Inc,
pg 731

ARIZONA

Arizona Cine Equipment, pg 688
Merestone, pg 823
Rodeo Video Inc, pg 876

ARKANSAS

White Diamond Productions LLC,
pg 937

CALIFORNIA

Ametron Audio/Video, pg 684
Antelope Valley Locations &
Production Services, pg 686
Bexel, an NEP Broadcast Services
Company, pg 704
Big Door, pg 705
Chapman/Leonard Studio
Equipment Inc, pg 720
Crystal Pyramid Productions™,
pg 735
DTC Lighting & Grip, pg 747
Express Media Inc, pg 757
First Camera, pg 761
FJ Productions Inc, pg 762
Gold Standard Productions, pg 772
Golden Gate Studios, pg 772
KTVU-Retail Services, pg 802
The Location Connection Inc,
pg 810
Lynch Communications, pg 813
Maximus Media Inc, pg 820
McCune Audio-Video-Lighting,
pg 821
Mole-Richardson Co, pg 829
New Circuit Films LLC, pg 839
Porter Productions, pg 859
Samy's Camera, pg 879
Santa Clarita Studios, pg 880
Sunset Bronson Studios, pg 904
Sunset Gower Studios, pg 904
Timestream Video, pg 914
Total Creative, pg 916
Twin Peaks Creative, pg 920
VMI Inc, pg 932
Warner Bros Entertainment Inc,
pg 934
Westcoast Video Productions Inc,
pg 936
Z-Ville Productions, pg 944

COLORADO

Chimera®, pg 722

CONNECTICUT

Videofilm Systems Inc, pg 929

DELAWARE

Ken-Del Productions Inc, pg 797

DISTRICT OF COLUMBIA

Interface Media Group, pg 789

FLORIDA

F&F Productions LLC, pg 759
Industrial Strength Inc, pg 787
Jordan Klein Film & Video (JKFV),
pg 795

VIDEO

Location Equipment & Facility Rentals (continued)

FLORIDA (continued)

Midtown Video Inc, pg 827
National Teleproductions Inc, pg 837
ONstage, pg 846
Universal Studios Florida® Production Group, pg 922
Mike Vasilinda Productions Inc, pg 925

GEORGIA

Convergent Media Systems, pg 731
Lighting & Production Equipment Inc, pg 807
Stage Front Presentation Systems, pg 899
WATL-TV Inc, pg 934

HAWAII

Sight & Sound Studios, pg 887

ILLINOIS

Atomic Imaging Inc/Golan Studios, pg 692
Backstar Creative Media Inc, pg 700
LITE-IT Grip Truck Rentals, pg 810
On Site Video, pg 846
Product Productions, pg 863
PSAV® Presentation Services (Hotel Services Division), pg 866
Resolution Productions Group, pg 874
SCI Television & Creative Media LLC, pg 882

INDIANA

Advanced Media Integration, pg 677

IOWA

Musco Lighting, pg 834

LOUISIANA

Digital FX Inc, pg 742
Moxie Media, pg 832
Pace Systems, pg 849
YES Productions, pg 944

MARYLAND

CPR MultiMedia Solutions, pg 732
Producers Video, pg 863

MASSACHUSETTS

High Output Inc, pg 779
Preston Productions Inc, pg 861
Small Planet Communications Inc, pg 890

MICHIGAN

City Events Group, pg 725
K&R All Media Productions LLC, pg 796
K&R's Recording Studios Inc, pg 796

MINNESOTA

Alpha Video & Audio Inc, pg 682
AVI Systems, pg 698
House of Cinemagraphics, pg 782

MISSOURI

Show-Me Audio-Visual, pg 887
Southwest Audio-Visual Inc, pg 895

NEVADA

Lefco Video Services Inc, pg 806

NEW HAMPSHIRE

Apertura, pg 686

NEW JERSEY

Earl Girls Inc, pg 749
Laurel Video Productions, pg 804
MediaMix Inc, pg 822
Vision Quest Productions Inc, pg 930

NEW YORK

Big Foot Productions Inc, pg 705
CP Communications, pg 732
Downtown Community Television Center (DCTV), pg 746
Long Island Video Enterprises Live Inc, pg 811
Manhattan Center Studios Inc, pg 816
PrimaLux Video Inc, pg 862
Visual Word Systems Inc, pg 932
WNET/New York Public Media, pg 940
Xtech Systems Inc, pg 943

NORTH CAROLINA

All Pro Media Inc, pg 680
Bill Barnes Video Productions LLC, pg 702
The Communications Group Inc, pg 729
Duke Media Services, pg 747
Microspace Communications Corp, pg 826
Moving Pictures, pg 832
On Location North Carolina, pg 846
Take One Productions Ltd, pg 906
Videowerks, pg 930

NORTH DAKOTA

Media Productions, pg 822

OHIO

CET, pg 720
Lyon Video Inc, pg 813
Mills James Productions, pg 828
R&B Communications Inc, pg 870
Vista Color Imaging Inc, pg 931

OKLAHOMA

Institute for Teaching & Learning Excellence (ITLE), pg 788
PDC Productions, pg 852

OREGON

Pacific Grip & Lighting Inc, pg 849

PENNSYLVANIA

FMP Media Solutions Inc, pg 763
Innovision Media Group, pg 788
JPL, pg 795
Location Camera Ltd, pg 810
Location Lighting Ltd, pg 810
Muderick Media, pg 833
Producers Management Television (PMTV), pg 863
The Videohouse Inc, pg 929
Videosmith Inc, pg 930
Visual Sound Inc, pg 931

SOUTH CAROLINA

Assignment Desk, pg 691

TENNESSEE

Love Shack Recording Studios, pg 811
Memphis Communications Corp, pg 823
Russ Sturgeon Productions/RSVP, pg 903
Technical Support Systems LLC, pg 908
United Methodist Productions, pg 921

TEXAS

AMS Pictures, pg 684
Earl Miller Productions Inc, pg 827
Muller Entertainment LLC, pg 833
Omega Productions, pg 845
Phillips Media Source, pg 855
South Coast Film & Video, pg 895
Stage Directions, pg 898
Texcam Inc, pg 911

VERMONT

Marlboro Productions, pg 817

VIRGINIA

Allied Media Corp, pg 681
Quince Imaging Inc, pg 868
Video Solutions, pg 928
WETA Production Center, pg 936

WASHINGTON

Kostov Productions, pg 801
Victory Studios, pg 927

WISCONSIN

Logan Productions Inc, pg 811
University of Wisconsin-Oshkosh Radio-TV-Film Dept, pg 923
USAV Group Inc, pg 923
Wisconsin Public Television, pg 940

WYOMING

Bridger Productions Inc, pg 710

ALBERTA

Global TV, pg 771

BRITISH COLUMBIA

Video Out Distribution, pg 928

ONTARIO

HD Source, pg 777
JIB Shots Equipment Inc, pg 794
Metalworks Recording Studios Inc, pg 824
RB Productions, pg 870

QUEBEC

Group PVP, pg 774

Location Equipment & Facility Repairs

CALIFORNIA

Ametron Audio/Video, pg 684
Mole-Richardson Co, pg 829

FLORIDA

Midtown Video Inc, pg 827

GEORGIA

Lighting & Production Equipment Inc, pg 807

ILLINOIS

Midwest Digital Corp, pg 827
On Site Video, pg 846

MICHIGAN

Studio Consulting & Construction Inc, pg 902
TEL Systems LLC, pg 909

MINNESOTA

Alpha Video & Audio Inc, pg 682
AVI Systems, pg 698

MISSOURI

Southwest Audio-Visual Inc, pg 895

NEW JERSEY

Earl Girls Inc, pg 749

NEW YORK

Xtech Systems Inc, pg 943

TENNESSEE

Memphis Communications Corp, pg 823
Technical Support Systems LLC, pg 908

TEXAS

Pro Video & Film Equipment Co Inc, pg 863

UTAH

RIA Corp, pg 874

WISCONSIN

Full Compass Systems, pg 767

Mastering, see Videodisc Mastering

Mixer Distributors

ARIZONA

EAR Professional Audio/Video, pg 749

ARKANSAS

White Diamond Productions LLC, pg 937

CALIFORNIA

Ametron Audio/Video, pg 684
Empire Pro, pg 753
Gravity Media, pg 773
JD Audio Visual Inc, pg 793
MediaPOINTE, pg 823
Promax Systems, pg 865
SNAP, pg 891
Southern California Sound Image Inc, pg 895
VMI Inc, pg 932
VTP Inc, pg 933
Westlake Recording Studios, pg 936

CONNECTICUT

Connecticut Audio & Theatrical Supply, pg 731

FLORIDA

Access Media Group, pg 673
A2D Solutions Inc, pg 692
AVI-SPL, pg 698
Digital Video Systems, pg 742
Harris Corp, pg 776
Hi-Tech Enterprises Inc, pg 779
Midtown Video Inc, pg 827
Recording Media & Equipment Inc
    (RM&E), pg 872

GEORGIA

Clark, pg 725
Lighting & Production Equipment
    Inc, pg 807
Stage Front Presentation Systems,
    pg 899

HAWAII

The Audio Visual Co (AVCO),
    pg 694

ILLINOIS

Quintessence Audio Ltd, pg 868

INDIANA

Sensory Technologies LLC, pg 884
SHP Electronics, pg 887

KENTUCKY

Barney Miller's Inc, pg 827
NOR-COM Inc, pg 841

LOUISIANA

Techkno Integration & Design
    Services LLC, pg 908

MARYLAND

Noventri, pg 843
Wiltronix Inc, pg 939

MASSACHUSETTS

Rule Boston Camera, pg 878

MICHIGAN

Olson Anderson Co, pg 685
On Stage Visuals, pg 846

MINNESOTA

Alpha Video & Audio Inc, pg 682

MISSOURI

Conference Technologies Inc,
    pg 730
Modern Communications Inc,
    pg 828
Schiller's Audio-Visual, pg 881
Southwest Audio-Visual Inc, pg 895

NEBRASKA

ATV Research Inc, pg 692
VSA Inc, pg 933

NEVADA

Aardvark Video & Media
    Productions, pg 671

NEW JERSEY

AlltecPro, pg 681
Audio Visual Associates, pg 694
HamiltonBuhl, pg 775
MCCOM Inc, pg 820
PatchAmp, pg 852
Starlite, pg 900

SYMCO Inc, pg 905
Total Video Products Inc, pg 916

NEW YORK

Audio-Video Corp, pg 694
B&H Photo Video, pg 701
Design Audio Visual Inc, pg 741
HAVE Inc, pg 777
Indigo Productions, pg 787
KVL Audio Visual Services Inc,
    pg 802
Markertek Video Supply, pg 817
TecNec Distributing, pg 909
Videoguys, pg 929
Visual Technologies Corp, pg 932

OHIO

Tri-State Audio Visual Co, pg 918

PENNSYLVANIA

Advanced AV LLC, pg 677
Clair Companies, pg 725
The Lerro Corp, pg 806

RHODE ISLAND

Shanix Inc, pg 885

TENNESSEE

Lowrance Sound Co Inc, pg 812
Zion Music Group, pg 945

TEXAS

AVES Audio Visual Systems Inc,
    pg 698
Pro Video & Film Equipment Co
    Inc, pg 863
Tarpley Media Systems, pg 907

UTAH

Performance Audio LLC, pg 854

VIRGINIA

Avitecture Inc, pg 699
Lee Hartman & Sons Inc, pg 805
StageSound, pg 899
The Whitlock Group, pg 937

WISCONSIN

Audio Visual of Milwaukee Inc,
    pg 694
Camera Corner Connecting Point,
    pg 715
Full Compass Systems, pg 767
Safe Harbor Computers, pg 879

ALBERTA

Infosat Communications Inc, pg 787

BRITISH COLUMBIA

Commercial Electronics Ltd, pg 728

MANITOBA

Inland Audio Visual Ltd, pg 788

ONTARIO

Cinema Stage Inc, pg 724
Westbury National Show Systems
    Ltd, pg 936

Mixer Manufacturers

CALIFORNIA

ALTINEX Inc, pg 682
Opticomm-EMCORE, pg 847

COLORADO

Liberty AV Solutions, pg 807

FLORIDA

Tel-Test, pg 909

MINNESOTA

Vaddio, pg 924

MISSOURI

GlobalStreams™ Corp, pg 771

NEW MEXICO

Burst Electronics Inc, pg 713

NEW YORK

Sima Products Corp, pg 888

PENNSYLVANIA

MicroImage Video Systems, pg 826

RHODE ISLAND

Rane, pg 870

BRITISH COLUMBIA

Triad Communications Ltd, pg 918

QUEBEC

Grass Valley, pg 773

Mixer Rentals

ALABAMA

Audio-Video Resources Inc, pg 694

ALASKA

Connections Film & Video Inc,
    pg 731

ARIZONA

Creative Backstage, pg 733
Merestone, pg 823
Video West Inc, pg 929

ARKANSAS

White Diamond Productions LLC,
    pg 937

CALIFORNIA

Absolute Rentals, pg 672
AGF Media Services, pg 678
Alternative Rentals, pg 682
Ametron Audio/Video, pg 684
Artichoke Productions, pg 690
Audio Rents, pg 693
AV Guys, pg 697
Big Door, pg 705
Express Media Inc, pg 757
Full Moon & High Tide Productions
    & Studios, pg 767
Golden Gate Studios, pg 772
Gravity Media, pg 773
Image Integration, pg 785
JD Audio Visual Inc, pg 793
Maximus Media Inc, pg 820
Munday & Collins AV, pg 834
Muse Presentation Technologies,
    pg 834
New Circuit Films LLC, pg 839
Pro HD Rentals, pg 863
Production Gear Rentals (PGR),
    pg 863
Radiant Images, pg 869
RetinaVision Productions, pg 874

Shooting Star Video, pg 886
SNAP, pg 891
Studio 637, pg 903
The Studios at Paramount, pg 903
Twin Peaks Creative, pg 920
VER, pg 926
Voice & Video Rentals, pg 932
Warner Bros Production Sound &
    Video Services, pg 934
Westcoast Video Productions Inc,
    pg 936

CONNECTICUT

A/V Davey, pg 697
Videofilm Systems Inc, pg 929

DISTRICT OF COLUMBIA

Metro Teleproductions Inc (MTI),
    pg 824

FLORIDA

Access Media Group, pg 673
AVI-SPL, pg 698
Hi-Tech Enterprises Inc, pg 779
Phat Planet Recording Studios,
    pg 855
Sight & Sound Productions, pg 887
Universal Studios Florida®
    Production Group, pg 922

GEORGIA

See Production Services, pg 883
Stage Front Presentation Systems,
    pg 899

HAWAII

Sight & Sound Studios, pg 887

ILLINOIS

RC Communications, pg 870
Resolution Productions Group,
    pg 874
SCI Television & Creative Media
    LLC, pg 882

IOWA

Pro Video, pg 863

KENTUCKY

Audio Visual Techniques Inc,
    pg 695
Idle Minds Productions Inc, pg 784

MARYLAND

CPR MultiMedia Solutions, pg 732
Event Tech, pg 756

MASSACHUSETTS

Preston Productions Inc, pg 861

MICHIGAN

Olson Anderson Co, pg 685
K&R All Media Productions LLC,
    pg 796
On Stage Visuals, pg 846

MINNESOTA

Alpha Video & Audio Inc, pg 682

MISSOURI

Show-Me Audio-Visual, pg 887

NEBRASKA

Dog & Pony Productions Inc,
    pg 744

VIDEO

Mixer Rentals (continued)

NEW JERSEY

Audio Visual Associates, pg 694
Audio Visual Dynamics®, pg 694
MiB MediaWorks, pg 825
Soundtracks Production Services
 LLC, pg 895
Starlite, pg 900

NEW MEXICO

Production Outfitters, pg 864

NEW YORK

Adorama Rental Co, pg 676
Big Foot Productions Inc, pg 705
CP Communications, pg 732
Design Audio Visual Inc, pg 741
KVL Audio Visual Services Inc,
 pg 802
PrimaLux Video Inc, pg 862
Production Central, pg 863

NORTH CAROLINA

All Pro Media Inc, pg 680
The Communications Group Inc,
 pg 729
Microspace Communications Corp,
 pg 826
On Location North Carolina, pg 846
Take One Productions Ltd, pg 906

NORTH DAKOTA

Media Productions, pg 822

OHIO

R&B Communications Inc, pg 870

OKLAHOMA

PDC Productions, pg 852

PENNSYLVANIA

Innovision Media Group, pg 788
Producers Management Television
 (PMTV), pg 863
The Videohouse Inc, pg 929
Viewpoint Production Services Inc,
 pg 930

TENNESSEE

Love Shack Recording Studios,
 pg 811

TEXAS

GEAR Cameras & Lighting, pg 769
Stage Directions, pg 898

UTAH

Ron Hill Imagery, pg 780

VERMONT

Dark Star Lighting & Production,
 pg 737

VIRGINIA

Quince Imaging Inc, pg 868

PUERTO RICO

Stage Crew Audiovisual Inc, pg 898

ALBERTA

L R Light & Sound, pg 802

MANITOBA

Inland Audio Visual Ltd, pg 788

ONTARIO

Wanted! Sound + Picture, pg 933
Westbury National Show Systems
 Ltd, pg 936
ZTV Broadcast Services Inc, pg 945

QUEBEC

Group PVP, pg 774

Mixer Repairs

CALIFORNIA

Ametron Audio/Video, pg 684
TV Pro Gear, pg 919
VMI Inc, pg 932

CONNECTICUT

A/V Davey, pg 697

FLORIDA

Digital Video Systems, pg 742
ELC Sales & Service Inc, pg 752
Hi-Tech Enterprises Inc, pg 779
Midtown Video Inc, pg 827
Phat Planet Recording Studios,
 pg 855
Tel-Test, pg 909

GEORGIA

Stage Front Presentation Systems,
 pg 899

ILLINOIS

Midwest Digital Corp, pg 827

KENTUCKY

NOR-COM Inc, pg 841

MARYLAND

Noventri, pg 843

MICHIGAN

TEL Systems LLC, pg 909

MINNESOTA

Alpha Video & Audio Inc, pg 682

MISSOURI

Southwest Audio-Visual Inc, pg 895

NEW JERSEY

Audio Visual Associates, pg 694
Starlite, pg 900

NEW YORK

Visual Technologies Corp, pg 932

OHIO

Tri-State Audio Visual Co, pg 918

OREGON

All Service Musical Electronics
 Repair, pg 680

TEXAS

Pro Video & Film Equipment Co
 Inc, pg 863
Tarpley Media Systems, pg 907

WISCONSIN

Full Compass Systems, pg 767

ALBERTA

Infosat Communications Inc, pg 787

BRITISH COLUMBIA

Commercial Electronics Ltd, pg 728

MANITOBA

Inland Audio Visual Ltd, pg 788

ONTARIO

Westbury National Show Systems
 Ltd, pg 936

Mixing—Stereo or Dolby Stereo

ALABAMA

Dogwood Productions Inc, pg 745

ARIZONA

Aardvark Productions LLC, pg 671
Allusion Studios & Pure Wave
 Audio, pg 681
Merestone, pg 823
Metropolitan Audio-Visual Inc,
 pg 824
Video West Inc, pg 929

ARKANSAS

White Diamond Productions LLC,
 pg 937

CALIFORNIA

AB Audio Visual Entertainment Inc,
 pg 672
Aliso Creek Productions Inc, pg 680
AlphaDogs Inc, pg 682
Artichoke Productions, pg 690
Berke Creative Inc, pg 704
Chace Audio by Deluxe, pg 720
Creative Media Recording, pg 733
Creative Technology, pg 733
Crystal Pyramid Productions™,
 pg 735
Custom Video Productions Inc,
 pg 736
Diamond Dreams Music
 Productions, pg 741
Digital Jungle, pg 742
digital OutPost, pg 742
Earwax Productions Inc, pg 749
Express Media Inc, pg 757
48 Windows, pg 764
Full Moon & High Tide Productions
 & Music, pg 767
Golden Gate Studios, pg 772
iCorpTv, pg 783
KPBS Public Broadcasting, pg 801
Ludlow Media, pg 812
Lynch Communications, pg 813
Maximus Media Inc, pg 820
McCune Audio-Video-Lighting,
 pg 821
New & Unique Videos™, pg 839
Nineteen87, pg 841
Nolte Media, pg 841
OTR Studios, pg 848
Palardo Productions, pg 850
PM Productions, pg 858
Polarity Post Production, pg 858
Private Island Audio Inc, pg 862
Pyramind Studios, pg 867
QRS Software Services, pg 867

COLORADO

Roundabout Entertainment Inc,
 pg 878
Shapeshifter, pg 885
SonicPool, pg 892
Sonora Recorders, pg 893
Staylor-Made Communications Inc,
 pg 900
Still N' Motion, pg 901
Studio 132, pg 902
Total Creative, pg 916
Twin Peaks Creative, pg 920
Universal Studios, pg 922

COLORADO

Tim Cissell Music, pg 725
Conly Productions, pg 730
Flashback Media Productions,
 pg 762

CONNECTICUT

Antenna International, pg 686
BRB Audiovisual Productions,
 pg 709
Ironik Design & Post, pg 791
Palace Production Center, pg 850
P&P Studios Inc, pg 851
T & M Digital Services LLC,
 pg 906

DELAWARE

Side Door Studio Inc, pg 887

DISTRICT OF COLUMBIA

Interface Media Group, pg 789

FLORIDA

Access Media Group, pg 673
Applebox Studio, pg 687
Civins Productions Inc, pg 725
Communications Concepts Inc
 (CCI), pg 729
Courter Films LLC, pg 732
The Kitchen, pg 799
Morrisound Recording, pg 830
Sound & Vision Communications
 Inc, pg 893
Sunfire Communications Inc,
 pg 904
Universal Studios Florida®
 Production Group, pg 922
Vistamax Productions, pg 931

GEORGIA

Beachwood Productions, pg 702
Beast Atlanta, pg 703
The DVI Group, pg 748
First Cut Communications LLC,
 pg 761
Guerrilla Productions LLC, pg 774
Staging Directions Inc, pg 899

ILLINOIS

ABSA Films, pg 672
CCore Media Inc, pg 718
IV Media Resources, pg 792
Multimedia Marketing Group,
 pg 833
Steven Samler Music & Sound,
 pg 879
SCI Television & Creative Media
 LLC, pg 882
Southern Illinois University, pg 895
Sparkfactor, pg 896
20/20 Communications Inc, pg 920
Video Impressions, pg 928

INDIANA

Advanced Media Integration, pg 677
Bright Ideas Creative Services,
    pg 710

LOUISIANA

Digital FX Inc, pg 742
Vidox Motion Imagery, pg 930
WVLA-TV, pg 942

MAINE

WGME-TV, pg 936

MARYLAND

CPR MultiMedia Solutions, pg 732
dbF a Media Company, pg 739
DBM Communications Inc, pg 739
Media Dimensions LLC, pg 821
Pro Cuts Editing Services, pg 862
Sheffield Audio/Video Productions,
    pg 885
Soundtrax Inc, pg 895

MASSACHUSETTS

Capron Lighting & Sound Co Inc,
    pg 716
Continental Recordings Inc, pg 731
Documentary Educational Resources
    Inc, pg 744
Labrecque Creative Sound, pg 803
Northern Light Productions (NLP),
    pg 842
Soundtrack Group, pg 895

MICHIGAN

Digi Sign Design LLC, pg 741
Digital Image Studios LLC, pg 742
GMP Music, pg 772
K&R's Recording Studios Inc,
    pg 796

MINNESOTA

The ADS Group, pg 676
BeyerSound & Essay Audio, pg 705
Worthwhile Films, pg 941

MISSOURI

Avatar Studios, pg 697
Show-Me Audio-Visual, pg 887

MONTANA

Jereco Studios Inc, pg 793

NEVADA

DVDs4Less, pg 748
Encore Event Technologies LLC,
    pg 754
JCS Video Productions, pg 793
Tanglewood Productions, pg 907

NEW HAMPSHIRE

Channell One Video, pg 720
Chip Taylor Communications LLC,
    pg 907

NEW JERSEY

AJS Events, pg 679
Allegro Productions Inc, pg 680
Broadcast Center Studios, pg 710
CFP Video Productions Inc, pg 720
Diversified, pg 744
Laurel Video Productions, pg 804
Mia Mind Music, pg 825
MiB MediaWorks, pg 825
Midnight Media Group Inc, pg 827
Milgrom Productions, pg 827

Ray Mueller Productions, pg 833
NFL Films Inc, pg 841
NFL Films Music Library, pg 841
Starlite, pg 900
Suede Interactive, pg 903
VCSvideo, pg 925

NEW MEXICO

Production Outfitters, pg 864

NEW YORK

Aural Gratification Inc, pg 695
The Big House Group, pg 705
Buffalo Video Production, pg 712
CP Communications, pg 732
Design Audio Visual Inc, pg 741
Digital Art Video Inc, pg 741
Downtown Community Television
    Center (DCTV), pg 746
Fingerpaint, pg 761
4-D Creative Media, pg 764
Hallel Communications, pg 775
HAVE Inc, pg 777
HB-Content, pg 777
KAS Music & Sound, pg 796
Magno Sound, pg 815
Mood Creations Ltd, pg 829
The Palmer Group, pg 850
PostWorks, pg 860
Teatown Communications Group,
    pg 908
Tiki Recording Studios Inc, pg 914
Visual Technologies Corp, pg 932

NORTH CAROLINA

Pat Appleson Studios Inc, pg 687
The Communications Group Inc,
    pg 729
Duke Media Services, pg 747
Franklin Video Inc, pg 765
Horizon Video Productions Inc,
    pg 781
Take One Productions Ltd, pg 906
2BruceStudio, pg 920

NORTH DAKOTA

Media Productions, pg 822

OHIO

Advent Media Inc, pg 677
Aztec Video Productions, pg 700
Lyon Video Inc, pg 813
Mills James Productions, pg 828
R&B Communications Inc, pg 870
The Telos Alliance, pg 910

OKLAHOMA

PDC Productions, pg 852

OREGON

KTVA Productions, pg 802
Production West, pg 864

PENNSYLVANIA

Audio Visual Communications Inc,
    pg 694
Beholder Productions Inc, pg 703
FMP Media Solutions Inc, pg 763
Innovision Media Group, pg 788
Laser Video Corp, pg 804
Panta Rhei Media Inc, pg 851
Production Masters Inc (PMI),
    pg 864
Right Coast Recording Inc, pg 875
The Videohouse Inc, pg 929
Visual Sound Inc, pg 931
WHYY Inc, pg 938

SOUTH CAROLINA

Genesis Creative, pg 769
Stages Video Productions, pg 899

TENNESSEE

American Blackguard Inc, pg 683
JamSync, pg 793
Love Shack Recording Studios,
    pg 811
Memphis Communications Corp,
    pg 823
Motion Picture Services, pg 831
Scripps Networks, pg 882
Stage Post, pg 899
Technical Support Systems LLC,
    pg 908
Zion Music Group, pg 945

TEXAS

The Editing Co, pg 750
McNee Productions Inc, pg 821
Mediaforce Productions, pg 822
Julye Newlin Productions Inc,
    pg 840
Out of the BLUE Media, pg 849
Phillips Media Source, pg 855
The Samuels Co, pg 879
The Sound Lab Inc, pg 894
Sound Works, pg 894
South Coast Film & Video, pg 895
Stage Directions, pg 898
Tropikal Productions, pg 918

UTAH

ImageWorks Communications,
    pg 785
One Stop CD Shop LLC, pg 846
Soularium Recording Studios,
    pg 893

VIRGINIA

AudioImage Recording, pg 695
Henninger Media Services, pg 779
Maniglia Media LLC, pg 816
Metro Productions, pg 824
Rocktown Media, pg 876

WASHINGTON

Bennett-Watt HD Productions Inc,
    pg 703
D A Sound, pg 737
North-by-Northwest - A Digital
    Studio, pg 842
Victory Studios, pg 927

WEST VIRGINIA

MotionMasters, pg 831
WSAZ-TV NewsChannel 3, pg 942

WISCONSIN

Audio Visual of Milwaukee Inc,
    pg 694
Concept Productions Inc, pg 730
5th Floor Recording Co, pg 760
USAV Group Inc, pg 923
Video Wisconsin Inc, pg 929

WYOMING

Bridger Productions Inc, pg 710

PUERTO RICO

Stage Crew Audiovisual Inc, pg 898

ALBERTA

Global TV, pg 771

BRITISH COLUMBIA

Pinewood Sound, pg 857
Triad Communications Ltd, pg 918

MANITOBA

DACAPO Productions Inc, pg 737
Spectra Video Productions Ltd,
    pg 897

NEWFOUNDLAND AND
LABRADOR

Vidcraft Productions Ltd, pg 927

ONTARIO

ADS Media, pg 677
GAPC (General Assembly
    Production Centre), pg 768
JFB Communications, pg 794
MCS Recording Studios, pg 821
Metalworks Recording Studios Inc,
    pg 824
Phase One Studios, pg 855
Silver Creek Media Inc, pg 888
Trebas Institute, pg 917
Video Excellence Productions,
    pg 927
VO2 Mix Audio Post, pg 932

QUEBEC

Group PVP, pg 774
Muse Entertainment Enterprises,
    pg 834
Trebas Institute, pg 917

Mixing—Stereo Surround
or Dolby Surround

ARIZONA

Allusion Studios & Pure Wave
    Audio, pg 681
Merestone, pg 823
Video West Inc, pg 929

ARKANSAS

White Diamond Productions LLC,
    pg 937

CALIFORNIA

AlphaDogs Inc, pg 682
Audio Mechanics, pg 693
Berke Creative Inc, pg 704
Berkeley Sound Artists Inc, pg 704
Chace Audio by Deluxe, pg 720
Creative Technology, pg 733
Crystal Pyramid Productions™,
    pg 735
Digital Jungle, pg 742
digital OutPost, pg 742
Earwax Productions Inc, pg 749
48 Windows, pg 764
Golden Gate Studios, pg 772
iCorpTv, pg 783
Maximus Media Inc, pg 820
OTR Studios, pg 848
Palardo Productions, pg 850
piXvfm Inc, pg 857
Polarity Post Production, pg 858
Private Island Audio Inc, pg 862
QRS Software Services, pg 867
Roundabout Entertainment Inc,
    pg 878
Shapeshifter, pg 885
SonicPool, pg 892
Staylor-Made Communications Inc,
    pg 900
Total Creative, pg 916
Twin Peaks Creative, pg 920
Universal Studios, pg 922

VIDEO

Mixing—Stereo Surround or Dolby Surround (continued)

COLORADO

Tim Cissell Music, pg 725

CONNECTICUT

Guymark Studios LLC, pg 775
Ironik Design & Post, pg 791
Palace Production Center, pg 850

DISTRICT OF COLUMBIA

Interface Media Group, pg 789

FLORIDA

Access Media Group, pg 673
Applebox Studio, pg 687
Audacity Recording Studios, pg 693
Communications Concepts Inc (CCI), pg 729
The Kitchen, pg 799
Morrisound Recording, pg 830
Sound & Vision Communications Inc, pg 893
Sunfire Communications Inc, pg 904

GEORGIA

Guerrilla Productions LLC, pg 774
Staging Directions Inc, pg 899

ILLINOIS

SCI Television & Creative Media LLC, pg 882
Southern Illinois University, pg 895
Video Impressions, pg 928

INDIANA

Bright Ideas Creative Services, pg 710
Alan Johnson Recording, pg 794
OMNI Productions, pg 845

LOUISIANA

Digital FX Inc, pg 742
Pace Systems, pg 849

MARYLAND

CPR MultiMedia Solutions, pg 732
dbF a Media Company, pg 739
Lion & Fox Recording Studios, pg 809
Sheffield Audio/Video Productions, pg 885

MASSACHUSETTS

Northern Light Productions (NLP), pg 842
Soundtrack Group, pg 895

MICHIGAN

Digi Sign Design LLC, pg 741
Digital Image Studios LLC, pg 742
GMP Music, pg 772
K&R's Recording Studios Inc, pg 796

MINNESOTA

The ADS Group, pg 676
Badiyan Inc, pg 700
Worthwhile Films, pg 941

MISSOURI

Show-Me Audio-Visual, pg 887

MONTANA

Jereco Studios Inc, pg 793

NEW HAMPSHIRE

Chip Taylor Communications LLC, pg 907

NEW JERSEY

Allegro Productions Inc, pg 680
Broadcast Center Studios, pg 710
CFP Video Productions Inc, pg 720
Diversified, pg 744
MiB MediaWorks, pg 825
Milgrom Productions, pg 827
NFL Films Inc, pg 841
Suede Interactive, pg 903

NEW MEXICO

Production Outfitters, pg 864

NEW YORK

The Big House Group, pg 705
CP Communications, pg 732
Design Audio Visual Inc, pg 741
Digital Art Video Inc, pg 741
Hallel Communications, pg 775
HAVE Inc, pg 777
Magno Sound Inc, pg 815
The Palmer Group, pg 850
PostWorks, pg 860
Zelman Studios Ltd, pg 945

NORTH CAROLINA

Pat Appleson Studios Inc, pg 687
Horizon Video Productions Inc, pg 781
Take One Productions Ltd, pg 906

OHIO

Aztec Video Productions, pg 700
Mills James Productions, pg 828
The Telos Alliance, pg 910

OKLAHOMA

PDC Productions, pg 852

OREGON

REX, pg 874

PENNSYLVANIA

Audio Visual Communications Inc, pg 694
FMP Media Solutions Inc, pg 763
Production Masters Inc (PMI), pg 864
Right Coast Recording Inc, pg 875

SOUTH CAROLINA

Genesis Creative, pg 769

TENNESSEE

American Blackguard Inc, pg 683
JamSync, pg 793
Love Shack Recording Studios, pg 811
Memphis Communications Corp, pg 823
Motion Picture Services, pg 831
Scripps Networks, pg 882
Stage Post, pg 899
Technical Support Systems LLC, pg 908

TEXAS

Mediaforce Productions, pg 822
The Samuels Co, pg 879
South Coast Film & Video, pg 895
Stage Directions, pg 898

UTAH

One Stop CD Shop LLC, pg 846
Soularium Recording Studios, pg 893

VIRGINIA

Metro Productions, pg 824

WASHINGTON

North-by-Northwest - A Digital Studio, pg 842
Victory Studios, pg 927

WISCONSIN

Audio Visual of Milwaukee Inc, pg 694
5th Floor Recording Co, pg 760

ALBERTA

Global TV, pg 771

BRITISH COLUMBIA

Pinewood Sound, pg 857

MANITOBA

DACAPO Productions Inc, pg 737

ONTARIO

ADS Media, pg 677
GAPC (General Assembly Production Centre), pg 768
Metalworks Recording Studios Inc, pg 824
Phase One Studios, pg 855
Silver Creek Media Inc, pg 888
VO2 Mix Audio Post, pg 932
Westbury National Show Systems Ltd, pg 936

QUEBEC

Muse Entertainment Enterprises, pg 834

Mixing—Videotapes

ARIZONA

Fox 10 Productions (KSAZ-TV), pg 765
Merestone, pg 823
Metropolitan Audio-Visual Inc, pg 824

ARKANSAS

Live'N'Loud, pg 810
White Diamond Productions LLC, pg 937

CALIFORNIA

Action Video, pg 675
All Video Productions, pg 680
AlphaDogs Inc, pg 682
Artichoke Productions, pg 690
Berke Creative Inc, pg 704
Berkeley Sound Artists Inc, pg 704
CCI Digital, a DVS Company, pg 718
Steve Chandler, pg 720
Creative Media Recording, pg 733

Crystal Pyramid Productions™, pg 735
Custom Video Productions Inc, pg 736
Diamond Dreams Music Productions, pg 741
Earwax Productions Inc, pg 749
Express Media Inc, pg 757
First Person Inc, pg 761
Gordon Productions Inc, pg 772
iCorpTv, pg 783
KPBS Public Broadcasting, pg 801
KTVU-Retail Services, pg 802
KVIE-Channel 6, pg 802
Ludlow Media, pg 812
Maximus Media Inc, pg 820
McCune Audio-Video-Lighting, pg 821
The Media Staff Inc, pg 822
Nolte Media, pg 841
On-Trax Inc, pg 846
Palardo Productions, pg 850
piXvfm Inc, pg 857
PM Productions, pg 858
Polarity Post Production, pg 858
PSI Inc, pg 866
QRS Software Services, pg 867
RetinaVision Productions, pg 874
Roundabout Entertainment Inc, pg 878
Shapeshifter, pg 885
SonicPool, pg 892
Total Creative, pg 916
Twin Peaks Creative, pg 920
Universal Studios, pg 922
Visions Plus, pg 931
West Coast Projections Inc, pg 935

COLORADO

Tim Cissell Music, pg 725
CSI Film & Video LLC, pg 735
Daylight Productions & Rentals, pg 739
Flashback Media Productions, pg 762
Open Media Foundation, pg 846
Transtar Entertainment Co Inc, pg 917

CONNECTICUT

BRB Audiovisual Productions, pg 709
Geomatrix Productions, pg 770
Ironik Design & Post, pg 791
MAVCO, pg 820

DELAWARE

Side Door Studio Inc, pg 887

DISTRICT OF COLUMBIA

Interface Media Group, pg 789

FLORIDA

Access Media Group, pg 673
Accord Productions, pg 673
Communications Concepts Inc (CCI), pg 729
Courter Films LLC, pg 732
Easy Edit Video Inc, pg 750
Jordan Klein Film & Video (JKFV), pg 795
The Kitchen, pg 799
Mach 1 Productions, pg 813
National Teleproductions Inc, pg 837
Sound & Vision Communications Inc, pg 893
Sunfire Communications Inc, pg 904
Universal Studios Florida® Production Group, pg 922

Mike Vasilinda Productions Inc,
pg 925
Video Techniques Inc, pg 928
Vistamax Productions, pg 931

GEORGIA

Beachwood Productions, pg 702
First Cut Communications LLC,
pg 761
Guerrilla Productions LLC, pg 774
Staging Directions Inc, pg 899

HAWAII

1013 Integrated, pg 911

IDAHO

KTVB-TV, pg 802
Wide Eye Productions, pg 938

ILLINOIS

Beatty TeleVisual Productions,
pg 703
Extraordinary Demos/Videos,
pg 757
Pepper Group, pg 854
PSAV® Presentation Services
(Hotel Services Division), pg 866
Steven Samler Music & Sound,
pg 879
SCI Television & Creative Media
LLC, pg 882
Tele-Time Systems, pg 910
20/20 Communications Inc, pg 920
Video I-D Teleproductions Inc,
pg 928
Video Impressions, pg 928
WEEK TV, pg 935

INDIANA

A-V-A Video Productions, pg 671
Advanced Media Integration, pg 677
Communication Ministries, pg 728

IOWA

Educational Technology & Media
Services, pg 751

KANSAS

KAKE-TV, pg 796

KENTUCKY

Barney Miller's Inc, pg 827
The PPS Group, pg 860

LOUISIANA

Digital FX Inc, pg 742
Louisiana State University Division
of Strategic Communications,
pg 811
Moxie Media, pg 832
Vidox Motion Imagery, pg 930
YES Productions, pg 944

MAINE

Headlight Audio Visual Inc, pg 777
WGME-TV, pg 936

MARYLAND

Adventure Productions LLC, pg 678
Bethesda Softworks LLC, pg 704
CAS Video Productions, pg 717
CPR MultiMedia Solutions, pg 732
dbF a Media Company, pg 739
Media Dimensions LLC, pg 821
Milner-Fenwick Inc, pg 828

Sheffield Audio/Video Productions,
pg 885
Welocalize, pg 935

MASSACHUSETTS

CommCreative, pg 728
Documentary Educational Resources
Inc, pg 744
HOME Inc, pg 781
Small Planet Communications Inc,
pg 890

MICHIGAN

Digi Sign Design LLC, pg 741
K&R's Recording Studios Inc,
pg 796
Michigan Recording Arts Institute
& Technologies, pg 825

MINNESOTA

The ADS Group, pg 676
GMI Productions, pg 771
MastCom, pg 819
Worthwhile Films, pg 941

MISSOURI

Avatar Studios, pg 697
Conference Technologies Inc,
pg 730
KPLR-TV, pg 801
Show-Me Audio-Visual, pg 887

MONTANA

Jereco Studios Inc, pg 793
KCFW Television, pg 797
KUSM TV, pg 802

NEVADA

Aardvark Video & Media
Productions, pg 671
DVDs4Less, pg 748
Encore Event Technologies LLC,
pg 754
JCS Video Productions, pg 793
Lefco Video Services Inc, pg 806

NEW HAMPSHIRE

Academic & Campus Technology
Services, pg 672
Apertura, pg 686
Channell One Video, pg 720
Chip Taylor Communications LLC,
pg 907
The Troupe, pg 918

NEW JERSEY

AJS Events, pg 679
Allegro Productions Inc, pg 680
Broadcast Center Studios, pg 710
CFP Video Productions Inc, pg 720
Diversified, pg 744
Laurel Video Productions, pg 804
MediaMix Inc, pg 822
Megavideo LLC, pg 823
MiB MediaWorks, pg 825
NFL Films Music Library, pg 841
Optisonics Productions, pg 847
Starlite, pg 900
Suede Interactive, pg 903
VCSvideo, pg 925
Video Corporation of America
(VCA), pg 927

NEW MEXICO

Production Outfitters, pg 864
30 Second Street Ltd, pg 912

NEW YORK

Adwar Video, pg 678
aurora productions, pg 696
The Big House Group, pg 705
Broadstreet Productions LLC,
pg 711
Chromavision Corp, pg 723
Design Audio Visual Inc, pg 741
Downtown Community Television
Center (DCTV), pg 746
4-D Creative Media, pg 764
HAVE Inc, pg 777
HB-Content, pg 777
KAS Music & Sound, pg 796
Ketchum Inc, pg 798
Long Island Video Enterprises Live
Inc, pg 811
Magno Sound Inc, pg 815
MRM//McCANN, pg 832
PostWorks, pg 860
Teatown Communications Group,
pg 908
Visual Technologies Corp, pg 932
Zelman Studios Ltd, pg 945

NORTH CAROLINA

Pat Appleson Studios Inc, pg 687
The Communications Group Inc,
pg 729
Duke Media Services, pg 747
Horizon Video Productions Inc,
pg 781
Moving Pictures, pg 832
NASCAR Productions LLC, pg 835
On Location North Carolina, pg 846
Take One Productions Ltd, pg 906
Trailblazer Studios®, pg 917

NORTH DAKOTA

Media Productions, pg 822

OHIO

Aztec Video Productions, pg 700
Cuyahoga Community College
Student Production Office (SPO),
pg 736
MainSail Production Services Inc,
pg 815
Mills James Productions, pg 828
Musicol Recording, pg 835
Take 1 Media Services, pg 906
Vista Color Imaging Inc, pg 931

OREGON

KPDX-TV Production Center,
pg 801
KTVA Productions, pg 802
Production West, pg 864
REX, pg 874

PENNSYLVANIA

Center City Film & Video Inc,
pg 719
FMP Media Solutions Inc, pg 763
Innovision Media Group, pg 788
Laser Video Corp, pg 804
Production Masters Inc (PMI),
pg 864
The Videohouse Inc, pg 929
Visual Sound Inc, pg 931
WHYY Inc, pg 938
WPHL-TV, pg 942

SOUTH CAROLINA

Genesis Creative, pg 769
Stages Video Productions, pg 899
Venture Media, pg 925

TENNESSEE

JamSync, pg 793
Love Shack Recording Studios,
pg 811
Memphis Communications Corp,
pg 823
Motion Picture Services, pg 831
Scripps Networks, pg 882
ST Productions, pg 898
Stage Post, pg 899

TEXAS

Cerutti Productions Inc, pg 720
Communication Arts Multimedia
Inc, pg 728
The Editing Co, pg 750
Horizon Film + Video Productions,
pg 781
McNee Productions Inc, pg 821
Mediaforce Productions, pg 822
Phillips Media Source, pg 855
The Samuels Co, pg 879
South Coast Film & Video, pg 895
Texas Heart Institute Visual
Communication Services, pg 911

VERMONT

University of Vermont, Instructional
Television Dept, pg 923

VIRGINIA

BES Studios, pg 704
CACI Integrated Communications,
pg 713
CVW Event Productions, pg 736

WASHINGTON

Robert McConnell Productions,
pg 820
North-by-Northwest - A Digital
Studio, pg 842
Victory Studios, pg 927

WEST VIRGINIA

WSAZ-TV NewsChannel 3, pg 942

WISCONSIN

Audio Visual of Milwaukee Inc,
pg 694
Learning Technology Services,
pg 805
Logan Productions Inc, pg 811
USAV Group Inc, pg 923
Video Wisconsin Inc, pg 929
Wisconsin Public Television, pg 940

WYOMING

Bridger Productions Inc, pg 710

PUERTO RICO

Stage Crew Audiovisual Inc, pg 898

BRITISH COLUMBIA

Pinewood Sound, pg 857
Triad Communications Ltd, pg 918
Video Out Distribution, pg 928

MANITOBA

Spectra Video Productions Ltd,
pg 897

NEWFOUNDLAND AND LABRADOR

Vidcraft Productions Ltd, pg 927

VIDEO

Mixing—Videotapes (continued)

ONTARIO

GAPC (General Assembly Production Centre), pg 768
JFB Communications, pg 794
Metalworks Recording Studios Inc, pg 824
Silver Creek Media Inc, pg 888
Spence-Thomas Audio Post, pg 897
Video Excellence Productions, pg 927
VO2 Mix Audio Post, pg 932

QUEBEC

Muse Entertainment Enterprises, pg 834

Mobile Production Vehicle Distributors

CALIFORNIA

Ametron Audio/Video, pg 684
Satellite Digital Teleproductions (SDTV), pg 881
SNAP, pg 891

FLORIDA

Digital Video Systems, pg 742
ONstage, pg 846

HAWAII

The Audio Visual Co (AVCO), pg 694

INDIANA

Sensory Technologies LLC, pg 884

MARYLAND

Absolute Hollywood, pg 672

MINNESOTA

Alpha Video & Audio Inc, pg 682

MISSOURI

Communitronics Corp, pg 729
Modern Communications Inc, pg 828
Southwest Audio-Visual Inc, pg 895

NEW JERSEY

Diversified, pg 744
Tele-Measurements Inc, pg 910
Turner Engineering Inc, pg 919

NEW YORK

Audio-Video Corp, pg 694

NORTH CAROLINA

Strategic Connections, pg 901

OHIO

iVideo Technologies, pg 792

PENNSYLVANIA

Advanced AV LLC, pg 677
The Lerro Corp, pg 806
Morefield Communications Inc, pg 830

TENNESSEE

Zion Music Group, pg 945

TEXAS

Pro Video & Film Equipment Co Inc, pg 863
Shook Mobile Technology LP, pg 886

UTAH

RIA Corp, pg 874

VIRGINIA

Quince Imaging Inc, pg 868

WISCONSIN

Demco Inc, pg 740
Safe Harbor Computers, pg 879

Mobile Production Vehicle Manufacturers

CALIFORNIA

Broadcast Microwave Services Inc (BMS), a StoneCalibre company, pg 710
Technical Services, pg 908

FLORIDA

Frontline Communications, pg 766

MARYLAND

Absolute Hollywood, pg 672

NEW YORK

CP Communications, pg 732

TEXAS

Exeltech Inc, pg 757
Shook Mobile Technology LP, pg 886

VIRGINIA

Quince Imaging Inc, pg 868

Mobile Production Vehicle Rentals

ARIZONA

Arizona Cine Equipment, pg 688
Cox Creative Studios, pg 732
Merestone, pg 823
Rodeo Video Inc, pg 876

CALIFORNIA

Aerial Video Systems, pg 678
Ametron Audio/Video, pg 684
CineVantage LLC, pg 724
Crystal Pyramid Productions™, pg 735
DTC Lighting & Grip, pg 747
Express Media Inc, pg 757
First Camera, pg 761
Golden Gate Studios, pg 772
Lynch Communications, pg 813
PSSI Global Services LLC, pg 866
RetinaVision Productions, pg 874
Santa Clarita Studios, pg 880
SNAP, pg 891
Stray Angel Films, pg 902
Total Creative, pg 916
Universal Satellite Communications Inc, pg 922
Z-Ville Productions, pg 944

COLORADO

Colorado Studios, pg 728

DISTRICT OF COLUMBIA

Interface Media Group, pg 789

FLORIDA

ACT Productions, pg 675
CopShopMiami.com, pg 731
Jordan Klein Film & Video (JKFV), pg 795
National Teleproductions Inc, pg 837
ONstage, pg 846
Skystorm Productions, pg 890
Trendy Studio LLC, pg 917

GEORGIA

ON Services, a GES Company, pg 846
Stage Front Presentation Systems, pg 899

HAWAII

FOTON Hawaii, pg 764
Sight & Sound Studios, pg 887

ILLINOIS

Atomic Imaging Inc/Golan Studios, pg 692
Big Shoulders Digital Video Productions, pg 705
Product Productions, pg 863
PSAV® Presentation Services (Hotel Services Division), pg 866
Satellite Technology Systems Inc, pg 881

INDIANA

Lakeshore Public Media, pg 803

KENTUCKY

WKYT-TV, pg 940

LOUISIANA

Digital FX Inc, pg 742
Moxie Media, pg 832
Satellite Center, pg 881
YES Productions, pg 944

MARYLAND

Absolute Hollywood, pg 672
CPR MultiMedia Solutions, pg 732
Producers Video, pg 863
Sheffield Audio/Video Productions, pg 885

MASSACHUSETTS

A/V Presentations Inc, pg 697

MICHIGAN

K&R All Media Productions LLC, pg 796
K&R's Recording Studios Inc, pg 796
WTVS, Detroit Public Television, pg 942

MISSOURI

Southwest Audio-Visual Inc, pg 895

NEBRASKA

Dog & Pony Productions Inc, pg 744

NEVADA

Lefco Video Services Inc, pg 806

NEW HAMPSHIRE

Channell One Video, pg 720

NEW JERSEY

E Video Productions LLC, pg 749
MediaMix Inc, pg 822
MiB MediaWorks, pg 825
Vision Quest Productions Inc, pg 930

NEW MEXICO

Production Outfitters, pg 864

NEW YORK

All Mobile Video Inc, pg 680
CP Communications, pg 732
Manhattan Center Studios Inc, pg 816
Sony Music Entertainment, pg 893
Visual Word Systems Inc, pg 932

NORTH CAROLINA

The Communications Group Inc, pg 729
On Location North Carolina, pg 846
Take One Productions Ltd, pg 906
Videowerks, pg 930

OHIO

Image Video Teleproductions Inc, pg 785
Lyon Video Inc, pg 813
Mills James Productions, pg 828

OKLAHOMA

Institute for Teaching & Learning Excellence (ITLE), pg 788

OREGON

Pacific Grip & Lighting Inc, pg 849

PENNSYLVANIA

FMP Media Solutions Inc, pg 763
Innovision Media Group, pg 788
Location Lighting Ltd, pg 810
NEP Group Inc, pg 838
Producers Management Television (PMTV), pg 863
Upstage Video, pg 923

SOUTH CAROLINA

Assignment Desk, pg 691

TENNESSEE

DR&A Inc, pg 746
Russ Sturgeon Productions/RSVP, pg 903
Technical Support Systems LLC, pg 908

TEXAS

AMS Pictures, pg 684
Imagine Communications Corp, pg 786
JWP Inc, pg 796
Earl Miller Productions Inc, pg 827
Muller Entertainment LLC, pg 833
Omega Productions, pg 845
Phillips Media Source, pg 855
Reelsound Recording Co, pg 872
Texcam Inc, pg 911

VIRGINIA

Quince Imaging Inc, pg 868

WASHINGTON

Victory Studios, pg 927

WISCONSIN

Logan Productions Inc, pg 811
Wisconsin Public Television, pg 940

ALBERTA

Global TV, pg 771

ONTARIO

JIB Shots Equipment Inc, pg 794

QUEBEC

Group PVP, pg 774

Mobile Production Vehicle Repairs

CALIFORNIA

Ametron Audio/Video, pg 684
Technical Services, pg 908

FLORIDA

ELC Sales & Service Inc, pg 752
JT Communications, pg 795

MICHIGAN

TEL Systems LLC, pg 909

MINNESOTA

Alpha Video & Audio Inc, pg 682

MISSOURI

Southwest Audio-Visual Inc, pg 895

NEW JERSEY

Turner Engineering Inc, pg 919

TENNESSEE

Technical Support Systems LLC,
 pg 908

TEXAS

Pro Video & Film Equipment Co
 Inc, pg 863
Shook Mobile Technology LP,
 pg 886

UTAH

RIA Corp, pg 874

VIRGINIA

Quince Imaging Inc, pg 868

Mobile Unit Distributors

CALIFORNIA

Ametron Audio/Video, pg 684
BigFoot Mobile Systems, pg 705
Satellite Digital Teleproductions
 (SDTV), pg 881

CONNECTICUT

Rockwell Communications Inc,
 pg 876

FLORIDA

Communications Concepts Inc
 (CCI), pg 729
Digital Video Systems, pg 742
L3Harris Technologies Inc, pg 812

GEORGIA

Convergent Media Systems, pg 731
Stage Front Presentation Systems,
 pg 899

ILLINOIS

Toko America Inc, pg 915

INDIANA

Sensory Technologies LLC, pg 884

MARYLAND

Nicholas P Pipino Associates Inc,
 pg 857

MINNESOTA

Alpha Video & Audio Inc, pg 682

MISSOURI

Communitronics Corp, pg 729
Modern Communications Inc,
 pg 828
Southwest Audio-Visual Inc, pg 895

NEW JERSEY

Diversified, pg 744
Turner Engineering Inc, pg 919

NEW YORK

Audio-Video Corp, pg 694
Visual Technologies Corp, pg 932

NORTH CAROLINA

Strategic Connections, pg 901

PENNSYLVANIA

Advanced AV LLC, pg 677
The Lerro Corp, pg 806
Morefield Communications Inc,
 pg 830
Wespen Audio Visual Co, pg 935

TENNESSEE

Lowrance Sound Co Inc, pg 812
WhisperRoom™ Inc, pg 937
Zion Music Group, pg 945

TEXAS

Heffernan Audio Visual, pg 778
Pro Video & Film Equipment Co
 Inc, pg 863
Shook Mobile Technology LP,
 pg 886

UTAH

RIA Corp, pg 874

VIRGINIA

Quince Imaging Inc, pg 868

WISCONSIN

Spectrum Industries Inc, pg 897

ONTARIO

Majortech Inc, pg 815

Mobile Unit Manufacturers

ARIZONA

Applied Integration Corp, pg 687

CALIFORNIA

Broadcast Microwave Services Inc
 (BMS), a StoneCalibre company,
 pg 710
Technical Services, pg 908
TV Pro Gear, pg 919

COLORADO

Display Devices Inc, pg 743

FLORIDA

Frontline Communications, pg 766

ILLINOIS

Dukane Corp, Audio Visual
 Products Division, pg 747
Toko America Inc, pg 915

IOWA

Winegard Co, pg 939

NEW YORK

Judson Rosebush Co Inc, pg 877

TENNESSEE

WhisperRoom™ Inc, pg 937

TEXAS

Exeltech Inc, pg 757
Shook Mobile Technology LP,
 pg 886
The Yesterday USA Radio
 Networks, pg 944

VIRGINIA

Quince Imaging Inc, pg 868

WISCONSIN

Spectrum Industries Inc, pg 897

QUEBEC

Matrox Video Products Group,
 pg 819

Mobile Unit Rentals

ALABAMA

AVS Media Group, pg 699

ARIZONA

Arizona Cine Equipment, pg 688
Crew West Inc, pg 734
Merestone, pg 823
Rodeo Video Inc, pg 876

CALIFORNIA

Acey Decy Lighting, pg 674
Aerial Video Systems, pg 678
Ametron Audio/Video, pg 684
Crash Video Productions, pg 733
Crystal Pyramid Productions™,
 pg 735
Digital Film Studios LLC, pg 742
DTC Lighting & Grip, pg 747
Express Media Inc, pg 757
Gear Monkey, pg 769
Golden Gate Studios, pg 772
Illuminate Studios, pg 784

KTVU-Retail Services, pg 802
Lynch Communications, pg 813
Maximus Media Inc, pg 820
McCune Audio-Video-Lighting,
 pg 821
Power & Light, pg 860
PSSI Global Services LLC, pg 866
RetinaVision Productions, pg 874
Shoulder High Productions, pg 886
SNAP, pg 891
Twin Peaks Creative, pg 920

COLORADO

Maniac Productions, pg 816
Open Media Foundation, pg 846

CONNECTICUT

Rockwell Communications Inc,
 pg 876

FLORIDA

Astoria Communications Inc,
 pg 691
Communications Concepts Inc
 (CCI), pg 729
Digital Comm Link Inc, pg 742
F&F Productions LLC, pg 759
Jordan Klein Film & Video (JKFV),
 pg 795
National Teleproductions Inc,
 pg 837
Phat Planet Recording Studios,
 pg 855

GEORGIA

Convergent Media Systems, pg 731
Stage Front Presentation Systems,
 pg 899
Studio Space Atlanta, pg 903

ILLINOIS

Big Shoulders Digital Video
 Productions, pg 705
On Site Video, pg 846
PSAV® Presentation Services
 (Hotel Services Division), pg 866

INDIANA

Midwest Uplink Inc, pg 827

KENTUCKY

WKYT-TV, pg 940

LOUISIANA

Digital FX Inc, pg 742
Moxie Media, pg 832
Pace Systems, pg 849
YES Productions, pg 944

MARYLAND

CPR MultiMedia Solutions, pg 732
Sheffield Audio/Video Productions,
 pg 885

MASSACHUSETTS

Red Sky Studios, pg 872

MICHIGAN

K&R All Media Productions LLC,
 pg 796
Lowing Light & Grip Inc, pg 812

MISSOURI

Southwest Audio-Visual Inc, pg 895

VIDEO

Mobile Unit Rentals (continued)

NEVADA

Lefco Video Services Inc, pg 806

NEW JERSEY

Ironbound Film & Television Studios LLC, pg 791
MediaMix Inc, pg 822
Vision Quest Productions Inc, pg 930

NEW MEXICO

Production Outfitters, pg 864

NEW YORK

CP Communications, pg 732
Gearhead Rentals, pg 769
Manhattan Center Studios Inc, pg 816
NBC Production Facilities, pg 837
PrimaLux Video Inc, pg 862
Scheimpflug Digital, pg 881
Visual Technologies Corp, pg 932
Visual Word Systems Inc, pg 932
WNET/New York Public Media, pg 940

NORTH CAROLINA

Bill Barnes Video Productions LLC, pg 702
On Location North Carolina, pg 846
Take One Productions Ltd, pg 906

NORTH DAKOTA

Media Productions, pg 822

OHIO

Image Video Teleproductions Inc, pg 785
Lyon Video Inc, pg 813
Mills James Productions, pg 828
OSV Studios, pg 848
Vista Color Imaging Inc, pg 931

OREGON

Pacific Grip & Lighting Inc, pg 849
Picture This Production Services, pg 856

PENNSYLVANIA

Innovision Media Group, pg 788
Liberty Uplink, pg 807
NEP Group Inc, pg 838
Videosmith Inc, pg 930
Viewpoint Production Services Inc, pg 930
WPHL-TV, pg 942

TENNESSEE

Russ Sturgeon Productions/RSVP, pg 903

TEXAS

Countdown Productions Inc, pg 732
Earl Miller Productions Inc, pg 827
Muller Entertainment LLC, pg 833
Omega Productions, pg 845
Stage Directions, pg 898

VIRGINIA

Quince Imaging Inc, pg 868

WISCONSIN

Logan Productions Inc, pg 811
Wisconsin Public Television, pg 940

ALBERTA

Global TV, pg 771

BRITISH COLUMBIA

Video Out Distribution, pg 928

Mobile Unit Repairs

CALIFORNIA

Ametron Audio/Video, pg 684
BigFoot Mobile Systems, pg 705
Technical Services, pg 908

FLORIDA

ELC Sales & Service Inc, pg 752

GEORGIA

Stage Front Presentation Systems, pg 899

ILLINOIS

On Site Video, pg 846

MICHIGAN

TEL Systems LLC, pg 909

MINNESOTA

Alpha Video & Audio Inc, pg 682

MISSOURI

Southwest Audio-Visual Inc, pg 895

NEW YORK

Visual Technologies Corp, pg 932

TEXAS

Shook Mobile Technology LP, pg 886
The Yesterday USA Radio Networks, pg 944

UTAH

RIA Corp, pg 874

VIRGINIA

Quince Imaging Inc, pg 868

Monitor, see Video Receiver & Monitor

Music Scoring

ALABAMA

Airwave Recording Studio, pg 679
Sound of Birmingham Productions, pg 894

ARIZONA

Creative Backstage, pg 733
Merestone, pg 823

ARKANSAS

Live'N'Loud, pg 810
White Diamond Productions LLC, pg 937

CALIFORNIA

AB Audio Visual Entertainment Inc, pg 672
Aliso Creek Productions Inc, pg 680
Berke Creative Inc, pg 704
Berkeley Sound Artists Inc, pg 704
CCI Digital, a DVS Company, pg 718
Steve Chandler, pg 720
Creative Media Recording, pg 733
Creative Support Services/CSS Music, pg 733
Creative Technology, pg 733
Crystal Pyramid Productions™, pg 735
Diamond Dreams Music Productions, pg 741
digital OutPost, pg 742
Earwax Productions Inc, pg 749
4th Street Recording, pg 764
GrooveWorx, pg 774
Steven Halpern's Inner Peace Music, pg 775
iCorpTv, pg 783
JDS Video & Media Productions Inc, pg 793
Kaleidosound, pg 796
Lynch Communications, pg 813
Maximus Media Inc, pg 820
The Media Staff Inc, pg 822
Megatrax, pg 823
The Music Kitchen Inc, pg 834
Joseph Nicoletti Consulting-Promotion, pg 841
OTR Studios, pg 848
Palardo Productions, pg 850
PM Productions, pg 858
Polarity Post Production, pg 858
Private Island Audio Inc, pg 862
Pyramind Studios, pg 867
QRS Software Services, pg 867
Reality Check Systems, pg 871
Russ InVision Co/AbridgeClub.com, pg 879
Sahara Records & Filmworks Entertainment Co, pg 879
Saturn Studios, pg 881
Sonic Gravy, pg 892
SonicPool, pg 892
Sonora Recorders, pg 893
Staylor-Made Communications Inc, pg 900
Still N' Motion, pg 901
Studio 132, pg 902
Timeless Productions, pg 914
Total Creative, pg 916
West Coast Projections Inc, pg 935

COLORADO

Tim Cissell Music, pg 725
Conly Productions, pg 730
Flashback Media Productions, pg 762
Los Angeles Post Music Inc, pg 811

CONNECTICUT

Guymark Studios LLC, pg 775
Palace Production Center, pg 850
P&P Studios Inc, pg 851

DELAWARE

Side Door Studio Inc, pg 887

DISTRICT OF COLUMBIA

Interface Media Group, pg 789
Yellow Cat Productions Inc, pg 944

FLORIDA

Applebox Studio, pg 687
Audacity Recording Studios, pg 693

CALIFORNIA

Kat Epple Music Productions, pg 755
Jordan Klein Film & Video (JKFV), pg 795
The Kitchen, pg 799
Mach 1 Productions, pg 813
Phat Planet Recording Studios, pg 855
Sunfire Communications Inc, pg 904
Mike Vasilinda Productions Inc, pg 925

GEORGIA

First Cut Communications LLC, pg 761
Staging Directions Inc, pg 899
White Dog Studios, pg 937

HAWAII

Media Bridge Gamekids, pg 821

ILLINOIS

ABS Enterprises, pg 672
CCore Media Inc, pg 718
Jim Passin Productions, pg 852
Pepper Group, pg 854
Steven Samler Music & Sound, pg 879
WEEK TV, pg 935
Woodside Avenue Music Productions Inc, pg 941

KENTUCKY

Broadway Digital, pg 711
Horizon Films & Media LLC, pg 781
The Media Collaboratory, pg 821

LOUISIANA

Digital FX Inc, pg 742
Vidox Motion Imagery, pg 930

MARYLAND

CPR MultiMedia Solutions, pg 732
CSPMedia.com, pg 735
dbF a Media Company, pg 739
Kramer Communications Video Production, pg 801
Satellite Media Production, pg 881

MASSACHUSETTS

CommCreative, pg 728
Continental Recordings Inc, pg 731
Cramer, pg 732
Green Mountain Post Films (GMP), pg 774
Northern Light Productions (NLP), pg 842
Penfield Productions Ltd, pg 853
Soundtrack Group, pg 895
TR Productions, pg 916

MICHIGAN

Digi Sign Design LLC, pg 741
GMP Music, pg 772
K&R's Recording Studios Inc, pg 796
Michigan Recording Arts Institute & Technologies, pg 825
RingSide Creative, pg 875

MINNESOTA

The ADS Group, pg 676
BeyerSound & Essay Audio, pg 705
Media Loft Inc, pg 822

MONTANA

Jereco Studios Inc, pg 793

NEVADA

Aardvark Video & Media
Productions, pg 671
Tanglewood Productions, pg 907

NEW HAMPSHIRE

Channell One Video, pg 720
Chip Taylor Communications LLC,
pg 907

NEW JERSEY

Allegro Productions Inc, pg 680
Broadcast Center Studios, pg 710
CFP Video Productions Inc, pg 720
Color Leasing Studios, pg 727
Milgrom Productions, pg 827
NFL Films Inc, pg 841
NFL Films Music Library, pg 841
Richard Reiter Productions Inc,
pg 873
Suede Interactive, pg 903
TRF Production Music Libraries,
pg 917
VCSvideo, pg 925
Video Corporation of America
(VCA), pg 927

NEW MEXICO

Production Outfitters, pg 864

NEW YORK

Air Sea Land Productions Inc
(ASL), pg 678
Aural Gratification Inc, pg 695
aurora productions, pg 696
The Big House Group, pg 705
Chromavision Corp, pg 723
Digital Arts NY, pg 742
Fingerpaint, pg 761
Hallel Communications, pg 775
Headroom Digital Audio, pg 777
Heavy Melody, pg 778
IAI Records & Video, pg 783
Icontent, pg 783
KAS Music & Sound, pg 796
Manhattan Center Studios Inc,
pg 816
Manhattan Production Music Inc,
pg 816
Jack Morton Worldwide, pg 830
New York Audio Productions,
pg 840
The Palmer Group, pg 850
PostWorks, pg 860
PrimeLight Productions Inc, pg 862
Elliot Sokolov Music, pg 892
Sony Music Entertainment, pg 893
Teatown Communications Group,
pg 908
Tiki Recording Studios Inc, pg 914
Zelman Studios Ltd, pg 945

NORTH CAROLINA

Audio Art, pg 693
The Communications Group Inc,
pg 729
Horizon Video Productions Inc,
pg 781
Trailblazer Studios®, pg 917
2BruceStudio, pg 920

NORTH DAKOTA

Media Productions, pg 822

OHIO

Aztec Video Productions, pg 700
Challenge Productions/Challenge
Aerial Imaging, pg 720
MainSail Production Services Inc,
pg 815
Mills James Productions, pg 828
Take 1 Media Services, pg 906

OREGON

Odyssey Productions Inc, pg 844
REX, pg 874

PENNSYLVANIA

Dreambox Media Inc, pg 746
Filmaker Technology, pg 760
Monster Tracks, pg 829
Production Masters Inc (PMI),
pg 864
WPHL-TV, pg 942

RHODE ISLAND

M-Audio, pg 813
Sound-FX-Design, pg 894

TENNESSEE

American Blackguard Inc, pg 683
Fricon Entertainment Co Inc,
pg 766
JamSync, pg 793
Motion Picture Services, pg 831
Scripps Networks, pg 882
Stage Post, pg 899

TEXAS

Audiomoxie®, pg 695
Communication Arts Multimedia
Inc, pg 728
The Editing Co, pg 750
Horizon Film + Video Productions,
pg 781
McNee Productions Inc, pg 821
Mediaforce Productions, pg 822
Phillips Media Source, pg 855
Reelsound Recording Co, pg 872
The Samuels Co, pg 879
The Sound Lab Inc, pg 894
Stage Directions, pg 898
TM Studios Inc, pg 915
Tropikal Productions, pg 918

UTAH

Soularium Recording Studios,
pg 893

VERMONT

University of Vermont, Instructional
Television Dept, pg 923

VIRGINIA

BES Studios, pg 704
Studio Center Corp, pg 902

WASHINGTON

Inland Audio Visual Co, pg 788
Kostov Productions, pg 801
North-by-Northwest - A Digital
Studio, pg 842
Sound Sound, pg 894

WISCONSIN

Audio Visual of Milwaukee Inc,
pg 694
5th Floor Recording Co, pg 760
USAV Group Inc, pg 923

WYOMING

Bridger Productions Inc, pg 710

BRITISH COLUMBIA

Pinewood Sound, pg 857

MANITOBA

DACAPO Productions Inc, pg 737
Spectra Video Productions Ltd,
pg 897

NEWFOUNDLAND AND LABRADOR

Vidcraft Productions Ltd, pg 927

ONTARIO

ADS Media, pg 677
GAPC (General Assembly
Production Centre), pg 768
Metalworks Recording Studios Inc,
pg 824
Nightingale Music Productions Inc,
pg 841
Silver Creek Media Inc, pg 888

Music Videos

ALABAMA

Diamond Studios, pg 741

ARIZONA

Arizona Studios, pg 688
Creative Backstage, pg 733
Film Creations Ltd, pg 760
Merestone, pg 823

ARKANSAS

Live'N'Loud, pg 810
Michael Mueller Video Productions,
pg 833
White Diamond Productions LLC,
pg 937

CALIFORNIA

A Go Go Films, pg 671
AB Audio Visual Entertainment Inc,
pg 672
Access Video in Berkeley, pg 673
Air Philosophy Inc, pg 678
All Video Productions, pg 680
Artichoke Productions, pg 690
Automated Entertainment, pg 696
Backstage Pass Entertainment Inc,
pg 700
Barber Tech Video Products, pg 701
Berke Creative Inc, pg 704
Big Door, pg 705
Blueyed Pictures Inc, pg 708
Steve Chandler, pg 720
Cherry Multimedia, pg 721
Concrete Images, pg 730
Creative Technology, pg 733
Crystal Pyramid Productions™,
pg 735
Custom Video Productions Inc,
pg 736
deKramer Productions Inc, pg 740
Diamond Dreams Music
Productions, pg 741
Direct Images Interactive Inc,
pg 743
Earwax Productions Inc, pg 749
First Camera, pg 761
First Person Inc, pg 761
Full Moon & High Tide Productions
& Music, pg 767
Glix Entertainment Inc, pg 771

Gold Standard Productions, pg 772
Bruce Goldberg Inc, pg 772
GrooveWorx, pg 774
Steven Halpern's Inner Peace
Music, pg 775
iCorpTv, pg 783
JDS Video & Media Productions
Inc, pg 793
The Jim Henson Co, pg 794
KVIE-Channel 6, pg 802
Laser Magic Productions, pg 804
Ludlow Media, pg 812
Lynch Communications, pg 813
Maximus Media Inc, pg 820
Media Magic, pg 822
Method Studios, pg 824
New & Unique Videos™, pg 839
Joseph Nicoletti Consulting-
Promotion, pg 841
Nineteen87, pg 841
On-Trax Inc, pg 846
OTR Studios, pg 848
Palardo Productions, pg 850
Playback Recording Studio, pg 858
PM Productions, pg 858
QRS Software Services, pg 867
Quality Clones, pg 867
Regent Press Publishers & Printers,
pg 873
RetinaVision Productions, pg 874
Sahara Records & Filmworks
Entertainment Co, pg 879
Saturn Studios, pg 881
Shapeshifter, pg 885
SNAP, pg 891
SonicPool, pg 892
Sonora Recorders, pg 893
Staylor-Made Communications Inc,
pg 900
Still N' Motion, pg 901
Tam Communications Inc, pg 906
Total Creative, pg 916
Twin Peaks Creative, pg 920
Two Door Productions LLC, pg 920
Universal Studios, pg 922
WARPed Pictures, pg 934
Wavemaker Media Design, pg 934
Z-Ville Productions, pg 944

COLORADO

Colorado Sound Recording Ltd,
pg 728
Conly Productions, pg 730
Denver Media Center, pg 740
Flashback Media Productions,
pg 762
Full Spectrum Arts & Services,
pg 767
Open Media Foundation, pg 846
Side 3 Studios, pg 887

CONNECTICUT

Digital Video Productions, pg 742
The Gary-Paul Agency, pg 768
Ironik Design & Post, pg 791
MAVCO, pg 820
New London Media, pg 839
P&P Studios Inc, pg 851

DISTRICT OF COLUMBIA

Interface Media Group, pg 789
Metro Teleproductions Inc (MTI),
pg 824

FLORIDA

Applebox Studio, pg 687
Audio Visual Imagineering Inc,
pg 694
Chatterbox Productions Inc, pg 721
Civins Productions Inc, pg 725

VIDEO

Music Videos (continued)

FLORIDA (continued)

Steven Cohen Motion Picture
　Production, pg 727
Communications Concepts Inc
　(CCI), pg 729
Courter Films LLC, pg 732
Kat Epple Music Productions,
　pg 755
Harmon's Audio-Visual Services,
　pg 776
Olympusat, pg 845
Sunfire Communications Inc,
　pg 904
Tricycle Studios, pg 918
Universal Studios Florida®
　Production Group, pg 922
Mike Vasilinda Productions Inc,
　pg 925
Venice Media Group, pg 925
Vistamax Productions, pg 931

GEORGIA

Beachwood Productions, pg 702
Beast Atlanta, pg 703
The DVI Group, pg 748
ECG Productions, pg 750
Guerrilla Productions LLC, pg 774
Myriad Productions, pg 835
On-Line Productions, pg 845

HAWAII

Hyperspective Studios Inc, pg 783
Media Bridge Gamekids, pg 821
Sight & Sound Studios, pg 887
1013 Integrated, pg 911

IDAHO

Wide Eye Productions, pg 938

ILLINOIS

ABSA Films, pg 672
AnswersMedia, pg 686
CCore Media Inc, pg 718
The Chicago Production Center,
　pg 721
Explore, pg 757
IV Media Resources, pg 792
Optimus, pg 847
Pepper Group, pg 854
Richter Studios, pg 875
Steven Samler Music & Sound,
　pg 879
SCI Television & Creative Media
　LLC, pg 882
20/20 Communications Inc, pg 920
Video Impressions, pg 928
Winter Productions, pg 939
Woodside Avenue Music
　Productions Inc, pg 941

INDIANA

A-V-A Video Productions, pg 671
PentaVision Communications Inc,
　pg 854

KENTUCKY

Hammond Communications Group
　Inc, pg 775
The Media Collaboratory, pg 821
The PPS Group, pg 860
Prosper Media Group Inc, pg 866

LOUISIANA

Digital FX Inc, pg 742
Moxie Media, pg 832
Vidox Motion Imagery, pg 930
YES Productions, pg 944

MARYLAND

Adventure Productions LLC, pg 678
CPR MultiMedia Solutions, pg 732
dbF a Media Company, pg 739
Kramer Communications Video
　Production, pg 801

MASSACHUSETTS

Extreme Reach Inc, pg 757
Green Mountain Post Films (GMP),
　pg 774
HOME Inc, pg 781
Penfield Productions Ltd, pg 853
Sound & Vision Media, pg 893
Soundtrack Group, pg 895
TVN-The Video Network, pg 919

MICHIGAN

Axis Films, pg 700
Digi Sign Design LLC, pg 741
Digital Image Studios LLC, pg 742
K&R's Recording Studios Inc,
　pg 796
Michigan Recording Arts Institute
　& Technologies, pg 825
On Stage Visuals, pg 846

MINNESOTA

Big Event Productions LLC, pg 705
MastCom, pg 819

MISSOURI

Avatar Studios, pg 697
Studio Worx Inc, pg 903

MONTANA

Jereco Studios Inc, pg 793
KCFW Television, pg 797
ooLite Media LLC, pg 846

NEVADA

Aardvark Video & Media
　Productions, pg 671
DVDs4Less, pg 748
JCS Video Productions, pg 793
Lefco Video Services Inc, pg 806
Tanglewood Productions, pg 907

NEW HAMPSHIRE

Channell One Video, pg 720
Chip Taylor Communications LLC,
　pg 907

NEW JERSEY

AJS Events, pg 679
Allegro Productions Inc, pg 680
Broadcast Center Studios, pg 710
CFP Video Productions Inc, pg 720
MediaMix Inc, pg 822
MediaNow Inc, pg 822
Megavideo LLC, pg 823
NFL Films Inc, pg 841
Optisonics Productions, pg 847
Richard Reiter Productions Inc,
　pg 873
Suede Interactive, pg 903
Telequest Inc, pg 910
VCSvideo, pg 925
Video Corporation of America
　(VCA), pg 927

NEW MEXICO

Production Outfitters, pg 864

NEW YORK

Air Sea Land Productions Inc
　(ASL), pg 678
aurora productions, pg 696
Bevilacqua Studios, pg 704
Big Foot Productions Inc, pg 705
The Big House Group, pg 705
Brooklyn Films, pg 711
Chromavision Corp, pg 723
CP Digital, pg 732
Design Audio Visual Inc, pg 741
Designomotion, pg 741
Digital Art Video Inc, pg 741
East of Hollywood NY, pg 749
Hello World Communications,
　pg 778
IAI Records & Video, pg 783
Icontent, pg 783
Long Island Video Enterprises Live
　Inc, pg 811
Lylofilm Productions, pg 813
Magnetic Music Publishing Co,
　pg 814
Manhattan Center Studios Inc,
　pg 816
Mood Creations Ltd, pg 829
New Horizon Studios, pg 839
The Palmer Group, pg 850
Peckham Productions Inc, pg 852
Pennebaker Hegedus Films Inc,
　pg 854
SmackDab Media, pg 890
Elliot Sokolov Music, pg 892
Sony Music Entertainment, pg 893
Teatown Communications Group,
　pg 908
Tiki Recording Studios Inc, pg 914
USA Studios, pg 923
VIEW Inc (Video International
　Entertainment World Inc), pg 930
Zelman Studios Ltd, pg 945

NORTH CAROLINA

Pat Appleson Studios Inc, pg 687
Bill Barnes Video Productions LLC,
　pg 702
The Communications Group Inc,
　pg 729
Crystal Pictures Inc, pg 735
Digital Rain LLC, pg 742
Duke Media Services, pg 747
Moving Pictures, pg 832
NASCAR Productions LLC, pg 835
On Location North Carolina, pg 846
Take One Productions Ltd, pg 906

NORTH DAKOTA

Media Productions, pg 822

OHIO

Advent Media Inc, pg 677
Aztec Video Productions, pg 700
Challenge Productions/Challenge
　Aerial Imaging, pg 720
Lyon Video Inc, pg 813
Mills James Productions, pg 828
R&B Communications Inc, pg 870
Take 1 Media Services, pg 906
Vista Color Imaging Inc, pg 931

OREGON

KPDX-TV Production Center,
　pg 801
REX, pg 874
Wilderness Video, pg 938

PENNSYLVANIA

Bang! Pictures Inc, pg 701
Center City Film & Video Inc,
　pg 719
CORTRON Media LLC, pg 732
Dreambox Media Inc, pg 746
FMP Media Solutions Inc, pg 763
Kensington Falls Animation, pg 797
Visual Sound Inc, pg 931
WHYY Inc, pg 938

RHODE ISLAND

Sound-FX-Design, pg 894

SOUTH CAROLINA

Genesis Creative, pg 769
Stages Video Productions, pg 899
Venture Media, pg 925

TENNESSEE

Fricon Entertainment Co Inc,
　pg 766
Griffith Productions, pg 774
Love Shack Recording Studios,
　pg 811
Motion Picture Services, pg 831
Stage Post, pg 899
Zion Music Group, pg 945

TEXAS

Biway Media, pg 706
Cerutti Productions Inc, pg 720
Communication Arts Multimedia
　Inc, pg 728
The Editing Co, pg 750
Epic Software Group Inc, pg 755
Eyecon Video Productions, pg 758
Horizon Film + Video Productions,
　pg 781
Maverick Video Productions, pg 820
McNee Productions Inc, pg 821
Mediaforce Productions, pg 822
Earl Miller Productions Inc, pg 827
Muller Entertainment LLC, pg 833
Out of the BLUE Media, pg 849
Phillips Media Source, pg 855
RuffHouse LLC, pg 878
The Samuels Co, pg 879
Sound Works, pg 894
South Coast Film & Video, pg 895
TopCat Records LLC, pg 915

UTAH

ImageWorks Communications,
　pg 785

VIRGINIA

BES Studios, pg 704
CACI Integrated Communications,
　pg 713
CVW Event Productions, pg 736
Goose Creek Music &
　Entertainment, pg 772
Henninger Media Services, pg 779
Limelight Communications Inc,
　pg 808
Rocktown Media, pg 876

WASHINGTON

Bennett-Watt HD Productions Inc,
　pg 703
North-by-Northwest - A Digital
　Studio, pg 842
Victory Studios, pg 927

WEST VIRGINIA

Blackwater Video Productions, pg 707
Sweetsong Productions, pg 905

WISCONSIN

Audio Visual of Milwaukee Inc, pg 694
Concept Productions Inc, pg 730
Meridian Studios, pg 824
Midland Video Productions Inc, pg 827
TBC Studios, pg 907
USAV Group Inc, pg 923
Video Wisconsin Inc, pg 929
Wisconsin Public Television, pg 940

WYOMING

Bridger Productions Inc, pg 710

ALBERTA

Black Media Works, pg 706
Global TV, pg 771

BRITISH COLUMBIA

Pinewood Sound, pg 857
Triad Communications Ltd, pg 918
24 Frames Film & Video, pg 920

MANITOBA

Manitoba Film & Music, pg 816
Spectra Video Productions Ltd, pg 897

ONTARIO

ADS Media, pg 677
GAPC (General Assembly Production Centre), pg 768
Image Video Services & Productions, pg 785
JFB Communications, pg 794
Legendary Entertainment, pg 806
Marblemedia, pg 816
Metalworks Recording Studios Inc, pg 824
Silver Creek Media Inc, pg 888
Spence-Thomas Audio Post, pg 897
Trebas Institute, pg 917
Video Excellence Productions, pg 927

QUEBEC

Trebas Institute, pg 917

Optical Effects, *see* Special Effects

Packaging & Storage— Cassette & Disc Distributors

ARIZONA

Troxell-CDI, pg 918

ARKANSAS

White Diamond Productions LLC, pg 937

CALIFORNIA

Ametron Audio/Video, pg 684
Audio/Video Supply Inc, pg 694
Christy's Editorial, pg 723
Polyline LLC, pg 859
VMI Inc, pg 932

COLORADO

Case Logic Inc, pg 717
ProLine Digital, pg 865
Rose Packaging & Design Inc, pg 877
Stanco Sales LLC, pg 899

FLORIDA

Digital Video Systems, pg 742
Midtown Video Inc, pg 827
Recording Media & Equipment Inc (RM&E), pg 872

GEORGIA

Blue Media Supply Inc, pg 707
Stage Front Presentation Systems, pg 899

ILLINOIS

LKG Industries Inc, pg 810

INDIANA

Lee Co Inc, pg 805
Sensory Technologies LLC, pg 884

KENTUCKY

American Recordable Media, pg 684
NOR-COM Inc, pg 841

MARYLAND

Ever-Ready Media Packaging, pg 757
Kipp Visual Systems Inc, pg 799

MASSACHUSETTS

Hannecke Display Systems Inc, pg 775
Rule Boston Camera, pg 878

MINNESOTA

Alpha Video & Audio Inc, pg 682

MISSOURI

Audio-VideoGraphics Inc, pg 694
Conference Technologies Inc, pg 730
Modern Communications Inc, pg 828
Southwest Audio-Visual Inc, pg 895

NEW JERSEY

AlltecPro, pg 681
AV Bluebook, pg 696

NEW YORK

Century Business Solutions, pg 720
Gaylord Archival, pg 768
HAVE Inc, pg 777
A Liss & Co, pg 809
Long Island Video Enterprises Live Inc, pg 811
Markertek Video Supply, pg 817
Sentry Industries Inc, pg 884
TecNec Distributing, pg 909

OHIO

Central Ohio Audio Video, pg 719
Univenture Inc, pg 921

OKLAHOMA

Piper Media Services Inc, pg 857

PENNSYLVANIA

Advanced AV LLC, pg 677
Bernie's Photo Center, pg 704
Brodart Co, pg 711
Morefield Communications Inc, pg 830
Visual Sound Inc, pg 931

SOUTH CAROLINA

Professional Label Inc, pg 865

TENNESSEE

Lowrance Sound Co Inc, pg 812

TEXAS

Crystal Clear Media Group, pg 735
Heffernan Audio Visual, pg 778

UTAH

RIA Corp, pg 874

VIRGINIA

Cybernetics, pg 736
Furnace MFG, pg 767
Lee Hartman & Sons Inc, pg 805

WISCONSIN

Camera Corner Connecting Point, pg 715
Full Compass Systems, pg 767

BRITISH COLUMBIA

Triad Communications Ltd, pg 918

ONTARIO

HD Source, pg 777

Packaging & Storage— Cassette & Disc Manufacturers

CALIFORNIA

El Mar Plastics Inc, pg 752
SF Global Sourcing, pg 885
Tasman Group Pacific Rim, pg 907

COLORADO

ProLine Digital, pg 865
Rose Packaging & Design Inc, pg 877

ILLINOIS

Flight Form Cases Inc, pg 762

INDIANA

Star Case Manufacturing Co Inc, pg 900

KENTUCKY

American Recordable Media, pg 684

MARYLAND

Ever-Ready Media Packaging, pg 757

MASSACHUSETTS

Hannecke Display Systems Inc, pg 775

MICHIGAN

Brilliance Audio, pg 710

MINNESOTA

Sunrise Packaging Inc, pg 904
Winsted Corp, pg 939

NEW JERSEY

Reed Presentations Inc (RPI), pg 872

NEW YORK

Century Business Solutions, pg 720

OHIO

Univenture Inc, pg 921

PENNSYLVANIA

Sandusky Lee Corp, pg 880

SOUTH CAROLINA

Professional Label Inc, pg 865

WISCONSIN

Bardes Products Inc, pg 702
Full Compass Systems, pg 767

ONTARIO

Can-Am Merchandising Systems, pg 715

Packaging & Storage— Cassette & Disc Rentals

CALIFORNIA

Express Media Inc, pg 757

NORTH CAROLINA

Take One Productions Ltd, pg 906

Packaging & Storage— Cassette & Disc Repairs

MICHIGAN

TEL Systems LLC, pg 909

Photography—Aerial

ALABAMA

Diamond Studios, pg 741

ALASKA

Connections Film & Video Inc, pg 731

ARIZONA

Direct Current Video Productions, pg 743
Fox 10 Productions (KSAZ-TV), pg 765
Merestone, pg 823

ARKANSAS

Live'N'Loud, pg 810
White Diamond Productions LLC, pg 937

CALIFORNIA

Action Sports/All Stock, pg 675
Aerial Video Systems, pg 678
All Video Productions, pg 680
Celebrity Helicopters Inc, pg 719
Classic Images Stock Footage LLC, pg 726

VIDEO

Photography—Aerial (continued)

CALIFORNIA (continued)

Concrete Images, pg 730
Creative Technology, pg 733
Crystal Pyramid Productions™, pg 735
Custom Video Productions Inc, pg 736
Dolphin MultiMedia Inc, pg 745
First Camera, pg 761
Goal Productions, pg 772
Gold Standard Productions, pg 772
iCorpTv, pg 783
Image Integration, pg 785
Indie Aerials, pg 787
JDS Video & Media Productions Inc, pg 793
KTVU-Retail Services, pg 802
Maximus Media Inc, pg 820
Media Magic, pg 822
New & Unique Videos™, pg 839
Nineteen87, pg 841
PK Productions, pg 857
Point of View Productions, pg 858
PSI Inc, pg 866
QRS Software Services, pg 867
Dick Reizner Film & Video, pg 873
RetinaVision Productions, pg 874
SpaceCam, pg 896
Stunt Wings Adventure Sports Talent & Equipment, pg 903
Total Creative, pg 916
Towards 2000 Inc, pg 916
Twin Peaks Creative, pg 920
Two Door Productions LLC, pg 920
Tyler Camera Systems, pg 920
WARPed Pictures, pg 934
West Coast Projections Inc, pg 935

COLORADO

Aerial Imaging Productions, pg 678
Flashback Media Productions, pg 762
Greg Hensley Productions, pg 779
Tatum Video, pg 907
Transtar Entertainment Co Inc, pg 917

CONNECTICUT

BRB Audiovisual Productions, pg 709
MAVCO, pg 820

FLORIDA

America By Air LLC, pg 682
Applebox Studio, pg 687
Civins Productions Inc, pg 725
Steven Cohen Motion Picture Production, pg 727
Communications Concepts Inc (CCI), pg 729
Courter Films LLC, pg 732
Fiddler Films, pg 759
Florida Film & Tape, pg 763
Glanz Technologies Inc, pg 771
Jordan Klein Film & Video (JKFV), pg 795
Norman Kent Productions, pg 798
Knowles Video Inc (KVI), pg 800
Midtown Video Inc, pg 827
National Teleproductions Inc, pg 837
NatureVision Stock Footage Library, pg 837
Paradise Video & Film, pg 851
Roger Scruggs Films, pg 883

Shooting Stars Post Inc, pg 886
Sunfire Communications Inc, pg 904
Sunrise Studios, pg 904
Universal Studios Florida® Production Group, pg 922
Mike Vasilinda Productions Inc, pg 925
Venice Media Group, pg 925
Video Techniques Inc, pg 928

GEORGIA

Beachwood Productions, pg 702
ECG Productions, pg 750
Guerrilla Productions LLC, pg 774
Imagers, pg 785
Visioneering International Inc, pg 931

HAWAII

Sight & Sound Studios, pg 887
1013 Integrated, pg 911
Tropical Visions Video Inc, pg 918

IDAHO

KTVB-TV, pg 802
Rex Morris Productions, pg 830
Brad Shaw Productions Inc, pg 885
Wide Eye Productions, pg 938

ILLINOIS

Airways Digital Media, pg 679
Breeze Productions Inc, pg 710
CCore Media Inc, pg 718
Mimi Productions, pg 828
PSAV® Presentation Services (Hotel Services Division), pg 866
Sparkfactor, pg 896
Video Impressions, pg 928
WEEK TV, pg 935
Winter Productions, pg 939

INDIANA

PentaVision Communications Inc, pg 854

IOWA

Educational Technology & Media Services, pg 751

KANSAS

KAKE-TV, pg 796

KENTUCKY

The Media Collaboratory, pg 821

LOUISIANA

Digital FX Inc, pg 742
Louisiana State University Division of Strategic Communications, pg 811
Moxie Media, pg 832
Vidox Motion Imagery, pg 930
WVLA-TV, pg 942

MAINE

Maine Imaging, pg 815

MARYLAND

CAS Video Productions, pg 717
Richard Chisolm Cinematography, pg 722
Kramer Communications Video Production, pg 801
Producers Video, pg 863

MASSACHUSETTS

Green Mountain Post Films (GMP), pg 774
Heliotrope Studios, pg 778
Northern Light Productions (NLP), pg 842
TR Productions, pg 916
WVP Boston, pg 942

MICHIGAN

Digi Sign Design LLC, pg 741
The Program Source International, pg 865

MINNESOTA

Badiyan Inc, pg 700
House of Cinemagraphics, pg 782
MastCom, pg 819

MISSOURI

Visionworks Design Services Inc, pg 931

NEBRASKA

Rainbow Video Productions Inc, pg 869

NEVADA

Aardvark Video & Media Productions, pg 671
DVDs4Less, pg 748

NEW HAMPSHIRE

Apertura, pg 686

NEW JERSEY

AJS Events, pg 679
Broadcast Center Studios, pg 710
CFP Video Productions Inc, pg 720
MediaMix Inc, pg 822
MiB MediaWorks, pg 825
Suede Interactive, pg 903
VCSvideo, pg 925

NEW MEXICO

Production Outfitters, pg 864

NEW YORK

aurora productions, pg 696
Broadstreet Productions LLC, pg 711
Buffalo Video Production, pg 712
Chromavision Corp, pg 723
CP Communications, pg 732
Golden Lamb Productions, pg 772
Hallel Communications, pg 775
Hover-Views Unlimited, pg 782
Icontent, pg 783
La Paloma Films, pg 803
Long Island Video Enterprises Live Inc, pg 811
Jack Morton Worldwide, pg 830
Peckham Productions Inc, pg 852
TeleTime Productions, pg 910

NORTH CAROLINA

Pat Appleson Studios Inc, pg 687
Bill Barnes Video Productions LLC, pg 702
The Communications Group Inc, pg 729
Horizon Video Productions Inc, pg 781
K2 Productions, pg 802
Moving Pictures, pg 832
NASCAR Productions LLC, pg 835

On Location North Carolina, pg 846
Take One Productions Ltd, pg 906

NORTH DAKOTA

Media Productions, pg 822

OHIO

Aztec Video Productions, pg 700
Challenge Productions/Challenge Aerial Imaging, pg 720
Lyon Video Inc, pg 813
Mills James Productions, pg 828

OKLAHOMA

Academic Media & Digital Services, pg 672

OREGON

Odyssey Productions Inc, pg 844
Wilderness Video, pg 938

PENNSYLVANIA

Argentine Productions Inc, pg 688
Audio Visions Inc, pg 694
FMP Media Solutions Inc, pg 763
Innovision Media Group, pg 788
JPL, pg 795
Production Masters Inc (PMI), pg 864
The Videohouse Inc, pg 929

SOUTH CAROLINA

Assignment Desk, pg 691
Genesis Creative, pg 769
Venture Media, pg 925

TENNESSEE

Motion Picture Services, pg 831
Phoenix Aerial Photography Inc, pg 855
Running Pony Productions LLC, pg 878
Scripps Networks, pg 882
Stage Post, pg 899
Zion Music Group, pg 945

TEXAS

AMS Pictures, pg 684
Castleview Productions, pg 717
Communication Arts Multimedia Inc, pg 728
Horizon Film + Video Productions, pg 781
Inferno Films, pg 787
McNee Productions Inc, pg 821
Earl Miller Productions Inc, pg 827
Julye Newlin Productions Inc, pg 840
Out of the BLUE Media, pg 849
Phillips Media Source, pg 855
Richie Media Productions LLC, pg 875
The Samuels Co, pg 879
South Coast Film & Video, pg 895
Video Perspective, pg 928

UTAH

ImageWorks Communications, pg 785

VIRGINIA

Advance Concepts Inc, pg 677
CACI Integrated Communications, pg 713
HeloAir Inc, pg 778
Metro Productions, pg 824

VIDEO

Photography—Location (continued)

KENTUCKY (continued)

Kentucky Grip & Lighting, pg 798
The Media Collaboratory, pg 821

LOUISIANA

Digital FX Inc, pg 742
Louisiana State University Division
  of Strategic Communications,
  pg 811
Moxie Media, pg 832
Vidox Motion Imagery, pg 930
WVLA-TV, pg 942
YES Productions, pg 944

MAINE

Maine Imaging, pg 815
WGME-TV, pg 936

MARYLAND

Absolute Hollywood, pg 672
Adventure Productions LLC, pg 678
CAS Video Productions, pg 717
Richard Chisolm Cinematography,
  pg 722
CPR MultiMedia Solutions, pg 732
dbF a Media Company, pg 739
DBM Communications Inc, pg 739
Kramer Communications Video
  Production, pg 801
Media Dimensions LLC, pg 821
Producers Video, pg 863
Quality Film & Video, pg 868
Sheffield Audio/Video Productions,
  pg 885
Spectrum Productions, pg 897

MASSACHUSETTS

Award Productions Inc, pg 699
Capron Lighting & Sound Co Inc,
  pg 716
CommCreative, pg 728
Documentary Educational Resources
  Inc, pg 744
Green Mountain Post Films (GMP),
  pg 774
Heliotrope Studios, pg 778
In the Wild Productions, pg 786
Northern Light Productions (NLP),
  pg 842
Small Planet Communications Inc,
  pg 890
TR Productions, pg 916
TVN-The Video Network, pg 919
VideoLink Inc, an AVI-SPL
  company, pg 929

MICHIGAN

Axis Films, pg 700
Digi Sign Design LLC, pg 741
K&R's Recording Studios Inc,
  pg 796
The Program Source International,
  pg 865

MINNESOTA

Badiyan Inc, pg 700
Big Event Productions LLC, pg 705
Butkowski Digital Imaging (BDI),
  pg 713
House of Cinemagraphics, pg 782
MastCom, pg 819
Media Loft Inc, pg 822
Rum Jungle Media, pg 878
Worthwhile Films, pg 941

MISSOURI

Avatar Studios, pg 697
Hardcastle Films & Video, pg 776
Visionworks Design Services Inc,
  pg 931

MONTANA

KCFW Television, pg 797

NEBRASKA

B & B Video Productions Inc,
  pg 700
Rainbow Video Productions Inc,
  pg 869
Three Pillars Media, pg 913

NEVADA

Aardvark Video & Media
  Productions, pg 671
DVDs4Less, pg 748
JCS Video Productions, pg 793

NEW HAMPSHIRE

Apertura, pg 686
Chip Taylor Communications LLC,
  pg 907

NEW JERSEY

AJS Events, pg 679
Allegro Productions Inc, pg 680
Broadcast Center Studios, pg 710
CFP Video Productions Inc, pg 720
Color Leasing Studios, pg 727
Early Films, pg 749
Euro-Pacific Film & Video
  Productions Inc, pg 756
Laurel Video Productions, pg 804
MediaMix Inc, pg 822
MiB MediaWorks, pg 825
Midnight Media Group Inc, pg 827
NFL Films Inc, pg 841
Allan Reider Photography & Video
  Productions, pg 873
Suede Interactive, pg 903
Telequest Inc, pg 910
VCSvideo, pg 925

NEW MEXICO

Production Outfitters, pg 864

NEW YORK

aurora productions, pg 696
BC Studio, pg 702
Big Film Design, pg 705
The Big House Group, pg 705
Brian Film Productions LLC,
  pg 710
Broadstreet Productions LLC,
  pg 711
Buffalo Video Production, pg 712
Chromavision Corp, pg 723
Cohn Creative Group LLC, pg 727
Debbie Regan Locations Ltd,
  pg 739
Digital Art Video Inc, pg 741
Douglas House Inc, pg 746
4-D Creative Media, pg 764
Golden Lamb Productions, pg 772
Hallel Communications, pg 775
HB-Content, pg 777
Icontent, pg 783
Ketchum Inc, pg 798
L A Bruell Inc, pg 802
La Paloma Films, pg 803
Long Island Video Enterprises Live
  Inc, pg 811
Mood Creations Ltd, pg 829
Jack Morton Worldwide, pg 830

New Horizon Studios, pg 839
News Broadcast Network Inc,
  pg 840
Peckham Productions Inc, pg 852
PrimaLux Video Inc, pg 862
PrimeLight Productions Inc, pg 862
Synaptic Digital, pg 905
TeleTime Productions, pg 910
Videograf, pg 929
Visual Technologies Corp, pg 932
Zelman Studios Ltd, pg 945

NORTH CAROLINA

All Pro Media Inc, pg 680
Pat Appleson Studios Inc, pg 687
Bill Barnes Video Productions LLC,
  pg 702
The Communications Group Inc,
  pg 729
Digital Rain LLC, pg 742
Duke Media Services, pg 747
Franklin Video Inc, pg 765
Horizon Video Productions Inc,
  pg 781
Image Associates Inc, pg 784
Kino Mountain Productions LLC,
  pg 799
Moving Pictures, pg 832
NASCAR Productions LLC, pg 835
On Location North Carolina, pg 846
Take One Productions Ltd, pg 906
Trailblazer Studios®, pg 917
Videowerks, pg 930

NORTH DAKOTA

Media Productions, pg 822

OHIO

Advent Media Inc, pg 677
Aztec Video Productions, pg 700
Russ Beckner Pictures, pg 703
Challenge Productions/Challenge
  Aerial Imaging, pg 720
Cinecraft Productions Inc, pg 723
Cuyahoga Community College
  Student Production Office (SPO),
  pg 736
Lyon Video Inc, pg 813
Mills James Productions, pg 828
Take 1 Media Services, pg 906
Treehaus Communications Inc,
  pg 917
Ungar Video & Film, pg 921

OKLAHOMA

Academic Media & Digital
  Services, pg 672
Garman Productions LLC, pg 768
Institute for Teaching & Learning
  Excellence (ITLE), pg 788
PDC Productions, pg 852

OREGON

CMD Agency, pg 726
KTVA Productions, pg 802
KVAL, pg 802
MediaFX, pg 822
Odyssey Productions Inc, pg 844
Wilderness Video, pg 938

PENNSYLVANIA

Argentine Productions Inc, pg 688
Audio Visions Inc, pg 694
Bang! Pictures Inc, pg 701
Beholder Productions Inc, pg 703
Center City Film & Video Inc,
  pg 719
FMP Media Solutions Inc, pg 763
Innovision Media Group, pg 788
JPL, pg 795

Main Point Productions, pg 815
Panta Rhei Media Inc, pg 851
Production Masters Inc (PMI),
  pg 864
The Videohouse Inc, pg 929

SOUTH CAROLINA

Assignment Desk, pg 691
Genesis Creative, pg 769
Venture Media, pg 925

TENNESSEE

Motion Picture Services, pg 831
Paradigm Marketing & Creative,
  pg 851
Phoenix Aerial Photography Inc,
  pg 855
Running Pony Productions LLC,
  pg 878
Scripps Networks, pg 882
Stage Post, pg 899
United Methodist Productions,
  pg 921

TEXAS

Alpha Video Productions, pg 682
AMS Pictures, pg 684
Best Film & Video, pg 704
Castleview Productions, pg 717
Cerutti Productions Inc, pg 720
Communication Arts Multimedia
  Inc, pg 728
Countdown Productions Inc, pg 732
Emergency Film Group, pg 753
Epic Software Group Inc, pg 755
Horizon Film + Video Productions,
  pg 781
Inferno Films, pg 787
Marx InDigital, pg 818
Maverick Video Productions, pg 820
McNee Productions Inc, pg 821
Mediaforce Productions, pg 822
Earl Miller Productions Inc, pg 827
Julye Newlin Productions Inc,
  pg 840
Out of the BLUE Media, pg 849
Phillips Media Source, pg 855
Prairie Pictures Film & Video,
  pg 860
The Samuels Co, pg 879
South Coast Film & Video, pg 895
South Trunk Studios, pg 895
Stage Directions, pg 898
Texas Heart Institute Visual
  Communication Services, pg 911
Video Perspective, pg 928

UTAH

ImageWorks Communications,
  pg 785

VERMONT

Marlboro Productions, pg 817
Wilson McLeran Inc, pg 939

VIRGINIA

Advance Concepts Inc, pg 677
BES Studios, pg 704
CACI Integrated Communications,
  pg 713
Limelight Communications Inc,
  pg 808
Metro Productions, pg 824
Rocktown Media, pg 876

WASHINGTON

Bennett-Watt HD Productions Inc,
  pg 703
Hamilton Studio, pg 775

VIDEO

Photography—Slow Motion (continued)

VIRGINIA

BES Studios, pg 704
CACI Integrated Communications, pg 713
Metro Productions, pg 824

WASHINGTON

Bennett-Watt HD Productions Inc, pg 703
Hamilton Studio, pg 775
North-by-Northwest - A Digital Studio, pg 842
Victory Studios, pg 927
White Rain Films Ltd, pg 937

WEST VIRGINIA

WSAZ-TV NewsChannel 3, pg 942

WISCONSIN

AVS Group, pg 699
Midland Video Productions Inc, pg 827
USAV Group Inc, pg 923
Video Wisconsin Inc, pg 929
Wisconsin Public Television, pg 940

WYOMING

Bridger Productions Inc, pg 710

ALBERTA

Black Media Works, pg 706
Global TV, pg 771
HDTV Productions Inc, pg 777

BRITISH COLUMBIA

Triad Communications Ltd, pg 918

MANITOBA

Spectra Video Productions Ltd, pg 897

NEWFOUNDLAND AND LABRADOR

Vidcraft Productions Ltd, pg 927

ONTARIO

GAPC (General Assembly Production Centre), pg 768
Video Excellence Productions, pg 927

Photography—Studio

ALABAMA

Diamond Studios, pg 741

ALASKA

Alaska Media Pros LLC, pg 679
Connections Film & Video Inc, pg 731

ARIZONA

Arizona Studios, pg 688
Direct Current Video Productions, pg 743
Merestone, pg 823
Metropolitan Audio-Visual Inc, pg 824

On-Site Video, pg 846
Rodeo Video Inc, pg 876

ARKANSAS

Live'N'Loud, pg 810
White Diamond Productions LLC, pg 937

CALIFORNIA

All Video Productions, pg 680
Artichoke Productions, pg 690
Big Door, pg 705
Cherry Multimedia, pg 721
Concrete Images, pg 730
Creative Technology, pg 733
Crystal Pyramid Productions™, pg 735
deKramer Productions Inc, pg 740
Design Media, pg 741
Direct Images Interactive Inc, pg 743
First Camera, pg 761
Goal Productions, pg 772
Golden Gate Studios, pg 772
Havas Edge, pg 777
iCorpTv, pg 783
Imageworks, pg 785
JDS Video & Media Productions Inc, pg 793
KTVU-Retail Services, pg 802
KVIE-Channel 6, pg 802
Main Street Media Inc, pg 815
Maximus Media Inc, pg 820
Media Magic, pg 822
The Media Staff Inc, pg 822
New & Unique Videos™, pg 839
New Circuit Films LLC, pg 839
Nineteen87, pg 841
Pacific Light Studios, pg 849
PM Productions, pg 858
James Porter Photography, pg 859
PSI Inc, pg 866
QRS Software Services, pg 867
Dick Reizner Film & Video, pg 873
RetinaVision Productions, pg 874
Saturn Studios, pg 881
Screen Door Entertainment Inc, pg 882
Sea Studios Foundation, pg 883
The Mack Sennett Studios, pg 883
Staylor-Made Communications Inc, pg 900
Still N' Motion, pg 901
Stray Angel Films, pg 902
The Studio of David Inocencio, pg 911
Total Creative, pg 916
Twin Peaks Creative, pg 920
Warner Bros Entertainment Inc, pg 934
WARPed Pictures, pg 934
Wavemaker Media Design, pg 934

COLORADO

CSI Film & Video LLC, pg 735
Daylight Productions & Rentals, pg 739
Flashback Media Productions, pg 762
Greg Hensley Productions, pg 779
Lightware Inc, pg 808
Tatum Video, pg 907

CONNECTICUT

BRB Audiovisual Productions, pg 709
Guymark Studios LLC, pg 775
MAVCO, pg 820
New London Media, pg 839

DISTRICT OF COLUMBIA

Metro Teleproductions Inc (MTI), pg 824

FLORIDA

A Cut Above Video Productions Inc, pg 671
Applebox Studio, pg 687
Bill Bachmann Studios, pg 705
C&I An Idea Agency, pg 716
Civins Productions Inc, pg 725
Steven Cohen Motion Picture Production, pg 727
Communications Concepts Inc (CCI), pg 729
Courter Films LLC, pg 732
The Great Southern Studios, pg 773
Jordan Klein Film & Video (JKFV), pg 795
JungleTV, pg 795
Midtown Video Inc, pg 827
Paradise Video & Film, pg 851
Shooting Stars Post Inc, pg 886
Sound*Light, pg 894
Sunfire Communications Inc, pg 904
Sunrise Studios, pg 904
Tricycle Studios, pg 918
Universal Studios Florida® Production Group, pg 922
Mike Vasilinda Productions Inc, pg 925
Venice Media Group, pg 925

GEORGIA

Beachwood Productions, pg 702
ECG Productions, pg 750
Guerrilla Productions LLC, pg 774
Malcolm Neal Productions, pg 837

HAWAII

Hyperspective Studios Inc, pg 783
Sight & Sound Studios, pg 887
1013 Integrated, pg 911

IDAHO

KTVB-TV, pg 802
Brad Shaw Productions Inc, pg 885
Wide Eye Productions, pg 938

ILLINOIS

Beatty TeleVisual Productions, pg 703
Breeze Productions Inc, pg 710
CCore Media Inc, pg 718
Film Police, pg 760
Mightybytes Inc, pg 827
Pepper Group, pg 854
PSAV® Presentation Services (Hotel Services Division), pg 866
SCI Television & Creative Media LLC, pg 882
20/20 Communications Inc, pg 920
Video Impressions, pg 928
WEEK TV, pg 935

INDIANA

A-V-A Video Productions, pg 671
Advanced Media Integration, pg 677

IOWA

Educational Technology & Media Services, pg 751

KANSAS

KAKE-TV, pg 796

KENTUCKY

Kentucky Grip & Lighting, pg 798
The Media Collaboratory, pg 821
Prosper Media Group Inc, pg 866

LOUISIANA

Digital FX Inc, pg 742
Louisiana State University Division of Strategic Communications, pg 811
Moxie Media, pg 832
Vidox Motion Imagery, pg 930
WVLA-TV, pg 942
YES Productions, pg 944

MAINE

WGME-TV, pg 936

MARYLAND

Adventure Productions LLC, pg 678
CAS Video Productions, pg 717
CPR MultiMedia Solutions, pg 732
DBM Communications Inc, pg 739
Kramer Communications Video Production, pg 801
Media Dimensions LLC, pg 821
Quality Film & Video, pg 868
Sheffield Audio/Video Productions, pg 885
Spectrum Productions, pg 897

MASSACHUSETTS

Award Productions Inc, pg 699
Heliotrope Studios, pg 778
National Boston, pg 836
Northern Light Productions (NLP), pg 842
PixMix Video Services, pg 857
Small Planet Communications Inc, pg 890
VideoLink Inc, an AVI-SPL company, pg 929
WVP Boston, pg 942

MICHIGAN

Digi Sign Design LLC, pg 741
K&R's Recording Studios Inc, pg 796
The Program Source International, pg 865

MINNESOTA

Badiyan Inc, pg 700
Big Event Productions LLC, pg 705
Butkowski Digital Imaging (BDI), pg 713
House of Cinemagraphics, pg 782
MastCom, pg 819
Media Loft Inc, pg 822

MISSOURI

Avatar Studios, pg 697
Hardcastle Films & Video, pg 776

MONTANA

KCFW Television, pg 797

NEBRASKA

Rainbow Video Productions Inc, pg 869
Three Pillars Media, pg 913

NEVADA

Aardvark Video & Media Productions, pg 671
DVDs4Less, pg 748
JCS Video Productions, pg 793

VIDEO

Photography—Underwater (continued)

ILLINOIS

Airways Digital Media, pg 679
Film Police, pg 760
Major Media Inc, pg 815

LOUISIANA

Digital FX Inc, pg 742
Louisiana State University Division of Strategic Communications, pg 811

MARYLAND

Adventure Productions LLC, pg 678
CAS Video Productions, pg 717
CPR MultiMedia Solutions, pg 732
Kramer Communications Video Production, pg 801
Pro Cuts Editing Services, pg 862

MASSACHUSETTS

Capron Lighting & Sound Co Inc, pg 716
CommCreative, pg 728
Northern Light Productions (NLP), pg 842

MICHIGAN

The Program Source International, pg 865

MINNESOTA

Badiyan Inc, pg 700
House of Cinemagraphics, pg 782
Babe Winkelman Productions Inc, pg 939

NEVADA

JCS Video Productions, pg 793

NEW HAMPSHIRE

Chip Taylor Communications LLC, pg 907

NEW JERSEY

Broadcast Center Studios, pg 710
MiB MediaWorks, pg 825
Suede Interactive, pg 903

NEW MEXICO

Production Outfitters, pg 864

NEW YORK

Air Sea Land Productions Inc (ASL), pg 678
Broadstreet Productions LLC, pg 711
Buffalo Video Production, pg 712
Chromavision Corp, pg 723
Digital Art Video Inc, pg 741
Ketchum Inc, pg 798
La Paloma Films, pg 803
Jack Morton Worldwide, pg 830
Videograf, pg 929

NORTH CAROLINA

Pat Appleson Studios Inc, pg 687
The Communications Group Inc, pg 729
Take One Productions Ltd, pg 906

NORTH DAKOTA

Media Productions, pg 822

OHIO

Aztec Video Productions, pg 700
Challenge Productions/Challenge Aerial Imaging, pg 720

OREGON

Odyssey Productions Inc, pg 844

PENNSYLVANIA

Argentine Productions Inc, pg 688
Audio Visions Inc, pg 694
Innovision Media Group, pg 788
The Videohouse Inc, pg 929
WPHL-TV, pg 942

SOUTH CAROLINA

Assignment Desk, pg 691

TENNESSEE

Motion Picture Services, pg 831
Scripps Networks, pg 882
Stage Post, pg 899

TEXAS

Horizon Film + Video Productions, pg 781
Julye Newlin Productions Inc, pg 840
Phillips Media Source, pg 855
Prairie Pictures Film & Video, pg 860
South Coast Film & Video, pg 895

VIRGINIA

CACI Integrated Communications, pg 713

WASHINGTON

Bennett-Watt HD Productions Inc, pg 703
Victory Studios, pg 927

WISCONSIN

Mirror 34 Productions, pg 828
Video Wisconsin Inc, pg 929
Wisconsin Public Television, pg 940

ALBERTA

Global TV, pg 771

NEWFOUNDLAND AND LABRADOR

Vidcraft Productions Ltd, pg 927

QUEBEC

Group PVP, pg 774
Kerrigan Productions Inc, pg 798

Post-Production Services

ALABAMA

AVS Media Group, pg 699
Diamond Studios, pg 741
Motion & Graphic Image Corp Inc (MAGIC), pg 831

ALASKA

Alaska Media Pros LLC, pg 679
Connections Film & Video Inc, pg 731
Imig Audio/Video Inc, pg 786

ARIZONA

Candee Productions Inc, pg 716
Cox Creative Studios, pg 732
Direct Current Video Productions, pg 743
Film Creations Ltd, pg 760
Fox 10 Productions (KSAZ-TV), pg 765
Merestone, pg 823
Metropolitan Audio-Visual Inc, pg 824
On-Site Video, pg 846
Rodeo Video Inc, pg 876
Star Video Duplicating, pg 900
Wild Visions Inc, pg 938

ARKANSAS

Live'N'Loud, pg 810
Michael Mueller Video Productions, pg 833
White Diamond Productions LLC, pg 937

CALIFORNIA

A Go Go Films, pg 671
AB Audio Visual Entertainment Inc, pg 672
Aberdeen Broadcast Services, pg 672
Access Video in Berkeley, pg 673
Action Video, pg 675
Advanced Media LLC, pg 677
All Video Productions, pg 680
AlphaDogs Inc, pg 682
Artichoke Productions, pg 690
ATV Video Center Inc, pg 692
Audio Mechanics, pg 693
Baldwin Productions Services Inc, pg 701
Berke Creative Inc, pg 704
Berkeley Sound Artists Inc, pg 704
Big Door, pg 705
BigFoot Mobile Systems, pg 705
Blind™, pg 707
CCI Digital, a DVS Company, pg 718
Steve Chandler, pg 720
Cherry Multimedia, pg 721
Christopher Gray Post Production, pg 722
Coastline Productions, pg 727
Creative Technology, pg 733
Crystal Pyramid Productions™, pg 735
Custom Video Productions Inc, pg 736
Deja View Video, pg 740
deKramer Productions Inc, pg 740
Deluxe Entertainment Services Group Inc, pg 740
Digital Jungle, pg 742
digital OutPost, pg 742
Direct Images Interactive Inc, pg 743
The Dreaming Tree, pg 746
DV Post, pg 748
eMotion Studios, pg 753
Express Media Inc, pg 757
Ferrari Productions, pg 759
First Camera, pg 761
First Person Inc, pg 761
FJ Productions Inc, pg 762
48 Windows, pg 764
4th Street Recording, pg 764
Fox Television Center, pg 765
Full Moon & High Tide Productions & Studios, pg 767
Glix Entertainment Inc, pg 771
Goal Productions, pg 772
Gold Standard Productions, pg 772
Golden Gate Studios, pg 772
Havas Edge, pg 777

Hollywood Vaults Inc, pg 781
Hybrid Studios, pg 783
iCorpTv, pg 783
Illuminate Post/Digital Finishing, pg 784
imageReal Pictures LLC, pg 785
Imageworks, pg 785
JDS Video & Media Productions Inc, pg 793
JFA Studio, pg 794
Kavich Reynolds Productions Inc, pg 797
KO Creative, pg 800
KPBS Public Broadcasting, pg 801
KTVU-Retail Services, pg 802
K2B2 Records, pg 802
KVIE-Channel 6, pg 802
Lightning Media, pg 808
Ludlow Media, pg 812
Main Street Media Inc, pg 815
Maximus Media Inc, pg 820
McCune Audio-Video-Lighting, pg 821
Media Magic, pg 822
The Media Staff Inc, pg 822
Medical Visual Creations (MVC), pg 823
Method Studios, pg 824
Nandar Entertainment Pictures, pg 835
New & Unique Videos™, pg 839
New Deal Studios, pg 839
Nineteen87, pg 841
Nolte Media, pg 841
On-Trax Inc, pg 846
Opticomm-EMCORE, pg 847
Pacific Light Studios, pg 849
Pacific Video Image, pg 849
Palardo Productions, pg 850
Penrose Productions, pg 854
PK Productions, pg 857
PM Productions, pg 858
Point.360, pg 858
PSI Inc, pg 866
Pyramind Studios, pg 867
QRS Software Services, pg 867
Reality Check Systems, pg 871
Renegade Animation Inc, pg 873
RetinaVision Productions, pg 874
Rough House, pg 878
Roundabout Entertainment Inc, pg 878
Sahara Records & Filmworks Entertainment Co, pg 879
Sand Box Studio, pg 880
Screen Door Entertainment Inc, pg 882
Shapeshifter, pg 885
Shoulder High Productions, pg 886
SonicPool, pg 892
Starburns Industries, pg 900
Staylor-Made Communications Inc, pg 900
Still N' Motion, pg 901
Studio 637, pg 903
The Studios at Paramount, pg 903
Tam Communications Inc, pg 906
TIMECODE Post Production, pg 914
Total Creative, pg 916
TVA Media Group, pg 919
Twin Peaks Creative, pg 920
Two Door Productions LLC, pg 920
Universal Satellite Communications Inc, pg 922
Universal Studios, pg 922
Via Verde Productions, pg 926
VidCan Media Solutions, pg 927
Video Movie Magic, pg 928
Videografix LLC, pg 929
Visions Plus, pg 931
Vitruvian Entertainment, pg 932

Warner Bros Entertainment Inc, pg 934
WARPed Pictures, pg 934
Wavemaker Media Design, pg 934
West Coast Projections Inc, pg 935

COLORADO

Aerial Imaging Productions, pg 678
Colorado Studios, pg 728
CSI Film & Video LLC, pg 735
Daylight Productions & Rentals, pg 739
Flashback Media Productions, pg 762
Old Army Press (OAP), pg 844
Open Media Foundation, pg 846
Rocky Mountain Audio/Video Productions Inc, pg 876
Spectrum Audio Visual Services, pg 897
Tatum Video, pg 907
Transtar Entertainment Co Inc, pg 917
Westworks Studios, pg 936
Z-Axis Corp, pg 944

CONNECTICUT

ACM Productions Ltd, pg 674
Antenna International, pg 686
BRB Audiovisual Productions, pg 709
Cine-Med Inc, pg 723
CMI Media Management, pg 727
Essex Television Group Inc, pg 755
Geomatrix Productions, pg 770
Guymark Studios LLC, pg 775
Ironik Design & Post, pg 791
MAVCO, pg 820
Moving Pictures, pg 832
Musivision Inc, pg 835
New London Media, pg 839
Palace Production Center, pg 850
Palace Productions MediaVision, pg 850
P&P Studios Inc, pg 851
Powerstation Events, pg 860
Sonalysts Media, pg 892
Bret Stern Productions, pg 900
UConn Health Multimedia Services, pg 920
Video Production Associates Inc, pg 928

DELAWARE

Cornerstone Media Productions Inc, pg 731

DISTRICT OF COLUMBIA

Hillmann & Carr Inc, pg 780
Interface Media Group, pg 789
Metro Teleproductions Inc (MTI), pg 824
Yellow Cat Productions Inc, pg 944

FLORIDA

A Cut Above Video Productions Inc, pg 671
Access Media Group, pg 673
Accord Productions, pg 673
ACT Productions, pg 675
Applebox Studio, pg 687
Audacity Recording Studios, pg 693
AVI-SPL, pg 698
Bill Bachmann Studios, pg 705
Civins Productions Inc, pg 725
Communications Concepts Inc (CCI), pg 729
Comtel Inc, pg 730
Courter Films LLC, pg 732
Digital Zoetrope Productions, pg 742

DME Studios, pg 744
Easy Edit Video Inc, pg 750
Kat Epple Music Productions, pg 755
Florida Digital Studios, pg 762
Florida Film & Tape, pg 763
Glanz Technologies Inc, pg 771
Harmon's Audio-Visual Services, pg 776
Hi-Tech Enterprises Inc, pg 779
Jordan Klein Film & Video (JKFV), pg 795
Norman Kent Productions, pg 798
Knowles Video Inc (KVI), pg 800
MAC Production Group, pg 813
National Teleproductions Inc, pg 837
The Newhouse Media Group, pg 840
Phat Planet Recording Studios, pg 855
Shooting Stars Post Inc, pg 886
Sound & Vision Communications Inc, pg 893
Sunfire Communications Inc, pg 904
Sunrise Studios, pg 904
Tricycle Studios, pg 918
Universal Studios Florida® Production Group, pg 922
Mike Vasilinda Productions Inc, pg 925
Video Techniques Inc, pg 928
Vistamax Productions, pg 931

GEORGIA

Beachwood Productions, pg 702
Beast Atlanta, pg 703
The DVI Group, pg 748
ECG Productions, pg 750
Guerrilla Productions LLC, pg 774
Imagers, pg 785
Magick Lantern, pg 814
Omega Media Group Inc, pg 845
On-Line Productions, pg 845
Video Copy Services Inc, pg 927
WATL-TV Inc, pg 934

HAWAII

Dot C Software Inc, pg 746
Hyperspective Studios Inc, pg 783
Media Bridge Gamekids, pg 821
Sight & Sound Studios, pg 887
1013 Integrated, pg 911
Tropical Visions Video Inc, pg 918

IDAHO

KTVB-TV, pg 802
Brad Shaw Productions Inc, pg 885
Wide Eye Productions, pg 938

ILLINOIS

ABSA Films, pg 672
Airways Digital Media, pg 679
AnswersMedia, pg 686
Atomic Imaging Inc/Golan Studios, pg 692
Backstar Creative Media Inc, pg 700
Beatty TeleVisual Productions, pg 703
Big Shoulders Digital Video Productions, pg 705
Breeze Productions Inc, pg 710
CCore Media Inc, pg 718
The Chicago Production Center, pg 721
Edit House Chicago, pg 750
Explore, pg 757
Freeman Pictures Inc, pg 765
IV Media Resources, pg 792

Manning Productions, pg 816
The Market Place, pg 817
Mightybytes Inc, pg 827
Mimi Productions, pg 828
Multimedia Marketing Group, pg 833
Optimus, pg 847
Rob Orr Productions Ltd, pg 848
Pepper Group, pg 854
PSAV® Presentation Services (Hotel Services Division), pg 866
RADMAR Inc, pg 869
RBR Productions, pg 870
Richter Studios, pg 875
SCI Television & Creative Media LLC, pg 882
Sound/Video Impressions Inc, pg 894
Sparkfactor, pg 896
Tele-Time Systems, pg 910
20/20 Communications Inc, pg 920
Video I-D Teleproductions Inc, pg 928
Video Impressions, pg 928
WIFR-TV, pg 938

INDIANA

A-V-A Video Productions, pg 671
Advanced Media Integration, pg 677
Bright Ideas Creative Services, pg 710
Educational Video Group Inc, pg 751
Lakeshore Public Media, pg 803
PentaVision Communications Inc, pg 854

IOWA

Educational Technology & Media Services, pg 751
Iowa State University-Information Technology Services, pg 791

KANSAS

KAKE-TV, pg 796

KENTUCKY

Broadway Digital, pg 711
Hammond Communications Group Inc, pg 775
Horizon Films & Media LLC, pg 781
The Media Collaboratory, pg 821
The PPS Group, pg 860
Prosper Media Group Inc, pg 866

LOUISIANA

Digital FX Inc, pg 742
Louisiana State University Division of Strategic Communications, pg 811
Moxie Media, pg 832
Pace Systems, pg 849
Vidox Motion Imagery, pg 930
WVLA-TV, pg 942
YES Productions, pg 944

MAINE

WGME-TV, pg 936

MARYLAND

Adventure Productions LLC, pg 678
CAS Video Productions, pg 717
CPR MultiMedia Solutions, pg 732
dbF a Media Company, pg 739
DBM Communications Inc, pg 739
James Agee Film Project, pg 792
Kramer Communications Video Production, pg 801

Media Dimensions LLC, pg 821
Mobile-Video Productions Inc, pg 828
Pro Cuts Editing Services, pg 862
Producers Video, pg 863
Quality Film & Video, pg 868
Sheffield Audio/Video Productions, pg 885
Sign Media Inc, pg 887
Spectrum Productions, pg 897

MASSACHUSETTS

Award Productions Inc, pg 699
Boston Productions Inc (BPI), pg 709
Continental Recordings Inc, pg 731
Documentary Educational Resources Inc, pg 744
Extreme Reach Inc, pg 757
Green Mountain Post Films (GMP), pg 774
Heliotrope Studios, pg 778
HOME Inc, pg 781
Labrecque Creative Sound, pg 803
Monadnock Media Inc, pg 829
MotionArt Studios, pg 831
Northern Light Productions (NLP), pg 842
Penfield Productions Ltd, pg 853
Gabriel Polonsky Studio, pg 859
Small Planet Communications Inc, pg 890
Sound & Vision Media, pg 893
Soundtrack Group, pg 895
TR Productions, pg 916
TVN-The Video Network, pg 919
VideoLink Inc, an AVI-SPL company, pg 929
WGBH Production Group, pg 936
WVP Boston, pg 942

MICHIGAN

Digi Sign Design LLC, pg 741
Digital Image Studios LLC, pg 742
K&R's Recording Studios Inc, pg 796
Lawrence Productions Inc, pg 804
Michigan Recording Arts Institute & Technologies, pg 825
The Program Source International, pg 865
RingSide Creative, pg 875
TGA Recording Co, pg 911
The Transfer Zone®, pg 917
WTVS, Detroit Public Television, pg 942

MINNESOTA

The ADS Group, pg 676
Big Event Productions LLC, pg 705
Blue Earth Pictures, pg 707
Freestyle Productions Inc, pg 765
GMI Productions, pg 771
House of Cinemagraphics, pg 782
MastCom, pg 819
Pro Media Productions, pg 863
Rum Jungle Media, pg 878
Babe Winkelman Productions Inc, pg 939
Worthwhile Films, pg 941

MISSOURI

Avatar Studios, pg 697
Communitronics Corp, pg 729
Conference Technologies Inc, pg 730
Hardcastle Films & Video, pg 776
KPLR-TV, pg 801
Spot Media Production Group, pg 898

VIDEO

Post-Production Services (continued)

Premastering, *see* Videodisc Premastering

Presentation System Distributors

VIDEO

Presentation System Distributors (continued)

VIRGINIA

Avitecture Inc, pg 699
Quince Imaging Inc, pg 868
The Whitlock Group, pg 937

WISCONSIN

Audio Visual of Milwaukee Inc, pg 694
Camera Corner Connecting Point, pg 715
Full Compass Systems, pg 767

PUERTO RICO

Audio Visual Concepts Inc, pg 694

MANITOBA

Inland Audio Visual Ltd, pg 788

ONTARIO

Cinema Stage Inc, pg 724
Corel Corp, pg 731
HD Source, pg 777
Image Video, pg 785
Technovision® Interactive Inc, pg 909
Westbury National Show Systems Ltd, pg 936

Presentation System Manufacturers

CALIFORNIA

Auton Motorized Systems, pg 696
Boland Communications Inc, pg 708
Extron Electronics, pg 758
Gefen, pg 769
Gyration, pg 775
Lasergraphics Inc, pg 804
Pioneer Electronics (USA) Inc, pg 857
RGB Spectrum, pg 874
Sonance, pg 892

CONNECTICUT

KOH Design Inc, pg 801
The Video Messenger Co, pg 928

FLORIDA

Florical Systems Inc, pg 762

GEORGIA

Barco Inc, pg 701
Comprehensive Technical Group, pg 729
PolyVision Corporation, pg 859
WolfVision Inc, pg 940

ILLINOIS

Dukane Corp, Audio Visual Products Division, pg 747
GBC Document Finishing, pg 768
NEC Display Solutions of America, pg 837

INDIANA

Da-Lite, a Legrand AV Inc brand, pg 737

KANSAS

Keywest Technology Inc, pg 798

MARYLAND

Absolute Hollywood, pg 672

MASSACHUSETTS

Elite Video Inc, pg 753

MINNESOTA

Vaddio, pg 924

NEW JERSEY

Crestron Electronics Inc, pg 734
FSR Inc, pg 766

NEW YORK

eMagin Corp, pg 753
Uniset LLC, pg 921

OHIO

Network Technologies Inc, pg 838
TV One Multimedia Solutions, pg 919

PENNSYLVANIA

AccuWeather Inc, pg 674
Interactive Products, pg 789
Scala Inc, pg 881

TENNESSEE

Adtec Digital Inc, pg 677

VIRGINIA

Quince Imaging Inc, pg 868

WASHINGTON

Avidex Inc, pg 699

ONTARIO

Corel Corp, pg 731
Image Video, pg 785

Presentation System Rentals

ALABAMA

Audio-Video Resources Inc, pg 694

ARIZONA

Merestone, pg 823

ARKANSAS

White Diamond Productions LLC, pg 937

CALIFORNIA

Associated Sound, pg 691
Express Media Inc, pg 757
JD Audio Visual Inc, pg 793
Munday & Collins AV, pg 834
Muse Presentation Technologies, pg 834
VER, pg 926
VMI Inc, pg 932

CONNECTICUT

A/V Davey, pg 697
Videofilm Systems Inc, pg 929

FLORIDA

Astoria Communications Inc, pg 691
Paradise Show & Design Inc, pg 851
Sight & Sound Productions, pg 887

GEORGIA

Stage Front Presentation Systems, pg 899

HAWAII

Hawaii Sound & Vision, pg 777

ILLINOIS

AV Chicago Inc, pg 696
RC Communications, pg 870
Resolution Productions Group, pg 874

KENTUCKY

Audio Visual Techniques Inc, pg 695

MARYLAND

CPR MultiMedia Solutions, pg 732
Event Tech, pg 756

MASSACHUSETTS

Preston Productions Inc, pg 861

MICHIGAN

K&R All Media Productions LLC, pg 796

MINNESOTA

Alpha Video & Audio Inc, pg 682

MISSOURI

Show-Me Audio-Visual, pg 887

NEW JERSEY

Earl Girls Inc, pg 749
Starlite, pg 900

NEW YORK

Design Audio Visual Inc, pg 741
KVL Audio Visual Services Inc, pg 802
Visual Word Systems Inc, pg 932

NORTH DAKOTA

Media Productions, pg 822

OHIO

Bartha, pg 702

OKLAHOMA

PDC Productions, pg 852

PENNSYLVANIA

Bernie's Photo Center, pg 704
Innovision Media Group, pg 788
Upstage Video, pg 923

TENNESSEE

Allstar Audio Systems Inc, pg 681
Technical Support Systems LLC, pg 908

TEXAS

Bright Star Productions Inc, pg 710
Stage Directions, pg 898

VIRGINIA

Advance Concepts Inc, pg 677
Quince Imaging Inc, pg 868

WISCONSIN

Audio Visual of Milwaukee Inc, pg 694

PUERTO RICO

Stage Crew Audiovisual Inc, pg 898

MANITOBA

Inland Audio Visual Ltd, pg 788

ONTARIO

HD Source, pg 777
Metalworks Recording Studios Inc, pg 824
RB Productions, pg 870
Westbury National Show Systems Ltd, pg 936

Presentation System Repairs

CALIFORNIA

Electrosonic Inc, pg 752
Sonance, pg 892
VMI Inc, pg 932

FLORIDA

ELC Sales & Service Inc, pg 752

GEORGIA

Stage Front Presentation Systems, pg 899

ILLINOIS

GBC Document Finishing, pg 768

KENTUCKY

Axxis Leasing Inc, pg 700
NOR-COM Inc, pg 841

MICHIGAN

TEL Systems LLC, pg 909

MINNESOTA

Alpha Video & Audio Inc, pg 682

MISSOURI

Schiller's Audio-Visual, pg 881
Southwest Audio-Visual Inc, pg 895

NEW JERSEY

Earl Girls Inc, pg 749
Starlite, pg 900

NEW YORK

Visual Technologies Corp, pg 932

OHIO

Network Technologies Inc, pg 838
Tri-State Audio Visual Co, pg 918

PENNSYLVANIA

Bernie's Photo Center, pg 704
J E Foss Co, pg 764

TENNESSEE

Technical Support Systems LLC, pg 908

VIRGINIA

Avitecture Inc, pg 699
Quince Imaging Inc, pg 868
The Whitlock Group, pg 937

WISCONSIN

Full Compass Systems, pg 767

MANITOBA

Inland Audio Visual Ltd, pg 788

ONTARIO

HD Source, pg 777
Westbury National Show Systems
Ltd, pg 936

Printing Videos, *see*
Volume Printing—Videos

Production Workshops

ARIZONA

Direct Current Video Productions,
pg 743
Film Creations Ltd, pg 760
Merestone, pg 823
Teaberry, pg 908

CALIFORNIA

Audio Visual Consultants, pg 694
Crystal Pyramid Productions™,
pg 735
Film TV Sound, pg 760
JDS Video & Media Productions
Inc, pg 793
Maximus Media Inc, pg 820
Palardo Productions, pg 850
QRS Software Services, pg 867
Quality Digest, pg 868
Dick Reizner Film & Video, pg 873
Russ InVision Co/AbridgeClub.com,
pg 879
Staylor-Made Communications Inc,
pg 900
Visual Communications - Southern
California Asian American
Studies Central Inc, pg 931

CONNECTICUT

BRB Audiovisual Productions,
pg 709
The Gary-Paul Agency, pg 768

DISTRICT OF COLUMBIA

Interface Media Group, pg 789

FLORIDA

Access Media Group, pg 673
Communications Concepts Inc
(CCI), pg 729

GEORGIA

Guerrilla Productions LLC, pg 774
Lighting & Production Equipment
Inc, pg 807
On-Line Productions, pg 845

HAWAII

Media Bridge Gamekids, pg 821

IDAHO

Wide Eye Productions, pg 938

ILLINOIS

Beatty TeleVisual Productions,
pg 703
CCore Media Inc, pg 718
PSAV® Presentation Services
(Hotel Services Division), pg 866

IOWA

Educational Technology & Media
Services, pg 751

LOUISIANA

Moxie Media, pg 832

MARYLAND

dbF a Media Company, pg 739

MASSACHUSETTS

Award Productions Inc, pg 699
HOME Inc, pg 781
MotionArt Studios, pg 831

MICHIGAN

Digi Sign Design LLC, pg 741
K&R's Recording Studios Inc,
pg 796
Michigan Recording Arts Institute
& Technologies, pg 825

MINNESOTA

House of Cinemagraphics, pg 782
Worthwhile Films, pg 941

NEVADA

Lefco Video Services Inc, pg 806

NEW HAMPSHIRE

Channell One Video, pg 720

NEW JERSEY

Diversified, pg 744
Euro-Pacific Film & Video
Productions Inc, pg 756
MiB MediaWorks, pg 825
Suede Interactive, pg 903
Yorktel, pg 944

NEW MEXICO

Blue Sky Stock Footage, pg 708

NEW YORK

Digital Art Video Inc, pg 741
Downtown Community Television
Center (DCTV), pg 746
HB-Content, pg 777
Richard Kaplan Productions, pg 796
La Paloma Films, pg 803
Teatown Communications Group,
pg 908
Third World Newsreel/Camera
News Inc, pg 912
Zelman Studios Ltd, pg 945

NORTH CAROLINA

Duke Media Services, pg 747

OHIO

Aztec Video Productions, pg 700
Cuyahoga Community College
Student Production Office (SPO),
pg 736
Vista Color Imaging Inc, pg 931

OREGON

Odyssey Productions Inc, pg 844

PENNSYLVANIA

Video/Film Associates, pg 928
The Videohouse Inc, pg 929
Visual Sound Inc, pg 931

RHODE ISLAND

Sound-FX-Design, pg 894

TENNESSEE

Stage Post, pg 899
Zion Music Group, pg 945

TEXAS

McNee Productions Inc, pg 821
Julye Newlin Productions Inc,
pg 840
Richie Media Productions LLC,
pg 875
Romar Learning Solutions LLC,
pg 877

VIRGINIA

Rocktown Media, pg 876

WASHINGTON

Victory Studios, pg 927

WISCONSIN

Audio Visual of Milwaukee Inc,
pg 694
AVS Group, pg 699
USAV Group Inc, pg 923
Wisconsin Public Television, pg 940

BRITISH COLUMBIA

Video Out Distribution, pg 928

ONTARIO

GAPC (General Assembly
Production Centre), pg 768
Image Video Services &
Productions, pg 785
Trebas Institute, pg 917

QUEBEC

Trebas Institute, pg 917

Projector & Projection System Distributors

ALABAMA

Curtis Company, pg 736

ARIZONA

EAR Professional Audio/Video,
pg 749
Metropolitan Audio-Visual Inc,
pg 824
Projector SuperStore LLC, pg 865
Troxell-CDI, pg 918
Ultimate Presentation Systems Inc,
pg 920

ARKANSAS

Carlton-Bates Co, pg 717
Jay S Stanley & Associates Inc,
pg 899
White Diamond Productions LLC,
pg 937

CALIFORNIA

Advanced Systems Group LLC,
pg 677
Ametron Audio/Video, pg 684
Associated Sound, pg 691
Assured Audio Visual, pg 691
Audio/Video Supply Inc, pg 694
AV Conferencing LLC (AVC),
pg 697
Barber Tech Video Products, pg 701
Be Media, pg 702
BigFoot Mobile Systems, pg 705
BroadcastStore.com, pg 711
California Tape Products Inc,
pg 714
Christie Digital Systems USA Inc,
pg 722
Christy's Editorial, pg 723
Cinema Equipment Sales of
California Inc, pg 724
Cinema Xenon International Inc,
pg 724
Electrosonic Inc, pg 752
Gluskin's Custom Audio Video,
pg 771
Instructional Materials & Equipment
Distributors (I-Med), pg 789
Inter Video, pg 789
JD Audio Visual Inc, pg 793
Lloyd F McKinney Associates Inc,
pg 821
Media Fabricators Inc, pg 822
MediaPOINTE, pg 823
Muse Presentation Technologies,
pg 834
PMP Marketing Inc, pg 858
Premier Lighting & Production Co,
pg 861
SNAP, pg 891
Sound Service Co, pg 894
Southern California Sound Image
Inc, pg 895
Stanislaus AV Inc, pg 899
SuperVision, pg 904
VMI Inc, pg 932

COLORADO

Ceavco Audio Visual Company Inc,
pg 719
Daylight Productions & Rentals,
pg 739
Mike's Camera, pg 827
Spectrum Audio Visual Services,
pg 897

CONNECTICUT

MAVCO, pg 820
Rockwell Communications Inc,
pg 876

DISTRICT OF COLUMBIA

Future View Inc, pg 767

FLORIDA

Access Media Group, pg 673
Altel Systems Group Inc, pg 682
A2D Solutions Inc, pg 692
AVI-SPL, pg 698
Cinema Equipment & Supplies Inc,
pg 724
Digital Video Systems, pg 742
Glanz Technologies Inc, pg 771
Harmon's Audio-Visual Services,
pg 776
Hollywood Theatre Equipment Inc,
pg 781
Industrial Strength Inc, pg 787
ONstage, pg 846
Photosound of Orlando Inc, pg 856
Tallahassee Audio Visual, pg 906
Techni-Lux Inc, pg 908

VIDEO

Projector & Projection System Distributors (continued)

GEORGIA

Audio Visual Resources Inc, pg 695
Baker Audio Visual, pg 700
Boxlight Inc, pg 709
Cinevision Corp, pg 725
Convergent Media Systems, pg 731
Digital Projection, pg 742
Lighting & Production Equipment Inc, pg 807
Stage Front Presentation Systems, pg 899

ILLINOIS

Allen Visual Systems Inc, pg 680
Chicago Spotlight Inc, pg 721
G T Luscombe Co Inc, pg 812
Quintessence Audio Ltd, pg 868
RC Communications, pg 870
The Screen Works®, pg 882
Tele-Time Systems, pg 910

INDIANA

Heart Breaker Entertainment LLC, pg 778
Lee Co Inc, pg 805
Sensory Technologies LLC, pg 884
SHP Electronics, pg 887

KANSAS

SKC Communication Products Inc, pg 890

KENTUCKY

Axxis Leasing Inc, pg 700
Barney Miller's Inc, pg 827
NOR-COM Inc, pg 841

LOUISIANA

Techkno Integration & Design Services LLC, pg 908

MAINE

Headlight Audio Visual Inc, pg 777

MARYLAND

Absolute Hollywood, pg 672
Cardinal Sound & Video, pg 717
Nelson White Systems Inc, pg 838
Nicholas P Pipino Associates Inc, pg 857
RTZ Audio Visual, pg 878

MASSACHUSETTS

Elite Video Inc, pg 753
General Electric Co, pg 769
Pro AV Systems, pg 862
Rule Boston Camera, pg 878

MICHIGAN

Olson Anderson Co, pg 685
ASC Systems, pg 690
Michigan Office Solutions (MOS), A Xerox Company, pg 825
TEL Systems LLC, pg 909

MINNESOTA

Alpha Video & Audio Inc, pg 682
AVI Systems, pg 698
New Life Communications Inc, pg 839

MISSISSIPPI

Bowie Audio Visual Enterprises Inc, pg 709
Jasper Ewing & Sons Inc, pg 757

MISSOURI

Communitronics Corp, pg 729
Conference Technologies Inc, pg 730
ITC, pg 791
Modern Communications Inc, pg 828
Production Support Services Inc, pg 864
Southwest Audio-Visual Inc, pg 895

NEBRASKA

ATV Research Inc, pg 692
VSA Inc, pg 933

NEVADA

Aardvark Video & Media Productions, pg 671
MeshTel, pg 824

NEW JERSEY

A-V Services Inc, pg 671
Alltec Stores, a Vcom IMC Company, pg 681
AlltecPro, pg 681
Argraph Corp, pg 688
Audio Visual Associates, pg 694
Audio Visual Dynamics®, pg 694
AV Bluebook, pg 696
Diversified, pg 744
Earl Girls Inc, pg 749
FlagHouse, pg 762
G&G Technologies Inc, pg 768
HamiltonBuhl, pg 775
Starlite, pg 900
SYMCO Inc, pg 905
Tele-Measurements Inc, pg 910
Total Video Products Inc, pg 916
Video Corporation of America (VCA), pg 927
Wired 4 Sound Inc, pg 940

NEW YORK

Adwar Video, pg 678
American Video Inc, pg 684
AV Workshop, pg 697
Canon USA Inc, pg 716
Crescendo Designs Inc, pg 734
Design Audio Visual Inc, pg 741
Gaylord Archival, pg 768
General Audio-Visual Inc (GAVI), pg 769
Indigo Productions, pg 787
Langie Audio Visual Systems, pg 803
Levy NYC Design & Production, pg 806
A Liss & Co, pg 809
Long Island Video Enterprises Live Inc, pg 811
Markertek Video Supply, pg 817
Neptune Photo Inc, pg 838
Presentation Products Inc, pg 861
Ray Supply Inc, pg 870
RNJ Electronics, pg 875
RTS Inc, pg 878
Sargent Welch, pg 880
Stampede Presentation Products Inc, pg 899
Topbulb, a Semmer Lighting Company, pg 915
Tri-Ed Distribution Inc, pg 918
Visual Technologies Corp, pg 932
Visual Word Systems Inc, pg 932

NORTH CAROLINA

Camcor Inc, pg 715
Carolina Biological Supply Co, pg 717
Strategic Connections, pg 901

OHIO

Audio Visual Media, pg 694
Copp Integrated Systems, pg 731
ITA Audio Visual Solutions, pg 791
Tri-State Audio Visual Co, pg 918
Tri-State Visual Products Inc, pg 918

OKLAHOMA

Ford AV, pg 763

OREGON

PLUS Corp of America, pg 858

PENNSYLVANIA

Advanced AV LLC, pg 677
Audio Visions Inc, pg 694
Bernie's Photo Center, pg 704
Brodart Co, pg 711
Clair Companies, pg 725
J E Foss Co, pg 764
Garcia Marketing Inc, pg 768
Hite Co, pg 780
The Lerro Corp, pg 806
Morefield Communications Inc, pg 830
RSS Distributors, pg 878
Vistacom Inc, pg 931
Visual Sound Inc, pg 931
Wespen Audio Visual Co, pg 935

RHODE ISLAND

Shanix Inc, pg 885

TENNESSEE

Continental Film, pg 731
Lowrance Sound Co Inc, pg 812
Memphis Communications Corp, pg 823
Technical Support Systems LLC, pg 908

TEXAS

Audio Visual Technologies Group (AVTG), pg 695
AVES Audio Visual Systems Inc, pg 698
Data Projections Inc, pg 738
Digital Display Solutions Inc, pg 742
Heffernan Audio Visual, pg 778
JSAV, pg 795
Tarpley Media Systems, pg 907

UTAH

Performance Audio LLC, pg 854
RIA Corp, pg 874
TV Specialists Inc, pg 919
Webb Audio Visual, pg 935

VIRGINIA

Avitecture Inc, pg 699
Boitnott Visual Communications Corp (BVC), pg 708
Intellidyne LLC, pg 789
Lee Hartman & Sons Inc, pg 805
Quince Imaging Inc, pg 868
StageSound, pg 899
The Whitlock Group, pg 937

WASHINGTON

Inland Audio Visual Co, pg 788
Laser Fantasy/HECK Industries/Photon Manufacturing, pg 804
Osum Event Rentals, pg 848

WISCONSIN

Audio Visual of Milwaukee Inc, pg 694
Camera Corner Connecting Point, pg 715
Demco Inc, pg 740
Full Compass Systems, pg 767
Safe Harbor Computers, pg 879

PUERTO RICO

Audio Visual Concepts Inc, pg 694

ALBERTA

Allstar Show Industries Inc, pg 681
Evolution AV, pg 757
Matrix Video Communications Corp (MVCC), pg 819
SMART Technologies ULC, pg 891

BRITISH COLUMBIA

DL Sound & Lighting Productions Ltd, pg 744

MANITOBA

Inland Audio Visual Ltd, pg 788

ONTARIO

Cinema Stage Inc, pg 724
HD Source, pg 777
Nationwide Audio Visual Co, pg 837
Westbury National Show Systems Ltd, pg 936

QUEBEC

Freeman Audio Visual, pg 765
Panavideo Inc, pg 850

Projector & Projection System Manufacturers

CALIFORNIA

Christie Digital Systems USA Inc, pg 722
Cinema Xenon International Inc, pg 724
Eiki International Inc, pg 751
Laser Magic Productions, pg 804
Stewart Filmscreen Corp, pg 901

CONNECTICUT

Collective Systems LLC, pg 727
KOH Design Inc, pg 801

FLORIDA

SVS Inc, pg 905
Vutec Corp, pg 933

GEORGIA

Digital Projection, pg 742

ILLINOIS

ACCO Brands Corp, pg 673
Dukane Corp, Audio Visual Products Division, pg 747
NEC Display Solutions of America, pg 837

MARYLAND

Absolute Hollywood, pg 672

MASSACHUSETTS

Elite Video Inc, pg 753
General Electric Co, pg 769

NEBRASKA

Strong Cinema Products, pg 902

NEVADA

MeshTel, pg 824

NEW JERSEY

AlltecPro, pg 681
CELCO, pg 719
Gerriets International, pg 770
RAMSA Professional Audio
    Systems, pg 870
Sharp Electronics Corp, Professional
    Display Division, pg 885
Sony Pro Audio, pg 893

NEW YORK

American Video Inc, pg 684
Canon USA Inc, pg 716
Hitachi Kokusai Electric America
    Ltd, pg 780
Levy NYC Design & Production,
    pg 806

PENNSYLVANIA

Questar Corp, pg 868

VIRGINIA

Optikinetics Ltd - The Americas,
    pg 847
Quince Imaging Inc, pg 868

ALBERTA

SMART Technologies ULC, pg 891

BRITISH COLUMBIA

Triad Communications Ltd, pg 918

Projector & Projection System Rentals

ALABAMA

Audio-Video Resources Inc, pg 694

ARIZONA

AV Concepts Inc, pg 696
Creative Backstage, pg 733
Merestone, pg 823
Metropolitan Audio-Visual Inc,
    pg 824
Ultimate Presentation Systems Inc,
    pg 920
Video West Inc, pg 929

ARKANSAS

White Diamond Productions LLC,
    pg 937

CALIFORNIA

Absolute Rentals, pg 672
Action Audio & Visual, pg 675
Action Video, pg 675
Advanced Media LLC, pg 677
AGF Media Services, pg 678
Alliant Event Services, pg 681
Alternative Rentals, pg 682
Ametron Audio/Video, pg 684

Associated Sound, pg 691
Assured Audio Visual, pg 691
ATV Video Center Inc, pg 692
AV Conferencing LLC (AVC),
    pg 697
AV Guys, pg 697
Barber Tech Video Products, pg 701
Cherry Multimedia, pg 721
Express Media Inc, pg 757
Express Video Supply Inc, pg 757
Fuller Street Productions, pg 767
Gluskin's Custom Audio Video,
    pg 771
Gold Standard Productions, pg 772
Alan Gordon Enterprises Inc,
    pg 772
Instructional Materials & Equipment
    Distributors (I-Med), pg 789
Inter Video, pg 789
JD Audio Visual Inc, pg 793
Lynch Communications, pg 813
McCune Audio-Video-Lighting,
    pg 821
Media Fabricators Inc, pg 822
Munday & Collins AV, pg 834
Muse Presentation Technologies,
    pg 834
Next Arts, pg 841
On-Trax Inc, pg 846
Premier Lighting & Production Co,
    pg 861
PSAV® Presentation Services,
    pg 866
Pyxis Industries Inc, pg 867
Sound Service Co, pg 894
Stanislaus AV Inc, pg 899
VER, pg 926
VMI Inc, pg 932

COLORADO

Ceavco Audio Visual Company Inc,
    pg 719
Daylight Productions & Rentals,
    pg 739
Mike's Camera, pg 827
Multimedia Audio Visual Inc,
    pg 833
Open Media Foundation, pg 846
Spectrum Audio Visual Services,
    pg 897

CONNECTICUT

A/V Davey, pg 697
Rockwell Communications Inc,
    pg 876
Videofilm Systems Inc, pg 929

DELAWARE

Ken-Del Productions Inc, pg 797
Showorks Audio Visual Inc, pg 887

DISTRICT OF COLUMBIA

Future View Inc, pg 767

FLORIDA

Access Media Group, pg 673
Astoria Communications Inc,
    pg 691
AVI-SPL, pg 698
Glanz Technologies Inc, pg 771
Harmon's Audio-Visual Services,
    pg 776
Industrial Strength Inc, pg 787
Jordan Klein Film & Video (JKFV),
    pg 795
Midtown Video Inc, pg 827
ONstage, pg 846
Paradise Show & Design Inc,
    pg 851
Photosound of Orlando Inc, pg 856

PRI Productions, pg 862
Sound*Light, pg 894
Style-City Music Inc, pg 903
Tallahassee Audio Visual, pg 906

GEORGIA

Audio Visual Resources Inc, pg 695
Cinevision Corp, pg 725
Convergent Media Systems, pg 731
Lighting & Production Equipment
    Inc, pg 807
ON Services, a GES Company,
    pg 846
Stage Front Presentation Systems,
    pg 899

HAWAII

Hawaii Sound & Vision, pg 777

ILLINOIS

Allen Visual Systems Inc, pg 680
Atomic Imaging Inc/Golan Studios,
    pg 692
AV Chicago Inc, pg 696
Backstar Creative Media Inc,
    pg 700
Beatty TeleVisual Productions,
    pg 703
Chicago Spotlight Inc, pg 721
Creative Technology (CT), pg 733
Meetinghouse Event Design &
    Production, pg 823
Pepper Group, pg 854
PSAV® Presentation Services
    (Hotel Services Division), pg 866
RC Communications, pg 870
Resolution Productions Group,
    pg 874
SCI Television & Creative Media
    LLC, pg 882
The Screen Works®, pg 882
2nd Cine Inc, pg 883
Staging Resources Inc, pg 899
Tele-Time Systems, pg 910

INDIANA

Advanced Media Integration, pg 677
Heart Breaker Entertainment LLC,
    pg 778
OMNI Productions, pg 845

IOWA

Central Lighting & Equipment Inc
    (CLE), pg 719
Pro Video, pg 863

KENTUCKY

Audio Visual Techniques Inc,
    pg 695
Barney Miller's Inc, pg 827

LOUISIANA

Clark Services Audio Visual &
    Exhibit Inc, pg 725
Digital FX Inc, pg 742
Pace Systems, pg 849

MAINE

Photo Finish, pg 856

MARYLAND

Absolute Hollywood, pg 672
Advance Audiovisual Presentation
    Ltd, pg 677
CPR MultiMedia Solutions, pg 732
Event Tech, pg 756
Hargrove Inc, pg 776

Nelson White Systems Inc, pg 838
RTZ Audio Visual, pg 878

MASSACHUSETTS

AVFX Inc, pg 698
Capron Lighting & Sound Co Inc,
    pg 716
Elite Video Inc, pg 753
General Electric Co, pg 769
massAV, pg 819
Preston Productions Inc, pg 861

MICHIGAN

Olson Anderson Co, pg 685
City Events Group, pg 725
K&R All Media Productions LLC,
    pg 796
K&R's Recording Studios Inc,
    pg 796
TEL Systems LLC, pg 909

MINNESOTA

Alpha Video & Audio Inc, pg 682
AVI Systems, pg 698

MISSISSIPPI

Bowie Audio Visual Enterprises Inc,
    pg 709

MISSOURI

Production Support Services Inc,
    pg 864
Schiller's Audio-Visual, pg 881
Show-Me Audio-Visual, pg 887
Southwest Audio-Visual Inc, pg 895
Switch, pg 905
Wise Audio Video, pg 940

NEBRASKA

Dog & Pony Productions Inc,
    pg 744

NEVADA

GES Audio Visual, pg 770
JCS Video Productions, pg 793
Lefco Video Services Inc, pg 806

NEW JERSEY

Audio Visual Associates, pg 694
Audio Visual Dynamics®, pg 694
Earl Girls Inc, pg 749
Gerriets International, pg 770
International Audio Visual Inc,
    pg 790
MB Productions, pg 820
PLS Staging, pg 858
Soundtracks Production Services
    LLC, pg 895
Starlite, pg 900
Video Corporation of America
    (VCA), pg 927
Wired 4 Sound Inc, pg 940

NEW YORK

Adwar Video, pg 678
American Video Inc, pg 684
AV Workshop, pg 697
CMI Communications, pg 727
Design Audio Visual Inc, pg 741
General Audio-Visual Inc (GAVI),
    pg 769
Hello World Communications,
    pg 778
Langie Audio Visual Systems,
    pg 803
Long Island Video Enterprises Live
    Inc, pg 811

VIDEO

Projector & Projection System Rentals (continued)

NEW YORK (continued)

Manhattan Center Studios Inc, pg 816
Production Central, pg 863
Specialized Audio-Visual Inc, pg 896
Tri-Ed Distribution Inc, pg 918
Visual Technologies Corp, pg 932
Visual Word Systems Inc, pg 932
WorldStage, pg 941

NORTH CAROLINA

All Pro Media Inc, pg 680
AV Connections Inc, pg 697
AV Metro Inc, pg 697
Special Event Services, pg 896
Strategic Connections, pg 901

NORTH DAKOTA

Media Productions, pg 822

OHIO

Audio Visual Media, pg 694
Hughie's Event Production Services, pg 782
ITA Audio Visual Solutions, pg 791
Mills James Productions, pg 828
OSV Studios, pg 848

OKLAHOMA

PDC Productions, pg 852

OREGON

Northwest Film Center, pg 842
Picture This Production Services, pg 856

PENNSYLVANIA

Advanced AV LLC, pg 677
Audio Visions Inc, pg 694
Audio Visual Communications Inc, pg 694
New York Camera & Video, pg 840
North Star Satellite Communications Inc, pg 842
Producers Management Television (PMTV), pg 863
Upstage Video, pg 923
Vistacom Inc, pg 931
Visual Sound Inc, pg 931

SOUTH CAROLINA

Impact Technology Group LLC, pg 786
Sound & Images Inc, pg 893

TENNESSEE

Memphis Communications Corp, pg 823
NuMynd Studios, pg 843
Russ Sturgeon Productions/RSVP, pg 903
Technical Support Systems LLC, pg 908

TEXAS

Alford Media Services, pg 680
Audio Visual Technologies Group (AVTG), pg 695

AVES Audio Visual Systems Inc, pg 698
Big House Sound Inc, pg 705
Bright Star Productions Inc, pg 710
FitzCo Sound Inc, pg 761
GEAR Cameras & Lighting, pg 769
JSAV, pg 795
Media Event Concepts, pg 822

UTAH

TV Specialists Inc, pg 919
Webb Audio Visual, pg 935

VERMONT

Dark Star Lighting & Production, pg 737

VIRGINIA

Advance Concepts Inc, pg 677
Audio Visual Actions Inc (AVA), pg 694
Boitnott Visual Communications Corp (BVC), pg 708
CVW Event Productions, pg 736
Lee Hartman & Sons Inc, pg 805
Projection, pg 865
Quince Imaging Inc, pg 868
StageSound, pg 899
The Whitlock Group, pg 937

WASHINGTON

Inland Audio Visual Co, pg 788
Kostov Productions, pg 801
Osum Event Rentals, pg 848

WISCONSIN

Audio Visual of Milwaukee Inc, pg 694
Event Essentials, pg 756
Full Compass Systems, pg 767
Logan Productions Inc, pg 811

PUERTO RICO

Stage Crew Audiovisual Inc, pg 898

ALBERTA

Allstar Show Industries Inc, pg 681
Cine Audio Visual Sales & Service Ltd, pg 723
Global TV, pg 771
L R Light & Sound, pg 802
Matrix Video Communications Corp (MVCC), pg 819
Unique Communications Ltd, pg 921

BRITISH COLUMBIA

Clark's Audio Visual Services Ltd, pg 725
Commercial Electronics Ltd, pg 728
DL Sound & Lighting Productions Ltd, pg 744
Triad Communications Ltd, pg 918
24 Frames Film & Video, pg 920
Video Out Distribution, pg 928

MANITOBA

Inland Audio Visual Ltd, pg 788

ONTARIO

HD Source, pg 777
Metalworks Recording Studios Inc, pg 824
MVI - MultiVision Inc, pg 835
RB Productions, pg 870

SIM Digital, pg 888
Westbury National Show Systems Ltd, pg 936

QUEBEC

Audio Visual Dynamics, pg 694
Freeman Audio Visual, pg 765
Panavideo Inc, pg 850

Projector & Projection System Repairs

CALIFORNIA

Advanced Media LLC, pg 677
Advanced Systems Group LLC, pg 677
Ametron Audio/Video, pg 684
Christie Digital Systems USA Inc, pg 722
Digitron Electronics, pg 743
Electrosonic Inc, pg 752
Instructional Materials & Equipment Distributors (I-Med), pg 789
Lloyd F McKinney Associates Inc, pg 821
VMI Inc, pg 932

COLORADO

Ceavco Audio Visual Company Inc, pg 719

CONNECTICUT

A/V Davey, pg 697
Rockwell Communications Inc, pg 876

FLORIDA

Digital Video Systems, pg 742
ELC Sales & Service Inc, pg 752
Glanz Technologies Inc, pg 771
Hi-Tech Enterprises Inc, pg 779
Tallahassee Audio Visual, pg 906

GEORGIA

Audio Visual Resources Inc, pg 695
Boxlight Inc, pg 709
Lighting & Production Equipment Inc, pg 807
Stage Front Presentation Systems, pg 899

ILLINOIS

Allen Visual Systems Inc, pg 680
Beatty TeleVisual Productions, pg 703
Chicago Spotlight Inc, pg 721
Midwest Digital Corp, pg 827
RC Communications, pg 870
Tele-Time Systems, pg 910

KENTUCKY

Axxis Leasing Inc, pg 700
Barney Miller's Inc, pg 827
NOR-COM Inc, pg 841

MARYLAND

Nelson White Systems Inc, pg 838
RTZ Audio Visual, pg 878

MASSACHUSETTS

Elite Video Inc, pg 753
General Electric Co, pg 769
Integrated Solutions Group, pg 789

MICHIGAN

Olson Anderson Co, pg 685
TEL Systems LLC, pg 909

MINNESOTA

Alpha Video & Audio Inc, pg 682
AVI Systems, pg 698

MISSISSIPPI

Bowie Audio Visual Enterprises Inc, pg 709

MISSOURI

Schiller's Audio-Visual, pg 881
Southwest Audio-Visual Inc, pg 895

NEW JERSEY

Audio Visual Associates, pg 694
Earl Girls Inc, pg 749
Starlite, pg 900

NEW YORK

Adwar Video, pg 678
American Video Inc, pg 684
Colortone Audio Visual, pg 728
General Audio-Visual Inc (GAVI), pg 769
Langie Audio Visual Systems, pg 803
Ray Supply Inc, pg 870
Tri-Ed Distribution Inc, pg 918
Visual Technologies Corp, pg 932

NORTH CAROLINA

Camcor Inc, pg 715
Strategic Connections, pg 901

OHIO

Audio Visual Media, pg 694
Copp Integrated Systems, pg 731
ITA Audio Visual Solutions, pg 791
Tri-State Audio Visual Co, pg 918
Tri-State Visual Products Inc, pg 918

PENNSYLVANIA

J E Foss Co, pg 764
Vistacom Inc, pg 931
Visual Sound Inc, pg 931

TENNESSEE

Memphis Communications Corp, pg 823
Technical Support Systems LLC, pg 908

TEXAS

Audio Visual Technologies Group (AVTG), pg 695
Digital Display Solutions Inc, pg 742
Tarpley Media Systems, pg 907

UTAH

TV Specialists Inc, pg 919

VIRGINIA

Avitecture Inc, pg 699
Boitnott Visual Communications Corp (BVC), pg 708
Lee Hartman & Sons Inc, pg 805
Metropolitan Audio Visual Co LLC, pg 824
Quince Imaging Inc, pg 868
The Whitlock Group, pg 937

WASHINGTON
Inland Audio Visual Co, pg 788

WISCONSIN
Full Compass Systems, pg 767

ALBERTA
Evolution AV, pg 757
Matrix Video Communications Corp (MVCC), pg 819

BRITISH COLUMBIA
Commercial Electronics Ltd, pg 728

MANITOBA
Inland Audio Visual Ltd, pg 788

ONTARIO
HD Source, pg 777
MVI - MultiVision Inc, pg 835
Westbury National Show Systems Ltd, pg 936

QUEBEC
Panavideo Inc, pg 850

Property Agencies— Television, *see* Talent & Property Agencies— Television

Raw Stock Distributors

ARIZONA
Metropolitan Audio-Visual Inc, pg 824

CALIFORNIA
Advanced Media LLC, pg 677
Advanced Systems Group LLC, pg 677
Ametron Audio/Video, pg 684
Audio/Video Supply Inc, pg 694
California Tape Products Inc, pg 714
Alan Gordon Enterprises Inc, pg 772
Media Fabricators Inc, pg 822

COLORADO
Stanco Sales LLC, pg 899

CONNECTICUT
Rockwell Communications Inc, pg 876

FLORIDA
Jordan Klein Film & Video (JKFV), pg 795
ONstage, pg 846
Summit Electronics Corp, pg 903

GEORGIA
Video Copy Services Inc, pg 927

HAWAII
Sight & Sound Studios, pg 887

ILLINOIS
Creative Technology (CT), pg 733

INDIANA
Sensory Technologies LLC, pg 884

KENTUCKY
American Recordable Media, pg 684

MARYLAND
Nicholas P Pipino Associates Inc, pg 857

MICHIGAN
TEL Systems LLC, pg 909

MINNESOTA
Cinequipt Inc, pg 724

MISSOURI
Southwest Audio-Visual Inc, pg 895

NEVADA
Aardvark Video & Media Productions, pg 671

NEW JERSEY
MiB MediaWorks, pg 825
Starlite, pg 900
Video Corporation of America (VCA), pg 927

NEW YORK
Aura Sonic Ltd (ASL), pg 695
Burlington A/V Recording Media, pg 712
Film Emporium, pg 760
HAVE Inc, pg 777
Long Island Video Enterprises Live Inc, pg 811
Rafik, pg 869
Tri-Ed Distribution Inc, pg 918

OHIO
iVideo Technologies, pg 792

OKLAHOMA
Piper Media Services Inc, pg 857

OREGON
Wilderness Video, pg 938

PENNSYLVANIA
Advanced AV LLC, pg 677
Morefield Communications Inc, pg 830
The Whale Video Co, pg 936

TENNESSEE
Memphis Communications Corp, pg 823
Phoenix Aerial Photography Inc, pg 855

TEXAS
Texcam Inc, pg 911

VIRGINIA
CVW Event Productions, pg 736

WISCONSIN
Audio Visual of Milwaukee Inc, pg 694
Camera Corner Connecting Point, pg 715
Full Compass Systems, pg 767

ONTARIO
FUJIFILM Canada Inc, pg 766
HD Source, pg 777

Raw Stock Manufacturers

COLORADO
InJoy Birth & Parenting Education, pg 788

FLORIDA
Vutec Corp, pg 933

KENTUCKY
American Recordable Media, pg 684

OREGON
Wilderness Video, pg 938

PENNSYLVANIA
FMP Media Solutions Inc, pg 763

WISCONSIN
Full Compass Systems, pg 767

ONTARIO
FUJIFILM Canada Inc, pg 766

Receiver, *see* Video Receiver & Monitor

Recorder, *see* Video Recorder & Player

Recording Facility Distributors

ILLINOIS
Major Media Inc, pg 815

Recording Facility Manufacturers

CALIFORNIA
Westlake Recording Studios, pg 936
Yanchar Design & Consulting Group, pg 943

ILLINOIS
IAC Acoustics, pg 783

MICHIGAN
Studio Consulting & Construction Inc, pg 902

NEW JERSEY
Radio Visions, pg 869

NEW YORK
CP Communications, pg 732

OKLAHOMA
Rees, pg 872

TEXAS
ETS-Lindgren, pg 756

VIRGINIA
Acoustics First Corp, pg 674

BRITISH COLUMBIA
Triad Communications Ltd, pg 918

Recording Facility Rentals

ALABAMA
AVS Media Group, pg 699

ARIZONA
Arizona Studios, pg 688
Cox Creative Studios, pg 732
Crew West Inc, pg 734
Glendale Media Center, pg 771
Loft 19, pg 811
Master Video Disc & Design, pg 819
Merestone, pg 823
Rodeo Video Inc, pg 876

ARKANSAS
White Diamond Productions LLC, pg 937

CALIFORNIA
Absolute Rentals, pg 672
Advanced Digital Design, pg 677
Ametron Audio/Video, pg 684
AMG Studios (Los Angeles), pg 684
Artichoke Productions, pg 690
Blue Lotus Temple Studio, pg 707
CenterStaging LLC, pg 719
Cherry Multimedia, pg 721
Crystal Pyramid Productions™, pg 735
Cutting Edge Productions, pg 736
Dystopian Studios, pg 748
5 Alarm Music, pg 762
Flip 2 Media Inc, pg 762
Full Moon & High Tide Productions & Studios, pg 767
Glendale Production Center, pg 771
Golden Gate Studios, pg 772
Greenery Studios, pg 774
Hampshire Street Studios, pg 775
Hybrid Studios, pg 783
Illuminate Studios, pg 784
Images in Motion Media Inc, pg 785
JFA Studio, pg 794
KTVU-Retail Services, pg 802
LA Castle Studios, pg 803
Laurel Canyon Stages, pg 804
Los Angeles Center Studios, pg 811
Loyal Studios, pg 812
Lynch Communications, pg 813
Maximus Media Inc, pg 820
McCune Audio-Video-Lighting, pg 821
MediaOne Studios, pg 823
New Deal Studios, pg 839
North County Media Center, pg 842
On-Trax Inc, pg 846
Opulen Studios, pg 847
Orange County Sound Stage, pg 847
Pacific Light Studios, pg 849
Photo Film Stage, pg 856
Playback Recording Studio, pg 858

VIDEO

Recording Facility Rentals (continued)

CALIFORNIA (continued)

Pollution Studios, pg 859
Pro HD Rentals, pg 863
The Producer's Loft, pg 863
RED Studios Hollywood, pg 872
Roundabout Entertainment Inc, pg 878
Sand Box Studio, pg 880
Santa Clarita Studios, pg 880
ShowBiz Studios, pg 887
Solar Studios, pg 892
Source Film Studio, pg 895
Still N' Motion, pg 901
Stray Angel Films, pg 902
Studio 1444, pg 902
Studio 637, pg 903
Sunset Bronson Studios, pg 904
Sunset Gower Studios, pg 904
Sunset Las Palmas Studios, pg 904
Total Creative, pg 916
TVA Media Group, pg 919
Valencia Studios, pg 924
Westlake Recording Studios, pg 936

COLORADO

Colorado Studios, pg 728
Daylight Productions & Rentals, pg 739
Denver Media Center, pg 740
EON247 Inc, pg 755
Side 3 Studios, pg 887
Westworks Studios, pg 936

CONNECTICUT

Sonalysts Media, pg 892
SoNo Studios, pg 892

DELAWARE

Cornerstone Media Productions Inc, pg 731
Ken-Del Productions Inc, pg 797

DISTRICT OF COLUMBIA

Flying Colors Broadcasts, pg 763
Interface Media Group, pg 789
Subject Matter, pg 903

FLORIDA

Accord Productions, pg 673
Adrenaline Films, pg 676
Aperture Studios Miami, pg 687
C&I An Idea Agency, pg 716
Cheuvront Studios, pg 721
Comtel Inc, pg 730
Digital Comm Link Inc, pg 742
Facet Media, pg 758
Fiddler Films, pg 759
The Great Southern Studios, pg 773
HD House, pg 777
Jordan Klein Film & Video (JKFV), pg 795
LHV Audio Services, pg 807
MAPS Production House, pg 816
Miami Daylight Studios, pg 825
National Teleproductions Inc, pg 837
Phat Planet Recording Studios, pg 855
South Florida Rehearsal Studios, pg 895
Trendy Studio LLC, pg 917
Universal Studios Florida® Production Group, pg 922

GEORGIA

Atlanta Filmworks, pg 692
ECG Productions, pg 750
Encyclomedia, pg 754
Lighting & Production Equipment Inc, pg 807
Magick Lantern, pg 814
Mailing Avenue Stageworks, pg 815
Stage Front Presentation Systems, pg 899
Studio Space Atlanta, pg 903
WATL-TV Inc, pg 934

HAWAII

FOTON Hawaii, pg 764

ILLINOIS

Beatty TeleVisual Productions, pg 703
Big Shoulders Digital Video Productions, pg 705
Delmark Records, pg 740
Firehouse Studios, pg 761
Magnanimous Media, pg 814
PSAV® Presentation Services (Hotel Services Division), pg 866
Resolution Productions Group, pg 874
ShiftFocus Productions, pg 886
Tele-Time Systems, pg 910

INDIANA

Lakeshore Public Media, pg 803
Midwest Uplink Inc, pg 827

LOUISIANA

Digital FX Inc, pg 742
Launch Media, pg 804
Second Line Stages, pg 883

MARYLAND

Bella Faccia Inc, pg 703
CPR MultiMedia Solutions, pg 732
Cre-a-tv Studios, pg 734
The Cutting Corporation, GraphicAudio® & Archival Sound Lab, pg 736
Quality Film & Video, pg 868
Sheffield Audio/Video Productions, pg 885

MASSACHUSETTS

HOME Inc, pg 781
Penfield Productions Ltd, pg 853
Preston Productions Inc, pg 861
Red Sky Studios, pg 872

MICHIGAN

Brilliance Audio, pg 710
City Events Group, pg 725
K&R's Recording Studios Inc, pg 796
Madonna University Information Technology, pg 814
Stage 3 Productions, pg 899
WTVS, Detroit Public Television, pg 942

MINNESOTA

Alpha Video & Audio Inc, pg 682

MISSOURI

Show-Me Audio-Visual, pg 887
Southwest Audio-Visual Inc, pg 895
Studio Worx Inc, pg 903

NEBRASKA

Lights On Nebraska, pg 808

NEVADA

DVDs4Less, pg 748
JCS Video Productions, pg 793
Lefco Video Services Inc, pg 806
MG Studio, pg 825

NEW JERSEY

Butter Tree Studios, pg 713
Color Leasing Studios, pg 727
E Video Productions LLC, pg 749
18 Label Studios, pg 751
Euro-Pacific Film & Video Productions Inc, pg 756
Ironbound Film & Television Studios LLC, pg 791
Laurel Video Productions, pg 804
MediaMix Inc, pg 822
Milgrom Productions, pg 827
Optisonics Productions, pg 847
Shamrock Communications, pg 885

NEW MEXICO

I-25 Studios, pg 783

NEW YORK

All Mobile Video Inc, pg 680
BC Studio, pg 702
Big Foot Productions Inc, pg 705
Bond Street Studio, pg 708
Bravo Studios, pg 709
Brooklyn Fire Proof, pg 711
Brooklyn Studios, pg 711
Camart, pg 714
CP Communications, pg 732
East of Hollywood NY, pg 749
Hayden 5 Media LLC, pg 777
LightBox-NY, pg 807
LightSpace Studios, pg 808
Location 05 Studios, pg 811
Long Island Video Enterprises Live Inc, pg 811
Manhattan Center Studios Inc, pg 816
Mark Custom Recording Service Inc, pg 817
Media 3 Ltd, pg 822
The Palmer Group, pg 850
Production Central, pg 863
Rollin Studios, pg 877
D S Simon Productions, pg 888
SmackDab Media, pg 890
Sony Music Entertainment, pg 893
Steiner Studios, pg 900
Video Dimensions Inc, pg 927
WNET/New York Public Media, pg 940

NORTH CAROLINA

Duke Media Services, pg 747
Evolve Inc, pg 757
K2 Productions, pg 802
Media-Comm, pg 821
Moving Pictures, pg 832
Take One Productions Ltd, pg 906

NORTH DAKOTA

Media Productions, pg 822

OHIO

Mills James Productions, pg 828
OSV Studios, pg 848
Vista Color Imaging Inc, pg 931

OKLAHOMA

Institute for Teaching & Learning Excellence (ITLE), pg 788

PENNSYLVANIA

JPL, pg 795
NEP Group Inc, pg 838
31st Street Studios, pg 912
The Videohouse Inc, pg 929
Visual Sound Inc, pg 931
WHYY Inc, pg 938

SOUTH CAROLINA

Genesis Creative, pg 769
Studio Charleston, pg 902

TENNESSEE

DR&A Inc, pg 746
Love Shack Recording Studios, pg 811
Memphis Communications Corp, pg 823
NuMynd Studios, pg 843
Technical Support Systems LLC, pg 908
United Methodist Productions, pg 921

TEXAS

AMS Pictures, pg 684
Digital Services Recording Studios, pg 742
Maverick Video Productions, pg 820
Earl Miller Productions Inc, pg 827
Omega Productions, pg 845
Photogroup Studios, pg 856
Reelsound Recording Co, pg 872
Saint Elmo Soundstage, pg 879
The Sound Lab Inc, pg 894
South Coast Film & Video, pg 895

VIRGINIA

Allied Media Corp, pg 681
Bias Studios, pg 705
WETA Production Center, pg 936

WASHINGTON

Avast! Recording Co, pg 697
The House Studios, pg 782
Kostov Productions, pg 801
Victory Studios, pg 927

WISCONSIN

Sound Strations Audio Productions Inc, pg 894
TBC Studios, pg 907
University of Wisconsin-Oshkosh Radio-TV-Film Dept, pg 923
Wisconsin Public Television, pg 940

WYOMING

Bridger Productions Inc, pg 710

ALBERTA

Global TV, pg 771

BRITISH COLUMBIA

Vancouver Film Studios Ltd, pg 924
Video Out Distribution, pg 928

ONTARIO

RB Productions, pg 870
Wanted! Sound + Picture, pg 933

Recording Facility Repairs

CALIFORNIA

Advanced Systems Group LLC, pg 677
Ametron Audio/Video, pg 684

ILLINOIS

Tele-Time Systems, pg 910

MICHIGAN

Studio Consulting & Construction Inc, pg 902
TEL Systems LLC, pg 909

MINNESOTA

Alpha Video & Audio Inc, pg 682

MISSOURI

Southwest Audio-Visual Inc, pg 895

NEW YORK

Manhattan Center Studios Inc, pg 816

TENNESSEE

Technical Support Systems LLC, pg 908

WISCONSIN

Full Compass Systems, pg 767

Recording—Videotapes

ARIZONA

Aardvark Productions LLC, pg 671
Film Creations Ltd, pg 760
Merestone, pg 823
Metropolitan Audio-Visual Inc, pg 824
On-Site Video, pg 846
Rodeo Video Inc, pg 876
Video West Inc, pg 929

ARKANSAS

White Diamond Productions LLC, pg 937

CALIFORNIA

Action Video, pg 675
All Video Productions, pg 680
Artichoke Productions, pg 690
Audio Visual Consultants, pg 694
CCI Digital, a DVS Company, pg 718
Steve Chandler, pg 720
Crystal Pyramid Productions™, pg 735
Custom Video Productions Inc, pg 736
Express Media Inc, pg 757
First Camera, pg 761
Full Moon & High Tide Productions & Studios, pg 767
Goal Productions, pg 772
Gold Standard Productions, pg 772
Golden Gate Studios, pg 772
Havas Edge, pg 777
ITV Productions, pg 792
JDS Video & Media Productions Inc, pg 793
KPBS Public Broadcasting, pg 801
KTVU-Retail Services, pg 802
KVIE-Channel 6, pg 802
Lynch Communications, pg 813
Maximus Media Inc, pg 820

McCune Audio-Video-Lighting, pg 821
Media Magic, pg 822
Munday & Collins AV, pg 834
New & Unique Videos™, pg 839
Nolte Media, pg 841
On-Trax Inc, pg 846
piXvfm Inc, pg 857
PM Productions, pg 858
Point of View Productions, pg 858
Prime Cut Productions, pg 862
QRS Software Services, pg 867
RetinaVision Productions, pg 874
Saturn Studios, pg 881
Shapeshifter, pg 885
Shokus Video, pg 886
SNAP, pg 891
SonicPool, pg 892
Still N' Motion, pg 901
Tam Communications Inc, pg 906
Todd-AO Studios, pg 915
Total Creative, pg 916
Twin Peaks Creative, pg 920
Video Movie Magic, pg 928
Visions Plus, pg 931
VMI Inc, pg 932
West Coast Projections Inc, pg 935

COLORADO

Apogee Communications Group, pg 687
Conly Productions, pg 730
Daylight Productions & Rentals, pg 739
Flashback Media Productions, pg 762
Old Army Press (OAP), pg 844
Open Media Foundation, pg 846

CONNECTICUT

BRB Audiovisual Productions, pg 709
Cine-Med Inc, pg 723
Digital Video Productions, pg 742
Geomatrix Productions, pg 770
MAVCO, pg 820
Rockwell Communications Inc, pg 876
Save the Children Federation Inc, pg 881
Video Production Associates Inc, pg 928

DISTRICT OF COLUMBIA

Interface Media Group, pg 789
Metro Teleproductions Inc (MTI), pg 824

FLORIDA

Access Media Group, pg 673
Applebox Studio, pg 687
Civins Productions Inc, pg 725
Steven Cohen Motion Picture Production, pg 727
Communications Concepts Inc (CCI), pg 729
Courter Films LLC, pg 732
Easy Edit Video Inc, pg 750
Florida Digital Studios, pg 762
Glanz Technologies Inc, pg 771
Harmon's Audio-Visual Services, pg 776
Jordan Klein Film & Video (JKFV), pg 795
The Kitchen, pg 799
Knowles Video Inc (KVI), pg 800
National Teleproductions Inc, pg 837
Phat Planet Recording Studios, pg 855
Roger Scruggs Films, pg 883

Sunfire Communications Inc, pg 904
Universal Studios Florida® Production Group, pg 922
University of Florida, Warrington College of Business Information Technology Support Programs, pg 922
Mike Vasilinda Productions Inc, pg 925
Video Techniques Inc, pg 928

GEORGIA

Beachwood Productions, pg 702
ECG Productions, pg 750
First Cut Communications LLC, pg 761
Guerrilla Productions LLC, pg 774
Myriad Productions, pg 835
WaveGuide Studios, pg 934

HAWAII

Hyperspective Studios Inc, pg 783
1013 Integrated, pg 911

IDAHO

KTVB-TV, pg 802
Wide Eye Productions, pg 938

ILLINOIS

ABSA Films, pg 672
Airways Digital Media, pg 679
Beatty TeleVisual Productions, pg 703
CCore Media Inc, pg 718
Creative Technology (CT), pg 733
Major Media Inc, pg 815
Manning Productions, pg 816
Multimedia Marketing Group, pg 833
On Site Video, pg 846
Jim Passin Productions, pg 852
Pepper Group, pg 854
PSAV® Presentation Services (Hotel Services Division), pg 866
RBR Productions, pg 870
SCI Television & Creative Media LLC, pg 882
Southern Illinois University, pg 895
Tele-Time Systems, pg 910
Video I-D Teleproductions Inc, pg 928
Video Impressions, pg 928
WEEK TV, pg 935

INDIANA

Advanced Media Integration, pg 677
Bright Ideas Creative Services, pg 710
Communication Ministries, pg 728
OMNI Productions, pg 845

IOWA

Educational Technology & Media Services, pg 751

KANSAS

KAKE-TV, pg 796

KENTUCKY

EKU Media, pg 752
Barney Miller's Inc, pg 827
The PPS Group, pg 860

LOUISIANA

Louisiana State University Division of Strategic Communications, pg 811
Moxie Media, pg 832
Vidox Motion Imagery, pg 930
WVLA-TV, pg 942

MAINE

WGME-TV, pg 936

MARYLAND

Adventure Productions LLC, pg 678
CAS Video Productions, pg 717
CPR MultiMedia Solutions, pg 732
CSPMedia.com, pg 735
dbF a Media Company, pg 739
Milner-Fenwick Inc, pg 828
Mobile-Video Productions Inc, pg 828
Sheffield Audio/Video Productions, pg 885
Spectrum Productions, pg 897

MASSACHUSETTS

Award Productions Inc, pg 699
Boston Productions Inc (BPI), pg 709
HOME Inc, pg 781
PixMix Video Services, pg 857
TR Productions, pg 916
TVN-The Video Network, pg 919
VideoLink Inc, an AVI-SPL company, pg 929

MICHIGAN

Digi Sign Design LLC, pg 741
K&R's Recording Studios Inc, pg 796
MessageMakers, pg 824
RingSide Creative, pg 875
The Transfer Zone®, pg 917
WTVS, Detroit Public Television, pg 942

MINNESOTA

The ADS Group, pg 676
Badiyan Inc, pg 700
GMI Productions, pg 771
House of Cinemagraphics, pg 782
MastCom, pg 819
Worthwhile Films, pg 941

MISSOURI

Avatar Studios, pg 697
Hardcastle Films & Video, pg 776
Show-Me Audio-Visual, pg 887

MONTANA

KCFW Television, pg 797
KUSM TV, pg 802

NEBRASKA

Rainbow Video Productions Inc, pg 869

NEVADA

Aardvark Video & Media Productions, pg 671
DVDs4Less, pg 748
Encore Event Technologies LLC, pg 754
JCS Video Productions, pg 793
Lefco Video Services Inc, pg 806
21st Century Video Productions, pg 919

VIDEO

Recording—Videotapes (continued)

NEW HAMPSHIRE

Apertura, pg 686
Channell One Video, pg 720
Chip Taylor Communications LLC, pg 907

NEW JERSEY

AJS Events, pg 679
Allegro Productions Inc, pg 680
CFP Video Productions Inc, pg 720
Diversified, pg 744
Laurel Video Productions, pg 804
Megavideo LLC, pg 823
MiB MediaWorks, pg 825
NFL Films Inc, pg 841
Optisonics Productions, pg 847
SES SA, pg 884
Suede Interactive, pg 903
Synergem, pg 905
VCSvideo, pg 925
Video Corporation of America (VCA), pg 927
Video Ideas Productions, pg 928

NEW MEXICO

Production Outfitters, pg 864

NEW YORK

Adwar Video, pg 678
Associated Press Television News, pg 691
aurora productions, pg 696
BC Studio, pg 702
Bellin Productions, pg 703
Bevilacqua Studios, pg 704
The Big House Group, pg 705
Broadstreet Productions LLC, pg 711
CP Digital, pg 732
Thomas Craven Film Corp, pg 733
Design Audio Visual Inc, pg 741
Downtown Community Television Center (DCTV), pg 746
Duplication Depot Inc, pg 748
4-D Creative Media, pg 764
HAVE Inc, pg 777
International Digital Centre, pg 790
La Paloma Films, pg 803
Magno Sound Inc, pg 815
NBC Production Facilities, pg 837
PrimaLux Video Inc, pg 862
Rafik, pg 869
Synaptic Digital, pg 905
Teatown Communications Group, pg 908
USA Studios, pg 923
Visual Technologies Corp, pg 932
Willow Mixed Media Inc, pg 939
WTL Productions, pg 942
Zelman Studios Ltd, pg 945

NORTH CAROLINA

Pat Appleson Studios Inc, pg 687
AV Connections Inc, pg 697
The Communications Group Inc, pg 729
Digital Rain LLC, pg 742
Duke Media Services, pg 747
Horizon Video Productions Inc, pg 781
Microspace Communications Corp, pg 826
Moving Pictures, pg 832
NASCAR Productions LLC, pg 835
On Location North Carolina, pg 846

Take One Productions Ltd, pg 906
Trailblazer Studios®, pg 917
Videowerks, pg 930

OHIO

Advent Media Inc, pg 677
Aztec Video Productions, pg 700
Russ Beckner Pictures, pg 703
Curtis Inc, pg 736
Cuyahoga Community College Student Production Office (SPO), pg 736
MainSail Production Services Inc, pg 815
Mills James Productions, pg 828
Musicol Recording, pg 835
R&B Communications Inc, pg 870
Take 1 Media Services, pg 906
Vista Color Imaging Inc, pg 931

OKLAHOMA

Academic Media & Digital Services, pg 672
Garman Productions LLC, pg 768
Institute for Teaching & Learning Excellence (ITLE), pg 788

OREGON

KPDX-TV Production Center, pg 801
KTVA Productions, pg 802
Odyssey Productions Inc, pg 844
Production West, pg 864
REX, pg 874

PENNSYLVANIA

Audio Visual Communications Inc, pg 694
Center City Film & Video Inc, pg 719
FMP Media Solutions Inc, pg 763
Innovision Media Group, pg 788
JPL, pg 795
Laser Video Corp, pg 804
Muderick Media, pg 833
Production Masters Inc (PMI), pg 864
The Videohouse Inc, pg 929
Visual Sound Inc, pg 931
WHYY Inc, pg 938
WPHL-TV, pg 942

SOUTH CAROLINA

Encore Video Productions, pg 754
Genesis Creative, pg 769
Venture Media, pg 925

TENNESSEE

Motion Picture Services, pg 831
Running Pony Productions LLC, pg 878
Scripps Networks, pg 882
ST Productions, pg 898
Stage Post, pg 899
Russ Sturgeon Productions/RSVP, pg 903
Zion Music Group, pg 945

TEXAS

Castleview Productions, pg 717
CEV Multimedia Ltd, pg 720
Communication Arts Multimedia Inc, pg 728
The Editing Co, pg 750
Eyecon Video Productions, pg 758
Horizon Film + Video Productions, pg 781
Marx InDigital, pg 818
Maverick Video Productions, pg 820

Media Event Concepts Inc, pg 822
Mediaforce Productions, pg 822
Earl Miller Productions Inc, pg 827
Replicopy Digital Media Center, pg 873
Romar Learning Solutions LLC, pg 877
South Coast Film & Video, pg 895
Texas Heart Institute Visual Communication Services, pg 911

UTAH

ImageWorks Communications, pg 785

VERMONT

University of Vermont, Instructional Television Dept, pg 923

VIRGINIA

American AV, pg 682
BES Studios, pg 704
CACI Integrated Communications, pg 713
CVW Event Productions, pg 736
Quince Imaging Inc, pg 868
WETA Production Center, pg 936

WASHINGTON

Hamilton Studio, pg 775
Small World Productions Inc, pg 890
Victory Studios, pg 927

WEST VIRGINIA

Blackwater Video Productions, pg 707

WISCONSIN

Audio Visual of Milwaukee Inc, pg 694
Learning Technology Services, pg 805
Meridian Studios, pg 824
University of Wisconsin-Oshkosh Radio-TV-Film Dept, pg 923
USAV Group Inc, pg 923
Video Wisconsin Inc, pg 929
Wisconsin Public Television, pg 940

WYOMING

Bridger Productions Inc, pg 710

PUERTO RICO

Stage Crew Audiovisual Inc, pg 898

ALBERTA

Black Media Works, pg 706
Global TV, pg 771

BRITISH COLUMBIA

Triad Communications Ltd, pg 918
Video Out Distribution, pg 928

MANITOBA

Spectra Video Productions Ltd, pg 897

NEWFOUNDLAND AND LABRADOR

Vidcraft Productions Ltd, pg 927

ONTARIO

Silver Creek Media Inc, pg 888
Video Excellence Productions, pg 927

QUEBEC

Muse Entertainment Enterprises, pg 834

Reel & Can Distributors

ARIZONA

Troxell-CDI, pg 918

CALIFORNIA

Christy's Editorial, pg 723
Cinema Equipment Sales of California Inc, pg 724
Hooper Camera & Imaging, pg 781
Zack Electronics Inc, pg 945

COLORADO

Goldberg Brothers Inc, pg 772
Stanco Sales LLC, pg 899

FLORIDA

Tallahassee Audio Visual, pg 906

ILLINOIS

Clark Wire & Cable, pg 725
Research Technology International (RTI), pg 873

MASSACHUSETTS

Hunt's Photo & Video, pg 782
University Products Inc, pg 923

MINNESOTA

Alpha Video & Audio Inc, pg 682

MISSISSIPPI

Jasper Ewing & Sons Inc, pg 757

MISSOURI

ITC, pg 791
Modern Communications Inc, pg 828
Southwest Audio-Visual Inc, pg 895

NEW JERSEY

AV Bluebook, pg 696
HamiltonBuhl, pg 775
Video Corporation of America (VCA), pg 927

NEW YORK

Burlington A/V Recording Media, pg 712
Film Emporium, pg 760
Gaylord Archival, pg 768
Markertek Video Supply, pg 817
Motion Picture Enterprises Inc, pg 831
Rafik, pg 869

NORTH CAROLINA

Camcor Inc, pg 715

PENNSYLVANIA

Advanced AV LLC, pg 677
Morefield Communications Inc, pg 830
Visual Sound Inc, pg 931

SOUTH CAROLINA

Professional Label Inc, pg 865

TENNESSEE
Memphis Communications Corp, pg 823

UTAH
Redman Movies & Stories, pg 872

VIRGINIA
Lee Hartman & Sons Inc, pg 805
The Whitlock Group, pg 937

WISCONSIN
Camera Corner Connecting Point, pg 715
Full Compass Systems, pg 767

PUERTO RICO
Bonnin Electronics Inc, pg 708

ONTARIO
Carr McLean Ltd, pg 717

QUEBEC
STIL Casing Solution, pg 901

Reel & Can Manufacturers

COLORADO
Goldberg Brothers Inc, pg 772

SOUTH CAROLINA
Professional Label Inc, pg 865

WISCONSIN
Regal Photo Products Inc/Arkay Corp, pg 873

QUEBEC
STIL Casing Solution, pg 901

Reel & Can Rentals

ARIZONA
Merestone, pg 823

FLORIDA
Jordan Klein Film & Video (JKFV), pg 795

LOUISIANA
Digital FX Inc, pg 742

MISSOURI
ITC, pg 791
Southwest Audio-Visual Inc, pg 895

NEW YORK
Long Island Video Enterprises Live Inc, pg 811

TEXAS
Stage Directions, pg 898

UTAH
Redman Movies & Stories, pg 872

ALBERTA
Global TV, pg 771

Rehearsal Studio Manufacturers

CALIFORNIA
Ametron Audio/Video, pg 684
Yanchar Design & Consulting Group, pg 943

GEORGIA
Lighting & Production Equipment Inc, pg 807

ILLINOIS
IAC Acoustics, pg 783

MICHIGAN
Studio Consulting & Construction Inc, pg 902

NEW YORK
CP Communications, pg 732

TEXAS
The Yesterday USA Radio Networks, pg 944

Rehearsal Studio Rentals

ARIZONA
Merestone, pg 823

CALIFORNIA
CenterStaging LLC, pg 719
Chapman/Leonard Studio Equipment Inc, pg 720
DTC Lighting & Grip, pg 747
Golden Gate Studios, pg 772
ShowBiz Studios, pg 887
Still N' Motion, pg 901
Studio 637, pg 903

CONNECTICUT
Videofilm Systems Inc, pg 929

DELAWARE
Ken-Del Productions Inc, pg 797

FLORIDA
CopShopMiami.com, pg 731
Jordan Klein Film & Video (JKFV), pg 795
National Teleproductions Inc, pg 837
South Florida Rehearsal Studios, pg 895

GEORGIA
ECG Productions, pg 750
Lighting & Production Equipment Inc, pg 807
Stage Front Presentation Systems, pg 899
WATL-TV Inc, pg 934

ILLINOIS
Resolution Productions Group, pg 874

LOUISIANA
Digital FX Inc, pg 742

MARYLAND
CPR MultiMedia Solutions, pg 732

MASSACHUSETTS
National Boston, pg 836
Penfield Productions Ltd, pg 853

MICHIGAN
City Events Group, pg 725
K&R All Media Productions LLC, pg 796
WTVS, Detroit Public Television, pg 942

MISSOURI
Show-Me Audio-Visual, pg 887
Southwest Audio-Visual Inc, pg 895

NEVADA
DVDs4Less, pg 748

NEW JERSEY
Audio Visual Dynamics®, pg 694

NEW MEXICO
Production Outfitters, pg 864

NEW YORK
Big Foot Productions Inc, pg 705
Long Island Video Enterprises Live Inc, pg 811
Manhattan Center Studios Inc, pg 816
SmackDab Media, pg 890
Sony Music Entertainment, pg 893
Studio Instrument Rentals (SIR), pg 902

NORTH CAROLINA
Duke Media Services, pg 747
Microspace Communications Corp, pg 826
Moving Pictures, pg 832
On Location North Carolina, pg 846
Take One Productions Ltd, pg 906

NORTH DAKOTA
Media Productions, pg 822

OHIO
CET, pg 720
Mills James Productions, pg 828
Vista Color Imaging Inc, pg 931

OREGON
Pacific Grip & Lighting Inc, pg 849

PENNSYLVANIA
JPL, pg 795

TENNESSEE
Memphis Communications Corp, pg 823
Technical Support Systems LLC, pg 908

TEXAS
Biway Media, pg 706
Maverick Video Productions, pg 820
Muller Entertainment LLC, pg 833
Stage Directions, pg 898

VIRGINIA
Allied Media Corp, pg 681

WISCONSIN
TBC Studios, pg 907
USAV Group Inc, pg 923
Wisconsin Public Television, pg 940

WYOMING
Bridger Productions Inc, pg 710

ALBERTA
Global TV, pg 771

BRITISH COLUMBIA
Video Out Distribution, pg 928

ONTARIO
JIB Shots Equipment Inc, pg 794

Rehearsal Studio Repairs

CALIFORNIA
Ametron Audio/Video, pg 684

FLORIDA
JT Communications, pg 795

MICHIGAN
Studio Consulting & Construction Inc, pg 902
TEL Systems LLC, pg 909

MINNESOTA
Alpha Video & Audio Inc, pg 682

MISSOURI
Southwest Audio-Visual Inc, pg 895

TENNESSEE
Technical Support Systems LLC, pg 908

Rewinder Distributors

CALIFORNIA
Ametron Audio/Video, pg 684
Garner Products Inc, pg 768
Alan Gordon Enterprises Inc, pg 772

FLORIDA
Access Media Group, pg 673
Digital Video Systems, pg 742

GEORGIA
Stage Front Presentation Systems, pg 899

ILLINOIS
Research Technology International (RTI), pg 873

INDIANA
Lee Co Inc, pg 805
Sensory Technologies LLC, pg 884

KENTUCKY
Barney Miller's Inc, pg 827

MASSACHUSETTS
Rule Boston Camera, pg 878

VIDEO

Rewinder Distributors (continued)

MINNESOTA
Alpha Video & Audio Inc, pg 682

MISSOURI
Modern Communications Inc, pg 828
Southwest Audio-Visual Inc, pg 895

NEW JERSEY
HamiltonBuhl, pg 775
MCCOM Inc, pg 820
Vcom IMC, pg 925

NEW YORK
B&H Photo Video, pg 701
Gaylord Archival, pg 768
HAVE Inc, pg 777
Markertek Video Supply, pg 817
RNJ Electronics, pg 875
TecNec Distributing, pg 909

PENNSYLVANIA
Advanced AV LLC, pg 677
Brodart Co, pg 711
J E Foss Co, pg 764

TENNESSEE
Lowrance Sound Co Inc, pg 812
Spring Arbor Distributors Inc, pg 898

TEXAS
Quality Audio Visual Service Inc, pg 867

WISCONSIN
Audio Visual of Milwaukee Inc, pg 694

Rewinder Manufacturers

CALIFORNIA
Ametron Audio/Video, pg 684

ILLINOIS
ACCO Brands Corp, pg 673
Research Technology International (RTI), pg 873

NEW YORK
Sima Products Corp, pg 888

Rewinder Rentals

ARIZONA
Merestone, pg 823

ARKANSAS
White Diamond Productions LLC, pg 937

CALIFORNIA
JD Audio Visual Inc, pg 793

GEORGIA
Stage Front Presentation Systems, pg 899

MINNESOTA
House of Cinemagraphics, pg 782

MISSOURI
Show-Me Audio-Visual, pg 887

NORTH CAROLINA
Take One Productions Ltd, pg 906

Rewinder Repairs

GEORGIA
Stage Front Presentation Systems, pg 899

KENTUCKY
NOR-COM Inc, pg 841

MICHIGAN
TEL Systems LLC, pg 909

Script Writing

ALABAMA
Diamond Studios, pg 741

ALASKA
Alaska Media Pros LLC, pg 679
Aurora Films, pg 696

ARIZONA
Candee Productions Inc, pg 716
Direct Current Video Productions, pg 743
Film Creations Ltd, pg 760
Fox 10 Productions (KSAZ-TV), pg 765
Merestone, pg 823
Metropolitan Audio-Visual Inc, pg 824
On-Site Video, pg 846
Teaberry, pg 908
Wild Visions Inc, pg 938

ARKANSAS
Live'N'Loud, pg 810
White Diamond Productions LLC, pg 937

CALIFORNIA
Action Video, pg 675
Steve Chandler, pg 720
Concrete Images, pg 730
Creative Technology, pg 733
Crystal Pyramid Productions™, pg 735
Custom Video Productions Inc, pg 736
Deja View Video, pg 740
deKramer Productions Inc, pg 740
Design Media, pg 741
digital OutPost, pg 742
Dolphin MultiMedia Inc, pg 745
Far West Media Services Inc, pg 759
Final Draft, A Cast & Crew Company, pg 761
FJ Productions Inc, pg 762
Full Moon & High Tide Productions & Studios, pg 767
Goal Productions, pg 772
Havas Edge, pg 777
iCorpTv, pg 783
Imageworks, pg 785

Increase Video/Silver Mine Video, pg 786
ITV Productions, pg 792
JDS Video & Media Productions Inc, pg 793
Joyce Media Inc, pg 795
Kavich Reynolds Productions Inc, pg 797
KO Creative, pg 800
KPBS Public Broadcasting, pg 801
KTVU-Retail Services, pg 802
KVIE-Channel 6, pg 802
Maximus Media Inc, pg 820
Media Magic, pg 822
The Media Staff Inc, pg 822
Nandar Entertainment Pictures, pg 835
New & Unique Videos™, pg 839
Nolte Media, pg 841
On-Trax Inc, pg 846
Pacific Light Studios, pg 849
Palardo Productions, pg 850
Penrose Productions, pg 854
piXvfm Inc, pg 857
PM Productions, pg 858
PSI Inc, pg 866
QRS Software Services, pg 867
Regent Press Publishers & Printers, pg 873
Sahara Records & Filmworks Entertainment Co, pg 879
Saturn Studios, pg 881
Staylor-Made Communications Inc, pg 900
Still N' Motion, pg 901
Tam Communications Inc, pg 906
Total Creative, pg 916
Twin Peaks Creative, pg 920
Via Verde Productions, pg 926
Videografix LLC, pg 929
Visions Plus, pg 931
West Coast Projections Inc, pg 935
WMS Media Inc, pg 940

COLORADO
Centre Communications Inc, pg 720
Daylight Productions & Rentals, pg 739
Flashback Media Productions, pg 762
Old Army Press (OAP), pg 844
Open Media Foundation, pg 846
Tatum Video, pg 907
Transtar Entertainment Co Inc, pg 917
Z-Axis Corp, pg 944

CONNECTICUT
ACM Productions Ltd, pg 674
Antenna International, pg 686
BRB Audiovisual Productions, pg 709
Cine-Med Inc, pg 723
Essex Television Group Inc, pg 755
The Gary-Paul Agency, pg 768
Geomatrix Productions, pg 770
Guymark Studios LLC, pg 775
Ironik Design & Post, pg 791
Palace Productions MediaVision, pg 850
P&P Studios Inc, pg 851
Powerstation Events, pg 860
Video Production Associates Inc, pg 928

DELAWARE
So Smart Productions, pg 891

DISTRICT OF COLUMBIA
Hillmann & Carr Inc, pg 780
Interface Media Group, pg 789

O'Keefe Communications Inc, pg 844
Yellow Cat Productions Inc, pg 944

FLORIDA
Accord Productions, pg 673
ACT Productions, pg 675
Applebox Studio, pg 687
Chatterbox Productions Inc, pg 721
Civins Productions Inc, pg 725
Communications Concepts Inc (CCI), pg 729
Courter Films LLC, pg 732
DME Studios, pg 744
Florida Digital Studios, pg 762
Gemstone Media Inc, pg 769
Jordan Klein Film & Video (JKFV), pg 795
National Teleproductions Inc, pg 837
The Newhouse Media Group, pg 840
Sound & Vision Communications Inc, pg 893
Sunfire Communications Inc, pg 904
Sunrise Studios, pg 904
Tricycle Studios, pg 918
Universal Studios Florida® Production Group, pg 922
Mike Vasilinda Productions Inc, pg 925
Video Techniques Inc, pg 928
Vistamax Productions, pg 931

GEORGIA
Beachwood Productions, pg 702
Burst Video/Film Inc, pg 713
The DVI Group, pg 748
ECG Productions, pg 750
Guerrilla Productions LLC, pg 774
Myriad Productions, pg 835
Malcolm Neal Productions, pg 837
On-Line Productions, pg 845
Visioneering International Inc, pg 931

HAWAII
FilmWorks Pacific, pg 761
Hyperspective Studios Inc, pg 783
Sight & Sound Studios, pg 887
1013 Integrated, pg 911
Tropical Visions Video Inc, pg 918

IDAHO
KTVB-TV, pg 802
Brad Shaw Productions Inc, pg 885
Wide Eye Productions, pg 938

ILLINOIS
ABSA Films, pg 672
Airways Digital Media, pg 679
Atomic Imaging Inc/Golan Studios, pg 692
Big Shoulders Digital Video Productions, pg 705
Breeze Productions Inc, pg 710
CCore Media Inc, pg 718
Edit House Chicago, pg 750
Explore, pg 757
Extraordinary Demos/Videos, pg 757
Film Police, pg 760
1st Financial Training Services Inc, pg 761
Freeman Pictures Inc, pg 765
IV Media Resources, pg 792
Major Media Productions Inc, pg 815
Manning Productions, pg 816

The Market Place, pg 817
Mightybytes Inc, pg 827
Mimi Productions, pg 828
Rob Orr Productions Ltd, pg 848
Production Craft Inc, pg 863
PSAV® Presentation Services
    (Hotel Services Division), pg 866
Richter Studios, pg 875
SCI Television & Creative Media
    LLC, pg 882
Sound/Video Impressions Inc,
    pg 894
Southern Illinois University, pg 895
Sparkfactor, pg 896
20/20 Communications Inc, pg 920
Video I-D Teleproductions Inc,
    pg 928
Video Impressions, pg 928
WEEK TV, pg 935
WIFR-TV, pg 938

INDIANA

A-V-A Video Productions, pg 671
Bright Ideas Creative Services,
    pg 710
Educational Video Group Inc,
    pg 751
PentaVision Communications Inc,
    pg 854

IOWA

Educational Technology & Media
    Services, pg 751

KANSAS

KAKE-TV, pg 796

KENTUCKY

Hammond Communications Group
    Inc, pg 775
Horizon Films & Media LLC,
    pg 781
Prosper Media Group Inc, pg 866

LOUISIANA

Digital FX Inc, pg 742
Launch Media, pg 804
Louisiana State University Division
    of Strategic Communications,
    pg 811
Moxie Media, pg 832
Vidox Motion Imagery, pg 930
WVLA-TV, pg 942

MAINE

Slim Goodbody Corp, pg 890
WGME-TV, pg 936

MARYLAND

Adventure Productions LLC, pg 678
CAS Video Productions, pg 717
CPR MultiMedia Solutions, pg 732
dbF a Media Company, pg 739
The Image Generators, pg 785
Kramer Communications Video
    Production, pg 801
Media Dimensions LLC, pg 821
Mobile-Video Productions Inc,
    pg 828
Pro Cuts Editing Services, pg 862
Quality Film & Video, pg 868
Sign Media Inc, pg 887
Spectrum Productions, pg 897

MASSACHUSETTS

Award Productions Inc, pg 699
CommCreative, pg 728
Green Mountain Post Films (GMP),
    pg 774

HOME Inc, pg 781
Monadnock Media Inc, pg 829
Northern Light Productions (NLP),
    pg 842
Penfield Productions Ltd, pg 853
Gabriel Polonsky Studio, pg 859
Preston Productions Inc, pg 861
Small Planet Communications Inc,
    pg 890
Sound & Vision Media, pg 893
TR Productions, pg 916
VideoLink Inc, an AVI-SPL
    company, pg 929

MICHIGAN

Digi Sign Design LLC, pg 741
K&R's Recording Studios Inc,
    pg 796
Madonna University Information
    Technology, pg 814
Michigan Recording Arts Institute
    & Technologies, pg 825
The Program Source International,
    pg 865

MINNESOTA

Badiyan Inc, pg 700
C Vision Productions, pg 713
MastCom, pg 819
Media Loft Inc, pg 822
Babe Winkelman Productions Inc,
    pg 939
Worthwhile Films, pg 941

MISSOURI

Communitronics Corp, pg 729
Studio Worx Inc, pg 903
Switch, pg 905

MONTANA

KCFW Television, pg 797

NEBRASKA

B & B Video Productions Inc,
    pg 700

NEVADA

Aardvark Video & Media
    Productions, pg 671
Encore Event Technologies LLC,
    pg 754

NEW HAMPSHIRE

Apertura, pg 686
Channell One Video, pg 720
Chip Taylor Communications LLC,
    pg 907

NEW JERSEY

AJS Events, pg 679
Allegro Productions Inc, pg 680
CFP Video Productions Inc, pg 720
Color Leasing Studios, pg 727
Creative Video, pg 734
Euro-Pacific Film & Video
    Productions Inc, pg 756
Laurel Video Productions, pg 804
MediaNow Inc, pg 822
Megavideo LLC, pg 823
MiB MediaWorks, pg 825
Midnight Media Group Inc, pg 827
Ray Mueller Productions, pg 833
NFL Films Inc, pg 841
Optisonics Productions, pg 847
PeopleVisionFX, pg 854
Reed Presentations Inc (RPI),
    pg 872
Selden Associates, pg 883

Shamrock Communications, pg 885
Suede Interactive, pg 903
Telequest Inc, pg 910
TimeSteps Productions Inc, pg 914
VCSvideo, pg 925

NEW MEXICO

Production Outfitters, pg 864

NEW YORK

Air Sea Land Productions Inc
    (ASL), pg 678
American Montage Inc, pg 683
aurora productions, pg 696
Bellin Productions, pg 703
Bevilacqua Studios, pg 704
Big Foot Productions Inc, pg 705
The Big House Group, pg 705
Broadstreet Productions LLC,
    pg 711
Brooklyn Films, pg 711
Buffalo Video Production, pg 712
Campus Productions, pg 715
Chromavision Corp, pg 723
Cohn Creative Group LLC, pg 727
Digital Art Video Inc, pg 741
Four Corners Productions, pg 764
4-D Creative Media, pg 764
Golden Lamb Productions, pg 772
HB-Content, pg 777
Icontent, pg 783
InterNation Inc, pg 789
Richard Kaplan Productions, pg 796
L A Bruell Inc, pg 802
La Paloma Films, pg 803
Manhattan Center Studios Inc,
    pg 816
Meltzer Media Productions, pg 823
Mood Creations Ltd, pg 829
Jack Morton Worldwide, pg 830
MRM//McCANN, pg 832
MRY, pg 832
New Horizon Studios, pg 839
News Broadcast Network Inc,
    pg 840
The Palmer Group, pg 850
Pat Kogan Productions Inc, pg 852
Peckham Productions, pg 852
PrimeLight Productions Inc, pg 862
Production Central, pg 863
Richter Productions Inc, pg 875
D S Simon Productions, pg 888
Synaptic Digital, pg 905
Teatown Communications Group,
    pg 908
TeleTime Productions, pg 910
Visual Technologies Corp, pg 932
WTL Productions, pg 942
Zelman Studios Ltd, pg 945

NORTH CAROLINA

All Pro Media Inc, pg 680
Pat Appleson Studios Inc, pg 687
Bill Barnes Video Productions LLC,
    pg 702
The Communications Group Inc,
    pg 729
Digital Rain LLC, pg 742
Duke Media Services, pg 747
Franklin Video Inc, pg 765
Horizon Video Productions Inc,
    pg 781
Image Associates Inc, pg 784
Kino Mountain Productions LLC,
    pg 799
K2 Productions, pg 802
L A Management Co LLC, pg 802
Moving Pictures, pg 832
NASCAR Productions LLC, pg 835
On Location North Carolina, pg 846
Take One Productions Ltd, pg 906

NORTH DAKOTA

Media Productions, pg 822
UND Television Center, pg 921

OHIO

Advent Media Inc, pg 677
Aztec Video Productions, pg 700
Bartha, pg 702
Russ Beckner Pictures, pg 703
Challenge Productions/Challenge
    Aerial Imaging, pg 720
Cinecraft Productions Inc, pg 723
Curtis Inc, pg 736
Cuyahoga Community College
    Student Production Office (SPO),
    pg 736
Lyon Video Inc, pg 813
MainSail Production Services Inc,
    pg 815
Mills James Productions, pg 828
Production Partners Media, pg 864
R&B Communications, pg 870
Shelburne Films, pg 885
Take 1 Media Services, pg 906
Treehaus Communications Inc,
    pg 917
Vista Color Imaging Inc, pg 931

OKLAHOMA

Academic Media & Digital
    Services, pg 672
PDC Productions, pg 852

OREGON

Ideascape Inc, pg 784
InterVision Media, pg 791
KPDX-TV Production Center,
    pg 801
KTVA Productions, pg 802
KVAL, pg 802
Limbo Films, pg 808
MediaFX, pg 822
Odyssey Productions Inc, pg 844
Production West, pg 864

PENNSYLVANIA

Argentine Productions Inc, pg 688
Audio Visions Inc, pg 694
Audio Visual Communications Inc,
    pg 694
Bang! Pictures Inc, pg 701
Beholder Productions Inc, pg 703
Center City Film & Video Inc,
    pg 719
FMP Media Solutions Inc, pg 763
Innovision Media Group, pg 788
JPL, pg 795
Muderick Media, pg 833
Panta Rhei Media Inc, pg 851
Production Masters Inc (PMI),
    pg 864
Video/Film Associates, pg 928
The Videohouse Inc, pg 929
Visual Sound Inc, pg 931
The Whale Video Co, pg 936
WPHL-TV, pg 942

SOUTH CAROLINA

American Production Services LLC,
    pg 684
Encore Video Productions, pg 754
Genesis Creative, pg 769
Sound & Images Inc, pg 893
Stages Video Productions, pg 899
Venture Media, pg 925

TENNESSEE

American Blackguard Inc, pg 683
Anode Inc, pg 686

VIDEO

Script Writing (continued)

TENNESSEE (continued)

Kingswood Productions, pg 799
Motion Picture Services, pg 831
Paradigm Marketing & Creative, pg 851
Running Pony Productions LLC, pg 878
Scripps Networks, pg 882
Stage Post, pg 899

TEXAS

Alexander Media Productions, pg 679
Alpha Video Productions, pg 682
AMS Pictures, pg 684
Anaphora Literary Press, pg 685
Best Film & Video, pg 704
Biway Media, pg 706
Castleview Productions, pg 717
Cerutti Productions Inc, pg 720
Communication Arts Multimedia Inc, pg 728
Dykeman Associates Inc, pg 748
The Editing Co, pg 750
Emergency Film Group, pg 753
Epic Software Group Inc, pg 755
Freeman, pg 765
Horizon Film + Video Productions, pg 781
JWP Inc, pg 796
Marx InDigital, pg 818
McNee Productions Inc, pg 821
Mediaforce Productions, pg 822
Earl Miller Productions Inc, pg 827
Out of the BLUE Media, pg 849
Phillips Media Source, pg 855
Prairie Pictures Film & Video, pg 860
Romar Learning Solutions LLC, pg 877
RuffHouse LLC, pg 878
The Samuels Co, pg 879
South Coast Film & Video, pg 895
Texas Heart Institute Visual Communication Services, pg 911
Video Perspective, pg 928

UTAH

ImageWorks Communications, pg 785

VERMONT

Wilson McLeran Inc, pg 939

VIRGINIA

Advance Concepts Inc, pg 677
Altruist Media LLC, pg 682
American AV, pg 682
BES Studios, pg 704
CACI Integrated Communications, pg 713
CDR Communications Inc, pg 719
CVW Event Productions, pg 736
Eagle Films, pg 749
Limelight Communications Inc, pg 808
Metro Productions, pg 824
Rocktown Media, pg 876
SoundView Services Inc, pg 895
Studio Center Corp, pg 902
Video Solutions, pg 928

WASHINGTON

Adams Creative & Production Services, pg 675
Bennett-Watt HD Productions Inc, pg 703
Kostov Productions, pg 801
Robert McConnell Productions, pg 820
Medical Media Systems, pg 823
North-by-Northwest - A Digital Studio, pg 842
Small World Productions Inc, pg 890
Sparkworks Media, pg 896
Victory Studios, pg 927
Washington State University College of Nursing, pg 934

WEST VIRGINIA

MotionMasters, pg 831

WISCONSIN

Audio Visual of Milwaukee Inc, pg 694
AVS Group, pg 699
Clear Focus Media LLC, pg 726
Meridian Studios, pg 824
Midland Video Productions Inc, pg 827
Mirror 34 Productions, pg 828
Rucinski Write!Now LLC, pg 878
USAV Group Inc, pg 923
Video Wisconsin Inc, pg 929
Watts Communications Inc, pg 934
Win Media Inc, pg 939
Wisconsin Public Television, pg 940

WYOMING

Bridger Productions Inc, pg 710

PUERTO RICO

Stage Crew Audiovisual Inc, pg 898

ALBERTA

Global TV, pg 771

BRITISH COLUMBIA

Triad Communications Ltd, pg 918

MANITOBA

Spectra Video Productions Ltd, pg 897

NEWFOUNDLAND AND LABRADOR

Vidcraft Productions Ltd, pg 927

NORTHWEST TERRITORIES

Yellowknife Films Inc, pg 944

ONTARIO

ADS Media, pg 677
DebsVoice, pg 739
GAPC (General Assembly Production Centre), pg 768
Image Video Services & Productions, pg 785
JFB Communications, pg 794
RB Productions, pg 870
Silver Creek Media Inc, pg 888
Video Excellence Productions, pg 927

QUEBEC

Muse Entertainment Enterprises, pg 834

Signal Processing Equipment Distributors

ALABAMA

PESA, pg 855

ARIZONA

EAR Professional Audio/Video, pg 749
Troxell-CDI, pg 918

CALIFORNIA

Ametron Audio/Video, pg 684
Audio/Video Supply Inc, pg 694
BigFoot Mobile Systems, pg 705
Computer Modules Inc, pg 729
Empire Pro, pg 753
Media Control Systems LLC, pg 821
Southern California Sound Image Inc, pg 895
SSL Industries, pg 898
Stanislaus AV Inc, pg 899
VMI Inc, pg 932
Westlake Recording Studios, pg 936

FLORIDA

Access Media Group, pg 673
Digital Video Systems, pg 742
Harris Corp, pg 776
Hi-Tech Enterprises Inc, pg 779
Midtown Video Inc, pg 827
Multicom Inc, pg 833
ONstage, pg 846
Recording Media & Equipment Inc (RM&E), pg 872

GEORGIA

Baker Audio Visual, pg 700
Barco Inc, pg 701
Clark, pg 725
Stage Front Presentation Systems, pg 899

INDIANA

Sensory Technologies LLC, pg 884
SHP Electronics, pg 887

KENTUCKY

NOR-COM Inc, pg 841

MARYLAND

Wiltronix Inc, pg 939

MASSACHUSETTS

Rule Boston Camera, pg 878

MICHIGAN

DAWNco, pg 739
Digi Sign Design LLC, pg 741
On Stage Visuals, pg 846

MINNESOTA

Alpha Video & Audio Inc, pg 682

MISSOURI

Communitronics Corp, pg 729
Modern Communications Inc, pg 828
Southwest Audio-Visual Inc, pg 895

NEBRASKA

ATV Research Inc, pg 692

NEVADA

Aardvark Video & Media Productions, pg 671

NEW JERSEY

A-V Services Inc, pg 671
American Fibertek Inc, pg 683
Comprehensive Cable & Connectivity Co, pg 729
Diversified, pg 744
FSR Inc, pg 766
MCCOM Inc, pg 820
PatchAmp, pg 852
Starlite, pg 900
SYMCO Inc, pg 905
Total Video Products Inc, pg 916
Video Corporation of America (VCA), pg 927
Wired 4 Sound Inc, pg 940

NEW YORK

AV Workshop, pg 697
HAVE Inc, pg 777
Long Island Video Enterprises Live Inc, pg 811
Markertek Video Supply, pg 817
Tri-Ed Distribution Inc, pg 918

OHIO

Copp Integrated Systems, pg 731
Tri-State Audio Visual Co, pg 918

PENNSYLVANIA

Advanced AV LLC, pg 677
Morefield Communications Inc, pg 830
Vistacom Inc, pg 931
Visual Sound Inc, pg 931

RHODE ISLAND

Shanix Inc, pg 885

SOUTH DAKOTA

Sencore Inc, pg 883

TENNESSEE

Lowrance Sound Co Inc, pg 812
Technical Support Systems LLC, pg 908

TEXAS

Audio Visual Technologies Group (AVTG), pg 695
Data Projections Inc, pg 738
FitzCo Sound Inc, pg 761
Pro Video & Film Equipment Co Inc, pg 863
Tarpley Media Systems, pg 907

UTAH

RIA Corp, pg 874

VIRGINIA

Quince Imaging Inc, pg 868

WISCONSIN

Audio Visual of Milwaukee Inc, pg 694
Camera Corner Connecting Point, pg 715
Full Compass Systems, pg 767

ALBERTA

McBain Camera Ltd, pg 820

BRITISH COLUMBIA
DL Sound & Lighting Productions Ltd, pg 744

ONTARIO
HD Source, pg 777
Westbury National Show Systems Ltd, pg 936

Signal Processing Equipment Manufacturers

ALABAMA
PESA, pg 855

ARIZONA
Covid Inc, pg 732

CALIFORNIA
ALTINEX Inc, pg 682
Computer Modules Inc, pg 729
DASAN Zhone Solutions (DZS) Inc, pg 737
DigiTech, pg 742
Ensemble Designs Inc, pg 754
ESE, pg 755
Extron Electronics, pg 758
FM Systems Inc, pg 763
For-A Corp of America, pg 763
Hotronic Inc, pg 782
JBL Professional, pg 793
Linkabit, pg 809
Loma Scientific International (LSI), pg 811
RF Industries, pg 874
Telestream Inc, pg 910
VITEC Multimedia, pg 932
Wohler Technologies Inc, pg 940
Xantech LLC, pg 943

COLORADO
Colorado Video Inc, pg 728
Liberty AV Solutions, pg 807
Vexcel Corp, pg 926
Video Accessory Corp, pg 927

CONNECTICUT
Xintekvideo Inc, pg 943

FLORIDA
Compuvideo Sales USA Ltd, pg 729
Sensormatic®, pg 884
Tel-Test, pg 909

GEORGIA
Barco Inc, pg 701

IOWA
Winegard Co, pg 939

MAINE
Dielectric, pg 741

MICHIGAN
ASC Systems, pg 690

MINNESOTA
Lynx Broadband, pg 813

MISSOURI
Link Electronics Inc, pg 809

NEW JERSEY
American Fibertek Inc, pg 683
Blonder Tongue Laboratories Inc, pg 707
CELCO, pg 719
Crestron Electronics Inc, pg 734
FSR Inc, pg 766
Kramer Electronics USA Inc, pg 801

NEW MEXICO
Burst Electronics Inc, pg 713

NEW YORK
Key Digital Systems, pg 798
Laird Digital Cinema, pg 803
MultiDyne Video & Fiber Optics Systems, pg 833
Judson Rosebush Co Inc, pg 877

OHIO
AV Toolbox, pg 697

PENNSYLVANIA
MicroImage Video Systems, pg 826
Prime Image Inc, pg 862

SOUTH DAKOTA
Sencore Inc, pg 883

TEXAS
Contemporary Research, pg 731
National Instruments Corp, pg 836

ONTARIO
Artaflex Inc, pg 690
Ward-Beck Systems Ltd, pg 933

QUEBEC
Matrox Video Products Group, pg 819

Signal Processing Equipment Rentals

ARIZONA
Merestone, pg 823
Metropolitan Audio-Visual Inc, pg 824
Video West Inc, pg 929

CALIFORNIA
Advanced Media LLC, pg 677
Ametron Audio/Video, pg 684
Artichoke Productions, pg 690
Bexel, an NEP Broadcast Services Company, pg 704
Express Media Inc, pg 757
Golden Gate Studios, pg 772
Imagecraft Productions, pg 785
Lynch Communications, pg 813
Maximus Media Inc, pg 820
McCune Audio-Video-Lighting, pg 821
Munday & Collins AV, pg 834
Muse Presentation Technologies, pg 834
On-Trax Inc, pg 846
RetinaVision Productions, pg 874
Stanislaus AV Inc, pg 899
VMI Inc, pg 932

COLORADO
Daylight Productions & Rentals, pg 739
Spectrum Audio Visual Services, pg 897

FLORIDA
Access Media Group, pg 673
All Comm Rentals Inc (ALLCOMM), pg 680
Midtown Video Inc, pg 827
ONstage, pg 846
Paradise Show & Design Inc, pg 851
Phat Planet Recording Studios, pg 855
Universal Studios Florida® Production Group, pg 922

GEORGIA
Stage Front Presentation Systems, pg 899

ILLINOIS
Backstar Creative Media Inc, pg 700
Resolution Productions Group, pg 874

LOUISIANA
Digital FX Inc, pg 742
Pace Systems, pg 849

MARYLAND
CPR MultiMedia Solutions, pg 732

MICHIGAN
Digi Sign Design LLC, pg 741
K&R All Media Productions LLC, pg 796
On Stage Visuals, pg 846

MINNESOTA
Alpha Video & Audio Inc, pg 682

MISSOURI
Show-Me Audio-Visual, pg 887
Southwest Audio-Visual Inc, pg 895

NEVADA
GES Audio Visual, pg 770
Lefco Video Services Inc, pg 806

NEW HAMPSHIRE
Apertura, pg 686

NEW JERSEY
MB Productions, pg 820
MediaMix Inc, pg 822
PLS Staging, pg 858
Starlite, pg 900
Video Corporation of America (VCA), pg 927
Wired 4 Sound Inc, pg 940

NEW YORK
AV Workshop, pg 697
Long Island Video Enterprises Live Inc, pg 811
Specialized Audio-Visual Inc, pg 896

NORTH CAROLINA
Special Event Services, pg 896
Take One Productions Ltd, pg 906

OHIO
Lyon Video Inc, pg 813

PENNSYLVANIA
Upstage Video, pg 923

TENNESSEE
Mr Mark's Used Musical, Stereo & Studio Equipment Store, pg 828
Technical Support Systems LLC, pg 908

TEXAS
Alford Media Services, pg 680
FitzCo Sound Inc, pg 761

VIRGINIA
Quince Imaging Inc, pg 868

WASHINGTON
Victory Studios, pg 927

WISCONSIN
Camera Corner Connecting Point, pg 715
Full Compass Systems, pg 767

WYOMING
Bridger Productions Inc, pg 710

PUERTO RICO
Stage Crew Audiovisual Inc, pg 898

BRITISH COLUMBIA
DL Sound & Lighting Productions Ltd, pg 744

ONTARIO
HD Source, pg 777
Westbury National Show Systems Ltd, pg 936

Signal Processing Equipment Repairs

CALIFORNIA
Advanced Media LLC, pg 677
Ametron Audio/Video, pg 684
SSL Industries Inc, pg 898
VMI Inc, pg 932

FLORIDA
Hi-Tech Enterprises Inc, pg 779
Midtown Video Inc, pg 827
Phat Planet Recording Studios, pg 855
Tel-Test, pg 909

GEORGIA
Stage Front Presentation Systems, pg 899

ILLINOIS
Beatty TeleVisual Productions, pg 703
Midwest Digital Corp, pg 827

KENTUCKY
NOR-COM Inc, pg 841

MICHIGAN
TEL Systems LLC, pg 909

VIDEO

Signal Processing Equipment Repairs (continued)

MINNESOTA

Alpha Video & Audio Inc, pg 682

MISSOURI

Southwest Audio-Visual Inc, pg 895

NEW JERSEY

Starlite, pg 900

OREGON

All Service Musical Electronics Repair, pg 680

TENNESSEE

Technical Support Systems LLC, pg 908

TEXAS

Tarpley Media Systems, pg 907

UTAH

RIA Corp, pg 874

WISCONSIN

Camera Corner Connecting Point, pg 715
Full Compass Systems, pg 767

ONTARIO

Westbury National Show Systems Ltd, pg 936

Slide to Video Transfers, *see* Transfers—Slide to Video

Slow Motion Photography, *see* Photography—Slow Motion

Special Effects

ALABAMA

Diamond Studios, pg 741

ARIZONA

Arizona Studios, pg 688
Creative Backstage, pg 733
Merestone, pg 823
Metropolitan Audio-Visual Inc, pg 824

ARKANSAS

Live'N'Loud, pg 810
White Diamond Productions LLC, pg 937

CALIFORNIA

Access Video in Berkeley, pg 673
Action Video, pg 675
Artichoke Productions, pg 690
Automated Entertainment, pg 696
Blind™, pg 707
Branam Enterprises Inc, pg 709

Buttercup Pictures, pg 713
Calbor Enterprises Two Inc, pg 713
Steve Chandler, pg 720
Cherry Multimedia, pg 721
Creative Technology, pg 733
Crystal Pyramid Productions™, pg 735
Custom Video Productions Inc, pg 736
deKramer Productions Inc, pg 740
Direct Images Interactive Inc, pg 743
Elektrashock, pg 753
First Person Inc, pg 761
Full Scale Effects, pg 767
iCorpTv, pg 783
JDS Video & Media Productions Inc, pg 793
Laser Magic Productions, pg 804
Lumeni Productions Inc, pg 812
Maximus Media Inc, pg 820
McCune Audio-Video-Lighting, pg 821
The Media Staff Inc, pg 822
Method Studios, pg 824
Moving Art by Louie Schwartzberg, pg 831
New & Unique Videos™, pg 839
New Deal Studios, pg 839
New Wave Entertainment, pg 839
Palardo Productions, pg 850
PSI Inc, pg 866
Pyro Spectaculars Inc, pg 867
QRS Software Services, pg 867
Reality Check Systems, pg 871
RetinaVision Productions, pg 874
Saturn Studios, pg 881
Shapeshifter, pg 885
SonicPool, pg 892
Special Effects Unlimited Inc, pg 896
Staylor-Made Communications Inc, pg 900
Still N' Motion, pg 901
Studio 637, pg 903
Tam Communications Inc, pg 906
Total Creative, pg 916
Twin Peaks Creative, pg 920
Two Door Productions LLC, pg 920
VidCan Media Solutions, pg 927
Videografix LLC, pg 929
Visions Plus, pg 931
Vitruvian Entertainment, pg 932
Wavemaker Media Design, pg 934
Mark Woollen & Associates, pg 941

COLORADO

Flashback Media Productions, pg 762
Full Spectrum Arts & Services, pg 767
Maniac Productions, pg 816
Z-Axis Corp, pg 944

CONNECTICUT

BRB Audiovisual Productions, pg 709
Guymark Studios LLC, pg 775
Ironik Design & Post, pg 791
MAVCO, pg 820
Musivision Inc, pg 835
Palace Production Center, pg 850
Think 3-D.com, pg 912

DISTRICT OF COLUMBIA

Interface Media Group, pg 789
Yellow Cat Productions Inc, pg 944

FLORIDA

Access Media Group, pg 673
Applebox Studio, pg 687

Audio Visual Imagineering Inc, pg 694
Civins Productions Inc, pg 725
Communications Concepts Inc (CCI), pg 729
Courter Films LLC, pg 732
Everlast Productions, pg 757
Hi-Tech Enterprises Inc, pg 779
Orlando Special Effects, pg 848
Sound & Vision Communications Inc, pg 893
Sunfire Communications Inc, pg 904
Sunrise Studios, pg 904
Tricycle Studios, pg 918
Vistamax Productions, pg 931

GEORGIA

The DVI Group, pg 748
First Cut Communications LLC, pg 761
Guerrilla Productions LLC, pg 774

HAWAII

Dot C Software Inc, pg 746
Hyperspective Studios Inc, pg 783
1013 Integrated, pg 911

ILLINOIS

ABSA Films, pg 672
Airways Digital Media, pg 679
AnswersMedia, pg 686
Backstar Creative Media Inc, pg 700
Chicago Spotlight Inc, pg 721
Consolidated Display Co Inc, pg 731
IV Media Resources, pg 792
Mightybytes Inc, pg 827
Multimedia Marketing Group, pg 833
Optimus, pg 847
Pepper Group, pg 854
PSAV® Presentation Services (Hotel Services Division), pg 866
Richter Studios, pg 875
20/20 Communications Inc, pg 920
Video Impressions, pg 928

INDIANA

A-V-A Video Productions, pg 671

KENTUCKY

The Media Collaboratory, pg 821
The PPS Group, pg 860
Theatre Effects, pg 911

LOUISIANA

Digital FX Inc, pg 742
Story Teller Effects Group LLC, pg 901
Vidox Motion Imagery, pg 930

MAINE

WGME-TV, pg 936

MARYLAND

Adventure Productions LLC, pg 678
CPR MultiMedia Solutions, pg 732
dbF a Media Company, pg 739
Kramer Communications Video Production, pg 801
Mobile-Video Productions Inc, pg 828
Producers Video, pg 863

MASSACHUSETTS

Award Productions Inc, pg 699
Northern Light Productions (NLP), pg 842

MICHIGAN

Digi Sign Design LLC, pg 741
Digital Image Studios LLC, pg 742
K&R's Recording Studios Inc, pg 796
Michigan Recording Arts Institute & Technologies, pg 825
The Program Source International, pg 865
RingSide Creative, pg 875

MINNESOTA

House of Cinemagraphics, pg 782
MastCom, pg 819

MISSOURI

Conference Technologies Inc, pg 730
Fantasy Creations FX, pg 759
Laser Rentals Inc, pg 804

MONTANA

Filmlites Montana, pg 760

NEVADA

Aardvark Video & Media Productions, pg 671
DVDs4Less, pg 748
Encore Event Technologies LLC, pg 754
GES Audio Visual, pg 770
MeshTel, pg 824
Ron Roy Productions/Moodtapes, pg 878

NEW HAMPSHIRE

Apertura, pg 686
Channell One Video, pg 720

NEW JERSEY

AJS Events, pg 679
Allegro Productions Inc, pg 680
Broadcast Center Studios, pg 710
CD Meyer Inc, pg 718
CELCO, pg 719
CFP Video Productions Inc, pg 720
Color Leasing Studios, pg 727
Early Films, pg 749
Euro-Pacific Film & Video Productions Inc, pg 756
Laurel Video Productions, pg 804
Megavideo LLC, pg 823
MiB MediaWorks, pg 825
Midnight Media Group Inc, pg 827
NFL Films Inc, pg 841
PeopleVisionFX, pg 854
Starlite, pg 900
Suede Interactive, pg 903
VCSvideo, pg 925

NEW MEXICO

Production Outfitters, pg 864

NEW YORK

Animotion Inc, pg 685
Big Film Design, pg 705
The Big House Group, pg 705
Broadstreet Productions LLC, pg 711
Buffalo Video Production, pg 712
Chromavision Corp, pg 723
Design Audio Visual Inc, pg 741

Designomotion, pg 741
Digital Art Video Inc, pg 741
4-D Creative Media, pg 764
HB-Content, pg 777
La Paloma Films, pg 803
Lylofilm Productions, pg 813
Mood Creations Ltd, pg 829
The Palmer Group, pg 850
PostWorks, pg 860
PrimaLux Video Inc, pg 862
Judson Rosebush Co Inc, pg 877
Teatown Communications Group, pg 908
Visual Technologies Corp, pg 932

NORTH CAROLINA

Pat Appleson Studios Inc, pg 687
The Communications Group Inc, pg 729
Horizon Video Productions Inc, pg 781
Moving Pictures, pg 832
NASCAR Productions LLC, pg 835
Take One Productions Ltd, pg 906
Trailblazer Studios®, pg 917

OHIO

Aztec Video Productions, pg 700
Cuyahoga Community College Student Production Office (SPO), pg 736
Mills James Productions, pg 828
R&B Communications Inc, pg 870
Take 1 Media Services, pg 906
Vista Color Imaging Inc, pg 931

OKLAHOMA

Garman Productions LLC, pg 768
PDC Productions, pg 852

OREGON

Artbeats, pg 690
InterVision Media, pg 791
KTVA Productions, pg 802
Production West, pg 864

PENNSYLVANIA

Bang! Pictures Inc, pg 701
Center City Film & Video Inc, pg 719
FMP Media Solutions Inc, pg 763
Panta Rhei Media Inc, pg 851
Production Masters Inc (PMI), pg 864
Shore Manufacturing Co, pg 886
31st Street Studios, pg 912
The Videohouse Inc, pg 929
WPHL-TV, pg 942

SOUTH CAROLINA

American Production Services LLC, pg 684
Genesis Creative, pg 769
Venture Media, pg 925

TENNESSEE

Griffith Productions, pg 774
High-Tech Special Effects Inc, pg 779
Motion Picture Services, pg 831
Paradigm Marketing & Creative, pg 851
Scripps Networks, pg 882
Stage Post, pg 899

TEXAS

Anaphora Literary Press, pg 685
Biway Media, pg 706

The Editing Co, pg 750
Julye Newlin Productions Inc, pg 840
The Samuels Co, pg 879
South Coast Film & Video, pg 895
Stage Directions, pg 898

UTAH

ImageWorks Communications, pg 785
Strata™, pg 901

VIRGINIA

Advance Concepts Inc, pg 677
Allied Media Corp, pg 681
BES Studios, pg 704
CVW Event Productions, pg 736
Eagle Films, pg 749
Limelight Communications Inc, pg 808
Metro Productions, pg 824

WASHINGTON

Laser Fantasy/HECK Industries/Photon Manufacturing, pg 804
North-by-Northwest - A Digital Studio, pg 842
Osum Event Rentals, pg 848
Victory Studios, pg 927

WISCONSIN

Audio Visual of Milwaukee Inc, pg 694
5th Floor Recording Co, pg 760
Meridian Studios, pg 824
USAV Group Inc, pg 923
Video Wisconsin Inc, pg 929

WYOMING

Bridger Productions Inc, pg 710

PUERTO RICO

Stage Crew Audiovisual Inc, pg 898

ALBERTA

Global TV, pg 771

BRITISH COLUMBIA

Triad Communications Ltd, pg 918

NEWFOUNDLAND AND LABRADOR

Vidcraft Productions Ltd, pg 927

ONTARIO

ADS Media, pg 677
GAPC (General Assembly Production Centre), pg 768
GestureTek, pg 770
Image Video Services & Productions, pg 785
RB Productions, pg 870
Silver Creek Media Inc, pg 888

QUEBEC

Muse Entertainment Enterprises, pg 834

Special Effects Generator Distributors

ARIZONA

EAR Professional Audio/Video, pg 749
Troxell-CDI, pg 918

CALIFORNIA

Advanced Systems Group LLC, pg 677
Ametron Audio/Video, pg 684
Audio/Video Supply Inc, pg 694
BigFoot Mobile Systems, pg 705
BroadcastStore.com, pg 711
Diaquest, pg 741
SNAP, pg 891

COLORADO

Spectrum Audio Visual Services, pg 897

CONNECTICUT

Rockwell Communications Inc, pg 876

FLORIDA

Access Media Group, pg 673
Digital Video Systems, pg 742
Glanz Technologies Inc, pg 771
Hi-Tech Enterprises Inc, pg 779
Midtown Video Inc, pg 827
ONstage, pg 846

GEORGIA

Baker Audio Visual, pg 700
Stage Front Presentation Systems, pg 899

ILLINOIS

Allen Visual Systems Inc, pg 680
Joseph Electronics, pg 795

INDIANA

Sensory Technologies LLC, pg 884

KENTUCKY

Barney Miller's Inc, pg 827
NOR-COM Inc, pg 841

MARYLAND

Image Logic Corp, pg 785
Wiltronix Inc, pg 939

MASSACHUSETTS

Rule Boston Camera, pg 878

MICHIGAN

ASC Systems, pg 690
Digi Sign Design LLC, pg 741
On Stage Visuals, pg 846

MINNESOTA

Alpha Video & Audio Inc, pg 682

MISSOURI

Communitronics Corp, pg 729
Modern Communications Inc, pg 828
Production Support Services Inc, pg 864
Southwest Audio-Visual Inc, pg 895

NEVADA

Aardvark Video & Media Productions, pg 671

NEW JERSEY

A-V Services Inc, pg 671
Alltec Stores, a Vcom IMC Company, pg 681
Comprehensive Cable & Connectivity Co, pg 729
Diversified, pg 744
G&G Technologies Inc, pg 768
HamiltonBuhl, pg 775
MCCOM Inc, pg 820
PatchAmp, pg 852
Starlite, pg 900
SYMCO Inc, pg 905
Total Video Products Inc, pg 916
Video Corporation of America (VCA), pg 927
Wired 4 Sound Inc, pg 940

NEW YORK

Adwar Video, pg 678
Audio-Video Corp, pg 694
AV Workshop, pg 697
Design Audio Visual Inc, pg 741
Long Island Video Enterprises Live Inc, pg 811
Markertek Video Supply, pg 817
Tri-Ed Distribution Inc, pg 918
Visual Technologies Corp, pg 932

OHIO

Tri-State Audio Visual Co, pg 918

PENNSYLVANIA

Advanced AV LLC, pg 677
The Lerro Corp, pg 806
Morefield Communications Inc, pg 830
Shore Manufacturing Co, pg 886
Visual Sound Inc, pg 931

TENNESSEE

Lowrance Sound Co Inc, pg 812

TEXAS

AVES Audio Visual Systems Inc, pg 698
Biway Media, pg 706
Pro Video & Film Equipment Co Inc, pg 863
Videotex Systems Inc, pg 930

UTAH

RIA Corp, pg 874
TV Specialists Inc, pg 919

VIRGINIA

Avitecture Inc, pg 699
The Whitlock Group, pg 937

WASHINGTON

Laser Fantasy/HECK Industries/Photon Manufacturing, pg 804

WISCONSIN

Audio Visual of Milwaukee Inc, pg 694
Camera Corner Connecting Point, pg 715
Full Compass Systems, pg 767

VIDEO

Special Effects Generator Distributors (continued)

ALBERTA

McBain Camera Ltd, pg 820

ONTARIO

Corel Corp, pg 731
HD Source, pg 777
Majortech Inc, pg 815
Nationwide Audio Visual Co,
pg 837

QUEBEC

Panavideo Inc, pg 850

Special Effects Generator Manufacturers

CALIFORNIA

Blackmagic Design Pty Ltd, pg 707
Diaquest, pg 741
For-A Corp of America, pg 763
Grande Vitesse Systems Inc (GVS),
pg 773

COLORADO

Colorado Video Inc, pg 728

FLORIDA

Compuvideo Sales USA Ltd,
pg 729
Florical Systems Inc, pg 762
Tel-Test, pg 909

MARYLAND

Image Logic Corp, pg 785

MISSOURI

GlobalStreams™ Corp, pg 771

NEW JERSEY

CELCO, pg 719

PENNSYLVANIA

Shore Manufacturing Co, pg 886

TEXAS

Biway Media, pg 706

VERMONT

Polhemus, pg 859

WASHINGTON

Laser Fantasy/HECK
Industries/Photon Manufacturing,
pg 804

BRITISH COLUMBIA

Triad Communications Ltd, pg 918

ONTARIO

Corel Corp, pg 731

Special Effects Generator Rentals

ARIZONA

Merestone, pg 823

CALIFORNIA

Ametron Audio/Video, pg 684
Artichoke Productions, pg 690
Express Media Inc, pg 757
Reality Check Systems, pg 871
RetinaVision Productions, pg 874

CONNECTICUT

Videofilm Systems Inc, pg 929

FLORIDA

Access Media Group, pg 673
Christie Lites, pg 722
Paradise Show & Design Inc,
pg 851

GEORGIA

Stage Front Presentation Systems,
pg 899

ILLINOIS

Resolution Productions Group,
pg 874

KENTUCKY

Audio Visual Techniques Inc,
pg 695

MARYLAND

CPR MultiMedia Solutions, pg 732

MICHIGAN

Digi Sign Design LLC, pg 741
On Stage Visuals, pg 846

MISSOURI

Production Support Services Inc,
pg 864
Show-Me Audio-Visual, pg 887

NEVADA

Lefco Video Services Inc, pg 806

NEW JERSEY

Soundtracks Production Services
LLC, pg 895
Starlite, pg 900
Wired 4 Sound Inc, pg 940

NEW YORK

Design Audio Visual Inc, pg 741
LightSpace Studios, pg 808

OKLAHOMA

PDC Productions, pg 852

PENNSYLVANIA

Producers Management Television
(PMTV), pg 863

UTAH

TV Specialists Inc, pg 919

ONTARIO

JIB Shots Equipment Inc, pg 794

SASKATCHEWAN

plan9films, pg 857

Special Effects Generator Repairs

CALIFORNIA

BroadcastStore.com, pg 711
VMI Inc, pg 932

FLORIDA

ELC Sales & Service Inc, pg 752
Glanz Technologies Inc, pg 771
Hi-Tech Enterprises Inc, pg 779
Midtown Video Inc, pg 827

GEORGIA

Stage Front Presentation Systems,
pg 899

ILLINOIS

Allen Visual Systems Inc, pg 680
Beatty TeleVisual Productions,
pg 703

KENTUCKY

Barney Miller's Inc, pg 827
NOR-COM Inc, pg 841

MICHIGAN

TEL Systems LLC, pg 909

MINNESOTA

Alpha Video & Audio Inc, pg 682

MISSOURI

Southwest Audio-Visual Inc, pg 895

NEW JERSEY

Starlite, pg 900

NEW YORK

Visual Technologies Corp, pg 932

TEXAS

Biway Media, pg 706

UTAH

RIA Corp, pg 874
TV Specialists Inc, pg 919

WISCONSIN

Camera Corner Connecting Point,
pg 715
Full Compass Systems, pg 767

BRITISH COLUMBIA

Commercial Electronics Ltd, pg 728

Standards Conversion, see Video Standards Conversion

Still Frame Storage Device Distributors

ARIZONA

Troxell-CDI, pg 918

CALIFORNIA

Advanced Systems Group LLC,
pg 677
Ametron Audio/Video, pg 684
Audio/Video Supply Inc, pg 694

FLORIDA

Access Media Group, pg 673
Digital Video Systems, pg 742
Midtown Video Inc, pg 827
ONstage, pg 846

GEORGIA

Baker Audio Visual, pg 700
Stage Front Presentation Systems,
pg 899

ILLINOIS

Tele-Time Systems, pg 910

INDIANA

Sensory Technologies LLC, pg 884

MARYLAND

Wiltronix Inc, pg 939

MINNESOTA

Alpha Video & Audio Inc, pg 682
AVI Systems, pg 698

MISSOURI

Communitronics Corp, pg 729
Modern Communications Inc,
pg 828
Southwest Audio-Visual Inc, pg 895

NEW JERSEY

Advanced Imaging Concepts Inc,
pg 677
G&G Technologies Inc, pg 768
MCCOM Inc, pg 820
PatchAmp, pg 852
SYMCO Inc, pg 905
Total Video Products Inc, pg 916
Video Corporation of America
(VCA), pg 927

NEW YORK

Audio-Video Corp, pg 694
AV Workshop, pg 697
Long Island Video Enterprises Live
Inc, pg 811
Tri-Ed Distribution Inc, pg 918
Vision Identics Systems Inc, pg 930

NORTH CAROLINA

Camcor Inc, pg 715

PENNSYLVANIA

Advanced AV LLC, pg 677
The Lerro Corp, pg 806
Morefield Communications Inc,
pg 830
Visual Sound Inc, pg 931

TENNESSEE

Memphis Communications Corp,
pg 823

TEXAS

Pro Video & Film Equipment Co
Inc, pg 863
Videotex Systems Inc, pg 930

UTAH

RIA Corp, pg 874

VIRGINIA

Avitecture Inc, pg 699
Quince Imaging Inc, pg 868
The Whitlock Group, pg 937

WISCONSIN

Audio Visual of Milwaukee Inc,
  pg 694
Camera Corner Connecting Point,
  pg 715
Full Compass Systems, pg 767

ALBERTA

McBain Camera Ltd, pg 820

ONTARIO

HD Source, pg 777
Majortech Inc, pg 815

Still Frame Storage Device Manufacturers

CALIFORNIA

Grande Vitesse Systems Inc (GVS),
  pg 773
Hotronic Inc, pg 782
Sony Electronics Inc, pg 893

COLORADO

Colorado Video Inc, pg 728

ILLINOIS

EPIX Inc, pg 755

MISSOURI

GlobalStreams™ Corp, pg 771

NEW JERSEY

Advanced Imaging Concepts Inc,
  pg 677
Transparent Office Products LLC,
  pg 917

NEW YORK

Eastman Kodak Co, pg 750

PENNSYLVANIA

MicroImage Video Systems, pg 826

BRITISH COLUMBIA

Triad Communications Ltd, pg 918

ONTARIO

Corel Corp, pg 731

QUEBEC

Grass Valley, pg 773

Still Frame Storage Device Rentals

ARIZONA

Merestone, pg 823

CALIFORNIA

Artichoke Productions, pg 690
Bexel, an NEP Broadcast Services
  Company, pg 704

Express Media Inc, pg 757
Golden Gate Studios, pg 772
Lynch Communications, pg 813
Main Street Media Inc, pg 815
McCune Audio-Video-Lighting,
  pg 821
RetinaVision Productions, pg 874
Twin Peaks Creative, pg 920

COLORADO

Daylight Productions & Rentals,
  pg 739
Multimedia Audio Visual Inc,
  pg 833

FLORIDA

Access Media Group, pg 673
Jordan Klein Film & Video (JKFV),
  pg 795
ONstage, pg 846

GEORGIA

Stage Front Presentation Systems,
  pg 899

ILLINOIS

Backstar Creative Media Inc,
  pg 700
Beatty TeleVisual Productions,
  pg 703
On Site Video, pg 846
Resolution Productions Group,
  pg 874
Tele-Time Systems, pg 910

KENTUCKY

Audio Visual Techniques Inc,
  pg 695

LOUISIANA

Digital FX Inc, pg 742
Pace Systems, pg 849

MARYLAND

CPR MultiMedia Solutions, pg 732

MASSACHUSETTS

HOME Inc, pg 781
massAV, pg 819
Preston Productions Inc, pg 861

MINNESOTA

Alpha Video & Audio Inc, pg 682
AVI Systems, pg 698

MISSOURI

Southwest Audio-Visual Inc, pg 895

NEVADA

GES Audio Visual, pg 770
Lefco Video Services Inc, pg 806

NEW JERSEY

MediaMix Inc, pg 822
PLS Staging, pg 858

NEW YORK

Ace Video, pg 674
AV Workshop, pg 697
Long Island Video Enterprises Live
  Inc, pg 811
Manhattan Center Studios Inc,
  pg 816
WNET/New York Public Media,
  pg 940

OHIO

Lyon Video Inc, pg 813
Vista Color Imaging Inc, pg 931

OKLAHOMA

PDC Productions, pg 852

PENNSYLVANIA

FMP Media Solutions Inc, pg 763

TENNESSEE

Russ Sturgeon Productions/RSVP,
  pg 903

TEXAS

Alford Media Services, pg 680
Earl Miller Productions Inc, pg 827
Stage Directions, pg 898

VIRGINIA

CVW Event Productions, pg 736
Quince Imaging Inc, pg 868

WYOMING

Bridger Productions Inc, pg 710

ALBERTA

Global TV, pg 771

ONTARIO

HD Source, pg 777

SASKATCHEWAN

plan9films, pg 857

Still Frame Storage Device Repairs

CALIFORNIA

VMI Inc, pg 932

FLORIDA

Midtown Video Inc, pg 827

GEORGIA

Stage Front Presentation Systems,
  pg 899

ILLINOIS

Beatty TeleVisual Productions,
  pg 703
On Site Video, pg 846

MARYLAND

RTZ Audio Visual, pg 878

MICHIGAN

TEL Systems LLC, pg 909

MINNESOTA

Alpha Video & Audio Inc, pg 682
AVI Systems, pg 698

MISSOURI

Southwest Audio-Visual Inc, pg 895

NEW YORK

Ace Video, pg 674

NORTH CAROLINA

Camcor Inc, pg 715

UTAH

RIA Corp, pg 874

VIRGINIA

The Whitlock Group, pg 937

WISCONSIN

Full Compass Systems, pg 767

Still Printer Distributors

ARKANSAS

Jay S Stanley & Associates Inc,
  pg 899

CALIFORNIA

Ametron Audio/Video, pg 684

FLORIDA

Access Media Group, pg 673
Digital Video Systems, pg 742
Midtown Video Inc, pg 827

GEORGIA

Stage Front Presentation Systems,
  pg 899

ILLINOIS

Allen Visual Systems Inc, pg 680

INDIANA

Sensory Technologies LLC, pg 884

MASSACHUSETTS

Hunt's Photo & Video, pg 782

MINNESOTA

Alpha Video & Audio Inc, pg 682

MISSOURI

Modern Communications Inc,
  pg 828
Southwest Audio-Visual Inc, pg 895

NEBRASKA

VSA Inc, pg 933

NEVADA

Aardvark Video & Media
  Productions, pg 671

NEW JERSEY

Advanced Imaging Concepts Inc,
  pg 677
SYMCO Inc, pg 905
Total Video Products Inc, pg 916

NEW YORK

B&H Photo Video, pg 701
TecNec Distributing, pg 909
Vision Identics Systems Inc, pg 930

PENNSYLVANIA

Advanced AV LLC, pg 677
The Lerro Corp, pg 806

VIDEO

Still Printer Distributors (continued)

WISCONSIN

Camera Corner Connecting Point, pg 715
Full Compass Systems, pg 767

ALBERTA

Matrix Video Communications Corp (MVCC), pg 819

Still Printer Manufacturers

BRITISH COLUMBIA

Triad Communications Ltd, pg 918

Still Printer Rentals

ARIZONA

Merestone, pg 823

CALIFORNIA

Express Media Inc, pg 757
RetinaVision Productions, pg 874
VMI Inc, pg 932

GEORGIA

Stage Front Presentation Systems, pg 899

KENTUCKY

Audio Visual Techniques Inc, pg 695

MARYLAND

CPR MultiMedia Solutions, pg 732

MISSOURI

Show-Me Audio-Visual, pg 887

Still Printer Repairs

CALIFORNIA

Ametron Audio/Video, pg 684
VMI Inc, pg 932

FLORIDA

ELC Sales & Service Inc, pg 752

GEORGIA

Stage Front Presentation Systems, pg 899

ILLINOIS

Allen Visual Systems Inc, pg 680

MICHIGAN

TEL Systems LLC, pg 909

MINNESOTA

Alpha Video & Audio Inc, pg 682

MISSOURI

Southwest Audio-Visual Inc, pg 895

VIRGINIA

Avitecture Inc, pg 699

WISCONSIN

Camera Corner Connecting Point, pg 715
Full Compass Systems, pg 767

Stock-Shot Libraries, *see* Libraries—Film or Stock-Shot

Storage Vault Distributors

FLORIDA

Midtown Video Inc, pg 827

INDIANA

Sensory Technologies LLC, pg 884

KANSAS

Desktop Video Systems, pg 741

MASSACHUSETTS

University Products Inc, pg 923

MINNESOTA

Alpha Video & Audio Inc, pg 682

MISSOURI

Southwest Audio-Visual Inc, pg 895

PENNSYLVANIA

Advanced AV LLC, pg 677
The Lerro Corp, pg 806

WISCONSIN

Audio Visual of Milwaukee Inc, pg 694

Storage Vault Manufacturers

KANSAS

Desktop Video Systems, pg 741

MISSOURI

GlobalStreams™ Corp, pg 771

Storage Vault Rentals

CALIFORNIA

Roundabout Entertainment Inc, pg 878

NORTH CAROLINA

Take One Productions Ltd, pg 906

Storage Vault Repairs

MICHIGAN

TEL Systems LLC, pg 909

Studio Photography, *see* Photography—Studio

Switcher & Matrix— Analog & Digital Distributors

ALABAMA

PESA, pg 855

ARIZONA

EAR Professional Audio/Video, pg 749

ARKANSAS

Jay S Stanley & Associates Inc, pg 899

CALIFORNIA

Ametron Audio/Video, pg 684
BigFoot Mobile Systems, pg 705
BroadcastStore.com, pg 711
California Tape Products Inc, pg 714
Cibola Systems, pg 723
JD Audio Visual Inc, pg 793
Marshall Electronics Inc, pg 817
Media Control Systems LLC, pg 821
SNAP, pg 891
Southern California Sound Image Inc, pg 895
Stanislaus AV Inc, pg 899
Videobotics, pg 929
VMI Inc, pg 932

COLORADO

Daylight Productions & Rentals, pg 739
Spectrum Audio Visual Services, pg 897

FLORIDA

Access Media Group, pg 673
Altel Systems Group Inc, pg 682
Digital Video Systems, pg 742
Harris Corp, pg 776
Hi-Tech Enterprises Inc, pg 779
Midtown Video Inc, pg 827
Multicom Inc, pg 833

GEORGIA

Clark, pg 725
Stage Front Presentation Systems, pg 899

ILLINOIS

Allen Visual Systems Inc, pg 680
Joseph Electronics, pg 795
Quintessence Audio Ltd, pg 868

INDIANA

Sensory Technologies LLC, pg 884
SHP Electronics, pg 887

KENTUCKY

NOR-COM Inc, pg 841

LOUISIANA

Techkno Integration & Design Services LLC, pg 908

MAINE

Independent Audio Inc, pg 786

MARYLAND

Human Circuit, pg 782
Wiltronix Inc, pg 939

MASSACHUSETTS

Antronics Inc, pg 686
Rule Boston Camera, pg 878

MICHIGAN

ASC Systems, pg 690
On Stage Visuals, pg 846

MINNESOTA

Alpha Video & Audio Inc, pg 682

MISSOURI

Modern Communications Inc, pg 828
Southwest Audio-Visual Inc, pg 895

NEBRASKA

ATV Research Inc, pg 692
VSA Inc, pg 933

NEW JERSEY

Alltec Stores, a Vcom IMC Company, pg 681
Diversified, pg 744
Earl Girls Inc, pg 749
HamiltonBuhl, pg 775
MCCOM Inc, pg 820
PatchAmp, pg 852
Starlite, pg 900
SYMCO Inc, pg 905
Total Video Products Inc, pg 916
Wired 4 Sound Inc, pg 940

NEW YORK

All Mobile Video Inc, pg 680
BTX Technologies, pg 712
Design Audio Visual Inc, pg 741
General Audio-Visual Inc (GAVI), pg 769
HAVE Inc, pg 777
Markertek Video Supply, pg 817
Stampede Presentation Products Inc, pg 899
TecNec Distributing, pg 909
Visual Word Systems Inc, pg 932

OHIO

ITA Audio Visual Solutions, pg 791

PENNSYLVANIA

AccuWeather Inc, pg 674
Advanced AV LLC, pg 677
The Lerro Corp, pg 806
Vistacom Inc, pg 931

RHODE ISLAND

Shanix Inc, pg 885

TENNESSEE

Allstar Audio Systems Inc, pg 681
Lowrance Sound Co Inc, pg 812
Technical Support Systems LLC, pg 908
Zion Music Group, pg 945

TEXAS

Audio Visual Technologies Group (AVTG), pg 695
AVES Audio Visual Systems Inc, pg 698
Data Projections Inc, pg 738
Digital Display Solutions Inc, pg 742
Pro Video & Film Equipment Co Inc, pg 863

Sundance Systems, Fibox Products Division, pg 904
Tarpley Media Systems, pg 907
Videotex Systems Inc, pg 930

VIRGINIA

Quince Imaging Inc, pg 868

WASHINGTON

Telect Inc, pg 910

WISCONSIN

Audio Visual of Milwaukee Inc, pg 694
Camera Corner Connecting Point, pg 715
Full Compass Systems, pg 767
Safe Harbor Computers, pg 879

MANITOBA

Advance Pro, pg 677

ONTARIO

Cinema Stage Inc, pg 724
Westbury National Show Systems Ltd, pg 936

Switcher & Matrix— Analog & Digital Manufacturers

ALABAMA

PESA, pg 855

ARIZONA

Applied Integration Corp, pg 687
Covid Inc, pg 732

CALIFORNIA

ALTINEX Inc, pg 682
AMX® by Harman, pg 685
Extron Electronics, pg 758
For-A Corp of America, pg 763
Gefen, pg 769
Hosa Technology Inc, pg 781
Marshall Electronics Inc, pg 817
Media Control Systems LLC, pg 821
RGB Spectrum, pg 874
Wohler Technologies Inc, pg 940

COLORADO

Liberty AV Solutions, pg 807

FLORIDA

Compuvideo Sales USA Ltd, pg 729
Tel-Test, pg 909

GEORGIA

Analog Way Inc, pg 685

MICHIGAN

Leightronix Inc, pg 806

MINNESOTA

Vaddio, pg 924

MISSOURI

GlobalStreams™ Corp, pg 771
Link Electronics Inc, pg 809

NEW JERSEY

Crestron Electronics Inc, pg 734
FSR Inc, pg 766
Kramer Electronics USA Inc, pg 801

NEW MEXICO

Adrienne Electronics Corp (AEC), pg 676
Burst Electronics Inc, pg 713

NEW YORK

Key Digital Systems, pg 798
Laird Digital Cinema, pg 803
Markertek Video Supply, pg 817
MultiDyne Video & Fiber Optics Systems, pg 833
Vicon Industries Inc, pg 926

NORTH CAROLINA

Crest Electronics Inc, pg 734

OHIO

TV One Multimedia Solutions, pg 919

PENNSYLVANIA

MicroImage Video Systems, pg 826

TENNESSEE

Adtec Digital Inc, pg 677

TEXAS

Sundance Systems, Fibox Products Division, pg 904

UTAH

Utah Scientific Inc, pg 924

VIRGINIA

Quince Imaging Inc, pg 868

WASHINGTON

Telect Inc, pg 910

BRITISH COLUMBIA

Richmond Sound Design Ltd, pg 875

Switcher & Matrix— Analog & Digital Rentals

ALABAMA

Audio-Video Resources Inc, pg 694

ARIZONA

Merestone, pg 823
Video West Inc, pg 929

CALIFORNIA

Ametron Audio/Video, pg 684
Artichoke Productions, pg 690
AV Guys, pg 697
Express Media Inc, pg 757
Full Moon & High Tide Productions & Studios, pg 767
Golden Gate Studios, pg 772
JD Audio Visual Inc, pg 793
MSI Production Services, pg 832
Muse Presentation Technologies, pg 834
RetinaVision Productions, pg 874

Voice & Video Rentals, pg 932
Westcoast Video Productions Inc, pg 936

CONNECTICUT

Videofilm Systems Inc, pg 929

FLORIDA

Access Media Group, pg 673
Paradise Show & Design Inc, pg 851
Sight & Sound Productions, pg 887

GEORGIA

Analog Way Inc, pg 685
Stage Front Presentation Systems, pg 899

ILLINOIS

Meetinghouse Event Design & Production, pg 823
Resolution Productions Group, pg 874
Staging Resources Inc, pg 899

KENTUCKY

Audio Visual Techniques Inc, pg 695

MARYLAND

CPR MultiMedia Solutions, pg 732
Event Tech, pg 756
Kramer Communications Video Production, pg 801

MASSACHUSETTS

Preston Productions Inc, pg 861

MICHIGAN

On Stage Visuals, pg 846

MISSOURI

Show-Me Audio-Visual, pg 887

NEBRASKA

Dog & Pony Productions Inc, pg 744

NEW JERSEY

Earl Girls Inc, pg 749
Starlite, pg 900
Wired 4 Sound Inc, pg 940

NEW YORK

All Mobile Video Inc, pg 680
Big Foot Productions Inc, pg 705
CP Communications, pg 732
Design Audio Visual Inc, pg 741
Visual Word Systems Inc, pg 932

NORTH CAROLINA

All Pro Media Inc, pg 680

NORTH DAKOTA

Media Productions, pg 822

OKLAHOMA

PDC Productions, pg 852

OREGON

Picture This Production Services, pg 856

PENNSYLVANIA

FMP Media Solutions Inc, pg 763
Innovision Media Group, pg 788
Upstage Video, pg 923

TENNESSEE

Allstar Audio Systems Inc, pg 681
Technical Support Systems LLC, pg 908

TEXAS

Alford Media Services, pg 680
Bright Star Productions Inc, pg 710
Stage Directions, pg 898

VIRGINIA

Advance Concepts Inc, pg 677
Quince Imaging Inc, pg 868

PUERTO RICO

Stage Crew Audiovisual Inc, pg 898

ONTARIO

JIB Shots Equipment Inc, pg 794
Westbury National Show Systems Ltd, pg 936

Switcher & Matrix— Analog & Digital Repairs

FLORIDA

ELC Sales & Service Inc, pg 752
Hi-Tech Enterprises Inc, pg 779

GEORGIA

Stage Front Presentation Systems, pg 899

ILLINOIS

Midwest Digital Corp, pg 827

KENTUCKY

NOR-COM Inc, pg 841

MICHIGAN

TEL Systems LLC, pg 909

NEW JERSEY

Starlite, pg 900

OREGON

All Service Musical Electronics Repair, pg 680

TENNESSEE

Technical Support Systems LLC, pg 908

TEXAS

Tarpley Media Systems, pg 907

ONTARIO

Westbury National Show Systems Ltd, pg 936

VIDEO

Switcher & Matrix— Mechanical & Electronic Distributors

ARIZONA

EAR Professional Audio/Video, pg 749

CALIFORNIA

Ametron Audio/Video, pg 684
BigFoot Mobile Systems, pg 705
BroadcastStore.com, pg 711
ChronTrol Corp, pg 723
JD Audio Visual Inc, pg 793
Media Control Systems LLC, pg 821
SNAP, pg 891
Stanislaus AV Inc, pg 899
VMI Inc, pg 932

COLORADO

Daylight Productions & Rentals, pg 739

FLORIDA

Access Media Group, pg 673
Altel Systems Group Inc, pg 682
Digital Video Systems, pg 742
Hi-Tech Enterprises Inc, pg 779
Midtown Video Inc, pg 827

GEORGIA

Stage Front Presentation Systems, pg 899

ILLINOIS

Allen Visual Systems Inc, pg 680
Joseph Electronics, pg 795

INDIANA

Sensory Technologies LLC, pg 884
SHP Electronics, pg 887

KENTUCKY

NOR-COM Inc, pg 841

LOUISIANA

Techkno Integration & Design Services LLC, pg 908

MAINE

Independent Audio Inc, pg 786

MARYLAND

Human Circuit, pg 782

MASSACHUSETTS

Antronics Inc, pg 686
Rule Boston Camera, pg 878

MICHIGAN

ASC Systems, pg 690
On Stage Visuals, pg 846

MINNESOTA

Alpha Video & Audio Inc, pg 682

MISSOURI

Conference Technologies Inc, pg 730
Modern Communications Inc, pg 828
Southwest Audio-Visual Inc, pg 895

NEBRASKA

ATV Research Inc, pg 692
VSA Inc, pg 933

NEW JERSEY

Diversified, pg 744
FSR Inc, pg 766
HamiltonBuhl, pg 775
MCCOM Inc, pg 820
PatchAmp, pg 852
Starlite, pg 900
SYMCO Inc, pg 905
Total Video Products Inc, pg 916
Wired 4 Sound Inc, pg 940

NEW YORK

Design Audio Visual Inc, pg 741
General Audio-Visual Inc (GAVI), pg 769
HAVE Inc, pg 777
Markertek Video Supply, pg 817
TecNec Distributing, pg 909
Visual Word Systems Inc, pg 932

PENNSYLVANIA

Advanced AV LLC, pg 677
Bernie's Photo Center, pg 704
The Lerro Corp, pg 806
Vistacom Inc, pg 931

TENNESSEE

Allstar Audio Systems Inc, pg 681
Lowrance Sound Co Inc, pg 812
Technical Support Systems LLC, pg 908

TEXAS

Audio Visual Technologies Group (AVTG), pg 695
Data Projections Inc, pg 738
Digital Display Solutions Inc, pg 742
Pro Video & Film Equipment Co Inc, pg 863
Sundance Systems, Fibox Products Division, pg 904
Tarpley Media Systems, pg 907

VIRGINIA

Quince Imaging Inc, pg 868

WASHINGTON

Telect Inc, pg 910

WISCONSIN

Audio Visual of Milwaukee Inc, pg 694
Camera Corner Connecting Point, pg 715
Full Compass Systems, pg 767

MANITOBA

Advance Pro, pg 677

ONTARIO

Cinema Stage Inc, pg 724

Switcher & Matrix— Mechanical & Electronic Manufacturers

ARIZONA

NKK Switches of America Inc, pg 841

CALIFORNIA

ALTINEX Inc, pg 682
ChronTrol Corp, pg 723
DiCon Fiberoptics Inc, pg 741
Dow-Key Microwave Corp, pg 746
For-A Corp of America, pg 763
Hosa Technology Inc, pg 781
Media Control Systems LLC, pg 821
Wohler Technologies Inc, pg 940

FLORIDA

Compuvideo Sales USA Ltd, pg 729
Tel-Test, pg 909

GEORGIA

Analog Way Inc, pg 685

MINNESOTA

Vaddio, pg 924

NEBRASKA

Veetronix Inc, pg 925

NEW JERSEY

FSR Inc, pg 766
Kramer Electronics USA Inc, pg 801

NEW MEXICO

Adrienne Electronics Corp (AEC), pg 676
Burst Electronics Inc, pg 713

NEW YORK

Markertek Video Supply, pg 817
MultiDyne Video & Fiber Optics Systems, pg 833

NORTH CAROLINA

Crest Electronics Inc, pg 734

OHIO

Network Technologies Inc, pg 838

PENNSYLVANIA

MicroImage Video Systems, pg 826

TEXAS

Sundance Systems, Fibox Products Division, pg 904

VIRGINIA

Quince Imaging Inc, pg 868

WASHINGTON

Telect Inc, pg 910

Switcher & Matrix— Mechanical & Electronic Rentals

ARIZONA

Merestone, pg 823

CALIFORNIA

Ametron Audio/Video, pg 684
Express Media Inc, pg 757
Golden Gate Studios, pg 772
JD Audio Visual Inc, pg 793
Muse Presentation Technologies, pg 834
RetinaVision Productions, pg 874

FLORIDA

Access Media Group, pg 673
Paradise Show & Design Inc, pg 851

GEORGIA

Analog Way Inc, pg 685
Stage Front Presentation Systems, pg 899

KENTUCKY

Audio Visual Techniques Inc, pg 695

MARYLAND

CPR MultiMedia Solutions, pg 732
Event Tech, pg 756

MASSACHUSETTS

Preston Productions Inc, pg 861

MICHIGAN

On Stage Visuals, pg 846

MISSOURI

Show-Me Audio-Visual, pg 887

NEW JERSEY

Starlite, pg 900
Wired 4 Sound Inc, pg 940

NEW YORK

CP Communications, pg 732
Design Audio Visual Inc, pg 741
Visual Word Systems Inc, pg 932

NORTH DAKOTA

Media Productions, pg 822

OKLAHOMA

PDC Productions, pg 852

PENNSYLVANIA

Innovision Media Group, pg 788

TENNESSEE

Allstar Audio Systems Inc, pg 681
Technical Support Systems LLC, pg 908

VIRGINIA

Quince Imaging Inc, pg 868

PUERTO RICO

Stage Crew Audiovisual Inc, pg 898

BRITISH COLUMBIA

Inspired Image Picture Co (IIPC), pg 788

ONTARIO

JIB Shots Equipment Inc, pg 794

Switcher & Matrix— Mechanical & Electronic Repairs

FLORIDA

ELC Sales & Service Inc, pg 752

GEORGIA

Stage Front Presentation Systems, pg 899

ILLINOIS

Midwest Digital Corp, pg 827

KENTUCKY

NOR-COM Inc, pg 841

MICHIGAN

TEL Systems LLC, pg 909

NEW JERSEY

Starlite, pg 900

OREGON

All Service Musical Electronics Repair, pg 680

TENNESSEE

Technical Support Systems LLC, pg 908

TEXAS

Tarpley Media Systems, pg 907

Syndication

ARIZONA

Merestone, pg 823

CALIFORNIA

Custom Video Productions Inc, pg 736
Full Moon & High Tide Productions & Studios, pg 767
JDS Video & Media Productions Inc, pg 793
New & Unique Videos™, pg 839
Point.360, pg 858
QRS Software Services, pg 867
Visions Plus, pg 931
The Wyland Group, pg 942

COLORADO

Flashback Media Productions, pg 762

FLORIDA

National Teleproductions Inc, pg 837

GEORGIA

Guerrilla Productions LLC, pg 774
On-Line Productions, pg 845

ILLINOIS

Moviecraft Inc, pg 831

LOUISIANA

Great Chefs/Leisure Jazz Video, pg 773
Leisure Video, pg 806

MASSACHUSETTS

Extreme Reach Inc, pg 757

MICHIGAN

K&R's Recording Studios Inc, pg 796

NEW HAMPSHIRE

Channell One Video, pg 720

NEW JERSEY

Broadcast Center Studios, pg 710
MiB MediaWorks, pg 825
Suede Interactive, pg 903

NEW YORK

Adwar Video, pg 678
Animotion Inc, pg 685
The Big House Group, pg 705
Jalbert Productions International, pg 792
Teatown Communications Group, pg 908
VIEW Inc (Video International Entertainment World Inc), pg 930

NORTH CAROLINA

Pat Appleson Studios Inc, pg 687
Crystal Pictures Inc, pg 735
NASCAR Productions LLC, pg 835

OHIO

Aztec Video Productions, pg 700

TENNESSEE

Motion Picture Services, pg 831
Scripps Networks, pg 882
Stage Post, pg 899

TEXAS

Phillips Media Source, pg 855
The Samuels Co, pg 879

VIRGINIA

CACI Integrated Communications, pg 713

WASHINGTON

Victory Studios, pg 927

WISCONSIN

Wisconsin Public Television, pg 940

WYOMING

Bridger Productions Inc, pg 710

ALBERTA

Global TV, pg 771

ONTARIO

Canamedia Inc, pg 715
GAPC (General Assembly Production Centre), pg 768

Talent & Property Agencies—Television

ALASKA

Alaska Media Pros LLC, pg 679

ARIZONA

Film Creations Ltd, pg 760
Merestone, pg 823

ARKANSAS

White Diamond Productions LLC, pg 937

CALIFORNIA

Creative Artists Agency LLC, pg 733
Havas Edge, pg 777
International Contact Inc, pg 790
JDS Video & Media Productions Inc, pg 793
KTVU-Retail Services, pg 802
The Location Connection Inc, pg 810
Joseph Nicoletti Consulting-Promotion, pg 841
Palardo Productions, pg 850
QRS Software Services, pg 867
Sahara Records & Filmworks Entertainment Co, pg 879
Santa Barbara Location Services, pg 880
SonicPool, pg 892

COLORADO

Flashback Media Productions, pg 762

CONNECTICUT

Ironik Design & Post, pg 791

HAWAII

Media Bridge Gamekids, pg 821

LOUISIANA

Digital FX Inc, pg 742
Great Chefs/Leisure Jazz Video, pg 773
Leisure Video, pg 806

MASSACHUSETTS

Preston Productions Inc, pg 861

MICHIGAN

K&R's Recording Studios Inc, pg 796

MINNESOTA

Moore Creative Talent Inc, pg 830

NEW HAMPSHIRE

Channell One Video, pg 720
Chip Taylor Communications LLC, pg 907

NEW JERSEY

Broadcast Center Studios, pg 710
Suede Interactive, pg 903

NEW YORK

InterNation Inc, pg 789
WNET/New York Public Media, pg 940

OHIO

Aztec Video Productions, pg 700
R&B Communications Inc, pg 870

RHODE ISLAND

Sound-FX-Design, pg 894

TENNESSEE

Anode Inc, pg 686
Motion Picture Services, pg 831
Stage Post, pg 899

TEXAS

The Campbell Agency, pg 715

VIRGINIA

CACI Integrated Communications, pg 713
Studio Center Corp, pg 902

WISCONSIN

Video Wisconsin Inc, pg 929

WYOMING

Bridger Productions Inc, pg 710

Tape Duplicator Distributors

ARKANSAS

White Diamond Productions LLC, pg 937

CALIFORNIA

Advanced Systems Group LLC, pg 677
Ametron Audio/Video, pg 684
Audio/Video Supply Inc, pg 694
BigFoot Mobile Systems, pg 705
BroadcastStore.com, pg 711
Christy's Editorial, pg 723
QRS Software Services, pg 867
SNAP, pg 891
Westlake Recording Studios, pg 936

COLORADO

Spectrum Audio Visual Services, pg 897

FLORIDA

Access Media Group, pg 673
Digital Video Systems, pg 742
Harris Corp, pg 776
Hi-Tech Import Export Corp, pg 779
Midtown Video Inc, pg 827
ONstage, pg 846
Recording Media & Equipment Inc (RM&E), pg 872

GEORGIA

Stage Front Presentation Systems, pg 899

ILLINOIS

Tele-Time Systems, pg 910

INDIANA

Lee Co Inc, pg 805
Sensory Technologies LLC, pg 884
SHP Electronics, pg 887

VIDEO

Tape Duplicator Distributors (continued)

KENTUCKY

Barney Miller's Inc, pg 827
NOR-COM Inc, pg 841

MAINE

Headlight Audio Visual Inc, pg 777

MARYLAND

RTZ Audio Visual, pg 878

MASSACHUSETTS

Rule Boston Camera, pg 878

MINNESOTA

Alpha Video & Audio Inc, pg 682
Cinequipt Inc, pg 724

MISSISSIPPI

Bowie Audio Visual Enterprises Inc,
  pg 709
Jasper Ewing & Sons Inc, pg 757

MISSOURI

Conference Technologies Inc,
  pg 730
Modern Communications Inc,
  pg 828
Southwest Audio-Visual Inc, pg 895

NEVADA

Aardvark Video & Media
  Productions, pg 671

NEW JERSEY

Audio Visual Associates, pg 694
Audio Visual Dynamics®, pg 694
Diversified, pg 744
G&G Technologies Inc, pg 768
HamiltonBuhl, pg 775
MCCOM Inc, pg 820
PatchAmp, pg 852
Reed Presentations Inc (RPI),
  pg 872
Starlite, pg 900
Total Video Products Inc, pg 916
Video Corporation of America
  (VCA), pg 927

NEW YORK

AV Workshop, pg 697
B&H Photo Video, pg 701
Burlington A/V Recording Media,
  pg 712
Gaylord Archival, pg 768
HAVE Inc, pg 777
TecNec Distributing, pg 909

NORTH CAROLINA

Camcor Inc, pg 715
Strategic Connections, pg 901

OHIO

iVideo Technologies, pg 792

PENNSYLVANIA

Advanced AV LLC, pg 677
Audio Visions Inc, pg 694
Audio Visual Communications Inc,
  pg 694
J E Foss Co, pg 764

Grise Audio Visual Center Inc,
  pg 774
The Lerro Corp, pg 806
Morefield Communications Inc,
  pg 830

TENNESSEE

Lowrance Sound Co Inc, pg 812
Memphis Communications Corp,
  pg 823
Technical Support Systems LLC,
  pg 908
Zion Music Group, pg 945

TEXAS

Pro Video & Film Equipment Co
  Inc, pg 863
Tarpley Media Systems, pg 907

UTAH

RIA Corp, pg 874

VIRGINIA

Lee Hartman & Sons Inc, pg 805
The Whitlock Group, pg 937

WISCONSIN

Audio Visual of Milwaukee Inc,
  pg 694
Full Compass Systems, pg 767

PUERTO RICO

Bonnin Electronics Inc, pg 708

ALBERTA

McBain Camera Ltd, pg 820

MANITOBA

Inland Audio Visual Ltd, pg 788

ONTARIO

Nationwide Audio Visual Co,
  pg 837
Westbury National Show Systems
  Ltd, pg 936

Tape Duplicator Manufacturers

CALIFORNIA

QRS Software Services, pg 867
Sony Electronics Inc, pg 893
TiVo Corp, pg 914

GEORGIA

Visix™ Inc, pg 931

MICHIGAN

Leightronix Inc, pg 806

NEW JERSEY

CELCO, pg 719

NEW YORK

TecNec Distributing, pg 909

TEXAS

World Media Group Inc, pg 941

BRITISH COLUMBIA

Triad Communications Ltd, pg 918

Tape Duplicator Rentals

ARIZONA

Merestone, pg 823
Metropolitan Audio-Visual Inc,
  pg 824

ARKANSAS

White Diamond Productions LLC,
  pg 937

CALIFORNIA

Advanced Media LLC, pg 677
AlphaDogs Inc, pg 682
Ametron Audio/Video, pg 684
Bexel, an NEP Broadcast Services
  Company, pg 704
Crystal Pyramid Productions™,
  pg 735
Express Media Inc, pg 757
Golden Gate Studios, pg 772
Maximus Media Inc, pg 820
Munday & Collins AV, pg 834
RetinaVision Productions, pg 874
Total Creative, pg 916
Twin Peaks Creative, pg 920
Voice & Video Rentals, pg 932

COLORADO

Daylight Productions & Rentals,
  pg 739
Spectrum Audio Visual Services,
  pg 897

CONNECTICUT

A/V Davey, pg 697
Videofilm Systems Inc, pg 929

DELAWARE

Ken-Del Productions Inc, pg 797

FLORIDA

Jordan Klein Film & Video (JKFV),
  pg 795
ONstage, pg 846

GEORGIA

ON Services, a GES Company,
  pg 846
Stage Front Presentation Systems,
  pg 899

KENTUCKY

The PPS Group, pg 860

LOUISIANA

Digital FX Inc, pg 742

MARYLAND

CPR MultiMedia Solutions, pg 732
RTZ Audio Visual, pg 878

MASSACHUSETTS

Capron Lighting & Sound Co Inc,
  pg 716
massAV, pg 819

MICHIGAN

Digi Sign Design LLC, pg 741
K&R All Media Productions LLC,
  pg 796

MINNESOTA

Alpha Video & Audio Inc, pg 682
AVI Systems, pg 698

MISSISSIPPI

Bowie Audio Visual Enterprises Inc,
  pg 709

MISSOURI

ITC, pg 791
Show-Me Audio-Visual, pg 887
Southwest Audio-Visual Inc, pg 895

NEVADA

JCS Video Productions, pg 793

NEW JERSEY

Audio Visual Associates, pg 694
Audio Visual Dynamics®, pg 694
MediaMix Inc, pg 822
Starlite, pg 900
Video Corporation of America
  (VCA), pg 927

NEW MEXICO

Production Outfitters, pg 864

NEW YORK

AV Workshop, pg 697
CMI Communications, pg 727
WNET/New York Public Media,
  pg 940

NORTH CAROLINA

Duke Media Services, pg 747
Special Event Services, pg 896
Strategic Connections, pg 901
Take One Productions Ltd, pg 906

OHIO

Hughie's Event Production Services,
  pg 782
Mills James Productions, pg 828
Vista Color Imaging Inc, pg 931

PENNSYLVANIA

Audio Visions Inc, pg 694
Audio Visual Communications Inc,
  pg 694
FMP Media Solutions Inc, pg 763
Grise Audio Visual Center Inc,
  pg 774
Innovision Media Group, pg 788

SOUTH CAROLINA

Sound & Images Inc, pg 893

TENNESSEE

Memphis Communications Corp,
  pg 823
Technical Support Systems LLC,
  pg 908

TEXAS

JSAV, pg 795
Earl Miller Productions Inc, pg 827
Stage Directions, pg 898

WASHINGTON

Kostov Productions, pg 801

WISCONSIN

Full Compass Systems, pg 767

WYOMING

Bridger Productions Inc, pg 710

ALBERTA
Global TV, pg 771

BRITISH COLUMBIA
Commercial Electronics Ltd, pg 728

MANITOBA
Inland Audio Visual Ltd, pg 788

ONTARIO
Wanted! Sound + Picture, pg 933
Westbury National Show Systems Ltd, pg 936

Tape Duplicator Repairs

CALIFORNIA
Advanced Media LLC, pg 677
Ametron Audio/Video, pg 684
BigFoot Mobile Systems, pg 705
BroadcastStore.com, pg 711
VMI Inc, pg 932

FLORIDA
ELC Sales & Service Inc, pg 752
JT Communications, pg 795

GEORGIA
Stage Front Presentation Systems, pg 899

ILLINOIS
Beatty TeleVisual Productions, pg 703

KENTUCKY
Barney Miller's Inc, pg 827
NOR-COM Inc, pg 841

MARYLAND
RTZ Audio Visual, pg 878

MICHIGAN
TEL Systems LLC, pg 909

MINNESOTA
Alpha Video & Audio Inc, pg 682
AVI Systems, pg 698

MISSOURI
Southwest Audio-Visual Inc, pg 895

NEW JERSEY
Starlite, pg 900

NORTH CAROLINA
Camcor Inc, pg 715

OHIO
Tri-State Audio Visual Co, pg 918

OREGON
All Service Musical Electronics Repair, pg 680

PENNSYLVANIA
Audio Visions Inc, pg 694
J E Foss Co, pg 764
Visual Sound Inc, pg 931

TENNESSEE
Memphis Communications Corp, pg 823
Technical Support Systems LLC, pg 908

TEXAS
Audio Visual Technologies Group (AVTG), pg 695
Tarpley Media Systems, pg 907

UTAH
RIA Corp, pg 874

VIRGINIA
The Whitlock Group, pg 937

WISCONSIN
Full Compass Systems, pg 767

MANITOBA
Inland Audio Visual Ltd, pg 788

ONTARIO
Westbury National Show Systems Ltd, pg 936

Tape Eraser Distributors

ARKANSAS
White Diamond Productions LLC, pg 937

CALIFORNIA
Ametron Audio/Video, pg 684
California Tape Products Inc, pg 714
Christy's Editorial, pg 723
QRS Software Services, pg 867
SNAP, pg 891
Westlake Recording Studios, pg 936

FLORIDA
Digital Video Systems, pg 742
Harris Corp, pg 776
Hi-Tech Import Export Corp, pg 779
Midtown Video Inc, pg 827
Recording Media & Equipment Inc (RM&E), pg 872
Sonar Radio Corp, pg 892

GEORGIA
Stage Front Presentation Systems, pg 899

INDIANA
Lee Co Inc, pg 805
Sensory Technologies LLC, pg 884

KENTUCKY
NOR-COM Inc, pg 841

MASSACHUSETTS
Rule Boston Camera, pg 878

MINNESOTA
Alpha Video & Audio Inc, pg 682

MISSOURI
Modern Communications Inc, pg 828
Southwest Audio-Visual Inc, pg 895

NEW JERSEY
AlltecPro, pg 681
AV Bluebook, pg 696
HamiltonBuhl, pg 775
Starlite, pg 900
Vcom IMC, pg 925

NEW YORK
B&H Photo Video, pg 701
HAVE Inc, pg 777
Markertek Video Supply, pg 817
TecNec Distributing, pg 909

PENNSYLVANIA
Advanced AV LLC, pg 677
Brodart Co, pg 711
J E Foss Co, pg 764
The Lerro Corp, pg 806

TENNESSEE
Lowrance Sound Co Inc, pg 812

TEXAS
Pro Video & Film Equipment Co Inc, pg 863

VIRGINIA
Lee Hartman & Sons Inc, pg 805

WISCONSIN
Audio Visual of Milwaukee Inc, pg 694
Full Compass Systems, pg 767

Tape Eraser Manufacturers

CALIFORNIA
Garner Products Inc, pg 768
QRS Software Services, pg 867

FLORIDA
Sonar Radio Corp, pg 892

ILLINOIS
Research Technology International (RTI), pg 873

INDIANA
R B Annis Instruments Inc, pg 686

NEBRASKA
Data Security Inc, pg 738

Tape Eraser Rentals

ARKANSAS
White Diamond Productions LLC, pg 937

CALIFORNIA
Ametron Audio/Video, pg 684
Artichoke Productions, pg 690
Garner Products Inc, pg 768
Golden Gate Studios, pg 772
Maximus Media Inc, pg 820
Twin Peaks Creative, pg 920

CONNECTICUT
A/V Davey, pg 697
Videofilm Systems Inc, pg 929

GEORGIA
Stage Front Presentation Systems, pg 899

MARYLAND
CPR MultiMedia Solutions, pg 732

MICHIGAN
Digi Sign Design LLC, pg 741
K&R All Media Productions LLC, pg 796

Tape Eraser Repairs

CALIFORNIA
Garner Products Inc, pg 768

GEORGIA
Stage Front Presentation Systems, pg 899

KENTUCKY
NOR-COM Inc, pg 841

MICHIGAN
TEL Systems LLC, pg 909

OREGON
All Service Musical Electronics Repair, pg 680

Tape Loading Equipment Distributors

ARKANSAS
White Diamond Productions LLC, pg 937

FLORIDA
Digital Video Systems, pg 742
ONstage, pg 846
Recording Media & Equipment Inc (RM&E), pg 872

INDIANA
Sensory Technologies LLC, pg 884

KENTUCKY
NOR-COM Inc, pg 841

NEW JERSEY
HamiltonBuhl, pg 775
Starlite, pg 900

NEW YORK
B&H Photo Video, pg 701

PENNSYLVANIA
Advanced AV LLC, pg 677
The Lerro Corp, pg 806

TENNESSEE
Lowrance Sound Co Inc, pg 812

VIRGINIA
Lee Hartman & Sons Inc, pg 805

WISCONSIN
Audio Visual of Milwaukee Inc, pg 694

VIDEO

Tape Loading Equipment Rentals

ARKANSAS

White Diamond Productions LLC, pg 937

CONNECTICUT

Videofilm Systems Inc, pg 929

FLORIDA

ONstage, pg 846

Tape Loading Equipment Repairs

KENTUCKY

NOR-COM Inc, pg 841

MICHIGAN

TEL Systems LLC, pg 909

WISCONSIN

Full Compass Systems, pg 767

Teleconferencing, see Virtual Conferencing

Teleconferencing Equipment Distributors

ARIZONA

ATCi (Antenna Technology Communication Solutions Inc), pg 692
EAR Professional Audio/Video, pg 749

ARKANSAS

Jay S Stanley & Associates Inc, pg 899
White Diamond Productions LLC, pg 937

CALIFORNIA

Advanced Systems Group LLC, pg 677
Ametron Audio/Video, pg 684
Audio/Video Supply Inc, pg 694
AV Conferencing LLC (AVC), pg 697
Cibola Systems, pg 723
Computer Modules Inc, pg 729
Empire Pro, pg 753
Lloyd F McKinney Associates Inc, pg 821
Media Fabricators Inc, pg 822
SSL Industries Inc, pg 898
Stanislaus AV Inc, pg 899
VMI Inc, pg 932
VTP Inc, pg 933
Westlake Recording Studios, pg 936

COLORADO

Spectrum Audio Visual Services, pg 897

FLORIDA

Access Media Group, pg 673
Altel Systems Group Inc, pg 682

AVI-SPL, pg 698
CircuitWerkes Inc, pg 725
Digital Video Systems, pg 742
Hi-Tech Enterprises Inc, pg 779
L3Harris Technologies Inc, pg 812
ONstage, pg 846
TAI Audio, pg 906

GEORGIA

Baker Audio Visual, pg 700
Convergent Media Systems, pg 731
Lighting & Production Equipment Inc, pg 807
PolyVision Corporation, pg 859
Stage Front Presentation Systems, pg 899
WolfVision Inc, pg 940

ILLINOIS

Allen Visual Systems Inc, pg 680
RC Communications, pg 870
Toko America Inc, pg 915

INDIANA

Sensory Technologies LLC, pg 884

KANSAS

SKC Communication Products Inc, pg 890

KENTUCKY

Axxis Leasing Inc, pg 700
NOR-COM Inc, pg 841

MAINE

Headlight Audio Visual Inc, pg 777

MARYLAND

Cardinal Sound & Video, pg 717
Human Circuit, pg 782
RTZ Audio Visual, pg 878

MICHIGAN

Digi Sign Design LLC, pg 741
On Stage Visuals, pg 846

MINNESOTA

Alpha Video & Audio Inc, pg 682
Vaddio, pg 924

MISSOURI

Communitronics Corp, pg 729
Conference Technologies Inc, pg 730
Southwest Audio-Visual Inc, pg 895

NEW JERSEY

A-V Services Inc, pg 671
Alltec Stores, a Vcom IMC Company, pg 681
AlltecPro, pg 681
Audio Visual Associates, pg 694
Diversified, pg 744
Radio Visions, pg 869
Starlite, pg 900
Telemetrics Inc, pg 910
Total Video Products Inc, pg 916
Wired 4 Sound Inc, pg 940

NEW YORK

American Video Inc, pg 684
Audio-Video Corp, pg 694
Colortone Audio Visual, pg 728
Design Audio Visual Inc, pg 741
Image Management Systems Inc, pg 785

KVL Audio Visual Services Inc, pg 802
Markertek Video Supply, pg 817
Presentation Products Inc, pg 861
Theatrical Services & Supplies Inc, pg 912
Visual Technologies Corp, pg 932

NORTH CAROLINA

Camcor Inc, pg 715
Strategic Connections, pg 901

OHIO

Copp Integrated Systems, pg 731
ITA Audio Visual Solutions, pg 791
The Telos Alliance, pg 910
Tri-State Audio Visual Co, pg 918
Tri-State Visual Products Inc, pg 918

OKLAHOMA

Ford AV, pg 763

PENNSYLVANIA

Advanced AV LLC, pg 677
Bernie's Photo Center, pg 704
Grise Audio Visual Center Inc, pg 774
The Lerro Corp, pg 806
Morefield Communications Inc, pg 830
North Star Satellite Communications Inc, pg 842
Vistacom Inc, pg 931
Visual Sound Inc, pg 931

RHODE ISLAND

Shanix Inc, pg 885

TENNESSEE

Allstar Audio Systems Inc, pg 681
Continental Film, pg 731
Lowrance Sound Co Inc, pg 812
Technical Support Systems LLC, pg 908

TEXAS

Audio Visual Technologies Group (AVTG), pg 695
Data Projections Inc, pg 738
Digital Display Solutions Inc, pg 742
Heffernan Audio Visual, pg 778
Tarpley Media Systems, pg 907

UTAH

RIA Corp, pg 874

VIRGINIA

Avitecture Inc, pg 699
Boitnott Visual Communications Corp (BVC), pg 708
Intellidyne LLC, pg 789
Lee Hartman & Sons Inc, pg 805
RGB Technology Inc, pg 874

WISCONSIN

Audio Visual of Milwaukee Inc, pg 694
Full Compass Systems, pg 767
Spectrum Industries Inc, pg 897

PUERTO RICO

Audio Visual Concepts Inc, pg 694

ALBERTA

Evolution AV, pg 757
Genesis Integration, pg 769
Infosat Communications Inc, pg 787
Matrix Video Communications Corp (MVCC), pg 819
SMART Technologies ULC, pg 891

BRITISH COLUMBIA

Commercial Electronics Ltd, pg 728

MANITOBA

Inland Audio Visual Ltd, pg 788

ONTARIO

GestureTek, pg 770
Westbury National Show Systems Ltd, pg 936

Teleconferencing Equipment Manufacturers

ARIZONA

Boeckeler Instruments Inc, pg 708
Covid Inc, pg 732

CALIFORNIA

ALTINEX Inc, pg 682
AMX® by Harman, pg 685
Computer Modules Inc, pg 729
DASAN Zhone Solutions (DZS) Inc, pg 737
ESE, pg 755
Hotronic Inc, pg 782
Opticomm-EMCORE, pg 847
RGB Spectrum, pg 874

COLORADO

Display Devices Inc, pg 743
Image Audiovisuals, pg 784

CONNECTICUT

Collective Systems LLC, pg 727
Sound Control Technologies Inc, pg 893

GEORGIA

PolyVision Corporation, pg 859
WolfVision Inc, pg 940

ILLINOIS

Bretford Manufacturing Inc, pg 710
NEC Display Solutions of America, pg 837
Toko America Inc, pg 915
Windel International/Weyel, pg 939

INDIANA

Draper Inc, pg 746

MICHIGAN

ASC Systems, pg 690

MINNESOTA

Vaddio, pg 924
Winsted Corp, pg 939

MISSOURI

Ken-A-Vision Manufacturing Co Inc, pg 797

NEW JERSEY

Crestron Electronics Inc, pg 734
FSR Inc, pg 766
Radio Visions, pg 869
Telemetrics Inc, pg 910
Turner Engineering Inc, pg 919

NEW YORK

ELMO USA Corp, pg 753
MultiDyne Video & Fiber Optics Systems, pg 833
Servoreeler Systems, pg 884

OHIO

The Telos Alliance, pg 910

PENNSYLVANIA

North Star Satellite Communications Inc, pg 842

TENNESSEE

Adtec Digital Inc, pg 677

TEXAS

Tellabs Inc, pg 910

UTAH

ClearOne Inc, pg 726

VIRGINIA

Avitecture Inc, pg 699
RGB Technology Inc, pg 874

WASHINGTON

Avidex Inc, pg 699

WISCONSIN

Spectrum Industries Inc, pg 897

ALBERTA

SMART Technologies ULC, pg 891

ONTARIO

GestureTek, pg 770

Teleconferencing Equipment Rentals

ARIZONA

Merestone, pg 823
Metropolitan Audio-Visual Inc, pg 824
Ultimate Presentation Systems Inc, pg 920

ARKANSAS

White Diamond Productions LLC, pg 937

CALIFORNIA

AGF Media Services, pg 678
Ametron Audio/Video, pg 684
AV Conferencing LLC (AVC), pg 697
AV Guys, pg 697
Cosumnes River College, pg 732
KTVU-Retail Services, pg 802
Lynch Communications, pg 813
McCune Audio-Video-Lighting, pg 821
Stanislaus AV Inc, pg 899
Twin Peaks Creative, pg 920
VER, pg 926

VMI Inc, pg 932
Voice & Video Rentals, pg 932

COLORADO

Spectrum Audio Visual Services, pg 897

CONNECTICUT

A/V Davey, pg 697
Videofilm Systems Inc, pg 929

FLORIDA

Digital Video Systems, pg 742
ONstage, pg 846
Sight & Sound Productions, pg 887
TAI Audio, pg 906

GEORGIA

Convergent Media Systems, pg 731
Lighting & Production Equipment Inc, pg 807
Stage Front Presentation Systems, pg 899
WATL-TV Inc, pg 934

ILLINOIS

Allen Visual Systems Inc, pg 680
RC Communications, pg 870

KENTUCKY

Audio Visual Techniques Inc, pg 695

LOUISIANA

Pace Systems, pg 849

MARYLAND

CPR MultiMedia Solutions, pg 732

MASSACHUSETTS

Capron Lighting & Sound Co Inc, pg 716
High Output Inc, pg 779
Preston Productions Inc, pg 861

MICHIGAN

Digi Sign Design LLC, pg 741
K&R All Media Productions LLC, pg 796

MINNESOTA

Alpha Video & Audio Inc, pg 682

MISSOURI

Show-Me Audio-Visual, pg 887
Wise Audio Video, pg 940

NEVADA

Lefco Video Services Inc, pg 806

NEW JERSEY

Audio Visual Associates, pg 694
Starlite, pg 900
Wired 4 Sound Inc, pg 940

NEW YORK

American Video Inc, pg 684
Big Foot Productions Inc, pg 705
Colortone Audio Visual, pg 728
CP Communications, pg 732
Design Audio Visual Inc, pg 741
KVL Audio Visual Services Inc, pg 802

Manhattan Center Studios Inc, pg 816
The Palmer Group, pg 850
PrimaLux Video Inc, pg 862
Visual Technologies Corp, pg 932

NORTH CAROLINA

AV Connections Inc, pg 697

OHIO

ITA Audio Visual Solutions, pg 791
Mills James Productions, pg 828

OKLAHOMA

Institute for Teaching & Learning Excellence (ITLE), pg 788

PENNSYLVANIA

Advanced AV LLC, pg 677
FMP Media Solutions Inc, pg 763
Grise Audio Visual Center Inc, pg 774
North Star Satellite Communications Inc, pg 842
Visual Sound Inc, pg 931
WHYY Inc, pg 938

SOUTH CAROLINA

Sound & Images Inc, pg 893

TENNESSEE

Allstar Audio Systems Inc, pg 681
Technical Support Systems LLC, pg 908
United Methodist Productions, pg 921

TEXAS

Audio Visual Technologies Group (AVTG), pg 695
Crossroads Audio Inc, pg 735
JSAV, pg 795
Earl Miller Productions Inc, pg 827
Omega Productions, pg 845

VIRGINIA

Boitnott Visual Communications Corp (BVC), pg 708
Projection, pg 865
WETA Production Center, pg 936

WISCONSIN

Event Essentials, pg 756
Full Compass Systems, pg 767
University of Wisconsin-Oshkosh Radio-TV-Film Dept, pg 923
Wisconsin Public Television, pg 940

PUERTO RICO

Stage Crew Audiovisual Inc, pg 898

ALBERTA

Cine Audio Visual Sales & Service Ltd, pg 723
Matrix Video Communications Corp (MVCC), pg 819

BRITISH COLUMBIA

Commercial Electronics Ltd, pg 728

MANITOBA

Inland Audio Visual Ltd, pg 788

ONTARIO

Westbury National Show Systems Ltd, pg 936

QUEBEC

Freeman Audio Visual, pg 765

Teleconferencing Equipment Repairs

CALIFORNIA

Ametron Audio/Video, pg 684
SSL Industries Inc, pg 898
VMI Inc, pg 932

CONNECTICUT

A/V Davey, pg 697

FLORIDA

ELC Sales & Service Inc, pg 752
Hi-Tech Enterprises Inc, pg 779
JT Communications, pg 795

GEORGIA

Lighting & Production Equipment Inc, pg 807
Stage Front Presentation Systems, pg 899

ILLINOIS

Allen Visual Systems Inc, pg 680

KENTUCKY

Axxis Leasing Inc, pg 700
NOR-COM Inc, pg 841

MICHIGAN

TEL Systems LLC, pg 909

NEW JERSEY

Audio Visual Associates, pg 694
Radio Visions, pg 869
Turner Engineering Inc, pg 919

NEW YORK

ELMO USA Corp, pg 753
Visual Technologies Corp, pg 932

OHIO

ITA Audio Visual Solutions, pg 791
Tri-State Audio Visual Co, pg 918

OREGON

All Service Musical Electronics Repair, pg 680

TENNESSEE

Technical Support Systems LLC, pg 908

TEXAS

Tarpley Media Systems, pg 907

VIRGINIA

Avitecture Inc, pg 699
Boitnott Visual Communications Corp (BVC), pg 708
Intellidyne LLC, pg 789

WISCONSIN

Full Compass Systems, pg 767

VIDEO

Teleconferencing Equipment Repairs (continued)

ALBERTA

Infosat Communications Inc, pg 787
Matrix Video Communications Corp (MVCC), pg 819

BRITISH COLUMBIA

Commercial Electronics Ltd, pg 728

MANITOBA

Inland Audio Visual Ltd, pg 788

ONTARIO

Westbury National Show Systems Ltd, pg 936

Teleprompting & Cueing System Distributors

ARIZONA

EAR Professional Audio/Video, pg 749

ARKANSAS

Jay S Stanley & Associates Inc, pg 899
White Diamond Productions LLC, pg 937

CALIFORNIA

Ametron Audio/Video, pg 684
Audio/Video Supply Inc, pg 694
Band Pro Film & Digital Inc, pg 701
Barber Tech Video Products, pg 701
Alan Gordon Enterprises Inc, pg 772
Jaguar Distribution Corp, pg 792
SSL Industries Inc, pg 898
Transvideo International, pg 917
VMI Inc, pg 932

FLORIDA

Access Media Group, pg 673
A2D Solutions Inc, pg 692
Digital Video Systems, pg 742
Enhanced View Services Inc, pg 754
Hi-Tech Enterprises Inc, pg 779
Midtown Video Inc, pg 827
ONstage, pg 846

GEORGIA

Lighting & Production Equipment Inc, pg 807
Stage Front Presentation Systems, pg 899
Visioneering International Inc, pg 931

ILLINOIS

Tele-Time Systems, pg 910

INDIANA

Sensory Technologies LLC, pg 884

KENTUCKY

Axxis Leasing Inc, pg 700
NOR-COM Inc, pg 841

MARYLAND

Human Circuit, pg 782
Kipp Visual Systems Inc, pg 799

MASSACHUSETTS

Rule Boston Camera, pg 878

MICHIGAN

On Stage Visuals, pg 846

MINNESOTA

Alpha Video & Audio Inc, pg 682

MISSOURI

Conference Technologies Inc, pg 730
Southwest Audio-Visual Inc, pg 895

NEBRASKA

VSA Inc, pg 933

NEVADA

Aardvark Video & Media Productions, pg 671

NEW JERSEY

Audio Visual Associates, pg 694
Audio Visual Dynamics®, pg 694
Diversified, pg 744
MiB MediaWorks, pg 825
PatchAmp, pg 852
Starlite, pg 900
SYMCO Inc, pg 905
Tele-Measurements Inc, pg 910
Wired 4 Sound Inc, pg 940

NEW YORK

Ace Video, pg 674
Audio-Video Corp, pg 694
AV Workshop, pg 697
Long Island Video Enterprises Live Inc, pg 811
Markertek Video Supply, pg 817
The Tiffen Co LLC, pg 914
Tri-Ed Distribution Inc, pg 918

NORTH CAROLINA

Strategic Connections, pg 901

OHIO

ITA Audio Visual Solutions, pg 791

PENNSYLVANIA

Advanced AV LLC, pg 677
The Lerro Corp, pg 806
Morefield Communications Inc, pg 830
Visual Sound Inc, pg 931

TENNESSEE

Allstar Audio Systems Inc, pg 681
Lowrance Sound Co Inc, pg 812

TEXAS

AVES Audio Visual Systems Inc, pg 698
Digital Display Solutions Inc, pg 742
Pro Video & Film Equipment Co Inc, pg 863

UTAH

Comtek Communications Technology Inc, pg 730
RIA Corp, pg 874

VIRGINIA

Lee Hartman & Sons Inc, pg 805

WEST VIRGINIA

Blackwater Video Productions, pg 707

WISCONSIN

Audio Visual of Milwaukee Inc, pg 694
Camera Corner Connecting Point, pg 715
Full Compass Systems, pg 767

ALBERTA

Matrix Video Communications Corp (MVCC), pg 819

MANITOBA

Inland Audio Visual Ltd, pg 788

QUEBEC

Panavideo Inc, pg 850

Teleprompting & Cueing System Manufacturers

CALIFORNIA

Barber Tech Video Products, pg 701
Boland Communications Inc, pg 708
Magic Teleprompting Inc, pg 814
Transvideo International, pg 917

CONNECTICUT

Autocue, pg 696

NEW JERSEY

Telescript International, pg 910

NEW YORK

The Tiffen Co LLC, pg 914

UTAH

Comtek Communications Technology Inc, pg 730

VIRGINIA

Quince Imaging Inc, pg 868

WISCONSIN

Comprompter Inc, pg 729

BRITISH COLUMBIA

Tekskil Industries Inc, pg 909

Teleprompting & Cueing System Rentals

ALASKA

Connections Film & Video Inc, pg 731

ARIZONA

Broadcast Rentals, pg 711
Glendale Media Center, pg 771

Merestone, pg 823
Metropolitan Audio-Visual Inc, pg 824

ARKANSAS

White Diamond Productions LLC, pg 937

CALIFORNIA

AGF Media Services, pg 678
Ametron Audio/Video, pg 684
Artichoke Productions, pg 690
AV Guys, pg 697
Barber Tech Video Products, pg 701
Bexel, an NEP Broadcast Services Company, pg 704
California Teleprompter, pg 714
Cherry Multimedia, pg 721
Crash Video Productions, pg 733
Crystal Pyramid Productions™, pg 735
Cue Tech Teleprompting Inc, pg 736
Golden Gate Studios, pg 772
Alan Gordon Enterprises Inc, pg 772
JFA Studio, pg 794
Lynch Communications, pg 813
McCune Audio-Video-Lighting, pg 821
Pro HD Rentals, pg 863
PSAV® Presentation Services, pg 866
Studio 637, pg 903
The Studios at Paramount, pg 903
Total Creative, pg 916
VER, pg 926
VMI Inc, pg 932
Voice & Video Rentals, pg 932

COLORADO

Daylight Productions & Rentals, pg 739
Spectrum Audio Visual Services, pg 897

CONNECTICUT

Autocue, pg 696
Videofilm Systems Inc, pg 929

FLORIDA

Accord Productions, pg 673
Budget Video Rentals, pg 712
Digital Zoetrope Productions, pg 742
Hi-Tech Enterprises Inc, pg 779
Industrial Strength Inc, pg 787
Jordan Klein Film & Video (JKFV), pg 795
JungleTV, pg 795
Midtown Video Inc, pg 827
ONstage, pg 846
Paradise Show & Design Inc, pg 851
PRI Productions, pg 862
Sight & Sound Productions, pg 887
Mike Vasilinda Productions Inc, pg 925

GEORGIA

Lighting & Production Equipment Inc, pg 807
ON Services, a GES Company, pg 846
See Production Services, pg 883
Stage Front Presentation Systems, pg 899

ILLINOIS

Atomic Imaging Inc/Golan Studios, pg 692
Backstar Creative Media Inc, pg 700
Beatty TeleVisual Productions, pg 703
Creative Technology (CT), pg 733
Firehouse Studios, pg 761
Resolution Productions Group, pg 874
SGW Teleprompter Solutions Inc, pg 885

KANSAS

Lights On, pg 808

KENTUCKY

Audio Visual Techniques Inc, pg 695

LOUISIANA

Digital FX Inc, pg 742
Moxie Media, pg 832
Pace Systems, pg 849

MARYLAND

CPR MultiMedia Solutions, pg 732
Kramer Communications Video Production, pg 801

MASSACHUSETTS

Capron Lighting & Sound Co Inc, pg 716

MICHIGAN

Digi Sign Design LLC, pg 741
K&R All Media Productions LLC, pg 796

MINNESOTA

Alpha Video & Audio Inc, pg 682
Big Event Productions LLC, pg 705

MISSOURI

Show-Me Audio-Visual, pg 887
Southwest Audio-Visual Inc, pg 895
Switch, pg 905

NEBRASKA

Dog & Pony Productions Inc, pg 744

NEVADA

GES Audio Visual, pg 770
JCS Video Productions, pg 793

NEW JERSEY

Audio Visual Associates, pg 694
Audio Visual Dynamics®, pg 694
MediaMix Inc, pg 822
MiB MediaWorks, pg 825
Starlite, pg 900
VCSvideo, pg 925
Video Corporation of America (VCA), pg 927
Wired 4 Sound Inc, pg 940

NEW MEXICO

Production Outfitters, pg 864

NEW YORK

Ace Video, pg 674
Ansonia Prompting Inc, pg 686
AV Workshop, pg 697

BC Studio, pg 702
Big Foot Productions Inc, pg 705
CSI Rentals, pg 735
Design Audio Visual Inc, pg 741
Digital Arts NY, pg 742
Gearhead Rentals, pg 769
Long Island Video Enterprises Live Inc, pg 811
Manhattan Center Studios Inc, pg 816
Media 3 Ltd, pg 822
PrimaLux Video Inc, pg 862
Visual Word Systems Inc, pg 932

NORTH CAROLINA

All Pro Media Inc, pg 680
The Communications Group Inc, pg 729
Moving Pictures, pg 832
On Location North Carolina, pg 846

OHIO

Bartha, pg 702
ITA Audio Visual Solutions, pg 791
Mills James Productions, pg 828
Ohio HD Video, pg 844
OSV Studios, pg 848
Vista Color Imaging Inc, pg 931

OREGON

Northwest Film Center, pg 842
Picture This Production Services, pg 856

PENNSYLVANIA

FMP Media Solutions Inc, pg 763
Innovision Media Group, pg 788
JPL, pg 795
Muderick Media, pg 833
New York Camera & Video, pg 840
Producers Management Television (PMTV), pg 863

SOUTH CAROLINA

Genesis Creative, pg 769
Sound & Images Inc, pg 893

TENNESSEE

Allstar Audio Systems Inc, pg 681
NuMynd Studios, pg 843
Tennessee Prompters, pg 911

TEXAS

Dallas Prompter, pg 737
Maverick Video Productions, pg 820
Media Event Concepts Inc, pg 822
South Coast Film & Video, pg 895
Stage Directions, pg 898

UTAH

Ron Hill Imagery, pg 780

VIRGINIA

Allied Media Corp, pg 681
Quince Imaging Inc, pg 868

WASHINGTON

Victory Studios, pg 927

WEST VIRGINIA

Blackwater Video Productions, pg 707

WISCONSIN

Logan Productions Inc, pg 811

WYOMING

Bridger Productions Inc, pg 710

PUERTO RICO

Stage Crew Audiovisual Inc, pg 898

ALBERTA

Global TV, pg 771

BRITISH COLUMBIA

24 Frames Film & Video, pg 920

MANITOBA

Inland Audio Visual Ltd, pg 788
MidCanada Production Services Inc (MidCan), pg 826

ONTARIO

Q-Prompt Inc, pg 867
RB Productions, pg 870

QUEBEC

Audio Visual Dynamics, pg 694
Freeman Audio Visual, pg 765

Teleprompting & Cueing System Repairs

CALIFORNIA

Ametron Audio/Video, pg 684
Barber Tech Video Products, pg 701
SSL Industries Inc, pg 898
Transvideo International, pg 917
VMI Inc, pg 932

CONNECTICUT

Autocue, pg 696

FLORIDA

Hi-Tech Enterprises Inc, pg 779
Midtown Video Inc, pg 827

GEORGIA

Lighting & Production Equipment Inc, pg 807
Stage Front Presentation Systems, pg 899

ILLINOIS

Beatty TeleVisual Productions, pg 703

KENTUCKY

Axxis Leasing Inc, pg 700
NOR-COM Inc, pg 841

MICHIGAN

TEL Systems LLC, pg 909

MINNESOTA

Alpha Video & Audio Inc, pg 682

MISSOURI

Southwest Audio-Visual Inc, pg 895

NEW YORK

Ace Video, pg 674

OHIO

ITA Audio Visual Solutions, pg 791

UTAH

RIA Corp, pg 874

VIRGINIA

Avitecture Inc, pg 699

MANITOBA

Inland Audio Visual Ltd, pg 788

Time Base Corrector Distributors

ARIZONA

EAR Professional Audio/Video, pg 749

ARKANSAS

Jay S Stanley & Associates Inc, pg 899

CALIFORNIA

Advanced Systems Group LLC, pg 677
Ametron Audio/Video, pg 684
Audio/Video Supply Inc, pg 694
BigFoot Mobile Systems, pg 705
BroadcastStore.com, pg 711
California Tape Products Inc, pg 714
Cibola Systems, pg 723
Computer Modules Inc, pg 729
Media Control Systems LLC, pg 821
SNAP, pg 891
SSL Industries Inc, pg 898
Stanislaus AV Inc, pg 899
VMI Inc, pg 932
Westlake Recording Studios, pg 936

FLORIDA

Access Media Group, pg 673
Digital Video Systems, pg 742
Harris Corp, pg 776
Hi-Tech Enterprises Inc, pg 779
Hi-Tech Import Export Corp, pg 779
Midtown Video Inc, pg 827
ONstage, pg 846

GEORGIA

Baker Audio Visual, pg 700
Stage Front Presentation Systems, pg 899

ILLINOIS

Allen Visual Systems Inc, pg 680

INDIANA

Sensory Technologies LLC, pg 884

KENTUCKY

NOR-COM Inc, pg 841

MARYLAND

Wiltronix Inc, pg 939

MASSACHUSETTS

Rule Boston Camera, pg 878

MICHIGAN

TEL Systems LLC, pg 909

VIDEO

Time Base Corrector Distributors (continued)

MINNESOTA

Alpha Video & Audio Inc, pg 682

MISSOURI

Communitronics Corp, pg 729
Conference Technologies Inc, pg 730
Southwest Audio-Visual Inc, pg 895

NEVADA

Aardvark Video & Media Productions, pg 671

NEW JERSEY

A-V Services Inc, pg 671
Audio Visual Associates, pg 694
Diversified, pg 744
Earl Girls Inc, pg 749
G&G Technologies Inc, pg 768
MCCOM, pg 820
PatchAmp, pg 852
SYMCO Inc, pg 905
Total Video Products Inc, pg 916
Wired 4 Sound Inc, pg 940

NEW YORK

Ace Video, pg 674
Audio-Video Corp, pg 694
AV Workshop, pg 697
B&H Photo Video, pg 701
Design Audio Visual Inc, pg 741
General Audio-Visual Inc (GAVI), pg 769
Long Island Video Enterprises Live Inc, pg 811
Markertek Video Supply, pg 817
TecNec Distributing, pg 909
Tri-Ed Distribution Inc, pg 918
Visual Technologies Corp, pg 932

OHIO

ITA Audio Visual Solutions, pg 791

PENNSYLVANIA

Advanced AV LLC, pg 677
The Lerro Corp, pg 806
Morefield Communications Inc, pg 830
Visual Sound Inc, pg 931

TENNESSEE

Lowrance Sound Co Inc, pg 812
Zion Music Group, pg 945

TEXAS

AVES Audio Visual Systems Inc, pg 698
Pro Video & Film Equipment Co Inc, pg 863
Videotex Systems Inc, pg 930

UTAH

RIA Corp, pg 874

VIRGINIA

Avitecture Inc, pg 699
Boitnott Visual Communications Corp (BVC), pg 708
The Whitlock Group, pg 937

WISCONSIN

Audio Visual of Milwaukee Inc, pg 694
Camera Corner Connecting Point, pg 715
Full Compass Systems, pg 767

ALBERTA

Infosat Communications Inc, pg 787
Matrix Video Communications Corp (MVCC), pg 819

MANITOBA

Inland Audio Visual Ltd, pg 788

ONTARIO

Cinema Stage Inc, pg 724
HD Source, pg 777
Majortech Inc, pg 815

QUEBEC

Panavideo Inc, pg 850

Time Base Corrector Manufacturers

ARIZONA

Applied Integration Corp, pg 687

CALIFORNIA

Ensemble Designs Inc, pg 754
Extron Electronics, pg 758
For-A Corp of America, pg 763
Hotronic Inc, pg 782

MISSOURI

GlobalStreams™ Corp, pg 771

NEW JERSEY

Kramer Electronics USA Inc, pg 801

NEW MEXICO

Burst Electronics Inc, pg 713

OHIO

TV One Multimedia Solutions, pg 919

PENNSYLVANIA

Prime Image Inc, pg 862

BRITISH COLUMBIA

Triad Communications Ltd, pg 918

Time Base Corrector Rentals

ARIZONA

Merestone, pg 823
Metropolitan Audio-Visual Inc, pg 824

ARKANSAS

White Diamond Productions LLC, pg 937

CALIFORNIA

Alliant Event Services, pg 681
Ametron Audio/Video, pg 684
AV Guys, pg 697

Bexel, an NEP Broadcast Services Company, pg 704
BroadcastStore.com, pg 711
Crystal Pyramid Productions™, pg 735
Express Media Inc, pg 757
Full Moon & High Tide Productions & Studios, pg 767
Golden Gate Studios, pg 772
Lynch Communications, pg 813
McCune Audio-Video-Lighting, pg 821
Munday & Collins AV, pg 834
On-Trax Inc, pg 846
RetinaVision Productions, pg 874
Total Creative, pg 916
Twin Peaks Creative, pg 920
VER, pg 926
VMI Inc, pg 932
Voice & Video Rentals, pg 932

COLORADO

Daylight Productions & Rentals, pg 739
Multimedia Audio Visual Inc, pg 833

CONNECTICUT

Videofilm Systems Inc, pg 929

DELAWARE

Showorks Audio Visual Inc, pg 887

FLORIDA

Knowles Video Inc (KVI), pg 800
Midtown Video Inc, pg 827
ONstage, pg 846
Paradise Show & Design Inc, pg 851

GEORGIA

ON Services, a GES Company, pg 846
Stage Front Presentation Systems, pg 899

ILLINOIS

Airways Digital Media, pg 679
Backstar Creative Media Inc, pg 700
Beatty TeleVisual Productions, pg 703
Resolution Productions Group, pg 874
Tele-Time Systems, pg 910

KENTUCKY

Audio Visual Techniques Inc, pg 695

LOUISIANA

Digital FX Inc, pg 742
Pace Systems, pg 849

MARYLAND

CPR MultiMedia Solutions, pg 732

MASSACHUSETTS

massAV, pg 819
Preston Productions Inc, pg 861

MICHIGAN

Digi Sign Design LLC, pg 741
K&R All Media Productions LLC, pg 796

K&R's Recording Studios Inc, pg 796

TEL Systems LLC, pg 909

MINNESOTA

Alpha Video & Audio Inc, pg 682

MISSOURI

Communitronics Corp, pg 729
Show-Me Audio-Visual, pg 887
Southwest Audio-Visual Inc, pg 895
Switch, pg 905

NEVADA

GES Audio Visual, pg 770

NEW JERSEY

Audio Visual Associates, pg 694
Earl Girls Inc, pg 749
MB Productions, pg 820
MediaMix Inc, pg 822
PLS Staging, pg 858
Video Corporation of America (VCA), pg 927
Wired 4 Sound Inc, pg 940

NEW MEXICO

Production Outfitters, pg 864

NEW YORK

Ace Video, pg 674
AV Workshop, pg 697
CP Communications, pg 732
Long Island Video Enterprises Live Inc, pg 811
Manhattan Center Studios Inc, pg 816
Visual Technologies Corp, pg 932
Visual Word Systems Inc, pg 932

NORTH CAROLINA

Moving Pictures, pg 832
Special Event Services, pg 896

NORTH DAKOTA

Media Productions, pg 822

OHIO

ITA Audio Visual Solutions, pg 791
Lyon Video Inc, pg 813

PENNSYLVANIA

FMP Media Solutions Inc, pg 763
Innovision Media Group, pg 788
JPL, pg 795

TENNESSEE

Russ Sturgeon Productions/RSVP, pg 903

TEXAS

FitzCo Sound Inc, pg 761
Media Event Concepts Inc, pg 822
Stage Directions, pg 898

VIRGINIA

Boitnott Visual Communications Corp (BVC), pg 708
CVW Event Productions, pg 736

WISCONSIN

Camera Corner Connecting Point, pg 715
Full Compass Systems, pg 767

WYOMING

Bridger Productions Inc, pg 710

PUERTO RICO

Stage Crew Audiovisual Inc, pg 898

ALBERTA

Cine Audio Visual Sales & Service Ltd, pg 723
Matrix Video Communications Corp (MVCC), pg 819

BRITISH COLUMBIA

Commercial Electronics Ltd, pg 728
Video Out Distribution, pg 928

MANITOBA

Inland Audio Visual Ltd, pg 788

ONTARIO

HD Source, pg 777
RB Productions, pg 870

QUEBEC

Panavideo Inc, pg 850

Time Base Corrector Repairs

CALIFORNIA

Ametron Audio/Video, pg 684
BigFoot Mobile Systems, pg 705
BroadcastStore.com, pg 711
SSL Industries Inc, pg 898
VMI Inc, pg 932

FLORIDA

ELC Sales & Service Inc, pg 752
Hi-Tech Enterprises Inc, pg 779

GEORGIA

Stage Front Presentation Systems, pg 899

ILLINOIS

Beatty TeleVisual Productions, pg 703
Midwest Digital Corp, pg 827

KENTUCKY

NOR-COM Inc, pg 841

MICHIGAN

TEL Systems LLC, pg 909

MINNESOTA

Alpha Video & Audio Inc, pg 682

MISSOURI

Communitronics Corp, pg 729
Southwest Audio-Visual Inc, pg 895

NEW YORK

Visual Technologies Corp, pg 932

OHIO

ITA Audio Visual Solutions, pg 791

UTAH

RIA Corp, pg 874

WISCONSIN

Camera Corner Connecting Point, pg 715
Full Compass Systems, pg 767

ALBERTA

Infosat Communications Inc, pg 787
Matrix Video Communications Corp (MVCC), pg 819

BRITISH COLUMBIA

Commercial Electronics Ltd, pg 728

MANITOBA

Inland Audio Visual Ltd, pg 788

ONTARIO

HD Source, pg 777

QUEBEC

Panavideo Inc, pg 850

Titling & Artwork Services, *see* Artwork & Titling Services

Transfer & Conversion Equipment Distributors

CALIFORNIA

Ametron Audio/Video, pg 684
BigFoot Mobile Systems, pg 705
Computer Modules Inc, pg 729
Promax Systems, pg 865
VITEC Multimedia, pg 932
Westlake Recording Studios, pg 936

FLORIDA

Access Media Group, pg 673
Digital Video Systems, pg 742
ONstage, pg 846

GEORGIA

Barco Inc, pg 701
Stage Front Presentation Systems, pg 899

INDIANA

Lee Co Inc, pg 805
Sensory Technologies LLC, pg 884

KENTUCKY

NOR-COM Inc, pg 841

MARYLAND

Wiltronix Inc, pg 939

MASSACHUSETTS

Rule Boston Camera, pg 878

MINNESOTA

Alpha Video & Audio Inc, pg 682

MISSOURI

Southwest Audio-Visual Inc, pg 895

NEVADA

Aardvark Video & Media Productions, pg 671

NEW JERSEY

Diversified, pg 744
Euro-Pacific Film & Video Productions Inc, pg 756
Starlite, pg 900
Tele-Measurements Inc, pg 910
Total Video Products Inc, pg 916

NEW YORK

Ace Video, pg 674
All Mobile Video Inc, pg 680
Audio-Video Corp, pg 694
Design Audio Visual Inc, pg 741
Markertek Video Supply, pg 817
Visual Technologies Corp, pg 932
Visual Word Systems Inc, pg 932

PENNSYLVANIA

Advanced AV LLC, pg 677
The Lerro Corp, pg 806

TENNESSEE

Lowrance Sound Co Inc, pg 812
Technical Support Systems LLC, pg 908

TEXAS

AVES Audio Visual Systems Inc, pg 698
GEAR Cameras & Lighting, pg 769
Graftek Imaging Inc, pg 773
Pro Video & Film Equipment Co Inc, pg 863

VIRGINIA

Avitecture Inc, pg 699
Lee Hartman & Sons Inc, pg 805

WASHINGTON

Macrosystem US Inc, pg 814

WISCONSIN

Audio Visual of Milwaukee Inc, pg 694
Full Compass Systems, pg 767
Safe Harbor Computers, pg 879

MANITOBA

Advance Pro, pg 677
Inland Audio Visual Ltd, pg 788

ONTARIO

Soundmaster Group, pg 894

Transfer & Conversion Equipment Manufacturers

CALIFORNIA

ALTINEX Inc, pg 682
DASAN Zhone Solutions (DZS) Inc, pg 737
Ensemble Designs Inc, pg 754
MediaPOINTE, pg 823
Nevion USA Inc, pg 838
RGB Spectrum, pg 874
Sprocket Digital, pg 898
Telestream Inc, pg 910
VITEC Multimedia, pg 932

CONNECTICUT

Xintekvideo Inc, pg 943

GEORGIA

Barco Inc, pg 701

MINNESOTA

Lynx Broadband, pg 813

NEW JERSEY

CELCO, pg 719
Kramer Electronics USA Inc, pg 801

NEW YORK

Laird Digital Cinema, pg 803
Judson Rosebush Co Inc, pg 877
Sima Products Corp, pg 888

OHIO

AV Toolbox, pg 697
TV One Multimedia Solutions, pg 919

PENNSYLVANIA

Prime Image Inc, pg 862

TENNESSEE

Adtec Digital Inc, pg 677

WASHINGTON

Macrosystem US Inc, pg 814

BRITISH COLUMBIA

Triad Communications Ltd, pg 918

ONTARIO

Evertz Microsystems Ltd, pg 757
Soundmaster Group, pg 894

QUEBEC

Grass Valley, pg 773
Matrox Video Products Group, pg 819

Transfer & Conversion Equipment Rentals

ARIZONA

Merestone, pg 823

ARKANSAS

White Diamond Productions LLC, pg 937

CALIFORNIA

Alliant Event Services, pg 681
Ametron Audio/Video, pg 684
Artichoke Productions, pg 690
Bexel, an NEP Broadcast Services Company, pg 704
Chater Camera Inc, pg 721
Express Media Inc, pg 757
Golden Gate Studios, pg 772
RetinaVision Productions, pg 874
SNAP, pg 891
Total Creative, pg 916
Twin Peaks Creative, pg 920
VER, pg 926
VMI Inc, pg 932

CONNECTICUT

Videofilm Systems Inc, pg 929

VIDEO

Transfer & Conversion Equipment Rentals (continued)

FLORIDA

Accord Productions, pg 673
ONstage, pg 846

GEORGIA

ON Services, a GES Company, pg 846
Stage Front Presentation Systems, pg 899

ILLINOIS

Backstar Creative Media Inc, pg 700
Resolution Productions Group, pg 874

KENTUCKY

Audio Visual Techniques Inc, pg 695

MARYLAND

CPR MultiMedia Solutions, pg 732

MICHIGAN

Digi Sign Design LLC, pg 741
K&R All Media Productions LLC, pg 796

MINNESOTA

Alpha Video & Audio Inc, pg 682

MISSOURI

Show-Me Audio-Visual, pg 887
Southwest Audio-Visual Inc, pg 895

NEVADA

JCS Video Productions, pg 793

NEW JERSEY

Euro-Pacific Film & Video Productions Inc, pg 756
Starlite, pg 900
Tele-Measurements Inc, pg 910

NEW YORK

Ace Video, pg 674
Colortone Audio Visual, pg 728
Design Audio Visual Inc, pg 741
Hello World Communications, pg 778
PrimaLux Video Inc, pg 862
Visual Technologies Corp, pg 932
Visual Word Systems Inc, pg 932

NORTH CAROLINA

Take One Productions Ltd, pg 906

OHIO

Mills James Productions, pg 828

PENNSYLVANIA

FMP Media Solutions Inc, pg 763
JPL, pg 795
The Videohouse Inc, pg 929

TENNESSEE

Technical Support Systems LLC, pg 908

TEXAS

Stage Directions, pg 898

VIRGINIA

Quince Imaging Inc, pg 868

WASHINGTON

Victory Studios, pg 927

WISCONSIN

Audio Visual of Milwaukee Inc, pg 694

PUERTO RICO

Stage Crew Audiovisual Inc, pg 898

BRITISH COLUMBIA

Commercial Electronics Ltd, pg 728

MANITOBA

Inland Audio Visual Ltd, pg 788

ONTARIO

RB Productions, pg 870

Transfer & Conversion Equipment Repairs

CALIFORNIA

Ametron Audio/Video, pg 684
VMI Inc, pg 932

FLORIDA

ELC Sales & Service Inc, pg 752

GEORGIA

Stage Front Presentation Systems, pg 899

KENTUCKY

NOR-COM Inc, pg 841

MICHIGAN

TEL Systems LLC, pg 909

MINNESOTA

Alpha Video & Audio Inc, pg 682

MISSOURI

Southwest Audio-Visual Inc, pg 895

NEW YORK

Visual Technologies Corp, pg 932

TENNESSEE

Technical Support Systems LLC, pg 908

TEXAS

Pro Video & Film Equipment Co Inc, pg 863

WASHINGTON

Macrosystem US Inc, pg 814

WISCONSIN

Full Compass Systems, pg 767

BRITISH COLUMBIA

Commercial Electronics Ltd, pg 728

MANITOBA

Inland Audio Visual Ltd, pg 788

Transfers—Film to Videotape

ARIZONA

Merestone, pg 823
Metropolitan Audio-Visual Inc, pg 824
On-Site Video, pg 846
Star Video Duplicating, pg 900

CALIFORNIA

Access Video in Berkeley, pg 673
Action Photo Digital Graphics, pg 675
Action Video, pg 675
Advanced Media LLC, pg 677
All Video Productions, pg 680
ALOM Technologies Corp, pg 681
Artichoke Productions, pg 690
Creative Technology, pg 733
Custom Video Productions Inc, pg 736
Havas Edge, pg 777
Hooper Camera & Imaging, pg 781
iCorpTv, pg 783
K2B2 Records, pg 802
Ludlow Media, pg 812
Method Studios, pg 824
Oddball Films Inc, pg 844
PM Productions, pg 858
Point.360, pg 858
Pro8mm, pg 862
QRS Software Services, pg 867
RetinaVision Productions, pg 874
RJ Video Productions, pg 875
SonicPool, pg 892
Universal Studios, pg 922
Wavemaker Media Design, pg 934
Yale Film & Video, pg 943

COLORADO

Rocky Mountain Audio/Video Productions Inc, pg 876

CONNECTICUT

A/V Davey, pg 697
Digital Video Productions, pg 742
The Gary-Paul Agency, pg 768
MAVCO, pg 820

DISTRICT OF COLUMBIA

Interface Media Group, pg 789
Library of Congress, Motion Picture, Broadcasting & Recorded Sound Division, pg 807

FLORIDA

Access Media Group, pg 673
Applebox Studio, pg 687
Civins Productions Inc, pg 725
Communications Concepts Inc (CCI), pg 729
Easy Edit Video Inc, pg 750
Hi-Tech Enterprises Inc, pg 779
Knowles Video Inc (KVI), pg 800
Photosound of Orlando Inc, pg 856
Sunrise Studios, pg 904
Video Techniques Inc, pg 928

IDAHO

KTVB-TV, pg 802

ILLINOIS

Intervideo Duplication Services, pg 791
Major Media Inc, pg 815
Moviecraft Inc, pg 831
Optimus, pg 847
Pepper Group, pg 854
Sound/Video Impressions Inc, pg 894
Southern Illinois University, pg 895
Video Impressions, pg 928
WEEK TV, pg 935

INDIANA

Advanced Media Integration, pg 677
Educational Video Group Inc, pg 751
Lighthouse Photo & Video Productions, pg 807

IOWA

Duplication Media, pg 748
Educational Technology & Media Services, pg 751

KENTUCKY

Audio Visual Techniques Inc, pg 695
Barney Miller's Inc, pg 827
The PPS Group, pg 860

LOUISIANA

Digital FX Inc, pg 742
Moxie Media, pg 832

MARYLAND

Carpel Video Inc, pg 717
CSPMedia.com, pg 735
Kramer Communications Video Production, pg 801
Pro Cuts Editing Services, pg 862
Quality Film & Video, pg 868
Saah Video, pg 879

MASSACHUSETTS

Capron Lighting & Sound Co Inc, pg 716

MICHIGAN

K&R's Recording Studios Inc, pg 796
The Transfer Zone®, pg 917

MISSISSIPPI

Jasper Ewing & Sons Inc, pg 757

MISSOURI

Communitronics Corp, pg 729
Conference Technologies Inc, pg 730
Schiller's Audio-Visual, pg 881
Show-Me Audio-Visual, pg 887

NEVADA

Aardvark Video & Media Productions, pg 671
JCS Video Productions, pg 793
Peterson's Video Transfer Services, pg 855
21st Century Video Productions, pg 919

NEW HAMPSHIRE

Apertura, pg 686
Channell One Video, pg 720

NEW JERSEY

AJS Events, pg 679
Broadcast Center Studios, pg 710
CFP Video Productions Inc, pg 720
Hogpenny Studios, pg 780
NFL Films Inc, pg 841
NFL Films Music Library, pg 841
Reed Presentations Inc (RPI),
 pg 872
Suede Interactive, pg 903
Video Corporation of America
 (VCA), pg 927

NEW YORK

Adwar Video, pg 678
aurora productions, pg 696
Buffalo Video Production, pg 712
CMI Communications, pg 727
Colortone Audio Visual, pg 728
Digital Art Video Inc, pg 741
DuArt Media Services, pg 747
Duplication Depot Inc, pg 748
Duplication Specialists Inc, pg 748
HAVE Inc, pg 777
International Digital Centre, pg 790
J&D Laboratories Inc, pg 793
Long Island Video Enterprises Live
 Inc, pg 811
Magno Sound Inc, pg 815
The Palmer Group, pg 850
PostWorks, pg 860
Rafik, pg 869
USA Studios, pg 923

NORTH CAROLINA

Camcor Inc, pg 715
Duke Media Services, pg 747

OHIO

Advent Media Inc, pg 677
Audio Visual Media, pg 694
Aztec Video Productions, pg 700
Russ Beckner Pictures, pg 703
MainSail Production Services Inc,
 pg 815
Take 1 Media Services, pg 906
Vista Color Imaging Inc, pg 931

OKLAHOMA

Academic Media & Digital
 Services, pg 672

OREGON

Nostalgia Family Video Inc, pg 843

PENNSYLVANIA

John E Allen Inc, pg 680
Audio Visions Inc, pg 694
Audio Visual Communications Inc,
 pg 694
Bernie's Photo Center, pg 704
Center City Film & Video Inc,
 pg 719
FMP Media Solutions Inc, pg 763
Visual Sound Inc, pg 931
WPHL-TV, pg 942

TENNESSEE

Motion Picture Services, pg 831
Stage Post, pg 899
Russ Sturgeon Productions/RSVP,
 pg 903

TEXAS

Dub King, pg 747
McNee Productions Inc, pg 821
Phillips Media Source, pg 855
Replicopy Digital Media Center,
 pg 873
The Samuels Co, pg 879
Texas Heart Institute Visual
 Communication Services, pg 911

VIRGINIA

BES Studios, pg 704
CDR Communications Inc, pg 719
Henninger Media Services, pg 779

WASHINGTON

Kostov Productions, pg 801
Victory Studios, pg 927

WISCONSIN

Audio Visual of Milwaukee Inc,
 pg 694
University of Wisconsin-Oshkosh
 Radio-TV-Film Dept, pg 923
USAV Group Inc, pg 923
Video Wisconsin Inc, pg 929
Wisconsin Public Television, pg 940

WYOMING

Bridger Productions Inc, pg 710

ALBERTA

Cine Audio Visual Sales & Service
 Ltd, pg 723

BRITISH COLUMBIA

Commercial Electronics Ltd, pg 728
Triad Communications Ltd, pg 918
24 Frames Film & Video, pg 920

ONTARIO

Silver Creek Media Inc, pg 888

QUEBEC

Group PVP, pg 774

Transfers—Slide to Video

ARIZONA

Merestone, pg 823
Metropolitan Audio-Visual Inc,
 pg 824
On-Site Video, pg 846
Star Video Duplicating, pg 900

ARKANSAS

White Diamond Productions LLC,
 pg 937

CALIFORNIA

Access Video in Berkeley, pg 673
All Video Productions, pg 680
Ametron Audio/Video, pg 684
Artichoke Productions, pg 690
CCI Digital, a DVS Company,
 pg 718
Steve Chandler, pg 720
Custom Video Productions Inc,
 pg 736
First Camera, pg 761
Gold Standard Productions, pg 772
Hooper Camera & Imaging, pg 781
iCorpTv, pg 783
ITV Productions, pg 792
KTVU-Retail Services, pg 802

McCune Audio-Video-Lighting,
 pg 821
Media Magic, pg 822
Method Studios, pg 824
On-Trax Inc, pg 846
Penrose Productions, pg 854
PM Productions, pg 858
PSI Inc, pg 866
QRS Software Services, pg 867
Dick Reizner Film & Video, pg 873
RetinaVision Productions, pg 874
RJ Video Productions, pg 875
Staylor-Made Communications Inc,
 pg 900
Tam Communications Inc, pg 906
Twin Peaks Creative, pg 920
West Coast Projections Inc, pg 935
WMS Media Inc, pg 940

COLORADO

Daylight Productions & Rentals,
 pg 739
Rocky Mountain Audio/Video
 Productions Inc, pg 876
Spectrum Audio Visual Services,
 pg 897
Tatum Video, pg 907

CONNECTICUT

Digital Video Productions, pg 742
The Gary-Paul Agency, pg 768
Guymark Studios LLC, pg 775
MAVCO, pg 820
Palace Production Center, pg 850

DISTRICT OF COLUMBIA

Interface Media Group, pg 789

FLORIDA

Access Media Group, pg 673
Applebox Studio, pg 687
Communications Concepts Inc
 (CCI), pg 729
Easy Edit Video Inc, pg 750
Hi-Tech Enterprises Inc, pg 779
Knowles Video Inc (KVI), pg 800
ONstage, pg 846
Sunrise Studios, pg 904
Venice Media Group, pg 925
Video Techniques Inc, pg 928
Vistamax Productions, pg 931

GEORGIA

Beachwood Productions, pg 702
Visioneering International Inc,
 pg 931

IDAHO

KTVB-TV, pg 802

ILLINOIS

Backstar Creative Media Inc,
 pg 700
IV Media Resources, pg 792
Major Media Inc, pg 815
Pepper Group, pg 854
PSAV® Presentation Services
 (Hotel Services Division), pg 866
Tele-Time Systems, pg 910
20/20 Communications Inc, pg 920
Video Impressions, pg 928
WEEK TV, pg 935

INDIANA

Advanced Media Integration, pg 677

IOWA

Duplication Media, pg 748
Educational Technology & Media
 Services, pg 751

KENTUCKY

Audio Visual Techniques Inc,
 pg 695
Barney Miller's Inc, pg 827
WKYT-TV, pg 940

LOUISIANA

Digital FX Inc, pg 742
Louisiana State University Division
 of Strategic Communications,
 pg 811
Moxie Media, pg 832
Vidox Motion Imagery, pg 930
WVLA-TV, pg 942

MAINE

Headlight Audio Visual Inc, pg 777

MARYLAND

Carpel Video Inc, pg 717
CSPMedia.com, pg 735
DBM Communications Inc, pg 739
Spectrum Productions, pg 897

MASSACHUSETTS

Award Productions Inc, pg 699
HOME Inc, pg 781
Small Planet Communications Inc,
 pg 890
TVN-The Video Network, pg 919

MICHIGAN

K&R's Recording Studios Inc,
 pg 796
The Program Source International,
 pg 865
RingSide Creative, pg 875
The Transfer Zone®, pg 917

MINNESOTA

The ADS Group, pg 676
Badiyan Inc, pg 700
GMI Productions, pg 771
Media Loft Inc, pg 822

MISSISSIPPI

Jasper Ewing & Sons Inc, pg 757

MISSOURI

Communitronics Corp, pg 729
Conference Technologies Inc,
 pg 730
Schiller's Audio-Visual, pg 881
Show-Me Audio-Visual, pg 887

NEVADA

Aardvark Video & Media
 Productions, pg 671
DVDs4Less, pg 748
Encore Event Technologies LLC,
 pg 754
JCS Video Productions, pg 793
Peterson's Video Transfer Services,
 pg 855
21st Century Video Productions,
 pg 919

NEW HAMPSHIRE

Apertura, pg 686
Channell One Video, pg 720
The Troupe, pg 918

VIDEO

Transfers—Slide to Video (continued)

NEW JERSEY

AJS Events, pg 679
Broadcast Center Studios, pg 710
Hogpenny Studios, pg 780
Laurel Video Productions, pg 804
Reed Presentations Inc (RPI), pg 872
Suede Interactive, pg 903
VCSvideo, pg 925

NEW MEXICO

30 Second Street Ltd, pg 912

NEW YORK

Ace Video, pg 674
Adwar Video, pg 678
aurora productions, pg 696
The Big House Group, pg 705
Buffalo Video Production, pg 712
Chromavision Corp, pg 723
CMI Communications, pg 727
Colortone Audio Visual, pg 728
Design Audio Visual Inc, pg 741
Digital Art Video Inc, pg 741
DuArt Media Services, pg 747
Duplication Depot Inc, pg 748
Duplication Specialists Inc, pg 748
HAVE Inc, pg 777
J&D Laboratories Inc, pg 793
Long Island Video Enterprises Live Inc, pg 811
Jack Morton Worldwide, pg 830
MRM//McCANN, pg 832
The Palmer Group, pg 850
PostWorks, pg 860
Rafik, pg 869
Teatown Communications Group, pg 908
Visual Technologies Corp, pg 932
Zelman Studios Ltd, pg 945

NORTH CAROLINA

Camcor Inc, pg 715
Duke Media Services, pg 747
On Location North Carolina, pg 846

OHIO

Advent Media Inc, pg 677
Aztec Video Productions, pg 700
Russ Beckner Pictures, pg 703
Cuyahoga Community College Student Production Office (SPO), pg 736
MainSail Production Services Inc, pg 815
Mills James Productions, pg 828
Take 1 Media Services, pg 906
Ungar Video & Film, pg 921
Vista Color Imaging Inc, pg 931

OKLAHOMA

Academic Media & Digital Services, pg 672

OREGON

KPDX-TV Production Center, pg 801
KTVA Productions, pg 802

PENNSYLVANIA

John E Allen Inc, pg 680
Audio Visions Inc, pg 694

Audio Visual Communications Inc, pg 694
Bernie's Photo Center, pg 704
Center City Film & Video Inc, pg 719
FMP Media Solutions Inc, pg 763
Muderick Media, pg 833
The Videohouse Inc, pg 929
Visual Sound Inc, pg 931
WPHL-TV, pg 942

TENNESSEE

Motion Picture Services, pg 831
Stage Post, pg 899
Russ Sturgeon Productions/RSVP, pg 903

TEXAS

Dub King, pg 747
The Editing Co, pg 750
JSAV, pg 795
McNee Productions Inc, pg 821
Replicopy Digital Media Center, pg 873
Romar Learning Solutions LLC, pg 877
The Samuels Co, pg 879
South Coast Film & Video, pg 895
Stage Directions, pg 898
Texas Heart Institute Visual Communication Services, pg 911

VIRGINIA

Advance Concepts Inc, pg 677
BES Studios, pg 704
CVW Event Productions, pg 736
Henninger Media Services, pg 779
Limelight Communications Inc, pg 808

WASHINGTON

Kostov Productions, pg 801

WISCONSIN

Audio Visual of Milwaukee Inc, pg 694
Mirror 34 Productions, pg 828
University of Wisconsin-Oshkosh Radio-TV-Film Dept, pg 923
USAV Group Inc, pg 923
Video Wisconsin Inc, pg 929
Wisconsin Public Television, pg 940

PUERTO RICO

Stage Crew Audiovisual Inc, pg 898

ALBERTA

Cine Audio Visual Sales & Service Ltd, pg 723
Global TV, pg 771

BRITISH COLUMBIA

Commercial Electronics Ltd, pg 728
Triad Communications Ltd, pg 918

ONTARIO

Silver Creek Media Inc, pg 888
Video Excellence Productions, pg 927

QUEBEC

Group PVP, pg 774

Transfers—Videotape to Film

ARIZONA

Merestone, pg 823
On-Site Video, pg 846
Star Video Duplicating, pg 900

CALIFORNIA

All Video Productions, pg 680
Artichoke Productions, pg 690
Havas Edge, pg 777
iCorpTv, pg 783
ITV Productions, pg 792
QRS Software Services, pg 867
RetinaVision Productions, pg 874
Roundabout Entertainment Inc, pg 878
SonicPool, pg 892

CONNECTICUT

MAVCO, pg 820

GEORGIA

Cinema Concepts, pg 724

INDIANA

Gary Camera & Digital, pg 768

LOUISIANA

Digital FX Inc, pg 742

MARYLAND

Kramer Communications Video Production, pg 801

MASSACHUSETTS

CommCreative, pg 728

MICHIGAN

K&R's Recording Studios Inc, pg 796
The Transfer Zone®, pg 917

NEVADA

JCS Video Productions, pg 793

NEW HAMPSHIRE

Apertura, pg 686

NEW JERSEY

AJS Events, pg 679
Broadcast Center Studios, pg 710
Suede Interactive, pg 903
Video Corporation of America (VCA), pg 927

NEW YORK

Adwar Video, pg 678
aurora productions, pg 696
DuArt Media Services, pg 747
HAVE Inc, pg 777
Jack Morton Worldwide, pg 830
The Palmer Group, pg 850
PostWorks, pg 860
Zelman Studios Ltd, pg 945

OHIO

Aztec Video Productions, pg 700

PENNSYLVANIA

Audio Visual Communications Inc, pg 694
Bernie's Photo Center, pg 704

FMP Media Solutions Inc, pg 763
Muderick Media, pg 833

TENNESSEE

Motion Picture Services, pg 831
Stage Post, pg 899

WISCONSIN

Audio Visual of Milwaukee Inc, pg 694
Video Wisconsin Inc, pg 929

ALBERTA

Cine Audio Visual Sales & Service Ltd, pg 723
Global TV, pg 771

ONTARIO

Silver Creek Media Inc, pg 888

Underwater Photography, see Photography—Underwater

VCR, see Videocassette Recorder & Player

Video Camera Distributors

ALABAMA

Curtis Company, pg 736

ARIZONA

EAR Professional Audio/Video, pg 749
Projector SuperStore LLC, pg 865
Tempe Camera, pg 910

CALIFORNIA

AbelCine, pg 672
Advanced Systems Group LLC, pg 677
Ametron Audio/Video, pg 684
Assured Audio Visual, pg 691
Audio/Video Supply Inc, pg 694
AV Conferencing LLC (AVC), pg 697
Band Pro Film & Digital Inc, pg 701
Barber Tech Video Products, pg 701
Be Media, pg 702
BigFoot Mobile Systems, pg 705
BroadcastStore.com, pg 711
Christy's Editorial, pg 723
Cibola Systems, pg 723
Computer Modules Inc, pg 729
Diaquest, pg 741
Educational Technology Services (ETS), pg 751
Gluskin's Custom Audio Video, pg 771
Alan Gordon Enterprises Inc, pg 772
Gravity Media, pg 773
Hooper Camera & Imaging, pg 781
Innovision Optics, pg 788
Inter Video, pg 789
Jameco Electronics, pg 792
JD Audio Visual Inc, pg 793
Kappa optronics Inc, pg 796
Marshall Electronics Inc, pg 817
MediaPOINTE, pg 823
Nortek Security & Control LLC, pg 842
Optronics®, pg 847

Photo-Sonics Inc, pg 856
Photodyne Technologies, pg 856
PMP Marketing Inc, pg 858
Promax Systems, pg 865
SNAP, pg 891
Sound Service Co, pg 894
Southern California Sound Image Inc, pg 895
SSL Industries Inc, pg 898
Videobotics, pg 929
VMI Inc, pg 932

COLORADO

Daylight Productions & Rentals, pg 739
G W Hannaway & Associates, pg 775
Spectrum Audio Visual Services, pg 897

FLORIDA

Access Media Group, pg 673
Altel Systems Group Inc, pg 682
A2D Solutions Inc, pg 692
AVI-SPL, pg 698
Digital Video Systems, pg 742
Encore Broadcast Solutions, pg 754
Enhanced View Services Inc, pg 754
Glanz Technologies Inc, pg 771
Harmon's Audio-Visual Services, pg 776
Harris Corp, pg 776
Hi-Tech Enterprises Inc, pg 779
Hi-Tech Import Export Corp, pg 779
Midtown Video Inc, pg 827
ONstage, pg 846
Recording Media & Equipment Inc (RM&E), pg 872
Reef Photo & Video, pg 872

GEORGIA

Baker Audio Visual, pg 700
Innocinema, pg 788
Stage Front Presentation Systems, pg 899
WolfVision Inc, pg 940

HAWAII

The Audio Visual Co (AVCO), pg 694

ILLINOIS

Allen Visual Systems Inc, pg 680
Cool-Lux, pg 731
RC Communications, pg 870

INDIANA

Lee Co Inc, pg 805
Sensory Technologies LLC, pg 884
SHP Electronics, pg 887

KENTUCKY

Axxis Leasing Inc, pg 700
Barney Miller's Inc, pg 827
NOR-COM Inc, pg 841

MARYLAND

Noventri, pg 843
Siqura Inc, pg 889

MASSACHUSETTS

Antronics Inc, pg 686
Hunt's Photo & Video, pg 782
Integrated Solutions Group, pg 789
Rule Boston Camera, pg 878

MICHIGAN

ASC Systems, pg 690
On Stage Visuals, pg 846
TEL Systems LLC, pg 909

MINNESOTA

Alpha Video & Audio Inc, pg 682
Vaddio, pg 924

MISSISSIPPI

Bowie Audio Visual Enterprises Inc, pg 709

MISSOURI

Communitronics Corp, pg 729
Conference Technologies Inc, pg 730
Modern Communications Inc, pg 828
Schiller's Audio-Visual, pg 881
Southwest Audio-Visual Inc, pg 895

NEBRASKA

ATV Research Inc, pg 692
VSA Inc, pg 933

NEVADA

Aardvark Video & Media Productions, pg 671

NEW JERSEY

A-V Services Inc, pg 671
Advanced Imaging Concepts Inc, pg 677
Alltec Stores, a Vcom IMC Company, pg 681
AlltecPro, pg 681
AV Bluebook, pg 696
Avtech Systems Inc, pg 699
Diversified, pg 744
Earl Girls Inc, pg 749
Entel Systems Inc, pg 754
Euro-Pacific Film & Video Productions Inc, pg 756
G&G Technologies Inc, pg 768
HamiltonBuhl, pg 775
MCCOM Inc, pg 820
PatchAmp, pg 852
Starlite, pg 900
SYMCO Inc, pg 905
Tele-Measurements Inc, pg 910
Total Video Products Inc, pg 916
Varto Technologies, pg 925
Yorktel, pg 944
ZGC Inc, pg 945

NEW YORK

All Mobile Video Inc, pg 680
American Video Inc, pg 684
Audio-Video Corp, pg 694
AV Workshop, pg 697
B&H Photo Video, pg 701
Colortone Audio Visual, pg 728
Design Audio Visual Inc, pg 741
KVL Audio Visual Services Inc, pg 802
Long Island Video Enterprises Live Inc, pg 811
Markertek Video Supply, pg 817
Neptune Photo Inc, pg 838
RNJ Electronics, pg 875
Scientifics Direct Inc, pg 882
TecNec Distributing, pg 909
Tri-Ed Distribution Inc, pg 918
Unitron Ltd, pg 921
Videoguys, pg 929
Vision Identics Systems Inc, pg 930
Visual Word Systems Inc, pg 932

OHIO

Copp Integrated Systems, pg 731
ITA Audio Visual Solutions, pg 791
Midwest Photo Exchange, pg 827
Tri-State Audio Visual Co, pg 918
Visual Products Inc, pg 931

OKLAHOMA

Ford AV, pg 763

OREGON

FLIR Systems Inc, pg 762

PENNSYLVANIA

Advanced AV LLC, pg 677
Audio Visions Inc, pg 694
Bernie's Photo Center, pg 704
Brodart Co, pg 711
Clair Companies, pg 725
J E Foss Co, pg 764
Grise Audio Visual Center Inc, pg 774
Innovision Media Group, pg 788
The Lerro Corp, pg 806
Morefield Communications Inc, pg 830
New York Camera & Video, pg 840
Questar Corp, pg 868
Visual Sound Inc, pg 931
Wespen Audio Visual Co, pg 935

TENNESSEE

Lowrance Sound Co Inc, pg 812
Technical Support Systems LLC, pg 908

TEXAS

AVES Audio Visual Systems Inc, pg 698
Biway Media, pg 706
CAM Audio Inc, pg 714
Data Projections Inc, pg 738
Digital Display Solutions Inc, pg 742
Graftek Imaging Inc, pg 773
Heffernan Audio Visual, pg 778
IVS Imaging, pg 792
Omega Broadcast Group, pg 845
Precision Camera & Video, pg 861
Pro Video & Film Equipment Co Inc, pg 863
Quality Audio Visual Service Inc, pg 867
Supercircuits, pg 904
Tarpley Media Systems, pg 907
Videotex Systems Inc, pg 930

UTAH

Performance Audio LLC, pg 854
RIA Corp, pg 874

VIRGINIA

Avitecture Inc, pg 699
Boitnott Visual Communications Corp (BVC), pg 708
Intellidyne LLC, pg 789
Lee Hartman & Sons Inc, pg 805
Quince Imaging Inc, pg 868
The Whitlock Group, pg 937

WASHINGTON

CCI Solutions, pg 718
Oppenheimer Camera Products, pg 847
ToteVision, pg 916

WISCONSIN

Audio Visual of Milwaukee Inc, pg 694
Camera Corner Connecting Point, pg 715
Full Compass Systems, pg 767
Safe Harbor Computers, pg 879

ALBERTA

Matrix Video Communications Corp (MVCC), pg 819
McBain Camera Ltd, pg 820

BRITISH COLUMBIA

Commercial Electronics Ltd, pg 728

MANITOBA

Advance Pro, pg 677
Inland Audio Visual Ltd, pg 788

ONTARIO

Cinema Stage Inc, pg 724
HD Source, pg 777
Henry's Camera, pg 779
L-3 WESCAM, pg 802
Majortech Inc, pg 815
Nationwide Audio Visual Co, pg 837

QUEBEC

Panavideo Inc, pg 850

Video Camera Manufacturers

CALIFORNIA

CohuHD Costar LLC, pg 727
Jerry Hill Steadicam Products, pg 780
Innovision Optics, pg 788
Jai Inc, pg 792
Kappa optronics Inc, pg 796
Marshall Electronics Inc, pg 817
Nortek Security & Control LLC, pg 842
Optronics®, pg 847
Photo-Sonics Inc, pg 856
Recortec Inc, pg 872
Sony Electronics Inc, pg 893
Visionary Solutions Inc, pg 931

GEORGIA

WolfVision Inc, pg 940

ILLINOIS

EPIX Inc, pg 755
FJW Optical Systems Inc, pg 762

MARYLAND

Siqura Inc, pg 889

MINNESOTA

Bosch Security Systems Inc, pg 709
Vaddio, pg 924

MISSOURI

Ken-A-Vision Manufacturing Co Inc, pg 797

NEW JERSEY

Ikegami Electronics (USA) Inc, pg 784
JVC Professional Products Co, pg 796

VIDEO

Video Camera Manufacturers (continued)

NEW YORK

Hitachi Kokusai Electric America Ltd, pg 780
Lenel Systems International Inc, pg 806
Vicon Industries Inc, pg 926

NORTH CAROLINA

Crest Electronics Inc, pg 734

OREGON

FLIR Systems Inc, pg 762

PENNSYLVANIA

MicroImage Video Systems, pg 826

TEXAS

IVS Imaging, pg 792

VIRGINIA

Charles A Hulcher Co Inc, pg 782
Quince Imaging Inc, pg 868

WASHINGTON

Aiphone Corp, pg 678
ToteVision, pg 916

BRITISH COLUMBIA

Triad Communications Ltd, pg 918

ONTARIO

PixeLINK, pg 857
Teledyne DALSA Inc, pg 910

QUEBEC

Grass Valley, pg 773

Video Camera Rentals

ALASKA

Connections Film & Video Inc, pg 731

ARIZONA

AV Concepts Inc, pg 696
Broadcast Rentals, pg 711
Creative Backstage, pg 733
Crew West Inc, pg 734
Loft 19, pg 811
Merestone, pg 823
Metropolitan Audio-Visual Inc, pg 824
Tempe Camera, pg 910
Ultimate Presentation Systems Inc, pg 920
Video West Inc, pg 929

ARKANSAS

White Diamond Productions LLC, pg 937

CALIFORNIA

AbelCine, pg 672
Absolute Rentals, pg 672
Action Audio & Visual, pg 675
Advanced Media LLC, pg 677
AGF Media Services, pg 678

Alliant Event Services, pg 681
Alternative Rentals, pg 682
Ametron Audio/Video, pg 684
Artichoke Productions, pg 690
Assured Audio Visual, pg 691
ATV Video Center Inc, pg 692
AV Conferencing LLC (AVC), pg 697
AV Guys, pg 697
Barber Tech Video Products, pg 701
Bexel, an NEP Broadcast Services Company, pg 704
Big Door, pg 705
BigFoot Mobile Systems, pg 705
Blue Lotus Temple Studio, pg 707
BroadcastStore.com, pg 711
The Camera Division, pg 715
Chater Camera Inc, pg 721
Cherry Multimedia, pg 721
Cinema Camera Rentals, pg 723
Clean Slate Video, pg 726
Crash Video Productions, pg 733
Crystal Pyramid Productions™, pg 735
Deck Hand Inc, pg 740
Digital Studios LLC, pg 742
The Dreaming Tree, pg 746
Dystopian Studios, pg 748
Express Media Inc, pg 757
Express Video Supply Inc, pg 757
First Camera, pg 761
FJ Productions Inc, pg 762
Flip 2 Media Inc, pg 762
Full Moon & High Tide Productions & Studios, pg 767
Gear Monkey, pg 769
Glendale Production Center, pg 771
Gluskin's Custom Audio Video, pg 771
Goal Productions, pg 772
Gold Standard Productions, pg 772
Golden Gate Studios, pg 772
Alan Gordon Enterprises Inc, pg 772
Gravity Media, pg 773
Greenery Studios, pg 774
HD Cinema, pg 777
HDrental.com, pg 777
iCorpTv, pg 783
Illuminate Studios, pg 784
Image Integration, pg 785
Imagecraft Productions, pg 785
Images in Motion Media Inc, pg 785
Innovision Optics, pg 788
Inter Video, pg 789
JD Audio Visual Inc, pg 793
JFA Studio, pg 794
Loyal Studios, pg 812
Lynch Communications, pg 813
Main Street Media Inc, pg 815
Maximus Media Inc, pg 820
McCune Audio-Video-Lighting, pg 821
MSI Production Services, pg 832
Munday & Collins AV, pg 834
New Circuit Films LLC, pg 839
Next Arts, pg 841
North County Media Center, pg 842
Old School Cameras, pg 844
Photo Film Stage, pg 856
Pollution Studios, pg 859
Prime Cut Productions, pg 862
Pro HD Rentals, pg 863
Production Gear Rentals (PGR), pg 863
PSAV® Presentation Services, pg 866
Radiant Images, pg 869
RetinaVision Productions, pg 874
Shooting Star Video, pg 886
Shoulder High Productions, pg 886
SNAP, pg 891

Sound Service Co, pg 894
Stray Angel Films, pg 902
Studio 637, pg 903
The Studios at Paramount, pg 903
T-stop Inc, pg 906
Total Creative, pg 916
Twin Peaks Creative, pg 920
VER, pg 926
Videofax, pg 929
VMI Inc, pg 932
Voice & Video Rentals, pg 932
Warner Bros Entertainment Inc, pg 934
Warner Bros Production Sound & Video Services, pg 934
Westcoast Video Productions Inc, pg 936
Z-Ville Productions, pg 944

COLORADO

Daylight Productions & Rentals, pg 739
Denver Media Center, pg 740
Open Media Foundation, pg 846
Spectrum Audio Visual Services, pg 897
Tatum Video, pg 907
Zelo Productions Inc, pg 945

CONNECTICUT

A/V Davey, pg 697
Digital Video Productions, pg 742
Presence Studios, pg 861
Videofilm Systems Inc, pg 929

DELAWARE

Cornerstone Media Productions Inc, pg 731
Ken-Del Productions Inc, pg 797
Showorks Audio Visual Inc, pg 887

DISTRICT OF COLUMBIA

Future View Inc, pg 767
Metro Teleproductions Inc (MTI), pg 824

FLORIDA

Access Media Group, pg 673
Accord Productions, pg 673
All Comm Rentals Inc (ALLCOMM), pg 680
Astoria Communications Inc, pg 691
AVI-SPL, pg 698
Budget Video Rentals, pg 712
C&I An Idea Agency, pg 716
CopShopMiami.com, pg 731
Digital Zoetrope Productions, pg 742
Facet Media, pg 758
Glanz Technologies Inc, pg 771
Harmon's Audio-Visual Services, pg 776
HD House, pg 777
Hi-Tech Enterprises Inc, pg 779
Industrial Strength Inc, pg 787
Knowles Video Inc (KVI), pg 800
Midtown Video Inc, pg 827
Moving Picture, pg 831
ONstage, pg 846
Paradise Show & Design Inc, pg 851
PRI Productions, pg 862
Sight & Sound Productions, pg 887
Universal Studios Florida® Production Group, pg 922
Mike Vasilinda Productions Inc, pg 925

GEORGIA

ECG Productions, pg 750
Lighting & Production Equipment Inc, pg 807
MAGNUM Companies Ltd, pg 815
ON Services, a GES Company, pg 846
See Production Services, pg 883
Stage Front Presentation Systems, pg 899

HAWAII

Sight & Sound Studios, pg 887

ILLINOIS

Allen Visual Systems Inc, pg 680
Atomic Imaging Inc/Golan Studios, pg 692
AV Chicago Inc, pg 696
Backstar Creative Media Inc, pg 700
Beatty TeleVisual Productions, pg 703
Creative Technology (CT), pg 733
Firehouse Studios, pg 761
LITE-IT Grip Truck Rentals, pg 810
Magnanimous Media, pg 814
RC Communications, pg 870
Resolution Productions Group, pg 874
SCI Television & Creative Media LLC, pg 882
2nd Cine Inc, pg 883
Staging Resources Inc, pg 899
Tele-Time Systems, pg 910
Zacuto, pg 945

IOWA

Pro Video, pg 863

KANSAS

Lights On, pg 808

KENTUCKY

Audio Visual Techniques Inc, pg 695
Idle Minds Productions Inc, pg 784
Kentucky Grip & Lighting, pg 798

LOUISIANA

Clark Services Audio Visual & Exhibit Inc, pg 725
Digital FX Inc, pg 742
Moxie Media, pg 832

MAINE

University of Maine Media Services, pg 922

MARYLAND

Advance Audiovisual Presentation Ltd, pg 677
Archai Media, pg 688
CPR MultiMedia Solutions, pg 732
Event Tech, pg 756
Kramer Communications Video Production, pg 801

MASSACHUSETTS

AVFX Inc, pg 698
Green Mountain Post Films (GMP), pg 774
Integrated Solutions Group, pg 789
massAV, pg 819
Preston Productions Inc, pg 861
Small Planet Communications Inc, pg 890

MICHIGAN

Digi Sign Design LLC, pg 741
K&R All Media Productions LLC,
    pg 796
K&R's Recording Studios Inc,
    pg 796
On Stage Visuals, pg 846
TEL Systems LLC, pg 909

MINNESOTA

Alpha Video & Audio Inc, pg 682
Big Event Productions LLC, pg 705
House of Cinemagraphics, pg 782
Pro Media Productions, pg 863

MISSISSIPPI

Bowie Audio Visual Enterprises Inc,
    pg 709

MISSOURI

Communitronics Corp, pg 729
Schiller's Audio-Visual, pg 881
Show-Me Audio-Visual, pg 887
Southwest Audio-Visual Inc, pg 895
Switch, pg 905

MONTANA

Filmlites Montana, pg 760

NEBRASKA

Dog & Pony Productions Inc,
    pg 744
Lights On Nebraska, pg 808

NEVADA

GES Audio Visual, pg 770
JCS Video Productions, pg 793
Lefco Video Services Inc, pg 806
MG Studio, pg 825

NEW JERSEY

Audio Visual Dynamics®, pg 694
CFP Video Productions Inc, pg 720
Earl Girls Inc, pg 749
Euro-Pacific Film & Video
    Productions Inc, pg 756
G&G Technologies Inc, pg 768
International Audio Visual Inc,
    pg 790
MB Productions, pg 820
PLS Staging, pg 858
Starlite, pg 900
Tele-Measurements Inc, pg 910
Video Corporation of America
    (VCA), pg 927

NEW MEXICO

Production Outfitters, pg 864

NEW YORK

Adorama Rental Co, pg 676
Air Sea Land Productions Inc
    (ASL), pg 678
All Mobile Video Inc, pg 680
American Video Inc, pg 684
AV Workshop, pg 697
Big Apple Films, pg 705
Big Foot Productions Inc, pg 705
Bond Street Studio, pg 708
Cinema-Vision, pg 724
Colortone Audio Visual, pg 728
CP Communications, pg 732
CSI Rentals, pg 735
Design Audio Visual, pg 741
Gearhead Rentals, pg 769
Hand Held Films, pg 775
HB-Content, pg 777

Hello World Communications,
    pg 778
KVL Audio Visual Services Inc,
    pg 802
LightHouse Films, pg 807
LightSpace Studios, pg 808
Long Island Video Enterprises Live
    Inc, pg 811
Manhattan Center Studios Inc,
    pg 816
Production Central, pg 863
Scheimpflug Digital, pg 881
The Visual Studies Workshop
    (VSW), pg 931
Visual Word Systems Inc, pg 932
WNET/New York Public Media,
    pg 940

NORTH CAROLINA

All Pro Media Inc, pg 680
AV Connections Inc, pg 697
AV Metro Inc, pg 697
The Communications Group Inc,
    pg 729
Digital Rain LLC, pg 742
Duke Media Services, pg 747
Moving Pictures, pg 832
On Location North Carolina, pg 846
Special Event Services, pg 896
Take One Productions Ltd, pg 906
Videowerks, pg 930

NORTH DAKOTA

Media Productions, pg 822

OHIO

Hughie's Event Production Services,
    pg 782
ITA Audio Visual Solutions, pg 791
Lyon Video Inc, pg 813
Mills James Productions, pg 828
Ohio HD Video, pg 844
OSV Studios, pg 848
R&B Communications Inc, pg 870

OKLAHOMA

PDC Productions, pg 852

OREGON

Koerner Camera Systems, pg 800
Northwest Film Center, pg 842
Picture This Production Services,
    pg 856

PENNSYLVANIA

Advanced AV LLC, pg 677
Argentine Productions Inc, pg 688
Audio Visions Inc, pg 694
Audio Visual Communications Inc,
    pg 694
Bang! Pictures Inc, pg 701
FirstGeneration Audio/Visual
    Services, pg 761
FMP Media Solutions Inc, pg 763
Grise Audio Visual Center Inc,
    pg 774
Innovision Media Group, pg 788
JPL, pg 795
Location Camera Ltd, pg 810
Muderick Media, pg 833
New York Camera & Video, pg 840
Producers Management Television
    (PMTV), pg 863
Upstage Video, pg 923
The Videohouse Inc, pg 929
Viewpoint Production Services Inc,
    pg 930
Visual Sound Inc, pg 931

SOUTH CAROLINA

Impact Technology Group LLC,
    pg 786

TENNESSEE

Nashville Production Rentals
    (NPR), pg 836
NuMynd Studios, pg 843
RentACamera.com, pg 873
Russ Sturgeon Productions/RSVP,
    pg 903
Technical Support Systems LLC,
    pg 908

TEXAS

Alford Media Services, pg 680
Big House Sound Inc, pg 705
Countdown Productions Inc, pg 732
GEAR Cameras & Lighting, pg 769
Media Event Concepts Inc, pg 822
Mediaforce Productions, pg 822
Earl Miller Productions, pg 827
Omega Broadcast Group, pg 845
Phillips Media Source, pg 855
Precision Camera & Video, pg 861
South Coast Film & Video, pg 895
Stage Directions, pg 898
Texcam Inc, pg 911
Video Perspective, pg 928

UTAH

Ron Hill Imagery, pg 780

VERMONT

Dark Star Lighting & Production,
    pg 737

VIRGINIA

Advance Concepts Inc, pg 677
Audio Visual Actions Inc (AVA),
    pg 694
Boitnott Visual Communications
    Corp (BVC), pg 708
CVW Event Productions, pg 736
Lee Hartman & Sons Inc, pg 805
Quince Imaging Inc, pg 868
StageSound, pg 899
The Whitlock Group, pg 937

WASHINGTON

The House Studios, pg 782
Kostov Productions, pg 801
Oppenheimer Camera Products,
    pg 847
Victory Studios, pg 927

WEST VIRGINIA

Blackwater Video Productions,
    pg 707

WISCONSIN

Audio Visual of Milwaukee Inc,
    pg 694
Camera Corner Connecting Point,
    pg 715
Event Essentials, pg 756
Full Compass Systems, pg 767
Logan Productions Inc, pg 811
MKE Production Rental, pg 828

WYOMING

Bridger Productions Inc, pg 710

PUERTO RICO

Stage Crew Audiovisual Inc, pg 898

ALBERTA

Allstar Show Industries Inc, pg 681
Evolution AV, pg 757
Matrix Video Communications Corp
    (MVCC), pg 819
Unique Communications Ltd,
    pg 921

BRITISH COLUMBIA

Clark's Audio Visual Services Ltd,
    pg 725
Commercial Electronics Ltd, pg 728
Video Out Distribution, pg 928

MANITOBA

Inland Audio Visual Ltd, pg 788
MidCanada Production Services Inc
    (MidCan), pg 826

ONTARIO

GAPC (General Assembly
    Production Centre), pg 768
HD Source, pg 777
JIB Shots Equipment Inc, pg 794
L-3 WESCAM, pg 802
Metalworks Recording Studios Inc,
    pg 824
RB Productions, pg 870
SIM Digital, pg 888
William F White International Inc,
    pg 937

QUEBEC

Audio Visual Dynamics, pg 694
Freeman Audio Visual, pg 765
Group PVP, pg 774
Panavideo Inc, pg 850

Video Camera Repairs

ARIZONA

Tempe Camera, pg 910

CALIFORNIA

Advanced Media LLC, pg 677
Ametron Audio/Video, pg 684
Band Pro Film & Digital Inc,
    pg 701
BigFoot Mobile Systems, pg 705
BroadcastStore.com, pg 711
Effective Engineering Inc, pg 751
Gluskin's Custom Audio Video,
    pg 771
Kappa optronics Inc, pg 796
McAlister Electronics, pg 820
Pro Camera Repair, pg 862
SSL Industries Inc, pg 898
Technical Services, pg 908
TEK Media Group, pg 909
VMI Inc, pg 932

COLORADO

Mike's Camera, pg 827

CONNECTICUT

A/V Davey, pg 697
Precision Camera & Video Repair
    Inc, pg 861

FLORIDA

Digital Video Systems, pg 742
ELC Sales & Service Inc, pg 752
Glanz Technologies Inc, pg 771
Hi-Tech Enterprises Inc, pg 779
Midtown Video Inc, pg 827

VIDEO

Video Camera Repairs (continued)

GEORGIA

Stage Front Presentation Systems, pg 899

ILLINOIS

Allen Visual Systems Inc, pg 680
Beatty TeleVisual Productions, pg 703
Midwest Digital Corp, pg 827
RC Communications, pg 870

KENTUCKY

Axxis Leasing Inc, pg 700
Barney Miller's Inc, pg 827
NOR-COM Inc, pg 841

MARYLAND

Noventri, pg 843

MASSACHUSETTS

Antronics Inc, pg 686
Integrated Solutions Group, pg 789

MICHIGAN

TEL Systems LLC, pg 909

MINNESOTA

Alpha Video & Audio Inc, pg 682

MISSOURI

Communitronics Corp, pg 729
Schiller's Audio-Visual, pg 881
Southwest Audio-Visual Inc, pg 895

NEW JERSEY

Entel Systems Inc, pg 754

OHIO

Copp Integrated Systems, pg 731
ITA Audio Visual Solutions, pg 791
Tri-State Audio Visual Co, pg 918

OREGON

FLIR Systems Inc, pg 762

PENNSYLVANIA

Audio Visions Inc, pg 694
Bernie's Photo Center, pg 704
Visual Sound Inc, pg 931

TENNESSEE

Technical Support Systems LLC, pg 908

TEXAS

Pro Video & Film Equipment Co Inc, pg 863
Quality Audio Visual Service Inc, pg 867
Tarpley Media Systems, pg 907

UTAH

RIA Corp, pg 874

VIRGINIA

Lee Hartman & Sons Inc, pg 805
Quince Imaging Inc, pg 868
The Whitlock Group, pg 937

WASHINGTON

Aiphone Corp, pg 678

WISCONSIN

Camera Corner Connecting Point, pg 715
Full Compass Systems, pg 767

ALBERTA

Matrix Video Communications Corp (MVCC), pg 819

BRITISH COLUMBIA

Commercial Electronics Ltd, pg 728

MANITOBA

Inland Audio Visual Ltd, pg 788

ONTARIO

HD Source, pg 777

QUEBEC

Panavideo Inc, pg 850

Video Presentation System Distributors

ALABAMA

CMEinfo™, pg 727
Curtis Company, pg 736

ARIZONA

EAR Professional Audio/Video, pg 749

ARKANSAS

Jay S Stanley & Associates Inc, pg 899

CALIFORNIA

Advanced Systems Group LLC, pg 677
AITech International, pg 679
Ametron Audio/Video, pg 684
Audio/Video Supply Inc, pg 694
AV Conferencing LLC (AVC), pg 697
Band Pro Film & Digital Inc, pg 701
Be Media, pg 702
Christy's Editorial, pg 723
Educational Technology Services (ETS), pg 751
Electrosonic Inc, pg 752
JD Audio Visual Inc, pg 793
Media Fabricators Inc, pg 822
Muse Presentation Technologies, pg 834
PMP Marketing Inc, pg 858
Promax Systems, pg 865
Sonance, pg 892
Southern California Sound Image Inc, pg 895
SSL Industries Inc, pg 898
Stanislaus AV Inc, pg 899
SuperVision, pg 904
VMI Inc, pg 932

COLORADO

Daylight Productions & Rentals, pg 739
Spectrum Audio Visual Services, pg 897

CONNECTICUT

MAVCO, pg 820
The Video Messenger Co, pg 928

FLORIDA

Access Media Group, pg 673
Altel Systems Group Inc, pg 682
AVI-SPL, pg 698
Digital Video Systems, pg 742
Harmon's Audio-Visual Services, pg 776
Hi-Tech Import Export Corp, pg 779
Industrial Strength Inc, pg 787
Midtown Video Inc, pg 827
ONstage, pg 846
Tallahassee Audio Visual, pg 906
Vela Research, pg 925

GEORGIA

Baker Audio Visual, pg 700
Barco Inc, pg 701
Stage Front Presentation Systems, pg 899
WolfVision Inc, pg 940

ILLINOIS

Allen Visual Systems Inc, pg 680
Tele-Time Systems, pg 910
Zenith Electronics LLC, pg 945

INDIANA

Lee Co Inc, pg 805
Sensory Technologies LLC, pg 884
SHP Electronics, pg 887

KENTUCKY

Axxis Leasing Inc, pg 700
Creative Realities Inc (CRI), pg 733
Barney Miller's Inc, pg 827
NOR-COM Inc, pg 841

LOUISIANA

Techkno Integration & Design Services LLC, pg 908

MAINE

Headlight Audio Visual Inc, pg 777

MARYLAND

Human Circuit, pg 782

MASSACHUSETTS

General Electric Co, pg 769
Integrated Solutions Group, pg 789
Pro AV Systems, pg 862
Rule Boston Camera, pg 878

MICHIGAN

ASC Systems, pg 690
Digi Sign Design LLC, pg 741
Michigan Office Solutions (MOS), A Xerox Company, pg 825
TEL Systems LLC, pg 909

MINNESOTA

Alpha Video & Audio Inc, pg 682

MISSISSIPPI

Bowie Audio Visual Enterprises Inc, pg 709

MISSOURI

Communitronics Corp, pg 729
Conference Technologies Inc, pg 730
Southwest Audio-Visual Inc, pg 895

NEVADA

Aardvark Video & Media Productions, pg 671

NEW HAMPSHIRE

Optics 1 Inc, pg 847

NEW JERSEY

A-V Services Inc, pg 671
Advanced Imaging Concepts Inc, pg 677
AlltecPro, pg 681
AV Bluebook, pg 696
Avtech Systems Inc, pg 699
Color Leasing Studios, pg 727
Diversified, pg 744
Earl Girls Inc, pg 749
HamiltonBuhl, pg 775
MCCOM, pg 820
MiB MediaWorks, pg 825
Starlite, pg 900
SYMCO Inc, pg 905
Tele-Measurements Inc, pg 910
Total Video Products Inc, pg 916
Yorktel, pg 944

NEW YORK

Ace Video, pg 674
Audio-Video Corp, pg 694
AV Workshop, pg 697
Colortone Audio Visual, pg 728
Crescendo Designs Inc, pg 734
Design Audio Visual Inc, pg 741
eMagin Corp, pg 753
KVL Audio Visual Services Inc, pg 802
Long Island Video Enterprises Live Inc, pg 811
Markertek Video Supply, pg 817
Neptune Photo Inc, pg 838
Presentation Products Inc, pg 861
Tri-Ed Distribution Inc, pg 918
Visual Word Systems Inc, pg 932

NORTH CAROLINA

Strategic Connections, pg 901

OHIO

Copp Integrated Systems, pg 731
ITA Audio Visual Solutions, pg 791
iVideo Technologies, pg 792
Tri-State Audio Visual Co, pg 918

OKLAHOMA

Ford AV, pg 763

PENNSYLVANIA

AccuWeather Inc, pg 674
Advanced AV LLC, pg 677
Audio Visions Inc, pg 694
Grise Audio Visual Center Inc, pg 774
The Lerro Corp, pg 806
Morefield Communications Inc, pg 830
Vistacom Inc, pg 931
Visual Sound Inc, pg 931
Wespen Audio Visual Co, pg 935

RHODE ISLAND

Shanix Inc, pg 885

TENNESSEE

Allstar Audio Systems Inc, pg 681
Lowrance Sound Co Inc, pg 812
Technical Support Systems LLC, pg 908

TEXAS

Audio Visual Technologies Group (AVTG), pg 695
AVES Audio Visual Systems Inc, pg 698
Biway Media, pg 706
Digital Display Solutions Inc, pg 742
Heffernan Audio Visual, pg 778
Tarpley Media Systems, pg 907

UTAH

RIA Corp, pg 874

VIRGINIA

Avitecture Inc, pg 699
Boitnott Visual Communications Corp (BVC), pg 708
Intellidyne LLC, pg 789
Lee Hartman & Sons Inc, pg 805
Quince Imaging Inc, pg 868
The Whitlock Group, pg 937

WASHINGTON

Macrosystem US Inc, pg 814
ToteVision, pg 916

WISCONSIN

Audio Visual of Milwaukee Inc, pg 694
Camera Corner Connecting Point, pg 715
Full Compass Systems, pg 767

ALBERTA

Evolution AV, pg 757
Genesis Integration, pg 769
Infosat Communications Inc, pg 787
Matrix Video Communications Corp (MVCC), pg 819

MANITOBA

Advance Pro, pg 677
Inland Audio Visual Ltd, pg 788

ONTARIO

Cinema Stage Inc, pg 724
HD Source, pg 777
Nationwide Audio Visual Co, pg 837
Technovision® Interactive Inc, pg 909
Westbury National Show Systems Ltd, pg 936

QUEBEC

Panavideo Inc, pg 850

Video Presentation System Manufacturers

ARIZONA

Boeckeler Instruments Inc, pg 708

CALIFORNIA

AITech International, pg 679
Extron Electronics, pg 758
Jupiter Systems, pg 795

Pioneer Electronics (USA) Inc, pg 857
RGB Spectrum, pg 874
Sonance, pg 892
Sony Electronics Inc, pg 893
Tatung Co of America Inc, pg 907

CONNECTICUT

The Video Messenger Co, pg 928

FLORIDA

Pangolin Laser Systems Inc, pg 851
Vela Research, pg 925
Vutec Corp, pg 933

GEORGIA

Barco Inc, pg 701
Visix™ Inc, pg 931
WolfVision Inc, pg 940

ILLINOIS

Dukane Corp, Audio Visual Products Division, pg 747
NEC Display Solutions of America, pg 837

INDIANA

Da-Lite, a Legrand AV Inc brand, pg 737
Draper Inc, pg 746

KANSAS

Keywest Technology Inc, pg 798

MARYLAND

Absolute Hollywood, pg 672

MASSACHUSETTS

Elite Video Inc, pg 753
General Electric Co, pg 769

MICHIGAN

ASC Systems, pg 690

MINNESOTA

Dotronix Technology Inc, pg 746
Vaddio, pg 924

MISSOURI

Ken-A-Vision Manufacturing Co Inc, pg 797

NEVADA

Keystone View, pg 798

NEW HAMPSHIRE

Optics 1 Inc, pg 847

NEW JERSEY

AlltecPro, pg 681
FSR Inc, pg 766
Sharp Electronics Corp, Professional Display Division, pg 885

NEW YORK

eMagin Corp, pg 753
Navitar Inc, pg 837

OHIO

TV One Multimedia Solutions, pg 919

PENNSYLVANIA

AccuWeather Inc, pg 674

TENNESSEE

Adtec Digital Inc, pg 677

TEXAS

Contemporary Research, pg 731

VIRGINIA

Quince Imaging Inc, pg 868

WASHINGTON

Macrosystem US Inc, pg 814
ToteVision, pg 916

BRITISH COLUMBIA

Triad Communications Ltd, pg 918

ONTARIO

Evertz Microsystems Ltd, pg 757

Video Presentation System Rentals

ALABAMA

Audio-Video Resources Inc, pg 694

ARIZONA

Creative Backstage, pg 733
Merestone, pg 823
Metropolitan Audio-Visual Inc, pg 824

ARKANSAS

White Diamond Productions LLC, pg 937

CALIFORNIA

Alliant Event Services, pg 681
Ametron Audio/Video, pg 684
AV Guys, pg 697
Christy's Editorial, pg 723
Crystal Pyramid Productions™, pg 735
Express Media Inc, pg 757
First Camera, pg 761
Golden Gate Studios, pg 772
JD Audio Visual Inc, pg 793
Lynch Communications, pg 813
McCune Audio-Video-Lighting, pg 821
Media Fabricators Inc, pg 822
Munday & Collins AV, pg 834
Muse Presentation Technologies, pg 834
On-Trax Inc, pg 846
PSAV® Presentation Services, pg 866
RetinaVision Productions, pg 874
SNAP, pg 891
Total Creative, pg 916
VER, pg 926
VMI Inc, pg 932
Voice & Video Rentals, pg 932

COLORADO

Daylight Productions & Rentals, pg 739
Spectrum Audio Visual Services, pg 897

CONNECTICUT

A/V Davey, pg 697
Videofilm Systems Inc, pg 929

DELAWARE

Ken-Del Productions Inc, pg 797

DISTRICT OF COLUMBIA

Future View Inc, pg 767
Metro Teleproductions Inc (MTI), pg 824

FLORIDA

AVI-SPL, pg 698
Budget Video Rentals, pg 712
Harmon's Audio-Visual Services, pg 776
Industrial Strength Inc, pg 787
Jordan Klein Film & Video (JKFV), pg 795
ONstage, pg 846
Paradise Show & Design Inc, pg 851
Sight & Sound Productions, pg 887

GEORGIA

MAGNUM Companies Ltd, pg 815
ON Services, a GES Company, pg 846
Stage Front Presentation Systems, pg 899

ILLINOIS

Airways Digital Media, pg 679
Allen Visual Systems Inc, pg 680
Atomic Imaging Inc/Golan Studios, pg 692
AV Chicago Inc, pg 696
Backstar Creative Media Inc, pg 700
Beatty TeleVisual Productions, pg 703
Creative Technology (CT), pg 733
RC Communications, pg 870
Resolution Productions Group, pg 874
SCI Television & Creative Media LLC, pg 882
Tele-Time Systems, pg 910

INDIANA

Advanced Media Integration, pg 677

KENTUCKY

Audio Visual Techniques Inc, pg 695

LOUISIANA

Clark Services Audio Visual & Exhibit Inc, pg 725
Digital FX Inc, pg 742

MAINE

Headlight Audio Visual Inc, pg 777

MARYLAND

Absolute Hollywood, pg 672
Advance Audiovisual Presentation Ltd, pg 677
CPR MultiMedia Solutions, pg 732
Event Tech, pg 756

MASSACHUSETTS

AVFX Inc, pg 698
Capron Lighting & Sound Co Inc, pg 716
Elite Video Inc, pg 753
General Electric Co, pg 769
massAV, pg 819
Preston Productions Inc, pg 861

VIDEO

Video Presentation System Rentals (continued)

MICHIGAN
Digi Sign Design LLC, pg 741
K&R All Media Productions LLC, pg 796
TEL Systems LLC, pg 909

MINNESOTA
Alpha Video & Audio Inc, pg 682
Big Event Productions LLC, pg 705

MISSISSIPPI
Bowie Audio Visual Enterprises Inc, pg 709

MISSOURI
Communitronics Corp, pg 729
Schiller's Audio-Visual, pg 881
Show-Me Audio-Visual, pg 887
Southwest Audio-Visual Inc, pg 895
Switch, pg 905

NEVADA
GES Audio Visual, pg 770
Lefco Video Services Inc, pg 806

NEW JERSEY
Audio Visual Dynamics®, pg 694
Color Leasing Studios, pg 727
Earl Girls Inc, pg 749
MB Productions, pg 820
MiB MediaWorks, pg 825
PLS Staging, pg 858
Starlite, pg 900
Tele-Measurements Inc, pg 910
Video Corporation of America (VCA), pg 927

NEW YORK
Ace Video, pg 674
AV Workshop, pg 697
Colortone Audio Visual, pg 728
Design Audio Visual Inc, pg 741
General Audio-Visual Inc (GAVI), pg 769
KVL Audio Visual Services Inc, pg 802
Long Island Video Enterprises Live Inc, pg 811
Manhattan Center Studios Inc, pg 816
Tri-Ed Distribution Inc, pg 918
Visual Word Systems Inc, pg 932
WorldStage, pg 941

NORTH CAROLINA
AV Metro Inc, pg 697
Special Event Services, pg 896

NORTH DAKOTA
Media Productions, pg 822

OHIO
Bartha, pg 702
Hughie's Event Production Services, pg 782
ITA Audio Visual Solutions, pg 791
Mills James Productions, pg 828
R&B Communications Inc, pg 870
Vista Color Imaging Inc, pg 931

OKLAHOMA
PDC Productions, pg 852

PENNSYLVANIA
Advanced AV LLC, pg 677
Audio Visions Inc, pg 694
FMP Media Solutions Inc, pg 763
Visual Sound Inc, pg 931

SOUTH CAROLINA
Impact Technology Group LLC, pg 786

TENNESSEE
Allstar Audio Systems Inc, pg 681
Russ Sturgeon Productions/RSVP, pg 903
Technical Support Systems LLC, pg 908

TEXAS
Bright Star Productions Inc, pg 710
Media Event Concepts Inc, pg 822
Stage Directions, pg 898

VIRGINIA
Advance Concepts Inc, pg 677
Boitnott Visual Communications Corp (BVC), pg 708
Quince Imaging Inc, pg 868
The Whitlock Group, pg 937

WASHINGTON
Victory Studios, pg 927

WISCONSIN
Audio Visual of Milwaukee Inc, pg 694
Camera Corner Connecting Point, pg 715
Event Essentials, pg 756
Full Compass Systems, pg 767

WYOMING
Bridger Productions Inc, pg 710

PUERTO RICO
Stage Crew Audiovisual Inc, pg 898

ALBERTA
Cine Audio Visual Sales & Service Ltd, pg 723
Global TV, pg 771
Matrix Video Communications Corp (MVCC), pg 819
Unique Communications Ltd, pg 921

BRITISH COLUMBIA
Clark's Audio Visual Services Ltd, pg 725
Video Out Distribution, pg 928

MANITOBA
Inland Audio Visual Ltd, pg 788

ONTARIO
HD Source, pg 777
Metalworks Recording Studios Inc, pg 824
RB Productions, pg 870
Westbury National Show Systems Ltd, pg 936

QUEBEC
Audio Visual Dynamics, pg 694
Panavideo Inc, pg 850

Video Presentation System Repairs

CALIFORNIA
Ametron Audio/Video, pg 684
Band Pro Film & Digital Inc, pg 701
Christy's Editorial, pg 723
Sonance, pg 892
SSL Industries Inc, pg 898
VMI Inc, pg 932

CONNECTICUT
A/V Davey, pg 697

DISTRICT OF COLUMBIA
Future View Inc, pg 767

FLORIDA
ELC Sales & Service Inc, pg 752
Midtown Video Inc, pg 827
Vela Research, pg 925

GEORGIA
Stage Front Presentation Systems, pg 899

ILLINOIS
Allen Visual Systems Inc, pg 680
Beatty TeleVisual Productions, pg 703
Midwest Digital Corp, pg 827

KENTUCKY
Axxis Leasing Inc, pg 700
Barney Miller's Inc, pg 827
NOR-COM Inc, pg 841

MASSACHUSETTS
Elite Video Inc, pg 753
General Electric Co, pg 769

MICHIGAN
TEL Systems LLC, pg 909

MINNESOTA
Alpha Video & Audio Inc, pg 682

MISSOURI
Communitronics Corp, pg 729
Schiller's Audio-Visual, pg 881
Southwest Audio-Visual Inc, pg 895

NEW YORK
Ace Video, pg 674
Tri-Ed Distribution Inc, pg 918

OHIO
Copp Integrated Systems, pg 731
ITA Audio Visual Solutions, pg 791
Tri-State Audio Visual Co, pg 918

PENNSYLVANIA
Audio Visions Inc, pg 694
Visual Sound Inc, pg 931

TENNESSEE
Technical Support Systems LLC, pg 908

TEXAS
Tarpley Media Systems, pg 907

UTAH
RIA Corp, pg 874

VIRGINIA
Avitecture Inc, pg 699
Boitnott Visual Communications Corp (BVC), pg 708
The Whitlock Group, pg 937

WASHINGTON
Macrosystem US Inc, pg 814

WISCONSIN
Camera Corner Connecting Point, pg 715
Full Compass Systems, pg 767

ALBERTA
Infosat Communications Inc, pg 787
Matrix Video Communications Corp (MVCC), pg 819

MANITOBA
Inland Audio Visual Ltd, pg 788

ONTARIO
Westbury National Show Systems Ltd, pg 936

QUEBEC
Panavideo Inc, pg 850

Video Receiver & Monitor Distributors

ALABAMA
Curtis Company, pg 736

ARIZONA
ATCi (Antenna Technology Communication Solutions Inc), pg 692
EAR Professional Audio/Video, pg 749

ARKANSAS
Jay S Stanley & Associates Inc, pg 899

CALIFORNIA
Advanced Systems Group LLC, pg 677
Ametron Audio/Video, pg 684
Audio/Video Supply Inc, pg 694
Band Pro Film & Digital Inc, pg 701
Be Media, pg 702
BroadcastStore.com, pg 711
Christy's Editorial, pg 723
Computer Modules Inc, pg 729
Diaquest, pg 741
Gluskin's Custom Audio Video, pg 771
HM Electronics Inc (HME), pg 780
Instructional Materials & Equipment Distributors (I-Med), pg 789
JD Audio Visual Inc, pg 793
Kappa optronics Inc, pg 796
Leader Instruments Corp, pg 805
Media Control Systems LLC, pg 821

Media Fabricators Inc, pg 822
Metro Video Systems Inc, pg 824
Photodyne Technologies, pg 856
Pioneer Electronics (USA) Inc,
pg 857
PMP Marketing Inc, pg 858
Promax Systems, pg 865
SNAP, pg 891
Southern California Sound Image
Inc, pg 895
SSL Industries Inc, pg 898
Stanislaus AV Inc, pg 899
SuperVision, pg 904
Transvideo International, pg 917
VMI Inc, pg 932

COLORADO

Daylight Productions & Rentals,
pg 739
Spectrum Audio Visual Services,
pg 897

CONNECTICUT

MAVCO, pg 820

DISTRICT OF COLUMBIA

Future View Inc, pg 767

FLORIDA

Access Media Group, pg 673
Altel Systems Group Inc, pg 682
A2D Solutions Inc, pg 692
AVI-SPL, pg 698
Digital Video Systems, pg 742
Glanz Technologies, pg 771
Hi-Tech Enterprises Inc, pg 779
Hi-Tech Import Export Corp,
pg 779
Industrial Strength Inc, pg 787
Midtown Video Inc, pg 827
ONstage, pg 846
Reef Photo & Video, pg 872
Tallahassee Audio Visual, pg 906
Vela Research, pg 925

GEORGIA

Baker Audio Visual, pg 700
Clark, pg 725
Innocinema, pg 788
Stage Front Presentation Systems,
pg 899

ILLINOIS

Allen Visual Systems Inc, pg 680
RC Communications, pg 870
Tele-Time Systems, pg 910
Woodside Avenue Music
Productions Inc, pg 941

INDIANA

Lee Co Inc, pg 805
Sensory Technologies LLC, pg 884
SHP Electronics, pg 887

KENTUCKY

Axxis Leasing Inc, pg 700
Barney Miller's Inc, pg 827
NOR-COM Inc, pg 841

MAINE

Headlight Audio Visual Inc, pg 777
Independent Audio Inc, pg 786

MARYLAND

Advance Audiovisual Presentation
Ltd, pg 677
Human Circuit, pg 782
Wiltronix Inc, pg 939

MASSACHUSETTS

Antronics Inc, pg 686
Rule Boston Camera, pg 878

MICHIGAN

ASC Systems, pg 690
Digi Sign Design LLC, pg 741
On Stage Visuals, pg 846
TEL Systems LLC, pg 909

MINNESOTA

Alpha Video & Audio Inc, pg 682

MISSISSIPPI

Bowie Audio Visual Enterprises Inc,
pg 709

MISSOURI

Communitronics Corp, pg 729
Conference Technologies Inc,
pg 730
Production Support Services Inc,
pg 864
Southwest Audio-Visual Inc, pg 895

NEBRASKA

ATV Research Inc, pg 692
VSA Inc, pg 933

NEVADA

Aardvark Video & Media
Productions, pg 671

NEW HAMPSHIRE

Optics 1 Inc, pg 847

NEW JERSEY

A-V Services Inc, pg 671
AlltecPro, pg 681
Audio Visual Dynamics®, pg 694
AV Bluebook, pg 696
Avtech Systems Inc, pg 699
Diversified, pg 744
Earl Girls Inc, pg 749
Euro-Pacific Film & Video
Productions Inc, pg 756
G&G Technologies Inc, pg 768
HamiltonBuhl, pg 775
MCCOM Inc, pg 820
PatchAmp, pg 852
Starlite, pg 900
Tele-Measurements Inc, pg 910
Total Video Products Inc, pg 916
Vcom IMC, pg 925
Yorktel, pg 944

NEW YORK

Ace Video, pg 674
Adwar Video, pg 678
American Video Inc, pg 684
Audio-Video Corp, pg 694
Audiovox®, pg 695
AV Workshop, pg 697
B&H Photo Video, pg 701
Colortone Audio Visual, pg 728
Design Audio Visual Inc, pg 741
General Audio-Visual Inc (GAVI),
pg 769
KVL Audio Visual Services Inc,
pg 802
Long Island Video Enterprises Live
Inc, pg 811
Markertek Video Supply, pg 817
Neptune Photo Inc, pg 838
Presentation Products Inc, pg 861
RNJ Electronics, pg 875
TecNec Distributing, pg 909

Tri-Ed Distribution Inc, pg 918
Videoguys, pg 929
Visual Word Systems Inc, pg 932

NORTH CAROLINA

Strategic Connections, pg 901

OHIO

Copp Integrated Systems, pg 731
ITA Audio Visual Solutions, pg 791
Tri-State Audio Visual Co, pg 918
Visual Products Inc, pg 931

OKLAHOMA

Ford AV, pg 763

PENNSYLVANIA

Advanced AV LLC, pg 677
Audio Visions Inc, pg 694
Audio Visual Communications Inc,
pg 694
Brodart Co, pg 711
J E Foss Co, pg 764
Grise Audio Visual Center Inc,
pg 774
The Lerro Corp, pg 806
Morefield Communications Inc,
pg 830
Questar Corp, pg 868
Vistacom Inc, pg 931
Visual Sound Inc, pg 931

TENNESSEE

Allstar Audio Systems Inc, pg 681
Lowrance Sound Co Inc, pg 812
Technical Support Systems LLC,
pg 908

TEXAS

Audio Visual Technologies Group
(AVTG), pg 695
AVES Audio Visual Systems Inc,
pg 698
CAM Audio Inc, pg 714
Data Projections Inc, pg 738
Digital Display Solutions Inc,
pg 742
Heffernan Audio Visual, pg 778
IVS Imaging, pg 792
Precision Camera & Video, pg 861
Pro Video & Film Equipment Co
Inc, pg 863
Replicopy Digital Media Center,
pg 873
Tarpley Media Systems, pg 907
Videotex Systems Inc, pg 930

UTAH

RIA Corp, pg 874

VIRGINIA

Avitecture Inc, pg 699
Boitnott Visual Communications
Corp (BVC), pg 708
Intellidyne LLC, pg 789
Quince Imaging Inc, pg 868
The Whitlock Group, pg 937

WASHINGTON

Oppenheimer Camera Products,
pg 847
ToteVision, pg 916

WISCONSIN

Audio Visual of Milwaukee Inc,
pg 694
Camera Corner Connecting Point,
pg 715

Demco Inc, pg 740
Full Compass Systems, pg 767
Safe Harbor Computers, pg 879

ALBERTA

Infosat Communications Inc, pg 787
Matrix Video Communications Corp
(MVCC), pg 819
McBain Camera Ltd, pg 820

MANITOBA

Advance Pro, pg 677
Inland Audio Visual Ltd, pg 788

ONTARIO

HD Source, pg 777
Henry's Camera, pg 779
Majortech Inc, pg 815
Nationwide Audio Visual Co,
pg 837
Westbury National Show Systems
Ltd, pg 936

QUEBEC

Panavideo Inc, pg 850

Video Receiver & Monitor Manufacturers

ARIZONA

Applied Integration Corp, pg 687

CALIFORNIA

AMX® by Harman, pg 685
Boland Communications Inc,
pg 708
Citizens Systems America Corp,
pg 725
DASAN Zhone Solutions (DZS)
Inc, pg 737
Hewlett-Packard Co, pg 779
Leader Instruments Corp, pg 805
Physical Optics Corp (POC), pg 856
Pioneer Electronics (USA) Inc,
pg 857
Sony Electronics Inc, pg 893
Tatung Co of America Inc, pg 907
Transvideo International, pg 917

CONNECTICUT

Harman International Industries Inc,
pg 776

FLORIDA

Compuvideo Sales USA Ltd,
pg 729
Domo Tactical Communications
(DTC) Ltd, pg 745
Vela Research, pg 925

ILLINOIS

Canvys™, pg 716
NEC Display Solutions of America,
pg 837

MASSACHUSETTS

Elite Video Inc, pg 753

MINNESOTA

Bosch Security Systems Inc, pg 709
Dotronix Technology Inc, pg 746

NEW HAMPSHIRE

Optics 1 Inc, pg 847

VIDEO

Video Receiver & Monitor Manufacturers (continued)

NEW JERSEY

Ikegami Electronics (USA) Inc, pg 784
JVC Professional Products Co, pg 796
Panasonic Consumer Electronics Co, pg 850
Sharp Electronics Corp, Professional Display Division, pg 885

NEW YORK

Hitachi Kokusai Electric America Ltd, pg 780
Vicon Industries Inc, pg 926

NORTH CAROLINA

Crest Electronics Inc, pg 734

TENNESSEE

Adtec Digital Inc, pg 677

TEXAS

Contemporary Research, pg 731

VIRGINIA

Quince Imaging Inc, pg 868

WASHINGTON

Aiphone Corp, pg 678
ToteVision, pg 916

BRITISH COLUMBIA

Triad Communications Ltd, pg 918

ONTARIO

Evertz Microsystems Ltd, pg 757

Video Receiver & Monitor Rentals

ALABAMA

Audio-Video Resources Inc, pg 694

ARIZONA

Broadcast Rentals, pg 711
Creative Backstage, pg 733
Merestone, pg 823
Metropolitan Audio-Visual Inc, pg 824
Video West Inc, pg 929

ARKANSAS

White Diamond Productions LLC, pg 937

CALIFORNIA

Action Audio & Visual, pg 675
Advanced Media LLC, pg 677
Alliant Event Services, pg 681
Alternative Rentals, pg 682
Ametron Audio/Video, pg 684
Artichoke Productions, pg 690
AV Guys, pg 697
Bexel, an NEP Broadcast Services Company, pg 704
Chater Camera Inc, pg 721
Cherry Multimedia, pg 721

Christy's Editorial, pg 723
Clean Slate Video, pg 726
Crystal Pyramid Productions™, pg 735
Deck Hand Inc, pg 740
Express Media Inc, pg 757
First Camera, pg 761
Flip 2 Media Inc, pg 762
Gear Monkey, pg 769
Gluskin's Custom Audio Video, pg 771
Gold Standard Productions, pg 772
Golden Gate Studios, pg 772
HD Cinema, pg 777
HDrental.com, pg 777
Image Integration, pg 785
Imagecraft Productions, pg 785
JD Audio Visual Inc, pg 793
Lynch Communications, pg 813
Main Street Media Inc, pg 815
McCune Audio-Video-Lighting, pg 821
Media Fabricators Inc, pg 822
Munday & Collins AV, pg 834
Muse Presentation Technologies, pg 834
Otto Nemenz International Inc, pg 838
On-Trax Inc, pg 846
Pro HD Rentals, pg 863
The Producer's Loft, pg 863
Production Gear Rentals (PGR), pg 863
PSAV® Presentation Services, pg 866
Radiant Images, pg 869
RetinaVision Productions, pg 874
Shooting Star Video, pg 886
Shoulder High Productions, pg 886
SNAP, pg 891
Stanislaus AV Inc, pg 899
Stray Angel Films, pg 902
The Studios at Paramount, pg 903
Synthesizer Rental Service, pg 906
T-stop Inc, pg 906
Total Creative, pg 916
Twin Peaks Creative, pg 920
VER, pg 926
Videofax, pg 929
VMI Inc, pg 932
Voice & Video Rentals, pg 932
Westcoast Video Productions Inc, pg 936

COLORADO

Daylight Productions & Rentals, pg 739
Spectrum Audio Visual Services, pg 897
Tatum Video, pg 907

CONNECTICUT

Videofilm Systems Inc, pg 929

DELAWARE

Ken-Del Productions Inc, pg 797
Showorks Audio Visual Inc, pg 887

DISTRICT OF COLUMBIA

Future View Inc, pg 767

FLORIDA

Access Media Group, pg 673
AVI-SPL, pg 698
Budget Video Rentals, pg 712
CopShopMiami.com, pg 731
Glanz Technologies Inc, pg 771
Industrial Strength Inc, pg 787
Jordan Klein Film & Video (JKFV), pg 795

Knowles Video Inc (KVI), pg 800
Midtown Video Inc, pg 827
Moving Picture, pg 831
ONstage, pg 846
Paradise Show & Design Inc, pg 851
Sight & Sound Productions, pg 887
Universal Studios Florida® Production Group, pg 922

GEORGIA

ECG Productions, pg 750
Lighting & Production Equipment Inc, pg 807
MAGNUM Companies Ltd, pg 815
ON Services, a GES Company, pg 846
See Production Services, pg 883
Stage Front Presentation Systems, pg 899

ILLINOIS

Allen Visual Systems Inc, pg 680
AV Chicago Inc, pg 696
Backstar Creative Media Inc, pg 700
Beatty TeleVisual Productions, pg 703
Creative Technology (CT), pg 733
Firehouse Studios, pg 761
LITE-IT Grip Truck Rentals, pg 810
Magnanimous Media, pg 814
On Site Video, pg 846
Product Productions, pg 863
RC Communications, pg 870
Resolution Productions Group, pg 874
2nd Cine Inc, pg 883
Staging Resources Inc, pg 899
Tele-Time Systems, pg 910
Woodside Avenue Music Productions Inc, pg 941
Zacuto, pg 945

INDIANA

Advanced Media Integration, pg 677

IOWA

Pro Video, pg 863

KANSAS

Lights On, pg 808

KENTUCKY

Audio Visual Techniques Inc, pg 695

LOUISIANA

Clark Services Audio Visual & Exhibit Inc, pg 725
Digital FX Inc, pg 742

MAINE

Headlight Audio Visual Inc, pg 777

MARYLAND

Advance Audiovisual Presentation Ltd, pg 677
CPR MultiMedia Solutions, pg 732
Event Tech, pg 756
Hargrove Inc, pg 776

MASSACHUSETTS

AVFX Inc, pg 698
Capron Lighting & Sound Co Inc, pg 716
Elite Video Inc, pg 753

Integrated Solutions Group, pg 789
massAV, pg 819
Preston Productions Inc, pg 861

MICHIGAN

Digi Sign Design LLC, pg 741
K&R All Media Productions LLC, pg 796
On Stage Visuals, pg 846
TEL Systems LLC, pg 909

MINNESOTA

Alpha Video & Audio Inc, pg 682

MISSISSIPPI

Bowie Audio Visual Enterprises Inc, pg 709

MISSOURI

Communitronics Corp, pg 729
Production Support Services Inc, pg 864
Schiller's Audio-Visual, pg 881
Show-Me Audio-Visual, pg 887
Southwest Audio-Visual Inc, pg 895
Switch, pg 905

NEBRASKA

Dog & Pony Productions Inc, pg 744
Lights On Nebraska, pg 808

NEVADA

GES Audio Visual, pg 770
Lefco Video Services Inc, pg 806
MG Studio, pg 825

NEW HAMPSHIRE

Apertura, pg 686

NEW JERSEY

Audio Visual Dynamics®, pg 694
Earl Girls Inc, pg 749
Euro-Pacific Film & Video Productions Inc, pg 756
G&G Technologies, pg 768
MB Productions, pg 820
PLS Staging, pg 858
Soundtracks Production Services LLC, pg 895
Starlite, pg 900
Tele-Measurements Inc, pg 910
Video Corporation of America (VCA), pg 927

NEW YORK

Ace Video, pg 674
Adorama Rental Co, pg 676
Adwar Video, pg 678
American Video Inc, pg 684
AV Workshop, pg 697
Big Apple Films, pg 705
Bond Street Studio, pg 708
Cinema-Vision, pg 724
Colortone Audio Visual, pg 728
CP Communications, pg 732
CPT Rental Inc, pg 732
Design Audio Visual Inc, pg 741
Gearhead Rentals, pg 769
Hand Held Films, pg 775
KVL Audio Visual Services Inc, pg 802
LightHouse Films, pg 807
Long Island Video Enterprises Live Inc, pg 811
Manhattan Center Studios Inc, pg 816
PrimaLux Video Inc, pg 862

Specialized Audio-Visual Inc, pg 896
Tri-Ed Distribution Inc, pg 918
Visual Word Systems Inc, pg 932

NORTH CAROLINA

AV Connections Inc, pg 697
AV Metro Inc, pg 697
Duke Media Services, pg 747
Moving Pictures, pg 832
On Location North Carolina, pg 846
Special Event Services, pg 896
Strategic Connections, pg 901

NORTH DAKOTA

Media Productions, pg 822

OHIO

Hughie's Event Production Services, pg 782
ITA Audio Visual Solutions, pg 791
Lyon Video Inc, pg 813
Mills James Productions, pg 828
Ohio HD Video, pg 844
OSV Studios, pg 848
R&B Communications Inc, pg 870
Vista Color Imaging Inc, pg 931

OKLAHOMA

PDC Productions, pg 852

OREGON

Koerner Camera Systems, pg 800

PENNSYLVANIA

Advanced AV LLC, pg 677
Audio Visions Inc, pg 694
Audio Visual Communications Inc, pg 694
FMP Media Solutions Inc, pg 763
Grise Audio Visual Center Inc, pg 774
New York Camera & Video, pg 840
Upstage Video, pg 923
The Videohouse Inc, pg 929
Viewpoint Production Services Inc, pg 930
Visual Sound Inc, pg 931

SOUTH CAROLINA

Impact Technology Group LLC, pg 786
Sound & Images Inc, pg 893

TENNESSEE

Allstar Audio Systems Inc, pg 681
Nashville Production Rentals (NPR), pg 836
RentACamera.com, pg 873
Technical Support Systems LLC, pg 908

TEXAS

Alford Media Services, pg 680
Audio Visual Technologies Group (AVTG), pg 695
Big House Sound Inc, pg 705
Bright Star Productions Inc, pg 710
FitzCo Sound Inc, pg 761
Heffernan Audio Visual, pg 778
Media Event Concepts Inc, pg 822
Stage Directions, pg 898
Texcam Inc, pg 911

UTAH

Ron Hill Imagery, pg 780

VERMONT

Dark Star Lighting & Production, pg 737

VIRGINIA

Boitnott Visual Communications Corp (BVC), pg 708
CVW Event Productions, pg 736
Quince Imaging Inc, pg 868

WASHINGTON

Oppenheimer Camera Products, pg 847
Victory Studios, pg 927

WISCONSIN

Audio Visual of Milwaukee Inc, pg 694
Camera Corner Connecting Point, pg 715
Event Essentials, pg 756
Full Compass Systems, pg 767

WYOMING

Bridger Productions Inc, pg 710

PUERTO RICO

Stage Crew Audiovisual Inc, pg 898

ALBERTA

Cine Audio Visual Sales & Service Ltd, pg 723
Global TV, pg 771
Matrix Video Communications Corp (MVCC), pg 819
Unique Communications Ltd, pg 921

BRITISH COLUMBIA

Clark's Audio Visual Services Ltd, pg 725
Commercial Electronics Ltd, pg 728
Video Out Distribution, pg 928

MANITOBA

Inland Audio Visual Ltd, pg 788

ONTARIO

HD Source, pg 777
JIB Shots Equipment Inc, pg 794
Metalworks Recording Studios Inc, pg 824
MVI - MultiVision Inc, pg 835
RB Productions, pg 870
SIM Digital, pg 888
Westbury National Show Systems Ltd, pg 936
ZTV Broadcast Services Inc, pg 945

QUEBEC

Audio Visual Dynamics, pg 694
Panavideo Inc, pg 850

Video Receiver & Monitor Repairs

CALIFORNIA

Advanced Media LLC, pg 677
Ametron Audio/Video, pg 684
Band Pro Film & Digital Inc, pg 701
BroadcastStore.com, pg 711
Christy's Editorial, pg 723
Gluskin's Custom Audio Video, pg 771

HM Electronics Inc (HME), pg 780
McAlister Electronics, pg 820
Metro Video Systems Inc, pg 824
SSL Industries Inc, pg 898
Technical Services, pg 908
TEK Media Group, pg 909
Transvideo International, pg 917
VMI Inc, pg 932

FLORIDA

Digital Video Systems, pg 742
ELC Sales & Service Inc, pg 752
Glanz Technologies Inc, pg 771
Hi-Tech Enterprises Inc, pg 779
Midtown Video Inc, pg 827

GEORGIA

Stage Front Presentation Systems, pg 899

ILLINOIS

Allen Visual Systems Inc, pg 680
Beatty TeleVisual Productions, pg 703
Midwest Digital Corp, pg 827
On Site Video, pg 846
RC Communications, pg 870
Tele-Time Systems, pg 910

KENTUCKY

Axxis Leasing Inc, pg 700
Barney Miller's Inc, pg 827
NOR-COM Inc, pg 841

MASSACHUSETTS

Antronics Inc, pg 686
Elite Video Inc, pg 753
Integrated Solutions Group, pg 789

MICHIGAN

TEL Systems LLC, pg 909

MINNESOTA

Alpha Video & Audio Inc, pg 682
Dotronix Technology Inc, pg 746

MISSOURI

Communitronics Corp, pg 729
Schiller's Audio-Visual, pg 881
Southwest Audio-Visual Inc, pg 895

NEW YORK

Adwar Video, pg 678
American Video Inc, pg 684
Tri-Ed Distribution Inc, pg 918

OHIO

Copp Integrated Systems, pg 731
ITA Audio Visual Solutions, pg 791
Tri-State Audio Visual Co, pg 918

PENNSYLVANIA

J E Foss Co, pg 764
Visual Sound Inc, pg 931

TENNESSEE

db electronics, pg 739
Technical Support Systems LLC, pg 908

TEXAS

Audio Visual Technologies Group (AVTG), pg 695
Pro Video & Film Equipment Co Inc, pg 863
Tarpley Media Systems, pg 907

UTAH

RIA Corp, pg 874

VIRGINIA

Avitecture Inc, pg 699
Boitnott Visual Communications Corp (BVC), pg 708
The Whitlock Group, pg 937

WASHINGTON

Aiphone Corp, pg 678
ToteVision, pg 916

WISCONSIN

Camera Corner Connecting Point, pg 715
Full Compass Systems, pg 767

ALBERTA

Infosat Communications Inc, pg 787
Matrix Video Communications Corp (MVCC), pg 819

BRITISH COLUMBIA

Commercial Electronics Ltd, pg 728

MANITOBA

Inland Audio Visual Ltd, pg 788

ONTARIO

HD Source, pg 777
MVI - MultiVision Inc, pg 835
Westbury National Show Systems Ltd, pg 936

QUEBEC

Panavideo Inc, pg 850

Video Recorder & Player Distributors

ALABAMA

Curtis Company, pg 736

ARIZONA

EAR Professional Audio/Video, pg 749
On-Site Video, pg 846

ARKANSAS

Carlton-Bates Co, pg 717
Jay S Stanley & Associates Inc, pg 899

CALIFORNIA

Advanced Systems Group LLC, pg 677
Ametron Audio/Video, pg 684
Assured Audio Visual, pg 691
Audio/Video Supply Inc, pg 694
Band Pro Film & Digital Inc, pg 701
Be Media, pg 702
BigFoot Mobile Systems, pg 705
BroadcastStore.com, pg 711
Computer Modules Inc, pg 729
Diaquest, pg 741
Educational Technology Services (ETS), pg 751
Gluskin's Custom Audio Video, pg 771
Gravity Media, pg 773
Instructional Materials & Equipment Distributors (I-Med), pg 789

VIDEO

Video Recorder & Player Distributors (continued)

CALIFORNIA (continued)

Jameco Electronics, pg 792
JD Audio Visual Inc, pg 793
Media Control Systems LLC, pg 821
Media Fabricators Inc, pg 822
Metro Video Systems Inc, pg 824
Photodyne Technologies, pg 856
PMP Marketing Inc, pg 858
Point of View Productions, pg 858
Promax Systems, pg 865
SNAP, pg 891
Southern California Sound Image Inc, pg 895
SSL Industries Inc, pg 898
SuperVision, pg 904
VMI Inc, pg 932

COLORADO

Ceavco Audio Visual Company Inc, pg 719
Daylight Productions & Rentals, pg 739
Spectrum Audio Visual Services, pg 897
Stanco Sales LLC, pg 899

CONNECTICUT

MAVCO, pg 820
Rockwell Communications Inc, pg 876

FLORIDA

Access Media Group, pg 673
Altel Systems Group Inc, pg 682
AVI-SPL, pg 698
Digital Video Systems, pg 742
Enhanced View Services Inc, pg 754
Glanz Technologies Inc, pg 771
Hi-Tech Enterprises Inc, pg 779
Hi-Tech Import Export Corp, pg 779
Industrial Strength Inc, pg 787
Midtown Video Inc, pg 827
ONstage, pg 846
Photosound of Orlando Inc, pg 856
Recording Media & Equipment Inc (RM&E), pg 872
Tallahassee Audio Visual, pg 906

GEORGIA

Audio Visual Resources Inc, pg 695
Baker Audio Visual, pg 700
Blue Media Supply Inc, pg 707
Clark, pg 725
Convergent Media Systems, pg 731
Stage Front Presentation Systems, pg 899

ILLINOIS

Allen Visual Systems Inc, pg 680
Creative Technology (CT), pg 733
Joseph Electronics, pg 795
Major Reproductions Equipment Co, pg 815
Tele-Time Systems, pg 910
Woodside Avenue Music Productions Inc, pg 941
Zenith Electronics LLC, pg 945

INDIANA

Lee Co Inc, pg 805
Sensory Technologies LLC, pg 884
SHP Electronics, pg 887

KENTUCKY

Axxis Leasing Inc, pg 700
Barney Miller's Inc, pg 827
NOR-COM Inc, pg 841

MAINE

Headlight Audio Visual Inc, pg 777

MARYLAND

Advance Audiovisual Presentation Ltd, pg 677
Human Circuit, pg 782
Nicholas P Pipino Associates Inc, pg 857
RTZ Audio Visual, pg 878

MASSACHUSETTS

Antronics Inc, pg 686
Hunt's Photo & Video, pg 782
Integrated Solutions Group, pg 789
Rule Boston Camera, pg 878

MICHIGAN

Olson Anderson Co, pg 685
ASC Systems, pg 690
Digi Sign Design LLC, pg 741
On Stage Visuals, pg 846
TEL Systems LLC, pg 909

MINNESOTA

Alpha Video & Audio Inc, pg 682
AVI Systems, pg 698
Cinequipt Inc, pg 724

MISSISSIPPI

Bowie Audio Visual Enterprises Inc, pg 709
Jasper Ewing & Sons Inc, pg 757

MISSOURI

Communitronics Corp, pg 729
Conference Technologies Inc, pg 730
ITC, pg 791
Production Support Services Inc, pg 864
Southwest Audio-Visual Inc, pg 895

NEBRASKA

ATV Research Inc, pg 692
VSA Inc, pg 933

NEVADA

Aardvark Video & Media Productions, pg 671

NEW JERSEY

A-V Services Inc, pg 671
Alltec Stores, a Vcom IMC Company, pg 681
Audio Visual Dynamics®, pg 694
AV Bluebook, pg 696
Diversified, pg 744
Earl Girls Inc, pg 749
Euro-Pacific Film & Video Productions Inc, pg 756
G&G Technologies Inc, pg 768
HamiltonBuhl, pg 775
MCCOM Inc, pg 820
PatchAmp, pg 852
Starlite, pg 900

SYMCO Inc, pg 905
Tele-Measurements Inc, pg 910
Total Video Products Inc, pg 916
Vcom IMC, pg 925
Video Corporation of America (VCA), pg 927
Yorktel, pg 944

NEW YORK

Adwar Video, pg 678
American Video Inc, pg 684
Audio-Video Corp, pg 694
Audiovox®, pg 695
AV Workshop, pg 697
B&H Photo Video, pg 701
Colortone Audio Visual, pg 728
Design Audio Visual Inc, pg 741
Flash Electronics Inc, pg 762
General Audio-Visual Inc (GAVI), pg 769
HAVE Inc, pg 777
Long Island Video Enterprises Live Inc, pg 811
Markertek Video Supply, pg 817
Neptune Photo Inc, pg 838
Presentation Products Inc, pg 861
Ray Supply Inc, pg 870
RNJ Electronics Inc, pg 875
TecNec Distributing, pg 909
Tri-Ed Distribution Inc, pg 918
Videoguys, pg 929
Visual Technologies Corp, pg 932
Visual Word Systems Inc, pg 932

NORTH CAROLINA

Camcor Inc, pg 715
Carolina Biological Supply Co, pg 717
Strategic Connections, pg 901

OHIO

Audio Visual Media, pg 694
Copp Integrated Systems, pg 731
ITA Audio Visual Solutions, pg 791
iVideo Technologies, pg 792
Tri-State Audio Visual Co, pg 918

PENNSYLVANIA

Advanced AV LLC, pg 677
Audio Visual Communications Inc, pg 694
Bernie's Photo Center, pg 704
J E Foss Co, pg 764
Grise Audio Visual Center Inc, pg 774
Hite Co, pg 780
The Lerro Corp, pg 806
Morefield Communications Inc, pg 830
Questar Corp, pg 868
Vistacom Inc, pg 931
Visual Sound Inc, pg 931
Wespen Audio Visual Co, pg 935

RHODE ISLAND

Shanix Inc, pg 885

TENNESSEE

Allstar Audio Systems Inc, pg 681
Continental Film, pg 731
Lowrance Sound Co Inc, pg 812
Memphis Communications Corp, pg 823
Technical Support Systems LLC, pg 908

TEXAS

Audio Visual Technologies Group (AVTG), pg 695
AVES Audio Visual Systems Inc, pg 698
Biway Media, pg 706
CAM Audio Inc, pg 714
Data Projections Inc, pg 738
Digital Display Solutions Inc, pg 742
Heffernan Audio Visual, pg 778
IVS Imaging, pg 792
JSAV, pg 795
Pro Video & Film Equipment Co Inc, pg 863
Replicopy Digital Media Center, pg 873
Tarpley Media Systems, pg 907
TWIST Integration Solutions Technology, pg 920
Videotex Systems Inc, pg 930

UTAH

Performance Audio LLC, pg 854
RIA Corp, pg 874
TV Specialists Inc, pg 919
Webb Audio Visual, pg 935

VIRGINIA

Avitecture Inc, pg 699
Boitnott Visual Communications Corp (BVC), pg 708
Intellidyne LLC, pg 789
Metropolitan Audio Visual Co LLC, pg 824
Quince Imaging Inc, pg 868
StageSound, pg 899
The Whitlock Group, pg 937

WASHINGTON

Inland Audio Visual Co, pg 788
Oppenheimer Camera Products, pg 847
Proforma Good Wood Marketing, pg 865

WISCONSIN

Audio Visual of Milwaukee Inc, pg 694
Camera Corner Connecting Point, pg 715
Demco Inc, pg 740
Full Compass Systems, pg 767
Safe Harbor Computers, pg 879

PUERTO RICO

Bonnin Electronics Inc, pg 708

ALBERTA

Allstar Show Industries Inc, pg 681
Matrix Video Communications Corp (MVCC), pg 819
McBain Camera Ltd, pg 820

BRITISH COLUMBIA

Triad Communications Ltd, pg 918

MANITOBA

Advance Pro, pg 677
Inland Audio Visual Ltd, pg 788

ONTARIO

Cinema Stage Inc, pg 724
Drastic Technologies Ltd, pg 746
HD Source, pg 777
Majortech Inc, pg 815

Nationwide Audio Visual Co, pg 837

Westbury National Show Systems Ltd, pg 936

QUEBEC

Panavideo Inc, pg 850

Video Recorder & Player Manufacturers

ARIZONA

Applied Integration Corp, pg 687

CALIFORNIA

Ampex Data Systems Corp, pg 684
FutureVideo, pg 767
Physical Optics Corp (POC), pg 856
Simon - Kaloi Engineering Ltd, pg 888
Sony Electronics Inc, pg 893
VITEC Multimedia, pg 932

FLORIDA

Domo Tactical Communications (DTC) Ltd, pg 745

MICHIGAN

Leightronix Inc, pg 806

MINNESOTA

Bosch Security Systems Inc, pg 709

NEW JERSEY

Emerson Radio Corp, pg 753
JVC Professional Products Co, pg 796
Konica Minolta Business Solutions, pg 801
Panasonic Consumer Electronics Co, pg 850
RAMSA Professional Audio Systems, pg 870
Starlite, pg 900

NEW YORK

Hitachi Kokusai Electric America Ltd, pg 780

NORTH CAROLINA

Crest Electronics Inc, pg 734

OKLAHOMA

BCD Associates Inc, pg 702

TENNESSEE

Adtec Digital Inc, pg 677

VIRGINIA

Quince Imaging Inc, pg 868

BRITISH COLUMBIA

Triad Communications Ltd, pg 918

ONTARIO

Drastic Technologies Ltd, pg 746

Video Recorder & Player Rentals

ALABAMA

Audio-Video Resources Inc, pg 694

ARIZONA

Broadcast Rentals, pg 711
Creative Backstage, pg 733
Glendale Media Center, pg 771
Merestone, pg 823
Metropolitan Audio-Visual Inc, pg 824
Video West Inc, pg 929

ARKANSAS

White Diamond Productions LLC, pg 937

CALIFORNIA

Absolute Rentals, pg 672
Action Video, pg 675
Advanced Media LLC, pg 677
AGF Media Services, pg 678
Alliant Event Services, pg 681
Alternative Rentals, pg 682
Ametron Audio/Video, pg 684
Artichoke Productions, pg 690
Assured Audio Visual, pg 691
AV Guys, pg 697
Bexel, an NEP Broadcast Services Company, pg 704
Big Door, pg 705
BigFoot Mobile Systems, pg 705
Chater Camera Inc, pg 721
Cherry Multimedia, pg 721
Clean Slate Video, pg 726
Crystal Pyramid Productions™, pg 735
Deck Hand Inc, pg 740
Express Media Inc, pg 757
First Camera, pg 761
FJ Productions Inc, pg 762
Gluskin's Custom Audio Video, pg 771
Gold Standard Productions, pg 772
Golden Gate Studios, pg 772
Alan Gordon Enterprises Inc, pg 772
Gravity Media, pg 773
Imagecraft Productions, pg 785
Instructional Materials & Equipment Distributors (I-Med), pg 789
JD Audio Visual Inc, pg 793
Lynch Communications, pg 813
Main Street Media Inc, pg 815
Maximus Media Inc, pg 820
McCune Audio-Video-Lighting, pg 821
Media Fabricators Inc, pg 822
Munday & Collins AV, pg 834
Muse Presentation Technologies, pg 834
Otto Nemenz International Inc, pg 838
On-Trax Inc, pg 846
PSAV® Presentation Services, pg 866
RetinaVision Productions, pg 874
SNAP, pg 891
Stanislaus AV Inc, pg 899
Synthesizer Rental Service, pg 906
Total Creative, pg 916
Twin Peaks Creative, pg 920
VER, pg 926
VMI Inc, pg 932
Voice & Video Rentals, pg 932
Warner Bros Production Sound & Video Services, pg 934
Westcoast Video Productions Inc, pg 936

COLORADO

Apogee Communications Group, pg 687
Ceavco Audio Visual Company Inc, pg 719

Daylight Productions & Rentals, pg 739
Spectrum Audio Visual Services, pg 897
Tatum Video, pg 907

CONNECTICUT

A/V Davey, pg 697
Rockwell Communications Inc, pg 876
Videofilm Systems Inc, pg 929

DELAWARE

Ken-Del Productions Inc, pg 797
Showorks Audio Visual Inc, pg 887

DISTRICT OF COLUMBIA

Future View Inc, pg 767

FLORIDA

Access Media Group, pg 673
Accord Productions, pg 673
AVI-SPL, pg 698
Budget Video Rentals, pg 712
Steven Cohen Motion Picture Production, pg 727
CopShopMiami.com, pg 731
Glanz Technologies Inc, pg 771
Hi-Tech Enterprises Inc, pg 779
Industrial Strength Inc, pg 787
Jordan Klein Film & Video (JKFV), pg 795
Knowles Video Inc (KVI), pg 800
Midtown Video Inc, pg 827
ONstage, pg 846
Paradise Show & Design Inc, pg 851
Photosound of Orlando Inc, pg 856
Sight & Sound Productions, pg 887
Tallahassee Audio Visual, pg 906
Universal Studios Florida® Production Group, pg 922

GEORGIA

Audio Visual Resources Inc, pg 695
Convergent Media Systems, pg 731
Lighting & Production Equipment Inc, pg 807
MAGNUM Companies Ltd, pg 815
ON Services, a GES Company, pg 846
Stage Front Presentation Systems, pg 899

ILLINOIS

Allen Visual Systems Inc, pg 680
AV Chicago Inc, pg 696
Backstar Creative Media Inc, pg 700
Beatty TeleVisual Productions, pg 703
Creative Technology (CT), pg 733
Helix Camera & Video, pg 778
Magnanimous Media, pg 814
On Site Video, pg 846
PSAV® Presentation Services (Hotel Services Division), pg 866
RC Communications, pg 870
Resolution Productions Group, pg 874
Staging Resources Inc, pg 899
Tele-Time Systems, pg 910

INDIANA

Advanced Media Integration, pg 677
Gary Camera & Digital, pg 768
OMNI Productions, pg 845

KENTUCKY

Audio Visual Techniques Inc, pg 695
Idle Minds Productions Inc, pg 784

LOUISIANA

Clark Services Audio Visual & Exhibit Inc, pg 725
Digital FX Inc, pg 742
Moxie Media, pg 832

MARYLAND

Archai Media, pg 688
CPR MultiMedia Solutions, pg 732
Event Tech, pg 756
Nelson White Systems Inc, pg 838
Producers Video, pg 863
Quality Film & Video, pg 868
RTZ Audio Visual, pg 878

MASSACHUSETTS

AVFX Inc, pg 698
Green Mountain Post Films (GMP), pg 774
Integrated Solutions Group, pg 789
massAV, pg 819
Preston Productions Inc, pg 861

MICHIGAN

Olson Anderson Co, pg 685
Digi Sign Design LLC, pg 741
K&R All Media Productions LLC, pg 796
K&R's Recording Studios Inc, pg 796
Madonna University Information Technology, pg 814
On Stage Visuals, pg 846
TEL Systems LLC, pg 909

MINNESOTA

Alpha Video & Audio Inc, pg 682
AVI Systems, pg 698
Big Event Productions LLC, pg 705
Pro Media Productions, pg 863

MISSISSIPPI

Bowie Audio Visual Enterprises Inc, pg 709
Jasper Ewing & Sons Inc, pg 757

MISSOURI

Production Support Services Inc, pg 864
Schiller's Audio-Visual, pg 881
Show-Me Audio-Visual, pg 887
Southwest Audio-Visual Inc, pg 895
Switch, pg 905

NEBRASKA

Dog & Pony Productions Inc, pg 744

NEVADA

GES Audio Visual, pg 770
Lefco Video Services Inc, pg 806

NEW HAMPSHIRE

Apertura, pg 686

NEW JERSEY

Audio Visual Dynamics®, pg 694
Earl Girls Inc, pg 749
Euro-Pacific Film & Video Productions Inc, pg 756
G&G Technologies Inc, pg 768

VIDEO

Video Recorder & Player Rentals (continued)

NEW JERSEY (continued)

MB Productions, pg 820
PLS Staging, pg 858
Starlite, pg 900
Tele-Measurements Inc, pg 910
Video Corporation of America (VCA), pg 927

NEW MEXICO

Production Outfitters, pg 864

NEW YORK

Adwar Video, pg 678
Air Sea Land Productions Inc (ASL), pg 678
American Video Inc, pg 684
AV Workshop, pg 697
Big Foot Productions Inc, pg 705
CMI Communications, pg 727
Colortone Audio Visual, pg 728
CP Communications, pg 732
Design Audio Visual Inc, pg 741
Gotham Sound & Communications Inc, pg 773
Long Island Video Enterprises Live Inc, pg 811
Manhattan Center Studios Inc, pg 816
PrimaLux Video Inc, pg 862
Production Central, pg 863
Ray Supply Inc, pg 870
Specialized Audio-Visual Inc, pg 896
Tri-Ed Distribution Inc, pg 918
Visual Technologies Corp, pg 932
Visual Word Systems Inc, pg 932
WNET/New York Public Media, pg 940
WorldStage, pg 941

NORTH CAROLINA

AV Connections Inc, pg 697
AV Metro Inc, pg 697
The Communications Group Inc, pg 729
Duke Media Services, pg 747
Moving Pictures, pg 832
On Location North Carolina, pg 846
Special Event Services, pg 896
Strategic Connections, pg 901
Take One Productions Ltd, pg 906
Trailblazer Studios®, pg 917

NORTH DAKOTA

Media Productions, pg 822

OHIO

Audio Visual Media, pg 694
CET, pg 720
Hughie's Event Production Services, pg 782
ITA Audio Visual Solutions, pg 791
iVideo Technologies, pg 792
Lyon Video Inc, pg 813
Mills James Productions, pg 828
Ohio HD Video, pg 844
R&B Communications Inc, pg 870
Vista Color Imaging Inc, pg 931

OKLAHOMA

PDC Productions, pg 852

OREGON

Northwest Film Center, pg 842
Picture This Production Services, pg 856

PENNSYLVANIA

Advanced AV LLC, pg 677
Audio Visions Inc, pg 694
Audio Visual Communications Inc, pg 694
FMP Media Solutions Inc, pg 763
Grise Audio Visual Center Inc, pg 774
JPL, pg 795
Muderick Media, pg 833
New York Camera & Video, pg 840
North Star Satellite Communications Inc, pg 842
Producers Management Television (PMTV), pg 863
Upstage Video, pg 923
The Videohouse Inc, pg 929
Videosmith Inc, pg 930
Visual Sound Inc, pg 931

SOUTH CAROLINA

Impact Technology Group LLC, pg 786

TENNESSEE

Allstar Audio Systems Inc, pg 681
Memphis Communications Corp, pg 823
Russ Sturgeon Productions/RSVP, pg 903
Technical Support Systems LLC, pg 908

TEXAS

Alford Media Services, pg 680
Audio Visual Technologies Group (AVTG), pg 695
Bright Star Productions Inc, pg 710
FitzCo Sound Inc, pg 761
Heffernan Audio Visual, pg 778
JSAV, pg 795
Media Event Concepts Inc, pg 822
Earl Miller Productions, pg 827
South Coast Film & Video, pg 895
Stage Directions, pg 898
Texcam Inc, pg 911

UTAH

TV Specialists Inc, pg 919
Webb Audio Visual, pg 935

VERMONT

Marlboro Productions, pg 817

VIRGINIA

Advance Concepts Inc, pg 677
Audio Visual Actions Inc (AVA), pg 694
Boitnott Visual Communications Corp (BVC), pg 708
CVW Event Productions, pg 736
Lee Hartman & Sons Inc, pg 805
Metropolitan Audio Visual Co LLC, pg 824
Projection, pg 865
Quince Imaging Inc, pg 868
The Whitlock Group, pg 937

WASHINGTON

Inland Audio Visual Co, pg 788
Intermedia Inc, pg 789

Oppenheimer Camera Products, pg 847
Victory Studios, pg 927

WISCONSIN

Audio Visual of Milwaukee Inc, pg 694
Camera Corner Connecting Point, pg 715
Event Essentials, pg 756
Full Compass Systems, pg 767
University of Wisconsin-Oshkosh Radio-TV-Film Dept, pg 923
USAV Group Inc, pg 923
Wisconsin Public Television, pg 940

WYOMING

Bridger Productions Inc, pg 710

PUERTO RICO

Stage Crew Audiovisual Inc, pg 898

ALBERTA

Cine Audio Visual Sales & Service Ltd, pg 723
Global TV, pg 771
Matrix Video Communications Corp (MVCC), pg 819
Unique Communications Ltd, pg 921

BRITISH COLUMBIA

Clark's Audio Visual Services Ltd, pg 725
Commercial Electronics Ltd, pg 728
Video Out Distribution, pg 928

MANITOBA

Inland Audio Visual Ltd, pg 788

ONTARIO

HD Source, pg 777
JIB Shots Equipment Inc, pg 794
MVI - MultiVision Inc, pg 835
Wanted! Sound + Picture, pg 933
Westbury National Show Systems Ltd, pg 936

QUEBEC

Audio Visual Dynamics, pg 694
Freeman Audio Visual, pg 765
Group PVP, pg 774
Kerrigan Productions Inc, pg 798
Panavideo Inc, pg 850

Video Recorder & Player Repairs

CALIFORNIA

Advanced Media LLC, pg 677
Advanced Systems Group LLC, pg 677
Ametron Audio/Video, pg 684
Band Pro Film & Digital Inc, pg 701
BigFoot Mobile Systems, pg 705
BroadcastStore.com, pg 711
Gluskin's Custom Audio Video, pg 771
Instructional Materials & Equipment Distributors (I-Med), pg 789
McAlister Electronics, pg 820
Metro Video Systems Inc, pg 824
Pro Camera Repair, pg 862
SSL Industries Inc, pg 898
Technical Services, pg 908
VMI Inc, pg 932

COLORADO

Ceavco Audio Visual Company Inc, pg 719

CONNECTICUT

A/V Davey, pg 697
Rockwell Communications Inc, pg 876

FLORIDA

Access Media Group, pg 673
Digital Video Systems, pg 742
ELC Sales & Service Inc, pg 752
Glanz Technologies Inc, pg 771
Hi-Tech Enterprises Inc, pg 779
Midtown Video Inc, pg 827
TAI Audio, pg 906
Tallahassee Audio Visual, pg 906

GEORGIA

Audio Visual Resources Inc, pg 695
Stage Front Presentation Systems, pg 899

ILLINOIS

Allen Visual Systems Inc, pg 680
Beatty TeleVisual Productions, pg 703
Central Audio-Visual Equipment Inc, pg 719
Midwest Digital Corp, pg 827
On Site Video, pg 846
Tele-Time Systems, pg 910

KENTUCKY

Axxis Leasing Inc, pg 700
Barney Miller's Inc, pg 827
NOR-COM Inc, pg 841

MARYLAND

RTZ Audio Visual, pg 878

MASSACHUSETTS

Antronics Inc, pg 686
Integrated Solutions Group, pg 789

MICHIGAN

Olson Anderson Co, pg 685
TEL Systems LLC, pg 909

MINNESOTA

Alpha Video & Audio Inc, pg 682
AVI Systems, pg 698

MISSOURI

Schiller's Audio-Visual, pg 881
Southwest Audio-Visual Inc, pg 895

NEW JERSEY

Konica Minolta Business Solutions, pg 801

NEW YORK

Adwar Video, pg 678
American Video Inc, pg 684
Colortone Audio Visual, pg 728
Ray Supply Inc, pg 870
Tri-Ed Distribution Inc, pg 918

NORTH CAROLINA

Camcor Inc, pg 715
Strategic Connections, pg 901

VIDEO

Video Standards Conversion (continued)

PENNSYLVANIA (continued)

The Videohouse Inc, pg 929
Visual Sound Inc, pg 931

SOUTH CAROLINA

American Production Services LLC, pg 684

TENNESSEE

Continental Film, pg 731
Motion Picture Services, pg 831
Stage Post, pg 899

TEXAS

CEV Multimedia Ltd, pg 720
Dub King, pg 747
The Editing Co, pg 750
Horizon Film + Video Productions, pg 781
McNee Productions Inc, pg 821
Mediaforce Productions, pg 822
Julye Newlin Productions Inc, pg 840
Replicopy Digital Media Center, pg 873
The Samuels Co, pg 879

UTAH

ImageWorks Communications, pg 785

VIRGINIA

Shakticom, pg 885

WASHINGTON

Bennett-Watt HD Productions Inc, pg 703
Victory Studios, pg 927

WEST VIRGINIA

Blackwater Video Productions, pg 707

WISCONSIN

Audio Visual of Milwaukee Inc, pg 694
AVS Group, pg 699

WYOMING

Bridger Productions Inc, pg 710

ALBERTA

Cine Audio Visual Sales & Service Ltd, pg 723

BRITISH COLUMBIA

Commercial Electronics Ltd, pg 728
Triad Communications Ltd, pg 918
24 Frames Film & Video, pg 920

NEWFOUNDLAND AND LABRADOR

Vidcraft Productions Ltd, pg 927

ONTARIO

Image Video Services & Productions, pg 785
Silver Creek Media Inc, pg 888

QUEBEC

Group PVP, pg 774

SASKATCHEWAN

Thomega Entertainment Inc, pg 913

Video Switcher Distributors

ALABAMA

PESA, pg 855

ARIZONA

ATCi (Antenna Technology Communication Solutions Inc), pg 692
EAR Professional Audio/Video, pg 749

ARKANSAS

Jay S Stanley & Associates Inc, pg 899

CALIFORNIA

Advanced Systems Group LLC, pg 677
Ametron Audio/Video, pg 684
Audio/Video Supply Inc, pg 694
AV Conferencing LLC (AVC), pg 697
Be Media, pg 702
BigFoot Mobile Systems, pg 705
BroadcastStore.com, pg 711
Cibola Systems, pg 723
Gravity Media, pg 773
Instructional Materials & Equipment Distributors (I-Med), pg 789
JD Audio Visual Inc, pg 793
Media Control Systems LLC, pg 821
Nortek Security & Control LLC, pg 842
Promax Systems, pg 865
SNAP, pg 891
Southern California Sound Image Inc, pg 895
SSL Industries Inc, pg 898
Stanislaus AV Inc, pg 899
Videobotics, pg 929
VMI Inc, pg 932

COLORADO

Spectrum Audio Visual Services, pg 897

FLORIDA

Access Media Group, pg 673
Altel Systems Group Inc, pg 682
A2D Solutions Inc, pg 692
AVI-SPL, pg 698
Digital Video Systems, pg 742
Encore Broadcast Solutions, pg 754
Glanz Technologies Inc, pg 771
Hi-Tech Enterprises Inc, pg 779
Midtown Video Inc, pg 827
Multicom Inc, pg 833
ONstage, pg 846

GEORGIA

Baker Audio Visual, pg 700
Barco Inc, pg 701
Clark, pg 725
Innocinema, pg 788
Stage Front Presentation Systems, pg 899

ILLINOIS

Allen Visual Systems Inc, pg 680
Dukane Corp, Audio Visual Products Division, pg 747
Joseph Electronics, pg 795
Quintessence Audio Ltd, pg 868

INDIANA

Lee Co Inc, pg 805
Sensory Technologies LLC, pg 884
SHP Electronics, pg 887

KENTUCKY

Axxis Leasing Inc, pg 700
Barney Miller's Inc, pg 827
NOR-COM Inc, pg 841

LOUISIANA

Techkno Integration & Design Services LLC, pg 908

MARYLAND

Human Circuit, pg 782
Noventri, pg 843
Wiltronix Inc, pg 939

MASSACHUSETTS

Rule Boston Camera, pg 878

MICHIGAN

On Stage Visuals, pg 846

MINNESOTA

Alpha Video & Audio Inc, pg 682

MISSISSIPPI

Bowie Audio Visual Enterprises Inc, pg 709

MISSOURI

Communitronics Corp, pg 729
Conference Technologies Inc, pg 730
Southwest Audio-Visual Inc, pg 895

NEBRASKA

ATV Research Inc, pg 692
VSA Inc, pg 933

NEVADA

Aardvark Video & Media Productions, pg 671

NEW JERSEY

A-V Services Inc, pg 671
Alltec Stores, a Vcom IMC Company, pg 681
AlltecPro, pg 681
Avtech Systems Inc, pg 699
Diversified, pg 744
Earl Girls Inc, pg 749
Euro-Pacific Film & Video Productions Inc, pg 756
G&G Technologies Inc, pg 768
HamiltonBuhl, pg 775
MCCOM Inc, pg 820
MiB MediaWorks, pg 825
PatchAmp, pg 852
Starlite, pg 900
SYMCO Inc, pg 905
Tele-Measurements Inc, pg 910
Total Video Products Inc, pg 916
Varto Technologies, pg 925
Yorktel, pg 944

NEW YORK

Audio-Video Corp, pg 694
AV Workshop, pg 697
B&H Photo Video, pg 701
BTX Technologies, pg 712
Design Audio Visual Inc, pg 741
General Audio-Visual Inc (GAVI), pg 769
KVL Audio Visual Services Inc, pg 802
Long Island Video Enterprises Live Inc, pg 811
Markertek Video Supply, pg 817
Presentation Products Inc, pg 861
RNJ Electronics, pg 875
TecNec Distributing, pg 909
Tri-Ed Distribution Inc, pg 918
Videoguys, pg 929
Visual Word Systems Inc, pg 932

NORTH CAROLINA

Crispin Corp, pg 734

OHIO

Copp Integrated Systems, pg 731
ITA Audio Visual Solutions, pg 791
iVideo Technologies, pg 792
Parts Express, pg 851
Tri-State Audio Visual Co, pg 918

PENNSYLVANIA

AccuWeather Inc, pg 674
Advanced AV LLC, pg 677
Audio Visions Inc, pg 694
Innovision Media Group, pg 788
The Lerro Corp, pg 806
Morefield Communications Inc, pg 830
Vistacom Inc, pg 931
Visual Sound Inc, pg 931

RHODE ISLAND

Shanix Inc, pg 885

TENNESSEE

Allstar Audio Systems Inc, pg 681
Lowrance Sound Co Inc, pg 812
Technical Support Systems LLC, pg 908
Zion Music Group, pg 945

TEXAS

Audio Visual Technologies Group (AVTG), pg 695
AVES Audio Visual Systems Inc, pg 698
Biway Media, pg 706
Data Projections Inc, pg 738
Digital Display Solutions Inc, pg 742
Pro Video & Film Equipment Co Inc, pg 863
Tarpley Media Systems, pg 907
TWIST Integration Solutions Technology, pg 920
Videotex Systems Inc, pg 930

UTAH

Performance Audio LLC, pg 854
RIA Corp, pg 874

VIRGINIA

Avitecture Inc, pg 699
Boitnott Visual Communications Corp (BVC), pg 708
Intellidyne LLC, pg 789
Quince Imaging Inc, pg 868

StageSound, pg 899
The Whitlock Group, pg 937

WASHINGTON

CCI Solutions, pg 718
PNTA, pg 858
Telect Inc, pg 910

WISCONSIN

Audio Visual of Milwaukee Inc,
pg 694
Camera Corner Connecting Point,
pg 715
Full Compass Systems, pg 767
Safe Harbor Computers, pg 879

ALBERTA

Allstar Show Industries Inc, pg 681
Matrix Video Communications Corp
(MVCC), pg 819
McBain Camera Ltd, pg 820

BRITISH COLUMBIA

DL Sound & Lighting Productions
Ltd, pg 744

MANITOBA

Advance Pro, pg 677
Inland Audio Visual Ltd, pg 788

ONTARIO

Cinema Stage Inc, pg 724
HD Source, pg 777
Majortech Inc, pg 815
Nationwide Audio Visual Co,
pg 837
Technovision® Interactive Inc,
pg 909
Westbury National Show Systems
Ltd, pg 936

QUEBEC

Panavideo Inc, pg 850

Video Switcher Manufacturers

ALABAMA

PESA, pg 855

ARIZONA

Applied Integration Corp, pg 687
ATCi (Antenna Technology
Communication Solutions Inc),
pg 692
Covid Inc, pg 732

CALIFORNIA

ALTINEX Inc, pg 682
Ampex Data Systems Corp, pg 684
DASAN Zhone Solutions (DZS)
Inc, pg 737
Extron Electronics, pg 758
FM Systems Inc, pg 763
For-A Corp of America, pg 763
Gefen, pg 769
Hosa Technology Inc, pg 781
Hotronic Inc, pg 782
Nortek Security & Control LLC,
pg 842
Physical Optics Corp (POC), pg 856
RGB Spectrum, pg 874
Sony Electronics Inc, pg 893

COLORADO

Liberty AV Solutions, pg 807
Video Accessory Corp, pg 927

FLORIDA

Hi-Tech Enterprises Inc, pg 779
Sensormatic®, pg 884
Tel-Test, pg 909

GEORGIA

Analog Way Inc, pg 685
Barco Inc, pg 701
Visix™ Inc, pg 931

ILLINOIS

NEC Display Solutions of America,
pg 837

MICHIGAN

Leightronix Inc, pg 806

MINNESOTA

Bosch Security Systems Inc, pg 709
CyberOptics Corp, pg 736
Vaddio, pg 924

MISSOURI

GlobalStreams™ Corp, pg 771
Link Electronics Inc, pg 809

NEW JERSEY

AlltecPro, pg 681
Comprehensive Cable &
Connectivity Co, pg 729
FSR Inc, pg 766
Kramer Electronics USA Inc,
pg 801

NEW MEXICO

Adrienne Electronics Corp (AEC),
pg 676
Burst Electronics Inc, pg 713

NEW YORK

Key Digital Systems, pg 798
Monroe Electronics Inc, pg 829
MultiDyne Video & Fiber Optics
Systems, pg 833
Judson Rosebush Co Inc, pg 877
TecNec Distributing, pg 909
Vicon Industries Inc, pg 926

NORTH CAROLINA

Crest Electronics Inc, pg 734

OHIO

AV Toolbox, pg 697
Network Technologies Inc, pg 838
TV One Multimedia Solutions,
pg 919

OKLAHOMA

Versatech Industries Inc, pg 926

PENNSYLVANIA

MicroImage Video Systems, pg 826

VIRGINIA

Quince Imaging Inc, pg 868

WASHINGTON

Telect Inc, pg 910

BRITISH COLUMBIA

Triad Communications Ltd, pg 918

ONTARIO

Semtech, pg 883
Technovision® Interactive Inc,
pg 909

QUEBEC

Grass Valley, pg 773
Matrox Video Products Group,
pg 819

Video Switcher Rentals

ARIZONA

AV Concepts Inc, pg 696
Creative Backstage, pg 733
Glendale Media Center, pg 771
Merestone, pg 823
Video West Inc, pg 929

ARKANSAS

White Diamond Productions LLC,
pg 937

CALIFORNIA

Alliant Event Services, pg 681
Ametron Audio/Video, pg 684
Artichoke Productions, pg 690
ATV Video Center Inc, pg 692
AV Conferencing LLC (AVC),
pg 697
AV Guys, pg 697
Express Media Inc, pg 757
Express Video Supply Inc, pg 757
First Camera, pg 761
Full Moon & High Tide Productions
& Studios, pg 767
Golden Gate Studios, pg 772
JD Audio Visual Inc, pg 793
Maximus Media Inc, pg 820
McCune Audio-Video-Lighting,
pg 821
Munday & Collins AV, pg 834
Muse Presentation Technologies,
pg 834
Production Gear Rentals (PGR),
pg 863
PSAV® Presentation Services,
pg 866
Pyxis Industries Inc, pg 867
RetinaVision Productions, pg 874
Shooting Star Video, pg 886
Shoulder High Productions, pg 886
SNAP, pg 891
The Studios at Paramount, pg 903
VER, pg 926
VMI Inc, pg 932
Voice & Video Rentals, pg 932
Warner Bros Production Sound &
Video Services, pg 934
Westcoast Video Productions Inc,
pg 936

COLORADO

Denver Media Center, pg 740

CONNECTICUT

A/V Davey, pg 697
Videofilm Systems Inc, pg 929

DISTRICT OF COLUMBIA

Metro Teleproductions Inc (MTI),
pg 824

FLORIDA

Access Media Group, pg 673
Accord Productions, pg 673
Budget Video Rentals, pg 712
Hi-Tech Enterprises Inc, pg 779
ONstage, pg 846
Paradise Show & Design Inc,
pg 851
Sight & Sound Productions, pg 887

GEORGIA

Analog Way Inc, pg 685
See Production Services, pg 883
Stage Front Presentation Systems,
pg 899

ILLINOIS

Allen Visual Systems Inc, pg 680
AV Chicago Inc, pg 696
Beatty TeleVisual Productions,
pg 703
Meetinghouse Event Design &
Production, pg 823
RC Communications, pg 870
Resolution Productions Group,
pg 874

IOWA

Pro Video, pg 863

KENTUCKY

Audio Visual Techniques Inc,
pg 695

MARYLAND

CPR MultiMedia Solutions, pg 732
Event Tech, pg 756
Kramer Communications Video
Production, pg 801

MASSACHUSETTS

massAV, pg 819
Preston Productions Inc, pg 861

MICHIGAN

K&R All Media Productions LLC,
pg 796
K&R's Recording Studios Inc,
pg 796
On Stage Visuals, pg 846

MINNESOTA

Alpha Video & Audio Inc, pg 682

MISSISSIPPI

Bowie Audio Visual Enterprises Inc,
pg 709

MISSOURI

Show-Me Audio-Visual, pg 887

NEBRASKA

Dog & Pony Productions Inc,
pg 744

NEW JERSEY

Audio Visual Dynamics®, pg 694
Earl Girls Inc, pg 749
Euro-Pacific Film & Video
Productions Inc, pg 756
Starlite, pg 900
Tele-Measurements Inc, pg 910

NEW MEXICO

Production Outfitters, pg 864

VIDEO

Video Switcher Rentals (continued)

NEW YORK

Big Foot Productions Inc, pg 705
CP Communications, pg 732
Design Audio Visual Inc, pg 741
KVL Audio Visual Services Inc, pg 802
Visual Word Systems Inc, pg 932

NORTH CAROLINA

All Pro Media Inc, pg 680
AV Connections Inc, pg 697
The Communications Group Inc, pg 729
On Location North Carolina, pg 846
Take One Productions Ltd, pg 906

NORTH DAKOTA

Media Productions, pg 822

OHIO

Lyon Video Inc, pg 813
Mills James Productions, pg 828

OKLAHOMA

PDC Productions, pg 852

OREGON

Picture This Production Services, pg 856

PENNSYLVANIA

Advanced AV LLC, pg 677
FirstGeneration Audio/Visual Services, pg 761
FMP Media Solutions Inc, pg 763
Grise Audio Visual Center Inc, pg 774
Innovision Media Group, pg 788
JPL, pg 795
New York Camera & Video, pg 840
Producers Management Television (PMTV), pg 863
Upstage Video, pg 923
The Videohouse Inc, pg 929
Viewpoint Production Services Inc, pg 930

SOUTH CAROLINA

Impact Technology Group LLC, pg 786

TENNESSEE

Allstar Audio Systems Inc, pg 681
Technical Support Systems LLC, pg 908

TEXAS

Alford Media Services, pg 680
Bright Star Productions Inc, pg 710
GEAR Cameras & Lighting, pg 769
Stage Directions, pg 898

VIRGINIA

Advance Concepts Inc, pg 677
Audio Visual Actions Inc (AVA), pg 694
Quince Imaging Inc, pg 868
StageSound, pg 899

WISCONSIN

Audio Visual of Milwaukee Inc, pg 694

PUERTO RICO

Stage Crew Audiovisual Inc, pg 898

ALBERTA

Allstar Show Industries Inc, pg 681
L R Light & Sound, pg 802
Matrix Video Communications Corp (MVCC), pg 819

BRITISH COLUMBIA

DL Sound & Lighting Productions Ltd, pg 744

MANITOBA

Inland Audio Visual Ltd, pg 788

ONTARIO

HD Source, pg 777
JIB Shots Equipment Inc, pg 794
SIM Digital, pg 888
Westbury National Show Systems Ltd, pg 936
ZTV Broadcast Services Inc, pg 945

Video Switcher Repairs

CALIFORNIA

Ametron Audio/Video, pg 684
BroadcastStore.com, pg 711
Effective Engineering Inc, pg 751
SSL Industries Inc, pg 898
Technical Services, pg 908
VMI Inc, pg 932

CONNECTICUT

A/V Davey, pg 697

FLORIDA

Access Media Group, pg 673
ELC Sales & Service Inc, pg 752
Glanz Technologies Inc, pg 771
Hi-Tech Enterprises Inc, pg 779
Midtown Video Inc, pg 827
Tel-Test, pg 909

GEORGIA

Stage Front Presentation Systems, pg 899

ILLINOIS

Beatty TeleVisual Productions, pg 703
Midwest Digital Corp, pg 827

KENTUCKY

Axxis Leasing Inc, pg 700
Barney Miller's Inc, pg 827
NOR-COM Inc, pg 841

MARYLAND

Noventri, pg 843

MASSACHUSETTS

Antronics Inc, pg 686

MICHIGAN

TEL Systems LLC, pg 909

MINNESOTA

Alpha Video & Audio Inc, pg 682

MISSOURI

Southwest Audio-Visual Inc, pg 895

OHIO

Copp Integrated Systems, pg 731
ITA Audio Visual Solutions, pg 791
Network Technologies Inc, pg 838

TENNESSEE

Technical Support Systems LLC, pg 908

TEXAS

Pro Video & Film Equipment Co Inc, pg 863
Tarpley Media Systems, pg 907

UTAH

RIA Corp, pg 874

VIRGINIA

Quince Imaging Inc, pg 868
The Whitlock Group, pg 937

WISCONSIN

Camera Corner Connecting Point, pg 715
Full Compass Systems, pg 767

ALBERTA

Matrix Video Communications Corp (MVCC), pg 819

MANITOBA

Inland Audio Visual Ltd, pg 788

ONTARIO

HD Source, pg 777
Westbury National Show Systems Ltd, pg 936

Video Wall & Control System Distributors

ARKANSAS

Jay S Stanley & Associates Inc, pg 899

CALIFORNIA

Ametron Audio/Video, pg 684
Assured Audio Visual, pg 691
Audio/Video Supply Inc, pg 694
Be Media, pg 702
Christie Digital Systems USA Inc, pg 722
Christy's Editorial, pg 723
Cibola Systems, pg 723
Computer Modules Inc, pg 729
Electrosonic Inc, pg 752
Multimedia LED, pg 833
Muse Presentation Technologies, pg 834
Sonance, pg 892
Southern California Sound Image Inc, pg 895
VITEC Multimedia, pg 932
VMI Inc, pg 932

COLORADO

Spectrum Audio Visual Services, pg 897
Stanco Sales LLC, pg 899

DISTRICT OF COLUMBIA

Future View Inc, pg 767

FLORIDA

Access Media Group, pg 673
Alcorn McBride Inc, pg 679
Altel Systems Group Inc, pg 682
AVI-SPL, pg 698
Digital Video Systems, pg 742
Hi-Tech Import Export Corp, pg 779
Multivision Video & Film, pg 833
ONstage, pg 846
Vela Research, pg 925

GEORGIA

Baker Audio Visual, pg 700
Clark, pg 725
Stage Front Presentation Systems, pg 899
Visioneering International Inc, pg 931

ILLINOIS

Allen Visual Systems Inc, pg 680
Joseph Electronics, pg 795
RC Communications, pg 870

INDIANA

Lee Co Inc, pg 805
Sensory Technologies LLC, pg 884
SHP Electronics, pg 887

KENTUCKY

Axxis Leasing Inc, pg 700
Creative Realities Inc (CRI), pg 733
NOR-COM Inc, pg 841

MARYLAND

Human Circuit, pg 782

MASSACHUSETTS

AVFX Inc, pg 698
Integrated Solutions Group, pg 789
Pro AV Systems, pg 862

MICHIGAN

Digi Sign Design LLC, pg 741

MINNESOTA

Alpha Video & Audio Inc, pg 682

MISSOURI

Communitronics Corp, pg 729
Southwest Audio-Visual Inc, pg 895

NEW JERSEY

A-V Services Inc, pg 671
Activu Corp, pg 675
Alltec Stores, a Vcom IMC Company, pg 681
Diversified, pg 744
Earl Girls Inc, pg 749
Euro-Pacific Film & Video Productions Inc, pg 756
HamiltonBuhl, pg 775
PatchAmp, pg 852
Starlite, pg 900
SYMCO Inc, pg 905
Tele-Measurements Inc, pg 910

Total Video Products Inc, pg 916
Wired 4 Sound Inc, pg 940
Yorktel, pg 944

NEW YORK

Ace Video, pg 674
American Video Inc, pg 684
Audio-Video Corp, pg 694
AV Workshop, pg 697
General Audio-Visual Inc (GAVI),
 pg 769
KVL Audio Visual Services Inc,
 pg 802
Long Island Video Enterprises Live
 Inc, pg 811
Presentation Products Inc, pg 861
Visual Word Systems Inc, pg 932

NORTH CAROLINA

The Godfrey Group Inc, pg 772
Strategic Connections, pg 901

OHIO

Copp Integrated Systems, pg 731
ITA Audio Visual Solutions, pg 791
iVideo Technologies, pg 792
Tri-State Audio Visual Co, pg 918

OKLAHOMA

Ford AV, pg 763

PENNSYLVANIA

Advanced AV LLC, pg 677
Audio Visions Inc, pg 694
Innovision Media Group, pg 788
The Lerro Corp, pg 806
Morefield Communications Inc,
 pg 830
SAPSIS Rigging Inc, pg 880
Vistacom Inc, pg 931

TENNESSEE

Allstar Audio Systems Inc, pg 681
Lowrance Sound Co Inc, pg 812
Technical Support Systems LLC,
 pg 908
Zion Music Group, pg 945

TEXAS

Audio Visual Technologies Group
 (AVTG), pg 695
Data Projections Inc, pg 738
Digital Display Solutions Inc,
 pg 742
Stage Directions, pg 898
Tarpley Media Systems, pg 907

UTAH

RIA Corp, pg 874

VIRGINIA

Avitecture Inc, pg 699
Intellidyne LLC, pg 789
Lee Hartman & Sons Inc, pg 805
Quince Imaging Inc, pg 868

WASHINGTON

PNTA, pg 858

WISCONSIN

Audio Visual of Milwaukee Inc,
 pg 694
Camera Corner Connecting Point,
 pg 715
Full Compass Systems, pg 767

PUERTO RICO

Audio Visual Concepts Inc, pg 694

ALBERTA

Evolution AV, pg 757
Genesis Integration, pg 769
Infosat Communications Inc, pg 787
Unique Communications Ltd,
 pg 921

MANITOBA

Advance Pro, pg 677
Inland Audio Visual Ltd, pg 788

ONTARIO

Cinema Stage Inc, pg 724
Image Video, pg 785
Technovision® Interactive Inc,
 pg 909
Westbury National Show Systems
 Ltd, pg 936

Video Wall & Control System Manufacturers

CALIFORNIA

Christie Digital Systems USA Inc,
 pg 722
Jupiter Systems, pg 795
Multimedia LED, pg 833
Physical Optics Corp (POC), pg 856
Pioneer Electronics (USA) Inc,
 pg 857
RGB Spectrum, pg 874
Sonance, pg 892
VITEC Multimedia, pg 932

COLORADO

Colorado Time Systems LLC,
 pg 728

CONNECTICUT

Collective Systems LLC, pg 727

FLORIDA

Alcorn McBride Inc, pg 679
Compuvideo Sales USA Ltd,
 pg 729
Vela Research, pg 925

INDIANA

Draper Inc, pg 746

MINNESOTA

Dotronix Technology Inc, pg 746
Winsted Corp, pg 939

NEW JERSEY

Activu Corp, pg 675
AlltecPro, pg 681
FSR Inc, pg 766

NEW YORK

Vicon Industries Inc, pg 926

PENNSYLVANIA

Video Visions Inc, pg 929

TENNESSEE

Adtec Digital Inc, pg 677

UTAH

ClearOne Inc, pg 726

ONTARIO

Image Video, pg 785
Technovision® Interactive Inc,
 pg 909

Video Wall & Control System Rentals

ARIZONA

AV Concepts Inc, pg 696
Merestone, pg 823

ARKANSAS

White Diamond Productions LLC,
 pg 937

CALIFORNIA

Alliant Event Services, pg 681
Ametron Audio/Video, pg 684
Express Media Inc, pg 757
Lynch Communications, pg 813
Multimedia LED, pg 833
Muse Presentation Technologies,
 pg 834
PSAV® Presentation Services,
 pg 866
SNAP, pg 891
VER, pg 926
VMI Inc, pg 932

COLORADO

Spectrum Audio Visual Services,
 pg 897

DISTRICT OF COLUMBIA

Future View Inc, pg 767

FLORIDA

Industrial Strength Inc, pg 787
Jordan Klein Film & Video (JKFV),
 pg 795
Midtown Video Inc, pg 827
Multivision Video & Film, pg 833
ONstage, pg 846

GEORGIA

MAGNUM Companies Ltd, pg 815
ON Services, a GES Company,
 pg 846
Stage Front Presentation Systems,
 pg 899

ILLINOIS

Atomic Imaging Inc/Golan Studios,
 pg 692
Backstar Creative Media Inc,
 pg 700
RC Communications, pg 870
SCI Television & Creative Media
 LLC, pg 882

LOUISIANA

Digital FX Inc, pg 742

MAINE

Headlight Audio Visual Inc, pg 777

MARYLAND

CPR MultiMedia Solutions, pg 732

MASSACHUSETTS

AVFX Inc, pg 698
Preston Productions Inc, pg 861

MICHIGAN

Digi Sign Design LLC, pg 741
K&R All Media Productions LLC,
 pg 796
K&R's Recording Studios Inc,
 pg 796

MINNESOTA

Freestyle Productions Inc, pg 765

MISSOURI

Communitronics Corp, pg 729
Southwest Audio-Visual Inc, pg 895

NEBRASKA

Dog & Pony Productions Inc,
 pg 744

NEVADA

GES Audio Visual, pg 770

NEW JERSEY

Audio Visual Dynamics®, pg 694
Earl Girls Inc, pg 749
Euro-Pacific Film & Video
 Productions Inc, pg 756
PLS Staging, pg 858
Starlite, pg 900
Tele-Measurements Inc, pg 910

NEW YORK

Ace Video, pg 674
American Video Inc, pg 684
AV Workshop, pg 697
CP Communications, pg 732
Design Audio Visual Inc, pg 741
KVL Audio Visual Services Inc,
 pg 802
Long Island Video Enterprises Live
 Inc, pg 811
PrimaLux Video Inc, pg 862
SmartSource Computer & AV
 Rentals, pg 891
Visual Word Systems Inc, pg 932
WorldStage, pg 941

NORTH CAROLINA

Special Event Services, pg 896

OHIO

Hughie's Event Production Services,
 pg 782
ITA Audio Visual Solutions, pg 791

PENNSYLVANIA

Advanced AV LLC, pg 677
FMP Media Solutions Inc, pg 763
Innovision Media Group, pg 788
Producers Management Television
 (PMTV), pg 863
Upstage Video, pg 923

TENNESSEE

Allstar Audio Systems Inc, pg 681
Technical Support Systems LLC,
 pg 908

TEXAS

Stage Directions, pg 898

VIRGINIA

Quince Imaging Inc, pg 868

VIDEO

Video Wall & Control System Rentals (continued)

WISCONSIN

Audio Visual of Milwaukee Inc, pg 694

ALBERTA

Unique Communications Ltd, pg 921

BRITISH COLUMBIA

Clark's Audio Visual Services Ltd, pg 725

MANITOBA

Inland Audio Visual Ltd, pg 788

ONTARIO

HD Source, pg 777
MVI - MultiVision Inc, pg 835
Westbury National Show Systems Ltd, pg 936

QUEBEC

Audio Visual Dynamics, pg 694
Freeman Audio Visual, pg 765

Video Wall & Control System Repairs

CALIFORNIA

Ametron Audio/Video, pg 684
Sonance, pg 892

FLORIDA

ELC Sales & Service Inc, pg 752
Multivision Video & Film, pg 833
Vela Research, pg 925

GEORGIA

Stage Front Presentation Systems, pg 899

ILLINOIS

RC Communications, pg 870

KENTUCKY

Axxis Leasing Inc, pg 700
NOR-COM Inc, pg 841

MICHIGAN

TEL Systems LLC, pg 909

MINNESOTA

Alpha Video & Audio Inc, pg 682
Dotronix Technology Inc, pg 746

OHIO

ITA Audio Visual Solutions, pg 791
Tri-State Audio Visual Co, pg 918

TENNESSEE

Technical Support Systems LLC, pg 908

TEXAS

Tarpley Media Systems, pg 907

UTAH

RIA Corp, pg 874

VIRGINIA

Avitecture Inc, pg 699
Quince Imaging Inc, pg 868

WISCONSIN

Full Compass Systems, pg 767

ALBERTA

Infosat Communications Inc, pg 787
Unique Communications Ltd, pg 921

MANITOBA

Inland Audio Visual Ltd, pg 788

ONTARIO

MVI - MultiVision Inc, pg 835
Westbury National Show Systems Ltd, pg 936

Videocassette—Blank Distributors

ALABAMA

Curtis Company, pg 736

ARIZONA

Metropolitan Audio-Visual Inc, pg 824
On-Site Video, pg 846
Rodeo Video Inc, pg 876

ARKANSAS

Carlton-Bates Co, pg 717

CALIFORNIA

Ametron Audio/Video, pg 684
Assured Audio Visual, pg 691
California Tape Products Inc, pg 714
Gluskin's Custom Audio Video, pg 771
Alan Gordon Enterprises Inc, pg 772
Instructional Materials & Equipment Distributors (I-Med), pg 789
JD Audio Visual Inc, pg 793
Lynch Communications, pg 813
Media Fabricators Inc, pg 822
MSE Media Solutions, pg 832
On-Trax Inc, pg 846
QRS Software Services, pg 867
Reel Picture, pg 872
RJ Video Productions, pg 875
SSL Industries Inc, pg 898
VMI Inc, pg 932

COLORADO

Daylight Productions & Rentals, pg 739
Spectrum Audio Visual Services, pg 897

CONNECTICUT

MAVCO, pg 820
Rockwell Communications Inc, pg 876

FLORIDA

Access Media Group, pg 673
Altel Systems Group Inc, pg 682

AVI-SPL, pg 698
Digital Video Systems, pg 742
Hi-Tech Import Export Corp, pg 779
Industrial Strength Inc, pg 787
Jordan Klein Film & Video (JKFV), pg 795
Midtown Video Inc, pg 827
ONstage, pg 846
Recording Media & Equipment Inc (RM&E), pg 872

GEORGIA

Audio Visual Resources Inc, pg 695
Convergent Media Systems, pg 731
Lighting & Production Equipment Inc, pg 807
Stage Front Presentation Systems, pg 899
Video Copy Services Inc, pg 927

ILLINOIS

Allen Visual Systems Inc, pg 680
Creative Technology (CT), pg 733
FUJIFILM Graphic Systems Division, pg 766
Joseph Electronics, pg 795
Major Reproductions Equipment Co, pg 815
Research Technology International (RTI), pg 873
Tele-Time Systems, pg 910

INDIANA

Lee Co Inc, pg 805
Sensory Technologies LLC, pg 884
SHP Electronics, pg 887

KANSAS

Lights On, pg 808

KENTUCKY

American Recordable Media, pg 684
Audio Visual Techniques Inc, pg 695
Axxis Leasing Inc, pg 700
Barney Miller's Inc, pg 827
NOR-COM Inc, pg 841
WaxWorks VideoWorks, pg 934

LOUISIANA

Digital FX Inc, pg 742

MARYLAND

Nicholas P Pipino Associates Inc, pg 857
RTZ Audio Visual, pg 878

MASSACHUSETTS

Antronics Inc, pg 686
Hunt's Photo & Video, pg 782
Integrated Solutions Group, pg 789
Rule Boston Camera, pg 878

MICHIGAN

TEL Systems LLC, pg 909

MINNESOTA

Cinequipt Inc, pg 724

MISSISSIPPI

Bowie Audio Visual Enterprises Inc, pg 709
Jasper Ewing & Sons Inc, pg 757

MISSOURI

Audio-VideoGraphics Inc, pg 694
Communitronics Corp, pg 729
Conference Technologies Inc, pg 730
Southwest Audio-Visual Inc, pg 895

NEBRASKA

VSA Inc, pg 933

NEW HAMPSHIRE

Channell One Video, pg 720

NEW JERSEY

Agfa Graphics, pg 678
AlltecPro, pg 681
Audio Visual Dynamics®, pg 694
AV Bluebook, pg 696
Comprehensive Cable & Connectivity Co, pg 729
G&G Technologies Inc, pg 768
Maxell Corp of America, pg 820
PatchAmp, pg 852
Starlite, pg 900
SYMCO Inc, pg 905
Tele-Measurements Inc, pg 910
Total Media Inc, pg 916
Total Video Products Inc, pg 916
Vcom IMC, pg 925

NEW YORK

Adwar Video, pg 678
AV Workshop, pg 697
Barbizon Electric Co Inc, pg 701
Burlington A/V Recording Media, pg 712
Colortone Audio Visual, pg 728
Design Audio Visual Inc, pg 741
Film Emporium, pg 760
Flash Electronics Inc, pg 762
Gaylord Archival, pg 768
HAVE Inc, pg 777
Long Island Video Enterprises Live Inc, pg 811
Markertek Video Supply, pg 817
Neptune Photo Inc, pg 838
Presentation Products Inc, pg 861
Rafik, pg 869
Ray Supply Inc, pg 870
Russell Industries Inc, pg 879
Sentry Industries Inc, pg 884
TecNec Distributing, pg 909
Tri-Ed Distribution Inc, pg 918
Visual Technologies Corp, pg 932

NORTH CAROLINA

Duke Media Services, pg 747
Strategic Connections, pg 901

OHIO

Audio Visual Media, pg 694
Copp Integrated Systems, pg 731
Hughie's Event Production Services, pg 782
Tri-State Audio Visual Co, pg 918

PENNSYLVANIA

Advanced AV LLC, pg 677
Audio Visual Communications Inc, pg 694
Bernie's Photo Center, pg 704
FMP Media Solutions Inc, pg 763
J E Foss Co, pg 764
Grise Audio Visual Center Inc, pg 774
Hite Co, pg 780
The Lerro Corp, pg 806

Morefield Communications Inc,
pg 830
Wespen Audio Visual Co, pg 935

TENNESSEE

Lowrance Sound Co Inc, pg 812
Memphis Communications Corp,
pg 823
Spring Arbor Distributors Inc,
pg 898

TEXAS

JSAV, pg 795
Stage Directions, pg 898

UTAH

RIA Corp, pg 874
TV Specialists Inc, pg 919
Webb Audio Visual, pg 935

VIRGINIA

Boitnott Visual Communications
Corp (BVC), pg 708
Lee Hartman & Sons Inc, pg 805
Metropolitan Audio Visual Co LLC,
pg 824
The Whitlock Group, pg 937

WASHINGTON

Inland Audio Visual Co, pg 788
Oppenheimer Camera Products,
pg 847

WISCONSIN

Demco Inc, pg 740
Full Compass Systems, pg 767
School Specialty Inc, pg 882

PUERTO RICO

Bonnin Electronics Inc, pg 708

ALBERTA

Infosat Communications Inc, pg 787
Matrix Video Communications Corp
(MVCC), pg 819
McBain Camera Ltd, pg 820

BRITISH COLUMBIA

Triad Communications Ltd, pg 918

MANITOBA

Advance Pro, pg 677
Inland Audio Visual Ltd, pg 788

ONTARIO

HD Source, pg 777
Nationwide Audio Visual Co,
pg 837

QUEBEC

Panavideo Inc, pg 850

Videocassette—Blank Manufacturers

CALIFORNIA

QRS Software Services, pg 867
Reel Picture, pg 872
Sony Electronics Inc, pg 893
Technicolor USA Inc, pg 908

KENTUCKY

American Recordable Media,
pg 684

MARYLAND

Saah Video, pg 879

NEW JERSEY

AlltecPro, pg 681
Konica Minolta Business Solutions,
pg 801
Maxell Corp of America, pg 820
Reed Presentations Inc (RPI),
pg 872
Synergem, pg 905

NEW YORK

FUJIFILM North America Corp,
pg 766

TEXAS

Adams Evidence Grade Technology
Inc, pg 675

WISCONSIN

Full Compass Systems, pg 767

Videocassette Duplication, *see* Duplication—Videocassettes

Videocassette Editing, *see* Editing—Videocassettes

Videocassette Recorder & Player Distributors

ARIZONA

EAR Professional Audio/Video,
pg 749

CALIFORNIA

Ametron Audio/Video, pg 684
Be Media, pg 702
BigFoot Mobile Systems, pg 705
Christy's Editorial, pg 723
Cibola Systems, pg 723
Diaquest, pg 741
Alan Gordon Enterprises Inc,
pg 772
Instructional Materials & Equipment
Distributors (I-Med), pg 789
JD Audio Visual Inc, pg 793
Southern California Sound Image
Inc, pg 895
VMI Inc, pg 932

COLORADO

Spectrum Audio Visual Services,
pg 897

FLORIDA

Access Media Group, pg 673
AVI-SPL, pg 698
Digital Video Systems, pg 742
Hi-Tech Import Export Corp,
pg 779
Midtown Video Inc, pg 827
ONstage, pg 846
Recording Media & Equipment Inc
(RM&E), pg 872

GEORGIA

Stage Front Presentation Systems,
pg 899

ILLINOIS

Joseph Electronics, pg 795
Woodside Avenue Music
Productions Inc, pg 941

INDIANA

Lee Co Inc, pg 805
Sensory Technologies LLC, pg 884
SHP Electronics, pg 887

KENTUCKY

Axxis Leasing Inc, pg 700
Barney Miller's Inc, pg 827
NOR-COM Inc, pg 841

MASSACHUSETTS

Rule Boston Camera, pg 878

MICHIGAN

Digi Sign Design LLC, pg 741
TEL Systems LLC, pg 909

MISSOURI

Southwest Audio-Visual Inc, pg 895

NEBRASKA

ATV Research Inc, pg 692
VSA Inc, pg 933

NEW JERSEY

Alltec Stores, a Vcom IMC
Company, pg 681
AlltecPro, pg 681
AV Bluebook, pg 696
Color Leasing Studios, pg 727
Diversified, pg 744
MCCOM Inc, pg 820
Starlite, pg 900
Tele-Measurements Inc, pg 910
Total Video Products Inc, pg 916

NEW YORK

B&H Photo Video, pg 701
Colortone Audio Visual, pg 728
Design Audio Visual Inc, pg 741
Gaylord Archival, pg 768
Markertek Video Supply, pg 817
Presentation Products Inc, pg 861
RNJ Electronics, pg 875
TecNec Distributing, pg 909
Visual Word Systems Inc, pg 932

OHIO

Tri-State Audio Visual Co, pg 918

PENNSYLVANIA

Advanced AV LLC, pg 677
Bernie's Photo Center, pg 704
Brodart Co, pg 711
J E Foss Co, pg 764
Grise Audio Visual Center Inc,
pg 774
The Lerro Corp, pg 806

TENNESSEE

Lowrance Sound Co Inc, pg 812
Technical Support Systems LLC,
pg 908

TEXAS

AVES Audio Visual Systems Inc,
pg 698
Digital Display Solutions Inc,
pg 742

Pro Video & Film Equipment Co
Inc, pg 863
Quality Audio Visual Service Inc,
pg 867
Videotex Systems Inc, pg 930

VIRGINIA

Lee Hartman & Sons Inc, pg 805

WASHINGTON

ToteVision, pg 916

WISCONSIN

Full Compass Systems, pg 767

ALBERTA

Matrix Video Communications Corp
(MVCC), pg 819

MANITOBA

Advance Pro, pg 677
Inland Audio Visual Ltd, pg 788

ONTARIO

Westbury National Show Systems
Ltd, pg 936

Videocassette Recorder & Player Manufacturers

NEW JERSEY

Panasonic Corporation of North
America, pg 850

WASHINGTON

ToteVision, pg 916

Videocassette Recorder & Player Rentals

ARIZONA

Merestone, pg 823

ARKANSAS

White Diamond Productions LLC,
pg 937

CALIFORNIA

Action Video, pg 675
Advanced Media LLC, pg 677
Ametron Audio/Video, pg 684
Artichoke Productions, pg 690
AV Guys, pg 697
Bexel, an NEP Broadcast Services
Company, pg 704
Big Door, pg 705
BigFoot Mobile Systems, pg 705
Deck Hand Inc, pg 740
Express Media Inc, pg 757
Golden Gate Studios, pg 772
Alan Gordon Enterprises Inc,
pg 772
Instructional Materials & Equipment
Distributors (I-Med), pg 789
JD Audio Visual Inc, pg 793
Lynch Communications, pg 813
Main Street Media Inc, pg 815
Maximus Media Inc, pg 820
Munday & Collins AV, pg 834
On-Trax Inc, pg 846
Prime Cut Productions, pg 862
PSAV® Presentation Services,
pg 866
RetinaVision Productions, pg 874
SNAP, pg 891

VIDEO

Videocassette Recorder & Player Rentals (continued)

CALIFORNIA (continued)

Twin Peaks Creative, pg 920
VMI Inc, pg 932
Voice & Video Rentals, pg 932
Warner Bros Production Sound & Video Services, pg 934
Westcoast Video Productions Inc, pg 936

COLORADO

Open Media Foundation, pg 846
Spectrum Audio Visual Services, pg 897

CONNECTICUT

A/V Davey, pg 697
Videofilm Systems Inc, pg 929

DISTRICT OF COLUMBIA

Metro Teleproductions Inc (MTI), pg 824

FLORIDA

Access Media Group, pg 673
Accord Productions, pg 673
All Comm Rentals Inc (ALLCOMM), pg 680
Midtown Video Inc, pg 827
ONstage, pg 846
Paradise Show & Design Inc, pg 851
Universal Studios Florida® Production Group, pg 922

GEORGIA

Lighting & Production Equipment Inc, pg 807
MAGNUM Companies Ltd, pg 815
Stage Front Presentation Systems, pg 899

ILLINOIS

Allen Visual Systems Inc, pg 680
AV Chicago Inc, pg 696
Backstar Creative Media Inc, pg 700
Creative Technology (CT), pg 733
RC Communications, pg 870
Resolution Productions Group, pg 874
Woodside Avenue Music Productions Inc, pg 941

KENTUCKY

Audio Visual Techniques Inc, pg 695

LOUISIANA

Moxie Media, pg 832

MARYLAND

CPR MultiMedia Solutions, pg 732

MASSACHUSETTS

AVFX Inc, pg 698
Green Mountain Post Films (GMP), pg 774
massAV, pg 819

MICHIGAN

Digi Sign Design LLC, pg 741
K&R All Media Productions LLC, pg 796
K&R's Recording Studios Inc, pg 796
TEL Systems LLC, pg 909

MISSISSIPPI

Bowie Audio Visual Enterprises Inc, pg 709

MISSOURI

Schiller's Audio-Visual, pg 881
Show-Me Audio-Visual, pg 887
Southwest Audio-Visual Inc, pg 895

NEVADA

GES Audio Visual, pg 770

NEW JERSEY

Color Leasing Studios, pg 727
International Audio Visual Inc, pg 790
PLS Staging, pg 858
Starlite, pg 900
Tele-Measurements Inc, pg 910

NEW YORK

Big Foot Productions Inc, pg 705
Colortone Audio Visual, pg 728
Design Audio Visual Inc, pg 741
Hello World Communications, pg 778
Manhattan Center Studios Inc, pg 816
PrimaLux Video Inc, pg 862
The Visual Studies Workshop (VSW), pg 931
Visual Word Systems Inc, pg 932

NORTH CAROLINA

AV Connections Inc, pg 697
AV Metro Inc, pg 697
Digital Rain LLC, pg 742
Duke Media Services, pg 747
On Location North Carolina, pg 846
Special Event Services, pg 896
Take One Productions Ltd, pg 906

OHIO

Hughie's Event Production Services, pg 782
R&B Communications Inc, pg 870

PENNSYLVANIA

Advanced AV LLC, pg 677
Audio Visual Communications Inc, pg 694
FMP Media Solutions Inc, pg 763
Grise Audio Visual Center Inc, pg 774
JPL, pg 795
Producers Management Television (PMTV), pg 863
The Videohouse Inc, pg 929

TENNESSEE

Technical Support Systems LLC, pg 908

TEXAS

Quality Audio Visual Service Inc, pg 867
South Coast Film & Video, pg 895
Stage Directions, pg 898

WASHINGTON

Victory Studios, pg 927

WISCONSIN

Full Compass Systems, pg 767

PUERTO RICO

Stage Crew Audiovisual Inc, pg 898

ALBERTA

Matrix Video Communications Corp (MVCC), pg 819

BRITISH COLUMBIA

Commercial Electronics Ltd, pg 728

MANITOBA

Inland Audio Visual Ltd, pg 788

ONTARIO

Westbury National Show Systems Ltd, pg 936

QUEBEC

Group PVP, pg 774

SASKATCHEWAN

plan9films, pg 857

Videocassette Recorder & Player Repairs

CALIFORNIA

Advanced Media LLC, pg 677
Ametron Audio/Video, pg 684
BigFoot Mobile Systems, pg 705
Effective Engineering Inc, pg 751
Instructional Materials & Equipment Distributors (I-Med), pg 789
McAlister Electronics, pg 820
Pro Camera Repair, pg 862
Towards 2000 Inc, pg 916
VMI Inc, pg 932

CONNECTICUT

A/V Davey, pg 697

FLORIDA

Access Media Group, pg 673
Digital Video Systems, pg 742
ELC Sales & Service Inc, pg 752
Midtown Video Inc, pg 827

GEORGIA

Stage Front Presentation Systems, pg 899

ILLINOIS

Midwest Digital Corp, pg 827

KENTUCKY

Axxis Leasing Inc, pg 700
Barney Miller's Inc, pg 827
NOR-COM Inc, pg 841

MICHIGAN

TEL Systems LLC, pg 909

MISSOURI

Schiller's Audio-Visual, pg 881
Southwest Audio-Visual Inc, pg 895

NEW JERSEY

Starlite, pg 900

OHIO

Tri-State Audio Visual Co, pg 918

PENNSYLVANIA

Bernie's Photo Center, pg 704
J E Foss Co, pg 764

TENNESSEE

Technical Support Systems LLC, pg 908

TEXAS

Pro Video & Film Equipment Co Inc, pg 863
Quality Audio Visual Service Inc, pg 867

WISCONSIN

Full Compass Systems, pg 767

ALBERTA

Matrix Video Communications Corp (MVCC), pg 819

BRITISH COLUMBIA

Commercial Electronics Ltd, pg 728

MANITOBA

Inland Audio Visual Ltd, pg 788

ONTARIO

Westbury National Show Systems Ltd, pg 936

Videodisc—Blank Distributors

CALIFORNIA

Ametron Audio/Video, pg 684
MSE Media Solutions, pg 832

FLORIDA

Digital Video Systems, pg 742

GEORGIA

Stage Front Presentation Systems, pg 899

ILLINOIS

Joseph Electronics, pg 795

INDIANA

Lee Co Inc, pg 805
Sensory Technologies LLC, pg 884
SHP Electronics, pg 887

KANSAS

Lights On, pg 808

KENTUCKY

NOR-COM Inc, pg 841

MARYLAND

Carpel Video Inc, pg 717

NEW JERSEY

Starlite, pg 900
Total Media Inc, pg 916

NEW YORK

Colortone Audio Visual, pg 728
Design Audio Visual Inc, pg 741
Film Emporium, pg 760

OHIO

Tri-State Audio Visual Co, pg 918

PENNSYLVANIA

Advanced AV LLC, pg 677
Brodart Co, pg 711

TENNESSEE

Lowrance Sound Co Inc, pg 812

VIRGINIA

Lee Hartman & Sons Inc, pg 805

MANITOBA

Advance Pro, pg 677
Inland Audio Visual Ltd, pg 788

Videodisc—Blank Manufacturers

TEXAS

Adams Evidence Grade Technology
Inc, pg 675

Videodisc Duplication, *see* Duplication—Videodiscs

Videodisc Mastering

ARIZONA

Merestone, pg 823

CALIFORNIA

All Video Productions, pg 680
Audio Visual Consultants, pg 694
Custom Video Productions Inc,
pg 736
Digital Jungle, pg 742
iCorpTv, pg 783
JDS Video & Media Productions
Inc, pg 793
Nineteen87, pg 841
Palardo Productions, pg 850
Point.360, pg 858
QRS Software Services, pg 867
RetinaVision Productions, pg 874
Roundabout Entertainment Inc,
pg 878

FLORIDA

Communications Concepts Inc
(CCI), pg 729
Sunfire Communications Inc,
pg 904

GEORGIA

Beachwood Productions, pg 702

ILLINOIS

Optimus, pg 847

KENTUCKY

The PPS Group, pg 860

LOUISIANA

Digital FX Inc, pg 742
Louisiana State University Division
of Strategic Communications,
pg 811

MASSACHUSETTS

HOME Inc, pg 781

MICHIGAN

Digi Sign Design LLC, pg 741
K&R's Recording Studios Inc,
pg 796

NEVADA

Encore Event Technologies LLC,
pg 754
JCS Video Productions, pg 793

NEW HAMPSHIRE

Academic & Campus Technology
Services, pg 672

NEW JERSEY

Allegro Productions Inc, pg 680
Broadcast Center Studios, pg 710
Suede Interactive, pg 903

NEW YORK

Duplication Specialists Inc, pg 748
Giant Interactive, pg 770
HAVE Inc, pg 777
PostWorks, pg 860
Teatown Communications Group,
pg 908

NORTH CAROLINA

Pat Appleson Studios Inc, pg 687

OHIO

Aztec Video Productions, pg 700

PENNSYLVANIA

FMP Media Solutions Inc, pg 763
Innovision Media Group, pg 788

TENNESSEE

Stage Post, pg 899

TEXAS

Castleview Productions, pg 717
The Editing Co, pg 750

VIRGINIA

CACI Integrated Communications,
pg 713

WASHINGTON

Bennett-Watt HD Productions Inc,
pg 703

WISCONSIN

Audio Visual of Milwaukee Inc,
pg 694
USAV Group Inc, pg 923
Video Wisconsin Inc, pg 929

WYOMING

Bridger Productions Inc, pg 710

ONTARIO

Technovision® Interactive Inc,
pg 909

Videodisc Premastering

ARIZONA

Merestone, pg 823

CALIFORNIA

Advanced Systems Group LLC,
pg 677
All Video Productions, pg 680
Custom Video Productions Inc,
pg 736
First Person Inc, pg 761
iCorpTv, pg 783
JDS Video & Media Productions
Inc, pg 793
QRS Software Services, pg 867
RetinaVision Productions, pg 874
Roundabout Entertainment Inc,
pg 878
Total Creative, pg 916

COLORADO

Z-Axis Corp, pg 944

CONNECTICUT

Palace Production Center, pg 850

DISTRICT OF COLUMBIA

Interface Media Group, pg 789

FLORIDA

Communications Concepts Inc
(CCI), pg 729
Knowles Video Inc (KVI), pg 800
Sunfire Communications Inc,
pg 904

GEORGIA

Beachwood Productions, pg 702

HAWAII

1013 Integrated, pg 911

ILLINOIS

Optimus, pg 847
Southern Illinois University, pg 895

LOUISIANA

Digital FX Inc, pg 742
Louisiana State University Division
of Strategic Communications,
pg 811

MARYLAND

Sign Media Inc, pg 887

MICHIGAN

Digi Sign Design LLC, pg 741
K&R's Recording Studios Inc,
pg 796
RingSide Creative, pg 875

NEVADA

Encore Event Technologies LLC,
pg 754
Lefco Video Services Inc, pg 806
21st Century Video Productions,
pg 919

NEW HAMPSHIRE

Academic & Campus Technology
Services, pg 672
The Troupe, pg 918

NEW JERSEY

Allegro Productions Inc, pg 680
Broadcast Center Studios, pg 710
MiB MediaWorks, pg 825
Midnight Media Group Inc, pg 827
Suede Interactive, pg 903
VCSvideo, pg 925

NEW YORK

Chromavision Corp, pg 723
Duplication Specialists Inc, pg 748
HAVE Inc, pg 777
PostWorks, pg 860
Teatown Communications Group,
pg 908

NORTH CAROLINA

Duke Media Services, pg 747
Trailblazer Studios®, pg 917

OHIO

Aztec Video Productions, pg 700
Cuyahoga Community College
Student Production Office (SPO),
pg 736

PENNSYLVANIA

Audio Visual Communications Inc,
pg 694
Center City Film & Video Inc,
pg 719
Innovision Media Group, pg 788
Production Masters Inc (PMI),
pg 864

TENNESSEE

Continental Film, pg 731
Stage Post, pg 899

TEXAS

The Editing Co, pg 750
Stage Directions, pg 898

VIRGINIA

BES Studios, pg 704
Henninger Media Services, pg 779

WASHINGTON

Bennett-Watt HD Productions Inc,
pg 703

WISCONSIN

Audio Visual of Milwaukee Inc,
pg 694
USAV Group Inc, pg 923
Video Wisconsin Inc, pg 929

WYOMING

Bridger Productions Inc, pg 710

ONTARIO

Technovision® Interactive Inc,
pg 909

Videodisc Recorder & Player Distributors

ARIZONA

EAR Professional Audio/Video,
pg 749

VIDEO

Videodisc Recorder & Player Distributors (continued)

CALIFORNIA

Advanced Systems Group LLC, pg 677
Ametron Audio/Video, pg 684
Audio/Video Supply Inc, pg 694
Be Media, pg 702
Diaquest, pg 741
Gluskin's Custom Audio Video, pg 771
Instructional Materials & Equipment Distributors (I-Med), pg 789
Jaguar Distribution Corp, pg 792
Media Fabricators Inc, pg 822
Pioneer Electronics (USA) Inc, pg 857
SNAP, pg 891
Southern California Sound Image Inc, pg 895
SSL Industries Inc, pg 898

COLORADO

Spectrum Audio Visual Services, pg 897

FLORIDA

AVI-SPL, pg 698
Digital Video Systems, pg 742
Hi-Tech Import Export Corp, pg 779
Midtown Video Inc, pg 827
ONstage, pg 846
Recording Media & Equipment Inc (RM&E), pg 872

GEORGIA

Clark, pg 725
Stage Front Presentation Systems, pg 899

ILLINOIS

Joseph Electronics, pg 795

INDIANA

Lee Co Inc, pg 805
Sensory Technologies LLC, pg 884
SHP Electronics, pg 887

KENTUCKY

Axxis Leasing Inc, pg 700
NOR-COM Inc, pg 841

MICHIGAN

ASC Systems, pg 690
Digi Sign Design LLC, pg 741

MISSOURI

Communitronics Corp, pg 729
Southwest Audio-Visual Inc, pg 895

NEBRASKA

VSA Inc, pg 933

NEVADA

Aardvark Video & Media Productions, pg 671

NEW JERSEY

A-V Services Inc, pg 671
AlltecPro, pg 681

MCCOM Inc, pg 820
Starlite, pg 900
Total Video Products Inc, pg 916

NEW YORK

American Video Inc, pg 684
AV Workshop, pg 697
B&H Photo Video, pg 701
Design Audio Visual Inc, pg 741
Gaylord Archival, pg 768
Gotham Sound & Communications Inc, pg 773
KVL Audio Visual Services Inc, pg 802
Neptune Photo Inc, pg 838
TecNec Distributing, pg 909
Tri-Ed Distribution Inc, pg 918
Visual Word Systems Inc, pg 932

OHIO

Tri-State Audio Visual Co, pg 918

PENNSYLVANIA

Advanced AV LLC, pg 677
The Lerro Corp, pg 806
Morefield Communications Inc, pg 830

TENNESSEE

Lowrance Sound Co Inc, pg 812
Technical Support Systems LLC, pg 908

TEXAS

Audio Visual Technologies Group (AVTG), pg 695
Digital Display Solutions Inc, pg 742
Stage Directions, pg 898
Videotex Systems Inc, pg 930

UTAH

RIA Corp, pg 874

VIRGINIA

Avitecture Inc, pg 699
Lee Hartman & Sons Inc, pg 805

WISCONSIN

Camera Corner Connecting Point, pg 715
Full Compass Systems, pg 767

MANITOBA

Advance Pro, pg 677
Inland Audio Visual Ltd, pg 788

ONTARIO

HD Source, pg 777
Technovision® Interactive Inc, pg 909

QUEBEC

Panavideo Inc, pg 850

Videodisc Recorder & Player Manufacturers

CALIFORNIA

Grande Vitesse Systems Inc (GVS), pg 773
Pioneer Electronics (USA) Inc, pg 857

MICHIGAN

Leightronix Inc, pg 806

NEW JERSEY

Panasonic Corporation of North America, pg 850

NEW YORK

Laird Digital Cinema, pg 803

TENNESSEE

Adtec Digital Inc, pg 677

Videodisc Recorder & Player Rentals

ARIZONA

Merestone, pg 823

ARKANSAS

White Diamond Productions LLC, pg 937

CALIFORNIA

Advanced Media LLC, pg 677
Alliant Event Services, pg 681
Ametron Audio/Video, pg 684
AV Guys, pg 697
Bexel, an NEP Broadcast Services Company, pg 704
BroadcastStore.com, pg 711
Golden Gate Studios, pg 772
Instructional Materials & Equipment Distributors (I-Med), pg 789
JD Audio Visual Inc, pg 793
Lynch Communications, pg 813
Main Street Media Inc, pg 815
McCune Audio-Video-Lighting, pg 821
Media Fabricators Inc, pg 822
Munday & Collins AV, pg 834
PSAV® Presentation Services, pg 866
RetinaVision Productions, pg 874
SNAP, pg 891
VER, pg 926
VMI Inc, pg 932
Voice & Video Rentals, pg 932

COLORADO

Spectrum Audio Visual Services, pg 897

DELAWARE

Showorks Audio Visual Inc, pg 887

FLORIDA

AVI-SPL, pg 698
Industrial Strength Inc, pg 787
ONstage, pg 846
Paradise Show & Design Inc, pg 851

GEORGIA

Lighting & Production Equipment Inc, pg 807
ON Services, a GES Company, pg 846
Stage Front Presentation Systems, pg 899

ILLINOIS

AV Chicago Inc, pg 696
Backstar Creative Media Inc, pg 700

Creative Technology (CT), pg 733
RC Communications, pg 870

LOUISIANA

Digital FX Inc, pg 742

MARYLAND

CPR MultiMedia Solutions, pg 732

MASSACHUSETTS

AVFX Inc, pg 698
Preston Productions Inc, pg 861

MICHIGAN

Digi Sign Design LLC, pg 741
K&R's Recording Studios Inc, pg 796
TEL Systems LLC, pg 909

MISSOURI

Schiller's Audio-Visual, pg 881
Southwest Audio-Visual Inc, pg 895

NEVADA

GES Audio Visual, pg 770

NEW JERSEY

PLS Staging, pg 858
Starlite, pg 900

NEW YORK

American Video Inc, pg 684
AV Workshop, pg 697
Design Audio Visual Inc, pg 741
KVL Audio Visual Services Inc, pg 802
Visual Word Systems Inc, pg 932

NORTH CAROLINA

AV Connections Inc, pg 697
On Location North Carolina, pg 846
Take One Productions Ltd, pg 906

OHIO

R&B Communications Inc, pg 870

PENNSYLVANIA

Advanced AV LLC, pg 677
FMP Media Solutions Inc, pg 763

TENNESSEE

Technical Support Systems LLC, pg 908

TEXAS

Alford Media Services, pg 680
Stage Directions, pg 898

WASHINGTON

Victory Studios, pg 927

WISCONSIN

Audio Visual of Milwaukee Inc, pg 694
Full Compass Systems, pg 767

PUERTO RICO

Stage Crew Audiovisual Inc, pg 898

MANITOBA

Inland Audio Visual Ltd, pg 788

ONTARIO

HD Source, pg 777
Technovision® Interactive Inc,
pg 909
Wanted! Sound + Picture, pg 933

QUEBEC

Panavideo Inc, pg 850

Videodisc Recorder & Player Repairs

CALIFORNIA

Advanced Media LLC, pg 677
Ametron Audio/Video, pg 684
McAlister Electronics, pg 820
SSL Industries Inc, pg 898
VMI Inc, pg 932

FLORIDA

ELC Sales & Service Inc, pg 752

GEORGIA

Stage Front Presentation Systems,
pg 899

ILLINOIS

Beatty TeleVisual Productions,
pg 703

KENTUCKY

Axxis Leasing Inc, pg 700
Barney Miller's Inc, pg 827
NOR-COM Inc, pg 841

MICHIGAN

TEL Systems LLC, pg 909

MINNESOTA

Alpha Video & Audio Inc, pg 682

MISSOURI

Schiller's Audio-Visual, pg 881
Southwest Audio-Visual Inc, pg 895

TENNESSEE

Technical Support Systems LLC,
pg 908

UTAH

RIA Corp, pg 874

WISCONSIN

Audio Visual of Milwaukee Inc,
pg 694
Full Compass Systems, pg 767

MANITOBA

Inland Audio Visual Ltd, pg 788

ONTARIO

HD Source, pg 777
Technovision® Interactive Inc,
pg 909

QUEBEC

Panavideo Inc, pg 850

Videodisc System— Hardware Distributors

ALABAMA

Curtis Company, pg 736

ARIZONA

EAR Professional Audio/Video,
pg 749

CALIFORNIA

Advanced Systems Group LLC,
pg 677
Ametron Audio/Video, pg 684
Audio/Video Supply Inc, pg 694
Be Media, pg 702
Diaquest, pg 741
Jaguar Distribution Corp, pg 792
Media Fabricators Inc, pg 822

COLORADO

Spectrum Audio Visual Services,
pg 897

CONNECTICUT

MAVCO, pg 820

FLORIDA

Alcorn McBride Inc, pg 679
Digital Video Systems, pg 742
Midtown Video Inc, pg 827
ONstage, pg 846
Tallahassee Audio Visual, pg 906

GEORGIA

Convergent Media Systems, pg 731
Stage Front Presentation Systems,
pg 899
Visioneering International Inc,
pg 931

ILLINOIS

Allen Visual Systems Inc, pg 680
RC Communications, pg 870
Tele-Time Systems, pg 910

INDIANA

Lee Co Inc, pg 805
Sensory Technologies LLC, pg 884
SHP Electronics, pg 887

KENTUCKY

Barney Miller's Inc, pg 827
NOR-COM Inc, pg 841

LOUISIANA

Digital FX Inc, pg 742

MARYLAND

RTZ Audio Visual, pg 878

MICHIGAN

ASC Systems, pg 690
Digi Sign Design LLC, pg 741
TEL Systems LLC, pg 909

MINNESOTA

Alpha Video & Audio Inc, pg 682
AVI Systems, pg 698

MISSOURI

Communitronics Corp, pg 729
Southwest Audio-Visual Inc, pg 895

NEW JERSEY

A-V Services Inc, pg 671
AlltecPro, pg 681
AV Bluebook, pg 696
G&G Technologies Inc, pg 768
Maxell Corp of America, pg 820
Starlite, pg 900
SYMCO Inc, pg 905
Total Video Products Inc, pg 916

NEW YORK

AV Workshop, pg 697
Design Audio Visual Inc, pg 741
Flash Electronics Inc, pg 762
Tri-Ed Distribution Inc, pg 918

OHIO

iVideo Technologies, pg 792

PENNSYLVANIA

Advanced AV LLC, pg 677
The Lerro Corp, pg 806
Morefield Communications Inc,
pg 830

TENNESSEE

Lowrance Sound Co Inc, pg 812
Memphis Communications Corp,
pg 823
Technical Support Systems LLC,
pg 908

TEXAS

Digital Display Solutions Inc,
pg 742
JSAV, pg 795
Stage Directions, pg 898
Videotex Systems Inc, pg 930

UTAH

RIA Corp, pg 874
Webb Audio Visual, pg 935

VIRGINIA

Avitecture Inc, pg 699
Lee Hartman & Sons Inc, pg 805
The Whitlock Group, pg 937

WISCONSIN

Camera Corner Connecting Point,
pg 715
Full Compass Systems, pg 767

MANITOBA

Advance Pro, pg 677
Inland Audio Visual Ltd, pg 788

ONTARIO

HD Source, pg 777
Nationwide Audio Visual Co,
pg 837
Technovision® Interactive Inc,
pg 909

QUEBEC

Panavideo Inc, pg 850

Videodisc System— Hardware Manufacturers

CALIFORNIA

Grande Vitesse Systems Inc (GVS),
pg 773
Pioneer Electronics (USA) Inc,
pg 857
Sony Electronics Inc, pg 893

FLORIDA

Alcorn McBride Inc, pg 679

GEORGIA

Visix™ Inc, pg 931

MICHIGAN

ASC Systems, pg 690
Leightronix Inc, pg 806

NEW JERSEY

Maxell Corp of America, pg 820

TENNESSEE

Adtec Digital Inc, pg 677

ONTARIO

Technovision® Interactive Inc,
pg 909

Videodisc System— Hardware Rentals

ARIZONA

Merestone, pg 823
Metropolitan Audio-Visual Inc,
pg 824

CALIFORNIA

Alliant Event Services, pg 681
Ametron Audio/Video, pg 684
Lynch Communications, pg 813
Main Street Media Inc, pg 815
Media Fabricators Inc, pg 822
Munday & Collins AV, pg 834
PSAV® Presentation Services,
pg 866
RetinaVision Productions, pg 874

COLORADO

Spectrum Audio Visual Services,
pg 897

CONNECTICUT

A/V Davey, pg 697

FLORIDA

ONstage, pg 846
Universal Studios Florida®
Production Group, pg 922

GEORGIA

Convergent Media Systems, pg 731
Lighting & Production Equipment
Inc, pg 807
Stage Front Presentation Systems,
pg 899

ILLINOIS

Allen Visual Systems Inc, pg 680
Backstar Creative Media Inc,
pg 700

447

VIDEO

Videodisc System—
Hardware Rentals
(continued)

ILLINOIS (continued)

RC Communications, pg 870
Tele-Time Systems, pg 910

KENTUCKY

Audio Visual Techniques Inc,
pg 695

LOUISIANA

Digital FX Inc, pg 742

MARYLAND

CPR MultiMedia Solutions, pg 732
RTZ Audio Visual, pg 878

MASSACHUSETTS

AVFX Inc, pg 698
Preston Productions Inc, pg 861

MICHIGAN

Digi Sign Design LLC, pg 741
TEL Systems LLC, pg 909

MISSOURI

Schiller's Audio-Visual, pg 881
Southwest Audio-Visual Inc, pg 895
Switch, pg 905

NEW JERSEY

PLS Staging, pg 858
Starlite, pg 900

NEW YORK

Adwar Video, pg 678
AV Workshop, pg 697

OHIO

ITA Audio Visual Solutions, pg 791

PENNSYLVANIA

FMP Media Solutions Inc, pg 763
Visual Sound Inc, pg 931

TENNESSEE

Technical Support Systems LLC,
pg 908

TEXAS

Stage Directions, pg 898

UTAH

Webb Audio Visual, pg 935

WASHINGTON

Victory Studios, pg 927

WISCONSIN

Full Compass Systems, pg 767

MANITOBA

Inland Audio Visual Ltd, pg 788

ONTARIO

HD Source, pg 777
Technovision® Interactive Inc,
pg 909

QUEBEC

Panavideo Inc, pg 850

Videodisc System—
Hardware Repairs

CALIFORNIA

Advanced Systems Group LLC,
pg 677
Ametron Audio/Video, pg 684
McAlister Electronics, pg 820

FLORIDA

ELC Sales & Service Inc, pg 752

GEORGIA

Stage Front Presentation Systems,
pg 899

KENTUCKY

Barney Miller's Inc, pg 827
NOR-COM Inc, pg 841

MARYLAND

RTZ Audio Visual, pg 878

MICHIGAN

TEL Systems LLC, pg 909

MINNESOTA

Alpha Video & Audio Inc, pg 682

MISSOURI

Schiller's Audio-Visual, pg 881
Southwest Audio-Visual Inc, pg 895

NEW YORK

Adwar Video, pg 678

PENNSYLVANIA

Visual Sound Inc, pg 931

TENNESSEE

Technical Support Systems LLC,
pg 908

UTAH

RIA Corp, pg 874

WISCONSIN

Full Compass Systems, pg 767

MANITOBA

Inland Audio Visual Ltd, pg 788

ONTARIO

Technovision® Interactive Inc,
pg 909

QUEBEC

Panavideo Inc, pg 850

Videodisc System—
Software Distributors

ARIZONA

EAR Professional Audio/Video,
pg 749

CALIFORNIA

Advanced Systems Group LLC,
pg 677
Ametron Audio/Video, pg 684
Audio/Video Supply Inc, pg 694
Be Media, pg 702
Diaquest, pg 741
Jaguar Distribution Corp, pg 792
Sony Pictures Home Entertainment,
pg 893

COLORADO

Spectrum Audio Visual Services,
pg 897

CONNECTICUT

MAVCO, pg 820

FLORIDA

Digital Video Systems, pg 742
ONstage, pg 846

GEORGIA

Stage Front Presentation Systems,
pg 899
Visioneering International Inc,
pg 931

ILLINOIS

Rand McNally Education, pg 870

INDIANA

Sensory Technologies LLC, pg 884

KENTUCKY

NOR-COM Inc, pg 841
WaxWorks VideoWorks, pg 934

LOUISIANA

Digital FX Inc, pg 742

MICHIGAN

Digi Sign Design LLC, pg 741

MINNESOTA

Alpha Video & Audio Inc, pg 682

MISSOURI

Communitronics Corp, pg 729
Southwest Audio-Visual Inc, pg 895

NEW JERSEY

AlltecPro, pg 681
AV Bluebook, pg 696

NEW YORK

AV Workshop, pg 697
Flash Electronics Inc, pg 762

PENNSYLVANIA

Advanced AV LLC, pg 677
The Lerro Corp, pg 806
Morefield Communications Inc,
pg 830

TENNESSEE

Lowrance Sound Co Inc, pg 812
Technical Support Systems LLC,
pg 908

TEXAS

Digital Display Solutions Inc,
pg 742
Videotex Systems Inc, pg 930

UTAH

RIA Corp, pg 874

VIRGINIA

Avitecture Inc, pg 699
Lee Hartman & Sons Inc, pg 805

WISCONSIN

Full Compass Systems, pg 767

MANITOBA

Advance Pro, pg 677

ONTARIO

Technovision® Interactive Inc,
pg 909

Videodisc System—
Software Manufacturers

CALIFORNIA

Grande Vitesse Systems Inc (GVS),
pg 773
Pioneer Electronics (USA) Inc,
pg 857
Sony Pictures Home Entertainment,
pg 893

ILLINOIS

Rand McNally Education, pg 870

MICHIGAN

Leightronix Inc, pg 806

NEW YORK

Lenel Systems International Inc,
pg 806

TENNESSEE

Adtec Digital Inc, pg 677

ONTARIO

Technovision® Interactive Inc,
pg 909

Videotape—Blank
Distributors

ALABAMA

Curtis Company, pg 736

ARIZONA

Metropolitan Audio-Visual Inc,
pg 824
On-Site Video, pg 846

CALIFORNIA

Advanced Systems Group LLC,
pg 677
Ametron Audio/Video, pg 684
Assured Audio Visual, pg 691

California Tape Products Inc, pg 714
Diaquest, pg 741
First Camera, pg 761
Gluskin's Custom Audio Video, pg 771
Alan Gordon Enterprises Inc, pg 772
Hooper Camera & Imaging, pg 781
Instructional Materials & Equipment Distributors (I-Med), pg 789
Jaguar Distribution Corp, pg 792
JD Audio Visual Inc, pg 793
Media Distributors, pg 822
Media Fabricators Inc, pg 822
MSE Media Solutions, pg 832
On-Trax Inc, pg 846
QRS Software Services, pg 867
Reel Picture, pg 872
SSL Industries Inc, pg 898
VMI Inc, pg 932
Westcoast Video Productions Inc, pg 936

COLORADO

Daylight Productions & Rentals, pg 739
Spectrum Audio Visual Services, pg 897
Stanco Sales LLC, pg 899

CONNECTICUT

MAVCO, pg 820
Rockwell Communications Inc, pg 876

FLORIDA

Access Media Group, pg 673
Digital Video Systems, pg 742
Hi-Tech Import Export Corp, pg 779
Jordan Klein Film & Video (JKFV), pg 795
Midtown Video Inc, pg 827
ONstage, pg 846
Recording Media & Equipment Inc (RM&E), pg 872

GEORGIA

Audio Visual Resources Inc, pg 695
Convergent Media Systems, pg 731
Lighting & Production Equipment Inc, pg 807
ON Services, a GES Company, pg 846
Stage Front Presentation Systems, pg 899
Video Copy Services Inc, pg 927

ILLINOIS

Allen Visual Systems Inc, pg 680
Creative Technology (CT), pg 733
FUJIFILM Graphic Systems Division, pg 766
Joseph Electronics, pg 795
Major Reproductions Equipment Co, pg 815
Tele-Time Systems, pg 910

INDIANA

Lee Co Inc, pg 805
Sensory Technologies LLC, pg 884
SHP Electronics, pg 887

KENTUCKY

American Recordable Media, pg 684
Barney Miller's Inc, pg 827

NOR-COM Inc, pg 841
WaxWorks VideoWorks, pg 934

LOUISIANA

Digital FX Inc, pg 742

MARYLAND

Nicholas P Pipino Associates Inc, pg 857
RTZ Audio Visual, pg 878

MASSACHUSETTS

Antronics Inc, pg 686
HOME Inc, pg 781
Integrated Solutions Group, pg 789
Rule Boston Camera, pg 878

MICHIGAN

TEL Systems LLC, pg 909

MINNESOTA

Alpha Video & Audio Inc, pg 682
Cinequipt Inc, pg 724

MISSISSIPPI

Bowie Audio Visual Enterprises Inc, pg 709
Jasper Ewing & Sons Inc, pg 757

MISSOURI

Audio-VideoGraphics Inc, pg 694
Communitronics Corp, pg 729
Southwest Audio-Visual Inc, pg 895

NEBRASKA

VSA Inc, pg 933

NEW JERSEY

Agfa Graphics, pg 678
AlltecPro, pg 681
Audio Visual Dynamics®, pg 694
AV Bluebook, pg 696
Comprehensive Cable & Connectivity Co, pg 729
G&G Technologies Inc, pg 768
Maxell Corp of America, pg 820
PatchAmp, pg 852
Tele-Measurements Inc, pg 910
Total Media Inc, pg 916
Total Video Products Inc, pg 916
Vcom IMC, pg 925
Video Corporation of America (VCA), pg 927

NEW YORK

Adwar Video, pg 678
Aura Sonic Ltd (ASL), pg 695
AV Workshop, pg 697
Burlington A/V Recording Media, pg 712
Canon USA Inc, pg 716
Colortone Audio Visual, pg 728
Design Audio Visual Inc, pg 741
Film Emporium, pg 760
Flash Electronics Inc, pg 762
Gaylord Archival, pg 768
HAVE Inc, pg 777
Long Island Video Enterprises Live Inc, pg 811
Markertek Video Supply, pg 817
Neptune Photo Inc, pg 838
Rafik, pg 869
Ray Supply Inc, pg 870
RNJ Electronics, pg 875
Russell Industries Inc, pg 879
TecNec Distributing, pg 909
Tri-Ed Distribution Inc, pg 918

Visual Technologies Corp, pg 932
Visual Word Systems Inc, pg 932

NORTH CAROLINA

Duke Media Services, pg 747
Strategic Connections, pg 901

OHIO

Copp Integrated Systems, pg 731
Hughie's Event Production Services, pg 782
Tri-State Audio Visual Co, pg 918

PENNSYLVANIA

Advanced AV LLC, pg 677
Audio Visual Communications Inc, pg 694
Bernie's Photo Center, pg 704
FMP Media Solutions Inc, pg 763
J E Foss Co, pg 764
Morefield Communications Inc, pg 830
Wespen Audio Visual Co, pg 935

TENNESSEE

Lowrance Sound Co Inc, pg 812
Memphis Communications Corp, pg 823
Spring Arbor Distributors Inc, pg 898

TEXAS

Quality Audio Visual Service Inc, pg 867
Replicopy Digital Media Center, pg 873
Texcam Inc, pg 911

UTAH

RIA Corp, pg 874
TV Specialists Inc, pg 919
Webb Audio Visual, pg 935

VIRGINIA

Lee Hartman & Sons Inc, pg 805
The Whitlock Group, pg 937

WASHINGTON

Inland Audio Visual Co, pg 788

WISCONSIN

Demco Inc, pg 740
Full Compass Systems, pg 767

PUERTO RICO

Bonnin Electronics Inc, pg 708

ALBERTA

Matrix Video Communications Corp (MVCC), pg 819
McBain Camera Ltd, pg 820
Unique Communications Ltd, pg 921

BRITISH COLUMBIA

Triad Communications Ltd, pg 918

MANITOBA

Advance Pro, pg 677
Inland Audio Visual Ltd, pg 788

ONTARIO

HD Source, pg 777
Majortech Inc, pg 815
Nationwide Audio Visual Co, pg 837

QUEBEC

Panavideo Inc, pg 850

Videotape—Blank Manufacturers

CALIFORNIA

Media Distributors, pg 822
MSE Media Solutions, pg 832
QRS Software Services, pg 867
Reel Picture, pg 872
Sony Electronics Inc, pg 893
Technicolor USA Inc, pg 908

KENTUCKY

American Recordable Media, pg 684

NEW JERSEY

AlltecPro, pg 681
Maxell Corp of America, pg 820
Synergem, pg 905

NEW YORK

FUJIFILM North America Corp, pg 766

WISCONSIN

Full Compass Systems, pg 767

Videotape Duplication, *see* Duplication—Videotapes

Videotape Editing, *see* Editing—Videotapes

Videotape Recording, *see* Recording—Videotapes

Videotape to Film Transfers, *see* Transfers—Videotape to Film

Virtual Conferencing

ARIZONA

Forensic Video Deposition Service, pg 764
Merestone, pg 823
Metropolitan Audio-Visual Inc, pg 824

ARKANSAS

White Diamond Productions LLC, pg 937

CALIFORNIA

All Video Productions, pg 680
AV Conferencing LLC (AVC), pg 697
Cibola Systems, pg 723
ITV Productions, pg 792

VIDEO

Virtual Conferencing (continued)

CALIFORNIA (continued)

JDS Video & Media Productions Inc, pg 793
KPBS Public Broadcasting, pg 801
KTVU-Retail Services, pg 802
KVIE-Channel 6, pg 802
Laser Magic Productions, pg 804
Ludlow Media, pg 812
Lynch Communications, pg 813
McCune Audio-Video-Lighting, pg 821
Opticomm-EMCORE, pg 847
Palardo Productions, pg 850
PSSI Global Services LLC, pg 866
QRS Software Services, pg 867
Still N' Motion, pg 901
Thorburn Associates (TA), pg 913
VMI Inc, pg 932

COLORADO

Level 3 Communications Inc, pg 806
Spectrum Audio Visual Services, pg 897

CONNECTICUT

Guymark Studios LLC, pg 775
UConn Health Multimedia Services, pg 920

DISTRICT OF COLUMBIA

Interface Media Group, pg 789
O'Keefe Communications Inc, pg 844

FLORIDA

All Comm Rentals Inc (ALLCOMM), pg 680
AVI-SPL, pg 698
Civins Productions Inc, pg 725
Communications Concepts Inc (CCI), pg 729
ONstage, pg 846
Sensormatic®, pg 884
Universal Studios Florida® Production Group, pg 922

GEORGIA

Digital Projection, pg 742
Myriad Productions, pg 835
Omega Media Group Inc, pg 845
On-Line Productions, pg 845

ILLINOIS

Atomic Imaging Inc/Golan Studios, pg 692
Production Craft Inc, pg 863
PSAV® Presentation Services (Hotel Services Division), pg 866
Satellite Technology Systems Inc, pg 881
Video I-D Teleproductions Inc, pg 928

IOWA

Educational Technology & Media Services, pg 751
Iowa State University-Information Technology Services, pg 791

KENTUCKY

Axxis Leasing Inc, pg 700
Hammond Communications Group Inc, pg 775
WKYT-TV, pg 940

LOUISIANA

Digital FX Inc, pg 742
Louisiana State University Division of Strategic Communications, pg 811
Pace Systems, pg 849

MARYLAND

Absolute Hollywood, pg 672
CPR MultiMedia Solutions, pg 732

MASSACHUSETTS

High Output Inc, pg 779
Preston Productions Inc, pg 861
TVN-The Video Network, pg 919
VideoLink Inc, an AVI-SPL company, pg 929
WVP Boston, pg 942

MICHIGAN

ASC Systems, pg 690
Digi Sign Design LLC, pg 741
K&R's Recording Studios Inc, pg 796
RingSide Creative, pg 875

MINNESOTA

Alpha Video & Audio Inc, pg 682
Vaddio, pg 924

MISSOURI

Communitronics Corp, pg 729
Conference Technologies Inc, pg 730

NEVADA

Encore Event Technologies LLC, pg 754
Lefco Video Services Inc, pg 806

NEW HAMPSHIRE

Academic & Campus Technology Services, pg 672

NEW JERSEY

Broadcast Center Studios, pg 710
Laurel Video Productions, pg 804
MiB MediaWorks, pg 825
NFL Films Inc, pg 841
Suede Interactive, pg 903
Tele-Measurements Inc, pg 910
Telemanagement Resources International Inc (TRI), pg 910
Total Video Products Inc, pg 916
Vision Quest Productions Inc, pg 930

NEW YORK

Adwar Video, pg 678
Associated Press Television News, pg 691
Broadstreet Productions LLC, pg 711
Colortone Audio Visual, pg 728
HBO Studio Productions, pg 777
Long Island Video Enterprises Live Inc, pg 811
Jack Morton Worldwide, pg 830
The Palmer Group, pg 850
Servoreeler Systems, pg 884

Synaptic Digital, pg 905
Visual Technologies Corp, pg 932

NORTH CAROLINA

Bill Barnes Video Productions LLC, pg 702
Lawrence Behr Associates Inc, pg 703
NASCAR Productions LLC, pg 835

OHIO

Aztec Video Productions, pg 700
CET, pg 720
Copp Integrated Systems, pg 731
Cuyahoga Community College Student Production Office (SPO), pg 736
Mills James Productions, pg 828
WOUB Public Media, pg 942

OKLAHOMA

Academic Media & Digital Services, pg 672
Institute for Teaching & Learning Excellence (ITLE), pg 788

OREGON

CMD Agency, pg 726
KTVA Productions, pg 802

PENNSYLVANIA

FMP Media Solutions Inc, pg 763
Innovision Media Group, pg 788
Luzerne County Community College, pg 813
Muderick Media, pg 833
Production Masters Inc (PMI), pg 864
Visual Sound Inc, pg 931
WHYY Inc, pg 938
WPHL-TV, pg 942
WQED-Multimedia, pg 942

SOUTH CAROLINA

Sound & Images Inc, pg 893
Venture Media, pg 925

TENNESSEE

Continental Film, pg 731
Stage Post, pg 899
United Methodist Productions, pg 921

TEXAS

AMS Pictures, pg 684
JSAV, pg 795
Earl Miller Productions Inc, pg 827
Romar Learning Solutions LLC, pg 877
Texas Heart Institute Visual Communication Services, pg 911

VIRGINIA

American AV, pg 682
CVW Event Productions, pg 736

WEST VIRGINIA

WSAZ-TV NewsChannel 3, pg 942

WISCONSIN

Audio Visual of Milwaukee Inc, pg 694
AVS Group, pg 699
University of Wisconsin-Oshkosh Radio-TV-Film Dept, pg 923
USAV Group Inc, pg 923

Video Wisconsin Inc, pg 929
Wisconsin Public Television, pg 940

ALBERTA

Cine Audio Visual Sales & Service Ltd, pg 723
Global TV, pg 771

ONTARIO

Cinema Stage Inc, pg 724
GestureTek, pg 770

Volume Printing—Videos

ARIZONA

Merestone, pg 823
On-Site Video, pg 846
Star Video Duplicating, pg 900

ARKANSAS

White Diamond Productions LLC, pg 937

CALIFORNIA

All Video Productions, pg 680
ALOM Technologies Corp, pg 681
Audio Visual Consultants, pg 694
Custom Video Productions Inc, pg 736
JDS Video & Media Productions Inc, pg 793
Lynch Communications, pg 813
New & Unique Videos™, pg 839
Point.360, pg 858
QRS Software Services, pg 867
SonicPool, pg 892
Total Creative, pg 916

COLORADO

Daylight Productions & Rentals, pg 739
Flashback Media Productions, pg 762

CONNECTICUT

BRB Audiovisual Productions, pg 709
CMI Media Management, pg 727
MAVCO, pg 820

FLORIDA

Florida Digital Studios, pg 762
Video Techniques Inc, pg 928

GEORGIA

Guerrilla Productions LLC, pg 774

INDIANA

Advanced Media Integration, pg 677

MARYLAND

dbF a Media Company, pg 739
DBM Communications Inc, pg 739

MASSACHUSETTS

Video Express, pg 928

MICHIGAN

Digi Sign Design LLC, pg 741
K&R's Recording Studios Inc, pg 796

MINNESOTA

The ADS Group, pg 676

MISSOURI

Schiller's Audio-Visual, pg 881

NEVADA

Aardvark Video & Media
    Productions, pg 671

NEW HAMPSHIRE

Channell One Video, pg 720
Chip Taylor Communications LLC,
    pg 907

NEW JERSEY

Allegro Productions Inc, pg 680
MiB MediaWorks, pg 825
Reed Presentations Inc (RPI),
    pg 872
Suede Interactive, pg 903
Yorktel, pg 944

NEW MEXICO

Production Outfitters, pg 864

NEW YORK

Ace Video, pg 674
DuArt Media Services, pg 747
HAVE Inc, pg 777
PostWorks, pg 860
USA Studios, pg 923

OHIO

Aztec Video Productions, pg 700
Central Ohio Audio Video, pg 719
Curtis Inc, pg 736
Take 1 Media Services, pg 906

PENNSYLVANIA

FMP Media Solutions Inc, pg 763
Innovision Media Group, pg 788

Laser Video Corp, pg 804
The Videohouse Inc, pg 929
Visual Sound Inc, pg 931

TENNESSEE

Stage Post, pg 899

TEXAS

Dub King, pg 747
Horizon Film + Video Productions,
    pg 781
Replicopy Digital Media Center,
    pg 873

VIRGINIA

BES Studios, pg 704

WASHINGTON

Victory Studios, pg 927

WISCONSIN

Audio Visual of Milwaukee Inc,
    pg 694
USAV Group Inc, pg 923

WYOMING

Bridger Productions Inc, pg 710

ONTARIO

Image Video Services &
    Productions, pg 785
Silver Creek Media Inc, pg 888

Workshops, *see* **Production
    Workshops**

PROGRAMMING — AUDIO

Audiobook Distributors

ARIZONA

Coyote Cowboy Co, pg 732
Valley of the Sun Publishing Co, pg 924

ARKANSAS

Master Books®, pg 819

CALIFORNIA

Audio Editions Books-On-Cassette & CD, pg 693
Bridge Publications Inc, pg 710
Dialect Accent Specialists Inc, pg 741
Hay House Inc, pg 777
Krishnamurti Foundation of America, pg 801
Maximus Media Inc, pg 820
monterey video, pg 829
M2 Communications, pg 833
Music World/Vocal Power School, pg 834
People Skills International, pg 854
QRS Software Services, pg 867
Redwood Audiobooks, pg 872
Regent Press Publishers & Printers, pg 873
The Wine Appreciation Guild Ltd, pg 939

CONNECTICUT

Tantor Media Inc, pg 907

FLORIDA

Effective Learning Systems LLC, pg 751
Health Communications Inc, pg 778
Times-Square Fantasy Theatre, pg 914

GEORGIA

August House Audio, pg 695
New Leaf Distributing Co, pg 839

HAWAII

Media Bridge Gamekids, pg 821

ILLINOIS

African American Images Inc, pg 678
CCore Media Inc, pg 718
Encyclopaedia Britannica Inc, pg 754
Follett School Solutions Inc, pg 763

LOUISIANA

Pelican Publishing Co, pg 853

MARYLAND

Audio Book Contractors LLC, pg 693
HighBridge Audio, pg 779
Recorded Books Inc, an RBmedia company, pg 871
RLJ Entertainment Inc, pg 875

MASSACHUSETTS

Pauline Books & Media, pg 852
Penfield Productions Ltd, pg 853

MICHIGAN

Brilliance Audio, pg 710
Digi Sign Design LLC, pg 741
Emery-Pratt Co, pg 753
University of Michigan, Center for Middle Eastern & North African Studies, pg 923

MINNESOTA

Hazelden Publishing & Educational Services, pg 777

MISSOURI

SOM Publishing Co, pg 892

NEW HAMPSHIRE

Captain Fiddle Music & Publications, pg 716
Chip Taylor Communications LLC, pg 907

NEW JERSEY

Alden Films, pg 679
Learning Ally, pg 805
Listen & Live Audio Inc, pg 809
Paulist Press, pg 852

NEW YORK

Beekman Books Inc, pg 703
Cross-Cultural Communications, pg 735
Digital Force Ltd, pg 742
Discovery Education Inc, pg 743
Listening Library, pg 810
Live Oak Media, pg 810
Penguin Random House Audio Publishing, pg 853
Posthorn Recordings, pg 859
RadioArt/Bob & Ray CDs & MP3 Files, pg 869
Random House Children's Books, pg 870
ZBS Foundation, pg 945

NORTH CAROLINA

Ladyslipper Music, pg 803

OHIO

Curtis Inc, pg 736
Twin Sisters® Digital Media™, pg 920

OREGON

Blackstone Audio Inc, pg 707
Downpour.com, pg 746
The Keyboard Workshop, pg 798
Sugar Mountain PR, pg 903

PENNSYLVANIA

Himalayan Institute Audio/Video, pg 780
Fred Rogers Productions, pg 876

SOUTH CAROLINA

BJU Press, pg 706
DaviSound, pg 739
University of South Carolina Press, pg 923

TENNESSEE

American Blackguard Inc, pg 683
Cokesbury, pg 727

Ingram Content Group LLC, pg 787
Spring Arbor Distributors Inc, pg 898

TEXAS

Milky Way Press, pg 827

VERMONT

Chelsea Green Publishing Co, pg 721
Trafalgar Square Books, pg 916

VIRGINIA

National Media Services Inc, pg 836

WASHINGTON

Books In Motion, pg 708

BRITISH COLUMBIA

Raincoast Books, pg 869
Timeless Books, pg 914

ONTARIO

Gospel Folio Press, pg 773
Penguin Random House Canada, pg 853

Audiobook Producers

ARIZONA

Allusion Studios & Pure Wave Audio, pg 681
Disney Consumer Products & Interactive Media (DCPI), pg 743
SPEAK HOUSE Audio™, pg 896
Teaberry, pg 908
Valley of the Sun Publishing Co, pg 924

ARKANSAS

Live'N'Loud, pg 810

CALIFORNIA

Ancient Future, pg 685
The Banquet Sound Studios, pg 701
Creative Media Recording, pg 733
Dialect Accent Specialists Inc, pg 741
4th Street Recording, pg 764
Hay House Inc, pg 777
International Contact Inc, pg 790
Kris Stevens Enterprises, pg 801
Krishnamurti Foundation of America, pg 801
Lynch Communications, pg 813
monterey video, pg 829
M2 Communications, pg 833
Music World/Vocal Power School, pg 834
OTR Studios, pg 848
QRS Software Services, pg 867
Redwood Audiobooks, pg 872
Regent Press Publishers & Printers, pg 873
Steve Shapiro Music, pg 885
Studio 132, pg 902
Webster Communications, pg 935

COLORADO

Rocky Mountain Audio/Video Productions Inc, pg 876
Shambhala Publications, pg 885

CONNECTICUT

Tantor Media Inc, pg 907

DISTRICT OF COLUMBIA

Biblical Archaeology Society (BAS), pg 705

FLORIDA

Blackburst Entertainment LLC, pg 706
Courter Films LLC, pg 732
Effective Learning Systems LLC, pg 751
Health Communications Inc, pg 778
LHV Audio Services, pg 807
Sunfire Communications Inc, pg 904
Sunrise Studios, pg 904
Times-Square Fantasy Theatre, pg 914

GEORGIA

August House Audio, pg 695
Guerrilla Productions LLC, pg 774

HAWAII

Media Bridge Gamekids, pg 821

ILLINOIS

African American Images Inc, pg 678
Audiobook Department, pg 695
CCore Media Inc, pg 718
Follett School Solutions Inc, pg 763
Steven Samler Music & Sound, pg 879

INDIANA

A-V-A Video Productions, pg 671

IOWA

Hedquist Productions Inc, pg 778

LOUISIANA

Pelican Publishing Co, pg 853

MARYLAND

Books on Tape™, pg 708
dbF a Media Company, pg 739
HighBridge Audio, pg 779
Recorded Books Inc, an RBmedia company, pg 871
RLJ Entertainment Inc, pg 875

MASSACHUSETTS

Pauline Books & Media, pg 852
Penfield Productions Ltd, pg 853
Soundtrack Group, pg 895

MICHIGAN

Brilliance Audio, pg 710
Digi Sign Design LLC, pg 741
K&R All Media Productions LLC, pg 796
K&R's Recording Studios Inc, pg 796

MINNESOTA

Hazelden Publishing & Educational Services, pg 777

MISSOURI

Audio-VideoGraphics Inc, pg 694
SOM Publishing Co, pg 892

MONTANA

Jereco Studios Inc, pg 793

NEVADA

Tanglewood Productions, pg 907
Tetrahedron LLC, pg 911

NEW HAMPSHIRE

Captain Fiddle Music &
   Publications, pg 716
Chip Taylor Communications LLC,
   pg 907

NEW JERSEY

CFP Video Productions Inc, pg 720
Learning Ally, pg 805
Listen & Live Audio Inc, pg 809
Milgrom Productions, pg 827
Optisonics Productions, pg 847
Paulist Press, pg 852

NEW YORK

Cross-Cultural Communications,
   pg 735
Digital Force Ltd, pg 742
Fingerpaint, pg 761
Listening Library, pg 810
Live Oak Media, pg 810
Macmillan Audio, pg 814
Mark Custom Recording Service
   Inc, pg 817
Jack Morton Worldwide, pg 830
New York Audio Productions,
   pg 840
Penguin Random House Audio
   Publishing, pg 853
RadioArt/Bob & Ray CDs & MP3
   Files, pg 869
Random House Children's Books,
   pg 870
Tiki Recording Studios Inc, pg 914
ZBS Foundation, pg 945

NORTH CAROLINA

Pat Appleson Studios Inc, pg 687
High Windy Audio/Banjoman Inc,
   pg 779

OHIO

Curtis Inc, pg 736
Dreamscape Media LLC, pg 746
Musicol Recording, pg 835
Twin Sisters® Digital Media™,
   pg 920

OKLAHOMA

Piper Media Services Inc, pg 857

OREGON

Blackstone Audio Inc, pg 707
Downpour.com, pg 746
REX, pg 874

PENNSYLVANIA

American Artist Studio, pg 682
Forge Recording LLC, pg 764
Himalayan Institute Audio/Video,
   pg 780
Muderick Media, pg 833

RHODE ISLAND

Sound-FX-Design, pg 894

SOUTH CAROLINA

BJU Press, pg 706
DaviSound, pg 739

TENNESSEE

American Blackguard Inc, pg 683
Cokesbury, pg 727
Love Shack Recording Studios,
   pg 811
Mr Mark's Used Musical, Stereo &
   Studio Equipment Store, pg 828

TEXAS

AMA Nystrom Printing/Finishing,
   pg 682
Epic Software Group Inc, pg 755
Milky Way Press, pg 827
The Music Bakery, pg 834
Planet Dallas Recording Studios,
   pg 857
Romar Learning Solutions LLC,
   pg 877
The Sound Lab Inc, pg 894
Sound Works, pg 894
Stage Directions, pg 898

VERMONT

Inner Traditions International,
   pg 788

VIRGINIA

Metro Productions, pg 824
National Media Services Inc,
   pg 836
Studio Center Corp, pg 902

WASHINGTON

Books In Motion, pg 708
Pacific Multimedia Inc, pg 849

WISCONSIN

Audio Visual of Milwaukee Inc,
   pg 694
5th Floor Recording Co, pg 760

WYOMING

Bridger Productions Inc, pg 710

BRITISH COLUMBIA

Timeless Books, pg 914

ONTARIO

ADS Media, pg 677
DebsVoice, pg 739
Penguin Random House Canada,
   pg 853

Audiobook Rentals

MICHIGAN

Digi Sign Design LLC, pg 741

NEW HAMPSHIRE

Chip Taylor Communications LLC,
   pg 907

NEW JERSEY

Alden Films, pg 679
Listen & Live Audio Inc, pg 809

ONTARIO

Simply Audiobooks, pg 889

Audiocassette Distributors

ARIZONA

Arizona Cine Equipment, pg 688

CALIFORNIA

Ametron Audio/Video, pg 684
Audio Editions Books-On-Cassette
   & CD, pg 693
California Language Laboratories,
   pg 714
Discovery Education - Los Angeles,
   pg 743
ECONEWS (Environmental
   Television Series) &
   (Environmental Directions Radio
   Series), pg 750
Gateways, pg 768
Bruce Goldberg Inc, pg 772
Health Education Services, pg 778
monterey media inc, pg 829
monterey video, pg 829
Motown®, pg 831
Music World/Vocal Power School,
   pg 834
Nilgiri Press, pg 841
People Skills International, pg 854
Prime Cut Productions, pg 862
Regent Press Publishers & Printers,
   pg 873
Rhythms Productions (Tom Thumb
   Music), pg 874
Sahara Records & Filmworks
   Entertainment Co, pg 879
Saturn Studios, pg 881
Sisters' Choice Press, pg 889
Sodanceabit, pg 892
Timeless Productions, pg 914
Valley Media, pg 924
Varese Sarabande Records Inc,
   pg 924
Welk Music Group, pg 935
The Wine Appreciation Guild Ltd,
   pg 939
The Writing Co, pg 942
The Wyland Group, pg 942

CONNECTICUT

Connecticut Audio & Theatrical
   Supply, pg 731

DELAWARE

So Smart Productions, pg 891

DISTRICT OF COLUMBIA

Biblical Archaeology Society
   (BAS), pg 705
Library of Congress, Motion
   Picture, Broadcasting & Recorded
   Sound Division, pg 807

FLORIDA

Hard Hat Radio Music Service,
   pg 776
I M P A C T Publishing Inc,
   pg 783

GEORGIA

Audio Visual Resources Inc, pg 695
School Media Associates LLC,
   pg 882

ILLINOIS

CCore Media Inc, pg 718
Earwig Music Co Inc, pg 749
National Safety Council (NSC),
   pg 836
Theosophical Publishing House,
   pg 912
Woodside Avenue Music
   Productions Inc, pg 941

INDIANA

Lee Co Inc, pg 805

LOUISIANA

Great Chefs/Leisure Jazz Video,
   pg 773
Leisure Video, pg 806

MARYLAND

Audio Book Contractors LLC,
   pg 693
dbF a Media Company, pg 739
Department of Education Resources,
   pg 740
HighBridge Audio, pg 779
MMI Marketing, pg 828
Nicholas P Pipino Associates Inc,
   pg 857
Recorded Books Inc, an RBmedia
   company, pg 871

MASSACHUSETTS

Cheng & Tsui Co, pg 721
Yellow Moon Press, pg 944

MICHIGAN

Brilliance Audio, pg 710
Digi Sign Design LLC, pg 741
Renaissance Unity, pg 873
Wayne State University Media
   Services, pg 934

MINNESOTA

American Choral Catalog Ltd,
   pg 683
GMI Productions, pg 771
Hazelden Publishing & Educational
   Services, pg 777

MISSOURI

Grace Church - St Louis, pg 773
Impact Christian Books Inc, pg 786
Mosby Inc, pg 831
Vedanta Society of St Louis, pg 925

NEBRASKA

AdventSource, pg 678
The Recruiters Library, pg 872

NEW HAMPSHIRE

Captain Fiddle Music &
   Publications, pg 716
Frey Scientific, pg 766
Chip Taylor Communications LLC,
   pg 907

NEW JERSEY

Dance Horizons Video, pg 737
Shanachie Entertainment Corp,
   pg 885
Tele-Measurements Inc, pg 910

NEW MEXICO

Indian House, pg 786

NEW YORK

Digital Force Ltd, pg 742
Dover Publications Inc, pg 746
Film Emporium, pg 760
Flash Electronics Inc, pg 762
Guilford Publications, pg 774
HB-Content, pg 777
Homespun Video, pg 781
Neptune Photo Inc, pg 838
Simon & Schuster, Inc, pg 888
SISU Home Entertainment Inc,
   pg 889
Sony Music Entertainment, pg 893
Spoken Arts Inc, pg 898
Synaptic Digital, pg 905

PROGRAMMING — AUDIO

Audiocassette Distributors (continued)

NEW YORK (continued)

Triumph Learning LLC, pg 918
United Nations Department of
Public Information-News &
Media Division, pg 921
Visual Technologies Corp, pg 932

NORTH CAROLINA

Carolina Biological Supply Co,
pg 717
Howard Hanger, pg 775

OHIO

Cuyahoga Community College
Student Production Office (SPO),
pg 736
Franciscan Media, pg 765
McGraw-Hill School Education
Group, pg 821

PENNSYLVANIA

Discovery Education - South
Burlington, pg 743
Dreambox Media Inc, pg 746
Forge Recording LLC, pg 764
Himalayan Institute Audio/Video,
pg 780
Library Video Company, pg 807
Newtown Psychological Center,
pg 840
TRC Interactive Inc, pg 917

SOUTH CAROLINA

DaviSound, pg 739

TENNESSEE

American Blackguard Inc, pg 683
Compass Records, pg 729
National School Products, pg 836
Provident Distribution, pg 866
Spring Arbor Distributors Inc,
pg 898
Word Label Group, pg 941

TEXAS

Lamb & Lion Ministries, pg 803
Milky Way Press, pg 827
Sound Works, pg 894
Stage Directions, pg 898
Texas Heart Institute Visual
Communication Services, pg 911

VIRGINIA

County Sales, pg 732
Rebel Records, pg 871

WISCONSIN

Aylmer Press, pg 700
Demco Inc, pg 740
School Specialty Inc, pg 882
Wisconsin Technical College
System Foundation Inc, pg 940

PUERTO RICO

Bonnin Electronics Inc, pg 708

BRITISH COLUMBIA

Thompson Rivers University
Marketing & Communications
Dept, pg 913

ONTARIO

Scholastic Canada Ltd, pg 882

Audiocassette Producers

ARIZONA

Merestone, pg 823
SPEAK HOUSE Audio™, pg 896
Truth Consciousness Publications,
pg 919

ARKANSAS

Live'N'Loud, pg 810
White Diamond Productions LLC,
pg 937

CALIFORNIA

ACDC Audio CD & Cassette,
pg 674
Artichoke Productions, pg 690
California Language Laboratories,
pg 714
Custom Video Productions Inc,
pg 736
Design Media, pg 741
Discovery Education - Los Angeles,
pg 743
4th Street Recording, pg 764
Gateways, pg 768
Gateways Books & Tapes, pg 768
Gold Standard Productions, pg 772
Bruce Goldberg Inc, pg 772
Lynch Communications, pg 813
Maximus Media Inc, pg 820
monterey media inc, pg 829
monterey video, pg 829
M2 Communications, pg 833
Music World/Vocal Power School,
pg 834
Nilgiri Press, pg 841
On-Trax Inc, pg 846
piXvfm Inc, pg 857
Prime Cut Productions, pg 862
Regent Press Publishers & Printers,
pg 873
Rhythms Productions (Tom Thumb
Music), pg 874
Sahara Records & Filmworks
Entertainment Co, pg 879
Saturn Studios, pg 881
Alwin Sauers Audio Productions
(ASAP), pg 881
Schroder Music Co, pg 882
Steve Shapiro Music, pg 885
Sisters' Choice Press, pg 889
Sodanceabit, pg 892
Timeless Productions, pg 914
Total Creative, pg 916
Twin Peaks Creative, pg 920
Vedanta Press & Catalog, pg 925
The Wyland Group, pg 942

COLORADO

Tim Cissell Music, pg 725
Daylight Productions & Rentals,
pg 739
Flashback Media Productions,
pg 762
Shambhala Publications, pg 885

DELAWARE

Ken-Del Productions Inc, pg 797
So Smart Productions, pg 891

DISTRICT OF COLUMBIA

Biblical Archaeology Society
(BAS), pg 705
Hillmann & Carr Inc, pg 780
Interface Media Group, pg 789

FLORIDA

Courter Films LLC, pg 732
Hard Hat Radio Music Service,
pg 776
LHV Audio Services, pg 807
Sunfire Communications Inc,
pg 904
Tel-Air Interests Inc, pg 909

GEORGIA

First Cut Communications LLC,
pg 761
Hottrax Records, pg 782

ILLINOIS

Audiobook Department, pg 695
CCore Media Inc, pg 718
Cresta Creative, pg 734
Delmark Records, pg 740
Earwig Music Co Inc, pg 749
Major Media Inc, pg 815
Jim Passin Productions, pg 852
PSAV® Presentation Services
(Hotel Services Division), pg 866
Theosophical Publishing House,
pg 912
Woodside Avenue Music
Productions Inc, pg 941

INDIANA

Bright Ideas Creative Services,
pg 710
Communication Ministries, pg 728
OMNI Productions, pg 845

IOWA

Educational Technology & Media
Services, pg 751
Iowa State University-Information
Technology Services, pg 791

KENTUCKY

Donna Lawrence Productions,
pg 804

LOUISIANA

Digital FX Inc, pg 742
Leisure Video, pg 806

MARYLAND

Books on Tape™, pg 708
The Cutting Corporation,
GraphicAudio® & Archival
Sound Lab, pg 736
dbF a Media Company, pg 739
Department of Education Resources,
pg 740
HighBridge Audio, pg 779
The Image Generators, pg 785
Recorded Books Inc, an RBmedia
company, pg 871

MASSACHUSETTS

Cheng & Tsui Co, pg 721
CommCreative, pg 728
Monadnock Media Inc, pg 829
Soundtrack Group, pg 895
Yellow Moon Press, pg 944

MICHIGAN

Brilliance Audio, pg 710
Digi Sign Design LLC, pg 741
K&R All Media Productions LLC,
pg 796
K&R's Recording Studios Inc,
pg 796
Renaissance Unity, pg 873
Wayne State University Media
Services, pg 934

MINNESOTA

American Choral Catalog Ltd,
pg 683
GMI Productions, pg 771
Hazelden Publishing & Educational
Services, pg 777

MISSOURI

Audio-VideoGraphics Inc, pg 694
Impact Christian Books Inc, pg 786
Mosby Inc, pg 831
SOM Publishing Co, pg 892
Vedanta Society of St Louis, pg 925

NEBRASKA

The Recruiters Library, pg 872

NEVADA

JCS Video Productions, pg 793
Tanglewood Productions, pg 907

NEW HAMPSHIRE

Academic & Campus Technology
Services, pg 672
Captain Fiddle Music &
Publications, pg 716
Frey Scientific, pg 766
Chip Taylor Communications LLC,
pg 907

NEW JERSEY

Broadcast Center Studios, pg 710
CFP Video Productions Inc, pg 720
Laurel Video Productions, pg 804
Optisonics Productions, pg 847
Shanachie Entertainment Corp,
pg 885
Suede Interactive, pg 903

NEW MEXICO

Indian House, pg 786

NEW YORK

Applause Learning Resources,
pg 687
Broadstreet Productions LLC,
pg 711
Thomas Craven Film Corp, pg 733
Digital Force Ltd, pg 742
Guilford Publications, pg 774
HB-Content, pg 777
International Digital Centre, pg 790
Long Island Video Enterprises Live
Inc, pg 811
New York Audio Productions,
pg 840
Oriental Records Inc, pg 848
David Rapkin Audio Production,
pg 870
Simon & Schuster, Inc, pg 888
SISU Home Entertainment Inc,
pg 889
Elliot Sokolov Music, pg 892
Sony Music Commercial Music
Group, pg 893
Sony Music Entertainment, pg 893
Split Image Productions, pg 898

Spoken Arts Inc, pg 898
Synaptic Digital, pg 905
TeleTime Productions, pg 910
Third World Newsreel/Camera
News Inc, pg 912
Zelman Studios Ltd, pg 945

NORTH CAROLINA

Pat Appleson Studios Inc, pg 687
The Communications Group Inc,
pg 729
Howard Hanger, pg 775
World Class Learning Materials Inc,
pg 941

OHIO

Cuyahoga Community College
Student Production Office (SPO),
pg 736
Franciscan Media, pg 765
McGraw-Hill School Education
Group, pg 821
Musicol Recording, pg 835
R&B Communications Inc, pg 870
Vista Color Imaging Inc, pg 931

OKLAHOMA

Academic Media & Digital
Services, pg 672

OREGON

Ideascape Inc, pg 784
KTVA Productions, pg 802
REX, pg 874

PENNSYLVANIA

American Artist Studio, pg 682
Audio Visual Communications Inc,
pg 694
Discovery Education - South
Burlington, pg 743
Dreambox Media Inc, pg 746
FMP Media Solutions Inc, pg 763
Forge Recording LLC, pg 764
Himalayan Institute Audio/Video,
pg 780
Innovision Media Group, pg 788
JPL, pg 795
Newtown Psychological Center,
pg 840
Production Masters Inc (PMI),
pg 864
The Videohouse Inc, pg 929

SOUTH CAROLINA

DaviSound, pg 739

TENNESSEE

Compass Records, pg 729
Memphis Communications Corp,
pg 823
Provident Distribution, pg 866
Word Label Group, pg 941

TEXAS

Lamb & Lion Ministries, pg 803
Milky Way Press, pg 827
Music Lab Inc, pg 834
Romar Learning Solutions LLC,
pg 877
The Samuels Co, pg 879
Sound Works, pg 894
Stage Directions, pg 898
Texas Heart Institute Visual
Communication Services, pg 911
Tropikal Productions, pg 918
The Yesterday USA Radio
Networks, pg 944

VERMONT

Inner Traditions International,
pg 788

VIRGINIA

AudioImage Recording, pg 695
BES Studios, pg 704
CACI Integrated Communications,
pg 713
County Sales, pg 732
Metro Productions, pg 824
Rebel Records, pg 871
Studio Center Corp, pg 902

WASHINGTON

Pacific Multimedia Inc, pg 849

WISCONSIN

5th Floor Recording Co, pg 760
Meridian Studios, pg 824
USAV Group Inc, pg 923
Video Wisconsin Inc, pg 929

WYOMING

Bridger Productions Inc, pg 710

BRITISH COLUMBIA

Thompson Rivers University
Marketing & Communications
Dept, pg 913

ONTARIO

Silver Creek Media Inc, pg 888

Audiocassette Rentals

CALIFORNIA

Ametron Audio/Video, pg 684
Medcom Inc, pg 821

DELAWARE

Side Door Studio Inc, pg 887

FLORIDA

Times-Square Fantasy Theatre,
pg 914

ILLINOIS

RBR Productions, pg 870
Woodside Avenue Music
Productions Inc, pg 941

MICHIGAN

Digi Sign Design LLC, pg 741
Wayne State University Media
Services, pg 934

NEW HAMPSHIRE

Chip Taylor Communications LLC,
pg 907

NEW YORK

United Nations Multimedia
Resources Unit, pg 921

WISCONSIN

Wisconsin Technical College
System Foundation Inc, pg 940

Audiotape Distributors

ARIZONA

Arizona Cine Equipment, pg 688
Drumbeat Indian Arts Inc, pg 747

CALIFORNIA

Ametron Audio/Video, pg 684
Audio Editions Books-On-Cassette
& CD, pg 693
Gateways, pg 768
Golden State Dance Teachers
Association (GSDTA), pg 772
Medcom Inc, pg 821
monterey video, pg 829
Music World/Vocal Power School,
pg 834
Joseph Nicoletti Consulting-
Promotion, pg 841
QRS Software Services, pg 867
Regent Press Publishers & Printers,
pg 873
Sahara Records & Filmworks
Entertainment Co, pg 879
Sodanceabit, pg 892
Valley Media, pg 924
Welk Music Group, pg 935

CONNECTICUT

Connecticut Audio & Theatrical
Supply, pg 731

DELAWARE

So Smart Productions, pg 891

DISTRICT OF COLUMBIA

Library of Congress, Motion
Picture, Broadcasting & Recorded
Sound Division, pg 807

FLORIDA

I M P A C T Publishing Inc,
pg 783
PAR Inc, pg 851

GEORGIA

Audio Visual Resources Inc, pg 695

ILLINOIS

Woodside Avenue Music
Productions Inc, pg 941

INDIANA

Lee Co Inc, pg 805

MARYLAND

HighBridge Audio, pg 779
Nicholas P Pipino Associates Inc,
pg 857
Recorded Books Inc, an RBmedia
company, pg 871

MICHIGAN

Brilliance Audio, pg 710
Digi Sign Design LLC, pg 741
MSU Technologies, pg 833
Renaissance Unity, pg 873
University of Michigan, Center for
Middle Eastern & North African
Studies, pg 923
Wayne State University Media
Services, pg 934

MINNESOTA

American Choral Catalog Ltd,
pg 683

NEW HAMPSHIRE

Chip Taylor Communications LLC,
pg 907

NEW YORK

Digital Force Ltd, pg 742
Film Emporium, pg 760
Flash Electronics Inc, pg 762
HB-Content, pg 777
Neptune Photo Inc, pg 838
SISU Home Entertainment Inc,
pg 889
Sony Music Entertainment, pg 893
Synaptic Digital, pg 905
Touchstone Center Publications,
pg 916
Visual Technologies Corp, pg 932

OHIO

Cuyahoga Community College
Student Production Office (SPO),
pg 736

PENNSYLVANIA

Forge Recording LLC, pg 764
Himalayan Institute Audio/Video,
pg 780

TENNESSEE

American Blackguard Inc, pg 683
Center for Southern Folklore Inc,
pg 719
Compass Records, pg 729
Spring Arbor Distributors Inc,
pg 898

TEXAS

Milky Way Press, pg 827
Sound Works, pg 894
Stage Directions, pg 898

VIRGINIA

County Sales, pg 732

WISCONSIN

Demco Inc, pg 740

PUERTO RICO

Bonnin Electronics Inc, pg 708

BRITISH COLUMBIA

Timeless Books, pg 914

ONTARIO

Entertainment One Distribution,
pg 754

Audiotape Producers

ARIZONA

Merestone, pg 823
SPEAK HOUSE Audio™, pg 896

ARKANSAS

Live'N'Loud, pg 810

CALIFORNIA

ACDC Audio CD & Cassette,
pg 674
Artichoke Productions, pg 690
The Banquet Sound Studios, pg 701
Custom Video Productions Inc,
pg 736
Design Media, pg 741

PROGRAMMING — AUDIO

Audiotape Producers (continued)

CALIFORNIA (continued)

4th Street Recording, pg 764
Gateways, pg 768
Gold Standard Productions, pg 772
International Contact Inc, pg 790
Lynch Communications, pg 813
Maximus Media Inc, pg 820
monterey video, pg 829
M2 Communications, pg 833
Music World/Vocal Power School, pg 834
Joseph Nicoletti Consulting-Promotion, pg 841
On-Trax Inc, pg 846
QRS Software Services, pg 867
Regent Press Publishers & Printers, pg 873
Rhythms Productions (Tom Thumb Music), pg 874
Sahara Records & Filmworks Entertainment Co, pg 879
Saturn Studios, pg 881
Steve Shapiro Music, pg 885
Sodanceabit, pg 892
Studio 132, pg 902
Total Creative, pg 916
Twin Peaks Creative, pg 920
Vedanta Press & Catalog, pg 925
Video Resources Inc, pg 928
Webster Communications, pg 935

COLORADO

Tim Cissell Music, pg 725
Daylight Productions & Rentals, pg 739
Flashback Media Productions, pg 762
Shambhala Publications, pg 885

DELAWARE

Ken-Del Productions Inc, pg 797
So Smart Productions, pg 891

DISTRICT OF COLUMBIA

Hillmann & Carr Inc, pg 780
Interface Media Group, pg 789

FLORIDA

Audio Visual Imagineering Inc, pg 694
Courter Films LLC, pg 732
LHV Audio Services, pg 807
PAR Inc, pg 851
Sunfire Communications Inc, pg 904
Tel-Air Interests Inc, pg 909

GEORGIA

First Cut Communications LLC, pg 761

ILLINOIS

Cresta Creative, pg 734
Major Media Inc, pg 815
Jim Passin Productions, pg 852
PSAV® Presentation Services (Hotel Services Division), pg 866
Woodside Avenue Music Productions Inc, pg 941

INDIANA

Bright Ideas Creative Services, pg 710
OMNI Productions, pg 845

IOWA

Educational Technology & Media Services, pg 751

KENTUCKY

Donna Lawrence Productions, pg 804

LOUISIANA

Leisure Video, pg 806

MARYLAND

Books on Tape™, pg 708
The Cutting Corporation, GraphicAudio® & Archival Sound Lab, pg 736
HighBridge Audio, pg 779
The Image Generators, pg 785
Recorded Books Inc, an RBmedia company, pg 871

MASSACHUSETTS

CommCreative, pg 728
Monadnock Media Inc, pg 829
Soundtrack Group, pg 895

MICHIGAN

Brilliance Audio, pg 710
Digi Sign Design LLC, pg 741
K&R All Media Productions LLC, pg 796
K&R's Recording Studios Inc, pg 796
MSU Technologies, pg 833
Renaissance Unity, pg 873
University of Michigan, Center for Middle Eastern & North African Studies, pg 923
Wayne State University Media Services, pg 934

MINNESOTA

American Choral Catalog Ltd, pg 683
GMI Productions, pg 771

MISSOURI

Audio-VideoGraphics Inc, pg 694

NEW HAMPSHIRE

Chip Taylor Communications LLC, pg 907

NEW JERSEY

Broadcast Center Studios, pg 710
CFP Video Productions Inc, pg 720
Optisonics Productions, pg 847
Suede Interactive, pg 903

NEW YORK

Applause Learning Resources, pg 687
Aural Gratification Inc, pg 695
Broadstreet Productions LLC, pg 711
Thomas Craven Film Corp, pg 733
Digital Force Ltd, pg 742
HB-Content, pg 777
International Digital Centre, pg 790
MRM//McCANN, pg 832

New York Audio Productions, pg 840
Sear Sound, pg 883
SISU Home Entertainment Inc, pg 889
Elliot Sokolov Music, pg 892
Sony Music Commercial Music Group, pg 893
Sony Music Entertainment, pg 893
Split Image Productions, pg 898
Synaptic Digital, pg 905
Touchstone Center Publications, pg 916
Zelman Studios Ltd, pg 945

NORTH CAROLINA

Pat Appleson Studios Inc, pg 687
The Communications Group Inc, pg 729

OHIO

Advent Media Inc, pg 677
Cuyahoga Community College Student Production Office (SPO), pg 736
Musicol Recording, pg 835
R&B Communications Inc, pg 870
Vista Color Imaging Inc, pg 931

OKLAHOMA

Academic Media & Digital Services, pg 672

OREGON

KTVA Productions, pg 802
REX, pg 874

PENNSYLVANIA

Audio Visual Communications Inc, pg 694
Canadian American Records, pg 715
FMP Media Solutions Inc, pg 763
Forge Recording LLC, pg 764
Himalayan Institute Audio/Video, pg 780
Innovision Media Group, pg 788
JPL, pg 795
Production Masters Inc (PMI), pg 864
The Videohouse Inc, pg 929

TENNESSEE

Center for Southern Folklore Inc, pg 719
Compass Records, pg 729
Memphis Communications Corp, pg 823

TEXAS

The Editing Co, pg 750
Milky Way Press, pg 827
Romar Learning Solutions LLC, pg 877
The Samuels Co, pg 879
Sound Works, pg 894
Stage Directions, pg 898
Texas Heart Institute Visual Communication Services, pg 911
Tropikal Productions, pg 918
The Yesterday USA Radio Networks, pg 944

VIRGINIA

AudioImage Recording, pg 695
BES Studios, pg 704
CACI Integrated Communications, pg 713

County Sales, pg 732
Studio Center Corp, pg 902

WISCONSIN

5th Floor Recording Co, pg 760
Meridian Studios, pg 824
USAV Group Inc, pg 923
Video Wisconsin Inc, pg 929

WYOMING

Bridger Productions Inc, pg 710

BRITISH COLUMBIA

Timeless Books, pg 914

ONTARIO

JFB Communications, pg 794
Silver Creek Media Inc, pg 888

Audiotape Rentals

CALIFORNIA

Ametron Audio/Video, pg 684
Medcom Inc, pg 821

ILLINOIS

RBR Productions, pg 870
Woodside Avenue Music Productions Inc, pg 941

MICHIGAN

Digi Sign Design LLC, pg 741
Wayne State University Media Services, pg 934

NEW HAMPSHIRE

Chip Taylor Communications LLC, pg 907

Business Program Distributors

ARIZONA

Personal Achievement Institute, pg 854

CALIFORNIA

Direct Cinema Ltd Inc, pg 743
Bruce Goldberg Inc, pg 772
Maximus Media Inc, pg 820
Publishers Group West (PGW), an Ingram brand, pg 866
QRS Software Services, pg 867

COLORADO

American Educational Products LLC, pg 683

CONNECTICUT

Tantor Media Inc, pg 907

FLORIDA

Effective Learning Systems LLC, pg 751

GEORGIA

Convergent Media Systems, pg 731
Playback Now Inc, pg 858
School Media Associates LLC, pg 882

HAWAII

Media Bridge Gamekids, pg 821

ILLINOIS

CCH Continuing Education, pg 718
CCore Media Inc, pg 718
Nightingale-Conant Corp, pg 841

IOWA

Long-Term Success Publishing,
  pg 811
Prositions Inc, pg 865

LOUISIANA

Pelican Publishing Co, pg 853

MAINE

Slim Goodbody Corp, pg 890

MARYLAND

HighBridge Audio, pg 779
Recorded Books Inc, an RBmedia
  company, pg 871

MASSACHUSETTS

Penfield Productions Ltd, pg 853

MICHIGAN

Digi Sign Design LLC, pg 741
Emery-Pratt Co, pg 753

MINNESOTA

Learning Strategies Corp, pg 805

NEVADA

DVDs4Less, pg 748

NEW HAMPSHIRE

Chip Taylor Communications LLC,
  pg 907

NEW JERSEY

Listen & Live Audio Inc, pg 809

NEW YORK

The Cinema Guild Inc, pg 724
Films Media Group, pg 760
HarperAudio, pg 776
HB-Content, pg 777
Practising Law Institute, pg 860
Synaptic Digital, pg 905
TeleTime Productions, pg 910
Visual Technologies Corp, pg 932

NORTH CAROLINA

AudioSolutionz LLC, pg 695
Speakers Unlimited, pg 896

OHIO

Curtis Inc, pg 736

OREGON

InterVision Media, pg 791

PENNSYLVANIA

FMP Media Solutions Inc, pg 763
Newtown Psychological Center,
  pg 840

SOUTH CAROLINA

DaviSound, pg 739

TENNESSEE

Continental Film, pg 731
Ingram Content Group LLC, pg 787
Zion Music Group, pg 945

TEXAS

Emergency Film Group, pg 753

VERMONT

Taylor Associates, pg 907

VIRGINIA

CACI Integrated Communications,
  pg 713

BRITISH COLUMBIA

Thompson Rivers University
  Marketing & Communications
  Dept, pg 913

ONTARIO

Canadian Learning Co Inc, pg 715

Business Program Producers

ALABAMA

Leo Ticheli Productions, pg 913

ARIZONA

Allusion Studios & Pure Wave
  Audio, pg 681
Candee Productions Inc, pg 716
Personal Achievement Institute,
  pg 854
SPEAK HOUSE Audio™, pg 896

CALIFORNIA

The Banquet Sound Studios, pg 701
Big Door, pg 705
Concrete Images, pg 730
Creative Media Recording, pg 733
Creative Technology, pg 733
Custom Video Productions Inc,
  pg 736
Design Media, pg 741
Direct Cinema Ltd Inc, pg 743
Goal Productions, pg 772
Gold Standard Productions, pg 772
Bruce Goldberg Inc, pg 772
Havas Edge, pg 777
Lynch Communications, pg 813
Maximus Media Inc, pg 820
Media Magic, pg 822
The Media Staff Inc, pg 822
OTR Studios, pg 848
piXvfm Inc, pg 857
PM Productions, pg 858
Point of View Productions, pg 858
Producers Group Ltd, pg 863
QRS Software Services, pg 867
Steve Shapiro Music, pg 885
Still N' Motion, pg 901
Studio 132, pg 902
Tam Communications Inc, pg 906
Total Creative, pg 916
Webster Communications, pg 935

COLORADO

American Educational Products
  LLC, pg 683
Daylight Productions & Rentals,
  pg 739
Flashback Media Productions,
  pg 762
Rocky Mountain Audio/Video
  Productions Inc, pg 876
Shambhala Publications, pg 885
Starwest Productions, pg 900

CONNECTICUT

P&P Studios Inc, pg 851
Tantor Media Inc, pg 907

DISTRICT OF COLUMBIA

Hillmann & Carr Inc, pg 780

FLORIDA

Audio Visual Imagineering Inc,
  pg 694
Blackburst Entertainment LLC,
  pg 706
Effective Learning Systems LLC,
  pg 751
LHV Audio Services, pg 807
Sunfire Communications Inc,
  pg 904
Sunrise Studios, pg 904
Tricycle Studios, pg 918
Universal Studios Florida®
  Production Group, pg 922

GEORGIA

Guerrilla Productions LLC, pg 774
Playback Now Inc, pg 858

HAWAII

Media Bridge Gamekids, pg 821

IDAHO

Wide Eye Productions, pg 938

ILLINOIS

ABS Enterprises, pg 672
Accenture, pg 672
Audiobook Department, pg 695
CCH Continuing Education, pg 718
CCore Media Inc, pg 718
Cresta Creative, pg 734
Major Media Productions Inc,
  pg 815
Nightingale-Conant Corp, pg 841
Pepper Group, pg 854
PSAV® Presentation Services
  (Hotel Services Division), pg 866
Steven Samler Music & Sound,
  pg 879
Sparkfactor, pg 896
Video Impressions, pg 928

INDIANA

A-V-A Video Productions, pg 671
Advanced Media Integration, pg 677
Bright Ideas Creative Services,
  pg 710
OMNI Productions, pg 845
PentaVision Communications Inc,
  pg 854

IOWA

Hedquist Productions Inc, pg 778
Long-Term Success Publishing,
  pg 811
Prositions Inc, pg 865

LOUISIANA

Disk Productions, pg 743

MARYLAND

CPR MultiMedia Solutions, pg 732
The Cutting Corporation,
  GraphicAudio® & Archival
  Sound Lab, pg 736
dbF a Media Company, pg 739
HighBridge Audio, pg 779
The Image Generators, pg 785

Kramer Communications Video
  Production, pg 801
Recorded Books Inc, an RBmedia
  company, pg 871

MASSACHUSETTS

CommCreative, pg 728
Heliotrope Studios, pg 778
Northern Light Productions (NLP),
  pg 842
Penfield Productions Ltd, pg 853
Preston Productions Inc, pg 861
Soundtrack Group, pg 895
TR Productions, pg 916
TVN-The Video Network, pg 919

MICHIGAN

Digi Sign Design LLC, pg 741
K&R All Media Productions LLC,
  pg 796
K&R's Recording Studios Inc,
  pg 796
MessageMakers, pg 824
TGA Recording Co, pg 911

MINNESOTA

Learning Strategies Corp, pg 805
MastCom, pg 819
Media Loft Inc, pg 822

MISSOURI

Audio-VideoGraphics Inc, pg 694

MONTANA

Jereco Studios Inc, pg 793

NEVADA

DVDs4Less, pg 748
JCS Video Productions, pg 793
Tanglewood Productions, pg 907

NEW HAMPSHIRE

Apertura, pg 686
Chip Taylor Communications LLC,
  pg 907

NEW JERSEY

Audio Vistas LLC, pg 694
CFP Video Productions Inc, pg 720
C2 Imaging, pg 735
Laurel Video Productions, pg 804
Listen & Live Audio Inc, pg 809
MiB MediaWorks, pg 825
Milgrom Productions, pg 827
Optisonics Productions, pg 847
Suede Interactive, pg 903

NEW YORK

Avekta Productions Inc, pg 697
Blue Barn Pictures Inc, pg 707
Broadstreet Productions LLC,
  pg 711
Cohn Creative Group LLC, pg 727
Thomas Craven Film Corp, pg 733
Digital Force Ltd, pg 742
Fingerpaint, pg 761
HarperAudio, pg 776
HB-Content, pg 777
Hello World Communications,
  pg 778
Icontent, pg 783
Ketchum, pg 798
L A Bruell Inc, pg 802
Jack Morton Worldwide, pg 830
MRM//McCANN, pg 832
MRY, pg 832
New York Audio Productions,
  pg 840

PROGRAMMING — AUDIO

Business Program Producers (continued)

NEW YORK (continued)

News Broadcast Network Inc, pg 840
The Palmer Group, pg 850
Pat Kogan Productions Inc, pg 852
Practising Law Institute, pg 860
David Rapkin Audio Production, pg 870
S&P Global Marketing Intelligence, pg 880
Elliot Sokolov Music, pg 892
Split Image Productions, pg 898
Suggs Media Productions Inc, pg 903
Synaptic Digital, pg 905
Tiki Recording Studios Inc, pg 914
Zelman Studios Ltd, pg 945

NORTH CAROLINA

Pat Appleson Studios Inc, pg 687
AudioSolutionz LLC, pg 695
The Communications Group Inc, pg 729
Sinclair Institute, pg 889
2BruceStudio, pg 920

OHIO

Curtis Inc, pg 736
Musicol Recording, pg 835
R&B Communications Inc, pg 870
Take 1 Media Services, pg 906
Vista Color Imaging Inc, pg 931

OKLAHOMA

Piper Media Services Inc, pg 857

OREGON

ERA Learning, pg 755
Ideascape Inc, pg 784
InterVision Media, pg 791
The Keyboard Workshop, pg 798
KTVA Productions, pg 802
REX, pg 874

PENNSYLVANIA

American Artist Studio, pg 682
FMP Media Solutions Inc, pg 763
Forge Recording LLC, pg 764
JPL, pg 795
Muderick Media, pg 833
Newtown Psychological Center, pg 840
Panta Rhei Media Inc, pg 851
Production Masters Inc (PMI), pg 864

RHODE ISLAND

Sound-FX-Design, pg 894

SOUTH CAROLINA

DaviSound, pg 739
Venture Media, pg 925

TENNESSEE

Continental Film, pg 731
Memphis Communications Corp, pg 823

TEXAS

AMA Nystrom Printing/Finishing, pg 682
Biway Media, pg 706
The Editing Co, pg 750
Emergency Film Group, pg 753
Epic Software Group Inc, pg 755
Matson Multi-Media, pg 820
Omega Productions, pg 845
Romar Learning Solutions LLC, pg 877
The Sound Lab Inc, pg 894
Sound Works, pg 894
South Coast Film & Video, pg 895
Stage Directions, pg 898
Tropikal Productions, pg 918

VIRGINIA

BES Studios, pg 704
CACI Integrated Communications, pg 713
Limelight Communications Inc, pg 808
Metro Productions, pg 824
National Media Services Inc, pg 836
Rocktown Media, pg 876
Video Solutions, pg 928

WASHINGTON

Getty Images, pg 770
Pacific Multimedia Inc, pg 849

WEST VIRGINIA

Blackwater Video Productions, pg 707

WISCONSIN

5th Floor Recording Co, pg 760
Meridian Studios, pg 824
USAV Group Inc, pg 923
Video Wisconsin Inc, pg 929
Watts Communications Inc, pg 934
Wisconsin Public Television, pg 940

WYOMING

Bridger Productions Inc, pg 710

BRITISH COLUMBIA

Thompson Rivers University Marketing & Communications Dept, pg 913

ONTARIO

ADS Media, pg 677
DebsVoice, pg 739
GAPC (General Assembly Production Centre), pg 768

QUEBEC

Kerrigan Productions Inc, pg 798

Business Program Rentals

CALIFORNIA

Direct Cinema Ltd Inc, pg 743

GEORGIA

Convergent Media Systems, pg 731

MASSACHUSETTS

Preston Productions Inc, pg 861

MICHIGAN

Digi Sign Design LLC, pg 741

NEW HAMPSHIRE

Chip Taylor Communications LLC, pg 907

NEW JERSEY

Alden Films, pg 679
Listen & Live Audio Inc, pg 809

UTAH

Webb Audio Visual, pg 935

ONTARIO

Simply Audiobooks, pg 889

Children's Program Distributors

ARIZONA

Drumbeat Indian Arts Inc, pg 747
Earth Mother Productions Inc™, pg 749

CALIFORNIA

Astronomical Society of the Pacific, pg 691
California Language Laboratories, pg 714
Clarity Sound & Light, pg 725
Direct Cinema Ltd Inc, pg 743
Educational Insights, pg 750
Gateways, pg 768
Steven Halpern's Inner Peace Music, pg 775
Maximus Media Inc, pg 820
monterey media inc, pg 829
monterey video, pg 829
Moose School Productions, pg 830
People Skills International, pg 854
Publishers Group West (PGW), an Ingram brand, pg 866
QRS Software Services, pg 867
Rhythms Productions (Tom Thumb Music), pg 874
Sound Feelings Records, pg 894
Warner Home Video Inc, pg 934

CONNECTICUT

American Melody, pg 683
Scholastic Library Publishing, pg 882
Tantor Media Inc, pg 907
Weston Woods Studios Inc, pg 936

DELAWARE

So Smart Productions, pg 891

FLORIDA

Effective Learning Systems LLC, pg 751
Potentials Unlimited, pg 860
Video Resources Software, pg 928

GEORGIA

August House Audio, pg 695
New Leaf Distributing Co, pg 839
School Media Associates LLC, pg 882

HAWAII

Media Bridge Gamekids, pg 821

NEW HAMPSHIRE

Chip Taylor Communications LLC, pg 907
Chip Taylor Communications LLC, pg 907

ILLINOIS

Jim Gill Music Inc, pg 771
Liturgy Training Publications, pg 810
Nightingale-Conant Corp, pg 841

LOUISIANA

Pelican Publishing Co, pg 853

MAINE

Slim Goodbody Corp, pg 890

MARYLAND

HighBridge Audio, pg 779
Recorded Books Inc, an RBmedia company, pg 871
RLJ Entertainment Inc, pg 875

MASSACHUSETTS

Cheng & Tsui Co, pg 721
Documentary Educational Resources Inc, pg 744
Pauline Books & Media, pg 852
Penfield Productions Ltd, pg 853
Revels Records, pg 874
Ben Rudnick and Friends, pg 878
Yellow Moon Press, pg 944

MICHIGAN

Digi Sign Design LLC, pg 741
Emery-Pratt Co, pg 753
Gemini, pg 769

MISSOURI

Marsh Media, pg 817
SOM Publishing Co, pg 892

NEBRASKA

Vision Maker Media, pg 930

NEW HAMPSHIRE

Chip Taylor Communications LLC, pg 907

NEW JERSEY

Allegro Productions Inc, pg 680
Kimbo Educational, pg 799
Listen & Live Audio Inc, pg 809

NEW YORK

Brooklyn Botanic Garden, pg 711
The Christophers, pg 722
De Nonno Productions Inc (DPI), pg 739
Educational Activities Inc, pg 750
A Gentle Wind, pg 770
Hallel Communications, pg 775
HarperAudio, pg 776
Homespun Video, pg 781
Janus Films Inc, pg 793
Klutz, pg 800
Listening Library, pg 810
Live Oak Media, pg 810
Random House Children's Books, pg 870
Scholastic Media, pg 882
SISU Home Entertainment Inc, pg 889
Spoken Arts Inc, pg 898
Synaptic Digital, pg 905
Visual Technologies Corp, pg 932

NORTH CAROLINA

Howard Hanger, pg 775
Ladyslipper Music, pg 803

OHIO

Alegra House Publishers, pg 679
Franciscan Media, pg 765
Twin Sisters® Digital Media™,
  pg 920

OREGON

Downpour.com, pg 746
InterVision Media, pg 791
Sugar Mountain PR, pg 903

PENNSYLVANIA

Discovery Education - South
  Burlington, pg 743
Fred Rogers Productions, pg 876

SOUTH CAROLINA

BJU Press, pg 706

SOUTH DAKOTA

Spizzirri Press Inc, pg 898

TENNESSEE

Abingdon Press, pg 672
American Blackguard Inc, pg 683
Capitol Christian Music Group,
  pg 716
Cokesbury, pg 727
Ingram Content Group LLC, pg 787
National School Products, pg 836
Provident Distribution, pg 866
Randall House Publications, pg 870
Spring Arbor Distributors Inc,
  pg 898
Word Label Group, pg 941

TEXAS

Institute of Texan Cultures, pg 788
Marengo Films, pg 817
Shadow Play Records & Video,
  pg 885

VERMONT

Taylor Associates, pg 907
Trafalgar Square Books, pg 916

WEST VIRGINIA

Focus on Animals, pg 763
Sweetsong Productions, pg 905

WISCONSIN

Aylmer Press, pg 700
Plank Road Publishing Inc, pg 857

ALBERTA

Global TV, pg 771

ONTARIO

Broughton's Church Supplies,
  Religious Books & Gifts, pg 711
Canadian Learning Co Inc, pg 715
The Children's Book Store
  Distribution (CBSD), pg 722
Novalis, pg 843

Children's Program Producers

ALABAMA

Dogwood Productions Inc, pg 745

ARIZONA

Candee Productions Inc, pg 716
Disney Consumer Products &
  Interactive Media (DCPI), pg 743
Earth Mother Productions Inc™,
  pg 749
Teaberry, pg 908

CALIFORNIA

Ancient Future, pg 685
Astronomical Society of the Pacific,
  pg 691
The Banquet Sound Studios, pg 701
Big Door, pg 705
California Language Laboratories,
  pg 714
Clarity Sound & Light, pg 725
Creative Technology, pg 733
Custom Video Productions Inc,
  pg 736
Direct Cinema Ltd Inc, pg 743
Gateways, pg 768
Steven Halpern's Inner Peace
  Music, pg 775
Lightyear Entertainment, pg 808
Lynch Communications, pg 813
Maximus Media Inc, pg 820
The Media Staff Inc, pg 822
monterey video, pg 829
Moose School Productions, pg 830
OTR Studios, pg 848
piXvfm Inc, pg 857
Producers Group Ltd, pg 863
QRS Software Services, pg 867
Rhythms Productions (Tom Thumb
  Music), pg 874
Steve Shapiro Music, pg 885
Sisters' Choice Press, pg 889
Sound Feelings Records, pg 894
Studio 132, pg 902
Total Creative, pg 916
Wavemaker Media Design, pg 934
Zamacona Productions, pg 945

COLORADO

Tim Cissell Music, pg 725
Flashback Media Productions,
  pg 762

CONNECTICUT

American Melody, pg 683
Scholastic Library Publishing,
  pg 882
T & M Digital Services LLC,
  pg 906
Tantor Media Inc, pg 907
Weston Woods Studios Inc, pg 936

DELAWARE

So Smart Productions, pg 891

FLORIDA

Blackburst Entertainment LLC,
  pg 706
Chatterbox Productions Inc, pg 721
Courter Films LLC, pg 732
Effective Learning Systems LLC,
  pg 751
I M P A C T Publishing Inc,
  pg 783
LHV Audio Services, pg 807
Potentials Unlimited, pg 860
Sunfire Communications Inc,
  pg 904
Sunrise Studios, pg 904
Video Resources Software, pg 928

GEORGIA

August House Audio, pg 695
Guerrilla Productions LLC, pg 774

HAWAII

Media Bridge Gamekids, pg 821

IDAHO

Wide Eye Productions, pg 938

ILLINOIS

ABS Enterprises, pg 672
Audiobook Department, pg 695
Jim Gill Music Inc, pg 771
Liturgy Training Publications,
  pg 810
Nightingale-Conant Corp, pg 841
Pepper Group, pg 854
Steven Samler Music & Sound,
  pg 879

INDIANA

A-V-A Video Productions, pg 671
OMNI Productions, pg 845

IOWA

Hedquist Productions Inc, pg 778

KANSAS

Rhythmic Medicine, pg 874

KENTUCKY

National Geographic Learning,
  pg 836

LOUISIANA

Disk Productions Inc, pg 743

MAINE

Slim Goodbody Corp, pg 890

MARYLAND

Books on Tape™, pg 708
CPR MultiMedia Solutions, pg 732
The Cutting Corporation,
  GraphicAudio® & Archival
  Sound Lab, pg 736
dbF a Media Company, pg 739
HighBridge Audio, pg 779
The Image Generators, pg 785
Kramer Communications Video
  Production, pg 801
Recorded Books Inc, an RBmedia
  company, pg 871

MASSACHUSETTS

Documentary Educational Resources
  Inc, pg 744
Heliotrope Studios, pg 778
HOME Inc, pg 781
Monadnock Media Inc, pg 829
Northern Light Productions (NLP),
  pg 842
Pauline Books & Media, pg 852
Penfield Productions Ltd, pg 853
Revels Records, pg 874
Ben Rudnick and Friends, pg 878
Soundtrack Group, pg 895
TVN-The Video Network, pg 919
Yellow Moon Press, pg 944

MICHIGAN

Digi Sign Design LLC, pg 741
Gemini, pg 769

K&R All Media Productions LLC,
  pg 796
K&R's Recording Studios Inc,
  pg 796

MISSOURI

Audio-VideoGraphics Inc, pg 694
Marsh Media, pg 817
SOM Publishing Co, pg 892

MONTANA

Jereco Studios Inc, pg 793

NEBRASKA

Vision Maker Media, pg 930

NEVADA

JCS Video Productions, pg 793

NEW HAMPSHIRE

Apertura, pg 686
Chip Taylor Communications LLC,
  pg 907

NEW JERSEY

Allegro Productions Inc, pg 680
CFP Video Productions Inc, pg 720
C2 Imaging, pg 735
Kimbo Educational, pg 799
Listen & Live Audio Inc, pg 809
Milgrom Productions, pg 827
Optisonics Productions, pg 847
Suede Interactive, pg 903

NEW MEXICO

Production Outfitters, pg 864
Rainbow International Inc, pg 869

NEW YORK

Air Sea Land Productions Inc
  (ASL), pg 678
American History Workshop (NY)
  Inc, pg 683
Avekta Productions Inc, pg 697
Brooklyn Botanic Garden, pg 711
Thomas Craven Film Corp, pg 733
De Nonno Productions Inc (DPI),
  pg 739
Digital Force Ltd, pg 742
Dyer-Bennet Records, pg 748
Educational Activities Inc, pg 750
Fingerpaint, pg 761
A Gentle Wind, pg 770
Hallel Communications, pg 775
HarperAudio, pg 776
Hello World Communications,
  pg 778
Klutz, pg 800
Listening Library, pg 810
Live Oak Media, pg 810
Jack Morton Worldwide, pg 830
MRY, pg 832
New York Audio Productions,
  pg 840
The Palmer Group, pg 850
Random House Children's Books,
  pg 870
David Rapkin Audio Production,
  pg 870
Elliot Sokolov Music, pg 892
Split Image Productions, pg 898
Spoken Arts Inc, pg 898
Synaptic Digital, pg 905
Tiki Recording Studios Inc, pg 914
Zelman Studios Ltd, pg 945

PROGRAMMING — AUDIO

Children's Program Producers (continued)

NORTH CAROLINA

Pat Appleson Studios Inc, pg 687
Howard Hanger, pg 775
High Windy Audio/Banjoman Inc, pg 779
World Class Learning Materials Inc, pg 941

OHIO

Alegra House Publishers, pg 679
Franciscan Media, pg 765
Twin Sisters® Digital Media™, pg 920
Vista Color Imaging Inc, pg 931

OKLAHOMA

Piper Media Services Inc, pg 857

OREGON

Downpour.com, pg 746
Ideascape Inc, pg 784
InterVision Media, pg 791
Odyssey Productions Inc, pg 844

PENNSYLVANIA

Discovery Education - South Burlington, pg 743
Forge Recording LLC, pg 764
Innovision Media Group, pg 788
Kensington Falls Animation, pg 797
Fred Rogers Productions, pg 876
WQED-Multimedia, pg 942

RHODE ISLAND

Sound-FX-Design, pg 894

SOUTH CAROLINA

BJU Press, pg 706

TENNESSEE

Abingdon Press, pg 672
American Blackguard Inc, pg 683
Capitol Christian Music Group, pg 716
Cokesbury, pg 727
Provident Distribution, pg 866
Word Label Group, pg 941

TEXAS

AMA Nystrom Printing/Finishing, pg 682
Biway Media, pg 706
Communication Arts Multimedia Inc, pg 728
Emergency Film Group, pg 753
Epic Software Group Inc, pg 755
Institute of Texan Cultures, pg 788
Omega Productions, pg 845
Shadow Play Records & Video, pg 885
The Sound Lab Inc, pg 894
Sound Works, pg 894
South Coast Film & Video, pg 895
Tropikal Productions, pg 918

VIRGINIA

BES Studios, pg 704
Metro Productions, pg 824

National Media Services Inc, pg 836
Rocktown Media, pg 876

WASHINGTON

Pacific Multimedia Inc, pg 849

WISCONSIN

5th Floor Recording Co, pg 760
Plank Road Publishing Inc, pg 857
Watts Communications Inc, pg 934
Wisconsin Public Television, pg 940

WYOMING

Bridger Productions Inc, pg 710

ALBERTA

Global TV, pg 771

ONTARIO

DebsVoice, pg 739
GAPC (General Assembly Production Centre), pg 768
Novalis, pg 843

QUEBEC

Kerrigan Productions Inc, pg 798

Children's Program Rentals

CALIFORNIA

Direct Cinema Ltd Inc, pg 743
Paulist Productions, pg 852

MASSACHUSETTS

Documentary Educational Resources Inc, pg 744

MICHIGAN

Digi Sign Design LLC, pg 741

NEBRASKA

Vision Maker Media, pg 930

NEW HAMPSHIRE

Chip Taylor Communications LLC, pg 907

NEW JERSEY

Listen & Live Audio Inc, pg 809

NEW YORK

Adwar Video, pg 678
Brooklyn Botanic Garden, pg 711
Hallel Communications, pg 775

UTAH

Webb Audio Visual, pg 935

ONTARIO

Simply Audiobooks, pg 889

Classic Radio Program, *see* Radio Program—Classic

Commercial, *see* Test Commercial

Compact Disc Distributors

ALABAMA

CMEinfo™, pg 727
Eternal Word Television Network (EWTN), pg 756

ARIZONA

Celestial Harmonies/Fortuna Records/Kuckuck Schallplatten/Black Sun Music/MonteVideo, pg 719
Coyote Cowboy Co, pg 732
Drumbeat Indian Arts Inc, pg 747
Earth Mother Productions Inc™, pg 749
Tom Hopkins International Inc, pg 781
Personal Achievement Institute, pg 854
Teaberry, pg 908
TSG Publishing Foundation Inc USA, pg 919
Valley of the Sun Publishing Co, pg 924

CALIFORNIA

Ametron Audio/Video, pg 684
Audio Editions Books-On-Cassette & CD, pg 693
California Language Laboratories, pg 714
Capitol Records, pg 716
Cibola Systems, pg 723
Clarity Sound & Light, pg 725
Concord Records, pg 730
Dialect Accent Specialists Inc, pg 741
ECONEWS (Environmental Television Series) & (Environmental Directions Radio Series), pg 750
Educational Insights, pg 750
Eye & I Productions, pg 758
Gateways, pg 768
GNP Crescendo Records, pg 772
Bruce Goldberg Inc, pg 772
Golden State Dance Teachers Association (GSDTA), pg 772
Harmonia Mundi USA, pg 776
Hay House Inc, pg 777
Interscope, Geffen, A&M Records, pg 790
Krishnamurti Foundation of America, pg 801
LANGUAGE/30™, pg 803
Lightworks Audio & Video Inc, pg 808
monterey video, pg 829
Motown®, pg 831
Music World/Vocal Power School, pg 834
Nilgiri Press, pg 841
Osho Viha Information Center & Book Distributors, pg 848
Prime Cut Productions, pg 862
QRS Software Services, pg 867
Randolf Productions Inc, pg 870
Sahara Records & Filmworks Entertainment Co, pg 879
Saturn Studios, pg 881
Sisters' Choice Press, pg 889
Sound Feelings Records, pg 894
Telarc International Corp, pg 909
Timeless Productions, pg 914
Universal Music Group, pg 922
Valley Media, pg 924
Varese Sarabande Records Inc, pg 924
Welk Music Group, pg 935
The Wyland Group, pg 942

COLORADO

Crown Ministries International, pg 735
National Institute for Trial Advocacy (NITA), pg 836
ProLine Digital, pg 865
White Swan Music Inc, pg 937

CONNECTICUT

Connecticut Audio & Theatrical Supply, pg 731
Tantor Media Inc, pg 907
Weston Woods Studios Inc, pg 936

DELAWARE

So Smart Productions, pg 891

DISTRICT OF COLUMBIA

American Chemical Society (ACS), pg 683
Library of Congress, Motion Picture, Broadcasting & Recorded Sound Division, pg 807

FLORIDA

Alliance Entertainment Corp (AEC) LLC, pg 680
Effective Learning Systems LLC, pg 751
Kat Epple Music Productions, pg 755
Hard Hat Radio Music Service, pg 776
I M P A C T Publishing Inc, pg 783
Times-Square Fantasy Theatre, pg 914

GEORGIA

The Alliance for Christian Media, pg 680
August House Audio, pg 695
New Leaf Distributing Co, pg 839
ON Services, a GES Company, pg 846

ILLINOIS

Bolchazy - Carducci Publishers Inc, pg 708
Britannica Digital Learning, pg 710
CCH Continuing Education, pg 718
CCore Media Inc, pg 718
Convenience, pg 731
Earwig Music Co Inc, pg 749
Film Ideas Inc, pg 760
Nightingale-Conant Corp, pg 841
Woodside Avenue Music Productions Inc, pg 941

INDIANA

Lee Co Inc, pg 805

IOWA

Long-Term Success Publishing, pg 811

KENTUCKY

Horizon Films & Media LLC, pg 781

LOUISIANA

Flat Town Music Co, pg 762
Great Chefs/Leisure Jazz Video, pg 773
Jin Records, pg 794
Leisure Video, pg 806
Maison de Soul Records, pg 815

Pelican Publishing Co, pg 853
Swallow, pg 905

MARYLAND

Adelphi Records Inc, pg 676
Audio Book Contractors LLC,
  pg 693
dbF a Media Company, pg 739
HighBridge Audio, pg 779
Recorded Books Inc, an RBmedia
  company, pg 871

MASSACHUSETTS

AirCraft Production Libraries,
  pg 679
Cheng & Tsui Co, pg 721
Pauline Books & Media, pg 852
Penfield Productions Ltd, pg 853
Revels Records, pg 874
Ben Rudnick and Friends, pg 878
Yellow Moon Press, pg 944

MICHIGAN

Brilliance Audio, pg 710
Digi Sign Design LLC, pg 741
Rebirth Inc, pg 871
Renaissance Unity, pg 873
Zondervan, pg 945

MINNESOTA

American Choral Catalog Ltd,
  pg 683
Augsburg Fortress, pg 695
Learning Strategies Corp, pg 805
Whole Person Associates Inc,
  pg 938

MISSOURI

American Optometric Association
  (AOA), pg 684
Grace Church - St Louis, pg 773
Impact Christian Books Inc, pg 786
New Letters on the Air, pg 839
Vedanta Society of St Louis, pg 925

MONTANA

Jereco Studios Inc, pg 793

NEBRASKA

AdventSource, pg 678
Back to the Bible, pg 700
The Recruiters Library, pg 872

NEVADA

Ron Roy Productions/Moodtapes,
  pg 878

NEW HAMPSHIRE

Captain Fiddle Music &
  Publications, pg 716
French American Music Enterprises,
  pg 765
Frey Scientific, pg 766
Chip Taylor Communications LLC,
  pg 907

NEW JERSEY

Alden Films, pg 679
Dance Horizons Video, pg 737
HamiltonBuhl, pg 775
Kimbo Educational, pg 799
Learning Ally, pg 805
Shanachie Entertainment Corp,
  pg 885

NEW MEXICO

Indian House, pg 786
Uncharted Country Publishing,
  pg 921

NEW YORK

Applause Learning Resources,
  pg 687
The Bureau for At-Risk Youth,
  pg 712
Cadence Jazz Records, pg 713
The Christophers, pg 722
Cornell Laboratory of Ornithology,
  pg 731
Digital Force Ltd, pg 742
Dover Publications Inc, pg 746
Dyer-Bennet Records, pg 748
Educational Activities Inc, pg 750
Entertainment One US, pg 754
Film Emporium, pg 760
A Gentle Wind, pg 770
Guilford Publications, pg 774
HB-Content, pg 777
Homespun Video, pg 781
Live Oak Media, pg 810
Manhattan Production Music Inc,
  pg 816
New World Records, pg 840
Oriental Records Inc, pg 848
RadioArt/Bob & Ray CDs & MP3
  Files, pg 869
Random House Children's Books,
  pg 870
Simon & Schuster, Inc, pg 888
SISU Home Entertainment Inc,
  pg 889
Sony Music Entertainment, pg 893
Spoken Arts Inc, pg 898
Tommy Boy Entertainment LLC,
  pg 915
Video Artists International & VAI
  Audio, pg 927
ZBS Foundation, pg 945

NORTH CAROLINA

Howard Hanger, pg 775
Ladyslipper Music, pg 803
Thinking Maps Inc, pg 912

OHIO

The American Classical League,
  pg 683

OKLAHOMA

Piper Media Services Inc, pg 857

OREGON

Downpour.com, pg 746
The Keyboard Workshop, pg 798

PENNSYLVANIA

Dreambox Media Inc, pg 746
Himalayan Institute Audio/Video,
  pg 780
Fred Rogers Productions, pg 876

SOUTH CAROLINA

BJU Press, pg 706
DaviSound, pg 739

SOUTH DAKOTA

Spizzirri Press Inc, pg 898

TENNESSEE

Abingdon Press, pg 672
American Blackguard Inc, pg 683

Capitol Christian Music Group,
  pg 716
Center for Southern Folklore Inc,
  pg 719
Cokesbury, pg 727
Compass Records, pg 729
Ingram Content Group LLC, pg 787
International Marketing Group,
  pg 790
National School Products, pg 836
Provident Distribution, pg 866
Rounder Records, pg 878
Spring Arbor Distributors Inc,
  pg 898
Word Label Group, pg 941
Zion Music Group, pg 945

TEXAS

Executive Development Systems
  Inc, pg 757
Lamb & Lion Ministries, pg 803
Marengo Films, pg 817
Milky Way Press, pg 827
Replicopy Digital Media Center,
  pg 873
SMI® Inc, pg 891
TM Studios Inc, pg 915
TopCat Records LLC, pg 915

VERMONT

Multicultural Media Inc, pg 833

VIRGINIA

Colonial Williamsburg Foundation,
  pg 727
Council on Foundations, pg 732
County Sales, pg 732
National Audiovisual Center (NAC),
  pg 836
National Media Services Inc,
  pg 836
Rebel Records, pg 871

WASHINGTON

Books In Motion, pg 708
Voyager Recordings & Publications,
  pg 932

WISCONSIN

Plank Road Publishing Inc, pg 857
School Specialty Inc, pg 882

PUERTO RICO

Bonnin Electronics Inc, pg 708

BRITISH COLUMBIA

Timeless Books, pg 914

ONTARIO

Broughton's Church Supplies,
  Religious Books & Gifts, pg 711
The Children's Book Store
  Distribution (CBSD), pg 722
Entertainment One Distribution,
  pg 754
GAPC (General Assembly
  Production Centre), pg 768
Mind Resources Inc, pg 828
Nelson Education Ltd, pg 837
Novalis, pg 843
Penguin Random House Canada,
  pg 853
Scholastic Canada Ltd, pg 882

Compact Disc Producers

ALABAMA

CMEinfo™, pg 727
Eternal Word Television Network
  (EWTN), pg 756

ARIZONA

Celestial Harmonies/Fortuna
  Records/Kuckuck
  Schallplatten/Black Sun
  Music/MonteVideo, pg 719
Drumbeat Indian Arts Inc, pg 747
Merestone, pg 823
Personal Achievement Institute,
  pg 854
SPEAK HOUSE Audio™, pg 896
Teaberry, pg 908
Truth Consciousness Publications,
  pg 919
TSG Publishing Foundation Inc
  USA, pg 919
Valley of the Sun Publishing Co,
  pg 924

ARKANSAS

Live'N'Loud, pg 810

CALIFORNIA

ACDC Audio CD & Cassette,
  pg 674
Ancient Future, pg 685
Artichoke Productions, pg 690
The Banquet Sound Studios, pg 701
California Language Laboratories,
  pg 714
Clarity Sound & Light, pg 725
Concord Jazz, pg 730
Concord Records, pg 730
Creative Media Recording, pg 733
Custom Video Productions Inc,
  pg 736
Dialect Accent Specialists Inc,
  pg 741
DiskFaktory, pg 743
ECONEWS (Environmental
  Television Series) &
  (Environmental Directions Radio
  Series), pg 750
Eye & I Productions, pg 758
4th Street Recording, pg 764
Gateways, pg 768
Gold Standard Productions, pg 772
Bruce Goldberg Inc, pg 772
Harmonia Mundi USA, pg 776
Hay House Inc, pg 777
Interscope, Geffen, A&M Records,
  pg 790
Krishnamurti Foundation of
  America, pg 801
K2B2 Records, pg 802
LANGUAGE/30™, pg 803
Lynch Communications, pg 813
Maximus Media Inc, pg 820
Media Magic, pg 822
monterey video, pg 829
M2 Communications, pg 833
Music World/Vocal Power School,
  pg 834
New Harbinger Publications, pg 839
Nilgiri Press, pg 841
On-Trax Inc, pg 846
Penrose Productions, pg 854
Prime Cut Productions, pg 862
QRS Software Services, pg 867
Randolf Productions Inc, pg 870
Reference Recordings, pg 872
Rhythms Productions (Tom Thumb
  Music), pg 874
Sahara Records & Filmworks
  Entertainment Co, pg 879

PROGRAMMING — AUDIO

Compact Disc Producers (continued)

CALIFORNIA (continued)

Saturn Studios, pg 881
Alwin Sauers Audio Productions (ASAP), pg 881
Schroder Music Co, pg 882
Steve Shapiro Music, pg 885
Sisters' Choice Press, pg 889
Sound Feelings Records, pg 894
Studio 132, pg 902
Tam Communications Inc, pg 906
Timeless Productions, pg 914
Total Creative, pg 916
Twin Peaks Creative, pg 920
Universal Music Group, pg 922
Varese Sarabande Records Inc, pg 924
Vedanta Press & Catalog, pg 925
Video Resources Inc, pg 928
Webster Communications, pg 935
The Wyland Group, pg 942

COLORADO

Tim Cissell Music, pg 725
Crown Ministries International, pg 735
Flashback Media Productions, pg 762
Los Angeles Post Music Inc, pg 811
Mike's Camera, pg 827
National Institute for Trial Advocacy (NITA), pg 836

CONNECTICUT

T & M Digital Services LLC, pg 906
Tantor Media Inc, pg 907
Weston Woods Studios Inc, pg 936

DELAWARE

Ken-Del Productions Inc, pg 797
So Smart Productions, pg 891

DISTRICT OF COLUMBIA

American Chemical Society (ACS), pg 683
Hillmann & Carr Inc, pg 780
Interface Media Group, pg 789
Smithsonian Folkways Recordings, pg 891

FLORIDA

Blackburst Entertainment LLC, pg 706
Courter Films LLC, pg 732
Effective Learning Systems LLC, pg 751
Kat Epple Music Productions, pg 755
Hard Hat Radio Music Service, pg 776
LHV Audio Services, pg 807
Sunfire Communications Inc, pg 904
Sunrise Studios, pg 904
Tight Line Productions, pg 914
Times-Square Fantasy Theatre, pg 914

GEORGIA

August House Audio, pg 695
Guerrilla Productions LLC, pg 774
Hottrax Records, pg 782

ILLINOIS

Audiobook Department, pg 695
Britannica Digital Learning, pg 710
CCore Media Inc, pg 718
Convenience, pg 731
Cresta Creative, pg 734
Delmark Records, pg 740
Earwig Music Co Inc, pg 749
Film Ideas Inc, pg 760
Major Media Inc, pg 815
Nightingale-Conant Corp, pg 841
Pepper Group, pg 854
RADMAR Inc, pg 869
Sparkfactor, pg 896
Video Impressions, pg 928
Woodside Avenue Music Productions Inc, pg 941

INDIANA

A-V-A Video Productions, pg 671
Bright Ideas Creative Services, pg 710

IOWA

Hedquist Productions Inc, pg 778
Long-Term Success Publishing, pg 811

KANSAS

Rhythmic Medicine, pg 874

KENTUCKY

Horizon Films & Media LLC, pg 781
Donna Lawrence Productions, pg 804
Prosper Media Group Inc, pg 866

LOUISIANA

Centaur Records Inc, pg 719
Flat Town Music Co, pg 762
Great Chefs/Leisure Jazz Video, pg 773
Jazzology, pg 793
Jin Records, pg 794
Leisure Video, pg 806
Louisiana State University Division of Strategic Communications, pg 811
Maison de Soul Records, pg 815
Swallow, pg 905

MAINE

Serendipity Recordings, pg 884

MARYLAND

Adelphi Records Inc, pg 676
Books on Tape™, pg 708
dbF a Media Company, pg 739
HighBridge Audio, pg 779
The Image Generators, pg 785
Lion & Fox Recording Studios, pg 809
Recorded Books Inc, an RBmedia company, pg 871

MASSACHUSETTS

Cheng & Tsui Co, pg 721
Labrecque Creative Sound, pg 803
Pauline Books & Media, pg 852
Penfield Productions Ltd, pg 853
Revels Records, pg 874
Ben Rudnick and Friends, pg 878
Soundtrack Group, pg 895
Rik Tinory Productions, pg 914
Yellow Moon Press, pg 944

MICHIGAN

Brilliance Audio, pg 710
Digi Sign Design LLC, pg 741
International Tae Kwon Do Association (ITA Institute), pg 790
K&R All Media Productions LLC, pg 796
K&R's Recording Studios Inc, pg 796
Rebirth Inc, pg 871
Renaissance Unity, pg 873
TGA Recording Co, pg 911
Zondervan, pg 945

MINNESOTA

American Choral Catalog Ltd, pg 683
Augsburg Fortress, pg 695
BeyerSound & Essay Audio, pg 705
Learning Strategies Corp, pg 805
Whole Person Associates Inc, pg 938

MISSOURI

American Optometric Association (AOA), pg 684
Audio-VideoGraphics Inc, pg 694
Impact Christian Books Inc, pg 786
New Letters on the Air, pg 839
SOM Publishing Co, pg 892
Vedanta Society of St Louis, pg 925

MONTANA

Jereco Studios Inc, pg 793

NEBRASKA

The Recruiters Library, pg 872

NEVADA

Ron Roy Productions/Moodtapes, pg 878
Tanglewood Productions, pg 907

NEW HAMPSHIRE

Captain Fiddle Music & Publications, pg 716
Frey Scientific, pg 766
Chip Taylor Communications LLC, pg 907

NEW JERSEY

Alden Films, pg 679
Audio Vistas LLC, pg 694
CFP Video Productions Inc, pg 720
Jeep Jazz Media Solutions, pg 793
Kimbo Educational, pg 799
Laurel Video Productions, pg 804
Learning Ally, pg 805
Ray Mueller Productions, pg 833
Presence Records, pg 861
Shanachie Entertainment Corp, pg 885
Suede Interactive, pg 903
VCSvideo, pg 925

NEW MEXICO

Indian House, pg 786
Production Outfitters, pg 864
Uncharted Country Publishing, pg 921

NEW YORK

Aural Gratification Inc, pg 695
Blue Barn Pictures Inc, pg 707
Blue Wave Records, pg 708
Bridge Records Inc, pg 710

The Bureau for At-Risk Youth, pg 712
Cadence Jazz Records, pg 713
The Christophers, pg 722
Cornell Laboratory of Ornithology, pg 731
Digital Force Ltd, pg 742
Dyer-Bennet Records, pg 748
Educational Activities Inc, pg 750
Entertainment One US, pg 754
Fingerpaint, pg 761
A Gentle Wind, pg 770
Guilford Publications, pg 774
HB-Content, pg 777
Homespun Video, pg 781
International Digital Centre, pg 790
L A Bruell Inc, pg 802
Live Oak Media, pg 810
Macmillan Audio, pg 814
Manhattan Production Music Inc, pg 816
Mark Custom Recording Service Inc, pg 817
New World Records, pg 840
New York Audio Productions, pg 840
Oriental Records Inc, pg 848
RadioArt/Bob & Ray CDs & MP3 Files, pg 869
Random House Children's Books, pg 870
RCA Records, pg 871
Simon & Schuster, Inc, pg 888
SISU Home Entertainment Inc, pg 889
Elliot Sokolov Music, pg 892
Spoken Arts Inc, pg 898
Sunnyside Communications Inc, pg 904
Tommy Boy Entertainment LLC, pg 915
United Nations Multimedia Resources Unit, pg 921
Verve Label Group, pg 926
ZBS Foundation, pg 945

NORTH CAROLINA

Pat Appleson Studios Inc, pg 687
Howard Hanger, pg 775
High Windy Audio/Banjoman Inc, pg 779
2BruceStudio, pg 920

OHIO

Lyon Video Inc, pg 813
Musicol Recording, pg 835
R&B Communications Inc, pg 870

OKLAHOMA

Piper Media Services Inc, pg 857

OREGON

Downpour.com, pg 746
ERA Learning, pg 755
Ideascape Inc, pg 784
The Keyboard Workshop, pg 798
KTVA Productions, pg 802
Odyssey Productions Inc, pg 844
REX, pg 874

PENNSYLVANIA

American Artist Studio, pg 682
Canadian American Records, pg 715
Dreambox Media Inc, pg 746
FMP Media Solutions Inc, pg 763
Forge Recording LLC, pg 764
Himalayan Institute Audio/Video, pg 780
Innovision Media Group, pg 788
JPL, pg 795

Production Masters Inc (PMI), pg 864
The Videohouse Inc, pg 929

SOUTH CAROLINA
BJU Press, pg 706
DaviSound, pg 739

TENNESSEE
Abingdon Press, pg 672
American Blackguard Inc, pg 683
Center for Southern Folklore Inc, pg 719
Cokesbury, pg 727
Compass Records, pg 729
High Water Records, pg 779
Provident Distribution, pg 866
Rounder Records, pg 878
Word Label Group, pg 941

TEXAS
Audiomoxie®, pg 695
Biway Media, pg 706
Milky Way Press, pg 827
Music Lab Inc, pg 834
Omni Intercommunications Inc, pg 845
Romar Learning Solutions LLC, pg 877
SMI® Inc, pg 891
The Sound Lab Inc, pg 894
Stage Directions, pg 898
TM Studios Inc, pg 915
TopCat Records LLC, pg 915
Tropikal Productions, pg 918
The Yesterday USA Radio Networks, pg 944

UTAH
One Stop CD Shop LLC, pg 846
San Juan School District Heritage Language Resource Center, pg 880

VERMONT
Inner Traditions International, pg 788
Lyrichord/Multicultural Media, pg 813
Multicultural Media Inc, pg 833

VIRGINIA
AudioImage Recording, pg 695
Council on Foundations, pg 732
County Sales, pg 732
National Media Services Inc, pg 836
Rebel Records, pg 871
Rocktown Media, pg 876
Studio Center Corp, pg 902

WASHINGTON
Books In Motion, pg 708
Center for Touch Drawing, pg 719
Voyager Recordings & Publications, pg 932

WISCONSIN
5th Floor Recording Co, pg 760
Meridian Studios, pg 824
Plank Road Publishing Inc, pg 857
Video Wisconsin Inc, pg 929
Watts Communications Inc, pg 934

WYOMING
Bridger Productions Inc, pg 710

BRITISH COLUMBIA
Timeless Books, pg 914

MANITOBA
DACAPO Productions Inc, pg 737
Manitoba Film & Music, pg 816

ONTARIO
ADS Media, pg 677
AMPLUS Productions, pg 684
DebsVoice, pg 739
Nelson Education Ltd, pg 837
Novalis, pg 843
Scholastic Canada Ltd, pg 882
Silver Creek Media Inc, pg 888

Compact Disc Rentals

ALABAMA
Audio-Video Resources Inc, pg 694

DELAWARE
Side Door Studio Inc, pg 887

MICHIGAN
Digi Sign Design LLC, pg 741

NEW HAMPSHIRE
Chip Taylor Communications LLC, pg 907

NEW JERSEY
Alden Films, pg 679

OREGON
The Keyboard Workshop, pg 798

ONTARIO
Simply Audiobooks, pg 889

Current Event Program Distributors

ARKANSAS
Master Books®, pg 819

CALIFORNIA
Direct Cinema Ltd Inc, pg 743
Maximus Media Inc, pg 820
Pacifica Radio Archives, pg 849
Publishers Group West (PGW), an Ingram brand, pg 866
QRS Software Services, pg 867
Social Studies School Service, pg 891

CONNECTICUT
Tantor Media Inc, pg 907

DISTRICT OF COLUMBIA
National Council of Churches, pg 836

GEORGIA
School Media Associates LLC, pg 882

HAWAII
Media Bridge Gamekids, pg 821

MARYLAND
HighBridge Audio, pg 779
Recorded Books Inc, an RBmedia company, pg 871

MICHIGAN
Digi Sign Design LLC, pg 741

NEW HAMPSHIRE
Chip Taylor Communications LLC, pg 907

NEW JERSEY
Listen & Live Audio Inc, pg 809

NEW YORK
The Cinema Guild Inc, pg 724
HarperAudio, pg 776
HB-Content, pg 777
Janus Films Inc, pg 793
News Broadcast Network Inc, pg 840
Practising Law Institute, pg 860
Timed Exposures Films, pg 914
United Nations Department of Public Information-News & Media Division, pg 921
United Nations Multimedia Resources Unit, pg 921

OREGON
InterVision Media, pg 791

TENNESSEE
Ingram Content Group LLC, pg 787
Spring Arbor Distributors Inc, pg 898

TEXAS
Emergency Film Group, pg 753

VIRGINIA
CACI Integrated Communications, pg 713
CDR Communications Inc, pg 719

ALBERTA
Global TV, pg 771

BRITISH COLUMBIA
Video Out Distribution, pg 928

ONTARIO
Canadian Learning Co Inc, pg 715
Life Cycle Books Ltd, pg 807

Current Event Program Producers

CALIFORNIA
Big Door, pg 705
Creative Technology, pg 733
Direct Cinema Ltd Inc, pg 743
Lynch Communications, pg 813
PM Productions, pg 858
Producers Group Ltd, pg 863
QRS Software Services, pg 867
Still N' Motion, pg 901
Studio 132, pg 902
Total Creative, pg 916
Video Resources Inc, pg 928
Wavemaker Media Design, pg 934
Webster Communications, pg 935

COLORADO
Apogee Communications Group, pg 687
Flashback Media Productions, pg 762

CONNECTICUT
Essex Television Group Inc, pg 755
Tantor Media Inc, pg 907

FLORIDA
Blackburst Entertainment LLC, pg 706
Courter Films LLC, pg 732
LHV Audio Services, pg 807
Sunfire Communications Inc, pg 904
Sunrise Studios, pg 904

GEORGIA
Guerrilla Productions LLC, pg 774

IDAHO
Wide Eye Productions, pg 938

ILLINOIS
ABS Enterprises, pg 672
Pepper Group, pg 854

INDIANA
A-V-A Video Productions, pg 671

KENTUCKY
National Geographic Learning, pg 836

MARYLAND
CPR MultiMedia Solutions, pg 732
The Cutting Corporation, GraphicAudio® & Archival Sound Lab, pg 736
dbF a Media Company, pg 739
HighBridge Audio, pg 779
The Image Generators, pg 785
Kramer Communications Video Production, pg 801
Recorded Books Inc, an RBmedia company, pg 871

MASSACHUSETTS
Heliotrope Studios, pg 778
Northern Light Productions (NLP), pg 842
Soundtrack Group, pg 895

MICHIGAN
Digi Sign Design LLC, pg 741
K&R All Media Productions LLC, pg 796
K&R's Recording Studios Inc, pg 796

MISSOURI
Hardcastle Films & Video, pg 776

NEVADA
JCS Video Productions, pg 793

NEW HAMPSHIRE
Apertura, pg 686
Chip Taylor Communications LLC, pg 907

PROGRAMMING — AUDIO

Current Event Program Producers (continued)

NEW JERSEY

CFP Video Productions Inc, pg 720
Listen & Live Audio Inc, pg 809
MiB MediaWorks, pg 825
Optisonics Productions, pg 847
Suede Interactive, pg 903

NEW MEXICO

Production Outfitters, pg 864

NEW YORK

Avekta Productions Inc, pg 697
Blue Barn Pictures Inc, pg 707
Broadstreet Productions LLC, pg 711
Digital Force Ltd, pg 742
HarperAudio, pg 776
HB-Content, pg 777
Jack Morton Worldwide, pg 830
New York Audio Productions, pg 840
News Broadcast Network Inc, pg 840
The Palmer Group, pg 850
Practising Law Institute, pg 860
David Rapkin Audio Production, pg 870
Split Image Productions, pg 898
Timed Exposures Films, pg 914
United Nations Multimedia Resources Unit, pg 921
Zelman Studios Ltd, pg 945

NORTH CAROLINA

Pat Appleson Studios Inc, pg 687

OHIO

R&B Communications Inc, pg 870
Vista Color Imaging Inc, pg 931

OKLAHOMA

Piper Media Services Inc, pg 857

OREGON

InterVision Media, pg 791

PENNSYLVANIA

Forge Recording LLC, pg 764
Innovision Media Group, pg 788
Production Masters Inc (PMI), pg 864

RHODE ISLAND

Sound-FX-Design, pg 894

TEXAS

Emergency Film Group, pg 753
Omega Productions, pg 845
The Sound Lab Inc, pg 894
Sound Works, pg 894
South Coast Film & Video, pg 895
Stage Directions, pg 898
Texas Rebel Radio Network, pg 911

VIRGINIA

BES Studios, pg 704
CACI Integrated Communications, pg 713
CDR Communications Inc, pg 719

Limelight Communications Inc, pg 808
Metro Productions, pg 824
Rocktown Media, pg 876

WISCONSIN

5th Floor Recording Co, pg 760
Knowledge Unlimited Inc, pg 800
Video Wisconsin Inc, pg 929
Wisconsin Public Television, pg 940

WYOMING

Bridger Productions Inc, pg 710

ALBERTA

Global TV, pg 771

ONTARIO

DebsVoice, pg 739

QUEBEC

Kerrigan Productions Inc, pg 798

Current Event Program Rentals

CALIFORNIA

Direct Cinema Ltd Inc, pg 743

MICHIGAN

Digi Sign Design LLC, pg 741

NEW HAMPSHIRE

Chip Taylor Communications LLC, pg 907

NEW JERSEY

Listen & Live Audio Inc, pg 809

NEW YORK

Timed Exposures Films, pg 914

BRITISH COLUMBIA

Video Out Distribution, pg 928

Digital Audio Distributors

CALIFORNIA

Ametron Audio/Video, pg 684
QRS Software Services, pg 867
Sisters' Choice Press, pg 889

CONNECTICUT

Connecticut Audio & Theatrical Supply, pg 731

FLORIDA

Times-Square Fantasy Theatre, pg 914

ILLINOIS

CCore Media Inc, pg 718

MARYLAND

Recorded Books Inc, an RBmedia company, pg 871

MICHIGAN

Brilliance Audio, pg 710
Digi Sign Design LLC, pg 741

NEW YORK

Digital Force Ltd, pg 742
Film Emporium, pg 760
RadioArt/Bob & Ray CDs & MP3 Files, pg 869
Synaptic Digital, pg 905

OHIO

Twin Sisters® Digital Media™, pg 920

TENNESSEE

American Blackguard Inc, pg 683

PUERTO RICO

Bonnin Electronics Inc, pg 708

ONTARIO

Entertainment One Distribution, pg 754

Digital Audio Producers

ARIZONA

Merestone, pg 823

CALIFORNIA

ACDC Audio CD & Cassette, pg 674
Ancient Future, pg 685
Artichoke Productions, pg 690
Custom Video Productions Inc, pg 736
K2B2 Records, pg 802
Lynch Communications, pg 813
Maximus Media Inc, pg 820
Media Magic, pg 822
On-Trax Inc, pg 846
QRS Software Services, pg 867
Saturn Studios, pg 881
Steve Shapiro Music, pg 885
Sisters' Choice Press, pg 889
Total Creative, pg 916
Twin Peaks Creative, pg 920
Video Resources Inc, pg 928

COLORADO

Tim Cissell Music, pg 725
Daylight Productions & Rentals, pg 739

DISTRICT OF COLUMBIA

Interface Media Group, pg 789

FLORIDA

LHV Audio Services, pg 807
Sunfire Communications Inc, pg 904

GEORGIA

Guerrilla Productions LLC, pg 774

ILLINOIS

CCore Media Inc, pg 718
Cresta Creative, pg 734
Major Media Inc, pg 815

INDIANA

Bright Ideas Creative Services, pg 710

MARYLAND

Books on Tape™, pg 708
The Image Generators, pg 785

Lion & Fox Recording Studios, pg 809
Recorded Books Inc, an RBmedia company, pg 871

MICHIGAN

Brilliance Audio, pg 710
Digi Sign Design LLC, pg 741
K&R All Media Productions LLC, pg 796
K&R's Recording Studios Inc, pg 796

NEW JERSEY

Jeep Jazz Media Solutions, pg 793
Laurel Video Productions, pg 804
Suede Interactive, pg 903

NEW YORK

Aural Gratification Inc, pg 695
Bridge Records Inc, pg 710
Digital Force Ltd, pg 742
Fingerpaint, pg 761
International Digital Centre, pg 790
RadioArt/Bob & Ray CDs & MP3 Files, pg 869
Sear Sound, pg 883
Synaptic Digital, pg 905

NORTH CAROLINA

Pat Appleson Studios Inc, pg 687

OHIO

Advent Media Inc, pg 677
Musicol Recording, pg 835
R&B Communications Inc, pg 870
Twin Sisters® Digital Media™, pg 920

OREGON

REX, pg 874

PENNSYLVANIA

Canadian American Records, pg 715
Forge Recording LLC, pg 764
Innovision Media Group, pg 788
JPL, pg 795
Production Masters Inc (PMI), pg 864

TEXAS

Biway Media, pg 706
Romar Learning Solutions LLC, pg 877
The Samuels Co, pg 879
Stage Directions, pg 898
Tropikal Productions, pg 918

VIRGINIA

Advance Concepts Inc, pg 677
AudioImage Recording, pg 695
Studio Center Corp, pg 902

WISCONSIN

5th Floor Recording Co, pg 760
Meridian Studios, pg 824

Digital Audio Rentals

DELAWARE

Side Door Studio Inc, pg 887

MICHIGAN

Digi Sign Design LLC, pg 741

Documentary Distributors

ARKANSAS
Master Books®, pg 819

CALIFORNIA
Astronomical Society of the Pacific, pg 691
Direct Cinema Ltd Inc, pg 743
ECONEWS (Environmental Television Series) & (Environmental Directions Radio Series), pg 750
Maximus Media Inc, pg 820
New Line Cinema, pg 839
Pacific Media, pg 849
Pacifica Radio Archives, pg 849
QRS Software Services, pg 867
Regent Press Publishers & Printers, pg 873
Sea Studios Foundation, pg 883
Social Studies School Service, pg 891
Warner Home Video Inc, pg 934
The Wine Appreciation Guild Ltd, pg 939

CONNECTICUT
Save the Children Federation Inc, pg 881

DISTRICT OF COLUMBIA
National Council of Churches, pg 836

GEORGIA
School Media Associates LLC, pg 882

HAWAII
Media Bridge Gamekids, pg 821

ILLINOIS
CCore Media Inc, pg 718
Theosophical Publishing House, pg 912

INDIANA
Communication Ministries, pg 728

KENTUCKY
Horizon Films & Media LLC, pg 781

MARYLAND
HighBridge Audio, pg 779
MMI Marketing, pg 828
Recorded Books Inc, an RBmedia company, pg 871
RLJ Entertainment Inc, pg 875
Special Archives Division, Motion Picture Branch, pg 896

MASSACHUSETTS
Documentary Educational Resources Inc, pg 744
Penfield Productions Ltd, pg 853

MICHIGAN
Digi Sign Design LLC, pg 741

MISSOURI
SOM Publishing Co, pg 892

MONTANA
High Plains Films, pg 779

NEBRASKA
Vision Maker Media, pg 930

NEVADA
DVDs4Less, pg 748

NEW HAMPSHIRE
Captain Fiddle Music & Publications, pg 716
Chip Taylor Communications LLC, pg 907

NEW JERSEY
Allegro Productions Inc, pg 680
Shanachie Entertainment Corp, pg 885

NEW YORK
The Cinema Guild Inc, pg 724
De Nonno Productions Inc (DPI), pg 739
Films Media Group, pg 760
Hallel Communications, pg 775
HB-Content, pg 777
Janus Films Inc, pg 793
Timed Exposures Films, pg 914
United Nations Department of Public Information-News & Media Division, pg 921
United Nations Multimedia Resources Unit, pg 921

NORTH CAROLINA
Ladyslipper Music, pg 803

OREGON
InterVision Media, pg 791

PENNSYLVANIA
FMP Media Solutions Inc, pg 763
S I Video Sales Group, pg 879

TENNESSEE
American Blackguard Inc, pg 683
Capitol Christian Music Group, pg 716
Center for Southern Folklore Inc, pg 719
Ingram Content Group LLC, pg 787
Spring Arbor Distributors Inc, pg 898

TEXAS
Emergency Film Group, pg 753

VIRGINIA
CACI Integrated Communications, pg 713

WISCONSIN
Her Own Words LLC, pg 779

ALBERTA
Global TV, pg 771

BRITISH COLUMBIA
Timeless Books, pg 914
Video Out Distribution, pg 928

ONTARIO
Canadian Learning Co Inc, pg 715
CBC/Radio-Canada, pg 717
Life Cycle Books Ltd, pg 807

Documentary Producers

ALABAMA
Dogwood Productions Inc, pg 745
Leo Ticheli Productions, pg 913

ARIZONA
Candee Productions Inc, pg 716
Teaberry, pg 908

ARKANSAS
Live'N'Loud, pg 810

CALIFORNIA
Ancient Future, pg 685
The Banquet Sound Studios, pg 701
Big Door, pg 705
Creative Technology, pg 733
Custom Video Productions Inc, pg 736
Design Media, pg 741
Direct Cinema Ltd Inc, pg 743
ECONEWS (Environmental Television Series) & (Environmental Directions Radio Series), pg 750
Goal Productions, pg 772
Gold Standard Productions, pg 772
imageReal Pictures LLC, pg 785
Kris Stevens Enterprises, pg 801
Lynch Communications, pg 813
Maximus Media Inc, pg 820
The Media Staff Inc, pg 822
New Circuit Films LLC, pg 839
On-Trax Inc, pg 846
Pacific Media, pg 849
PM Productions, pg 858
Point of View Productions, pg 858
Prime Cut Productions, pg 862
Producers Group Ltd, pg 863
QRS Software Services, pg 867
Regent Press Publishers & Printers, pg 873
Sea Studios Foundation, pg 883
Steve Shapiro Music, pg 885
Still N' Motion, pg 901
Studio 132, pg 902
Timestream Video, pg 914
Total Creative, pg 916
Wavemaker Media Design, pg 934
Webster Communications, pg 935
Zamacona Productions, pg 945

COLORADO
Apogee Communications Group, pg 687
Tim Cissell Music, pg 725
Daylight Productions & Rentals, pg 739
Flashback Media Productions, pg 762
Shambhala Publications, pg 885
Starwest Productions, pg 900
Tatum Video, pg 907

CONNECTICUT
ACM Productions Ltd, pg 674
Essex Television Group Inc, pg 755
The Gary-Paul Agency, pg 768
P&P Studios Inc, pg 851
Save the Children Federation Inc, pg 881
UConn Health Multimedia Services, pg 920

DISTRICT OF COLUMBIA
Hillmann & Carr Inc, pg 780

FLORIDA
Blackburst Entertainment LLC, pg 706
Communications Concepts Inc (CCI), pg 729
Courter Films LLC, pg 732
LHV Audio Services, pg 807
Roger Scruggs Films, pg 883
Sunfire Communications Inc, pg 904
Sunrise Studios, pg 904

GEORGIA
Guerrilla Productions LLC, pg 774

HAWAII
Media Bridge Gamekids, pg 821

IDAHO
Wide Eye Productions, pg 938

ILLINOIS
ABS Enterprises, pg 672
Jim Passin Productions, pg 852
Pepper Group, pg 854
Steven Samler Music & Sound, pg 879
Theosophical Publishing House, pg 912
20/20 Communications Inc, pg 920

INDIANA
A-V-A Video Productions, pg 671
Bright Ideas Creative Services, pg 710
Communication Ministries, pg 728
PentaVision Communications Inc, pg 854

IOWA
Educational Technology & Media Services, pg 751
Iowa State University-Information Technology Services, pg 791

KENTUCKY
Horizon Films & Media LLC, pg 781
Donna Lawrence Productions, pg 804

LOUISIANA
Digital FX Inc, pg 742
Moxie Media, pg 832

MARYLAND
CPR MultiMedia Solutions, pg 732
The Cutting Corporation, GraphicAudio® & Archival Sound Lab, pg 736
dbF a Media Company, pg 739
HighBridge Audio, pg 779
The Image Generators, pg 785
Kramer Communications Video Production, pg 801
Recorded Books Inc, an RBmedia company, pg 871
RLJ Entertainment Inc, pg 875

MASSACHUSETTS
CommCreative, pg 728
Documentary Educational Resources Inc, pg 744

PROGRAMMING — AUDIO

Documentary Producers (continued)

MASSACHUSETTS (continued)

Heliotrope Studios, pg 778
HOME Inc, pg 781
Monadnock Media Inc, pg 829
Northern Light Productions (NLP), pg 842
Penfield Productions Ltd, pg 853
Soundtrack Group, pg 895
TR Productions, pg 916

MICHIGAN

Digi Sign Design LLC, pg 741
K&R All Media Productions LLC, pg 796
K&R's Recording Studios Inc, pg 796
MessageMakers, pg 824

MINNESOTA

MastCom, pg 819
Media Loft Inc, pg 822

MISSOURI

Hardcastle Films & Video, pg 776
SOM Publishing Co, pg 892

MONTANA

High Plains Films, pg 779

NEBRASKA

Vision Maker Media, pg 930

NEVADA

DVDs4Less, pg 748
JCS Video Productions, pg 793

NEW HAMPSHIRE

Apertura, pg 686
Captain Fiddle Music & Publications, pg 716
Chip Taylor Communications LLC, pg 907

NEW JERSEY

Allegro Productions Inc, pg 680
CFP Video Productions Inc, pg 720
MiB MediaWorks, pg 825
Optisonics Productions, pg 847
Shanachie Entertainment Corp, pg 885
Suede Interactive, pg 903

NEW MEXICO

Production Outfitters, pg 864

NEW YORK

American History Workshop (NY) Inc, pg 683
Avekta Productions Inc, pg 697
Blue Barn Pictures Inc, pg 707
Broadstreet Productions LLC, pg 711
Clarity Media Group, pg 725
Thomas Craven Film Corp, pg 733
De Nonno Productions Inc (DPI), pg 739
Digital Force Ltd, pg 742
Downtown Community Television Center (DCTV), pg 746

Dyer-Bennet Records, pg 748
Fingerpaint, pg 761
Hallel Communications, pg 775
HB-Content, pg 777
Hello World Communications, pg 778
Ketchum Inc, pg 798
L A Bruell Inc, pg 802
Lavine Production Group, pg 804
Mood Creations Ltd, pg 829
Jack Morton Worldwide, pg 830
MRY, pg 832
New York Audio Productions, pg 840
The Palmer Group, pg 850
Pat Kogan Productions Inc, pg 852
David Rapkin Audio Production, pg 870
Elliot Sokolov Music, pg 892
Split Image Productions, pg 898
Spoken Arts Inc, pg 898
Suggs Media Productions Inc, pg 903
Third World Newsreel/Camera News Inc, pg 912
Timed Exposures Films, pg 914
United Nations Multimedia Resources Unit, pg 921
Videograf, pg 929
Zelman Studios Ltd, pg 945

NORTH CAROLINA

Pat Appleson Studios Inc, pg 687
Digital Rain LLC, pg 742
Trailblazer Studios®, pg 917
2BruceStudio, pg 920

OHIO

R&B Communications Inc, pg 870
Take 1 Media Services, pg 906
Vista Color Imaging Inc, pg 931

OKLAHOMA

Piper Media Services Inc, pg 857

OREGON

Ideascape Inc, pg 784
InterVision Media, pg 791
Odyssey Productions Inc, pg 844

PENNSYLVANIA

Bang! Pictures Inc, pg 701
FMP Media Solutions Inc, pg 763
Innovision Media Group, pg 788
Muderick Media, pg 833
Panta Rhei Media Inc, pg 851
Production Masters Inc (PMI), pg 864
S I Video Sales Group, pg 879
Videosmith Inc, pg 930
WQED-Multimedia, pg 942

RHODE ISLAND

Sound-FX-Design, pg 894

SOUTH CAROLINA

Stages Video Productions, pg 899

TENNESSEE

American Blackguard Inc, pg 683
Continental Film, pg 731

TEXAS

The Editing Co, pg 750
Emergency Film Group, pg 753
Omega Productions, pg 845
The Sound Lab Inc, pg 894
Sound Works, pg 894

South Coast Film & Video, pg 895
Tropikal Productions, pg 918

VIRGINIA

BES Studios, pg 704
CACI Integrated Communications, pg 713
Limelight Communications Inc, pg 808
Metro Productions, pg 824
Rocktown Media, pg 876

WASHINGTON

Getty Images, pg 770

WEST VIRGINIA

Blackwater Video Productions, pg 707

WISCONSIN

5th Floor Recording Co, pg 760
USAV Group Inc, pg 923
Watts Communications Inc, pg 934
Wisconsin Public Television, pg 940

WYOMING

Bridger Productions Inc, pg 710

ALBERTA

Black Media Works, pg 706
Global TV, pg 771

BRITISH COLUMBIA

Timeless Books, pg 914

ONTARIO

ADS Media, pg 677
Art Gallery of Ontario, pg 690
CBC/Radio-Canada, pg 717
DebsVoice, pg 739
GAPC (General Assembly Production Centre), pg 768

QUEBEC

Kerrigan Productions Inc, pg 798

Documentary Rentals

CALIFORNIA

Direct Cinema Ltd Inc, pg 743
New Line Cinema, pg 839
Point of View Productions, pg 858

MASSACHUSETTS

Documentary Educational Resources Inc, pg 744

MICHIGAN

Digi Sign Design LLC, pg 741

NEBRASKA

Vision Maker Media, pg 930

NEW HAMPSHIRE

Chip Taylor Communications LLC, pg 907

NEW JERSEY

Alden Films, pg 679

NEW YORK

Adwar Video, pg 678
Downtown Community Television Center (DCTV), pg 746
Hallel Communications, pg 775
Timed Exposures Films, pg 914

WISCONSIN

Her Own Words LLC, pg 779

BRITISH COLUMBIA

Video Out Distribution, pg 928

ONTARIO

Simply Audiobooks, pg 889

Educational Program Distributors

ARIZONA

Arizona Public Media, pg 688
CyberIconics International, pg 736
Drumbeat Indian Arts Inc, pg 747
Tom Hopkins International Inc, pg 781
Personal Achievement Institute, pg 854
TSG Publishing Foundation Inc USA, pg 919

ARKANSAS

Master Books®, pg 819

CALIFORNIA

Academy Savant, pg 672
Astronomical Society of the Pacific, pg 691
California Language Laboratories, pg 714
Clarity Sound & Light, pg 725
Crystal Pyramid Productions™, pg 735
Deja View Video, pg 740
Dialect Accent Specialists Inc, pg 741
Direct Cinema Ltd Inc, pg 743
ECONEWS (Environmental Television Series) & (Environmental Directions Radio Series), pg 750
Educational Insights, pg 750
Educational Technology Services (ETS), pg 751
Feldenkrais® Resources, pg 759
Gateways, pg 768
Bruce Goldberg Inc, pg 772
Golden State Dance Teachers Association (GSDTA), pg 772
Health Education Services, pg 778
Joyce Media Inc, pg 795
Krishnamurti Foundation of America, pg 801
LANGUAGE/30™, pg 803
Lightyear Entertainment, pg 808
Maximus Media Inc, pg 820
Medcom Inc, pg 821
monterey media inc, pg 829
Moose School Productions, pg 830
Music World/Vocal Power School, pg 834
Pacific Media, pg 849
Pacifica Radio Archives, pg 849
Paulist Productions, pg 852
QRS Software Services, pg 867
Redwood Audiobooks, pg 872
Regent Press Publishers & Printers, pg 873

Rhythms Productions (Tom Thumb Music), pg 874
Sea Studios Foundation, pg 883
Social Studies School Service, pg 891
Sodanceabit, pg 892
Sound Feelings Records, pg 894
The Wine Appreciation Guild Ltd, pg 939
The Writing Co, pg 942

COLORADO

American Educational Products LLC, pg 683
Crown Ministries International, pg 735
MakeMusic® Inc, pg 815
National Institute for Trial Advocacy (NITA), pg 836

CONNECTICUT

Scholastic Library Publishing, pg 882
Weston Woods Studios Inc, pg 936

DELAWARE

Intercollegiate Studies Institute Inc (ISI), pg 789
So Smart Productions, pg 891

DISTRICT OF COLUMBIA

American Chemical Society (ACS), pg 683
Biblical Archaeology Society (BAS), pg 705
National Council of Churches, pg 836

FLORIDA

Bisk Education, pg 706
Effective Learning Systems LLC, pg 751
I M P A C T Publishing Inc, pg 783
PAR Inc, pg 851
Potentials Unlimited, pg 860
Video Resources Software, pg 928

GEORGIA

August House Audio, pg 695
New Leaf Distributing Co, pg 839
Playback Now Inc, pg 858
School Media Associates LLC, pg 882

HAWAII

Media Bridge Gamekids, pg 821
Source School of Tantra Yoga Inc, pg 895

ILLINOIS

CCH Continuing Education, pg 718
Liturgy Training Publications, pg 810
National Safety Council (NSC), pg 836
Nightingale-Conant Corp, pg 841
Research Press, pg 873
Theosophical Publishing House, pg 912

INDIANA

Indiana University Press, pg 786
Purdue University Digital Education, pg 866

IOWA

Accelerated Learning Foundation, pg 672
Long-Term Success Publishing, pg 811
Perfection Learning Corp, pg 854

KENTUCKY

The Learning House Inc, pg 805

MAINE

Slim Goodbody Corp, pg 890

MARYLAND

Department of Education Resources, pg 740
Hearing Loss Association of America (HLAA), pg 778
HighBridge Audio, pg 779
James Agee Film Project, pg 792
Milner-Fenwick Inc, pg 828
MMI Marketing, pg 828
Nicholas P Pipino Associates Inc, pg 857
Recorded Books Inc, an RBmedia company, pg 871

MASSACHUSETTS

Brookline Books, pg 711
Cheng & Tsui Co, pg 721
Documentary Educational Resources Inc, pg 744
Pauline Books & Media, pg 852
Penfield Productions Ltd, pg 853
Ben Rudnick and Friends, pg 878
Yellow Moon Press, pg 944

MICHIGAN

Digi Sign Design LLC, pg 741
Emery-Pratt Co, pg 753
HighScope Press, pg 780
Madonna University Information Technology, pg 814
Zondervan, pg 945

MINNESOTA

EMC Publishing LLC, pg 753
Learning Strategies Corp, pg 805
Science Museum of Minnesota, pg 882

MISSOURI

Marsh Media, pg 817
Mosby Inc, pg 831
New Letters on the Air, pg 839
SOM Publishing Co, pg 892
Vedanta Society of St Louis, pg 925

MONTANA

High Plains Films, pg 779

NEBRASKA

Vision Maker Media, pg 930

NEVADA

DVDs4Less, pg 748

NEW HAMPSHIRE

Captain Fiddle Music & Publications, pg 716
French American Music Enterprises, pg 765
Chip Taylor Communications LLC, pg 907

NEW JERSEY

Allegro Productions Inc, pg 680
Jointure for Community Adult Education Inc, pg 794
Learning Ally, pg 805
Listen & Live Audio Inc, pg 809
Shanachie Entertainment Corp, pg 885

NEW MEXICO

Uncharted Country Publishing, pg 921

NEW YORK

Asia Society, pg 691
Beekman Books Inc, pg 703
Brooklyn Botanic Garden, pg 711
Cambridge University Press, pg 715
The Cinema Guild Inc, pg 724
Cross-Cultural Communications, pg 735
Dover Publications Inc, pg 746
Educational Activities Inc, pg 750
Albert Ellis Institute (AEI), pg 753
Films Media Group, pg 760
Guilford Publications, pg 774
Hallel Communications, pg 775
Homespun Video, pg 781
Janus Films Inc, pg 793
Klutz, pg 800
Listening Library, pg 810
March of Dimes Foundation, pg 816
Practising Law Institute, pg 860
Random House Children's Books, pg 870
Scholastic Media, pg 882
TeleTime Productions, pg 910
Timed Exposures Films, pg 914
Triumph Learning LLC, pg 918
United Nations Multimedia Resources Unit, pg 921
Visual Technologies Corp, pg 932
Weigl Publishers Inc, pg 935

NORTH CAROLINA

AudioSolutionz LLC, pg 695
Ladyslipper Music, pg 803
Sinclair Institute, pg 889
Thinking Maps Inc, pg 912

OHIO

Alegra House Publishers, pg 679
The American Classical League, pg 683
McGraw-Hill School Education Group, pg 821
Twin Sisters® Digital Media™, pg 920

OREGON

InterVision Media, pg 791
The Keyboard Workshop, pg 798

PENNSYLVANIA

Discovery Education - South Burlington, pg 743
FMP Media Solutions Inc, pg 763
Newtown Psychological Center, pg 840
S I Video Sales Group, pg 879

SOUTH CAROLINA

BJU Press, pg 706

SOUTH DAKOTA

Spizzirri Press Inc, pg 898

TENNESSEE

Abingdon Press, pg 672
American Blackguard Inc, pg 683
Center for Southern Folklore Inc, pg 719
Ingram Content Group LLC, pg 787
National School Products, pg 836
Spring Arbor Distributors Inc, pg 898

TEXAS

Educational Video Network, pg 751
Emergency Film Group, pg 753
Executive Development Systems Inc, pg 757
Institute of Texan Cultures, pg 788
Lamb & Lion Ministries, pg 803
Marengo Films, pg 817
Milky Way Press, pg 827
Shadow Play Records & Video, pg 885
SMI® Inc, pg 891

UTAH

San Juan School District Heritage Language Resource Center, pg 880

VERMONT

Multicultural Media Inc, pg 833
Taylor Associates, pg 907

VIRGINIA

CACI Integrated Communications, pg 713

WISCONSIN

Her Own Words LLC, pg 779
Plank Road Publishing Inc, pg 857
School Specialty Inc, pg 882

ALBERTA

Global TV, pg 771

BRITISH COLUMBIA

Thompson Rivers University Marketing & Communications Dept, pg 913
Video Out Distribution, pg 928

ONTARIO

Canadian Learning Co Inc, pg 715
CBC/Radio-Canada, pg 717
The Children's Book Store Distribution (CBSD), pg 722
Life Cycle Books Ltd, pg 807
Mind Resources Inc, pg 828
Nelson Education Ltd, pg 837
Novalis, pg 843
Wintergreen Learning Materials, pg 939

Educational Program Producers

ALABAMA

Leo Ticheli Productions, pg 913

ARIZONA

Arizona Public Media, pg 688
Candee Productions Inc, pg 716
CyberIconics International, pg 736
Drumbeat Indian Arts Inc, pg 747
Personal Achievement Institute, pg 854

PROGRAMMING — AUDIO

Educational Program Producers (continued)

ARIZONA (continued)

Teaberry, pg 908
TSG Publishing Foundation Inc USA, pg 919

ARKANSAS

Live'N'Loud, pg 810

CALIFORNIA

Academy Savant, pg 672
Ancient Future, pg 685
Astronomical Society of the Pacific, pg 691
The Banquet Sound Studios, pg 701
Big Door, pg 705
California Language Laboratories, pg 714
Clarity Sound & Light, pg 725
Creative Media Recording, pg 733
Creative Technology, pg 733
Crystal Pyramid Productions™, pg 735
Custom Video Productions Inc, pg 736
Deja View Video, pg 740
Design Media, pg 741
Dialect Accent Specialists Inc, pg 741
Direct Cinema Ltd Inc, pg 743
ECONEWS (Environmental Television Series) & (Environmental Directions Radio Series), pg 750
Educational Technology Services (ETS), pg 751
Feldenkrais® Resources, pg 759
Gateways, pg 768
Gateways Books & Tapes, pg 768
Goal Productions, pg 772
Gold Standard Productions, pg 772
Bruce Goldberg Inc, pg 772
Havas Edge, pg 777
imageReal Pictures LLC, pg 785
Joyce Media Inc, pg 795
Krishnamurti Foundation of America, pg 801
LANGUAGE/30™, pg 803
Lynch Communications, pg 813
Maximus Media Inc, pg 820
Medcom Inc, pg 821
Media Magic, pg 822
The Media Staff Inc, pg 822
Moose School Productions, pg 830
Music World/Vocal Power School, pg 834
On-Trax Inc, pg 846
Pacific Media, pg 849
Paulist Productions, pg 852
piXvfm Inc, pg 857
PM Productions, pg 858
Point of View Productions, pg 858
Prime Cut Productions, pg 862
Producers Group Ltd, pg 863
QRS Software Services, pg 867
Redwood Audiobooks, pg 872
Regent Press Publishers & Printers, pg 873
Rhythms Productions (Tom Thumb Music), pg 874
Sea Studios Foundation, pg 883
Steve Shapiro Music, pg 885
Sodanceabit, pg 892
Sound Feelings Records, pg 894
Still N' Motion, pg 901

Studio 132, pg 902
Timestream Video, pg 914
Total Creative, pg 916
Video Resources Inc, pg 928
Webster Communications, pg 935
Zamacona Productions, pg 945

COLORADO

American Educational Products LLC, pg 683
Apogee Communications Group, pg 687
Crown Ministries International, pg 735
Daylight Productions & Rentals, pg 739
Flashback Media Productions, pg 762
Jeppesen, pg 793
National Institute for Trial Advocacy (NITA), pg 836
Shambhala Publications, pg 885

CONNECTICUT

ACM Productions Ltd, pg 674
Antenna International, pg 686
Essex Television Group Inc, pg 755
The Gary-Paul Agency, pg 768
P&P Studios Inc, pg 851
Scholastic Library Publishing, pg 882
T & M Digital Services LLC, pg 906
UConn Health Multimedia Services, pg 920
Weston Woods Studios Inc, pg 936

DELAWARE

Intercollegiate Studies Institute Inc (ISI), pg 789
So Smart Productions, pg 891

DISTRICT OF COLUMBIA

American Chemical Society (ACS), pg 683
Biblical Archaeology Society (BAS), pg 705
Hillmann & Carr Inc, pg 780

FLORIDA

Audacity Recording Studios, pg 693
Audio Visual Imagineering Inc, pg 694
Bisk Education, pg 706
Communications Concepts Inc (CCI), pg 729
Courter Films LLC, pg 732
Effective Learning Systems LLC, pg 751
I M P A C T Publishing Inc, pg 783
LHV Audio Services, pg 807
Potentials Unlimited, pg 860
Sunfire Communications Inc, pg 904
Sunrise Studios, pg 904
Tricycle Studios, pg 918
Video Resources Software, pg 928

GEORGIA

August House Audio, pg 695
Guerrilla Productions LLC, pg 774
Playback Now Inc, pg 858
WaveGuide Studios, pg 934

HAWAII

Media Bridge Gamekids, pg 821
Source School of Tantra Yoga Inc, pg 895

IDAHO

Wide Eye Productions, pg 938

ILLINOIS

ABS Enterprises, pg 672
Accenture, pg 672
Audiobook Department, pg 695
CCH Continuing Education, pg 718
CCore Media Inc, pg 718
Esoteric Sound, pg 755
Liturgy Training Publications, pg 810
Major Media Productions Inc, pg 815
Manning Productions, pg 816
Multimedia Marketing Group, pg 833
Nightingale-Conant Corp, pg 841
Jim Passin Productions, pg 852
Pepper Group, pg 854
PSAV® Presentation Services (Hotel Services Division), pg 866
Rand McNally Education, pg 870
Research Press, pg 873
Theosophical Publishing House, pg 912
Video Impressions, pg 928

INDIANA

A-V-A Video Productions, pg 671
Bright Ideas Creative Services, pg 710
OMNI Productions, pg 845
PentaVision Communications Inc, pg 854
Purdue University Digital Education, pg 866

IOWA

Accelerated Learning Foundation, pg 672
Educational Technology & Media Services, pg 751
Hedquist Productions Inc, pg 778
Iowa State University-Information Technology Services, pg 791
Long-Term Success Publishing, pg 811

KENTUCKY

Donna Lawrence Productions, pg 804
The Learning House Inc, pg 805
National Geographic Learning, pg 836

LOUISIANA

Digital FX Inc, pg 742

MAINE

Slim Goodbody Corp, pg 890

MARYLAND

CPR MultiMedia Solutions, pg 732
The Cutting Corporation, GraphicAudio® & Archival Sound Lab, pg 736
dbF a Media Company, pg 739
Department of Education Resources, pg 740
HighBridge Audio, pg 779
The Image Generators, pg 785
James Agee Film Project, pg 792
Kramer Communications Video Production, pg 801
Milner-Fenwick Inc, pg 828
MMI Marketing, pg 828
Recorded Books Inc, an RBmedia company, pg 871

MASSACHUSETTS

Cheng & Tsui Co, pg 721
CommCreative, pg 728
Documentary Educational Resources Inc, pg 744
Heliotrope Studios, pg 778
HOME Inc, pg 781
Monadnock Media Inc, pg 829
Pauline Books & Media, pg 852
Penfield Productions Ltd, pg 853
Soundtrack Group, pg 895
TR Productions, pg 916

MICHIGAN

Digi Sign Design LLC, pg 741
HighScope Press, pg 780
International Tae Kwon Do Association (ITA Institute), pg 790
K&R All Media Productions LLC, pg 796
K&R's Recording Studios Inc, pg 796
Madonna University Information Technology, pg 814
MessageMakers, pg 824
TGA Recording Co, pg 911
University of Michigan, Center for Middle Eastern & North African Studies, pg 923
Zondervan, pg 945

MINNESOTA

EMC Publishing LLC, pg 753
Learning Strategies Corp, pg 805
MastCom, pg 819
Science Museum of Minnesota, pg 882

MISSOURI

Audio-VideoGraphics Inc, pg 694
Hardcastle Films & Video, pg 776
Marsh Media, pg 817
Mosby Inc, pg 831
New Letters on the Air, pg 839
SOM Publishing Co, pg 892
Vedanta Society of St Louis, pg 925

MONTANA

High Plains Films, pg 779

NEBRASKA

AdventSource, pg 678
Vision Maker Media, pg 930

NEVADA

DVDs4Less, pg 748
JCS Video Productions, pg 793
Tetrahedron LLC, pg 911

NEW HAMPSHIRE

Academic & Campus Technology Services, pg 672
Apertura, pg 686
Captain Fiddle Music & Publications, pg 716
Chip Taylor Communications LLC, pg 907

NEW JERSEY

Allegro Productions Inc, pg 680
Audio Vistas LLC, pg 694
Broadcast Center Studios, pg 710
CFP Video Productions Inc, pg 720
C2 Imaging, pg 735
Laurel Video Productions, pg 804

Learning Ally, pg 805
Listen & Live Audio Inc, pg 809
MiB MediaWorks, pg 825
Optisonics Productions, pg 847
Shanachie Entertainment Corp, pg 885
Suede Interactive, pg 903

NEW MEXICO

Lannan Foundation, pg 803
Production Outfitters, pg 864
Rainbow International, pg 869
Uncharted Country Publishing, pg 921

NEW YORK

American History Workshop (NY) Inc, pg 683
Asia Society, pg 691
Avekta Productions Inc, pg 697
Blue Barn Pictures Inc, pg 707
Broadstreet Productions LLC, pg 711
Brooklyn Botanic Garden, pg 711
Thomas Craven Film Corp, pg 733
Cross-Cultural Communications, pg 735
Digital Force Ltd, pg 742
Downtown Community Television Center (DCTV), pg 746
Dyer-Bennet Records, pg 748
Educational Activities Inc, pg 750
Albert Ellis Institute (AEI), pg 753
Eye on Dance, pg 758
Films Media Group, pg 760
Fingerpaint, pg 761
Guilford Publications, pg 774
Hallel Communications, pg 775
Hello World Communications, pg 778
Homespun Video, pg 781
Human Relations Media, pg 782
Icontent, pg 783
Ketchum Inc, pg 798
Klutz, pg 800
L A Bruell Inc, pg 802
Lavine Production Group, pg 804
Listening Library, pg 810
March of Dimes Foundation, pg 816
Mark Custom Recording Service Inc, pg 817
Jack Morton Worldwide, pg 830
MRY, pg 832
New York Audio Productions, pg 840
The Palmer Group, pg 850
Pat Kogan Productions Inc, pg 852
Practising Law Institute, pg 860
Random House Children's Books, pg 870
David Rapkin Audio Production, pg 870
Elliot Sokolov Music, pg 892
Split Image Productions, pg 898
Spoken Arts Inc, pg 898
Suggs Media Productions Inc, pg 903
Tiki Recording Studios Inc, pg 914
Timed Exposures Films, pg 914
Triumph Learning LLC, pg 918
United Nations Multimedia Resources Unit, pg 921
Videograf, pg 929
Weigl Publishers Inc, pg 935
WorldView Software, pg 941
Zelman Studios Ltd, pg 945

NORTH CAROLINA

Pat Appleson Studios Inc, pg 687
AudioSolutionz LLC, pg 695
The Communications Group Inc, pg 729

Digital Rain LLC, pg 742
The International Society of Automation (ISA), pg 790
Sinclair Institute, pg 889
World Class Learning Materials Inc, pg 941

OHIO

Advent Media Inc, pg 677
Alegra House Publishers, pg 679
Cuyahoga Community College Student Production Office (SPO), pg 736
McGraw-Hill School Education Group, pg 821
Musicol Recording, pg 835
Take 1 Media Services, pg 906
Twin Sisters® Digital Media™, pg 920
Vista Color Imaging Inc, pg 931

OKLAHOMA

Academic Media & Digital Services, pg 672
Piper Media Services Inc, pg 857

OREGON

ADD Plus, pg 676
ERA Learning, pg 755
Ideascape Inc, pg 784
InterVision Media, pg 791
The Keyboard Workshop, pg 798
KTVA Productions, pg 802
Odyssey Productions Inc, pg 844

PENNSYLVANIA

American Artist Studio, pg 682
Discovery Education - South Burlington, pg 743
FMP Media Solutions Inc, pg 763
Forge Recording LLC, pg 764
Innovision Media Group, pg 788
JPL, pg 795
Kensington Falls Animation, pg 797
Newtown Psychological Center, pg 840
Panta Rhei Media Inc, pg 851
Production Masters Inc (PMI), pg 864
Fred Rogers Productions, pg 876
S I Video Sales Group, pg 879
The Videohouse Inc, pg 929
Videosmith Inc, pg 930
WQED-Multimedia, pg 942

RHODE ISLAND

Sound-FX-Design, pg 894

SOUTH CAROLINA

BJU Press, pg 706
Venture Media, pg 925

TENNESSEE

Abingdon Press, pg 672
American Blackguard Inc, pg 683
Continental Film, pg 731
Memphis Communications Corp, pg 823

TEXAS

AMA Nystrom Printing/Finishing, pg 682
The Editing Co, pg 750
Educational Video Network, pg 751
Emergency Film Group, pg 753
Epic Software Group Inc, pg 755
Institute of Texan Cultures, pg 788
Lamb & Lion Ministries, pg 803

Matson Multi-Media, pg 820
Milky Way Press, pg 827
Omega Productions, pg 845
Romar Learning Solutions LLC, pg 877
Shadow Play Records & Video, pg 885
SMI® Inc, pg 891
The Sound Lab Inc, pg 894
Sound Works, pg 894
South Coast Film & Video, pg 895
Stage Directions, pg 898
Texas Heart Institute Visual Communication Services, pg 911
Tropikal Productions, pg 918
Writer's AudioShop/Davenport Productions, pg 942

UTAH

San Juan School District Heritage Language Resource Center, pg 880

VIRGINIA

BES Studios, pg 704
CACI Integrated Communications, pg 713
Limelight Communications Inc, pg 808
Metro Productions, pg 824
National Media Services Inc, pg 836
Rocktown Media, pg 876

WASHINGTON

Center for Touch Drawing, pg 719

WEST VIRGINIA

Blackwater Video Productions, pg 707

WISCONSIN

5th Floor Recording Co, pg 760
Knowledge Unlimited Inc, pg 800
Meridian Studios, pg 824
Plank Road Publishing Inc, pg 857
USAV Group Inc, pg 923
Watts Communications Inc, pg 934
Wisconsin Public Television, pg 940

WYOMING

Bridger Productions Inc, pg 710

ALBERTA

Black Media Works, pg 706

BRITISH COLUMBIA

Thompson Rivers University Marketing & Communications Dept, pg 913
Video Out Distribution, pg 928

ONTARIO

ADS Media, pg 677
Art Gallery of Ontario, pg 690
CBC/Radio-Canada, pg 717
DebsVoice, pg 739
Nelson Education Ltd, pg 837
Novalis, pg 843
Pearson Education Canada, pg 852

QUEBEC

Les Editions CEC Inc, pg 750
Kerrigan Productions, pg 798

Educational Program Rentals

ARIZONA

Arizona Public Media, pg 688

CALIFORNIA

Direct Cinema Ltd Inc, pg 743
ECONEWS (Environmental Television Series) & (Environmental Directions Radio Series), pg 750
Educational Technology Services (ETS), pg 751
Medcom Inc, pg 821
Paulist Productions, pg 852
Point of View Productions, pg 858

MARYLAND

James Agee Film Project, pg 792

MASSACHUSETTS

Documentary Educational Resources Inc, pg 744

MICHIGAN

Digi Sign Design LLC, pg 741

NEBRASKA

Vision Maker Media, pg 930

NEW HAMPSHIRE

Chip Taylor Communications LLC, pg 907

NEW JERSEY

Alden Films, pg 679
Listen & Live Audio Inc, pg 809

NEW YORK

Brooklyn Botanic Garden, pg 711
Downtown Community Television Center (DCTV), pg 746
Hallel Communications, pg 775
Timed Exposures Films, pg 914

WISCONSIN

Her Own Words LLC, pg 779

ONTARIO

Simply Audiobooks, pg 889

Feature Program Distributors

CALIFORNIA

Direct Cinema Ltd Inc, pg 743
Bruce Goldberg Inc, pg 772
Jaguar Distribution Corp, pg 792
Maximus Media Inc, pg 820
Moose School Productions, pg 830
New Line Cinema, pg 839
Pacific Media, pg 849
Pacifica Radio Archives, pg 849
Palardo Productions, pg 850
Publishers Group West (PGW), an Ingram brand, pg 866
QRS Software Services, pg 867
Varese Sarabande Records Inc, pg 924
Warner Home Video Inc, pg 934

PROGRAMMING — AUDIO

Feature Program Distributors (continued)

DELAWARE

Intercollegiate Studies Institute Inc (ISI), pg 789

ILLINOIS

CCore Media Inc, pg 718

IOWA

American Visions, pg 684
Right Stuf Inc, pg 875

MARYLAND

HighBridge Audio, pg 779
Recorded Books Inc, an RBmedia company, pg 871

MISSOURI

SOM Publishing Co, pg 892

MONTANA

High Plains Films, pg 779

NEBRASKA

Vision Maker Media, pg 930

NEVADA

DVDs4Less, pg 748

NEW HAMPSHIRE

Chip Taylor Communications LLC, pg 907

NEW YORK

The Cinema Guild Inc, pg 724
Albert Ellis Institute (AEI), pg 753
HarperAudio, pg 776
HB-Content, pg 777
Janus Films Inc, pg 793
RadioArt/Bob & Ray CDs & MP3 Files, pg 869
Simon & Schuster, Inc, pg 888
Synaptic Digital, pg 905

OREGON

InterVision Media, pg 791

TENNESSEE

American Blackguard Inc, pg 683
Ingram Content Group LLC, pg 787
Spring Arbor Distributors Inc, pg 898

VIRGINIA

CACI Integrated Communications, pg 713

ALBERTA

Global TV, pg 771

ONTARIO

CBC/Radio-Canada, pg 717
Life Cycle Books Ltd, pg 807

Feature Program Producers

ARIZONA

Disney Consumer Products & Interactive Media (DCPI), pg 743

ARKANSAS

Live'N'Loud, pg 810

CALIFORNIA

The Banquet Sound Studios, pg 701
Big Door, pg 705
Catapult Films Inc, pg 717
Creative Technology, pg 733
Custom Video Productions Inc, pg 736
Direct Cinema Ltd Inc, pg 743
Bruce Goldberg Inc, pg 772
imageReal Pictures LLC, pg 785
Jaguar Distribution Corp, pg 792
Lynch Communications, pg 813
Maximus Media Inc, pg 820
Moose School Productions, pg 830
New Line Cinema, pg 839
Pacific Media, pg 849
Palardo Productions, pg 850
PM Productions, pg 858
Producers Group Ltd, pg 863
QRS Software Services, pg 867
Studio 132, pg 902
Total Creative, pg 916
Video Resources Inc, pg 928
Webster Communications, pg 935

COLORADO

Tim Cissell Music, pg 725
Shambhala Publications, pg 885
Starwest Productions, pg 900
Tatum Video, pg 907

CONNECTICUT

Essex Television Group Inc, pg 755
The Gary-Paul Agency, pg 768

FLORIDA

Blackburst Entertainment LLC, pg 706
Chatterbox Productions Inc, pg 721
Communications Concepts Inc (CCI), pg 729
Courter Films LLC, pg 732
LHV Audio Services, pg 807
Sunfire Communications Inc, pg 904

GEORGIA

Guerrilla Productions LLC, pg 774

IDAHO

Wide Eye Productions, pg 938

ILLINOIS

CCore Media Inc, pg 718
Pepper Group, pg 854

INDIANA

A-V-A Video Productions, pg 671

IOWA

American Visions, pg 684
Right Stuf Inc, pg 875

MARYLAND

The Cutting Corporation, GraphicAudio® & Archival Sound Lab, pg 736
dbF a Media Company, pg 739
HighBridge Audio, pg 779
Kramer Communications Video Production, pg 801
Recorded Books Inc, an RBmedia company, pg 871

MASSACHUSETTS

Heliotrope Studios, pg 778
Monadnock Media Inc, pg 829
Penfield Productions Ltd, pg 853
Soundtrack Group, pg 895

MICHIGAN

K&R All Media Productions LLC, pg 796
K&R's Recording Studios Inc, pg 796

MISSOURI

SOM Publishing Co, pg 892

MONTANA

High Plains Films, pg 779

NEBRASKA

AdventSource, pg 678

NEVADA

DVDs4Less, pg 748

NEW HAMPSHIRE

Chip Taylor Communications LLC, pg 907

NEW JERSEY

CFP Video Productions Inc, pg 720
MiB MediaWorks, pg 825
Optisonics Productions, pg 847
Suede Interactive, pg 903

NEW MEXICO

Production Outfitters, pg 864

NEW YORK

Big Fish Production US, pg 705
Broadstreet Productions LLC, pg 711
CompuWeather Inc, pg 729
Digital Force Ltd, pg 742
Albert Ellis Institute (AEI), pg 753
HarperAudio, pg 776
HB-Content, pg 777
Jack Morton Worldwide, pg 830
The Palmer Group, pg 850
David Rapkin Audio Production, pg 870
Simon & Schuster, Inc, pg 888
Elliot Sokolov Music, pg 892
Split Image Productions, pg 898
Suggs Media Productions Inc, pg 903
Synaptic Digital, pg 905
Zelman Studios Ltd, pg 945

NORTH CAROLINA

Digital Rain LLC, pg 742
Trailblazer Studios®, pg 917
2BruceStudio, pg 920

OHIO

R&B Communications Inc, pg 870
Vista Color Imaging Inc, pg 931

OKLAHOMA

Piper Media Services Inc, pg 857

OREGON

Ideascape Inc, pg 784
InterVision Media, pg 791

PENNSYLVANIA

Innovision Media Group, pg 788
WQED-Multimedia, pg 942

RHODE ISLAND

Sound-FX-Design, pg 894

TENNESSEE

American Blackguard Inc, pg 683

TEXAS

Cinestate, pg 724
Educational Video Network, pg 751
Emergency Film Group, pg 753
Omega Productions, pg 845
The Sound Lab Inc, pg 894
Sound Works, pg 894

VIRGINIA

BES Studios, pg 704
CACI Integrated Communications, pg 713
Metro Productions, pg 824

WISCONSIN

5th Floor Recording Co, pg 760
Knowledge Unlimited Inc, pg 800
Wisconsin Public Television, pg 940

WYOMING

Bridger Productions Inc, pg 710

ALBERTA

Global TV, pg 771

ONTARIO

ADS Media, pg 677
CBC/Radio-Canada, pg 717

QUEBEC

Kerrigan Productions Inc, pg 798

Feature Program Rentals

CALIFORNIA

Direct Cinema Ltd Inc, pg 743
New Line Cinema, pg 839
Palardo Productions, pg 850

NEBRASKA

Vision Maker Media, pg 930

NEW HAMPSHIRE

Chip Taylor Communications LLC, pg 907

NEW YORK

Adwar Video, pg 678

Foreign Program Distributors

ARIZONA

Drumbeat Indian Arts Inc, pg 747

CALIFORNIA

Jaguar Distribution Corp, pg 792
LANGUAGE/30™, pg 803
Maximus Media Inc, pg 820
Pacifica Radio Archives, pg 849
QRS Software Services, pg 867
Warner Home Video Inc, pg 934

DISTRICT OF COLUMBIA

Biblical Archaeology Society
(BAS), pg 705

MARYLAND

Recorded Books Inc, an RBmedia
company, pg 871

MASSACHUSETTS

Documentary Educational Resources
Inc, pg 744

MICHIGAN

Digi Sign Design LLC, pg 741

NEW HAMPSHIRE

Chip Taylor Communications LLC,
pg 907

NEW YORK

Applause Learning Resources,
pg 687
Beekman Books Inc, pg 703
The Cinema Guild Inc, pg 724
Cross-Cultural Communications,
pg 735
Dover Publications Inc, pg 746
Hallel Communications, pg 775
Janus Films Inc, pg 793
Live Oak Media, pg 810
SISU Home Entertainment Inc,
pg 889

NORTH CAROLINA

Ladyslipper Music, pg 803

PENNSYLVANIA

FMP Media Solutions Inc, pg 763
S I Video Sales Group, pg 879

TENNESSEE

Ingram Content Group LLC, pg 787
Spring Arbor Distributors Inc,
pg 898

TEXAS

Educational Video Network, pg 751

VERMONT

Trafalgar Square Books, pg 916

WISCONSIN

Plank Road Publishing Inc, pg 857

ALBERTA

Global TV, pg 771

BRITISH COLUMBIA

Video Out Distribution, pg 928

Foreign Program Producers

CALIFORNIA

Ancient Future, pg 685
Creative Technology, pg 733
Custom Video Productions Inc,
pg 736
Jaguar Distribution Corp, pg 792
LANGUAGE/30™, pg 803
Lynch Communications, pg 813
Prime Cut Productions, pg 862
Producers Group Ltd, pg 863
QRS Software Services, pg 867
Studio 132, pg 902
Total Creative, pg 916

COLORADO

Tim Cissell Music, pg 725

DISTRICT OF COLUMBIA

Biblical Archaeology Society
(BAS), pg 705
Hillmann & Carr Inc, pg 780

FLORIDA

Blackburst Entertainment LLC,
pg 706
Courter Films LLC, pg 732
LHV Audio Services, pg 807
Sunfire Communications Inc,
pg 904

GEORGIA

Guerrilla Productions LLC, pg 774

IDAHO

Wide Eye Productions, pg 938

ILLINOIS

ABS Enterprises, pg 672
Pepper Group, pg 854

INDIANA

A-V-A Video Productions, pg 671

IOWA

Right Stuf Inc, pg 875

MARYLAND

The Cutting Corporation,
GraphicAudio® & Archival
Sound Lab, pg 736
Recorded Books Inc, an RBmedia
company, pg 871

MASSACHUSETTS

Documentary Educational Resources
Inc, pg 744
Heliotrope Studios, pg 778
Penfield Productions Ltd, pg 853
Soundtrack Group, pg 895

MICHIGAN

Digi Sign Design LLC, pg 741
K&R All Media Productions LLC,
pg 796
K&R's Recording Studios Inc,
pg 796

MINNESOTA

MastCom, pg 819

NEW HAMPSHIRE

Apertura, pg 686
Chip Taylor Communications LLC,
pg 907

NEW JERSEY

CFP Video Productions Inc, pg 720
MiB MediaWorks, pg 825
Suede Interactive, pg 903

NEW YORK

Applause Learning Resources,
pg 687
Avekta Productions Inc, pg 697
Cross-Cultural Communications,
pg 735
Digital Force Ltd, pg 742
Downtown Community Television
Center (DCTV), pg 746
Fingerpaint, pg 761
Hallel Communications, pg 775
Live Oak Media, pg 810
Jack Morton Worldwide, pg 830
New York Audio Productions,
pg 840
The Palmer Group, pg 850
SISU Home Entertainment Inc,
pg 889
Split Image Productions, pg 898
Spoken Arts Inc, pg 898
Zelman Studios Ltd, pg 945

NORTH CAROLINA

Pat Appleson Studios Inc, pg 687

OHIO

Vista Color Imaging Inc, pg 931

OKLAHOMA

Piper Media Services Inc, pg 857

PENNSYLVANIA

FMP Media Solutions Inc, pg 763

RHODE ISLAND

Sound-FX-Design, pg 894

TEXAS

Omega Productions, pg 845
Omni Intercommunications Inc,
pg 845
Romar Learning Solutions LLC,
pg 877
The Sound Lab Inc, pg 894
Tropikal Productions, pg 918

VERMONT

Inner Traditions International,
pg 788

WASHINGTON

Kostov Productions, pg 801

WISCONSIN

5th Floor Recording Co, pg 760
Wisconsin Public Television, pg 940

WYOMING

Bridger Productions Inc, pg 710

QUEBEC

Kerrigan Productions Inc, pg 798

Foreign Program Rentals

CALIFORNIA

New Line Cinema, pg 839

MASSACHUSETTS

Documentary Educational Resources
Inc, pg 744

MICHIGAN

Digi Sign Design LLC, pg 741

NEW HAMPSHIRE

Chip Taylor Communications LLC,
pg 907

NEW JERSEY

Alden Films, pg 679

NEW YORK

Downtown Community Television
Center (DCTV), pg 746
Hallel Communications, pg 775

BRITISH COLUMBIA

Video Out Distribution, pg 928

ONTARIO

Simply Audiobooks, pg 889

Government Program Distributors

CALIFORNIA

Direct Cinema Ltd Inc, pg 743
Maximus Media Inc, pg 820
QRS Software Services, pg 867

FLORIDA

Bisk Education, pg 706

ILLINOIS

CCH Inc, A Wolters Kluwer
business, pg 718
CCore Media Inc, pg 718
Cool-Lux, pg 731

MARYLAND

Recorded Books Inc, an RBmedia
company, pg 871
Special Archives Division, Motion
Picture Branch, pg 896

MICHIGAN

Digi Sign Design LLC, pg 741

MONTANA

Jereco Studios Inc, pg 793

NEVADA

DVDs4Less, pg 748

NEW HAMPSHIRE

Chip Taylor Communications LLC,
pg 907

NEW JERSEY

Allegro Productions Inc, pg 680

PROGRAMMING — AUDIO

Government Program Distributors (continued)

NEW YORK

Films Media Group, pg 760
Janus Films Inc, pg 793
Synaptic Digital, pg 905
Visual Technologies Corp, pg 932

OHIO

Curtis Inc, pg 736

OREGON

InterVision Media, pg 791

PENNSYLVANIA

FMP Media Solutions Inc, pg 763

VIRGINIA

CACI Integrated Communications, pg 713
CDR Communications Inc, pg 719

Government Program Producers

CALIFORNIA

Creative Media Recording, pg 733
Creative Technology, pg 733
Custom Video Productions Inc, pg 736
Design Media, pg 741
Direct Cinema Ltd Inc, pg 743
Havas Edge, pg 777
Jaguar Distribution Corp, pg 792
Lynch Communications, pg 813
Maximus Media Inc, pg 820
The Media Staff Inc, pg 822
On-Trax Inc, pg 846
piXvfm Inc, pg 857
PM Productions, pg 858
QRS Software Services, pg 867
Steve Shapiro Music, pg 885
Still N' Motion, pg 901
Studio 132, pg 902
Total Creative, pg 916

COLORADO

Daylight Productions & Rentals, pg 739
Flashback Media Productions, pg 762
Tatum Video, pg 907

CONNECTICUT

UConn Health Multimedia Services, pg 920

DISTRICT OF COLUMBIA

Hillmann & Carr Inc, pg 780

FLORIDA

Audio Visual Imagineering Inc, pg 694
Bisk Education, pg 706
Blackburst Entertainment LLC, pg 706
Communications Concepts Inc (CCI), pg 729
Courter Films LLC, pg 732
LHV Audio Services, pg 807

Sunfire Communications Inc, pg 904
Sunrise Studios, pg 904

GEORGIA

Guerrilla Productions LLC, pg 774

IDAHO

Wide Eye Productions, pg 938

ILLINOIS

ABS Enterprises, pg 672
Accenture, pg 672
CCH Inc, A Wolters Kluwer business, pg 718
CCore Media Inc, pg 718
Pepper Group, pg 854
Video Impressions, pg 928

INDIANA

A-V-A Video Productions, pg 671
OMNI Productions, pg 845

IOWA

Educational Technology & Media Services, pg 751

LOUISIANA

Moxie Media, pg 832

MARYLAND

CPR MultiMedia Solutions, pg 732
The Cutting Corporation, GraphicAudio® & Archival Sound Lab, pg 736
dbF a Media Company, pg 739
The Image Generators, pg 785
Kramer Communications Video Production, pg 801
Milner-Fenwick Inc, pg 828
Recorded Books Inc, an RBmedia company, pg 871

MASSACHUSETTS

Monadnock Media Inc, pg 829
Penfield Productions Ltd, pg 853
Soundtrack Group, pg 895
TR Productions, pg 916

MICHIGAN

Digi Sign Design LLC, pg 741
K&R All Media Productions LLC, pg 796
K&R's Recording Studios Inc, pg 796
MessageMakers, pg 824

MINNESOTA

MastCom, pg 819

MISSOURI

Audio-VideoGraphics Inc, pg 694
Hardcastle Films & Video, pg 776

MONTANA

Jereco Studios Inc, pg 793

NEVADA

DVDs4Less, pg 748
JCS Video Productions, pg 793

NEW HAMPSHIRE

Apertura, pg 686
Chip Taylor Communications LLC, pg 907

NEW JERSEY

Allegro Productions Inc, pg 680
CFP Video Productions Inc, pg 720
C2 Imaging, pg 735
MiB MediaWorks, pg 825
Optisonics Productions, pg 847
Suede Interactive, pg 903

NEW YORK

Avekta Productions Inc, pg 697
Thomas Craven Film Corp, pg 733
Digital Force Ltd, pg 742
Ketchum Inc, pg 798
Mood Creations Ltd, pg 829
Jack Morton Worldwide, pg 830
MRY, pg 832
New York Audio Productions, pg 840
The Palmer Group, pg 850
Split Image Productions, pg 898
Suggs Media Productions Inc, pg 903
Synaptic Digital, pg 905
Zelman Studios Ltd, pg 945

NORTH CAROLINA

Pat Appleson Studios Inc, pg 687
Digital Rain LLC, pg 742
2BruceStudio, pg 920

OHIO

Curtis Inc, pg 736
R&B Communications Inc, pg 870
Take 1 Media Services, pg 906
Vista Color Imaging Inc, pg 931

OKLAHOMA

Academic Media & Digital Services, pg 672
Piper Media Services Inc, pg 857

OREGON

ERA Learning, pg 755
Ideascape Inc, pg 784
InterVision Media, pg 791
KTVA Productions, pg 802
Odyssey Productions Inc, pg 844

PENNSYLVANIA

Audio Visual Communications Inc, pg 694
FMP Media Solutions Inc, pg 763
JPL, pg 795

RHODE ISLAND

Sound-FX-Design, pg 894

SOUTH CAROLINA

Venture Media, pg 925

TENNESSEE

Continental Film, pg 731
Memphis Communications Corp, pg 823

TEXAS

The Editing Co, pg 750
Emergency Film Group, pg 753
Epic Software Group Inc, pg 755
Omega Productions, pg 845
Romar Learning Solutions LLC, pg 877
The Sound Lab Inc, pg 894
Sound Works, pg 894
South Coast Film & Video, pg 895
Stage Directions, pg 898

VIRGINIA

BES Studios, pg 704
CACI Integrated Communications, pg 713
CDR Communications Inc, pg 719
Limelight Communications Inc, pg 808
Metro Productions, pg 824
National Media Services Inc, pg 836
Rocktown Media, pg 876

WASHINGTON

Kostov Productions, pg 801

WEST VIRGINIA

Blackwater Video Productions, pg 707

WISCONSIN

5th Floor Recording Co, pg 760
Meridian Studios, pg 824
USAV Group Inc, pg 923
Watts Communications Inc, pg 934
Wisconsin Public Television, pg 940

WYOMING

Bridger Productions Inc, pg 710

ALBERTA

Black Media Works, pg 706

ONTARIO

DebsVoice, pg 739
GAPC (General Assembly Production Centre), pg 768

QUEBEC

Kerrigan Productions Inc, pg 798

Government Program Rentals

CALIFORNIA

Direct Cinema Ltd Inc, pg 743

MICHIGAN

Digi Sign Design LLC, pg 741

NEW HAMPSHIRE

Chip Taylor Communications LLC, pg 907

UTAH

Webb Audio Visual, pg 935

Industrial Program Distributors

CALIFORNIA

Academy Savant, pg 672
Deja View Video, pg 740
Maximus Media Inc, pg 820
QRS Software Services, pg 867
The Wine Appreciation Guild Ltd, pg 939

FLORIDA

Video Resources Software, pg 928

GEORGIA

Convergent Media Systems, pg 731

PROGRAMMING — AUDIO

Industrial Program Producers (continued)

NORTH CAROLINA (continued)

PACE Worldwide, pg 849
Sinclair Institute, pg 889
Trailblazer Studios®, pg 917
2BruceStudio, pg 920

OHIO

Curtis Inc, pg 736
Cuyahoga Community College Student Production Office (SPO), pg 736
R&B Communications Inc, pg 870
Take 1 Media Services, pg 906
Vista Color Imaging Inc, pg 931

OKLAHOMA

Piper Media Services Inc, pg 857

OREGON

Ideascape Inc, pg 784
InterVision Media, pg 791
KTVA Productions, pg 802
Odyssey Productions Inc, pg 844

PENNSYLVANIA

Audio Visual Communications Inc, pg 694
FMP Media Solutions Inc, pg 763
Forge Recording LLC, pg 764
JPL, pg 795
Kensington Falls Animation, pg 797
Muderick Media, pg 833
Newtown Psychological Center, pg 840
Panta Rhei Media Inc, pg 851
Production Masters Inc (PMI), pg 864
Videosmith Inc, pg 930
Visual Sound Inc, pg 931
WQED-Multimedia, pg 942

RHODE ISLAND

Sound-FX-Design, pg 894

SOUTH CAROLINA

DaviSound, pg 739
Stages Video Productions, pg 899
Venture Media, pg 925

TENNESSEE

Continental Film, pg 731
Memphis Communications Corp, pg 823

TEXAS

AMA Nystrom Printing/Finishing, pg 682
Dykeman Associates Inc, pg 748
The Editing Co, pg 750
Emergency Film Group, pg 753
Epic Software Group Inc, pg 755
Omega Productions, pg 845
Romar Learning Solutions LLC, pg 877
The Sound Lab Inc, pg 894
Sound Works, pg 894
South Coast Film & Video, pg 895
Stage Directions, pg 898
Tropikal Productions, pg 918

VIRGINIA

Advance Concepts Inc, pg 677
BES Studios, pg 704
CACI Integrated Communications, pg 713
Limelight Communications Inc, pg 808
Metro Productions, pg 824
National Media Services Inc, pg 836
Rocktown Media, pg 876
Studio Center Corp, pg 902

WASHINGTON

Getty Images, pg 770
Hamilton Studio, pg 775
Kostov Productions, pg 801

WEST VIRGINIA

Blackwater Video Productions, pg 707

WISCONSIN

5th Floor Recording Co, pg 760
Meridian Studios, pg 824
USAV Group Inc, pg 923
Video Wisconsin Inc, pg 929
Watts Communications Inc, pg 934
Wisconsin Public Television, pg 940

WYOMING

Bridger Productions Inc, pg 710

ALBERTA

Black Media Works, pg 706

BRITISH COLUMBIA

Thompson Rivers University Marketing & Communications Dept, pg 913

ONTARIO

ADS Media, pg 677
DebsVoice, pg 739
GAPC (General Assembly Production Centre), pg 768

QUEBEC

Kerrigan Productions Inc, pg 798

Industrial Program Rentals

CALIFORNIA

Direct Cinema Ltd Inc, pg 743

GEORGIA

Convergent Media Systems, pg 731

ILLINOIS

Creative Technology (CT), pg 733

MASSACHUSETTS

Preston Productions Inc, pg 861

MICHIGAN

Digi Sign Design LLC, pg 741

NEW HAMPSHIRE

Chip Taylor Communications LLC, pg 907

NEW JERSEY

Alden Films, pg 679

UTAH

Webb Audio Visual, pg 935

ONTARIO

Simply Audiobooks, pg 889

Literature, *see* Feature Program

Medical Program Distributors

CALIFORNIA

Academy Savant, pg 672
Educational Technology Services (ETS), pg 751
Bruce Goldberg Inc, pg 772
Joyce Media Inc, pg 795
Maximus Media Inc, pg 820
Moose School Productions, pg 830
QRS Software Services, pg 867
Sound Feelings Records, pg 894

COLORADO

American Educational Products LLC, pg 683

FLORIDA

Bisk Education, pg 706

ILLINOIS

CCore Media Inc, pg 718

IOWA

Long-Term Success Publishing, pg 811

MARYLAND

Milner-Fenwick Inc, pg 828

MICHIGAN

Digi Sign Design LLC, pg 741
Emery-Pratt Co, pg 753
Phoenix Society for Burn Survivors Inc, pg 856

MISSOURI

Marsh Media, pg 817
Mosby Inc, pg 831
University of Missouri-Kansas City School of Dentistry, pg 923

NEW HAMPSHIRE

Chip Taylor Communications LLC, pg 907

NEW JERSEY

Allegro Productions Inc, pg 680

NEW YORK

Billy Budd Films Inc, pg 712
The Cinema Guild Inc, pg 724
Films Media Group, pg 760
Guilford Publications, pg 774
HB-Content, pg 777
Synaptic Digital, pg 905
Visual Technologies Corp, pg 932

NORTH CAROLINA

Sinclair Institute, pg 889

OHIO

Curtis Inc, pg 736

OREGON

InterVision Media, pg 791

PENNSYLVANIA

FMP Media Solutions Inc, pg 763
Lippincott Williams & Wilkins, pg 809
S I Video Sales Group, pg 879

TEXAS

Emergency Film Group, pg 753
Texas Heart Institute Visual Communication Services, pg 911

VIRGINIA

CACI Integrated Communications, pg 713

WASHINGTON

Medical Media Systems, pg 823

ONTARIO

Canadian Learning Co Inc, pg 715
Life Cycle Books Ltd, pg 807

Medical Program Producers

ALABAMA

Leo Ticheli Productions, pg 913

ARIZONA

SPEAK HOUSE Audio™, pg 896
Teaberry, pg 908

CALIFORNIA

Academy Savant, pg 672
The Banquet Sound Studios, pg 701
Big Door, pg 705
Creative Technology, pg 733
Custom Video Productions Inc, pg 736
Design Media, pg 741
Direct Cinema Ltd Inc, pg 743
Educational Technology Services (ETS), pg 751
Gold Standard Productions, pg 772
Bruce Goldberg Inc, pg 772
Havas Edge, pg 777
imageReal Pictures LLC, pg 785
Jaguar Distribution Corp, pg 792
Joyce Media Inc, pg 795
Lynch Communications, pg 813
Maximus Media Inc, pg 820
The Media Staff Inc, pg 822
Moose School Productions, pg 830
On-Trax Inc, pg 846
piXvfm Inc, pg 857
PM Productions, pg 858
Point of View Productions, pg 858
Producers Group Ltd, pg 863
QRS Software Services, pg 867
Steve Shapiro Music, pg 885
Sound Feelings Records, pg 894
Still N' Motion, pg 901
Studio 132, pg 902
Total Creative, pg 916
Video Resources Inc, pg 928
Wavemaker Media Design, pg 934

COLORADO

American Educational Products LLC, pg 683
Apogee Communications Group, pg 687
Daylight Productions & Rentals, pg 739
Flashback Media Productions, pg 762
Starwest Productions, pg 900

CONNECTICUT

ACM Productions Ltd, pg 674
Essex Television Group Inc, pg 755
The Gary-Paul Agency, pg 768
P&P Studios Inc, pg 851
UConn Health Multimedia Services, pg 920

FLORIDA

Audio Visual Imagineering Inc, pg 694
Bisk Education, pg 706
Blackburst Entertainment LLC, pg 706
Courter Films LLC, pg 732
LHV Audio Services, pg 807
Sunfire Communications Inc, pg 904
Sunrise Studios, pg 904
Tricycle Studios, pg 918

GEORGIA

Guerrilla Productions LLC, pg 774
WaveGuide Studios, pg 934

IDAHO

Wide Eye Productions, pg 938

ILLINOIS

ABS Enterprises, pg 672
CCore Media Inc, pg 718
Major Media Productions Inc, pg 815
Multimedia Marketing Group, pg 833
Pepper Group, pg 854
20/20 Communications Inc, pg 920
Video Impressions, pg 928

INDIANA

A-V-A Video Productions, pg 671
Bright Ideas Creative Services, pg 710
OMNI Productions, pg 845
PentaVision Communications Inc, pg 854

IOWA

Hedquist Productions Inc, pg 778
Long-Term Success Publishing, pg 811

LOUISIANA

Louisiana State University Division of Strategic Communications, pg 811

MARYLAND

The Cutting Corporation, GraphicAudio® & Archival Sound Lab, pg 736
dbF a Media Company, pg 739
The Image Generators, pg 785
Kramer Communications Video Production, pg 801
Milner-Fenwick Inc, pg 828

MASSACHUSETTS

Heliotrope Studios, pg 778
Penfield Productions Ltd, pg 853
Preston Productions Inc, pg 861
Soundtrack Group, pg 895
TR Productions, pg 916
TVN-The Video Network, pg 919

MICHIGAN

Digi Sign Design LLC, pg 741
K&R All Media Productions LLC, pg 796
K&R's Recording Studios Inc, pg 796
Phoenix Society for Burn Survivors Inc, pg 856

MINNESOTA

Media Loft Inc, pg 822

MISSOURI

Audio-VideoGraphics Inc, pg 694
Marsh Media, pg 817
Mosby Inc, pg 831
University of Missouri-Kansas City School of Dentistry, pg 923

NEVADA

JCS Video Productions, pg 793
Tetrahedron LLC, pg 911

NEW HAMPSHIRE

Apertura, pg 686
Chip Taylor Communications LLC, pg 907

NEW JERSEY

Allegro Productions Inc, pg 680
CFP Video Productions Inc, pg 720
C2 Imaging, pg 735
Laurel Video Productions, pg 804
MiB MediaWorks, pg 825
Optisonics Productions, pg 847
Projects in Knowledge Inc, pg 865
Suede Interactive, pg 903

NEW MEXICO

Production Outfitters, pg 864

NEW YORK

Aural Gratification Inc, pg 695
Avekta Productions Inc, pg 697
Broadstreet Productions LLC, pg 711
Billy Budd Films Inc, pg 712
Cohn Creative Group LLC, pg 727
Digital Force Ltd, pg 742
Downtown Community Television Center (DCTV), pg 746
Fingerpaint, pg 761
Guilford Publications, pg 774
HB-Content, pg 777
Hello World Communications, pg 778
Icontent, pg 783
Ketchum Inc, pg 798
L A Bruell Inc, pg 802
Mood Creations Ltd, pg 829
Jack Morton Worldwide, pg 830
MRY, pg 832
News Broadcast Network Inc, pg 840
The Palmer Group, pg 850
Pat Kogan Productions Inc, pg 852
Elliot Sokolov Music, pg 892
Split Image Productions, pg 898
Synaptic Digital, pg 905
Tiki Recording Studios Inc, pg 914

Videograf, pg 929
Zelman Studios Ltd, pg 945

NORTH CAROLINA

Pat Appleson Studios Inc, pg 687
Digital Rain LLC, pg 742
Sinclair Institute, pg 889
Trailblazer Studios®, pg 917
2BruceStudio, pg 920

OHIO

Curtis Inc, pg 736
Cuyahoga Community College Student Production Office (SPO), pg 736
R&B Communications Inc, pg 870
Take 1 Media Services, pg 906
Vista Color Imaging Inc, pg 931

OKLAHOMA

Academic Media & Digital Services, pg 672
Piper Media Services Inc, pg 857

OREGON

ERA Learning, pg 755
Ideascape Inc, pg 784
InterVision Media, pg 791

PENNSYLVANIA

Audio Visual Communications Inc, pg 694
FMP Media Solutions Inc, pg 763
Forge Recording LLC, pg 764
Innovision Media Group, pg 788
JPL, pg 795
Kensington Falls Animation, pg 797
Lippincott Williams & Wilkins, pg 809
Panta Rhei Media Inc, pg 851
S I Video Sales Group, pg 879
WQED-Multimedia, pg 942

RHODE ISLAND

Sound-FX-Design, pg 894

SOUTH CAROLINA

Venture Media, pg 925

TENNESSEE

Continental Film, pg 731
Memphis Communications Corp, pg 823

TEXAS

The Editing Co, pg 750
Emergency Film Group, pg 753
Epic Software Group Inc, pg 755
Omega Productions, pg 845
Romar Learning Solutions LLC, pg 877
The Sound Lab Inc, pg 894
South Coast Film & Video, pg 895
Stage Directions, pg 898
Texas Heart Institute Visual Communication Services, pg 911

VIRGINIA

BES Studios, pg 704
CACI Integrated Communications, pg 713
Limelight Communications Inc, pg 808
Metro Productions, pg 824
National Media Services Inc, pg 836

Rocktown Media, pg 876
Studio Center Corp, pg 902

WASHINGTON

Kostov Productions, pg 801
Medical Media Systems, pg 823

WEST VIRGINIA

Blackwater Video Productions, pg 707

WISCONSIN

5th Floor Recording Co, pg 760
Meridian Studios, pg 824
USAV Group Inc, pg 923
Video Wisconsin Inc, pg 929
Watts Communications Inc, pg 934
Wisconsin Public Television, pg 940

WYOMING

Bridger Productions Inc, pg 710

ONTARIO

ADS Media, pg 677
DebsVoice, pg 739
GAPC (General Assembly Production Centre), pg 768

QUEBEC

Kerrigan Productions Inc, pg 798

Medical Program Rentals

CALIFORNIA

Direct Cinema Ltd Inc, pg 743
Educational Technology Services (ETS), pg 751
Point of View Productions, pg 858

MASSACHUSETTS

Preston Productions Inc, pg 861

MICHIGAN

Digi Sign Design LLC, pg 741

MISSOURI

University of Missouri-Kansas City School of Dentistry, pg 923

NEW HAMPSHIRE

Chip Taylor Communications LLC, pg 907

NEW JERSEY

Alden Films, pg 679

NEW YORK

Downtown Community Television Center (DCTV), pg 746

TEXAS

Romar Learning Solutions LLC, pg 877

Multimedia, CD-ROM & DVD Interactive Program Distributors

ARKANSAS

Mullikin Agency, pg 833

PROGRAMMING — AUDIO

Multimedia, CD-ROM & DVD Interactive Program Distributors (continued)

CALIFORNIA
Astronomical Society of the Pacific, pg 691
Eye & I Productions, pg 758
Maximus Media Inc, pg 820
QRS Software Services, pg 867
TiVo Corp, pg 914

COLORADO
American Educational Products LLC, pg 683

FLORIDA
Video Resources Software, pg 928

GEORGIA
Convergent Media Systems, pg 731
School Media Associates LLC, pg 882

HAWAII
Media Bridge Gamekids, pg 821

ILLINOIS
Britannica Digital Learning, pg 710
CCore Media Inc, pg 718

IOWA
Right Stuf Inc, pg 875

MARYLAND
Department of Education Resources, pg 740

MASSACHUSETTS
Cheng & Tsui Co, pg 721
Documentary Educational Resources Inc, pg 744
Nuance Communications Inc, pg 843
Penfield Productions Ltd, pg 853

MICHIGAN
Digi Sign Design LLC, pg 741

MINNESOTA
BeyerSound & Essay Audio, pg 705

MISSOURI
Mosby Inc, pg 831

NEW HAMPSHIRE
Chip Taylor Communications LLC, pg 907

NEW JERSEY
Allegro Productions Inc, pg 680

NEW YORK
Films Media Group, pg 760
HB-Content, pg 777

OREGON
InterVision Media, pg 791

PENNSYLVANIA
Anchor Distributors, pg 685
Discovery Education - South Burlington, pg 743
FMP Media Solutions Inc, pg 763

TENNESSEE
Center for Southern Folklore Inc, pg 719
Spring Arbor Distributors Inc, pg 898

TEXAS
Emergency Film Group, pg 753
Replicopy Digital Media Center, pg 873

UTAH
Strata™, pg 901
Webb Audio Visual, pg 935

VERMONT
Multicultural Media Inc, pg 833

WASHINGTON
Proforma Good Wood Marketing, pg 865

BRITISH COLUMBIA
Video Out Distribution, pg 928

ONTARIO
Canadian Learning Co Inc, pg 715

Multimedia, CD-ROM & DVD Interactive Program Producers

ARIZONA
Merestone, pg 823

ARKANSAS
Live'N'Loud, pg 810
Mullikin Agency, pg 833

CALIFORNIA
Ancient Future, pg 685
Berkeley Sound Artists Inc, pg 704
Big Door, pg 705
Concrete Images, pg 730
Creative Media Recording, pg 733
Creative Technology, pg 733
Custom Video Productions Inc, pg 736
Design Media, pg 741
Eye & I Productions, pg 758
Gold Standard Productions, pg 772
Havas Edge, pg 777
International Contact Inc, pg 790
Lynch Communications, pg 813
Maximus Media Inc, pg 820
Media Magic, pg 822
New Circuit Films LLC, pg 839
OTR Studios, pg 848
Palardo Productions, pg 850
piXvfm Inc, pg 857
Producers Group Ltd, pg 863
QRS Software Services, pg 867
Steve Shapiro Music, pg 885
Still N' Motion, pg 901
Studio 132, pg 902
Tam Communications Inc, pg 906

The Studio of David Inocencio, pg 911
Total Creative, pg 916
Video Movie Magic, pg 928
Video Resources Inc, pg 928
Wavemaker Media Design, pg 934
Webster Communications, pg 935
The Wine Appreciation Guild Ltd, pg 939

COLORADO
American Educational Products LLC, pg 683
Flashback Media Productions, pg 762
Starwest Productions, pg 900

CONNECTICUT
Moving Pictures, pg 832

DISTRICT OF COLUMBIA
Hillmann & Carr Inc, pg 780

FLORIDA
Audacity Recording Studios, pg 693
Audio Visual Imagineering Inc, pg 694
Blackburst Entertainment LLC, pg 706
CD ROM™ Inc, pg 718
Communications Concepts Inc (CCI), pg 729
Courter Films LLC, pg 732
LHV Audio Services, pg 807
Sunfire Communications Inc, pg 904
Sunrise Studios, pg 904
Tricycle Studios, pg 918
Video Resources Software, pg 928
Z-Systems Audio Engineering, pg 944

GEORGIA
Guerrilla Productions LLC, pg 774
Myriad Productions, pg 835
WaveGuide Studios, pg 934

HAWAII
Media Bridge Gamekids, pg 821

IDAHO
Wide Eye Productions, pg 938

ILLINOIS
ABS Enterprises, pg 672
Advanced Audio Technology, pg 677
Airways Digital Media, pg 679
Britannica Digital Learning, pg 710
CCore Media Inc, pg 718
Cresta Creative, pg 734
Major Media Inc, pg 815
Major Media Productions Inc, pg 815
Pepper Group, pg 854
PSAV® Presentation Services (Hotel Services Division), pg 866
Sparkfactor, pg 896
20/20 Communications Inc, pg 920
Video Impressions, pg 928

INDIANA
Advanced Media Integration, pg 677
Bright Ideas Creative Services, pg 710
Communication Ministries, pg 728

OMNI Productions, pg 845
PentaVision Communications Inc, pg 854

IOWA
Educational Technology & Media Services, pg 751
Right Stuf Inc, pg 875

KENTUCKY
Hammond Communications Group Inc, pg 775
Donna Lawrence Productions, pg 804

LOUISIANA
Digital FX Inc, pg 742
Louisiana State University Division of Strategic Communications, pg 811

MARYLAND
CPR MultiMedia Solutions, pg 732
The Cutting Corporation, GraphicAudio® & Archival Sound Lab, pg 736
dbF a Media Company, pg 739
Department of Education Resources, pg 740
The Image Generators, pg 785
Kramer Communications Video Production, pg 801
Media Dimensions LLC, pg 821

MASSACHUSETTS
Cheng & Tsui Co, pg 721
CommCreative, pg 728
Documentary Educational Resources Inc, pg 744
HOME Inc, pg 781
Monadnock Media Inc, pg 829
Northern Light Productions (NLP), pg 842
Penfield Productions Ltd, pg 853
Preston Productions Inc, pg 861
Soundtrack Group, pg 895
TR Productions, pg 916
TVN-The Video Network, pg 919

MICHIGAN
Digi Sign Design LLC, pg 741
K&R All Media Productions LLC, pg 796
K&R's Recording Studios Inc, pg 796
MessageMakers, pg 824
TGA Recording Co, pg 911

MINNESOTA
BeyerSound & Essay Audio, pg 705
Media Loft Inc, pg 822

MISSOURI
Mosby Inc, pg 831

NEBRASKA
Rainbow Video Productions Inc, pg 869

NEVADA
JCS Video Productions, pg 793

NEW HAMPSHIRE
Apertura, pg 686
Chip Taylor Communications LLC, pg 907

NEW JERSEY

Allegro Productions Inc, pg 680
Audio Vistas LLC, pg 694
Broadcast Center Studios, pg 710
C2 Imaging, pg 735
MiB MediaWorks, pg 825
Midnight Media Group Inc, pg 827
Optisonics Productions, pg 847
Outside The Box Interactive LLC, pg 849
Suede Interactive, pg 903
VCSvideo, pg 925

NEW MEXICO

Production Outfitters, pg 864

NEW YORK

Aural Gratification Inc, pg 695
Avekta Productions Inc, pg 697
Blue Barn Pictures Inc, pg 707
Broadstreet Productions LLC, pg 711
Cohn Creative Group LLC, pg 727
Digital Force Ltd, pg 742
Duplication Depot Inc, pg 748
Films Media Group, pg 760
Fingerpaint, pg 761
HB-Content, pg 777
Icontent, pg 783
Image Zone Inc, pg 785
L A Bruell Inc, pg 802
Jack Morton Worldwide, pg 830
MRY, pg 832
New York Audio Productions, pg 840
David Rapkin Audio Production, pg 870
Judson Rosebush Co Inc, pg 877
Elliot Sokolov Music, pg 892
Split Image Productions, pg 898
Spoken Arts Inc, pg 898
Tiki Recording Studios Inc, pg 914
Zelman Studios Ltd, pg 945

NORTH CAROLINA

Pat Appleson Studios Inc, pg 687
Image Associates Inc, pg 784
NASCAR Productions LLC, pg 835
2BruceStudio, pg 920
World Class Learning Materials Inc, pg 941

OHIO

Advent Media Inc, pg 677
R&B Communications Inc, pg 870
Take 1 Media Services, pg 906
Vista Color Imaging Inc, pg 931

OKLAHOMA

Piper Media Services Inc, pg 857

OREGON

ERA Learning, pg 755
Ideascape Inc, pg 784
InterVision Media, pg 791
NeoSoft Corp, pg 838
Odyssey Productions Inc, pg 844
REX, pg 874

PENNSYLVANIA

Audio Visual Communications Inc, pg 694
Discovery Education - South Burlington, pg 743
FMP Media Solutions Inc, pg 763
Innovision Media Group, pg 788
JPL, pg 795
New Horizons Computer Learning Centers Inc, pg 839

Production Masters Inc (PMI), pg 864
Scala Inc, pg 881
Visual Sound Inc, pg 931

RHODE ISLAND

Sound-FX-Design, pg 894

SOUTH CAROLINA

Venture Media, pg 925

TENNESSEE

Anode Inc, pg 686
Continental Film, pg 731
Love Shack Recording Studios, pg 811
Memphis Communications Corp, pg 823
Russ Sturgeon Productions/RSVP, pg 903

TEXAS

Biway Media, pg 706
Emergency Film Group, pg 753
Epic Software Group Inc, pg 755
Matson Multi-Media, pg 820
Omega Productions, pg 845
Romar Learning Solutions LLC, pg 877
The Sound Lab Inc, pg 894
Sound Works, pg 894
Stage Directions, pg 898

UTAH

Webb Audio Visual, pg 935

VIRGINIA

Advance Concepts Inc, pg 677
Metro Productions, pg 824
Studio Center Corp, pg 902

WASHINGTON

Inland Audio Visual Co, pg 788
Kostov Productions, pg 801

WISCONSIN

AVS Group, pg 699
5th Floor Recording Co, pg 760
USAV Group Inc, pg 923
Video Wisconsin Inc, pg 929
Watts Communications Inc, pg 934
Wisconsin Public Television, pg 940

WYOMING

Bridger Productions Inc, pg 710

NEWFOUNDLAND AND LABRADOR

Vidcraft Productions Ltd, pg 927

ONTARIO

ADS Media, pg 677
Art Gallery of Ontario, pg 690
DebsVoice, pg 739
GAPC (General Assembly Production Centre), pg 768
JFB Communications, pg 794
Marblemedia, pg 816

QUEBEC

Kerrigan Productions Inc, pg 798

Multimedia, CD-ROM & DVD Interactive Program Rentals

DELAWARE

Side Door Studio Inc, pg 887

GEORGIA

Convergent Media Systems, pg 731

MASSACHUSETTS

Documentary Educational Resources Inc, pg 744
Preston Productions Inc, pg 861

MICHIGAN

Digi Sign Design LLC, pg 741

NEW HAMPSHIRE

Chip Taylor Communications LLC, pg 907

UTAH

Webb Audio Visual, pg 935

News Program Distributors

CALIFORNIA

Maximus Media Inc, pg 820
Pacifica Radio Archives, pg 849

GEORGIA

School Media Associates LLC, pg 882

INDIANA

Communication Ministries, pg 728

MICHIGAN

Digi Sign Design LLC, pg 741

NEBRASKA

Vision Maker Media, pg 930

NEW YORK

De Nonno Productions Inc (DPI), pg 739
HB-Content, pg 777
News Broadcast Network Inc, pg 840
United Nations Multimedia Resources Unit, pg 921

PENNSYLVANIA

AccuWeather Inc, pg 674

VIRGINIA

CACI Integrated Communications, pg 713

ALBERTA

Global TV, pg 771

News Program Producers

CALIFORNIA

Big Door, pg 705
Creative Technology, pg 733
Direct Cinema Ltd Inc, pg 743
Gold Standard Productions, pg 772
Jaguar Distribution Corp, pg 792

Lynch Communications, pg 813
PM Productions, pg 858
Steve Shapiro Music, pg 885
Studio 132, pg 902
Total Creative, pg 916
Webster Communications, pg 935

COLORADO

Apogee Communications Group, pg 687

CONNECTICUT

Essex Television Group Inc, pg 755
P&P Studios Inc, pg 851

FLORIDA

Blackburst Entertainment LLC, pg 706
Communications Concepts Inc (CCI), pg 729
LHV Audio Services, pg 807
Roger Scruggs Films, pg 883
Sunfire Communications Inc, pg 904

GEORGIA

Guerrilla Productions LLC, pg 774

IDAHO

Wide Eye Productions, pg 938

ILLINOIS

ABS Enterprises, pg 672
Pepper Group, pg 854

INDIANA

A-V-A Video Productions, pg 671
Communication Ministries, pg 728

KANSAS

KAKE-TV, pg 796

LOUISIANA

Digital FX Inc, pg 742

MARYLAND

CPR MultiMedia Solutions, pg 732
The Cutting Corporation, GraphicAudio® & Archival Sound Lab, pg 736
dbF a Media Company, pg 739
The Image Generators, pg 785
Kramer Communications Video Production, pg 801

MASSACHUSETTS

Soundtrack Group, pg 895
TVN-The Video Network, pg 919

MICHIGAN

Digi Sign Design LLC, pg 741
K&R All Media Productions LLC, pg 796
K&R's Recording Studios Inc, pg 796

NEVADA

JCS Video Productions, pg 793

NEW JERSEY

CFP Video Productions Inc, pg 720
Laurel Video Productions, pg 804
MiB MediaWorks, pg 825
Optisonics Productions, pg 847

PROGRAMMING — AUDIO

News Program Producers (continued)

NEW MEXICO
Production Outfitters, pg 864

NEW YORK
CompuWeather Inc, pg 729
De Nonno Productions Inc (DPI), pg 739
Digital Force Ltd, pg 742
Downtown Community Television Center (DCTV), pg 746
HB-Content, pg 777
Hello World Communications, pg 778
Jack Morton Worldwide, pg 830
New York Audio Productions, pg 840
News Broadcast Network Inc, pg 840
The Palmer Group, pg 850
David Rapkin Audio Production, pg 870
Split Image Productions, pg 898
Suggs Media Productions Inc, pg 903
United Nations Multimedia Resources Unit, pg 921
Zelman Studios Ltd, pg 945

NORTH CAROLINA
Pat Appleson Studios Inc, pg 687
Digital Rain LLC, pg 742

OHIO
R&B Communications Inc, pg 870
Vista Color Imaging Inc, pg 931

OKLAHOMA
Piper Media Services Inc, pg 857

OREGON
InterVision Media, pg 791

PENNSYLVANIA
AccuWeather Inc, pg 674
Scala Inc, pg 881
The Videohouse Inc, pg 929

RHODE ISLAND
Sound-FX-Design, pg 894

SOUTH CAROLINA
Stages Video Productions, pg 899

TEXAS
Dykeman Associates Inc, pg 748
Emergency Film Group, pg 753
Epic Software Group Inc, pg 755
Omega Productions, pg 845
Romar Learning Solutions LLC, pg 877
The Sound Lab Inc, pg 894
Sound Works, pg 894
Stage Directions, pg 898
Texas Heart Institute Visual Communication Services, pg 911

VIRGINIA
CACI Integrated Communications, pg 713
Limelight Communications Inc, pg 808
National Media Services Inc, pg 836
Rocktown Media, pg 876

WEST VIRGINIA
Blackwater Video Productions, pg 707

WISCONSIN
5th Floor Recording Co, pg 760
University of Wisconsin-Oshkosh Radio-TV-Film Dept, pg 923
Video Wisconsin Inc, pg 929
Watts Communications Inc, pg 934
Wisconsin Public Television, pg 940

WYOMING
Bridger Productions Inc, pg 710

ALBERTA
Global TV, pg 771

ONTARIO
DebsVoice, pg 739

QUEBEC
Kerrigan Productions Inc, pg 798

News Program Rentals

CALIFORNIA
Direct Cinema Ltd Inc, pg 743

MICHIGAN
Digi Sign Design LLC, pg 741

NEBRASKA
Vision Maker Media, pg 930

NEW JERSEY
Alden Films, pg 679

NEW YORK
Downtown Community Television Center (DCTV), pg 746

UTAH
Webb Audio Visual, pg 935

Phonograph Record Distributors

CALIFORNIA
Ametron Audio/Video, pg 684
GNP Crescendo Records, pg 772
Harmonia Mundi USA, pg 776
Sahara Records & Filmworks Entertainment Co, pg 879
Universal Music Group, pg 922
Welk Music Group, pg 935

COLORADO
White Swan Music Inc, pg 937

CONNECTICUT
Original Cast Records, pg 848

DISTRICT OF COLUMBIA
Library of Congress, Motion Picture, Broadcasting & Recorded Sound Division, pg 807

FLORIDA
Kat Epple Music Productions, pg 755
Times-Square Fantasy Theatre, pg 914

ILLINOIS
Earwig Music Co Inc, pg 749

MARYLAND
Adelphi Records Inc, pg 676

NEW YORK
Cadence Jazz Records, pg 713
Digital Force Ltd, pg 742
Dyer-Bennet Records, pg 748
Sony Music Entertainment, pg 893
Tommy Boy Entertainment LLC, pg 915

NORTH CAROLINA
Howard Hanger, pg 775

PENNSYLVANIA
Dreambox Media Inc, pg 746

TENNESSEE
Center for Southern Folklore Inc, pg 719
Rounder Records, pg 878
Spring Arbor Distributors Inc, pg 898

VIRGINIA
County Sales, pg 732
Rebel Records, pg 871

WISCONSIN
School Specialty Inc, pg 882

ONTARIO
Entertainment One Distribution, pg 754

Phonograph Record Producers

CALIFORNIA
4th Street Recording, pg 764
Lynch Communications, pg 813
Maximus Media Inc, pg 820
OTR Studios, pg 848
Reference Recordings, pg 872
Sahara Records & Filmworks Entertainment Co, pg 879
Schroder Music Co, pg 882
Universal Music Group, pg 922
Webster Communications, pg 935

COLORADO
Tim Cissell Music, pg 725

DELAWARE
Ken-Del Productions Inc, pg 797

FLORIDA
Kat Epple Music Productions, pg 755
Times-Square Fantasy Theatre, pg 914

GEORGIA
Hottrax Records, pg 782

ILLINOIS
Delmark Records, pg 740
Earwig Music Co Inc, pg 749
Major Media Inc, pg 815

LOUISIANA
Jazzology, pg 793

MAINE
Serendipity Recordings, pg 884

MARYLAND
Adelphi Records Inc, pg 676

MICHIGAN
K&R All Media Productions LLC, pg 796
K&R's Recording Studios Inc, pg 796

NEW JERSEY
Presence Records, pg 861
Suede Interactive, pg 903

NEW YORK
Digital Force Ltd, pg 742
Dyer-Bennet Records, pg 748
Fingerpaint, pg 761
Oriental Records Inc, pg 848
Elliot Sokolov Music, pg 892
Sony Music Commercial Music Group, pg 893
Sony Music Entertainment, pg 893
Tommy Boy Entertainment LLC, pg 915

NORTH CAROLINA
Howard Hanger, pg 775

OHIO
Musicol Recording, pg 835

PENNSYLVANIA
Dreambox Media Inc, pg 746
Innovision Media Group, pg 788

TENNESSEE
Center for Southern Folklore Inc, pg 719

TEXAS
The Samuels Co, pg 879

VIRGINIA
County Sales, pg 732
Rebel Records, pg 871

Phonograph Record Rentals

CALIFORNIA
Ametron Audio/Video, pg 684

FLORIDA

Times-Square Fantasy Theatre, pg 914

MISSOURI

Show-Me Audio-Visual, pg 887

Public Relations Program Distributors

ARKANSAS

Mullikin Agency, pg 833

CALIFORNIA

Direct Cinema Ltd Inc, pg 743
Maximus Media Inc, pg 820
Joseph Nicoletti Consulting-Promotion, pg 841
QRS Software Services, pg 867

GEORGIA

Convergent Media Systems, pg 731

ILLINOIS

CCore Media Inc, pg 718

MASSACHUSETTS

Penfield Productions Ltd, pg 853

MICHIGAN

Digi Sign Design LLC, pg 741

NEVADA

DVDs4Less, pg 748

NEW HAMPSHIRE

Chip Taylor Communications LLC, pg 907

NEW JERSEY

Allegro Productions Inc, pg 680

NEW YORK

HB-Content, pg 777
Janus Films Inc, pg 793
News Broadcast Network Inc, pg 840
Synaptic Digital, pg 905

OREGON

InterVision Media, pg 791

PENNSYLVANIA

FMP Media Solutions Inc, pg 763

SOUTH CAROLINA

DaviSound, pg 739

TENNESSEE

American Blackguard Inc, pg 683

TEXAS

Emergency Film Group, pg 753

VIRGINIA

CACI Integrated Communications, pg 713

WISCONSIN

Wisconsin Public Television, pg 940

ALBERTA

Global TV, pg 771

Public Relations Program Producers

ALABAMA

Leo Ticheli Productions, pg 913

ARIZONA

Candee Productions Inc, pg 716
Metropolitan Audio-Visual Inc, pg 824
SPEAK HOUSE Audio™, pg 896

ARKANSAS

Live'N'Loud, pg 810
Mullikin Agency, pg 833

CALIFORNIA

Big Door, pg 705
Creative Media Recording, pg 733
Creative Technology, pg 733
Custom Video Productions Inc, pg 736
Design Media, pg 741
Direct Cinema Ltd Inc, pg 743
Goal Productions, pg 772
Gold Standard Productions, pg 772
International Contact Inc, pg 790
Lynch Communications, pg 813
The Media Staff Inc, pg 822
Joseph Nicoletti Consulting-Promotion, pg 841
On-Trax Inc, pg 846
piXvfm Inc, pg 857
Point of View Productions, pg 858
Prime Cut Productions, pg 862
Producers Group Ltd, pg 863
QRS Software Services, pg 867
Steve Shapiro Music, pg 885
Still N' Motion, pg 901
Studio 132, pg 902
Total Creative, pg 916
Video Resources Inc, pg 928
Wavemaker Media Design, pg 934
Webster Communications, pg 935
Zamacona Productions, pg 945

COLORADO

Apogee Communications Group, pg 687
Daylight Productions & Rentals, pg 739
Flashback Media Productions, pg 762
Starwest Productions, pg 900
Tatum Video, pg 907

CONNECTICUT

ACM Productions Ltd, pg 674
The Gary-Paul Agency, pg 768
P&P Studios Inc, pg 851
UConn Health Multimedia Services, pg 920

DISTRICT OF COLUMBIA

Hillmann & Carr Inc, pg 780

FLORIDA

Audio Visual Imagineering Inc, pg 694
Blackburst Entertainment LLC, pg 706
Communications Concepts Inc (CCI), pg 729
LHV Audio Services, pg 807

Sunfire Communications Inc, pg 904
Sunrise Studios, pg 904
Tricycle Studios, pg 918
Mike Vasilinda Productions Inc, pg 925

GEORGIA

Guerrilla Productions LLC, pg 774

IDAHO

Wide Eye Productions, pg 938

ILLINOIS

ABS Enterprises, pg 672
CCore Media Inc, pg 718
Cresta Creative, pg 734
Major Media Productions Inc, pg 815
Multimedia Marketing Group, pg 833
Jim Passin Productions, pg 852
Pepper Group, pg 854
PSAV® Presentation Services (Hotel Services Division), pg 866
20/20 Communications Inc, pg 920
Video Impressions, pg 928

INDIANA

A-V-A Video Productions, pg 671
PentaVision Communications Inc, pg 854

IOWA

Hedquist Productions Inc, pg 778

LOUISIANA

Digital FX Inc, pg 742
Louisiana State University Division of Strategic Communications, pg 811

MARYLAND

CPR MultiMedia Solutions, pg 732
The Cutting Corporation, GraphicAudio® & Archival Sound Lab, pg 736
dbF a Media Company, pg 739
The Image Generators, pg 785
Kramer Communications Video Production, pg 801

MASSACHUSETTS

CommCreative, pg 728
Heliotrope Studios, pg 778
HOME Inc, pg 781
Monadnock Media Inc, pg 829
Penfield Productions Ltd, pg 853
Preston Productions Inc, pg 861
Soundtrack Group, pg 895
TR Productions, pg 916
TVN-The Video Network, pg 919

MICHIGAN

Digi Sign Design LLC, pg 741
K&R All Media Productions LLC, pg 796
K&R's Recording Studios Inc, pg 796

MINNESOTA

Media Loft Inc, pg 822

MISSOURI

Audio-VideoGraphics Inc, pg 694
Clayton-Davis & Associates, pg 726

NEVADA

DVDs4Less, pg 748
JCS Video Productions, pg 793

NEW HAMPSHIRE

Apertura, pg 686
Chip Taylor Communications LLC, pg 907

NEW JERSEY

Allegro Productions Inc, pg 680
CFP Video Productions Inc, pg 720
C2 Imaging, pg 735
Laurel Video Productions, pg 804
MiB MediaWorks, pg 825
Midnight Media Group Inc, pg 827
Optisonics Productions, pg 847

NEW YORK

Avekta Productions Inc, pg 697
Blue Barn Pictures Inc, pg 707
Broadstreet Productions LLC, pg 711
Cohn Creative Group LLC, pg 727
Thomas Craven Film Corp, pg 733
Digital Force Ltd, pg 742
HB-Content, pg 777
Icontent, pg 783
Ketchum Inc, pg 798
L A Bruell Inc, pg 802
Jack Morton Worldwide, pg 830
New York Audio Productions, pg 840
News Broadcast Network Inc, pg 840
The Palmer Group, pg 850
Pat Kogan Productions Inc, pg 852
David Rapkin Audio Production, pg 870
Elliot Sokolov Music, pg 892
Split Image Productions, pg 898
Suggs Media Productions Inc, pg 903
Synaptic Digital, pg 905
Tiki Recording Studios Inc, pg 914
Zelman Studios Ltd, pg 945

NORTH CAROLINA

Pat Appleson Studios Inc, pg 687
The Communications Group Inc, pg 729
Trailblazer Studios®, pg 917
2BruceStudio, pg 920

OHIO

MainSail Production Services Inc, pg 815
R&B Communications Inc, pg 870
Take 1 Media Services, pg 906
Vista Color Imaging Inc, pg 931

OKLAHOMA

Piper Media Services Inc, pg 857

OREGON

Ideascape Inc, pg 784
InterVision Media, pg 791
Odyssey Productions Inc, pg 844

PENNSYLVANIA

Audio Visual Communications Inc, pg 694
FMP Media Solutions Inc, pg 763
Innovision Media Group, pg 788
JPL, pg 795
Muderick Media, pg 833
Panta Rhei Media Inc, pg 851

PROGRAMMING — AUDIO

Public Relations Program Producers (continued)

PENNSYLVANIA (continued)
Production Masters Inc (PMI), pg 864
The Videohouse Inc, pg 929
Visual Sound Inc, pg 931

RHODE ISLAND
Sound-FX-Design, pg 894

SOUTH CAROLINA
DaviSound, pg 739
Stages Video Productions, pg 899
Venture Media, pg 925

TENNESSEE
American Blackguard Inc, pg 683
Continental Film, pg 731
Memphis Communications Corp, pg 823

TEXAS
Biway Media, pg 706
Dykeman Associates Inc, pg 748
The Editing Co, pg 750
Emergency Film Group, pg 753
Epic Software Group Inc, pg 755
Omega Productions, pg 845
The Sound Lab Inc, pg 894
Sound Works, pg 894
Texas Heart Institute Visual Communication Services, pg 911
Tropikal Productions, pg 918

VIRGINIA
BES Studios, pg 704
CACI Integrated Communications, pg 713
Limelight Communications Inc, pg 808
Metro Productions, pg 824
National Media Services Inc, pg 836
Rocktown Media, pg 876
Studio Center Corp, pg 902

WASHINGTON
Kostov Productions, pg 801
Pacific Multimedia Inc, pg 849

WEST VIRGINIA
Blackwater Video Productions, pg 707

WISCONSIN
5th Floor Recording Co, pg 760
Meridian Studios, pg 824
USAV Group Inc, pg 923
Video Wisconsin Inc, pg 929
Watts Communications Inc, pg 934
Wisconsin Public Television, pg 940

WYOMING
Bridger Productions Inc, pg 710

ALBERTA
Black Media Works, pg 706
Global TV, pg 771

NEWFOUNDLAND AND LABRADOR
Vidcraft Productions Ltd, pg 927

ONTARIO
DebsVoice, pg 739

QUEBEC
Kerrigan Productions Inc, pg 798

Public Relations Program Rentals

CALIFORNIA
Direct Cinema Ltd Inc, pg 743

GEORGIA
Convergent Media Systems, pg 731

MASSACHUSETTS
Preston Productions Inc, pg 861

MICHIGAN
Digi Sign Design LLC, pg 741

NEW HAMPSHIRE
Chip Taylor Communications LLC, pg 907

UTAH
Webb Audio Visual, pg 935

Public Service Announcement Distributors

CALIFORNIA
ECONEWS (Environmental Television Series) & (Environmental Directions Radio Series), pg 750
Maximus Media Inc, pg 820
QRS Software Services, pg 867
The Wyland Group, pg 942

CONNECTICUT
Save the Children Federation Inc, pg 881

FLORIDA
Mike Vasilinda Productions Inc, pg 925

INDIANA
Communication Ministries, pg 728

MASSACHUSETTS
Penfield Productions Ltd, pg 853

MICHIGAN
Digi Sign Design LLC, pg 741
Zondervan, pg 945

NEVADA
DVDs4Less, pg 748

NEW HAMPSHIRE
Chip Taylor Communications LLC, pg 907

NEW YORK
The Christophers, pg 722
De Nonno Productions Inc (DPI), pg 739
HB-Content, pg 777
March of Dimes Foundation, pg 816
News Broadcast Network Inc, pg 840
Synaptic Digital, pg 905
United Nations Multimedia Resources Unit, pg 921
Visual Technologies Corp, pg 932

OHIO
Franciscan Media, pg 765

SOUTH CAROLINA
DaviSound, pg 739

TENNESSEE
American Blackguard Inc, pg 683

TEXAS
Institute of Texan Cultures, pg 788
TM Studios Inc, pg 915

VIRGINIA
CACI Integrated Communications, pg 713
CDR Communications Inc, pg 719

WISCONSIN
Wisconsin Public Television, pg 940

Public Service Announcement Producers

ARIZONA
Candee Productions Inc, pg 716
Metropolitan Audio-Visual Inc, pg 824

ARKANSAS
Live'N'Loud, pg 810

CALIFORNIA
Big Door, pg 705
Concrete Images, pg 730
Creative Media Recording, pg 733
Creative Technology, pg 733
Custom Video Productions Inc, pg 736
Direct Cinema Ltd Inc, pg 743
ECONEWS (Environmental Television Series) & (Environmental Directions Radio Series), pg 750
4th Street Recording, pg 764
imageReal Pictures LLC, pg 785
Kris Stevens Enterprises, pg 801
KTVU-Retail Services, pg 802
Lynch Communications, pg 813
Maximus Media Inc, pg 820
Media Magic, pg 822
The Media Staff Inc, pg 822
On-Trax Inc, pg 846
OTR Studios, pg 848
PM Productions, pg 858
Point of View Productions, pg 858
Producers Group Ltd, pg 863
QRS Software Services, pg 867
Steve Shapiro Music, pg 885
Still N' Motion, pg 901
Studio 132, pg 902
Tam Communications Inc, pg 906

COLORADO
Apogee Communications Group, pg 687

CONNECTICUT
The Gary-Paul Agency, pg 768
Moving Pictures, pg 832
P&P Studios Inc, pg 851
Save the Children Federation Inc, pg 881
UConn Health Multimedia Services, pg 920

DISTRICT OF COLUMBIA
Hillmann & Carr Inc, pg 780

FLORIDA
Blackburst Entertainment LLC, pg 706
Communications Concepts Inc (CCI), pg 729
LHV Audio Services, pg 807
Sunfire Communications Inc, pg 904
Sunrise Studios, pg 904
Tricycle Studios, pg 918
Mike Vasilinda Productions Inc, pg 925

GEORGIA
Guerrilla Productions LLC, pg 774

IDAHO
Wide Eye Productions, pg 938

ILLINOIS
ABS Enterprises, pg 672
Cresta Creative, pg 734
Major Media Productions Inc, pg 815
Multimedia Marketing Group, pg 833
Jim Passin Productions, pg 852
Pepper Group, pg 854
PSAV® Presentation Services (Hotel Services Division), pg 866
Steven Samler Music & Sound, pg 879
Sparkfactor, pg 896
20/20 Communications Inc, pg 920

INDIANA
A-V-A Video Productions, pg 671
Communication Ministries, pg 728
OMNI Productions, pg 845

IOWA
Hedquist Productions Inc, pg 778

LOUISIANA
Disk Productions Inc, pg 743
Louisiana State University Division of Strategic Communications, pg 811

MARYLAND
CPR MultiMedia Solutions, pg 732
The Cutting Corporation, GraphicAudio® & Archival Sound Lab, pg 736
dbF a Media Company, pg 739

Total Creative, pg 916
Wavemaker Media Design, pg 934
Webster Communications, pg 935
The Wyland Group, pg 942

The Image Generators, pg 785
Kramer Communications Video
Production, pg 801

MASSACHUSETTS

Documentary Educational Resources
Inc, pg 744
Heliotrope Studios, pg 778
HOME Inc, pg 781
Labrecque Creative Sound, pg 803
Penfield Productions Ltd, pg 853
Soundtrack Group, pg 895
TR Productions, pg 916
TVN-The Video Network, pg 919

MICHIGAN

Digi Sign Design LLC, pg 741
K&R All Media Productions LLC,
pg 796
K&R's Recording Studios Inc,
pg 796
MessageMakers, pg 824
Zondervan, pg 945

MINNESOTA

MastCom, pg 819

MISSOURI

Audio-VideoGraphics Inc, pg 694

NEVADA

DVDs4Less, pg 748
JCS Video Productions, pg 793

NEW HAMPSHIRE

Apertura, pg 686
Chip Taylor Communications LLC,
pg 907

NEW JERSEY

Audio Vistas LLC, pg 694
Broadcast Center Studios, pg 710
CFP Video Productions Inc, pg 720
MiB MediaWorks, pg 825
Midnight Media Group Inc, pg 827
Optisonics Productions, pg 847
Presence Records, pg 861
Suede Interactive, pg 903

NEW MEXICO

Production Outfitters, pg 864

NEW YORK

Aural Gratification Inc, pg 695
Avekta Productions Inc, pg 697
Blue Barn Pictures Inc, pg 707
Broadstreet Productions LLC,
pg 711
The Christophers, pg 722
Clarity Media Group, pg 725
Thomas Craven Film Corp, pg 733
De Nonno Productions Inc (DPI),
pg 739
Digital Force Ltd, pg 742
Downtown Community Television
Center (DCTV), pg 746
Fingerpaint, pg 761
HB-Content, pg 777
L A Bruell Inc, pg 802
March of Dimes Foundation, pg 816
Jack Morton Worldwide, pg 830
MRM//McCANN, pg 832
New York Audio Productions,
pg 840
News Broadcast Network Inc,
pg 840
The Palmer Group, pg 850
Pat Kogan Productions Inc, pg 852

David Rapkin Audio Production,
pg 870
Elliot Sokolov Music, pg 892
Split Image Productions, pg 898
Suggs Media Productions Inc,
pg 903
Synaptic Digital, pg 905
Tiki Recording Studios Inc, pg 914
United Nations Multimedia
Resources Unit, pg 921
Zelman Studios Ltd, pg 945

NORTH CAROLINA

Pat Appleson Studios Inc, pg 687
The Communications Group Inc,
pg 729
Digital Rain LLC, pg 742
Trailblazer Studios®, pg 917
2BruceStudio, pg 920

OHIO

Cuyahoga Community College
Student Production Office (SPO),
pg 736
Franciscan Media, pg 765
MainSail Production Services Inc,
pg 815
R&B Communications Inc, pg 870
Take 1 Media Services, pg 906
Vista Color Imaging Inc, pg 931

OKLAHOMA

Academic Media & Digital
Services, pg 672
Piper Media Services Inc, pg 857

OREGON

Ideascape Inc, pg 784
InterVision Media, pg 791
Odyssey Productions Inc, pg 844

PENNSYLVANIA

Audio Visual Communications Inc,
pg 694
Forge Recording LLC, pg 764
Innovision Media Group, pg 788
JPL, pg 795
Kensington Falls Animation, pg 797
Muderick Media, pg 833
Panta Rhei Media Inc, pg 851
Production Masters Inc (PMI),
pg 864
The Videohouse Inc, pg 929
WQED-Multimedia, pg 942

RHODE ISLAND

Sound-FX-Design, pg 894

SOUTH CAROLINA

DaviSound, pg 739
Stages Video Productions, pg 899
Venture Media, pg 925

TENNESSEE

American Blackguard Inc, pg 683
Continental Film, pg 731

TEXAS

Biway Media, pg 706
Communication Arts Multimedia
Inc, pg 728
Dykeman Associates Inc, pg 748
The Editing Co, pg 750
Emergency Film Group, pg 753
Epic Software Group Inc, pg 755
Institute of Texan Cultures, pg 788
Omega Productions, pg 845
The Sound Lab Inc, pg 894

Sound Works, pg 894
Stage Directions, pg 898
TM Studios Inc, pg 915
Tropikal Productions, pg 918

VIRGINIA

CACI Integrated Communications,
pg 713
CDR Communications Inc, pg 719
Limelight Communications Inc,
pg 808
Metro Productions, pg 824
National Media Services Inc,
pg 836
Rocktown Media, pg 876
Studio Center Corp, pg 902

WASHINGTON

Hamilton Studio, pg 775
Kostov Productions, pg 801
Pacific Multimedia Inc, pg 849

WEST VIRGINIA

Blackwater Video Productions,
pg 707

WISCONSIN

5th Floor Recording Co, pg 760
Meridian Studios, pg 824
University of Wisconsin-Oshkosh
Radio-TV-Film Dept, pg 923
USAV Group Inc, pg 923
Video Wisconsin Inc, pg 929
Watts Communications Inc, pg 934
Wisconsin Public Television, pg 940

WYOMING

Bridger Productions Inc, pg 710

ALBERTA

Black Media Works, pg 706
Global TV, pg 771

*NEWFOUNDLAND AND
LABRADOR*

Vidcraft Productions Ltd, pg 927

ONTARIO

ADS Media, pg 677
DebsVoice, pg 739
GAPC (General Assembly
Production Centre), pg 768

QUEBEC

Kerrigan Productions Inc, pg 798

Public Service
Announcement Rentals

CALIFORNIA

Direct Cinema Ltd Inc, pg 743

MICHIGAN

Digi Sign Design LLC, pg 741

NEW HAMPSHIRE

Chip Taylor Communications LLC,
pg 907

Radio Commercial
Distributors

CALIFORNIA

Far West Media Services Inc,
pg 759
Maximus Media Inc, pg 820
QRS Software Services, pg 867

ILLINOIS

Woodside Avenue Music
Productions Inc, pg 941

MASSACHUSETTS

Penfield Productions Ltd, pg 853

MICHIGAN

Digi Sign Design LLC, pg 741

NEVADA

DVDs4Less, pg 748

NEW HAMPSHIRE

Chip Taylor Communications LLC,
pg 907

NEW YORK

HB-Content, pg 777

SOUTH CAROLINA

DaviSound, pg 739

TENNESSEE

American Blackguard Inc, pg 683
Zion Music Group, pg 945

TEXAS

TM Studios Inc, pg 915

Radio Commercial
Producers

ALABAMA

Dogwood Productions Inc, pg 745
Leo Ticheli Productions, pg 913

ARIZONA

KOOL-FM Radio, pg 801
SPEAK HOUSE Audio™, pg 896

ARKANSAS

Live'N'Loud, pg 810
White Diamond Productions LLC,
pg 937

CALIFORNIA

The Banquet Sound Studios, pg 701
Creative Media Recording, pg 733
Custom Video Productions Inc,
pg 736
Far West Media Services Inc,
pg 759
4th Street Recording, pg 764
Havas Edge, pg 777
International Contact Inc, pg 790
Kris Stevens Enterprises, pg 801
KTVU-Retail Services, pg 802
Lynch Communications, pg 813
Maximus Media Inc, pg 820
Media Magic, pg 822
The Media Staff Inc, pg 822
On-Trax Inc, pg 846
OTR Studios, pg 848

PROGRAMMING — AUDIO

Radio Commercial Producers (continued)

CALIFORNIA (continued)

piXvfm Inc, pg 857
PM Productions, pg 858
QRS Software Services, pg 867
Steve Shapiro Music, pg 885
Still N' Motion, pg 901
Studio 132, pg 902
Tam Communications Inc, pg 906
Total Creative, pg 916
Webster Communications, pg 935

COLORADO

Tim Cissell Music, pg 725
Daylight Productions & Rentals, pg 739

CONNECTICUT

Moving Pictures, pg 832
P&P Studios Inc, pg 851
Powerstation Events, pg 860

FLORIDA

Blackburst Entertainment LLC, pg 706
Communications Concepts Inc (CCI), pg 729
Digital Zoetrope Productions, pg 742
LHV Audio Services, pg 807
Sunfire Communications Inc, pg 904
Sunrise Studios, pg 904
Tricycle Studios, pg 918
Universal Studios Florida® Production Group, pg 922

GEORGIA

Guerrilla Productions LLC, pg 774
White Dog Studios, pg 937

ILLINOIS

ABS Enterprises, pg 672
CCore Media Inc, pg 718
Cresta Creative, pg 734
Major Media Productions Inc, pg 815
Multimedia Marketing Group, pg 833
Jim Passin Productions, pg 852
Pepper Group, pg 854
Steven Samler Music & Sound, pg 879
Video Impressions, pg 928
Woodside Avenue Music Productions Inc, pg 941

INDIANA

A-V-A Video Productions, pg 671
Advanced Media Integration, pg 677

IOWA

Hedquist Productions Inc, pg 778

LOUISIANA

Digital FX Inc, pg 742
Disk Productions Inc, pg 743

MAINE

Serendipity Recordings, pg 884

MARYLAND

CPR MultiMedia Solutions, pg 732
The Cutting Corporation, GraphicAudio® & Archival Sound Lab, pg 736
dbF a Media Company, pg 739
The Image Generators, pg 785

MASSACHUSETTS

Labrecque Creative Sound, pg 803
Penfield Productions Ltd, pg 853
Soundtrack Group, pg 895
Rik Tinory Productions, pg 914
TR Productions, pg 916
TVN-The Video Network, pg 919

MICHIGAN

Digi Sign Design LLC, pg 741
K&R All Media Productions LLC, pg 796
K&R's Recording Studios Inc, pg 796
MessageMakers, pg 824

MISSOURI

Audio-VideoGraphics Inc, pg 694

NEVADA

DVDs4Less, pg 748
JCS Video Productions, pg 793

NEW HAMPSHIRE

Apertura, pg 686
Chip Taylor Communications LLC, pg 907

NEW JERSEY

CFP Video Productions Inc, pg 720
Euro-Pacific Film & Video Productions Inc, pg 756
Laurel Video Productions, pg 804
Midnight Media Group Inc, pg 827
Optisonics Productions, pg 847
Presence Records, pg 861
Suede Interactive, pg 903
VCSvideo, pg 925

NEW MEXICO

Production Outfitters, pg 864

NEW YORK

Big Fish Production US, pg 705
Blue Barn Pictures Inc, pg 707
Thomas Craven Film Corp, pg 733
Digital Force Ltd, pg 742
Fingerpaint, pg 761
HB-Content, pg 777
Mood Creations Ltd, pg 829
Jack Morton Worldwide, pg 830
New York Audio Productions, pg 840
The Palmer Group, pg 850
RadioArt/Bob & Ray CDs & MP3 Files, pg 869
David Rapkin Audio Production, pg 870
Elliot Sokolov Music, pg 892
Split Image Productions, pg 898
Suggs Media Productions Inc, pg 903
Tiki Recording Studios Inc, pg 914
Zelman Studios Ltd, pg 945

NORTH CAROLINA

Pat Appleson Studios Inc, pg 687
The Communications Group Inc, pg 729

Trailblazer Studios®, pg 917
2BruceStudio, pg 920

OHIO

Musicol Recording, pg 835
Take 1 Media Services, pg 906
Vista Color Imaging Inc, pg 931

OKLAHOMA

Piper Media Services Inc, pg 857

OREGON

Ideascape Inc, pg 784
KTVA Productions, pg 802
Odyssey Productions Inc, pg 844
REX, pg 874

PENNSYLVANIA

Audio Visual Communications Inc, pg 694
Forge Recording LLC, pg 764
Innovision Media Group, pg 788
JPL, pg 795
Production Masters Inc (PMI), pg 864
The Videohouse Inc, pg 929

RHODE ISLAND

Sound-FX-Design, pg 894

SOUTH CAROLINA

DaviSound, pg 739
Venture Media, pg 925

TENNESSEE

American Blackguard Inc, pg 683
Continental Film, pg 731
Love Shack Recording Studios, pg 811

TEXAS

Audiomoxie®, pg 695
Communication Arts Multimedia Inc, pg 728
Dykeman Associates Inc, pg 748
The Editing Co, pg 750
James Loupas Associates Inc, pg 811
Music Lab Inc, pg 834
Omega Productions, pg 845
Radio Vision Inc, pg 869
The Sound Lab Inc, pg 894
Sound Works, pg 894
Stage Directions, pg 898
TM Studios Inc, pg 915
Tropikal Productions, pg 918
The Yesterday USA Radio Networks, pg 944

VIRGINIA

Limelight Communications Inc, pg 808
Metro Productions, pg 824
National Media Services Inc, pg 836
Rocktown Media, pg 876
Studio Center Corp, pg 902

WASHINGTON

Hamilton Studio, pg 775
Kostov Productions, pg 801
Pacific Multimedia Inc, pg 849

WISCONSIN

5th Floor Recording Co, pg 760
Meridian Studios, pg 824

University of Wisconsin-Oshkosh Radio-TV-Film Dept, pg 923
USAV Group Inc, pg 923
Video Wisconsin Inc, pg 929
Watts Communications Inc, pg 934

WYOMING

Bridger Productions Inc, pg 710

NEWFOUNDLAND AND LABRADOR

Vidcraft Productions Ltd, pg 927

ONTARIO

ADS Media, pg 677
DebsVoice, pg 739
GAPC (General Assembly Production Centre), pg 768

Radio Commercial Rentals

ILLINOIS

Woodside Avenue Music Productions Inc, pg 941

MICHIGAN

Digi Sign Design LLC, pg 741

NEW HAMPSHIRE

Chip Taylor Communications LLC, pg 907

UTAH

Webb Audio Visual, pg 935

Radio Program—Classic Distributors

ARIZONA

Valley of the Sun Publishing Co, pg 924

CALIFORNIA

Pacifica Radio Archives, pg 849
QRS Software Services, pg 867

ILLINOIS

Major Media Inc, pg 815

MARYLAND

HighBridge Audio, pg 779

MASSACHUSETTS

Penfield Productions Ltd, pg 853

MICHIGAN

Digi Sign Design LLC, pg 741

NEW YORK

RadioArt/Bob & Ray CDs & MP3 Files, pg 869

SOUTH CAROLINA

DaviSound, pg 739

TEXAS

Endtime Ministries Inc, pg 754
Lamb & Lion Ministries, pg 803
Marengo Films, pg 817
TM Studios Inc, pg 915

Radio Program—Classic Producers

ARIZONA

KOOL-FM Radio, pg 801

CALIFORNIA

Ancient Future, pg 685
Creative Media Recording, pg 733
Kris Stevens Enterprises, pg 801
Lynch Communications, pg 813
Maximus Media Inc, pg 820
QRS Software Services, pg 867
Steve Shapiro Music, pg 885
Total Creative, pg 916

FLORIDA

LHV Audio Services, pg 807
Sunfire Communications Inc,
    pg 904

GEORGIA

Guerrilla Productions LLC, pg 774

ILLINOIS

Major Media Inc, pg 815

INDIANA

A-V-A Video Productions, pg 671

MARYLAND

dbF a Media Company, pg 739
HighBridge Audio, pg 779

MASSACHUSETTS

Penfield Productions Ltd, pg 853
Soundtrack Group, pg 895

MICHIGAN

Digi Sign Design LLC, pg 741
K&R All Media Productions LLC,
    pg 796
K&R's Recording Studios Inc,
    pg 796

NEVADA

JCS Video Productions, pg 793

NEW JERSEY

Suede Interactive, pg 903

NEW YORK

Digital Force Ltd, pg 742
RadioArt/Bob & Ray CDs & MP3
    Files, pg 869

NORTH CAROLINA

Pat Appleson Studios Inc, pg 687

OHIO

Musicol Recording, pg 835
Take 1 Media Services, pg 906

PENNSYLVANIA

Forge Recording LLC, pg 764

RHODE ISLAND

Sound-FX-Design, pg 894

SOUTH CAROLINA

DaviSound, pg 739

TENNESSEE

Love Shack Recording Studios,
    pg 811

TEXAS

Central Texas College KNCT-Radio
    FM, pg 719
Endtime Ministries Inc, pg 754
Lamb & Lion Ministries, pg 803
The Sound Lab Inc, pg 894
Texas Rebel Radio Network, pg 911
TM Studios Inc, pg 915
The Yesterday USA Radio
    Networks, pg 944

VIRGINIA

National Media Services Inc,
    pg 836
Rocktown Media, pg 876

WISCONSIN

5th Floor Recording Co, pg 760

ONTARIO

DebsVoice, pg 739
GAPC (General Assembly
    Production Centre), pg 768

Radio Program—Classic Rentals

MICHIGAN

Digi Sign Design LLC, pg 741

Religious Program Distributors

ALABAMA

Eternal Word Television Network
    (EWTN), pg 756

ARIZONA

Drumbeat Indian Arts Inc, pg 747
TSG Publishing Foundation Inc
    USA, pg 919

CALIFORNIA

Christian Media Network, pg 722
Clarity Sound & Light, pg 725
Direct Cinema Ltd Inc, pg 743
Hay House Inc, pg 777
Maximus Media Inc, pg 820
Nilgiri Press, pg 841
Osho Viha Information Center &
    Book Distributors, pg 848
Pacifica Radio Archives, pg 849
Paulist Productions, pg 852
QRS Software Services, pg 867
Vedanta Press & Catalog, pg 925
The Wyland Group, pg 942

COLORADO

Crown Ministries International,
    pg 735

DISTRICT OF COLUMBIA

Biblical Archaeology Society
    (BAS), pg 705
National Council of Churches,
    pg 836
USCCB Publishing, pg 923

FLORIDA

Children of Mary, pg 722

GEORGIA

Dake Publishing Inc, pg 737
New Leaf Distributing Co, pg 839

HAWAII

Media Bridge Gamekids, pg 821

ILLINOIS

ACTA Publications, pg 675
Baha'i Distribution Service (BDS),
    pg 700
CCore Media Inc, pg 718
Film Ideas Inc, pg 760
Institute on Religious Life Inc,
    pg 788
Liturgy Training Publications,
    pg 810
Theosophical Publishing House,
    pg 912

INDIANA

Communication Ministries, pg 728

MARYLAND

HighBridge Audio, pg 779

MASSACHUSETTS

Pauline Books & Media, pg 852

MICHIGAN

Digi Sign Design LLC, pg 741
Emery-Pratt Co, pg 753
Gemini, pg 769
Renaissance Unity, pg 873
Jack Van Impe Ministries
    International, pg 924
Zondervan, pg 945

MINNESOTA

Augsburg Fortress, pg 695

MISSOURI

Grace Church - St Louis, pg 773
Impact Christian Books Inc, pg 786
SOM Publishing Co, pg 892
Vedanta Society of St Louis, pg 925

NEBRASKA

Back to the Bible, pg 700

NEW HAMPSHIRE

Chip Taylor Communications LLC,
    pg 907

NEW JERSEY

Listen & Live Audio Inc, pg 809
Paulist Press, pg 852

NEW YORK

Billy Budd Films Inc, pg 712
Hallel Communications, pg 775
HarperAudio, pg 776
Janus Films Inc, pg 793
SISU Home Entertainment Inc,
    pg 889

NORTH CAROLINA

Howard Hanger, pg 775

OHIO

Franciscan Media, pg 765
Twin Sisters® Digital Media™,
    pg 920

PENNSYLVANIA

Anchor Distributors, pg 685
Chinmaya Publications, pg 722
FMP Media Solutions Inc, pg 763
Himalayan Institute Audio/Video,
    pg 780
Pendle Hill Bookstore, pg 853

TENNESSEE

Abingdon Press, pg 672
Capitol Christian Music Group,
    pg 716
Cokesbury, pg 727
Randall House Publications, pg 870
Spring Arbor Distributors Inc,
    pg 898
Word Label Group, pg 941
Zion Music Group, pg 945

TEXAS

Educational Video Network, pg 751
Endtime Ministries Inc, pg 754
Lamb & Lion Ministries, pg 803

VIRGINIA

CDR Communications Inc, pg 719
Shakticom, pg 885

BRITISH COLUMBIA

Timeless Books, pg 914

ONTARIO

Broughton's Church Supplies,
    Religious Books & Gifts, pg 711
Canadian Learning Co Inc, pg 715
Gospel Folio Press, pg 773
Life Cycle Books Ltd, pg 807
Novalis, pg 843

Religious Program Producers

ALABAMA

Dogwood Productions Inc, pg 745
Eternal Word Television Network
    (EWTN), pg 756

ARIZONA

CyberIconics International, pg 736
Truth Consciousness Publications,
    pg 919
TSG Publishing Foundation Inc
    USA, pg 919

ARKANSAS

White Diamond Productions LLC,
    pg 937

CALIFORNIA

The Banquet Sound Studios, pg 701
Christian Media Network, pg 722
Clarity Sound & Light, pg 725
Custom Video Productions Inc,
    pg 736
Direct Cinema Ltd Inc, pg 743
Gateways Books & Tapes, pg 768
Hay House Inc, pg 777
Lynch Communications, pg 813
Maximus Media Inc, pg 820
Osho Viha Information Center &
    Book Distributors, pg 848
Paulist Productions, pg 852
piXvfm Inc, pg 857
PM Productions, pg 858
QRS Software Services, pg 867
Studio 132, pg 902
Total Creative, pg 916

PROGRAMMING — AUDIO

Religious Program Producers (continued)

CALIFORNIA (continued)
Vedanta Press & Catalog, pg 925
The Wyland Group, pg 942

COLORADO
Crown Ministries International, pg 735

DISTRICT OF COLUMBIA
Biblical Archaeology Society (BAS), pg 705
USCCB Publishing, pg 923

FLORIDA
Blackburst Entertainment LLC, pg 706
LHV Audio Services, pg 807
Sunfire Communications Inc, pg 904
Sunrise Studios, pg 904

GEORGIA
The Alliance for Christian Media, pg 680
Dake Publishing Inc, pg 737
Guerrilla Productions LLC, pg 774

HAWAII
Media Bridge Gamekids, pg 821

ILLINOIS
ACTA Publications, pg 675
CCore Media Inc, pg 718
Liturgy Training Publications, pg 810
Major Media Productions Inc, pg 815
Pepper Group, pg 854
Theosophical Publishing House, pg 912
20/20 Communications Inc, pg 920
Video Impressions, pg 928

INDIANA
A-V-A Video Productions, pg 671
Communication Ministries, pg 728
OMNI Productions, pg 845
PentaVision Communications Inc, pg 854

LOUISIANA
Disk Productions Inc, pg 743

MARYLAND
The Cutting Corporation, GraphicAudio® & Archival Sound Lab, pg 736
dbF a Media Company, pg 739
HighBridge Audio, pg 779

MASSACHUSETTS
Pauline Books & Media, pg 852
Soundtrack Group, pg 895

MICHIGAN
Digi Sign Design LLC, pg 741
Gemini, pg 769
K&R All Media Productions LLC, pg 796

K&R's Recording Studios Inc, pg 796
Renaissance Unity, pg 873
Zondervan, pg 945

MINNESOTA
Augsburg Fortress, pg 695

MISSOURI
Audio-VideoGraphics Inc, pg 694
Grace Church - St Louis, pg 773
Impact Christian Books Inc, pg 786
SOM Publishing Co, pg 892
Vedanta Society of St Louis, pg 925

NEVADA
JCS Video Productions, pg 793

NEW HAMPSHIRE
Apertura, pg 686
Chip Taylor Communications LLC, pg 907

NEW JERSEY
Audio Vistas LLC, pg 694
CFP Video Productions Inc, pg 720
C2 Imaging, pg 735
Laurel Video Productions, pg 804
Listen & Live Audio Inc, pg 809
MiB MediaWorks, pg 825
Optisonics Productions, pg 847
Paulist Press, pg 852
Suede Interactive, pg 903

NEW YORK
Thomas Craven Film Corp, pg 733
Digital Force Ltd, pg 742
Hallel Communications, pg 775
HarperAudio, pg 776
Lavine Production Group, pg 804
Jack Morton Worldwide, pg 830
The Palmer Group, pg 850
SISU Home Entertainment Inc, pg 889
Split Image Productions, pg 898
Spoken Arts Inc, pg 898
Tiki Recording Studios Inc, pg 914
Zelman Studios Ltd, pg 945

NORTH CAROLINA
Howard Hanger, pg 775

OHIO
Franciscan Media, pg 765
MainSail Production Services Inc, pg 815
Musicol Recording, pg 835
Take 1 Media Services, pg 906
Twin Sisters® Digital Media™, pg 920
Vista Color Imaging Inc, pg 931

OKLAHOMA
Piper Media Services Inc, pg 857

PENNSYLVANIA
Chinmaya Publications, pg 722
FMP Media Solutions Inc, pg 763
Forge Recording LLC, pg 764
Himalayan Institute Audio/Video, pg 780
JPL, pg 795

RHODE ISLAND
Sound-FX-Design, pg 894

TENNESSEE
Abingdon Press, pg 672
Capitol Christian Music Group, pg 716
Cokesbury, pg 727
Continental Film, pg 731
Memphis Communications Corp, pg 823
Mr Mark's Used Musical, Stereo & Studio Equipment Store, pg 828
Spring Arbor Distributors Inc, pg 898
Word Label Group, pg 941

TEXAS
AMA Nystrom Printing/Finishing, pg 682
The Editing Co, pg 750
Educational Video Network, pg 751
Endtime Ministries Inc, pg 754
Lamb & Lion Ministries, pg 803
Omega Productions, pg 845
Reelsound Recording Co, pg 872
The Sound Lab Inc, pg 894
Sound Works, pg 894
Stage Directions, pg 898
Tropikal Productions, pg 918

VERMONT
Inner Traditions International, pg 788

VIRGINIA
CDR Communications Inc, pg 719
Metro Productions, pg 824
National Media Services Inc, pg 836
Rocktown Media, pg 876
Shakticom, pg 885

WASHINGTON
Kostov Productions, pg 801
Pacific Multimedia Inc, pg 849

WISCONSIN
5th Floor Recording Co, pg 760
USAV Group Inc, pg 923
Watts Communications Inc, pg 934

WYOMING
Bridger Productions Inc, pg 710

BRITISH COLUMBIA
Timeless Books, pg 914

ONTARIO
ADS Media, pg 677
DebsVoice, pg 739
Novalis, pg 843

QUEBEC
Kerrigan Productions Inc, pg 798

Religious Program Rentals

CALIFORNIA
Direct Cinema Ltd Inc, pg 743
Paulist Productions, pg 852

MICHIGAN
Digi Sign Design LLC, pg 741

NEW HAMPSHIRE
Chip Taylor Communications LLC, pg 907

NEW JERSEY
Alden Films, pg 679
Listen & Live Audio Inc, pg 809

NEW YORK
Hallel Communications, pg 775

ONTARIO
Simply Audiobooks, pg 889

Research—Technical Program, see Technical Research Program

Sales Promotion & Training Program Distributors

ARIZONA
Tom Hopkins International Inc, pg 781
Personal Achievement Institute, pg 854

CALIFORNIA
Direct Cinema Ltd Inc, pg 743
Maximus Media Inc, pg 820
People Skills International, pg 854
QRS Software Services, pg 867

FLORIDA
Effective Learning Systems LLC, pg 751
PAR Inc, pg 851
Potentials Unlimited, pg 860

GEORGIA
Playback Now Inc, pg 858

ILLINOIS
ABS Enterprises, pg 672
CCore Media Inc, pg 718
Nightingale-Conant Corp, pg 841

IOWA
Prositions Inc, pg 865

MASSACHUSETTS
Penfield Productions Ltd, pg 853

MICHIGAN
Digi Sign Design LLC, pg 741

MINNESOTA
Learning Strategies Corp, pg 805

MISSOURI
SOM Publishing Co, pg 892

MONTANA
Jereco Studios Inc, pg 793

NEVADA
DVDs4Less, pg 748

NEW HAMPSHIRE
Chip Taylor Communications LLC, pg 907

NEW JERSEY

Listen & Live Audio Inc, pg 809

NEW YORK

The Cinema Guild Inc, pg 724
Albert Ellis Institute (AEI), pg 753
HarperAudio, pg 776
HB-Content, pg 777
Synaptic Digital, pg 905
Visual Technologies Corp, pg 932

NORTH CAROLINA

AudioSolutionz LLC, pg 695
Speakers Unlimited, pg 896

OREGON

InterVision Media, pg 791

PENNSYLVANIA

FMP Media Solutions Inc, pg 763

TENNESSEE

American Blackguard Inc, pg 683
Continental Film, pg 731

TEXAS

Emergency Film Group, pg 753
Executive Development Systems
   Inc, pg 757

VIRGINIA

CACI Integrated Communications,
   pg 713

BRITISH COLUMBIA

Thompson Rivers University
   Marketing & Communications
   Dept, pg 913

ONTARIO

Canadian Learning Co Inc, pg 715

Sales Promotion & Training Program Producers

ALABAMA

Dogwood Productions Inc, pg 745
Leo Ticheli Productions, pg 913

ARIZONA

Allusion Studios & Pure Wave
   Audio, pg 681
Candee Productions Inc, pg 716
Tom Hopkins International Inc,
   pg 781
Metropolitan Audio-Visual Inc,
   pg 824
Personal Achievement Institute,
   pg 854
SPEAK HOUSE Audio™, pg 896

ARKANSAS

White Diamond Productions LLC,
   pg 937

CALIFORNIA

Aaron Marcus and Associates,
   pg 671
The Banquet Sound Studios, pg 701
Big Door, pg 705
Creative Media Recording, pg 733
Creative Technology, pg 733

Custom Video Productions Inc,
   pg 736
Design Media, pg 741
Direct Cinema Ltd Inc, pg 743
Goal Productions, pg 772
Gold Standard Productions, pg 772
International Contact Inc, pg 790
Kavich Reynolds Productions Inc,
   pg 797
KTVU-Retail Services, pg 802
Lynch Communications, pg 813
Maximus Media Inc, pg 820
Media Magic, pg 822
The Media Staff Inc, pg 822
piXvfm Inc, pg 857
Point of View Productions, pg 858
Producers Group Ltd, pg 863
QRS Software Services, pg 867
Steve Shapiro Music, pg 885
Still N' Motion, pg 901
Studio 132, pg 902
Tam Communications Inc, pg 906
Total Creative, pg 916
Video Resources Inc, pg 928
Wavemaker Media Design, pg 934
Webster Communications, pg 935
Zamacona Productions, pg 945

COLORADO

Apogee Communications Group,
   pg 687
Daylight Productions & Rentals,
   pg 739
Flashback Media Productions,
   pg 762

CONNECTICUT

ACM Productions Ltd, pg 674
The Gary-Paul Agency, pg 768
Moving Pictures, pg 832
P&P Studios Inc, pg 851

FLORIDA

Audacity Recording Studios, pg 693
Audio Visual Imagineering Inc,
   pg 694
Blackburst Entertainment LLC,
   pg 706
Communications Concepts Inc
   (CCI), pg 729
Effective Learning Systems LLC,
   pg 751
I M P A C T Publishing Inc,
   pg 783
LHV Audio Services, pg 807
Roger Scruggs Films, pg 883
Sunfire Communications Inc,
   pg 904
Sunrise Studios, pg 904
Tricycle Studios, pg 918
Universal Studios Florida®
   Production Group, pg 922
Mike Vasilinda Productions Inc,
   pg 925

GEORGIA

Guerrilla Productions LLC, pg 774
Playback Now Inc, pg 858
WaveGuide Studios, pg 934

IDAHO

Wide Eye Productions, pg 938

ILLINOIS

ABS Enterprises, pg 672
Accenture, pg 672
CCore Media Inc, pg 718
Cresta Creative, pg 734
Major Media Productions Inc,
   pg 815

Multimedia Marketing Group,
   pg 833
Nightingale-Conant Corp, pg 841
Pepper Group, pg 854
PSAV® Presentation Services
   (Hotel Services Division), pg 866
Steven Samler Music & Sound,
   pg 879
Sparkfactor, pg 896
20/20 Communications Inc, pg 920
Video Impressions, pg 928

INDIANA

A-V-A Video Productions, pg 671
Advanced Media Integration, pg 677
Bright Ideas Creative Services,
   pg 710
OMNI Productions, pg 845
PentaVision Communications Inc,
   pg 854

IOWA

Hedquist Productions Inc, pg 778
Prositions Inc, pg 865

LOUISIANA

Digital FX Inc, pg 742

MARYLAND

CPR MultiMedia Solutions, pg 732
The Cutting Corporation,
   GraphicAudio® & Archival
   Sound Lab, pg 736
dbF a Media Company, pg 739
The Image Generators, pg 785
Kramer Communications Video
   Production, pg 801
Milner-Fenwick Inc, pg 828
Mobile-Video Productions Inc,
   pg 828

MASSACHUSETTS

CommCreative, pg 728
Penfield Productions Ltd, pg 853
Preston Productions Inc, pg 861
Soundtrack Group, pg 895
TR Productions, pg 916
TVN-The Video Network, pg 919

MICHIGAN

Digi Sign Design LLC, pg 741
K&R All Media Productions LLC,
   pg 796
K&R's Recording Studios Inc,
   pg 796
MessageMakers, pg 824
TGA Recording Co, pg 911

MINNESOTA

GMI Productions, pg 771
Learning Strategies Corp, pg 805
Media Loft Inc, pg 822

MISSOURI

Audio-VideoGraphics Inc, pg 694
Hardcastle Films & Video, pg 776
SOM Publishing Co, pg 892

MONTANA

Jereco Studios Inc, pg 793

NEVADA

DVDs4Less, pg 748
JCS Video Productions, pg 793

NEW HAMPSHIRE

Apertura, pg 686
Chip Taylor Communications LLC,
   pg 907

NEW JERSEY

Audio Vistas LLC, pg 694
CFP Video Productions Inc, pg 720
C2 Imaging, pg 735
Laurel Video Productions, pg 804
Listen & Live Audio Inc, pg 809
MiB MediaWorks, pg 825
Optisonics Productions, pg 847
Projects in Knowledge Inc, pg 865
Suede Interactive, pg 903

NEW YORK

Avekta Productions Inc, pg 697
Broadstreet Productions LLC,
   pg 711
Cohn Creative Group LLC, pg 727
Digital Force Ltd, pg 742
Albert Ellis Institute (AEI), pg 753
Fingerpaint, pg 761
HarperAudio, pg 776
HB-Content, pg 777
Hello World Communications,
   pg 778
Icontent, pg 783
Ketchum Inc, pg 798
Jack Morton Worldwide, pg 830
MRM//McCANN, pg 832
MRY, pg 832
New York Audio Productions,
   pg 840
News Broadcast Network Inc,
   pg 840
The Palmer Group, pg 850
Pat Kogan Productions Inc, pg 852
David Rapkin Audio Production,
   pg 870
Split Image Productions, pg 898
Suggs Media Productions Inc,
   pg 903
Synaptic Digital, pg 905
Tiki Recording Studios Inc, pg 914
Zelman Studios Ltd, pg 945

NORTH CAROLINA

Pat Appleson Studios Inc, pg 687
AudioSolutionz LLC, pg 695
The Communications Group Inc,
   pg 729
Sinclair Institute, pg 889
Trailblazer Studios®, pg 917
2BruceStudio, pg 920

OHIO

Advent Media Inc, pg 677
MainSail Production Services Inc,
   pg 815
Musicol Recording, pg 835
R&B Communications Inc, pg 870
Take 1 Media Services, pg 906
Vista Color Imaging Inc, pg 931

OKLAHOMA

Piper Media Services Inc, pg 857

OREGON

Ideascape Inc, pg 784
InterVision Media, pg 791
KTVA Productions, pg 802
Odyssey Productions Inc, pg 844
REX, pg 874

PROGRAMMING — AUDIO

Sales Promotion & Training Program Producers (continued)

PENNSYLVANIA

American Artist Studio, pg 682
Audio Visual Communications Inc, pg 694
Bang! Pictures Inc, pg 701
FMP Media Solutions Inc, pg 763
Forge Recording LLC, pg 764
Innovision Media Group, pg 788
JPL, pg 795
Kensington Falls Animation, pg 797
Muderick Media, pg 833
Panta Rhei Media Inc, pg 851
Production Masters Inc (PMI), pg 864
The Videohouse Inc, pg 929
Visual Sound Inc, pg 931

RHODE ISLAND

Sound-FX-Design, pg 894

SOUTH CAROLINA

Stages Video Productions, pg 899
Venture Media, pg 925

TENNESSEE

American Blackguard Inc, pg 683
Continental Film, pg 731
Memphis Communications Corp, pg 823
Stage Post, pg 899
Russ Sturgeon Productions/RSVP, pg 903

TEXAS

AMA Nystrom Printing/Finishing, pg 682
Biway Media, pg 706
Dykeman Associates Inc, pg 748
The Editing Co, pg 750
Emergency Film Group, pg 753
Epic Software Group Inc, pg 755
Omega Productions, pg 845
Romar Learning Solutions LLC, pg 877
The Sound Lab Inc, pg 894
Sound Works, pg 894
Stage Directions, pg 898

VIRGINIA

Advance Concepts Inc, pg 677
CACI Integrated Communications, pg 713
Limelight Communications Inc, pg 808
Metro Productions, pg 824
National Media Services Inc, pg 836
Rocktown Media, pg 876

WASHINGTON

Kostov Productions, pg 801
Pacific Multimedia Inc, pg 849

WISCONSIN

Audio Visual of Milwaukee Inc, pg 694
5th Floor Recording Co, pg 760
Meridian Studios, pg 824
USAV Group Inc, pg 923
Video Wisconsin Inc, pg 929

Watts Communications Inc, pg 934
Wisconsin Public Television, pg 940

WYOMING

Bridger Productions Inc, pg 710

ALBERTA

Black Media Works, pg 706

BRITISH COLUMBIA

Thompson Rivers University Marketing & Communications Dept, pg 913

NEWFOUNDLAND AND LABRADOR

Vidcraft Productions Ltd, pg 927

ONTARIO

ADS Media, pg 677
DebsVoice, pg 739
GAPC (General Assembly Production Centre), pg 768
JFB Communications, pg 794

QUEBEC

Kerrigan Productions Inc, pg 798

Sales Promotion & Training Program Rentals

CALIFORNIA

Direct Cinema Ltd Inc, pg 743

MASSACHUSETTS

Preston Productions Inc, pg 861

MICHIGAN

Digi Sign Design LLC, pg 741

NEW HAMPSHIRE

Chip Taylor Communications LLC, pg 907

NEW JERSEY

Alden Films, pg 679
Listen & Live Audio Inc, pg 809

UTAH

Webb Audio Visual, pg 935

ONTARIO

Simply Audiobooks, pg 889

Scientific Program Distributors

CALIFORNIA

Astronomical Society of the Pacific, pg 691
Direct Cinema Ltd Inc, pg 743
Gateways, pg 768
Bruce Goldberg Inc, pg 772
Maximus Media Inc, pg 820
Pacifica Radio Archives, pg 849
QRS Software Services, pg 867
The Wine Appreciation Guild Ltd, pg 939

COLORADO

American Educational Products LLC, pg 683

CONNECTICUT

Tantor Media Inc, pg 907

DISTRICT OF COLUMBIA

American Chemical Society (ACS), pg 683

FLORIDA

Video Resources Software, pg 928

GEORGIA

School Media Associates LLC, pg 882

KENTUCKY

Horizon Films & Media LLC, pg 781

MARYLAND

MMI Marketing, pg 828

MASSACHUSETTS

Penfield Productions Ltd, pg 853

MICHIGAN

Digi Sign Design LLC, pg 741
Emery-Pratt Co, pg 753

MINNESOTA

Science Museum of Minnesota, pg 882

MONTANA

High Plains Films, pg 779

NEW HAMPSHIRE

Chip Taylor Communications LLC, pg 907

NEW JERSEY

Allegro Productions Inc, pg 680

NEW YORK

Cambridge University Press, pg 715
Films Media Group, pg 760
Guilford Publications, pg 774
March of Dimes Foundation, pg 816

PENNSYLVANIA

FMP Media Solutions Inc, pg 763

TEXAS

Educational Video Network, pg 751
Emergency Film Group, pg 753

VIRGINIA

CACI Integrated Communications, pg 713

ONTARIO

Canadian Learning Co Inc, pg 715

Scientific Program Producers

CALIFORNIA

Astronomical Society of the Pacific, pg 691
Big Door, pg 705
Custom Video Productions Inc, pg 736
Direct Cinema Ltd Inc, pg 743
Bruce Goldberg Inc, pg 772
imageReal Pictures LLC, pg 785
Lynch Communications, pg 813
The Media Staff Inc, pg 822
piXvfm Inc, pg 857
Producers Group Ltd, pg 863
QRS Software Services, pg 867
Steve Shapiro Music, pg 885
Still N' Motion, pg 901
Studio 132, pg 902
Total Creative, pg 916
Video Resources Inc, pg 928
Wavemaker Media Design, pg 934
Webster Communications, pg 935

COLORADO

American Educational Products LLC, pg 683
Apogee Communications Group, pg 687
Daylight Productions & Rentals, pg 739
Flashback Media Productions, pg 762

CONNECTICUT

ACM Productions Ltd, pg 674
Tantor Media Inc, pg 907

DISTRICT OF COLUMBIA

American Chemical Society (ACS), pg 683
Hillmann & Carr Inc, pg 780

FLORIDA

Audio Visual Imagineering Inc, pg 694
Blackburst Entertainment LLC, pg 706
LHV Audio Services, pg 807
Sunfire Communications Inc, pg 904
Sunrise Studios, pg 904
Tricycle Studios, pg 918
Video Resources Software, pg 928

GEORGIA

Guerrilla Productions LLC, pg 774

IDAHO

Wide Eye Productions, pg 938

ILLINOIS

ABS Enterprises, pg 672
Major Media Productions Inc, pg 815
Pepper Group, pg 854
20/20 Communications Inc, pg 920
Video Impressions, pg 928

INDIANA

A-V-A Video Productions, pg 671

IOWA

Hedquist Productions Inc, pg 778

KENTUCKY

Horizon Films & Media LLC, pg 781
National Geographic Learning, pg 836

LOUISIANA

Louisiana State University Division of Strategic Communications, pg 811

MARYLAND

The Cutting Corporation, GraphicAudio® & Archival Sound Lab, pg 736
dbF a Media Company, pg 739
The Image Generators, pg 785
Kramer Communications Video Production, pg 801
MMI Marketing, pg 828

MASSACHUSETTS

Heliotrope Studios, pg 778
Monadnock Media Inc, pg 829
Penfield Productions Ltd, pg 853
Soundtrack Group, pg 895
TR Productions, pg 916

MICHIGAN

Digi Sign Design LLC, pg 741
K&R All Media Productions LLC, pg 796
K&R's Recording Studios Inc, pg 796

MINNESOTA

Science Museum of Minnesota, pg 882

MONTANA

High Plains Films, pg 779

NEVADA

JCS Video Productions, pg 793
Tetrahedron LLC, pg 911

NEW HAMPSHIRE

Apertura, pg 686
Chip Taylor Communications LLC, pg 907

NEW JERSEY

Allegro Productions Inc, pg 680
Audio Vistas LLC, pg 694
CFP Video Productions Inc, pg 720
C2 Imaging, pg 735
Laurel Video Productions, pg 804
MiB MediaWorks, pg 825
Optisonics Productions, pg 847
Suede Interactive, pg 903

NEW YORK

Avekta Productions Inc, pg 697
Broadstreet Productions LLC, pg 711
CompuWeather Inc, pg 729
Digital Force Ltd, pg 742
Fingerpaint, pg 761
Guilford Publications, pg 774
Icontent, pg 783
March of Dimes Foundation, pg 816
Jack Morton Worldwide, pg 830
MRY, pg 832
New York Audio Productions, pg 840
News Broadcast Network Inc, pg 840

The Palmer Group, pg 850
Pat Kogan Productions Inc, pg 852
David Rapkin Audio Production, pg 870
Split Image Productions, pg 898
Tiki Recording Studios Inc, pg 914
Videograf, pg 929
Zelman Studios Ltd, pg 945

NORTH CAROLINA

Pat Appleson Studios Inc, pg 687
Trailblazer Studios®, pg 917
2BruceStudio, pg 920

OHIO

R&B Communications Inc, pg 870
Take 1 Media Services, pg 906
Vista Color Imaging Inc, pg 931

OKLAHOMA

Piper Media Services Inc, pg 857

OREGON

ERA Learning, pg 755
Ideascape Inc, pg 784
Odyssey Productions Inc, pg 844

PENNSYLVANIA

Audio Visual Communications Inc, pg 694
FMP Media Solutions Inc, pg 763
Forge Recording LLC, pg 764
JPL, pg 795
Production Masters Inc (PMI), pg 864

RHODE ISLAND

Sound-FX-Design, pg 894

SOUTH CAROLINA

Venture Media, pg 925

TENNESSEE

Continental Film, pg 731
Memphis Communications Corp, pg 823

TEXAS

Educational Video Network, pg 751
Emergency Film Group, pg 753
Omega Productions, pg 845
Romar Learning Solutions LLC, pg 877
The Sound Lab Inc, pg 894
Sound Works, pg 894
Texas Heart Institute Visual Communication Services, pg 911

VIRGINIA

CACI Integrated Communications, pg 713
Limelight Communications Inc, pg 808
Metro Productions, pg 824
National Media Services Inc, pg 836
Rocktown Media, pg 876

WASHINGTON

Pacific Multimedia Inc, pg 849

WISCONSIN

5th Floor Recording Co, pg 760
USAV Group Inc, pg 923
Wisconsin Public Television, pg 940

WYOMING

Bridger Productions Inc, pg 710

ONTARIO

ADS Media, pg 677
JFB Communications, pg 794

QUEBEC

Kerrigan Productions Inc, pg 798

Scientific Program Rentals

CALIFORNIA

Direct Cinema Ltd Inc, pg 743

MICHIGAN

Digi Sign Design LLC, pg 741

NEW HAMPSHIRE

Chip Taylor Communications LLC, pg 907

UTAH

Webb Audio Visual, pg 935

Sponsored Program Distributors

CALIFORNIA

Direct Cinema Ltd Inc, pg 743
Maximus Media Inc, pg 820
Medcom Inc, pg 821
QRS Software Services, pg 867

ILLINOIS

CCore Media Inc, pg 718

MASSACHUSETTS

Penfield Productions Ltd, pg 853

MICHIGAN

Digi Sign Design LLC, pg 741

NEW HAMPSHIRE

Chip Taylor Communications LLC, pg 907

NEW JERSEY

Allegro Productions Inc, pg 680

NEW YORK

Hallel Communications, pg 775
HB-Content, pg 777
Synaptic Digital, pg 905

OREGON

InterVision Media, pg 791

PENNSYLVANIA

FMP Media Solutions Inc, pg 763

SOUTH CAROLINA

DaviSound, pg 739

TENNESSEE

American Blackguard Inc, pg 683
Continental Film, pg 731

ALBERTA

Global TV, pg 771

Sponsored Program Producers

ALABAMA

Leo Ticheli Productions, pg 913

CALIFORNIA

Big Door, pg 705
Creative Media Recording, pg 733
Creative Technology, pg 733
Custom Video Productions Inc, pg 736
Direct Cinema Ltd Inc, pg 743
imageReal Pictures LLC, pg 785
KTVU-Retail Services, pg 802
Lynch Communications, pg 813
Maximus Media Inc, pg 820
Medcom Inc, pg 821
The Media Staff Inc, pg 822
Producers Group Ltd, pg 863
QRS Software Services, pg 867
Still N' Motion, pg 901
Studio 132, pg 902
Total Creative, pg 916
Video Resources Inc, pg 928
Webster Communications, pg 935
Zamacona Productions, pg 945

COLORADO

Apogee Communications Group, pg 687
Tatum Video, pg 907

CONNECTICUT

ACM Productions Ltd, pg 674
Moving Pictures, pg 832

DISTRICT OF COLUMBIA

Hillmann & Carr Inc, pg 780

FLORIDA

Audio Visual Imagineering Inc, pg 694
Blackburst Entertainment LLC, pg 706
Communications Concepts Inc (CCI), pg 729
LHV Audio Services, pg 807
Roger Scruggs Films, pg 883
Sunfire Communications Inc, pg 904
Sunrise Studios, pg 904
Tricycle Studios, pg 918

GEORGIA

Guerrilla Productions LLC, pg 774

IDAHO

Wide Eye Productions, pg 938

ILLINOIS

CCore Media Inc, pg 718
Nightingale-Conant Corp, pg 841
Jim Passin Productions, pg 852
Pepper Group, pg 854
PSAV® Presentation Services (Hotel Services Division), pg 866
Video Impressions, pg 928

INDIANA

A-V-A Video Productions, pg 671

IOWA

Educational Technology & Media Services, pg 751

PROGRAMMING — AUDIO

Sponsored Program Producers (continued)

MARYLAND

CPR MultiMedia Solutions, pg 732
The Cutting Corporation, GraphicAudio® & Archival Sound Lab, pg 736
dbF a Media Company, pg 739
The Image Generators, pg 785

MASSACHUSETTS

Penfield Productions Ltd, pg 853
Preston Productions Inc, pg 861
Soundtrack Group, pg 895
TR Productions, pg 916

MICHIGAN

Digi Sign Design LLC, pg 741
K&R All Media Productions LLC, pg 796
K&R's Recording Studios Inc, pg 796

NEVADA

JCS Video Productions, pg 793

NEW HAMPSHIRE

Apertura, pg 686
Chip Taylor Communications LLC, pg 907

NEW JERSEY

Allegro Productions Inc, pg 680
CFP Video Productions Inc, pg 720
Laurel Video Productions, pg 804
Optisonics Productions, pg 847
Suede Interactive, pg 903

NEW YORK

Avekta Productions Inc, pg 697
Blue Barn Pictures Inc, pg 707
Broadstreet Productions LLC, pg 711
Cohn Creative Group LLC, pg 727
Digital Force Ltd, pg 742
Hallel Communications, pg 775
HB-Content, pg 777
Ketchum Inc, pg 798
Jack Morton Worldwide, pg 830
New York Audio Productions, pg 840
News Broadcast Network Inc, pg 840
The Palmer Group, pg 850
Pat Kogan Productions Inc, pg 852
David Rapkin Audio Production, pg 870
Elliot Sokolov Music, pg 892
Split Image Productions, pg 898
Suggs Media Productions Inc, pg 903
Synaptic Digital, pg 905
Videograf, pg 929
Zelman Studios Ltd, pg 945

NORTH CAROLINA

Pat Appleson Studios Inc, pg 687

OHIO

R&B Communications Inc, pg 870
Take 1 Media Services, pg 906
Vista Color Imaging Inc, pg 931

OKLAHOMA

Piper Media Services Inc, pg 857

OREGON

Ideascape Inc, pg 784
InterVision Media, pg 791
Odyssey Productions Inc, pg 844

PENNSYLVANIA

FMP Media Solutions Inc, pg 763
Forge Recording LLC, pg 764
JPL, pg 795
Production Masters Inc (PMI), pg 864

RHODE ISLAND

Sound-FX-Design, pg 894

SOUTH CAROLINA

DaviSound, pg 739

TENNESSEE

American Blackguard Inc, pg 683

TEXAS

Emergency Film Group, pg 753
Omega Productions, pg 845
Romar Learning Solutions LLC, pg 877
The Sound Lab Inc, pg 894
Sound Works, pg 894
South Coast Film & Video, pg 895
Texas Heart Institute Visual Communication Services, pg 911

VIRGINIA

Metro Productions, pg 824
National Media Services Inc, pg 836
Rocktown Media, pg 876

WISCONSIN

5th Floor Recording Co, pg 760
Video Wisconsin Inc, pg 929
Watts Communications Inc, pg 934

WYOMING

Bridger Productions Inc, pg 710

ALBERTA

Global TV, pg 771

ONTARIO

GAPC (General Assembly Production Centre), pg 768
JFB Communications, pg 794

QUEBEC

Kerrigan Productions Inc, pg 798

Sponsored Program Rentals

CALIFORNIA

Direct Cinema Ltd Inc, pg 743
Medcom Inc, pg 821

MASSACHUSETTS

Preston Productions Inc, pg 861

MICHIGAN

Digi Sign Design LLC, pg 741

NEW HAMPSHIRE

Chip Taylor Communications LLC, pg 907

NEW YORK

Hallel Communications, pg 775

UTAH

Webb Audio Visual, pg 935

Sports Program Distributors

CALIFORNIA

Crystal Pyramid Productions™, pg 735
Deja View Video, pg 740
Maximus Media Inc, pg 820
QRS Software Services, pg 867
Sodanceabit, pg 892

FLORIDA

Effective Learning Systems LLC, pg 751
I M P A C T Publishing Inc, pg 783
Potentials Unlimited, pg 860

ILLINOIS

Nightingale-Conant Corp, pg 841

IOWA

Championship Productions Inc, pg 720

MARYLAND

HighBridge Audio, pg 779

MASSACHUSETTS

Penfield Productions Ltd, pg 853

MICHIGAN

Digi Sign Design LLC, pg 741

NEW HAMPSHIRE

Chip Taylor Communications LLC, pg 907

NEW JERSEY

Listen & Live Audio Inc, pg 809

NEW YORK

HarperAudio, pg 776
HB-Content, pg 777
Madison Square Garden, pg 814
Synaptic Digital, pg 905

NORTH CAROLINA

Motor Racing Network, pg 831

OREGON

InterVision Media, pg 791

PENNSYLVANIA

FMP Media Solutions Inc, pg 763

TENNESSEE

Spring Arbor Distributors Inc, pg 898

VIRGINIA

CACI Integrated Communications, pg 713

ALBERTA

Global TV, pg 771

ONTARIO

Canadian Learning Co Inc, pg 715

Sports Program Producers

ARKANSAS

White Diamond Productions LLC, pg 937

CALIFORNIA

A Go Go Films, pg 671
Big Door, pg 705
Creative Technology, pg 733
Crystal Pyramid Productions™, pg 735
Custom Video Productions Inc, pg 736
Deja View Video, pg 740
Direct Cinema Ltd Inc, pg 743
Havas Edge, pg 777
Lynch Communications, pg 813
On-Trax Inc, pg 846
Producers Group Ltd, pg 863
QRS Software Services, pg 867
Reality Check Systems, pg 871
Steve Shapiro Music, pg 885
Sodanceabit, pg 892
Studio 132, pg 902
Total Creative, pg 916
Video Resources Inc, pg 928
Webster Communications, pg 935

COLORADO

Tatum Video, pg 907

CONNECTICUT

ACM Productions Ltd, pg 674
The Gary-Paul Agency, pg 768

FLORIDA

Blackburst Entertainment LLC, pg 706
Communications Concepts Inc (CCI), pg 729
Effective Learning Systems LLC, pg 751
I M P A C T Publishing Inc, pg 783
LHV Audio Services, pg 807
Roger Scruggs Films, pg 883
Sunfire Communications Inc, pg 904
Sunrise Studios, pg 904

GEORGIA

Guerrilla Productions LLC, pg 774
Myriad Productions, pg 835

IDAHO

Wide Eye Productions, pg 938

ILLINOIS

ABS Enterprises, pg 672
Nightingale-Conant Corp, pg 841
Pepper Group, pg 854
20/20 Communications Inc, pg 920

INDIANA
A-V-A Video Productions, pg 671
PentaVision Communications Inc, pg 854

IOWA
Championship Productions Inc, pg 720

LOUISIANA
Disk Productions Inc, pg 743

MARYLAND
CPR MultiMedia Solutions, pg 732
The Cutting Corporation, GraphicAudio® & Archival Sound Lab, pg 736
dbF a Media Company, pg 739
HighBridge Audio, pg 779
Kramer Communications Video Production, pg 801

MASSACHUSETTS
Penfield Productions Ltd, pg 853
Soundtrack Group, pg 895

MICHIGAN
Digi Sign Design LLC, pg 741
K&R All Media Productions LLC, pg 796
K&R's Recording Studios Inc, pg 796

NEVADA
JCS Video Productions, pg 793

NEW HAMPSHIRE
Apertura, pg 686
Chip Taylor Communications LLC, pg 907

NEW JERSEY
CFP Video Productions Inc, pg 720
C2 Imaging, pg 735
Listen & Live Audio Inc, pg 809
Optisonics Productions, pg 847
Suede Interactive, pg 903

NEW YORK
Avekta Productions Inc, pg 697
Broadstreet Productions LLC, pg 711
Digital Force Ltd, pg 742
HarperAudio, pg 776
HB-Content, pg 777
Hello World Communications, pg 778
Madison Square Garden, pg 814
Jack Morton Worldwide, pg 830
MRY, pg 832
New York Audio Productions, pg 840
The Palmer Group, pg 850
Synaptic Digital, pg 905
Zelman Studios Ltd, pg 945

NORTH CAROLINA
Pat Appleson Studios Inc, pg 687
Digital Rain LLC, pg 742
Motor Racing Network, pg 831

OHIO
R&B Communications Inc, pg 870

OKLAHOMA
Piper Media Services Inc, pg 857

OREGON
InterVision Media, pg 791
Odyssey Productions Inc, pg 844

PENNSYLVANIA
FMP Media Solutions Inc, pg 763
Innovision Media Group, pg 788
Production Masters Inc (PMI), pg 864

RHODE ISLAND
Sound-FX-Design, pg 894

TENNESSEE
Continental Film, pg 731
Russ Sturgeon Productions/RSVP, pg 903

TEXAS
Emergency Film Group, pg 753
Epic Software Group Inc, pg 755
The Music Bakery, pg 834
Omega Productions, pg 845
Oncourt Offcourt Ltd, pg 846
The Sound Lab Inc, pg 894
Sound Works, pg 894
Tropikal Productions, pg 918

VERMONT
Trafalgar Square Books, pg 916

VIRGINIA
CACI Integrated Communications, pg 713
Metro Productions, pg 824

WEST VIRGINIA
Blackwater Video Productions, pg 707

WISCONSIN
5th Floor Recording Co, pg 760
Watts Communications Inc, pg 934
Wisconsin Public Television, pg 940

WYOMING
Bridger Productions Inc, pg 710

ALBERTA
Black Media Works, pg 706
Global TV, pg 771

ONTARIO
ADS Media, pg 677

QUEBEC
Kerrigan Productions Inc, pg 798

Sports Program Rentals

CALIFORNIA
Direct Cinema Ltd Inc, pg 743

MICHIGAN
Digi Sign Design LLC, pg 741

NEW HAMPSHIRE
Chip Taylor Communications LLC, pg 907

NEW JERSEY
Listen & Live Audio Inc, pg 809

UTAH
Webb Audio Visual, pg 935

ONTARIO
Simply Audiobooks, pg 889

Technical Research Program Distributors

CALIFORNIA
Maximus Media Inc, pg 820
QRS Software Services, pg 867

DISTRICT OF COLUMBIA
American Chemical Society (ACS), pg 683

ILLINOIS
CCH Continuing Education, pg 718

MASSACHUSETTS
Penfield Productions Ltd, pg 853

MICHIGAN
Digi Sign Design LLC, pg 741

NEW HAMPSHIRE
Chip Taylor Communications LLC, pg 907

NEW YORK
Synaptic Digital, pg 905

TEXAS
Emergency Film Group, pg 753

Technical Research Program Producers

CALIFORNIA
Big Door, pg 705
Creative Media Recording, pg 733
Creative Technology, pg 733
Custom Video Productions Inc, pg 736
Design Media, pg 741
Havas Edge, pg 777
Lynch Communications, pg 813
QRS Software Services, pg 867
Still N' Motion, pg 901
Studio 132, pg 902
Timestream Video, pg 914
Total Creative, pg 916

COLORADO
Daylight Productions & Rentals, pg 739
Flashback Media Productions, pg 762

DISTRICT OF COLUMBIA
American Chemical Society (ACS), pg 683

FLORIDA
LHV Audio Services, pg 807
Sunfire Communications Inc, pg 904
Sunrise Studios, pg 904

GEORGIA
Guerrilla Productions LLC, pg 774

ILLINOIS
ABS Enterprises, pg 672
CCH Continuing Education, pg 718
Major Media Productions Inc, pg 815
Pepper Group, pg 854
20/20 Communications Inc, pg 920
Video Impressions, pg 928

INDIANA
A-V-A Video Productions, pg 671

LOUISIANA
Louisiana State University Division of Strategic Communications, pg 811

MARYLAND
CPR MultiMedia Solutions, pg 732
The Cutting Corporation, GraphicAudio® & Archival Sound Lab, pg 736
dbF a Media Company, pg 739
Kramer Communications Video Production, pg 801

MASSACHUSETTS
Heliotrope Studios, pg 778
Penfield Productions Ltd, pg 853
Soundtrack Group, pg 895

MICHIGAN
Digi Sign Design LLC, pg 741
K&R All Media Productions LLC, pg 796
K&R's Recording Studios Inc, pg 796

MINNESOTA
GMI Productions, pg 771

NEW HAMPSHIRE
Apertura, pg 686
Chip Taylor Communications LLC, pg 907

NEW JERSEY
CFP Video Productions Inc, pg 720
Optisonics Productions, pg 847
Suede Interactive, pg 903

NEW YORK
Avekta Productions Inc, pg 697
Digital Force Ltd, pg 742
Fingerpaint, pg 761
Jack Morton Worldwide, pg 830
The Palmer Group, pg 850
Split Image Productions, pg 898
Synaptic Digital, pg 905
Tiki Recording Studios Inc, pg 914
Videograf, pg 929
Zelman Studios Ltd, pg 945

NORTH CAROLINA
Pat Appleson Studios Inc, pg 687
Trailblazer Studios®, pg 917

OHIO
Advent Media Inc, pg 677
R&B Communications Inc, pg 870
Vista Color Imaging Inc, pg 931

OKLAHOMA
Piper Media Services Inc, pg 857

PROGRAMMING — AUDIO

Technical Research Program Producers (continued)

OREGON

Ideascape Inc, pg 784
InterVision Media, pg 791

PENNSYLVANIA

Muderick Media, pg 833
Panta Rhei Media Inc, pg 851

RHODE ISLAND

Sound-FX-Design, pg 894

TEXAS

Emergency Film Group, pg 753
James Loupas Associates Inc,
  pg 811
The Music Bakery, pg 834
Omega Productions, pg 845
Romar Learning Solutions LLC,
  pg 877
The Sound Lab Inc, pg 894
Texas Heart Institute Visual
  Communication Services, pg 911

WISCONSIN

5th Floor Recording Co, pg 760
USAV Group Inc, pg 923
Wisconsin Public Television, pg 940

WYOMING

Bridger Productions Inc, pg 710

ALBERTA

Global TV, pg 771

QUEBEC

Kerrigan Productions Inc, pg 798

Technical Research Program Rentals

MICHIGAN

Digi Sign Design LLC, pg 741

NEW HAMPSHIRE

Chip Taylor Communications LLC,
  pg 907

UTAH

Webb Audio Visual, pg 935

Test Commercial Distributors

CALIFORNIA

Maximus Media Inc, pg 820
QRS Software Services, pg 867

MASSACHUSETTS

Penfield Productions Ltd, pg 853

MICHIGAN

Digi Sign Design LLC, pg 741

NEVADA

DVDs4Less, pg 748

NEW YORK

HB-Content, pg 777
Janus Films Inc, pg 793

TEXAS

TM Studios Inc, pg 915

Test Commercial Producers

ARIZONA

Candee Productions Inc, pg 716

ARKANSAS

Live'N'Loud, pg 810

CALIFORNIA

A Go Go Films, pg 671
Big Door, pg 705
Concrete Images, pg 730
Creative Media Recording, pg 733
Creative Technology, pg 733
Custom Video Productions Inc,
  pg 736
Design Media, pg 741
Havas Edge, pg 777
KTVU-Retail Services, pg 802
Lynch Communications, pg 813
Maximus Media Inc, pg 820
Media Magic, pg 822
QRS Software Services, pg 867
Steve Shapiro Music, pg 885
Still N' Motion, pg 901
Studio 132, pg 902
Total Creative, pg 916
Video Resources Inc, pg 928
Webster Communications, pg 935
Zamacona Productions, pg 945

COLORADO

Tim Cissell Music, pg 725
Flashback Media Productions,
  pg 762

CONNECTICUT

P&P Studios Inc, pg 851

FLORIDA

Blackburst Entertainment LLC,
  pg 706
LHV Audio Services, pg 807
Sunfire Communications Inc,
  pg 904
Sunrise Studios, pg 904
Tricycle Studios, pg 918

GEORGIA

Guerrilla Productions LLC, pg 774
WaveGuide Studios, pg 934

IDAHO

Wide Eye Productions, pg 938

ILLINOIS

ABS Enterprises, pg 672
Pepper Group, pg 854
Steven Samler Music & Sound,
  pg 879
Video Impressions, pg 928

INDIANA

A-V-A Video Productions, pg 671

KANSAS

KAKE-TV, pg 796

MAINE

Serendipity Recordings, pg 884

MARYLAND

CPR MultiMedia Solutions, pg 732
The Cutting Corporation,
  GraphicAudio® & Archival
  Sound Lab, pg 736
dbF a Media Company, pg 739
The Image Generators, pg 785

MASSACHUSETTS

Labrecque Creative Sound, pg 803
Penfield Productions Ltd, pg 853
Soundtrack Group, pg 895

MICHIGAN

Digi Sign Design LLC, pg 741
K&R All Media Productions LLC,
  pg 796
K&R's Recording Studios Inc,
  pg 796

MINNESOTA

GMI Productions, pg 771

MISSOURI

Hardcastle Films & Video, pg 776

NEVADA

DVDs4Less, pg 748

NEW JERSEY

CFP Video Productions Inc, pg 720
Euro-Pacific Film & Video
  Productions Inc, pg 756
Optisonics Productions, pg 847
Suede Interactive, pg 903

NEW YORK

Avekta Productions Inc, pg 697
Thomas Craven Film Corp, pg 733
Digital Force Ltd, pg 742
HB-Content, pg 777
Hello World Communications,
  pg 778
Icontent, pg 783
Mood Creations Ltd, pg 829
Jack Morton Worldwide, pg 830
MRY, pg 832
The Palmer Group, pg 850
Pat Kogan Productions Inc, pg 852
David Rapkin Audio Production,
  pg 870
Elliot Sokolov Music, pg 892
Split Image Productions, pg 898
Suggs Media Productions Inc,
  pg 903
Zelman Studios Ltd, pg 945

NORTH CAROLINA

2BruceStudio, pg 920

OHIO

Musicol Recording, pg 835
Take 1 Media Services, pg 906
Vista Color Imaging Inc, pg 931

OKLAHOMA

Piper Media Services Inc, pg 857

PENNSYLVANIA

Forge Recording LLC, pg 764
Innovision Media Group, pg 788
JPL, pg 795
The Videohouse Inc, pg 929

RHODE ISLAND

Sound-FX-Design, pg 894

SOUTH CAROLINA

Stages Video Productions, pg 899

TEXAS

Audiomoxie®, pg 695
Communication Arts Multimedia
  Inc, pg 728
Emergency Film Group, pg 753
The Music Bakery, pg 834
Omega Productions, pg 845
The Sound Lab Inc, pg 894
South Coast Film & Video, pg 895
Stage Directions, pg 898
TM Studios Inc, pg 915

VIRGINIA

Limelight Communications Inc,
  pg 808
Metro Productions, pg 824
Rocktown Media, pg 876
Studio Center Corp, pg 902

WISCONSIN

5th Floor Recording Co, pg 760
Video Wisconsin Inc, pg 929

WYOMING

Bridger Productions Inc, pg 710

ALBERTA

Global TV, pg 771

ONTARIO

DebsVoice, pg 739

QUEBEC

Kerrigan Productions Inc, pg 798

Test Commercial Rentals

MICHIGAN

Digi Sign Design LLC, pg 741

UTAH

Webb Audio Visual, pg 935

Training Program Distributors

ARIZONA

Tom Hopkins International Inc,
  pg 781
Video Learning Library, pg 928

CALIFORNIA

California Language Laboratories,
  pg 714
Dialect Accent Specialists Inc,
  pg 741
Golden State Dance Teachers
  Association (GSDTA), pg 772
Maximus Media Inc, pg 820
Medcom Inc, pg 821
People Skills International, pg 854

QRS Software Services, pg 867
The Wine Appreciation Guild Ltd,
  pg 939

COLORADO

National Institute for Trial
  Advocacy (NITA), pg 836

CONNECTICUT

Gold Line/TEF, pg 772

FLORIDA

Bisk Education, pg 706
PAR Inc, pg 851

HAWAII

Source School of Tantra Yoga Inc,
  pg 895

ILLINOIS

CCH Continuing Education, pg 718
CCore Media Inc, pg 718
Film Ideas Inc, pg 760
Liturgy Training Publications,
  pg 810
National Safety Council (NSC),
  pg 836
Nightingale-Conant Corp, pg 841

IOWA

Prositions Inc, pg 865

MARYLAND

MMI Marketing, pg 828

MASSACHUSETTS

Penfield Productions Ltd, pg 853

MICHIGAN

Digi Sign Design LLC, pg 741

MINNESOTA

Whole Person Associates Inc,
  pg 938

NEVADA

DVDs4Less, pg 748

NEW HAMPSHIRE

Chip Taylor Communications LLC,
  pg 907

NEW YORK

Albert Ellis Institute (AEI), pg 753
Guidance Associates Inc Center for
  Humanities, pg 774
Guilford Publications, pg 774
HB-Content, pg 777
Homespun Video, pg 781
TeleTime Productions, pg 910

NORTH CAROLINA

AudioSolutionz LLC, pg 695
Speakers Unlimited, pg 896

OREGON

InterVision Media, pg 791
The Keyboard Workshop, pg 798

PENNSYLVANIA

American Law Institute Continuing
  Legal Education (ALI CLE),
  pg 683
FMP Media Solutions Inc, pg 763
TRC Interactive Inc, pg 917

SOUTH CAROLINA

DaviSound, pg 739

TENNESSEE

American Blackguard Inc, pg 683
Randall House Publications, pg 870
Spring Arbor Distributors Inc,
  pg 898

TEXAS

Emergency Film Group, pg 753
Executive Development Systems
  Inc, pg 757
Teleometrics International, pg 910

VIRGINIA

CACI Integrated Communications,
  pg 713

BRITISH COLUMBIA

Thompson Rivers University
  Marketing & Communications
  Dept, pg 913

ONTARIO

Canadian Learning Co Inc, pg 715

Training Program
Producers

ALABAMA

Leo Ticheli Productions, pg 913

ARIZONA

Candee Productions Inc, pg 716
Tom Hopkins International Inc,
  pg 781
Metropolitan Audio-Visual Inc,
  pg 824
SPEAK HOUSE Audio™, pg 896
Video Learning Library, pg 928

ARKANSAS

Live'N'Loud, pg 810
White Diamond Productions LLC,
  pg 937

CALIFORNIA

Aaron Marcus and Associates,
  pg 671
Ancient Future, pg 685
The Banquet Sound Studios, pg 701
Big Door, pg 705
California Language Laboratories,
  pg 714
Creative Media Recording, pg 733
Creative Support Services/CSS
  Music, pg 733
Creative Technology, pg 733
Custom Video Productions Inc,
  pg 736
Design Media, pg 741
Dialect Accent Specialists Inc,
  pg 741
Havas Edge, pg 777
imageReal Pictures LLC, pg 785
International Contact Inc, pg 790
Lynch Communications, pg 813
Maximus Media Inc, pg 820

Medcom Inc, pg 821
Media Magic, pg 822
The Media Staff Inc, pg 822
On-Trax Inc, pg 846
Prime Cut Productions, pg 862
QRS Software Services, pg 867
Steve Shapiro Music, pg 885
Still N' Motion, pg 901
Studio 132, pg 902
Tam Communications Inc, pg 906
Total Creative, pg 916
Video Resources Inc, pg 928
Wavemaker Media Design, pg 934
Webster Communications, pg 935

COLORADO

Daylight Productions & Rentals,
  pg 739
Flashback Media Productions,
  pg 762
National Institute for Trial
  Advocacy (NITA), pg 836

CONNECTICUT

The Gary-Paul Agency, pg 768
Gold Line/TEF, pg 772
Moving Pictures, pg 832
UConn Health Multimedia Services,
  pg 920

FLORIDA

Bisk Education, pg 706
Blackburst Entertainment LLC,
  pg 706
Communications Concepts Inc
  (CCI), pg 729
LHV Audio Services, pg 807
Sunfire Communications Inc,
  pg 904
Sunrise Studios, pg 904
Tricycle Studios, pg 918
Mike Vasilinda Productions Inc,
  pg 925

GEORGIA

Guerrilla Productions LLC, pg 774

HAWAII

Source School of Tantra Yoga Inc,
  pg 895

IDAHO

Wide Eye Productions, pg 938

ILLINOIS

Accenture, pg 672
Audiobook Department, pg 695
CCH Continuing Education, pg 718
CCore Media Inc, pg 718
Liturgy Training Publications,
  pg 810
Major Media Productions Inc,
  pg 815
Multimedia Marketing Group,
  pg 833
Nightingale-Conant Corp, pg 841
Pepper Group, pg 854
Steven Samler Music & Sound,
  pg 879
Sparkfactor, pg 896
20/20 Communications Inc, pg 920
Video Impressions, pg 928

INDIANA

A-V-A Video Productions, pg 671
Advanced Media Integration, pg 677
Bright Ideas Creative Services,
  pg 710

PentaVision Communications Inc,
  pg 854
SynAudCon, pg 905

IOWA

Educational Technology & Media
  Services, pg 751
Prositions Inc, pg 865

LOUISIANA

Digital FX Inc, pg 742
Louisiana State University Division
  of Strategic Communications,
  pg 811

MARYLAND

CPR MultiMedia Solutions, pg 732
The Cutting Corporation,
  GraphicAudio® & Archival
  Sound Lab, pg 736
dbF a Media Company, pg 739
The Image Generators, pg 785
Kramer Communications Video
  Production, pg 801

MASSACHUSETTS

CommCreative, pg 728
HOME Inc, pg 781
Penfield Productions Ltd, pg 853
Soundtrack Group, pg 895
TVN-The Video Network, pg 919

MICHIGAN

Digi Sign Design LLC, pg 741
K&R All Media Productions LLC,
  pg 796
K&R's Recording Studios Inc,
  pg 796
TGA Recording Co, pg 911

MINNESOTA

GMI Productions, pg 771
MastCom, pg 819
Media Loft Inc, pg 822
Whole Person Associates Inc,
  pg 938

MISSOURI

Audio-VideoGraphics Inc, pg 694
Hardcastle Films & Video, pg 776

NEVADA

DVDs4Less, pg 748
JCS Video Productions, pg 793

NEW HAMPSHIRE

Apertura, pg 686
Chip Taylor Communications LLC,
  pg 907

NEW JERSEY

CFP Video Productions Inc, pg 720
Laurel Video Productions, pg 804
MiB MediaWorks, pg 825
Optisonics Productions, pg 847
Selden Associates, pg 883
Suede Interactive, pg 903
Telemanagement Resources
  International Inc (TRI), pg 910

NEW MEXICO

Production Outfitters, pg 864

PROGRAMMING — AUDIO

Training Program Producers (continued)

NEW YORK

Blue Barn Pictures Inc, pg 707
Broadstreet Productions LLC, pg 711
Cohn Creative Group LLC, pg 727
Digital Force Ltd, pg 742
Albert Ellis Institute (AEI), pg 753
Guidance Associates Inc Center for Humanities, pg 774
Guilford Publications, pg 774
HB-Content, pg 777
Hello World Communications, pg 778
Ketchum Inc, pg 798
L A Bruell Inc, pg 802
Mood Creations Ltd, pg 829
Jack Morton Worldwide, pg 830
MRM//McCANN, pg 832
MRY, pg 832
New York Audio Productions, pg 840
News Broadcast Network Inc, pg 840
The Palmer Group, pg 850
Pat Kogan Productions Inc, pg 852
Tiki Recording Studios Inc, pg 914
Videograf, pg 929
Zelman Studios Ltd, pg 945

NORTH CAROLINA

Pat Appleson Studios Inc, pg 687
AudioSolutionz LLC, pg 695
Digital Rain LLC, pg 742

OHIO

Advent Media Inc, pg 677
Cuyahoga Community College Student Production Office (SPO), pg 736
MainSail Production Services Inc, pg 815
R&B Communications Inc, pg 870
Take 1 Media Services, pg 906
Vista Color Imaging Inc, pg 931

OKLAHOMA

Piper Media Services Inc, pg 857

OREGON

ERA Learning, pg 755
Ideascape Inc, pg 784
InterVision Media, pg 791
The Keyboard Workshop, pg 798
KTVA Productions, pg 802

PENNSYLVANIA

American Law Institute Continuing Legal Education (ALI CLE), pg 683
Audio Visual Communications Inc, pg 694
FMP Media Solutions Inc, pg 763
Innovision Media Group, pg 788
JPL, pg 795
Muderick Media, pg 833
Newtown Psychological Center, pg 840
Panta Rhei Media Inc, pg 851
Production Masters Inc (PMI), pg 864
Scala Inc, pg 881
The Videohouse Inc, pg 929

RHODE ISLAND

Sound-FX-Design, pg 894

SOUTH CAROLINA

DaviSound, pg 739
Stages Video Productions, pg 899
Venture Media, pg 925

TENNESSEE

American Blackguard Inc, pg 683
Continental Film, pg 731
Memphis Communications Corp, pg 823
Spring Arbor Distributors Inc, pg 898
Stage Post, pg 899

TEXAS

AMA Nystrom Printing/Finishing, pg 682
Audiomoxie®, pg 695
Biway Media, pg 706
Dykeman Associates Inc, pg 748
The Editing Co, pg 750
The Music Bakery, pg 834
Omega Productions, pg 845
Romar Learning Solutions LLC, pg 877
The Sound Lab Inc, pg 894
Sound Works, pg 894
South Coast Film & Video, pg 895
Stage Directions, pg 898
Teleometrics International, pg 910
The Yesterday USA Radio Networks, pg 944

VIRGINIA

CACI Integrated Communications, pg 713
Limelight Communications Inc, pg 808
Metro Productions, pg 824
National Media Services Inc, pg 836
Rocktown Media, pg 876
Studio Center Corp, pg 902

WASHINGTON

Kostov Productions, pg 801
Pacific Multimedia Inc, pg 849

WISCONSIN

5th Floor Recording Co, pg 760
Meridian Studios, pg 824
USAV Group Inc, pg 923
Video Wisconsin Inc, pg 929
Watts Communications Inc, pg 934
Wisconsin Public Television, pg 940

WYOMING

Bridger Productions Inc, pg 710

ALBERTA

Black Media Works, pg 706
Global TV, pg 771

BRITISH COLUMBIA

Thompson Rivers University Marketing & Communications Dept, pg 913

ONTARIO

ADS Media, pg 677
DebsVoice, pg 739
GAPC (General Assembly Production Centre), pg 768

JFB Communications, pg 794
Silver Creek Media Inc, pg 888

QUEBEC

Kerrigan Productions Inc, pg 798

Training Program Rentals

CALIFORNIA

Medcom Inc, pg 821

MICHIGAN

Digi Sign Design LLC, pg 741

NEW HAMPSHIRE

Chip Taylor Communications LLC, pg 907

OREGON

The Keyboard Workshop, pg 798

UTAH

Webb Audio Visual, pg 935

Travelog Distributors

ARIZONA

Video Learning Library, pg 928

CALIFORNIA

Jaguar Distribution Corp, pg 792
Maximus Media Inc, pg 820
QRS Software Services, pg 867

MASSACHUSETTS

Penfield Productions Ltd, pg 853

MICHIGAN

Digi Sign Design LLC, pg 741

NEW HAMPSHIRE

Chip Taylor Communications LLC, pg 907

PENNSYLVANIA

FMP Media Solutions Inc, pg 763

SOUTH CAROLINA

DaviSound, pg 739

TENNESSEE

American Blackguard Inc, pg 683
Spring Arbor Distributors Inc, pg 898

TEXAS

Educational Video Network, pg 751

VIRGINIA

CACI Integrated Communications, pg 713

ONTARIO

Canadian Learning Co Inc, pg 715

Travelog Producers

ARIZONA

Video Learning Library, pg 928

CALIFORNIA

Ancient Future, pg 685
The Banquet Sound Studios, pg 701
Big Door, pg 705
Creative Technology, pg 733
Gold Standard Productions, pg 772
Jaguar Distribution Corp, pg 792
Lynch Communications, pg 813
On-Trax Inc, pg 846
PM Productions, pg 858
Producers Group Ltd, pg 863
QRS Software Services, pg 867
Studio 132, pg 902
Total Creative, pg 916
Wavemaker Media Design, pg 934
Webster Communications, pg 935

COLORADO

Apogee Communications Group, pg 687
Tatum Video, pg 907

CONNECTICUT

The Gary-Paul Agency, pg 768

FLORIDA

Blackburst Entertainment LLC, pg 706
LHV Audio Services, pg 807
Sunfire Communications Inc, pg 904

GEORGIA

Guerrilla Productions LLC, pg 774

HAWAII

Source School of Tantra Yoga Inc, pg 895

IDAHO

Wide Eye Productions, pg 938

ILLINOIS

Pepper Group, pg 854
PSAV® Presentation Services (Hotel Services Division), pg 866
Steven Samler Music & Sound, pg 879
Video Impressions, pg 928

INDIANA

A-V-A Video Productions, pg 671

MARYLAND

CPR MultiMedia Solutions, pg 732
The Cutting Corporation, GraphicAudio® & Archival Sound Lab, pg 736
dbF a Media Company, pg 739
The Image Generators, pg 785

MASSACHUSETTS

Penfield Productions Ltd, pg 853
Soundtrack Group, pg 895
TVN-The Video Network, pg 919

MICHIGAN

Digi Sign Design LLC, pg 741
K&R All Media Productions LLC, pg 796
K&R's Recording Studios Inc, pg 796

MISSOURI

Audio-VideoGraphics Inc, pg 694

NEW HAMPSHIRE

Chip Taylor Communications LLC, pg 907

NEW JERSEY

CFP Video Productions Inc, pg 720
MiB MediaWorks, pg 825
Optisonics Productions, pg 847
Suede Interactive, pg 903

NEW MEXICO

Production Outfitters, pg 864
Rainbow International Inc, pg 869

NEW YORK

Avekta Productions Inc, pg 697
Thomas Craven Film Corp, pg 733
De Nonno Productions Inc (DPI), pg 739
Digital Force Ltd, pg 742
Icontent, pg 783
Mood Creations Ltd, pg 829
Jack Morton Worldwide, pg 830
MRY, pg 832
New York Audio Productions, pg 840
News Broadcast Network Inc, pg 840
The Palmer Group, pg 850
Pat Kogan Productions Inc, pg 852
Split Image Productions, pg 898
Suggs Media Productions Inc, pg 903
Videograf, pg 929
Zelman Studios Ltd, pg 945

NORTH CAROLINA

Pat Appleson Studios Inc, pg 687
Digital Rain LLC, pg 742

OHIO

Advent Media Inc, pg 677
MainSail Production Services Inc, pg 815
R&B Communications Inc, pg 870

OKLAHOMA

Piper Media Services Inc, pg 857

OREGON

Odyssey Productions Inc, pg 844

PENNSYLVANIA

FMP Media Solutions Inc, pg 763
Forge Recording LLC, pg 764
JPL, pg 795
Production Masters Inc (PMI), pg 864

RHODE ISLAND

Sound-FX-Design, pg 894

SOUTH CAROLINA

DaviSound, pg 739
Stages Video Productions, pg 899

TENNESSEE

American Blackguard Inc, pg 683

TEXAS

Educational Video Network, pg 751
The Music Bakery, pg 834
Omega Productions, pg 845
The Sound Lab Inc, pg 894
Sound Works, pg 894

South Coast Film & Video, pg 895
Stage Directions, pg 898

VIRGINIA

CACI Integrated Communications, pg 713
Limelight Communications Inc, pg 808
Rocktown Media, pg 876
Studio Center Corp, pg 902

WISCONSIN

5th Floor Recording Co, pg 760
Wisconsin Public Television, pg 940

WYOMING

Bridger Productions Inc, pg 710

ALBERTA

Global TV, pg 771

QUEBEC

Kerrigan Productions Inc, pg 798

Travelog Rentals

CALIFORNIA

Jaguar Distribution Corp, pg 792

MICHIGAN

Digi Sign Design LLC, pg 741

NEW HAMPSHIRE

Chip Taylor Communications LLC, pg 907

NEW JERSEY

Alden Films, pg 679

Vocational Program Distributors

CALIFORNIA

Direct Cinema Ltd Inc, pg 743
Maximus Media Inc, pg 820
Medcom Inc, pg 821
QRS Software Services, pg 867

FLORIDA

PAR Inc, pg 851
Video Resources Software, pg 928

GEORGIA

Convergent Media Systems, pg 731
School Media Associates LLC, pg 882

ILLINOIS

Film Ideas Inc, pg 760
National Safety Council (NSC), pg 836

MASSACHUSETTS

Penfield Productions Ltd, pg 853

MICHIGAN

Digi Sign Design LLC, pg 741

MINNESOTA

EMC Publishing LLC, pg 753

MISSOURI

Mosby Inc, pg 831

NEW HAMPSHIRE

Chip Taylor Communications LLC, pg 907

NEW YORK

Films Media Group, pg 760
Guidance Associates Inc Center for Humanities, pg 774
March of Dimes Foundation, pg 816
TeleTime Productions, pg 910

OHIO

McGraw-Hill School Education Group, pg 821

OREGON

InterVision Media, pg 791

PENNSYLVANIA

Bullfrog Films Inc, pg 712
FMP Media Solutions Inc, pg 763

TENNESSEE

American Blackguard Inc, pg 683

TEXAS

Educational Video Network, pg 751
Emergency Film Group, pg 753

VERMONT

Taylor Associates, pg 907

VIRGINIA

CACI Integrated Communications, pg 713

WISCONSIN

Wisconsin Technical College System Foundation Inc, pg 940

ONTARIO

Canadian Learning Co Inc, pg 715

Vocational Program Producers

CALIFORNIA

Aaron Marcus and Associates, pg 671
Big Door, pg 705
Custom Video Productions Inc, pg 736
Design Media, pg 741
Direct Cinema Ltd Inc, pg 743
Gold Standard Productions, pg 772
imageReal Pictures LLC, pg 785
Lynch Communications, pg 813
Maximus Media Inc, pg 820
Medcom Inc, pg 821
The Media Staff Inc, pg 822
On-Trax Inc, pg 846
PM Productions, pg 858
QRS Software Services, pg 867
Still N' Motion, pg 901
Studio 132, pg 902
Timestream Video, pg 914
Total Creative, pg 916
Wavemaker Media Design, pg 934
Webster Communications, pg 935

COLORADO

Apogee Communications Group, pg 687
Daylight Productions & Rentals, pg 739

CONNECTICUT

The Gary-Paul Agency, pg 768

FLORIDA

LHV Audio Services, pg 807
Sunfire Communications Inc, pg 904
Sunrise Studios, pg 904
Video Resources Software, pg 928

GEORGIA

Guerrilla Productions LLC, pg 774

IDAHO

Wide Eye Productions, pg 938

ILLINOIS

ABS Enterprises, pg 672
Major Media Productions Inc, pg 815
Pepper Group, pg 854
20/20 Communications Inc, pg 920

INDIANA

A-V-A Video Productions, pg 671

KENTUCKY

NIMCO Inc, pg 841

MARYLAND

CPR MultiMedia Solutions, pg 732
The Cutting Corporation, GraphicAudio® & Archival Sound Lab, pg 736
dbF a Media Company, pg 739
The Image Generators, pg 785

MASSACHUSETTS

Penfield Productions Ltd, pg 853
Soundtrack Group, pg 895

MICHIGAN

Digi Sign Design LLC, pg 741
K&R All Media Productions LLC, pg 796
K&R's Recording Studios Inc, pg 796

MINNESOTA

EMC Publishing LLC, pg 753
MastCom, pg 819

MISSOURI

Audio-VideoGraphics Inc, pg 694

NEVADA

JCS Video Productions, pg 793

NEW HAMPSHIRE

Apertura, pg 686
Chip Taylor Communications LLC, pg 907

NEW JERSEY

Audio Vistas LLC, pg 694
CFP Video Productions Inc, pg 720
Laurel Video Productions, pg 804
MiB MediaWorks, pg 825

PROGRAMMING — AUDIO

Vocational Program Producers (continued)

NEW JERSEY (continued)

Optisonics Productions, pg 847
Suede Interactive, pg 903

NEW YORK

Avekta Productions Inc, pg 697
De Nonno Productions Inc (DPI), pg 739
Digital Force Ltd, pg 742
Films Media Group, pg 760
Guidance Associates Inc Center for Humanities, pg 774
Ketchum Inc, pg 798
March of Dimes Foundation, pg 816
Jack Morton Worldwide, pg 830
The Palmer Group, pg 850
Pat Kogan Productions Inc, pg 852
Elliot Sokolov Music, pg 892
Split Image Productions, pg 898
Triumph Learning LLC, pg 918
Videograf, pg 929

NORTH CAROLINA

Pat Appleson Studios Inc, pg 687
Digital Rain LLC, pg 742

OHIO

Advent Media Inc, pg 677
MainSail Production Services Inc, pg 815
McGraw-Hill School Education Group, pg 821
R&B Communications Inc, pg 870
Take 1 Media Services, pg 906
Vista Color Imaging Inc, pg 931

OKLAHOMA

Piper Media Services Inc, pg 857

OREGON

ERA Learning, pg 755
Ideascape Inc, pg 784
InterVision Media, pg 791
KTVA Productions, pg 802

PENNSYLVANIA

FMP Media Solutions Inc, pg 763
JPL, pg 795
Production Masters Inc (PMI), pg 864

RHODE ISLAND

Sound-FX-Design, pg 894

SOUTH CAROLINA

Stages Video Productions, pg 899

TENNESSEE

American Blackguard Inc, pg 683
Continental Film, pg 731
Memphis Communications Corp, pg 823

TEXAS

AMA Nystrom Printing/Finishing, pg 682
Educational Video Network, pg 751
Emergency Film Group, pg 753
The Music Bakery, pg 834
Omega Productions, pg 845
The Sound Lab Inc, pg 894
Sound Works, pg 894

VIRGINIA

CACI Integrated Communications, pg 713
Limelight Communications Inc, pg 808
Metro Productions, pg 824
National Media Services Inc, pg 836
Rocktown Media, pg 876

WISCONSIN

5th Floor Recording Co, pg 760
USAV Group Inc, pg 923
Video Wisconsin Inc, pg 929
Wisconsin Public Television, pg 940
Wisconsin Technical College System Foundation Inc, pg 940

WYOMING

Bridger Productions Inc, pg 710

ALBERTA

Global TV, pg 771

ONTARIO

DebsVoice, pg 739

QUEBEC

Kerrigan Productions Inc, pg 798

Vocational Program Rentals

CALIFORNIA

Direct Cinema Ltd Inc, pg 743
Medcom Inc, pg 821

GEORGIA

Convergent Media Systems, pg 731

MICHIGAN

Digi Sign Design LLC, pg 741

NEW HAMPSHIRE

Chip Taylor Communications LLC, pg 907

UTAH

Webb Audio Visual, pg 935

WISCONSIN

Wisconsin Technical College System Foundation Inc, pg 940

PROGRAMMING — AUDIO/VISUAL

Business Program Distributors

ARIZONA

Video Learning Library, pg 928

CALIFORNIA

Crystal Pyramid Productions™, pg 735
Deja View Video, pg 740
Discovery Education - Los Angeles, pg 743
Bruce Goldberg Inc, pg 772
Griggs Productions Inc, pg 774
Kantola Productions LLC, pg 796
New & Unique Videos™, pg 839
TMW Media Group, pg 915
Westlake Recording Studios, pg 936

COLORADO

Vital Learning LLC, pg 932

CONNECTICUT

Book Marketing Works LLC, pg 708

FLORIDA

Video Resources Software, pg 928

GEORGIA

Convergent Media Systems, pg 731
School Media Associates LLC, pg 882

HAWAII

Media Bridge Gamekids, pg 821

ILLINOIS

CCH Continuing Education, pg 718
CCH Inc, A Wolters Kluwer business, pg 718
CCore Media Inc, pg 718
Cool-Lux, pg 731
Film Ideas Inc, pg 760
1st Financial Training Services Inc, pg 761

IOWA

Prositions Inc, pg 865

KENTUCKY

KET The Kentucky Network, pg 798

MASSACHUSETTS

Preston Productions Inc, pg 861

MICHIGAN

Digi Sign Design LLC, pg 741
Emery-Pratt Co, pg 753
MSU Technologies, pg 833

NEW HAMPSHIRE

Frey Scientific, pg 766
Chip Taylor Communications LLC, pg 907

NEW JERSEY

Allegro Productions Inc, pg 680
Euro-Pacific Film & Video Productions Inc, pg 756

NEW MEXICO

The Phoenix Learning Group Inc, pg 855

NEW YORK

Fanlight Productions, pg 759
Films Media Group, pg 760
Guidance Associates Inc Center for Humanities, pg 774
HB-Content, pg 777
Meridian Education Corp, pg 823
Practising Law Institute, pg 860
Shopware, pg 886
TeleTime Productions, pg 910

PENNSYLVANIA

FMP Media Solutions Inc, pg 763

SOUTH CAROLINA

DaviSound, pg 739

TENNESSEE

Zion Music Group, pg 945

TEXAS

Educational Video Network, pg 751
The Samuels Co, pg 879
Stage Directions, pg 898

VERMONT

Wilson McLeran Inc, pg 939

VIRGINIA

Design & Production Inc, pg 740
PBS Video, pg 852

ONTARIO

BBC Worldwide Canada Ltd, pg 702
Canadian Learning Co Inc, pg 715
Kineticvideo.com, pg 799

Business Program Producers

ALABAMA

AVS Media Group, pg 699

ARIZONA

Aardvark Productions LLC, pg 671
Candee Productions Inc, pg 716
Creative Backstage, pg 733
Video Learning Library, pg 928

ARKANSAS

White Diamond Productions LLC, pg 937

CALIFORNIA

Creative Technology, pg 733
Crystal Pyramid Productions™, pg 735
Design Media, pg 741
Direct Images Interactive Inc, pg 743
Discovery Education - Los Angeles, pg 743
Dolphin MultiMedia Inc, pg 745
imageReal Pictures LLC, pg 785

Kantola Productions LLC, pg 796
Lynch Communications, pg 813
Main Street Media Inc, pg 815
Media Magic, pg 822
The Media Staff Inc, pg 822
New Circuit Films LLC, pg 839
PM Productions, pg 858
SNAP, pg 891
Tam Communications Inc, pg 906
TMW Media Group, pg 915
Total Creative, pg 916
Vineyard Video & Photography, pg 930
Wavemaker Media Design, pg 934
Webster Communications, pg 935
West Coast Projections Inc, pg 935

COLORADO

Daylight Productions & Rentals, pg 739
Flashback Media Productions, pg 762
Vital Learning LLC, pg 932

CONNECTICUT

New London Media, pg 839

DISTRICT OF COLUMBIA

O'Keefe Communications Inc, pg 844

FLORIDA

Applebox Studio, pg 687
Communications Concepts Inc (CCI), pg 729
Sunfire Communications Inc, pg 904
Tricycle Studios, pg 918
Universal Studios Florida® Production Group, pg 922
Video Resources Software, pg 928

GEORGIA

Beachwood Productions, pg 702
Guerrilla Productions LLC, pg 774
Myriad Productions, pg 835

HAWAII

Hyperspective Studios Inc, pg 783
Media Bridge Gamekids, pg 821

ILLINOIS

Airways Digital Media, pg 679
Atomic Imaging Inc/Golan Studios, pg 692
CCH Continuing Education, pg 718
CCH Inc, A Wolters Kluwer business, pg 718
CCore Media Inc, pg 718
Cresta Creative, pg 734
1st Financial Training Services Inc, pg 761
Major Media Productions Inc, pg 815
Manning Productions, pg 816
Multimedia Marketing Group, pg 833
Pepper Group, pg 854
PSAV® Presentation Services (Hotel Services Division), pg 866
SCI Television & Creative Media LLC, pg 882
Sparkfactor, pg 896
20/20 Communications Inc, pg 920
Video Impressions, pg 928

INDIANA

A-V-A Video Productions, pg 671

IOWA

Prositions Inc, pg 865

KENTUCKY

Idle Minds Productions Inc, pg 784
KET The Kentucky Network, pg 798

LOUISIANA

Digital FX Inc, pg 742
Disk Productions Inc, pg 743

MARYLAND

The Cutting Corporation, GraphicAudio® & Archival Sound Lab, pg 736
dbF a Media Company, pg 739
The Image Generators, pg 785
Mobile-Video Productions Inc, pg 828

MASSACHUSETTS

CommCreative, pg 728
Cramer, pg 732
Soundtrack Group, pg 895
TVN-The Video Network, pg 919
WGBH Production Group, pg 936

MICHIGAN

Digi Sign Design LLC, pg 741
K&R All Media Productions LLC, pg 796
K&R's Recording Studios Inc, pg 796

MINNESOTA

Live Spark Inc, pg 810
MastCom, pg 819
Media Loft Inc, pg 822

NEVADA

JCS Video Productions, pg 793

NEW HAMPSHIRE

Apertura, pg 686
Chip Taylor Communications LLC, pg 907

NEW JERSEY

Allegro Productions Inc, pg 680
Broadcast Center Studios, pg 710
Laurel Video Productions, pg 804
Milgrom Productions, pg 827
Optisonics Productions, pg 847
Outside The Box Interactive LLC, pg 849
TimeSteps Productions Inc, pg 914

NEW MEXICO

The Phoenix Learning Group Inc, pg 855

NEW YORK

Blue Barn Pictures Inc, pg 707
Broadstreet Productions LLC, pg 711
De Nonno Productions Inc (DPI), pg 739
Duggal Visual Solutions Inc, pg 747
Fanlight Productions, pg 759
Films Media Group, pg 760
Guidance Associates Inc Center for Humanities, pg 774
Havas Creative, pg 776
HB-Content, pg 777

PROGRAMMING — AUDIO/VISUAL

Business Program Producers (continued)

NEW YORK (continued)

Hello World Communications, pg 778
Image Zone Inc, pg 785
Ketchum Inc, pg 798
Long Island Video Enterprises Live Inc, pg 811
Jack Morton Worldwide, pg 830
MRY, pg 832
News Broadcast Network Inc, pg 840
Northeast Video Productions Inc, pg 842
The Palmer Group, pg 850
Practising Law Institute, pg 860
Total Impact Multimedia Group Ltd, pg 916
Zelman Studios Ltd, pg 945

NORTH CAROLINA

Pat Appleson Studios Inc, pg 687
The Communications Group Inc, pg 729
Digital Rain LLC, pg 742
Image Associates Inc, pg 784
Kino Mountain Productions LLC, pg 799
Moving Pictures, pg 832
Sinclair Institute, pg 889

OHIO

MainSail Production Services Inc, pg 815
R&B Communications Inc, pg 870
Take 1 Media Services, pg 906
Vista Color Imaging Inc, pg 931

OREGON

ERA Learning, pg 755
Ideascape Inc, pg 784
KTVA Productions, pg 802
Odyssey Productions Inc, pg 844
REX, pg 874

PENNSYLVANIA

AccuWeather Inc, pg 674
Audio Visual Communications Inc, pg 694
Bang! Pictures Inc, pg 701
FMP Media Solutions Inc, pg 763
JPL, pg 795
Main Point Productions, pg 815
Muderick Media, pg 833
New Horizons Computer Learning Centers Inc, pg 839
Panta Rhei Media Inc, pg 851
Production Masters Inc (PMI), pg 864

RHODE ISLAND

Sound-FX-Design, pg 894

SOUTH CAROLINA

DaviSound, pg 739

TENNESSEE

Continental Film, pg 731
Running Pony Productions LLC, pg 878
Russ Sturgeon Productions/RSVP, pg 903

TEXAS

Biway Media, pg 706
Educational Video Network, pg 751
Epic Software Group Inc, pg 755
Mediaforce Productions, pg 822
The Samuels Co, pg 879
South Coast Film & Video, pg 895
Stage Directions, pg 898
Stockyard Photos/Jim Olive Photography, pg 901
Tropikal Productions, pg 918

VERMONT

Wilson McLeran Inc, pg 939

VIRGINIA

Altruist Media LLC, pg 682
Metro Productions, pg 824

WASHINGTON

Adams Creative & Production Services, pg 675
Kostov Productions, pg 801
Laser Fantasy/HECK Industries/Photon Manufacturing, pg 804

WISCONSIN

Audio Visual of Milwaukee Inc, pg 694
AVS Group, pg 699
Clear Focus Media LLC, pg 726
USAV Group Inc, pg 923
Video Wisconsin Inc, pg 929
Watts Communications Inc, pg 934
Wisconsin Public Television, pg 940

WYOMING

Bridger Productions Inc, pg 710

ALBERTA

Black Media Works, pg 706

BRITISH COLUMBIA

West Eagle Films Inc, pg 935

NEWFOUNDLAND AND LABRADOR

Vidcraft Productions Ltd, pg 927

ONTARIO

BBC Worldwide Canada Ltd, pg 702
DebsVoice, pg 739
JFB Communications, pg 794
Mediaimage Communications Group, pg 822

QUEBEC

Kerrigan Productions Inc, pg 798

Business Program Rentals

GEORGIA

Convergent Media Systems, pg 731
ON Services, a GES Company, pg 846

ILLINOIS

1st Financial Training Services Inc, pg 761

MASSACHUSETTS

Preston Productions Inc, pg 861

MICHIGAN

Digi Sign Design LLC, pg 741

NEW HAMPSHIRE

Chip Taylor Communications LLC, pg 907

NEW JERSEY

Euro-Pacific Film & Video Productions Inc, pg 756

NEW YORK

Historic Films, pg 780

TEXAS

Stage Directions, pg 898

UTAH

Webb Audio Visual, pg 935

Chart Distributors

CALIFORNIA

Ametron Audio/Video, pg 684
Astronomical Society of the Pacific, pg 691
Health Education Services, pg 778
Medcom Inc, pg 821
QRS Software Services, pg 867
Social Studies School Service, pg 891
The Writing Co, pg 942

COLORADO

American Educational Products LLC, pg 683

FLORIDA

PAR Inc, pg 851

GEORGIA

School Media Associates LLC, pg 882

ILLINOIS

CCore Media Inc, pg 718

MAINE

Headlight Audio Visual Inc, pg 777

MARYLAND

MMI Marketing, pg 828
Nicholas P Pipino Associates Inc, pg 857

NEW HAMPSHIRE

Frey Scientific, pg 766

NORTH CAROLINA

Carolina Biological Supply Co, pg 717

OREGON

The Keyboard Workshop, pg 798

PENNSYLVANIA

AccuWeather Inc, pg 674

SOUTH CAROLINA

BJU Press, pg 706

TENNESSEE

Randall House Publications, pg 870

TEXAS

Audio Visual Technologies Group (AVTG), pg 695

WISCONSIN

Knowledge Unlimited Inc, pg 800
School Specialty Inc, pg 882

Chart Producers

CALIFORNIA

Dolphin MultiMedia Inc, pg 745
Geddes Productions LLC, pg 769
Lynch Communications, pg 813
QRS Software Services, pg 867
Total Creative, pg 916
The Wine Appreciation Guild Ltd, pg 939

COLORADO

American Educational Products LLC, pg 683
Starwest Productions, pg 900
Stretching Inc, pg 902

FLORIDA

Tricycle Studios, pg 918

GEORGIA

Guerrilla Productions LLC, pg 774
Imagers, pg 785

ILLINOIS

Cresta Creative, pg 734
Rand McNally Education, pg 870

INDIANA

Bright Ideas Creative Services, pg 710
OMNI Productions, pg 845

IOWA

Educational Technology & Media Services, pg 751

KENTUCKY

National Geographic Learning, pg 836

LOUISIANA

Digital FX Inc, pg 742

MASSACHUSETTS

CommCreative, pg 728
TR Productions, pg 916

MICHIGAN

K&R All Media Productions LLC, pg 796
K&R's Recording Studios Inc, pg 796

MISSOURI

Switch, pg 905

NEW HAMPSHIRE

Frey Scientific, pg 766

NEW JERSEY

Optisonics Productions, pg 847
Outside The Box Interactive LLC, pg 849

NEW YORK

Applause Learning Resources, pg 687
Blue Barn Pictures Inc, pg 707
Broadstreet Productions LLC, pg 711
SMP Digital Graphics, pg 891

NORTH CAROLINA

Carolina Biological Supply Co, pg 717
World Class Learning Materials Inc, pg 941

OHIO

Cuyahoga Community College Student Production Office (SPO), pg 736
Take 1 Media Services, pg 906
Vista Color Imaging Inc, pg 931

OREGON

The Keyboard Workshop, pg 798

PENNSYLVANIA

AccuWeather Inc, pg 674
Kensington Falls Animation, pg 797

SOUTH CAROLINA

BJU Press, pg 706

TEXAS

Romar Learning Solutions LLC, pg 877

VIRGINIA

Advance Concepts Inc, pg 677
Blair Inc, pg 707

WASHINGTON

Kostov Productions, pg 801

WISCONSIN

USAV Group Inc, pg 923

Chart Rentals

CALIFORNIA

Ametron Audio/Video, pg 684

COLORADO

Spectrum Audio Visual Services, pg 897

MAINE

Headlight Audio Visual Inc, pg 777

MISSOURI

Show-Me Audio-Visual, pg 887

NEW JERSEY

PLS Staging, pg 858
Video Corporation of America (VCA), pg 927

NORTH CAROLINA

Special Event Services, pg 896

Children's Program Distributors

ARIZONA

Video Learning Library, pg 928

CALIFORNIA

Astronomical Society of the Pacific, pg 691
California Language Laboratories, pg 714
Crystal Pyramid Productions™, pg 735
Discovery Education - Los Angeles, pg 743
Educational Insights, pg 750
ETR, pg 756
Glenn Photo Supply, pg 771
Main Street Media Inc, pg 815
MarVista Entertainment Inc, pg 818
monterey video, pg 829
Moose School Productions, pg 830
Music Rhapsody, pg 834
Music World/Vocal Power School, pg 834
New & Unique Videos™, pg 839
Nystrom Education, pg 844
Rhythms Productions (Tom Thumb Music), pg 874
Sea Studios Foundation, pg 883
TMW Media Group, pg 915

COLORADO

Crystal Productions, pg 735

CONNECTICUT

Weston Woods Studios Inc, pg 936

FLORIDA

Video Resources Software, pg 928

GEORGIA

School Media Associates LLC, pg 882

HAWAII

Media Bridge Gamekids, pg 821

ILLINOIS

Discovery Education - Chicago, pg 743
Film Ideas Inc, pg 760

KENTUCKY

Horizon Films & Media LLC, pg 781
KET The Kentucky Network, pg 798
National Geographic Learning, pg 836

MAINE

Slim Goodbody Corp, pg 890

MASSACHUSETTS

Cheng & Tsui Co, pg 721
Documentary Educational Resources Inc, pg 744
Pauline Books & Media, pg 852

MICHIGAN

Digi Sign Design LLC, pg 741
Emery-Pratt Co, pg 753

MISSOURI

Marsh Media, pg 817

NEW HAMPSHIRE

Chip Taylor Communications LLC, pg 907

NEW JERSEY

Allegro Productions Inc, pg 680

NEW MEXICO

The Phoenix Learning Group Inc, pg 855

NEW YORK

Brooklyn Botanic Garden, pg 711
The Bureau for At-Risk Youth, pg 712
De Nonno Productions Inc (DPI), pg 739
Educational Activities Inc, pg 750
Guidance Associates Inc Center for Humanities, pg 774
Hallel Communications, pg 775
Human Relations Media, pg 782
Janson Media Inc, pg 793
Listening Library, pg 810
Live Oak Media, pg 810
Random House Children's Books, pg 870
VIEW Inc (Video International Entertainment World Inc), pg 930

OHIO

Alegra House Publishers, pg 679
Franciscan Media, pg 765
Treehaus Communications Inc, pg 917

PENNSYLVANIA

Discovery Education - South Burlington, pg 743
Media Inc, pg 822

TENNESSEE

American Blackguard Inc, pg 683
National School Products, pg 836
Randall House Publications, pg 870
Spring Arbor Distributors Inc, pg 898

TEXAS

Educational Video Network, pg 751
Horizon Film + Video Productions, pg 781
Institute of Texan Cultures, pg 788
Marengo Films, pg 817

VIRGINIA

Design & Production Inc, pg 740
PBS Video, pg 852

WISCONSIN

Aylmer Press, pg 700

ONTARIO

BBC Worldwide Canada Ltd, pg 702
Broughton's Church Supplies, Religious Books & Gifts, pg 711
Canadian Learning Co Inc, pg 715
Canamedia Inc, pg 715
The Children's Book Store Distribution (CBSD), pg 722
Kineticvideo.com, pg 799

McIntyre Media Inc, pg 821
Novalis, pg 843

Children's Program Producers

ARIZONA

Aardvark Productions LLC, pg 671
Candee Productions Inc, pg 716

CALIFORNIA

Ancient Future, pg 685
Creative Technology, pg 733
Crystal Pyramid Productions™, pg 735
Discovery Education - Los Angeles, pg 743
Lynch Communications, pg 813
Main Street Media Inc, pg 815
Media Magic, pg 822
The Media Staff Inc, pg 822
Music Rhapsody, pg 834
Music World/Vocal Power School, pg 834
Nystrom Education, pg 844
PM Productions, pg 858
Rhythms Productions (Tom Thumb Music), pg 874
Screen Door Entertainment Inc, pg 882
Sea Studios Foundation, pg 883
TMW Media Group, pg 915
Total Creative, pg 916
Vineyard Video & Photography, pg 930
Wavemaker Media Design, pg 934
Webster Communications, pg 935

COLORADO

Crystal Productions, pg 735
Flashback Media Productions, pg 762

CONNECTICUT

Weston Woods Studios Inc, pg 936

DISTRICT OF COLUMBIA

Hillmann & Carr Inc, pg 780

FLORIDA

Applebox Studio, pg 687
Sunfire Communications Inc, pg 904
Tricycle Studios, pg 918
Video Resources Software, pg 928

GEORGIA

Beachwood Productions, pg 702
Guerrilla Productions LLC, pg 774

HAWAII

Hyperspective Studios Inc, pg 783
Media Bridge Gamekids, pg 821

ILLINOIS

Atomic Imaging Inc/Golan Studios, pg 692
Discovery Education - Chicago, pg 743
Manning Productions, pg 816
Pepper Group, pg 854
20/20 Communications Inc, pg 920

KANSAS

Sagebrush Video Productions, pg 879

PROGRAMMING — AUDIO/VISUAL

Children's Program Producers (continued)

KENTUCKY

Horizon Films & Media LLC, pg 781
KET The Kentucky Network, pg 798
National Geographic Learning, pg 836

LOUISIANA

Disk Productions Inc, pg 743

MAINE

Slim Goodbody Corp, pg 890

MARYLAND

The Cutting Corporation, GraphicAudio® & Archival Sound Lab, pg 736

MASSACHUSETTS

Documentary Educational Resources Inc, pg 744
Monadnock Media Inc, pg 829
MotionArt Studios, pg 831
Pauline Books & Media, pg 852
Soundtrack Group, pg 895
WGBH Production Group, pg 936

MICHIGAN

Blue Mouse Studio, pg 707
Digi Sign Design LLC, pg 741
K&R All Media Productions LLC, pg 796
K&R's Recording Studios Inc, pg 796

MISSOURI

Marsh Media, pg 817

NEVADA

JCS Video Productions, pg 793

NEW HAMPSHIRE

Apertura, pg 686
Chip Taylor Communications LLC, pg 907

NEW JERSEY

Allegro Productions Inc, pg 680
Milgrom Productions, pg 827
Optisonics Productions, pg 847
Outside The Box Interactive LLC, pg 849

NEW MEXICO

The Phoenix Learning Group Inc, pg 855

NEW YORK

Air Sea Land Productions Inc (ASL), pg 678
American History Workshop (NY) Inc, pg 683
Brooklyn Botanic Garden, pg 711
The Bureau for At-Risk Youth, pg 712
De Nonno Productions Inc (DPI), pg 739
Duggal Visual Solutions Inc, pg 747

Educational Activities Inc, pg 750
Fanlight Productions, pg 759
Guidance Associates Inc Center for Humanities, pg 774
Hallel Communications, pg 775
Havas Creative, pg 776
Hello World Communications, pg 778
Human Relations Media, pg 782
Listening Library, pg 810
Live Oak Media, pg 810
Manhattan Center Studios Inc, pg 816
Jack Morton Worldwide, pg 830
MRY, pg 832
The Palmer Group, pg 850
Polestar Films & Associated Arts Ltd, pg 859
Random House Children's Books, pg 870
Spoken Arts Inc, pg 898
VIEW Inc (Video International Entertainment World Inc), pg 930
Zelman Studios Ltd, pg 945

NORTH CAROLINA

Pat Appleson Studios Inc, pg 687
Digital Rain LLC, pg 742
Kino Mountain Productions LLC, pg 799
Moving Pictures, pg 832

OHIO

Alegra House Publishers, pg 679
Franciscan Media, pg 765
Lyon Video Inc, pg 813
MainSail Production Services Inc, pg 815
R&B Communications Inc, pg 870
Take 1 Media Services, pg 906
Treehaus Communications Inc, pg 917
Vista Color Imaging Inc, pg 931

OREGON

Ideascape Inc, pg 784
Odyssey Productions Inc, pg 844

PENNSYLVANIA

Discovery Education - South Burlington, pg 743
Media Inc, pg 822
Production Masters Inc (PMI), pg 864

RHODE ISLAND

Sound-FX-Design, pg 894

SOUTH CAROLINA

BJU Press, pg 706

TENNESSEE

American Blackguard Inc, pg 683

TEXAS

Biway Media, pg 706
Communication Arts Multimedia Inc, pg 728
Educational Video Network, pg 751
Epic Software Group Inc, pg 755
Horizon Film + Video Productions, pg 781
Institute of Texan Cultures, pg 788
Mediaforce Productions, pg 822
Tropikal Productions, pg 918

VIRGINIA

Metro Productions, pg 824

WISCONSIN

Aylmer Press, pg 700
Watts Communications Inc, pg 934
Wisconsin Public Television, pg 940

WYOMING

Bridger Productions Inc, pg 710

BRITISH COLUMBIA

West Eagle Films Inc, pg 935

NEWFOUNDLAND AND LABRADOR

Vidcraft Productions Ltd, pg 927

ONTARIO

BBC Worldwide Canada Ltd, pg 702
Canamedia Inc, pg 715
DebsVoice, pg 739
Novalis, pg 843
Weston Woods Canada, pg 936

QUEBEC

Kerrigan Productions Inc, pg 798

Children's Program Rentals

CALIFORNIA

Glenn Photo Supply, pg 771

ILLINOIS

Discovery Education - Chicago, pg 743

MASSACHUSETTS

Documentary Educational Resources Inc, pg 744

MICHIGAN

Digi Sign Design LLC, pg 741

NEW HAMPSHIRE

Chip Taylor Communications LLC, pg 907

NEW YORK

Brooklyn Botanic Garden, pg 711
Hallel Communications, pg 775

OHIO

Treehaus Communications Inc, pg 917

WISCONSIN

Her Own Words LLC, pg 779

Current Event Program Distributors

ARIZONA

Video Learning Library, pg 928

CALIFORNIA

Crystal Pyramid Productions™, pg 735

GEORGIA

School Media Associates LLC, pg 882

ILLINOIS

Discovery Education - Chicago, pg 743
Film Ideas Inc, pg 760

KANSAS

Sagebrush Video Productions, pg 879

MASSACHUSETTS

WGBH Production Group, pg 936

MICHIGAN

Digi Sign Design LLC, pg 741

MONTANA

High Plains Films, pg 779

NEW HAMPSHIRE

Chip Taylor Communications LLC, pg 907

NEW MEXICO

The Phoenix Learning Group Inc, pg 855

NEW YORK

De Nonno Productions Inc (DPI), pg 739
Guidance Associates Inc Center for Humanities, pg 774
HB-Content, pg 777
Janson Media Inc, pg 793
News Broadcast Network Inc, pg 840
Practising Law Institute, pg 860
Women Make Movies Inc, pg 941

PENNSYLVANIA

Media Inc, pg 822

TENNESSEE

Spring Arbor Distributors Inc, pg 898

VIRGINIA

PBS Video, pg 852

WISCONSIN

Knowledge Unlimited Inc, pg 800

ONTARIO

BBC Worldwide Canada Ltd, pg 702
Canadian Learning Co Inc, pg 715
Canamedia Inc, pg 715
Kineticvideo.com, pg 799
Life Cycle Books Ltd, pg 807

Current Event Program Producers

ARIZONA

Aardvark Productions LLC, pg 671
Candee Productions Inc, pg 716

CALIFORNIA

Creative Technology, pg 733
Crystal Pyramid Productions™, pg 735
Lynch Communications, pg 813
Main Street Media Inc, pg 815

PM Productions, pg 858
Total Creative, pg 916
Vineyard Video & Photography,
pg 930
Webster Communications, pg 935

COLORADO

Flashback Media Productions,
pg 762

CONNECTICUT

New London Media, pg 839

DISTRICT OF COLUMBIA

Hillmann & Carr Inc, pg 780

FLORIDA

Applebox Studio, pg 687
NewsBank Inc, pg 840
Sunfire Communications Inc,
pg 904

GEORGIA

Beachwood Productions, pg 702
Guerrilla Productions LLC, pg 774

ILLINOIS

Discovery Education - Chicago,
pg 743
Manning Productions, pg 816
Pepper Group, pg 854
SCI Television & Creative Media
LLC, pg 882

KANSAS

Sagebrush Video Productions,
pg 879

KENTUCKY

Idle Minds Productions Inc, pg 784

MARYLAND

dbF a Media Company, pg 739

MASSACHUSETTS

Soundtrack Group, pg 895
WGBH Production Group, pg 936

MICHIGAN

Digi Sign Design LLC, pg 741
K&R All Media Productions LLC,
pg 796
K&R's Recording Studios Inc,
pg 796

MONTANA

High Plains Films, pg 779

NEVADA

JCS Video Productions, pg 793

NEW HAMPSHIRE

Apertura, pg 686
Chip Taylor Communications LLC,
pg 907

NEW JERSEY

Allegro Productions Inc, pg 680
Optisonics Productions, pg 847

NEW MEXICO

The Phoenix Learning Group Inc,
pg 855

NEW YORK

Broadstreet Productions LLC,
pg 711
De Nonno Productions Inc (DPI),
pg 739
Duggal Visual Solutions Inc, pg 747
Fanlight Productions, pg 759
Guidance Associates Inc Center for
Humanities, pg 774
Havas Creative, pg 776
HB-Content, pg 777
Hello World Communications,
pg 778
The Independent Production Fund,
pg 786
Ketchum Inc, pg 798
Manhattan Center Studios Inc,
pg 816
Jack Morton Worldwide, pg 830
News Broadcast Network Inc,
pg 840
The Palmer Group, pg 850
Practising Law Institute, pg 860
Zelman Studios Ltd, pg 945

NORTH CAROLINA

Pat Appleson Studios Inc, pg 687

OHIO

Lyon Video Inc, pg 813
MainSail Production Services Inc,
pg 815
R&B Communications Inc, pg 870
Take 1 Media Services, pg 906
Vista Color Imaging Inc, pg 931

PENNSYLVANIA

FMP Media Solutions Inc, pg 763
Production Masters Inc (PMI),
pg 864

RHODE ISLAND

Sound-FX-Design, pg 894

TENNESSEE

Running Pony Productions LLC,
pg 878

TEXAS

Epic Software Group Inc, pg 755
Mediaforce Productions, pg 822
South Coast Film & Video, pg 895
Stage Directions, pg 898

VIRGINIA

Metro Productions, pg 824

WISCONSIN

Knowledge Unlimited Inc, pg 800
USAV Group Inc, pg 923
Wisconsin Public Television, pg 940

WYOMING

Bridger Productions Inc, pg 710

ALBERTA

Black Media Works, pg 706

BRITISH COLUMBIA

West Eagle Films Inc, pg 935

ONTARIO

BBC Worldwide Canada Ltd,
pg 702
Canamedia Inc, pg 715

QUEBEC

Kerrigan Productions Inc, pg 798

Current Event Program Rentals

ILLINOIS

Discovery Education - Chicago,
pg 743

MICHIGAN

Digi Sign Design LLC, pg 741

NEW HAMPSHIRE

Chip Taylor Communications LLC,
pg 907

NEW YORK

Historic Films, pg 780

Documentary Distributors

ARIZONA

Video Learning Library, pg 928

CALIFORNIA

Astronomical Society of the Pacific,
pg 691
Les Blank Films Inc, pg 707
California Newsreel, pg 714
Crystal Pyramid Productions™,
pg 735
Discovery Education - Los Angeles,
pg 743
ETR, pg 756
Glenn Photo Supply, pg 771
MarVista Entertainment Inc, pg 818
monterey video, pg 829
New & Unique Videos™, pg 839
Regent Press Publishers & Printers,
pg 873
Sea Studios Foundation, pg 883
TMW Media Group, pg 915
The Wine Appreciation Guild Ltd,
pg 939

CONNECTICUT

Hartley Film Foundation, pg 776

DISTRICT OF COLUMBIA

Art Museum of the Americas,
pg 690
Biblical Archaeology Society
(BAS), pg 705
USCCB Publishing, pg 923

GEORGIA

School Media Associates LLC,
pg 882

HAWAII

Media Bridge Gamekids, pg 821

ILLINOIS

Discovery Education - Chicago,
pg 743
Film Ideas Inc, pg 760
International Historic Films Inc,
pg 790
Questar Entertainment Inc, pg 868
Terra Nova Films Inc, pg 911

KANSAS

Sagebrush Video Productions,
pg 879

KENTUCKY

Horizon Films & Media LLC,
pg 781
KET The Kentucky Network,
pg 798
National Geographic Learning,
pg 836

MARYLAND

James Agee Film Project, pg 792
MMI Marketing, pg 828
Special Archives Division, Motion
Picture Branch, pg 896

MASSACHUSETTS

Documentary Educational Resources
Inc, pg 744
The New Film Company Inc,
pg 839
WGBH Production Group, pg 936

MICHIGAN

Digi Sign Design LLC, pg 741

MONTANA

High Plains Films, pg 779

NEW HAMPSHIRE

Captain Fiddle Music &
Publications, pg 716
Chip Taylor Communications LLC,
pg 907

NEW JERSEY

Allegro Productions Inc, pg 680
Euro-Pacific Film & Video
Productions Inc, pg 756

NEW MEXICO

The Phoenix Learning Group Inc,
pg 855

NEW YORK

Michael Blackwood Productions
Inc, pg 707
De Nonno Productions Inc (DPI),
pg 739
Downtown Community Television
Center (DCTV), pg 746
Fanlight Productions, pg 759
Films Media Group, pg 760
William Greaves Productions Inc,
pg 774
Guidance Associates Inc Center for
Humanities, pg 774
Hallel Communications, pg 775
HB-Content, pg 777
Human Relations Media, pg 782
Janson Media Inc, pg 793
Meridian Education Corp, pg 823
Monad Trainer's Aide Inc, pg 829
News Broadcast Network Inc,
pg 840
Shopware, pg 886
VIEW Inc (Video International
Entertainment World Inc), pg 930
Women Make Movies Inc, pg 941
Wonderwomen™ Enterprises,
pg 941

OHIO

Treehaus Communications Inc,
pg 917

PROGRAMMING — AUDIO/VISUAL

Documentary Distributors (continued)

OREGON

TeleVideos, pg 910

PENNSYLVANIA

FMP Media Solutions Inc, pg 763
Media Inc, pg 822

SOUTH CAROLINA

BJU Press, pg 706

TENNESSEE

American Blackguard Inc, pg 683
Center for Southern Folklore Inc, pg 719
Spring Arbor Distributors Inc, pg 898

TEXAS

Educational Video Network, pg 751
The Samuels Co, pg 879

VIRGINIA

National Audiovisual Center (NAC), pg 836
PBS Video, pg 852

WASHINGTON

Intermedia Inc, pg 789

WEST VIRGINIA

Focus on Animals, pg 763

WISCONSIN

Knowledge Unlimited Inc, pg 800

ONTARIO

BBC Worldwide Canada Ltd, pg 702
Canadian Learning Co Inc, pg 715
Canamedia Inc, pg 715
Kineticvideo.com, pg 799
Life Cycle Books Ltd, pg 807
McIntyre Media Inc, pg 821

Documentary Producers

ARIZONA

Aardvark Productions LLC, pg 671
Candee Productions Inc, pg 716
Creative Backstage, pg 733

ARKANSAS

Live'N'Loud, pg 810
White Diamond Productions LLC, pg 937

CALIFORNIA

Ancient Future, pg 685
Les Blank Films Inc, pg 707
Creative Technology, pg 733
Crystal Pyramid Productions™, pg 735
Design Media, pg 741
Direct Images Interactive Inc, pg 743
Discovery Education - Los Angeles, pg 743

imageReal Pictures LLC, pg 785
Lynch Communications, pg 813
Main Street Media Inc, pg 815
The Media Staff Inc, pg 822
New Circuit Films LLC, pg 839
PM Productions, pg 858
Prime Cut Productions, pg 862
Regent Press Publishers & Printers, pg 873
Screen Door Entertainment Inc, pg 882
Sea Studios Foundation, pg 883
SNAP, pg 891
TMW Media Group, pg 915
Total Creative, pg 916
Vineyard Video & Photography, pg 930
Webster Communications, pg 935

COLORADO

Flashback Media Productions, pg 762
Tatum Video, pg 907

CONNECTICUT

Hartley Film Foundation, pg 776
UConn Health Multimedia Services, pg 920

DISTRICT OF COLUMBIA

Art Museum of the Americas, pg 690
Biblical Archaeology Society (BAS), pg 705
Hillmann & Carr Inc, pg 780
O'Keefe Communications Inc, pg 844

FLORIDA

Applebox Studio, pg 687
Communications Concepts Inc (CCI), pg 729
Sunfire Communications Inc, pg 904

GEORGIA

Beachwood Productions, pg 702
Guerrilla Productions LLC, pg 774

HAWAII

Hyperspective Studios Inc, pg 783
Media Bridge Gamekids, pg 821

ILLINOIS

Discovery Education - Chicago, pg 743
Manning Productions, pg 816
Pepper Group, pg 854
Questar Entertainment Inc, pg 868
SCI Television & Creative Media LLC, pg 882
Terra Nova Films Inc, pg 911
20/20 Communications Inc, pg 920
Video Impressions, pg 928

INDIANA

A-V-A Video Productions, pg 671

IOWA

Educational Technology & Media Services, pg 751

KANSAS

Sagebrush Video Productions, pg 879

KENTUCKY

Horizon Films & Media LLC, pg 781
Idle Minds Productions Inc, pg 784
KET The Kentucky Network, pg 798
National Geographic Learning, pg 836

LOUISIANA

Digital FX Inc, pg 742
Disk Productions Inc, pg 743

MARYLAND

The Cutting Corporation, GraphicAudio® & Archival Sound Lab, pg 736
dbF a Media Company, pg 739
James Agee Film Project, pg 792

MASSACHUSETTS

CommCreative, pg 728
Documentary Educational Resources Inc, pg 744
Monadnock Media Inc, pg 829
The New Film Company Inc, pg 839
Soundtrack Group, pg 895
TVN-The Video Network, pg 919
WGBH Production Group, pg 936

MICHIGAN

Digi Sign Design LLC, pg 741
K&R All Media Productions LLC, pg 796
K&R's Recording Studios Inc, pg 796

MINNESOTA

MastCom, pg 819
Media Loft Inc, pg 822

MONTANA

High Plains Films, pg 779

NEVADA

JCS Video Productions, pg 793
Tanglewood Productions, pg 907

NEW HAMPSHIRE

Apertura, pg 686
Chip Taylor Communications LLC, pg 907

NEW JERSEY

Allegro Productions Inc, pg 680
Laurel Video Productions, pg 804
Optisonics Productions, pg 847

NEW MEXICO

The Phoenix Learning Group Inc, pg 855

NEW YORK

Air Sea Land Productions Inc (ASL), pg 678
American History Workshop (NY) Inc, pg 683
Michael Blackwood Productions Inc, pg 707
Blue Barn Pictures Inc, pg 707
Broadstreet Productions LLC, pg 711
Castillo Theatre, pg 717
Clarity Media Group, pg 725

De Nonno Productions Inc (DPI), pg 739
Downtown Community Television Center (DCTV), pg 746
Duggal Visual Solutions Inc, pg 747
Fanlight Productions, pg 759
Films Media Group, pg 760
William Greaves Productions Inc, pg 774
Guidance Associates Inc Center for Humanities, pg 774
Hallel Communications, pg 775
Havas Creative, pg 776
HB-Content, pg 777
Human Relations Media, pg 782
The Independent Production Fund, pg 786
Janson Media Inc, pg 793
Ketchum Inc, pg 798
Manhattan Center Studios Inc, pg 816
Jack Morton Worldwide, pg 830
MRY, pg 832
News Broadcast Network Inc, pg 840
The Palmer Group, pg 850
Polestar Films & Associated Arts Ltd, pg 859
Vanguard Documentaries, pg 924
VIEW Inc (Video International Entertainment World Inc), pg 930
Wonderwomen™ Enterprises, pg 941
Zelman Studios Ltd, pg 945

NORTH CAROLINA

Pat Appleson Studios Inc, pg 687
The Communications Group Inc, pg 729
Digital Rain LLC, pg 742
Kino Mountain Productions LLC, pg 799
Moving Pictures, pg 832

OHIO

Lyon Video Inc, pg 813
MainSail Production Services Inc, pg 815
R&B Communications Inc, pg 870
Take 1 Media Services, pg 906
Treehaus Communications Inc, pg 917
Vista Color Imaging Inc, pg 931

OREGON

Ideascape Inc, pg 784
Odyssey Productions Inc, pg 844
TeleVideos, pg 910

PENNSYLVANIA

Bang! Pictures Inc, pg 701
FMP Media Solutions Inc, pg 763
Main Point Productions, pg 815
Panta Rhei Media Inc, pg 851
Production Masters Inc (PMI), pg 864

RHODE ISLAND

Sound-FX-Design, pg 894

TENNESSEE

American Blackguard Inc, pg 683
Continental Film, pg 731
Running Pony Productions LLC, pg 878

TEXAS

Dykeman Associates Inc, pg 748
Educational Video Network, pg 751

Mediaforce Productions, pg 822
The Samuels Co, pg 879
South Coast Film & Video, pg 895
Stage Directions, pg 898
Tropikal Productions, pg 918

VIRGINIA

Metro Productions, pg 824

WASHINGTON

Intermedia Inc, pg 789
Kostov Productions, pg 801

WEST VIRGINIA

Focus on Animals, pg 763

WISCONSIN

Knowledge Unlimited Inc, pg 800
USAV Group Inc, pg 923
Watts Communications Inc, pg 934
Wisconsin Public Television, pg 940

WYOMING

Bridger Productions Inc, pg 710

ALBERTA

Black Media Works, pg 706

BRITISH COLUMBIA

West Eagle Films Inc, pg 935

*NEWFOUNDLAND AND
LABRADOR*

Vidcraft Productions Ltd, pg 927

ONTARIO

BBC Worldwide Canada Ltd,
pg 702
Canamedia Inc, pg 715
DebsVoice, pg 739

QUEBEC

Kerrigan Productions Inc, pg 798

Documentary Rentals

CALIFORNIA

Les Blank Films Inc, pg 707
Glenn Photo Supply, pg 771

ILLINOIS

Discovery Education - Chicago,
pg 743
Terra Nova Films Inc, pg 911

MARYLAND

James Agee Film Project, pg 792

MASSACHUSETTS

Documentary Educational Resources
Inc, pg 744

MICHIGAN

Digi Sign Design LLC, pg 741

NEW HAMPSHIRE

Chip Taylor Communications LLC,
pg 907

NEW JERSEY

Euro-Pacific Film & Video
Productions Inc, pg 756

NEW YORK

Downtown Community Television
Center (DCTV), pg 746
Fanlight Productions, pg 759
William Greaves Productions Inc,
pg 774
Hallel Communications, pg 775
Historic Films, pg 780

WASHINGTON

Intermedia Inc, pg 789

Educational Program Distributors

ARIZONA

Video Learning Library, pg 928

CALIFORNIA

Academy Savant, pg 672
Astronomical Society of the Pacific,
pg 691
Les Blank Films Inc, pg 707
California Newsreel, pg 714
Crystal Pyramid Productions™,
pg 735
Davidson Productions, pg 738
Deja View Video, pg 740
Dialect Accent Specialists Inc,
pg 741
Discovery Education - Los Angeles,
pg 743
Educational Insights, pg 750
ETR, pg 756
Geddes Productions LLC, pg 769
Glenn Photo Supply, pg 771
Bruce Goldberg Inc, pg 772
Golden State Dance Teachers
Association (GSDTA), pg 772
Griggs Productions Inc, pg 774
Joyce Media Inc, pg 795
Kantola Productions LLC, pg 796
Learn Quickly, pg 805
MarVista Entertainment Inc, pg 818
monterey video, pg 829
Moose School Productions, pg 830
Music World/Vocal Power School,
pg 834
New & Unique Videos™, pg 839
Nystrom Education, pg 844
Regent Press Publishers & Printers,
pg 873
Rhythms Productions (Tom Thumb
Music), pg 874
Sea Studios Foundation, pg 883
TMW Media Group, pg 915
The Wine Appreciation Guild Ltd,
pg 939

COLORADO

Crystal Productions, pg 735
Vital Learning LLC, pg 932

CONNECTICUT

Cine-Med Inc, pg 723
Hartley Film Foundation, pg 776
Weston Woods Studios Inc, pg 936

DISTRICT OF COLUMBIA

Art Museum of the Americas,
pg 690
Biblical Archaeology Society
(BAS), pg 705
Systems Impact Inc, pg 906

FLORIDA

Video Resources Software, pg 928

GEORGIA

School Media Associates LLC,
pg 882

HAWAII

Media Bridge Gamekids, pg 821
Source School of Tantra Yoga Inc,
pg 895

ILLINOIS

Britannica Digital Learning, pg 710
CCH Continuing Education, pg 718
CCore Media Inc, pg 718
Discovery Education - Chicago,
pg 743
Encyclopaedia Britannica Inc,
pg 754
Film Ideas Inc, pg 760
Learning Seed, pg 805
National Safety Council (NSC),
pg 836
Questar Entertainment Inc, pg 868
RADMAR Inc, pg 869
Terra Nova Films Inc, pg 911

INDIANA

Solution Tree, pg 892

KANSAS

Sagebrush Video Productions,
pg 879

KENTUCKY

KET The Kentucky Network,
pg 798
National Geographic Learning,
pg 836

MARYLAND

Department of Education Resources,
pg 740
James Agee Film Project, pg 792
MMI Marketing, pg 828

MASSACHUSETTS

Cheng & Tsui Co, pg 721
Davis Art Images, pg 738
Documentary Educational Resources
Inc, pg 744
The New Film Company Inc,
pg 839
WGBH Production Group, pg 936

MICHIGAN

Digi Sign Design LLC, pg 741
Emery-Pratt Co, pg 753
HighScope Press, pg 780
Madonna University Information
Technology, pg 814
MSU Technologies, pg 833
The Program Source International,
pg 865

MINNESOTA

American Choral Catalog Ltd,
pg 683
EMC Publishing LLC, pg 753
Hazelden Publishing & Educational
Services, pg 777

MISSOURI

Marsh Media, pg 817
SOM Publishing Co, pg 892

MONTANA

High Plains Films, pg 779

NEW HAMPSHIRE

Captain Fiddle Music &
Publications, pg 716
Frey Scientific, pg 766
Heinemann, pg 778
Chip Taylor Communications LLC,
pg 907

NEW JERSEY

Allegro Productions Inc, pg 680

NEW MEXICO

The Phoenix Learning Group Inc,
pg 855

NEW YORK

Beekman Books Inc, pg 703
Michael Blackwood Productions
Inc, pg 707
Brooklyn Botanic Garden, pg 711
The Bureau for At-Risk Youth,
pg 712
Cornell Laboratory of Ornithology,
pg 731
Criterion Collection, pg 735
De Nonno Productions Inc (DPI),
pg 739
Downtown Community Television
Center (DCTV), pg 746
Educational Activities Inc, pg 750
Fanlight Productions, pg 759
Films Media Group, pg 760
William Greaves Productions Inc,
pg 774
Guidance Associates Inc Center for
Humanities, pg 774
Hallel Communications, pg 775
Homespun Video, pg 781
Human Relations Media, pg 782
Janson Media Inc, pg 793
Listening Library, pg 810
March of Dimes Foundation, pg 816
Practising Law Institute, pg 860
TeleTime Productions, pg 910
VIEW Inc (Video International
Entertainment World Inc), pg 930
Women Make Movies Inc, pg 941
Wonderwomen™ Enterprises,
pg 941

NORTH CAROLINA

Carolina Biological Supply Co,
pg 717

OHIO

Alegra House Publishers, pg 679
Franciscan Media, pg 765
McGraw-Hill School Education
Group, pg 821
Treehaus Communications Inc,
pg 917

OREGON

CNS Productions Inc, pg 727
Getty-Dubay Productions, pg 770
The Keyboard Workshop, pg 798
TeleVideos, pg 910

PENNSYLVANIA

Discovery Education - South
Burlington, pg 743
FMP Media Solutions Inc, pg 763
Media Inc, pg 822

SOUTH CAROLINA

BJU Press, pg 706

PROGRAMMING — AUDIO/VISUAL

Educational Program Distributors (continued)

TENNESSEE

American Blackguard Inc, pg 683
Center for Southern Folklore Inc, pg 719
National School Products, pg 836
Spring Arbor Distributors Inc, pg 898

TEXAS

Educational Video Network, pg 751
Institute of Texan Cultures, pg 788
PetroSkills | RDC Solutions, pg 855
University of Texas at Austin - Petroleum Extension Service, pg 923

VERMONT

Wilson McLeran Inc, pg 939

VIRGINIA

Design & Production Inc, pg 740
National Audiovisual Center (NAC), pg 836
PBS Video, pg 852

WASHINGTON

Intermedia Inc, pg 789

WEST VIRGINIA

Focus on Animals, pg 763
Harpers Ferry Historical Association, pg 776

WISCONSIN

Her Own Words LLC, pg 779
Knowledge Unlimited Inc, pg 800

BRITISH COLUMBIA

Credo Interactive Inc, pg 734

ONTARIO

BBC Worldwide Canada Ltd, pg 702
Canadian Learning Co Inc, pg 715
Canamedia Inc, pg 715
Kineticvideo.com, pg 799
Life Cycle Books Ltd, pg 807
McIntyre Media Inc, pg 821
Novalis, pg 843

QUEBEC

Editions Hurtubise HMH Ltee, pg 782

Educational Program Producers

ALABAMA

AVS Media Group, pg 699

ARIZONA

Aardvark Productions LLC, pg 671
Candee Productions Inc, pg 716

ARKANSAS

White Diamond Productions LLC, pg 937

CALIFORNIA

Academy Savant, pg 672
Ancient Future, pg 685
Astronomical Society of the Pacific, pg 691
Les Blank Films Inc, pg 707
Creative Technology, pg 733
Crystal Pyramid Productions™, pg 735
Davidson Productions, pg 738
Design Media, pg 741
Dialect Accent Specialists Inc, pg 741
Direct Images Interactive Inc, pg 743
Discovery Education - Los Angeles, pg 743
Dolphin MultiMedia Inc, pg 745
Geddes Productions LLC, pg 769
imageReal Pictures LLC, pg 785
Joyce Media Inc, pg 795
Kantola Productions LLC, pg 796
Lynch Communications, pg 813
Main Street Media Inc, pg 815
Media Magic, pg 822
The Media Staff Inc, pg 822
Music World/Vocal Power School, pg 834
Nystrom Education, pg 844
PM Productions, pg 858
Prime Cut Productions, pg 862
Regent Press Publishers & Printers, pg 873
Rhythms Productions (Tom Thumb Music), pg 874
Sea Studios Foundation, pg 883
SNAP, pg 891
Tam Communications Inc, pg 906
TMW Media Group, pg 915
Total Creative, pg 916
Vineyard Video & Photography, pg 930
Wavemaker Media Design, pg 934
Webster Communications, pg 935
West Coast Projections Inc, pg 935

COLORADO

Crystal Productions, pg 735
Flashback Media Productions, pg 762
Jeppesen, pg 793
Vital Learning LLC, pg 932

CONNECTICUT

Cine-Med Inc, pg 723
Hartley Film Foundation, pg 776
UConn Health Multimedia Services, pg 920
Weston Woods Studios Inc, pg 936

DISTRICT OF COLUMBIA

Art Museum of the Americas, pg 690
Biblical Archaeology Society (BAS), pg 705
Hillmann & Carr Inc, pg 780
O'Keefe Communications Inc, pg 844
Systems Impact Inc, pg 906

FLORIDA

Applebox Studio, pg 687
Audio Visual Imagineering Inc, pg 694
ITC Learning LLC, pg 791
Sunfire Communications Inc, pg 904
Teach America Corp, pg 908
Tricycle Studios, pg 918
Video Resources Software, pg 928

GEORGIA

Beachwood Productions, pg 702
Guerrilla Productions LLC, pg 774

HAWAII

Hyperspective Studios Inc, pg 783
Media Bridge Gamekids, pg 821
Source School of Tantra Yoga Inc, pg 895

ILLINOIS

Accenture, pg 672
Airways Digital Media, pg 679
Britannica Digital Learning, pg 710
CCH Continuing Education, pg 718
CCore Media Inc, pg 718
Cresta Creative, pg 734
Discovery Education - Chicago, pg 743
1st Financial Training Services Inc, pg 761
Learning Seed, pg 805
Major Media Productions Inc, pg 815
Manning Productions, pg 816
National Safety Council (NSC), pg 836
Pepper Group, pg 854
PSAV® Presentation Services (Hotel Services Division), pg 866
Questar Entertainment Inc, pg 868
Rand McNally Education, pg 870
Steven Samler Music & Sound, pg 879
SCI Television & Creative Media LLC, pg 882
Terra Nova Films Inc, pg 911
20/20 Communications Inc, pg 920
Video Impressions, pg 928

INDIANA

Solution Tree, pg 892

IOWA

Educational Technology & Media Services, pg 751

KANSAS

Sagebrush Video Productions, pg 879

KENTUCKY

Idle Minds Productions Inc, pg 784
KET The Kentucky Network, pg 798
National Geographic Learning, pg 836
NIMCO Inc, pg 841

LOUISIANA

Disk Productions Inc, pg 743

MARYLAND

The Cutting Corporation, GraphicAudio® & Archival Sound Lab, pg 736
dbF a Media Company, pg 739
Department of Education Resources, pg 740
The Image Generators, pg 785
James Agee Film Project, pg 792
MMI Marketing, pg 828
Mobile-Video Productions Inc, pg 828

MASSACHUSETTS

Cheng & Tsui Co, pg 721
Documentary Educational Resources Inc, pg 744
Monadnock Media Inc, pg 829
The New Film Company Inc, pg 839
Soundtrack Group, pg 895
TVN-The Video Network, pg 919
WGBH Production Group, pg 936

MICHIGAN

Digi Sign Design LLC, pg 741
HighScope Press, pg 780
K&R All Media Productions LLC, pg 796
K&R's Recording Studios Inc, pg 796
Madonna University Information Technology, pg 814

MINNESOTA

American Choral Catalog Ltd, pg 683
EMC Publishing LLC, pg 753
Hazelden Publishing & Educational Services, pg 777
MastCom, pg 819
Media Loft Inc, pg 822
Vaddio, pg 924

MISSOURI

Marsh Media, pg 817
SOM Publishing Co, pg 892

MONTANA

High Plains Films, pg 779

NEVADA

JCS Video Productions, pg 793

NEW HAMPSHIRE

Academic & Campus Technology Services, pg 672
Apertura, pg 686
Captain Fiddle Music & Publications, pg 716
Heinemann, pg 778
Chip Taylor Communications LLC, pg 907

NEW JERSEY

Allegro Productions Inc, pg 680
Laurel Video Productions, pg 804
Optisonics Productions, pg 847

NEW MEXICO

The Phoenix Learning Group Inc, pg 855

NEW YORK

American History Workshop (NY) Inc, pg 683
Blue Barn Pictures Inc, pg 707
Broadstreet Productions LLC, pg 711
Brooklyn Botanic Garden, pg 711
The Bureau for At-Risk Youth, pg 712
Cornell Laboratory of Ornithology, pg 731
Criterion Collection, pg 735
De Nonno Productions Inc (DPI), pg 739
Downtown Community Television Center (DCTV), pg 746
Duggal Visual Solutions Inc, pg 747

Educational Activities Inc, pg 750
Fanlight Productions, pg 759
Films Media Group, pg 760
The Food & Beverage Institute,
 pg 763
William Greaves Productions Inc,
 pg 774
Guidance Associates Inc Center for
 Humanities, pg 774
Hallel Communications, pg 775
Havas Creative, pg 776
Human Relations Media, pg 782
The Independent Production Fund,
 pg 786
Ketchum Inc, pg 798
Listening Library, pg 810
Long Island Video Enterprises Live
 Inc, pg 811
Manhattan Center Studios Inc,
 pg 816
March of Dimes Foundation, pg 816
Jack Morton Worldwide, pg 830
MRY, pg 832
New York Audio Productions,
 pg 840
News Broadcast Network Inc,
 pg 840
The Palmer Group, pg 850
Polestar Films & Associated Arts
 Ltd, pg 859
Practising Law Institute, pg 860
Spoken Arts Inc, pg 898
Triumph Learning LLC, pg 918
VIEW Inc (Video International
 Entertainment World Inc), pg 930
Weigl Publishers Inc, pg 935
Wonderwomen™ Enterprises,
 pg 941
Zelman Studios Ltd, pg 945

NORTH CAROLINA

Pat Appleson Studios Inc, pg 687
Carolina Biological Supply Co,
 pg 717
The Communications Group Inc,
 pg 729
Digital Rain LLC, pg 742
Kino Mountain Productions LLC,
 pg 799
Laurel Hill Press, pg 804
Moving Pictures, pg 832
PACE Worldwide, pg 849
Sinclair Institute, pg 889

OHIO

Alegra House Publishers, pg 679
Cuyahoga Community College
 Student Production Office (SPO),
 pg 736
Franciscan Media, pg 765
Lyon Video Inc, pg 813
MainSail Production Services Inc,
 pg 815
McGraw-Hill School Education
 Group, pg 821
R&B Communications Inc, pg 870
Take 1 Media Services, pg 906
Treehaus Communications Inc,
 pg 917
Vista Color Imaging Inc, pg 931

OKLAHOMA

CSI/Orion, pg 735

OREGON

CNS Productions Inc, pg 727
Getty-Dubay Productions, pg 770
Ideascape, pg 784
The Keyboard Workshop, pg 798
KTVA Productions, pg 802

Odyssey Productions Inc, pg 844
TeleVideos, pg 910

PENNSYLVANIA

Bang! Pictures Inc, pg 701
Discovery Education - South
 Burlington, pg 743
FMP Media Solutions Inc, pg 763
JPL, pg 795
Kensington Falls Animation, pg 797
Main Point Productions, pg 815
Media Inc, pg 822
Muderick Media, pg 833
Panta Rhei Media Inc, pg 851
Production Masters Inc (PMI),
 pg 864

RHODE ISLAND

Sound-FX-Design, pg 894

SOUTH CAROLINA

BJU Press, pg 706

TENNESSEE

American Blackguard Inc, pg 683
Running Pony Productions LLC,
 pg 878
Russ Sturgeon Productions/RSVP,
 pg 903

TEXAS

Educational Video Network, pg 751
Institute of Texan Cultures, pg 788
Mediaforce Productions, pg 822
PetroSkills | RDC Solutions, pg 855
Romar Learning Solutions LLC,
 pg 877
Stage Directions, pg 898
Stockyard Photos/Jim Olive
 Photography, pg 901
Tropikal Productions, pg 918
University of Texas at Austin -
 Petroleum Extension Service,
 pg 923

VERMONT

Wilson McLeran Inc, pg 939

VIRGINIA

Altruist Media LLC, pg 682
Metro Productions, pg 824

WASHINGTON

Intermedia Inc, pg 789
Laser Fantasy/HECK
 Industries/Photon Manufacturing,
 pg 804

WEST VIRGINIA

Focus on Animals, pg 763

WISCONSIN

Her Own Words LLC, pg 779
Knowledge Unlimited Inc, pg 800
USAV Group Inc, pg 923
Video Wisconsin Inc, pg 929
Watts Communications Inc, pg 934
Wisconsin Public Television, pg 940

WYOMING

Bridger Productions Inc, pg 710

ALBERTA

Black Media Works, pg 706

BRITISH COLUMBIA

West Eagle Films Inc, pg 935

*NEWFOUNDLAND AND
 LABRADOR*

Vidcraft Productions Ltd, pg 927

NORTHWEST TERRITORIES

Yellowknife Films Inc, pg 944

ONTARIO

Art Gallery of Ontario, pg 690
BBC Worldwide Canada Ltd,
 pg 702
Canamedia Inc, pg 715
DebsVoice, pg 739
Doomsday Studios Limited, pg 745
McIntyre Media Inc, pg 821
Novalis, pg 843
Pearson Education Canada, pg 852

QUEBEC

Kerrigan Productions Inc, pg 798

Educational Program
Rentals

CALIFORNIA

Les Blank Films Inc, pg 707
Davidson Productions, pg 738
Glenn Photo Supply, pg 771

ILLINOIS

Discovery Education - Chicago,
 pg 743
1st Financial Training Services Inc,
 pg 761
National Safety Council (NSC),
 pg 836
Terra Nova Films Inc, pg 911

MARYLAND

James Agee Film Project, pg 792

MASSACHUSETTS

Documentary Educational Resources
 Inc, pg 744

MICHIGAN

Digi Sign Design LLC, pg 741
HighScope Press, pg 780

MINNESOTA

American Choral Catalog Ltd,
 pg 683
Hazelden Publishing & Educational
 Services, pg 777

NEW HAMPSHIRE

Academic & Campus Technology
 Services, pg 672
Heinemann, pg 778
Chip Taylor Communications LLC,
 pg 907

NEW YORK

Brooklyn Botanic Garden, pg 711
Downtown Community Television
 Center (DCTV), pg 746
Fanlight Productions, pg 759
William Greaves Productions Inc,
 pg 774
Hallel Communications, pg 775
Historic Films, pg 780

OHIO

Franciscan Media, pg 765
Treehaus Communications Inc,
 pg 917

WASHINGTON

Intermedia Inc, pg 789

WEST VIRGINIA

Harpers Ferry Historical
 Association, pg 776

WISCONSIN

Her Own Words LLC, pg 779

Feature Program
Distributors

CALIFORNIA

Les Blank Films Inc, pg 707
Crystal Pyramid Productions™,
 pg 735
Glenn Photo Supply, pg 771
Bruce Goldberg Inc, pg 772
MarVista Entertainment Inc, pg 818
monterey video, pg 829
Moose School Productions, pg 830

GEORGIA

Visioneering International Inc,
 pg 931

IOWA

Right Stuf Inc, pg 875

KENTUCKY

KET The Kentucky Network,
 pg 798

MONTANA

High Plains Films, pg 779

NEW HAMPSHIRE

Chip Taylor Communications LLC,
 pg 907

NEW YORK

Criterion Collection, pg 735
Guidance Associates Inc Center for
 Humanities, pg 774
HB-Content, pg 777
Janson Media Inc, pg 793
VIEW Inc (Video International
 Entertainment World Inc), pg 930
Women Make Movies Inc, pg 941

SOUTH CAROLINA

BJU Press, pg 706

TENNESSEE

American Blackguard Inc, pg 683
Spring Arbor Distributors Inc,
 pg 898

TEXAS

The Samuels Co, pg 879

ONTARIO

Canadian Learning Co Inc, pg 715
Life Cycle Books Ltd, pg 807

PROGRAMMING — AUDIO/VISUAL

Feature Program Producers

ARIZONA

Aardvark Productions LLC, pg 671

CALIFORNIA

Les Blank Films Inc, pg 707
Creative Technology, pg 733
Crystal Pyramid Productions™, pg 735
imageReal Pictures LLC, pg 785
Jaguar Distribution Corp, pg 792
Lynch Communications, pg 813
PM Productions, pg 858
RKO Pictures Inc, pg 875
Screen Door Entertainment Inc, pg 882
Total Creative, pg 916
Vineyard Video & Photography, pg 930

COLORADO

Flashback Media Productions, pg 762
Tatum Video, pg 907

CONNECTICUT

Hartley Film Foundation, pg 776

FLORIDA

Applebox Studio, pg 687
Communications Concepts Inc (CCI), pg 729
Sunfire Communications Inc, pg 904

GEORGIA

Guerrilla Productions LLC, pg 774
Visioneering International Inc, pg 931

HAWAII

Hyperspective Studios Inc, pg 783

ILLINOIS

Manning Productions, pg 816
Pepper Group, pg 854

IOWA

Right Stuf Inc, pg 875

KENTUCKY

KET The Kentucky Network, pg 798

MASSACHUSETTS

Monadnock Media Inc, pg 829
Soundtrack Group, pg 895

MICHIGAN

K&R All Media Productions LLC, pg 796
K&R's Recording Studios Inc, pg 796

MONTANA

High Plains Films, pg 779

NEW HAMPSHIRE

Chip Taylor Communications LLC, pg 907

NEW JERSEY

Optisonics Productions, pg 847

NEW YORK

Blue Barn Pictures Inc, pg 707
Broadstreet Productions LLC, pg 711
CompuWeather Inc, pg 729
Criterion Collection, pg 735
Duggal Visual Solutions Inc, pg 747
William Greaves Productions Inc, pg 774
Havas Creative, pg 776
HB-Content, pg 777
Jack Morton Worldwide, pg 830
News Broadcast Network Inc, pg 840
The Palmer Group, pg 850
Vanguard Documentaries, pg 924
VIEW Inc (Video International Entertainment World Inc), pg 930
Zelman Studios Ltd, pg 945

NORTH CAROLINA

Pat Appleson Studios Inc, pg 687
Digital Rain LLC, pg 742

OHIO

Image Video Teleproductions Inc, pg 785
Lyon Video Inc, pg 813
R&B Communications Inc, pg 870
Vista Color Imaging Inc, pg 931

OREGON

Ideascape Inc, pg 784

PENNSYLVANIA

Kensington Falls Animation, pg 797
Production Masters Inc (PMI), pg 864

RHODE ISLAND

Sound-FX-Design, pg 894

SOUTH CAROLINA

BJU Press, pg 706

TENNESSEE

American Blackguard Inc, pg 683
Running Pony Productions LLC, pg 878

TEXAS

Epic Software Group Inc, pg 755
The Samuels Co, pg 879
Stage Directions, pg 898
Stockyard Photos/Jim Olive Photography, pg 901

VIRGINIA

Metro Productions, pg 824

WASHINGTON

Laser Fantasy/HECK Industries/Photon Manufacturing, pg 804

WISCONSIN

Wisconsin Public Television, pg 940

WYOMING

Bridger Productions Inc, pg 710

NEWFOUNDLAND AND LABRADOR

Vidcraft Productions Ltd, pg 927

ONTARIO

Doomsday Studios Limited, pg 745

QUEBEC

Kerrigan Productions Inc, pg 798

Feature Program Rentals

CALIFORNIA

Les Blank Films Inc, pg 707
Glenn Photo Supply, pg 771

NEW HAMPSHIRE

Chip Taylor Communications LLC, pg 907

NEW YORK

Historic Films, pg 780

Film Loop Distributors

CALIFORNIA

Ametron Audio/Video, pg 684
QRS Software Services, pg 867

INDIANA

Lee Co Inc, pg 805

NEW YORK

Janus Films Inc, pg 793
Visual Technologies Corp, pg 932

Film Loop Producers

CALIFORNIA

International Contact Inc, pg 790
QRS Software Services, pg 867

FLORIDA

Blackburst Entertainment LLC, pg 706
The Kitchen, pg 799

GEORGIA

Guerrilla Productions LLC, pg 774

ILLINOIS

Cresta Creative, pg 734

IOWA

Educational Technology & Media Services, pg 751

MASSACHUSETTS

TR Productions, pg 916

MICHIGAN

K&R All Media Productions LLC, pg 796
K&R's Recording Studios Inc, pg 796

NEW YORK

Duggal Visual Solutions Inc, pg 747
Split Image Productions, pg 898
Zelman Studios Ltd, pg 945

TENNESSEE

Memphis Communications Corp, pg 823
Running Pony Productions LLC, pg 878

TEXAS

Romar Learning Solutions LLC, pg 877

WISCONSIN

USAV Group Inc, pg 923

Film Loop Rentals

CALIFORNIA

Ametron Audio/Video, pg 684

Filmstrip—Silent Distributors

Ametron Audio/Video, pg 684
Discovery Education - Los Angeles, pg 743
QRS Software Services, pg 867
Sea Studios Foundation, pg 883

COLORADO

American Educational Products LLC, pg 683

DISTRICT OF COLUMBIA

Biblical Archaeology Society (BAS), pg 705

MICHIGAN

Michigan Office Solutions (MOS), A Xerox Company, pg 825
Wayne State University Media Services, pg 934

NEW YORK

Visual Technologies Corp, pg 932

TENNESSEE

Spring Arbor Distributors Inc, pg 898

TEXAS

Audio Visual Technologies Group (AVTG), pg 695

VIRGINIA

Colonial Williamsburg Foundation, pg 727

WISCONSIN

School Specialty Inc, pg 882

Filmstrip—Silent Producers

CALIFORNIA

Discovery Education - Los Angeles, pg 743
Lynch Communications, pg 813
QRS Software Services, pg 867
Sea Studios Foundation, pg 883

COLORADO

American Educational Products LLC, pg 683

DISTRICT OF COLUMBIA

Biblical Archaeology Society (BAS), pg 705

GEORGIA

Guerrilla Productions LLC, pg 774

INDIANA

OMNI Productions, pg 845

MASSACHUSETTS

CommCreative, pg 728
TR Productions, pg 916

MICHIGAN

Blue Mouse Studio, pg 707
K&R All Media Productions LLC, pg 796
Wayne State University Media Services, pg 934

NEW HAMPSHIRE

Apertura, pg 686

NEW JERSEY

Optisonics Productions, pg 847

NEW YORK

Applause Learning Resources, pg 687
Duggal Visual Solutions Inc, pg 747
Jack Morton Worldwide, pg 830
Split Image Productions, pg 898
Triumph Learning LLC, pg 918
Zelman Studios Ltd, pg 945

OHIO

Treehaus Communications Inc, pg 917

PENNSYLVANIA

FMP Media Solutions Inc, pg 763

TENNESSEE

Memphis Communications Corp, pg 823
Running Pony Productions LLC, pg 878

TEXAS

Romar Learning Solutions LLC, pg 877

VIRGINIA

Blair Inc, pg 707

WISCONSIN

USAV Group Inc, pg 923

Filmstrip—Silent Rentals

CALIFORNIA

Ametron Audio/Video, pg 684

MICHIGAN

Wayne State University Media Services, pg 934

Filmstrip—Sound Distributors

CALIFORNIA

Ametron Audio/Video, pg 684
Discovery Education - Los Angeles, pg 743
QRS Software Services, pg 867
Sea Studios Foundation, pg 883
Visual Communications - Southern California Asian American Studies Central Inc, pg 931

GEORGIA

School Media Associates LLC, pg 882

KENTUCKY

National Geographic Learning, pg 836

MICHIGAN

Michigan Office Solutions (MOS), A Xerox Company, pg 825

MISSOURI

Mosby Inc, pg 831

NEW HAMPSHIRE

Frey Scientific, pg 766

NEW YORK

Brooklyn Botanic Garden, pg 711
Triumph Learning LLC, pg 918
Visual Technologies Corp, pg 932

NORTH CAROLINA

Carolina Biological Supply Co, pg 717

OHIO

McGraw-Hill School Education Group, pg 821
Treehaus Communications Inc, pg 917

PENNSYLVANIA

Discovery Education - South Burlington, pg 743

TENNESSEE

Spring Arbor Distributors Inc, pg 898

TEXAS

Audio Visual Technologies Group (AVTG), pg 695
Stage Directions, pg 898

WISCONSIN

School Specialty Inc, pg 882

ONTARIO

Canadian Learning Co Inc, pg 715

Filmstrip—Sound Producers

CALIFORNIA

Discovery Education - Los Angeles, pg 743
Lynch Communications, pg 813
QRS Software Services, pg 867
Sea Studios Foundation, pg 883
Steve Shapiro Music, pg 885

GEORGIA

Guerrilla Productions LLC, pg 774

INDIANA

OMNI Productions, pg 845

KENTUCKY

National Geographic Learning, pg 836

MASSACHUSETTS

CommCreative, pg 728
TR Productions, pg 916

MICHIGAN

K&R All Media Productions LLC, pg 796
K&R's Recording Studios Inc, pg 796

MISSOURI

Mosby Inc, pg 831
Switch, pg 905

NEW HAMPSHIRE

Apertura, pg 686
Frey Scientific, pg 766

NEW JERSEY

Optisonics Productions, pg 847

NEW YORK

Applause Learning Resources, pg 687
Brooklyn Botanic Garden, pg 711
Duggal Visual Solutions Inc, pg 747
Jack Morton Worldwide, pg 830
David Rapkin Audio Production, pg 870
Split Image Productions, pg 898
Zelman Studios Ltd, pg 945

OHIO

McGraw-Hill School Education Group, pg 821
Treehaus Communications Inc, pg 917

PENNSYLVANIA

FMP Media Solutions Inc, pg 763

TENNESSEE

Memphis Communications Corp, pg 823
Running Pony Productions LLC, pg 878

TEXAS

Romar Learning Solutions LLC, pg 877
The Sound Lab Inc, pg 894
Tropikal Productions, pg 918

VIRGINIA

Blair Inc, pg 707

WASHINGTON

Kostov Productions, pg 801

WISCONSIN

USAV Group Inc, pg 923

BRITISH COLUMBIA

West Eagle Films Inc, pg 935

ONTARIO

Weston Woods Canada, pg 936

Filmstrip—Sound Rentals

CALIFORNIA

Ametron Audio/Video, pg 684
Visual Communications - Southern California Asian American Studies Central Inc, pg 931

NEW YORK

Brooklyn Botanic Garden, pg 711

Foreign Program Distributors

CALIFORNIA

Crystal Pyramid Productions™, pg 735
Discovery Education - Los Angeles, pg 743
Glenn Photo Supply, pg 771
MarVista Entertainment Inc, pg 818
New & Unique Videos™, pg 839
The Wine Appreciation Guild Ltd, pg 939

DISTRICT OF COLUMBIA

Biblical Archaeology Society (BAS), pg 705

GEORGIA

Visioneering International Inc, pg 931

ILLINOIS

International Historic Films Inc, pg 790

IOWA

Right Stuf Inc, pg 875

MASSACHUSETTS

Cheng & Tsui Co, pg 721
Documentary Educational Resources Inc, pg 744

MICHIGAN

Digi Sign Design LLC, pg 741

NEW HAMPSHIRE

Chip Taylor Communications LLC, pg 907

NEW JERSEY

Euro-Pacific Film & Video Productions Inc, pg 756

NEW YORK

Applause Learning Resources, pg 687
Hallel Communications, pg 775
Janson Media Inc, pg 793
VIEW Inc (Video International Entertainment World Inc), pg 930
Women Make Movies Inc, pg 941

PROGRAMMING — AUDIO/VISUAL

Foreign Program Distributors (continued)

PENNSYLVANIA

FMP Media Solutions Inc, pg 763

TENNESSEE

Spring Arbor Distributors Inc, pg 898

TEXAS

Educational Video Network, pg 751

VIRGINIA

National Audiovisual Center (NAC), pg 836

ONTARIO

Canadian Learning Co Inc, pg 715

Foreign Program Producers

ARIZONA

Aardvark Productions LLC, pg 671

CALIFORNIA

Ancient Future, pg 685
Creative Technology, pg 733
Crystal Pyramid Productions™, pg 735
Discovery Education - Los Angeles, pg 743
Dolphin MultiMedia Inc, pg 745
International Contact Inc, pg 790
Jaguar Distribution Corp, pg 792
Lynch Communications, pg 813
Prime Cut Productions, pg 862
Total Creative, pg 916
Vineyard Video & Photography, pg 930
Webster Communications, pg 935

DISTRICT OF COLUMBIA

Biblical Archaeology Society (BAS), pg 705
Hillmann & Carr Inc, pg 780

FLORIDA

Sunfire Communications Inc, pg 904

GEORGIA

Guerrilla Productions LLC, pg 774
Visioneering International Inc, pg 931

ILLINOIS

Manning Productions, pg 816
Pepper Group, pg 854
20/20 Communications Inc, pg 920

IOWA

Right Stuf Inc, pg 875

MASSACHUSETTS

Documentary Educational Resources Inc, pg 744
Soundtrack Group, pg 895

MICHIGAN

Digi Sign Design LLC, pg 741
K&R All Media Productions LLC, pg 796
K&R's Recording Studios Inc, pg 796

MINNESOTA

MastCom, pg 819

NEW HAMPSHIRE

Apertura, pg 686
Chip Taylor Communications LLC, pg 907

NEW YORK

Applause Learning Resources, pg 687
Hallel Communications, pg 775
Havas Creative, pg 776
Manhattan Center Studios Inc, pg 816
Jack Morton Worldwide, pg 830
The Palmer Group, pg 850
VIEW Inc (Video International Entertainment World Inc), pg 930
Zelman Studios Ltd, pg 945

NORTH CAROLINA

Pat Appleson Studios Inc, pg 687

OHIO

Take 1 Media Services, pg 906
Vista Color Imaging Inc, pg 931

PENNSYLVANIA

FMP Media Solutions Inc, pg 763

RHODE ISLAND

Sound-FX-Design, pg 894

TEXAS

Educational Video Network, pg 751
Stage Directions, pg 898
Tropikal Productions, pg 918

VIRGINIA

Metro Productions, pg 824

WASHINGTON

Kostov Productions, pg 801

WISCONSIN

Wisconsin Public Television, pg 940

WYOMING

Bridger Productions Inc, pg 710

ONTARIO

Doomsday Studios Limited, pg 745

QUEBEC

Kerrigan Productions Inc, pg 798

Foreign Program Rentals

CALIFORNIA

Glenn Photo Supply, pg 771

MASSACHUSETTS

Documentary Educational Resources Inc, pg 744

MICHIGAN

Digi Sign Design LLC, pg 741

NEW HAMPSHIRE

Chip Taylor Communications LLC, pg 907

NEW JERSEY

Euro-Pacific Film & Video Productions Inc, pg 756

NEW YORK

Fanlight Productions, pg 759
Hallel Communications, pg 775

Globe Distributors

CALIFORNIA

Educational Insights, pg 750
Nystrom Education, pg 844
QRS Software Services, pg 867
Social Studies School Service, pg 891

KENTUCKY

National Geographic Learning, pg 836

MARYLAND

Absolute Hollywood, pg 672
MMI Marketing, pg 828

NORTH CAROLINA

Carolina Biological Supply Co, pg 717

WISCONSIN

Demco Inc, pg 740
School Specialty Inc, pg 882

Globe Producers

CALIFORNIA

Creative Technology, pg 733
Nystrom Education, pg 844
QRS Software Services, pg 867
Total Creative, pg 916

ILLINOIS

Rand McNally Education, pg 870

KENTUCKY

National Geographic Learning, pg 836

MARYLAND

Absolute Hollywood, pg 672

MICHIGAN

K&R's Recording Studios Inc, pg 796

OHIO

Vista Color Imaging Inc, pg 931

PENNSYLVANIA

Main Point Productions, pg 815

TENNESSEE

Running Pony Productions LLC, pg 878

TEXAS

The Music Bakery, pg 834

VIRGINIA

Advance Concepts Inc, pg 677

Globe Rentals

MARYLAND

Absolute Hollywood, pg 672

Government Program Distributors

CALIFORNIA

Crystal Pyramid Productions™, pg 735
Discovery Education - Los Angeles, pg 743
Glenn Photo Supply, pg 771

COLORADO

Vital Learning LLC, pg 932

FLORIDA

Video Resources Software, pg 928

GEORGIA

Visioneering International Inc, pg 931

ILLINOIS

CCH Inc, A Wolters Kluwer business, pg 718
CCore Media Inc, pg 718
Film Ideas Inc, pg 760

MARYLAND

Special Archives Division, Motion Picture Branch, pg 896

MICHIGAN

Digi Sign Design LLC, pg 741

NEW HAMPSHIRE

Chip Taylor Communications LLC, pg 907

NEW JERSEY

Allegro Productions Inc, pg 680

NEW MEXICO

The Phoenix Learning Group Inc, pg 855

NEW YORK

Monad Trainer's Aide Inc, pg 829
Women Make Movies Inc, pg 941

OHIO

Treehaus Communications Inc, pg 917

PENNSYLVANIA

FMP Media Solutions Inc, pg 763

VIRGINIA

National Audiovisual Center (NAC), pg 836

ONTARIO

Kineticvideo.com, pg 799

Government Program Producers

ARIZONA

Aardvark Productions LLC, pg 671

ARKANSAS

White Diamond Productions LLC, pg 937

CALIFORNIA

Creative Technology, pg 733
Crystal Pyramid Productions™, pg 735
Design Media, pg 741
Discovery Education - Los Angeles, pg 743
Jaguar Distribution Corp, pg 792
Lynch Communications, pg 813
The Media Staff Inc, pg 822
PM Productions, pg 858
Total Creative, pg 916
Vineyard Video & Photography, pg 930

COLORADO

Daylight Productions & Rentals, pg 739
Flashback Media Productions, pg 762
Tatum Video, pg 907
Vital Learning LLC, pg 932

CONNECTICUT

UConn Health Multimedia Services, pg 920

DISTRICT OF COLUMBIA

Hillmann & Carr Inc, pg 780
O'Keefe Communications Inc, pg 844

FLORIDA

Applebox Studio, pg 687
Communications Concepts Inc (CCI), pg 729
Sunfire Communications Inc, pg 904
Video Resources Software, pg 928
Video Techniques Inc, pg 928

GEORGIA

Beachwood Productions, pg 702
Guerrilla Productions LLC, pg 774
Visioneering International Inc, pg 931

HAWAII

Hyperspective Studios Inc, pg 783

ILLINOIS

Airways Digital Media, pg 679
CCH Inc, A Wolters Kluwer business, pg 718
CCore Media Inc, pg 718
Pepper Group, pg 854
Video Impressions, pg 928

INDIANA

A-V-A Video Productions, pg 671

IOWA

Educational Technology & Media Services, pg 751

KANSAS

Sagebrush Video Productions, pg 879

LOUISIANA

Digital FX Inc, pg 742

MARYLAND

The Cutting Corporation, GraphicAudio® & Archival Sound Lab, pg 736
dbF a Media Company, pg 739
The Image Generators, pg 785
Mobile-Video Productions Inc, pg 828

MASSACHUSETTS

Cramer, pg 732
Monadnock Media Inc, pg 829
Soundtrack Group, pg 895
TVN-The Video Network, pg 919

MICHIGAN

Digi Sign Design LLC, pg 741
K&R All Media Productions LLC, pg 796
K&R's Recording Studios Inc, pg 796

MINNESOTA

Live Spark Inc, pg 810
MastCom, pg 819
Vaddio, pg 924

NEVADA

JCS Video Productions, pg 793

NEW HAMPSHIRE

Apertura, pg 686
Chip Taylor Communications LLC, pg 907

NEW JERSEY

Laurel Video Productions, pg 804
Optisonics Productions, pg 847
Suede Interactive, pg 903

NEW MEXICO

The Phoenix Learning Group Inc, pg 855

NEW YORK

Blue Barn Pictures Inc, pg 707
Duggal Visual Solutions Inc, pg 747
Havas Creative, pg 776
Ketchum Inc, pg 798
Jack Morton Worldwide, pg 830
MRY, pg 832
Northeast Video Productions Inc, pg 842
The Palmer Group, pg 850
Zelman Studios Ltd, pg 945

NORTH CAROLINA

Pat Appleson Studios Inc, pg 687
The Communications Group Inc, pg 729
Digital Rain LLC, pg 742
Kino Mountain Productions LLC, pg 799

OHIO

Image Video Teleproductions Inc, pg 785
Lyon Video Inc, pg 813
MainSail Production Services Inc, pg 815
R&B Communications Inc, pg 870
Take 1 Media Services, pg 906
Treehaus Communications Inc, pg 917
Vista Color Imaging Inc, pg 931

OREGON

Ideascape Inc, pg 784
KTVA Productions, pg 802
Odyssey Productions Inc, pg 844

PENNSYLVANIA

Audio Visual Communications Inc, pg 694
Bang! Pictures Inc, pg 701
FMP Media Solutions Inc, pg 763
JPL, pg 795

RHODE ISLAND

Sound-FX-Design, pg 894

TENNESSEE

Continental Film, pg 731
Running Pony Productions LLC, pg 878

TEXAS

Biway Media, pg 706
Epic Software Group Inc, pg 755
Mediaforce Productions, pg 822
Romar Learning Solutions LLC, pg 877
Stage Directions, pg 898

VIRGINIA

Advance Concepts Inc, pg 677
Altruist Media LLC, pg 682
Metro Productions, pg 824

WASHINGTON

Kostov Productions, pg 801

WISCONSIN

Audio Visual of Milwaukee Inc, pg 694
USAV Group Inc, pg 923
Video Wisconsin Inc, pg 929
Watts Communications Inc, pg 934
Wisconsin Public Television, pg 940

WYOMING

Bridger Productions Inc, pg 710

ALBERTA

Black Media Works, pg 706

BRITISH COLUMBIA

West Eagle Films Inc, pg 935

NEWFOUNDLAND AND LABRADOR

Vidcraft Productions Ltd, pg 927

QUEBEC

Kerrigan Productions Inc, pg 798

Government Program Rentals

CALIFORNIA

Glenn Photo Supply, pg 771

GEORGIA

ON Services, a GES Company, pg 846

MICHIGAN

Digi Sign Design LLC, pg 741

NEW HAMPSHIRE

Chip Taylor Communications LLC, pg 907

NEW YORK

Historic Films, pg 780

UTAH

Webb Audio Visual, pg 935

Industrial Program Distributors

ARIZONA

Video Learning Library, pg 928

CALIFORNIA

Academy Savant, pg 672
Crystal Pyramid Productions™, pg 735
Deja View Video, pg 740
Discovery Education - Los Angeles, pg 743
Glenn Photo Supply, pg 771
New & Unique Videos™, pg 839

COLORADO

Vital Learning LLC, pg 932

FLORIDA

Video Resources Software, pg 928

GEORGIA

Convergent Media Systems, pg 731
Visioneering International Inc, pg 931

ILLINOIS

CCore Media Inc, pg 718
National Safety Council (NSC), pg 836
Woodside Avenue Music Productions Inc, pg 941

KENTUCKY

Hammond Communications Group Inc, pg 775

MASSACHUSETTS

Preston Productions Inc, pg 861

MICHIGAN

Digi Sign Design LLC, pg 741

NEW HAMPSHIRE

Chip Taylor Communications LLC, pg 907

PROGRAMMING — AUDIO/VISUAL

Industrial Program Distributors (continued)

NEW JERSEY

Advanced Imaging Concepts Inc, pg 677
Allegro Productions Inc, pg 680
Euro-Pacific Film & Video Productions Inc, pg 756

NEW MEXICO

The Phoenix Learning Group Inc, pg 855

NEW YORK

Fanlight Productions, pg 759
Guidance Associates Inc Center for Humanities, pg 774
HB-Content, pg 777
Monad Trainer's Aide Inc, pg 829
TeleTime Productions, pg 910

OHIO

Treehaus Communications Inc, pg 917

PENNSYLVANIA

FMP Media Solutions Inc, pg 763
Media Inc, pg 822

SOUTH CAROLINA

DaviSound, pg 739

TEXAS

PetroSkills | RDC Solutions, pg 855
The Samuels Co, pg 879
University of Texas at Austin - Petroleum Extension Service, pg 923

WISCONSIN

Wisconsin Technical College System Foundation Inc, pg 940

ONTARIO

BBC Worldwide Canada Ltd, pg 702
Canadian Learning Co Inc, pg 715
Kineticvideo.com, pg 799

Industrial Program Producers

ARIZONA

Aardvark Productions LLC, pg 671
Candee Productions Inc, pg 716

ARKANSAS

Live'N'Loud, pg 810
White Diamond Productions LLC, pg 937

CALIFORNIA

Academy Savant, pg 672
Creative Technology, pg 733
Crystal Pyramid Productions™, pg 735
Design Media, pg 741
Direct Images Interactive Inc, pg 743

Discovery Education - Los Angeles, pg 743
Dolphin MultiMedia Inc, pg 745
imageReal Pictures LLC, pg 785
Jaguar Distribution Corp, pg 792
Kavich Reynolds Productions Inc, pg 797
Lynch Communications, pg 813
Media Magic, pg 822
The Media Staff Inc, pg 822
PM Productions, pg 858
Screen Door Entertainment Inc, pg 882
SNAP, pg 891
Tam Communications Inc, pg 906
Total Creative, pg 916
Vineyard Video & Photography, pg 930
Wavemaker Media Design, pg 934
Webster Communications, pg 935
West Coast Projections Inc, pg 935

COLORADO

Daylight Productions & Rentals, pg 739
Flashback Media Productions, pg 762
Vital Learning LLC, pg 932

CONNECTICUT

UConn Health Multimedia Services, pg 920

DISTRICT OF COLUMBIA

Hillmann & Carr Inc, pg 780
O'Keefe Communications Inc, pg 844

FLORIDA

Applebox Studio, pg 687
ITC Learning LLC, pg 791
Sunfire Communications Inc, pg 904
Tricycle Studios, pg 918
Universal Studios Florida® Production Group, pg 922
Video Resources Software, pg 928
Video Techniques Inc, pg 928

GEORGIA

Beachwood Productions, pg 702
Guerrilla Productions LLC, pg 774
Visioneering International Inc, pg 931

HAWAII

Hyperspective Studios Inc, pg 783

ILLINOIS

Airways Digital Media, pg 679
CCore Media Inc, pg 718
Cresta Creative, pg 734
1st Financial Training Services Inc, pg 761
Major Media Productions Inc, pg 815
National Safety Council (NSC), pg 836
Pepper Group, pg 854
PSAV® Presentation Services (Hotel Services Division), pg 866
20/20 Communications Inc, pg 920
Video Impressions, pg 928
Woodside Avenue Music Productions Inc, pg 941

INDIANA

A-V-A Video Productions, pg 671

KANSAS

Sagebrush Video Productions, pg 879

KENTUCKY

Idle Minds Productions Inc, pg 784
NIMCO Inc, pg 841

LOUISIANA

Digital FX Inc, pg 742
Disk Productions Inc, pg 743

MARYLAND

The Cutting Corporation, GraphicAudio® & Archival Sound Lab, pg 736
dbF a Media Company, pg 739
The Image Generators, pg 785
Mobile-Video Productions Inc, pg 828

MASSACHUSETTS

CommCreative, pg 728
Cramer, pg 732
Soundtrack Group, pg 895
TVN-The Video Network, pg 919

MICHIGAN

Digi Sign Design LLC, pg 741
K&R All Media Productions LLC, pg 796
K&R's Recording Studios Inc, pg 796

MINNESOTA

Big Event Productions LLC, pg 705
Live Spark Inc, pg 810
MastCom, pg 819

NEVADA

JCS Video Productions, pg 793
Tanglewood Productions, pg 907

NEW HAMPSHIRE

Apertura, pg 686
Chip Taylor Communications LLC, pg 907

NEW JERSEY

Advanced Imaging Concepts Inc, pg 677
Allegro Productions Inc, pg 680
Laurel Video Productions, pg 804
Optisonics Productions, pg 847
Suede Interactive, pg 903

NEW MEXICO

The Phoenix Learning Group Inc, pg 855

NEW YORK

Blue Barn Pictures Inc, pg 707
Broadstreet Productions LLC, pg 711
Castillo Theatre, pg 717
Duggal Visual Solutions Inc, pg 747
Fanlight Productions, pg 759
Guidance Associates Inc Center for Humanities, pg 774
Havas Creative, pg 776
HB-Content, pg 777
Hello World Communications, pg 778
Image Zone Inc, pg 785
The Independent Production Fund, pg 786

Ketchum Inc, pg 798
Long Island Video Enterprises Live Inc, pg 811
Manhattan Center Studios Inc, pg 816
Jack Morton Worldwide, pg 830
MRY, pg 832
New York Audio Productions, pg 840
News Broadcast Network Inc, pg 840
Northeast Video Productions Inc, pg 842
The Palmer Group, pg 850
Polestar Films & Associated Arts Ltd, pg 859
Zelman Studios Ltd, pg 945

NORTH CAROLINA

Pat Appleson Studios Inc, pg 687
The Communications Group Inc, pg 729
Digital Rain LLC, pg 742
Kino Mountain Productions LLC, pg 799
Moving Pictures, pg 832
PACE Worldwide, pg 849

OHIO

Cuyahoga Community College Student Production Office (SPO), pg 736
Image Video Teleproductions Inc, pg 785
Lyon Video Inc, pg 813
MainSail Production Services Inc, pg 815
R&B Communications Inc, pg 870
Take 1 Media Services, pg 906
Treehaus Communications Inc, pg 917
Vista Color Imaging Inc, pg 931

OREGON

Ideascape Inc, pg 784
KTVA Productions, pg 802
Odyssey Productions Inc, pg 844

PENNSYLVANIA

Audio Visual Communications Inc, pg 694
Bang! Pictures Inc, pg 701
FMP Media Solutions Inc, pg 763
JPL, pg 795
Kensington Falls Animation, pg 797
Main Point Productions, pg 815
Muderick Media, pg 833
Panta Rhei Media Inc, pg 851
Production Masters Inc (PMI), pg 864

RHODE ISLAND

Sound-FX-Design, pg 894

SOUTH CAROLINA

DaviSound, pg 739

TENNESSEE

Continental Film, pg 731
Running Pony Productions LLC, pg 878

TEXAS

Biway Media, pg 706
Dykeman Associates Inc, pg 748
Epic Software Group Inc, pg 755
Mediaforce Productions, pg 822
PetroSkills | RDC Solutions, pg 855

Romar Learning Solutions LLC, pg 877
The Samuels Co, pg 879
South Coast Film & Video, pg 895
Stage Directions, pg 898
Stockyard Photos/Jim Olive Photography, pg 901
Tropikal Productions, pg 918
University of Texas at Austin - Petroleum Extension Service, pg 923

VIRGINIA

Advance Concepts Inc, pg 677
Altruist Media LLC, pg 682
Metro Productions, pg 824

WASHINGTON

Adams Creative & Production Services, pg 675
Kostov Productions, pg 801

WISCONSIN

Audio Visual of Milwaukee Inc, pg 694
AVS Group, pg 699
Logan Productions Inc, pg 811
USAV Group Inc, pg 923
Video Wisconsin Inc, pg 929
Watts Communications Inc, pg 934
Wisconsin Public Television, pg 940
Wisconsin Technical College System Foundation Inc, pg 940

WYOMING

Bridger Productions Inc, pg 710

ALBERTA

Black Media Works, pg 706

BRITISH COLUMBIA

West Eagle Films Inc, pg 935

NEWFOUNDLAND AND LABRADOR

Vidcraft Productions Ltd, pg 927

ONTARIO

BBC Worldwide Canada Ltd, pg 702
DebsVoice, pg 739
Mediaimage Communications Group, pg 822

QUEBEC

Kerrigan Productions Inc, pg 798

Industrial Program Rentals

CALIFORNIA

Glenn Photo Supply, pg 771

GEORGIA

Convergent Media Systems, pg 731
ON Services, a GES Company, pg 846

ILLINOIS

National Safety Council (NSC), pg 836
Woodside Avenue Music Productions Inc, pg 941

MASSACHUSETTS

Preston Productions Inc, pg 861

MICHIGAN

Digi Sign Design LLC, pg 741

NEW HAMPSHIRE

Chip Taylor Communications LLC, pg 907

NEW JERSEY

Euro-Pacific Film & Video Productions Inc, pg 756

NEW YORK

Fanlight Productions, pg 759
Historic Films, pg 780

UTAH

Webb Audio Visual, pg 935

Literature, *see* Feature Program

Map Distributors

ARIZONA

Arizona Cine Equipment, pg 688

CALIFORNIA

Astronomical Society of the Pacific, pg 691
Health Education Services, pg 778
Nystrom Education, pg 844
QRS Software Services, pg 867
Social Studies School Service, pg 891

FLORIDA

Kappa Map Group LLC, pg 796

KENTUCKY

National Geographic Learning, pg 836

MARYLAND

MMI Marketing, pg 828

NEW HAMPSHIRE

Frey Scientific, pg 766

NORTH CAROLINA

Carolina Biological Supply Co, pg 717

PENNSYLVANIA

AccuWeather Inc, pg 674

SOUTH CAROLINA

BJU Press, pg 706

TENNESSEE

B&H Publishing Group, pg 701
Randall House Publications, pg 870
Spring Arbor Distributors Inc, pg 898

WISCONSIN

School Specialty Inc, pg 882

Map Producers

CALIFORNIA

Creative Technology, pg 733
Nystrom Education, pg 844
QRS Software Services, pg 867
Total Creative, pg 916
The Wine Appreciation Guild Ltd, pg 939

COLORADO

Flashback Media Productions, pg 762

FLORIDA

Kappa Map Group LLC, pg 796

GEORGIA

Imagers, pg 785

ILLINOIS

Rand McNally Education, pg 870

INDIANA

Bright Ideas Creative Services, pg 710

KENTUCKY

National Geographic Learning, pg 836

MASSACHUSETTS

CommCreative, pg 728

MICHIGAN

K&R's Recording Studios Inc, pg 796

NEW JERSEY

Fiber Optic Systems Inc (FOSI), pg 759

NEW YORK

Applause Learning Resources, pg 687

OHIO

Vista Color Imaging Inc, pg 931

OREGON

InterVision Media, pg 791

PENNSYLVANIA

AccuWeather Inc, pg 674
Kensington Falls Animation, pg 797
Main Point Productions, pg 815

SOUTH CAROLINA

BJU Press, pg 706

TENNESSEE

Running Pony Productions LLC, pg 878

VIRGINIA

Advance Concepts Inc, pg 677
Blair Inc, pg 707

WISCONSIN

USAV Group Inc, pg 923

Medical Program Distributors

ARIZONA

Video Learning Library, pg 928

CALIFORNIA

Academy Savant, pg 672
Crystal Pyramid Productions™, pg 735
Davies Publishing Inc, pg 738
Discovery Education - Los Angeles, pg 743
ETR, pg 756
Geddes Productions LLC, pg 769
Glenn Photo Supply, pg 771
Bruce Goldberg Inc, pg 772
Joyce Media Inc, pg 795
Medcom Inc, pg 821
New & Unique Videos™, pg 839
TMW Media Group, pg 915

COLORADO

Vital Learning LLC, pg 932

CONNECTICUT

Cine-Med Inc, pg 723

ILLINOIS

CCore Media Inc, pg 718
Film Ideas Inc, pg 760

LOUISIANA

Louisiana State University Division of Strategic Communications, pg 811

MASSACHUSETTS

Preston Productions Inc, pg 861

MICHIGAN

Digi Sign Design LLC, pg 741
Emery-Pratt Co, pg 753
MSU Technologies, pg 833
Phoenix Society for Burn Survivors Inc, pg 856

MISSOURI

Marsh Media, pg 817
Mosby Inc, pg 831
University of Missouri-Kansas City School of Dentistry, pg 923

NEW HAMPSHIRE

Frey Scientific, pg 766
Chip Taylor Communications LLC, pg 907

NEW JERSEY

Advanced Imaging Concepts Inc, pg 677
Allegro Productions Inc, pg 680
Euro-Pacific Film & Video Productions Inc, pg 756

NEW MEXICO

The Phoenix Learning Group Inc, pg 855

NEW YORK

Fanlight Productions, pg 759
Guidance Associates Inc Center for Humanities, pg 774
HB-Content, pg 777
Monad Trainer's Aide Inc, pg 829

PROGRAMMING — AUDIO/VISUAL

Medical Program Distributors (continued)

NEW YORK (continued)

News Broadcast Network Inc, pg 840
VIEW Inc (Video International Entertainment World Inc), pg 930
Women Make Movies Inc, pg 941

NORTH CAROLINA

Sinclair Institute, pg 889

PENNSYLVANIA

FMP Media Solutions Inc, pg 763
Lippincott Williams & Wilkins, pg 809
Media Inc, pg 822

VIRGINIA

PBS Video, pg 852

WASHINGTON

Medical Media Systems, pg 823

ONTARIO

BBC Worldwide Canada Ltd, pg 702
Canadian Learning Co Inc, pg 715
Kineticvideo.com, pg 799
Life Cycle Books Ltd, pg 807

Medical Program Producers

ARIZONA

Aardvark Productions LLC, pg 671
Candee Productions Inc, pg 716

ARKANSAS

White Diamond Productions LLC, pg 937

CALIFORNIA

Academy Savant, pg 672
Creative Technology, pg 733
Crystal Pyramid Productions™, pg 735
Design Media, pg 741
Direct Images Interactive Inc, pg 743
Discovery Education - Los Angeles, pg 743
Dolphin MultiMedia Inc, pg 745
Geddes Productions LLC, pg 769
imageReal Pictures LLC, pg 785
Jaguar Distribution Corp, pg 792
Joyce Media Inc, pg 795
Lynch Communications, pg 813
Medcom Inc, pg 821
The Media Staff Inc, pg 822
PM Productions, pg 858
SNAP, pg 891
TMW Media Group, pg 915
Total Creative, pg 916
Vineyard Video & Photography, pg 930
Wavemaker Media Design, pg 934
West Coast Projections Inc, pg 935

COLORADO

Daylight Productions & Rentals, pg 739
Flashback Media Productions, pg 762
Vital Learning LLC, pg 932

CONNECTICUT

Cine-Med Inc, pg 723
New London Media, pg 839
UConn Health Multimedia Services, pg 920

DISTRICT OF COLUMBIA

Hillmann & Carr Inc, pg 780
O'Keefe Communications Inc, pg 844

FLORIDA

Sunfire Communications Inc, pg 904
Teach America Corp, pg 908
Tricycle Studios, pg 918
Video Techniques Inc, pg 928

GEORGIA

Beachwood Productions, pg 702
Guerrilla Productions LLC, pg 774

HAWAII

Hyperspective Studios Inc, pg 783

ILLINOIS

Airways Digital Media, pg 679
CCore Media Inc, pg 718
Major Media Productions Inc, pg 815
Manning Productions, pg 816
Pepper Group, pg 854
SCI Television & Creative Media LLC, pg 882
20/20 Communications Inc, pg 920
Video Impressions, pg 928

INDIANA

A-V-A Video Productions, pg 671

KENTUCKY

Idle Minds Productions Inc, pg 784

LOUISIANA

Digital FX Inc, pg 742
Louisiana State University Division of Strategic Communications, pg 811

MARYLAND

The Cutting Corporation, GraphicAudio® & Archival Sound Lab, pg 736
dbF a Media Company, pg 739
The Image Generators, pg 785
Mobile-Video Productions Inc, pg 828

MASSACHUSETTS

Cramer, pg 732
Soundtrack Group, pg 895
TVN-The Video Network, pg 919

MICHIGAN

Digi Sign Design LLC, pg 741
K&R All Media Productions LLC, pg 796

K&R's Recording Studios Inc, pg 796
Phoenix Society for Burn Survivors Inc, pg 856

MINNESOTA

Media Loft Inc, pg 822
Vaddio, pg 924

MISSOURI

Marsh Media, pg 817
Mosby Inc, pg 831
University of Missouri-Kansas City School of Dentistry, pg 923

NEVADA

JCS Video Productions, pg 793

NEW HAMPSHIRE

Apertura, pg 686
Chip Taylor Communications LLC, pg 907

NEW JERSEY

Advanced Imaging Concepts Inc, pg 677
Laurel Video Productions, pg 804
Optisonics Productions, pg 847
Outside The Box Interactive LLC, pg 849
Suede Interactive, pg 903

NEW MEXICO

The Phoenix Learning Group Inc, pg 855

NEW YORK

Broadstreet Productions LLC, pg 711
Duggal Visual Solutions Inc, pg 747
Fanlight Productions, pg 759
Guidance Associates Inc Center for Humanities, pg 774
Havas Creative, pg 776
HB-Content, pg 777
Hello World Communications, pg 778
Image Zone Inc, pg 785
The Independent Production Fund, pg 786
Ketchum Inc, pg 798
Long Island Video Enterprises Live Inc, pg 811
Jack Morton Worldwide, pg 830
News Broadcast Network Inc, pg 840
Northeast Video Productions Inc, pg 842
The Palmer Group, pg 850
VIEW Inc (Video International Entertainment World Inc), pg 930
Zelman Studios Ltd, pg 945

NORTH CAROLINA

Pat Appleson Studios Inc, pg 687
The Communications Group Inc, pg 729
Digital Rain LLC, pg 742
Kino Mountain Productions LLC, pg 799
Moving Pictures, pg 832
Sinclair Institute, pg 889

OHIO

Cuyahoga Community College Student Production Office (SPO), pg 736
Image Video Teleproductions Inc, pg 785
Lyon Video Inc, pg 813
MainSail Production Services Inc, pg 815
R&B Communications Inc, pg 870
Take 1 Media Services, pg 906
Vista Color Imaging Inc, pg 931

OKLAHOMA

CSI/Orion, pg 735

OREGON

Ideascape Inc, pg 784

PENNSYLVANIA

Audio Visual Communications Inc, pg 694
Bang! Pictures Inc, pg 701
FMP Media Solutions Inc, pg 763
JPL, pg 795
Kensington Falls Animation, pg 797
Lippincott Williams & Wilkins, pg 809
Media Inc, pg 822
Panta Rhei Media Inc, pg 851
Production Masters Inc (PMI), pg 864

RHODE ISLAND

Sound-FX-Design, pg 894

TENNESSEE

Continental Film, pg 731
Running Pony Productions LLC, pg 878

TEXAS

Dykeman Associates Inc, pg 748
Epic Software Group Inc, pg 755
Mediaforce Productions, pg 822
Romar Learning Solutions LLC, pg 877
South Coast Film & Video, pg 895
Stage Directions, pg 898
Texas Heart Institute Visual Communication Services, pg 911

VIRGINIA

Advance Concepts Inc, pg 677
Altruist Media LLC, pg 682
Metro Productions, pg 824

WASHINGTON

Adams Creative & Production Services, pg 675
Kostov Productions, pg 801
Medical Media Systems, pg 823

WISCONSIN

Audio Visual of Milwaukee Inc, pg 694
USAV Group Inc, pg 923
Video Wisconsin Inc, pg 929
Watts Communications Inc, pg 934
Wisconsin Public Television, pg 940

WYOMING

Bridger Productions Inc, pg 710

*NEWFOUNDLAND AND
LABRADOR*
Vidcraft Productions Ltd, pg 927

ONTARIO
BBC Worldwide Canada Ltd,
pg 702
JFB Communications, pg 794

QUEBEC
Kerrigan Productions Inc, pg 798

Medical Program Rentals

CALIFORNIA
Glenn Photo Supply, pg 771
Medcom Inc, pg 821

GEORGIA
ON Services, a GES Company,
pg 846

MASSACHUSETTS
Preston Productions Inc, pg 861

MICHIGAN
Digi Sign Design LLC, pg 741

MISSOURI
University of Missouri-Kansas City
School of Dentistry, pg 923

NEW HAMPSHIRE
Chip Taylor Communications LLC,
pg 907

NEW JERSEY
Euro-Pacific Film & Video
Productions Inc, pg 756

NEW YORK
Fanlight Productions, pg 759
Historic Films, pg 780

UTAH
Webb Audio Visual, pg 935

Model & Mock-up
Distributors

CALIFORNIA
Health Education Services, pg 778
Medcom Inc, pg 821
QRS Software Services, pg 867
Social Studies School Service,
pg 891

COLORADO
American Educational Products
LLC, pg 683

FLORIDA
PAR Inc, pg 851

GEORGIA
School Media Associates LLC,
pg 882

MARYLAND
MMI Marketing, pg 828

MICHIGAN
Digi Sign Design LLC, pg 741

NEW HAMPSHIRE
Frey Scientific, pg 766

NORTH CAROLINA
Carolina Biological Supply Co,
pg 717

UTAH
Strata™, pg 901

WISCONSIN
School Specialty Inc, pg 882

Model & Mock-up
Producers

ARIZONA
Merestone, pg 823

CALIFORNIA
Classic Images Stock Footage LLC,
pg 726
Creative Technology, pg 733
QRS Software Services, pg 867

COLORADO
American Educational Products
LLC, pg 683
Starwest Productions, pg 900

HAWAII
Hyperspective Studios Inc, pg 783

INDIANA
A-V-A Video Productions, pg 671

LOUISIANA
Moxie Media, pg 832

MICHIGAN
Digi Sign Design LLC, pg 741
K&R All Media Productions LLC,
pg 796
K&R's Recording Studios Inc,
pg 796

MISSOURI
Switch, pg 905

NEW JERSEY
Fiber Optic Systems Inc (FOSI),
pg 759

OHIO
Vista Color Imaging Inc, pg 931

OREGON
InterVision Media, pg 791

VIRGINIA
Blair Inc, pg 707

WISCONSIN
USAV Group Inc, pg 923

Model & Mock-up Rentals

MICHIGAN
Digi Sign Design LLC, pg 741

Multimedia, CD-ROM &
DVD Interactive
Program Distributors

CALIFORNIA
Astronomical Society of the Pacific,
pg 691
California Language Laboratories,
pg 714
Crystal Pyramid Productions™,
pg 735
Davies Publishing Inc, pg 738
Discovery Education - Los Angeles,
pg 743
Educational Insights, pg 750
Griggs Productions Inc, pg 774
MarVista Entertainment Inc, pg 818
Medcom Inc, pg 821
Nystrom Education, pg 844
QRS Software Services, pg 867
TiVo Corp, pg 914
The Wine Appreciation Guild Ltd,
pg 939

COLORADO
American Educational Products
LLC, pg 683
Vital Learning LLC, pg 932

CONNECTICUT
Cine-Med Inc, pg 723

FLORIDA
CD ROM™ Inc, pg 718
Video Aided Instruction Inc, pg 927
Video Resources Software, pg 928

GEORGIA
Convergent Media Systems, pg 731
School Media Associates LLC,
pg 882
Visioneering International Inc,
pg 931

HAWAII
Media Bridge Gamekids, pg 821

ILLINOIS
Britannica Digital Learning, pg 710
CCore Media Inc, pg 718
National Safety Council (NSC),
pg 836

IOWA
Prositions Inc, pg 865
Right Stuf Inc, pg 875

KENTUCKY
National Geographic Learning,
pg 836

MARYLAND
MMI Marketing, pg 828

MASSACHUSETTS
Documentary Educational Resources
Inc, pg 744
Nuance Communications Inc,
pg 843

Preston Productions Inc, pg 861
Sinauer Associates, pg 889

MICHIGAN
Digi Sign Design LLC, pg 741
MSU Technologies, pg 833
Zondervan, pg 945

MINNESOTA
BeyerSound & Essay Audio, pg 705
EMC Publishing LLC, pg 753
JIST Publishing, pg 794

NEW HAMPSHIRE
Frey Scientific, pg 766
Chip Taylor Communications LLC,
pg 907

NEW JERSEY
Allegro Productions Inc, pg 680
Euro-Pacific Film & Video
Productions Inc, pg 756

NEW MEXICO
The Phoenix Learning Group Inc,
pg 855

NEW YORK
Brooklyn Botanic Garden, pg 711
The Bureau for At-Risk Youth,
pg 712
Future US Inc, pg 767
Guidance Associates Inc Center for
Humanities, pg 774
HB-Content, pg 777
Human Relations Media, pg 782
Magnetic Music Publishing Co,
pg 814
Marshad Technology Group, pg 817
Meridian Education Corp, pg 823
Monad Trainer's Aide Inc, pg 829
Scholastic Media, pg 882
Shopware, pg 886
Trans-Lux Multimedia Corp, pg 917

OREGON
Wilderness Video, pg 938

PENNSYLVANIA
AccuWeather Inc, pg 674
Discovery Education - South
Burlington, pg 743
FMP Media Solutions Inc, pg 763
MVD Entertainment Group, pg 835
New Horizons Computer Learning
Centers Inc, pg 839

TENNESSEE
Spring Arbor Distributors Inc,
pg 898

TEXAS
Replicopy Digital Media Center,
pg 873

UTAH
Strata™, pg 901

VERMONT
Multicultural Media Inc, pg 833

VIRGINIA
National Audiovisual Center (NAC),
pg 836

PROGRAMMING — AUDIO/VISUAL

Multimedia, CD-ROM & DVD Interactive Program Distributors (continued)

WASHINGTON

Intermedia Inc, pg 789

WISCONSIN

Wisconsin Technical College System Foundation Inc, pg 940

MANITOBA

Inland Audio Visual Ltd, pg 788
Tek Gear, pg 909

ONTARIO

Canadian Learning Co Inc, pg 715
The Children's Book Store Distribution (CBSD), pg 722
Corel Corp, pg 731
McIntyre Media Inc, pg 821

Multimedia, CD-ROM & DVD Interactive Program Producers

ARIZONA

Aardvark Productions LLC, pg 671

CALIFORNIA

Ancient Future, pg 685
Astronomical Society of the Pacific, pg 691
California Language Laboratories, pg 714
Creative Technology, pg 733
Crystal Pyramid Productions™, pg 735
Design Media, pg 741
Direct Images Interactive Inc, pg 743
Discovery Education - Los Angeles, pg 743
Dolphin MultiMedia Inc, pg 745
IEEE Computer Society Press, pg 784
Lumeni Productions Inc, pg 812
Lynch Communications, pg 813
Medcom Inc, pg 821
Media Magic, pg 822
The Media Staff Inc, pg 822
New Circuit Films LLC, pg 839
Nystrom Education, pg 844
QRS Software Services, pg 867
SNAP, pg 891
Tam Communications Inc, pg 906
Total Creative, pg 916
Towards 2000 Inc, pg 916
Video Movie Magic, pg 928
Vineyard Video & Photography, pg 930
Wavemaker Media Design, pg 934
Webster Communications, pg 935
West Coast Projections Inc, pg 935
WMS Media Inc, pg 940

COLORADO

American Educational Products LLC, pg 683
Daylight Productions & Rentals, pg 739

Flashback Media Productions, pg 762
Vital Learning LLC, pg 932

CONNECTICUT

Cine-Med Inc, pg 723
VRSim Inc, pg 933

DISTRICT OF COLUMBIA

Hillmann & Carr Inc, pg 780
O'Keefe Communications Inc, pg 844

FLORIDA

Audio Visual Imagineering Inc, pg 694
CD ROM™ Inc, pg 718
Communications Concepts Inc (CCI), pg 729
ITC Learning LLC, pg 791
Sunfire Communications Inc, pg 904
Tricycle Studios, pg 918
Video Aided Instruction Inc, pg 927
Video Resources Software, pg 928
Video Techniques Inc, pg 928

GEORGIA

ADAM Inc, pg 675
Beachwood Productions, pg 702
Guerrilla Productions LLC, pg 774
Myriad Productions, pg 835
Visioneering International Inc, pg 931

HAWAII

Hyperspective Studios Inc, pg 783
Media Bridge Gamekids, pg 821

ILLINOIS

Airways Digital Media, pg 679
Atomic Imaging Inc/Golan Studios, pg 692
Bolchazy - Carducci Publishers Inc, pg 708
Britannica Digital Learning, pg 710
CCore Media Inc, pg 718
Cresta Creative, pg 734
Major Media Productions Inc, pg 815
Manning Productions, pg 816
Multimedia Marketing Group, pg 833
National Safety Council (NSC), pg 836
Pepper Group, pg 854
PSAV® Presentation Services (Hotel Services Division), pg 866
Sparkfactor, pg 896
20/20 Communications Inc, pg 920
Video Impressions, pg 928

INDIANA

A-V-A Video Productions, pg 671

IOWA

Educational Technology & Media Services, pg 751
Prositions Inc, pg 865
Right Stuf Inc, pg 875

KANSAS

KAKE-TV, pg 796

KENTUCKY

Hammond Communications Group Inc, pg 775
National Geographic Learning, pg 836

LOUISIANA

Digital FX Inc, pg 742
Louisiana State University Division of Strategic Communications, pg 811

MARYLAND

dbF a Media Company, pg 739
The Image Generators, pg 785
Mobile-Video Productions Inc, pg 828

MASSACHUSETTS

Cheng & Tsui Co, pg 721
CommCreative, pg 728
Documentary Educational Resources Inc, pg 744
Monadnock Media Inc, pg 829
New England Technology Group Inc (NETG), pg 839
Sinauer Associates, pg 889
Soundtrack Group, pg 895
TVN-The Video Network, pg 919

MICHIGAN

Digi Sign Design LLC, pg 741
K&R All Media Productions LLC, pg 796
K&R's Recording Studios Inc, pg 796
Zondervan, pg 945

MINNESOTA

Badiyan Inc, pg 700
BeyerSound & Essay Audio, pg 705
EMC Publishing LLC, pg 753
JIST Publishing, pg 794
Live Spark Inc, pg 810
Media Loft Inc, pg 822

NEBRASKA

Rainbow Video Productions Inc, pg 869

NEVADA

Encore Event Technologies LLC, pg 754
JCS Video Productions, pg 793

NEW HAMPSHIRE

Apertura, pg 686
Chip Taylor Communications LLC, pg 907

NEW JERSEY

Allegro Productions Inc, pg 680
Laurel Video Productions, pg 804
MediaNow Inc, pg 822
Megavideo LLC, pg 823
Optisonics Productions, pg 847
Outside The Box Interactive LLC, pg 849
Suede Interactive, pg 903
VCSvideo, pg 925

NEW MEXICO

The Phoenix Learning Group Inc, pg 855

NEW YORK

Blue Barn Pictures Inc, pg 707
Broadstreet Productions LLC, pg 711
Brooklyn Botanic Garden, pg 711
The Bureau for At-Risk Youth, pg 712
Duggal Visual Solutions Inc, pg 747
Educational Activities Inc, pg 750
Future US Inc, pg 767
Havas Creative, pg 776
HB-Content, pg 777
Human Relations Media, pg 782
Image Zone Inc, pg 785
The Independent Production Fund, pg 786
Ketchum Inc, pg 798
Magnetic Music Publishing Co, pg 814
Manhattan Center Studios Inc, pg 816
Meridian Education Corp, pg 823
Jack Morton Worldwide, pg 830
MRY, pg 832
Northeast Video Productions Inc, pg 842
The Palmer Group, pg 850
Judson Rosebush Co Inc, pg 877
Shopware, pg 886
Tiki Recording Studios Inc, pg 914
Trans-Lux Multimedia Corp, pg 917
Zelman Studios Ltd, pg 945

NORTH CAROLINA

Pat Appleson Studios Inc, pg 687
The Communications Group Inc, pg 729
Image Associates Inc, pg 784
Moving Pictures, pg 832

OHIO

Advent Media Inc, pg 677
Cuyahoga Community College Student Production Office (SPO), pg 736
R&B Communications Inc, pg 870
Take 1 Media Services, pg 906
Thread Marketing Group, pg 913
Treehaus Communications Inc, pg 917
Vista Color Imaging Inc, pg 931

OKLAHOMA

BCD Associates Inc, pg 702

OREGON

Ideascape Inc, pg 784
NeoSoft Corp, pg 838
Odyssey Productions Inc, pg 844
REX, pg 874
Wilderness Video, pg 938

PENNSYLVANIA

AccuWeather Inc, pg 674
Audio Visual Communications Inc, pg 694
Discovery Education - South Burlington, pg 743
FMP Media Solutions Inc, pg 763
JPL, pg 795
New Horizons Computer Learning Centers Inc, pg 839
Production Masters Inc (PMI), pg 864
Scala Inc, pg 881

RHODE ISLAND

Sound-FX-Design, pg 894

TENNESSEE

Continental Film, pg 731
Running Pony Productions LLC, pg 878
Spring Arbor Distributors Inc, pg 898
Russ Sturgeon Productions/RSVP, pg 903

TEXAS

Biway Media, pg 706
Communication Arts Multimedia Inc, pg 728
Epic Software Group Inc, pg 755
Horizon Film + Video Productions, pg 781
Mediaforce Productions, pg 822
Romar Learning Solutions LLC, pg 877
South Coast Film & Video, pg 895
Stage Directions, pg 898
Stockyard Photos/Jim Olive Photography, pg 901

VIRGINIA

Advance Concepts Inc, pg 677
Altruist Media LLC, pg 682
Metro Productions, pg 824

WASHINGTON

Adams Creative & Production Services, pg 675
Intermedia Inc, pg 789
Kostov Productions, pg 801

WISCONSIN

Audio Visual of Milwaukee Inc, pg 694
Logan Productions Inc, pg 811
USAV Group Inc, pg 923
Video Wisconsin Inc, pg 929
Watts Communications Inc, pg 934
Wisconsin Public Television, pg 940
Wisconsin Technical College System Foundation Inc, pg 940

WYOMING

Bridger Productions Inc, pg 710

ALBERTA

Black Media Works, pg 706

BRITISH COLUMBIA

West Eagle Films Inc, pg 935

MANITOBA

Tek Gear, pg 909

NEWFOUNDLAND AND LABRADOR

Vidcraft Productions Ltd, pg 927

ONTARIO

Corel Corp, pg 731
DebsVoice, pg 739
GAPC (General Assembly Production Centre), pg 768
GestureTek, pg 770
JFB Communications, pg 794
Mediaimage Communications Group, pg 822
Silver Creek Media Inc, pg 888

QUEBEC

Kerrigan Productions Inc, pg 798

Multimedia, CD-ROM & DVD Interactive Program Rentals

DELAWARE

Side Door Studio Inc, pg 887

GEORGIA

Convergent Media Systems, pg 731

MASSACHUSETTS

Documentary Educational Resources Inc, pg 744
Preston Productions Inc, pg 861

MICHIGAN

Digi Sign Design LLC, pg 741

NEW HAMPSHIRE

Chip Taylor Communications LLC, pg 907

NEW JERSEY

Euro-Pacific Film & Video Productions Inc, pg 756

NEW YORK

Brooklyn Botanic Garden, pg 711

UTAH

Webb Audio Visual, pg 935

WASHINGTON

Intermedia Inc, pg 789

MANITOBA

Tek Gear, pg 909

Multimedia Kit Distributors

ARIZONA

Arizona Cine Equipment, pg 688

CALIFORNIA

Ametron Audio/Video, pg 684
Astronomical Society of the Pacific, pg 691
Discovery Education - Los Angeles, pg 743
Educational Insights, pg 750
Nystrom Education, pg 844
QRS Software Services, pg 867
Rhythms Productions (Tom Thumb Music), pg 874
Social Studies School Service, pg 891
The Wine Appreciation Guild Ltd, pg 939

COLORADO

American Educational Products LLC, pg 683
Crystal Productions, pg 735
Vital Learning LLC, pg 932

GEORGIA

School Media Associates LLC, pg 882

ILLINOIS

National Safety Council (NSC), pg 836
Sunburst Digital Inc, pg 903

KENTUCKY

National Geographic Learning, pg 836

MARYLAND

Department of Education Resources, pg 740
MMI Marketing, pg 828
Nicholas P Pipino Associates Inc, pg 857

MASSACHUSETTS

Cheng & Tsui Co, pg 721

MICHIGAN

Digi Sign Design LLC, pg 741

MISSOURI

Marsh Media, pg 817
Mosby Inc, pg 831

NEW HAMPSHIRE

Frey Scientific, pg 766

NEW YORK

Brooklyn Botanic Garden, pg 711
Criterion Collection, pg 735
Educational Activities Inc, pg 750
Guidance Associates Inc Center for Humanities, pg 774
Human Relations Media, pg 782
Magnetic Music Publishing Co, pg 814
Triumph Learning LLC, pg 918

NORTH CAROLINA

Carolina Biological Supply Co, pg 717

OHIO

McGraw-Hill School Education Group, pg 821
Treehaus Communications Inc, pg 917

PENNSYLVANIA

Discovery Education - South Burlington, pg 743
TRC Interactive Inc, pg 917

TEXAS

Lamb & Lion Ministries, pg 803
Stage Directions, pg 898

VERMONT

Taylor Associates, pg 907
Wilson McLeran Inc, pg 939

VIRGINIA

National Audiovisual Center (NAC), pg 836

WISCONSIN

Knowledge Unlimited Inc, pg 800
Plank Road Publishing Inc, pg 857
School Specialty Inc, pg 882

ONTARIO

Canadian Learning Co Inc, pg 715

QUEBEC

National Film Board of Canada/Office National du Film du Canada, pg 836

Multimedia Kit Producers

ARIZONA

Aardvark Productions LLC, pg 671

ARKANSAS

Live'N'Loud, pg 810

CALIFORNIA

Astronomical Society of the Pacific, pg 691
Custom Video Productions Inc, pg 736
Design Media, pg 741
Direct Images Interactive Inc, pg 743
Discovery Education - Los Angeles, pg 743
Dolphin MultiMedia Inc, pg 745
International Contact Inc, pg 790
Main Street Media Inc, pg 815
Media Magic, pg 822
Nystrom Education, pg 844
piXvfm Inc, pg 857
QRS Software Services, pg 867
Rhythms Productions (Tom Thumb Music), pg 874
Tam Communications Inc, pg 906
Wavemaker Media Design, pg 934

COLORADO

American Educational Products LLC, pg 683
Starwest Productions, pg 900
Vital Learning LLC, pg 932

CONNECTICUT

Antenna International, pg 686

DISTRICT OF COLUMBIA

Hillmann & Carr Inc, pg 780
O'Keefe Communications Inc, pg 844

FLORIDA

Tricycle Studios, pg 918

GEORGIA

First Cut Communications LLC, pg 761
Guerrilla Productions LLC, pg 774
Imagers, pg 785

HAWAII

Hyperspective Studios Inc, pg 783

ILLINOIS

ABS Enterprises, pg 672
Airways Digital Media, pg 679
National Safety Council (NSC), pg 836
Rand McNally Education, pg 870
Sparkfactor, pg 896
Sunburst Digital Inc, pg 903

INDIANA

OMNI Productions, pg 845

PROGRAMMING — AUDIO/VISUAL

Multimedia Kit Producers (continued)

IOWA

Educational Technology & Media Services, pg 751

KENTUCKY

National Geographic Learning, pg 836
Prosper Media Group Inc, pg 866

LOUISIANA

Louisiana State University Division of Strategic Communications, pg 811

MARYLAND

Department of Education Resources, pg 740
Milner-Fenwick Inc, pg 828

MASSACHUSETTS

Capron Lighting & Sound Co Inc, pg 716
TR Productions, pg 916

MICHIGAN

Digi Sign Design LLC, pg 741
K&R All Media Productions LLC, pg 796
K&R's Recording Studios Inc, pg 796
MessageMakers, pg 824

MISSOURI

Marsh Media, pg 817
Mosby Inc, pg 831
Switch, pg 905

NEVADA

Encore Event Technologies LLC, pg 754
JCS Video Productions, pg 793

NEW HAMPSHIRE

Frey Scientific, pg 766

NEW JERSEY

Optisonics Productions, pg 847
Outside The Box Interactive LLC, pg 849

NEW YORK

Blue Barn Pictures Inc, pg 707
Broadstreet Productions LLC, pg 711
Criterion Collection, pg 735
Educational Activities Inc, pg 750
Guidance Associates Inc Center for Humanities, pg 774
Havas Creative, pg 776
Human Relations Media, pg 782
The Independent Production Fund, pg 786
Ketchum Inc, pg 798
L A Bruell Inc, pg 802
Magnetic Music Publishing Co, pg 814
Jack Morton Worldwide, pg 830
MRY, pg 832
Scholastic Media, pg 882

WorldView Software, pg 941
Zelman Studios Ltd, pg 945

NORTH CAROLINA

Carolina Biological Supply Co, pg 717
The Communications Group Inc, pg 729
Image Associates Inc, pg 784
2BruceStudio, pg 920
World Class Learning Materials Inc, pg 941

OHIO

McGraw-Hill School Education Group, pg 821
Treehaus Communications Inc, pg 917
Vista Color Imaging Inc, pg 931

OREGON

ERA Learning, pg 755
Ideascape Inc, pg 784
NeoSoft Corp, pg 838

PENNSYLVANIA

Audio Visual Communications Inc, pg 694
Beholder Productions Inc, pg 703
Discovery Education - South Burlington, pg 743
FMP Media Solutions Inc, pg 763
JPL, pg 795
Main Point Productions, pg 815
Production Masters Inc (PMI), pg 864
Scala Inc, pg 881

TENNESSEE

Center for Southern Folklore Inc, pg 719
Memphis Communications Corp, pg 823

TEXAS

Lamb & Lion Ministries, pg 803
Mediaforce Productions, pg 822
The Music Bakery, pg 834
Omni Intercommunications Inc, pg 845
Romar Learning Solutions LLC, pg 877

VERMONT

Wilson McLeran Inc, pg 939

VIRGINIA

Advance Concepts Inc, pg 677

WISCONSIN

Knowledge Unlimited Inc, pg 800
Plank Road Publishing Inc, pg 857
USAV Group Inc, pg 923
Video Wisconsin Inc, pg 929
Watts Communications Inc, pg 934

NEWFOUNDLAND AND LABRADOR

Vidcraft Productions Ltd, pg 927

ONTARIO

Art Gallery of Ontario, pg 690
Image Video Services & Productions, pg 785

QUEBEC

Group PVP, pg 774
National Film Board of Canada/Office National du Film du Canada, pg 836

Multimedia Kit Rentals

ARIZONA

Arizona Cine Equipment, pg 688

CALIFORNIA

Ametron Audio/Video, pg 684
deKramer Productions Inc, pg 740

ILLINOIS

Pepper Group, pg 854

MICHIGAN

Digi Sign Design LLC, pg 741

NEW JERSEY

PLS Staging, pg 858

WYOMING

Bridger Productions Inc, pg 710

News Program Distributors

CALIFORNIA

Crystal Pyramid Productions™, pg 735

ILLINOIS

CCore Media Inc, pg 718

MICHIGAN

Digi Sign Design LLC, pg 741

NEW HAMPSHIRE

Chip Taylor Communications LLC, pg 907

NEW JERSEY

Allegro Productions Inc, pg 680

NEW YORK

HB-Content, pg 777
News Broadcast Network Inc, pg 840
Women Make Movies Inc, pg 941

VIRGINIA

PBS Video, pg 852

News Program Producers

ARIZONA

Aardvark Productions LLC, pg 671

CALIFORNIA

Creative Technology, pg 733
Crystal Pyramid Productions™, pg 735
Direct Images Interactive Inc, pg 743
Jaguar Distribution Corp, pg 792
Lynch Communications, pg 813
PM Productions, pg 858
Total Creative, pg 916

Vineyard Video & Photography, pg 930
Webster Communications, pg 935

COLORADO

Flashback Media Productions, pg 762
Tatum Video, pg 907

CONNECTICUT

Fox 61, pg 765

FLORIDA

CD ROM™ Inc, pg 718
Communications Concepts Inc (CCI), pg 729
Sunfire Communications Inc, pg 904
Video Techniques Inc, pg 928

GEORGIA

Beachwood Productions, pg 702
Guerrilla Productions LLC, pg 774

ILLINOIS

CCore Media Inc, pg 718
Manning Productions, pg 816
Multimedia Marketing Group, pg 833
Pepper Group, pg 854

KENTUCKY

Idle Minds Productions Inc, pg 784

LOUISIANA

Digital FX Inc, pg 742

MARYLAND

The Image Generators, pg 785

MASSACHUSETTS

Soundtrack Group, pg 895

MICHIGAN

Digi Sign Design LLC, pg 741
K&R All Media Productions LLC, pg 796
K&R's Recording Studios Inc, pg 796

MINNESOTA

Vaddio, pg 924

NEVADA

JCS Video Productions, pg 793

NEW HAMPSHIRE

Chip Taylor Communications LLC, pg 907

NEW JERSEY

Allegro Productions Inc, pg 680
Laurel Video Productions, pg 804
Optisonics Productions, pg 847

NEW YORK

Castillo Theatre, pg 717
CompuWeather Inc, pg 729
Havas Creative, pg 776
HB-Content, pg 777
Hello World Communications, pg 778
Manhattan Center Studios Inc, pg 816

Jack Morton Worldwide, pg 830
News Broadcast Network Inc,
   pg 840
Northeast Video Productions Inc,
   pg 842
The Palmer Group, pg 850
SMP Digital Graphics, pg 891
Zelman Studios Ltd, pg 945

NORTH CAROLINA

Pat Appleson Studios Inc, pg 687
Digital Rain LLC, pg 742
Moving Pictures, pg 832

OHIO

MainSail Production Services Inc,
   pg 815
R&B Communications Inc, pg 870
Take 1 Media Services, pg 906
Vista Color Imaging Inc, pg 931

PENNSYLVANIA

FMP Media Solutions Inc, pg 763
Main Point Productions, pg 815

RHODE ISLAND

Sound-FX-Design, pg 894

TENNESSEE

Running Pony Productions LLC,
   pg 878

TEXAS

Epic Software Group Inc, pg 755
Romar Learning Solutions LLC,
   pg 877
The Samuels Co, pg 879
Stage Directions, pg 898

WISCONSIN

Video Wisconsin Inc, pg 929
Watts Communications Inc, pg 934
Wisconsin Public Television, pg 940

WYOMING

Bridger Productions Inc, pg 710

ALBERTA

Black Media Works, pg 706

QUEBEC

Kerrigan Productions Inc, pg 798

News Program Rentals

MICHIGAN

Digi Sign Design LLC, pg 741

NEW HAMPSHIRE

Chip Taylor Communications LLC,
   pg 907

UTAH

Webb Audio Visual, pg 935

Overhead Transparency Distributors

ARIZONA

Arizona Cine Equipment, pg 688

CALIFORNIA

Ametron Audio/Video, pg 684
Educational Insights, pg 750
QRS Software Services, pg 867

CONNECTICUT

USI Inc, pg 924

FLORIDA

AVI-SPL, pg 698
ONstage, pg 846

GEORGIA

Audio Visual Resources Inc, pg 695
ON Services, a GES Company,
   pg 846
School Media Associates LLC,
   pg 882

MAINE

Headlight Audio Visual Inc, pg 777

MARYLAND

Nicholas P Pipino Associates Inc,
   pg 857

MICHIGAN

Michigan Office Solutions (MOS),
   A Xerox Company, pg 825

MISSOURI

Southwest Binding & Laminating,
   pg 896

NEW HAMPSHIRE

Frey Scientific, pg 766

NEW YORK

Human Relations Media, pg 782
Visual Technologies Corp, pg 932

OHIO

McGraw-Hill School Education
   Group, pg 821

PENNSYLVANIA

TRC Interactive Inc, pg 917

TENNESSEE

Randall House Publications, pg 870
Spring Arbor Distributors Inc,
   pg 898

WISCONSIN

Demco Inc, pg 740
Knowledge Unlimited Inc, pg 800
School Specialty Inc, pg 882

ONTARIO

Nelson Education Ltd, pg 837

Overhead Transparency Producers

ARIZONA

Merestone, pg 823

CALIFORNIA

Geddes Productions LLC, pg 769
Lynch Communications, pg 813
QRS Software Services, pg 867

GEORGIA

Guerrilla Productions LLC, pg 774
Imagers, pg 785

ILLINOIS

CCore Media Inc, pg 718
Jim Passin Productions, pg 852
Rand McNally Education, pg 870

INDIANA

OMNI Productions, pg 845

IOWA

Educational Technology & Media
   Services, pg 751

KENTUCKY

NIMCO Inc, pg 841

LOUISIANA

Digital FX Inc, pg 742
Louisiana State University Division
   of Strategic Communications,
   pg 811

MAINE

Headlight Audio Visual Inc, pg 777

MASSACHUSETTS

DGI-Invisuals LLC, pg 741
TR Productions, pg 916

MICHIGAN

K&R All Media Productions LLC,
   pg 796
K&R's Recording Studios Inc,
   pg 796

NEW HAMPSHIRE

Academic & Campus Technology
   Services, pg 672

NEW JERSEY

C2 Imaging, pg 735
Optisonics Productions, pg 847

NEW YORK

Blue Barn Pictures Inc, pg 707
Broadstreet Productions LLC,
   pg 711
Duggal Visual Solutions Inc, pg 747
Human Relations Media, pg 782
SMP Digital Graphics, pg 891

OHIO

Cuyahoga Community College
   Student Production Office (SPO),
   pg 736
McGraw-Hill School Education
   Group, pg 821
Thread Marketing Group, pg 913
Vista Color Imaging Inc, pg 931

OREGON

Ideascape Inc, pg 784

PENNSYLVANIA

Audio Visual Communications Inc,
   pg 694

TENNESSEE

Memphis Communications Corp,
   pg 823

VIRGINIA

Blair Inc, pg 707

WASHINGTON

Kostov Productions, pg 801

WISCONSIN

Knowledge Unlimited Inc, pg 800
USAV Group Inc, pg 923

Overhead Transparency Rentals

ARIZONA

Arizona Cine Equipment, pg 688

CALIFORNIA

Ametron Audio/Video, pg 684

FLORIDA

ONstage, pg 846

MICHIGAN

Wayne State University Media
   Services, pg 934

NEW YORK

The New York Historical Society,
   pg 840

Public Relations Program Distributors

ARIZONA

Video Learning Library, pg 928

CALIFORNIA

Crystal Pyramid Productions™,
   pg 735

GEORGIA

Convergent Media Systems, pg 731

ILLINOIS

CCore Media Inc, pg 718

MICHIGAN

Digi Sign Design LLC, pg 741

NEW HAMPSHIRE

Chip Taylor Communications LLC,
   pg 907

NEW JERSEY

Allegro Productions Inc, pg 680

NEW YORK

Hallel Communications, pg 775
HB-Content, pg 777
News Broadcast Network Inc,
   pg 840

TENNESSEE

American Blackguard Inc, pg 683

ONTARIO

BBC Worldwide Canada Ltd,
   pg 702

PROGRAMMING — AUDIO/VISUAL

Public Relations Program Producers

ARIZONA

Candee Productions Inc, pg 716
Teaberry, pg 908

ARKANSAS

Live'N'Loud, pg 810

CALIFORNIA

Creative Technology, pg 733
Crystal Pyramid Productions™, pg 735
Design Media, pg 741
Direct Images Interactive Inc, pg 743
Dolphin MultiMedia Inc, pg 745
Kavich Reynolds Productions Inc, pg 797
Lynch Communications, pg 813
Media Magic, pg 822
The Media Staff Inc, pg 822
New & Unique Videos™, pg 839
PM Productions, pg 858
Prime Cut Productions, pg 862
SNAP, pg 891
Total Creative, pg 916
Vineyard Video & Photography, pg 930
Wavemaker Media Design, pg 934
Webster Communications, pg 935
West Coast Projections Inc, pg 935

COLORADO

Daylight Productions & Rentals, pg 739
Flashback Media Productions, pg 762
Tatum Video, pg 907

CONNECTICUT

UConn Health Multimedia Services, pg 920

DISTRICT OF COLUMBIA

Hillmann & Carr Inc, pg 780
O'Keefe Communications Inc, pg 844

FLORIDA

Applebox Studio, pg 687
Audio Visual Imagineering Inc, pg 694
CD ROM™ Inc, pg 718
Communications Concepts Inc (CCI), pg 729
Sunfire Communications Inc, pg 904
Tricycle Studios, pg 918
Universal Studios Florida® Production Group, pg 922
Video Techniques Inc, pg 928

GEORGIA

Beachwood Productions, pg 702
Guerrilla Productions LLC, pg 774
Visioneering International Inc, pg 931

HAWAII

Hyperspective Studios Inc, pg 783

ILLINOIS

Airways Digital Media, pg 679
CCore Media Inc, pg 718
Major Media Productions Inc, pg 815
Manning Productions, pg 816
Multimedia Marketing Group, pg 833
Pepper Group, pg 854
PSAV® Presentation Services (Hotel Services Division), pg 866
SCI Television & Creative Media LLC, pg 882
20/20 Communications Inc, pg 920
Video Impressions, pg 928

INDIANA

A-V-A Video Productions, pg 671

LOUISIANA

Digital FX Inc, pg 742

MARYLAND

The Image Generators, pg 785
Mobile-Video Productions Inc, pg 828

MASSACHUSETTS

CommCreative, pg 728
Cramer, pg 732
Monadnock Media Inc, pg 829
Soundtrack Group, pg 895

MICHIGAN

Digi Sign Design LLC, pg 741
K&R All Media Productions LLC, pg 796
K&R's Recording Studios Inc, pg 796

MINNESOTA

Big Event Productions LLC, pg 705
GMI Productions, pg 771
Live Spark Inc, pg 810
Media Loft Inc, pg 822

NEVADA

JCS Video Productions, pg 793

NEW HAMPSHIRE

Apertura, pg 686
Chip Taylor Communications LLC, pg 907

NEW JERSEY

Allegro Productions Inc, pg 680
Laurel Video Productions, pg 804
Optisonics Productions, pg 847
Outside The Box Interactive LLC, pg 849

NEW YORK

Broadstreet Productions LLC, pg 711
Duggal Visual Solutions Inc, pg 747
Hallel Communications, pg 775
Havas Creative, pg 776
HB-Content, pg 777
Ketchum Inc, pg 798
Manhattan Center Studios Inc, pg 816
Jack Morton Worldwide, pg 830
News Broadcast Network Inc, pg 840
Northeast Video Productions Inc, pg 842
The Palmer Group, pg 850

SMP Digital Graphics, pg 891
Zelman Studios Ltd, pg 945

NORTH CAROLINA

Pat Appleson Studios Inc, pg 687
The Communications Group Inc, pg 729
Kino Mountain Productions LLC, pg 799

OHIO

MainSail Production Services Inc, pg 815
R&B Communications Inc, pg 870
Take 1 Media Services, pg 906
Thread Marketing Group, pg 913
Treehaus Communications Inc, pg 917
Vista Color Imaging Inc, pg 931

OREGON

Ideascape Inc, pg 784
Odyssey Productions Inc, pg 844
REX, pg 874

PENNSYLVANIA

FMP Media Solutions Inc, pg 763
JPL, pg 795
Main Point Productions, pg 815
Panta Rhei Media Inc, pg 851
Production Masters Inc (PMI), pg 864

RHODE ISLAND

Sound-FX-Design, pg 894

TENNESSEE

American Blackguard Inc, pg 683
Continental Film, pg 731
Running Pony Productions LLC, pg 878

TEXAS

Epic Software Group Inc, pg 755
Mediaforce Productions, pg 822
The Samuels Co, pg 879
South Coast Film & Video, pg 895
Stage Directions, pg 898
Stockyard Photos/Jim Olive Photography, pg 901

VIRGINIA

Advance Concepts Inc, pg 677
Altruist Media LLC, pg 682
Metro Productions, pg 824

WASHINGTON

Adams Creative & Production Services, pg 675
Kostov Productions, pg 801

WISCONSIN

AVS Group, pg 699
USAV Group Inc, pg 923
Video Wisconsin Inc, pg 929
Watts Communications Inc, pg 934
Wisconsin Public Television, pg 940

WYOMING

Bridger Productions Inc, pg 710

ALBERTA

Black Media Works, pg 706

BRITISH COLUMBIA

West Eagle Films Inc, pg 935

NEWFOUNDLAND AND LABRADOR

Vidcraft Productions Ltd, pg 927

ONTARIO

BBC Worldwide Canada Ltd, pg 702
Mediaimage Communications Group, pg 822

QUEBEC

Kerrigan Productions Inc, pg 798

Public Relations Program Rentals

GEORGIA

Convergent Media Systems, pg 731

MICHIGAN

Digi Sign Design LLC, pg 741

NEW HAMPSHIRE

Chip Taylor Communications LLC, pg 907

NEW YORK

Hallel Communications, pg 775

UTAH

Webb Audio Visual, pg 935

Public Service Announcement Distributors

CALIFORNIA

Crystal Pyramid Productions™, pg 735
New & Unique Videos™, pg 839

LOUISIANA

Louisiana State University Division of Strategic Communications, pg 811

MICHIGAN

Digi Sign Design LLC, pg 741

NEW HAMPSHIRE

Chip Taylor Communications LLC, pg 907

NEW YORK

HB-Content, pg 777
March of Dimes Foundation, pg 816
News Broadcast Network Inc, pg 840

OHIO

Franciscan Media, pg 765

TENNESSEE

American Blackguard Inc, pg 683

TEXAS

Institute of Texan Cultures, pg 788

WISCONSIN

Wisconsin Public Television, pg 940

Public Service Announcement Producers

ARIZONA

Candee Productions Inc, pg 716
Teaberry, pg 908

ARKANSAS

Live'N'Loud, pg 810

CALIFORNIA

Creative Technology, pg 733
Crystal Pyramid Productions™, pg 735
Direct Images Interactive Inc, pg 743
Lynch Communications, pg 813
Media Magic, pg 822
The Media Staff Inc, pg 822
New & Unique Videos™, pg 839
New Circuit Films LLC, pg 839
PM Productions, pg 858
Total Creative, pg 916
Vineyard Video & Photography, pg 930
Wavemaker Media Design, pg 934

COLORADO

Flashback Media Productions, pg 762
Tatum Video, pg 907

DISTRICT OF COLUMBIA

Hillmann & Carr Inc, pg 780

FLORIDA

Applebox Studio, pg 687
Communications Concepts Inc (CCI), pg 729
Paradise Video & Film, pg 851
Sunfire Communications Inc, pg 904
Tricycle Studios, pg 918
Video Techniques Inc, pg 928

GEORGIA

Beachwood Productions, pg 702
Guerrilla Productions LLC, pg 774
Visioneering International Inc, pg 931

HAWAII

Hyperspective Studios Inc, pg 783

ILLINOIS

Cresta Creative, pg 734
Major Media Productions Inc, pg 815
Multimedia Marketing Group, pg 833
Pepper Group, pg 854
SCI Television & Creative Media LLC, pg 882
Sparkfactor, pg 896
20/20 Communications Inc, pg 920

INDIANA

A-V-A Video Productions, pg 671

IOWA

Hellman Associates Inc, pg 778

LOUISIANA

Digital FX Inc, pg 742
Louisiana State University Division of Strategic Communications, pg 811

MARYLAND

dbF a Media Company, pg 739
The Image Generators, pg 785

MASSACHUSETTS

Cramer, pg 732
Documentary Educational Resources Inc, pg 744
Soundtrack Group, pg 895
TVN-The Video Network, pg 919

MICHIGAN

Digi Sign Design LLC, pg 741
K&R All Media Productions LLC, pg 796
K&R's Recording Studios Inc, pg 796

MINNESOTA

Big Event Productions LLC, pg 705
MastCom, pg 819

NEVADA

JCS Video Productions, pg 793

NEW HAMPSHIRE

Apertura, pg 686
Chip Taylor Communications LLC, pg 907

NEW JERSEY

Allegro Productions Inc, pg 680
Optisonics Productions, pg 847

NEW YORK

Blue Barn Pictures Inc, pg 707
Broadstreet Productions LLC, pg 711
Fanlight Productions, pg 759
Florentine Films, pg 762
Havas Creative, pg 776
HB-Content, pg 777
Hello World Communications, pg 778
Ketchum Inc, pg 798
Long Island Video Enterprises Live Inc, pg 811
Manhattan Center Studios Inc, pg 816
March of Dimes Foundation, pg 816
Jack Morton Worldwide, pg 830
News Broadcast Network Inc, pg 840
The Palmer Group, pg 850
Polestar Films & Associated Arts Ltd, pg 859
Alan Weiss Productions, pg 935
Zelman Studios Ltd, pg 945

NORTH CAROLINA

Pat Appleson Studios Inc, pg 687
Digital Rain LLC, pg 742
Kino Mountain Productions LLC, pg 799
Laurel Hill Press, pg 804

OHIO

Cuyahoga Community College Student Production Office (SPO), pg 736
Franciscan Media, pg 765

MainSail Production Services Inc, pg 815
R&B Communications Inc, pg 870
Take 1 Media Services, pg 906
Vista Color Imaging Inc, pg 931

OREGON

Ideascape Inc, pg 784
Odyssey Productions Inc, pg 844
REX, pg 874

PENNSYLVANIA

Audio Visual Communications Inc, pg 694
Bang! Pictures Inc, pg 701
FMP Media Solutions Inc, pg 763
JPL, pg 795
Kensington Falls Animation, pg 797
Panta Rhei Media Inc, pg 851
Production Masters Inc (PMI), pg 864

RHODE ISLAND

Sound-FX-Design, pg 894

TENNESSEE

American Blackguard Inc, pg 683
Continental Film, pg 731
Running Pony Productions LLC, pg 878

TEXAS

Biway Media, pg 706
Horizon Film + Video Productions, pg 781
Institute of Texan Cultures, pg 788
Mediaforce Productions, pg 822
The Samuels Co, pg 879
Stage Directions, pg 898
Tropikal Productions, pg 918

VIRGINIA

Altruist Media LLC, pg 682
Metro Productions, pg 824

WASHINGTON

Kostov Productions, pg 801
White Rain Films Ltd, pg 937

WISCONSIN

USAV Group Inc, pg 923
Video Wisconsin Inc, pg 929
Watts Communications Inc, pg 934
Wisconsin Public Television, pg 940

WYOMING

Bridger Productions Inc, pg 710

ALBERTA

Black Media Works, pg 706

NEWFOUNDLAND AND LABRADOR

Vidcraft Productions Ltd, pg 927

ONTARIO

DebsVoice, pg 739
Mediaimage Communications Group, pg 822

QUEBEC

Kerrigan Productions Inc, pg 798

Public Service Announcement Rentals

CALIFORNIA

ETR, pg 756

MICHIGAN

Digi Sign Design LLC, pg 741

NEW HAMPSHIRE

Chip Taylor Communications LLC, pg 907

UTAH

Webb Audio Visual, pg 935

Realia Distributors

CALIFORNIA

QRS Software Services, pg 867

COLORADO

American Educational Products LLC, pg 683

MARYLAND

MMI Marketing, pg 828

NORTH CAROLINA

Carolina Biological Supply Co, pg 717

Realia Producers

CALIFORNIA

QRS Software Services, pg 867

COLORADO

American Educational Products LLC, pg 683

Religious Program Distributors

ARIZONA

CyberIconics International, pg 736
Video Learning Library, pg 928

CALIFORNIA

Clarity Sound & Light, pg 725
Discovery Education - Los Angeles, pg 743
Glenn Photo Supply, pg 771
Joyce Media Inc, pg 795
monterey video, pg 829

DISTRICT OF COLUMBIA

Biblical Archaeology Society (BAS), pg 705

HAWAII

Media Bridge Gamekids, pg 821

ILLINOIS

ACTA Publications, pg 675
Baha'i Distribution Service (BDS), pg 700
CCore Media Inc, pg 718
Film Ideas Inc, pg 760

PROGRAMMING — AUDIO/VISUAL

Religious Program Distributors (continued)

ILLINOIS (continued)

Institute on Religious Life Inc, pg 788
RADMAR Inc, pg 869

MASSACHUSETTS

Pauline Books & Media, pg 852

MICHIGAN

Digi Sign Design LLC, pg 741
Emery-Pratt Co, pg 753
The Program Source International, pg 865
Zondervan, pg 945

MINNESOTA

Augsburg Fortress, pg 695

NEW HAMPSHIRE

Chip Taylor Communications LLC, pg 907

NEW YORK

Janson Media Inc, pg 793
Women Make Movies Inc, pg 941

NORTH CAROLINA

Howard Hanger, pg 775
World Wide Pictures Inc, pg 941

OHIO

Franciscan Media, pg 765
Treehaus Communications Inc, pg 917

TENNESSEE

Abingdon Press, pg 672
Capitol Christian Music Group, pg 716
Randall House Publications, pg 870
Spring Arbor Distributors Inc, pg 898
Zion Music Group, pg 945

TEXAS

Endtime Ministries Inc, pg 754
Lamb & Lion Ministries, pg 803

ONTARIO

Broughton's Church Supplies, Religious Books & Gifts, pg 711
Canadian Learning Co Inc, pg 715
Gospel Folio Press, pg 773
Kineticvideo.com, pg 799
Life Cycle Books Ltd, pg 807
Novalis, pg 843

Religious Program Producers

ALABAMA

AVS Media Group, pg 699

ARKANSAS

White Diamond Productions LLC, pg 937

CALIFORNIA

Clarity Sound & Light, pg 725
Discovery Education - Los Angeles, pg 743
Dolphin MultiMedia Inc, pg 745
Joyce Media Inc, pg 795
Lynch Communications, pg 813
PM Productions, pg 858
SNAP, pg 891
Total Creative, pg 916
Vineyard Video & Photography, pg 930

COLORADO

Flashback Media Productions, pg 762

DISTRICT OF COLUMBIA

Biblical Archaeology Society (BAS), pg 705

FLORIDA

Applebox Studio, pg 687
Audio Visual Imagineering Inc, pg 694
Sunfire Communications Inc, pg 904

GEORGIA

Beachwood Productions, pg 702
Guerrilla Productions LLC, pg 774

HAWAII

Hyperspective Studios Inc, pg 783
Media Bridge Gamekids, pg 821

ILLINOIS

ACTA Publications, pg 675
CCore Media Inc, pg 718
Major Media Productions Inc, pg 815
Multimedia Marketing Group, pg 833
Pepper Group, pg 854
20/20 Communications Inc, pg 920
Video Impressions, pg 928

MASSACHUSETTS

Pauline Books & Media, pg 852
Soundtrack Group, pg 895

MICHIGAN

Digi Sign Design LLC, pg 741
K&R All Media Productions LLC, pg 796
K&R's Recording Studios Inc, pg 796
Zondervan, pg 945

MINNESOTA

Augsburg Fortress, pg 695
Vaddio, pg 924

NEVADA

JCS Video Productions, pg 793

NEW HAMPSHIRE

Apertura, pg 686
Chip Taylor Communications LLC, pg 907

NEW JERSEY

Laurel Video Productions, pg 804
Optisonics Productions, pg 847

NEW YORK

Havas Creative, pg 776
Manhattan Center Studios Inc, pg 816
Jack Morton Worldwide, pg 830
The Palmer Group, pg 850
Spoken Arts Inc, pg 898
Zelman Studios Ltd, pg 945

NORTH CAROLINA

Pat Appleson Studios Inc, pg 687
Howard Hanger, pg 775

OHIO

Franciscan Media, pg 765
MainSail Production Services Inc, pg 815
Take 1 Media Services, pg 906
Treehaus Communications Inc, pg 917
Vista Color Imaging Inc, pg 931

PENNSYLVANIA

Audio Visual Communications Inc, pg 694
Bang! Pictures Inc, pg 701
FMP Media Solutions Inc, pg 763
JPL, pg 795

RHODE ISLAND

Sound-FX-Design, pg 894

SOUTH CAROLINA

BJU Press, pg 706

TENNESSEE

Abingdon Press, pg 672
Capitol Christian Music Group, pg 716
Continental Film, pg 731
Running Pony Productions LLC, pg 878
Spring Arbor Distributors Inc, pg 898
Russ Sturgeon Productions/RSVP, pg 903

TEXAS

Endtime Ministries Inc, pg 754
Lamb & Lion Ministries, pg 803
Mediaforce Productions, pg 822
Stage Directions, pg 898

VIRGINIA

Metro Productions, pg 824

WASHINGTON

Kostov Productions, pg 801

WISCONSIN

Video Wisconsin Inc, pg 929

WYOMING

Bridger Productions Inc, pg 710

ONTARIO

Novalis, pg 843

QUEBEC

Kerrigan Productions Inc, pg 798

Religious Program Rentals

CALIFORNIA

Glenn Photo Supply, pg 771

MICHIGAN

Digi Sign Design LLC, pg 741

NEW HAMPSHIRE

Chip Taylor Communications LLC, pg 907

NORTH CAROLINA

World Wide Pictures Inc, pg 941

OHIO

Franciscan Media, pg 765
Treehaus Communications Inc, pg 917

UTAH

Webb Audio Visual, pg 935

Research—Technical Program, *see* Technical Research Program

Sales Promotion & Training Program Distributors

ARIZONA

Video Learning Library, pg 928

CALIFORNIA

Crystal Pyramid Productions™, pg 735
Discovery Education - Los Angeles, pg 743
Kantola Productions LLC, pg 796

COLORADO

Vital Learning LLC, pg 932

FLORIDA

Video Resources Software, pg 928

ILLINOIS

CCore Media Inc, pg 718
1st Financial Training Services Inc, pg 761

IOWA

Prositions Inc, pg 865

MICHIGAN

Digi Sign Design LLC, pg 741

NEW HAMPSHIRE

Chip Taylor Communications LLC, pg 907

NEW JERSEY

Allegro Productions Inc, pg 680

NEW YORK

HB-Content, pg 777
Monad Trainer's Aide Inc, pg 829

PENNSYLVANIA

FMP Media Solutions Inc, pg 763

TENNESSEE

American Blackguard Inc, pg 683

ONTARIO

BBC Worldwide Canada Ltd,
pg 702
Canadian Learning Co Inc, pg 715
Kineticvideo.com, pg 799

Sales Promotion & Training Program Producers

ARIZONA

Aardvark Productions LLC, pg 671
Candee Productions Inc, pg 716
Creative Backstage, pg 733

CALIFORNIA

Aaron Marcus and Associates,
pg 671
Creative Technology, pg 733
Crystal Pyramid Productions™,
pg 735
Design Media, pg 741
Direct Images Interactive Inc,
pg 743
Discovery Education - Los Angeles,
pg 743
Dolphin MultiMedia Inc, pg 745
IEEE Computer Society Press,
pg 784
Kantola Productions LLC, pg 796
Kavich Reynolds Productions Inc,
pg 797
Lynch Communications, pg 813
Media Magic, pg 822
The Media Staff Inc, pg 822
New & Unique Videos™, pg 839
PM Productions, pg 858
SNAP, pg 891
Tam Communications Inc, pg 906
Total Creative, pg 916
Vineyard Video & Photography,
pg 930
Wavemaker Media Design, pg 934
Webster Communications, pg 935
West Coast Projections Inc, pg 935

COLORADO

Daylight Productions & Rentals,
pg 739
Flashback Media Productions,
pg 762
Vital Learning LLC, pg 932

CONNECTICUT

Cine-Med Inc, pg 723

DISTRICT OF COLUMBIA

O'Keefe Communications Inc,
pg 844

FLORIDA

Applebox Studio, pg 687
Audio Visual Imagineering Inc,
pg 694
CD ROM™ Inc, pg 718
Communications Concepts Inc
(CCI), pg 729
Paradise Video & Film, pg 851
Sunfire Communications Inc,
pg 904

Teach America Corp, pg 908
Tricycle Studios, pg 918
Universal Studios Florida®
Production Group, pg 922
Video Resources Software, pg 928
Video Techniques Inc, pg 928

GEORGIA

Beachwood Productions, pg 702
Guerrilla Productions LLC, pg 774

HAWAII

Hyperspective Studios Inc, pg 783

ILLINOIS

Airways Digital Media, pg 679
CCore Media Inc, pg 718
Cresta Creative, pg 734
1st Financial Training Services Inc,
pg 761
Major Media Productions Inc,
pg 815
Manning Productions, pg 816
Multimedia Marketing Group,
pg 833
Pepper Group, pg 854
PSAV® Presentation Services
(Hotel Services Division), pg 866
SCI Television & Creative Media
LLC, pg 882
Sparkfactor, pg 896
20/20 Communications Inc, pg 920
Video Impressions, pg 928

INDIANA

A-V-A Video Productions, pg 671

IOWA

Hellman Associates Inc, pg 778
Prositions Inc, pg 865

KENTUCKY

Hammond Communications Group
Inc, pg 775

LOUISIANA

Digital FX Inc, pg 742

MARYLAND

The Cutting Corporation,
GraphicAudio® & Archival
Sound Lab, pg 736
The Image Generators, pg 785
Mobile-Video Productions Inc,
pg 828

MASSACHUSETTS

CommCreative, pg 728
Cramer, pg 732
Soundtrack Group, pg 895
TVN-The Video Network, pg 919

MICHIGAN

Digi Sign Design LLC, pg 741
K&R All Media Productions LLC,
pg 796
K&R's Recording Studios Inc,
pg 796

MINNESOTA

Badiyan Inc, pg 700
Big Event Productions LLC, pg 705
Live Spark Inc, pg 810
Media Loft Inc, pg 822

NEBRASKA

Rainbow Video Productions Inc,
pg 869

NEVADA

JCS Video Productions, pg 793

NEW HAMPSHIRE

Apertura, pg 686
Chip Taylor Communications LLC,
pg 907

NEW JERSEY

Allegro Productions Inc, pg 680
Laurel Video Productions, pg 804
Optisonics Productions, pg 847
Outside The Box Interactive LLC,
pg 849

NEW YORK

Blue Barn Pictures Inc, pg 707
Duggal Visual Solutions Inc, pg 747
Havas Creative, pg 776
HB-Content, pg 777
Hello World Communications,
pg 778
Ketchum Inc, pg 798
Manhattan Center Studios Inc,
pg 816
Jack Morton Worldwide, pg 830
News Broadcast Network Inc,
pg 840
Northeast Video Productions Inc,
pg 842
The Palmer Group, pg 850
SMP Digital Graphics, pg 891
Total Impact Multimedia Group Ltd,
pg 916
WorldView Software, pg 941
Zelman Studios Ltd, pg 945

NORTH CAROLINA

Pat Appleson Studios Inc, pg 687
The Communications Group Inc,
pg 729
Digital Rain LLC, pg 742
Image Associates Inc, pg 784
Kino Mountain Productions LLC,
pg 799
Moving Pictures, pg 832
PACE Worldwide, pg 849

OHIO

Cuyahoga Community College
Student Production Office (SPO),
pg 736
Image Video Teleproductions Inc,
pg 785
MainSail Production Services Inc,
pg 815
R&B Communications Inc, pg 870
Take 1 Media Services, pg 906
Thread Marketing Group, pg 913
Vista Color Imaging Inc, pg 931

OREGON

Ideascape Inc, pg 784
KTVA Productions, pg 802
Odyssey Productions Inc, pg 844

PENNSYLVANIA

Audio Visual Communications Inc,
pg 694
Bang! Pictures Inc, pg 701
FMP Media Solutions Inc, pg 763
JPL, pg 795
Kensington Falls Animation, pg 797
Main Point Productions, pg 815

New Horizons Computer Learning
Centers Inc, pg 839
Panta Rhei Media Inc, pg 851
Production Masters Inc (PMI),
pg 864
Scala Inc, pg 881

RHODE ISLAND

Sound-FX-Design, pg 894

TENNESSEE

American Blackguard Inc, pg 683
Continental Film, pg 731
Running Pony Productions LLC,
pg 878

TEXAS

Biway Media, pg 706
Epic Software Group Inc, pg 755
Horizon Film + Video Productions,
pg 781
Mediaforce Productions, pg 822
Romar Learning Solutions LLC,
pg 877
The Samuels Co, pg 879
Stage Directions, pg 898
Stockyard Photos/Jim Olive
Photography, pg 901

VIRGINIA

Advance Concepts Inc, pg 677
Altruist Media LLC, pg 682
Metro Productions, pg 824

WASHINGTON

Adams Creative & Production
Services, pg 675
Kostov Productions, pg 801
Medical Media Systems, pg 823
White Rain Films Ltd, pg 937

WISCONSIN

Audio Visual of Milwaukee Inc,
pg 694
AVS Group, pg 699
Clear Focus Media LLC, pg 726
Logan Productions Inc, pg 811
USAV Group Inc, pg 923
Video Wisconsin Inc, pg 929
Watts Communications Inc, pg 934
Wisconsin Public Television, pg 940

WYOMING

Bridger Productions Inc, pg 710

ALBERTA

Black Media Works, pg 706

*NEWFOUNDLAND AND
LABRADOR*

Vidcraft Productions Ltd, pg 927

ONTARIO

BBC Worldwide Canada Ltd,
pg 702
DebsVoice, pg 739
JFB Communications, pg 794
Mediaimage Communications
Group, pg 822

QUEBEC

Kerrigan Productions Inc, pg 798

PROGRAMMING — AUDIO/VISUAL

Sales Promotion & Training Program Rentals

ILLINOIS

1st Financial Training Services Inc, pg 761

MICHIGAN

Digi Sign Design LLC, pg 741

NEW HAMPSHIRE

Chip Taylor Communications LLC, pg 907

NORTH CAROLINA

Image Associates Inc, pg 784

UTAH

Webb Audio Visual, pg 935

Scientific Program Distributors

CALIFORNIA

Academy Savant, pg 672
Astronomical Society of the Pacific, pg 691
Crystal Pyramid Productions™, pg 735
Deja View Video, pg 740
Discovery Education - Los Angeles, pg 743
Glenn Photo Supply, pg 771
Bruce Goldberg Inc, pg 772
Joyce Media Inc, pg 795
Sea Studios Foundation, pg 883
The Wine Appreciation Guild Ltd, pg 939

COLORADO

American Educational Products LLC, pg 683

FLORIDA

PAR Inc, pg 851
Video Resources Software, pg 928

GEORGIA

School Media Associates LLC, pg 882

KENTUCKY

National Geographic Learning, pg 836

MARYLAND

MMI Marketing, pg 828

MASSACHUSETTS

Documentary Educational Resources Inc, pg 744
Sinauer Associates, pg 889

MICHIGAN

Digi Sign Design LLC, pg 741
Emery-Pratt Co, pg 753
MSU Technologies, pg 833

NEW HAMPSHIRE

Chip Taylor Communications LLC, pg 907

NEW JERSEY

Advanced Imaging Concepts Inc, pg 677
Allegro Productions Inc, pg 680

NEW YORK

Human Relations Media, pg 782
Janson Media Inc, pg 793
March of Dimes Foundation, pg 816
Meridian Education Corp, pg 823
Shopware, pg 886

NORTH CAROLINA

Carolina Biological Supply Co, pg 717

PENNSYLVANIA

AccuWeather Inc, pg 674
FMP Media Solutions Inc, pg 763
Media Inc, pg 822

VIRGINIA

PBS Video, pg 852

ONTARIO

BBC Worldwide Canada Ltd, pg 702
Canadian Learning Co Inc, pg 715
Kineticvideo.com, pg 799
McIntyre Media Inc, pg 821

Scientific Program Producers

ARIZONA

Aardvark Productions LLC, pg 671

CALIFORNIA

Academy Savant, pg 672
Astronomical Society of the Pacific, pg 691
Creative Technology, pg 733
Crystal Pyramid Productions™, pg 735
Direct Images Interactive Inc, pg 743
Discovery Education - Los Angeles, pg 743
Dolphin MultiMedia Inc, pg 745
imageReal Pictures LLC, pg 785
Joyce Media Inc, pg 795
Lynch Communications, pg 813
The Media Staff Inc, pg 822
New & Unique Videos™, pg 839
PM Productions, pg 858
Sea Studios Foundation, pg 883
Total Creative, pg 916
Vineyard Video & Photography, pg 930
Wavemaker Media Design, pg 934
Webster Communications, pg 935
West Coast Projections Inc, pg 935

COLORADO

American Educational Products LLC, pg 683
Daylight Productions & Rentals, pg 739
Flashback Media Productions, pg 762

DISTRICT OF COLUMBIA

Hillmann & Carr Inc, pg 780

FLORIDA

CD ROM™ Inc, pg 718
Sunfire Communications Inc, pg 904
Tricycle Studios, pg 918
Video Resources Software, pg 928

GEORGIA

Beachwood Productions, pg 702
Guerrilla Productions LLC, pg 774

HAWAII

Hyperspective Studios Inc, pg 783

ILLINOIS

Airways Digital Media, pg 679
Major Media Productions Inc, pg 815
Multimedia Marketing Group, pg 833
Pepper Group, pg 854
20/20 Communications Inc, pg 920
Video Impressions, pg 928

KENTUCKY

National Geographic Learning, pg 836

LOUISIANA

Louisiana State University Division of Strategic Communications, pg 811

MARYLAND

The Image Generators, pg 785
MMI Marketing, pg 828

MASSACHUSETTS

Documentary Educational Resources Inc, pg 744
Monadnock Media Inc, pg 829
Sinauer Associates, pg 889
Soundtrack Group, pg 895
TVN-The Video Network, pg 919

MICHIGAN

Digi Sign Design LLC, pg 741
K&R All Media Productions LLC, pg 796
K&R's Recording Studios Inc, pg 796

NEVADA

JCS Video Productions, pg 793

NEW HAMPSHIRE

Apertura, pg 686
Chip Taylor Communications LLC, pg 907

NEW JERSEY

Advanced Imaging Concepts Inc, pg 677
Allegro Productions Inc, pg 680
Laurel Video Productions, pg 804
Optisonics Productions, pg 847

NEW YORK

Blue Barn Pictures Inc, pg 707
Broadstreet Productions LLC, pg 711
CompuWeather Inc, pg 729

Duggal Visual Solutions Inc, pg 747
Florentine Films, pg 762
Havas Creative, pg 776
Hello World Communications, pg 778
Human Relations Media, pg 782
March of Dimes Foundation, pg 816
Jack Morton Worldwide, pg 830
MRY, pg 832
News Broadcast Network Inc, pg 840
The Palmer Group, pg 850
Zelman Studios Ltd, pg 945

NORTH CAROLINA

Pat Appleson Studios Inc, pg 687
Carolina Biological Supply Co, pg 717
Digital Rain LLC, pg 742
Kino Mountain Productions LLC, pg 799

OHIO

R&B Communications Inc, pg 870
Take 1 Media Services, pg 906
Vista Color Imaging Inc, pg 931

OREGON

Ideascape Inc, pg 784
Odyssey Productions Inc, pg 844

PENNSYLVANIA

AccuWeather Inc, pg 674
Audio Visual Communications Inc, pg 694
FMP Media Solutions Inc, pg 763
JPL, pg 795
Panta Rhei Media Inc, pg 851
Production Masters Inc (PMI), pg 864

RHODE ISLAND

Sound-FX-Design, pg 894

TENNESSEE

Continental Film, pg 731
Running Pony Productions LLC, pg 878

TEXAS

Epic Software Group Inc, pg 755
Mediaforce Productions, pg 822
Romar Learning Solutions LLC, pg 877
Stage Directions, pg 898
Texas Heart Institute Visual Communication Services, pg 911

VIRGINIA

Metro Productions, pg 824

WISCONSIN

USAV Group Inc, pg 923
Video Wisconsin Inc, pg 929
Wisconsin Public Television, pg 940

WYOMING

Bridger Productions Inc, pg 710

BRITISH COLUMBIA

West Eagle Films Inc, pg 935

ONTARIO

BBC Worldwide Canada Ltd, pg 702

QUEBEC

Kerrigan Productions Inc, pg 798

Scientific Program Rentals

CALIFORNIA

Glenn Photo Supply, pg 771

MASSACHUSETTS

Documentary Educational Resources Inc, pg 744

MICHIGAN

Digi Sign Design LLC, pg 741

NEW HAMPSHIRE

Chip Taylor Communications LLC, pg 907

UTAH

Webb Audio Visual, pg 935

Silent Filmstrip, *see* Filmstrip—Silent

Slide Distributors

ARIZONA

Arizona Cine Equipment, pg 688

CALIFORNIA

Academy Savant, pg 672
Ametron Audio/Video, pg 684
Astronomical Society of the Pacific, pg 691
Discovery Education - Los Angeles, pg 743
Medcom Inc, pg 821
QRS Software Services, pg 867
RJ Video Productions, pg 875
Sea Studios Foundation, pg 883
Social Studies School Service, pg 891

FLORIDA

ONstage, pg 846

GEORGIA

First Cut Communications LLC, pg 761
School Media Associates LLC, pg 882

ILLINOIS

CCore Media Inc, pg 718
National Safety Council (NSC), pg 836

MARYLAND

Department of Education Resources, pg 740
Milner-Fenwick Inc, pg 828
MMI Marketing, pg 828

MICHIGAN

Michigan Office Solutions (MOS), A Xerox Company, pg 825
MSU Technologies, pg 833

MISSOURI

Mosby Inc, pg 831

NEW HAMPSHIRE

Frey Scientific, pg 766

NEW YORK

Janus Films Inc, pg 793
Light Impressions, pg 807
Triumph Learning LLC, pg 918
United Nations Department of Public Information-News & Media Division, pg 921
Visual Technologies Corp, pg 932

NORTH CAROLINA

Carolina Biological Supply Co, pg 717

TENNESSEE

Spring Arbor Distributors Inc, pg 898

TEXAS

Stage Directions, pg 898
University of Texas at Austin - Petroleum Extension Service, pg 923

VIRGINIA

Colonial Williamsburg Foundation, pg 727

WISCONSIN

Demco Inc, pg 740
School Specialty Inc, pg 882

QUEBEC

Editions Hurtubise HMH Ltee, pg 782

Slide Producers

ARIZONA

Video Learning Library, pg 928

CALIFORNIA

Astronomical Society of the Pacific, pg 691
deKramer Productions Inc, pg 740
Design Media, pg 741
Discovery Education - Los Angeles, pg 743
Dolphin MultiMedia Inc, pg 745
Geddes Productions LLC, pg 769
Lynch Communications, pg 813
QRS Software Services, pg 867
Dick Reizner Film & Video, pg 873
Sea Studios Foundation, pg 883
Webster Communications, pg 935

COLORADO

Starwest Productions, pg 900

DISTRICT OF COLUMBIA

Biblical Archaeology Society (BAS), pg 705
Hillmann & Carr Inc, pg 780
O'Keefe Communications Inc, pg 844

FLORIDA

Roger Scruggs Films, pg 883

GEORGIA

First Cut Communications LLC, pg 761
Imagers, pg 785

HAWAII

Hyperspective Studios Inc, pg 783

ILLINOIS

CCore Media Inc, pg 718
National Safety Council (NSC), pg 836
Jim Passin Productions, pg 852
PSAV® Presentation Services (Hotel Services Division), pg 866

INDIANA

Communication Ministries, pg 728
OMNI Productions, pg 845

IOWA

Educational Technology & Media Services, pg 751
Iowa State University-Information Technology Services, pg 791

LOUISIANA

Digital FX Inc, pg 742
Louisiana State University Division of Strategic Communications, pg 811

MARYLAND

Department of Education Resources, pg 740
Milner-Fenwick Inc, pg 828
MMI Marketing, pg 828

MASSACHUSETTS

CommCreative, pg 728
DGI-Invisuals LLC, pg 741
Preston Productions Inc, pg 861
TR Productions, pg 916

MICHIGAN

K&R All Media Productions LLC, pg 796
K&R's Recording Studios Inc, pg 796
MessageMakers, pg 824
Michigan Office Solutions (MOS), A Xerox Company, pg 825
MSU Technologies, pg 833

MINNESOTA

Linhoff Photo & Digital Imaging, pg 809

MISSOURI

Mosby Inc, pg 831
Switch, pg 905

NEBRASKA

Telepro Video Inc, pg 910

NEVADA

Encore Event Technologies LLC, pg 754

NEW HAMPSHIRE

Academic & Campus Technology Services, pg 672
Apertura, pg 686

NEW JERSEY

The Bergman Collection of Medical/Technical/Scientific Stock Images, pg 704
Laurel Video Productions, pg 804
Optisonics Productions, pg 847

NEW YORK

Applause Learning Resources, pg 687
Blue Barn Pictures Inc, pg 707
Broadstreet Productions LLC, pg 711
Cornell Laboratory of Ornithology, pg 731
Icontent, pg 783
Jack Morton Worldwide, pg 830
SMP Digital Graphics, pg 891
Zelman Studios Ltd, pg 945

NORTH CAROLINA

Aon Hewitt, pg 686
Carolina Biological Supply Co, pg 717
Image Associates Inc, pg 784

OHIO

Cuyahoga Community College Student Production Office (SPO), pg 736
Treehaus Communications Inc, pg 917
Vista Color Imaging Inc, pg 931

OREGON

Ideascape Inc, pg 784

PENNSYLVANIA

Audio Visual Communications Inc, pg 694
FMP Media Solutions Inc, pg 763
JPL, pg 795
Kensington Falls Animation, pg 797
Main Point Productions, pg 815

TENNESSEE

Center for Southern Folklore Inc, pg 719
Memphis Communications Corp, pg 823

TEXAS

Omni Intercommunications Inc, pg 845
Romar Learning Solutions LLC, pg 877
Stage Directions, pg 898
Texas Heart Institute Visual Communication Services, pg 911
University of Texas at Austin - Petroleum Extension Service, pg 923

VIRGINIA

Advance Concepts Inc, pg 677
Blair Inc, pg 707

WASHINGTON

Kostov Productions, pg 801

WISCONSIN

AVS Group, pg 699
USAV Group Inc, pg 923
Video Wisconsin Inc, pg 929

ONTARIO

Mediaimage Communications
  Group, pg 822
Silver Creek Media Inc, pg 888

QUEBEC

Kerrigan Productions Inc, pg 798

Slide Show Rentals

ILLINOIS

National Safety Council (NSC),
  pg 836

MASSACHUSETTS

Preston Productions Inc, pg 861

MICHIGAN

Digi Sign Design LLC, pg 741

NEW HAMPSHIRE

Chip Taylor Communications LLC,
  pg 907

NEW YORK

Brooklyn Botanic Garden, pg 711

NORTH CAROLINA

Image Associates Inc, pg 784

UTAH

Webb Audio Visual, pg 935

Sound Filmstrip, *see* Filmstrip—Sound

Sponsored Program Distributors

CALIFORNIA

Crystal Pyramid Productions™,
  pg 735
Medcom Inc, pg 821
New & Unique Videos™, pg 839

ILLINOIS

CCore Media Inc, pg 718
Terra Nova Films Inc, pg 911

MASSACHUSETTS

Preston Productions Inc, pg 861

MICHIGAN

Digi Sign Design LLC, pg 741

NEW HAMPSHIRE

Chip Taylor Communications LLC,
  pg 907

NEW JERSEY

Allegro Productions Inc, pg 680
Euro-Pacific Film & Video
  Productions Inc, pg 756

NEW YORK

William Greaves Productions Inc,
  pg 774
HB-Content, pg 777

TENNESSEE

American Blackguard Inc, pg 683

ONTARIO

Canadian Learning Co Inc, pg 715

Sponsored Program Producers

ARIZONA

Candee Productions Inc, pg 716
Teaberry, pg 908

CALIFORNIA

Creative Technology, pg 733
Crystal Pyramid Productions™,
  pg 735
Direct Images Interactive Inc,
  pg 743
imageReal Pictures LLC, pg 785
Lynch Communications, pg 813
The Media Staff Inc, pg 822
New & Unique Videos™, pg 839
Screen Door Entertainment Inc,
  pg 882
Total Creative, pg 916
Vineyard Video & Photography,
  pg 930
Webster Communications, pg 935

COLORADO

Flashback Media Productions,
  pg 762
Tatum Video, pg 907

CONNECTICUT

Cine-Med Inc, pg 723

FLORIDA

Applebox Studio, pg 687
Audio Visual Imagineering Inc,
  pg 694
Communications Concepts Inc
  (CCI), pg 729
Sunfire Communications Inc,
  pg 904
Tricycle Studios, pg 918

GEORGIA

Beachwood Productions, pg 702
Guerrilla Productions LLC, pg 774
Visioneering International Inc,
  pg 931

HAWAII

Hyperspective Studios Inc, pg 783

ILLINOIS

CCore Media Inc, pg 718
Manning Productions, pg 816
Multimedia Marketing Group,
  pg 833
Pepper Group, pg 854
PSAV® Presentation Services
  (Hotel Services Division), pg 866
Terra Nova Films Inc, pg 911
Video Impressions, pg 928

INDIANA

A-V-A Video Productions, pg 671

IOWA

Educational Technology & Media
  Services, pg 751

MARYLAND

The Image Generators, pg 785

MASSACHUSETTS

Soundtrack Group, pg 895

MICHIGAN

Digi Sign Design LLC, pg 741
K&R All Media Productions LLC,
  pg 796
K&R's Recording Studios Inc,
  pg 796

NEVADA

JCS Video Productions, pg 793

NEW HAMPSHIRE

Apertura, pg 686
Chip Taylor Communications LLC,
  pg 907

NEW JERSEY

Allegro Productions Inc, pg 680
Laurel Video Productions, pg 804
Optisonics Productions, pg 847

NEW YORK

Blue Barn Pictures Inc, pg 707
Broadstreet Productions LLC,
  pg 711
Castillo Theatre, pg 717
William Greaves Productions Inc,
  pg 774
Havas Creative, pg 776
HB-Content, pg 777
Ketchum Inc, pg 798
Jack Morton Worldwide, pg 830
News Broadcast Network Inc,
  pg 840
The Palmer Group, pg 850
Zelman Studios Ltd, pg 945

NORTH CAROLINA

Pat Appleson Studios Inc, pg 687
Digital Rain LLC, pg 742
Kino Mountain Productions LLC,
  pg 799
Moving Pictures, pg 832

OHIO

Advent Media Inc, pg 677
R&B Communications Inc, pg 870
Take 1 Media Services, pg 906
Vista Color Imaging Inc, pg 931

OREGON

Ideascape Inc, pg 784
Odyssey Productions Inc, pg 844
REX, pg 874

PENNSYLVANIA

Bang! Pictures Inc, pg 701
FMP Media Solutions Inc, pg 763
JPL, pg 795
Kensington Falls Animation, pg 797
Main Point Productions, pg 815
Production Masters Inc (PMI),
  pg 864

RHODE ISLAND

Sound-FX-Design, pg 894

TENNESSEE

American Blackguard Inc, pg 683
Continental Film, pg 731
Running Pony Productions LLC,
  pg 878

TEXAS

Epic Software Group Inc, pg 755
Mediaforce Productions, pg 822
Romar Learning Solutions LLC,
  pg 877
The Samuels Co, pg 879
South Coast Film & Video, pg 895

VIRGINIA

Advance Concepts Inc, pg 677
Altruist Media LLC, pg 682
Metro Productions, pg 824

WASHINGTON

Laser Fantasy/HECK
  Industries/Photon Manufacturing,
  pg 804

WISCONSIN

Watts Communications Inc, pg 934

WYOMING

Bridger Productions Inc, pg 710

ALBERTA

Black Media Works, pg 706

QUEBEC

Kerrigan Productions Inc, pg 798

Sponsored Program Rentals

CALIFORNIA

Medcom Inc, pg 821

ILLINOIS

Terra Nova Films Inc, pg 911

MASSACHUSETTS

Preston Productions Inc, pg 861

MICHIGAN

Digi Sign Design LLC, pg 741

NEW HAMPSHIRE

Chip Taylor Communications LLC,
  pg 907

NEW JERSEY

Euro-Pacific Film & Video
  Productions Inc, pg 756

NEW YORK

William Greaves Productions Inc,
  pg 774

UTAH

Webb Audio Visual, pg 935

Sports Program Distributors

ARIZONA

Video Learning Library, pg 928

PROGRAMMING — AUDIO/VISUAL

Sports Program Distributors (continued)

CALIFORNIA

Crystal Pyramid Productions™, pg 735
Discovery Education - Los Angeles, pg 743
monterey video, pg 829
New & Unique Videos™, pg 839

ILLINOIS

Film Ideas Inc, pg 760

IOWA

Championship Productions Inc, pg 720

MICHIGAN

Digi Sign Design LLC, pg 741

NEW HAMPSHIRE

Chip Taylor Communications LLC, pg 907

NEW YORK

HB-Content, pg 777
Janson Media Inc, pg 793
VIEW Inc (Video International Entertainment World Inc), pg 930
Women Make Movies Inc, pg 941

PENNSYLVANIA

FMP Media Solutions Inc, pg 763

ONTARIO

Canadian Learning Co Inc, pg 715
Canamedia Inc, pg 715
Kineticvideo.com, pg 799

Sports Program Producers

ARIZONA

Aardvark Productions LLC, pg 671
Candee Productions Inc, pg 716

CALIFORNIA

Creative Technology, pg 733
Crystal Pyramid Productions™, pg 735
Discovery Education - Los Angeles, pg 743
Lynch Communications, pg 813
New & Unique Videos™, pg 839
Total Creative, pg 916
Vineyard Video & Photography, pg 930
Webster Communications, pg 935

COLORADO

Tatum Video, pg 907

FLORIDA

Communications Concepts Inc (CCI), pg 729
Sunfire Communications Inc, pg 904

GEORGIA

Beachwood Productions, pg 702
Guerrilla Productions LLC, pg 774
Myriad Productions, pg 835

HAWAII

Hyperspective Studios Inc, pg 783

ILLINOIS

Multimedia Marketing Group, pg 833
Pepper Group, pg 854
20/20 Communications Inc, pg 920

IOWA

Championship Productions Inc, pg 720

KENTUCKY

Idle Minds Productions Inc, pg 784

MASSACHUSETTS

Cramer, pg 732
Soundtrack Group, pg 895

MICHIGAN

Digi Sign Design LLC, pg 741
K&R All Media Productions LLC, pg 796
K&R's Recording Studios Inc, pg 796

NEW HAMPSHIRE

Apertura, pg 686
Chip Taylor Communications LLC, pg 907

NEW JERSEY

Allegro Productions Inc, pg 680
Optisonics Productions, pg 847

NEW YORK

Broadstreet Productions LLC, pg 711
Florentine Films, pg 762
Havas Creative, pg 776
HB-Content, pg 777
Jack Morton Worldwide, pg 830
MRY, pg 832
The Palmer Group, pg 850
VIEW Inc (Video International Entertainment World Inc), pg 930
Zelman Studios Ltd, pg 945

NORTH CAROLINA

Pat Appleson Studios Inc, pg 687
Digital Rain LLC, pg 742
Kino Mountain Productions LLC, pg 799

OHIO

Image Video Teleproductions Inc, pg 785
MainSail Production Services Inc, pg 815
R&B Communications Inc, pg 870

OREGON

Odyssey Productions Inc, pg 844

PENNSYLVANIA

Bang! Pictures Inc, pg 701
FMP Media Solutions Inc, pg 763

Kensington Falls Animation, pg 797
Production Masters Inc (PMI), pg 864

RHODE ISLAND

Sound-FX-Design, pg 894

TENNESSEE

Continental Film, pg 731
Running Pony Productions LLC, pg 878

TEXAS

Epic Software Group Inc, pg 755
Mediaforce Productions, pg 822
Tropikal Productions, pg 918

VIRGINIA

Metro Productions, pg 824

WISCONSIN

Watts Communications Inc, pg 934
Wisconsin Public Television, pg 940

WYOMING

Bridger Productions Inc, pg 710

ALBERTA

Black Media Works, pg 706

NEWFOUNDLAND AND LABRADOR

Vidcraft Productions Ltd, pg 927

QUEBEC

Kerrigan Productions Inc, pg 798

Sports Program Rentals

MICHIGAN

Digi Sign Design LLC, pg 741

NEW HAMPSHIRE

Chip Taylor Communications LLC, pg 907

UTAH

Webb Audio Visual, pg 935

Talking Filmstrip, *see* Filmstrip—Sound

Technical Research Program Distributors

CALIFORNIA

Crystal Pyramid Productions™, pg 735

DISTRICT OF COLUMBIA

American Chemical Society (ACS), pg 683

ILLINOIS

CCH Continuing Education, pg 718

MASSACHUSETTS

Documentary Educational Resources Inc, pg 744

MICHIGAN

Digi Sign Design LLC, pg 741

NEW HAMPSHIRE

Chip Taylor Communications LLC, pg 907

PENNSYLVANIA

FMP Media Solutions Inc, pg 763

VIRGINIA

National Audiovisual Center (NAC), pg 836

ONTARIO

BBC Worldwide Canada Ltd, pg 702

Technical Research Program Producers

ARIZONA

Aardvark Productions LLC, pg 671
Candee Productions Inc, pg 716

CALIFORNIA

Creative Technology, pg 733
Crystal Pyramid Productions™, pg 735
Design Media, pg 741
IEEE Computer Society Press, pg 784
Lynch Communications, pg 813
New & Unique Videos™, pg 839
Total Creative, pg 916
Vineyard Video & Photography, pg 930
Wavemaker Media Design, pg 934
West Coast Projections Inc, pg 935

COLORADO

Daylight Productions & Rentals, pg 739
Flashback Media Productions, pg 762

DISTRICT OF COLUMBIA

American Chemical Society (ACS), pg 683

FLORIDA

Sunfire Communications Inc, pg 904

GEORGIA

Beachwood Productions, pg 702
Guerrilla Productions LLC, pg 774
Visioneering International Inc, pg 931

HAWAII

Hyperspective Studios Inc, pg 783

ILLINOIS

Accenture, pg 672
CCH Continuing Education, pg 718
Major Media Productions Inc, pg 815
Pepper Group, pg 854
20/20 Communications Inc, pg 920
Video Impressions, pg 928

INDIANA

A-V-A Video Productions, pg 671

LOUISIANA

Louisiana State University Division
of Strategic Communications,
pg 811

MASSACHUSETTS

Documentary Educational Resources
Inc, pg 744
Soundtrack Group, pg 895

MICHIGAN

Digi Sign Design LLC, pg 741
K&R All Media Productions LLC,
pg 796
K&R's Recording Studios Inc,
pg 796

MINNESOTA

Badiyan Inc, pg 700

NEBRASKA

Rainbow Video Productions Inc,
pg 869

NEW HAMPSHIRE

Apertura, pg 686
Chip Taylor Communications LLC,
pg 907

NEW JERSEY

Allegro Productions Inc, pg 680
Broadcast Center Studios, pg 710
Optisonics Productions, pg 847

NEW YORK

Havas Creative, pg 776
Jack Morton Worldwide, pg 830
The Palmer Group, pg 850
Zelman Studios Ltd, pg 945

NORTH CAROLINA

Pat Appleson Studios Inc, pg 687
Kino Mountain Productions LLC,
pg 799

OHIO

Advent Media Inc, pg 677
R&B Communications Inc, pg 870
Take 1 Media Services, pg 906
Vista Color Imaging Inc, pg 931

OREGON

Ideascape Inc, pg 784

PENNSYLVANIA

FMP Media Solutions Inc, pg 763
Panta Rhei Media Inc, pg 851
Production Masters Inc (PMI),
pg 864

RHODE ISLAND

Sound-FX-Design, pg 894

TENNESSEE

Continental Film, pg 731
Running Pony Productions LLC,
pg 878

TEXAS

Mediaforce Productions, pg 822
Romar Learning Solutions LLC,
pg 877

Stage Directions, pg 898
Stockyard Photos/Jim Olive
Photography, pg 901

WISCONSIN

Wisconsin Public Television, pg 940

WYOMING

Bridger Productions Inc, pg 710

ONTARIO

BBC Worldwide Canada Ltd,
pg 702

QUEBEC

Kerrigan Productions Inc, pg 798

Technical Research Program Rentals

MASSACHUSETTS

Documentary Educational Resources
Inc, pg 744

MICHIGAN

Digi Sign Design LLC, pg 741

NEW HAMPSHIRE

Chip Taylor Communications LLC,
pg 907

UTAH

Webb Audio Visual, pg 935

Training Program Distributors

ARIZONA

Video Learning Library, pg 928

CALIFORNIA

Academy Savant, pg 672
Crystal Pyramid Productions™,
pg 735
Deja View Video, pg 740
Dialect Accent Specialists Inc,
pg 741
Discovery Education - Los Angeles,
pg 743
Kantola Productions LLC, pg 796
Medcom Inc, pg 821
Semiconductor Services, pg 883
The Wine Appreciation Guild Ltd,
pg 939

COLORADO

American Educational Products
LLC, pg 683
MVP International Inc, pg 835
Vital Learning LLC, pg 932

DISTRICT OF COLUMBIA

Theatrical Technicians Inc (TTI),
pg 912

FLORIDA

PAR Inc, pg 851
Video Resources Software, pg 928

HAWAII

Media Bridge Gamekids, pg 821
Source School of Tantra Yoga Inc,
pg 895

ILLINOIS

CCH Continuing Education, pg 718
CCore Media Inc, pg 718
Film Ideas Inc, pg 760
National Safety Council (NSC),
pg 836

IOWA

Prositions Inc, pg 865

KENTUCKY

KET The Kentucky Network,
pg 798

MARYLAND

MMI Marketing, pg 828

MICHIGAN

Digi Sign Design LLC, pg 741
The Program Source International,
pg 865

NEW HAMPSHIRE

Captain Fiddle Music &
Publications, pg 716
Chip Taylor Communications LLC,
pg 907

NEW JERSEY

FlagHouse, pg 762

NEW MEXICO

The Phoenix Learning Group Inc,
pg 855

NEW YORK

Guidance Associates Inc Center for
Humanities, pg 774
HB-Content, pg 777
Monad Trainer's Aide Inc, pg 829
VIEW Inc (Video International
Entertainment World Inc), pg 930

PENNSYLVANIA

American Law Institute Continuing
Legal Education (ALI CLE),
pg 683
FMP Media Solutions Inc, pg 763
Media Inc, pg 822
TRC Interactive Inc, pg 917

TENNESSEE

American Blackguard Inc, pg 683
Spring Arbor Distributors Inc,
pg 898
Zion Music Group, pg 945

TEXAS

PetroSkills | RDC Solutions, pg 855
University of Texas at Austin -
Petroleum Extension Service,
pg 923

WASHINGTON

Intermedia Inc, pg 789

WISCONSIN

Wisconsin Technical College
System Foundation Inc, pg 940

ONTARIO

BBC Worldwide Canada Ltd,
pg 702
Canadian Learning Co Inc, pg 715
Kineticvideo.com, pg 799

Training Program Producers

ARIZONA

Aardvark Productions LLC, pg 671
Candee Productions Inc, pg 716
Creative Backstage, pg 733
Teaberry, pg 908

ARKANSAS

Live'N'Loud, pg 810
White Diamond Productions LLC,
pg 937

CALIFORNIA

Aaron Marcus and Associates,
pg 671
Academy Savant, pg 672
Ancient Future, pg 685
California Language Laboratories,
pg 714
Creative Technology, pg 733
Crystal Pyramid Productions™,
pg 735
Design Media, pg 741
Dialect Accent Specialists Inc,
pg 741
Direct Images Interactive Inc,
pg 743
Discovery Education - Los Angeles,
pg 743
Dolphin MultiMedia Inc, pg 745
imageReal Pictures LLC, pg 785
International Contact Inc, pg 790
Kantola Productions LLC, pg 796
Kavich Reynolds Productions Inc,
pg 797
Lynch Communications, pg 813
Medcom Inc, pg 821
Media Magic, pg 822
The Media Staff Inc, pg 822
New & Unique Videos™, pg 839
New Circuit Films LLC, pg 839
Prime Cut Productions, pg 862
Tam Communications Inc, pg 906
Total Creative, pg 916
Vineyard Video & Photography,
pg 930
Wavemaker Media Design, pg 934
Webster Communications, pg 935
West Coast Projections Inc, pg 935

COLORADO

American Educational Products
LLC, pg 683
Daylight Productions & Rentals,
pg 739
Flashback Media Productions,
pg 762
MVP International Inc, pg 835
Vital Learning LLC, pg 932

CONNECTICUT

Cine-Med Inc, pg 723

DISTRICT OF COLUMBIA

O'Keefe Communications Inc,
pg 844
Theatrical Technicians Inc (TTI),
pg 912

PROGRAMMING — AUDIO/VISUAL

Training Program Producers (continued)

FLORIDA

Applebox Studio, pg 687
CD ROM™ Inc, pg 718
Communications Concepts Inc (CCI), pg 729
ITC Learning LLC, pg 791
Paradise Video & Film, pg 851
Sunfire Communications Inc, pg 904
Teach America Corp, pg 908
Tricycle Studios, pg 918
Video Resources Software, pg 928
Video Techniques Inc, pg 928

GEORGIA

Beachwood Productions, pg 702
Guerrilla Productions LLC, pg 774

HAWAII

Hyperspective Studios Inc, pg 783
Media Bridge Gamekids, pg 821
Source School of Tantra Yoga Inc, pg 895

ILLINOIS

Accenture, pg 672
Airways Digital Media, pg 679
Atomic Imaging Inc/Golan Studios, pg 692
CCH Continuing Education, pg 718
CCore Media Inc, pg 718
1st Financial Training Services Inc, pg 761
Major Media Productions Inc, pg 815
Manning Productions, pg 816
Multimedia Marketing Group, pg 833
National Safety Council (NSC), pg 836
Pepper Group, pg 854
PSAV® Presentation Services (Hotel Services Division), pg 866
SCI Television & Creative Media LLC, pg 882
Sparkfactor, pg 896
20/20 Communications Inc, pg 920
Video Impressions, pg 928

INDIANA

A-V-A Video Productions, pg 671

IOWA

Educational Technology & Media Services, pg 751
Prositions Inc, pg 865

KENTUCKY

Idle Minds Productions Inc, pg 784
KET The Kentucky Network, pg 798
NIMCO Inc, pg 841

LOUISIANA

Digital FX Inc, pg 742
Louisiana State University Division of Strategic Communications, pg 811

MARYLAND

The Cutting Corporation, GraphicAudio® & Archival Sound Lab, pg 736
dbF a Media Company, pg 739
The Image Generators, pg 785
Mobile-Video Productions Inc, pg 828

MASSACHUSETTS

CommCreative, pg 728
Cramer, pg 732
Soundtrack Group, pg 895
TVN-The Video Network, pg 919

MICHIGAN

Digi Sign Design LLC, pg 741
K&R All Media Productions LLC, pg 796
K&R's Recording Studios Inc, pg 796

MINNESOTA

Badiyan Inc, pg 700
Big Event Productions LLC, pg 705
Live Spark Inc, pg 810
MastCom, pg 819
Media Loft Inc, pg 822

NEVADA

JCS Video Productions, pg 793

NEW HAMPSHIRE

Apertura, pg 686
Chip Taylor Communications LLC, pg 907

NEW JERSEY

Allegro Productions Inc, pg 680
Broadcast Center Studios, pg 710
Laurel Video Productions, pg 804
Optisonics Productions, pg 847
Selden Associates, pg 883
Telemanagement Resources International Inc (TRI), pg 910

NEW MEXICO

The Phoenix Learning Group Inc, pg 855

NEW YORK

Blue Barn Pictures Inc, pg 707
Broadstreet Productions LLC, pg 711
Duggal Visual Solutions Inc, pg 747
Guidance Associates Inc Center for Humanities, pg 774
Havas Creative, pg 776
HB-Content, pg 777
Hello World Communications, pg 778
Ketchum Inc, pg 798
Jack Morton Worldwide, pg 830
MRY, pg 832
News Broadcast Network Inc, pg 840
Northeast Video Productions Inc, pg 842
The Palmer Group, pg 850
VIEW Inc (Video International Entertainment World Inc), pg 930
Zelman Studios Ltd, pg 945

NORTH CAROLINA

Pat Appleson Studios Inc, pg 687
The Communications Group Inc, pg 729

Digital Rain LLC, pg 742
Image Associates Inc, pg 784
Kino Mountain Productions LLC, pg 799
Moving Pictures, pg 832
PACE Worldwide, pg 849

OHIO

Cuyahoga Community College Student Production Office (SPO), pg 736
MainSail Production Services Inc, pg 815
R&B Communications Inc, pg 870
Take 1 Media Services, pg 906
Thread Marketing Group, pg 913
Treehaus Communications Inc, pg 917
Vista Color Imaging Inc, pg 931

OREGON

Ideascape Inc, pg 784
KTVA Productions, pg 802
REX, pg 874

PENNSYLVANIA

American Law Institute Continuing Legal Education (ALI CLE), pg 683
Audio Visual Communications Inc, pg 694
Bang! Pictures Inc, pg 701
FMP Media Solutions Inc, pg 763
JPL, pg 795
Main Point Productions, pg 815
Panta Rhei Media Inc, pg 851
Production Masters Inc (PMI), pg 864

RHODE ISLAND

Sound-FX-Design, pg 894

TENNESSEE

American Blackguard Inc, pg 683
Continental Film, pg 731
Running Pony Productions LLC, pg 878
Spring Arbor Distributors Inc, pg 898

TEXAS

Biway Media, pg 706
Horizon Film + Video Productions, pg 781
Mediaforce Productions, pg 822
PetroSkills | RDC Solutions, pg 855
Romar Learning Solutions LLC, pg 877
Stage Directions, pg 898
Stockyard Photos/Jim Olive Photography, pg 901
University of Texas at Austin - Petroleum Extension Service, pg 923

VIRGINIA

Advance Concepts Inc, pg 677
Altruist Media LLC, pg 682
Metro Productions, pg 824

WASHINGTON

Adams Creative & Production Services, pg 675
Intermedia Inc, pg 789
Kostov Productions, pg 801

WISCONSIN

Audio Visual of Milwaukee Inc, pg 694
USAV Group Inc, pg 923
Watts Communications Inc, pg 934
Wisconsin Public Television, pg 940
Wisconsin Technical College System Foundation Inc, pg 940

WYOMING

Bridger Productions Inc, pg 710

ALBERTA

Black Media Works, pg 706

NEWFOUNDLAND AND LABRADOR

Vidcraft Productions Ltd, pg 927

NORTHWEST TERRITORIES

Yellowknife Films Inc, pg 944

ONTARIO

BBC Worldwide Canada Ltd, pg 702
JFB Communications, pg 794
Silver Creek Media Inc, pg 888

QUEBEC

Kerrigan Productions Inc, pg 798

Training Program Rentals

CALIFORNIA

Academy Savant, pg 672
ETR, pg 756
Medcom Inc, pg 821
Semiconductor Services, pg 883

COLORADO

MVP International Inc, pg 835

ILLINOIS

1st Financial Training Services Inc, pg 761
National Safety Council (NSC), pg 836

MICHIGAN

Digi Sign Design LLC, pg 741

NEW HAMPSHIRE

Chip Taylor Communications LLC, pg 907

UTAH

Webb Audio Visual, pg 935

WASHINGTON

Intermedia Inc, pg 789

Transparency, *see* Overhead Transparency

Travelog Distributors

ARIZONA

Video Learning Library, pg 928

CALIFORNIA

Crystal Pyramid Productions™,
  pg 735
Glenn Photo Supply, pg 771
Jaguar Distribution Corp, pg 792
New & Unique Videos™, pg 839

DISTRICT OF COLUMBIA

Biblical Archaeology Society
  (BAS), pg 705

ILLINOIS

Film Ideas Inc, pg 760

KENTUCKY

Horizon Films & Media LLC,
  pg 781

MICHIGAN

Digi Sign Design LLC, pg 741

NEW HAMPSHIRE

Chip Taylor Communications LLC,
  pg 907

NEW JERSEY

Euro-Pacific Film & Video
  Productions Inc, pg 756

NEW YORK

Janson Media Inc, pg 793
Videofashion Network, pg 929

OREGON

TeleVideos, pg 910

PENNSYLVANIA

FMP Media Solutions Inc, pg 763

TENNESSEE

American Blackguard Inc, pg 683

TEXAS

Educational Video Network, pg 751

ONTARIO

Canadian Learning Co Inc, pg 715

Travelog Producers

ALABAMA

AVS Media Group, pg 699

ARIZONA

Aardvark Productions LLC, pg 671
Teaberry, pg 908

CALIFORNIA

Ancient Future, pg 685
Crystal Pyramid Productions™,
  pg 735
Dolphin MultiMedia Inc, pg 745
Jaguar Distribution Corp, pg 792
Lynch Communications, pg 813
New & Unique Videos™, pg 839
Prime Cut Productions, pg 862
Screen Door Entertainment Inc,
  pg 882
Total Creative, pg 916
Vineyard Video & Photography,
  pg 930
Wavemaker Media Design, pg 934

Webster Communications, pg 935
West Coast Projections Inc, pg 935

COLORADO

Flashback Media Productions,
  pg 762
Tatum Video, pg 907

DISTRICT OF COLUMBIA

O'Keefe Communications Inc,
  pg 844

FLORIDA

Applebox Studio, pg 687
Sunfire Communications Inc,
  pg 904

GEORGIA

Beachwood Productions, pg 702
Guerrilla Productions LLC, pg 774

HAWAII

Hyperspective Studios Inc, pg 783

ILLINOIS

Multimedia Marketing Group,
  pg 833
Pepper Group, pg 854
PSAV® Presentation Services
  (Hotel Services Division), pg 866
SCI Television & Creative Media
  LLC, pg 882
20/20 Communications Inc, pg 920
Video Impressions, pg 928

KENTUCKY

Horizon Films & Media LLC,
  pg 781

MARYLAND

The Image Generators, pg 785

MASSACHUSETTS

Soundtrack Group, pg 895
TVN-The Video Network, pg 919

MICHIGAN

Digi Sign Design LLC, pg 741
K&R All Media Productions LLC,
  pg 796
K&R's Recording Studios Inc,
  pg 796

NEW HAMPSHIRE

Chip Taylor Communications LLC,
  pg 907

NEW JERSEY

Allegro Productions Inc, pg 680
Broadcast Center Studios, pg 710
Optisonics Productions, pg 847

NEW YORK

Jack Morton Worldwide, pg 830
MRY, pg 832
News Broadcast Network Inc,
  pg 840
The Palmer Group, pg 850
Videofashion Network, pg 929
Zelman Studios Ltd, pg 945

NORTH CAROLINA

Pat Appleson Studios Inc, pg 687
Digital Rain LLC, pg 742
Kino Mountain Productions LLC,
  pg 799

OHIO

MainSail Production Services Inc,
  pg 815
R&B Communications Inc, pg 870
Take 1 Media Services, pg 906
Treehaus Communications Inc,
  pg 917

OREGON

Odyssey Productions Inc, pg 844
TeleVideos, pg 910

PENNSYLVANIA

FMP Media Solutions Inc, pg 763
JPL, pg 795
Muderick Media, pg 833
Production Masters Inc (PMI),
  pg 864

RHODE ISLAND

Sound-FX-Design, pg 894

TENNESSEE

American Blackguard Inc, pg 683
Running Pony Productions LLC,
  pg 878

TEXAS

Educational Video Network, pg 751
Horizon Film + Video Productions,
  pg 781
Mediaforce Productions, pg 822
Stage Directions, pg 898

WASHINGTON

White Rain Films Ltd, pg 937

WISCONSIN

Wisconsin Public Television, pg 940

WYOMING

Bridger Productions Inc, pg 710

*NEWFOUNDLAND AND
LABRADOR*

Vidcraft Productions Ltd, pg 927

NORTHWEST TERRITORIES

Yellowknife Films Inc, pg 944

QUEBEC

Kerrigan Productions Inc, pg 798

Travelog Rentals

CALIFORNIA

Glenn Photo Supply, pg 771

MICHIGAN

Digi Sign Design LLC, pg 741

NEW HAMPSHIRE

Chip Taylor Communications LLC,
  pg 907

NEW JERSEY

Euro-Pacific Film & Video
  Productions Inc, pg 756

UTAH

Webb Audio Visual, pg 935

Vocational Program
Distributors

ARIZONA

Video Learning Library, pg 928

CALIFORNIA

Crystal Pyramid Productions™,
  pg 735
Discovery Education - Los Angeles,
  pg 743

FLORIDA

Video Resources Software, pg 928

GEORGIA

Convergent Media Systems, pg 731
School Media Associates LLC,
  pg 882

ILLINOIS

Film Ideas Inc, pg 760
National Safety Council (NSC),
  pg 836

MICHIGAN

Digi Sign Design LLC, pg 741

NEW HAMPSHIRE

Frey Scientific, pg 766
Chip Taylor Communications LLC,
  pg 907

NEW MEXICO

The Phoenix Learning Group Inc,
  pg 855

NEW YORK

Films Media Group, pg 760
Guidance Associates Inc Center for
  Humanities, pg 774
Human Relations Media, pg 782
March of Dimes Foundation, pg 816
Meridian Education Corp, pg 823
Shopware, pg 886
VIEW Inc (Video International
  Entertainment World Inc), pg 930

OHIO

McGraw-Hill School Education
  Group, pg 821

PENNSYLVANIA

FMP Media Solutions Inc, pg 763

TENNESSEE

American Blackguard Inc, pg 683

TEXAS

University of Texas at Austin -
  Petroleum Extension Service,
  pg 923

WISCONSIN

Wisconsin Technical College
  System Foundation Inc, pg 940

PROGRAMMING — AUDIO/VISUAL

Vocational Program Distributors (continued)

ONTARIO

Canadian Learning Co Inc, pg 715
Kineticvideo.com, pg 799
McIntyre Media Inc, pg 821

Vocational Program Producers

ARIZONA

Aardvark Productions LLC, pg 671

CALIFORNIA

Aaron Marcus and Associates, pg 671
Crystal Pyramid Productions™, pg 735
Discovery Education - Los Angeles, pg 743
imageReal Pictures LLC, pg 785
Lynch Communications, pg 813
The Media Staff Inc, pg 822
New & Unique Videos™, pg 839
Total Creative, pg 916
Vineyard Video & Photography, pg 930
Wavemaker Media Design, pg 934
Webster Communications, pg 935
West Coast Projections Inc, pg 935

COLORADO

Flashback Media Productions, pg 762

FLORIDA

Applebox Studio, pg 687
Sunfire Communications Inc, pg 904
Video Resources Software, pg 928

GEORGIA

Beachwood Productions, pg 702
Guerrilla Productions LLC, pg 774

HAWAII

Hyperspective Studios Inc, pg 783

ILLINOIS

1st Financial Training Services Inc, pg 761
Major Media Productions Inc, pg 815
National Safety Council (NSC), pg 836
Pepper Group, pg 854
20/20 Communications Inc, pg 920

KENTUCKY

NIMCO Inc, pg 841

MARYLAND

dbF a Media Company, pg 739
The Image Generators, pg 785

MASSACHUSETTS

Soundtrack Group, pg 895

MICHIGAN

Digi Sign Design LLC, pg 741
K&R All Media Productions LLC, pg 796
K&R's Recording Studios Inc, pg 796

MINNESOTA

Badiyan Inc, pg 700
MastCom, pg 819

NEVADA

JCS Video Productions, pg 793

NEW HAMPSHIRE

Apertura, pg 686
Frey Scientific, pg 766
Chip Taylor Communications LLC, pg 907

NEW JERSEY

Allegro Productions Inc, pg 680
Laurel Video Productions, pg 804
Optisonics Productions, pg 847

NEW MEXICO

The Phoenix Learning Group Inc, pg 855

NEW YORK

Films Media Group, pg 760
The Food & Beverage Institute, pg 763

Guidance Associates Inc Center for Humanities, pg 774
Havas Creative, pg 776
Hello World Communications, pg 778
Human Relations Media, pg 782
Ketchum Inc, pg 798
March of Dimes Foundation, pg 816
Jack Morton Worldwide, pg 830
The Palmer Group, pg 850
Triumph Learning LLC, pg 918
VIEW Inc (Video International Entertainment World Inc), pg 930
Zelman Studios Ltd, pg 945

NORTH CAROLINA

Pat Appleson Studios Inc, pg 687
Kino Mountain Productions LLC, pg 799
Moving Pictures, pg 832

OHIO

MainSail Production Services Inc, pg 815
McGraw-Hill School Education Group, pg 821
R&B Communications Inc, pg 870
Take 1 Media Services, pg 906
Treehaus Communications Inc, pg 917
Vista Color Imaging Inc, pg 931

OREGON

ERA Learning, pg 755
Ideascape Inc, pg 784
KTVA Productions, pg 802

PENNSYLVANIA

FMP Media Solutions Inc, pg 763
JPL, pg 795
Muderick Media, pg 833
Production Masters Inc (PMI), pg 864

RHODE ISLAND

Sound-FX-Design, pg 894

TENNESSEE

American Blackguard Inc, pg 683
Continental Film, pg 731
Running Pony Productions LLC, pg 878

TEXAS

Epic Software Group Inc, pg 755
Horizon Film + Video Productions, pg 781
Mediaforce Productions, pg 822
Stage Directions, pg 898
University of Texas at Austin - Petroleum Extension Service, pg 923

VIRGINIA

Metro Productions, pg 824

WISCONSIN

Video Wisconsin Inc, pg 929
Wisconsin Public Television, pg 940
Wisconsin Technical College System Foundation Inc, pg 940

WYOMING

Bridger Productions Inc, pg 710

NEWFOUNDLAND AND LABRADOR

Vidcraft Productions Ltd, pg 927

QUEBEC

Kerrigan Productions Inc, pg 798

Vocational Program Rentals

GEORGIA

Convergent Media Systems, pg 731

ILLINOIS

1st Financial Training Services Inc, pg 761
National Safety Council (NSC), pg 836

MICHIGAN

Digi Sign Design LLC, pg 741

NEW HAMPSHIRE

Chip Taylor Communications LLC, pg 907

UTAH

Webb Audio Visual, pg 935

PROGRAMMING — FILM

Business Program Distributors

ARIZONA

Video Learning Library, pg 928

CALIFORNIA

Allied Artists International Inc, pg 681
Crystal Pyramid Productions™, pg 735
Direct Cinema Ltd Inc, pg 743
eFootage LLC, pg 751
Jaguar Distribution Corp, pg 792
New & Unique Videos™, pg 839
TMW Media Group, pg 915

GEORGIA

Convergent Media Systems, pg 731

HAWAII

Media Bridge Gamekids, pg 821

ILLINOIS

ABSA Films, pg 672

MICHIGAN

Emery-Pratt Co, pg 753

MINNESOTA

Service Quality Institute, pg 884

NEVADA

DVDs4Less, pg 748

NEW MEXICO

The Phoenix Learning Group Inc, pg 855

NEW YORK

Broadstreet Productions LLC, pg 711
Films Media Group, pg 760
Guidance Associates Inc Center for Humanities, pg 774
HB-Content, pg 777
Richter Productions Inc, pg 875
VIEW Inc (Video International Entertainment World Inc), pg 930

PENNSYLVANIA

FMP Media Solutions Inc, pg 763

TEXAS

Emergency Film Group, pg 753

VIRGINIA

CACI Integrated Communications, pg 713

ONTARIO

Kineticvideo.com, pg 799
McNabb & Connolly, pg 821

Business Program Producers

ALABAMA

Leo Ticheli Productions, pg 913

ALASKA

Aurora Films, pg 696

ARIZONA

Candee Productions Inc, pg 716
Film Creations Ltd, pg 760

CALIFORNIA

Classic Images Stock Footage LLC, pg 726
Creative Technology, pg 733
Crystal Pyramid Productions™, pg 735
Dolphin MultiMedia Inc, pg 745
Havas Edge, pg 777
imageReal Pictures LLC, pg 785
Kavich Reynolds Productions Inc, pg 797
Main Street Media Inc, pg 815
The Media Staff Inc, pg 822
New & Unique Videos™, pg 839
PK Productions, pg 857
Dick Reizner Film & Video, pg 873
Glenn Roland Films, pg 876
Tam Communications Inc, pg 906
TMW Media Group, pg 915
Utopia Films, pg 924
Vineyard Video & Photography, pg 930
Webster Communications, pg 935

COLORADO

Apogee Communications Group, pg 687
Flashback Media Productions, pg 762
Transtar Entertainment Co Inc, pg 917

CONNECTICUT

ACM Productions Ltd, pg 674
Moving Pictures, pg 832

DISTRICT OF COLUMBIA

Hillmann & Carr Inc, pg 780
Yellow Cat Productions Inc, pg 944

FLORIDA

Civins Productions Inc, pg 725
Jordan Klein Film & Video (JKFV), pg 795
Universal Studios Florida® Production Group, pg 922

GEORGIA

Beachwood Productions, pg 702
Burst Video/Film Inc, pg 713
Guerrilla Productions LLC, pg 774
Myriad Productions, pg 835

HAWAII

Hyperspective Studios Inc, pg 783
Media Bridge Gamekids, pg 821
1013 Integrated, pg 911

ILLINOIS

ABSA Films, pg 672
Cresta Creative, pg 734
Film Police, pg 760
Manning Productions, pg 816

Mightybytes Inc, pg 827
Multimedia Marketing Group, pg 833
SCI Television & Creative Media LLC, pg 882
Winter Productions, pg 939

INDIANA

A-V-A Video Productions, pg 671
Road Pictures, pg 876

LOUISIANA

Digital FX Inc, pg 742

MARYLAND

Richard Chisolm Cinematography, pg 722
dbF a Media Company, pg 739
The Image Generators, pg 785

MASSACHUSETTS

CommCreative, pg 728
Green Mountain Post Films (GMP), pg 774
Heliotrope Studios, pg 778

MINNESOTA

House of Cinemagraphics, pg 782
Service Quality Institute, pg 884

NEVADA

DVDs4Less, pg 748

NEW HAMPSHIRE

Apertura, pg 686

NEW JERSEY

Telequest Inc, pg 910
TimeSteps Productions Inc, pg 914

NEW MEXICO

The Phoenix Learning Group Inc, pg 855

NEW YORK

aurora productions, pg 696
Brian Film Productions LLC, pg 710
Broadstreet Productions LLC, pg 711
De Nonno Productions Inc (DPI), pg 739
Fanlight Productions, pg 759
Films Media Group, pg 760
Florentine Films, pg 762
Havas Creative, pg 776
HB-Content, pg 777
Hello World Communications, pg 778
Image Zone Inc, pg 785
Ketchum Inc, pg 798
Jack Morton Worldwide, pg 830
MRY, pg 832
New Horizon Studios, pg 839
News Broadcast Network Inc, pg 840
Northeast Video Productions Inc, pg 842
The Palmer Group, pg 850
Pat Kogan Productions Inc, pg 852
Polestar Films & Associated Arts Ltd, pg 859
PrimeLight Productions Inc, pg 862
Richter Productions Inc, pg 875
VIEW Inc (Video International Entertainment World Inc), pg 930
Zelman Studios Ltd, pg 945

NORTH CAROLINA

The Communications Group Inc, pg 729
Kino Mountain Productions LLC, pg 799

OHIO

Advent Media Inc, pg 677
Take 1 Media Services, pg 906

OREGON

Ideascape Inc, pg 784
Odyssey Productions Inc, pg 844

PENNSYLVANIA

Bang! Pictures Inc, pg 701
FMP Media Solutions Inc, pg 763
JPL, pg 795
Main Point Productions, pg 815
Muderick Media, pg 833
Production Masters Inc (PMI), pg 864
Video/Film Associates, pg 928

RHODE ISLAND

Sound-FX-Design, pg 894

TENNESSEE

Continental Film, pg 731
Memphis Communications Corp, pg 823
Scripps Networks, pg 882

TEXAS

Alexander Media Productions, pg 679
AMS Pictures, pg 684
Aries Productions Inc, pg 688
Castleview Productions, pg 717
Cerutti Productions Inc, pg 720
Dykeman Associates Inc, pg 748
The Editing Co, pg 750
Emergency Film Group, pg 753
Marx InDigital, pg 818
Earl Miller Productions Inc, pg 827
South Coast Film & Video, pg 895
Stage Directions, pg 898

VERMONT

Marlboro Productions, pg 817

VIRGINIA

Altruist Media LLC, pg 682
BES Studios, pg 704
CACI Integrated Communications, pg 713

WASHINGTON

Adams Creative & Production Services, pg 675
White Rain Films Ltd, pg 937

WISCONSIN

Meridian Studios, pg 824
University of Wisconsin-Oshkosh Radio-TV-Film Dept, pg 923
Video Wisconsin Inc, pg 929
Wisconsin Public Television, pg 940

WYOMING

Bridger Productions Inc, pg 710

ALBERTA

Global TV, pg 771

PROGRAMMING — FILM

Business Program Producers (continued)

BRITISH COLUMBIA

West Eagle Films Inc, pg 935

ONTARIO

JFB Communications, pg 794
Mediaimage Communications Group, pg 822

QUEBEC

Kerrigan Productions Inc, pg 798

SASKATCHEWAN

plan9films, pg 857

Business Program Rentals

CALIFORNIA

Direct Cinema Ltd Inc, pg 743

GEORGIA

Convergent Media Systems, pg 731

MISSOURI

University of Missouri-Columbia, pg 923

NEW YORK

Films Media Group, pg 760
Richter Productions Inc, pg 875
VIEW Inc (Video International Entertainment World Inc), pg 930

ONTARIO

Kineticvideo.com, pg 799

Children's Program Distributors

ARIZONA

Video Learning Library, pg 928

CALIFORNIA

Crystal Pyramid Productions™, pg 735
Direct Cinema Ltd Inc, pg 743
Em Gee Film Library, pg 753
Glenn Photo Supply, pg 771
Joyce Media Inc, pg 795
Main Street Media Inc, pg 815
MarVista Entertainment Inc, pg 818
Moose School Productions, pg 830
New & Unique Videos™, pg 839
TMW Media Group, pg 915
Universal Pictures Home Entertainment, pg 922
Visual Communications - Southern California Asian American Studies Central Inc, pg 931

CONNECTICUT

Weston Woods Studios Inc, pg 936

HAWAII

Media Bridge Gamekids, pg 821

ILLINOIS

Discovery Education - Chicago, pg 743
Encyclopaedia Britannica Inc, pg 754
Film Ideas Inc, pg 760
Film Police, pg 760

KENTUCKY

National Geographic Learning, pg 836

MASSACHUSETTS

Green Mountain Post Films (GMP), pg 774

MICHIGAN

Emery-Pratt Co, pg 753

NEW JERSEY

Ergo Media Inc, pg 755

NEW MEXICO

The Phoenix Learning Group Inc, pg 855

NEW YORK

Broadstreet Productions LLC, pg 711
Brooklyn Botanic Garden, pg 711
Billy Budd Films Inc, pg 712
Guidance Associates Inc Center for Humanities, pg 774
Hallel Communications, pg 775
Hearst Entertainment & Syndication, pg 778
Icarus Films Inc, pg 783
Janson Media Inc, pg 793
Third World Newsreel/Camera News Inc, pg 912
VIEW Inc (Video International Entertainment World Inc), pg 930

NORTH CAROLINA

Crystal Pictures Inc, pg 735

PENNSYLVANIA

Bullfrog Films Inc, pg 712

TENNESSEE

American Blackguard Inc, pg 683
Spring Arbor Distributors Inc, pg 898

TEXAS

Marengo Films, pg 817

WISCONSIN

Wisconsin Public Television, pg 940

ALBERTA

Global TV, pg 771

ONTARIO

Canadian Filmmakers Distribution Center (CFMDC), pg 715
CCI Entertainment Ltd, pg 718
The Children's Book Store Distribution (CBSD), pg 722
Kineticvideo.com, pg 799
McIntyre Media Inc, pg 821
McNabb & Connolly, pg 821
Sullivan Home Entertainment, pg 903

QUEBEC

Les Productions Via Le Monde (Daniel Bertolino) Inc, pg 864

Children's Program Producers

ARIZONA

Candee Productions Inc, pg 716
Teaberry, pg 908

CALIFORNIA

Burrud Productions Inc, pg 713
Cinevest, pg 725
Classic Images Stock Footage LLC, pg 726
Creative Technology, pg 733
Crystal Pyramid Productions™, pg 735
The Jim Henson Co, pg 794
Joyce Media Inc, pg 795
Main Street Media Inc, pg 815
The Media Staff Inc, pg 822
Moose School Productions, pg 830
New & Unique Videos™, pg 839
Dick Reizner Film & Video, pg 873
Glenn Roland Films, pg 876
TMW Media Group, pg 915
Universal Pictures Home Entertainment, pg 922
Vineyard Video & Photography, pg 930
Visual Communications - Southern California Asian American Studies Central Inc, pg 931

COLORADO

CSI Film & Video LLC, pg 735
Flashback Media Productions, pg 762
Transtar Entertainment Co Inc, pg 917

CONNECTICUT

ACM Productions Ltd, pg 674
The Gary-Paul Agency, pg 768
Weston Woods Studios Inc, pg 936

DISTRICT OF COLUMBIA

Hillmann & Carr Inc, pg 780

FLORIDA

Chatterbox Productions Inc, pg 721
Jordan Klein Film & Video (JKFV), pg 795

GEORGIA

Beachwood Productions, pg 702
Burst Video/Film Inc, pg 713
Guerrilla Productions LLC, pg 774

HAWAII

Hyperspective Studios Inc, pg 783
Media Bridge Gamekids, pg 821

ILLINOIS

Discovery Education - Chicago, pg 743
Encyclopaedia Britannica Inc, pg 754
Film Police, pg 760
The Market Place, pg 817
Mightybytes Inc, pg 827
Multimedia Marketing Group, pg 833

INDIANA

Perennial Pictures Film Corp, pg 854

KENTUCKY

National Geographic Learning, pg 836

MARYLAND

dbF a Media Company, pg 739

MASSACHUSETTS

Green Mountain Post Films (GMP), pg 774
Heliotrope Studios, pg 778

MINNESOTA

House of Cinemagraphics, pg 782

NEW HAMPSHIRE

Apertura, pg 686

NEW JERSEY

Telequest Inc, pg 910

NEW MEXICO

The Phoenix Learning Group Inc, pg 855
Rainbow International Inc, pg 869

NEW YORK

American History Workshop (NY) Inc, pg 683
aurora productions, pg 696
Brian Film Productions LLC, pg 710
Brooklyn Botanic Garden, pg 711
Billy Budd Films Inc, pg 712
Buzzco Associates Inc, pg 713
De Nonno Productions Inc (DPI), pg 739
Fanlight Productions, pg 759
Florentine Films, pg 762
Hallel Communications, pg 775
Havas Creative, pg 776
Hearst Entertainment & Syndication, pg 778
Hello World Communications, pg 778
Jack Morton Worldwide, pg 830
The Palmer Group, pg 850
Pat Kogan Productions Inc, pg 852
Polestar Films & Associated Arts Ltd, pg 859
Scholastic Media, pg 882
Third World Newsreel/Camera News Inc, pg 912
VIEW Inc (Video International Entertainment World Inc), pg 930
Zelman Studios Ltd, pg 945

NORTH CAROLINA

The Communications Group Inc, pg 729
Crystal Pictures Inc, pg 735
Kino Mountain Productions LLC, pg 799

OHIO

Take 1 Media Services, pg 906

OREGON

Ideascape Inc, pg 784

PENNSYLVANIA

Kensington Falls Animation, pg 797
Production Masters Inc (PMI),
  pg 864

RHODE ISLAND

Sound-FX-Design, pg 894

TENNESSEE

American Blackguard Inc, pg 683

TEXAS

Alexander Media Productions,
  pg 679
Cerutti Productions Inc, pg 720
Marx InDigital, pg 818
Earl Miller Productions Inc, pg 827

VERMONT

Marlboro Productions, pg 817

VIRGINIA

Altruist Media LLC, pg 682
BES Studios, pg 704

WISCONSIN

Wisconsin Public Television, pg 940

WYOMING

Bridger Productions Inc, pg 710

ALBERTA

Global TV, pg 771

BRITISH COLUMBIA

West Eagle Films Inc, pg 935

NOVA SCOTIA

WildBrain™, pg 938

QUEBEC

Kerrigan Productions Inc, pg 798
Les Productions Via Le Monde
  (Daniel Bertolino) Inc, pg 864

SASKATCHEWAN

plan9films, pg 857

Children's Program Rentals

CALIFORNIA

Direct Cinema Ltd Inc, pg 743
Em Gee Film Library, pg 753
Glenn Photo Supply, pg 771
Visual Communications - Southern
  California Asian American
  Studies Central Inc, pg 931

ILLINOIS

Discovery Education - Chicago,
  pg 743

MISSOURI

University of Missouri-Columbia,
  pg 923

NEW YORK

Brooklyn Botanic Garden, pg 711
Hallel Communications, pg 775

Third World Newsreel/Camera
  News Inc, pg 912
VIEW Inc (Video International
  Entertainment World Inc), pg 930

NORTH CAROLINA

Crystal Pictures Inc, pg 735

PENNSYLVANIA

Bullfrog Films Inc, pg 712

ONTARIO

Kineticvideo.com, pg 799

QUEBEC

Les Productions Via Le Monde
  (Daniel Bertolino) Inc, pg 864

Classic Program Distributors

CALIFORNIA

Increase Video/Silver Mine Video,
  pg 786
MarVista Entertainment Inc, pg 818
MGM Home Entertainment, pg 825
TMW Media Group, pg 915
Visual Communications - Southern
  California Asian American
  Studies Central Inc, pg 931
Worldwide Entertainment Corp,
  pg 941

IDAHO

Lagoon Video, pg 803

ILLINOIS

Cool-Lux, pg 731
International Historic Films Inc,
  pg 790
Movies Unlimited, pg 831

MASSACHUSETTS

Documentary Educational Resources
  Inc, pg 744

NEBRASKA

Mary Riepma Ross Media Arts
  Center, pg 877

NORTH CAROLINA

Crystal Pictures Inc, pg 735

PENNSYLVANIA

Library Video Company, pg 807
MVD Entertainment Group, pg 835

TENNESSEE

Spring Arbor Distributors Inc,
  pg 898

TEXAS

Marengo Films, pg 817

ONTARIO

CCI Entertainment Ltd, pg 718
Universal Studios Canada Inc,
  pg 922

Classic Program Producers

CALIFORNIA

Backstage Pass Entertainment Inc,
  pg 700
Creative Technology, pg 733
Glenn Roland Films, pg 876
TMW Media Group, pg 915
Total Creative, pg 916
Visual Communications - Southern
  California Asian American
  Studies Central Inc, pg 931

FLORIDA

Chatterbox Productions Inc, pg 721

GEORGIA

Guerrilla Productions LLC, pg 774

MARYLAND

dbF a Media Company, pg 739

MASSACHUSETTS

Heliotrope Studios, pg 778

MICHIGAN

K&R's Recording Studios Inc,
  pg 796

MINNESOTA

House of Cinemagraphics, pg 782

NEW YORK

De Nonno Productions Inc (DPI),
  pg 739
Havas Creative, pg 776

NORTH CAROLINA

The Communications Group Inc,
  pg 729
Crystal Pictures Inc, pg 735

OHIO

Take 1 Media Services, pg 906

PENNSYLVANIA

Production Masters Inc (PMI),
  pg 864

RHODE ISLAND

Sound-FX-Design, pg 894

TEXAS

Alexander Media Productions,
  pg 679
Castleview Productions, pg 717

WYOMING

Bridger Productions Inc, pg 710

BRITISH COLUMBIA

West Eagle Films Inc, pg 935

QUEBEC

Kerrigan Productions Inc, pg 798

Classic Program Rentals

CALIFORNIA

Visual Communications - Southern
  California Asian American
  Studies Central Inc, pg 931
Worldwide Entertainment Corp,
  pg 941

MISSOURI

University of Missouri-Columbia,
  pg 923

NORTH CAROLINA

Crystal Pictures Inc, pg 735

Commercial, *see* Test Commercial

Current Event Program Distributors

CALIFORNIA

Crystal Pyramid Productions™,
  pg 735
Direct Cinema Ltd Inc, pg 743
New & Unique Videos™, pg 839
TMW Media Group, pg 915
Visual Communications - Southern
  California Asian American
  Studies Central Inc, pg 931

ILLINOIS

Film Ideas Inc, pg 760

MASSACHUSETTS

Green Mountain Post Films (GMP),
  pg 774

NEW MEXICO

The Phoenix Learning Group Inc,
  pg 855

NEW YORK

Guidance Associates Inc Center for
  Humanities, pg 774
HB-Content, pg 777
Icarus Films Inc, pg 783
Janson Media Inc, pg 793
Kino International Corp, pg 799
News Broadcast Network Inc,
  pg 840
Pennebaker Hegedus Films Inc,
  pg 854
Richter Productions Inc, pg 875
Third World Newsreel/Camera
  News Inc, pg 912
VIEW Inc (Video International
  Entertainment World Inc), pg 930
Women Make Movies Inc, pg 941

PENNSYLVANIA

Bullfrog Films Inc, pg 712

TENNESSEE

Spring Arbor Distributors Inc,
  pg 898

VIRGINIA

CACI Integrated Communications,
  pg 713

PROGRAMMING — FILM

Current Event Program Distributors (continued)

ALBERTA

Global TV, pg 771

ONTARIO

Kineticvideo.com, pg 799

QUEBEC

Les Productions Via Le Monde (Daniel Bertolino) Inc, pg 864

Current Event Program Producers

ARIZONA

Candee Productions Inc, pg 716
Film Creations Ltd, pg 760

CALIFORNIA

A Go Go Films, pg 671
Big Door, pg 705
Creative Technology, pg 733
Crystal Pyramid Productions™, pg 735
Durrin Productions Inc, pg 748
Main Street Media Inc, pg 815
New & Unique Videos™, pg 839
PK Productions, pg 857
QRS Software Services, pg 867
Glenn Roland Films, pg 876
TMW Media Group, pg 915
Vineyard Video & Photography, pg 930
Visual Communications - Southern California Asian American Studies Central Inc, pg 931
Zamacona Productions, pg 945

COLORADO

Flashback Media Productions, pg 762

CONNECTICUT

Essex Television Group Inc, pg 755
The Gary-Paul Agency, pg 768
New London Media, pg 839

DISTRICT OF COLUMBIA

Hillmann & Carr Inc, pg 780

FLORIDA

Accord Productions, pg 673
Blackburst Entertainment LLC, pg 706
CopShopMiami.com, pg 731
Jordan Klein Film & Video (JKFV), pg 795

GEORGIA

Beachwood Productions, pg 702
Guerrilla Productions LLC, pg 774
Myriad Productions, pg 835

ILLINOIS

SCI Television & Creative Media LLC, pg 882
Winter Productions, pg 939

MARYLAND

Absolute Hollywood, pg 672
Richard Chisolm Cinematography, pg 722
dbF a Media Company, pg 739

MASSACHUSETTS

Green Mountain Post Films (GMP), pg 774
Heliotrope Studios, pg 778
Northern Light Productions (NLP), pg 842

MICHIGAN

K&R All Media Productions LLC, pg 796

MINNESOTA

House of Cinemagraphics, pg 782

NEW HAMPSHIRE

Apertura, pg 686

NEW JERSEY

Telequest Inc, pg 910

NEW MEXICO

The Phoenix Learning Group Inc, pg 855

NEW YORK

aurora productions, pg 696
Blue Barn Pictures Inc, pg 707
Brian Film Productions LLC, pg 710
Broadstreet Productions LLC, pg 711
De Nonno Productions Inc (DPI), pg 739
Fanlight Productions, pg 759
Florentine Films, pg 762
Four Corners Productions, pg 764
Havas Creative, pg 776
HB-Content, pg 777
Ketchum Inc, pg 798
Jack Morton Worldwide, pg 830
News Broadcast Network Inc, pg 840
The Palmer Group, pg 850
Pennebaker Hegedus Films Inc, pg 854
Richter Productions Inc, pg 875
Third World Newsreel/Camera News Inc, pg 912
VIEW Inc (Video International Entertainment World Inc), pg 930
Zelman Studios Ltd, pg 945

NORTH CAROLINA

Pat Appleson Studios Inc, pg 687
The Communications Group Inc, pg 729

OHIO

Take 1 Media Services, pg 906

OREGON

Odyssey Productions Inc, pg 844

PENNSYLVANIA

Innovision Media Group, pg 788
Production Masters Inc (PMI), pg 864

RHODE ISLAND

Sound-FX-Design, pg 894

TENNESSEE

Scripps Networks, pg 882

TEXAS

Cerutti Productions Inc, pg 720
Earl Miller Productions Inc, pg 827
South Coast Film & Video, pg 895

VIRGINIA

Altruist Media LLC, pg 682
BES Studios, pg 704
CACI Integrated Communications, pg 713
Metro Productions, pg 824

WISCONSIN

5th Floor Recording Co, pg 760
Wisconsin Public Television, pg 940

WYOMING

Bridger Productions Inc, pg 710

ALBERTA

Black Media Works, pg 706
Global TV, pg 771
HDTV Productions Inc, pg 777

BRITISH COLUMBIA

West Eagle Films Inc, pg 935

QUEBEC

Kerrigan Productions Inc, pg 798
Les Productions Via Le Monde (Daniel Bertolino) Inc, pg 864

Current Event Program Rentals

CALIFORNIA

Direct Cinema Ltd Inc, pg 743
Visual Communications - Southern California Asian American Studies Central Inc, pg 931

NEW YORK

Pennebaker Hegedus Films Inc, pg 854
Richter Productions Inc, pg 875
Third World Newsreel/Camera News Inc, pg 912
VIEW Inc (Video International Entertainment World Inc), pg 930

PENNSYLVANIA

Bullfrog Films Inc, pg 712

ONTARIO

Kineticvideo.com, pg 799

QUEBEC

Les Productions Via Le Monde (Daniel Bertolino) Inc, pg 864

Documentary Distributors

ARIZONA

Teaberry, pg 908

CALIFORNIA

Allied Artists International Inc, pg 681
Les Blank Films Inc, pg 707
California Newsreel, pg 714

Cambridge Documentary Films Inc, pg 714
Crystal Pyramid Productions™, pg 735
Direct Cinema Ltd Inc, pg 743
eFootage LLC, pg 751
Em Gee Film Library, pg 753
Glenn Photo Supply, pg 771
Goal Productions, pg 772
Ishtar Films, pg 791
Main Street Media Inc, pg 815
MarVista Entertainment Inc, pg 818
New & Unique Videos™, pg 839
Nineteen87, pg 841
Regent Press Publishers & Printers, pg 873
TMW Media Group, pg 915
Universal Pictures Home Entertainment, pg 922
Visual Communications - Southern California Asian American Studies Central Inc, pg 931
The Wine Appreciation Guild Ltd, pg 939

COLORADO

Tatum Video, pg 907

CONNECTICUT

Hartley Film Foundation, pg 776

DELAWARE

University Media Services, pg 922

FLORIDA

Accord Productions, pg 673

HAWAII

Media Bridge Gamekids, pg 821

IDAHO

Lagoon Video, pg 803

ILLINOIS

ABSA Films, pg 672
Film Ideas Inc, pg 760
Terra Nova Films Inc, pg 911

KENTUCKY

Horizon Films & Media LLC, pg 781
National Geographic Learning, pg 836

MARYLAND

DSR Computer Technology Specialists Inc, pg 747
James Agee Film Project, pg 792
Special Archives Division, Motion Picture Branch, pg 896

MASSACHUSETTS

Documentary Educational Resources Inc, pg 744
Green Mountain Post Films (GMP), pg 774
The New Film Company Inc, pg 839
Northern Light Productions (NLP), pg 842

MINNESOTA

Festival Films, pg 759

NEBRASKA

Mary Riepma Ross Media Arts Center, pg 877

NEVADA

DVDs4Less, pg 748

NEW HAMPSHIRE

Captain Fiddle Music & Publications, pg 716

NEW JERSEY

Alden Films, pg 679
Ergo Media Inc, pg 755
Euro-Pacific Film & Video Productions Inc, pg 756
Milestone Film & Video Inc, pg 827

NEW MEXICO

The Phoenix Learning Group Inc, pg 855
SouthWest Organizing Project (SWOP), pg 896

NEW YORK

Michael Blackwood Productions Inc, pg 707
Broadstreet Productions LLC, pg 711
Billy Budd Films Inc, pg 712
Circulating Film & Video Library, pg 725
FACE Foundation, pg 758
Fanlight Productions, pg 759
Films Media Group, pg 760
First Run Features, pg 761
William Greaves Productions Inc, pg 774
Hallel Communications, pg 775
HB-Content, pg 777
Hearst Entertainment & Syndication, pg 778
Icarus Films Inc, pg 783
Janson Media Inc, pg 793
Richard Kaplan Productions, pg 796
Kino International Corp, pg 799
Mastervision Inc, pg 819
New Day Films, pg 839
News Broadcast Network Inc, pg 840
Pennebaker Hegedus Films Inc, pg 854
Richter Productions Inc, pg 875
Third World Newsreel/Camera News Inc, pg 912
VIEW Inc (Video International Entertainment World Inc), pg 930
Women Make Movies Inc, pg 941
Wonderwomen™ Enterprises, pg 941
Zeitgeist Films Ltd, pg 945

NORTH CAROLINA

Crystal Pictures Inc, pg 735

OHIO

Griesinger Films LLC, pg 774

PENNSYLVANIA

Bullfrog Films Inc, pg 712
FMP Media Solutions Inc, pg 763
Rahlic Publishing Co, pg 869

TENNESSEE

American Blackguard Inc, pg 683
Center for Southern Folklore Inc, pg 719
Spring Arbor Distributors Inc, pg 898

TEXAS

Emergency Film Group, pg 753

VERMONT

Dorothy Tod Films, pg 915

VIRGINIA

CACI Integrated Communications, pg 713

WASHINGTON

North-by-Northwest - A Digital Studio, pg 842
White Rain Films Ltd, pg 937

WEST VIRGINIA

Focus on Animals, pg 763

WISCONSIN

Wisconsin Public Television, pg 940

ALBERTA

Global TV, pg 771

NORTHWEST TERRITORIES

Yellowknife Films Inc, pg 944

ONTARIO

Canadian Filmmakers Distribution Center (CFMDC), pg 715
CCI Entertainment Ltd, pg 718
IMAX Corp, pg 786
Kineticvideo.com, pg 799
McIntyre Media Inc, pg 821
McNabb & Connolly, pg 821
Sullivan Home Entertainment, pg 903

QUEBEC

National Film Board of Canada/Office National du Film du Canada, pg 836
Les Productions Via Le Monde (Daniel Bertolino) Inc, pg 864

Documentary Producers

ALASKA

Aurora Films, pg 696

ARIZONA

Candee Productions Inc, pg 716
Film Creations Ltd, pg 760
Teaberry, pg 908

ARKANSAS

Live'N'Loud, pg 810

CALIFORNIA

Allied Artists International Inc, pg 681
Artichoke Productions, pg 690
Big Door, pg 705
Les Blank Films Inc, pg 707
Burrud Productions Inc, pg 713
Cambridge Documentary Films Inc, pg 714

Catapult Films Inc, pg 717
Cinevest, pg 725
Classic Images Stock Footage LLC, pg 726
Concoction Lab, pg 730
Concrete Images, pg 730
Creative Technology, pg 733
Crystal Pyramid Productions™, pg 735
Custom Video Productions Inc, pg 736
Design Media, pg 741
Durrin Productions Inc, pg 748
GAMfilm Productions, pg 768
Goal Productions, pg 772
imageReal Pictures LLC, pg 785
Ingenuity Films LLC, pg 787
Ishtar Films, pg 791
Jaguar Distribution Corp, pg 792
Kavich Reynolds Productions Inc, pg 797
Main Street Media Inc, pg 815
The Media Staff Inc, pg 822
Moving Art by Louie Schwartzberg, pg 831
New & Unique Videos™, pg 839
New Circuit Films LLC, pg 839
Nineteen87, pg 841
Point of View Productions, pg 858
Prime Cut Productions, pg 862
QRS Software Services, pg 867
Regent Press Publishers & Printers, pg 873
Dick Reizner Film & Video, pg 873
RetinaVision Productions, pg 874
Roadside Attractions, pg 876
Glenn Roland Films, pg 876
Santa Barbara Location Services, pg 880
SNAP, pg 891
Tam Communications Inc, pg 906
TMW Media Group, pg 915
Universal Pictures Home Entertainment, pg 922
Utopia Films, pg 924
Video Resources Inc, pg 928
Vineyard Video & Photography, pg 930
Visual Communications - Southern California Asian American Studies Central Inc, pg 931
Webster Communications, pg 935
Zamacona Productions, pg 945

COLORADO

Blue River Productions, pg 708
Flashback Media Productions, pg 762
Greg Hensley Productions, pg 779
Tatum Video, pg 907
Transtar Entertainment Co Inc, pg 917

CONNECTICUT

Essex Television Group Inc, pg 755
The Gary-Paul Agency, pg 768
Hartley Film Foundation, pg 776
Moving Pictures, pg 832
New London Media, pg 839

DELAWARE

University Media Services, pg 922

DISTRICT OF COLUMBIA

Dorst MediaWorks Inc, pg 746
Hillmann & Carr Inc, pg 780

FLORIDA

Accord Productions, pg 673
Blackburst Entertainment LLC, pg 706

Chatterbox Productions Inc, pg 721
Communications Concepts Inc (CCI), pg 729
CopShopMiami.com, pg 731
Jordan Klein Film & Video (JKFV), pg 795
Karst Productions Inc, pg 796
Tel-Air Interests Inc, pg 909

GEORGIA

Beachwood Productions, pg 702
Burst Video/Film Inc, pg 713
Guerrilla Productions LLC, pg 774
Myriad Productions, pg 835

HAWAII

Hyperspective Studios Inc, pg 783
Media Bridge Gamekids, pg 821
1013 Integrated, pg 911

IDAHO

Lagoon Video, pg 803

ILLINOIS

ABSA Films, pg 672
Film Police, pg 760
The Market Place, pg 817
Multimedia Marketing Group, pg 833
SCI Television & Creative Media LLC, pg 882
Terra Nova Films Inc, pg 911
Winter Productions, pg 939

INDIANA

A-V-A Video Productions, pg 671

IOWA

Educational Technology & Media Services, pg 751
Iowa State University-Information Technology Services, pg 791

KENTUCKY

Horizon Films & Media LLC, pg 781
Donna Lawrence Productions, pg 804
National Geographic Learning, pg 836

LOUISIANA

Digital FX Inc, pg 742
Moxie Media, pg 832

MAINE

Films by Huey, pg 760

MARYLAND

Absolute Hollywood, pg 672
Richard Chisolm Cinematography, pg 722
dbF a Media Company, pg 739
DSR Computer Technology Specialists Inc, pg 747
The Image Generators, pg 785
James Agee Film Project, pg 792

MASSACHUSETTS

Cramer, pg 732
Documentary Educational Resources Inc, pg 744
Green Mountain Post Films (GMP), pg 774
Heliotrope Studios, pg 778

PROGRAMMING — FILM

Documentary Producers (continued)

MASSACHUSETTS (continued)

The New Film Company Inc, pg 839
Northern Light Productions (NLP), pg 842

MICHIGAN

K&R All Media Productions LLC, pg 796
Zondervan, pg 945

MINNESOTA

House of Cinemagraphics, pg 782

MISSOURI

Hardcastle Films & Video, pg 776

NEVADA

DVDs4Less, pg 748

NEW HAMPSHIRE

Apertura, pg 686
Captain Fiddle Music & Publications, pg 716

NEW JERSEY

Alden Films, pg 679
Broadcast Center Studios, pg 710
CELCO, pg 719
Euro-Pacific Film & Video Productions Inc, pg 756
MiB MediaWorks, pg 825
Telequest Inc, pg 910
TimeSteps Productions Inc, pg 914

NEW MEXICO

The Phoenix Learning Group Inc, pg 855

NEW YORK

Ace Video, pg 674
American History Workshop (NY) Inc, pg 683
aurora productions, pg 696
Michael Blackwood Productions Inc, pg 707
Blue Barn Pictures Inc, pg 707
Brian Film Productions LLC, pg 710
Broadstreet Productions LLC, pg 711
Brooklyn Films, pg 711
Billy Budd Films Inc, pg 712
De Nonno Productions Inc (DPI), pg 739
Fanlight Productions, pg 759
Films Media Group, pg 760
Florentine Films, pg 762
Four Corners Productions, pg 764
William Greaves Productions Inc, pg 774
Greenwich Entertainment, pg 774
Hallel Communications, pg 775
Havas Creative, pg 776
HB-Content, pg 777
Hearst Entertainment & Syndication, pg 778
Historic Films, pg 780
Janson Media Inc, pg 793
Richard Kaplan Productions, pg 796

Ketchum Inc, pg 798
Kinetic Arts, pg 799
Manhattan Center Studios Inc, pg 816
Mastervision Inc, pg 819
Jack Morton Worldwide, pg 830
New Horizon Studios, pg 839
News Broadcast Network Inc, pg 840
The Palmer Group, pg 850
Pat Kogan Productions Inc, pg 852
Peckham Productions Inc, pg 852
Pennebaker Hegedus Films Inc, pg 854
Polestar Films & Associated Arts Ltd, pg 859
R/GA, pg 868
RAVA Films, pg 870
Richter Productions Inc, pg 875
Third World Newsreel/Camera News Inc, pg 912
VIEW Inc (Video International Entertainment World Inc), pg 930
Wonderwomen™ Enterprises, pg 941
Zelman Studios Ltd, pg 945

NORTH CAROLINA

Pat Appleson Studios Inc, pg 687
The Communications Group Inc, pg 729
Crystal Pictures Inc, pg 735
Horizon Video Productions Inc, pg 781
Kino Mountain Productions LLC, pg 799

OHIO

Advent Media Inc, pg 677
Griesinger Films LLC, pg 774
Take 1 Media Services, pg 906

OREGON

Ideascape Inc, pg 784
Odyssey Productions Inc, pg 844

PENNSYLVANIA

Argentine Productions Inc, pg 688
Bang! Pictures Inc, pg 701
FMP Media Solutions Inc, pg 763
Innovision Media Group, pg 788
Main Point Productions, pg 815
Production Masters Inc (PMI), pg 864
Rahlic Publishing Co, pg 869
Video/Film Associates, pg 928

RHODE ISLAND

Sound-FX-Design, pg 894

TENNESSEE

American Blackguard Inc, pg 683
Center for Southern Folklore Inc, pg 719
Continental Film, pg 731
Scripps Networks, pg 882

TEXAS

Alexander Media Productions, pg 679
Castleview Productions, pg 717
Cerutti Productions Inc, pg 720
Dykeman Associates Inc, pg 748
The Editing Co, pg 750
Emergency Film Group, pg 753
Horizon Film + Video Productions, pg 781
Earl Miller Productions Inc, pg 827
Rich-Heape Films Inc, pg 875

South Coast Film & Video, pg 895
Stage Directions, pg 898
Texas Heart Institute Visual Communication Services, pg 911

VERMONT

Marlboro Productions, pg 817
Dorothy Tod Films, pg 915

VIRGINIA

Altruist Media LLC, pg 682
BES Studios, pg 704
CACI Integrated Communications, pg 713
Metro Productions, pg 824

WASHINGTON

Hamilton Studio, pg 775
North-by-Northwest - A Digital Studio, pg 842
Pal Productions Inc, pg 850
White Rain Films Ltd, pg 937

WISCONSIN

Clear Focus Media LLC, pg 726
5th Floor Recording Co, pg 760
University of Wisconsin-Oshkosh Radio-TV-Film Dept, pg 923
Wisconsin Public Television, pg 940

WYOMING

Bridger Productions Inc, pg 710

ALBERTA

Black Media Works, pg 706
Global TV, pg 771

BRITISH COLUMBIA

Network Entertainment Inc, pg 838
West Eagle Films Inc, pg 935

MANITOBA

Lank/Beach Productions Inc, pg 803

NORTHWEST TERRITORIES

Yellowknife Films Inc, pg 944

ONTARIO

Doomsday Studios Limited, pg 745
IMAX Corp, pg 786

QUEBEC

Kerrigan Productions Inc, pg 798
Muse Entertainment Enterprises, pg 834
National Film Board of Canada/Office National du Film du Canada, pg 836
Productions Grand Nord Quebec Inc, pg 864
Les Productions Via Le Monde (Daniel Bertolino) Inc, pg 864

Documentary Rentals

CALIFORNIA

Les Blank Films Inc, pg 707
Cambridge Documentary Films Inc, pg 714
Direct Cinema Ltd Inc, pg 743
Em Gee Film Library, pg 753
Glenn Photo Supply, pg 771
Point of View Productions, pg 858
Visual Communications - Southern California Asian American Studies Central Inc, pg 931

COLORADO

Tatum Video, pg 907

DELAWARE

University Media Services, pg 922

ILLINOIS

Terra Nova Films Inc, pg 911

KENTUCKY

National Geographic Learning, pg 836

MARYLAND

James Agee Film Project, pg 792

MASSACHUSETTS

Documentary Educational Resources Inc, pg 744

MISSOURI

University of Missouri-Columbia, pg 923

NEW JERSEY

Alden Films, pg 679
Euro-Pacific Film & Video Productions Inc, pg 756
Milestone Film & Video Inc, pg 827

NEW YORK

American Museum of Natural History (AMNH), pg 683
Circulating Film & Video Library, pg 725
Fanlight Productions, pg 759
The Film-Makers' Cooperative, pg 760
Films Media Group, pg 760
First Run Features, pg 761
William Greaves Productions Inc, pg 774
Hallel Communications, pg 775
Icarus Films Inc, pg 783
Kino International Corp, pg 799
New Day Films, pg 839
Pennebaker Hegedus Films Inc, pg 854
Richter Productions Inc, pg 875
Third World Newsreel/Camera News Inc, pg 912
VIEW Inc (Video International Entertainment World Inc), pg 930

NORTH CAROLINA

Crystal Pictures Inc, pg 735

PENNSYLVANIA

Bullfrog Films Inc, pg 712
Rahlic Publishing Co, pg 869

TENNESSEE

Center for Southern Folklore Inc, pg 719

ONTARIO

Kineticvideo.com, pg 799
McNabb & Connolly, pg 821

QUEBEC

Les Productions Via Le Monde (Daniel Bertolino) Inc, pg 864

Educational Program Distributors

ARIZONA

Teaberry, pg 908

CALIFORNIA

Allied Artists International Inc, pg 681
Les Blank Films Inc, pg 707
California Newsreel, pg 714
Cambridge Documentary Films Inc, pg 714
Crystal Pyramid Productions™, pg 735
Davidson Productions, pg 738
Direct Cinema Ltd Inc, pg 743
eFootage LLC, pg 751
Em Gee Film Library, pg 753
Glenn Photo Supply, pg 771
Ishtar Films, pg 791
Joyce Media Inc, pg 795
Main Street Media Inc, pg 815
MarVista Entertainment Inc, pg 818
Moose School Productions, pg 830
New & Unique Videos™, pg 839
TMW Media Group, pg 915
Visual Communications - Southern California Asian American Studies Central Inc, pg 931
The Wine Appreciation Guild Ltd, pg 939

COLORADO

Crystal Productions, pg 735

CONNECTICUT

Hartley Film Foundation, pg 776
Weston Woods Studios Inc, pg 936

DELAWARE

University Media Services, pg 922

HAWAII

Media Bridge Gamekids, pg 821

ILLINOIS

ABSA Films, pg 672
Discovery Education - Chicago, pg 743
Encyclopaedia Britannica Inc, pg 754
Film Ideas Inc, pg 760
National Safety Council (NSC), pg 836
Terra Nova Films Inc, pg 911

KENTUCKY

Horizon Films & Media LLC, pg 781
The Learning House Inc, pg 805
National Geographic Learning, pg 836

MARYLAND

Department of Education Resources, pg 740
DSR Computer Technology Specialists Inc, pg 747
James Agee Film Project, pg 792

MASSACHUSETTS

Documentary Educational Resources Inc, pg 744
Green Mountain Post Films (GMP), pg 774

The New Film Company Inc, pg 839
Northern Light Productions (NLP), pg 842

MICHIGAN

Emery-Pratt Co, pg 753
HighScope Press, pg 780

MINNESOTA

Festival Films, pg 759
Hazelden Publishing & Educational Services, pg 777

NEBRASKA

Peak Performance Publishing, pg 852

NEW HAMPSHIRE

Captain Fiddle Music & Publications, pg 716

NEW JERSEY

Allegro Productions Inc, pg 680
Ergo Media Inc, pg 755

NEW MEXICO

The Phoenix Learning Group Inc, pg 855

NEW YORK

Michael Blackwood Productions Inc, pg 707
Broadstreet Productions LLC, pg 711
Brooklyn Botanic Garden, pg 711
Billy Budd Films Inc, pg 712
Fanlight Productions, pg 759
Films Media Group, pg 760
William Greaves Productions Inc, pg 774
Guidance Associates Inc Center for Humanities, pg 774
Hallel Communications, pg 775
Icarus Films Inc, pg 783
Janson Media Inc, pg 793
Mastervision Inc, pg 819
Richter Productions Inc, pg 875
Third World Newsreel/Camera News Inc, pg 912
VIEW Inc (Video International Entertainment World Inc), pg 930
Women Make Movies Inc, pg 941
Wonderwomen™ Enterprises, pg 941

NORTH CAROLINA

Crystal Pictures Inc, pg 735
Sinclair Institute, pg 889
World Wide Pictures Inc, pg 941

OHIO

Franciscan Media, pg 765
Griesinger Films LLC, pg 774

OREGON

Wilderness Video, pg 938

PENNSYLVANIA

Bullfrog Films Inc, pg 712
FMP Media Solutions Inc, pg 763
Rahlic Publishing Co, pg 869

TENNESSEE

American Blackguard Inc, pg 683
Center for Southern Folklore Inc, pg 719
Spring Arbor Distributors Inc, pg 898

TEXAS

CEV Multimedia Ltd, pg 720
Emergency Film Group, pg 753
University of Texas at Austin - Petroleum Extension Service, pg 923

VERMONT

Dorothy Tod Films, pg 915

VIRGINIA

CACI Integrated Communications, pg 713
Filmakers Library, pg 760

WEST VIRGINIA

Focus on Animals, pg 763
Harpers Ferry Historical Association, pg 776

WISCONSIN

Wisconsin Public Television, pg 940

ONTARIO

Canadian Filmmakers Distribution Center (CFMDC), pg 715
IMAX Corp, pg 786
Kineticvideo.com, pg 799
McIntyre Media Inc, pg 821
McNabb & Connolly, pg 821
Nelson Education Ltd, pg 837
Sullivan Home Entertainment, pg 903
University of Toronto, Classroom Technology Support, pg 923

QUEBEC

National Film Board of Canada/Office National du Film du Canada, pg 836
Les Productions Via Le Monde (Daniel Bertolino) Inc, pg 864

Educational Program Producers

ALABAMA

Leo Ticheli Productions, pg 913

ALASKA

Aurora Films, pg 696

ARIZONA

Candee Productions Inc, pg 716
Film Creations Ltd, pg 760
Teaberry, pg 908

CALIFORNIA

A Go Go Films, pg 671
Allied Artists International Inc, pg 681
Big Door, pg 705
Les Blank Films Inc, pg 707
Burrud Productions Inc, pg 713
Cambridge Documentary Films Inc, pg 714
Cinevest, pg 725

Classic Images Stock Footage LLC, pg 726
Concrete Images, pg 730
Creative Technology, pg 733
Crystal Pyramid Productions™, pg 735
Custom Video Productions Inc, pg 736
Davidson Productions, pg 738
Design Media, pg 741
Dolphin MultiMedia Inc, pg 745
Durrin Productions Inc, pg 748
Goal Productions, pg 772
Havas Edge, pg 777
imageReal Pictures LLC, pg 785
Ishtar Films, pg 791
Jaguar Distribution Corp, pg 792
The Jim Henson Co, pg 794
Joyce Media Inc, pg 795
Kavich Reynolds Productions Inc, pg 797
Main Street Media Inc, pg 815
The Media Staff Inc, pg 822
Moose School Productions, pg 830
New & Unique Videos™, pg 839
Point of View Productions, pg 858
QRS Software Services, pg 867
Glenn Roland Films, pg 876
Santa Barbara Location Services, pg 880
SNAP, pg 891
Tam Communications Inc, pg 906
TMW Media Group, pg 915
Video Resources Inc, pg 928
Vineyard Video & Photography, pg 930
Visual Communications - Southern California Asian American Studies Central Inc, pg 931
Webster Communications, pg 935
Zamacona Productions, pg 945

COLORADO

Crystal Productions, pg 735
CSI Film & Video LLC, pg 735
Flashback Media Productions, pg 762
Jeppesen, pg 793
Transtar Entertainment Co Inc, pg 917

CONNECTICUT

Essex Television Group Inc, pg 755
The Gary-Paul Agency, pg 768
Hartley Film Foundation, pg 776
New London Media, pg 839
Weston Woods Studios Inc, pg 936

DELAWARE

University Media Services, pg 922

DISTRICT OF COLUMBIA

Hillmann & Carr Inc, pg 780

FLORIDA

Accord Productions, pg 673
Blackburst Entertainment LLC, pg 706
Civins Productions Inc, pg 725
CopShopMiami.com, pg 731
Jordan Klein Film & Video (JKFV), pg 795
Tel-Air Interests Inc, pg 909

GEORGIA

Beachwood Productions, pg 702
Burst Video/Film Inc, pg 713
Guerrilla Productions LLC, pg 774

PROGRAMMING — FILM

Educational Program Producers (continued)

HAWAII

Hyperspective Studios Inc, pg 783
Media Bridge Gamekids, pg 821

ILLINOIS

ABSA Films, pg 672
Accenture, pg 672
Cresta Creative, pg 734
Discovery Education - Chicago, pg 743
Encyclopaedia Britannica Inc, pg 754
Film Police, pg 760
The Market Place, pg 817
Mightybytes Inc, pg 827
Multimedia Marketing Group, pg 833
National Safety Council (NSC), pg 836
SCI Television & Creative Media LLC, pg 882
Terra Nova Films Inc, pg 911
Winter Productions, pg 939

INDIANA

Road Pictures, pg 876

IOWA

Educational Technology & Media Services, pg 751
Iowa State University-Information Technology Services, pg 791

KENTUCKY

Horizon Films & Media LLC, pg 781
Donna Lawrence Productions, pg 804
The Learning House Inc, pg 805
National Geographic Learning, pg 836

LOUISIANA

Digital FX Inc, pg 742
Moxie Media, pg 832

MAINE

Films by Huey, pg 760

MARYLAND

Absolute Hollywood, pg 672
Richard Chisolm Cinematography, pg 722
dbF a Media Company, pg 739
Department of Education Resources, pg 740
DSR Computer Technology Specialists Inc, pg 747
The Image Generators, pg 785
James Agee Film Project, pg 792

MASSACHUSETTS

Cramer, pg 732
Documentary Educational Resources Inc, pg 744
Green Mountain Post Films (GMP), pg 774
Heliotrope Studios, pg 778

The New Film Company Inc, pg 839
Northern Light Productions (NLP), pg 842

MICHIGAN

HighScope Press, pg 780
K&R All Media Productions LLC, pg 796
Lawrence Productions Inc, pg 804

MINNESOTA

Hazelden Publishing & Educational Services, pg 777
House of Cinemagraphics, pg 782

MISSOURI

Hardcastle Films & Video, pg 776

NEBRASKA

Peak Performance Publishing, pg 852

NEW HAMPSHIRE

Academic & Campus Technology Services, pg 672
Apertura, pg 686
Captain Fiddle Music & Publications, pg 716

NEW JERSEY

Allegro Productions Inc, pg 680
Broadcast Center Studios, pg 710
MiB MediaWorks, pg 825
Telequest Inc, pg 910
TimeSteps Productions Inc, pg 914

NEW MEXICO

The Phoenix Learning Group Inc, pg 855

NEW YORK

Ace Video, pg 674
American History Workshop (NY) Inc, pg 683
aurora productions, pg 696
Michael Blackwood Productions Inc, pg 707
Blue Barn Pictures Inc, pg 707
Brian Film Productions LLC, pg 710
Broadstreet Productions LLC, pg 711
Brooklyn Botanic Garden, pg 711
Billy Budd Films Inc, pg 712
Buzzco Associates Inc, pg 713
De Nonno Productions Inc (DPI), pg 739
Fanlight Productions, pg 759
Films Media Group, pg 760
Florentine Films, pg 762
Four Corners Productions, pg 764
William Greaves Productions Inc, pg 774
Hallel Communications, pg 775
Havas Creative, pg 776
Ketchum Inc, pg 798
Mastervision Inc, pg 819
Jack Morton Worldwide, pg 830
News Broadcast Network Inc, pg 840
The Palmer Group, pg 850
Pat Kogan Productions Inc, pg 852
Peckham Productions Inc, pg 852
Polestar Films & Associated Arts Ltd, pg 859
R/GA, pg 868
Richter Productions Inc, pg 875

Scholastic Media, pg 882
Third World Newsreel/Camera News Inc, pg 912
VIEW Inc (Video International Entertainment World Inc), pg 930
Wonderwomen™ Enterprises, pg 941
Zelman Studios Ltd, pg 945

NORTH CAROLINA

Pat Appleson Studios Inc, pg 687
The Communications Group Inc, pg 729
Crystal Pictures Inc, pg 735
Horizon Video Productions Inc, pg 781
Kino Mountain Productions LLC, pg 799
Sinclair Institute, pg 889

OHIO

Advent Media Inc, pg 677
Franciscan Media, pg 765
Griesinger Films LLC, pg 774
Take 1 Media Services, pg 906

OKLAHOMA

CSI/Orion, pg 735

OREGON

Ideascape Inc, pg 784
Odyssey Productions Inc, pg 844
Wilderness Video, pg 938

PENNSYLVANIA

Argentine Productions Inc, pg 688
Bang! Pictures Inc, pg 701
FMP Media Solutions Inc, pg 763
Innovision Media Group, pg 788
JPL, pg 795
Kensington Falls Animation, pg 797
Main Point Productions, pg 815
Muderick Media, pg 833
Production Masters Inc (PMI), pg 864
Rahlic Publishing Co, pg 869
Video/Film Associates, pg 928

RHODE ISLAND

Sound-FX-Design, pg 894

TENNESSEE

American Blackguard Inc, pg 683
Center for Southern Folklore Inc, pg 719
Continental Film, pg 731
Memphis Communications Corp, pg 823
Scripps Networks, pg 882

TEXAS

Castleview Productions, pg 717
Cerutti Productions Inc, pg 720
CEV Multimedia Ltd, pg 720
The Editing Co, pg 750
Emergency Film Group, pg 753
Horizon Film + Video Productions, pg 781
Marx InDigital, pg 818
Earl Miller Productions Inc, pg 827
Romar Learning Solutions LLC, pg 877
South Coast Film & Video, pg 895
Stage Directions, pg 898
Texas Heart Institute Visual Communication Services, pg 911
University of Texas at Austin - Petroleum Extension Service, pg 923

VERMONT

Marlboro Productions, pg 817
Dorothy Tod Films, pg 915

VIRGINIA

Altruist Media LLC, pg 682
BES Studios, pg 704
CACI Integrated Communications, pg 713
Metro Productions, pg 824

WASHINGTON

North-by-Northwest - A Digital Studio, pg 842
White Rain Films Ltd, pg 937

WISCONSIN

Clear Focus Media LLC, pg 726
5th Floor Recording Co, pg 760
Meridian Studios, pg 824
University of Wisconsin-Oshkosh Radio-TV-Film Dept, pg 923
Video Wisconsin Inc, pg 929
Wisconsin Public Television, pg 940

WYOMING

Bridger Productions Inc, pg 710

ALBERTA

Black Media Works, pg 706
Global TV, pg 771

BRITISH COLUMBIA

West Eagle Films Inc, pg 935

MANITOBA

Lank/Beach Productions Inc, pg 803

NOVA SCOTIA

WildBrain™, pg 938

ONTARIO

IMAX Corp, pg 786
Pearson Education Canada, pg 852

QUEBEC

Kerrigan Productions Inc, pg 798
National Film Board of Canada/Office National du Film du Canada, pg 836
Productions Grand Nord Quebec Inc, pg 864
Les Productions Via Le Monde (Daniel Bertolino) Inc, pg 864

Educational Program Rentals

CALIFORNIA

Les Blank Films Inc, pg 707
Cambridge Documentary Films Inc, pg 714
Davidson Productions, pg 738
Direct Cinema Ltd Inc, pg 743
Em Gee Film Library, pg 753
Glenn Photo Supply, pg 771
Point of View Productions, pg 858
Visual Communications - Southern California Asian American Studies Central Inc, pg 931

DELAWARE

University Media Services, pg 922

PROGRAMMING — FILM

Feature Program Producers (continued)

FLORIDA (continued)
CopShopMiami.com, pg 731
Jordan Klein Film & Video (JKFV), pg 795

GEORGIA
Burst Video/Film Inc, pg 713
Guerrilla Productions LLC, pg 774
Myriad Productions, pg 835

HAWAII
Hyperspective Studios Inc, pg 783

IDAHO
Lagoon Video, pg 803

ILLINOIS
Film Police, pg 760
Multimedia Marketing Group, pg 833
Winter Productions, pg 939

IOWA
Right Stuf Inc, pg 875

KENTUCKY
Donna Lawrence Productions, pg 804

MARYLAND
Absolute Hollywood, pg 672
dbF a Media Company, pg 739
DSR Computer Technology Specialists Inc, pg 747

MASSACHUSETTS
Green Mountain Post Films (GMP), pg 774
Heliotrope Studios, pg 778

MICHIGAN
K&R All Media Productions LLC, pg 796

MINNESOTA
House of Cinemagraphics, pg 782

NEW JERSEY
Broadcast Center Studios, pg 710
CELCO, pg 719

NEW MEXICO
I-25 Studios, pg 783

NEW YORK
Blue Barn Pictures Inc, pg 707
Broadstreet Productions LLC, pg 711
Brooklyn Films, pg 711
De Nonno Productions Inc (DPI), pg 739
FilmNation Entertainment, pg 760
William Greaves Productions Inc, pg 774
Greenwich Entertainment, pg 774
Havas Creative, pg 776
HB-Content, pg 777
Richard Kaplan Productions, pg 796

Kinetic Arts, pg 799
Jack Morton Worldwide, pg 830
New Horizon Studios, pg 839
The Palmer Group, pg 850
Pennebaker Hegedus Films Inc, pg 854
Scholastic Media, pg 882
VIEW Inc (Video International Entertainment World Inc), pg 930
The Visual Studies Workshop (VSW), pg 931
Zelman Studios Ltd, pg 945

NORTH CAROLINA
The Communications Group Inc, pg 729

OREGON
Ideascape Inc, pg 784

PENNSYLVANIA
Innovision Media Group, pg 788
Kensington Falls Animation, pg 797
Production Masters Inc (PMI), pg 864

RHODE ISLAND
Sound-FX-Design, pg 894

TENNESSEE
American Blackguard Inc, pg 683
Cinemarr Entertainment, pg 724

TEXAS
Aries Productions Inc, pg 688
Castleview Productions, pg 717
Cerutti Productions Inc, pg 720
Cinestate, pg 724
Rich-Heape Films Inc, pg 875

VERMONT
Edgewood Studios, pg 750

VIRGINIA
BES Studios, pg 704
CACI Integrated Communications, pg 713
Metro Productions, pg 824

WASHINGTON
Hamilton Studio, pg 775
North-by-Northwest - A Digital Studio, pg 842
Pal Productions Inc, pg 850
Victory Studios, pg 927

WISCONSIN
5th Floor Recording Co, pg 760
Wisconsin Public Television, pg 940

WYOMING
Bridger Productions Inc, pg 710

ALBERTA
Global TV, pg 771

BRITISH COLUMBIA
Network Entertainment Inc, pg 838

MANITOBA
Lank/Beach Productions Inc, pg 803

ONTARIO
Doomsday Studios Limited, pg 745
IMAX Corp, pg 786

QUEBEC
Kerrigan Productions Inc, pg 798
Max Films Inc, pg 820
Muse Entertainment Enterprises, pg 834
Productions Grand Nord Quebec Inc, pg 864
Les Productions Via Le Monde (Daniel Bertolino) Inc, pg 864
Reel One International Ltd, pg 872

Feature Program Rentals

CALIFORNIA
Les Blank Films Inc, pg 707
Direct Cinema Ltd Inc, pg 743
Em Gee Film Library, pg 753
Glenn Photo Supply, pg 771
Palardo Productions, pg 850
Visual Communications - Southern California Asian American Studies Central Inc, pg 931
Worldwide Entertainment Corp, pg 941

IDAHO
Lagoon Video, pg 803

MISSOURI
University of Missouri-Columbia, pg 923

NEW YORK
Circulating Film & Video Library, pg 725
The Film-Makers' Cooperative, pg 760
First Run Features, pg 761
Icarus Films Inc, pg 783
Kino International Corp, pg 799
Pennebaker Hegedus Films Inc, pg 854
Third World Newsreel/Camera News Inc, pg 912
VIEW Inc (Video International Entertainment World Inc), pg 930

NORTH CAROLINA
Crystal Pictures Inc, pg 735
World Wide Pictures Inc, pg 941

PENNSYLVANIA
Bullfrog Films Inc, pg 712

ONTARIO
L-3 WESCAM, pg 802
McNabb & Connolly, pg 821

QUEBEC
Les Productions Via Le Monde (Daniel Bertolino) Inc, pg 864

Film Short, *see* Theatrical Short

Films—8mm Distributors

CALIFORNIA
Canyon Cinema Inc, pg 716
QRS Software Services, pg 867
Visual Communications - Southern California Asian American Studies Central Inc, pg 931

KENTUCKY
National Geographic Learning, pg 836

MARYLAND
Milner-Fenwick Inc, pg 828
Nicholas P Pipino Associates Inc, pg 857

NEW YORK
Film Emporium, pg 760
Janus Films Inc, pg 793
Visual Technologies Corp, pg 932

NORTH CAROLINA
Crystal Pictures Inc, pg 735

WASHINGTON
White Rain Films Ltd, pg 937

ONTARIO
Canadian Filmmakers Distribution Center (CFMDC), pg 715

Films—8mm Producers

ARKANSAS
White Diamond Productions LLC, pg 937

CALIFORNIA
Concrete Images, pg 730
Custom Video Productions Inc, pg 736
Design Media, pg 741
Main Street Media Inc, pg 815
New Circuit Films LLC, pg 839
QRS Software Services, pg 867
Visual Communications - Southern California Asian American Studies Central Inc, pg 931

COLORADO
Starwest Productions, pg 900

CONNECTICUT
The Gary-Paul Agency, pg 768

FLORIDA
Chatterbox Productions Inc, pg 721

INDIANA
OMNI Productions, pg 845

IOWA
Educational Technology & Media Services, pg 751

MARYLAND
Milner-Fenwick Inc, pg 828

NEW YORK
aurora productions, pg 696
Blue Barn Pictures Inc, pg 707

Split Image Productions, pg 898
Zelman Studios Ltd, pg 945

NORTH CAROLINA

The Communications Group Inc,
pg 729

PENNSYLVANIA

Argentine Productions Inc, pg 688
Production Masters Inc (PMI),
pg 864

TENNESSEE

American Blackguard Inc, pg 683
Memphis Communications Corp,
pg 823

TEXAS

South Coast Film & Video, pg 895

WASHINGTON

Adams Creative & Production
Services, pg 675
White Rain Films Ltd, pg 937

WYOMING

Bridger Productions Inc, pg 710

Films—8mm Rentals

CALIFORNIA

Canyon Cinema Inc, pg 716
Classic Images Stock Footage LLC,
pg 726
New Circuit Films LLC, pg 839
Visual Communications - Southern
California Asian American
Studies Central Inc, pg 931

FLORIDA

Jordan Klein Film & Video (JKFV),
pg 795

GEORGIA

Staging Directions Inc, pg 899

NEW YORK

The Film-Makers' Cooperative,
pg 760

Films—16mm Distributors

CALIFORNIA

Ametron Audio/Video, pg 684
Cambridge Documentary Films Inc,
pg 714
Canyon Cinema Inc, pg 716
Direct Cinema Ltd Inc, pg 743
Discovery Education - Los Angeles,
pg 743
The Walt Disney Co, pg 743
Em Gee Film Library, pg 753
Glenn Photo Supply, pg 771
New & Unique Videos™, pg 839
Palardo Productions, pg 850
Paulist Productions, pg 852
Point of View Productions, pg 858
QRS Software Services, pg 867
Sony Pictures Entertainment Inc,
pg 893
Twentieth Century Fox Film Corp,
pg 919

Visual Communications - Southern
California Asian American
Studies Central Inc, pg 931
Warner Bros Entertainment Inc,
pg 934

DELAWARE

University Media Services, pg 922

FLORIDA

Courter Films LLC, pg 732

ILLINOIS

Film Ideas Inc, pg 760
National Safety Council (NSC),
pg 836
Terra Nova Films Inc, pg 911

KENTUCKY

National Geographic Learning,
pg 836

MAINE

Headlight Audio Visual Inc, pg 777

MARYLAND

Department of Education Resources,
pg 740
DSR Computer Technology
Specialists Inc, pg 747
Milner-Fenwick Inc, pg 828
Nicholas P Pipino Associates Inc,
pg 857

MASSACHUSETTS

Documentary Educational Resources
Inc, pg 744
Green Mountain Post Films (GMP),
pg 774

NEVADA

DVDs4Less, pg 748

NEW JERSEY

Milestone Film & Video Inc,
pg 827

NEW YORK

Applause Learning Resources,
pg 687
ATA Trading Corp/Favorite TV Inc,
pg 691
The Cinema Guild Inc, pg 724
Circulating Film & Video Library,
pg 725
Thomas Craven Film Corp, pg 733
FACE Foundation, pg 758
Film Emporium, pg 760
First Run Features, pg 761
Gene Friedman, pg 766
Hallel Communications, pg 775
HB-Content, pg 777
Icarus Films Inc, pg 783
Janus Films Inc, pg 793
Richard Kaplan Productions, pg 796
Kino International Corp, pg 799
New Day Films, pg 839
Richter Productions Inc, pg 875
Third World Newsreel/Camera
News Inc, pg 912
Timed Exposures Films, pg 914
Tisch School of the Arts, pg 914
United Nations Department of
Public Information-News &
Media Division, pg 921
Visual Technologies Corp, pg 932

Women Make Movies Inc, pg 941
Worldview Entertainment Holdings
Inc, pg 941

NORTH CAROLINA

Crystal Pictures Inc, pg 735

OHIO

Griesinger Films LLC, pg 774

PENNSYLVANIA

FMP Media Solutions Inc, pg 763
Rahlic Publishing Co, pg 869

TENNESSEE

American Blackguard Inc, pg 683
Center for Southern Folklore Inc,
pg 719

TEXAS

Emergency Film Group, pg 753
Stage Directions, pg 898
Texas Heart Institute Visual
Communication Services, pg 911

VERMONT

Dorothy Tod Films, pg 915

WASHINGTON

White Rain Films Ltd, pg 937

WISCONSIN

Wisconsin Public Television, pg 940

ONTARIO

Canadian Filmmakers Distribution
Center (CFMDC), pg 715
Canamedia Inc, pg 715
Kineticvideo.com, pg 799

QUEBEC

National Film Board of
Canada/Office National du Film
du Canada, pg 836
Les Productions Via Le Monde
(Daniel Bertolino) Inc, pg 864

Films—16mm Producers

ALASKA

Aurora Films, pg 696

ARKANSAS

White Diamond Productions LLC,
pg 937

CALIFORNIA

Artichoke Productions, pg 690
Big Door, pg 705
Cambridge Documentary Films Inc,
pg 714
Concrete Images, pg 730
Creative Technology, pg 733
Custom Video Productions Inc,
pg 736
deKramer Productions Inc, pg 740
Design Media, pg 741
Direct Cinema Ltd Inc, pg 743
Discovery Education - Los Angeles,
pg 743
The Walt Disney Co, pg 743
Dolphin MultiMedia Inc, pg 745
imageReal Pictures LLC, pg 785
Joyce Media Inc, pg 795

Kavich Reynolds Productions Inc,
pg 797
KTVU-Retail Services, pg 802
Main Street Media Inc, pg 815
New & Unique Videos™, pg 839
New Circuit Films LLC, pg 839
Palardo Productions, pg 850
Paulist Productions, pg 852
Point of View Productions, pg 858
Prime Cut Productions, pg 862
Producers Group Ltd, pg 863
QRS Software Services, pg 867
RetinaVision Productions, pg 874
Glenn Roland Films, pg 876
SNAP, pg 891
Sony Pictures Entertainment Inc,
pg 893
Tam Communications Inc, pg 906
Twentieth Century Fox Film Corp,
pg 919
Visual Communications - Southern
California Asian American
Studies Central Inc, pg 931
Zamacona Productions, pg 945

COLORADO

Starwest Productions, pg 900
Tatum Video, pg 907
Transtar Entertainment Co Inc,
pg 917

CONNECTICUT

ACM Productions Ltd, pg 674
The Gary-Paul Agency, pg 768

DELAWARE

University Media Services, pg 922

DISTRICT OF COLUMBIA

Hillmann & Carr Inc, pg 780

FLORIDA

Chatterbox Productions Inc, pg 721
Roger Scruggs Films, pg 883
Tel-Air Interests Inc, pg 909

GEORGIA

Burst Video/Film Inc, pg 713
Myriad Productions, pg 835

ILLINOIS

Multimedia Marketing Group,
pg 833
National Safety Council (NSC),
pg 836
PSAV® Presentation Services
(Hotel Services Division), pg 866
Terra Nova Films Inc, pg 911
Winter Productions, pg 939

INDIANA

A-V-A Video Productions, pg 671
OMNI Productions, pg 845
Road Pictures, pg 876

IOWA

Educational Technology & Media
Services, pg 751
Hellman Associates Inc, pg 778

KENTUCKY

Horizon Films & Media LLC,
pg 781
Donna Lawrence Productions,
pg 804
National Geographic Learning,
pg 836

PROGRAMMING — FILM

Films—16mm Producers (continued)

LOUISIANA

Digital FX Inc, pg 742
Moxie Media, pg 832

MARYLAND

Richard Chisolm Cinematography, pg 722
Department of Education Resources, pg 740
DSR Computer Technology Specialists Inc, pg 747
Milner-Fenwick Inc, pg 828

MASSACHUSETTS

Capron Lighting & Sound Co Inc, pg 716
CommCreative, pg 728
Documentary Educational Resources Inc, pg 744
Green Mountain Post Films (GMP), pg 774
Heliotrope Studios, pg 778
Monadnock Media Inc, pg 829
TR Productions, pg 916

MICHIGAN

Lawrence Productions Inc, pg 804
MessageMakers, pg 824

MINNESOTA

Badiyan Inc, pg 700
House of Cinemagraphics, pg 782

MONTANA

KUSM TV, pg 802

NEVADA

DVDs4Less, pg 748

NEW HAMPSHIRE

Apertura, pg 686

NEW JERSEY

Euro-Pacific Film & Video Productions Inc, pg 756
Telequest Inc, pg 910

NEW MEXICO

Rainbow International Inc, pg 869

NEW YORK

Applause Learning Resources, pg 687
aurora productions, pg 696
Blue Barn Pictures Inc, pg 707
Brooklyn Films, pg 711
Thomas Craven Film Corp, pg 733
Four Corners Productions, pg 764
Gene Friedman, pg 766
William Greaves Productions Inc, pg 774
Guidance Associates Inc Center for Humanities, pg 774
Hallel Communications, pg 775
HB-Content, pg 777
Icontent, pg 783
Richard Kaplan Productions, pg 796
Kinetic Arts, pg 799
Jack Morton Worldwide, pg 830

Northeast Video Productions Inc, pg 842
The Palmer Group, pg 850
Pat Kogan Productions Inc, pg 852
Peckham Productions Inc, pg 852
Richter Productions Inc, pg 875
Split Image Productions, pg 898
Third World Newsreel/Camera News Inc, pg 912
Timed Exposures Films, pg 914
Zelman Studios Ltd, pg 945

NORTH CAROLINA

The Communications Group Inc, pg 729
Crystal Pictures Inc, pg 735
Trailblazer Studios®, pg 917

OHIO

Griesinger Films LLC, pg 774
Lyon Video Inc, pg 813

OREGON

Ideascape Inc, pg 784
Odyssey Productions Inc, pg 844
Production West, pg 864

PENNSYLVANIA

Argentine Productions Inc, pg 688
Aztech Productions LLC, pg 700
Bang! Pictures Inc, pg 701
FMP Media Solutions Inc, pg 763
JPL, pg 795
Kensington Falls Animation, pg 797
Main Point Productions, pg 815
Production Masters Inc (PMI), pg 864
Rahlic Publishing Co, pg 869
Video/Film Associates, pg 928

SOUTH CAROLINA

Venture Media, pg 925

TENNESSEE

American Blackguard Inc, pg 683
Center for Southern Folklore Inc, pg 719
Memphis Communications Corp, pg 823
Scripps Networks, pg 882
United Methodist Productions, pg 921

TEXAS

Alexander Media Productions, pg 679
AMS Pictures, pg 684
Emergency Film Group, pg 753
Marx InDigital, pg 818
South Coast Film & Video, pg 895
Stage Directions, pg 898
Texas Heart Institute Visual Communication Services, pg 911

VERMONT

Dorothy Tod Films, pg 915

VIRGINIA

CACI Integrated Communications, pg 713

WASHINGTON

Adams Creative & Production Services, pg 675
Getty Images, pg 770
White Rain Films Ltd, pg 937

WISCONSIN

Meridian Studios, pg 824
University of Wisconsin-Oshkosh Radio-TV-Film Dept, pg 923
Video Wisconsin Inc, pg 929
Wisconsin Public Television, pg 940

WYOMING

Bridger Productions Inc, pg 710

ALBERTA

Black Media Works, pg 706
Global TV, pg 771

NORTHWEST TERRITORIES

Yellowknife Films Inc, pg 944

ONTARIO

Canamedia Inc, pg 715
Doomsday Studios Limited, pg 745

QUEBEC

National Film Board of Canada/Office National du Film du Canada, pg 836
Les Productions Via Le Monde (Daniel Bertolino) Inc, pg 864

Films—16mm Rentals

CALIFORNIA

Ametron Audio/Video, pg 684
Cambridge Documentary Films Inc, pg 714
Canyon Cinema Inc, pg 716
Classic Images Stock Footage LLC, pg 726
Direct Cinema Ltd Inc, pg 743
Discovery Education - Los Angeles, pg 743
Em Gee Film Library, pg 753
Glenn Photo Supply, pg 771
New Circuit Films LLC, pg 839
New Line Cinema, pg 839
Palardo Productions, pg 850
Visual Communications - Southern California Asian American Studies Central Inc, pg 931

CONNECTICUT

Rockwell Communications Inc, pg 876

DELAWARE

University Media Services, pg 922

FLORIDA

Jordan Klein Film & Video (JKFV), pg 795

GEORGIA

Staging Directions Inc, pg 899

ILLINOIS

National Safety Council (NSC), pg 836
Terra Nova Films Inc, pg 911

MAINE

Headlight Audio Visual Inc, pg 777

MASSACHUSETTS

Documentary Educational Resources Inc, pg 744

MINNESOTA

Science Museum of Minnesota, pg 882

NEW YORK

Circulating Film & Video Library, pg 725
FACE Foundation, pg 758
The Film-Makers' Cooperative, pg 760
First Run Features, pg 761
Gene Friedman, pg 766
William Greaves Productions Inc, pg 774
Hallel Communications, pg 775
Icarus Films Inc, pg 783
Kino International Corp, pg 799
New Day Films, pg 839
Richter Productions Inc, pg 875
Third World Newsreel/Camera News Inc, pg 912
Timed Exposures Films, pg 914

NORTH CAROLINA

Crystal Pictures Inc, pg 735

OHIO

Franciscan Media, pg 765

PENNSYLVANIA

Rahlic Publishing Co, pg 869

TENNESSEE

Center for Southern Folklore Inc, pg 719

TEXAS

University of Texas at Austin - Petroleum Extension Service, pg 923

WISCONSIN

Wisconsin Public Television, pg 940

ONTARIO

Kineticvideo.com, pg 799

QUEBEC

National Film Board of Canada/Office National du Film du Canada, pg 836
Les Productions Via Le Monde (Daniel Bertolino) Inc, pg 864

Films—35mm Distributors

CALIFORNIA

Air Bud Entertainment, pg 678
Canyon Cinema Inc, pg 716
Direct Cinema Ltd Inc, pg 743
New & Unique Videos™, pg 839
Palardo Productions, pg 850
Visual Communications - Southern California Asian American Studies Central Inc, pg 931
Warner Bros Entertainment Inc, pg 934

COLORADO

American Educational Products LLC, pg 683
Greg Hensley Productions, pg 779

IDAHO

Lagoon Video, pg 803

PROGRAMMING — FILM

Films—35mm Rentals (continued)

NEW YORK (continued)
Kino International Corp, pg 799
Pennebaker Hegedus Films Inc, pg 854
Third World Newsreel/Camera News Inc, pg 912

NORTH CAROLINA
Crystal Pictures Inc, pg 735

QUEBEC
National Film Board of Canada/Office National du Film du Canada, pg 836
Les Productions Via Le Monde (Daniel Bertolino) Inc, pg 864

Films—70mm Distributors

CALIFORNIA
Cinevest, pg 725
MacGillivray Freeman Films Inc, pg 813
Sony Pictures Entertainment Inc, pg 893

NEW YORK
FACE Foundation, pg 758
Janus Films Inc, pg 793
Paramount Motion Pictures Group, pg 851
Visual Technologies Corp, pg 932

ONTARIO
IMAX Corp, pg 786

Films—70mm Producers

CALIFORNIA
Cinevest, pg 725
Creative Technology, pg 733
MacGillivray Freeman Films Inc, pg 813
Moving Art by Louie Schwartzberg, pg 831
Producers Group Ltd, pg 863
RetinaVision Productions, pg 874
Rhythm & Hues Studios Inc, pg 874
Sony Pictures Entertainment Inc, pg 893

KENTUCKY
Donna Lawrence Productions, pg 804

NEW YORK
aurora productions, pg 696
Blue Barn Pictures Inc, pg 707
Guidance Associates Inc Center for Humanities, pg 774
The Palmer Group, pg 850
Paramount Motion Pictures Group, pg 851
Scholastic Media, pg 882
Split Image Productions, pg 898

PENNSYLVANIA
Argentine Productions Inc, pg 688

WYOMING
Bridger Productions Inc, pg 710

BRITISH COLUMBIA
West Eagle Films Inc, pg 935

ONTARIO
IMAX Corp, pg 786

Films—70mm Rentals

CALIFORNIA
Classic Images Stock Footage LLC, pg 726

GEORGIA
Staging Directions Inc, pg 899

Foreign Program Distributors

CALIFORNIA
Allied Artists International Inc, pg 681
Les Blank Films Inc, pg 707
Crystal Pyramid Productions™, pg 735
Em Gee Film Library, pg 753
Glenn Photo Supply, pg 771
MarVista Entertainment Inc, pg 818
New & Unique Videos™, pg 839

CONNECTICUT
Really Good Stuff, pg 871

IDAHO
Lagoon Video, pg 803

IOWA
Right Stuf Inc, pg 875

MARYLAND
DSR Computer Technology Specialists Inc, pg 747
Recorded Books Inc, an RBmedia company, pg 871

MASSACHUSETTS
Documentary Educational Resources Inc, pg 744

MINNESOTA
Festival Films, pg 759

NEBRASKA
Mary Riepma Ross Media Arts Center, pg 877

NEW JERSEY
Alden Films, pg 679
Ergo Media Inc, pg 755
Milestone Film & Video Inc, pg 827

NEW YORK
Applause Learning Resources, pg 687
Circulating Film & Video Library, pg 725
FACE Foundation, pg 758
Fanlight Productions, pg 759
First Run Features, pg 761
Hallel Communications, pg 775

Icarus Films Inc, pg 783
Janson Media Inc, pg 793
Kino International Corp, pg 799
Mastervision Inc, pg 819
Richter Productions Inc, pg 875
SISU Home Entertainment Inc, pg 889
Third World Newsreel/Camera News Inc, pg 912
VIEW Inc (Video International Entertainment World Inc), pg 930
Women Make Movies Inc, pg 941
Zeitgeist Films Ltd, pg 945

NORTH CAROLINA
Crystal Pictures Inc, pg 735

OHIO
Network Technologies Inc, pg 838

PENNSYLVANIA
Bullfrog Films Inc, pg 712
FMP Media Solutions Inc, pg 763

ALBERTA
Global TV, pg 771

ONTARIO
Canadian Filmmakers Distribution Center (CFMDC), pg 715
CCI Entertainment Ltd, pg 718
IMAX Corp, pg 786

QUEBEC
Les Productions Via Le Monde (Daniel Bertolino) Inc, pg 864

Foreign Program Producers

CALIFORNIA
Classic Images Stock Footage LLC, pg 726
Creative Technology, pg 733
Crystal Pyramid Productions™, pg 735
Custom Video Productions Inc, pg 736
International Contact Inc, pg 790
Jaguar Distribution Corp, pg 792
Main Street Media Inc, pg 815
New & Unique Videos™, pg 839
QRS Software Services, pg 867
Vineyard Video & Photography, pg 930

CONNECTICUT
The Gary-Paul Agency, pg 768

DISTRICT OF COLUMBIA
Hillmann & Carr Inc, pg 780

FLORIDA
Blackburst Entertainment LLC, pg 706
Jordan Klein Film & Video (JKFV), pg 795

GEORGIA
Guerrilla Productions LLC, pg 774

IOWA
Right Stuf Inc, pg 875

LOUISIANA
Moxie Media, pg 832

MARYLAND
Absolute Hollywood, pg 672
Richard Chisolm Cinematography, pg 722
dbF a Media Company, pg 739
DSR Computer Technology Specialists Inc, pg 747

MASSACHUSETTS
Documentary Educational Resources Inc, pg 744
Heliotrope Studios, pg 778

MICHIGAN
K&R All Media Productions LLC, pg 796

MINNESOTA
House of Cinemagraphics, pg 782

NEW HAMPSHIRE
Apertura, pg 686

NEW YORK
Ace Video, pg 674
Applause Learning Resources, pg 687
Blue Barn Pictures Inc, pg 707
Hallel Communications, pg 775
Havas Creative, pg 776
Kinetic Arts, pg 799
Mastervision Inc, pg 819
Jack Morton Worldwide, pg 830
The Palmer Group, pg 850
Pat Kogan Productions Inc, pg 852
Richter Productions Inc, pg 875
VIEW Inc (Video International Entertainment World Inc), pg 930
Zelman Studios Ltd, pg 945

NORTH CAROLINA
Pat Appleson Studios Inc, pg 687
The Communications Group Inc, pg 729

PENNSYLVANIA
FMP Media Solutions Inc, pg 763

RHODE ISLAND
Sound-FX-Design, pg 894

TEXAS
Cerutti Productions Inc, pg 720
Stage Directions, pg 898

VIRGINIA
Metro Productions, pg 824

WISCONSIN
5th Floor Recording Co, pg 760
Wisconsin Public Television, pg 940

WYOMING
Bridger Productions Inc, pg 710

ALBERTA
Global TV, pg 771

BRITISH COLUMBIA
West Eagle Films Inc, pg 935

QUEBEC

Kerrigan Productions Inc, pg 798

Foreign Program Rentals

CALIFORNIA

Les Blank Films Inc, pg 707
Em Gee Film Library, pg 753
Glenn Photo Supply, pg 771

MASSACHUSETTS

Documentary Educational Resources
Inc, pg 744

MISSOURI

University of Missouri-Columbia,
pg 923

NEW JERSEY

Alden Films, pg 679

NEW YORK

Circulating Film & Video Library,
pg 725
The Film-Makers' Cooperative,
pg 760
First Run Features, pg 761
Hallel Communications, pg 775
Icarus Films Inc, pg 783
Kino International Corp, pg 799
Richter Productions Inc, pg 875
Third World Newsreel/Camera
News Inc, pg 912
VIEW Inc (Video International
Entertainment World Inc), pg 930

NORTH CAROLINA

Crystal Pictures Inc, pg 735

QUEBEC

Les Productions Via Le Monde
(Daniel Bertolino) Inc, pg 864

Government Program Distributors

CALIFORNIA

Crystal Pyramid Productions™,
pg 735
Em Gee Film Library, pg 753
Glenn Photo Supply, pg 771

ILLINOIS

ABSA Films, pg 672

MARYLAND

DSR Computer Technology
Specialists Inc, pg 747
Special Archives Division, Motion
Picture Branch, pg 896

NEVADA

DVDs4Less, pg 748

NEW MEXICO

The Phoenix Learning Group Inc,
pg 855

NEW YORK

Broadstreet Productions LLC,
pg 711
Films Media Group, pg 760

VIEW Inc (Video International
Entertainment World Inc), pg 930
Women Make Movies Inc, pg 941

PENNSYLVANIA

FMP Media Solutions Inc, pg 763

TEXAS

CEV Multimedia Ltd, pg 720

VIRGINIA

CACI Integrated Communications,
pg 713

WISCONSIN

Wisconsin Public Television, pg 940

ONTARIO

Kineticvideo.com, pg 799

Government Program Producers

ALASKA

Aurora Films, pg 696

ARIZONA

Film Creations Ltd, pg 760

CALIFORNIA

Big Door, pg 705
Classic Images Stock Footage LLC,
pg 726
Creative Technology, pg 733
Crystal Pyramid Productions™,
pg 735
Custom Video Productions Inc,
pg 736
Design Media, pg 741
Goal Productions, pg 772
Havas Edge, pg 777
The Media Staff Inc, pg 822
New & Unique Videos™, pg 839
QRS Software Services, pg 867
Dick Reizner Film & Video, pg 873
Glenn Roland Films, pg 876
Santa Barbara Location Services,
pg 880
Utopia Films, pg 924
Video Resources Inc, pg 928
Vineyard Video & Photography,
pg 930

COLORADO

Blue River Productions, pg 708
Flashback Media Productions,
pg 762
Tatum Video, pg 907
Transtar Entertainment Co Inc,
pg 917

CONNECTICUT

The Gary-Paul Agency, pg 768
Moving Pictures, pg 832
New London Media, pg 839

DISTRICT OF COLUMBIA

Hillmann & Carr Inc, pg 780
O'Keefe Communications Inc,
pg 844

FLORIDA

Accord Productions, pg 673
Blackburst Entertainment LLC,
pg 706

Communications Concepts Inc
(CCI), pg 729
CopShopMiami.com, pg 731
Jordan Klein Film & Video (JKFV),
pg 795
Tel-Air Interests Inc, pg 909
Video Techniques Inc, pg 928

GEORGIA

Beachwood Productions, pg 702
Burst Video/Film Inc, pg 713
Guerrilla Productions LLC, pg 774

HAWAII

Hyperspective Studios Inc, pg 783

ILLINOIS

ABSA Films, pg 672
Film Police, pg 760
Multimedia Marketing Group,
pg 833
SCI Television & Creative Media
LLC, pg 882

INDIANA

Road Pictures, pg 876

IOWA

Educational Technology & Media
Services, pg 751

LOUISIANA

Digital FX Inc, pg 742
Moxie Media, pg 832

MARYLAND

Absolute Hollywood, pg 672
dbF a Media Company, pg 739
DSR Computer Technology
Specialists Inc, pg 747

MASSACHUSETTS

Green Mountain Post Films (GMP),
pg 774
Northern Light Productions (NLP),
pg 842

MICHIGAN

K&R All Media Productions LLC,
pg 796

MINNESOTA

House of Cinemagraphics, pg 782

MISSOURI

Hardcastle Films & Video, pg 776

NEVADA

DVDs4Less, pg 748

NEW HAMPSHIRE

Apertura, pg 686

NEW JERSEY

Suede Interactive, pg 903

NEW MEXICO

The Phoenix Learning Group Inc,
pg 855

NEW YORK

Ace Video, pg 674
Blue Barn Pictures Inc, pg 707

Brian Film Productions LLC,
pg 710
Films Media Group, pg 760
Havas Creative, pg 776
Ketchum Inc, pg 798
Jack Morton Worldwide, pg 830
The Palmer Group, pg 850
Peckham Productions Inc, pg 852
Third World Newsreel/Camera
News Inc, pg 912
VIEW Inc (Video International
Entertainment World Inc), pg 930
Zelman Studios Ltd, pg 945

NORTH CAROLINA

Pat Appleson Studios Inc, pg 687
The Communications Group Inc,
pg 729
Kino Mountain Productions LLC,
pg 799

OHIO

Advent Media Inc, pg 677
Take 1 Media Services, pg 906

OREGON

Ideascape Inc, pg 784
Odyssey Productions Inc, pg 844

PENNSYLVANIA

FMP Media Solutions Inc, pg 763
Innovision Media Group, pg 788
JPL, pg 795
Video/Film Associates, pg 928

RHODE ISLAND

Sound-FX-Design, pg 894

TENNESSEE

Continental Film, pg 731
Memphis Communications Corp,
pg 823
Scripps Networks, pg 882

TEXAS

AMS Pictures, pg 684
Aries Productions Inc, pg 688
Castleview Productions, pg 717
Cerutti Productions Inc, pg 720
CEV Multimedia Ltd, pg 720
The Editing Co, pg 750
Horizon Film + Video Productions,
pg 781
Earl Miller Productions Inc, pg 827
Romar Learning Solutions LLC,
pg 877
South Coast Film & Video, pg 895

VIRGINIA

Altruist Media LLC, pg 682
BES Studios, pg 704
CACI Integrated Communications,
pg 713
Metro Productions, pg 824

WASHINGTON

North-by-Northwest - A Digital
Studio, pg 842
Victory Studios, pg 927

WISCONSIN

5th Floor Recording Co, pg 760
Meridian Studios, pg 824
Video Wisconsin Inc, pg 929
Wisconsin Public Television, pg 940

PROGRAMMING — FILM

Government Program Producers (continued)

WYOMING

Bridger Productions Inc, pg 710

ALBERTA

Black Media Works, pg 706

BRITISH COLUMBIA

West Eagle Films Inc, pg 935

MANITOBA

Lank/Beach Productions Inc, pg 803

NORTHWEST TERRITORIES

Yellowknife Films Inc, pg 944

QUEBEC

Kerrigan Productions Inc, pg 798

Government Program Rentals

CALIFORNIA

Em Gee Film Library, pg 753
Glenn Photo Supply, pg 771

MISSOURI

University of Missouri-Columbia, pg 923

NEW YORK

Films Media Group, pg 760
VIEW Inc (Video International Entertainment World Inc), pg 930

ONTARIO

Kineticvideo.com, pg 799
L-3 WESCAM, pg 802

Industrial Program Distributors

ARIZONA

Teaberry, pg 908

CALIFORNIA

Crystal Pyramid Productions™, pg 735
Em Gee Film Library, pg 753
Glenn Photo Supply, pg 771
Nineteen87, pg 841

GEORGIA

Convergent Media Systems, pg 731

ILLINOIS

ABSA Films, pg 672
National Safety Council (NSC), pg 836

NEVADA

DVDs4Less, pg 748

NEW JERSEY

MiB MediaWorks, pg 825

NEW MEXICO

The Phoenix Learning Group Inc, pg 855

NEW YORK

Broadstreet Productions LLC, pg 711
Fanlight Productions, pg 759
Films Media Group, pg 760
HB-Content, pg 777
VIEW Inc (Video International Entertainment World Inc), pg 930

PENNSYLVANIA

FMP Media Solutions Inc, pg 763

TEXAS

CEV Multimedia Ltd, pg 720
Emergency Film Group, pg 753
University of Texas at Austin - Petroleum Extension Service, pg 923

VIRGINIA

CACI Integrated Communications, pg 713

ONTARIO

Kineticvideo.com, pg 799

QUEBEC

Les Productions Via Le Monde (Daniel Bertolino) Inc, pg 864

Industrial Program Producers

ALABAMA

Leo Ticheli Productions, pg 913

ALASKA

Aurora Films, pg 696

ARIZONA

Candee Productions Inc, pg 716
Film Creations Ltd, pg 760
Teaberry, pg 908

CALIFORNIA

A Go Go Films, pg 671
Big Door, pg 705
Classic Images Stock Footage LLC, pg 726
Concrete Images, pg 730
Creative Technology, pg 733
Crystal Pyramid Productions™, pg 735
Custom Video Productions Inc, pg 736
Davidson Productions, pg 738
Design Media, pg 741
Dolphin MultiMedia Inc, pg 745
Goal Productions, pg 772
Havas Edge, pg 777
imageReal Pictures LLC, pg 785
Jaguar Distribution Corp, pg 792
Kavich Reynolds Productions Inc, pg 797
Main Street Media Inc, pg 815
The Media Staff Inc, pg 822
New & Unique Videos™, pg 839
Nineteen87, pg 841
Point of View Productions, pg 858
QRS Software Services, pg 867
Dick Reizner Film & Video, pg 873
RetinaVision Productions, pg 874

Glenn Roland Films, pg 876
Santa Barbara Location Services, pg 880
SNAP, pg 891
Tam Communications Inc, pg 906
Video Resources Inc, pg 928
Vineyard Video & Photography, pg 930
Webster Communications, pg 935

COLORADO

Flashback Media Productions, pg 762
Transtar Entertainment Co Inc, pg 917

CONNECTICUT

The Gary-Paul Agency, pg 768
Moving Pictures, pg 832
New London Media, pg 839

DISTRICT OF COLUMBIA

Hillmann & Carr Inc, pg 780

FLORIDA

Accord Productions, pg 673
Blackburst Entertainment LLC, pg 706
Civins Productions Inc, pg 725
CopShopMiami.com, pg 731
Jordan Klein Film & Video (JKFV), pg 795
Tel-Air Interests Inc, pg 909
Universal Studios Florida® Production Group, pg 922

GEORGIA

Beachwood Productions, pg 702
Burst Video/Film Inc, pg 713
Guerrilla Productions LLC, pg 774
Myriad Productions, pg 835

HAWAII

Hyperspective Studios Inc, pg 783

ILLINOIS

ABSA Films, pg 672
Cresta Creative, pg 734
Film Police, pg 760
Manning Productions, pg 816
Multimedia Marketing Group, pg 833
National Safety Council (NSC), pg 836
Richter Studios, pg 875
SCI Television & Creative Media LLC, pg 882
Winter Productions, pg 939

INDIANA

Road Pictures, pg 876

IOWA

Hellman Associates Inc, pg 778

LOUISIANA

Digital FX Inc, pg 742
Moxie Media, pg 832

MARYLAND

Absolute Hollywood, pg 672
dbF a Media Company, pg 739
The Image Generators, pg 785

MASSACHUSETTS

CommCreative, pg 728
Green Mountain Post Films (GMP), pg 774
Heliotrope Studios, pg 778
Northern Light Productions (NLP), pg 842

MICHIGAN

K&R All Media Productions LLC, pg 796
Lawrence Productions Inc, pg 804

MINNESOTA

House of Cinemagraphics, pg 782

MISSOURI

Hardcastle Films & Video, pg 776

NEVADA

DVDs4Less, pg 748

NEW HAMPSHIRE

Apertura, pg 686

NEW JERSEY

MiB MediaWorks, pg 825
Suede Interactive, pg 903
Telequest Inc, pg 910
TimeSteps Productions Inc, pg 914

NEW MEXICO

The Phoenix Learning Group Inc, pg 855

NEW YORK

Ace Video, pg 674
aurora productions, pg 696
Blue Barn Pictures Inc, pg 707
Brian Film Productions LLC, pg 710
Broadstreet Productions LLC, pg 711
Fanlight Productions, pg 759
Films Media Group, pg 760
Florentine Films, pg 762
Havas Creative, pg 776
HB-Content, pg 777
Ketchum Inc, pg 798
Mark X Productions Inc, pg 817
Jack Morton Worldwide, pg 830
News Broadcast Network Inc, pg 840
The Palmer Group, pg 850
Pat Kogan Productions Inc, pg 852
Peckham Productions Inc, pg 852
Polestar Films & Associated Arts Ltd, pg 859
PrimeLight Productions Inc, pg 862
R/GA, pg 868
Third World Newsreel/Camera News Inc, pg 912
VIEW Inc (Video International Entertainment World Inc), pg 930
Zelman Studios Ltd, pg 945

NORTH CAROLINA

Pat Appleson Studios Inc, pg 687
The Communications Group Inc, pg 729
Horizon Video Productions Inc, pg 781
Kino Mountain Productions LLC, pg 799

OHIO

Advent Media Inc, pg 677
Lyon Video Inc, pg 813
Take 1 Media Services, pg 906

OREGON

Ideascape Inc, pg 784
Odyssey Productions Inc, pg 844
Production West, pg 864

PENNSYLVANIA

Bang! Pictures Inc, pg 701
FMP Media Solutions Inc, pg 763
Innovision Media Group, pg 788
JPL, pg 795
Kensington Falls Animation, pg 797
Main Point Productions, pg 815
Muderick Media, pg 833
Production Masters Inc (PMI),
  pg 864
Video/Film Associates, pg 928

RHODE ISLAND

Sound-FX-Design, pg 894

TENNESSEE

Continental Film, pg 731
Memphis Communications Corp,
  pg 823
Scripps Networks, pg 882

TEXAS

Alexander Media Productions,
  pg 679
AMS Pictures, pg 684
Aries Productions Inc, pg 688
Biway Media, pg 706
Castleview Productions, pg 717
Cerutti Productions Inc, pg 720
CEV Multimedia Ltd, pg 720
Dykeman Associates Inc, pg 748
The Editing Co, pg 750
Emergency Film Group, pg 753
Epic Software Group Inc, pg 755
Horizon Film + Video Productions,
  pg 781
Marx InDigital, pg 818
Earl Miller Productions Inc, pg 827
Romar Learning Solutions LLC,
  pg 877
South Coast Film & Video, pg 895
Stage Directions, pg 898
University of Texas at Austin -
  Petroleum Extension Service,
  pg 923

VERMONT

Marlboro Productions, pg 817

VIRGINIA

Altruist Media LLC, pg 682
BES Studios, pg 704
CACI Integrated Communications,
  pg 713
Metro Productions, pg 824

WASHINGTON

Adams Creative & Production
  Services, pg 675
Hamilton Studio, pg 775
North-by-Northwest - A Digital
  Studio, pg 842
Pal Productions Inc, pg 850
Victory Studios, pg 927
White Rain Films Ltd, pg 937

WISCONSIN

Audio Visual of Milwaukee Inc,
  pg 694
5th Floor Recording Co, pg 760
Meridian Studios, pg 824
University of Wisconsin-Oshkosh
  Radio-TV-Film Dept, pg 923
Video Wisconsin Inc, pg 929
Wisconsin Public Television, pg 940

WYOMING

Bridger Productions Inc, pg 710

ALBERTA

Black Media Works, pg 706

BRITISH COLUMBIA

West Eagle Films Inc, pg 935

MANITOBA

Lank/Beach Productions Inc, pg 803

NORTHWEST TERRITORIES

Yellowknife Films Inc, pg 944

ONTARIO

Mediaimage Communications
  Group, pg 822

QUEBEC

Kerrigan Productions Inc, pg 798
Les Productions Via Le Monde
  (Daniel Bertolino) Inc, pg 864

Industrial Program Rentals

CALIFORNIA

Em Gee Film Library, pg 753
Glenn Photo Supply, pg 771

GEORGIA

Convergent Media Systems, pg 731

ILLINOIS

National Safety Council (NSC),
  pg 836

MISSOURI

University of Missouri-Columbia,
  pg 923

NEW YORK

Fanlight Productions, pg 759
Films Media Group, pg 760
Richter Productions Inc, pg 875
VIEW Inc (Video International
  Entertainment World Inc), pg 930

ONTARIO

Kineticvideo.com, pg 799

Kinescope Producers

KENTUCKY

Donna Lawrence Productions,
  pg 804

NEW YORK

The Palmer Group, pg 850

Kinescope Rentals

CALIFORNIA

Classic Images Stock Footage LLC,
  pg 726

GEORGIA

Staging Directions Inc, pg 899

Literature, *see* Feature Program

Medical Program Distributors

ARIZONA

Teaberry, pg 908

CALIFORNIA

Crystal Pyramid Productions™,
  pg 735
Davidson Productions, pg 738
Direct Cinema Ltd Inc, pg 743
Glenn Photo Supply, pg 771
Joyce Media Inc, pg 795
TMW Media Group, pg 915

ILLINOIS

Film Ideas Inc, pg 760

MARYLAND

DSR Computer Technology
  Specialists Inc, pg 747

MICHIGAN

Emery-Pratt Co, pg 753
Phoenix Society for Burn Survivors
  Inc, pg 856

NEW JERSEY

MiB MediaWorks, pg 825

NEW MEXICO

The Phoenix Learning Group Inc,
  pg 855

NEW YORK

Broadstreet Productions LLC,
  pg 711
Fanlight Productions, pg 759
Films Media Group, pg 760
HB-Content, pg 777
News Broadcast Network Inc,
  pg 840
Richter Productions Inc, pg 875
VIEW Inc (Video International
  Entertainment World Inc), pg 930
Women Make Movies Inc, pg 941

NORTH CAROLINA

Sinclair Institute, pg 889

PENNSYLVANIA

Bullfrog Films Inc, pg 712
FMP Media Solutions Inc, pg 763

TEXAS

CEV Multimedia Ltd, pg 720
Emergency Film Group, pg 753
Texas Heart Institute Visual
  Communication Services, pg 911

VIRGINIA

CACI Integrated Communications,
  pg 713

ONTARIO

Kineticvideo.com, pg 799

Medical Program Producers

ALABAMA

Leo Ticheli Productions, pg 913

ARIZONA

Film Creations Ltd, pg 760
Teaberry, pg 908

CALIFORNIA

Big Door, pg 705
Classic Images Stock Footage LLC,
  pg 726
Creative Technology, pg 733
Crystal Pyramid Productions™,
  pg 735
Custom Video Productions Inc,
  pg 736
Davidson Productions, pg 738
Design Media, pg 741
Dolphin MultiMedia Inc, pg 745
Havas Edge, pg 777
imageReal Pictures LLC, pg 785
Joyce Media Inc, pg 795
Kavich Reynolds Productions Inc,
  pg 797
Main Street Media Inc, pg 815
The Media Staff Inc, pg 822
New & Unique Videos™, pg 839
Point of View Productions, pg 858
QRS Software Services, pg 867
Dick Reizner Film & Video, pg 873
RetinaVision Productions, pg 874
Glenn Roland Films, pg 876
SNAP, pg 891
Tam Communications Inc, pg 906
TMW Media Group, pg 915
Video Resources Inc, pg 928

COLORADO

Flashback Media Productions,
  pg 762
Transtar Entertainment Co Inc,
  pg 917

CONNECTICUT

The Gary-Paul Agency, pg 768
Moving Pictures, pg 832
New London Media, pg 839

DISTRICT OF COLUMBIA

Hillmann & Carr Inc, pg 780
O'Keefe Communications Inc,
  pg 844

FLORIDA

Accord Productions, pg 673
Blackburst Entertainment LLC,
  pg 706
CopShopMiami.com, pg 731
Jordan Klein Film & Video (JKFV),
  pg 795

GEORGIA

Beachwood Productions, pg 702
Burst Video/Film Inc, pg 713
Guerrilla Productions LLC, pg 774

PROGRAMMING — FILM

Medical Program Producers (continued)

HAWAII

Hyperspective Studios Inc, pg 783

ILLINOIS

Film Police, pg 760
Manning Productions, pg 816
Multimedia Marketing Group, pg 833
SCI Television & Creative Media LLC, pg 882
Winter Productions, pg 939

INDIANA

Road Pictures, pg 876

KENTUCKY

Idle Minds Productions Inc, pg 784

LOUISIANA

Digital FX Inc, pg 742
Moxie Media, pg 832

MARYLAND

Absolute Hollywood, pg 672
Richard Chisolm Cinematography, pg 722
dbF a Media Company, pg 739
DSR Computer Technology Specialists Inc, pg 747
The Image Generators, pg 785

MASSACHUSETTS

Green Mountain Post Films (GMP), pg 774
Heliotrope Studios, pg 778
Northern Light Productions (NLP), pg 842

MICHIGAN

K&R All Media Productions LLC, pg 796

MINNESOTA

House of Cinemagraphics, pg 782

NEW HAMPSHIRE

Apertura, pg 686

NEW JERSEY

MiB MediaWorks, pg 825
Suede Interactive, pg 903
Telequest Inc, pg 910
TimeSteps Productions Inc, pg 914

NEW MEXICO

The Phoenix Learning Group Inc, pg 855
Rainbow International Inc, pg 869

NEW YORK

Ace Video, pg 674
aurora productions, pg 696
Brian Film Productions LLC, pg 710
Broadstreet Productions LLC, pg 711
Fanlight Productions, pg 759
Films Media Group, pg 760

Havas Creative, pg 776
HB-Content, pg 777
Image Zone Inc, pg 785
Ketchum Inc, pg 798
Jack Morton Worldwide, pg 830
News Broadcast Network Inc, pg 840
The Palmer Group, pg 850
Pat Kogan Productions Inc, pg 852
Peckham Productions Inc, pg 852
R/GA, pg 868
Richter Productions Inc, pg 875
VIEW Inc (Video International Entertainment World Inc), pg 930
Zelman Studios Ltd, pg 945

NORTH CAROLINA

Pat Appleson Studios Inc, pg 687
The Communications Group Inc, pg 729
Horizon Video Productions Inc, pg 781
Kino Mountain Productions LLC, pg 799
Sinclair Institute, pg 889

OHIO

Advent Media Inc, pg 677
Take 1 Media Services, pg 906

OKLAHOMA

CSI/Orion, pg 735

OREGON

Ideascape Inc, pg 784

PENNSYLVANIA

Bang! Pictures Inc, pg 701
FMP Media Solutions Inc, pg 763
Innovision Media Group, pg 788
JPL, pg 795
Kensington Falls Animation, pg 797
Production Masters Inc (PMI), pg 864
Video/Film Associates, pg 928

RHODE ISLAND

Sound-FX-Design, pg 894

TENNESSEE

Continental Film, pg 731
Memphis Communications Corp, pg 823
Scripps Networks, pg 882

TEXAS

Alexander Media Productions, pg 679
AMS Pictures, pg 684
Castleview Productions, pg 717
Cerutti Productions Inc, pg 720
CEV Multimedia Ltd, pg 720
Dykeman Associates Inc, pg 748
The Editing Co, pg 750
Emergency Film Group, pg 753
Horizon Film + Video Productions, pg 781
Marx InDigital, pg 818
Earl Miller Productions Inc, pg 827
Romar Learning Solutions LLC, pg 877
South Coast Film & Video, pg 895
Texas Heart Institute Visual Communication Services, pg 911

VERMONT

Marlboro Productions, pg 817

VIRGINIA

Altruist Media LLC, pg 682
BES Studios, pg 704
CACI Integrated Communications, pg 713
Metro Productions, pg 824

WASHINGTON

Adams Creative & Production Services, pg 675
Hamilton Studio, pg 775
North-by-Northwest - A Digital Studio, pg 842
Victory Studios, pg 927

WISCONSIN

Audio Visual of Milwaukee Inc, pg 694
5th Floor Recording Co, pg 760
Meridian Studios, pg 824
Video Wisconsin Inc, pg 929
Wisconsin Public Television, pg 940

WYOMING

Bridger Productions Inc, pg 710

MANITOBA

Lank/Beach Productions Inc, pg 803

QUEBEC

Kerrigan Productions Inc, pg 798

Medical Program Rentals

CALIFORNIA

Davidson Productions, pg 738
Direct Cinema Ltd Inc, pg 743
Glenn Photo Supply, pg 771
Point of View Productions, pg 858

MISSOURI

University of Missouri-Columbia, pg 923

NEW YORK

Fanlight Productions, pg 759
Films Media Group, pg 760
Richter Productions Inc, pg 875

NORTH CAROLINA

Sinclair Institute, pg 889

PENNSYLVANIA

Bullfrog Films Inc, pg 712

ONTARIO

Kineticvideo.com, pg 799

Multimedia, CD-ROM & DVD Interactive Program Distributors

CALIFORNIA

Crystal Pyramid Productions™, pg 735
Focus Features, pg 763
MarVista Entertainment Inc, pg 818
TiVo Corp, pg 914

GEORGIA

Convergent Media Systems, pg 731

ILLINOIS

ABSA Films, pg 672
Britannica Digital Learning, pg 710
National Safety Council (NSC), pg 836

MASSACHUSETTS

Documentary Educational Resources Inc, pg 744

NEW JERSEY

Allegro Productions Inc, pg 680

NEW MEXICO

The Phoenix Learning Group Inc, pg 855

NEW YORK

Brooklyn Botanic Garden, pg 711
Films Media Group, pg 760
HB-Content, pg 777

OREGON

Wilderness Video, pg 938

PENNSYLVANIA

FMP Media Solutions Inc, pg 763
New Horizons Computer Learning Centers Inc, pg 839

TENNESSEE

Center for Southern Folklore Inc, pg 719
Spring Arbor Distributors Inc, pg 898

TEXAS

CEV Multimedia Ltd, pg 720
Replicopy Digital Media Center, pg 873

UTAH

Strata™, pg 901

ONTARIO

McIntyre Media Inc, pg 821

Multimedia, CD-ROM & DVD Interactive Program Producers

ARIZONA

Film Creations Ltd, pg 760

CALIFORNIA

Big Door, pg 705
Concrete Images, pg 730
Creative Technology, pg 733
Crystal Pyramid Productions™, pg 735
Custom Video Productions Inc, pg 736
Design Media, pg 741
Direct Images Interactive Inc, pg 743
Dolphin MultiMedia Inc, pg 745
Focus Features, pg 763
Havas Edge, pg 777
The Jim Henson Co, pg 794
Kavich Reynolds Productions Inc, pg 797
Lumeni Productions Inc, pg 812
Main Street Media Inc, pg 815
The Media Staff Inc, pg 822

New Circuit Films LLC, pg 839
Palardo Productions, pg 850
QRS Software Services, pg 867
RetinaVision Productions, pg 874
Glenn Roland Films, pg 876
SNAP, pg 891
Tam Communications Inc, pg 906
Video Movie Magic, pg 928
Webster Communications, pg 935

COLORADO

Flashback Media Productions,
pg 762

CONNECTICUT

Moving Pictures, pg 832
New London Media, pg 839
T & M Digital Services LLC,
pg 906
VRSim Inc, pg 933

DISTRICT OF COLUMBIA

Hillmann & Carr Inc, pg 780
O'Keefe Communications Inc,
pg 844
USCCB Publishing, pg 923

FLORIDA

Blackburst Entertainment LLC,
pg 706
CD ROM™ Inc, pg 718
Civins Productions Inc, pg 725
Communications Concepts Inc
(CCI), pg 729
Jordan Klein Film & Video (JKFV),
pg 795
Video Techniques Inc, pg 928

GEORGIA

Beachwood Productions, pg 702
Burst Video/Film Inc, pg 713
Guerrilla Productions LLC, pg 774
Myriad Productions, pg 835

HAWAII

Hyperspective Studios Inc, pg 783

ILLINOIS

ABSA Films, pg 672
Accenture, pg 672
Britannica Digital Learning, pg 710
Cresta Creative, pg 734
Manning Productions, pg 816
Mightybytes Inc, pg 827
Multimedia Marketing Group,
pg 833
National Safety Council (NSC),
pg 836
Richter Studios, pg 875
SCI Television & Creative Media
LLC, pg 882

IOWA

Educational Technology & Media
Services, pg 751

KENTUCKY

Donna Lawrence Productions,
pg 804

LOUISIANA

Digital FX Inc, pg 742

MARYLAND

Absolute Hollywood, pg 672
dbF a Media Company, pg 739
Satellite Media Production, pg 881

MASSACHUSETTS

CommCreative, pg 728
Documentary Educational Resources
Inc, pg 744
Northern Light Productions (NLP),
pg 842

MICHIGAN

Arbor Oakland Group, pg 688
K&R All Media Productions LLC,
pg 796

MINNESOTA

House of Cinemagraphics, pg 782

NEW HAMPSHIRE

Apertura, pg 686

NEW JERSEY

Allegro Productions Inc, pg 680
Outside The Box Interactive LLC,
pg 849
Suede Interactive, pg 903

NEW MEXICO

The Phoenix Learning Group Inc,
pg 855

NEW YORK

Blue Barn Pictures Inc, pg 707
Broadstreet Productions LLC,
pg 711
Brooklyn Botanic Garden, pg 711
Films Media Group, pg 760
Havas Creative, pg 776
HB-Content, pg 777
Image Zone Inc, pg 785
Jack Morton Worldwide, pg 830
MRY, pg 832
The Palmer Group, pg 850
Pat Kogan Productions Inc, pg 852
R/GA, pg 868
Judson Rosebush Co Inc, pg 877
Zelman Studios Ltd, pg 945

NORTH CAROLINA

Pat Appleson Studios Inc, pg 687
The Communications Group Inc,
pg 729
Horizon Video Productions Inc,
pg 781
Moving Pictures, pg 832
NASCAR Productions LLC, pg 835

OHIO

Advent Media Inc, pg 677
Take 1 Media Services, pg 906

OREGON

Ideascape Inc, pg 784
Odyssey Productions Inc, pg 844
Wilderness Video, pg 938

PENNSYLVANIA

Argentine Productions Inc, pg 688
FMP Media Solutions Inc, pg 763
Innovision Media Group, pg 788
JPL, pg 795
New Horizons Computer Learning
Centers Inc, pg 839
Production Masters Inc (PMI),
pg 864

RHODE ISLAND

Sound-FX-Design, pg 894

TENNESSEE

Anode Inc, pg 686
Continental Film, pg 731
Memphis Communications Corp,
pg 823
Scripps Networks, pg 882

TEXAS

Castleview Productions, pg 717
CEV Multimedia Ltd, pg 720
The Editing Co, pg 750
Epic Software Group Inc, pg 755
Horizon Film + Video Productions,
pg 781
Romar Learning Solutions LLC,
pg 877
South Coast Film & Video, pg 895

VIRGINIA

Altruist Media LLC, pg 682
Metro Productions, pg 824

WASHINGTON

Adams Creative & Production
Services, pg 675
Hamilton Studio, pg 775
North-by-Northwest - A Digital
Studio, pg 842

WISCONSIN

Audio Visual of Milwaukee Inc,
pg 694
5th Floor Recording Co, pg 760
Video Wisconsin Inc, pg 929
Wisconsin Public Television, pg 940

WYOMING

Bridger Productions Inc, pg 710

ALBERTA

Black Media Works, pg 706

ONTARIO

GAPC (General Assembly
Production Centre), pg 768
Silver Creek Media Inc, pg 888

QUEBEC

Kerrigan Productions Inc, pg 798

Multimedia, CD-ROM & DVD Interactive Program Rentals

DELAWARE

Side Door Studio Inc, pg 887

GEORGIA

Convergent Media Systems, pg 731

MASSACHUSETTS

Documentary Educational Resources
Inc, pg 744

NEW YORK

Brooklyn Botanic Garden, pg 711
Films Media Group, pg 760

OREGON

Wilderness Video, pg 938

News Program Distributors

CALIFORNIA

Crystal Pyramid Productions™,
pg 735

GEORGIA

School Media Associates LLC,
pg 882

NEW JERSEY

MiB MediaWorks, pg 825

NEW YORK

Icarus Films Inc, pg 783
News Broadcast Network Inc,
pg 840
Richter Productions Inc, pg 875
Women Make Movies Inc, pg 941

VIRGINIA

CACI Integrated Communications,
pg 713

ALBERTA

Global TV, pg 771

News Program Producers

CALIFORNIA

Big Door, pg 705
Crystal Pyramid Productions™,
pg 735
Jaguar Distribution Corp, pg 792
New & Unique Videos™, pg 839
QRS Software Services, pg 867
SNAP, pg 891
Vineyard Video & Photography,
pg 930
Webster Communications, pg 935

COLORADO

Flashback Media Productions,
pg 762
Tatum Video, pg 907

CONNECTICUT

Essex Television Group Inc, pg 755
New London Media, pg 839

DISTRICT OF COLUMBIA

Hillmann & Carr Inc, pg 780
O'Keefe Communications Inc,
pg 844

FLORIDA

Blackburst Entertainment LLC,
pg 706
Civins Productions Inc, pg 725
Communications Concepts Inc
(CCI), pg 729
CopShopMiami.com, pg 731
Jordan Klein Film & Video (JKFV),
pg 795
Video Techniques Inc, pg 928

GEORGIA

Beachwood Productions, pg 702
Guerrilla Productions LLC, pg 774
Myriad Productions, pg 835

PROGRAMMING — FILM

News Program Producers (continued)

ILLINOIS

Multimedia Marketing Group, pg 833
SCI Television & Creative Media LLC, pg 882

KENTUCKY

Idle Minds Productions Inc, pg 784

LOUISIANA

Digital FX Inc, pg 742

MARYLAND

Absolute Hollywood, pg 672
Richard Chisolm Cinematography, pg 722
dbF a Media Company, pg 739

MICHIGAN

K&R All Media Productions LLC, pg 796

MINNESOTA

House of Cinemagraphics, pg 782

NEW JERSEY

MiB MediaWorks, pg 825
Telequest Inc, pg 910

NEW YORK

Ace Video, pg 674
aurora productions, pg 696
De Nonno Productions Inc (DPI), pg 739
Havas Creative, pg 776
Jack Morton Worldwide, pg 830
News Broadcast Network Inc, pg 840
The Palmer Group, pg 850
Richter Productions Inc, pg 875
Zelman Studios Ltd, pg 945

NORTH CAROLINA

Pat Appleson Studios Inc, pg 687
The Communications Group Inc, pg 729

PENNSYLVANIA

Innovision Media Group, pg 788
Production Masters Inc (PMI), pg 864

RHODE ISLAND

Sound-FX-Design, pg 894

TENNESSEE

Continental Film, pg 731

TEXAS

Cerutti Productions Inc, pg 720
Horizon Film + Video Productions, pg 781
Romar Learning Solutions LLC, pg 877
Stage Directions, pg 898
Texas Heart Institute Visual Communication Services, pg 911

VIRGINIA

CACI Integrated Communications, pg 713
Metro Productions, pg 824

WISCONSIN

5th Floor Recording Co, pg 760
Wisconsin Public Television, pg 940

WYOMING

Bridger Productions Inc, pg 710

ALBERTA

Black Media Works, pg 706
Global TV, pg 771

QUEBEC

Kerrigan Productions Inc, pg 798

News Program Rentals

NEW YORK

Richter Productions Inc, pg 875

ONTARIO

L-3 WESCAM, pg 802

Public Relations Program Distributors

CALIFORNIA

Christian Media Network, pg 722
Crystal Pyramid Productions™, pg 735
Direct Cinema Ltd Inc, pg 743
eFootage LLC, pg 751
Joseph Nicoletti Consulting-Promotion, pg 841

GEORGIA

Convergent Media Systems, pg 731

ILLINOIS

ABSA Films, pg 672

NEVADA

DVDs4Less, pg 748

NEW JERSEY

Allegro Productions Inc, pg 680

NEW YORK

Broadstreet Productions LLC, pg 711
HB-Content, pg 777
News Broadcast Network Inc, pg 840

PENNSYLVANIA

FMP Media Solutions Inc, pg 763

TENNESSEE

American Blackguard Inc, pg 683

VIRGINIA

CACI Integrated Communications, pg 713

ALBERTA

Global TV, pg 771

Public Relations Program Producers

ALABAMA

Leo Ticheli Productions, pg 913

ALASKA

Aurora Films, pg 696

ARIZONA

Candee Productions Inc, pg 716
Metropolitan Audio-Visual Inc, pg 824
Teaberry, pg 908

CALIFORNIA

Big Door, pg 705
Christian Media Network, pg 722
Classic Images Stock Footage LLC, pg 726
Crystal Pyramid Productions™, pg 735
Dolphin MultiMedia Inc, pg 745
Goal Productions, pg 772
Kavich Reynolds Productions Inc, pg 797
Main Street Media Inc, pg 815
The Media Staff Inc, pg 822
New & Unique Videos™, pg 839
Joseph Nicoletti Consulting-Promotion, pg 841
Point of View Productions, pg 858
QRS Software Services, pg 867
Dick Reizner Film & Video, pg 873
Glenn Roland Films, pg 876
Santa Barbara Location Services, pg 880
SNAP, pg 891
Tam Communications Inc, pg 906
Vineyard Video & Photography, pg 930
Webster Communications, pg 935
Zamacona Productions, pg 945

COLORADO

Flashback Media Productions, pg 762
Tatum Video, pg 907
Transtar Entertainment Co Inc, pg 917

CONNECTICUT

The Gary-Paul Agency, pg 768
New London Media, pg 839

DISTRICT OF COLUMBIA

Hillmann & Carr Inc, pg 780

FLORIDA

Accord Productions, pg 673
Blackburst Entertainment LLC, pg 706
Civins Productions Inc, pg 725
Communications Concepts Inc (CCI), pg 729
Jordan Klein Film & Video (JKFV), pg 795
Tel-Air Interests Inc, pg 909
Video Techniques Inc, pg 928

GEORGIA

Beachwood Productions, pg 702
Burst Video/Film Inc, pg 713
Guerrilla Productions LLC, pg 774
Myriad Productions, pg 835

HAWAII

Hyperspective Studios Inc, pg 783
1013 Integrated, pg 911

ILLINOIS

ABSA Films, pg 672
Cresta Creative, pg 734
Film Police, pg 760
Manning Productions, pg 816
Multimedia Marketing Group, pg 833
SCI Television & Creative Media LLC, pg 882
WEEK TV, pg 935
Winter Productions, pg 939

INDIANA

Road Pictures, pg 876

IOWA

Hellman Associates Inc, pg 778

KENTUCKY

Horizon Films & Media LLC, pg 781
Idle Minds Productions Inc, pg 784
Donna Lawrence Productions, pg 804

LOUISIANA

Digital FX Inc, pg 742
Moxie Media, pg 832

MARYLAND

Absolute Hollywood, pg 672
Richard Chisolm Cinematography, pg 722
dbF a Media Company, pg 739

MASSACHUSETTS

Green Mountain Post Films (GMP), pg 774
Heliotrope Studios, pg 778

MICHIGAN

K&R All Media Productions LLC, pg 796

MINNESOTA

House of Cinemagraphics, pg 782

NEVADA

DVDs4Less, pg 748

NEW HAMPSHIRE

Apertura, pg 686

NEW JERSEY

Allegro Productions Inc, pg 680
Concepts TV Productions Inc, pg 730
Telequest Inc, pg 910
TimeSteps Productions Inc, pg 914

NEW YORK

Ace Video, pg 674
aurora productions, pg 696
Blue Barn Pictures Inc, pg 707
Brian Film Productions LLC, pg 710
Broadstreet Productions LLC, pg 711
Buzzco Associates Inc, pg 713
Florentine Films, pg 762
Havas Creative, pg 776

HB-Content, pg 777
Ketchum Inc, pg 798
Kinetic Arts, pg 799
Jack Morton Worldwide, pg 830
News Broadcast Network Inc,
    pg 840
Northeast Video Productions Inc,
    pg 842
The Palmer Group, pg 850
Peckham Productions Inc, pg 852
Richter Productions Inc, pg 875
Zelman Studios Ltd, pg 945

NORTH CAROLINA

Pat Appleson Studios Inc, pg 687
The Communications Group Inc,
    pg 729
Horizon Video Productions Inc,
    pg 781
Kino Mountain Productions LLC,
    pg 799

OHIO

Advent Media Inc, pg 677

OREGON

Ideascape Inc, pg 784
Odyssey Productions Inc, pg 844

PENNSYLVANIA

FMP Media Solutions Inc, pg 763
Innovision Media Group, pg 788
JPL, pg 795
Main Point Productions, pg 815
Production Masters Inc (PMI),
    pg 864
Video/Film Associates, pg 928

RHODE ISLAND

Sound-FX-Design, pg 894

TENNESSEE

American Blackguard Inc, pg 683
Continental Film, pg 731
Memphis Communications Corp,
    pg 823
Scripps Networks, pg 882

TEXAS

AMS Pictures, pg 684
Biway Media, pg 706
Castleview Productions, pg 717
Cerutti Productions Inc, pg 720
The Editing Co, pg 750
Horizon Film + Video Productions,
    pg 781
Marx InDigital, pg 818
Earl Miller Productions Inc, pg 827
South Coast Film & Video, pg 895
Stage Directions, pg 898
Texas Heart Institute Visual
    Communication Services, pg 911

VIRGINIA

Altruist Media LLC, pg 682
BES Studios, pg 704
CACI Integrated Communications,
    pg 713
Metro Productions, pg 824

WASHINGTON

Adams Creative & Production
    Services, pg 675
Hamilton Studio, pg 775
North-by-Northwest - A Digital
    Studio, pg 842

WISCONSIN

5th Floor Recording Co, pg 760
Meridian Studios, pg 824
Video Wisconsin Inc, pg 929
Wisconsin Public Television, pg 940

WYOMING

Bridger Productions Inc, pg 710

ALBERTA

Black Media Works, pg 706
Global TV, pg 771

NORTHWEST TERRITORIES

Yellowknife Films Inc, pg 944

QUEBEC

Kerrigan Productions Inc, pg 798

Public Relations Program Rentals

CALIFORNIA

Direct Cinema Ltd Inc, pg 743

GEORGIA

Convergent Media Systems, pg 731

Public Service Announcement Distributors

CALIFORNIA

Crystal Pyramid Productions™,
    pg 735
New & Unique Videos™, pg 839

ILLINOIS

ABSA Films, pg 672

NEVADA

DVDs4Less, pg 748

NEW JERSEY

Allegro Productions Inc, pg 680

NEW YORK

HB-Content, pg 777
News Broadcast Network Inc,
    pg 840

OHIO

Franciscan Media, pg 765

TENNESSEE

American Blackguard Inc, pg 683

VIRGINIA

CACI Integrated Communications,
    pg 713

WISCONSIN

Wisconsin Public Television, pg 940

ALBERTA

Global TV, pg 771

Public Service Announcement Producers

ALASKA

Aurora Films, pg 696

ARIZONA

Candee Productions Inc, pg 716
Film Creations Ltd, pg 760
Metropolitan Audio-Visual Inc,
    pg 824

CALIFORNIA

Big Door, pg 705
Classic Images Stock Footage LLC,
    pg 726
Concrete Images, pg 730
Crystal Pyramid Productions™,
    pg 735
Custom Video Productions Inc,
    pg 736
GAMfilm Productions, pg 768
imageReal Pictures LLC, pg 785
Kavich Reynolds Productions Inc,
    pg 797
KTVU-Retail Services, pg 802
Main Street Media Inc, pg 815
The Media Staff Inc, pg 822
New & Unique Videos™, pg 839
New Circuit Films LLC, pg 839
Point of View Productions, pg 858
QRS Software Services, pg 867
Glenn Roland Films, pg 876
Santa Barbara Location Services,
    pg 880
SNAP, pg 891
Tam Communications Inc, pg 906
Video Resources Inc, pg 928
Vineyard Video & Photography,
    pg 930
Webster Communications, pg 935
Zamacona Productions, pg 945

COLORADO

Flashback Media Productions,
    pg 762
Transtar Entertainment Co Inc,
    pg 917

CONNECTICUT

ACM Productions Ltd, pg 674
The Gary-Paul Agency, pg 768
Moving Pictures, pg 832

DISTRICT OF COLUMBIA

Hillmann & Carr Inc, pg 780

FLORIDA

Accord Productions, pg 673
Blackburst Entertainment LLC,
    pg 706
Civins Productions Inc, pg 725
Communications Concepts Inc
    (CCI), pg 729
CopShopMiami.com, pg 731
Jordan Klein Film & Video (JKFV),
    pg 795
Tel-Air Interests Inc, pg 909
Video Techniques Inc, pg 928

GEORGIA

Beachwood Productions, pg 702
Burst Video/Film Inc, pg 713
Guerrilla Productions LLC, pg 774

HAWAII

Hyperspective Studios Inc, pg 783

ILLINOIS

ABSA Films, pg 672
Film Police, pg 760
Manning Productions, pg 816
Multimedia Marketing Group,
    pg 833
SCI Television & Creative Media
    LLC, pg 882
Winter Productions, pg 939

INDIANA

Road Pictures, pg 876

KENTUCKY

Idle Minds Productions Inc, pg 784

LOUISIANA

Digital FX Inc, pg 742
Moxie Media, pg 832

MARYLAND

Absolute Hollywood, pg 672
Richard Chisolm Cinematography,
    pg 722
dbF a Media Company, pg 739
The Image Generators, pg 785

MASSACHUSETTS

Green Mountain Post Films (GMP),
    pg 774
Heliotrope Studios, pg 778
MotionArt Studios, pg 831
Northern Light Productions (NLP),
    pg 842

MICHIGAN

K&R All Media Productions LLC,
    pg 796

MINNESOTA

House of Cinemagraphics, pg 782

NEVADA

DVDs4Less, pg 748

NEW HAMPSHIRE

Apertura, pg 686

NEW JERSEY

Allegro Productions Inc, pg 680
TimeSteps Productions Inc, pg 914

NEW YORK

aurora productions, pg 696
Blue Barn Pictures Inc, pg 707
Broadstreet Productions LLC,
    pg 711
De Nonno Productions Inc (DPI),
    pg 739
Fanlight Productions, pg 759
Florentine Films, pg 762
Havas Creative, pg 776
HB-Content, pg 777
Ketchum Inc, pg 798
Kinetic Arts, pg 799
Jack Morton Worldwide, pg 830
News Broadcast Network Inc,
    pg 840
The Palmer Group, pg 850
Pat Kogan Productions Inc, pg 852
Polestar Films & Associated Arts
    Ltd, pg 859

PROGRAMMING — FILM

Public Service Announcement Producers (continued)

NEW YORK (continued)

Alan Weiss Productions, pg 935
Zelman Studios Ltd, pg 945

NORTH CAROLINA

Pat Appleson Studios Inc, pg 687
The Communications Group Inc, pg 729
Horizon Video Productions Inc, pg 781
Kino Mountain Productions LLC, pg 799

OHIO

Advent Media Inc, pg 677
Franciscan Media, pg 765
Lyon Video Inc, pg 813
Take 1 Media Services, pg 906

OREGON

Ideascape Inc, pg 784
Odyssey Productions Inc, pg 844
Production West, pg 864

PENNSYLVANIA

Bang! Pictures Inc, pg 701
Innovision Media Group, pg 788
JPL, pg 795
Kensington Falls Animation, pg 797
Muderick Media, pg 833
Production Masters Inc (PMI), pg 864
Video/Film Associates, pg 928

RHODE ISLAND

Sound-FX-Design, pg 894

TENNESSEE

American Blackguard Inc, pg 683
Continental Film, pg 731

TEXAS

AMS Pictures, pg 684
Biway Media, pg 706
Castleview Productions, pg 717
Cerutti Productions Inc, pg 720
The Editing Co, pg 750
Horizon Film + Video Productions, pg 781
Stage Directions, pg 898
Texas Heart Institute Visual Communication Services, pg 911

VIRGINIA

Altruist Media LLC, pg 682
BES Studios, pg 704
CACI Integrated Communications, pg 713
Metro Productions, pg 824
Studio Center Corp, pg 902

WASHINGTON

Hamilton Studio, pg 775
Victory Studios, pg 927
White Rain Films Ltd, pg 937

WISCONSIN

5th Floor Recording Co, pg 760
Meridian Studios, pg 824
University of Wisconsin-Oshkosh Radio-TV-Film Dept, pg 923
Wisconsin Public Television, pg 940

WYOMING

Bridger Productions Inc, pg 710

ALBERTA

Black Media Works, pg 706
Global TV, pg 771

ONTARIO

Mediaimage Communications Group, pg 822

QUEBEC

Kerrigan Productions Inc, pg 798

Religious Program Distributors

ARIZONA

Teaberry, pg 908

CALIFORNIA

Christian Media Network, pg 722
Direct Cinema Ltd Inc, pg 743
Joyce Media Inc, pg 795

CONNECTICUT

Hartley Film Foundation, pg 776

DISTRICT OF COLUMBIA

USCCB Publishing, pg 923

HAWAII

Media Bridge Gamekids, pg 821

ILLINOIS

Baha'i Distribution Service (BDS), pg 700
Film Ideas Inc, pg 760

MASSACHUSETTS

Documentary Educational Resources Inc, pg 744

MICHIGAN

Emery-Pratt Co, pg 753

MINNESOTA

Festival Films, pg 759

NEW JERSEY

Alden Films, pg 679
Ergo Media Inc, pg 755

NEW YORK

First Run Features, pg 761
Hallel Communications, pg 775
Janson Media Inc, pg 793
SISU Home Entertainment Inc, pg 889
Women Make Movies Inc, pg 941

NORTH CAROLINA

World Wide Pictures Inc, pg 941

OHIO

Franciscan Media, pg 765

PENNSYLVANIA

Bullfrog Films Inc, pg 712
FMP Media Solutions Inc, pg 763

TENNESSEE

Spring Arbor Distributors Inc, pg 898

TEXAS

Lamb & Lion Ministries, pg 803

Religious Program Producers

ALASKA

Aurora Films, pg 696

CALIFORNIA

Christian Media Network, pg 722
Classic Images Stock Footage LLC, pg 726
Custom Video Productions Inc, pg 736
Dolphin MultiMedia Inc, pg 745
Joyce Media Inc, pg 795
QRS Software Services, pg 867
Roadside Attractions, pg 876
Glenn Roland Films, pg 876
SNAP, pg 891
TVA Media Group, pg 919
Video Resources Inc, pg 928

COLORADO

Flashback Media Productions, pg 762

CONNECTICUT

The Gary-Paul Agency, pg 768
Hartley Film Foundation, pg 776

DISTRICT OF COLUMBIA

USCCB Publishing, pg 923

FLORIDA

Blackburst Entertainment LLC, pg 706
CopShopMiami.com, pg 731
Jordan Klein Film & Video (JKFV), pg 795
Tel-Air Interests Inc, pg 909

GEORGIA

Beachwood Productions, pg 702
Burst Video/Film Inc, pg 713
Guerrilla Productions LLC, pg 774

HAWAII

Hyperspective Studios Inc, pg 783
Media Bridge Gamekids, pg 821

ILLINOIS

The Market Place, pg 817
Multimedia Marketing Group, pg 833
SCI Television & Creative Media LLC, pg 882
Winter Productions, pg 939

KENTUCKY

Idle Minds Productions Inc, pg 784

LOUISIANA

Moxie Media, pg 832

MARYLAND

Absolute Hollywood, pg 672
dbF a Media Company, pg 739

MASSACHUSETTS

Documentary Educational Resources Inc, pg 744

MICHIGAN

K&R All Media Productions LLC, pg 796

MINNESOTA

House of Cinemagraphics, pg 782

NEW HAMPSHIRE

Apertura, pg 686

NEW JERSEY

Alden Films, pg 679

NEW YORK

aurora productions, pg 696
Brian Film Productions LLC, pg 710
Hallel Communications, pg 775
Havas Creative, pg 776
Jack Morton Worldwide, pg 830
The Palmer Group, pg 850
Richter Productions Inc, pg 875
Zelman Studios Ltd, pg 945

NORTH CAROLINA

Pat Appleson Studios Inc, pg 687
The Communications Group Inc, pg 729

OHIO

Franciscan Media, pg 765
Take 1 Media Services, pg 906

PENNSYLVANIA

FMP Media Solutions Inc, pg 763
JPL, pg 795

RHODE ISLAND

Sound-FX-Design, pg 894

TENNESSEE

Continental Film, pg 731
Memphis Communications Corp, pg 823

TEXAS

Cerutti Productions Inc, pg 720
The Editing Co, pg 750
Horizon Film + Video Productions, pg 781
Lamb & Lion Ministries, pg 803
Earl Miller Productions Inc, pg 827
South Coast Film & Video, pg 895
Stage Directions, pg 898

VIRGINIA

Altruist Media LLC, pg 682
Metro Productions, pg 824

WISCONSIN

5th Floor Recording Co, pg 760

WYOMING
Bridger Productions Inc, pg 710

QUEBEC
Kerrigan Productions Inc, pg 798

Religious Program Rentals

CALIFORNIA
Direct Cinema Ltd Inc, pg 743

MASSACHUSETTS
Documentary Educational Resources Inc, pg 744

MISSOURI
University of Missouri-Columbia, pg 923

NEW JERSEY
Alden Films, pg 679

NEW YORK
First Run Features, pg 761
Hallel Communications, pg 775

NORTH CAROLINA
World Wide Pictures Inc, pg 941

OHIO
Franciscan Media, pg 765

PENNSYLVANIA
Bullfrog Films, pg 712

Research—Technical Program, *see* Technical Research Program

Sales Promotion & Training Program Distributors

CALIFORNIA
Christian Media Network, pg 722
Crystal Pyramid Productions™, pg 735
Direct Cinema Ltd Inc, pg 743
Em Gee Film Library, pg 753
New & Unique Videos™, pg 839

ILLINOIS
ABSA Films, pg 672

NEVADA
DVDs4Less, pg 748

NEW JERSEY
Allegro Productions Inc, pg 680
MiB MediaWorks, pg 825

NEW YORK
HB-Content, pg 777

PENNSYLVANIA
FMP Media Solutions Inc, pg 763
New Horizons Computer Learning Centers Inc, pg 839

TENNESSEE
American Blackguard Inc, pg 683

VIRGINIA
CACI Integrated Communications, pg 713

ONTARIO
Kineticvideo.com, pg 799

Sales Promotion & Training Program Producers

ALABAMA
Leo Ticheli Productions, pg 913

ARIZONA
Candee Productions Inc, pg 716
Film Creations Ltd, pg 760
Metropolitan Audio-Visual Inc, pg 824

CALIFORNIA
Aaron Marcus and Associates, pg 671
Big Door, pg 705
Christian Media Network, pg 722
Classic Images Stock Footage LLC, pg 726
Concrete Images, pg 730
Crystal Pyramid Productions™, pg 735
Custom Video Productions Inc, pg 736
Design Media, pg 741
Dolphin MultiMedia Inc, pg 745
Kavich Reynolds Productions Inc, pg 797
KTVU-Retail Services, pg 802
Main Street Media Inc, pg 815
The Media Staff Inc, pg 822
New & Unique Videos™, pg 839
People Skills International, pg 854
PK Productions, pg 857
Point of View Productions, pg 858
QRS Software Services, pg 867
Dick Reizner Film & Video, pg 873
RetinaVision Productions, pg 874
Glenn Roland Films, pg 876
Santa Barbara Location Services, pg 880
SNAP, pg 891
Tam Communications Inc, pg 906
Vineyard Video & Photography, pg 930
Webster Communications, pg 935
Zamacona Productions, pg 945

COLORADO
Flashback Media Productions, pg 762
Transtar Entertainment Co Inc, pg 917

CONNECTICUT
The Gary-Paul Agency, pg 768

FLORIDA
Accord Productions, pg 673
Blackburst Entertainment LLC, pg 706
Communications Concepts Inc (CCI), pg 729
Jordan Klein Film & Video (JKFV), pg 795

Tel-Air Interests Inc, pg 909
Video Techniques Inc, pg 928

GEORGIA
Beachwood Productions, pg 702
Burst Video/Film Inc, pg 713
Guerrilla Productions LLC, pg 774
Myriad Productions, pg 835

HAWAII
Hyperspective Studios Inc, pg 783

ILLINOIS
ABSA Films, pg 672
Cresta Creative, pg 734
Film Police, pg 760
Manning Productions, pg 816
Mightybytes Inc, pg 827
Multimedia Marketing Group, pg 833
Richter Studios, pg 875
SCI Television & Creative Media LLC, pg 882
Winter Productions, pg 939

INDIANA
Road Pictures, pg 876

IOWA
Hellman Associates Inc, pg 778

KENTUCKY
Idle Minds Productions Inc, pg 784

LOUISIANA
Digital FX Inc, pg 742
Moxie Media, pg 832

MARYLAND
Absolute Hollywood, pg 672
Richard Chisolm Cinematography, pg 722
dbF a Media Company, pg 739
The Image Generators, pg 785

MASSACHUSETTS
CommCreative, pg 728
Green Mountain Post Films (GMP), pg 774
Northern Light Productions (NLP), pg 842

MICHIGAN
K&R All Media Productions LLC, pg 796
Lawrence Productions Inc, pg 804

MINNESOTA
House of Cinemagraphics, pg 782

MISSOURI
Hardcastle Films & Video, pg 776

NEVADA
DVDs4Less, pg 748

NEW HAMPSHIRE
Apertura, pg 686

NEW JERSEY
Allegro Productions Inc, pg 680
Concepts TV Productions Inc, pg 730
MiB MediaWorks, pg 825

Telequest Inc, pg 910
TimeSteps Productions Inc, pg 914

NEW MEXICO
Rainbow International Inc, pg 869

NEW YORK
Ace Video, pg 674
aurora productions, pg 696
Blue Barn Pictures Inc, pg 707
Brian Film Productions LLC, pg 710
Broadstreet Productions LLC, pg 711
Havas Creative, pg 776
HB-Content, pg 777
Ketchum Inc, pg 798
Jack Morton Worldwide, pg 830
News Broadcast Network Inc, pg 840
Northeast Video Productions Inc, pg 842
The Palmer Group, pg 850
Pat Kogan Productions Inc, pg 852
Peckham Productions Inc, pg 852
Zelman Studios Ltd, pg 945

NORTH CAROLINA
Pat Appleson Studios Inc, pg 687
The Communications Group Inc, pg 729
Horizon Video Productions Inc, pg 781
Kino Mountain Productions LLC, pg 799

OHIO
Advent Media Inc, pg 677
Lyon Video Inc, pg 813
Take 1 Media Services, pg 906

OREGON
Ideascape Inc, pg 784
Odyssey Productions Inc, pg 844

PENNSYLVANIA
Argentine Productions Inc, pg 688
FMP Media Solutions Inc, pg 763
Innovision Media Group, pg 788
JPL, pg 795
Kensington Falls Animation, pg 797
Main Point Productions, pg 815
Muderick Media, pg 833
New Horizons Computer Learning Centers Inc, pg 839
Production Masters Inc (PMI), pg 864
Video/Film Associates, pg 928

RHODE ISLAND
Sound-FX-Design, pg 894

TENNESSEE
American Blackguard Inc, pg 683
Continental Film, pg 731
Memphis Communications Corp, pg 823
Scripps Networks, pg 882
Stage Post, pg 899

TEXAS
Aries Productions Inc, pg 688
Biway Media, pg 706
Castleview Productions, pg 717
Cerutti Productions Inc, pg 720
The Editing Co, pg 750
Horizon Film + Video Productions, pg 781

PROGRAMMING — FILM

Sales Promotion & Training Program Producers (continued)

TEXAS (continued)

Marx InDigital, pg 818
Earl Miller Productions Inc, pg 827
Romar Learning Solutions LLC, pg 877
South Coast Film & Video, pg 895

VERMONT

Marlboro Productions, pg 817

VIRGINIA

Altruist Media LLC, pg 682
BES Studios, pg 704
CACI Integrated Communications, pg 713
Metro Productions, pg 824

WASHINGTON

Adams Creative & Production Services, pg 675
Hamilton Studio, pg 775
North-by-Northwest - A Digital Studio, pg 842
Victory Studios, pg 927
White Rain Films Ltd, pg 937

WISCONSIN

Audio Visual of Milwaukee Inc, pg 694
Clear Focus Media LLC, pg 726
5th Floor Recording Co, pg 760
Meridian Studios, pg 824
University of Wisconsin-Oshkosh Radio-TV-Film Dept, pg 923
Wisconsin Public Television, pg 940

WYOMING

Bridger Productions Inc, pg 710

ALBERTA

Black Media Works, pg 706

QUEBEC

Kerrigan Productions Inc, pg 798

Sales Promotion & Training Program Rentals

CALIFORNIA

Direct Cinema Ltd Inc, pg 743
Em Gee Film Library, pg 753

Scientific Program Distributors

Allied Artists International Inc, pg 681
Crystal Pyramid Productions™, pg 735
Direct Cinema Ltd Inc, pg 743
Em Gee Film Library, pg 753
Glenn Photo Supply, pg 771
New & Unique Videos™, pg 839
TMW Media Group, pg 915
The Wine Appreciation Guild Ltd, pg 939

GEORGIA

School Media Associates LLC, pg 882

KENTUCKY

National Geographic Learning, pg 836

MASSACHUSETTS

Documentary Educational Resources Inc, pg 744

MICHIGAN

Emery-Pratt Co, pg 753

NEW JERSEY

Allegro Productions Inc, pg 680

NEW YORK

Films Media Group, pg 760
Icarus Films Inc, pg 783
Janson Media Inc, pg 793
Mastervision Inc, pg 819
Richter Productions Inc, pg 875
VIEW Inc (Video International Entertainment World Inc), pg 930

PENNSYLVANIA

Bullfrog Films Inc, pg 712
FMP Media Solutions Inc, pg 763

TEXAS

CEV Multimedia Ltd, pg 720
Emergency Film Group, pg 753
Texas Heart Institute Visual Communication Services, pg 911

VIRGINIA

CACI Integrated Communications, pg 713

ONTARIO

IMAX Corp, pg 786
Kineticvideo.com, pg 799
McIntyre Media Inc, pg 821

QUEBEC

Les Productions Via Le Monde (Daniel Bertolino) Inc, pg 864

Scientific Program Producers

ARIZONA

Film Creations Ltd, pg 760
Teaberry, pg 908

CALIFORNIA

Allied Artists International Inc, pg 681
Big Door, pg 705
Classic Images Stock Footage LLC, pg 726
Crystal Pyramid Productions™, pg 735
Custom Video Productions Inc, pg 736
Davidson Productions, pg 738
Dolphin MultiMedia Inc, pg 745
Goal Productions, pg 772
imageReal Pictures LLC, pg 785
Kavich Reynolds Productions Inc, pg 797
Main Street Media Inc, pg 815

The Media Staff Inc, pg 822
New & Unique Videos™, pg 839
Point of View Productions, pg 858
QRS Software Services, pg 867
RetinaVision Productions, pg 874
Glenn Roland Films, pg 876
SNAP, pg 891
TMW Media Group, pg 915

COLORADO

Flashback Media Productions, pg 762
Transtar Entertainment Co Inc, pg 917

DISTRICT OF COLUMBIA

Hillmann & Carr Inc, pg 780

FLORIDA

Accord Productions, pg 673
Blackburst Entertainment LLC, pg 706
Civins Productions Inc, pg 725
Jordan Klein Film & Video (JKFV), pg 795
Karst Productions Inc, pg 796

GEORGIA

Beachwood Productions, pg 702
Guerrilla Productions LLC, pg 774

HAWAII

Hyperspective Studios Inc, pg 783

ILLINOIS

Film Police, pg 760
SCI Television & Creative Media LLC, pg 882

KENTUCKY

Donna Lawrence Productions, pg 804
National Geographic Learning, pg 836

LOUISIANA

Moxie Media, pg 832

MARYLAND

Absolute Hollywood, pg 672
Richard Chisolm Cinematography, pg 722
dbF a Media Company, pg 739

MASSACHUSETTS

Documentary Educational Resources Inc, pg 744
Green Mountain Post Films (GMP), pg 774
Heliotrope Studios, pg 778
Northern Light Productions (NLP), pg 842

MICHIGAN

K&R All Media Productions LLC, pg 796

MINNESOTA

House of Cinemagraphics, pg 782

NEW HAMPSHIRE

Apertura, pg 686

NEW JERSEY

Allegro Productions Inc, pg 680

NEW YORK

Ace Video, pg 674
aurora productions, pg 696
Blue Barn Pictures Inc, pg 707
Brian Film Productions LLC, pg 710
Broadstreet Productions LLC, pg 711
Films Media Group, pg 760
Havas Creative, pg 776
Ketchum Inc, pg 798
Mastervision Inc, pg 819
Jack Morton Worldwide, pg 830
News Broadcast Network Inc, pg 840
The Palmer Group, pg 850
Peckham Productions Inc, pg 852
Richter Productions Inc, pg 875
VIEW Inc (Video International Entertainment World Inc), pg 930
Zelman Studios Ltd, pg 945

NORTH CAROLINA

Pat Appleson Studios Inc, pg 687
The Communications Group Inc, pg 729
Kino Mountain Productions LLC, pg 799

OHIO

Take 1 Media Services, pg 906

OREGON

Ideascape Inc, pg 784
Odyssey Productions Inc, pg 844

PENNSYLVANIA

FMP Media Solutions Inc, pg 763
Innovision Media Group, pg 788
Production Masters Inc (PMI), pg 864

RHODE ISLAND

Sound-FX-Design, pg 894

TENNESSEE

Continental Film, pg 731
Memphis Communications Corp, pg 823
Scripps Networks, pg 882

TEXAS

Cerutti Productions Inc, pg 720
CEV Multimedia Ltd, pg 720
The Editing Co, pg 750
Emergency Film Group, pg 753
Epic Software Group Inc, pg 755
Horizon Film + Video Productions, pg 781
Earl Miller Productions Inc, pg 827
Romar Learning Solutions LLC, pg 877
Texas Heart Institute Visual Communication Services, pg 911

VIRGINIA

Altruist Media LLC, pg 682
CACI Integrated Communications, pg 713
Metro Productions, pg 824

WISCONSIN

5th Floor Recording Co, pg 760
Wisconsin Public Television, pg 940

WYOMING

Bridger Productions Inc, pg 710

ALBERTA
Black Media Works, pg 706

BRITISH COLUMBIA
West Eagle Films Inc, pg 935

NORTHWEST TERRITORIES
Yellowknife Films Inc, pg 944

ONTARIO
IMAX Corp, pg 786

QUEBEC
Kerrigan Productions Inc, pg 798
Les Productions Via Le Monde
  (Daniel Bertolino) Inc, pg 864

Scientific Program Rentals

CALIFORNIA
Direct Cinema Ltd Inc, pg 743
Em Gee Film Library, pg 753
Glenn Photo Supply, pg 771

KENTUCKY
National Geographic Learning,
  pg 836

MASSACHUSETTS
Documentary Educational Resources
  Inc, pg 744

MINNESOTA
Science Museum of Minnesota,
  pg 882

MISSOURI
University of Missouri-Columbia,
  pg 923

NEW YORK
American Museum of Natural
  History (AMNH), pg 683
Films Media Group, pg 760
Richter Productions Inc, pg 875

PENNSYLVANIA
Bullfrog Films Inc, pg 712

QUEBEC
Les Productions Via Le Monde
  (Daniel Bertolino) Inc, pg 864

Seventy mm Films, *see* Films—70mm

Short Film, *see* Theatrical Short

Sixteen mm Films, *see* Films—16mm

Sponsored Program Distributors

CALIFORNIA
Crystal Pyramid Productions™,
  pg 735
Direct Cinema Ltd Inc, pg 743

New & Unique Videos™, pg 839
Visual Communications - Southern
  California Asian American
  Studies Central Inc, pg 931

ILLINOIS
Terra Nova Films Inc, pg 911

MARYLAND
DSR Computer Technology
  Specialists Inc, pg 747

NEVADA
DVDs4Less, pg 748

NEW JERSEY
Allegro Productions Inc, pg 680

NEW YORK
Broadstreet Productions LLC,
  pg 711
William Greaves Productions Inc,
  pg 774
HB-Content, pg 777
VIEW Inc (Video International
  Entertainment World Inc), pg 930

PENNSYLVANIA
Bullfrog Films Inc, pg 712

TENNESSEE
American Blackguard Inc, pg 683

QUEBEC
Les Productions Via Le Monde
  (Daniel Bertolino) Inc, pg 864

Sponsored Program Producers

ALABAMA
Leo Ticheli Productions, pg 913

CALIFORNIA
A Go Go Films, pg 671
Big Door, pg 705
Classic Images Stock Footage LLC,
  pg 726
Crystal Pyramid Productions™,
  pg 735
Custom Video Productions Inc,
  pg 736
Davidson Productions, pg 738
imageReal Pictures LLC, pg 785
KTVU-Retail Services, pg 802
Main Street Media Inc, pg 815
The Media Staff Inc, pg 822
New & Unique Videos™, pg 839
Point of View Productions, pg 858
QRS Software Services, pg 867
Glenn Roland Films, pg 876
SNAP, pg 891
Visual Communications - Southern
  California Asian American
  Studies Central Inc, pg 931

COLORADO
Flashback Media Productions,
  pg 762
Transtar Entertainment Co Inc,
  pg 917

DISTRICT OF COLUMBIA
Hillmann & Carr Inc, pg 780

FLORIDA
Accord Productions, pg 673
Blackburst Entertainment LLC,
  pg 706
Communications Concepts Inc
  (CCI), pg 729
Courter Films LLC, pg 732
Jordan Klein Film & Video (JKFV),
  pg 795
Karst Productions Inc, pg 796
Tel-Air Interests Inc, pg 909

GEORGIA
Beachwood Productions, pg 702
Burst Video/Film Inc, pg 713
Guerrilla Productions LLC, pg 774
Myriad Productions, pg 835

HAWAII
Hyperspective Studios Inc, pg 783
1013 Integrated, pg 911

ILLINOIS
Film Police, pg 760
Multimedia Marketing Group,
  pg 833
SCI Television & Creative Media
  LLC, pg 882
Terra Nova Films Inc, pg 911
Winter Productions, pg 939

INDIANA
Road Pictures, pg 876

KENTUCKY
Donna Lawrence Productions,
  pg 804

LOUISIANA
Moxie Media, pg 832

MARYLAND
Absolute Hollywood, pg 672
Richard Chisolm Cinematography,
  pg 722
dbF a Media Company, pg 739
DSR Computer Technology
  Specialists Inc, pg 747

MASSACHUSETTS
Green Mountain Post Films (GMP),
  pg 773
Heliotrope Studios, pg 778

MICHIGAN
K&R All Media Productions LLC,
  pg 796

MINNESOTA
House of Cinemagraphics, pg 782

NEVADA
DVDs4Less, pg 748

NEW HAMPSHIRE
Apertura, pg 686

NEW JERSEY
Allegro Productions Inc, pg 680
Telequest Inc, pg 910
TimeSteps Productions Inc, pg 914

NEW YORK
Ace Video, pg 674
aurora productions, pg 696
Blue Barn Pictures Inc, pg 707
Brian Film Productions LLC,
  pg 710
Broadstreet Productions LLC,
  pg 711
Florentine Films, pg 762
William Greaves Productions Inc,
  pg 774
HB-Content, pg 777
Ketchum Inc, pg 798
Jack Morton Worldwide, pg 830
News Broadcast Network Inc,
  pg 840
The Palmer Group, pg 850
Pat Kogan Productions Inc, pg 852
Peckham Productions Inc, pg 852
R/GA, pg 868
Richter Productions Inc, pg 875
VIEW Inc (Video International
  Entertainment World Inc), pg 930
Zelman Studios Ltd, pg 945

NORTH CAROLINA
Pat Appleson Studios Inc, pg 687
The Communications Group Inc,
  pg 729

OHIO
Advent Media Inc, pg 677
Lyon Video Inc, pg 813
Take 1 Media Services, pg 906

OREGON
Ideascape Inc, pg 784
Odyssey Productions Inc, pg 844

PENNSYLVANIA
Innovision Media Group, pg 788
JPL, pg 795
Production Masters Inc (PMI),
  pg 864
Video/Film Associates, pg 928

RHODE ISLAND
Sound-FX-Design, pg 894

TENNESSEE
American Blackguard Inc, pg 683
Continental Film, pg 731
Scripps Networks, pg 882

TEXAS
AMS Pictures, pg 684
Cerutti Productions Inc, pg 720
Horizon Film + Video Productions,
  pg 781
Earl Miller Productions Inc, pg 827
Romar Learning Solutions LLC,
  pg 877
South Coast Film & Video, pg 895
Texas Heart Institute Visual
  Communication Services, pg 911

VIRGINIA
Altruist Media LLC, pg 682
BES Studios, pg 704
Metro Productions, pg 824

WASHINGTON
Victory Studios, pg 927

PROGRAMMING — FILM

Sponsored Program Producers (continued)

WISCONSIN

Audio Visual of Milwaukee Inc, pg 694
5th Floor Recording Co, pg 760

WYOMING

Bridger Productions Inc, pg 710

ALBERTA

Global TV, pg 771

BRITISH COLUMBIA

West Eagle Films Inc, pg 935

QUEBEC

Kerrigan Productions Inc, pg 798
Les Productions Via Le Monde (Daniel Bertolino) Inc, pg 864

Sponsored Program Rentals

CALIFORNIA

Direct Cinema Ltd Inc, pg 743
Visual Communications - Southern California Asian American Studies Central Inc, pg 931

ILLINOIS

Terra Nova Films Inc, pg 911

NEW YORK

William Greaves Productions Inc, pg 774
VIEW Inc (Video International Entertainment World Inc), pg 930

PENNSYLVANIA

Bullfrog Films Inc, pg 712

Sports Program Distributors

CALIFORNIA

Allied Artists International Inc, pg 681
Crystal Pyramid Productions™, pg 735
Direct Cinema Ltd Inc, pg 743
Em Gee Film Library, pg 753
Glenn Photo Supply, pg 771
Goal Productions, pg 772
MarVista Entertainment Inc, pg 818
New & Unique Videos™, pg 839
Nineteen87, pg 841
Glenn Roland Films, pg 876
TMW Media Group, pg 915
Universal Pictures Home Entertainment, pg 922

COLORADO

Tatum Video, pg 907

FLORIDA

Accord Productions, pg 673

IOWA

Championship Productions Inc, pg 720

MASSACHUSETTS

The New Film Company Inc, pg 839

NEBRASKA

The Recruiters Library, pg 872

NEW HAMPSHIRE

YMAA Publication Center Inc, pg 944

NEW JERSEY

Allegro Productions Inc, pg 680
Euro-Pacific Film & Video Productions Inc, pg 756

NEW YORK

Broadstreet Productions LLC, pg 711
HB-Content, pg 777
Janson Media Inc, pg 793
Mastervision Inc, pg 819
VIEW Inc (Video International Entertainment World Inc), pg 930
Women Make Movies Inc, pg 941

PENNSYLVANIA

Bullfrog Films Inc, pg 712
FMP Media Solutions Inc, pg 763

TENNESSEE

Spring Arbor Distributors Inc, pg 898

VIRGINIA

CACI Integrated Communications, pg 713

ALBERTA

Global TV, pg 771

ONTARIO

Sullivan Home Entertainment, pg 903

Sports Program Producers

ARIZONA

Candee Productions Inc, pg 716

CALIFORNIA

A Go Go Films, pg 671
Allied Artists International Inc, pg 681
Big Door, pg 705
Cinevest, pg 725
Classic Images Stock Footage LLC, pg 726
Crystal Pyramid Productions™, pg 735
Custom Video Productions Inc, pg 736
Goal Productions, pg 772
Havas Edge, pg 777
Jaguar Distribution Corp, pg 792
Kavich Reynolds Productions Inc, pg 797
New & Unique Videos™, pg 839
Nineteen87, pg 841
QRS Software Services, pg 867
Glenn Roland Films, pg 876

SNAP, pg 891
TMW Media Group, pg 915
Universal Pictures Home Entertainment, pg 922
Webster Communications, pg 935

COLORADO

CSI Film & Video LLC, pg 735
Tatum Video, pg 907
Transtar Entertainment Co Inc, pg 917

CONNECTICUT

The Gary-Paul Agency, pg 768

FLORIDA

Accord Productions, pg 673
Blackburst Entertainment LLC, pg 706
Communications Concepts Inc (CCI), pg 729
Courter Films LLC, pg 732
Jordan Klein Film & Video (JKFV), pg 795
Tel-Air Interests Inc, pg 909

GEORGIA

Beachwood Productions, pg 702
Guerrilla Productions LLC, pg 774
Myriad Productions, pg 835

HAWAII

Hyperspective Studios Inc, pg 783

ILLINOIS

Film Police, pg 760
SCI Television & Creative Media LLC, pg 882

IOWA

Championship Productions Inc, pg 720

KENTUCKY

Idle Minds Productions Inc, pg 784
Donna Lawrence Productions, pg 804

LOUISIANA

Moxie Media, pg 832

MARYLAND

Absolute Hollywood, pg 672
dbF a Media Company, pg 739

MASSACHUSETTS

Green Mountain Post Films (GMP), pg 774

MICHIGAN

K&R All Media Productions LLC, pg 796

MINNESOTA

House of Cinemagraphics, pg 782

NEBRASKA

The Recruiters Library, pg 872

NEW HAMPSHIRE

Apertura, pg 686
YMAA Publication Center Inc, pg 944

NEW JERSEY

Allegro Productions Inc, pg 680
Euro-Pacific Film & Video Productions Inc, pg 756

NEW YORK

aurora productions, pg 696
Blue Barn Pictures Inc, pg 707
Brian Film Productions LLC, pg 710
Broadstreet Productions LLC, pg 711
Florentine Films, pg 762
Havas Creative, pg 776
HB-Content, pg 777
Jalbert Productions International, pg 792
Mastervision Inc, pg 819
Jack Morton Worldwide, pg 830
The Palmer Group, pg 850
Peckham Productions Inc, pg 852
VIEW Inc (Video International Entertainment World Inc), pg 930
Zelman Studios Ltd, pg 945

NORTH CAROLINA

Pat Appleson Studios Inc, pg 687
The Communications Group Inc, pg 729
Kino Mountain Productions LLC, pg 799

OREGON

Odyssey Productions Inc, pg 844

PENNSYLVANIA

Bang! Pictures Inc, pg 701
FMP Media Solutions Inc, pg 763
Innovision Media Group, pg 788
Kensington Falls Animation, pg 797
Production Masters Inc (PMI), pg 864

RHODE ISLAND

Sound-FX-Design, pg 894

TENNESSEE

Continental Film, pg 731

TEXAS

Cerutti Productions Inc, pg 720
Horizon Film + Video Productions, pg 781
Earl Miller Productions Inc, pg 827

VIRGINIA

CACI Integrated Communications, pg 713
Metro Productions, pg 824

WASHINGTON

Victory Studios, pg 927

WISCONSIN

5th Floor Recording Co, pg 760
Wisconsin Public Television, pg 940

WYOMING

Bridger Productions Inc, pg 710

ALBERTA

Black Media Works, pg 706
Global TV, pg 771

BRITISH COLUMBIA

Network Entertainment Inc, pg 838

QUEBEC

Kerrigan Productions Inc, pg 798

Sports Program Rentals

CALIFORNIA

Direct Cinema Ltd Inc, pg 743
Em Gee Film Library, pg 753
Glenn Photo Supply, pg 771

COLORADO

Tatum Video, pg 907

MISSOURI

University of Missouri-Columbia,
pg 923

NEW JERSEY

Euro-Pacific Film & Video
Productions Inc, pg 756

PENNSYLVANIA

Bullfrog Films Inc, pg 712

ONTARIO

L-3 WESCAM, pg 802

Technical Research Program Distributors

CALIFORNIA

Crystal Pyramid Productions™,
pg 735

DISTRICT OF COLUMBIA

American Chemical Society (ACS),
pg 683

ILLINOIS

ABSA Films, pg 672

MASSACHUSETTS

Documentary Educational Resources
Inc, pg 744

PENNSYLVANIA

FMP Media Solutions Inc, pg 763

TEXAS

Emergency Film Group, pg 753

VIRGINIA

CACI Integrated Communications,
pg 713

Technical Research Program Producers

CALIFORNIA

Big Door, pg 705
Classic Images Stock Footage LLC,
pg 726
Creative Technology, pg 733
Crystal Pyramid Productions™,
pg 735
Custom Video Productions Inc,
pg 736
Design Media, pg 741

Havas Edge, pg 777
New & Unique Videos™, pg 839
QRS Software Services, pg 867
Glenn Roland Films, pg 876
SNAP, pg 891

COLORADO

Flashback Media Productions,
pg 762
Transtar Entertainment Co Inc,
pg 917

DISTRICT OF COLUMBIA

American Chemical Society (ACS),
pg 683

FLORIDA

Accord Productions, pg 673
Civins Productions Inc, pg 725
Courter Films LLC, pg 732
Jordan Klein Film & Video (JKFV),
pg 795

GEORGIA

Beachwood Productions, pg 702
Guerrilla Productions LLC, pg 774

HAWAII

Hyperspective Studios Inc, pg 783

ILLINOIS

ABSA Films, pg 672
Accenture, pg 672

LOUISIANA

Moxie Media, pg 832

MARYLAND

Absolute Hollywood, pg 672
dbF a Media Company, pg 739

MASSACHUSETTS

Documentary Educational Resources
Inc, pg 744
Green Mountain Post Films (GMP),
pg 774
Heliotrope Studios, pg 778
Northern Light Productions (NLP),
pg 842

MICHIGAN

K&R All Media Productions LLC,
pg 796

MINNESOTA

House of Cinemagraphics, pg 782

NEW HAMPSHIRE

Apertura, pg 686

NEW YORK

Ace Video, pg 674
Jack Morton Worldwide, pg 830
The Palmer Group, pg 850
Peckham Productions Inc, pg 852
Zelman Studios Ltd, pg 945

NORTH CAROLINA

Pat Appleson Studios Inc, pg 687
The Communications Group Inc,
pg 729
Kino Mountain Productions LLC,
pg 799
Moving Pictures, pg 832

OHIO

Advent Media Inc, pg 677
Take 1 Media Services, pg 906

PENNSYLVANIA

FMP Media Solutions Inc, pg 763
Innovision Media Group, pg 788
Muderick Media, pg 833
Production Masters Inc (PMI),
pg 864

RHODE ISLAND

Sound-FX-Design, pg 894

TENNESSEE

Continental Film, pg 731
Memphis Communications Corp,
pg 823
Scripps Networks, pg 882

TEXAS

Emergency Film Group, pg 753
Horizon Film + Video Productions,
pg 781
Romar Learning Solutions LLC,
pg 877
Texas Heart Institute Visual
Communication Services, pg 911

VIRGINIA

Altruist Media LLC, pg 682
CACI Integrated Communications,
pg 713
Metro Productions, pg 824

WISCONSIN

5th Floor Recording Co, pg 760
Wisconsin Public Television, pg 940

WYOMING

Bridger Productions Inc, pg 710

ALBERTA

Global TV, pg 771

BRITISH COLUMBIA

West Eagle Films Inc, pg 935

QUEBEC

Kerrigan Productions Inc, pg 798

Technical Research Program Rentals

MASSACHUSETTS

Documentary Educational Resources
Inc, pg 744

Test Commercial Distributors

CALIFORNIA

Crystal Pyramid Productions™,
pg 735
Far West Media Services Inc,
pg 759

ILLINOIS

ABSA Films, pg 672

NEVADA

DVDs4Less, pg 748

NEW YORK

HB-Content, pg 777

Test Commercial Producers

ARIZONA

Candee Productions Inc, pg 716

CALIFORNIA

A Go Go Films, pg 671
Big Door, pg 705
Classic Images Stock Footage LLC,
pg 726
Concrete Images, pg 730
Creative Technology, pg 733
Crystal Pyramid Productions™,
pg 735
Custom Video Productions Inc,
pg 736
Design Media, pg 741
Far West Media Services Inc,
pg 759
Havas Edge, pg 777
KTVU-Retail Services, pg 802
Main Street Media Inc, pg 815
Moving Art by Louie Schwartzberg,
pg 831
New & Unique Videos™, pg 839
QRS Software Services, pg 867
Glenn Roland Films, pg 876
SNAP, pg 891
Vineyard Video & Photography,
pg 930

COLORADO

Flashback Media Productions,
pg 762
Transtar Entertainment Co Inc,
pg 917

CONNECTICUT

The Gary-Paul Agency, pg 768

FLORIDA

Blackburst Entertainment LLC,
pg 706
Chatterbox Productions Inc, pg 721
Civins Productions Inc, pg 725
CopShopMiami.com, pg 731
Courter Films LLC, pg 732
Jordan Klein Film & Video (JKFV),
pg 795

GEORGIA

Beachwood Productions, pg 702
Guerrilla Productions LLC, pg 774

HAWAII

Hyperspective Studios Inc, pg 783

ILLINOIS

ABSA Films, pg 672
Film Police, pg 760
Multimedia Marketing Group,
pg 833
SCI Television & Creative Media
LLC, pg 882
Winter Productions, pg 939

IOWA

Hellman Associates Inc, pg 778

MARYLAND

Absolute Hollywood, pg 672
dbF a Media Company, pg 739

PROGRAMMING — FILM

Test Commercial Producers (continued)

MASSACHUSETTS

Green Mountain Post Films (GMP), pg 774

MICHIGAN

K&R All Media Productions LLC, pg 796

MINNESOTA

GMI Productions, pg 771
House of Cinemagraphics, pg 782

MISSOURI

Hardcastle Films & Video, pg 776

NEVADA

DVDs4Less, pg 748

NEW JERSEY

Allegro Productions Inc, pg 680
Broadcast Center Studios, pg 710
CELCO, pg 719
Concepts TV Productions Inc, pg 730
Suede Interactive, pg 903

NEW YORK

Ace Video, pg 674
aurora productions, pg 696
Blue Barn Pictures Inc, pg 707
Brooklyn Films, pg 711
HB-Content, pg 777
Kinetic Arts, pg 799
Jack Morton Worldwide, pg 830
New Horizon Studios, pg 839
Northeast Video Productions Inc, pg 842
The Palmer Group, pg 850
Pat Kogan Productions Inc, pg 852
Peckham Productions Inc, pg 852
PrimeLight Productions Inc, pg 862
R/GA, pg 868
Zelman Studios Ltd, pg 945

NORTH CAROLINA

The Communications Group Inc, pg 729

OHIO

Advent Media Inc, pg 677
Take 1 Media Services, pg 906

PENNSYLVANIA

Bang! Pictures Inc, pg 701
JPL, pg 795
Kensington Falls Animation, pg 797
Production Masters Inc (PMI), pg 864

RHODE ISLAND

Sound-FX-Design, pg 894

TEXAS

Biway Media, pg 706
Cerutti Productions Inc, pg 720
The Editing Co, pg 750
Horizon Film + Video Productions, pg 781
South Coast Film & Video, pg 895

VIRGINIA

Metro Productions, pg 824
Video Solutions, pg 928

WASHINGTON

Adams Creative & Production Services, pg 675

WISCONSIN

5th Floor Recording Co, pg 760

WYOMING

Bridger Productions Inc, pg 710

ALBERTA

Global TV, pg 771

MANITOBA

Lank/Beach Productions Inc, pg 803

QUEBEC

Kerrigan Productions Inc, pg 798

Theatrical Short Distributors

CALIFORNIA

Crystal Pyramid Productions™, pg 735
Direct Cinema Ltd Inc, pg 743
Em Gee Film Library, pg 753
Glenn Photo Supply, pg 771
New & Unique Videos™, pg 839
Nineteen87, pg 841
Palardo Productions, pg 850
Visual Communications - Southern California Asian American Studies Central Inc, pg 931

NEW JERSEY

Ergo Media Inc, pg 755

NEW YORK

ATA Trading Corp/Favorite TV Inc, pg 691
Circulating Film & Video Library, pg 725
HB-Content, pg 777
Janus Films Inc, pg 793
Kino International Corp, pg 799
Pennebaker Hegedus Films Inc, pg 854
Richter Productions Inc, pg 875
Telemotions LLC, pg 910
Third World Newsreel/Camera News Inc, pg 912
VIEW Inc (Video International Entertainment World Inc), pg 930
Women Make Movies Inc, pg 941

NORTH CAROLINA

Crystal Pictures Inc, pg 735

TENNESSEE

American Blackguard Inc, pg 683

VIRGINIA

CACI Integrated Communications, pg 713

WASHINGTON

White Rain Films Ltd, pg 937

BRITISH COLUMBIA

Credo Interactive Inc, pg 734

ONTARIO

Canadian Filmmakers Distribution Center (CFMDC), pg 715
IMAX Corp, pg 786

QUEBEC

Les Productions Via Le Monde (Daniel Bertolino) Inc, pg 864

Theatrical Short Producers

ARKANSAS

Live'N'Loud, pg 810

CALIFORNIA

Artichoke Productions, pg 690
Big Door, pg 705
Cinevest, pg 725
Classic Images Stock Footage LLC, pg 726
Concrete Images, pg 730
Creative Technology, pg 733
Crystal Pyramid Productions™, pg 735
Custom Video Productions Inc, pg 736
Direct Cinema Ltd Inc, pg 743
GAMfilm Productions, pg 768
imageReal Pictures LLC, pg 785
Jaguar Distribution Corp, pg 792
Main Street Media Inc, pg 815
Moving Art by Louie Schwartzberg, pg 831
New & Unique Videos™, pg 839
New Deal Studios, pg 839
Nineteen87, pg 841
Palardo Productions, pg 850
Point of View Productions, pg 858
QRS Software Services, pg 867
RetinaVision Productions, pg 874
Rhythm & Hues Studios Inc, pg 874
Glenn Roland Films, pg 876
Santa Barbara Location Services, pg 880
SNAP, pg 891
Visual Communications - Southern California Asian American Studies Central Inc, pg 931

COLORADO

Starwest Productions, pg 900
Transtar Entertainment Co Inc, pg 917

CONNECTICUT

ACM Productions Ltd, pg 674
The Gary-Paul Agency, pg 768

FLORIDA

Accord Productions, pg 673
Chatterbox Productions Inc, pg 721
CopShopMiami.com, pg 731
Courter Films LLC, pg 732
Jordan Klein Film & Video (JKFV), pg 795
Tel-Air Interests Inc, pg 909

GEORGIA

Burst Video/Film Inc, pg 713
Guerrilla Productions LLC, pg 774
Myriad Productions, pg 835

HAWAII

Hyperspective Studios Inc, pg 783

ILLINOIS

ABS Enterprises, pg 672
Film Police, pg 760
Multimedia Marketing Group, pg 833
Winter Productions, pg 939

INDIANA

Perennial Pictures Film Corp, pg 854

LOUISIANA

Moxie Media, pg 832

MARYLAND

Absolute Hollywood, pg 672
Richard Chisolm Cinematography, pg 722
dbF a Media Company, pg 739

MASSACHUSETTS

Green Mountain Post Films (GMP), pg 774
Heliotrope Studios, pg 778

MICHIGAN

K&R All Media Productions LLC, pg 796

MINNESOTA

House of Cinemagraphics, pg 782

NEW HAMPSHIRE

Apertura, pg 686

NEW MEXICO

Rainbow International Inc, pg 869

NEW YORK

aurora productions, pg 696
Blue Barn Pictures Inc, pg 707
Brian Film Productions LLC, pg 710
Brooklyn Films, pg 711
Thomas Craven Film Corp, pg 733
Florentine Films, pg 762
William Greaves Productions Inc, pg 774
HB-Content, pg 777
Kinetic Arts, pg 799
Jack Morton Worldwide, pg 830
The Palmer Group, pg 850
Peckham Productions Inc, pg 852
Pennebaker Hegedus Films Inc, pg 854
Polestar Films & Associated Arts Ltd, pg 859
R/GA, pg 868
Richter Productions Inc, pg 875
Split Image Productions, pg 898
Third World Newsreel/Camera News Inc, pg 912
VIEW Inc (Video International Entertainment World Inc), pg 930
Zelman Studios Ltd, pg 945

NORTH CAROLINA

The Communications Group Inc, pg 729
Crystal Pictures Inc, pg 735
Kino Mountain Productions LLC, pg 799
Trailblazer Studios®, pg 917

OREGON
Ideascape Inc, pg 784

PENNSYLVANIA
Innovision Media Group, pg 788
JPL, pg 795
Kensington Falls Animation, pg 797
Production Masters Inc (PMI),
    pg 864

RHODE ISLAND
Sound-FX-Design, pg 894

TENNESSEE
American Blackguard Inc, pg 683

TEXAS
Biway Media, pg 706
Cerutti Productions Inc, pg 720

VIRGINIA
Altruist Media LLC, pg 682
CACI Integrated Communications,
    pg 713
Metro Productions, pg 824

WISCONSIN
5th Floor Recording Co, pg 760
Wisconsin Public Television, pg 940

WYOMING
Bridger Productions Inc, pg 710

ALBERTA
Black Media Works, pg 706

MANITOBA
Lank/Beach Productions Inc, pg 803

ONTARIO
IMAX Corp, pg 786

QUEBEC
Kerrigan Productions Inc, pg 798
Les Productions Via Le Monde
    (Daniel Bertolino) Inc, pg 864

Theatrical Short Rentals

CALIFORNIA
Direct Cinema Ltd Inc, pg 743
Em Gee Film Library, pg 753
Glenn Photo Supply, pg 771
Palardo Productions, pg 850
Point of View Productions, pg 858
Visual Communications - Southern
    California Asian American
    Studies Central Inc, pg 931

MISSOURI
University of Missouri-Columbia,
    pg 923

NEW YORK
Circulating Film & Video Library,
    pg 725
Kino International Corp, pg 799
Pennebaker Hegedus Films Inc,
    pg 854
Richter Productions Inc, pg 875
Third World Newsreel/Camera
    News Inc, pg 912
VIEW Inc (Video International
    Entertainment World Inc), pg 930

NORTH CAROLINA
Crystal Pictures Inc, pg 735

QUEBEC
Les Productions Via Le Monde
    (Daniel Bertolino) Inc, pg 864

Thirty-Five mm Films, *see* Films—35mm

Trailer Distributors

CALIFORNIA
Crystal Pyramid Productions™,
    pg 735
Em Gee Film Library, pg 753
Focus Features, pg 763
Glenn Photo Supply, pg 771
Lions Gate Entertainment Corp,
    pg 809
New & Unique Videos™, pg 839

NEW YORK
ATA Trading Corp/Favorite TV Inc,
    pg 691
HB-Content, pg 777
Janus Films Inc, pg 793
Kino International Corp, pg 799
Women Make Movies Inc, pg 941

TENNESSEE
American Blackguard Inc, pg 683

VIRGINIA
CACI Integrated Communications,
    pg 713

QUEBEC
Les Productions Via Le Monde
    (Daniel Bertolino) Inc, pg 864

Trailer Producers

ARIZONA
Teaberry, pg 908

CALIFORNIA
Anonymous Content, pg 686
Artichoke Productions, pg 690
Big Door, pg 705
Classic Images Stock Footage LLC,
    pg 726
Concoction Lab, pg 730
Concrete Images, pg 730
Creative Technology, pg 733
Crystal Pyramid Productions™,
    pg 735
Custom Video Productions Inc,
    pg 736
Focus Features, pg 763
KO Creative, pg 800
Lions Gate Entertainment Corp,
    pg 809
Lumeni Productions Inc, pg 812
Main Street Media Inc, pg 815
New & Unique Videos™, pg 839
Nineteen87, pg 841
Producers Group Ltd, pg 863
QRS Software Services, pg 867
RetinaVision Productions, pg 874
Glenn Roland Films, pg 876
SNAP, pg 891
Vineyard Video & Photography,
    pg 930

Warner Bros Entertainment Inc,
    pg 934
Webster Communications, pg 935
Zamacona Productions, pg 945

COLORADO
CSI Film & Video LLC, pg 735
Flashback Media Productions,
    pg 762

CONNECTICUT
New London Media, pg 839

FLORIDA
Accord Productions, pg 673
Blackburst Entertainment LLC,
    pg 706
CopShopMiami.com, pg 731
Courter Films LLC, pg 732
Jordan Klein Film & Video (JKFV),
    pg 795

GEORGIA
Guerrilla Productions LLC, pg 774

HAWAII
Hyperspective Studios Inc, pg 783

ILLINOIS
Film Police, pg 760
Multimedia Marketing Group,
    pg 833
Richter Studios, pg 875

MARYLAND
Absolute Hollywood, pg 672
dbF a Media Company, pg 739

MASSACHUSETTS
Documentary Educational Resources
    Inc, pg 744
Green Mountain Post Films (GMP),
    pg 774
Northern Light Productions (NLP),
    pg 842

MICHIGAN
K&R All Media Productions LLC,
    pg 796

MINNESOTA
House of Cinemagraphics, pg 782

NEW JERSEY
Audio Vistas LLC, pg 694

NEW YORK
Avekta Productions Inc, pg 697
Blue Barn Pictures Inc, pg 707
Thomas Craven Film Corp, pg 733
HB-Content, pg 777
Jack Morton Worldwide, pg 830
The Palmer Group, pg 850
Pennebaker Hegedus Films Inc,
    pg 854
Polestar Films & Associated Arts
    Ltd, pg 859
R/GA, pg 868
David Rapkin Audio Production,
    pg 870
Split Image Productions, pg 898
Tiki Recording Studios Inc, pg 914
Zelman Studios Ltd, pg 945

NORTH CAROLINA
The Communications Group Inc,
    pg 729
Kino Mountain Productions LLC,
    pg 799

OHIO
Take 1 Media Services, pg 906

PENNSYLVANIA
Bang! Pictures Inc, pg 701
Innovision Media Group, pg 788
JPL, pg 795
Kensington Falls Animation, pg 797

RHODE ISLAND
Sound-FX-Design, pg 894

TENNESSEE
American Blackguard Inc, pg 683
Cinemarr Entertainment, pg 724
Continental Film, pg 731

TEXAS
Cerutti Productions Inc, pg 720
The Editing Co, pg 750
Horizon Film + Video Productions,
    pg 781
Stage Directions, pg 898

VERMONT
Edgewood Studios, pg 750

VIRGINIA
CACI Integrated Communications,
    pg 713
Metro Productions, pg 824

WASHINGTON
Hamilton Studio, pg 775
North-by-Northwest - A Digital
    Studio, pg 842

WISCONSIN
Clear Focus Media LLC, pg 726
5th Floor Recording Co, pg 760

WYOMING
Bridger Productions Inc, pg 710

BRITISH COLUMBIA
West Eagle Films Inc, pg 935

QUEBEC
Kerrigan Productions Inc, pg 798
Les Productions Via Le Monde
    (Daniel Bertolino) Inc, pg 864

Trailer Rentals

CALIFORNIA
Em Gee Film Library, pg 753
Glenn Photo Supply, pg 771

Training Program Distributors

CALIFORNIA
Crystal Pyramid Productions™,
    pg 735
Direct Cinema Ltd Inc, pg 743
Em Gee Film Library, pg 753
Goal Productions, pg 772
Increase Video/Silver Mine Video,
    pg 786

PROGRAMMING — FILM

New & Unique Videos™, pg 839
People Skills International, pg 854

CONNECTICUT

Digital Video Productions, pg 742

DELAWARE

University Media Services, pg 922

ILLINOIS

ABSA Films, pg 672
CCH Inc, A Wolters Kluwer business, pg 718
National Safety Council (NSC), pg 836

NEVADA

DVDs4Less, pg 748

NEW HAMPSHIRE

Captain Fiddle Music & Publications, pg 716

NEW MEXICO

The Phoenix Learning Group Inc, pg 855

NEW YORK

HB-Content, pg 777

PENNSYLVANIA

FMP Media Solutions Inc, pg 763

TENNESSEE

American Blackguard Inc, pg 683
Spring Arbor Distributors Inc, pg 898

TEXAS

CEV Multimedia Ltd, pg 720
Emergency Film Group, pg 753
Teleometrics International, pg 910
University of Texas at Austin - Petroleum Extension Service, pg 923

VIRGINIA

CACI Integrated Communications, pg 713

ONTARIO

Kineticvideo.com, pg 799

Training Program Producers

ALABAMA

Leo Ticheli Productions, pg 913

ALASKA

Aurora Films, pg 696

ARIZONA

Candee Productions Inc, pg 716
Film Creations Ltd, pg 760
Metropolitan Audio-Visual Inc, pg 824
Teaberry, pg 908

CALIFORNIA

Aaron Marcus and Associates, pg 671
Big Door, pg 705
Classic Images Stock Footage LLC, pg 726
Concrete Images, pg 730
Creative Technology, pg 733
Crystal Pyramid Productions™, pg 735
Custom Video Productions Inc, pg 736
Design Media, pg 741
Dolphin MultiMedia Inc, pg 745
Goal Productions, pg 772
Havas Edge, pg 777
imageReal Pictures LLC, pg 785
Kavich Reynolds Productions Inc, pg 797
KTVU-Retail Services, pg 802
Main Street Media Inc, pg 815
The Media Staff Inc, pg 822
New & Unique Videos™, pg 839
New Circuit Films LLC, pg 839
QRS Software Services, pg 867
RetinaVision Productions, pg 874
Glenn Roland Films, pg 876
SNAP, pg 891
Tam Communications Inc, pg 906
Videografix LLC, pg 929
Webster Communications, pg 935

COLORADO

CSI Film & Video LLC, pg 735
Flashback Media Productions, pg 762
Transtar Entertainment Co Inc, pg 917

CONNECTICUT

ACM Productions Ltd, pg 674
The Gary-Paul Agency, pg 768

DELAWARE

University Media Services, pg 922

DISTRICT OF COLUMBIA

O'Keefe Communications Inc, pg 844

FLORIDA

Accord Productions, pg 673
Blackburst Entertainment LLC, pg 706
Communications Concepts Inc (CCI), pg 729
CopShopMiami.com, pg 731
Courter Films LLC, pg 732
Jordan Klein Film & Video (JKFV), pg 795
Video Techniques Inc, pg 928

GEORGIA

Beachwood Productions, pg 702
Guerrilla Productions LLC, pg 774
Myriad Productions, pg 835

HAWAII

Hyperspective Studios Inc, pg 783

ILLINOIS

ABSA Films, pg 672
Accenture, pg 672
CCH Inc, A Wolters Kluwer business, pg 718
Film Police, pg 760
Manning Productions, pg 816
Mightybytes Inc, pg 827

Multimedia Marketing Group, pg 833
National Safety Council (NSC), pg 836
SCI Television & Creative Media LLC, pg 882
Winter Productions, pg 939

IOWA

Educational Technology & Media Services, pg 751

KENTUCKY

Idle Minds Productions Inc, pg 784

LOUISIANA

Digital FX Inc, pg 742
Moxie Media, pg 832

MARYLAND

Absolute Hollywood, pg 672
dbF a Media Company, pg 739

MASSACHUSETTS

CommCreative, pg 728
Documentary Educational Resources Inc, pg 744
Green Mountain Post Films (GMP), pg 774
Northern Light Productions (NLP), pg 842

MICHIGAN

K&R All Media Productions LLC, pg 796

MINNESOTA

House of Cinemagraphics, pg 782

NEVADA

DVDs4Less, pg 748

NEW HAMPSHIRE

Apertura, pg 686
Captain Fiddle Music & Publications, pg 716

NEW JERSEY

Broadcast Center Studios, pg 710
Concepts TV Productions Inc, pg 730
Selden Associates, pg 883
Telemanagement Resources International Inc (TRI), pg 910
Telequest Inc, pg 910
TimeSteps Productions Inc, pg 914

NEW MEXICO

The Phoenix Learning Group Inc, pg 855

NEW YORK

aurora productions, pg 696
Blue Barn Pictures Inc, pg 707
Broadstreet Productions LLC, pg 711
HB-Content, pg 777
Ketchum Inc, pg 798
Jack Morton Worldwide, pg 830
News Broadcast Network Inc, pg 840
The Palmer Group, pg 850
Peckham Productions Inc, pg 852
Zelman Studios Ltd, pg 945

NORTH CAROLINA

Pat Appleson Studios Inc, pg 687
The Communications Group Inc, pg 729
Horizon Video Productions Inc, pg 781
Kino Mountain Productions LLC, pg 799

OHIO

Advent Media Inc, pg 677
Take 1 Media Services, pg 906

OREGON

Ideascape Inc, pg 784

PENNSYLVANIA

Bang! Pictures Inc, pg 701
FMP Media Solutions Inc, pg 763
Innovision Media Group, pg 788
JPL, pg 795
Kensington Falls Animation, pg 797
Main Point Productions, pg 815
Muderick Media, pg 833
Video/Film Associates, pg 928

RHODE ISLAND

Sound-FX-Design, pg 894

TENNESSEE

American Blackguard Inc, pg 683
Cinemarr Entertainment, pg 724
Continental Film, pg 731
Memphis Communications Corp, pg 823
Scripps Networks, pg 882
Stage Post, pg 899

TEXAS

Aries Productions Inc, pg 688
Castleview Productions, pg 717
Cerutti Productions Inc, pg 720
CEV Multimedia Ltd, pg 720
The Editing Co, pg 750
Emergency Film Group, pg 753
Horizon Film + Video Productions, pg 781
Marx InDigital, pg 818
Earl Miller Productions Inc, pg 827
Romar Learning Solutions LLC, pg 877
Stage Directions, pg 898
Teleometrics International, pg 910
University of Texas at Austin - Petroleum Extension Service, pg 923

VIRGINIA

Altruist Media LLC, pg 682
CACI Integrated Communications, pg 713
Metro Productions, pg 824

WASHINGTON

Adams Creative & Production Services, pg 675
North-by-Northwest - A Digital Studio, pg 842

WISCONSIN

Audio Visual of Milwaukee Inc, pg 694
5th Floor Recording Co, pg 760
Meridian Studios, pg 824
Wisconsin Public Television, pg 940

WYOMING

Bridger Productions Inc, pg 710

ALBERTA

Black Media Works, pg 706
Global TV, pg 771

MANITOBA

Lank/Beach Productions Inc, pg 803

ONTARIO

Silver Creek Media Inc, pg 888

QUEBEC

Kerrigan Productions Inc, pg 798

Training Program Rentals

CALIFORNIA

Direct Cinema Ltd Inc, pg 743
Em Gee Film Library, pg 753

DELAWARE

University Media Services, pg 922

ILLINOIS

National Safety Council (NSC),
  pg 836

MISSOURI

University of Missouri-Columbia,
  pg 923

Travelog Distributors

ARIZONA

Video Learning Library, pg 928

CALIFORNIA

Crystal Pyramid Productions™,
  pg 735
Direct Cinema Ltd Inc, pg 743
Glenn Photo Supply, pg 771
Goal Productions, pg 772
Jaguar Distribution Corp, pg 792
New & Unique Videos™, pg 839

ILLINOIS

ABSA Films, pg 672

KENTUCKY

Horizon Films & Media LLC,
  pg 781

NEW JERSEY

Ergo Media Inc, pg 755

NEW YORK

Janson Media Inc, pg 793
VIEW Inc (Video International
  Entertainment World Inc), pg 930

OREGON

Wilderness Video, pg 938

PENNSYLVANIA

FMP Media Solutions Inc, pg 763

TENNESSEE

American Blackguard Inc, pg 683
Spring Arbor Distributors Inc,
  pg 898

VIRGINIA

CACI Integrated Communications,
  pg 713

NORTHWEST TERRITORIES

Yellowknife Films Inc, pg 944

ONTARIO

IMAX Corp, pg 786

Travelog Producers

ALASKA

Aurora Films, pg 696

ARIZONA

Teaberry, pg 908

CALIFORNIA

Artichoke Productions, pg 690
Big Door, pg 705
Cinevest, pg 725
Classic Images Stock Footage LLC,
  pg 726
Creative Technology, pg 733
Crystal Pyramid Productions™,
  pg 735
Dolphin MultiMedia Inc, pg 745
Goal Productions, pg 772
Jaguar Distribution Corp, pg 792
Kavich Reynolds Productions Inc,
  pg 797
Main Street Media Inc, pg 815
New & Unique Videos™, pg 839
Point of View Productions, pg 858
QRS Software Services, pg 867
Dick Reizner Film & Video, pg 873
RetinaVision Productions, pg 874
Glenn Roland Films, pg 876
Santa Barbara Location Services,
  pg 880
SNAP, pg 891
Video Resources Inc, pg 928
Videografix LLC, pg 929
Webster Communications, pg 935

COLORADO

Flashback Media Productions,
  pg 762
Tatum Video, pg 907

CONNECTICUT

The Gary-Paul Agency, pg 768

DISTRICT OF COLUMBIA

O'Keefe Communications Inc,
  pg 844

FLORIDA

Blackburst Entertainment LLC,
  pg 706
Courter Films LLC, pg 732
Jordan Klein Film & Video (JKFV),
  pg 795
Tel-Air Interests Inc, pg 909

GEORGIA

Beachwood Productions, pg 702
Burst Video/Film Inc, pg 713
Guerrilla Productions LLC, pg 774

HAWAII

Hyperspective Studios Inc, pg 783

ILLINOIS

ABSA Films, pg 672
Film Police, pg 760
SCI Television & Creative Media
  LLC, pg 882
Winter Productions, pg 939

INDIANA

Road Pictures, pg 876

KENTUCKY

Horizon Films & Media LLC,
  pg 781

LOUISIANA

Moxie Media, pg 832

MARYLAND

Absolute Hollywood, pg 672
Richard Chisolm Cinematography,
  pg 722
dbF a Media Company, pg 739

MASSACHUSETTS

Green Mountain Post Films (GMP),
  pg 774

MICHIGAN

K&R All Media Productions LLC,
  pg 796

MINNESOTA

House of Cinemagraphics, pg 782

NEW JERSEY

Broadcast Center Studios, pg 710

NEW YORK

aurora productions, pg 696
Blue Barn Pictures Inc, pg 707
Florentine Films, pg 762
Janson Media Inc, pg 793
Jack Morton Worldwide, pg 830
News Broadcast Network Inc,
  pg 840
The Palmer Group, pg 850
Pat Kogan Productions Inc, pg 852
Peckham Productions Inc, pg 852
VIEW Inc (Video International
  Entertainment World Inc), pg 930
Zelman Studios Ltd, pg 945

NORTH CAROLINA

Pat Appleson Studios Inc, pg 687
The Communications Group Inc,
  pg 729
Kino Mountain Productions LLC,
  pg 799

OHIO

Take 1 Media Services, pg 906

OREGON

Odyssey Productions Inc, pg 844
Wilderness Video, pg 938

PENNSYLVANIA

Bang! Pictures Inc, pg 701
FMP Media Solutions Inc, pg 763
JPL, pg 795
Main Point Productions, pg 815

RHODE ISLAND

Sound-FX-Design, pg 894

TENNESSEE

American Blackguard Inc, pg 683

TEXAS

Cerutti Productions Inc, pg 720
Horizon Film + Video Productions,
  pg 781
Earl Miller Productions Inc, pg 827

VERMONT

Marlboro Productions, pg 817

VIRGINIA

Altruist Media LLC, pg 682
CACI Integrated Communications,
  pg 713
Metro Productions, pg 824

WISCONSIN

5th Floor Recording Co, pg 760
Wisconsin Public Television, pg 940

WYOMING

Bridger Productions Inc, pg 710

ALBERTA

Global TV, pg 771

NORTHWEST TERRITORIES

Yellowknife Films Inc, pg 944

ONTARIO

IMAX Corp, pg 786

QUEBEC

Kerrigan Productions Inc, pg 798

Travelog Rentals

CALIFORNIA

Direct Cinema Ltd Inc, pg 743
Em Gee Film Library, pg 753
Glenn Photo Supply, pg 771

MISSOURI

University of Missouri-Columbia,
  pg 923

NEW YORK

VIEW Inc (Video International
  Entertainment World Inc), pg 930

OREGON

Wilderness Video, pg 938

Vocational Program Distributors

CALIFORNIA

Crystal Pyramid Productions™,
  pg 735
Direct Cinema Ltd Inc, pg 743
Increase Video/Silver Mine Video,
  pg 786
New & Unique Videos™, pg 839
The Wine Appreciation Guild Ltd,
  pg 939

PROGRAMMING — FILM

Vocational Program Distributors (continued)

DELAWARE
University Media Services, pg 922

GEORGIA
Convergent Media Systems, pg 731

ILLINOIS
Film Ideas Inc, pg 760
National Safety Council (NSC), pg 836

NEW MEXICO
The Phoenix Learning Group Inc, pg 855

NEW YORK
Films Media Group, pg 760
VIEW Inc (Video International Entertainment World Inc), pg 930

PENNSYLVANIA
Bullfrog Films Inc, pg 712
FMP Media Solutions Inc, pg 763

TEXAS
CEV Multimedia Ltd, pg 720
Emergency Film Group, pg 753
University of Texas at Austin - Petroleum Extension Service, pg 923

VIRGINIA
CACI Integrated Communications, pg 713

ONTARIO
Kineticvideo.com, pg 799

Vocational Program Producers

ALASKA
Aurora Films, pg 696

CALIFORNIA
Aaron Marcus and Associates, pg 671
Big Door, pg 705
Classic Images Stock Footage LLC, pg 726

Crystal Pyramid Productions™, pg 735
imageReal Pictures LLC, pg 785
Main Street Media Inc, pg 815
The Media Staff Inc, pg 822
New & Unique Videos™, pg 839
QRS Software Services, pg 867
Dick Reizner Film & Video, pg 873
Glenn Roland Films, pg 876
Santa Barbara Location Services, pg 880
SNAP, pg 891
Webster Communications, pg 935

COLORADO
Flashback Media Productions, pg 762

CONNECTICUT
The Gary-Paul Agency, pg 768

DELAWARE
University Media Services, pg 922

FLORIDA
Blackburst Entertainment LLC, pg 706
Civins Productions Inc, pg 725
CopShopMiami.com, pg 731
Courter Films LLC, pg 732
Jordan Klein Film & Video (JKFV), pg 795

GEORGIA
Beachwood Productions, pg 702
Guerrilla Productions LLC, pg 774

HAWAII
Hyperspective Studios Inc, pg 783

ILLINOIS
National Safety Council (NSC), pg 836

INDIANA
Road Pictures, pg 876

LOUISIANA
Moxie Media, pg 832

MARYLAND
Absolute Hollywood, pg 672
dbF a Media Company, pg 739

MICHIGAN
K&R All Media Productions LLC, pg 796

MINNESOTA
House of Cinemagraphics, pg 782

NEW HAMPSHIRE
Apertura, pg 686

NEW JERSEY
Broadcast Center Studios, pg 710
Telequest Inc, pg 910

NEW MEXICO
The Phoenix Learning Group Inc, pg 855

NEW YORK
aurora productions, pg 696
Blue Barn Pictures Inc, pg 707
Films Media Group, pg 760
Jack Morton Worldwide, pg 830
The Palmer Group, pg 850
Pat Kogan Productions Inc, pg 852
Peckham Productions Inc, pg 852
VIEW Inc (Video International Entertainment World Inc), pg 930
Zelman Studios Ltd, pg 945

NORTH CAROLINA
Pat Appleson Studios Inc, pg 687
The Communications Group Inc, pg 729
Kino Mountain Productions LLC, pg 799

OHIO
Advent Media Inc, pg 677
Take 1 Media Services, pg 906

OREGON
Ideascape Inc, pg 784

PENNSYLVANIA
FMP Media Solutions Inc, pg 763
JPL, pg 795

RHODE ISLAND
Sound-FX-Design, pg 894

TENNESSEE
Continental Film, pg 731
Memphis Communications Corp, pg 823

TEXAS
Cerutti Productions Inc, pg 720
CEV Multimedia Ltd, pg 720
The Editing Co, pg 750
Emergency Film Group, pg 753

Horizon Film + Video Productions, pg 781
Earl Miller Productions Inc, pg 827
University of Texas at Austin - Petroleum Extension Service, pg 923

VIRGINIA
Altruist Media LLC, pg 682
CACI Integrated Communications, pg 713
Metro Productions, pg 824

WISCONSIN
5th Floor Recording Co, pg 760
Wisconsin Public Television, pg 940

WYOMING
Bridger Productions Inc, pg 710

ALBERTA
Global TV, pg 771

QUEBEC
Kerrigan Productions Inc, pg 798

Vocational Program Rentals

CALIFORNIA
Direct Cinema Ltd Inc, pg 743

DELAWARE
University Media Services, pg 922

GEORGIA
Convergent Media Systems, pg 731

ILLINOIS
National Safety Council (NSC), pg 836

MISSOURI
University of Missouri-Columbia, pg 923

NEW YORK
Films Media Group, pg 760

PENNSYLVANIA
Bullfrog Films Inc, pg 712

PROGRAMMING — VIDEO

Animated Television Commercials, *see* Television Commercial—Animated

Business Program Distributors

ALABAMA

CMEinfo™, pg 727

ARIZONA

CyberIconics International, pg 736
Video Learning Library, pg 928

CALIFORNIA

Crystal Pyramid Productions™, pg 735
Custom Video Productions Inc, pg 736
Direct Cinema Ltd Inc, pg 743
Discovery Education - Los Angeles, pg 743
Ferrari Productions, pg 759
411 Video Information, pg 764
Increase Video/Silver Mine Video, pg 786
Kantola Productions LLC, pg 796
KPBS Public Broadcasting, pg 801
New & Unique Videos™, pg 839
People Skills International, pg 854
Pyramid Media, pg 867
Quality Digest, pg 868
Thinking Allowed Productions, pg 912
TMW Media Group, pg 915
Valley Media, pg 924

COLORADO

Jeppesen, pg 793

CONNECTICUT

Book Marketing Works LLC, pg 708

FLORIDA

Video Resources Software, pg 928

GEORGIA

Convergent Media Systems, pg 731
LYRASIS, pg 813
School Media Associates LLC, pg 882

ILLINOIS

ABSA Films, pg 672
CCH Continuing Education, pg 718
CCH Inc, A Wolters Kluwer business, pg 718
CCore Media Inc, pg 718
Film Ideas Inc, pg 760
Moviecraft Inc, pg 831
Movies Unlimited, pg 831
Nightingale-Conant Corp, pg 841
Questar Entertainment Inc, pg 868

INDIANA

Educational Video Group Inc, pg 751

IOWA

Prositions Inc, pg 865

KENTUCKY

KET The Kentucky Network, pg 798
WaxWorks VideoWorks, pg 934

MARYLAND

Total AV Systems, pg 916

MASSACHUSETTS

Commonwealth Films Inc, pg 728
Enterprise Media LLC, pg 754
Merrimack Films, pg 824
Penfield Productions Ltd, pg 853

MICHIGAN

Digi Sign Design LLC, pg 741
Emery-Pratt Co, pg 753
MSU Technologies, pg 833
The Program Source International, pg 865
Society of Manufacturing Engineers (SME), pg 891

MINNESOTA

JIST Publishing, pg 794
Service Quality Institute, pg 884

NEBRASKA

B & B Video Productions Inc, pg 700

NEVADA

Aardvark Video & Media Productions, pg 671
DVDs4Less, pg 748

NEW HAMPSHIRE

Channell One Video, pg 720
Frey Scientific, pg 766
Chip Taylor Communications LLC, pg 907

NEW JERSEY

Euro-Pacific Film & Video Productions Inc, pg 756
MiB MediaWorks, pg 825
SES SA, pg 884

NEW MEXICO

The Phoenix Learning Group Inc, pg 855

NEW YORK

A-List Quality Videographer, pg 671
American Management Association® (AMA), pg 683
Broadstreet Productions LLC, pg 711
De Nonno Productions Inc (DPI), pg 739
Films Media Group, pg 760
Guidance Associates Inc Center for Humanities, pg 774
HB-Content, pg 777
Mastervision Inc, pg 819
Meridian Education Corp, pg 823
Practising Law Institute, pg 860
Richter Productions Inc, pg 875
Shopware, pg 886
Synaptic Digital, pg 905

Video Catalogue Co Inc, pg 927
VIEW Inc (Video International Entertainment World Inc), pg 930

NORTH CAROLINA

AudioSolutionz LLC, pg 695
Crystal Pictures Inc, pg 735

OHIO

Curtis Inc, pg 736

OREGON

InterVision Media, pg 791
The Keyboard Workshop, pg 798

PENNSYLVANIA

Beholder Productions Inc, pg 703
FMP Media Solutions Inc, pg 763
Library Video Company, pg 807
S I Video Sales Group, pg 879

SOUTH CAROLINA

American Production Services LLC, pg 684

TENNESSEE

National School Products, pg 836
Zion Music Group, pg 945

TEXAS

CEV Multimedia Ltd, pg 720
Educational Video Network, pg 751
Emergency Film Group, pg 753

VERMONT

University of Vermont, Instructional Television Dept, pg 923
Wilson McLeran Inc, pg 939

VIRGINIA

CACI Integrated Communications, pg 713
WETA Production Center, pg 936

WASHINGTON

Bennett-Watt HD Productions Inc, pg 703
Intermedia Inc, pg 789

WEST VIRGINIA

Sweetsong Productions, pg 905

ONTARIO

Canadian Learning Co Inc, pg 715
Kineticvideo.com, pg 799
McIntyre Media Inc, pg 821
McNabb & Connolly, pg 821

Business Program Producers

ALABAMA

CMEinfo™, pg 727
Leo Ticheli Productions, pg 913

ALASKA

Aurora Films, pg 696
Imig Audio/Video Inc, pg 786

ARIZONA

Aardvark Productions LLC, pg 671
Candee Productions Inc, pg 716
Creative Backstage, pg 733

CyberIconics International, pg 736
Direct Current Video Productions, pg 743
Fox 10 Productions (KSAZ-TV), pg 765
Metropolitan Audio-Visual Inc, pg 824
On-Site Video, pg 846
Teaberry, pg 908

CALIFORNIA

Access Video in Berkeley, pg 673
Action Video, pg 675
Air Philosophy Inc, pg 678
Artichoke Productions, pg 690
Big Door, pg 705
Cavalcade Productions Inc, pg 717
Steve Chandler, pg 720
Classic Images Stock Footage LLC, pg 726
Coastline Productions, pg 727
Creative Technology, pg 733
Crystal Pyramid Productions™, pg 735
Custom Video Productions Inc, pg 736
digital OutPost, pg 742
Direct Images Interactive Inc, pg 743
Discovery Education - Los Angeles, pg 743
Dolphin MultiMedia Inc, pg 745
Durrin Productions Inc, pg 748
First Camera, pg 761
Goal Productions, pg 772
Havas Edge, pg 777
imageReal Pictures LLC, pg 785
Imageworks, pg 785
ITV Productions, pg 792
Kantola Productions LLC, pg 796
Kavich Reynolds Productions Inc, pg 797
KPBS Public Broadcasting, pg 801
Lieberman Productions, pg 807
Ludlow Media, pg 812
Maximus Media Inc, pg 820
McCune Audio-Video-Lighting, pg 821
Media Magic, pg 822
The Media Staff Inc, pg 822
New & Unique Videos™, pg 839
New Circuit Films LLC, pg 839
Nolte Media, pg 841
Penrose Productions, pg 854
PK Productions, pg 857
Quality Digest, pg 868
Dick Reizner Film & Video, pg 873
RetinaVision Productions, pg 874
Glenn Roland Films, pg 876
Screen Door Entertainment Inc, pg 882
Shot Glass Films, pg 886
SNAP, pg 891
Staylor-Made Communications Inc, pg 900
Still N' Motion, pg 901
Tam Communications Inc, pg 906
Thinking Allowed Productions, pg 912
Timestream Video, pg 914
TMW Media Group, pg 915
Total Creative, pg 916
TVA Media Group, pg 919
Twin Peaks Creative, pg 920
Vineyard Video & Photography, pg 930
Visions Plus, pg 931
Webster Communications, pg 935
West Coast Projections Inc, pg 935
Yada/Levine Video Productions, pg 943
Zamacona Productions, pg 945

PROGRAMMING — VIDEO

Business Program Producers (continued)

COLORADO

Apogee Communications Group, pg 687
Blue River Productions, pg 708
Centre Communications Inc, pg 720
Daylight Productions & Rentals, pg 739
Flashback Media Productions, pg 762
People Productions, pg 854
Rocky Mountain Audio/Video Productions Inc, pg 876
Transtar Entertainment Co Inc, pg 917

CONNECTICUT

ACM Productions Ltd, pg 674
Business & Legal Reports Inc, pg 713
Geomatrix Productions, pg 770
Ironik Design & Post, pg 791
Moving Pictures, pg 832
New London Media, pg 839
Palace Productions MediaVision, pg 850
P&P Studios Inc, pg 851
Powerstation Events, pg 860
Bret Stern Productions, pg 900
Video Production Associates Inc, pg 928

DISTRICT OF COLUMBIA

Hillmann & Carr Inc, pg 780
O'Keefe Communications Inc, pg 844
Yellow Cat Productions Inc, pg 944

FLORIDA

Applebox Studio, pg 687
Astoria Communications Inc, pg 691
Blackburst Entertainment LLC, pg 706
Civins Productions Inc, pg 725
Courter Films LLC, pg 732
DME Studios, pg 744
EarthDesign Inc, pg 749
Easy Edit Video Inc, pg 750
Jordan Klein Film & Video (JKFV), pg 795
National Teleproductions Inc, pg 837
Paradise Video & Film, pg 851
Skystorm Productions, pg 890
Sunfire Communications Inc, pg 904
Sunrise Studios, pg 904
Tel-Air Interests Inc, pg 909
Tricycle Studios, pg 918
Universal Studios Florida® Production Group, pg 922
Mike Vasilinda Productions Inc, pg 925
Video Resources Software, pg 928
Video Techniques Inc, pg 928

GEORGIA

Beachwood Productions, pg 702
Burst Video/Film Inc, pg 713
Cox Media, pg 732
ECG Productions, pg 750
GP Studios, pg 773
Guerrilla Productions LLC, pg 774

KEF Media, pg 797
Myriad Productions, pg 835
Malcolm Neal Productions, pg 837
On-Line Productions, pg 845

HAWAII

Hyperspective Studios Inc, pg 783
Sight & Sound Studios, pg 887
1013 Integrated, pg 911

IDAHO

Brad Shaw Productions Inc, pg 885
Wide Eye Productions, pg 938

ILLINOIS

Abacus Group of Saint Louis LLC, pg 672
ABSA Films, pg 672
Airways Digital Media, pg 679
Atomic Imaging Inc/Golan Studios, pg 692
Beatty TeleVisual Productions, pg 703
CCH Continuing Education, pg 718
CCH Inc, A Wolters Kluwer business, pg 718
The Chicago Production Center, pg 721
Cresta Creative, pg 734
Film Police, pg 760
1st Financial Training Services Inc, pg 761
IV Media Resources, pg 792
Major Media Productions Inc, pg 815
Manning Productions, pg 816
Mimi Productions, pg 828
Multimedia Marketing Group, pg 833
Nightingale-Conant Corp, pg 841
Rob Orr Productions Ltd, pg 848
Pepper Group, pg 854
Production Craft Inc, pg 863
PSAV® Presentation Services (Hotel Services Division), pg 866
Richter Studios, pg 875
SCI Television & Creative Media LLC, pg 882
20/20 Communications Inc, pg 920
Video I-D Teleproductions Inc, pg 928
Video Impressions, pg 928
WEEK TV, pg 935
Winter Productions, pg 939

INDIANA

A-V-A Video Productions, pg 671
Advanced Media Integration, pg 677
Bright Ideas Creative Services, pg 710
Educational Video Group Inc, pg 751
PentaVision Communications Inc, pg 854
Road Pictures, pg 876

IOWA

Kuhn Productions LLC, pg 802
Prositions Inc, pg 865

KANSAS

KAKE-TV, pg 796

KENTUCKY

Hammond Communications Group Inc, pg 775
Idle Minds Productions Inc, pg 784
KET The Kentucky Network, pg 798

The Media Collaboratory, pg 821
Prosper Media Group Inc, pg 866

LOUISIANA

Digital FX Inc, pg 742
Launch Media, pg 804
Moxie Media, pg 832

MAINE

WGME-TV, pg 936

MARYLAND

Absolute Hollywood, pg 672
Adventure Productions LLC, pg 678
CAS Video Productions, pg 717
Richard Chisolm Cinematography, pg 722
CPR MultiMedia Solutions, pg 732
dbF a Media Company, pg 739
The Image Generators, pg 785
Media Dimensions LLC, pg 821
Quality Film & Video, pg 868

MASSACHUSETTS

Award Productions Inc, pg 699
CommCreative, pg 728
Commonwealth Films Inc, pg 728
Enterprise Media LLC, pg 754
Green Mountain Post Films (GMP), pg 774
Heliotrope Studios, pg 778
Merrimack Films, pg 824
Northern Light Productions (NLP), pg 842
Penfield Productions Ltd, pg 853
Preston Productions Inc, pg 861
TVN-The Video Network, pg 919
VideoLink Inc, an AVI-SPL company, pg 929
WGBH Production Group, pg 936
WVP Boston, pg 942

MICHIGAN

Digi Sign Design LLC, pg 741
K&R All Media Productions LLC, pg 796
K&R's Recording Studios Inc, pg 796
MSU Technologies, pg 833
The Program Source International, pg 865
Society of Manufacturing Engineers (SME), pg 891
TGA Recording Co, pg 911
WTVS, Detroit Public Television, pg 942

MINNESOTA

GMI Productions, pg 771
House of Cinemagraphics, pg 782
JIST Publishing, pg 794
MastCom, pg 819
Media Loft Inc, pg 822
Service Quality Institute, pg 884
Vaddio, pg 924
Babe Winkelman Productions Inc, pg 939

MISSOURI

Audio-VideoGraphics Inc, pg 694
Communitronics Corp, pg 729

MONTANA

ooLite Media LLC, pg 846

NEBRASKA

B & B Video Productions Inc, pg 700
Envision Communications Inc, pg 755
Rainbow Video Productions Inc, pg 869

NEVADA

Aardvark Video & Media Productions, pg 671
DVDs4Less, pg 748
Encore Event Technologies LLC, pg 754
JCS Video Productions, pg 793
Skyfire Video, pg 890
Tanglewood Productions, pg 907

NEW HAMPSHIRE

Apertura, pg 686
Channell One Video, pg 720
Chip Taylor Communications LLC, pg 907
The Troupe, pg 918

NEW JERSEY

Broadcast Center Studios, pg 710
CFP Video Productions Inc, pg 720
Euro-Pacific Film & Video Productions Inc, pg 756
Laurel Video Productions, pg 804
MediaNow Inc, pg 822
Megavideo LLC, pg 823
MiB MediaWorks, pg 825
Ray Mueller Productions, pg 833
Optisonics Productions, pg 847
Suede Interactive, pg 903
Telequest Inc, pg 910
TimeSteps Productions Inc, pg 914
VCSvideo, pg 925

NEW MEXICO

The Phoenix Learning Group Inc, pg 855
Production Outfitters, pg 864
Rainbow International Inc, pg 869

NEW YORK

Ace Video, pg 674
American Management Association® (AMA), pg 683
Associated Press Television News, pg 691
aurora productions, pg 696
Blue Barn Pictures Inc, pg 707
Brian Film Productions LLC, pg 710
Broadstreet Productions LLC, pg 711
Charlex Inc, pg 721
Cohn Creative Group LLC, pg 727
De Nonno Productions Inc (DPI), pg 739
Duplication Depot Inc, pg 748
Fanlight Productions, pg 759
Films Media Group, pg 760
Florentine Films, pg 762
Guidance Associates Inc Center for Humanities, pg 774
Havas Creative, pg 776
HB-Content, pg 777
Hello World Communications, pg 778
Image Zone Inc, pg 785
Ketchum Inc, pg 798
L A Bruell Inc, pg 802
Long Island Video Enterprises Live Inc, pg 811
Mastervision Inc, pg 819
Jack Morton Worldwide, pg 830

MRM//McCANN, pg 832
MRY, pg 832
New Horizon Studios, pg 839
News Broadcast Network Inc,
  pg 840
Northeast Video Productions Inc,
  pg 842
The Palmer Group, pg 850
Pat Kogan Productions Inc, pg 852
Peckham Productions Inc, pg 852
Polestar Films & Associated Arts
  Ltd, pg 859
Practising Law Institute, pg 860
PrimaLux Video Inc, pg 862
PrimeLight Productions Inc, pg 862
Richter Productions Inc, pg 875
Spoken Arts Inc, pg 898
Suggs Media Productions Inc,
  pg 903
Synaptic Digital, pg 905
TeleTime Productions, pg 910
Video Catalogue Co Inc, pg 927
VIEW Inc (Video International
  Entertainment World Inc), pg 930
Alan Weiss Productions, pg 935
WNET/New York Public Media,
  pg 940
Zelman Studios Ltd, pg 945

NORTH CAROLINA

All Pro Media Inc, pg 680
Pat Appleson Studios Inc, pg 687
AudioSolutionz LLC, pg 695
Bill Barnes Video Productions LLC,
  pg 702
The Communications Group Inc,
  pg 729
Digital Rain LLC, pg 742
Kino Mountain Productions LLC,
  pg 799
Moving Pictures, pg 832
Sinclair Institute, pg 889
Videowerks, pg 930

OHIO

Advent Media Inc, pg 677
Russ Beckner Pictures, pg 703
CET, pg 720
Curtis Inc, pg 736
Image Video Teleproductions Inc,
  pg 785
Lyon Video Inc, pg 813
MainSail Production Services Inc,
  pg 815
Take 1 Media Services, pg 906
Treehaus Communications Inc,
  pg 917
Vista Color Imaging Inc, pg 931

OKLAHOMA

Institute for Teaching & Learning
  Excellence (ITLE), pg 788

OREGON

CMD Agency, pg 726
ERA Learning, pg 755
InterVision Media, pg 791
The Keyboard Workshop, pg 798
KPDX-TV Production Center,
  pg 801
KTVA Productions, pg 802
KVAL, pg 802
Odyssey Productions Inc, pg 844
Production West, pg 864
REX, pg 874

PENNSYLVANIA

Audio Visual Communications Inc,
  pg 694
Bang! Pictures Inc, pg 701

Beholder Productions Inc, pg 703
CCI Communications Inc, pg 718
FMP Media Solutions Inc, pg 763
JPL, pg 795
Main Point Productions, pg 815
Muderick Media, pg 833
Panta Rhei Media Inc, pg 851
Production Masters Inc (PMI),
  pg 864
Video/Film Associates, pg 928
The Videohouse Inc, pg 929
Visual Sound Inc, pg 931
WHYY Inc, pg 938

RHODE ISLAND

Sound-FX-Design, pg 894

SOUTH CAROLINA

American Production Services LLC,
  pg 684
Encore Video Productions, pg 754
Go To Team, pg 772
Stages Video Productions, pg 899
Venture Media, pg 925

TENNESSEE

Continental Film, pg 731
Memphis Communications Corp,
  pg 823
Paradigm Marketing & Creative,
  pg 851
Running Pony Productions LLC,
  pg 878
Scripps Networks, pg 882

TEXAS

Alpha Video Productions, pg 682
AMS Pictures, pg 684
Biway Media, pg 706
Castleview Productions, pg 717
Cerutti Productions Inc, pg 720
CEV Multimedia Ltd, pg 720
Communication Arts Multimedia
  Inc, pg 728
Countdown Productions Inc, pg 732
Dub King, pg 747
Dykeman Associates Inc, pg 748
The Editing Co, pg 750
Educational Video Network, pg 751
Emergency Film Group, pg 753
Eyecon Video Productions, pg 758
Horizon Film + Video Productions,
  pg 781
JSAV, pg 795
Marx InDigital, pg 818
Matson Multi-Media, pg 820
Mediaforce Productions, pg 822
Earl Miller Productions Inc, pg 827
Julye Newlin Productions Inc,
  pg 840
Omega Productions, pg 845
Omni Intercommunications Inc,
  pg 845
Richie Media Productions LLC,
  pg 875
South Coast Film & Video, pg 895
Sportsmen on Film Inc, pg 898
Stage Directions, pg 898

VERMONT

Marlboro Productions, pg 817
University of Vermont, Instructional
  Television Dept, pg 923
Wilson McLeran Inc, pg 939

VIRGINIA

Advance Concepts Inc, pg 677
Altruist Media LLC, pg 682
BES Studios, pg 704
Cinebar Productions Inc, pg 723

CVW Event Productions, pg 736
Limelight Communications Inc,
  pg 808
Metro Productions, pg 824
National Media Services Inc,
  pg 836
Rocktown Media, pg 876
Video Solutions, pg 928
WETA Production Center, pg 936

WASHINGTON

Adams Creative & Production
  Services, pg 675
Bennett-Watt HD Productions Inc,
  pg 703
Intermedia Inc, pg 789
Pal Productions Inc, pg 850
Victory Studios, pg 927

WISCONSIN

Audio Visual of Milwaukee Inc,
  pg 694
AVS Group, pg 699
Meridian Studios, pg 824
Midland Video Productions Inc,
  pg 827
Mirror 34 Productions, pg 828
Rucinski Write!Now LLC, pg 878
University of Wisconsin-Oshkosh
  Radio-TV-Film Dept, pg 923
USAV Group Inc, pg 923
Video Wisconsin Inc, pg 929
Watts Communications Inc, pg 934
Wisconsin Public Television, pg 940

WYOMING

Bridger Productions Inc, pg 710

ALBERTA

Global TV, pg 771
HDTV Productions Inc, pg 777

BRITISH COLUMBIA

Triad Communications Ltd, pg 918

MANITOBA

Spectra Video Productions Ltd,
  pg 897

ONTARIO

ADS Media, pg 677
DebsVoice, pg 739
Image Video Services &
  Productions, pg 785
Jams Productions Inc, pg 793
JFB Communications, pg 794
Mediaimage Communications
  Group, pg 822
RB Productions, pg 870
Video Advantage, pg 927
Video Excellence Productions,
  pg 927

QUEBEC

Kerrigan Productions Inc, pg 798

SASKATCHEWAN

plan9films, pg 857

Business Program Rentals

ARIZONA

Video Learning Library, pg 928

CALIFORNIA

Direct Cinema Ltd Inc, pg 743

GEORGIA

Convergent Media Systems, pg 731

ILLINOIS

1st Financial Training Services Inc,
  pg 761

MASSACHUSETTS

Commonwealth Films Inc, pg 728
Enterprise Media LLC, pg 754
Merrimack Films, pg 824

MICHIGAN

Digi Sign Design LLC, pg 741

MINNESOTA

Service Quality Institute, pg 884

MISSOURI

University of Missouri-Columbia,
  pg 923

NEW JERSEY

Euro-Pacific Film & Video
  Productions Inc, pg 756

NEW YORK

Films Media Group, pg 760
Richter Productions Inc, pg 875
VIEW Inc (Video International
  Entertainment World Inc), pg 930

OREGON

The Keyboard Workshop, pg 798

VERMONT

University of Vermont, Instructional
  Television Dept, pg 923

ONTARIO

Kineticvideo.com, pg 799
McNabb & Connolly, pg 821

Cable TV Program Distributors

ALABAMA

Eternal Word Television Network
  (EWTN), pg 756

ARIZONA

Arizona Cine Equipment, pg 688

ARKANSAS

Mullikin Agency, pg 833

CALIFORNIA

Ametron Audio/Video, pg 684
Custom Video Productions Inc,
  pg 736
411 Video Information, pg 764
Krishnamurti Foundation of
  America, pg 801
Lions Gate Entertainment Corp,
  pg 809
New & Unique Videos™, pg 839
Prime Cut Productions, pg 862
Pyramid Media, pg 867

COLORADO

Apogee Communications Group,
  pg 687

PROGRAMMING — VIDEO

Cable TV Program Distributors (continued)

CONNECTICUT
ESPN Inc, pg 755

FLORIDA
Lighting Sales Connection Inc, pg 808

GEORGIA
Turner Broadcasting System Inc, A Time Warner Company, pg 919

ILLINOIS
Moviecraft Inc, pg 831

INDIANA
Communication Ministries, pg 728

IOWA
Right Stuf Inc, pg 875

KENTUCKY
EKU Media, pg 752

MARYLAND
Recorded Books Inc, an RBmedia company, pg 871
Total AV Systems, pg 916

MASSACHUSETTS
Documentary Educational Resources Inc, pg 744

MICHIGAN
Digi Sign Design LLC, pg 741

MINNESOTA
American Choral Catalog Ltd, pg 683

NEVADA
Aardvark Video & Media Productions, pg 671
DVDs4Less, pg 748

NEW HAMPSHIRE
Channell One Video, pg 720
Chip Taylor Communications LLC, pg 907

NEW JERSEY
Alden Films, pg 679
MiB MediaWorks, pg 825
SES SA, pg 884

NEW YORK
A&E Home Video, pg 671
A&E Television Networks LLC, pg 671
ATA Trading Corp/Favorite TV Inc, pg 691
HB-Content, pg 777
Lifetime Television®, pg 807
Mastervision Inc, pg 819
Showtime Networks Inc, pg 887
SISU Home Entertainment Inc, pg 889
Spectrum Enterprise, pg 897

Third World Newsreel/Camera News Inc, pg 912
VIEW Inc (Video International Entertainment World Inc), pg 930

NORTH DAKOTA
UND Television Center, pg 921

PENNSYLVANIA
AccuWeather Inc, pg 674

TENNESSEE
American Blackguard Inc, pg 683
Center for Southern Folklore Inc, pg 719
Zion Music Group, pg 945

TEXAS
Lamb & Lion Ministries, pg 803
Marengo Films, pg 817

WASHINGTON
Bennett-Watt HD Productions Inc, pg 703
Victory Studios, pg 927

WISCONSIN
Wisconsin Public Television, pg 940

QUEBEC
Whalley-Abbey Media Holdings Inc, pg 937

Cable TV Program Producers

ALABAMA
Eternal Word Television Network (EWTN), pg 756

ARIZONA
Aardvark Productions LLC, pg 671
Direct Current Video Productions, pg 743

ARKANSAS
Live'N'Loud, pg 810
Mullikin Agency, pg 833

CALIFORNIA
Action Video, pg 675
Anonymous Content, pg 686
Big Door, pg 705
Burrud Productions Inc, pg 713
Creative Technology, pg 733
Custom Video Productions Inc, pg 736
Direct Images Interactive Inc, pg 743
Image Integration, pg 785
imageReal Pictures LLC, pg 785
ITV Productions, pg 792
Krishnamurti Foundation of America, pg 801
KTVU-Retail Services, pg 802
Lions Gate Entertainment Corp, pg 809
Ludlow Media, pg 812
Media Magic, pg 822
New & Unique Videos™, pg 839
On-Trax Inc, pg 846
Prime Cut Productions, pg 862
RED Studios Hollywood, pg 872
RetinaVision Productions, pg 874
Glenn Roland Films, pg 876
Saturn Studios, pg 881

Screen Door Entertainment Inc, pg 882
SNAP, pg 891
Staylor-Made Communications Inc, pg 900
Tam Communications Inc, pg 906
Timestream Video, pg 914
Total Creative, pg 916
TVA Media Group, pg 919
Twin Peaks Creative, pg 920
Vineyard Video & Photography, pg 930

COLORADO
Apogee Communications Group, pg 687
CSI Film & Video LLC, pg 735
Daylight Productions & Rentals, pg 739
Flashback Media Productions, pg 762
Rocky Mountain Audio/Video Productions Inc, pg 876
Tatum Video, pg 907

CONNECTICUT
ESPN Inc, pg 755
Ironik Design & Post, pg 791
Moving Pictures, pg 832
New London Media, pg 839

FLORIDA
Applebox Studio, pg 687
Blackburst Entertainment LLC, pg 706
Courter Films LLC, pg 732
Sunfire Communications Inc, pg 904
Sunrise Studios, pg 904
Tel-Air Interests Inc, pg 909
Tricycle Studios, pg 918

GEORGIA
ECG Productions, pg 750
Guerrilla Productions LLC, pg 774
Myriad Productions, pg 835
Malcolm Neal Productions, pg 837
On-Line Productions, pg 845

HAWAII
Hyperspective Studios Inc, pg 783
Sight & Sound Studios, pg 887
Tropical Visions Video Inc, pg 918

IDAHO
Brad Shaw Productions Inc, pg 885
Wide Eye Productions, pg 938

ILLINOIS
Airways Digital Media, pg 679
Atomic Imaging Inc/Golan Studios, pg 692
Film Police, pg 760
IV Media Resources, pg 792
Mimi Productions, pg 828
Moviecraft Inc, pg 831
Pepper Group, pg 854
PSAV® Presentation Services (Hotel Services Division), pg 866
SCI Television & Creative Media LLC, pg 882
20/20 Communications Inc, pg 920
Video Impressions, pg 928
Winter Productions, pg 939

INDIANA
A-V-A Video Productions, pg 671
Advanced Media Integration, pg 677

IOWA
Right Stuf Inc, pg 875

KANSAS
KAKE-TV, pg 796

KENTUCKY
EKU Media, pg 752
Prosper Media Group Inc, pg 866

LOUISIANA
Digital FX Inc, pg 742
Moxie Media, pg 832

MARYLAND
Absolute Hollywood, pg 672
Adventure Productions LLC, pg 678
CAS Video Productions, pg 717
CPR MultiMedia Solutions, pg 732
dbF a Media Company, pg 739

MASSACHUSETTS
Documentary Educational Resources Inc, pg 744
HOME Inc, pg 781
Penfield Productions Ltd, pg 853
VideoLink Inc, an AVI-SPL company, pg 929

MICHIGAN
Digi Sign Design LLC, pg 741
K&R All Media Productions LLC, pg 796
K&R's Recording Studios Inc, pg 796

MINNESOTA
American Choral Catalog Ltd, pg 683
House of Cinemagraphics, pg 782

NEVADA
Aardvark Video & Media Productions, pg 671
DVDs4Less, pg 748
JCS Video Productions, pg 793

NEW HAMPSHIRE
Channell One Video, pg 720
Chip Taylor Communications LLC, pg 907

NEW JERSEY
Alden Films, pg 679
Broadcast Center Studios, pg 710
CFP Video Productions Inc, pg 720
Euro-Pacific Film & Video Productions Inc, pg 756
MiB MediaWorks, pg 825
Suede Interactive, pg 903
TimeSteps Productions Inc, pg 914

NEW MEXICO
Production Outfitters, pg 864

NEW YORK
A&E Home Video, pg 671
Artistic Video, pg 690
aurora productions, pg 696
Blue Barn Pictures Inc, pg 707
Buzzco Associates Inc, pg 713
HB-Content, pg 777
Hello World Communications, pg 778

The Independent Production Fund, pg 786
Kinetic Arts, pg 799
Manhattan Center Studios Inc, pg 816
Mastervision Inc, pg 819
Mood Creations Ltd, pg 829
News Broadcast Network Inc, pg 840
News Corp, pg 840
Nickelodeon, pg 841
The Palmer Group, pg 850
Pat Kogan Productions Inc, pg 852
PrimaLux Video Inc, pg 862
SISU Home Entertainment Inc, pg 889
Suggs Media Productions Inc, pg 903
VIEW Inc (Video International Entertainment World Inc), pg 930
Zelman Studios Ltd, pg 945

NORTH CAROLINA

The Communications Group Inc, pg 729
Digital Rain LLC, pg 742
Kino Mountain Productions LLC, pg 799
NASCAR Productions LLC, pg 835
Videowerks, pg 930

NORTH DAKOTA

UND Television Center, pg 921

OHIO

CET, pg 720
Curtis Inc, pg 736
Cuyahoga Community College Student Production Office (SPO), pg 736
Lyon Video Inc, pg 813
MainSail Production Services Inc, pg 815
Take 1 Media Services, pg 906
Vista Color Imaging Inc, pg 931

OREGON

KTVA Productions, pg 802
Production West, pg 864
REX, pg 874

PENNSYLVANIA

AccuWeather Inc, pg 674
Beholder Productions Inc, pg 703
JPL, pg 795
Production Masters Inc (PMI), pg 864
The Videohouse Inc, pg 929

RHODE ISLAND

Sound-FX-Design, pg 894

SOUTH CAROLINA

Encore Video Productions, pg 754
Go To Team, pg 772
Stages Video Productions, pg 899
Venture Media, pg 925

TENNESSEE

American Blackguard Inc, pg 683
Center for Southern Folklore Inc, pg 719
Running Pony Productions LLC, pg 878
Scripps Networks, pg 882

TEXAS

Biway Media, pg 706
Communication Arts Multimedia Inc, pg 728
Dub King, pg 747
Horizon Film + Video Productions, pg 781
Lamb & Lion Ministries, pg 803
Earl Miller Productions Inc, pg 827
Reelsound Recording Co, pg 872

VIRGINIA

BES Studios, pg 704
CACI Integrated Communications, pg 713
Metro Productions, pg 824
Rocktown Media, pg 876
Video Solutions, pg 928

WASHINGTON

Bennett-Watt HD Productions Inc, pg 703
White Rain Films Ltd, pg 937

WISCONSIN

Audio Visual of Milwaukee Inc, pg 694
University of Wisconsin-Oshkosh Radio-TV-Film Dept, pg 923
Watts Communications Inc, pg 934
Wisconsin Public Television, pg 940

WYOMING

Bridger Productions Inc, pg 710

ONTARIO

Marblemedia, pg 816

QUEBEC

Kerrigan Productions Inc, pg 798
Whalley-Abbey Media Holdings Inc, pg 937

SASKATCHEWAN

plan9films, pg 857

Cable TV Program Rentals

CALIFORNIA

Ametron Audio/Video, pg 684

FLORIDA

Lighting Sales Connection Inc, pg 808

GEORGIA

Staging Directions Inc, pg 899

MASSACHUSETTS

Documentary Educational Resources Inc, pg 744

MICHIGAN

Digi Sign Design LLC, pg 741

NEW JERSEY

Alden Films, pg 679

NEW YORK

Third World Newsreel/Camera News Inc, pg 912

TENNESSEE

Center for Southern Folklore Inc, pg 719

WISCONSIN

Wisconsin Public Television, pg 940

Children's Program Distributors

ALASKA

Alaska Video Postcards Inc, pg 679

ARIZONA

Video Learning Library, pg 928

CALIFORNIA

Astronomical Society of the Pacific, pg 691
Backstage Pass Entertainment Inc, pg 700
C & M Publishing Co, pg 713
California Language Laboratories, pg 714
Concept Associates Inc, pg 730
Crystal Pyramid Productions™, pg 735
Direct Cinema Ltd Inc, pg 743
Discovery Education - Los Angeles, pg 743
Durrin Productions Inc, pg 748
Em Gee Film Library, pg 753
ETR, pg 756
411 Video Information, pg 764
Glenn Video Vistas Ltd, pg 771
Increase Video/Silver Mine Video, pg 786
Joyce Media Inc, pg 795
Lightyear Entertainment, pg 808
Live Wire Media, pg 810
MarVista Entertainment Inc, pg 818
MGM Home Entertainment, pg 825
monterey media inc, pg 829
monterey video, pg 829
Moose School Productions, pg 830
Music Rhapsody, pg 834
New & Unique Videos™, pg 839
People Skills International, pg 854
Publishers Group West (PGW), an Ingram brand, pg 866
Pyramid Media, pg 867
Regent Press Publishers & Printers, pg 873
Rhythms Productions (Tom Thumb Music), pg 874
Russ InVision Co/AbridgeClub.com, pg 879
Sea Studios Foundation, pg 883
TMW Media Group, pg 915
Universal Pictures Home Entertainment, pg 922
The Video Project, pg 928
Visual Communications - Southern California Asian American Studies Central Inc, pg 931
Warner Home Video Inc, pg 934
Xenon Pictures Inc, pg 943

COLORADO

Crystal Productions, pg 735
InJoy Birth & Parenting Education, pg 788

CONNECTICUT

Really Good Stuff, pg 871
Weston Woods Studios Inc, pg 936

DELAWARE

So Smart Productions, pg 891

DISTRICT OF COLUMBIA

Biblical Archaeology Society (BAS), pg 705
Systems Impact Inc, pg 906
USCCB Publishing, pg 923

FLORIDA

I M P A C T Publishing Inc, pg 783
Potentials Unlimited, pg 860
Video Aided Instruction Inc, pg 927
Video Resources Software, pg 928

GEORGIA

Gingerbread Group Holdings LLC, pg 771
Little Mammoth Media, pg 810
New Leaf Distributing Co, pg 839
School Media Associates LLC, pg 882

ILLINOIS

Britannica Digital Learning, pg 710
Discovery Education - Chicago, pg 743
Encyclopaedia Britannica Inc, pg 754
Facets Multi-Media Inc, pg 758
Film Ideas Inc, pg 760
The Market Place, pg 817
Moviecraft Inc, pg 831
Movies Unlimited, pg 831
Nightingale-Conant Corp, pg 841
Questar Entertainment Inc, pg 868

INDIANA

Perennial Pictures Film Corp, pg 854

KENTUCKY

KET The Kentucky Network, pg 798
National Geographic Learning, pg 836
WaxWorks VideoWorks, pg 934

MAINE

Slim Goodbody Corp, pg 890

MARYLAND

Adventure Productions LLC, pg 678
Recorded Books Inc, an RBmedia company, pg 871
RLJ Entertainment Inc, pg 875
Sign Media Inc, pg 887

MASSACHUSETTS

Documentary Educational Resources Inc, pg 744
HOME Inc, pg 781
Pauline Books & Media, pg 852
Yellow Moon Press, pg 944

MICHIGAN

Digi Sign Design LLC, pg 741
Emery-Pratt Co, pg 753
Gemini, pg 769
Zondervan, pg 945

MINNESOTA

Harris Communications Inc, pg 776

PROGRAMMING — VIDEO

Children's Program Distributors (continued)

MISSOURI

Marsh Media, pg 817
SOM Publishing Co, pg 892

NEBRASKA

Vision Maker Media, pg 930

NEW HAMPSHIRE

Chip Taylor Communications LLC, pg 907

NEW JERSEY

Dance Horizons Video, pg 737
Ergo Media Inc, pg 755
Milestone Film & Video Inc, pg 827

NEW MEXICO

The Phoenix Learning Group Inc, pg 855

NEW YORK

Ambrose Video Publishing Inc, pg 682
ATA Trading Corp/Favorite TV Inc, pg 691
Broadstreet Productions LLC, pg 711
Brooklyn Botanic Garden, pg 711
Billy Budd Films Inc, pg 712
The Bureau for At-Risk Youth, pg 712
The Christophers, pg 722
De Nonno Productions Inc (DPI), pg 739
Educational Activities Inc, pg 750
FACE Foundation, pg 758
Guidance Associates Inc Center for Humanities, pg 774
Hallel Communications, pg 775
Hearst Entertainment & Syndication, pg 778
Homespun Video, pg 781
Human Relations Media, pg 782
IAI Records & Video, pg 783
Janson Media Inc, pg 793
L&S Video Inc, pg 803
Live Oak Media, pg 810
Mastervision Inc, pg 819
Random House Children's Books, pg 870
Scholastic Media, pg 882
SISU Home Entertainment Inc, pg 889
Spoken Arts Inc, pg 898
Synaptic Digital, pg 905
Third World Newsreel/Camera News Inc, pg 912
VIEW Inc (Video International Entertainment World Inc), pg 930

NORTH CAROLINA

Crystal Pictures Inc, pg 735
Ladyslipper Music, pg 803

OHIO

Alegra House Publishers, pg 679
Curtis Inc, pg 736
Treehaus Communications Inc, pg 917

OREGON

Encounter Video Inc, pg 754
InterVision Media, pg 791
Nostalgia Family Video Inc, pg 843
Sugar Mountain PR, pg 903

PENNSYLVANIA

Anchor Distributors, pg 685
Beholder Productions Inc, pg 703
Bullfrog Films Inc, pg 712
Corinth Films Inc, pg 731
Discovery Education - South Burlington, pg 743
Library Video Company, pg 807
MVD Entertainment Group, pg 835
Fred Rogers Productions, pg 876
S I Video Sales Group, pg 879
Schlessinger Media, pg 881
Vision Video, pg 930
The Whale Video Co, pg 936

SOUTH CAROLINA

American Production Services LLC, pg 684
BJU Press, pg 706

TENNESSEE

Abingdon Press, pg 672
American Blackguard Inc, pg 683
Capitol Christian Music Group, pg 716
Cokesbury, pg 727
National School Products, pg 836
Randall House Publications, pg 870
Spring Arbor Distributors Inc, pg 898
Word Label Group, pg 941

TEXAS

Educational Video Network, pg 751
Horizon Film + Video Productions, pg 781
Marengo Films, pg 817
Shadow Play Records & Video, pg 885

VERMONT

University of Vermont, Instructional Television Dept, pg 923

WASHINGTON

Intermedia Inc, pg 789
John McLean Media, pg 794
Victory Studios, pg 927

WEST VIRGINIA

Focus on Animals, pg 763
Sweetsong Productions, pg 905

WISCONSIN

Aylmer Press, pg 700
Knowledge Unlimited Inc, pg 800
NEWIST/CESA 7, pg 840
Wisconsin Public Television, pg 940

ALBERTA

Global TV, pg 771

BRITISH COLUMBIA

Thompson Rivers University Marketing & Communications Dept, pg 913

ONTARIO

Broughton's Church Supplies, Religious Books & Gifts, pg 711
Canadian Filmmakers Distribution Center (CFMDC), pg 715
Canadian Learning Co Inc, pg 715
Canamedia Inc, pg 715
CCI Entertainment Ltd, pg 718
The Children's Book Store Distribution (CBSD), pg 722
Kineticvideo.com, pg 799
Life Cycle Books Ltd, pg 807
McIntyre Media Inc, pg 821
McNabb & Connolly, pg 821
Novalis, pg 843
Sullivan Home Entertainment, pg 903
Universal Studios Canada Inc, pg 922

QUEBEC

Les Productions Via Le Monde (Daniel Bertolino) Inc, pg 864

Children's Program Producers

ALASKA

Alaska Video Postcards Inc, pg 679

ARIZONA

Aardvark Productions LLC, pg 671
Candee Productions Inc, pg 716
Teaberry, pg 908

CALIFORNIA

Action Video, pg 675
Allied Artists International Inc, pg 681
Big Door, pg 705
Burrud Productions Inc, pg 713
C & M Publishing Co, pg 713
California Language Laboratories, pg 714
Classic Images Stock Footage LLC, pg 726
Concept Associates Inc, pg 730
Creative Technology, pg 733
Crystal Pyramid Productions™, pg 735
Custom Video Productions Inc, pg 736
Discovery Education - Los Angeles, pg 743
Durrin Productions Inc, pg 748
Increase Video/Silver Mine Video, pg 786
ITV Productions, pg 792
Joyce Media Inc, pg 795
Lightyear Entertainment, pg 808
Live Wire Media, pg 810
Ludlow Media, pg 812
Main Street Media Inc, pg 815
MarVista Entertainment Inc, pg 818
Maximus Media Inc, pg 820
McCune Audio-Video-Lighting, pg 821
Media Magic, pg 822
The Media Staff Inc, pg 822
monterey media inc, pg 829
Moose School Productions, pg 830
The Mother Co, pg 831
Music Rhapsody, pg 834
New & Unique Videos™, pg 839
Pyramid Media, pg 867
Regent Press Publishers & Printers, pg 873
Rhythms Productions (Tom Thumb Music), pg 874

Glenn Roland Films, pg 876
Russ InVision Co/AbridgeClub.com, pg 879
Saturn Studios, pg 881
Screen Door Entertainment Inc, pg 882
Sea Studios Foundation, pg 883
SNAP, pg 891
Staylor-Made Communications Inc, pg 900
Still N' Motion, pg 901
Tam Communications Inc, pg 906
TMW Media Group, pg 915
Total Creative, pg 916
TVA Media Group, pg 919
Twin Peaks Creative, pg 920
Universal Pictures Home Entertainment, pg 922
Vineyard Video & Photography, pg 930
Visual Communications - Southern California Asian American Studies Central Inc, pg 931
Webster Communications, pg 935
Xenon Pictures Inc, pg 943
Zamacona Productions, pg 945

COLORADO

Apogee Communications Group, pg 687
Centre Communications Inc, pg 720
Crystal Productions, pg 735
CSI Film & Video LLC, pg 735
Flashback Media Productions, pg 762
InJoy Birth & Parenting Education, pg 788
Rocky Mountain Audio/Video Productions Inc, pg 876
Transtar Entertainment Co Inc, pg 917

CONNECTICUT

ACM Productions Ltd, pg 674
Geomatrix Productions, pg 770
Ironik Design & Post, pg 791
Spectrum, pg 897
Weston Woods Studios Inc, pg 936

DELAWARE

So Smart Productions, pg 891

DISTRICT OF COLUMBIA

Hillmann & Carr Inc, pg 780
Systems Impact Inc, pg 906

FLORIDA

Applebox Studio, pg 687
Blackburst Entertainment LLC, pg 706
Chatterbox Productions Inc, pg 721
Civins Productions Inc, pg 725
Courter Films LLC, pg 732
Global Cyber-Visions, pg 771
Jordan Klein Film & Video (JKFV), pg 795
National Teleproductions Inc, pg 837
Paradise Video & Film, pg 851
Sunfire Communications Inc, pg 904
Sunrise Studios, pg 904
Tricycle Studios, pg 918
Video Aided Instruction Inc, pg 927
Video Resources Software, pg 928

GEORGIA

Beachwood Productions, pg 702
Burst Video/Film Inc, pg 713
Cox Media, pg 732

Gingerbread Group Holdings LLC, pg 771
Guerrilla Productions LLC, pg 774
Little Mammoth Media, pg 810
Malcolm Neal Productions, pg 837
On-Line Productions, pg 845

HAWAII

Hyperspective Studios Inc, pg 783

IDAHO

Brad Shaw Productions Inc, pg 885
Wide Eye Productions, pg 938

ILLINOIS

Britannica Digital Learning, pg 710
The Chicago Production Center, pg 721
Discovery Education - Chicago, pg 743
Encyclopaedia Britannica Inc, pg 754
Film Police, pg 760
IV Media Resources, pg 792
Manning Productions, pg 816
Nightingale-Conant Corp, pg 841
Pepper Group, pg 854
Production Craft Inc, pg 863
SCI Television & Creative Media LLC, pg 882
20/20 Communications Inc, pg 920
Video Impressions, pg 928
Winter Productions, pg 939

INDIANA

A-V-A Video Productions, pg 671
Bright Ideas Creative Services, pg 710

KANSAS

KAKE-TV, pg 796

KENTUCKY

KET The Kentucky Network, pg 798
National Geographic Learning, pg 836

LOUISIANA

Moxie Media, pg 832

MAINE

Slim Goodbody Corp, pg 890

MARYLAND

Absolute Hollywood, pg 672
Adventure Productions LLC, pg 678
dbF a Media Company, pg 739
Sign Media Inc, pg 887

MASSACHUSETTS

Green Mountain Post Films (GMP), pg 774
Heliotrope Studios, pg 778
HOME Inc, pg 781
Northern Light Productions (NLP), pg 842
Pauline Books & Media, pg 852
Penfield Productions Ltd, pg 853
TVN-The Video Network, pg 919
VideoLink Inc, an AVI-SPL company, pg 929
WGBH Production Group, pg 936
WVP Boston, pg 942

MICHIGAN

Digi Sign Design LLC, pg 741
Gemini, pg 769
K&R All Media Productions LLC, pg 796
K&R's Recording Studios Inc, pg 796
Zondervan, pg 945

MINNESOTA

House of Cinemagraphics, pg 782
MastCom, pg 819
Worthwhile Films, pg 941

MISSOURI

Audio-VideoGraphics Inc, pg 694
Marsh Media, pg 817
SOM Publishing Co, pg 892

NEBRASKA

Vision Maker Media, pg 930

NEVADA

Encore Event Technologies LLC, pg 754
JCS Video Productions, pg 793

NEW HAMPSHIRE

Apertura, pg 686
Chip Taylor Communications LLC, pg 907

NEW JERSEY

Broadcast Center Studios, pg 710
CFP Video Productions Inc, pg 720
Optisonics Productions, pg 847
Telequest Inc, pg 910
VCSvideo, pg 925

NEW MEXICO

The Phoenix Learning Group Inc, pg 855
Production Outfitters, pg 864
Rainbow International Inc, pg 869

NEW YORK

Ace Video, pg 674
Air Sea Land Productions Inc (ASL), pg 678
American History Workshop (NY) Inc, pg 683
aurora productions, pg 696
Blue Barn Pictures Inc, pg 707
Brian Film Productions LLC, pg 710
Brooklyn Botanic Garden, pg 711
Billy Budd Films Inc, pg 712
The Bureau for At-Risk Youth, pg 712
Buzzco Associates Inc, pg 713
De Nonno Productions Inc (DPI), pg 739
Educational Activities Inc, pg 750
Fabled Films LLC, pg 758
Fanlight Productions, pg 759
Florentine Films, pg 762
Guidance Associates Inc Center for Humanities, pg 774
Hallel Communications, pg 775
Hearst Entertainment & Syndication, pg 778
Hello World Communications, pg 778
Homespun Video, pg 781
Human Relations Media, pg 782
IAI Records & Video, pg 783
L A Bruell Inc, pg 802
L&S Video Inc, pg 803

Live Oak Media, pg 810
Manhattan Center Studios Inc, pg 816
Mastervision Inc, pg 819
Mood Creations Ltd, pg 829
Jack Morton Worldwide, pg 830
MRY, pg 832
Nickelodeon, pg 841
The Palmer Group, pg 850
Pat Kogan Productions Inc, pg 852
Peckham Productions Inc, pg 852
Polestar Films & Associated Arts Ltd, pg 859
PrimaLux Video Inc, pg 862
Random House Children's Books, pg 870
Scholastic Media, pg 882
SISU Home Entertainment Inc, pg 889
Spoken Arts Inc, pg 898
Synaptic Digital, pg 905
Third World Newsreel/Camera News Inc, pg 912
VIEW Inc (Video International Entertainment World Inc), pg 930
Alan Weiss Productions, pg 935
WNET/New York Public Media, pg 940
Zelman Studios Ltd, pg 945

NORTH CAROLINA

The Communications Group Inc, pg 729
Crystal Pictures Inc, pg 735
Digital Rain LLC, pg 742
High Windy Audio/Banjoman Inc, pg 779
Kino Mountain Productions LLC, pg 799
Moving Pictures, pg 832
Videowerks, pg 930

OHIO

Alegra House Publishers, pg 679
Russ Beckner Pictures, pg 703
CET, pg 720
Curtis Inc, pg 736
Dreamscape Media LLC, pg 746
Image Video Teleproductions Inc, pg 785
Lyon Video Inc, pg 813
MainSail Production Services Inc, pg 815
Take 1 Media Services, pg 906
Treehaus Communications Inc, pg 917
Vista Color Imaging Inc, pg 931

OKLAHOMA

Academic Media & Digital Services, pg 672

OREGON

Encounter Video Inc, pg 754
InterVision Media, pg 791
KPDX-TV Production Center, pg 801
KTVA Productions, pg 802
Odyssey Productions Inc, pg 844
Wallace Creative LLC, pg 933

PENNSYLVANIA

Beholder Productions Inc, pg 703
CCI Communications Inc, pg 718
Discovery Education - South Burlington, pg 743
Kensington Falls Animation, pg 797
Muderick Media, pg 833
Production Masters Inc (PMI), pg 864

Fred Rogers Productions, pg 876
Schlessinger Media, pg 881
The Videohouse Inc, pg 929
Vision Video, pg 930
The Whale Video Co, pg 936

RHODE ISLAND

Sound-FX-Design, pg 894

SOUTH CAROLINA

American Production Services LLC, pg 684
BJU Press, pg 706
Venture Media, pg 925

TENNESSEE

Abingdon Press, pg 672
American Blackguard Inc, pg 683
Capitol Christian Music Group, pg 716
Cokesbury, pg 727
Running Pony Productions LLC, pg 878
United Methodist Productions, pg 921
Word Label Group, pg 941

TEXAS

AMS Pictures, pg 684
Cerutti Productions Inc, pg 720
Communication Arts Multimedia Inc, pg 728
The Editing Co, pg 750
Educational Video Network, pg 751
Horizon Film + Video Productions, pg 781
Marx InDigital, pg 818
Mediaforce Productions, pg 822
Earl Miller Productions Inc, pg 827
Julye Newlin Productions Inc, pg 840
Omega Productions, pg 845
Shadow Play Records & Video, pg 885
South Coast Film & Video, pg 895

VERMONT

Marlboro Productions, pg 817
University of Vermont, Instructional Television Dept, pg 923

VIRGINIA

BES Studios, pg 704
Limelight Communications Inc, pg 808
Rocktown Media, pg 876
Video Solutions, pg 928

WASHINGTON

Pal Productions Inc, pg 850

WEST VIRGINIA

Sweetsong Productions, pg 905

WISCONSIN

Aylmer Press, pg 700
Midland Video Productions Inc, pg 827
Mirror 34 Productions, pg 828
NEWIST/CESA 7, pg 840
Watts Communications Inc, pg 934
Wisconsin Public Television, pg 940

WYOMING

Bridger Productions Inc, pg 710

PROGRAMMING — VIDEO

Children's Program Producers (continued)

ALBERTA
Global TV, pg 771

BRITISH COLUMBIA
Thompson Rivers University Marketing & Communications Dept, pg 913
Triad Communications Ltd, pg 918

MANITOBA
Spectra Video Productions Ltd, pg 897

ONTARIO
ADS Media, pg 677
Canamedia Inc, pg 715
Jams Productions Inc, pg 793
Marblemedia, pg 816
Mediaimage Communications Group, pg 822
Novalis, pg 843
Weston Woods Canada, pg 936

QUEBEC
Kerrigan Productions Inc, pg 798
Les Productions Via Le Monde (Daniel Bertolino) Inc, pg 864

SASKATCHEWAN
plan9films, pg 857

Children's Program Rentals

ARIZONA
Video Learning Library, pg 928

CALIFORNIA
Direct Cinema Ltd Inc, pg 743
Durrin Productions Inc, pg 748
Visual Communications - Southern California Asian American Studies Central Inc, pg 931

ILLINOIS
Discovery Education - Chicago, pg 743
Facets Multi-Media Inc, pg 758

MASSACHUSETTS
Pauline Books & Media, pg 852

MICHIGAN
Digi Sign Design LLC, pg 741

MISSOURI
University of Missouri-Columbia, pg 923

NEBRASKA
Vision Maker Media, pg 930

NEW YORK
Brooklyn Botanic Garden, pg 711
Hallel Communications, pg 775

Third World Newsreel/Camera News Inc, pg 912
VIEW Inc (Video International Entertainment World Inc), pg 930

NORTH CAROLINA
Crystal Pictures Inc, pg 735

OHIO
Treehaus Communications Inc, pg 917

OREGON
Nostalgia Family Video Inc, pg 843

PENNSYLVANIA
Bullfrog Films Inc, pg 712

VERMONT
University of Vermont, Instructional Television Dept, pg 923

WISCONSIN
NEWIST/CESA 7, pg 840

MANITOBA
Spectra Video Productions Ltd, pg 897

ONTARIO
Kineticvideo.com, pg 799
McNabb & Connolly, pg 821

QUEBEC
Les Productions Via Le Monde (Daniel Bertolino) Inc, pg 864

Classic Television Program, see Television Program— Classic

Commercial, see Test Commercial

Commercials—Animated, Television, see Television Commercial—Animated

Commercials—Live, Television, see Television Commercial—Live

Current Event Program Distributors

ARIZONA
Video Learning Library, pg 928

ARKANSAS
Master Books®, pg 819

CALIFORNIA
Crystal Pyramid Productions™, pg 735
Direct Cinema Ltd Inc, pg 743
Durrin Productions Inc, pg 748
eFootage LLC, pg 751
411 Video Information, pg 764

New & Unique Videos™, pg 839
Publishers Group West (PGW), an Ingram brand, pg 866
Pyramid Media, pg 867
Regent Press Publishers & Printers, pg 873
Social Studies School Service, pg 891
TMW Media Group, pg 915
Visual Communications - Southern California Asian American Studies Central Inc, pg 931

CONNECTICUT
Really Good Stuff, pg 871

DISTRICT OF COLUMBIA
National Council of Churches, pg 836

GEORGIA
School Media Associates LLC, pg 882

ILLINOIS
CCore Media Inc, pg 718
Film Ideas Inc, pg 760
Moviecraft Inc, pg 831
Movies Unlimited, pg 831
Questar Entertainment Inc, pg 868

INDIANA
Educational Video Group Inc, pg 751
Our Sunday Visitor Inc, pg 849

KENTUCKY
WaxWorks VideoWorks, pg 934

MARYLAND
Recorded Books Inc, an RBmedia company, pg 871

MASSACHUSETTS
WGBH Production Group, pg 936

MICHIGAN
Digi Sign Design LLC, pg 741

MONTANA
High Plains Films, pg 779

NEVADA
Aardvark Video & Media Productions, pg 671

NEW HAMPSHIRE
Channell One Video, pg 720
Chip Taylor Communications LLC, pg 907

NEW JERSEY
Allegro Productions Inc, pg 680
MiB MediaWorks, pg 825

NEW MEXICO
The Phoenix Learning Group Inc, pg 855

NEW YORK
ATA Trading Corp/Favorite TV Inc, pg 691
Broadstreet Productions LLC, pg 711

De Nonno Productions Inc (DPI), pg 739
Guidance Associates Inc Center for Humanities, pg 774
HB-Content, pg 777
Icarus Films Inc, pg 783
Janson Media Inc, pg 793
Kino International Corp, pg 799
Mastervision Inc, pg 819
Meridian Education Corp, pg 823
News Broadcast Network Inc, pg 840
Richter Productions Inc, pg 875
Shopware, pg 886
SISU Home Entertainment Inc, pg 889
Synaptic Digital, pg 905
Third World Newsreel/Camera News Inc, pg 912
United Nations Department of Public Information-News & Media Division, pg 921
VIEW Inc (Video International Entertainment World Inc), pg 930
Women Make Movies Inc, pg 941

OREGON
InterVision Media, pg 791

PENNSYLVANIA
Bullfrog Films Inc, pg 712
FMP Media Solutions Inc, pg 763
Library Video Company, pg 807

TENNESSEE
National School Products, pg 836
Spring Arbor Distributors Inc, pg 898

VIRGINIA
CACI Integrated Communications, pg 713
Close Up Foundation, pg 726
Filmakers Library, pg 760
WETA Production Center, pg 936

WASHINGTON
Bennett-Watt HD Productions Inc, pg 703
Intermedia Inc, pg 789

ALBERTA
Global TV, pg 771

BRITISH COLUMBIA
Video Out Distribution, pg 928

ONTARIO
Canadian Learning Co Inc, pg 715
Canamedia Inc, pg 715
CCI Entertainment Ltd, pg 718
Kineticvideo.com, pg 799
Life Cycle Books Ltd, pg 807

QUEBEC
Les Productions Via Le Monde (Daniel Bertolino) Inc, pg 864

Current Event Program Producers

ALASKA
Aurora Films, pg 696

ARIZONA

Aardvark Productions LLC, pg 671
Candee Productions Inc, pg 716
Film Creations Ltd, pg 760
Master Video Disc & Design, pg 819

CALIFORNIA

A Go Go Films, pg 671
Big Door, pg 705
Classic Images Stock Footage LLC, pg 726
Creative Technology, pg 733
Crystal Pyramid Productions™, pg 735
digital OutPost, pg 742
Direct Images Interactive Inc, pg 743
Durrin Productions Inc, pg 748
Goal Productions, pg 772
Image Integration, pg 785
ITV Productions, pg 792
Main Street Media Inc, pg 815
McCune Audio-Video-Lighting, pg 821
Media Magic, pg 822
New & Unique Videos™, pg 839
New Circuit Films LLC, pg 839
Nineteen87, pg 841
PK Productions, pg 857
PM Productions, pg 858
QRS Software Services, pg 867
Regent Press Publishers & Printers, pg 873
Dick Reizner Film & Video, pg 873
Glenn Roland Films, pg 876
Screen Door Entertainment Inc, pg 882
SNAP, pg 891
Still N' Motion, pg 901
Tam Communications Inc, pg 906
TMW Media Group, pg 915
Total Creative, pg 916
Vineyard Video & Photography, pg 930
Visual Communications - Southern California Asian American Studies Central Inc, pg 931
Webster Communications, pg 935
Zamacona Productions, pg 945

COLORADO

Apogee Communications Group, pg 687
Flashback Media Productions, pg 762
Rocky Mountain Audio/Video Productions Inc, pg 876

CONNECTICUT

Essex Television Group Inc, pg 755
Ironik Design & Post, pg 791
New London Media, pg 839

DISTRICT OF COLUMBIA

Hillmann & Carr Inc, pg 780
Yellow Cat Productions Inc, pg 944

FLORIDA

Accord Productions, pg 673
Blackburst Entertainment LLC, pg 706
Civins Productions Inc, pg 725
Courter Films LLC, pg 732
Jordan Klein Film & Video (JKFV), pg 795
National Teleproductions Inc, pg 837
Paradise Video & Film, pg 851
Sound*Light, pg 894

Sunfire Communications Inc, pg 904
Tel-Air Interests Inc, pg 909

GEORGIA

Beachwood Productions, pg 702
Burst Video/Film Inc, pg 713
Guerrilla Productions LLC, pg 774
Myriad Productions, pg 835
On-Line Productions, pg 845

HAWAII

Hyperspective Studios Inc, pg 783

IDAHO

Wide Eye Productions, pg 938

ILLINOIS

CCore Media Inc, pg 718
The Chicago Production Center, pg 721
Manning Productions, pg 816
Mimi Productions, pg 828
Pepper Group, pg 854
SCI Television & Creative Media LLC, pg 882

INDIANA

A-V-A Video Productions, pg 671
Educational Video Group Inc, pg 751

KANSAS

KAKE-TV, pg 796

KENTUCKY

Idle Minds Productions Inc, pg 784

LOUISIANA

Moxie Media, pg 832

MARYLAND

Absolute Hollywood, pg 672
Adventure Productions LLC, pg 678
CAS Video Productions, pg 717
Richard Chisolm Cinematography, pg 722
CPR MultiMedia Solutions, pg 732
dbF a Media Company, pg 739
Kramer Communications Video Production, pg 801

MASSACHUSETTS

Award Productions Inc, pg 699
Green Mountain Post Films (GMP), pg 774
Heliotrope Studios, pg 778
Northern Light Productions (NLP), pg 842
TVN-The Video Network, pg 919
VideoLink Inc, an AVI-SPL company, pg 929
WGBH Production Group, pg 936
WVP Boston, pg 942

MICHIGAN

Digi Sign Design LLC, pg 741
K&R All Media Productions LLC, pg 796
K&R's Recording Studios Inc, pg 796

MINNESOTA

House of Cinemagraphics, pg 782
MastCom, pg 819
Worthwhile Films, pg 941

MONTANA

High Plains Films, pg 779

NEBRASKA

Mason Video, pg 819

NEVADA

Aardvark Video & Media Productions, pg 671
Encore Event Technologies LLC, pg 754
JCS Video Productions, pg 793

NEW HAMPSHIRE

Apertura, pg 686
Channell One Video, pg 720
Chip Taylor Communications LLC, pg 907

NEW JERSEY

Allegro Productions Inc, pg 680
Broadcast Center Studios, pg 710
CFP Video Productions Inc, pg 720
Laurel Video Productions, pg 804
MiB MediaWorks, pg 825
Optisonics Productions, pg 847
Telequest Inc, pg 910
VCSvideo, pg 925

NEW MEXICO

The Phoenix Learning Group Inc, pg 855
Production Outfitters, pg 864

NEW YORK

Ace Video, pg 674
aurora productions, pg 696
Brian Film Productions LLC, pg 710
Broadstreet Productions LLC, pg 711
Clarity Media Group, pg 725
De Nonno Productions Inc (DPI), pg 739
Fanlight Productions, pg 759
Florentine Films, pg 762
Guidance Associates Inc Center for Humanities, pg 774
HB-Content, pg 777
Hello World Communications, pg 778
The Independent Production Fund, pg 786
Manhattan Center Studios Inc, pg 816
Mastervision Inc, pg 819
Jack Morton Worldwide, pg 830
MRY, pg 832
News Broadcast Network Inc, pg 840
The Palmer Group, pg 850
PrimaLux Video Inc, pg 862
PrimeLight Productions Inc, pg 862
Richter Productions Inc, pg 875
Suggs Media Productions Inc, pg 903
Synaptic Digital, pg 905
Third World Newsreel/Camera News Inc, pg 912
Videograf, pg 929
VIEW Inc (Video International Entertainment World Inc), pg 930
WNET/New York Public Media, pg 940
Zelman Studios Ltd, pg 945

NORTH CAROLINA

Pat Appleson Studios Inc, pg 687
Bill Barnes Video Productions LLC, pg 702
The Communications Group Inc, pg 729
Digital Rain LLC, pg 742
Videowerks, pg 930

OHIO

CET, pg 720
Image Video Teleproductions Inc, pg 785
Lyon Video Inc, pg 813
MainSail Production Services Inc, pg 815
R&B Communications Inc, pg 870
Take 1 Media Services, pg 906
Vista Color Imaging Inc, pg 931

OREGON

InterVision Media, pg 791
KPDX-TV Production Center, pg 801
Odyssey Productions Inc, pg 844
Production West, pg 864

PENNSYLVANIA

Beholder Productions Inc, pg 703
CCI Communications Inc, pg 718
FMP Media Solutions Inc, pg 763
Innovision Media Group, pg 788
Muderick Media, pg 833
NEP Group Inc, pg 838
Production Masters Inc (PMI), pg 864
The Videohouse Inc, pg 929
WHYY Inc, pg 938

RHODE ISLAND

Sound-FX-Design, pg 894

SOUTH CAROLINA

Go To Team, pg 772
Venture Media, pg 925

TENNESSEE

Running Pony Productions LLC, pg 878
United Methodist Productions, pg 921

TEXAS

Cerutti Productions Inc, pg 720
Countdown Productions Inc, pg 732
Epic Software Group Inc, pg 755
Horizon Film + Video Productions, pg 781
Mediaforce Productions, pg 822
Earl Miller Productions Inc, pg 827
Julye Newlin Productions Inc, pg 840
Omega Productions, pg 845
South Coast Film & Video, pg 895
Stage Directions, pg 898

VIRGINIA

BES Studios, pg 704
Close Up Foundation, pg 726
Limelight Communications Inc, pg 808
Metro Productions, pg 824
Rocktown Media, pg 876
Video Solutions, pg 928
WETA Production Center, pg 936

PROGRAMMING — VIDEO

Current Event Program Producers (continued)

WASHINGTON

Bennett-Watt HD Productions Inc, pg 703
Intermedia Inc, pg 789

WEST VIRGINIA

Blackwater Video Productions, pg 707
Sweetsong Productions, pg 905

WISCONSIN

5th Floor Recording Co, pg 760
Midland Video Productions Inc, pg 827
Mirror 34 Productions, pg 828
Wisconsin Public Television, pg 940

WYOMING

Bridger Productions Inc, pg 710

ALBERTA

Black Media Works, pg 706
Global TV, pg 771

BRITISH COLUMBIA

Triad Communications Ltd, pg 918

NEWFOUNDLAND AND LABRADOR

Vidcraft Productions Ltd, pg 927

ONTARIO

Canamedia Inc, pg 715
GAPC (General Assembly Production Centre), pg 768
Image Video Services & Productions, pg 785
Video Excellence Productions, pg 927

QUEBEC

Kerrigan Productions Inc, pg 798
Les Productions Via Le Monde (Daniel Bertolino) Inc, pg 864

Current Event Program Rentals

ARIZONA

Video Learning Library, pg 928

CALIFORNIA

Direct Cinema Ltd Inc, pg 743
Visual Communications - Southern California Asian American Studies Central Inc, pg 931

MICHIGAN

Digi Sign Design LLC, pg 741

MISSOURI

University of Missouri-Columbia, pg 923

NEW YORK

Icarus Films Inc, pg 783
Kino International Corp, pg 799

Richter Productions Inc, pg 875
Third World Newsreel/Camera News Inc, pg 912
VIEW Inc (Video International Entertainment World Inc), pg 930

PENNSYLVANIA

Bullfrog Films Inc, pg 712

VIRGINIA

Filmakers Library, pg 760

BRITISH COLUMBIA

Video Out Distribution, pg 928

ONTARIO

Kineticvideo.com, pg 799

QUEBEC

Les Productions Via Le Monde (Daniel Bertolino) Inc, pg 864

Documentary Distributors

ARIZONA

Drumbeat Indian Arts Inc, pg 747
Teaberry, pg 908
Video Learning Library, pg 928

ARKANSAS

Master Books®, pg 819

CALIFORNIA

Allied Artists International Inc, pg 681
Ark Media Group Ltd, pg 689
Astronomical Society of the Pacific, pg 691
Les Blank Films Inc, pg 707
Cambridge Documentary Films Inc, pg 714
Crystal Pyramid Productions™, pg 735
Deja View Video, pg 740
Direct Cinema Ltd Inc, pg 743
Discovery Education - Los Angeles, pg 743
Durrin Productions Inc, pg 748
ECONEWS (Environmental Television Series) & (Environmental Directions Radio Series), pg 750
Em Gee Film Library, pg 753
ETR, pg 756
411 Video Information, pg 764
Glenn Photo Supply, pg 771
Glenn Video Vistas Ltd, pg 771
Increase Video/Silver Mine Video, pg 786
Ishtar Films, pg 791
KPBS Public Broadcasting, pg 801
Main Street Media Inc, pg 815
MarVista Entertainment Inc, pg 818
MGM Home Entertainment, pg 825
monterey media inc, pg 829
monterey video, pg 829
New & Unique Videos™, pg 839
Nineteen87, pg 841
Pacific Media, pg 849
Pentrex Media Group LLC, pg 854
Pyramid Media, pg 867
Regent Press Publishers & Printers, pg 873
Sea Studios Foundation, pg 883
Social Studies School Service, pg 891
TMW Media Group, pg 915

Universal Pictures Home Entertainment, pg 922
The Video Project, pg 928
Visual Communications - Southern California Asian American Studies Central Inc, pg 931
Warner Home Video Inc, pg 934
The Wine Appreciation Guild Ltd, pg 939
Xenon Pictures Inc, pg 943

COLORADO

Tatum Video, pg 907

CONNECTICUT

Creative Arts Television, pg 733
Hartley Film Foundation, pg 776
Really Good Stuff, pg 871

DELAWARE

University Media Services, pg 922

DISTRICT OF COLUMBIA

Art Museum of the Americas, pg 690
Biblical Archaeology Society (BAS), pg 705
Department of VSA & Accessibility at the John F Kennedy Center for the Performing Arts, pg 740
National Council of Churches, pg 836
US Holocaust Memorial Museum, pg 923
USCCB Publishing, pg 923

FLORIDA

Accord Productions, pg 673
America By Air LLC, pg 682
NatureVision Stock Footage Library, pg 837

GEORGIA

On-Line Productions, pg 845
School Media Associates LLC, pg 882
Skyhoundz, pg 890

HAWAII

Ka Io Productions Inc, pg 796
Tropical Visions Video Inc, pg 918

IDAHO

Lagoon Video, pg 803

ILLINOIS

ABSA Films, pg 672
Facets Multi-Media Inc, pg 758
Film Ideas Inc, pg 760
International Historic Films Inc, pg 790
Moviecraft Inc, pg 831
Movies Unlimited, pg 831
Questar Entertainment Inc, pg 868
Terra Nova Films Inc, pg 911
Theosophical Publishing House, pg 912

INDIANA

Educational Video Group Inc, pg 751

IOWA

American Visions, pg 684

KENTUCKY

Horizon Films & Media LLC, pg 781
KET The Kentucky Network, pg 798
National Geographic Learning, pg 836
WaxWorks VideoWorks, pg 934

LOUISIANA

Great Chefs/Leisure Jazz Video, pg 773
Leisure Video, pg 806

MARYLAND

Adventure Productions LLC, pg 678
DSR Computer Technology Specialists Inc, pg 747
James Agee Film Project, pg 792
MMI Marketing, pg 828
Recorded Books Inc, an RBmedia company, pg 871
RLJ Entertainment Inc, pg 875
Special Archives Division, Motion Picture Branch, pg 896
Total AV Systems, pg 916

MASSACHUSETTS

Award Productions Inc, pg 699
Documentary Educational Resources Inc, pg 744
Enterprise Media LLC, pg 754
Merrimack Films, pg 824
The New Film Company Inc, pg 839
Pauline Books & Media, pg 852
Penfield Productions Ltd, pg 853
WGBH Production Group, pg 936

MICHIGAN

Digi Sign Design LLC, pg 741
The Program Source International, pg 865
Zondervan, pg 945

MINNESOTA

Festival Films, pg 759
Harris Communications Inc, pg 776

MISSOURI

SOM Publishing Co, pg 892
Vedanta Society of St Louis, pg 925

MONTANA

High Plains Films, pg 779

NEBRASKA

B & B Video Productions Inc, pg 700
Mary Riepma Ross Media Arts Center, pg 877
Vision Maker Media, pg 930

NEVADA

DVDs4Less, pg 748

NEW HAMPSHIRE

Channell One Video, pg 720
Chip Taylor Communications LLC, pg 907

NEW JERSEY

Alden Films, pg 679
Allegro Productions Inc, pg 680
Comex Systems Inc, pg 728
Dance Horizons Video, pg 737

Ergo Media Inc, pg 755
Euro-Pacific Film & Video
   Productions Inc, pg 756
Kultur International Films Ltd Inc,
   pg 802
MiB MediaWorks, pg 825
Milestone Film & Video Inc,
   pg 827
Princeton Book Company,
   Publishers, pg 862
Shanachie Entertainment Corp,
   pg 885

NEW MEXICO

The Phoenix Learning Group Inc,
   pg 855

NEW YORK

A&E Home Video, pg 671
Ambrose Video Publishing Inc,
   pg 682
Artistic Video, pg 690
ATA Trading Corp/Favorite TV Inc,
   pg 691
Michael Blackwood Productions
   Inc, pg 707
Billy Budd Films Inc, pg 712
Circulating Film & Video Library,
   pg 725
Downtown Community Television
   Center (DCTV), pg 746
FACE Foundation, pg 758
The Film-Makers' Cooperative,
   pg 760
Films Media Group, pg 760
First Run Features, pg 761
William Greaves Productions Inc,
   pg 774
Guidance Associates Inc Center for
   Humanities, pg 774
Hallel Communications, pg 775
HB-Content, pg 777
Hearst Entertainment &
   Syndication, pg 778
Human Relations Media, pg 782
IAI Records & Video, pg 783
Icarus Films Inc, pg 783
The Institute Inc, pg 788
Janson Media Inc, pg 793
Richard Kaplan Productions, pg 796
Kino International Corp, pg 799
L&S Video Inc, pg 803
Mastervision, pg 819
Meridian Education Corp, pg 823
Monad Trainer's Aide Inc, pg 829
New Day Films, pg 839
News Broadcast Network Inc,
   pg 840
Richter Productions Inc, pg 875
Shopware, pg 886
SISU Home Entertainment Inc,
   pg 889
Synaptic Digital, pg 905
Third World Newsreel/Camera
   News Inc, pg 912
Transformational Education
   Initiatives, pg 917
United Nations Department of
   Public Information-News &
   Media Division, pg 921
Video Artists International & VAI
   Audio, pg 927
Video Catalogue Co Inc, pg 927
VIEW Inc (Video International
   Entertainment World Inc), pg 930
Willow Mixed Media Inc, pg 939
Women Make Movies Inc, pg 941
Wonderwomen™ Enterprises,
   pg 941
Zeitgeist Films Ltd, pg 945

NORTH CAROLINA

Carolina Biological Supply Co,
   pg 717
Crystal Pictures Inc, pg 735
Ladyslipper Music, pg 803
World Wide Pictures Inc, pg 941

OHIO

Franciscan Media, pg 765
Griesinger Films LLC, pg 774
Shelburne Films, pg 885
Treehaus Communications Inc,
   pg 917

OKLAHOMA

Academic Media & Digital
   Services, pg 672
VCI Entertainment, pg 925

OREGON

Encounter Video Inc, pg 754
InterVision Media, pg 791
Nostalgia Family Video Inc, pg 843
Wilderness Video, pg 938

PENNSYLVANIA

Anchor Distributors, pg 685
Beholder Productions Inc, pg 703
Bullfrog Films Inc, pg 712
Corinth Films Inc, pg 731
FMP Media Solutions Inc, pg 763
Gary Gentile Productions (GGP),
   pg 770
Himalayan Institute Audio/Video,
   pg 780
Library Video Company, pg 807
MVD Entertainment Group, pg 835
Rahlic Publishing Co, pg 869
Fred Rogers Productions, pg 876
S I Video Sales Group, pg 879
Schlessinger Media, pg 881
Vision Video, pg 930
The Whale Video Co, pg 936

TENNESSEE

American Blackguard Inc, pg 683
Center for Southern Folklore Inc,
   pg 719
National School Products, pg 836
Spring Arbor Distributors Inc,
   pg 898

TEXAS

Educational Video Network, pg 751
EduMedia of Sugar Land, Texas,
   pg 751
Emergency Film Group, pg 753
Three Rivers Publishing Co, pg 913

VERMONT

Multicultural Media Inc, pg 833
Dorothy Tod Films, pg 915
University of Vermont, Instructional
   Television Dept, pg 923

VIRGINIA

CACI Integrated Communications,
   pg 713
CDR Communications Inc, pg 719
Filmakers Library, pg 760
National Audiovisual Center (NAC),
   pg 836

WASHINGTON

Bennett-Watt HD Productions Inc,
   pg 703
Intermedia Inc, pg 789

John McLean Media, pg 794
North-by-Northwest - A Digital
   Studio, pg 842
Victory Studios, pg 927
White Rain Films Ltd, pg 937

WISCONSIN

Her Own Words LLC, pg 779
NEWIST/CESA 7, pg 840
Wisconsin Public Television, pg 940

ALBERTA

Global TV, pg 771

BRITISH COLUMBIA

Timeless Books, pg 914
Video Out Distribution, pg 928

NORTHWEST TERRITORIES

Yellowknife Films Inc, pg 944

ONTARIO

Canadian Filmmakers Distribution
   Center (CFMDC), pg 715
Canadian Learning Co Inc, pg 715
Canamedia Inc, pg 715
CCI Entertainment Ltd, pg 718
Doomsday Studios Limited, pg 745
Kineticvideo.com, pg 799
Life Cycle Books Ltd, pg 807
McIntyre Media Inc, pg 821
McNabb & Connolly, pg 821
Sullivan Home Entertainment,
   pg 903

QUEBEC

National Film Board of
   Canada/Office National du Film
   du Canada, pg 836
Les Productions Via Le Monde
   (Daniel Bertolino) Inc, pg 864
Reel One International Ltd, pg 872

Documentary Producers

ALASKA

Alaska Media Pros LLC, pg 679
Aurora Films, pg 696

ARIZONA

Aardvark Productions LLC, pg 671
Candee Productions Inc, pg 716
Creative Backstage, pg 733
Film Creations Ltd, pg 760
Forensic Video Deposition Service,
   pg 764
Fox 10 Productions (KSAZ-TV),
   pg 765
Merestone, pg 823
Teaberry, pg 908

ARKANSAS

Live'N'Loud, pg 810
White Diamond Productions LLC,
   pg 937

CALIFORNIA

Access Video in Berkeley, pg 673
Action Video, pg 675
Allied Artists International Inc,
   pg 681
Artichoke Productions, pg 690
Big Door, pg 705
Les Blank Films Inc, pg 707
Burrud Productions Inc, pg 713
Cambridge Documentary Films Inc,
   pg 714

Cavalcade Productions Inc, pg 717
Steve Chandler, pg 720
Classic Images Stock Footage LLC,
   pg 726
Coastline Productions, pg 727
Concept Associates Inc, pg 730
Concoction Lab, pg 730
Concrete Images, pg 730
Creative Technology, pg 733
Crystal Pyramid Productions™,
   pg 735
Custom Video Productions Inc,
   pg 736
Deja View Video, pg 740
Design Media, pg 741
digital OutPost, pg 742
Direct Images Interactive Inc,
   pg 743
Discovery Education - Los Angeles,
   pg 743
Durrin Productions Inc, pg 748
ECONEWS (Environmental
   Television Series) &
   (Environmental Directions Radio
   Series), pg 750
FIDM Productions, pg 759
First Camera, pg 761
GAMfilm Productions, pg 768
Goal Productions, pg 772
Howard Hall Productions, pg 775
Image Integration, pg 785
imageReal Pictures LLC, pg 785
Imageworks, pg 785
Increase Video/Silver Mine Video,
   pg 786
Ishtar Films, pg 791
ITV Productions, pg 792
Kavich Reynolds Productions Inc,
   pg 797
Main Street Media Inc, pg 815
Maximus Media Inc, pg 820
McCune Audio-Video-Lighting,
   pg 821
Media Magic, pg 822
The Media Staff Inc, pg 822
monterey media inc, pg 829
Moving Art by Louie Schwartzberg,
   pg 831
New & Unique Videos™, pg 839
New Circuit Films LLC, pg 839
Nineteen87, pg 841
Nolte Media, pg 841
On-Trax Inc, pg 846
Pacific Media, pg 849
Penrose Productions, pg 854
Pentrex Media Group LLC, pg 854
PM Productions, pg 858
Point of View Productions, pg 858
Prime Cut Productions, pg 862
Pyramid Media, pg 867
QRS Software Services, pg 867
Regent Press Publishers & Printers,
   pg 873
Dick Reizner Film & Video, pg 873
RJ Video Productions, pg 875
Glenn Roland Films, pg 876
Screen Door Entertainment Inc,
   pg 882
Sea Studios Foundation, pg 883
SNAP, pg 891
Still N' Motion, pg 901
Tam Communications Inc, pg 906
Timestream Media, pg 914
TMW Media Group, pg 915
Total Creative, pg 916
TVA Media Group, pg 919
Twin Peaks Creative, pg 920
Universal Pictures Home
   Entertainment, pg 922
Utopia Films, pg 924
Vineyard Video & Photography,
   pg 930
Visions Plus, pg 931

PROGRAMMING — VIDEO

Documentary Producers (continued)

CALIFORNIA (continued)

Visual Communications - Southern California Asian American Studies Central Inc, pg 931
Wavemaker Media Design, pg 934
Webster Communications, pg 935
The Wine Appreciation Guild Ltd, pg 939
Xenon Pictures Inc, pg 943
Zamacona Productions, pg 945

COLORADO

Apogee Communications Group, pg 687
Blue River Productions, pg 708
Centre Communications Inc, pg 720
Daylight Productions & Rentals, pg 739
Flashback Media Productions, pg 762
Greg Hensley Productions, pg 779
Renaissance Media, pg 873
Side 3 Studios, pg 887
Tatum Video, pg 907
Transtar Entertainment Co Inc, pg 917

CONNECTICUT

Creative Arts Television, pg 733
Essex Television Group Inc, pg 755
The Gary-Paul Agency, pg 768
Geomatrix Productions, pg 770
Hartley Film Foundation, pg 776
Ironik Design & Post, pg 791
Moving Pictures, pg 832
New London Media, pg 839
Palace Productions MediaVision, pg 850
P&P Studios Inc, pg 851
Spectrum, pg 897
Bret Stern Productions, pg 900
UConn Health Multimedia Services, pg 920

DELAWARE

University Media Services, pg 922

DISTRICT OF COLUMBIA

Art Museum of the Americas, pg 690
Biblical Archaeology Society (BAS), pg 705
Department of VSA & Accessibility at the John F Kennedy Center for the Performing Arts, pg 740
Hillmann & Carr Inc, pg 780
O'Keefe Communications Inc, pg 844
US Holocaust Memorial Museum, pg 923
Yellow Cat Productions Inc, pg 944

FLORIDA

Accord Productions, pg 673
America By Air LLC, pg 682
Applebox Studio, pg 687
Blackburst Entertainment LLC, pg 706
Civins Productions Inc, pg 725
Communications Concepts Inc (CCI), pg 729
CopShopMiami.com, pg 731

Courter Films LLC, pg 732
EarthDesign Inc, pg 749
Global Cyber-Visions, pg 771
Jordan Klein Film & Video (JKFV), pg 795
National Teleproductions Inc, pg 837
NatureVision Stock Footage Library, pg 837
Paradise Video & Film, pg 851
Sunfire Communications Inc, pg 904
Sunrise Studios, pg 904
Tel-Air Interests Inc, pg 909

GEORGIA

Beachwood Productions, pg 702
Burst Video/Film Inc, pg 713
Cox Media, pg 732
ECG Productions, pg 750
Guerrilla Productions LLC, pg 774
Myriad Productions, pg 835
Malcolm Neal Productions, pg 837
On-Line Productions, pg 845
Skyhoundz, pg 890

HAWAII

Hyperspective Studios Inc, pg 783
Ka Io Productions Inc, pg 796
Sight & Sound Studios, pg 887
1013 Integrated, pg 911
Tropical Visions Video Inc, pg 918

IDAHO

Brad Shaw Productions Inc, pg 885
Wide Eye Productions, pg 938

ILLINOIS

ABSA Films, pg 672
Airways Digital Media, pg 679
The Chicago Production Center, pg 721
Explore, pg 757
Film Police, pg 760
IV Media Resources, pg 792
Manning Productions, pg 816
The Market Place, pg 817
Mimi Productions, pg 828
Rob Orr Productions Ltd, pg 848
Pepper Group, pg 854
Questar Entertainment Inc, pg 868
SCI Television & Creative Media LLC, pg 882
Southern Illinois University, pg 895
Terra Nova Films Inc, pg 911
Theosophical Publishing House, pg 912
20/20 Communications Inc, pg 920
WEEK TV, pg 935
Winter Productions, pg 939

INDIANA

A-V-A Video Productions, pg 671
Bright Ideas Creative Services, pg 710
Educational Video Group Inc, pg 751
Lighthouse Photo & Video Productions, pg 807
PentaVision Communications Inc, pg 854

IOWA

American Visions, pg 684
Educational Technology & Media Services, pg 751
Iowa State University-Information Technology Services, pg 791
Kuhn Productions LLC, pg 802

KANSAS

KAKE-TV, pg 796

KENTUCKY

Horizon Films & Media LLC, pg 781
Idle Minds Productions Inc, pg 784
KET The Kentucky Network, pg 798
Donna Lawrence Productions, pg 804
The Media Collaboratory, pg 821
National Geographic Learning, pg 836
Prosper Media Group Inc, pg 866

LOUISIANA

Digital FX Inc, pg 742
Great Chefs/Leisure Jazz Video, pg 773
Launch Media, pg 804
Leisure Video, pg 806
Moxie Media, pg 832

MAINE

Films by Huey, pg 760
WGME-TV, pg 936

MARYLAND

Absolute Hollywood, pg 672
Adventure Productions LLC, pg 678
CAS Video Productions, pg 717
Richard Chisolm Cinematography, pg 722
CPR MultiMedia Solutions, pg 732
CSPMedia.com, pg 735
dbF a Media Company, pg 739
DSR Computer Technology Specialists Inc, pg 747
James Agee Film Project, pg 792
Kramer Communications Video Production, pg 801
Media Dimensions LLC, pg 821

MASSACHUSETTS

Award Productions Inc, pg 699
CommCreative, pg 728
Documentary Educational Resources Inc, pg 744
Enterprise Media LLC, pg 754
Green Mountain Post Films (GMP), pg 774
Heliotrope Studios, pg 778
HOME Inc, pg 781
In the Wild Productions, pg 786
Merrimack Films, pg 824
Monadnock Media Inc, pg 829
The New Film Company Inc, pg 839
Northern Light Productions (NLP), pg 842
Pauline Books & Media, pg 852
Penfield Productions Ltd, pg 853
TVN-The Video Network, pg 919
WGBH Production Group, pg 936
WVP Boston, pg 942

MICHIGAN

Digi Sign Design LLC, pg 741
K&R All Media Productions LLC, pg 796
K&R's Recording Studios Inc, pg 796
The Program Source International, pg 865
WTVS, Detroit Public Television, pg 942
Zondervan, pg 945

MINNESOTA

House of Cinemagraphics, pg 782
MastCom, pg 819
Media Loft Inc, pg 822
Worthwhile Films, pg 941

MISSOURI

Hardcastle Films & Video, pg 776
SOM Publishing Co, pg 892
Vedanta Society of St Louis, pg 925

MONTANA

High Plains Films, pg 779
KUSM TV, pg 802
ooLite Media LLC, pg 846

NEBRASKA

B & B Video Productions Inc, pg 700
Envision Communications Inc, pg 755
Mason Video, pg 819
Rainbow Video Productions Inc, pg 869
Vision Maker Media, pg 930

NEVADA

Aardvark Video & Media Productions, pg 671
DVDs4Less, pg 748
Encore Event Technologies LLC, pg 754
JCS Video Productions, pg 793
Tanglewood Productions, pg 907

NEW HAMPSHIRE

Apertura, pg 686
Channell One Video, pg 720
Chip Taylor Communications LLC, pg 907
The Troupe, pg 918

NEW JERSEY

Alden Films, pg 679
Allegro Productions Inc, pg 680
Audio Vistas LLC, pg 694
CELCO, pg 719
CFP Video Productions Inc, pg 720
Comex Systems Inc, pg 728
Dance Horizons Video, pg 737
Euro-Pacific Film & Video Productions Inc, pg 756
Laurel Video Productions, pg 804
MiB MediaWorks, pg 825
Ray Mueller Productions, pg 833
Optisonics Productions, pg 847
Shanachie Entertainment Corp, pg 885
Suede Interactive, pg 903
Telequest Inc, pg 910
TimeSteps Productions Inc, pg 914
VCSvideo, pg 925

NEW MEXICO

The Phoenix Learning Group Inc, pg 855
Production Outfitters, pg 864

NEW YORK

A&E Home Video, pg 671
Ace Video, pg 674
Air Sea Land Productions Inc (ASL), pg 678
American History Workshop (NY) Inc, pg 683
American Montage Inc, pg 683
Artistic Video, pg 690
aurora productions, pg 696

PROGRAMMING — VIDEO

Documentary Producers (continued)

QUEBEC (continued)

Les Productions Via Le Monde (Daniel Bertolino) Inc, pg 864
Reel One International Ltd, pg 872

SASKATCHEWAN

plan9films, pg 857

Documentary Rentals

ARIZONA

Video Learning Library, pg 928

CALIFORNIA

Les Blank Films Inc, pg 707
Cambridge Documentary Films Inc, pg 714
Direct Cinema Ltd Inc, pg 743
Durrin Productions Inc, pg 748
ECONEWS (Environmental Television Series) & (Environmental Directions Radio Series), pg 750
Point of View Productions, pg 858
Visual Communications - Southern California Asian American Studies Central Inc, pg 931

COLORADO

Tatum Video, pg 907

DELAWARE

University Media Services, pg 922

GEORGIA

On-Line Productions, pg 845

ILLINOIS

Facets Multi-Media Inc, pg 758
Terra Nova Films Inc, pg 911

MARYLAND

James Agee Film Project, pg 792

MASSACHUSETTS

Documentary Educational Resources Inc, pg 744
Enterprise Media LLC, pg 754
Merrimack Films, pg 824
Pauline Books & Media, pg 852

MICHIGAN

Digi Sign Design LLC, pg 741

MISSOURI

University of Missouri-Columbia, pg 923

NEBRASKA

Vision Maker Media, pg 930

NEW JERSEY

Euro-Pacific Film & Video Productions Inc, pg 756

NEW YORK

BC Studio, pg 702
Circulating Film & Video Library, pg 725
Downtown Community Television Center (DCTV), pg 746
Fanlight Productions, pg 759
Films Media Group, pg 760
First Run Features, pg 761
William Greaves Productions Inc, pg 774
Hallel Communications, pg 775
Icarus Films Inc, pg 783
Kino International Corp, pg 799
New Day Films, pg 839
Richter Productions Inc, pg 875
Third World Newsreel/Camera News Inc, pg 912
VIEW Inc (Video International Entertainment World Inc), pg 930

NORTH CAROLINA

Crystal Pictures Inc, pg 735
World Wide Pictures Inc, pg 941

OREGON

Nostalgia Family Video Inc, pg 843
Wilderness Video, pg 938

PENNSYLVANIA

Bullfrog Films Inc, pg 712
Rahlic Publishing Co, pg 869

TENNESSEE

Center for Southern Folklore Inc, pg 719

TEXAS

Three Rivers Publishing Co, pg 913

VERMONT

University of Vermont, Instructional Television Dept, pg 923

VIRGINIA

Filmakers Library, pg 760

WASHINGTON

Intermedia Inc, pg 789

WISCONSIN

Her Own Words LLC, pg 779
NEWIST/CESA 7, pg 840

BRITISH COLUMBIA

Video Out Distribution, pg 928

MANITOBA

Spectra Video Productions Ltd, pg 897

ONTARIO

Kineticvideo.com, pg 799
McNabb & Connolly, pg 821

QUEBEC

Les Productions Via Le Monde (Daniel Bertolino) Inc, pg 864

DVD Distributors

ALABAMA

Eternal Word Television Network (EWTN), pg 756

ARIZONA

Arizona Public Media, pg 688
Celestial Harmonies/Fortuna Records/Kuckuck Schallplatten/Black Sun Music/MonteVideo, pg 719
Coyote Cowboy Co, pg 732
Drumbeat Indian Arts Inc, pg 747
Tom Hopkins International Inc, pg 781
Mother Basilea Films, pg 831
Teaberry, pg 908
Valley of the Sun Publishing Co, pg 924

CALIFORNIA

Ariztical Entertainment Inc, pg 689
Ark Media Group Ltd, pg 689
Astronomical Society of the Pacific, pg 691
Les Blank Films Inc, pg 707
Bridge Publications Inc, pg 710
California Language Laboratories, pg 714
California Newsreel, pg 714
Cambridge Documentary Films Inc, pg 714
Canyon Cinema Inc, pg 716
Cavalcade Productions Inc, pg 717
Coast Learning Systems, pg 727
Davidson Productions, pg 738
DawnSignPress, pg 739
Deja View Video, pg 740
Deluxe Entertainment Services Group Inc, pg 740
Dialect Accent Specialists Inc, pg 741
Direct Cinema Ltd Inc, pg 743
The Walt Disney Studios, pg 743
Eastman Corp, pg 749
ECONEWS (Environmental Television Series) & (Environmental Directions Radio Series), pg 750
Educational Technology Services (ETS), pg 751
Em Gee Film Library, pg 753
ETR, pg 756
Focus Features, pg 763
Forte Productions, pg 764
411 Video Information, pg 764
Glenn Photo Supply, pg 771
Golden State Dance Teachers Association (GSDTA), pg 772
Griggs Productions Inc, pg 774
Steven Halpern's Inner Peace Music, pg 775
Hay House Inc, pg 777
Health Education Services, pg 778
Image Entertainment, pg 785
Increase Video/Silver Mine Video, pg 786
Ishtar Films, pg 791
Joyce Media Inc, pg 795
Krishnamurti Foundation of America, pg 801
Latham Foundation Publications, pg 804
Learn Quickly, pg 805
Lightworks Audio & Video Inc, pg 808
Live Wire Media, pg 810
MarVista Entertainment Inc, pg 818
MGM Home Entertainment, pg 825
monterey media inc, pg 829
Nilgiri Press, pg 841
Nineteen87, pg 841
Pacific Media, pg 849
Paulist Productions, pg 852
Pyramid Media, pg 867
Randolf Productions Inc, pg 870
Revelli, pg 874

Rhythms Productions (Tom Thumb Music), pg 874
Sea Studios Foundation, pg 883
Shokus Video, pg 886
Social Studies School Service, pg 891
Staylor-Made Communications Inc, pg 900
Theatre Arts Video Library, pg 911
Thinking Allowed Productions, pg 912
Valley Media, pg 924
Visual Communications - Southern California Asian American Studies Central Inc, pg 931
Warner Bros Entertainment Inc, pg 934
Warner Home Video Inc, pg 934
The Wine Appreciation Guild Ltd, pg 939
The Writing Co, pg 942
Xenon Pictures Inc, pg 943
Zamacona Productions, pg 945

COLORADO

Crown Ministries International, pg 735
Crystal Productions, pg 735
Greg Hensley Productions, pg 779
InJoy Birth & Parenting Education, pg 788
Jeppesen, pg 793
National Institute for Trial Advocacy (NITA), pg 836
Stretching Inc, pg 902
Tatum Video, pg 907
White Swan Music Inc, pg 937

CONNECTICUT

Cine-Med Inc, pg 723
Ironik Design & Post, pg 791
The Taunton Press Inc, pg 907
Weston Woods Studios Inc, pg 936

DISTRICT OF COLUMBIA

Dorst MediaWorks Inc, pg 746
Sano Videos, pg 880

FLORIDA

Alliance Entertainment Corp (AEC) LLC, pg 680
America By Air LLC, pg 682
Catholic Books & Tapes, pg 717
Children of Mary, pg 722
Karst Productions Inc, pg 796
MTI Home Video, pg 833
NatureVision Stock Footage Library, pg 837
Video Aided Instruction Inc, pg 927

GEORGIA

The Alliance for Christian Media, pg 680
New Leaf Distributing Co, pg 839
Skyhoundz, pg 890

HAWAII

Ka Io Productions Inc, pg 796

ILLINOIS

ABSA Films, pg 672
Bolchazy - Carducci Publishers Inc, pg 708
Encyclopaedia Britannica Inc, pg 754
Film Ideas Inc, pg 760
Follett School Solutions Inc, pg 763
Learning Seed, pg 805
Nightingale-Conant Corp, pg 841

Questar Entertainment Inc, pg 868
Research Press, pg 873
Sunburst Digital Inc, pg 903
Terra Nova Films Inc, pg 911

INDIANA

Educational Video Group Inc,
   pg 751

KANSAS

Yarn Barn of Kansas, pg 943

KENTUCKY

American Recordable Media,
   pg 684
Horizon Films & Media LLC,
   pg 781
WaxWorks VideoWorks, pg 934

LOUISIANA

Great Chefs/Leisure Jazz Video,
   pg 773
Leisure Video, pg 806
Moxie Media, pg 832

MARYLAND

dbF a Media Company, pg 739
Hearing Loss Association of
   America (HLAA), pg 778
Human Circuit, pg 782
MMI Marketing, pg 828
Nicholas P Pipino Associates Inc,
   pg 857
Recorded Books Inc, an RBmedia
   company, pg 871
RLJ Entertainment Inc, pg 875
Total AV Systems, pg 916

MASSACHUSETTS

Cheng & Tsui Co, pg 721
Documentary Educational Resources
   Inc, pg 744
Education Development Center Inc
   (EDC), pg 750
Merrimack Films, pg 824
National Fire Protection Association
   (NFPA), pg 836
The New Film Company Inc,
   pg 839
Pauline Books & Media, pg 852
Video Express, pg 928

MICHIGAN

Digi Sign Design LLC, pg 741
MSU Technologies, pg 833
The Program Source International,
   pg 865
Rebirth Inc, pg 871
Society of Manufacturing Engineers
   (SME), pg 891
Jack Van Impe Ministries
   International, pg 924
Zondervan, pg 945

MINNESOTA

Augsburg Fortress, pg 695
Festival Films, pg 759
Harris Communications Inc, pg 776
Hazelden Publishing & Educational
   Services, pg 777
JIST Publishing, pg 794
Learning Strategies Corp, pg 805
MastCom, pg 819
Whole Person Associates Inc,
   pg 938

MISSOURI

American Optometric Association
   (AOA), pg 684
Annenberg Learner, pg 685
Marsh Media, pg 817
SOM Publishing Co, pg 892
Vedanta Society of St Louis, pg 925

NEBRASKA

AdventSource, pg 678
Peak Performance Publishing,
   pg 852
The Recruiters Library, pg 872

NEVADA

DVDs4Less, pg 748
Ron Roy Productions/Moodtapes,
   pg 878

NEW HAMPSHIRE

Captain Fiddle Music &
   Publications, pg 716
Channell One Video, pg 720
French American Music Enterprises,
   pg 765
Heinemann, pg 778
Chip Taylor Communications LLC,
   pg 907
YMAA Publication Center Inc,
   pg 944

NEW JERSEY

Alden Films, pg 679
Allegro Productions Inc, pg 680
Business Education Films, pg 713
Comex Systems Inc, pg 728
Dance Horizons Video, pg 737
Ergo Media Inc, pg 755
Euro-Pacific Film & Video
   Productions Inc, pg 756
Jointure for Community Adult
   Education Inc, pg 794
Kimbo Educational, pg 799
Kultur International Films Ltd Inc,
   pg 802
Milestone Film & Video Inc,
   pg 827
Shanachie Entertainment Corp,
   pg 885
John Wiley & Sons Inc, pg 938

NEW MEXICO

The Phoenix Learning Group Inc,
   pg 855
SouthWest Organizing Project
   (SWOP), pg 896
Uncharted Country Publishing,
   pg 921

NEW YORK

A&E Home Video, pg 671
A&E Television Networks LLC,
   pg 671
Applause Learning Resources,
   pg 687
Michael Blackwood Productions
   Inc, pg 707
Billy Budd Films Inc, pg 712
The Bureau for At-Risk Youth,
   pg 712
The Christophers, pg 722
The Cinema Guild Inc, pg 724
Cornell Laboratory of Ornithology,
   pg 731
Criterion Collection, pg 735
Educational Activities Inc, pg 750
Entertainment One US, pg 754
Fanlight Productions, pg 759
Film Emporium, pg 760

The Film-Makers' Cooperative,
   pg 760
William Greaves Productions Inc,
   pg 774
Guilford Publications, pg 774
Hallel Communications, pg 775
HB-Content, pg 777
HBO Home Entertainment Inc,
   pg 777
Homespun Video, pg 781
Human Relations Media, pg 782
Icarus Films Inc, pg 783
Janson Media Inc, pg 793
L&S Video Inc, pg 803
Live Oak Media, pg 810
Magnetic Music Publishing Co,
   pg 814
Mastervision Inc, pg 819
Mathmadeeasy.com, pg 819
Monad Trainer's Aide Inc, pg 829
New Day Films, pg 839
Random House Children's Books,
   pg 870
Richter Productions Inc, pg 875
The Fulton J Sheen Co Inc, pg 885
SISU Home Entertainment Inc,
   pg 889
Third World Newsreel/Camera
   News Inc, pg 912
Tommy Boy Entertainment LLC,
   pg 915
Transformational Education
   Initiatives, pg 917
United Nations Department of
   Public Information-News &
   Media Division, pg 921
Video Artists International & VAI
   Audio, pg 927
Video Catalogue Co Inc, pg 927
VIEW Inc (Video International
   Entertainment World Inc), pg 930
Visual Technologies Corp, pg 932
Women Make Movies Inc, pg 941
Wonderwomen™ Enterprises,
   pg 941

NORTH CAROLINA

AudioSolutionz LLC, pg 695
Carolina Biological Supply Co,
   pg 717
Sinclair Institute, pg 889
World Wide Pictures Inc, pg 941

OHIO

The American Classical League,
   pg 683
Griesinger Films LLC, pg 774

OKLAHOMA

VCI Entertainment, pg 925

OREGON

CNS Productions Inc, pg 727
Getty-Dubay Productions, pg 770
The Keyboard Workshop, pg 798
TeleVideos, pg 910

PENNSYLVANIA

Bergwall Productions Inc, pg 704
Corinth Films Inc, pg 731
Himalayan Institute Audio/Video,
   pg 780
Vision Video, pg 930
The Whale Video Co, pg 936

SOUTH CAROLINA

American Production Services LLC,
   pg 684
BJU Press, pg 706

TENNESSEE

Abingdon Press, pg 672
American Blackguard Inc, pg 683
B&H Publishing Group, pg 701
Cokesbury, pg 727
Ingram Entertainment Inc, pg 787
National School Products, pg 836
Word Label Group, pg 941
Zion Music Group, pg 945

TEXAS

CEV Multimedia Ltd, pg 720
Chalk Dust Co, pg 720
Educational Video Network, pg 751
Emergency Film Group, pg 753
Executive Development Systems
   Inc, pg 757
Marengo Films, pg 817
Replicopy Digital Media Center,
   pg 873
Sentai Filmworks LLC, pg 884
TopCat Records LLC, pg 915

VERMONT

Multicultural Media Inc, pg 833
Wilson McLeran Inc, pg 939

VIRGINIA

Coastal Training Technologies Corp,
   pg 727
Colonial Williamsburg Foundation,
   pg 727
County Sales, pg 732
Filmakers Library, pg 760
National Media Services Inc,
   pg 836
Rocktown Media, pg 876

WASHINGTON

Bennett-Watt HD Productions Inc,
   pg 703
Intermedia Inc, pg 789
Medifecta Healthcare Training,
   pg 823
Washington State University College
   of Nursing, pg 934

WEST VIRGINIA

Focus on Animals, pg 763
Harpers Ferry Historical
   Association, pg 776

WISCONSIN

Aylmer Press, pg 700
Her Own Words LLC, pg 779
NEWIST/CESA 7, pg 840
Plank Road Publishing Inc, pg 857

ONTARIO

Broughton's Church Supplies,
   Religious Books & Gifts, pg 711
Canadian Learning Co Inc, pg 715
Canamedia Inc, pg 715
CBC/Radio-Canada, pg 717
The Children's Book Store
   Distribution (CBSD), pg 722
Life Cycle Books Ltd, pg 807
McIntyre Media Inc, pg 821
McNabb & Connolly, pg 821
Mind Resources Inc, pg 828
Nelson Education Ltd, pg 837
Novalis, pg 843
Penguin Random House Canada,
   pg 853
TVO/Ontario Educational
   Communications Authority
   (OECA), pg 919

PROGRAMMING — VIDEO

DVD Distributors (continued)

QUEBEC

National Film Board of Canada/Office National du Film du Canada, pg 836

DVD Producers

ALABAMA

Eternal Word Television Network (EWTN), pg 756

ALASKA

Aurora Films, pg 696

ARIZONA

Aardvark Productions LLC, pg 671
Arizona Public Media, pg 688
Celestial Harmonies/Fortuna Records/Kuckuck Schallplatten/Black Sun Music/MonteVideo, pg 719
Film Creations Ltd, pg 760
Forensic Video Deposition Service, pg 764
Merestone, pg 823
Teaberry, pg 908
Valley of the Sun Publishing Co, pg 924

ARKANSAS

Live'N'Loud, pg 810
White Diamond Productions LLC, pg 937

CALIFORNIA

Access Video in Berkeley, pg 673
ACDC Audio CD & Cassette, pg 674
Ariztical Entertainment Inc, pg 689
Artichoke Productions, pg 690
Astronomical Society of the Pacific, pg 691
Big Door, pg 705
Les Blank Films Inc, pg 707
California Language Laboratories, pg 714
Cambridge Documentary Films Inc, pg 714
Cavalcade Productions Inc, pg 717
Center for the Collaborative Classroom, pg 719
Steve Chandler, pg 720
Coast Learning Systems, pg 727
Concrete Images, pg 730
Custom Video Productions Inc, pg 736
Davidson Productions, pg 738
DawnSignPress, pg 739
Deja View Video, pg 740
Deluxe Entertainment Services Group Inc, pg 740
Dialect Accent Specialists Inc, pg 741
digital OutPost, pg 742
Direct Cinema Ltd Inc, pg 743
Direct Images Interactive Inc, pg 743
DiskFaktory, pg 743
Eastman Corp, pg 749

ECONEWS (Environmental Television Series) & (Environmental Directions Radio Series), pg 750
Educational Technology Services (ETS), pg 751
Focus Features, pg 763
Forte Productions, pg 764
411 Video Information, pg 764
Geddes Productions LLC, pg 769
Gold Standard Productions, pg 772
Griggs Productions Inc, pg 774
Steven Halpern's Inner Peace Music, pg 775
Havas Edge, pg 777
imageReal Pictures LLC, pg 785
Imageworks, pg 785
Increase Video/Silver Mine Video, pg 786
ITV Productions, pg 792
Joyce Media Inc, pg 795
Krishnamurti Foundation of America, pg 801
K2B2 Records, pg 802
Latham Foundation Publications, pg 804
Learn Quickly, pg 805
Live Wire Media, pg 810
Ludlow Media, pg 812
Main Street Media Inc, pg 815
Maximus Media Inc, pg 820
Media Magic, pg 822
MGM Home Entertainment, pg 825
monterey media inc, pg 829
The Mother Co, pg 831
M2 Communications, pg 833
Music World/Vocal Power School, pg 834
Nilgiri Press, pg 841
Nineteen87, pg 841
On-Trax Inc, pg 846
Pacific Media, pg 849
Paulist Productions, pg 852
Penrose Productions, pg 854
Pentrex Media Group LLC, pg 854
PM Productions, pg 858
Pyramid Media, pg 867
QRS Software Services, pg 867
Randolf Productions Inc, pg 870
RetinaVision Productions, pg 874
Revelli, pg 874
Rhythms Productions (Tom Thumb Music), pg 874
Glenn Roland Films, pg 876
Saturn Studios, pg 881
Screen Door Entertainment Inc, pg 882
Sea Studios Foundation, pg 883
Shokus Video, pg 886
Staylor-Made Communications Inc, pg 900
Tam Communications Inc, pg 906
Theatre Arts Video Library, pg 911
Thinking Allowed Productions, pg 912
Timestream Video, pg 914
Total Creative, pg 916
Vedanta Press & Catalog, pg 925
Video Resources Inc, pg 928
Warner Bros Entertainment Inc, pg 934
Wavemaker Media Design, pg 934
Xenon Pictures Inc, pg 943
Zamacona Productions, pg 945

COLORADO

Blue Onion Media, pg 708
Crown Ministries International, pg 735
Flashback Media Productions, pg 762
InJoy Birth & Parenting Education, pg 788

Jeppesen, pg 793
Mike's Camera, pg 827
National Institute for Trial Advocacy (NITA), pg 836
Side 3 Studios, pg 887
Tatum Video, pg 907

CONNECTICUT

ACM Productions Ltd, pg 674
Cine-Med Inc, pg 723
Essex Television Group Inc, pg 755
Geomatrix Productions, pg 770
Ironik Design & Post, pg 791
New London Media, pg 839
The Taunton Press Inc, pg 907
UConn Health Multimedia Services, pg 920
Weston Woods Studios Inc, pg 936

DISTRICT OF COLUMBIA

Dorst MediaWorks Inc, pg 746
USCCB Publishing, pg 923
Yellow Cat Productions Inc, pg 944

FLORIDA

Accord Productions, pg 673
America By Air LLC, pg 682
Applebox Studio, pg 687
Blackburst Entertainment LLC, pg 706
Chatterbox Productions Inc, pg 721
Civins Productions Inc, pg 725
Courter Films LLC, pg 732
Easy Edit Video Inc, pg 750
MTI Home Video, pg 833
Multivision Video & Film, pg 833
National Teleproductions Inc, pg 837
NatureVision Stock Footage Library, pg 837
Sound & Vision Communications Inc, pg 893
Sunfire Communications Inc, pg 904
Sunrise Studios, pg 904
Tight Line Productions, pg 914
Tricycle Studios, pg 918
Universal Studios Florida® Production Group, pg 922
Video Aided Instruction Inc, pg 927
Video Techniques Inc, pg 928

GEORGIA

Burst Video/Film Inc, pg 713
ECG Productions, pg 750
Guerrilla Productions LLC, pg 774
Myriad Productions, pg 835
On-Line Productions, pg 845
Skyhoundz, pg 890

HAWAII

Hyperspective Studios Inc, pg 783
Ka Io Productions Inc, pg 796
Sight & Sound Studios, pg 887

IDAHO

Brad Shaw Productions Inc, pg 885

ILLINOIS

ABSA Films, pg 672
Airways Digital Media, pg 679
American Hospital Association, pg 683
Beatty TeleVisual Productions, pg 703
Cresta Creative, pg 734
Encyclopaedia Britannica Inc, pg 754

Extraordinary Demos/Videos, pg 757
Film Police, pg 760
Follett School Solutions Inc, pg 763
IV Media Resources, pg 792
Learning Seed, pg 805
Major Media Inc, pg 815
Manning Productions, pg 816
Nightingale-Conant Corp, pg 841
Jim Passin Productions, pg 852
Questar Entertainment Inc, pg 868
RADMAR Inc, pg 869
Research Press, pg 873
Richter Studios, pg 875
Sparkfactor, pg 896
Sunburst Digital Inc, pg 903
Terra Nova Films Inc, pg 911
Video Impressions, pg 928
Winter Productions, pg 939

INDIANA

A-V-A Video Productions, pg 671
Bright Ideas Creative Services, pg 710
Educational Video Group Inc, pg 751
Indiana University Press, pg 786
PentaVision Communications Inc, pg 854
Road Pictures, pg 876

IOWA

American Visions, pg 684
Right Stuf Inc, pg 875

KANSAS

KAKE-TV, pg 796
Yarn Barn of Kansas, pg 943

KENTUCKY

American Recordable Media, pg 684
Blood-Horse Publications, pg 707
Horizon Films & Media LLC, pg 781
Prosper Media Group Inc, pg 866

LOUISIANA

Great Chefs/Leisure Jazz Video, pg 773
Jazzology, pg 793
Leisure Video, pg 806
Louisiana State University Division of Strategic Communications, pg 811
Moxie Media, pg 832

MARYLAND

CPR MultiMedia Solutions, pg 732
dbF a Media Company, pg 739
The Image Generators, pg 785
Kramer Communications Video Production, pg 801
Lion & Fox Recording Studios, pg 809
Media Dimensions LLC, pg 821
RLJ Entertainment Inc, pg 875

MASSACHUSETTS

Cheng & Tsui Co, pg 721
Education Development Center Inc (EDC), pg 750
Heliotrope Studios, pg 778
In the Wild Productions, pg 786
Merrimack Films, pg 824
Monadnock Media Inc, pg 829
Pauline Books & Media, pg 852
Preston Productions Inc, pg 861
TR Productions, pg 916

MICHIGAN

Digi Sign Design LLC, pg 741
International Tae Kwon Do
    Association (ITA Institute),
    pg 790
K&R All Media Productions LLC,
    pg 796
MSU Technologies, pg 833
The Program Source International,
    pg 865
Rebirth Inc, pg 871
Society of Manufacturing Engineers
    (SME), pg 891
TGA Recording Co, pg 911
Zondervan, pg 945

MINNESOTA

Augsburg Fortress, pg 695
Hazelden Publishing & Educational
    Services, pg 777
House of Cinemagraphics, pg 782
JIST Publishing, pg 794
Learning Strategies Corp, pg 805
Whole Person Associates Inc,
    pg 938
Babe Winkelman Productions Inc,
    pg 939
Worthwhile Films, pg 941

MISSOURI

American Optometric Association
    (AOA), pg 684
Annenberg Learner, pg 685
Marsh Media, pg 817
SOM Publishing Co, pg 892
Vedanta Society of St Louis, pg 925

NEBRASKA

AdventSource, pg 678
Envision Communications Inc,
    pg 755
Peak Performance Publishing,
    pg 852
Rainbow Video Productions Inc,
    pg 869
The Recruiters Library, pg 872

NEVADA

Encore Event Technologies LLC,
    pg 754
JCS Video Productions, pg 793
Ron Roy Productions/Moodtapes,
    pg 878
Tanglewood Productions, pg 907

NEW HAMPSHIRE

Captain Fiddle Music &
    Publications, pg 716
Channell One Video, pg 720
Chip Taylor Communications LLC,
    pg 907
YMAA Publication Center Inc,
    pg 944

NEW JERSEY

Allegro Productions Inc, pg 680
Audio Vistas LLC, pg 694
Comex Systems Inc, pg 728
Dance Horizons Video, pg 737
Euro-Pacific Film & Video
    Productions Inc, pg 756
Kimbo Educational, pg 799
Midnight Media Group Inc, pg 827
Ray Mueller Productions, pg 833
Outside The Box Interactive LLC,
    pg 849
Shanachie Entertainment Corp,
    pg 885
TimeSteps Productions Inc, pg 914

VCSvideo, pg 925
John Wiley & Sons Inc, pg 938

NEW MEXICO

The Phoenix Learning Group Inc,
    pg 855
Production Outfitters, pg 864
Uncharted Country Publishing,
    pg 921

NEW YORK

A&E Home Video, pg 671
Air Sea Land Productions Inc
    (ASL), pg 678
Applause Learning Resources,
    pg 687
Asia Society, pg 691
BC Studio, pg 702
Michael Blackwood Productions
    Inc, pg 707
Blue Barn Pictures Inc, pg 707
Bridge Records Inc, pg 710
Brooklyn Films, pg 711
Billy Budd Films Inc, pg 712
The Bureau for At-Risk Youth,
    pg 712
Cornell Laboratory of Ornithology,
    pg 731
Thomas Craven Film Corp, pg 733
Criterion Collection, pg 735
Downtown Community Television
    Center (DCTV), pg 746
Duplication Depot Inc, pg 748
Educational Activities Inc, pg 750
Entertainment One US, pg 754
Eye on Dance, pg 758
The Food & Beverage Institute,
    pg 763
Guidance Associates Inc Center for
    Humanities, pg 774
Guilford Publications, pg 774
Hallel Communications, pg 775
HB-Content, pg 777
HBO Home Entertainment Inc,
    pg 777
Homespun Video, pg 781
Human Relations Media, pg 782
The Independent Production Fund,
    pg 786
International Digital Centre, pg 790
Richard Kaplan Productions, pg 796
L A Bruell Inc, pg 802
L&S Video Inc, pg 803
Live Oak Media, pg 810
Magnetic Music Publishing Co,
    pg 814
Mastervision Inc, pg 819
Mathmadeeasy.com, pg 819
Jack Morton Worldwide, pg 830
Pat Kogan Productions Inc, pg 852
PrimaLux Video Inc, pg 862
Random House Children's Books,
    pg 870
Richter Productions Inc, pg 875
The Fulton J Sheen Co Inc, pg 885
Suggs Media Productions Inc,
    pg 903
Third World Newsreel/Camera
    News Inc, pg 912
Tommy Boy Entertainment LLC,
    pg 915
United Nations Multimedia
    Resources Unit, pg 921
Video Catalogue Co Inc, pg 927
VIEW Inc (Video International
    Entertainment World Inc), pg 930
Willow Mixed Media Inc, pg 939
Wonderwomen™ Enterprises,
    pg 941

NORTH CAROLINA

Pat Appleson Studios Inc, pg 687
AudioSolutionz LLC, pg 695
Carolina Biological Supply Co,
    pg 717
The Communications Group Inc,
    pg 729
Digital Rain LLC, pg 742
Horizon Video Productions Inc,
    pg 781
Moving Pictures, pg 832
Sinclair Institute, pg 889
2BruceStudio, pg 920
Videowerks, pg 930

OHIO

Advent Media Inc, pg 677
CET, pg 720
Griesinger Films LLC, pg 774
Lyon Video Inc, pg 813
Musicol Recording, pg 835
R&B Communications Inc, pg 870
Vista Color Imaging Inc, pg 931

OKLAHOMA

VCI Entertainment, pg 925

OREGON

CNS Productions Inc, pg 727
Getty-Dubay Productions, pg 770
Ideascape Inc, pg 784
InterVision Media, pg 791
The Keyboard Workshop, pg 798
Odyssey Productions Inc, pg 844
REX, pg 874
TeleVideos, pg 910

PENNSYLVANIA

Argentine Productions Inc, pg 688
Bang! Pictures Inc, pg 701
Beholder Productions Inc, pg 703
Bergwall Productions Inc, pg 704
CORTRON Media LLC, pg 732
Himalayan Institute Audio/Video,
    pg 780
Innovision Media Group, pg 788
JPL, pg 795
Main Point Productions, pg 815
Video/Film Associates, pg 928
The Videohouse Inc, pg 929
Videosmith Inc, pg 930
Vision Video, pg 930
The Whale Video Co, pg 936

SOUTH CAROLINA

American Production Services LLC,
    pg 684
BJU Press, pg 706
Encore Video Productions, pg 754
Go To Team, pg 772
Stages Video Productions, pg 899
Venture Media, pg 925

TENNESSEE

Abingdon Press, pg 672
American Blackguard Inc, pg 683
Cokesbury, pg 727
Running Pony Productions LLC,
    pg 878
Word Label Group, pg 941

TEXAS

CEV Multimedia Ltd, pg 720
Chalk Dust Co, pg 720
Communication Arts Multimedia
    Inc, pg 728
The Editing Co, pg 750
Educational Video Network, pg 751

Emergency Film Group, pg 753
McNee Productions Inc, pg 821
Mediaforce Productions, pg 822
Julye Newlin Productions Inc,
    pg 840
Sentai Filmworks LLC, pg 884
Sportsmen on Film Inc, pg 898
Stage Directions, pg 898
TopCat Records LLC, pg 915

UTAH

One Stop CD Shop LLC, pg 846
San Juan School District Heritage
    Language Resource Center,
    pg 880

VERMONT

Edgewood Studios, pg 750
Lyrichord/Multicultural Media,
    pg 813
Multicultural Media Inc, pg 833
Wilson McLeran Inc, pg 939

VIRGINIA

Cinebar Productions Inc, pg 723
Coastal Training Technologies Corp,
    pg 727
County Sales, pg 732
Limelight Communications Inc,
    pg 808
Metro Productions, pg 824
National Media Services Inc,
    pg 836
PBS Video, pg 852
Rocktown Media, pg 876

WASHINGTON

Bennett-Watt HD Productions Inc,
    pg 703
Center for Touch Drawing, pg 719
Medifecta Healthcare Training,
    pg 823
Victory Studios, pg 927
Washington State University College
    of Nursing, pg 934

WISCONSIN

Audio Visual of Milwaukee Inc,
    pg 694
Aylmer Press, pg 700
Excel Duplication Services, pg 757
Her Own Words LLC, pg 779
Knowledge Unlimited Inc, pg 800
Meridian Studios, pg 824
NEWIST/CESA 7, pg 840
Plank Road Publishing Inc, pg 857
USAV Group Inc, pg 923
Video Wisconsin Inc, pg 929
Watts Communications Inc, pg 934

ALBERTA

Black Media Works, pg 706
HDTV Productions Inc, pg 777

BRITISH COLUMBIA

Triad Communications Ltd, pg 918
West Eagle Films Inc, pg 935

NEWFOUNDLAND AND
LABRADOR

Vidcraft Productions Ltd, pg 927

ONTARIO

ADS Media, pg 677
Art Gallery of Ontario, pg 690
CBC/Radio-Canada, pg 717
DebsVoice, pg 739

PROGRAMMING — VIDEO

DVD Producers (continued)

ONTARIO (continued)

GAPC (General Assembly Production Centre), pg 768
Image Video Services & Productions, pg 785
McNabb & Connolly, pg 821
Novalis, pg 843
RB Productions, pg 870
Silver Creek Media Inc, pg 888
Weston Woods Canada, pg 936

QUEBEC

National Film Board of Canada/Office National du Film du Canada, pg 836

SASKATCHEWAN

plan9films, pg 857

DVD Rentals

ARIZONA

Arizona Public Media, pg 688

CALIFORNIA

Les Blank Films Inc, pg 707
Cavalcade Productions Inc, pg 717
Educational Technology Services (ETS), pg 751
Griggs Productions Inc, pg 774
Visual Communications - Southern California Asian American Studies Central Inc, pg 931

ILLINOIS

RBR Productions, pg 870
Terra Nova Films Inc, pg 911

MARYLAND

Kramer Communications Video Production, pg 801

MASSACHUSETTS

Documentary Educational Resources Inc, pg 744
Merrimack Films, pg 824

MICHIGAN

Digi Sign Design LLC, pg 741

MISSOURI

Show-Me Audio-Visual, pg 887

NEW HAMPSHIRE

Chip Taylor Communications LLC, pg 907

NEW JERSEY

Alden Films, pg 679
Business Education Films, pg 713
Euro-Pacific Film & Video Productions Inc, pg 756

NEW YORK

Fanlight Productions, pg 759
Icarus Films Inc, pg 783

New Day Films, pg 839
Third World Newsreel/Camera News Inc, pg 912

OREGON

The Keyboard Workshop, pg 798

PENNSYLVANIA

Bullfrog Films Inc, pg 712

VIRGINIA

Filmakers Library, pg 760

WISCONSIN

Her Own Words LLC, pg 779
NEWIST/CESA 7, pg 840

ONTARIO

McNabb & Connolly, pg 821

QUEBEC

National Film Board of Canada/Office National du Film du Canada, pg 836

Educational Program Distributors

ALABAMA

CMEinfo™, pg 727

ARIZONA

Clever Cleaver Productions, pg 726
CyberIconics International, pg 736
Drumbeat Indian Arts Inc, pg 747
Teaberry, pg 908
TSG Publishing Foundation Inc USA, pg 919

ARKANSAS

Master Books®, pg 819
Mullikin Agency, pg 833

CALIFORNIA

Allied Artists International Inc, pg 681
Ark Media Group Ltd, pg 689
Astronomical Society of the Pacific, pg 691
Backstage Pass Entertainment Inc, pg 700
Les Blank Films Inc, pg 707
C & M Publishing Co, pg 713
California Language Laboratories, pg 714
Cambridge Documentary Films Inc, pg 714
Clarity Sound & Light, pg 725
Coast Learning Systems, pg 727
Concept Associates Inc, pg 730
Crystal Pyramid Productions™, pg 735
Davidson Productions, pg 738
DawnSignPress, pg 739
Deja View Video, pg 740
Dialect Accent Specialists Inc, pg 741
Direct Cinema Ltd Inc, pg 743
Discovery Education - Los Angeles, pg 743
Durrin Productions Inc, pg 748
Eastman Corp, pg 749
ECONEWS (Environmental Television Series) & (Environmental Directions Radio Series), pg 750

eFootage LLC, pg 751
Em Gee Film Library, pg 753
ETR, pg 756
Feldenkrais® Resources, pg 759
Ferrari Productions, pg 759
Forte Productions, pg 764
411 Video Information, pg 764
Geddes Productions LLC, pg 769
Glenn Photo Supply, pg 771
Glenn Video Vistas Ltd, pg 771
Golden State Dance Teachers Association (GSDTA), pg 772
Hay House Inc, pg 777
Increase Video/Silver Mine Video, pg 786
Institute of Precision Muscle Balancing, pg 788
Ishtar Films, pg 791
Joyce Media Inc, pg 795
Kantola Productions LLC, pg 796
KPBS Public Broadcasting, pg 801
Krishnamurti Foundation of America, pg 801
Latham Foundation Publications, pg 804
Learn Quickly, pg 805
Live Wire Media, pg 810
Main Street Media Inc, pg 815
MarVista Entertainment Inc, pg 818
Medcom Inc, pg 821
monterey media inc, pg 829
monterey video, pg 829
Moose School Productions, pg 830
Music World/Vocal Power School, pg 834
New & Unique Videos™, pg 839
Nolte Media, pg 841
Noontide Press, pg 841
Pacific Media, pg 849
Pentrex Media Group LLC, pg 854
People Skills International, pg 854
Pyramid Media, pg 867
Quality Digest, pg 868
Regent Press Publishers & Printers, pg 873
Revelli, pg 874
Rhythms Productions (Tom Thumb Music), pg 874
Russ InVision Co/AbridgeClub.com, pg 879
Sea Studios Foundation, pg 883
Social Studies School Service, pg 891
Sodanceabit, pg 892
Theatre Arts Video Library, pg 911
Thinking Allowed Productions, pg 912
TMW Media Group, pg 915
The Video Project, pg 928
Visual Communications - Southern California Asian American Studies Central Inc, pg 931
ViVi Co, pg 932
Warner Home Video Inc, pg 934
Xenon Pictures Inc, pg 943

COLORADO

Crown Ministries International, pg 735
Crystal Productions, pg 735
InJoy Birth & Parenting Education, pg 788
Jeppesen, pg 793
National Institute for Trial Advocacy (NITA), pg 836
Stretching Inc, pg 902

CONNECTICUT

Cine-Med Inc, pg 723
Creative Arts Television, pg 733
Hartley Film Foundation, pg 776
Really Good Stuff, pg 871

The Taunton Press Inc, pg 907
Weston Woods Studios Inc, pg 936

DELAWARE

Intercollegiate Studies Institute Inc (ISI), pg 789
So Smart Productions, pg 891
University Media Services, pg 922

DISTRICT OF COLUMBIA

American Chemical Society (ACS), pg 683
Art Museum of the Americas, pg 690
Biblical Archaeology Society (BAS), pg 705
Department of VSA & Accessibility at the John F Kennedy Center for the Performing Arts, pg 740
National Council of Churches, pg 836
Sano Videos, pg 880
Systems Impact Inc, pg 906
USCCB Publishing, pg 923

FLORIDA

America By Air LLC, pg 682
Bisk Education, pg 706
EarthDesign Inc, pg 749
I M P A C T Publishing Inc, pg 783
Potentials Unlimited, pg 860
Video Aided Instruction Inc, pg 927
Video Resources Software, pg 928

GEORGIA

American Association for Vocational Instructional Materials (AAVIM), pg 682
Benedetto Guitars, pg 703
Gingerbread Group Holdings LLC, pg 771
Little Mammoth Media, pg 810
LYRASIS, pg 813
New Leaf Distributing Co, pg 839
School Media Associates LLC, pg 882
Skyhoundz, pg 890

HAWAII

Ka Io Productions Inc, pg 796
Source School of Tantra Yoga Inc, pg 895

IDAHO

University of Idaho Engineering Outreach, pg 922

ILLINOIS

ABSA Films, pg 672
African American Images Inc, pg 678
Britannica Digital Learning, pg 710
Cahokia Mounds Museum Society, pg 713
CCH Continuing Education, pg 718
CCore Media Inc, pg 718
Discovery Education - Chicago, pg 743
Encyclopaedia Britannica Inc, pg 754
Film Ideas Inc, pg 760
1st Financial Training Services Inc, pg 761
International Historic Films Inc, pg 790
Learning Seed, pg 805
Liturgy Training Publications, pg 810

Moviecraft Inc, pg 831
Movies Unlimited, pg 831
National Safety Council (NSC), pg 836
Nightingale-Conant Corp, pg 841
Questar Entertainment Inc, pg 868
Research Press, pg 873
Terra Nova Films Inc, pg 911
Theosophical Publishing House, pg 912

INDIANA

Educational Video Group Inc, pg 751
Indiana University Press, pg 786
Purdue University Digital Education, pg 866
Solution Tree, pg 892

IOWA

Accelerated Learning Foundation, pg 672
Championship Productions Inc, pg 720
Kendall Hunt Publishing Co, pg 797
Kirkwood Community College, pg 799
Perfection Learning Corp, pg 854

KANSAS

Yarn Barn of Kansas, pg 943

KENTUCKY

EKU Media, pg 752
Hammond Communications Group Inc, pg 775
KET The Kentucky Network, pg 798
The Learning House Inc, pg 805
National Geographic Learning, pg 836
WaxWorks VideoWorks, pg 934

MAINE

Slim Goodbody Corp, pg 890
WoodenBoat Publications, pg 941

MARYLAND

Adventure Productions LLC, pg 678
Paul H Brookes Publishing Co, pg 711
DSR Computer Technology Specialists Inc, pg 747
Hearing Loss Association of America (HLAA), pg 778
James Agee Film Project, pg 792
MMI Marketing, pg 828
Recorded Books Inc, an RBmedia company, pg 871
RLJ Entertainment Inc, pg 875
Sign Media Inc, pg 887
Total AV Systems, pg 916

MASSACHUSETTS

Award Productions Inc, pg 699
Cheng & Tsui Co, pg 721
Commonwealth Films Inc, pg 728
Documentary Educational Resources Inc, pg 744
Education Development Center Inc (EDC), pg 750
HOME Inc, pg 781
In the Wild Productions, pg 786
Limelight Production® Inc, pg 809
Merrimack Films, pg 824
National Fire Protection Association (NFPA), pg 836
The New Film Company Inc, pg 839

Penfield Productions Ltd, pg 853
Sinauer Associates, pg 889
WGBH Production Group, pg 936

MICHIGAN

Digi Sign Design LLC, pg 741
Emery-Pratt Co, pg 753
HighScope Press, pg 780
Madonna University Information Technology, pg 814
MSU Technologies, pg 833
Prakken Publications Inc, pg 861
The Program Source International, pg 865
Society of Manufacturing Engineers (SME), pg 891
VMS Inc, pg 932
Zondervan, pg 945

MINNESOTA

American Choral Catalog Ltd, pg 683
EMC Publishing LLC, pg 753
Festival Films, pg 759
Harris Communications Inc, pg 776
Hazelden Publishing & Educational Services, pg 777
JIST Publishing, pg 794
Whole Person Associates Inc, pg 938

MISSOURI

Annenberg Learner, pg 685
ASET - The Neurodiagnostic Society, pg 690
Marsh Media, pg 817
SOM Publishing Co, pg 892
Vedanta Society of St Louis, pg 925

MONTANA

High Plains Films, pg 779

NEBRASKA

B & B Video Productions Inc, pg 700
Vision Maker Media, pg 930

NEVADA

DVDs4Less, pg 748

NEW HAMPSHIRE

Captain Fiddle Music & Publications, pg 716
French American Music Enterprises, pg 765
Frey Scientific, pg 766
Heinemann, pg 778
Chip Taylor Communications LLC, pg 907

NEW JERSEY

Alden Films, pg 679
Allegro Productions Inc, pg 680
Comex Systems Inc, pg 728
Dance Horizons Video, pg 737
Ergo Media Inc, pg 755
Euro-Pacific Film & Video Productions Inc, pg 756
Jointure for Community Adult Education Inc, pg 794
Kultur International Films Ltd Inc, pg 802
MiB MediaWorks, pg 825
Milestone Film & Video Inc, pg 827
Princeton Book Company, Publishers, pg 862
SES SA, pg 884

Shanachie Entertainment Corp, pg 885
John Wiley & Sons Inc, pg 938

NEW MEXICO

The Phoenix Learning Group Inc, pg 855
Uncharted Country Publishing, pg 921

NEW YORK

Ambrose Video Publishing Inc, pg 682
American Management Association® (AMA), pg 683
Artistic Video, pg 690
Asia Society, pg 691
ATA Trading Corp/Favorite TV Inc, pg 691
Beekman Books Inc, pg 703
Michael Blackwood Productions Inc, pg 707
Broadstreet Productions LLC, pg 711
Brooklyn Botanic Garden, pg 711
Billy Budd Films Inc, pg 712
The Bureau for At-Risk Youth, pg 712
Criterion Collection, pg 735
Cross-Cultural Communications, pg 735
De Nonno Productions Inc (DPI), pg 739
Downtown Community Television Center (DCTV), pg 746
Educational Activities Inc, pg 750
Albert Ellis Institute (AEI), pg 753
FACE Foundation, pg 758
The Film-Makers' Cooperative, pg 760
Films Media Group, pg 760
William Greaves Productions Inc, pg 774
Guidance Associates Inc Center for Humanities, pg 774
Guilford Publications, pg 774
Hallel Communications, pg 775
Homespun Video, pg 781
Human Relations Media, pg 782
IAI Records & Video, pg 783
Icarus Films Inc, pg 783
The Institute Inc, pg 788
Janson Media Inc, pg 793
L&S Video Inc, pg 803
Lifetime Television®, pg 807
March of Dimes Foundation, pg 816
Mastervision Inc, pg 819
Mathmadeeasy.com, pg 819
Meridian Education Corp, pg 823
Metropolitan Opera Guild Inc, pg 824
Practising Law Institute, pg 860
Random House Children's Books, pg 870
Richter Productions Inc, pg 875
SciMedTv, pg 882
Shopware, pg 886
SISU Home Entertainment Inc, pg 889
Third World Newsreel/Camera News Inc, pg 912
Transformational Education Initiatives, pg 917
Video Catalogue Co Inc, pg 927
Videofashion Network, pg 929
VIEW Inc (Video International Entertainment World Inc), pg 930
Willow Mixed Media Inc, pg 939
Women Make Movies Inc, pg 941
Wonderwomen™ Enterprises, pg 941
Zeitgeist Films Ltd, pg 945

NORTH CAROLINA

AudioSolutionz LLC, pg 695
Carolina Biological Supply Co, pg 717
Crystal Pictures Inc, pg 735
Ladyslipper Music, pg 803
Laurel Hill Press, pg 804
Sinclair Institute, pg 889
Thinking Maps Inc, pg 912
World Wide Pictures Inc, pg 941

NORTH DAKOTA

UND Television Center, pg 921

OHIO

Alegra House Publishers, pg 679
Curtis Inc, pg 736
Franciscan Media, pg 765
Griesinger Films LLC, pg 774
McGraw-Hill School Education Group, pg 821
Shelburne Films, pg 885
Treehaus Communications Inc, pg 917
WOUB Public Media, pg 942

OKLAHOMA

Academic Media & Digital Services, pg 672
VCI Entertainment, pg 925

OREGON

CNS Productions Inc, pg 727
Cooking by the Book, pg 731
Encounter Video Inc, pg 754
Garden Valley Productions, pg 768
Getty-Dubay Productions, pg 770
InterVision Media, pg 791
The Keyboard Workshop, pg 798
Sugar Mountain PR, pg 903

PENNSYLVANIA

Bergwall Productions Inc, pg 704
Bullfrog Films Inc, pg 712
Corinth Films Inc, pg 731
CORTRON Media LLC, pg 732
Discovery Education - South Burlington, pg 743
FMP Media Solutions Inc, pg 763
MVD Entertainment Group, pg 835
Rahlic Publishing Co, pg 869
Fred Rogers Productions, pg 876
S I Video Sales Group, pg 879
Schlessinger Media, pg 881
Vision Video, pg 930
The Whale Video Co, pg 936

SOUTH CAROLINA

American Production Services LLC, pg 684

TENNESSEE

Abingdon Press, pg 672
American Blackguard Inc, pg 683
Center for Southern Folklore Inc, pg 719
National School Products, pg 836
Spring Arbor Distributors Inc, pg 898

TEXAS

CEV Multimedia Ltd, pg 720
Chalk Dust Co, pg 720
Educational Video Network, pg 751
EduMedia of Sugar Land, Texas, pg 751
Emergency Film Group, pg 753

PROGRAMMING — VIDEO

Educational Program Distributors (continued)

TEXAS (continued)

Executive Development Systems Inc, pg 757
PetroSkills | RDC Solutions, pg 855
Shadow Play Records & Video, pg 885
Teleometrics International, pg 910
University of Texas at Austin - Petroleum Extension Service, pg 923

UTAH

San Juan School District Heritage Language Resource Center, pg 880

VERMONT

Multicultural Media Inc, pg 833
Dorothy Tod Films, pg 915
University of Vermont, Instructional Television Dept, pg 923
Wilson McLeran Inc, pg 939

VIRGINIA

CACI Integrated Communications, pg 713
CDR Communications Inc, pg 719
Close Up Foundation, pg 726
Filmakers Library, pg 760
National Audiovisual Center (NAC), pg 836

WASHINGTON

Bennett-Watt HD Productions Inc, pg 703
Intermedia Inc, pg 789
John McLean Media, pg 794
Robert McConnell Productions, pg 820
Medifecta Healthcare Training, pg 823
Washington State University College of Nursing, pg 934

WEST VIRGINIA

Focus on Animals, pg 763
Harpers Ferry Historical Association, pg 776

WISCONSIN

Attainment Co Inc, pg 692
Aylmer Press, pg 700
Her Own Words LLC, pg 779
Knowledge Unlimited Inc, pg 800
NEWIST/CESA 7, pg 840
Plank Road Publishing Inc, pg 857

ALBERTA

Global TV, pg 771

BRITISH COLUMBIA

Credo Interactive Inc, pg 734
Thompson Rivers University Marketing & Communications Dept, pg 913

ONTARIO

Canadian Filmmakers Distribution Center (CFMDC), pg 715
Canadian Learning Co Inc, pg 715

Canamedia Inc, pg 715
Entertainment One Distribution, pg 754
Kineticvideo.com, pg 799
Life Cycle Books Ltd, pg 807
McIntyre Media Inc, pg 821
McNabb & Connolly, pg 821
Novalis, pg 843
Scholastic Canada Ltd, pg 882
Sullivan Home Entertainment, pg 903
TVO/Ontario Educational Communications Authority (OECA), pg 919
University of Toronto, Classroom Technology Support, pg 923
Wintergreen Learning Materials, pg 939

QUEBEC

National Film Board of Canada/Office National du Film du Canada, pg 836
Les Productions Via Le Monde (Daniel Bertolino) Inc, pg 864
Whalley-Abbey Media Holdings Inc, pg 937

Educational Program Producers

ALABAMA

AVS Media Group, pg 699
CMEinfo™, pg 727
Leo Ticheli Productions, pg 913

ALASKA

Alaska Media Pros LLC, pg 679
Aurora Films, pg 696

ARIZONA

Aardvark Productions LLC, pg 671
Candee Productions Inc, pg 716
CyberIconics International, pg 736
Direct Current Video Productions, pg 743
Film Creations Ltd, pg 760
Fox 10 Productions (KSAZ-TV), pg 765
Merestone, pg 823
Teaberry, pg 908
TSG Publishing Foundation Inc USA, pg 919

ARKANSAS

Live'N'Loud, pg 810
Mullikin Agency, pg 833
White Diamond Productions LLC, pg 937

CALIFORNIA

A Go Go Films, pg 671
Access Video in Berkeley, pg 673
Action Video, pg 675
Allied Artists International Inc, pg 681
Artichoke Productions, pg 690
Astronomical Society of the Pacific, pg 691
Backstage Pass Entertainment Inc, pg 700
Big Door, pg 705
Les Blank Films Inc, pg 707
Burrud Productions Inc, pg 713
C & M Publishing Co, pg 713
California Language Laboratories, pg 714
Cambridge Documentary Films Inc, pg 714

Cavalcade Productions Inc, pg 717
Center for the Collaborative Classroom, pg 719
Steve Chandler, pg 720
Chick Russell Communications, pg 721
Clarity Sound & Light, pg 725
Classic Images Stock Footage LLC, pg 726
Coast Learning Systems, pg 727
Coastline Productions, pg 727
Concept Associates Inc, pg 730
Concrete Images, pg 730
Creative Technology, pg 733
Crystal Pyramid Productions™, pg 735
Custom Video Productions Inc, pg 736
Davidson Productions, pg 738
DawnSignPress, pg 739
Deja View Video, pg 740
Design Media, pg 741
Dialect Accent Specialists Inc, pg 741
digital OutPost, pg 742
Direct Images Interactive Inc, pg 743
Discovery Education - Los Angeles, pg 743
Dolphin MultiMedia Inc, pg 745
Durrin Productions Inc, pg 748
Eastman Corp, pg 749
ECONEWS (Environmental Television Series) & (Environmental Directions Radio Series), pg 750
Feldenkrais® Resources, pg 759
First Camera, pg 761
Forte Productions, pg 764
Gateways Books & Tapes, pg 768
Geddes Productions LLC, pg 769
Goal Productions, pg 772
Bruce Goldberg Inc, pg 772
Havas Edge, pg 777
Hay House Inc, pg 777
imageReal Pictures LLC, pg 785
Images in Motion Media Inc, pg 785
Imageworks, pg 785
Increase Video/Silver Mine Video, pg 786
Institute of Precision Muscle Balancing, pg 788
Ishtar Films, pg 791
ITV Productions, pg 792
Joyce Media Inc, pg 795
Kantola Productions LLC, pg 796
Kavich Reynolds Productions Inc, pg 797
KPBS Public Broadcasting, pg 801
Krishnamurti Foundation of America, pg 801
Latham Foundation Publications, pg 804
Learn Quickly, pg 805
Live Wire Media, pg 810
Main Street Media Inc, pg 815
Maximus Media Inc, pg 820
McCune Audio-Video-Lighting, pg 821
Medcom Inc, pg 821
Media Magic, pg 822
The Media Staff Inc, pg 822
monterey media inc, pg 829
Moose School Productions, pg 830
Music World/Vocal Power School, pg 834
New & Unique Videos™, pg 839
New Circuit Films LLC, pg 839
Nolte Media, pg 841
Noontide Press, pg 841
On-Trax Inc, pg 846
Pacific Media, pg 849

Penrose Productions, pg 854
Pentrex Media Group LLC, pg 854
PM Productions, pg 858
Point of View Productions, pg 858
Prime Cut Productions, pg 862
Pyramid Media, pg 867
QRS Software Services, pg 867
Quality Digest, pg 868
Quilt in a Day, pg 868
Regent Press Publishers & Printers, pg 873
Dick Reizner Film & Video, pg 873
RetinaVision Productions, pg 874
Revelli, pg 874
Rhythms Productions (Tom Thumb Music), pg 874
Glenn Roland Films, pg 876
Russ InVision Co/AbridgeClub.com, pg 879
Sea Studios Foundation, pg 883
SNAP, pg 891
Sodanceabit, pg 892
Staylor-Made Communications Inc, pg 900
Still N' Motion, pg 901
Tam Communications Inc, pg 906
Theatre Arts Video Library, pg 911
Thinking Allowed Productions, pg 912
Timestream Video, pg 914
TMW Media Group, pg 915
Total Creative, pg 916
Twin Peaks Creative, pg 920
Vineyard Video & Photography, pg 930
Visions Plus, pg 931
Visual Communications - Southern California Asian American Studies Central Inc, pg 931
ViVi Co, pg 932
Wavemaker Media Design, pg 934
Webster Communications, pg 935
West Coast Projections Inc, pg 935
The Wine Appreciation Guild Ltd, pg 939
Xenon Pictures Inc, pg 943
Zamacona Productions, pg 945

COLORADO

Apogee Communications Group, pg 687
Centre Communications Inc, pg 720
Crown Ministries International, pg 735
Crystal Productions, pg 735
Daylight Productions & Rentals, pg 739
Flashback Media Productions, pg 762
Greg Hensley Productions, pg 779
InJoy Birth & Parenting Education, pg 788
Jeppesen, pg 793
National Institute for Trial Advocacy (NITA), pg 836
Renaissance Media, pg 873
Rocky Mountain Audio/Video Productions Inc, pg 876
Scott Resources Inc, pg 882
Stretching Inc, pg 902
Transtar Entertainment Co Inc, pg 917

CONNECTICUT

Antenna International, pg 686
Cine-Med Inc, pg 723
Creative Arts Television, pg 733
Essex Television Group Inc, pg 755
The Gary-Paul Agency, pg 768
Geomatrix Productions, pg 770
Hartley Film Foundation, pg 776
Ironik Design & Post, pg 791
Moving Pictures, pg 832

New London Media, pg 839
Palace Productions MediaVision, pg 850
P&P Studios Inc, pg 851
The Taunton Press Inc, pg 907
UConn Health Multimedia Services, pg 920
Weston Woods Studios Inc, pg 936

DELAWARE

So Smart Productions, pg 891
University Media Services, pg 922

DISTRICT OF COLUMBIA

American Chemical Society (ACS), pg 683
Art Museum of the Americas, pg 690
Biblical Archaeology Society (BAS), pg 705
Department of VSA & Accessibility at the John F Kennedy Center for the Performing Arts, pg 740
Hillmann & Carr Inc, pg 780
National Education Association (NEA), pg 836
O'Keefe Communications Inc, pg 844
Sano Videos, pg 880
Systems Impact Inc, pg 906
Yellow Cat Productions Inc, pg 944

FLORIDA

Accord Productions, pg 673
America By Air LLC, pg 682
Applebox Studio, pg 687
Bisk Education, pg 706
Blackburst Entertainment LLC, pg 706
Civins Productions Inc, pg 725
CopShopMiami.com, pg 731
Courter Films LLC, pg 732
DME Studios, pg 744
EarthDesign Inc, pg 749
Easy Edit Video Inc, pg 750
Global Cyber-Visions, pg 771
I M P A C T Publishing Inc, pg 783
ITC Learning LLC, pg 791
Jordan Klein Film & Video (JKFV), pg 795
National Teleproductions Inc, pg 837
Paradise Video & Film, pg 851
Sound*Light, pg 894
Sunfire Communications Inc, pg 904
Sunrise Studios, pg 904
Tel-Air Interests Inc, pg 909
Tricycle Studios, pg 918
Video Aided Instruction Inc, pg 927
Video Resources Software, pg 928

GEORGIA

ADAM Inc, pg 675
Beachwood Productions, pg 702
Burst Video/Film Inc, pg 713
Cox Media, pg 732
ECG Productions, pg 750
Gingerbread Group Holdings LLC, pg 771
GP Studios, pg 773
Guerrilla Productions LLC, pg 774
Little Mammoth Media, pg 810
Malcolm Neal Productions, pg 837
On-Line Productions, pg 845
Skyhoundz, pg 890

HAWAII

Hyperspective Studios Inc, pg 783
Ka Io Productions Inc, pg 796

Sight & Sound Studios, pg 887
Source School of Tantra Yoga Inc, pg 895
1013 Integrated, pg 911

IDAHO

Brad Shaw Productions Inc, pg 885
University of Idaho Engineering Outreach, pg 922
Wide Eye Productions, pg 938

ILLINOIS

ABSA Films, pg 672
Accenture, pg 672
African American Images Inc, pg 678
Airways Digital Media, pg 679
Beatty TeleVisual Productions, pg 703
Britannica Digital Learning, pg 710
Cahokia Mounds Museum Society, pg 713
CCH Continuing Education, pg 718
CCore Media Inc, pg 718
The Chicago Production Center, pg 721
Cresta Creative, pg 734
Discovery Education - Chicago, pg 743
Encyclopaedia Britannica Inc, pg 754
Explore, pg 757
Extraordinary Demos/Videos, pg 757
Film Police, pg 760
1st Financial Training Services Inc, pg 761
IV Media Resources, pg 792
Learning Seed, pg 805
Liturgy Training Publications, pg 810
Major Media Productions Inc, pg 815
Manning Productions, pg 816
Mightybytes Inc, pg 827
Mimi Productions, pg 828
Multimedia Marketing Group, pg 833
National Safety Council (NSC), pg 836
Nightingale-Conant Corp, pg 841
Rob Orr Productions Ltd, pg 848
Pepper Group, pg 854
PSAV® Presentation Services (Hotel Services Division), pg 866
Questar Entertainment Inc, pg 868
Research Press, pg 873
SCI Television & Creative Media LLC, pg 882
Southern Illinois University, pg 895
Sparkfactor, pg 896
Terra Nova Films Inc, pg 911
Theosophical Publishing House, pg 912
20/20 Communications Inc, pg 920
Video I-D Teleproductions Inc, pg 928
Video Impressions, pg 928
Winter Productions, pg 939

INDIANA

A-V-A Video Productions, pg 671
Bright Ideas Creative Services, pg 710
Educational Video Group Inc, pg 751
PentaVision Communications Inc, pg 854
Purdue University Digital Education, pg 866
Road Pictures, pg 876
Solution Tree, pg 892

IOWA

Accelerated Learning Foundation, pg 672
Championship Productions Inc, pg 720
Educational Technology & Media Services, pg 751
Iowa State University-Information Technology Services, pg 791
Kirkwood Community College, pg 799
Kuhn Productions LLC, pg 802

KANSAS

KAKE-TV, pg 796
Rhythmic Medicine, pg 874
Yarn Barn of Kansas, pg 943

KENTUCKY

Blood-Horse Publications, pg 707
EKU Media, pg 752
Hammond Communications Group Inc, pg 775
Idle Minds Productions Inc, pg 784
KET The Kentucky Network, pg 798
Donna Lawrence Productions, pg 804
The Learning House Inc, pg 805
National Geographic Learning, pg 836
NIMCO Inc, pg 841

LOUISIANA

Great Chefs/Leisure Jazz Video, pg 773
Leisure Video, pg 806
Moxie Media, pg 832

MAINE

Films by Huey, pg 760
Slim Goodbody Corp, pg 890
WGME-TV, pg 936

MARYLAND

Absolute Hollywood, pg 672
Adventure Productions LLC, pg 678
CAS Video Productions, pg 717
Richard Chisolm Cinematography, pg 722
CPR MultiMedia Solutions, pg 732
dbF a Media Company, pg 739
DSR Computer Technology Specialists Inc, pg 747
The Image Generators, pg 785
James Agee Film Project, pg 792
Kramer Communications Video Production, pg 801
Media Dimensions LLC, pg 821
MMI Marketing, pg 828
Mobile-Video Productions Inc, pg 828
Producers Video, pg 863
Recorded Books Inc, an RBmedia company, pg 871
Sign Media Inc, pg 887

MASSACHUSETTS

Award Productions Inc, pg 699
Cheng & Tsui Co, pg 721
CommCreative, pg 728
Commonwealth Films Inc, pg 728
Documentary Educational Resources Inc, pg 744
Education Development Center Inc (EDC), pg 750
Green Mountain Post Films (GMP), pg 774
Heliotrope Studios, pg 778

HOME Inc, pg 781
In the Wild Productions, pg 786
Merrimack Films, pg 824
Monadnock Media Inc, pg 829
The New Film Company Inc, pg 839
Northern Light Productions (NLP), pg 842
Penfield Productions Ltd, pg 853
PixMix Video Services, pg 857
Sinauer Associates, pg 889
TVN-The Video Network, pg 919
VideoLink Inc, an AVI-SPL company, pg 929
WGBH Production Group, pg 936
WVP Boston, pg 942

MICHIGAN

Digi Sign Design LLC, pg 741
HighScope Press, pg 780
International Tae Kwon Do Association (ITA Institute), pg 790
K&R All Media Productions LLC, pg 796
K&R's Recording Studios Inc, pg 796
Lawrence Productions Inc, pg 804
Madonna University Information Technology, pg 814
MSU Technologies, pg 833
Prakken Publications Inc, pg 861
The Program Source International, pg 865
Society of Manufacturing Engineers (SME), pg 891
TGA Recording Co, pg 911
VMS Inc, pg 932
WTVS, Detroit Public Television, pg 942
Zondervan, pg 945

MINNESOTA

American Choral Catalog Ltd, pg 683
EMC Publishing LLC, pg 753
Hazelden Publishing & Educational Services, pg 777
House of Cinemagraphics, pg 782
JIST Publishing, pg 794
MastCom, pg 819
Media Loft Inc, pg 822
Whole Person Associates Inc, pg 938
Babe Winkelman Productions Inc, pg 939
Worthwhile Films, pg 941

MISSOURI

Annenberg Learner, pg 685
ASET - The Neurodiagnostic Society, pg 690
Audio-VideoGraphics Inc, pg 694
Communitronics Corp, pg 729
Hardcastle Films & Video, pg 776
Marsh Media, pg 817
SOM Publishing Co, pg 892
University of Missouri-Columbia, pg 923
Vedanta Society of St Louis, pg 925

MONTANA

High Plains Films, pg 779

NEBRASKA

AdventSource, pg 678
B & B Video Productions Inc, pg 700

PROGRAMMING — VIDEO

Educational Program Producers (continued)

NEBRASKA (continued)
Mason Video, pg 819
Rainbow Video Productions Inc, pg 869

NEVADA

Aardvark Video & Media Productions, pg 671
DVDs4Less, pg 748
Encore Event Technologies LLC, pg 754
JCS Video Productions, pg 793
Tetrahedron LLC, pg 911

NEW HAMPSHIRE

Academic & Campus Technology Services, pg 672
Apertura, pg 686
Captain Fiddle Music & Publications, pg 716
Channell One Video, pg 720
Chip Taylor Communications LLC, pg 907
The Troupe, pg 918

NEW JERSEY

Alden Films, pg 679
Allegro Productions Inc, pg 680
CFP Video Productions Inc, pg 720
Comex Systems Inc, pg 728
Dance Horizons Video, pg 737
Euro-Pacific Film & Video Productions Inc, pg 756
Laurel Video Productions, pg 804
Megavideo LLC, pg 823
MiB MediaWorks, pg 825
Ray Mueller Productions, pg 833
Optisonics Productions, pg 847
Selden Associates, pg 883
Shamrock Communications, pg 885
Shanachie Entertainment Corp, pg 885
Suede Interactive, pg 903
Telequest Inc, pg 910
TimeSteps Productions Inc, pg 914
VCSvideo, pg 925
John Wiley & Sons Inc, pg 938

NEW MEXICO

Lannan Foundation, pg 803
The Phoenix Learning Group Inc, pg 855
Production Outfitters, pg 864
Rainbow International Inc, pg 869
Uncharted Country Publishing, pg 921

NEW YORK

American History Workshop (NY) Inc, pg 683
American Management Association® (AMA), pg 683
American Montage Inc, pg 683
Artistic Video, pg 690
Asia Society, pg 691
aurora productions, pg 696
BC Studio, pg 702
Bevilacqua Studios, pg 704
Michael Blackwood Productions Inc, pg 707
Brian Film Productions LLC, pg 710

Broadstreet Productions LLC, pg 711
Brooklyn Botanic Garden, pg 711
Billy Budd Films Inc, pg 712
The Bureau for At-Risk Youth, pg 712
Buzzco Associates Inc, pg 713
Clarity Media Group, pg 725
Criterion Collection, pg 735
Cross-Cultural Communications, pg 735
De Nonno Productions Inc (DPI), pg 739
Discovery Education Inc, pg 743
Downtown Community Television Center (DCTV), pg 746
Educational Activities Inc, pg 750
Eye on Dance, pg 758
Fanlight Productions, pg 759
Films Media Group, pg 760
Florentine Films, pg 762
Golf Digest Publications, pg 772
William Greaves Productions Inc, pg 774
Guidance Associates Inc Center for Humanities, pg 774
Guilford Publications, pg 774
Hallel Communications, pg 775
Hello World Communications, pg 778
Homespun Video, pg 781
Human Relations Media, pg 782
IAI Records & Video, pg 783
The Independent Production Fund, pg 786
The Institute Inc, pg 788
Ketchum Inc, pg 798
L A Bruell Inc, pg 802
L&S Video Inc, pg 803
Lavine Production Group, pg 804
Lifetime Television®, pg 807
Long Island Video Enterprises Live Inc, pg 811
March of Dimes Foundation, pg 816
Mastervision Inc, pg 819
Mathmadeeasy.com, pg 819
Meridian Education Corp, pg 823
Mood Creations Ltd, pg 829
Jack Morton Worldwide, pg 830
MRY, pg 832
New Horizon Studios, pg 839
News Broadcast Network Inc, pg 840
Northeast Video Productions Inc, pg 842
The Palmer Group, pg 850
Pat Kogan Productions Inc, pg 852
Peckham Productions Inc, pg 852
Polestar Films & Associated Arts Ltd, pg 859
Practising Law Institute, pg 860
PrimaLux Video Inc, pg 862
PrimeLight Productions Inc, pg 862
Random House Children's Books, pg 870
Richter Productions Inc, pg 875
SciMedTv, pg 882
Shopware, pg 886
D S Simon Productions, pg 888
SISU Home Entertainment Inc, pg 889
Spoken Arts Inc, pg 898
Suggs Media Productions Inc, pg 903
TeleTime Productions, pg 910
Third World Newsreel/Camera News Inc, pg 912
Triumph Learning LLC, pg 918
Video Catalogue Co Inc, pg 927
Videofashion Network, pg 929
Videograf, pg 929
Vidicom Inc, pg 930
VIEW Inc (Video International Entertainment World Inc), pg 930

Weigl Publishers Inc, pg 935
Alan Weiss Productions, pg 935
Willow Mixed Media Inc, pg 939
WNET/New York Public Media, pg 940
Wonderwomen™ Enterprises, pg 941
Zelman Studios Ltd, pg 945

NORTH CAROLINA

All Pro Media Inc, pg 680
Pat Appleson Studios Inc, pg 687
AudioSolutionz LLC, pg 695
The Communications Group Inc, pg 729
Crystal Pictures Inc, pg 735
Digital Rain LLC, pg 742
Horizon Video Productions Inc, pg 781
Kino Mountain Productions LLC, pg 799
Laurel Hill Press, pg 804
Moving Pictures, pg 832
PACE Worldwide, pg 849
Sinclair Institute, pg 889
Videowerks, pg 930

NORTH DAKOTA

UND Television Center, pg 921

OHIO

Advent Media Inc, pg 677
Alegra House Publishers, pg 679
Russ Beckner Pictures, pg 703
CET, pg 720
Curtis Inc, pg 736
Cuyahoga Community College Student Production Office (SPO), pg 736
Dreamscape Media LLC, pg 746
Franciscan Media, pg 765
Griesinger Films LLC, pg 774
Image Video Teleproductions Inc, pg 785
Lyon Video Inc, pg 813
MainSail Production Services Inc, pg 815
McGraw-Hill School Education Group, pg 821
R&B Communications Inc, pg 870
Shelburne Films, pg 885
Take 1 Media Services, pg 906
Treehaus Communications Inc, pg 917
Vista Color Imaging Inc, pg 931
WOUB Public Media, pg 942

OKLAHOMA

Academic Media & Digital Services, pg 672
CSI/Orion, pg 735
Institute for Teaching & Learning Excellence (ITLE), pg 788
VCI Entertainment, pg 925

OREGON

ADD Plus, pg 676
CNS Productions Inc, pg 727
Cooking by the Book, pg 731
Encounter Video Inc, pg 754
Garden Valley Productions, pg 768
Getty-Dubay Productions, pg 770
Ideascape Inc, pg 784
InterVision Media, pg 791
The Keyboard Workshop, pg 798
KPDX-TV Production Center, pg 801
KTVA Productions, pg 802
KVAL, pg 802
Odyssey Productions Inc, pg 844

Production West, pg 864
Spirit Media, pg 897

PENNSYLVANIA

Argentine Productions Inc, pg 688
Bang! Pictures Inc, pg 701
Beholder Productions Inc, pg 703
Bergwall Productions Inc, pg 704
CCI Communications Inc, pg 718
CORTRON Media LLC, pg 732
Discovery Education - South Burlington, pg 743
FMP Media Solutions Inc, pg 763
Innovision Media Group, pg 788
JPL, pg 795
Kensington Falls Animation, pg 797
Main Point Productions, pg 815
Muderick Media, pg 833
Panta Rhei Media Inc, pg 851
Production Masters Inc (PMI), pg 864
Rahlic Publishing Co, pg 869
S I Video Sales Group, pg 879
Scala Inc, pg 881
Schlessinger Media, pg 881
Video/Film Associates, pg 928
The Videohouse Inc, pg 929
Vision Video, pg 930
Visual Sound Inc, pg 931
The Whale Video Co, pg 936
WHYY Inc, pg 938

RHODE ISLAND

Sound-FX-Design, pg 894

SOUTH CAROLINA

American Production Services LLC, pg 684
BJU Press, pg 706
Encore Video Productions, pg 754
Stages Video Productions, pg 899
Venture Media, pg 925

TENNESSEE

Abingdon Press, pg 672
American Blackguard Inc, pg 683
Center for Southern Folklore Inc, pg 719
Continental Film, pg 731
Memphis Communications Corp, pg 823
Paradigm Marketing & Creative, pg 851
Running Pony Productions LLC, pg 878
Scripps Networks, pg 882
Russ Sturgeon Productions/RSVP, pg 903
United Methodist Productions, pg 921

TEXAS

Alpha Video Productions, pg 682
Castleview Productions, pg 717
Cerutti Productions Inc, pg 720
CEV Multimedia Ltd, pg 720
Chalk Dust Co, pg 720
Communication Arts Multimedia Inc, pg 728
Dub King, pg 747
The Editing Co, pg 750
Educational Video Network, pg 751
EduMedia of Sugar Land, Texas, pg 751
Emergency Film Group, pg 753
Epic Software Group Inc, pg 755
Horizon Film + Video Productions, pg 781
JSAV, pg 795
Marx InDigital, pg 818

Matson Multi-Media, pg 820
Mediaforce Productions, pg 822
Earl Miller Productions Inc, pg 827
Julye Newlin Productions Inc,
 pg 840
Omega Productions, pg 845
Omni Intercommunications Inc,
 pg 845
PetroSkills | RDC Solutions, pg 855
Romar Learning Solutions LLC,
 pg 877
Shadow Play Records & Video,
 pg 885
South Coast Film & Video, pg 895
Sportsmen on Film Inc, pg 898
Teleometrics International, pg 910
Texas Heart Institute Visual
 Communication Services, pg 911
University of Texas at Austin -
 Petroleum Extension Service,
 pg 923

UTAH

San Juan School District Heritage
 Language Resource Center,
 pg 880

VERMONT

Marlboro Productions, pg 817
Dorothy Tod Films, pg 915
University of Vermont, Instructional
 Television Dept, pg 923
Wilson McLeran Inc, pg 939

VIRGINIA

Altruist Media LLC, pg 682
American Counseling Association,
 pg 683
BES Studios, pg 704
CDR Communications Inc, pg 719
Cinebar Productions Inc, pg 723
Close Up Foundation, pg 726
CVW Event Productions, pg 736
Limelight Communications Inc,
 pg 808
Metro Productions, pg 824
National Media Services Inc,
 pg 836
Rocktown Media, pg 876
Video Solutions, pg 928

WASHINGTON

Bennett-Watt HD Productions Inc,
 pg 703
Center for Touch Drawing, pg 719
Hamilton Studio, pg 775
Intermedia Inc, pg 789
Robert McConnell Productions,
 pg 820
Medifecta Healthcare Training,
 pg 823
North-by-Northwest - A Digital
 Studio, pg 842
Washington State University College
 of Nursing, pg 934
White Rain Films Ltd, pg 937

WEST VIRGINIA

Blackwater Video Productions,
 pg 707

WISCONSIN

Attainment Co Inc, pg 692
Aylmer Press, pg 700
5th Floor Recording Co, pg 760
Her Own Words LLC, pg 779
Knowledge Unlimited Inc, pg 800
Meridian Studios, pg 824
Midland Video Productions Inc,
 pg 827

Mirror 34 Productions, pg 828
NEWIST/CESA 7, pg 840
Plank Road Publishing Inc, pg 857
University of Wisconsin-Oshkosh
 Radio-TV-Film Dept, pg 923
USAV Group Inc, pg 923
Video Wisconsin Inc, pg 929
Watts Communications Inc, pg 934
Wisconsin Public Television, pg 940

WYOMING

Bridger Productions Inc, pg 710

ALBERTA

Black Media Works, pg 706
Global TV, pg 771
HDTV Productions Inc, pg 777

BRITISH COLUMBIA

Inspired Image Picture Co (IIPC),
 pg 788
Thompson Rivers University
 Marketing & Communications
 Dept, pg 913
Triad Communications Ltd, pg 918

MANITOBA

Spectra Video Productions Ltd,
 pg 897

*NEWFOUNDLAND AND
 LABRADOR*

Vidcraft Productions Ltd, pg 927

ONTARIO

ADS Media, pg 677
Art Gallery of Ontario, pg 690
Associated Producers Ltd, pg 691
Canamedia, pg 715
DebsVoice, pg 739
GAPC (General Assembly
 Production Centre), pg 768
Image Video Services &
 Productions, pg 785
Marblemedia, pg 816
Novalis, pg 843
Pearson Education Canada, pg 852
RB Productions, pg 870
Scholastic Canada Ltd, pg 882
University of Toronto, Classroom
 Technology Support, pg 923
Video Excellence Productions,
 pg 927
YAP Films, pg 943

QUEBEC

Les Editions CEC Inc, pg 750
Group PVP, pg 774
Kerrigan Productions Inc, pg 798
National Film Board of
 Canada/Office National du Film
 du Canada, pg 836
Productions Grand Nord Quebec
 Inc, pg 864
Les Productions Via Le Monde
 (Daniel Bertolino) Inc, pg 864
Whalley-Abbey Media Holdings
 Inc, pg 937

SASKATCHEWAN

plan9films, pg 857

Educational Program
Rentals

ARIZONA

Video Learning Library, pg 928

CALIFORNIA

Les Blank Films Inc, pg 707
Cambridge Documentary Films Inc,
 pg 714
Clarity Sound & Light, pg 725
Davidson Productions, pg 738
Direct Cinema Ltd Inc, pg 743
Durrin Productions Inc, pg 748
ECONEWS (Environmental
 Television Series) &
 (Environmental Directions Radio
 Series), pg 750
Medcom Inc, pg 821
Point of View Productions, pg 858
Visual Communications - Southern
 California Asian American
 Studies Central Inc, pg 931

ILLINOIS

Discovery Education - Chicago,
 pg 743
1st Financial Training Services Inc,
 pg 761
National Safety Council (NSC),
 pg 836
Research Press, pg 873
Terra Nova Films Inc, pg 911

MAINE

WoodenBoat Publications, pg 941

MARYLAND

James Agee Film Project, pg 792

MASSACHUSETTS

Commonwealth Films Inc, pg 728
Documentary Educational Resources
 Inc, pg 744
Merrimack Films, pg 824

MICHIGAN

Digi Sign Design LLC, pg 741
HighScope Press, pg 780

MINNESOTA

American Choral Catalog Ltd,
 pg 683

MISSOURI

University of Missouri-Columbia,
 pg 923

NEBRASKA

Vision Maker Media, pg 930

NEW HAMPSHIRE

Academic & Campus Technology
 Services, pg 672

NEW JERSEY

Euro-Pacific Film & Video
 Productions Inc, pg 756

NEW YORK

BC Studio, pg 702
Brooklyn Botanic Garden, pg 711
Downtown Community Television
 Center (DCTV), pg 746
Fanlight Productions, pg 759
Films Media Group, pg 760
William Greaves Productions Inc,
 pg 774
Hallel Communications, pg 775
Icarus Films Inc, pg 783
Richter Productions Inc, pg 875

Third World Newsreel/Camera
 News Inc, pg 912
VIEW Inc (Video International
 Entertainment World Inc), pg 930

NORTH CAROLINA

Crystal Pictures Inc, pg 735
Sinclair Institute, pg 889
World Wide Pictures Inc, pg 941

OHIO

Franciscan Media, pg 765
Treehaus Communications Inc,
 pg 917
WOUB Public Media, pg 942

OREGON

The Keyboard Workshop, pg 798

PENNSYLVANIA

Bullfrog Films Inc, pg 712
Rahlic Publishing Co, pg 869

TENNESSEE

Center for Southern Folklore Inc,
 pg 719

VERMONT

University of Vermont, Instructional
 Television Dept, pg 923

VIRGINIA

Filmakers Library, pg 760

WASHINGTON

Intermedia Inc, pg 789

WISCONSIN

Her Own Words LLC, pg 779
NEWIST/CESA 7, pg 840

MANITOBA

Spectra Video Productions Ltd,
 pg 897

ONTARIO

Kineticvideo.com, pg 799
McNabb & Connolly, pg 821
University of Toronto, Classroom
 Technology Support, pg 923

QUEBEC

Les Productions Via Le Monde
 (Daniel Bertolino) Inc, pg 864

Feature Program
Distributors

ARIZONA

Drumbeat Indian Arts Inc, pg 747

CALIFORNIA

Allied Artists International Inc,
 pg 681
Ariztical Entertainment Inc, pg 689
Les Blank Films Inc, pg 707
Crystal Pyramid Productions™,
 pg 735
Direct Cinema Ltd Inc, pg 743
Em Gee Film Library, pg 753
411 Video Information, pg 764
Glenn Photo Supply, pg 771
Glenn Video Vistas Ltd, pg 771

PROGRAMMING — VIDEO

Feature Program Distributors (continued)

CALIFORNIA (continued)

Increase Video/Silver Mine Video, pg 786
MarVista Entertainment Inc, pg 818
MGM Home Entertainment, pg 825
monterey media inc, pg 829
monterey video, pg 829
Noontide Press, pg 841
Pacific Media, pg 849
Palardo Productions, pg 850
Universal Pictures Home Entertainment, pg 922
Warner Home Video Inc, pg 934
Worldwide Entertainment Corp, pg 941
Xenon Pictures Inc, pg 943

COLORADO

Crown Ministries International, pg 735
Inferno Film Productions LLC, pg 787

CONNECTICUT

Really Good Stuff, pg 871

IDAHO

Lagoon Video, pg 803

ILLINOIS

CCore Media Inc, pg 718
Facets Multi-Media Inc, pg 758
Film Ideas Inc, pg 760
Moviecraft Inc, pg 831
Movies Unlimited, pg 831

IOWA

Right Stuf Inc, pg 875

KENTUCKY

KET The Kentucky Network, pg 798
WaxWorks VideoWorks, pg 934

MARYLAND

DSR Computer Technology Specialists Inc, pg 747
Recorded Books Inc, an RBmedia company, pg 871
RLJ Entertainment Inc, pg 875

MASSACHUSETTS

Award Productions Inc, pg 699
Penfield Productions Ltd, pg 853

MINNESOTA

Festival Films, pg 759

MONTANA

High Plains Films, pg 779

NEBRASKA

B & B Video Productions Inc, pg 700

NEVADA

DVDs4Less, pg 748

NEW HAMPSHIRE

Chip Taylor Communications LLC, pg 907

NEW JERSEY

Dance Horizons Video, pg 737
Ergo Media Inc, pg 755
MiB MediaWorks, pg 825
Milestone Film & Video Inc, pg 827

NEW YORK

A&E Television Networks LLC, pg 671
ATA Trading Corp/Favorite TV Inc, pg 691
Criterion Collection, pg 735
FACE Foundation, pg 758
The Film-Makers' Cooperative, pg 760
First Run Features, pg 761
Guidance Associates Inc Center for Humanities, pg 774
HB-Content, pg 777
HBO Home Entertainment Inc, pg 777
Icarus Films Inc, pg 783
Janson Media Inc, pg 793
Kino International Corp, pg 799
Mastervision Inc, pg 819
SISU Home Entertainment Inc, pg 889
Synaptic Digital, pg 905
Third World Newsreel/Camera News Inc, pg 912
VIEW Inc (Video International Entertainment World Inc), pg 930
Women Make Movies Inc, pg 941

NORTH CAROLINA

Crystal Pictures Inc, pg 735
Ladyslipper Music, pg 803
World Wide Pictures Inc, pg 941

OHIO

Network Technologies Inc, pg 838

OKLAHOMA

VCI Entertainment, pg 925

OREGON

InterVision Media, pg 791
Nostalgia Family Video Inc, pg 843

PENNSYLVANIA

Corinth Films Inc, pg 731
MVD Entertainment Group, pg 835

SOUTH CAROLINA

BJU Press, pg 706

TENNESSEE

American Blackguard Inc, pg 683
Spring Arbor Distributors Inc, pg 898

TEXAS

Marengo Films, pg 817

VIRGINIA

CACI Integrated Communications, pg 713

WASHINGTON

Bennett-Watt HD Productions Inc, pg 703
White Rain Films Ltd, pg 937

WISCONSIN

Knowledge Unlimited Inc, pg 800

ALBERTA

Global TV, pg 771

ONTARIO

Canadian Filmmakers Distribution Center (CFMDC), pg 715
Canadian Learning Co Inc, pg 715
CCI Entertainment Ltd, pg 718
Entertainment One Distribution, pg 754
Life Cycle Books Ltd, pg 807
McNabb & Connolly, pg 821
Sullivan Home Entertainment, pg 903
Universal Studios Canada Inc, pg 922

QUEBEC

Les Productions Via Le Monde (Daniel Bertolino) Inc, pg 864
Reel One International Ltd, pg 872

Feature Program Producers

ALASKA

Aurora Films, pg 696

ARIZONA

Aardvark Productions LLC, pg 671
Candee Productions Inc, pg 716
Film Creations Ltd, pg 760

ARKANSAS

Live'N'Loud, pg 810

CALIFORNIA

Allied Artists International Inc, pg 681
Artichoke Productions, pg 690
Big Door, pg 705
Les Blank Films Inc, pg 707
Burrud Productions Inc, pg 713
Classic Images Stock Footage LLC, pg 726
Concrete Images, pg 730
Creative Technology, pg 733
Crystal Pyramid Productions™, pg 735
Custom Video Productions Inc, pg 736
Howard Hall Productions, pg 775
imageReal Pictures LLC, pg 785
Imageworks, pg 785
ITV Productions, pg 792
Main Street Media Inc, pg 815
Maximus Media Inc, pg 820
McCune Audio-Video-Lighting, pg 821
New & Unique Videos™, pg 839
New Deal Studios, pg 839
New Wave Entertainment, pg 839
Noontide Press, pg 841
On-Trax Inc, pg 846
Pacific Media, pg 849
Palardo Productions, pg 850
Picturestart, pg 856
Playboy Entertainment Group Inc, pg 858

PM Productions, pg 858
QRS Software Services, pg 867
RKO Pictures Inc, pg 875
Glenn Roland Films, pg 876
Screen Door Entertainment Inc, pg 882
Total Creative, pg 916
Universal Pictures Home Entertainment, pg 922
Vineyard Video & Photography, pg 930
Webster Communications, pg 935
Xenon Pictures Inc, pg 943

COLORADO

Centre Communications Inc, pg 720
Inferno Film Productions LLC, pg 787
Tatum Video, pg 907

CONNECTICUT

Essex Television Group Inc, pg 755
The Gary-Paul Agency, pg 768
Ironik Design & Post, pg 791

FLORIDA

Applebox Studio, pg 687
Blackburst Entertainment LLC, pg 706
Chatterbox Productions Inc, pg 721
Civins Productions Inc, pg 725
Communications Concepts Inc (CCI), pg 729
CopShopMiami.com, pg 731
Courter Films LLC, pg 732
Jordan Klein Film & Video (JKFV), pg 795
National Teleproductions Inc, pg 837
Sunfire Communications Inc, pg 904

GEORGIA

Beachwood Productions, pg 702
Cox Media, pg 732
ECG Productions, pg 750
Guerrilla Productions LLC, pg 774
Myriad Productions, pg 835

HAWAII

Hyperspective Studios Inc, pg 783
Sight & Sound Studios, pg 887

IDAHO

Lagoon Video, pg 803
Brad Shaw Productions Inc, pg 885
Wide Eye Productions, pg 938

ILLINOIS

ABSA Films, pg 672
CCore Media Inc, pg 718
Film Police, pg 760
Multimedia Marketing Group, pg 833
Pepper Group, pg 854
Winter Productions, pg 939

INDIANA

A-V-A Video Productions, pg 671

IOWA

Right Stuf Inc, pg 875

KANSAS

KAKE-TV, pg 796

KENTUCKY

KET The Kentucky Network, pg 798
Donna Lawrence Productions, pg 804

LOUISIANA

Moxie Media, pg 832

MARYLAND

Absolute Hollywood, pg 672
Adventure Productions LLC, pg 678
dbF a Media Company, pg 739
DSR Computer Technology Specialists Inc, pg 747
Kramer Communications Video Production, pg 801

MASSACHUSETTS

Award Productions Inc, pg 699
Green Mountain Post Films (GMP), pg 774
Heliotrope Studios, pg 778
Monadnock Media Inc, pg 829
Penfield Productions Ltd, pg 853

MICHIGAN

K&R All Media Productions LLC, pg 796
K&R's Recording Studios Inc, pg 796

MINNESOTA

House of Cinemagraphics, pg 782

MONTANA

High Plains Films, pg 779

NEBRASKA

B & B Video Productions Inc, pg 700

NEVADA

Aardvark Video & Media Productions, pg 671
DVDs4Less, pg 748
Encore Event Technologies LLC, pg 754

NEW HAMPSHIRE

Chip Taylor Communications LLC, pg 907

NEW JERSEY

Broadcast Center Studios, pg 710
CELCO, pg 719
CFP Video Productions Inc, pg 720
MiB MediaWorks, pg 825
Optisonics Productions, pg 847
Suede Interactive, pg 903

NEW MEXICO

I-25 Studios, pg 783
Production Outfitters, pg 864

NEW YORK

A&E Television Networks LLC, pg 671
American Montage Inc, pg 683
aurora productions, pg 696
Bevilacqua Studios, pg 704
Blue Barn Pictures Inc, pg 707
Broadstreet Productions LLC, pg 711
Brooklyn Films, pg 711

CompuWeather Inc, pg 729
Criterion Collection, pg 735
De Nonno Productions Inc (DPI), pg 739
HB-Content, pg 777
HBO Home Entertainment Inc, pg 777
Kinetic Arts, pg 799
Mastervision Inc, pg 819
Jack Morton Worldwide, pg 830
News Broadcast Network Inc, pg 840
News Corp, pg 840
Nickelodeon, pg 841
The Palmer Group, pg 850
Paradoxal Inc, pg 851
PrimaLux Video Inc, pg 862
Suggs Media Productions Inc, pg 903
Synaptic Digital, pg 905
Videograf, pg 929
VIEW Inc (Video International Entertainment World Inc), pg 930

NORTH CAROLINA

The Communications Group Inc, pg 729
Digital Rain LLC, pg 742
Videowerks, pg 930

OHIO

R&B Communications Inc, pg 870
Vista Color Imaging Inc, pg 931

OKLAHOMA

VCI Entertainment, pg 925

OREGON

Ideascape Inc, pg 784
InterVision Media, pg 791
KPDX-TV Production Center, pg 801
Production West, pg 864

PENNSYLVANIA

Innovision Media Group, pg 788
Kensington Falls Animation, pg 797
Muderick Media, pg 833
Production Masters Inc (PMI), pg 864
The Videohouse Inc, pg 929

RHODE ISLAND

Sound-FX-Design, pg 894

SOUTH CAROLINA

BJU Press, pg 706
Go To Team, pg 772

TENNESSEE

American Blackguard Inc, pg 683
Running Pony Productions LLC, pg 878
Scripps Networks, pg 882

TEXAS

Castleview Productions, pg 717
Cerutti Productions Inc, pg 720
Communication Arts Multimedia Inc, pg 728
Dykeman Associates Inc, pg 748
The Editing Co, pg 750
Epic Software Group Inc, pg 755
Horizon Film + Video Productions, pg 781
Earl Miller Productions Inc, pg 827
Julye Newlin Productions Inc, pg 840

Omega Productions, pg 845
Stage Directions, pg 898

VIRGINIA

BES Studios, pg 704
Metro Productions, pg 824

WASHINGTON

Bennett-Watt HD Productions Inc, pg 703
Hamilton Studio, pg 775
Victory Studios, pg 927

WISCONSIN

5th Floor Recording Co, pg 760
Knowledge Unlimited Inc, pg 800
Wisconsin Public Television, pg 940

WYOMING

Bridger Productions Inc, pg 710

ALBERTA

Global TV, pg 771
HDTV Productions Inc, pg 777

BRITISH COLUMBIA

Inspired Image Picture Co (IIPC), pg 788

NEWFOUNDLAND AND LABRADOR

Vidcraft Productions Ltd, pg 927

ONTARIO

GAPC (General Assembly Production Centre), pg 768
Image Video Services & Productions, pg 785

QUEBEC

Kerrigan Productions Inc, pg 798
Productions Grand Nord Quebec Inc, pg 864
Les Productions Via Le Monde (Daniel Bertolino) Inc, pg 864
Reel One International Ltd, pg 872

Feature Program Rentals

CALIFORNIA

Les Blank Films Inc, pg 707
Direct Cinema Ltd Inc, pg 743

ILLINOIS

Facets Multi-Media Inc, pg 758

MISSOURI

University of Missouri-Columbia, pg 923

NEW YORK

First Run Features, pg 761
Icarus Films Inc, pg 783
Kino International Corp, pg 799
Third World Newsreel/Camera News Inc, pg 912
VIEW Inc (Video International Entertainment World Inc), pg 930

NORTH CAROLINA

Crystal Pictures Inc, pg 735
World Wide Pictures Inc, pg 941

OREGON

Nostalgia Family Video Inc, pg 843

BRITISH COLUMBIA

Video Out Distribution, pg 928

ONTARIO

L-3 WESCAM, pg 802
McNabb & Connolly, pg 821

QUEBEC

Les Productions Via Le Monde (Daniel Bertolino) Inc, pg 864

Film on Videocassette Distributors

CALIFORNIA

Ametron Audio/Video, pg 684
California Language Laboratories, pg 714
Cambridge Documentary Films Inc, pg 714
411 Video Information, pg 764
Increase Video/Silver Mine Video, pg 786
Ishtar Films, pg 791
MarVista Entertainment Inc, pg 818
monterey media inc, pg 829
Nineteen87, pg 841
QRS Software Services, pg 867
Regent Press Publishers & Printers, pg 873
Revelli, pg 874
Visual Communications - Southern California Asian American Studies Central Inc, pg 931

CONNECTICUT

Cine-Med Inc, pg 723
Ironik Design & Post, pg 791

DISTRICT OF COLUMBIA

Library of Congress, Motion Picture, Broadcasting & Recorded Sound Division, pg 807

GEORGIA

School Media Associates LLC, pg 882

ILLINOIS

Britannica Digital Learning, pg 710
Film Ideas Inc, pg 760

MARYLAND

dbF a Media Company, pg 739

MISSOURI

SOM Publishing Co, pg 892

NEW HAMPSHIRE

Chip Taylor Communications LLC, pg 907

NEW YORK

Michael Blackwood Productions Inc, pg 707
FACE Foundation, pg 758
Flash Electronics Inc, pg 762
HB-Content, pg 777
Human Relations Media, pg 782
Mastervision Inc, pg 819
SISU Home Entertainment Inc, pg 889

PROGRAMMING — VIDEO

Film on Videocassette Distributors (continued)

NEW YORK (continued)

Spoken Arts Inc, pg 898
Tisch School of the Arts, pg 914
Women Make Movies Inc, pg 941

OREGON

Nostalgia Family Video Inc, pg 843

TEXAS

Lamb & Lion Ministries, pg 803

VIRGINIA

National Audiovisual Center (NAC), pg 836

WASHINGTON

Intermedia Inc, pg 789
White Rain Films Ltd, pg 937

WEST VIRGINIA

Focus on Animals, pg 763

ONTARIO

Entertainment One Distribution, pg 754
Life Cycle Books Ltd, pg 807

Film on Videocassette Producers

ARIZONA

Merestone, pg 823

ARKANSAS

Live'N'Loud, pg 810

CALIFORNIA

ACDC Audio CD & Cassette, pg 674
Artichoke Productions, pg 690
ATV Video Center Inc, pg 692
Big Door, pg 705
Les Blank Films Inc, pg 707
California Language Laboratories, pg 714
Cambridge Documentary Films Inc, pg 714
Concrete Images, pg 730
Creative Technology, pg 733
Havas Edge, pg 777
Ishtar Films, pg 791
Main Street Media Inc, pg 815
monterey media inc, pg 829
Nineteen87, pg 841
QRS Software Services, pg 867
Regent Press Publishers & Printers, pg 873
RetinaVision Productions, pg 874
Revelli, pg 874
Glenn Roland Films, pg 876
Tam Communications Inc, pg 906
TVA Media Group, pg 919
Vedanta Press & Catalog, pg 925
Video Resources Inc, pg 928
Visual Communications - Southern California Asian American Studies Central Inc, pg 931
Wavemaker Media Design, pg 934

COLORADO

CSI Film & Video LLC, pg 735

CONNECTICUT

Cine-Med Inc, pg 723
The Gary-Paul Agency, pg 768
Ironik Design & Post, pg 791

DISTRICT OF COLUMBIA

Hillmann & Carr Inc, pg 780
USCCB Publishing, pg 923

FLORIDA

Chatterbox Productions Inc, pg 721
Civins Productions Inc, pg 725
Courter Films LLC, pg 732
Sunfire Communications Inc, pg 904
Tight Line Productions, pg 914

HAWAII

Hyperspective Studios Inc, pg 783

ILLINOIS

Britannica Digital Learning, pg 710
Cresta Creative, pg 734
Richter Studios, pg 875
Video Impressions, pg 928

KENTUCKY

Idle Minds Productions Inc, pg 784
Donna Lawrence Productions, pg 804
Prosper Media Group Inc, pg 866

MARYLAND

dbF a Media Company, pg 739

MASSACHUSETTS

Heliotrope Studios Inc, pg 778
In the Wild Productions, pg 786

MICHIGAN

K&R All Media Productions LLC, pg 796

MINNESOTA

House of Cinemagraphics, pg 782
Worthwhile Films, pg 941

MISSOURI

SOM Publishing Co, pg 892

NEW HAMPSHIRE

Chip Taylor Communications LLC, pg 907

NEW JERSEY

Suede Interactive, pg 903

NEW YORK

Michael Blackwood Productions Inc, pg 707
Blue Barn Pictures Inc, pg 707
Duplication Depot Inc, pg 748
William Greaves Productions Inc, pg 774
HB-Content, pg 777
Human Relations Media, pg 782
Kinetic Arts, pg 799
Mastervision Inc, pg 819
Polestar Films & Associated Arts Ltd, pg 859

COLORADO (cont.)

SISU Home Entertainment Inc, pg 889
Spoken Arts Inc, pg 898

NORTH CAROLINA

Pat Appleson Studios Inc, pg 687
The Communications Group Inc, pg 729
Digital Rain LLC, pg 742
Moving Pictures, pg 832

OHIO

Musicol Recording, pg 835
R&B Communications Inc, pg 870
Take 1 Media Services, pg 906

OREGON

Ideascape Inc, pg 784
Odyssey Productions Inc, pg 844
REX, pg 874

PENNSYLVANIA

Argentine Productions Inc, pg 688
FMP Media Solutions Inc, pg 763
Innovision Media Group, pg 788

SOUTH CAROLINA

Encore Video Productions, pg 754

TENNESSEE

American Blackguard Inc, pg 683

TEXAS

The Editing Co, pg 750
Lamb & Lion Ministries, pg 803
Romar Learning Solutions LLC, pg 877
Stage Directions, pg 898

VIRGINIA

Metro Productions, pg 824

WASHINGTON

Bennett-Watt HD Productions Inc, pg 703
White Rain Films Ltd, pg 937

WISCONSIN

Meridian Studios, pg 824
Video Wisconsin Inc, pg 929

ALBERTA

Black Media Works, pg 706

BRITISH COLUMBIA

Triad Communications Ltd, pg 918

NEWFOUNDLAND AND LABRADOR

Vidcraft Productions Ltd, pg 927

NORTHWEST TERRITORIES

Yellowknife Films Inc, pg 944

Film on Videocassette Rentals

ARIZONA

Video Learning Library, pg 928

CALIFORNIA

Ametron Audio/Video, pg 684
Les Blank Films Inc, pg 707

Cambridge Documentary Films Inc, pg 714
Regent Press Publishers & Printers, pg 873
Visual Communications - Southern California Asian American Studies Central Inc, pg 931

MASSACHUSETTS

Documentary Educational Resources Inc, pg 744

NEW HAMPSHIRE

Chip Taylor Communications LLC, pg 907

NEW YORK

William Greaves Productions Inc, pg 774

OREGON

Nostalgia Family Video Inc, pg 843

Film Short, see Theatrical Short

Film—Television, see Television Film

Foreign Program Distributors

ARIZONA

Drumbeat Indian Arts Inc, pg 747

CALIFORNIA

Allied Artists International Inc, pg 681
Ariztical Entertainment Inc, pg 689
Backstage Pass Entertainment Inc, pg 700
Les Blank Films Inc, pg 707
Crystal Pyramid Productions™, pg 735
Discovery Education - Los Angeles, pg 743
Em Gee Film Library, pg 753
411 Video Information, pg 764
Glenn Photo Supply, pg 771
Glenn Video Vistas Ltd, pg 771
MarVista Entertainment Inc, pg 818
New & Unique Videos™, pg 839
Pacific Media, pg 849

CONNECTICUT

Really Good Stuff, pg 871

DISTRICT OF COLUMBIA

Art Museum of the Americas, pg 690
Biblical Archaeology Society (BAS), pg 705
Sano Videos, pg 880

GEORGIA

On-Line Productions, pg 845

ILLINOIS

Facets Multi-Media Inc, pg 758
International Historic Films Inc, pg 790
Moviecraft Inc, pg 831
Movies Unlimited, pg 831

IOWA

Right Stuf Inc, pg 875

KENTUCKY

WaxWorks VideoWorks, pg 934

MARYLAND

DSR Computer Technology
Specialists Inc, pg 747
Recorded Books Inc, an RBmedia
company, pg 871

MASSACHUSETTS

Cheng & Tsui Co, pg 721
Documentary Educational Resources
Inc, pg 744

MICHIGAN

Digi Sign Design LLC, pg 741

MINNESOTA

Festival Films, pg 759

NEBRASKA

Mary Riepma Ross Media Arts
Center, pg 877

NEW HAMPSHIRE

Chip Taylor Communications LLC,
pg 907

NEW JERSEY

Ergo Media Inc, pg 755
Euro-Pacific Film & Video
Productions Inc, pg 756
Kultur International Films Ltd Inc,
pg 802
Milestone Film & Video Inc,
pg 827

NEW YORK

Applause Learning Resources,
pg 687
ATA Trading Corp/Favorite TV Inc,
pg 691
Criterion Collection, pg 735
Cross-Cultural Communications,
pg 735
Downtown Community Television
Center (DCTV), pg 746
FACE Foundation, pg 758
Fanlight Productions, pg 759
The Film-Makers' Cooperative,
pg 760
First Run Features, pg 761
Hallel Communications, pg 775
Icarus Films Inc, pg 783
Janson Media Inc, pg 793
Kino International Corp, pg 799
Mastervision Inc, pg 819
Meridian Education Corp, pg 823
Richter Productions Inc, pg 875
Shopware, pg 886
SISU Home Entertainment Inc,
pg 889
Third World Newsreel/Camera
News Inc, pg 912
VIEW Inc (Video International
Entertainment World Inc), pg 930
Women Make Movies Inc, pg 941

NORTH CAROLINA

Crystal Pictures Inc, pg 735

OHIO

Network Technologies Inc, pg 838

OREGON

Nostalgia Family Video Inc, pg 843

PENNSYLVANIA

Anchor Distributors, pg 685
Bullfrog Films Inc, pg 712
Corinth Films Inc, pg 731
FMP Media Solutions Inc, pg 763
MVD Entertainment Group, pg 835
S I Video Sales Group, pg 879

TENNESSEE

Spring Arbor Distributors Inc,
pg 898

TEXAS

Educational Video Network, pg 751
Marengo Films, pg 817

VIRGINIA

National Audiovisual Center (NAC),
pg 836

WASHINGTON

Bennett-Watt HD Productions Inc,
pg 703

WISCONSIN

Plank Road Publishing Inc, pg 857

BRITISH COLUMBIA

Video Out Distribution, pg 928

ONTARIO

Canadian Filmmakers Distribution
Center (CFMDC), pg 715
CCI Entertainment Ltd, pg 718
Entertainment One Distribution,
pg 754

QUEBEC

Les Productions Via Le Monde
(Daniel Bertolino) Inc, pg 864

Foreign Program Producers

ARIZONA

Aardvark Productions LLC, pg 671
Candee Productions Inc, pg 716

CALIFORNIA

Classic Images Stock Footage LLC,
pg 726
Creative Technology, pg 733
Crystal Pyramid Productions™,
pg 735
Custom Video Productions Inc,
pg 736
Discovery Education - Los Angeles,
pg 743
International Contact Inc, pg 790
ITV Productions, pg 792
Lightyear Entertainment, pg 808
McCune Audio-Video-Lighting,
pg 821
New & Unique Videos™, pg 839
New Circuit Films LLC, pg 839
Pacific Media, pg 849
Prime Cut Productions, pg 862
QRS Software Services, pg 867
Total Creative, pg 916
TVA Media Group, pg 919
Twin Peaks Creative, pg 920

Vineyard Video & Photography,
pg 930
Webster Communications, pg 935

CONNECTICUT

Ironik Design & Post, pg 791

DISTRICT OF COLUMBIA

Art Museum of the Americas,
pg 690
Biblical Archaeology Society
(BAS), pg 705
Hillmann & Carr Inc, pg 780
Sano Videos, pg 880
Yellow Cat Productions Inc, pg 944

FLORIDA

Blackburst Entertainment LLC,
pg 706
Civins Productions Inc, pg 725
CopShopMiami.com, pg 731
Courter Films LLC, pg 732
Jordan Klein Film & Video (JKFV),
pg 795
Sunfire Communications Inc,
pg 904

GEORGIA

Guerrilla Productions LLC, pg 774
Malcolm Neal Productions, pg 837
On-Line Productions, pg 845

IDAHO

Wide Eye Productions, pg 938

ILLINOIS

Film Police, pg 760
Pepper Group, pg 854
20/20 Communications Inc, pg 920

INDIANA

A-V-A Video Productions, pg 671
Road Pictures, pg 876

IOWA

Right Stuf Inc, pg 875

LOUISIANA

Moxie Media, pg 832

MARYLAND

Absolute Hollywood, pg 672
Richard Chisolm Cinematography,
pg 722
dbF a Media Company, pg 739
DSR Computer Technology
Specialists Inc, pg 747
Kramer Communications Video
Production, pg 801

MASSACHUSETTS

Documentary Educational Resources
Inc, pg 744
Heliotrope Studios, pg 778

MICHIGAN

Digi Sign Design LLC, pg 741
K&R All Media Productions LLC,
pg 796
K&R's Recording Studios Inc,
pg 796

MINNESOTA

House of Cinemagraphics, pg 782
MastCom, pg 819
Worthwhile Films, pg 941

NEVADA

Aardvark Video & Media
Productions, pg 671
Encore Event Technologies LLC,
pg 754

NEW HAMPSHIRE

Apertura, pg 686
Chip Taylor Communications LLC,
pg 907

NEW JERSEY

Euro-Pacific Film & Video
Productions Inc, pg 756
MiB MediaWorks, pg 825
Suede Interactive, pg 903
Video Ideas Productions, pg 928

NEW YORK

Applause Learning Resources,
pg 687
Blue Barn Pictures Inc, pg 707
Criterion Collection, pg 735
Cross-Cultural Communications,
pg 735
Downtown Community Television
Center (DCTV), pg 746
Hallel Communications, pg 775
Manhattan Center Studios Inc,
pg 816
Mastervision Inc, pg 819
Jack Morton Worldwide, pg 830
The Palmer Group, pg 850
Pat Kogan Productions Inc, pg 852
PrimaLux Video Inc, pg 862
Richter Productions Inc, pg 875
VIEW Inc (Video International
Entertainment World Inc), pg 930

NORTH CAROLINA

Pat Appleson Studios Inc, pg 687
The Communications Group Inc,
pg 729
Videowerks, pg 930

OHIO

Take 1 Media Services, pg 906

PENNSYLVANIA

FMP Media Solutions Inc, pg 763
Muderick Media, pg 833
S I Video Sales Group, pg 879

RHODE ISLAND

Sound-FX-Design, pg 894

TENNESSEE

Scripps Networks, pg 882

TEXAS

Alpha Video Productions, pg 682
Cerutti Productions Inc, pg 720
Educational Video Network, pg 751
Omega Productions, pg 845
Omni Intercommunications Inc,
pg 845
South Coast Film & Video, pg 895
Stage Directions, pg 898

VIRGINIA

Metro Productions, pg 824

WASHINGTON

Bennett-Watt HD Productions Inc,
pg 703

PROGRAMMING — VIDEO

Foreign Program Producers (continued)

WISCONSIN

5th Floor Recording Co, pg 760
Midland Video Productions Inc, pg 827
Wisconsin Public Television, pg 940

WYOMING

Bridger Productions Inc, pg 710

ONTARIO

GAPC (General Assembly Production Centre), pg 768

QUEBEC

Kerrigan Productions Inc, pg 798

Foreign Program Rentals

CALIFORNIA

Les Blank Films Inc, pg 707

GEORGIA

On-Line Productions, pg 845

ILLINOIS

Facets Multi-Media Inc, pg 758

MASSACHUSETTS

Documentary Educational Resources Inc, pg 744

MICHIGAN

Digi Sign Design LLC, pg 741

MISSOURI

University of Missouri-Columbia, pg 923

NEW JERSEY

Euro-Pacific Film & Video Productions Inc, pg 756

NEW YORK

Downtown Community Television Center (DCTV), pg 746
Fanlight Productions, pg 759
First Run Features, pg 761
Hallel Communications, pg 775
Icarus Films Inc, pg 783
Kino International Corp, pg 799
Richter Productions Inc, pg 875
Third World Newsreel/Camera News Inc, pg 912
VIEW Inc (Video International Entertainment World Inc), pg 930

NORTH CAROLINA

Crystal Pictures Inc, pg 735

OREGON

Nostalgia Family Video Inc, pg 843

PENNSYLVANIA

Bullfrog Films Inc, pg 712

BRITISH COLUMBIA

Video Out Distribution, pg 928

QUEBEC

Les Productions Via Le Monde (Daniel Bertolino) Inc, pg 864

Game, see Video Game

Government Program Distributors

CALIFORNIA

Crystal Pyramid Productions™, pg 735
Discovery Education - Los Angeles, pg 743
Em Gee Film Library, pg 753
411 Video Information, pg 764
Glenn Video Vistas Ltd, pg 771
Pyramid Media, pg 867

FLORIDA

Bisk Education, pg 706
Video Resources Software, pg 928

ILLINOIS

ABSA Films, pg 672
CCH Inc, A Wolters Kluwer business, pg 718
CCore Media Inc, pg 718
Film Ideas Inc, pg 760

KENTUCKY

WaxWorks VideoWorks, pg 934

MARYLAND

DSR Computer Technology Specialists Inc, pg 747
Special Archives Division, Motion Picture Branch, pg 896

MASSACHUSETTS

Enterprise Media LLC, pg 754
Merrimack Films, pg 824
Penfield Productions Ltd, pg 853

MICHIGAN

Digi Sign Design LLC, pg 741

MINNESOTA

Service Quality Institute, pg 884

NEVADA

DVDs4Less, pg 748

NEW HAMPSHIRE

Chip Taylor Communications LLC, pg 907

NEW JERSEY

Allegro Productions Inc, pg 680
Comex Systems Inc, pg 728

NEW MEXICO

The Phoenix Learning Group Inc, pg 855

NEW YORK

Broadstreet Productions LLC, pg 711
Downtown Community Television Center (DCTV), pg 746
Films Media Group, pg 760
Monad Trainer's Aide Inc, pg 829
Synaptic Digital, pg 905
VIEW Inc (Video International Entertainment World Inc), pg 930
Women Make Movies Inc, pg 941

OHIO

Curtis Inc, pg 736

OKLAHOMA

Academic Media & Digital Services, pg 672

OREGON

InterVision Media, pg 791

PENNSYLVANIA

FMP Media Solutions Inc, pg 763

TEXAS

CEV Multimedia Ltd, pg 720

VERMONT

University of Vermont, Instructional Television Dept, pg 923

VIRGINIA

CACI Integrated Communications, pg 713
National Audiovisual Center (NAC), pg 836
WETA Production Center, pg 936

WASHINGTON

Bennett-Watt HD Productions Inc, pg 703

WEST VIRGINIA

Sweetsong Productions, pg 905

ONTARIO

Entertainment One Distribution, pg 754
Kineticvideo.com, pg 799

Government Program Producers

ALASKA

Aurora Films, pg 696

ARIZONA

Aardvark Productions LLC, pg 671
Direct Current Video Productions, pg 743
Film Creations Ltd, pg 760

ARKANSAS

White Diamond Productions LLC, pg 937

CALIFORNIA

Access Video in Berkeley, pg 673
Action Video, pg 675
Big Door, pg 705
Cavalcade Productions Inc, pg 717

Classic Images Stock Footage LLC, pg 726
Concrete Images, pg 730
Creative Technology, pg 733
Crystal Pyramid Productions™, pg 735
Custom Video Productions Inc, pg 736
Design Media, pg 741
digital OutPost, pg 742
Discovery Education - Los Angeles, pg 743
Durrin Productions Inc, pg 748
Goal Productions Inc, pg 772
Havas Edge, pg 777
Imageworks, pg 785
ITV Productions, pg 792
Maximus Media Inc, pg 820
McCune Audio-Video-Lighting, pg 821
Media Magic, pg 822
The Media Staff Inc, pg 822
New & Unique Videos™, pg 839
On-Trax Inc, pg 846
Opticomm-EMCORE, pg 847
PM Productions, pg 858
QRS Software Services, pg 867
Dick Reizner Film & Video, pg 873
Glenn Roland Films, pg 876
Shot Glass Films, pg 886
SNAP, pg 891
Staylor-Made Communications Inc, pg 900
Still N' Motion, pg 901
Tam Communications Inc, pg 906
Timestream Video, pg 914
Total Creative, pg 916
TVA Media Group, pg 919
Twin Peaks Creative, pg 920
Utopia Films, pg 924
Vineyard Video & Photography, pg 930
Visions Plus, pg 931
Zamacona Productions, pg 945

COLORADO

Apogee Communications Group, pg 687
Daylight Productions & Rentals, pg 739
Flashback Media Productions, pg 762
Tatum Video, pg 907
Transtar Entertainment Co Inc, pg 917

CONNECTICUT

The Gary-Paul Agency, pg 768
Ironik Design & Post, pg 791
Moving Pictures, pg 832
New London Media, pg 839
Spectrum, pg 897
UConn Health Multimedia Services, pg 920

DISTRICT OF COLUMBIA

Hillmann & Carr Inc, pg 780
O'Keefe Communications Inc, pg 844
Yellow Cat Productions Inc, pg 944

FLORIDA

Applebox Studio, pg 687
Bisk Education, pg 706
Blackburst Entertainment LLC, pg 706
Civins Productions Inc, pg 725
Communications Concepts Inc (CCI), pg 729
CopShopMiami.com, pg 731
Courter Films LLC, pg 732

Easy Edit Video Inc, pg 750
Jordan Klein Film & Video (JKFV), pg 795
Roger Scruggs Films, pg 883
Sunfire Communications Inc, pg 904
Sunrise Studios, pg 904
Tel-Air Interests Inc, pg 909
Video Resources Software, pg 928
Video Techniques Inc, pg 928

GEORGIA

Beachwood Productions, pg 702
Burst Video/Film Inc, pg 713
Cox Media, pg 732
Guerrilla Productions LLC, pg 774
On-Line Productions, pg 845

HAWAII

Hyperspective Studios Inc, pg 783

IDAHO

Brad Shaw Productions Inc, pg 885
Wide Eye Productions, pg 938

ILLINOIS

ABSA Films, pg 672
Accenture, pg 672
Airways Digital Media, pg 679
Beatty TeleVisual Productions, pg 703
CCH Inc, A Wolters Kluwer business, pg 718
CCore Media Inc, pg 718
Film Police, pg 760
IV Media Resources, pg 792
Manning Productions, pg 816
Mimi Productions, pg 828
Pepper Group, pg 854
PSAV® Presentation Services (Hotel Services Division), pg 866
Richter Studios, pg 875
SCI Television & Creative Media LLC, pg 882
Southern Illinois University, pg 895
Video I-D Teleproductions Inc, pg 928
Video Impressions, pg 928

INDIANA

A-V-A Video Productions, pg 671
Advanced Media Integration, pg 677
Road Pictures, pg 876

IOWA

Educational Technology & Media Services, pg 751

KENTUCKY

Hammond Communications Group Inc, pg 775
Idle Minds Productions Inc, pg 784
The Media Collaboratory, pg 821

LOUISIANA

Moxie Media, pg 832

MAINE

WGME-TV, pg 936

MARYLAND

Absolute Hollywood, pg 672
CAS Video Productions, pg 717
CPR MultiMedia Solutions, pg 732
dbF a Media Company, pg 739
DSR Computer Technology Specialists Inc, pg 747

The Image Generators, pg 785
Kramer Communications Video Production, pg 801
Mobile-Video Productions Inc, pg 828

MASSACHUSETTS

Award Productions Inc, pg 699
Enterprise Media LLC, pg 754
Merrimack Films, pg 824
Monadnock Media Inc, pg 829
Northern Light Productions (NLP), pg 842
Penfield Productions Ltd, pg 853
TVN-The Video Network, pg 919

MICHIGAN

Digi Sign Design LLC, pg 741
K&R All Media Productions LLC, pg 796
K&R's Recording Studios Inc, pg 796

MINNESOTA

House of Cinemagraphics, pg 782
MastCom, pg 819
Service Quality Institute, pg 884
Vaddio, pg 924
Worthwhile Films, pg 941

MISSOURI

Audio-VideoGraphics Inc, pg 694
Hardcastle Films & Video, pg 776

MONTANA

ooLite Media LLC, pg 846

NEBRASKA

Rainbow Video Productions Inc, pg 869

NEVADA

Aardvark Video & Media Productions, pg 671
DVDs4Less, pg 748
Encore Event Technologies LLC, pg 754
JCS Video Productions, pg 793

NEW HAMPSHIRE

Apertura, pg 686
Channell One Video, pg 720
Chip Taylor Communications LLC, pg 907
The Troupe, pg 918

NEW JERSEY

Allegro Productions Inc, pg 680
Broadcast Center Studios, pg 710
Comex Systems Inc, pg 728
Laurel Video Productions, pg 804
MiB MediaWorks, pg 825
Optisonics Productions, pg 847
Suede Interactive, pg 903
Telequest Inc, pg 910
VCSvideo, pg 925

NEW MEXICO

The Phoenix Learning Group Inc, pg 855
Production Outfitters, pg 864

NEW YORK

Ace Video, pg 674
Associated Press Television News, pg 691
aurora productions, pg 696

Blue Barn Pictures Inc, pg 707
Brian Film Productions LLC, pg 710
Clarity Media Group, pg 725
Downtown Community Television Center (DCTV), pg 746
Films Media Group, pg 760
Golden Lamb Productions, pg 772
Hello World Communications, pg 778
Ketchum Inc, pg 798
Mood Creations Ltd, pg 829
Jack Morton Worldwide, pg 830
MRY, pg 832
Northeast Video Productions Inc, pg 842
The Palmer Group, pg 850
PrimaLux Video Inc, pg 862
PrimeLight Productions Inc, pg 862
Richter Productions Inc, pg 875
Suggs Media Productions Inc, pg 903
Synaptic Digital, pg 905
Third World Newsreel/Camera News Inc, pg 912
VIEW Inc (Video International Entertainment World Inc), pg 930
Alan Weiss Productions, pg 935
WNET/New York Public Media, pg 940

NORTH CAROLINA

Pat Appleson Studios Inc, pg 687
The Communications Group Inc, pg 729
Digital Rain LLC, pg 742
Horizon Video Productions Inc, pg 781
Kino Mountain Productions LLC, pg 799
Moving Pictures, pg 832
Videowerks, pg 930

OHIO

Advent Media Inc, pg 677
Russ Beckner Pictures, pg 703
Curtis Inc, pg 736
Image Video Teleproductions Inc, pg 785
Lyon Video Inc, pg 813
R&B Communications Inc, pg 870
Take 1 Media Services, pg 906
Treehaus Communications Inc, pg 917
Vista Color Imaging Inc, pg 931

OKLAHOMA

Academic Media & Digital Services, pg 672
Institute for Teaching & Learning Excellence (ITLE), pg 788

OREGON

Ideascape Inc, pg 784
InterVision Media, pg 791
KTVA Productions, pg 802
Odyssey Productions Inc, pg 844
Production West, pg 864

PENNSYLVANIA

Audio Visual Communications Inc, pg 694
Beholder Productions Inc, pg 703
CCI Communications Inc, pg 718
FMP Media Solutions Inc, pg 763
Innovision Media Group, pg 788
JPL, pg 795
Muderick Media, pg 833
Visual Sound Inc, pg 931

RHODE ISLAND

Sound-FX-Design, pg 894

SOUTH CAROLINA

Encore Video Productions, pg 754
Go To Team, pg 772
Venture Media, pg 925

TENNESSEE

Continental Film, pg 731
Memphis Communications Corp, pg 823
Paradigm Marketing & Creative, pg 851
Running Pony Productions LLC, pg 878
Scripps Networks, pg 882
Russ Sturgeon Productions/RSVP, pg 903

TEXAS

AMS Pictures, pg 684
Castleview Productions, pg 717
Cerutti Productions Inc, pg 720
CEV Multimedia Ltd, pg 720
Countdown Productions Inc, pg 732
The Editing Co, pg 750
Epic Software Group Inc, pg 755
Horizon Film + Video Productions, pg 781
Mediaforce Productions, pg 822
Earl Miller Productions Inc, pg 827
Omega Productions, pg 845
Richie Media Productions LLC, pg 875
Romar Learning Solutions LLC, pg 877
South Coast Film & Video, pg 895
Stage Directions, pg 898

VERMONT

University of Vermont, Instructional Television Dept, pg 923

VIRGINIA

Advance Concepts Inc, pg 677
Altruist Media LLC, pg 682
BES Studios, pg 704
CVW Event Productions, pg 736
DXC Technology Co, pg 748
Limelight Communications Inc, pg 808
Metro Productions, pg 824
Rocktown Media, pg 876
Video Solutions, pg 928
WETA Production Center, pg 936

WASHINGTON

Bennett-Watt HD Productions Inc, pg 703
Hamilton Studio, pg 775
North-by-Northwest - A Digital Studio, pg 842
Sparkworks Media, pg 896
Victory Studios, pg 927

WEST VIRGINIA

Blackwater Video Productions, pg 707

WISCONSIN

AVS Group, pg 699
5th Floor Recording Co, pg 760
Meridian Studios, pg 824
Mirror 34 Productions, pg 828
USAV Group Inc, pg 923
Watts Communications Inc, pg 934
Wisconsin Public Television, pg 940

PROGRAMMING — VIDEO

Government Program Producers (continued)

WYOMING

Bridger Productions Inc, pg 710

ALBERTA

Black Media Works, pg 706
Global TV, pg 771

BRITISH COLUMBIA

Inspired Image Picture Co (IIPC), pg 788
Triad Communications Ltd, pg 918

MANITOBA

Spectra Video Productions Ltd, pg 897

NEWFOUNDLAND AND LABRADOR

Vidcraft Productions Ltd, pg 927

NORTHWEST TERRITORIES

Yellowknife Films Inc, pg 944

ONTARIO

GAPC (General Assembly Production Centre), pg 768
Image Video Services & Productions, pg 785
RB Productions, pg 870
Video Excellence Productions, pg 927

QUEBEC

Kerrigan Productions Inc, pg 798

Government Program Rentals

MASSACHUSETTS

Enterprise Media LLC, pg 754
Merrimack Films, pg 824

MICHIGAN

Digi Sign Design LLC, pg 741

MINNESOTA

Service Quality Institute, pg 884

MISSOURI

University of Missouri-Columbia, pg 923

NEW YORK

Downtown Community Television Center (DCTV), pg 746
Films Media Group, pg 760
VIEW Inc (Video International Entertainment World Inc), pg 930

VERMONT

University of Vermont, Instructional Television Dept, pg 923

ONTARIO

Kineticvideo.com, pg 799

Industrial Program Distributors

ARIZONA

CyberIconics International, pg 736
Video Learning Library, pg 928

ARKANSAS

Mullikin Agency, pg 833

CALIFORNIA

Academy Savant, pg 672
Crystal Pyramid Productions™, pg 735
Deja View Video, pg 740
Discovery Education - Los Angeles, pg 743
411 Video Information, pg 764
Increase Video/Silver Mine Video, pg 786
New & Unique Videos™, pg 839
Pyramid Media, pg 867
The Wine Appreciation Guild Ltd, pg 939

FLORIDA

Accord Productions, pg 673
Video Resources Software, pg 928

GEORGIA

Convergent Media Systems, pg 731

ILLINOIS

ABSA Films, pg 672
CCore Media Inc, pg 718
National Safety Council (NSC), pg 836
RADMAR Inc, pg 869

IOWA

Kirkwood Community College, pg 799

KENTUCKY

WaxWorks VideoWorks, pg 934

MARYLAND

Sign Media Inc, pg 887
Total AV Systems, pg 916

MASSACHUSETTS

Penfield Productions Ltd, pg 853

MICHIGAN

Digi Sign Design LLC, pg 741
The Program Source International, pg 865
Society of Manufacturing Engineers (SME), pg 891
VMS Inc, pg 932

NEBRASKA

B & B Video Productions Inc, pg 700

NEVADA

DVDs4Less, pg 748

NEW HAMPSHIRE

Channell One Video, pg 720
Frey Scientific, pg 766
Chip Taylor Communications LLC, pg 907

NEW JERSEY

Allegro Productions Inc, pg 680
MiB MediaWorks, pg 825

NEW MEXICO

The Phoenix Learning Group Inc, pg 855

NEW YORK

Broadstreet Productions LLC, pg 711
Fanlight Productions, pg 759
Films Media Group, pg 760
Guidance Associates Inc Center for Humanities, pg 774
HB-Content, pg 777
Monad Trainer's Aide Inc, pg 829
Richter Productions Inc, pg 875
Synaptic Digital, pg 905
VIEW Inc (Video International Entertainment World Inc), pg 930

NORTH CAROLINA

The International Society of Automation (ISA), pg 790

NORTH DAKOTA

UND Television Center, pg 921

OHIO

Curtis Inc, pg 736

OREGON

InterVision Media, pg 791

PENNSYLVANIA

Bergwall Productions Inc, pg 704
FMP Media Solutions Inc, pg 763

TENNESSEE

Zion Music Group, pg 945

TEXAS

CEV Multimedia Ltd, pg 720
Dykeman Associates Inc, pg 748
Emergency Film Group, pg 753
PetroSkills | RDC Solutions, pg 855
University of Texas at Austin - Petroleum Extension Service, pg 923

VERMONT

University of Vermont, Instructional Television Dept, pg 923
Wilson McLeran Inc, pg 939

VIRGINIA

CACI Integrated Communications, pg 713
Coastal Training Technologies Corp, pg 727
WETA Production Center, pg 936

WASHINGTON

Bennett-Watt HD Productions Inc, pg 703

ONTARIO

Canadian Learning Co Inc, pg 715
Kineticvideo.com, pg 799

QUEBEC

Les Productions Via Le Monde (Daniel Bertolino) Inc, pg 864

Industrial Program Producers

ALABAMA

Leo Ticheli Productions, pg 913

ALASKA

Alaska Video Postcards Inc, pg 679
Aurora Films, pg 696

ARIZONA

Aardvark Productions LLC, pg 671
Candee Productions Inc, pg 716
CyberIconics International, pg 736
Direct Current Video Productions, pg 743
Film Creations Ltd, pg 760
Fox 10 Productions (KSAZ-TV), pg 765
Merestone, pg 823
On-Site Video, pg 846

ARKANSAS

Live'N'Loud, pg 810
Mullikin Agency, pg 833
White Diamond Productions LLC, pg 937

CALIFORNIA

A Go Go Films, pg 671
Academy Savant, pg 672
Access Video in Berkeley, pg 673
Action Video, pg 675
Artichoke Productions, pg 690
Big Door, pg 705
Cavalcade Productions Inc, pg 717
Steve Chandler, pg 720
Chick Russell Communications, pg 721
Classic Images Stock Footage LLC, pg 726
Coastline Productions, pg 727
Concrete Images, pg 730
Creative Technology, pg 733
Crystal Pyramid Productions™, pg 735
Custom Video Productions Inc, pg 736
Davidson Productions, pg 738
Deja View Video, pg 740
Design Media, pg 741
digital OutPost, pg 742
Direct Images Interactive Inc, pg 743
Discovery Education - Los Angeles, pg 743
Dolphin MultiMedia Inc, pg 745
Durrin Productions Inc, pg 748
First Camera, pg 761
Goal Productions, pg 772
Havas Edge, pg 777
Image Integration, pg 785
imageReal Pictures LLC, pg 785
Imageworks, pg 785
Increase Video/Silver Mine Video, pg 786
ITV Productions, pg 792
Kavich Reynolds Productions Inc, pg 797
Main Street Media Inc, pg 815
Maximus Media Inc, pg 820
McCune Audio-Video-Lighting, pg 821
Media Magic, pg 822
The Media Staff Inc, pg 822
New & Unique Videos™, pg 839
Nineteen87, pg 841
Nolte Media, pg 841
On-Trax Inc, pg 846

PROGRAMMING — VIDEO

Industrial Program Producers (continued)

NEW YORK (continued)

Cohn Creative Group LLC, pg 727
De Nonno Productions Inc (DPI), pg 739
Fanlight Productions, pg 759
Films Media Group, pg 760
Florentine Films, pg 762
Golden Lamb Productions, pg 772
Guidance Associates Inc Center for Humanities, pg 774
Havas Creative, pg 776
HB-Content, pg 777
Hello World Communications, pg 778
The Independent Production Fund, pg 786
Ketchum Inc, pg 798
Kinetic Arts, pg 799
L A Bruell Inc, pg 802
Long Island Video Enterprises Live Inc, pg 811
Mark X Productions Inc, pg 817
Mood Creations Ltd, pg 829
Jack Morton Worldwide, pg 830
MRM//McCANN, pg 832
MRY, pg 832
News Broadcast Network Inc, pg 840
Northeast Video Productions Inc, pg 842
The Palmer Group, pg 850
Pat Kogan Productions Inc, pg 852
Peckham Productions Inc, pg 852
Polestar Films & Associated Arts Ltd, pg 859
PrimaLux Video Inc, pg 862
PrimeLight Productions Inc, pg 862
Richter Productions Inc, pg 875
Suggs Media Productions Inc, pg 903
Synaptic Digital, pg 905
TeleTime Productions, pg 910
Third World Newsreel/Camera News Inc, pg 912
Videograf, pg 929
VIEW Inc (Video International Entertainment World Inc), pg 930
Alan Weiss Productions, pg 935
WNET/New York Public Media, pg 940

NORTH CAROLINA

All Pro Media Inc, pg 680
Pat Appleson Studios Inc, pg 687
Bill Barnes Video Productions LLC, pg 702
The Communications Group Inc, pg 729
Digital Rain LLC, pg 742
Horizon Video Productions Inc, pg 781
Kino Mountain Productions LLC, pg 799
Moving Pictures, pg 832
Videowerks, pg 930

NORTH DAKOTA

UND Television Center, pg 921

OHIO

Advent Media Inc, pg 677
Russ Beckner Pictures, pg 703
CET, pg 720

Curtis Inc, pg 736
Cuyahoga Community College Student Production Office (SPO), pg 736
Image Video Teleproductions Inc, pg 785
Lyon Video Inc, pg 813
MainSail Production Services Inc, pg 815
R&B Communications Inc, pg 870
Shelburne Films, pg 885
Take 1 Media Services, pg 906
Treehaus Communications Inc, pg 917
Vista Color Imaging Inc, pg 931

OKLAHOMA

Institute for Teaching & Learning Excellence (ITLE), pg 788

OREGON

Ideascape Inc, pg 784
InterVision Media, pg 791
KPDX-TV Production Center, pg 801
KTVA Productions, pg 802
KVAL, pg 802
Odyssey Productions Inc, pg 844
Production West, pg 864
REX, pg 874

PENNSYLVANIA

Audio Visual Communications Inc, pg 694
Beholder Productions Inc, pg 703
Bergwall Productions Inc, pg 704
CCI Communications Inc, pg 718
FMP Media Solutions Inc, pg 763
Innovision Media Group, pg 788
JPL, pg 795
Kensington Falls Animation, pg 797
Main Point Productions, pg 815
Muderick Media, pg 833
Panta Rhei Media Inc, pg 851
Production Masters Inc (PMI), pg 864
Video/Film Associates, pg 928
The Videohouse Inc, pg 929
Visual Sound Inc, pg 931
WHYY Inc, pg 938

RHODE ISLAND

Sound-FX-Design, pg 894

SOUTH CAROLINA

Encore Video Productions, pg 754
Go To Team, pg 772
Stages Video Productions, pg 899
Venture Media, pg 925

TENNESSEE

Continental Film, pg 731
Griffith Productions, pg 774
Memphis Communications Corp, pg 823
Paradigm Marketing & Creative, pg 851
Running Pony Productions LLC, pg 878
Scripps Networks, pg 882

TEXAS

Alpha Video Productions, pg 682
Biway Media, pg 706
Castleview Productions, pg 717
Cerutti Productions Inc, pg 720
CEV Multimedia Ltd, pg 720
Communication Arts Multimedia Inc, pg 728

Countdown Productions Inc, pg 732
Dykeman Associates Inc, pg 748
The Editing Co, pg 750
Emergency Film Group, pg 753
Epic Software Group Inc, pg 755
Horizon Film + Video Productions, pg 781
JSAV, pg 795
Marx InDigital, pg 818
Mediaforce Productions, pg 822
Earl Miller Productions Inc, pg 827
Julye Newlin Productions Inc, pg 840
Omega Productions, pg 845
Omni Intercommunications Inc, pg 845
PetroSkills | RDC Solutions, pg 855
Richie Media Productions LLC, pg 875
Romar Learning Solutions LLC, pg 877
South Coast Film & Video, pg 895
Sportsmen on Film Inc, pg 898
Stage Directions, pg 898
University of Texas at Austin - Petroleum Extension Service, pg 923

UTAH

ImageWorks Communications, pg 785

VERMONT

Marlboro Productions, pg 817
University of Vermont, Instructional Television Dept, pg 923
Wilson McLeran Inc, pg 939

VIRGINIA

Advance Concepts Inc, pg 677
Altruist Media LLC, pg 682
BES Studios, pg 704
Cinebar Productions Inc, pg 723
Coastal Training Technologies Corp, pg 727
CVW Event Productions, pg 736
DXC Technology Co, pg 748
Limelight Communications Inc, pg 808
Metro Productions, pg 824
National Media Services Inc, pg 836
Rocktown Media, pg 876
Video Solutions, pg 928
WETA Production Center, pg 936

WASHINGTON

Adams Creative & Production Services, pg 675
Bennett-Watt HD Productions Inc, pg 703
Hamilton Studio, pg 775
North-by-Northwest - A Digital Studio, pg 842
Sparkworks Media, pg 896
Victory Studios, pg 927
White Rain Films Ltd, pg 937

WEST VIRGINIA

Blackwater Video Productions, pg 707

WISCONSIN

AVS Group, pg 699
5th Floor Recording Co, pg 760
Logan Productions Inc, pg 811
Meridian Studios, pg 824
Midland Video Productions Inc, pg 827
Mirror 34 Productions, pg 828

Rucinski Write!Now LLC, pg 878
University of Wisconsin-Oshkosh Radio-TV-Film Dept, pg 923
USAV Group Inc, pg 923
Watts Communications Inc, pg 934
Wisconsin Public Television, pg 940

WYOMING

Bridger Productions Inc, pg 710

ALBERTA

Black Media Works, pg 706
Global TV, pg 771

BRITISH COLUMBIA

Triad Communications Ltd, pg 918

MANITOBA

Spectra Video Productions Ltd, pg 897

NEWFOUNDLAND AND LABRADOR

Vidcraft Productions Ltd, pg 927

NORTHWEST TERRITORIES

Yellowknife Films Inc, pg 944

ONTARIO

ADS Media, pg 677
DebsVoice, pg 739
GAPC (General Assembly Production Centre), pg 768
Image Video Services & Productions, pg 785
Jams Productions Inc, pg 793
JFB Communications, pg 794
Mediaimage Communications Group, pg 822
RB Productions, pg 870
Silver Creek Media Inc, pg 888
Video Excellence Productions, pg 927

QUEBEC

Group PVP, pg 774
Kerrigan Productions Inc, pg 798
Les Productions Via Le Monde (Daniel Bertolino) Inc, pg 864

SASKATCHEWAN

plan9films, pg 857

Industrial Program Rentals

ARIZONA

Video Learning Library, pg 928

GEORGIA

Convergent Media Systems, pg 731

ILLINOIS

National Safety Council (NSC), pg 836

LOUISIANA

WVLA-TV, pg 942

MICHIGAN

Digi Sign Design LLC, pg 741

MISSOURI

University of Missouri-Columbia, pg 923

PROGRAMMING — VIDEO

Medical Program Producers (continued)

CALIFORNIA (continued)

Discovery Education - Los Angeles, pg 743
Dolphin MultiMedia Inc, pg 745
First Camera, pg 761
Geddes Productions LLC, pg 769
Steven Halpern's Inner Peace Music, pg 775
Havas Edge, pg 777
imageReal Pictures LLC, pg 785
Imageworks, pg 785
Increase Video/Silver Mine Video, pg 786
Institute of Precision Muscle Balancing, pg 788
ITV Productions, pg 792
Joyce Media Inc, pg 795
Kavich Reynolds Productions Inc, pg 797
KPBS Public Broadcasting, pg 801
Main Street Media Inc, pg 815
Maximus Media Inc, pg 820
McCune Audio-Video-Lighting, pg 821
Medcom Inc, pg 821
Media Magic, pg 822
The Media Staff Inc, pg 822
New & Unique Videos™, pg 839
On-Trax Inc, pg 846
Opticomm-EMCORE, pg 847
PM Productions, pg 858
Point of View Productions, pg 858
Pyramid Media, pg 867
QRS Software Services, pg 867
Regent Press Publishers & Printers, pg 873
Dick Reizner Film & Video, pg 873
RetinaVision Productions, pg 874
Glenn Roland Films, pg 876
Screen Door Entertainment Inc, pg 882
SNAP, pg 891
Staylor-Made Communications Inc, pg 900
Still N' Motion, pg 901
Tam Communications Inc, pg 906
Timestream Video, pg 914
TMW Media Group, pg 915
Total Creative, pg 916
Twin Peaks Creative, pg 920
Vineyard Video & Photography, pg 930
Visions Plus, pg 931
Wavemaker Media Design, pg 934
Webster Communications, pg 935
West Coast Projections Inc, pg 935
Zamacona Productions, pg 945

COLORADO

Apogee Communications Group, pg 687
Centre Communications Inc, pg 720
Daylight Productions & Rentals, pg 739
Flashback Media Productions, pg 762
InJoy Birth & Parenting Education, pg 788
Rocky Mountain Audio/Video Productions Inc, pg 876
Transtar Entertainment Co Inc, pg 917

CONNECTICUT

Cine-Med Inc, pg 723
Essex Television Group Inc, pg 755
The Gary-Paul Agency, pg 768
Geomatrix Productions, pg 770
Ironik Design & Post, pg 791
Moving Pictures, pg 832
New London Media, pg 839
P&P Studios Inc, pg 851
UConn Health Multimedia Services, pg 920
Video Production Associates Inc, pg 928

DISTRICT OF COLUMBIA

Hillmann & Carr Inc, pg 780
O'Keefe Communications Inc, pg 844
Yellow Cat Productions Inc, pg 944

FLORIDA

Accord Productions, pg 673
Applebox Studio, pg 687
Bisk Education, pg 706
Blackburst Entertainment LLC, pg 706
Civins Productions Inc, pg 725
CopShopMiami.com, pg 731
Courter Films LLC, pg 732
DME Studios, pg 744
Easy Edit Video Inc, pg 750
Jordan Klein Film & Video (JKFV), pg 795
National Teleproductions Inc, pg 837
Paradise Video & Film, pg 851
Sound & Vision Communications Inc, pg 893
Sunfire Communications Inc, pg 904
Sunrise Studios, pg 904
Tight Line Productions, pg 914
Tricycle Studios, pg 918
Video Resources Software, pg 928

GEORGIA

ADAM Inc, pg 675
Beachwood Productions, pg 702
Burst Video/Film Inc, pg 713
Cox Media, pg 732
GP Studios, pg 773
Guerrilla Productions LLC, pg 774
On-Line Productions, pg 845

HAWAII

Hyperspective Studios Inc, pg 783

IDAHO

Brad Shaw Productions Inc, pg 885
Wide Eye Productions, pg 938

ILLINOIS

ABSA Films, pg 672
Airways Digital Media, pg 679
American Hospital Association, pg 683
CCore Media Inc, pg 718
The Chicago Production Center, pg 721
Explore, pg 757
Film Police, pg 760
IV Media Resources, pg 792
Major Media Productions Inc, pg 815
Manning Productions, pg 816
The Market Place, pg 817
Mimi Productions, pg 828
Multimedia Marketing Group, pg 833

Rob Orr Productions Ltd, pg 848
Pepper Group, pg 854
SCI Television & Creative Media LLC, pg 882
20/20 Communications Inc, pg 920
Video I-D Teleproductions Inc, pg 928
Video Impressions, pg 928
WEEK TV, pg 935
Winter Productions, pg 939

INDIANA

A-V-A Video Productions, pg 671
Advanced Media Integration, pg 677
Bright Ideas Creative Services, pg 710
PentaVision Communications Inc, pg 854
Purdue University Digital Education, pg 866
Road Pictures, pg 876

KANSAS

KAKE-TV, pg 796

KENTUCKY

Idle Minds Productions Inc, pg 784
The Media Collaboratory, pg 821

LOUISIANA

Digital FX Inc, pg 742
Louisiana State University Division of Strategic Communications, pg 811
Moxie Media, pg 832

MAINE

WGME-TV, pg 936

MARYLAND

Adventure Productions LLC, pg 678
CAS Video Productions, pg 717
Richard Chisolm Cinematography, pg 722
dbF a Media Company, pg 739
DSR Computer Technology Specialists Inc, pg 747
The Image Generators, pg 785
Kramer Communications Video Production, pg 801
Mobile-Video Productions Inc, pg 828

MASSACHUSETTS

Award Productions Inc, pg 699
Green Mountain Post Films (GMP), pg 774
Heliotrope Studios, pg 778
Northern Light Productions (NLP), pg 842
Pauline Books & Media, pg 852
Penfield Productions Ltd, pg 853
PixMix Video Services, pg 857
Preston Productions Inc, pg 861
TVN-The Video Network, pg 919
VideoLink Inc, an AVI-SPL company, pg 925
WVP Boston, pg 942

MICHIGAN

Digi Sign Design LLC, pg 741
K&R All Media Productions LLC, pg 796
K&R's Recording Studios Inc, pg 796
MSU Technologies, pg 833
Phoenix Society for Burn Survivors Inc, pg 856

MINNESOTA

House of Cinemagraphics, pg 782
MastCom, pg 819
Media Loft Inc, pg 822
Service Quality Institute, pg 884
Vaddio, pg 924
Worthwhile Films, pg 941

MISSOURI

Audio-VideoGraphics Inc, pg 694
Communitronics Corp, pg 729
Marsh Media, pg 817
Mosby Inc, pg 831
University of Missouri-Kansas City School of Dentistry, pg 923

NEBRASKA

B & B Video Productions Inc, pg 700
Rainbow Video Productions Inc, pg 869

NEVADA

Aardvark Video & Media Productions, pg 671
DVDs4Less, pg 748
Encore Event Technologies LLC, pg 754
JCS Video Productions, pg 793
Ron Roy Productions/Moodtapes, pg 878
Tetrahedron LLC, pg 911

NEW HAMPSHIRE

Apertura, pg 686
Chip Taylor Communications LLC, pg 907

NEW JERSEY

Allegro Productions Inc, pg 680
Broadcast Center Studios, pg 710
CFP Video Productions Inc, pg 720
Euro-Pacific Film & Video Productions Inc, pg 756
Laurel Video Productions, pg 804
MediaNow Inc, pg 822
Megavideo LLC, pg 823
MiB MediaWorks, pg 825
Midnight Media Group Inc, pg 827
Optisonics Productions, pg 847
Projects in Knowledge Inc, pg 865
Telequest Inc, pg 910
TimeSteps Productions Inc, pg 914
VCSvideo, pg 925

NEW MEXICO

The Phoenix Learning Group Inc, pg 855
Production Outfitters, pg 864
Rainbow International Inc, pg 869

NEW YORK

Ace Video, pg 674
Associated Press Television News, pg 691
aurora productions, pg 696
BC Studio, pg 702
Brian Film Productions LLC, pg 710
Broadstreet Productions LLC, pg 711
Clarity Media Group, pg 725
Cohn Creative Group LLC, pg 727
Fanlight Productions, pg 759
Films Media Group, pg 760
Guidance Associates Inc Center for Humanities, pg 774
Guilford Publications, pg 774

HB-Content, pg 777
Hello World Communications, pg 778
Image Zone Inc, pg 785
The Independent Production Fund, pg 786
Ketchum Inc, pg 798
L A Bruell Inc, pg 802
Long Island Video Enterprises Live Inc, pg 811
Mood Creations Ltd, pg 829
MRY, pg 832
News Broadcast Network Inc, pg 840
Northeast Video Productions Inc, pg 842
The Palmer Group, pg 850
Pat Kogan Productions Inc, pg 852
Peckham Productions Inc, pg 852
PrimaLux Video Inc, pg 862
PrimeLight Productions Inc, pg 862
Richter Productions Inc, pg 875
Suggs Media Productions Inc, pg 903
Synaptic Digital, pg 905
TeleTime Productions, pg 910
Videograf, pg 929
VIEW Inc (Video International Entertainment World Inc), pg 930
Alan Weiss Productions, pg 935
Willow Mixed Media Inc, pg 939
WNET/New York Public Media, pg 940

NORTH CAROLINA

Pat Appleson Studios Inc, pg 687
Bill Barnes Video Productions LLC, pg 702
The Communications Group Inc, pg 729
Digital Rain LLC, pg 742
Horizon Video Productions Inc, pg 781
Kino Mountain Productions LLC, pg 799
Moving Pictures, pg 832
Sinclair Institute, pg 889
Videowerks, pg 930

OHIO

CET, pg 720
Curtis Inc, pg 736
Image Video Teleproductions Inc, pg 785
Lyon Video Inc, pg 813
MainSail Production Services Inc, pg 815
R&B Communications Inc, pg 870
Take 1 Media Services, pg 906
Vista Color Imaging Inc, pg 931

OKLAHOMA

Academic Media & Digital Services, pg 672
CSI/Orion, pg 735

OREGON

Ideascape Inc, pg 784
InterVision Media, pg 791
Production West, pg 864

PENNSYLVANIA

Audio Visual Communications Inc, pg 694
Beholder Productions Inc, pg 703
CCI Communications Inc, pg 718
FMP Media Solutions Inc, pg 763
Innovision Media Group, pg 788
JPL, pg 795
Kensington Falls Animation, pg 797

Lippincott Williams & Wilkins, pg 809
Muderick Media, pg 833
Panta Rhei Media Inc, pg 851
Production Masters Inc (PMI), pg 864
S I Video Sales Group, pg 879
Video/Film Associates, pg 928
The Videohouse Inc, pg 929
Videosmith Inc, pg 930
WHYY Inc, pg 938

RHODE ISLAND

Sound-FX-Design, pg 894

SOUTH CAROLINA

Encore Video Productions, pg 754
Go To Team, pg 772
Venture Media, pg 925

TENNESSEE

Continental Film, pg 731
Griffith Productions, pg 774
Memphis Communications Corp, pg 823
Paradigm Marketing & Creative, pg 851
Running Pony Productions LLC, pg 878
Scripps Networks, pg 882
Russ Sturgeon Productions/RSVP, pg 903

TEXAS

Alpha Video Productions, pg 682
Castleview Productions, pg 717
Cerutti Productions Inc, pg 720
CEV Multimedia Ltd, pg 720
Communication Arts Multimedia Inc, pg 728
The Editing Co, pg 750
Emergency Film Group, pg 753
Epic Software Group Inc, pg 755
Horizon Film + Video Productions, pg 781
Mediaforce Productions, pg 822
Earl Miller Productions Inc, pg 827
Julye Newlin Productions Inc, pg 840
Omega Productions, pg 845
Omni Intercommunications Inc, pg 845
Romar Learning Solutions LLC, pg 877
South Coast Film & Video, pg 895
Sportsmen on Film Inc, pg 898
Stage Directions, pg 898
Texas Heart Institute Visual Communication Services, pg 911

VERMONT

Marlboro Productions, pg 817
University of Vermont, Instructional Television Dept, pg 923

VIRGINIA

Advance Concepts Inc, pg 677
Alexander Street, a ProQuest Company, pg 679
Altruist Media LLC, pg 682
BES Studios, pg 704
Coastal Training Technologies Corp, pg 727
CVW Event Productions, pg 736
Family Health Media, pg 758
Limelight Communications Inc, pg 808
Metro Productions, pg 824
Rocktown Media, pg 876
Video Solutions, pg 928

WASHINGTON

Adams Creative & Production Services, pg 675
Bennett-Watt HD Productions Inc, pg 703
Hamilton Studio, pg 775
Medical Media Systems, pg 823
Medifecta Healthcare Training, pg 823
North-by-Northwest - A Digital Studio, pg 842
Sparkworks Media, pg 896
Victory Studios, pg 927
Washington State University College of Nursing, pg 934

WEST VIRGINIA

Blackwater Video Productions, pg 707

WISCONSIN

5th Floor Recording Co, pg 760
Meridian Studios, pg 824
Midland Video Productions Inc, pg 827
Mirror 34 Productions, pg 828
Rucinski Write!Now LLC, pg 878
USAV Group Inc, pg 923
Video Wisconsin Inc, pg 929
Watts Communications Inc, pg 934
Wisconsin Public Television, pg 940

WYOMING

Bridger Productions Inc, pg 710

ALBERTA

Global TV, pg 771

BRITISH COLUMBIA

Thompson Rivers University Marketing & Communications Dept, pg 913
Triad Communications Ltd, pg 918

MANITOBA

Spectra Video Productions Ltd, pg 897

NEWFOUNDLAND AND LABRADOR

Vidcraft Productions Ltd, pg 927

ONTARIO

ADS Media, pg 677
Associated Producers Ltd, pg 691
GAPC (General Assembly Production Centre), pg 768
Image Video Services & Productions, pg 785
JFB Communications, pg 794
Video Excellence Productions, pg 927
YAP Films, pg 943

QUEBEC

Kerrigan Productions Inc, pg 798

Medical Program Rentals

ARIZONA

Video Learning Library, pg 928

CALIFORNIA

Cavalcade Productions Inc, pg 717
Davidson Productions, pg 738

Direct Cinema Ltd Inc, pg 743
Medcom Inc, pg 821
Point of View Productions, pg 858

MICHIGAN

Digi Sign Design LLC, pg 741

MINNESOTA

Service Quality Institute, pg 884

MISSOURI

University of Missouri-Columbia, pg 923
University of Missouri-Kansas City School of Dentistry, pg 923

NEW JERSEY

Euro-Pacific Film & Video Productions Inc, pg 756

NEW YORK

BC Studio, pg 702
Fanlight Productions, pg 759
Films Media Group, pg 760
Richter Productions Inc, pg 875

NORTH CAROLINA

Sinclair Institute, pg 889

PENNSYLVANIA

Bullfrog Films Inc, pg 712

VERMONT

University of Vermont, Instructional Television Dept, pg 923

VIRGINIA

Alexander Street, a ProQuest Company, pg 679
Filmakers Library, pg 760

ONTARIO

Kineticvideo.com, pg 799

Multimedia, CD-ROM & DVD Interactive Program Distributors

ARIZONA

Valley of the Sun Publishing Co, pg 924

ARKANSAS

Master Books®, pg 819

CALIFORNIA

Ariztical Entertainment Inc, pg 689
Astronomical Society of the Pacific, pg 691
California Language Laboratories, pg 714
Christian Media Network, pg 722
Crystal Pyramid Productions™, pg 735
Davies Publishing Inc, pg 738
Ferrari Productions, pg 759
411 Video Information, pg 764
MarVista Entertainment Inc, pg 818
Music World/Vocal Power School, pg 834
QRS Software Services, pg 867
Sea Studios Foundation, pg 883
TiVo Corp, pg 914
Videobotics, pg 929

PROGRAMMING — VIDEO

Multimedia, CD-ROM & DVD Interactive Program Distributors (continued)

COLORADO

American Educational Products LLC, pg 683
Crystal Productions, pg 735

CONNECTICUT

Cine-Med Inc, pg 723
Really Good Stuff, pg 871

FLORIDA

Video Resources Software, pg 928

GEORGIA

Convergent Media Systems, pg 731
School Media Associates LLC, pg 882

ILLINOIS

Britannica Digital Learning, pg 710
CCore Media Inc, pg 718
National Safety Council (NSC), pg 836

INDIANA

Educational Video Group Inc, pg 751

IOWA

Prositions Inc, pg 865
Right Stuf Inc, pg 875

KENTUCKY

WaxWorks VideoWorks, pg 934

LOUISIANA

Great Chefs/Leisure Jazz Video, pg 773
Leisure Video, pg 806

MASSACHUSETTS

Cheng & Tsui Co, pg 721
Documentary Educational Resources Inc, pg 744
Penfield Productions Ltd, pg 853

MICHIGAN

Digi Sign Design LLC, pg 741
MSU Technologies, pg 833
Prakken Publications Inc, pg 861
VMS Inc, pg 932

MINNESOTA

BeyerSound & Essay Audio, pg 705
Harris Communications Inc, pg 776
JIST Publishing, pg 794

NEBRASKA

B & B Video Productions Inc, pg 700

NEW HAMPSHIRE

French American Music Enterprises, pg 765
Frey Scientific, pg 766
Chip Taylor Communications LLC, pg 907

NEW JERSEY

Allegro Productions Inc, pg 680
Comex Systems Inc, pg 728
MiB MediaWorks, pg 825

NEW MEXICO

The Phoenix Learning Group Inc, pg 855

NEW YORK

Broadstreet Productions LLC, pg 711
Brooklyn Botanic Garden, pg 711
The Bureau for At-Risk Youth, pg 712
FACE Foundation, pg 758
Films Media Group, pg 760
Guidance Associates Inc Center for Humanities, pg 774
HB-Content, pg 777
Human Relations Media, pg 782
IAI Records & Video, pg 783
Magnetic Music Publishing Co, pg 814
Meridian Education Corp, pg 823
Monad Trainer's Aide Inc, pg 829
Shopware, pg 886
SISU Home Entertainment Inc, pg 889
Videofashion Network, pg 929
Women Make Movies Inc, pg 941

OHIO

Treehaus Communications Inc, pg 917

OREGON

InterVision Media, pg 791

PENNSYLVANIA

Anchor Distributors, pg 685
Bullfrog Films Inc, pg 712
Discovery Education - South Burlington, pg 743
FMP Media Solutions Inc, pg 763
Library Video Company, pg 807
MVD Entertainment Group, pg 835
S I Video Sales Group, pg 879
Schlessinger Media, pg 881

SOUTH CAROLINA

American Production Services LLC, pg 684

TENNESSEE

Center for Southern Folklore Inc, pg 719
National School Products, pg 836
Spring Arbor Distributors Inc, pg 898

TEXAS

CEV Multimedia Ltd, pg 720

UTAH

Strata™, pg 901

VERMONT

Multicultural Media Inc, pg 833
University of Vermont, Instructional Television Dept, pg 923

VIRGINIA

National Audiovisual Center (NAC), pg 836

WASHINGTON

Bennett-Watt HD Productions Inc, pg 703
Intermedia Inc, pg 789

ALBERTA

Global TV, pg 771

ONTARIO

Canadian Learning Co Inc, pg 715
McIntyre Media Inc, pg 821
Universal Studios Canada Inc, pg 922

Multimedia, CD-ROM & DVD Interactive Program Producers

ALASKA

Alaska Media Pros LLC, pg 679
Imig Audio/Video Inc, pg 786

ARIZONA

Aardvark Productions LLC, pg 671
Film Creations Ltd, pg 760
Forensic Video Deposition Service, pg 764
Merestone, pg 823
Valley of the Sun Publishing Co, pg 924

ARKANSAS

Live'N'Loud, pg 810

CALIFORNIA

Access Video in Berkeley, pg 673
Action Video, pg 675
Artichoke Productions, pg 690
Astronomical Society of the Pacific, pg 691
Big Door, pg 705
California Language Laboratories, pg 714
Christian Media Network, pg 722
Classic Images Stock Footage LLC, pg 726
Coastline Productions, pg 727
Concrete Images, pg 730
Creative Technology, pg 733
Crystal Pyramid Productions™, pg 735
Custom Video Productions Inc, pg 736
Design Media, pg 741
digital OutPost, pg 742
Direct Images Interactive Inc, pg 743
Dolphin MultiMedia Inc, pg 745
First Camera, pg 761
Gateways Books & Tapes, pg 768
Havas Edge, pg 777
Imageworks, pg 785
ITV Productions, pg 792
Kavich Reynolds Productions Inc, pg 797
Lieberman Productions, pg 807
Lumeni Productions Inc, pg 812

Main Street Media Inc, pg 815
Maximus Media Inc, pg 820
McCune Audio-Video-Lighting, pg 821
Media Magic, pg 822
Music World/Vocal Power School, pg 834
Nolte Media, pg 841
Prime Cut Productions, pg 862
PSI Inc, pg 866
QRS Software Services, pg 867
RetinaVision Productions, pg 874
Glenn Roland Films, pg 876
Sea Studios Foundation, pg 883
SNAP, pg 891
Staylor-Made Communications Inc, pg 900
Still N' Motion, pg 901
Tam Communications Inc, pg 906
Total Creative, pg 916
Towards 2000 Inc, pg 916
Video Movie Magic, pg 928
Vineyard Video & Photography, pg 930
Visions Plus, pg 931
ViVi Co, pg 932
Wavemaker Media Design, pg 934
Webster Communications, pg 935
West Coast Projections Inc, pg 935
The Wine Appreciation Guild Ltd, pg 939
WMS Media Inc, pg 940
Zamacona Productions, pg 945

COLORADO

American Educational Products LLC, pg 683
Daylight Productions & Rentals, pg 739
Flashback Media Productions, pg 762

CONNECTICUT

ACM Productions Ltd, pg 674
Cine-Med Inc, pg 723
Ironik Design & Post, pg 791
Moving Pictures, pg 832
New London Media, pg 839
VRSim Inc, pg 933

DISTRICT OF COLUMBIA

Hillmann & Carr Inc, pg 780
O'Keefe Communications Inc, pg 844
USCCB Publishing, pg 923

FLORIDA

Accord Productions, pg 673
Applebox Studio, pg 687
Astoria Communications Inc, pg 691
Blackburst Entertainment LLC, pg 706
Civins Productions Inc, pg 725
Communications Concepts Inc (CCI), pg 729
Courter Films LLC, pg 732
DME Studios, pg 744
ITC Learning LLC, pg 791
Jordan Klein Film & Video (JKFV), pg 795
Skystorm Productions, pg 890
Sound & Vision Communications Inc, pg 893
Sunfire Communications Inc, pg 904
Sunrise Studios, pg 904
Teach America Corp, pg 908
Tricycle Studios, pg 918
Video Resources Software, pg 928
Video Techniques Inc, pg 928

GEORGIA

ADAM Inc, pg 675
Beachwood Productions, pg 702
Burst Video/Film Inc, pg 713
ECG Productions, pg 750
Guerrilla Productions LLC, pg 774
Myriad Productions, pg 835
On-Line Productions, pg 845

HAWAII

Hyperspective Studios Inc, pg 783
1013 Integrated, pg 911

IDAHO

Brad Shaw Productions Inc, pg 885
Wide Eye Productions, pg 938

ILLINOIS

Airways Digital Media, pg 679
Atomic Imaging Inc/Golan Studios,
    pg 692
Britannica Digital Learning, pg 710
CCore Media Inc, pg 718
Cresta Creative, pg 734
Explore, pg 757
Extraordinary Demos/Videos,
    pg 757
IV Media Resources, pg 792
Major Media Productions Inc,
    pg 815
Manning Productions, pg 816
Mightybytes Inc, pg 827
Multimedia Marketing Group,
    pg 833
National Safety Council (NSC),
    pg 836
Jim Passin Productions, pg 852
Pepper Group, pg 854
PSAV® Presentation Services
    (Hotel Services Division), pg 866
Richter Studios, pg 875
SCI Television & Creative Media
    LLC, pg 882
Southern Illinois University, pg 895
Sparkfactor, pg 896
20/20 Communications Inc, pg 920
Video I-D Teleproductions Inc,
    pg 928
Video Impressions, pg 928

INDIANA

Advanced Media Integration, pg 677
Bright Ideas Creative Services,
    pg 710
PentaVision Communications Inc,
    pg 854

IOWA

Educational Technology & Media
    Services, pg 751
Prositions Inc, pg 865
Right Stuf Inc, pg 875

KANSAS

KAKE-TV, pg 796

KENTUCKY

Hammond Communications Group
    Inc, pg 775
Donna Lawrence Productions,
    pg 804
NIMCO Inc, pg 841
Prosper Media Group Inc, pg 866

LOUISIANA

Digital FX Inc, pg 742
Leisure Video, pg 806
Louisiana State University Division
    of Strategic Communications,
    pg 811

MARYLAND

Absolute Hollywood, pg 672
CPR MultiMedia Solutions, pg 732
CSPMedia.com, pg 735
dbF a Media Company, pg 739
Kramer Communications Video
    Production, pg 801
Media Dimensions LLC, pg 821
Mobile-Video Productions Inc,
    pg 828

MASSACHUSETTS

Cheng & Tsui Co, pg 721
CommCreative, pg 728
Documentary Educational Resources
    Inc, pg 744
Green Mountain Post Films (GMP),
    pg 774
Monadnock Media Inc, pg 829
Northern Light Productions (NLP),
    pg 842
Penfield Productions Ltd, pg 853
Preston Productions Inc, pg 861
TVN-The Video Network, pg 919
WGBH Production Group, pg 936

MICHIGAN

Digi Sign Design LLC, pg 741
K&R All Media Productions LLC,
    pg 796
K&R's Recording Studios Inc,
    pg 796
TGA Recording Co, pg 911
VMS Inc, pg 932

MINNESOTA

Badiyan Inc, pg 700
BeyerSound & Essay Audio, pg 705
House of Cinemagraphics, pg 782
JIST Publishing, pg 794
Live Spark Inc, pg 810
MastCom, pg 819
Worthwhile Films, pg 941

NEBRASKA

B & B Video Productions Inc,
    pg 700
Rainbow Video Productions Inc,
    pg 869

NEVADA

Aardvark Video & Media
    Productions, pg 671
Encore Event Technologies LLC,
    pg 754
JCS Video Productions, pg 793

NEW HAMPSHIRE

Apertura, pg 686
Chip Taylor Communications LLC,
    pg 907

NEW JERSEY

Allegro Productions Inc, pg 680
Comex Systems Inc, pg 728
Euro-Pacific Film & Video
    Productions Inc, pg 756
Laurel Video Productions, pg 804
MediaNow Inc, pg 822
MiB MediaWorks, pg 825
Midnight Media Group Inc, pg 827

Optisonics Productions, pg 847
Outside The Box Interactive LLC,
    pg 849
Suede Interactive, pg 903
VCSvideo, pg 925
Video Ideas Productions, pg 928

NEW MEXICO

The Phoenix Learning Group Inc,
    pg 855
Production Outfitters, pg 864
Rainbow International Inc, pg 869

NEW YORK

Ace Video, pg 674
Big Fish Production US, pg 705
Blue Barn Pictures Inc, pg 707
Broadstreet Productions LLC,
    pg 711
Brooklyn Botanic Garden, pg 711
Brooklyn Films, pg 711
The Bureau for At-Risk Youth,
    pg 712
Cohn Creative Group LLC, pg 727
Digital Force Ltd, pg 742
Duplication Depot Inc, pg 748
Films Media Group, pg 760
Guidance Associates Inc Center for
    Humanities, pg 774
Havas Creative, pg 776
HB-Content, pg 777
Human Relations Media, pg 782
IAI Records & Video, pg 783
Image Zone Inc, pg 785
The Independent Production Fund,
    pg 786
Ketchum Inc, pg 798
L A Bruell Inc, pg 802
Long Island Video Enterprises Live
    Inc, pg 811
Magnetic Music Publishing Co,
    pg 814
Meridian Education Corp, pg 823
MRY, pg 832
New Horizon Studios, pg 839
Northeast Video Productions Inc,
    pg 842
The Palmer Group, pg 850
PrimaLux Video Inc, pg 862
R/GA, pg 868
Judson Rosebush Co Inc, pg 877
Shopware, pg 886
Suggs Media Productions Inc,
    pg 903
Tiki Recording Studios Inc, pg 914
Videofashion Network, pg 929
Vidicom Inc, pg 930

NORTH CAROLINA

Pat Appleson Studios Inc, pg 687
The Communications Group Inc,
    pg 729
Horizon Video Productions Inc,
    pg 781
Image Associates Inc, pg 784
Moving Pictures, pg 832
NASCAR Productions LLC, pg 835
Videowerks, pg 930

OHIO

Advent Media Inc, pg 677
Cuyahoga Community College
    Student Production Office (SPO),
    pg 736
Lyon Video Inc, pg 813
R&B Communications Inc, pg 870
Take 1 Media Services, pg 906
Treehaus Communications Inc,
    pg 917
Vista Color Imaging Inc, pg 931

OKLAHOMA

BCD Associates Inc, pg 702

OREGON

ERA Learning, pg 755
Ideascape Inc, pg 784
InterVision Media, pg 791
KTVA Productions, pg 802
Odyssey Productions Inc, pg 844
REX, pg 874
Wallace Creative LLC, pg 933

PENNSYLVANIA

Argentine Productions Inc, pg 688
Audio Visual Communications Inc,
    pg 694
Beholder Productions Inc, pg 703
CCI Communications Inc, pg 718
Discovery Education - South
    Burlington, pg 743
FMP Media Solutions Inc, pg 763
Innovision Media Group, pg 788
JPL, pg 795
Kensington Falls Animation, pg 797
Muderick Media, pg 833
Production Masters Inc (PMI),
    pg 864
S I Video Sales Group, pg 879
Scala Inc, pg 881
Visual Sound Inc, pg 931

RHODE ISLAND

Sound-FX-Design, pg 894

SOUTH CAROLINA

American Production Services LLC,
    pg 684

TENNESSEE

Anode Inc, pg 686
Center for Southern Folklore Inc,
    pg 719
Continental Film, pg 731
Griffith Productions, pg 774
Memphis Communications Corp,
    pg 823
Paradigm Marketing & Creative,
    pg 851
Running Pony Productions LLC,
    pg 878
Scripps Networks, pg 882
Spring Arbor Distributors Inc,
    pg 898
Russ Sturgeon Productions/RSVP,
    pg 903

TEXAS

Biway Media, pg 706
Castleview Productions, pg 717
CEV Multimedia Ltd, pg 720
Communication Arts Multimedia
    Inc, pg 728
Dykeman Associates Inc, pg 748
The Editing Co, pg 750
Epic Software Group Inc, pg 755
Horizon Film + Video Productions,
    pg 781
JSAV, pg 795
Mediaforce Productions, pg 822
Julye Newlin Productions Inc,
    pg 840
Omega Productions, pg 845
Omni Intercommunications Inc,
    pg 845
Romar Learning Solutions LLC,
    pg 877
South Coast Film & Video, pg 895

PROGRAMMING — VIDEO

Multimedia, CD-ROM & DVD Interactive Program Producers (continued)

TEXAS (continued)

Stage Directions, pg 898
Texas Heart Institute Visual Communication Services, pg 911

VERMONT

University of Vermont, Instructional Television Dept, pg 923

VIRGINIA

Advance Concepts Inc, pg 677
Altruist Media LLC, pg 682
DXC Technology Co, pg 748
Metro Productions, pg 824
Video Solutions, pg 928

WASHINGTON

Adams Creative & Production Services, pg 675
Bennett-Watt HD Productions Inc, pg 703
Evia, pg 757
Hamilton Studio, pg 775
Intermedia Inc, pg 789
North-by-Northwest - A Digital Studio, pg 842

WISCONSIN

AVS Group, pg 699
5th Floor Recording Co, pg 760
Logan Productions Inc, pg 811
USAV Group Inc, pg 923
Video Wisconsin Inc, pg 929
Watts Communications Inc, pg 934
Wisconsin Public Television, pg 940

WYOMING

Bridger Productions Inc, pg 710

ALBERTA

Black Media Works, pg 706

BRITISH COLUMBIA

Triad Communications Ltd, pg 918

NEWFOUNDLAND AND LABRADOR

Vidcraft Productions Ltd, pg 927

ONTARIO

ADS Media, pg 677
DebsVoice, pg 739
GAPC (General Assembly Production Centre), pg 768
GestureTek, pg 770
Image Video Services & Productions, pg 785
JFB Communications, pg 794
Marblemedia, pg 816
RB Productions, pg 870
Silver Creek Media Inc, pg 888
Video Excellence Productions, pg 927

QUEBEC

Group PVP, pg 774
Kerrigan Productions Inc, pg 798

SASKATCHEWAN

plan9films, pg 857

Multimedia, CD-ROM & DVD Interactive Program Rentals

DELAWARE

Side Door Studio Inc, pg 887

GEORGIA

Convergent Media Systems, pg 731

MASSACHUSETTS

Documentary Educational Resources Inc, pg 744

MICHIGAN

Digi Sign Design LLC, pg 741

NEW YORK

Brooklyn Botanic Garden, pg 711
Films Media Group, pg 760

TENNESSEE

Center for Southern Folklore Inc, pg 719

VERMONT

University of Vermont, Instructional Television Dept, pg 923

WASHINGTON

Intermedia Inc, pg 789

Music Video Distributors

ARIZONA

Drumbeat Indian Arts Inc, pg 747
Video Learning Library, pg 928

CALIFORNIA

Allied Artists International Inc, pg 681
Ark Media Group Ltd, pg 689
Backstage Pass Entertainment Inc, pg 700
Crystal Pyramid Productions™, pg 735
411 Video Information, pg 764
Glenn Photo Supply, pg 771
Glenn Video Vistas Ltd, pg 771
Steven Halpern's Inner Peace Music, pg 775
Increase Video/Silver Mine Video, pg 786
Lightyear Entertainment, pg 808
MarVista Entertainment Inc, pg 818
MGM Home Entertainment, pg 825
monterey media inc, pg 829
monterey video, pg 829
Moose School Productions, pg 830
New & Unique Videos™, pg 839
Palardo Productions, pg 850
QRS Software Services, pg 867
Regent Press Publishers & Printers, pg 873
Sahara Records & Filmworks Entertainment Co, pg 879
Sodanceabit, pg 892
Valley Media, pg 924
Xenon Pictures Inc, pg 943

DISTRICT OF COLUMBIA

Sano Videos, pg 880

GEORGIA

New Leaf Distributing Co, pg 839

ILLINOIS

ABSA Films, pg 672
CCore Media Inc, pg 718
Movies Unlimited, pg 831

KENTUCKY

WaxWorks VideoWorks, pg 934

LOUISIANA

Great Chefs/Leisure Jazz Video, pg 773
Leisure Video, pg 806

MASSACHUSETTS

Penfield Productions Ltd, pg 853

MICHIGAN

Digi Sign Design LLC, pg 741

NEVADA

DVDs4Less, pg 748

NEW HAMPSHIRE

Captain Fiddle Music & Publications, pg 716
Channell One Video, pg 720
Chip Taylor Communications LLC, pg 907

NEW JERSEY

Ergo Media Inc, pg 755
Kultur International Films Ltd Inc, pg 802
Shanachie Entertainment Corp, pg 885

NEW YORK

ATA Trading Corp/Favorite TV Inc, pg 691
Beekman Books Inc, pg 703
Hallel Communications, pg 775
HB-Content, pg 777
Homespun Video, pg 781
IAI Records & Video, pg 783
Magnetic Music Publishing Co, pg 814
Mastervision Inc, pg 819
Music Sales Corp, pg 834
RCA Records, pg 871
VIEW Inc (Video International Entertainment World Inc), pg 930

NORTH CAROLINA

Crystal Pictures Inc, pg 735
Ladyslipper Music, pg 803

OHIO

WOUB Public Media, pg 942

OREGON

TeleVideos, pg 910
Wilderness Video, pg 938

PENNSYLVANIA

Anchor Distributors, pg 685
CORTRON Media LLC, pg 732
Discovery Education - South Burlington, pg 743
FMP Media Solutions Inc, pg 763
MVD Entertainment Group, pg 835
Vision Video, pg 930

TENNESSEE

American Blackguard Inc, pg 683
Spring Arbor Distributors Inc, pg 898
Word Label Group, pg 941

TEXAS

Marengo Films, pg 817

VERMONT

Multicultural Media Inc, pg 833

VIRGINIA

CACI Integrated Communications, pg 713

WASHINGTON

Bennett-Watt HD Productions Inc, pg 703

WISCONSIN

Aylmer Press, pg 700

ALBERTA

Global TV, pg 771

BRITISH COLUMBIA

Video Out Distribution, pg 928

ONTARIO

Entertainment One Distribution, pg 754
Universal Studios Canada Inc, pg 922

Music Video Producers

ALASKA

Aurora Films, pg 696

ARIZONA

Aardvark Productions LLC, pg 671
Candee Productions Inc, pg 716
Creative Backstage, pg 733
Direct Current Video Productions, pg 743
Film Creations Ltd, pg 760

ARKANSAS

Live'N'Loud, pg 810

CALIFORNIA

Access Video in Berkeley, pg 673
Action Video, pg 675
Air Philosophy Inc, pg 678
Allied Artists International Inc, pg 681
Anonymous Content, pg 686
Artichoke Productions, pg 690
Backstage Pass Entertainment Inc, pg 700
Big Door, pg 705
Steve Chandler, pg 720
Classic Images Stock Footage LLC, pg 726
Concrete Images, pg 730
Creative Technology, pg 733
Crystal Pyramid Productions™, pg 735
Custom Video Productions Inc, pg 736

PROGRAMMING — VIDEO

Music Video Producers (continued)

RHODE ISLAND

Sound-FX-Design, pg 894

SOUTH CAROLINA

Go To Team, pg 772
Stages Video Productions, pg 899

TENNESSEE

American Blackguard Inc, pg 683
Continental Film, pg 731
Griffith Productions, pg 774
Russ Sturgeon Productions/RSVP, pg 903
Word Label Group, pg 941

TEXAS

Biway Media, pg 706
Cerutti Productions Inc, pg 720
Countdown Productions Inc, pg 732
The Editing Co, pg 750
Eyecon Video Productions, pg 758
Horizon Film + Video Productions, pg 781
Mediaforce Productions, pg 822
Earl Miller Productions Inc, pg 827
Julye Newlin Productions Inc, pg 840
Omega Productions, pg 845
Reelsound Recording Co, pg 872
The Samuels Co, pg 879
South Coast Film & Video, pg 895
Sportsmen on Film Inc, pg 898
Stage Directions, pg 898

VERMONT

Multicultural Media Inc, pg 833

VIRGINIA

CACI Integrated Communications, pg 713
CVW Event Productions, pg 736
Limelight Communications Inc, pg 808
Metro Productions, pg 824
Rocktown Media, pg 876

WASHINGTON

Bennett-Watt HD Productions Inc, pg 703
Center for Touch Drawing, pg 719
Hamilton Studio, pg 775
North-by-Northwest - A Digital Studio, pg 842

WEST VIRGINIA

Blackwater Video Productions, pg 707
Sweetsong Productions, pg 905

WISCONSIN

Aylmer Press, pg 700
5th Floor Recording Co, pg 760
Meridian Studios, pg 824
Midland Video Productions Inc, pg 827
Mirror 34 Productions, pg 828
USAV Group Inc, pg 923
Wisconsin Public Television, pg 940

WYOMING

Bridger Productions Inc, pg 710

ALBERTA

Black Media Works, pg 706
Global TV, pg 771

MANITOBA

Spectra Video Productions Ltd, pg 897

ONTARIO

ADS Media, pg 677
GAPC (General Assembly Production Centre), pg 768
Image Video Services & Productions, pg 785
Marblemedia, pg 816
Pendulum Entertainment, pg 853
RB Productions, pg 870
Trebas Institute, pg 917
Video Excellence Productions, pg 927

QUEBEC

Kerrigan Productions Inc, pg 798
Trebas Institute, pg 917

SASKATCHEWAN

plan9films, pg 857

Music Video Rentals

ARIZONA

Video Learning Library, pg 928

MICHIGAN

Digi Sign Design LLC, pg 741

NEW YORK

BC Studio, pg 702
Hallel Communications, pg 775
Icarus Films Inc, pg 783
VIEW Inc (Video International Entertainment World Inc), pg 930

NORTH CAROLINA

Crystal Pictures Inc, pg 735

OHIO

WOUB Public Media, pg 942

BRITISH COLUMBIA

Video Out Distribution, pg 928

News Program Distributors

ARIZONA

Video Learning Library, pg 928

CALIFORNIA

Crystal Pyramid Productions™, pg 735
411 Video Information, pg 764
New & Unique Videos™, pg 839
Regent Press Publishers & Printers, pg 873

FLORIDA

Mike Vasilinda Productions Inc, pg 925

ILLINOIS

Movies Unlimited, pg 831

KENTUCKY

WaxWorks VideoWorks, pg 934

MARYLAND

Total AV Systems, pg 916

MICHIGAN

Digi Sign Design LLC, pg 741

NEW HAMPSHIRE

Channell One Video, pg 720
Chip Taylor Communications LLC, pg 907

NEW JERSEY

Allegro Productions Inc, pg 680
MiB MediaWorks, pg 825
SES SA, pg 884

NEW YORK

AP Images, pg 686
Downtown Community Television Center (DCTV), pg 746
HB-Content, pg 777
News Broadcast Network Inc, pg 840
Richter Productions Inc, pg 875
VIEW Inc (Video International Entertainment World Inc), pg 930
Women Make Movies Inc, pg 941

NORTH DAKOTA

UND Television Center, pg 921

PENNSYLVANIA

AccuWeather Inc, pg 674

TENNESSEE

National School Products, pg 836

VIRGINIA

CACI Integrated Communications, pg 713

WASHINGTON

Bennett-Watt HD Productions Inc, pg 703

ALBERTA

Global TV, pg 771

QUEBEC

Reel One International Ltd, pg 872

News Program Producers

ALABAMA

AVS Media Group, pg 699

ARIZONA

Aardvark Productions LLC, pg 671
Fox 10 Productions (KSAZ-TV), pg 765
KPHO-TV CBS 5, pg 801

ARKANSAS

KTHV-TV, pg 802

CALIFORNIA

Big Door, pg 705
Classic Images Stock Footage LLC, pg 726
Creative Technology, pg 733
Crystal Pyramid Productions™, pg 735
Custom Video Productions Inc, pg 736
Direct Images Interactive Inc, pg 743
First Camera, pg 761
Goal Productions, pg 772
Image Integration, pg 785
ITV Productions, pg 792
KION-TV, pg 799
McCune Audio-Video-Lighting, pg 821
Media Magic, pg 822
New & Unique Videos™, pg 839
Penrose Productions, pg 854
PM Productions, pg 858
QRS Software Services, pg 867
Regent Press Publishers & Printers, pg 873
Dick Reizner Film & Video, pg 873
SNAP, pg 891
Still N' Motion, pg 901
Tam Communications Inc, pg 906
Total Creative, pg 916
Twin Peaks Creative, pg 920
Vineyard Video & Photography, pg 930

COLORADO

Apogee Communications Group, pg 687
Flashback Media Productions, pg 762
Tatum Video, pg 907

CONNECTICUT

Essex Television Group Inc, pg 755
Fox 61, pg 765
Ironik Design & Post, pg 791
New London Media, pg 839
P&P Studios Inc, pg 851

DISTRICT OF COLUMBIA

UPN 20 WDCA-TV, pg 923

FLORIDA

Blackburst Entertainment LLC, pg 706
Civins Productions Inc, pg 725
Communications Concepts Inc (CCI), pg 729
CopShopMiami.com, pg 731
Jordan Klein Film & Video (JKFV), pg 795
National Teleproductions Inc, pg 837
Roger Scruggs Films, pg 883
Sunfire Communications Inc, pg 904
Mike Vasilinda Productions Inc, pg 925
Video Techniques Inc, pg 928
WCJB TV20, pg 934

GEORGIA

Beachwood Productions, pg 702
Guerrilla Productions LLC, pg 774
KEF Media, pg 797
Myriad Productions, pg 835
On-Line Productions, pg 845

HAWAII

KHNL/KGMB, pg 798

IDAHO

Brad Shaw Productions Inc, pg 885
Wide Eye Productions, pg 938

ILLINOIS

Abacus Group of Saint Louis LLC, pg 672
ABSA Films, pg 672
CCore Media Inc, pg 718
The Chicago Production Center, pg 721
Film Police, pg 760
Manning Productions, pg 816
Pepper Group, pg 854
Production Craft Inc, pg 863
PSAV® Presentation Services (Hotel Services Division), pg 866
SCI Television & Creative Media LLC, pg 882

INDIANA

A-V-A Video Productions, pg 671

KANSAS

KAKE-TV, pg 796

KENTUCKY

Idle Minds Productions Inc, pg 784

LOUISIANA

Digital FX Inc, pg 742

MAINE

WGME-TV, pg 936

MARYLAND

Adventure Productions LLC, pg 678
Richard Chisolm Cinematography, pg 722
CPR MultiMedia Solutions, pg 732
dbF a Media Company, pg 739
The Image Generators, pg 785
Kramer Communications Video Production, pg 801
WMAR-TV, pg 940

MASSACHUSETTS

Award Productions Inc, pg 699
HOME Inc, pg 781
TVN-The Video Network, pg 919
VideoLink Inc, an AVI-SPL company, pg 929
WVP Boston, pg 942

MICHIGAN

Digi Sign Design LLC, pg 741
K&R All Media Productions LLC, pg 796
K&R's Recording Studios Inc, pg 796

MINNESOTA

House of Cinemagraphics, pg 782
MastCom, pg 819
Worthwhile Films, pg 941

NEBRASKA

Mason Video, pg 819

NEVADA

Aardvark Video & Media Productions, pg 671
Encore Event Technologies LLC, pg 754
JCS Video Productions, pg 793

NEW HAMPSHIRE

Apertura, pg 686
Chip Taylor Communications LLC, pg 907

NEW JERSEY

Allegro Productions Inc, pg 680
Broadcast Center Studios, pg 710
CFP Video Productions Inc, pg 720
Laurel Video Productions, pg 804
MiB MediaWorks, pg 825
Optisonics Productions, pg 847
Telequest Inc, pg 910
VCSvideo, pg 925

NEW MEXICO

Production Outfitters, pg 864

NEW YORK

Ace Video, pg 674
Associated Press Television News, pg 691
aurora productions, pg 696
Clarity Media Group, pg 725
CompuWeather Inc, pg 729
De Nonno Productions Inc (DPI), pg 739
Downtown Community Television Center (DCTV), pg 746
Havas Creative, pg 776
HB-Content, pg 777
Hello World Communications, pg 778
Manhattan Center Studios Inc, pg 816
MHS-TV, pg 825
MRY, pg 832
News Broadcast Network Inc, pg 840
News Corp, pg 840
Northeast Video Productions Inc, pg 842
The Palmer Group, pg 850
PrimaLux Video Inc, pg 862
Richter Productions Inc, pg 875
VIEW Inc (Video International Entertainment World Inc), pg 930
Alan Weiss Productions, pg 935
WNET/New York Public Media, pg 940

NORTH CAROLINA

Pat Appleson Studios Inc, pg 687
Bill Barnes Video Productions LLC, pg 702
The Communications Group Inc, pg 729
Digital Rain LLC, pg 742
Videowerks, pg 930

NORTH DAKOTA

UND Television Center, pg 921

OHIO

CET, pg 720
Image Video Teleproductions Inc, pg 785
Lyon Video Inc, pg 813
MainSail Production Services Inc, pg 815
R&B Communications Inc, pg 870
Shelburne Films, pg 885
Vista Color Imaging Inc, pg 931

OREGON

Production West, pg 864

PENNSYLVANIA

AccuWeather Inc, pg 674
Beholder Productions Inc, pg 703
CCI Communications Inc, pg 718
FMP Media Solutions Inc, pg 763
Innovision Media Group, pg 788
Muderick Media, pg 833
Production Masters Inc (PMI), pg 864
The Videohouse Inc, pg 929

RHODE ISLAND

Sound-FX-Design, pg 894

SOUTH CAROLINA

Encore Video Productions, pg 754
Go To Team, pg 772
Stages Video Productions, pg 899
Venture Media, pg 925

TENNESSEE

Continental Film, pg 731
Running Pony Productions LLC, pg 878

TEXAS

Cerutti Productions Inc, pg 720
Communication Arts Multimedia Inc, pg 728
Countdown Productions Inc, pg 732
Epic Software Group Inc, pg 755
Horizon Film + Video Productions, pg 781
Julye Newlin Productions Inc, pg 840
Omega Productions, pg 845
South Coast Film & Video, pg 895
Stage Directions, pg 898
Texas Heart Institute Visual Communication Services, pg 911

VIRGINIA

CACI Integrated Communications, pg 713
Limelight Communications Inc, pg 808
Metro Productions, pg 824
Rocktown Media, pg 876
Video Solutions, pg 928

WASHINGTON

Bennett-Watt HD Productions Inc, pg 703
North-by-Northwest - A Digital Studio, pg 842
Sparkworks Media, pg 896

WEST VIRGINIA

Blackwater Video Productions, pg 707

WISCONSIN

5th Floor Recording Co, pg 760
Mirror 34 Productions, pg 828
University of Wisconsin-Oshkosh Radio-TV-Film Dept, pg 923
Wisconsin Public Television, pg 940
WTMJ-TV, pg 942

WYOMING

Bridger Productions Inc, pg 710

ALBERTA

Black Media Works, pg 706
Global TV, pg 771

BRITISH COLUMBIA

Triad Communications Ltd, pg 918

NEWFOUNDLAND AND LABRADOR

Vidcraft Productions Ltd, pg 927

NORTHWEST TERRITORIES

Yellowknife Films Inc, pg 944

ONTARIO

GAPC (General Assembly Production Centre), pg 768
Video Excellence Productions, pg 927

QUEBEC

Kerrigan Productions Inc, pg 798
Reel One International Ltd, pg 872

News Program Rentals

ARIZONA

Video Learning Library, pg 928

MICHIGAN

Digi Sign Design LLC, pg 741

NEW YORK

Downtown Community Television Center (DCTV), pg 746
Icarus Films Inc, pg 783
Richter Productions Inc, pg 875
VIEW Inc (Video International Entertainment World Inc), pg 930

ONTARIO

L-3 WESCAM, pg 802

Program—Television, see Television Program

Public Relations Program Distributors

ARIZONA

Video Learning Library, pg 928

ARKANSAS

Mullikin Agency, pg 833

CALIFORNIA

Crystal Pyramid Productions™, pg 735
Direct Cinema Ltd Inc, pg 743
eFootage LLC, pg 751
411 Video Information, pg 764
New & Unique Videos™, pg 839

GEORGIA

Convergent Media Systems, pg 731
On-Line Productions, pg 845

ILLINOIS

ABSA Films, pg 672
CCore Media Inc, pg 718

KENTUCKY

WaxWorks VideoWorks, pg 934

PROGRAMMING — VIDEO

Public Relations Program Distributors (continued)

MASSACHUSETTS

Penfield Productions Ltd, pg 853

MICHIGAN

Digi Sign Design LLC, pg 741

NEBRASKA

B & B Video Productions Inc, pg 700

NEVADA

DVDs4Less, pg 748

NEW HAMPSHIRE

Channell One Video, pg 720
Chip Taylor Communications LLC, pg 907

NEW JERSEY

Allegro Productions Inc, pg 680
MiB MediaWorks, pg 825
SES SA, pg 884

NEW YORK

Broadstreet Productions LLC, pg 711
HB-Content, pg 777
News Broadcast Network Inc, pg 840
Synaptic Digital, pg 905

OHIO

Treehaus Communications Inc, pg 917

OKLAHOMA

Academic Media & Digital Services, pg 672

OREGON

Sugar Mountain PR, pg 903

PENNSYLVANIA

FMP Media Solutions Inc, pg 763

TENNESSEE

American Blackguard Inc, pg 683

VERMONT

University of Vermont, Instructional Television Dept, pg 923

VIRGINIA

CACI Integrated Communications, pg 713
WETA Production Center, pg 936

WASHINGTON

Bennett-Watt HD Productions Inc, pg 703

ALBERTA

Global TV, pg 771

Public Relations Program Producers

ALASKA

Aurora Films, pg 696

ARIZONA

Aardvark Productions LLC, pg 671
Candee Productions Inc, pg 716
Direct Current Video Productions, pg 743
Fox 10 Productions (KSAZ-TV), pg 765
Merestone, pg 823
Metropolitan Audio-Visual Inc, pg 824

ARKANSAS

Live'N'Loud, pg 810
Mullikin Agency, pg 833
White Diamond Productions LLC, pg 937

CALIFORNIA

Aaron Marcus and Associates, pg 671
Action Video, pg 675
Big Door, pg 705
Cavalcade Productions Inc, pg 717
Steve Chandler, pg 720
Chick Russell Communications, pg 721
Classic Images Stock Footage LLC, pg 726
Creative Technology, pg 733
Crystal Pyramid Productions™, pg 735
Custom Video Productions Inc, pg 736
Design Media, pg 741
digital OutPost, pg 742
Direct Images Interactive Inc, pg 743
Dolphin MultiMedia Inc, pg 745
First Camera, pg 761
Goal Productions, pg 772
Imageworks, pg 785
ITV Productions, pg 792
Kavich Reynolds Productions Inc, pg 797
Main Street Media Inc, pg 815
Maximus Media Inc, pg 820
McCune Audio-Video-Lighting, pg 821
Media Magic, pg 822
The Media Staff Inc, pg 822
Nolte Media, pg 841
On-Trax Inc, pg 846
Prime Cut Productions, pg 862
QRS Software Services, pg 867
Dick Reizner Film & Video, pg 873
Glenn Roland Films, pg 876
SNAP, pg 891
Staylor-Made Communications Inc, pg 900
Still N' Motion, pg 901
Tam Communications Inc, pg 906
Total Creative, pg 916
TVA Media Group, pg 919
Twin Peaks Creative, pg 920
Vineyard Video & Photography, pg 930
Visions Plus, pg 931
Wavemaker Media Design, pg 934
West Coast Projections Inc, pg 935
WMS Media Inc, pg 940
Yada/Levine Video Productions, pg 943
Zamacona Productions, pg 945

COLORADO

Apogee Communications Group, pg 687
Daylight Productions & Rentals, pg 739
Flashback Media Productions, pg 762
Rocky Mountain Audio/Video Productions Inc, pg 876
Tatum Video, pg 907
Transtar Entertainment Co Inc, pg 917

CONNECTICUT

The Gary-Paul Agency, pg 768
Geomatrix Productions, pg 770
Ironik Design & Post, pg 791
Moving Pictures, pg 832
New London Media, pg 839
P&P Studios Inc, pg 851
Spectrum, pg 897
UConn Health Multimedia Services, pg 920
Video Production Associates Inc, pg 928

DISTRICT OF COLUMBIA

Hillmann & Carr Inc, pg 780
O'Keefe Communications Inc, pg 844
Yellow Cat Productions Inc, pg 944

FLORIDA

Accord Productions, pg 673
Applebox Studio, pg 687
Blackburst Entertainment LLC, pg 706
Civins Productions Inc, pg 725
Communications Concepts Inc (CCI), pg 729
CopShopMiami.com, pg 731
Courter Films LLC, pg 732
Easy Edit Video Inc, pg 750
Jordan Klein Film & Video (JKFV), pg 795
National Teleproductions Inc, pg 837
Paradise Video & Film, pg 851
Sound & Vision Communications Inc, pg 893
Sound*Light, pg 894
Sunfire Communications Inc, pg 904
Sunrise Studios, pg 904
Tel-Air Interests Inc, pg 909
Tricycle Studios, pg 918
Universal Studios Florida® Production Group, pg 922
Mike Vasilinda Productions Inc, pg 925
Video Techniques Inc, pg 928

GEORGIA

Beachwood Productions, pg 702
Burst Video/Film Inc, pg 713
ECG Productions, pg 750
GP Studios, pg 773
Guerrilla Productions LLC, pg 774
Myriad Productions, pg 835
Malcolm Neal Productions, pg 837
On-Line Productions, pg 845

HAWAII

Hyperspective Studios Inc, pg 783
1013 Integrated, pg 911

IDAHO

Brad Shaw Productions Inc, pg 885
Wide Eye Productions, pg 938

ILLINOIS

Abacus Group of Saint Louis LLC, pg 672
ABSA Films, pg 672
Airways Digital Media, pg 679
Atomic Imaging Inc/Golan Studios, pg 692
Beatty TeleVisual Productions, pg 703
CCore Media Inc, pg 718
The Chicago Production Center, pg 721
Cresta Creative, pg 734
Explore, pg 757
Extraordinary Demos/Videos, pg 757
Film Police, pg 760
IV Media Resources, pg 792
Major Media Productions Inc, pg 815
Manning Productions, pg 816
Mimi Productions, pg 828
Multimedia Marketing Group, pg 833
Rob Orr Productions Ltd, pg 848
Pepper Group, pg 854
Production Craft Inc, pg 863
PSAV® Presentation Services (Hotel Services Division), pg 866
SCI Television & Creative Media LLC, pg 882
20/20 Communications Inc, pg 920
Video I-D Teleproductions Inc, pg 928
Video Impressions, pg 928
WEEK TV, pg 935
Winter Productions, pg 939

INDIANA

A-V-A Video Productions, pg 671
PentaVision Communications Inc, pg 854

KANSAS

KAKE-TV, pg 796

KENTUCKY

Horizon Films & Media LLC, pg 781
Idle Minds Productions Inc, pg 784
Donna Lawrence Productions, pg 804
The Media Collaboratory, pg 821

LOUISIANA

Digital FX Inc, pg 742
Louisiana State University Division of Strategic Communications, pg 811
Moxie Media, pg 832

MAINE

WGME-TV, pg 936

MARYLAND

Absolute Hollywood, pg 672
Adventure Productions LLC, pg 678
CAS Video Productions, pg 717
Richard Chisolm Cinematography, pg 722
CPR MultiMedia Solutions, pg 732
dbF a Media Company, pg 739
The Image Generators, pg 785
Kramer Communications Video Production, pg 801

MASSACHUSETTS

Award Productions Inc, pg 699
CommCreative, pg 728

PROGRAMMING — VIDEO

Public Relations Program Rentals

CALIFORNIA
Direct Cinema Ltd Inc, pg 743

GEORGIA
Convergent Media Systems, pg 731

MICHIGAN
Digi Sign Design LLC, pg 741

VERMONT
University of Vermont, Instructional Television Dept, pg 923

Public Service Announcement Distributors

ARKANSAS
Mullikin Agency, pg 833

CALIFORNIA
Crystal Pyramid Productions™, pg 735
eFootage LLC, pg 751
ETR, pg 756
New & Unique Videos™, pg 839
Visual Communications - Southern California Asian American Studies Central Inc, pg 931
The Wyland Group, pg 942

DISTRICT OF COLUMBIA
US Holocaust Memorial Museum, pg 923
USCCB Publishing, pg 923

FLORIDA
Mike Vasilinda Productions Inc, pg 925

GEORGIA
On-Line Productions, pg 845

ILLINOIS
ABSA Films, pg 672

KENTUCKY
EKU Media, pg 752

MARYLAND
Recorded Books Inc, an RBmedia company, pg 871
Sign Media Inc, pg 887

MASSACHUSETTS
HOME Inc, pg 781
Penfield Productions Ltd, pg 853

MICHIGAN
Digi Sign Design LLC, pg 741

NEVADA
DVDs4Less, pg 748

NEW HAMPSHIRE
Channell One Video, pg 720
Chip Taylor Communications LLC, pg 907

NEW JERSEY
Allegro Productions Inc, pg 680

NEW YORK
Brooklyn Botanic Garden, pg 711
Downtown Community Television Center (DCTV), pg 746
HB-Content, pg 777
March of Dimes Foundation, pg 816
News Broadcast Network Inc, pg 840
Synaptic Digital, pg 905
Vidicom Inc, pg 930

PENNSYLVANIA
CORTRON Media LLC, pg 732

TENNESSEE
American Blackguard Inc, pg 683

VERMONT
University of Vermont, Instructional Television Dept, pg 923

VIRGINIA
CACI Integrated Communications, pg 713
CDR Communications Inc, pg 719

WEST VIRGINIA
Focus on Animals, pg 763

WISCONSIN
Wisconsin Public Television, pg 940

Public Service Announcement Producers

ALASKA
Alaska Media Pros LLC, pg 679
Aurora Films, pg 696

ARIZONA
Aardvark Productions LLC, pg 671
Candee Productions Inc, pg 716
Direct Current Video Productions, pg 743
Film Creations Ltd, pg 760
Fox 10 Productions (KSAZ-TV), pg 765
Metropolitan Audio-Visual Inc, pg 824
On-Site Video, pg 846

ARKANSAS
Live'N'Loud, pg 810
Mullikin Agency, pg 833
White Diamond Productions LLC, pg 937

CALIFORNIA
Access Video in Berkeley, pg 673
Action Video, pg 675
Artichoke Productions, pg 690
Big Door, pg 705
Cavalcade Productions Inc, pg 717
Steve Chandler, pg 720

Classic Images Stock Footage LLC, pg 726
Coastline Productions, pg 727
Concrete Images, pg 730
Creative Technology, pg 733
Crystal Pyramid Productions™, pg 735
Custom Video Productions Inc, pg 736
Direct Images Interactive Inc, pg 743
First Camera, pg 761
GAMfilm Productions, pg 768
Image Integration, pg 785
imageReal Pictures LLC, pg 785
Imageworks, pg 785
ITV Productions, pg 792
Kavich Reynolds Productions Inc, pg 797
KTVU-Retail Services, pg 802
Main Street Media Inc, pg 815
Maximus Media Inc, pg 820
McCune Audio-Video-Lighting, pg 821
Media Magic, pg 822
The Media Staff Inc, pg 822
New & Unique Videos™, pg 839
New Circuit Films LLC, pg 839
Nineteen87, pg 841
Nolte Media, pg 841
On-Trax Inc, pg 846
Point of View Productions, pg 858
QRS Software Services, pg 867
Dick Reizner Film & Video, pg 873
Glenn Roland Films, pg 876
Screen Door Entertainment Inc, pg 882
SNAP, pg 891
Staylor-Made Communications Inc, pg 900
Still N' Motion, pg 901
Tam Communications Inc, pg 906
Timestream Video, pg 914
Total Creative, pg 916
Twin Peaks Creative, pg 920
Vineyard Video & Photography, pg 930
Visions Plus, pg 931
Visual Communications - Southern California Asian American Studies Central Inc, pg 931
Wavemaker Media Design, pg 934
The Wyland Group, pg 942
Zamacona Productions, pg 945

COLORADO
Daylight Productions & Rentals, pg 739
Flashback Media Productions, pg 762
Rocky Mountain Audio/Video Productions Inc, pg 876
Tatum Video, pg 907
Transtar Entertainment Co Inc, pg 917

CONNECTICUT
ACM Productions Ltd, pg 674
The Gary-Paul Agency, pg 768
Geomatrix Productions, pg 770
Ironik Design & Post, pg 791
Moving Pictures, pg 832
P&P Studios Inc, pg 851
Spectrum, pg 897
UConn Health Multimedia Services, pg 920
Video Production Associates Inc, pg 928

DISTRICT OF COLUMBIA
Hillmann & Carr Inc, pg 780
O'Keefe Communications Inc, pg 844
US Holocaust Memorial Museum, pg 923
Yellow Cat Productions Inc, pg 944

FLORIDA
Applebox Studio, pg 687
Blackburst Entertainment LLC, pg 706
Civins Productions Inc, pg 725
Communications Concepts Inc (CCI), pg 729
CopShopMiami.com, pg 731
Courter Films LLC, pg 732
Jordan Klein Film & Video (JKFV), pg 795
National Teleproductions Inc, pg 837
Paradise Video & Film, pg 851
Sunfire Communications Inc, pg 904
Sunrise Studios, pg 904
Tel-Air Interests Inc, pg 909
Tricycle Studios, pg 918
Mike Vasilinda Productions Inc, pg 925
Video Techniques Inc, pg 928

GEORGIA
Beachwood Productions, pg 702
Burst Video/Film Inc, pg 713
Cox Media, pg 732
GP Studios, pg 773
Guerrilla Productions LLC, pg 774
On-Line Productions, pg 845

HAWAII
Hyperspective Studios Inc, pg 783
1013 Integrated, pg 911

IDAHO
Brad Shaw Productions Inc, pg 885
Wide Eye Productions, pg 938

ILLINOIS
ABSA Films, pg 672
Airways Digital Media, pg 679
CCore Media Inc, pg 718
The Chicago Production Center, pg 721
Explore, pg 757
Film Police, pg 760
IV Media Resources, pg 792
Major Media Productions Inc, pg 815
Manning Productions, pg 816
Pepper Group, pg 854
Production Craft Inc, pg 863
PSAV® Presentation Services (Hotel Services Division), pg 866
SCI Television & Creative Media LLC, pg 882
Sparkfactor, pg 896
20/20 Communications Inc, pg 920
Video I-D Teleproductions Inc, pg 928
WEEK TV, pg 935
Winter Productions, pg 939

INDIANA
A-V-A Video Productions, pg 671
Bright Ideas Creative Services, pg 710
Road Pictures, pg 876

PROGRAMMING — VIDEO

Public Service Announcement Producers (continued)

NEWFOUNDLAND AND LABRADOR

Vidcraft Productions Ltd, pg 927

NORTHWEST TERRITORIES

Yellowknife Films Inc, pg 944

ONTARIO

ADS Media, pg 677
DebsVoice, pg 739
GAPC (General Assembly Production Centre), pg 768
Image Video Services & Productions, pg 785
Video Excellence Productions, pg 927

QUEBEC

Kerrigan Productions Inc, pg 798

SASKATCHEWAN

plan9films, pg 857

Public Service Announcement Rentals

CALIFORNIA

Visual Communications - Southern California Asian American Studies Central Inc, pg 931

GEORGIA

On-Line Productions, pg 845

MICHIGAN

Digi Sign Design LLC, pg 741

NEW YORK

BC Studio, pg 702

VERMONT

University of Vermont, Instructional Television Dept, pg 923

Religious Program Distributors

ALABAMA

Eternal Word Television Network (EWTN), pg 756

ARIZONA

Mother Basilea Films, pg 831
TSG Publishing Foundation Inc USA, pg 919

ARKANSAS

Mullikin Agency, pg 833

CALIFORNIA

Christian Media Network, pg 722
Clarity Sound & Light, pg 725
Direct Cinema Ltd Inc, pg 743

Discovery Education - Los Angeles, pg 743
411 Video Information, pg 764
Increase Video/Silver Mine Video, pg 786
monterey media inc, pg 829
monterey video, pg 829
Nilgiri Press, pg 841
Osho Viha Information Center & Book Distributors, pg 848
People Skills International, pg 854
Pyramid Media, pg 867
Thinking Allowed Productions, pg 912
Vedanta Press & Catalog, pg 925
The Wyland Group, pg 942
Xenon Pictures Inc, pg 943

COLORADO

Crown Ministries International, pg 735

CONNECTICUT

Hartley Film Foundation, pg 776

DISTRICT OF COLUMBIA

Biblical Archaeology Society (BAS), pg 705
National Council of Churches, pg 836
USCCB Publishing, pg 923

FLORIDA

Children of Mary, pg 722

GEORGIA

Gingerbread Group Holdings LLC, pg 771
New Leaf Distributing Co, pg 839

ILLINOIS

ACTA Publications, pg 675
Baha'i Distribution Service (BDS), pg 700
CCore Media Inc, pg 718
Film Ideas Inc, pg 760
International Historic Films Inc, pg 790
Liturgy Training Publications, pg 810
The Market Place, pg 817
Movies Unlimited, pg 831
Questar Entertainment Inc, pg 868
Theosophical Publishing House, pg 912

KENTUCKY

WaxWorks VideoWorks, pg 934

MARYLAND

RLJ Entertainment Inc, pg 875
Total AV Systems, pg 916

MASSACHUSETTS

Pauline Books & Media, pg 852

MICHIGAN

Digi Sign Design LLC, pg 741
Emery-Pratt Co, pg 753
The Program Source International, pg 865
Jack Van Impe Ministries International, pg 924
Zondervan, pg 945

MINNESOTA

Augsburg Fortress, pg 695
Harris Communications Inc, pg 776

MISSOURI

Vedanta Society of St Louis, pg 925

NEBRASKA

B & B Video Productions Inc, pg 700

NEW HAMPSHIRE

Chip Taylor Communications LLC, pg 907

NEW JERSEY

Ergo Media Inc, pg 755
SES SA, pg 884

NEW YORK

The Christophers, pg 722
First Run Features, pg 761
Hallel Communications, pg 775
Janson Media Inc, pg 793
Mastervision Inc, pg 819
The Fulton J Sheen Co Inc, pg 885
SISU Home Entertainment Inc, pg 889
Women Make Movies Inc, pg 941

NORTH CAROLINA

World Wide Pictures Inc, pg 941

OHIO

Franciscan Media, pg 765
Treehaus Communications Inc, pg 917

OKLAHOMA

VCI Entertainment, pg 925

OREGON

Cooking by the Book, pg 731

PENNSYLVANIA

Anchor Distributors, pg 685
Bullfrog Films Inc, pg 712
Chinmaya Publications, pg 722
FMP Media Solutions Inc, pg 763
Himalayan Institute Audio/Video, pg 780
MVD Entertainment Group, pg 835
Vision Video, pg 930

SOUTH CAROLINA

ACS Technologies, pg 674
American Production Services LLC, pg 684

TENNESSEE

Abingdon Press, pg 672
Capitol Christian Music Group, pg 716
Cokesbury, pg 727
Randall House Publications, pg 870
Spring Arbor Distributors Inc, pg 898
Zion Music Group, pg 945

TEXAS

Endtime Ministries Inc, pg 754
Lamb & Lion Ministries, pg 803

MINNESOTA

Augsburg Fortress, pg 695
Harris Communications Inc, pg 776

VIRGINIA

Shakticom, pg 885

WASHINGTON

Linguist's Software Inc, pg 809

BRITISH COLUMBIA

Timeless Books, pg 914

ONTARIO

Broughton's Church Supplies, Religious Books & Gifts, pg 711
Canadian Learning Co Inc, pg 715
Gospel Folio Press, pg 773
Life Cycle Books Ltd, pg 807
Novalis, pg 843

Religious Program Producers

ALABAMA

AVS Media Group, pg 699
Eternal Word Television Network (EWTN), pg 756

ALASKA

Aurora Films, pg 696

ARIZONA

Aardvark Productions LLC, pg 671
CyberIconics International, pg 736
Merestone, pg 823
Mother Basilea Films, pg 831
TSG Publishing Foundation Inc USA, pg 919

ARKANSAS

Mullikin Agency, pg 833
White Diamond Productions LLC, pg 937

CALIFORNIA

Action Video, pg 675
Cavalcade Productions Inc, pg 717
Christian Media Network, pg 722
Clarity Sound & Light, pg 725
Classic Images Stock Footage LLC, pg 726
Custom Video Productions Inc, pg 736
Discovery Education - Los Angeles, pg 743
Gateways Books & Tapes, pg 768
ITV Productions, pg 792
Maximus Media Inc, pg 820
McCune Audio-Video-Lighting, pg 821
Nilgiri Press, pg 841
Osho Viha Information Center & Book Distributors, pg 848
PM Productions, pg 858
QRS Software Services, pg 867
Dick Reizner Film & Video, pg 873
Glenn Roland Films, pg 876
Screen Door Entertainment Inc, pg 882
SNAP, pg 891
Still N' Motion, pg 901
Total Creative, pg 916
TVA Media Group, pg 919
Vedanta Press & Catalog, pg 925
Vineyard Video & Photography, pg 930
The Wyland Group, pg 942
Xenon Pictures Inc, pg 943

COLORADO

Centre Communications Inc, pg 720
Crown Ministries International, pg 735
Flashback Media Productions, pg 762

CONNECTICUT

Geomatrix Productions, pg 770
Hartley Film Foundation, pg 776
Ironik Design & Post, pg 791
Spectrum, pg 897

DISTRICT OF COLUMBIA

Biblical Archaeology Society (BAS), pg 705
USCCB Publishing, pg 923

FLORIDA

Applebox Studio, pg 687
Blackburst Entertainment LLC, pg 706
Civins Productions Inc, pg 725
CopShopMiami.com, pg 731
Courter Films LLC, pg 732
Jordan Klein Film & Video (JKFV), pg 795
Sound*Light, pg 894
Sunfire Communications Inc, pg 904
Sunrise Studios, pg 904
Tel-Air Interests Inc, pg 909

GEORGIA

The Alliance for Christian Media, pg 680
Beachwood Productions, pg 702
Burst Video/Film Inc, pg 713
Cox Media, pg 732
Gingerbread Group Holdings LLC, pg 771
Guerrilla Productions LLC, pg 774
Malcolm Neal Productions, pg 837
On-Line Productions, pg 845

HAWAII

Hyperspective Studios Inc, pg 783

ILLINOIS

ACTA Publications, pg 675
Beatty TeleVisual Productions, pg 703
CCore Media Inc, pg 718
Explore, pg 757
Film Police, pg 760
IV Media Resources, pg 792
Liturgy Training Publications, pg 810
Pepper Group, pg 854
PSAV® Presentation Services (Hotel Services Division), pg 866
Questar Entertainment Inc, pg 868
RADMAR Inc, pg 869
SCI Television & Creative Media LLC, pg 882
Theosophical Publishing House, pg 912
20/20 Communications Inc, pg 920
Video Impressions, pg 928
WEEK TV, pg 935
Winter Productions, pg 939

INDIANA

A-V-A Video Productions, pg 671
PentaVision Communications Inc, pg 854

IOWA

Kuhn Productions LLC, pg 802

KANSAS

KAKE-TV, pg 796

KENTUCKY

Idle Minds Productions Inc, pg 784
Prosper Media Group Inc, pg 866

LOUISIANA

Moxie Media, pg 832

MARYLAND

Adventure Productions LLC, pg 678
CPR MultiMedia Solutions, pg 732
dbF a Media Company, pg 739

MASSACHUSETTS

Award Productions Inc, pg 699
Heliotrope Studios, pg 778
Pauline Books & Media, pg 852
VideoLink Inc, an AVI-SPL company, pg 929

MICHIGAN

Digi Sign Design LLC, pg 741
K&R All Media Productions LLC, pg 796
K&R's Recording Studios Inc, pg 796
Zondervan, pg 945

MINNESOTA

Augsburg Fortress, pg 695
House of Cinemagraphics, pg 782
MastCom, pg 819
Vaddio, pg 924

MISSOURI

Audio-VideoGraphics Inc, pg 694
Communitronics Corp, pg 729
Vedanta Society of St Louis, pg 925

NEBRASKA

B & B Video Productions Inc, pg 700
Rainbow Video Productions Inc, pg 869

NEVADA

Aardvark Video & Media Productions, pg 671
Encore Event Technologies LLC, pg 754
JCS Video Productions, pg 793

NEW HAMPSHIRE

Apertura, pg 686
Chip Taylor Communications LLC, pg 907

NEW JERSEY

CFP Video Productions Inc, pg 720
Euro-Pacific Film & Video Productions Inc, pg 756
MiB MediaWorks, pg 825
Ray Mueller Productions, pg 833
Optisonics Productions, pg 847
Paulist Press, pg 852
VCSvideo, pg 925

NEW MEXICO

Production Outfitters, pg 864

NEW YORK

aurora productions, pg 696
Brian Film Productions LLC, pg 710
Golden Lamb Productions, pg 772
Hallel Communications, pg 775
Lavine Production Group, pg 804
Manhattan Center Studios Inc, pg 816
Mastervision Inc, pg 819
The Palmer Group, pg 850
Richter Productions Inc, pg 875
The Fulton J Sheen Co Inc, pg 885
SISU Home Entertainment Inc, pg 889

NORTH CAROLINA

All Pro Media Inc, pg 680
Pat Appleson Studios Inc, pg 687
The Communications Group Inc, pg 729
Horizon Video Productions Inc, pg 781
Videowerks, pg 930

OHIO

Russ Beckner Pictures, pg 703
Franciscan Media, pg 765
Image Video Teleproductions Inc, pg 785
MainSail Production Services Inc, pg 815
Take 1 Media Services, pg 906
Treehaus Communications Inc, pg 917
Vista Color Imaging Inc, pg 931

OKLAHOMA

VCI Entertainment, pg 925

OREGON

KTVA Productions, pg 802
Production West, pg 864

PENNSYLVANIA

Beholder Productions Inc, pg 703
CCI Communications Inc, pg 718
Chinmaya Publications, pg 722
FMP Media Solutions Inc, pg 763
Himalayan Institute Audio/Video, pg 780
JPL, pg 795
Muderick Media, pg 833
The Videohouse Inc, pg 929
Vision Video, pg 930
Visual Sound Inc, pg 931

RHODE ISLAND

Sound-FX-Design, pg 894

SOUTH CAROLINA

ACS Technologies, pg 674
BJU Press, pg 706

TENNESSEE

Abingdon Press, pg 672
Capitol Christian Music Group, pg 716
Continental Film, pg 731
Memphis Communications Corp, pg 823
Running Pony Productions LLC, pg 878
Russ Sturgeon Productions/RSVP, pg 903
United Methodist Productions, pg 921

TEXAS

Alpha Video Productions, pg 682
Cerutti Productions Inc, pg 720
Communication Arts Multimedia Inc, pg 728
The Editing Co, pg 750
Endtime Ministries Inc, pg 754
Horizon Film + Video Productions, pg 781
Lamb & Lion Ministries, pg 803
Mediaforce Productions, pg 822
Earl Miller Productions Inc, pg 827
Omega Productions, pg 845
Reelsound Recording Co, pg 872
South Coast Film & Video, pg 895

VIRGINIA

CVW Event Productions, pg 736
Metro Productions, pg 824
National Media Services Inc, pg 836
Rocktown Media, pg 876
Shakticom, pg 885

WASHINGTON

Bennett-Watt HD Productions Inc, pg 703
Linguist's Software Inc, pg 809

WISCONSIN

5th Floor Recording Co, pg 760
Midland Video Productions Inc, pg 827
Video Wisconsin Inc, pg 929
Watts Communications Inc, pg 934

WYOMING

Bridger Productions Inc, pg 710

BRITISH COLUMBIA

Timeless Books, pg 914

ONTARIO

ADS Media, pg 677
GAPC (General Assembly Production Centre), pg 768
Image Video Services & Productions, pg 785
Jams Productions Inc, pg 793
Novalis, pg 843

QUEBEC

Kerrigan Productions Inc, pg 798

Religious Program Rentals

ARIZONA

Video Learning Library, pg 928

CALIFORNIA

Clarity Sound & Light, pg 725
Direct Cinema Ltd Inc, pg 743

MASSACHUSETTS

Pauline Books & Media, pg 852

MICHIGAN

Digi Sign Design LLC, pg 741

MISSOURI

University of Missouri-Columbia, pg 923

PROGRAMMING — VIDEO

Religious Program Rentals (continued)

NEW YORK

First Run Features, pg 761
Hallel Communications, pg 775
Icarus Films Inc, pg 783

NORTH CAROLINA

World Wide Pictures Inc, pg 941

OHIO

Franciscan Media, pg 765
Treehaus Communications Inc, pg 917

PENNSYLVANIA

Bullfrog Films Inc, pg 712

Research—Technical Program, *see* Technical Research Program

Sales Promotion & Training Program Distributors

ARIZONA

Video Learning Library, pg 928

ARKANSAS

Mullikin Agency, pg 833

CALIFORNIA

Crystal Pyramid Productions™, pg 735
Deja View Video, pg 740
Direct Cinema Ltd Inc, pg 743
Discovery Education - Los Angeles, pg 743
Ferrari Productions, pg 759
411 Video Information, pg 764
New & Unique Videos™, pg 839
TMW Media Group, pg 915

CONNECTICUT

Cine-Med Inc, pg 723

FLORIDA

Potentials Unlimited, pg 860
Video Resources Software, pg 928

GEORGIA

On-Line Productions, pg 845

ILLINOIS

ABSA Films, pg 672
CCore Media Inc, pg 718
1st Financial Training Services Inc, pg 761
Nightingale-Conant Corp, pg 841

IOWA

Prositions Inc, pg 865

KENTUCKY

KET The Kentucky Network, pg 798

MARYLAND

Sign Media Inc, pg 887
Total AV Systems, pg 916

MASSACHUSETTS

Penfield Productions Ltd, pg 853

MICHIGAN

Digi Sign Design LLC, pg 741
VMS Inc, pg 932

NEBRASKA

B & B Video Productions Inc, pg 700

NEVADA

DVDs4Less, pg 748

NEW HAMPSHIRE

Chip Taylor Communications LLC, pg 907

NEW JERSEY

Allegro Productions Inc, pg 680

NEW YORK

Broadstreet Productions LLC, pg 711
HB-Content, pg 777
Monad Trainer's Aide Inc, pg 829
Video Catalogue Co Inc, pg 927

NORTH CAROLINA

AudioSolutionz LLC, pg 695
Speakers Unlimited, pg 896

PENNSYLVANIA

CORTRON Media LLC, pg 732
FMP Media Solutions Inc, pg 763

TENNESSEE

American Blackguard Inc, pg 683

TEXAS

Executive Development Systems Inc, pg 757

VERMONT

University of Vermont, Instructional Television Dept, pg 923
Wilson McLeran Inc, pg 939

VIRGINIA

CACI Integrated Communications, pg 713
CDR Communications Inc, pg 719
WETA Production Center, pg 936

WASHINGTON

Bennett-Watt HD Productions Inc, pg 703

ONTARIO

Kineticvideo.com, pg 799

Sales Promotion & Training Program Producers

ALABAMA

Leo Ticheli Productions, pg 913

ARIZONA

Aardvark Productions LLC, pg 671
Candee Productions Inc, pg 716
Creative Backstage, pg 733
Direct Current Video Productions, pg 743
Film Creations Ltd, pg 760
Fox 10 Productions (KSAZ-TV), pg 765
Master Video Disc & Design, pg 819
Merestone, pg 823
Metropolitan Audio-Visual Inc, pg 824
On-Site Video, pg 846

ARKANSAS

Live'N'Loud, pg 810
Mullikin Agency, pg 833
White Diamond Productions LLC, pg 937

CALIFORNIA

Aaron Marcus and Associates, pg 671
Access Video in Berkeley, pg 673
Action Video, pg 675
Artichoke Productions, pg 690
Big Door, pg 705
Cavalcade Productions Inc, pg 717
Steve Chandler, pg 720
Chick Russell Communications, pg 721
Classic Images Stock Footage LLC, pg 726
Coastline Productions, pg 727
Creative Technology, pg 733
Crystal Pyramid Productions™, pg 735
Custom Video Productions Inc, pg 736
Deja View Video, pg 740
Design Media, pg 741
digital OutPost, pg 742
Direct Images Interactive Inc, pg 743
Discovery Education - Los Angeles, pg 743
Dolphin MultiMedia Inc, pg 745
ECONEWS (Environmental Television Series) & (Environmental Directions Radio Series), pg 750
Imageworks, pg 785
International Contact Inc, pg 790
ITV Productions, pg 792
Kavich Reynolds Productions Inc, pg 797
KTVU-Retail Services, pg 802
Main Street Media Inc, pg 815
Maximus Media Inc, pg 820
McCune Audio-Video-Lighting, pg 821
Media Magic, pg 822
The Media Staff Inc, pg 822
New & Unique Videos™, pg 839
On-Trax Inc, pg 846
Penrose Productions, pg 854
PK Productions, pg 857
PSI Inc, pg 866
QRS Software Services, pg 867
Dick Reizner Film & Video, pg 873
RetinaVision Productions, pg 874
Glenn Roland Films, pg 876
SNAP, pg 891
Staylor-Made Communications Inc, pg 900
Still N' Motion, pg 901
Tam Communications Inc, pg 906
TMW Media Group, pg 915
Total Creative, pg 916
TVA Media Group, pg 919

Twin Peaks Creative, pg 920
Videografix LLC, pg 929
Vineyard Video & Photography, pg 930
Visions Plus, pg 931
Wavemaker Media Design, pg 934
West Coast Projections Inc, pg 935
WMS Media Inc, pg 940
Yada/Levine Video Productions, pg 943
Zamacona Productions, pg 945

COLORADO

Apogee Communications Group, pg 687
Daylight Productions & Rentals, pg 739
Flashback Media Productions, pg 762
People Productions, pg 854
Transtar Entertainment Co Inc, pg 917

CONNECTICUT

Cine-Med Inc, pg 723
Digital Video Productions, pg 742
The Gary-Paul Agency, pg 768
Geomatrix Productions, pg 770
Ironik Design & Post, pg 791
Moving Pictures, pg 832
P&P Studios Inc, pg 851
Powerstation Events, pg 860
UConn Health Multimedia Services, pg 920
Video Production Associates Inc, pg 928

DISTRICT OF COLUMBIA

O'Keefe Communications Inc, pg 844
Yellow Cat Productions Inc, pg 944

FLORIDA

Applebox Studio, pg 687
Blackburst Entertainment LLC, pg 706
Civins Productions Inc, pg 725
Communications Concepts Inc (CCI), pg 729
CopShopMiami.com, pg 731
Courter Films LLC, pg 732
Easy Edit Video Inc, pg 750
I M P A C T Publishing Inc, pg 783
Jordan Klein Film & Video (JKFV), pg 795
National Teleproductions Inc, pg 837
Paradise Video & Film, pg 851
Sound & Vision Communications Inc, pg 893
Sound*Light, pg 894
Sunfire Communications Inc, pg 904
Sunrise Studios, pg 904
Tel-Air Interests Inc, pg 909
Tight Line Productions, pg 914
Tricycle Studios, pg 918
Mike Vasilinda Productions Inc, pg 925
Video Resources Software, pg 928
Video Techniques Inc, pg 928

GEORGIA

Beachwood Productions, pg 702
Burst Video/Film Inc, pg 713
Cox Media, pg 732
ECG Productions, pg 750
GP Studios, pg 773
Guerrilla Productions LLC, pg 774

PROGRAMMING — VIDEO

Sales Promotion & Training Program Producers (continued)

TENNESSEE (continued)

Paradigm Marketing & Creative, pg 851
Running Pony Productions LLC, pg 878
Scripps Networks, pg 882

TEXAS

Alpha Video Productions, pg 682
AMS Pictures, pg 684
Biway Media, pg 706
Castleview Productions, pg 717
Cerutti Productions Inc, pg 720
Communication Arts Multimedia Inc, pg 728
Countdown Productions Inc, pg 732
Dykeman Associates Inc, pg 748
The Editing Co, pg 750
Epic Software Group Inc, pg 755
Horizon Film + Video Productions, pg 781
JSAV, pg 795
Marx InDigital, pg 818
Mediaforce Productions, pg 822
Earl Miller Productions Inc, pg 827
Julye Newlin Productions Inc, pg 840
Omega Productions, pg 845
Omni Intercommunications Inc, pg 845
Romar Learning Solutions LLC, pg 877
The Samuels Co, pg 879
South Coast Film & Video, pg 895
Sportsmen on Film Inc, pg 898
Stage Directions, pg 898

VERMONT

Marlboro Productions, pg 817
University of Vermont, Instructional Television Dept, pg 923
Wilson McLeran Inc, pg 939

VIRGINIA

Advance Concepts Inc, pg 677
Altruist Media LLC, pg 682
CACI Integrated Communications, pg 713
CDR Communications Inc, pg 719
Cinebar Productions Inc, pg 723
CVW Event Productions, pg 736
Limelight Communications Inc, pg 808
Metro Productions, pg 824
National Media Services Inc, pg 836
Rocktown Media, pg 876
Studio Center Corp, pg 902
Video Solutions, pg 928
WETA Production Center, pg 936

WASHINGTON

Adams Creative & Production Services, pg 675
Bennett-Watt HD Productions Inc, pg 703
Hamilton Studio, pg 775
Intermedia Inc, pg 789
Medical Media Systems, pg 823
North-by-Northwest - A Digital Studio, pg 842

Sparkworks Media, pg 896
Victory Studios, pg 927

WEST VIRGINIA

Blackwater Video Productions, pg 707

WISCONSIN

AVS Group, pg 699
5th Floor Recording Co, pg 760
Logan Productions Inc, pg 811
Meridian Studios, pg 824
Midland Video Productions Inc, pg 827
Mirror 34 Productions, pg 828
University of Wisconsin-Oshkosh Radio-TV-Film Dept, pg 923
USAV Group Inc, pg 923
Video Wisconsin Inc, pg 929
Watts Communications Inc, pg 934
Wisconsin Public Television, pg 940

WYOMING

Bridger Productions Inc, pg 710

ALBERTA

Black Media Works, pg 706
Global TV, pg 771
HDTV Productions Inc, pg 777

BRITISH COLUMBIA

Triad Communications Ltd, pg 918

MANITOBA

Spectra Video Productions Ltd, pg 897

NEWFOUNDLAND AND LABRADOR

Vidcraft Productions Ltd, pg 927

ONTARIO

DebsVoice, pg 739
GAPC (General Assembly Production Centre), pg 768
Image Video Services & Productions, pg 785
Jams Productions Inc, pg 793
JFB Communications, pg 794
Mediaimage Communications Group, pg 822
RB Productions, pg 870
Silver Creek Media Inc, pg 888
Video Excellence Productions, pg 927

QUEBEC

Kerrigan Productions Inc, pg 798

SASKATCHEWAN

plan9films, pg 857

Sales Promotion & Training Program Rentals

ARIZONA

Video Learning Library, pg 928

CALIFORNIA

Direct Cinema Ltd Inc, pg 743

ILLINOIS

1st Financial Training Services Inc, pg 761

MICHIGAN

Digi Sign Design LLC, pg 741

NEW YORK

BC Studio, pg 702

NORTH CAROLINA

Image Associates Inc, pg 784

VERMONT

University of Vermont, Instructional Television Dept, pg 923

Scientific Program Distributors

ALABAMA

CMEinfo™, pg 727

ARIZONA

Video Learning Library, pg 928

CALIFORNIA

Academy Savant, pg 672
Allied Artists International Inc, pg 681
Astronomical Society of the Pacific, pg 691
Crystal Pyramid Productions™, pg 735
Deja View Video, pg 740
Direct Cinema Ltd Inc, pg 743
Discovery Education - Los Angeles, pg 743
Increase Video/Silver Mine Video, pg 786
New & Unique Videos™, pg 839
Pyramid Media, pg 867
Sea Studios Foundation, pg 883
TMW Media Group, pg 915
The Video Project, pg 928
The Wine Appreciation Guild Ltd, pg 939

DISTRICT OF COLUMBIA

American Chemical Society (ACS), pg 683

FLORIDA

PAR Inc, pg 851
Video Resources Software, pg 928

HAWAII

Ka Io Productions Inc, pg 796

ILLINOIS

ABSA Films, pg 672
Cahokia Mounds Museum Society, pg 713
Film Ideas Inc, pg 760

KENTUCKY

National Geographic Learning, pg 836
WaxWorks VideoWorks, pg 934

MARYLAND

MMI Marketing, pg 828

MASSACHUSETTS

Documentary Educational Resources Inc, pg 744
Penfield Productions Ltd, pg 853
Sinauer Associates, pg 889

MICHIGAN

Digi Sign Design LLC, pg 741
Emery-Pratt Co, pg 753
MSU Technologies, pg 833

MISSOURI

ASET - The Neurodiagnostic Society, pg 690

NEVADA

DVDs4Less, pg 748

NEW HAMPSHIRE

Chip Taylor Communications LLC, pg 907

NEW JERSEY

Allegro Productions Inc, pg 680

NEW YORK

FACE Foundation, pg 758
Films Media Group, pg 760
Guilford Publications, pg 774
Human Relations Media, pg 782
Janson Media Inc, pg 793
March of Dimes Foundation, pg 816
Mastervision Inc, pg 819
Richter Productions Inc, pg 875
SciMedTv, pg 882
Synaptic Digital, pg 905
VIEW Inc (Video International Entertainment World Inc), pg 930

NORTH CAROLINA

Carolina Biological Supply Co, pg 717

PENNSYLVANIA

Bullfrog Films Inc, pg 712
Discovery Education - South Burlington, pg 743
FMP Media Solutions Inc, pg 763

TEXAS

CEV Multimedia Ltd, pg 720
Emergency Film Group, pg 753

VERMONT

University of Vermont, Instructional Television Dept, pg 923

VIRGINIA

CACI Integrated Communications, pg 713
Filmakers Library, pg 760
WETA Production Center, pg 936

WASHINGTON

Bennett-Watt HD Productions Inc, pg 703
Linguist's Software Inc, pg 809

BRITISH COLUMBIA

Thompson Rivers University Marketing & Communications Dept, pg 913

ONTARIO

Canadian Learning Co Inc, pg 715
Kineticvideo.com, pg 799
Life Cycle Books Ltd, pg 807
McIntyre Media Inc, pg 821

QUEBEC

Les Productions Via Le Monde
(Daniel Bertolino) Inc, pg 864

Scientific Program Producers

ALABAMA

CMEinfo™, pg 727

ALASKA

Alaska Media Pros LLC, pg 679

ARIZONA

Aardvark Productions LLC, pg 671
Film Creations Ltd, pg 760

CALIFORNIA

Academy Savant, pg 672
Access Video in Berkeley, pg 673
Action Video, pg 675
Allied Artists International Inc,
   pg 681
Artichoke Productions, pg 690
Astronomical Society of the Pacific,
   pg 691
Big Door, pg 705
Classic Images Stock Footage LLC,
   pg 726
Creative Technology, pg 733
Crystal Pyramid Productions™,
   pg 735
Custom Video Productions Inc,
   pg 736
Davidson Productions, pg 738
Deja View Video, pg 740
Direct Images Interactive Inc,
   pg 743
Discovery Education - Los Angeles,
   pg 743
Dolphin MultiMedia Inc, pg 745
imageReal Pictures LLC, pg 785
ITV Productions, pg 792
Kavich Reynolds Productions Inc,
   pg 797
Main Street Media Inc, pg 815
Maximus Media Inc, pg 820
McCune Audio-Video-Lighting,
   pg 821
The Media Staff Inc, pg 822
New & Unique Videos™, pg 839
Penrose Productions, pg 854
QRS Software Services, pg 867
Dick Reizner Film & Video, pg 873
Screen Door Entertainment Inc,
   pg 882
Sea Studios Foundation, pg 883
SNAP, pg 891
Staylor-Made Communications Inc,
   pg 900
Still N' Motion, pg 901
Tam Communications Inc, pg 906
TMW Media Group, pg 915
Total Creative, pg 916
Twin Peaks Creative, pg 920
Vineyard Video & Photography,
   pg 930
Visions Plus, pg 931
Wavemaker Media Design, pg 934
West Coast Projections Inc, pg 935

COLORADO

Apogee Communications Group,
   pg 687
Daylight Productions & Rentals,
   pg 739
Flashback Media Productions,
   pg 762
Transtar Entertainment Co Inc,
   pg 917

CONNECTICUT

Ironik Design & Post, pg 791
P&P Studios Inc, pg 851

DISTRICT OF COLUMBIA

American Chemical Society (ACS),
   pg 683
Hillmann & Carr Inc, pg 780
Yellow Cat Productions Inc, pg 944

FLORIDA

Blackburst Entertainment LLC,
   pg 706
Civins Productions Inc, pg 725
CopShopMiami.com, pg 731
Courter Films LLC, pg 732
Jordan Klein Film & Video (JKFV),
   pg 795
National Teleproductions Inc,
   pg 837
Sound & Vision Communications
   Inc, pg 893
Sunfire Communications Inc,
   pg 904
Sunrise Studios, pg 904
Tricycle Studios, pg 918
Video Resources Software, pg 928

GEORGIA

Beachwood Productions, pg 702
Cox Media, pg 732
GP Studios, pg 773
Guerrilla Productions LLC, pg 774
On-Line Productions, pg 845

HAWAII

Hyperspective Studios Inc, pg 783
Ka Io Productions Inc, pg 796
Sight & Sound Studios, pg 887

IDAHO

Brad Shaw Productions Inc, pg 885
Wide Eye Productions, pg 938

ILLINOIS

ABSA Films, pg 672
Cahokia Mounds Museum Society,
   pg 713
Explore, pg 757
Film Police, pg 760
IV Media Resources, pg 792
Manning Productions, pg 816
Mimi Productions, pg 828
Pepper Group, pg 854
SCI Television & Creative Media
   LLC, pg 882
20/20 Communications Inc, pg 920
Video Impressions, pg 928

INDIANA

A-V-A Video Productions, pg 671
Road Pictures, pg 876

KANSAS

KAKE-TV, pg 796

KENTUCKY

Idle Minds Productions Inc, pg 784
Donna Lawrence Productions,
   pg 804
National Geographic Learning,
   pg 836
NIMCO Inc, pg 841

LOUISIANA

Louisiana State University Division
   of Strategic Communications,
   pg 811
Moxie Media, pg 832

MARYLAND

Adventure Productions LLC, pg 678
Richard Chisolm Cinematography,
   pg 722
dbF a Media Company, pg 739
The Image Generators, pg 785
Kramer Communications Video
   Production, pg 801
MMI Marketing, pg 828

MASSACHUSETTS

Award Productions Inc, pg 699
Documentary Educational Resources
   Inc, pg 744
Green Mountain Post Films (GMP),
   pg 774
Heliotrope Studios, pg 778
In the Wild Productions, pg 786
Monadnock Media Inc, pg 829
Northern Light Productions (NLP),
   pg 842
Penfield Productions Ltd, pg 853
Sinauer Associates, pg 889
TVN-The Video Network, pg 919
VideoLink Inc, an AVI-SPL
   company, pg 929
WVP Boston, pg 942

MICHIGAN

Digi Sign Design LLC, pg 741
K&R All Media Productions LLC,
   pg 796
K&R's Recording Studios Inc,
   pg 796

MINNESOTA

House of Cinemagraphics, pg 782
MastCom, pg 819
Worthwhile Films, pg 941

MISSOURI

ASET - The Neurodiagnostic
   Society, pg 690

NEBRASKA

Rainbow Video Productions Inc,
   pg 869

NEVADA

Aardvark Video & Media
   Productions, pg 671
DVDs4Less, pg 748
Encore Event Technologies LLC,
   pg 754
JCS Video Productions, pg 793
Tetrahedron LLC, pg 911

NEW HAMPSHIRE

Apertura, pg 686
Channell One Video, pg 720
Chip Taylor Communications LLC,
   pg 907

NEW JERSEY

Allegro Productions Inc, pg 680
CFP Video Productions Inc, pg 720
Euro-Pacific Film & Video
   Productions Inc, pg 756
Laurel Video Productions, pg 804
MiB MediaWorks, pg 825
Midnight Media Group Inc, pg 827
Optisonics Productions, pg 847
Telequest Inc, pg 910
VCSvideo, pg 925

NEW MEXICO

Production Outfitters, pg 864

NEW YORK

aurora productions, pg 696
Brian Film Productions LLC,
   pg 710
Clarity Media Group, pg 725
CompuWeather Inc, pg 729
Criterion Collection, pg 735
Films Media Group, pg 760
Florentine Films, pg 762
Guilford Publications, pg 774
Hello World Communications,
   pg 778
Human Relations Media, pg 782
Ketchum Inc, pg 798
L A Bruell Inc, pg 802
March of Dimes Foundation, pg 816
Mastervision Inc, pg 819
MRY, pg 832
News Broadcast Network Inc,
   pg 840
The Palmer Group, pg 850
Pat Kogan Productions Inc, pg 852
Peckham Productions Inc, pg 852
PrimaLux Video Inc, pg 862
Richter Productions Inc, pg 875
SciMedTv, pg 882
Synaptic Digital, pg 905
Videograf, pg 929
VIEW Inc (Video International
   Entertainment World Inc), pg 930

NORTH CAROLINA

Pat Appleson Studios Inc, pg 687
Carolina Biological Supply Co,
   pg 717
The Communications Group Inc,
   pg 729
Horizon Video Productions Inc,
   pg 781
Kino Mountain Productions LLC,
   pg 799
Videowerks, pg 930

OHIO

Image Video Teleproductions Inc,
   pg 785
Lyon Video Inc, pg 813
MainSail Production Services Inc,
   pg 815
R&B Communications Inc, pg 870
Take 1 Media Services, pg 906
Vista Color Imaging Inc, pg 931

OREGON

Ideascape Inc, pg 784
Odyssey Productions Inc, pg 844
Production West, pg 864

PENNSYLVANIA

Audio Visual Communications Inc,
   pg 694
Beholder Productions Inc, pg 703
CCI Communications Inc, pg 718

PROGRAMMING — VIDEO

Scientific Program Producers (continued)

PENNSYLVANIA (continued)

Discovery Education - South Burlington, pg 743
FMP Media Solutions Inc, pg 763
Innovision Media Group, pg 788
Muderick Media, pg 833
Panta Rhei Media Inc, pg 851
Production Masters Inc (PMI), pg 864
The Videohouse Inc, pg 929

RHODE ISLAND

Sound-FX-Design, pg 894

SOUTH CAROLINA

Venture Media, pg 925

TENNESSEE

Continental Film, pg 731
Paradigm Marketing & Creative, pg 851
Running Pony Productions LLC, pg 878
Scripps Networks, pg 882

TEXAS

Alpha Video Productions, pg 682
Cerutti Productions Inc, pg 720
CEV Multimedia Ltd, pg 720
Communication Arts Multimedia Inc, pg 728
The Editing Co, pg 750
Emergency Film Group, pg 753
Horizon Film + Video Productions, pg 781
Mediaforce Productions, pg 822
Earl Miller Productions Inc, pg 827
Julye Newlin Productions Inc, pg 840
Omega Productions, pg 845
Omni Intercommunications Inc, pg 845
Romar Learning Solutions LLC, pg 877
South Coast Film & Video, pg 895
Sportsmen on Film Inc, pg 898
Texas Heart Institute Visual Communication Services, pg 911

VERMONT

University of Vermont, Instructional Television Dept, pg 923

VIRGINIA

CACI Integrated Communications, pg 713
Limelight Communications Inc, pg 808
Metro Productions, pg 824
National Media Services Inc, pg 836
Rocktown Media, pg 876
Video Solutions, pg 928
WETA Production Center, pg 936

WASHINGTON

Bennett-Watt HD Productions Inc, pg 703
Linguist's Software Inc, pg 809

WISCONSIN

5th Floor Recording Co, pg 760
USAV Group Inc, pg 923
Video Wisconsin Inc, pg 929
Wisconsin Public Television, pg 940

WYOMING

Bridger Productions Inc, pg 710

ALBERTA

Global TV, pg 771

BRITISH COLUMBIA

Thompson Rivers University Marketing & Communications Dept, pg 913

NEWFOUNDLAND AND LABRADOR

Vidcraft Productions Ltd, pg 927

NORTHWEST TERRITORIES

Yellowknife Films Inc, pg 944

ONTARIO

ADS Media, pg 677
JFB Communications, pg 794
Video Excellence Productions, pg 927

QUEBEC

Kerrigan Productions Inc, pg 798
Les Productions Via Le Monde (Daniel Bertolino) Inc, pg 864

SASKATCHEWAN

plan9films, pg 857

Scientific Program Rentals

ARIZONA

Video Learning Library, pg 928

CALIFORNIA

Direct Cinema Ltd Inc, pg 743

MASSACHUSETTS

Documentary Educational Resources Inc, pg 744

MICHIGAN

Digi Sign Design LLC, pg 741

MISSOURI

University of Missouri-Columbia, pg 923

NEW YORK

Films Media Group, pg 760
Icarus Films Inc, pg 783
Richter Productions Inc, pg 875
VIEW Inc (Video International Entertainment World Inc), pg 930

PENNSYLVANIA

Bullfrog Films Inc, pg 712

VERMONT

University of Vermont, Instructional Television Dept, pg 923

VIRGINIA

Filmakers Library, pg 760

QUEBEC

Les Productions Via Le Monde (Daniel Bertolino) Inc, pg 864

Short Film, see Theatrical Short

Sponsored Program Distributors

CALIFORNIA

Crystal Pyramid Productions™, pg 735
Direct Cinema Ltd Inc, pg 743
Medcom Inc, pg 821
New & Unique Videos™, pg 839
Pyramid Media, pg 867
Visual Communications - Southern California Asian American Studies Central Inc, pg 931

CONNECTICUT

Cine-Med Inc, pg 723

DISTRICT OF COLUMBIA

Department of VSA & Accessibility at the John F Kennedy Center for the Performing Arts, pg 740

GEORGIA

On-Line Productions, pg 845

ILLINOIS

Professional Education Institute (PEI), pg 865
Terra Nova Films Inc, pg 911

MARYLAND

Adventure Productions LLC, pg 678
DSR Computer Technology Specialists Inc, pg 747

MASSACHUSETTS

HOME Inc, pg 781
Penfield Productions Ltd, pg 853

MICHIGAN

Digi Sign Design LLC, pg 741

NEVADA

DVDs4Less, pg 748

NEW HAMPSHIRE

Chip Taylor Communications LLC, pg 907

NEW JERSEY

Allegro Productions Inc, pg 680
Euro-Pacific Film & Video Productions Inc, pg 756

NEW YORK

Broadstreet Productions LLC, pg 711
William Greaves Productions Inc, pg 774
HB-Content, pg 777
Mastervision Inc, pg 819
Synaptic Digital, pg 905

VIRGINIA

Video Catalogue Co Inc, pg 927
VIEW Inc (Video International Entertainment World Inc), pg 930

NORTH CAROLINA

NASCAR Productions LLC, pg 835

OREGON

Cooking by the Book, pg 731

PENNSYLVANIA

Beholder Productions Inc, pg 703
Bullfrog Films Inc, pg 712
FMP Media Solutions Inc, pg 763

TENNESSEE

American Blackguard Inc, pg 683

VIRGINIA

WETA Production Center, pg 936

WASHINGTON

Bennett-Watt HD Productions Inc, pg 703

QUEBEC

Les Productions Via Le Monde (Daniel Bertolino) Inc, pg 864

Sponsored Program Producers

ALABAMA

Leo Ticheli Productions, pg 913

ARIZONA

Fox 10 Productions (KSAZ-TV), pg 765

ARKANSAS

White Diamond Productions LLC, pg 937

CALIFORNIA

A Go Go Films, pg 671
Action Video, pg 675
Big Door, pg 705
Cavalcade Productions Inc, pg 717
Classic Images Stock Footage LLC, pg 726
Creative Technology, pg 733
Crystal Pyramid Productions™, pg 735
Custom Video Productions Inc, pg 736
Direct Images Interactive Inc, pg 743
Durrin Productions Inc, pg 748
imageReal Pictures LLC, pg 785
ITV Productions, pg 792
Kavich Reynolds Productions Inc, pg 797
KTVU-Retail Services, pg 802
Main Street Media Inc, pg 815
Maximus Media Inc, pg 820
McCune Audio-Video-Lighting, pg 821
Medcom Inc, pg 821
Media Magic, pg 822
The Media Staff Inc, pg 822
New & Unique Videos™, pg 839
Nineteen87, pg 841
Point of View Productions, pg 858
QRS Software Services, pg 867
Dick Reizner Film & Video, pg 873
Glenn Roland Films, pg 876

Screen Door Entertainment Inc, pg 882
SNAP, pg 891
Staylor-Made Communications Inc, pg 900
Still N' Motion, pg 901
Total Creative, pg 916
Twin Peaks Creative, pg 920
Vineyard Video & Photography, pg 930
Visual Communications - Southern California Asian American Studies Central Inc, pg 931
Wavemaker Media Design, pg 934
Zamacona Productions, pg 945

COLORADO

Apogee Communications Group, pg 687
Flashback Media Productions, pg 762
Tatum Video, pg 907
Transtar Entertainment Co Inc, pg 917

CONNECTICUT

Cine-Med Inc, pg 723
Ironik Design & Post, pg 791
Moving Pictures, pg 832

DISTRICT OF COLUMBIA

Department of VSA & Accessibility at the John F Kennedy Center for the Performing Arts, pg 740
Hillmann & Carr Inc, pg 780

FLORIDA

Applebox Studio, pg 687
Blackburst Entertainment LLC, pg 706
CD ROM™ Inc, pg 718
Civins Productions Inc, pg 725
Communications Concepts Inc (CCI), pg 729
CopShopMiami.com, pg 731
Courter Films LLC, pg 732
Jordan Klein Film & Video (JKFV), pg 795
National Teleproductions Inc, pg 837
Paradise Video & Film, pg 851
Sound & Vision Communications Inc, pg 893
Sunfire Communications Inc, pg 904
Sunrise Studios, pg 904
Tel-Air Interests Inc, pg 909
Tricycle Studios, pg 918

GEORGIA

Beachwood Productions, pg 702
Burst Video/Film Inc, pg 713
Guerrilla Productions LLC, pg 774
Myriad Productions, pg 835
Malcolm Neal Productions, pg 837
On-Line Productions, pg 845

HAWAII

Hyperspective Studios Inc, pg 783
Sight & Sound Studios, pg 887
1013 Integrated, pg 911

IDAHO

Brad Shaw Productions Inc, pg 885
Wide Eye Productions, pg 938

ILLINOIS

Airways Digital Media, pg 679
Film Police, pg 760

Manning Productions, pg 816
Rob Orr Productions Ltd, pg 848
Pepper Group, pg 854
Professional Education Institute (PEI), pg 865
PSAV® Presentation Services (Hotel Services Division), pg 866
SCI Television & Creative Media LLC, pg 882
Terra Nova Films Inc, pg 911
Video Impressions, pg 928
WEEK TV, pg 935
Winter Productions, pg 939

INDIANA

A-V-A Video Productions, pg 671
Advanced Media Integration, pg 677
Road Pictures, pg 876

IOWA

Educational Technology & Media Services, pg 751

KANSAS

KAKE-TV, pg 796

KENTUCKY

Donna Lawrence Productions, pg 804

LOUISIANA

Moxie Media, pg 832

MAINE

WGME-TV, pg 936

MARYLAND

Adventure Productions LLC, pg 678
Richard Chisolm Cinematography, pg 722
CPR MultiMedia Solutions, pg 732
dbF a Media Company, pg 739
DSR Computer Technology Specialists Inc, pg 747
Kramer Communications Video Production, pg 801

MASSACHUSETTS

Award Productions Inc, pg 699
Green Mountain Post Films (GMP), pg 774
Heliotrope Studios, pg 778
HOME Inc, pg 781
Penfield Productions Ltd, pg 853
TVN-The Video Network, pg 919

MICHIGAN

Digi Sign Design LLC, pg 741
K&R All Media Productions LLC, pg 796
K&R's Recording Studios Inc, pg 796

MINNESOTA

House of Cinemagraphics, pg 782
MastCom, pg 819

MONTANA

KUSM TV, pg 802

NEVADA

Aardvark Video & Media Productions, pg 671
DVDs4Less, pg 748

Encore Event Technologies LLC, pg 754
JCS Video Productions, pg 793

NEW HAMPSHIRE

Apertura, pg 686
Channell One Video, pg 720
Chip Taylor Communications LLC, pg 907

NEW JERSEY

Allegro Productions Inc, pg 680
Broadcast Center Studios, pg 710
CFP Video Productions Inc, pg 720
Euro-Pacific Film & Video Productions Inc, pg 756
Laurel Video Productions, pg 804
MiB MediaWorks, pg 825
Midnight Media Group Inc, pg 827
Optisonics Productions, pg 847
Telequest Inc, pg 910
VCSvideo, pg 925

NEW MEXICO

Production Outfitters, pg 864

NEW YORK

Associated Press Television News, pg 691
aurora productions, pg 696
Brian Film Productions LLC, pg 710
Broadstreet Productions LLC, pg 711
Cohn Creative Group LLC, pg 727
Florentine Films, pg 762
William Greaves Productions Inc, pg 774
HB-Content, pg 777
Ketchum Inc, pg 798
Mastervision Inc, pg 819
MRY, pg 832
News Broadcast Network Inc, pg 840
The Palmer Group, pg 850
Pat Kogan Productions Inc, pg 852
Peckham Productions Inc, pg 852
PrimaLux Video Inc, pg 862
Richter Productions Inc, pg 875
Suggs Media Productions Inc, pg 903
Synaptic Digital, pg 905
TeleTime Productions, pg 910
Third World Newsreel/Camera News Inc, pg 912
Video Catalogue Co Inc, pg 927
Videograf, pg 929
VIEW Inc (Video International Entertainment World Inc), pg 930
WNET/New York Public Media, pg 940

NORTH CAROLINA

Pat Appleson Studios Inc, pg 687
The Communications Group Inc, pg 729
Digital Rain LLC, pg 742
Horizon Video Productions Inc, pg 781
Kino Mountain Productions LLC, pg 799
Moving Pictures, pg 832
NASCAR Productions LLC, pg 835
Videowerks, pg 930

OHIO

Advent Media Inc, pg 677
Russ Beckner Pictures, pg 703
Image Video Teleproductions Inc, pg 785

Lyon Video Inc, pg 813
MainSail Production Services Inc, pg 815
R&B Communications Inc, pg 870
Take 1 Media Services, pg 906
Vista Color Imaging Inc, pg 931

OREGON

CMD Agency, pg 726
Ideascape Inc, pg 784
KPDX-TV Production Center, pg 801
Odyssey Productions Inc, pg 844
Production West, pg 864
REX, pg 874

PENNSYLVANIA

Beholder Productions Inc, pg 703
CCI Communications Inc, pg 718
FMP Media Solutions Inc, pg 763
Innovision Media Group, pg 788
JPL, pg 795
Kensington Falls Animation, pg 797
Muderick Media, pg 833
NEP Group Inc, pg 838
Production Masters Inc (PMI), pg 864
Video/Film Associates, pg 928
The Videohouse Inc, pg 929
Visual Sound Inc, pg 931

RHODE ISLAND

Sound-FX-Design, pg 894

SOUTH CAROLINA

Stages Video Productions, pg 899

TENNESSEE

American Blackguard Inc, pg 683
Continental Film, pg 731
Running Pony Productions LLC, pg 878
Scripps Networks, pg 882

TEXAS

Cerutti Productions Inc, pg 720
Horizon Film + Video Productions, pg 781
Mediaforce Productions, pg 822
Earl Miller Productions Inc, pg 827
Julye Newlin Productions Inc, pg 840
Omega Productions, pg 845
Romar Learning Solutions LLC, pg 877
South Coast Film & Video, pg 895
Texas Heart Institute Visual Communication Services, pg 911

VIRGINIA

Altruist Media LLC, pg 682
CVW Event Productions, pg 736
Limelight Communications Inc, pg 808
Metro Productions, pg 824
Rocktown Media, pg 876
Video Solutions, pg 928
WETA Production Center, pg 936

WASHINGTON

Bennett-Watt HD Productions Inc, pg 703
Intermedia Inc, pg 789
Sparkworks Media, pg 896
Victory Studios, pg 927

PROGRAMMING — VIDEO

Sponsored Program Producers (continued)

WISCONSIN

5th Floor Recording Co, pg 760
Video Wisconsin Inc, pg 929
Watts Communications Inc, pg 934

WYOMING

Bridger Productions Inc, pg 710

ALBERTA

Black Media Works, pg 706
Global TV, pg 771
HDTV Productions Inc, pg 777

BRITISH COLUMBIA

Triad Communications Ltd, pg 918

MANITOBA

Spectra Video Productions Ltd, pg 897

NEWFOUNDLAND AND LABRADOR

Vidcraft Productions Ltd, pg 927

ONTARIO

GAPC (General Assembly Production Centre), pg 768
JFB Communications, pg 794
Marblemedia, pg 816

QUEBEC

Kerrigan Productions Inc, pg 798
Les Productions Via Le Monde (Daniel Bertolino) Inc, pg 864

SASKATCHEWAN

plan9films, pg 857

Sponsored Program Rentals

CALIFORNIA

Direct Cinema Ltd Inc, pg 743
Medcom Inc, pg 821
Visual Communications - Southern California Asian American Studies Central Inc, pg 931

GEORGIA

On-Line Productions, pg 845

ILLINOIS

Terra Nova Films Inc, pg 911

MICHIGAN

Digi Sign Design LLC, pg 741

NEW JERSEY

Euro-Pacific Film & Video Productions Inc, pg 756

NEW YORK

William Greaves Productions Inc, pg 774
VIEW Inc (Video International Entertainment World Inc), pg 930

PENNSYLVANIA

Bullfrog Films Inc, pg 712

Sports Program Distributors

ARIZONA

Rodeo Video Inc, pg 876
Video Learning Library, pg 928

CALIFORNIA

Allied Artists International Inc, pg 681
Crystal Pyramid Productions™, pg 735
Deja View Video, pg 740
Direct Cinema Ltd Inc, pg 743
411 Video Information, pg 764
Golden State Dance Teachers Association (GSDTA), pg 772
Increase Video/Silver Mine Video, pg 786
MarVista Entertainment Inc, pg 818
MGM Home Entertainment, pg 825
monterey media inc, pg 829
monterey video, pg 829
Publishers Group West (PGW), an Ingram brand, pg 866
Pyramid Media, pg 867
Glenn Roland Films, pg 876
Sodanceabit, pg 892
TMW Media Group, pg 915
Universal Pictures Home Entertainment, pg 922
Valley Media, pg 924
Warner Home Video Inc, pg 934

COLORADO

Tatum Video, pg 907

DISTRICT OF COLUMBIA

Department of VSA & Accessibility at the John F Kennedy Center for the Performing Arts, pg 740

FLORIDA

Accord Productions, pg 673
I M P A C T Publishing Inc, pg 783
Potentials Unlimited, pg 860

GEORGIA

School Media Associates LLC, pg 882

ILLINOIS

Cool-Lux, pg 731
Movies Unlimited, pg 831
Nightingale-Conant Corp, pg 841

IOWA

Championship Productions Inc, pg 720

KENTUCKY

WaxWorks VideoWorks, pg 934

MARYLAND

RLJ Entertainment Inc, pg 875
Total AV Systems, pg 916

MASSACHUSETTS

The New Film Company Inc, pg 839
Penfield Productions Ltd, pg 853

MICHIGAN

Digi Sign Design LLC, pg 741

NEW HAMPSHIRE

Channell One Video, pg 720
Chip Taylor Communications LLC, pg 907
YMAA Publication Center Inc, pg 944

NEW JERSEY

Allegro Productions Inc, pg 680
Euro-Pacific Film & Video Productions Inc, pg 756
NBA Entertainment Inc, pg 837
SES SA, pg 884

NEW YORK

Ace Video, pg 674
Broadstreet Productions LLC, pg 711
HB-Content, pg 777
Janson Media Inc, pg 793
Madison Square Garden, pg 814
Mastervision Inc, pg 819
Synaptic Digital, pg 905
VIEW Inc (Video International Entertainment World Inc), pg 930
Women Make Movies Inc, pg 941

NORTH CAROLINA

NASCAR Productions LLC, pg 835

NORTH DAKOTA

UND Television Center, pg 921

OKLAHOMA

VCI Entertainment, pg 925

PENNSYLVANIA

Bullfrog Films Inc, pg 712
CCI Communications Inc, pg 718
FMP Media Solutions Inc, pg 763
Library Video Company, pg 807
S I Video Sales Group, pg 879

SOUTH CAROLINA

American Production Services LLC, pg 684

TENNESSEE

Spring Arbor Distributors Inc, pg 898

TEXAS

Oncourt Offcourt Ltd, pg 846

VERMONT

Trafalgar Square Books, pg 916

VIRGINIA

CACI Integrated Communications, pg 713

WASHINGTON

Bennett-Watt HD Productions Inc, pg 703
John McLean Media, pg 794

WYOMING

Bridger Productions Inc, pg 710

ALBERTA

Global TV, pg 771

ONTARIO

Canadian Learning Co Inc, pg 715
Canamedia Inc, pg 715

Sports Program Producers

ALASKA

Aurora Films, pg 696

ARIZONA

Aardvark Productions LLC, pg 671
Candee Productions Inc, pg 716
Film Creations Ltd, pg 760
Fox 10 Productions (KSAZ-TV), pg 765
Rodeo Video Inc, pg 876

ARKANSAS

Live'N'Loud, pg 810
White Diamond Productions LLC, pg 937

CALIFORNIA

A Go Go Films, pg 671
Allied Artists International Inc, pg 681
Big Door, pg 705
Classic Images Stock Footage LLC, pg 726
Creative Technology, pg 733
Crystal Pyramid Productions™, pg 735
Custom Video Productions Inc, pg 736
Deja View Video, pg 740
Discovery Education - Los Angeles, pg 743
First Camera, pg 761
Goal Productions, pg 772
Havas Edge, pg 777
Image Integration, pg 785
ITV Productions, pg 792
Kavich Reynolds Productions Inc, pg 797
McCune Audio-Video-Lighting, pg 821
New & Unique Videos™, pg 839
New Circuit Films LLC, pg 839
New Wave Entertainment, pg 839
Nineteen87, pg 841
On-Trax Inc, pg 846
Penrose Productions, pg 854
PME Audio/Video, pg 858
QRS Software Services, pg 867
Glenn Roland Films, pg 876
Screen Door Entertainment Inc, pg 882
SNAP, pg 891
Sodanceabit, pg 892
TMW Media Group, pg 915
Total Creative, pg 916
Twin Peaks Creative, pg 920
Universal Pictures Home Entertainment, pg 922
Vineyard Video & Photography, pg 930

COLORADO

Apogee Communications Group, pg 687
Centre Communications Inc, pg 720
CSI Film & Video LLC, pg 735
Flashback Media Productions, pg 762
Tatum Video, pg 907
Transtar Entertainment Co Inc, pg 917

CONNECTICUT

Digital Video Productions, pg 742
Ironik Design & Post, pg 791
Spectrum, pg 897
Video Production Associates Inc, pg 928

DISTRICT OF COLUMBIA

Department of VSA & Accessibility at the John F Kennedy Center for the Performing Arts, pg 740

FLORIDA

Accord Productions, pg 673
Blackburst Entertainment LLC, pg 706
Civins Productions Inc, pg 725
Communications Concepts Inc (CCI), pg 729
CopShopMiami.com, pg 731
Courter Films LLC, pg 732
DME Studios, pg 744
Easy Edit Video Inc, pg 750
I M P A C T Publishing Inc, pg 783
Jordan Klein Film & Video (JKFV), pg 795
National Teleproductions Inc, pg 837
Olympusat, pg 845
Sunfire Communications Inc, pg 904
Sunrise Studios, pg 904
Tel-Air Interests Inc, pg 909
Venice Media Group, pg 925
WCJB TV20, pg 934

GEORGIA

Beachwood Productions, pg 702
Cox Media, pg 732
ECG Productions, pg 750
GP Studios, pg 773
Guerrila Productions LLC, pg 774
Myriad Productions, pg 835
On-Line Productions, pg 845

HAWAII

Hyperspective Studios Inc, pg 783
Sight & Sound Studios, pg 887

IDAHO

Brad Shaw Productions Inc, pg 885
Wide Eye Productions, pg 938

ILLINOIS

Explore, pg 757
Film Police, pg 760
IV Media Resources, pg 792
Nightingale-Conant Corp, pg 841
Pepper Group, pg 854
SCI Television & Creative Media LLC, pg 882
20/20 Communications Inc, pg 920
Video I-D Teleproductions Inc, pg 928
WEEK TV, pg 935

INDIANA

A-V-A Video Productions, pg 671
PentaVision Communications Inc, pg 854

IOWA

Championship Productions Inc, pg 720

KANSAS

KAKE-TV, pg 796

KENTUCKY

Idle Minds Productions Inc, pg 784
Donna Lawrence Productions, pg 804

LOUISIANA

Moxie Media, pg 832

MARYLAND

Absolute Hollywood, pg 672
Adventure Productions LLC, pg 678
dbF a Media Company, pg 739
Kramer Communications Video Production, pg 801
Quality Film & Video, pg 868

MASSACHUSETTS

Award Productions Inc, pg 699
Green Mountain Post Films (GMP), pg 774
Penfield Productions Ltd, pg 853
TVN-The Video Network, pg 919
VideoLink Inc, an AVI-SPL company, pg 929

MICHIGAN

Digi Sign Design LLC, pg 741
K&R All Media Productions LLC, pg 796
K&R's Recording Studios Inc, pg 796
Lawrence Productions, pg 804

MINNESOTA

House of Cinemagraphics, pg 782

NEBRASKA

Mason Video, pg 819

NEVADA

Aardvark Video & Media Productions, pg 671
Encore Event Technologies LLC, pg 754
JCS Video Productions, pg 793
Skyfire Video, pg 890

NEW HAMPSHIRE

Apertura, pg 686
Channell One Video, pg 720
Chip Taylor Communications LLC, pg 907
YMAA Publication Center Inc, pg 944

NEW JERSEY

Allegro Productions Inc, pg 680
CFP Video Productions Inc, pg 720
Euro-Pacific Film & Video Productions Inc, pg 756
MiB MediaWorks, pg 825
NBA Entertainment Inc, pg 837
Optisonics Productions, pg 847
VCSvideo, pg 925

NEW MEXICO

Production Outfitters, pg 864

NEW YORK

Ace Video, pg 674
Associated Press Television News, pg 691
aurora productions, pg 696
Brian Film Productions LLC, pg 710

Broadstreet Productions LLC, pg 711
Florentine Films, pg 762
Golf Digest Publications, pg 772
HB-Content, pg 777
Jalbert Productions International, pg 792
Madison Square Garden, pg 814
Mastervision Inc, pg 819
MRY, pg 832
The Palmer Group, pg 850
Peckham Productions Inc, pg 852
PrimaLux Video Inc, pg 862
Synaptic Digital, pg 905
VIEW Inc (Video International Entertainment World Inc), pg 930

NORTH CAROLINA

Pat Appleson Studios Inc, pg 687
The Communications Group Inc, pg 729
Digital Rain LLC, pg 742
NASCAR Productions LLC, pg 835
Videowerks, pg 930

NORTH DAKOTA

UND Television Center, pg 921

OHIO

CET, pg 720
Image Video Teleproductions Inc, pg 785
Lyon Video Inc, pg 813
MainSail Production Services Inc, pg 815
R&B Communications Inc, pg 870

OKLAHOMA

Institute for Teaching & Learning Excellence (ITLE), pg 788
VCI Entertainment, pg 925

OREGON

KPDX-TV Production Center, pg 801
KVAL, pg 802
Odyssey Productions Inc, pg 844
Production West, pg 864

PENNSYLVANIA

Bang! Pictures Inc, pg 701
CCI Communications Inc, pg 718
FMP Media Solutions Inc, pg 763
Innovision Media Group, pg 788
Kensington Falls Animation, pg 797
Muderick Media, pg 833
NEP Group Inc, pg 838
Producers Management Television (PMTV), pg 863
Production Masters Inc (PMI), pg 864
S I Video Sales Group, pg 879
The Videohouse Inc, pg 929

RHODE ISLAND

Sound-FX-Design, pg 894

SOUTH CAROLINA

American Production Services LLC, pg 684
Encore Video Productions, pg 754
Go To Team, pg 772

TENNESSEE

Continental Film, pg 731
Running Pony Productions LLC, pg 878
Russ Sturgeon Productions/RSVP, pg 903

TEXAS

AMS Pictures, pg 684
Cerutti Productions Inc, pg 720
Communication Arts Multimedia Inc, pg 728
Countdown Productions Inc, pg 732
Dub King, pg 747
Epic Software Group Inc, pg 755
Horizon Film + Video Productions, pg 781
Mediaforce Productions, pg 822
Earl Miller Productions Inc, pg 827
Omega Productions, pg 845
Oncourt Offcourt Ltd, pg 846
South Coast Film & Video, pg 895
Sportsmen on Film Inc, pg 898

UTAH

ImageWorks Communications, pg 785

VERMONT

Trafalgar Square Books, pg 916

VIRGINIA

CACI Integrated Communications, pg 713
CVW Event Productions, pg 736
Limelight Communications Inc, pg 808
Metro Productions, pg 824

WASHINGTON

Bennett-Watt HD Productions Inc, pg 703
Pal Productions Inc, pg 850
Victory Studios, pg 927

WEST VIRGINIA

Blackwater Video Productions, pg 707

WISCONSIN

5th Floor Recording Co, pg 760
Watts Communications Inc, pg 934
Wisconsin Public Television, pg 940

WYOMING

Bridger Productions Inc, pg 710

ALBERTA

Black Media Works, pg 706
Global TV, pg 771

NEWFOUNDLAND AND LABRADOR

Vidcraft Productions Ltd, pg 927

ONTARIO

ADS Media, pg 677
Image Video Services & Productions, pg 785
Video Excellence Productions, pg 927

QUEBEC

Kerrigan Productions Inc, pg 798

PROGRAMMING — VIDEO

Sports Program Producers (continued)

SASKATCHEWAN

plan9films, pg 857

Sports Program Rentals

ARIZONA

Video Learning Library, pg 928

CALIFORNIA

Direct Cinema Ltd Inc, pg 743

COLORADO

Tatum Video, pg 907

MICHIGAN

Digi Sign Design LLC, pg 741

MISSOURI

University of Missouri-Columbia, pg 923

NEW HAMPSHIRE

Channell One Video, pg 720

NEW JERSEY

Euro-Pacific Film & Video Productions Inc, pg 756

NEW YORK

VIEW Inc (Video International Entertainment World Inc), pg 930

PENNSYLVANIA

Bullfrog Films Inc, pg 712

ONTARIO

L-3 WESCAM, pg 802

Technical Research Program Distributors

CALIFORNIA

Astronomical Society of the Pacific, pg 691
Crystal Pyramid Productions™, pg 735

DISTRICT OF COLUMBIA

American Chemical Society (ACS), pg 683

ILLINOIS

ABSA Films, pg 672
CCH Continuing Education, pg 718

MASSACHUSETTS

Documentary Educational Resources Inc, pg 744
Penfield Productions Ltd, pg 853

MICHIGAN

Digi Sign Design LLC, pg 741

NEVADA

DVDs4Less, pg 748

NEW HAMPSHIRE

Chip Taylor Communications LLC, pg 907

NEW JERSEY

Avtech Systems Inc, pg 699

NEW YORK

SciMedTv, pg 882
Synaptic Digital, pg 905

PENNSYLVANIA

FMP Media Solutions Inc, pg 763

TEXAS

Emergency Film Group, pg 753

VERMONT

University of Vermont, Instructional Television Dept, pg 923

VIRGINIA

CACI Integrated Communications, pg 713

WASHINGTON

Bennett-Watt HD Productions Inc, pg 703

Technical Research Program Producers

ALASKA

Alaska Media Pros LLC, pg 679

ARIZONA

Aardvark Productions LLC, pg 671
Candee Productions Inc, pg 716
Film Creations Ltd, pg 760

CALIFORNIA

Access Video in Berkeley, pg 673
Astronomical Society of the Pacific, pg 691
Big Door, pg 705
Classic Images Stock Footage LLC, pg 726
Creative Technology, pg 733
Crystal Pyramid Productions™, pg 735
Custom Video Productions Inc, pg 736
Design Media, pg 741
ITV Productions, pg 792
Main Street Media Inc, pg 815
Maximus Media Inc, pg 820
McCune Audio-Video-Lighting, pg 821
New & Unique Videos™, pg 839
QRS Software Services, pg 867
Dick Reizner Film & Video, pg 873
SNAP, pg 891
Still N' Motion, pg 901
Timestream Video, pg 914
Total Creative, pg 916
TVA Media Group, pg 919
Vineyard Video & Photography, pg 930
West Coast Projections Inc, pg 935

COLORADO

Daylight Productions & Rentals, pg 739
Flashback Media Productions, pg 762
Transtar Entertainment Co Inc, pg 917

CONNECTICUT

Ironik Design & Post, pg 791
Video Production Associates Inc, pg 928

DISTRICT OF COLUMBIA

American Chemical Society (ACS), pg 683

FLORIDA

Accord Productions, pg 673
Civins Productions Inc, pg 725
CopShopMiami.com, pg 731
Courter Films LLC, pg 732
Jordan Klein Film & Video (JKFV), pg 795
National Teleproductions Inc, pg 837
Sunfire Communications Inc, pg 904
Sunrise Studios, pg 904

GEORGIA

Beachwood Productions, pg 702
Cox Media, pg 732
Guerrilla Productions LLC, pg 774
On-Line Productions, pg 845

HAWAII

Hyperspective Studios Inc, pg 783
Sight & Sound Studios, pg 887

ILLINOIS

ABSA Films, pg 672
Accenture, pg 672
Airways Digital Media, pg 679
CCH Continuing Education, pg 718
Film Police, pg 760
IV Media Resources, pg 792
Pepper Group, pg 854
20/20 Communications Inc, pg 920
Video Impressions, pg 928

INDIANA

A-V-A Video Productions, pg 671
PentaVision Communications Inc, pg 854

LOUISIANA

Louisiana State University Division of Strategic Communications, pg 811
Moxie Media, pg 832

MARYLAND

dbF a Media Company, pg 739
Kramer Communications Video Production, pg 801

MASSACHUSETTS

Award Productions Inc, pg 699
Documentary Educational Resources Inc, pg 744
Green Mountain Post Films (GMP), pg 774
Heliotrope Studios, pg 778
Northern Light Productions (NLP), pg 842

Penfield Productions Ltd, pg 853
TVN-The Video Network, pg 919

MICHIGAN

Digi Sign Design LLC, pg 741
K&R All Media Productions LLC, pg 796
K&R's Recording Studios Inc, pg 796

MINNESOTA

House of Cinemagraphics, pg 782

NEBRASKA

Rainbow Video Productions Inc, pg 869

NEVADA

Aardvark Video & Media Productions, pg 671
DVDs4Less, pg 748
Encore Event Technologies LLC, pg 754
JCS Video Productions, pg 793

NEW HAMPSHIRE

Apertura, pg 686
ProPhotonix Ltd, pg 865
Chip Taylor Communications LLC, pg 907
The Troupe, pg 918

NEW JERSEY

CFP Video Productions Inc, pg 720
Laurel Video Productions, pg 804
MiB MediaWorks, pg 825
Optisonics Productions, pg 847
Suede Interactive, pg 903
VCSvideo, pg 925

NEW MEXICO

Production Outfitters, pg 864

NEW YORK

aurora productions, pg 696
Broadstreet Productions LLC, pg 711
The Palmer Group, pg 850
Peckham Productions Inc, pg 852
SciMedTv, pg 882
Synaptic Digital, pg 905
TeleTime Productions, pg 910
Videograf, pg 929

NORTH CAROLINA

Pat Appleson Studios Inc, pg 687
The Communications Group Inc, pg 729
Kino Mountain Productions LLC, pg 799
Moving Pictures, pg 832
Videowerks, pg 930

OHIO

Advent Media Inc, pg 677
Image Video Teleproductions Inc, pg 785
Lyon Video Inc, pg 813
MainSail Production Services Inc, pg 815
R&B Communications Inc, pg 870
Take 1 Media Services, pg 906
Vista Color Imaging Inc, pg 931

OREGON

Ideascape Inc, pg 784
Production West, pg 864

PROGRAMMING — VIDEO

Television Commercial— Animated Producers (continued)

NEW YORK (continued)
Buzzco Associates Inc, pg 713
Charlex Inc, pg 721
HB-Content, pg 777
Kinetic Arts, pg 799
Manhattan Center Studios Inc, pg 816
The Palmer Group, pg 850
Polestar Films & Associated Arts Ltd, pg 859
R/GA, pg 868
David Rapkin Audio Production, pg 870
TeleTime Productions, pg 910

NORTH CAROLINA
The Communications Group Inc, pg 729
Kino Mountain Productions LLC, pg 799
Videowerks, pg 930

OHIO
Advent Media Inc, pg 677
Image Video Teleproductions Inc, pg 785
Lyon Video Inc, pg 813
R&B Communications Inc, pg 870
Take 1 Media Services, pg 906

OKLAHOMA
KFOR-TV, pg 798

OREGON
KPDX-TV Production Center, pg 801
Odyssey Productions Inc, pg 844
Wallace Creative LLC, pg 933

PENNSYLVANIA
Bang! Pictures Inc, pg 701
FMP Media Solutions Inc, pg 763
Innovision Media Group, pg 788
JPL, pg 795
Kensington Falls Animation, pg 797
Muderick Media, pg 833
Production Masters Inc (PMI), pg 864
The Videohouse Inc, pg 929

RHODE ISLAND
Sound-FX-Design, pg 894

SOUTH CAROLINA
American Production Services LLC, pg 684

TENNESSEE
Continental Film, pg 731
Paradigm Marketing & Creative, pg 851
Running Pony Productions LLC, pg 878
Scripps Networks, pg 882

TEXAS
Biway Media, pg 706
The Editing Co, pg 750

Horizon Film + Video Productions, pg 781
Omega Productions, pg 845
Omni Intercommunications Inc, pg 845
The Samuels Co, pg 879
South Coast Film & Video, pg 895
Stage Directions, pg 898

VIRGINIA
Metro Productions, pg 824

WASHINGTON
Bennett-Watt HD Productions Inc, pg 703
Hamilton Studio, pg 775
North-by-Northwest - A Digital Studio, pg 842
Victory Studios, pg 927

WISCONSIN
5th Floor Recording Co, pg 760
Meridian Studios, pg 824
Midland Video Productions Inc, pg 827
Mirror 34 Productions, pg 828
USAV Group Inc, pg 923
Video Wisconsin Inc, pg 929
Watts Communications Inc, pg 934

WYOMING
Bridger Productions Inc, pg 710

ALBERTA
Black Media Works, pg 706
Global TV, pg 771

NEWFOUNDLAND AND LABRADOR
Vidcraft Productions Ltd, pg 927

ONTARIO
ADS Media, pg 677
GAPC (General Assembly Production Centre), pg 768

QUEBEC
Kerrigan Productions Inc, pg 798

SASKATCHEWAN
plan9films, pg 857

Television Commercial— Animated Rentals

MICHIGAN
Digi Sign Design LLC, pg 741

MISSOURI
University of Missouri-Columbia, pg 923

Television Commercial— Live Distributors

ARKANSAS
Mullikin Agency, pg 833

CALIFORNIA
Crystal Pyramid Productions™, pg 735
Far West Media Services Inc, pg 759
Shokus Video, pg 886

ILLINOIS
ABS Enterprises, pg 672
ABSA Films, pg 672
Movies Unlimited, pg 831

MARYLAND
Total AV Systems, pg 916

MASSACHUSETTS
Penfield Productions Ltd, pg 853

MICHIGAN
Digi Sign Design LLC, pg 741

NEVADA
DVDs4Less, pg 748

NEW HAMPSHIRE
Chip Taylor Communications LLC, pg 907

NEW JERSEY
Allegro Productions Inc, pg 680
MiB MediaWorks, pg 825
SES SA, pg 884

NEW YORK
HB-Content, pg 777
Janus Films Inc, pg 793
Lifetime Television®, pg 807

PENNSYLVANIA
CORTRON Media LLC, pg 732
FMP Media Solutions Inc, pg 763

TENNESSEE
American Blackguard Inc, pg 683

VIRGINIA
CACI Integrated Communications, pg 713

ALBERTA
Global TV, pg 771

Television Commercial— Live Producers

ALASKA
Alaska Media Pros LLC, pg 679
Aurora Films, pg 696
Imig Audio/Video Inc, pg 786

ARIZONA
Aardvark Productions LLC, pg 671
Candee Productions Inc, pg 716
Direct Current Video Productions, pg 743
Film Creations Ltd, pg 760
Fox 10 Productions (KSAZ-TV), pg 765
Metropolitan Audio-Visual Inc, pg 824
Rodeo Video Inc, pg 876

ARKANSAS
Live'N'Loud, pg 810
Mullikin Agency, pg 833
White Diamond Productions LLC, pg 937

CALIFORNIA
A Go Go Films, pg 671
Anonymous Content, pg 686
Artichoke Productions, pg 690
Big Door, pg 705
Steve Chandler, pg 720
Classic Images Stock Footage LLC, pg 726
Concrete Images, pg 730
Crystal Pyramid Productions™, pg 735
Custom Video Productions Inc, pg 736
Direct Images Interactive Inc, pg 743
Dolphin MultiMedia Inc, pg 745
Far West Media Services Inc, pg 759
GAMfilm Productions, pg 768
Havas Edge, pg 777
Images in Motion Media Inc, pg 785
Imageworks, pg 785
ITV Productions, pg 792
Kavich Reynolds Productions Inc, pg 797
KTVU-Retail Services, pg 802
Lieberman Productions, pg 807
Main Street Media Inc, pg 815
Maximus Media Inc, pg 820
McCune Audio-Video-Lighting, pg 821
Media Magic, pg 822
Moving Art by Louie Schwartzberg, pg 831
New & Unique Videos™, pg 839
New Deal Studios, pg 839
Nolte Media, pg 841
On-Trax Inc, pg 846
Opticomm-EMCORE, pg 847
Penrose Productions, pg 854
PK Productions, pg 857
PM Productions, pg 858
Producers Group Ltd, pg 863
QRS Software Services, pg 867
Dick Reizner Film & Video, pg 873
RetinaVision Productions, pg 874
Glenn Roland Films, pg 876
Sahara Records & Filmworks Entertainment Co, pg 879
Santa Barbara Location Services, pg 880
Santa Clarita Studios, pg 880
Shot Glass Films, pg 886
SNAP, pg 891
Staylor-Made Communications Inc, pg 900
Still N' Motion, pg 901
Tam Communications Inc, pg 906
Timestream Video, pg 914
Total Creative, pg 916
TVA Media Group, pg 919
Vineyard Video & Photography, pg 930
Wavemaker Media Design, pg 934
Yada/Levine Video Productions, pg 943
Zamacona Productions, pg 945

COLORADO
Apogee Communications Group, pg 687
Blue River Productions, pg 708
CSI Film & Video LLC, pg 735
Daylight Productions & Rentals, pg 739
Flashback Media Productions, pg 762
People Productions, pg 854
Side 3 Studios, pg 887
Starwest Productions, pg 900
Transtar Entertainment Co Inc, pg 917

CONNECTICUT

ACM Productions Ltd, pg 674
Ironik Design & Post, pg 791
Moving Pictures, pg 832
Palace Productions MediaVision, pg 850
P&P Studios Inc, pg 851
Powerstation Events, pg 860
Video Production Associates Inc, pg 928

DISTRICT OF COLUMBIA

Dorst MediaWorks Inc, pg 746

FLORIDA

Applebox Studio, pg 687
Astoria Communications Inc, pg 691
Blackburst Entertainment LLC, pg 706
CD ROM™ Inc, pg 718
Chatterbox Productions Inc, pg 721
Civins Productions Inc, pg 725
CopShopMiami.com, pg 731
Courter Films LLC, pg 732
Digital Zoetrope Productions, pg 742
Jordan Klein Film & Video (JKFV), pg 795
National Teleproductions Inc, pg 837
Olympusat, pg 845
Roger Scruggs Films, pg 883
Skystorm Productions, pg 890
Sunfire Communications Inc, pg 904
Sunrise Studios, pg 904
Tel-Air Interests Inc, pg 909
Tight Line Productions, pg 914
Tricycle Studios, pg 918
Universal Studios Florida®
    Production Group, pg 922
Mike Vasilinda Productions Inc, pg 925
Venice Media Group, pg 925

GEORGIA

Beachwood Productions, pg 702
Burst Video/Film Inc, pg 713
Cox Media, pg 732
ECG Productions, pg 750
GP Studios, pg 773
Guerrilla Productions LLC, pg 774
On-Line Productions, pg 845
Pogo Pictures, pg 858
WaveGuide Studios, pg 934

HAWAII

Hyperspective Studios Inc, pg 783
Sight & Sound Studios, pg 887
1013 Integrated, pg 911

IDAHO

Brad Shaw Productions Inc, pg 885

ILLINOIS

Abacus Group of Saint Louis LLC, pg 672
ABS Enterprises, pg 672
ABSA Films, pg 672
Atomic Imaging Inc/Golan Studios, pg 692
The Chicago Production Center, pg 721
Cresta Creative, pg 734
Explore, pg 757
Film Police, pg 760
IV Media Resources, pg 792
Manning Productions, pg 816

The Market Place, pg 817
Mimi Productions, pg 828
Multimedia Marketing Group, pg 833
Jim Passin Productions, pg 852
Pepper Group, pg 854
SCI Television & Creative Media LLC, pg 882
Sparkfactor, pg 896
Video Impressions, pg 928
WEEK TV, pg 935
Winter Productions, pg 939

INDIANA

A-V-A Video Productions, pg 671
Advanced Media Integration, pg 677
OMNI Productions, pg 845
PentaVision Communications Inc, pg 854
Road Pictures, pg 876

KANSAS

KAKE-TV, pg 796
Walterscheid Productions, pg 933

KENTUCKY

Idle Minds Productions Inc, pg 784
Prosper Media Group Inc, pg 866

LOUISIANA

Digital FX Inc, pg 742
Moxie Media, pg 832

MARYLAND

Adventure Productions LLC, pg 678
Richard Chisolm Cinematography, pg 722
CPR MultiMedia Solutions, pg 732
dbF a Media Company, pg 739
The Image Generators, pg 785
Kramer Communications Video Production, pg 801
Media Dimensions LLC, pg 821
Producers Video, pg 863

MASSACHUSETTS

Award Productions Inc, pg 699
Cramer, pg 732
Green Mountain Post Films (GMP), pg 774
Heliotrope Studios, pg 778
Penfield Productions Ltd, pg 853
PixMix Video Services, pg 857
Gabriel Polonsky Studio, pg 859
TVN-The Video Network, pg 919
VideoLink Inc, an AVI-SPL company, pg 929

MICHIGAN

Digi Sign Design LLC, pg 741
K&R All Media Productions LLC, pg 796
K&R's Recording Studios Inc, pg 796
Lawrence Productions Inc, pg 804

MINNESOTA

Big Event Productions LLC, pg 705
GMI Productions, pg 771
House of Cinemagraphics, pg 782

MISSOURI

Avatar Studios, pg 697
Hardcastle Films & Video, pg 776

MONTANA

ooLite Media LLC, pg 846

NEBRASKA

Mason Video, pg 819
Telepro Video Inc, pg 910

NEVADA

Aardvark Video & Media Productions, pg 671
DVDs4Less, pg 748
Encore Event Technologies LLC, pg 754
JCS Video Productions, pg 793
Ron Roy Productions/Moodtapes, pg 878
Tanglewood Productions, pg 907

NEW HAMPSHIRE

Apertura, pg 686
Channell One Video, pg 720
Chip Taylor Communications LLC, pg 907
The Troupe, pg 918

NEW JERSEY

Allegro Productions Inc, pg 680
Broadcast Center Studios, pg 710
Color Leasing Studios, pg 727
Concepts TV Productions Inc, pg 730
Euro-Pacific Film & Video Productions Inc, pg 756
MediaNow Inc, pg 822
MiB MediaWorks, pg 825
Optisonics Productions, pg 847
Shamrock Communications, pg 885
Suede Interactive, pg 903
TimeSteps Productions Inc, pg 914
VCSvideo, pg 925

NEW MEXICO

Stevens Design & Animation LLC, pg 900

NEW YORK

Air Sea Land Productions Inc (ASL), pg 678
American Montage Inc, pg 683
aurora productions, pg 696
Avekta Productions Inc, pg 697
Bevilacqua Studios, pg 704
Big Fish Production US, pg 705
Blue Barn Pictures Inc, pg 707
Broadstreet Productions LLC, pg 711
Brooklyn Films, pg 711
Charlex Inc, pg 721
De Nonno Productions Inc (DPI), pg 739
East of Hollywood NY, pg 749
Golden Lamb Productions, pg 772
HB-Content, pg 777
Hello World Communications, pg 778
HOThead, pg 782
Kinetic Arts, pg 799
L A Bruell Inc, pg 802
Lifetime Television®, pg 807
Long Island Video Enterprises Live Inc, pg 811
Mark X Productions Inc, pg 817
McGuane Studio Inc, pg 821
Meltzer Media Productions, pg 823
Mood Creations Ltd, pg 829
New Horizon Studios, pg 839
News Broadcast Network Inc, pg 840
Northeast Video Productions Inc, pg 842
The Palmer Group, pg 850
Paradoxal Inc, pg 851
Pat Kogan Productions Inc, pg 852

Peckham Productions Inc, pg 852
PrimaLux Video Inc, pg 862
Production Central, pg 863
R/GA, pg 868
Split Image Productions, pg 898
Suggs Media Productions Inc, pg 903
TeleTime Productions, pg 910
Zelman Studios Ltd, pg 945

NORTH CAROLINA

All Pro Media Inc, pg 680
The Communications Group Inc, pg 729
Digital Rain LLC, pg 742
Kino Mountain Productions LLC, pg 799
Moving Pictures, pg 832
Trailblazer Studios®, pg 917
Videowerks, pg 930

OHIO

Advent Media Inc, pg 677
Russ Beckner Pictures, pg 703
CET, pg 720
Clear Choice Creative Corp, pg 726
Image Video Teleproductions Inc, pg 785
Lyon Video Inc, pg 813
R&B Communications Inc, pg 870
Shelburne Films, pg 885
Take 1 Media Services, pg 906
Treehaus Communications Inc, pg 917
Vista Color Imaging Inc, pg 931

OKLAHOMA

KFOR-TV, pg 798

OREGON

CMD Agency, pg 726
Ideascape Inc, pg 784
InterVision Media, pg 791
KPDX-TV Production Center, pg 801
KVAL, pg 802
Odyssey Productions Inc, pg 844
Production West, pg 864
REX, pg 874

PENNSYLVANIA

Bang! Pictures Inc, pg 701
Beholder Productions Inc, pg 703
CCI Communications Inc, pg 718
CORTRON Media LLC, pg 732
FMP Media Solutions Inc, pg 763
Innovision Media Group, pg 788
JPL, pg 795
Muderick Media, pg 833
Production Masters Inc (PMI), pg 864
The Videohouse Inc, pg 929
Visual Sound Inc, pg 931
WHYY Inc, pg 938

RHODE ISLAND

Sound-FX-Design, pg 894

SOUTH CAROLINA

Encore Video Productions, pg 754
Stages Video Productions, pg 899
Venture Media, pg 925

TENNESSEE

American Blackguard Inc, pg 683
Cinemarr Entertainment, pg 724
Continental Film, pg 731

PROGRAMMING — VIDEO

Television Commercial— Live Producers (continued)

TENNESSEE (continued)
Paradigm Marketing & Creative, pg 851
Running Pony Productions LLC, pg 878
Scripps Networks, pg 882
Stage Post, pg 899
Russ Sturgeon Productions/RSVP, pg 903

TEXAS
Alexander Media Productions, pg 679
AMS Pictures, pg 684
Biway Media, pg 706
Cerutti Productions Inc, pg 720
Communication Arts Multimedia Inc, pg 728
Countdown Productions Inc, pg 732
Dykeman Associates Inc, pg 748
The Editing Co, pg 750
Eyecon Video Productions, pg 758
Horizon Film + Video Productions, pg 781
Marx InDigital, pg 818
Mediaforce Productions, pg 822
Earl Miller Productions Inc, pg 827
NBC-5, pg 837
Omega Productions, pg 845
Omni Intercommunications Inc, pg 845
Radio Vision Inc, pg 869
The Samuels Co, pg 879
South Coast Film & Video, pg 895
Stage Directions, pg 898
Zachry Associates Inc, pg 944

VERMONT
Marlboro Productions, pg 817

VIRGINIA
CACI Integrated Communications, pg 713
Limelight Communications Inc, pg 808
Metro Productions, pg 824
Rocktown Media, pg 876
Video Solutions, pg 928

WASHINGTON
Adams Creative & Production Services, pg 675
Bennett-Watt HD Productions Inc, pg 703
Hamilton Studio, pg 775
North-by-Northwest - A Digital Studio, pg 842
Pal Productions Inc, pg 850
Victory Studios, pg 927

WEST VIRGINIA
Blackwater Video Productions, pg 707

WISCONSIN
5th Floor Recording Co, pg 760
Logan Productions Inc, pg 811
Meridian Studios, pg 824
Midland Video Productions Inc, pg 827
Mirror 34 Productions, pg 828

University of Wisconsin-Oshkosh Radio-TV-Film Dept, pg 923
USAV Group Inc, pg 923
Watts Communications Inc, pg 934

WYOMING
Bridger Productions Inc, pg 710

ALBERTA
Black Media Works, pg 706
Global TV, pg 771

MANITOBA
Lank/Beach Productions Inc, pg 803
Spectra Video Productions Ltd, pg 897

NEWFOUNDLAND AND LABRADOR
Vidcraft Productions Ltd, pg 927

ONTARIO
ADS Media, pg 677
DebsVoice, pg 739
GAPC (General Assembly Production Centre), pg 768
Image Video Services & Productions, pg 785
Pendulum Entertainment, pg 853
RB Productions, pg 870
Video Excellence Productions, pg 927

QUEBEC
Auriga Productions Ltd, pg 696
Kerrigan Productions Inc, pg 798

SASKATCHEWAN
plan9films, pg 857

Television Commercial— Live Rentals

MICHIGAN
Digi Sign Design LLC, pg 741

MISSOURI
University of Missouri-Columbia, pg 923

Television Film Distributors

CALIFORNIA
Agrama Film Enterprises Inc, pg 678
Astronomical Society of the Pacific, pg 691
Direct Cinema Ltd Inc, pg 743
ECONEWS (Environmental Television Series) & (Environmental Directions Radio Series), pg 750
eFootage LLC, pg 751
Glenn Photo Supply, pg 771
Glenn Video Vistas Ltd, pg 771
MarVista Entertainment Inc, pg 818
MGM Home Entertainment, pg 825
Nineteen87, pg 841
Paulist Productions, pg 852
Pyramid Media, pg 867
Regent Press Publishers & Printers, pg 873
Universal Pictures Home Entertainment, pg 922

DISTRICT OF COLUMBIA
Department of VSA & Accessibility at the John F Kennedy Center for the Performing Arts, pg 740

ILLINOIS
Moviecraft Inc, pg 831
Movies Unlimited, pg 831

KENTUCKY
WaxWorks VideoWorks, pg 934

MARYLAND
RLJ Entertainment Inc, pg 875

MASSACHUSETTS
Documentary Educational Resources Inc, pg 744

NEVADA
DVDs4Less, pg 748

NEW HAMPSHIRE
Chip Taylor Communications LLC, pg 907

NEW JERSEY
Ergo Media Inc, pg 755
Euro-Pacific Film & Video Productions Inc, pg 756

NEW YORK
ATA Trading Corp/Favorite TV Inc, pg 691
William Greaves Productions Inc, pg 774
HB-Content, pg 777
Hearst Entertainment & Syndication, pg 778
Janus Films Inc, pg 793
Kino International Corp, pg 799
Mastervision Inc, pg 819
Richter Productions Inc, pg 875
SISU Home Entertainment Inc, pg 889
United Nations Multimedia Resources Unit, pg 921
VIEW Inc (Video International Entertainment World Inc), pg 930
Women Make Movies Inc, pg 941

NORTH CAROLINA
Crystal Pictures Inc, pg 735

PENNSYLVANIA
Bullfrog Films Inc, pg 712
MVD Entertainment Group, pg 835
S I Video Sales Group, pg 879

TENNESSEE
American Blackguard Inc, pg 683
Spring Arbor Distributors Inc, pg 898

TEXAS
Marengo Films, pg 817

VIRGINIA
CACI Integrated Communications, pg 713

WEST VIRGINIA
Focus on Animals, pg 763

ALBERTA
Global TV, pg 771

ONTARIO
Canadian Learning Co Inc, pg 715
Canamedia Inc, pg 715
CCI Entertainment Ltd, pg 718
Sullivan Home Entertainment, pg 903
TVO/Ontario Educational Communications Authority (OECA), pg 919

QUEBEC
Les Productions Via Le Monde (Daniel Bertolino) Inc, pg 864

Television Film Producers

ALABAMA
Leo Ticheli Productions, pg 913

ALASKA
Alaska Media Pros LLC, pg 679
Aurora Films, pg 696

ARIZONA
Candee Productions Inc, pg 716
Film Creations Ltd, pg 760

ARKANSAS
Live'N'Loud, pg 810

CALIFORNIA
A Go Go Films, pg 671
Agrama Film Enterprises Inc, pg 678
Allied Artists International Inc, pg 681
Big Door, pg 705
Burrud Productions Inc, pg 713
Catapult Films Inc, pg 717
Classic Images Stock Footage LLC, pg 726
Creative Technology, pg 733
Custom Video Productions Inc, pg 736
GAMfilm Productions, pg 768
imageReal Pictures LLC, pg 785
ITV Productions, pg 792
Main Street Media Inc, pg 815
McCune Audio-Video-Lighting, pg 821
New & Unique Videos™, pg 839
Nineteen87, pg 841
Paulist Productions, pg 852
Point of View Productions, pg 858
Producers Group Ltd, pg 863
QRS Software Services, pg 867
Regent Press Publishers & Printers, pg 873
Glenn Roland Films, pg 876
Santa Barbara Location Services, pg 880
SNAP, pg 891
Tam Communications Inc, pg 906
Total Creative, pg 916
Universal Pictures Home Entertainment, pg 922
Utopia Films, pg 924
Vineyard Video & Photography, pg 930

COLORADO
Centre Communications Inc, pg 720
CSI Film & Video LLC, pg 735
Renaissance Media, pg 873

Tatum Video, pg 907
Transtar Entertainment Co Inc,
pg 917

CONNECTICUT

ACM Productions Ltd, pg 674
Ironik Design & Post, pg 791

DISTRICT OF COLUMBIA

Department of VSA & Accessibility
at the John F Kennedy Center for
the Performing Arts, pg 740

FLORIDA

Blackburst Entertainment LLC,
pg 706
Chatterbox Productions Inc, pg 721
Civins Productions Inc, pg 725
CopShopMiami.com, pg 731
Courter Films LLC, pg 732
Jordan Klein Film & Video (JKFV),
pg 795
National Teleproductions Inc,
pg 837
Sunfire Communications Inc,
pg 904

GEORGIA

Beachwood Productions, pg 702
Burst Video/Film Inc, pg 713
Cox Media, pg 732
ECG Productions, pg 750
GP Studios, pg 773
Guerrilla Productions LLC, pg 774
Myriad Productions, pg 835
On-Line Productions, pg 845

HAWAII

Hyperspective Studios Inc, pg 783
Sight & Sound Studios, pg 887

IDAHO

Brad Shaw Productions Inc, pg 885

ILLINOIS

ABS Enterprises, pg 672
Film Police, pg 760
Moviecraft Inc, pg 831
Pepper Group, pg 854
SCI Television & Creative Media
LLC, pg 882

INDIANA

A-V-A Video Productions, pg 671

LOUISIANA

Moxie Media, pg 832

MARYLAND

Richard Chisolm Cinematography,
pg 722
dbF a Media Company, pg 739
Kramer Communications Video
Production, pg 801
Mobile-Video Productions Inc,
pg 828

MASSACHUSETTS

Documentary Educational Resources
Inc, pg 744
Green Mountain Post Films (GMP),
pg 774
Heliotrope Studios, pg 778
Pauline Books & Media, pg 852

MICHIGAN

K&R All Media Productions LLC,
pg 796
K&R's Recording Studios Inc,
pg 796

MINNESOTA

House of Cinemagraphics, pg 782

NEBRASKA

Telepro Video Inc, pg 910

NEVADA

DVDs4Less, pg 748
Encore Event Technologies LLC,
pg 754

NEW HAMPSHIRE

Apertura, pg 686
Chip Taylor Communications LLC,
pg 907

NEW JERSEY

Euro-Pacific Film & Video
Productions Inc, pg 756
MiB MediaWorks, pg 825
Optisonics Productions, pg 847
Suede Interactive, pg 903

NEW MEXICO

Stevens Design & Animation LLC,
pg 900

NEW YORK

aurora productions, pg 696
Big Fish Production US, pg 705
Brian Film Productions LLC,
pg 710
Broadstreet Productions LLC,
pg 711
Thomas Craven Film Corp, pg 733
De Nonno Productions Inc (DPI),
pg 739
Florentine Films, pg 762
William Greaves Productions Inc,
pg 774
HB-Content, pg 777
Hearst Entertainment &
Syndication, pg 778
Kinetic Arts, pg 799
Mastervision Inc, pg 819
McGuane Studio Inc, pg 821
The Palmer Group, pg 850
David Rapkin Audio Production,
pg 870
Richter Productions Inc, pg 875
Scholastic Media, pg 882
Split Image Productions, pg 898
Suggs Media Productions Inc,
pg 903
Third World Newsreel/Camera
News Inc, pg 906
United Nations Multimedia
Resources Unit, pg 921
VIEW Inc (Video International
Entertainment World Inc), pg 930

NORTH CAROLINA

The Communications Group Inc,
pg 729
Crystal Pictures Inc, pg 735
Digital Rain LLC, pg 742
Moving Pictures, pg 832
Trailblazer Studios®, pg 917
Videowerks, pg 930

OHIO

Advent Media Inc, pg 677
Lyon Video Inc, pg 813
R&B Communications Inc, pg 870
Take 1 Media Services, pg 906

OKLAHOMA

KFOR-TV, pg 798

OREGON

Ideascape Inc, pg 784
Odyssey Productions Inc, pg 844
Production West, pg 864
REX, pg 874

PENNSYLVANIA

Bang! Pictures Inc, pg 701
FMP Media Solutions Inc, pg 763
Innovision Media Group, pg 788
JPL, pg 795
Kensington Falls Animation, pg 797
Muderick Media, pg 833
Production Masters Inc (PMI),
pg 864
Video/Film Associates, pg 928

RHODE ISLAND

Sound-FX-Design, pg 894

TENNESSEE

American Blackguard Inc, pg 683
Running Pony Productions LLC,
pg 878
Scripps Networks, pg 882

TEXAS

Cerutti Productions Inc, pg 720
Emergency Film Group, pg 753
Horizon Film + Video Productions,
pg 781
Julye Newlin Productions Inc,
pg 840
Omega Productions, pg 845
Stage Directions, pg 898

VERMONT

Marlboro Productions, pg 817

VIRGINIA

CACI Integrated Communications,
pg 713
Metro Productions, pg 824

WASHINGTON

Bennett-Watt HD Productions Inc,
pg 703
North-by-Northwest - A Digital
Studio, pg 842
Pal Productions Inc, pg 850

WISCONSIN

5th Floor Recording Co, pg 760
Video Wisconsin Inc, pg 929
Wisconsin Public Television, pg 940

WYOMING

Bridger Productions Inc, pg 710

ALBERTA

Black Media Works, pg 706
Global TV, pg 771
HDTV Productions Inc, pg 777

MANITOBA

Spectra Video Productions Ltd,
pg 897

ONTARIO

Canamedia Inc, pg 715
Doomsday Studios Limited, pg 745
RB Productions, pg 870

QUEBEC

Kerrigan Productions Inc, pg 798
Max Films Inc, pg 820
Les Productions Via Le Monde
(Daniel Bertolino) Inc, pg 864

Television Film Rentals

CALIFORNIA

Direct Cinema Ltd Inc, pg 743
Paulist Productions, pg 852
Point of View Productions, pg 858

MASSACHUSETTS

Documentary Educational Resources
Inc, pg 744

MISSOURI

University of Missouri-Columbia,
pg 923

NEW JERSEY

Alden Films, pg 679

NEW YORK

Kino International Corp, pg 799
Richter Productions Inc, pg 875
VIEW Inc (Video International
Entertainment World Inc), pg 930

NORTH CAROLINA

Crystal Pictures Inc, pg 735

PENNSYLVANIA

Bullfrog Films Inc, pg 712

QUEBEC

Les Productions Via Le Monde
(Daniel Bertolino) Inc, pg 864

Television Program
Distributors

ALABAMA

Eternal Word Television Network
(EWTN), pg 756

CALIFORNIA

Ariztical Entertainment Inc, pg 689
Astronomical Society of the Pacific,
pg 691
Direct Cinema Ltd Inc, pg 743
411 Video Information, pg 764
Lions Gate Entertainment Corp,
pg 809
Live Wire Media, pg 810
MarVista Entertainment Inc, pg 818
MGM Home Entertainment, pg 825
Nineteen87, pg 841
Paramount Pictures Corporation,
pg 851
Prime Cut Productions, pg 862
Pyramid Media, pg 867
Regent Press Publishers & Printers,
pg 873

PROGRAMMING — VIDEO

Television Program Distributors (continued)

CALIFORNIA (continued)

Sahara Records & Filmworks Entertainment Co, pg 879
Shokus Video, pg 886
Thinking Allowed Productions, pg 912
Universal Pictures Home Entertainment, pg 922
Warner Home Video Inc, pg 934
The Wyland Group, pg 942

CONNECTICUT

CMI Media Management, pg 727

DISTRICT OF COLUMBIA

Department of VSA & Accessibility at the John F Kennedy Center for the Performing Arts, pg 740

FLORIDA

Accord Productions, pg 673
NatureVision Stock Footage Library, pg 837

GEORGIA

New Leaf Distributing Co, pg 839
On-Line Productions, pg 845

ILLINOIS

Facets Multi-Media Inc, pg 758
Movies Unlimited, pg 831
Questar Entertainment Inc, pg 868

INDIANA

Communication Ministries, pg 728
Perennial Pictures Film Corp, pg 854

IOWA

American Visions, pg 684
Right Stuf Inc, pg 875

LOUISIANA

Great Chefs/Leisure Jazz Video, pg 773
Leisure Video, pg 806

MARYLAND

Adventure Productions LLC, pg 678
RLJ Entertainment Inc, pg 875
Total AV Systems, pg 916

MASSACHUSETTS

Award Productions Inc, pg 699
Documentary Educational Resources Inc, pg 744
Enterprise Media LLC, pg 754
Penfield Productions Ltd, pg 853

MICHIGAN

Digi Sign Design LLC, pg 741
VMS Inc, pg 932

MISSOURI

WEP LLC, pg 935

MONTANA

High Plains Films, pg 779

NEBRASKA

Vision Maker Media, pg 930

NEW HAMPSHIRE

Channell One Video, pg 720
Chip Taylor Communications LLC, pg 907

NEW JERSEY

Euro-Pacific Film & Video Productions Inc, pg 756
MiB MediaWorks, pg 825
SES SA, pg 884
Shanachie Entertainment Corp, pg 885

NEW YORK

A&E Home Video, pg 671
A&E Television Networks LLC, pg 671
ATA Trading Corp/Favorite TV Inc, pg 691
The Christophers, pg 722
HB-Content, pg 777
Hearst Entertainment & Syndication, pg 778
Icarus Films Inc, pg 783
Janson Media Inc, pg 793
Janus Films Inc, pg 793
Lifetime Television®, pg 807
Mastervision Inc, pg 819
Scholastic Media, pg 882
SISU Home Entertainment Inc, pg 889
Third World Newsreel/Camera News Inc, pg 912
Timed Exposures Films, pg 914
United Nations Multimedia Resources Unit, pg 921
Videofashion Network, pg 929
VIEW Inc (Video International Entertainment World Inc), pg 930

NORTH DAKOTA

UND Television Center, pg 921

OREGON

Cooking by the Book, pg 731
Nostalgia Family Video Inc, pg 843

PENNSYLVANIA

Beholder Productions Inc, pg 703
Corinth Films Inc, pg 731
CORTRON Media LLC, pg 732
MVD Entertainment Group, pg 835
Rahlic Publishing Co, pg 869
Fred Rogers Productions, pg 876
Schlessinger Media, pg 881

SOUTH CAROLINA

American Production Services LLC, pg 684

TENNESSEE

American Blackguard Inc, pg 683
Spring Arbor Distributors Inc, pg 898

VIRGINIA

CACI Integrated Communications, pg 713

WASHINGTON

Bennett-Watt HD Productions Inc, pg 703
John McLean Media, pg 794
Victory Studios, pg 927

WEST VIRGINIA

Focus on Animals, pg 763

WISCONSIN

NEWIST/CESA 7, pg 840
Wisconsin Public Television, pg 940

ALBERTA

Global TV, pg 771

ONTARIO

Canadian Learning Co Inc, pg 715
Canamedia Inc, pg 715
CCI Entertainment Ltd, pg 718
Sullivan Home Entertainment, pg 903

QUEBEC

Les Productions Via Le Monde (Daniel Bertolino) Inc, pg 864
Reel One International Ltd, pg 872

Television Program Producers

ALABAMA

AVS Media Group, pg 699
Eternal Word Television Network (EWTN), pg 756
Leo Ticheli Productions, pg 913

ALASKA

Alaska Media Pros LLC, pg 679
Alaska Video Postcards Inc, pg 679
Aurora Films, pg 696

ARIZONA

Aardvark Productions LLC, pg 671
Candee Productions Inc, pg 716
Direct Current Video Productions, pg 743
Film Creations Ltd, pg 760
Fox 10 Productions (KSAZ-TV), pg 765
Teaberry, pg 908

ARKANSAS

Live'N'Loud, pg 810
White Diamond Productions LLC, pg 937

CALIFORNIA

A Go Go Films, pg 671
Access Video in Berkeley, pg 673
Air Philosophy Inc, pg 678
Big Door, pg 705
Burrud Productions Inc, pg 713
Catapult Films Inc, pg 717
Cavalcade Productions Inc, pg 717
Steve Chandler, pg 720
CineVantage LLC, pg 724
Classic Images Stock Footage LLC, pg 726
Coastline Productions, pg 727
Concept Associates Inc, pg 730
Concrete Images, pg 730
Creative Technology, pg 733
Custom Video Productions Inc, pg 736
Direct Images Interactive Inc, pg 743
Durrin Productions Inc, pg 748
ECONEWS (Environmental Television Series) & (Environmental Directions Radio Series), pg 750

Fox Television Center, pg 765
FremantleMedia North America, pg 765
GAMfilm Productions, pg 768
Goal Productions, pg 772
Image Integration, pg 785
imageReal Pictures LLC, pg 785
Images in Motion Media Inc, pg 785
Imageworks, pg 785
ITV Productions, pg 792
The Jim Henson Co, pg 794
Kaboom Productions, pg 796
KO Creative, pg 800
KTVU-Retail Services, pg 802
Legendary Pictures, pg 806
Lions Gate Entertainment Corp, pg 809
Live Wire Media, pg 810
Main Street Media Inc, pg 815
MarVista Entertainment Inc, pg 818
Maximus Media Inc, pg 820
McCune Audio-Video-Lighting, pg 821
Media Magic, pg 822
The Media Staff Inc, pg 822
The Mother Co, pg 831
New & Unique Videos™, pg 839
New Wave Entertainment, pg 839
Nineteen87, pg 841
Paramount Pictures Corporation, pg 851
PM Productions, pg 858
Point of View Productions, pg 858
Prime Cut Productions, pg 862
Producers Group Ltd, pg 863
QRS Software Services, pg 867
Regent Press Publishers & Printers, pg 873
RJ Video Productions, pg 875
Glenn Roland Films, pg 876
Sahara Records & Filmworks Entertainment Co, pg 879
Santa Barbara Location Services, pg 880
Santa Clarita Studios, pg 880
Saturn Studios, pg 881
Screen Door Entertainment Inc, pg 882
Shokus Video, pg 886
SNAP, pg 891
Still N' Motion, pg 901
Tam Communications Inc, pg 906
Thinking Allowed Productions, pg 912
Total Creative, pg 916
TVA Media Group, pg 919
Twin Peaks Creative, pg 920
Universal Pictures Home Entertainment, pg 922
Vineyard Video & Photography, pg 930
Wavemaker Media Design, pg 934
WMS Media Inc, pg 940
The Wyland Group, pg 942
Zamacona Productions, pg 945

COLORADO

Apogee Communications Group, pg 687
Centre Communications Inc, pg 720
CSI Film & Video LLC, pg 735
Daylight Productions & Rentals, pg 739
Denver Media Center, pg 740
Flashback Media Productions, pg 762
Greg Hensley Productions, pg 779
Renaissance Media, pg 873
Tatum Video, pg 907

PROGRAMMING — VIDEO

Television Program Producers (continued)

OREGON (continued)

KPDX-TV Production Center, pg 801
KTVA Productions, pg 802
Odyssey Productions Inc, pg 844
Production West, pg 864
REX, pg 874

PENNSYLVANIA

Bang! Pictures Inc, pg 701
Beholder Productions Inc, pg 703
CCI Communications Inc, pg 718
CORTRON Media LLC, pg 732
FMP Media Solutions Inc, pg 763
Innovision Media Group, pg 788
Kensington Falls Animation, pg 797
Muderick Media, pg 833
NEP Group Inc, pg 838
Production Masters Inc (PMI), pg 864
Rahlic Publishing Co, pg 869
Schlessinger Media, pg 881
Video/Film Associates, pg 928
The Videohouse Inc, pg 929
Videosmith Inc, pg 930
WHYY Inc, pg 938
WQED-Multimedia, pg 942

RHODE ISLAND

Sound-FX-Design, pg 894

SOUTH CAROLINA

American Production Services LLC, pg 684
Go To Team, pg 772
Venture Media, pg 925

TENNESSEE

American Blackguard Inc, pg 683
Cinemarr Entertainment, pg 724
Running Pony Productions LLC, pg 878
Scripps Networks, pg 882
United Methodist Productions, pg 921

TEXAS

Biway Media, pg 706
Cerutti Productions Inc, pg 720
Communication Arts Multimedia Inc, pg 728
Countdown Productions Inc, pg 732
Dub King, pg 747
The Editing Co, pg 750
Emergency Film Group, pg 753
Horizon Film + Video Productions, pg 781
Mediaforce Productions, pg 822
Earl Miller Productions Inc, pg 827
Julye Newlin Productions Inc, pg 840
Omega Productions, pg 845
South Coast Film & Video, pg 895
Stage Directions, pg 898

VERMONT

Marlboro Productions, pg 817

VIRGINIA

CACI Integrated Communications, pg 713
Cinebar Productions Inc, pg 723
Limelight Communications Inc, pg 808
Metro Productions, pg 824
Rocktown Media, pg 876

WASHINGTON

Bennett-Watt HD Productions Inc, pg 703
Medical Media Systems, pg 823
North-by-Northwest - A Digital Studio, pg 842
Pal Productions Inc, pg 850
Victory Studios, pg 927

WEST VIRGINIA

Blackwater Video Productions, pg 707

WISCONSIN

5th Floor Recording Co, pg 760
Mirror 34 Productions, pg 828
NEWIST/CESA 7, pg 840
Video Wisconsin Inc, pg 929
Watts Communications Inc, pg 934
Wisconsin Public Television, pg 940

WYOMING

Bridger Productions Inc, pg 710

ALBERTA

Black Media Works, pg 706
Global TV, pg 771

BRITISH COLUMBIA

Inspired Image Picture Co (IIPC), pg 788

MANITOBA

Spectra Video Productions Ltd, pg 897

NEWFOUNDLAND AND LABRADOR

Vidcraft Productions Ltd, pg 927

ONTARIO

ADS Media, pg 677
Canamedia Inc, pg 715
Doomsday Studios Limited, pg 745
GAPC (General Assembly Production Centre), pg 768
Jams Productions Inc, pg 793
Marblemedia, pg 816
Mediaimage Communications Group, pg 822

QUEBEC

Auriga Productions Ltd, pg 696
Kerrigan Productions Inc, pg 798
Muse Entertainment Enterprises, pg 834
Les Productions Via Le Monde (Daniel Bertolino) Inc, pg 864
Reel One International Ltd, pg 872

SASKATCHEWAN

plan9films, pg 857

Television Program Rentals

CALIFORNIA

Direct Cinema Ltd Inc, pg 743
ECONEWS (Environmental Television Series) & (Environmental Directions Radio Series), pg 750
Point of View Productions, pg 858

GEORGIA

On-Line Productions, pg 845

ILLINOIS

Facets Multi-Media Inc, pg 758

LOUISIANA

Great Chefs/Leisure Jazz Video, pg 773
Leisure Video, pg 806

MASSACHUSETTS

Documentary Educational Resources Inc, pg 744
Enterprise Media LLC, pg 754

MICHIGAN

Digi Sign Design LLC, pg 741

MISSOURI

University of Missouri-Columbia, pg 923

NEW HAMPSHIRE

Channell One Video, pg 720

NEW YORK

Icarus Films Inc, pg 783
Third World Newsreel/Camera News Inc, pg 912
Timed Exposures Films, pg 914
VIEW Inc (Video International Entertainment World Inc), pg 930

OREGON

Nostalgia Family Video Inc, pg 843

PENNSYLVANIA

Bullfrog Films Inc, pg 712
Rahlic Publishing Co, pg 869

WISCONSIN

NEWIST/CESA 7, pg 840

QUEBEC

Les Productions Via Le Monde (Daniel Bertolino) Inc, pg 864

Television Program— Classic Distributors

CALIFORNIA

MarVista Entertainment Inc, pg 818
MGM Home Entertainment, pg 825

FLORIDA

Accord Productions, pg 673

ILLINOIS

International Historic Films Inc, pg 790
Movies Unlimited, pg 831

MARYLAND

Recorded Books Inc, an RBmedia company, pg 871
Total AV Systems, pg 916

MICHIGAN

Digi Sign Design LLC, pg 741

NEW HAMPSHIRE

Chip Taylor Communications LLC, pg 907

NEW YORK

A&E Television Networks LLC, pg 671
Mastervision Inc, pg 819

PENNSYLVANIA

Corinth Films Inc, pg 731
MVD Entertainment Group, pg 835
Fred Rogers Productions, pg 876

ONTARIO

Canamedia Inc, pg 715

Television Program— Classic Producers

ARIZONA

Aardvark Productions LLC, pg 671

CALIFORNIA

Big Door, pg 705
Creative Technology, pg 733
Main Street Media Inc, pg 815
QRS Software Services, pg 867
Glenn Roland Films, pg 876
Total Creative, pg 916
Vineyard Video & Photography, pg 930

COLORADO

Tatum Video, pg 907

CONNECTICUT

Ironik Design & Post, pg 791

FLORIDA

Accord Productions, pg 673
Chatterbox Productions Inc, pg 721
Courter Films LLC, pg 732
Sunfire Communications Inc, pg 904
Tricycle Studios, pg 918

GEORGIA

Guerrilla Productions LLC, pg 774
On-Line Productions, pg 845

IDAHO

Wide Eye Productions, pg 938

ILLINOIS

Manning Productions, pg 816

INDIANA

A-V-A Video Productions, pg 671

MARYLAND

dbF a Media Company, pg 739
Kramer Communications Video Production, pg 801

MASSACHUSETTS

Heliotrope Studios, pg 778

MICHIGAN

Digi Sign Design LLC, pg 741
K&R All Media Productions LLC, pg 796
K&R's Recording Studios Inc, pg 796

MINNESOTA

House of Cinemagraphics, pg 782

NEVADA

JCS Video Productions, pg 793

NEW HAMPSHIRE

Chip Taylor Communications LLC, pg 907

NEW JERSEY

MiB MediaWorks, pg 825

NEW MEXICO

Production Outfitters, pg 864

NEW YORK

Mastervision Inc, pg 819

NORTH CAROLINA

The Communications Group Inc, pg 729
Digital Rain LLC, pg 742
Videowerks, pg 930

OHIO

R&B Communications Inc, pg 870
Take 1 Media Services, pg 906

PENNSYLVANIA

Bang! Pictures Inc, pg 701
FMP Media Solutions Inc, pg 763
Production Masters Inc (PMI), pg 864

RHODE ISLAND

Sound-FX-Design, pg 894

TEXAS

Mediaforce Productions, pg 822

VIRGINIA

Metro Productions, pg 824
Rocktown Media, pg 876

WASHINGTON

Bennett-Watt HD Productions Inc, pg 703

WISCONSIN

5th Floor Recording Co, pg 760
Watts Communications Inc, pg 934

WYOMING

Bridger Productions Inc, pg 710

ALBERTA

HDTV Productions Inc, pg 777

ONTARIO

Canamedia Inc, pg 715
GAPC (General Assembly Production Centre), pg 768

QUEBEC

Kerrigan Productions Inc, pg 798

Television Program— Classic Rentals

MICHIGAN

Digi Sign Design LLC, pg 741

Test Commercial Distributors

CALIFORNIA

Far West Media Services Inc, pg 759

MASSACHUSETTS

Penfield Productions Ltd, pg 853

MICHIGAN

Digi Sign Design LLC, pg 741

NEVADA

DVDs4Less, pg 748

NEW HAMPSHIRE

Chip Taylor Communications LLC, pg 907

NEW JERSEY

Allegro Productions Inc, pg 680

NEW YORK

HB-Content, pg 777

VIRGINIA

CACI Integrated Communications, pg 713

Test Commercial Producers

ARIZONA

Aardvark Productions LLC, pg 671
Candee Productions Inc, pg 716
Film Creations Ltd, pg 760
Rodeo Video Inc, pg 876

ARKANSAS

Live'N'Loud, pg 810

CALIFORNIA

A Go Go Films, pg 671
Action Video, pg 675
Artichoke Productions, pg 690
Big Door, pg 705
Classic Images Stock Footage LLC, pg 726
Concrete Images, pg 730
Creative Technology, pg 733
Custom Video Productions Inc, pg 736
Design Media, pg 741
Direct Images Interactive Inc, pg 743
Far West Media Services Inc, pg 759
Havas Edge, pg 777

ITV Productions, pg 792
KTVU-Retail Services, pg 802
Main Street Media Inc, pg 815
Maximus Media Inc, pg 820
McCune Audio-Video-Lighting, pg 821
Media Magic, pg 822
New & Unique Videos™, pg 839
New Circuit Films LLC, pg 839
QRS Software Services, pg 867
Dick Reizner Film & Video, pg 873
RetinaVision Productions, pg 874
Glenn Roland Films, pg 876
SNAP, pg 891
Still N' Motion, pg 901
Tam Communications Inc, pg 906
Timestream Video, pg 914
Total Creative, pg 916
Vineyard Video & Photography, pg 930
Zamacona Productions, pg 945

COLORADO

Flashback Media Productions, pg 762
Transtar Entertainment Co Inc, pg 917

CONNECTICUT

Ironik Design & Post, pg 791
P&P Studios Inc, pg 851
Video Production Associates Inc, pg 928

FLORIDA

Applebox Studio, pg 687
Blackburst Entertainment LLC, pg 706
Chatterbox Productions Inc, pg 721
Civins Productions Inc, pg 725
CopShopMiami.com, pg 731
Courter Films LLC, pg 732
Jordan Klein Film & Video (JKFV), pg 795
Sunfire Communications Inc, pg 904
Sunrise Studios, pg 904
Tricycle Studios, pg 918
Universal Studios Florida® Production Group, pg 922

GEORGIA

Beachwood Productions, pg 702
ECG Productions, pg 750
GP Studios, pg 773
Guerrilla Productions LLC, pg 774
On-Line Productions, pg 845
WATL-TV Inc, pg 934

HAWAII

Hyperspective Studios Inc, pg 783

IDAHO

Brad Shaw Productions Inc, pg 885
Wide Eye Productions, pg 938

ILLINOIS

Atomic Imaging Inc/Golan Studios, pg 692
Film Police, pg 760
Pepper Group, pg 854
PSAV® Presentation Services (Hotel Services Division), pg 866
Richter Studios, pg 875
SCI Television & Creative Media LLC, pg 882
20/20 Communications Inc, pg 920
Video Impressions, pg 928

WEEK TV, pg 935
Winter Productions, pg 939

INDIANA

A-V-A Video Productions, pg 671
Road Pictures, pg 876

KANSAS

KAKE-TV, pg 796

LOUISIANA

Moxie Media, pg 832

MARYLAND

CPR MultiMedia Solutions, pg 732
dbF a Media Company, pg 739
The Image Generators, pg 785
Kramer Communications Video Production, pg 801

MASSACHUSETTS

Green Mountain Post Films (GMP), pg 774
Penfield Productions Ltd, pg 853

MICHIGAN

Digi Sign Design LLC, pg 741
K&R All Media Productions LLC, pg 796
K&R's Recording Studios Inc, pg 796

MINNESOTA

Big Event Productions LLC, pg 705
GMI Productions, pg 771
House of Cinemagraphics, pg 782
MastCom, pg 819

MISSOURI

Hardcastle Films & Video, pg 776

NEVADA

DVDs4Less, pg 748
Encore Event Technologies LLC, pg 754
JCS Video Productions, pg 793

NEW HAMPSHIRE

Chip Taylor Communications LLC, pg 907

NEW JERSEY

Allegro Productions Inc, pg 680
Broadcast Center Studios, pg 710
CFP Video Productions Inc, pg 720
Euro-Pacific Film & Video Productions Inc, pg 756
Laurel Video Productions, pg 804
MediaNow Inc, pg 822
MiB MediaWorks, pg 825
Optisonics Productions, pg 847
Suede Interactive, pg 903
VCSvideo, pg 925

NEW MEXICO

Production Outfitters, pg 864

NEW YORK

aurora productions, pg 696
Blue Barn Pictures Inc, pg 707
Brooklyn Films, pg 711
Charlex Inc, pg 721
HB-Content, pg 777
Hello World Communications, pg 778

PROGRAMMING — VIDEO

Test Commercial Producers (continued)

NEW YORK (continued)

Long Island Video Enterprises Live Inc, pg 811
Mood Creations Ltd, pg 829
MRM//McCANN, pg 832
MRY, pg 832
New Horizon Studios, pg 839
Northeast Video Productions Inc, pg 842
The Palmer Group, pg 850
Pat Kogan Productions Inc, pg 852
PrimaLux Video Inc, pg 862
Suggs Media Productions Inc, pg 903
TeleTime Productions, pg 910

NORTH CAROLINA

The Communications Group Inc, pg 729
Digital Rain LLC, pg 742
Kino Mountain Productions LLC, pg 799
PACE Worldwide, pg 849
Videowerks, pg 930

OHIO

Advent Media Inc, pg 677
CET, pg 720
Lyon Video Inc, pg 813
R&B Communications Inc, pg 870
Take 1 Media Services, pg 906
Vista Color Imaging Inc, pg 931

PENNSYLVANIA

Bang! Pictures Inc, pg 701
FMP Media Solutions Inc, pg 763
JPL, pg 795
Kensington Falls Animation, pg 797
Muderick Media, pg 833
Production Masters Inc (PMI), pg 864
Visual Sound Inc, pg 931
WHYY Inc, pg 938

RHODE ISLAND

Sound-FX-Design, pg 894

TEXAS

Biway Media, pg 706
Cerutti Productions Inc, pg 720
Communication Arts Multimedia Inc, pg 728
Horizon Film + Video Productions, pg 781
Marx InDigital, pg 818
Mediaforce Productions, pg 822
Omega Productions, pg 845
South Coast Film & Video, pg 895

VIRGINIA

CACI Integrated Communications, pg 713
Limelight Communications Inc, pg 808
Metro Productions, pg 824
Rocktown Media, pg 876

WASHINGTON

Adams Creative & Production Services, pg 675
Bennett-Watt HD Productions Inc, pg 703

WISCONSIN

5th Floor Recording Co, pg 760
Mirror 34 Productions, pg 828
USAV Group Inc, pg 923
Video Wisconsin Inc, pg 929

WYOMING

Bridger Productions Inc, pg 710

MANITOBA

Spectra Video Productions Ltd, pg 897

NEWFOUNDLAND AND LABRADOR

Vidcraft Productions Ltd, pg 927

ONTARIO

DebsVoice, pg 739
Video Excellence Productions, pg 927

QUEBEC

Kerrigan Productions Inc, pg 798

SASKATCHEWAN

plan9films, pg 857

Test Commercial Rentals

MICHIGAN

Digi Sign Design LLC, pg 741

Theatrical Short Distributors

CALIFORNIA

Direct Cinema Ltd Inc, pg 743
Em Gee Film Library, pg 753
Glenn Photo Supply, pg 771
Glenn Video Vistas Ltd, pg 771
MarVista Entertainment Inc, pg 818
New & Unique Videos™, pg 839
Pyramid Media, pg 867
Visual Communications - Southern California Asian American Studies Central Inc, pg 931
Warner Home Video Inc, pg 934

GEORGIA

On-Line Productions, pg 845

ILLINOIS

Film Ideas Inc, pg 760
Film Police, pg 760
Movies Unlimited, pg 831

INDIANA

Perennial Pictures Film Corp, pg 854

MICHIGAN

Digi Sign Design LLC, pg 741

NEW HAMPSHIRE

Chip Taylor Communications LLC, pg 907

NEW JERSEY

Ergo Media Inc, pg 755

NEW YORK

ATA Trading Corp/Favorite TV Inc, pg 691
Castillo Theatre, pg 717
Circulating Film & Video Library, pg 725
HB-Content, pg 777
Kino International Corp, pg 799
Third World Newsreel/Camera News Inc, pg 912
VIEW Inc (Video International Entertainment World Inc), pg 930
Women Make Movies Inc, pg 941
Zeitgeist Films Ltd, pg 945

NORTH CAROLINA

Crystal Pictures Inc, pg 735

TENNESSEE

American Blackguard Inc, pg 683

VIRGINIA

CACI Integrated Communications, pg 713

WASHINGTON

White Rain Films Ltd, pg 937

ONTARIO

Canadian Filmmakers Distribution Center (CFMDC), pg 715
Canadian Learning Co Inc, pg 715
CCI Entertainment Ltd, pg 718
Doomsday Studios Limited, pg 745

QUEBEC

Les Productions Via Le Monde (Daniel Bertolino) Inc, pg 864

Theatrical Short Producers

ALASKA

Alaska Media Pros LLC, pg 679

ARIZONA

Aardvark Productions LLC, pg 671

ARKANSAS

Live'N'Loud, pg 810

CALIFORNIA

Artichoke Productions, pg 690
Big Door, pg 705
Steve Chandler, pg 720
Classic Images Stock Footage LLC, pg 726
Concrete Images, pg 730
Creative Technology, pg 733
Custom Video Productions Inc, pg 736
digital OutPost, pg 742
imageReal Pictures LLC, pg 785
ITV Productions, pg 792
McCune Audio-Video-Lighting, pg 821
Media Magic, pg 822
Moving Art by Louie Schwartzberg, pg 831
New & Unique Videos™, pg 839
New Deal Studios, pg 839
Nineteen87, pg 841
PM Productions, pg 858

Point of View Productions, pg 858
QRS Software Services, pg 867
Glenn Roland Films, pg 876
SNAP, pg 891
Total Creative, pg 916
Vineyard Video & Photography, pg 930
Visual Communications - Southern California Asian American Studies Central Inc, pg 931
Wavemaker Media Design, pg 934

CONNECTICUT

Ironik Design & Post, pg 791

FLORIDA

Chatterbox Productions Inc, pg 721
CopShopMiami.com, pg 731
Courter Films LLC, pg 732
Jordan Klein Film & Video (JKFV), pg 795
Sunfire Communications Inc, pg 904
Tel-Air Interests Inc, pg 909

GEORGIA

Beachwood Productions, pg 702
Guerrilla Productions LLC, pg 774
Myriad Productions, pg 835
On-Line Productions, pg 845

HAWAII

Hyperspective Studios Inc, pg 783

IDAHO

Wide Eye Productions, pg 938

ILLINOIS

Film Police, pg 760
Pepper Group, pg 854
Winter Productions, pg 939

INDIANA

A-V-A Video Productions, pg 671

LOUISIANA

Moxie Media, pg 832

MARYLAND

Absolute Hollywood, pg 672
Richard Chisolm Cinematography, pg 722
CPR MultiMedia Solutions, pg 732
dbF a Media Company, pg 739
Kramer Communications Video Production, pg 801

MASSACHUSETTS

Green Mountain Post Films (GMP), pg 774
Heliotrope Studios, pg 778
HOME Inc, pg 781
Preston Productions Inc, pg 861

MICHIGAN

Digi Sign Design LLC, pg 741
K&R All Media Productions LLC, pg 796
K&R's Recording Studios Inc, pg 796

MINNESOTA

House of Cinemagraphics, pg 782

NEVADA

Aardvark Video & Media
Productions, pg 671
Encore Event Technologies LLC,
pg 754

NEW HAMPSHIRE

Apertura, pg 686
Chip Taylor Communications LLC,
pg 907

NEW JERSEY

Broadcast Center Studios, pg 710
CFP Video Productions Inc, pg 720
MiB MediaWorks, pg 825
Optisonics Productions, pg 847

NEW YORK

Air Sea Land Productions Inc
(ASL), pg 678
aurora productions, pg 696
Big Fish Production US, pg 705
Blue Barn Pictures Inc, pg 707
Brooklyn Films, pg 711
Buzzco Associates Inc, pg 713
Castillo Theatre, pg 717
HB-Content, pg 777
Kinetic Arts, pg 799
The Palmer Group, pg 850
Peckham Productions Inc, pg 852
Third World Newsreel/Camera
News Inc, pg 912
VIEW Inc (Video International
Entertainment World Inc), pg 930

NORTH CAROLINA

The Communications Group Inc,
pg 729
Crystal Pictures Inc, pg 735
Digital Rain LLC, pg 742
Videowerks, pg 930

OHIO

R&B Communications Inc, pg 870
Vista Color Imaging Inc, pg 931

OKLAHOMA

Institute for Teaching & Learning
Excellence (ITLE), pg 788

OREGON

Ideascape Inc, pg 784

PENNSYLVANIA

Bang! Pictures Inc, pg 701
FMP Media Solutions Inc, pg 763
Innovision Media Group, pg 788
Kensington Falls Animation, pg 797
Muderick Media, pg 833
Production Masters Inc (PMI),
pg 864

RHODE ISLAND

Sound-FX-Design, pg 894

TENNESSEE

American Blackguard Inc, pg 683
Continental Film, pg 731

TEXAS

Cerutti Productions Inc, pg 720
Horizon Film + Video Productions,
pg 781
Mediaforce Productions, pg 822
Omega Productions, pg 845
Stage Directions, pg 898

VIRGINIA

CACI Integrated Communications,
pg 713
Limelight Communications Inc,
pg 808
Metro Productions, pg 824

WASHINGTON

Bennett-Watt HD Productions Inc,
pg 703
Intermedia Inc, pg 789

WISCONSIN

5th Floor Recording Co, pg 760
Wisconsin Public Television, pg 940

WYOMING

Bridger Productions Inc, pg 710

ONTARIO

Doomsday Studios Limited, pg 745
GAPC (General Assembly
Production Centre), pg 768
Image Video Services &
Productions, pg 785
RB Productions, pg 870

QUEBEC

Kerrigan Productions Inc, pg 798
Les Productions Via Le Monde
(Daniel Bertolino) Inc, pg 864

SASKATCHEWAN

plan9films, pg 857

Theatrical Short Rentals

CALIFORNIA

Direct Cinema Ltd Inc, pg 743
Point of View Productions, pg 858
Visual Communications - Southern
California Asian American
Studies Central Inc, pg 931

GEORGIA

On-Line Productions, pg 845

MICHIGAN

Digi Sign Design LLC, pg 741

NEW YORK

Circulating Film & Video Library,
pg 725
Kino International Corp, pg 799
Third World Newsreel/Camera
News Inc, pg 912
VIEW Inc (Video International
Entertainment World Inc), pg 930

NORTH CAROLINA

Crystal Pictures Inc, pg 735

ONTARIO

Doomsday Studios Limited, pg 745

QUEBEC

Les Productions Via Le Monde
(Daniel Bertolino) Inc, pg 864

Training Program
Distributors

ALABAMA

CMEinfo™, pg 727

ARIZONA

Rodeo Video Inc, pg 876
Valley of the Sun Publishing Co,
pg 924
Video Learning Library, pg 928

ARKANSAS

Mullikin Agency, pg 833

CALIFORNIA

Academy Savant, pg 672
Backstage Pass Entertainment Inc,
pg 700
California Language Laboratories,
pg 714
Cavalcade Productions Inc, pg 717
Deja View Video, pg 740
Dialect Accent Specialists Inc,
pg 741
Direct Cinema Ltd Inc, pg 743
Discovery Education - Los Angeles,
pg 743
ETR, pg 756
Ferrari Productions, pg 759
Forte Productions, pg 764
Golden State Dance Teachers
Association (GSDTA), pg 772
Increase Video/Silver Mine Video,
pg 786
Kantola Productions LLC, pg 796
MarVista Entertainment Inc, pg 818
Medcom Inc, pg 821
Moose School Productions, pg 830
New & Unique Videos™, pg 839
Pacific Media, pg 849
People Skills International, pg 854
Pyramid Media, pg 867
Quality Digest, pg 868
Revelli, pg 874
Russ InVision Co/AbridgeClub.com,
pg 879
Semiconductor Services, pg 883
Theatre Arts Video Library, pg 911
TMW Media Group, pg 915
The Wine Appreciation Guild Ltd,
pg 939

COLORADO

InJoy Birth & Parenting Education,
pg 788
Jeppesen, pg 793
National Institute for Trial
Advocacy (NITA), pg 836

DELAWARE

University Media Services, pg 922

DISTRICT OF COLUMBIA

American Chemical Society (ACS),
pg 683

FLORIDA

PAR Inc, pg 851
Video Aided Instruction Inc, pg 927
Video Resources Software, pg 928

GEORGIA

LYRASIS, pg 813
On-Line Productions, pg 845

HAWAII

Source School of Tantra Yoga Inc,
pg 895

ILLINOIS

ABSA Films, pg 672
CCH Continuing Education, pg 718
CCore Media Inc, pg 718
Film Ideas Inc, pg 760
1st Financial Training Services Inc,
pg 761
Movies Unlimited, pg 831
National Safety Council (NSC),
pg 836
Nightingale-Conant Corp, pg 841
RADMAR Inc, pg 869

INDIANA

Purdue University Digital
Education, pg 866

IOWA

Kirkwood Community College,
pg 799
Prositions Inc, pg 865

KENTUCKY

EKU Media, pg 752
KET The Kentucky Network,
pg 798
WaxWorks VideoWorks, pg 934

MARYLAND

MMI Marketing, pg 828
Total AV Systems, pg 916

MASSACHUSETTS

Commonwealth Films Inc, pg 728
Enterprise Media LLC, pg 754
National Fire Protection Association
(NFPA), pg 836
Penfield Productions Ltd, pg 853

MICHIGAN

Digi Sign Design LLC, pg 741
MSU Technologies, pg 833
Prakken Publications Inc, pg 861
The Program Source International,
pg 865
Society of Manufacturing Engineers
(SME), pg 891
VMS Inc, pg 932

MINNESOTA

Harris Communications Inc, pg 776
JIST Publishing, pg 794
Service Quality Institute, pg 884
Whole Person Associates Inc,
pg 938

MISSOURI

Annenberg Learner, pg 685

NEBRASKA

B & B Video Productions Inc,
pg 700

NEVADA

DVDs4Less, pg 748

NEW HAMPSHIRE

Chip Taylor Communications LLC,
pg 907

PROGRAMMING — VIDEO

Training Program Distributors (continued)

NEW JERSEY

Dance Horizons Video, pg 737
Euro-Pacific Film & Video Productions Inc, pg 756
FlagHouse, pg 762
MiB MediaWorks, pg 825
SES SA, pg 884

NEW MEXICO

The Phoenix Learning Group Inc, pg 855

NEW YORK

American Management Association® (AMA), pg 683
Artistic Video, pg 690
Broadstreet Productions LLC, pg 711
Albert Ellis Institute (AEI), pg 753
Guidance Associates Inc Center for Humanities, pg 774
Guilford Publications, pg 774
HB-Content, pg 777
Homespun Video, pg 781
Mastervision Inc, pg 819
Monad Trainer's Aide Inc, pg 829
Shopware, pg 886
Video Catalogue Co Inc, pg 927
Willow Mixed Media Inc, pg 939

NORTH CAROLINA

AudioSolutionz LLC, pg 695
The International Society of Automation (ISA), pg 790
Speakers Unlimited, pg 896

OKLAHOMA

Academic Media & Digital Services, pg 672

OREGON

InterVision Media, pg 791

PENNSYLVANIA

American Law Institute Continuing Legal Education (ALI CLE), pg 683
Bergwall Productions Inc, pg 704
The Computer Language Co Inc, pg 729
CORTRON Media LLC, pg 732
FMP Media Solutions Inc, pg 763
Fred Rogers Productions, pg 876
S I Video Sales Group, pg 879
TRC Interactive Inc, pg 917

TENNESSEE

American Blackguard Inc, pg 683

TEXAS

CEV Multimedia Ltd, pg 720
Chalk Dust Co, pg 720
Communication Arts Multimedia Inc, pg 728
Emergency Film Group, pg 753
Executive Development Systems Inc, pg 757
PetroSkills | RDC Solutions, pg 855

Teleometrics International, pg 910
University of Texas at Austin - Petroleum Extension Service, pg 923

VERMONT

Wilson McLeran Inc, pg 939

VIRGINIA

CACI Integrated Communications, pg 713
CDR Communications Inc, pg 719
Coastal Training Technologies Corp, pg 727
National Audiovisual Center (NAC), pg 836
WETA Production Center, pg 936

WASHINGTON

Bennett-Watt HD Productions Inc, pg 703
Intermedia Inc, pg 789
Medifecta Healthcare Training, pg 823

BRITISH COLUMBIA

Credo Interactive Inc, pg 734
Thompson Rivers University Marketing & Communications Dept, pg 913

ONTARIO

Canadian Learning Co Inc, pg 715
Kineticvideo.com, pg 799

Training Program Producers

ALABAMA

CMEinfo™, pg 727
Leo Ticheli Productions, pg 913

ALASKA

Aurora Films, pg 696
Imig Audio/Video Inc, pg 786

ARIZONA

Aardvark Productions LLC, pg 671
Candee Productions Inc, pg 716
Creative Backstage, pg 733
Direct Current Video Productions, pg 743
Film Creations Ltd, pg 760
Fox 10 Productions (KSAZ-TV), pg 765
Master Video Disc & Design, pg 819
Merestone, pg 823
Metropolitan Audio-Visual Inc, pg 824
On-Site Video, pg 846
Rodeo Video Inc, pg 876
Valley of the Sun Publishing Co, pg 924
Video Learning Library, pg 928

ARKANSAS

Live'N'Loud, pg 810
Mullikin Agency, pg 833
White Diamond Productions LLC, pg 937

CALIFORNIA

A Go Go Films, pg 671
Academy Savant, pg 672
Access Video in Berkeley, pg 673

Action Video, pg 675
Artichoke Productions, pg 690
Backstage Pass Entertainment Inc, pg 700
Big Door, pg 705
California Language Laboratories, pg 714
Cavalcade Productions Inc, pg 717
Center for the Collaborative Classroom, pg 719
Steve Chandler, pg 720
Classic Images Stock Footage LLC, pg 726
Coastline Productions, pg 727
Concrete Images, pg 730
Creative Technology, pg 733
Custom Video Productions Inc, pg 736
Deja View Video, pg 740
Design Media, pg 741
Dialect Accent Specialists Inc, pg 741
Direct Images Interactive Inc, pg 743
Discovery Education - Los Angeles, pg 743
Dolphin MultiMedia Inc, pg 745
Forte Productions, pg 764
Glix Entertainment Inc, pg 771
Havas Edge, pg 777
imageReal Pictures LLC, pg 785
Increase Video/Silver Mine Video, pg 786
ITV Productions, pg 792
Kantola Productions LLC, pg 796
Kavich Reynolds Productions Inc, pg 797
KPBS Public Broadcasting, pg 801
KTVU-Retail Services, pg 802
Main Street Media Inc, pg 815
Maximus Media Inc, pg 820
McCune Audio-Video-Lighting, pg 821
Medcom Inc, pg 821
Media Magic, pg 822
The Media Staff Inc, pg 822
Moose School Productions, pg 830
New & Unique Videos™, pg 839
New Circuit Films LLC, pg 839
Nineteen87, pg 841
Nolte Media, pg 841
On-Trax Inc, pg 846
Pacific Media, pg 849
Penrose Productions, pg 854
PM Productions, pg 858
Pyramid Media, pg 867
QRS Software Services, pg 867
Quality Digest, pg 868
Dick Reizner Film & Video, pg 873
RetinaVision Productions, pg 874
Revelli, pg 874
Glenn Roland Films, pg 876
Russ InVision Co/AbridgeClub.com, pg 879
SNAP, pg 891
Staylor-Made Communications Inc, pg 900
Still N' Motion, pg 901
Tam Communications Inc, pg 906
Theatre Arts Video Library, pg 911
TMW Media Group, pg 915
Total Creative, pg 916
TVA Media Group, pg 919
Twin Peaks Creative, pg 920
Videografix LLC, pg 929
Vineyard Video & Photography, pg 930
Visions Plus, pg 931
Wavemaker Media Design, pg 934
West Coast Projections Inc, pg 935
Zamacona Productions, pg 945

COLORADO

Daylight Productions & Rentals, pg 739
Flashback Media Productions, pg 762
InJoy Birth & Parenting Education, pg 788
National Institute for Trial Advocacy (NITA), pg 836
People Productions, pg 854
Rocky Mountain Audio/Video Productions Inc, pg 876
Transtar Entertainment Co Inc, pg 917

CONNECTICUT

ACM Productions Ltd, pg 674
Business & Legal Reports Inc, pg 713
Cine-Med Inc, pg 723
Digital Video Productions, pg 742
The Gary-Paul Agency, pg 768
Geomatrix Productions, pg 770
Ironik Design & Post, pg 791
Moving Pictures, pg 832
Palace Productions MediaVision, pg 850
P&P Studios Inc, pg 851
UConn Health Multimedia Services, pg 920
Video Production Associates Inc, pg 928

DELAWARE

University Media Services, pg 922

DISTRICT OF COLUMBIA

American Chemical Society (ACS), pg 683
O'Keefe Communications Inc, pg 844
Yellow Cat Productions Inc, pg 944

FLORIDA

Accord Productions, pg 673
Applebox Studio, pg 687
Astoria Communications Inc, pg 691
Blackburst Entertainment LLC, pg 706
Civins Productions Inc, pg 725
Communications Concepts Inc (CCI), pg 729
CopShopMiami.com, pg 731
Courter Films LLC, pg 732
Easy Edit Video Inc, pg 750
ITC Learning LLC, pg 791
Jordan Klein Film & Video (JKFV), pg 795
National Teleproductions Inc, pg 837
Paradise Video & Film, pg 851
Roger Scruggs Films, pg 883
Skystorm Productions, pg 890
Sound & Vision Communications Inc, pg 893
Sunfire Communications Inc, pg 904
Sunrise Studios, pg 904
Teach America Corp, pg 908
Tel-Air Interests Inc, pg 909
Tight Line Productions, pg 914
Tricycle Studios, pg 918
Universal Studios Florida® Production Group, pg 922
Mike Vasilinda Productions Inc, pg 925
Video Aided Instruction Inc, pg 927
Video Resources Software, pg 928
Video Techniques Inc, pg 928

GEORGIA

Beachwood Productions, pg 702
Cox Media, pg 732
ECG Productions, pg 750
GP Studios, pg 773
Guerrilla Productions LLC, pg 774
Myriad Productions, pg 835
On-Line Productions, pg 845

HAWAII

Hyperspective Studios Inc, pg 783
Source School of Tantra Yoga Inc, pg 895

IDAHO

Brad Shaw Productions Inc, pg 885
Wide Eye Productions, pg 938

ILLINOIS

ABSA Films, pg 672
Accenture, pg 672
Airways Digital Media, pg 679
Atomic Imaging Inc/Golan Studios, pg 692
Beatty TeleVisual Productions, pg 703
CCH Continuing Education, pg 718
CCore Media Inc, pg 718
The Chicago Production Center, pg 721
Extraordinary Demos/Videos, pg 757
Film Police, pg 760
1st Financial Training Services Inc, pg 761
IV Media Resources, pg 792
Major Media Productions Inc, pg 815
Manning Productions, pg 816
Mightybytes Inc, pg 827
Mimi Productions, pg 828
Multimedia Marketing Group, pg 833
National Safety Council (NSC), pg 836
Nightingale-Conant Corp, pg 841
Pepper Group, pg 854
Production Craft Inc, pg 863
PSAV® Presentation Services (Hotel Services Division), pg 866
RADMAR Inc, pg 869
Richter Studios, pg 875
SCI Television & Creative Media LLC, pg 882
Southern Illinois University, pg 895
Sparkfactor, pg 896
20/20 Communications Inc, pg 920
Video I-D Teleproductions Inc, pg 928
Video Impressions, pg 928
WEEK TV, pg 935
Winter Productions, pg 939

INDIANA

A-V-A Video Productions, pg 671
Advanced Media Integration, pg 677
Lighthouse Photo & Video Productions, pg 807
PentaVision Communications Inc, pg 854
Purdue University Digital Education, pg 866

IOWA

Educational Technology & Media Services, pg 751
Kirkwood Community College, pg 799
Prositions Inc, pg 865

KENTUCKY

EKU Media, pg 752
Idle Minds Productions Inc, pg 784
KET The Kentucky Network, pg 798
The Media Collaboratory, pg 821
Prosper Media Group Inc, pg 866

LOUISIANA

Digital FX Inc, pg 742
Launch Media, pg 804
Louisiana State University Division of Strategic Communications, pg 811
Moxie Media, pg 832

MAINE

WGME-TV, pg 936

MARYLAND

Adventure Productions LLC, pg 678
CAS Video Productions, pg 717
Richard Chisolm Cinematography, pg 722
CPR MultiMedia Solutions, pg 732
dbF a Media Company, pg 739
The Image Generators, pg 785
Kramer Communications Video Production, pg 801
Media Dimensions LLC, pg 821
Mobile-Video Productions Inc, pg 828
Quality Film & Video, pg 868

MASSACHUSETTS

Award Productions Inc, pg 699
CommCreative, pg 728
Commonwealth Films Inc, pg 728
Enterprise Media LLC, pg 754
Green Mountain Post Films (GMP), pg 774
HOME Inc, pg 781
Northern Light Productions (NLP), pg 842
Penfield Productions Ltd, pg 853
TVN-The Video Network, pg 919
VideoLink Inc, an AVI-SPL company, pg 929
WVP Boston, pg 942

MICHIGAN

Digi Sign Design LLC, pg 741
K&R All Media Productions LLC, pg 796
K&R's Recording Studios Inc, pg 796
Lawrence Productions Inc, pg 804
Prakken Publications Inc, pg 861
The Program Source International, pg 865
Society of Manufacturing Engineers (SME), pg 891
TGA Recording Co, pg 911
VMS Inc, pg 932

MINNESOTA

Big Event Productions LLC, pg 705
GMI Productions, pg 771
House of Cinemagraphics, pg 782
JIST Publishing, pg 794
Live Spark Inc, pg 810
MastCom, pg 819
Media Loft Inc, pg 822
Service Quality Institute, pg 884
Whole Person Associates Inc, pg 938
Worthwhile Films, pg 941

MISSOURI

Annenberg Learner, pg 685
Audio-VideoGraphics Inc, pg 694
Communitronics Corp, pg 729
Hardcastle Films & Video, pg 776

NEBRASKA

B & B Video Productions Inc, pg 700
Envision Communications Inc, pg 755
Rainbow Video Productions Inc, pg 869

NEVADA

Aardvark Video & Media Productions, pg 671
DVDs4Less, pg 748
Encore Event Technologies LLC, pg 754
JCS Video Productions, pg 793
Tanglewood Productions, pg 907

NEW HAMPSHIRE

Apertura, pg 686
Channell One Video, pg 720
Chip Taylor Communications LLC, pg 907
The Troupe, pg 918

NEW JERSEY

Broadcast Center Studios, pg 710
CFP Video Productions Inc, pg 720
Color Leasing Studios, pg 727
Euro-Pacific Film & Video Productions Inc, pg 756
Laurel Video Productions, pg 804
MiB MediaWorks, pg 825
Midnight Media Group Inc, pg 827
Ray Mueller Productions, pg 833
Optisonics Productions, pg 847
Selden Associates, pg 883
Shamrock Communications, pg 885
Suede Interactive, pg 903
Telemanagement Resources International Inc (TRI), pg 910
Telequest Inc, pg 910
TimeSteps Productions, pg 914
VCSvideo, pg 925
Video Ideas Productions, pg 928

NEW MEXICO

The Phoenix Learning Group Inc, pg 855
Production Outfitters, pg 864

NEW YORK

American Management Association® (AMA), pg 683
Artistic Video, pg 690
aurora productions, pg 696
BC Studio, pg 702
Blue Barn Pictures Inc, pg 707
Broadstreet Productions LLC, pg 711
Buzzco Associates Inc, pg 713
Campus Productions, pg 715
Cohn Creative Group LLC, pg 727
Guidance Associates Inc Center for Humanities, pg 774
Guilford Publications, pg 774
Havas Creative, pg 776
HB-Content, pg 777
Ketchum Inc, pg 798
L A Bruell Inc, pg 802
LightHouse Films, pg 807
Mastervision Inc, pg 819
Mood Creations Ltd, pg 829
MRM//McCANN, pg 832

MRY, pg 832
News Broadcast Network Inc, pg 840
Northeast Video Productions Inc, pg 842
The Palmer Group, pg 850
Pat Kogan Productions Inc, pg 852
Peckham Productions Inc, pg 852
PrimaLux Video Inc, pg 862
PrimeLight Productions Inc, pg 862
Shopware, pg 886
Suggs Media Productions Inc, pg 903
TeleTime Productions, pg 910
Video Catalogue Co Inc, pg 927
Videograf, pg 929
Alan Weiss Productions, pg 935
Willow Mixed Media Inc, pg 939
WNET/New York Public Media, pg 940

NORTH CAROLINA

All Pro Media Inc, pg 680
Pat Appleson Studios Inc, pg 687
AudioSolutionz LLC, pg 695
Bill Barnes Video Productions LLC, pg 702
The Communications Group Inc, pg 729
Digital Rain LLC, pg 742
Horizon Video Productions Inc, pg 781
Image Associates Inc, pg 784
Kino Mountain Productions LLC, pg 799
Moving Pictures, pg 832
NASCAR Productions LLC, pg 835
PACE Worldwide, pg 849
Videowerks, pg 930

OHIO

Advent Media Inc, pg 677
Russ Beckner Pictures, pg 703
CET, pg 720
Clear Choice Creative Corp, pg 726
Cuyahoga Community College Student Production Office (SPO), pg 736
Image Video Teleproductions Inc, pg 785
Lyon Video Inc, pg 813
MainSail Production Services Inc, pg 815
R&B Communications Inc, pg 870
Shelburne Films, pg 885
Take 1 Media Services, pg 906
Vista Color Imaging Inc, pg 931

OKLAHOMA

Academic Media & Digital Services, pg 672

OREGON

CMD Agency, pg 726
Ideascape Inc, pg 784
InterVision Media, pg 791
KPDX-TV Production Center, pg 801
KTVA Productions, pg 802
Production West, pg 864

PENNSYLVANIA

American Law Institute Continuing Legal Education (ALI CLE), pg 683
Audio Visual Communications Inc, pg 694
Beholder Productions Inc, pg 703
Bergwall Productions Inc, pg 704
CORTRON Media LLC, pg 732

PROGRAMMING — VIDEO

Training Program Producers (continued)

PENNSYLVANIA (continued)

FMP Media Solutions Inc, pg 763
Innovision Media Group, pg 788
JPL, pg 795
Kensington Falls Animation, pg 797
Main Point Productions, pg 815
Muderick Media, pg 833
Panta Rhei Media Inc, pg 851
Production Masters Inc (PMI), pg 864
Fred Rogers Productions, pg 876
S I Video Sales Group, pg 879
Video/Film Associates, pg 928
The Videohouse Inc, pg 929
Videosmith Inc, pg 930
Visual Sound Inc, pg 931

RHODE ISLAND

Sound-FX-Design, pg 894

SOUTH CAROLINA

Encore Video Productions, pg 754
Stages Video Productions, pg 899
Venture Media, pg 925

TENNESSEE

American Blackguard Inc, pg 683
Continental Film, pg 731
Memphis Communications Corp, pg 823
Paradigm Marketing & Creative, pg 851
Running Pony Productions LLC, pg 878
Scripps Networks, pg 882
Stage Post, pg 899
Russ Sturgeon Productions/RSVP, pg 903

TEXAS

Alpha Video Productions, pg 682
AMS Pictures, pg 684
Biway Media, pg 706
Castleview Productions, pg 717
Cerutti Productions Inc, pg 720
CEV Multimedia Ltd, pg 720
Chalk Dust Co, pg 720
Communication Arts Multimedia Inc, pg 728
Countdown Productions Inc, pg 732
Dub King, pg 747
Dykeman Associates Inc, pg 748
The Editing Co, pg 750
Emergency Film Group, pg 753
Epic Software Group Inc, pg 755
Eyecon Video Productions, pg 758
Horizon Film + Video Productions, pg 781
JSAV, pg 795
Marx InDigital, pg 818
Mediaforce Productions, pg 822
Earl Miller Productions Inc, pg 827
Julye Newlin Productions Inc, pg 840
Omega Productions, pg 845
Omni Intercommunications Inc, pg 845
PetroSkills | RDC Solutions, pg 855
Richie Media Productions LLC, pg 875
Romar Learning Solutions LLC, pg 877
South Coast Film & Video, pg 895

Sportsmen on Film Inc, pg 898
Stage Directions, pg 898
Teleometrics International, pg 910
University of Texas at Austin - Petroleum Extension Service, pg 923

VERMONT

Wilson McLeran Inc, pg 939

VIRGINIA

Altruist Media LLC, pg 682
American Counseling Association, pg 683
CACI Integrated Communications, pg 713
CDR Communications Inc, pg 719
Cinebar Productions Inc, pg 723
Coastal Training Technologies Corp, pg 727
CVW Event Productions, pg 736
DXC Technology Co, pg 748
Limelight Communications Inc, pg 808
Metro Productions, pg 824
National Association of Elementary School Principals (NAESP), pg 836
National Media Services Inc, pg 836
Rocktown Media, pg 876
Video Solutions, pg 928
WETA Production Center, pg 936

WASHINGTON

Adams Creative & Production Services, pg 675
Bennett-Watt HD Productions Inc, pg 703
Hamilton Studio, pg 775
Intermedia Inc, pg 789
Medifecta Healthcare Training, pg 823
North-by-Northwest - A Digital Studio, pg 842
Sparkworks Media, pg 896
White Rain Films Ltd, pg 937

WEST VIRGINIA

Blackwater Video Productions, pg 707
Sweetsong Productions, pg 905

WISCONSIN

AVS Group, pg 699
5th Floor Recording Co, pg 760
Logan Productions Inc, pg 811
Meridian Studios, pg 824
Midland Video Productions Inc, pg 827
Mirror 34 Productions, pg 828
USAV Group Inc, pg 923
Video Wisconsin Inc, pg 929
Watts Communications Inc, pg 934
Wisconsin Public Television, pg 940

WYOMING

Bridger Productions Inc, pg 710

ALBERTA

Black Media Works, pg 706
HDTV Productions Inc, pg 777

BRITISH COLUMBIA

Thompson Rivers University Marketing & Communications Dept, pg 913
Triad Communications Ltd, pg 918

NEWFOUNDLAND AND LABRADOR

Vidcraft Productions Ltd, pg 927

ONTARIO

ADS Media, pg 677
GAPC (General Assembly Production Centre), pg 768
Image Video Services & Productions, pg 785
JFB Communications, pg 794
RB Productions, pg 870
Silver Creek Media Inc, pg 888
Video Excellence Productions, pg 927

QUEBEC

Kerrigan Productions Inc, pg 798

SASKATCHEWAN

plan9films, pg 857

Training Program Rentals

CALIFORNIA

Cavalcade Productions Inc, pg 717
Direct Cinema Ltd Inc, pg 743
Medcom Inc, pg 821
Semiconductor Services, pg 883

DELAWARE

University Media Services, pg 922

ILLINOIS

1st Financial Training Services Inc, pg 761
National Safety Council (NSC), pg 836

MASSACHUSETTS

Commonwealth Films Inc, pg 728
Enterprise Media LLC, pg 754

MICHIGAN

Digi Sign Design LLC, pg 741

MINNESOTA

Service Quality Institute, pg 884

NEW JERSEY

Euro-Pacific Film & Video Productions Inc, pg 756

NEW YORK

BC Studio, pg 702

NORTH CAROLINA

Image Associates Inc, pg 784

WASHINGTON

Intermedia Inc, pg 789

Travelog Distributors

ALASKA

Alaska Video Postcards Inc, pg 679

ARIZONA

Video Learning Library, pg 928

CALIFORNIA

Direct Cinema Ltd Inc, pg 743
ECONEWS (Environmental Television Series) & (Environmental Directions Radio Series), pg 750
eFootage LLC, pg 751
Em Gee Film Library, pg 753
411 Video Information, pg 764
Glenn Video Vistas Ltd, pg 771
MarVista Entertainment Inc, pg 818
New & Unique Videos™, pg 839
TMW Media Group, pg 915

COLORADO

Tatum Video, pg 907

DISTRICT OF COLUMBIA

Biblical Archaeology Society (BAS), pg 705

FLORIDA

America By Air LLC, pg 682
NatureVision Stock Footage Library, pg 837

GEORGIA

On-Line Productions, pg 845

ILLINOIS

ABSA Films, pg 672
Film Ideas Inc, pg 760
Moviecraft Inc, pg 831
Movies Unlimited, pg 831
Questar Entertainment Inc, pg 868

IOWA

American Visions, pg 684

KENTUCKY

Horizon Films & Media LLC, pg 781
WaxWorks VideoWorks, pg 934

MARYLAND

Recorded Books Inc, an RBmedia company, pg 871
RLJ Entertainment Inc, pg 875

MASSACHUSETTS

Penfield Productions Ltd, pg 853

MICHIGAN

Digi Sign Design LLC, pg 741
The Program Source International, pg 865

NEW HAMPSHIRE

Chip Taylor Communications LLC, pg 907

NEW JERSEY

Ergo Media Inc, pg 755
Euro-Pacific Film & Video Productions Inc, pg 756
MiB MediaWorks, pg 825

NEW YORK

Janson Media Inc, pg 793
Metropolitan Opera Guild Inc, pg 824
Random House Children's Books, pg 870

SISU Home Entertainment Inc, pg 889
VIEW Inc (Video International Entertainment World Inc), pg 930

OHIO

Shelburne Films, pg 885

OREGON

Encounter Video Inc, pg 754
Wilderness Video, pg 938

PENNSYLVANIA

Beholder Productions Inc, pg 703
CCI Communications Inc, pg 718
FMP Media Solutions Inc, pg 763
Library Video Company, pg 807

SOUTH CAROLINA

American Production Services LLC, pg 684

TENNESSEE

American Blackguard Inc, pg 683
Spring Arbor Distributors Inc, pg 898

TEXAS

Educational Video Network, pg 751

VIRGINIA

CACI Integrated Communications, pg 713

WASHINGTON

Bennett-Watt HD Productions Inc, pg 703
John McLean Media, pg 794
Small World Productions Inc, pg 890

WEST VIRGINIA

Harpers Ferry Historical Association, pg 776

ONTARIO

Canadian Learning Co Inc, pg 715
Canamedia Inc, pg 715

QUEBEC

Ulysses Travel Guides Inc, pg 920

Travelog Producers

ALABAMA

AVS Media Group, pg 699

ALASKA

Alaska Media Pros LLC, pg 679
Alaska Video Postcards Inc, pg 679
Aurora Films, pg 696

ARIZONA

Aardvark Productions LLC, pg 671
Video Learning Library, pg 928

CALIFORNIA

Access Video in Berkeley, pg 673
Action Video, pg 675
Artichoke Productions, pg 690
Big Door, pg 705
Steve Chandler, pg 720
Classic Images Stock Footage LLC, pg 726

Coastline Productions, pg 727
Creative Technology, pg 733
Dolphin MultiMedia Inc, pg 745
ECONEWS (Environmental Television Series) & (Environmental Directions Radio Series), pg 750
First Camera, pg 761
Goal Productions, pg 772
International Contact Inc, pg 790
ITV Productions, pg 792
Kavich Reynolds Productions Inc, pg 797
Main Street Media Inc, pg 815
MarVista Entertainment Inc, pg 818
McCune Audio-Video-Lighting, pg 821
Media Magic, pg 822
New & Unique Videos™, pg 839
Nineteen87, pg 841
On-Trax Inc, pg 846
Penrose Productions, pg 854
PM Productions, pg 858
Point of View Productions, pg 858
Prime Cut Productions, pg 862
QRS Software Services, pg 867
Dick Reizner Film & Video, pg 873
RetinaVision Productions, pg 874
Glenn Roland Films, pg 876
Screen Door Entertainment Inc, pg 882
SNAP, pg 891
Tam Communications Inc, pg 906
TMW Media Group, pg 915
Total Creative, pg 916
Twin Peaks Creative, pg 920
Videografix LLC, pg 929
Vineyard Video & Photography, pg 930
Wavemaker Media Design, pg 934
West Coast Projections Inc, pg 935
The Wine Appreciation Guild Ltd, pg 939
WMS Media Inc, pg 940

COLORADO

Centre Communications Inc, pg 720
Flashback Media Productions, pg 762
Tatum Video, pg 907

CONNECTICUT

Digital Video Productions, pg 742
The Gary-Paul Agency, pg 768
Ironik Design & Post, pg 791

DISTRICT OF COLUMBIA

O'Keefe Communications Inc, pg 844

FLORIDA

America By Air LLC, pg 682
Blackburst Entertainment LLC, pg 706
Civins Productions Inc, pg 725
Courter Films LLC, pg 732
Jordan Klein Film & Video (JKFV), pg 795
NatureVision Stock Footage Library, pg 837
Paradise Video & Film, pg 851
Sunfire Communications Inc, pg 904
Tel-Air Interests Inc, pg 909

GEORGIA

Beachwood Productions, pg 702
Burst Video/Film Inc, pg 713
Cox Media, pg 732
ECG Productions, pg 750

GP Studios, pg 773
Guerrilla Productions LLC, pg 774
Myriad Productions, pg 835
Malcolm Neal Productions, pg 837
On-Line Productions, pg 845

HAWAII

Hyperspective Studios Inc, pg 783
1013 Integrated, pg 911

IDAHO

Brad Shaw Productions Inc, pg 885
Wide Eye Productions, pg 938

ILLINOIS

ABSA Films, pg 672
Film Police, pg 760
IV Media Resources, pg 792
Manning Productions, pg 816
Mightybytes Inc, pg 827
Pepper Group, pg 854
PSAV® Presentation Services (Hotel Services Division), pg 866
Questar Entertainment Inc, pg 868
SCI Television & Creative Media LLC, pg 882
20/20 Communications Inc, pg 920
Video Impressions, pg 928
WEEK TV, pg 935
Winter Productions, pg 939

INDIANA

A-V-A Video Productions, pg 671
Road Pictures, pg 876

IOWA

American Visions, pg 684

KENTUCKY

Horizon Films & Media LLC, pg 781

LOUISIANA

Moxie Media, pg 832

MARYLAND

Adventure Productions LLC, pg 678
Richard Chisolm Cinematography, pg 722
CPR MultiMedia Solutions, pg 732
dbF a Media Company, pg 739
Kramer Communications Video Production, pg 801

MASSACHUSETTS

Award Productions Inc, pg 699
Green Mountain Post Films (GMP), pg 774
In the Wild Productions, pg 786
Penfield Productions Ltd, pg 853
TVN-The Video Network, pg 919

MICHIGAN

Digi Sign Design LLC, pg 741
K&R All Media Productions LLC, pg 796
K&R's Recording Studios Inc, pg 796

MINNESOTA

House of Cinemagraphics, pg 782
MastCom, pg 819

MISSOURI

Audio-VideoGraphics Inc, pg 694

NEVADA

Aardvark Video & Media Productions, pg 671
Encore Event Technologies LLC, pg 754

NEW HAMPSHIRE

Chip Taylor Communications LLC, pg 907

NEW JERSEY

Broadcast Center Studios, pg 710
CFP Video Productions Inc, pg 720
Euro-Pacific Film & Video Productions Inc, pg 756
Laurel Video Productions, pg 804
MiB MediaWorks, pg 825
Ray Mueller Productions, pg 833
Optisonics Productions, pg 847

NEW MEXICO

Production Outfitters, pg 864
Rainbow International Inc, pg 869

NEW YORK

aurora productions, pg 696
Blue Barn Pictures Inc, pg 707
Florentine Films, pg 762
Janson Media Inc, pg 793
Mood Creations Ltd, pg 829
MRY, pg 832
News Broadcast Network Inc, pg 840
The Palmer Group, pg 850
Pat Kogan Productions Inc, pg 852
Peckham Productions Inc, pg 852
PrimaLux Video Inc, pg 862
Random House Children's Books, pg 870
SISU Home Entertainment Inc, pg 889
Suggs Media Productions Inc, pg 903
TeleTime Productions, pg 910
Videograf, pg 929
VIEW Inc (Video International Entertainment World Inc), pg 930

NORTH CAROLINA

Pat Appleson Studios Inc, pg 687
The Communications Group Inc, pg 729
Digital Rain LLC, pg 742
Kino Mountain Productions LLC, pg 799
Videowerks, pg 930

OHIO

Advent Media Inc, pg 677
MainSail Production Services Inc, pg 815
R&B Communications Inc, pg 870
Shelburne Films, pg 885
Treehaus Communications Inc, pg 917

OREGON

Encounter Video Inc, pg 754
KPDX-TV Production Center, pg 801
Odyssey Productions Inc, pg 844
Production West, pg 864
REX, pg 874
Wilderness Video, pg 938

PENNSYLVANIA

Bang! Pictures Inc, pg 701
Beholder Productions Inc, pg 703

PROGRAMMING — VIDEO

Travelog Producers (continued)

PENNSYLVANIA (continued)

CCI Communications Inc, pg 718
FMP Media Solutions Inc, pg 763
Innovision Media Group, pg 788
JPL, pg 795
Main Point Productions, pg 815
Muderick Media, pg 833
Production Masters Inc (PMI), pg 864
The Videohouse Inc, pg 929

RHODE ISLAND

Sound-FX-Design, pg 894

SOUTH CAROLINA

American Production Services LLC, pg 684
Stages Video Productions, pg 899
Venture Media, pg 925

TENNESSEE

American Blackguard Inc, pg 683
Griffith Productions, pg 774
Running Pony Productions LLC, pg 878
Scripps Networks, pg 882

TEXAS

Cerutti Productions Inc, pg 720
Communication Arts Multimedia Inc, pg 728
Educational Video Network, pg 751
Horizon Film + Video Productions, pg 781
Mediaforce Productions, pg 822
Earl Miller Productions Inc, pg 827
Julye Newlin Productions Inc, pg 840
Omega Productions, pg 845
South Coast Film & Video, pg 895
Sportsmen on Film Inc, pg 898
Stage Directions, pg 898

VERMONT

Marlboro Productions, pg 817

VIRGINIA

CACI Integrated Communications, pg 713
Cinebar Productions Inc, pg 723
Limelight Communications Inc, pg 808
Metro Productions, pg 824
Rocktown Media, pg 876

WASHINGTON

Bennett-Watt HD Productions Inc, pg 703
Small World Productions Inc, pg 890
White Rain Films Ltd, pg 937

WISCONSIN

5th Floor Recording Co, pg 760
Mirror 34 Productions, pg 828
Wisconsin Public Television, pg 940

WYOMING

Bridger Productions Inc, pg 710

NEWFOUNDLAND AND LABRADOR

Vidcraft Productions Ltd, pg 927

ONTARIO

Canamedia Inc, pg 715
GAPC (General Assembly Production Centre), pg 768
Image Video Services & Productions, pg 785
Video Excellence Productions, pg 927

QUEBEC

Kerrigan Productions Inc, pg 798

Travelog Rentals

ARIZONA

Video Learning Library, pg 928

CALIFORNIA

Direct Cinema Ltd Inc, pg 743
ECONEWS (Environmental Television Series) & (Environmental Directions Radio Series), pg 750

COLORADO

Tatum Video, pg 907

MICHIGAN

Digi Sign Design LLC, pg 741

NEW JERSEY

Euro-Pacific Film & Video Productions Inc, pg 756

NEW YORK

VIEW Inc (Video International Entertainment World Inc), pg 930

OREGON

Wilderness Video, pg 938

Video Game Distributors

CALIFORNIA

Allied Artists International Inc, pg 681

KENTUCKY

WaxWorks VideoWorks, pg 934

MARYLAND

Recorded Books Inc, an RBmedia company, pg 871

TENNESSEE

Spring Arbor Distributors Inc, pg 898

WISCONSIN

Aylmer Press, pg 700

ONTARIO

GestureTek, pg 770

Video Game Producers

CALIFORNIA

Allied Artists International Inc, pg 681
Classic Images Stock Footage LLC, pg 726
Creative Technology, pg 733
Gateways Books & Tapes, pg 768
ITV Productions, pg 792
Kavich Reynolds Productions Inc, pg 797
McCune Audio-Video-Lighting, pg 821
Opticomm-EMCORE, pg 847
Palardo Productions, pg 850
QRS Software Services, pg 867
Total Creative, pg 916

FLORIDA

Jordan Klein Film & Video (JKFV), pg 795
Tricycle Studios, pg 918

GEORGIA

Beachwood Productions, pg 702
Cox Media, pg 732
Guerrilla Productions LLC, pg 774

HAWAII

Hyperspective Studios Inc, pg 783

ILLINOIS

Pepper Group, pg 854

MARYLAND

Absolute Hollywood, pg 672

MICHIGAN

K&R All Media Productions LLC, pg 796

MINNESOTA

House of Cinemagraphics, pg 782

NEVADA

Encore Event Technologies LLC, pg 754

NEW HAMPSHIRE

The Troupe, pg 918

NEW JERSEY

Optisonics Productions, pg 847
Outside The Box Interactive LLC, pg 849

NEW YORK

MRY, pg 832
R/GA, pg 868
Split Image Productions, pg 898

NORTH CAROLINA

Pat Appleson Studios Inc, pg 687
Moving Pictures, pg 832

OHIO

Vista Color Imaging Inc, pg 931

OREGON

InterVision Media, pg 791

PENNSYLVANIA

Innovision Media Group, pg 788
Muderick Media, pg 833

SOUTH CAROLINA

Venture Media, pg 925

TEXAS

Omega Productions, pg 845
Romar Learning Solutions LLC, pg 877

VIRGINIA

Advance Concepts Inc, pg 677
CACI Integrated Communications, pg 713

WISCONSIN

Aylmer Press, pg 700

BRITISH COLUMBIA

Credo Interactive Inc, pg 734

ONTARIO

GestureTek, pg 770
RB Productions, pg 870

Video Game Rentals

GestureTek, pg 770

Videocassette Distributors

ARIZONA

Arizona Cine Equipment, pg 688
Arizona Public Media, pg 688
Mother Basilea Films, pg 831
Valley of the Sun Publishing Co, pg 924
Video Learning Library, pg 928

CALIFORNIA

Ametron Audio/Video, pg 684
Les Blank Films Inc, pg 707
Cambridge Documentary Films Inc, pg 714
Cavalcade Productions Inc, pg 717
Coast Learning Systems, pg 727
Deja View Video, pg 740
Direct Cinema Ltd Inc, pg 743
Discovery Education - Los Angeles, pg 743
The Walt Disney Studios, pg 743
Durrin Productions Inc, pg 748
Eastman Corp, pg 749
Em Gee Film Library, pg 753
Forte Productions, pg 764
411 Video Information, pg 764
Glenn Photo Supply, pg 771
Bruce Goldberg Inc, pg 772
Gordon Productions Inc, pg 772
Hay House Inc, pg 777
Health Education Services, pg 778
Increase Video/Silver Mine Video, pg 786
Ishtar Films, pg 791
Joyce Media Inc, pg 795
MarVista Entertainment Inc, pg 818
monterey media inc, pg 829
Music World/Vocal Power School, pg 834
New & Unique Videos™, pg 839
Joseph Nicoletti Consulting-Promotion, pg 841
Nilgiri Press, pg 841
Nineteen87, pg 841
Palardo Productions, pg 850

Point of View Productions, pg 858
Prime Cut Productions, pg 862
Regent Press Publishers & Printers, pg 873
RJ Video Productions, pg 875
Sea Studios Foundation, pg 883
Shokus Video, pg 886
Sodanceabit, pg 892
Universal Music Group, pg 922
Valley Media, pg 924
Visual Communications - Southern California Asian American Studies Central Inc, pg 931
Warner Home Video Inc, pg 934
The Wine Appreciation Guild Ltd, pg 939
The Writing Co, pg 942
The Wyland Group, pg 942

COLORADO

Greg Hensley Productions, pg 779
Tatum Video, pg 907

CONNECTICUT

Ironik Design & Post, pg 791
Scholastic Library Publishing, pg 882

DELAWARE

So Smart Productions, pg 891
University Media Services, pg 922

DISTRICT OF COLUMBIA

Biblical Archaeology Society (BAS), pg 705
Sano Videos, pg 880

GEORGIA

American Association for Vocational Instructional Materials (AAVIM), pg 682
Audio Visual Resources Inc, pg 695
First Cut Communications LLC, pg 761
Gingerbread Group Holdings LLC, pg 771
School Media Associates LLC, pg 882

IDAHO

Lagoon Video, pg 803

ILLINOIS

ABSA Films, pg 672
Britannica Digital Learning, pg 710
CCore Media Inc, pg 718
Encyclopaedia Britannica Inc, pg 754
Film Ideas Inc, pg 760
Moviecraft Inc, pg 831
National Safety Council (NSC), pg 836
Terra Nova Films Inc, pg 911
Theosophical Publishing House, pg 912

INDIANA

Communication Ministries, pg 728
Educational Video Group Inc, pg 751
Lee Co Inc, pg 805
Our Sunday Visitor Inc, pg 849
Perennial Pictures Film Corp, pg 854

KENTUCKY

EKU Media, pg 752
National Geographic Learning, pg 836
WaxWorks VideoWorks, pg 934

LOUISIANA

Great Chefs/Leisure Jazz Video, pg 773
Leisure Video, pg 806
Moxie Media, pg 832

MAINE

Headlight Audio Visual Inc, pg 777

MARYLAND

The Cutting Corporation, GraphicAudio® & Archival Sound Lab, pg 736
DSR Computer Technology Specialists Inc, pg 747
Human Circuit, pg 782
Milner-Fenwick Inc, pg 828
MMI Marketing, pg 828
Nicholas P Pipino Associates Inc, pg 857
Sign Media Inc, pg 887

MASSACHUSETTS

Green Mountain Post Films (GMP), pg 774
Video Express, pg 928

MICHIGAN

Jack Van Impe Ministries International, pg 924
Wayne State University Media Services, pg 934

MINNESOTA

Hazelden Publishing & Educational Services, pg 777

MISSOURI

Annenberg Learner, pg 685
Marsh Media, pg 817
Mosby Inc, pg 831
SOM Publishing Co, pg 892
Vedanta Society of St Louis, pg 925

NEBRASKA

The Recruiters Library, pg 872
Vision Maker Media, pg 930

NEVADA

DVDs4Less, pg 748

NEW HAMPSHIRE

Channell One Video, pg 720
Frey Scientific, pg 766
Heinemann, pg 778
Chip Taylor Communications LLC, pg 907

NEW JERSEY

Business Education Films, pg 713
Shanachie Entertainment Corp, pg 885

NEW YORK

ATA Trading Corp/Favorite TV Inc, pg 691
Brooklyn Botanic Garden, pg 711
Circulating Film & Video Library, pg 725

Thomas Craven Film Corp, pg 733
Discovery Education Inc, pg 743
FACE Foundation, pg 758
First Run Features, pg 761
Flash Electronics Inc, pg 762
Guidance Associates Inc Center for Humanities, pg 774
Guilford Publications, pg 774
HB-Content, pg 777
Human Relations Media, pg 782
Icarus Films Inc, pg 783
Kino International Corp, pg 799
Magnetic Music Publishing Co, pg 814
Mastervision Inc, pg 819
Richter Productions Inc, pg 875
The Fulton J Sheen Co Inc, pg 885
SISU Home Entertainment Inc, pg 889
Third World Newsreel/Camera News Inc, pg 912
Timed Exposures Films, pg 914
Tommy Boy Entertainment LLC, pg 915
United Nations Department of Public Information-News & Media Division, pg 921
Video Catalogue Co Inc, pg 927
Videofashion Network, pg 929
Visual Technologies Corp, pg 932
WNET/New York Public Media, pg 940
Women Make Movies Inc, pg 941

NORTH CAROLINA

Carolina Biological Supply Co, pg 717
Speakers Unlimited, pg 896

NORTH DAKOTA

UND Television Center, pg 921

OHIO

Franciscan Media, pg 765
Griesinger Films LLC, pg 774
McGraw-Hill School Education Group, pg 821
Treehaus Communications Inc, pg 917
WOUB Public Media, pg 942

OREGON

InterVision Media, pg 791
Wilderness Video, pg 938

PENNSYLVANIA

Corinth Films Inc, pg 731
Discovery Education - South Burlington, pg 743
Dreambox Media Inc, pg 746
FMP Media Solutions Inc, pg 763
Himalayan Institute Audio/Video, pg 780
Library Video Company, pg 807
Rahlic Publishing Co, pg 869
Schlessinger Media, pg 881
TRC Interactive Inc, pg 917

TENNESSEE

Spring Arbor Distributors Inc, pg 898
Word Label Group, pg 941

TEXAS

Educational Video Network, pg 751
Stage Directions, pg 898
Texas Heart Institute Visual Communication Services, pg 911

VERMONT

Dorothy Tod Films, pg 915
University of Vermont, Instructional Television Dept, pg 923
Wilson McLeran Inc, pg 939

VIRGINIA

County Sales, pg 732
WETA Production Center, pg 936

WASHINGTON

Bennett-Watt HD Productions Inc, pg 703
Intermedia Inc, pg 789
Victory Studios, pg 927

WEST VIRGINIA

Focus on Animals, pg 763
Harpers Ferry Historical Association, pg 776

WISCONSIN

Aylmer Press, pg 700
Full Compass Systems, pg 767
NEWIST/CESA 7, pg 840
Wisconsin Public Television, pg 940

BRITISH COLUMBIA

Thompson Rivers University Marketing & Communications Dept, pg 913
Video Out Distribution, pg 928

ONTARIO

BBC Worldwide Canada Ltd, pg 702
Canadian Learning Co Inc, pg 715
Scholastic Canada Ltd, pg 882
University of Toronto, Classroom Technology Support, pg 923

QUEBEC

Les Productions Via Le Monde (Daniel Bertolino) Inc, pg 864
Whalley-Abbey Media Holdings Inc, pg 937

Videocassette Producers

ARIZONA

Arizona Public Media, pg 688
Valley of the Sun Publishing Co, pg 924

ARKANSAS

Live'N'Loud, pg 810
White Diamond Productions LLC, pg 937

CALIFORNIA

Access Video in Berkeley, pg 673
ACDC Audio CD & Cassette, pg 674
Big Door, pg 705
Cambridge Documentary Films Inc, pg 714
Cavalcade Productions Inc, pg 717
Coast Learning Systems, pg 727
Creative Technology, pg 733
Custom Video Productions Inc, pg 736
Deja View Video, pg 740
Design Media, pg 741
Direct Cinema Ltd Inc, pg 743
Discovery Education - Los Angeles, pg 743

PROGRAMMING — VIDEO

Videocassette Producers (continued)

CALIFORNIA (continued)

Dolphin MultiMedia Inc, pg 745
Durrin Productions Inc, pg 748
Eastman Corp, pg 749
Em Gee Film Library, pg 753
Forte Productions, pg 764
411 Video Information, pg 764
Gateways Books & Tapes, pg 768
Geddes Productions LLC, pg 769
Goal Productions, pg 772
Gold Standard Productions, pg 772
Bruce Goldberg Inc, pg 772
Gordon Productions Inc, pg 772
Havas Edge, pg 777
Hay House Inc, pg 777
Imageworks, pg 785
Increase Video/Silver Mine Video, pg 786
Ishtar Films, pg 791
ITV Productions, pg 792
Joyce Media Inc, pg 795
KTVU-Retail Services, pg 802
K2B2 Records, pg 802
Ludlow Media, pg 812
Lynch Communications, pg 813
Main Street Media Inc, pg 815
Maximus Media Inc, pg 820
Media Magic, pg 822
monterey media inc, pg 829
Music World/Vocal Power School, pg 834
New & Unique Videos™, pg 839
Nilgiri Press, pg 841
Nineteen87, pg 841
On-Trax Inc, pg 846
Palardo Productions, pg 850
piXvfm Inc, pg 857
PM Productions, pg 858
Point of View Productions, pg 858
Prime Cut Productions, pg 862
Producers Group Ltd, pg 863
QRS Software Services, pg 867
Randolf Productions Inc, pg 870
Regent Press Publishers & Printers, pg 873
RetinaVision Productions, pg 874
Glenn Roland Films, pg 876
Screen Door Entertainment Inc, pg 882
Sea Studios Foundation, pg 883
Shokus Video, pg 886
SNAP, pg 891
Sodanceabit, pg 892
Tam Communications Inc, pg 906
Timestream Video, pg 914
Total Creative, pg 916
Universal Music Group, pg 922
Video Resources Inc, pg 928
Visual Communications - Southern California Asian American Studies Central Inc, pg 931
Wavemaker Media Design, pg 934
Webster Communications, pg 935
The Wyland Group, pg 942

COLORADO

Centre Communications Inc, pg 720
Daylight Productions & Rentals, pg 739
Flashback Media Productions, pg 762
Tatum Video, pg 907
Transtar Entertainment Co Inc, pg 917

CONNECTICUT

Ironik Design & Post, pg 791
Scholastic Library Publishing, pg 882

DELAWARE

So Smart Productions, pg 891
University Media Services, pg 922

DISTRICT OF COLUMBIA

Biblical Archaeology Society (BAS), pg 705
Hillmann & Carr Inc, pg 780
USCCB Publishing, pg 923

FLORIDA

Courter Films LLC, pg 732
EarthDesign Inc, pg 749
Multivision Video & Film, pg 833
National Teleproductions Inc, pg 837
Sound*Light, pg 894
Sunfire Communications Inc, pg 904
Tel-Air Interests Inc, pg 909
Universal Studios Florida® Production Group, pg 922
Video Techniques Inc, pg 928

GEORGIA

Beachwood Productions, pg 702
Burst Video/Film Inc, pg 713
ECG Productions, pg 750
First Cut Communications LLC, pg 761
Gingerbread Group Holdings LLC, pg 771
Myriad Productions, pg 835
WaveGuide Studios, pg 934

HAWAII

1013 Integrated, pg 911

IDAHO

Brad Shaw Productions Inc, pg 885

ILLINOIS

ABSA Films, pg 672
Beatty TeleVisual Productions, pg 703
Britannica Digital Learning, pg 710
CCore Media Inc, pg 718
Cresta Creative, pg 734
Encyclopaedia Britannica Inc, pg 754
Major Media Inc, pg 815
Manning Productions, pg 816
Moviecraft Inc, pg 831
National Safety Council (NSC), pg 836
Jim Passin Productions, pg 852
Pepper Group, pg 854
PSAV® Presentation Services (Hotel Services Division), pg 866
Sparkfactor, pg 896
Terra Nova Films Inc, pg 911
Theosophical Publishing House, pg 912
Video Impressions, pg 928

INDIANA

Advanced Media Integration, pg 677
Communication Ministries, pg 728
OMNI Productions, pg 845

IOWA

Educational Technology & Media Services, pg 751
Hellman Associates Inc, pg 778
Iowa State University-Information Technology Services, pg 791

KENTUCKY

EKU Media, pg 752
Idle Minds Productions Inc, pg 784
Donna Lawrence Productions, pg 804
National Geographic Learning, pg 836

LOUISIANA

Digital FX Inc, pg 742
Great Chefs/Leisure Jazz Video, pg 773
Leisure Video, pg 806
Louisiana State University Division of Strategic Communications, pg 811
Moxie Media, pg 832

MAINE

WGME-TV, pg 936

MARYLAND

Richard Chisolm Cinematography, pg 722
CPR MultiMedia Solutions, pg 732
DSR Computer Technology Specialists Inc, pg 747
Milner-Fenwick Inc, pg 828
Mobile-Video Productions Inc, pg 828
Sign Media Inc, pg 887

MASSACHUSETTS

CommCreative, pg 728
Green Mountain Post Films (GMP), pg 774
HOME Inc, pg 781
Monadnock Media Inc, pg 829

MICHIGAN

K&R All Media Productions LLC, pg 796
K&R's Recording Studios Inc, pg 796
MessageMakers, pg 824
Wayne State University Media Services, pg 934
WTVS, Detroit Public Television, pg 942

MINNESOTA

GMI Productions, pg 771
Hazelden Publishing & Educational Services, pg 777
House of Cinemagraphics, pg 782
Worthwhile Films, pg 941

MISSOURI

Annenberg Learner, pg 685
Marsh Media, pg 817
Mosby Inc, pg 831
SOM Publishing Co, pg 892
Vedanta Society of St Louis, pg 925

NEBRASKA

The Recruiters Library, pg 872
Telepro Video Inc, pg 910
Vision Maker Media, pg 930

NEVADA

DVDs4Less, pg 748
Encore Event Technologies LLC, pg 754
Tanglewood Productions, pg 907

NEW HAMPSHIRE

Academic & Campus Technology Services, pg 672
Apertura, pg 686
Channell One Video, pg 720
Chip Taylor Communications LLC, pg 907
The Troupe, pg 918

NEW JERSEY

Alden Films, pg 679
Broadcast Center Studios, pg 710
CFP Video Productions Inc, pg 720
Euro-Pacific Film & Video Productions Inc, pg 756
Laurel Video Productions, pg 804
Optisonics Productions, pg 847
Reed Presentations Inc (RPI), pg 872
Shanachie Entertainment Corp, pg 885
VCSvideo, pg 925

NEW MEXICO

Production Outfitters, pg 864

NEW YORK

aurora productions, pg 696
BC Studio, pg 702
Blue Barn Pictures Inc, pg 707
Brooklyn Botanic Garden, pg 711
Thomas Craven Film Corp, pg 733
Discovery Education Inc, pg 743
Guidance Associates Inc Center for Humanities, pg 774
Guilford Publications, pg 774
HB-Content, pg 777
Human Relations Media, pg 782
Icontent, pg 783
The Independent Production Fund, pg 786
International Digital Centre, pg 790
Long Island Video Enterprises Live Inc, pg 811
Magnetic Music Publishing Co, pg 814
Mastervision Inc, pg 819
Jack Morton Worldwide, pg 830
Pat Kogan Productions Inc, pg 852
Richter Productions Inc, pg 875
Scholastic Media, pg 882
The Fulton J Sheen Co Inc, pg 885
SISU Home Entertainment Inc, pg 889
Split Image Productions, pg 898
TeleTime Productions, pg 910
Third World Newsreel/Camera News Inc, pg 912
Tisch School of the Arts, pg 914
Tommy Boy Entertainment LLC, pg 915
Triumph Learning LLC, pg 918
United Nations Multimedia Resources Unit, pg 921
Video Catalogue Co Inc, pg 927
Videofashion Network, pg 929
Zelman Studios Ltd, pg 945

NORTH CAROLINA

Pat Appleson Studios Inc, pg 687
Carolina Biological Supply Co, pg 717
The Communications Group Inc, pg 729

Moving Pictures, pg 832
Trailblazer Studios®, pg 917
Videowerks, pg 930

NORTH DAKOTA

UND Television Center, pg 921

OHIO

CET, pg 720
Cuyahoga Community College
  Student Production Office (SPO),
  pg 736
Franciscan Media, pg 765
Griesinger Films LLC, pg 774
MainSail Production Services Inc,
  pg 815
McGraw-Hill School Education
  Group, pg 821
Musicol Recording, pg 835
R&B Communications Inc, pg 870
Take 1 Media Services, pg 906
Vista Color Imaging Inc, pg 931
WOUB Public Media, pg 942

OKLAHOMA

Academic Media & Digital
  Services, pg 672

OREGON

Ideascape Inc, pg 784
InterVision Media, pg 791
KPDX-TV Production Center,
  pg 801
Odyssey Productions Inc, pg 844
REX, pg 874
Wilderness Video, pg 938

PENNSYLVANIA

Argentine Productions Inc, pg 688
Audio Visual Communications Inc,
  pg 694
Discovery Education - South
  Burlington, pg 743
Dreambox Media Inc, pg 746
FMP Media Solutions Inc, pg 763
Himalayan Institute Audio/Video,
  pg 780
Innovision Media Group, pg 788
JPL, pg 795
Main Point Productions, pg 815
Muderick Media, pg 833
Production Masters Inc (PMI),
  pg 864
Rahlic Publishing Co, pg 869
Schlessinger Media, pg 881
Video/Film Associates, pg 928
Visual Sound Inc, pg 931

SOUTH CAROLINA

Stages Video Productions, pg 899
Venture Media, pg 925

TENNESSEE

Memphis Communications Corp,
  pg 823
Scripps Networks, pg 882
United Methodist Productions,
  pg 921
Word Label Group, pg 941

TEXAS

Communication Arts Multimedia
  Inc, pg 728
The Editing Co, pg 750
Educational Video Network, pg 751
JSAV, pg 795
Marx InDigital, pg 818
Mediaforce Productions, pg 822

Earl Miller Productions Inc, pg 827
Romar Learning Solutions LLC,
  pg 877
Stage Directions, pg 898
Texas Heart Institute Visual
  Communication Services, pg 911

VERMONT

University of Vermont, Instructional
  Television Dept, pg 923
Wilson McLeran Inc, pg 939

VIRGINIA

BES Studios, pg 704
CACI Integrated Communications,
  pg 713
CVW Event Productions, pg 736
Limelight Communications Inc,
  pg 808
WETA Production Center, pg 936

WASHINGTON

Bennett-Watt HD Productions Inc,
  pg 703
Intermedia Inc, pg 789
Victory Studios, pg 927

WISCONSIN

Aylmer Press, pg 700
Excel Duplication Services, pg 757
Meridian Studios, pg 824
Mirror 34 Productions, pg 828
NEWIST/CESA 7, pg 840
University of Wisconsin-Oshkosh
  Radio-TV-Film Dept, pg 923
USAV Group Inc, pg 923
Video Wisconsin Inc, pg 929
Watts Communications Inc, pg 934
Wisconsin Public Television, pg 940

WYOMING

Bridger Productions Inc, pg 710

ALBERTA

Black Media Works, pg 706

BRITISH COLUMBIA

Thompson Rivers University
  Marketing & Communications
  Dept, pg 913
Triad Communications Ltd, pg 918

*NEWFOUNDLAND AND
  LABRADOR*

Vidcraft Productions Ltd, pg 927

ONTARIO

BBC Worldwide Canada Ltd,
  pg 702
RB Productions, pg 870
Silver Creek Media Inc, pg 888
University of Toronto, Classroom
  Technology Support, pg 923

QUEBEC

Les Productions Via Le Monde
  (Daniel Bertolino) Inc, pg 864
Whalley-Abbey Media Holdings
  Inc, pg 937

SASKATCHEWAN

plan9films, pg 857

Videocassette Rentals

ARIZONA

Arizona Public Media, pg 688
Video Learning Library, pg 928

CALIFORNIA

Ametron Audio/Video, pg 684
Cambridge Documentary Films Inc,
  pg 714
Cavalcade Productions Inc, pg 717
Direct Cinema Ltd Inc, pg 743
Durrin Productions Inc, pg 748
Medcom Inc, pg 821
Palardo Productions, pg 850
Regent Press Publishers & Printers,
  pg 873
Visual Communications - Southern
  California Asian American
  Studies Central Inc, pg 931
The Wyland Group, pg 942

DELAWARE

University Media Services, pg 922

GEORGIA

Staging Directions Inc, pg 899

ILLINOIS

National Safety Council (NSC),
  pg 836
Terra Nova Films Inc, pg 911

MASSACHUSETTS

Documentary Educational Resources
  Inc, pg 744

MICHIGAN

The Program Source International,
  pg 865
Wayne State University Media
  Services, pg 934

MINNESOTA

Hazelden Publishing & Educational
  Services, pg 777

NEBRASKA

Vision Maker Media, pg 930

NEW HAMPSHIRE

Chip Taylor Communications LLC,
  pg 907

NEW JERSEY

Business Education Films, pg 713
Euro-Pacific Film & Video
  Productions Inc, pg 756

NEW YORK

Adwar Video, pg 678
Brooklyn Botanic Garden, pg 711
Circulating Film & Video Library,
  pg 725
First Run Features, pg 761
Icarus Films Inc, pg 783
Kino International Corp, pg 799
Richter Productions Inc, pg 875
Third World Newsreel/Camera
  News Inc, pg 912

OHIO

Franciscan Media, pg 765

OREGON

Wilderness Video, pg 938

PENNSYLVANIA

Rahlic Publishing Co, pg 869

VERMONT

University of Vermont, Instructional
  Television Dept, pg 923

WISCONSIN

NEWIST/CESA 7, pg 840
Wisconsin Public Television, pg 940

BRITISH COLUMBIA

Video Out Distribution, pg 928

QUEBEC

Les Productions Via Le Monde
  (Daniel Bertolino) Inc, pg 864

Videodisc Distributors

ARIZONA

Arizona Cine Equipment, pg 688

CALIFORNIA

Ametron Audio/Video, pg 684
Health Education Services, pg 778
Joyce Media Inc, pg 795
Medcom Inc, pg 821
QRS Software Services, pg 867
Valley Media, pg 924
Warner Home Video Inc, pg 934
The Writing Co, pg 942

CONNECTICUT

Ironik Design & Post, pg 791
Scholastic Library Publishing,
  pg 882

DELAWARE

University Media Services, pg 922

GEORGIA

School Media Associates LLC,
  pg 882

ILLINOIS

Britannica Digital Learning, pg 710
Encyclopaedia Britannica Inc,
  pg 754
Film Ideas Inc, pg 760

KENTUCKY

National Geographic Learning,
  pg 836

LOUISIANA

Great Chefs/Leisure Jazz Video,
  pg 773
Leisure Video, pg 806

NEW HAMPSHIRE

Academic & Campus Technology
  Services, pg 672

NEW YORK

Thomas Craven Film Corp, pg 733
Discovery Education Inc, pg 743
Flash Electronics Inc, pg 762
Human Relations Media, pg 782
Mastervision Inc, pg 819

PROGRAMMING — VIDEO

Videodisc Distributors (continued)

NEW YORK (continued)

Visual Technologies Corp, pg 932
Women Make Movies Inc, pg 941

NORTH CAROLINA

Carolina Biological Supply Co, pg 717

PENNSYLVANIA

Schlessinger Media, pg 881

TEXAS

Stage Directions, pg 898

VERMONT

University of Vermont, Instructional Television Dept, pg 923

ONTARIO

Entertainment One Distribution, pg 754
Technovision® Interactive Inc, pg 909

Videodisc Producers

ARIZONA

Film Creations Ltd, pg 760

ARKANSAS

White Diamond Productions LLC, pg 937

CALIFORNIA

Big Door, pg 705
Creative Technology, pg 733
Custom Video Productions Inc, pg 736
Joyce Media Inc, pg 795
Main Street Media Inc, pg 815
piXvfm Inc, pg 857
PM Productions, pg 858
Producers Group Ltd, pg 863
QRS Software Services, pg 867
RetinaVision Productions, pg 874
Glenn Roland Films, pg 876
Screen Door Entertainment Inc, pg 882
Sea Studios Foundation, pg 883
SNAP, pg 891
Tam Communications Inc, pg 906
Total Creative, pg 916
Wavemaker Media Design, pg 934
WMS Media Inc, pg 940

COLORADO

Daylight Productions & Rentals, pg 739
Flashback Media Productions, pg 762
Tatum Video, pg 907

CONNECTICUT

ACM Productions Ltd, pg 674
Ironik Design & Post, pg 791
Scholastic Library Publishing, pg 882

DELAWARE

University Media Services, pg 922

DISTRICT OF COLUMBIA

Hillmann & Carr Inc, pg 780

FLORIDA

Blackburst Entertainment LLC, pg 706
National Teleproductions Inc, pg 837
Sunfire Communications Inc, pg 904

GEORGIA

Beachwood Productions, pg 702
WaveGuide Studios, pg 934

HAWAII

1013 Integrated, pg 911

IDAHO

Brad Shaw Productions Inc, pg 885

ILLINOIS

Britannica Digital Learning, pg 710
Encyclopaedia Britannica Inc, pg 754
Major Media Inc, pg 815
Video Impressions, pg 928

KENTUCKY

Donna Lawrence Productions, pg 804
National Geographic Learning, pg 836

LOUISIANA

Digital FX Inc, pg 742
Great Chefs/Leisure Jazz Video, pg 773
Moxie Media, pg 832

MASSACHUSETTS

Capron Lighting & Sound Co Inc, pg 716
CommCreative, pg 728
Penfield Productions Ltd, pg 853

MICHIGAN

K&R All Media Productions LLC, pg 796
K&R's Recording Studios Inc, pg 796

MINNESOTA

House of Cinemagraphics, pg 782

NEVADA

Encore Event Technologies LLC, pg 754

NEW HAMPSHIRE

Academic & Campus Technology Services, pg 672
Apertura, pg 686
The Troupe, pg 918

NEW JERSEY

CFP Video Productions Inc, pg 720

NEW YORK

Thomas Craven Film Corp, pg 733
Discovery Education Inc, pg 743

Human Relations Media, pg 782
Mastervision Inc, pg 819
Jack Morton Worldwide, pg 830
MRY, pg 832
Split Image Productions, pg 898
Suggs Media Productions Inc, pg 903
TeleTime Productions, pg 910

NORTH CAROLINA

Pat Appleson Studios Inc, pg 687
Carolina Biological Supply Co, pg 717
The Communications Group Inc, pg 729
Videowerks, pg 930

OHIO

Take 1 Media Services, pg 906

OREGON

Odyssey Productions Inc, pg 844
REX, pg 874

PENNSYLVANIA

Innovision Media Group, pg 788
Production Masters Inc (PMI), pg 864
Schlessinger Media, pg 881
Video/Film Associates, pg 928
Videosmith Inc, pg 930

SOUTH CAROLINA

Venture Media, pg 925

TENNESSEE

Scripps Networks, pg 882

TEXAS

The Editing Co, pg 750
Mediaforce Productions, pg 822
Romar Learning Solutions LLC, pg 877
Stage Directions, pg 898

VERMONT

University of Vermont, Instructional Television Dept, pg 923

VIRGINIA

DXC Technology Co, pg 748

WASHINGTON

Sparkworks Media, pg 896
Victory Studios, pg 927

WISCONSIN

USAV Group Inc, pg 923
Video Wisconsin Inc, pg 929
Wisconsin Public Television, pg 940

ALBERTA

Black Media Works, pg 706

NEWFOUNDLAND AND LABRADOR

Vidcraft Productions Ltd, pg 927

ONTARIO

Technovision® Interactive Inc, pg 909

Videodisc Rentals

CALIFORNIA

Ametron Audio/Video, pg 684
Medcom Inc, pg 821

DELAWARE

University Media Services, pg 922

GEORGIA

Staging Directions Inc, pg 899

TEXAS

Stage Directions, pg 898

VERMONT

University of Vermont, Instructional Television Dept, pg 923

VIRGINIA

Lee Hartman & Sons Inc, pg 805

ONTARIO

Technovision® Interactive Inc, pg 909

Videotape Distributors

ARIZONA

Arizona Cine Equipment, pg 688

CALIFORNIA

Air Bud Entertainment, pg 678
Ametron Audio/Video, pg 684
Coast Learning Systems, pg 727
DawnSignPress, pg 739
Deja View Video, pg 740
Direct Cinema Ltd Inc, pg 743
Durrin Productions Inc, pg 748
Bruce Goldberg Inc, pg 772
Golden State Dance Teachers Association (GSDTA), pg 772
Griggs Productions Inc, pg 774
Increase Video/Silver Mine Video, pg 786
Joyce Media Inc, pg 795
Main Street Media Inc, pg 815
Medcom Inc, pg 821
monterey media inc, pg 829
Music World/Vocal Power School, pg 834
Joseph Nicoletti Consulting-Promotion, pg 841
Nilgiri Press, pg 841
Nineteen87, pg 841
Point of View Productions, pg 858
Regent Press Publishers & Printers, pg 873
Sahara Records & Filmworks Entertainment Co, pg 879
Sea Studios Foundation, pg 883
Technicolor USA Inc, pg 908
Valley Media, pg 924
Warner Bros Production Sound & Video Services, pg 934
Warner Home Video Inc, pg 934

COLORADO

Stretching Inc, pg 902

CONNECTICUT

Cine-Med Inc, pg 723
Ironik Design & Post, pg 791

DELAWARE

University Media Services, pg 922

DISTRICT OF COLUMBIA

Library of Congress, Motion Picture, Broadcasting & Recorded Sound Division, pg 807

FLORIDA

AVI-SPL, pg 698
Courter Films LLC, pg 732
EarthDesign Inc, pg 749
MTI Home Video, pg 833
NatureVision TV, pg 837

GEORGIA

Audio Visual Resources Inc, pg 695
First Cut Communications LLC, pg 761
School Media Associates LLC, pg 882

ILLINOIS

CCore Media Inc, pg 718
Encyclopaedia Britannica Inc, pg 754
Film Ideas Inc, pg 760
Moviecraft Inc, pg 831
National Safety Council (NSC), pg 836

INDIANA

Lee Co Inc, pg 805

IOWA

Accelerated Learning Foundation, pg 672

KENTUCKY

EKU Media, pg 752
National Geographic Learning, pg 836
WaxWorks VideoWorks, pg 934

LOUISIANA

Leisure Video, pg 806
Louisiana State University Division of Strategic Communications, pg 811
Moxie Media, pg 832

MARYLAND

Milner-Fenwick Inc, pg 828
Nicholas P Pipino Associates Inc, pg 857
Sign Media Inc, pg 887
Total AV Systems, pg 916

MASSACHUSETTS

Education Development Center Inc (EDC), pg 750
Video Express, pg 928

MICHIGAN

Digi Sign Design LLC, pg 741
MSU Technologies, pg 833
Prakken Publications Inc, pg 861
Wayne State University Media Services, pg 934

MINNESOTA

American Choral Catalog Ltd, pg 683
MastCom, pg 819

MISSOURI

SOM Publishing Co, pg 892

NEBRASKA

Vision Maker Media, pg 930

NEVADA

DVDs4Less, pg 748

NEW HAMPSHIRE

Channell One Video, pg 720
Chip Taylor Communications LLC, pg 907
YMAA Publication Center Inc, pg 944

NEW JERSEY

Business Education Films, pg 713
Comex Systems Inc, pg 728
SES SA, pg 884
Shanachie Entertainment Corp, pg 885

NEW YORK

Thomas Craven Film Corp, pg 733
FACE Foundation, pg 758
Flash Electronics Inc, pg 762
William Greaves Productions Inc, pg 774
Homespun Video, pg 781
Human Relations Media, pg 782
Icarus Films Inc, pg 783
Kino International Corp, pg 799
Mastervision Inc, pg 819
New Day Films, pg 839
Pennebaker Hegedus Films Inc, pg 854
Richter Productions Inc, pg 875
SISU Home Entertainment Inc, pg 889
Timed Exposures Films, pg 914
United Nations Department of Public Information-News & Media Division, pg 921
Videofashion Network, pg 929
Visual Technologies Corp, pg 932
WNET/New York Public Media, pg 940
Women Make Movies Inc, pg 941

NORTH CAROLINA

Carolina Biological Supply Co, pg 717
Speakers Unlimited, pg 896

OHIO

The American Classical League, pg 683
Franciscan Media, pg 765

OREGON

InterVision Media, pg 791
Nostalgia Family Video Inc, pg 843
Wilderness Video, pg 938

PENNSYLVANIA

Corinth Films Inc, pg 731
FMP Media Solutions Inc, pg 763
Rahlic Publishing Co, pg 869
Schlessinger Media, pg 881

SOUTH CAROLINA

American Production Services LLC, pg 684

TENNESSEE

Center for Southern Folklore Inc, pg 719
Spring Arbor Distributors Inc, pg 898
Zion Music Group, pg 945

TEXAS

Lamb & Lion Ministries, pg 803
Marengo Films, pg 817
Stage Directions, pg 898
University of Texas at Austin - Petroleum Extension Service, pg 923

VERMONT

Wilson McLeran Inc, pg 939

WASHINGTON

Bennett-Watt HD Productions Inc, pg 703
Medifecta Healthcare Training, pg 823
Victory Studios, pg 927
White Rain Films Ltd, pg 937

WEST VIRGINIA

Focus on Animals, pg 763

WISCONSIN

Aylmer Press, pg 700
Full Compass Systems, pg 767
School Specialty Inc, pg 882
Wisconsin Public Television, pg 940

BRITISH COLUMBIA

Timeless Books, pg 914
Video Out Distribution, pg 928

NEWFOUNDLAND AND LABRADOR

Vidcraft Productions Ltd, pg 927

ONTARIO

Canadian Filmmakers Distribution Center (CFMDC), pg 715
Canadian Learning Co Inc, pg 715
Entertainment One Distribution, pg 754
Kineticvideo.com, pg 799
Life Cycle Books Ltd, pg 807

QUEBEC

Les Productions Via Le Monde (Daniel Bertolino) Inc, pg 864

Videotape Producers

ARIZONA

Aardvark Productions LLC, pg 671
Direct Current Video Productions, pg 743
Film Creations Ltd, pg 760
Metropolitan Audio-Visual Inc, pg 824

ARKANSAS

Live'N'Loud, pg 810
White Diamond Productions LLC, pg 937

CALIFORNIA

Access Video in Berkeley, pg 673
Air Bud Entertainment, pg 678
Artichoke Productions, pg 690

Big Door, pg 705
Burrud Productions Inc, pg 713
Steve Chandler, pg 720
Coast Learning Systems, pg 727
Creative Technology, pg 733
Custom Video Productions Inc, pg 736
Deja View Video, pg 740
Design Media, pg 741
Direct Cinema Ltd Inc, pg 743
Dolphin MultiMedia Inc, pg 745
Durrin Productions Inc, pg 748
First Camera, pg 761
Fox Television Center, pg 765
Geddes Productions LLC, pg 769
Goal Productions, pg 772
Gold Standard Productions, pg 772
Bruce Goldberg Inc, pg 772
Griggs Productions Inc, pg 774
Havas Edge, pg 777
Imageworks, pg 785
Increase Video/Silver Mine Video, pg 786
International Contact Inc, pg 790
ITV Productions, pg 792
Joyce Media Inc, pg 795
Kavich Reynolds Productions Inc, pg 797
KTVU-Retail Services, pg 802
K2B2 Records, pg 802
Ludlow Media, pg 812
Lynch Communications, pg 813
Main Street Media Inc, pg 815
Maximus Media Inc, pg 820
Media Magic, pg 822
monterey media inc, pg 829
Music World/Vocal Power School, pg 834
New & Unique Videos™, pg 839
Nilgiri Press, pg 841
Nineteen87, pg 841
On-Trax Inc, pg 846
Palardo Productions, pg 850
piXvfm Inc, pg 857
Point of View Productions, pg 858
Producers Group Ltd, pg 863
QRS Software Services, pg 867
Quality Digest, pg 868
Regent Press Publishers & Printers, pg 873
RetinaVision Productions, pg 874
Glenn Roland Films, pg 876
Sahara Records & Filmworks Entertainment Co, pg 879
Screen Door Entertainment Inc, pg 882
Sea Studios Foundation, pg 883
SNAP, pg 891
Technicolor USA Inc, pg 908
Timestream Video, pg 914
Total Creative, pg 916
Warner Bros Production Sound & Video Services, pg 934
Wavemaker Media Design, pg 934
Webster Communications, pg 935
WMS Media Inc, pg 940
The Wyland Group, pg 942

COLORADO

Centre Communications Inc, pg 720
Daylight Productions & Rentals, pg 739
Flashback Media Productions, pg 762
Tatum Video, pg 907
Transtar Entertainment Co Inc, pg 917

CONNECTICUT

ACM Productions Ltd, pg 674
Antenna International, pg 686
Cine-Med Inc, pg 723

PROGRAMMING — VIDEO

Videotape Producers (continued)

CONNECTICUT (continued)

Geomatrix Productions, pg 770
Ironik Design & Post, pg 791
New London Media, pg 839

DELAWARE

Ken-Del Productions Inc, pg 797
University Media Services, pg 922

DISTRICT OF COLUMBIA

Hillmann & Carr Inc, pg 780
USCCB Publishing, pg 923

FLORIDA

Applebox Studio, pg 687
Civins Productions Inc, pg 725
Courter Films LLC, pg 732
I M P A C T Publishing Inc, pg 783
MTI Home Video, pg 833
National Teleproductions Inc, pg 837
NatureVision TV, pg 837
Roger Scruggs Films, pg 883
Sound & Vision Communications Inc, pg 893
Sunfire Communications Inc, pg 904
Video Techniques Inc, pg 928

GEORGIA

Beachwood Productions, pg 702
Burst Video/Film Inc, pg 713
ECG Productions, pg 750
First Cut Communications LLC, pg 761
Myriad Productions, pg 835
WaveGuide Studios, pg 934

IDAHO

Brad Shaw Productions Inc, pg 885

ILLINOIS

CCore Media Inc, pg 718
Cresta Creative, pg 734
Encyclopaedia Britannica Inc, pg 754
Major Media Inc, pg 815
Manning Productions, pg 816
Moviecraft Inc, pg 831
National Safety Council (NSC), pg 836
Jim Passin Productions, pg 852
Pepper Group, pg 854
PSAV® Presentation Services (Hotel Services Division), pg 866
Sparkfactor, pg 896
Terra Nova Films Inc, pg 911
Video Impressions, pg 928

INDIANA

OMNI Productions, pg 845

IOWA

Accelerated Learning Foundation, pg 672
Educational Technology & Media Services, pg 751

KENTUCKY

EKU Media, pg 752
Donna Lawrence Productions, pg 804
National Geographic Learning, pg 836
Prosper Media Group Inc, pg 866

LOUISIANA

Digital FX Inc, pg 742
Great Chefs/Leisure Jazz Video, pg 773
Leisure Video, pg 806
Louisiana State University Division of Strategic Communications, pg 811
Moxie Media, pg 832

MAINE

WGME-TV, pg 936

MARYLAND

CPR MultiMedia Solutions, pg 732
Media Dimensions LLC, pg 821
Milner-Fenwick Inc, pg 828
Mobile-Video Productions Inc, pg 828
Sign Media Inc, pg 887

MASSACHUSETTS

Capron Lighting & Sound Co Inc, pg 716
CommCreative, pg 728
Cramer, pg 732
Education Development Center Inc (EDC), pg 750
Heliotrope Studios, pg 778
HOME Inc, pg 781
Preston Productions Inc, pg 861

MICHIGAN

Digi Sign Design LLC, pg 741
K&R All Media Productions LLC, pg 796
K&R's Recording Studios Inc, pg 796
Lawrence Productions Inc, pg 804
MessageMakers, pg 824
MSU Technologies, pg 833
Prakken Publications Inc, pg 861
Wayne State University Media Services, pg 934
WTVS, Detroit Public Television, pg 942

MINNESOTA

American Choral Catalog Ltd, pg 683
GMI Productions, pg 771
House of Cinemagraphics, pg 782
Worthwhile Films, pg 941

MISSOURI

Marsh Media, pg 817
SOM Publishing Co, pg 892

NEBRASKA

Envision Communications Inc, pg 755
Rainbow Video Productions Inc, pg 869
Telepro Video Inc, pg 910
Vision Maker Media, pg 930

NEVADA

DVDs4Less, pg 748
Encore Event Technologies LLC, pg 754

KENTUCKY

JCS Video Productions, pg 793
Tanglewood Productions, pg 907

NEW HAMPSHIRE

Apertura, pg 686
Channell One Video, pg 720
Chip Taylor Communications LLC, pg 907
The Troupe, pg 918
YMAA Publication Center Inc, pg 944

NEW JERSEY

Alden Films, pg 679
Broadcast Center Studios, pg 710
CFP Video Productions Inc, pg 720
Comex Systems Inc, pg 728
Euro-Pacific Film & Video Productions Inc, pg 756
Laurel Video Productions, pg 804
MiB MediaWorks, pg 825
Ray Mueller Productions, pg 833
Optisonics Productions, pg 847
Telequest Inc, pg 910
VCSvideo, pg 925

NEW MEXICO

Production Outfitters, pg 864
Rainbow International Inc, pg 869

NEW YORK

Ace Video, pg 674
aurora productions, pg 696
Blue Barn Pictures Inc, pg 707
Buzzco Associates Inc, pg 713
Thomas Craven Film Corp, pg 733
Duplication Depot Inc, pg 748
The Food & Beverage Institute, pg 763
Four Corners Productions, pg 764
William Greaves Productions Inc, pg 774
Homespun Video, pg 781
Human Relations Media, pg 782
IAI Records & Video, pg 783
Icontent, pg 783
The Independent Production Fund, pg 786
International Digital Centre, pg 790
Richard Kaplan Productions, pg 796
Long Island Video Enterprises Live Inc, pg 811
Manhattan Center Studios Inc, pg 816
Mastervision Inc, pg 819
Jack Morton Worldwide, pg 830
MRM//McCANN, pg 832
MRY, pg 832
News Broadcast Network Inc, pg 840
Pat Kogan Productions Inc, pg 852
Peckham Productions Inc, pg 852
PrimaLux Video Inc, pg 862
PrimeLight Productions Inc, pg 862
Richter Productions Inc, pg 875
SISU Home Entertainment Inc, pg 889
Split Image Productions, pg 898
TeleTime Productions, pg 910
Videofashion Network, pg 929
The Visual Studies Workshop (VSW), pg 931
Zelman Studios Ltd, pg 945

NORTH CAROLINA

Pat Appleson Studios Inc, pg 687
Carolina Biological Supply Co, pg 717
The Communications Group Inc, pg 729

Horizon Video Productions Inc, pg 781
NASCAR Productions LLC, pg 835
Trailblazer Studios®, pg 917
Videowerks, pg 930

OHIO

CET, pg 720
Cuyahoga Community College Student Production Office (SPO), pg 736
Franciscan Media, pg 765
MainSail Production Services Inc, pg 815
Musicol Recording, pg 835
R&B Communications Inc, pg 870
Take 1 Media Services, pg 906

OREGON

CMD Agency, pg 726
Garden Valley Productions, pg 768
InterVision Media, pg 791
KPDX-TV Production Center, pg 801
Odyssey Productions Inc, pg 844
REX, pg 874
Wilderness Video, pg 938

PENNSYLVANIA

Argentine Productions Inc, pg 688
Audio Visual Communications Inc, pg 694
FMP Media Solutions Inc, pg 763
Main Point Productions, pg 815
Muderick Media, pg 833
Production Masters Inc (PMI), pg 864
Rahlic Publishing Co, pg 869
Schlessinger Media, pg 881
Video/Film Associates, pg 928
The Videohouse Inc, pg 929

SOUTH CAROLINA

American Production Services LLC, pg 684
Stages Video Productions, pg 899
Venture Media, pg 925

TENNESSEE

Center for Southern Folklore Inc, pg 719
Memphis Communications Corp, pg 823
Running Pony Productions LLC, pg 878
Scripps Networks, pg 882
United Methodist Productions, pg 921

TEXAS

Biway Media, pg 706
Communication Arts Multimedia Inc, pg 728
The Editing Co, pg 750
Lamb & Lion Ministries, pg 803
Marx InDigital, pg 818
Mediaforce Productions, pg 822
Earl Miller Productions Inc, pg 827
Omni Intercommunications Inc, pg 845
Romar Learning Solutions LLC, pg 877
Stage Directions, pg 898
Texas Heart Institute Visual Communication Services, pg 911
University of Texas at Austin - Petroleum Extension Service, pg 923

VERMONT

Dorothy Tod Films, pg 915
Wilson McLeran Inc, pg 939

VIRGINIA

Altruist Media LLC, pg 682
BES Studios, pg 704
CACI Integrated Communications, pg 713
DXC Technology Co, pg 748
Limelight Communications Inc, pg 808

WASHINGTON

Adams Creative & Production Services, pg 675
Bennett-Watt HD Productions Inc, pg 703
Center for Touch Drawing, pg 719
Medifecta Healthcare Training, pg 823
Victory Studios, pg 927

WISCONSIN

Excel Duplication Services, pg 757
Meridian Studios, pg 824
Mirror 34 Productions, pg 828
USAV Group Inc, pg 923
Video Wisconsin Inc, pg 929
Watts Communications Inc, pg 934
Wisconsin Public Television, pg 940

WYOMING

Bridger Productions Inc, pg 710

ALBERTA

Black Media Works, pg 706
Global TV, pg 771

BRITISH COLUMBIA

Timeless Books, pg 914
Triad Communications Ltd, pg 918

NEWFOUNDLAND AND LABRADOR

Vidcraft Productions Ltd, pg 927

NORTHWEST TERRITORIES

Yellowknife Films Inc, pg 944

ONTARIO

RB Productions, pg 870
Silver Creek Media Inc, pg 888

QUEBEC

Les Productions Via Le Monde (Daniel Bertolino) Inc, pg 864

SASKATCHEWAN

plan9films, pg 857

Videotape Rentals

ARIZONA

Video Learning Library, pg 928

CALIFORNIA

Ametron Audio/Video, pg 684
Direct Cinema Ltd Inc, pg 743
Durrin Productions Inc, pg 748
Griggs Productions, pg 774
Medcom Inc, pg 821

Regent Press Publishers & Printers, pg 873
The Wyland Group, pg 942

CONNECTICUT

Ironik Design & Post, pg 791

DELAWARE

University Media Services, pg 922

FLORIDA

Courter Films LLC, pg 732
Jordan Klein Film & Video (JKFV), pg 795

GEORGIA

Staging Directions Inc, pg 899

ILLINOIS

National Safety Council (NSC), pg 836
RBR Productions, pg 870

MASSACHUSETTS

Documentary Educational Resources Inc, pg 744

MICHIGAN

Digi Sign Design LLC, pg 741
Wayne State University Media Services, pg 934

MINNESOTA

American Choral Catalog Ltd, pg 683
Science Museum of Minnesota, pg 882

NEBRASKA

Vision Maker Media, pg 930

NEW HAMPSHIRE

Chip Taylor Communications LLC, pg 907

NEW JERSEY

Business Education Films, pg 713
Euro-Pacific Film & Video Productions Inc, pg 756

NEW YORK

Adwar Video, pg 678
William Greaves Productions Inc, pg 774
Icarus Films Inc, pg 783
Kino International Corp, pg 799
New Day Films, pg 839
Richter Productions Inc, pg 875
Timed Exposures Films, pg 914

OHIO

Franciscan Media, pg 765

OREGON

Nostalgia Family Video Inc, pg 843
Wilderness Video, pg 938

PENNSYLVANIA

Rahlic Publishing Co, pg 869

TENNESSEE

Center for Southern Folklore Inc, pg 719

TEXAS

University of Texas at Austin - Petroleum Extension Service, pg 923

WISCONSIN

Wisconsin Public Television, pg 940

ALBERTA

Global TV, pg 771

BRITISH COLUMBIA

Video Out Distribution, pg 928

ONTARIO

Kineticvideo.com, pg 799

QUEBEC

Les Productions Via Le Monde (Daniel Bertolino) Inc, pg 864

Vocational Program Distributors

ARIZONA

Video Learning Library, pg 928

CALIFORNIA

Direct Cinema Ltd Inc, pg 743
Discovery Education - Los Angeles, pg 743
411 Video Information, pg 764
Increase Video/Silver Mine Video, pg 786
New & Unique Videos™, pg 839
Pyramid Media, pg 867
TMW Media Group, pg 915
The Wine Appreciation Guild Ltd, pg 939

COLORADO

InJoy Birth & Parenting Education, pg 788

CONNECTICUT

The Taunton Press Inc, pg 907

DELAWARE

University Media Services, pg 922

DISTRICT OF COLUMBIA

Department of VSA & Accessibility at the John F Kennedy Center for the Performing Arts, pg 740

FLORIDA

EarthDesign Inc, pg 749
PAR Inc, pg 851
Video Resources Software, pg 928

GEORGIA

Convergent Media Systems, pg 731
On-Line Productions, pg 845

ILLINOIS

ABSA Films, pg 672
Film Ideas Inc, pg 760
Movies Unlimited, pg 831
National Safety Council (NSC), pg 836

INDIANA

Purdue University Digital Education, pg 866

IOWA

Kirkwood Community College, pg 799

KENTUCKY

WaxWorks VideoWorks, pg 934

MAINE

WoodenBoat Publications, pg 941

MASSACHUSETTS

Penfield Productions Ltd, pg 853

MICHIGAN

Digi Sign Design LLC, pg 741
Prakken Publications Inc, pg 861
Society of Manufacturing Engineers (SME), pg 891
VMS Inc, pg 932

MINNESOTA

EMC Publishing LLC, pg 753
JIST Publishing, pg 794

NEVADA

DVDs4Less, pg 748

NEW HAMPSHIRE

Chip Taylor Communications LLC, pg 907

NEW JERSEY

Alden Films, pg 679
Comex Systems Inc, pg 728
MiB MediaWorks, pg 825

NEW MEXICO

The Phoenix Learning Group Inc, pg 855

NEW YORK

Brooklyn Botanic Garden, pg 711
The Bureau for At-Risk Youth, pg 712
Films Media Group, pg 760
Guidance Associates Inc Center for Humanities, pg 774
Human Relations Media, pg 782
March of Dimes Foundation, pg 816
Shopware, pg 886
SISU Home Entertainment Inc, pg 889
Video Catalogue Co Inc, pg 927
VIEW Inc (Video International Entertainment World Inc), pg 930
Willow Mixed Media Inc, pg 939

OHIO

McGraw-Hill School Education Group, pg 821
Shelburne Films, pg 885
WOUB Public Media, pg 942

PENNSYLVANIA

Bergwall Productions Inc, pg 704
Bullfrog Films Inc, pg 712
Discovery Education - South Burlington, pg 743
FMP Media Solutions Inc, pg 763

PROGRAMMING — VIDEO

Vocational Program Distributors (continued)

TENNESSEE

American Blackguard Inc, pg 683

TEXAS

CEV Multimedia Ltd, pg 720
University of Texas at Austin - Petroleum Extension Service, pg 923

VERMONT

University of Vermont, Instructional Television Dept, pg 923
Wilson McLeran Inc, pg 939

VIRGINIA

CACI Integrated Communications, pg 713

ONTARIO

Canadian Learning Co Inc, pg 715
Kineticvideo.com, pg 799
McIntyre Media Inc, pg 821

Vocational Program Producers

ALASKA

Aurora Films, pg 696

ARIZONA

Aardvark Productions LLC, pg 671

CALIFORNIA

Access Video in Berkeley, pg 673
Action Video, pg 675
Big Door, pg 705
Steve Chandler, pg 720
Classic Images Stock Footage LLC, pg 726
Coastline Productions, pg 727
Creative Technology, pg 733
Custom Video Productions Inc, pg 736
Design Media, pg 741
Discovery Education - Los Angeles, pg 743
imageReal Pictures LLC, pg 785
ITV Productions, pg 792
Main Street Media Inc, pg 815
Maximus Media Inc, pg 820
McCune Audio-Video-Lighting, pg 821
Media Magic, pg 822
The Media Staff Inc, pg 822
New & Unique Videos™, pg 839
New Circuit Films LLC, pg 839
Nineteen87, pg 841
Nolte Media, pg 841
On-Trax Inc, pg 846
Penrose Productions, pg 854
PM Productions, pg 858
Point of View Productions, pg 858
QRS Software Services, pg 867
Dick Reizner Film & Video, pg 873
Glenn Roland Films, pg 876
SNAP, pg 891
Tam Communications Inc, pg 906
Timestream Video, pg 914
TMW Media Group, pg 915
Total Creative, pg 916

Vineyard Video & Photography, pg 930
Wavemaker Media Design, pg 934
West Coast Projections Inc, pg 935
Zamacona Productions, pg 945

COLORADO

Daylight Productions & Rentals, pg 739
Flashback Media Productions, pg 762
InJoy Birth & Parenting Education, pg 788

CONNECTICUT

The Gary-Paul Agency, pg 768
Ironik Design & Post, pg 791
The Taunton Press Inc, pg 907

DELAWARE

University Media Services, pg 922

DISTRICT OF COLUMBIA

Department of VSA & Accessibility at the John F Kennedy Center for the Performing Arts, pg 740
Hillmann & Carr Inc, pg 780

FLORIDA

Blackburst Entertainment LLC, pg 706
Civins Productions Inc, pg 725
CopShopMiami.com, pg 731
Courter Films LLC, pg 732
EarthDesign Inc, pg 749
Easy Edit Video Inc, pg 750
Jordan Klein Film & Video (JKFV), pg 795
Sunfire Communications Inc, pg 904
Sunrise Studios, pg 904
Tricycle Studios, pg 918
Video Resources Software, pg 928

GEORGIA

Beachwood Productions, pg 702
Cox Media, pg 732
Guerrilla Productions LLC, pg 774
On-Line Productions, pg 845

HAWAII

Hyperspective Studios Inc, pg 783
Source School of Tantra Yoga Inc, pg 895

IDAHO

Brad Shaw Productions Inc, pg 885
Wide Eye Productions, pg 938

ILLINOIS

ABSA Films, pg 672
Film Police, pg 760
IV Media Resources, pg 792
Major Media Productions Inc, pg 815
National Safety Council (NSC), pg 836
Pepper Group, pg 854
SCI Television & Creative Media LLC, pg 882
Southern Illinois University, pg 895
20/20 Communications Inc, pg 920

INDIANA

A-V-A Video Productions, pg 671
PentaVision Communications Inc, pg 854

Purdue University Digital Education, pg 866
Road Pictures, pg 876

IOWA

Educational Technology & Media Services, pg 751
Kirkwood Community College, pg 799

KENTUCKY

NIMCO Inc, pg 841

LOUISIANA

Moxie Media, pg 832

MARYLAND

CPR MultiMedia Solutions, pg 732
dbF a Media Company, pg 739
The Image Generators, pg 785
Kramer Communications Video Production, pg 801

MASSACHUSETTS

Award Productions Inc, pg 699
Green Mountain Post Films (GMP), pg 774
Penfield Productions Ltd, pg 853

MICHIGAN

Digi Sign Design LLC, pg 741
K&R All Media Productions LLC, pg 796
K&R's Recording Studios Inc, pg 796
Prakken Publications Inc, pg 861
Society of Manufacturing Engineers (SME), pg 891
VMS Inc, pg 932

MINNESOTA

EMC Publishing LLC, pg 753
House of Cinemagraphics, pg 782
JIST Publishing, pg 794
MastCom, pg 819

MISSOURI

Audio-VideoGraphics Inc, pg 694

MONTANA

KUSM TV, pg 802

NEVADA

Aardvark Video & Media Productions, pg 671
DVDs4Less, pg 748
Encore Event Technologies LLC, pg 754
JCS Video Productions, pg 793
Tanglewood Productions, pg 907

NEW HAMPSHIRE

Apertura, pg 686
Chip Taylor Communications LLC, pg 907

NEW JERSEY

Alden Films, pg 679
Broadcast Center Studios, pg 710
CFP Video Productions Inc, pg 720
Comex Systems Inc, pg 728
Laurel Video Productions, pg 804
MiB MediaWorks, pg 825
Optisonics Productions, pg 847
Suede Interactive, pg 903

Telequest Inc, pg 910
VCSvideo, pg 925

NEW MEXICO

The Phoenix Learning Group Inc, pg 855
Production Outfitters, pg 864

NEW YORK

aurora productions, pg 696
BC Studio, pg 702
Blue Barn Pictures Inc, pg 707
Brooklyn Botanic Garden, pg 711
The Bureau for At-Risk Youth, pg 712
Films Media Group, pg 760
Guidance Associates Inc Center for Humanities, pg 774
Hello World Communications, pg 778
Human Relations Media, pg 782
March of Dimes Foundation, pg 816
The Palmer Group, pg 850
Pat Kogan Productions Inc, pg 852
Peckham Productions Inc, pg 852
PrimaLux Video Inc, pg 862
Shopware, pg 886
TeleTime Productions, pg 910
Triumph Learning LLC, pg 918
Video Catalogue Co Inc, pg 927
Videograf, pg 929
VIEW Inc (Video International Entertainment World Inc), pg 930
Alan Weiss Productions, pg 935
Willow Mixed Media Inc, pg 939

NORTH CAROLINA

Pat Appleson Studios Inc, pg 687
The Communications Group Inc, pg 729
Digital Rain LLC, pg 742
Kino Mountain Productions LLC, pg 799
Moving Pictures, pg 832
Videowerks, pg 930

OHIO

Advent Media Inc, pg 677
Lyon Video Inc, pg 813
MainSail Production Services Inc, pg 815
McGraw-Hill School Education Group, pg 821
R&B Communications Inc, pg 870
Shelburne Films, pg 885
Treehaus Communications Inc, pg 917
Vista Color Imaging Inc, pg 931
WOUB Public Media, pg 942

OREGON

ERA Learning, pg 755
Ideascape Inc, pg 784
KPDX-TV Production Center, pg 801
KTVA Productions, pg 802
Production West, pg 864
REX, pg 874

PENNSYLVANIA

Bergwall Productions Inc, pg 704
CCI Communications Inc, pg 718
FMP Media Solutions Inc, pg 763
Innovision Media Group, pg 788
JPL, pg 795
Muderick Media, pg 833
Panta Rhei Media Inc, pg 851
The Videohouse Inc, pg 929

PROGRAMMING — MISCELLANEOUS

Computer Multimedia, CD-ROM & DVD Interactive Program Distributors

CALIFORNIA

Academy Savant, pg 672
Ametron Audio/Video, pg 684
Animated Software Co, pg 685
Astronomical Society of the Pacific, pg 691
Christian Media Network, pg 722
Deja View Video, pg 740
Educational Insights, pg 750
Electronic Arts Inc, pg 752
ETR, pg 756
Eye & I Productions, pg 758
Steven Halpern's Inner Peace Music, pg 775
MarVista Entertainment Inc, pg 818
Social Studies School Service, pg 891
Staylor-Made Communications Inc, pg 900
TiVo Corp, pg 914
Videobotics, pg 929

COLORADO

Aspen Systems Inc, pg 691

CONNECTICUT

Cine-Med Inc, pg 723
Ironik Design & Post, pg 791

DISTRICT OF COLUMBIA

Theatrical Technicians Inc (TTI), pg 912

FLORIDA

CD ROM™ Inc, pg 718
Communications Concepts Inc (CCI), pg 729
Times-Square Fantasy Theatre, pg 914

ILLINOIS

Britannica Digital Learning, pg 710
CCore Media Inc, pg 718
Encyclopaedia Britannica Inc, pg 754
Film Ideas Inc, pg 760
Learning Seed, pg 805
Rand McNally Education, pg 870
Richter Studios, pg 875

IOWA

Perfection Learning Corp, pg 854
Right Stuf Inc, pg 875

LOUISIANA

Great Chefs/Leisure Jazz Video, pg 773
Leisure Video, pg 806

MARYLAND

dbF a Media Company, pg 739
MMI Marketing, pg 828

MASSACHUSETTS

Cramer, pg 732
Documentary Educational Resources Inc, pg 744
Pauline Books & Media, pg 852
Penfield Productions Ltd, pg 853

MICHIGAN

Digi Sign Design LLC, pg 741
Prakken Publications Inc, pg 861
Zondervan, pg 945

MINNESOTA

BeyerSound & Essay Audio, pg 705
Harris Communications Inc, pg 776
JIST Publishing, pg 794

NEW JERSEY

Allegro Productions Inc, pg 680
Paulist Press, pg 852

NEW YORK

The Bureau for At-Risk Youth, pg 712
Criterion Collection, pg 735
Digital Force Ltd, pg 742
Discovery Education Inc, pg 743
FACE Foundation, pg 758
HB-Content, pg 777
Human Relations Media, pg 782
Monad Trainer's Aide Inc, pg 829
SISU Home Entertainment Inc, pg 889

OREGON

Wilderness Video, pg 938

PENNSYLVANIA

AccuWeather Inc, pg 674
Bullfrog Films Inc, pg 712
Discovery Education - South Burlington, pg 743
FMP Media Solutions Inc, pg 763
Library Video Company, pg 807
MVD Entertainment Group, pg 835
Scala Inc, pg 881
Schlessinger Media, pg 881

SOUTH DAKOTA

Sencore Inc, pg 883

TENNESSEE

American Blackguard Inc, pg 683
National School Products, pg 836
Spring Arbor Distributors Inc, pg 898
Zion Music Group, pg 945

TEXAS

CEV Multimedia Ltd, pg 720
Emergency Film Group, pg 753
Epic Software Group Inc, pg 755
Lamb & Lion Ministries, pg 803
Replicopy Digital Media Center, pg 873

UTAH

Strata™, pg 901

VIRGINIA

Design & Production Inc, pg 740
National Audiovisual Center (NAC), pg 836

WISCONSIN

Meridian Studios, pg 824

BRITISH COLUMBIA

Credo Interactive Inc, pg 734

Computer Multimedia, CD-ROM & DVD Interactive Program Producers

ALABAMA

CMEinfo™, pg 727

ARIZONA

Aardvark Productions LLC, pg 671
Merestone, pg 823
MindPlay, pg 828

ARKANSAS

Live'N'Loud, pg 810

CALIFORNIA

Animated Software Co, pg 685
Astronomical Society of the Pacific, pg 691
Big Door, pg 705
Christian Media Network, pg 722
Coloredge Inc, pg 728
Creative Technology, pg 733
Custom Video Productions Inc, pg 736
Deja View Video, pg 740
digital OutPost, pg 742
Direct Images Interactive Inc, pg 743
Dolphin MultiMedia Inc, pg 745
Electronic Arts Inc, pg 752
Eye & I Productions, pg 758
Gateways Books & Tapes, pg 768
Steven Halpern's Inner Peace Music, pg 775
Havas Edge, pg 777
Imageworks, pg 785
International Contact Inc, pg 790
Ludlow Media, pg 812
Lumeni Productions Inc, pg 812
Lynch Communications, pg 813
Main Street Media Inc, pg 815
Maximus Media Inc, pg 820
Media Magic, pg 822
QRS Software Services, pg 867
RetinaVision Productions, pg 874
Glenn Roland Films, pg 876
Staylor-Made Communications Inc, pg 900
Still N' Motion, pg 901
Tam Communications Inc, pg 906
Three D Graphics Inc, pg 913
Tickets.com, pg 913
Total Creative, pg 916
Towards 2000 Inc, pg 916
Videobotics, pg 929
Wavemaker Media Design, pg 934
WMS Media Inc, pg 940

COLORADO

Flashback Media Productions, pg 762

CONNECTICUT

Cine-Med Inc, pg 723
Geomatrix Productions, pg 770
Ironik Design & Post, pg 791
Musivision Inc, pg 835
New London Media, pg 839
Palace Production Center, pg 850

DISTRICT OF COLUMBIA

Hillmann & Carr Inc, pg 780
National Education Association (NEA), pg 836
Theatrical Technicians Inc (TTI), pg 912
USCCB Publishing, pg 923

FLORIDA

AVI-SPL, pg 698
Blackburst Entertainment LLC, pg 706
CD ROM™ Inc, pg 718
Civins Productions Inc, pg 725
ITC Learning LLC, pg 791
Sunfire Communications Inc, pg 904
Sunrise Studios, pg 904
Teach America Corp, pg 908
Times-Square Fantasy Theatre, pg 914
Tricycle Studios, pg 918
Video Techniques Inc, pg 928

GEORGIA

Beachwood Productions, pg 702
ECG Productions, pg 750
Guerrilla Productions LLC, pg 774
Imagers, pg 785
On-Line Productions, pg 845

HAWAII

Hyperspective Studios Inc, pg 783

IDAHO

Marketron Broadcast Solutions, pg 817

ILLINOIS

ABSA Films, pg 672
Advanced Audio Technology, pg 677
Airways Digital Media, pg 679
AnswersMedia, pg 686
Atomic Imaging Inc/Golan Studios, pg 692
Britannica Digital Learning, pg 710
CCore Media Inc, pg 718
Cresta Creative, pg 734
Encyclopaedia Britannica Inc, pg 754
Extraordinary Demos/Videos, pg 757
IV Media Resources, pg 792
Learning Seed, pg 805
Major Media Inc, pg 815
Mightybytes Inc, pg 827
Multimedia Marketing Group, pg 833
RADMAR Inc, pg 869
Rand McNally Education, pg 870
Richter Studios, pg 875
Sparkfactor, pg 896
Video Impressions, pg 928

INDIANA

A-V-A Video Productions, pg 671
Bright Ideas Creative Services, pg 710
PentaVision Communications Inc, pg 854

IOWA

Right Stuf Inc, pg 875

KANSAS

KAKE-TV, pg 796

PROGRAMMING — MISCELLANEOUS

Microcomputer Software & Courseware Distributors (continued)

CALIFORNIA (continued)
Astronomical Society of the Pacific, pg 691
Autodesk Inc, pg 696
CADint, pg 713
Joyce Media Inc, pg 795
Social Studies School Service, pg 891
Unique Business Systems, pg 921
Videobotics, pg 929
Xytech Systems Corp, pg 943

CONNECTICUT
Scholastic Library Publishing, pg 882

DELAWARE
University Media Services, pg 922

FLORIDA
Medina Software Inc, pg 823

GEORGIA
LYRASIS, pg 813
School Media Associates LLC, pg 882

ILLINOIS
CCH Inc, A Wolters Kluwer business, pg 718
Creative Technology (CT), pg 733
Encyclopaedia Britannica Inc, pg 754
Film Ideas Inc, pg 760
1st Financial Training Services Inc, pg 761
Follett School Solutions Inc, pg 763
National Safety Council (NSC), pg 836
Rand McNally Education, pg 870
Sunburst Digital Inc, pg 903

IOWA
Accelerated Learning Foundation, pg 672

KENTUCKY
The Learning House Inc, pg 805
National Geographic Learning, pg 836

MARYLAND
MMI Marketing, pg 828
Nicholas P Pipino Associates Inc, pg 857

MASSACHUSETTS
Cheng & Tsui Co, pg 721
Duxbury Systems Inc, pg 748
Monotype Imaging Inc, pg 829

MICHIGAN
MSU Technologies, pg 833
Prakken Publications Inc, pg 861

MINNESOTA
BeyerSound & Essay Audio, pg 705
Harris Communications Inc, pg 776

NEW HAMPSHIRE
Frey Scientific, pg 766

NEW JERSEY
Advanced Imaging Concepts Inc, pg 677
Argraph Corp, pg 688
John Wiley & Sons Inc, pg 938

NEW MEXICO
VidCAD LLC, pg 927

NEW YORK
Applause Learning Resources, pg 687
Monad Trainer's Aide Inc, pg 829
WorldView Software, pg 941

NORTH CAROLINA
Carolina Biological Supply Co, pg 717

OHIO
McGraw-Hill School Education Group, pg 821

PENNSYLVANIA
AccuWeather Inc, pg 674
Discovery Education - South Burlington, pg 743
TRC Interactive Inc, pg 917
Visual Sound Inc, pg 931

SOUTH CAROLINA
ACS Technologies, pg 674
BJU Press, pg 706

TENNESSEE
Cokesbury, pg 727
Randall House Publications, pg 870

TEXAS
CEV Multimedia Ltd, pg 720
Epic Software Group Inc, pg 755
MusicMaster Inc, pg 835

VERMONT
Taylor Associates, pg 907

WISCONSIN
School Specialty Inc, pg 882
Wisconsin Technical College System Foundation Inc, pg 940

BRITISH COLUMBIA
Thompson Rivers University Marketing & Communications Dept, pg 913

ONTARIO
Canadian Learning Co Inc, pg 715
OpenText Corp, pg 846
Technovision® Interactive Inc, pg 909

Microcomputer Software & Courseware Producers

ARIZONA
Edgenuity Inc, pg 750
MindPlay, pg 828

CALIFORNIA
Academy Savant, pg 672
Adobe Systems Inc, pg 676
Apple Inc, pg 687
Astronomical Society of the Pacific, pg 691
Autodesk Inc, pg 696
CADint, pg 713
Creative Technology, pg 733
Joyce Media Inc, pg 795
Palardo Productions, pg 850
QRS Software Services, pg 867
Three D Graphics Inc, pg 913
Unique Business Systems, pg 921
Videobotics, pg 929
Xytech Systems Corp, pg 943

CONNECTICUT
Scholastic Library Publishing, pg 882

DELAWARE
University Media Services, pg 922

FLORIDA
Medina Software Inc, pg 823
Teach America Corp, pg 908

ILLINOIS
CCH Inc, A Wolters Kluwer business, pg 718
Encyclopaedia Britannica Inc, pg 754
1st Financial Training Services Inc, pg 761
Follett School Solutions Inc, pg 763
Major Media Inc, pg 815
National Safety Council (NSC), pg 836
Rand McNally Education, pg 870
Sunburst Digital Inc, pg 903
Video Impressions, pg 928

INDIANA
OMNI Productions, pg 845

IOWA
Accelerated Learning Foundation, pg 672
Educational Technology & Media Services, pg 751

KENTUCKY
The Learning House Inc, pg 805
National Geographic Learning, pg 836

MASSACHUSETTS
Cheng & Tsui Co, pg 721
Duxbury Systems Inc, pg 748
Monotype Imaging Inc, pg 829

MICHIGAN
Digi Sign Design LLC, pg 741
K&R All Media Productions LLC, pg 796
Wayne State University Media Services, pg 934
Zondervan, pg 945

MINNESOTA
Badiyan Inc, pg 700
BeyerSound & Essay Audio, pg 705

NEVADA
Encore Event Technologies LLC, pg 754

NEW JERSEY
Adcis Inc, pg 675
Advanced Imaging Concepts Inc, pg 677
Outside The Box Interactive LLC, pg 849
John Wiley & Sons Inc, pg 938

NEW MEXICO
VidCAD LLC, pg 927

NEW YORK
Criterion Collection, pg 735
IBM Collaboration Solutions, pg 783
MRY, pg 832
The Palmer Group, pg 850
Judson Rosebush Co Inc, pg 877
WorldView Software, pg 941

NORTH CAROLINA
Alien Skin Software LLC, pg 680
SAS Institute Inc, pg 880

OHIO
Advent Media Inc, pg 677
McGraw-Hill School Education Group, pg 821
R&B Communications Inc, pg 870

OREGON
ERA Learning, pg 755
InterVision Media, pg 791
NeoSoft Corp, pg 838

PENNSYLVANIA
AccuWeather Inc, pg 674
FMP Media Solutions Inc, pg 763
Innovision Media Group, pg 788
JPL, pg 795
Scala Inc, pg 881

RHODE ISLAND
Sound-FX-Design, pg 894

SOUTH CAROLINA
ACS Technologies, pg 674
BJU Press, pg 706

TENNESSEE
Cokesbury, pg 727
Memphis Communications Corp, pg 823

TEXAS
CEV Multimedia Ltd, pg 720
Communication Arts Multimedia Inc, pg 728
Epic Software Group Inc, pg 755
Romar Learning Solutions LLC, pg 877
Videotex Systems Inc, pg 930

UTAH
Micro Focus, pg 825

VIRGINIA
DXC Technology Co, pg 748

WISCONSIN
DNASTAR Inc, pg 744
USAV Group Inc, pg 923
Wisconsin Technical College
System Foundation Inc, pg 940

WYOMING
Bridger Productions Inc, pg 710

BRITISH COLUMBIA
Thompson Rivers University
Marketing & Communications
Dept, pg 913

ONTARIO
Canadian Learning Co Inc, pg 715
OpenText Corp, pg 846
RB Productions, pg 870
Technovision® Interactive Inc,
pg 909

QUEBEC
Orion Software, pg 848

Microcomputer Software & Courseware Rentals

DELAWARE
University Media Services, pg 922

GEORGIA
Staging Directions Inc, pg 899

ILLINOIS
1st Financial Training Services Inc,
pg 761

MICHIGAN
Wayne State University Media
Services, pg 934

WISCONSIN
Wisconsin Technical College
System Foundation Inc, pg 940

QUEBEC
Orion Software, pg 848

Print—Study, *see* Study Print

Reading & Tachistoscopic Equipment & Learning System Distributors

CALIFORNIA
Ametron Audio/Video, pg 684
Educational Insights, pg 750

COLORADO
Vital Learning LLC, pg 932

MARYLAND
Nicholas P Pipino Associates Inc,
pg 857

MASSACHUSETTS
Duxbury Systems Inc, pg 748

NEW YORK
Visual Technologies Corp, pg 932

ONTARIO
Technovision® Interactive Inc,
pg 909

Reading & Tachistoscopic Equipment & Learning System Producers

CALIFORNIA
QRS Software Services, pg 867

COLORADO
Vital Learning LLC, pg 932

GEORGIA
Guerrilla Productions LLC, pg 774

MASSACHUSETTS
Duxbury Systems Inc, pg 748

MICHIGAN
K&R All Media Productions LLC,
pg 796

OHIO
R&B Communications Inc, pg 870

RHODE ISLAND
Sound-FX-Design, pg 894

ONTARIO
Technovision® Interactive Inc,
pg 909

Reading & Tachistoscopic Equipment & Learning System Rentals

CALIFORNIA
Ametron Audio/Video, pg 684

GEORGIA
Staging Directions Inc, pg 899

Software & Courseware— Microcomputer, *see* Microcomputer Software & Courseware

Study Print Distributors

CALIFORNIA
Health Education Services, pg 778
Social Studies School Service,
pg 891

ILLINOIS
Encyclopaedia Britannica Inc,
pg 754

MARYLAND
Department of Education Resources,
pg 740

NORTH CAROLINA
Carolina Biological Supply Co,
pg 717

WISCONSIN
School Specialty Inc, pg 882

Study Print Producers

CALIFORNIA
QRS Software Services, pg 867

COLORADO
Crystal Productions, pg 735

GEORGIA
Guerrilla Productions LLC, pg 774

KENTUCKY
National Geographic Learning,
pg 836

MARYLAND
Department of Education Resources,
pg 740

MICHIGAN
K&R All Media Productions LLC,
pg 796

NORTH CAROLINA
Carolina Biological Supply Co,
pg 717
World Class Learning Materials Inc,
pg 941

OHIO
R&B Communications Inc, pg 870

PENNSYLVANIA
Innovision Media Group, pg 788
JPL, pg 795

RHODE ISLAND
Sound-FX-Design, pg 894

Study Print Rentals

GEORGIA
Staging Directions Inc, pg 899

Tachistoscopic Equipment, *see* Reading & Tachistoscopic Equipment & Learning System

MISCELLANEOUS

Analyzer, *see* **Battery, Charger & Analyzer**

Battery, Charger & Analyzer Distributors

ARIZONA

EAR Professional Audio/Video, pg 749
Metropolitan Audio-Visual Inc, pg 824
Troxell-CDI, pg 918

CALIFORNIA

Ametron Audio/Video, pg 684
Audio/Video Supply Inc, pg 694
Band Pro Film & Digital Inc, pg 701
BigFoot Mobile Systems, pg 705
BroadcastStore.com, pg 711
California Tape Products Inc, pg 714
Christy's Editorial, pg 723
CinemaGear, pg 724
Filmtools®, pg 761
Gluskin's Custom Audio Video, pg 771
Alan Gordon Enterprises Inc, pg 772
Hooper Camera & Imaging, pg 781
IDX System Technology Inc, pg 784
Jameco Electronics, pg 792
JD Audio Visual Inc, pg 793
Kappa optronics, pg 796
Location Sound Corp, pg 810
Mole-Richardson Co, pg 829
Orvac Electronics, pg 848
Pacific Radio Electronics, pg 849
Point of View Productions, pg 858
Pro Camera Repair, pg 862
Pro Power Products Inc, pg 863
Promax Systems, pg 865
SimpliPhi Power Inc, pg 889
SNAP, pg 891
Sound Service Co, pg 894
SSL Industries Inc, pg 898
Total Concept Sales, pg 916
VTP Inc, pg 933
Zack Electronics Inc, pg 945

COLORADO

Daylight Productions & Rentals, pg 739
Mike's Camera, pg 827
Spectrum Audio Visual Services, pg 897
Stanco Sales LLC, pg 899

CONNECTICUT

MAVCO, pg 820
Sennheiser Electronic Corp, pg 884
Vitec Videocom Inc, pg 932

FLORIDA

Access Media Group, pg 673
AudioVideoElectric, pg 695
Digital Video Systems, pg 742
Enhanced View Services Inc, pg 754
Hi-Tech Enterprises Inc, pg 779
Hi-Tech Import Export Corp, pg 779
Midtown Video Inc, pg 827
ONstage, pg 846
Recording Media & Equipment Inc (RM&E), pg 872
Reef Photo & Video, pg 872
TAI Audio, pg 906
Techni-Lux Inc, pg 908
Test Equipment Connection, pg 911

GEORGIA

Blue Media Supply Inc, pg 707
Boxlight Inc, pg 709
Lighting & Production Equipment Inc, pg 807
Stage Front Presentation Systems, pg 899
Synergistic Batteries Inc, pg 906

ILLINOIS

Joseph Electronics, pg 795
Tele-Time Systems, pg 910

INDIANA

Jack's Camera Shop, pg 792
Lee Co Inc, pg 805

IOWA

Sitler's Supplies Inc, pg 890

KANSAS

Lights On, pg 808

KENTUCKY

Barney Miller's Inc, pg 827
NOR-COM Inc, pg 841

MARYLAND

Noventri, pg 843

MASSACHUSETTS

Advanced Battery Systems Inc, pg 677
Terry Hanley Audio Systems Inc, pg 775
Hunt's Photo & Video, pg 782
Integrated Solutions Group, pg 789
JENSEN Tools + Supply, pg 793
Rule Boston Camera, pg 878

MICHIGAN

Lowing Light & Grip Inc, pg 812

MINNESOTA

Alpha Video & Audio Inc, pg 682

MISSISSIPPI

Bowie Audio Visual Enterprises Inc, pg 709

MISSOURI

Communitronics Corp, pg 729
Southwest Audio-Visual Inc, pg 895

NEBRASKA

VSA Inc, pg 933

NEVADA

Aardvark Video & Media Productions, pg 671
L E Nelson Sales Corp, pg 838
Power Sonic Corp, pg 860

NEW JERSEY

Alltec Stores, a Vcom IMC Company, pg 681
AlltecPro, pg 681
Argraph Corp, pg 688
Audio Visual Associates, pg 694
AV Bluebook, pg 696
Comprehensive Cable & Connectivity Co, pg 729
Frezzi Energy Systems, pg 766
G&G Technologies Inc, pg 768
HamiltonBuhl, pg 775
MCCOM Inc, pg 820
Panasonic Industrial Devices Sales Company of America, pg 850
Starlite, pg 900
SYMCO Inc, pg 905
ToCad America Inc, pg 915
Total Video Products Inc, pg 916

NEW YORK

Adwar Video, pg 678
Audio-Video Corp, pg 694
AV Workshop, pg 697
B&H Photo Video, pg 701
Barbizon Electric Co Inc, pg 701
BTX Technologies, pg 712
Bulbtronics Inc, pg 712
Creative Stage Lighting Co Inc, pg 733
Film Emporium, pg 760
Gaylord Archival, pg 768
HAVE Inc, pg 777
Long Island Video Enterprises Live Inc, pg 811
Markertek Video Supply, pg 817
Neptune Photo Inc, pg 838
RNJ Electronics, pg 875
RTS Inc, pg 878
Russell Industries Inc, pg 879
Scientifics Direct Inc, pg 882
TecNec Distributing, pg 909
The Tiffen Co LLC, pg 914
Topbulb, a Semmer Lighting Company, pg 915
Tri-Ed Distribution Inc, pg 918
VARTA Microbattery Inc, pg 925
Visual Technologies Corp, pg 932
Visual Word Systems Inc, pg 932
Xtech Systems Inc, pg 943

NORTH CAROLINA

Harrison Brothers, pg 776
Strategic Connections, pg 901
Verbatim Americas LLC, pg 926

OHIO

Copp Integrated Systems, pg 731
Midwest Photo Exchange, pg 827
Parts Express, pg 851
Tri-State Audio Visual Co, pg 918
Vanner Inc, pg 924

OKLAHOMA

Ford AV, pg 763

PENNSYLVANIA

Advanced AV LLC, pg 677
Audio Visions Inc, pg 694
Bernie's Photo Center, pg 704
J E Foss Co, pg 764
Garcia Marketing Inc, pg 768
The Lerro Corp, pg 806
Morefield Communications Inc, pg 830
New York Camera & Video, pg 840
Techni-Tool, a TestEquity LLC company, pg 908
Wire X 17 LLC, pg 940

TENNESSEE

Allstar Audio Systems Inc, pg 681
Lowrance Sound Co Inc, pg 812

TEXAS

Audio Visual Technologies Group (AVTG), pg 695
MarathonNorco Aerospace Inc, pg 816
Omega Broadcast Group, pg 845
Precision Camera & Video, pg 861
Pro Video & Film Equipment Co Inc, pg 863
Specialized Products Co, pg 896
Tarpley Media Systems, pg 907
TWIST Integration Solutions Technology, pg 920

UTAH

Performance Audio LLC, pg 854
Redman Movies & Stories, pg 872
RIA Corp, pg 874

VERMONT

Production Advantage Inc, pg 863

VIRGINIA

Avitecture Inc, pg 699
Boitnott Visual Communications Corp (BVC), pg 708
Lee Hartman & Sons Inc, pg 805
Thomas & Betts Power Solutions LLC, pg 912

WASHINGTON

Alpha Technologies Inc, pg 681
Oppenheimer Camera Products, pg 847
Proforma Good Wood Marketing, pg 865

WISCONSIN

Alpha Source Inc, pg 681
Audio Visual of Milwaukee Inc, pg 694
Camera Corner Connecting Point, pg 715
Full Compass Systems, pg 767
Safe Harbor Computers, pg 879

PUERTO RICO

Bonnin Electronics Inc, pg 708

ALBERTA

Infosat Communications Inc, pg 787
Matrix Video Communications Corp (MVCC), pg 819
McBain Camera Ltd, pg 820

BRITISH COLUMBIA

Cadex Electronics Inc, pg 713

MANITOBA

Inland Audio Visual Ltd, pg 788

ONTARIO

HD Source, pg 777
Henry's Camera, pg 779
Nationwide Audio Visual Co, pg 837

QUEBEC

Panavideo Inc, pg 850
SC Media Canada, pg 881

Battery, Charger & Analyzer Manufacturers

CALIFORNIA

Apogee Electronics Corp, pg 687
FrontRow, pg 766
IDX System Technology Inc, pg 784
Kappa optronics Inc, pg 796
Pro Power Products Inc, pg 863
SimpliPhi Power Inc, pg 889
Visual Instrumentation Corp, pg 931

COLORADO

Liberty AV Solutions, pg 807

CONNECTICUT

Anton/Bauer®, pg 686

FLORIDA

Chauvet Lighting, pg 721

GEORGIA

Synergistic Batteries Inc, pg 906

ILLINOIS

Cool-Lux, pg 731
Smith-Victor Corp, pg 891
Tripp Lite, pg 918

NEVADA

Power Sonic Corp, pg 860

NEW JERSEY

Dyna-Lite Inc, pg 748
Frezzi Energy Systems, pg 766
Nova Electric, pg 843
Panasonic Industrial Devices Sales Company of America, pg 850
ToCad America Inc, pg 915

NEW YORK

Cine 60 Inc, pg 723
Sima Products Corp, pg 888
Ultralife Corporation, pg 920
VARTA Microbattery Inc, pg 925

NORTH CAROLINA

Verbatim Americas LLC, pg 926

OHIO

Vanner Inc, pg 924

PENNSYLVANIA

Wire X 17 LLC, pg 940

RHODE ISLAND

APC by Schneider Electric, pg 686

TEXAS

Exeltech Inc, pg 757
MarathonNorco Aerospace Inc, pg 816

VIRGINIA

Thomas & Betts Power Solutions LLC, pg 912

WASHINGTON

Alpha Technologies Inc, pg 681
Oppenheimer Camera Products, pg 847

WISCONSIN

Marinco Electrical Group, pg 817

BRITISH COLUMBIA

Cadex Electronics Inc, pg 713

Battery, Charger & Analyzer Rentals

ALASKA

Connections Film & Video Inc, pg 731

ARIZONA

Merestone, pg 823
Metropolitan Audio-Visual Inc, pg 824
Reel Men Rentals Inc, pg 872

ARKANSAS

White Diamond Productions LLC, pg 937

CALIFORNIA

Acey Decy Lighting, pg 674
Action Audio & Visual, pg 675
Alternative Rentals, pg 682
Ametron Audio/Video, pg 684
Artichoke Productions, pg 690
Bexel, an NEP Broadcast Services Company, pg 704
Chater Camera Inc, pg 721
Crystal Pyramid Productions™, pg 735
Express Media Inc, pg 757
First Camera, pg 761
Full Moon & High Tide Productions & Studios, pg 767
Gear Monkey, pg 769
Gold Standard Productions, pg 772
Alan Gordon Enterprises Inc, pg 772
iCorpTv, pg 783
Image Integration, pg 785
Main Street Media Inc, pg 815
Munday & Collins AV, pg 834
Otto Nemenz International Inc, pg 838
Next Arts, pg 841
Old School Cameras, pg 844
Prime Cut Productions, pg 862
Pro HD Rentals, pg 863
Radiant Images, pg 869
RetinaVision Productions, pg 874
Samy's Camera, pg 879
Shooting Star Video, pg 886
SNAP, pg 891
Stray Angel Films, pg 902
T-stop Inc, pg 906
Total Creative, pg 916
Twin Peaks Creative, pg 920
VER, pg 926
Visual Instrumentation Corp, pg 931
VMI Inc, pg 932
Voice & Video Rentals, pg 932
Westcoast Video Productions Inc, pg 936

COLORADO

Daylight Productions & Rentals, pg 739
Tatum Video, pg 907

CONNECTICUT

A/V Davey, pg 697
Videofilm Systems Inc, pg 929

FLORIDA

Access Media Group, pg 673
Budget Video Rentals, pg 712
Jordan Klein Film & Video (JKFV), pg 795
Knowles Video Inc (KVI), pg 800
Midtown Video Inc, pg 827
ONstage, pg 846
Universal Studios Florida® Production Group, pg 922

GEORGIA

Lighting & Production Equipment Inc, pg 807
Stage Front Presentation Systems, pg 899

HAWAII

Sight & Sound Studios, pg 887

ILLINOIS

Backstar Creative Media Inc, pg 700
Beatty TeleVisual Productions, pg 703
On Site Video, pg 846
RC Communications, pg 870
Resolution Productions Group, pg 874
Tele-Time Systems, pg 910

KANSAS

Lights On, pg 808

KENTUCKY

Audio Visual Techniques Inc, pg 695
Kentucky Grip & Lighting, pg 798

LOUISIANA

Pace Systems, pg 849

MARYLAND

Archai Media, pg 688

MASSACHUSETTS

Capron Lighting & Sound Co Inc, pg 716
Terry Hanley Audio Systems Inc, pg 775
Integrated Solutions Group, pg 789
WVP Boston, pg 942

MICHIGAN

Digi Sign Design LLC, pg 741
K&R All Media Productions LLC, pg 796
K&R's Recording Studios Inc, pg 796
Lowing Light & Grip Inc, pg 812

MINNESOTA

Pro Media Productions, pg 863

MISSISSIPPI

Bowie Audio Visual Enterprises Inc, pg 709

MISSOURI

Show-Me Audio-Visual, pg 887

NEBRASKA

Lights On Nebraska, pg 808

NEW HAMPSHIRE

Apertura, pg 686

NEW JERSEY

CFP Video Productions Inc, pg 720
Dyna-Lite Inc, pg 748
Video Corporation of America (VCA), pg 927

NEW MEXICO

Production Outfitters, pg 864

NEW YORK

Adorama Rental Co, pg 676
Adwar Video, pg 678
Big Foot Productions Inc, pg 705
Bond Street Studio, pg 708
Cine 60 Inc, pg 723
Cinema-Vision, pg 724
CPT Rental Inc, pg 732
CSI Rentals, pg 735
Hand Held Films, pg 775
LightHouse Films, pg 807
Long Island Video Enterprises Live Inc, pg 811
Scheimpflug Digital, pg 881
Tri-Ed Distribution Inc, pg 918
Visual Technologies Corp, pg 932
Xtech Systems Inc, pg 943

NORTH CAROLINA

The Communications Group Inc, pg 729
Duke Media Services, pg 747
Moving Pictures, pg 832
On Location North Carolina, pg 846
Special Event Services, pg 896
Take One Productions Ltd, pg 906

NORTH DAKOTA

Media Productions, pg 822

OHIO

ITA Audio Visual Solutions, pg 791
Lyon Video Inc, pg 813
Ohio HD Video, pg 844
R&B Communications Inc, pg 870

OKLAHOMA

PDC Productions, pg 852

OREGON

Koerner Camera Systems, pg 800
Northwest Film Center, pg 842

PENNSYLVANIA

Advanced AV LLC, pg 677
Bernie's Photo Center, pg 704
JPL, pg 795
Location Camera Ltd, pg 810
Location Lighting Ltd, pg 810
Muderick Media, pg 833
New York Camera & Video, pg 840
The Videohouse Inc, pg 929
Visual Sound Inc, pg 931

TENNESSEE

Allstar Audio Systems Inc, pg 681
RentACamera.com, pg 873

TEXAS

GEAR Cameras & Lighting, pg 769
Omega Broadcast Group, pg 845
South Coast Film & Video, pg 895
Stage Directions, pg 898

MISCELLANEOUS

Battery, Charger & Analyzer Rentals (continued)

TEXAS (continued)

Texcam Inc, pg 911
Video Perspective, pg 928

UTAH

Ron Hill Imagery, pg 780
Performance Audio LLC, pg 854
Redman Movies & Stories, pg 872

VERMONT

Dark Star Lighting & Production, pg 737

WASHINGTON

Oppenheimer Camera Products, pg 847

WISCONSIN

Camera Corner Connecting Point, pg 715
Full Compass Systems, pg 767

WYOMING

Bridger Productions Inc, pg 710

ALBERTA

Global TV, pg 771

BRITISH COLUMBIA

Triad Communications Ltd, pg 918
Video Out Distribution, pg 928

ONTARIO

HD Source, pg 777
JIB Shots Equipment Inc, pg 794
RB Productions, pg 870
William F White International Inc, pg 937
ZTV Broadcast Services Inc, pg 945

QUEBEC

Group PVP, pg 774

Battery, Charger & Analyzer Repairs

CALIFORNIA

Ametron Audio/Video, pg 684
BroadcastStore.com, pg 711
McAlister Electronics, pg 820
Pro Power Products Inc, pg 863
TEK Media Group, pg 909
Visual Instrumentation Corp, pg 931

CONNECTICUT

Vitec Videocom Inc, pg 932

FLORIDA

ELC Sales & Service Inc, pg 752

GEORGIA

Stage Front Presentation Systems, pg 899

ILLINOIS

Midwest Digital Corp, pg 827
On Site Video, pg 846

KENTUCKY

NOR-COM Inc, pg 841

MICHIGAN

Lowing Light & Grip Inc, pg 812

NEW JERSEY

Dyna-Lite Inc, pg 748
Frezzi Energy Systems, pg 766

NEW YORK

Adwar Video, pg 678
Cine 60 Inc, pg 723
CPT Rental Inc, pg 732
Visual Technologies Corp, pg 932
Xtech Systems Inc, pg 943

OHIO

Vanner Inc, pg 924

PENNSYLVANIA

Bernie's Photo Center, pg 704

TEXAS

MarathonNorco Aerospace Inc, pg 816
Pro Video & Film Equipment Co Inc, pg 863
Tarpley Media Systems, pg 907

UTAH

RIA Corp, pg 874

WASHINGTON

Alpha Technologies Inc, pg 681
Oppenheimer Camera Products, pg 847

WISCONSIN

Camera Corner Connecting Point, pg 715
Full Compass Systems, pg 767

ALBERTA

Infosat Communications Inc, pg 787

ONTARIO

HD Source, pg 777

Blinds, see Room-Darkening Drape & Blind

Cabinet—Storage, see Storage Cabinet

Carrying Case, see Shipping, Packaging, Carrying & Storage Case

Charger, see Battery, Charger & Analyzer

Clock, see Timer & Clock

Control Equipment, see Lighting Fixture & Control Equipment

Drapes, see Room-Darkening Drape & Blind

Dust Elimination Equipment Distributors

CALIFORNIA

Educational Technology Services (ETS), pg 751
Gluskin's Custom Audio Video, pg 771
Jameco Electronics, pg 792
Media Fabricators Inc, pg 822
Samy's Camera, pg 879

CONNECTICUT

MAVCO, pg 820

FLORIDA

Midtown Video Inc, pg 827

GEORGIA

Stage Front Presentation Systems, pg 899

KENTUCKY

K&R PhotoDigital, pg 796
NOR-COM Inc, pg 841
WaxWorks VideoWorks, pg 934

MASSACHUSETTS

Hunt's Photo & Video, pg 782
Spirig Advanced Technologies Inc (SAT), pg 897

NEW JERSEY

AlltecPro, pg 681
Argraph Corp, pg 688
AV Bluebook, pg 696
Falcon Safety Products Inc, pg 758

NEW YORK

AV Workshop, pg 697
Get Smart Products, pg 770
Light Impressions, pg 807
Markertek Video Supply, pg 817
NRD Static Control LLC, pg 843
TecNec Distributing, pg 909
Tri-Ed Distribution Inc, pg 918

PENNSYLVANIA

Bernie's Photo Center, pg 704
Charles Beseler Co, pg 721
Techni-Tool, a TestEquity LLC company, pg 908

TEXAS

Specialized Products Co, pg 896

VIRGINIA

Lee Hartman & Sons Inc, pg 805

WISCONSIN

Full Compass Systems, pg 767

PUERTO RICO

Bonnin Electronics Inc, pg 708

ALBERTA

McBain Camera Ltd, pg 820

QUEBEC

SC Media Canada, pg 881

Dust Elimination Equipment Manufacturers

FLORIDA

Kinetronics Corp, pg 799

ILLINOIS

Sprayway Inc, pg 898

MASSACHUSETTS

Spirig Advanced Technologies Inc (SAT), pg 897

NEW JERSEY

Falcon Safety Products Inc, pg 758

NEW YORK

NRD Static Control LLC, pg 843

PENNSYLVANIA

Nilfisk Inc, pg 841

Dust Elimination Equipment Rentals

FLORIDA

Jordan Klein Film & Video (JKFV), pg 795

GEORGIA

Stage Front Presentation Systems, pg 899

NORTH CAROLINA

Take One Productions Ltd, pg 906

PENNSYLVANIA

Bernie's Photo Center, pg 704

UTAH

Redman Movies & Stories, pg 872

Dust Elimination Equipment Repairs

GEORGIA

Stage Front Presentation Systems, pg 899

KENTUCKY

NOR-COM Inc, pg 841

PENNSYLVANIA

Bernie's Photo Center, pg 704

Electrical Generator Distributors

CALIFORNIA

Ametron Audio/Video, pg 684
Angstrom Lighting, pg 685
Mole-Richardson Co, pg 829
Phoebus Manufacturing, pg 855

FLORIDA

ONstage, pg 846
Recording Media & Equipment Inc
 (RM&E), pg 872

GEORGIA

Lighting & Production Equipment
 Inc, pg 807

ILLINOIS

Joseph Electronics, pg 795

MARYLAND

Absolute Hollywood, pg 672

MASSACHUSETTS

High Output Inc, pg 779

NEW YORK

All Mobile Video Inc, pg 680
Long Island Video Enterprises Live
 Inc, pg 811

PENNSYLVANIA

Techni-Tool, a TestEquity LLC
 company, pg 908

TENNESSEE

Allstar Audio Systems Inc, pg 681

TEXAS

MQ Power Corp, pg 832
Pro Video & Film Equipment Co
 Inc, pg 863
Specialized Products Co, pg 896

UTAH

RIA Corp, pg 874

PUERTO RICO

Bonnin Electronics Inc, pg 708

ALBERTA

McBain Camera Ltd, pg 820

BRITISH COLUMBIA

DL Sound & Lighting Productions
 Ltd, pg 744

ONTARIO

Nationwide Audio Visual Co,
 pg 837

Electrical Generator Manufacturers

CALIFORNIA

Mole-Richardson Co, pg 829
Phoebus Manufacturing, pg 855

FLORIDA

Compuvideo Sales USA Ltd,
 pg 729

MARYLAND

Teledyne Energy Systems Inc,
 pg 910

NEW JERSEY

Nova Electric, pg 843

OHIO

Norlake Manufacturing Co, pg 842

TEXAS

MQ Power Corp, pg 832

Electrical Generator Rentals

ALABAMA

Audio-Video Resources Inc, pg 694

ARIZONA

Arizona Cine Equipment, pg 688

CALIFORNIA

Acey Decy Lighting, pg 674
AGF Media Services, pg 678
Ametron Audio/Video, pg 684
Angstrom Lighting, pg 685
Cherry Multimedia, pg 721
Dadco, pg 737
DTC Lighting & Grip, pg 747
Gear Monkey, pg 769
JD Audio Visual Inc, pg 793
Main Street Media Inc, pg 815
McCune Audio-Video-Lighting,
 pg 821
Mole-Richardson Co, pg 829
Panavision, pg 850
PSAV® Presentation Services,
 pg 866
RetinaVision Productions, pg 874
Total Creative, pg 916

COLORADO

Zelo Productions Inc, pg 945

CONNECTICUT

A/V Davey, pg 697
Videofilm Systems Inc, pg 929

FLORIDA

Budget Video Rentals, pg 712
Jordan Klein Film & Video (JKFV),
 pg 795
MAPS Production House, pg 816
ONstage, pg 846

GEORGIA

Lighting & Production Equipment
 Inc, pg 807
Stage Front Presentation Systems,
 pg 899

HAWAII

FOTON Hawaii, pg 764

ILLINOIS

AV Chicago Inc, pg 696
LITE-IT Grip Truck Rentals, pg 810
On Site Video, pg 846

KANSAS

Lights On, pg 808

KENTUCKY

Audio Visual Techniques Inc,
 pg 695

LOUISIANA

Moxie Media, pg 832
Pace Systems, pg 849

MARYLAND

Event Tech, pg 756

MASSACHUSETTS

Advanced Lighting & Production
 Services Inc (ALPS), pg 677
Capron Lighting & Sound Co Inc,
 pg 716
High Output Inc, pg 779
Limelight Production® Inc, pg 809
massAV, pg 819

MICHIGAN

Digi Sign Design LLC, pg 741
Lowing Light & Grip Inc, pg 812
On Stage Visuals, pg 846

MISSOURI

Show-Me Audio-Visual, pg 887
Sight & Sound Production Services
 Inc, pg 887

NEW JERSEY

CFP Video Productions Inc, pg 720
Ironbound Film & Television
 Studios LLC, pg 791
Starlite, pg 900

NEW YORK

All Terrain Power Co Inc, pg 680
Bond Street Studio, pg 708
Design Audio Visual Inc, pg 741
Eastern Effects Inc, pg 749
Gearhead Rentals, pg 769
LightSpace Studios, pg 808
Long Island Video Enterprises Live
 Inc, pg 811
Production Resource Group LLC
 (PRG), pg 864

NORTH CAROLINA

On Location North Carolina, pg 846
Take One Productions Ltd, pg 906

OKLAHOMA

PDC Productions, pg 852

OREGON

Pacific Grip & Lighting Inc, pg 849
Picture This Production Services,
 pg 856

PENNSYLVANIA

Location Camera Ltd, pg 810
Location Lighting Ltd, pg 810

SOUTH CAROLINA

Studio Charleston, pg 902

TENNESSEE

Allstar Audio Systems Inc, pg 681
DR&A Inc, pg 746

TEXAS

GEAR Cameras & Lighting, pg 769
Muller Entertainment LLC, pg 833
Texcam Inc, pg 911

UTAH

Redman Movies & Stories, pg 872

PUERTO RICO

Stage Crew Audiovisual Inc, pg 898

ALBERTA

Global TV, pg 771

BRITISH COLUMBIA

DL Sound & Lighting Productions
 Ltd, pg 744

ONTARIO

JIB Shots Equipment Inc, pg 794

Electrical Generator Repairs

CALIFORNIA

Ametron Audio/Video, pg 684
Mole-Richardson Co, pg 829

GEORGIA

Lighting & Production Equipment
 Inc, pg 807

MARYLAND

Teledyne Energy Systems Inc,
 pg 910

MASSACHUSETTS

Capron Lighting & Sound Co Inc,
 pg 716
Limelight Production® Inc, pg 809

TEXAS

Pro Video & Film Equipment Co
 Inc, pg 863

UTAH

RIA Corp, pg 874

Equipment Inspection & Testing Device Distributors

CALIFORNIA

Ametron Audio/Video, pg 684
Cinematography Electronics Inc,
 pg 724
Jameco Electronics, pg 792
VTP Inc, pg 933

CONNECTICUT

Gold Line/TEF, pg 772

FLORIDA

Access Media Group, pg 673
Alcorn McBride Inc, pg 679
Digital Video Systems, pg 742
ONstage, pg 846

ILLINOIS

Joseph Electronics, pg 795

MISCELLANEOUS

Equipment Inspection & Testing Device Distributors (continued)

KENTUCKY
NOR-COM Inc, pg 841

MASSACHUSETTS
JENSEN Tools + Supply, pg 793
Rule Boston Camera, pg 878

MICHIGAN
ASC Systems, pg 690

NEW JERSEY
Starlite, pg 900

NEW YORK
Gage-Line Technology Inc, pg 767
Markertek Video Supply, pg 817
Scientifics Direct Inc, pg 882

OHIO
Parts Express, pg 851

PENNSYLVANIA
Techni-Tool, a TestEquity LLC
   company, pg 908

SOUTH DAKOTA
Sencore Inc, pg 883

TEXAS
Specialized Products Co, pg 896

VIRGINIA
Lee Hartman & Sons Inc, pg 805

WISCONSIN
Full Compass Systems, pg 767

Equipment Inspection & Testing Device Manufacturers

ARIZONA
Applied Integration Corp, pg 687
East Arizona Good Luck Enterprises
   Inc, pg 749

CALIFORNIA
Ametek Programmable Power Inc,
   pg 684
Cinematography Electronics Inc,
   pg 724
Emlight Design, pg 753
Extron Electronics, pg 758

CONNECTICUT
Gold Line/TEF, pg 772

FLORIDA
Alcorn McBride Inc, pg 679
Compuvideo Sales USA Ltd,
   pg 729

INDIANA
R B Annis Instruments Inc, pg 686

MINNESOTA
CyberOptics Corp, pg 736

NEW HAMPSHIRE
Monarch Instrument, pg 829

NEW YORK
Broadcast Devices Inc, pg 710
Gage-Line Technology Inc, pg 767
Navitar Inc, pg 837

PENNSYLVANIA
Tobias Associates Inc, pg 915

SOUTH DAKOTA
Sencore Inc, pg 883

TEXAS
National Instruments Corp, pg 836

Equipment Inspection & Testing Device Rentals

CALIFORNIA
Ametron Audio/Video, pg 684
Express Media Inc, pg 757
RetinaVision Productions, pg 874
Twin Peaks Creative, pg 920

CONNECTICUT
Videofilm Systems Inc, pg 929

FLORIDA
Access Media Group, pg 673
ONstage, pg 846

GEORGIA
Stage Front Presentation Systems,
   pg 899

NEW JERSEY
Starlite, pg 900

NORTH CAROLINA
Take One Productions Ltd, pg 906

OHIO
Lyon Video Inc, pg 813

TEXAS
GEAR Cameras & Lighting, pg 769
Texcam Inc, pg 911

WISCONSIN
Full Compass Systems, pg 767

Equipment Inspection & Testing Device Repairs

CALIFORNIA
Ametron Audio/Video, pg 684

KENTUCKY
NOR-COM Inc, pg 841

WISCONSIN
Full Compass Systems, pg 767

Generator, *see* Electrical Generator

Kiosk Distributors

ARKANSAS
Jay S Stanley & Associates Inc,
   pg 899

CALIFORNIA
Cibola Systems, pg 723

COLORADO
KD Kanopy Inc, pg 797

FLORIDA
Alcorn McBride Inc, pg 679
Digital Video Systems, pg 742

KENTUCKY
Axxis Leasing Inc, pg 700
NOR-COM Inc, pg 841

MARYLAND
Noventri, pg 843

MICHIGAN
Digi Sign Design LLC, pg 741

NEW JERSEY
MiB MediaWorks, pg 825

NEW YORK
General Audio-Visual Inc (GAVI),
   pg 769
Visual Technologies Corp, pg 932

NORTH CAROLINA
DNP Imagingcomm America Corp
   (DNP IAM), pg 744

PENNSYLVANIA
Advanced AV LLC, pg 677
Innovision Media Group, pg 788

TENNESSEE
Spring Arbor Distributors Inc,
   pg 898

WISCONSIN
Spectrum Industries Inc, pg 897

MANITOBA
Tek Gear, pg 909

ONTARIO
Cinema Stage Inc, pg 724
GestureTek, pg 770
Technovision® Interactive Inc,
   pg 909

Kiosk Manufacturers

ALABAMA
ExpoDisplays, pg 757
Marco Inc, pg 816

CALIFORNIA
Grande Vitesse Systems Inc (GVS),
   pg 773
International E-Z UP Inc, pg 790

COLORADO
Display Devices Inc, pg 743

CONNECTICUT
Alarmco Intelligent Message
   Repeaters, pg 679

FLORIDA
Alcorn McBride Inc, pg 679
CD ROM™ Inc, pg 718

ILLINOIS
Bretford Manufacturing Inc, pg 710
Marshall Furniture Inc, pg 817

KANSAS
Keywest Technology Inc, pg 798

MARYLAND
Quatrefoil Associates Inc, pg 868

MINNESOTA
Emcor Enclosures-Crenlo, pg 753

NORTH CAROLINA
DNP Imagingcomm America Corp
   (DNP IAM), pg 744

OHIO
Mills James Productions, pg 828

OKLAHOMA
DD Audio, pg 739

TENNESSEE
Adtec Digital Inc, pg 677
Spring Arbor Distributors Inc,
   pg 898

VIRGINIA
Optikinetics Ltd - The Americas,
   pg 847

WISCONSIN
Spectrum Industries Inc, pg 897

BRITISH COLUMBIA
Kodak Graphic Communications
   Canada Co, pg 800

MANITOBA
Big Deal Custom Casings, pg 705
Tek Gear, pg 909

ONTARIO
GestureTek, pg 770
Technovision® Interactive Inc,
   pg 909
Versatruss, pg 926

Kiosk Rentals

CALIFORNIA
Muse Presentation Technologies,
   pg 834

GEORGIA
Stage Front Presentation Systems,
   pg 899

MICHIGAN
Digi Sign Design LLC, pg 741

NEW YORK
Design Audio Visual Inc, pg 741
SmartSource Computer & AV
Rentals, pg 891
Visual Technologies Corp, pg 932

PENNSYLVANIA
Advanced AV LLC, pg 677
FMP Media Solutions Inc, pg 763
Innovision Media Group, pg 788

WISCONSIN
Logan Productions Inc, pg 811

MANITOBA
Tek Gear, pg 909

Kiosk Repairs

KENTUCKY
Axxis Leasing Inc, pg 700
NOR-COM Inc, pg 841

MANITOBA
Big Deal Custom Casings, pg 705
Tek Gear, pg 909

Learning System, *see* Reading & Tachistoscopic Equipment & Learning System

Light Meter Distributors

ARIZONA
Troxell-CDI, pg 918

CALIFORNIA
Ametron Audio/Video, pg 684
Angstrom Lighting, pg 685
Educational Technology Services
(ETS), pg 751
Filmtools®, pg 761
Alan Gordon Enterprises Inc,
pg 772
Hooper Camera & Imaging, pg 781
Mole-Richardson Co, pg 829
Point of View Productions, pg 858
Sacramento Theatrical Lighting Ltd
(STL), pg 879

COLORADO
Mike's Camera, pg 827

CONNECTICUT
Connecticut Audio & Theatrical
Supply, pg 731

FLORIDA
Access Media Group, pg 673
AudioVideoElectric, pg 695
Bay Stage Lighting Co Inc, pg 702
Digital Video Systems, pg 742
ONstage, pg 846
Recording Media & Equipment Inc
(RM&E), pg 872
Test Equipment Connection, pg 911

ILLINOIS
Chicago Spotlight Inc, pg 721
Joseph Electronics, pg 795

KANSAS
Lights On, pg 808

KENTUCKY
NOR-COM Inc, pg 841

MASSACHUSETTS
Hunt's Photo & Video, pg 782
International Light Technologies
Inc, pg 790
JENSEN Tools + Supply, pg 793
Rule Boston Camera, pg 878
University Products Inc, pg 923

MICHIGAN
Fantasee Lighting, pg 759

NEVADA
MeshTel, pg 824

NEW JERSEY
Argraph Corp, pg 688
Manfrotto Distribution Inc, pg 816
Starlite, pg 900

NEW MEXICO
Quickbeam Systems Inc (QSI),
pg 868

NEW YORK
B&H Photo Video, pg 701
Barbizon Electric Co Inc, pg 701
Creative Stage Lighting Co Inc,
pg 733
Markertek Video Supply, pg 817
Neptune Photo Inc, pg 838
RTS Inc, pg 878
Scientifics Direct Inc, pg 882
Sekonic, pg 883
TecNec Distributing, pg 909

OHIO
Midwest Photo Exchange, pg 827

PENNSYLVANIA
Bernie's Photo Center, pg 704
Techni-Tool, a TestEquity LLC
company, pg 908

SOUTH DAKOTA
Sencore Inc, pg 883

TEXAS
Olden Lighting, pg 845
Precision Camera & Video, pg 861
Pro Video & Film Equipment Co
Inc, pg 863

VIRGINIA
Lee Hartman & Sons Inc, pg 805

WASHINGTON
Oppenheimer Camera Products,
pg 847

WISCONSIN
Full Compass Systems, pg 767

MANITOBA
Inland Audio Visual Ltd, pg 788

ONTARIO
Henry's Camera, pg 779

Light Meter Manufacturers

CALIFORNIA
Spectra Cine Inc, pg 897

MASSACHUSETTS
AEMC Instruments, pg 678
International Light Technologies
Inc, pg 790

MICHIGAN
PCO-TECH Inc, pg 852

NEVADA
MeshTel, pg 824

NEW YORK
RTS Inc, pg 878

SOUTH DAKOTA
Sencore Inc, pg 883

ONTARIO
The Optikon Corp, pg 847

QUEBEC
Grass Valley, pg 773

Light Meter Rentals

ARIZONA
Arizona Cine Equipment, pg 688

ARKANSAS
White Diamond Productions LLC,
pg 937

CALIFORNIA
Artichoke Productions, pg 690
Cherry Multimedia, pg 721
Full Moon & High Tide Productions
& Studios, pg 767
Golden Gate Studios, pg 772
New Circuit Films LLC, pg 839

FLORIDA
MAPS Production House, pg 816
ONstage, pg 846

GEORGIA
Stage Front Presentation Systems,
pg 899

HAWAII
FOTON Hawaii, pg 764

LOUISIANA
Available Lighting & Motion
Picture Services Inc, pg 697

MICHIGAN
Fantasee Lighting, pg 759
Lowing Light & Grip Inc, pg 812

NEW JERSEY
Starlite, pg 900

NEW YORK
Bond Street Studio, pg 708

NORTH CAROLINA
Take One Productions Ltd, pg 906

OHIO
Lyon Video Inc, pg 813

OREGON
Northwest Film Center, pg 842

TEXAS
Muller Entertainment LLC, pg 833
Precision Camera & Video, pg 861

UTAH
Redman Movies & Stories, pg 872

MANITOBA
Inland Audio Visual Ltd, pg 788

Light Meter Repairs

CALIFORNIA
Pro Camera Repair, pg 862
Spectra Cine Inc, pg 897

KENTUCKY
NOR-COM Inc, pg 841

MASSACHUSETTS
International Light Technologies
Inc, pg 790

MICHIGAN
Fantasee Lighting, pg 759

NEW YORK
Sekonic, pg 883

TEXAS
Pro Video & Film Equipment Co
Inc, pg 863

Lighting Fixture & Control Equipment Distributors

ARIZONA
Metropolitan Audio-Visual Inc,
pg 824
Tempe Camera, pg 910
David Wexler & Co, pg 936

ARKANSAS
Carlton-Bates Co, pg 717
Jay S Stanley & Associates Inc,
pg 899

CALIFORNIA
Advanced Systems Group LLC,
pg 677
Ametron Audio/Video, pg 684
Angstrom Lighting, pg 685
ARRI Inc, pg 689
Audio/Video Supply Inc, pg 694
Automated Entertainment, pg 696

MISCELLANEOUS

Lighting Fixture & Control Equipment Distributors (continued)

CALIFORNIA (continued)

Band Pro Film & Digital Inc, pg 701
Barger-Lite, pg 702
Birns & Sawyer Inc, pg 706
ChronTrol Corp, pg 723
Cinemills Corp, pg 724
DTC Lighting & Grip, pg 747
Filmtools®, pg 761
Freestyle Photographic Supplies, pg 765
Gluskin's Custom Audio Video, pg 771
Alan Gordon Enterprises Inc, pg 772
Gravity Media, pg 773
Kino Flo Lighting Systems, pg 799
LTM Corp of America, pg 812
Matthews Studio Equipment Inc, pg 820
Mole-Richardson Co, pg 829
Pacific Radio Electronics, pg 849
Phoebus Manufacturing, pg 855
Premier Lighting & Production Co, pg 861
Sacramento Theatrical Lighting Ltd (STL), pg 879
San Diego Stage & Lighting Supply Inc, pg 879
SNAP, pg 891
Thin-Lite Corp, pg 912
Ushio America Inc, pg 924
Visual Instrumentation Corp, pg 931
VTP Inc, pg 933
Wildfire Lighting & Visual Effects, pg 938

COLORADO

Ceavco Audio Visual Company Inc, pg 719
Chimera®, pg 722
Mike's Camera, pg 827
Plume Ltd, pg 858
Spectrum Audio Visual Services, pg 897

CONNECTICUT

Connecticut Audio & Theatrical Supply, pg 731
Lex Products Corp, pg 807
MAVCO, pg 820
Revolution Lighting Technologies Inc, pg 874
Rockwell Communications Inc, pg 876
Vitec Videocom Inc, pg 932

DELAWARE

Actors Attic, pg 675

DISTRICT OF COLUMBIA

Theatrical Technicians Inc (TTI), pg 912

FLORIDA

Access Media Group, pg 673
Alcorn McBride Inc, pg 679
A2D Solutions Inc, pg 692
AudioVideoElectric, pg 695
Bay Stage Lighting Co Inc, pg 702
Digital Lighting Systems Inc, pg 742

Digital Video Systems, pg 742
Enhanced View Services Inc, pg 754
Hi-Tech Enterprises Inc, pg 779
Martin Professional Inc, pg 818
Miami Stagecraft Inc, pg 825
Midtown Video Inc, pg 827
ONstage, pg 846
P&H Crystalite LLC, pg 850
Reef Photo & Video, pg 872
Stage Equipment & Lighting Inc, pg 898
Tallahassee Audio Visual, pg 906
Techni-Lux Inc, pg 908
Union Connector Co Inc, pg 921

GEORGIA

Convergent Media Systems, pg 731
Innocinema, pg 788
Lighting & Production Equipment Inc, pg 807
MAGNUM Companies Ltd, pg 815
Stage Front Presentation Systems, pg 899
WolfVision Inc, pg 940

ILLINOIS

Chicago Spotlight Inc, pg 721
Duray Lighting, pg 748
Grand Stage Co Inc, pg 773
Leedal Inc, pg 805
Photoflex Inc, pg 856
Robertson Worldwide, pg 876
Tele-Time Systems, pg 910

INDIANA

Heart Breaker Entertainment LLC, pg 778
Lee Co Inc, pg 805

KANSAS

EiKO Global LLC, pg 752
Theatrical Services Inc, pg 912

KENTUCKY

NOR-COM Inc, pg 841
Theatre Effects, pg 911
Theatre House Inc, pg 911

LOUISIANA

Available Lighting & Motion Picture Services Inc, pg 697

MARYLAND

Cannon Stage Lighting Inc, pg 716
Event Tech, pg 756
Noventri, pg 843
Parlights Inc, pg 851
RTZ Audio Visual, pg 878
Theatre Service & Supply Corp, pg 912

MASSACHUSETTS

Advanced Lighting & Production Services Inc (ALPS), pg 677
Capron Lighting & Sound Co Inc, pg 716
High Output Inc, pg 779
International Light Technologies Inc, pg 790
Limelight Production® Inc, pg 809
Osram Sylvania Inc, pg 848
Rule Boston Camera, pg 878
Savant Systems LLC, pg 881

MICHIGAN

Fantasee Lighting, pg 759
Lowing Light & Grip Inc, pg 812

On Stage Visuals, pg 846
TEL Systems LLC, pg 909
Tobins Lake Sales, pg 915

MINNESOTA

Alpha Video & Audio Inc, pg 682
AVI Systems, pg 698
Cinequipt Inc, pg 724
Norcostco Inc, pg 842

MISSISSIPPI

Jasper Ewing & Sons Inc, pg 757

MISSOURI

A to Z Theatrical Supply & Service, pg 671
Communitronics Corp, pg 729
Conference Technologies Inc, pg 730
ITC, pg 791
Production Support Services Inc, pg 864
The RapcoHorizon Co, pg 870
Southwest Audio-Visual Inc, pg 895

NEBRASKA

VSA Inc, pg 933

NEVADA

Aardvark Video & Media Productions, pg 671
4 Wall Entertainment, pg 764
L E Nelson Sales Corp, pg 838
Selco Products Co, pg 883

NEW HAMPSHIRE

APS Lighting-Sound-AV, pg 688

NEW JERSEY

AlltecPro, pg 681
Argraph Corp, pg 688
Audio Visual Dynamics®, pg 694
Dazian LLC, pg 739
Dyna-Lite Inc, pg 748
Earl Girls Inc, pg 749
Euro-Pacific Film & Video Productions Inc, pg 756
FlagHouse, pg 762
Frezzi Energy Systems, pg 766
G&G Technologies Inc, pg 768
Leucos USA Inc, pg 806
MCCOM Inc, pg 820
Nelson Enterprises Theatrical Supply Co, pg 838
Outwater Plastics Industries Inc, pg 849
Ritz Camera & Image, pg 875
Starlite, pg 900
SYMCO Inc, pg 905
Total Video Products Inc, pg 916
Varto Technologies, pg 925
Video Corporation of America (VCA), pg 927

NEW MEXICO

Quickbeam Systems Inc (QSI), pg 868

NEW YORK

Ace Video, pg 674
Adwar Video, pg 678
Barbizon Electric Co Inc, pg 701
Bestek Lighting & Staging, pg 704
BMI Supply, pg 708
Bowens USA, pg 709
Bulbtronics Inc, pg 712
Colortone Audio Visual, pg 728

Creative Stage Lighting Co Inc, pg 733
Crescendo Designs Inc, pg 734
Design Audio Visual Inc, pg 741
Just Bulbs - The Light Bulb Store, pg 795
KVL Audio Visual Services Inc, pg 802
Levy NYC Design & Production, pg 806
Long Island Video Enterprises Live Inc, pg 811
MAC Group, pg 813
Markertek Video Supply, pg 817
Mutual Hardware, pg 835
Neptune Photo Inc, pg 838
Production Resource Group LLC (PRG), pg 864
RTS Inc, pg 878
Specialty Bulb Co Inc, pg 896
Syracuse Scenery & Stage Lighting Co Inc, pg 906
TecNec Distributing, pg 909
Theatrical Services & Supplies Inc, pg 912
Topbulb, a Semmer Lighting Company, pg 915
TPR Enterprises Ltd, pg 916
Tri-Ed Distribution Inc, pg 918
Visual Technologies Corp, pg 932

NORTH CAROLINA

Camcor Inc, pg 715
Strategic Connections, pg 901

OHIO

Copp Integrated Systems, pg 731
Future Light Inc, pg 767
ITA Audio Visual Solutions, pg 791
Midwest Photo Exchange, pg 827
Partech Lighting Systems Inc, pg 851
Vincent Lighting Systems, pg 930

OKLAHOMA

Ford AV, pg 763

OREGON

Hollywood Lights Inc, pg 780
Pacific Grip & Lighting Inc, pg 849

PENNSYLVANIA

Advanced AV LLC, pg 677
Audio Visions Inc, pg 694
Bernie's Photo Center, pg 704
Charles Beseler Co, pg 721
Garcia Marketing Inc, pg 768
Hite Co, pg 780
Lehigh Electric Products Co, pg 806
Location Lighting Ltd, pg 810
New York Camera & Video, pg 840
Vistacom Inc, pg 931

TENNESSEE

Allstar Audio Systems Inc, pg 681
Kozmic Lazer Show LLC, pg 801
Lowrance Sound Co Inc, pg 812
Memphis Communications Corp, pg 823
Technical Support Systems LLC, pg 908
TOMCAT USA Inc, pg 915

TEXAS

Audio Visual Technologies Group (AVTG), pg 695
Biway Media, pg 706
Cinema Antiques, pg 723
Communilux Productions, pg 729

Crossroads Audio Inc, pg 735
High End Systems Inc, pg 779
Hisco Inc, pg 780
Olden Lighting, pg 845
Omega Broadcast Group, pg 845
Philips Entertainment Lighting, pg 855
Precision Camera & Video, pg 861
Pro Video & Film Equipment Co Inc, pg 863
Sky-View Search Lights & Promotions, pg 890
Strand Lighting Inc, pg 901
Tarpley Media Systems, pg 907
TWIST Integration Solutions Technology, pg 920

UTAH

Performance Audio LLC, pg 854
Redman Movies & Stories, pg 872
RIA Corp, pg 874

VERMONT

Dark Star Lighting & Production, pg 737
Production Advantage Inc, pg 863

VIRGINIA

Avitecture Inc, pg 699
Intellidyne LLC, pg 789
Lee Hartman & Sons Inc, pg 805
StageSound, pg 899
The Whitlock Group, pg 937

WASHINGTON

CCI Solutions, pg 718
Inland Audio Visual Co, pg 788
Oppenheimer Camera Products, pg 847
PNTA, pg 858

WEST VIRGINIA

United Sound & Electronics, pg 921

WISCONSIN

Audio Visual of Milwaukee Inc, pg 694
Camera Corner Connecting Point, pg 715
Full Compass Systems, pg 767

ALBERTA

Allstar Show Industries Inc, pg 681
Evolution AV, pg 757
Johnson Systems Inc (JSI), pg 794
McBain Camera Ltd, pg 820

MANITOBA

Inland Audio Visual Ltd, pg 788
Lank/Beach Productions Inc, pg 803

ONTARIO

AC Lighting Inc, pg 672
Cinema Stage Inc, pg 724
The Fluorescent Co Inc, pg 763
HD Source, pg 777
Henry's Camera, pg 779
Kingsway Motion Picture Inc, pg 799
Nationwide Audio Visual Co, pg 837
Westbury National Show Systems Ltd, pg 936

Lighting Fixture & Control Equipment Manufacturers

ALABAMA

Centralite Systems Inc, pg 719

CALIFORNIA

AMX® by Harman, pg 685
ARRI Inc, pg 689
Automated Entertainment, pg 696
Auton Motorized Systems, pg 696
B-K Lighting, pg 700
Barger-Lite, pg 702
California Stainless Manufacturing Inc, pg 714
ChronTrol Corp, pg 723
Cinemills Corp, pg 724
Dreamscape Lighting Mfg Inc, pg 746
Doug Fleenor Design Inc, pg 762
Kino Flo Lighting Systems, pg 799
LEDtronics Inc, pg 805
The Lighting Design Alliance, pg 807
LTM Corp of America, pg 812
Luminys Systems Corp, pg 812
Matthews Studio Equipment Inc, pg 820
Mole-Richardson Co, pg 829
Phoebus Manufacturing, pg 855
Spectra Cine Inc, pg 897
Thin-Lite Corp, pg 912
Ushio America Inc, pg 924
Videssence, pg 930
Visual Instrumentation Corp, pg 931
Wildfire Lighting & Visual Effects, pg 938

COLORADO

Chimera®, pg 722
Plume Ltd, pg 858
Ultimate Support Systems Inc, pg 920

CONNECTICUT

Anton/Bauer®, pg 686
Hubbell Wiring Device-Kellems, pg 782
ITT Veam LLC, pg 791
Lex Products Corp, pg 807
Revolution Lighting Technologies Inc, pg 874
Superior Electric, pg 904
Titus Technological Laboratories (TTL), pg 914

DISTRICT OF COLUMBIA

Theatrical Technicians Inc (TTI), pg 912

FLORIDA

Alcorn McBride Inc, pg 679
Chauvet Lighting, pg 721
Digital Lighting Systems Inc, pg 742
Martin Professional Inc, pg 818
P&H Crystalite LLC, pg 850
Techni-Lux Inc, pg 908
Union Connector Co Inc, pg 921
Vutec Corp, pg 933

GEORGIA

Acuity Brands Lighting Inc, pg 675
WolfVision Inc, pg 940

ILLINOIS

Cool-Lux, pg 731
Duray Lighting, pg 748
Helix Camera & Video, pg 778
Leedal Inc, pg 805
Photoflex Inc, pg 856
Photogenic Professional Lighting, pg 856
Robertson Worldwide, pg 876
Smith-Victor Corp, pg 891

KANSAS

EiKO Global LLC, pg 752

MARYLAND

Absolute Hollywood, pg 672

MASSACHUSETTS

Capron Lighting & Sound Co Inc, pg 716
Dedotec USA Inc, pg 740
International Light Technologies Inc, pg 790
Osram Sylvania Inc, pg 848
Pelican Products Inc, pg 853
Savant Systems LLC, pg 881

MICHIGAN

Leprecon®, pg 806
Littlite LLC, pg 810
Lowing Light & Grip Inc, pg 812

MINNESOTA

Emcor Enclosures-Crenlo, pg 753

MISSOURI

Dazor Lighting Technology LLC, pg 739

NEBRASKA

Strong Cinema Products, pg 902

NEW HAMPSHIRE

ProPhotonix Ltd, pg 865

NEW JERSEY

AlltecPro, pg 681
Crestron Electronics Inc, pg 734
Dazian LLC, pg 739
De Sisti Lighting/I-Light Corp USA, pg 739
Dyna-Lite Inc, pg 748
Frezzi Energy Systems, pg 766
Hanovia Specialty Lighting LLC, pg 775
Hasselblad Bron Inc, pg 776
Leucos USA Inc, pg 806
Philips Lightolier, pg 855
Philips Stonco, pg 855
Pro-Tape & Specialities Inc, pg 863

NEW YORK

Creative Stage Lighting Co Inc, pg 733
Edison Price Lighting Inc, pg 750
Estiluz Inc, pg 755
Gagne Inc, pg 767
Group One Ltd, pg 774
GTI (Graphic Technology Inc), pg 774
Legion Lighting Co Inc, pg 806
Levy NYC Design & Production, pg 806
Lighting Services Inc, pg 808
LightTech Group Inc, pg 808
Navitar Inc, pg 837
Swivelier, pg 905

Theatrical Services & Supplies Inc, pg 912
The Tiffen Co LLC, pg 914
TPR Enterprises Ltd, pg 916
WAC Lighting Co, pg 933

NORTH CAROLINA

Strategic Connections, pg 901
Sunnex Inc, pg 904

OHIO

Future Light Inc, pg 767
Janson Industries, pg 793
The Will-Burt Co, pg 938

OREGON

Leviton LES (Lighting & Energy Solutions), pg 806
Magic Gadgets™, pg 814

PENNSYLVANIA

Brightline LP, pg 710
Charles Beseler Co, pg 721
Lehigh Electric Products Co, pg 806

SOUTH CAROLINA

Columbia Lighting, pg 728
Prescolite, pg 861

TENNESSEE

Kozmic Lazer Show LLC, pg 801
Mystery Electronics LLC, pg 835
TOMCAT USA Inc, pg 915

TEXAS

High End Systems Inc, pg 779
Philips Entertainment Lighting, pg 855
Philips Lighting Controls, pg 855
Sky-View Search Lights & Promotions, pg 890
Strand Lighting Inc, pg 901
Texas Scenic Co Inc, pg 911

UTAH

Vantage Controls, a Legrand AV Inc brand, pg 924

VERMONT

Verilux® - The Healthy Lighting Co, pg 926

VIRGINIA

Applied Electronics, pg 687
Lightronics Inc, pg 808
Optikinetics Ltd - The Americas, pg 847

WISCONSIN

ETC, pg 756

ALBERTA

Johnson Systems Inc (JSI), pg 794
Pathway Connectivity, pg 852

ONTARIO

The Fluorescent Co Inc, pg 763
Osram Sylvania Ltd/Ltee, pg 848
Technovision® Interactive Inc, pg 909

MISCELLANEOUS

Lighting Fixture & Control Equipment Rentals

ALASKA

Imig Audio/Video Inc, pg 786

ARIZONA

Arizona Cine Equipment, pg 688
AV Concepts Inc, pg 696
Broadcast Rentals, pg 711
Creative Backstage, pg 733
Glendale Media Center, pg 771
Merestone, pg 823
Metropolitan Audio-Visual Inc, pg 824
Reel Men Rentals Inc, pg 872
Tempe Camera, pg 910
Video West Inc, pg 929

CALIFORNIA

Absolute Rentals, pg 672
Acey Decy Lighting, pg 674
Action Audio & Visual, pg 675
AGF Media Services, pg 678
All Access Staging & Productions, pg 680
Alternative Rentals, pg 682
Ametron Audio/Video, pg 684
Angstrom Lighting, pg 685
Arc Light Efx Inc, pg 688
Artichoke Productions, pg 690
ATV Video Center Inc, pg 692
Automated Entertainment, pg 696
AV Guys, pg 697
Birns & Sawyer Inc, pg 706
The Camera Division, pg 715
Chater Camera Inc, pg 721
Cherry Multimedia, pg 721
Cinema Camera Rentals, pg 723
Cinemills Corp, pg 724
Clean Slate Video, pg 726
Crash Video Productions, pg 733
Crystal Pyramid Productions™, pg 735
Dadco, pg 737
Digital Film Studios LLC, pg 742
DTC Lighting & Grip, pg 747
Dystopian Studios, pg 748
Express Video Supply Inc, pg 757
Flashback Stage Lighting (FBSL), pg 762
Flip 2 Media Inc, pg 762
Fuller Street Productions, pg 767
Gear Monkey, pg 769
Gold Standard Productions, pg 772
Golden Gate Studios, pg 772
Alan Gordon Enterprises Inc, pg 772
Greenery Studios, pg 774
HDrental.com, pg 777
iCorpTv, pg 783
Illuminate Studios, pg 784
Imagecraft Productions, pg 785
Images in Motion Media Inc, pg 785
JFA Studio, pg 794
Laurel Canyon Stages, pg 804
Loyal Studios, pg 812
Luminys Systems Corp, pg 812
Main Street Media Inc, pg 815
McCune Audio-Video-Lighting, pg 821
Mole-Richardson Co, pg 829
MSI Production Services, pg 832
Next Arts, pg 841
North County Media Center, pg 842
On-Trax Inc, pg 846
Panavision, pg 850

Photo Film Stage, pg 856
Pollution Studios, pg 859
Power & Light, pg 860
Premier Lighting & Production Co, pg 861
Pro HD Rentals, pg 863
The Producer's Loft, pg 863
Production Gear Rentals (PGR), pg 863
Pyxis Industries Inc, pg 867
RED Studios Hollywood, pg 872
The Rosenthal Group, pg 877
Sacramento Theatrical Lighting Ltd (STL), pg 879
Samy's Camera, pg 879
San Diego Stage & Lighting Supply Inc, pg 879
Santa Clarita Studios, pg 880
Shooting Star Video, pg 886
Shoulder High Productions, pg 886
SNAP, pg 891
Source Film Studio, pg 895
Stray Angel Films, pg 902
Studio 1444, pg 902
Studio 637, pg 903
The Studios at Paramount, pg 903
Sunset Las Palmas Studios, pg 904
T-stop Inc, pg 906
Towards 2000 Inc, pg 916
Twin Peaks Creative, pg 920
Universal Studios, pg 922
Valencia Studios, pg 924
Visual Instrumentation Corp, pg 931
Vitruvian Entertainment, pg 932
VMI Inc, pg 932
Voice & Video Rentals, pg 932
Warner Bros Entertainment Inc, pg 934
Wildfire Lighting & Visual Effects, pg 938
Z-Ville Productions, pg 944

COLORADO

Chimera®, pg 722
Denver Media Center, pg 740
EON247 Inc, pg 755
Maniac Productions, pg 816
Mike's Camera, pg 827
Tatum Video, pg 907
Westworks Studios, pg 936
Zelo Productions Inc, pg 945

CONNECTICUT

Connecticut Audio & Theatrical Supply, pg 731
Digital Video Productions, pg 742
KJfilms LLC, pg 799
Revolution Lighting Technologies Inc, pg 874
Videofilm Systems Inc, pg 929

DELAWARE

Actors Attic, pg 675
Cornerstone Media Productions Inc, pg 731

DISTRICT OF COLUMBIA

Metro Teleproductions Inc (MTI), pg 824

FLORIDA

Access Media Group, pg 673
Adrenaline Films, pg 676
All Comm Rentals Inc (ALLCOMM), pg 680
Aperture Studios Miami, pg 687
Bay Stage Lighting Co Inc, pg 702
Budget Video Rentals, pg 712
Canavan Scenic & Light LLC, pg 716

Christie Lites, pg 722
Steven Cohen Motion Picture Production, pg 727
Digital Zoetrope Productions, pg 742
Facet Media, pg 758
Fiddler Films, pg 759
The Great Southern Studios, pg 773
HD House, pg 777
Illuminart Lighting, pg 784
Jordan Klein Film & Video (JKFV), pg 795
JungleTV, pg 795
Knowles Video Inc (KVI), pg 800
MAPS Production House, pg 816
Miami Daylight Studios, pg 825
Miami Stagecraft Inc, pg 825
Moving Picture, pg 831
ONstage, pg 846
Paradise Show & Design Inc, pg 851
Photosound of Orlando Inc, pg 856
PRI Productions, pg 862
Stage Equipment & Lighting Inc, pg 898
Style-City Music Inc, pg 903
Universal Studios Florida® Production Group, pg 922
Zebedee Productions, pg 945

GEORGIA

Convergent Media Systems, pg 731
First Cut Communications LLC, pg 761
In Concert Production Inc (ICP), pg 786
Lighting & Production Equipment Inc, pg 807
Magick Lantern, pg 814
MAGNUM Companies Ltd, pg 815
See Production Services, pg 883
Stage Front Presentation Systems, pg 899
Studio Space Atlanta, pg 903

HAWAII

FOTON Hawaii, pg 764
Hawaii Sound & Vision, pg 777
Sight & Sound Studios, pg 887

ILLINOIS

Chicago Spotlight Inc, pg 721
Firehouse Studios, pg 761
Grand Stage Co Inc, pg 773
Helix Camera & Video, pg 778
LITE-IT Grip Truck Rentals, pg 810
Magnanimous Media, pg 814
Product Productions, pg 863
PSAV® Presentation Services (Hotel Services Division), pg 866
Resolution Productions Group, pg 874
2nd Cine Inc, pg 883
Staging Resources Inc, pg 899
Tele-Time Systems, pg 910
Zacuto, pg 945

INDIANA

Heart Breaker Entertainment LLC, pg 778
Jack's Camera Shop, pg 792
OMNI Productions, pg 845

IOWA

Central Lighting & Equipment Inc (CLE), pg 719
Musco Lighting, pg 834
Pro Video, pg 863

KANSAS

Lights On, pg 808
Theatrical Services Inc, pg 912

KENTUCKY

Audio Visual Techniques Inc, pg 695
Kentucky Grip & Lighting, pg 798
Theatre House Inc, pg 911

LOUISIANA

Available Lighting & Motion Picture Services Inc, pg 697
Pace Systems, pg 849

MARYLAND

Archai Media, pg 688
Cannon Stage Lighting Inc, pg 716
CPR MultiMedia Solutions, pg 732
RTZ Audio Visual, pg 878

MASSACHUSETTS

Advanced Lighting & Production Services Inc (ALPS), pg 677
AVFX Inc, pg 698
Capron Lighting & Sound Co Inc, pg 716
Fastlane Productions LLC, pg 759
Green Mountain Post Films (GMP), pg 774
High Output Inc, pg 779
HOME Inc, pg 781
Integrated Solutions Group, pg 789
Limelight Production® Inc, pg 809
Preston Productions Inc, pg 861

MICHIGAN

Fantasee Lighting, pg 759
K&R All Media Productions LLC, pg 796
Lowing Light & Grip Inc, pg 812
Magnicon Media/Image d'Or, pg 815
On Stage Visuals, pg 846
TEL Systems LLC, pg 909

MINNESOTA

AVI Systems, pg 698
Freestyle Productions Inc, pg 765
House of Cinemagraphics, pg 782
Norcostco Inc, pg 842
Pro Media Productions, pg 863

MISSOURI

A to Z Theatrical Supply & Service, pg 671
EZ Scenic, pg 758
Production Support Services Inc, pg 864
Show-Me Audio-Visual, pg 887
Sight & Sound Production Services Inc, pg 887
Switch, pg 905
Wise Audio Video, pg 940

MONTANA

Filmlites Montana, pg 760

NEBRASKA

Lights On Nebraska, pg 808

NEVADA

4 Wall Entertainment, pg 764
GES Audio Visual, pg 770
MG Studio, pg 825

Lighting Fixture & Control Equipment Repairs

MISCELLANEOUS

Lighting Fixture & Control Equipment Repairs (continued)

MINNESOTA

AVI Systems, pg 698
Norcostco Inc, pg 842

MISSOURI

A to Z Theatrical Supply & Service, pg 671

NEVADA

4 Wall Entertainment, pg 764

NEW JERSEY

Dazian LLC, pg 739
Dyna-Lite Inc, pg 748
Earl Girls Inc, pg 749
Frezzi Energy Systems, pg 766
Nelson Enterprises Theatrical Supply Co, pg 838
Starlite, pg 900

NEW MEXICO

Quickbeam Systems Inc (QSI), pg 868

NEW YORK

Adwar Video, pg 678
Bowens USA, pg 709
Levy NYC Design & Production, pg 806
MAC Group, pg 813
Production Resource Group LLC (PRG), pg 864
Theatrical Services & Supplies Inc, pg 912

NORTH CAROLINA

Strategic Connections, pg 901

OHIO

Partech Lighting Systems Inc, pg 851
Vincent Lighting Systems, pg 930

OREGON

All Service Musical Electronics Repair, pg 680
Hollywood Lights Inc, pg 780

PENNSYLVANIA

Location Lighting Ltd, pg 810

TENNESSEE

Kozmic Lazer Show LLC, pg 801
Technical Support Systems LLC, pg 908

TEXAS

Communilux Productions, pg 729
Crossroads Audio Inc, pg 735
Olden Lighting, pg 845
Pro Video & Film Equipment Co Inc, pg 863
Sky-View Search Lights & Promotions, pg 890
Strand Lighting Inc, pg 901
Tarpley Media Systems, pg 907

UTAH

RIA Corp, pg 874

VIRGINIA

Intellidyne LLC, pg 789

WEST VIRGINIA

United Sound & Electronics, pg 921

WISCONSIN

Full Compass Systems, pg 767

ALBERTA

Allstar Show Industries Inc, pg 681

NOVA SCOTIA

Atlantic Illumination Entertainment Lighting, pg 692

ONTARIO

The Fluorescent Co Inc, pg 763
Westbury National Show Systems Ltd, pg 936

Microform Projector & Reader Distributors

ARIZONA

Troxell-CDI, pg 918

CALIFORNIA

Ametron Audio/Video, pg 684
Media Fabricators Inc, pg 822

COLORADO

Ceavco Audio Visual Company Inc, pg 719

CONNECTICUT

MAVCO, pg 820

KENTUCKY

NOR-COM Inc, pg 841

MARYLAND

Nicholas P Pipino Associates Inc, pg 857

MICHIGAN

Michigan Office Solutions (MOS), A Xerox Company, pg 825

NEVADA

Bulbman Inc, pg 712

NEW YORK

Gaylord Archival, pg 768
Topbulb, a Semmer Lighting Company, pg 915

OHIO

Audio Visual Media, pg 694
Thread Marketing Group, pg 913

PENNSYLVANIA

Brodart Co, pg 711

SOUTH CAROLINA

Keymark Inc, pg 798

TENNESSEE

Spring Arbor Distributors Inc, pg 898

TEXAS

Audio Visual Technologies Group (AVTG), pg 695

VIRGINIA

Lee Hartman & Sons Inc, pg 805
The Whitlock Group, pg 937

WISCONSIN

Demco Inc, pg 740
Indus International Inc, pg 787

ONTARIO

Carr McLean Ltd, pg 717

Microform Projector & Reader Manufacturers

WISCONSIN

Indus International Inc, pg 787

BRITISH COLUMBIA

Kodak Graphic Communications Canada Co, pg 800

Microform Projector & Reader Rentals

CALIFORNIA

Ametron Audio/Video, pg 684
Crystal Pyramid Productions™, pg 735
Media Fabricators Inc, pg 822

COLORADO

Ceavco Audio Visual Company Inc, pg 719

FLORIDA

Jordan Klein Film & Video (JKFV), pg 795

GEORGIA

Stage Front Presentation Systems, pg 899

OHIO

Audio Visual Media, pg 694
Thread Marketing Group, pg 913

SOUTH CAROLINA

Keymark Inc, pg 798

VIRGINIA

Projection, pg 865

ALBERTA

Global TV, pg 771

Microform Projector & Reader Repairs

CALIFORNIA

Ametron Audio/Video, pg 684

COLORADO

Ceavco Audio Visual Company Inc, pg 719

KENTUCKY

NOR-COM Inc, pg 841

OHIO

Audio Visual Media, pg 694

SOUTH CAROLINA

Keymark Inc, pg 798

VIRGINIA

The Whitlock Group, pg 937

WASHINGTON

Inland Audio Visual Co, pg 788

Microform Reader, *see* Microform Projector & Reader

Phase Converter—Rotary Distributors

FLORIDA

Access Media Group, pg 673

KENTUCKY

NOR-COM Inc, pg 841

NEW JERSEY

Earl Girls Inc, pg 749

Phase Converter—Rotary Manufacturers

CALIFORNIA

OnLine Power Inc, pg 846

INDIANA

Kay Industries Inc, pg 797

Phase Converter—Rotary Rentals

CALIFORNIA

PSAV® Presentation Services, pg 866

GEORGIA

Stage Front Presentation Systems, pg 899

MICHIGAN

Lowing Light & Grip Inc, pg 812

NEW JERSEY

Earl Girls Inc, pg 749

Phase Converter—Rotary Repairs

KENTUCKY

NOR-COM Inc, pg 841

MICHIGAN

Lowing Light & Grip Inc, pg 812

Power Quality & Control Equipment Distributors

CALIFORNIA

Ametron Audio/Video, pg 684
Band Pro Film & Digital Inc, pg 701
Filmtools®, pg 761
Furman®, pg 767
Orvac Electronics, pg 848
Promax Systems, pg 865
Seagate Technology LLC, pg 883
Skjonberg Controls Inc, pg 890
Yanchar Design & Consulting Group, pg 943
Zack Electronics Inc, pg 945

COLORADO

Lightning Eliminators & Consultants Inc, pg 808

CONNECTICUT

Connecticut Audio & Theatrical Supply, pg 731

FLORIDA

Access Media Group, pg 673
Digital Video Systems, pg 742
Test Equipment Connection, pg 911

GEORGIA

Innocinema, pg 788
Stage Front Presentation Systems, pg 899

ILLINOIS

AmpliVox Portable Sound Systems, pg 684
Chicago Spotlight Inc, pg 721
Joseph Electronics, pg 795

KENTUCKY

NOR-COM Inc, pg 841

MASSACHUSETTS

JENSEN Tools + Supply, pg 793

MICHIGAN

ASC Systems, pg 690

NEVADA

Selco Products Co, pg 883

NEW JERSEY

Earl Girls Inc, pg 749
Total Video Products Inc, pg 916

NEW YORK

BTX Technologies, pg 712

NORTH CAROLINA

Power Integrity Corporation, pg 860
SurgeX, pg 904

OKLAHOMA

Ford AV, pg 763

PENNSYLVANIA

Techni-Tool, a TestEquity LLC company, pg 908

TENNESSEE

Lowrance Sound Co Inc, pg 812
Technical Support Systems LLC, pg 908

TEXAS

Juice Goose, pg 795
Specialized Products Co, pg 896

VIRGINIA

Avitecture Inc, pg 699
Lee Hartman & Sons Inc, pg 805

WASHINGTON

Alpha Technologies Inc, pg 681
Asentria Corp, pg 690
PNTA, pg 858

WISCONSIN

Alpha Source Inc, pg 681
Full Compass Systems, pg 767

ALBERTA

Johnson Systems Inc (JSI), pg 794

ONTARIO

Cinema Stage Inc, pg 724
VFGadgets Inc, pg 926
Westbury National Show Systems Ltd, pg 936

Power Quality & Control Equipment Manufacturers

CALIFORNIA

Ametek Programmable Power Inc, pg 684
ESL Power Systems, pg 755
Furman®, pg 767
Henry Engineering, pg 779
OnLine Power Inc, pg 846
Skjonberg Controls Inc, pg 890

COLORADO

Lightning Eliminators & Consultants Inc, pg 808

CONNECTICUT

Hubbell Wiring Device-Kellems, pg 782
Superior Electric, pg 904

FLORIDA

Compuvideo Sales USA Ltd, pg 729
Lightning Master Corp, pg 808
Vutec Corp, pg 933

IDAHO

Transtector Systems Inc, pg 917

ILLINOIS

AmpliVox Portable Sound Systems, pg 684
Tripp Lite, pg 918

MASSACHUSETTS

AEMC Instruments, pg 678
L-3 ESSCO, pg 802

MINNESOTA

Emcor Enclosures-Crenlo, pg 753

MISSOURI

Lowell Manufacturing, pg 812

NEW JERSEY

FSR Inc, pg 766
Nova Electric, pg 843

NEW YORK

Creative Stage Lighting Co Inc, pg 733
Moog Inc, pg 830

NORTH CAROLINA

Eaton Corp, pg 750
Power Integrity Corporation, pg 860

OHIO

Staco Energy Products Co, pg 898
Vertiv, pg 926

OREGON

Equi=Tech Corp, pg 755
Leviton LES (Lighting & Energy Solutions), pg 806
Magic Gadgets™, pg 814

PENNSYLVANIA

Kalglo Electronics Co Inc, pg 796

RHODE ISLAND

APC by Schneider Electric, pg 686

TEXAS

ETA Systems, pg 756
Exeltech Inc, pg 757
Juice Goose, pg 795

WASHINGTON

Alpha Technologies Inc, pg 681

ALBERTA

Johnson Systems Inc (JSI), pg 794

Power Quality & Control Equipment Rentals

CALIFORNIA

Acey Decy Lighting, pg 674
AGF Media Services, pg 678
Ametron Audio/Video, pg 684
Imagecraft Productions, pg 785
Main Street Media Inc, pg 815
Muse Presentation Technologies, pg 834
Next Arts, pg 841
PSAV® Presentation Services, pg 866

COLORADO

Zelo Productions Inc, pg 945

GEORGIA

Stage Front Presentation Systems, pg 899

ILLINOIS

Chicago Spotlight Inc, pg 721
Resolution Productions Group, pg 874

KENTUCKY

Audio Visual Techniques Inc, pg 695

MARYLAND

CPR MultiMedia Solutions, pg 732

MICHIGAN

Lowing Light & Grip Inc, pg 812

MONTANA

Jereco Studios Inc, pg 793

NEW JERSEY

Earl Girls Inc, pg 749

OHIO

Bartha, pg 702

OKLAHOMA

PDC Productions, pg 852

VERMONT

Dark Star Lighting & Production, pg 737

ALBERTA

Johnson Systems Inc (JSI), pg 794

ONTARIO

Westbury National Show Systems Ltd, pg 936

Power Quality & Control Equipment Repairs

CALIFORNIA

Ametron Audio/Video, pg 684
Effective Engineering Inc, pg 751
TEK Media Group, pg 909

GEORGIA

Stage Front Presentation Systems, pg 899

ILLINOIS

Chicago Spotlight Inc, pg 721

KENTUCKY

NOR-COM Inc, pg 841

MICHIGAN

Lowing Light & Grip Inc, pg 812

OHIO

ITA Audio Visual Solutions, pg 791

TENNESSEE

Technical Support Systems LLC, pg 908

WASHINGTON

Alpha Technologies Inc, pg 681

WISCONSIN

Full Compass Systems, pg 767

ONTARIO

Westbury National Show Systems Ltd, pg 936

MISCELLANEOUS

Properties (Props) Distributors

ARIZONA

Arizona Cine Equipment, pg 688
Mardi Gras Costume Shop, pg 817

CALIFORNIA

Ametron Audio/Video, pg 684
Apex Jr, pg 687
Automated Entertainment, pg 696
Omnirax Furniture Co, pg 845
Silvestri California, pg 888
Studio Dynamics, pg 902
Stunt Wings Adventure Sports
 Talent & Equipment, pg 903

CONNECTICUT

MAVCO, pg 820

FLORIDA

The Great Southern Studios, pg 773
ONstage, pg 846

ILLINOIS

Grand Stage Co Inc, pg 773

MASSACHUSETTS

Limelight Production® Inc, pg 809

MICHIGAN

AirBrands Event & Marketing
 Group, pg 679
Digi Sign Design LLC, pg 741
Tobins Lake Sales, pg 915

MISSOURI

A to Z Theatrical Supply & Service,
 pg 671
Production Support Services Inc,
 pg 864

NEVADA

DVDs4Less, pg 748

NEW HAMPSHIRE

APS Lighting-Sound-AV, pg 688

NEW JERSEY

Earl Girls Inc, pg 749
Showman Fabricators Inc, pg 887
Starlite, pg 900

NEW YORK

Barbizon Electric Co Inc, pg 701
Rafik, pg 869
M Schwartz & Gettinger Feather
 Inc, pg 882
Uniset LLC, pg 921

NORTH CAROLINA

The Godfrey Group Inc, pg 772

OHIO

Cleveland Costume & Display Corp,
 pg 726

PENNSYLVANIA

Shore Manufacturing Co, pg 886

TEXAS

Pro Video & Film Equipment Co
 Inc, pg 863
Starline Costumes, pg 900

VERMONT

Dark Star Lighting & Production,
 pg 737

VIRGINIA

Blair Inc, pg 707

WISCONSIN

Demco Inc, pg 740
Wisconsin Public Television, pg 940

Properties (Props) Manufacturers

ARIZONA

Merestone, pg 823

CALIFORNIA

The Set Shop, pg 884

NEW YORK

Cobalt Studios Inc, pg 727
Uniset LLC, pg 921

OREGON

Magic Gadgets™, pg 814

TEXAS

Communilux Productions, pg 729

Properties (Props) Rentals

ARIZONA

Arizona Cine Equipment, pg 688
Mardi Gras Costume Shop, pg 817
Merestone, pg 823

CALIFORNIA

Ametron Audio/Video, pg 684
Antelope Valley Locations &
 Production Services, pg 686
Artichoke Productions, pg 690
Automated Entertainment, pg 696
Digital Film Studios LLC, pg 742
Dystopian Studios, pg 748
Fuller Street Productions, pg 767
Golden Gate Studios, pg 772
JFA Studio, pg 794
Loyal Studios, pg 812
Palace Costume & Prop Co, pg 850
Pro HD Rentals, pg 863
The Mack Sennett Studios, pg 883
Studio Dynamics, pg 902
Stunt Wings Adventure Sports
 Talent & Equipment, pg 903
Universal Studios, pg 922
Warner Bros Entertainment Inc,
 pg 934

CONNECTICUT

MAVCO, pg 820

DISTRICT OF COLUMBIA

Metro Teleproductions Inc (MTI),
 pg 824

FLORIDA

Canavan Scenic & Light LLC,
 pg 716
The Great Southern Studios, pg 773
Jordan Klein Film & Video (JKFV),
 pg 795
ONstage, pg 846
PRI Productions, pg 862
Sight & Sound Productions, pg 887
Universal Studios Florida®
 Production Group, pg 922
Zebedee Productions, pg 945

GEORGIA

Lighting & Production Equipment
 Inc, pg 807
Studio Space Atlanta, pg 903

ILLINOIS

Broadway Costumes Inc, pg 711
WEEK TV, pg 935

MASSACHUSETTS

Capron Lighting & Sound Co Inc,
 pg 716

MICHIGAN

AirBrands Event & Marketing
 Group, pg 679
Digi Sign Design LLC, pg 741
K&R All Media Productions LLC,
 pg 796
K&R's Recording Studios Inc,
 pg 796
On Stage Visuals, pg 846

MISSOURI

A to Z Theatrical Supply & Service,
 pg 671
Production Support Services Inc,
 pg 864

NEW HAMPSHIRE

APS Lighting-Sound-AV, pg 688

NEW JERSEY

Earl Girls Inc, pg 749
Starlite, pg 900

NEW YORK

Automobile Film Club of America
 Inc, pg 696
Brooklyn Studios, pg 711
East of Hollywood NY, pg 749
modprop.com, pg 828
The Old Rhinebeck Aerodome®,
 pg 844

NORTH CAROLINA

The Godfrey Group Inc, pg 772
Take One Productions Ltd, pg 906

PENNSYLVANIA

Innovision Media Group, pg 788

TENNESSEE

Center for Southern Folklore Inc,
 pg 719

TEXAS

Communilux Productions, pg 729
Starline Costumes, pg 900
The Yesterday USA Radio
 Networks, pg 944

WASHINGTON

The House Studios, pg 782
Osum Event Rentals, pg 848
PNTA, pg 858

WISCONSIN

Wisconsin Public Television, pg 940

ALBERTA

Global TV, pg 771

BRITISH COLUMBIA

MicrophoneRentals.com, pg 826

ONTARIO

RB Productions, pg 870

Properties (Props) Repairs

ARIZONA

Merestone, pg 823

NEW YORK

Cobalt Studios Inc, pg 727

Reading & Tachistoscopic Equipment & Learning System Distributors

CALIFORNIA

Ametron Audio/Video, pg 684
Instructional Materials & Equipment
 Distributors (I-Med), pg 789

CONNECTICUT

MAVCO, pg 820

MARYLAND

Nicholas P Pipino Associates Inc,
 pg 857

MASSACHUSETTS

Duxbury Systems Inc, pg 748

NEW YORK

Langie Audio Visual Systems,
 pg 803

TENNESSEE

Memphis Communications Corp,
 pg 823

ONTARIO

Carr McLean Ltd, pg 717

Reading & Tachistoscopic Equipment & Learning System Manufacturers

MASSACHUSETTS

Duxbury Systems Inc, pg 748

Reading & Tachistoscopic Equipment & Learning System Rentals

CALIFORNIA

Ametron Audio/Video, pg 684
Instructional Materials & Equipment Distributors (I-Med), pg 789

TENNESSEE

Memphis Communications Corp, pg 823

Reading & Tachistoscopic Equipment & Learning System Repairs

CALIFORNIA

Ametron Audio/Video, pg 684
Instructional Materials & Equipment Distributors (I-Med), pg 789

MINNESOTA

AVI Systems, pg 698

TENNESSEE

Memphis Communications Corp, pg 823

Room-Darkening Drape & Blind Distributors

ARIZONA

Metropolitan Audio-Visual Inc, pg 824

ARKANSAS

Jay S Stanley & Associates Inc, pg 899

CALIFORNIA

Ametron Audio/Video, pg 684
Camera Essentials, pg 715
Instructional Materials & Equipment Distributors (I-Med), pg 789
Matthews Studio Equipment Inc, pg 820
San Diego Stage & Lighting Supply Inc, pg 879

CONNECTICUT

MAVCO, pg 820

DELAWARE

Actors Attic, pg 675

FLORIDA

Bay Stage Lighting Co Inc, pg 702
ONstage, pg 846

GEORGIA

Lighting & Production Equipment Inc, pg 807

ILLINOIS

Grand Stage Co Inc, pg 773

INDIANA

Lee Co Inc, pg 805

KANSAS

KK Office Solutions Inc, pg 799

KENTUCKY

Barney Miller's Inc, pg 827
NOR-COM Inc, pg 841

LOUISIANA

Techkno Integration & Design Services LLC, pg 908

MARYLAND

Nicholas P Pipino Associates Inc, pg 857
Theatre Service & Supply Corp, pg 912

MASSACHUSETTS

Advanced Lighting & Production Services Inc (ALPS), pg 677
International Display & Exhibit Corp (IDEC), pg 790
Rule Boston Camera, pg 878

MICHIGAN

Fantasee Lighting, pg 759
Lowing Light & Grip Inc, pg 812

MISSOURI

A to Z Theatrical Supply & Service, pg 671
Production Support Services Inc, pg 864
Southwest Audio-Visual Inc, pg 895

NEW HAMPSHIRE

APS Lighting-Sound-AV, pg 688

NEW JERSEY

Argraph Corp, pg 688
Audio Visual Associates, pg 694
Audio Visual Dynamics®, pg 694
Dazian LLC, pg 739
FlagHouse, pg 762
Wired 4 Sound Inc, pg 940

NEW MEXICO

Quickbeam Systems Inc (QSI), pg 868

NEW YORK

AV Workshop, pg 697
Bestek Lighting & Staging, pg 704
BMI Supply, pg 708
Colortone Audio Visual, pg 728
Crescendo Designs Inc, pg 734
Design Audio Visual Inc, pg 741
Mutual Hardware, pg 835
PASCO, pg 851
Visual Technologies Corp, pg 932
Visual Word Systems Inc, pg 932

OHIO

Copp Integrated Systems, pg 731
ITA Audio Visual Solutions, pg 791

PENNSYLVANIA

Audio Visions Inc, pg 694
Bernie's Photo Center, pg 704
SAPSIS Rigging Inc, pg 880

TENNESSEE

Memphis Communications Corp, pg 823
Technical Support Systems LLC, pg 908

TEXAS

Audio Visual Technologies Group (AVTG), pg 695
Heffernan Audio Visual, pg 778
Tarpley Media Systems, pg 907

VERMONT

Production Advantage Inc, pg 863

VIRGINIA

Boitnott Visual Communications Corp (BVC), pg 708

WISCONSIN

Audio Visual of Milwaukee Inc, pg 694

ALBERTA

Evolution AV, pg 757

MANITOBA

Inland Audio Visual Ltd, pg 788

ONTARIO

Cinema Stage Inc, pg 724
Westbury National Show Systems Ltd, pg 936

Room-Darkening Drape & Blind Manufacturers

ARIZONA

Merestone, pg 823

CALIFORNIA

Automated Entertainment, pg 696
Camera Essentials, pg 715
Matthews Studio Equipment Inc, pg 820

FLORIDA

Vutec Corp, pg 933

ILLINOIS

Chicago Spotlight Inc, pg 721

INDIANA

Draper Inc, pg 746

MARYLAND

Baron Stage Curtain & Equipment Co Inc, pg 702
Theatre Service & Supply Corp, pg 912

MICHIGAN

North Coast Studios Inc, pg 842

MISSOURI

A to Z Theatrical Supply & Service, pg 671

NEW JERSEY

Dazian LLC, pg 739
Gerriets International, pg 770
Showman Fabricators Inc, pg 887

NEW YORK

Syracuse Scenery & Stage Lighting Co Inc, pg 906

OHIO

Janson Industries, pg 793

TEXAS

Communilux Productions, pg 729
Texas Scenic Co Inc, pg 911

VIRGINIA

LuXout Stage Curtains, pg 813

WISCONSIN

Regal Photo Products Inc/Arkay Corp, pg 873

Room-Darkening Drape & Blind Rentals

ARIZONA

Merestone, pg 823
Metropolitan Audio-Visual Inc, pg 824

CALIFORNIA

AGF Media Services, pg 678
All Access Staging & Productions, pg 680
Fuller Street Productions, pg 767
Golden Gate Studios, pg 772
McCune Audio-Video-Lighting, pg 821
Next Arts, pg 841
San Diego Stage & Lighting Supply Inc, pg 879
Warner Bros Entertainment Inc, pg 934

FLORIDA

All Comm Rentals Inc (ALLCOMM), pg 680
ONstage, pg 846
Paradise Show & Design Inc, pg 851
PRI Productions, pg 862
Style-City Music Inc, pg 903

GEORGIA

Lighting & Production Equipment Inc, pg 807
Stage Front Presentation Systems, pg 899

ILLINOIS

Grand Stage Co Inc, pg 773

MASSACHUSETTS

AVFX Inc, pg 698

MICHIGAN

Lowing Light & Grip Inc, pg 812

MINNESOTA

Freestyle Productions Inc, pg 765

MISSOURI

Production Support Services Inc, pg 864

NEW HAMPSHIRE

APS Lighting-Sound-AV, pg 688

MISCELLANEOUS

Room-Darkening Drape & Blind Rentals (continued)

NEW JERSEY

Dazian LLC, pg 739
Showman Fabricators Inc, pg 887

NEW MEXICO

Quickbeam Systems Inc (QSI), pg 868

NEW YORK

Albany Theatre Supply Co Inc, pg 679
Bestek Lighting & Staging, pg 704
Design Audio Visual Inc, pg 741
Visual Word Systems Inc, pg 932

NORTH CAROLINA

AV Connections Inc, pg 697
Special Event Services, pg 896
Take One Productions Ltd, pg 906

OKLAHOMA

PDC Productions, pg 852

PENNSYLVANIA

Bernie's Photo Center, pg 704
The Videohouse Inc, pg 929

TENNESSEE

Memphis Communications Corp, pg 823

TEXAS

Communilux Productions, pg 729

VIRGINIA

StageSound, pg 899

WASHINGTON

PNTA, pg 858

ALBERTA

Allstar Show Industries Inc, pg 681
Evolution AV, pg 757
Global TV, pg 771

BRITISH COLUMBIA

Clark's Audio Visual Services Ltd, pg 725
Inspired Image Picture Co (IIPC), pg 788

ONTARIO

Westbury National Show Systems Ltd, pg 936

QUEBEC

Freeman Audio Visual, pg 765

Room-Darkening Drape & Blind Repairs

ARIZONA

Merestone, pg 823

CALIFORNIA

Matthews Studio Equipment Inc, pg 820
Lloyd F McKinney Associates Inc, pg 821
San Diego Stage & Lighting Supply Inc, pg 879

DELAWARE

Actors Attic, pg 675

GEORGIA

Lighting & Production Equipment Inc, pg 807

ILLINOIS

Chicago Spotlight Inc, pg 721

KENTUCKY

NOR-COM Inc, pg 841

MARYLAND

Baron Stage Curtain & Equipment Co Inc, pg 702

MICHIGAN

Fantasee Lighting, pg 759
Lowing Light & Grip Inc, pg 812

NEW JERSEY

Dazian LLC, pg 739
Showman Fabricators Inc, pg 887

PENNSYLVANIA

Bernie's Photo Center, pg 704

TENNESSEE

Memphis Communications Corp, pg 823
Technical Support Systems LLC, pg 908

TEXAS

Tarpley Media Systems, pg 907

VIRGINIA

Avitecture Inc, pg 699

Satellite Earth Station Equipment Distributors

CALIFORNIA

SNAP, pg 891

COLORADO

Vexcel Corp, pg 926

DISTRICT OF COLUMBIA

NPR Distribution Services, pg 843

FLORIDA

Digital Video Systems, pg 742
L3Harris Technologies Inc, pg 812
Multicom Inc, pg 833
Recording Media & Equipment Inc (RM&E), pg 872

IOWA

EASI, pg 749
Winegard Co, pg 939

MASSACHUSETTS

Antronics Inc, pg 686

MICHIGAN

DAWNco, pg 739

NEBRASKA

ATV Research Inc, pg 692

NEW JERSEY

Diversified, pg 744

PENNSYLVANIA

North Star Satellite Communications Inc, pg 842

TEXAS

Pro Video & Film Equipment Co Inc, pg 863

VIRGINIA

Lee Hartman & Sons Inc, pg 805

WISCONSIN

DH Satellite, pg 741

BRITISH COLUMBIA

Norsat International Inc, pg 842

Satellite Earth Station Equipment Manufacturers

CALIFORNIA

Broadcast Microwave Services Inc (BMS), a StoneCalibre company, pg 710
CPI Malibu, pg 732
FM Systems Inc, pg 763
Intersil Americas LLC, pg 790

COLORADO

Vexcel Corp, pg 926

GEORGIA

Wegener Communications Inc, pg 935

IOWA

EASI, pg 749
Winegard Co, pg 939

MICHIGAN

DAWNco, pg 739

NEW JERSEY

CELCO, pg 719

NORTH CAROLINA

Eaton Corp, pg 750

PENNSYLVANIA

North Star Satellite Communications Inc, pg 842

WISCONSIN

DH Satellite, pg 741

BRITISH COLUMBIA

Norsat International Inc, pg 842

ONTARIO

ATX Networks, pg 692
Communications & Power Industries (CPI), Satcom & Medical Products Division, pg 728
International Datacasting, pg 790

Satellite Earth Station Equipment Rentals

CALIFORNIA

Cosumnes River College, pg 732
FJ Productions Inc, pg 762
Lynch Communications, pg 813
PSSI Global Services LLC, pg 866

GEORGIA

Stage Front Presentation Systems, pg 899

NORTH CAROLINA

Microspace Communications Corp, pg 826

PENNSYLVANIA

North Star Satellite Communications Inc, pg 842

SOUTH CAROLINA

Assignment Desk, pg 691

Satellite Earth Station Equipment Repairs

IOWA

EASI, pg 749

PENNSYLVANIA

North Star Satellite Communications Inc, pg 842

TEXAS

The Yesterday USA Radio Networks, pg 944

ONTARIO

Communications & Power Industries (CPI), Satcom & Medical Products Division, pg 728

Satellite News Vehicle Distributors

CALIFORNIA

Satellite Digital Teleproductions (SDTV), pg 881
SNAP, pg 891

FLORIDA

Digital Video Systems, pg 742

MICHIGAN

DAWNco, pg 739

NEW JERSEY

Diversified, pg 744

TEXAS

Pro Video & Film Equipment Co
Inc, pg 863
Shook Mobile Technology LP,
pg 886

Satellite News Vehicle Manufacturers

CALIFORNIA

Broadcast Microwave Services Inc
(BMS), a StoneCalibre company,
pg 710

FLORIDA

Frontline Communications, pg 766

GEORGIA

Wegener Communications Inc,
pg 935

TEXAS

Shook Mobile Technology LP,
pg 886

Satellite News Vehicle Rentals

CALIFORNIA

PSSI Global Services LLC, pg 866

GEORGIA

Stage Front Presentation Systems,
pg 899

LOUISIANA

Satellite Center, pg 881

MICHIGAN

Digi Sign Design LLC, pg 741

NEW JERSEY

Vision Quest Productions Inc,
pg 930

NEW MEXICO

Production Outfitters, pg 864

NORTH CAROLINA

Microspace Communications Corp,
pg 826

SOUTH CAROLINA

Assignment Desk, pg 691

TEXAS

AMS Pictures, pg 684

Satellite News Vehicle Repairs

Shook Mobile Technology LP,
pg 886
The Yesterday USA Radio
Networks, pg 944

Satellite Teleport Service Distributors

FLORIDA

Digital Video Systems, pg 742
L3Harris Technologies Inc, pg 812

MICHIGAN

ASC Systems, pg 690
DAWNco, pg 739

NEW JERSEY

Diversified, pg 744
MiB MediaWorks, pg 825
SES SA, pg 884

ONTARIO

International Datacasting, pg 790

Satellite Teleport Service Manufacturers

FLORIDA

L3Harris Technologies Inc, pg 812

Satellite Teleport Service Rentals

ARIZONA

Crew West Inc, pg 734

CALIFORNIA

PSSI Global Services LLC, pg 866
Universal Satellite Communications
Inc, pg 922

COLORADO

Maniac Productions, pg 816

FLORIDA

Mike Vasilinda Productions Inc,
pg 925

GEORGIA

Stage Front Presentation Systems,
pg 899

ILLINOIS

Satellite Technology Systems Inc,
pg 881

INDIANA

Midwest Uplink Inc, pg 827

MISSOURI

Show-Me Audio-Visual, pg 887

NORTH CAROLINA

Microspace Communications Corp,
pg 826

OHIO

Mills James Productions, pg 828

PENNSYLVANIA

Liberty Uplink, pg 807

Satellite Teleport Service Repairs

TEXAS

The Yesterday USA Radio
Networks, pg 944

Satellite Transmission Equipment Distributors

CALIFORNIA

Computer Modules Inc, pg 729
Satellite Digital Teleproductions
(SDTV), pg 881

CONNECTICUT

Newtec America Inc, pg 840

DISTRICT OF COLUMBIA

NPR Distribution Services, pg 843

FLORIDA

Digital Video Systems, pg 742
L3Harris Technologies Inc, pg 812
Multicom Inc, pg 833
ONstage, pg 846
Recording Media & Equipment Inc
(RM&E), pg 872

IOWA

EASI, pg 749

MICHIGAN

DAWNco, pg 739

NEW JERSEY

Diversified, pg 744
DSI RF Systems Inc, pg 747
MiB MediaWorks, pg 825

NEW YORK

Image Management Systems Inc,
pg 785

PENNSYLVANIA

North Star Satellite Communications
Inc, pg 842

TEXAS

Pro Video & Film Equipment Co
Inc, pg 863

BRITISH COLUMBIA

Norsat International Inc, pg 842

Satellite Transmission Equipment Manufacturers

CALIFORNIA

FM Systems Inc, pg 763
Intersil Americas LLC, pg 790
TiVo Corp, pg 914

CONNECTICUT

Newtec America Inc, pg 840

FLORIDA

L3Harris Technologies Inc, pg 812

GEORGIA

Wegener Communications Inc,
pg 935

MASSACHUSETTS

L-3 ESSCO, pg 802

PENNSYLVANIA

North Star Satellite Communications
Inc, pg 842

TENNESSEE

Adtec Digital Inc, pg 677

ONTARIO

Communications & Power
Industries (CPI), Satcom &
Medical Products Division,
pg 728
International Datacasting, pg 790

Satellite Transmission Equipment Rentals

CALIFORNIA

Cosumnes River College, pg 732
Golden Gate Studios, pg 772
Lynch Communications, pg 813
PSSI Global Services LLC, pg 866

FLORIDA

ONstage, pg 846

LOUISIANA

Satellite Center, pg 881

MICHIGAN

Digi Sign Design LLC, pg 741
K&R All Media Productions LLC,
pg 796

NEW JERSEY

Vision Quest Productions Inc,
pg 930

NEW YORK

Image Management Systems Inc,
pg 785

NORTH CAROLINA

Microspace Communications Corp,
pg 826

OHIO

Cuyahoga Community College
Student Production Office (SPO),
pg 736

PENNSYLVANIA

FMP Media Solutions Inc, pg 763
North Star Satellite Communications
Inc, pg 842

Satellite Transmission Equipment Repairs

DISTRICT OF COLUMBIA

NPR Distribution Services, pg 843

PENNSYLVANIA

North Star Satellite Communications
Inc, pg 842

MISCELLANEOUS

Satellite Transmission Equipment Repairs (continued)

ONTARIO

Communications & Power Industries (CPI), Satcom & Medical Products Division, pg 728

Satellite Transponder Space Segment Distributors

CALIFORNIA

Satellite Digital Teleproductions (SDTV), pg 881

FLORIDA

L3Harris Technologies Inc, pg 812

NEW JERSEY

Diversified, pg 744
SES SA, pg 884

NEW YORK

Associated Press Television News, pg 691

PENNSYLVANIA

North Star Satellite Communications Inc, pg 842

Satellite Transponder Space Segment Rentals

CALIFORNIA

PSSI Global Services LLC, pg 866

DISTRICT OF COLUMBIA

NPR Distribution Services, pg 843

MICHIGAN

Digi Sign Design LLC, pg 741

NEW JERSEY

Vision Quest Productions Inc, pg 930

NEW YORK

Associated Press Television News, pg 691

NORTH CAROLINA

Microspace Communications Corp, pg 826

PENNSYLVANIA

North Star Satellite Communications Inc, pg 842

Shipping, Packaging, Carrying & Storage Case Distributors

ARIZONA

EAR Professional Audio/Video, pg 749
Troxell-CDI, pg 918

CALIFORNIA

Ametron Audio/Video, pg 684
Assured Audio Visual, pg 691
Audio/Video Supply Inc, pg 694
Band Pro Film & Digital Inc, pg 701
Christy's Editorial, pg 723
Filmtools®, pg 761
Gravity Media, pg 773
J & R Film Co, pg 792
Jameco Electronics, pg 792
McCune Audio-Video-Lighting, pg 821
Media Fabricators Inc, pg 822
Melmat Inc, pg 823
Mole-Richardson Co, pg 829
Nalpak Inc, pg 835
Orvac Electronics, pg 848
Pacific Radio Electronics, pg 849
Polyline LLC, pg 859
San Diego Stage & Lighting Supply Inc, pg 879
Thermodyne Cases, pg 912
Zack Electronics Inc, pg 945

COLORADO

Case Logic Inc, pg 717
Ceavco Audio Visual Company Inc, pg 719
Lightware Inc, pg 808
Mike's Camera, pg 827
Rose Packaging & Design Inc, pg 877
Stanco Sales LLC, pg 899

CONNECTICUT

Calzone Case Co, pg 714
MAVCO, pg 820
Monaco LLC, pg 829
Rockwell Communications Inc, pg 876

DELAWARE

Actors Attic, pg 675

FLORIDA

Access Media Group, pg 673
Digital Video Systems, pg 742
Olympic Case Co, pg 845
ONstage, pg 846
Recording Media & Equipment Inc (RM&E), pg 872
TAI Audio, pg 906

GEORGIA

Audio Visual Resources Inc, pg 695
Lighting & Production Equipment Inc, pg 807

ILLINOIS

Chicago Spotlight Inc, pg 721
Creative Technology (CT), pg 733
Joseph Electronics, pg 795
Platt Luggage Inc, pg 858
RC Communications, pg 870
Research Technology International (RTI), pg 873
Tele-Time Systems, pg 910

INDIANA

Jack's Camera Shop, pg 792
Lee Co Inc, pg 805

KENTUCKY

Axxis Leasing Inc, pg 700
NOR-COM Inc, pg 841

LOUISIANA

Techkno Integration & Design Services LLC, pg 908

MARYLAND

Cardinal Sound & Video, pg 717
RTZ Audio Visual, pg 878

MASSACHUSETTS

Terry Hanley Audio Systems Inc, pg 775
High Output Inc, pg 779
Integrated Solutions Group, pg 789
JENSEN Tools + Supply, pg 793
Rule Boston Camera, pg 878
University Products Inc, pg 923

MICHIGAN

On Stage Visuals, pg 846
TEL Systems LLC, pg 909

MINNESOTA

AVI Systems, pg 698

MISSISSIPPI

Bowie Audio Visual Enterprises Inc, pg 709
Jasper Ewing & Sons Inc, pg 757

MISSOURI

A to Z Theatrical Supply & Service, pg 671
Communitronics Corp, pg 729
Southwest Audio-Visual Inc, pg 895

NEBRASKA

VSA Inc, pg 933
Wilson Case Inc, pg 939

NEW HAMPSHIRE

Channell One Video, pg 720

NEW JERSEY

AlltecPro, pg 681
Audio Visual Associates, pg 694
Comprehensive Cable & Connectivity Co, pg 729
Nelson Enterprises Theatrical Supply Co, pg 838
Starlite, pg 900
ToCad America Inc, pg 915
Total Video Products Inc, pg 916

NEW YORK

Barbizon Electric Co Inc, pg 701
Century Business Solutions, pg 720
Colortone Audio Visual, pg 728
Design Audio Visual Inc, pg 741
DSan Corp, pg 747
Gotham Sound & Communications Inc, pg 773
Langie Audio Visual Systems, pg 803
Light Impressions, pg 807
Long Island Video Enterprises Live Inc, pg 811
MAC Group, pg 813

Motion Picture Enterprises Inc

Motion Picture Enterprises Inc, pg 831
Rafik, pg 869
Road Cases USA Inc, pg 876
Talas, pg 906
TecNec Distributing, pg 909
Tenba, pg 911
Visual Technologies Corp, pg 932
Visual Word Systems Inc, pg 932
Willoughby's® Camera, pg 939

NORTH CAROLINA

Camcor Inc, pg 715
Verbatim Americas LLC, pg 926

OHIO

Copp Integrated Systems, pg 731
Tri-State Audio Visual Co, pg 918
Univenture Inc, pg 921

OKLAHOMA

Ford AV, pg 763

PENNSYLVANIA

Audio Visions Inc, pg 694
Brodart Co, pg 711
Charles Beseler Co, pg 721
Electron Microscopy Sciences (EMS), pg 752
J E Foss Co, pg 764
The Lerro Corp, pg 806
New York Camera & Video, pg 840
RSS Distributors, pg 878
Techni-Tool, a TestEquity LLC company, pg 908

SOUTH CAROLINA

Professional Label Inc, pg 865

TENNESSEE

Memphis Communications Corp, pg 823
Spring Arbor Distributors Inc, pg 898
Technical Support Systems LLC, pg 908

TEXAS

Audio Visual Technologies Group (AVTG), pg 695
Cinema Antiques, pg 723
JSAV, pg 795
Pro Video & Film Equipment Co Inc, pg 863
Specialized Products Co, pg 896

UTAH

Performance Audio LLC, pg 854

VERMONT

Production Advantage Inc, pg 863

VIRGINIA

Avitecture Inc, pg 699
Boitnott Visual Communications Corp (BVC), pg 708
Lee Hartman & Sons Inc, pg 805
The Whitlock Group, pg 937

WASHINGTON

Allsop Inc, pg 681
Inland Audio Visual Co, pg 788
Proforma Good Wood Marketing, pg 865

Shipping, Packaging, Carrying & Storage Case Manufacturers

Shipping, Packaging, Carrying & Storage Case Rentals

Shipping, Packaging, Carrying & Storage Case Repairs

MISCELLANEOUS

Shipping, Packaging, Carrying & Storage Case Repairs (continued)

CALIFORNIA (continued)

Jan-Al Cases, pg 793
Mole-Richardson Co, pg 829

COLORADO

Ceavco Audio Visual Company Inc, pg 719

CONNECTICUT

Calzone Case Co, pg 714

FLORIDA

Olympic Case Co, pg 845

GEORGIA

Lighting & Production Equipment Inc, pg 807

ILLINOIS

R & R Cases & Cabinets, pg 868

KENTUCKY

Axxis Leasing Inc, pg 700
NOR-COM Inc, pg 841

NEBRASKA

Wilson Case Inc, pg 939

NEW JERSEY

Nelson Enterprises Theatrical Supply Co, pg 838

NEW YORK

Langie Audio Visual Systems, pg 803
Tenba, pg 911

NORTH CAROLINA

US Case Corp, pg 923

OHIO

Cabbage Cases Inc, pg 713

TENNESSEE

Memphis Communications Corp, pg 823

VIRGINIA

Avitecture Inc, pg 699

WISCONSIN

Full Compass Systems, pg 767

MANITOBA

Big Deal Custom Casings, pg 705

Stage Distributors

ALABAMA

Curtis Company, pg 736

CALIFORNIA

Sacramento Theatrical Lighting Ltd (STL), pg 879
San Diego Stage & Lighting Supply Inc, pg 879
Steeldeck® Inc, pg 900

DISTRICT OF COLUMBIA

Theatrical Technicians Inc (TTI), pg 912

FLORIDA

Bay Stage Lighting Co Inc, pg 702
ONstage, pg 846
Techni-Lux Inc, pg 908

GEORGIA

MAGNUM Companies Ltd, pg 815

ILLINOIS

Chicago Spotlight Inc, pg 721

INDIANA

Lee Co Inc, pg 805

KENTUCKY

Theatre Effects, pg 911

MARYLAND

Event Tech, pg 756
Theatre Service & Supply Corp, pg 912

MASSACHUSETTS

Limelight Production® Inc, pg 809

MICHIGAN

AirBrands Event & Marketing Group, pg 679
Fantasee Lighting, pg 759
On Stage Visuals, pg 846
Tobins Lake Sales, pg 915

NEW JERSEY

Audio Visual Dynamics®, pg 694
Earl Girls Inc, pg 749
MiB MediaWorks, pg 825
Nelson Enterprises Theatrical Supply Co, pg 838
Starlite, pg 900

NEW MEXICO

Quickbeam Systems Inc (QSI), pg 868

NEW YORK

Bestek Lighting & Staging, pg 704
BMI Supply, pg 708
Design Audio Visual Inc, pg 741
KVL Audio Visual Services Inc, pg 802

OKLAHOMA

Ford AV, pg 763

PENNSYLVANIA

Advanced AV LLC, pg 677
Audio Visions Inc, pg 694
SAPSIS Rigging Inc, pg 880
Stagestep Inc, pg 899

TENNESSEE

Allstar Audio Systems Inc, pg 681

TEXAS

L'AIR International, pg 802

VERMONT

Production Advantage Inc, pg 863

WASHINGTON

CCI Solutions, pg 718
PNTA, pg 858

WEST VIRGINIA

United Sound & Electronics, pg 921

WISCONSIN

Full Compass Systems, pg 767

ALBERTA

Allstar Show Industries Inc, pg 681

BRITISH COLUMBIA

DL Sound & Lighting Productions Ltd, pg 744

ONTARIO

Cinema Stage Inc, pg 724
HD Source, pg 777
Westbury National Show Systems Ltd, pg 936

QUEBEC

Stageline Mobile Stage Inc, pg 899

Stage Manufacturers

ARIZONA

Merestone, pg 823

CALIFORNIA

Brown United Inc, pg 711
CMI, pg 727
The Set Shop, pg 884
Steeldeck® Inc, pg 900

DISTRICT OF COLUMBIA

Theatrical Technicians Inc (TTI), pg 912

GEORGIA

Lighting & Production Equipment Inc, pg 807
Staging Directions Inc, pg 899

ILLINOIS

Chicago Scenic Studios Inc, pg 721

MARYLAND

Theatre Service & Supply Corp, pg 912

MICHIGAN

AirBrands Event & Marketing Group, pg 679
Stageright Corp, a Rogers Group brand, pg 899
Studio Consulting & Construction Inc, pg 902

MINNESOTA

Staging Concepts, pg 899

NEVADA

Pignose-Gorilla, pg 856

NEW JERSEY

American Harlequin Corp, pg 683

NEW YORK

Bestek Lighting & Staging, pg 704
Pook Diemont & Ohl Inc, pg 859
Uniset LLC, pg 921

OHIO

Bil-Jax Inc, pg 705
Janson Industries, pg 793

OREGON

Leviton LES (Lighting & Energy Solutions), pg 806

TENNESSEE

TOMCAT USA Inc, pg 915

TEXAS

Chelsea Decorative Metal Co, pg 721
Communilux Productions, pg 729
L'AIR International, pg 802
Texas Scenic Co Inc, pg 911

VIRGINIA

Applied Electronics, pg 687
Spider Support Systems, pg 897

ONTARIO

Versatruss, pg 926
Westbury National Show Systems Ltd, pg 936

QUEBEC

Stageline Mobile Stage Inc, pg 899

Stage Rentals

ARIZONA

Arizona Cine Equipment, pg 688
Creative Backstage, pg 733
Merestone, pg 823

CALIFORNIA

AGF Media Services, pg 678
All Access Staging & Productions, pg 680
Artichoke Productions, pg 690
ATV Video Center Inc, pg 692
Big Door, pg 705
Chapman/Leonard Studio Equipment Inc, pg 720
Digital Film Studios LLC, pg 742
DTC Lighting & Grip, pg 747
Full Moon & High Tide Productions & Studios, pg 767
Fuller Street Productions, pg 767
Golden Gate Studios, pg 772
KTVU-Retail Services, pg 802
McCune Audio-Video-Lighting, pg 821
Next Arts, pg 841
Premier Lighting & Production Co, pg 861
The Production Group Studios, pg 863
Pyxis Industries Inc, pg 867
Sacramento Theatrical Lighting Ltd (STL), pg 879
Samy's Camera, pg 879
San Diego Stage & Lighting Supply Inc, pg 879
The Mack Sennett Studios, pg 883
SNAP, pg 891

Stanislaus AV Inc, pg 899
Steeldeck® Inc, pg 900
The Studios at Paramount, pg 903
Universal Studios, pg 922

CONNECTICUT

A/V Davey, pg 697
Videofilm Systems Inc, pg 929

DELAWARE

Ken-Del Productions Inc, pg 797

FLORIDA

Canavan Scenic & Light LLC,
    pg 716
The Great Southern Studios, pg 773
Jordan Klein Film & Video (JKFV),
    pg 795
Mobile Stage Rentals Inc, pg 828
National Teleproductions Inc,
    pg 837
ONstage, pg 846
Paradise Show & Design Inc,
    pg 851
PRI Productions, pg 862
Sight & Sound Productions, pg 887
Universal Studios Florida®
    Production Group, pg 922
Mike Vasilinda Productions Inc,
    pg 925
Zebedee Productions, pg 945

GEORGIA

In Concert Production Inc (ICP),
    pg 786
Lighting & Production Equipment
    Inc, pg 807
MAGNUM Companies Ltd, pg 815
PC&E, pg 852
Stage Front Presentation Systems,
    pg 899

ILLINOIS

Chicago Scenic Studios Inc, pg 721
Resolution Productions Group,
    pg 874

IOWA

Central Lighting & Equipment Inc
    (CLE), pg 719

LOUISIANA

Pace Systems, pg 849

MARYLAND

CPR MultiMedia Solutions, pg 732

MASSACHUSETTS

Advanced Lighting & Production
    Services Inc (ALPS), pg 677
High Output Inc, pg 779
Limelight Production® Inc, pg 809

MICHIGAN

AirBrands Event & Marketing
    Group, pg 679
Digi Sign Design LLC, pg 741
Fantasee Lighting, pg 759
K&R All Media Productions LLC,
    pg 796
On Stage Visuals, pg 846

MINNESOTA

Freestyle Productions Inc, pg 765

MISSOURI

EZ Scenic, pg 758
Switch, pg 905

NEW JERSEY

Audio Visual Dynamics®, pg 694
Earl Girls Inc, pg 749
MiB MediaWorks, pg 825
PLS Staging, pg 858
Showman Fabricators Inc, pg 887
Starlite, pg 900

NEW MEXICO

Quickbeam Systems Inc (QSI),
    pg 868

NEW YORK

Bestek Lighting & Staging, pg 704
Design Audio Visual Inc, pg 741
KVL Audio Visual Services Inc,
    pg 802
Manhattan Center Studios Inc,
    pg 816
Mood Creations Ltd, pg 829
NBC Production Facilities, pg 837
Studio Instrument Rentals (SIR),
    pg 902
Visual Word Systems Inc, pg 932

NORTH CAROLINA

Moving Pictures, pg 832
Special Event Services, pg 896

OHIO

Bartha, pg 702
CET, pg 720
Mills James Productions, pg 828
Thread Marketing Group, pg 913
Vista Color Imaging Inc, pg 931

OREGON

Pacific Grip & Lighting Inc, pg 849

PENNSYLVANIA

Advanced AV LLC, pg 677
FMP Media Solutions Inc, pg 763
Raven Rental, pg 870
Stagestep Inc, pg 899
WQED-Multimedia, pg 942

TENNESSEE

Allstar Audio Systems Inc, pg 681
Brantley Sound Associates Inc,
    pg 709
United Methodist Productions,
    pg 921

TEXAS

Big House Sound Inc, pg 705
Communilux Productions, pg 729
Freeman, pg 765
Onstage Systems, pg 846
Phillips Media Source, pg 855
Power Factory Productions, pg 860
South Coast Film & Video, pg 895
Stage Directions, pg 898
Texcam Inc, pg 911

VERMONT

Dark Star Lighting & Production,
    pg 737

VIRGINIA

American AV, pg 682
CVW Event Productions, pg 736

StageSound, pg 899
WETA Production Center, pg 936

WASHINGTON

PNTA, pg 858

WEST VIRGINIA

United Sound & Electronics, pg 921

WISCONSIN

Event Essentials, pg 756
Full Compass Systems, pg 767
Logan Productions Inc, pg 811

ALBERTA

Allstar Show Industries Inc, pg 681
Global TV, pg 771

BRITISH COLUMBIA

DL Sound & Lighting Productions
    Ltd, pg 744

ONTARIO

HD Source, pg 777
Westbury National Show Systems
    Ltd, pg 936

Stage Repairs

CALIFORNIA

San Diego Stage & Lighting Supply
    Inc, pg 879
Steeldeck® Inc, pg 900

FLORIDA

Tel-Test, pg 909

GEORGIA

Lighting & Production Equipment
    Inc, pg 807

MICHIGAN

Fantasee Lighting, pg 759
Studio Consulting & Construction
    Inc, pg 902

WISCONSIN

Full Compass Systems, pg 767

ONTARIO

Westbury National Show Systems
    Ltd, pg 936

Static Eliminator Distributors

CALIFORNIA

Ametron Audio/Video, pg 684
Christy's Editorial, pg 723
Jameco Electronics, pg 792

COLORADO

Stanco Sales LLC, pg 899

CONNECTICUT

MAVCO, pg 820

FLORIDA

Lightning Master Corp, pg 808

ILLINOIS

FUJIFILM Graphic Systems
    Division, pg 766

INDIANA

Lee Co Inc, pg 805

KANSAS

Nazdar®, pg 837

KENTUCKY

NOR-COM Inc, pg 841

MASSACHUSETTS

Spirig Advanced Technologies Inc
    (SAT), pg 897

NEBRASKA

ATV Research Inc, pg 692

NEW JERSEY

Argraph Corp, pg 688
Falcon Safety Products Inc, pg 758
Vcom IMC, pg 925

NEW YORK

Colortone Audio Visual, pg 728
Light Impressions, pg 807
NRD Static Control LLC, pg 843

PENNSYLVANIA

Techni-Tool, a TestEquity LLC
    company, pg 908

VIRGINIA

Lee Hartman & Sons Inc, pg 805

WISCONSIN

Associated Bag Co, pg 691
School Specialty Inc, pg 882

PUERTO RICO

Bonnin Electronics Inc, pg 708

Static Eliminator Manufacturers

ARIZONA

Zippertubing® Co, pg 945

FLORIDA

Kinetronics Corp, pg 799
Lightning Master Corp, pg 808

ILLINOIS

Sprayway Inc, pg 898

MASSACHUSETTS

Spirig Advanced Technologies Inc
    (SAT), pg 897

NEW JERSEY

Falcon Safety Products Inc, pg 758
Master Bond, pg 819

NEW YORK

NRD Static Control LLC, pg 843

PENNSYLVANIA

Simco-Ion, pg 888

MISCELLANEOUS

Static Eliminator Rentals

GEORGIA

Stage Front Presentation Systems, pg 899

OHIO

Hughie's Event Production Services, pg 782

Static Eliminator Repairs

KENTUCKY

NOR-COM Inc, pg 841

Storage Cabinet Distributors

ARIZONA

Troxell-CDI, pg 918

ARKANSAS

Jay S Stanley & Associates Inc, pg 899

CALIFORNIA

Advanced Systems Group LLC, pg 677
ARS Electronics, pg 690
Christy's Editorial, pg 723
Compact Storage Systems Inc, pg 729
Instructional Materials & Equipment Distributors (I-Med), pg 789
Media Fabricators Inc, pg 822
Promax Systems, pg 865
Russ Bassett Corp, pg 878
Zack Electronics Inc, pg 945

COLORADO

Ceavco Audio Visual Company Inc, pg 719
Stanco Sales LLC, pg 899

CONNECTICUT

MAVCO, pg 820
Rockwell Communications Inc, pg 876

FLORIDA

Access Media Group, pg 673
Digital Video Systems, pg 742
Hi-Tech Import Export Corp, pg 779
Multicom Inc, pg 833
Photosound of Orlando Inc, pg 856

GEORGIA

Audio Visual Resources Inc, pg 695

ILLINOIS

Joseph Electronics, pg 795
G T Luscombe Co Inc, pg 812
Research Technology International (RTI), pg 873
Woodside Avenue Music Productions Inc, pg 941

INDIANA

Lee Co Inc, pg 805

KANSAS

Nazdar®, pg 837

MARYLAND

Cardinal Sound & Video, pg 717
Nicholas P Pipino Associates Inc, pg 857
RTZ Audio Visual, pg 878

MASSACHUSETTS

Hannecke Display Systems Inc, pg 775
Integrated Solutions Group, pg 789
Rule Boston Camera, pg 878
University Products Inc, pg 923

MICHIGAN

Olson Anderson Co, pg 685

MINNESOTA

Alpha Video & Audio Inc, pg 682

MISSISSIPPI

Bowie Audio Visual Enterprises Inc, pg 709
Jasper Ewing & Sons Inc, pg 757

MISSOURI

ITC, pg 791
Southwest Audio-Visual Inc, pg 895

NEW JERSEY

Audio Visual Associates, pg 694
Audio Visual Dynamics®, pg 694
Comprehensive Cable & Connectivity Co, pg 729
Total Video Products Inc, pg 916
Vcom IMC, pg 925
Video Corporation of America (VCA), pg 927

NEW YORK

AV Workshop, pg 697
Biomorph Desks, pg 706
Colortone Audio Visual, pg 728
Design Audio Visual Inc, pg 741
Flash Electronics Inc, pg 762
Light Impressions, pg 807
A Liss & Co, pg 809
Long Island Video Enterprises Live Inc, pg 811
Markertek Video Supply, pg 817
Motion Picture Enterprises Inc, pg 831
Neptune Photo Inc, pg 838
Sargent Welch, pg 880
Sentry Industries Inc, pg 884
Talas, pg 906
Visual Technologies Corp, pg 932

NORTH CAROLINA

Camcor Inc, pg 715
Carolina Biological Supply Co, pg 717

OHIO

Copp Integrated Systems, pg 731

PENNSYLVANIA

Audio Visions Inc, pg 694
Brodart Co, pg 711
The Lerro Corp, pg 806
Morefield Communications Inc, pg 830

Techni-Tool, a TestEquity LLC company, pg 908
Wespen Audio Visual Co, pg 935

TENNESSEE

Lowrance Sound Co Inc, pg 812
Memphis Communications Corp, pg 823

TEXAS

Audio Visual Technologies Group (AVTG), pg 695
Heffernan Audio Visual, pg 778
JSAV, pg 795
Specialized Products Co, pg 896
TopCat Records LLC, pg 915

UTAH

RIA Corp, pg 874

VIRGINIA

Avitecture Inc, pg 699
Boitnott Visual Communications Corp (BVC), pg 708
Lee Hartman & Sons Inc, pg 805
Metropolitan Audio Visual Co LLC, pg 824

WASHINGTON

Inland Audio Visual Co, pg 788

WISCONSIN

Demco Inc, pg 740
Full Compass Systems, pg 767
School Specialty Inc, pg 882
Spectrum Industries Inc, pg 897

PUERTO RICO

Bonnin Electronics Inc, pg 708

ALBERTA

McBain Camera Ltd, pg 820

ONTARIO

Carr McLean Ltd, pg 717
CBM Ltd, pg 718

Storage Cabinet Manufacturers

ALABAMA

Omni International Inc, pg 845

CALIFORNIA

A & J Cases, pg 671
Russ Bassett Corp, pg 878
Tasman Group Pacific Rim, pg 907

COLORADO

Liberty AV Solutions, pg 807
ProLine Digital, pg 865

FLORIDA

Harris Corp, pg 776

ILLINOIS

Bretford Manufacturing Inc, pg 710
Luxor, pg 812
Lyon Workspace Products LLC, pg 813
Marshall Furniture Inc, pg 817
Smith-Victor Corp, pg 891
Tripp Lite, pg 918

INDIANA

General Devices Co Inc, pg 769
Star Case Manufacturing Co Inc, pg 900

MASSACHUSETTS

Hannecke Display Systems Inc, pg 775

MINNESOTA

Emcor Enclosures-Crenlo, pg 753
Winsted Corp, pg 939

MISSOURI

Shure Manufacturing Corp, pg 887

NEW YORK

Biomorph Desks, pg 706
TBC Consoles Inc, pg 907

NORTH CAROLINA

Newton Instrument Co Inc, pg 840

OHIO

Vertiv, pg 926

PENNSYLVANIA

A/S Custom Furniture, pg 671
Electron Microscopy Sciences (EMS), pg 752
Sandusky Lee Corp, pg 880

TENNESSEE

Mystery Electronics LLC, pg 835

TEXAS

TopCat Records LLC, pg 915

VIRGINIA

Opterna, a Belden brand, pg 847

WASHINGTON

Watson Desking, pg 934

WISCONSIN

Spectrum Industries Inc, pg 897

MANITOBA

Big Deal Custom Casings, pg 705

ONTARIO

Can-Am Merchandising Systems, pg 715
CBM Ltd, pg 718
Egan Visual Inc/Egan TeamBoard Inc, pg 751

Storage Cabinet Rentals

FLORIDA

Jordan Klein Film & Video (JKFV), pg 795

GEORGIA

Stage Front Presentation Systems, pg 899

ILLINOIS

Woodside Avenue Music Productions Inc, pg 941

NEW YORK
Visual Technologies Corp, pg 932

NORTH CAROLINA
Take One Productions Ltd, pg 906

TENNESSEE
Memphis Communications Corp, pg 823

VIRGINIA
Lee Hartman & Sons Inc, pg 805

Storage Cabinet Repairs

TENNESSEE
Memphis Communications Corp, pg 823

VIRGINIA
Avitecture Inc, pg 699
Lee Hartman & Sons Inc, pg 805

WISCONSIN
Full Compass Systems, pg 767

Storage Case, *see* Shipping, Packaging, Carrying & Storage Case

Studio Furniture Distributors

ARIZONA
EAR Professional Audio/Video, pg 749
Troxell-CDI, pg 918

CALIFORNIA
BigFoot Mobile Systems, pg 705
Christy's Editorial, pg 723
Fusion Consoles/Eurotech Seating, pg 767
Marketec, pg 817
Omnirax Furniture Co, pg 845
Steeldeck® Inc, pg 900
VTP, pg 933
Zack Electronics Inc, pg 945

FLORIDA
Access Media Group, pg 673
Digital Video Systems, pg 742
Recording Media & Equipment Inc (RM&E), pg 872
Tallahassee Audio Visual, pg 906

GEORGIA
Lighting & Production Equipment Inc, pg 807

ILLINOIS
Chicago Spotlight Inc, pg 721
Leedal Inc, pg 805
Woodside Avenue Music Productions Inc, pg 941

INDIANA
Lee Co Inc, pg 805

KENTUCKY
Axxis Leasing Inc, pg 700
NOR-COM Inc, pg 841

MARYLAND
Cardinal Sound & Video, pg 717

MASSACHUSETTS
Professional Audio Design Inc, pg 865
Rule Boston Camera, pg 878

MINNESOTA
Alpha Video & Audio Inc, pg 682

MISSOURI
Production Support Services Inc, pg 864

NEW HAMPSHIRE
Technet® Systems Group, pg 908

NEW JERSEY
Alltec Stores, a Vcom IMC Company, pg 681
Diversified, pg 744
PatchAmp, pg 852
Starlite, pg 900
Total Video Products Inc, pg 916
Wired 4 Sound Inc, pg 940

NEW YORK
Biomorph Desks, pg 706
BTX Technologies, pg 712
Design Audio Visual Inc, pg 741
A Liss & Co, pg 809
Markertek Video Supply, pg 817
Neptune Photo Inc, pg 838
TecNec Distributing, pg 909

OREGON
ASC-Tube Trap, pg 690

PENNSYLVANIA
A/S Custom Furniture, pg 671
Audio Visions Inc, pg 694
The Lerro Corp, pg 806

SOUTH CAROLINA
DaviSound, pg 739

TENNESSEE
Lowrance Sound Co Inc, pg 812
Technical Support Systems LLC, pg 908
WhisperRoom™ Inc, pg 937

UTAH
Performance Audio LLC, pg 854

VIRGINIA
Avitecture Inc, pg 699
Lee Hartman & Sons Inc, pg 805

WASHINGTON
CCI Solutions, pg 718
PNTA, pg 858

WISCONSIN
Full Compass Systems, pg 767
Spectrum Industries Inc, pg 897

ALBERTA
Infosat Communications Inc, pg 787

ONTARIO
Cinema Stage Inc, pg 724

Studio Furniture Manufacturers

ALABAMA
Marco Inc, pg 816

ARIZONA
David Wexler & Co, pg 936

CALIFORNIA
Omnirax Furniture Co, pg 845
Steeldeck® Inc, pg 900

COLORADO
Arrakis Systems, pg 689

CONNECTICUT
Titus Technological Laboratories (TTL), pg 914

FLORIDA
Harris Corp, pg 776

ILLINOIS
Bretford Manufacturing Inc, pg 710
Chicago Scenic Studios Inc, pg 721
Leedal Inc, pg 805
Marshall Furniture Inc, pg 817

INDIANA
HSA Inc, pg 782

MINNESOTA
Artograph Inc, pg 690
Winsted Corp, pg 939

NEW JERSEY
Middle Atlantic Products, a Legrand AV Inc brand, pg 826

NEW YORK
Biomorph Desks, pg 706
TBC Consoles Inc, pg 907
Uniset LLC, pg 921

NORTH CAROLINA
Wheatstone Corp, pg 937

OREGON
ASC-Tube Trap, pg 690

PENNSYLVANIA
A/S Custom Furniture, pg 671

SOUTH CAROLINA
DaviSound, pg 739

TENNESSEE
WhisperRoom™ Inc, pg 937

WASHINGTON
PNTA, pg 858

WISCONSIN
Spectrum Industries Inc, pg 897

MANITOBA
Big Deal Custom Casings, pg 705

Studio Furniture Rentals

ARIZONA
Merestone, pg 823

CALIFORNIA
Golden Gate Studios, pg 772
Steeldeck® Inc, pg 900

CONNECTICUT
Videofilm Systems Inc, pg 929

GEORGIA
Stage Front Presentation Systems, pg 899

MICHIGAN
Digi Sign Design LLC, pg 741

MISSOURI
Production Support Services Inc, pg 864

NEW YORK
modprop.com, pg 828
Production Central, pg 863

NORTH CAROLINA
Take One Productions Ltd, pg 906

TENNESSEE
Technical Support Systems LLC, pg 908

Studio Furniture Repairs

CALIFORNIA
Steeldeck® Inc, pg 900

KENTUCKY
NOR-COM Inc, pg 841

Tachistoscopic Equipment, *see* Reading & Tachistoscopic Equipment & Learning System

Test Scoring Equipment Distributors

FLORIDA
Access Media Group, pg 673

GEORGIA
Convergent Media Systems, pg 731

ILLINOIS
Allen Visual Systems Inc, pg 680

NEW JERSEY
A-V Services Inc, pg 671

PENNSYLVANIA
Hite Co, pg 780

VIRGINIA
Lee Hartman & Sons Inc, pg 805

MISCELLANEOUS

Test Scoring Equipment Rentals

CALIFORNIA
VER, pg 926

GEORGIA
Convergent Media Systems, pg 731

Timer & Clock Distributors

ARIZONA
Troxell-CDI, pg 918

CALIFORNIA
Ametron Audio/Video, pg 684
ChronTrol Corp, pg 723
HM Electronics Inc (HME), pg 780
Instructional Materials & Equipment
 Distributors (I-Med), pg 789
Lloyd F McKinney Associates Inc,
 pg 821

FLORIDA
Access Media Group, pg 673
Digital Video Systems, pg 742
Hi-Tech Enterprises Inc, pg 779
Hi-Tech Import Export Corp,
 pg 779
Recording Media & Equipment Inc
 (RM&E), pg 872

INDIANA
Lee Co Inc, pg 805

KENTUCKY
NOR-COM Inc, pg 841

MARYLAND
Image Logic Corp, pg 785
Wiltronix Inc, pg 939

MASSACHUSETTS
Capron Lighting & Sound Co Inc,
 pg 716
Rule Boston Camera, pg 878
Spirig Advanced Technologies Inc
 (SAT), pg 897

MISSOURI
Southwest Audio-Visual Inc, pg 895

NEW HAMPSHIRE
Technet® Systems Group, pg 908

NEW JERSEY
Diversified, pg 744
SDI Technologies Inc, pg 883
Starlite, pg 900

NEW YORK
B&H Photo Video, pg 701
DSan Corp, pg 747
KVL Audio Visual Services Inc,
 pg 802
Markertek Video Supply, pg 817
Neptune Photo Inc, pg 838
Scientifics Direct Inc, pg 882

TecNec Distributing, pg 909
Tri-Ed Distribution Inc, pg 918
Visual Word Systems Inc, pg 932

OHIO
Copp Integrated Systems, pg 731

PENNSYLVANIA
Bernie's Photo Center, pg 704
The Lerro Corp, pg 806

TEXAS
Pro Video & Film Equipment Co
 Inc, pg 863

UTAH
RIA Corp, pg 874

VIRGINIA
Lee Hartman & Sons Inc, pg 805
Quince Imaging Inc, pg 868

WASHINGTON
Broadcast Supply World Wide,
 pg 711

WEST VIRGINIA
United Sound & Electronics, pg 921

WISCONSIN
Audio Visual of Milwaukee Inc,
 pg 694
Full Compass Systems, pg 767

PUERTO RICO
Bonnin Electronics Inc, pg 708

ALBERTA
Genesis Integration, pg 769
McBain Camera Ltd, pg 820

ONTARIO
Cinema Stage Inc, pg 724

Timer & Clock Manufacturers

ARKANSAS
Autogram/CRL, pg 696

CALIFORNIA
ChronTrol Corp, pg 723
Denecke Inc, pg 740
ESE, pg 755
For-A Corp of America, pg 763
HM Electronics Inc (HME), pg 780
Horita Co Inc, pg 781
Microsemi Corp, pg 826

COLORADO
Colorado Time Systems LLC,
 pg 728

CONNECTICUT
Alarmco Intelligent Message
 Repeaters, pg 679
Industrial Timer Co, pg 787

GEORGIA
Staging Directions Inc, pg 899
Visix™ Inc, pg 931

ILLINOIS
Rauland-Borg Corp, pg 870

MARYLAND
Image Logic Corp, pg 785

MASSACHUSETTS
Spirig Advanced Technologies Inc
 (SAT), pg 897

MICHIGAN
Leightronix Inc, pg 806

MISSOURI
Masterclock Inc, pg 819

NEW JERSEY
Bogen Communications Inc, pg 708
Radio Systems Inc, pg 869
SDI Technologies Inc, pg 883

NEW YORK
DSan Corp, pg 747
Monroe Electronics Inc, pg 829

OHIO
DimcoGray Co, pg 743

PENNSYLVANIA
MicroImage Video Systems, pg 826

ONTARIO
Evertz Microsystems Ltd, pg 757
Torpey Time, pg 915

QUEBEC
Skotel Corp, pg 890

Timer & Clock Rentals

ARIZONA
Merestone, pg 823

CALIFORNIA
Ametron Audio/Video, pg 684
Associated Sound, pg 691
AV Guys, pg 697
Lynch Communications, pg 813
McCune Audio-Video-Lighting,
 pg 821
VER, pg 926

COLORADO
Daylight Productions & Rentals,
 pg 739
Spectrum Audio Visual Services,
 pg 897

DELAWARE
Ken-Del Productions Inc, pg 797

FLORIDA
Jordan Klein Film & Video (JKFV),
 pg 795
Sight & Sound Productions, pg 887

GEORGIA
Stage Front Presentation Systems,
 pg 899

ILLINOIS
AV Chicago Inc, pg 696
Resolution Productions Group,
 pg 874

LOUISIANA
Pace Systems, pg 849

MASSACHUSETTS
Capron Lighting & Sound Co Inc,
 pg 716

NEVADA
GES Audio Visual, pg 770

NEW YORK
KVL Audio Visual Services Inc,
 pg 802
Visual Word Systems Inc, pg 932

NORTH CAROLINA
Special Event Services, pg 896

OHIO
Bartha, pg 702
Mills James Productions, pg 828

PENNSYLVANIA
Bernie's Photo Center, pg 704
FMP Media Solutions Inc, pg 763

VIRGINIA
Quince Imaging Inc, pg 868

WISCONSIN
Event Essentials, pg 756

BRITISH COLUMBIA
Clark's Audio Visual Services Ltd,
 pg 725

Timer & Clock Repairs

CALIFORNIA
Ametron Audio/Video, pg 684
HM Electronics Inc (HME), pg 780

KENTUCKY
NOR-COM Inc, pg 841

MASSACHUSETTS
Capron Lighting & Sound Co Inc,
 pg 716

PENNSYLVANIA
Bernie's Photo Center, pg 704

VIRGINIA
Quince Imaging Inc, pg 868

WEST VIRGINIA
United Sound & Electronics, pg 921

WISCONSIN
Full Compass Systems, pg 767

Sections

AV Product & Service Providers
Associations
Film & Television Commissions
Awards & Festivals
Calendar of Events
Periodicals for the Trade
Reference Books for the Trade

Sections

AV Product & Service Providers

This section contains full entries for companies active in the AV trade. Entries are sorted by company name and generally contain name, address, telecommunications data, key personnel, branch office and catalog information.

A & J Cases
11121 Hindry Ave, Los Angeles, CA 90045
Tel: 310-216-2170 *Toll Free Tel:* 800-537-4000
Fax: 310-216-2694
Web Site: www.ajcases.com
Online catalog(s) available

A Cut Above Video Productions Inc
4450 W Eau Gallie Blvd, Suite 220, Melbourne, FL 32934
Tel: 321-253-5677
Web Site: www.acutabovevideo.com
Key Personnel
Pres: Bill Williams *E-mail:* bill@acutabovevideo.com
Founded: 1988
Video production company. Broadcast HD ENG/EFP camera, cinema style camera/lenses, insert studio, Premiere & Final Cut post.
Membership(s): American Advertising Federation

A Go Go Films
907 Fourth St, Santa Monica, CA 90403
Tel: 310-387-1659
E-mail: art@agogofilms.com
Web Site: www.agogofilms.com
Key Personnel
Prodr: Art Brown *E-mail:* artieb60@gmail.com
Founded: 1997
Commercial, music video production & fitness videos.

A KTVA Production LLC, see KTVA Productions

A-List Quality Videographer
Division of Loftin Productions
33 Saint Mark's Place, New York, NY 10003
Tel: 917-825-5412; 917-399-8501
E-mail: loftin.productions@gmail.com
Web Site: www.loftinpro.com
Key Personnel
Cameraman: Don Loftin
Founded: 1999
Provides a cost-effective service to bring visual capture to life. Video shoots are events, interviews, celebrities, performances, fashion, training videos, product demonstrations, video presentations, the red carpet, parties, documentaries, discoveries & new inventions.
Video(s) available

A M Graphics Products, see Affton Graphics Inc

A/S Custom Furniture
364-C Valley Rd, Warrington, PA 18976
Tel: 215-491-3100 *Fax:* 215-491-3107
E-mail: sales@ascustom.com
Web Site: www.ascustom.com
Key Personnel
Co-Owner: Matt Smith; Roy Smith, Jr
Design & manufacturing of custom technical furniture; control rooms & audio rooms.
Membership(s): SBE

A to Z Theatrical Supply & Service
800 E Meyer Blvd, Kansas City, MO 64131

Tel: 816-523-1655 *Toll Free Tel:* 800-732-8252
Fax: 816-523-1690
E-mail: info@atoztheatrical.com
Web Site: www.atoztheatrical.com
Key Personnel
Pres: Alex Perry
VP, Sales: Brad Schmitz
A theatrical supply company offering design, sales, installation, service & rentals in lighting, rigging, curtain, costume & scenic supplies. Lighting & costume rentals for individuals, schools, churches & corporate productions. 2,000 inventory items from makeup to paint, lamps to hardware are available for immediate shipping.
Catalog(s) available
Membership(s): National Costumers Association; Professional Lighting & Sound Association; USITT

A-V-A Video Productions
4760 E 65 St, Indianapolis, IN 46220
Tel: 317-253-8562; 317-370-1794 (cell)
E-mail: avaprods@comcast.net
Web Site: www.avavideoproductions.com
Key Personnel
Owner: Bud Osborne
Founded: 1980
Catalog(s) available
Membership(s): AES; Digital Cinema Society; NATAS; PPA

A-V Services Inc
99 Fairfield Rd, Fairfield, NJ 07004
Tel: 973-575-5222 *Fax:* 973-575-0857
E-mail: sales@avservices.net
Web Site: www.avservices.net
Key Personnel
CEO: Charles Rodriguez *E-mail:* crodriguez@avservices.net
Pres: Ralph Capria *E-mail:* rcapria@avservices.net
VP, Engg: Joseph Shewchuk *E-mail:* jshewchuk@avservices.net
VP, Fin: Stephen J Inge *E-mail:* singe@avservices.net
VP, Sales: Gary Lanzet *E-mail:* glanzet@avservices.net
Founded: 1960
Provide end-to-end AV solutions from individual "smart rooms" to linked corporate campuses, from local installation to a global multi-site network.
Branch Office(s)
36 Mill Plain Rd, Suite 310, Danbury, CT 06811
1560 Broadway, Suite 1108, New York, NY 10036

A&E Home Video
Subsidiary of A&E Networks
235 E 45 St, New York, NY 10017
Tel: 212-210-1400 *Toll Free Tel:* 877-447-4253
Fax: 212-907-9418
Web Site: www.aetv.com
Key Personnel
Pres & CEO: Nancy Dubuc
EVP, Corp Communs: Michael Feeney
Catalog(s) available

A&E Networks, see A&E Television Networks LLC

A&E Television Networks LLC
Affiliate of Hearst/Disney-ABC Television Group
235 E 45 St, New York, NY 10017
Tel: 212-210-1400
Web Site: www.aetv.com
Key Personnel
Pres & CEO: Paul Buccieri
SVP, Publicity: Dan Silberman
Branch Office(s)
2049 Century Park E, Suite 1000, Los Angeles, CA 90067 *Tel:* 310-556-7500

A&I - Fine Art & Photography
6844 Vineland Ave, North Hollywood, CA 91605
Tel: 818-848-9001
E-mail: support@aandi.com
Web Site: www.aandi.com
Key Personnel
Pres: Phillip Goldner
Founded: 2004
Photographic & digital imaging lab. Fine art photographic printing, photobooks, cards, calendars & head shots.

A&I - ISGO, see A&I - Fine Art & Photography

Aardvark Productions LLC
6738 S La Rosa Dr, Tempe, AZ 85283-3737
Tel: 480-775-8237 *Fax:* 480-775-8237
E-mail: aardvarkproductions@cox.net
Web Site: www.aardvarkproductionsllc.com
Key Personnel
Pres: Jeff H Haymes *Tel:* 310-301-3040 (cell)
World class TV crew, pre-production & production staff. Full line of television production equipment available as well as still production equipment.
Membership(s): IBEW; International Alliance of Theatrical Stage Employees; NABET-CWA; NATAS; Television Academy

Aardvark Video & Media Productions
17 Winding Rd, Henderson, NV 89052
Tel: 702-897-4477 *Toll Free Tel:* 800-692-4445
E-mail: creators@computer.net
Web Site: aardvarkvideolasvegas.com
Founded: 1987
Video production in Las Vegas.
Membership(s): Las Vegas Metro Chamber of Commerce; Las Vegas Videographers Association; WEVA

Aaron Marcus and Associates
1196 Euclid Ave, Berkeley, CA 94708-1640
Tel: 510-599-3195 (cell) *Fax:* 510-527-1994
Web Site: www.bamanda.com
Key Personnel
Principal: Aaron Marcus *E-mail:* aaron.marcus@bamanda.com
Founded: 1982
User-interface design, web design & information visualization. Video editing (conceptual, visual, verbal & story boarding). Interactive media & presentation editing (conceptual, visual & verbal).
Membership(s): AIGA, the professional association for design; Association for Computing Machinery; Special Interest Group for Computer Human Interaction; User Experience Professionals Association

AAVIM, see American Association for Vocational Instructional Materials (AAVIM)

AB Audio Visual Entertainment Inc
PO Box 8020, Long Beach, CA 90808
Tel: 562-429-1042 *Toll Free Tel:* 877-222-8346
Fax: 562-429-2401
E-mail: media@abaudio.com
Web Site: www.abaudio.com
Key Personnel
Pres: Arlan Boll
Founded: 1990

AB Systems Amplifiers
6120 Brace Rd, Loomis, CA 95650
Tel: 916-223-1133
E-mail: absales@abamps.com
Web Site: www.abamps.net
Founded: 1978
High-end home theater, studio & home audio amplifiers.
Membership(s): AES; NAMM, the National Association of Music Merchants; NSCA

Abacus Group of Saint Louis LLC
11 Tower Lane, Glen Carbon, IL 62034
Tel: 314-583-3747
E-mail: abacusgroup@agstl.com
Web Site: www.agstl.com
Key Personnel
Owner: Susan Elliot
Founded: 1971
Motion picture/video/image production & editing company with over 40 years of experience serving national & international clients.
Membership(s): IBEW; International Alliance of Theatrical Stage Employees; NABET-CWA

AbelCine
801 S Main St, Burbank, CA 91506
Toll Free Tel: 888-700-4416
E-mail: orders@abelcine.com; customerservice@abelcine.com
Web Site: www.abelcine.com
Key Personnel
Co-Founder, CEO & Mktg Dir: Pete Abel
Co-Founder & COO: Rich Abel
CFO: Henry Jiang
Dir of Prod Strategies: Joe Facchini
Dir of Sales Opers: Tzvi Gerstle
Dir of Educ: Jeff Lee
Dir of HR: Gala Napakh
Dir of Tech Devt: Jesse Rosen
Dir of Sales: Dawn Terranova
Founded: 1989
Provider of products & services to the production, broadcast & new media industries.
Branch Office(s)
Cinespace Film Studios, 2602 W 16 St, 4th fl, Chicago, IL 60608 *Toll Free Tel:* 877-880-4267
Industry City, 88 35 St, 4th fl, Brooklyn, NY 11232 *Toll Free Tel:* 888-223-1599

Aberdeen Broadcast Services
30071 Tomas, Suite 100, Rancho Santa Margarita, CA 92688
Tel: 949-858-4463 *Toll Free Tel:* 800-688-6621
Fax: 949-858-4405
E-mail: info@abercap.com
Web Site: www.abercap.com
Founded: 2001
Digital file delivery, closed captioning & subtitling, multi-language subtitling.
Membership(s): NRB

Abingdon Press
2222 Rosa L Parks Blvd, Nashville, TN 37228
Mailing Address: PO Box 801, Nashville, TN 37202-0801
Tel: 615-749-6000 *Toll Free Tel:* 800-251-3320
E-mail: orders@abingdonpress.com
Web Site: www.abingdonpress.com
Key Personnel
Exec Dir, Mktg: Tamara Crabtree
Religious publisher, including DVDs, CDs & CD-ROMs.
Catalog(s) available

ABS Enterprises
PO Box 5127, Evanston, IL 60204-5127
Tel: 847-982-1414
Key Personnel
Owner: Alan Soell *E-mail:* alansoell@comcast.net
Full service marketing communications firm.
Membership(s): AECT; AMC; Biomedical Photographers Association; Chicago Audio-Visual Association; Cinema Chicago; IIAC

ABSA Films
757 N Orleans St, No 1001, Chicago, IL 60654
Tel: 312-488-1089
E-mail: info@absafilms.com
Web Site: www.absafilms.com
Key Personnel
Prodr/Dir: Yamil Ahuile
Founded: 1999
Full service video production company.

Absolute Hollywood
10232 Harvest Fields Dr, Woodstock, MD 21163
Tel: 443-341-6424
E-mail: events@absolutehollywood.com
Web Site: absolutehollywood.com
Key Personnel
CEO: James Lanier
Founded: 1993
3D video projection, filming & event production. World's largest video dome, air structures & immersive 360 video display screen structures.

Absolute Rentals
2633 N San Fernando Blvd, Burbank, CA 91504
Tel: 818-842-2828
Web Site: absoluterentals.com
Key Personnel
CEO: Dave Rosen *E-mail:* dave@absoluteliveproductions.com
Founded: 1995
Live streaming & live production services.

Ac-cetera Inc
5049 Center Dr, Bldg D-1, Latrobe, PA 15650
Mailing Address: PO Box 900, Luxor, PA 15662
Tel: 724-532-3362 *Toll Free Tel:* 800-537-3491
Fax: 724-532-3364
Web Site: www.ac-cetera.com
Key Personnel
Owner & Pres: Mike Kairys *E-mail:* mike@mic-eze.com
Founded: 1989
Manufactures work lights, microphone holders & goosenecks, iPads, iPhone & Smart Phone holders.

AC Lighting Inc
88 Horner Ave, Toronto, ON M8Z 5Y3, Canada
Tel: 416-255-9494 *Fax:* 416-255-3514
E-mail: northamerica@aclighting.com
Web Site: www.aclighting.com
Key Personnel
CFO: Michael Krzywicki
VP, US Sales & Mktg: Fred Mikeska *Tel:* 518-321-9672
Mng Dir: J F Canuel
Gen Mgr: Tracey Hill
Distribute stage, studio & event lighting, accessories & consumables.

Academic & Campus Technology Services
Division of Dartmouth College
4 Currier Place, Suite 201, Hanover, NH 03755
Tel: 603-646-2999 (help desk); 603-646-2643
E-mail: itc@dartmouth.edu
Web Site: itc.dartmouth.edu
Key Personnel
Assoc Dir, Classroom Technol Servs: Andrew G Faunce *Tel:* 603-646-3614 *E-mail:* andrew.g.faunce@dartmouth.edu

Academic Media & Digital Services
Affiliate of The University of Oklahoma Health Sciences Center
1105 N Stonewall Ave, Rm 251, Oklahoma City, OK 73117-1221
Tel: 405-271-2318
E-mail: amds@ouhsc.edu
Web Site: www.ouhsc.edu/amds
Lecture capture, videoconferencing, video production, poster printing & AV design/installation services.
Catalog(s) available

Academy Savant
PO Box 3670, Fullerton, CA 92834-3670
Tel: 714-870-7880 *Toll Free Tel:* 800-472-8268
Fax: 714-526-7400
E-mail: info@academysavant.com
Web Site: www.academysavant.com
Key Personnel
Pres: Robin D Lai
Founded: 1977
Develop, publish & distribute computer based AV training programs for analytical laboratories.
Catalog(s) available
Online catalog(s) available

Accelerated Learning Foundation
402 N Third St, Fairfield, IA 52556
Tel: 641-954-5443 *Toll Free Tel:* 800-289-2377
Fax: 641-954-5851
E-mail: info@gamesforthinkers.org
Web Site: www.gamesforthinkers.org
Key Personnel
Pres & Dir, Sales & Training: Layman G (Buzz) Allen
Central Off & Warehouse Mgr: Gail Crotta
Produce & distribute educational games & puzzles.
Catalog(s) available

Accenture
161 N Clark St, Chicago, IL 60601
Tel: 312-693-0161 *Toll Free Tel:* 877-889-9009
Fax: 312-693-0507
Web Site: www.accenture.com
Key Personnel
CEO, North America: Julie Sweet
CFO: David P Rowland
COO: Ju Deblaere
Chief Leadership & HR Offr: Ellyn J Shook
Chief Mktg & Communs Offr: Roxanne Taylor
Chief of Staff, Off of Chmn & CEO: Laurence Morvan
Chief Strategy Offr: Omar Abbosh
Chief Technol & Innovation Offr: Paul R Daugherty
Gen Coun & Chief Compliance Offr: Chad T Jerdee
Group Chief Exec, Accenture Digital: Michael R Sutcliff
Group Chief Exec, Accenture Opers: Debra A Polishook
Group Chief Exec, Accenture Strategy: Mark A Knickrehm
Group Chief Exec, Accenture Technol Servs: Bhaskar Ghosh
Group Chief Exec, Communs, Media & Technol: Robert E Sell
Group Chief Exec, Fin Servs: Richard Lumb
Group Chief Exec, Growth Mkts: Gianfranco Casati
Group Chief Exec, Health & Public Serv: Dan T London

Group Chief Exec, Prods: Sander Van't Noordende

Group Chief Exec, Resources: Jean-Marc Ollasnier

Global professional services company, providing a broad range of services & solutions in strategy, consulting, digital, technology & operations.
Branch Office(s)
3200 E Camelback, Suite 245, Phoenix, AZ 85018 *Tel:* 602-337-4000 *Fax:* 602-337-4444
2141 Rosecrans Ave, Suite 3100, El Segundo, CA 90245 *Tel:* 310-726-2700 *Fax:* 310-726-2950
1415 "L" St, Suite 700, Sacramento, CA 95814 *Tel:* 916-557-2200
750 "B" St, Suite 2820, San Diego, CA 92101
1700 Sea Port Blvd, Redwood City, San Francisco, CA 94063
50 W San Fernando St, Suite 1200, San Jose, CA 95113 *Tel:* 408-817-2700
1400 16 St, Suite 500, Denver, CO 80202 *Tel:* 720-359-6500 *Fax:* 720-359-6750
One Financial Plaza, Suite 1600, Hartford, CT 06103 *Tel:* 860-756-2000 *Fax:* 860-756-2890
501 Carr Rd, Wilmington, DE 19809 *Tel:* 302-830-5800 *Fax:* 302-830-5801
800 Connecticut Ave NW, Suite 600, Washington, DC 20006 *Tel:* 202-533-1100 *Fax:* 202-533-1111
5201 Blue Lagoon Dr, Suite 250, Miami, FL 33126 *Tel:* 786-425-7000 *Fax:* 305-358-3122
75 Fifth St NW, Suite 1100, Atlanta, GA 30308 *Tel:* 678-657-8000 *Fax:* 678-657-4050
Rogus City Ctr, 201 N Illinois St, 16th fl, South Tower, Indianapolis, IN 46204 *Tel:* 317-267-3400 *Fax:* 317-267-3450
Prudential Tower, Suite 2300, 800 Boylston St, Boston, MA 02199 *Tel:* 617-488-4000 *Fax:* 617-488-4001
3000 Town Ctr, Suite 2400, Southfield, MI 48075 *Tel:* 313-887-2000 *Fax:* 313-887-2050
333 S Seventh St, Minneapolis, MN 55402 *Tel:* 612-277-0000 *Fax:* 612-277-1010
Marquette Bldg, 300 N Broadway, St Louis, MO 63102 *Tel:* 314-345-3000 *Fax:* 314-345-3505
500 Campus Dr, Florham Park, NJ 07932 *Tel:* 973-301-1000 *Fax:* 973-301-1005
1345 Avenue of the Americas, New York, NY 10105 *Tel:* 917-452-4400 *Fax:* 917-527-9915
201 S College St, Suite 1900, Charlotte, NC 28244 *Tel:* 704-332-6411 *Fax:* 704-370-5700
One Renaissance Ctr, Suite 503, 3301 Benson Dr, Raleigh, NC 27609 *Tel:* 919-836-1200 *Fax:* 919-821-0561
Atrium One, 201 E Fourth St, Suite 1600, Cincinnati, OH 45202-1604 *Tel:* 513-455-1000 *Fax:* 513-455-1604
1400 W Tenth St, Suite 400, Cleveland, OH 44113 *Tel:* 216-535-5000 *Fax:* 216-535-5350
400 W Nationwide Blvd, Suite 100, Columbus, OH 43215 *Tel:* 614-629-2000 *Fax:* 614-629-2001
One Commerce Sq, 15th fl, 2005 Market St, Philadelphia, PA 19103 *Tel:* 267-216-1000 *Fax:* 267-216-0100
K&L Gates Ctr, 210 Sixth Ave, Suite 3650, Pittsburgh, PA 15222 *Tel:* 412-937-6000 *Fax:* 412-937-6005
1501 S MoPac Expwy, Suite 300, Austin, TX 78746 *Tel:* 512-732-5300 *Fax:* 512-476-7765
1301 Fannin St, Suite 1900, Houston, TX 77002 *Tel:* 713-483-9090 *Fax:* 713-483-9091
5221 N O'Connor Blvd, Suite 1400, Irving, TX 75039 *Tel:* 469-665-0000 *Fax:* 469-665-2000
BPO, 6415 Babcock Rd, Suite 100, San Antonio, TX 78249 *Tel:* 210-699-2400
800 N Glebe Rd, Suite 300, Arlington, VA 22203 *Tel:* 703-947-2000 *Fax:* 703-947-2200
818 Stewart St, Suite 400, Seattle, WA 98101 *Tel:* 206-839-2000 *Fax:* 206-839-2008
111 E Kilbourn, Suite 1200, Milwaukee, WI 53202 *Tel:* 414-212-1000 *Fax:* 414-212-3620

Access Media Group
Division of Hi-Tech Enterprises Inc

4250 114 Terr N, Clearwater, FL 33762
Tel: 727-573-9600 *Toll Free Tel:* 888-354-2510
Fax: 727-573-9606
E-mail: hitech@videoequipment.com
Web Site: www.videoequipment.com
Founded: 1984
Video production, rentals, editing & duplication.
Membership(s): Media Professionals of Florida Inc

Access Video in Berkeley
1442 A Walnut St, Berkeley, CA 94709
Tel: 510-528-6044
E-mail: accessvideo@hotmail.com
Web Site: www.accessvideoproductions.com
Key Personnel
Prodn: David Karp
A full service video production & post-production facility. Services include event videography, live video streaming & Avid video editing.

ACCO Brands Corp
4 Corporate Dr, Lake Zurick, IL 60047-8997
Toll Free Tel: 800-541-0094; 800-222-6462
Toll Free Fax: 800-941-4463
E-mail: contactus@acco.com (cust serv)
Web Site: www.accobrands.com
Key Personnel
Chmn, Pres & CEO: Boris Elisman
EVP & CFO: Neal V Fenwick
SVP & CIO: Joseph S Pekala
EVP & Pres, ACCO Brands North America: Thomas W Tedford
EVP & Pres, ACCO Brands International: Patrick Buchenroth
EVP & Pres, EMEA: Cezary L Monko
SVP & Global Chief People Offr: Ralph Hargrow
SVP, Corp Devt: Mark C Anderson
SVP, Gen Coun & Corp Secy: Pamela R Schneider
SVP & Mng Dir, Australia & New Zealand: Bruce Haynes
SVP & Corp Cont: Kathleen D Schnaedter
SVP, Global Prods: Greg McCormack
SVP, Strategic Initiatives: Neil McLachlan
VP & Treas: Jagannath Bobji
VP, Corp Communs: Richard Nelson
VP, Investor Rel: Jennifer Rice
VP, Premium Prods Group: Scott Buttle
Brands include Quartet® whiteboard, bulletin & chalkboard products.
Catalog(s) available
Membership(s): Audiovisual and Integrated Experience Association; Business Technology Association; The Imaging Alliance; NAB; NOPA

Accord Productions
2140 S Dixie Hwy, Suite 301, Miami, FL 33133
Tel: 305-856-1245; 305-985-5842
Toll Free Tel: 800-833-1245 *Fax:* 305-856-9101
E-mail: mail@accordvideo.com
Web Site: www.accordproductions.com
Key Personnel
Pres: William Wyler
VP: Rocky Wyler
Mktg Dir: Max Wyler *E-mail:* max@accordvideo.com
Opers Mgr: Jeff Somerstein
Post-Prodn Supv: Michael Ball
Founded: 1988
Video & audio production & post-production, digital asset management system (ADAM), digitization & duplication services.
Membership(s): Independent Media Producers Association

Accu-Tech
11350 Old Roswell Rd, Suite 100, Roswell, GA 30009
Toll Free Tel: 888-222-8832
Web Site: www.accu-tech.com

Key Personnel
Pres: Brian Michel
VP, Natl Accts: Keith Hopkins
Dir, Mktg: Brian Brown
Dir, Security Solutions: Joe Essma
Founded: 1984
Distributor of voice, data, AV, wireless & security solutions.
Online catalog(s) available
Branch Office(s)
660 Hembree Pkwy, Suite 100, Roswell, GA 30076, Mgr: Todd Delavie *Tel:* 770-751-9473 *Toll Free Tel:* 800-221-4767
241 Lyon Lane, Birmingham, AL 35211, Mgr: Brad Moore *Tel:* 205-942-0366 *Toll Free Tel:* 800-368-0265
2360 W Broadway Rd, Suite 102, Mesa, AZ 85202-1885, Mgr: David Gay *Tel:* 480-615-4804 *Toll Free Tel:* 800-824-0180
2351 Lincoln Ave, Hayward, CA 94545, Mgr: Jesse Friedman *Tel:* 510-477-8060 *Toll Free Tel:* 800-470-2759
16801 Knott Ave, No D, La Mirada, CA 90638, Mgr: Shannon Van Malsen *Tel:* 714-994-8000 *Toll Free Tel:* 866-293-2514
830 W National Dr, Suite 100, Sacramento, CA 95834, Mgr: Jesse Friedman *Tel:* 916-574-9257 *Toll Free Tel:* 800-470-2759
7025 S Revere Pkwy, Suite 300, Centennial, CO 80112, Mgr: Jennifer Hall *Tel:* 720-460-3400 *Toll Free Tel:* 844-209-9273
6631 Executive Park Ct, Suite 208, Jacksonville, FL 32216, Mgr: Chris Havel *Tel:* 904-281-9834 *Toll Free Tel:* 855-291-9834
1571 W Copans Rd, Suite 102, Pompano Beach, FL 33064-2054, Mgr: Trent Little *Tel:* 954-788-0016 *Toll Free Tel:* 800-951-5966
119 Hamilton Dr, Tallahassee, FL 32304, Mgr: John Campbell *Tel:* 850-210-0168 *Toll Free Tel:* 888-838-3166
9220 Palm River Rd, Bldg 1, Suite 103, Tampa, FL 33619-4426, Mgr: Josh Dobnikar *Tel:* 813-664-1919 *Toll Free Tel:* 800-493-8328
1660 Wall St, Suite 200, Mount Prospect, IL 60056, Mgr: Nate Schuller *Tel:* 630-226-0133 *Toll Free Tel:* 866-417-0133
15731 W 100 Terr, Bldg 3, Lenexa, KS 66219, Mgr: Kevin Weiss *Tel:* 913-894-0444 *Toll Free Tel:* 800-810-5666
1328 Charwood Rd, Suite 600, Hanover, MD 21076-3113, Mgr: Josh McCullough *Tel:* 410-694-9621 *Toll Free Tel:* 800-490-4580
23R Rainin Rd, Woburn, MA 01801, Mgr: Chris DeFeo *Tel:* 617-894-2826 *Toll Free Tel:* 866-822-8656
13114 Waco Ct, Livonia, MI 48150-1460, Mgr: Dan Walker *Tel:* 734-524-8385 *Toll Free Tel:* 800-228-1016
9775 85 Ave N, Maple Grove, MN 55369, Mgr: Tom Quanbeck *Tel:* 612-656-7912
13231 Centennial Rd, Suite 3, Omaha, NE 68138, Mgr: Tom Regan *Tel:* 402-408-4580 *Toll Free Tel:* 855-533-7260
109 Amfresco Dr, Plainview, NY 11803, Mgr: Kevin Lynch *Tel:* 516-249-5790 *Toll Free Tel:* 800-880-9517
2801-A Hutchison-McDonald Rd, Charlotte, NC 28269, Mgr: Dion Roberts *Tel:* 704-599-9997 *Toll Free Tel:* 800-770-0006
200 Innovation Ave, Suite 110, Morrisville, NC 27560, Mgr: Darrell Davis *Tel:* 919-484-8500 *Toll Free Tel:* 866-243-3916
2305 International St, Columbus, OH 43228-4622, Mgr: Jon Park *Tel:* 614-527-9600 *Toll Free Tel:* 800-414-3777
235 Hope St, Carnegie, PA 15106, Mgr: Brandon Apple *Tel:* 412-275-8526 *Toll Free Tel:* 888-456-4206
Essex Bldg, Darby Commons, Bay 6, Folcroft, PA 19032, Mgr: Vince Rizzo *Tel:* 610-583-7789 *Toll Free Tel:* 866-858-0838
7260 Peppermill Pkwy, Charleston, SC 29418, Mgr: Hank Frailey *Tel:* 843-767-1771 *Toll Free Tel:* 866-851-9468

5200 Pelham Rd, Suite B, Greenville, SC 29615, Mgr: Brian Hughes *Tel:* 864-288-3765 *Toll Free Tel:* 888-457-2900

1417 Donelson Pike, Nashville, TN 37217-2957, Mgr: Patrick Laughter *Tel:* 615-399-2123 *Toll Free Tel:* 800-227-0628

1500 Luna Rd, Suite 108, Carrollton, TX 75006, Mgr: Brent Campbell *Tel:* 972-488-9233 *Toll Free Tel:* 800-895-5792

8790 West Rd, Suite 190, Houston, TX 77064, Mgr: Steve Bellew *Tel:* 713-647-9995 *Toll Free Tel:* 800-909-5995

1421 Wells Branch Pkwy, Suite 100, Pflugerville, TX 78660, Mgr: Greg Huffman *Tel:* 512-719-3155 *Toll Free Tel:* 800-432-0325

12625 Wetmore Rd, Suite 207, San Antonio, TX 78247, Mgr: Mark Garcia *Tel:* 210-402-0316 *Toll Free Tel:* 877-803-0162

901 Live Oak Dr, Chesapeake, VA 23320, Mgr: Dave Rivera *Tel:* 757-523-4100 *Toll Free Tel:* 800-362-6612

2256 Dabney Rd, Suite A, Richmond, VA 23230, Mgr: Walter Baker *Tel:* 804-204-1507 *Toll Free Tel:* 866-255-7876

1109 Andover Park W, Tukwila, WA 98188, Mgr: Sean Mallery *Tel:* 206-575-2820 *Toll Free Tel:* 866-423-2590

Accusoft
4001 N Riverside Dr, Tampa, FL 33603
Tel: 813-875-7575 *Toll Free Tel:* 800-875-7009
  Fax: 813-875-7705
E-mail: sales@accusoft.com
Web Site: www.accusoft.com
Key Personnel
Founder, Pres & CEO: Jack Berlin
CFO: Anthony Sanchez
VP, Architecture & Chief of Staff: Jim Bean
VP, Engg & Dir, SaaS: Susan Gorman
VP, Prod: Steve Wilson
VP, Sales: Russ Puskaric
Dir, HR: Christine Hairelson
Dir, SDKs: Tom Setzer
Dir, Self-Hosted Solutions: John Armenia
Founded: 1991
Provide document & imaging technology for developers.
Branch Office(s)
4 Mount Royal Ave, Suite 110, Marlborough, MA 01752

AccuWeather Inc
385 Science Park Rd, State College, PA 16803
Tel: 814-237-0309 *Toll Free Tel:* 800-566-6606
E-mail: sales@accuweather.com
Web Site: www.accuweather.com
Key Personnel
Founder & Pres: Dr Joel N Myers
CEO: Barry Myers
COO: Evan A Myers
Founded: 1962
Weather forecasts, video, customized content & presentations through smartphones, tablets, free & wired mobile Internet sites.

ACDC Audio CD & Cassette
606 Alamo Pintado Rd, Suite 3-281, Solvang, CA 93463
Tel: 818-762-ACDC (762-2232)
Web Site: www.acdc-cdr.com
Key Personnel
Owner: Steve Mitchell *E-mail:* steve@acdc-cdr.com
Founded: 1983
Audio & video duplication.

Ace Video
178 Columbus Ave, No 237072, New York, NY 10023
Tel: 212-727-7969
E-mail: acevideonyc@gmail.com
Web Site: www.acevideonyc.com

Key Personnel
Mgr: Michael Temmer
Founded: 1968
Consult, maintain & repair AV installations & manage event productions. Rent equipment & personnel for AV events & retail installations.
Online catalog(s) available
Membership(s): AES; SMPTE®

Acey Decy Lighting
200 Parkside Dr, San Fernando, CA 91340
Tel: 818-408-4444 *Fax:* 818-408-2777
Web Site: www.aceydecy.com
Founded: 1963
Equipment, rental, sales & service for film, television, theatre, concerts & events. Specialize in grip trucks, moving lights, special effects & dimmers. Factory authorized sales & service center for high-end, ETC & strand lighting. Complete line of expendables for all your needs.
Online catalog(s) available

ACM Productions Ltd
38 Bob Hill Rd, Ridgefield, CT 06877
Tel: 203-431-9575
E-mail: info@acmproductions.tv
Web Site: www.acmproductions.tv
Key Personnel
Pres: A J Mikhitarian
VP: Craig Mikhitarian

Acme Filmworks Inc
3347 Motor Ave, Los Angeles, CA 90034
Tel: 323-464-7805 *Fax:* 323-464-6614
E-mail: pr@acmefilmworks.com (publicity)
Web Site: www.acmefilmworks.com
Key Personnel
Exec Prodr: Ron Diamond *E-mail:* rjd@acmefilmworks.com
Prodr: Tara Beyhm *E-mail:* tara@acmefilmworks.com
Animation studio producing commercials, short films, feature films, music videos, title sequences & interactive media.

Acme Recording Studios Inc
112 W Boston Post Rd, Mamaroneck, NY 10543
Web Site: www.acmerec.com
Key Personnel
Owner, Prodr & Engr: Peter Denenberg
  E-mail: pdenenberg@acmerec.com
Founded: 1979

ACO Pacific Inc
2604 Read Ave, Belmont, CA 94002
Tel: 650-595-8588 *Fax:* 650-591-2891
E-mail: sales@acopacific.com; info@acopacific.com; support@acopacific.com
Web Site: www.acopacific.com
Key Personnel
Pres: Noland L Lewis
Founded: 1978
Manufacturer of measurement mics & systems, sound level alarms & monitors, noise generators.
Catalog(s) available
Membership(s): AES; ASA; CAS; INCE

Acorn Productions
13330 Noel Rd, No 1428, Dallas, TX 75240
Tel: 972-385-9977 *Fax:* 972-385-9944
E-mail: acornprod@aol.com
Key Personnel
Owner & Pres: Tony Metcalfe
Video production, AV services, sound & lighting for corporate events.

acouStaCorp
Division of Texas Scenic Co Inc
701 E 132 St, Bronx, NY 10454

Tel: 718-402-2677 *Fax:* 718-402-2859
E-mail: info@texasscenic.com
Web Site: acoustacorp.texasscenic.com
Key Personnel
CEO: Barbara Pook
Dir, Engg & Prodn: Tony Diemont
Sales & Serv: Kevin Cushing *E-mail:* k.cushing@texasscenic.com
Sales: Mark McKinney *E-mail:* m.mckinney@texasscenic.com
Founded: 2009
Design & manufacture variable acoustic products.
Online catalog(s) available
Membership(s): National Council of Acoustical Consultants

Acoustical Solutions LLC
2420 Grenoble Rd, Richmond, VA 23294
Tel: 804-346-8350 *Toll Free Tel:* 800-782-5742
  Fax: 804-346-8808
E-mail: info@acousticalsolutions.com
Web Site: www.acousticalsolutions.com
Key Personnel
Pres: Joe Niemann
VP, Sales: Gary Hudson
Sound & noise control products & acoustical materials.
Catalog(s) available
Membership(s): Audiovisual and Integrated Experience Association; NAB

Acoustics First Corp
2247 Tomlyn St, Richmond, VA 23230-3334
Tel: 804-342-2900 *Toll Free Tel:* 888-765-2900
  Fax: 804-342-1107
E-mail: info@acousticsfirst.com
Web Site: www.acousticsfirst.com
Key Personnel
Pres, Sales: Rebecca Colleran
Mktg Dir: Nick Colleran
Accoustical materials.
Catalog(s) available

Acoustone Corp
140 58 St, Suite W, Brooklyn, NY 11220
Tel: 718-782-5560 *Toll Free Tel:* 800-782-5742
  Fax: 718-782-7367
E-mail: acoustone@newcastlefabrics.com; info@acousticalsolutions.com
Web Site: www.acoustonegrillecloth.com
Key Personnel
VP: Larry Lubliner
Manufacturer of grille cloth designed for acoustical panels, wall treatments & ceilings.
Catalog(s) available

ACS Professional Education, see American Chemical Society (ACS)

ACS Technologies
180 Dunbarton Dr, Florence, SC 29501
Tel: 843-662-1681 *Toll Free Tel:* 800-736-7425
  (sales); 800-669-2309 (support) *Fax:* 843-669-7513
E-mail: info@acstechnologies.com
Web Site: www.acstechnologies.com
Key Personnel
Chmn of the Bd & VP: Paige Tuttle
CFO: Craig Hearon
Chief Busn Devt Offr: Steve Kriter
Pres: Marvin Owen
VP: Tommy Rogers
Sr Dir, Catholic Mkt: Johnny Stoupenos
Sr Dir, Cust Satisfaction: Donna Howell
Sr Dir, Enterprise Churches: Pattie White
Sr Dir, HR: Cary Ashworth
Sr Dir, IT: Dean Lisenby
Sr Dir, Mktg: John Gilman
Sr Dir, R&D: Steve Cumbia
Sr Dir, Sales: Art Wright
Sr Dir, Schools & Organizations: Calvin Moreau
Founded: 1978

Information management solutions for churches, schools & other faith-based organizations.
Catalog(s) available

ACT Productions
407 Lincoln Rd, Suite 302, Miami Beach, FL 33139
Tel: 305-538-3809 *Fax:* 305-538-3814
E-mail: info@actproductions.com
Web Site: www.actproductions.com
Key Personnel
Pres & CEO: Bruce Orosz
Dir, Opers: Barbara Goicoechea
Digital Media Dir: Aram Velazquez
Commercial, corporate video, documentary, film, photo shoot & TV production support.

ACTA Publications
4848 N Clark St, Chicago, IL 60640
Tel: 773-271-1030 *Toll Free Tel:* 800-397-2282
Fax: 773-271-7399 *Toll Free Fax:* 800-397-0079
E-mail: actapublications@actapublications.com
Web Site: www.actapublications.com
Key Personnel
Pres & Publr: Gregory F Augustine-Pierce
Founded: 1957
A religious book, audio & video publishing company & distributor of select religious AV products produced by others.
Catalog(s) available
Membership(s): Association of Catholic Publishers Inc

Action Audio & Visual
5907 Yarmouth Ave, Encino, CA 91316
Tel: 818-760-2585
E-mail: info@actionaudioandvisual.com
Web Site: www.actionaudioandvisual.com
Founded: 2001
Audio, camera, AV presentation, lighting, grip & projector rentals. Crew & event services.

Action Photo Digital Graphics
1741 Clayton Rd, Concord, CA 94520
Tel: 925-676-7777
E-mail: actionps@sbcglobal.net
Web Site: www.actionphotoservice.com
Key Personnel
Owner: Dennis Hamilton
Founded: 1963
Professional full service photo lab & digital imaging specialists.
Online catalog(s) available
Membership(s): The Imaging Alliance

Action Sports/All Stock
Subsidiary of All-Stock Footage
PO Box 301, Malibu, CA 90265-0301
Tel: 310-459-2526
E-mail: info@actionsportsstockfootage.com
Web Site: www.actionsportsstockfootage.com; www.allstockfootage.com
Key Personnel
Owner & Pres: Scott Dittrich
Content Mgr: Ellen Runnell
Founded: 1985
Stock library & production services.

Action Video
2373 Walnut Blvd, Walnut Creek, CA 94597
Tel: 925-934-4366
E-mail: actvid@aol.com
Web Site: actionvideo.biz
Key Personnel
Owner: Lester Howard
Founded: 1983
Video production & duplication.

Activu Corp
301 Roundhill Dr, Rockaway, NJ 07866
Tel: 973-366-5550 *Toll Free Tel:* 888-ACTIVU1 (228-4881) *Fax:* 973-625-7775
E-mail: facebook@activu.com
Web Site: activu.com
Key Personnel
Founder & CEO: Paul Noble
COO: Bob Hinkle
CTO: Chris Bryczkowski
VP, Prodn Mgmt: John Stark
VP, Sales: John Desmond
Mktg Mgr: Avery Quayle
Founded: 1983
Delivers a scalable visualization platform for control rooms & mobile devices. Our solution integrates with other applications to provide information when & where it's needed in order to provide greater situational awareness & collaboration.
Online catalog(s) available
Branch Office(s)
1100 Wilson Blvd, Suite 1225, Arlington, VA 22209 *Tel:* 703-527-4440 *Fax:* 571-312-7581
Membership(s): Audiovisual and Integrated Experience Association

Actors Attic
540 Otis Dr, Dover, DE 19901
Tel: 302-734-8214 *Fax:* 302-734-8207
E-mail: sales@actorsattic.com
Web Site: www.actorsattic.com
Key Personnel
Owner: Susan Betts; Mark Fels
Founded: 1981
Everything for stage & theatre—costume, makeup, staging & lighting rentals & sales.

Acuity Brands Lighting Inc
One Lithonia Way, Conyers, GA 30012
Tel: 770-922-9000
E-mail: info@acuitybrands.com
Web Site: www.acuitybrands.com
Lighting solutions include luminaries, lighting controls, lighting components, power supplies & skylights. Building management solutions include controls for building systems (HVAC, lighting, shades & access control).
Online catalog(s) available
Branch Office(s)
1170 Peachtree St, Suite 2300, Atlanta, GA 30309 *Toll Free Tel:* 800-922-9641 (corp headquarters)

ADAM Inc
Unit of Ebix Inc
One Ebix Way, Johns Creek, GA 30097
Tel: 770-625-3450 *Toll Free Tel:* 800-755-ADAM (755-2326)
E-mail: aod-info@ebix.com
Web Site: www.adam.com
Key Personnel
Chmn & CEO: Robin Raina
Founded: 1990
Health care information & multimedia visual learning assets.
Branch Office(s)
6855 De L'Epee, Suite 200, Montreal, QC H3N 2C7, Canada *Toll Free Tel:* 888-278-9614
Foreign Office(s): Evoma Business Ctr, No 14, Bhattrahali, Old Madras Rd, K R Puram, Bangalore 560 049, India *Tel:* (080) 4190-3696
122/123 NSEZ Phase II, Noida 201 305, India *Tel:* (0120) 468-8400 *Fax:* (0120) 246-0870

Adams Creative & Production Services
PO Box 98636, Des Moines, WA 98198-0636
Tel: 206-300-1094 (cell) *Fax:* 206-824-7036
Key Personnel
Owner, Pres & Creative Dir: Dan Adams
E-mail: adamsdl@comcast.net
Founded: 1976
Business communications media design & production.

D L Adams Associates Inc
1536 Ogden St, Denver, CO 80218
Tel: 303-455-1900
E-mail: infodenver@dlaa.com
Web Site: www.dlaa.com
Key Personnel
Principal & Engr: Ben Bridgewater; Stephanie Adams-Ball
Founded: 1979
Acoustical, AV, theater design & technology engineering consultants.
Branch Office(s)
D L Adams Associates Ltd, 970 N Kalaheo Ave, Suite A-311, Kailua, HI 96734, Principal & Engr: David Adams *Tel:* 808-254-3318
E-mail: infohawaii@dlaa.com (subsidiary)
Membership(s): AES; ASA; Audiovisual and Integrated Experience Association; Entertainment Services and Technology Association; National Council of Acoustical Consultants; USITT

D L Adams Associates Ltd
Subsidiary of D L Adams Associates Inc
970 N Kalaheo Ave, Suite A-311, Kailua, HI 96734
Tel: 808-254-3318
E-mail: infohawaii@dlaa.com
Web Site: www.dlaa.com
Key Personnel
Principal & Engr: David Adams
Founded: 1990
Acoustical, AV, theater design & technology engineering consultants.
Membership(s): AES; ASA; Audiovisual and Integrated Experience Association; Entertainment Services and Technology Association; National Council of Acoustical Consultants; USITT

Adams Evidence Grade Technology Inc
4123 N Little Creek Rd, Utopia, TX 78884
Mailing Address: PO Box 1216, Utopia, TX 78884-1216
Tel: 830-966-4210 *Toll Free Tel:* 877-643-4900
Fax: 830-966-4214
E-mail: info1@evidencegrade.com; customerservice@evidencegrade.com
Web Site: www.evidencegrade.com
Key Personnel
Pres: Brian Gilliam *E-mail:* brian@evidencegrade.com
Founded: 1981
Optical media & evidence towers for government & law enforcement.
Online catalog(s) available

Adaptive Technologies Group Inc
1635 E Burnett St, Signal Hill, CA 90755
Tel: 562-424-1100
E-mail: sales@adaptivetechnologiesgroup.com
Web Site: www.adaptivetechnologiesgroup.com
Key Personnel
Pres: Paul Allen
Founded: 1987
Designer of certified, pre-engineered professional loudspeaker mounts & rigging systems for permanent installations & live performances. Creates digital signage video wall frames & structures. Design, engineer & manufacture custom & standard cinema-centered mounts.
Online catalog(s) available

Adcis Inc
Subsidiary of ADCIS SA
PO Box 6473, Monroe Township, NJ 08831-6473
Tel: 609-944-8855 *Toll Free Tel:* 877-664-8772
E-mail: info@adcis.net
Web Site: www.adcis.net
Founded: 1986

Develop & market image processing/analysis software products.
Foreign Office(s): 3 rue Martin Luther King, 14280 Saint-Contest, France, Pres & CEO: Bruno Lay *Tel:* 02 31 06 23 00

ADD Plus
488 Glacier Way S, Monmouth, OR 97361
Toll Free Tel: 800-847-1233 *Fax:* 503-838-1608
Web Site: www.add-plus.com
Key Personnel
Dir: Dr John Taylor *E-mail:* drtaylor@add-plus.com
Founded: 1993
Training & resources for Attention Deficit Hyperactivity Disorder (ADHD) & related conditions.
Online catalog(s) available

Adelphi Records Inc
PO Box 7688, Silver Spring, MD 20907-7688
Tel: 301-434-6958 *Fax:* 301-434-3056
E-mail: adelphi@adelphirecords.com
Web Site: www.adelphirecords.com
Key Personnel
CEO & Pres: Gene Rosenthal *E-mail:* gene@adelphirecords.com
Busn Mgr: Hap Passman *E-mail:* hap@adelphirecords.com

ADI Global Distribution
263 Old Country Rd, Melville, NY 11747
Toll Free Tel: 800-233-6261 (sales/serv); 800-234-7971 (prod/systems)
E-mail: awebadmin@adi-dist.com
Web Site: adiglobal.us
Wholesale distributor of security & low voltage products, including closed circuit TV, commercial sound & intercom products & video surveillance equipment. Over 100 North America branch locations.

ADI Systems Inc, see ADI Global Distribution

Adobe Systems Inc
345 Park Ave, San Jose, CA 95110-2704
Tel: 408-536-6000 *Fax:* 408-537-6000
Web Site: www.adobe.com
Key Personnel
Founder & Chmn of the Bd: Dr Charles M Geschke; Dr John E Warnock
Pres & CEO: Shantanu Narayen
EVP, Gen Coun & Corp Secy: Michael Dillon
EVP & CFO: Mark Garrett
EVP & CTO: Abhay Paranis
EVP & Chief Mktg Offr: Ann Lewnes
EVP & Gen Mgr, Digital Mktg: Brad Rencher
EVP & Gen Mgr, Digital Media: Bryan Lamkin
EVP, Cust & Employee Experience: Donna Morris
EVP, Worldwide Field Opers: Matt Thompson
SVP, Engg Technol Group: Digby Horner
Founded: 1982
Branch Office(s)
601 Townsend St, San Francisco, CA 94103
  Tel: 415-832-2000 *Fax:* 415-832-2020
275 Washington St, 3rd fl, Newton, MA 02458
  Tel: 617-766-2360 *Fax:* 617-658-2190 (Boston off)
3900 Northwoods, 3rd fl, Arden Hills, MN
  Tel: 651-766-4700 *Fax:* 651-766-4750
1540 Broadway, 17th fl, New York, NY 10036
  Tel: 212-471-0904 *Fax:* 212-471-0990
532 Broadway, 7th fl, New York, NY 10036
  Tel: 646-918-7738 *Fax:* 646-861-6495
18 E 16 St, 7th fl, New York, NY 10003
  Tel: 646-480-3670 *Fax:* 212-242-3273
3900 Adobe Way, Lehi, UT 84043 *Tel:* 385-345-0000
7930 Jones Branch Dr, 5th fl, McLean, VA 22102
  Tel: 571-765-5400 *Fax:* 571-765-5450 (Washington, DC off)

801 N 34 St, Seattle, WA 98103 *Tel:* 206-675-7000
Adobe Systems Canada, 343 Preston St, Ottawa, ON K1S 1N4, Canada *Tel:* 613-940-3676 *Fax:* 613-594-8886
Foreign Office(s): Adobe Systems Pty Ltd, Tower 2, Level 27, 201 Sussex St, Sydney, NSW 2000, Australia *Tel:* (02) 9778 4100 *Fax:* (02) 9778 4190
Adobe Systems Pty Ltd, One Queens Rd, Suite 1001, Melbourne, Victoria 3004, Australia *Tel:* (03) 9778 4162 *Fax:* (03) 9863 8010
Adobe Systems Benelux BV, Park Lane Bldg F, 1st fl, Culliganlaan 2F, 1831 Diegem, Belgium *Tel:* (02) 416 40 00 *Fax:* (02) 416 40 09
Adobe Systems Brazil, Rua James Joule 65, Conjunto 141, Condominio Edificio Torre Sul, 04576-080 Sao Paulo-SP, Brazil *Tel:* (011) 2175 9595 *Fax:* (011) 3842 9539
0909, 9/F, China World Tower, No 1 Jian-GuoMenWai Ave, Beijing 100004, China *Tel:* (010) 58657700 *Fax:* (010) 58657701
35/F Citic Sq, 1168 Nanjing Rd W, Shanghai 200041, China *Tel:* (010) 58657700 *Fax:* (021) 52524616
Avenir Business Park, Radlicka 714/113a, 158 00 Prague 5, Czechia *Tel:* 225 020 900 *Fax:* 225 020 909
Adobe Systems Danmark ApS, Islands Brygge 57, 2300 Copenhagen, Denmark *Tel:* 3231 6000 *Fax:* 3231 6001
Adobe Systems France SAS, Tour Maine Montparnasse, 112, ave Kleber, 75784 Paris Cedex 16, France *Tel:* 01 56 54 99 00 *Fax:* 01 56 54 99 01
Adobe Sytems Engineering GmbH, Grosse Elbstr 27, 22767 Hamburg, Germany *Tel:* (040) 306 36 0 *Fax:* (040) 306 36 333
Adobe Systems GmbH, Georg-Brauchle-Ring 58, 80992 Munich, Germany *Tel:* (089) 31 70 50 *Fax:* (089) 31 70 57 05
The Lee Gardens, Suite 4102, 41/F, 33 Hysan Ave, Causeway Bay, Hong Kong *Tel:* 2916 2100 *Fax:* 2970 2277
Salarpuria Infinity, 3rd fl, 5 Bannerghatta Rd, Bangalore 560 029, India *Tel:* (080) 41939500 *Fax:* (080) 41939505 *Web Site:* www.adobeindia.com
518/519 Midas Sahar Plaza Complex, Andheri (E), Mumbai 400 059, India *Tel:* (022) 40308809 *Fax:* (022) 28365167
Adobe Systems India Pvt Ltd, Adobe Towers, I-1A City Centre, Sector 25A, Noida 201 301, India *Tel:* (0120) 244 4711 *Fax:* (0120) 433 3427 *Web Site:* www.adobeindia.com
Adobe Systems Software Ireland Ltd, 4-6 Riverwalk, Citywest Business Campus, Dublin 24, Ireland *Tel:* (01) 242 6700 *Fax:* (01) 242 6711
Adobe Systems Israel, 8 Aba Even Blvd, 46725 Herzlia, Israel *Tel:* (09) 9614025
Adobe Systems Italia SRL, Viale Colleoni 5, Centro Direzlionale Colleoni, Palazzo Taurus A3, 20041 Milan MI, Italy *Tel:* (02) 039 6550 1 *Fax:* (02) 039 6550 50
Adobe Systems Roma, c/o Tiempo Business Ctr, Via Leone XIII 95, 00165 Rome, Italy *Tel:* (06) 3280 3650 *Fax:* (06) 454 39899
Adobe Systems Co Ltd, Gate City Osaki, East Tower, 1-11-2 Osaki, Shinagawa-ku, Tokyo 141-0032, Japan *Tel:* (03) 5740 2400
ICS Adobe Systems SRL, Business Center Le Roi, 29 Sfatul Tarii St, 2012 Chisinau, Moldova *Tel:* (032) 283 9878 *Fax:* (032) 283 9877
Adobe Systems Benelux BV, Europlaza, Hoogoorddreef 54a, 1101 BE Amsterdam, Netherlands *Tel:* (020) 65 11 200 *Fax:* (020) 65 11 300
171 Featherston St, Wellington 6011, New Zealand *Tel:* (04) 894 8538
Adobe Systems Norge AS, Karenslyst alle 8 B, 0278 Oslo, Norway *Tel:* 23 16 28 81 *Fax:* 23 16 28 82

Regus Business Ctr, ul Prusa 2, 00-493 Warsaw, Poland *Tel:* (22) 657 0173 *Fax:* (22) 657 0111
Adobe Systems Romania, Anchor Plaza, 9th fl, 26Z Timisoara Blvd, 061331 Bucharest, Romania *Tel:* (031) 413 35 00 *Fax:* (021) 413 36 26
Adobe Systems Russia, Kosmodamianskaya nab 52, Bldg 1B, 115054 Moscow, Russia *Tel:* (495) 782 97 00 *Fax:* (495) 503 66 90
No 8 Temasek Blvd, Suntec Tower 3, 06-02, Singapore 038988, Singapore *Tel:* 6511 5500 *Fax:* 6333 8023
Adobe Systems South Africa (Pty) Ltd, The Campus Twickenham Bldg, Corner Sloane & Main Rd, Bryanston 2021, South Africa *Tel:* (011) 573 0008 *Fax:* (011) 541 0842
16F, A, Kyobo Kangnam Tower, 1303-22 Seochodong, Seocho-gu, Seoul 137-070, South Korea *Tel:* (02) 530 8000 *Fax:* (02) 530 8001
Adobe Systems Iberica SL, Torre Mapfre, Villa Olimpica C/ Marina 16-18, Planta 20, 08005 Barcelona, Spain *Tel:* 933 268 400 *Fax:* 933 268 420
Adobe Systems Nordic AB, Knarrarnasgatan 7, 164 93 Kista, Sweden *Tel:* (08) 752 3300 *Fax:* (08) 751 4955
Adobe Research Schweiz AG, Barfusserplatz 6, 4051 Basel, Switzerland *Tel:* (061) 226 5500 *Fax:* (061) 226 5539
Buyukdere Cad No 191, Apa Giz Ofis Binasi Kat 16, 34394 Levent Istanbul, Turkey *Tel:* (0212) 371 05 00 *Fax:* (0212) 371 05 99
Festival City, Festival Business Tower 19th fl, PO Box 36605, Dubai, United Arab Emirates *Tel:* (04) 293 26 13 *Fax:* (04) 293 25 25
Adobe Systems Europe Ltd, 34-38 Market St, Maidenhead, Berks SL6 8AD, United Kingdom *Tel:* (01628) 590 000 *Fax:* (01628) 590 100

Adorama Rental Co
50 W 17 St, Ground fl, New York, NY 10011
Tel: 212-627-8487 *Fax:* 212-929-9013
E-mail: rent@adorama.com
Web Site: www.adoramarentals.com
Founded: 1988
Rents & supports a full range of still & motion cameras & accessories, lighting & grip equipment.

Adrenaline Films
5224 S Orange Ave, Orlando, FL 32809
Tel: 407-850-0711 *Fax:* 407-859-6527
E-mail: contact@adrenalinefilms.com
Web Site: www.adrenalinefilms.com
Key Personnel
Pres: Michael Murray
Gen Mgr: Tim Bartlett
Prodn Mgr & Prodr: Mary Rosa
Post-Prodn Mgr: Dennis Larkin
Location production, specialty shooting, camera crews, lighting & grip equipment. Post-production services include video editing, sound design, color grading & visual effects.

Adrienne Electronics Corp (AEC)
HC 65 Box 254, 1008 York Ranch Rd, Pie Town, NM 87827
Tel: 575-772-2572 *Toll Free Tel:* 800-782-2321 *Fax:* 575-772-2575
E-mail: info@adrielec.com; orders@adrielec.com; support@adrielec.com
Web Site: www.adrielec.com
Key Personnel
Founder & Owner: Bruce E Waggoner
Founded: 1986
Manufacturer of computer based time code products.
Online catalog(s) available
Membership(s): NAB

The ADS Group
2155 Niagara Lane N, Suite 120, Plymouth, MN 55447

Tel: 763-449-5500 *Toll Free Tel:* 800-759-0992
  Fax: 763-449-5555
E-mail: sales@theadsgroup.com
Web Site: theadsgroup.com
Key Personnel
COO: Connie Comeau
Prodr: Kerry Johnson
Sales Acct Exec & Cust Rel: Kristin Swartout
Sales Assoc: Lisa Libby
Founded: 1989
Full service AV production company, including a
  music library. Manufacture DVDs, CDs & USB
  drives.
Catalog(s) available
Membership(s): Audiovisual and Integrated Expe-
  rience Association; AVDA; Content Delivery &
  Storage Association

ADS Media
Division of ADS Studio Productions Inc
620 Trinity Church Rd, Hamilton, ON L0R 1P0,
  Canada
Tel: 905-692-2960 *Fax:* 905-692-2961
E-mail: info@adsmedia.ca
Web Site: www.adsmedia.ca
Key Personnel
Pres & CEO: Ken Vandevrie
Founded: 1989
Multimedia production.

Adtec Digital Inc
408 Russell St, Nashville, TN 37206
Tel: 615-256-6619 *Fax:* 615-256-6593
E-mail: sales@adtecinc.com
Web Site: www.adtecinc.com
Key Personnel
VP, Mktg: Ron Johnson *E-mail:* ronj@adtecinc.
  com
Founded: 1985
Manufacturer of MPEG-2 based digital video
  players, single-channel commercial insertion
  controllers, automated video control systems &
  streaming video encoders.
Online catalog(s) available
Branch Office(s)
2231-3 Corporate Square Blvd, Jacksonville, FL
  32216 *Tel:* 904-720-2003 ext 4606 *Fax:* 904-
  239-3199

Advance Audiovisual Presentation Ltd
5 Rothschild Ct, Gaithersburg, MD 20878
Tel: 301-937-0900 *Fax:* 301-330-2937
E-mail: aaplav@outlook.com
Web Site: aaplav.com
Key Personnel
Pres: Robert J Ziobro
Founded: 1993
AV equipment rentals & sales.
Online catalog(s) available

Advance Concepts Inc
8453 Tyco Rd, Suite N, Vienna, VA 22182-2623
Tel: 703-448-0445 *Fax:* 703-893-8049
Web Site: www.advanceconcepts.com
Key Personnel
Pres: Philip Joseph *E-mail:* phil@
  advanceconcepts.com
VP, Servs: Rebecca Draznin *E-mail:* rebecca@
  advanceconcepts.com
Founded: 1982
AV production for live events, conferences
  & meetings. Specialize in medical confer-
  ences/CME.
Membership(s): Audiovisual and Integrated Ex-
  perience Association; Television, Internet &
  Video Association of DC Inc

Advance Pro
Division of Advance Electronics
62 Sucurfield Blvd, Unit 12 & 14, Winnipeg, MB
  R3Y 1M5, Canada

Tel: 204-772-0386 *Toll Free Tel:* 800-392-1295
  Fax: 204-783-2177
E-mail: ap@advance.mb.ca
Web Site: advance-pro.com
Key Personnel
Mng Partner: Peter Bernatsky
Founded: 1971
Membership(s): Audiovisual and Integrated Expe-
  rience Association; Manitoba Electrical League;
  NAB; NSCA

Advanced Audio Technology
200 Easy St, Carol Stream, IL 60188
Tel: 630-665-3344 *Fax:* 630-665-3347
E-mail: aat@ameritech.net
Web Site: www.advancedaudio.net
Key Personnel
Owner: Robert Atkins
CD & DVD production, USB duplication, onsite
  recording, media conversion, specialty printing
  & multimedia authoring. Printing for police,
  medical imaging & crime files.
Online catalog(s) available

Advanced AV LLC
208 Carter Dr, Suite 7, West Chester, PA 19382
Toll Free Tel: 877-696-7700 *Fax:* 610-692-8421
E-mail: sales@advancedav.com
Web Site: www.advancedav.com
Key Personnel
Founder: Paul Grafinger
CEO: Michael Boettcher
VP, Sales & Mktg: John P Green
VP, Tech Opers: Travis A Lisk
Founded: 1985
Specialized integrator of professional AV systems
  for business, education, government & worship
  facilities.
Catalog(s) available
Membership(s): Audiovisual and Integrated Expe-
  rience Association

Advanced Battery Systems Inc
516 Bedford St, East Bridgewater, MA 02333
Tel: 508-378-2284
E-mail: abs@batteryprice.com
Web Site: www.batteryprice.com
Portable equipment batteries.
Online catalog(s) available

Advanced Designs Corp
1169 W Second St, Bloomington, IN 47403
Tel: 812-333-1922 *Fax:* 812-333-2030
E-mail: service@doprad.com
Web Site: www.doprad.com
Key Personnel
Pres: Matt McGrath *E-mail:* mmcgrath@doprad.
  com
Founded: 1982
Doppler weather radar, weather display systems
  & computer graphics.
Membership(s): American Meteorological Soci-
  ety; NAB

Advanced Digital Design
6429 Independence Ave, Woodland Hills, CA
  91367
Web Site: advanced-digital-design.com
Key Personnel
Pres: Paul Formanek *Tel:* 818-822-1939 (cell)
  E-mail: paulfadd@att.net
Full service post-production studio with editing
  services, screening room & soundstage.

Advanced Imaging Concepts Inc
301 N Harrison St, No 9F 266, Princeton, NJ
  08540
Tel: 609-921-3629; 609-529-9200 *Fax:* 609-924-
  3010
E-mail: info@aic-imagecentral.com; sales@aic-
  imagecentral.com

Web Site: www.aic-imagecentral.com
Key Personnel
Sales Mgr: Scott E Berman *E-mail:* sberman@
  aic-imagecentral.com
Founded: 1989
Digital imaging for optical microscopes.
Online catalog(s) available

Advanced Lighting & Production Services Inc (ALPS)
125 Shamut Rd, Canton, MA 02021
Tel: 781-961-3066 *Toll Free Tel:* 866-961-3066
  Fax: 781-961-3256
E-mail: info@alpsweb.com
Web Site: www.alpsweb.com
Key Personnel
Pres: Steven F Way
VP: James A deVeer
Mgr: Chad Winship
Founded: 1981
Sales, installations, rentals, repairs & production
  services of theatrical lighting supplies & related
  equipment. Rigging & truss, staging & produc-
  tion management.
Online catalog(s) available
Membership(s): International Live Events Associ-
  ation; Professional Lighting & Sound Associa-
  tion

Advanced Media Integration
2300 Meyer Rd, Fort Wayne, IN 46805
Tel: 260-428-2698 *Toll Free Tel:* 877-428-2610
E-mail: info@amifw.com
Web Site: amifw.com
Key Personnel
Owner: Vince Tippmann
Founded: 1976
DVD, CD & Blu-ray replication & duplication,
  video production & photography.

Advanced Media LLC
369 N Fairfax Ave, Suite A, Los Angeles, CA
  90036
Tel: 323-658-6102
E-mail: info@advancedmediallc.com
Web Site: www.advancedmediallc.com; www.
  gomemoriesforever.com
Key Personnel
Exec Mgr: Jesse Kelly
Founded: 1984
Video, DVD, film & media services.

Advanced Sound
4611 Central Ave Pike, Suite F, Knoxville, TN
  37912
Tel: 865-661-5961
Web Site: www.advancedsound.com
Key Personnel
Owner: Robert Craton *E-mail:* robert_20072001@
  yahoo.com
Founded: 1983

Advanced Systems Group LLC
1226 Powell St, Emeryville, CA 94608-2618
Tel: 510-654-8300 *Fax:* 510-654-8370
Web Site: www.asgllc.com
Key Personnel
CFO: Amy Zeno *E-mail:* amy@asgllc.com
Pres & Sales: Dave Van Hoy *E-mail:* dvh@asgllc.
  com
Founded: 1997
Membership(s): SMPTE®

Advantech B+B SmartWorx, see B+B
SmartWorx

Advent Media Inc
5629 Fraley Ct, Columbus, OH 43235
Tel: 614-538-1622 *Toll Free Tel:* 877-538-1622
  Fax: 614-538-1621
Web Site: www.adventmediainc.com

Key Personnel
Owner & Pres: Stephen F Puffenberger
VP: David Puffenberger
Founded: 1982
Helps organizations nationwide reach customers +/or colleagues with creative multimedia content.

AdventSource
5120 Prescott Ave, Lincoln, NE 68506
Tel: 402-486-8800 *Toll Free Tel:* 800-328-0525
    Fax: 402-486-8819
E-mail: service@adventsource.org
Web Site: www.adventsource.org
Key Personnel
Exec Dir: Brad Forbes
Leadership resource center for the Seventh-Day Adventist Church in North America, including CDs & DVDs.
Online catalog(s) available

Adventure Productions LLC
5910 York Rd, Lower Level, Baltimore, MD 21212
Tel: 410-878-1261; 410-961-5942 (cell) *Fax:* 410-878-1263
Web Site: www.adventureproductions.com
Key Personnel
Owner & Dir, Photog: George A Stover, III
    E-mail: george@adventureproductions.com
Owner & Mktg Dir: Carol L Stover
    E-mail: carol@adventureproductions.com
Founded: 1993
Full service TV & video production company. Complete electronic gathering equipment & editing facilities, lighting & audio packages, green screen studio, music libraries.
Membership(s): ASCAP; IBEW; NATAS

Adwar Video
125 Gazza Blvd, Farmingdale, NY 11735
Tel: 631-777-7070 *Toll Free Tel:* 877-GOADWAR (462-3927) *Fax:* 631-777-7011
E-mail: sales@adwarvideo.com
Web Site: adwarvideo.com
Key Personnel
Pres: Michael Adwar
Supplier of professional AV equipment & services.
Online catalog(s) available

AEMC Instruments
200 Foxborough Blvd, Foxborough, MA 02035
Tel: 508-698-2115 *Toll Free Tel:* 800-343-1391
    Fax: 508-698-2118
E-mail: sales@aemc.com
Web Site: www.aemc.com
Founded: 1893
Manufacturer of electrical testing equipment.

Aerial Imaging Productions
4258 Tennyson St, Unit 101, Denver, CO 80212
Tel: 720-255-1195
E-mail: info@aerialimagingproductions.com
Web Site: www.aerialimagingproductions.com
Founded: 2007
HD low-altitude videography.

Aerial Video Systems
3200 W Valhalla Dr, Burbank, CA 91505
Tel: 818-954-8842 *Fax:* 818-954-8842
E-mail: info@aerialvideo.com
Web Site: aerialvideo.com
Key Personnel
Founder: Randy Hermes
Customized HD solutions for the broadcasting industry. Specialize in aerial camera platforms, point-of-view cameras, microwave systems & HD wireless video.

Affton Graphics Inc
400 E 85 St, Unit 3F, New York, NY 10028
Mailing Address: PO Box 28, Gracie Sta, New York, NY 10028
Tel: 718-401-4040 *Toll Free Tel:* 800-777-0539
E-mail: amproducts@aol.com
Web Site: amgraphics-classe.com
Key Personnel
Pres: A V Classe
Founded: 1973
Specialize in the manufacturing of interior architectural signage. Also provides engraving services.
Online catalog(s) available

African American Images Inc
PO Box 1799, Sauk Village, IL 60412
Tel: 708-672-4909 *Toll Free Tel:* 800-552-1991
    Fax: 708-672-0466
E-mail: customer@africanamericanimages.com
Web Site: africanamericanimages.com
Key Personnel
Pres: Jawanza Kunjufu
Online catalog(s) available
Membership(s): The Association of Publishers for Special Sales; The Imaging Alliance; Reading Recovery Council of North America

AGF Media Services
21522 Osborne St, Canoga Park, CA 91304
Tel: 818-780-7400 *Fax:* 818-904-9905
E-mail: info@agfmedia.com
Web Site: www.agfmedia.com
Key Personnel
CEO: Aaron J Baker
Dir: Jeffrey Baker
Founded: 1967
AV production services & equipment rental & staging for corporate, nonprofit & social events.
Branch Office(s)
9641 Sunset Blvd, Beverly Hills, CA 90210
    Tel: 310-281-2969 *Fax:* 310-887-2508
Membership(s): Audiovisual and Integrated Experience Association

Agfa Graphics
Unit of Agfa-Gevaert Group
611 River Dr, Ctr 3, Elmwood Park, NJ 07407
Tel: 201-440-2500 *Toll Free Tel:* 800-540-2432; 888-274-8626 (cust serv)
E-mail: graphics@agfa.com
Web Site: www.agfa.com; www.agfagraphics.com
Key Personnel
Pres, Regl North America: Gunther Muertens
VP, North America Opers: Jonathan Ashton
Dir, Opers: Jeffrey Aurichio
Dir, Supply Chain, North America: Adam Szewc
HR Dir: Nadine Lauzon-Rosato
Founded: 2003
Digital printing solutions for sign & display & industrial printing. Integrated prepress solutions.
Online catalog(s) available

Agrama Film Enterprises Inc
Division of Harmony Gold USA Inc
7655 Sunset Blvd, Los Angeles, CA 90046
Tel: 323-851-4900 *Fax:* 323-851-5599
E-mail: sales@harmonygold.com
Web Site: harmonygold.com
Key Personnel
Chmn & CEO: Frank Agrama
VP, Busn & Legal Aff: Christy Duran
Online catalog(s) available

Ahead Stereo Inc
7428 Beverly Blvd, Los Angeles, CA 90036
Tel: 323-931-8873
E-mail: sales@aheadstereo.com
Web Site: www.aheadstereo.com
Key Personnel
Owner & Custom Design Mgr: Phil Werbin
    Tel: 323-939-8081

Sales Mgr: Brian Bloom
Founded: 1971

AheadTeK
6410 Via Del Oro, San Jose, CA 95119
Tel: 408-226-9800; 408-226-9991
    Toll Free Tel: 800-971-9191 *Fax:* 408-226-9195
Web Site: www.aheadtek.com
Key Personnel
CFO: Ed Soldani
Pres: Tim Higgins
EVP, Busn Devt: Patrick Johnston *E-mail:* patj@aheadtek.com
Dir, Engg: Howard Temple
Dir, HR: Yolanda Verdugo
Dir, Mfg: Hristo Mishkov
Television broadcast, video production & computer & data storage equipment.
Online catalog(s) available

AIEL, see Atlantic Illumination Entertainment Lighting

Aiphone Corp
6670 185 Ave NE, Redmond, WA 98052
Tel: 425-455-0510 *Toll Free Tel:* 800-692-0200
    Fax: 425-455-0071 *Toll Free Fax:* 800-525-3372 (cust serv)
E-mail: info@aiphone.com; cs@aiphone.com
Web Site: www.aiphone.com/home
Key Personnel
Sr Mktg Specialist: Brad Kamcheff
Founded: 1970
Manufacture intercom solutions for communication & security.
Online catalog(s) available

Air Bud Entertainment
22525 Pacific Coast Hwy, Malibu, CA 90265
Tel: 310-317-4883
Web Site: www.airbud.com
Key Personnel
CEO: Robert Vince
Pres: Anna McRoberts
Founded: 1996
Film producers & post-production facility.
Branch Office(s)
300-2339 Columbia St, Vancouver, BC V5Y 3Y3, Canada *Tel:* 604-873-9739 *Fax:* 604-873-5919

Air Philosophy Inc
1933 S Broadway, Suite 1107B, Los Angeles, CA 90007
Tel: 310-980-3902
E-mail: info@airphilosophy.com
Web Site: airphilosophy.com
Key Personnel
Chief Creative Offr: Kawai Matthews
Prodr: Chanel Urban
Prodn: Kofa Boyah
Digital production company. Specialize in video & photography for marketing, advertising, promotional & experiential campaigns.

Air Sea Land Productions Inc (ASL)
19-69 Steinway St, Astoria, NY 11105-1108
Tel: 718-626-2646 *Toll Free Tel:* 888-ASL-LENS (275-5367)
E-mail: info@airsealand.com
Web Site: www.airsealand.com
Key Personnel
Pres & CEO: Anthony S Lenzo
    E-mail: anthonyl@airsealand.com
VP: Edward Lenzo *E-mail:* camraguy@gmail.com
Dir, Opers: Michael Warner *E-mail:* mwarner@airsealand.com
Opers Mgr: Gary Costantino *E-mail:* gary@airsealand.com
Founded: 1994
Production company & rental house. DVD & digital programming.

AirBrands Event & Marketing Group
Affiliate of Dynamic Displays Inc
6470 Wyoming St, Suite 2024, Dearborn, MI
48126
Tel: 519-254-9563 *Toll Free Tel:* 800-411-6200
(ext 26) *Fax:* 519-735-5446
Web Site: www.airbrandsmarketing.com;
famousinflatables.com
Key Personnel
Pres: Steve Thomson *Tel:* 519-254-9563 ext 26
E-mail: steve@airbrandsmarketing.com
Founded: 1962
Design, manufacture, install, management &
staffing for inflatable props.
Online catalog(s) available
Branch Office(s)
1805 Wilson Ave, No 212, Toronto, ON M9M
1A2, Canada
1775 Sylvestre Dr, Windsor, ON N8N 2L9,
Canada

Aircraft Music Library, see AirCraft Production
Libraries

AirCraft Production Libraries
Division of CAV Corp
162 Columbus Ave, Boston, MA 02116-5222
Tel: 617-303-7600 *Toll Free Tel:* 800-343-2514
Fax: 617-303-7555
E-mail: info@aircraftmusiclibrary.com; acsales@
aircraftmusiclibrary.com
Web Site: www.aircraftmusiclibrary.com
Key Personnel
Engr & Prodr: Tim Reppert
Founded: 1985
Production music: aircraft, The American Music
Series, Ads Up-Music for Commercials, Cine-
music & Rock Sweepers.
Online catalog(s) available

Airwave Recording Studio
5176 Hollow Log Lane, Birmingham, AL 35244
Tel: 205-427-4675
Key Personnel
Pres: Marc Phillips

Airways Digital Media
4055 W Peterson Ave, Chicago, IL 60646
Tel: 773-539-8400
E-mail: info@airwaysdigital.com
Web Site: www.airwaysdigital.com
Key Personnel
Pres: Steve Zaransky
Founded: 1981
Specialize in digital media creation for businesses
of all sizes, including web site development,
online learning & application development for
mobile devices.

AITech International
1973 O'Toole Way, San Jose, CA 95131
Tel: 408-991-9699 *Fax:* 408-991-9691
E-mail: sales@aitech.com
Web Site: www.aitech.com
Key Personnel
Chmn & CEO: Dr Michael J Chen
SVP: Jennifer H Chen
Founded: 1987
Development & delivery of PC to TV scan con-
version technology.

AJA Video Systems Inc
180 Litton Dr, Grass Valley, CA 95945
Mailing Address: PO Box 1033, Grass Valley, CA
95945-1033
Tel: 530-274-2048 *Fax:* 530-274-9442
E-mail: sales@aja.com
Web Site: www.aja.com
Founded: 1993

AJS Events
317 Forsgate Dr, Unit C, Monroe Township, NJ
08831
Tel: 732-382-2333
Web Site: www.alljerseystudios.com
Key Personnel
Pres: James J O'Keefe *E-mail:* jim@ajsevents.
com
Founded: 2001
Full event services including photography
& video, media transfers, moving video
biographies/montages & photo restora-
tion/enhancement.

Akai Professional
Subsidiary of inMusic Brands Inc
200 Scenic View Dr, Cumberland, RI 02864
Tel: 401-658-3131
E-mail: pressrelations@akaipro.com
Web Site: www.akaipro.com
Founded: 1984
Digital personal studios, digital audio recording
& editing systems. Samplers, the MPC & Midi
production center.
Online catalog(s) available

AKG Acoustics US
Division of Harman Professional Solutions
8500 Balboa Blvd, Northridge, CA 91329
Tel: 818-920-3212 *Toll Free Tel:* 888-452-4254
Web Site: www.akg.com/pro
Key Personnel
VP, Prod & Prog Mgmt: Brian Divine
Founded: 1947
Manufacture high-quality microphones, head-
phones & wireless equipment.
Online catalog(s) available

Alarmco Intelligent Message Repeaters
One Bailey Dr, Guilford, CT 06437
Tel: 203-458-2646 *Toll Free Tel:* 800-824-5006
E-mail: info@messagerepeaters.com
Web Site: www.messagerepeaters.com
Message repeaters, paging system feedback elimi-
nator.

Alaska Media Pros LLC
11050 Cange St, Anchorage, AK 99516
Mailing Address: PO Box 110163, Anchorage,
AK 99511-0163
Tel: 907-230-8839
E-mail: ifilm@alaska.net
Web Site: www.alaskamediapros.com
Key Personnel
Owner & Prodn Mgr: Deborah Schildt
Gen Mgr, Location Mgr & Scout: Bob Crockett
Tel: 907-223-3740
Founded: 1983
Boutique production company. HD camera, edit-
ing suite. Location scouting, casting, produc-
ing, directing & editing. Digital video (HD
& Digi Beta & DV). Television, educational-
commercials & documentary. Sales offices in
Alaska & Kenora, ON, CN.
Membership(s): Alaska Film Group; International
Alliance of Theatrical Stage Employees

Alaska Video Postcards Inc
11405 Discovery Park Dr, Anchorage, AK 99515
Mailing Address: PO Box 112808, Anchorage,
AK 99511-2808
Tel: 907-349-8002 *Toll Free Tel:* 800-248-2624
Key Personnel
Pres: Todd Hardesty
Founded: 1987

Albany Theatre Supply Co Inc
445 N Pearl St, Albany, NY 12204
Tel: 518-229-7899
E-mail: sales@albanytheatresupply.com
Web Site: www.albanytheatresupply.com

Key Personnel
Pres: Dick McGrath
VP: Thomas McGrath *E-mail:* tom@
albanytheatresupply.com
Founded: 1946
Lighting, sound equipment, theatre supplies, stage
curtains & rigging.

Albumx Corp, see Renaissance Albums

Alcorn McBride Inc
3300 S Hiawassee Rd, Bldg 105, Orlando, FL
32835
Tel: 407-296-5800 *Fax:* 407-296-5801
E-mail: info@alcorn.com; sales@alcorn.com
Web Site: www.alcorn.com
Key Personnel
COO: Loren Barrows
Chief Innovation Offr: Scott Harkless
Prod Mgr: Alan Wheeler
Founded: 1986
Largest manufacturer of show control, au-
dio/video playback & lighting control equip-
ment used in theme parks, museums, retail
stores, casinos, visitor centers, themed restau-
rants & transportation systems worldwide. Our
systems are reliable & cost-effective.
Online catalog(s) available

Alden Films
PO Box 449, Clarksburg, NJ 08510-0449
Tel: 732-462-3522 *Toll Free Tel:* 800-832-0980
Fax: 732-294-0330
E-mail: info@aldenfilms.com
Web Site: www.aldenfilms.com
Key Personnel
Pres: Paul Weinberg
Founded: 1952
Video & audio programming on Israel, Judaica &
Jewish studies.
Online catalog(s) available

Alegra House Publishers
Subsidiary of Kaya Books
PO Box 1443, Warren, OH 44482-1443
Tel: 330-372-2951 *Fax:* 330-399-1619
Key Personnel
Pres: Robert Prokop
Ed-in-Chief: Linda Marado
Mng Ed: Robert C Peters
Catalog(s) available
Shipping Address: 641 Fairway NE, Warren, OH
44483
Membership(s): Independent Book Publishers As-
sociation

Alexander Media Productions
1901 Diamond Ridge Dr, Carrollton, TX 75010
Tel: 214-274-3456
Web Site: www.heatheralexander.net
Key Personnel
Prodn Coord: Heather Alexander
E-mail: halexander74@gmail.com
Specialize in script writing for television & film.

Alexander Street, a ProQuest Company
99 Canal Center Plaza, Suite 200, Alexandria, VA
22314
Tel: 703-212-8520 *Toll Free Tel:* 800-889-5937
E-mail: sales@alexanderstreet.com; marketing@
alexanderstreet.com; info@alexanderstreet.com
Web Site: alexanderstreet.com;
academicvideostore.com
Key Personnel
Sr Dir, Prod Mgmt: David Parker
E-mail: dparker@alexanderstreet.com
Media producers. Over 800 films on healthcare
issues, including new films on DVD, streaming
& online education.
Catalog(s) available

Alford Media Services
296 Freeport Pkwy, Coppell, TX 75019
Tel: 972-538-9400 *Toll Free Tel:* 800-554-9144
E-mail: info@alfordmedia.com; sales@
alfordmedia.com
Web Site: www.alfordmedia.com
Key Personnel
Founder & Pres: Steve Alford
Video Tech Dir: Michael Hare
Gen Mgr: Tom Alford
Prodn & Travel Mgr: Nora Donohue
Acct Coord: Wade Diebold; Pam Schoen
Audio Engr: Matt Dietzler
Lighting Designer: Dominic Fanelli
Founded: 1984
Audio/video/lighting rental & event staging.
Membership(s): Audiovisual and Integrated Expe-
rience Association; IABC; National Foundation
of Independent Businesses

Alien Skin Software LLC
1111 Haynes St, Suite 113, Raleigh, NC 27604
Tel: 919-832-4124 *Toll Free Tel:* 888-921-7546
Fax: 919-832-4065
E-mail: sales@alienskin.com
Web Site: www.alienskin.com
Key Personnel
CEO: Finley Lee
Founded: 1993
Manufacture graphics software.

Aliso Creek Productions Inc
4106 W Burbank Blvd, Burbank, CA 91510
Mailing Address: PO Box 10006, Burbank, CA
91510-0006
Tel: 818-954-9931
Web Site: www.alisocreek.net
Key Personnel
Founder: William Williams
Founded: 1987
Voice-over workshops, live action & animation
shorts, web site design.

All Access Staging & Productions
1320 Storm Pkwy, Torrance, CA 90501
Tel: 310-784-2464 *Toll Free Tel:* 877-784-2464
Fax: 310-517-0899
E-mail: sales@allaccessinc.com
Web Site: www.allaccessinc.com
Key Personnel
CEO & COO: Clive Forrester *E-mail:* clivef@
allaccessinc.com
Pres/Versa Stage Creative Sales Exec: Erik East-
land *E-mail:* erike@allaccessinc.com
VP, Versa Stage/Sr Sales Exec: Bob Hughes
E-mail: bobh@allaccessinc.com
VP: Robert Achlimbari *E-mail:* robert@
allaccessinc.com
VP/East Coast Opers: Jennifer Davies
E-mail: jenniferd@allaccessinc.com
Tech VP/Sales Exec: David Agar *E-mail:* davea@
allaccessinc.com
Sales Mgr: Bryan Schluntz *E-mail:* bryans@
allaccessinc.com
Founded: 1991
Rental & sales of custom staging, sets, camera
platforms & accessories. Additional services include custom low-res & high-res displays, soft
goods, lifts, elevators, turntables & plexidecks.
Versastage, CM hoists, hippotizer media server,
colorkinetics, SL Flex power supplies & video
system management.
Branch Office(s)
2 N Park Dr, Newton, NJ 07860 *Tel:* 973-579-
0067 *Fax:* 973-579-0068
Foreign Office(s): 23 Demand Ave, Arundel, Qld
4214, Australia, Dir: Ross Butler *Tel:* (0411)
656 462 *E-mail:* rossb@allaccessinc.com
Unit 12, Woking Business Park, Albert Dr, Woking, Surrey GU21 5JY, United Kingdom,

Mng Dir: Guy Forrester *Tel:* (01483) 765 305
E-mail: guyf@allaccessinc.com
Membership(s): Entertainment Services and Tech-
nology Association; Professional Lighting &
Sound Association; USITT

All Comm Rentals Inc (ALLCOMM)
1402 SW 13 Ct, Pompano Beach, FL 33069
Tel: 954-788-9555
Web Site: www.allcommrentals.com
Key Personnel
Pres: Lou Selesnick *E-mail:* louis@
allcommrentals.com
VP, Event Prodn: Damein Futch
E-mail: damein@allcommrentals.com
Tech Dir: Kris Bauersfeld *E-mail:* kris@
allcommrentals.com
Founded: 1993
Rental of audio, video & lighting equipment.
Also provides full production services.

All Mobile Video Inc
221 W 26 St, New York, NY 10001
Tel: 212-727-1234 *Fax:* 212-255-6644
E-mail: contact@amvchelsea.com
Web Site: allmobilevideo.com
Key Personnel
Pres: Eric Duke *E-mail:* eduke@amvchelsea.com
Mobile production, post-production, equipment
sales & rental, internet streaming & digital me-
dia.
Branch Office(s)
AMV Field Operations, 272 State Rte 17 S, Lodi,
NJ 07644 *Tel:* 201-488-4181 *Fax:* 201-488-
3709

All Pro Media Inc
422 S Spring St, Burlington, NC 27215
Mailing Address: PO Box 2566, Burlington, NC
27216-2566
Tel: 336-229-7700 *Toll Free Tel:* 800-270-2207
Fax: 336-229-7778
Web Site: www.allpromedia.com
Key Personnel
Pres: Alan Kirby *E-mail:* alan@allpromedia.com
Founded: 1990
Video production, web design, advertising &
equipment rental.

All Service Musical Electronics Repair
33470 SW Chinook Plaza, PMB 154, Scapoose,
OR 97056
Tel: 503-231-6552
E-mail: service@asmusic.org
Web Site: www.all-service-musical.com
Key Personnel
Owner: Randy Morgan
Founded: 1981
Electronic repair.

All Terrain Power Co Inc
3055 49 St, Astoria, NY 11103
Tel: 718-852-4922 *Fax:* 718-267-0002
Web Site: www.allterrainpower.com
Key Personnel
Owner/Operator: John Kuegel *E-mail:* jwkco@
yahoo.com
Founded: 2000
On location electric power generator & distri-
bution rentals. Specialize in off-road location
shoots.

All Video Productions
726 Santa Monica Blvd, Suite 212, Santa Monica,
CA 90401
Tel: 310-656-1155 *Fax:* 310-656-1155
E-mail: info@allvideoproductions.com
Web Site: www.allvideoproductions.com
Key Personnel
Pres: Pascal Sangary

Founded: 1989
Video production services.

ALLCOMM, see All Comm Rentals Inc
(ALLCOMM)

Allegro Productions Inc
347 Main St, Chester, NJ 07930
Tel: 908-879-0428 *Toll Free Tel:* 800-232-2133
Web Site: www.allegrovideo.com
Key Personnel
Pres: Scott J Forman
Founded: 1957
Online catalog(s) available

Allen Avionics Inc
255 E Second St, Mineola, NY 11501
Tel: 516-248-8080 *Fax:* 516-747-6724
E-mail: info@allenavionics.com
Web Site: www.allenavionics.com
Key Personnel
VP: Jim Lyons *E-mail:* jim@allenavionics.com
Online catalog(s) available
Membership(s): AES; NAB; SMPTE®

John E Allen Inc
PO Box 452, Newfoundland, PA 18445
Tel: 570-676-4152 *Fax:* 570-676-9194
E-mail: jeainc@gmail.com
Web Site: www.allenarchive.com/wordpress
Key Personnel
Pres: John E Allen
Stock shot(s) available, by specific request
Online catalog(s) available
Membership(s): Association of Moving Image
Archivists

Allen Products Co Inc, see Adaptive
Technologies Group Inc

Allen Visual Systems Inc
1405 Busch Pkwy, Buffalo Grove, IL 60089
Tel: 847-520-4960 *Fax:* 847-520-7370
E-mail: sales@allenvisual.com
Web Site: www.allenvisual.com
Founded: 1971
Single source for equipment, design, engineering,
installation, maintenance & support for inte-
grated AV/IT technologies.
Online catalog(s) available
Membership(s): ATD; Audiovisual and Integrated
Experience Association; International Facilities
Management Association; NSCA; Professional
Systems Network International

Alliance Entertainment Corp (AEC) LLC
1401 NW 136 Ave, Suite 100, Sunrise, FL 33323
Toll Free Tel: 800-329-7664
Web Site: www.aent.com
Key Personnel
CEO: Jeff Walker *Tel:* 954-255-4403
E-mail: jeffw@sdcd.com
CFO: George Campagna *Tel:* 954-255-4031
E-mail: george.campagna@aent.com
VP, Busn Devt: Bobby Miranda *Tel:* 530-668-
3470 ext 6206 *E-mail:* bobby.miranda@aent.
com
Founded: 1990
Wholesale distributor of home entertainment au-
dio & video software.

The Alliance for Christian Media
2715 Peachtree Rd NE, Atlanta, GA 30305
Toll Free Tel: 888-411-DAY-1 (411-3291)
E-mail: info@day1.org
Web Site: day1.org
Key Personnel
CFO: Thomas Keuneke
Pres & Exec Prodr: Reverend Peter Wallace
Prodn Coord: Donal Jones

Founded: 2004
Lectionary-based sermons in text & AV resources.
Day 1 is a radio program & podcast presenting
preachers from the mainline Protestant denomi-
nations.
Online catalog(s) available

Alliant Event Services
196 University Pkwy, Pomona, CA 91768
Tel: 909-622-3306 *Toll Free Tel:* 800-851-5415
 Fax: 909-622-3917
E-mail: marketing@alliantevents.com
Web Site: www.alliantevents.com
Key Personnel
Pres: Sanjay Patel *E-mail:* sanjay.patel@
 alliantevents.com
Opers Mgr: Brian Carter *E-mail:* brian.carter@
 alliantevents.com
Founded: 1984
Complete audio, visual, lighting, computer, dis-
 play rental, staging services, design sets &
 LED walls.

Allied Artists International Inc
Production Services Ctr, 15810 E Gale Ave, Suite
 133, Hacienda Heights, CA 91745
Tel: 626-330-0600 *Fax:* 626-961-0411
Key Personnel
CEO & Chmn of the Bd: Kim Richards
CFO, Entertainment Group: Jerry Sifuentes
Pres: Robert Fitzpatrick
VP & CTO: Greg Hammond
Catalog(s) available
Branch Office(s)
Allied Artists Music Group, Attn: A & R, PO
 Box 2035, City of Industry, CA 91746 (demo
 submissions)
445 Park Ave, 9th fl, New York, NY 10022
 Tel: 646-350-0009
Membership(s): Music Business Association;
 RIAA

Allied Media Corp
5252 Cherokee Ave, Suite 200, Alexandria, VA
 22312
Tel: 703-333-2008 *Fax:* 703-997-7539
E-mail: info@allied-media.com; contact@allied-
 media.com
Web Site: www.allied-media.com
Key Personnel
Pres & CEO: Mostapha Saout
Founded: 1998
Communication & creative multimedia produc-
 tion.

Allied Photocolor Co
3728 Market St, Suite 100, St Louis, MO 63110
Tel: 314-652-4000 *Fax:* 314-652-8203
E-mail: aimaging@alliedphotocolor.com
Web Site: alliedphotocolor.com
Key Personnel
Pres & CEO: Robert Little
Digital photographic imaging services.
Online catalog(s) available
Membership(s): The Imaging Alliance; PPA

Alligator Records & Artist Management Inc
1441 W Devon Ave, Chicago, IL 60660
Mailing Address: PO Box 60234, Chicago, IL
 60660
Tel: 773-973-7736
E-mail: info@allig.com; publicity@allig.com
Web Site: www.alligator.com
Key Personnel
Pres: Bruce Iglauer
Natl Sales & Ad Dir: Kerry Peace
Dir, Publicity: Marc Lipkin
Founded: 1971
Blues & roots rock record label.
Catalog(s) available
Online catalog(s) available

Allsop Inc
PO Box 23, Bellingham, WA 98227-0023
Tel: 360-734-9090 *Toll Free Tel:* 800-426-4303
 Fax: 360-734-9858
E-mail: info@allsop.com
Web Site: www.allsop.com
Founded: 1965
Online catalog(s) available
Foreign Office(s): Allsop Europe Ltd, IDA Indus-
 trial Park, Waterford, Ireland *Tel:* (051) 355091
 Fax: (051) 377717 *E-mail:* info@allsop.eu *Web
 Site:* www.allsop.eu

Allstar Audio Systems Inc
750 Cowan St, Nashville, TN 37017
Tel: 615-804-7800
Web Site: allstaraudio.com
Key Personnel
Pres: Mike Borne *E-mail:* mike@allstaraudio.com
Founded: 1984
AV equipment rental service & production com-
 pany.

Allstar Show Industries Inc
10331 176 St, Edmonton, AB T5S 2E4, Canada
Tel: 780-486-4000 *Toll Free Tel:* 800-663-4063
 (CN & US)
E-mail: info@allstar-show.com
Web Site: www.allstar-show.com
Key Personnel
Owner: Rodger Boyce
Purchaser: Dave Nay
Founded: 1979
Sale, rental & service of professional audio, video
 (large format LED & projection), stage light-
 ing, staging, rigging & control systems. Pro-
 vides a full range of production & design ser-
 vices for events, tours & integrated system in-
 stallations.
Online catalog(s) available
Branch Office(s)
6029 Fourth St SE, Calgary, AB T2H 2A5,
 Canada *Tel:* 403-258-2000
1131 William St, Vancouver, BC V6A 2J1,
 Canada *Tel:* 604-255-5787
Membership(s): AES; International Live Events
 Association; NAMM, the National Association
 of Music Merchants; NSCA

Alltec Stores, a Vcom IMC Company
80 Little Falls Rd, Fairfield, NJ 07004
Toll Free Tel: 800-637-3181 *Toll Free Fax:* 800-
 965-7836
E-mail: sales@alltecstores.com
Web Site: www.alltecstores.com
Key Personnel
Pres: Shelly Goldstein
Sales: Ezra Hiller *Tel:* 800-637-3181 ext 1046
Founded: 1958
AV & technology equipment distributors.
Catalog(s) available
CD-ROM catalog(s) available
Membership(s): Custom Electronic Design & In-
 stallation Association; NSCA

AlltecPro
Division of Vcom IMC
80 Little Falls Rd, Fairfield, NJ 07004
Toll Free Tel: 800-243-2518
E-mail: sales@alltecpro.com
Web Site: www.alltecpro.com
Manufacturer & distributor of consumer technol-
 ogy & professional AV products, equipment &
 accessories for commercial & residential appli-
 cations.

Allusion Studios & Pure Wave Audio
Division of Allusion Enterprises
248 W Elm St, Tucson, AZ 85705
Tel: 520-622-3895
E-mail: contact@allusionstudios.com

Web Site: www.allusionstudios.com; www.
 purewaveaudio.com
Key Personnel
Owner & Operator: Jim Pavett
Commercial studio including transfers & forensic
 audio.

ALOM Technologies Corp
48105 Warm Springs Blvd, Fremont, CA 94539-
 7498
Tel: 510-360-3600 *Toll Free Tel:* 800-500-9991
 Fax: 510-226-7617
E-mail: customerservice@alom.com
Web Site: www.alom.com
Key Personnel
Pres & CEO: Hannah Kain
CFO: Jack Sexton
CTO: Brandon Marugg
VP, Cust Rel: Rick Mizzo
VP, Opers: Subu Subramanian
Quality: Rajeev Mehta
Founded: 1997
A logistics company, packaging, shipping & me-
 dia duplication.

Alpec®
3098 Kenneth St, Santa Clara, CA 95054
Tel: 408-735-6180 *Toll Free Tel:* 800-854-6686
 Fax: 408-735-6190
E-mail: info@alpec.com
Web Site: www.alpec.com
Key Personnel
Pres: Sunil Prafullchandra
Founded: 1991
Manufacturer of laser pointer, laser projection
 equipment & presentation systems.
Online catalog(s) available

Alpha Source Inc
6619 W Calumet Rd, Milwaukee, WI 53223-4186
Tel: 414-760-2222 *Toll Free Tel:* 800-654-9845
E-mail: customer.service@alphasource.com;
 info@alphasource.com
Web Site: www.alphasource.com
Key Personnel
CEO: Rick Lytle
COO: Rich Springer
CFO: Karen Tichy
VP, HR: Sue Fiegel
VP, Mktg & Cust Experience: Kirsten Corbell
VP, Serv: Don Smith
Founded: 1986
LCD projector lamps, AV lamps & batteries for
 medical equipment.
Online catalog(s) available

Alpha Technologies Inc
Division of EnerSys
3767 Alpha Way, Bellingham, WA 98226
Tel: 360-647-2360 *Toll Free Tel:* 800-322-5742
E-mail: alpha@alpha.com
Web Site: www.alpha.com
Key Personnel
Pres: Drew Zogby
VP, Broadband & Cable: John Hewitt
VP, Fin: Michael Perica
VP, Mktg & Prod Mgmt: Grant Clark
VP, Servs: Gary Tremblay
Founded: 1975
Full line of power supplies, status monitoring
 products, surge suppressors, batteries & enclo-
 sures for use in cable TV/broadband, industrial,
 renewable energy & FTTx industries.
Online catalog(s) available
Branch Office(s)
Alpha Energy, 1628 W Williams Dr, Phoenix, AZ
 85027 *Tel:* 623-251-3000 *Fax:* 623-249-7833
Alpha Industrial Power Inc, 1075 Satellite Blvd
 NW, Suite 400, Suwanee, GA 30024 *Tel:* 678-
 475-3995 *Fax:* 678-584-9259
Alpha Technologies Ltd, 7700 Riverfront Gate,
 Burnaby, BC V5J 5M4, Canada *Tel:* 604-436-

5900 *Toll Free Tel:* 800-667-8743 *Fax:* 604-436-1233 *E-mail:* sales@alpha.ca *Web Site:* www.alpha.ca
Foreign Office(s): Alpha Technologies Australia, 91 Phillip St, Parramatta, NSW 2150, Australia *Tel:* (02) 8599 6960 *E-mail:* ata@alpha.com
Alpha Innovations Brazil, Rua Manoel da Nobrega, 598-CJ 88/89, 09910-720 Diadema-SP, Brazil *Tel:* (011) 2476 0150 *E-mail:* vendas@alphabrasil.net *Web Site:* www.alphabrasil.net
Alpha Tech Energy Solutions India Pvt Ltd, Vikas Plaza, Plot No 38/1A (4), Electronic City Phase 2, Hosur Rd, Bangalore, Karnataka 560 100, India *Tel:* (080) 4123 0299; 95380 25325 (cell) *E-mail:* sales.india@alpha.com
Membership(s): SCTE

Alpha Video & Audio Inc
7690 Golden Triangle Dr, Eden Prairie, MN 55344
Tel: 952-896-9898 *Toll Free Tel:* 800-388-0008 *Fax:* 952-896-9899
E-mail: info@alphavideo.com
Web Site: www.alphavideo.com
Key Personnel
Owner & CEO: Kevin Groves *E-mail:* kevin.groves@alphavideo.com
Founded: 1970
Leading video systems integrator & provider of visual communications solutions.
Membership(s): Audiovisual and Integrated Experience Association; NSCA; PSNI

Alpha Video Productions
441 Biscay Dr, Garland, TX 75043
Tel: 972-497-9959
E-mail: alphaghb@sbcglobal.net
Web Site: www.alphavideo.net
Key Personnel
Founder & Owner: Gary H Bauer
Founder, Writer & Prodr: Susan Bauer
Founded: 1981
Award winning video production company serving the US & international clients, including broadcast, corporate & nonprofit. HD & HD-DVcam camera packages & Avid Media Composer edit system.

Alpha Wire Co
Division of Belden Wire & Cable Co
711 Lidgerwood Ave, Elizabeth, NJ 07207-0711
Tel: 908-925-8000 *Toll Free Tel:* 800-52-ALPHA (522-5742) *Fax:* 908-925-6923
E-mail: info@alphawire.com
Web Site: www.alphawire.com
Key Personnel
Dir, Mktg: Paul Barsa
Catalog(s) available
Online catalog(s) available
Foreign Office(s): Silver Ctr, Rm 1708, N Shanxi Rd 1388, Shanghai 200060, China *Tel:* (021) 61498201 *Fax:* (021) 61498001 *E-mail:* apac@alphawire.com
Alpha Wire International, Saxon House, One Downside, Sudbury-on-Thames, Middx TW16 6RT, United Kingdom *Toll Free Tel:* 800-288-8809 *Toll Free Fax:* 800-288-8810 *E-mail:* europe@alphawire.com

AlphaDogs Inc
1612 W Olive Ave, Suite 200, Burbank, CA 91506-2462
Tel: 818-729-9262 *Fax:* 818-729-8537
Web Site: www.alphadogs.tv
Key Personnel
Founder & Pres: Terence Curren *E-mail:* terry@alphadogs.tv
Gen Mgr: Paul De Cham *E-mail:* paul@alphadogs.tv
Founded: 2002
Full service post-production & design boutique.

Alpine Optics Inc
14 Helping Hands Way, Pisgah Forest, NC 28768
Tel: 828-884-5822
E-mail: info@alpine-optics.com
Web Site: www.alpine-optics.com
Key Personnel
Pres: Michael Millsap
Treas & Busn Dir: Yamile Florez
Secy: Gabriele Jung
Founded: 1989
Premier servicer of Cannon & Fuji broadcasting lenses & accessories.
Online catalog(s) available

ALPS, see Advanced Lighting & Production Services Inc (ALPS)

Altaria Inc, see Alpec®

Altel Systems Group Inc
2856 Broadway Center Blvd, Brandon, FL 33510
Tel: 813-628-6100 *Fax:* 813-628-8949
Web Site: www.asg-av.com
Key Personnel
Pres/Owner: Bruce Vitale *E-mail:* avitale@asg-av.com
Founded: 1998
Membership(s): AES; Audiovisual and Integrated Experience Association; NSCA; SMPTE®

Alternative Rentals
5805 W Jefferson Blvd, Los Angeles, CA 90016
Tel: 310-204-3388 *Fax:* 310-204-3384
E-mail: info@alternativerentals.com
Web Site: www.alternativerentals.com
Rents high-end digital equipment for the feature film, television & commercial industries.
Branch Office(s)
1600 Roswell St, Suite 5, Smyrna, GA 30080 *Tel:* 770-438-0912 *Fax:* 770-438-0916

ALTINEX Inc
592 Apollo St, Brea, CA 92821
Tel: 714-990-2300 *Toll Free Tel:* 800-ALTINEX (258-4639) *Fax:* 714-990-3303
E-mail: sales@altinex.com
Web Site: www.altinex.com
Key Personnel
Pres: Jack Gershfield
Founded: 1993
Leading manufacturer of AV signal management equipment & design software.
Online catalog(s) available
Membership(s): Audiovisual and Integrated Experience Association; NSCA

Altruist Media LLC
2601A Wilson Blvd, Arlington, VA 22201
Tel: 703-812-8813
Key Personnel
Creative Dir: Frank Beach

AM Stock-Cameo Film Library
12340 Santa Monica Blvd, Suite 212, Los Angeles, CA 90025
Tel: 310-479-4800 *Fax:* 310-933-6979
E-mail: researcher@amstockcameo.com
Web Site: www.amstockcameo.com
Key Personnel
Pres: Chris Angelich *E-mail:* chris@amstockcameo.com
35mm & HD stock footage film library; over 1.5 million feet of 35mm film. Shoot custom stock & second unit footage for over 50 different series.
Catalog(s) available

AMA, see American Management Association® (AMA)

AMA Nystrom Printing/Finishing
920 N Valley Mills Dr, Waco, TX 76710
Tel: 254-776-8860 *Toll Free Tel:* 800-369-9226 *Fax:* 254-751-2127
E-mail: info@amanystrom.com
Web Site: www.amanystrom.com
Key Personnel
Pres: Morris Shaw

AM+A, see Aaron Marcus and Associates

Ambrose Video Publishing Inc
1202 Lexington Ave, Suite 171, New York, NY 10028
Tel: 212-768-7373 *Toll Free Tel:* 800-526-4663 *Fax:* 212-768-9282
E-mail: customerservice@ambrosevideo.com
Web Site: www.ambrosevideo.com
Key Personnel
Pres: William V Ambrose
Catalog(s) available
Shipping Address: Karol Fulfillment, 375 Stewart Rd, Wilkes-Barre, PA 18706

America By Air LLC
5390 Venetia Ct, Unit D, Boynton Beach, FL 33437
Tel: 386-663-4567
E-mail: footage@americabyair.com
Web Site: www.americabyair.com
Key Personnel
Owner: Douglas Kahan
B2B video & still image production & licensing. Stock footage in HD, UHD & Cinema 4K, including aerials, ground based terrestrial imagery, point of view, time-lapse, slow motion & historical footage.

American Artist Studio
1114 W 26 St, Erie, PA 16508-1518
Mailing Address: PO Box 131, Erie, PA 16512-0131
Tel: 814-455-4796 *Toll Free Tel:* 888-462-7813
Web Site: americanartiststudio.com
Key Personnel
Owner: Skip Niebauer *E-mail:* skipniebauer@gmail.com
Founded: 1972

American Artists Representatives Inc
One Chatsworth Ave, No 518, Larchmont, NY 10538
Tel: 646-286-5633 (cell); 212-682-2462
E-mail: info@aareps.com
Web Site: www.aareps.com
Key Personnel
Mng Dir: Michael R Mendelsohn
Sales Mgr: Antonio Adriao
Digital creative production for interactive, motion & print.

American Association for Vocational Instructional Materials (AAVIM)
220 Smithonia Rd, Winterville, GA 30683
Tel: 706-742-5355 *Fax:* 706-742-7005
E-mail: sales@aavim.com
Web Site: www.aavim.com
Key Personnel
Dir: Gary Farmer
Founded: 1949
Produce instructional materials in the vocational areas including agriculture education. Distribute CD-ROMs & videos.
Catalog(s) available
Membership(s): National Association of Agriculture Educators

American AV
8005 Haute Ct, Springfield, VA 22150
Tel: 703-573-6910 *Fax:* 703-573-3539
E-mail: sales@aavevents.com

Web Site: www.aavevents.com
Key Personnel
Gen Mgr: Colin Babej *E-mail:* cbabej@aavevents.
com
Regl Mgr: Colin Harrell *E-mail:* charrell@
aavevents.com
Sales: Erik Blum *E-mail:* eblum@aavevents.com
Founded: 1972
Branch Office(s)
800 Briar Creek Rd, Suite EE-206, Charlotte, NC
28205, Sales: Colin Bobby *Tel:* 704-339-0030
Fax: 704-339-0506 *E-mail:* cbobby@aavevents.
com
Sheraton Imperial Hotel, 4700 Emperor Blvd,
Durham, NC 27703, Mgr: Eric Hauge *Tel:* 919-
941-8112 *Fax:* 919-941-9109 *E-mail:* ehauge@
aavevents.com
151 Kitty Hawk Dr, Morrisville, NC 27560,
Regl Mgr: Michael Murphy *Tel:* 919-361-
1151 *Fax:* 919-405-2380 *E-mail:* mmurphy@
aavevents.com

American Blackguard Inc
PO Box 680686, Franklin, TN 37068-0686
Tel: 615-599-4032
E-mail: contact@americanblackguard.com
Web Site: www.americanblackguard.com
Key Personnel
Pres & CEO: Clay Stafford
CFO: Jacqueline Stafford
Founded: 1978
Motion picture & television development, produc-
tion & support.

American Chemical Society (ACS)
Dept of Professional Education, 1155 16 St NW,
Washington, DC 20036
Tel: 202-872-4508 *Toll Free Tel:* 800-ACS-5558
(227-5558 ext 4508) *Fax:* 202-872-6336
E-mail: proed@acs.org
Web Site: proed.acs.org
Key Personnel
Admin: Andrea Adams
Founded: 1876

American Choral Catalog Ltd
205 S Water St, Northfield, MN 55057
Mailing Address: PO Box 528, Northfield, MN
55057-0528
Tel: 507-645-4695 *Fax:* 507-645-2474
E-mail: info@americanchoral.com
Web Site: www.americanchoral.com
Key Personnel
Pres: Peter Dahlen
Catalog(s) available
Membership(s): Music Business Association; The
Recording Academy

The American Classical League
860 NW Washington Blvd, Suite A, Hamilton,
OH 45013
Tel: 513-529-7741 *Fax:* 513-529-7742
E-mail: info@aclclassics.org
Web Site: www.aclclassics.org
Key Personnel
Pres: Kathy Elifrits *E-mail:* president@aclclassics.
org
VP: John Gruber-Miller *E-mail:* vicepresident@
aclclassics.org
Exec Dir: Sherwin Little
Founded: 1919
Educational materials, books, software & student
resources.
Online catalog(s) available
Catalog(s) available

American Color Imaging (ACI)
715 E 18 St, Cedar Falls, IA 50613
Tel: 319-277-3655 *Toll Free Tel:* 800-728-2722
Fax: 319-277-6522
E-mail: sales@acilab.com

Web Site: www.acilab.com
Key Personnel
Pres: Mark Lane
VP: Lisa Lane
HR Dir: Jenny Jensen
Cust Serv Mgr: Paul Kestel
Mktg Mgr: Len Searfoss
Natl Sales Mgr: Pat Cahill
Founded: 1967
Membership(s): The Imaging Alliance; PPA

American Counseling Association
6101 Stevenson Ave, Suite 600, Alexandria, VA
22304
Tel: 703-823-9800 (ext 222) *Toll Free Tel:* 800-
347-6647 (ext 222) *Fax:* 703-823-0252
E-mail: membership@counseling.org
Web Site: www.counseling.org
Key Personnel
CEO: Richard Yep
Assoc Publr: Carolyn C Baker *Tel:* 703-823-9800
ext 356 *E-mail:* cbaker@counseling.org
Founded: 1952
Professional association. Produce online educa-
tional & training programs.
Catalog(s) available, free, annual
Online catalog(s) available

American Educational Products LLC
401 Hickory St, Fort Collins, CO 80524
Tel: 970-484-7445 *Toll Free Tel:* 800-289-9299
Fax: 970-484-1198
E-mail: custserv@amep.com
Web Site: www.amep.com
Key Personnel
Pres: Michael Warring
Catalog(s) available

American Fibertek Inc
120 Belmont Dr, Somerset, NJ 08873-4243
Tel: 732-302-0660 *Toll Free Tel:* 877-234-7200
Fax: 732-302-0667
E-mail: websales@americanfibertek.com
Web Site: www.americanfibertek.com
Founded: 1984
Manufacture IP video systems & video manage-
ment systems. CCTV - Fiber optic transmis-
sion.
Catalog(s) available
Membership(s): American Society for Industrial
Security

American Harlequin Corp
1531 Glen Ave, Moorestown, NJ 08057
Tel: 856-234-5505 *Toll Free Tel:* 800-642-6440
Fax: 856-231-4403
E-mail: dance@harlequinfloors.com; contact@
harlequinfloors.com
Web Site: us.harlequinfloors.com
Key Personnel
EVP: Patricia Basileo
Acct Exec: Marlyn Kress
PR & Mktg: Ester Rodriguez
Catalog(s) available

American History Workshop (NY) Inc
588 Seventh St, Brooklyn, NY 11215-3707
Tel: 718-499-6500
E-mail: info@americanhistoryworkshop.com
Web Site: www.americanhistoryworkshop.com
Key Personnel
Pres: Richard Rabinowitz
Media Dir & Planner: Lynda B Kaplan
Founded: 1980
Produces public programs to connect Americans
with their past.
Membership(s): AASCH; American Alliance of
Museums; NAME

American Hospital Association
155 N Wacker Dr, Suite 400, Chicago, IL 60606-
1725
Tel: 312-422-3000 *Fax:* 312-422-4700
Web Site: www.aha.org
Key Personnel
Dir, Info & Knowledge Servs: Brenda Stenger
Tel: 312-422-2017 *E-mail:* bstenger@aha.org
Founded: 1898
Online catalog(s) available
Branch Office(s)
800 Tenth St NW, Two CityCenter, Suite 400,
Washington, DC 20001-4956 *Tel:* 202-638-
1100

**American Law Institute Continuing Legal
Education (ALI CLE)**
4025 Chestnut St, Philadelphia, PA 19104-3099
Toll Free Tel: 800-CLE-NEWS (253-6397)
Fax: 215-243-1664
E-mail: custserv@ali-cle.org
Web Site: www.ali-cle.org
Key Personnel
Dir & CFO: Julie Scribner *Tel:* 215-243-1672
E-mail: jscribner@ali-cle.org
Dir, HR: Diane Schnitzer *Tel:* 215-243-4000
E-mail: dschnitzer@ali-cle.org
Founded: 1947
Legal training products & services.

American Management Association® (AMA)
1601 Broadway, New York, NY 10019
Tel: 212-586-8100 *Toll Free Tel:* 877-566-9441
(cust serv) *Fax:* 212-903-8168; 518-891-0368
(cust serv)
E-mail: customerservice@amanet.org
Web Site: www.amanet.org
Key Personnel
Pres & CEO: Edward T Reilly
PR Mgr: Roger Kelleher
Founded: 1923
Brochure(s) available

American Melody
PO Box 270, Guilford, CT 06437-0270
Tel: 203-457-0881
E-mail: studio@americanmelody.com
Web Site: www.americanmelody.com
Key Personnel
Pres: Phil Rosenthal *E-mail:* phil@
americanmelody.com
Founded: 1985
Recording company producing bluegrass & folk
music for children & families.

American Montage Inc
PO Box 1042, New York, NY 10003
Tel: 212-334-8283
Web Site: americanmontage.com
Key Personnel
Pres: Eric A Marciano *E-mail:* eric@
americanmontage.com
Founded: 1984
Motion picture media creation & storytelling
company.

**American Museum of Natural History
(AMNH)**
c/o Special Collections, Library Services Dept,
Central Park W & 79 St, New York, NY
10024-5192
Tel: 212-769-5420 *Fax:* 212-769-5009
E-mail: speccol@amnh.org
Web Site: www.amnh.org
Key Personnel
Spec Collections Libn: Gregory Raml
E-mail: graml@amnh.org
Online catalog(s) available

American Music & Sound (AM&S)
925 Broadbeck Dr, No 220, Newbury Park, CA 91320
Toll Free Tel: 800-431-2609 *Toll Free Fax:* 866-707-0717
E-mail: info@americanmusicandsound.com
Web Site: www.americanmusicandsound.com
Key Personnel
Pres: Lynn Martin
Independent distributor of pro audio equipment & musical instruments, including products from Allen & Heath, Alpine Hearing Protection, CAD Audio, dB Technologies, Focusrite, Fostex, Kurzweil, Lewitt, Nord, Novation, Reloop, Studiologic & Xone.

American Music Environments Inc (AME)
1133 W Long Lake Rd, Suite 200, Bloomfield Hills, MI 48302
Tel: 248-646-2020 *Toll Free Tel:* 888-AME-5005 (263-5005) *Toll Free Fax:* 888-AME-6006 (263-6006)
E-mail: info@amemusic.com
Web Site: www.amemusic.com
Founded: 1996
Background music & messaging & in-store video services. Full line of audio equipment including speakers, amplifiers, wire, microphones & much more.

American Optometric Association (AOA)
243 N Lindbergh Blvd, 1st fl, St Louis, MO 63141-7881
Tel: 314-991-4100 *Toll Free Tel:* 800-365-2219 *Fax:* 314-991-4101
Web Site: www.aoa.org
Key Personnel
Exec Dir: Jon Hymes
Founded: 1898
Leading authority on quality care, representing more than 44,000 doctors of optometry, professionals & students, providing training materials & resources.
Online catalog(s) available
Branch Office(s)
1505 Prince St, Suite 300, Alexandria, VA 22314
Tel: 703-739-9200 *Fax:* 703-739-9497

American Playback Images
27748 Caraway Lane, Santa Clarita, CA 91350
Tel: 818-427-8292 *Fax:* 661-263-2387
E-mail: americanplayback@aol.com
Web Site: americanplayback.com
Key Personnel
Mgr: Mike Anglim
Stock footage clips & photos. Specialize in historical, retro, vintage & hard to find images for use in TV shows, feature films, commercials, educational films, corporate projects & web content.

American Production Services LLC
1763 Earl Dr, Fort Mill, SC 29715
Tel: 803-548-2290 *Fax:* 803-548-3406
Web Site: www.apsvideo.com
Key Personnel
Pres: Bruce A Moody *E-mail:* bmoody@apsvideo.com
Founded: 1995
Legal video production.

American Recordable Media
110 Dewey Dr, Suite A, Nicholasville, KY 40356
Tel: 859-881-1036 *Toll Free Tel:* 800-598-8273 *Fax:* 859-881-1035
E-mail: info@americanrecordablemedia.com
Web Site: www.americanrecordablemedia.com
Key Personnel
Prodn Mgr: Ryan Wendt
Founded: 1983

Manufacturer & distribute recordable media, custom CD & DVD printing solutions, full color, waterproof graphics, UV cured technology, cover media backup, duplication & replication.

The American University
Dept of Performing Arts, 4400 Massachusetts Ave NW, Washington, DC 20016-8053
Tel: 202-885-3420 *Fax:* 202-885-1092
Web Site: www.american.edu
Key Personnel
Dir, Audio Technol Progs: Michael Harvey
Tel: 202-885-6302 *E-mail:* mharvey@american.edu

American Video Inc
780 Third Ave, 5th fl, New York, NY 10017-2024
Tel: 212-527-9000
E-mail: sales@accnewyork.com
Key Personnel
Pres: Greg Sherman
Founded: 1979
Design, produce, install & manage display advertising, augmented reality, video conferencing facilities, webcasting services, webinars, conference AV & lighting, technical services.
Online catalog(s) available
Membership(s): Audiovisual and Integrated Experience Association

American Visions
One Deerfield Lane, Cedar Rapids, IA 52403
Tel: 319-360-3211
Web Site: www.americanvisions.org
Key Personnel
Exec Prodr & Dir: Thomas D Hedges
Exec Prodr & Dir, Busn Devt: Stevie Ballard
E-mail: stevie.ballard@stamats.com
Creators & producers of documentaries for public television programming.

Amerinex Applied Imaging Inc, see Adcis Inc

Ametek Programmable Power Inc
9250 Brown Deer Rd, San Diego, CA 92121
Tel: 858-450-0085; 858-458-0223 *Toll Free Tel:* 888-608-0992 *Fax:* 858-458-0267
E-mail: sales.ppd@ametek.com
Web Site: programmablepower.com
Founded: 1961
Manufacturer of precision AC & DC power supplies & test instrumentation products for applications where stable, controllable & reliable power is needed.
Online catalog(s) available

Ametron Audio/Video
Division of Ametron/American Electronic Supply Inc
1546 N Argyle Ave, Hollywood, CA 90028-6410
Tel: 323-466-4321 *Fax:* 323-871-0127
E-mail: info@ametron.com
Web Site: www.ametron.com
Key Personnel
Owner: Fred Rosenthal
Online catalog(s) available

AMG Studios (Los Angeles)
Member of Asset Media Group Inc
2225 E 28 St, Suite 511, Signal Hill, CA 90755
Tel: 562-424-0824
Web Site: www.amgstudiosla.com
Key Personnel
Founder & CEO: Marcus Guy
Co-Founder & Pres: Melissa Guy
Creative Dir: Chris Valcarel
Studio rental for film production or photography.

AMP Services Inc
3111 Fortune Way, Suite B-18, West Palm Beach, FL 33414
Tel: 561-333-0335 *Fax:* 561-333-0370
Web Site: www.audiomagnetics.com
Key Personnel
Pres: Tom Rappolt *E-mail:* tomampservices@comcast.net
Founded: 1985
Head relapping, reel to reel & motor rebuilding for AV equipment, keyboards, mixing consoles, speakers, amplifiers & most professional audio equipment.
Catalog(s) available

Ampex Data Systems Corp
26460 Corporate Ave, Hayward, CA 94545
Tel: 650-367-2011
E-mail: info@ampex.com
Web Site: www.ampex.com
Key Personnel
Gen Mgr: Jim Orahood
Founded: 1944
Manufacture cameras for aircrafts.

Amplifier Technologies Inc (ATI)
1749 Chapin Rd, Montebello, CA 90640
Tel: 323-278-0001 *Fax:* 323-278-0083
E-mail: sales@ati-amp.com
Web Site: www.ati-amp.com
Key Personnel
Founder & Pres: Morris Kessler
Founded: 1993
Membership(s): Consumer Technology Association™; Custom Electronic Design & Installation Association; International Theatre Equipment Association; NAMM, the National Association of Music Merchants

AmpliVox Portable Sound Systems
650 Anthony Trail, Suite D, Northbrook, IL 60062-2512
Tel: 847-498-9000 *Toll Free Tel:* 800-267-5486 *Toll Free Fax:* 800-267-5489
E-mail: info@ampli.com
Web Site: www.ampli.com
Key Personnel
CEO & Pres: Don Roth
Founded: 1952
Design engineering, manufacturing all electronics & audio, UL/CUL & CE, portable sound systems & lecterns.
Online catalog(s) available
Membership(s): Audiovisual and Integrated Experience Association; BPIA; Business Technology Association; Education Market Association

AMPLUS Productions
1484 Liveoak Dr, Mississauga, ON L5E 2X1, Canada
Tel: 416-889-7664 *Fax:* 905-274-7687
Web Site: www.amplusproductions.com
Key Personnel
Pres: Brian Allen *E-mail:* brian@amplusproductions.com
Music production, composition, business consultation.
Membership(s): Canadian Country Music Association; Country Music Association of Ontario; The Society of Composers, Authors and Music Publishers of Canada; Songwriters Association of Canada

AMS Pictures
16986 N Dallas Pkwy, Dallas, TX 75248
Tel: 972-818-7400 *Toll Free Tel:* 866-691-3660 *Fax:* 972-818-1257
Web Site: amspictures.com
Key Personnel
Founder & CEO: Andy Streitfeld

VP, Exec Creative Dir, Alchemy at AMS: Mark McGovern
Founded: 1982
Premiere film, video, HD interactive services & multimedia production company in the Southwestern US. Specialize in creative communication solutions for clients.
Online catalog(s) available
Branch Office(s)
4407 Bee Caves Rd, Suite 612, Austin, TX 78746 *Tel:* 512-330-9434 *Toll Free Tel:* 866-691-3660

AMV/Unitel Studios
515 W 57 St, New York, NY 10019
Tel: 212-265-3600 (studios); 212-586-8616 (sales)
Fax: 212-246-5059
E-mail: hdsales@allmobilevideo.com
Web Site: www.allmobilevideo.com
Key Personnel
AVM Broadcast Sales: Erik Thielking
E-mail: ethielking@allmobilevideo.com
Founded: 1976
Television production facility.
Online catalog(s) available
Branch Office(s)
433 W 53 St, New York, NY 10019 *Tel:* 212-246-5040

AMX® by Harman
Division of Harman Professional Solutions
8500 Balboa Blvd, Northridge, CA 91329
Toll Free Tel: 800-222-0193 (cust care); 844-776-4899 (tech support)
E-mail: hprotechsupportusa@harman.com
Web Site: www.amx.com
Control & automation, system-wide switching & AV signal distribution, digital signage & technology management.
Catalog(s) available
Online catalog(s) available
Membership(s): Audiovisual and Integrated Experience Association; Consumer Technology Association™; Custom Electronic Design & Installation Association; NSCA; US Green Building Council

Analog Man Recording Studio
PO Box 70245, Nashville, TN 37207
Tel: 615-596-6094
E-mail: mrmarksmusic@gmail.com
Key Personnel
Engr & Prodr: Mark Hughes
E-mail: mrmarksmusic@aol.com
Founded: 1980
Analog electronics with over 25 pieces of vintage mike preamps (most of which have been customized by Stephen Hazelton from The Mastering Lab in LA), console & effects, recording to digital recorders. 55 synthesizers. Lotsa outboard. Production & musicians also available.
Membership(s): NAMM, the National Association of Music Merchants

Analog Way Inc
3047 Summer Oak Place, Buford, GA 30518
Tel: 212-269-1902 *Fax:* 212-269-1943
E-mail: salesusa@analogway.com
Web Site: www.analogway.com
Founded: 1989
Manufacturer of innovative signal converters & AV switchers.
Online catalog(s) available
Foreign Office(s): Analog Way SAS, 2/4 rue Georges Besse, 92160 Antony, France *Tel:* 01 81 89 08 60 *Fax:* 01 57 19 04 54
Analog Way Italy, Via Volta N 18, 20026 Novate Milanese MI, Italy *Tel:* (02) 39493943 *Fax:* (02) 39493943
Analog Way Pte Ltd, 152 Beach Rd, 15-03 Gateway E, Singapore 189721, Singapore *Tel:* 6292 5800 *Fax:* 6292 5202

Analog Way UK, North London Business Park, Oakleigh Rd S, N11 1NP London, United Kingdom *Tel:* (020) 3668 1574
Membership(s): Audiovisual and Integrated Experience Association; IEEE; NAB; SMPTE®; VESA

Anaphora Literary Press
1108 W Third St, Quanah, TX 79252
Tel: 470-289-6395
Web Site: anaphoraliterary.com
Key Personnel
Dir: Dr Anna Faktorovich *E-mail:* director@anaphoraliterary.com
Founded: 2009
Anaphora offers audio & visual services to anybody in need of inexpensive solutions. Video book trailers, audio books & other services are provided as part of the standard publishing package to authors working with Anaphora Literary Press. Anaphora has also created animated cartoons, original techno music, & other motion & sound projects posted on its YouTube channel. Anaphora's Director, Dr Anna Faktorovich, wrote & produced a short, "My Sister, the Psychopath," which won international awards.
E-mail for pricing information with details about your needs.

Anchor Audio Inc
5931 Darwin Ct, Carlsbad, CA 92008
Tel: 760-827-7100 *Toll Free Tel:* 800-262-4671
Fax: 760-827-7105
E-mail: sales@anchoraudio.com
Web Site: www.anchoraudio.com
Key Personnel
Pres: Alex Jacobs
VP, Mktg: Emily Golding
Dir, Sales: Nick Craig
Founded: 1975
Portable sound system manufacturer. Wired & wireless intercom manufacturer.
Online catalog(s) available
Membership(s): Audiovisual and Integrated Experience Association

Anchor Distributors
Division of Whitaker House
1030 Hunt Valley Circle, New Kensington, PA 15068
Tel: 724-334-7000 *Toll Free Tel:* 800-444-4484
Fax: 724-334-1200 *Toll Free Fax:* 800-765-1960
E-mail: customercare@anchordistributors.com; marketing@anchordistributors.com
Web Site: www.whitakerhouse.com; www.anchordistributors.com
Key Personnel
Pres: Robert Whitaker, Sr
Founded: 1970
Distributors of Christian products.
Catalog(s) available, free, biannual, available upon request

Ancient Future
PO Box 264, Kentfield, CA 94914-0264
Tel: 415-459-1892
E-mail: info@ancient-future.com
Web Site: www.ancient-future.com
Key Personnel
Dir: Matthew Montfort
Online catalog(s) available

Olson Anderson Co
3124 Kochville Rd, Suite 121, Saginaw, MI 48604-9305
Tel: 989-399-3024
E-mail: oac100@aol.com
Web Site: www.olsonanderson.com

Key Personnel
CFO & Cont: Michael Bracey
Founded: 1931
Membership(s): National Association of Sound Contractors

Angenieux
140 Centennial Ave, Piscataway, NJ 08854
Tel: 973-812-3858
E-mail: angenieux@tccus.com
Web Site: www.angenieux.com
Founded: 1935
Online catalog(s) available
Foreign Office(s): Blvd Ravel de Malval, 42570 Saint-Heand, France *Tel:* 04 77 90 78 00 *Fax:* 04 77 90 78 03 *E-mail:* angenieux@fr.thalesgroup.com (headquarters)
Thales Japan KK, Akasaka Tameike Tower 8F, 2-17-7 Akasaka, Minato-ku, Tokyo 107-0052, Japan *Tel:* (090) 8943 2557 *E-mail:* yasuhiko.mikami@asia.thalesgroup.com
Thales Solutions Asia Pte Ltd, 21 Changi North Rise, Singapore 498788, Singapore *Tel:* 9632 6225 *E-mail:* frank.goh@asia.thalesgroup.com
Membership(s): NAB; SBE; SMPTE®

Angstrom Lighting
12224 Montague St, Pacoima, CA 91331
Tel: 323-462-4246
E-mail: info@angstromlighting.com
Web Site: www.angstromlighting.com
Key Personnel
Owner & Pres: Alton Butler
Opers Mgr: John McQuay
Founded: 1977
Full service lighting & special effects supplier serving the entertainment industry. Rentals, sales, service, design & education.
Membership(s): Professional Lighting & Sound Association; USITT

Animated Software Co
PO Box 1936, Carlsbad, CA 92018-1936
Tel: 760-720-7261 *Toll Free Tel:* 800-551-2726
Web Site: www.animatedsoftware.com
Key Personnel
Owner: Ace Hoffman *E-mail:* rhoffman@animatedsoftware.com
Founded: 1984
Interactive & educational animation.
Online catalog(s) available

Animotion Inc
501 W Fayette St, Syracuse, NY 13204
Tel: 315-471-3533
E-mail: info@animotioninc.com
Web Site: animotioninc.com
Key Personnel
Pres: David Hicock; Larry Royer
VP, Opers: Peter Wynn
Founded: 1983
Traditional animation, animation for the web & motion graphics.

Anixter Inc
2301 Patriot Blvd, Glenview, IL 60026
Tel: 224-521-8000 *Toll Free Tel:* 800-323-8167
Fax: 224-521-8100
Web Site: www.anixter.com
Key Personnel
Pres & CEO: William A Galvin
Founded: 1957
Global supplier of communications & security products.

Annenberg Learner
Division of Annenberg Foundation
PO Box 26983, St Louis, MO 63118
Tel: 202-783-0500 (outside US)
Toll Free Tel: 800-LEARNER (532-7637)
Fax: 202-783-0333

E-mail: order@learner.org
Web Site: www.learner.org
Key Personnel
Sr Prog Offr: Michele McLeod
    E-mail: mmcleod@learner.org
Sr Coord, Mktg & Communs: Stacie Pierpoint
    E-mail: spierpoint@learner.org
Opers Analyst: Kristine Inchausti
    E-mail: kinchausti@learner.org
Development & distribution of multimedia resources for teaching & learning.
Online catalog(s) available

R B Annis Instruments Inc
117 W Franklin St, Greencastle, IN 46135-1223
Tel: 765-848-1621 *Fax:* 765-848-1625
E-mail: info@rbannis.com
Web Site: www.rbannis.com
Key Personnel
Pres: Michael Scott
Online catalog(s) available

Anode Inc
926 Main St, Nashville, TN 37206
Tel: 615-742-1490 *Fax:* 615-742-1487
E-mail: inquiry@anode.com
Web Site: www.anode.com
Key Personnel
Pres: Mark Magnuson
Founded: 1991
Provides clients with digital solutions, develops marketing & sales tools, produces meetings & creates interactive media for corporations & institutions.

Anonymous Content
3532 Hayden Ave, Culver City, CA 90232
Tel: 310-558-6000 *Fax:* 310-558-2724
E-mail: filmtv@anonymouscontent.com
Web Site: www.anonymouscontent.com
Key Personnel
CEO: Steve Golin
Mng Dir: Eric Stern *Tel:* 310-558-6215
    E-mail: eric@anonymouscontent.com
Sr Exec Prodr: Gina Zapata *Tel:* 310-558-6282
    E-mail: gzapata@anonymouscontent.com
Exec Prodr/Prodn: SueEllen Clair *Tel:* 310-558-6006 *E-mail:* sueellen@anonymouscontent.com
Head, Prodn: Kerry Haynie *Tel:* 310-558-6241
    E-mail: kerry@anonymouscontent.com
Prodr, Music Video/Content: Nina Soriano *Tel:* 310-558-6227 *E-mail:* nina@anonymouscontent.com
Founded: 1999
Production & talent management company.
Branch Office(s)
155 Spring St, 3rd fl, New York, NY 10012
    Tel: 212-925-0055 *Fax:* 212-925-5030

Ansonia Prompting Inc
39 W 29 St, Suite 305, New York, NY 10001
Tel: 212-594-0500 *Fax:* 212-202-4925
E-mail: info@ansoniaprompting.com
Web Site: www.ansoniaprompting.com
Key Personnel
Owner & Pres: Sandy Garfunkel
Founded: 1995
Offer complete teleprompter services. Branch office in Orlando, FL.

AnswersMedia
30 N Racine Ave, Suite 300, Chicago, IL 60607
Tel: 312-421-0113
E-mail: contactus@answersmediainc.com
Web Site: www.answersmediainc.com
Key Personnel
CEO: Jeff Bohnson
Pres: Sean Murray *E-mail:* sean@answersmediainc.com
Founded: 2004

Full service video production & post-production company.
Online catalog(s) available

Antelope Valley Locations & Production Services
42848 150 St E, Lancaster, CA 93535
Tel: 661-946-1515 *Fax:* 661-946-0454
E-mail: clubed@avlocations.com
Web Site: www.avlocations.com
Key Personnel
Owner & Mgr: Randy Czajkowski *Tel:* 661-917-1587 (cell)
Founded: 1990
Provide locations, services & props for movie, commercial, music videos & still photography.

Antenna International
383 Main Ave, Norwalk, CT 06851
Tel: 203-523-0320
E-mail: inquiry@antennainternational.com; marketing@antennainternational.com
Web Site: www.antennainternational.com
Key Personnel
Pres & CEO: David A Falter
Global Cont: Jack Orlando
EVP & Chief Innovation Offr: Sean Lentner
EVP, Creative Servs & Global Chief Mktg Offr: Gordon Montgomery
EVP, Global Human Capital, Retail Opers & Admin: Bob Moran
SVP, Global Sales: Christopher Bazley
Head, Interactive Design: James Morgan
Dir, Creative Strategies, Americas: Alice Walker
Acctg Mgr: Tricia McGovern
Regl Retail Mgr: Danielle Brooks
Tech Servs Mgr: Ryan Bruce
Creates audio tours, mobile apps, multimedia guides, podcasts, interactives & unrivalled story-driven content for the museum & cultural sector.
Online catalog(s) available
Foreign Office(s): 3 rue des dechargeurs, 75001 Paris, France *Tel:* 01 42 86 68 10 *Fax:* 01 42 86 04 08 *E-mail:* fr@antennainternational.com
Fasanenstr 37, 10719 Berlin, Germany *Tel:* (030) 8871 360 *Fax:* (030) 8871 3626 *E-mail:* de@antennainternational.com
Via Properzio, 5, 4th fl, 00193 Rome, Italy *Tel:* (06) 9765 7850 *Fax:* (06) 9765 7851 *E-mail:* it@antennainternational.com
Antenna Internacional de RL de CV, Presidente Masaryk No 111, Primer Piso, Col Polanco, Delegacion Miguel Hidalgo, 11570 Mexico, DF, Mexico *E-mail:* mx@antennainternational.com
Stadhouderskade 60, 1072 AC Amsterdam, Netherlands *Tel:* (020) 673 6824 *E-mail:* nl@antennainternational.com
Ak, Jerozolimskie 56c, 00-803 Warsaw, Poland *Tel:* (61) 2251502 *E-mail:* pl@antennainternational.com
Calle La Granada del Penedes, 25, 6e 1a, 08006 Barcelona, Spain *Tel:* 932 182 094 *E-mail:* es@antennainternational.com
The Office Group, 20 Eastbourne Terr, Paddington, London W2 6LG, United Kingdom, Exec Dir: Haydn Pinnell *Tel:* (020) 3365 8600 *E-mail:* uk@antennainternational.com

Anton/Bauer®
Division of Vitec Videocom Inc
14 Progress Dr, Shelton, CT 06484
Tel: 203-929-1100 *Toll Free Tel:* 800-422-3473
    Fax: 203-929-9935
E-mail: salessupport_USA@vitecgroup.com
Web Site: www.antonbauer.com
Founded: 1970
Portable power systems for professional broadcast, digital cinema, video & healthcare indus-

tries. Foreign offices in Brazil, France, Japan, Netherlands, Singapore & UK.
Online catalog(s) available

Antronics Inc
25 Summer Ave, Waltham, MA 02452-5634
Mailing Address: PO Box 540429, Waltham, MA 02454-0429
Tel: 781-891-7525 *Fax:* 781-647-3667
E-mail: info@antronics.net
Web Site: www.antronics.net
Key Personnel
Pres: Chris Karimbakas
Gen Mgr: Jim Karimbakas
Founded: 1955
Sales, service & systems integration.

Anvil Cases
Subsidiary of Calzone Case Co
1242 E Edna Place, Covina, CA 91724
Tel: 626-968-4100 *Toll Free Tel:* 800-FLYANVIL (359-2684) *Fax:* 626-968-1703
E-mail: web.sales@anvilcase.com
Web Site: www.calzoneandanvil.com
Key Personnel
Pres (Bridgeport, CT): Joseph Calzone
Founded: 1952
Manufacture & repair reusable shipping, packaging, carrying & storage cases & containers.
Online catalog(s) available
Membership(s): Audiovisual and Integrated Experience Association; NAB; NAMM, the National Association of Music Merchants; Percussive Arts Society; Professional Lighting & Sound Association

Aon Hewitt
Affiliate of Aon Corp
1100 Reynolds Blvd, Winston-Salem, NC 27105-3400
Mailing Address: PO Box 66, Winston-Salem, NC 27102-0066
Tel: 336-748-1120 *Fax:* 847-953-4854
Web Site: www.aon.com
Produce sales presentations with slides.
Membership(s): American Business Communication Association; IABC; Industrial Communication Council

AP Images
Division of Associated Press (AP)
200 Liberty St, New York, NY 10281
Tel: 212-621-1930 *Fax:* 212-621-1955
Web Site: www.apimages.com; apimagesblog.com
Visual content for purchase (historical & contemporary photographs). Still photography & assignment photography.

APC by Schneider Electric
132 Fairgrounds Rd, West Kingston, RI 02892
Tel: 401-789-5735 *Toll Free Tel:* 800-800-4272
    Fax: 401-789-3710
Web Site: www.apc.com
Founded: 1981
Worldwide leader in the designing, manufacturing & marketing of power protection & management solutions for nonstop networking. The product range includes surge suppressors, uninterruptible power supplies, DC power supplies, power conditioning equipment & related software for computer & computer-related equipment.
Online catalog(s) available

Apertura
535 Main St, Orford, NH 03777
Mailing Address: PO Box 12, Orford, NH 03777-0012
Tel: 603-353-9067
Web Site: www.apertura.org

Key Personnel
Prodr & Filmmaker: John Karol *E-mail:* karol@
apertura.org
Founded: 1969
Film/video/sound production & production ser-
vices.
Catalog(s) available
Membership(s): SMPTE®

Aperture Studios Miami
385 NE 59 St, Miami, FL 33137
Tel: 305-759-4327 *Fax:* 305-757-1198
E-mail: rental@aperturepro.com
Web Site: aperturepro.com
Founded: 1993
Studio & equipment rentals, including cameras,
computer & DSLR accessories, lighting & grip.

Apex Jr
1450 W 228 St, Unit 4, Torrance, CA 90501
Tel: 818-248-0416 *Toll Free Tel:* 866-4-ApexJr
(427-3957) *Fax:* 424-263-4614
E-mail: steve.apexjr@prodigy.net
Web Site: www.apexjr.com
Founded: 1992
New surplus electronics.

Apex Machine Co Inc
3000 NE 12 Terr, Fort Lauderdale, FL 33334
Tel: 954-566-1572 *Fax:* 954-563-2844
E-mail: email@apexmachine.com
Web Site: www.apexmachine.com
Key Personnel
CEO: A Robert Coningsby, III
Pres: Todd Coningsby
Founded: 1903
Custom printing for CD-ROMs.
Brochure(s) available
Membership(s): Content Delivery & Storage As-
sociation; PMMI: The Association for Packag-
ing and Processing Technologies; WIMA

Aphex
Division of DWV Entertainment
PO Box 91028, Long Beach, CA 90809-1028
Tel: 562-364-7400 *Toll Free Fax:* 888-412-4664
E-mail: info@aphex.com
Web Site: www.aphex.com
Key Personnel
CEO: David Wiener
Founded: 1975
Audio system manufacturer.
Online catalog(s) available
Foreign Office(s): 107 Carnarvon St, Silverwater,
NSW 2128, Australia *Tel:* (02) 9648 5855
Membership(s): AES; NAB; NAMM, the Na-
tional Association of Music Merchants; NSCA;
SMPTE®

API
8301 Patuxent Range Rd, Jessup, MD 20794
Tel: 301-776-7879 *Fax:* 301-776-8117
E-mail: service@apiaudio.com
Web Site: www.apiaudio.com
Key Personnel
Pres: Larry Droppa *E-mail:* larry@apiaudio.com
Mng Dir: Gordon Smart *E-mail:* gordon@
apiaudio.com
Dir, Sales: Dan Zimbelman *Tel:* 410-330-8079
E-mail: zimbel@apiaudio.com
Dir, Serv: Radovan Maricic *E-mail:* rmaricic@
apiaudio.com
Sales: Mark Seman *E-mail:* mark@apiaudio.com
Founded: 1968
Audio broadcast console manufacturer for radio
& TV networks.
Membership(s): AES

APM Music, see Associated Production Music
LLC

Apogee Communications Group
159 Alpine Way, Boulder, CO 80304
Tel: 303-443-8473 *Toll Free Tel:* 800-210-5700
Fax: 303-443-0500
E-mail: sales@apogeevideo.com; contact@
apogeecommunicationsgroup.com
Web Site: www.apogeevideo.com;
apogeecommunicationsgroup.com
Key Personnel
Owner, Prodr & Dir, Photog: Arthur J Levy
Health & safety videos & DVDs. HD & SD
video production services for television, cor-
porate, medical & educational clients including
HD vertical & horizontal digital signage & 4K
HD production.
Online catalog(s) available

Apogee Electronics Corp
1715 Berkeley St, Santa Monica, CA 90404
Tel: 310-584-9394 *Fax:* 310-584-9385
E-mail: info@apogeedigital.com
Web Site: www.apogeedigital.com
Key Personnel
Pres: Betty Bennett
Creative Dir: Sean McArthur
Founded: 1985
Design, manufacture & distribute analog & digital
converters.

Apogee Sound International LLC
Subsidiary of Bogen Communications Interna-
tional Inc
1200 MacArthur Blvd, Suite 304, Mahwah, NJ
07430-2331
Toll Free Tel: 800-443-3979 *Toll Free Fax:* 800-
999-9016
E-mail: info@apogee-sound.com
Web Site: www.apogee-sound.com
Key Personnel
SVP, Sales: Dave Chambers *E-mail:* dchambers@
bogen.com
Founded: 1985
Membership(s): AES; NAMM, the National Asso-
ciation of Music Merchants; NSCA

Apollo Design Technology Inc
4130 Fourier Dr, Fort Wayne, IN 46818
Tel: 260-497-9191 *Fax:* 260-497-9192
E-mail: sales@apollodesign.net
Web Site: www.apollodesign.net
Founded: 1992
Innovator, manufacturer & distributor of gobos,
LED fixtures, color filters & related equipment
& accessories for the lighting industry.
Online catalog(s) available
Membership(s): Entertainment Services and Tech-
nology Association; Professional Lighting &
Sound Association; Themed Entertainment As-
sociation; USITT

Applause Learning Resources
85 Fernwood Lane, Roslyn, NY 11576
Tel: 516-625-1145 *Toll Free Tel:* 800-277-5287
Toll Free Fax: 877-365-7484
E-mail: info@applauselearning.com
Web Site: www.applauselearning.com
Key Personnel
Dir: Michael Pollack
Sales Dir: Evelyn Pollack
Foreign language teaching products, including
textbooks, DVDs, study guides, books, read-
ers, dictionaries, games, audio CDs, maps &
posters.
Catalog(s) available
Membership(s): American Council on the Teach-
ing of Foreign Languages

Applause Productions & Publications
PO Box 820024, Dallas, TX 75382-0024
Tel: 214-652-4300
E-mail: info@applauseproductions.com

Web Site: applauseproductions.com
Key Personnel
Pres: Lisa Owen *E-mail:* lisa@
applauseproductions.com
Founded: 1983
Specialize in corporate event production. Pro-
ducer of the annual Partyfest Extravaganza
Tradeshow.
Catalog(s) available

Apple Inc
One Infinite Loop, Cupertino, CA 95014
Tel: 408-996-1010
Web Site: www.apple.com
Key Personnel
CEO: Timothy D Cook
CFO & SVP: Luca Maestri
SVP, Internet Software & Servs: Eddy Cue
SVP, Software Engg: Craig Federighi
SVP, Worldwide Mktg: Philip W Schiller
Founded: 1976

Applebox Studio
379 53 Circle, Vero Beach, FL 32968
Tel: 203-803-9115
Web Site: www.appleboxstudio.com
Key Personnel
Pres: Jim Jontz *E-mail:* jim@appleboxstudio.com
Founded: 1990
Video & photography production company.

Pat Appleson Studios Inc
2359 Hwy 70 SE, Suite 102, Hickory, NC 28602
Tel: 828-461-3003 (cell); 828-994-4361
Web Site: www.appleson.com
Key Personnel
Pres: Patrick G Appleson *E-mail:* pat@appleson.
com
PR Dir: Jayne Kilgore
Full service broadcast production company.
Membership(s): AES; NAB; SBE; SMPTE®

Applied Electronics
722 Blue Crab Rd, Newport News, VA 23606
Tel: 757-591-9371 *Toll Free Tel:* 800-883-0008
Fax: 757-591-9514
E-mail: sales@appliednn.com
Web Site: www.appliednn.com
Key Personnel
COO: Mike Rampmeyer *E-mail:* mike@
appliednn.com
Manufactures & distributes trussing, portable
crank lifts, ground support systems, roof sys-
tems, dimmers, lighting controllers, power dis-
tribution & other accessories.
Catalog(s) available

Applied Electronics Ltd
1260 Kamato Rd, Mississauga, ON L4W 1Y1,
Canada
Tel: 905-625-4321 *Fax:* 905-625-4333
E-mail: ael.toronto@appliedelectronics.com
Web Site: www.appliedelectronics.com
Key Personnel
Pres: Paul Stechly
VP, AV Systems Div: Mike Dalton
Designer, supplier & integrator of professional
AV, broadcast & post-production technology.

Applied Integration Corp
3930 W New York Dr, Tucson, AZ 85745
Tel: 520-743-3095
E-mail: info@appliedi.com
Web Site: www.appliedi.com
Key Personnel
Pres: Frederick Pingal
Dir: Karen Bock
Founded: 1993
Developer & manufacturer of mobile & remote
access digital video surveillance systems.

Applied Research & Technology Inc, see ART (Applied Research & Technology Inc)

Applied Voice & Speech Technologies Inc (AVST)
27042 Towne Centre Dr, Suite 200, Foothill Ranch, CA 92610-2810
Tel: 949-699-2300 *Toll Free Tel:* 866-368-0400
Fax: 949-699-2301
E-mail: info@avst.com; sales@avst.com
Web Site: www.avst.com
Key Personnel
Pres & CEO: Jean Champagne
CFO: Jeff Dick
SVP, Global Sales: Jean Pierre Filion
VP, Mktg & Communs: Stephane Vidal
VP, Support & Servs: Dan Ravetto
Gen Mgr: Tom Minifie
Founded: 2003
Developer of software-based Unified Communications (UC) solutions for businesses of all sizes.
Branch Office(s)
20000 North Creek Pkwy, Suite 200, Bothell, WA 98011 *Tel:* 425-951-1600 *Fax:* 425-951-1597

APS Lighting-Sound-AV
901 Columbia Circle, Merrimack, NH 03054
Tel: 603-424-9198 *Toll Free Tel:* 800-837-0005
Fax: 603-423-9816
E-mail: info@apslightingnh.com
Web Site: www.apslightingnh.com
Key Personnel
Owner: Norm St Germain
Founded: 2000
Full service theatrical & special event production company providing the sale, installation & rental of quality stage/video lighting, AV, special effects & theatrical equipment.
Product sheet(s) available, free
Membership(s): National Foundation of Independent Businesses; Professional Lighting & Sound Association; USITT

Arbor Oakland Group
4303 Normandy Ct, Royal Oak, MI 48073-2266
Tel: 248-549-0150 *Toll Free Tel:* 800-886-5661
Fax: 248-549-5270
E-mail: info@arboroakland.com
Web Site: www.arboroakland.com
Key Personnel
Pres: Don Kirkland
Full service photo & digital imaging lab specializing in direct to board printing, digital die cutting, full color grand format printing on cloth, mesh canvas & vinyl - used for curtains, wallcoverings, backdrops & props.
Catalog(s) available
Membership(s): The Imaging Alliance

ARC Document Solutions
1981 N Broadway, Suite 385, Walnut Creek, CA 94596
Tel: 925-949-5100 *Toll Free Tel:* 855-500-0660
E-mail: contact@e-arc.com
Web Site: www.e-arc.com
Key Personnel
Chmn, Pres & CEO: Suri Suriyakumar
COO: Dilo Wijesuriya
CFO: Jorge Avalos
CTO: Rahul Roy
EVP, Global Servs: Ted Buscaglia
EVP, North America Opers: John Zulli
EVP, Technol Solutions: Brian Bailard
SVP, Corp Admin, Opers & Procurement: Ken Gini
SVP, Mergers & Acqs: Theodore Carlson
VP, Sr Corp Coun & Corp Secy: Jeffery Grimes
VP, ARC Technol Solutions: Kumar Wiratunga
VP, Corp Communs & Investor Rel: David Stickney
VP, HR: John Herb
VP, Tech Servs: Greg Schiemann

Gen Mgr & Dir, Engg & R&D: Srinivas Mukkamala
Founded: 1988
Reprographics company which provides business-to-business document management services.
Catalog(s) available
Online catalog(s) available

Arc Light Efx Inc
9338 San Fernando Rd, Sun Valley, CA 91352
Tel: 818-394-6330 *Fax:* 818-252-3486
E-mail: gaslights@arclightefx.com
Web Site: www.arclightefx.com
Key Personnel
CEO & Pres: Greg Smith
CFO: Kary Smith
Founded: 1989
Lighting equipment rental company.
Online catalog(s) available

Archai Media
31E Patrick St, Frederick, MD 21701
Tel: 301-401-8117
E-mail: rentals@archaimedia.com
Web Site: archaimedia.com
Rent cameras & accessories for any production.

Arcor Electronics Co
5689 W Howard St, Niles, IL 60714
Tel: 847-588-0088 *Fax:* 847-588-0080
E-mail: sales@arcorelectronics.com
Web Site: www.arcorelectronics.com
Key Personnel
Pres: David Heuberger
Founded: 2009
Specialty wire & cable distributor specializing in bulk wire.

Arcube Multimedia Inc
1845 Summit Ave, Suite 407, Plano, TX 75074
Tel: 972-267-1800 *Toll Free Tel:* 877-677-9582
Fax: 972-267-1922
E-mail: sales@arcube.com
Web Site: www.arcube.com
Founded: 1999
CD/DVD manufacturing services. Branch offices in Austin & Houston.
Membership(s): International Disc Duplicating Association

Ardent Music LLC
2000 Madison Ave, Memphis, TN 38104
Tel: 901-725-0855 *Fax:* 901-725-7011
E-mail: info@ardentmusic.com
Web Site: www.ardentmusic.com
Key Personnel
Pres: Patrick Scholes
Gen Mgr: Ryan Wiley *E-mail:* rwiley@ardentmusic.com
Founded: 1959
Membership(s): The Recording Academy

Ardent Studios Inc
2000 Madison Ave, Memphis, TN 38104
Tel: 901-725-0855 *Fax:* 901-725-7011
E-mail: info@ardentstudios.com
Web Site: www.ardentstudios.com
Key Personnel
Pres: Keith Sykes *E-mail:* ksykes@ardentmusic.com
Studio Mgr: Jody Stephens *E-mail:* jstephens@ardentmusic.com
Full service recording & mixing studio.
Online catalog(s) available

ARF! ARF!
PO Box 465, Middleboro, MA 02346-0465
Tel: 508-947-7387 *Fax:* 508-947-7387
E-mail: page@arfarfrecords.com
Web Site: www.arfarfrecords.com

Key Personnel
Pres: Erik Lindgren
Re-issues of '60s rock.
Online catalog(s) available

Argentine Productions Inc
111 Mayfair Dr, Pittsburgh, PA 15228
Tel: 412-341-6448
E-mail: engage@argentineproductions.com
Web Site: argentineproductions.com
Key Personnel
Prodr, Writer & Dir: Peter Argentine
Prodr & Ed: Per Argentine
Prodr, Busn Devt: Mia Boccella Hartle
Assoc Prodr & Writer: Erik Argentine
Dir, Photog: Jeff Garton; Jeff Hogan
Create cinematic theater films, immersive media & interactive environments, soundscapes, 3D animations & historical reenactments.

Argraph Corp
111 Asia Place, Carlstadt, NJ 07072
Tel: 201-939-7722 *Toll Free Tel:* 800-526-6290
Fax: 201-939-7782
E-mail: info@argraph.com; sales@argraph.com
Web Site: www.argraph.com
Key Personnel
CEO: Mark Roth
Natl Sales Mgr: Martin Lipton
Founded: 1953
Manufacturer & distributor of photographic & imaging products.
Online catalog(s) available
Membership(s): The Imaging Alliance

Aries Productions Inc
1110 Avenue "H" E, Suite 200, Arlington, TX 76011
Tel: 817-640-9955; 817-300-5255 (cell)
Web Site: www.aries-prods.com
Key Personnel
Pres & Prodn Mgr: Wynn Winberg
E-mail: wynn@aries-prods.com
Founded: 1980
Video, film & multimedia production & post-production.
Online catalog(s) available
Membership(s): Dallas Producers Association

Arizona Cine Equipment
2125 E 20 St, Tucson, AZ 85719
Tel: 520-623-8268 *Fax:* 520-623-1092
Web Site: www.azcine.com
Key Personnel
Pres: Lee Oliver
Convention Servs Sales Mgr: Linda Oliver
AV equipment sales & rentals.
Branch Office(s)
3532 E Elwood St, Phoenix, AZ 85040 *Tel:* 602-437-0221

Arizona Public Media
1423 E University, MLB67, Rm 223, Tucson, AZ 85719
Mailing Address: PO Box 210067, MLB67, Tucson, AZ 85721
Tel: 520-621-5828; 520-621-5836 (sales)
Fax: 520-621-3360
Web Site: www.azpm.org
Key Personnel
Dir & Gen Mgr: Jack Gibson
Prodr: Christopher Conover
Television & radio production & broadcast.
Online catalog(s) available

Arizona Studios
4614 E McDowell Rd, Phoenix, AZ 85008
Tel: 602-275-9100
E-mail: info@arizonastudios.com
Web Site: arizonastudios.com
Key Personnel
CEO: Kevin Mayer

Prodn Mgr: Alyssa Eshelman
Digital Media Artist: Nero Manalo
Animator: Ashley Rangel
Cinematographer/Editor: Christopher Nez
Full service video production studio offering 3D animation, graphic design, motion graphics & video effects.

Ariztical Entertainment Inc
12400 Ventura Blvd, Suite 686, Studio City, CA 91604-2406
Tel: 818-760-3740 *Fax:* 818-760-3581
E-mail: info@ariztical.com; customerservice@ariztical.com; sales@ariztical.com
Web Site: www.ariztical.com
Key Personnel
Pres: Michael Jack Shoel *E-mail:* mjshoel@ariztical.com
Distribute & produce LGBT, independent & art house films.

Ark Media Group Ltd
PO Box 410685, San Francisco, CA 94141-0685
Tel: 415-863-7200; 415-863-3555 *Fax:* 415-864-5437
E-mail: sales@arkmedia.com
Web Site: www.arkmedia.com
Key Personnel
Pres: Allan Kessler
Founded: 1985
Multimedia sales company.
Online catalog(s) available
Shipping Address: 425 Alabama St, San Francisco, CA 94110

Arkon Resources Inc
20 La Porte St, Arcadia, CA 91006
Tel: 626-254-9005 *Toll Free Tel:* 800-841-0884
Fax: 626-254-9266
E-mail: arkon8@arkon.com
Web Site: www.arkon.com
Key Personnel
Pres & CEO: Paul Brassard
VP, Sales & Mktg: Aaron Roth
Dir, Sales & Sr Acct Mgr: Benjamin Arana
Tel: 626-400-6767
Founded: 1988
Manufacture & supplier of mobile mounting solutions & accessories designed for use with tablets, smartphones, cameras, GPS, satellite radios & other mobile communication & portable devices. Offices located in Belgium, South Korea & Taiwan.
Online catalog(s) available

Arrakis Systems
6604 Powell St, Loveland, CO 80538
Tel: 970-461-0730
E-mail: sales@arrakis-systems.com
Web Site: www.arrakis-systems.com
Key Personnel
VP, Sales: Ben Palmer
Leading manufacturer of electronic & furniture products for the radio broadcast & Internet streaming industries.
Catalog(s) available
Online catalog(s) available

ARRI Inc
Subsidiary of Arnold & Richter Cine Technik
600 N Victory Blvd, Burbank, CA 91502-1639
Tel: 818-841-7070 *Fax:* 818-848-4028
E-mail: info@arri.com
Web Site: www.arri.com
Key Personnel
Pres: Glenn Kennel
VP, Intl Mktg: Franz Wieser *E-mail:* fwieser@arri.com
Founded: 1917

Design & manufacture camera & lighting systems for the film & broadcast industry.
Membership(s): AICP; NAB; Professional Film & Video Equipment Association; SMPTE®

ARRIS Group Inc
3871 Lakefield Dr, Suwanee, GA 30024
Tel: 678-473-2907 *Toll Free Tel:* 866-36-ARRIS (362-7747); 877-466-8646 (tech) *Fax:* 678-473-8470
E-mail: marketing@arris.com
Web Site: www.arris.com
Key Personnel
CEO: Bruce McClelland
Exec Chmn & Chmn of the Bd: Robert J Stanzione
EVP & CFO: David B Potts
SVP & CIO: Phil Baldock
SVP, Gen Coun & Secy: Patrick Macken
SVP, HR: Vicki Brewster
Digital & AM fiber optics, RF amplifiers, network management systems, modems, passives & 90-volt powering options. Services include network analysis & design, field engineering, installation & maintenance assistance, technical training, equipment repair, 48-hour emergency repair service & a 24-hour emergency hotline.
Catalog(s) available
Branch Office(s)
1101 Marina Village Pkwy, Alameda, CA 94501
1560 B S Baker Ave, Ontario, CA 91761
6450 Sequence Dr, San Diego, CA 92121 *Toll Free Tel:* 800-225-9446
1764 Automation Pkwy, San Jose, CA 95131 *Tel:* 408-428-9500 *Fax:* 408-428-9590
General Instrument Corp, 2450 Walsh Ave, Santa Clara, CA 95051 *Tel:* 408-235-5500
9800 E Geddes Ave, Suite A-100, Englewood, CO 80112 *Tel:* 720-895-7000 *Toll Free Tel:* 888-353-9473 *Fax:* 720-895-7106
15 Sterling Dr, Wallingford, CT 06492 *Tel:* 203-303-6400 *Fax:* 203-303-6411
3701 FAU Blvd, Suite 200, Boca Raton, FL 33431 *Tel:* 561-995-6000 *Fax:* 561-995-6001
2400 Ogden Ave, Suite 180, Lisle, IL 60532 *Tel:* 630-281-3000 *Fax:* 630-281-3362
1321 Wakarusa Dr, Lawrence, KS 66049
900 Chelmsford St, Lowell, MA 01851 *Tel:* 978-614-2900
101 Stamford Dr, Cary, NC 27513
1825 NW 167 Place, Beaverton, OR 97006 *Tel:* 503-495-9240
101 Tournament Dr, Horsham, PA 19044 *Tel:* 215-323-1000
100 N 18 St, Suite 1810, Philadelphia, PA 19103 *Tel:* 215-209-6160
4516 Seton Center Pkwy, Suite 185, Austin, TX 78759 *Tel:* 512-837-7400
5300 Hollister St, Suite 210, Houston, TX 77040
ARRIS Canada Inc, 90 Matheson Blvd W, 4th fl, Mississauga, ON L5R 3R3, Canada
Foreign Office(s): ARRIS de Argentina SA, Bartolome Cruz 1850-Vicente Lopez, 1st fl, B1638BHR Buenos Aires, Argentina
ARRIS Group Australia Pty Ltd, 460 Bourke St, Level 4, Melbourne 3000, Australia
ARRIS Group Australia Pty Ltd, 10a Julius Ave, Level 1, North Ryde 2113, Australia *Tel:* (02) 9078 1200 *Fax:* (02) 9078 1284
ARRIS Belgium BVBA, Diegem Industrie Excelsiorlaan 89, Pav 813, 1930 Zaventem, Belgium
ARRIS Telecomunicacoes do Brazil, Av das Nacoes Unidas, 12399, Sala 11B, Edificio Landmark, 04578-000 Sao Paulo-SP, Brazil *Tel:* (011) 3027-3757
ARRIS Telecomunicaciones Chile Ltda, Av Cerro el Plomo 5680, Torre 6, oficina 1901, 7500742 Las Condes, Santiago, Chile *Tel:* (02) 26784500 *Fax:* (02) 23352791
ARRIS Technology (Hangzhou) Co Ltd, No 1 Wang Jing East Rd, Chao Yang District, Beijing 100102, China

ARRIS Technology (Hangzhou) Co Ltd, 2/F Back Area, Bldg D, No 68 Eastcom Rd, Bin Jiang District, Hangzhou 310053, China
ARRIS Technology (Hangzhou) Ltd, No 27 Xin Jin Qiao Rd, 5th fl, 11th Bldg, Pudong New District, Shanghai 200021, China *Tel:* (021) 5116 2945 *Fax:* (021) 5116 2960
ARRIS Technology (Shenzhen) Co Ltd, South & East Wing, 4/F, Block 2, Vision (Shenzhen) Business Park, Shenzhen, China *Tel:* (0755) 2671 6300 *Fax:* (0755) 2671 6307
ARRIS de Colombia SAS, Av Carrera 9, No 113-52 Off 1606, Edificio Torres Unidas II, Bogota, Colombia *Tel:* (01) 7460127
ARRIS France SAS, 5 Blvd Gallieni, Immeuble DUEO, 92130 Issy-les-Moulineaux, France
ARRIS Global Procurement Ltd, Rm 1607B, 16/F, Two Harbourfront, 22 Tak Fung St, Hunghom, Kowloon, Hong Kong
ARRIS Hong Kong Ltd, Rm 1607C-1609, 16/F, Two Harbourfront, 22 Tak Fung St, Hunghom, Kowloon, Hong Kong
ARRIS Group India Pvt Ltd, "The Senate," 3rd fl, No 33/1, Ulsoor Rd, Bangalore 560 042, India *Tel:* (080) 67737908 *Fax:* (080) 67738380
ARRIS India Pvt Ltd, "The Senate," Ground, 1st & 2nd fl, No 33/1, Ulsoor Rd, Bangalore 560 042, India *Tel:* (080) 67738500 *Fax:* (080) 67737900
ARRIS Communications Ireland Ltd, 4300 Cork Airport Business Park, Kinsale Rd, Cork, Ireland *Tel:* (021) 7305800 *Fax:* (021) 4321972
ARRIS Broadband Solutions Ltd Research & Development, 28 Ha Barzel St, 69710 Tel Aviv, Israel *Tel:* (03) 607 1111 *Fax:* (03) 607 1222
ARRIS Group Japan KK, Shinagawa East One Tower 21F, 2-16-1 Konan, Minato-ku, Tokyo 108-0075, Japan *Tel:* (03) 5461-7300 *Fax:* (03) 5461-2270
ARRIS Solutions Malaysia Sdn Bhd, Jl Puteri 2/7, Unit 19-3, Bandar Puteri, Puchong, 47100 Selangor, Malaysia
ARRIS de Mexico SA de CV, Via de Innovacion 402, Parque de Investigacion e Innocation Tecnologica, 66628 Apodaca, Nuevo Leon, Mexico *Tel:* (0181) 2281 8500
ARRIS de Mexico SA de CV, Blvd Manuel Avila Camacho, 126, Piso 2, Colonia Lomas de Chapultepec III sseccion, Delegacion Miguel Hidalgo, 11000 Mexico, DF, Mexico *Tel:* (0155) 41255400
ARRIS Manufacturing Facility, ARRIS Group de Mexico SA de CV, Av De La Paz 11721-B, Parque Industrial Pacifico, 22643 Tijuana, Mexico *Tel:* (0664) 104-7200 *Fax:* (0664) 104-7294
ARRIS Group BV, Atlas Arena Bldg Azie, Hoogoorddreef 5, 1101 BA Amsterdam, Netherlands *Tel:* (020) 311 2500 *Fax:* (020) 311 2501
ARRIS New Zealand Ltd, 117 St Georges Bay Rd, Parnell, Auckland, New Zealand
ARRIS Group Russia, 216 Regus Krasnaya Roza, Timura Frunze 11, Bldg 2, 119021 Moscow, Russia *Tel:* (495) 988 47 64
ARRIS Singapore Pte Ltd, UE BizHub Central Block A, No 03-01, 12 Ang Mo Kio St 64, Ang Mo Kio Industrial Park 3, Singapore 569088, Singapore *Tel:* 63357299
ARRIS Group Korea Inc, Parkview Off Tower, No 1507, Jeongja-dong, Bundang-gu, Seongnam-si, Gyeonggi-do, Korea 463-863, South Korea *Tel:* (031) 740-4217 *Fax:* (031) 783-4896
ARRIS Solutions Spain SLU, Calle Garrotxa No 10-12, Fl 1, Mod 4B, Oceano 1, 08820 Barcelona, Spain *Tel:* 93 378 9140 *Fax:* 93 378 9147
ARRIS Solutions Spain SLU, Calle Martinez Villergas 52, Bldg 3, 2nd fl, Madrid, Spain *Tel:* 91 4233800 *Fax:* 91 4233901
ARRIS Sweden AB, Teknikringen 2, 583 30 Linkoping, Sweden *Tel:* (013) 367600
ARRIS Taiwan Ltd, No 1, Lane 232, Baoqiao Rd, Xindian District, New Taipai City 23145, Taiwan *Tel:* (02) 29189145 *Fax:* (02) 29159561

ARRIS Turkey Telekomunikasyon Ltd Sir-
keti, Sterling Off, No 127 Astoria Tower A,
Buyukdere Caddesi, 34394 Istanbul, Turkey
50 Stranmills Embankment, Belfast BT95FL,
United Kingdom *Tel:* (028) 90998240
ARRIS Solutions UK Ltd, 710 Wharfedale Rd,
Wokingham, Berks RG41 5TP, United King-
dom *Tel:* (0118) 921 5500
ARRIS Global Ltd, Victoria Rd, Saltaire,
W Yorks BD18 3LF, United Kingdom
Tel: (01274) 532000 *Fax:* (01274) 532010

ARS Electronics
7110 DeCelis Place, Van Nuys, CA 91406
Tel: 818-997-6279 *Fax:* 818-997-6158
E-mail: info@arselectronics.com
Web Site: www.arselectronics.com
Key Personnel
Sales Mgr: Martin Sanett
Founded: 1947
Catalog(s) available

ART (Applied Research & Technology Inc)
Division of Yorkville Sound Inc
4625 Witmer Industrial Estate, Niagara Falls, NY
14305
Tel: 716-297-2920 *Fax:* 716-297-3689
E-mail: usa@yorkville.com
Web Site: www.artproaudio.com; www.yorkville.
com
Key Personnel
Gen Mgr: Betty VanDenBosch
Founded: 1984
Audio equipment manufacturer.
Online catalog(s) available

Art Gallery of Ontario
317 Dundas St W, Toronto, ON M5T 1G4,
Canada
Tel: 416-979-6648 *Toll Free Tel:* 877-225-4246
Web Site: ago.ca
Key Personnel
Michael & Sonja Koerner Dir & CEO: Stephen
Jost
CFO, Fin & IT: Rocco Saverino
Pres: Tony Gagliano
Chief, Communs & Brand: Lisa Clements
Chief, Exhibitions & Collections: Christy Thomp-
son
Richard & Elizabeth Currrie Chief, Public Pro-
gramming & Learning: Judy Koke
Chief of Staff & Corp Secy: Erin Prendergast
Exec Dir, Corp Spec Projs & Dir, Opers: Mike
Mahoney
Dir, Staff & Volunteer Resources: Deborah
O'Leary
Deputy Dir & Chief Advancement Offr: Alicia
Vandermeer
Online catalog(s) available
Membership(s): Visual Resources Association

Art Museum of the Americas
201 18 St, Washington, DC 20006
Mailing Address: 1889 "F" St NW, Washington,
DC 20006
Tel: 202-370-0147
E-mail: artmus@oas.org
Web Site: www.amamuseum.org
Key Personnel
Dir: Pablo Zuniga
Admin, Public & Media Rel: Gregory Svitil
E-mail: gsvitil@oas.org
Online catalog(s) available

Art Resource
65 Bleecker St, 12th fl, New York, NY 10012
Tel: 212-505-8700 *Toll Free Tel:* 888-505-8666
Fax: 212-505-2053
E-mail: requests@artres.com
Web Site: www.artres.com
Founded: 1968

Fine art images, digital & analog.
Online catalog(s) available
Membership(s): American Society of Picture Pro-
fessionals; ASMP

Artaflex Inc
174 W Beaver Creek Rd, Richmond Hill, ON
L4B 1B4, Canada
Tel: 905-470-0109 *Toll Free Tel:* 866-502-3378
Fax: 905-470-0621
E-mail: sales@artaflex.com; general@artaflex.com
Web Site: www.artaflex.com
Key Personnel
Owner & CEO: Paul Walker
Owner & Pres: Gerry Iuliano
EVP: Trent Carruthers
Founded: 1985
Online catalog(s) available
Branch Office(s)
360 Terry Fox Dr, Kanata, ON K2K 2P5, Canada
Tel: 613-744-3043 *Toll Free Tel:* 888-773-7832
Fax: 905-470-0621
Membership(s): AES; IEEE; PEO; SMPTE®

Artbeats
1405 N Myrtle Rd, Myrtle Creek, OR 97457
Tel: 541-863-4429 *Fax:* 541-863-4547
E-mail: info@artbeats.com
Web Site: www.artbeats.com
Key Personnel
CEO: Phil Bates
COO: Laura Hollifield
Dir, Technol: Sebastian Rabern
Global Dist Mgr: Peggy Nichols
E-mail: pnichols@artbeats.com
Ad & Mktg: Julie Hill *E-mail:* julie@artbeats.
com
Founded: 1989
Leading provider of royalty free stock-footage for
broadcast, desktop video & multimedia.

Artech Electronics Ltd
PO Box 1547, Williston, VT 05495-1547
Toll Free Tel: 800-631-6448 *Toll Free Fax:* 800-
631-6448
E-mail: info@artech-electronics.com
Web Site: www.artech-electronics.com
Key Personnel
Pres: David Lang
Founded: 1971
Importer & distributor of high quality audio &
AV consumer products.
Online catalog(s) available
Branch Office(s)
PO Box 218, Sta CSL, Montreal, QC H4V 2Y4,
Canada

Artel Video Systems
5B Lyberty Way, Westford, MA 01886
Tel: 978-263-5775 *Toll Free Tel:* 800-225-0228
Fax: 978-263-9755
E-mail: sales@artel.com
Web Site: www.artel.com
Key Personnel
Mktg Mgr: Karen Menard *E-mail:* kmenard@
artel.com
Founded: 1981
Manufacture & distribute video & Ethernet trans-
port equipment.
Online catalog(s) available
Membership(s): NAB; SCTE; SMPTE®; Video
Services Forum

Artichoke Productions
4114 Linden St, Oakland, CA 94608
Tel: 510-655-1283
Web Site: www.artichokepro.com
Key Personnel
Prodr & Dir: Paul Kalbach
Founded: 1981

Artistic Video
87 Tyler Ave, Sound Beach, NY 11789
Tel: 631-744-5999 *Toll Free Tel:* 888-982-4244
Fax: 631-744-5993
E-mail: info@movementsofmagic.com
Web Site: www.movementsofmagic.com
Key Personnel
Pres: Bob Klein *E-mail:* bobklein5@yahoo.com
Founded: 1985
Over 100 instructional videos & DVDs on health
& fitness, martial arts & Tai-Chi.
Online catalog(s) available

Artograph Inc
525 Ninth St S, Delano, MN 55328-8624
Tel: 763-553-1112 *Toll Free Tel:* 888-975-9555
Fax: 763-553-1262
E-mail: sales@artograph.com; info@artograph.
com
Web Site: www.artograph.com
Key Personnel
Pres: Donald Dow
Founded: 1947
Manufacturer of art projectors, light boxes & ac-
cessories.
Online catalog(s) available
Sales list(s) available
Membership(s): NAMTA

ASC Systems
Mack Place, 566, St Clair Shores, MI 48080-0566
Tel: 313-882-1133
E-mail: ascsystems@live.com
Key Personnel
Mktg Mgr: D Leadore
Systems Mgr: R Martin
Video graphics systems, imaging systems, fa-
cilities & security monitoring & video Inter-
net broadcasting & web broadcasting, wire-
less/video networking, broadband networks &
cloud computing.
Catalog(s) available

ASC-Tube Trap
Division of Acoustic Sciences Corp
4275 W Fifth Ave, Eugene, OR 97402
Mailing Address: PO Box 1189, Eugene, OR
97440
Tel: 541-343-9727 *Toll Free Tel:* 800-272-8823
Fax: 541-343-9245
E-mail: info@acousticsciences.com
Web Site: www.acousticsciences.com
Key Personnel
Pres: Arthur Noxon
CFO: Pearl Chang
Distribute & manufacture acoustic control prod-
ucts.
Online catalog(s) available
Membership(s): AES; Custom Electronic Design
& Installation Association

Asentria Corp
1200 N 96 St, Seattle, WA 98103
Tel: 206-344-8800 *Fax:* 206-344-2116
E-mail: sales@asentria.com
Web Site: www.asentria.com
Remote site monitoring & telecommunications
equipment.
Online catalog(s) available

ASET - The Neurodiagnostic Society
402 E Bannister Rd, Suite A, Kansas City, MO
64131-3019
Tel: 816-931-1120 *Fax:* 816-931-1145
E-mail: info@aset.org
Web Site: www.aset.org
Key Personnel
Exec Dir: Arlen Reimnitz
Mktg & Communs Coord: Sarah Dolezilek
Founded: 1959
Nonprofit organization. Distribute continuing edu-
cation programs.
Online catalog(s) available

Ashly Audio Inc
Division of Jam Industries
847 Holt Rd, Webster, NY 14580-9103
Tel: 585-872-0010 *Toll Free Tel:* 800-828-6308
  Fax: 585-872-0739
E-mail: info@ashly.com; sales@ashly.com;
  service@ashly.com
Web Site: ashly.com
Key Personnel
CEO: Mark Wentling
Dir, Mktg: Anthony Errigo *Tel:* 585-872-0010 ext
  106
Founded: 1974
Design & manufacture quality signal processing
  equipment.
Catalog(s) available
Online catalog(s) available
Membership(s): AES; Audiovisual and Integrated
  Experience Association; NAMM, the National
  Association of Music Merchants; NSCA

Asia Society
725 Park Ave, New York, NY 10021
Tel: 212-288-6400 *Fax:* 212-517-8315
E-mail: info@asiasociety.org
Web Site: www.asiasociety.org; www.asiasociety.
  org/video
Key Personnel
Pres & CEO: Josette Sheeran
SVP, Opers & CFO: Don Nagle
EVP: Tom Nagorski
Communs & Mktg Mgr: Christine Hsieh
  E-mail: chsieh@asiasociety.org
Founded: 1956
Videos online.

Aspen Systems Inc
3900 Youngfield St, Wheat Ridge, CO 80033-
  3865
Tel: 303-431-4606 *Toll Free Tel:* 800-992-9242
  Fax: 303-431-7196
E-mail: sales@aspsys.com
Web Site: www.aspsys.com
Key Personnel
CEO: Steven L Spring
Founded: 1982
Leading solutions for High Performance Comput-
  ing (HPC) users & administrators.
Online catalog(s) available

Assignment Desk
665 Johnnie Dodds Blvd, Suite 201, Mount
  Pleasant, SC 29464
Tel: 312-464-8600 *Toll Free Tel:* 800-959-DESK
  (959-3375) *Fax:* 312-464-8605
E-mail: crew@assignmentdesk.com
Web Site: www.assignmentdesk.com
Founded: 1992
Booking agency for video production personnel &
  camera crews worldwide.

Associated Bag Co
400 W Boden St, Milwaukee, WI 53207
Tel: 414-769-1000 *Toll Free Tel:* 800-926-6100
  Fax: 414-769-6530 *Toll Free Fax:* 800-926-
  4610
E-mail: customerservice@associatedbag.com
Web Site: www.associatedbag.com
Key Personnel
Pres: Herb Rubenstein
Cust Serv Mgr: Ellen Virta
Mktg Designer: Kory Beavers *Tel:* 414-769-1000
  ext 186
Packaging & shipping products.
Catalog(s) available

Associated Press Television News
200 Liberty St, New York, NY 10281
Tel: 212-621-1500 *Fax:* 212-621-7419
E-mail: info@ap.org
Web Site: www.aptn.com

Key Personnel
VP, Natl & Latin America Media Mkts: Sara Tro-
  hanis *Tel:* 212-621-7863 *E-mail:* strohanis@ap.
  org
Dir, Natl Networks & Major Accts: Ivett Chicas
  Tel: 212-621-1876 *E-mail:* ichicas@ap.org
Natl Entertainment Video Mgr: Robert Merrill
  Tel: 212-621-7258 *E-mail:* rmerrill@ap.org
SNTV North America Ed: Rick Haas *Tel:* 212-
  621-7417 *E-mail:* rhaas@ap.org
News production services for media clients.

Associated Producers Ltd
210 St Clair Ave W, 4th fl, Toronto, ON M4V
  1R2, Canada
Tel: 416-504-6662 *Fax:* 416-504-6667
E-mail: general@apltd.ca
Web Site: www.apltd.ca
Key Personnel
Partner & Dir: Simcha Jacobovici *Tel:* 416-504-
  6662 ext 230
Also produce reality TV programs & episodic
  television. Documentary & factual program-
  ming for cable & digital broadcasters.

Associated Production Music LLC
6255 Sunset Blvd, Suite 900, Hollywood, CA
  90028
Tel: 323-461-3211 *Fax:* 323-461-9102
E-mail: info@apmmusic.com; clientservices@
  apmmusic.com
Web Site: www.apmmusic.com
Key Personnel
Pres: Adam Taylor *E-mail:* ataylor@apmmusic.
  com
VP, Fin: Sarah Konkoski *E-mail:* skonkoski@
  apmmusic.com
VP, Sales & Revenue Opers: Chad Elbert
  E-mail: celbert@apmmusic.com
VP, Technol: Josh Roach *E-mail:* jroach@
  apmmusic.com
Production music library & music services com-
  pany.
Branch Office(s)
381 Park Ave S, Suite 1101, New York, NY
  10016 *Tel:* 212-856-9800 *Fax:* 212-856-9807
Membership(s): BME; Entertainment Merchants
  Association; NAB; NATPE; NCTA - The In-
  ternet & Television Association; Production
  Music Association; Promax

Associated Sound
1417 Del Paso Blvd, Sacramento, CA 95815
Tel: 916-649-8040 *Toll Free Tel:* 800-492-6800
  Fax: 916-649-0243
E-mail: sales@associatedsound.com
Web Site: www.associatedsound.com
Key Personnel
Pres & Rental Dept Mgr: Brad Clark
Sales Mgr: Anthony Brown
Founded: 1968
Pro audio & AV systems & equipment. Media &
  sports events a specialty.
Membership(s): NAMM, the National Association
  of Music Merchants

Assured Audio Visual
2941 E Miraloma Ave, Suite 3, Anaheim, CA
  92806
Tel: 714-535-1414 *Fax:* 714-630-3518
E-mail: sales@assuredav.com
Web Site: www.assuredav.com
Key Personnel
Pres: Susan P Ellis
Sales Mgr: Andrew Ellis
Founded: 1985
Distribute, rent, install, service & repair LCD
  projectors & AV presentation equipment.
Catalog(s) available, annual
Membership(s): Audiovisual and Integrated Expe-
  rience Association

Astoria Communications Inc
5553 Ravenswood Rd, Suite 101, Fort Laud-
  erdale, FL 33312
Tel: 305-728-4280 *Toll Free Tel:* 877-GETMEAV
  (438-6328) *Fax:* 954-367-5883
E-mail: info@astoria.productions
Web Site: www.getmeav.com
Key Personnel
Pres & Owner: Ron Spiegel *E-mail:* ron@
  getmeav.com
Sr Proj Mgr: Hector Arocho *E-mail:* hectorjr@
  getmeav.com
Founded: 1997
Full service production company. Rent profes-
  sional video & AV live event products & crew.
Branch Office(s)
195A Central Ave, Farmingdale, NY 11735, Op-
  ers Mgr: Nicholas Somma *Tel:* 631-694-3334
  Toll Free Tel: 800-886-1328

Astrodyne TDI
36 Newburgh Rd, Hackettstown, NJ 07840
Tel: 908-850-5088 *Fax:* 908-850-1607
E-mail: lpcs@astrodynetdi.com (cust serv, low
  power prods); hpcs@astrodynetdi.com (cust
  serv, high power prods); emifiltersales@
  astrodynetdi.com (cust serv, EMI filters)
Web Site: www.tdipower.com
Key Personnel
VP, Global Sales: Bill Gray *E-mail:* bill.gray@
  astrodynetdi.com
Designs & manufactures innovative power solutions for demanding applications worldwide.
  Products include power supplies & EMI filters for industrial, semiconductor manufacturing, medical, consumer appliance, military,
  aerospace & many varied markets. With over
  50 years of power supply design experience,
  Astrodyne TDI is headquartered in Nashua, NH
  & has engineering & manufacturing centers in
  the US & Canada.
Catalog(s) available
Foreign Office(s): Fuitian Trade Free Zone, China
  E-mail: ruby.li@astrodynetdi.com

Astronomical Society of the Pacific
390 Ashton Ave, San Francisco, CA 94112
Tel: 415-337-1100 *Toll Free Tel:* 800-335-2624
  Fax: 415-337-5205
Web Site: astrosociety.org
Key Personnel
CEO: Dr Linda Shore *Tel:* 415-715-1411
  E-mail: lshore@astrosociety.org
CFO: Cyrille Betant *Tel:* 415-715-1412
  E-mail: cbetant@astrosociety.org
Dir, Membership, Mktg & Communs: Joycelin
  Craig *E-mail:* jcraig@astrosociety.org
Dir, Museum, Parks & Lib Progs: Anna Hurst
  Tel: 415-715-1408 *E-mail:* ahurst@astrosociety.
  org
Dir, Teacher Learning Ctr & Formal Educ
  Progs: Brian Kruse *Tel:* 415-715-1426
  E-mail: bkruse@astrosociety.org
Sr Scientist & Educator: Greg Schultz *Tel:* 415-
  715-1425 *E-mail:* gschultz@astrosociety.org
Founded: 1889
Design & deliver astronomy & space science ed-
  ucation & outreach programs, workshops, ma-
  terials, toolkits & publications throughout the
  US.

ATA Trading Corp/Favorite TV Inc
877 Oceanfront, Long Beach, NY 11561-1542
Tel: 516-431-2302
E-mail: atat@verizon.net
Key Personnel
Pres: Harold G Lewis
Will sell rights to entire library of programs in
  perpetuity.
Catalog(s) available

ATCi (Antenna Technology Communication Solutions Inc)
450 N McKemy Ave, Chandler, AZ 85226
Tel: 480-844-8501
Web Site: www.atci.com
Founded: 1979
Supplier & integrator of ground-based fixed & mobile satellite communications systems, commercial video broadcast systems, satellite teleport services & fiber optic links.
Online catalog(s) available
Membership(s): NAB; NCTA - The Internet & Television Association; SCTE; World Teleport Association

ATI Audio
Subsidiary of DaySequerra Corp
7209 Browning Rd, Pennsauken, NJ 08091
Tel: 856-719-9900
E-mail: sales@daysequerra.com
Web Site: www.atiaudio.com
Key Personnel
Pres: David Day
VP, Busn Devt: Mike Pappas
Opers Mgr: Sandra Martin
Founded: 1979
Audio equipment manufacturer.
Membership(s): NAB; NSCA; SBE

Atlanta Filmworks
4280 Northeast Expwy, Atlanta, GA 30340
E-mail: info@atlantafilmworks.com
Web Site: atlantafilmworks.com
Key Personnel
Partner: Mark Henderson *Tel:* 678-677-1257; Daniel Minchew *Tel:* 404-630-0508
Founded: 2013
Feature film & TV program production & rental studio.

Atlantic Illumination Entertainment Lighting
80 Fairbanks St, Dartmouth, NS B3A 1C4, Canada
Tel: 902-463-7418
E-mail: aiel@chebucto.biz
Web Site: aiel.chebucto.biz
Key Personnel
Company Dir: Richard Bonner
Founded: 1977
Sales, rental & repair of stage lighting, theatrical & stage accessories & related equipment.
Membership(s): Theatre Nova Scotia

AtlasIED
Subsidiary of MiTek Corporation
4545 E Baseline Rd, Phoenix, AZ 85042
Toll Free Tel: 800-876-3333
E-mail: support@atlasied.com
Web Site: www.atlasied.com
Key Personnel
Pres & CEO: John Ivey
VP Mktg & Corp Communs: Gina Sansivero
E-mail: gina.sansivero@atlasied.com
Founded: 1934
Manufactures communications products for the commercial, broadcast, industrial, institutional, security, custom installation (home) & music markets.
Online catalog(s) available
Branch Office(s)
9701 Taylorsville Rd, Louisville, KY 40299
Tel: 502-267-7436 (mfg)
1601 Jack McKay Blvd, Ennis, TX 75119 (R&D)
AtlasIED Canada, 102-26712 Gouchester Way, Langley, BC V4W 3V6, Canada *Toll Free Tel:* 800-663-2511 *E-mail:* canadasupport@atlasied.com
Membership(s): AAAE; AES; Audiovisual and Integrated Experience Association; Custom Electronic Design & Installation Association;

IBMA; International Association of Assembly Managers; IPMA; NAMM, the National Association of Music Merchants; NSCA

ATM Flyware, see Adaptive Technologies Group Inc

Atma-Sphere Music Systems Inc
1742 Selby Ave, St Paul, MN 55104
Tel: 651-690-2246
Web Site: www.atma-sphere.com
Key Personnel
Founder, Owner & CEO: Ralph Karsten
E-mail: ralph@atma-sphere.com
Founded: 1978
Manufacture preamplifiers & amplifiers.

Atomic Imaging Inc/Golan Studios
1501 N Magnolia Ave, Chicago, IL 60642
Tel: 312-649-1800 *Fax:* 312-642-7441
Web Site: www.atomicimaging.com
Key Personnel
Film/Video Prodn: Candice Gerber *Tel:* 312-649-1800 ext 5703 *E-mail:* candice@golan.tv
Live Events: Ari Golan *Tel:* 312-649-1800 ext 5701 *E-mail:* ari@atomicimaging.com
Studio/Sound Stages & Equip Rental: Kevin Olson *Tel:* 312-649-1800 ext 5704 *E-mail:* kevin@golan.tv
Founded: 1985
International full service emerging technologies solution provider & digital media production facility.

ATS Cases Inc
172 Otis St, Northborough, MA 01532
Tel: 508-393-9110 *Toll Free Tel:* 800-451-4242; 800-519-2771 *Fax:* 508-393-9508
E-mail: casemakers@mac.com
Web Site: atscases.com
Key Personnel
Founder & Pres: Ron Orlando
Founded: 1975
Designs & manufactures custom shipping cases, OEM carrying cases, material handling containers & reusable packaging for commercial & military applications.

Attainment Co Inc
504 Commerce Pkwy, Verona, WI 53593
Mailing Address: PO Box 930160, Verona, WI 53593-0160
Tel: 608-845-7880 *Toll Free Tel:* 800-327-4269 *Fax:* 608-845-8040 *Toll Free Fax:* 800-942-3865
E-mail: customerservice@attainmentcompany.com; international@attainmentcompany.com
Web Site: www.attainmentcompany.com
Key Personnel
Pres: Autumn Garza *E-mail:* autumn@attainmentcompany.com
Founded: 1979
Creating, scripting, producing, editing, distributing & soliciting distributors for in-house video products; do not produce for others. The areas covered are youth at risk, early childhood & special education, especially people with developmental disabilities.
Catalog(s) available, free
Online catalog(s) available, PDF

ATTO Technology Inc
155 CrossPoint Pkwy, Amherst, NY 14068
Tel: 716-691-1999 *Fax:* 716-691-9353
Web Site: www.atto.com
Key Personnel
Co-Founder, Pres & CEO: Timothy J Klein
Co-Founder, VP, Engg & CTO: David A Snell
VP, Fin & HR: James F Masiello
VP, Opers: Timothy J Boser
Founded: 1988

Provide storage connectivity & infrastructure solutions for data intensive computing environments.
Online catalog(s) available
Membership(s): Computer Technology Industry Association; Fibre Channel Industry Association; SMPTE®

ATV Research Inc
1301 Broadway, Dakota City, NE 68731
Mailing Address: PO Box 620, Dakota City, NE 68731-0620
Tel: 402-987-3771 *Toll Free Tel:* 800-392-3922 *Fax:* 402-987-3709
E-mail: sales@atvresearch.com
Web Site: www.atvresearch.com
Key Personnel
Pres: Melvin Shadbolt
VP: Scott Shadbolt
Founded: 1964
Nationwide video distributors & system consultants on CCTV, MATV & SMATV.
Online catalog(s) available

ATV Video Center Inc
2424 Glendale Lane, Sacramento, CA 95825
Tel: 916-973-9100 *Toll Free Tel:* 800-635-1266
E-mail: info@atv.net
Web Site: www.atv.net
Key Personnel
Founder & Owner: Gary Jones
Opers Mgr/Prodn Coord: Rachel "Ryan" Behrman *E-mail:* rachel@atv.net
Sales Mgr: Robert Leven *E-mail:* robert@atv.net
Founded: 1986
Professional AV sales, rental, production & installation.
Online catalog(s) available
Membership(s): Audiovisual and Integrated Experience Association

A2D Solutions Inc
Member of Fedele Group
20200 NW Second Ave, Suite 403, Miami Gardens, FL 33169
Tel: 305-895-5888 *Toll Free Tel:* 866-223-7253
E-mail: sales@a2dsolutions.com
Web Site: a2dsolutions.com
Founded: 2000
Worldwide business-to-business equipment supplier, distributor & systems integration firm serving clients from high-end broadcast & film to defense & security systems.

ATX Networks
8-1602 Tricont Ave, Whitby, ON L1N 7C3, Canada
Tel: 289-204-7800 *Toll Free Tel:* 866-968-7289
E-mail: info@atx.com
Web Site: atx.com
Key Personnel
Pres & CEO: Charlie Vogt
CFO: Christina Kotsios
Chief People Offr: John Higgins
Chief Sales Offr: Jeff Liening
Chief Technol & Strategy Offr: Jay Lee
EVP, Mktg: Kim Lee
VP, Global Opers: Sanjay Sood
Gen Mgr & CTO, Media Broadcast: Jose Rivero
Gen Mgr & CTO, Media Dist: Andrew Isherwood
Gen Mgr, Access Networking: Kevin Rossi
Founded: 1985
Broadband, broadcast & telecom products.
Catalog(s) available
Branch Office(s)
8880 Rehco Rd, San Diego, CA 92121 *Tel:* 858-546-5050
5850 Hellyer Ave, San Jose, CA 95138 *Tel:* 408-227-3400
1125 Legacy Dr, Suite 350, Frisco, TX 75034
Tel: 469-850-5900

Audacity Recording Studios
2734 Polk St, Suite B, Hollywood, FL 33020
Tel: 954-920-4418
Web Site: www.audacityrecordingstudios.com
Key Personnel
Co-Owner: Linda Thornberg *E-mail:* linda@
audacityrecording.com; John Jay Martyn
Founded: 1986
Audio for film & television, original music com-
position, ADR, artist production.
Membership(s): The Recording Academy

Audience Response Systems Inc
5611-C E Morgan Ave, Evansville, IN 47715
Tel: 812-479-7507 *Toll Free Tel:* 800-INVOLVE
(468-6583) *Fax:* 812-479-1057
E-mail: arsales@audienceresponse.com
Web Site: www.audienceresponse.com
Key Personnel
Pres: Steve Campus
EVP: Steve Knapp
VP, Sales: Debbie Minor
IT Mgr: Jeff Osborne
Pulse Systems Mgr: Brad Copes
Founded: 1984
Membership(s): Audiovisual and Integrated Expe-
rience Association

Audio Accessories Inc
25 Mill St, Marlow, NH 03456
Mailing Address: PO Box 360, Marlow, NH
03456-0360
Tel: 603-446-3335 *Fax:* 603-446-7543
E-mail: audioacc@patchbays.com
Web Site: www.patchbays.com
Key Personnel
Pres: M B Hall
Opers Mgr: Timothy J Symonds
Audio patch panels & video panels.
Online catalog(s) available
Membership(s): NAB

Audio & Light
2209 Randleman Rd, Greensboro, NC 27406
Tel: 336-274-1234 *Fax:* 336-274-4022
E-mail: info@audio-light.com
Web Site: www.audio-light.com
Key Personnel
Pres: Jim Hoyle *E-mail:* jhoyle@audio-light.com
VP, Sales: Brian Cox
Dir, Opers/Rental Div: Ernest Grey
E-mail: egrey@audio-light.com
Tech Dir: Charlie Starr
Founded: 1984
Audio, video & lighting systems. Specialize in
live events.

Audio Art
124 Forsythe Dr, Chapel Hill, NC 27517
Tel: 919-260-1507
Key Personnel
Owner: Jon Paul McClellan
E-mail: jonpaulmcclellan@gmail.com
Sound mixing for concerts.

Audio Book Contractors LLC
PO Box 96, Riverdale, MD 20738-0096
Tel: 301-439-5830 *Fax:* 301-439-5830
E-mail: info@audiobookcontractors.com;
audiobookcontractors@verizon.net
Web Site: www.audiobookcontractors.com
Key Personnel
Owner & Mgr: Robert Butler
Founded: 1983
Sells unabridged classic novels, children's books,
poetry, plays & collections of short stories for
use by the general public, schools & libraries
on cassette & CD. Downloads available on au-
dible.com.
Online catalog(s) available

Audio Consultant Services Inc
4020 S Spruce St, Denver, CO 80237
Tel: 303-437-0308
Web Site: www.audio-consultants.com
Key Personnel
Pres: David Soran *E-mail:* dsoran@comcast.net
Founded: 1993
Engineering services for location recording.
Online catalog(s) available

The Audio Department Inc
324 Mills Place, Wycloff, NJ 07481
Tel: 212-586-3503 *Fax:* 212-245-1675
E-mail: scheduling@theaudiodepartment.com
Web Site: www.theaudiodepartment.com
Key Personnel
Pres: Robert Chapman
Studio Mgr: Aimee Christie
Sound Engr: Donald Hoffman
Audio post-production studio.

Audio Editions Books-On-Cassette & CD
Division of The Audio Partners Inc
131 E Placer St, Auburn, CA 95603
Mailing Address: PO Box 6930, Auburn, CA
95604-6930
Tel: 530-888-7801 *Toll Free Tel:* 800-231-4261
Toll Free Fax: 800-882-1840
E-mail: info@audioeditions.com
Web Site: audioeditions.com; audioeditionslibrary.
com
Key Personnel
Mgr & Lib Servs Supv: Kirby Desha
Founded: 1987
Audiobook supplier offering personal customer
service for 19,000 audiobooks from 100 pub-
lishers. Also distributes MP3 CDs & Play-
aways.
Catalog(s) available, monthly
Membership(s): ALA; Audio Publishers Associa-
tion

Audio Graphic Services
1516 Ferris Ave, Royal Oak, MI 48067
Tel: 248-544-1793
E-mail: netmail@audiographicservices.com
Web Site: www.audiographicservices.com
Key Personnel
Owner, Pres & COO: Edward J Wolfrum
Owner: Susan E Wolfrum
Founded: 1967
Audio, technical & recording services.
Online catalog(s) available
Membership(s): The Recording Academy

Audio Images Corp
701 Bryant St, 2nd fl, San Francisco, CA 94107
Tel: 415-957-9131 *Fax:* 415-957-1531
Web Site: www.facebook.com/Audio-Images-
Corporation-262409103085/
Key Personnel
Partner: James C Chen
Founded: 1986
Retail professional audio store. AV system instal-
lation & service.

Audio Mechanics
1200 W Magnolia Blvd, Burbank, CA 91506
Tel: 818-846-5525 *Fax:* 818-846-5501
E-mail: info@audiomechanics.com
Web Site: audiomechanics.com
Key Personnel
Owner & Chief Engr: John Polito *E-mail:* john@
audiomechanics.com
Founded: 1991
Music mastering & sound restoration.

Audio Media Productions
6739 Kirby Trace Cove, Memphis, TN 38119
Tel: 901-751-2363
E-mail: ampman@aol.com

Web Site: www.audiomediaproductions.net
Key Personnel
Owner/Soundmixer: Andy Black
Soundmixer: Nathan Black; Michael Hunkele
Founded: 1994
Specialize in sound for film, video & radio. Lo-
cation sound mixing. Complete sound packages
for film & video.

Audio Network US Inc
48 W 25 St, 10th fl, New York, NY 10010
Tel: 646-688-4320
E-mail: nyoffice@audionetwork.com
Web Site: us.audionetwork.com
Key Personnel
CEO: Robb Smith
Head, East Coast Sales, NY: Cindy Chao
Head, West Coast Sales, Los Angeles: Brad Burn-
side
Sr Mgr, Creative Licensing: Matt McMullian
Sr Mgr, Hispanic Mkts, Latin America: Carolina
Arenas
Gen Mgr, The Americas: Mary-Liz McDonald
Founded: 2001
Production & stock music for TV, film advertising
& corporate video.
Branch Office(s)
811 W Seventh St, Suite 1050, Los Angeles, CA
90017 *Tel:* 310-889-0109
Audio Network Canada, Robert Attersley Dr E,
Whitby, ON L1R 3E3, Canada, VP: Randi
Gold *Tel:* 905-425-3011 *E-mail:* randi.gold@
audionetwork.com
Foreign Office(s): Audio Network Australia Ltd,
2 Kings Lane, Suite 11, Level 4, Darlinghurst,
Sydney, NSW 2010, Australia *Tel:* (02) 8204
0100
Audio Network France SAS, 33 Rue La Fayette,
75009 Paris, France *Tel:* 01 42 21 18 60
E-mail: contact.fr@audionetwork.com (com-
mercial)
Audio Network France SAS, Parc Gouraud, Im-
meuble les Alizes, 8 allee de l'Innovation,
02200 Soissons, France (admin)
Audio Network GmbH, Tal 36, 80331 Munich, Germany *Tel:* (089) 21 75 12441
E-mail: infode@audionetwork.com
Audiofficina Sample SAS, Via Canonica 69,
20154 Milan MI, Italy *Tel:* (045) 92 34 105
E-mail: info@audiofficinasample.it
Audio Network Holland BV, Weteringschans 165,
1017 XD Amsterdam, Netherlands *Tel:* (020)
808 2984 *E-mail:* nl@audionetwork.com
Audio Network UK, The Johnson Bldg, 77 Hat-
ton Garden, London EC1N 8JS, United Kingdom *Tel:* (020) 7566 1441 (licenses & cust
serv)
Audio Network UK, The Washington Ctr, Unit
7-9, 112-116 Broadway, Salford M50 2UW,
United Kingdom *Tel:* (0161) 729 1060 (licenses & cust serv)

Audio Precision
5750 SW Arctic Dr, Beaverton, OR 97005
Tel: 503-627-0832 *Toll Free Tel:* 800-231-7350
E-mail: message@ap.com
Web Site: www.ap.com
Key Personnel
CEO: David Schmoldt
VP, Sales & Mktg: Spyros Lazaris
Founded: 1984
Audio test & measurement equipment manufac-
turer.
Foreign Office(s): South Fens Business Ctr, Suite
L13, Fenton Way, Chatteris, Cambs PE16 6TT,
United Kingdom, Dir: James Kelly *Tel:* (0740)
307 9426 *E-mail:* jamesk@ap.com
Membership(s): AES

Audio Rents
4209 E Vanowen Pl, Burbank, CA 91505
Tel: 323-874-1000 *Fax:* 323-460-2676
E-mail: info@audiorents.com

Web Site: www.audiorents.com
Key Personnel
Mgr: Traci Bradford
Founded: 1986
Recording & post-production audio equipment & music rentals.

Audio-Technica US Inc
Subsidiary of Audio-Technica Corp
1221 Commerce Dr, Stow, OH 44224
Tel: 330-686-2600 *Fax:* 330-686-0719
E-mail: pro@atus.com
Web Site: www.audio-technica.com
Key Personnel
Pres: Philip Cajka
Design, manufacture, marketing & distribution of problem-solving audio equipment.
Membership(s): AES; NAB; NAMM, the National Association of Music Merchants; NSCA

Audio Upgrades
6982 Mimosa Dr, Carlsbad, CA 92011
Tel: 818-780-1222
Web Site: www.audioupgrades.com
Key Personnel
Owner: Jim Williams *E-mail:* jwilliams3@earthlink.net
Founded: 1990
Component level upgrades for the recording industry & design services.

Audio-Video Corp
213 Broadway, Albany, NY 12204
Tel: 518-449-7213 *Fax:* 518-449-1205
E-mail: info@audiovideocorp.com; sales@audiovideocorp.com; service@audiovideocorp.com
Web Site: www.audiovideocorp.com
Key Personnel
Pres & CEO: Ted Klarsfeld
Provider of high-end AV presentation equipment.
Online catalog(s) available
Branch Office(s)
6365 Collamer Dr, East Syracuse, NY 13057
    Tel: 315-463-1946 *Fax:* 315-463-2999
145 Pine Haven Shores Rd, Suite 1053, Shelburne, VT 05482 *Tel:* 802-316-6375 *Fax:* 315-463-2999

Audio-Video Resources Inc
1043 Adams Ave, Montgomery, AL 36104
Mailing Address: PO Box 2371, Montgomery, AL 36102-2371
Tel: 334-262-4806 *Fax:* 334-240-0000
E-mail: avrinc@bellsouth.net
Key Personnel
Owner & Pres: Rick Martin
Sr Partner & VP: Charles E McCoy
Founded: 1990
Industrial AV rental house only.

Audio/Video Supply Inc
4575 Ruffner St, San Diego, CA 92111
Tel: 858-565-1101 *Toll Free Tel:* 800-284-2288
    Fax: 858-565-7845
E-mail: sales@avsupply.com
Web Site: www.avsupply.com
Founded: 1968
Dealer of professional AV equipment & accessories.
Membership(s): Audiovisual and Integrated Experience Association

Audio-VideoGraphics Inc
17501 E 40 Hwy, Suite 219, Independence, MO 64055
Tel: 816-350-0800 *Toll Free Tel:* 800-322-2832
    Fax: 816-350-0804
Web Site: www.avginc.com

Key Personnel
Pres: Greg Azorsky
Online catalog(s) available

Audio Visions Inc
1501 N George St, York, PA 17404
Tel: 717-747-1898
Key Personnel
Pres: Ray R Snyder

Audio Vistas LLC
170 N Woods Dr, South Orange, NJ 07079
Tel: 212-586-2177
E-mail: info@audiovistas.com
Web Site: www.audiovistas.com
Key Personnel
Pres: Charles D Wantman *E-mail:* charles@audiovistas.com
Founded: 1977
Produce HD video.
Online catalog(s) available

Audio Visual Actions Inc (AVA)
5641-C General Washington Dr, Alexandria, VA 22312
Tel: 703-750-0950 *Toll Free Tel:* 866-893-5382
    Fax: 703-750-0954
E-mail: info@avactions.com
Web Site: avactions.com
Event staging. Video, audio equipment, conferencing, lighting & general AV rentals.

Audio Visual Associates
One Stewart Ct, Denville, NJ 07834
Toll Free Tel: 888-435-6678 *Fax:* 973-442-0888
E-mail: sales@avaonline.com; info@avaonline.com
Web Site: www.avaonline.com
Key Personnel
Pres: Ed Susco *E-mail:* esusco@avaonline.com
Founded: 1988
AV sales, service, design, installation & rental.
Membership(s): Audiovisual and Integrated Experience Association

Audio Visual Communications Inc
1336 Cherry St, Boothwyn, PA 19061
Tel: 610-272-8500
E-mail: audiovc@verizon.net
Web Site: www.audiovc.com
Key Personnel
Pres: Frank Matys

The Audio Visual Co (AVCO)
98-810 Moanalua Rd, Aiea, HI 96701
Tel: 808-485-3200 *Fax:* 808-487-0733
Web Site: www.theavco.com
Key Personnel
Pres: Thomas Lee *E-mail:* tlee@theavco.net
Proj Mgr: Wade Higa *Tel:* 808-485-3238
    E-mail: whiga@theavco.net
Founded: 1970
Membership(s): Audiovisual and Integrated Experience Association; General Contractors Association of Hawaii; Professional Systems Network International

Audio Visual Concepts Inc
Rd 1, Km 29.3, Rio Canas, Caguas, PR 00725
Mailing Address: PO Box 3915, Guaynabo, PR 00970-3915
Tel: 787-753-7700 *Fax:* 787-766-4578
Web Site: www.mig-avc.com
Key Personnel
Partner & VP: Jose Antonio Alvarado-Cancel
    E-mail: talvarado@mig-avc.com
VP, Busn & Educ Solutions: Fernando Cruz Strazzara *E-mail:* fernancruz@mig-avc.com
VP, Tech Support & Servs: Ivan Mendoza
    E-mail: imendoza@mig-avc.com

Admin Dir: Sarely Rivera *E-mail:* srivera@mig-avc.com
Founded: 1982
AV/IT/System Integrators.
Membership(s): PR Industrial Association

Audio Visual Consultants
3207 Lakeshore Ave, 2nd fl, Oakland, CA 94610
Tel: 510-839-2020
E-mail: info@avconsultants.com
Web Site: www.avconsultants.com
Key Personnel
Owner: Stuart Sweetow *E-mail:* sweetow@avconsultants.com
Founded: 1983

Audio Visual Dynamics®
424 Sand Shore Rd, Hackettstown, NJ 07840
Tel: 973-993-8500 *Fax:* 973-984-0644
Web Site: www.avdusa.com
Key Personnel
Pres: Chris Broening *E-mail:* cbroening@avdusa.com
VP, Admin: Tracey Brown
VP, Devt: Robyn Broening
VP, Opers & Technol: Frank Revfi
Dir, Busn Devt: Steve Levin
Dir, Warehousing & Logistics: Mark Heeman
Head, Audio Opers: Rich Cramer
Head, Video Opers: Tim Burke
Founded: 1964
Full service AV staging & rental company.
Online catalog(s) available
Membership(s): Audiovisual and Integrated Experience Association

Audio Visual Dynamics
Division of Total Events
2360 23 Ave, Lachine, QC H8T 0A3, Canada
Tel: 514-332-6440 *Fax:* 514-332-2009
E-mail: service@avd.ca
Web Site: www.avd.ca
Key Personnel
Consultant: Philip Hamilton
AV staging & rentals.

Audio Visual Imagineering Inc
6565 Hazeltine National Dr, Suite 2, Orlando, FL 32822
Tel: 407-859-8166 *Fax:* 407-859-8254
Web Site: www.av-imagineering.com
Key Personnel
Owner & Mng Dir: Joanne Young
    E-mail: joanne@av-imagineering.com
Founded: 1978
Manufacture laser projection equipment & produce laser shows. Full animation studio producing classical 2D animation & computer graphics. Design planetariums throughout the US.
Membership(s): International Planetarium Society

Audio Visual Media
1141 Lexington Ave, Mansfield, OH 44907
Mailing Address: PO Box 3526, Mansfield, OH 44907-0526
Tel: 419-756-2698
E-mail: avm2698@aol.com
Web Site: audiovisualmedia.net
Key Personnel
Owner: Mark Stallsmith
Founded: 1957
Services include videography, film transfer, video editing, format conversion & video photo montages. Rents AV presentation equipment for business meetings & special events.

Audio Visual of Milwaukee Inc
285 N Janacek Rd, Brookfield, WI 53045
Tel: 262-432-1077 *Toll Free Tel:* 800-236-6909
    Fax: 262-432-1078

E-mail: avm@avmonline.com
Web Site: www.avmonline.com
Key Personnel
Pres: Mark Powell
Systems Engr: Charles Powell
Event Coord: Dan Oseman
Prodn: Mike Hartwig
Founded: 1980
AV sales & installation, rental, production & service.
Branch Office(s)
333 W Main St, Green Bay, WI 54301 *Tel:* 920-448-1890
2410 Daniels St, Suite C, Madison, WI 53718
Tel: 608-277-8883

Audio Visual Resources Inc
3932 Ogeechee Rd, Savannah, GA 31405
Tel: 912-447-5656
E-mail: aaavr@aol.com
Web Site: www.avrsav.com
Online catalog(s) available

Audio Visual Sales & Service Inc
2601 Curry Rd, Schenectady, NY 12303
Tel: 518-688-0640 *Fax:* 518-688-0634
E-mail: info@avssi.com
Key Personnel
CEO: Leo Lupien

Audio Visual Techniques Inc
905 Georgetown St, Lexington, KY 40511
Tel: 859-254-8954 *Fax:* 859-233-4754
E-mail: info@avtav.com
Web Site: avtav.com
Key Personnel
Pres: Bradley Abney *E-mail:* brad@avtav.com
Founded: 1983
AV rentals & staging.
Membership(s): Audiovisual and Integrated Experience Association

Audio Visual Technologies Group (AVTG)
12502 Exchange Dr, Suite 404, Stafford, TX 77477
Mailing Address: PO Box 2307, Stafford, TX 77497-2307
Tel: 281-240-2329 *Toll Free Tel:* 800-522-3687
E-mail: info@avtg.com
Web Site: www.avtg.com
Key Personnel
Pres: Ashley Brown *E-mail:* abrown@avtg.com
Founded: 1952
Provides advanced AV, digital signage & video conferencing technologies.
Online catalog(s) available
Membership(s): Audiovisual and Integrated Experience Association

Audioarts Engineering
Division of Wheatstone Corp
600 Industrial Dr, New Bern, NC 28562
Tel: 252-638-7000 *Fax:* 252-635-4857 (sales); 252-637-1285
E-mail: sales@wheatstone.com
Web Site: www.wheatstone.com
Key Personnel
Dir, Intl Sales: Brad Harrison

Audiobook Department
6429 N Talman Ave, Chicago, IL 60645
Tel: 773-338-8813 *Fax:* 773-338-8813
Web Site: www.judithwest.com
Key Personnel
Owner & Prodr: Judith West *E-mail:* judith@judithwest.com
Founded: 2000
Full service audiobook development & production with a diverse talent pool & on-site production facilities. Special consulting for publishers new to audiobooks: from concept to design, through

digital or hard copy formats, reviewers & special markets. Free estimates available.
Membership(s): The Association of Publishers for Special Sales; Audio Publishers Association; The Authors Guild; Chicago Women in Publishing

AudioControl® Inc
22410 70 Ave W, Mountlake Terrace, WA 98043
Tel: 425-775-8461 *Fax:* 425-778-3166
E-mail: sound.great@audiocontrol.com
Web Site: www.audiocontrol.com
Key Personnel
CEO: Alex Camara
Mgr, Sales & Mktg: Chris Kane *E-mail:* chris.k@audiocontrol.com
Founded: 1977
Designer & manufacturer of audio products for home & car audio systems.
Online catalog(s) available
Membership(s): AES; Consumer Technology Association™; Custom Electronic Design & Installation Association; NSCA

AudioImage Recording
110 N Jefferson St, Richmond, VA 23220-5022
Tel: 804-644-7700 *Fax:* 804-644-8801
E-mail: info@audioimagerecording.com
Web Site: www.audioimagerecording.com
Key Personnel
Pres: John Valentine *E-mail:* john@audioimagerecording.com
Client Servs: Coral Preston *E-mail:* coral@audioimagerecording.com
Founded: 1980
Digital audio production studio, also do ISDN & IPDPL.

Audiomoxie®
PO Box 304, Georgetown, TX 78627
E-mail: info@audiomoxie.com
Web Site: www.audiomoxie.com
Key Personnel
Founder & Creative Dir: James Laurance
Founded: 2000
Music production.
Membership(s): ASCAP; BMI

AudioSolutionz LLC
Division of ProEdTech LLC
2222 Sedwick Rd, Durham, NC 27713
Toll Free Tel: 800-223-8720 *Fax:* 919-287-2643
E-mail: support@audiosolutionz.com
Web Site: www.audiosolutionz.com
Online business training programs. Specialize in webinars, DVDs, books & other training tools & products.

AudioVideoElectric
3907 Peppervine Dr, Orlando, FL 32828
Toll Free Tel: 888-792-9283 *Fax:* 407-381-5610
E-mail: sales@audiovideoelectric.com
Web Site: www.audiovideoelectric.com
Key Personnel
Pres: Jeffrey D Bova
Commercial bulk wire & cable distributor.
Online catalog(s) available

Audiovox®
180 Marcus Blvd, Hauppauge, NY 11788
Tel: 631-231-7750 *Toll Free Tel:* 800-645-4994
Web Site: www.voxxelectronics.com; www.voxxintl.com
VOXX International brand.

Audix Microphones
Unit of Audix Corp
9400 SW Barber St, Wilsonville, OR 97070
Mailing Address: PO Box 4010, Wilsonville, OR 97070-4010

Tel: 503-682-6933 *Toll Free Tel:* 800-966-8261
Fax: 503-682-7114
E-mail: info@audixusa.com
Web Site: audixusa.com
Founded: 1984
Professional microphones for installed sound, pro audio & house of worship markets as well as OEM manufacturing. Audix manufactures, designs & assembles at the headquarters in Wilsonville, OR.
Catalog(s) available
Membership(s): AES; NAMM, the National Association of Music Merchants

Augsburg Fortress
Unit of 1517 Media
510 Marquette Ave, Suite 800, Minneapolis, MN 55402
Mailing Address: PO Box 1209, Minneapolis, MN 55440-1209
Tel: 612-330-3300 *Toll Free Tel:* 800-328-4648
Toll Free Fax: 800-722-7766
E-mail: customercare@augsburgfortress.org; salesandservice@augsburgfortress.org
Web Site: www.augsburgfortress.org
Key Personnel
VP & Publr, Congregational Resources: Martin A Seltz
Supplies & creates substantive & innovative materials to support the ministries of faith communities within Lutheran congregations.
Online catalog(s) available
Membership(s): ICVM

August House Audio
Subsidiary of August House Inc
3500 Piedmont Rd NE, Suite 310, Atlanta, GA 30305
Tel: 404-442-4420 *Toll Free Tel:* 800-284-8784
Fax: 404-442-4435
E-mail: ahinfo@augusthouse.com
Web Site: www.augusthouse.com
Key Personnel
CEO: Steve Floyd *E-mail:* steve@augusthouse.com
EVP & Creative Dir: Graham Anthony *E-mail:* graham@augusthouse.com
Dir, Devt: Rob Cleveland *E-mail:* rob@storycove.com
Online catalog(s) available
Membership(s): Audio Publishers Association

Aura Sonic Ltd (ASL)
PO Box 520791, Flushing, NY 11352-0791
Tel: 718-886-6500
E-mail: somebody@aurasonic.com
Web Site: www.aurasonicltd.com
Key Personnel
Owner: Steven Remote
Established in the late 1970s to provide a variety of location audio recording & production ventures. ASL provides an efficient & economical way to integrate quality audio components with the finest "On Location" audio production techniques. ASL is dedicated to satisfying the needs of our colleagues & clients. We invite you to call +/or e-mail us with any questions, concerns or suggestions you may have. Analog & digital recording is available via 3 mobile audio trucks & various remote recording packages. Additional services include sound reinforcement, audio production & audio equipment sales.

Aural Gratification Inc
32 Nissen Lane, West Hurley, NY 12491-5903
Tel: 845-679-5674
E-mail: auralg@gmail.com
Key Personnel
Pres: Kevin Bartlett
Recording studio & record label. Specialize in custom music production for TV & film as

well as album production & recording for artists.
Online catalog(s) available
Membership(s): BMI

Auralex Acoustics Inc
9955 Westpoint Dr, Suite 101, Indianapolis, IN 46256
Tel: 317-842-2600 *Toll Free Tel:* 800-95-WEDGE (959-3343, orders) *Fax:* 317-842-2760
E-mail: info@auralex.com
Web Site: www.auralex.com
Key Personnel
Pres: Eric Smith
Founded: 1977
Manufacture & distribute acoustical foams, sound barriers, diffusors, adhesives & related sound control items.
Online catalog(s) available

Auriga Productions Ltd
2856 rue du Comtois, Ste-Lazare, QC J7T 0E7, Canada
Tel: 514-984-4202
E-mail: aurigapix@gmail.com
Web Site: www.aurigapix.com
Key Personnel
Founder & Pres: Francois Ouimet

Aurora Films
324 E Dowling Rd, Suite 4, Anchorage, AK 99518
Tel: 907-258-4686
E-mail: aurorafilms@gci.net
Key Personnel
Prodr: Laurence Goldin
Founded: 1974
Documentary film production, writing, direction & location scouting.
Membership(s): Alaska Film Group; Writers Guild of America, West

aurora productions
315 Walt Whitman Rd, Suite 210, Huntington Station, NY 11746-4112
Tel: 631-549-8933
E-mail: info@auroraproductions.tv
Web Site: www.auroraproductions.tv
Key Personnel
Founder & Prodr/Dir: Richard H Poggioli
  E-mail: richpogg@optonline.net
Membership(s): SMPTE®

Autocue
Affiliate of Vitec Group PLC
14 Progress Dr, Shelton, CT 06484
Tel: 212-929-7755 *Fax:* 212-929-2105
Web Site: www.autocue.com/teleprompter
Key Personnel
Busn Devt Mgr: Aaron Brady *E-mail:* aaron. brady@vitecgroup.com
Founded: 1955
Leader supplier of teleprompting hardware & software for purchase & rentals.
Membership(s): Production Equipment Rental Association

Autodesk Inc
111 McInnis Pkwy, San Rafael, CA 94903
Tel: 415-507-5000 *Fax:* 415-507-5100
Web Site: www.autodesk.com
Key Personnel
Pres & CEO: Andrew Anagnost
SVP & CFO: R Scott Herren
SVP & CTO: Scott Borduin
SVP, Busn Strategy & Mktg & Chief Mktg Offr: Lisa Campbell
SVP & Chief Digital Offr: Jeff Kinder
SVP & Chief HR Offr: Carmel Galvin
SVP, Corp Aff, Chief Legal Offr & Corp Secy: Pascal W Di Fronzo

SVP, Design & Creation Prods: Amy Bunszel
SVP, Mfg, Cloud & Prodn Prods: Scott Reese
SVP, Worldwide Field Opers: Steve Blum
VP & Gen Mgr, Autodesk Construction Solutions: Jim Lynch
Branch Office(s)
The Landmark, One Market St, Suite 500, San Francisco, CA 94105 *Tel:* 415-356-0700 *Fax:* 415-547-2222
23 Drydock Ave, Suite 610E, Boston, MA 02210 *Tel:* 857-263-5401 *Fax:* 857-263-5403 *Web Site:* www.autodesk.com/careers/boston
100 Commercial St, Manchester, NH 03101 *Tel:* 603-621-3100 *Fax:* 603-621-3383
221 SE Ankeny St, Portland, OR 97214 *Tel:* 503-833-3500 *Fax:* 503-746-9292
275 S Temple, No 305, Salt Lake City, UT 84111 *Tel:* 801-575-6021 *Toll Free Tel:* 877-335-2261 *E-mail:* na_mfg@autodesk.com *Web Site:* we-make.autodesk.com
Autodesk Canada Co, 6227 Second St SE, Unit 107, Calgary, AB T2H 1J5, Canada *Tel:* 403-294-0090 *Fax:* 403-264-1442
Autodesk Canada Co, 661 University Ave, Suite 200, Toronto, ON M5G 1M1, Canada *Tel:* 416-362-9181 *Fax:* 416-369-6140
Autodesk Canada Co, 3280 Electricity Dr, Windsor, ON N8W 5J1, Canada *Tel:* 819-823-9944 (French speaking) *Toll Free Tel:* 877-335-2261 *E-mail:* na_mfg@autodesk.com *Web Site:* we-make.autodesk.com
Autodesk Canada Co, 75 rue Anne (930 rue Wellington), Montreal, QC H3C 1T8, Canada *Tel:* 514-393-1616 *Fax:* 514-393-0110
Autodesk Canada Co, 10 rue Duke, Montreal, QC H3C 2L7, Canada *Tel:* 514-393-1616 *Toll Free Tel:* 800-869-3504 (sales) *Fax:* 514-393-0110
Autodesk Canada Co, 90 rue Queen, Montreal, QC H3C 6X4, Canada *Tel:* 514-393-1616 *Fax:* 514-393-0110
Foreign Office(s): Autodesk Ireland Operations Ltd, One Windmill Lane, 2nd fl, Dublin D02 F206, Ireland *Tel:* (01) 571 8800 (EMEA headquarters)
Autodesk Asia Pte Ltd, 3 Fusionopolis Way, 10-21 Symbosis, Singapore 138633, Singapore *Tel:* 6461 8100 *Fax:* 6735 3866 (APAC headquarters)

AutoDesSys Inc
3518 Riverside Dr, Suite 206, Columbus, OH 43221
Tel: 614-488-8838 *Fax:* 614-488-0848
E-mail: sales@formz.com; marketing@formz.com
Web Site: www.formz.com
Key Personnel
Pres & CEO: David Kropp
Founded: 1989
3D modeling software development.

Autogram/CRL
920 Edison Ave, Benton, AR 72015
Tel: 501-794-6994 *Fax:* 501-776-0357
E-mail: support@autogram.net
Web Site: www.autogram.net
Design & manufacture professional audio consoles.
Online catalog(s) available
Membership(s): NAB

Automated Entertainment
PO Box 1079, Littlerock, CA 95343-1079
Tel: 661-944-2299 *Toll Free Tel:* 800-880-6567 (orders)
E-mail: questions@automatedhd.com
Web Site: www.automatedhd.com
Key Personnel
Principal & Owner: Jeffrey W Hillinger
Founded: 1987
Catalog(s) available

Automatic Devices Co (ADC)
2121 S 12 St, Allentown, PA 18103
Tel: 610-797-6000 *Toll Free Tel:* 800-360-2321 *Fax:* 610-797-4088
E-mail: info@automaticdevices.com
Web Site: www.automaticdevices.com
Key Personnel
Cust Serv Mgr: Stan Nemeth *Tel:* 610-797-6000 ext 576 *E-mail:* stan.nemeth@automaticdevices. com
Purch: Robert Buchman *Tel:* 610-797-6000 ext 583 *E-mail:* robert.buchman@automaticdevices. com
Tech Sales: Robert Jones *Tel:* 610-797-6000 ext 579 *E-mail:* bob.jones@automaticdevices.com
Founded: 1919
Manufacture stage curtain track systems.
Online catalog(s) available

Automobile Film Club of America Inc
10 Cross St, Staten Island, NY 10304
Tel: 718-447-2255
E-mail: contact@autofilmclub.com
Web Site: www.autofilmclub.com
Key Personnel
Founder: Ralph Lucci
Pres: Margaret Lucci
Founded: 1992
Supplier of vehicles & equipment for the film industry.

Auton Motorized Systems
24856 Avenue Rockefeller, Valencia, CA 91355
Tel: 661-257-9282 *Fax:* 661-295-5638
E-mail: info@auton.com
Web Site: auton.com
Key Personnel
Pres & CEO: Art Walker
Founded: 1955
Manufacturer of television lifts.
Catalog(s) available, on request
CD-ROM catalog(s) available
Membership(s): Custom Electronic Design & Installation Association

AV Bluebook
80 Little Falls Rd, Fairfield, NJ 07004
Mailing Address: PO Box 10005, Fairfield, NJ 07004
Toll Free Tel: 800-631-7791 *Toll Free Fax:* 800-332-5871
E-mail: info@avbluebook.com; sales@ avbluebook.com
Web Site: www.avbluebook.com
Key Personnel
Sales Rep: Eddie Stern *E-mail:* estern@ avbluebook.com
Founded: 1976
Distributor for AV presentation products.
Catalog(s) available
Membership(s): Audiovisual and Integrated Experience Association; BPIA; The Imaging Alliance; National Art Materials Trade Association; NSCA

AV Chicago Inc
619 W Taylor St, Chicago, IL 60607
Tel: 312-229-4100 *Toll Free Tel:* 888-709-9599 *Fax:* 312-229-5642
Web Site: avchicago.com
Key Personnel
Owner & Pres: Andrew Brode; Justin Frick
Founded: 1982
Event technology partners. Full service production solution.
Online catalog(s) available
Membership(s): Audiovisual and Integrated Experience Association; Better Business Bureau; Chicago Convention & Tourism Bureau (Choose Chicago®)

AV Concepts Inc
1917 W First St, Tempe, AZ 85281

Tel: 480-557-6000; 480-646-4216 (sales & serv)
Toll Free Tel: 866-927-7590
E-mail: exhibitorservices@avconcepts.com
Web Site: www.avconcepts.com
Key Personnel
Pres: Nick Smith
Chief Revenue Offr: Jim Thornton
VP, Technol: Alex Howes
Dir, Sales & Staging: Mitch Teitelbaum
Founded: 1987
Full service provider of AV, staging & technical solutions for meetings, conventions & trade shows.

AV Conferencing LLC (AVC)
PO Box 21606, Concord, CA 94521
Tel: 925-216-6319 *Fax:* 801-382-5573
E-mail: sales@avconferencing.com
Web Site: www.avconferencing.com
Founded: 1989
Design, installation, sales & rental of audio conferencing, video conferencing & presentation systems.

AV Connections Inc
245 Executive Park Blvd, Winston-Salem, NC 27103
Tel: 336-768-5454 *Fax:* 336-768-5054
E-mail: avrentals@avconnectionsusa.com
Web Site: avconnectionsusa.com
Key Personnel
CFO: Marjorie Luckhart *E-mail:* margie@avconnectionsusa.com
Pres: Brad Luckhart *E-mail:* brad@avconnectionsusa.com
VP: Jared Luckhart *E-mail:* jluckhart@avconnectionssc.com
Video Prodn Mgr: Trent Perry *E-mail:* trent@avconnectionsusa.com
Logistics Coord: Marilyn Wilson
E-mail: marilyn@avconnectionsusa.com
Founded: 1985
Branch Office(s)
AV Connections, 1012 Saint Andrews Blvd, Suite C, Charleston, SC 29407, Br Mgr: Jared Luckhart *Tel:* 843-573-1174 *Fax:* 843-573-1176
E-mail: avrentals@avconnectionssc.com

A/V Davey
71 Clifton Place, Bridgeport, CT 06606
Tel: 203-372-3286 *Fax:* 203-372-3307
Web Site: avdavey.com
Key Personnel
Pres: David M Katz *Tel:* 203-372-3286 ext 12
E-mail: davey@avdavey.com
Founded: 1989
AV equipment installation, video production, equipment service & repairs, rental & staging.
Online catalog(s) available

AV Guys
1641 Pacific Rim Ct, Suite A, San Diego, CA 92154
Tel: 619-474-5050 *Fax:* 619-474-5454
Web Site: www.avguys.com
Key Personnel
Owner: Pete Pandit *E-mail:* pete@avguys.com
Founded: 2000
AV equipment rentals & sales.
Foreign Office(s): SAV Mision de Loreto No 26-B, Zona Rio, 22320 Tijuana, Mexico, Contact: Carlos Portilla *Tel:* (01664) 634 21 81 *Fax:* (01664) 634 39 71 *E-mail:* sav@solucionesaudiovisuales.com *Web Site:* www.solucionesaudiovisuales.com

AV Metro Inc
5401 Etta Burke Ct, Raleigh, NC 27606
Tel: 919-233-1901 *Fax:* 919-233-1804
E-mail: info@avmetro.com
Web Site: www.avmetro.com

Key Personnel
Pres: Frank Thompson *E-mail:* ft@avmetro.com
Sr Proj Mgr: Jon Singletary *E-mail:* jon@avmetro.com
Brochure(s) available
Membership(s): Audiovisual and Integrated Experience Association

A/V Presentations Inc
104 Otis St, Suite 30, Northborough, MA 01532
Tel: 508-393-9767 *Toll Free Tel:* 800-648-7176
Fax: 508-393-6698
E-mail: staff@avpresentations.com
Web Site: www.avpresentations.com
Key Personnel
Owner: Morris Beverly *E-mail:* bmorris@avpresentations.com; Rod Callahan
E-mail: rodc@avpresentations.com
Pres, CEO & Treas: James R Callahan
Secy & Dir: Clyde M Beverly
Corporate event & staging assistance. Specialize in user & video conferencing, tradeshows, partner services, corporate & general AV.
Online catalog(s) available

AV Toolbox
Division of TV One Multimedia Solutions
621 Wilmer Ave, Cincinnati, OH 45226
Tel: 859-282-7303 *Toll Free Tel:* 800-235-3280; 800-721-4044
E-mail: sales@avtoolbox.com
Web Site: www.avtoolbox.com

AV Workshop
500 W 37 St, 3rd fl, New York, NY 10018
Tel: 212-643-0040 *Fax:* 212-564-5277
E-mail: sales@avworkshop.com
Web Site: avworkshop.com
Key Personnel
VP: Jason Lieberman *E-mail:* jlieberman@avworkshop.com
Founded: 1978
Catalog(s) available
Membership(s): Audiovisual and Integrated Experience Association

Available Light
29-20 37 Ave, Long Island City, NY 11101
Tel: 718-707-9670; 718-707-9671 *Fax:* 718-707-9693
E-mail: contactus@alny.net
Web Site: www.alny.net

Available Light
Division of JT Services
5251 Dixon Rd, Oceanside, CA 92056-2319
Tel: 760-505-1605
E-mail: availablelight@cox.net
Web Site: www.availablelightandgrip.com
Key Personnel
Owner & Operator: James Teiper
Founded: 1986
Mobile grip & lighting.

Available Lighting & Motion Picture Services Inc
826 Jefferson Hwy, New Orleans, LA 70121
Tel: 504-831-5214 *Fax:* 504-831-5361
E-mail: avlight@bellsouth.net
Web Site: www.availablelighting.com
Key Personnel
Pres: Billy Bragg
Rental Mgr: Jose Sanchez
Founded: 1984
Lighting, grip, generators for rental.

Avalon Acoustics
2800 Wilderness Place, Boulder, CO 80301
Tel: 303-440-0422

Web Site: avalonacoustics.com
Key Personnel
Pres: Neil Patel

Avast! Recording Co
601 NW 80 St, Seattle, WA 98117
Fax: 206-789-7569
E-mail: avast@comcast.net
Web Site: www.avastrecording.com
Key Personnel
Owner: Stuart Hallerman
Staff Engr: Adam Burd *E-mail:* adam.burd@gmail.com
Founded: 1990
Recording studio.

Avatar Studios
2675 Scott Ave, Suite G, St Louis, MO 63103
Tel: 314-533-2242 *Fax:* 314-533-3349
E-mail: info@avatar-studios.com
Web Site: avatar-studios.com
Key Personnel
Pres: Bill Faris
VP, Opers: Brad Shelton *E-mail:* bshelton@avatar-studios.com
Dir, Photog: Doug Hastings
Ed: Jack Larson
Founded: 1999
Provides creative & engaging video, audio & interactive communications solutions for clients across all media delivery platforms.

Avaya Inc
4655 Great American Pkwy, Santa Clara, CA 95054
Tel: 908-953-6000 *Toll Free Tel:* 866-GO-AVAYA (462-8292 US & CN)
Web Site: www.avaya.com
Key Personnel
Pres & CEO: Jim Chirico
SVP & CFO: Patrick O'Malley
SVP, Chief Admin Offr & Gen Coun: Shefali Shah
SVP, Corp Strategy, Devt & Mktg: Nikos Nikolopoulos
SVP, Opers: Jerry Glembocki
SVP & Gen Mgr, Solutions & Technol: Laurent Philonenko
Gen Mgr, Americas Sales & Servs: James J Geary
Media Rel: Alex Alias
Founded: 2000
Global provider of business collaboration & communications solutions.
Branch Office(s)
8744 Lucent Blvd, Highlands Ranch, CO 80129
12121 Grant St, Thornton, CO 80241
1000 NW 57 Ct, Suite 500, Miami, FL 33126
1145 Sanctuary Pkwy, Alpharetta, GA 30009
350 Mount Kemble Ave, Morristown, NJ 07960
Two Penn Plaza, New York, NY 10121
2605 Meridian Pkwy, Suite 200, Durham, NC 27713
1111 Freeport Pkwy, Coppell, TX 75019-4451

Avekta Productions Inc
One Rock Place, Yonkers, NY 10705
Tel: 914-378-8000
Web Site: avekta.com
Key Personnel
Pres: Maria Avgerakis *E-mail:* maria@avekta.com
VP & Creative Dir: George Avgerakis
Prodr: Carlyle Gifford; Patricia Pastorelli
Founded: 1976
E-media consultancy producing video, Internet content & print in English & all foreign languages.
Membership(s): IABC

AVerMedia Technologies Inc
47358 Fremont Blvd, Fremont, CA 94538

Tel: 510-403-0006 *Fax:* 510-403-0022
E-mail: avtsales.usa@avermedia.com
Web Site: www.avermedia.com
Key Personnel
Chmn of the Bd, Pres & CEO: Michael Kuo
VP & CTO: Ted Dai
Founded: 1990
Provides PC, tablet & mobile TV-viewing solutions, HD video & real-time AV product designs, manufacturing & marketing.
Online catalog(s) available

AVES Audio Visual Systems Inc
PO Box 500, Sugar Land, TX 77487-0500
Tel: 281-295-1300 *Toll Free Tel:* 800-365-AVES (365-2837) *Fax:* 281-295-1311
E-mail: sales@avesav.com
Web Site: www.avesav.com
Founded: 1963
AV, digital signage & conferencing technologies.
Membership(s): Audiovisual and Integrated Experience Association

AVFX Inc
96 Holton St, Boston, MA 02135
Tel: 617-254-0770 *Toll Free Tel:* 888-254-0770
E-mail: info@avfx.com
Web Site: www.avfx.com
Key Personnel
Founder & CEO: Murray Lapides
Pres: Steve Halling
VP, Busn Devt: Cecil Dorman
Gen Mgr: Tom Peckham
Systems Design Mgr: Robert Sicklick
Sr Tech Prodr: Kevin Reilly
Tech Prodr: Rich Keefe; Ken Quigley
Founded: 1984
Membership(s): Audiovisual and Integrated Experience Association; EDPA; MPI; TESA

AVI-SPL
6301 Benjamin Rd, Suite 101, Tampa, FL 33634
Tel: 813-884-7168 *Toll Free Tel:* 866-708-5034; 866-925-8298 (cust serv); 866-559-8197 (sales)
E-mail: contact@avispl.com; sales@avispl.com; customerservice@avispl.com
Web Site: www.avispl.com
Key Personnel
CEO: John Zettel
CFO: Steve Palmer
COO: John Murphy
EVP: Steve Benjamin
EVP, Sales & Mktg: Dale Bottcher
Founded: 1979
Full service AV company providing the following services: AV system design/build & installation, product sales, rental & repair, rental & event staging & logistic management.
Online catalog(s) available, PDF
Branch Office(s)
337 Northlake Blvd, Suite 1004, Altamonte Springs, FL 32701 *Tel:* 407-786-5000
772 S Military Trail, Deerfield Beach, FL 33442 *Tel:* 954-938-9382
9143 Philips Hwy, Suite 350, Jacksonville, FL 32256 *Tel:* 904-281-2714
4600 E Washington, Suite 300, Phoenix, AZ 85034 *Tel:* 602-772-3983
904 Pardee St, Berkeley, CA 94710 *Tel:* 510-652-5030
10775 Business Center Dr, Suite 150, Cypress, CA 90630 *Tel:* 714-799-7166
4225 Hopyard Rd, Suite 1, Pleasanton, CA 94588 *Tel:* 925-404-0440
9332 Tech Center Dr, Suite 200, Sacramento, CA 95826 *Tel:* 916-438-5400
5735 Kearny Villa Rd, Suite 114, San Diego, CA 92123 *Tel:* 858-277-1751
7367 S Revere Pkwy, Unit 2B, Centennial, CO 80112 *Tel:* 303-792-3090
3079 Premier Pkwy, Suite 170, Duluth, GA 30096 *Tel:* 678-542-2201

2266 Palmer Dr, Schaumburg, IL 60173 *Tel:* 847-437-7712
9160 Rumsey Rd, Suite B-12, Columbia, MD 21045 *Tel:* 410-964-8100
101 Billerica Ave, Bldg 6, North Billerica, MA 01862 *Toll Free Tel:* 866-296-0418
160-162 E 19 St, Suite A, Holland, MI 49423 *Toll Free Tel:* 866-843-0536
28900 Beck Rd, Wixom, MI 48393 *Tel:* 248-669-4286
2730 Arthur St, Roseville, MN 55113 *Tel:* 651-287-7000
10-40 45 Ave, Long Island City, NY 11101 *Tel:* 718-806-4040
8301 Arrowridge Blvd, Suite B, Charlotte, NC 28273 *Tel:* 704-523-5886
4524 Green Point Dr, Suite 104, Greensboro, NC 27410 *Tel:* 336-605-4760
335 Ken-Mar Industrial Pkwy, Broadview Heights, OH 44147 *Tel:* 440-740-0630
761 Crossroads Ct, Vandalia, OH 45377 *Tel:* 937-847-5558
207 Commerce Park Dr, Cranberry Township, PA 16066 *Tel:* 724-776-3877
2550 Eisenhower Ave, Suite A200, Audubon, PA 19403 *Tel:* 610-270-1545
13859 Diplomat Dr, Suite 180, Dallas, TX 75234 *Tel:* 972-243-4422
4333 W Sam Houston Pkwy N, Suite 150, Houston, TX 77043 *Tel:* 281-902-3933
540 Huntmar Park, Suite B, Herndon, VA 20170 *Tel:* 703-796-9011 *Fax:* 703-796-9047
21312 30 Dr SE, Suite 102, Bothell, WA 98021 *Tel:* 425-861-5564
Bay 3 - 5030 13 St SE, Calgary, AB T2G 5M9, Canada *Tel:* 403-255-4123
4415 Juneau St, Burnaby, BC V5C 4C4, Canada *Tel:* 604-877-1400
883 Boyd Ave, Suite 200, Ottawa, ON K2A E2E, Canada *Tel:* 613-714-1100
Foreign Office(s): Im Gefierth 11, 63303 Dreieich, Germany *Tel:* (0151) 74474777
FNC Compound, DIP 2, Bldg 8, Unit 1, Makani No 18839 62382, Dubai Investment Park 21000, Dubai, United Arab Emirates *Tel:* (04) 810-8100
Armstrong Mall, Unit 12, Farnborough, Hants GU14 0NR, United Kingdom *Tel:* 0800 181 4425 (European headquarters)
Membership(s): ABC; AES; AFCEA; American Institute of Architects; ASA; Audiovisual and Integrated Experience Association; Buy-Out Music Association; Illuminating Engineering Society; International Facilities Management Association; NSCA

AVI Systems
9675 W 76 St, Suite 130, Eden Prairie, MN 55344
Tel: 952-949-3700 *Toll Free Tel:* 800-488-4954 (support); 855-521-0050 *Fax:* 952-949-6000
E-mail: info@avisystems.com
Web Site: www.avisystems.com
Key Personnel
Chmn: Joe Stoebner
Pres & CEO: Jeff Stoebner
COO: Joel Lehman
CFO: Christopher Mounts
Area VP: Brian Van Der Hagen *Tel:* 952-949-6035 *E-mail:* brian.vanderhagen@avisystems.com
VP, Sales: Donald Mastro
Tech Servs Mgr: Travis Kjerstad *Tel:* 952-949-6048 *E-mail:* travis.kjerstad@avisystems.com
Branch Admin: Blair Schipper *Tel:* 952-949-6003 *E-mail:* blair.schipper@avisystems.com
Catalog(s) available
Branch Office(s)
208 N Broadway Ave, Rochester, MN 55906, Area VP: Brian Van Der Hagen *Tel:* 952-949-6034 *E-mail:* brian.vanderhagen@avisystems.com

44150 S Grimmer Blvd, Fremont, CA 94538, Area VP: Rich Marlenee *Tel:* 415-915-2070 *E-mail:* rich.marlenee@avisystems.com
10070 Willow Creek Rd, San Diego, CA 92131, Area VP: David Bunting *Tel:* 858-653-4300 *Fax:* 858-695-7844 *E-mail:* david.bunting@avisystems.com
355 Inverness Dr S, Unit 355-A, Englewood, CO 80112, Area VP: Patrick Hart *Tel:* 303-792-4800 *Fax:* 303-792-4801 *E-mail:* patrick.hart@avisystems.com
2975 Gateway Dr, Suite 110, Peachtree Corners, GA 30071, Area VP: Rick Landry *Tel:* 470-705-2445 *Fax:* 470-300-7789 *E-mail:* rick.landry@avisystems.com
717 W Algonquin Rd, Arlington Heights, IL 60005, Area VP: Tom Melms *Tel:* 630-477-2300 *Fax:* 630-477-2301 *E-mail:* tom.melms@avisystems.com
3001 104 St, Urbandale, IA 50322, Area VP: Roland Schlegel *Tel:* 515-254-9850 *Fax:* 215-254-9981 *E-mail:* roland.schlegel@avisystems.com
8019 Bond St, Lenexa, KS 66214, Area VP: Tom Madsen *Tel:* 913-495-9494 *Fax:* 913-495-9479 *E-mail:* tom.madsen@avisystems.com
48679 Alpha Dr, Suite 140, Wixom, MI 48393, Area VP: Aaron Campbell *Tel:* 248-957-6150 *Fax:* 248-957-6151 *E-mail:* aaron.campbell@avisystems.com
9 Sunnen Dr, Suite 300, Maplewood, MO 63143, Area VP: Tom Madsen *Tel:* 314-647-0009 *Fax:* 314-647-1465 *E-mail:* tom.madsen@avisystems.com
5055 S 111 St, Omaha, NE 68137, Area VP: Roland Schlegel *Tel:* 402-593-6500 *Fax:* 402-593-8500 *E-mail:* roland.schlegel@avisystems.com
1930 E Century Ave, Bismarck, ND 58503, Area VP: Trent Slyter *Tel:* 701-258-6360 *E-mail:* trent.slyter@avisystems.com
3002 Fiechtner Dr, Suite D, Fargo, ND 58103 *Tel:* 701-237-4427
7139 E Kemper Rd, Cincinnati, OH 45249, Area VP: Dave Wesco *Tel:* 513-578-6550 *Fax:* 513-578-6551 *E-mail:* dave.wesco@avisystems.com
2300 E 54 St N, Suite 2, Sioux Falls, SD 57104, Area VP: Michael Safranski *Tel:* 605-782-4141 *E-mail:* michael.safranski@avisystems.com
8801 Jameel St, Suite 140, Houston, TX 77040, Regl VP: David Walshe *Tel:* 469-359-4100 *E-mail:* david.walshe@avisystems.com
4040 W Royal Lane, Suite 136, Irving, TX 75063, Regl VP: David Walshe *Tel:* 469-359-4100 *Fax:* 469-359-4099 *E-mail:* david.walshe@avisystems.com
4321 W College Ave, Suite 200, Appleton, WI 54914, Area VP: Jane Phillips *Tel:* 920-393-9500 *Fax:* 920-273-6061 *E-mail:* jane.phillips@avisystems.com
3275 Intertech Dr, Suite 500, Brookfield, WI 53045, Area VP: Jane Phillips *Tel:* 262-207-1300 *Fax:* 262-207-1301 *E-mail:* jane.phillips@avisystems.com
5201 Femrite Dr, Madison, WI 53718, Area VP: Jane Phillips *Tel:* 608-221-8888 *Fax:* 608-221-9252 *E-mail:* jane.phillips@avisystems.com
Membership(s): Audiovisual and Integrated Experience Association

Avid Technology Inc
65-75 Network Dr, Burlington, MA 01830
Tel: 978-640-6789
Web Site: www.avid.com
Key Personnel
Pres & CEO: Jeff Rosica
CFO & EVP: Ken Gayron
EVP, Chief Legal & Admin Offr: Jason Duva
SVP & Chief Mktg Offr: Melissa Puls
SVP & Chief Prod Offr: Dana Ruzicka
SVP, Global Sales: Tom Cordiner
SVP, Global Servs & Support: Peter Ennis
SVP, Global Supply Chain Opers: Dave Perillo

VP & Chief HR Offr: Diana Brunelle
Founded: 1987
Audio & video technology for media organizations & independent professionals.
Branch Office(s)
2600 Tenth St, Suite 200, Berkeley, CA 94710
Tel: 510-229-1000 *Fax:* 510-229-1010
101 S First St, Suite 200, Burbank, CA 91502
Tel: 818-557-2520 *Fax:* 818-557-2558
3140 Old Mountain View-Alviso Rd, Santa Clara, CA 95054 *Tel:* 408-855-3800 *Fax:* 408-855-3830
2903 Bunker Hill Lane, No 100, Santa Clara, CA 95054
1101 Pennsylvania Ave NW, Suite 600, Washington, DC 20004 *Tel:* 202-756-4599 *Fax:* 202-318-4593
One Grand Central Place, 60 E 42 St, Suite 600, New York, NY 10165 *Tel:* 212-983-2424 *Fax:* 212-430-0378
3510 Saint Laurent Blvd, Suite 300, Montreal, QC H2X 2V2, Canada *Tel:* 514-845-1636 *Fax:* 514-845-5676
Foreign Office(s): Northpoint Tower, 100 Miller St, North Sydney 2060, Australia *Tel:* (02) 9931 6841; (02) 9420 3066 (support)
Grand Pacific Bldg, Rm 706, Tower C, Jia 8 GuangHua Rd, Chaoyang District, Beijing 100026, China *Tel:* (010) 6581 8199
Parkview Green, 9 Dongdaqiao Rd, Off Bldg A, Beijing 100020, China *Tel:* (010) 5730 6096 (audio); (010) 5730 6095 (video)
Pasilan Visio Kiintiesto Oy, Televisiokatu 3, 00100 Helsinki, Finland *Tel:* (040) 511 9477
Immeuble Place de Seine, 157 rue Anatole France, 8ieme etage, 92300 Levallois-Perret, France *Tel:* 01 41 49 40 00 *Fax:* 01 47 57 15 27
Takustr 1-3, 50825 Cologne, Germany *Tel:* (0221) 3795060
Europallee 10, 67657 Kaiserslautern, Germany *Tel:* (0631) 680-3500 *Fax:* (0631) 680-35099
Paul-Heyse Str 29, 2nd fl, 80336 Munich, Germany *Tel:* (089) 50 20 60 *Fax:* (089) 50 20 6140
ChaseGold Tower, 14th fl, Hunghom, Hong Kong *Tel:* 2363 9263 *Fax:* 2364 5536
306/326 Regus, Level 3 Neo Vikram, New Link Rd, Andheri West, Mumbai 400 053, India *Tel:* (022) 6198 4946
Citywest Business Campus, 4051 Kingswood Dr, Dublin D24 T021, Ireland *Tel:* (01) 466 9600 *Fax:* (01) 479 6140
Atir Yeda 15, Kfar Saba, Israel *Tel:* (09) 7676862 *Fax:* (09) 7676861
ATT Bldg 4F, 2-11-7 Akasaka, Minato-ku, Tokyo 107-0052, Japan *Tel:* (03) 3505 7937 *Fax:* (03) 3505 7938
Vreelandseweg 42A, 1216 CH Hilversum, Netherlands *Tel:* (035) 772 35 61 *Fax:* (035) 625 00 90
10F Uptown Tower 1, 1634 Taguig City, Manila, Philippines *Tel:* (02) 317 2300
Bulwar M Beniowskiego 5a, 70-642 Szczecin, Poland *Tel:* (91) 464 8619 *Fax:* (91) 881 2189
ul Robotnicza 68c, 53-608 Warsaw, Poland
Sime Darby Business Ctr, 315 Alexandra Rd, Suite 03-01, Singapore 159944, Singapore *Tel:* 6476 7666 *Fax:* 6475 7666
3F, DongSung Bldg, 17-8 Youido-dong, Youngdeugpo-gu, Seoul 150-874, South Korea *Tel:* (02) 782 4210 *Fax:* (02) 782 4214
Centro Empresarial VK, Locales A & B, Camino de la Zarzuela 21, 3a Planta, 28023 Madrid, Spain *Tel:* 91 762 86 00 *Fax:* 91 183 66 50
Calle Luis de la Mata, 14 D Off 4, 28042 Madrid, Spain *Tel:* 91 742 92 13
Malmo Grabroder 22, Grabrodersgatan 9, 211 21 Malmo, Sweden
Hus E, Plan 3, Linnegatan 87B, 11523 Stockholm, Sweden *Tel:* (08) 442 55 70 *Fax:* (08) 442 55 87
6F, No 300 Yangguang St, Neihu District, Taipei 114, Taiwan

36/F CRC Tower, All Seasons Place, Off 46, 87/2 Wireless Rd, Phathumwan, Bangkok 10330, Thailand *Tel:* (02) 625 3119
Aurora Tower, 19th fl, 1903, PO Box 500646, Dubai Media City, United Arab Emirates *Tel:* (04) 559 0600
Pinewood Studios, West Side Complex, Pinewood Rd, Iver Heath, Bucks SL0 0NH, United Kingdom *Tel:* (01753) 655 999 *Fax:* (01753) 654 999
32 The Maltings, Lower Charlton Trading Estate, Charlot Rd, Shepton Mallet, Somerset BA4 5QE, United Kingdom *Tel:* (01483) 280208 *Fax:* (01749) 330047
Thorncroft Manor, Leatherhead, Surrey KT22 8JB, United Kingdom *Tel:* (03333) 44 11 42
Membership(s): NAB

Avidex Inc
Subsidiary of ITOCHU International Inc
13555 Bel-Red Rd, Suite 226, Bellevue, WA 98005
Tel: 425-643-0330 *Toll Free Tel:* 800-798-0330 *Fax:* 425-274-7091
E-mail: info@avidexav.com
Web Site: www.avidexav.com
Key Personnel
CEO: Joel Harris
Provides project management, equipment procurement, programming, installation, rental & staging services.
Branch Office(s)
6100 Stewart Ave, Fremont, CA 94538 *Tel:* 510-279-7100 *Toll Free Tel:* 800-999-8590 *Fax:* 510-279-7101
4308A Wiley Post Rd, Suite 100, Addison, TX 75001 *Tel:* 972-212-6870

Aviom Inc
1157 Phoenixville Pike, Suite 201, West Chester, PA 19380-4254
Tel: 610-738-9005 *Fax:* 610-738-9950
E-mail: info@aviom.com
Web Site: www.aviom.com
Key Personnel
Founder & CEO: Carl Bader
Devt Mgr & Prod Res: Ray Legnini
Founded: 2002
Manufacturer of distributed audio network products.

Avitecture Inc
One Export Dr, Sterling, VA 20164-4421
Tel: 703-404-8900 *Fax:* 703-404-8940
E-mail: info@avitecture.com
Web Site: www.avitecture.com
Key Personnel
Chmn: Sidney L Lissner *E-mail:* sidney.lissner@avitecture.com
CFO: Debra Jones *E-mail:* deb.jones@avitecture.com
VP & CTO: Jason Nichols *E-mail:* jason.nichols@avitecture.com
Pres: Greg Boyd *E-mail:* greg.boyd@avitecture.com
VP, Sales & Mktg: Bruce Pittman *E-mail:* bruce.pittman@avitecture.com
Founded: 1979
Design, build, install & support integrated AV-IT systems.
Membership(s): American Alliance of Museums; American Institute of Architects; Audiovisual and Integrated Experience Association; BICSI; International Facilities Management Association; Mid-Atlantic Association of Museums; Northern Virginia Technology Council; NSCA; SEMC; US Green Building Council; VAM

AVL Systems Design LLC
14901 Bristol Park Blvd, Edmond, OK 73013
Tel: 405-749-1866 *Fax:* 405-749-1851
E-mail: dnix@avl1.com

Web Site: www.avl1.com
Key Personnel
CFO: Stacy Pierce
Pres: Marc Pierce
Dir, Engg: Ryan Zemke
Cust Rel & Mktg Mgr: Danny Nix
Founded: 2000
Provides quality designs for audio, acoustics, video projection, production video, intercom systems & lighting systems.
Membership(s): AES; American Institute of Architects; Audiovisual and Integrated Experience Association; BICSI; HAA; IEEE; Imaging Science Foundation; LDI; NAB; NSCA; Synergetic Audio Concepts

AVP Mfg & Supply Inc
2288-B7 Dumfries Rd, RR2, Cambridge, ON N1R 5S3, Canada
Tel: 519-740-7966 *Toll Free Tel:* 800-481-2493 *Fax:* 519-740-0131
E-mail: sales@jackfields.com
Web Site: www.jackfields.com
Key Personnel
Dir, Admin: Wim Vanvoorst
Dir, Sales: Brian Ferri *Tel:* 416-529-3623 (cell) *E-mail:* brian.ferri@jackfields.com
Founded: 1985
Manufacturer of commercial broadcast, telecom & satellite equipment.
Catalog(s) available, free, PDF download

AVS Group
3120 South Ave, Suite 133, La Crosse, WI 54601
Tel: 608-780-7019 *Fax:* 608-787-0012
E-mail: info@avsgroup.com
Web Site: www.avsgroup.com
Key Personnel
Owner & Gen Mgr: Ed Wais
Founded: 1988
Full service video production, from pre-planning & script writing to filming, editing & duplication.

AVS Media Group
11193 Old Hwy 31, Suite 1, Spanish Fort, AL 36527
Tel: 251-621-1200
E-mail: info@avsmediagroup.com
Web Site: www.avsmediagroup.com
Key Personnel
Pres: Steve King *E-mail:* steve@avsmediagroup.com
Video production & post-production.

AVST, An XMedius Company, see Applied Voice & Speech Technologies Inc (AVST)

Avtech Systems Inc
7-1 Bellair Ave, Fair Lawn, NJ 07410
Tel: 201-833-8777
Founded: 1978
Catalog(s) available

AVW-TELAV Audio Visual Solutions, see Freeman Audio Visual

Award Productions Inc
164 Great Rd, Acton, MA 01720
Tel: 978-635-8000
E-mail: web@awardprod.com
Web Site: www.awardproductions.com
Key Personnel
Founder & Pres: Al Ward
Dir, Prodn & Opers: Peter Koziell
Sales Dir: Barry Kane
Sr Proj Mgr, Prodr & Sr Artistic Designer: Ursula Kane
Prodn Coord & Asst Ed: Jaime Therriault

Video Ed & Audio Technician: Heather Anderson
Full service video production company offering a full range of media services from script development to post-production.

Axis Films
3138 Cumberland Rd, Berkley, MI 48072
Tel: 248-722-1734
Web Site: www.axisfilms.tv
Key Personnel
Owner: Steve Oatley *E-mail:* steveoatley@yahoo.com
Founded: 1991
Film & video production.

Axxis Leasing Inc
845 S Ninth St, Louisville, KY 40203
Tel: 502-568-6030 *Fax:* 502-568-6204
E-mail: info@axxisinc.com
Web Site: www.axxisinc.com
Key Personnel
CFO: Joseph M Smith
Pres: Steve Smith
Secy-Treas: Mike Smith
Full service video production company.
Membership(s): Audiovisual and Integrated Experience Association; NSCA

Aydin Displays, a Sparton Company
One Riga Lane, Birdsboro, PA 19508
Tel: 610-404-7400 *Toll Free Tel:* 866-367-2934
Fax: 610-404-8190
E-mail: sales@spartonre.com
Web Site: www.spartonre.com
Key Personnel
Prog Mgr: Brent Smith
Founded: 1967
Catalog(s) available

Aylmer Press
PO Box 2302, Madison, WI 53701-2302
Tel: 608-441-5277 *Fax:* 608-251-0890
Web Site: www.signit2.com
Key Personnel
Pres: Steve Kokette
Founded: 1992
Produces videos & DVDs to teach kids sign language.
Catalog(s) available

AZ Spectrum
53-53 62 St, Maspeth, NY 11378
Tel: 718-779-1892 *Fax:* 718-779-1892
E-mail: az@az-spectrum.com; azspectrum@aol.com
Web Site: www.az-spectrum.com
Key Personnel
Owner: Andrew Zorawski
Founded: 1994
Accessories for professional motion picture cameras as well as electronics repair services.

Aztec Video Productions
2967 Montana Ave, Cincinnati, OH 45211
Tel: 513-481-5004
E-mail: aztec@fuse.net
Web Site: www.aztecvideo.com
Founded: 1980
Film, tape, picture & slide transfers, DVD & CD duplication, photos & music to video, custom audio work.
Branch Office(s)
9435 Waterstone Blvd, Suite 140, Cincinnati, OH 45249 *Tel:* 513-489-5554

Aztech Productions LLC
6 Hillcrest Ave, Erdenheim, PA 19038
Tel: 215-836-5490
Web Site: aztechproductions.com

Key Personnel
Owner & CEO: Linda Mattice *E-mail:* lmattice@aztechproductions.com
Owner: Kevin Mattice
Film & video production, multimedia design & post-production studio.

Aztek Inc
13765-F Alton Pkwy, Irvine, CA 92618
Tel: 949-770-8787 *Toll Free Tel:* 800-GRAPH-55 (472-7455) *Fax:* 949-770-4986
E-mail: mail@aztek.com
Web Site: www.aztek.com
Key Personnel
Founder: Phil Lippincott
VP & VP, Engg: Evan Lippincott
Founded: 1980
Provide professional, quality integrated turnkey image production systems & software.
Catalog(s) available
Membership(s): ACM SIGGRAPH; Audiovisual and Integrated Experience Association; DIMA; The Imaging Alliance

B & B Video Productions Inc
233 N Main St, West Point, NE 68788
Tel: 402-380-9042
Web Site: www.bandbvideo.com
Key Personnel
Pres: Brian Kreikemeier *E-mail:* brian@bandbvideo.com
Founded: 1987
Documentary style productions for businesses & organizations.

B-K Lighting
40429 Brickyard Dr, Madera, CA 93636
Tel: 559-438-5800 *Fax:* 559-438-5900
E-mail: info@bklighting.com
Web Site: www.bklighting.com
Key Personnel
Founder: Doug Hagen
Pres & CEO: Nathan Sloan
Founded: 1984
Manufacturer of outdoor lighting fixtures.
Online catalog(s) available

The Baby School, see So Smart Productions

Back to the Bible
6400 Cornhusker Hwy, Suite 100, Lincoln, NE 68507
Mailing Address: PO Box 82808, Lincoln, NE 68501-2808
Tel: 402-464-7200 *Toll Free Tel:* 800-759-6655
Fax: 402-464-7474
E-mail: info@backtothebible.org
Web Site: www.backtothebible.org
Key Personnel
CEO: Dr Arnie Cole
Founded: 1939
Worldwide Christian ministry bringing people together through media & technology.
Online catalog(s) available

Backdrop Outlet
3540 Seagate Way, Oceanside, CA 92056
Tel: 760-547-2900 *Toll Free Tel:* 800-466-1755
Fax: 760-547-2899
E-mail: cs@backdropoutlet.com
Web Site: backdropoutlet.com
Key Personnel
Pres: Jay Gupta
Founded: 1991
Backgrounds, props, lighting & studio accessories for photography & video.

Backstage Equipment Inc
8052 Lankershim Blvd, North Hollywood, CA 91605

Tel: 818-504-6026 *Toll Free Tel:* 800-692-2787
Fax: 818-504-6180
E-mail: info@backstageweb.com
Web Site: www.backstageweb.com
Key Personnel
Pres & Chief Designer: Cary Griffith
Opers Mgr: Sig Guzman
Founded: 1979
Manufacture specialized carts to transport motion picture equipment.
Catalog(s) available, free

Backstage Pass Entertainment Inc
Unit of Hailing Frequency Productions Inc
7438 Shoshone Ave, Lake Balboa, CA 91406-2340
Tel: 818-881-9888 *Toll Free Tel:* 800-664-6555
Fax: 818-881-0555
E-mail: blowinsmokeband@ktb.net
Key Personnel
Owner & Pres: Larry Weisberg
Catalog(s) available

Backstar Creative Media Inc
70 W Hubbard St, Suite 203, Chicago, IL 60654
Tel: 312-467-0425 *Toll Free Tel:* 800-955-8900
E-mail: solutions@backstar.com
Web Site: www.backstar.com
Key Personnel
Pres: Mitch Norinsky
Founded: 2002
Digital media solutions for broadcast.

Badiyan Inc
720 W 94 St, Bloomington, MN 55420
Tel: 952-888-5507 *Fax:* 952-888-0360
E-mail: info@badiyan.com
Web Site: www.badiyan.com
Key Personnel
Owner & Pres: Fred Badiyan
CFO: Rolo Mahabadi
Founded: 1974

Bag End Loudspeakers
1201 Armstrong St, Algonquin, IL 60102
Tel: 847-658-8888 *Fax:* 847-658-5008
Web Site: www.bagend.com
Key Personnel
Pres: Jim Wischmeyer
Founded: 1976
Online catalog(s) available

Baha'i Distribution Service (BDS)
Subsidiary of Baha'i Publishing Trust of India
401 Greenleaf Ave, Wilmette, IL 60091
Tel: 847-425-7950; 847-853-7899
Toll Free Tel: 800-999-9019
E-mail: bds@usbnc.org
Web Site: www.bahaibookstore.com
Founded: 1902
Primary distributor for Baha'i World Center publications. Print & ebook titles available as well as digital media in a variety of formats.

Baker Audio Visual
2195 N Norcross Tucker Rd, Norcross, GA 30071
Tel: 770-441-2000 *Toll Free Tel:* 800-847-3523
Fax: 770-449-7719
E-mail: support@bakeraudiovisual.com
Web Site: www.bakeraudiovisual.com
Key Personnel
CEO: Keith Hicks, III
Pres: Joe Schuch
EVP: Dave Davis
Cust Support Mgr: Jacki Kirsch
Mktg Mgr: Kasie Grant
Founded: 1953
Provide innovative sight & sound communication solutions.

Baldwin Productions Services Inc
160 Tioga Lane, Greenbrae, CA 94904
Tel: 415-699-0729
Web Site: www.baldwinproductionsinc.com
Key Personnel
Owner: Jim Baldwin *E-mail:* jim@
baldwinproductionsinc.com
Film, location services & still photography.

Ballantyne Strong Inc
11422 Miracle Hills Dr, Suite 300, Omaha, NE
68154
Tel: 402-453-4444 *Toll Free Tel:* 800-424-1215;
800-722-0046
E-mail: customerservice@btn-inc.com
Web Site: ballantynestrong.com
Key Personnel
Chmn & CEO: D Kyle Cerminara *Tel:* 402-829-
9403
SVP & CFO: Lance Schulz *Tel:* 402-829-9427
Founded: 1932
Designs, integrates & installs technology solu-
tions for a broad range of applications includ-
ing digital projection & digital signage.
Online catalog(s) available
Membership(s): International Cinema Technology
Association; Theatre Equipment Association

Band Pro Film & Digital Inc
3403 W Pacific Ave, Burbank, CA 91505
Tel: 818-841-9655 *Toll Free Tel:* 888-BANDPRO
(226-3776) *Fax:* 818-841-7649
E-mail: info@bandpro.com; customercare@
bandpro.com
Web Site: www.bandpro.com
Key Personnel
Pres & CEO: Amnon H Band *E-mail:* amnon.
band@bandpro.com
EVP & COO: Renee Contreras *E-mail:* rene.
contreras@bandpro.com
VP, Tech Servs & CTO: Jeff Cree *E-mail:* jeff.
cree@bandpro.com
Cont: Amy Miller *E-mail:* amy.miller@bandpro.
com
VP, Key Accts: Nir Reches *E-mail:* nir.reches@
bandpro.com
Mktg Dir: Brett Gillespie *E-mail:* brett.gillespie@
bandpro.com
Founded: 1984
Digital cinematography, broadcast & ENG equipment.
Branch Office(s)
330 W 38 St, Ground flr, New York, NY 10018
Tel: 212-227-8577
Foreign Office(s): Max-Planck-Str 6, 85609 Dor-
nach, Munich, Germany *Tel:* (089) 94548490
Fax: (089) 94548499 *Web Site:* www.bandpro.
de
3 Hasolelim St, 67897 Tel Aviv, Israel *Tel:* (03)
5621631 *Fax:* (03) 5621632 *Web Site:* www.
bandpro.co.il

B+B SmartWorx
707 Dayton Rd, Ottawa, IL 61350
Mailing Address: PO Box 1040, Ottawa, IL
61350-6040
Tel: 815-433-5100 *Toll Free Tel:* 800-346-3119
Fax: 815-433-5109
E-mail: info@advantech-bb.com; orders@
advantech-bb.com
Web Site: advantech-bb.com
Key Personnel
Pres & CEO: Jerry O'Gorman
Founded: 1981
Manufacturer of rugged, reliable, wired & wire-
less connectivity & communications solutions.
Catalog(s) available, free, semiannual
Online catalog(s) available
Foreign Office(s): Westlink Commercial Park,
Oranmore, Co Galway, Ireland *Tel:* (091)
792444 *Fax:* (091) 792445 *E-mail:* esales@
advantech-bb.com (intl sales)

No 1, Alley 20, Lane 26, Reuiguang Rd, Neihu
District, Taipei 11491, Taiwan *Tel:* (02) 2792-
7818; 0800-777-111 (toll-free) (corp headquarters)

B&H Photo Video
420 Ninth Ave, New York, NY 10001
Tel: 212-444-5000; 212-444-6615
Toll Free Tel: 800-606-6969 *Fax:* 212-239-7770
Toll Free Fax: 800-947-7008
Web Site: www.bhphotovideo.com
Key Personnel
Pres: Samuel Goldstein
Founded: 1973
Catalog(s) available

B&H Publishing Group
Division of LifeWay Christian Resources
One LifeWay Plaza, Nashville, TN 37234
Tel: 615-251-2520 *Fax:* 615-251-5004
Web Site: www.bhpublishinggroup.com
Key Personnel
Pres & Publr, LifeWay Christian Resources:
Thom S Rainer
VP, Intl Sales: Craig Featherstone
VP, Mktg: Dave Schroeder
Founded: 1934
Publisher of Bible-centered content, including re-
ligious & children's programming on DVD.
Online catalog(s) available

B&K AV Ltd
Division of Amplifier Technologies Inc
140-12031 Horsheshoe Way, Richmond, BC V7A
4V4, Canada
Tel: 604-274-7711 (intl) *Toll Free Tel:* 800-949-
3344 (US) *Fax:* 323-278-0083
E-mail: info@bandkav.com
Web Site: www.bandkav.com
Founded: 1981
Manufacturer of high-end audio & home theater
components.

Bang! Pictures Inc
78 Graterford Rd, Schwenksville, PA 19473
Tel: 610-357-1015
Web Site: www.bangpictures.com
Key Personnel
Exec Prodr & Dir: Mark Eaton *E-mail:* mark@
bangpictures.com; John Swarr *Tel:* 610-888-
5656 *E-mail:* john@bangpictures.com
Dir: Gerry Creighton

The Banquet Sound Studios
5870 McFarland Rd, Sebastopol, CA 95472
Tel: 707-823-3500
E-mail: main@banquetstudios.com
Web Site: www.banquetstudios.com
Key Personnel
Owner & Prodr: Warren Dennis Kahn
E-mail: warren@banquetstudios.com
Mgr: Shanin Jones
Digital audio recording studio.
Membership(s): AES; The Recording Academy

Barber Tech Video Products
5111 Via Corona St, East Los Angeles, CA
90022
Tel: 818-982-7775
E-mail: info@barbertvp.com; info@barbertech.
com
Key Personnel
Owner: Eddie Barber *E-mail:* eddie@barbertvp.
com

Barbizon Electric Co Inc
456 W 55 St, New York, NY 10019-4403
Tel: 212-586-1620 *Toll Free Tel:* 800-582-9941
Fax: 212-247-8818
E-mail: benysales@barbizon.com
Web Site: www.barbizon.com

Key Personnel
Dir, Intl Sales: Michael Lieberman
Sales Mgr: Danny Quiles
Founded: 1947
Sales, service, installation & integration of lighting equipment & accessories for the performing
arts, themed environments, live productions,
film & television.
Branch Office(s)
1320 S Priest Dr, Suite 105, Tempe, AZ
85281, Sales & Off Mgr: Mark Schneider *Tel:* 480-237-0470 *Fax:* 480-237-0475
E-mail: bwrsales@barbizon.com
8269 E 23 Ave, Suite 111, Denver, CO 80238,
Gen Mgr: Rick Loudenberg *Tel:* 303-394-
9875 *Fax:* 303-355-5996 *E-mail:* bwrsales@
barbizon.com
11551 Interchange Circle S, Miramar, FL 33025,
Gen Mgr: Nick Cohen *Tel:* 954-919-6495
Fax: 954-919-6606 *E-mail:* flasales@barbizon.
com
3309 Bartlett Blvd, Orlando, FL 32811, Systems Mgr: Drew Bongiorno *Tel:* 407-999-2647
Fax: 407-999-7685 *E-mail:* flasales@barbizon.
com
1483 Chattahoochee Ave NW, Suite D, Atlanta,
GA 30318, Contact: Damian Vaudo *Tel:* 404-
681-5124 *Fax:* 404-681-5315 *E-mail:* atlsales@
barbizon.com
2525 N Elston Ave, Suite D220, Chicago, IL
60647, Sales & New Busn Devt Mgr: Mike
Moore *Tel:* 773-276-8500 *Fax:* 773-276-8504
E-mail: chisales@barbizon.com
3 Draper St, Woburn, MA 01801, Gen Mgr: Peter
McNamee *Tel:* 781-935-3920 *Fax:* 781-935-
9273 *E-mail:* blonesales@barbizon.com
1016 McClelland Ct, Charlotte, NC 28206,
Contact: Jeff Montgomerie *Tel:* 704-372-
2122 *Fax:* 704-372-7422 *E-mail:* charsales@
barbizon.com
2225 E Beltline Rd, Suite 309, Carrollton,
TX 75006, Gen Mgr: Rick Loundenberg
Tel: 972-416-9930 *Fax:* 972-416-9924
E-mail: bwrsales@barbizon.com
6437 G General Greenway, Alexandria, VA
22312, Gen Mgr: Tom Madden *Tel:* 703-750-
3900 *Fax:* 703-750-1448 *E-mail:* capitolsales@
barbizon.com
Foreign Office(s): Barbizon Australia Pty Ltd, 652
Botany Rd, Alexandria, NSW 2015, Australia,
Contact: Marshall Harrington *Tel:* (02) 9700
9590 *E-mail:* australia@barbizon.com
9/1 Corporation Rd, Ashmore, Qld 4214, Australia, Contact: Marshall Harrington *Tel:* (07)
5564 5000 *E-mail:* queensland@barbizon.com
Melbourne, Victoria 3000, Australia, Contact:
Marshall Harrington *Tel:* (04) 3706 7022
E-mail: victoria@barbizon.com
India, Proj Mgr & Field Servs Tech: Vasanth Kumar *Tel:* 9008628028 (cell) *E-mail:* india@
barbizon.com
The Saracen Industrial Estate, Mark Rd, Unit
12, Hemel Hempstead, Herts HP2 7BJ, United
Kingdom, Gen Mgr: Phil Bullock *Tel:* (01442)
260600 *Fax:* (01442) 243457 *E-mail:* europe@
barbizon.com

Barbizon Lighting Co, see Barbizon Electric Co
Inc

Barco Inc
3059 Premiere Pkwy, Suite 400, Duluth, GA
30097
Tel: 916-859-2500; 678-475-8000
Toll Free Tel: 888-414-7226
E-mail: sales.events.us@barco.com
Web Site: www.barco.com
Key Personnel
Corp Mktg Dir, North America: Tyler West
Tel: 678-512-6107 *E-mail:* tyler.west@barco.
com
Designs & develops visualization solutions for
the medical imaging, media & entertainment,

infrastructure & utilities, traffic & transportation, defense & security, education & training & corporate AV markets.
Branch Office(s)
47817 Fremont Blvd, Fremont, CA 94538 *Tel:* 510-490-1005 *Fax:* 510-490-1151
3078 Prospect Park Dr, Rancho Cordova, CA 95670 *Toll Free Tel:* 888-414-7226
9125 SW Gemini Dr, Suite 200, Beaverton, OR 97008
750 Justin Rd, Rockwall, TX 75087 *Tel:* 214-935-2416

Bardes Products Inc
5245 W Clinton Ave, Milwaukee, WI 53223 *Tel:* 414-354-9000 *Toll Free Tel:* 800-223-1357 *Fax:* 414-354-1921
E-mail: sales@bardes.com
Web Site: www.bardes.com
Key Personnel
Custom Prods Mgr: Scott Hallberg
Founded: 1978
Manufacturer of heat-sealed vinyl envelopes, pouches, production jackets, sleeves etc.
Catalog(s) available, free, annual, by request
Membership(s): Ophthalmic Photographers Society

Barger-Lite
12023 Victory Blvd, Los Angeles, CA 91606 *Tel:* 310-401-0633
E-mail: sales@bargerlite.com
Web Site: www.bargerlite.com
Key Personnel
Owner: Ed Barger
Founded: 2000
Manufacture, sell & rent lighting equipment for motion picture & TV production.

Bill Barnes Video Productions LLC
14238 Honeysuckle Ridge, Matthews, NC 28105-6403
Tel: 704-847-8685
E-mail: bill@bbvp.tv
Web Site: www.bbvp.tv
Key Personnel
Owner: William R Barnes
Prodr: Charlotte Barnes
Founded: 1988

Baron Stage Curtain & Equipment Co Inc
1910 Light St, Baltimore, MD 21230 *Tel:* 410-327-6962 *Toll Free Tel:* 800-249-6464
E-mail: curtains@baronstage.com
Web Site: www.baronstage.com
Key Personnel
Pres: Joe Stelmack
Custom stage curtains for schools, churches & theaters.
Catalog(s) available

Carl Barth Images
PO Box 5325, Santa Barbara, CA 93150-5325 *Tel:* 805-637-0881
E-mail: carlbarthimages@cox.net
Key Personnel
Owner: Carl Barth
Archive of footage 1960-2005 on film, then digital custom stock shots & special projects.

Bartha
600 N Cassady Ave, Columbus, OH 43219 *Tel:* 614-252-7455 *Toll Free Tel:* 800-363-2698 *Fax:* 614-252-7641
E-mail: info@bartha.com
Web Site: www.bartha.com
Key Personnel
Owner & Pres: Dan Bashore
Owner: Tom Gabbert; John Killacky
Founded: 1946

Event planning & production.
Membership(s): Audiovisual and Integrated Experience Association

Bay Photo Lab
920 Disc Dr, Scotts Valley, CA 95066 *Tel:* 831-475-6686 *Toll Free Tel:* 800-435-6686 *Fax:* 831-475-5275
E-mail: support@bayphoto.com (cust serv); sales@bayphoto.com
Web Site: www.bayphoto.com
Key Personnel
Owner & Pres: Larry Abitbol *E-mail:* larry@bayphoto.com
Cust Serv Mgr: Tiffanie Morrasy *E-mail:* tiffanie@bayphoto.com
Catalog(s) available
Membership(s): The Imaging Alliance

Bay Records
3365 S Lucille Lane, Lafayette, CA 94549 *Tel:* 925-284-7797
Web Site: www.bayrec.com
Key Personnel
Owner: Michael Cogan *E-mail:* mcogan@bayrec.com
Audio recording, mastering & CD production.
Catalog(s) available
Membership(s): The Recording Academy

Bay Stage Lighting Co Inc
4008 W Alva St, Tampa, FL 33614 *Tel:* 813-877-1089 *Fax:* 813-875-8837
Web Site: www.baystagelive.com
Key Personnel
Co-Owner & Pres: Yvonne Felicione Justo *E-mail:* yvonne@baystagelive.com
Co-Owner: Brian Justo *E-mail:* brian@baystagelive.com
Dir, Busn Devt: Nicole Justo Idziak *E-mail:* nicole@baystagelive.com
Founded: 1957
Rental & production of stage lighting equipment.

BBC Worldwide Canada Ltd
Subsidiary of British Broadcasting Corp (BBC)
401-409 King St W, 5th fl, Toronto, ON M5V 1K1, Canada
Tel: 416-204-0500
E-mail: canada.sales@bbc.com (sales)
Web Site: www.bbcworldwide.com
Key Personnel
VP, Content Sales: Sandra Murphy
Catalog(s) available

BBC Worldwide Learning
1120 Avenue of the Americas, 5th fl, New York, NY 10036
Tel: 212-339-1700
E-mail: bbcwlearningamericas@bbc.com
Web Site: www.bbcworldwidelearning.com
Rights-cleared video solutions tailored for education, from clip licensing to fully produced short form video segments.

BBE Sound Inc
2548 Fender Ave, Fullerton, CA 92831 *Tel:* 714-897-6766 *Toll Free Tel:* 800-233-8346 *Fax:* 714-895-6728
Web Site: www.bbesound.com
Key Personnel
Chmn: John C McLaren
Pres & CEO: David C McLaren *E-mail:* dmclaren@bbesound.com
Founded: 1985
Audio technology company.
Online catalog(s) available

BC Studio
Affiliate of BC Video Inc
152 W 25 St, 2nd fl, New York, NY 10001

Tel: 212-242-4065 *Fax:* 212-242-4190
E-mail: info@bcvideo.com
Web Site: www.greenscreenproductionnyc.com
Key Personnel
Pres: Bill Cote *E-mail:* bill@bcvideo.com
Founded: 1981
Complete green screen production facitlity including realistic sets; kitchen, living room & dining room: for videos, DVDs, television & DVD authoring. Cameras, video, film & final cut pro-editing.

BCD Associates Inc
2800 NW 36 St, Suite 220, Oklahoma City, OK 73112
Tel: 405-702-6888 *Toll Free Tel:* 800-223-6734
E-mail: salesweb@bcdusa.com; sales@bcdusa.com
Web Site: www.bcdusa.com
Key Personnel
Pres: Diane Howard *E-mail:* diane@bcdusa.com
VP, Devt: Robert Howard
Founded: 1980
Manufacture high resolution video & DVD recorders.
Online catalog(s) available
Membership(s): Association for Computing Machinery; Audiovisual and Integrated Experience Association

The BD Co
PO Box 2048, Chandler, AZ 85225-2048 *Tel:* 480-632-1160 *Toll Free Tel:* 800-704-3072 *Fax:* 480-632-1163
Web Site: bdbackgrounds.com
Manufacturer of professional photography backdrops, background stands & studio accessories.
Catalog(s) available
Membership(s): The Imaging Alliance; PPA

Be Media
9729 Lurline Ave, Chatsworth, CA 91311 *Tel:* 310-725-8500 *Toll Free Tel:* 877-210-7664 *Fax:* 310-725-9500
Web Site: www.bemedia.com
Key Personnel
Pres & CEO: Mohammad Ahmadi
VP, Opers: David Sayah
Founded: 1998
AV & lighting systems integration, design, engineer, install & service. Sales offices located in Atlanta, GA, Columbus, OH, Toronto, ON, CN & Nassau, Bahamas.
Membership(s): International Association of Amusement Parks and Attractions; NSCA; Themed Entertainment Association

BeachTek Inc
480 Osprey Ave, Kelowna, BC V1Y 5A5, Canada
Tel: 778-478-9872
E-mail: info@beachtek.com
Web Site: www.beachtek.com
Key Personnel
Pres: Harry Kaufmann
Founded: 1997
Manufacturer of audio adapters for camcorders.

Beachwood Productions
1500 Mill Creek Ct SW, Marietta, GA 30008 *Tel:* 770-432-6563; 404-324-7271 (cell)
Web Site: www.beachwoodproductions.com
Key Personnel
Contact: Peter Wilcox *E-mail:* beachwoodpeter@gmail.com
Founded: 1985
Full service video production.

Bear Creek Studio & Music Production Inc
6313 Maltby Rd, Woodinville, WA 98072 *Tel:* 425-481-4100 *Fax:* 425-486-2718
E-mail: bearcreek@seanet.com
Web Site: bearcreekstudio.com

Key Personnel
Prodr, Composer & Engr: Joe Hadlock
  E-mail: joehadlock@hotmail.com; Ryan Hadlock *E-mail:* ryanhadlock@hotmail.com
Studio Mgr & Engr: Taylor Carroll
  E-mail: taylor.james.carroll@gmail.com
Busn Aff: Manny Hadlock
  E-mail: mannyhadlock@hotmail.com
Founded: 1977
Music production, licensing & supervision. Full analog & digital studio for music recording.

Beast Atlanta
Division of Deluxe Entertainment Services Group Inc
3399 Peachtree Rd NE, Suite 200, Atlanta, GA 30326-1149
Tel: 404-237-9977 *Fax:* 404-237-3923
Web Site: www.beast.tv
Key Personnel
Mng Dir: Billy Gabor *Tel:* 917-608-7548 (cell)
Sr Creative Ed: Matt Barron; Eddie Kesler
Founded: 1984
Offers content, concept & design creation services in a boutique work environment. Beast is also located in Los Angeles & San Francisco, CA, Chicago, IL, Detroit, MI, New York, NY & Austin, TX.
Membership(s): AICP

Beatty TeleVisual Productions
Division of Beatty TeleVisual Inc
1287 Wabash Ave, Springfield, IL 62704
Tel: 217-787-4747 *Fax:* 217-787-4857
Web Site: www.beattytelevisual.com
Key Personnel
CEO: Wilma Beatty
Pres: Bill Beatty
Admin Asst: Debbie Beatty *E-mail:* debkb@beattytelevisual.com
Founded: 1958
Audio & video equipment sales & rentals.

Russ Beckner Pictures
2100 Heatherwood Ct, Middletown, OH 45042
Tel: 513-422-9552
E-mail: rdbvideo@gmail.com
Web Site: russbeckner.com
Key Personnel
Owner & Exec Prodr: Russ Beckner
Busn Mgr: Jenni Beckner
Founded: 2003

Beekman Books Inc
300 Old All Angels Hill Rd, Wappingers Falls, NY 12590
Tel: 845-297-2690 *Fax:* 845-297-1002
E-mail: beekmanbooks@yahoo.com
Key Personnel
Pres: Michael Arthur
Founded: 1972

Beholder Productions Inc
1769 Old York Rd, Abington, PA 19001
Toll Free Tel: 844-BEHOLD-R (234-6537)
E-mail: info@beholderproductions.com
Web Site: www.beholderagency.com
Key Personnel
Co-Founder, Pres & CEO: Craig Andrews
Co-Founder & COO: Emilia Andrews
Founded: 1999
Integrated marketing agency with specialties in integrated marketing, content development, digital, branding, video & social media marketing.
Membership(s): Alliance for Women in Media; Business Clubs America

Lawrence Behr Associates Inc
Division of LBA Group Inc
3400 Tupper Dr, Greenville, NC 27834

Mailing Address: PO Box 8026, Greenville, NC 27835-8026
Tel: 252-757-0279 *Toll Free Tel:* 800-522-4464
  Fax: 252-752-9155
E-mail: lbagrp@lbagroup.com
Web Site: www.lbagroup.com/associates
Key Personnel
COO & VP, Sales: Mike Britner *E-mail:* mike.britner@lbagroup.com
CTO: Chris Horne *E-mail:* chris.horne@lbagroup.com
Busn Devt: Michael Senn *E-mail:* michael.senn@lbagroup.com
Founded: 1963
Offer infrastructure support services for the wireless communications industry worldwide.

Bel Fuse Inc
Division of Cinch Connectivity Solutions Inc
299 Johnson Ave, Suite 100, Waseca, MN 56093
Tel: 507-833-8822 *Fax:* 507-833-6287
E-mail: ccsorders@us.cinch.com
Web Site: cinch.com
Key Personnel
Pres & CEO: Daniel Bernstein
HR Mgr: Lisa Hanson
Founded: 1960
Manufacturer of RF coax, triax & twinax transmission line connectors, electronic components, fiber optics & cables.
Catalog(s) available

Belar Electronics Laboratory Inc
1140 McDermott Dr, Suite 105, West Chester, PA 19380-4043
Mailing Address: PO Box 1689, West Chester, PA 19380-0055
Tel: 610-687-5550 *Fax:* 610-687-2686
E-mail: sales@belar.com
Web Site: www.belar.com
Key Personnel
CEO: Mark Grant
COO: Erich Meyer
Founded: 1964
Manufacture modulation monitors & related equipment for the broadcast industry. Belar products are used by radio & TV stations globally to monitor broadcast signals with accuracy & reliability. These benefits are also recognized worldwide by manufacturers of transmitters & audio processors, which regularly rely on Belar monitors as test instruments to ensure their products meet specifications.
Membership(s): NAB

Belden Inc
401 Pennsylvania Pkwy, Suite 200, Indianapolis, IN 46280
Tel: 317-818-6300 *Toll Free Tel:* 800-235-3362; 800-BELDEN-1 (235-3361) *Fax:* 317-818-6365
E-mail: info@belden.com
Web Site: www.belden.com
Key Personnel
Pres: Glenn Pennycook
Founded: 1902
Manufactures speciality cables for AV applications.
Online catalog(s) available

Belew Enterprises
524 Vance Dr, Bristol, TN 37620
Mailing Address: PO Box 3167, Bristol, TN 37625
Tel: 423-764-4116
E-mail: bsv@tricon.net
Key Personnel
Pres: Sam B Belew

Bell and Howell LLC
3791 S Alston Ave, Durham, NC 27713

Toll Free Tel: 800-220-3030; 800-792-4782 (cust care)
E-mail: info@bhemail.com
Web Site: www.bellhowell.net
Key Personnel
Pres & CEO: Larry Blue
CFO & COO: Arthur Bergens
SVP, Global Serv Solutions: Jim Feely
VP, Mfg & Engg: Joe Zuech
VP, Mktg: Brian Irish
Founded: 1907
Provider of solutions & services for paper-based & digital messaging.

Bella Faccia Inc
5137 Lawrence Place, Hyattsville, MD 20781
Tel: 202-291-1932
E-mail: contact@bellafaccia.net
Web Site: www.bellafaccia.net
Key Personnel
Pres: Paul Falcon
Founded: 2000
Production design & fabrication for the television, film & theatrical industries.

Bellin Productions
109 Mosher Rd, Glenmont, NY 12077
Tel: 518-472-0037; 914-980-6322 (cell)
  Toll Free Tel: 888-834-5520
E-mail: info@bellinproductions.com
Web Site: www.bellinproductions.com
Key Personnel
Prodr/Dir: Gil Bellin
Video & digital services to corporations & small businesses.

Ben Nye Makeup
3655 Lenawee Ave, Los Angeles, CA 90016
Tel: 310-839-1984 *Fax:* 310-839-2640
Web Site: www.bennye.com
Makeup for theater, film & video.
Catalog(s) available
Online catalog(s) available

Benchmark Media Systems Inc
203 E Hampton Place, Suite 2, Syracuse, NY 13206
Tel: 315-437-6300 *Toll Free Tel:* 800-262-4675
  Fax: 315-437-8119
E-mail: sales@benchmarkmedia.com
Web Site: www.benchmarkmedia.com
Key Personnel
Sales Mgr: Rory Rall
Membership(s): AES; NAMM, the National Association of Music Merchants

Benedetto Guitars
10 Mall Terr, Suite A, Savannah, GA 31406
Tel: 912-692-1400 *Fax:* 912-692-1403
Web Site: www.benedettoguitars.com
Key Personnel
Pres & CEO: Howard Paul *E-mail:* hpaul@benedettoguitars.com
Founded: 1968
Guitar making & consulting.
Online catalog(s) available
Membership(s): Association of Stringed Instrument Artisans; NAMM, the National Association of Music Merchants

Bennett-Watt HD Productions Inc
Affiliate of Bennett-Watt Entertainment Inc
13021 244 Ave SE, Issaquah, WA 98027
Tel: 425-392-3935 *Toll Free Tel:* 800-327-2893
  Fax: 425-526-5851
E-mail: info@bennett-watt.com
Web Site: www.bennett-watt.com
Key Personnel
Pres: Kelly Watt
VP: Jim Watt

Founded: 1978
Complete HD video production services for broadcast, in-house or media. Aerial drone service available.

Benro
Division of MAC Group
75 Virginia Rd, Suite 1, North White Plains, NY 10603
Tel: 914-347-3300 *Fax:* 914-347-3309
E-mail: info@benrousa.com
Web Site: www.benrousa.com
Key Personnel
Pres, MAC Group: Jan Lederman
Photographic tripods, monopods, heads & photographic support gear.

The Bergman Collection of Medical/Technical/Scientific Stock Images
Division of Project Masters Inc
134 Leabrook Lane, Princeton, NJ 08540-3622
Tel: 609-921-0749
E-mail: information@pmiprinceton.com
Web Site: pmiprinceton.com
Key Personnel
Owner & Pres: Richard I Bergman
Owner & VP: Victoria B Bergman

Bergwall Productions Inc
120 N Church St, Suite 106, West Chester, PA 19380
E-mail: info@bergwall.com
Web Site: www.bergwall.com
Founded: 1970
Provide training to vocational/career & technical education teachers & students by providing online training videos & DVDs.
Online catalog(s) available

Berke Creative Inc
50 Mendell St, Suite 11, San Francisco, CA 94124
Tel: 415-312-2476
Web Site: www.berkecreative.com
Key Personnel
CEO: Stephen Berke *E-mail:* stephen@berkecreative.com
Founded: 1970

Berkeley Sound Artists Inc
2600 Tenth St, Suite 312, Berkeley, CA 94710
Tel: 510-486-2290
E-mail: info@berkeleysoundartists.com
Web Site: www.berkeleysoundartists.com
Key Personnel
Pres: James LeBrecht
Founded: 1996
Full service post-production audio facility serving film, television, multimedia, corporate, exhibition & music. Audio forensics & media transfers.
Membership(s): IDA; San Francisco Film Society

Bernie's Photo Center
525 E Ohio St, Pittsburgh, PA 15212
Tel: 412-231-1717 *Toll Free Tel:* 800-346-8884
Fax: 412-231-1217
E-mail: berniesphotocenter.info@gmail.com
Web Site: www.berniesphoto.com
Key Personnel
Pres: Bruce M Klein
Off Mgr: Donna Downie
Founded: 1958
Photographic equipment & supplies.
Online catalog(s) available

Berry & Homer
2035 Richmond St, Philadelphia, PA 19125
Tel: 215-425-0888
Web Site: www.berryandhomer.com

Key Personnel
Pres: Brett Roe
Dir, Opers: Melissa DeLicci
Prod Mgr: Ralph Frangipani
Sales Mgr: Eric J Shields *E-mail:* eric.shields@berryandhomer.com
Founded: 1898
Large format digital printing, fabrication & installation.
Branch Office(s)
4390 Parliament Place, Suite G, Lanham, MD 20706, Gen Mgr, Sales: Jared Selles *Tel:* 301-459-4500
Membership(s): EDPA

Daniel Bertolino Inc, see Les Productions Via Le Monde (Daniel Bertolino) Inc

BES Studios
5711 Old Osbourne Tpke, Henrico, VA 23231
Tel: 804-276-0806 *Toll Free Tel:* 800-995-2371
E-mail: info@besstudios.com
Web Site: www.besstudios.com
Key Personnel
Exec Prodr: Mark Remes *E-mail:* mark@besstudios.com

Beseler Photo
Division of Charles Beseler Co
2018 W Main St, Stroudsburg, PA 18360
Mailing Address: PO Box 431, Stroudsburg, PA 18360
Toll Free Tel: 800-237-3537 *Toll Free Fax:* 800-966-4515
Web Site: www.beselerphoto.com
Key Personnel
Pres: Bob Deinarowicz *E-mail:* bob@beseler.com
Membership(s): Society for Photographic Education

Best Film & Video
3913 Fall Wheat Dr, Plano, TX 75075
Tel: 214-395-4070
Web Site: www.bestfilmandvideo.com
Key Personnel
Owner: Alan J Lefebvre *E-mail:* alan@bestfilmandvideo.com
Turnkey film & video production, all formats. Individual services include: acquisition, writing & editing. Production in HD.

Bestek Lighting & Staging
98 Mahan St, West Babylon, NY 11704
Tel: 631-643-0707 *Fax:* 631-643-0764
E-mail: production@bestek.com
Web Site: www.bestek.com
Key Personnel
Pres: Abott Finkle
Gen Mgr: Kevin O'Brian
Membership(s): International Live Events Association; MPI; Professional Lighting & Sound Association

Bestwell Optical Instrument Corp
46 Henry St, Merrick, NY 11566
Tel: 516-889-1178 *Fax:* 516-706-1744
Web Site: www.bestwelloptical.com
Key Personnel
Founder & Inventor: Murray Rosenberg
Pres & CEO: Irene Rosenfeld
VP & COO: Lisa Weingarten
E-mail: lisaweingarten@bestwelloptical.com
Founded: 1950
Manufacture grain focusers & image magnifiers for darkroom photography.

Beta Electronics Inc
318 Bronze, Irvine, CA 92618
Tel: 614-538-8207 *Toll Free Tel:* 800-546-2382
Fax: 614-358-9945 *Toll Free Fax:* 888-329-2382

E-mail: sales@betalaser.com
Web Site: www.betalaser.com
Key Personnel
Pres: Ming Liou
Manufacture laser pointers. Produces electronic interactive whiteboards.
Online catalog(s) available

Bethesda Softworks LLC
Division of ZeniMax Media Inc
1370 Piccard Dr, Suite 120, Rockville, MD 20850
Tel: 301-926-8300
E-mail: info@bethsoft.com; press@bethsoft.com
Web Site: bethesda.net
Key Personnel
Pres: Vlatko Andonov
Publisher of interactive entertainment software.
Catalog(s) available
Membership(s): AES; SMPTE®

Bevilacqua Studios
202 E 42 St, New York, NY 10017
Tel: 212-490-0355 *Fax:* 212-490-0355
Key Personnel
Pres & Prodr: Joe Bevilacqua
E-mail: joebev202@aol.com
Feature film production, writing, creation & commercials.
Membership(s): ASMP

Bexel, an NEP Broadcast Services Company
2701 N Ontario St, Burbank, CA 91504
Tel: 818-565-4322 *Toll Free Tel:* 800-225-6185 (tech support)
E-mail: services@bexel.com
Web Site: bexel.com
Key Personnel
CTO: Tom Dickinson
VP & Gen Mgr, Bexel ESS: Scott Nardelli
VP, Engg & Opers: Edd Bonner
VP, Opers: Craig Schiller
VP, Servs Fulfillment: Kirsten Ballard
Founded: 1981
Provider of broadcast services.
Catalog(s) available
Branch Office(s)
Brexel Dallas/Fort Worth, 1000 Nolen Dr, Suite 100, Grapevine, TX 76051 *Tel:* 972-870-2339
Membership(s): NAB

Bext Inc
1045 Tenth Ave, San Diego, CA 92101
Tel: 619-BEXTINC (239-8462)
Toll Free Tel: 888-BEXTINC (239-8462)
Fax: 619-239-8474
E-mail: bext@bext.com
Web Site: www.bext.com
Key Personnel
CEO: Dennis Pieri
Founded: 1985
Specialize in high quality RF equipment for radio, television & industrial or scientific applications.
Membership(s): NAB

beyerdynamic Inc
56 Central Ave, Farmingdale, NY 11735
Tel: 631-293-3200 *Fax:* 631-293-3288
E-mail: info@beyerdynamic-usa.com
Web Site: north-america.beyerdynamic.com
Key Personnel
Dir: Alan Feckanin *E-mail:* alan@beyerdynamic.com
Founded: 1924
Manufacturer of headphones, microphones & conference systems.
Online catalog(s) available
Data sheet(s) available
Membership(s): AES; NAB; NAMM, the National Association of Music Merchants; NSCA; SBE

BeyerSound & Essay Audio
Division of BeyerSound Computing
PO Box 120442, St Paul, MN 55112-0018
Tel: 651-633-3933
E-mail: info@essayaudio.com
Web Site: www.essayaudio.com
Key Personnel
Owner & Founder: Scott Beyers
Founded: 1989
Audio post-production with focus on live & re-
mote recording.

BIAMP Systems
9300 SW Gemini Dr, Beaverton, OR 97008
Tel: 503-641-7287 *Toll Free Tel:* 800-826-1457
(US & CN)
E-mail: biampinfo@biamp.com
Web Site: www.biamp.com
Key Personnel
Pres & CEO: Rashid Skaf
VP & CFO: Alex Buchanan-Munro
EVP, Corp Devt: Joe Andrulis
VP, Global Sales: Ron Camden
Founded: 1976
Manufacture AV systems & products.
Online catalog(s) available
Membership(s): AES; NSCA

Bias Studios
5400 Carolina Place, Springfield, VA 22151
Tel: 703-941-3333
E-mail: info@biasstudios.com
Web Site: www.biasstudios.com
Key Personnel
Owner, Prodr & Engr: Bob Dawson
Studio Mgr: Gloria Dawson
Founded: 1973
Audio recording, 2 multitrack audio studios.

Biblical Archaeology Society (BAS)
4710 41 St NW, Washington, DC 20016
Tel: 202-364-3300 *Toll Free Tel:* 800-221-4644
Fax: 202-364-2636
E-mail: bas@bib-arch.org; merchandise@bib-
arch.org
Web Site: www.biblicalarchaeology.org
Key Personnel
Publr: Susan Laden
Ed: Hershel Shanks
Prodn Mgr: Heather Metzger
Founded: 1974
A nonprofit, nondenominational educational orga-
nization dedicated to the dissemination of in-
formation about archaeology in the Bible lands.
Online catalog(s) available

Big Apple Films
636 W 28 St, New York, NY 10001
E-mail: info@bigapplefilms.com
Web Site: www.bigapplefilms.com
Key Personnel
Owner: Daniel Dacian *Tel:* 917-386-8322 (cell)
Mng Dir: Corey Scott Rutledge
Film production, camera rentals & accessories.
Editing & color correction services.

Big Deal Custom Casings
100 Durand Rd, Winnipeg, MB R2J 3T2, Canada
Tel: 204-663-4870 *Toll Free Tel:* 800-337-3325
Fax: 204-668-7404
E-mail: info@bigdealcases.com
Web Site: bigdealcases.ca
Key Personnel
Pres: Gary Dealey *E-mail:* gdealey@bigdealcases.
com
Founded: 1976
Design & manufacture custom cases ranging from
aerospace & utilities to theatre & sports clubs.
Specialize in large theatre productions & com-
plete show packaging.
Online catalog(s) available

Big Door
114 Sheldon St, El Segundo, CA 90245
Tel: 310-546-6100 *Fax:* 310-906-4585
E-mail: sales@bigdoor.tv
Web Site: www.bigdoor.tv; www.bigdoorstudio.tv
Key Personnel
Principal, Prodr & Dir: Max Yoffe *E-mail:* max@
bigdoor.tv
Partner & Exec in Charge: Jaromy Siporen
E-mail: js@bigdoor.tv
Sr Prodr & Ed: Tom Herrick
Staff Prodr & Ed: Chip Hiden
Prodn Mgr: Audra Kirk
Founded: 1993
Full service production company. Specialize in
live streaming, video & post-production, web
series & branded entertainment.

Big Event Productions LLC
77 13 Ave NE, Studio 101, Minneapolis, MN
55413
Tel: 612-623-7800
Web Site: www.bigeventpros.com
Key Personnel
Prodr & Tech Dir: Bob Chouinard
E-mail: bobc@bigeventpros.com
Prodr/Video: Steve Friederichsen
Lighting Designer: Ross Gish
Founded: 2003
Video production & event staging company.

Big Film Design
375 South End Ave, Suite 3H, New York, NY
10280
Tel: 212-627-3430
E-mail: info@bigfilmdesign.com
Web Site: www.bigfilmdesign.com
Key Personnel
Owner, Pres & Chief Creative Offr: Randall
Balsmeyer
Founded: 2001
Design & production of title sequences & visual
effects for feature films & television.
Membership(s): DGA; International Cinematogra-
phers Guild; Visual Effects Society

Big Fish Production US
PO Box 782, Bronx, NY 10462-0782
Tel: 347-526-5211
E-mail: bigfishproductionus@gmail.com
Web Site: www.bigfishproductionus.com
Key Personnel
Pres, CEO & Gen Mgr: James Carter
E-mail: jcarter89129@gmail.com
VP: Isaiah M Carter
Gen Mgr: Belinda McCoy
Mixed media company. Specialize in artist devel-
opment & production.
Membership(s): Actors' Equity Association; AS-
CAP; SAG-AFTRA

Big Foot Productions Inc
37-09 36 Ave, Long Island City, NY 11101
Tel: 718-729-1900
E-mail: info@bigfootnyc.com
Web Site: www.bigfootnyc.com
Key Personnel
Owner: Steven Mosovic *E-mail:* steve@
bigfootnyc.com
Prodn Mgr: Marcia Hahn Foley *E-mail:* marcia@
bigfootnyc.com
Prodr & Sound Engr: Paul Turlick *E-mail:* paul@
bigfootnyc.com
Prodr & Writer: Brad Rothschild
Founded: 1994
Video production services.

The Big House Group
17 Waller Ave, Ossining, NY 10562
Tel: 914-944-4011 *Fax:* 914-944-8044
Web Site: www.bighousetv.com

Key Personnel
Pres: Jacqueline Weir *Tel:* 914-589-1660 (cell)
E-mail: jackie@bighousetv.com
Founded: 1993
Emmy award winning production company. AVID
Symphony, creative editorial, graphic design &
visual effects.

Big House Sound Inc
4001 Drossett Dr, Austin, TX 78744
Tel: 512-443-0019 *Fax:* 512-443-0916
Web Site: www.bighousesound.com
Key Personnel
Principal: Roy Kircher *E-mail:* roy@
bighousesound.com; Rod Nielsen *E-mail:* rod@
bighousesound.com
Opers Mgr: Bobby Filarowicz *E-mail:* bobby@
bighousesound.com
Founded: 1991
Specialize in production services for concerts
& corporate events. Provides sound systems,
video production, staging, backline & lighting
equipment.

Big Shoulders Digital Video Productions
875 N Michigan Ave, Suite 3750, Chicago, IL
60611
Tel: 312-540-5400
E-mail: info@bigshoulders.com; sales@
bigshoulders.com
Web Site: www.bigshoulders.com
Key Personnel
Pres: Frank Hanes *Tel:* 312-540-5400 ext 222
E-mail: frankh@bigshoulders.com
VP: Brad Fox *Tel:* 312-540-5400 ext 218
E-mail: bradf@bigshoulders.com
Dir, Photog: Don Murphy
Equip Mgr: Matt Hacker
Intl Sales Mgr: Maria Colapinto
Prodn Mgr: Amy Stewart
Founded: 1995
Specialize in remote video production. Full edit-
ing & post-production services, design & audio
sound engineering. Television studio available.
Webcasting, time lapse video & other addi-
tional services available.

BigFoot Mobile Systems
4015 Blackthorn Dr, Vacaville, CA 95688
Tel: 707-602-5548 *Fax:* 707-602-5549
E-mail: info@bigfootmobilecarts.com
Web Site: www.bigfootmobilecarts.com
Key Personnel
Pres: Doug Solis *E-mail:* doug@
bigfootmobilecarts.com
Creative Servs Coord: Amber Solis
E-mail: amber@bigfootmobilecarts.com
AV equipment sales.

Bil-Jax Inc
125 Taylor Pkwy, Archbold, OH 43502
Tel: 419-445-8915 *Toll Free Tel:* 800-537-0540
Fax: 419-445-0367
E-mail: sales@biljax.com
Web Site: www.biljax.com
Key Personnel
Sr Mktg, Events & Indirect Channels Dir: Jeannie
McCarthy *E-mail:* jeanniemccarthy@biljax.com
Founded: 1946
Manufacturing of scaffold & event products (scaf-
fold, scaffolding towers, Pro-Jax units, staging,
etc).
Catalog(s) available, free, annual, PDF downloads

Bill Bachmann Studios
PO Box 950833, Lake Mary, FL 32795
Tel: 407-333-9988
Web Site: www.billbachmann.com
Key Personnel
Owner & Photog: Bill Bachmann
Studio Mgr: Michele Rene
PR: Bob Schlussler

Founded: 1984
Photography & videography studios.
Membership(s): ASMP; PPA

BingoLewis
5828 N Lombard St, Portland, OR 97203
Tel: 503-223-2224
E-mail: info@bingolewis.com
Web Site: www.bingolewis.com
Key Personnel
Pres: Nancy Anderson
VP: Rob Anderson *E-mail:* rob@bingolewis.com
Video post-production services. Editing, color
grading, DVD & Blu-ray authoring; video edit-
ing suites available.

Biomorph Desks
11 Broadway, Rm 905, New York, NY 10004
Tel: 212-809-4323 *Toll Free Tel:* 888-302-DESK
(302-3375) *Toll Free Fax:* 888-652-7137
E-mail: info@biomorphdesk.com
Web Site: www.biomorphdesk.com
Key Personnel
Pres & Design Dir: Stephen Lawson
Founded: 1978
Ergonomic height-adjustable office/studio fur-
niture designing & manufacturing business.
Showroom located in New York City.
Catalog(s) available

Birds & Animals Unlimited
34145 Pacific Coast Hwy, No 761, Dana Point,
CA 92629
Tel: 661-269-0148 *Toll Free Tel:* 877-542-1355
Toll Free Fax: 866-212-7899
E-mail: california@birdsandanimals.com
Web Site: www.birdsandanimals.com
35mm original stock film of North American &
African wildlife in their natural habitat.

Birns & Sawyer Inc
3039 Roswell St, Los Angeles, CA 90065
Tel: 323-466-8211
E-mail: info@birnsandsawyer.com
Web Site: www.birnsandsawyer.com
Key Personnel
Owner & Cinematographer: Bill Meurer
Dir, Rentals: Jeff Jackson *E-mail:* jjackson@
birnsandsawyer.com
Dir, Sales: Mari Acevedo *E-mail:* macevedo@
birnsandsawyer.com
Online catalog(s) available
Membership(s): SMPTE®

Bisk Education
9417 Princess Palm Ave, Tampa, FL 33619
Toll Free Tel: 800-280-9718
E-mail: media@bisk.com
Web Site: www.bisk.com
Key Personnel
CEO: Michael D Bisk
CFO: William Geary, III
EVP & COO: Joseph Smith
Chief Corp Advisor: Andrew Titen
Chief Growth Offr: Chad Bandy
Gen Coun: Srini Medi
VP & Corp Coun: Alison Bisk
VP, Communs & Culture: Misty Brown
VP, Mktg: Gilles Argivier
Founded: 1971
Online education.
Catalog(s) available

Bismeaux Studios
PO Box 463, Austin, TX 78767-0463
Tel: 512-444-9885
Web Site: www.bismeauxstudios.com
Key Personnel
Studio Mgr: Tyler Merriman *Tel:* 512-444-9885
ext 131 *E-mail:* tyler@bismeaux.com
Founded: 1991

Premier recording facility serving the music, film
& advertising agencies.
Membership(s): The Recording Academy

Bitcentral Inc
4340 Von Karman Ave, Suite 400, Newport
Beach, CA 92660
Tel: 949-253-9000 *Toll Free Tel:* 800-272-4004
(support)
E-mail: sales@bitcentral.com; support@bitcentral.
com
Web Site: www.bitcentral.com
Key Personnel
Founder, CEO, Bd Chair & New Ventures
Lead Advisor: Fred Fourcher *E-mail:* fred@
bitcentral.com
VP, Advanced Technologies: Michael Petersen;
Daniel Pugh
VP, Devt & Quality Assurance: Jonathan Clarke
VP, Opers: Sameer Mohiuddin
VP, Sales Engg: John King
Founded: 1998
Software company that provides efficient media
workflows & customized solutions to maximize
the value of video content. Our Core News™
solution is the No 1 news production platform
in the US reaching millions every day; Central
Control™ provides flexible toolset for master
control operation with modules to execute all
the processes that converge into playout; while
FUEL™, our most innovative & industry-
changing Linear on Demand™ streaming solution, is creating an easy path to new digital
revenue.
Online catalog(s) available

BitFlow Inc
400 W Cummings Park, Suite 5050, Woburn, MA
01801
Tel: 781-932-2900 *Fax:* 781-933-9965
E-mail: sales@bitflow.com
Web Site: www.bitflow.com
Key Personnel
Co-Founder & CEO: Avner Butnaru
Co-Founder & Pres: Reynold Dodson
Dir, Sales: Donal Waide
Founded: 1993
Leading manufacturer of digital Camera Link &
CoaXPress frame grabbers.
Membership(s): Automated Imaging Association;
SPIE

Biway Media
5803 Sovereign, Suite 204, Houston, TX 77036
Tel: 713-271-4036 *Toll Free Tel:* 877-BIWAY DV
(249-2938)
E-mail: info@biwaymedia.com; sales@
biwaymedia.com
Web Site: www.biwaymedia.com
Key Personnel
Mgr: Joseph Wang *E-mail:* joseph@biwaymedia.
com
Founded: 1995
Non-Linear Video Editing (NLE) systems for professional video & film production applications
& turnkey Digital Audio Workstation (DAW)
systems for musicians & audio production applications. Video production services with 20
x 30 studio with light grid & edit suites with
latest NLE & DAW systems. Host 3D animation user groups & daily training sessions for
production tools.
Membership(s): Texas Association of Motion Media Professionals

BJU Press
1430 Wade Hampton Blvd, Greenville, SC 29609
Tel: 864-770-1317 *Toll Free Tel:* 800-845-5731
Fax: 864-271-8151 *Toll Free Fax:* 800-525-
8398
E-mail: bjupinfo@bjupress.com

Web Site: www.bjupress.com; www.
bjupresshomeschool.com
Founded: 1974
Provides K-12 educational materials that are aca-
demically rigorous, develop a biblical worldview, promote critical thinking & inspire a love
of learning.
Catalog(s) available

The Black Academy of Arts & Letters Inc
Dallas Convention Ctr Theater Complex, 1309
Canton St, Dallas, TX 75201
Mailing Address: Dallas Convention Ctr Theater
Complex, 650 S Griffin St, Dallas, TX 75202
Tel: 214-743-2440 *Fax:* 214-743-2451
E-mail: info@tbaal.org
Web Site: www.tbaal.org
Key Personnel
Founder & Pres: Curtis L King
Founded: 1977
Create & enhance awareness & understanding of
artistic, cultural & aesthetic differences utiliz-
ing the framework of African-American arts &
letters.

Black Film Center/Archive
Unit of Indiana University
Indiana University, Wells Library, Rm 044, 1320
E Tenth St, Bloomington, IN 47405
Tel: 812-855-6041 *Fax:* 812-856-5832
E-mail: bfca@indiana.edu
Web Site: www.indiana.edu/~bfca
Key Personnel
Dir: Terri Francis, PhD *E-mail:* francist@indiana.
edu
Off & Fin Asst: Ja Quita Joy Roberts
E-mail: jjrob@indiana.edu
Archivist: Ronda Sewald *Tel:* 812-855-8058
E-mail: rsewald@indiana.edu
Founded: 1981
Collect, preserve & make available historically
& culturally significant films by & about black
people.
Newsletter(s) available, 2 issues/yr, PDF down-
load

Black Media Works
534 21 Ave SW, Calgary, AB T2S 0H1, Canada
Tel: 403-802-0010
E-mail: info@blackmediaworks.com
Web Site: www.blackmediaworks.com
Key Personnel
Prodr & Dir: Darold Black
Writer & Prodr: John Nursall
Videography & non-linear editing, full production
services from script to screen.
Membership(s): Director's Guild of Canada

Black Star Publishing Co Inc
333 Mamaroneck Ave, No 175, White Plains, NY
10605
Tel: 212-679-3288 *Fax:* 212-889-2052
Web Site: www.blackstar.com
Key Personnel
Pres: Benjamin J Chapnick
EVP: John P Chapnick
Provide location photography, stock photography
& Internet development.

Blackburst Entertainment LLC
1011 E Colonial Dr, No 304, Orlando, FL 32803
Tel: 321-439-2844
E-mail: contact@blackburstentertainment.com
Web Site: blackburstentertainment.com
Key Personnel
Founder & Pres: Walter Lowe
Founded: 2001
Full service television, film, commercial & video
production company.

Blackmagic Design Pty Ltd
2875 Bayview Dr, Fremont, CA 94538
Tel: 408-954-0500 *Fax:* 408-954-0508
E-mail: info-usa@blackmagicdesign.com
Web Site: www.blackmagicdesign.com
Key Personnel
CEO: Grant Petty
Dir, Mktg: Terry Frechette *Tel:* 408-954-0500 ext
    321 *E-mail:* terryf@blackmagicdesign.com
Head of Communs, Americas: Stephanie
    Hueter *Tel:* 408-954-0500 ext 339
    E-mail: stephanieh@blackmagicdesign.com
Brochure(s) available
Branch Office(s)
333 N Glenoaks Blvd, Suite 250, Burbank, CA
    91502, Video Prod Sales USA, CN & South
    America: Dan May *Tel:* 408-954-0500 *Toll
    Free Tel:* 877-717-5248 *Fax:* 408-954-0508
Foreign Office(s): 11 Gateway Ct, Port Mel-
    bourne, Victoria 3207, Australia *Tel:* (03) 9682
    4770; (03) 9722 9700 (support) *Fax:* (03) 9682
    4790
Brewery International Art Garden, D-1003 fl, Bei-
    huqu, Anwai Beiyuan, Chaoyang District, Bei-
    jing 100012, China, Video Prod Sales: Aaron
    Zhang *Tel:* (010) 5166 1116; (0189) 1123 3633
    (cell)
8F OS Bldg, 3-6-4 Sotokanda, Chiyoda-ku, Tokyo
    101-0021, Japan, Video Prod Sales: Rie Moro-
    hara *Tel:* (03) 5295 5660; (03) 5295 5661 (sup-
    port) *Fax:* (03) 5295 5662 (tech support/ship-
    ping)
4F A2 Tsuruta Keyaki Bldg, 1-1-5 Akasaka,
    Chuo-ku, Fukuoka-shi 810-0042, Japan, Video
    Prod Sales: Yusuke Hata *Tel:* (092) 406 9780;
    (03) 5295 5661 (support) *Fax:* (092) 406 9780
4F Take Bldg 11, 1-9-1 Shinjuku, Shinjuku-ku,
    Tokyo 160-0022, Japan, Video Prod Sales: Rie
    Morohara *Tel:* (03) 5361 6312; (03) 5295 5661
    (support) *Fax:* (03) 5361 6313 (regional sales
    office)
31 Tannery Lane, No 08-01, HB Centre II, Sin-
    gapore 347788, Singapore, Video Prod Sales,
    Asia & Sub-Continent: Richard Lim *Tel:* 6339
    2171 *Fax:* 6339 2172
Mere Hall Business Ctr, Unit 3, Bucklow Hill
    Lane, Mere, Knutsford, Cheshire WA16 6LE,
    United Kingdom, Video Prod Sales: Stuart
    Ashton *Tel:* (01565) 830049 *Fax:* (01565)
    830739
Membership(s): NAB; RTDNA; SMPTE®

Blackstone Audio Inc
31 Mistletoe Rd, Ashland, OR 97520
Toll Free Tel: 800-621-0182 *Toll Free Fax:* 877-
    492-0793
E-mail: libraryservices@blackstoneaudio.com
Web Site: www.blackstoneaudio.com; www.
    blackstonelibrary.com
Key Personnel
Founder & Pres: Craig Black
Founded: 1987
Audiobooks on CD, MP3-CD & digital down-
    load.
Online catalog(s) available

Blackwater Video Productions
PO Box 909, Morgantown, WV 26507
Tel: 304-296-4048
E-mail: blackwatervideo@hotmail.com
Web Site: www.blackwatervideo.com
Key Personnel
Owner & Founder: Daniel McMullen

Michael Blackwood Productions Inc
6 W 18 St, Suite 2B, New York, NY 10011
Tel: 212-242-1805 *Fax:* 212-242-1671
E-mail: blackwoodfilm@aol.com
Web Site: www.michaelblackwoodproductions.
    com
Key Personnel
CEO, Prodr & Dir: Michael Blackwood

Dist Mgr: Elinor Feist
Founded: 1966
Producer of documentaries on the arts. HD equip-
    ment & facilities, complete HD services.

Blair Inc
7001 Loisdale Rd, Springfield, VA 22150
Tel: 703-922-0200 *Fax:* 703-924-0765
E-mail: info@blairinc.com
Web Site: www.blairinc.com
Key Personnel
VP: R Scott Jackson
Founded: 1952

Les Blank Films Inc
10341 San Pablo Ave, El Cerrito, CA 94530-3123
Tel: 510-525-0942
E-mail: lesblankfilmsinc@gmail.com
Web Site: lesblank.com
Key Personnel
Pres: Harrod Blank
Dir & Ed: Gina Leibrecht
Dir & Prodr: David Silberberg
Founded: 1967
Films by Les Blank & others, nonfiction, music,
    art, cooking, filmmaking, folklore, creativity &
    vitality.
Catalog(s) available
Membership(s): American Film & Video Associa-
    tion; International Documentary Association

Blind™
1702 Olympic Blvd, Santa Monica, CA 90404
Tel: 310-314-1618 *Fax:* 310-314-1718
Web Site: www.blind.com
Key Personnel
CEO, Chief Strategist & Exec Creative Dir: Chris
    Do
Creative Dir: Matthew Encina; Greg Gunn
Exec Prodr/Head of Prodn: Scott Rothstein
Digital Dir: Ben Burns
Founded: 1995
Motion graphics studio & design consultancy.

Blonder Tongue Laboratories Inc
One Jake Brown Rd, Old Bridge, NJ 08857
Tel: 732-679-4000 *Toll Free Tel:* 800-523-6049
    Fax: 732-679-4353
E-mail: custsvc@blondertongue.com;
    btglobalsales@blondertongue.com (outside US
    & CN); information@blondertongue.com
Web Site: www.blondertongue.com
Key Personnel
CEO: Robert J Palle *E-mail:* bpalle@
    blondertongue.com
Pres & COO: Ted Grauch *E-mail:* tgrauch@
    blondertongue.com
SVP & CFO: Eric Skolnik *E-mail:* eskolnik@
    blondertongue.com
VP, Engg & CTO: Ronald Alterio
VP, Opers: Allen Horvath
VP, Sales: Jeffrey Smith *Tel:* 732-491-5657 (cell)
    E-mail: jsmith@blondertongue.com
Mgr, Sales & Serv Communs: Liz Rapelye
    E-mail: lrapelye@blondertongue.com
Founded: 1950
Cable television communications, serving the pro-
    fessional video markets with comprehensive so-
    lutions for content contribution, distribution &
    video delivery. The company designs, manufac-
    tures, sells & supports digital video solutions
    & core analog-video as well as high-speed data
    solutions for distribution over coax, fiber & IP
    networks.
Online catalog(s) available

Blood-Horse Publications
Subsidiary of Thoroughbred Owners & Breeders
    Association
3101 Beaumont Centre Circle, Lexington, KY
    40513

Toll Free Tel: 800-866-2361; 800-582-5604
E-mail: advertise@bloodhorse.com;
    customerservice@bloodhorse.com
Web Site: www.bloodhorse.com
Key Personnel
Ed-in-Chief: John Keitt *Tel:* 859-276-6770
    E-mail: jkeitt@bloodhorse.com
News Ed: Frank Angst *Tel:* 859-276-6879
    E-mail: fangst@bloodhorse.com
Founded: 1916
Offer a vast selection of thoroughbred & equine
    publications, products & services.
Online catalog(s) available

Blue Barn Pictures Inc
68 Jay St, Suite 311, Brooklyn, NY 11201
Web Site: www.bluebarnpictures.com
Key Personnel
CEO: Jim Baker *E-mail:* jimbaker@
    bluebarnpictures.com
Creative Dir: David Castillo
Multimedia production company including HD,
    green screen, editing & effects.

Blue Earth Pictures
5532 Code Ave, Minneapolis, MN 55436
Tel: 612-619-5909
E-mail: missioncontrol@blueearthpictures.com
Web Site: www.blueearthpictures.com
Key Personnel
Pres & Dir: James Ankeny *E-mail:* jankeny@
    blueearthpictures.com
Founded: 1990
Pre-production, production & post-production ser-
    vices.

Blue Lotus Temple Studio
PO Box 888, Boulder Creek, CA 95006
Tel: 831-338-2544
E-mail: info@bluelotustemple.com
Web Site: www.bluelotustemple.com
Key Personnel
Art Dir: Penny Slinger
Design & Prodn: Dhiren Dasu
Studio facilities include a chromakey video stu-
    dio/photo studio, control room, vocal booth,
    edit suite, scoring studio & viewing/projection
    lounge. Digital film & video cameras for rent
    on a project basis.

Blue Media Supply Inc
3511 Church St, Suite F, Atlanta, GA 30021
Tel: 404-622-6709 *Toll Free Tel:* 866-717-6334
    Fax: 404-622-1008
E-mail: sales@bluemediasupply.com
Web Site: www.bluemediasupply.com
Distributor of recordable media products, dupli-
    cation equipment, audio video equipment &
    accessories.

Blue Mouse Studio
26829 37 St, Gobles, MI 49055
Tel: 269-628-5160
E-mail: frogville@earthlink.net; mwivi@earthlink.
    net
Key Personnel
Mgr: Chris Buchman
Art Dir: Rex Schneider
Founded: 1979
Creates all manner of illustrations but special-
    izing in children's picture books, classic chil-
    dren's literature & educational material; cel
    animation & backgrounds for filmstrips & ani-
    mated films; title artwork; slides from original
    artwork; computer graphics & also restores
    old photographs. We now offer the following:
    Computer Graphics, Power Point Presentation,
    Storyboards, Art (DVD, CD) Covers, DVD
    Production-enquire.
Catalog(s) available

Blue Onion Media
940 Wadsworth Blvd, 3rd fl, Lakewood, CO 80214
Tel: 303-597-9661 *Fax:* 303-232-2241
Web Site: www.blueonionmedia.com
Key Personnel
VP, Busn Devt: Peter TenEyck *Tel:* 303-232-1100
   E-mail: petert@blueonionmedia.com
Founded: 1985
Online catalog(s) available

Blue River Productions
Subsidiary of Lukacs & Associates
PO Box 1535, Breckenridge, CO 80424-1535
Tel: 970-390-8568
E-mail: filmbreckenridge@gmail.com
Founded: 1990
Handles permits, scouting & locations, hotel accommodations, production support & casting.
Membership(s): Location Managers Guild International

Blue Room Post
MBS Raleigh Studios, Bldg 5-A, Suite 100, 1600 Rosecrans Ave, Manhattan Beach, CA 90266
Tel: 310-727-2600
Web Site: www.blueroompost.com
Key Personnel
Owner: John Harris *Tel:* 310-941-0221 (cell)
   E-mail: john@blueroompost.com
Founded: 2010
DVD & Blu-ray authoring services, 5.1 audio encoding, CD & DVD replication, graphic design, visual effects, offline & online.
Branch Office(s)
Raleigh Studios, Chaplin Bldg, 2nd fl, 5300 Melrose Ave, Hollywood, CA 90038

Blue Sky Stock Footage
PO Box 177, Santa Fe, NM 87504-0177
Tel: 310-859-4709
E-mail: sales@blueskyfootage.com
Web Site: www.blueskyfootage.com
Key Personnel
Owner & Cinematographer: Bill Mitchell
COO: Laurie Schrader
Prodn Mgr: Linda Giella
Founded: 1993
35mm film & HD sourced stock footage available for immediate download: 4K & 1080p HD. Designed to service feature films, commercials, television shows & multimedia productions.

Blue Wave Records
3221 Perryville Rd, Baldwinsville, NY 13027
Tel: 315-638-4286
E-mail: bluewave@localnet.com
Web Site: www.bluewaverecords.com
Key Personnel
Owner: Greg Spencer
Founded: 1985
Artist oriented, non-commercial independent music label with a common thread of blues related music.

Blueyed Pictures Inc
8950 W Olympic Blvd, Suite 324, Beverly Hills, CA 90211
Tel: 310-295-0848
E-mail: la@blueyedpictures.com
Web Site: www.blueyedpictures.com
Key Personnel
Founder & Exec Prodr: Jamee Natella
   E-mail: jnatella@blueyedpictures.com
Founded: 1998
Specialize in creating award-winning commercials, digital branded content, corporate films & multimedia entertainment.
Foreign Office(s): MBE No 316, Atago Green Hills, Mori Tower 1F, 2-5-1 Atago, Minato-ku, Tokyo 105-0002, Japan *Tel:* (0904) 4745 7121
   (cell) *Fax:* (03) 3431 6233 *E-mail:* tokyo@ blueyedpictures.com
77 Beak St, Suite 160, Soho, London W1F 7QP, United Kingdom, Exec Prodr: Chris Ellis
   Tel: (07534) 32 6559 (cell) *Fax:* (020) 8043 2154 *E-mail:* london@blueyedpictures.com
Membership(s): AICP; DGA; Producers Guild of America; Women in Film

BMI Supply
571 Queensbury Ave, Queensbury, NY 12804
Tel: 518-793-6706 *Toll Free Tel:* 800-836-0524
   Fax: 518-793-6181
E-mail: bminy@bmisupply.com
Web Site: www.bmisupply.com
Key Personnel
Pres: Cindy Barber *E-mail:* cindy.barber@ bmisupply.com
Dir, Mktg & Devt: Steve Roudebush
   E-mail: steve.roudebush@bmisupply.com
Sr Sales Mgr: Matt Williams *E-mail:* matt. williams@bmisupply.com
Sales Mgr: Dave Durbin; Paul Martini
   E-mail: paul.martini@bmisupply.com; Mark Ross *E-mail:* mark.ross@bmisupply.com
Founded: 1987
Theatrical supply & installation company that offers stage lighting, rigging, stage hardware, paint, special effects, draperies, stage/studio lamps, intercom & more.
Catalog(s) available, free, annual, US only
Online catalog(s) available
Membership(s): Professional Lighting & Sound Association; USITT

Boeckeler Instruments Inc
4650 S Butterfield Dr, Tucson, AZ 85714
Tel: 520-745-0001 *Toll Free Tel:* 800-552-2262
   Fax: 520-745-0004
E-mail: info@boeckeler.com
Web Site: www.boeckeler.com
Key Personnel
Pres: Pat Brey
Founded: 1942
Manufacturer of precision measuring devices, video measuring & software.
Data sheet(s) available
Membership(s): Audiovisual and Integrated Experience Association; PRSA; RTDNA

Bogen Communications Inc
1200 MacArthur Blvd, Suite 304, Mahwah, NJ 07430
Tel: 201-934-8500 *Toll Free Tel:* 800-999-2809
E-mail: info@bogen.com; customerservice@ bogen.com
Web Site: www.bogen.com
Founded: 1932
Catalog(s) available, free, annual
Membership(s): IPMA; NSCA

Boitnott Visual Communications Corp (BVC)
14201 Justice Rd, Midlothian, VA 23113
Mailing Address: PO Box 655, Midlothian, VA 23113-0655
Tel: 804-379-9400 *Fax:* 804-379-9413
Web Site: www.boitnottvisual.com
Key Personnel
Pres & CEO: Keith Boitnott *E-mail:* kboitnott@ boitnottvisual.com
Founded: 1969
AV rentals, systems integrators & LED projection screen rentals.

Boland Communications Inc
16 Rancho Circle, Lake Forest, CA 92630
Tel: 949-465-9911 *Toll Free Tel:* 800-918-9090
E-mail: sales@bolandcom.com
Web Site: www.bolandcom.com
Key Personnel
Pres: Michael J Boland
Dir, Sales: Gary Litwin
Premium quality LCD monitor manufacturer.
Brochure(s) available, online
Membership(s): Audiovisual and Integrated Experience Association; NAB; SID; SMPTE®

Bolchazy - Carducci Publishers Inc
1570 Baskin Rd, Mundelein, IL 60060
Tel: 847-526-4344 *Fax:* 847-526-2867
E-mail: info@bolchazy.com
Web Site: www.bolchazy.com
Key Personnel
Owner: Marie C Bolchazy, EdD
Pres: Bridget Dean, PhD *E-mail:* bridget@ bolchazy.com
Online catalog(s) available

Bond Street Studio
235 Bond St, Brooklyn, NY 11217
Tel: 718-858-2238
E-mail: info@bondstreetstudio.com
Web Site: www.bondstreetstudio.com
Key Personnel
Owner: Robert DiScalfani
Studio space for film, still photography & music video shoots. Full array of professional camera, lighting & grip equipment available.

Bonnin Electronics Inc
619 Hipodromo St, San Juan, PR 00909
Mailing Address: PO Box 13846, San Juan, PR 00908-3846
Tel: 787-725-4765 *Fax:* 787-725-0840
E-mail: sales@bonninelectronics.com
Web Site: www.bonninelectronics.com
Key Personnel
Pres & CEO: Carlos Bonnin *E-mail:* carlos@ bonninelectronics.com
Founded: 1970
Home entertainment systems, professional multimedia systems & educational systems.
Catalog(s) available

Book Marketing Works LLC
50 Lovely St, Avon, CT 06001
Mailing Address: PO Box 715, Avon, CT 06001-0715
Tel: 860-675-1344
Web Site: www.bookmarketingworks.com
Key Personnel
Pres & Publr: Brian Jud *E-mail:* brianjud@ bookmarketing.com
Book marketing products & services.
Online catalog(s) available
Membership(s): The Association of Publishers for Special Sales; Connecticut Authors & Publishers Association; Independent Book Publishers Association

Books In Motion
Division of Classic Ventures Ltd
9922 E Montgomery Dr, Suite 31, Spokane Valley, WA 99206
Tel: 509-922-1646 *Toll Free Tel:* 800-752-3199
   Fax: 509-922-1445
E-mail: sales@booksinmotion.com
Web Site: www.booksinmotion.com
Key Personnel
Pres: Gary Challender
Founded: 1980
Publish, record & market audiobooks. Distribute & produce MP3 downloads.

Books on Tape™
Division of Penguin Random House Inc
c/o Library & School Servs, 400 Hahn Rd, Westminster, MD 21157
Toll Free Tel: 800-733-3000 *Toll Free Fax:* 800-940-7046
E-mail: csbot@penguinrandomhouse.com
Web Site: www.booksontape.com

Key Personnel
Mktg Dir: Heather Dalton *E-mail:* hdalton@penguinrandomhouse.com
Founded: 1975
Adult, children's & teen unabridged audiobook productions of bestselling, award-winning titles. CDs, digital downloads & flexible standing order plan available.
Catalog(s) available, seasonal

Boonton Electronics
Subsidiary of Wireless Telecom Group Co
25 Eastmans Rd, Parsippany, NJ 07054
Tel: 973-386-9696 *Fax:* 973-386-9191
E-mail: info@boonton.com
Web Site: www.boonton.com
Key Personnel
CEO: Timothy Whelan
CFO: Michael Kandell
Founded: 1947
Manufacturer of test equipment for RF & microwave systems used in both military & commercial sectors. Also manufactures impendance measuring instruments, RF voltmeters & audio analyzers.
Catalog(s) available
Foreign Office(s): Landmark House, Station Rd, Cheadle Hulme, Cheadle, Cheshire SK8 7BS, United Kingdom *Tel:* (0777) 229 0389 *Fax:* (0161) 486 3301 *E-mail:* info.uk@boonton.com

Bosch Security Systems Inc
Subsidiary of Bosch Group
12000 Portland Ave S, Burnsville, MN 35337
Toll Free Tel: 800-289-0096
E-mail: buv.orders@us.bosch.com
Web Site: us.boschsecurity.com
Brands include: Bosch (conferencing & public address), Dynacord (professional audio), Electro-Voice (professional audio), RTS (intercom systems) & Telex (aviation headsets & radio dispatch systems).
Catalog(s) available
Membership(s): AES; NAB; NAMM, the National Association of Music Merchants

Bose Corp
The Mountain, MS 2C3, Framingham, MA 01701-8863
Tel: 508-879-7330; 508-766-6885 (sales outside US) *Toll Free Tel:* 800-999-2673; 800-379-2073 (sales)
E-mail: support@bose.com
Web Site: www.bose.com
Founded: 1964
Audio solutions for the home, office & mobile devices.
Membership(s): AES; ASA; NSCA

Boston Acoustics
Subsidiary of Sound United LLC
One Viper Way, Suite C, Vista, CA 92081
Toll Free Tel: 877-924-5817 (tech/prod support)
Web Site: www.bostonacoustics.com
Founded: 1979
Design & manufacture high-performance loudspeakers, tabletop products & advanced car audio systems.

The Boston Connection Inc
7 High St, Cotuit, MA 02635
Mailing Address: PO Box 1835, Cotuit, MA 02635
Tel: 617-908-6258 *Fax:* 508-428-2036
E-mail: bconnect@cutfilm.com
Web Site: www.cutfilm.com
Key Personnel
Owner: Dwight Cody
Founded: 1983
Film editing equipment supplier.

Boston Light & Sound Inc
290 N Beacon St, Boston, MA 02135-1990
Tel: 617-787-3131 *Fax:* 617-787-4257
E-mail: info@blsi.com
Web Site: www.blsi.com
Key Personnel
Mktg & Off Mgr: Christina Gaita *Tel:* 617-787-3131 ext 103 *E-mail:* christina@blsi.com
Prodn Mgr: Jon Newlander *Tel:* 617-787-3131 ext 114 *E-mail:* jnewlander@blsi.com
Design, installation & integration of sound systems along with film/video projection systems.

Boston Productions Inc (BPI)
290 Vanderbilt Ave, Suite 1, Norwood, MA 02062
Tel: 781-255-1555; 720-233-1250 (sales)
E-mail: info@bostonproductions.com
Web Site: www.bostonproductions.com
Key Personnel
CEO: Robert Noll
EVP, Client Servs: Deb Noll
Head, Opers: Janel Cuneen
Creative Dir: Mark Dorgan
Dir, AV Integration: Dan Lee
Dir, Busn Devt: Candy Moulton
Dir, Post-Prodn: Mike Rafferty
Full service production services.

Bowens USA
Division of MAC Group
75 Virginia Rd, North White Plains, NY 10603
Tel: 914-347-3300 *Fax:* 914-347-3309
Key Personnel
Pres, MAC Group: Jan Lederman
Photographic lighting & light modifiers.

Bowie Audio Visual Enterprises Inc
290 Highpoint Dr, Ridgeland, MS 39157
Tel: 601-957-6566 *Toll Free Tel:* 800-748-9030 *Fax:* 601-957-7042 *Toll Free Fax:* 800-748-3401
E-mail: sales@bowieav.com; info@bowieav.com
Web Site: www.bowieav.com
Key Personnel
Pres: Robert Smylie
Founded: 1976
Sales & rentals of AV equipment.
Catalog(s) available
Membership(s): Audiovisual and Integrated Experience Association

Boxlight Inc
1045 Progress Circle, Lawrenceville, GA 30043
Toll Free Tel: 866-972-1549
E-mail: service@boxlight.com; marketing@boxlight.com
Web Site: mimio.boxlight.com
Key Personnel
CEO & Dir: Mark Elliott
COO: Hank Nance
Pres & Dir: Michael Pope
EVP, Sales: John Patrick Henry
Founded: 1985
AV digital projection equipment for classroom use. Software, touch boards, interactive displays & whiteboards.
Catalog(s) available
Branch Office(s)
19472 Powder Hill Place, Suite 110, Poulsbo, WA 98370
Membership(s): Audiovisual and Integrated Experience Association

Boyce Nemec Designs
PO Box 566, Norfolk, CT 06058-0566
Tel: 860-542-5937
Web Site: www.boycenemec.com
Key Personnel
Principal: Andrew Smith *E-mail:* andy@boycenemec.com
Design & consulting services.

Bradley Broadcast & Pro Audio
Division of SCMS Inc
PO Box 756, New Market, MD 21774
Tel: 301-682-8700 *Toll Free Tel:* 800-732-7665 *Fax:* 301-263-7042
E-mail: beburg@bradleybroadcast.com
Web Site: www.bradleybroadcast.com
Key Personnel
Gen Mgr: Art Reed *E-mail:* areed@bradleybroadcast.com
Audio, RF & broadcast equipment supplier.
Online catalog(s) available

Brady Corp
6555 W Good Hope Rd, Milwaukee, WI 53201-0571
Tel: 414-358-6600 *Toll Free Tel:* 888-250-3082
E-mail: bradyusa@bradycorp.com (cust serv & sales)
Web Site: www.bradyid.com
Key Personnel
Pres, CEO & Dir: Michael Nauman
CFO & Treas: Aaron Pearce
CIO & VP, Digital Busn: Bentley Curran
Pres, Identification Solutions: Russell Shaller
Pres, Workplace Safety: Thomas J Felmer
SVP, Gen Coun & Secy: Louis Bolognini
SVP, HR: Helena Nelligan
Founded: 1914
Manufacturer & marketer of complete identification solutions that help companies improve productivity, performance, safety & security.
Catalog(s) available
Membership(s): Content Delivery & Storage Association

Branam Enterprises Inc
9152 Independence Ave, Chatsworth, CA 91311
Tel: 818-885-6474 *Toll Free Tel:* 877-295-3390 *Fax:* 818-885-6475
E-mail: info@branament.com
Web Site: www.branament.com
Founded: 1978
Theatrical rigging & special effects. Rigging & grip equipment rental, fabrication, special flying effects & stunts. Aerial camera rigs, CM chain motors, truss, curtain track, decks, I-beam track, fall protection & rigging accessories.
Online catalog(s) available

Brantley Sound Associates Inc
115 Duluth Ave, Nashville, TN 37209-1207
Tel: 615-256-6260
Web Site: www.brantleysound.com
Key Personnel
Pres: Bobby Brantley
Gen Mgr/Sales: Keith Beck
Labor & Logistics Mgr: Stephen Beck
Warehouse Mgr/Rentals: Zachariah Orbin
Founded: 1983
Provider of high-end full production services throughout the US & Canada. Specialize in audio, staging, lighting & scenic.

Bravo Studios
40 W 27 St, 2nd fl, New York, NY 10001
Tel: 212-563-0054
E-mail: info@newyorkgreenscreen.com
Web Site: www.newyorkgreenscreen.com
Two film studios with production support. Cameras, lighting & grip equipment as well as video production & post-production services.
Branch Office(s)
145 W 28 St, 2nd fl, New York, NY 10001

BRB Audiovisual Productions
135 Punkup Rd, Oxford, CT 06478-1747

Tel: 203-881-3577 *Toll Free Tel:* 800-587-7521
Fax: 203-828-0732
E-mail: services@brbaudiovisual.com
Web Site: www.brbaudiovisual.com
Founded: 1984
Audio & video production company.
Membership(s): NAB; WEVA

Breeze Productions Inc
1660 Edgewood Rd, Highland Park, IL 60035
Web Site: www.breezeprod.com
Key Personnel
Founder & Pres: Mel Levy *Tel:* 312-860-1710
(cell) *E-mail:* mel@breezeprod.com
Founded: 1993
Full service video production company. Specialize
in corporate visual communications.

Bretford Manufacturing Inc
11000 Seymour Ave, Franklin Park, IL 60131
Tel: 847-678-2545 *Toll Free Tel:* 800-521-9614
Fax: 847-678-0852 *Toll Free Fax:* 800-343-
1779
E-mail: customerservice@bretford.com
Web Site: www.bretford.com
Key Personnel
Pres & CEO: Chris Petrick
Founded: 1948
Design & manufacture AV carts, whiteboards,
mounts & presenters.
Online catalog(s) available
Foreign Office(s): Bretford Manufacturing
Ltd, 2 Eatongate, 110 Windsor Rd, Slough,
Berks, United Kingdom *Tel:* (01753) 539955
Fax: (01753) 539478 *E-mail:* ukmarketing@
bretford.com
Membership(s): Audiovisual and Integrated Expe-
rience Association; Education Market Associa-
tion

Brian Film Productions LLC
254 W 25 St, Suite 6-A, New York, NY 10001-
7325
Tel: 212-645-8795
Key Personnel
Owner: Brian Kellman
Membership(s): New York Women in Film &
Television

Bridge Publications Inc
5600 E Olympic Blvd, Los Angeles, CA 90022
Tel: 323-888-6200 *Toll Free Tel:* 800-722-1733
Fax: 323-888-6202
E-mail: info@bridgepub.com
Web Site: www.bridgepub.com
Founded: 1981
Publish audio books & DVDs of the nonfiction
works of L Ron Hubbard.
Online catalog(s) available
Membership(s): Audio Publishers Association

Bridge Records Inc
200 Clinton Ave, New Rochelle, NY 10801
Tel: 914-654-9270
Web Site: www.bridgerecords.com
Key Personnel
Pres: Becky Starobin
Founder & Dir, Artists & Repertoire: David
Starobin
VP: Robert Starobin
Founded: 1981
Issue CDs, DVDs & digital downloads. Also a
publishing arm & artist management.
Online catalog(s) available

Bridger Productions Inc
4150 Glory View Lane, Jackson, WY 83001
Mailing Address: PO Box 8131, Jackson, WY
83002
Tel: 307-733-7871
E-mail: bridgerproductions@gmail.com

Web Site: www.bridgerproductions.com
Key Personnel
Founder & Pres: Michael Emmer
Prodr: Henry Silverio
Founded: 1990
Full service film & video production company.

Bright Ideas Creative Services
107 W Maple St, Suite 206, Jeffersonville, IN
47130
Mailing Address: PO Box 446, Jeffersonville, IN
47131
Tel: 812-282-9900; 502-693-9900 (cell)
Toll Free Fax: 866-593-5753
Web Site: www.brightideascreative.com
Key Personnel
Owner: William Tyler Thomas *E-mail:* bill@
brightideascreative.com
Founded: 1986
Complete AV production services.

Bright Star Productions Inc
2420 Center St, Houston, TX 77007
Tel: 713-529-2757 *Fax:* 713-529-2329
Web Site: www.brightstarproductions.com
Key Personnel
Prodn Mgr: Malcolm Hackney
E-mail: malcolm@brightstarproductions.com
Provides highest quality production services for
major social events, corporate affairs, concerts,
weddings, fashion shows & fundraising bene-
fits.

Brightline LP
580 Mayer St, Bldg 7, Bridgeville, PA 15017
Tel: 412-206-0106 *Fax:* 412-206-0146
E-mail: information@brightlines.com
Web Site: www.brightlines.com
Founded: 1997
Energy efficient specialty lighting manufacturer.
Light fixtures for broadcast, video conference,
telemedicine, telepsychology, distance educa-
tion (e-learning) & architectural applications.
Catalog(s) available, free, as requested, full line
binder

Brilliance Audio
1704 Eaton Dr, Grand Haven, MI 49417
Tel: 616-846-5256 *Toll Free Tel:* 800-648-2312
(orders) *Fax:* 616-846-0630
E-mail: help@audiobookstand.com
Web Site: www.brillianceaudio.com
Key Personnel
Gen Mgr & Publr: Mark Pereira
Studio Mgr: Brian Pepera
Founded: 1984
Audio publishing; CDs, MP3 CDs & downloads.
Catalog(s) available, consumer; retail; library
products
Membership(s): Audio Publishers Association;
The Recording Academy

Brim Electronics
120 Home Place, Lodi, NJ 07644
Tel: 201-796-2886 *Fax:* 973-778-2792
E-mail: info@brimelectronics.com
Web Site: www.brimelectronics.com
Key Personnel
Sales Mgr: B Brown
Founded: 1975

Britannica Digital Learning
Division of Encyclopaedia Britannica Inc
325 N La Salle St, Suite 200, Chicago, IL 60654
Toll Free Tel: 800-621-3900 *Toll Free Fax:* 800-
344-9624
E-mail: contact@eb.com; bdlpress@eb.com
Web Site: britannicalearn.com
Key Personnel
Chief Prod Offr: Greg Healy

Exec Dir, Instl: Rick Lumsden
E-mail: rlumsden@eb.com
Global educational publisher with online products
that promote knowledge & learning.
Catalog(s) available
Online catalog(s) available

Broadcast Center Studios
700 Millbridge Gardens, Clementon, NJ 08021
Tel: 856-751-3500
Key Personnel
Pres: Larry Scott

Broadcast Devices Inc
Westchester Industrial Complex, 3199 Albany
Post Rd, Suite 122, Buchanan, NY 10511-1639
Tel: 914-737-5032 *Fax:* 914-736-6916
E-mail: sales@broadcast-devices.com; customer.
service@broadcast-devices.com
Web Site: www.broadcast-devices.com
Key Personnel
Owner & Pres: Bob Tarsio *E-mail:* bob@
broadcast-devices.com
Founded: 1985
Equipment for the broadcast industry; RF & au-
dio products, RF monitor protection systems.

Broadcast Electronics
4100 N 24 St, Quincy, IL 62305
Mailing Address: PO Box 3606, Quincy, IL
62305-3606
Tel: 217-224-9600 *Fax:* 217-224-9607
E-mail: bdcast@bdcast.com
Web Site: www.bdcast.com
Key Personnel
Pres & CEO: Tom Beck *E-mail:* tombeck@
bdcast.com
CFO: Becky Keck *E-mail:* bkeck@bdcast.com
VP, Engg: Brian Lindemann
E-mail: blindemann@bdcast.com
VP, Opers & RF Tech Servs: Brent Whelan
E-mail: bwhelan@bdcast.com
HR Mgr: Tina Zanger *E-mail:* tzanger@bdcast.
com
Mktg Mgr & Sr Prod Mgr, Studio Systems: Jim
Roberts *E-mail:* jroberts@bdcast.com
Founded: 1959
Radio broadcast equipment manufacturer.
Online catalog(s) available
Membership(s): NAB; SBE; Texas Association of
Broadcasters

Broadcast Management Group
718 Seventh St NW, Washington, DC 20001
Tel: 202-609-7757
E-mail: info@broadcastmgmt.com
Web Site: www.broadcastmgmt.com
Key Personnel
CEO: Todd Mason
EVP, Prodn: Andrew Ryback
Exec Prodr: Driss Sekkat
Tech Dir: David Roman
Digital Media Prodr: Aaron Eastbrook
Live Series & Broadcast Specials Prodr: Gregory
Branch
Founded: 2005
Television production management services, stu-
dio facility management, remote production
services & social media integration.
Branch Office(s)
2600 W Olive Ave, 5th fl, Burbank, CA 91505
Tel: 310-807-4635
20 W Kinzie St, Chicago, IL 60654 *Tel:* 312-586-
7366
381 Park Ave S, Suite 1214, New York, NY
10016 *Tel:* 212-784-6020

**Broadcast Microwave Services Inc (BMS), a
StoneCalibre company**
12305 Crosthwaite Circle, Poway, CA 92064
Tel: 858-391-3050 *Toll Free Tel:* 800-669-9667
(US) *Fax:* 858-391-3049
E-mail: sales@bms-inc.com

Web Site: www.bms-inc.com
Key Personnel
Pres & VP, Engg: Graham Bunney
Founded: 1982
System customization services including: portable & fixed site microwave communication equipment links & manufacturing.
Online catalog(s) available
Foreign Office(s): In Der Au 19, 61440 Oberursel, Germany *Tel:* (06171) 7408 224; (0177) 7288 304 (hotline)

Broadcast Rentals
2343 W University Dr, Suite 101, Tempe, AZ 85281
Tel: 480-894-1456 *Toll Free Tel:* 888-686-7368
Fax: 480-894-1023
E-mail: rent@broadcastrentals.com
Web Site: www.broadcastrentals.com
Key Personnel
Owner: Deborah Oslund; Steve Oslund
Founded: 1994
Rents broadcast & support equipment. Supply projection, teleprompting, audio & support equipment for corporate meetings & events. Also media duplication & replication services & used gear for sale.

Broadcast Supply World Wide
2237 S 19 St, Tacoma, WA 98405
Tel: 253-565-2301 (intl) *Toll Free Tel:* 800-426-8434 (intl) *Fax:* 253-565-8114 (intl)
Toll Free Fax: 800-231-7055
E-mail: sales@bswusa.com; info@bswusa.com; customersupport@bswusa.com
Web Site: www.bswusa.com
Key Personnel
Pres: Tim Schwieger
Sales Mgr: Shannon Nichols *E-mail:* shannon@bswusa.com
Audio equipment dealer.
Catalog(s) available
Online catalog(s) available
Membership(s): NAMM, the National Association of Music Merchants; SBE

Broadcasters General Store Inc
2480 SE 52 St, Ocala, FL 34480
Tel: 352-622-7700 *Fax:* 352-629-7000
E-mail: sales@bgs.cc (orders)
Web Site: www.bgs.cc
Key Personnel
Pres: Kerry Kerstin
Sales Mgr: Buck Waters *E-mail:* buck@bgs.cc
Sales: Jonathan Shute *E-mail:* jon@bgs.cc
Founded: 1979
Audio & video equipment sales.
Membership(s): NAB; SBE

BroadcastStore.com
9420 Lurline Ave, Unit C, Chatsworth, CA 91311
Tel: 818-998-9100 *Fax:* 818-998-9106
E-mail: sales@broadcaststore.com
Web Site: www.broadcaststore.com
Key Personnel
CEO: Lou Claude
Founded: 1984
New & used professional AV equipment.
Online catalog(s) available
Membership(s): NAB; SMPTE®; STE

Broadstreet Productions LLC
242 W 30 St, 2nd fl, New York, NY 10001
Tel: 212-780-5700
E-mail: newyork@broadstreet.com; admin@broadstreet.com
Web Site: www.broadstreet.com
Key Personnel
CEO & Mng Partner: Mark Baltazar
COO & Partner: Claudia Rodriguez Tressler
CFO & Partner: Ed Gibbons

Deliver strategic communications planning, meetings & events, brand experiences, employee engagement & leadership development, learning & performance improvement programs, digital/social media & creative collateral.

Broadview Software Inc
110 Adelaide St E, Toronto, ON M5C 1K9, Canada
Tel: 647-255-3500 *Fax:* 416-778-0648
E-mail: sales@broadviewsoftware.com
Web Site: www.broadviewsoftware.com
Key Personnel
Pres: Michael Atkin *E-mail:* michael@broadviewsoftware.com
Provide software for television & radio broadcasters with a solution for traffic, scheduling, programming, rights management & ad management.

Broadway Costumes Inc
1100 W Cermak Rd, 2nd fl, Chicago, IL 60608
Tel: 312-829-6400 *Fax:* 312-829-8621
E-mail: rentals@broadwaycostumes.com
Web Site: www.broadwaycostumes.com
Key Personnel
Pres: R C Schramm
Rentals Mgr: Rachel Snypnawski
Founded: 1886
Costume rentals.

Broadway Digital
1014 E Broadway, Louisville, KY 40204
Mailing Address: 1611 Deerwood Ave, Louisville, KY 40205
Tel: 502-540-5301 *Fax:* 502-540-5565
E-mail: msworkscm@mindspring.com
Web Site: www.broadwaydigital.us
Key Personnel
Pres: Charles Miesner
Fiber & satellite uplinks. Additional studio locations in Phoenix, AZ, Indianapolis, IN, New York, NY, Austin, TX & Dallas, TX.

Brodart Co
500 Arch St, Williamsport, PA 17701
Tel: 570-326-2461 *Toll Free Tel:* 888-820-4377
Toll Free Fax: 800-283-6087
E-mail: supplies.customerservice@brodart.com
Web Site: www.shopbrodart.com
Key Personnel
Pres & COO: Robert McAndrew
Founded: 1939
AV equipment, media supplies & cases.
Catalog(s) available
Online catalog(s) available
Membership(s): ALA

Paul H Brookes Publishing Co
PO Box 10624, Baltimore, MD 21285-0624
Tel: 410-337-9580 *Toll Free Tel:* 800-638-3775 (cust serv) *Fax:* 410-337-8539
E-mail: custserv@brookespublishing.com
Web Site: www.brookespublishing.com
Key Personnel
Mktg Dir: Jessica Reighard *E-mail:* jreighard@brookespublishing.com
Founded: 1978
Early childhood education products.
Catalog(s) available, free, annual, books & videos

Brookline Books
8 Trumbull Rd, Suite B-001, Northampton, MA 01060
Tel: 413-584-0184; 603-669-7032 (orders)
Toll Free Tel: 800-666-BOOK (666-2665 cust serv) *Fax:* 413-584-6184
E-mail: brbooks@yahoo.com
Web Site: www.brooklinebks.com
Founded: 1983

Distribute educational programs & ebooks.
Online catalog(s) available

Brooklyn Botanic Garden
1000 Washington Ave, Brooklyn, NY 11225
Tel: 718-623-7200
E-mail: feedback@bbg.org
Web Site: www.bbg.org
Educational programming.

Brooklyn College Television Center
Division of City University of New York (CUNY)
Whitehead Hall, Rm 018, 2900 Bedford Ave, Brooklyn, NY 11210
Tel: 718-951-5585
E-mail: tvcenter@brooklyn.cuny.edu
Web Site: www.bctvcenter.org
Key Personnel
Dir: Jeanine Corbet *E-mail:* jcorbet@brooklyn.cuny.edu
Founded: 1964
TV post-production facility that supports academic functions.

Brooklyn Films
PO Box 20412, New York, NY 10021-0066
E-mail: connect@brooklynfilms.com
Web Site: www.brooklynfilms.com
Key Personnel
Founder & Exec Dir: Michael Helman *E-mail:* michael.helman@brooklynfilms.com
Founded: 1987
Entertainment & technology company.

Brooklyn Fire Proof
119 Ingraham St, Brooklyn, NY 11237
Tel: 718-456-7570
E-mail: hello@brooklynfireproof.com
Web Site: www.brooklynfireproof.com
Rents full service film & television sound & workspaces.

Brooklyn Studios
8-16 43 Ave, Long Island City, NY 11101
Tel: 718-392-1007 *Fax:* 718-392-1008
E-mail: info@brooklynstudios.net
Web Site: www.brooklynstudios.net
Relocated & renovated 15,000 sq ft production facility. Rental studios & equipment for photography, video, film, commercials, music videos & events.

The Brookwood Studio Inc
6870 N Territorial Rd, Plymouth, MI 48170
Tel: 734-358-6071
E-mail: info@brookwoodstudio.com
Web Site: www.brookwoodstudio.com
Key Personnel
Owner, Pres & Chief Engr: David Lau *E-mail:* david@brookwoodstudio.com
Founded: 1978
Fine arts audio recording, including on-location.

Broughton's Church Supplies, Religious Books & Gifts
322 Consumers Rd, North York, ON M2J 1P8, Canada
Tel: 416-690-4777 *Toll Free Tel:* 800-268-4449 *Fax:* 416-690-5357
E-mail: sales@bbroughton.com
Web Site: www.bbroughton.com
Key Personnel
Owner: Brian Broughton
Founded: 1970
Books & AV materials on religious education for church, home & school.
Catalog(s) available, every 5 yrs

Brown United Inc
PO Box 1700, Monrovia, CA 91017-5700

Tel: 626-357-1161 *Toll Free Tel:* 800-44-BROWN (442-7696) *Fax:* 626-358-3064
Web Site: www.brownunited.com
Key Personnel
Pres & CEO: John Brown *E-mail:* john.brown@ brownunited.com
VP: Jeff Llamas
Founded: 1979
AV support (structural) services, concert roofs, staging, seating, scaffolding & more.

Bryston Ltd
677 Neal Dr, Peterborough, ON K9J 6X7, Canada
Mailing Address: PO Box 2170, Peterborough, ON K9J 7Y4, Canada
Tel: 705-742-5325 *Toll Free Tel:* 800-632-8217 *Fax:* 705-742-0882
Web Site: www.bryston.com
Key Personnel
CEO: Christopher Russell
Pres: Brian W Russell
VP, Sales & Mktg: James Tanner
State of the art audio equipment manufacturer.
Online catalog(s) available

BTX Technologies
5 Skyline Dr, Hawthorne, NY 10532
Tel: 914-592-1800 *Toll Free Tel:* 800-666-0996 *Toll Free Fax:* 800-569-4244
E-mail: info@btx.com
Web Site: www.btx.com
Key Personnel
Sr Mktg Mgr: Kim Robbins *E-mail:* kimr@btx.com
Founded: 1967
Distributor & manufacturer of the industry's cutting edge interface & integration products for audio, video & data systems.
Catalog(s) available
Online catalog(s) available
Membership(s): Audiovisual and Integrated Experience Association; Custom Electronic Design & Installation Association; Electronic Components Industry Association; NSCA; SMPTE®

Bud Industries
4605 E 355 St, Willoughby, OH 44094
Tel: 440-946-3200 *Fax:* 440-951-4015
E-mail: saleseast@budind.com
Web Site: www.budind.com
Manufacture enclosures in various materials, small boxes to large racks.
Online catalog(s) available

Billy Budd Films Inc
235 E 57 St, New York, NY 10022
Tel: 212-755-3968
E-mail: info@billybuddfilms.com
Web Site: www.billybuddfilms.com
Key Personnel
Pres: Frank Moynihan
Produce clay animated classics.

Budget Films Stock Footage Inc
706 N Vendome St, Suite 6, Los Angeles, CA 90026
Tel: 323-660-0187 *Fax:* 323-660-5571
E-mail: filmclip@aol.com; info@budgetfilms.com
Web Site: www.budgetfilms.com
Key Personnel
Mgr: Layne J Drebin-Murphy
Founded: 1962
Stock footage library.
Membership(s): Association of Moving Image Archivists

Budget Video Rentals
Division of SuperGroup International
1825 NE 149 St, Miami, FL 33181
Tel: 305-945-8888 *Toll Free Tel:* 800-772-1111 *Fax:* 305-945-0300

E-mail: rentals@budgetvideo.com
Web Site: budgetvideo.com
Rental house for cameras, accessories & production tools.

BUF Technology
12335 World Trade Dr, Suite 11, San Diego, CA 92128
Tel: 858-451-1350 *Fax:* 858-451-6589
E-mail: info@buftek.com
Web Site: www.buftek.com
Key Personnel
Pres: Bruce Bredon
VP, Mktg: Tracey H Bredon
Founded: 1991
Manufacturer of control systems for broadcast & professional television equipment. Instant replay systems, server control, VTR/DDR control & router controls.
Membership(s): NAB; SMPTE®

Buffalo Video Production
233 Fillmore Ave, Suite 8, Tonawanda, NY 14150
Tel: 716-807-1510
Web Site: www.buffalovideoproduction.com
Key Personnel
Chief Creative Offr: Jon Ferrari *E-mail:* jon@ buffalovideoproduction.com
Exec Prodr: Katherine Lucas *E-mail:* katherine@ buffalovideoproduction.com
Sr Media Ed: David Halm *E-mail:* dave@ buffalovideoproduction.com
AV content for television, radio, web sites, social media & print.

Bulbman Inc
630 Sunshine Lane, Reno, NV 89502
Mailing Address: PO Box 12280, Reno, NV 89510-2280
Tel: 775-788-5661 *Toll Free Tel:* 800-648-1163 *Fax:* 775-329-6599 *Toll Free Fax:* 800-548-6216
E-mail: service@bulbman.com
Web Site: www.bulbman.com
Key Personnel
CEO: Dee Ann Harn
Replacement bulbs for all projectors; stage & studio lighting.
Branch Office(s)
Bulbman Vegas, 4305 W Post Rd, Las Vegas, NV 89118 *Tel:* 702-364-9000 *Fax:* 702-364-0138 *Toll Free Fax:* 800-548-6216
Bulbman Sacramento, 3101 Orange Grove, North Highlands, CA 95660, Contact: Dennis Curran *Tel:* 916-920-3234 *Toll Free Tel:* 800-648-1163 *Toll Free Fax:* 800-548-6216

Bulbtronics Inc
45 Banfi Plaza N, Farmingdale, NY 11735
Tel: 631-249-2272 *Toll Free Tel:* 800-654-8542 (sales); 800-588-2852
E-mail: sftv@bulbtronics.com
Web Site: www.bulbtronics.com
Key Personnel
Pres & CEO: Bruce R Thaw
SVP: Lee Vestrich
Founded: 1976
Replacement lamps, bulbs & batteries for all applications.
Online catalog(s) available
Branch Office(s)
2210 N Screenland Dr, Burbank, CA 91505 *Tel:* 323-461-6262
9990 NW 14 St, Suite 106, Miami, FL 33172, VP: John Dahdouh *Tel:* 305-704-7163 *E-mail:* jdahdouh@bulbtronics.com
6185 S Valley View Dr, Suite O, Las Vegas, NV 89118 *Tel:* 702-586-9993

Bullfrog Films Inc
372 Dautrich Rd, Reading, PA 19606

Mailing Address: PO Box 149, Oley, PA 19547-0149
Tel: 610-779-8226 *Toll Free Tel:* 800-543-3764 *Fax:* 610-370-1978
E-mail: info@bullfrogfilms.com; video@ bullfrogfilms.com
Web Site: www.bullfrogfilms.com
Key Personnel
Principal, Acqs & Filmmaker Rel: John Hoskyns-Abrahall *E-mail:* john@bullfrogfilms.com
Principal, Mktg & Promos: Winifred Scherrer *E-mail:* winnie@bullfrogfilms.com
VP & Dir, Bullfrog Communities: Alex Hoskyns-Abrahall *E-mail:* alex@bullfrogfilms.com
Graphics Mgr, Writer & DVD Technician: Mark Martelli *E-mail:* mark@bullfrogfilms.com
Off Mgr, Order Processing & IT: Cheryl Gillam Woolley *E-mail:* cheryl@bullfrogfilms.com
Reviews Coord, Outreach & Cust Rel: Stephanie Miller *E-mail:* stephanie@bullfrogfilms.com
Founded: 1973
Educational video & DVD distributor.
Online catalog(s) available
Membership(s): ALA; Consortium of College & University Media Centers; National Association of Media & Technology Centers; PAECT

Richard W Burden Associates
20944 Sherman Way, Canoga Park, CA 91303
Tel: 818-340-4590
Key Personnel
Principal: Richard W Burden
Low power broadcast systems for theatres; equipment & facilities consulting.
Membership(s): AES; SBE; SMPTE®

The Bureau for At-Risk Youth
Division of The Guidance Group
40 Aero Rd, Suite 2, Bohemia, NY 11716
Toll Free Tel: 800-99-YOUTH (999-6884) *Fax:* 631-389-2511 *Toll Free Fax:* 800-262-1886
Web Site: www.guidance-group.com; www.at-risk.com
Educational publishing company that develops guidance & health videos, DVD games, activity books, curricula, pamphlets & print materials for the K-12 school market.
Catalog(s) available
Online catalog(s) available

Burk Technology Inc
7 Beaver Brook Rd, Littleton, MA 01460
Tel: 978-486-0086 *Fax:* 978-486-0081
E-mail: sales@burk.com; orders@burk.com; support@burk.com
Web Site: www.burk.com
Key Personnel
Dir, Opers: Kevin Frappier
Dir, Sales: Matt Leland
Founded: 1985
Remote monitoring & control system manufacturer.
Online catalog(s) available

Burlington A/V Recording Media
106 Mott St, Oceanside, NY 11572
Tel: 516-678-4414 *Fax:* 516-678-8959
E-mail: shopping@recordingstore.com
Web Site: www.recordingstore.com
Key Personnel
Pres: Jan Schwartz
Gen Mgr: Tom Marchetti *Tel:* 800-331-3191 ext 122
Founded: 1970
Distributor of pro audio, home audio, headphones, recording & DJ equipment, musical gear, musical instruments, recording media, audio & video tape formats & hard drives. Leading seller of air purifiers. Serving consumers & professionals.

Burrud Productions Inc
468 N Camden Dr, 2nd fl, Beverly Hills, CA
  90210
Key Personnel
Pres & CEO: John Burrud
Founded: 1954
Film & interactive media solutions including
  broadcast & web programs, commercials, exhibition videos, internal communications &
  2D/3D motion graphics.
Branch Office(s)
3620 Long Beach Blvd, Suite C1, Long Beach,
  CA 90807 (prodn facility & billing)

Burst Electronics Inc
PO Box 820, Edgewood, NM 87015
Tel: 505-898-1455
E-mail: sales@burstelectronics.com
Web Site: www.burstelectronics.com
Key Personnel
Pres: Brad Hamlin
Founded: 1985
Manufacture professional video & broadcasting
  equipment.
Online catalog(s) available
Membership(s): NAB; SMPTE®

Burst Video/Film Inc
1104 Alta Ave NE, Atlanta, GA 30307
Key Personnel
CEO: Fran Burst-Terranella
CFO & Secy: Anthony Terranella
Founded: 1981
Membership(s): Georgia Production Partnership;
  NATAS

Business & Legal Reports Inc
141 Mill Rock Rd E, Old Saybrook, CT 06475
Tel: 860-510-0100 *Toll Free Tel:* 800-727-5257
  Toll Free Fax: 800-785-9212
E-mail: service@blr.com
Web Site: www.blr.com
Key Personnel
Pres: Rafael Cardoso
VP, Sales: Beth Greene
Membership(s): Instructional Systems Association

Business Education Films
Division of Paulicia Enterprises
PO Box 449, Clarksburg, NJ 08510-0449
Tel: 732-462-3522 *Fax:* 732-294-0330
E-mail: info@aldenfilms.com
Web Site: www.aldenfilms.com
Key Personnel
Pres: Paul Weinberg
VP: Felicia Weinberg
Films & audios of Israel & Judaica.

Butkowski Digital Imaging (BDI)
2229 Roosevelt Rd, St Cloud, MN 56301
Tel: 320-333-1520
E-mail: info@bdiphoto.com
Web Site: www.bdiphoto.com
Key Personnel
Owner: Joel Butkowski
Contemporary commercial photography.

Butter Tree Studios
32 Merry Lane, East Hanover, NJ 07936
Tel: 973-585-7632 *Fax:* 973-585-7633
Web Site: www.buttertreestudios.com
Film & soundstage rental for video, film & pho-
  tography shoots.

Buttercup Pictures
206 N Bundy Dr, Los Angeles, CA 90049
Tel: 310-869-9405
Web Site: cargocollective.com/buttercup
Key Personnel
Co-Founder, Dir & Visual Effects Supv: Nick
  Bates *E-mail:* nick@buttercuppictures.com

Exec Prodr: Carolyn Bates *E-mail:* carolyn@
  buttercuppictures.com
Specialize in complex 2D animation, CG visual
  effects, live action production & compositing for feature films, commercials & specialty
  venue projects.

Buzzco Associates Inc
33 Bleecker St, New York, NY 10012
Tel: 212-473-8800 *Fax:* 212-473-8891
E-mail: info@buzzzco.com
Web Site: www.buzzzco.com
Key Personnel
Owner, Dir & Prodr: Candy Kugel
Prodr: Marilyn Kraemer *E-mail:* marilynk@
  buzzzco.com
Founded: 1985
Animation production, complete 2D animation.

BZ/Rights & Permissions Inc
145 W 86 St, New York, NY 10024
Tel: 212-924-3000 *Fax:* 212-924-2525
E-mail: info@bzrights.com
Web Site: www.bzrights.com; www.
  thepublicdomainsite.com
Key Personnel
Pres: Barbara Zimmerman *E-mail:* bz@bzrights.
  com
Rights clearance service–books, lyrics, music,
  film & TV clips, photos & art–anything that is
  copyrighted, plus celebrities. Our subsidiary,
  The BZ/Rights Stuff Inc publishes lists of music & literature in the public domain. Articles
  on rights clearance on web site.
Membership(s): Association of Independent Music Publishers; CLEAR; The Copyright Society
  of the USA

C & M Publishing Co
Subsidiary of Curriculum Media Inc
1076 Torrey Pines Rd, Chula Vista, CA 91915
Tel: 619-656-6462
Key Personnel
CEO: Robert Pike *E-mail:* rpike63@aol.com
Children's video programming.
Membership(s): American Checker Federation

C-Ducer/C T Audio
54 Old Lakeside Rd S, Hewitt, NJ 07421
Tel: 973-728-1743 *Toll Free Tel:* 800-282-8346
E-mail: meow54@rocketmail.com
Web Site: www.c-ducer.com
Key Personnel
Owner: Jack Waligora
US distributor for contact microphones.

C Vision Productions
5533 144 Ave NW, Ramsey, MN 55303-5646
Tel: 763-577-1358 *Toll Free Tel:* 888-827-3287
E-mail: laskovideo@yahoo.com
Web Site: www.cvisionproductions.com
Key Personnel
Owner: Chris Laskowski *E-mail:* clasko@
  cvisionproductions.com
Founded: 1990
Multimedia video production company.

CAA, see Creative Artists Agency LLC

Cabbage Cases Inc
1166-C Steelwood Rd, Columbus, OH 43212-
  1356
Tel: 614-486-2495 *Toll Free Tel:* 800-888-2495
  Fax: 614-486-2788
E-mail: sales@cabbagecases.com
Web Site: www.cabbagecases.com
Key Personnel
Sales Mgr: Michael Hannah *E-mail:* mhannah@
  cabbagecases.com

Founded: 1974
Manufacturer of custom shipping & carrying
  cases.

CACI Integrated Communications
Subsidiary of CACI International Inc
14370 Newbrook Dr, Chantilly, VA 20151
Tel: 703-679-4221 *Fax:* 703-679-3434
E-mail: cicinfo@caci.com
Web Site: www.caci.com/cic
Founded: 1985
Video production & duplication.
Catalog(s) available

CAD Audio
6573 Cochran Rd, Bldg I, Solon, OH 44139
Tel: 440-349-4900 *Fax:* 440-248-4904
E-mail: info@cadaudio.com
Web Site: cadaudio.com
Design & manufacture professional microphones
  for stage & studio.
Online catalog(s) available

Cadence Jazz Records
Subsidiary of CadNor Ltd
Cadence Bldg, Redwood, NY 13679
Tel: 315-287-2852 *Fax:* 315-287-2860
E-mail: cjr@cadencebuilding.com; cadence@
  cadencebuilding.com; orders@cadencebuilding.
  com
Web Site: www.cadencejazzworld.com
Founded: 1980
Catalog(s) available

Cadex Electronics Inc
22000 Fraserwood Way, Richmond, BC V6W
  1J6, Canada
Tel: 604-231-7777 *Toll Free Tel:* 800-565-5228
  Fax: 604-231-7755
E-mail: info@cadex.com
Web Site: www.cadex.com
Key Personnel
Mktg Communs Mgr: John Bradshaw *Tel:* 604-
  231-7777 ext 314 *E-mail:* john.bradshaw@
  cadex.com
Founded: 1982
Design & manufacture battery chargers & analyz-
  ers, as well as advanced rapid-test & monitor-
  ing systems.

CADint
5719 Mallardview Way, Elk Grove, CA 95757
Tel: 209-606-0660 *Toll Free Tel:* 800-553-1177
  (sales)
E-mail: support@cadint.com; sales@cadint.com
Web Site: www.cadint.com
Supplier of CAD/CAE software.
Online catalog(s) available

Cahokia Mounds Museum Society
Affiliate of Cahokia Mounds World Heritage Site
30 Ramey Dr, Collinsville, IL 62234
Tel: 618-344-7316 *Fax:* 618-346-5162
E-mail: museumsociety@cahokiamounds.org
Web Site: www.cahokiamounds.org
Key Personnel
Exec Dir: Lori Belknap
Founded: 1976
Online catalog(s) available

Calbor Enterprises Two Inc
10646 Chiquita St, Toluca Lake, CA 91602
Tel: 818-760-3222
Key Personnel
Pres: John Bordeaux
Founded: 1973
Pyrotechnic special effects & design effects for
  film, video, theatrical & concerts & provide
  licensed operator.

Membership(s): Alliance of Special Effects & Pyrotechnics Operators; National Fire Protection Association; National Fireworks Association; Pyrotechnics Guild International

Calculated Industries Inc
4840 Hytech Dr, Carson City, NV 89706
Tel: 775-885-4900 *Toll Free Tel:* 800-854-8075
 Fax: 775-885-4949
E-mail: info@calculated.com
Web Site: www.calculated.com
Key Personnel
Mktg & Commns Mgr: Jennifer Goedde
 E-mail: jenniferg@calculated.com
Founded: 1978
Advanced time-code calculator for film, video & audio editing.
Catalog(s) available
Membership(s): NAB

Calger Lighting Inc
200 Lexington Ave, Suite 434, New York, NY 10016
Tel: 212-689-9511 *Fax:* 212-779-0721
E-mail: sales@calgerlighting.com
Web Site: www.calgerlighting.com
Key Personnel
Pres & Mgr: Carmela Califano *E-mail:* carmela@calgerlighting.com
Founded: 1981
Catalog(s) available

Califone International Inc
9135 Alabama Ave, Suite B, Chatsworth, CA 91311
Tel: 818-407-2400 *Toll Free Tel:* 800-722-0500
 Fax: 818-407-2405 *Toll Free Fax:* 877-402-2248
Web Site: www.califone.com
Key Personnel
Key Accts Mgr: Terry Davis
Mktg Mgr: Scott Evans
Sales & Mktg Mgr: Grace Sun
Founded: 1946
Design, development & manufacturing of AV & supplemental curriculum products for use in education & presentation settings. Product lines include DVD/CD/cassette players; cassette recorders; stereo, monaural & cordless headphones; wired & wireless public address systems; listening centers; record players; computer lab peripherals & other communications wares.
Catalog(s) available
Online catalog(s) available
Membership(s): Audiovisual and Integrated Experience Association

California Communications Inc, see CCI Digital, a DVS Company

California Language Laboratories
6170 Palmero Circle, Cameron Park, CA 95682
Toll Free Tel: 800-327-1147 *Fax:* 530-350-8072
E-mail: info@esltapes.com
Web Site: www.esltapes.com
Key Personnel
Owner & Dir: Barbara Sullivan
Founded: 1980
English as a second language materials from 30 languages. Interactive Citizenship DVDs for the new citizenship exam in 28 languages plus English only. Job seekers DVDs in 22 languages plus English only.
Online catalog(s) available

California Newsreel
44 Gough St, Suite 303, San Francisco, CA 94103
Tel: 415-284-7800 *Fax:* 415-284-7801
E-mail: contact@newsreel.org

Web Site: www.newsreel.org
Key Personnel
COO: Steve Guy
Co-Dir: Cornelious Moore
Nonprofit organization distributing social change educational documentaries to institutional theme markets.
Online catalog(s) available
Sales Office(s): PO Box 3400, Lancaster, PA 17604-3400 *Toll Free Tel:* 877-811-7495
 Fax: 717-285-6363 (order dept & fulfillment ctr)

California Stainless Manufacturing Inc
32 N Wood Rd, Camarillo, CA 93010
Tel: 805-484-1038 *Toll Free Tel:* 888-712-7035
 Fax: 805-484-1030
E-mail: calstainless@aol.com
Web Site: www.calstainless.com
Founded: 1960
Manufacture revolving darkroom doors & stainless steel photographic sinks.
Online catalog(s) available
Catalog(s) available

California Tape Products Inc
Subsidiary of Kollner Corp
PO Box 177, Forest Falls, CA 92339-0177
Tel: 909-794-6524
E-mail: info@caltape.com
Web Site: www.caltape.com
Key Personnel
Pres: David Druck
Supplies magnetic media & related products throughout the nation to the video professional as well as government, education & the entertainment industry.

California Teleprompter
PO Box 13024, La Jolla, CA 92039-3024
Tel: 858-945-2076
E-mail: caprompter@aol.com
Web Site: www.sandiegoteleprompter.com
Key Personnel
Owner: Maia McQuillan
Teleprompter equipment rental & services for Southern California, San Diego, Palm Springs & Orange County.

Callen Photo Mount Corp
185 Sixth Ave, Paterson, NJ 07524
Tel: 973-925-2390 *Toll Free Tel:* 800-225-5360
 Fax: 973-925-9615
Key Personnel
VP: Dennis Callen
Founded: 1938
Manufacture & sale of photo mats & mounting boards to major retailers, small photo retailers & craft stores.
Online catalog(s) available

Calrad Electronics
819 N Highland Ave, Los Angeles, CA 90038
Tel: 323-465-2131 *Fax:* 323-465-3504
E-mail: sales@calrad.com
Web Site: www.calrad.com
Key Personnel
Pres: Robert Shupper
VP, Sales: Alma Munoz
Gen Mgr: Mike Karten
Founded: 1951
Audio video distributor.
Online catalog(s) available

Calumet Carton Co
16920 State St, South Holland, IL 60473
Tel: 708-333-6521
E-mail: info@calumetcarton.com
Web Site: www.calumetcarton.com
Key Personnel
Pres: John Inwood

Sales: Gina Inwood
Founded: 1930
Packaging manufacturer for all industries, including electronics & multimedia.
Catalog(s) available
Online catalog(s) available

Calzone Case Co
225 Black Rock Ave, Bridgeport, CT 06605
Toll Free Tel: 800-243-5152 *Fax:* 203-336-4406
Web Site: www.calzoneandanvil.com
Key Personnel
Pres: Joe Calzone
VP: Vincent Calzone
Corp Strategy & Devt: Don Sessions *E-mail:* don. sessions@calzonecase.com
Founded: 1952
Manufacture reusable shipping, packaging, carrying, storage cases & containers, including: racks, monitor cases, plasma screen cases, video camera cases, audio console cases, etc.
Online catalog(s) available
Branch Office(s)
Anvil Cases, 1242 E Edna Place, Covina, CA 91724, Gen Mgr: Deborah Visokay *Tel:* 626-968-4100 *Toll Free Tel:* 800-359-2684
 Fax: 626-968-1703
Tampa Anvil/Calzone Case Co, 11208 Marvelwood Rd, Tampa, FL 34614 *Toll Free Tel:* 800-243-5152
Anvil/Calzone Case Co, 1430 Bradley Lane, Carrollton, TX 75007, Sales Mgr: Frank Bravico *Toll Free Tel:* 800-852-4983 *Fax:* 972-241-3998
Membership(s): Audiovisual and Integrated Experience Association; NAB; NAMM, the National Association of Music Merchants; Percussive Arts Society

CAM Audio Inc
2210 Executive Dr, Garland, TX 75041
Tel: 972-271-2800 *Toll Free Tel:* 800-527-3458
 Fax: 972-271-1555
E-mail: sales@camaudio.com
Web Site: www.camaudio.com
Founded: 1968
Discount audio, video, sound, media & packaging dealer.
Branch Office(s)
WM Sales, 124 W Fairmeadows, Duncanville, TX 75116 *Tel:* 972-296-2773 *Toll Free Tel:* 800-836-7745 *Fax:* 972-709-1514 *E-mail:* sales@wmsales.com *Web Site:* www.wmsales.com

Camart
6 W 20 St, New York, NY 10011
Tel: 212-691-8840
E-mail: rentals@camart.com
Web Site: www.camart.com
Key Personnel
Owner: John Carriglio
Photography studio rental, including cameras, lighting & accessories.

Cambium Catalyst International, see CCI Entertainment Ltd

Cambridge Documentary Films Inc
3099 Hidden Valley Lane, Santa Barbara, CA 93108
Mailing Address: PO Box 390385, Cambridge, MA 02139-0004
Tel: 617-484-3993
E-mail: info@cambridgedocumentaryfilms.org; mail@cambridgedocumentaryfilms.org
Web Site: www.cambridgedocumentaryfilms.org
Key Personnel
Pres: Carol Belding
Exec Dir: Margaret Lazarus
Prodr: R Wunderlich
Secy: E Shub
Treas: Joan Sawyer
Founded: 1974

Nonprofit production & distribution organizations.
Online catalog(s) available
Membership(s): AMPAS

Cambridge University Press
One Liberty Plaza, 20th fl, New York, NY 10006
Tel: 212-337-5000 *Toll Free Tel:* 800-221-4512;
800-872-7423
E-mail: information@cambridge.org;
customer_service@cambridge.org
Web Site: www.cambridge.org
Key Personnel
Mng Dir, ELT & Americas: Michael Peluse
Distributor of educational & scientific programming.
Online catalog(s) available
Foreign Office(s): University Printing House,
Shaftesbury Rd, Cambridge CB2 8BS, United
Kingdom *Tel:* (01223) 358331
Membership(s): American Association of University Presses; Association of American Publishers

Camcor Inc
2273 S Church St, Burlington, NC 27215
Mailing Address: PO Box 1899, Burlington, NC
27216-1899
Tel: 336-228-0251 *Toll Free Tel:* 800-868-2462
Fax: 336-222-8011 *Toll Free Fax:* 800-298-1181
E-mail: info@camcor.com
Web Site: www.camcor.com
Key Personnel
Pres: Ray E Bailey, Sr
Treas: Glenda Bailey
Founded: 1949
AV, photographic, digital imaging & technology solutions.
Branch Office(s)
1212 Belmont St, Burlington, NC 27215 (warehouse)

Camera Corner Connecting Point
PO Box 248, Green Bay, WI 54305-0248
Tel: 920-435-5353 *Toll Free Tel:* 800-236-4950
(orders) *Fax:* 920-438-0389
E-mail: salessupport@cccp.com; contactus@cccp.com
Web Site: www.cccp.com
Key Personnel
CEO: Rick Chernick
Founded: 1953
Online catalog(s) available
Shipping Address: 529 N Monroe Ave, Green
Bay, WI 54301
Membership(s): Audiovisual and Integrated Experience Association

The Camera Division
7351 Fulton Ave, North Hollywood, CA 91605
Tel: 323-465-7700 *Fax:* 818-997-3802
E-mail: rentals@thecameradivision.com
Web Site: thecameradivision.com
Key Personnel
Gen Mgr: Brad Miller
Rents digital cinema cameras, lenses & support technology for productions of all sizes.

Camera Essentials
91 N Daisy Ave, Pasadena, CA 91107-3705
Tel: 626-844-3722 *Fax:* 323-686-5230
E-mail: info@cameraessentials.com
Web Site: www.cameraessentials.com
Founded: 1987
Manufacture & distributor of Harrison film changing tents, Harrison changing bags & photographic accessories, film equipment & accessories & large format photographic accessories.
Online catalog(s) available

CamMate Systems
425 E Comstock, Chandler, AZ 85225
Tel: 480-813-9500 *Fax:* 480-813-9292
Web Site: www.cammate.com
Key Personnel
Pres: Linda Mitchell
Founded: 1987
Manufacture, sell & service camera cranes & accessories for video & film cameras.
Online catalog(s) available
Membership(s): A2 Production Association; NAB

The Campbell Agency
Hidden Grove Bldg, 12404 Park Central Dr, Suite
222 S, Dallas, TX 75251
Tel: 214-522-8991 *Fax:* 214-522-8997
Web Site: www.thecampbellagency.com
Key Personnel
Agency Pres: Nancy Campbell
E-mail: nancycampbell@thecampbellagency.com
Talent Dir/Voice Over & On Camera
Agent: Sharon Hendricks Howell
E-mail: sharonhowell@thecampbellagency.com
Film/TV & On Camera Agent: Bridgette Poe
Talent Assoc, Kids/Teens Div: Shannon McHale-Horan
Asst, Talent Divisions: Shelby Taylor
Founded: 1989
Full service model/talent agency.
Membership(s): Dallas Producers Association;
Texas Association of Motion Media Professionals; Women in Film

Campus Productions
Division of Campus Group Companies Inc
42 Oak Ave, Tuckahoe, NY 10707
Tel: 914-395-1010 *Fax:* 914-395-1095
E-mail: sales@campusgroup.com
Web Site: www.campusgroup.com
Key Personnel
Pres: Steven Campus
VP, New Busn Devt, Interactive Conferencing
Network: Gina Nelson
Treas: Jordan Campus
Prodr & Dir, Opers: Sanjay Prakash
Video production for product promotion, education & training. Produce corporate meetings.

CamTec Motion Picture Cameras
4221 W Magnolia Blvd, Burbank, CA 91505
Tel: 818-841-8700 *Fax:* 818-841-8777
Web Site: www.camtec.tv
Key Personnel
Rental Dept Mgr: Scott Travers *E-mail:* scott@camtec.tv
Rental Agent: Will Moritz *E-mail:* will@camtec.tv
Founded: 1989
Rents cameras, new & vintage lenses & accessories for the film industry.

Can-Am Merchandising Systems
70 Shields Ct, Markham, ON L3R 9T5, Canada
Tel: 905-475-6622 *Toll Free Tel:* 800-387-9790
Fax: 905-475-1154
E-mail: mail@can-am.ca
Web Site: www.can-am.ca
Key Personnel
Pres: Jerry Pila
Founded: 1979
Modular media furniture manufacturer.
Online catalog(s) available

Canadian American Records
PO Box 808, Lititz, PA 17543-0538
Tel: 717-627-4800
E-mail: canadianamerican@dejazzd.com
Web Site: www.canadianamericanrecords.net;
www.canadianamericanrecordcompany.com

Key Personnel
Owner & CEO: Joey Welz *E-mail:* joeywelz@dejazzd.com
Pres, A&R: Phil Schwartz
VP/A&R Dir: Michael Patrick
VP, Prodr: Gabriel Maciocia
VP & Gen Mgr: David Vann
VP, Catalog: Danny Burden
Tech Dir: Andrew Lingenfelter
Founded: 1958
Record label, publishing, production & CD manufacturing & recording studio.
Catalog(s) available, oldies & current artists
Membership(s): American Federation of Musicians; ASCAP; BMI; The Recording Academy

**Canadian Filmmakers Distribution Center
(CFMDC)**
401 Richmond St W, Toronto, ON M5V 3A8,
Canada
Tel: 416-588-0725
E-mail: info@cfmdc.org
Web Site: www.cfmdc.org
Key Personnel
Exec Dir: Lauren Howes *E-mail:* director@cfmdc.org
Deputy Dir: Genne Speers *E-mail:* genne@cfmdc.org
Dist Coord: Jesse Brossoit
Tech Coord: Edward Fawcett Sharpe
Founded: 1967
Distribute independent short cinema.
Online catalog(s) available

Canadian Learning Co Inc
95 Vansittart Ave, Woodstock, ON N4S 6E3,
Canada
Tel: 519-537-2360 *Toll Free Tel:* 800-267-2977
(CN) *Fax:* 519-537-1035
Web Site: www.canlearn.com
Founded: 1978
Producer & distributor of educational media.
Online catalog(s) available
Membership(s): Educational Media Producers &
Distributors Association of Canada

Canamedia Inc
Division of Magic Lantern Media Inc
1540 Cornwall Rd, Suite 216, Oakville, ON L6J
7W5, Canada
Tel: 416-363-6765 *Toll Free Tel:* 866-999-5292
Fax: 416-363-7834
Web Site: www.canamedia.com
Key Personnel
Pres & COO: Doug Connolly *Tel:* 416-363-6147
E-mail: doug.connolly@magiclanternmedia.com
VP: Brad Schroeder *Tel:* 416-363-5681
E-mail: brad.schroeder@magiclanternmedia.com
Sr Exec Prodr, Content Devt: Daniel D'or
E-mail: dan.or@canamedia.com
Mng Dir, Intl Sales & Acqs: Andrea Stokes
Tel: 416-363-8683 *E-mail:* andrea_stokes@magiclanternmedia.com
Founded: 1978
Television, music & archive film distribution. TV
production. Pump audio music library.
Online catalog(s) available, PDF download
Branch Office(s)
7820 Venture St, Burnaby, BC V5A 1V3, Canada,
VP, Global Sales & Acqs: Bill McGowan
Tel: 604-523-6677 *Toll Free Tel:* 800-665-4121
Fax: 604-523-6688 *Toll Free Fax:* 800-665-2909 *E-mail:* bill.mcgowan@distributionaccess.com
Hilyard Place Bldg A, Suite 120, 560 Main St,
St John, NB E2K 1J5, Canada, Dir, Access
Digital Media: Greg Abrams *Tel:* 506-633-6038 *Toll Free Tel:* 800-595-MPEG (595-6734)

Fax: 506-633-7493 *E-mail:* greg.abrams@
distributionaccess.com
Membership(s): Canadian Film & Television Production Association

Canare Corporation of America
45 Commerce Way, Unit C, Totowa, NJ 07512
Tel: 973-837-0070 *Fax:* 973-837-0080
E-mail: sales@canare.com
Web Site: www.canare.com
Founded: 1983
Manufacture broadcasting cables & connectors including SMPTE hybrid fiberoptic cables & assemblies & panels.
Catalog(s) available
Online catalog(s) available

Canavan Scenic & Light LLC
2440 Dinneen Ave, Orlando, FL 32804
Tel: 407-888-8002
Web Site: www.csandl.com
Key Personnel
CEO: Michael Canavan *E-mail:* mikec@csandl.com
Founded: 1996
Scenery & lighting services for business meetings & trade shows.

Candee Productions Inc
301 W Deer Valley Rd, Suite 7, Phoenix, AZ 85027
Tel: 623-266-3070
Web Site: candeeproductionsinc.wordpress.com
Key Personnel
Proj Mgr & Dir: Rees W Candee
E-mail: rwcandee@gmail.com
Ed & Cameraman: Darren Ito
Ed & Field Audio: Kyle Belousek
Founded: 1979
Full service television production studio.
Online catalog(s) available

C&I An Idea Agency
541 NW First Ave, Fort Lauderdale, FL 33301
Tel: 954-357-3934
E-mail: contact@c-istudios.com
Web Site: www.c-istudios.com
Key Personnel
CEO: Joshua Miller
COO: Ian Dawson
Prodr & Event Dir: Amy Miller
Gen Mgr: Joseph Miller
Chief Mktg Offr: Justin Mein
Mktg Mgr: Ricardo Salazar Vega
Brand Devt Mgr: Sarah Dreyer
Studio Opers: Celina Rose
Pre- to post-production services in the photographic, design, audio & video/film industries.
Branch Office(s)
743 Santee St, Los Angeles, CA 90014 *Tel:* 323-844-3336
716 Broadway, 2nd fl, Baltimore, MD 21231
Tel: 240-893-0177

C&I Studios, see C&I An Idea Agency

Cannon Stage Lighting Inc
7110 Ambassador Rd, Windsor Mill, MD 21244
Tel: 410-298-0636 *Fax:* 410-298-7950
E-mail: cannonstage@gmail.com
Web Site: www.cannonstage.com
Key Personnel
Pres: George Cannon, Jr
Founded: 1981
Provide rental, sales & service of stage light equipment.

Canon USA Inc
One Canon Park, Melville, NY 11747
Toll Free Tel: 800-652-2666
E-mail: pr@cusa.canon.com

Web Site: www.usa.canon.com
Key Personnel
Chmn & CEO: Joe Adachi
Pres & COO: Kazuto Ogawa
EVP, Chief Admin Offr, Gen Coun & Secy: Seymour Liebman
SVP, Busn Imaging Solutions Group: Sam Yoshida
SVP, Imaging Technologies & Communs Group: Eliott Peck
Leading provider of consumer, business-to-business & industrial digital imaging solutions.
Online catalog(s) available

Cantrax Recorders
2119 Fidler Ave, Long Beach, CA 90815
Tel: 562-498-6492
E-mail: cantrax@verizon.net
Key Personnel
Owner & Pres: Richard Cannata
Chief Engr: Martin Carman
All recording services.

Canvys™
Division of Richardson Electronics
40W267 Keslinger Rd, LaFox, IL 60147-0393
Mailing Address: PO Box 393, LaFox, IL 60147-0393
Tel: 508-460-5400 *Toll Free Tel:* 800-291-1344
Fax: 508-460-5470
Web Site: www.canvys.com
Key Personnel
EVP & Gen Mgr: Jens Ruppert
VP, Global Engg: Brian Blanchette
Founded: 1988
Visual technology solutions for customers in a wide array of industries, including: Medical OEM; entertainment & gaming; transportation; automation & industrial; military defense & aerospace; touch screen displays; retail.
Brochure(s) available
Online catalog(s) available
Data sheet(s) available
Branch Office(s)
753 Forest St, Suite 100, Marlborough, MA 01752 *E-mail:* info@canvys.com
Foreign Office(s): Raiffeisenstr 5, 78166 Donaueschingen, Germany *Tel:* (0771) 8300-0 *Fax:* (0771) 8300-80 *E-mail:* info-europe@canvys.com
St Swithin's Ct, Suite 2, One Flavian Rd, Nettleham Rd, Lincoln LN2 4GR, United Kingdom, Sales Mgr: Andrew Perez *Tel:* (01623) 792286 *Fax:* (01522) 545453 *E-mail:* andrew.perez@canvys.com

Canyon Cinema Inc
1777 Yosemite Ave, Suite 210, San Francisco, CA 94124
Tel: 415-626-2255
E-mail: info@canyoncinema.com
Web Site: canyoncinema.com
Key Personnel
Dir: Antonella Bonfanti *E-mail:* antonella@canyoncinema.com
Collection Mgr: Seth Mitter *E-mail:* seth@canyoncinema.com
Founded: 1967
Rental distribution of Super 8mm, 16mm & 35mm films by independent film artists. Also lease those films & their DVD transfers.
Online catalog(s) available

Capitol Christian Music Group
Division of Capitol Music Group
101 Winners Circle, Brentwood, TN 37027
Tel: 615-371-4300 *Toll Free Tel:* 800-877-4443 (sales) *Fax:* 615-371-6980 (sales)
E-mail: ccmgdistribution@umusic.com (sales)
Web Site: www.capitolchristianmusicgroup.com
Key Personnel
Pres & CEO: Bill Hearn

Founded: 1994
Online catalog(s) available

Capitol Records
Member of Capitol Music Group
1750 N Vine St, Hollywood, CA 90028
Tel: 323-871-5001
Web Site: www.capitolrecords.com
Founded: 1942
Hollywood record label.

Caprock Developments Inc
475 Speedwell, Morris Plains, NJ 07950
Mailing Address: PO Box 95, Morris Plains, NJ 07950
Tel: 973-267-9292 *Toll Free Tel:* 800-222-0325
Fax: 973-292-0614
E-mail: info@caprockdev.com
Web Site: www.caprockdev.com
Key Personnel
Pres: Alan Schwartz
Founded: 1953
Supplier of speciality lamps, magnifiers & microscopes, hanna PH, conductivity & ORP (Redux) meters, thickness gages & digital micrometers, anti-moire filters & other measuring devices.
Online catalog(s) available, PDF download
Membership(s): Association for Print Technologies; Epicomm; NACASA; Specialty Graphic Imaging Association

Capron Lighting & Sound Co Inc
278 West St, Needham, MA 02494
Tel: 781-444-8850
E-mail: info@capron.net
Web Site: www.capron.net
Key Personnel
Pres: Richard Larond
Full service special events contractor.

Captain Fiddle Music & Publications
94 Wiswall Rd, Lee, NH 03861
Tel: 603-659-2658
E-mail: cfiddle@tiac.net
Web Site: captainfiddle.com
Key Personnel
Owner: Ryan Thomson
Founded: 1985
Publisher of books packaged with audio & video recordings.
Catalog(s) available, upon request

CaptionMax
2438 27 Ave S, Minneapolis, MN 55406
Tel: 612-341-3566
Web Site: www.captionmax.com
Key Personnel
Founder & CEO: Max Duckler
Pres & COO: Gerald Freda
EVP, Busn Devt: Donna Horn
Dir, Busn Devt: Lindsay Beiriger
Founded: 1993
Closed captioning & audio description production services.
Branch Office(s)
425 W Broadway, No 450, Glendale, CA 91204
Tel: 818-295-2500
1115 Broadway, 12th fl, New York, NY 10010
Tel: 212-462-0060

Captions & Subtitle Services Ltd
5113 S Harper, Suite 2C, Chicago, IL 60615
Tel: 872-222-9057
E-mail: quote@capsubservices.com
Web Site: www.capsubservices.com
Key Personnel
Pres: Angie N Russell
Natl Sales & Mktg Mgr: Terry Thomas

Founded: 2000
Captions & subtitles produced for video, DVD & webcasts.

Cardinal Sound & Video
7510 Rickenbacker Dr, Gaithersburg, MD 20879
Tel: 301-589-3700 *Fax:* 301-740-7820
E-mail: info@cardinalsound.us
Web Site: www.cardinalsoundvideo.com
Key Personnel
Pres: Scott Reidinger
Founded: 1970
Professional sound & video system design, sales, installation & service. Offer sound system rentals for small- to medium-sized events.
Online catalog(s) available
Membership(s): NSCA

Carlton-Bates Co
Subsidiary of Wesco International Inc
3600 W 69 St, Little Rock, AR 72209
Tel: 501-562-9100 *Toll Free Tel:* 866-600-6040
E-mail: customerservicecb@carltonbates.com; sales@carltonbates.com
Web Site: www.carltonbates.com
Founded: 1957
Offers electrical OEM products to the electronic & electromechanical industries.
Catalog(s) available, free
Online catalog(s) available

Carolina Biological Supply Co
2700 York Rd, Burlington, NC 27215-3398
Tel: 336-586-4399 (intl sales) *Toll Free Tel:* 800-334-5551 *Toll Free Fax:* 800-222-7112
E-mail: customer_service@carolina.com; internationalsales@carolina.com
Web Site: www.carolina.com
Key Personnel
Direct Mktg Mgr: Gray Amick
Founded: 1927
Curriculum resources for science classrooms.
Catalog(s) available
Online catalog(s) available
Membership(s): National Science Teachers Association

Carpel Video Inc
429 E Patrick St, Frederick, MD 21701
Tel: 301-694-3500 *Toll Free Tel:* 800-238-4300
Fax: 301-694-9510
Web Site: www.carpelvideoonline.com
Key Personnel
Pres: Andy Carpel *E-mail:* acarpel@aol.com
Sales Mgr: Vicki Fearnow *E-mail:* vfearnow@outlook.com
Founded: 1978
Video production, film & tape transferring, DVD & CD duplication & video tape wholesaling.
Online catalog(s) available

Carr McLean Ltd
461 Horner Ave, Toronto, ON M8W 4X2, Canada
Tel: 416-252-3371 *Toll Free Tel:* 800-268-2123 (CN) *Fax:* 416-252-9203 *Toll Free Fax:* 800-871-2397
E-mail: sales@carrmclean.ca
Web Site: www.carrmclean.ca
Key Personnel
Pres: Paul Barclay
Mktg Mgr: David Gudnason
Purch Offr: Nicole Van Engelen
National library & museum supply distributor, including AV equipment, packaging & supplies.
Catalog(s) available
Online catalog(s) available
Membership(s): ALA; Audiovisual and Integrated Experience Association; NOPA

Carvin Amps & Audio
16262 W Bernardo Dr, San Diego, CA 92127

Tel: 858-751-4884
Web Site: carvinaudio.com
Key Personnel
Pres: Joel Kiesel
VP: Kristen Kiesel Lieurance
Founded: 1946
Professional audio equipment & guitar pedals.
Online catalog(s) available

CAS Video Productions
820 White Marsh Ct, Huntingtown, MD 20639
Tel: 301-674-2000 (cell)
E-mail: info@casvideo.com
Web Site: www.casvideo.com
Key Personnel
Owner: Chris Sciannella *E-mail:* chris@casvideo.com
Founded: 1984
Full service production company.
Membership(s): Television, Internet & Video Association of DC Inc; Women in Film & Video

Case Design Corp
333 School Lane, Telford, PA 18969
Tel: 215-703-0130 *Toll Free Tel:* 800-847-4176
Fax: 215-703-0139
E-mail: sales@casedesigncorp.com
Web Site: www.casedesigncorp.com
Key Personnel
Pres: Roger Ernst
VP, Sales: Paul Lowman
Catalog(s) available, free
Membership(s): Audiovisual and Integrated Experience Association; NAB

Case Logic Inc
6303 Dry Creek Pkwy, Longmont, CO 80503
Tel: 303-652-1000 *Toll Free Tel:* 800-925-8111
E-mail: help.na@caselogic.com
Web Site: www.caselogic.com
Founded: 1984
Online catalog(s) available

Casio America Inc
570 Mount Pleasant Ave, Dover, NJ 07801
Tel: 973-361-5400
Web Site: www.casioprojector.com
Key Personnel
Dir, Prod Mktg: Joseph Gillio *Tel:* 973-361-5400 ext 4145 *E-mail:* jgillio@casio.com
Founded: 1957

Castillo Theatre
543 W 42 St, New York, NY 10036
Tel: 212-941-5800 *Toll Free Tel:* 800-435-7453
Web Site: www.castillo.org
Key Personnel
Mng Dir: Diane Stiles *Tel:* 212-356-8412 *E-mail:* dstiles@allstars.org
Assoc Mng Dir: John Rankin *Tel:* 212-356-8430 *E-mail:* jrankin@allstars.org
Artistic Dir: Dan Friedman *Tel:* 212-356-8450 *E-mail:* dfriedman@allstars.org
Tech Dir: Joseph Spirito *Tel:* 212-356-8406 *E-mail:* jspirito@allstars.org
Founded: 1984
Theatre production company.

Castleview Productions
1100 W 41 St, Austin, TX 78756
Tel: 512-442-9944 *Fax:* 512-442-8823
E-mail: contact@castleviewproductions.com
Web Site: castleviewproductions.com
Key Personnel
Pres & Exec Prodr: Ted Barnhill
Creative Dir: Carter Pagel
Head, Devt: Heather Mansfield
Head, Opers & Prodn: Sonia Anguiano
Head, Post: Dan Towell
Head, Sales & Mktg: Derek Castillo

Founded: 1999
Video, film & interactive media production.

Catapult Films Inc
832 Third St, Suite 303, Santa Monica, CA 90403
Tel: 310-395-1470
Key Personnel
Pres: Lawrence Levy
Prodr: Lisa Josefsberg
Membership(s): DGA; Independent Film Project/West; Writers Guild of America

Catholic Books & Tapes
Subsidiary of Children of Mary
PO Box 350333, Fort Lauderdale, FL 33335-0333
Tel: 954-583-5108 *Fax:* 954-583-5108
E-mail: mascmen7@yahoo.com
Web Site: www.catholicbook.com
Key Personnel
Owner & CEO: John Walsh
Catholic traditional books & conspiracy books on who rules the world.

Cavalcade Productions Inc
PO Box 2480, Nevada City, CA 95959-1948
Tel: 530-477-0701 (outside US & CN)
Toll Free Tel: 800-345-5530 *Fax:* 530-477-0701 (outside US & CN) *Toll Free Fax:* 800-345-5530
E-mail: info@cavalcadeproductions.com
Web Site: www.cavalcadeproductions.com
Key Personnel
Pres: Bruce McCulley
Founded: 1948
Video production & distribution, specializing in programs on psychological trauma.
Online catalog(s) available

Cavanaugh Tocci Associates Inc
327F Boston Post Rd, Sudbury, MA 01776
Tel: 978-443-7871
E-mail: cta@cavtocci.com
Web Site: www.cavtocci.com
Key Personnel
Pres: Douglas Bell
Sr Principal Consultant: Nicholas Browse
Founded: 1975
Acoustical, theatrical & AV consulting firm.

Cavision Enterprises Ltd
2323 Boundary Rd, Suite 210, Vancouver, BC V5M 4V8, Canada
Tel: 604-298-9053
E-mail: info@cavision.com
Web Site: www.cavision.com
Founded: 1993
Design & manufacture a wide variety of accessories for professional cameras.
Online catalog(s) available
Membership(s): NAB

CBC/Radio-Canada
181 Queen St, Ottawa, ON K1P 1K9, Canada
Mailing Address: PO Box 3220, Sta C, Ottawa, ON K1Y 1E4, Canada
Tel: 613-288-6000; 613-288-6445 (newsroom)
Toll Free Tel: 866-306-4636 (CN only)
E-mail: cbcnewsottawa@cbc.ca
Web Site: cbc.radio-canada.ca
Key Personnel
Pres & CEO: Catherine Tait
EVP & CFO: Judith Purves
EVP, CBC: Barbara Williams
EVP, Corp Devt: Claude Galipeau
EVP, Media Technol & Infrastructure Servs: Daniel Boudreau
EVP, Radio-Canada: Michel Bissonnette
VP, Legal Servs, Gen Coun & Corp Secy: Sylvie Gadoury
VP, People & Culture: Marco Dube

Founded: 1936
Broadcast company.
Branch Office(s)
PO Box 3220, Sta "C", Ottawa, ON
  K1Y 1E4, Canada *Tel:* 613-288-6445
  E-mail: cbcnewsottawa@cbc.ca
118 James St N, Hamilton, ON L8R 2K7, Canada
  Tel: 905-524-1985 *E-mail:* hamilton@cbc.ca
117 King St W, Kitchener, ON N2G 1A7, Canada
  Tel: 519-581-1384
251 Dundas St, London, ON N6A 6H9, Canada
  Tel: 519-931-3163 *E-mail:* londonnewstips@
  cbc.ca
43 Elm St, Unit 120, Sudbury, ON P3C 1S4,
  Canada *Tel:* 705-688-3240 *Toll Free Tel:* 800-
  461-1138 *E-mail:* sudburynews@cbc.ca
213 Miles St E, Thunder Bay, ON P7C 1J5,
  Canada *Tel:* 807-625-5000
205 Wellington St W, Rm 4E301-B, PO Box 500,
  Sta A, Toronto, ON M5W 1E6, Canada
825 Riverside Dr W, Windsor, ON N9A 5K9,
  Canada *Tel:* 519-255-3456 *E-mail:* windsor@
  cbc.ca
PO Box 2640, Calgary, AB, Canada *Tel:* 403-
  521-6340 *E-mail:* calgarynewstips@cbc.ca
123 Edmonton City Centre, 10062-102 Ave, Edmonton, AB T5J 2Y8, Canada *Tel:* 780-468-
  2300 *E-mail:* newsedmonton@cbc.ca
700 Hamilton St, Vancouver, BC V6B
  4A2, Canada *Tel:* 604-662-6000
  E-mail: cbcnewsvancouver@cbc.ca (broadcast
  ctr)
541 Portage Ave, Winnipeg, MB R3C 2H1,
  Canada *Tel:* 204-788-3641 *E-mail:* talkback@
  cbc.ca
1160 Regent St, PO Box 2200, Fredericton, NB
  E3B 5G4, Canada *Tel:* 506-451-4000
165 Main St, Suite 15, Moncton, NB E1C 1B8,
  Canada *Tel:* 506-853-6666
Brunswick Sq, 39 King St, Suite A500A, St John,
  NB E2L 4W3, Canada *Tel:* 506-632-7710
PO Box 12010, Sta "A", St John's, NL A1B 3T8,
  Canada *Tel:* 709-576-5225 *Fax:* 709-576-5011
  E-mail: radionews@cbc.ca
5002 Forrest Dr, Yellowknife, NT X1A 2A9,
  Canada *Tel:* 867-920-5465 (news desk); 867-
  920-5449 (Talkback) *Toll Free Tel:* 866-271-
  9957 (Talkback)
6940 Mumford Rd, Suite 100, Halifax, NS B3L
  0B7, Canada *Tel:* 902-420-4100 *Fax:* 902-420-
  4137 *E-mail:* cbcns@cbc.ca
500 George St, Sydney, NS B1P 1K6, Canada
  Tel: 902-563-4100 *Fax:* 902-539-1562
  E-mail: cbcns@cbc.ca
Box 490, Iqaluit, NU X0A 0H0, Canada *Tel:* 867-
  979-6110 (news desk); 867-979-6101 (Talkback) *Toll Free Tel:* 888-896-3135 (Talkback)
PO Box 2230, Charlottetown, PE C1A 8B9,
  Canada *Tel:* 902-629-6403 *E-mail:* compass@
  cbc.ca
PO Box 6000, Montreal, QC H3C 3A8, Canada
  Tel: 514-597-6300 *Fax:* 514-597-7600
  E-mail: assignmentmontreal@cbc.ca
1400 Rene-Levesque E, A-46-60, Montreal, QC
  H2L 2M2, Canada *Tel:* 514-597-4370; 514-
  597-4988 (news desk) *Toll Free Tel:* 877-597-
  4369 *Fax:* 514-597-4501
PO Box 18800, Quebec City, QC G1K 9L4,
  Canada *Toll Free Tel:* 866-691-3620 *Fax:* 418-
  691-3610
2440 Broad St, Box 540, Regina, SK S4P 4A1,
  Canada *Tel:* 306-347-9666 (Regina); 306-956-
  7414 (Saskatoon) *E-mail:* sasknews@cbc.ca
100-128th Fourth Ave S, Saskatoon, SK S7K
  1M8, Canada *Tel:* 306-956-7414; 306-347-9651
  (assignment desk) *E-mail:* sasknews@cbc.ca
3103 Third Ave, Whitehorse, YT Y1A 1E5,
  Canada *Tel:* 867-668-8470 (news desk); 867-
  668-8400 (news desk); 867-668-8460 (listener
  line) *Toll Free Tel:* 877-222-9856 (listener line)
  E-mail: cbcnorth@cbc.ca

CBM Ltd
High Point Business Park, 8750 Holgate Cresent,
  Milton, ON L9T 0K3, Canada
Tel: 905-878-0648 *Toll Free Tel:* 800-387-4834
  Fax: 905-878-6748 *Toll Free Fax:* 888-554-
  5501
E-mail: sales@cbmmetal.com
Web Site: www.cbmmetal.com
Key Personnel
VP, Sales & Mktg: Jeff Williams
Dir, Sales: Bruce Hosker
Sr Proj Mgr: David Bruce
Founded: 1927
Design driven manufacturing. AV mounts, stands
  & accessories for all applications.
Catalog(s) available
Membership(s): Audiovisual and Integrated Expe-
  rience Association

CCH Continuing Education
Division of CCH Inc, A Wolters Kluwer business
2700 Lake Cook Rd, Riverwoods, IL 60015
Tel: 773-866-3648 *Toll Free Tel:* 800-248-3248
  Fax: 773-866-3084
Web Site: www.cch.com
Key Personnel
Mng Ed: Gwen Hefty *E-mail:* gwen.hefty@
  wolterskluwer.com
Tax & legal publications.

CCH Inc, A Wolters Kluwer business
2700 Lake Cook Rd, Riverwoods, IL 60015
Tel: 847-267-7000 *Toll Free Tel:* 888-224-7377
E-mail: press@wolterskluwer.com
Web Site: www.cch.com; taxna.wolterskluwer.com
Key Personnel
VP, Corp Communs: Leslie Bonacum *Tel:* 847-
  267-7153
Founded: 1913
Provider of tax, accounting & audit information
  & software solutions for tax & accounting pro-
  fessionals.
Catalog(s) available
Branch Office(s)
CCH Washington Service Bureau, 1015 15 St
  NW, 10th fl, Washington, DC 20005 *Tel:* 202-
  842-7355 *Toll Free Tel:* 800-289-1057 *Web
  Site:* www.wsb.com
Foreign Office(s): CCH Australia Ltd, 66 Talavera
  Rd, Ground fl, Macquarie Park, NSW 2113,
  Australia *Tel:* (02) 9857 1300 *E-mail:* au-
  support@wolterskluwer.com *Web Site:* www.
  cch.com.au
CCH Asia Pte Ltd, 03-00 Link (THM) Bldg, 8
  Chang Charn Rd, Singapore 159637, Singa-
  pore *Toll Free Tel:* 800-6162-161 *E-mail:* sg-
  support@wolterskluwer.com *Web Site:* www.
  wolterskluwer.com.sg

CCI Communications Inc
643 Swedesford Rd, Malvern, PA 19355
Tel: 610-296-7233 *Fax:* 610-296-7358
E-mail: info@ccivideo.com
Web Site: www.ccivideo.com
Key Personnel
Pres: Kenneth R Selinger
Founded: 1982
Television production with location shooting &
  editing utilizing a mobile production unit.

CCI Digital, a DVS Company
2921 W Alameda Ave, Burbank, CA 91505
Tel: 818-562-6300
E-mail: info@ccidigital.com
Web Site: www.ccidigital.com
Full service post-production facility.
Online catalog(s) available
Membership(s): IAA-VC

CCI Entertainment Ltd
210 St Clair Ave W, 4th fl, Toronto, ON M4V
  1R2, Canada

Tel: 416-964-8750
E-mail: info@ccientertainment.com
Web Site: www.ccientertainment.com
Key Personnel
Co-Founder & Exec Prodr: Charles Falzon; Arnie
  Zipursky
Founded: 2002
Producer & distributor of children's, family, TV
  movies & lifestyle programming.
Membership(s): Canadian Film & Television Pro-
  duction Association; NATPE

CCI Solutions
1342 88 Ave SE, Olympia, WA 98501
Mailing Address: PO Box 481, Olympia, WA
  98507
Tel: 360-943-5378 *Toll Free Tel:* 800-562-6006
  Fax: 360-754-1566
E-mail: info@ccisolutions.com
Web Site: www.ccisolutions.com
Key Personnel
VP, Sales & Integration: Duke DeJong
Systems Opers Dir: Todd Gathany
Founded: 1976
Acoustical consulting, equipment sales, recording
  media & design-build/installation services to
  churches, schools & government agencies.
Online catalog(s) available
Membership(s): NAMM, the National Association
  of Music Merchants; National Systems Con-
  tractors Association

CCore Media Inc
1421 Lowe Dr, Algonquin, IL 60102
Tel: 815-219-0424
Web Site: www.creativecore.com
Key Personnel
Exec Prodr: Robert L Sandidge
Founded: 1982
Media producer, publisher & distributor.
Catalog(s) available
Membership(s): Chicago Area Producers Associa-
  tion; SPARC

CD Meyer Inc
15 Oak Rd, No 202, Fairfield, NJ 07004
E-mail: info@cdmeyer.com
Web Site: www.cdmeyer.com; www.point2explore.
  com; museumdigitalsignage.com
Key Personnel
Pres: Chris Meyer *E-mail:* chris@cdmeyer.com
Founded: 1988
Corporate web site development, digital signage
  content creation, touch screen programs &
  games, exhibit multimedia, DVD & video pro-
  duction services.

The CD Recycling Center of America
68 E Stiles Rd, Salem, NH 03079
Tel: 603-894-5553 *Fax:* 603-898-4319
E-mail: info@cdrecyclingcenter.com
Web Site: www.cdrecyclingcenter.com
Founded: 2006
Founded to promote public awareness of the im-
  portance of recycling CDs & DVDs & their
  packaging. Collection center will accept un-
  wanted & obsolete CDs, DVDs & their packaging. Online information center, with onsite
  collection of materials.

CD ROM™ Inc
3131 E Riverside Dr, Fort Myers, FL 33916
Toll Free Tel: 866-662-3766 (orders) *Fax:* 239-
  332-2808
E-mail: sales@cdrominc.com
Web Site: www.cdrominc.com
Key Personnel
Pres & CEO: Roger S Hutchison, PhD
  E-mail: rshutch@cdrominc.com
Founded: 1988
Manufactures DX-CD2 optical disc destruction
  device & DX-CD manual optical disc destruc-
  tion device. Distributes Hammer, hard drive

secure ease device, SCSI Hammer, hard drive secure erase device & PSI Clone, hard drive forensic imaging device.
Catalog(s) available
Foreign Office(s): CRSI Pte Ltd, International Plaza, No 23-14, 10 Anson Rd, Singapore, Singapore, Consultant: Dr Philip Teo *Tel:* 9616 5632 *Fax:* 745 2009

CDI Technologies, see Troxell-CDI

CDR Communications Inc
9310B/9302C Old Keene Mill Rd, Burke, VA 22015
Tel: 703-569-3400 *Toll Free Tel:* 800-729-2237 *Fax:* 703-569-3448
E-mail: info@cdrcommunications.com
Web Site: www.cdrcommunications.com
Key Personnel
Pres: Christopher D Rogers *E-mail:* chris@cdrcommunications.com
VP & Mgr: Nancy Rogers *E-mail:* nancy@cdrcommunications.com
Founded: 1984
Full service film & video production company.
Membership(s): ICVM

Ceavco Audio Visual Company Inc
6240 W 54 Ave, Arvada, CO 80002
Tel: 303-539-3500
E-mail: solutions@ceavco.com
Web Site: ceavco.com
Key Personnel
Pres: Matt Emerson
Founded: 1961
Full service audio, video & lighting solutions provider specializing in AV production for live events & system integration for clients nationwide.
Online catalog(s) available
Membership(s): Audiovisual and Integrated Experience Association; AV Alliance; Rental & Staging Network

CELCO
14 Industrial Ave, Mahwah, NJ 07430
Web Site: www.celco.com
Founded: 1950
Develops, manufactures & deploys high-resolution digital film imaging solutions.
Online catalog(s) available, yokes, coils, deflection components
Branch Office(s)
CELCO Pacific, 10291-A Trademark St, Rancho Cucamonga, CA 91730, Gen Mgr: Michael Constantine *Tel:* 909-481-4648 *Fax:* 909-481-6899 *E-mail:* info@celco.com
Membership(s): IBC; IEEE; NAB; SID; SMPTE®; SPIE

Celebrity Helicopters Inc
961 W Alondra Blvd, Compton, CA 90220
Tel: 310-618-1155 *Toll Free Tel:* 877-999-2099 *Fax:* 424-785-8768 *Toll Free Fax:* 877-999-2099
Web Site: www.celebheli.com
Key Personnel
CEO: Robin Petgrave *E-mail:* robin@celebheli.com
Aerial production services, executive transportation & location scouting, flight training & sightseeing flights.

Celestial Harmonies/Fortuna Records/Kuckuck Schallplatten/Black Sun Music/MonteVideo
Division of Mayflower Music Corp
1951 N Wilmot Rd, Bldg 2, Unit 7, Tucson, AZ 85712-8000
Mailing Address: PO Box 30122, Tucson, AZ 85751-0122
Tel: 520-326-4400 *Fax:* 520-326-3333

E-mail: celestial@harmonies.com
Web Site: www.harmonies.com
Key Personnel
Pres: Eckart Rahn
Gen Mgr: Tony Eckstat
Online catalog(s) available
Membership(s): ASCAP; BMI; RIAA

Celestial Mechanix Inc, see CMI

Centaur Records Inc
136 Saint Joseph St, Baton Rouge, LA 70802
Tel: 225-336-4877 *Fax:* 225-336-9678
E-mail: info@centaurrecords.com
Web Site: www.centaurrecords.com
Key Personnel
Pres: Victor E Sachse
VP: Dan Cassin
Founded: 1976
Audio production.
Membership(s): The Recording Academy

Center City Film & Video Inc
1501-1503 Walnut St, Philadelphia, PA 19102
Tel: 215-568-4134 *Fax:* 215-568-6011
E-mail: info@ccfv.com; sales@ccfv.com
Web Site: www.ccfv.com
Key Personnel
Founder, CEO & Pres: Jordan M Schwartz
Full service video & interactive production company.
Membership(s): Television Radio Advertising Club

Center for Southern Folklore Inc
119 S Main St, Memphis, TN 38103
Tel: 901-525-3655 *Fax:* 901-544-9965
E-mail: info@southernfolklore.com
Web Site: www.southernfolklore.com
Key Personnel
Exec Dir: Judy Peiser *E-mail:* jlpeiser@gmail.com
Nonprofit multimedia organization documenting culture of the Memphis delta region of the South.

Center for the Collaborative Classroom
Formerly Developmental Studies Center
1001 Marina Village Pkwy, Suite 110, Alameda, CA 94501-1042
Tel: 510-533-0213 *Toll Free Tel:* 800-666-7270 *Fax:* 510-464-3670
E-mail: info@collaborativeclassroom.org
Web Site: www.collaborativeclassroom.org
Key Personnel
Pres & CEO: Roger King
COO: Kelly Stuart
CTO: Tim Millen
SVP & CFO: Brent Welling
VP, Mktg: Sofia Roman
VP, Organizational Learning: Peter Brunn
VP, Prog Devt & Publg Servs: Valerie Fraser
Founded: 1980
Educational products.
Online catalog(s) available

Center for Touch Drawing
PO Box 1595, Langley, WA 98260
Tel: 360-221-5745
E-mail: center@touchdrawing.com
Web Site: www.touchdrawing.com
Key Personnel
Founder & Owner: Deborah Koff-Chapin
Produces multimedia educational materials to encourage the use of the creative healing art form of Touch Drawing. Also publishes the visual & musical artistic productions of its founder, Deborah Koff-Chapin.
Online catalog(s) available

Shipping Address: 628 First St, Langley, WA 98260
Membership(s): International Expressive Arts Therapy Association®

CenterStaging LLC
3407 Winona Ave, Burbank, CA 91504
Tel: 818-559-4333 *Fax:* 818-848-4016
E-mail: info@centerstaging.com
Web Site: centerstaging.com
Key Personnel
Co-Owner & Pres: Mitch Clark
Co-Owner: Scott Scovill
Gen Mgr: James "Jimbo" Neal
Opers Mgr: Robert Lowndes
Studio Mgr: Jr Tagle
Audio Dept Mgr: Doug Dubin
Founded: 2009
Studio, soundstage & equipment rentals. Specialize in production & technical support for television & live performances.
Branch Office(s)
2517 N Ontario St, Burbank, CA 91504, Proj Coord: Ben Fenton *E-mail:* ben.fenton@centerstaging.com (rentals)
23-41 Borden Ave, Long Island City, NY 11101, Proj Coord: Ben Clark *Tel:* 212-651-1290 *Fax:* 718-729-4778 *E-mail:* ben.clark@centerstaging.com (rentals)

Central Audio-Visual Equipment Inc
375 Roma Jean Pkwy, Streamwood, IL 60107
Tel: 630-372-8100 *Toll Free Tel:* 800-323-4239 *Fax:* 630-372-9281
Web Site: www.cavinc.com
Key Personnel
Pres: Michael Bashir
VP: Irene Bashir
Sales: Jonathan Bashir *E-mail:* jbashir@cavinc.com
Founded: 1958
Catalog(s) available

Central Lighting & Equipment Inc (CLE)
4103 E 16 St, Des Moines, IA 50313
Tel: 515-277-4190 *Toll Free Tel:* 877-977-4190 *Fax:* 515-277-2295
E-mail: info@cleproductions.com
Web Site: cleproductions.com
Key Personnel
Pres: Arren C Wetzel
Mktg Dir: Emily Giunta
Opers Dir: Kris Churchill
Founded: 2002
Full service event production company including indoor/outdoor LED walls, floating screens & wall-to-wall video displays.
Membership(s): Professional Lighting & Sound Association

Central Ohio Audio Video
6650 Busch Rd, Columbus, OH 43229
Toll Free Tel: 877-432-8273
Web Site: www.centralohav.com
Founded: 1999
CD & DVD duplication, video equipment sales & AV integration.

Central Texas College KNCT-Radio FM
PO Box 1800, Killeen, TX 76540-1800
Tel: 254-526-1176
E-mail: knct@knct.org
Web Site: www.knct.org
Key Personnel
Gen Mgr: Lynn Woolley *E-mail:* lynn.woolley@knct.org
Radio programming.
Program guide(s) available

Centralite Systems Inc
1701 Industrial Park Dr, Mobile, AL 36693

Tel: 251-607-9119 *Toll Free Tel:* 877-466-5483
Fax: 251-607-9117
E-mail: info@centralite.com
Web Site: centralite.com
Key Personnel
Pres & CEO: Sean Bryant
Founded: 1997
Manufacturer of wireless connected home devices, including lighting control systems.

Centre Communications Inc
75 Manhattan Dr, Suite 200, Boulder, CO 80303
Tel: 303-444-1166
E-mail: centre@ecentral.com
Web Site: www.centrecommunicationinc.com;
www.centredm.com
Key Personnel
Pres: Ron Meyer
Online catalog(s) available
Membership(s): IAA-VC

Century Business Solutions
Division of FDM Brands
100 Carlson Rd, Rochester, NY 14610
Toll Free Tel: 844-656-3476 *Toll Free Fax:* 866-592-8642 (orders)
E-mail: info@centurybusinesssolutions.com;
help@fdmbrands.com
Web Site: www.centurybusinesssolutions.com
Founded: 1954
Products for organization, presentation & storage, including digital media storage & photographic archiving.
Online catalog(s) available
Catalog(s) available, by request

Century Color Labs Inc
494 School St, East Hartford, CT 06108
Tel: 860-289-9501 *Toll Free Tel:* 800-242-9501
Fax: 860-291-9098
E-mail: production@centurycolor.com
Web Site: www.centurycolor.com
Key Personnel
Pres: Greg Der Boghosian
Founded: 1968
Online catalog(s) available

Cerutti Productions Inc
18211 Bulverde Rd, Suite 10202, San Antonio, TX 78259-3625
Tel: 210-403-0800
Web Site: www.cerutti.org
Key Personnel
Pres: Marc Cerutti *E-mail:* marc@cerutti.org
Video production, post, editing & technical services.
Membership(s): International Alliance of Theatrical Stage Employees; NATAS

Cerwin-Vega! Inc
Division of Gibson Pro Audio
c/o Gibson Pro Audio, 309 Park Plus Blvd, Nashville, TN 37217
Toll Free Tel: 800-4GIBSON (444-2766)
E-mail: service@gibson.com (cust serv)
Web Site: www.cerwinvega.com
Founded: 1954
Professional, home & mobile audio products & accessories.
Online catalog(s) available

CES, see Cinema Equipment & Supplies Inc

CET
Division of Public Media Connect
1223 Central Pkwy, Cincinnati, OH 45214
Tel: 513-381-4033
E-mail: comments@cetconnect.org
Web Site: www.cetconnect.org
Key Personnel
CFO: Lee Weinel *E-mail:* lweinel@cetconnect.org

COO: Kitty Lensman *Tel:* 937-220-1600
E-mail: klensman@cetconnect.org
Prodn Dir: Jason Garrison *Tel:* 513-345-6531
E-mail: jgarrison@cetconnect.org
Cincinnati's PBS station presenting educational TV stations in HD.

CEV Multimedia Ltd
1020 SE Loop 289, Lubbock, TX 79404
Toll Free Tel: 877-610-5017 *Toll Free Fax:* 800-243-6398
E-mail: customersupport@cevmultimedia.com
Web Site: www.cevmultimedia.com
Key Personnel
Partner & Pres: Jeff Lansdell *E-mail:* jeff.lansdell@cevmultimedia.com
Founded: 1984
Online catalog(s) available

CFP Video Productions Inc
149 Meriden Rd, Boonton, NJ 07005
Tel: 973-226-2481
Web Site: cfpvideo.com
Key Personnel
Pres: Don Spitzmiller *E-mail:* don.spitzmiller@verizon.net
Founded: 1983
Membership(s): American Guild of Court Videographers; IEEE; NAB

Chace Audio by Deluxe
Division of Deluxe Entertainment Services Group
900 Seward St, Hollywood, CA 90038
Toll Free Tel: 800-842-8346
Web Site: www.bydeluxe.com
Key Personnel
VP, Audio/DDM: Rich Cusano
Founded: 1984
Full audio post-production services.
Membership(s): AES; Association of Moving Image Archivists; SMPTE®

Chalk Dust Co
16107 Kensington Dr, PMB 256, Sugar Land, TX 77479-4401
Tel: 281-265-2495 *Toll Free Tel:* 800-588-7564
Fax: 281-265-3197
E-mail: sales@chalkdust.com
Web Site: www.chalkdust.com
Key Personnel
Owner & Pres: Dana Mosely *E-mail:* dana@chalkdust.com
Owner & VP: Richard Mosely *E-mail:* richard@chalkdust.com
Founded: 1994
Manufacturing & marketing of comprehensive math DVDs for 14 separate courses including Basic Math, Prealgebra, Algebra 1, Geometry, ACT-SAT™ Math Review, Algebra 2, College Algebra, Trigonometry, Precalculus, Calculus 1 & Statistics.
Online catalog(s) available

Challenge Productions/Challenge Aerial Imaging
400 E George St, Marion, OH 43302
Tel: 740-531-3077
E-mail: info@challenge-pro.com
Web Site: challenge-pro.com
Key Personnel
Owner: Terry Cline *E-mail:* terry@challenge-pro.com
Creation of film, music & video from concept & execution to distribution.

Championship Productions Inc
Ames Community Development Park, 2730 Graham St, Ames, IA 50010
Tel: 515-232-3687 *Toll Free Tel:* 800-873-2730
Fax: 515-232-3739
E-mail: info@championshipproductions.com

Web Site: www.championshipproductions.com
Key Personnel
Founder & Pres: William Bergan
Founded: 1976
Catalog(s) available, upon request

Steve Chandler
798 W 26 St, San Bernardino, CA 92405
Tel: 909-882-1621
E-mail: stevevldy@aol.com
Founded: 1970
Full service production & post-production. Beta SP & digital cameras, lighting, etc. Final cut production editing, analog & HD. Transfer film to DVD, DVD duplication.
Price list(s) available

Channell One Video
PO Box 399, Epping, NH 03042-0399
Tel: 603-679-6796
E-mail: racevid@earthlink.net
Key Personnel
Pres: Bill Channell
VP: Kathleen Channell
VP, Prodn: Bill Harris
Founded: 1971
Video & post-production.
Shipping Address: 9 Old State Rd, Epping, NH 03042
Membership(s): Alliance for Community Media; Race Videographers Association; Seacoast Professional Videographers Association

Chapman/Leonard Studio Equipment Inc
12950 Raymer St, North Hollywood, CA 91605
Tel: 818-764-6726 *Toll Free Tel:* 888-883-6559
Fax: 818-764-6730
E-mail: marketing@chapman-leonard.com
Web Site: www.chapman-leonard.com
Key Personnel
Sr Mktg & Outside Opers Mgr: Christine Chapman-Huenergardt *E-mail:* christine@chapman-leonard.com
Acctg Mgr: Michael Chapman *E-mail:* mchapman@chapman-leonard.com
Mktg Mgr: Nichole Huenergardt *E-mail:* nicholeh@chapman-leonard.com
Prodn Mgr: Charles L Huenergardt *E-mail:* charlesl@chapman-leonard.com
Asst Gen Mgr: Susan Weinmuller *E-mail:* susanw@chapman-leonard.com
Mktg/Screen Credit Supv: Jaqueline Sunshine *E-mail:* jackies@chapman-leonard.com
Founded: 1945
Specialize in camera cranes, arms, bases, dollies, pedestals & remote camera systems for motion picture & TV production. State-of-the-art soundstage & production center at the Orlando location.
Catalog(s) available
Branch Office(s)
9460 Delegates Dr, Orlando, FL 32837, Contact: Juan Escribano *Tel:* 407-851-3456 *Toll Free Tel:* 888-337-8243 *Fax:* 407-855-1653 *E-mail:* juane@chapman-leonard.com
500 Sandy Creek Rd, Bldg 2004, Suite 101, Fayetteville, GA 30214, Contact: Joe Velasquez *Toll Free Tel:* 888-758-4826 *Fax:* 770-716-9787 *E-mail:* joev@chapman-leonard.com
Elmwood Business Park, 668 Distributors Row, Suite E, New Orleans, LA 70123, Contact: David Bullard *Tel:* 504-731-6050 *Toll Free Tel:* 888-758-4826 *E-mail:* davidb@chapman-leonard.com
1701 Aspen Ave NW, Units J & O, Albuquerque, NM 87104, Contact: Ian Curry *Fax:* 505-243-9904 *E-mail:* ianc@chapman-leonard.com
1901 E 51 St, Austin, TX 78723, Contact: Joe Datri *Tel:* 512-473-0084 *Toll Free Tel:* 888-758-4826 *Fax:* 512-473-0042 *E-mail:* joed@chapman-leonard.com
Foreign Office(s): Chapman/Leonard Studio Equipment Ltd, North Orbital Commer-

cial Park, Unit 2, Napsbury Lane, Saint Albans, Herts AL1 1XB, United Kingdom, Mng Dir: Dennis Fraser *Tel:* (01727) 838424 *Fax:* (01727) 852241 *E-mail:* dennis@ chapmanleonard.com
Membership(s): AICP; ASC; SMPTE®; Society of Camera Operators; Women in Film

Charles Beseler Co
2018 W Main St, Stroudsburg, PA 18360
Mailing Address: PO Box 431, Stroudsburg, PA 18360
Toll Free Tel: 800-237-3537 *Toll Free Fax:* 800-966-4515
Web Site: www.beselerphoto.com
Key Personnel
Pres: Bob Deinarowicz *E-mail:* bob@beseler.com
Founded: 1869
Membership(s): Society for Photographic Education

Charles M Salter Associates Inc
130 Sutter St, 5th fl, San Francisco, CA 94104
Tel: 415-397-0442 *Fax:* 415-397-0454
E-mail: info@cmsalter.com
Web Site: www.cmsalter.com
Key Personnel
Pres: Charles M Salter
SVP: Eric B Mori; Philip N Sanders; Thomas Schindler; David R Schwind; Ken W Graven
Founded: 1975
Branch Office(s)
100 W San Fernando, Suite 595, San Jose, CA 95113 *Tel:* 408-295-4944 *Fax:* 408-295-4949
Membership(s): AES; ASA; Audio Publishers Association; Audiovisual and Integrated Experience Association; BICSI; SMPTE®

Charlex Inc
2 W 45 St, 7th fl, New York, NY 10036
Tel: 212-719-4600
E-mail: info@chrlx.com
Web Site: www.chrlx.com
Key Personnel
Pres: Chris Byrnes

Chartpak Inc
One River Rd, Leeds, MA 01053
Tel: 413-584-5446 *Toll Free Tel:* 800-628-1910
E-mail: info@chartpak.com
Web Site: www.chartpak.com
Key Personnel
Pres: Steven Roth
VP & Gen Mgr: Bob Rodak
Founded: 1949
Catalog(s) available
Online catalog(s) available

Chater Camera Inc
1336 Ninth St, Berkeley, CA 94710
Tel: 510-525-5400 *Fax:* 510-295-2478
E-mail: rentals@chatercamera.com
Web Site: www.chatercamera.com
Key Personnel
Owner: John Chater *E-mail:* john@chatercamera.com
Owner & Engr: Jay Farrington *E-mail:* jay@ chatercamera.com
Busn Mgr: Erin Anderson *E-mail:* erin@ chatercamera.com
Full service film, video, digital cinema & 35mm lens rental house.

Chatterbox Productions Inc
5305 Johnson St, Hollywood, FL 33021-5721
Tel: 754-816-5432
Web Site: www.facebook.com/ chatterboxproductions
Key Personnel
Prodr & Script Writer: Marjory E Leposky *E-mail:* meleposky@aol.com

Founded: 1996
TV & film production, music videos, infomercials, casting, short films & feature films.

Chauvet Lighting
5200 NW 108 Ave, Sunrise, FL 33351-8040
Tel: 954-577-4455 *Toll Free Tel:* 800-762-1084 *Fax:* 954-929-5560 *Toll Free Fax:* 800-544-4898
E-mail: marketing@chauvetlighting.com
Web Site: www.chauvetlighting.com
Founded: 1990
Lighting manufacturer.
Catalog(s) available, free, semiannual
Online catalog(s) available
Branch Office(s)
7555 N San Fernando Rd, Burbank, CA 91505
Foreign Office(s): Stokstr 18, 9770 Kruishoutem, Belgium *Tel:* (09) 3889397
3, Rue Ampere, 91380 Chilly-Mazarin, France *Tel:* 01 78 85 33 59
Bruno-Buergel-Str 11, 28759 Bremen, Germany *Tel:* (0421) 62 60 20
Av de las Partidas 34, 3-B (Entrance by Calle 2), Zona Industrial Lerma, 52000 Lerma, MEX, Mexico *Tel:* (01728) 690-2010
Brookhill Rd Industrial Estate, Pinxton, Nottingham NG16 6NT, United Kingdom *Tel:* (01773) 511115

Checkers Safety Group
620 Compton St, Broomfield, CO 80020
Toll Free Tel: 800-438-9336; 877-384-6103
E-mail: sales@checkers-safety.com
Web Site: www.checkers-safety.com
Key Personnel
Pres & CEO: Ray Torres
Manufacture cable protectors, grip equipment, ground protection solutions, motion & vehicle safety.
Online catalog(s) available
Membership(s): ARA; International Association of Amusement Parks and Attractions; NAB

Chelsea Decorative Metal Co
Division of Pressed Tin Ceiling Co
8212 Braewick Dr, Dept AV, Houston, TX 77074
Tel: 713-721-9200 *Fax:* 713-776-8661
E-mail: tinman83@earthlink.net
Web Site: www.tinman.com
Key Personnel
Owner: Glenn Eldridge
Ceiling material backdrops; Victorian styles & scenic accessories for movie sets or backgrounds.
Catalog(s) available

Chelsea Green Publishing Co
85 N Main St, Suite 120, White River Junction, VT 05001
Tel: 802-295-6300 *Toll Free Tel:* 800-639-4099 (orders) *Fax:* 802-295-6444
E-mail: customerservice@chelseagreen.com
Web Site: www.chelseagreen.com
Key Personnel
Pres & Publr: Margo Baldwin *E-mail:* mbaldwin@chelseagreen.com
Busn & Dist Dir: Sandi Eaton *E-mail:* seaton@ chelseagreen.com
Dir, Mktg: Sean Maher *E-mail:* smaher@ chelseagreen.com
Dir, Rts & Ancillary Revenue: Eliza Haun *E-mail:* ehaun@chelseagreen.com
Prodn Dir: Patricia Stone *E-mail:* pstone@ chelseagreen.com
Subs Rts & Audio Asst: Cassidy Seidler *E-mail:* cseidler@chelseagreen.com
Founded: 1984
Audiobook publisher on the topics of politics & practice of sustainable living.
Online catalog(s) available

Foreign Office(s): South Wing, Somerset House, Strand, London WC2R 1LA, United Kingdom, Mng Dir: Matt Haslum *E-mail:* mhaslum@ chelseagreen.com

Cheng & Tsui Co
25 West St, 2nd fl, Boston, MA 02111-1213
Tel: 617-988-2400 *Toll Free Tel:* 800-554-1963 (orders) *Fax:* 617-426-3669
E-mail: orders@cheng-tsui.com
Web Site: www.cheng-tsui.com
Key Personnel
Pres: Jill Cheng
Founded: 1987
Catalog(s) available
Online catalog(s) available

Cherry Multimedia
2129 Colorado Blvd, Los Angeles, CA 90041
Toll Free Tel: 800-378-7598
E-mail: info@cherrymultimedia.com
Web Site: cherrymultimedia.com
Key Personnel
CEO: Lee Cherry
Full service production company & rental studios.

Cheuvront Studios
4607 NW Sixth St Ext, Studio I, Gainesville, FL 32609
Tel: 352-378-4671 *Fax:* 352-338-9215
E-mail: allen@cheuvront.com
Web Site: www.cheuvront.com
Full service commercial photography studio.

The Chicago Production Center
Division of WTTW Communications Inc
5400 N Saint Louis Ave, Chicago, IL 60625-4698
Tel: 773-509-5571 *Fax:* 773-509-5303
Web Site: www.wttw.com
Key Personnel
Pres & CEO: Daniel J Schmidt
COO: Reese P Marcusson
Dir, Prodn Servs: Kim Mattes
Online catalog(s) available
Membership(s): NAB; NATAS

Chicago Scenic Studios Inc
955 W Cermak Rd, Chicago, IL 60608
Tel: 312-274-9900 *Fax:* 312-274-9901
E-mail: info@chicagoscenic.com
Web Site: www.chicagoscenic.com
Key Personnel
Pres: Bob Doepel *E-mail:* rdoepel@ chicagoscenic.com
Founded: 1978
A full service organization providing design, fabrication & production management to the special event, trade show, theatrical & entertainment industries.

Chicago Spotlight Inc
3418 N Knox Ave, Chicago, IL 60641
Tel: 312-455-1171
Web Site: www.grandstage.com
Key Personnel
Pres: Greg Becker *E-mail:* grbecker@grandstage.com
Mktg Mgr: Todd Koeppl *E-mail:* tkoeppl@ grandstage.com
Rental Mgr: Cassius Wright *E-mail:* cwright@ grandstage.com
Sales Mgr: Hope Kass *E-mail:* hkass@ grandstage.com
Sales: Ruth Hudson *E-mail:* rhudson@grandstage.com
Online catalog(s) available
Membership(s): Illinois Theatre Association; Professional Lighting & Sound Association; USITT

Chick Russell Communications
490 Castano Ave, Pasadena, CA 91107

E-mail: info@chickrussell.com
Web Site: www.chickrussell.com
Key Personnel
Pres: Chick Russell
Creative development of world-class destination experiences.

Chief, a Legrand AV Inc brand
6436 City West Pkwy, Eden Prairie, MN 55344
Tel: 952-894-6280 *Toll Free Tel:* 866-977-3901
 Toll Free Fax: 877-894-6918
E-mail: av.chief.support@legrand.com
Web Site: www.legrandav.com/products/chief
Key Personnel
Pres: Scott Gill
Dir, Facilities: Ron Jensen
Founded: 1978
Complete line of mounts, racks & accessories for TVs, displays, projectors & other AV components.
Online catalog(s) available
Membership(s): Audiovisual and Integrated Experience Association

Children of Mary
PO Box 350333, Fort Lauderdale, FL 33335-0333
Tel: 954-583-5108 *Fax:* 954-583-5108
E-mail: mascmen7@yahoo.com
Web Site: www.catholicbook.com
Key Personnel
Owner & CEO: John R Walsh
Founded: 1985
Distribute DVDs, Catholic traditional books & conspiracy books on who rules the world.

The Children's Book Store Distribution (CBSD)
Division of IDLA Associated Label Distribution
23 Griffin St, Waterdown, ON L0R 2H0, Canada
Mailing Address: PO Box 170, Waterdown, ON L0R 2H0, Canada
Tel: 905-690-9397 (ext 237) *Toll Free Tel:* 800-757-8372 (cust serv, CN & US) *Fax:* 905-690-3419
E-mail: info@childrensgroup.com; sales@idla.ca
Web Site: www.childrensgroup.com
Key Personnel
Sales: Judy Smyth
Classical music entertainment for children through a collection of CDs, DVDs, illustrated books, live concerts & educational resources.
Online catalog(s) available
Membership(s): Education Market Association; NAMM, the National Association of Music Merchants

Chimera®
1067 Telleen Ave, Erie, CO 80516
Tel: 303-444-8000 *Toll Free Tel:* 888-444-1812
 Fax: 303-444-8303
E-mail: info@chimeralighting.com
Web Site: chimeralighting.com
Key Personnel
Dir, Sales & Mktg: John Fuller *Tel:* 303-444-8000 ext 120
Gen Mgr: Ron Hunt *Tel:* 303-444-8000 ext 115
Prod Coord: Matt Pevear *Tel:* 303-444-8000 ext 121
Catalog(s) available
Online catalog(s) available
Membership(s): NAB

Chinmaya Publications
Division of Chinmaya Mission West
560 Bridgetown Pike, Langhorne, PA 19053-7210
Tel: 215-396-0390 *Toll Free Tel:* 888-CMW-READ (269-7323) *Fax:* 215-396-9710
E-mail: publications@chinmayamission.org
Web Site: www.chinmayamission.org; www.chinmayapublications.org

Key Personnel
Dir: Reverend Swami Siddhananda
Catalog(s) available
Online catalog(s) available

Richard Chisolm Cinematography
311 Somerset Rd, Baltimore, MD 21210
Tel: 410-340-5308
E-mail: chisolmcamera@gmail.com
Web Site: www.richardchisolm.com
Key Personnel
Dir, Photog: Richard Chisolm

CHK Electronics Ltd
836A Southampton Rd, No 260, Benicia, CA 94510
Tel: 707-750-8446 *Fax:* 707-361-0230
E-mail: sales@chk-electronics.com
Web Site: www.chk-electronics.com
Founded: 1991
Warehouse & distribute professional quality electronic components & connectors throughout North & South America.
Foreign Office(s): Seaview Commercial Bldg, Rm 1301-2, 21-24 Connaught Rd W, Sheung Wan, Hong Kong *Tel:* 2780 4576 *Fax:* 3013 8793
E-mail: sales.hk@chk-electronics.com (headquarters)
Membership(s): NAMM, the National Association of Music Merchants

Christian Media Network
PO Box 728, Garberville, CA 95542-8728
Tel: 541-899-8888
Web Site: www.christianmedianetwork.com
Key Personnel
Owner: James Lloyd *E-mail:* james@christianmedianetwork.com
Christian music & videos.

Christie Digital Systems USA Inc
10550 Camden Dr, Cypress, CA 90630
Tel: 714-236-8610 *Toll Free Tel:* 866-880-4462 (cust serv) *Fax:* 714-503-3375
E-mail: sales-us@christiedigital.com; orders@christiedigital.com
Web Site: www.christiedigital.com
Key Personnel
Chmn, Pres & CEO: Jack Kline
CFO & Secy: Takeshi Suzuki
EVP, Busn Devt & Strategic Planning: Craig Sholder
EVP, Content Mgmt & Processing: Clark Williams
EVP, Global HR: Brian Gifford
EVP, Global Mkt Solutions: Zoran Veselic
EVP, Global Prof Servs: Sean James
VP, Global Opers: Clint Carter
VP, Global Quality: Al-Karim Shariff
EVP, Global Sales: Dale Miller
VP, EMEA: Simon Smith
VP, Global & Corp Mktg: Kathryn Cress
VP, Global Engg: Mike Esch
VP, Global Info Systems: David Hsieh
VP, HR: Anna Escudero
VP, Prod Mgmt, Global Cinema: Brian Claypool
VP, Sales, Asia Pacific: Lin Yu
VP, Sales, Cinema-Americas: Susie Beiersdorf
VP, Sales, Enterprise Solutions-Americas: Dave Muscat
Founded: 1929
Manufacturers of high resolution projection systems for digital & film applications.
Branch Office(s)
2001 W Melinda Lane, Phoenix, AZ 85027
 Tel: 602-943-5700 *Fax:* 623-582-3571
Christie Digital Systems Canada Inc, 809 Wellington St N, Kitchener, ON N2G 4Y7,

Canada *Tel:* 519-744-8005 *Toll Free Tel:* 800-221-2025 (cust care) *Fax:* 519-749-3321
Christie 360 Experiential Studios, 1001 Lenoir St, Suite B-528, Montreal, QC H4C 2Z6, Canada *Tel:* 514-389-1515 *Toll Free Tel:* 877-979-9024

Christie Lites
6990 Lake Ellenor Dr, Orlando, FL 32809
Tel: 407-856-0016 *Fax:* 407-856-0765
Web Site: www.christielites.com
Key Personnel
CEO: Huntly Christie
Mktg Mgr: Sheila Grant
Founded: 1985
Stage lighting services & lighting equipment rentals for theater, concerts, trade shows, TV & film, corporate presentations & special events.
Catalog(s) available
Branch Office(s)
Christie Lites Orlando, 2479 Eunice Ave, Orlando, FL 32808, Opers Mgr: Fred Foster *Tel:* 407-856-0016
Christie Lites Chicago, 1000 Davey Rd, Suite 500, Woodbridge, IL 60517, Opers Mgr: Anthony Deleon *Tel:* 630-863-7067
Christie Lites Las Vegas, 4850 Statz St, Suite 103, North Las Vegas, NV 89081, Opers Mgr: Cory Ausiello *Tel:* 702-222-0363
Christie Lites Broadway, 40 Whelan Rd, East Rutherford, NJ 07073, Opers Mgr: Pete Hulin *Tel:* 201-438-6700
Christie Lites New York, 150 Western Rd, Suite 100, Kearny, NJ 07032, Opers Mgr: Keith Smith *Tel:* 201-941-8370
Christie Lites Nashville, 6050 Dana Way, Suite 250, Antioch, TN 37013, Opers Mgr: Troy Rigney *Tel:* 615-280-5450 *Fax:* 615-641-5143
Christie Lites Dallas, 12121 N Stemmons Fwy, No 100, Dallas, TX 75234-5860, Opers Mgr: Bucky Glance *Tel:* 214-637-3535
Christie Lites Seattle, 7815 S 208 St, Suite 101, Kent, WA 98032-1303, Opers Mgr: Tim Haack *Tel:* 206-223-7200
Christie Lites Calgary, 4900 64 Ave SE, Bay 60, Calgary, AB T2C 4V3, Canada, Opers Mgr: Todd Hucul *Tel:* 403-243-2688
Christie Lites Vancouver, 4154 McConnell Dr, Bay 14, Burnaby, BC V5A 3Y9, Canada, Opers Mgr: Kevan Bull *Tel:* 604-255-9943 *Fax:* 604-420-1130
Christie Lites Winnipeg, 25 Terracon Place, Winnipeg, MB R2J 4B3, Canada, Regl Opers Mgr: A-Lynn Thompson *Tel:* 204-231-3921 *Fax:* 204-233-7965
Christie Lites Ottawa, 1157 Parisien St, Ottawa, ON K1B 4W4, Canada *Tel:* 613-594-5804 (by appt only)
Christie Lites Toronto, 100 Carson St, Unit A, Toronto, ON M8W 3R9, Canada, Opers Mgr: Drew McElary *Tel:* 416-644-1010 *Fax:* 416-644-0404 (Canadian headquarters)
Foreign Office(s): Christie Lites Coventry, 40 Sayer Dr, Unit B, Lyons Park, Coventry CV5 9PF, United Kingdom, Opers Mgr: Andy Mitchinson *Tel:* (02476) 017 270
Membership(s): Professional Lighting & Sound Association

Christopher Gray Post Production
3918 Michael Ave, Los Angeles, CA 90066
Tel: 310-395-9845
E-mail: cgray@cgpost.com
Web Site: www.cgpost.com
Founded: 1980
Post-production services.
Membership(s): SMPTE®

The Christophers
5 Hanover Sq, 22nd fl, New York, NY 10004
Tel: 212-759-4050 *Toll Free Tel:* 888-298-4050 (orders) *Fax:* 212-838-5073
E-mail: mail@christophers.org

Web Site: www.christophers.org
Key Personnel
Prodr: Tony Rossi *E-mail:* t.rossi@christophers.org
Founded: 1945
Online catalog(s) available
Brochure(s) available

Christy's Editorial
Affiliate of Atomic Film Co
3625 W Pacific Ave, Burbank, CA 91505
Tel: 818-845-1755 *Toll Free Tel:* 800-468-6391;
    800-556-5706 (CA) *Fax:* 818-845-1756
E-mail: info@christys.net
Web Site: www.christys.net
Key Personnel
Pres & Ad Mgr: Craig Christy
Founded: 1969
Rent, sell & repair traditional film equipment &
    supplies. Also rent Avid editing systems, stor-
    age & decks.
Online catalog(s) available

CHRLX, see Charlex Inc

Chromavision Corp
The Radio Wave Bldg, Suite 900, 49 W 27 St,
    New York, NY 10001
Tel: 212-686-7366
E-mail: info@chromavision.net
Web Site: www.chromavision.net
Key Personnel
Owner & Pres: Bruce Testa *E-mail:* btesta@
    chromavision.net
Online catalog(s) available

ChronTrol Corp
7525-K Mission Gorge Rd, San Diego, CA 92120
Mailing Address: PO Box 19537, San Diego, CA
    92159-0537
Tel: 619-282-8686 *Toll Free Tel:* 800-854-1999
    Fax: 619-563-6563
E-mail: info@chrontrol.com
Web Site: www.chrontrol.com
Key Personnel
VP, Engg: James G Durham *E-mail:* jgd@
    chrontrol.com
Mgr, Prodn: Chris McDuff
Founded: 1977
Online catalog(s) available

ChyronHego Corp
5 Hub Dr, Melville, NY 11747
Tel: 631-845-2000
E-mail: info@chyronhego.com; sales@
    chryonhego.com
Web Site: chyronhego.com
Key Personnel
Exec Chmn: Johan Apel *E-mail:* johan.apel@
    chyronhego.com
CEO: Marco Lopez *E-mail:* marco.lopez@
    chyronhego.com
Chief Mktg Offr: Jesper Gawell *E-mail:* jesper.
    gawell@chyronhego.com
Chief Prod Offr: Boromy Ung *E-mail:* boromy.
    ung@chyronhego.com
CTO: Soren Kjellin *E-mail:* soren.kjellin@
    chyronhego.com
Pres, Sports: Rickard Ohrn *E-mail:* rickard.ohrn@
    chyronhego.com
SVP, Fin, Acctg, IT & Legal: Mike Truex
    E-mail: mike.truex@chyronhego.com
VP, Sales, North America: Paul Weiser *Tel:* 631-
    845-2040 *E-mail:* paul.weiser@chyronhego.
    com
Head, HR: Barri Grisolia
Broadcast graphics creation, playout & real-time
    data visualization offering a wide variety of
    products & services for live television, news,
    sports, corporate & government video produc-
    tion.

Online catalog(s) available
Branch Office(s)
411 Fifth Ave, New York, NY 10016
800-1199 W Hastings St, Vancouver, BC V6E
    3T5, Canada
Foreign Office(s): Purkynova 2855/97a,
    612 00 Brno, Czechia *Tel:* 731 963 534
    E-mail: czech@chyronhego.com
Neue Weyerstr 6, 50676 Cologne, Germany
    Tel: (06122) 170 9660 *Fax:* (06122) 411 87729
    E-mail: germany@chyronhego.com
Borsigstr 11-13, 65205 Wiesbaden, Germany
    Tel: (06122) 170 9660 *Fax:* (06122) 411 87729
    E-mail: germany@chyronhego.com
Naritaweg 108, 1043 CA Amsterdam, Nether-
    lands *Tel:* (020) 8200 611 *Fax:* (020) 8200 610
    E-mail: netherlands@chyronhego.com
Sandakerveien 114a, 0484 Oslo, Nor-
    way *Tel:* 2279 7030 *Fax:* 2279 7034
    E-mail: norway@chyronhego.com
Vajanskeho 43, 080 01 Presov, Slovakia *Tel:* 692
    003 451 *Fax:* 905 477 354 *E-mail:* slovakia@
    chyronhego.com
Tegeluddsvagen 3, 115 41 Stockholm, Swe-
    den *Tel:* (08) 534 883 00 *E-mail:* sweden@
    chyronhego.com
Ironbridge House, Unit 1, Windmill Place, Lon-
    don UB2 4NJ, United Kingdom *Tel:* (020)
    8867 9050 *E-mail:* unitedkingdom@
    chyronhego.com

Cibola Systems
180 S Cypress St, Orange, CA 92866
Tel: 714-480-0272 *Fax:* 714-480-0768
E-mail: info@cibolasystems.com
Web Site: cibolasystems.com
Key Personnel
CEO: Lisa Perrine *Tel:* 714-480-0272 ext 101
VP, Engg: Diana Theron
Sr Design Engr: Benjamin Djou
Sr Field Engr: Viktor Shafer
Control Systems Programmer/Engr: Scott Stetzko
Electrical Design Engr: Christopher Bertell
Systems Engr: Craig Eady
Proj Design Lead: JoAn Kenmotsu
Purch Mgr: Doug Kotkin
Serv Coord: Ramon Duran
Founded: 1971
AV design & integration.
Brochure(s) available

Cine Audio Visual Sales & Service Ltd
10251 106 St NW, Edmonton, AB T5J 1H5,
    Canada
Tel: 780-423-5081 *Toll Free Tel:* 877-423-5081
    Fax: 780-424-0309
E-mail: cineav@cineav.com; sales@cineav.com;
    info@cineav.com
Web Site: www.cineav.com
Key Personnel
Gen Mgr: Scott Zubko
Founded: 1958
Branch Office(s)
5655 Tenth St NE, Bay No 131, Calgary, AB
    T2E 8W7, Canada, Gen Mgr: Daryl Zubko
    Tel: 403-777-1070 *Toll Free Tel:* 877-777-1070
    Fax: 403-777-1074

Cine Magnetics Inc, see CMI Media
Management

Cine-Med Inc
127 Main St N, Woodbury, CT 06798
Mailing Address: PO Box 745, Woodbury, CT
    06798
Tel: 203-263-0006 *Toll Free Tel:* 800-253-7657
    Fax: 203-263-4839
E-mail: support@cine-med.net
Web Site: www.cine-med.com
Key Personnel
Pres: Kevin McGovern *E-mail:* kmcgovern@cine-
    med.net

Founded: 1980
Book publishing providing continuing medical
    education DVDs, books & meeting services.
Catalog(s) available

Cine 60 Inc
630 Ninth Ave, New York, NY 10036
Tel: 347-673-3240
E-mail: cine60nyc@gmail.com
Web Site: cine60.jimdo.com
Founded: 1960
Manufacture & distribute film, video, lighting
    equipment & supplies.
Online catalog(s) available

CineBags Inc
825 Western Ave, Suite 17, Glendale, CA 91201
Tel: 818-662-0605
E-mail: sales@cinebags.com
Web Site: www.cinebags.com
Key Personnel
Pres: Markus Davids
Founded: 2001
Production bags.
Catalog(s) available

Cinebar Productions Inc
10 San Jose Dr, Suite 4-C, Newport News, VA
    23606
Tel: 757-873-3232
E-mail: cinebar@cinebarproductions.com
Key Personnel
Principal: Richard D Borenstein *E-mail:* rich@
    cinebarproductions.com; Sherri Fisher-Staples
    E-mail: sherri@cinebarproductions.com
Founded: 1987
Media production for museums & not-for-profits
    ranging from interactive exhibits to broadcast
    documentaries.
Membership(s): SEMC; VAM

Cinecraft Productions Inc
2515 Franklin Blvd, Cleveland, OH 44113
Tel: 216-781-2300 *Toll Free Tel:* 800-959-2463
    Fax: 216-781-1067
E-mail: info@cinecraft.com
Web Site: cinecraft.com
Key Personnel
Chmn: Neil G McCormick *E-mail:* neil@
    cinecraft.com
Founded: 1939
Corporate & film video production company that
    also produces DVDs & provides web develop-
    ment.
Membership(s): AMA; IABC; SME

Cinema Antiques
11425 Mathis Ave, Studio 404, Dallas, TX 75234
Tel: 972-869-0011
E-mail: gallery@cinemaantiques.com
Web Site: www.cinemaantiques.com
Key Personnel
Pres & Curator: Bill Reiter
Founded: 1969
Dedicated to antique & collectible equipment &
    artifacts of the motion picture industry. Spe-
    cialize in rare, artifact-sculpture, authentic, cer-
    tified, collectible, vintage, displayable, iconic
    & re-purposed equipment antiques of the 20th
    Century Hollywood Film Studios & The Inter-
    national Motion Picture Production Industry.
    Curate & represent antiques from the Machine
    Age, Art Deco Age, Streamline Age & Mid
    Century Modern Age.
Affiliated with the Decorative Arts Society & the
    Silent Cinema Society.
Membership(s): Historic Vehicle Association; So-
    ciety for Cinema and Media Studies

Cinema Camera Rentals
4700 W Jefferson Blvd, Suite 102, Los Angeles,
    CA 90016

Tel: 323-795-0300
E-mail: info@cinemacamerarentals.com
Web Site: www.cinemacamerarentals.com
Camera rental facility carrying ARRI Alexa, RED Epic, RED Scarlet, RED MX & a wide selection of lenses.

Cinema Concepts
Subsidiary of Cinema Concepts Theater Service Co Inc
2030 Powers Ferry Rd, Suite 214, Atlanta, GA 30339
Tel: 770-956-7460 *Toll Free Tel:* 800-SHOWADS (746-9237) *Fax:* 770-956-8358
E-mail: info@cinemaconcepts.com
Web Site: www.cinemaconcepts.com
Key Personnel
CEO: Sharron Harnell
VP & Studio Dir: John Price
Creative Dir: Mike Tremble
Founded: 1977
Film, D-Cinema, 3D Stereoscopic & HD resolution post-production, digital intermediate solutions, 35mm, DCI-compliant & HD theatre with on-screen editing & finishing. Film recording & digital encoding services. Smoke 2K, Avid DS/HD Nitris, DVS Clipster 4K, Final Cut HD, 2D & 3D animation suites, multi-resolution conversion, D-Cinema encoding, DVD replication, fulfillment.
Membership(s): Cinema Advertising Council; Digital Cinema Initiatives; SMPTE®; Women in Film/Atlanta

Cinema Equipment & Supplies Inc
12457 SW 130 St, Miami, FL 33186
Tel: 305-232-8182
E-mail: sales@cinemaequip.com
Web Site: www.cinemaequip.com
Key Personnel
VP, Sales: Alex Younger
Founded: 1984
Distributor of movie theatre equipment.
Membership(s): Theatre Equipment Association

Cinema Equipment Sales of California Inc
31858 Castaic Rd, No 326, Castaic, CA 91384
Tel: 949-470-0298 *Fax:* 949-470-0835
E-mail: cinemadealer@cinemadealer.com
Key Personnel
Pres: Paula Smith *E-mail:* paula@cinemadealer. com
Gen Mgr: Michael Smith *E-mail:* mike@ cinemadealer.com
Founded: 1986
Provide & install all equipment, furnishings & accessories for commercial cinemas, professional screening rooms & home cinemas (worldwide).

The Cinema Guild Inc
2803 Ocean Ave, Brooklyn, NY 11229
Tel: 212-685-6242 *Toll Free Tel:* 800-723-5522
E-mail: info@cinemaguild.com
Web Site: www.cinemaguild.com
Key Personnel
Founder: Philip Hobel; Mary-Ann Hobel
Owner & Pres: Peter Kelly
Founded: 1984

Cinema Rentals Inc
25876 The Old Rd, Suite 174, Stevenson Ranch, CA 91381
Tel: 661-222-7342
E-mail: ocxinc@gmail.com
Web Site: www.cinemarentals.com
Key Personnel
Owner & CEO: Jim Pearson *E-mail:* jpearson@ cinema-aquatics.com
Founded: 1969
Filming service.

Cinema Stage Inc
110 Saunders Rd, Unit 4, Barrie, ON L4N 9A8, Canada
Tel: 705-733-8740 *Toll Free Tel:* 800-387-6205 *Fax:* 705-733-8742
E-mail: info@cinemastage.ca
Web Site: www.cinemastage.ca
Key Personnel
Sales Mgr: Karl Hergert
Founded: 1981
Supply & install motion picture systems, sound systems, specialty lighting systems, complex control systems, board rooms, training facilities, simulator theatres, lecture theatres, specialized video walls & plasma LCD technology, digital signage video projection, rigging, large projection screens, wall acoustical treatment & motorized drapery systems.
Membership(s): Audiovisual and Integrated Experience Association; NSCA

Cinema-Vision
424 W 33 St, Suite 370, New York, NY 10001
Tel: 212-620-8191 *Fax:* 212-620-8198
E-mail: info@motionpicturerentals.com
Web Site: www.motionpicturerentals.com
Rental house for digital & film cameras, lenses, filters & more.

Cinema Xenon International Inc
261 Valley Vista Dr, Camarillo, CA 93010-1655
Tel: 805-383-5548 *Toll Free Tel:* 888-669-7271 *Fax:* 805-389-9611
E-mail: info@cxilamps.com
Web Site: www.cxilamps.com
Key Personnel
Founder & Pres: Dick Stockton
Founded: 1995
Exclusive distributor for YUMEX™ Xenon arc lamps. Complete line of high quality, competitively priced xenon, mercury & metal halide arc lamps, flash lamps & power supplies.

CinemaGear.com
14737 Arminta St, Unit B, Panorama City, CA 91402
Tel: 818-780-5404 *Fax:* 818-780-5405
E-mail: cinemagear@cinemagear.com
Web Site: www.cinemagear.com
Key Personnel
Pres: Richard Bennett
Founded: 1999
Motion picture camera sales & repair, motion picture lens sales & repairs, motion picture equipment supply & sales. Film camera repair, modifications & sales. Live action DP & visual effects DP.
Online catalog(s) available
Membership(s): AFI; SMPTE®; Television Academy

Cinemarr Entertainment
711 Dolly Parton Pkwy, Box 5941, Sevierville, TN 37864
E-mail: cinemarrstudios@aol.com
Web Site: cinemarrstudios.com
Key Personnel
Prodr & Dir: Shane Marr
Contact: Doris Marr
Founded: 1999
Video production & post-production.

Cinemat Inc
2520 NW 112 Ave, Doral, FL 33172
Tel: 305-887-7726
E-mail: info@cinematusa.com
Web Site: cinematusa.com
Key Personnel
Owner: Eduardo Scheuren; Jose Vicente Scheuren
Founded: 1997
Television production company that produces original scripted & non-scripted programming.

Cinematography Electronics Inc
5321 Derry Ave, Suite G, Agoura Hills, CA 91301
Tel: 818-706-3334 *Fax:* 818-706-3335
E-mail: info@cinemaelec.com
Web Site: cinemaelec.com
Key Personnel
Pres: Larry Barton
Founded: 1976
Catalog(s) available

Cinemills Corp
2021 N Lincoln St, Burbank, CA 91504
Tel: 818-843-4560 *Toll Free Tel:* 877-CMC-HMIS (262-4647) *Fax:* 818-843-7834
E-mail: sales@cinemills.com
Web Site: www.cinemills.com
Key Personnel
Dir, Sales & Mktg: Matthew M De Mattos
Design & manufacture state-of-the-art lighting instruments for the motion picture & television industries.
Online catalog(s) available
Branch Office(s)
2650 Walnut Ave, Unit F, Tustin, CA 92780
6415 S Tenaya Way, Las Vegas, NV 89113
Tel: 805-238-9056
1720 Redwood Rd, Suite B, San Marcos, TX 78666 *Tel:* 512-537-7049 *E-mail:* sales@ cinemillstx.com *Web Site:* www.cinemillstx. com

Cinequipt Inc
2601 49 Ave N, Suite 500, Minneapolis, MN 55430
Tel: 612-627-9080 *Toll Free Tel:* 800-809-9080 *Fax:* 612-627-9789
Web Site: www.cinequipt.com
Key Personnel
Pres: Dawn Mans *E-mail:* dawn@cinequipt.com
Membership(s): AICP; Production Equipment Rental Association

Cinestate
4100 Swiss Ave, Dallas, TX 75204
E-mail: info@cinestate.com
Web Site: cinestate.com
Key Personnel
Co-Founder & Pres: Will Evans
Co-Founder & Prodr: Dallas Sonnier
Founded: 2016
Entertainment company producing content for books, film & audio.

CineTel Films Inc
8484 Wilshire Blvd, Suite 850C, Beverly Hills, CA 90211
Tel: 323-654-4000 *Fax:* 323-650-6400
E-mail: info@cinetelfilms.com
Web Site: cinetelfilms.com
Key Personnel
Pres & CEO: Paul Hertzberg
Pres, Prodn: Lisa M Hansen
Founded: 1988
Film production & distribution.
Catalog(s) available
Membership(s): Independent Film & Television Alliance®

CineVantage LLC
8560 W Sunset Blvd, 5th fl, West Hollywood, CA 90069
Tel: 323-904-9363 *Toll Free Tel:* 888-518-7571
Web Site: cinevantage.com
Key Personnel
Founder & Prodr: Honnie Korngold
E-mail: hkorngold@cinevantage.com

Full service television production company, supplying reality & nonfiction programming to networks in the US & internationally. Branch office in Denver, CO.

Cinevest
PO Box 261112, Encino, CA 91426
Tel: 310-913-0284
Web Site: www.cinevest.com
Key Personnel
Pres & CEO: Andrew Gellis *E-mail:* agellis@cinevest.com
Distribute & produce IMAX/large format films & glasses-free 3D displays & digital signage content.
Membership(s): AMPAS

CineVideotech Inc
14458 Commerce Way, Miami Lakes, FL 33016
Tel: 305-754-2611 *Fax:* 305-573-5587
Web Site: www.cinevideotech.com
Key Personnel
Pres: Egon Stephan, Jr *E-mail:* estephanjr@cinevideotech.com
Founded: 1968
Catalog(s) available
Membership(s): AICP; Professional Film & Video Equipment Association; SMPTE®

Cinevision Corp
3300 Northeast Expwy NE, Bldg 2, Suite A, Atlanta, GA 30341
Tel: 770-455-8988 *Fax:* 770-455-4066
Web Site: www.cinevisionatlanta.com
Key Personnel
Pres: Stephen A Newton
VP: Saundra Conner
Sales, rentals & service for motion picture projection & sound equipment. Also distributes digital video equipment.
Catalog(s) available
Online catalog(s) available

Cintrex Audio Visual
101 Weldon Pkwy, Maryland Heights, MO 63043
Toll Free Tel: 800-325-9541
E-mail: websales@cintrexav.com
Web Site: www.cintrexav.com
Founded: 1979
Media conversion.

CircuitWerkes Inc
2805 NW Sixth St, Gainesville, FL 32609
Tel: 352-335-6555 *Fax:* 352-380-0230
E-mail: sales@circuitwerkes.com
Web Site: www.broadcastboxes.com; www.circuitwerkes.com
Key Personnel
Pres: Kyle Magrill
Electronic interface gear for professional broadcasting & industrial use. Product line includes telecommunication & audio signaling devices & remote controls.
Online catalog(s) available

Circulating Film & Video Library
Affiliate of The Museum of Modern Art
11 W 53 St, New York, NY 10019-5401
Tel: 212-708-9530 *Fax:* 212-708-9531
E-mail: circfilm@moma.org
Web Site: www.moma.org
Key Personnel
Contact: Kitty Cleary
Catalog(s) available

Tim Cissell Music
10732 W 107 Circle, Westminster, CO 80021
Tel: 303-955-4436
E-mail: tim@cissellmusic.com
Web Site: www.cissellmusic.com

Key Personnel
Owner: Tim Cissell
Founded: 1989
Original music composition & production.

Citizens Systems America Corp
Subsidiary of Citizens Systems Japan
363 Van Ness Way, Suite 404, Torrance, CA 90501
Tel: 310-781-1460 *Toll Free Tel:* 800-421-6516
Fax: 310-781-9152
Web Site: www.citizen-systems.com
Key Personnel
VP, Mktg & Prod Mgmt: Glenn Williams *E-mail:* gwilliams@citizen-systems.com
Label printers for industrial environments, compact desktop & portable POS units for retail, fast, powerful mobile printers for reliable on-the-spot printing, high quality photo printers That meet the needs of professional photographers & kiosk print mechanisms.
Catalog(s) available

City Events Group
57 Park Dr, Troy, MI 48083-2724
Tel: 248-589-0600 *Toll Free Tel:* 800-872-8295
Fax: 248-589-2020
E-mail: info@cityeventsgroup.com
Web Site: www.cityeventsgroup.com
Key Personnel
Pres & CEO: Eric D Schultz *E-mail:* eschultz@cityeventsgroup.com
Founded: 1959
Full service AV rental & staging.

Civins Productions Inc
5881 NW 122 Dr, Coral Springs, FL 33076
Tel: 954-938-8600
E-mail: info@civins.com
Web Site: www.civins.com
Key Personnel
Pres: Gary Civins *E-mail:* gary@civins.com
Founded: 1984
Video pre-production project analysis & strategy, management & scheduling, asset creation, post-production & distribution services. Commercials, corporate communications, training, marketing & viral videos.

Clair Brothers Audio Systems Inc, see Clair Companies

Clair Companies
One Clair Blvd, Manheim, PA 17545
Tel: 717-665-4000 *Fax:* 717-665-8000
E-mail: contact@clairbrothers.com; sales@clairbrothers.com
Web Site: www.claircompanies.com; www.clairbrothers.com; www.clairsolutions.com
Design & install comprehensive AV & lighting systems.
Online catalog(s) available, PDF
Branch Office(s)
3335 Ambrose Ave, Nashville, TN 37207
Tel: 615-227-9881 *Fax:* 615-227-7989
4904 Sharp St, Dallas, TX 75247 *Tel:* 214-922-0289 *Fax:* 214-922-9225

Clair Solutions, see Clair Companies

Clarity Media Group
166 Fifth Ave, 6th & 7th fl, New York, NY 10010
Tel: 212-262-7015
E-mail: info@claritymediagroup.com
Web Site: www.claritymediagroup.com
Key Personnel
Founder & CEO: Bill McGowan
Mng Dir: Mariko Takahashi
Exec Dir, Client Rel: Melissa Hellen
Dir, Training Servs: Chelsea Lobue

Founded: 2001
Full service media training, presentations & communications training.

Clarity Sound & Light
Division of Crystal Clarity Publishers
14618 Tyler Foote Rd, Nevada City, CA 95959
Tel: 530-478-7600 *Toll Free Tel:* 800-424-1055
E-mail: seva@crystalclarity.com
Web Site: www.crystalclarity.com
Teach principles & practices that help individuals develop an expanded, divine awareness & to demonstrate practically how to apply these principles to every facet of life. Produce CDs & DVDs.

Clark
1225 Old Alpharetta Rd, Suite 295, Alpharetta, GA 30005
Tel: 770-888-5088 *Toll Free Tel:* 888-621-8841
E-mail: info@clark.is
Web Site: www.clark.is
Key Personnel
Off Mgr: Anna Cardinal *E-mail:* anna.cardinal@clark.is
Founded: 2009
National performance engineering firm, headquartered in Atlanta, specializing in solutions for venues in the 1,500-8,000 seat range. Clients are primarily churches, ranging from contemporary to traditional, who value technical excellence as a key part of their overall worship experience.
Branch Office(s)
2803 Taylor St, Dallas, TX 75226 *Tel:* 214-377-0573

Clark Services Audio Visual & Exhibit Inc
113 Board Rd, Lafayette, LA 70508
Mailing Address: PO Box 91265, Lafayette, LA 70509-1265
Tel: 337-234-5653 *Fax:* 337-232-0243
E-mail: clarkservices@bellsouth.net
Key Personnel
Owner & Pres: James M Clark
Founded: 1981
Convention services.
Membership(s): Greater Lafayette Chamber of Commerce; Lafayette Convention & Visitors Commission; Louisianna Society of Association Executives

Clark Wire & Cable
408 Washington Blvd, Mundelein, IL 60060-3102
Tel: 847-949-9944 *Toll Free Tel:* 800-222-5348
Fax: 847-949-9595
E-mail: sales@clarkwire.com
Web Site: www.clarkwire.com
Founded: 1989
Membership(s): NAB; SBE

Clark's Audio Visual Services Ltd
1615 Venables St, Vancouver, BC V5L 2H1, Canada
Tel: 604-877-8558 *Toll Free Tel:* 800-667-1819
Fax: 604-879-2993 *Toll Free Fax:* 800-665-2932
E-mail: info@clarksav.com
Web Site: www.clarksav.com
Key Personnel
Mng Dir: James Downey
Founded: 1981
Supplier of AV equipment & technical support services for the convention & meeting industry.
Online catalog(s) available
Branch Office(s)
7030 Woodbine Ave, Suite 500, Markham, ON L3R 6G2, Canada *Tel:* 647-620-8558
Membership(s): AMA; Audiovisual and Integrated Experience Association; MPI

Clarkson Studio
401 N Hoback St, Helena, MT 59601
Web Site: www.clarksonstudio.com
Key Personnel
Owner: Robert N Clarkson *E-mail:* clarkson@mt.
net
Founded: 1974
Imaging for commercial media & public relations, private portraiture, stock images & Internet web pages.

Classic Images Stock Footage LLC
469 1/2 S Bedford Dr, Beverly Hills, CA 90212
Tel: 310-277-0400 *Toll Free Tel:* 800-949-CLIP (949-2547) *Fax:* 310-277-0412
E-mail: sales@classicimg.com
Web Site: www.classicimg.com
Key Personnel
Pres: Marcie Alexander
Vintage & contemporary stock footage library.

ClassicStock.com/Robertstock.com
4203 Locust St, Philadelphia, PA 19104
Tel: 215-386-6300 *Toll Free Tel:* 800-786-6300
Toll Free Fax: 800-786-1920
E-mail: info@robertstock.com; info@classicstock.
com
Web Site: www.robertstock.com; www.
classicstock.com
Key Personnel
Pres: Bob Roberts
Stock photography; contemporary, retro, vintage, historical; color/B&W.
Online catalog(s) available
Membership(s): ASMP

Clayton-Davis & Associates
4 Warridge Dr, St Louis, MO 63124
Tel: 314-862-7800
Key Personnel
Pres: Jennifer Davis Jermak
Founded: 1953
Full circle service in advertising, public relations & marketing.

Clean Slate Video
3070 Kerner Blvd, Unit O, San Rafael, CA 94901
Tel: 415-485-0727
E-mail: info@cleanslatevideo.com
Web Site: www.cleanslatevideo.com
Key Personnel
Owner: Eli Adler
Founded: 1981
Full service video production rentals & staffing.

Clear Choice Creative Corp
260 Monroe St, NW, Warren, OH 44483
Tel: 330-469-9542; 330-469-9524
E-mail: info@clearchoicecreative.com
Web Site: www.clearchoicecreative.com
Web design, search engine optimization, marketing & advertising, social media marketing, video production, public relations & graphic design.

Clear-Com® LLC
Division of HM Electronics Inc (HME)
1301 Marina Village Pkwy, Suite 105, Alameda, CA 94501
Tel: 510-337-6600 *Toll Free Tel:* 800-462-HELP (462-4357) *Fax:* 510-337-6699
E-mail: salessupportus@clearcom.com
Web Site: www.clearcom.com
Key Personnel
Dir, Mktg: Rachel Archibald *E-mail:* rachel.
archibald@clearcom.com
Mktg & Brand Specialist: Mitzi Sterchele
E-mail: mitzi.sterchele@clearcom.com
Founded: 1968
Global provider of professional real-time communication solutions & services. Innovate

market-proven technologies that connect teams together through wired & wireless systems. Clear-Com® products facilitate the seamless coordination of any activity all while maintaining a level of reliability, security & simplicity.
Branch Office(s)
1430 Hocquart, Suite 101, St-Bruno-de-Montarville, QC J3V 6E1, Canada *Tel:* 450-653-9669
Foreign Office(s): Clear-Com LLC, Rm 810, Block B, N Tower, Soho Shangdu, No 8, Dongdaqiao Rd, Chaoyang District, Beijing 100020, China *Tel:* (010) 59002608
HME Clear-Com Ltd, Cambridge Research Park, 2000 Beach Dr, Cambridge CB25 9TP, United Kingdom *Tel:* (01223) 815000 *Fax:* (01223) 815001 *E-mail:* salessupportemea@clearcom.com (Africa, Europe & Middle East headquarters)

Clear Focus Media LLC
6402 Creel Dr, Weston, WI 54476
Tel: 715-212-6239
Web Site: www.clearfocus.media
Key Personnel
Writer, Dir & Prodr: Susan Reetz *E-mail:* susan@
clearfocus.media
Freelance writing, film directing & producing, project coordination for web & print.

Clearlast, see Bardes Products Inc

ClearOne Inc
Edgewater Corporate Park, South Tower, Suite 500, 5225 Wiley Post Way, Salt Lake City, UT 84116
Tel: 801-975-7200 *Fax:* 801-303-5711
E-mail: contact@clearone.com; marketing@
clearone.com
Web Site: www.clearone.com
Key Personnel
Chmn of the Bd & CEO: Ms Zee Hakimoglu
Mktg Mgr: Brent Johnson
Design, develop & sell conferencing, collaboration & network streaming solutions for AV communications.
Branch locations in Gainesville, FL & Austin, TX. Foreign offices in China, Hong Kong, India, Spain & United Arab Emirates.
Online catalog(s) available
Membership(s): Audiovisual and Integrated Experience Association; US Green Building Council; USDLA

Wally Cleaver's Recording Service
2200 Airport Ave, Fredericksburg, VA 22401-7220
Tel: 540-846-6382
E-mail: wallycleavers@mac.com
Web Site: www.facebook.com/wallycleavers
Key Personnel
Owner: Jeff Covert
Catalog(s) available
Membership(s): AES; American Federation of Musicians

Cleveland Costume & Display Corp
1271 Pearl Rd, Brunswick, OH 44212
Tel: 440-846-9292

Clever Cleaver Productions
7050 E Sunrise Dr, Suite 2101, Tucson, AZ 85750
Tel: 520-333-8403
Key Personnel
Principal: Lee Gerovitz *E-mail:* lee@
clevercleaver.com
Founded: 1984
Program producer & distributor.

Clever Devices Ltd
300 Crossways Park Dr, Woodbury, NY 11797
Tel: 516-433-6100 *Toll Free Tel:* 800-872-6129
Web Site: www.cleverdevices.com
Key Personnel
CEO: Frank Ingrassia
COO: Andrew Stanton
Chief Cust Offr: Buddy Coleman
Chief People Offr: Linda Amper
Chief Strategy Offr: Michael Elgarten
SVP, Busn Devt: Saundra Graman; Craig Lang
SVP, Busn Opers: Monica Malhotra
SVP, Engg: Dean Soucy
SVP, New Ventures: Joe Saporita
VP, Engg: Christos Karanicolas
VP, Prod Mgmt: Kirk Shore
Helping the transit industry work with products that keep buses on track & on time, monitor fuel consumption & emissions & keep rider comfortable. Some products are: IVN®; BusTime™-Bus arrival prediction technology; AVM™; CleverCAD®; CleverAnalytics™; SpeakEasy®; AVA®. Fully compliant with the Americans with Disabilities Act of 1990.
Branch Office(s)
575 Fifth Ave, 15th fl, New York, NY 10017
101 Callan Ave, Suite 220, San Leandro, CA 94577
8770 W Bryn Mawr Ave, Suite 1300, Chicago, IL 60631-3515 *Tel:* 773-867-8022
598 Airport Rd, Suite 300, Morrisville, NC 27703 *Tel:* 919-313-3000
RSM Services, 12603 SW Freeway, Suite 255, Stafford, TX 77477 *Tel:* 713-650-0654 (div)
1703 N Parham Rd, Suite 201, Richmond, VA 23229 *Tel:* 804-673-5220
112 S Spruce St, Burlington, WA 98233 *Tel:* 360-856-5315
Clever Devices Canada ULC, 44 Victoria St, Suite 801, Toronto, ON M5C 1Y2, Canada *Tel:* 416-583-5833

Close Up Foundation
1330 Braddock Place, Suite 400, Alexandria, VA 22314
Tel: 703-706-3300 *Toll Free Tel:* 800-CLOSEUP (256-7387)
E-mail: info@closeup.org
Web Site: www.closeup.org
Key Personnel
Pres & CEO: Timothy S Davis, Esq
Treas & CFO: Stephanie Stargell
COO: Eric Adydan
Chief Devt Offr: Mia Charity
VP, Mktg, IT & Transportation: Jodi Stewart Miteva
VP, Sales & Prog Servs: Justin Anderson
Founded: 1971
Partner with educators, schools & youth organizations throughout the country to help young people develop the skills & attitudes to become informed & engaged citizens.

CMD Agency
1631 NW Thurman St, Portland, OR 97209
Tel: 503-223-6794
E-mail: info@cmdagency.com
Web Site: www.cmdagency.com
Key Personnel
Pres: Darren Rankin
Group Acct Dir: Maria Ekstrand; Randy Woloshin
Group Creative Dir: John O'Connell; Jon Stengle
Mng Dir, Film & Video: Mike Pool
Mng Dir, Paid Media: Patti Cody
Mng Dir, Technol & Digital Servs: David Kohn
Dir, User Experience: Sharon Huber
HR Mgr: Paula Ordway
Founded: 1978
Full service creative agency specializing in analytics & metrics, promotion marketing, channel & sales enablement, strategy & planning, content strategy & marketing, technology ser-

vices, creative services, user experience, film & video, paid & earned media.
Catalog(s) available
Branch Office(s)
1201 First Ave S, No 316, Seattle, WA 98134
Membership(s): Oregon Media Production Association; SMPTE®

CMEinfo™
Division of EBIX | Oakstone Publishing
2 Perimeter Park S, Suite 160E, Birmingham, AL 35243
Toll Free Tel: 800-633-4743
E-mail: oakstoneservice@ebix.com
Web Site: www.cmeinfo.com
Medical continuing education products.
Online catalog(s) available

CMI
612 Hampton Dr, Venice, CA 90291
Tel: 310-392-8771
E-mail: cmi@cmifilms.com
Web Site: www.cmifilms.com
Key Personnel
Owner & Dir: Robert Benderson
Make commercials for radio stations & the radio industry.
Membership(s): AICP

CMI Communications
400 Mile Crossing Blvd, Rochester, NY 14624
Tel: 585-424-1900 *Toll Free Tel:* 888-736-8264
Fax: 585-424-1913
E-mail: info@cmiav.com
Web Site: www.cmiav.com
Key Personnel
Pres: Eric M Smith *E-mail:* esmith@cmiav.com
AV services for trade shows, conferences & corporate events.
Branch Office(s)
14 Jupiter Lane, Suite 1, Albany, NY 12205
Tel: 518-867-3288 *Fax:* 518-867-3290
E-mail: albany@cmiav.com
9901 Business Pkwy, Suite J, Lanham, MD 20706 *Tel:* 202-600-4777 *E-mail:* dc@cmiav.com
Membership(s): ASAE; Audiovisual and Integrated Experience Association; The Business Council of New York State Inc; MPI; Professional Convention Management Association; Rental & Staging Network

CMI Media Management
9 W Broad St, Stamford, CT 06902
Tel: 203-989-9955 *Toll Free Tel:* 800-431-1102
Fax: 203-316-8353
Web Site: www.cminyla.com
Key Personnel
CEO: Haitham Wahab
CTO: John O'Connor
Pres: Kenneth Wynne
Dir, Busn Devt: David Kirk
Dir, Client Servs: Deborah DiGiasante
Dir, Digital Delivery: Chris McKenzie
Dir, IT Servs: Andrea DeBellis
Dir, Localization Servs: Yalena Makarczyk
Sr Sales Exec: Bob Bowen
Founded: 1961
Provider of localization services offering subtitling, captioning & dubbing. Digital delivery & media fulfillment.
Branch Office(s)
3765 Cahuenga Blvd W, Studio City, CA 91604-3504 *Tel:* 818-623-2560 *Fax:* 818-623-2565
Membership(s): Airline Passenger Experience Association; American Independent Media Manufacturers Association; International Disc Duplicating Association; National Veteran-Owned Business Association

CNS Productions Inc
897 Royal Ave, Suite A, Medford, OR 97504
Tel: 541-779-3361 *Toll Free Tel:* 800-888-0617
Fax: 541-773-5905
E-mail: info@cnsproductions.com
Web Site: www.cnsproductions.com
Key Personnel
Dir, Res & Educ: Dr Darryl Inaba
Founded: 1980
Comprehensive library of educational textbooks & DVDs.
Online catalog(s) available

Coast Learning Systems
Division of Coastline Community College/Coast Community College District
11460 Warner Ave, Fountain Valley, CA 92708
Tel: 714-241-6109 *Toll Free Tel:* 800-547-4748
E-mail: coastlearning@coastline.edu
Web Site: www.coastlearning.org
Key Personnel
Dir, Mktg & Partnerships: Lynn M Dahnke
Tel: 714-241-6231 *E-mail:* ldahnke@coastline.edu
Founded: 1973
Educational courseware producer. Full production. Products sold online.
Online catalog(s) available

Coastal Training Technologies Corp
Subsidiary of DuPont Sustainable Solutions
500 Studio Dr, Virginia Beach, VA 23452
Tel: 757-498-9014 *Toll Free Tel:* 877-262-7825
Fax: 757-498-3657
E-mail: support@training.consultdss.com
Web Site: www.coastalflix.com
Key Personnel
Global E-Learning Commercial Prod Mgr: Steve Zuckerman
Founded: 1984
CoastalFlix streaming video & content delivery platform. E-learning courses, training DVDs/videos & streaming videos in the areas of workplace safety, sustainable operations, employee training & clean technologies.

Coastline Productions
2647 Gateway Rd, No 105-355, Carlsbad, CA 92009
Tel: 760-598-1860 *Toll Free Tel:* 888-781-5714
E-mail: productions@coastlinevideo.com
Web Site: www.coastlinevideo.com
Key Personnel
Owner & Prodr: Simone Hogan *Tel:* 760-599-9792 (cell)
Founded: 1993
Video production company providing video location production services & HD recording.

Cobalt Studios Inc
134 Royce Rd, White Lake, NY 12786
Mailing Address: PO Box 79, White Lake, NY 12786
Tel: 845-583-7025 *Fax:* 845-583-7025
E-mail: mail@cobaltstudios.net
Web Site: www.cobaltstudios.net
Key Personnel
Co-Founder & Owner: Rachel Keebler
Founded: 1988
Professional scenic painting/decorative painting school & studio, custom-painted backdrops.
Membership(s): Association for Theatre in Higher Education; Educational Theatre Association; USITT

Steven Cohen Motion Picture Production
1182 Coral Club Dr, Coral Springs, FL 33071
Tel: 954-346-7370 *Fax:* 954-346-7370
Membership(s): International Alliance of Theatrical Stage Employees; NATAS; SMPTE®

Cohn Creative Group LLC
630 Ninth Ave, Suite 806, New York, NY 10036
Tel: 212-333-3241 *Fax:* 212-246-5727
E-mail: info@cohncreative.com
Web Site: cohncreative.com
Key Personnel
Pres: Roy B Cohn *E-mail:* roy@cohncreative.com
Founded: 1986
Corporate video & meeting production.

CohuHD Costar LLC
Subsidiary of Costar Technologies Inc
7330 Trade St, San Diego, CA 92121
Tel: 858-391-1800
E-mail: info@cohuhd.com
Web Site: www.cohuhd.com
Key Personnel
SVP & Gen Mgr: Doug Means
Dir, Global Software Engg: Neil Alan
Founded: 1946
Manufacturer of HD CCTV video surveillance camera systems for use in mission-critical sensitive environments.
Online catalog(s) available

Cokesbury
Division of United Methodist Publishing House
2222 Rosa Parks Blvd, Nashville, TN 37228
Tel: 615-749-6000 (UMPH) *Toll Free Tel:* 800-672-1789; 844-381-2708 (cust care) *Fax:* 615-749-6578 *Toll Free Fax:* 800-445-8189
E-mail: cokes_serv@cokesbury.com; customerhelp@cokesbury.com
Web Site: www.cokesbury.com
Key Personnel
Exec Dir, Mktg: Blake Aldridge
E-mail: baldridge@cokesbury.com
Exec Dir, Mdse: Mary McCarthy
E-mail: mmccarthy@umpublishing.org
Exec Dir, Opers: Jeff Barnes *E-mail:* jbarnes@umpublishing.org
Producers of religious & children's programs.

Cole Wire & Cable Co Inc
620 Margate Dr, Lincolnshire, IL 60069-4247
Toll Free Tel: 800-323-1403 *Fax:* 847-634-4988; 847-634-4300
E-mail: sales@colewire.com
Web Site: www.colewire.com
Key Personnel
Owner & Pres: Leo Cole
Founded: 1979

Collaborative Classroom, see Center for the Collaborative Classroom

Collective Systems LLC
76 Progress Dr, Suite 270, Stamford, CT 06902
Tel: 203-973-7011 *Fax:* 203-323-8078
E-mail: sales@collectivesys.com
Web Site: www.cs-av.com
Key Personnel
Owner: Erik VanderPoel *E-mail:* erik@cs-av.com
Full service design/build integrator of conference & AV systems.

Colonial Williamsburg Foundation
PO Box 1776, Williamsburg, VA 23187-1776
Tel: 757-229-1000 *Toll Free Tel:* 888-974-7926
E-mail: social@cwf.org
Web Site: www.colonialwilliamsburg.org; www.history.org/foundation
Key Personnel
Pres & CEO: Mitchell B Reiss
PR Mgr: Joseph Straw *Tel:* 757-220-7287
E-mail: jstraw@cwf.org
Preserves & interprets the historic area through books, videos, recordings & other media.

Color Leasing Studios
330 Rte 46 E, Fairfield, NJ 07004
Tel: 973-575-1118 *Fax:* 973-575-1170
Web Site: www.colorleasingstudios.com

Key Personnel
Prodr: Jack Berberian
Founded: 1966
Product demos, TV spots & corporate marketing; video NLE post services; video location & studio recording & rental.

Colorado Display Systems, see Colorado Time Systems LLC

Colorado Sound Recording Ltd
3100 W 71 Ave, Westminster, CO 80030
Tel: 303-430-8811
E-mail: colosnd@coloradosound.com
Web Site: www.coloradosound.com
Key Personnel
Owner & Studio Mgr: Kevin Clock
Founded: 1977
Full service recording studio with video lock.

Colorado Studios
8455 Highfield Pkwy, Englewood, CO 80112
Fax: 303-388-9600
E-mail: info@coloradostudios.com
Web Site: coloradostudios.info
Key Personnel
Pres & COO: Phillip Garvin *E-mail:* pgarvin@ coloradostudios.com
Contact: Nick Garvin *Tel:* 303-388-8500
    E-mail: ngarvin@coloradostudios.com
Design & build mobile TV trucks.

Colorado Time Systems LLC
1551 E 11 St, Loveland, CO 80537
Tel: 970-667-1000; 970-612-3573 (intl sales)
    Toll Free Tel: 800-279-0111 *Fax:* 970-667-5876; 970-667-1788 (intl sales)
E-mail: info@coloradotime.com
Web Site: www.coloradotime.com
Key Personnel
VP & Gen Mgr: Rick Connell
Proj Mgr: John William
Founded: 1972
A wide range of displays for commercial & sporting applications.
Catalog(s) available

Colorado Video Inc
PO Box 952, Longmont, CO 80502
Tel: 303-530-9580 *Fax:* 303-530-9569
E-mail: sales@colorado-video.com
Web Site: www.colorado-video.com
Key Personnel
Pres & Mktg Mgr: Kirk Fowler
Founded: 1965
Video equipment manufacturer with the ability to provide custom designs for special requirements.
Online catalog(s) available

Coloredge Inc
1919 W Empire Ave, Burbank, CA 91504
Tel: 818-842-1121 *Toll Free Tel:* 800-321-8864
E-mail: lainfo@coloredge.com
Web Site: coloredge.com
Full service graphic arts & visual communications agency.
Catalog(s) available
Branch Office(s)
120 Interstate North Pkwy, Atlanta, GA 30339
    Tel: 404-876-3330 *E-mail:* atlinfo@coloredge. com
190 Jony Dr, Carlstadt, NJ 07072 *Tel:* 201-716-5200 *E-mail:* njinfo@coloredge.com (prodn)
132 W 31 St, New York, NY 10001 *Tel:* 212-594-4800 *E-mail:* nycinfo@coloredge.com
Membership(s): Bay Area Association of Professional Laboratories; Bay Area Association of Professional Photographers; The Imaging Alliance; Society of Industrial Photographers

Colortek of Boston
727 Atlantic Ave, Boston, MA 02111
Tel: 617-451-0894
E-mail: info@colortekofboston.com
Web Site: www.colortekofboston.com
Key Personnel
Owner: Jackie Anderson *E-mail:* jackie@ colortekofboston.com
Full service color lab.

Colortone Audio Visual
181 Westchester Ave, Suite 408B, Port Chester, NY 10573
Tel: 914-592-4151 *Fax:* 914-592-2833
Web Site: www.colortone-av.com
Key Personnel
Pres & CEO: Olivier Peardon
VP, Opers: Steve Bodner
Sales Dir: Stephen Edelman
Founded: 1946
Specialists in custom design & installation.
Catalog(s) available
Membership(s): Audiovisual and Integrated Experience Association

Columbia Lighting
Division of Hubbell Lighting
701 Millennium Blvd, Greenville, SC 29607
Tel: 864-678-1000; 864-678-1664 (cust support)
    Toll Free Fax: 866-898-0131
Web Site: www.columbialighting.com
Key Personnel
Mgr, Mktg Communs: Jill Mungovan
    E-mail: jmungovan@hubbell.com
Founded: 1897
Lighting manufacturer. Manufacturing factories in Juarez & Tijuana, Mexico.

Columbia Pictures Inc
Division of Sony Pictures Entertainment
10202 W Washington Blvd, Culver City, CA 90232
Tel: 310-244-4000
Web Site: www.sonypictures.com
Founded: 1918

Comex Systems Inc
101 Pleasant Hill Rd, Chester, NJ 07930
Tel: 908-881-6301 (cell)
E-mail: mail@comexsystems.com
Web Site: www.comexsystems.com
Key Personnel
VP: Doug Prybylowski
Producer of educational videos & CD-ROMs.
Catalog(s) available

Comm-Arts Inc
2512 E 71 St, Suite A, Tulsa, OK 74136
Tel: 918-493-5700
E-mail: marketing@comm-arts.com
Web Site: www.comm-arts.com
Founded: 1985
Full service marketing, communications & advertising company. Broadcasts TV documentaries & commercials.

CommCreative
75 Fountain St, Framingham, MA 01702
Tel: 508-620-6664 *Toll Free Tel:* 877-620-6664
    Fax: 508-620-0592
E-mail: info@commcreative.com
Web Site: www.commcreative.com
Key Personnel
Pres: Ashley Depaolo
Agency Partner/CFO: Janet Sefakis
Agency Partner/Brand Strategy: Alex Nosevich
Agency Partner/Strategy: Joanna Bittle
VP, Strategy: Amy Grucela
Exec Creative Dir: George Koukkos
Creative Dir, Art: Carter Kasdon

Dir, Digital Mktg: Patrick Negrini
Founded: 1990

Commercial Electronics Ltd
1565 W Seventh St, Vancouver, BC V6J 1S1, Canada
Tel: 604-669-5525
E-mail: info@commercialelectronics.ca
Web Site: commercialelectronics.ca
Key Personnel
Pres: Susanne Adam
Founded: 1957
Electronic sales, installation, service & rental company.
Membership(s): AES; Audiovisual and Integrated Experience Association; Custom Electronic Design & Installation Association; NSCA

Commonwealth Films Inc
223 Commonwealth Ave, Boston, MA 02116
Tel: 617-262-5634
E-mail: info@commonwealthfilms.com
Web Site: www.commonwealthfilms.com
Educational digital media producer & publisher.

CommScope Inc
1100 CommScope Place SE, Hickory, NC 28602
Tel: 828-324-2200 *Toll Free Tel:* 800-982-1708
E-mail: publicrelations@commscope.com
Web Site: www.commscope.com
Key Personnel
Chmn of the Bd: Frank M Drendel
Pres & CEO: Marvin (Eddie) S Edwards, Jr
EVP & CFO: Alexander W Pease
EVP & CTO: Morgan C S Kurk
SVP & Chief Acctg Offr: Brook B Clark
SVP & CIO: Karen K Renner
SVP & Chief HR Offr: Robyn T Mingle
SVP, Gen Coun & Secy: Frank (Burk) B Wyatt, II
SVP, Global Mktg: Fiona Nolan
SVP, Tax: Suzan M Campbell
VP, Corp Audit & Advisory: Wendy Taylor
Founded: 1976
Enterprise network solutions: in-building wireless coverage, structured cabling solutions, automated infrastructure management & power over Ethernet solutions.

Communication Arts Multimedia Inc
1618 Williams Dr, No 5, Georgetown, TX 78628
Tel: 512-868-0548 *Fax:* 512-868-0548
E-mail: mail@commartsmultimedia.com
Web Site: commartsmultimedia.com
Key Personnel
Pres: Eugene Vasconi

Communication Ministries
Division of Christian Church (Disciples of Christ)
PO Box 1986, Indianapolis, IN 46206-1986
Tel: 317-713-2492
Web Site: disciples.org/dns
Shipping Address: 1099 N Meridian, Suite 700, Indianapolis, IN 46204
Membership(s): National Council of Churches Communication Commission; Religious Public Relations Council; World Association for Christian Communication

Communications & Power Industries (CPI), Satcom & Medical Products Division
45 River Dr, Georgetown, ON L7G 2J4, Canada
Tel: 905-877-0161 *Fax:* 905-877-5327
E-mail: satcommarketing@cpii.com
Web Site: www.cpii.com
Key Personnel
Pres: Andrew E Tafler
Uplink amplifier products & systems for satellite communications.
Catalog(s) available

Branch Office(s)
6385 San Ignacio Ave, San Jose, CA 95119-1206 *Tel:* 669-275-2744
MCL Service Ctr, 1938 University Lane, Unit C, Lisle, IL 60532-2314 *Tel:* 630-759-9500 *Fax:* 630-759-5980
176 Technology Dr, Suite 200, Boalsburg, PA 16827-1530 *Tel:* 814-466-6275 *Fax:* 814-466-1104 *E-mail:* bdc@cpii.com
Foreign Office(s): 5-7 Rasheed Ave, Newton, SA 5074, Australia *Tel:* (08) 8337 7805 *E-mail:* adelaide.support@cpii.com

Communications Concepts Inc (CCI)
7980 N Atlantic Ave, Suite 101, Cape Canaveral, FL 32920
Tel: 321-783-5232
Web Site: cci321.com
Key Personnel
Founder & Pres: Jim Lewis
Opers Mgr: Robin Champagne
Founded: 1978
Florida-based digital media company. Specializes in corporate communications, e-learning, HD & 4K video production, web site development & AV rentals.
Catalog(s) available
Membership(s): Florida Motion Picture & Television Association

Communications Design Associates
437 Turnpike St, Canton, MA 02021
Tel: 339-502-6551
Web Site: www.cdaconsultants.com
Key Personnel
Founding Principal: Greg T Vincent
Principal: Cynthia D Oliver; Stewart B Randall *E-mail:* srandall@cdaconsultants.com
Founded: 1993
Consultants for AV, IT infrastructure & broadcast/production video system design, engineering & management services.
Membership(s): Audiovisual and Integrated Experience Association; The Boston Society of Architects

The Communications Group Inc
502 S West St, Raleigh, NC 27601
Mailing Address: PO Box 50157, Raleigh, NC 27650-6157
Tel: 919-828-4086 *Toll Free Tel:* 800-595-2937
E-mail: info@cgfilm.com
Web Site: cgroupfilm.tv
Key Personnel
Principal: Jay Spain *E-mail:* jay@cgfilm.com
Founded: 1982
Documentary film production.
Membership(s): Independent Documentary Association

Communilux Productions
4001 East Side Ave, Dallas, TX 75226
Tel: 214-821-8706 *Toll Free Tel:* 877-323-5189 *Fax:* 214-827-6306
E-mail: info@communilux.com
Web Site: www.communilux.com
Key Personnel
Owner & Pres: Warren Cunningham
Founded: 1982
Theatrical production services.
Membership(s): Professional Lighting & Sound Association

Communitronics Corp
970 Bolger Ct, Fenton, MO 63026
Tel: 314-771-7160 *Fax:* 314-771-9144
E-mail: info@communitronics.com
Web Site: www.communitronics.com
Key Personnel
Pres: Rita Leitensdorfer

Founded: 1969
Newsletter(s) available, quarterly

Community Professional Loudspeakers
333 E Fifth St, Chester, PA 19013-4511
Tel: 610-876-3400 *Toll Free Tel:* 800-523-4934 *Fax:* 610-874-0190 *Toll Free Fax:* 800-220-3661 (orders)
E-mail: info@communitypro.com; sales@communitypro.com
Web Site: www.communitypro.com
Key Personnel
Dir, Sales & Mktg: Julia Lee
Founded: 1968
Manufacturer of sound devices.
Online catalog(s) available
Membership(s): AES; Audiovisual and Integrated Experience Association; International Association of Assembly Managers; NAMM, the National Association of Music Merchants; NSCA

Compact Storage Systems Inc
9757 Reseda Blvd, Suite 68, Northridge, CA 91324
Tel: 818-772-0996
E-mail: info@halfthespace.com
Web Site: www.halfthespace.com
Key Personnel
Co-Owner: Paul Jemielita; Betty M Leonard
Distribute AV cabinetry & storage.

Compass Records
916 19 Ave S, Nashville, TN 37212
Tel: 615-320-7672 *Fax:* 615-320-7378
E-mail: info@compassrecords.com
Web Site: www.compassrecords.com
Key Personnel
Dir: Alison Brown; Garry West
Founded: 1976
Produce & market Celtic music.
Catalog(s) available, free

Compix Media Inc
5151 California Ave, Suite 100, Irvine, CA 92617
Tel: 949-585-0055
E-mail: info@compix.tv
Web Site: www.compix.tv
Founded: 1986
Manufacture & distribution of video character generators.

Composer Louis Anthony deLise
83 Park Dr, Cherry Hill, NJ 08002-3002
Tel: 856-616-2867
E-mail: louis@bocagemusic.com
Web Site: www.louisanthonydelise.com
Key Personnel
Contact: Louis Anthony deLise
Award-winning composer & producer of music for film, television & recordings. Clients include: McNeil Pharma, Janssen Pharma, DuPont Co, Capital Cities Communications & local PBS, ABC & CBS affiliates. Hit records on various labels, including Mercury, Casablanca, Vanguard, Centaur, Def-Soul, EM & BBE. Producer of the Bocage Music Library.

Comprehensive Cable & Connectivity Co
Division of Vcom IMC
80 Little Falls Rd, Fairfield, NJ 07004
Toll Free Tel: 800-526-0242 *Fax:* 201-814-0510
E-mail: sales@comprehensiveco.com; customerservice@comprehensiveco.com
Web Site: www.comprehensiveco.com
Key Personnel
Pres: Scott Schaefer
Founded: 1974
Multimedia sales solutions.
Online catalog(s) available
Membership(s): Audiovisual and Integrated Experience Association; NAB; NSCA; SBE

Comprehensive Technical Group
2030 Powers Ferry Rd SE, Suite 130, Atlanta, GA 30339
Tel: 404-352-3000 *Toll Free Tel:* 888-557-4284 *Fax:* 404-352-2962
E-mail: info@ctgatlanta.com
Web Site: www.ctgatlanta.com
Founded: 1991
Professional broadcast & AV solutions, including sales & consultation, system design & integration, service & repair.
Branch Office(s)
340 Summer Cove Circle, St Augustine, FL 32086, Sr Acct Mgr: Edward Kothera *Tel:* 904-794-2735 *E-mail:* ekothera@ctgatlanta.com
Membership(s): PSNI

Comprompter Inc
1601 Caledonia St, Suite E, La Crosse, WI 54601
Tel: 608-785-7766
E-mail: sales@comprompter.com
Web Site: www.comprompter.com
Key Personnel
Pres: Ralph King *E-mail:* ralph@comprompter.com
Founded: 1985
Newsroom & automation systems.
Catalog(s) available
Membership(s): Minnesota Broadcasters Association; NAB; Wisconsin Broadcasters Association

Computer Dynamics
Division of CIMTEC Automation LLC
3030 Whitehall Park Dr, Charlotte, NC 28273
Tel: 704-227-4600 *Toll Free Tel:* 866-599-6512 *Fax:* 704-583-9671
Web Site: www.cdynamics.com
Founded: 1981
Manufacture flat panel display systems, both computers & monitors.
Online catalog(s) available

The Computer Language Co Inc
5521 State Park Rd, Point Pleasant, PA 18950
Tel: 215-297-8082
E-mail: sales@computerlanguage.com; comments@computerlanguage.com
Web Site: www.computerlanguage.com
Key Personnel
Pres: Alan Freedman
VP: Irma Morrison
Founded: 1978
Distributor of the computer desktop encyclopedia for Windows, iPhone & Android.

Computer Modules Inc
11409 W Bernardo Ct, San Diego, CA 92127
Tel: 858-613-1818 *Fax:* 858-613-1815
E-mail: info@dveo.com
Web Site: www.dveo.com
Key Personnel
Pres: Laszlo "Les" Zoltan
Founded: 1982
AV sales & service.
Membership(s): ATSC; Electronic Retailing Association; NAB; SBE; SMPTE®

Compuvideo Sales USA Ltd
7255 Brunswick Circle, Boynton Beach, FL 33472
Tel: 561-733-4780
E-mail: sales@compuvideo.com; customerservice@compuvideo.com
Web Site: www.compuvideo.com
Manufacture professional test & measurement video equipment.

CompuWeather Inc
Member of FleetWeather Group
2566 Rte 52, Hopewell Junction, NY 12533

Tel: 845-227-8500 *Toll Free Tel:* 800-825-4445 *Fax:* 845-227-8400 *Toll Free Fax:* 800-825-4441
E-mail: info@compuweather.com
Web Site: www.compuweather.com
Key Personnel
Dir, Forensic Div: Steve Roberts
  E-mail: sroberts@compuweather.com
Sr Acct Mgr: Patti Robertson
  E-mail: probertson@compuweather.com
Founded: 1976
Membership(s): AICP; CWSA

Comrex Corp
19 Pine Rd, Devens, MA 01434
Tel: 978-784-1776 (intl) *Toll Free Tel:* 800-237-1776 *Fax:* 978-784-1717
E-mail: info@comrex.com
Web Site: www.comrex.com
Key Personnel
Mng Dir: Kris Specht
Sr Dir, Sales & Mktg: Chris Crump *Tel:* 410-610-5954 *E-mail:* chris@comrex.com
Founded: 1961
Innovator in communications & telephony technologies, providing reliable solutions to meet the demands of live broadcast. Thousands of radio & TV stations trust the quality of our products every day for news, sports & entertainment audio. Headquartered near Boston, MA, our products are offered & supported by a worldwide network of dealers.
Online catalog(s) available
Membership(s): SBE

Comtek Communications Technology Inc
357 W 2700 S, Salt Lake City, UT 84115
Tel: 801-466-3463 *Toll Free Tel:* 800-496-3463
  Fax: 801-484-6906
E-mail: sales@comtek.com
Web Site: www.comtek.com
Key Personnel
Pres: Ralph Belgique
Sales Dir: Laurel Robertson
Communs Dir: Jon Belgique
Assistive listening supplies & professional sound systems.
Membership(s): NAB; NSCA

Comtel Inc
14901 NE 20 Ave, North Miami, FL 33181
Tel: 305-424-4160 (facility servs); 305-424-4178 (local inquiries); 516-816-5152 (natl inquiries)
Web Site: www.comtelinc.com; www.facebook.com/comtelinc/
Key Personnel
VP of Engg: Gene Tally
Mng Dir: Scott Michaeloff
Dir, TV Prodn Servs: Mary Pat Lang
Tech Dir: David Fahey
Sr Ed & Tech Dir: Brian Zeikowitz
Prodn Mgr & Dir: Bill Wasko
Mgr, Creative Servs Admin: Norma Quintero
Proj Mgr: David Fruitman
Sales Mgr, Facility Servs: Bernard Cottle
Mgr, Media Rel & Prodr/Talent: Laura DeAngelis
Sr Prodr: Kendra O'Connor
Founded: 1981
Full service state-of-the art HD production & post-production facility. Service & staffing for television, film & digital media needs. Comtel has 2 of the largest sound stages in South Florida, complete HD editing facilities & one of the only facilities in South Florida where you can transmit in HD. Offers a choice of 2 studios, both with dedicated control rooms.
Branch Office(s)
3401 S Congress Ave, Boynton Beach, FL 33426 (Palm Beach studios)

Concept Associates Inc
5371 Punta Alta, Unit 1E, Laguna Woods, CA 92637
Key Personnel
CEO: William J Connell
Founded: 1972
Award winning children's programming.
Catalog(s) available

Concept Productions Inc
7878 Big Sky Dr, Madison, WI 53719
Tel: 608-833-8273
E-mail: info@conceptpro.biz
Web Site: www.conceptpro.biz
Key Personnel
Audio Engr: Doug Schoebel
Full service digital audio post-production & music recording studio.
Rate card(s) available
Membership(s): American Advertising Federation

Concepts TV Productions Inc
53 Indian Lane E, Towaco, NJ 07082
Tel: 973-331-1500 *Fax:* 973-331-1550
E-mail: sales@conceptstv.com
Web Site: conceptstv.com
Key Personnel
Pres & Creative Dir: Collette Liantonio
CFO: Laraine Lamicella
VP, Sr Ed: James Nolan
VP of Opers: Jon Calderaro
Dir of Busn Devt: Lauren Fahey
Dir of Prodn: Heather Eyrich
Visual Effects Dir: Steven T Miller
Art Dir: Jon Gregory
Post-Prodn Supv: Cheron Walden
Prodr: Rachel Leskanic
Soc Media Spec: Catarina Neto
Founded: 1983
Direct Response Television experts specializing in the production of commercials & infomercials for over 25 years. Most recent award winners include: Bottle Top, Emery Cat & Amish Heat Surge Fireplace. Production & post-production facilities.
Membership(s): Electronic Retailing Association

Concoction Lab
520 Frederick St, No 8, San Francisco, CA 94117
Tel: 415-997-9649 *Fax:* 415-294-2178
E-mail: info@concoctionlab.com
Web Site: www.concoctionlab.com
Theatrical & TV trailers, documentaries, broadcast promos, product launches, sizzle reels.

Concord Jazz
Member of Concord Music Group Inc
5750 Wilshire Blvd, Suite 450, Los Angeles, CA 90036
Tel: 310-385-4455
Web Site: concord.com/labels/concord-jazz
Key Personnel
Pres & CEO: Glen Barros
Founded: 1973
Jazz recording label.
Membership(s): Music Business Association

Concord Records
Member of Concord Music Group Inc
5750 Wilshire Blvd, Suite 450, Los Angeles, CA 90036
Tel: 310-385-4455
Web Site: concord.com/labels/concord-records
Key Personnel
Pres & CEO: Glen Barros
Founded: 1969
Record label.
Membership(s): Music Business Association

Concrete Images
1301 Main St, Venice, CA 90291

Tel: 310-452-9655 *Fax:* 310-452-9866
E-mail: office@concreteimages.com
Web Site: www.concreteimages.com
Key Personnel
Pres & Exec Prodr: Hani Selim *E-mail:* hs@concreteimages.com
Founded: 1998
Line production services.

Conex Electro Systems Inc
789 W Smith Rd, Bellingham, WA 98226-9613
Tel: 360-734-4323 *Toll Free Tel:* 800-645-1061
  Fax: 360-676-4822
E-mail: sales@conex-electro.com
Web Site: www.conex-electro.com
Key Personnel
Pres: John Plattner *E-mail:* john@conex-electro.com
Broadcast equipment manufacturer.
Online catalog(s) available

Conference Technologies Inc
11653 Adie Rd, Maryland Heights, MO 63043
Tel: 314-993-1400 *Toll Free Tel:* 800-743-6051
  Toll Free Fax: 855-329-2844
E-mail: info@conferencetech.com
Web Site: www.conferencetech.com
Founded: 1988
Design & install AV systems; also service, maintenance & support.
Online catalog(s) available
Branch Office(s)
1419 Westpark Dr, Suite A, Little Rock, AR 72204 *Tel:* 501-375-2800
3164 S Country Club Dr, Mesa, AZ 85210
  Tel: 480-816-7526
46727 Fremont Blvd, Fremont, CA 94538
  Tel: 510-935-9424
512 High Point Lane, East Peoria, IL 61611
  Tel: 309-698-8150
1501 Ardmore Ave, Itasca, IL 60143 *Tel:* 630-467-1500
5783 Park Plaza Ct, Indianapolis, IN 46220
  Tel: 317-360-0636
3513 Vine Ct, Davenport, IA 52806 *Tel:* 563-359-1825
333 SW Ninth St, Suite N, Des Moines, IA 50309 *Tel:* 515-280-9800
820 N 15 Ave, Suite 102, Hiawatha, IA 52233
  Tel: 319-363-8144
13228 W 99 St, Lenexa, KS 66215 *Tel:* 913-894-2500
248 N Cleveland Ave, Wichita, KS 67214
  Tel: 316-651-0119
3883 Linden Ave SE, Suite A&B, Wyoming, MI 49548 *Tel:* 616-258-2858
14990 Shepard St, Suite 600, Omaha, NE 68138
  Tel: 402-592-6750
520 Third Ave, Suite 1, Brookings, SD 57006
  Tel: 605-692-2667
2013 Fletcher Creek, Memphis, TN 38133
  Tel: 314-993-1400
5211 Linbar Dr, Suite 506B, Nashville, TN 37211
  Tel: 615-913-3289
3706 Arapaho Rd, Addison, TX 75001 *Tel:* 469-941-4130
11525 Stonehollow Dr, Suite 155A, Austin, TX 78758
4508 W Burnham St, West Milwaukee, WI 53214
  Tel: 262-790-1130
Membership(s): Professional Systems Network International

Conly Productions
1563 Oneida St, Denver, CO 80220
Tel: 303-393-6240 *Fax:* 303-393-6240
Key Personnel
CEO: Paul Conly
Mktg Dir: Maura Adler
Founded: 1980
Recording studio & equipment.

Connecticut Audio & Theatrical Supply
125-F Old Iron Ore Rd, Bloomfield, CT 06002
Tel: 860-206-9555 *Fax:* 860-206-0485
Web Site: www.ctaudio.com
Key Personnel
Owner & Pres: Douglas Fay *E-mail:* doug@
ctaudio.com
Sound system, stages, lighting, LCD video pro-
jectors & plasma screens.
Membership(s): International Alliance of Theatri-
cal Stage Employees

Connections Film & Video Inc
PO Box 110929, Anchorage, AK 99511
Tel: 907-561-6450
Web Site: www.filmalaska.com
Key Personnel
Owner: Jerry LaVine
HD & film production services & rentals.

Conquest Sound Co Inc
209 Cypress Dr, Manteno, IL 60950
Tel: 708-534-0390 *Toll Free Tel:* 800-323-7671
 Fax: 708-534-0398
E-mail: info@conquestsound.com
Web Site: www.conquestsound.com
Key Personnel
Opers: Sue Woolum *E-mail:* sue@conquestsound.
 com
Purch: Michelle Borvan *E-mail:* michelle@
 conquestsound.com
Designer & manufacturer of audio, video & data
 wiring systems & cables.
Online catalog(s) available, PDF download
Membership(s): NAB; NAMM, the National As-
 sociation of Music Merchants; NSCA

Consolidated Communications Consultants
1837 SE Harold St, Portland, OR 97202-4932
Tel: 503-232-9787 *Toll Free Tel:* 800-929-5119
 Fax: 503-232-9787 *Toll Free Fax:* 800-929-
 5119
E-mail: acmrl@myexcel.com
Web Site: www.acmusicresearch.com
Key Personnel
VP & Gen Mgr: Eric Norberg
Founded: 1980
Radio programming, management consulting &
 music research.

Consolidated Display Co Inc
1210 US Hwy 34, Oswego, IL 60543
Mailing Address: PO Box 4108, Naperville, IL
 60567-4108
Tel: 630-851-8666 *Toll Free Tel:* 888-851-7669
 Fax: 630-851-8756
E-mail: info@letitsnow.com
Web Site: www.letitsnow.com
Key Personnel
Pres: Sebastian J Puccio
Full service display company.
Catalog(s) available

Constantine Engineering Labs Co, see CELCO

Contemporary Research
4355 Excel Pkwy, Suite 600, Addison, TX 75001
Tel: 972-931-2728 *Toll Free Tel:* 888-972-2728
E-mail: contact@crwww.com
Web Site: contemporaryresearch.com
Key Personnel
Pres & Chief Engr: Scott Hetzler
Founded: 1994
Designs & manufactures HD AV control prod-
 ucts, HD tuners, HD modulators & software for
 integrated systems solutions applicable to stad-
 iums, arenas, control rooms, corporate facilities,
 education & church facilities, to name a few.
Online catalog(s) available
Membership(s): Audiovisual and Integrated Expe-
 rience Association; NAB; SCTE

Continental Film
1466 Riverside Dr, Suite E, Chattanooga, TN
 37406
Mailing Address: PO Box 5126, Chattanooga, TN
 37406
Tel: 423-622-1193 *Toll Free Tel:* 888-909-3456
 Fax: 423-629-0853
E-mail: info@continentalfilm.com
Web Site: www.continentalfilm.com
Key Personnel
Pres: James L Webster *E-mail:* jim.webster@
 continentalfilm.com
Founded: 1951
AV systems integration.
Online catalog(s) available
Membership(s): Audiovisual and Integrated Expe-
 rience Association

Continental Recordings Inc
23 Mirimichi St, Plainville, MA 02762
Tel: 508-699-0003 *Toll Free Tel:* 888-729-3130
 Fax: 508-699-0004
Key Personnel
Pres & Sales Mgr: L Daniel Flynn
 E-mail: danf31@earthlink.net
Founded: 1963
Recording studio.

Convenience
3012 N Long Ave, Chicago, IL 60641-4930
Tel: 773-545-3073
Key Personnel
Owner & Dir: John A Mazovick
Founded: 1984
Music production, CD release & production
 wholesale.

Convergent Media Systems
Division of Ballantyne Strong Inc
190 Bluegrass Valley Pkwy, Alpharetta, GA
 30005-2204
Tel: 770-369-9000 *Fax:* 770-369-9100
Web Site: www.convergent.com
Key Personnel
Pres: Steve Schilling
SVP, Plan & Busn Opers: Jorge L Rosado
SVP, Sales & Mktg: Gary Johns
VP, Cust Engagement: Brian Williams
VP, Sales & Mktg: Gregg Davis
Sr Dir, Engg: Trevor Davies
Creative Dir: Adam Shilling
Dir, Mktg: Kris Konrath
Mktg Mgr: Whitney Gandara
Provider of broadband platforms.
Brochure(s) available
Branch Office(s)
49 Ontario St, Suite 503, Toronto, ON M5A 2V1,
 Canada *Tel:* 647-349-0723 *Fax:* 770-369-9100
Membership(s): IMCCA

Cooking by the Book
13475 N Applegate Rd, Grants Pass, OR 97527
Tel: 541-846-0654 *Toll Free Tel:* 800-655-9071
 Fax: 541-846-0654
Web Site: www.atasteofnature.org
Key Personnel
Owner & Author: Marcella O Lynch
 E-mail: lynchmarcella@gmail.com
Vegetarian cookbook, vegetarian cooking DVDs
 & television programs.
Brochure(s) available

Cool-Lux
Division of PromarkBRANDS Inc
1268 Humbracht Circle, Bartlett, IL 60103
Toll Free Tel: 800-ACDC-LUX (223-2589)
 Fax: 630-830-2525
Web Site: www.cool-lux.com
Key Personnel
Pres: Ken Orlando

Founded: 1977
Products & services for professional videographers.

Copp Integrated Systems
123 S Keowee St, Dayton, OH 45402
Tel: 937-228-4188 *Toll Free Tel:* 877-450-2677
 Fax: 937-228-2901
Web Site: www.copp.com
Key Personnel
Owner & CEO: William DeFries
Pres: David Markham
Sr Sales Engr: Jeff Perretta *E-mail:* jep@copp.
 com
Production & repair services.
Membership(s): Audiovisual and Integrated Expe-
 rience Association; IBMA; NSCA

CopShopMiami.com
160 E 35 St, Hialeah, FL 33013
Tel: 305-333-5791
E-mail: omar@copshopmiami.com
Web Site: www.copshopmiami.com
Founded: 1989
One stop police props.
Online catalog(s) available
Membership(s): DGA; SAG-AFTRA; Writers
 Guild of America

Corel Corp
1600 Carling Ave, Ottawa, ON K1Z 8R7, Canada
Toll Free Tel: 877-582-6735
Web Site: www.corel.com
Key Personnel
CEO: Patrick Nichols
COO: Prasannaa Ganesan
CFO: Brad Jewett
Gen Coun: Chris Carsen
EVP, Global E-Commerce & Digital Mktg: Rob
 Charlebois
EVP, Global Prods: Gerard Metrailler
EVP, Sales & Mktg: Jason Wesbecher
Founded: 1985
Graphics, digital painting, photo, video & office
 software.
Online catalog(s) available

Corinth Films Inc
3117 Bursonville Rd, Riegelsville, PA 18077
E-mail: john@corinthfilms.com
Web Site: www.corinthreleasing.com; www.
 corinthfilms.com
Key Personnel
Pres & CEO: John Poole, Sr *E-mail:* johnsr@
 corinthfilms.com
Founded: 1977
Distribution of independent & foreign movies.
Online catalog(s) available

Cornell Laboratory of Ornithology
Division of Cornell University Audio-Visual Re-
 source Center
Cornell University, 159 Sapsucker Woods Rd,
 Ithaca, NY 14850
Toll Free Tel: 866-989-BIRD (989-2473)
Web Site: www.birds.cornell.edu
Key Personnel
Exec Dir: John Fitzpatrick *Tel:* 607-254-2449
 E-mail: jwf7@cornell.edu
Educational programming.
Catalog(s) available

Cornerstone Media Productions Inc
306 W Market St, Georgetown, DE 19947
Tel: 302-855-9380
Web Site: www.cornerstonemedia.com
Key Personnel
CEO: Rick Greenberg *E-mail:* rick@
 cornerstonemedia.com
Video, audio & multimedia production services.

Corporate Color Graphics Inc
3525 Lousma Dr SE, Grand Rapids, MI 49548
Tel: 616-774-9583 *Toll Free Tel:* 800-776-9583
E-mail: production@corpcolor.com
Web Site: www.corpcolor.com
Key Personnel
Sr Acct Exec: Kevin Wells *Tel:* 616-774-9583 ext
3117 *E-mail:* kevin.wells@corpcolor.com
Large format printing company.
Catalog(s) available
Membership(s): The Imaging Alliance

CORTRON Media LLC
320 Fort Duquesne Blvd, Suite 100, Pittsburgh,
PA 15222-1146
Tel: 412-565-3471 (ext 3)
Web Site: cortronmedia.com
Key Personnel
Founder & Pres: Louis D Cordera
E-mail: lcordera@cortronmedia.com
Sales Mgr: Doug Malcolm *E-mail:* dmalcolm@
cortronmedia.com
Prodn Specialist: Robert O'Brien
Dir of Opers: Don Wright
Camera Operator: Frank D'Oratio
Founded: 2005
Full service video production & digital media
company. Also offers consulting services for
designing & equipping studios for video pro-
duction, recording & live transmission.

Cosumnes River College
Subsidiary of Los Rios Community College Dis-
trict
8401 Center Pkwy, Sacramento, CA 95823
Tel: 916-691-7474
Web Site: www.crc.losrios.edu
College resource center, including fiber optics &
satellite transmission capabilities.

Council on Foundations
2121 Crystal Dr, Suite 700, Arlington, VA 22202
Toll Free Tel: 800-673-9036
E-mail: membership@cof.org
Web Site: www.cof.org
Catalog(s) available

Countdown Productions Inc
PO Box 180220, Dallas, TX 75218
Tel: 214-321-3233; 214-808-9988 (cell)
E-mail: info@countdownproductions.com
Web Site: www.countdownproductions.com
Key Personnel
Pres: Thomas C Crocker *E-mail:* tom@
countdownproductions.com
Founded: 1986
Professional video, web & corporate productions.

Countryman Associates Inc
195 Constitution Dr, Menlo Park, CA 94025
Tel: 650-364-9988 *Toll Free Tel:* 800-669-1422
Fax: 650-364-2794
E-mail: sales@countryman.com
Web Site: www.countryman.com
Key Personnel
Mktg Dir: Mary Anderson
Microphone manufacturers.
Online catalog(s) available

County Sales
117A W Main St, Floyd, VA 24091
Mailing Address: PO Box 191, Floyd, VA 24091-
0191
Tel: 540-745-2001 *Fax:* 540-745-2008
E-mail: info@countysales.com
Web Site: www.countysales.com
Key Personnel
Pres: Dylan Locke *E-mail:* dylan@countysales.
com
Founded: 1965

Bluegrass, old time & country music distributor.
Catalog(s) available

Courter Films LLC
1145 N Stoney Point, Crystal River, FL 34429
Tel: 352-563-7888 (cell)
E-mail: info@courterfilms.com
Web Site: www.courterfilms.com
Key Personnel
Dir & Ed: Philip R Courter *E-mail:* phil@
courterfilms.com
Exec Prodr: Gay Courter *E-mail:* gay@
courterfilms.com
Founded: 1971
Full service production company.
Catalog(s) available

Coustic
Unit of MiTek Consumer Electronics Group
4545 E Baseline Rd, Phoenix, AZ 85042
Toll Free Tel: 800-225-5689; 800-372-3029 (or-
ders)
E-mail: mtx@mtx.com; orders@mtx.com
Web Site: www.coustic.com
Key Personnel
Pres & CEO: John Ivey
Automobile audio systems.
Online catalog(s) available

Covid Inc
1723 W Fourth St, Tempe, AZ 85281
Tel: 480-966-2221 *Toll Free Tel:* 800-638-6104
Fax: 480-966-6728
E-mail: sales@covid.com
Web Site: www.covid.com
Key Personnel
CFO: Saima Dolphin
Pres: Norm Carson
VP, Prod Devt: Chee Guan Chew
Opers Mgr: John Sullivan
Busn Devt Mgr: Ryan Carson
Mktg Mgr: George Schneider
Manufacturer of AV integration products.
Catalog(s) available
Membership(s): Audiovisual and Integrated Expe-
rience Association

Cox Creative Studios
17602 N Black Canyon Hwy, Phoenix, AZ 85053
Tel: 623-328-4778
Web Site: www.coxcreativestudios.com
Founded: 1982
HDTV production & broadcast facility. Studio,
equipment & truck rentals.

Cox Media
6205 Peachtree Dunwoody Rd, No B17, Atlanta,
GA 30328
Toll Free Tel: 855-755-2691
Web Site: www.coxmedia.com
Key Personnel
SVP: Billy Farina
VP, Busn Devt & Opers: Mike Zeigler
VP, Fin & Busn Opers: Heather Purvis
VP, Mktg: Nicole Buie
Cable networks, television, video & display ad-
vertising, creative services.

Coyote Cowboy Co
PO Box 2190, Benson, AZ 85602-2190
Tel: 520-586-1077 *Toll Free Tel:* 800-654-2550
Web Site: baxterblack.com
Founded: 1982
Audiobooks, CDs & DVDs of performances by
Baxter Black, cowboy poet & author.
Catalog(s) available, annual

CP Communications
15 Ninnie Dr, Wappingers Falls, NY 12590
Tel: 914-345-9292 *Toll Free Tel:* 800-762-4254
Fax: 914-345-9222

E-mail: info@cpcomms.com; sales@cpcomms.
com
Web Site: www.cpcomms.com
Key Personnel
CEO: Kurt Heitmann *E-mail:* kurt.heitmann@
cpcomms.com
Pres: Michael Mason *Tel:* 845-440-0525
E-mail: michael.mason@cpcomms.com
Gen Mgr: Aaron Segarra *E-mail:* aaron.segarra@
cpcomms.com
Founded: 1980
Production communications equipment rentals &
custom engineering solutions.
Branch Office(s)
3506 St Valentine Way, Unit 6, Orlando, FL
32811 *Tel:* 407-843-4225 *Toll Free Tel:* 800-
373-6827 *Fax:* 407-843-4921
9965 18 St N, Suite 2 & 3, St Petersburg, FL
33716

CP Digital
102 Madison Ave, New York, NY 10016
Tel: 212-686-9570
Web Site: www.cpdigital.com
Online & interactive development & production.

CPI Malibu
Division of Communications & Power Industries
(CPI)
3760-A Calle Tecate, Camarillo, CA 93012-5060
Tel: 805-383-1829 *Fax:* 805-383-1859
E-mail: malibu.sales@cpii.com
Web Site: www.cpii.com/division.cfm/10
Founded: 1975
Satellite terminal provider.

CPR MultiMedia Solutions
7812 Cessna Ave, Gaithersburg, MD 20879
Tel: 301-590-9400 *Fax:* 301-590-9402
E-mail: info@cprmms.com
Web Site: www.cprmms.com
Key Personnel
Owner & Pres: Jeff Studley *E-mail:* jstudley@
cprmms.com
Founded: 1988
Full service media component distributor.
Online catalog(s) available
Membership(s): ASAE; Audiovisual and Inte-
grated Experience Association; International
Live Events Association; MPI

CPT Rental Inc
36-01A 48 Ave, Long Island City, NY 11101
Tel: 718-424-1600
E-mail: rental@cptrental.com
Web Site: www.cptrental.com
Key Personnel
Pres: Aaron Fidan
Rent & repair movie equipment.

Craig Recording Studios
2381 Philmont Ave, Suite 112, Huntingdon Val-
ley, PA 19006
Tel: 215-947-8900
Web Site: www.craigrecording.com; www.
craigrecordingstudios.com
Key Personnel
Owner: Michael Gallagher *E-mail:* mike@
craigrecording.com
Recording studios.

Cramer
425 University Ave, Norwood, MA 02062
Tel: 781-278-2300
E-mail: theteam@cramer.com
Web Site: cramer.com
Key Personnel
CEO: Thom Faria
Pres: Rich Sturchio
SVP, Busn Solutions: Scott Connolly
SVP, Mktg Strategy & Technol: Brent Turner

SVP, Opers: Julie Ogles
EVP, Opers: Tim Martin
Exec Creative Dir: Mark Wilson
Dir, Mktg: Kate Romano
Founded: 1982
Full service AV production company & digital marketing.

Crash Video Productions
713 N Mansfield Ave, Los Angeles, CA 90038
Tel: 310-489-6848
E-mail: crash@crashproductions.com
Web Site: www.crashproductions.com
Key Personnel
Owner: Michael Levine
Founded: 1995
Provides camera crews to the television industry.
Branch Office(s)
6775 Santa Monica Blvd, No 4-229, Los Angeles, CA 90038 *Tel:* 310-489-6949

Thomas Craven Film Corp
5 W 19 St, 3rd fl, New York, NY 10011-4216
Tel: 212-463-7190 *Fax:* 212-627-4761
E-mail: info@cravenfilms.com
Web Site: cravenfilms.com
Key Personnel
Pres: Michael Craven *E-mail:* michael@cravenfilms.com
VP, Prodn: Penny Craven
VP, Sales: Ernest Barbieri
Founded: 1952
Complete video, film & webcasting services from script & development through duplication & distribution.
Catalog(s) available

Crawford Media Services Inc
6 W Druid Hills Dr NE, Atlanta, GA 30329
Tel: 404-876-0333 *Toll Free Tel:* 800-831-8029
E-mail: bookit@crawford.com
Web Site: audio.crawford.com; www.facebook.com/crawfordmediaservices
Key Personnel
CEO: Jesse Crawford
Founded: 1981
Post-production audio services.
Membership(s): AES; NATAS; The Recording Academy; SMPTE®; SPARS

Creation Technologies Inc
8999 Fraserton Ct, Burnaby, BC V5J 5H8, Canada
Tel: 604-430-4336 *Toll Free Tel:* 800-736-1271
E-mail: info@creationtech.com; sales@creationtech.com
Web Site: www.creationtech.com
Key Personnel
Pres & CEO: Ashley Dafel
CFO: Annette Cusworth
COO: Todd Baggett
Chief People & Culture Offr: Heather Ohlinger
Chief Sales & Mktg Offr: David Longshore
Founded: 1991
Electronics manufacturer.
Catalog(s) available
Membership(s): AES; NAMM, the National Association of Music Merchants

Creative Artists Agency LLC
2000 Avenue of the Stars, Los Angeles, CA 90067
Tel: 424-288-2000 *Fax:* 424-288-2900
E-mail: info@caa.com
Web Site: www.caa.com
Founded: 1975
Talent agency representing actors, directors, writers, producers, musical artists, comedians, authors, athletes, coaches, broadcasters & more.
Branch Office(s)
3652 S Third St, Suite 200, Jacksonville Beach,

FL 32250 *Tel:* 904-339-0435 *Fax:* 904-758-0562
420 Lincoln Rd, Suite 347, Miami Beach, FL 33139 *Tel:* 305-538-7535
3560 Lenox Rd, Suite 1525, Atlanta, GA 30326 *Tel:* 404-816-2722
444 N Michigan Ave, Suite 3540, Chicago, IL 60611 *Tel:* 312-242-2700
405 Lexington Ave, 19th fl, New York, NY 10174 *Tel:* 212-277-9000 *Fax:* 212-277-9099
6075 Poplar Ave, Suite 410, Memphis, TN 38119 *Tel:* 901-763-4900
401 Commerce St, Penthouse, Nashville, TN 37219 *Tel:* 615-383-8787 *Fax:* 615-383-4937
Foreign Office(s): No 1, E Changan Ave, 6th fl, Rm 601, Dongcheng District, Beijing 100006, China *Tel:* (010) 85247500 *Fax:* (010) 85247599
Shanghai Ctr, 8th fl, Rm 804, 1376 Nanjing Rd W, Shanghai 200040, China *Tel:* (021) 3211 2888
Infanteriestr 11A, Haus C, 80797 Munich, Germany *Tel:* (089) 26 209 7900
CAA Sports Sweden AB, Bryggavagen 133, 178 51 Ekero, Sweden *Tel:* (08) 667 4110
CAA Eleven SARL, Allee de la Petite Prairie 8-10, 1260 Nyon, Switzerland *Tel:* (022) 308 51 51
12 Hammersmith Grove, London W6 7AP, United Kingdom *Tel:* (020) 8846 3000 *Fax:* (020) 8846 3090

Creative Arts Television
PO Box 739, Kent, CT 06757-0739
E-mail: info@catarchive.com
Web Site: www.catarchive.com
Founded: 1950
Educational programming. Archives of filmed & videotaped arts documentaries from 1950 to present.

Creative Backstage
4829 S 36 St, Suite 1, Phoenix, AZ 85040
Tel: 480-580-2222
E-mail: sales@creativebackstage.com
Web Site: www.creativebackstage.com
Key Personnel
Owner: John Garberson *E-mail:* john@creativebackstage.com
Creative production services: lighting, sound, video & staging.

Creative Media Recording
11105 Knott Ave, Suite G, Cypress, CA 90630
Tel: 714-892-9469
E-mail: info@creativemediarecording.com
Web Site: www.creativemediarecording.com
Key Personnel
Opers Dir: Tim Keenan
Prodn Coord: Linda Keenan
Founded: 1970
Digital audio post-production.
Membership(s): SoCal Media Pros

Creative Realities Inc (CRI)
13100 Magisterial Dr, Suite 100, Louisville, KY 40223
Tel: 502-791-8800
Web Site: cri.com
Key Personnel
CEO: Rick Mills
CFO: Will Logan
COO: John Walpuck
SVP, Client Solutions: Alan Buterbaugh
SVP, Mktg & Experience Planning: Beth Warren
SVP, Sales: Alan Buterbaugh
VP, Servs: Troy Walls
Founded: 1997
Digital in-store merchandising, digital signage & marketing solutions for retailers & brands using the latest technologies.

Creative Sound Corp
5515 Medea Valley Dr, Agoura Hills, CA 91301
Tel: 818-707-8986
E-mail: info@csoundcorp.com
Web Site: www.csoundcorp.com
Key Personnel
CEO: Bob Cotterell
Founded: 1983
Manufacture CDs & DVDs - replication, graphics, printing & packaging.

Creative Specialists Inc, see CSI/Orion

Creative Stage Lighting Co Inc
149 Rte 28 N, North Creek, NY 12853
Mailing Address: PO Box 567, North Creek, NY 12853-0567
Tel: 518-251-3302 *Fax:* 518-251-2908
E-mail: info@creativestagelighting.com
Web Site: www.creativestagelighting.com
Key Personnel
Mktg: Dan Sudnicky
Lighting distributor & manufacturer.
Membership(s): Professional Lighting & Sound Association; USITT

Creative Support Services/CSS Music
1948 Riverside Dr, Los Angeles, CA 90039
Tel: 323-666-7968 *Toll Free Tel:* 800-468-6874
Fax: 323-660-2070
E-mail: info@cssmusic.com
Web Site: www.cssmusic.com
Key Personnel
Owner & Chief Mktg Offr: Michael M Fuller
E-mail: mfuller@cssmusic.com
Catalog(s) available
Membership(s): AES; Audiovisual and Integrated Experience Association; Buy-Out Music Association; The Copyright Society of the USA; IAA-VC; NAB; NATPE

Creative Technology
222 Front St, 2nd fl, San Francisco, CA 94111
Tel: 415-513-5918
E-mail: studio@ct-sf.com
Web Site: www.ct-sf.com
Key Personnel
Exec Prodr: Melanie Bass *E-mail:* melanie@ct-sf.com
Prodr: Felicia Libby
Founded: 2011
Boutique post-production studio offering VFX, color grading & finishing services to the advertising & feature film industries.

Creative Technology (CT)
Subsidiary of NEP Group Inc
2200 S Mount Prospect Rd, Unit A, Des Plaines, IL 60018
Tel: 847-671-9670
E-mail: info@ctus.com
Web Site: www.ct-group.com
Key Personnel
Dir, Opers: Jason O'Donnell *E-mail:* jodonnell@ctus.com
Gen Mgr: Scott Heins *E-mail:* sheins@ctus.com
Labor Coord: Chai Abdennabi
E-mail: cabdennabi@ctus.com
New Busn Devt: Josh Anderson
E-mail: janderson@ctus.com
Systems Integration: Steve Rodgers
E-mail: srodgers@ctus.com
Professional full service AV staging company providing turnkey solutions for corporate & special events, trade shows & exhibits, conferences & general sessions, product launches & award ceremonies.
Catalog(s) available
Branch Office(s)
1320 Harbor Bay Pkwy, Suite 135, Alameda, CA 94502, Gen Mgr: David Skaff *Tel:* 510-618-5100 *E-mail:* dskaff@ctus.com

14000 Arminta St, Panorama City, CA 91402, Natl Busn Devt Dir: Curt Petty *Tel:* 818-779-2400 *E-mail:* cpetty@ctus.com

1425 Oakbrook Dr, Suite 100, Norcross, GA 30093, Gen Mgr: Augie Dellapi *Tel:* 770-407-1681 *E-mail:* adellapi@ctus.com

Patrick Commerce Ctr, 6171 S McLeod Dr, Bldg E, Las Vegas, NV 89120, Gen Mgr: Herb Brandt *Tel:* 702-450-3600 *E-mail:* hbrandt@ctus.com

Foreign Office(s): 659 Yin Xing Rd, Bldg 4, Pu Tuo District, Shanghai 201802, China, Mng Dir: Chris Burke *Tel:* (021) 6695 8661 *Fax:* (021) 6695 1328 *E-mail:* cburke@ctasiapacific.com

CT Creative Technology GmbH & Co KG, Kelterstr 69, 73265 Dettingen/Teck, Germany *Tel:* (07022) 253-0 *Fax:* (07022) 253-100 *E-mail:* info@ctgermany.com

3/F, Regency Centre II, 41-43 Wong Chuk Hang Rd, Aberdeen, Hong Kong, Mng Dir: Chris Burke *Tel:* 2989 9300 *E-mail:* cburke@ctasiapacific.com

Doko Bldg 2F, 3-3-4 Minamisuna, Koto-ku, Tokyo 136-0076, Japan *Tel:* (070) 3194-7620 *E-mail:* info@ctasiapacific.com

Argon 21a, 4751 XC Oud Gastel, Netherlands *Tel:* (088) 32 23 764 *E-mail:* info@ctholland.com

Estrada da Lage, n14 armz/cv, 2705-736 Lisbon, Portugal *Tel:* 913296064 *E-mail:* info@ctportugal.com

Video Technology Qatar LLC, Regus Busn Ctr, Off 122, D-Ring Rd, 1st fl, PO Box 24863, Doha, Qatar, Gen Mgr: Irum Ashraf *Tel:* 4423 1221 *E-mail:* iashraf@ctme.co

61 Ubi Ave 1, No 02-01 UB Point, Singapore 408941, Singapore, Mng Dir: Chris Burke *Tel:* 6295 0562 *E-mail:* cburke@ctasiapacific.com

C/ Ciencias 153-155, L'Hospitalet de Llobregat, 08908 Barcelona, Spain, Mng Dir: Frederic Mouffe *Tel:* 93 408 0793 *E-mail:* fred@ctspain.com

Calle Mario Roso de Luna 29, nave 9, 28022 Madrid, Spain *Tel:* 912 465 288 *E-mail:* info@ctspain.com

C Constitucion, 2, 46136 Museros, Valencia, Spain *Tel:* 622 475 395 *E-mail:* info@ctspain.com

Creative Technology-Emirates LLC, Dubai Investment Park 2, Plot 597978, Units 1-3, PO Box 282572, Dubai, United Arab Emirates, Mng Dir: Andy Reardon *Tel:* (04) 885 6020 *E-mail:* areardon@ctme.com

Creative Technology Ltd, Sussex Manor Business Park, Unit E2, Gatwick Rd, Crawley RH10 9NH, United Kingdom, Mng Dir: Mark Elliott *Tel:* (01293) 582000 *E-mail:* mark.elliott@ctlondon.com

Membership(s): Audiovisual and Integrated Experience Association

Creative Video
26 Colonial Ave, Woodbury, NJ 08096
Tel: 856-848-0046 *Fax:* 856-848-8905
E-mail: contact@creativevideo.org
Web Site: www.creativevideo.org
Founded: 1991
Full service corporate video production company & studio.

Cre-a-tv Studios
1393 Progress Way, Eldersburg, MD 21784
Toll Free Tel: 800-628-0112
E-mail: production@cre-a-tv.com
Web Site: cre-a-tv.com
Key Personnel
Pres: Tina Apellaniz Waganer
Dir & Prodr: Richard Waganer *E-mail:* rich@cre-a-tv.com
Premier live events arena & video production studio.

Credo Interactive Inc
4612 Strathcona Rd, North Vancouver, BC V7O 1G3, Canada
E-mail: info@charactermotion.com
Web Site: www.charactermotion.com
Key Personnel
CEO: Tom Calvert
Founded: 1995
Creates innovative content, products, solutions & choreography for 3D character animation applications.
Online catalog(s) available

Crescendo Designs Inc
641 County Rd 39-A, Southampton, NY 11968
Tel: 631-283-2133 *Fax:* 631-204-1066
E-mail: sales@crescendodesigns.com; service@crescendodesigns.com
Web Site: www.crescendodesigns.com
Key Personnel
Pres & Co-Founder: Chris Brody
VP & Co-Founder: Mike Brody
Founded: 2002
Sales & installation of home theatre equipment.
Brochure(s) available, PDF
Branch Office(s)
21 E 26 St, New York, NY 10010 *Tel:* 212-786-5755

Crest Audio Inc
Division of Peavey Commercial Audio
5022 Hwy 493, Meridian, MS 39305
Toll Free Tel: 866-812-7378 *Fax:* 601-486-1380
E-mail: webmaster@peavey.com
Web Site: www.peaveycommercialaudio.com
Manufacture amps, consoles & control products.

Crest Electronics Inc
3703 Alliance Dr, Suite A, Greensboro, NC 27407
Tel: 336-855-6422 *Toll Free Tel:* 888-502-7378 *Fax:* 336-855-6676
Web Site: www.crestelectronics.com
Key Personnel
Off Mgr: Suzie Woodring
Founded: 1974
Video security products & accessories manufacturer.
Catalog(s) available

Cresta Creative
1050 N State St, Chicago, IL 60610
Tel: 312-944-4700 *Fax:* 312-944-1582
E-mail: info@crestagroup.com
Web Site: www.crestacreative.com
Key Personnel
Mng Partner: Joan Beugen
Founded: 1987
Corporate & marketing communications.
Branch Office(s)
6815 Willoughby Ave, Suite 102, Los Angeles, CA 90038 *Tel:* 323-939-7003
Membership(s): BMA; IABC

Crestron Electronics Inc
15 Volvo Dr, Rockleigh, NJ 07647
Tel: 201-767-3400 (sales & support); 201-750-7004 (admin) *Toll Free Tel:* 800-237-2041; 855-791-5322 *Fax:* 201-767-1903 (sales & support); 201-767-8872 (admin)
E-mail: inquiries@crestron.com
Web Site: www.crestron.com
Key Personnel
Pres & CEO: Randy Klein
EVP, Fin: David Hakula
VP, Mktg: Josh Stene
Exec Dir, Sales Strategy & Commun: Raymond Coneys
Founded: 1971
Control & automation systems manufacturer.
Online catalog(s) available

Branch Office(s)
4050 E Cotton Center Blvd, Suite 77, Phoenix, AZ 85040 *Toll Free Tel:* 866-278-0676 *Fax:* 602-437-1766 *E-mail:* khrabczuk@crestron.com

5660 Katella Ave, Suite 150, Cypress, CA 90630 *Toll Free Tel:* 800-827-2188 *Fax:* 562-596-0713 *E-mail:* sflynn@crestron.com

3950 Civic Center Dr, Suite 110, San Rafael, CA 94903 *Toll Free Tel:* 866-634-0904 *Fax:* 415-479-2542 *E-mail:* sflynn@crestron.com

Pacific Design Ctr, 8687 Melrose Ave, Suite G-288, West Hollywood, CA 90069 *Tel:* 562-340-0105 *E-mail:* showroom@crestron.com

5995 Greenwood Plaza Blvd, Suite 190, Greenwood Village, CO 80111 *Tel:* 303-305-4080 *Toll Free Tel:* 866-947-6443 *Fax:* 303-740-2098 *E-mail:* akilgore@crestron.com

1855 Griffin Rd, Suite B-108, Dania Beach, FL 33004 *Tel:* 754-208-5100 *E-mail:* showroom@crestron.com

1060 Maitland Center Commons, Suite 150, Maitland, FL 32751 *Tel:* 407-261-0459 *Toll Free Tel:* 866-273-7876 *Fax:* 407-261-0913 *E-mail:* nvillamil@crestron.com

11660 Alpharetta Hwy, Suite 740, Roswell, GA 30076 *Toll Free Tel:* 877-339-0060 *Fax:* 678-339-0066 *E-mail:* dbowen@crestron.com

Parkway Corporate Place, 935 National Pkwy, Schaumburg, IL 60173 *Tel:* 847-273-0700 *Toll Free Tel:* 800-949-3465 *Fax:* 847-273-0701 *E-mail:* lroulo@crestron.com

8161 Maple Lawn Blvd, Suite 100, Fulton, MD 20759 *Toll Free Tel:* 866-537-6298 *Fax:* 301-725-0629 *E-mail:* dharvey@crestron.com

3763 Howard Hughes Pkwy, Suite 100, Las Vegas, NV 89169 *Toll Free Tel:* 866-634-0903 *Fax:* 702-731-1297 *E-mail:* ajuarez@crestron.com

Decoration & Design Bldg, 979 Third Ave, Suite 407, New York, NY 10022 *Tel:* 212-223-2434 *E-mail:* showroom@crestron.com

1200 Lakeside Pkwy, Suite 250, Flower Mound, TX 75028 *Tel:* 972-538-2638 *Toll Free Tel:* 866-999-1300 *Fax:* 972-724-2580 *E-mail:* scuna@crestron.com

5120 Woodway, Suite 119, Houston, TX 77056 *Toll Free Tel:* 800-237-2041 *E-mail:* showroom@crestron.com

7250 Dallas Pkwy, Suite 600, Plano, TX 75024 *Toll Free Tel:* 800-237-2041 *E-mail:* planohq2@crestron.com

10 Carlson Ct, Suite 800, Toronto, ON M9W 6L2, Canada *Tel:* 416-213-1477 *Toll Free Tel:* 877-732-7378 *Fax:* 416-213-0217 *E-mail:* cprueckel@crestron.com

Membership(s): American Institute of Architects; Audiovisual and Integrated Experience Association; Consortium of College & University Media Centers; Consumer Technology Association™; Custom Electronic Design & Installation Association; EDUCAUSE®; IALD; Illuminating Engineering Society; NSCA; Society for College and University Planning; US Green Building Council

Crew West Inc
1515 W Deer Valley Rd, Suite C-109, Phoenix, AZ 85027
Tel: 480-367-6888 *Toll Free Tel:* 888-444-2739 *Fax:* 480-367-6688
E-mail: tvcrews@crewwestinc.com
Web Site: www.crewwestinc.com
Key Personnel
Corp Pres & Dir, Photog: Jim Farrell
Busn Mgr: Nancy Morningstar *E-mail:* nancym@crewwestinc.com
Network level HDTV & production video crews. Satellite trucks & live uplink studio.

Crispin Corp
600 Wade Ave, Raleigh, NC 27605
Tel: 919-845-7744 *Fax:* 919-845-7766

E-mail: welisten@crispincorp.com; support@
crispincorp.com
Web Site: www.crispincorp.com
Key Personnel
CEO: David Jones
CTO: Jim Zagrobelny
VP, Sales & Busn Strategy: Jill Walters
Sr Dir, Mktg & Opers: Sara DeVaney
Sr Dir, Tech Servs: Joe Walker
Dir, Software Devt: Ed Molina
Founded: 1997
Supplier of master control automation, asset man-
agement solutions for broadcasters, cable oper-
ators & other TV & media operations.

Criterion Collection
215 Park Ave S, 5th fl, New York, NY 10003
Tel: 212-756-8822
E-mail: orders@criterion.com; press@criterion.
com
Web Site: www.criterion.com
Founded: 1984
Classic & contemporary film publishing.
Online catalog(s) available

Cross-Cultural Communications
Subsidiary of Cross-Cultural Communications
Publications Corp
239 Wynsum Ave, Merrick, NY 11566-4725
Tel: 516-868-5635 *Fax:* 516-379-1901
E-mail: info@cross-culturalcommunications.com
Web Site: www.cross-culturalcommunications.com
Key Personnel
Publr & Ed-in-Chief: Stanley H Barkan
Art Dir: Bebe Barkan
Publicity Dir: Mia Barkan Clarke
Founded: 1972
Distribute & publish audiocassettes, videocas-
settes, CDs, records & DVDs.
Flyer(s) available, free, continuous
Foreign Office(s): Via Tripoli 13, 90138 Palermo
PA, Italy, Contact: Nicolo D'Alessandro
Tel: (091) 322030
Membership(s): American Literary Translators
Association

Crossroads Audio Inc
2623 Myrtle Springs Ave, Dallas, TX 75220
Tel: 214-358-2623 *Toll Free Tel:* 800-287-0436
Fax: 214-358-0185
E-mail: mail@crossroadsaudio.com
Web Site: www.crossroadsaudio.com
Key Personnel
Dir, Opers, Chief Engr & Partner: Ed Spoto
Pres, Gen Mgr & Partner: Robin Magruder
Sr Engr-at-Large & Partner: Stewart Bennett
Chief Engr: Dave Bell
Concerts & Event Servs Mgr: Mike Ponczek
Mgr, Rentals & Sales Depts: Chris Rodriguez
Founded: 1972
Professional audio sales, rentals & event services.
Membership(s): AES; NAMM, the National Asso-
ciation of Music Merchants

Crown Ministries International
Division of Youth With a Mission, International
Communications Network
PO Box 26479, Colorado Springs, CO 80936-
6479
Toll Free Tel: 800-433-4685
E-mail: crownmin@intlcom.org
Web Site: www.crownmin.org
Founded: 1979
Religious educational programming.
Catalog(s) available
Membership(s): ICVM

CRT Custom Products Inc
7532 Hickory Hills Ct, Whites Creek, TN 37189
Tel: 615-876-5490 *Toll Free Tel:* 800-453-2533
Fax: 615-876-0096

E-mail: sales@crtcustomproducts.com
Web Site: www.crtcustomproducts.com
Key Personnel
CEO: Brandee Wilson *Tel:* 615-876-5490 ext 132
E-mail: bwilson@crtcustomproducts.com
Mktg Dir: Cory Harkins *Tel:* 615-876-5490 ext
152 *E-mail:* coryharkins@crtcustomproducts.
com
Founded: 1979
Manufacturing, printing, packaging & fulfillment.

Crystal Clear Media Group
7370 Dogwood Park, Richland Hills, TX 76118
Toll Free Tel: 800-880-0073
E-mail: information@crystalclearcds.com
Web Site: www.crystalclearcds.com
Key Personnel
Head, Sales: Jim Cocke *Tel:* 214-349-0081
E-mail: jim@crystalclearcds.com
Manufacturer & distributor of CDs & DVDs.
Catalog(s) available

Crystal Pictures Inc
2000 Riverside Dr, Asheville, NC 28804
Tel: 828-285-9995 *Toll Free Tel:* 800-669-4057
Fax: 828-285-9997
E-mail: cryspic@aol.com
Web Site: ivyvideo.com
Key Personnel
Pres: Joshua Tager
Video sales & rentals.
Catalog(s) available, free

Crystal Productions
401 Hickory St, Fort Collins, CO 80524
Toll Free Tel: 800-289-9299
E-mail: custserv@crystalproductions.com
Web Site: www.crystalproductions.com
Key Personnel
Pres: Amy Woodworth
Produces & distributes educational materials per-
taining to art.
Online catalog(s) available

Crystal Pyramid Productions™
Subsidiary of Crystal Pyramid Inc
7323 Rondel Ct, San Diego, CA 92119-1530
Tel: 619-644-3000
E-mail: info@crystalpyramid.com
Web Site: sandiegovideoproduction.com
Key Personnel
CEO: Mark Schulze
CFO & COO: Patty Mooney
Founded: 1981
Full service video production company. Equip-
ment includes HD to 4K camera systems,
sound & grip gear.
Membership(s): SDMediaPros

Crystal Records Inc
28818 NE Hancock Rd, Camas, WA 98607
Tel: 360-834-7022 *Fax:* 360-834-9680
E-mail: info@crystalrecords.com
Web Site: www.crystalrecords.com
Key Personnel
Pres: Peter Christ
Founded: 1966
Record producers.
Catalog(s) available, free, 1-2 times/yr

CSI Film & Video LLC
1913 Sonora St, Fort Collins, CO 80525
Tel: 970-310-9039
Web Site: csifilms.com
Key Personnel
Prodr & Dir: Blake Miller *E-mail:* blake@
csifilms.com
Creative Dir: Rob Aukerman
Dir, Photog: Randy Pfizenmaier

Photog: Tom Bol
Production company shooting outdoor themed
films.

CSI Films, see CSI Film & Video LLC

CSI/Orion
1709 Utica Sq, Tulsa, OK 74114
Tel: 918-743-7881 *Toll Free Tel:* 888-579-1850
Web Site: www.csihealthcarecommunications.com;
www.csiorion.com
Founded: 1970
Web-based communications tools for organiza-
tions in healthcare & other key industries.

CSI Rentals
133 W 19 St, Ground Level, New York, NY
10011
Tel: 212-243-7368 *Fax:* 212-243-2102
E-mail: orders@csirentals.com
Web Site: www.csirentals.com
Photo & video equipment featuring camera &
lighting rentals for still & video as well as expendables, photo & video supplies.
Branch Office(s)
1138 Flushing Ave, Ground Level, Brooklyn, NY
11237 *Tel:* 718-366-7368 *Fax:* 718-366-1721
E-mail: ordersbk@csirentals.com

CSPI
175 Cabot St, Suite 210, Lowell, MA 01854
Tel: 978-663-7598; 978-954-5038
Toll Free Tel: 800-325-3110
E-mail: hello@cspi.com
Web Site: www.cspi.com
Key Personnel
CEO & Gen Mgr, IT Managed Servs: Victor
Dellovo
CFO: Gary Levine
Chief Acctg Offr: Mike Newbanks
Gen Mgr, Cybersecurity Div: Gary Southwell
Founded: 1968
Professional IT services for entire IT life cycle
delivering innovative technology solutions for
data centers, advanced security, wireless & mo-
bility, unified collaboration & networking.
Online catalog(s) available

CSPMedia.com
9411 Gumtree Park St, Capitol Heights, MD
20743
Tel: 301-350-3181
Web Site: www.soundstore.com; www.cspmedia.
com
Key Personnel
Owner: Nolan C Church
Legal multimedia-forensic audio/video, editing,
archiving, format conversion & webcasting.
Online catalog(s) available

CTGaudio
2100 Constitution Blvd, Sarasota, FL 34231
Tel: 941-922-2322 *Toll Free Fax:* 866-871-6874
E-mail: orders@ctgaudio.com; info@ctgaudio.
com
Web Site: ctgaudio.com
Key Personnel
Pres & CEO: Dave J Newman
Founded: 1995
Manufacture installed sound systems for telecon-
ferencing.
Brochure(s) available, annual
Membership(s): Audiovisual and Integrated Expe-
rience Association

C2 Imaging
2 Harborside, 200 Hudson St, Suite 201, Jersey
City, NJ 07311
Tel: 646-557-6300
Web Site: www.c2spark.com

Key Personnel
Pres: Mark Auth
E-business provider of media graphics.
Brochure(s) available
Price list(s) available

Cue Tech Teleprompting Inc
5527 Satsuma Ave, North Hollywood, CA 91601
Tel: 818-487-2700 *Fax:* 818-487-2750
E-mail: info@cue-tech.com
Web Site: www.cue-tech.com
Key Personnel
Owner: Pamela Kutsunai
Teleprompter systems.

Curb Entertainment International Corp
3907 W Alameda Ave, Burbank, CA 91505
Tel: 818-843-8580 *Fax:* 818-566-1719
Web Site: www.curbentertainment.com
Key Personnel
Chmn: Mike Curb
Pres: Carole Curb Nemoy *E-mail:* ccurb@curb.
com
Dir/Head, Dist & Post Servs: Mona Kirton
E-mail: mkirton@curb.com
Worldwide Servicing Coord: Eddie Francis
E-mail: efrancis@curb.com
Founded: 1984
Film production & distribution.
Membership(s): Independent Film & Television
Alliance®

Curtis Company
886 Plantation Way, Montgomery, AL 36117
Mailing Address: PO Box 210-215, Montgomery,
AL 36121
Tel: 334-279-7127 *Toll Free Tel:* 800-228-5937
Fax: 334-270-8787 *Toll Free Fax:* 800-325-
6341
Web Site: www.curtisav.com
Key Personnel
Owner & Pres: Larry Huffstetter *E-mail:* larryh@
curtisav.com
Educational AV equipment.
Online catalog(s) available

Curtis Inc
1105 Western Ave, Cincinnati, OH 45203
Tel: 513-621-8895 *Toll Free Tel:* 800-733-2878
Fax: 513-621-0942
E-mail: info@curtisinc.com
Web Site: www.curtisinc.com
Key Personnel
VP: Karen Sellers *E-mail:* ksellers@curtisinc.com
Founded: 1985
Visual communications provider.

Custom Color Corp
14320 W 101 Terr, Lenexa, KS 66215
Tel: 913-730-3100 *Fax:* 913-730-3101
E-mail: info@customcolor.com
Web Site: www.customcolor.com
Key Personnel
Pres & CEO: Matt Keith
COO: Mike Lecus
VP: Jason Milbourne
VP, Fin & Devt: Brett Saunders
Prodn Mgr: Rodney Mulick
Founded: 1969
Comprehensive full service digital printing com-
pany.
Catalog(s) available

Custom Computer Specialists Inc
70 Suffolk Ct, Hauppauge, NY 11788
Tel: 631-864-6699 *Toll Free Tel:* 800-589-8989
Fax: 401-765-6440 *Toll Free Fax:* 800-986-
5518
E-mail: info@customtech.com; support@
customtech.com
Web Site: www.customonline.com

Key Personnel
Pres & CEO: Gregory G Galdi
Pres, IT Div: Dennis Callagy
VP, Fin: Christine Bergold
VP, Support Servs: Tom Franson
VP, Technol & NY Gen Mgr: Kyriakos Kaimis
Founded: 1979
Technology solutions to corporate, education,
government & healthcare clients.
Branch Office(s)
One Penn Plaza, 36th fl, Suite 3622, New York,
NY 10019 *Tel:* 212-786-7462
33 Wood Ave S, Suite 600, Iselin, NJ 08830
Fax: 401-765-6440
6 Blackstone Valley Place, Suite 402, Lincoln,
RI 02865, Gen Mgr: Suzanne McLaughlin
Fax: 401-765-6440

Custom Video Productions Inc
Division of South Bay Custom Video Productions
Inc
707 Torrance Blvd, Suite 105, Redondo Beach,
CA 90277
Tel: 310-543-4901
E-mail: info@customvideo.tv
Web Site: www.customvideo.tv
Key Personnel
Exec Prodr: Michael Ude *E-mail:* michael@
customvideo.tv
Sr Mktg Dir & Prodr: Hugh Malay
E-mail: hugh@customvideo.tv
Founded: 1990
Video production, duplication, transfer, replication
& packaging services. Media placement.

Custom Video Productions Inc
15 Lake Shore Dr, Red Bank, NJ 07701
Tel: 732-936-1001
E-mail: info@cvpnj.com
Web Site: www.cvpnj.com
Key Personnel
Pres: Frank Farrell
Busn Devt Mgr: Noreen Miller
Founded: 1978
Full service multimedia production company of-
fering services to corporations. Complete mu-
sic & sound effects library, scripting, camera,
editing, multimedia, high quality duplication,
professional narrators & studio sound booth.

**The Cutting Corporation, GraphicAudio® &
Archival Sound Lab**
7520 Standish Place, Suite 100, Rockville, MD
20855
Tel: 301-654-CUTS (654-2887) *Fax:* 301-444-
4519
E-mail: sales@graphicaudio.net
Web Site: cuttingcorporation.com; www.
graphicaudio.net
Key Personnel
GraphicAudio & Archival Sound Lab VP & Exec
Prodr: Anji Cornette
Archival Sound Lab Dir: Aaron Coe
Founded: 1971
Audiobook publisher, production & duplication;
audio preservation services.
Catalog(s) available

Cutting Edge Productions
22904 Lockness Ave, Torrance, CA 90501
Tel: 310-326-4500; 818-503-0400
E-mail: info@cuttingedgeproductions.tv
Web Site: www.cuttingedgeproductions.tv
Full service broadcast, meeting & event technol-
ogy company. Supplies video, audio & lighting
services nationwide & operates a TV studio.

**Cuyahoga Community College Student
Production Office (SPO)**
Unit of Television & Video Production Dept
(TVP)

Metro Campus Media Ctr, 2900 Community College Ave, Cleveland, OH 44115
Tel: 216-987-6000
Web Site: www.tri-c.edu
Key Personnel
Prog Mgr: Mike Pella *Tel:* 216-987-0245
E-mail: michael.pella2@tri-c.edu; Linda Lee
Will *Tel:* 216-987-0252 *E-mail:* linda.will@tri-
c.edu
Provides students in the Creative Arts disciplines
with a media production experience in both a
professional & educational setting. Students are
hired by the college as a paid intern with the
option to receive course credit. These student
assistants are assigned to various media arts &
graphic design projects, live events & broadcast programs for several college departments
& partners.

CVW Event Productions
470 Spring Park Place, Suite 900, Herndon, VA
20170
Tel: 703-891-2620 *Fax:* 703-891-2625
E-mail: info@cvwevents.com
Web Site: cvwevents.com
Key Personnel
Pres & Exec Prodr: Kirby Whyte *E-mail:* kw@
cvwevents.com
Ed/Prodr: Adam Harris
Acct Exec: Kathleen Murphy
Founded: 1981
Full service AV production company.
Membership(s): Television, Internet & Video As-
sociation of DC Inc

CyberIconics International
1752 N 74 Place, Mesa, AZ 85207-2932
Tel: 480-396-8731
Key Personnel
Pres: Ron L McIntyre
Religious educational programming producer.

Cybernetics
111 Cybernetics Way, Yorktown, VA 23693
Tel: 757-833-9000 *Fax:* 757-833-9300
E-mail: techsales@cybernetics.com;
customer_service@cybernetics.com; media@
cybernetics.com
Web Site: www.cybernetics.com
Founded: 1978
Design & manufacture high performance disk,
tape & virtual tape storage & backup solutions.

CyberOptics Corp
5900 Golden Hills Dr, Minneapolis, MN 55416
Tel: 763-542-5000 *Fax:* 763-542-5100
E-mail: info@cyberoptics.com
Web Site: cyberoptics.com
Key Personnel
Pres & CEO: Dr Subodh Kulkarni
COO, CFO & VP, Fin: Jeffrey Bertelsen
VP, Technol & Busn Devt: Timothy Skunes
VP, Worldwide Opers: Corey Felber
Founded: 1984
Global developer & manufacturer of high preci-
sion sensing technology solutions use in gen-
eral purpose metrology & 3D scanning, surface
mount technology (SMT) & semiconductor
markets to significantly improve yields & pro-
ductivity.
Foreign Office(s): CyberOptics (China) Co Ltd,
No 1395 Hengshan Rd, Kunshan, Jiangsu
215300, China *Tel:* (0512) 50156306
CyberOptics (Singapore) Pte Ltd, No 21 Ubi Rd
1, Suite 02-01, Singapore 408724, Singapore
Tel: 6744 3021 *Fax:* 6844 5331
CyberOptics Ltd, 15a, Hornbeam Park Oval,
Hornbeam Park, Harrogate, N Yorks HG2
8RB, United Kingdom *Tel:* (01423) 871411
Fax: (01756) 700440

Membership(s): IPC —Association Connecting Electronics Industries®; Semiconductor Equipment & Materials International; SPIE; Surface Mount Technology Association

Czar Productions Inc
809 New Britain Ave, Hartford, CT 06106
Tel: 860-953-0809
E-mail: czar.productions@snet.net
Key Personnel
Owner & Mktg Mgr: Gene Czarnecki
Video production company.

D A S Audio of America Inc
6900 NW 52 St, Miami, FL 33166
Tel: 305-436-0521 *Fax:* 305-436-0528
E-mail: infousa@dasaudio.com
Web Site: www.dasaudio.com
Key Personnel
Gen Mgr: Jaime Villegas
Speaker distributor.

D A Sound
12932 SE Kent Kangley Rd, Box 460, Kent, WA 98030
Tel: 206-632-7773 *Toll Free Tel:* 855-DASOUND (327-6863)
E-mail: info@dasound.biz
Web Site: www.dasound.biz
Key Personnel
Owner: David Hunter *Tel:* 253-569-5560
    E-mail: david@dasound.biz; Mark Szczerba *Tel:* 253-880-4699 *E-mail:* mark@dasound.biz
Founded: 1987
Audio sales & rentals.

Da-Lite, a Legrand AV Inc brand
3100 N Detroit St, Warsaw, IN 46582
Tel: 574-267-8101 *Toll Free Tel:* 866-977-3901
E-mail: av.da-lite.support@legrand.com
Web Site: www.legrandav.com/products/da-lite
Key Personnel
Dir, Prod Mgmt: Wendy Cox *E-mail:* wendy.cox@legrand.com
Sr Mgr, Prod Mktg: Sarah Baum *E-mail:* sarah.baum@legrand.com
Founded: 1909
World leader in projection screen design & surface technology. Product lines include custom surface solutions, manual & electric front projection screens as well as rear projection screens, lecterns, computer furniture, easels, projection carts & stands, TV/AV carts & simulation.
Catalog(s) available, free
Online catalog(s) available
Branch Office(s)
11500 Williamson Rd, Blue Ash, OH 45241
Tel: 513-489-3222
Membership(s): Audiovisual and Integrated Experience Association; Consumer Technology Association™; Custom Electronic Design & Installation Association; NAB; NAPM; NSCA

Daburn Electronics & Cable Corp
44 Richboynton Rd, Dover, NJ 07801
Tel: 973-328-3200 *Fax:* 973-328-3130
E-mail: daburn@daburn.com
Web Site: www.daburn.com
Founded: 1964
Supplier of wire, cable & associated hardware, shrinkable tubing, sleeving & cold shrinking tape.
Online catalog(s) available

DACAPO Productions Inc
516 Hargrave St, Winnipeg, MB R3A 0X8, Canada
Tel: 204-956-2867 *Fax:* 204-956-2869
Web Site: www.dacapo.ca

Key Personnel
Mgr, Opers: Clinton Skibitzky
Music Prodr & Composer: Olaf Pyttlik
Voice Dir: Nolan Balzer
Audio Engr: Nicholas Mann
Audio Engr & Prodn Mgr: Kristen Martin
Audio Engr & SFX Designer: Giselle Nazareno
Commercial Audio Engr: Steve Payne
Founded: 1998
Complete digital audio service from original music to voice-overs for everything from TV & film to advertising campaigns & web multimedia.

Dadco
11078 Fleetwood St, Sun Valley, CA 91352
Tel: 818-768-8886
Web Site: www.dadcopowerandlights.com
Founded: 1995
Manufacturer of portable power distribution systems & cable assemblies. Lighting & equipment rentals & sales. Generator rentals, tractor rentals & production vehicle rentals. Manufacturer of Sunray Lighting. Repair department available.

Dage-MTI
701 N Roeske Ave, Michigan City, IN 46360
Tel: 219-872-5514 *Fax:* 219-872-5559
E-mail: info@dagemti.com
Web Site: dagemti.com
Key Personnel
Pres: John Moore
VP: Peggy Moore
VP, Busn Devt: Nate Jones
Founded: 1952
Design advanced HD microscope cameras & digital streaming solutions.
Online catalog(s) available

Daily Electronics Corp
PO Box 822437, Vancouver, WA 98682-0053
Tel: 360-896-8856 *Toll Free Tel:* 800-346-6667
    Fax: 360-896-5476
E-mail: daily@worldaccessnet.com
Web Site: dailyelectronics.net
Key Personnel
Pres: Jim Grimes
Transmitting & camera tubes, electron tubes & accessories.

Dake Publishing Inc
764 Martins Chapel Rd, Lawrenceville, GA 30046
Toll Free Tel: 800-241-1239
E-mail: info@dake.com
Web Site: www.dake.com
Key Personnel
Dir, Prod Devt: Mark Allison *E-mail:* mark@dake.com
Gen Mgr: Derrick Germaine *E-mail:* derrick@dake.com
Founded: 1961
Religious publishing.
Catalog(s) available
Membership(s): Evangelical Christian Publishers Association

Dalet Digital Media Systems
88 Pine St, 8th fl, New York, NY 10005
Tel: 212-269-6700
E-mail: ddms@dalet.com
Web Site: www.dalet.com
Founded: 1990
Developer of audio, video & multimedia software solutions for the broadcast industry, government agencies, corporations & educational institutions.
Membership(s): NAB; RTDNA

Dalet US, see Dalet Digital Media Systems

Dallas Prompter
PO Box 571233, Dallas, TX 75357
Tel: 214-275-9000
Web Site: www.dallasprompter.com
Key Personnel
Pres: Greg Stephenson *E-mail:* g@dallasprompter.com
Founded: 1985
Provide teleprompter services & equipment for meetings, conventions & video projects.
Membership(s): Dallas Producers Association; Texas Association of Motion Media Professionals

Dance Horizons Video
Division of Princeton Book Company, Publishers
15 W Front St, 3rd fl, Trenton, NJ 08608
Tel: 609-426-0602 *Toll Free Tel:* 800-220-7149
    Fax: 609-426-1344
E-mail: pbc@dancehorizons.com
Web Site: www.dancehorizons.com
Key Personnel
Pres: Charles H Woodford
Cust Serv: Anju Lad
Dance DVDs & videos, music CDs.
Online catalog(s) available

Dark Star Lighting & Production
102 Commerce St, Hinesburg, VT 05461
Tel: 802-482-4802 *Toll Free Tel:* 877-375-7827
E-mail: sales@darkstarlighting.com
Web Site: www.darkstarlighting.com
Founded: 1995
Technical design, equipment rentals & sales, onsite event management. Specialize in corporate event AV & mobile stage rentals.

DASAN Zhone Solutions (DZS) Inc
7195 Oakport St, Oakland, CA 94621
Tel: 510-777-7000 *Toll Free Tel:* 877-ZHONE-20 (946-6320, US & CN) *Fax:* 510-777-7001
Web Site: dasanzhone.com
Key Personnel
CEO: Yung Kim
Corp Treas & Secy: Kirk Misaka
SVP, Americas & Europe: Michael Fischer
SVP, Asia Sales: Daniel Won
VP, Global Serv & Support: Joe Fortin
VP, Mgmt Innovation: Jun Bahk
VP, Mktg Communs & Enterprise Sales: Monique Apter
VP, Opers: YoungBae Jo
VP, Prod Mgmt & Strategy: Keith Nauman
VP, R&D: Seungdong Lee
Online catalog(s) available
Branch Office(s)
801 Brickell Ave, 9th fl, Miami, FL 33131
Tel: 305-789-6680 *Fax:* 305-371-0084
E-mail: ajonusas@zhone.com
7340 Bryan Dairy Rd, Suite 150, Seminole, FL 33777-1550 *Tel:* 727-530-2545
1360 Bluegrass Lakes Pkwy, Suite 100, Alpharetta, GA 30004-3395
Calle Sol No 310, Old San Juan, PR *Tel:* 787-723-3217 *Fax:* 786-431-5244
Foreign Office(s): Av Libertador 2442, 3 y 4 piso, B1636DSR Olivos, Buenos Aires, Argentina *Tel:* (011) 4711 8769 *Fax:* (011) 4711 8201
Kleine Bollostr 21, 3120 Tremelo, Belgium *Tel:* (0478) 675390
Ave Das Nacoes Unidas 12551, 17º andar Chacara Itaim, 04578-000 Sao Paulo-SP, Brazil *Tel:* (011) 3443 7445; (011) 96903 3455
201-203, Block D, Unis Science & Technology, Langshan Rd 13, Hi-Tech Industrial Park (North), Nanshan District, Shenzhen, China *Tel:* (0755) 2167 9529
Zhone Technologies de Colombia Ltda, Cra 18, No 86-A 14, Bogota, Colombia *Tel:* (01) 638-6186 *Fax:* (01) 616-3030
Zhone Technologies International Inc, 19 El Shahid Helmy El Masry St, 2nd fl, Off No

6-Almaza, Heliopolis, Cairo, Egypt *Tel:* (02) 22912218 *Fax:* (02) 24187273

Zhone Technologies GmbH, Jaegerstr 27a, 92318 Neumark/Opf, Germany *Tel:* (09181) 698 6899 *Fax:* (09181) 698 6890

Zhone Technologies Ltd, Level 54, Hopewell Ctr, 183 Queen's Rd E, Hong Kong *Tel:* 9422 9990 *Fax:* 3011 5440

No 92, ZED Sq, 2nd fl, Jyothi Nivas College Rd, 5th Block, Koramangla Industrial Layout, Bangalore 560 095, India *Tel:* (077) 6013 5566

Zhone Technologies SRL, Via Alfredo Catalani 5, 20900 Monza MB, Italy *Tel:* (0335) 582 9734

6F, Nihonbashi Tomizawacho 7-13, Chuo-ku, Tokyo, Japan *Tel:* (03) 5643 6030

Reforma 350 Piso 11 (Torre Angel), Col Juarez, 06600 Mexico, DF, Mexico *Tel:* (0155) 9171-1480 *Fax:* (0155) 5209-8499

16 Collyer Quay, No 17-00, Income at Raffles, Singapore 049318, Singapore *Tel:* 9422 9990 *Fax:* 3011 5440

DASAN Tower, 49 Daewangpangyo-ro 644 Beongil, Bundang-gu, Seongnam-si, Gyeonggi-do, South Korea *Tel:* (070) 7010 1000

Zhone Technologies AB, Kopmangatan 19, 64130 Katrineholm, Sweden *Tel:* (073) 39 91 166

4F-1, Neihu 433, Ruiguang Rd, Taipei, Taiwan *Tel:* (02) 7721 2220

Zhone Technologies International Inc, Dubai Media City, Busn Central Towers, Tower B, Off 2701, PO Box 9456, Dubai, United Arab Emirates *Tel:* (04) 449 4017 *Fax:* (04) 449 4018

West St, Midhurst GU29 9NQ, United Kingdom *Tel:* (07557) 948908

12402 DASAN Networks, 12A fl, Indochina Plaza Hanoi, 241 Xuan Thuy Str, Cau Giay District, Hanoi, Vietnam *Tel:* (04) 3768 9330

Membership(s): IEEE; The Optical Society; SMPTE®; SPIE

Data Projections Inc
3700 W Sam Houston Pkwy S, Suite 525, Houston, TX 77042
Tel: 713-781-1999 *Toll Free Tel:* 866-225-5374
  Fax: 713-781-3338
E-mail: dpiweb@dataprojections.com
Web Site: www.dataprojections.com
Key Personnel
Pres: Matthew Zaleski *E-mail:* mzaleski@ dataprojections.com
EVP, Sales & Mktg: Robby Turner *E-mail:* rturner@dataprojections.com
VP, Opers: Megan Stasio
Regl VP: Kris Begnaud *E-mail:* kbegnaud@ dataprojections.com
Founded: 1987
Visual systems designer & integrator providing advanced communications products, support services & technology solutions.
Branch Office(s)
4616 W Howard Lane, Suite 140, Austin, TX 78728, Regl VP: Kris Begnaud *Tel:* 512-420-8856 *Fax:* 512-420-9185 *E-mail:* kbegnaud@ dataprojections.com
14452 W Beltwood Pkwy, Dallas, TX 75244, EVP, Sales & Mktg: Robby Turner *Tel:* 972-386-7686 *Fax:* 972-386-7685 *E-mail:* rturner@ dataprojections.com
16120 College Oak, Suite 107, San Antonio, TX 78249, Regl VP: Kris Begnaud *Tel:* 210-408-2860 *Fax:* 210-408-4598 *E-mail:* kbegnaud@ dataprojections.com
Membership(s): Audiovisual and Integrated Experience Association

Data Security Inc
300 S Seventh St, Lincoln, NE 68508
Tel: 402-434-5959 *Toll Free Tel:* 800-225-7554
  Fax: 402-434-3291
E-mail: sales@telesis-inc.com
Web Site: www.datasecurityinc.com
Key Personnel
CEO: Brian K Boles

Dir, Sales & Mktg: Renee Schafer
Founded: 1985
Manufacturer & supplier of hard drive degaussers, magnetic tape degaussers & hard drive & solid state destruction devices.

Data Translation
Subsidiary of Measurement Computing Corporation (MCC)
10 Commerce Way, Norton, MA 02766
Tel: 508-946-5100 *Toll Free Tel:* 800-234-4232
  Fax: 508-946-9500
E-mail: info@mccdaq.com
Web Site: www.mccdaq.com/data-translation
Founded: 1973
Design, manufacture & provide data acquisition solutions for test & measurement.

DataDirect Networks
9351 Deering Ave, Chatsworth, CA 91311
Tel: 818-700-4000 *Toll Free Tel:* 800-TERABYTE (837-2298)
E-mail: info@ddn.com; sales@ddn.com
Web Site: www.ddn.com
Key Personnel
Co-Founder, Chmn & CEO: Alex Bouzari
Co-Founder & Pres: Paul Bloch
CFO: Ian Angelo
Chief Res Offr: Sven Oehme
EVP, Global Engg Opers & CTO: Bret Weber
SVP, Field Sales, Americas & Europe: Dean Koester
SVP, Global Sales, Mktg & Field Servs: Robert Triendl
SVP, Prods: James Coomer
VP, Worldwide Pre-Sale, Serv & Support: Mark Canepa
Dir, Mktg: Kurt Kuckein
Founded: 1998
Manufacture high-performance, cross-platform data storage & networking systems for the open systems, network attached computer environment.
Branch Office(s)
2929 Patrick Henry Dr, Santa Clara, CA 95054
Tel: 408-419-2800
9950 Federal Dr, Suite 150, Colorado Springs, CO 80921 *Tel:* 719-598-9792
8320 Guilford Rd, Suite D, Columbia, MD 21046
Tel: 410-309-9300
Foreign Office(s): Level 36 Riparian Plaza, 71 Eagle St, Brisbane, Qld 4000, Australia *Tel:* (07) 243 280 248
Rm 1003 & 1005, Bldg 2, No 99, Danba Rd, Putuo District, Shanghai, China
Immeuble le Dynasteur, 2eme Etage, 10-12, rue Andras Beck, 92360 Meudon-La-Foret, France *Tel:* 01 75 95 10 95
Noerdlicher Zubringer 9, 40470 Duesseldorf, Germany *Tel:* (06196) 5868580
DataDirect India Pvt Ltd, Nyati Emporius, 8th fl, Pashan Hwy Side Rd, Mahalunge, Pune, Maharashtra 411 045, India *Tel:* (020) 67320700
Tokyo Bancho Bldg 8F, 6-2 Yonban-cho, Chiyoda-ku, Tokyo 102-0081, Japan *Tel:* (03) 3261-9101 *Fax:* (03) 3261-9140
TOZ Busn Ctr, 5th, Hwanghwa B/D 320, Gangnam-daero, Suite S548, Gangnam-gu, Seoul 06252, South Korea *Tel:* (010) 3837 1957
Dubai Media City, Al Thuraya Tower 1, Off 504, Dubai, United Arab Emirates *Tel:* (04) 390-2576
DataDirect Networks UK Ltd, 5 New Street Sq, London EC4A 3TW, United Kingdom

Dav Tronics Ltd
Subsidiary of S W Davis Broadcast Technical Services Ltd
1543 Venables St, Suite 200, Vancouver, BC V5L 2G8, Canada
Tel: 604-255-2200

Web Site: www.broadcasttechnical.com
Key Personnel
Supv: Dan Roach
Manufacture broadcasting equipment.
Data sheet(s) available

Davenport Music Library
PO Box 690536, Charlotte, NC 28227-7009
Web Site: www.davenportmusic.com
Key Personnel
Owner & Pres: Neal Davenport
Founded: 1992
Royalty free tracks & CDs.
Catalog(s) available

David Clark Co Inc
360 Franklin St, Worcester, MA 01604
Mailing Address: PO Box 15054, Worcester, MA 01615-0054
Tel: 508-751-5800 *Toll Free Tel:* 800-900-3434
  Fax: 508-753-5827
E-mail: sales@davidclark.com
Web Site: www.davidclark.com
Key Personnel
Prod Mgr: John Tasi
Manufacturer of headsets & communication equipment.

Davidson Productions
1180 Vista Del Lago, San Luis Obispo, CA 93405
Tel: 415-886-7540
E-mail: dfi@davidsonfilms.com
Web Site: davidsonfilms.com
Key Personnel
CEO: Jean Davidson *E-mail:* jean@ davidsonfilms.com
CFO: Trent Johnson *E-mail:* trent@davidsonfilms.com
Founded: 1955
Produce & distribute educational documentaries for the university market specializing in psychology, neuroscience & education.
Online catalog(s) available, PDF

Davies Publishing Inc
32 S Raymond Ave, Suites 4-5, Pasadena, CA 91105
Tel: 626-792-3046 *Toll Free Tel:* 877-792-0005 (US only) *Fax:* 626-792-5308
E-mail: info@daviespublishing.com
Web Site: daviespublishing.com
Key Personnel
Pres & Publr: Michael Davies
Art Dir: Bill Murawski
Mgr, Digital Mktg & Media: Daniel Liota
Opers Mgr: Janet Heard *E-mail:* janetheard@ daviespublishing.com
Prod Devt Specialist: Christian Jones
Founded: 1981
Publisher & purveyor of registry reviews, study aids, textbooks, videos, software & CME solutions for ultrasound professionals.
Catalog(s) available, free upon request, annual
Online catalog(s) available

Davis Art Images
Division of Davis Publications Inc
50 Portland St, Worcester, MA 01608
Tel: 508-754-7201 *Toll Free Tel:* 800-533-2847
  Fax: 508-753-3834
E-mail: contactus@davisart.com; das@davisart.com
Web Site: www.davisart.com
Key Personnel
Pres: Julian Davis Wade
Curator, Images: Karl Cole *E-mail:* kcole@ davisart.com
Assoc Curator: Lydia Keene-Kendrick *E-mail:* lkeenekendrick@davisart.com
Founded: 1901

Educational resources. Over 35,000 digital fine art images from leading museum & galleries.
Online catalog(s) available

John J Davis & Associates Consulting Engineers
PO Box 128, Sierra Madre, CA 91025-0128
Tel: 626-355-6909
Key Personnel
Owner & Pres: John J Davis

DaviSound
PO Box 521, Newberry, SC 29108-0521
Tel: 803-944-7972 (messages only)
Web Site: www.davisound.com
Key Personnel
Founder: Hayne Davis
Founded: 1970

DAWNco
7111 Dixie Hwy, Suite 118, Clarkston, MI 48346
Tel: 248-391-9200; 248-391-9207
  Toll Free Tel: 800-866-6969 *Fax:* 248-391-9206
E-mail: sales@dawnco.com
Web Site: www.dawnco.com
Key Personnel
Dir, Sales & Mktg: John A Joslin
Providing satellite & fiber optic communication products.
Catalog(s) available, semiannual

DawnSignPress
6130 Nancy Ridge Dr, San Diego, CA 92121-3223
Tel: 858-625-0600 *Toll Free Tel:* 800-549-5350
  Fax: 858-625-2336
E-mail: contactus@dawnsign.com
Web Site: www.dawnsign.com
Key Personnel
Mktg Dir: Becky Ryan *E-mail:* beckyr@dawnsign.com
Founded: 1979
Creates, develops & publishes American Sign Language (ASL) & Deaf culture-related DVDs & books.
Online catalog(s) available

Day 1, see The Alliance for Christian Media

Daylight Productions & Rentals
4700 Sterling Dr, Suite I, Boulder, CO 80301
Tel: 303-440-3334
E-mail: info@daylightav.com
Web Site: www.daylightav.com
Key Personnel
Pres: Brian Day
Founded: 2004
Video production, video & AV rentals.
Catalog(s) available
Membership(s): Audiovisual and Integrated Experience Association; Mountain Film & Video Association

Dazian Creative Fabric Environments, see Dazian LLC

Dazian LLC
18 Central Blvd, South Hackensack, NJ 07606
Toll Free Tel: 877-232-9426 *Fax:* 201-641-2728; 201-549-1055 (efax)
E-mail: info@dazian.com
Web Site: www.dazian.com
Key Personnel
CEO/Pres: Jon Weingarten
CFO/COO: Chris Diaz
Mktg Dir: Karen Loftus
Digital Mktg Mgr: Melissa Chute
Founded: 1842
Manufacture, sell, install & rent theatrical drapery & LED lighting elements.

Online catalog(s) available
Branch Office(s)
10671 Lorne St, Sun Valley, CA 91352 *Tel:* 818-287-3800 *Toll Free Tel:* 877-432-9426
  Fax: 818-287-3810 (efax)
7100 TPC Dr, Suite 650, Orlando, FL 32822
  Tel: 321-206-0084 *Toll Free Tel:* 888-318-2904
  Fax: 407-219-9679
Membership(s): EDPA; Industrial Fabrics Association International; International Association of Exhibitions and Events; International Live Events Association; Meeting Planners International; National Fire Protection Association; Set Decorators Society of America; Shop Environments Association; Specialty Graphic Imaging Association; USITT; Visit Orlando

Dazor Lighting Technology LLC
2360 Chaffee Dr, St Louis, MO 63146
Tel: 314-652-2400 *Toll Free Tel:* 800-345-9103
  Fax: 314-652-2069
E-mail: info@dazor.com
Web Site: www.dazor.com
Founded: 1938
Illumination & magnification tools.

Dazor Manufacturing Corp, see Dazor Lighting Technology LLC

db electronics
4611G Central Ave Pike, Knoxville, TN 37912
Tel: 865-588-9532
E-mail: service@dbelectronics.com
Web Site: dbelectronics.com
Founded: 1976
Specialize in repair & restoration of precision audio electronics. Service many makes & models of equipment including Altec Lansing, Mark Levinson, Bose & Auratron Systems.

db interactive Inc
PO Box 302064, Austin, TX 78703
Tel: 512-436-8586
E-mail: info@dbinteractive.com
Web Site: dbinteractive.com
Key Personnel
Founder: Dan Brown
Founded: 1999
Web site design & management.

dbF a Media Company
9683 Charles St, La Plata, MD 20646
Tel: 301-645-6110 *Fax:* 301-392-6111
E-mail: service@dbfmedia.com
Web Site: www.dbfmedia.com
Key Personnel
Pres: Randy Runyon
VP: Wendy Runyon
Founded: 1981
Audio & video production services.
Membership(s): Business Alliance of Charles County

DBM Communications Inc
606 Baltimore Ave, Suite 200, Towson, MD 21204
Mailing Address: PO Box 20115, Towson, MD 21284
Tel: 410-825-7400 *Fax:* 443-269-0213
Web Site: www.dbmcommunications.com
Key Personnel
Dir, Prodr & Exec Prodr: Douglas B Maddox
Dir, Sales & Mktg/Prodr: Robert Koenig
Cinematographer & Ed: Evan DeVita
Writer & Sales Prodr: Jason Richards
Designer: Sherri Joyce
Designer & Programmer: Lance Janocha
Founded: 1990
Offer production services including film, video, marketing design, print, new media & web.

DCTV, see Downtown Community Television Center (DCTV)

DD Audio
Division of Resonance Inc
4025 NW 36 St, Oklahoma City, OK 73112
Tel: 405-239-2800 *Fax:* 405-239-7100
E-mail: service@ddaudio.com
Web Site: ddaudio.com
Key Personnel
Owner & Intl Sales Mgr: Jassa Langford
Founded: 1986
Manufacture audio products for industrial, professional, marine, mobile, home & OEM applications.
Online catalog(s) available
Membership(s): NAMM, the National Association of Music Merchants

De Nonno Productions Inc (DPI)
7119 Shore Rd, Suite 6-F, Brooklyn, NY 11209
Tel: 917-304-6610
Web Site: www.denonnoprod.com; www.denonnoscelebrityphotos.com
Key Personnel
Pres & Dir: Tony De Nonno
Founded: 1978
Video, TV, film, music, photographic production & distribution.
Online catalog(s) available

De Sisti Lighting/I-Light Corp USA
1011 Rte 22 E, Unit D, Mountainside, NJ 07092
Tel: 908-317-0020 *Fax:* 908-317-0021
Web Site: www.desisti.it
Key Personnel
Pres & CEO: Frank Kosuda *E-mail:* fkosuda@desistiusa.com
Founded: 1982
Lighting equipment manufacturer.
Catalog(s) available
Foreign Office(s): ILT, via Cancelliera 10/A, 00041 Albano Laziale, Rome RM, Italy, Contact: Fabio De Sisti *Tel:* (06) 902901 *Fax:* (06) 90231051 *E-mail:* desisti@desisti.it
Membership(s): NAB; Professional Lighting & Sound Association

de Wolfe Music USA
37 W 17 St, 7th fl, Suite E, New York, NY 10011
Tel: 212-259-0524
E-mail: info@dewolfemusicusa.com
Web Site: dewolfemusic.com
Catalog(s) available
Membership(s): NAB

Debbie Regan Locations Ltd
PO Box 353, Old Westbury, NY 11568
Tel: 516-626-1928; 212-591-1313 *Fax:* 516-626-2337
E-mail: DRLNYC@gmail.com
Web Site: www.debbiereganlocations.com
Key Personnel
Owner & Pres: Debbie Regan
NYC location scout. 6,000 locations in NYC, NY, NJ & CT. Location library online. Film photo, TV, video, webisodes, print & events.

DebsVoice
19 Park Trail, Midhurst, ON L0L 1X0, Canada
Tel: 604-459-5559 (cell)
Web Site: www.debsvoice.com; www.voiceactortraining.com
Key Personnel
Owner & Voice-over Talent: Debbie Munro *E-mail:* deb@debsvoice.com
Passionate production company for audio & video needs. International full-time voice talent & voice instructor & motivational speaker.
Membership(s): AMPIA; WIFT

DecisionOne Corp
640 Lee Rd, 3rd fl, Wayne, PA 19087
Tel: 610-296-6000 *Toll Free Tel:* 800-767-2876;
    800-777-8800 (cust serv); 888-287-9202
    (sales); 800-554-5179 (CN) *Fax:* 610-296-2910
E-mail: sales@decisionone.com
Web Site: www.decisionone.com
Key Personnel
Pres: Michael P Horne
EVP, Opers: Pat Croce
EVP, Sales: Dan DellaVentura
SVP, Fin: Tom Darling
SVP, Logistics: Wayne Smith
VP, HR: Kimberly Burke
Dir, IT: Jack Greenleaf
Dir, Mktg & Communs: Larry Quinn
Founded: 1958
Provider of IT infrastructure services.
Branch Office(s)
1013 Lucerne Ave, Lake Worth, FL 33460 (call
    ctr/help desk)
1325 American Blvd E, Suite 1, Bloomington,
    MN 55425 *Tel:* 952-814-5750 (call ctr/help
    desk)
3425 Urbancrest Industrial Dr, Urbancrest, OH
    43123 *Tel:* 614-883-0041 (technol ctr)
44 E Beaver Creek Rd, Unit 19, Richmond Hill,
    ON L4B 1G8, Canada *Tel:* 905-882-1555

Deck Hand Inc
1905 S Victory Blvd, Suite 8, Glendale, CA
    91201
Tel: 818-557-8403 *Fax:* 818-557-8406
E-mail: info@deckhand.com
Web Site: www.deckhand.com
Key Personnel
Owner: Joseph Mealey
Founded: 2002
Digital filmmaking equipment rentals.

Dedotec USA Inc
48 Sheffield Business Park, Ashley Falls, MA
    01222
Tel: 413-229-2550
E-mail: info@dedolight.com
Web Site: www.dedolight.com
Key Personnel
Pres: Paul Tepper
Manufacture Dedolight precision lighting instru-
    ments.
Online catalog(s) available
Membership(s): NAB

Deerfield Laboratory Inc
7 Millbrae Ave, San Anselmo, CA 94960
Tel: 650-632-4090
Web Site: www.deerfieldlab.com
Key Personnel
Pres & CEO: Daniel Krakauer *E-mail:* danielk@
    deerfieldlab.com
Founded: 1995
Video isolation transformer.
Online catalog(s) available

Definitive Technology LLP
One Viper Way, Vista, CA 92081
Tel: 410-363-7148 *Toll Free Tel:* 800-228-7148
E-mail: info@definitivetech.com
Web Site: www.definitivetech.com
Key Personnel
Cust Serv Mgr: Chet Pelkowski *Tel:* 410-363-
    7148 ext 5562 *E-mail:* chet.pelkowski@
    soundunited.com
Founded: 1990
Manufacturer of high-end loudspeakers.
Branch Office(s)
11500 Cronridge Dr, Suite 110, Owings Mills,
    MD 21117-2294
Membership(s): Consumer Technology Associa-
    tion™; Custom Electronic Design & Installa-
    tion Association

Deja View Video
417 S Eldorado St, San Mateo, CA 94402-1374
Tel: 650-343-8899
Web Site: www.dejaview.com
Key Personnel
Owner: William Krone
Producing video programs & distributor of in-
    structional videos.
Online catalog(s) available
Membership(s): CLVS; NABET-CWA; SMPTE®

deKramer Productions Inc
515 Western Ave, Petaluma, CA 94952
Tel: 707-765-0888
E-mail: dekramer@sonic.net
Web Site: www.dekramerproductions.com
Key Personnel
Pres: Peter deKramer *E-mail:* peter@
    dekramerproductions.com
Founded: 1978
Stage, film & video direction.

Louis Anthony deLise, see Composer Louis
    Anthony deLise

Delmark Records
4121 N Rockwell, Chicago, IL 60618
Tel: 773-539-5001 *Fax:* 773-539-5004
E-mail: info@delmark.com
Web Site: www.delmark.com
Key Personnel
Pres & CEO: Julia A Miller *E-mail:* julia@
    delmark.com
VP & Artistic Dir: Elbio Barilari *E-mail:* elbio@
    delmark.com
Label & Studio Mgr: Steve Wagner
    E-mail: delmark@delmark.com
Founded: 1953
Recording studio & record company. Provide
    sound recordings - magnetic & digital.
Catalog(s) available, quarterly

Delta Electronics Inc
5730 General Washington Dr, Alexandria, VA
    22312
Mailing Address: PO Box 11268, Alexandria, VA
    22312
Tel: 703-354-3350 *Toll Free Tel:* 800-8-DELTA-8
    (833-5828) *Fax:* 703-354-0216
E-mail: sales@deltaelectronics.com
Web Site: www.deltaelectronics.com
Founded: 1962
Manufacture test equipment, high power RF
    switches & meters & operating impedance
    bridges.
Catalog(s) available

Deluxe Entertainment Services Group Inc
2400 W Empire Ave, 2nd fl, Burbank, CA 91504
Tel: 818-260-7005; 818-526-3700
    Toll Free Tel: 800-99-FILMS (993-4567)
E-mail: ddchelp@bydeluxe.com; pr@bydeluxe.
    com
Web Site: www.bydeluxe.com
Key Personnel
CEO: John Wallace
COO, Dist: Justin Beaudin
CFO: Eric Cummins
CIO: Cindy McKenzie
Chief Prod Offr: Andy Shenkler
Pres, Deluxe Creative Services: Jamie Haggarty
EVP & Gen Coun: Stefani Liquori
EVP, Sales: Daniel Gray
Founded: 1915
Video creation to distribution company offering
    global end-to-end services & technology. Vi-
    sual effects, post-production, 2D-3D conver-
    sion, digital, theatrical & physical distribution.

Demco Inc
4810 Forest Run Rd, Madison, WI 53704
Mailing Address: PO Box 7488, Madison, WI
    53707-7488
Tel: 608-241-1201 *Toll Free Tel:* 800-962-4463;
    800-279-1586 *Toll Free Fax:* 800-245-1329
Web Site: www.demco.com
Key Personnel
Pres: Nedra Sadorf *E-mail:* president@demco.
    com
Founded: 1905
Catalog(s) available, annual
Online catalog(s) available
Membership(s): NOPA

Denecke Inc
25209 Ave Tibbitts, Valencia, CA 91355
Tel: 661-607-0206 *Fax:* 661-257-2236
E-mail: info@denecke.com
Web Site: www.denecke.com
Key Personnel
Off Mgr: Kimberly Parra
Time code equipment for the entertainment indus-
    try.

Denver Media Center
2601 Lemay, Suite 7, PMB 227, Fort Collins, CO
    80525
Tel: 720-255-1640 (ext 101)
Web Site: denvermediacenter.com
Key Personnel
Founder & Exec Prodr: Blaine Howerton
    Tel: 720-255-1640 ext 101 *E-mail:* blaine@
    denvermediacenter.com
Founder & Dir: Nick Arnold
Founded: 2013
Full service audio & video recording studio. Mix-
    ing, mastering, replicating & distribution ser-
    vices, video production equipment rental &
    closed captioning services.

Department of Education Resources
Division of National Gallery of Art
2000B S Club Dr, Landover, MD 20785
Tel: 202-842-6706 *Fax:* 202-842-6937
E-mail: edresources@nga.gov
Web Site: www.nga.gov/education.html
Key Personnel
Head, Dept of Educ Resources: Leo Kasun
Provides free loan teaching packets with image
    CDs, DVDs & video programs to individuals,
    educational institutions, community groups &
    nonprofit television stations.
Catalog(s) available, free
Online catalog(s) available

**Department of VSA & Accessibility at the
    John F Kennedy Center for the Performing
    Arts**
2700 "F" St NW, Washington, DC 20566
E-mail: vsainfo@kennedy-center.org
Web Site: education.kennedy-center.org/education/
    vsa
Key Personnel
Dir, VSA & Accessibility: Betty Siegel
Founded: 1974
Creating a society for people with disabilities to
    learn, participate in & enjoy the arts.

Derksen (USA) Inc
4934 Pathway Ct, Fair Oaks, CA 95628
Tel: 916-903-7515 *Fax:* 916-903-7022
E-mail: info@derksen.com
Web Site: www.derksen.com
Distributor of Derksen line of projection systems.
Catalog(s) available

Design & Production Inc
7110 Rainwater Place, Lorton, VA 22079
Tel: 703-550-8640 *Fax:* 703-339-0296
E-mail: email@d-and-p.com
Web Site: www.d-and-p.com

Key Personnel
SVP: L Sue Lepp *E-mail:* lslepp@d-and-p.com
Membership(s): Audiovisual and Integrated Experience Association; EDPA; NSCA

Design Audio Visual Inc
Division of Astoria Communications Inc
195-A Central Ave, Farmingdale, NY 11735
Tel: 631-694-3334 *Toll Free Tel:* 800-886-1328
  Fax: 631-694-3549
Web Site: www.design-av.com
Key Personnel
Pres: Chuck Weinstein *E-mail:* chuck@design-av.
  com
Founded: 1981
Online catalog(s) available, rental & sales
Brochure(s) available, free
Membership(s): ATD; Audiovisual and Integrated
  Experience Association; HSMAI; IABC; International Live Events Association; MPI

Design Media
650 Alabama St, Suite 203, San Francisco, CA
  94110-2038
Tel: 415-641-4848 *Fax:* 415-641-5245
E-mail: info@designmedia.com
Web Site: www.designmedia.com
Key Personnel
Pres & CEO: Pamela May *E-mail:* pmay@
  designmedia.com
Multimedia solutions for business, education &
  government.

Designomotion
67 E 11 St, Suite 324, New York, NY 10003
Tel: 917-532-0738
E-mail: info@designomotion.com
Web Site: designomotion.com
Key Personnel
Founder & Creative Dir: Joseph Silver
  E-mail: jsilver@designomotion.com
Founded: 2006
Motion graphics production.

Desktop Video Systems
9052 Parkhill, Lenexa, KS 66215
Tel: 913-782-8888
Key Personnel
Owner: Tom O'Connor *E-mail:* toconnor@
  outlook.com
Professional video equipment sales.

Destiny Recordings, see Inner Traditions
  International

Developmental Studies Center, see Center for
  the Collaborative Classroom

DGI-Invisuals LLC
Division of DGI Communications Co
101 Billerica Ave, Bldg 6, North Billerica, MA
  01862
Toll Free Tel: 800-344-0432 *Fax:* 781-270-3663
E-mail: sales@dgi-invisuals.com
Web Site: www.dgi-invisuals.com
Key Personnel
Owner & Pres: James Dadmun
Gen Mgr: Glen Fairbanks *E-mail:* gfairbanks@
  dgi-invisuals.com
Founded: 1994
Large format digital printing & photo imaging.
Online catalog(s) available
Membership(s): The Imaging Alliance

DH Satellite
600 N Marquette Rd, Prairie du Chien, WI 53821
Mailing Address: PO Box 239, Prairie du Chien,
  WI 53821-0239
Tel: 608-326-8406 *Toll Free Tel:* 800-627-9443
  Fax: 608-326-4233

E-mail: dhsat@mhtc.net; sales@dhsatellite.com
Web Site: www.dhsatellite.com
Key Personnel
Sales: Cindy Wille *E-mail:* cwille@dhsatellite.
  com
Manufacture satellite spun aluminum parabolic
  antennas, one piece or sectional.
Catalog(s) available

Dialect Accent Specialists Inc
7048 Timberrose Way, Roseville, CA 95747
Toll Free Tel: 800-753-1016
E-mail: dasinc@kingcon.com; info@
  dialectaccentspecialists.com
Web Site: www.dialectaccentspecialists.com;
  www.learnaccent.com
Key Personnel
Mgr: Peggy Voakes
Mail order educational audiotapes, booklets &
  CDs teaching learning/losing accents, dialects
  & general speech improvement.

Diamond Displays Inc, see ExpoDisplays

Diamond Dreams Music Productions
North Ocean County, Carbon Canyon, Chino
  Hills, CA 91709
Tel: 909-393-6120 *Fax:* 909-606-5779
E-mail: diamonddreamsmusic@yahoo.com
Web Site: www.diamonddreamsmusic.com
Key Personnel
Owner & Prodr: Raphael DeGiorgio
Founded: 1999
Membership(s): ASCAP

Diamond Studios
Woods Point 1, 1855 Data Dr, Suite 255, Hoover,
  AL 35244
Tel: 205-987-2121 *Fax:* 205-987-2128
Web Site: www.tvstuff.com
Key Personnel
CEO: Joe Miele *Tel:* 205-987-2121 ext 1
  E-mail: joe@tvstuff.com
Founded: 1982
HD & web video, TV, multimedia & technology
  company. Viral, corporate, marketing, training
  & orientation videos.
Online catalog(s) available

Diaquest
Subsidiary of Advanced Systems Group
5808 Vallejo St, Emeryville, CA 94608
Tel: 510-547-4544 *Fax:* 510-654-8370
E-mail: sales@diaquest.com; support@diaquest.
  com
Web Site: www.diaquest.com
Key Personnel
Pres: David Van Hoy
Founded: 1982
Develop mission critical software for the video,
  film & broadcast industries. Develop software as an OEM for several manufacturers as
  well as custom software tools for a variety of
  clients. Also provide professional-level support
  of related software & hardware products.
Online catalog(s) available
Membership(s): SMPTE®

Dickensheets Design Associates
10919 Conchos Trail, Suite 100, Austin, TX
  78726-1431
Tel: 512-331-8977
Web Site: www.dickensheets.com
Key Personnel
VP: Ken Dickensheets *E-mail:* ken@dickensheets.
  com
Founded: 1985
Design of AV systems, acoustics, noise control &
  IT.
Membership(s): AES; ASA; NCAC; NSCA;
  SMPTE®

DiCon Fiberoptics Inc
1689 Regatta Blvd, Richmond, CA 94804
Tel: 510-620-5000; 510-620-5200 (sales)
  Fax: 510-620-4100; 510-620-4102 (sales)
E-mail: sales@diconfiberoptics.com
Web Site: www.diconfiberoptics.com
Key Personnel
Pres, CEO & Dir: Ho-Shang Lee
VP, Prod Devt: Robert Schleicher
Founded: 1986
Supplier of passive components, modules & test
  instruments for the fiber optic communications
  industry.
Catalog(s) available
Foreign Office(s): Global Fiberoptics Inc, 6F, 248-
  28 Hsing Shen Rd, Cheng-Jeng District, Kaoh-
  siung, Taiwan *Tel:* (07) 815-8055 *Fax:* (07)
  815-8456

Dielectric
Division of Sinclair Broadcast Group Inc
22 Tower Rd, Raymond, ME 04071
Tel: 207-655-4555 *Toll Free Tel:* 800-341-9678
  Fax: 207-655-8173
E-mail: PF-dielec-sales@sbgtv.com
Web Site: www.dielectric.com
Key Personnel
Dir, Busn Devt: Kim Savage *E-mail:* kim.
  savage@dielectric.com
Founded: 1942
Manufacturer of radio & TV equipment.
Online catalog(s) available

Diemer Amp & Keyboard Repair
12814 Landale St, Studio City, CA 91604-1351
Tel: 818-762-0804
Web Site: bustedgear.com
Key Personnel
Owner: Richard Diemer *E-mail:* rich@bustedgear.
  com
Online catalog(s) available

Different Fur Recording Ltd
3470 19 St, San Francisco, CA 94110
Tel: 415-828-4060 (bookings)
Web Site: differentfurstudios.com
Key Personnel
Owner, Prodr & Engr: Patrick Brown
Head Engr: Sean Paulson
Engr/Prodr: Lien Do
Studio Mgr/Engr: Jorge Hernandez
  E-mail: jorge@differentfurstudios.com
Recording studio.

Digi Sign Design LLC
Subsidiary of K&R All Media Productions LLC
28533 Greenfield Rd, Southfield, MI 48076
Web Site: www.digisigndesign.com
Key Personnel
Pres: Ken Glaza
Outside & inside digital signage design & net-
  working.
Online catalog(s) available

Digimation
1515 International Pkwy, Suite 2013, Lake Mary,
  FL 32746
Tel: 407-833-0600
E-mail: sales@digimation.com
Web Site: digimation.com
Key Personnel
Pres: David Avgikos
Founded: 1992
Virtual training & simulation, 3D content & soft-
  ware tools for 3D users.

Digital Art Video Inc
8506 60 Ave, 3rd fl, Middle Village, NY 11379-
  5430
Tel: 718-457-5388
E-mail: production@digitalartvideo.com

Web Site: www.digitalartvideo.com
Key Personnel
Founder & Pres: Kim E Wang
Full service film & video production & post-production.

Digital Arts NY
130 W 29 St, New York, NY 10001
Tel: 212-460-9600 *Fax:* 212-660-3600
Web Site: digitalartsny.com
Key Personnel
Founder & CEO: Axel Ericson *E-mail:* axel@digitalartsny.com
Dir, Prodn: Brian Donnelly
Sr Prodr: Lauren Boyle
Finishing Ed/Tech Engr: Mark Spano
Colorist: Gary Scarpulla
Sound Designer/Mixer: Brian Beatrice; Frank Verderosa
Specialize in audio & image finishing in 4K, 2K & HD, as well as sound design & mixing for feature films, scripted & unscripted television, commercials, trailers & video games.

Digital Audio Labs
1266 Park Rd, Chanhassen, MN 55317
Tel: 952-401-7700 *Fax:* 952-401-7725
E-mail: sales@digitalaudio.com; contact@digitalaudio.com
Web Site: www.digitalaudio.com
Key Personnel
Pres: Ted Klein
Opers Mgr: Jeff Gedden
Founded: 1988
Developer & manufacturer of Livemix personal monitoring system, PowerShape integrated amplifiers & LaChapell Audio microphone preamps.
Membership(s): Audiovisual and Integrated Experience Association; NAMM, the National Association of Music Merchants

Digital Comm Link Inc
10450 W State Rd 84, Davie, FL 33324-4206
Tel: 954-236-2993 *Toll Free Tel:* 877-532-5438
Fax: 954-236-3633
E-mail: bookings@dclinc.net
Web Site: www.dclinc.net
Key Personnel
VP, Opers: Robert Mendes *E-mail:* rmendes@dclinc.net
VP, Mktg: Said Khan *E-mail:* skhan@dclinc.net
Founded: 1995
Colocation, ISP, production, satellite/teleport, mobile satellite, studio, VoIP, FTP & video streaming services.

Digital Designs, see DD Audio

Digital Display Solutions Inc
2840, 12223 San Pedro Ave, San Antonio, TX 78216
Tel: 210-404-1233 *Fax:* 210-979-6585
E-mail: info@ddsav.com
Web Site: ddsav.com
Key Personnel
Pres: Lisa Harbert *E-mail:* lharbert@ddsav.com
VP: Roger Harbert *E-mail:* rharbert@ddsav.com
Founded: 2001

Digital Film Studios LLC
11800 Sheldon St, Unit C/D, Sun Valley, CA 91352
Tel: 818-771-0019
Web Site: www.digitalfilmstudios.com
Key Personnel
Owner: Ted Hayash
Owner & Mgr: Dan Toback
Complete lighting, grip & small stage rental.

Digital Force Ltd
248 W 35 St, 14th fl, New York, NY 10001
Tel: 212-252-9300 *Toll Free Tel:* 877-DISC-USA (347-2872) *Fax:* 212-252-7377
E-mail: frontdesk@digitalforce.com
Web Site: digitalforce.com
Key Personnel
Pres: Jerome Bunke
Founded: 1994
Specialize in media replication & duplication.
Membership(s): The Recording Academy

Digital FX Inc
6010 Perkins Rd, Suite B, Baton Rouge, LA 70808
Tel: 225-763-6010 *Toll Free Tel:* 888-898-6010
E-mail: info@digitalfx.tv; rentals@digitalfx.tv
Web Site: www.digitalfx.tv
Key Personnel
Founder & Pres: Greg Milneck
Full service AV production company.
Membership(s): PPA

Digital Image Studios LLC
22915 Commerce Dr, Farmington Hills, MI 48335
Tel: 248-477-5600 *Toll Free Tel:* 888-434-7839
Fax: 248-477-4322
Web Site: www.dimage.com
Founded: 1990

Digital Jungle
28348 Constellation Rd, Suite 880, Santa Clara, CA 91355
Tel: 323-962-0867 *Fax:* 323-962-9960
E-mail: info@digijungle.com
Web Site: www.digijungle.com
4K, 2K, HD & SD post-production services for film, television & commercials-servicing studios, networks & independent content providers.

Digital Lighting Systems Inc
12302 SW 128 Ct, Suite 105, Miami, FL 33186
Tel: 305-969-8442 *Fax:* 305-969-8675
E-mail: info@digitallighting.com; sales@digitallighting.com
Web Site: www.digitallighting.com
Key Personnel
Pres & Head, Engg: Mr Elie Khawand *E-mail:* elie@digitallighting.com
Founded: 1978
Architectural & animation dimmers & lighting control systems.
Online catalog(s) available

Digital Music Corp
3165 Coffey Lane, Santa Rosa, CA 95403
Tel: 707-545-0600 *Fax:* 707-545-9777
E-mail: info@voodoolab.com
Web Site: www.voodoolab.com
Key Personnel
Pres & Mktg Mgr: Josh Fiden
Sales Mgr: Tony Motta
Founded: 1986
Guitar effects & electronics.

digital OutPost
2772 Loker Ave W, Carlsbad, CA 92010
Tel: 760-431-3575 *Toll Free Tel:* 800-464-6434
E-mail: sales@dop.com
Web Site: www.dop.com
Key Personnel
Pres: Brian Douglas
Founded: 1996
DVD authoring, post-production facility, full production, multimedia design, encoding house & video for the web.

Digital Projection
55 Chastain Rd, Suite 115, Kennesaw, GA 30144

Tel: 770-420-1350 *Fax:* 770-420-1360
E-mail: contact@digitalprojection.com
Web Site: www.digitalprojection.com
Key Personnel
Mktg & Communs Mgr: Kyle Greetham *E-mail:* kgreetham@digitalprojection.com
Founded: 1987
Projection equipment manufacturer.
Membership(s): Audiovisual and Integrated Experience Association; Custom Electronic Design & Installation Association

Digital Rain LLC
253 Lagoda Dr, Locust, NC 28097
Tel: 980-354-1209
Web Site: www.digitalrainllc.com
Key Personnel
Owner: Rodney A Myers *E-mail:* rodney@digitalrainllc.com
Founded: 1998
Video post-production.

Digital Services Recording Studios
1601 S Cherry St, Tomball, TX 77375
Tel: 832-463-5781
E-mail: studio@dsrecordings.com
Web Site: www.dsrecordings.com
Key Personnel
Owner: Charlie Ray *E-mail:* charlie@dsrecordings.com
Full service recording, mixing, mastering & production services.
Membership(s): AES

Digital Video Productions
257 Federal Rd, Brookfield, CT 06804
Tel: 203-743-7663 *Fax:* 203-743-1658
E-mail: info@dvpllc.com
Web Site: dvpllc.com
Key Personnel
Founder & Partner: Paul Ayoub *E-mail:* paul@dvpllc.com
Mng Partner & Dir: Mike Evans *E-mail:* mike@dvpllc.com
Founded: 1995
Video production services & video transfers.
Membership(s): WEVA

Digital Video Systems
3270 Executive Way, Miramar, FL 33025
Tel: 954-239-4410 *Fax:* 954-239-4486
E-mail: info@digitalvideosystems.net
Web Site: digitalvideosystems.net
Key Personnel
COO: Kathleen McGovern
Pres: Charles E Sackermann, Jr
VP, Opers: Dino Marikos
VP, Sales & Mktg: Jorge J Necuze, Sr *E-mail:* jorgen@digitalvideosystems.net
Dir, Opers: Cristian Tache
Proj Engr: Jason Taormina
Founded: 1975
Broadcast, satellite & AV systems integrator.
Online catalog(s) available
Membership(s): Audiovisual and Integrated Experience Association; NAB; SMPTE®

Digital Zoetrope Productions
1902 Oak St, Melbourne, FL 32901
Tel: 321-821-7404 *Fax:* 321-821-2287
Web Site: digitalzoetrope.com
Key Personnel
Owner: Michael Misconi
Full service video production company & advertising agency. Video production equipment rental.

DigiTech
Division of Harman Professional Solutions
8500 Balboa Blvd, Northridge, CA 91329
Toll Free Tel: 800-222-0193 (cust care); 844-776-4899 (tech support)

E-mail: hprotechsupportusa@harman.com
Web Site: digitech.com
Manufacturer of guitar products.
Membership(s): AES; NAMM, the National Association of Music Merchants; NSCA

Digitron Electronics
7801 E Telegraph Rd, Montebello, CA 90640
Tel: 323-629-4518 *Fax:* 323-887-0891
E-mail: repairs@digitronelectronics.com
Web Site: digitronelectronics.com
Founded: 1991
Repairs for broadcast & film, musicians & DJs, studio & event production, projectors, CCTV cameras, industrial & medical imaging equipment.

DimcoGray Co
900 Dimco Way, Centerville, OH 45458
Tel: 937-433-7600 *Fax:* 937-433-0520
E-mail: dgsales@dimcogray.com
Web Site: www.dimcogray.com
Founded: 1924
Custom molded thermoplastic parts.
Catalog(s) available
Membership(s): The Imaging Alliance

Direct Cinema Ltd Inc
PO Box 10003, Santa Monica, CA 90410-1003
Tel: 310-636-8200 *Fax:* 310-636-8228
E-mail: dclvideo@aol.com
Web Site: www.directcinema.com
Key Personnel
Pres: Mitchell W Block
Founded: 1974
Video production & rentals.
Online catalog(s) available
Membership(s): AECT; ALA; American Association for the Arts; AMPAS; Consortium of College & University Media Centers; National Association of Media & Technology Centers; NFM; University Film & Video Association

Direct Current Video Productions
1928 E Highland Ave, Suite F104-448, Phoenix, AZ 85016
Tel: 602-263-7717
Web Site: www.directcurrentproductions.com
Key Personnel
Owner: Ginny Temple *E-mail:* ginny@ directcurrentproductions.com
Founded: 1988
Complete video production services for television, corporations & independent producers.
Membership(s): Arizona Production Association

Direct Images Interactive Inc
1933 Davis St, Suite 308, San Leandro, CA 94577
Tel: 510-613-8299
E-mail: info@directimages.com
Web Site: www.directimages.com
Key Personnel
Prodr: Bill Knowland
Founded: 1988
Multimedia design & video production.

Directed Electronics
Unit of DEI Holdings Inc
One Viper Way, Suite A, Vista, CA 92081
Tel: 760-598-6200 *Toll Free Tel:* 800-876-0800
E-mail: pr@directed.com
Web Site: www.directed.com
Key Personnel
CEO: Robert J Struble
SVP, Sales & Cust Serv: Glenn R Busse
Founded: 1982
Vehicle security & control telematics.
Branch Office(s)
2113 32e Ave, Lachine, QC H8T 3J1, Canada
Toll Free Tel: 800-361-7271

Disc Makers
Division of DiY Media Group Inc
7905 N Crescent Blvd, Pennsauken, NJ 08110-1402
Tel: 856-663-9030 *Toll Free Tel:* 800-468-9353
Fax: 856-661-3450
E-mail: info@discmakers.com
Web Site: www.discmakers.com
Key Personnel
EVP: David Olinsky
Founded: 1946
CD & DVD manufacturer.
Catalog(s) available
Membership(s): Content Delivery & Storage Association; The Recording Academy; SPARS

Discovery Education - Chicago
111 E Wacker Dr, Suite 3000, Chicago, IL 60601-4803
Web Site: www.discoveryeducation.com
Key Personnel
SVP, Partnerships: Coni Rechner
Catalog(s) available

Discovery Education Inc
230 Park Ave S, New York, NY 10003
Toll Free Tel: 800-323-9084 *Toll Free Fax:* 855-495-6542
E-mail: education_info@discoveryed.com
Web Site: www.discoveryeducation.com
Key Personnel
CEO: Bill Goodwyn
Standards-based digital curriculum resources for K-12 classrooms worldwide.

Discovery Education - Los Angeles
10100 Santa Monica Blvd, Suite 1500, Los Angeles, CA 90067
Tel: 310-551-1611 *Fax:* 310-551-1684
Web Site: www.discoveryeducation.com
Catalog(s) available

Discovery Education - South Burlington
700 Indian Springs Dr, Lancaster, PA 17601
Toll Free Tel: 888-892-3484 *Toll Free Fax:* 877-324-6830
E-mail: education_info@discovery.com
Web Site: store.discoveryeducation.com
Catalog(s) available

Disk Productions Inc
1100 Perkins Rd, Baton Rouge, LA 70802
Tel: 225-343-5438
E-mail: disk_productions@yahoo.com
Key Personnel
Owner: Joe Decker
Audio production studio.
Membership(s): AES; American Advertising Association

DiskFaktory
1145 Polk St, Suite DF, San Francisco, CA 94109
Toll Free Tel: 855-273-4263
E-mail: customercare@diskfaktory.com
Web Site: diskfaktory.com
Customized disc products & promotional items for musicians, indie musicians, filmmakers & marketing professionals.
Online catalog(s) available

Disney Consumer Products & Interactive Media (DCPI)
Subsidiary of The Walt Disney Co
1201 Flower St, Glendale, AZ 91201
Tel: 818-544-0000
Web Site: dcpi.disney.com
Key Personnel
Chmn: James Pitaro
EVP & CFO: Ignace Lahoud
EVP, Global Licensing: Josh Silverman

EVP, Publishing & Digital Media: Andrew Sugerman
EVP, Retail: Paul Gainer
SVP & CTO: Michael White
SVP, Communs: Tasia Filippatos
SVP, Franchise: Mark L Walker
SVP, Games & Interactive Experiences: Kyle Laughlin
SVP, Global Creative: Luis Fernandez
SVP, HR: Garry Randall
VP, Busn Insights & Optimization: Robert Vanderhyde
VP, Off Chmn: Sarah Weisinger
Deputy Gen Coun: Suzanne Wilson
Founded: 1929
Brings stories & characters to life through innovative & engaging physical products & digital experiences from toys to apps, books & console games.
Online catalog(s) available

The Walt Disney Co
500 S Buena Vista St, Burbank, CA 91521
Tel: 818-560-1000
Web Site: disney.com; thewaltdisneycompany.com
Key Personnel
Chmn & CEO: Robert A Iger
Chmn, Walt Disney Intl, The Walt Disney Co: Andy Bird
SVP, Gen Coun & Secy: Alan Braverman
SVP & CFO: Christine M McCarthy
SVP & Chief Communs Offr: Zenia Mucha
SVP & Chief HR Offr: Jayne Parker
SVP & Chief Strategy Offr: Kevin Mayer
SVP, Global Security: Ronald L Iden
Founded: 1923
International family entertainment & media enterprise including segments: media networks, parks & resorts, studio entertainment, consumer products & interactive media.

The Walt Disney Studios
500 S Buena Vista St, Burbank, CA 91521
Tel: 818-560-1000
Web Site: studioservices.go.com; waltdisneystudios.com
Key Personnel
Chmn: Alan Horn
Pres: Alan Bergman
Pres, Mktg: Ricky Strauss
SVP, HR: Carolyn Wilson
Founded: 1923
Disney production & post-production facilities.

Display Devices Inc
21075 Westgate Rd, Golden, CO 80403
Tel: 303-412-0399
E-mail: sales@displaydevices.com; tech@ displaydevices.com
Web Site: www.displaydevices.com
Founded: 1989
Design, engineer & manufacture commercial AV equipment & display products.
Online catalog(s) available
Membership(s): Audiovisual and Integrated Experience Association; NAB

Display Systems International
Division of TV Media Inc
2214 Hanselman Ave, Saskatoon, SK S7L 6A4, Canada
Tel: 306-934-6884 *Toll Free Tel:* 877-934-6884
Fax: 306-934-6447 *Toll Free Fax:* 800-410-4419
E-mail: sales@displaysystemsintl.com
Web Site: www.displaysystemsintl.com
Key Personnel
Owner, Pres & CEO: Dale Lemke
Founded: 1983
Scrolling TV guides, character generators & digital signage systems.

Online catalog(s) available
Branch Office(s)
500 Lacolle Way, Ottawa K4A 0N9, ON, Canada

Scott Dittrich Films, see Action Sports/All Stock

Diversified
37 Market St, Kenilworth, NJ 07033
Tel: 908-245-4833 *Fax:* 908-245-0011
E-mail: customerservice@diversifiedus.com;
 info@diversifiedus.com
Web Site: diversifiedus.com
Key Personnel
Chmn & CEO: Fred D'Alessandro
Exec VChmn: Mike Landrum
Pres & COO: Kevin Collins
EVP & CFO: Bruce Herman
CTO: Karl Paulsen
Pres, Media Group: John Melillo
SVP, Mktg: Anthony Cuellar
Founded: 1993
Provide aggregated media, technology consulting, engineering, management & integration
 services to broadcast & cable, Fortune 500,
 sports & entertainment, out of home advertising, education, government, retail & healthcare
 markets.
Branch Office(s)
140 Business Center Dr, Birmingham, AL
 35244, Contact: David Berndt *Tel:* 205-582-
 5900 *Fax:* 205-985-4756 *E-mail:* dberndt@
 diversifiedus.com
440 W Cypress St, Glendale, CA 91204 *Tel:* 818-
 863-8150 *Fax:* 818-863-8205 *E-mail:* kyu@
 diversifiedus.com
198 Cirby Way, Suite 180, Roseville, CA 95678
 Tel: 916-782-7339 *E-mail:* jchrisco-brown@
 diversifiedus.com
101 Glacier Point Rd, Suite B, San Rafael, CA
 94901 *Tel:* 415-257-8480 *E-mail:* jberitzhoff@
 diversifiedus.com
3275 Edward Ave, Santa Clara, CA 95054
 Tel: 408-969-1972 *Fax:* 408-969-1985
 E-mail: dyoslov@diversifiedus.com
PO Box 4476, Greenwood Village, CO 80155
 Tel: 303-536-7809, ext 2 *E-mail:* pcatterson@
 diversifiedus.com
9555 Holsberry Lane, Unit 3, Pensacola,
 FL 32534, Contact: David Berndt *Toll
 Free Tel:* 800-554-5440 *E-mail:* dberndt@
 diversifiedus.com
2975 Northwoods Pkwy, Atlanta, GA
 30071, Contact: Tom Spearman *Toll Free
 Tel:* 800-554-5440 *Fax:* 770-441-5285
 E-mail: tspearman@diversifiedus.com
1400 Michael Dr, Suite C, Wood Dale, IL
 60191 *Tel:* 630-741-4620 *Fax:* 630-860-8010
 E-mail: ctaylor@diversifiedus.com
9801-G Southern Pine Blvd, Charlotte, NC
 28273, Contact: Dan Lumsden *Tel:* 704-944-
 3115 *E-mail:* dlumsden@diversifiedus.com
10404 Chapel Hill Rd, Suite 107, Morrisville, NC
 27560, Contact: Dan Lumsden *Tel:* 919-462-
 9300 *Fax:* 916-462-9455 *E-mail:* dlumsden@
 diversifiedus.com
1600 Century Center Pkwy, Bldg B, Suite
 106, Memphis, TN 38134, Contact: David
 Berndt *Tel:* 901-345-5971 *Fax:* 901-969-0170
 E-mail: dberndt@diversifiedus.com
1449 Donelson Pike, Nashville, TN 37217,
 Contact: David Berndt *Tel:* 615-244-3933
 Fax: 615-244-1031 *E-mail:* dberndt@
 diversifiedus.com
1801 Royal Lane, Dallas, TX 75229 *Tel:* 972-
 409-0900 *E-mail:* rdungan@diversifiedus.com
6120 West by Northwest Blvd, Suite 160,
 Houston, TX 77040, Contact: Chad Cog-
 burn *Tel:* 713-325-6819 *E-mail:* ccogburn@
 diversifiedus.com
3635 Concorde Pkwy, Suite 300, Chantilly,
 VA 20151, David Berndt *Tel:* 703-579-3902
 E-mail: dberndt@diversifiedus.com

23475 Rockhaven Way, Suite 140, Dulles, VA
 20166 *Tel:* 703-552-6900 *Fax:* 703-552-6990
 E-mail: fpansolini@diversifiedus.com
Foreign Office(s): 501, Endeavor Bldg, 74-gil
 45, Seochodaero, Seocho-Gu, Seoul 06626,
 South Korea, Contact: Jay Park *E-mail:* jpark@
 diversifiedus.com
Membership(s): Audiovisual and Integrated Experience Association; NAB; SBE; SMPTE®

DL Acoustics
14301 Middletown Lane, Westminster, CA 92683
Tel: 714-373-3050 *Fax:* 714-373-3050
Web Site: www.dlacoustics.biz
Key Personnel
Pres: David Lubman *E-mail:* dlubman@
 dlacoustics.com
Acoustical consultant specializing in certified
 sound measurement & analysis.
Membership(s): ASA; INCE; National Council of
 Acoustical Consultants

DL Sound & Lighting Productions Ltd
450 Banga Place, Victoria, BC V8Z 6X5, Canada
Mailing Address: PO Box 1173, Victoria, BC
 V8W 2T6, Canada
Tel: 250-216-7898
Web Site: www.dlsound.net
Key Personnel
Owner & Pres: Doug Lyngard *E-mail:* doug@
 dlsound.net
Founded: 1984
Sales, rentals & productions.
Branch Office(s)
Vancouver, BC, Canada *Tel:* 604-561-3528

DME Studios
1025 Greenwood Blvd, Suite 191, Lake Mary, FL
 32746
Tel: 407-585-7500
E-mail: creativeteam@dmestudios.com
Web Site: www.dmestudios.com
Integrated marketing communications & video
 production.

DNASTAR Inc
3801 Regent St, Madison, WI 53705-5204
Tel: 608-258-7420 *Toll Free Tel:* 866-511-5090
 Fax: 608-258-7439
E-mail: info@dnastar.com
Web Site: www.dnastar.com
Key Personnel
Pres: Frederick Blattner
Founded: 1984
Global software company for life scientists.
Catalog(s) available

DNP Imagingcomm America Corp (DNP IAM)
Subsidiary of DNP Group
4524 Enterprise Dr NW, Concord, NC 28027
Tel: 704-784-8100 *Toll Free Tel:* 800-814-4672
 Fax: 704-784-7196
E-mail: sales_marketing@dnp.imgcomm.com
Web Site: www.dnpimagingcomm.com; www.
 dnpphoto.com
Key Personnel
Pres: Shinichi Yamashita
Founded: 1992
Printer & media solutions for retailers, event pho-
 tographers & photo booth operators.
Online catalog(s) available
Foreign Office(s): DNP International Trading
 (Shanghai) Co Ltd, Shanghai Mall, 603B, 1376
 Nanjing West Rd, Shanghai, China *Tel:* (021)
 62798711 *E-mail:* zhang-d@dnp-cn.com *Web
 Site:* dnpphoto.com/china
DNP Photo Imaging Europe, Z I Paris Nord 2,
 22, Avenue des Nations, CS 51077, 95948
 Roissy CDG Cedex, France *Tel:* 01 49 38
 65 50 *Fax:* 01 49 89 00 81 *Web Site:* www.
 dnpphoto.eu

DNP Photo Imaging Japan Co Ltd, 3-35-13 Yay-
 oicho, Nakano-ku, Tokyo 164-0013, Japan
 Tel: (0120) 37-2010 *Fax:* (03) 3299-1201 *Web
 Site:* dnpphoto.jp
DNP Imagingcomm Asia Sdn Bhd, PLO 676, Jl
 Nikel 4, Kawasan Perindustrian Pasir Gudang,
 81707 Pasir Gudang, Johor, Malaysia *Tel:* (07)
 257 8400 *E-mail:* photosales@dnp.imgcomm.
 asia *Web Site:* dnpimagingcomm.asia

Docter Optics Inc
Subsidiary of Docter Optics SE
1425 W Elliot Rd, Suite A-105, Gilbert, AZ
 85233
Tel: 480-844-7585 *Fax:* 480-844-7826
E-mail: doi@docteroptics.com
Web Site: www.docteroptics.com
Optical components, systems & services.
Catalog(s) available
Foreign Office(s): Docter Optics SE, Mittelweg
 29, 07806 Neustadt an der Orla, Germany
 Tel: (0364) 81-27-0 *Fax:* (0364) 81-27-270
 (headquarters)

Documentary Educational Resources Inc
108 Water St, Suite 5A, Watertown, MA 02472
Tel: 617-926-0491 *Toll Free Tel:* 800-569-6621
 Fax: 617-926-9519
E-mail: info@der.org
Web Site: www.der.org
Key Personnel
Exec Dir: Alice Apley *E-mail:* alice@der.org
Founded: 1968
Produce, distribute & promote ethnographic &
 documentary films from around the world.
Online catalog(s) available
Catalog(s) available, free on request
Printed material(s) available, free, new releases
Membership(s): The Alliance for Media Arts and
 Culture; American Anthropological Associa-
 tion; IFP; International Documentary Associa-
 tion

DocuWare Corp
4 Crotty Lane, Suite 200, New Windsor, NY
 12553
Tel: 845-563-9045 *Toll Free Tel:* 888-565-5907
 Fax: 845-563-9046
E-mail: info@docuware.com; dwsales@docuware.
 com
Web Site: www.docuware.com
Key Personnel
Mktg Communs Mgr: Mary K Williams *Tel:* 845-
 563-9045 ext 221 *E-mail:* mary.williams@
 docuware.com
Founded: 1988
Document management software for companies
 seeking to digitize, automate & transform key
 document-centric processes without the need
 for IT resources.
Branch Office(s)
35 Thorpe Ave, Suite 201, Wallingford, CT
 06492 *Tel:* 203-871-4984 *Fax:* 203-269-0322
 E-mail: fortissupport@docuware.com
Foreign Office(s): DocuWare SARL, 17 rue du
 Colisee, 75008 Paris, France *Tel:* 01 57 19 03
 23 *E-mail:* infoline@docuware.com
DocuWare GmbH, Therese-Giehse-Platz 2, 82110
 Germering, Germany, Mng Dir: Juergen Bif-
 far *Tel:* (089) 894433-0 *Fax:* (089) 8419966
 E-mail: docuware@docuware.com (headquar-
 ters)
DocuWare SL, Casp, 90 3° 1a, 08010 Barcelona,
 Spain *Tel:* 933171771 *E-mail:* infoline@
 docuware.com
DocuWare Ltd, Chiltern Chambers, 37 St Peters
 Ave, Caversham, United Kingdom *Tel:* (0115)
 7180353 *E-mail:* infoline@docuware.com
Membership(s): AIIM

Dog & Pony Productions Inc
8928 "L" St, Omaha, NE 68127

Tel: 402-391-7691 *Fax:* 402-341-2751
E-mail: dognponyinc@aol.com
Web Site: www.dogandponyinc.com
Key Personnel
CFO: Susan Gilstrap
Pres: Mike Gilstrap
Founded: 1988
AV rentals & productions.

Dogwood Productions Inc
Formerly Dogwood Recording Studios
757 Government St, Mobile, AL 36602
Tel: 251-476-0858 *Toll Free Tel:* 800-254-9903
Fax: 251-479-0364
E-mail: info@dogwoodproductions.com
Web Site: www.dogwoodproductions.com
Key Personnel
Audio Dir: Ray Norman *E-mail:* raynorman@
  dogwoodproductions.com
Creative Dir: Jason Cruthirds *E-mail:* jason@
  dogwoodproductions.com
New Busn Dir: Tad Denson *E-mail:* tad@
  dogwoodproductions.com
Audio Engr: Charlie Mitchell *E-mail:* charlie@
  dogwoodproductions.com
Interactive Designer: Phillip Davis
  E-mail: phillip@dogwoodproductions.com
Multimedia Designer: Amy Collins
  E-mail: amy@dogwoodproductions.com
Founded: 1981
Audio production facility. Specialize in products
  for advertising, broadcast, multimedia & film.

Dogwood Recording Studios, see Dogwood
  Productions Inc

Dolby Laboratories Inc
1275 Market St, San Francisco, CA 94103-1410
Tel: 415-558-0200 *Fax:* 415-645-4000
Web Site: www.dolby.com
Key Personnel
Pres & CEO: Kevin Yeaman
EVP & CFO: Lewis Chew
EVP, Gen Coun & Corp Secy: Andy Sherman
SVP & Chief Mktg Offr: Todd Pendleton
SVP, Advanced Technol Group: Steven E Forshay
SVP, Cinema Busn Group: Doug Darrow
SVP, Commercial Partnerships: John Couling
SVP, Consumer Entertainment: Giles Baker
SVP, HR: Linda Rogers
VP, Communs Busn Group: Andrew Border
Founded: 1965
Online catalog(s) available
Branch Office(s)
1020 Chestnut St, Burbank, CA 91506 *Tel:* 818-
  562-1101 *Fax:* 818-562-1109
3601 W Alameda Ave, Burbank, CA 91505-5300
  Tel: 818-823-2800 *Fax:* 818-557-0890
4000 W Alameda Ave, Suite 500, Burbank, CA
  91505 *Tel:* 818-391-1100 *Fax:* 818-391-1100
432 Lakeside Dr, Sunnyvale, CA 94085 *Tel:* 408-
  330-3300 *Fax:* 408-330-3200
8021 Knue Rd, Suite 113, Indianapolis, IN 46250
  Tel: 317-585-3912 *Fax:* 317-585-3912
SLS Audio, 1650 W Jackson St, Ozark, MO
  65721 *Tel:* 417-323-7000 *Fax:* 417-485-3744
  (div)
1350 Avenue of the Americas, Suite 2400, New
  York, NY 10019-4703 *Tel:* 212-767-1700
  Fax: 212-767-1705
Foreign Office(s): Dolby Australia Pty Ltd, 35
  Mitchell St, Level 3, McMahons Point, NSW
  2060, Australia *Tel:* (02) 9101 7900 *Fax:* (02)
  9101 7800
Rua Paulo Orozimbo, 260 Aclimacao, 01535-000
  Sao Paulo-SP, Brazil *Tel:* (011) 2872-5600
Dolby Laboratories International Services (Bei-
  jing) Co Ltd, World Financial Ctr, West Bldg,
  Rm 907-916, Level 9, No 1 E 3rd Ring Middle
  Rd, Chaoyang District, Beijing 100020, China
  Tel: (010) 5910-3000 *Fax:* (010) 5910-3001

Dolby Laboratories International Services (Shang-
  hai) Co Ltd, 09-128, Tower A, ONE ITC, 1901
  Huashan Rd, Xuhui District, Shanghai 200030,
  China *Tel:* (021) 6113-3456 *Fax:* (021) 6113-
  3400
Dolby Laboratories International Services Inc,
  Kerry Plaza, 18F, Tower 1, No 1 Zhong Xin Si
  Rd, Futian District, Shenzhen 518048, China
  Tel: (0755) 3698-5900 *Fax:* (0755) 3698-5901
Dolby France, 18 Rue de Londres, 75009 Paris,
  France *Tel:* 04 22 10 67 00 *Fax:* 04 22 10 67
  00
Dolby France SAS, 2400, Route des Cretes,
  Sophia Antipolis, 06560 Valbonne, France
  Tel: 04 22 10 67 00 *Fax:* 04 22 10 67 01
Dolby Germany GmbH, Rheinstr 45, Aufgang 1,
  12161 Berlin, Germany *Tel:* (030) 89061-8000
  Fax: (030) 89061-8001
Dolby Germany GmbH, Arnulfstr 122, 80636
  Munich, Germany *Tel:* (089) 244100-200
  Fax: (089) 244100-201
Dolby Germany GmbH, Deutschherrnstr 15-19,
  90429 Nuremberg, Germany *Tel:* (0911) 928-
  91-0 *Fax:* (0911) 928-91-99
Dolby Laboratories Hong Kong Ltd, Central
  Plaza, Suite 5407, 18 Harbour Rd, Wanchai,
  Hong Kong *Tel:* 2519 0888 *Fax:* 2519 8988
Dolby Technology India Pvt Ltd, Prestige Pal-
  ladium Bayan, Level 5, Greams Rd, Chennai
  600 006, India *Tel:* (044) 4654-9227 *Fax:* (044)
  4654-9394
Dolby Technology India Pvt Ltd, Solitaire Cor-
  porate Park, S14, 5th fl, 167, Guru Hargovindji
  Marg Chakala, Andheri (E), Mumbai 400 093,
  India *Tel:* (022) 4919-2400 *Fax:* (022) 4973-
  3965
Dolby Technology India Pvt Ltd, Regus, Level
  15, SB Tower, 1A/1, Sec 16A, Film City,
  Noida 201 301, India *Tel:* (0120) 4804819
  Fax: (0120) 4804949
Dolby Japan KK, Hankyu Terminal Bldg, 16th fl,
  1-1-4 Shibata, Kita-ku, Osaka 530-0012, Japan
  Tel: (06) 7222-3772 *Fax:* (06) 7222-3701
Dolby Japan KK, NBF Higashi-Ginza Sq 3F,
  1-13-14 Tsukiji, Chuo-ku, Tokyo 104-0045,
  Japan *Tel:* (03) 3524-7300 *Fax:* (03) 3524-7389
Dolby International AB, Apollo Bldg, 3E,
  Herikerbergweg 1-35, 1101 CN Amsterdam
  Zuidoost, Netherlands *Tel:* (020) 6511 800
  Fax: (020) 6511 801
Dolby Poland Sp zoo, Business Garden, Bldg
  G, ul Legknicka 48, 54-202 Wroclaw, Poland
  Tel: (071) 7352-300 *Fax:* (071) 7352-301
Dolby CIS LLC, Smolensky Passage, Smolen-
  skaya Sq, 3, fl 7, 121099 Moscow, Russia *Tel:* (495) 937-8485
  Fax: (495) 937-8290
Dolby Singapore Pte Ltd, UIC Bldg 10-01, 5
  Shenton Way, Singapore 068808, Singapore
  Tel: 6911 6610 *Fax:* 6911 6611
Dolby Laboratories International Services Inc, 14,
  Teheran-ro, 26-gil, Gangnam-gu, Seoul 06236,
  South Korea
Dolby Iberia SL, Edificio Imagina, Av Diago-
  nal, 177, Planta 10, 08018 Barcelona, Spain
  Tel: 934-867-600 *Fax:* 934-867-601
Dolby Iberia SL, Paseo de la Castellana 93,
  28046 Madrid, Spain *Tel:* 91-047-9310
  Fax: 91-793-2999
Dolby Sweden AB, Gaevlegatan 12A, 113 30
  Stockholm, Sweden *Tel:* (08) 442 91 60
  Fax: (08) 442 91 90
Dolby Laboratories International Services Inc,
  Neihu New Century Bldg, Level 04, No 55,
  Zhouzi St, Taipei 114, Taiwan *Tel:* (02) 8758
  2785 *Fax:* (02) 8758 2728
Dolby Middle East FZ LLC, Dubai Media City,
  Bldg 5, Off 110, 502444 Dubai, United Arab
  Emirates *Tel:* (04) 455-6900 *Fax:* (040 455-
  6901
Dolby Europe Ltd, 4-6 Soho Sq, London W1D
  3PZ, United Kingdom *Tel:* (020) 7406 3200
  Fax: (020) 7406 3201

Dolby Europe Ltd, Royal Wootton Bassett,
  Swindon, Wilts SN4 8QJ, United Kingdom
  Tel: (01793) 842100 *Fax:* (01793) 842101
Membership(s): AES; SMPTE®

Dolphin MultiMedia Inc
1660 Belleville Way, Sunnyvale, CA 94087
Tel: 650-354-0800 *Fax:* 408-737-8404
Web Site: dolphinmm.com
Key Personnel
Pres: Cynthia Kondratieff *E-mail:* cynthia@
  dolphinmm.com
Founded: 1972
Delivers visual communications to clients that
  drive their message home in dramatic & pow-
  erful ways. Modes of delivery include film,
  video, multi-image programs, interactive CD-
  ROMs, presentations, print & web.

Domo Tactical Communications (DTC) Ltd
3845 Gateway Centre Blvd, Suite 360, Pinellas
  Park, FL 33782
Tel: 727-741-6900 *Toll Free Tel:* 800-665-4648
E-mail: tampa.info@domotactical.com
Web Site: domotactical.com
Key Personnel
Regl VP, Sales (Americas): Marc Whalen
Founded: 2016
Surveillance operations within high performance
  overt & covert video, audio, tracking & cellular
  solutions, along with developing cutting edge
  technologies for the wireless broadcast market.
Online catalog(s) available

Donnelly Sound Inc
59 Hylan Blvd, Apt 1C, Staten Island, NY 10305
Tel: 917-496-7752
E-mail: donnellysound@gmail.com
Web Site: billdonnelly.com
Key Personnel
Owner & Pres: Bill Donnelly
Founded: 2005
Sound designer & mixer.
Membership(s): AES

Doomsday Studios Limited
212 James St, Ottawa, ON K1R 5M7, Canada
Tel: 613-230-9769 *Fax:* 613-230-6004
E-mail: info@doomsdaystudios.com
Key Personnel
Pres & Exec Prodr: Ramona Macdonald
Founded: 1978
Membership(s): Canadian Media Production As-
  sociation; WIFT

Dorfman Museum Figures Inc
6224 Holabird Ave, Baltimore, MD 21224
Tel: 410-284-3248 *Toll Free Tel:* 800-634-4873
  Fax: 410-284-3249
E-mail: info@museumfigures.com
Web Site: www.museumfigures.com
Key Personnel
Pres: Robert Dorfman
Founded: 1957
Create lifesize life-like human figures for
  museums, visitor centers & collectors &
  ETHAFOAM™ conservation forms for display
  & storage of high value artifacts.
Online catalog(s) available

Dorian Color
Division of Hunt's Photo & Video
100 Main St, Melrose, MA 02176
Tel: 781-648-8040
E-mail: images@doriancolor.com
Web Site: www.doriancolor.com
Key Personnel
Dir, Photo Imaging Servs: Alan Asadorian
  E-mail: aasadorian@huntsphoto.com
Prodn Mgr: Jim Munn *E-mail:* jmunn@
  huntsphoto.com

Imaging Specialist: Rodney Soares
  E-mail: rsoares@huntsphoto.com
Founded: 1973
Full service professional photographic printing &
  framing company.
Catalog(s) available
Membership(s): The Imaging Alliance

Dorrough Electronics Inc
5221 Collier Place, Woodland Hills, CA 91364
Tel: 818-998-2824
E-mail: dorroughel@aol.com
Web Site: www.dorrough.com
Key Personnel
Partner: Kay Dorrough
Pres: Michael Dorrough
Manufacture audio level meters & sound record-
  ing.
Online catalog(s) available
Membership(s): AES; NAB

Dorst MediaWorks Inc
1219 Blagden Alley NW, 2nd fl, Washington, DC
  20001
Tel: 202-258-9612
Web Site: dorstmediaworks.com
Key Personnel
Pres, Dir, Prodr & Ed: Steve Dorst
  E-mail: steve@dorstmediaworks.com
Founded: 2000
Script-to-screen full service video production
  company.
Membership(s): Women in Film & Video

Dot C Software Inc
117 Waihili Place, Honolulu, HI 96825
E-mail: info@dotcsw.com
Web Site: www.dotcsw.com
Key Personnel
Pres: Cheryl M LaMont E-mail: cheryl@dotcsw.
  com
Founded: 1992
Development & sale of computer graphics soft-
  ware tools & services.

Dotronix Technology Inc
160 First St SE, New Brighton, MN 55112
Tel: 651-633-1742
E-mail: service@dotronix.com; sales@dotronix.
  com
Web Site: www.dotronix.com
Key Personnel
Owner: Kurt Sadler E-mail: ksadler@dotronix.
  com
Founded: 1980
Sell new replacement monitors & service nearly
  any CRT-based monitor.

Douglas House Inc
275 Kings Hwy, Orangeburg, NY 10962
Tel: 845-359-1477 Fax: 845-359-2945
E-mail: thedouglashouse@earthlink.net
Web Site: www.thedouglashouse.com
Key Personnel
CEO: Heather Douglas
Founded: 1981
Commercial, fully propped film production facil-
  ity.

Dover Publications Inc
Subsidiary of Courier Corp
31 E Second St, Mineola, NY 11501
Tel: 516-294-7000 Fax: 516-742-5049 (wholesale
  orders); 516-742-6953 (cust care)
Web Site: store.doverpublications.com
Founded: 1941
Catalog(s) available

Dow-Key Microwave Corp
Subsidiary of Dover Corp
4822 McGrath St, Ventura, CA 93003

Tel: 805-650-0260 Toll Free Tel: 800-266-3695
  Fax: 805-650-1734
E-mail: askdk@dowkey.com
Web Site: www.dowkey.com
Founded: 1945
Manufacture electromechanical switches for
  the commercial, military, government, space,
  telecommications, automated test equipment,
  avionics, ground-based satellite communica-
  tions & broadcasting industries.
Online catalog(s) available

Downpour.com
31 Mistletoe Rd, Ashland, OR 97520
Toll Free Tel: 855-369-6768 Toll Free Fax: 800-
  482-9294
E-mail: customercare@downpour.com
Web Site: www.downpour.com
Founded: 1987
Produce audiobooks in CD & download.

**Downtown Community Television Center
(DCTV)**
87 Lafayette St, New York, NY 10013
Tel: 212-966-4510 Fax: 212-226-3053
E-mail: info@dctvny.org
Web Site: www.dctvny.org
Key Personnel
Co-Founder, Co-Exec Dir & Pres: Jon Alpert
  E-mail: jonny@dctvny.org
Co-Founder & Co-Exec Dir: Keiko Tsuno
  Tel: 212-996-4510 ext 622 E-mail: ktsuno@
  dctvny.org
Film Prodr & Dir: Matthew O'Neill Tel: 212-996-
  4510 ext 636 E-mail: matthew@dctvny.org
Founded: 1972
Foster diverse viewpoints by providing profes-
  sional training, state-of-the-industry resources
  & by creating outstanding documentary produc-
  tions, with the belief that diversity of expres-
  sion strengthens our democracy & enhances
  civil society.

R L Drake Co
710 Pleasant Valley Dr, Springboro, OH 45066
Tel: 937-746-4556 Fax: 937-806-1510
E-mail: salesgroup@rldrake.net
Web Site: www.rldrake.com
Key Personnel
Inside Sales Mgr: Philip Hawkins
Founded: 1943
Manufacturer of cable television products.
Online catalog(s) available

DR&A Inc
45 Willow St, Nashville, TN 37210
Tel: 615-256-6200 Fax: 615-256-6236
Web Site: www.griptruck.com
Key Personnel
Contact: Shaun Anweiler E-mail: shaun@
  griptruck.com; Doug Rice E-mail: drice@
  griptruck.com
Founded: 1985
Television & film production services.

Draper Inc
411 S Pearl St, Spiceland, IN 47385
Tel: 765-987-7999 Toll Free Tel: 800-238-7999
  Fax: 765-987-7142
E-mail: av@draperinc.com
Web Site: www.draperinc.com; blog.draperinc.
  com
Key Personnel
Dir, AV Mkts: Bob Mathes E-mail: bmathes@
  draperinc.com
Dir, Sales: Lee Denhart E-mail: ldenhart@
  draperinc.com
Mktg Mgr: Penny Sitler E-mail: psitler@
  draperinc.com
Mktg Admin: Amy Bradway E-mail: abradway@
  draperinc.com

Founded: 1902
Creates core & tailored solutions for the profes-
  sional AV marketplace, including projection
  screens, custom AV structures, supports, en-
  closures & lifts, as well as window shades &
  video conferencing solutions.
Online catalog(s) available
Sales Office(s): 151 N Kraemer Blvd, Suite 101,
  Placentia, CA 92870, AV Regl Sales Mgr:
  Randy Reece Tel: 714-577-0088 Fax: 714-577-
  0044 E-mail: rreece@draperinc.com
Membership(s): Audiovisual and Integrated Expe-
  rience Association; Custom Electronic Design
  & Installation Association

Drastic Technologies Ltd
523 The Queensway, Suite 102, Toronto, ON
  M8Y 1J7, Canada
Tel: 416-255-5636 Fax: 416-255-8780
E-mail: sales@drastictech.com
Web Site: www.drastic.tv
Key Personnel
CTO & OEM Support: James Brooks
  E-mail: james@drastictech.com
Pres: Robert Brooks E-mail: bob@drastictech.
  com
Mgr, Admin: Bret Pearson E-mail: bret@
  drastictech.com
Sales Support Coord: Corey D Cousineau
Founded: 1991
Offer hardware & software products for digital
  video capture, control, conversion & delivery.

Dreambox Media Inc
PO Box 8132, Philadelphia, PA 19101-8132
E-mail: mail@dreamboxmedia.com
Web Site: www.dreamboxmedia.com
Key Personnel
Founder: James Miller Tel: 267-250-8506
Founded: 1995
Independent musicians' recording label dedicated
  to promoting the rich tradition of distinctively
  original & creative Philadelphia Jazz artists.

The Dreaming Tree
1112 Chestnut St, Unit B, Burbank, CA 91506
Tel: 818-845-3230
E-mail: info@dreamingtreeproductions.com
Web Site: www.dreamingtreeproductions.com
Key Personnel
Dir & Dir, Photog: Oktay Ortabasi
Ed/Colorist: Leslie Ortabasi
Production company.

Dreamscape Lighting Mfg Inc
5521 W Washington Blvd, Los Angeles, CA
  90016
Tel: 323-933-5760 Fax: 323-933-3607
E-mail: info@dreamscapelighting.com
Web Site: dreamscapelighting.com
Key Personnel
VP: Victor Kelmelis
Founded: 1988
Manufacture linear, landscape, architectural light-
  ing & linear LED.
Online catalog(s) available, PDF

Dreamscape Media LLC
1417 Timberwolf Dr, Holland, OH 43528
Tel: 419-867-6965 Toll Free Tel: 877-983-7326
E-mail: info@dreamscapeab.com
Web Site: www.dreamscapeab.com
Key Personnel
Publr: Tammy Faxel Tel: 419-491-1166
  E-mail: tfaxel@dreamscapeab.com
Exec Dir, Content & Strategy: Cat Zappa
Founded: 2010
Distribution, marketing & production services for
  audiobooks, ebooks, film & documentaries.

DRM: sir reel sound
2952 Cohoba Dr, Austin, TX 78748

Tel: 469-360-1443 (studio)
E-mail: drmuzik@mac.com
Web Site: drm-sirreelsound.com
Key Personnel
Founder, Pres, Sound Designer & Music Prodr:
   David Rosenblad
Founded: 1989
Provides comprehensive post audio, sound & music production services for film, video, TV, radio, album & multimedia.
Membership(s): AES; The Recording Academy

Mark Druck Productions, see Mark X
   Productions Inc

Drumbeat Indian Arts Inc
4143 N 16 St, Phoenix, AZ 85016
Tel: 602-266-4823 *Toll Free Tel:* 800-895-4859
   Fax: 602-265-2402
E-mail: info@drumbeatindianarts.com
Web Site: drumbeatindianarts.com
Key Personnel
Owner & Pres: Robert Nuss
Founded: 1984
Wholesale & retail source for authentic traditional & contemporary American Indian music. Also a major supplier of American Indian religious herbs, craft supplies & books.
Online catalog(s) available

Drytac Corp
5601 Eastport Blvd, Richmond, VA 23231
Tel: 804-222-3094 *Toll Free Tel:* 800-280-6013
E-mail: customerservice@drytac.com
Web Site: www.drytac.com
Key Personnel
Chmn: Richard Kelley
CEO: Hayden Kelley
VP, Busn Devt: Jerry Hill
VP, Fin: Tim Rader
VP, US Sales: Wayne Colbath
Global Mktg Mgr: Amanda Brown
Prod Support Specialist: Steve Yarbrough
Founded: 1976
Manufacturer & distributor of mounting & laminating materials & equipment.
Online catalog(s) available, PDF download
Branch Office(s)
14067 Stage Rd, Santa Fe Springs, CA 90670
   Tel: 562-921-0450
30 Driver Rd, Brampton, ON L6T 5V2, Canada
   Toll Free Tel: 800-353-2883 *E-mail:* toronto@
   drytac.com
Foreign Office(s): Drytac Europe Ltd, Filwood Rd, Fishponds, Bristol BS16 3RY, United Kingdom *Tel:* (0117) 958-6500
   E-mail: bristol@drytac.com
Membership(s): Alberta Sign Association; Association of International Metallizers, Coaters & Laminators; International Sign Association; ISA-UK; National Association of Sign Supply Distributors; Shop Environments Association; Specialty Graphic Imaging Association; Virginia Sign Association

DSan Corp
142 Mineola Ave, Roslyn Heights, NY 11577
Tel: 516-625-5608 *Fax:* 516-625-0878
E-mail: sales@dsan.com
Web Site: www.dsan.com
Key Personnel
Pres: Kelvin J Swarth
Mktg Dir: Rodger Swarth
Manufacturer of unique presentation tools.
   Speaker timers are used by the US Congress, Supreme Court, city councils, government agencies & corporations everywhere. Cue lights for remote control of presentations have become industry standards for their solid RF links & flexible setups. Ultra bright green laser pointers suitable for institutions & the rental market & several handy audio adapters for

getting sound-accompanied presentations into house audio systems. Sells direct worldwide & through AV dealers.
Online catalog(s) available

DSI RF Systems Inc
249 Homestead Rd, Hillsborough, NJ 08844
Tel: 732-563-1144 *Fax:* 732-563-1818
E-mail: sales@dsirf.com; info@dsirf.com
Web Site: www.dsirf.com
Key Personnel
Pres: Joe Giardina *E-mail:* jgiardina@dsirf.com
Provide technical & engineering solutions to the broadcast industry.

DSR Computer Technology Specialists Inc
961-M Mercantile Dr, Hanover, MD 21076
Tel: 410-579-4508 *Toll Free Tel:* 800-875-0037
   Fax: 410-579-8412
E-mail: dsr@dsr-inc.com
Web Site: www.dsr-inc.com
Key Personnel
Pres & CEO: Dan Hogan *Tel:* 410-540-4015
   E-mail: dhogan@dsr-inc.com
Founded: 1986
Business computer sales, networking & computer repair.

DTC Grip & Electric, see DTC Lighting & Grip

DTC Lighting & Grip
1280 65 St, Emeryville, CA 94608
Tel: 510-595-0770 *Fax:* 510-595-0772
E-mail: sales@dtcgrip.com; rentals@dtcgrip.com
Web Site: www.dtcgrip.com
Key Personnel
Pres: Steve Condiotti *E-mail:* stevec@dtcgrip.com
Mktg Coord: Audrey Onesta *E-mail:* audrey@
   dtcgrip.com
Founded: 1983
Lighting & grip equipment rentals & sales.
Online catalog(s) available

DuArt Media Services
245 W 55 St, New York, NY 10019
Tel: 212-757-4580 *Fax:* 212-977-5609
E-mail: info@duart.com
Web Site: www.duart.com
Key Personnel
Pres & CEO: Linda Young *E-mail:* lyoung@
   duart.com
Pres, Audiobook Div: Lou Gutierrez *Tel:* 973-204-3787
SVP, Sales: Nick Marucci *Tel:* 917-522-5645
Dir, Audio Servs: Allan Gus *Tel:* 917-522-5674
Facilities Dir: Susan Gallo *Tel:* 917-522-5679
Founded: 1922
Post-production facility. Specialize in broadcast post-production, editing, finishing, equipment rentals & other services.
Membership(s): IAA-VC; SMPTE®

Dub King
8133 Callaghan Rd, San Antonio, TX 78230
Tel: 210-979-8779
E-mail: dubking@dubking.com
Web Site: www.dubking.com
Key Personnel
Owner: Kimble Dement *E-mail:* kimble@
   dubking.com; Brian Howell *E-mail:* brian@
   dubking.com
Mgr: Nick Delgado *E-mail:* nick@dubking.com
Founded: 1981
DVD & AV transfers along with other multimedia services.
Branch Office(s)
1925 Rutland Dr, Suite E, Austin, TX 78758,
   Mgr: Paul Lippa *Tel:* 512-451-3827
   E-mail: paul@dubking.com
Membership(s): Association of Professional Videographers

Dan Dugan Sound Design Inc
290 Napoleon St, Suite E, San Francisco, CA 94124
Tel: 415-821-9776 *Fax:* 415-826-7699
Web Site: www.dandugan.com
Key Personnel
CEO & Proprietor: Dan Dugan *E-mail:* dan@
   dandugan.com
Manufacturing, editing & CD mastering.
Membership(s): AES; NAB; NSCA; SMPTE®

Duggal Visual Solutions Inc
Brooklyn Navy Yard, 63 Flushing Ave, Bldg 25,
   Brooklyn, NY 11205
Tel: 212-924-8100 (prodn); 212-242-7000 (corp)
   Fax: 212-486-1399
E-mail: info@duggal.com
Web Site: duggal.com
Key Personnel
CEO: Michael Duggal
SVP & Creative Dir: Glenn Rabbach *Tel:* 212-924-8100 ext 1009
Founded: 1963
Supplier of printing, digital imaging, multimedia, wide format graphics & graphic display services.
Branch Office(s)
43 W 24 St, New York, NY 10010 (retail space)
10300 SW Herman Rd, Tualatin, OR 97062
   Tel: 503-820-0120

Dukane Corp, Audio Visual Products Division
Division of Dukane Corp
2900 Dukane Dr, St Charles, IL 60174
Tel: 630-762-4040 *Toll Free Tel:* 888-245-1966
   Fax: 630-584-5156
E-mail: avsales@dukane.com
Web Site: dukaneav.com
Key Personnel
Pres: James Locascio *Tel:* 800-265-4607; 630-846-1102 (cell) *E-mail:* jlocascio@dukane.com
Dir, Prods & Technol: Ron Ohlhaber
Natl Sales Mgr: Scott Doornbos *Tel:* 800-269-9715 *E-mail:* sdoornbos@dukane.com
Founded: 1945
Supplies data video projectors, document cameras, visual presenters, interactive products, wireless microphones, technology carts & accessories for businesses, governments, churches & educational institutions.
Membership(s): Audiovisual and Integrated Experience Association; BPIA; Computer Technology Industry Association; Education Market Association; NSCA

Duke Media Services
Division of Duke University
0052 Bryan Ctr, Durham, NC 27708
Tel: 919-660-1740 *Fax:* 919-660-1719
E-mail: dms-info@duke.edu
Web Site: sites.duke.edu/mediaservices
Key Personnel
Tech & Media Servs Mgr: Selden Smith
   E-mail: selden.smith@duke.edu
Prodn Coord: Greg Hobbs *Tel:* 919-660-1749
   E-mail: greg.hobbs@duke.edu
Prodn Supv: Tom Wilson *Tel:* 919-660-1742
   E-mail: t.wilson@duke.edu

Dunning Photo Equipment Inc
605 W Needles St, Bixby, OK 74008
Tel: 918-366-4917 *Fax:* 918-366-4918
Web Site: www.dunningphoto.com
Key Personnel
Owner & Sales: Ernie Dunning *E-mail:* ernie@
   dunningphoto.com
Founded: 1975
Dealer & rebuilder of kreonite color print processors & color film processors.
Membership(s): The Imaging Alliance; PPA

Duplication Depot Inc
7 Plane Tree Lane, St James, NY 11780
Tel: 631-752-0608
E-mail: copymydisc@gmail.com
Web Site: www.duplicationdepot.com
Founded: 2010
CD/DVD duplication & replication, media conversions & video production.
Price sheet(s) available

Duplication Media
8126 Douglas Ave, Urbandale, IA 50322
Tel: 515-334-DUPS (334-3877)
E-mail: info@duplicationmedia.com
Web Site: www.duplicationmedia.com
Key Personnel
Owner: Jason Olson
Founded: 2003
Duplication service company offering CD & DVD duplications, audio to CD transfers, video to DVD transfers, slide transfers, photo scanning, picture videos, film transfers, online video services & more.

Duplication Specialists Inc
843 Merrick Rd, Baldwin, NY 11510
Tel: 516-867-7300
E-mail: sales@dupespec.com
Web Site: dupespec.com
Key Personnel
Pres: David Schwartz
Founded: 1986
Full service media creation & manufacturing facility.
Online catalog(s) available

Duray Lighting
Division of Weslite Inc
500 E Touhy Ave, Suite F, Des Plaines, IL 60018
Tel: 773-271-2800 *Fax:* 773-271-4410
E-mail: info@duraylighting.com; sales@duraylighting.com
Web Site: www.duraylighting.com
Key Personnel
Gen Mgr: Ken Spalla *E-mail:* kspalla@duraylighting.com
Founded: 1946
Designer & manufacturer of standard & custom flourescent & LED lighting fixtures.
Online catalog(s) available

Durrin Productions Inc
6443 Wynkoop St, Los Angeles, CA 90045
Tel: 202-413-8971
Web Site: www.durrinproductions.com
Key Personnel
Owner & Pres: Ginny Durrin *E-mail:* gdurrin@durrinproductions.com
Film & video company producing social issue media for broadcast.
Membership(s): Women in Film & Video

Duxbury Systems Inc
270 Littleton Rd, Unit 6, Westford, MA 01886-3523
Tel: 978-692-3000 *Fax:* 978-692-7912
E-mail: info@duxsys.com
Web Site: www.duxburysystems.com
Key Personnel
Pres: Joe Sullivan
VP, Software Devt: Peter Sullivan
Mktg Dir: Neal Kuniansky
Founded: 1976
Software engineering, Braille software, Braille translation software, 3195 & NT, Macintosh, DOS & UNIX.
Online catalog(s) available

DV Post
505 N Tustin Ave, Suite 220, Santa Ana, CA 92705

Tel: 714-550-0925
Web Site: www.dvpostvideo.com
Key Personnel
Owner: John Primm *E-mail:* john@dvpostvideo.com
Founded: 1999
Nonlinear video editing & production services.
Membership(s): Media Alliance of Orange County

DVDs4Less
6519 Jamon Dr, Sparks, NV 89436-9142
Mailing Address: PO Box 2266, Sparks, NV 89432-2266
Tel: 775-323-0965 *Toll Free Tel:* 800-852-2330
Fax: 775-323-1055
E-mail: info@dvds4less.net
Web Site: www.dvds4less.net
Key Personnel
Pres: James F Mitchell
Prodn Mgr: Ramm Francis
Founded: 1967
Production & post-production.
Membership(s): AICP; American Marketing Association

The DVI Group
1486 Mecaslin St NW, Atlanta, GA 30309
Tel: 404-873-6283 *Toll Free Tel:* 888-736-7384
E-mail: makeitbetter@thedvigroup.com
Web Site: www.thedvigroup.com
Key Personnel
CEO: Matthew Lopes
Partner & Busn Devt: Suzanne Kosak
Creative Dir: Stuart Fleisher
Dir, Sales & Mktg: Craig D'Egidio
Founded: 1999
Visual communications company which specializes in video production & has built a reputation on a proven ability to create effective video productions driven by innovative creative concepts, designed to reach the target audience. Full service corporate productions from creative to all delivery formats: broadcast, promotional videos, training, event & trade show on disc, web, iPod, e-mail & mobile phones. Multilingual & formats that offer advanced tracking technology for marketing or training analysis.

DVS InteleStream
2600 W Olive Ave, Burbank, CA 91505
Tel: 818-566-4151
E-mail: info@dvs.tv
Web Site: www.dvs.tv
Key Personnel
Pres: Richard Appell
Founded: 2000
Digital media distribution company. Services include encoding, encryption, transcoding, archiving & analysis.
Catalog(s) available
Branch Office(s)
216 E 45 St, 7th fl, New York, NY 10017
Tel: 212-629-6971 *Fax:* 212-629-6976

DW Electrochemicals Ltd
3-97 Newkirk Rd N, Richmond Hill, ON L4C 3G4, Canada
Tel: 905-508-7500 *Fax:* 905-508-7502
E-mail: dwel@stabilant.com
Web Site: www.stabilant.com
Key Personnel
Pres: Wm M Wright
Intl Mktg Mgr: Betty Gordon
Founded: 1986
Handle the Stabilant 22, which is an electronic contact enhancer used to ensure long-term connector reliability. It is an easy to use, cost-effective, active resident contact treatment when assembling or servicing audio & video equipment. Stabilant 22 can improve sound quality by increasing the signal-to-noise ratio

as well as reducing thin-film rectification effects which cause RF demodulation.
Information sheet(s) available

DWD Theatre Design & Consulting
Suite 485, 425 Carrall St, Vancouver, BC V6B 6E3, Canada
Tel: 604-874-0552
E-mail: info@d-w-d.com
Web Site: www.d-w-d.com
Key Personnel
Co-Owner: Robert Hamilton; Scott Miller
Design & technical consulting for the performing arts & related industries.

DXC Technology Co
1775 Tysons Blvd, Tysons, VA 22102
Tel: 317-331-1197
Web Site: www.dxc.technology
Key Personnel
Chmn, Pres & CEO: Mike Lawrie
EVP & CFO: Paul N Saleh
EVP & Chief HR Offr: Jo Mason
EVP, Gen Coun & Secy: William L Deckelman, Jr
SVP & CIO: Erich Windmuller
SVP & CTO: Dan Hushon
SVP & Chief Mktg & Communs Offr: Gary Stockman
Founded: 2017
Independent end-to-end IT services company.
Branch Office(s)
1501 Page Mill Rd, Palo Alto, CA 94304
Foreign Office(s): 26 Talavera Rd, Macquarie Park, NSW 2113, Australia *Tel:* (02) 9034 3000
Tour Carpe Diem, 31 Place Des Corolles, CS 40075, 92098 Paris la Defense Cedex, France *Tel:* 01 55 70 70 70
Schickardstr 32, 71034 Boeblingen, Germany
One Depot Close, No 03-01, Singapore 109841, Singapore *Tel:* 68099 000
One Pancras Sq, 4th fl, London N1C 4AG, United Kingdom *Tel:* (020) 3882 4422

Dyer-Bennet Records
792 Columbus Ave, Rm 16-0, New York, NY 10025
Tel: 212-866-3675
Key Personnel
Mgr: Harvey Cort *E-mail:* hcort@msn.com
Distributed by the Smithsonian Folkways.
Membership(s): BMI

Dykeman Associates Inc
4115 Rawlins St, Dallas, TX 75219
E-mail: info@dykemanassociates.com
Web Site: www.dykemanassociates.com
Founded: 1974
Full service results-oriented firm which provides public relations, advertising, video production & other related services.
Brochure(s) available, free
Membership(s): Public Relations Society of America Inc; Religion Communicators Council

Dyna-Lite Inc
1050 Commerce Ave, Union, NJ 07083
Tel: 908-687-8800 *Toll Free Tel:* 800-722-6638
E-mail: flash@dynalite.com
Web Site: www.dynalite.com
Key Personnel
Pres: Peter Poremba
Founded: 1970
Manufacturer of electronic flash equipment for the lighting industry.
Online catalog(s) available
Membership(s): The Imaging Alliance

Dystopian Studios
651 Clover St, Bldg 1, Los Angeles, CA 90031
Tel: 310-503-2365

Web Site: dystopianstudios.com
Key Personnel
Owner: Kevin Flint *E-mail:* kevin@
dystopianstudios.com
Founded: 2004
Facility & equipment rentals, including cameras,
lighting & sound recording equipment.
Branch Office(s)
670 Moulton Ave, No 9, Los Angeles, CA 90031

E Video Productions LLC
17 Washington St, Toms River, NJ 08753
Mailing Address: PO Box 322, Forked River, NJ
08731
Tel: 732-349-4762 *Toll Free Tel:* 877-384-3365
E-mail: info@evideoproductions.net
Web Site: www.evideoproductions.net
Key Personnel
Owner: Kristopher King
Owner & Exec Prodr: Darcie King
Lead Editor: Joe Ferrara
Prodn Mgr: Meghan Caputo
Founded: 2001
Corporate video production. Specialize in Web-
mercials. In-studio & mobile studio rental.

Eagle Camera Support Systems Ltd
2787 Norland Ave, Burnaby, BC V5B 3A9,
Canada
Tel: 604-649-6350
E-mail: info@eaglecss.com
Web Site: eaglecss.com
Key Personnel
CEO: Ken Woznow
Founded: 1995
Camera support & cranes rental.

Eagle Films
2806 Cameron Rd, Falls Church, VA 22042-2004
Tel: 703-237-8160
Web Site: www.eaglefilms.com
Key Personnel
Owner: Phillip Cook *E-mail:* philcook@
eaglefilms.com
Visual effects & animation.

EAGLE Inc, see East Arizona Good Luck
Enterprises Inc

Eagle Photographics & Digital Imaging Inc
3612 W Swann Ave, Tampa, FL 33609
Tel: 813-870-2495
Web Site: www.eaglefineartimaging.com
Key Personnel
Owner & Pres: George Cott *E-mail:* george@
eaglefineartimaging.com
Inkjet prints, photographic digital prints, large
format display, high resolution scanning & dig-
ital scanning.

EAR Professional Audio/Video
2641 E McDowell Rd, Phoenix, AZ 85008
Tel: 602-267-0600 *Toll Free Tel:* 800-473-6914
Fax: 602-275-3277
E-mail: info@ear.net
Web Site: ear.net
Key Personnel
Owner: Edward Vogt
Founded: 1978
Systems integrator & reseller of professional au-
dio & video products.
Catalog(s) available

Earl Girls Inc
1648 White Horse Pike, Egg Harbor City, NJ
08215
Mailing Address: PO Box 297, Egg Harbor City,
NJ 08215-0297
Tel: 609-965-6900
Web Site: earlgirlsinc.com

Key Personnel
Pres: Don Earl *Tel:* 609-965-6900 ext 112
E-mail: don@egipro.com
Rental & Sales Mgr: Ted Oponski *Tel:* 609-965-
6900 ext 115 *E-mail:* ted@egipro.com
Shop Foreman: Roy Egrie *Tel:* 609-965-6900 ext
118 *E-mail:* roy@egipro.com
Prodn & Serv Technician: Cory Williams
Tel: 609-965-6900 ext 121 *E-mail:* cory@
egipro.com
Founded: 1991
Sales, rental, installation & production services of
entertainment audio, video, lighting, drapery &
rigging.

Early Films
9 Richter St, Randolph, NJ 07869-3309
Tel: 973-361-5817
E-mail: info@earlyfilms.net
Web Site: www.earlyfilms.net
Key Personnel
Owner: Bruce Bertrand *E-mail:* bruceb@
earlyfilms.net
Film & video editing.

Earth Mother Productions Inc™
PO Box 43204, Tucson, AZ 85733-3204
Tel: 520-365-3608
E-mail: art4wall@aol.com
Web Site: www.earthmotherproductions.com
Key Personnel
Pres: Pamala Ballingham
VP: Tim Ballingham
Catalog(s) available

EarthDesign Inc
9 Riverfront Dr, Venice, FL 34293
Tel: 941-276-8689 *Toll Free Tel:* 800-327-8433
E-mail: gp@jamilin.com
Web Site: jamilin.com
Key Personnel
Owner: Jami Lin
Production of decorating, design, landscaping,
educational, documentary & vocational videos.
Catalog(s) available

Earthworks Inc
37 Wilton Rd, Suite 1, Milford, NH 03055
Tel: 603-654-1512 (sales); 603-654-2433
Fax: 603-654-6107
E-mail: info@earthworksaudio.com
Web Site: www.earthworksaudio.com
Key Personnel
Pres: Heidi B Robichaud
Microphone manufacturer.
Membership(s): AES; Audiovisual and Integrated
Experience Association; NAMM, the National
Association of Music Merchants

Earwax Productions Inc
916 Kearny St, San Francisco, CA 94133
Tel: 415-860-9403 (cell)
Web Site: www.earwaxproductions.com
Key Personnel
Owner & Prodr: Jim McKee *E-mail:* jim@
earwaxproductions.com
Founded: 1983
Sound design for film, television, Internet, radio,
as well as audio for tours, installations, toys &
electronics.

Earwig Music Co Inc
2054 W Farwell Ave, Unit G, Chicago, IL 60645
Tel: 773-262-0278
E-mail: orders@earwigmusic.com
Web Site: www.earwigmusic.com
Key Personnel
Pres & CEO: Michael Frank *Tel:* 773-960-7064
(cell) *E-mail:* mfrank@earwigmusic.com
Founded: 1978

Produce & distribute blues, jazz & folktales on
CD & cassette. Shipping is billed to customer.
Catalog(s) available, free, annual
Online catalog(s) available
Membership(s): The Blues Foundation; The
Recording Academy

EASI
21477 Orchid Ave, Mason City, IA 50401
Tel: 641-424-5079 *Toll Free Tel:* 888-327-4797
Fax: 641-424-8869
Web Site: easisat.com
Key Personnel
Owner & Pres: Tim Hedrick
Founded: 1993
Satellite equipment, systems & integration from
conception to completion.

East Arizona Good Luck Enterprises Inc
PO Box 579, Clarkdale, AZ 86324
Tel: 928-204-2597 *Fax:* 928-204-2568
E-mail: hier_bosch@yahoo.com
Key Personnel
Pres/CEO: James S Beck
Prodn Mgr: Richard A Cain
Founded: 1975
Manufacturer of instruments to measure electric-
ity.
Catalog(s) available

East of Hollywood NY
140 53 St, Brooklyn, NY 11232
Tel: 718-492-7400 *Fax:* 718-439-3930
Web Site: www.eastofhollywoodny.com
Key Personnel
Owner: Simon Srybnik
Property Mgr: Angela Correa
Founded: 1996
Film & television production facility. Sound
stages offer onsite production offices & ex-
tensive set, prop & wardrobe storage areas.

Eastern Acoustic Works Inc (EAW)
One Main St, Bldg 13, Whitinsville, MA 01588-
2238
Tel: 508-234-6158 *Toll Free Tel:* 800-992-5013
Toll Free Fax: 800-322-8251
Web Site: www.eaw.com
Key Personnel
Pres: TJ Smith
VP, Global Sales: James Newhouse *Tel:* 774-280-
9297 *E-mail:* james.newhouse@eaw.com
Founded: 1978
Loudspeaker system design & manufacture.
Online catalog(s) available

Eastern Effects Inc
99 Ninth St, Brooklyn, NY 11215
Tel: 718-855-1197 *Toll Free Fax:* 888-566-6547
Web Site: easterneffects.com
Key Personnel
Founder & Pres: Scott Levy *E-mail:* scott@
easterneffects.com
Mng Partner: Laura Gahrahmat *E-mail:* laura@
easterneffects.com; Chris Hayes *E-mail:* chris@
easterneffects.com
Dir, Opers: Ian Defibaugh *E-mail:* ian@
easterneffects.com
Inside Sales Mgr: Phillip Warren *E-mail:* phil@
easterneffects.com
Founded: 1998
Film & television equipment, office & studio
rental.
Branch Office(s)
210 Douglas St, Brooklyn, NY 11217 (sound
stages & prodn off)
302 Shefield Ave, Brooklyn, NY 11207 (sound
stages)

Eastman Corp
7447 Via de Fortuna, Carlsbad, CA 92009

Tel: 760-603-8646
Web Site: www.kbwfoundation.com
Key Personnel
Pres: Kay Weiner *E-mail:* kayeastman@aol.com
Founded: 1992

Eastman Kodak Co
343 State St, Rochester, NY 14650
Toll Free Tel: 800-698-3324
Web Site: www.kodak.com
Key Personnel
CEO: Jeff Clarke
SVP & CFO: David Bullwinkle
SVP & CIO: Kim VanGelder
SVP & CTO: Terry R Taber, PhD
SVP & Chief HR Offr: Mark Green
SVP & Chief Mktg Offr: Steven Overman
SVP, Gen Coun & Secy: Sharon E Underberg
VP: Christopher Payne
Hardware, software, consumables & services to
   customers in graphic arts, commercial print,
   publishing, packaging, electronic displays, en-
   tertainment & commercial films & consumer
   products markets.
Online catalog(s) available

Easy Edit Video Inc
8431 Baymeadows Way, Jacksonville, FL 32256
Tel: 904-730-9999
Web Site: www.easyeditvideo.com
Key Personnel
Owner & Pres: David Zuckerman *E-mail:* david@
   easyeditvideo.com
Founded: 1993
Professionally operated, affordably priced, we
   are Northeast Florida's largest DVD duplica-
   tion center, also offering production & post-
   production services for business clients. Two
   non-linear edit suites equipped with Final Cut
   Pro 7.0 & Adobe Creative Suite 6.0.

Easy Street Productions LLC
118 Redhaven Ct, Thurmont, MD 21788
Tel: 301-471-8058
E-mail: info@publicdomainfootage.com
Web Site: www.publicdomainfootage.com
Key Personnel
Pres & Creative Dir: Peter Ferraro
Provider of public domain & royalty free con-
   temporary & archival stock footage. Writing,
   producing & stock footage archival research.
Membership(s): NATAS

Eaton Corp
8609 Six Forks Rd, Raleigh, NC 27615
Tel: 919-872-3020 *Toll Free Tel:* 800-356-5794
Web Site: powerquality.eaton.com
Key Personnel
Pres, Electrical Systems & Servs Group: Brian
   Brickhouse
Power distribution solution company.
Catalog(s) available

ECG Productions
120 Interstate N Pkwy SE, Suite 435, Atlanta,
   GA 30339
Tel: 678-855-5169 *Toll Free Tel:* 855-787-4487
E-mail: info@ecgprod.com
Web Site: www.ecgprod.com
Key Personnel
Prodr & Dir: Jason Sirotin *E-mail:* sirotin@
   ecgprod.com
Principal & Head, Post-Prodn Opers: Jason Mar-
   raccini *E-mail:* jason@ecgprod.com
Principal & Dir, Animation: Trey Gregory
   E-mail: trey@ecgprod.com
Founded: 2006
Full service video production, post-production &
   animation. National & international shipping.
   Greenscreen & Cyc wall facility. Equipment

rental. Also offers compositing & 3D anima-
   tion services as well as Blu-ray programming.
Membership(s): Georgia Production Partnership;
   Metro Atlanta Chamber of Commerce

**ECONEWS (Environmental Television Series)
   & (Environmental Directions Radio Series)**
Subsidiary of Educational Communications
PO Box 351419, Los Angeles, CA 90035-9119
Tel: 310-559-9160
E-mail: ecnp@aol.com
Web Site: www.ecoprojects.org
Key Personnel
Exec Prodr & Exec Dir: Nancy Pearlman
Founded: 1958
Produce & distribute Econews television series &
   Environmental Directions radio series. Produce,
   distribute & give away both DVDs/MP4 &
   CDs/MP3 of environmental radio & television
   programs. We also do documentaries & public
   service announcements & have an archive of
   over 3,000 tapes, DVDs & CDs from 1977 to
   present.
Online catalog(s) available

Edgenuity Inc
8860 E Chaparral Rd, Scottsdale, AZ 85250
Toll Free Tel: 877-725-4257 (sales)
E-mail: customersupport@edgenuity.com;
   solutions@edgenuity.com (sales)
Web Site: www.edgenuity.com
Key Personnel
CEO: Sari Factor
CTO: Dhiraj Rattan
EVP, Busn Devt: Michael Humphrey
SVP, Sales: Andy Caulo
VP, Fin & Admin: David Alderslade
VP, Instrl Servs: Kinsey Rawe
VP, Mktg & Cust Experience: Leslie Sobon
VP, Prod Devt: Jack Shira
VP, Prod Mgmt & Strategy: Deborah Rayow
Founded: 1998
K-12 online learning solutions.
Branch Office(s)
352 Seventh Ave, No 12a, New York, NY 10001
11501 Domain Dr, Suite 160, Austin, TX 78758

Edgewood Studios
One Scale Ave, Suite 90, Unit 309, Bldg 3, Rut-
   land, VT 05701
Tel: 802-773-0510
E-mail: flicks@edgewoodstudios.com
Web Site: www.edgewoodstudios.com
Key Personnel
Owner: David Giancola
Founded: 1987
Film production.

Edison Price Lighting Inc
41-50 22 St, Long Island City, NY 11101
Tel: 718-685-0700
E-mail: orders@epl.com; info@epl.com
Web Site: www.epl.com
Key Personnel
Pres: Emma Price *E-mail:* eprice@epl.com
EVP, Mktg & Sales: Joel R Siegel
   E-mail: jsiegel@epl.com
Founded: 1952
Design & manufacture innovative, energy-efficient
   architectural lighting fixtures.
Catalog(s) available

Edit House Chicago
5325 W Berenice Ave, Chicago, IL 60641
Tel: 773-725-1525
E-mail: info@edithousechicago.com
Web Site: www.edithousechicago.com
Key Personnel
Co-Owner: Jeff Hellyer; Leny Hellyer
Video & media production & post-production ser-
   vices.

The Editing Co
7030 Empire Central Dr, Houston, TX 77040
Tel: 713-783-2655 *Fax:* 713-783-8642
Web Site: www.editingco.com
Key Personnel
Pres: Nancy Clinton
Founded: 1979
All new award-winning television & corporate
   communications facility with 3 edit suites, Pro
   Tools audio suite, large area network server &
   film/video production services. Fast closed cap-
   tioning in HD, 14 video formats, compressions,
   web development, DVD/CD authoring & dupli-
   cation. Subtitling & narrations in 60 languages,
   30' x 30' studio.
Membership(s): WIFT

Les Editions CEC Inc
Subsidiary of Quebecor Media Inc
9001 Louis-H-La Fontaine Blvd, Anjou, QC H1J
   2C5, Canada
Tel: 514-351-6010 *Toll Free Tel:* 800-363-0494
   Fax: 514-351-3534 *Toll Free Fax:* 877-913-
   5920
E-mail: sac@editionscec.com
Web Site: www.editionscec.com
Key Personnel
VP, Sales & Mktg: Gilles Lefebvre
Founded: 1956
Online catalog(s) available

Education Development Center Inc (EDC)
43 Foundry Ave, Waltham, MA 02453-8313
Tel: 617-969-7100 *Fax:* 617-969-5979
E-mail: contact@edc.org
Web Site: www.edc.org
Key Personnel
Pres & CEO: David Offensend
VP & Deputy to Pres: Siobhan Murphy
Founded: 1958
Branch Office(s)
1025 Thomas Jefferson St NW, Suite 700, Wash-
   ington, DC 20007 *Tel:* 202-572-3700 *Fax:* 202-
   223-4059
770 N Halsted St, Suite 205, Chicago, IL 60642
   Tel: 312-962-4500
96 Morton St, 7th fl, New York, NY 10014
   Tel: 212-807-4200 *Fax:* 212-633-8804

Educational Activities Inc
PO Box 87, Baldwin, NY 11510-0087
Tel: 516-223-4666 *Toll Free Tel:* 800-797-3223
   Fax: 516-623-9282
Web Site: edact.com
Key Personnel
CEO: Al Harris
Pres: Carol Stern
Founded: 1948
Publishes engaging early childhood music &
   movement recordings, DVDs, software & other
   educational media.
Online catalog(s) available

Educational Insights
152 W Walnut St, Suite 201, Gardena, CA 90248
Toll Free Tel: 800-995-4436 *Toll Free Fax:* 888-
   498-8670
E-mail: sales@educationalinsights.com
Web Site: www.educationalinsights.com
Key Personnel
Creative Dir: Michael Sherman *Tel:* 847-968-3710
Founded: 1962
Kid-powered play through innovative toys, games
   & educational tools. Products include light fil-
   ters, electronic games, interactive storybooks,
   microscopes, black light illuminators, tele-
   scopes, projectors, lasers, binoculars & more.
Online catalog(s) available
Catalog(s) available
Branch Office(s)
Learning Resources Inc, 380 N Fairway Dr,
   Vernon Hills, IL 60061 *Tel:* 847-990-3341
   Fax: 847-281-1720 *E-mail:* intlorders@

learningresources.com (Asia, Australia, Latin America & New Zealand)
Foreign Office(s): Learning Resources Ltd, 51A Bergen Way, King's Lynn, Norfolk PE30 2JG, United Kingdom *Tel:* (01553) 762276 *Fax:* (01553) 769943 *E-mail:* sales@learning-resources.co.uk (Africa, Europe, Middle East & UK)
Membership(s): American Specialty Toy Retailing Association; Audiovisual and Integrated Experience Association; Education Market Association

Educational Technology & Media Services
Unit of University of Northern Iowa, Department of Information Technology
University of Northern Iowa, Inno Teaching & Technol Ctr 101, Cedar Falls, IA 50614-0301
Web Site: it.uni.edu/educational-technology-media-services
Key Personnel
Mgr, Media Servs: Keith Kennedy *Tel:* 319-273-6192 *E-mail:* keith.kennedy@uni.edu
Media services area supports the AV needs of the University for live events, AV editing & production level media production.
Membership(s): Consortium of College & University Media Centers

Educational Technology Services (ETS)
Division of University of California, San Francisco
Medical Sciences, Rm SB-43, 513 Parnassus Ave, San Francisco, CA 94143-0702
Tel: 415-476-4310 *Fax:* 415-514-3735
E-mail: edtech@ucsf.edu
Web Site: edtech.ucsf.edu
Key Personnel
Dir: John DeAngelo
Founded: 2011
Provide support, technology & a full suite of media services of UCSF instructional environment.

Educational Video Group Inc
291 Southwind Way, Greenwood, IN 46142-9190
Tel: 317-889-8253 *Fax:* 317-888-5857
E-mail: service@evgonline.com
Web Site: www.evgonline.com
Key Personnel
VP: Roger Cook
Production services & educational programming.
Online catalog(s) available

Educational Video Network
1401 19 St, Huntsville, TX 77340
Tel: 936-295-5767 *Toll Free Tel:* 800-762-0060
Fax: 936-294-0233
Web Site: www.evndirect.com
Key Personnel
CEO: George H Russell
Catalog(s) available
Membership(s): Entertainment Merchants Association

EduMedia of Sugar Land, Texas
PO Box 2428, Sugar Land, TX 77487-2428
Tel: 281-756-7510
E-mail: service@history2u.com
Web Site: www.history2u.com
Key Personnel
Pres: Bryan Hardesty
Founded: 1995

EEG Enterprises Inc
586 Main St, Farmingdale, NY 11735
Tel: 516-293-7472 *Fax:* 516-293-7417
E-mail: sales@eegent.com
Web Site: www.eegent.com

Key Personnel
VP, Sales: Stephen Eric McErlain
E-mail: ericm@eegent.com
Manufacture TV broadcast equipment, closed caption decoders & encoders.
Online catalog(s) available
Branch Office(s)
68 Jay St, Brooklyn, NY 11201
Membership(s): NAB

Effective Engineering Inc
2805 W Empire Ave, Burbank, CA 91504
Tel: 818-841-4437 *Fax:* 818-841-4389
E-mail: info@effeng.com
Web Site: www.effeng.com
Out-source repair services for manufacturers; engineering & logistics services.
Catalog(s) available
Membership(s): NAB

Effective Learning Audio, see Effective Learning Systems LLC

Effective Learning Systems LLC
Formerly Effective Learning Audio
PO Box 366666, Bonita Springs, FL 34136
Tel: 612-513-0760
Web Site: www.effectivelearning.com
Key Personnel
Founder & Mgr: Bob Griswold
Mgr: Deirdre Griswold
E-mail: deirdregriswold99@gmail.com
Founded: 1972
Self-help audio programs.
Online catalog(s) available

Efficient Antenna Systems Inc, see EASI

eFootage LLC
530 S Lake Ave, Suite 450, Pasadena, CA 91101
Tel: 626-395-9593 *Fax:* 626-792-5394
E-mail: info@efootage.com
Web Site: www.efootage.com
Key Personnel
Mgr: Paul Lisy
Founded: 1967
Premier HD, film & video, stock footage archive (contemporary & vintage).
Membership(s): Association of Moving Image Archivists

EFX Media
2300 S Ninth St, Suite 136, Arlington, VA 22204
Tel: 703-486-2303
E-mail: info@efxmedia.com; sales@efxmedia.com
Web Site: www.efxmedia.com
Key Personnel
CEO & Pres: James Franco
Founded: 1983
Core business revolves around full service video production, interactive solutions, media services & online video.
Membership(s): Women in Film & Video

Egan Visual Inc/Egan TeamBoard Inc
300 Hanlan Rd, Woodbridge, ON L4L 3P6, Canada
Tel: 905-851-2826 *Toll Free Tel:* 800-263-2387 (CN & US) *Toll Free Fax:* 888-609-8886
E-mail: sales@teamboard.com
Web Site: www.egan.com
Founded: 1967
Manufacture interactive whiteboards, protection capable dry erase whiteboards, flat panels & lecterns.
Catalog(s) available

Eggplant Pictures & Sound
Division of Eggplant Collective

157 Princess St, Toronto, ON M5A 4M4, Canada
Tel: 416-214-9911 *Fax:* 416-214-9912
Web Site: www.eggplantps.com
Key Personnel
Pres: David Colon
Founded: 1996
Full service audio & video post-production, motion graphics, animation, VFX & 360/VR.

Egripment USA
2009 O'Neil Rd, Hudson, WI 54016
Tel: 715-386-0777
E-mail: egripment@egripment.com
Web Site: www.egripment.com
Manufacturer of camera support equipment, including remote systems.
Product sheet(s) available
Foreign Office(s): Egripment Deutschland, Immendorfer Str 1, 50354 Huerth, Germany *Tel:* (02233) 6877-0 *Fax:* (02233) 6877-11 *E-mail:* egripment@egripment.de
Egripment Holland, Machineweg 22, Nederhorst den Berg City, 1394 AV Holland, Netherlands *Tel:* (0294) 253988 *Fax:* (0294) 254635 *E-mail:* egripment@egripment.nl (headquarters)
Membership(s): IBC; NAB

18 Label Studios
18 Label St, Montclair, NJ 07042
Tel: 973-744-7382
E-mail: info@18label.com
Web Site: 18label.com
Key Personnel
Contact: Elizabeth Sardinsky
Photography studio & event space designed to cater to photographers, agencies, producers, filmmakers & brands.

Eiki International Inc
Subsidiary of Eiki Industrial Co Ltd (Japan)
30251 Esperanza, Rancho Santa Margarita, CA 92688-2132
Tel: 949-457-0200 *Toll Free Tel:* 800-242-3454 *Fax:* 949-457-7878 *Toll Free Fax:* 800-457-3454
E-mail: usa@eiki.com; orders-usa@eiki.com
Web Site: www.eiki.com
Key Personnel
Pres & CEO: Bill Blair
Founded: 1974
Online catalog(s) available
Branch Office(s)
Megatech Integrated Services Ltd, 351 Steelcase Rd W, Unit 8, Markham, ON L3R 4H9, Canada *Tel:* 905-470-8183 *Fax:* 905-479-8010 *E-mail:* orders@megatech-int.com
Foreign Office(s): Eiki Australia Pty Ltd, Level 5, 11 Queens Rd, Melbourne, Victoria 3004, Australia *Tel:* (06) 8530 7048 *Fax:* (06) 9820 5834 *E-mail:* sales@eiki.net.au
Eiki (Shanghai) Co Ltd, Lakeside Oasis Middle Ring Business Centre, Block 1, Rm 606, 1628 Jin Sha Jiang Rd, Shanghai 200333, China *Tel:* (021) 3251-3993; (021) 3251-3995 *Fax:* (021) 3251-3997 *E-mail:* info@eiki-china.com
Eiki Czech Spol sro, Nad Cementarnou 1163/4a, 147 00 Podoli, Prague 4, Czechia *Tel:* 241 410 928; 241 403 095 *Fax:* 241 409 435 *E-mail:* info@eiki.cz
Eiki Deutschland GmbH, Am Frauwald 12, 65510 Idstein, Germany *Tel:* (06126) 9371-0 *Fax:* (06126) 9371-11 *E-mail:* info@eiki.de
Eiki Industrial Co Ltd, 6-23 Teramoto, Itami-shi, Hyogo 664-0026, Japan *Tel:* (072) 782-7492 *Fax:* (072) 781-5435 (corp headquarters)
Eiki Industrial (M) Sdn Bhd, No 11, Nouvelle Industrial Park, Lorong Teknologi B, Taman Sains, Selangor 1, Kota Damansara PJU5, 47810 Petaling Jaya, Selangor Darul Ehsan,

Malaysia *Tel:* (03) 6157-9330 *Fax:* (03) 6157-1320 *E-mail:* sales@eiki.my
Membership(s): Association of Audio-Visual Service Technicians; Audiovisual and Integrated Experience Association; SMPTE®

EiKO Global LLC
23220 W 84 St, Shawnee, KS 66227
Toll Free Tel: 800-852-2217 *Fax:* 913-441-6679
E-mail: orders@eiko.com; info@eikom.com
Web Site: www.eiko.com
Key Personnel
VP, Prod Mgmt: Rick Laird
Founded: 1978
Lighting manufacturer for commercial & industrial end-users. Traditional lighting products & LED lamps & fixtures.
Branch Office(s)
1485 Southern Way, Sparks, NV 89431 (dist ctr)
933-43 Hylton Rd, Pennsauken, NJ 08110 (dist ctr)
2634-45 Ave SE, Unit 121, Calgary, AB T2B 3M1, Canada (dist ctr)
81 King St, Barrie, ON L4N 6B5, Canada *Toll Free Tel:* 888-410-8151 *Toll Free Fax:* 888-705-1335 *E-mail:* orderdesk@eiko.com
Foreign Office(s): Mittelwegring 20, 76751 Jockgrim, Germany *Tel:* (07271) 7607-0 *Fax:* (07271) 7607-29 *E-mail:* info@eiko-europe.de *Web Site:* www.eiko-europe.de
25F, No 29-1, Sec 2, Zhongzheng E Rd, Danshuei Jen, Taipei, Taiwan *Tel:* (02) 8809-9966 *Fax:* (02) 8809-8372 *E-mail:* eiko@eiko-ltd.com.tw *Web Site:* www.eiko-ltd.com.tw
Membership(s): Illuminating Engineering Society; Industry Data Exchange Association Inc; National Association of Electrical Distributors; National Association of Energy Service Companies; National Association of Independent Lighting Distributors; National Electrical Manufacturers Association; National Electrical Manufacturers Representatives Association

EKU Media
Division of Eastern Kentucky University
102 Perkins Bldg, 521 Lancaster Ave, Richmond, KY 40475
Tel: 859-622-6671
Web Site: video.eku.edu
Key Personnel
Prodn Mgr/Prodr: Leonard K Nave *Tel:* 859-622-6447 *E-mail:* leonard.nave@eku.edu
Sr Media Specialist: Dwayne Bolin *Tel:* 859-622-6286 *E-mail:* dwayne.bolin@eku.edu
College resource center.
Catalog(s) available

El Mar Plastics Inc
833 E Walnut St, Carson, CA 90746
Tel: 310-436-6444 *Toll Free Tel:* 800-255-5210 *Fax:* 310-436-6445
E-mail: sales@elmarplastics.com
Web Site: www.elmarplastics.com
Key Personnel
Pres: Allen Schor *E-mail:* allen@elmarplastics.com
Founded: 1966
Manufacture audio jewel boxes, handle & ship spindles for video. Also distribute DVD boxes.
Catalog(s) available

ELC Sales & Service Inc
3100 S Congress Ave, Suite 6, Boynton Beach, FL 33426
Tel: 561-756-2210
E-mail: tvman@gate.net
Key Personnel
Pres: Gary Braisted
AV, marine installation repair & service.

Electric Lady Studios
52 W Eighth St, New York, NY 10011

Tel: 212-677-4700
Web Site: electricladystudios.com
Key Personnel
Partner & Gen Mgr: Lee Foster *E-mail:* lee.foster@electricladystudios.com
Asst Mgr: Iris Sofia *E-mail:* iris@electricladystudios.com
Artist Mgr: Kirby Lee *E-mail:* kirby@electricladystudios.com; Erika Wolf *E-mail:* erika@electricladystudios.com
Prodr Mgr: Nicole Ficenec *E-mail:* nicole@electricladystudios.com
Founded: 1970
Oldest working & flourishing recording studio in NYC founded by Jimi Hendrix.

Electriduct Inc
1650 NW 18 St, Unit 801, Pompano Beach, FL 33069
Tel: 954-867-9100 *Toll Free Tel:* 866-673-9590 *Fax:* 954-206-0799
E-mail: sales@electriduct.com
Web Site: www.electriduct.com
Key Personnel
Pres: Joseph Proto *E-mail:* joe@electriduct.com
Founded: 2006
Online catalog(s) available

Electro Impulse Laboratory Inc
1805 Rte 33, Neptune, NJ 07754
Mailing Address: PO Box 278, Neptune, NJ 07754-0278
Tel: 732-776-5800 *Fax:* 732-776-6793
E-mail: sales@electroimpulse.com
Web Site: www.electroimpulse.com
Key Personnel
CEO & Pres: Mark Rubin
Founded: 1949
Catalog(s) available

Electron Microscopy Sciences (EMS)
Subsidiary of Negafile Systems
1560 Industry Rd, Hatfield, PA 19440
Mailing Address: PO Box 550, Hatfield, PA 19440
Tel: 215-412-8400 *Toll Free Tel:* 800-523-5874 *Fax:* 215-412-8450
E-mail: info@emsdiasum.com
Web Site: www.emsdiasum.com/microscopy
Key Personnel
Pres: Stacie Kirsch *E-mail:* stacie@ems-secure.com
Founded: 1988
Manufacturing, preparation & distribution of laboratory chemicals & microscopy supplies & equipment for electron microscopy, light microscopy & histology.
Online catalog(s) available

Electronic Arts Inc
209 Redwood Shores Pkwy, Redwood City, CA 94065
Tel: 650-628-1500
Web Site: www.ea.com
Key Personnel
CEO: Andrew Wilson
COO & CFO: Blake Jorgensen
Chief Mktg Offr: Chris Bruzzo
Chief People Offr: Mala Singh
Chief Studios Offr: Laura Miele
CTO: Ken Moss
EVP, Gen Coun & Corp Secy: Jacob Schatz
EVP, Strategic Growth: Matt Bilbey
EVP, Worldwide Busn Aff: Joel Linzner
SVP & Chief Acctg Offr: Ken Barker
Founded: 1982
Publish, develop & distribute digital interactive entertainment worldwide.

Electronic Design Solutions Inc
41785 Elm St, Suite 201, Murrieta, CA 92562

Tel: 951-304-3879 *Toll Free Tel:* 888-611-1741 *Fax:* 951-304-0608
E-mail: sales@myedsinc.com
Web Site: www.gmfsound.com; www.myedsinc.com
Key Personnel
Pres: James Carroll *E-mail:* jim@myedsinc.com
Gen Mgr: Wayne Trouten *E-mail:* wayne@myedsinc.com
Founded: 1972
Distribute AV equipment.

Electronic Theatre Controls Inc, see ETC

Electrosonic Inc
3320 N San Fernando Blvd, Burbank, CA 91504
Tel: 818-333-3600 *Toll Free Tel:* 888-343-3604 (sales)
E-mail: contactus@electrosonic.com
Web Site: www.electrosonic.com
Key Personnel
Pres: Bryan Hinckley
Founded: 1964
AV company providing systems integration services, engineering, project management & AV design.
Branch Office(s)
137 E Airway Blvd, Suite 167, Livermore, CA 94551 *Tel:* 915-482-3190
4501 Vineland Rd, Suite 105, Orlando, FL 32811 *Tel:* 407-839-1154
12400 Whitewater Dr, Suite 140, Minnetonka, MN 55343-9048 *Tel:* 952-931-7500
187 E Warm Springs Rd, Suite C, Las Vegas, NV 89119 *Tel:* 702-605-1402
1239 Parkway Ave, Suite 202, Ewing, NJ 08628
318 W 39 St, 9th fl, New York, NY 10018 *Tel:* 646-545-6200
478 Elden St, PMB 117, Herndon, VA 20170
Foreign Office(s): Electrosonic Ltd, 12/F Shun Point Commercial Bldg, Unit B, 5-11 Thomson Rd, Wan Chai, Hong Kong *Tel:* 2525 1828
Electrosonic LLC, PO Box 62425, Dubai, United Arab Emirates *Tel:* (04) 4295700
Electrosonic Ltd, Cults Busn Park, Unit 3, Station Rd, Cults, Aberdeen, United Kingdom *Tel:* (01224) 531340
Electrosonic Ltd, Indian Queens Trading Estate, Unit 9, Warren Rd, St Columb, Cornwall TR9 6TL, United Kingdom *Tel:* (01637) 875824
Electrosonic Ltd, 107-109 Whitehouse Loan, Edinburgh EH9 1AT, United Kingdom *Tel:* (0131) 4476211
Electrosonic Ltd, Hawley Mill, Hawley Rd, Dartford, Kent DA2 7SY, United Kingdom *Tel:* (01322) 222211 *E-mail:* info@electrosonic.com *Web Site:* www.electrosonic.co.uk
Membership(s): AFCEA; American Institute of Architects; Association of Science-Technology Centers; Audiovisual and Integrated Experience Association; International Association of Amusement Parks and Attractions; NSCA; Themed Entertainment Association

Elegant Packaging
5253 W Roosevelt Rd, Cicero, IL 60804
Tel: 708-652-3400 *Toll Free Tel:* 800-367-5493 *Fax:* 708-652-6444
E-mail: info@elegantpackaging.com
Web Site: www.elegantpackaging.com
Key Personnel
Pres: Mario Denado
Founded: 1910
Design & manufacture customized rigid specialty boxes, presentation binders, soft sewn packaging & compression thermal forming. These products are sold to various industries including the advertising, computer, confections, cosmetics, education, electronics, entertainment, medical, publishing, software & toy/game industries.

Catalog(s) available
Membership(s): AICC, The Independent Packaging Association; Retail Packaging Association

Elektrashock
1320 Main St, Venice, CA 90291
Tel: 310-399-4985
E-mail: info@elektrashock.com
Web Site: www.elektrashock.com
Key Personnel
Dir: Darnell Williams
Founded: 1997
Cinematics, motion design & visual effects for feature film, television, games & integrated media.

Eli Research Group, see AudioSolutionz LLC

Elite Video Inc
209 E Emerson Rd, Lexington, MA 02420
Tel: 781-862-6606
Key Personnel
Pres: Eric Geller
Founded: 1999
Manufacturer/distributor/VAR/installer of large screen displays for home & business.
Membership(s): Custom Electronic Design & Installation Association

Elkind+Sweet Communications Inc, see Live Wire Media

Albert Ellis Institute (AEI)
145 E 32 St, 9th fl, New York, NY 10016
Tel: 212-535-0822 *Fax:* 212-249-3582
E-mail: info@albertellis.org
Web Site: albertellis.org
Key Personnel
Exec Dir: Kristene Doyle
Founded: 1959

ELMO USA Corp
Subsidiary of ELMO Co Ltd
1478 Old Country Rd, Plainview, NY 11803
Tel: 516-501-1400 *Toll Free Tel:* 800-947-3566
Fax: 516-501-0429
E-mail: elmo@elmousa.com
Web Site: www.elmousa.com
Foreign Office(s): ELMO Europe SAS, Immeuble Elysees la Defense, 7C, Place du Dome, 92056 Paris la Defense, France *Tel:* 01 73 02 67 06 *Fax:* 01 73 02 67 10 *E-mail:* info@ elmoeurope.fr *Web Site:* www.elmoeurope.com
ELMO Europe SAS, Hansaallee 201, 40549 Dusseldorf, Germany *Tel:* (0211) 544 756 40 *Fax:* (0211) 544 756 60 *E-mail:* info@elmo-germany.de *Web Site:* elmo-germany.de
ELMO Co Ltd, 3-12-16 Mita, Minato-ku, Tokyo 108-0073, Japan *Tel:* (03) 3453 6471 *Fax:* (03) 3453 6479 *Web Site:* www.elmo.co.jp
ELMO Russia, 121170 Moscow, Russia *Tel:* (495) 743 2620 *E-mail:* info@elmorussia. com *Web Site:* elmorussia.com

Elo TouchSystems
670 N McCarthy Blvd, Milpitas, CA 95035
Toll Free Tel: 800-356-8682; 800-557-1458
Fax: 650-361-4722
E-mail: eloinfo@elotouch.com; customerservice@ elotouch.com
Web Site: www.elotouch.com
Key Personnel
CEO: Craig Witsoe
Founded: 1971
Branch Office(s)
2245 Brighton Henrietta Trail Rd, Rochester, NY 14623 *Tel:* 585-272-3100
Membership(s): SID

ELS Productions Inc
627 W Olympic Lane, Elk Ridge, UT 84651
Tel: 801-676-0807 *Toll Free Tel:* 800-927-3472
Web Site: www.elsproductions.com
Key Personnel
Owner & Pres: Mark McLelland
Owner & VP: Dawn McLelland
Short run & large run CD, DVD & Blu-ray duplication, retail packaging & design. Bulk discs & generic packaging replication.

Em Gee Film Library
13502 Erwin St, Van Nuys, CA 91401
Tel: 818-997-0410
Key Personnel
Owner & Mgr: Murray Glass
E-mail: murray713@hotmail.com
Founded: 1954
16mm film rental library; 16mm film sales; video sales.
Affiliate companies: Glenn Photo Supply; Glenn Video Vistas Ltd.
Catalog(s) available, $5

eMagin Corp
700 South Dr, Suite 201, Hopewell Junction, NY 12533
Tel: 845-838-7900 *Fax:* 845-838-7901
E-mail: info@emagin.com; sales@emagin.com; customersupport@emagin.com
Web Site: www.emagin.com
Key Personnel
CEO: Andrew G Sculley, Jr
Pres & CFO: Jeffrey P Lucas
SVP & CTO: Dr Amal Ghosh
SVP, Display Opers, Design & Devt: Olivier Prache
SVP, Opers: Joe Saltarelli
VP, Busn Devt: Doug Hughes
Founded: 1996
Leading manufacturer of active matrix OLED-on-silicon microdisplays.
Catalog(s) available
Branch Office(s)
3080 Olcott St, Suite C100, Santa Clara, CA 95054 (engg & design)

EMC Publishing LLC
Division of Carnegie Learning Inc
875 Montreal Way, St Paul, MN 55102
Tel: 651-290-2800 (corp) *Toll Free Tel:* 888-851-7094
E-mail: info@carnegielearning.com
Web Site: www.emcp.com
Key Personnel
CEO: Eric Cantor
Founded: 1954
K-12 textbook programs in world languages, business education, literature & language arts & social studies with supplementary & multimedia materials.
Online catalog(s) available

Emcor Enclosures-Crenlo
1600 Fourth Ave NW, Rochester, MN 55901
Tel: 507-289-3371; 507-216-9245 (cust serv)
Fax: 507-287-3405
Web Site: www.crenlo.com/emcor
Electronic equipment racks & consoles.
Online catalog(s) available

Emergency Film Group
Division of Detrick Lawrence Corp
1811 Bering Dr, Suite 430, Houston, TX 77057
Tel: 713-621-1100 (cust support); 713-952-1156 (direct sales) *Toll Free Tel:* 866-427-2467
Fax: 713-621-7500
E-mail: info@efilmgroup.com
Web Site: www.efilmgroup.com
Key Personnel
Pres & Dir: Gordon Massingham
E-mail: gordon@efilmgroup.com

Founded: 1987
Produce & distribute training films, DVDs & videos of interest to the hazardous materials, counter terrorism, environmental, emergency management & emergency response communities in both the public & private sector.
Membership(s): IAFC; ISFSI; National Fire Protection Association

Emerson Network Power, see Vertiv

Emerson Radio Corp
Affiliate of H H Scott Division Audio Equipment
3 University Plaza, Suite 405, Hackensack, NJ 07601
Tel: 973-884-5800 *Toll Free Tel:* 800-909-1240 (cust serv) *Fax:* 973-428-2067
E-mail: internet@emersonradio.com
Web Site: www.emersonradio.com
Key Personnel
CEO: Duncan Hon
EVP: Michael Binney
Treas & Asst Secy: Barry Smith
Founded: 1948
Consumer electronic sales including home theater systems, DVD players & televisions.

Emery-Pratt Co
1966 W M 21, Owosso, MI 48867-9317
Tel: 989-723-5291 *Toll Free Tel:* 800-248-3887
Fax: 989-723-4677 *Toll Free Fax:* 800-523-6379
Web Site: www.emery-pratt.com
Key Personnel
Dir, Busn Devt: Byron E Shattuck
Natl Sales Dir: Avery Weaver
Distributes audiobooks & videos to libraries.
Membership(s): ALA

Emlight Design
1179 N Eastman Ave, Suite 1, Los Angeles, CA 90063
Tel: 323-261-5162 *Toll Free Fax:* 866-728-9164
E-mail: service@dimmer.com; service@ emlightdesign.com
Web Site: www.dimmer.com; www.emlightdesign. com
Key Personnel
Owner: Maurice Garcia
Founded: 1999
Service dimmers: architectural, theatrical, motion picture & television lighting.

eMotion Studios
85 Liberty Ship Way, Suite 110, Sausalito, CA 94965
Tel: 415-331-6975
E-mail: info@emotionstudios.com
Web Site: www.emotionstudios.com
Key Personnel
Dir & CEO: Glen Janssens *E-mail:* glen@ emotionstudios.com
Pres & Creative Dir: Paul Lundahl *E-mail:* paul@ emotionstudios.com
Founded: 1993
Marketing, communications & creative services agency.

Empire Pro
Formerly Empire Wholesale Inc
5675 Mansfield Way, Bell, CA 90201
Tel: 213-748-5200 *Toll Free Tel:* 866-748-5200
Fax: 213-748-5505
E-mail: sales@empirepro.com
Web Site: www.empirepro.com
Key Personnel
Pres: Edmond Khanian *Tel:* 213-748-5200 ext 103

Distributor of professional audio, lighting & video products.
Membership(s): Audiovisual and Integrated Experience Association; NAMM, the National Association of Music Merchants

Empire Wholesale Inc, see Empire Pro

ENCO Systems Inc
29444 Northwestern Hwy, Southfield, MI 48034
Tel: 248-827-4440 *Toll Free Tel:* 800-362-6797 (sales) *Fax:* 248-827-4441
E-mail: sales@enco.com; support@enco.com
Web Site: www.enco.com
Key Personnel
Pres: Eugene Novacek
Founded: 1983
Provider of playout, automation & captioning solutions to the broadcast & AV industry.

Encore A & S Case Co
Formerly Encore Cases
8818 Lankershim Blvd, Sun Valley, CA 91352
Tel: 818-768-8803
E-mail: info@encorecases.com
Web Site: www.encorecases.com
Key Personnel
Founder & Pres: Gary Peterson *E-mail:* gary@encorecases.com
Prodn Mgr: Karo Ovasapyan *E-mail:* karo@encorecases.com
Founded: 1988
Design & manufacture custom road cases for the following industries: touring, theatrical, production, photo & video production, corporate events, aerospace & military.
Online catalog(s) available

Encore Broadcast Solutions
2104 W Kennedy Blvd, Tampa, FL 33606
Tel: 813-253-2774 *Toll Free Tel:* 800-780-8857 *Fax:* 813-254-5907
Web Site: www.encorebroadcast.com
Founded: 1992
Serving all broadcast, government, education, religion & corporate markets. Video equipment sales, design, installation & services.
Branch Office(s)
1110 Douglas Ave, Suite 1001, Altamonte Springs, FL 32714 *Tel:* 407-327-9006 *Fax:* 407-327-2202
213 Hoffman Ave, Bridgeport, AL 35740 *Tel:* 423-544-1821 (cell)

Encore Cases, see Encore A & S Case Co

Encore Event Technologies LLC
8850 W Sunset Rd, 3rd fl, Las Vegas, NV 89148
Tel: 702-739-8803 *Fax:* 702-739-8831
Web Site: www.encoreglobal.com/us
Key Personnel
CEO: Phillip Cooper
COO: Andy Nichols
Pres & CFO: Eddy Eisenberg
Pres, Casino Div: Bill Dayton
VP, Prodn: Rob Stout

Encore Productions Inc, see Encore Event Technologies LLC

Encore Video Productions
811 Main St, Myrtle Beach, SC 29577
Tel: 843-448-9900
Web Site: www.encorevideo.biz
Key Personnel
Pres: Rik Dickinson *E-mail:* rik@encorevideo.biz
Founded: 1980
Full service video production, AV equipment & operation.

Encounter Video Inc
1761 N Jantzen Ave, Portland, OR 97217
Web Site: www.encountervideo.com
Key Personnel
Pres: Dennis Burkhart
Founded: 1983
Specialize in national park programs, natural history documentaries & world travel videos.
Catalog(s) available

Encyclomedia
1526 Dekalb Ave, Atlanta, GA 30307
Tel: 404-527-3600 *Fax:* 404-584-5171
E-mail: info@encyclomedia.net
Web Site: www.encyclomedia.net
Key Personnel
Mng Partner/Prodr: Lance Holland
Mktg Dir: Tiffany Farmer
Dir, Photog: Kent Maxey
Prodr: Burt Holland
Soundstage & editing suite rental. Camera crew for hire.

Encyclopaedia Britannica Inc
325 N La Salle St, Suite 200, Chicago, IL 60654
Tel: 312-347-7000 (all other countries) *Toll Free Tel:* 800-323-1229 (US & CN) *Fax:* 312-294-2104
Web Site: www.britannica.com
Key Personnel
EVP, Gen Coun & Corp Secy: Doug Eveleigh
VP, Consumer Mkts: Chris Mayland
VP, Sales: Matthew Krise
Exec Dir, Core Edit Group: J E Luebering
Exec Ed & Chief Devt Offr: Theodore Pappas
Exec Ed, Curriculum, Media & Prodn: Marsha Mackenzie
Catalog(s) available
Foreign Office(s): Encyclopaedia Britannica Australia Ltd, 9 Help St, Level 1, Chatswood, NSW 2067, Australia *Tel:* (02) 9915 8800 *Fax:* (02) 9419 5247 *E-mail:* sales@eb.com.au *Web Site:* britannica.com.au (Australia & Asia Pacific)
Britannica Japan Co Ltd, Nishi-Gotanda 8 Chome Bldg, 8-3-16 Nishi-Gotanda, Shinagawa, Tokyo 141-0031, Japan *Tel:* (03) 5436 1388 (consumers); (03) 5436 1390 (instns) *Fax:* (03) 5436 1380 *E-mail:* info@britannica.co.jp *Web Site:* www.britannica.co.jp
Encyclopaedia Britannica (UK) Ltd, Unity Wharf, Mill St, 2nd fl, London SE1 2BH, United Kingdom *Tel:* (020) 7500 7800 (cust support); (020) 7500 7843 (consumer sales outside UK) *Toll Free Tel:* 800 282433 (consumer sales UK only) *Fax:* (020) 7500 7878 *E-mail:* enquiries@britannica.co.uk *Web Site:* britannica.co.uk (Africa, Europe & Middle East)
Membership(s): ALA; Audiovisual and Integrated Experience Association

Endtime Ministries Inc
PO Box 940729, Plano, TX 75094-0729
Tel: 972-422-0857 *Toll Free Tel:* 833-563-6063; 800-363-8463 (cust serv)
E-mail: endtime@endtime.com
Web Site: www.endtime.com
Key Personnel
Founder & Pres: Irvin Baxter, Jr
VP: Dave Robbins
Founded: 1991
Audio & AV programming including distribution & production of religious & political radio programs, specifically Prophecy.

Enhanced View Services Inc
12360 SW 132 Ct, Suite 114, Miami, FL 33186
Tel: 305-971-2916 *Toll Free Tel:* 877-873-3843
Dealers of professional broadcast audio & video equipment.

Ensemble Designs Inc
870 Gold Flat Rd, Nevada City, CA 95959
Mailing Address: PO Box 993, Grass Valley, CA 95945-0993
Tel: 530-478-1830 *Fax:* 530-478-1832
E-mail: info@ensembledesigns.com; service@ensembledesigns.com
Web Site: www.ensembledesigns.com
Key Personnel
Pres: David Wood
Dir, Sales: Mondae Hott *E-mail:* mondae@ensembledesigns.com
Mktg: Lisa Cowden *Tel:* 530-478-8328 *E-mail:* lisa@ensembledesigns.com
Founded: 1989
Catalog(s) available, free
CD-ROM catalog(s) available, free
Membership(s): IABM; NAB; SMPTE®

Entel Systems Inc
230 W Parkway, Pompton Plains, NJ 07444
Tel: 201-447-2000 *Toll Free Tel:* 888-914-7100 *Fax:* 201-447-2880
E-mail: service@entelsystems.com
Web Site: www.entelsystems.com
Key Personnel
Owner & VP: Don Giordano
Owner: Enzo Stampone
Founded: 1992
Branch Office(s)
17 Arcadian Way, Paramus, NJ 07652

Enterprise Media LLC
91 Harvey St, Cambridge, MA 02140
Tel: 617-354-0017 *Toll Free Tel:* 800-423-6021 *Fax:* 617-354-1637
E-mail: orders@enterprisemedia.com
Web Site: www.enterprisemedia.com
Key Personnel
Pres: Stewart B Clifford *E-mail:* stewart@enterprisemedia.com
Partner: Dini Coffin *E-mail:* dini@enterprisemedia.com
Founded: 1986
Catalog(s) available, by request

Entertainment One Distribution
70 Driver Rd, Unit 1, Brampton, ON L6T 5V2, Canada
Tel: 905-624-7337 *Toll Free Tel:* 800-387-0184 *Fax:* 905-624-7310
Web Site: entertainmentone.com
Key Personnel
CEO: Darren Throop *Tel:* 905-624-7337 ext 4130
Founded: 1973
Acquisition, production & distribution of film & television content.
Branch Office(s)
134 Peter St, Suite 700, Toronto, ON M5V 2H2, Canada
16 E Third Ave, 2nd fl, Vancouver, BC V5T 1B1, Canada
Les Films Christal/Les Films Seville/Videoglobe 1, 455 rue St Antoine W, 3rd fl, Montreal, QC H2Z 1J1, Canada
Membership(s): Canadian Academy of Recording Arts & Sciences

Entertainment One US
10 Harbor Park Dr, Port Washington, NY 11050
Tel: 516-484-1000
Web Site: entertainmentone.com
Key Personnel
Corp Communs: Jackie Rubin *E-mail:* jrubin@entonegroup.com
Physical & digital music & video distribution company for independent record labels & studios.
Catalog(s) available
Branch Office(s)
150 S El Camino Dr, Suite 300, Beverly Hills, CA 90212

9378 Wilshire Blvd, Suite 210, Beverly Hills, CA 90212

4641 Leahy St, Culver City, CA 90232

4201 Wilshire Blvd, Suite 400, Los Angeles, CA 90010

1447 Cloverfield Blvd, Suite 201, Santa Monica, CA 90404

Renegade 83, 12925 Riverside Dr, 3rd fl, Sherman Oaks, CA 91423

200 Varick St, New York, NY 10014

801 Fifth Ave S, Suite 206, Nashville, TN 37203

Dualtone Records, 3 Mcferrin Ave, Nashville, TN 37206

16 E Third Ave, 2nd fl, Vancouver, BC V5T 1B1, Canada

70 Driver Rd, Unit 1, Brampton, ON L6T 5V2, Canada

134 Peter St, Suite 700, Toronto, ON M5V 2H2, Canada

Les Films Seville, 455 rue St Antoine W, 3rd fl, Montreal, QC H2Z 1J1, Canada

Videoglobe1, 455 rue St Antoine W, 3rd fl, Montreal, QC H2Z 1J1, Canada

Les Films Christal, 455 rue St Antoine W, 3rd fl, Montreal, QC H2Z 1J1, Canada

Foreign Office(s): 28-30 Queen St, Level 2, Chippendale, NSW 2008, Australia

9 Yarra St, Suite 11.06, 11th fl, South Yarra, Victoria 3141, Australia

Leonardo da Vincilaan 9, 1930 Zaventem, Brussels, Belgium

Av Paulista, 1374, 12° andar, Bela Vista, 01310-100 Sao Paulo-SP, Brazil

Oskar-von-Miller-Ring 20, 80333 Munich, Germany

20/F, Tower 535, 535 Jaffe Rd, Causeway Bay, Hong Kong

Bergweg 46, 1217 SC Hilversum, Netherlands

Avda De Burgos, n° 12, 10a Planta, 28036 Madrid, Spain

45 Warren St, London W1T 6AG, United Kingdom

The Smiths Bldg, 5th fl, 179 Great Portland St, London W1W 5PL, United Kingdom

Whizz Kid Entertainment, 4 Kingly St, London W1B 5PE, United Kingdom

Membership(s): Music Business Association

Envision Communications Inc
2002 N 204 St, Elkhorn, NE 68022
Tel: 402-289-2220
Key Personnel
Pres: Verle G Peterson *Tel:* 402-289-2220 ext 201 *E-mail:* verle@envision-com.com
Motion picture film services.

eOne, see Entertainment One Distribution

eOne, see Entertainment One US

EON247 Inc
1245 Champa St, Basement, Denver, CO 80204
Tel: 720-935-7497
E-mail: info@eon247.com
Web Site: www.eon247.com
Key Personnel
CEO/CTO: Brandon Naughton
Creative Dir: Chris Eng
Mktg Dir: Christopher Leirer
Full 4K UHD production facility providing end to end services. Studio rental, lighting & production services, live HD streaming & virtual reality experiences.

Epic Software Group Inc
701 Sawdust Rd, The Woodlands, TX 77380
Tel: 281-363-3742
E-mail: epic@epicsoftware.com
Web Site: www.epicsoftware.com
Key Personnel
Pres: Vic Cherubini

3D animation & multimedia production studio & NewTek reseller.
Membership(s): BMA

Epitome Pictures Inc, see WildBrain™

EPIX Inc
381 Lexington Dr, Buffalo Grove, IL 60089
Tel: 847-465-1818 *Fax:* 847-465-1919
E-mail: epix@epixinc.com; orders@epixinc.com
Web Site: epixinc.com
Key Personnel
Off Mgr: Kirsten Gimm
Founded: 1983
Designs & manufactures frame grabbers, cameras, image acquisition & processing software, camera kits & video to disk computer systems for machine vision, medical imaging & high speed video analysis applications.
Online catalog(s) available

Kat Epple Music Productions
PO Box 3156, North Fort Myers, FL 33918-3156
Tel: 239-997-0323
E-mail: music@katepple.com
Web Site: www.katepple.com
Key Personnel
Pres: Kat Epple *E-mail:* katepple@comcast.net
Film score music & production.

Equi=Tech Corp
PO Box 249, Selma, OR 97538-0249
Tel: 541-218-6900 (tech support, cust serv); 541-291-9253 *Toll Free Tel:* 877-EQUITECH (378-4832) *Fax:* 541-787-8740
E-mail: sales@equitech.com; customerservice@equitech.com; marketing@equitech.com
Web Site: www.equitech.com
Key Personnel
Pres: Martin Glasband *E-mail:* martin.g@equitech.com
Prodn Mgr: Erik Praytor *E-mail:* erik.p@equitech.com
Founded: 1992
Shipping Address: 18258 Redwood Hwy, Selma, OR 97538

ERA Learning
Division of Educational Research Associates
PO Box 3428, Hillsboro, OR 97123
Tel: 503-228-6345 *Toll Free Tel:* 800-827-2499 (orders) *Fax:* 810-885-5811
E-mail: info@eralearning.com; customerservice@eralearning.com; sales@eralearning.com
Web Site: www.eralearning.com
Key Personnel
Exec Dir: Mark Salser
Founded: 1965
Publish instructional materials including a wide range of individualized multimedia programs.
Catalog(s) available
Sales Office(s): PO Box 8795, Portland, OR 97207-8795

Ergo Media Inc
668 American Legion Dr, Teaneck, NJ 07666
Mailing Address: PO Box 2132, Teaneck, NJ 07666-1437
Tel: 201-692-0404 *Fax:* 201-692-0663
E-mail: info@jewishvideo.com
Web Site: www.jewishvideo.com
Key Personnel
Pres: Eric Goldman
Founded: 1986
Jewish oriented DVDs & films.
Online catalog(s) available

ESE
142 Sierra St, El Segundo, CA 90245
Tel: 310-322-2136 *Fax:* 310-322-8127
E-mail: ese@ese-web.com

Web Site: www.ese-web.com
Key Personnel
Pres: Brian Way
Founded: 1971
Provider of time control solutions & distribution products: GPS based master clocks, SMPTE Time Code products, audio & video distribution amplifiers, analog & digital remote displays, NTP Time Servers, frequency standards & audio level indicators & interfaces.
Online catalog(s) available
Membership(s): NAB

ESECO Speedmaster
730 E Eseco Rd, Cushing, OK 74023-5505
Tel: 918-225-1266 *Toll Free Tel:* 800-331-5904 (US & CN)
E-mail: info@eseco-speedmaster.com
Web Site: www.eseco-speedmaster.com
Key Personnel
Pres: Wallace Hallman *E-mail:* wallace@eseco-speedmaster.com
EVP: Jerry Kaminshine *E-mail:* jerry@eseco-speedmaster.com
Founded: 1956
Electronic systems engineering company. Manufactures & markets in the photographic, graphic arts & x-ray industries.

ESL Power Systems
2800 Palisades Dr, Corona, CA 92880-9427
Tel: 951-739-7000 *Toll Free Tel:* 800-922-4188 *Fax:* 951-739-7048
E-mail: sales@eslpwr.com; info@eslpwr.com
Web Site: eslpwr.com
Key Personnel
Owner: David Hellmers; Michael Hellmers
Manufacture temporary power equipment.

Esoteric Sound
1608 Hemstock Ave, Wheaton, IL 60189
Tel: 630-933-9801 *Fax:* 630-933-9801
E-mail: esoterictt@aol.com
Web Site: www.esotericsound.com
Founded: 1981
Catalog(s) available

ESPN Inc
Subsidiary of The Walt Disney Co
ESPN Plaza, 545 Middle St, Bristol, CT 06010
Tel: 860-766-2000
Web Site: www.espn.com
Founded: 1979
Membership(s): Cable Television Advertising Bureau; NAB; NATAS; NCTA - The Internet & Television Association; SMPTE®

ESSCO, see L-3 ESSCO

Essex Television Group Inc
7 Vista Dr, Old Lyme, CT 06371
Mailing Address: PO Box 454, Old Lyme, CT 06371-0454
Tel: 860-434-7200 *Fax:* 860-434-7210
E-mail: contact@essextelevision.com
Web Site: www.essextelevision.com
Key Personnel
Pres: Daniel Carey *E-mail:* dcarey@essextelevision.com
Busn Mgr: Jennifer Gobey *E-mail:* jgobey@essextelevision.com
Founded: 1998
Full production company. Corporate video, documentaries & HD programs.

Estiluz Inc
330 W 38 St, Suite 710, New York, NY 10018
Tel: 201-641-1997; 646-454-1285 *Fax:* 201-641-2092; 646-454-1799
E-mail: info@estiluzusa.com
Web Site: www.estiluzusa.com

Key Personnel
EVP: Albert Grabulosa
Founded: 1993
Manufacture contemporary decorative lighting products.
Foreign Office(s): Estiluz SA, Crta Ogassa s/n, St Joan de les Abadesses, 17860 Girona, Spain *Tel:* 972 720 125 *Fax:* 972 720 796
E-mail: estiluz@estiluz.com (headquarters)

ETA Systems
Subsidiary of MiTek Corporation
1601 Jack McKay Blvd, Ennis, TX 75119
Toll Free Tel: 800-321-6699 *Toll Free Fax:* 800-996-3821
Founded: 1977
Manufacturer of rack mounted power protection & management products designed to protect the ultrasensitive digital electronic equipment used in audio & video applications.

ETC
3031 Pleasant View Rd, Middleton, WI 53562-4809
Mailing Address: PO Box 620979, Middleton, WI 53562-0979
Tel: 608-831-4116 *Toll Free Tel:* 800-688-4116
Fax: 608-836-1736
Web Site: www.etcconnect.com
Key Personnel
Pres & CEO: Dick Titus
COO: Julie Cymbalak
VP, Busn Resources: Bob Tollefson
VP, Commercial & Indust Opers: Jake Dunnum
VP, Fin: Jeffrey Welch
VP, Intl Opers: Durrell Ramer
VP, Mfg: Bill McGivern
VP, Mktg: David Lincecum
VP, Prof Servs: Sarah Danke
VP, R&D: Dennis Varian
VP, World Sales: Mark Vassallo
Founded: 1975
Manufacture of lighting & rigging technology for entertainment & architectural applications.
Catalog(s) available
Branch Office(s)
711 ETC Dr, Mazomanie, WI 53560 *Tel:* 608-824-5656 *Fax:* 608-836-1736
1120 Scott Rd, Burbank, CA 91504 *Tel:* 323-461-0216 *Fax:* 323-461-7830 (western regl off)
4501 Vineland Rd, Suite 101-102, Orlando, FL 32811 *Tel:* 407-843-7770 *Fax:* 407-843-0337 (southeast regl off)
630 Ninth Ave, Suite 1001, New York, NY 10036 *Tel:* 212-397-8080 *Fax:* 212-397-4340 (northeast regl off)
Foreign Office(s): 62-64 rue Danielle Casanova, 93200 Saint-Denis Cedex, France *Tel:* 01 42 43 35 35 *Fax:* 01 42 43 08 05
ETC GmbH, Ohmstr 3, 83607 Holzkirchen, Germany, Gen Mgr: Philipp Schaeffer *Tel:* (08024) 47 00-0 *Fax:* (08024) 47 00-3 00
Enterprise Sq, 18/F, Tower I, Rm 1801, 9 Sheung Yuet Rd, Kowloon Bay, Kowloon, Hong Kong, Gen Mgr: Wynne Cheung *Tel:* 2799 1220 *Fax:* 2799 9325
ETC Italia SRL, Via Bruno Pontecorvo, 10, Guidonia Montecelio, 00012 Rome RM, Italy *Tel:* (063) 211 1683 *Fax:* (020) 87528486
Studio 2, Zee Tower, Media City, Dubai, United Arab Emirates *Tel:* (020) 8896 1000 *Fax:* (020) 8896 2000
ETC Ltd, 26-28 Victoria Industrial Estate, Victoria Rd, London W3 6UU, United Kingdom, Gen Mgr: Matthew Brookfield *Tel:* (020) 8896 1000 *Fax:* (020) 8896 2000

Eternal Word Television Network (EWTN)
5817 Old Leeds Rd, Irondale, AL 35210-2164
Tel: 205-271-2900 *Fax:* 205-271-2920
E-mail: viewer@ewtn.com
Web Site: www.ewtn.com

Key Personnel
Chmn of the Bd & CEO: Michael P Warsaw
COO & Pres: Doug Keck
Dir, Mktg Support: Julia Muscari
Founded: 1981
Now offer in-house production on EWTN Home Video.
Branch Office(s)
PO Box 157, Sta A, Etobicoke, ON M9C 4V2, Canada
Membership(s): NCTA - The Internet & Television Association

ETR
100 Enterprise Way, Suite G 300, Scotts Valley, CA 95066
Toll Free Tel: 800-620-8884 *Fax:* 831-438-4284
E-mail: customerservice@etr.org
Key Personnel
CEO: Vignetta Charles
CFO: Kathy Pedersen
CIO: Eric Blanke
VP, Busn Devt: Coleen Cantwell
Chief Science Offr: Karin Coyle, PhD
Publish & distribute health promotion & health education materials used in health care settings & schools.
Catalog(s) available
Online catalog(s) available
Branch Office(s)
1333 Broadway, Suite P110, Oakland, CA 94612 *Tel:* 510-291-4559
5495 Carlson Dr, Suite D, Sacramento, CA 95819 *Tel:* 916-642-1187 *Fax:* 916-739-8925

ETS-Lindgren
1301 Arrow Point Dr, Cedar Park, TX 78613
Tel: 512-531-6400; 512-531-2609 (serv)
Fax: 512-531-6500
E-mail: sales@ets-lindgren.com
Web Site: www.ets-lindgren.com
Key Personnel
Dir, Global Mktg & Communs: Glenn Watkins
Test, measurement & shielding company for wireless, automotive, military, medical, aerospace, acoustical & EMC. Supplies shielding solutions for electromagnetic & radio frequency (EMI/RFI), creates acoustic testing rooms & measure exposure to electromagnetic & magnetic sources.
Online catalog(s) available
Branch Office(s)
1360 N Wood Dale Rd, Suite G, Wood Dale, IL 60191 *Tel:* 630-307-7200 *Fax:* 630-307-7571
Foreign Office(s): Rm 1016-1018, 10th fl, Jin Ao International Bldg, No 17 Ma Dian East Rd, Haidian District, Beijing 100088, China *Tel:* (010) 82730877 *Fax:* (010) 82730880 *E-mail:* china@ets-lindgren.com
Rm 805, Bldg 8, No 28 Tongxin Rd, Hongkou District, Shanghai 200083, China *Tel:* (021) 52045795 *Fax:* (021) 52045796 *E-mail:* shanghai@ets-lindgren.com
B412-3 Tian'an Chuangxin, Technology Plaza, Chegongmiao, Futian District, Shenzhen, China *Tel:* (0755) 26758955 *Fax:* (0755) 267589300 *E-mail:* shenzhen@ets-lindgren.com
Mekaanikontie 1, 27510 Eura, Finland *Tel:* (02) 8383 300 *Fax:* (02) 8651 233 *E-mail:* euinfo@ets-lindgren.com
No 73, Service Rd, West of Chord Rd, Mahalakshmipuram, Bangalore 560 086, India *Tel:* (080) 4341 8600 *Fax:* (080) 4341 8611 *E-mail:* indiainfo@ets-lindgren.com
4-2-6, Kohinata, Bunkyo-ku, Tokyo 112-0006, Japan *Tel:* (03) 38137100 *Fax:* (03) 38138068 *E-mail:* japan@ets-lindgren.com
7500A Beach Rd, No 07-303, The Plaza, Singapore 199591, Singapore *Tel:* 6391 0026 *Fax:* 6291 7311 *E-mail:* singapore@ets-lindgren.com
8F-1, No 380, Sec 1, Fu-Hsing South Rd, Virtuoso Enterprise Bldg, Taipei 106, Taiwan

Tel: (02) 27023389 *Fax:* (02) 27023055
E-mail: taiwan@ets-lindgren.com
Jumeirah Lakes Towers, Platinum Tower, Off No 2702, PO Box 9082, Dubai, United Arab Emirates *Tel:* (055) 610 4055

EUE/Screen Gems Studios
Division of EUE/Screen Gems Ltd
1223 N 23 St, Wilmington, NC 28405
Tel: 910-343-3500 *Fax:* 910-343-3574
Web Site: euescreengems.com
Key Personnel
EVP: Bill Vassar *E-mail:* bvassar@euescreengems.com
Film, television & commercial production.
Branch Office(s)
50 NW 14 St, Miami, FL 33136, Gen Mgr: Christian Lovschal *Tel:* 786-774-4007 *E-mail:* clovschal@euescreengems.com
175 Lakewood Way, Atlanta, GA 30315, EVP: Kris Bagwell *Tel:* 404-333-6506 *E-mail:* kbagwell@euescreengems.com
603 Greenwich St, New York, NY 10014, COO: Chris Cooney *Tel:* 212-450-1600 *Fax:* 212-450-1610 *E-mail:* info@euescreengems.com (headquarters)

Euro-Pacific Film & Video Productions Inc
101 Crawfords Corner Rd, Suite 4-101R, Holmdel, NJ 07733
Tel: 732-530-4451 *Toll Free Tel:* 800-387-6776
E-mail: info@euro-pacific.com
Web Site: www.euro-pacific.com
Key Personnel
Pres & Exec Sr Prodr: David Calderwood *E-mail:* david@euro-pacific.com
VP & Exec Sr Prodr: Lisa Moss Calderwood
Promos Mktg Specialist: E B Moss
Founded: 1990
Multimedia production & web site development. Foreign offices located in Auckland, New Zealand.
Membership(s): NATAS

Eurotech Seating, see Fusion Consoles/Eurotech Seating

Event Essentials
Division of A to Z RentAll & Sales Inc
6485 Blanchar's Crossing, Windsor, WI 53598
Tel: 608-846-5004 *Toll Free Tel:* 800-220-4991
Fax: 608-222-5063
Web Site: www.eventessentials.com
Key Personnel
Owner: Kevin Hoffman
Gen Mgr: Greg Goke *E-mail:* greg@eventessentials.com
Catalog(s) available

Event Tech
7601 Brandon Woods Blvd, Baltimore, MD 21226
Tel: 410-360-5006 *Toll Free Tel:* 866-950-8343
E-mail: info@eventtech.com
Web Site: www.eventtech.com
Key Personnel
Pres: Eric Maynard
VP, Opers: Matt Totaro
Founded: 1986
Full production services & equipment rentals for special events nationwide.
Membership(s): International Live Events Association; Professional Lighting & Sound Association

Eventide Inc
One Alsan Way, Little Ferry, NJ 07643
Tel: 201-641-1200 *Fax:* 201-641-1640
E-mail: audio@eventide.com; support@eventide.com
Web Site: www.eventide.com

Key Personnel
VP, Sales & Mktg: Ray Maxwell
Manufacture audio hardware & software, including stompboxes.
Catalog(s) available
Membership(s): AES; NAB; NAMM, the National Association of Music Merchants

Ever-Ready Media Packaging
Unit of Reliance Corrugated Container Corp
8192 Gatherly Circle, Easton, MD 21601
Mailing Address: PO Box 1643, Easton, MD 21601
Tel: 973-566-9333
E-mail: packages@erpack.com
Web Site: www.erpack.com
Key Personnel
Pres: Marshall Weingarden
Founded: 1963
Manufacture & distribute CD, DVD, HD-DVD & Blu-ray disc packaging.
Sample(s) available, free, annual
Online catalog(s) available
Shipping Address: 920 N Ridge Ave, Unit C-3, Lombard, IL 60148

Everlast Productions
59 SW 12 Ave, Unit 110, Dania Beach, FL 33004
Tel: 954-456-7167 *Fax:* 954-456-1243
E-mail: info@everlastproductions.com
Web Site: everlastproductions.com
Key Personnel
CEO: Washington Arias
Sales Dir: Letty Dexter
Tech Dir: David McCrainie
Gen Mgr: Dave Jones

Evertz Microsystems Ltd
5292 John Lucas Dr, Burlington, ON L7L 5Z9, Canada
Tel: 905-335-3700 *Toll Free Tel:* 877-995-3700
Fax: 905-335-3573
E-mail: sales@evertz.com
Web Site: www.evertz.com
Key Personnel
Sr Regl Sales Mgr: Paul Soares *E-mail:* paul@evertz.com
Founded: 1966
Design & manufacture audio & video infrastructure equipment for the television broadcast & film industry. Offers HD, 3G & Ultra HD end-to-end solutions including: master control systems, large, medium & small routers, branding, RF, master sync generation, terminal gear, fiber optics, multi-display monitoring, production tools & interfaces & closed captioning. Also provides solutions for post-production, production & mobile production, IPTV, OTT, transport & distribution equipment & broadcast, satellite & cable applications. Branch offices in Los Angeles & San Jose, CA, Washington, DC & New York, NY. Foreign offices in Australia, Germany, Hong Kong, India, New Zealand, United Arab Emirates & UK.
Catalog(s) available, free, annual
Membership(s): IABM; SMPTE®

Evia
8424 154 Ave NE, Redmond, WA 98052
Tel: 425-284-3888 *Toll Free Tel:* 800-206-2547
Fax: 425-883-3887
E-mail: hello@evia.events
Web Site: www.tri-digital.com
Key Personnel
Pres: Hilary Laney
Multimedia service bureau video compression & CD-ROM title developer.
Catalog(s) available
Membership(s): Washington Software Association

Evolution AV
Formerly Evolution Presentation Technologies

129, 2312-52 Ave SE, Calgary, AB T2C 0A3, Canada
Tel: 403-259-3793 *Toll Free Tel:* 800-561-9820
Fax: 403-259-2374 *Toll Free Fax:* 800-561-9820
Web Site: www.evolutionav.ca
Key Personnel
Pres: Steve Read
Founded: 1969
AV rentals & staging, sales & installation.
Branch Office(s)
11668 154 St NW, Edmonton, AB T5M 3N8, Canada *Tel:* 780-451-4688
No 1388, 100-535 Thurlow St, Vancouver, BC V6E 3L6, Canada
525 Madison St, Winnipeg, MB R3H 0L6, Canada *Tel:* 204-775-6662
340 B Waterloo St N, Thunder Bay, ON P7C 5Y3, Canada *Tel:* 807-627-5604
901 King St, Suite 400, Toronto, ON M5V 3H5, Canada
1817 McDonald St, Regina, SK S4N 7A2, Canada *Tel:* 306-525-6133
110-2366 Ave "C" N, Saskatoon, SK S7L 5X5, Canada *Tel:* 306-244-2999
Membership(s): Audiovisual and Integrated Experience Association; MPI; Professional Systems Network International

Evolution Presentation Technologies, see Evolution AV

Evolve Inc
1210 E Arlington Blvd, Greenville, NC 27858
Tel: 252-754-2957 *Fax:* 252-754-2832
Web Site: www.evolveinc.com
Key Personnel
Pres: Will Daugherty
Creative Dir: Brian Taylor
Founded: 2002
Full service advertising agency. Specialize in brand management & marketing strategy through the integrated use of marketing, advertising & public relations. Video & radio production.

Jasper Ewing & Sons Inc
PO Box 12853, Jackson, MS 39236
Tel: 601-942-3325
E-mail: info@jasperewing.com
Web Site: jasperewing.com
Key Personnel
Pres: Malcolm P Ewing, Jr
Founded: 1906

EWTN, see Eternal Word Television Network (EWTN)

Excel Duplication Services
1219 N Cass St, Milwaukee, WI 53202
Tel: 414-225-9235
Founded: 1986
DVD & CD duplication.

Executive Development Systems Inc
3818 Vinecrest Dr, Dallas, TX 75229
Tel: 214-351-0055 *Toll Free Tel:* 800-955-7353
Web Site: www.edforeman.com
Key Personnel
Co-Founder & Pres: Ed Foreman *E-mail:* edf@edforeman.com
Co-Founder & EVP: Earlene Vining *E-mail:* earlene@edforeman.com
Contact: Linda Barrett *E-mail:* linda@edforeman.com
Online catalog(s) available

Exeltech Inc
7317 Jack Newell Blvd N, Fort Worth, TX 76118
Tel: 817-595-4969 *Toll Free Tel:* 800-886-4683
Fax: 817-595-1290

Web Site: www.exeltech.com
Founded: 1990
Manufacture true-sine-wave power inverters, rack mount systems, & accessories.
Catalog(s) available

Explore
Formerly Explore Media LLC
311 W Superior St, Suite 218, Chicago, IL 60610
Tel: 312-818-2101
E-mail: info@explore-media.com
Web Site: www.explore-media.com
Key Personnel
Exec Prodr: Jeremy Pinckert *E-mail:* jeremy@explore-media.com
Commercial production company.

Explore Media LLC, see Explore

ExpoDisplays
3401 Mary Taylor Rd, Birmingham, AL 35235
Toll Free Tel: 800-747-3976
E-mail: info@expodisplays.com
Web Site: www.expodisplays.com
Key Personnel
CEO: Jeff Culton
Pres: David Holladay
VP: Jay Burkette
Design Dir: Nate Preg
Dir, Trade Show Proj Mgmt: Branan Mercer
Exhibit Mgmt Dir: Ann Thomas
Mktg Dir: Melissa Johnson
Gen Mgr: Lonnie Miller
Founded: 1970
Full service custom exhibit house & manufacturer of innovative portable & modular displays.
Branch Office(s)
1003 Production Ct, Madison, AL 35758
8910 N Dale Mabry Hwy, Suite 15, Tampa, FL 33614
3664 Trousdale Dr, Nashville, TN 37204

Express Media Inc
2225 Palou Ave, San Francisco, CA 94124
Tel: 415-255-9883 *Fax:* 415-255-0139
Web Site: expressmedia.tv
Key Personnel
CFO: Maria Stepanenko
Pres: Steven Barger
Dir: Buddy Scauzzo
Founded: 1989
Broadcast & industrial video equipment rentals. Also offers a wide range of production & post services.
Rate card(s) available, free, quarterly
Membership(s): Northern California Production Community

Express Video Supply Inc
1819 Victory Blvd, Glendale, CA 91201
Tel: 818-552-4590 *Toll Free Tel:* 800-238-8480
Fax: 818-552-4591
E-mail: rentals@evsonline.com; sales@evsonline.com; studios@evsonline.com
Web Site: www.evsonline.com
Founded: 1991
Catalog(s) available

Extraordinary Demos/Videos
2131 Yellowstar Lane, Naperville, IL 60564-5330
Tel: 630-904-3636
Web Site: www.extraordinaryvideos.com
Key Personnel
Owner & Pres: Fred Harms *E-mail:* demofred@aol.com
Founded: 1985
Multimedia & training-audio & video.

Extreme Reach Inc
75 Second Ave, Suite 720, Needham, MA 02494
Tel: 781-577-2016 *Toll Free Tel:* 877-769-9382

E-mail: sales@extremereach.com; support@ extremereach.com
Web Site: extremereach.com
Key Personnel
Chmn & CEO: John Roland
COO: Tim Conley
Interim CFO: Jorge Martell
CTO: Dan Brackett
Chief Client Offr: Patrick Hanavan
Chief Mktg Offr: Melinda McLaughlin
Chief Talent Offr: Tim Hale
VP, HR: Jennifer Wambold
TV & digital video advertising.
Branch Office(s)
2323 N Valley St, Burbank, CA 91505 *Tel:* 818-729-2900
2000 Powell St, Suite 970, Emeryville, CA 94608 *Tel:* 510-400-8200
3330 Cahuenga Blvd W, 4th fl, Los Angeles, CA 90068 *Tel:* 323-603-5220
450 Corporate Blvd, Newark, DE 19702 *Tel:* 302-368-0002
245 Hembree Park Dr, Roswell, GA 30076 *Tel:* 770-619-0801
111 W Jackson Blvd, Suite 1525, Chicago, IL 60604 *Tel:* 312-846-6255
8130 River Dr, Morton Grove, IL 60053 *Tel:* 312-624-7539
3309 Gilmore Industrial Blvd, Louisville, KY 40213 *Toll Free Tel:* 877-769-9382
200 Galleria Officentre, Suite 109, Southfield, MI 48034
721 Second St S, Great Falls, MT 59405 *Tel:* 406-761-7877
1633 Broadway, 6th fl, New York, NY 10019 *Tel:* 646-344-3400
2525 McKinnon St, Suite 530, Dallas, TX 75201
107 Spring St, Seattle, WA 98104
Extreme Reach, 635 Queen St E, Toronto, ON M4M 1G4, Canada *Tel:* 416-964-7539
Foreign Office(s): 37 Sun St, 4th fl, London EC2M 2PL, United Kingdom *Tel:* (0747) 871 9903

Extron Electronics
1025 E Ball Rd, Suite 100, Anaheim, CA 92805-5957
Tel: 714-491-1500 *Toll Free Tel:* 800-633-9876 (sales & tech support); 800-633-9873 (order support) *Fax:* 714-491-1517
E-mail: sales-usa@extron.com
Web Site: www.extron.com
Key Personnel
VP, Busn Devt: Art Garcia
VP, Worldwide Sales & Mktg: Casey Hall
PR/Media Coord: Tracy Barillas
Founded: 1983
Leading manufacturer of Pro AV system integration products including AV control systems, matrix switchers, distribution amplifiers, fiber optic systems, videowall processors, video signal processors, streaming products, audio amplifiers & signal processors, speakers & cables.
Catalog(s) available
Branch Office(s)
2500 N Raleigh Blvd, Raleigh, NC 27604 *Tel:* 919-850-1000 *Fax:* 919-850-1001
3855 Centerview Dr, Suite 400A, Chantilly, VA 20151
Foreign Office(s): Extron Europe, Hanzeboulevard 10, 3825 PH Amersfoort, Netherlands *Tel:* (033) 453 4040 *Toll Free Tel:* 800 3987 6673 (inside Europe only) *Fax:* (033) 453 4050
Extron Electronics Asia Pte Ltd, PM Industrial Bldg, Suite 04-01, 135 Joo Seng Rd, Singapore 368363, Singapore *Tel:* 6383 4400 *Fax:* 6383 4664
Membership(s): Audiovisual and Integrated Experience Association; NAB

Eye & I Productions
1250 Kay Lane, Oakley, CA 94561
Tel: 925-625-7888 *Toll Free Tel:* 800-720-9014

E-mail: contact@voicecrystal.com
Web Site: www.voicecrystal.com
Key Personnel
Gen Mgr: Mark Wiens
Founded: 1987
Voice Crystal® music synthesizer, sampler, midi & multimedia products. Sound design consultants. Synthesizer spec & implementation & general midi soundset design. Full sound design studio Mac & PC. Full line of sample CDs & synthesizer sound banks & cards, SoundFont libraries & DLS.
Online catalog(s) available

Eye on Dance
Subsidiary of Arts Resources in Collaboration Inc (ARC)
70 E Tenth St, Suite 19-D, New York, NY 10003
Tel: 212-206-6492
E-mail: info@eyeondance.org
Web Site: www.eyeondance.org
Key Personnel
Founder & Dir: Jeff Bush; Celia Ipiotis
Founded: 1981
Arts television series & video library.
Online catalog(s) available

Eyecon Video Productions
1865 Summit Ave, Suite 605, Plano, TX 75074
Tel: 972-881-3200 *Toll Free Tel:* 877-704-1517
E-mail: info@eyeconvideo.com
Web Site: www.eyeconvideo.com
Key Personnel
Owner: Greg Coon *E-mail:* greg@eyeconadvertising.com
Founded: 1991
Full service video production company.
Membership(s): National Press Photographers Association; Texas Association of Motion Media Professionals

Eyeline Teleprompting
1313 Mound St, Alameda, CA 94501
Tel: 510-205-6762
E-mail: info@eyeline.tv
Web Site: www.eyeline.tv
Key Personnel
Owner & Operator: Conchita Perales *E-mail:* conchita@eyeline.tv
Founded: 2000
Teleprompting equipment rental & operator services for video, film, events, conventions & webcasts. Bilingual operators.

EZ FX Inc
Division of EZ FX Jib Arm
324 Maguire Rd, Ocoee, FL 34761
Tel: 407-877-2335 *Toll Free Tel:* 800-541-5706
E-mail: sales@ezfx.com
Web Site: ezfx.com
Key Personnel
Contact: Steve G Bonin *E-mail:* steve@ezfx.com
Founded: 1993
Manufacture camera cranes, jib arms & slider dolly.
Catalog(s) available
Demo video(s) available

EZ Scenic
834 NW 1911 Rd, Lone Jack, MO 64070
Tel: 816-861-4200
Web Site: www.ezscenic.com
Key Personnel
Owner: Daryn Cashmark *E-mail:* daryn@cashmarkmedia.com
Specialty scenic & rental stage sets.

Fabled Films LLC
200 Park Ave S, 15th fl, New York, NY 10003
Tel: 212-220-5804
E-mail: info@fabledfilms.com

Web Site: www.fabledfilms.com
Key Personnel
Creative Dir: Tracey Hecht *E-mail:* traceyhecht@fabledfilms.com
Sales, Mktg & Opers: Stacey Ashton *E-mail:* staceyashton@fabledfilms.com
Media & entertainment company, creating spirited characters for children & young adult audiences. Expertise in writing, illustration, visual design, filmmaking, digital animation, app creation, brand building, sales strategy, digital marketing, publishing & licensed products. Subsidiary publishing company: Fabled Films Press.

FACE Foundation
972 Fifth Ave, New York, NY 10075
Tel: 212-439-1439
E-mail: info@face-foundation.org
Web Site: www.face-foundation.org
Key Personnel
Chmn of the Bd: Patrick Pagni
Acting Exec Dir: Laurent Auffret *E-mail:* laurent.auffret@face-foundation.org
Admin Mgr: Oisin Muldowney *E-mail:* oisin.muldowney@face-foundation.org
Founded: 1955

Facet Media
408 NE Sixth St, Fort Lauderdale, FL 33304
Tel: 954-593-0411
E-mail: info@facetmedia.com
Web Site: www.facetmedia.com
Key Personnel
Contact: Andrae Palmer *E-mail:* andrae@facetmedia.com
Digital cinema services & RED EPIC rentals. Lighting & grip services & crews, studio rental, camera rentals & accessories.

Facets Multi-Media Inc
1517 W Fullerton Ave, Chicago, IL 60614
Tel: 773-281-9075 *Fax:* 773-929-5437
E-mail: sales@facets.org; press@facets.org
Web Site: www.facets.org
Key Personnel
Founder: Milos Stehlik
Dir, Opers: Matt Silcock *E-mail:* matt@facets.org
Mktg Dir: Paul Gonter *Tel:* 773-281-9075 ext 106 *E-mail:* paul@facets.org
Founded: 1975
Connect people to independent ideas through film.
Online catalog(s) available
Membership(s): Entertainment Merchants Association

Falcon Safety Products Inc
25 Imclone Dr, Branchburg, NJ 08876
Tel: 908-707-4900 *Toll Free Tel:* 800-332-5266 (ext 220, cust serv) *Fax:* 908-707-8855
Web Site: www.falconsafety.com; www.shopfalcon.com
Key Personnel
Pres & CEO: Philip Lapin
SVP, Sales: Steve Smith
Dir, Mktg: Jennifer Rappaport
Founded: 1953
Catalog(s) available

Family Health Media
PO Box 5832, Charlottesville, VA 22905-5832
Tel: 434-566-0123 *Toll Free Tel:* 800-366-3641 *Toll Free Fax:* 888-234-2579
E-mail: support@familyhealthmedia.com
Web Site: www.familyhealthmedia.com
Key Personnel
Owner: Andy Spratt *E-mail:* andy@familyhealthmedia.com
Founded: 1992
Produce & publish health education media.

Online catalog(s) available
Shipping Address: 4320 Burton Rd, North Garden, VA 22959

F&F Productions LLC
Subsidiary of Hubbard Broadcasting Inc
14333 Myerlake Circle, Clearwater, FL 33760
Tel: 727-530-5000 *Fax:* 727-535-6547
E-mail: info@fandfhd.tv
Web Site: www.fandfhd.tv
Key Personnel
Pres & CEO: George Orgera *E-mail:* georgeo@fandfhd.tv
VP & Gen Mgr: Marc Orgera *E-mail:* marco@fandfhd.tv
VP, Engg: Bill McKechney *E-mail:* billm@fandfhd.tv
Dir, Busn Devt: Joe Scionti *Tel:* 847-372-0487 *E-mail:* joes@fandfhd.tv
Dir, Engg: Donald Adydan *E-mail:* donalda@fandfhd.tv
Dir, Sales & Mktg: Connie Vizaro *Tel:* 727-743-5249 *E-mail:* conniev@fandfhd.tv
Busn Devt Mgr: Leann Stiver *Tel:* 716-909-5499 (cell) *E-mail:* leanns@fandfhd.tv
Mgr, Engg Opers: Mike Anthony *E-mail:* mikea@fandfhd.tv
Opers Mgr: Brian Hawley *E-mail:* brianh@fandfhd.tv
Opers Coord: Sue Molner *E-mail:* suem@fandfhd.tv
Founded: 1981
Provider of HD remote production facilities for the television broadcasting industry.
Online catalog(s) available
Membership(s): NAB

Fanlight Productions
Subsidiary of Icarus Films Inc
c/o Icarus Films, 32 Court St, Brooklyn, NY 11201
Tel: 718-488-8900 *Fax:* 781-488-8642
E-mail: info@fanlight.com; sales@icarusfilms.com; rentals@icarusfilms.com
Web Site: www.fanlight.com; www.icarusfilms.com
Founded: 1978
Film & video distributor with a focus on healthcare.
Catalog(s) available
Membership(s): IMDA

Fantasee Lighting
14857 Martinsville Rd, Belleville, MI 48111
Tel: 734-699-7200 *Fax:* 734-699-7400
E-mail: info@fantaseelighting.com
Web Site: fantaseelighting.com
Key Personnel
Opers Mgr: Colin Brandt *Tel:* 734-699-7200 ext 119 *E-mail:* cbrandt@fantaseelighting.com
Founded: 1977
Rent, sell & service theatrical lighting systems & special effects.
Membership(s): USITT

Fantasy Creations FX
Division of Studio 2060
2060 E McDaniel St, Springfield, MO 65802
Tel: 417-619-1138
E-mail: fcfxmike@yahoo.com
Web Site: www.fantasycreationsfx.com
Key Personnel
Owner: Mike Strain, Jr
Founded: 1987
Create special makeup effects & pyrotechnics.
Catalog(s) available, $2, annual, makeup FX & expendables
Online catalog(s) available, makeup FX & expendables

Far West Media Services Inc
904 Silver Spur Rd, No 804, Rolling Hills Estates, CA 90274
Tel: 562-496-3342 *Fax:* 562-496-4329
Web Site: www.farwestmedia.com
Key Personnel
Pres & Dir: Robert Ranaldi
Radio & television advertising short & long form.

Fastlane Productions LLC
7 Riverdale Rd, Billerica, MA 01821
Tel: 978-667-8399 *Fax:* 978-667-8398
E-mail: info@fastlaneproductions.net
Web Site: www.fastlaneproductions.net
Sound, lighting & production company. Services include sales, installations & rentals for all audio & lighting needs.

Fax Animation Co
Division of Alan Gordon Enterprises Inc
5625 Melrose Ave, Hollywood, CA 90038
Tel: 323-466-3561 *Fax:* 323-871-2193
E-mail: contactus@alangordon.com
Web Site: www.alangordon.com
Key Personnel
Co-Owner: Grant Loucks; Don Sahlein
Manufacture, sales & rental of animation stands, animation desks, animation discs, backlites, pegboards & pegbars.
Catalog(s) available
Online catalog(s) available

D W Fearn
Division of Hazelrigg Industries
124 Tartan Terr, Chalfont, PA 18914
Tel: 567-DWFEARN (393-3276)
E-mail: support@hazelriggindustries.com
Web Site: www.dwfearn.com
Key Personnel
Founder & Consultant: Douglas W Fearn
Founded: 1993
Manufacturer of professional vacuum tube audio recording equipment.
Catalog(s) available

Feldenkrais® Institute of San Diego, see Feldenkrais® Resources

Feldenkrais® Resources
3680 Sixth Ave, San Diego, CA 92103
Tel: 619-220-8776 *Toll Free Tel:* 800-765-1907 *Fax:* 619-330-4993
E-mail: info@feldenkraisresources.com
Web Site: feldenkraisresources.com
Key Personnel
Founder & Educ Dir: Elizabeth Beringer
Sales Dir: Ryan Etzel
Off Mgr: Deirdre O'Shea
Somatic education organization & publisher of audio home programs & DVDs by Moshe Feldenkrais & other Feldenkrais teachers.
Online catalog(s) available
Branch Office(s)
Feldenkrais® Resources Training Institute, 830 Bancroft Way, Suite 112, Berkeley, CA 94710 *Tel:* 510-540-7600 *Web Site:* frtiberkeley.com
Feldenkrais® Institute of New York, 134 W 26 St, 2nd fl, New York, NY 10001 *Tel:* 212-727-1014 *Web Site:* www.feldenkraisinstitute.com

Fender Musical Instruments Corp
17600 N Perimeter Dr, Suite 100, Scottsdale, AZ 85255
Tel: 480-596-9690 *Toll Free Tel:* 800-856-9801 (consumer rel)
E-mail: consumerrelations@fender.com
Web Site: www.fender.com
Key Personnel
Chief Mktg Offr: Evan Jones
Founded: 1946

Design & manufacture musical instruments.
Catalog(s) available

Ferrari Color®, see Signs.com

Ferrari Productions
13323 Deer Canyon Place, San Diego, CA 92129
Tel: 858-354-8888
E-mail: info@ferrariproductions.com; sales@ferrariproductions.com
Web Site: www.ferrariproductions.com
Key Personnel
Owner: Phillip Ferrari *E-mail:* phil@ferrariproductions.com
Founded: 1989
AV production & staging, video production & editing.

Festival Films
6115 Chestnut Terr, Shorewood, MN 55331
Tel: 952-470-2172
E-mail: fesfilms@aol.com
Web Site: www.fesfilms.com
Key Personnel
Pres: Ron Hall
Founded: 1976
Distribute public domain feature films & 1950s TV shows.
Catalog(s) available

Fiber Optic Cable Shop
Affiliate of Support Systems International Corp
136 S Second St, Richmond, CA 94804
Tel: 510-234-9090 *Toll Free Tel:* 800-777-6269 *Fax:* 510-233-8888
E-mail: sales@fibermailbox.com
Web Site: www.fiberopticcableshop.com
Key Personnel
Gen Mgr: Ben Parsons
Founded: 1976
Manufactures & distributes custom & standard fiber optic cable assemblies, media converters, switches, patch panels, enclosures & associated equipment.

Fiber Optic Systems Inc (FOSI)
2 Railroad Ave, Whitehouse Station, NJ 08889
Tel: 908-534-5500 *Toll Free Tel:* 800-809-3674 *Fax:* 908-534-2272
E-mail: info@fosi.com
Web Site: www.fosi.com
Key Personnel
Owner: Cyr A Ryan
Founded: 1970
Design & manufacture interactive fiber optic exhibits, optic lighting & special effects.
Catalog(s) available

Fiddler Films
1111 Fifth Ave S, Naples, FL 34102
Tel: 239-435-1818
E-mail: lou@fiddlerfilms.com
Web Site: www.fiddlerfilms.com
Provides rental of facilities & lighting. Offers DVD & Blu-ray production, aerial & underwater shooting & voice-over casting; from pre-production to post-production.

FIDM Productions
Division of Fashion Institute of Design & Merchandising
919 S Grand Ave, Los Angeles, CA 90015-1421
Tel: 213-624-1201 *Toll Free Tel:* 800-624-1200 *Fax:* 213-624-4799
Web Site: fidm.edu
Key Personnel
Exec Dir: Gene Lebrock
Founded: 1969

5th Floor Recording Co
316 N Milwaukee St, Suite 501, Milwaukee, WI 53202
Tel: 414-276-1919 *Fax:* 414-271-6621
Web Site: www.5thfloorrecording.com
Key Personnel
Owner & Engr: Ray Fister *Tel:* 414-412-4056 (cell) *E-mail:* ray@5thfloorrecording.com
Founded: 1997
Offers professional commercial & industrial audio for advertising agencies as well as the corporate world. Produce TV & radio commercials, industrial DVD/videos & original music.

FILM Archives Inc
35 W 35 St, Suite 904, New York, NY 10001-2238
Tel: 212-696-2616 *Fax:* 503-210-9927
E-mail: info@filmarchivesonline.com
Web Site: www.filmarchivesonline.com
Key Personnel
Founding Partner & Pres: Mark Trost
Founded: 1988
Stock footage library.
Online catalog(s) available

Film Creations Ltd
4349 E Fifth St, Tucson, AZ 85711
Tel: 520-624-4444 *Toll Free Tel:* 888-877-2490
    Fax: 520-624-9659
E-mail: info@filmcreations.com
Web Site: www.filmcreations.com
Key Personnel
Pres & CEO: Richard A Rose *E-mail:* rarose@filmcreations.com
Prodr & Dir: Will Hunter *E-mail:* will@filmcreations.com
Post-Prodn Supv & Ed: Steven Koeppen
    E-mail: steve@filmcreations.com
Founded: 1978
Full service video production company. Specialize in corporate videos, promotional videos & commercials, politics & government, educational & training videos, documentaries, fundraiser & event videos & creative video editing.

Film Emporium
1890 Palmer Ave, Suite 403, Larchmont, NY 10538
Tel: 914-833-2433 *Toll Free Tel:* 800-371-2555
    Fax: 914-833-2430
E-mail: info@filmemporium.com
Web Site: www.filmemporium.com
Founded: 1995
Motion picture film stock, video/audio tape & production insurance. Competitive rates.

Film House Inc
810 Dominican Dr, Nashville, TN 37228
Tel: 615-255-4000 *Fax:* 615-255-4111
E-mail: results@filmhouse.com
Web Site: www.filmhouse.com
Key Personnel
CEO: Curt Hahn
CFO: Andy Cohen
Dir, Post-Prodn: Dave Donnelly
    E-mail: davedonnelly@filmhouse.com
Founded: 1976
Film production company-movies, television commercials, films for the US government, feature length documentaries, corporate & real estate videos.

Film Ideas Inc
308 N Wolf Rd, Wheeling, IL 60090
Tel: 847-419-0255 *Toll Free Tel:* 800-475-3456
    (US only) *Fax:* 847-419-8933
E-mail: info@filmideas.com; orders@filmideas.com (cust serv)
Web Site: www.filmideas.com

Key Personnel
Mng Dir: Bob Norris *E-mail:* bobn@filmideas.com
Dir, Busn Devt & Acqs: Chris Collins
    E-mail: chrisc@filmideas.com
Sales Mgr: Paul Molidor *E-mail:* paulm@filmideas.com
Regl Sales Mgr: Evan Hirsh *E-mail:* evanh@filmideas.com
Founded: 1979
DVD, digital rights, hosted streaming, broadcast (HD).
Online catalog(s) available
Membership(s): Consortium of College & University Media Centers; National Association of Media & Technology Centers

The Film-Makers' Cooperative
Division of New American Cinema Group Inc
475 Park Ave S, 6th fl, New York, NY 10016
Tel: 212-267-5665
E-mail: filmmakerscoop@gmail.com; info@film-makerscoop.com
Web Site: film-makerscoop.com
Key Personnel
Exec Dir: MM Serra
Founded: 1961
Distributor of independent & avant-garde films.
Online catalog(s) available
Membership(s): National Association of Media Arts Centers

Film Marketing Services Inc
4640 Admiralty Way, Suite 500, Marina del Rey, CA 90292
E-mail: info@filmmarketingservices.com
Web Site: filmmarketingservices.com
Distribution consultant.

Film Police
Division of Koch/Marshall Productions Inc
2558 W 16 St, Chicago, IL 60608
Tel: 773-463-4010
E-mail: info@filmpolice.com
Web Site: www.filmpolice.com
Key Personnel
Pres: Phillip Koch *E-mail:* phil@filmpolice.com
VP: Sally Marschall *E-mail:* sally@filmpolice.com
Founded: 1980
Full service film & video production company specializing in high quality programs.
Membership(s): DGA; Independent Feature Project

Film TV Sound
Division of EQE Media & Consulting Group
PO Box 950207, Mission Hills, CA 91395-0207
Tel: 818-231-1038 *Fax:* 818-892-9236
E-mail: editorial@filmtvsound.com; eqe-media@filmtvsound.com
Web Site: www.filmtvsound.com
Key Personnel
Pres: Fred Ginsburg
Educational web site for production sound & video production. Tips, tricks, tutorials. Workshops & seminars. Online articles & tutorials available.
Membership(s): Cinema Audio Society; Law Enforcement Video Association; University Film & Video Association

Filmaker Technology
606 W Broad St, Bethlehem, PA 18018
Tel: 610-691-0900 *Fax:* 610-691-0952
E-mail: enquire@filmaker.com
Web Site: www.filmaker.com
Key Personnel
Pres & CTO: Robin Miller
Founded: 1970

Provides consulting engineering services in immersive entertainment technology applied research, surround audio recording, production & exhibition systems design & integration & marketing communications.
Membership(s): AES; SMPTE®

Filmakers Library
Division of Alexander Street, a ProQuest Company
3212 Duke St, Alexandria, VA 22314
Tel: 703-212-8520
E-mail: sales@alexanderstreet.com; orders@alexanderstreet.com; info@alexanderstreet.com
Web Site: www.academicvideostore.com; www.academicvideostore.com/filmakers
Key Personnel
Dir: Andrea Traubner
Educational distributors.
Online catalog(s) available
Membership(s): AFVA; ALA; Consortium of College & University Media Centers; National Association of Media & Technology Centers; New York Film/Video Council; New York Women in Film & Television

Filmlites Montana
6465 River Rd, Bozeman, MT 59718
Tel: 406-587-0226 *Fax:* 406-551-4555
E-mail: info@filmlitesmt.com
Web Site: www.filmlitesmt.com
Key Personnel
Founder & Dir: J P Gabriel
Founded: 1989
Film & video production rental equipment; HD video/film production; events & lighting.

FilmNation Entertainment
150 W 22 St, 9th fl, New York, NY 10011
Web Site: www.filmnation.com
Key Personnel
CEO: Glen Basner
COO: Milan Popelka
Co-Pres, Prodn & Acqs: Aaron Ryder; Ben Browning
EVP, Mktg & Dist: Richard Baker
EVP, Prodn: Karen Lunder
EVP, Post-Prodn: Mike Jackman
SVP, Intl Dist Servs: Stefan Zorich
SVP, Mktg & Dist: Pauline Piechota
VP: Patrick Chu
VP, Sales: Robert Carney
Dir, Publicity: Selena Saldana
Coord, Mktg, Publicity & Dist: Colby Leopard
Founded: 2008
Film production company & international film sales agent.
Branch Office(s)
6430 W Sunset Blvd, Suite 1025, Los Angeles, CA 90028

Films by Huey
103 Montrose Ave, Portland, ME 04103
Tel: 207-773-1130
E-mail: huey@filmsbyhuey.com
Web Site: www.filmsbyhuey.com
Key Personnel
Dir: James "Huey" Coleman
Award winning independent film & video producer. Conducts workshops & residencies as a teaching artist for K-12 schools & educators.

Films Media Group
Division of Infobase Learning
132 W 31 St, 16th fl, New York, NY 10001
Toll Free Tel: 800-322-8755 *Toll Free Fax:* 800-678-3633
E-mail: custserv@films.com
Web Site: www.films.com
DVDs & streaming video on academic, vocational & life skills topics.
Online catalog(s) available

Filmtools®
Division of Moviola
1400 W Burbank Blvd, Burbank, CA 91506
Tel: 818-845-8066 *Toll Free Tel:* 888-807-1900
  Fax: 818-845-4237
E-mail: sales@filmtools.com; customerservice@
  filmtools.com
Web Site: www.filmtools.com
Key Personnel
Owner: Jorge Jimenez
Founded: 1986
Film production equipment including camera
  support, lighting, studio carts, grip, electrical,
  recordable media, hard drive & memory card
  storage, audio equipment & on-set expendables.
Online catalog(s) available
Branch Office(s)
4514 Vanowen St, Burbank, CA 91505 (ware-
  house)

FilmWorks Pacific
PO Box 61281, Honolulu, HI 96839-1281
Tel: 808-221-2255
E-mail: studio@filmworkspacific.com
Web Site: filmworkspacific.com
Key Personnel
Writer & Dir: Edgy Lee
Develop, produce & package film, television pro-
  gramming, commercials, music & books for
  domestic & international distribution.
Membership(s): Association of Commercial Stock
  Image Licensors

Final Draft, A Cast & Crew Company
2300 Empire Ave, Burbank, CA 91504
Tel: 818-995-8995; 818-906-8930 (tech support)
  Toll Free Tel: 800-231-4055
E-mail: info@finaldraft.com
Web Site: www.finaldraft.com
Key Personnel
Pres: Scott McMenamin
VP, Prod Devt: Joe Jarvis
VP, Sales & Mktg: Shelly Mellott
VP, Tech Support: Joel Levin
Founded: 1990
Screenwriting software design, production &
  sales.

Fingerpaint
13 Walker Way, Albany, NY 12205
Tel: 518-869-1968
Web Site: fingerpaintmarketing.com
Key Personnel
Audio & Video Servs: Margherita Petti Krug
  Tel: 518-693-6960 ext 3002 *E-mail:* mkrug@
  fingerpaintmarketing.com
Founded: 2008
Full service marketing agency. Services include
  brand & product development, strategic plan-
  ning, digital & multichannel marketing, audio
  & video production, social media, public rela-
  tions & brand journalism.
Branch Office(s)
395 Broadway, Saratoga Springs, NY 12866
Membership(s): The Ad Club; Alliance for
  Women in Media; AMA; SPARS

Stuart Finley Films
3428 Mansfield Rd, Falls Church, VA 22041
Tel: 703-820-7700
Key Personnel
Pres: Robert Finley *E-mail:* rsf@finfam.com
Stock footage.
Catalog(s) available

Fire Power Music LLC
3400 S Mill Ave, No 29, Tempe, AZ 85282
Tel: 602-463-2988
Key Personnel
CEO: Douglas Robertson

Founded: 2005
Recording studio specializing in all types of music & vocal presentation. Also provide PA
  rentals & audio consultation.

Fire Station Studios
224 N Guadalupe St, San Marcos, TX 78666
Tel: 512-396-1144 *Fax:* 512-396-1169
E-mail: info@firestationstudios.com
Web Site: www.firestationstudios.com
Key Personnel
Studio Mgr: Mark C Erickson *E-mail:* mark@
  firestationstudios.com
Engr: Gary Hickinbotham *E-mail:* gary@
  firestationstudios.com

Firehouse Studios
1545 W Rosemont Ave, Chicago, IL 60660
Tel: 773-271-3100
E-mail: folks@firehousestudios.com
Web Site: firehousestudios.com
Studio, lighting, video & audio equipment rentals
  & crew.

First Camera
2472 Third St, San Francisco, CA 94107
Tel: 415-647-3400 *Fax:* 415-647-3410
E-mail: sfvideo@firstcamera.com
Web Site: www.firstcamera.com
Key Personnel
Owner: Vaughn Kilgore *E-mail:* vaughn@
  firstcamera.com
Video production & equipment rental.

First Cut Communications LLC
301 W Broome St, Suite 100, LaGrange, GA
  30240
Mailing Address: PO Box 49, LaGrange, GA
  30241
Tel: 706-882-5581 *Fax:* 706-407-4528
E-mail: info@firstcutcommunications.com
Web Site: www.firstcutcommunications.com
Key Personnel
Client Devt Mgmt & Opers: Matt French
Video production. Specialize in contract negoti-
  ations, employee orientations/onboarding, employee benefits, labor relations, positive employee relations, plant tours, sales meetings,
  training, union avoidance & web sites.

1st Financial Training Services Inc
1515 E Woodfield Rd, Suite 345, Schaumburg, IL
  60173
Tel: 847-969-0900 *Toll Free Tel:* 800-442-8662
  Fax: 847-969-0521
E-mail: info@1stfinancialtraining.com
Web Site: www.1stfinancialtraining.com
Key Personnel
Pres: Bonnie Eidsin
Founded: 1986
Streaming video e-learning, DVD video & print
  training solutions for banks & credit unions.
Catalog(s) available

First Person Inc
550 Bryant St, San Francisco, CA 94107
Tel: 415-495-5595
E-mail: hi@firstperson.is
Web Site: firstperson.is
Key Personnel
Pres & CEO: Drew Fiero
Chief, Busn Devt: Brandon Grande
Exec Creative Dir: Marcello Grande
Founded: 2013
Creative design agency providing interactive &
  visual technology for building & maintaining
  brand relevance.
Brochure(s) available
Membership(s): AICP; San Francisco Ad Club

First Run Features
The Film Center Bldg, Suite 1213, 630 Ninth
  Ave, New York, NY 10036-3708
Tel: 212-243-0600 *Fax:* 212-989-7649
E-mail: info@firstrunfeatures.com
Web Site: www.firstrunfeatures.com
Key Personnel
Pres: Seymour Wishman
VP, Home Media Sales: John Bione
Dir, Theatrical Bookings: Marc Mauceri
Founded: 1979
Independent film distributor.
Catalog(s) available
Membership(s): Entertainment Merchants Associ-
  ation

1st Wave Productions
2017 Pacific Ave, Venice, CA 90291
Tel: 310-279-7059
Web Site: www.1stwaveproductions.com
Key Personnel
Owner: Luann Barry *E-mail:* luann@
  1stwaveproductions.com
Founded: 1999
Production services, co-production & office space.

FirstCom Music
Division of Universal Publishing Production Mu-
  sic
14860 Montfort Dr, Suite 260, Dallas, TX 75254
Tel: 972-446-8742 *Toll Free Tel:* 800-858-8880
E-mail: info@firstcom.com; musicsearch@
  firstcom.com
Web Site: www.firstcom.com
Key Personnel
Exec Prodr: Ken Nelson
VP, Sales & Mktg: Billy Stover *Tel:* 972-389-
  2822 *E-mail:* billy.stover@firstcom.com
Sr Dir, Mktg: Cristy Coffey *E-mail:* cristyc@
  firstcom.com
Sr Music Dir: John Lentz
Founded: 1980
Provider of production music for film, broadcast,
  digital media & corporate productions. Mu-
  sic collection is comprised of 48 labels & over
  275,000 titles available for licensing.
Online catalog(s) available
Branch Office(s)
2110 Colorado Ave, Santa Monica, CA 90404
  Tel: 310-865-4437
1755 Broadway, No 6, New York, NY 10019
  Tel: 212-333-1330
Membership(s): Dallas Producers Association;
  Guild of Music Supervisors; Independent Doc-
  umentary Association; NAB; Production Music
  Association; Promax

FirstGeneration Audio/Visual Services
410 Allentown Dr, Allentown, PA 18109
Tel: 610-437-4300 *Fax:* 610-437-3200
E-mail: information@firstgencom.com; contact@
  firstgencom.com
Web Site: www.firstgencom.com
Key Personnel
Dir, New Technol: Steve White
Sr Prodr/Dir: John Costello
Sr Ed: Wayne Persing
Equipment rentals - audio, data projection &
  video, event lighting & general presentation
  AV.

Fish Films Footage World
4548 Van Noord Ave, Studio City, CA 91604
Tel: 818-905-1071
E-mail: footageworld@aol.com
Web Site: www.footageworld.com
Key Personnel
Pres: David Fishbein
Off Mgr: Gloria Lopez
Online catalog(s) available

FitzCo Sound Inc
4300 W Wall St, Bldg B, Midland, TX 79703

Mailing Address: PO Box 10645, Midland, TX
 79702
Tel: 432-684-0861 *Fax:* 432-682-9978
Web Site: www.fitzcosound.com
Key Personnel
Owner: Milt Hathaway
Founded: 1981

5 Alarm Music
Division of Anthem Entertainment
3500 W Olive Ave, Suite 810, Burbank, CA
 91505
Tel: 626-304-1698 *Toll Free Tel:* 800-322-7879
 Fax: 626-795-2058
E-mail: info@5alarmmusic.com
Web Site: www.5alarmmusic.com
Key Personnel
Dir, Opers: TerriLynn Massey *Tel:* 626-304-1698
 ext 5542 *E-mail:* terrilynn@rescuerecords.net
Gen Mgr: J D Adams *Tel:* 626-304-1698 ext
 5511 *E-mail:* jd@5alarmmusic.com
Founded: 1997
Production music library.
Catalog(s) available, licensed library
Membership(s): Association of Independent Mu-
 sic Publishers; The Imaging Alliance

FJ Productions Inc
14900 Ventura Blvd, Suite 350, Sherman Oaks,
 CA 91403-3465
Tel: 818-788-0153
E-mail: contact@fjproductions.com
Web Site: www.fjproductions.com
Key Personnel
SVP, Unscripted Devt: Johnny Healey
Exec Prodr: Fabio Golombek *Tel:* 818-788-0153
 ext 16 *E-mail:* fgolombek@fjproductions.com
Full service film & television production com-
 pany.

FJW Optical Systems Inc
322 N Woodwork Lane, Palatine, IL 60067-4933
Tel: 847-358-2500 *Toll Free Tel:* 800-355-4FJW
 (355-4359) *Fax:* 847-358-2533
E-mail: irsales@findrscope.com
Web Site: www.findrscope.com
Key Personnel
Pres: Barry F Warzak
Founded: 1945
Manufacture infrared video camera.
Online catalog(s) available

FlagHouse
601 Flaghouse Dr, Hasbrouck Heights, NJ 07604-
 3116
Tel: 201-288-7600 *Toll Free Tel:* 800-793-7900
 Fax: 201-288-7887 *Toll Free Fax:* 800-793-
 7922
E-mail: sales@flaghouse.com; info@flaghouse.
 com
Web Site: www.flaghouse.com
Key Personnel
Owner: George Carmel
COO: Douglas Carmel
Founded: 1954
Products for multi-sensory environments, includ-
 ing music systems, DVDs, black lights, fiber
 optics, interactive panels, lighting effects, pro-
 jectors & accessories.
Catalog(s) available, free, by request
Online catalog(s) available

Flash Electronics Inc
Brooklyn Army Terminal, Suite 1-A, Mail Box 3,
 140 58 St, Brooklyn, NY 11220
Tel: 718-492-4040 *Toll Free Tel:* 800-831-3127
 Fax: 718-492-4590
E-mail: customercare@flashdistributors.com
Web Site: www.flashdistributors.com
Key Personnel
Pres: Steven V Scavelli

VP: Frank Rampino
Catalog(s) available
Membership(s): Entertainment Merchants Associ-
 ation

Flashback Media Productions
Division of Strassner Media Group LLC
1172 Lombardi St, Erie, CO 80516
Tel: 303-545-9955
E-mail: info@flashbackmedia.tv
Web Site: www.flashbackmedia.tv
Key Personnel
COO: Norman Strassner
Pres: Bunnie Strassner *E-mail:* bunnie@
 flashbackmedia.tv
Founded: 1987
Video & film production services.

Flashback Stage Lighting (FBSL)
1124 Bay Blvd, Suite A, Chula Vista, CA 91911-
 7155
Tel: 619-697-2729 *Fax:* 619-697-2782
E-mail: mail@flashbackstagelighting.com
Web Site: flashbackstagelighting.com
Key Personnel
Pres: Matthew Short
Founded: 1979
Event lighting & rigging company.
Online catalog(s) available

Flat Town Music Co
Division of Swallow Publications Inc
700 S Chataignier St, Ville Platte, LA 70586
Mailing Address: PO Drawer 10, Ville Platte, LA
 70586-0010
Tel: 337-363-2177 *Toll Free Tel:* 800-738-8668
 Fax: 337-363-2094
E-mail: info@flattownmusic.com; order@
 flattownmusic.com
Web Site: www.flattownmusic.com
Key Personnel
Pres: Floyd Soileau
Founded: 1957
Music libraries, Cajun, Zydeco, Swamp-Pop.
Online catalog(s) available

Doug Fleenor Design Inc
396 Corbett Canyon Rd, Arroyo Grande, CA
 93420
Tel: 805-481-9599 *Toll Free Tel:* 888-436-9512
 Fax: 805-481-9599
E-mail: info@dfd.com
Web Site: www.dfd.com
Key Personnel
Pres: Doug Fleenor
Cont: Cindy Fleenor *E-mail:* cindy@dfd.com
Opers Mgr: Matt Walker *E-mail:* matt@dfd.com
Founded: 1990
Manufacture lighting control equipment.

Fleetwood Group Inc
11832 James St, Holland, MI 49424
Mailing Address: PO Box 1259, Holland, MI
 49422-1259
Tel: 616-396-1142 *Toll Free Tel:* 800-257-6390
 Fax: 616-820-8300
Web Site: www.fleetwoodgroup.com;
 www.fleetwoodelectronics.com; www.
 fleetwoodfurniture.com
Key Personnel
Pres & CEO: Jason Grant
VP, Engg: Brian Harvey
VP, Opers: Travis Wilson
Prodn Mgr: Kerri Courson
Electronics design & low-power electronic device
 manufacturing. Furniture manufacturer part-
 nering with schools to create effective learning
 environments.

Flight Form Cases Inc
Division of AW Enterprises Inc

6543 S Laramie Ave, Bedford Park, IL 60638
Tel: 708-458-8989 *Toll Free Tel:* 800-334-4884
 Fax: 708-458-9023
Key Personnel
Pres: Edward Otrusina
Founded: 1962
Catalog(s) available
Membership(s): GAMMA; Music Distributors As-
 sociation; NAMM, the National Association of
 Music Merchants

Flip 2 Media Inc
1067 Serpentine Lane, Pleasanton, CA 94566-
 4759
Tel: 925-417-1420
E-mail: info@flip2media.com
Web Site: www.flip2media.com
Key Personnel
CTO: Doug Mann
Sr Prodr/Dir: Thaddeus Coburg
Dir, Post Prodn: Glen Shockley
Founded: 2014
Full service media & video production company
 offering content development, production, post-
 production & electronic file delivery. Also mar-
 keting & advertising services.

FLIR Systems Inc
27700 SW Parkway Ave, Wilsonville, OR 97070
Tel: 503-498-3547 *Toll Free Tel:* 800-322-3731
 Fax: 503-498-3904
Web Site: www.flir.com
Key Personnel
Mgr: Ashley Walker
Global leader in infrared technology.
Catalog(s) available
Branch Office(s)
25 Esquire Rd, North Billerica, MA 01862 *Toll
 Free Tel:* 800-464-6372
108 Kountz Lane, Freeport, PA 16229, Con-
 tact: Michael Matzko *Tel:* 724-295-2880
 E-mail: michael.matzko@flir.com
5230 S Service Rd, Suite 125, Burlington, ON
 L7L 5K2, Canada *Toll Free Tel:* 800-613-0507
Foreign Office(s): FLIR Systems AB, Anten-
 nvagen 6, 187 66 Taby, Sweden *Tel:* (08) 753
 2500 *Fax:* (08) 753 0752

Flo-Co, see The Fluorescent Co Inc

Florentine Films
136 E 56 St, Suite 4-B, New York, NY 10022
Tel: 212-980-5966 *Fax:* 212-980-5944
E-mail: Sherman.Pictures@florentinefilms.com
Web Site: www.florentinefilms.com/sherman
Key Personnel
Prodr & Dir: Roger Sherman *E-mail:* Roger.
 Sherman@florentinefilms.com
Founded: 1976
Catalog(s) available

Florical Systems Inc
Division of RCS Sound Software
4500 NW 27 Ave, Bldg B-1, Gainesville, FL
 32606
Tel: 352-372-8326 *Fax:* 352-375-0859
E-mail: sales@florical.com
Web Site: www.florical.com
Key Personnel
Pres & CEO: Philippe Generali
VP & Gen Mgr, Opers: Shawn Maynard
VP, R&D: Eric Piard
Founded: 1995
TV automation for TV stations & cable networks.
Membership(s): Alliance for IP Media Solutions

Florida Digital Studios
6677 13 Ave N, Suite 3C, St Petersburg, FL
 33710
Tel: 727-546-7900
Web Site: www.floridadigitalstudios.com

Key Personnel
Exec Prodr & Mng Partner: Jay Gross
Dir, Sales & Mktg: Kathy Fishback
E-mail: kathy@floridadigitalstudios.com
Founded: 1982
Studio & on location videography, motion graphics, 3D animation, DVD duplication.

Florida Film & Tape
3417 Lake Breeze Rd, Orlando, FL 32808
Tel: 407-297-0091
E-mail: info@ffandt.com
Web Site: ffandt.com
Key Personnel
Pres, Creative Dir & Exec Prodr: Brad Fuller
Tel: 310-491-1420 *E-mail:* brad@ffandt.com
Dir & Photog: Michael Fuller *Tel:* 407-257-8435
E-mail: mike.fuller@mikefullergroup.com
Dir, Photog: George Burkitt *Tel:* 407-421-6833
E-mail: gburkitt@ffandt.com
Dir, Videographer & Ed: Cleve Cooney *Tel:* 407-491-9786 *E-mail:* cleve@ffandt.com
Prodr, Stylist & Gen Mgr: Patti Miller *Tel:* 407-353-4848 *E-mail:* patti.miller@mikefullergroup.com
Founded: 1980
Video production & post-production. Specialize in aviation & marine photography & videos.

Florida Film & Video
4461 38 Way S, St Petersburg, FL 33711
Tel: 727-369-0732
E-mail: info@flhd.tv
Web Site: www.flhd.tv
Key Personnel
Pres: Bill Mills
Founded: 1985
Film & video production.

Fluke Corp
Subsidiary of Danaher Corp
6920 Seaway Blvd, Everett, WA 98203
Mailing Address: PO Box 9090, Everett, WA 98206-9090
Tel: 425-347-6100 *Toll Free Tel:* 800-443-5853
Fax: 425-446-5116
E-mail: fluke-info@fluke.com
Web Site: www.fluke.com
Key Personnel
PR Mgr: Leah Friberg
Electronics test & measurement company.
Catalog(s) available
Foreign Office(s): PO Box 1186, Eindhoven, Netherlands *Tel:* (040) 267 5200 *Fax:* (040) 267 5222

The Fluorescent Co Inc
c/o Red*D*Mix Rentals Inc, 388 Carlaw Ave, Suite 116, Toronto, ON M4M 2T4, Canada
Tel: 416-879-3761 *Fax:* 905-681-8520
E-mail: reddmix@cogeco.ca
Web Site: www.flo-co.com
Key Personnel
Visual Effects Prodr & Supv: Ray McMillan
Manufacture specialty fluorescent lighting for motion picture, TV & entertainment industries.
Catalog(s) available

Flying Colors Broadcasts
2000 "M" St NW, Suite 345, Washington, DC 20036
Tel: 202-293-5300
E-mail: info@fc-tv.com
Web Site: www.fc-tv.com
Key Personnel
Co-Owner & Pres: Constance Chatfield-Taylor
Co-Owner & VP: Lynn Knieriem
Dir, Prodn & Mktg: Erin Powers
Sales & Satellite Servs Dir: Susan Chavarria
Specialize in video production, live domestic & international event broadcasts, business television networks & broadcasting.

FM Systems Inc
3877 S Main St, Santa Ana, CA 92707
Tel: 714-979-3355 *Toll Free Tel:* 800-235-6960
Fax: 714-979-0913
E-mail: fmsystemsinc@sbcglobal.net
Web Site: www.fmsystems-inc.com
Key Personnel
COO: Donald McClatchie
Pres: Frank McClatchie
Founded: 1978
Catalog(s) available

FMP Media Solutions Inc
3600 Horizon Dr, Suite 180, King of Prussia, PA 19406
Tel: 610-825-4000 *Toll Free Tel:* 800-346-5071
Fax: 610-825-4430
E-mail: info@fmpmedia.com
Web Site: www.fmpmedia.com
Key Personnel
Pres: Ronald Giannone
VP, Creative Media: Don Cox
Dir, FMP Langs Translation/Narration: Bill Groce
Founded: 1966
Digital media & event production company that develops visually-driven business communications for their clients. Outfit productions & video shoots but do not rent equipment without providing management & staff.
Catalog(s) available
Membership(s): AFI; SMPTE®

Focus Features
Division of NBCUniversal
100 Universal City Plaza, Bldg 2160, Suite 7-C, Los Angeles, CA 90068
Web Site: www.focusfeatures.com
Founded: 2002
Branch Office(s)
c/o NBCUniversal, 30 Rockefeller Plaza, Bldg 5TS, 10th fl, New York, NY 10112

Focus on Animals
Division of National Humane Education Society (NHES)
PO Box 340, Charles Town, WV 25414-0340
Tel: 304-725-0506 *Fax:* 304-725-1523
E-mail: information@nhes.org; education@nhes.org
Web Site: www.nhes.org
Key Personnel
Devt Coord: Amanda Bowers
Founded: 1948
Educational videos & films for people with a reverence for life, animal rights & welfare issues.
Catalog(s) available, free

Folk-Legacy, see Smithsonian Folkways Recordings

Follett School Solutions Inc
Division of Follett Corporation
1340 Ridgeview Dr, McHenry, IL 60050
Tel: 815-759-1700 *Toll Free Tel:* 888-511-5114 (cust serv); 877-899-8550 (sales) *Fax:* 815-759-9831 *Toll Free Fax:* 800-852-5458
E-mail: info@follettlearning.com; customerservice@follett.com
Web Site: www.follettlearning.com; www.follett.com/prek12; www.titlewave.com
Key Personnel
EVP: Britten Follett
Sales Exec: Erica Moore
Digital resources, ebooks & AV materials to PreK-12 libraries, classrooms, learning centers & school districts.
Online catalog(s) available

The Food & Beverage Institute
Division of The Culinary Institute of America
1946 Campus Dr, Hyde Park, NY 12538
Tel: 845-452-9600 *Toll Free Tel:* 800-888-7850
Fax: 845-451-1078
E-mail: ciachef@culinary.edu
Web Site: www.ciachef.edu; www.ciaprochef.com
Catalog(s) available

FootageBank HD
13470 Washington Blvd, Suite 210, Marina del Rey, CA 90292
Tel: 310-822-1400 *Fax:* 310-822-4100
E-mail: info@footagebank.com
Web Site: www.footagebank.com
Key Personnel
Founder & Pres: Paula Lumbard *Tel:* 310-822-1400 ext 105 *E-mail:* paulal@footagebank.com
VP: Carol Martin *Tel:* 310-822-1400 ext 102
E-mail: carolm@footagebank.com
Content Coord & Off Mgr: Erik Dahlgren *Tel:* 310-822-1400 ext 107 *E-mail:* erikd@footagebank.com
Founded: 2002
Supplier of large format & HD images to television, theatrical, mobile, independent & corporate media buyers.

Foothill Digital Inc
217 Storer Ave, New Rochelle, NY 10801
Tel: 914-235-5670
E-mail: info@foothilldigital.com
Web Site: www.foothilldigital.com; www.tuckersound.com
Key Personnel
Owner: Allan Tucker *E-mail:* tucker@foothilldigital.com
Founded: 1988
Digital mastering & authoring for CD & DVD.

For-A Corp of America
Subsidiary of For-A Co Ltd
11155 Knott Ave, Suite G & H, Cypress, CA 90630
Tel: 714-894-3311 *Fax:* 714-894-5399
E-mail: info@for-a.com
Web Site: www.for-a.com
Key Personnel
Pres: Ken Truong
Manufacturer & distributor of AV systems.
Catalog(s) available
Branch Office(s)
2400 NE Waldo Rd, Gainesville, FL 32609-3329
Tel: 352-371-1505 (support ctr)
1360 Clifton Ave, Clifton, NJ 07012 *Tel:* 973-220-8471
Membership(s): Audiovisual and Integrated Experience Association; NAB

Ford Audio-Video LLC, see Ford AV

Ford AV
4800 W Interstate 40, Oklahoma City, OK 73128
Tel: 405-946-9966 *Toll Free Tel:* 800-654-6744
Web Site: www.fordav.com
Key Personnel
Pres: James A Ford
Founded: 1973
Commercial AV integrator.
Online catalog(s) available
Branch Office(s)
8349 E 51 St, Tulsa, OK 74145 *Tel:* 918-664-2420
920 E Madison St, Phoenix, AZ 85034 *Tel:* 602-643-4200
48551 Warm Springs Blvd, Fremont, CA 94539
4230 Carson St, Denver, CO 80239 *Tel:* 720-374-2345
2180 Satellite Blvd, Duluth, GA 30097
Daniel K Inouye Intl Airport, Honolulu, HI 96819
4640 Forbes Blvd, Lanham, MD 20706
6255 S Sandhill Rd, Las Vegas, NV 89120
Tel: 702-369-9965

341 Rte 168 S, Turnersville, NJ 08012
200 Park Ave, New York, NY 10166 *Tel:* 646-354-6519
7901 E Riverside Dr, Suite 125, Austin, TX 78744 *Tel:* 512-447-1103
4380 Blalock Rd, Houston, TX 77041 *Tel:* 713-690-0555
4901 Statesman Dr, Irving, TX 75063-2412 *Tel:* 972-241-9966
Greater Salt Lake City Area, Salt Lake City, UT 84101 *Tel:* 801-401-9966

Forensic Video Deposition Service
11111 N Scottsdale Rd, Suite 205, Scottsdale, AZ 85254
Tel: 602-840-1222 *Fax:* 480-360-1421
E-mail: office@forensicvideo.net
Web Site: forensicvideo.net
Key Personnel
Pres: John Lynch *E-mail:* jlynch@forensicvideo.net
Legal video & video conferencing.

Foresight Imaging
One Executive Dr, Suite 202, Chelmsford, MA 01824
Tel: 978-458-4624 *Fax:* 978-458-5488
E-mail: info@fi-llc.com
Web Site: www.fi-llc.com
Key Personnel
Co-Founder, Pres/CEO: Mark Mariotti
Co-Founder, VP, Engg: Jack Melville
Co-Founder, VP, Sales & Mktg: Tony Molinari
Co-Owner, VP, Procurement & Mfg: Mike Carroll
Founded: 1985
Specializes in frame grabbers & video streamers.
Catalog(s) available

Forge Recording LLC
100 Mill Rd, Oreland, PA 19075
Tel: 215-885-7000 *Fax:* 215-887-3501
E-mail: info@forgerecording.com
Web Site: www.forgerecording.com
Founded: 1979
Recording & duplication services.
Catalog(s) available

Forte Productions
PO Box 17, San Geronimo, CA 94963-0325
Tel: 415-488-9446 *Fax:* 415-488-9446
Web Site: www.pianovideos.com
Key Personnel
Pres: Talc Tolchin *E-mail:* talc.tolchin@gmail.com
Catalog(s) available

48 Windows
1661 N Lincoln Blvd, Suite 220, Santa Monica, CA 90404
Tel: 310-392-9545 *Fax:* 310-392-9445
E-mail: ziv@48windows.com
Web Site: www.48windows.com
Key Personnel
Pres & Owner: Eric Garcia *E-mail:* ericg@48windows.com
Mng Partner: Ziv Fisher

J E Foss Co
3328-B Industrial Blvd, Bethel Park, PA 15102
Mailing Address: PO Box 357, Bethel Park, PA 15102-0357
Tel: 412-564-5644 *Toll Free Tel:* 800-245-6240
Fax: 412-564-5646
E-mail: jefoss@earthlink.net
Web Site: www.jefoss.com
Key Personnel
Pres: Gary Spezialetti
Founded: 1925
Multimedia projectors.
Catalog(s) available

FotoKem
Division of Foto-Kem Industries Inc
2801 W Alameda Ave, Burbank, CA 91505
Tel: 818-846-3101 *Toll Free Tel:* 800-FOTOKEM (368-6536)
E-mail: info@fotokem.com
Web Site: www.fotokem.com
Key Personnel
Pres: William F Brodersen
Founded: 1963
Full service motion picture & video post-production facility: 35mm & 16mm film processing, answer prints, digital intermediates, preservation & restoration, telecine, duplication, scanning & recording, HD transfers, DVD pre-mastering & tape-to-film transfer.
Branch Office(s)
6855 Santa Monica Blvd, Hollywood, CA 90038 *Tel:* 818-441-5100; 818-441-5111 (tech support) (nonlinear servs)
1661 Lincoln Blvd, No 240, Santa Monica, CA 90404 *Tel:* 818-846-3101
715 Peachtree St NE, Suite 150, Atlanta, GA 30308 *Tel:* 404-334-3660
800 Richard St, Suite 2R, New Orleans, LA 70130 *Tel:* 504-299-4545

FOTON Hawaii
98-021 Kamehameha Hwy, Aiea, HI 96701
Tel: 808-206-5244
E-mail: rentals@fotonhawaii.com
Web Site: www.fotonhawaii.com
Lighting & grip rentals, serving the needs of professional photographers & still photo shoots. Other services include photo assistant referral, studio rental, motorhomes & production supplies.

Fotosearch Stock Photography
21155 Watertown Rd, Waukesha, WI 53186
Tel: 262-717-0740 *Toll Free Tel:* 800-827-3920
Fax: 262-717-0745
E-mail: fotosearch@fotosearch.com
Web Site: www.fotosearch.com
Provider of royalty free & rights managed stock photography, illustrations & audio.

Four Corners Productions
101 W 90 St, No 6J, New York, NY 10024
Tel: 212-228-6492 *Fax:* 212-228-6492
Web Site: www.operatitles.net; www.gracepaleyvideo.com
Key Personnel
Owner: Sonya Friedman *E-mail:* friedman4c@verizon.net
Opera supertitles. Subtitles for film & video. Producer & director for film & video.
Membership(s): New York Women in Film & Television

4-D Creative Media
16 W 46 St, 12th fl, New York, NY 10036
Tel: 646-483-7768
Web Site: www.4-dcreative.com
Key Personnel
Owner & Pres: Rob Carbone
Exec Prodr: Peter Cascone *E-mail:* peter@4-dcreative.com
Ed/Prodr: Michael Griffin
Creative production film/video. Avid, Final Cut Pro, Combustion, Hal, Digi Beta Deck & Davinci Premier. Branch office in Madrid, Spain.
Online catalog(s) available, NY411 Production Guide

411 Video Information
PO Box 1223, Pebble Beach, CA 93953-1223
Tel: 408-671-2859 (cell)
Web Site: www.411videoinfo.com
Key Personnel
Pres: Leslie McClure *E-mail:* leslie@411videoinfo.com
Founded: 1988
Health & fitness, how-to, special interest, theatrical & non-theatrical video sales & marketing, as well as DVD, CD-ROM, VHS, Blu-ray, Internet, etc. Publicity, marketing & consulting.
Online catalog(s) available
Shipping Address: 81 Cuesta Vista Dr, Monterey, CA 93940

4 Wall Entertainment
3165 W Sunset Rd, Suite 100, Las Vegas, NV 89118
Tel: 702-263-3858 *Toll Free Tel:* 877-789-8167 (Western US) *Fax:* 702-263-3863
E-mail: info@4wall.com; info@usedlighting.com
Web Site: www.4wall.com; www.usedlighting.com
Key Personnel
CEO: Kathy Cluxton
CFO: Marc Morris
Pres & COO: Wes Bailey
SVP, Busn Devt: Bob Gaynor
VP, Mktg & Sales: Dan Abdalla
Opers Mgr: Bob Velasquez
Founded: 1999
Provider of architectural & entertainment lighting systems - including rentals, sales, service, design, consultation & project management.
Branch Office(s)
5435 W San Fernando Rd, Los Angeles, CA 90039, Opers Mgr: Hector Lasso *Tel:* 818-252-7481 *Fax:* 818-252-7642
9652 Oak Crossing Rd, Suite 800, Orlando, FL 32837, Opers Mgr: Ami-Jo Mazur *Tel:* 407-850-5959 *Fax:* 407-965-4094
5607 Hiatus Rd, Suite 500, Tamarac, FL 33321, Opers Mgr: Omar Malpica *Tel:* 954-933-9210
9525 Berger Rd, Suite G, Columbia, MD 21046, Gen Mgr: Doug Mackenzie *Tel:* 410-242-3322 *Fax:* 410-247-5589
125 Shawmut Rd, Canton, MA 02021, Gen Mgr: Steve Way *Tel:* 781-961-3066 *Fax:* 781-298-7417
30082 Research Dr, New Hudson, MI 48165, Opers Mgr: John Ward *Tel:* 248-685-0102
One Carol Place, Moonachie, NJ 07074, Opers Mgr: Pete Harrison *Tel:* 201-329-9878 *Toll Free Tel:* 866-492-5540 *Fax:* 201-329-9890
425 Front St, Lititz, PA 17543, Opers Mgr: Justin Vanderbeck *Tel:* 717-626-5265 *Fax:* 717-625-1329
820 Cowan St, Nashville, TN 37207, Cross-Rental Agent: Stephen Wells *Tel:* 615-453-2332 *Fax:* 615-645-7424
16505 Air Center Blvd, Houston, TX 77032, Opers Mgr: Brian Luftig *Tel:* 281-209-1944 *Fax:* 281-209-2928
Foreign Office(s): Arndtstr 3, 38118 Braunschweig, Lower Saxony, Germany, VP, Busn Devt: Graham Hill *Tel:* (0531) 480 34 750
Glenfield Business Park, Unit E&F, Philips Rd, Blackburn, Lancs BB1 5PF, United Kingdom, Opers Mgr: Tom Smith-Hollins *Tel:* (0125) 469 8808
Membership(s): Professional Lighting & Sound Association

4th Street Recording
1211 Fourth St, Santa Monica, CA 90401
Tel: 310-395-9114
E-mail: info@4thstreetrecording.com
Web Site: www.4thstreetrecording.com
Key Personnel
Studio Mgr: Kathleen Wirt *E-mail:* kathleen@4thstreetrecording.com
Founded: 1989
Recording studio.

Fox 40 KTXL TV
Subsidiary of Nexstar Broadcasting Inc
4655 Fruitridge Rd, Sacramento, CA 95820

Tel: 916-454-4422 Fax: 916-739-1079
E-mail: foxprogramming@fox40.com
Web Site: www.fox40.com
Founded: 1968
Television programming.

Fox 61
Subsidiary of Tribune Broadcasting
285 Broad St, Hartford, CT 06115
Tel: 860-527-6161 Fax: 860-727-0158
Web Site: www.fox61.com
Key Personnel
Prodn Mgr: Frank Zakrzewski Tel: 860-723-2171
TV program productions.

Fox Television Center
Division of Fox Television Stations LLC
1999 S Bundy Dr, Los Angeles, CA 90025
Tel: 310-584-2000 Fax: 310-584-2023
Web Site: www.foxla.com
Key Personnel
VP & Gen Mgr: Bob Cook
Television programming.
Membership(s): NATPE

Fox 10 Productions (KSAZ-TV)
511 W Adams St, Phoenix, AZ 85003
Tel: 602-257-1234 Fax: 602-262-0177
E-mail: fox10.desk@foxtv.com
Web Site: www.fox10phoenix.com
TV station.

Frame 30 Productions Ltd
10816A-82 Ave, No 202, Edmonton, AB T6E
2B3, Canada
Tel: 780-439-5322
E-mail: frame30@frame30.com
Web Site: www.frame30.com
Key Personnel
Prodr & Dir: Michael Hamm E-mail: michael@
frame30.com
Prodr: Kerrie Long
Prodn: Kailla MacLellan
Founded: 1980

Framepool
175 Varick St, New York, NY 10014
Tel: 646-701-7472 Toll Free Tel: 800-331-1314
E-mail: newyork@framepool.com
Web Site: www.framepool.com
Key Personnel
Opers Dir: Joe Marrone E-mail: joe.marrone@
framepool.com
Founded: 2001
Stock footage library & agency.

Franciscan Media
28 W Liberty St, Cincinnati, OH 45202-6498
Tel: 513-241-5615 Toll Free Tel: 800-488-0488
Fax: 513-241-0399
E-mail: info@franciscanmedia.org
Web Site: www.americancatholic.org
Key Personnel
CEO & Publr: Fr Dan Kroger
COO: Thomas Shumate
Catalog(s) available

Franklin Video Inc
931 Marilyn Dr, Raleigh, NC 27607
Tel: 919-833-8888; 919-621-0400 (cell)
Web Site: www.franklinvideo.com
Key Personnel
Pres: Frank Smith E-mail: frank@franklinvideo.
com
Founded: 1985
Full service production company also offering
non-linear editing, digital video & web design.

Freeman
1600 Viceroy, Suite 100, Dallas, TX 75235

Mailing Address: PO Box 660613, Dallas, TX
75266-0613
Tel: 214-445-1000
Web Site: www.freeman.com
Key Personnel
Chmn: Donald S Freeman, Jr
Vice Chair: Carrie Freeman Parsons
CEO: Joseph V Popolo, Jr
Chief Design Offr: Bruce Mau
Chief Devt Offr: Ken Sanders
Pres & COO: Bob Priest-Heck
Pres, Expositions: Albert Chew
Pres, FreemanXP: Daniel Hoffend, Jr
EVP & Chief Digital Offr: Richard Maranville
EVP & CFO: Phil Rehkemper
EVP & Chief Growth Offr: Janet Dell
EVP & Chief Legal & Admin Offr: Dawn Repp
EVP & Chief Marketing Officer: Chris Ca-
vanaugh
EVP & COO, Expositions: Chris Schimek
EVP & COO, Freeman Audio Visual: John
Kennedy
EVP & COO, FreemanXP & Expositions: Mike
O'Neil
EVP & Chief People & Inclusion Offr: Martha
May
EVP & Chief Sales Offr, Exposition Servs: Mar-
tin Moggre
EVP & Chief Sales Offr, Freeman Audio Visual:
Larry Luteran
EVP, Busn Devt: Steve Anderson
EVP, Busn Devt, Expositions: Daniel Steenstrup
EVP, Sales, Freeman Audio Visual: Jim Russell
SVP & CIO: Michelle Johnson
VP, Cust Experience: Bobbie Caldwell
Founded: 1927
Integrated marketing solutions for live engage-
ments including expositions, conventions, cor-
porate events & exhibits. State-of-the-art AV
equipment & production services.

Freeman Audio Visual
Formerly AVW-TELAV Audio Visual Solutions
2056 32 Ave, Montreal, QC H8T 3H7, Canada
Tel: 514-631-1821 Toll Free Tel: 800-868-6886
Web Site: freemanav-ca.com
Key Personnel
Gen Mgr, Montreal & Regl Dir, Eastern Reg:
Bernard Carignan E-mail: bernard.carignan@
freemanco.com
Dir, Sales: Carol Deeb E-mail: carol.deeb@
freemanco.com
Founded: 1959
Offers a full range of AV & presentation technol-
ogy services in over 30 cities throughout North
America.
Online catalog(s) available
Branch Office(s)
2025 Rue Lavoisier, Suite 100, Quebec, QC
G1N 4L6, Canada, Dir, Opers: Andre Cantin
Tel: 418-687-9055 E-mail: andre.cantin@
freemanco.com
2931 Fifth Ave NE, Calgary, AB T2A 6T8,
Canada, Gen Mgr: Mike T O'Brien Tel: 403-
235-1563 E-mail: miket.obrien@freemanco.
com
118 Ave NW, No 7515, Edmonton, AB T5B 0J2,
Canada Tel: 780-454-8840
395 W Eighth Ave, Vancouver, BC V5Y 1N7,
Canada, Gen Mgr: Kevin Mackillop Tel: 604-
255-1151 E-mail: kevin.mackillop@freemanco.
com
1950 Government St, No 15, Victoria, BC V8T
4N8, Canada Tel: 778-410-2522
375 York Ave, Suite 210, Winnipeg, MB R3C
3J3, Canada Tel: 204-775-6198
125 Whiting Rd, Unit 2G, Fredericton, NB E3B
5Y5, Canada Tel: 506-459-1117
61-10 Akerley Blvd, Dartmouth, NS B3B 1J4,
Canada Tel: 902-468-4485
1110 Dearness Dr, Unit 5D, London, ON N6E
1N9, Canada, Br Mgr: Dan McGrath Tel: 519-
668-7745 E-mail: dan.mcgrath@freemanco.com

2365 Matheson Blvd E, Mississauga, ON L4W
5B3, Canada, Asst Dir, Sales: Melissa Deslau-
riers Tel: 905-366-9200 E-mail: melissa.
deslauriers@freemanco.com
3020 Hawthorne Rd, No 300A, Ottawa, ON K1G
3J6, Canada, Gen Mgr: Kevin Wolfe Tel: 613-
526-3121 E-mail: kevin.wolfe@freemanco.com
418A 50 St E, Bay 105, Saskatoon, SK S7K 6L7,
Canada Tel: 306-665-7874
Membership(s): Audiovisual and Integrated Experience Association; Global Presence Alliance

Freeman Pictures Inc
1234 Sherman Ave, Suite 211, Evanston, IL
60602-1375
Tel: 847-733-0717
E-mail: info@freemanpictures.com
Web Site: www.freemanpictures.com
Key Personnel
Dir: Barbara Freeman
Founded: 1991
Film & video production, post-production & still
photography.
Membership(s): DGA

Freestyle Photographic Supplies
5124 Sunset Blvd, Los Angeles, CA 90027
Tel: 323-660-3460 Toll Free Tel: 800-292-6137
Fax: 323-660-4885
Web Site: www.freestylephoto.biz
Founded: 1946
Photographic equipment & supplies, including
cameras, films, papers & darkroom supplies.

Freestyle Productions Inc
3268 Winpark Dr, Minneapolis, MN 55427
Tel: 763-417-9575
E-mail: info@freestyleproductions.com
Web Site: freestyleproductions.com
Key Personnel
VP, Sales: Carrie O'Keefe E-mail: carrie@
freestyleproductions.com
Founded: 1990
Event design & management, live event produc-
tion services, fashion show production, video &
web production, social media & digital signage.

Freewheelin' Films
44895 Hwy 82, Aspen, CO 81611
Tel: 970-925-2640 Fax: 970-925-9369
Web Site: www.fwf.com
Key Personnel
Principal & Exec Prodr: Rodney H Jacobs
SVP: Kayla B Hoffman-Cook E-mail: kayla@
fwf.com
Dir: Peter Sellers

FremantleMedia North America
Division of RTL Group
2900 W Alameda Ave, Suite 800, Burbank, CA
91505
Tel: 818-748-1100
Web Site: www.fremantlemedia.com
Key Personnel
Co-CEO: Craig Cegielski; Jennifer Mullin
Founded: 1917
Create, produce & distribute content across tradi-
tional TV & digital platforms.
Foreign Office(s): Fremantle Media Ltd, One
Stephen St, London W1T 1AL, United King-
dom Tel: (020) 7691 6000
Membership(s): Television Academy

French American Music Enterprises
5 Junkins Ave, Suite 106, Portsmouth, NH 03801
Tel: 603-430-9524
Web Site: www.luciet.com
Key Personnel
Owner: Lucie Therrien E-mail: lth@star.net
Distribute CDs, DVDs & publications.
Brochure(s) available

Fresh Music Library
320 South St, Agawam, MA 01001
Toll Free Tel: 888-211-8576
Web Site: www.freshmusic.com
Key Personnel
Owner: Bob Casinghino *E-mail:* bob@
freshmusic.com
Founded: 1990
Royalty free music.

Frey Scientific
Division of School Specialty Inc
80 Northwest Blvd, Nashua, NH 03063-4067
Mailing Address: PO Box 3000, Nashua, NH
03061-3000
Toll Free Tel: 800-225-3739; 800-258-1302
Toll Free Fax: 877-256-3739; 800-282-9560
E-mail: customercare.frey@schoolspecialty.com;
social@schoolspecialty.com
Web Site: www.freyscientific.com
Key Personnel
VP, Sales: Doug Welles *Tel:* 800-225-3739 ext
3589 *E-mail:* doug.welles@schoolspecialty.com
Founded: 1962
Educational programs.
Catalog(s) available
Membership(s): Audiovisual and Integrated Experience Association

Frezzi Energy Systems
Division of Frezzolini Electronics Inc
7 Valley St, Hawthorne, NJ 07506
Tel: 973-427-1160 *Fax:* 973-427-0934
E-mail: info@frezzi.com
Web Site: www.frezzi.com
Key Personnel
Chmn of the Bd & Pres: James Crawford
VP, Engg & New Prods: Kevin Crawford
VP, Sales: Edward Kuhn
Lighting & power equipment manufacturer for broadcast industry, system integration.
Online catalog(s) available
Membership(s): NAB

Fricon Entertainment Co Inc
134 Bluegrass Circle, Hendersonville, TN 37075
Tel: 615-826-2288 *Fax:* 615-826-0500
Key Personnel
Pres: Terri Fricon *E-mail:* fricon@comcast.net
Dir, Opers: Jan Morales
Founded: 1981
Contact for quote on catalog. Music clearances.
Membership(s): American Federation of Musicians; ASCAP; BMI; SESAC

Robert Fried Photography
610 Eldridge Ct, Novato, CA 94947
Tel: 415-898-6153 *Fax:* 415-897-0353
Web Site: www.robertfriedphotography.com
Key Personnel
CEO: Robert Fried *E-mail:* rob@
robertfriedphotography.com

Gene Friedman
PO Box 275, Wainscott, NY 11975-0275
Tel: 631-537-0178
E-mail: genfried@optonline.net
Shipping Address: 425 Montauk Hwy, Wainscott, NY 11975

Frontier Communications Corp
PO Box 939, Portland, OR 97207-0939
Tel: 503-246-8080
Key Personnel
Pres: Bob McClanathan
Founded: 1974
Designing & building radio & TV broadcast systems & operating communication towers.
Branch Office(s)
PO Box 1810, Sisters, OR 97759-1810

Frontline Communications
Division of Pierce Manufacturing Inc
12770 44 St N, Clearwater, FL 33762
Tel: 727-573-0400 *Fax:* 727-571-3295
Web Site: www.frontlinecomm.com
Key Personnel
Gen Mgr: Andy Callaway *Tel:* 727-573-0400 ext
38803 *E-mail:* acallaway@frontlinecomm.com
Founded: 1985
Catalog(s) available
Membership(s): NAB; RTDNA

FrontRow
1690 Corporate Circle, Petaluma, CA 94954
Tel: 707-769-1110 *Toll Free Tel:* 800-227-0735
Fax: 707-769-9624
E-mail: customercare@gofrontrow.com
Web Site: www.gofrontrow.com
Key Personnel
Pres: Jens Holstebro
VP, Engg: Leo Stearns
VP, Opers: Graham Askew
VP, US Sales: Mark Jones
Sr Dir, Mktg: Christopher Bundy
Founded: 1963
Communications technology for teaching environments using classroom audio, lesson capture & sharing, integrated AV management & network paging, bells & control.
Branch Office(s)
1600-4950 Yonge St, Toronto, ON M2N 6K1,
Canada *Toll Free Tel:* 800-340-9894 *Fax:* 905-
677-7760 *E-mail:* information@gofrontrow.com
Foreign Office(s): 629 Nudgee Rd, Nundah, Qld
4012, Australia *Tel:* 1800 746 642 *Fax:* 1300
737 983 *E-mail:* info@gofrontrow.com.au
Oticon AB, Lofstroms allee 5, Box 1262, 172
25 Sundbyberg, Sweden *Tel:* (08) 545 22
750 *Fax:* (08) 545 22 751 *E-mail:* mail@
gofrontrow.se
Cadzow Industrial Estate, Low Waters Rd, Hamilton, Lanarkshire ML3 7QE, United Kingdom *Tel:* (01698) 208268 *E-mail:* uksales@
gofrontrow.com

FSR Inc
244 Bergen Blvd, Woodland Park, NJ 07424
Tel: 973-785-4347 *Toll Free Tel:* 800-332-3771
(tech support) *Fax:* 973-785-4207
E-mail: sales@fsrinc.com
Web Site: www.fsrinc.com
Key Personnel
Pres: Janice Sandri *E-mail:* jan@fsrinc.com
Founded: 1981
Catalog(s) available
Membership(s): Audiovisual and Integrated Experience Association; BICSI; NSCA

Fugro
6100 Hillcroft Ave, Houston, TX 77081
Tel: 713-369-5600
Web Site: www.fugro.com
Arial mapping in natural resources management, urban planning, economic development, emergency response, environmental & engineering activities. Satellite monitoring & mapping to support land management, infrastructure planning, natural resources exploration & development, civil engineering & environmental monitoring. Terrestrial survey & geospatial GIS solutions.
Branch Office(s)
10350 Richmond Ave, Suite 800, Houston, TX
77042 *Tel:* 713-904-2244
6671 Southwest Fwy, Suite 700, Houston, TX
77074 *Tel:* 713-346-3700
8613 Cross Park Dr, Austin, TX 78754 *Tel:* 512-
977-1800
5360 Washington Blvd, Beaumont, TX 77707
Tel: 409-840-5551
2880 Virgo Lane, Dallas, TX 75229 *Tel:* 972-484-
8301

2517 East Loop 820 N, Ft Worth, TX 76118
Tel: 817-284-9595
11009 Osgood St, San Antonio, TX 78233
Tel: 210-655-9516
5761 Silverado Way, Suite O, Anchorage, AK
99518 *Tel:* 907-561-3478
5855 Rickenbacker Rd, Commerce, CA 90040
Tel: 323-591-6210
17752 Skypark Circle, Suite 240, Irvine, CA
92614 *Tel:* 949-536-5175
2420 Del Paso Rd, Suite 250, Roseville, CA
95834 *Tel:* 916-773-2600
4820 McGrath St, Suite 100, Ventura, CA 93003
Tel: 805-650-7000
1777 Botelho Dr, Suite 262, Walnut Creek, CA
94596 *Tel:* 925-949-7100
1658 Cole Blvd, Suite 190, Lakewood, CO 80401
Tel: 303-824-1458
2631 NW 41 St, D-1, Gainesville, FL 32606
Tel: 352-339-7700
4233 Rhoda Dr, Baton Rouge, LA 70816
Tel: 225-292-5084
226 Dulles Dr, Suite 110, Lafayette, LA 70506
Tel: 337-237-1300
916 Sampson St, Suite E, Westlake, LA 70669
Tel: 337-439-1731
7320 Executive Way, Frederick, MD 21704
Tel: 301-948-8550
4350 Airport Rd, Rapid City, SD 57703 *Tel:* 605-
393-8300
World Trade Ctr, 101 W Main St, Suite 350, Norfolk, VA 23510 *Tel:* 757-625-3350
3104 Northside Ave, Richmond, VA 23228
Tel: 804-335-6248

Fugro Geospatial, see Fugro

FUJIFILM Canada Inc
Subsidiary of FUJIFILM North America Corp
600 Suffolk Ct, Mississauga, ON L5R 4G4,
Canada
Tel: 905-890-6611 *Toll Free Tel:* 800-263-5018
Fax: 905-890-6446
Web Site: www.fujifilm.ca
Key Personnel
Pres: Michio Kondo
Founded: 1934
Photographic film & paper, film cameras, digital cameras, minilab systems, graphic systems, recording media, motion picture films.

FUJIFILM Graphic Systems Division
Division of FUJIFILM North America Corp
850 Central Ave, Hanover Park, IL 60133
Tel: 630-259-7200 *Toll Free Tel:* 800-877-0555
Fax: 630-259-7078
Web Site: www.fujifilmusa.com
Key Personnel
Regl Sales Mgr: Anthony Aquino
Graphic arts & printing.

FUJIFILM North America Corp
Subsidiary of FUJIFILM Holdings America Corp
200 Summit Lake Dr, Valhalla, NY 10595-1356
Tel: 914-789-8100 *Toll Free Tel:* 800-755-3854
Fax: 914-789-8530
Web Site: www.fujifilmusa.com/northamerica
Key Personnel
CEO & Pres: Go Miyazaki
AV media, cameras, film & graphics.
Membership(s): NAB; SBE; SMPTE®

FUJIFILM Optical Devices Division
Division of FUJIFILM North America Corp
10 High Point Dr, Wayne, NJ 07470
Tel: 973-633-5600 *Fax:* 973-633-5216
Web Site: www.fujifilmusa.com/products/
optical_devices
Broadcast lenses, Cine lenses & pan & tilt systems.
Catalog(s) available

Branch Office(s)
2621 Manhattan Beach Blvd, Redondo Beach, CA 90278-1604, Contact: Miles Shozuya
Tel: 310-536-0800 *Fax:* 310-536-0022
E-mail: mshozuya@fujifilm.com
18601 LBJ Fwy, Suite 100, Mesquite, TX 75150, Contact: David Waddell *Tel:* 972-385-8902 *Fax:* 972-392-3251 *E-mail:* dwaddell@fujifilm. com

Full Compass Systems
9770 Silicon Prairie Pkwy, Madison, WI 53593
Tel: 608-831-7330 *Toll Free Tel:* 800-356-5844
E-mail: customerservice@fullcompass.com
Web Site: www.fullcompass.com
Key Personnel
Chmn: Susan W Lipp
CEO: Jonathan Lipp *E-mail:* jon@fullcompass. com
Founded: 1977
Dealer of professional audio, video, lighting & musical instrument equipment; rents audio & video equipment. Rentals in WI only.
Catalog(s) available, 2 times/yr
Online catalog(s) available
Membership(s): AES; Audiovisual and Integrated Experience Association; GSA; NAB; NAMM, the National Association of Music Merchants; NSCA; SBE

Full Moon & High Tide Productions & Studios
424 Main St, El Segundo, CA 90245-3002
Tel: 310-647-1958 *Fax:* 310-647-1960
Web Site: fmht.net
Key Personnel
Owner: Jake Pentland *E-mail:* jakep@fmht.net
Production studio.

Full Scale Effects
6869 Tujunga Ave, North Hollywood, CA 91605
Tel: 818-760-0875; 818-760-0042 *Fax:* 818-760-0876
Web Site: fullscalefx.com
Key Personnel
Gen Mgr: Dave Peterson *E-mail:* dave@fullscalefx.com
Opers Mgr: Mike Craven *E-mail:* mike@fullscalefx.com
Full service special effects company that specializes in the highest quality physical effects, design, manufacturing, rentals & set operations.

Full Spectrum Arts & Services
PO Box 1032, Littleton, CO 80160
Tel: 303-798-7906 (voicemail only); 720-326-2043 (cell)
Web Site: www.fullspectrumarts.com
Key Personnel
Owner: David Magoun *E-mail:* dave@fullspectrumarts.com
Founded: 1989
A "one stop shop" for all your creative needs. Graphic arts, fine arts, animation, advertising, multimedia or recording.

Fuller Street Productions
12131 Shoemaker Ave, Santa Fe Springs, CA 90670
Toll Free Tel: 877-637-8733 *Toll Free Fax:* 877-637-8733
E-mail: contact@fullerstreet.com
Web Site: www.fullerstreet.com
Key Personnel
Dir, Sales: Daniel Smith *E-mail:* daniel@fullerstreet.com
Prodn Mgr: Brad Cook *E-mail:* brad@fullerstreet.com
Founded: 2005
Full service event production & equipment rental company.

Furman®
Division of Nortek Security & Control LLC
1800 S McDowell Blvd, Petaluma, CA 94954
Tel: 707-283-5900 *Toll Free Tel:* 800-472-5555 *Fax:* 707-283-5901
E-mail: powertechsupport@corebrands.com
Web Site: www.furmanpower.com
Key Personnel
Sr Dir, Mktg: Bill Hensley
Founded: 1974
Power conditioning, regulation, sequencing & distribution for audio, video & broadcast professionals.
Online catalog(s) available

Furnace MFG
2719-B Dorr Ave, Fairfax, VA 22031
Mailing Address: PO Box 3268, Merrifield, VA 22116
Tel: 703-205-0007 *Toll Free Tel:* 888-599-9883 *Fax:* 703-205-2951
E-mail: sales@furnacemfg.com
Web Site: www.furnacemfg.com
Key Personnel
CEO & Pres: Eric Astor
Prodn Mgr: Ali Miller
Founded: 1996
Small disc manufacturing business. CD/DVD replication & duplication (graphic design, mastering & DVD authoring services), vinyl LP production.

Fusion Brand Experiences, see Freeman

Fusion Consoles/Eurotech Seating
c/o Marketec, No 601, 3784 Mission Ave, Suite 148, Oceanside, CA 92058
Toll Free Tel: 800-557-8861 *Toll Free Fax:* 888-262-1726
E-mail: info@marketec.com
Web Site: www.marketec.com
Key Personnel
Pres: Penny Russell
AV seating.

Future Disc LLC
15851 NW Willis Rd, McMinnville, OR 97128
Tel: 213-361-0603 *Fax:* 503-472-1951
Web Site: www.futurediscsystems.com
Key Personnel
Owner & Mastering Engr: Steve Hall *E-mail:* steve@futurediscsystems.com
Studio Coord: Laura Hall *E-mail:* laura@futurediscsystems.com
Founded: 1981
Surround & stereo mastering.

Future Light Inc
21887 Lorain Rd, Suite 200, Cleveland, OH 44126
Tel: 440-801-1310 *Toll Free Tel:* 800-581-5536 *Fax:* 440-779-4159
E-mail: info@future-light.com
Web Site: www.future-light.com
Key Personnel
Pres: John Seaman *E-mail:* jseaman@future-light.com
Manufacturing lighting equipment.
Online catalog(s) available
Membership(s): Illuminating Engineering Society; Professional Lighting & Sound Association; SBE

Future US Inc
Subsidiary of Future PLC
11 W 42 St, 15th fl, New York, NY 10036
Tel: 212-378-0448 *Toll Free Tel:* 844-779-2822 (subns)
Web Site: www.futureplc.com
Key Personnel
COO: Claire Maclellan

Mng Dir & SVP, B2B: Christine Shaw
Founded: 1985
Gaming, entertainment & technology.
Catalog(s) available

Future View Inc
6035 Blair Rd NW, Washington, DC 20011
Tel: 202-882-7400 *Fax:* 202-882-7450
E-mail: info@futureview.com
Web Site: www.futureview.com
Key Personnel
CEO: Dave Hanrahan
Pres & Co-Owner: Chris Shelton
Founded: 1976
Provide video production services & equipment, large screen display & event staging.

FutureVideo
28202 Cabot Rd, Suite 300, Laguna Niguel, CA 92677
Mailing Address: PO Box 6251, Laguna Niguel, CA 92607-6251
Tel: 949-363-1686 *Toll Free Fax:* 866-261-1686
E-mail: sales@futurevideo.com
Web Site: www.futurevideo.com; www.futurevideo.tv
Key Personnel
Dir, Busn Devt: Stephen Godfrey
Founded: 1986
Design, engineer & manufacture V-Station HD multi-channel production DVR systems for multi-cam recording in industry, government & academia.
Catalog(s) available

Gage-Line Technology Inc
121 LaGrange Ave, Rochester, NY 14613-1577
Tel: 585-458-2000 *Toll Free Tel:* 800-291-3724 *Fax:* 585-458-0524
E-mail: sales@gage-line.com
Web Site: www.gage-line.com
Key Personnel
Pres: Frank Dombrowski
Founded: 1972
Design & manufacture precision imaged, optical, gaging & calibration products, test arrays & used photographic equipment.
Catalog(s) available
Membership(s): Optics & Electro Optics Standards Counsel; Rochester Regional Photomics Cluster; SPIE

Gagne Inc
41 Commercial Dr, Johnson City, NY 13790
Tel: 607-729-3366 *Toll Free Tel:* 800-800-5954 *Fax:* 607-729-7644
E-mail: sales@gagneinc.com
Web Site: www.gagneinc.com
Key Personnel
Pres: Mary Ann Holland
Natl Sales Mgr: Kim Prentice
Sales Engr: Dick Fletcher
Founded: 1950
Manufacturers of portable light boxes & freestanding light tables.
Catalog(s) available

Gaither Studios LLC
1705 S Park Ave, Alexandria, IN 46001
Mailing Address: PO Box 119, Alexandria, IN 46001
Toll Free Tel: 800-333-7859
E-mail: info@gaitherstudios.com
Key Personnel
Owner: Bill Gaither; Gloria Gaither
Music equipment sales & rentals & digital recording studio.

Galaxy Audio
601 E Pawnee Ave, Wichita, KS 67211
Mailing Address: PO Box 16285, Wichita, KS 67216-0285

Tel: 316-263-2852 *Toll Free Tel:* 800-369-7768
Fax: 316-263-0642
E-mail: sales@galaxyaudio.com; orders@
galaxyaudio.com
Web Site: www.galaxyaudio.com
Key Personnel
Founder & Pres: Brock M Jabara *E-mail:* brock@
galaxyaudio.com
Founded: 1977
Audio sound systems.
Catalog(s) available
Membership(s): AES; NAMM, the National Association of Music Merchants; NSCA

Gallien-Krueger
2234 Industrial Dr, Stockton, CA 95206
Tel: 209-234-7300 *Fax:* 209-234-8420
E-mail: sales@gallien.com
Web Site: www.gallien-krueger.com
Key Personnel
Pres: Robert Gallien
Founded: 1968
Manufacture & distribute sound systems-guitar
bass amplifiers & cabinets.
Online catalog(s) available
Membership(s): AES

GAMfilm Productions
7559 Willoughby Ave, Suite 5, Los Angeles, CA
90046
Tel: 213-840-6212
E-mail: gamfilm@gmail.com
Web Site: director-writer-producer.com
Key Personnel
Dir & Prodr: A G Melkom
Full service production in documentaries, commercials & music videos.

Gamma Imaging
222 N DesPlaines St, Chicago, IL 60661
Tel: 312-441-0091 *Toll Free Tel:* 877-441-4830
Fax: 312-441-0092
E-mail: digital@gammaimaging.com
Web Site: gammaimaging.com
Key Personnel
Pres: Doug Goddard
Founded: 1962
Digital & graphic imaging services.
Catalog(s) available
Membership(s): American Association of Magazine Photographers; The Imaging Alliance

G&G Technologies Inc
280 N Midland Ave, Bldg F, Suite 202, Saddle
Brook, NJ 07663
Tel: 201-791-1400 *Toll Free Tel:* 800-422-2920
Fax: 201-791-1401
E-mail: staff@ggvideo.com
Web Site: www.ggvideo.com
Key Personnel
Pres: Robert Greenberg
Founded: 1988
Professional AV equipment sales & rentals.
Catalog(s) available

GAPC (General Assembly Production Centre)
1550 Laperriere Ave, Suite 102, Ottawa, ON K1Z
7T2, Canada
Tel: 613-723-3316 *Fax:* 613-723-8583
Web Site: www.gapc.com
Key Personnel
Pres & Exec Prodr: Ken Stewart *Tel:* 613-723-
3316 ext 224 *E-mail:* kstewart@gapc.com
Sr Prodr: Hoda Elatawi *E-mail:* helatawi@gapc.
com
Founded: 1983
Full service video agency providing turn-key audio, video & transmedia production with in-house facilities as well as on-location filming services, live event production & service production for international producers.

Catalog(s) available
Membership(s): Canadian Media Production Association

Garcia Marketing Inc
400 Ninth St, Conway, PA 15027-1663
Tel: 724-869-0100 *Toll Free Tel:* 800-683-1925
Fax: 724-869-1925
E-mail: gmavfoto@verizon.net
Key Personnel
Owner: Jean Garcia
VP: Thomas C Garcia
Mgr: Cathy Stewart
AV equipment distribution & installation.
Catalog(s) available
Membership(s): Audiovisual and Integrated Experience Association; The Imaging Alliance

Garden Valley Productions
240 Crystal Springs Lane, Roseburg, OR 97471
Tel: 541-440-1926 *Fax:* 541-440-1008
Key Personnel
Partner & Opers Mgr: Woody Lane
E-mail: woody@woodylane.com

Garman Productions LLC
2828 NW 58 St, Oklahoma City, OK 73112
Tel: 405-254-2500 *Toll Free Tel:* 800-747-5699
Fax: 405-254-2507
E-mail: info@garman.com
Web Site: www.garman.com
Key Personnel
Owner & CEO: Steve Garman *E-mail:* steve@
garman.com
Founded: 1981
Full service AV production, post-production &
new media company. Facilities include 3 nonlinear, 2 digital audio, new media & graphics animation suites. Additional production services available are DVD authoring, DVD burning, video compression, web site development, closed captioning, remote & studio shooting, ISDN & Pro Tools 11 HD.

Garner Products Inc
10620 Industrial Ave, Suite 100, Roseville, CA
95678
Tel: 916-784-0200 *Toll Free Tel:* 800-624-1903
Fax: 916-784-1425
E-mail: info@garner-products.com
Web Site: www.garner-products.com
Key Personnel
CEO: Ronald A Stofan *E-mail:* ron@garner-
products.com
Founded: 1959
Manufacturer of degaussing equipment for audio,
video, hard drive & computer industries.

Gary Camera & Digital
6750 Broadway Ave, Merrillville, IN 46410
Tel: 219-769-2451 *Fax:* 219-769-2488
E-mail: garycamera@gmail.com
Web Site: garycameradigital.com
Key Personnel
VP: Barry Blane; Mark Blane
Founded: 1940
Catalog(s) available

The Gary-Paul Agency
1549 Main St, Stratford, CT 06615
Tel: 203-345-6167
Web Site: www.thegarypaulagency.com; www.
nutmegpictures.com
Key Personnel
Owner: Gary Maynard *E-mail:* garret@
thegarypaulagency.com
Founded: 1994
Full service production company: post-production,
avid editing suite & archivist. Represents & promotes screenplays. Specialize in script development. WGAE signatory.

Branch Office(s)
127 Horseshoe Rd, Fayston, VT 05660
Membership(s): Writers Guild of America, East

GatesAir
5300 Kings Island Dr, Suite 101, Mason, OH
45040
Tel: 513-459-3400 *Toll Free Tel:* 800-622-0022
Fax: 513-459-3796
E-mail: information@gatesair.com; orders@
gatesair.com; support@gatesair.com
Web Site: www.gatesair.com
Key Personnel
CEO: Bruce Swail
Chief Prod Offr: Rich Redmond
VP, HR: Kim Ratcliffe
VP, Opers: Bryant Burke
VP, Sales-Americas: Joseph Mack *E-mail:* joe@
gatesair.com
VP, Sales-Europe, Middle East, Asia & Africa:
Darren Frearson
Founded: 1922
Over-the-air TV & radio technology, including
transmitters, exciters & shelters.
Company formed from the rebranding of Harris Broadcast which split into two companies, GatesAir & Imagine Communications.
Branch Office(s)
3200 Wismann Lane, Quincy, IL 62301 *Tel:* 217-
222-8200

Gateways
Subsidiary of G W Fulfillment
PO Box 1706, Ojai, CA 93024-1706
Tel: 805-649-5367 *Toll Free Tel:* 800-477-8908
Fax: 805-649-5302
Key Personnel
Owner: Karen Schumann
Children's self-improvement & educational audio
programs.
Catalog(s) available
Shipping Address: 699 Highland Dr, Ojai, CA
93023

Gateways Books & Tapes
Division of Institute for the Development of the
Harmonious Human Being Inc
PO Box 370, Nevada City, CA 95959
Tel: 530-271-2239 *Toll Free Tel:* 800-869-0658
Fax: 530-272-0184
E-mail: info@gatewaysbooksandtapes.com
Web Site: www.gatewaysbooksandtapes.com
Key Personnel
Sr Ed: Iven Lourie *Tel:* 530-477-8101
Founded: 1971
Educational & religious programs.
Catalog(s) available
Membership(s): Reading Recovery Council of
North America

Gaylord Archival
PO Box 4901, Syracuse, NY 13221-4901
Tel: 315-634-8125 (intl) *Toll Free Tel:* 800-448-
6160 (cust serv) *Fax:* 315-453-5030 (intl)
Toll Free Fax: 800-272-3412
E-mail: customerservice@gaylord.com
Web Site: www.gaylord.com; www.facebook.com/
gaylordarchival
Key Personnel
CEO: Keith George
Regl Sales Mgr: Paul Randall
Founded: 1896
Provide library & archival supplies.
Catalog(s) available
Shipping Address: 7282 William Barry Blvd,
North Syracuse, NY 13212

GBC Document Finishing
Division of ACCO Brands Corp
4 Corporate Dr, Lake Zurich, IL 60047
Toll Free Tel: 800-723-4000 (orders & serv)
Toll Free Fax: 800-914-8178
Web Site: www.gbcconnect.com; www.gbc.com

Key Personnel
VP, Mktg: Adam Smith *E-mail:* adam.smith@
acco.com
Founded: 1947
Complete document finishing solutions.
Branch Office(s)
GBC Canada, 7381 Bramalea Rd, Mississauga,
ON L5S 1C4, Canada *Toll Free Tel:* 800-
463-2545 *Toll Free Fax:* 800-463-2545
E-mail: customer.service@acco.com *Web
Site:* www.gbccanada.com
Foreign Office(s): GBC Australia, Unit 1, Block
Q, Regents Park Estate, Princes Rd E, Regents
Park, NSW 2143, Australia *Tel:* (02) 9738
4000 *Fax:* (02) 9738 4100 *E-mail:* enquiry.
nsw@acco.com *Web Site:* www.gbcaustralia.
com.au
Pelikan Art Line, 2 Coronation Ave, Kings Park,
NSW 2214, Australia *Tel:* (02) 9674 0900
Fax: (02) 9674 0910 *E-mail:* custsupport@
pelikanartline.com
ACCO Brands Japan KK, 14F Harmony Tower
Bldg, 1-32-2 Honcho, Nakano-Ku, Tokyo 164-
8721, Japan *Tel:* (03) 5351 1810 *Fax:* (03)
5351 1831 *E-mail:* raymond.tan@acco.com
Web Site: www.accobrands.co.jp
GBC Mexicana SA de C V, Neptuno No 43,
Colonia Nueva Industrial Vallejo, Delegacion
Gustavo A Madero, 07700 Mexico, CDMX,
Mexico *Tel:* (0155) 1500-5700; (0155) 1500-
5778 (tech support) *Fax:* (0155) 1500-5701
E-mail: yadira.escamilla@acco.com
GBC Asia Pte Ltd, 47 Ayer Rajah Cres-
cent, No 05-08/17, Singapore 139947, Sin-
gapore *Tel:* 6776 0195 *Fax:* 6779 1041
E-mail: raymond.tan@acco.com *Web
Site:* www.accobrandsasia.com
GBC Asian Films Group, 98-18 Shin Hang Ri,
Doon Po Myun, Asan City, Choong Nam
336-873, South Korea *Tel:* (041) 531 1830
Fax: (041) 531 1831 *E-mail:* raymond.tan@
acco.com
Acco Brands Europe, Oxford House, Oxford Rd,
Aylesbury, Bucks HP21 8SZ, United Kingdom
Tel: (01296) 397444 *Fax:* (01296) 311000
E-mail: orders@acco.com *Web Site:* www.
gbceurope.com

GEAR Cameras & Lighting
4822 E Cesar Chavez, Austin, TX 78702
Tel: 512-485-3131 *Fax:* 512-474-6098
E-mail: austin@hdgear.tv
Web Site: www.hdgear.tv
Rents cameras, lenses, support, lighting & grip
equipment.

Gear Monkey
2650 Walnut Ave, Suite F, Tustin, CA 92780
Tel: 714-705-6088 *Toll Free Tel:* 877-411-4445
Fax: 714-705-6080
Web Site: www.gearmonkey.tv
Production equipment rentals & sales.

Gearhead Rentals
69 O'Conner Rd, Suite 6, Fairport, NY 14450
Tel: 585-236-4272
E-mail: info@gearheadrentals.com
Web Site: www.gearheadrentals.com
Key Personnel
Contact: Mike Drago *E-mail:* mdrago@
gearheadrentals.com
Rents cameras, lenses, filters, tripods, monitors,
recorders, microphones, teleprompters, lighting,
grip equipment.

Gearhouse Broadcast LLC, see Gravity Media

Geddes Productions LLC
PO Box 41761, Los Angeles, CA 90041-0761
Tel: 323-344-8045 *Fax:* 323-257-7209
E-mail: orders@geddesproduction.com

Web Site: www.geddesproduction.com
Key Personnel
Pres: Kittie Frantz *E-mail:* frantz@usc.edu
Founded: 1986
Produce & distribute informational materials
(videos, DVDs, slides, overheads, patient hand-
outs, pocket cards, CDs, posters & books) related to breastfeeding. Breastfeeding or lac-
tation would be key words. Most films are
streaming on web site on a pay per view basis.
Online catalog(s) available

Gefen
Subsidiary of Core Brands LLC
20600 Nordhoff St, Chatsworth, CA 91311
Tel: 818-772-9100 *Toll Free Tel:* 800-545-6900;
800-472-5555 *Fax:* 818-772-9120
E-mail: sales@gefen.com; support@gefen.com
Web Site: www.gefen.com
Key Personnel
Pres: Tony Dowzall
Sales Dir: Aaron R Hernandez
Founded: 1995
Supplies a wide selection of signal switchers,
splitters, extenders, scalers, converters, KVM,
digital signage & home theater accessories that
enable audio/video & computer systems to be
easily integrated, extended, distributed & opti-
mized to maximize performance.
Catalog(s) available
Membership(s): AES; Audiovisual and Integrated
Experience Association; Consumer Technology
Association™; Custom Electronic Design &
Installation Association; NAB; NSCA

Gemini
2000 Penncraft Ct, Ann Arbor, MI 48103
Toll Free Tel: 800-317-9929 *Fax:* 734-786-4007
E-mail: info@geminichildrensmusic.com
Web Site: www.geminichildrensmusic.com
Key Personnel
Owner: Laszlo Slomovits; Sandor Slomovits
Recordings & videos for children & families.
Catalog(s) available

Gemini Sound
107 Trumbull St, Bldg F-8, 2nd fl, Elizabeth, NJ
07206-2171
Tel: 732-346-0061 *Fax:* 732-346-0065
E-mail: sales@geminisound.com
Web Site: www.geminisound.com
Key Personnel
CEO: Artie Cabasso
Founded: 1974
Manufacturer of equipment including studio
monitors, media controllers, DJ mixers, head-
phones, power amps, passive & active loud
speakers, CD players, turntables.
Online catalog(s) available

Gemstone Media Inc
8280 Princeton Square Blvd W, Suite 4, Jack-
sonville, FL 32256
Tel: 904-354-1500
E-mail: service@gemstonemediainc.com
Web Site: www.gemstonemediainc.com
Key Personnel
Exec Prodr: Ray Hays
Founded: 1988
Film, video & interactive media production.

General Audio-Visual Inc (GAVI)
92 E Merrick Rd, Freeport, NY 11520
Tel: 516-623-8500 *Fax:* 516-623-9155
Web Site: www.gavi.com
Key Personnel
Chmn: Angelo Dituri
Pres: Michael Dituri *E-mail:* miked@gavi.com
Online catalog(s) available
Membership(s): Audiovisual and Integrated Expe-
rience Association

General Cable
4 Tesseneer Dr, Highland Heights, KY 41076
Tel: 859-572-8000
E-mail: info@generalcable.com
Web Site: www.generalcable.com
Founded: 1981
Catalog(s) available
Membership(s): AES; NAB; NSCA; SBE;
SMPTE®

General Devices Co Inc
1410 S Post Rd, Indianapolis, IN 46239
Mailing Address: PO Box 39100, Indianapolis, IN
46239
Tel: 317-897-7000 *Fax:* 317-898-2917
E-mail: sales@generaldevices.com
Web Site: www.generaldevices.com
Key Personnel
Owner & EVP: Martin Fall
CEO: Maxwell Fall
Dir, Sales & Mktg: Dan McCauley
Founded: 1953
Electronic hardware manufacturers.
Catalog(s) available, free

General Electric Co
41 Farnsworth St, Boston, MA 02210
Tel: 203-373-2211; 617-443-3000
Web Site: www.ge.com
Key Personnel
Chmn & CEO: John Flannery
VChmn-Busn, Innovations: Beth Comstock
SVP & Gen Coun: Alex Dimitrief
Projection systems.
Branch Office(s)
Lighting Division, Nela Park, Bldg 308, Cleve-
land, OH 44112 *Tel:* 216-266-2121 *Fax:* 216-
266-2310

General Production Services
Division of GPS Inc
883 S East St, Anaheim, CA 92805
Tel: 714-535-2271 *Fax:* 714-535-0952
E-mail: lensclens@yahoo.com; sales@lensclens.
com
Web Site: www.lensclens.com
Key Personnel
Pres: Jerry Tochilin
Founded: 1971
Manufacturer of cleaning solutions & supplies for
optics.
Online catalog(s) available

Genesis Creative
1006 Hafely Ct, Cayce, SC 29033
Tel: 803-796-9666
E-mail: geninfo@gencreative.com
Web Site: genesisstudiossc.com
Key Personnel
Pres & Prodn Dir: Cliff Springs
Founded: 1993
Full service advertising & production. Graphic
design, animation, web design, interactive,
video & film production - all in-house. 4,000
feet of studio space. Canon C300 Mkii, Canon
C300, Panasonic HPX500, Canon 5D Mkii,
cine-rime lenses, Steadicam, Ronin, Jib, Dollies, 5 edit suites. Work with clients from concept to completion or as a production resource
for other agencies.

Genesis Integration
14721 123 Ave NW, Edmonton, AB T5L 2Y6,
Canada
Toll Free Tel: 877-283-2253 (Toronto); 866-622-
2966 (Quebec); 844-436-4681 (rest of CN)
E-mail: marketing@genint.com
Web Site: www.genint.com
Key Personnel
Chmn: Mr Kelly McCarthy
CEO: Andrew Turner

Pres & COO: Marc Vinet
EVP: Gabriel Gely
Dir, Design & Programming: Dan Moran
Dir, Fin & Admin: Lynn Walker
Dir, Sales: Kevin McKay
Dir, Serv Delivery: Robert Belisle
Founded: 1990
Systems integration company.
Catalog(s) available
Branch Office(s)
Bay 13, 6143 Fourth St SE, Calgary, AB T2H
 2H9, Canada
18380 McCartney Way, Richmond, BC V6W
 0A1, Canada
2740 Matheson Blvd E, Unit 5, Mississauga, ON
 L4W 4X3, Canada
22 Gurdwara Rd, Units 13 & 14, Ottawa, ON
 K2E 8A2, Canada
31 Durward Place, Unit C, Waterloo, ON N2L
 4E5, Canada
360 Eugenie St E, Unit 212, Windsor, ON N8X
 2Y1, Canada
5005 blvd Metropolitain E, Montreal, QC H1R
 1Z7, Canada
771 rue des Rocailles, Quebec City, QC G2J
 1A2, Canada

Gary Gentile Productions (GGP)
3 Lehigh Gorge Dr, Jim Thorpe, PA 18229
Tel: 252-694-6974
Web Site: www.ggentile.com
Key Personnel
Owner: Gary Gentile E-mail: gary@ggentile.com
Founded: 1989
Video distribution.

A Gentle Wind
14 S Pine Ave, Albany, NY 12208
Mailing Address: PO Box 3103, Albany, NY
 12203-0103
Tel: 518-482-9023 Toll Free Tel: 888-FUN-SONG
 (386-7664, orders)
E-mail: hello@gentlewind.com
Web Site: www.gentlewind.com
Key Personnel
Owner: Donald Person
Record label for children's music & stories.
Catalog(s) available, free, annual or by request

Geomatrix Productions
270 Amity Rd, Woodbridge, CT 06525-2267
Tel: 203-389-0001
E-mail: info@geomatrixproductions.com
Web Site: www.geomatrixproductions.com
Key Personnel
Pres: Cathie Reese E-mail: cathie@
 geomatrixproductions.com
Prodr: Edgar Smith; Patrick Volk
Founded: 1978
Video production company.

Georgia-Pacific Television & Photography, see
 GP Studios

Gerriets International
130 Winterwood Ave, Ewing, NJ 08638
Tel: 609-771-8111 Fax: 609-771-8118
E-mail: info@gerriets.us
Web Site: www.gerriets.us
Key Personnel
New Prods Mgr: Nick Pagliante
Manufacturer of front & rear projection screens &
 stage products.
Online catalog(s) available

GES Audio Visual
Subsidiary of The Viad Corp
7000 Lindell Rd, Las Vegas, NV 89118
Tel: 702-515-5500 Fax: 702-515-5765
E-mail: lasvegas@ges.com; info@ges.com
Web Site: ges.com

Key Personnel
Pres: Steve Moster
EVP, Global Mktg: Wendy Gibson
SVP, AV Servs: Paul Wedesky
Opers: Brian Larson
Full service AV equipment rentals.

GestureTek
317 Adelaide St W, Suite 903, Toronto, ON M5V
 1P9, Canada
Tel: 416-340-9290 Toll Free Tel: 800-315-1189
 Fax: 416-348-9809
E-mail: info@gesturetek.com; sales@gesturetek.
 com
Web Site: www.gesturetek.com
Key Personnel
Founder & CEO: John Vincent
Pres: Erol Vekil E-mail: erol@gesturetek.com
Founded: 1986
Video(s) available
Branch Office(s)
5255 Stevens Creek Blvd, Suite 162, Santa Clara,
 CA 95051 Tel: 408-506-2206 Fax: 408-732-
 3977
240 Catherine St, Suite 305, Ottawa, ON K2P
 2G8, Canada Tel: 613-233-2022 Fax: 815-361-
 4123

Get Smart Products
30 S Highland Ave, Ossining, NY 10562
Mailing Address: PO Box 0018, Maryknoll, NY
 10545
Tel: 914-762-3500 Toll Free Tel: 800-827-0673
 Fax: 914-923-5818 Toll Free Fax: 866-827-
 0673
E-mail: getsmart@pfile.com
Web Site: www.pfile.com
Key Personnel
Pres: Steve Weisbart
Founded: 1988
Retailer for archival photo storage supplies.
Online catalog(s) available
Shipping Address: 807 Airport Access Rd, Unit
 D, Traverse City, MI 49686

Getty-Dubay Productions
c/o Handwriting Success LLC, PO Box 91088,
 Portland, OR 97280
Tel: 971-254-8695
E-mail: info@handwritingsuccess.com; info@
 allport.com (orders)
Web Site: www.handwritingsuccess.com; www.
 allport.com (orders)
Key Personnel
Owner: Jonathan Dubay
Founded: 1995
Educational program in DVD-handwriting.
Online catalog(s) available,
 www.handwritingsuccess.com

Getty Images
605 Fifth Ave S, Suite 400, Seattle, WA 98104
Tel: 206-925-5000 Toll Free Tel: 888-888-5889;
 800-462-4379 (sales)
E-mail: sales.na@gettyimages.com
Web Site: www.gettyimages.com
Key Personnel
CEO: Craig Peters
CFO: Rik Powell
Chief People Offr: Lizanne Vaughan
Chief Technol & Prod Offr: Nate Gandert
SVP & Chief Commercial Offr: Pam Woehrle
SVP & Chief Mktg Offr: Gene Foca
SVP & Gen Coun: Kjelti Kellough
SVP, Content: Ken Mainardis
SVP, Creative Content: Andrew Saunders
SVP, Global Strategic Devt: Lee Martin
SVP, Strategic Devt: Peter Orlowsky
Founded: 1995
Provide imagery, film & digital services.
Online catalog(s) available

Branch Office(s)
6300 Wilshire Blvd, 16th fl, Los Angeles, CA
 90048 Tel: 323-202-4200
55 E Monroe St, 17th fl, Suite 1700, Chicago, IL
 60603 Tel: 312-344-4500
195 Broadway, New York, NY 10007 Tel: 646-
 613-4000

Getty Images Music
Division of Getty Images
75 Varick St, New York, NY 10013
Tel: 646-613-4000
E-mail: music@gettyimages.com
Web Site: www.gettyimages.com/music
Founded: 2012
Royalty-free music & audio clips.

GGP, see Gary Gentile Productions (GGP)

Ghent Manufacturing
Affiliate of GMi
2999 Henkle Dr, Lebanon, OH 45036-9260
Tel: 513-932-3445 Toll Free Tel: 800-543-0550
 Fax: 513-932-9252
E-mail: customer_service@ghent.com; sales@
 ghent.com
Web Site: www.ghent.com
Key Personnel
Chmn: George Leasure E-mail: gleasure@ghent.
 com
CEO: Mark Leasure E-mail: markl@ghent.com
Pres: Janet Collins E-mail: jcollins@ghent.com
VP: Jim Harter E-mail: jharter@ghent.com
Dir, Mfg: John Kurtz E-mail: johnk@ghent.com
Dir, Prodn: Scott Bowers E-mail: bowers@ghent.
 com
Founded: 1976
Produce visual communication products.
Catalog(s) available
Membership(s): Business + Institutional Furniture
 Manufacturers Association

GHO Group LLC
340 W 55 St, Suite 5E, New York, NY 10019
Tel: 212-319-7716
E-mail: info@ghogroup.com
Web Site: www.ghogroup.com
Key Personnel
Principal: Gary H Olson
Owner representative & project management.

Giant Interactive
133 W 19 St, 3rd fl, New York, NY 10011
Tel: 212-675-7300
E-mail: info@giant-interactive.com
Web Site: www.giant-interactive.com
Key Personnel
Co-Founder & Pres: Jeff Stabenau
Co-Founder & VP: David Anthony
Founded: 2005
Digital studio offering creative & technical production services for the entertainment, media
 & sports markets. Services include digital/VOD
 prep & delivery; OTT platform development;
 Blu-ray/DVD design & authoring; web site design & development; mobile, table app & tvOS
 design & development; original content production.
Branch Office(s)
2950 N Hollywood Way, Suite 125, Burbank, CA
 91505 Tel: 818-446-9100
2724 Walnut St, Denver, CO 80205 Tel: 303-458-
 6000
Membership(s): Entertainment Merchants Association

GigaSonic
260 E Gish Rd, San Jose, CA 95112
Tel: 408-573-1400 Toll Free Tel: 888-246-4442
 Fax: 408-573-0602
E-mail: info@gigasonic.com

Web Site: www.gigasonic.com
Music recording equipment & musical instrument distributor.

Gilderfluke & Co Inc
205 S Flower St, Burbank, CA 91502
Tel: 818-840-9484 *Toll Free Tel:* 800-776-5972
Fax: 818-840-9485
E-mail: info@gilderfluke.com
Web Site: www.gilderfluke.com
Key Personnel
CEO & Pres: Douglas C Mobley
CFO & VP: Carolyn Rowley *E-mail:* carolyn@gilderfluke.com
Founded: 1981
Designs & manufactures animation control systems, CD-quality digital audio repeaters & intelligent public address systems for themed amusement park, themed restaurants, museums, churches & movies. PC MAC systems, using Microsoft Windows & a standard PC compatible computer, creates a complete animation control system.
Catalog(s) available

Jim Gill Music Inc
PO Box 2263, Oak Park, IL 60303-2263
Tel: 708-763-9864 *Fax:* 708-763-9888
Web Site: www.jimgill.com
Key Personnel
Owner: Jim Gill *E-mail:* jimgill@jimgill.com
Produce children's music.
Catalog(s) available

Gingerbread Group Holdings LLC
1337 Kittredge Ct, Atlanta, GA 30329
Tel: 404-634-8678; 404-663-9050
E-mail: books2gogh@gmail.com
Key Personnel
Exec Prodr & Dir, Mktg: Evi Reznick
Founded: 1996
Produce & distribute children's videos.

Glanz Technologies Inc
687 NE 124 St, North Miami, FL 33161
Tel: 305-893-1269 *Fax:* 305-899-8526
E-mail: mglanz@glanztech.com
Web Site: www.glanztechnologies.com
Key Personnel
Pres: Mark Glanz
Founded: 1981
Rent & distribute video equipment & projection systems.

Glendale Media Center
9494 W Maryland Ave, Glendale, AZ 85305
Tel: 623-930-4512
Web Site: www.glendalemediacenter.com
Key Personnel
Chief Broadcast Engr: Dave Rainey
E-mail: drainey@glendaleaz.com
Rental studios & HD production for video, films, advertising, commercials, studio audience shows & more.

Glendale Production Center
1239 S Glendale Ave, Glendale, CA 91205
Tel: 818-550-6000
E-mail: info@glendalestudios.com
Soundstages, production office & AV rentals.

Glenn Photo Supply
13502 Erwin St, Van Nuys, CA 91401
Tel: 818-997-0410
Web Site: www.emgee.freeyellow.com
Key Personnel
Owner & Mgr: Murray Glass
E-mail: murray713@hotmail.com
Founded: 1950
16mm film sales.

Affiliate companies: Em Gee Film Library; Glenn Video Vistas Ltd.
Catalog(s) available, $5

Glenn Video Vistas Ltd
13502 Erwin St, Van Nuys, CA 91401
Tel: 818-997-0410
Web Site: www.emgee.freeyellow.com
Key Personnel
Owner & Mgr: Murray Glass
E-mail: murray713@hotmail.com
Video sales.
Affiliate companies: Em Gee Film Library; Glenn Photo Supply.
Catalog(s) available, $5

GLI Sound Systems
2691 W 15 St, Brooklyn, NY 11224
Tel: 718-372-7849 *Toll Free Tel:* 800-GLI-PRO-1 (454-7761) *Fax:* 718-946-4151
E-mail: info@glipro.com; sales@glipro.com
Web Site: www.glipro.com
Key Personnel
Pres: David Harari
Dir, Opers: Paul Arking *Tel:* 718-946-4134
Sales: Morris Shalom *E-mail:* mshalom@glipro.com
Manufacture DJ equipment.
Catalog(s) available

Glidecam Industries Inc
23 Joseph St, Kingston, MA 02364
Tel: 781-585-7900 *Toll Free Tel:* 800-949-2089; 800-600-2011 *Fax:* 781-585-7903
E-mail: info@glidecam.com
Web Site: glidecam.com
Key Personnel
VP, Sales & Mktg: Thomas Howie
Founded: 1992
Manufacture camera stabilizers & cranes.
Catalog(s) available
Membership(s): NAB

GliPro, see Harbro Corp

Glix Entertainment Inc
503 S Flower St, Burbank, CA 91502
Tel: 323-905-GLIX (905-4549)
E-mail: info@glixstudios.com
Web Site: www.glixent.com
Full service video production, post-production, Blu-ray & DVD authoring & duplication; grip & electric rentals.

Glix Studios, see Glix Entertainment Inc

Global Cyber-Visions
Subsidiary of The Venus Project
21 Valley Lane, Venus, FL 33960
Tel: 863-465-0321
E-mail: tvp@thevenusproject.com
Web Site: www.thevenusproject.com
Key Personnel
Founder & Mktg Dir: Roxanne Meadows
E-mail: meadows@thevenusproject.com
Produce educational programs.

Global ImageWorks LLC
65 Beacon St, Haworth, NJ 07641
Tel: 201-384-7715 *Fax:* 201-501-8971
E-mail: info@globalimageworks.com
Web Site: www.globalimageworks.com
Key Personnel
Pres: Jessica Berman-Bogdan *E-mail:* jessica@globalimageworks.com
Independent multi-service media business that licenses Rights Managed & Royalty Free contemporary & historic footage & photos. Subjects includes: 9/11, aerials, climate change, destinations, extreme sports, fire, global con-

flict, historic travel films, home movies, interviews, lifestyle, music, nature, pop culture, reenactments, rock n roll, extreme weather, science, time lapse, US cities, wildlife. Premium collections include The Dick Cavett Show, Austin City Limits & Omnibus, Films of Robert Mugge, The Harold Lloyd Collection & The History of Rock n' Roll Interviews. Also provides a full range of AV research, rights & clearance services.
Catalog(s) available
Membership(s): Association of Commercial Stock Image Licensors; Association of Moving Image Archivists; BAFTA; Digital Media Licensing Association; The Federation of Commercial Audiovisual Libraries Ltd; IDA

Global TV
Division of Corus Entertainment Inc
5325 Allard Way, Edmonton, AB T6H 5B8, Canada
Tel: 780-436-1250 *Fax:* 587-525-9257
E-mail: edmonton@globalnews.ca
Web Site: www.globaltv.com
Key Personnel
News Dir & Gen Mgr: Jim Haskins
Produce TV programs.

Global TV
Division of Corus Entertainment Inc
222 23 St NE, Calgary, AB T2E 7N2, Canada
Tel: 403-235-7777
E-mail: calgary@globalnews.ca
Web Site: www.globaltv.com
Founded: 1974

GlobalStreams™ Corp
2432 Heartland Ave, St Louis, MO 63114
Tel: 314-997-5100 *Toll Free Tel:* 800-788-7205
E-mail: sales@globalstreams.com
Web Site: www.globalstreams.com
Founded: 2000
Provider of video communications hardware & software for the video production professional.
Branch Office(s)
141 Millwell Dr, Suite A, St Louis, MO 63043 (cust support)

Globe Photos LLC
6445 Tenaya Way, B-130, Las Vegas, NV 89113
Tel: 702-210-6208 *Fax:* 631-321-4063
E-mail: info@globephotos.com
Web Site: www.globephotos.com
Key Personnel
CEO: Stuart Scheinman
Dir, Licensing: Regina Feiler
Founded: 1939
Stock celebrity photos.
Catalog(s) available

Gluskin's Custom Audio Video
Division of Gluskin's Inc
2051 Pacific Ave, Stockton, CA 95204
Tel: 209-888-4609 *Fax:* 209-888-4629
E-mail: info@gluskinsav.com
Web Site: www.gluskins.com; www.gluskinsav.com
Key Personnel
Owner: Greg Dooley
Founded: 2008
Photographic equipment design, installation, service & repair.
Membership(s): Custom Electronic Design & Installation Association

GMI Productions
Division of General Mills Inc
One General Mills Blvd, Minneapolis, MN 55426
Mailing Address: PO Box 9452, Minneapolis, MN 55440

Tel: 763-764-7600 *Toll Free Tel:* 800-248-7310
  Fax: 763-764-8330
Web Site: www.generalmills.com
Key Personnel
Mgr, AV & Video Prodn Servs: Eric Swenson
  E-mail: eric.swenson@genmills.com
Audio & video resources relating to General
  Mills brands.

GMP, see Green Mountain Post Films (GMP)

GMP Music
Division of Gene Michael Productions Inc
1103 North St, Niles, MI 49120
Tel: 269-687-9100 *Toll Free Tel:* 800-955-0619
  Fax: 269-687-9200
E-mail: info@gmpmusic.com
Web Site: www.gmpmusic.com; www.
  reservemusic.com
Key Personnel
Owner: Gene Ort
Founded: 1989
Production music library.
Catalog(s) available

GNP Crescendo Records
1405 N Avon St, Burbank, CA 91505-1885
Tel: 818-566-8900
E-mail: gnpcrescendo@gmail.com
Web Site: www.gnpcrescendo.com
Key Personnel
Pres: Neil Norman
Founded: 1954
Music & soundtracks.
Catalog(s) available, free

Go To Team
665 Johnnie Dodds Blvd, Suite 201, Mount
  Pleasant, SC 29464
Tel: 843-884-6222 *Toll Free Tel:* 888-455-4333
E-mail: crew@gototeam.com
Web Site: www.gototeam.com
Key Personnel
Mng Partner: Shawn Moffatt *E-mail:* smoffatt@
  gototeam.com
Partner: Patrick Bryant
Dir, Photog: Dave Baker
Founded: 1997
On location videography. High-end broadcast
  video crews located throughout the country.

Goal Productions
1905 Victory Blvd, Suite 6, Glendale, CA 91201
Tel: 818-588-3900 *Fax:* 818-588-3903
E-mail: info@goalproductions.com
Web Site: www.goalproductions.com
Key Personnel
Pres: Robert Ballo *E-mail:* rballo@
  goalproductions.com
Mktg Dir: Alysia Camp *E-mail:* acamp@
  goalproductions.com
Prodr: Griff Partington *E-mail:* gpartington@
  goalproductions.com
Founded: 1969
Digital video & film production company.
Membership(s): Television Academy

Goddard Design Co
51 Nassau Ave, Brooklyn, NY 11222
Tel: 718-599-0170 *Fax:* 718-599-0172
E-mail: sales@goddarddesign.com
Web Site: www.goddarddesign.com
Key Personnel
Owner: Bob Goddard
Off Mgr: Rosemary F Heath
Founded: 1972
Manufacture & sales of electronic test & control
  equipment for theater. Manufacture RDM &
  DMX 512 test equipment & DMX 512/RDM
  processing & distribution equipment. We ship
  worldwide.

Online catalog(s) available
Membership(s): Professional Lighting & Sound
  Association; USITT

The Godfrey Group Inc
113 Roseroot Ct, Holly Springs, NC 27540
Tel: 919-544-6504 *Toll Free Tel:* 800-789-9394
E-mail: sales@godfreygroup.com
Web Site: www.godfreygroup.com
Key Personnel
Pres: Will Daniel Godfrey
Founded: 1970
Design trade show display exhibits using custom
  design graphics, photography & more.
Catalog(s) available

Gold Line/TEF
PO Box 500, West Redding, CT 06896-0500
Tel: 203-938-2588 *Fax:* 203-938-8740
E-mail: sales@gold-line.com
Web Site: www.gold-line.com
Founded: 1961
Manufacture audio test equipment & equalizers
  for the sound installer.
Online catalog(s) available
Membership(s): AES; Custom Electronic Design
  & Installation Association

Gold Link Productions Inc
1457 Pembroke Dr, Oakville, ON L6H 1V6,
  Canada
Tel: 416-560-3864
E-mail: goldlinkproductions@gmail.com; info@
  torontocameramanservices.com
Web Site: www.torontocameramanservices.com
Key Personnel
Camera Operator: Silvio Bulgaretti
Founded: 1993
Freelance camera operator: EFP for broadcast &
  corporate.
Membership(s): International Cinematographers
  Guild

Gold Standard Productions
Division of Gold Standard Enterprises
12952 Miriam Place, Santa Ana, CA 92705-1334
Tel: 714-544-7000 *Fax:* 714-544-7010
Web Site: www.goldstandardproductions.com
Key Personnel
Dir, Photog: Gary Stone *E-mail:* gkstone@
  earthlink.net
Full service audio & video production.
Membership(s): AOPA

Goldberg Brothers Inc
10488 W Centennial Rd, Suite 100, Littleton, CO
  80127
Tel: 303-321-1099
E-mail: reelservice@goldbergbrothers.com
Web Site: www.goldbergbrothers.com
Key Personnel
Pres: John Golesh
Founded: 1897
Movie theater & home theater equipment, decor
  & accessories.
Catalog(s) available

Bruce Goldberg Inc
5354 Quakertown Ave, Woodland Hills, CA
  91364
Tel: 818-713-8190 *Toll Free Tel:* 800-527-6248
  Fax: 818-704-9189
E-mail: drbg@sbcglobal.net
Web Site: www.drbrucegoldberg.com
Key Personnel
Dir: Bruce Goldberg
Catalog(s) available

Golden Gate Studios
Division of KTLN-TV
100 Pelican Way, Suite E, San Rafael, CA 94901

Tel: 415-485-5856 *Fax:* 415-256-9262
Web Site: www.goldengatestudios.com
Key Personnel
Admin Asst: Lara Peterson *E-mail:* lpeterson@
  tln.com
Founded: 1974

Golden Lamb Productions
47 Schoolhouse Rd, Nassau, NY 12123
Tel: 518-766-4358
Web Site: www.glpvideoproduction.com
Key Personnel
Pres: Dow Haynor
Founded: 1986
Provide SD & HD camera crews throughout the
  Northeast. Complete SD & HD production.

**Golden State Dance Teachers Association
  (GSDTA)**
Division of Alterra Publishing
10804 Woodruff Ave, Downey, CA 90241-3910
Tel: 562-869-8949
Web Site: www.swingworld.com
Key Personnel
Owner: Skippy Blair *E-mail:* skippy@skippyblair.
  com
Dance education.
Catalog(s) available

Golf Digest Publications
Division of Conde Nast
One World Trade Center, 27th fl, New York, NY
  10007-0090
Tel: 212-286-2860 *Toll Free Tel:* 800-962-5513
Web Site: www.golfdigest.com
Key Personnel
Chmn & Ed-in-Chief: Jerry Tarde
Publr: Dan Robertson
Ed, Golf Digest Resource Ctr: Cliff Schrock
Educational golf videos & books.
Catalog(s) available

Goose Creek Music & Entertainment
17723 Tranquility Rd, Purcellville, VA 20132
Tel: 540-751-1395
E-mail: info@goosecreekmusic.com
Web Site: www.goosecreekmusic.com
Key Personnel
Pres & COO: Mike Pugh
Head, Busn Devt: Paul Shreve
Founded: 2008
Audio & video recordings of original Americana
  music by emerging artists. Specialize in record-
  ing live performances.

Alan Gordon Enterprises Inc
5625 Melrose Ave, Hollywood, CA 90038
Tel: 323-466-3561 *Fax:* 323-871-2193
E-mail: contactus@alangordon.com
Web Site: www.alangordon.com
Key Personnel
Co-Owner: Grant Loucks; Don Sahlein
Pres: Wayne Loucks
EVP: Stacey Sahlein
Founded: 1947
Manufacture, sales & rental of professional mo-
  tion picture & video equipment.
Online catalog(s) available
Membership(s): American Society for Photogram-
  metry and Remote Sensing; American Society
  of Cinematographers; NAB

Gordon Productions Inc
469 Magellan Ave, San Francisco, CA 94116
Tel: 415-776-7484
Web Site: www.gpvideo.com; www.vimeo.
  com/gordonproductions
Key Personnel
Pres: John T Gordon *E-mail:* john@gpvideo.com
Corporate video production.
Membership(s): National Association of Broad-
  cast Communications

Gospel Folio Press
304 Killaly St W, Port Colborne, ON L3K 6A6, Canada
Tel: 905-835-9166 *Toll Free Tel:* 800-952-2382
    Fax: 905-834-0012
E-mail: info@gospelfolio.com; orders@
    gospelfolio.com
Web Site: www.gospelfolio.com
Key Personnel
Sales Mgr: Sam Cairns
Founded: 1923
Religious programming distribution.
Catalog(s) available

Gotham Sound & Communications Inc
35-10 36 Ave, 2nd fl, Long Island City, NY 11106
Tel: 212-629-9430 *Toll Free Tel:* 866-468-4268
    Fax: 212-629-9436
E-mail: nyc@gothamsound.com
Web Site: www.gothamsound.com
Key Personnel
Owner: Jim Guzzi; Peter Schneider
Gen Mgr: Joe Mulica
Founded: 2002
Audio solution company that rents, sells & repairs audio equipment.
Branch Office(s)
500 Bishop St NW, Suite F-5, Atlanta, GA
    30318 *Tel:* 404-855-2255 *Fax:* 404-855-2256
    E-mail: atl@gothamsound.com

GP Studios
Formerly Georgia-Pacific Television & Photography
Subsidiary of Georgia-Pacific LLC
133 Peachtree St NE, 1st fl, Atlanta, GA 30303
Tel: 404-652-5690
E-mail: gpstudios@gapac.com
Web Site: www.gpstudios.tv
Full service production facility.

Grace Church - St Louis
2695 Creve Coeur Mill Rd, Maryland Heights, MO 63043
Tel: 314-292-8300 *Fax:* 314-291-0918
E-mail: info@gracestl.org
Web Site: www.gracestl.org
Key Personnel
Sr Pastor: Ron Tucker *Tel:* 314-292-8300 ext
    2119 *E-mail:* ront@gracestl.org
Personnel Dir: Mike Schmidt *Tel:* 314-292-8300
    ext 2115 *E-mail:* mikes@gracestl.org
Tech Dir: Ron Krause *Tel:* 314-292-8300 ext
    2196 *E-mail:* ronk@gracestl.org
Founded: 1978
Religious audio programs (pastor's sermons).

Grafco Inc
Division of Toledo Furniture
2018 W Main St, Stroudsburg, PA 18360
Mailing Address: PO Box 431, Stroudsburg, PA 18360
Toll Free Tel: 800-367-6169 *Fax:* 570-213-0369
    Toll Free Fax: 800-443-4329
E-mail: info@toledofurniture.com
Web Site: www.toledofurniture.com
Key Personnel
Pres: Steve Mavin
Computer tables for schools with cable management.
Catalog(s) available

Graftek Imaging Inc
8900 Shoal Creek Blvd, Bldg 300, Suite B, Austin, TX 78757
Tel: 512-416-1099 *Toll Free Tel:* 800-441-2118
    Fax: 512-416-1014
E-mail: graftek@graftek.com
Web Site: www.graftek.com

Key Personnel
CFO: Jane Sims *Tel:* 512-416-1099 ext 103
Founded: 1984
Machine vision hardware & software solutions.
Catalog(s) available

Grand Stage Co Inc
3418 N Knox Ave, Chicago, IL 60641
Tel: 312-332-5611 *Toll Free Tel:* 800-621-2181
    Fax: 312-332-3655
E-mail: marketing@grandstage.com
Web Site: www.grandstage.com
Key Personnel
Pres & Mktg: Gregory Becker *Tel:* 312-332-5611
    ext 155 *E-mail:* grbecker@grandstage.com
Rentals Mgr: Ruth Hudson *Tel:* 312-332-5611 ext
    127 *E-mail:* rhudson@grandstage.com
Sales Mgr: Hope Kass *Tel:* 312-332-5611 ext 129
    E-mail: hkass@grandstage.com
Founded: 1947
Stage lighting distribution.
Online catalog(s) available
Branch Office(s)
1319 W Grand Ave, Chicago, IL 60642 (quick
    serv store)
Membership(s): Entertainment Services and Technology Association; Professional Lighting & Sound Association

Grande Vitesse Systems Inc (GVS)
390 Fremont St, San Francisco, CA 94105-2316
Tel: 415-777-0320; 415-777-9937 (intl); 917-
    744-4270 (rental); 818-823-1760 (sales)
    Toll Free Tel: 800-794-4622 (sales) *Fax:* 415-
    777-9544
Web Site: www.gvs9000.com; www.gvsf.com
Founded: 1989
Develop & manufacture digital acquisition, storage & distribution units for thousands of clients worldwide.

GRANGER - Historical Picture Archive
Division of The Granger Collection Ltd
25 Chapel St, Suite 605, New York, NY 11201
Tel: 212-447-1789 *Fax:* 212-447-1492
E-mail: grangerinfo@granger.com
Web Site: www.granger.com
Founded: 1964
Archival image library providing image content to educational publishers, news organizations, documentary producers, etc. Collection of historical prints & photographs from prehistoric times through the recent past. NB stills only, no film footage.
Online catalog(s) available
Membership(s): American Society of Picture Professionals; Digital Media Licensing Association

Graphic Laminating LLC
6185 Cochran Rd, Solon, OH 44139
Tel: 440-498-3400 *Toll Free Tel:* 800-345-5300
    Fax: 440-498-3410
E-mail: info@graphiclaminating.com
Web Site: www.graphiclaminating.com
Key Personnel
Pres: Michael Hannon
Admin Mgr: Ginger Hannon
Manufactures laminating equipment (LEDCO Division), films & paper. Also provides laminating services.
Catalog(s) available
Membership(s): Education Market Association

Graphic Technology Inc, see GTI (Graphic
    Technology Inc)

Graphx Inc
400 W Cummings Park, Woburn, MA 01801
Tel: 781-932-0430 *Fax:* 781-932-0855
E-mail: support@graphx.com
Web Site: photogize.net

Key Personnel
Founder & CTO: Pete Traversy
Pres & CEO: Joseph Kowalik
Founded: 1986
Software digital printers & RIP for digital printers. Web based print fulfillment for digital mini-labs.
Membership(s): DIMA; The Imaging Alliance

Grass Valley
3499 Douglas-B-Floreani, Montreal, QC H4S 2C6, Canada
Tel: 514-333-1772 *Fax:* 514-333-9828
Web Site: www.grassvalley.com
Key Personnel
Mktg Communs & PR: Elaine Tipping
    E-mail: elaine.tipping@grassvalley.com
Founded: 1959
Broadcast media.
Catalog(s) available
Membership(s): Alliance for IP Media Solutions;
    European Broadcasting Union; IABM; IBC;
    NAB; SMPTE®; Video Services Forum

Gravity Media
7701 Haskell Ave, Van Nuys, CA 91406
Tel: 818-955-9449; 747-258-4100 *Fax:* 818-955-
    9779
E-mail: enquiries@gravitymedia.com
Web Site: www.gravitymedia.com
Key Personnel
Pres, US Opers: Michael Harabin
    E-mail: michael.harabin@gravitymedia.com
Founded: 2000
Specialize in media services & facilities, production & content, equipment rental & sales.

Great Chefs/Leisure Jazz Video
Division of GCI Inc
747 Magazine St, New Orleans, LA 70130
Tel: 504-581-5000 *Toll Free Tel:* 800-321-1499
    Fax: 504-581-1188
E-mail: info@greatchefs.com
Web Site: www.greatchefs.com
Key Personnel
Chmn & CEO: John Shoup *E-mail:* shoup@
    greatchefs.com
Cooking technique shows.
Membership(s): Entertainment Merchants Association; MIP; NATPE

Great Recordings LLC
1812 Procter St, Port Arthur, TX 77640
Mailing Address: PO Box 1436, Port Arthur, TX 77641-1436
Tel: 409-982-7121
E-mail: music@great-recordings.com
Web Site: www.great-recordings.com
Key Personnel
Owner: Floyd J Badeaux
Founded: 1957
CD premastering & audio noise reduction.

Great River Electronics
164 Hardman Ave S, South St Paul, MN 55075
Tel: 651-455-1846 *Fax:* 651-455-3224
E-mail: info@greweb.com
Web Site: www.greatriverelectronics.com
Key Personnel
Founder & CEO: Dan Kennedy
    E-mail: dkennedy@greweb.com
Founded: 1994

The Great Southern Studios
15221 NE 21 Ave, North Miami Beach, FL 33162
Tel: 305-944-2464 *Fax:* 305-944-9920
E-mail: info@gssmiami.com
Web Site: www.greatsouthernstudios.com
Key Personnel
Owner & Pres: Arlene Gillen

Owner: Phil Gillen
Founded: 1978
Scenery, studios, concept & design & lighting
    equipment rentals.
Catalog(s) available
Membership(s): AICP

William Greaves Productions Inc
475 W 57 St, No 17A, New York, NY 10019
Toll Free Tel: 800-874-8314 *Fax:* 212-315-0027
Web Site: www.williamgreaves.com
Key Personnel
Pres: Louise Greaves
Founded: 1964
Production of educational videos & documen-
    taries.
Online catalog(s) available

Green Dot Audio Electronics
PO Box 290609, Nashville, TN 37229-0609
Tel: 615-366-5964 *Fax:* 615-366-7069
E-mail: greendotaudio@bellsouth.net
Web Site: www.greendotaudio.com
Key Personnel
Owner: Mark Nadlin
Founded: 1989
Distributor of Neutrik/Rean/Switchcraft/EDAC
    parts.

Green Mountain Post Films (GMP)
PO Box 229, Turners Falls, MA 01376-0229
Tel: 413-863-4754 *Fax:* 413-863-8248
E-mail: info@gmpfilms.com
Web Site: www.gmpfilms.com
Key Personnel
Pres: Daniel Keller
VP & Ad Mgr: Charles Light
Founded: 1975
Complete film & video production & distribution.
Catalog(s) available
Shipping Address: 23 Unity St, Turners Falls, MA
    01376

Dr Ida Greene, see People Skills International

Greenery Studios
7764 San Fernando Rd, Burbank, CA 91352
Tel: 818-253-9990
E-mail: info@greenerystudios.com
Web Site: greenerystudios.com
Service for motion pictures, TV, commercials,
    music videos & photography.

Greenwich Entertainment
610 Fifth Ave, 3rd fl, New York, NY 10020
E-mail: info@greenwichentertainment.com;
    booking@greenwichentertainment.com;
    publicity@greenwichentertainment.com;
    acquisitions@greenwichentertainment.com
Web Site: greenwichentertainment.com
Key Personnel
Pres: Edmondo Schwartz
Co-Mng Dir: Ed Arentz; Andy Bohn
Founded: 2017
Independent film distribution company. Special-
    ize in distinctive, theatrical-quality narrative &
    documentary features.

GretagMacbeth, see X-Rite

Griesinger Films LLC
7300 Old Mill Rd, Gates Mills, OH 44040
Tel: 440-423-1601 *Toll Free Tel:* 800-872-4456
    Fax: 440-423-1601
E-mail: orders@griesingerfilms.com
Web Site: www.griesingerfilms.com
Key Personnel
Prodr & Dir: Peter Root Griesinger
    E-mail: peterg@griesingerfilms.com

Founded: 1974
Unique environmental films from an economic
    perspective.

Griffith Productions
1750 Donelson Dr, Eads, TN 38028
Tel: 901-351-1899 *Fax:* 901-465-1787
E-mail: info@griffithproductions.tv
Web Site: www.griffithproductions.tv
Key Personnel
Pres: Ed Griffith
Founded: 1992
Video production for TV, music, video, commer-
    cials, corporate & documentary.

Griggs Productions Inc
Kappas Marina, 29 W Pier, Sausalito, CA 94965
Tel: 415-999-1079 *Toll Free Tel:* 800-210-4200
Web Site: www.griggs.com
Key Personnel
Prodr & CEO: Lewis Brown Griggs
Founded: 1983
Diversity, culture & relationship training. Videos,
    DVDs, CD-ROMs & online programs as well
    as workshops & speaking.
Catalog(s) available

Grise Audio Visual Center Inc
2402 Cherry St, Erie, PA 16507
Tel: 814-452-4465
E-mail: grise@erie.net
Web Site: griseav.com
Key Personnel
CEO: Jim Grise
Pres & Sr AV Technician: Don Grise
Founded: 1947
Full service AV production company.
Catalog(s) available
Membership(s): Audiovisual and Integrated Expe-
    rience Association

GrooveWorx
1200 Chickory Lane, Santa Monica, CA 90049
Tel: 310-260-2626 *Fax:* 310-260-2662
E-mail: info@grooveworx.com
Web Site: grooveworx.com
Key Personnel
Pres: Dain Blair
Founded: 1997
Music production studio. Scoring for television
    shows, feature film trailers & national commer-
    cials. Radio imaging services.

Ground Support Equipment (US) Ltd, see
    Biomorph Desks

Group One Ltd
70 Sea Lane, Farmingdale, NY 11735
Tel: 631-396-0195 (audio div); 631-396-0184
    (lighting div) *Fax:* 631-396-0190
E-mail: sales@g1limited.com
Web Site: www.g1limited.com
Key Personnel
Pres: Jack Kelly *E-mail:* jackk@g1limited.com
VP, US Sales-Audio: Chris Fichera *Tel:* 310-927-
    7788 *E-mail:* chris@abluesky.com
VP, US Sales-Lighting: Vincent Finnegan
    E-mail: vinnyf@g1limited.com
Import & distribute audio & lighting products.
Catalog(s) available
Membership(s): AES; NAB; NAMM, the Na-
    tional Association of Music Merchants; Profes-
    sional Lighting & Sound Association

Group PVP
296 Saint Pierre St, Matane, QC G4W 2B9,
    Canada
Tel: 418-566-2040 *Toll Free Tel:* 877-320-2040
    Fax: 418-562-4643
E-mail: info@pvp.ca
Web Site: www.pvp.ca

Key Personnel
Pres & Prodr: Vic Pelletier
VP & Prodr: Vincent Leroux
VP, Devt: Robert Tremblay
Founded: 1985
Produce documentaries for television, animation
    film & series, fiction, web sites.
Branch Office(s)
67 Elizabeth St, Longueuil, QC J4H 1J3, Canada
    Tel: 450-670-5858 *Fax:* 450-670-5859
Membership(s): APFTQ

GTI (Graphic Technology Inc)
PO Box 3138, Newburgh, NY 12550-0651
Tel: 845-562-7066 *Toll Free Tel:* 888-562-7066
    Fax: 845-562-2543
E-mail: sales@gtilite.com
Web Site: www.gtilite.com
Key Personnel
Pres: Robert McCurdy
Sales Mktg Coord: Linda Sutherland
Online catalog(s) available
Shipping Address: 211 Dupont Ave, Newburgh,
    NY 12550

Guerrilla Productions LLC
1119 E 50 St, Savannah, GA 31404
Tel: 912-354-1518 *Fax:* 404-585-5692
E-mail: info@guerrillapro.com
Web Site: guerrillapro.com
Key Personnel
Pres: Wil Kazary
Founded: 2001
Video & television production.
Branch Office(s)
PO Box 20852, Raleigh, NC 27619 *Tel:* 919-349-
    7643

Guerrilla Video Solutions, see Buffalo Video
    Production

**Guidance Associates Inc Center for
    Humanities**
31 Pine View Rd, Mount Kisco, NY 10549
Tel: 914-420-2363 *Toll Free Tel:* 800-431-1242
    Fax: 914-666-5319
Web Site: www.guidanceassociates.com
Key Personnel
Pres: Will Goodman *E-mail:* willg1961@gmail.
    com
Publish educational videos & DVDs.
Catalog(s) available
Membership(s): American Personnel & Guidance
    Association; Audiovisual and Integrated Expe-
    rience Association

Guilford Publications
370 Seventh Ave, Suite 1200, New York, NY
    10001-1020
Tel: 212-431-9800 *Toll Free Tel:* 800-365-7006
    Fax: 212-966-6708
E-mail: info@guilford.com
Web Site: www.guilford.com
Key Personnel
Mktg Dir: Marian Robinson
Acct Mgr: Estefeni Estremera *Tel:* 212-431-9800
    ext 258 *E-mail:* estefeni.estremera@guilford.
    com
Sales Mgr: Anne Patota *E-mail:* anne.patota@
    guilford.com
Publisher of books, periodicals, software & DVDs
    in mental health, education, geography & re-
    search methods.
Catalog(s) available
Foreign Office(s): Footprint Books, 1/6a Pros-
    perity Parade, Warriewood, NSW 2102, Aus-
    tralia *Tel:* (02) 9997 3973 *Fax:* (02) 9997 3185
    E-mail: info@footprint.com.au *Web Site:* www.
    footprint.com.au
Taylor & Francis Asia Pacific, No 06-09 Siemens
    Ctr, Block 1, 60 MacPherson Rd, Singapore
    348574, Singapore *Tel:* 6741 5166 *Fax:* 6742
    9356 *E-mail:* info@tandf.com.sg (Brunei, Cam-

bodia, China, Hong Kong, Indonesia, Korea, Laos, Malaysia, Myanmar, Philippines, Singapore, Thailand, Vietnam)
Juta & Co Ltd, Sunclare Bldg, 1st fl, 21 Dreyer St, Claremont, Cape Town 7708, South Africa *Tel:* (021) 659 2300 *Fax:* (021) 659 2360 *E-mail:* orders@juta.co.za
Unifacmanu Trading, 4F, No 19 Ho-Ping E Rd, Section 1, Taipei 10609, Taiwan *Tel:* (02) 2391 4280 *Fax:* (02) 2394 3103 *E-mail:* unifacmu@ms34.hinet.net *Web Site:* www.unifacmanu.com.tw
Taylor & Francis, c/o Bookpoint Ltd, 130 Milton Park, Abingdon, Oxon OX14 4SB, United Kingdom *Tel:* (01235) 400 524 *Fax:* (01235) 400 525 *E-mail:* tandf@bookpoint.co.uk *Web Site:* www.guilfordpress.co.uk

Guymark Studios LLC
3019 Dixwell Ave, Hamden, CT 06518
Mailing Address: PO Box 5037, Hamden, CT 06518-5037
Tel: 203-248-9323 *Fax:* 203-248-9325
E-mail: guymark.studios@snet.net
Web Site: www.guymarkstudios.com
Key Personnel
Owner & VP: Mark L Guarino
Pres: Anthony Guy Guarino
Off Mgr: Susan Guarino
Founded: 1950
Full AV production studio.
Online catalog(s) available

GVISION USA Inc
20532 Crescent Bay Dr, Lake Forest, CA 92630
Tel: 949-586-3338 *Fax:* 949-272-4594
E-mail: info@gvision-usa.com
Web Site: gvision-usa.com
Key Personnel
Gen Mgr: Darren Somo
Founded: 1999
LCD monitors, touch screens, open frame units, stands & mounts.

Gyration
3601 Calle Tecate, Suite B, Camarillo, CA 93012
Toll Free Tel: 888-340-0033 (tech support)
E-mail: gsupport@smkusa.com; info@smkusa.com
Web Site: www.gyration.com
Key Personnel
Gen Mgr: John Blair
Founded: 1989
Manufacture & distribute motion-sensing technology for in-air navigation & cursor control on a television screen or monitor.
Online catalog(s) available
Brochure(s) available

Howard Hall Productions
2171 La Amatista Rd, Del Mar, CA 92014-3031
Tel: 858-259-8989
Web Site: www.howardhall.com
Key Personnel
Owner: Howard Hall; Michele Hall
Founded: 1988
TV & IMAX film production; natural history wildlife stock footage library - originated in HD. Shoot special assignments. Time lapse underwater & topside photography.
Membership(s): AMPAS; DGA; Television Academy

Hall Productions
951 Front St, Grover Beach, CA 93433
Mailing Address: PO Box 645, Grover Beach, CA 93483
Tel: 805-473-1042 *Fax:* 805-473-2202
Web Site: hallpro.com
Key Personnel
Pres: Dan Hall *E-mail:* dan@hallpro.com

Handcrafted light boxes & light tables.
Online catalog(s) available
Membership(s): The Imaging Alliance

Hallel Communications
Hallel Institute, 175 Rte 340, Sparkill, NY 10976-1047
Tel: 845-365-2277 *Toll Free Tel:* 800-445-7477 *Fax:* 845-365-2279
E-mail: hallel@hallel.net; info@hallelvideos.com
Web Site: www.hallelvideos.com
Key Personnel
Pres: George Torok
Founded: 1974
Full service video production company.
Online catalog(s) available

Steven Halpern's Inner Peace Music
PO Box 2644, San Anselmo, CA 94979-2644
Toll Free Tel: 800-909-0707 (orders)
E-mail: info@innerpeacemusic.com
Web Site: www.innerpeacemusic.com
Key Personnel
COO: Diana Ziegler *Tel:* 415-485-5321 *E-mail:* dvz@innerpeacemusic.com
Private record label.
Online catalog(s) available
Shipping Address: 701 Mistletoe Rd, Ashland, OR 97520 *Toll Free Tel:* 888-765-9697

Hamilton Studio
1427 W Dean Ave, Spokane, WA 99201
Tel: 509-327-9501
E-mail: info@hamiltonstudio.com
Web Site: www.hamiltonstudio.com
Key Personnel
Prodr: Don Hamilton *E-mail:* don@hamiltonstudio.com; Lorna St John *E-mail:* lorna@hamiltonstudio.com
Film/video production & commercial photography.
Membership(s): ASMP

HamiltonBuhl
Division of Vcom IMC
80 Little Falls Rd, Fairfield, NJ 07004
Toll Free Tel: 800-631-0868 *Toll Free Fax:* 800-398-1812 (cust serv & sales)
E-mail: customerservice@hamiltonbuhl.com; info@hamiltonbuhl.com; sales@hamiltonbuhl.com
Web Site: www.hamiltonbuhl.com
Founded: 1933
Design & manufacture of electronics & presentation equipment for education & industry.
Online catalog(s) available
Membership(s): Audiovisual and Integrated Experience Association; Education Market Association

Hammond Communications Group Inc
173 Trade St, Lexington, KY 40511
Tel: 859-254-1878
E-mail: info@hammondcg.com
Web Site: hammondcg.com
Key Personnel
Pres: Ron Mossotti
VP, Interactive Media: Craig Miller *Tel:* 859-254-1878 ext 119 *E-mail:* craig@hammondcg.com
VP, Video Prodn: Jesse Kelsey *Tel:* 859-254-1878 ext 109 *E-mail:* jkelsey@hammondcg.com
Prodn Coord: Angie Poole
Founded: 1980
Multimedia production facility specializing in digital signage, live events/broadcast productions, media support services & web/interactive.

Hampshire Street Studios
540A Hampshire St, San Francisco, CA 94110
Tel: 415-643-5580
E-mail: info@hampshirestreetstudios.com

Web Site: www.hampshirestreetstudios.com
Soundstage & facilities rental.

Hand Held Films
129 W 27 St, New York, NY 10001
Tel: 212-627-2781; 212-502-0900 (rentals) *Fax:* 212-502-0906
E-mail: rentals@handheldfilms.com
Web Site: handheldfilms.com
Founded: 1987
Offers rental of digital HD cameras, lenses & accessories, film equipment, grip & lighting.

Howard Hanger
Affiliate of Jazz Fantasy
31 Park Ave N, Asheville, NC 28801
Tel: 828-280-8419
E-mail: howardhangerhall@gmail.com
Web Site: www.contacthoward.com
Catalog(s) available

Terry Hanley Audio Systems Inc
20 Industrial Pkwy, Woburn, MA 01801
Tel: 781-932-5300 *Fax:* 781-932-5354
E-mail: mail@terryhanleyaudio.com
Web Site: www.terryhanleyaudio.com
Key Personnel
CEO & Pres: Terrence Hanley
Gen Mgr & Acct Mgr: John Doerschuk *E-mail:* john@terryhanleyaudio.com
Sales Mgr & Chief Engr: Daniel Kidwell
Founded: 1969

G W Hannaway & Associates
839 Pearl St, Boulder, CO 80302
Tel: 303-440-9631 *Fax:* 303-440-4421
E-mail: sales@gwha.com; services@gwha.com; technology@gwha.com
Web Site: www.gwha.com
Key Personnel
Busn Mgr: Sarah Anderson
Founded: 1975

Hannay Reels Inc
553 State Rte 143, Westerlo, NY 12193-0159
Tel: 518-797-3791 *Toll Free Tel:* 877-467-3357 *Fax:* 518-797-3259 *Toll Free Fax:* 800-733-5464
E-mail: reels@hannay.com
Web Site: www.hannay.com
Key Personnel
Pres & CEO: Eric Hannay
Mktg Mgr: Jennifer Wing
Founded: 1933
World's leading manufacturer of quality cable reels & AV reels. Offers infinite variety, built to order & delivered on time.
Catalog(s) available, free
Online catalog(s) available

Hannecke Display Systems Inc
Subsidiary of Hannecke Display Systems GmbH & Co KG
210 Grove St, Franklin, MA 02038
Tel: 774-235-2329 *Fax:* 508-528-0913
E-mail: info@hannecke.com
Web Site: www.hannecke.de/us
Online catalog(s) available
Membership(s): National Association of College Stores; Reading Recovery Council of North America; Shop Environments Association

Hanovia Specialty Lighting LLC
6 Evans St, Fairfield, NJ 07004
Tel: 973-651-5510 *Fax:* 973-651-5550
E-mail: sales@hanovia-uv.com
Web Site: www.hanovia-uv.com
Key Personnel
Mng Dir: Liming Du
Founded: 1905
Manufacture UV lamps & equipment.

Catalog(s) available
Foreign Office(s): 27-B Yifu Rd, Jiuting Songjiang, Shanghai 201615, China *Tel:* (021) 6762 7720 *Fax:* (021) 6762 7730

Harbro Corp
2691 W 15 St, Brooklyn, NY 11224-2705
Tel: 718-946-4134 *Toll Free Tel:* 800-GLI-PRO-1 (454-7761) *Fax:* 718-946-4151
E-mail: info@glipro.com
Web Site: www.glipro.com
Key Personnel
CEO: David Harari

Hard Hat Radio Music Service
519 N Halifax Ave, Daytona Beach, FL 32118-4017
Tel: 386-252-0381 *Fax:* 386-252-0381
E-mail: hardhatrecords@aol.com; hardhatrecords@bellsouth.net
Web Site: www.hardhatrecords.com
Key Personnel
CEO: Bobby Lee Cude
Founded: 1948
Membership(s): Alliance of Artists & Recording Companies; BMI; National Music Publishers' Association; The Recording Academy; SoundExchange

Hardcastle Films & Video
7319 Wise Ave, St Louis, MO 63117-1718
Tel: 314-647-4200
Key Personnel
Partner: Jeff Hardcastle
Founded: 1930

Hargrove Inc
One Hargrove Dr, Lanham, MD 20706
Tel: 301-306-9000 *Fax:* 301-306-9318
E-mail: exhibitorservices@hargroveinc.com
Web Site: www.hargroveinc.com
Key Personnel
CEO: Tim McGill
Pres & COO: Carla Hargrove McGill
Special events, exhibits & trade show company.
Catalog(s) available
Membership(s): EDPA; IAEM

Harman International Industries Inc
Subsidiary of Samsung Electronics Co Ltd
400 Atlantic St, 15th fl, Stamford, CT 06901
Tel: 203-328-3500
Web Site: www.harman.com
Key Personnel
CEO: Dinesh C Paliwal
EVP & CFO: Sandra E Rowland

Harman Pro North America, see Harman Professional Solutions

Harman Professional Solutions
Subsidiary of Harman International Industries Inc
8500 Balboa Blvd, Northridge, CA 91329
Tel: 818-893-8411 *Toll Free Tel:* 888-234-5450 (order support) *Fax:* 818-830-2921
E-mail: info@harman.com
Web Site: www.harman.com; shop.harmanpro.com; pro.harman.com
US distributor for AKG, AMX, BSS, Crown, dbx, DigiTech, JBL Professional, Lexicon, Martin, Soundcraft & Studer.
Catalog(s) available
Membership(s): AES; NSCA

Harmonia Mundi USA
Unit of PIAS
1117 Chestnut St, Burbank, CA 91506
Tel: 818-333-1500
E-mail: info-usa@harmoniamundi.com
Web Site: www.harmoniamundi.com

Key Personnel
Pres: Rene Goiffon
Dir, Press & PR: Sarah Folger *E-mail:* sfolger@harmoniamundi.com
Gen Mgr: Matthew Owen *E-mail:* mowen@harmoniamundi.com
Founded: 1958
Catalog(s) available

Harmon's Audio-Visual Services
Division of Jim Harmon Enterprises Inc
2533 Crystal Dr, Fort Myers, FL 33966
Mailing Address: PO Box 61127, Fort Myers, FL 33906-1127
Tel: 239-939-2273 *Fax:* 239-939-5966
E-mail: info@harmonsav.com
Web Site: www.harmonsav.com
Key Personnel
Owner: James R Harmon *E-mail:* jim@harmonsav.com
Prodn Mgr: Bobby Harmon *E-mail:* bobby@harmonsav.com
Founded: 2003
Full service audio, visual & lighting solution provider.
Membership(s): Audiovisual and Integrated Experience Association

Harnel Case Co
1600 Marshall Ave SE, Grand Rapids, MI 49507
Tel: 616-452-4522 *Fax:* 616-452-5514
E-mail: info@harnelcase.com
Web Site: www.harnelcase.com
Key Personnel
Owner: Doug Spencer
Contact: Mike Novy *E-mail:* mobrik@comcast.net
Founded: 1947
Quality custom case manufacturer.
Product sheet(s) available

HarperAudio
Division of HarperCollins Publishers Inc
10 E 53 St, New York, NY 10022
Tel: 212-207-7000 *Toll Free Tel:* 800-242-7737 *Fax:* 212-207-2582 *Toll Free Fax:* 800-822-4090
Web Site: www.harpercollins.com
Key Personnel
Chief Digital Offr: Chantal Restivo-Alessi
VP/Publr: Ana Marie Allessi
Exec Prodr: Caitlin Garing
Sr Prodr: Katie Ostrowka
Mktg Dir, Audio: Beth Ives *Tel:* 212-207-7286
Mng Ed: Karen Radner
Catalog(s) available

Harpers Ferry Historical Association
c/o National Park Bookshop, 723 Shenandoah St, Harpers Ferry, WV 25425
Mailing Address: PO Box 197, Harpers Ferry, WV 25425-0197
Tel: 304-535-6881 *Fax:* 304-535-6749
E-mail: info@hfpawv.org
Web Site: www.harpersferryhistory.org
Key Personnel
Exec Dir: Deborah Piscitelli
Film Libn: Whitney Richards
Founded: 1971
Online catalog(s) available

Harris Communications Inc
15155 Technology Dr, Eden Prairie, MN 55344
Tel: 952-906-1180 *Toll Free Tel:* 800-825-6758 *Fax:* 952-906-1099
E-mail: info@harriscomm.com
Web Site: www.harriscomm.com
Distribution of products including DVDs for deaf & hard-of-hearing individuals as well as the interpreters & hearing healthcare workers who associate with them.
Catalog(s) available, free, annual

Harris Corp
1025 W NASA Blvd, Melbourne, FL 32919-0001
Tel: 321-727-9100
E-mail: webmaster@harris.com
Web Site: www.harris.com
Key Personnel
Pres & CEO: William Brown
SVP & CFO: Rahul Ghai
An international communications & information technology company that serves government & commercial markets throughout the world.
Catalog(s) available

Harrison Brothers
47 N Chatham Pkwy, Chapel Hill, NC 27517
Toll Free Tel: 866-386-8335; 800-327-4414 *Toll Free Fax:* 800-327-6651
E-mail: info@harrisonbros.com
Web Site: www.thetapeworks.com
Key Personnel
Contact: Jeff Harrison *E-mail:* jeff@harrisonbros.com
Founded: 1986
Catalog(s) available

Harrison Consoles
1024 Firestone Pkwy, La Vergne, TN 37086-3505
Tel: 615-641-7200 *Fax:* 615-641-7224
E-mail: info@harrisonconsoles.com
Web Site: www.harrisonconsoles.com
Key Personnel
Sales/Advanced Prod Mgr: Gary Thielman *E-mail:* mixbus@harrisonconsoles.com
Founded: 1971
Brochure(s) available

Hartley Film Foundation
49 Richmondville Ave, Suite 204, Westport, CT 06880
Tel: 203-226-9500 *Toll Free Tel:* 800-937-1819 *Fax:* 203-227-6938
E-mail: info@hartleyfoundation.org
Web Site: hartleyfoundation.org
Key Personnel
Mng Dir: Sarah Masters
Off Mgr: Laura Healy
Documentary & audio meditation sales.
Online catalog(s) available

Hasselblad Bron Inc
Subsidiary of Victor Hasselblad AB (Denmark)
1080A Garden State Rd, Union, NJ 07083
Tel: 908-754-5800 *Toll Free Tel:* 800-367-6434; 800-456-0203 *Fax:* 908-754-5807
E-mail: sales@hasselbladbron.com; servicedept@hasselbladbron.com; productinfo@hasselbladbron.com
Web Site: www.hasselbladbron.com
Key Personnel
Pres & CEO: Michael Hejtmanek
VP: Joe Robinson *Tel:* 800-367-6434 ext 231
Photographic gear supplier. Products include studio & portable power packs, light reflectors & modifiers, tripod, shooting stand & grip gear & continuous lighting systems used for broadcast & cinema.
Catalog(s) available

Havas Creative
200 Hudson St, New York, NY 10013
Tel: 212-886-2000; 212-886-4100 *Fax:* 212-886-5013
Web Site: havas.com
Key Personnel
Chmn & CEO: Yannick Bollore
Chief Network Initiatives & Communs Offr: Yvonne Bond *E-mail:* yvonne.bond@havas.com
Advertising, marketing, corporate communications, design, digital & social media solutions.

Havas Edge
2386 Faraday Ave, Suite 200, Carlsbad, CA 92008
Tel: 760-929-0041
E-mail: info@havasedge.com
Web Site: www.havasedge.com
Key Personnel
CEO: Steve Netzley
Pres & COO: Greg Johnson
CFO: Eric Bush
EVP, Busn Devt: Shannon Ellis *E-mail:* shannon.ellis@havasedge.com
EVP, Client Strategy: Jim Lyons
Commns Mgr: Amber Boone *E-mail:* amber.boone@havasedge.com
Founded: 1988
Full service direct response agency with expertise across all digital, broadcast & media domains.
Branch Office(s)
6922 Hollywood Blvd, 2nd fl, Los Angeles, CA 90028 *Tel:* 310-734-1333
10 Summer St, Boston, MA 02110 *Tel:* 617-585-3000
200 Hudson St, New York, NY 10013

HAVE Inc
309 Power Ave, Hudson, NY 12534
Tel: 518-828-2000 *Toll Free Tel:* 888-999-HAVE (999-4283) *Fax:* 518-828-2008
E-mail: pro_sales@haveinc.com; have@haveinc.com
Web Site: www.haveinc.com
Key Personnel
Pres: Nancy Gordon *E-mail:* ngordon@haveinc.com
VP: Paul Swedenburg
Mktg Mgr: Kevin Stein *E-mail:* kstein@haveinc.com
Founded: 1977
Catalog(s) available
Membership(s): SBE

Hawaii Sound & Vision
PO Box 2267, Kailua-Kona, HI 96745
Tel: 808-982-8330 *Toll Free Tel:* 877-982-8330
Fax: 808-982-8340
E-mail: aloha@hawaiisav.com
Web Site: www.hawaiisav.com
AV equipment rental, full service entertainment crew & event enhancements.

Hay House Inc
PO Box 5100, Carlsbad, CA 92018-5100
Tel: 760-431-7695 (ext 2, intl) *Toll Free Tel:* 800-654-5126 (ext 2, US); 800-650-5115
Web Site: www.hayhouse.com
Key Personnel
Pres & CEO: Reid Tracy
Founded: 1984
International leader in inspirational & self-help publishing.
Catalog(s) available
Branch Office(s)
250 Park Ave S, Suite 201, New York, NY 10003
Tel: 646-484-4950 *Fax:* 646-484-4956

Hayden 5 Media LLC
22 W 27 St, 6th fl, New York, NY 10001
Tel: 212-871-9316
E-mail: hi@hayden5.com
Web Site: www.hayden5.com
Key Personnel
Co-Founder & Exec Prodr: Milos Silber; Todd Wiseman, Jr
Provides rental of studio & services for production & post-production.

Hazelden Publishing & Educational Services
Division of The Hazelden Betty Ford Foundation
15251 Pleasant Valley Rd, Center City, MN 55012-0011

Mailing Address: PO Box 176, Center City, MN 55012-0176
Tel: 651-213-4215 *Toll Free Tel:* 800-328-9000
Fax: 651-213-4404
E-mail: info@hazelden.org; customersupport@hazelden.org
Web Site: www.hazeldenbettyford.org
Key Personnel
SVP, Publg & Mktg Mgr: Helen Al Said
Catalog(s) available

HB Communications Inc
Affiliate of HB Group Inc
60 Dodge Ave, North Haven, CT 06473
Tel: 203-234-9246 *Toll Free Tel:* 800-243-4414
Fax: 203-234-2013
E-mail: info@hbcommunications.com
Web Site: hbcommunications.com
Key Personnel
Pres & Founder: Mackey Barron
CEO: Dana Barron
CFO: John Martin
EVP: George Bing; James Burke
Founded: 1946
Premier AV systems integration company. Satellite offices in New York, NY, Providence, RI & Waterford, VT.
Catalog(s) available
Branch Office(s)
1432 Main St, Waltham, MA 02451 *Tel:* 781-890-6046 *Fax:* 781-890-6048
1130 Globe Ave, Mountainside, NJ 07092
Tel: 908-654-3600 *Fax:* 908-654-9273
Membership(s): ATD; Audiovisual and Integrated Experience Association; International Facilities Management Association; NSCA

HB-Content
105 Butler St, Suite 2B, Brooklyn, NY 11231
Tel: 212-213-8824
E-mail: hb@hb-content.com
Web Site: www.hb-content.com; vimeopro.com/hbcontent
Key Personnel
Founder & Creative Dir: David Ragsdale
E-mail: david@hb-content.com
Founded: 2008
Full service film, video, new media & event production; video/film editing, audio editing & original music production.

HBO Home Entertainment Inc
1100 Avenue of the Americas, New York, NY 10036
Tel: 212-512-1000
Web Site: www.hbo.com
Founded: 1985

HBO Studio Productions
Division of Home Box Office
120-A E 23 St, New York, NY 10010
Tel: 212-512-7800
Web Site: www.hbostudio.com
Key Personnel
Dir, Studio Opers: Peter Consiglio
Founded: 1972
Full service production & post-production facility, studio & stage.
Shipping Address: 115 E 22 St, New York, NY 10010

HD Cinema
12233 W Olympic Blvd, Suite 158, Los Angeles, CA 90064
Tel: 310-434-9500 *Fax:* 310-499-5237 (efax)
Web Site: www.hd-cinema.com
Key Personnel
Contact: Jeff Blauvelt *E-mail:* jeff@hd-cinema.com
Founded: 1998

Production & post-production rental house with a vision for the creative use of 4K & HD technology for digital cinema & broadcast programming.

HD House
6312 NW 77 Ct, Miami, FL 33166
Tel: 305-597-7359 *Fax:* 305-597-7027
Web Site: thehdhouse.com
Key Personnel
CEO: Tony Perez *E-mail:* tony@thehdhouse.com
CTO: Gaston Fazio *E-mail:* gaston@thehdhouse.com
Dir, Opers: Samantha Harter *E-mail:* samantha@thehdhouse.com
Founded: 2008
Provides HD & digital cinema equipment rental packages, audio & lighting gear, portable post-production suites, crewing, technical & logistical support & studio space.

HD Source
1670 Enterprise Rd, Mississauga, ON L4W 4L4, Canada
Tel: 905-890-6905; 905-290-4430 (ZTV rentals)
E-mail: info@hdsource.ca
Web Site: www.hdsource.ca
Key Personnel
Owner: Steve Zajaczkiwsky
Specialize in professional products & services for broadcast, film & production. Offers complete state-of-the-art digital signage, AV products & solutions.
Online catalog(s) available
Membership(s): Canadian Society of Cinematographers; CCTA; MTCVA; SMPTE®

HDrental.com
Division of United Broadcast Group
16129 Covello St, Van Nuys, CA 91406
Tel: 818-994-3461
Web Site: hdrental.com
Key Personnel
CEO: John Schneider *Tel:* 818-625-4231 (cell)
E-mail: jon@hdrental.com
Sales Mgr: Nick Teti *Tel:* 484-390-0279 (cell)
E-mail: nick@hdrental.com
Film & television production equipment rentals.

HDTV Productions Inc
132-250 Shawville Blvd SE, No 209, Calgary, AB T2Y 2Z7, Canada
Tel: 403-931-1936
Web Site: www.hdtvproductions.com
Key Personnel
Dir, Photog: Douglas Munro *Tel:* 587-215-5511 (cell)
Ed: Margot McMaster *Tel:* 403-860-4184 (cell)
Founded: 1997
HD production services, cameras & HD editing.
Membership(s): International Alliance of Theatrical Stage Employees

Headlight Audio Visual Inc
74 Evergreen Dr, Portland, ME 04103-1066
Tel: 207-774-5998 *Toll Free Tel:* 800-247-0540
Fax: 207-774-4917
Web Site: www.headlightav.com
Key Personnel
Pres & CEO: Andrew Bruns *E-mail:* abruns@headlightav.com
COO: David P Coffin *E-mail:* dcoffin@headlightav.com
Founded: 1975
Catalog(s) available
Membership(s): Audiovisual and Integrated Experience Association

Headroom Digital Audio
Subsidiary of Plotkin Music Associates Inc
11 E 26 St, 19th fl, New York, NY 10010

Tel: 212-246-8400
E-mail: info@headroom.nyc
Web Site: www.headroom.nyc
Key Personnel
Pres: Jerry Plotkin
Studio Mgr: Darcy Becker
Sample(s) available

Health Communications Inc

3201 SW 15 St, Deerfield Beach, FL 33442-8124
Tel: 954-360-0909 *Toll Free Tel:* 800-441-5569
Fax: 954-360-0034
Web Site: www.hcibooks.com
Key Personnel
Pres: Peter Vegso
Founded: 1977
Catalog(s) available

Health Education Services

Division of Social Studies School Service
10200 Jefferson Blvd, Culver City, CA 90232
Mailing Address: PO Box 802, Culver City, CA
90232-0802
Tel: 310-839-2436 *Toll Free Tel:* 800-421-4246
Fax: 310-839-2249 *Toll Free Fax:* 800-944-
5432
E-mail: access@socialstudies.com;
customerservice@socialstudies.com
Web Site: www.socialstudies.com
Key Personnel
CEO: David Weiner
Chief Educ Offr: Dr Aaron Willis
Founded: 1965
Distributing supplementary educational materials.
Catalog(s) available

Hearing Loss Association of America (HLAA)

7910 Woodmont Ave, Suite 1200, Bethesda, MD
20814
Tel: 301-657-2248 *Fax:* 301-913-9413
E-mail: inquiry@hearingloss.org
Web Site: www.hearingloss.org
Key Personnel
Exec Dir: Barbara Kelley *E-mail:* bkelley@
hearingloss.org
Dir, Public Policy: Lise Hamlin
Natl Chapter & Membership Coord: Carla Beyer-
Smolin
Founded: 1979
Educational webinars & DVDs.

Hearst Entertainment & Syndication

Subsidiary of Hearst Corp
300 W 57 St, New York, NY 10019-5238
Web Site: www.hearst.com/entertainment-
syndication
Key Personnel
Pres: Neeraj Khemlani
SVP & CFO: Michael Bachmann
Cable television networks, digital video entertainment, cable television & digital video production, subscription video-on-demand services,
streaming music publishing & platform services, comics syndication & character licensing.
Online catalog(s) available
Membership(s): Entertainment Merchants Association; INTV; NAB; NATPE

Heart Breaker Entertainment LLC

10094 Lacy Rd, Hagerstown, IN 47346
Tel: 765-489-4048; 765-489-5558
Toll Free Tel: 800-843-3635 *Fax:* 765-489-4899
E-mail: info@videodj.com
Web Site: videodj.com
Key Personnel
Owner: Larry Black
Founded: 1978
Service provider for production services such as
stage, lighting, audio rentals & also a retailer
for top brands in the industry.

Heart Music Inc

PO Box 160326, Austin, TX 78716-0326
Tel: 512-795-2375 *Fax:* 512-795-9573
E-mail: info@heartmusic.com
Web Site: www.heartmusic.com
Key Personnel
Owner: Tab Bartling *E-mail:* tab@heartmusic.com
Phonograph record label.
Catalog(s) available
Membership(s): BMI; The Recording Academy

Heavy Melody

307 Seventh Ave, Suite 1203, New York, NY
10001
Tel: 212-675-9585 *Fax:* 212-675-9565
E-mail: contact_hm@heavymelodymusic.com
(studio inquiries)
Web Site: www.heavymelodymusic.com
Key Personnel
Creative Dir: Dave Fraser
Contact: Neil Goldberg
Founded: 2003
Composing original music for film, TV & video
games.

Hedquist Productions Inc

PO Box 1475, Fairfield, IA 52556-1475
Tel: 641-472-6708 *Toll Free Fax:* 855-510-5726
Web Site: www.hedquist.com
Key Personnel
Pres & Creative Dir: Jeffrey P Hedquist
E-mail: jeffrey@hedquist.com
Founded: 1985
Audio creation & production for all media. Cast-
ing, directing, talent payment, recording, edit-
ing & distribution.
Shipping Address: 2108 150 St, Fairfield, IA
52556

Heffernan Audio Visual

616 W Rhapsody, San Antonio, TX 78216
Tel: 210-732-4333
Key Personnel
Pres: Paul Heffernan
Presentation AV dealer & distributor.
Catalog(s) available

Heffernan Supply Co Inc, see Heffernan Audio
Visual

Grant Heilman Photography Inc

506 W Lincoln Ave, Lititz, PA 17543
Mailing Address: PO Box 317, Lititz, PA 17543
Tel: 717-626-0296 *Toll Free Tel:* 800-622-2046
Fax: 717-626-0971
E-mail: info@heilmanphoto.com
Web Site: www.heilmanphoto.com
Key Personnel
Pres & CEO: Sonia S Wasco *E-mail:* sw@
heilmanphoto.com
Founded: 1948
Stock photography.
Membership(s): AAAE; American Society of
Picture Professionals; North American Nature
Photography Association

Heinemann

Division of Houghton Mifflin Harcourt
361 Hanover St, Portsmouth, NH 03801-3912
Mailing Address: PO Box 6926, Portsmouth, NH
03802-6926
Tel: 603-431-7894 *Toll Free Tel:* 800-225-5800
Fax: 603-431-2214 *Toll Free Fax:* 877-231-
6980
E-mail: custserv@heinemann.com
Web Site: www.heinemann.com
Key Personnel
SVP & Publr: Vicki Boyd
VP, Mktg: Stephen Perepeluk
Dir, Sales: Terry Thomas

Sales Serv Mgr: Lori Lampert *E-mail:* lori.
lampert@heinemann.com
Founded: 1978
Publisher of professional resources for teachers.
Catalog(s) available

Heliotrope Studios

44 Oak St, Newton Upper Falls, MA 02464
Tel: 617-964-8181
E-mail: heliotropestudios@earthlink.net
Web Site: www.heliotropestudios.com
Key Personnel
Pres: Boyd Estus *E-mail:* boydestus@sprintmail.
com
Founded: 1984
Film & video production services; all formats:
film, digital video, analog video & HD.
Membership(s): International Alliance of Theatri-
cal Stage Employees

Helix Camera & Video

100 N Walnut St, Itasca, IL 60134
Tel: 312-421-6000 *Toll Free Tel:* 800-33-HELIX
(334-3549 orders) *Fax:* 312-421-1586
E-mail: info@helixcamera.com
Web Site: www.helixcamera.com
Key Personnel
Pres: Val Maros
Founded: 1963
Full service camera & video retailer.
Online catalog(s) available

Hellman Associates Inc

1225 W Fourth St, Waterloo, IA 50702
Mailing Address: PO Box 627, Waterloo, IA
50704-0627
Tel: 319-234-7055 *Toll Free Tel:* 800-747-7055
Fax: 319-234-2089
E-mail: info@hellman.com
Web Site: www.hellman.com
Key Personnel
Founder & Chmn: Robert B Hellman
Co-Pres: Tony Luetkehans; David McNurlen
VP, Busn Devt: Ross Bruno
Founded: 1981
Demo reel(s) available
Branch Office(s)
PO Box 17746, Golden, CO 80402 *Tel:* 303-726-
5031 *Fax:* 303-731-4883
The Gilbert Bldg, 413 Wacouta St, Suite 250, St
Paul, MN 55101 *Tel:* 651-256-1149 *Fax:* 651-
256-1158

Hello World Communications

118 W 22 St, 2nd fl, New York, NY 10011
Tel: 212-243-8800 *Fax:* 212-691-6961
E-mail: excitable01@gmail.com
Web Site: hwc.tv
Key Personnel
Dir: Ron Yoshida *Tel:* 917-566-0000 (cell)
E-mail: elronyo@msn.com
Mgr: Corbin DeBerry
Founded: 1992
Video production, editing, duplication DVD au-
thoring & audio/video/communications rental.
Membership(s): AICP; IFP

HeloAir Inc

5721 Gulfstream Rd, Richmond, VA 23250
Tel: 804-226-3400 *Toll Free Tel:* 888-FLY-HELO
(359-4356) *Fax:* 804-226-3494
E-mail: info@heloair.com
Web Site: www.heloair.com
Key Personnel
Pres: Whit Baldwin *E-mail:* whit@heloair.com
Founded: 1992
Six Bell helicopter aerials, WESCAM, FLIR,
Cineflex. Branch offices in Norfolk, VA &
Washington, DC.

Henninger Media Services
1320 N Courthouse Rd, Suite 130, Arlington, VA
22201
Tel: 703-243-3444 *Toll Free Tel:* 888-243-3444
E-mail: info@henninger.com
Web Site: www.henninger.com
Key Personnel
Pres & CEO: Robert L Henninger
Founded: 1983
Full service video production & post-production.
Catalog(s) available
Membership(s): IABC

Henry Engineering
PO Box 3796, Seal Beach, CA 90740
Tel: 562-493-3589
Web Site: www.henryeng.com
Key Personnel
Pres & CEO: Hank Landsberg
    E-mail: henryeng@aol.com
Founded: 1982
Manufacturer of professional audio & broadcast
    studio equipment.
Membership(s): NAB

Henry's Camera
119 Church St, Toronto, ON M5C 2G5, Canada
Tel: 416-941-0579 *Toll Free Tel:* 800-461-7960
    Fax: 416-868-4951 *Toll Free Fax:* 800-645-
    6431
E-mail: info@henrys.com
Web Site: www.henrys.com
Founded: 1909
Photographic & digital retailer.

Greg Hensley Productions
200 S "E" Ave, Unit 113, New Castle, CO 81647
Tel: 970-984-3158
E-mail: hensley@sopris.net
Key Personnel
Owner & Filmmaker: Greg Hensley
Founded: 1991
35mm film shot, Arriflex, video HD cameras.
    Stock footage library available as HD & SD.
    Produce wildlife nature films, plus all video
    formats & subjects. Multimedia as available,
    stills production services, illustration, art work,
    music & made to order wildlife sounds.
Catalog(s) available, weekly

Her Own Words LLC
PO Box 5264, Madison, WI 53705-0264
Tel: 608-271-7083 *Fax:* 608-271-0209
Web Site: herownwords.com;
    nontraditionalcareers.com
Key Personnel
Pres: Jocelyn Riley
Founded: 1986
Catalog(s) available
Online catalog(s) available

Here-in Our Motives Evolve Inc, see HOME
    Inc

Herman Pro AV
10110 USA Today Way, Miramar, FL 33025
Tel: 305-477-0063 *Toll Free Tel:* 888-736-6888
    Fax: 305-392-3377
E-mail: support@hermanproav.com
Web Site: www.hermanproav.com
Key Personnel
Owner & Pres: David Wolf
Owner & EVP: Jeffrey Wolf
Founded: 1963
Leading provider of professional AV products &
    labor resources to the commercial AV industry.
    Distribution facilities in FL, GA, NV & NJ.
Membership(s): Audiovisual and Integrated Expe-
    rience Association; NAB; NSCA

Hewlett-Packard Co
3000 Hanover St, Palo Alto, CA 94304-1185
Tel: 650-857-1501 *Toll Free Tel:* 800-752-0900
    Fax: 650-857-5518
Web Site: www.hp.com
Key Personnel
CEO & Pres: Meg Whitman
Catalog(s) available

Hi-Tech Audio Systems Inc
3382 Enterprise Ave, Hayward, CA 94545
Tel: 650-742-9166 *Fax:* 650-648-0573
Web Site: www.hi-techaudio.com
Key Personnel
Pres: Louis Adamo *E-mail:* louis@hi-techaudio.
    com

Hi-Tech Enterprises Inc
4250 114 Terr N, Clearwater, FL 33762
Mailing Address: PO Box 1752, Pinellas Park, FL
    33780
Tel: 727-573-9600
E-mail: hitech@videoequipment.tv
Web Site: www.videoequipment.tv
Key Personnel
Pres: Angela Reischmann
Founded: 1984
New & used video production equipment & ser-
    vices.
Catalog(s) available

Hi-Tech Import Export Corp
1101 W McNab Rd, Pompano Beach, FL 33069
Tel: 954-946-0603 *Fax:* 954-946-0652
Key Personnel
Pres: Jay Shah *E-mail:* jayhitec@bellsouth.net
Catalog(s) available

Hi-Tech Lamps Inc
922 San Leandro Ave, Suite B, Mountain View,
    CA 94043
Tel: 650-961-9031 *Toll Free Tel:* 800-229-6509
    Fax: 650-961-9033
E-mail: info@hi-techlamps.com
Web Site: www.hi-techlamps.com
Key Personnel
Pres: Wes Moloney
Distributor specializing in technical lamps, bulbs,
    sockets, photo-detectors & optical equipment
    for customers in manufacturing, science, educa-
    tion & government.
Catalog(s) available

High End Systems Inc
Division of ETC
2105 Gracy Farms Lane, Austin, TX 78758
Tel: 512-836-2242 *Toll Free Tel:* 800-890-8989
Web Site: www.highend.com
Key Personnel
VP, Sales: Mark Vassallo *Tel:* 608-824-5011
    E-mail: mark.vassallo@highend.com
Gen Mgr: Becky Koester
Mgr/Sales & Serv Opers Mgr: Betsy Childers
    Tel: 512-491-4211 *E-mail:* betsy.childers@
    highend.com
Natl Sales Mgr: Sean Hoey *Tel:* 512-491-4270
    E-mail: sean.hoey@highend.com
Founded: 1988
High power LED automated lighting, digital
    lighting fixtures & industry preferred lighting
    controllers for live event & concert touring ap-
    plications.
Online catalog(s) available
Membership(s): IALD; Professional Lighting &
    Sound Association

High Output Inc
495 Turnpike St, Canton, MA 02021
Tel: 781-364-1800 *Fax:* 781-364-1900
Web Site: www.highoutput.com

Key Personnel
System Sales Mgr: Mark Shore
Online catalog(s) available
Branch Office(s)
83 Bell St, Portland, ME 04013, Regl Mgr: J P
    Gagnone *Tel:* 207-854-4737 *Fax:* 207-854-4746
301 Iron Horse Way, Bldg 62, Providence, RI
    02908, Acct Mgr: Patrick Adam *Tel:* 401-521-
    0676 *Fax:* 401-521-0776
62 Bridge St, Suite A-5, Charleston, SC 29403,
    Regl Mgr: Martin Bluford *Tel:* 843-772-3600
    Toll Free Tel: 888-744-1400 *Fax:* 843-722-3607
Membership(s): Production Equipment Rental
    Association; Professional Lighting & Sound
    Association; USITT

High Plains Films
PO Box 8796, Missoula, MT 59807
Tel: 406-543-6726
E-mail: yak@highplainsfilms.org
Web Site: www.highplainsfilms.org
Key Personnel
Dir & Ed: Drury Gunn Carr *E-mail:* dru@
    highplainsfilms.org; Doug Hawes-Davis
    E-mail: dhd@highplainsfilms.org
Founded: 1992
Full service film production.

High-Tech Special Effects Inc
PO Box 193, Eads, TN 38028-0193
Tel: 901-850-5522 *Fax:* 901-850-8315
Web Site: www.hightechspecialeffects.com
Key Personnel
Owner & Pres: Randy Bast *E-mail:* randybast@
    bellsouth.net
Off Mgr: Rick Inghram
Provide special effects, fireworks, pyrotechnics &
    lasers to the corporate & entertainment indus-
    try. Fog & gas systems.

High Water Records
Division of University of Memphis
University of Memphis, Rudi E Scheidt School of
    Music, 121 Music Bldg, Memphis, TN 38152
Tel: 901-678-3317 *Fax:* 901-678-3096
Key Personnel
Gen Mgr: Richard Ranta
Prodr: David Evans *E-mail:* dhevans@memphis.
    edu
Founded: 1980
Catalog(s) available

High Windy Audio/Banjoman Inc
PO Box 553, Fairview, NC 28730
Tel: 828-628-1728 *Toll Free Tel:* 800-637-8679
    Fax: 828-628-4435
E-mail: office@davidholt.com
Web Site: www.davidholt.com
Key Personnel
Owner & Pres: David Holt
Booking: Betty Nichols
Founded: 1986
Audio production.
Online catalog(s) available
Membership(s): ABA; Audio Publishers Associa-
    tion

HighBridge Audio
Division of Recorded Books Inc, an RBmedia
    company
270 Skipjack Rd, Prince Frederick, MD 20678
Toll Free Tel: 800-755-8532 *Fax:* 410-535-5499
E-mail: highbridge@highbridgeaudio.com;
    customerservice@recordedbooks.com
Web Site: www.highbridgeaudio.com
Publisher of unabridged audiobooks & public ra-
    dio collections.
Catalog(s) available
Membership(s): Audio Publishers Association;
    Reading Recovery Council of North America

HighScope Press
Division of HighScope Educational Research
Foundation
600 N River St, Ypsilanti, MI 48198-2898
Tel: 734-485-2000 *Toll Free Tel:* 800-407-7377
Fax: 734-485-0704 *Toll Free Fax:* 800-442-
4329
E-mail: info@highscope.org; press@highscope.
org
Web Site: www.highscope.org
Key Personnel
Pres: Cheryl Polk *E-mail:* cpolk@highscope.org
Founded: 1970
Books, videos, CDs, cassettes & software for the
early childhood market.
Catalog(s) available

Hilferty & Associates Inc
14240 State Rte 550, Athens, OH 45701
Tel: 740-448-3821 *Fax:* 740-448-2331
E-mail: gha@hilferty.com
Web Site: www.hilferty.com
Key Personnel
Pres: Gerard Hilferty
Museum planning & exhibit design.
Membership(s): ASTEC; ICON

Jerry Hill Steadicam Products
19160 Arminta St, Reseda, CA 91335-1105
Tel: 818-772-9256 *Fax:* 818-772-9251
E-mail: jerry@steadimoves.com
Web Site: steadimoves.com
Key Personnel
Owner: Jerry Hill
Founded: 1980
Manufacturer of Steadicam accessories & camera
related products.
Online catalog(s) available

Ron Hill Imagery
2994 S Richards St, Salt Lake City, UT 84115
Tel: 801-486-3300 *Fax:* 801-486-3310
Web Site: ronhillimagery.com
Television, film & video production equipment
rentals, directing, crewing, on-site technical
assistance, pre & post-production services,
web/graphic design & support, photography.

Hillmann & Carr Inc
2233 Wisconsin Ave, Washington, DC 20007
Tel: 202-342-0001 *Fax:* 202-342-0117
E-mail: mail@hillmanncarr.com
Web Site: www.hillmanncarr.com
Key Personnel
Principal & Pres: Alfred J Hillmann
VP & Treas: Michal Brand Carr
E-mail: michalcarr@hillmanncarr.com
Founded: 1974
Production of film, video, interactive, audio, vide-
owall & multimedia & new media presenta-
tions. Full service production & project man-
agement. Creative track record with expertise
in expositions, museums, visitor centers, spe-
cial exhibits & multi-language international
projects in traditional & non-traditional stan-
dard formats. Experience includes AV systems,
design, integration & installation.
Membership(s): AASLH; American Alliance of
Museums; ASIFA; ASTEC; Audiovisual and
Integrated Experience Association; Washington Film & Video Council; Women in Film &
Video

Himalayan Institute Audio/Video
Division of Himalayan Institute
952 Bethany Tpke, Honesdale, PA 18431
Tel: 570-253-5551 *Toll Free Tel:* 800-822-4547
E-mail: info@himalayaninstitute.org
Web Site: www.himalayaninstitute.org
Key Personnel
IT Mgr: Josh Wolfenberg *E-mail:* jwolfenberg@
himalayaninstitute.org

Founded: 1971
Video production.
Online catalog(s) available

Hisco Inc
6650 Concord Park Dr, Houston, TX 77040-4098
Tel: 713-934-1700 *Toll Free Tel:* 844-807-1902
(web orders); 877-447-2650 (cust support)
Fax: 713-934-1790
E-mail: info@hiscoinc.com
Web Site: www.hiscoinc.com
Key Personnel
Pres & CEO: Bob Dill
Founded: 1940
Distribute industrial supply products for the elec-
tronic assembly & other industrial markets
including lighting/magnification products. 38
North American branch locations including
Canada & Mexico.
Online catalog(s) available

Historic Films
211 Third St, Greenport, NY 11944
Tel: 631-477-9700 *Toll Free Tel:* 800-249-1940
Fax: 631-477-9800
E-mail: info@historicfilms.com
Web Site: www.historicfilms.com
Key Personnel
Pres: Joseph Lauro
Sales Dir: Mark Heidemann *E-mail:* mark@
historicfilms.com
Founded: 1991
Stock footage film archives.
Online catalog(s) available
Membership(s): The Federation of Commercial
Audiovisual Libraries Ltd

Hitachi Kokusai Electric America Ltd
Subsidiary of Hitachi Kokusai Electric Inc
150 Crossways Park Dr, Woodbury, NY 11797
Tel: 516-921-7200 *Toll Free Tel:* 855-891-5179
Fax: 516-496-3718
E-mail: info@hitachikokusai.us
Web Site: hitachikokusai.us
Key Personnel
Pres: Toshihiro Matsuzaka
VP, Sales & COO: Sean Moran
Specialize in broadcasting & production cameras.
Branch Office(s)
11258 Monarch St, Unit H, Garden Grove, CA
92841, Regl Sales Mgr: Kenneth Cyr *Tel:* 714-
895-6116 *Fax:* 714-895-6252
PO Box 5, Wadsworth, OH 44281 *Tel:* 330-334-
4115 *Fax:* 330-334-0574
One Select Ave, Unit 11, Scarborough, ON M1V
5J3, Canada, Natl Sales Mgr: Richard Kraemer
Tel: 416-299-5900 ext 223 *Fax:* 416-299-0450
Membership(s): NAB; SMPTE®

Hite Co
Division of Mayer Electric
3101 Beale Ave, Altoona, PA 16601
Tel: 814-944-6121 *Toll Free Tel:* 800-252-3598
Fax: 814-944-3052
E-mail: altoona@mayerelectric.com
Web Site: www.hiteco.com
Key Personnel
Prod Specialist: Tim Merritts *E-mail:* tmerritts@
mayerelectric.com
Founded: 1949
Sells lighting, professional AV equipment & elec-
trical products.
Catalog(s) available

HM Electronics Inc (HME)
14110 Stowe Dr, Poway, CA 92064
Tel: 858-535-6000 *Toll Free Tel:* 800-848-4468
(dom sales) *Fax:* 858-452-7207; 858-552-0139
(dom sales)
E-mail: info@hme.com
Web Site: www.hme.com

Key Personnel
CEO: Chuck Miyahira
VP, Sales: Paul Foley
Dir, Mktg: Daren Haas
Founded: 1971
Brochure(s) available
Branch Office(s)
117 Vista Dr, Streetsville, ON L5M 1C4, Canada
Tel: 905-542-1115 *Toll Free Tel:* 800-383-3945
Membership(s): American Electronics Association

Hogpenny Studios
Ship Bottom Studio Ctr, 123 E 14 St, Ship Bot-
tom, Long Beach Island, NJ 08008
Tel: 609-494-6640
E-mail: hogpenny@verizon.net
Web Site: hogpennytv.com
Key Personnel
Exec Prodr: Jim De Francesco
Founded: 1975
Video & audio production & duplication.

The Hollaender Manufacturing Co
10285 Wayne Ave, Cincinnati, OH 45215
Mailing Address: PO Box 156399, Cincinnati,
OH 45215-6399
Tel: 513-772-8800 *Toll Free Tel:* 800-772-8800
(orders) *Fax:* 513-772-8806
Web Site: www.hollaender.com
Key Personnel
CEO: Robert P Hollaender, II
COO & Pres: Marc E Cetrulo
VP, Sales & Mktg: Ron Crebo
Admin Asst: Robin Keller *E-mail:* robink@
hollaender.com
Founded: 1946
Manufacturer of structural aluminum slip-on pipe
fittings & handrail systems.
Catalog(s) available

The Hollywood Edge
Division of Sound Ideas
c/o Sound Ideas, 105 W Beaver Creek Rd, Suite
4, Richmond Hill, ON L4B 1C6, Canada
Tel: 905-886-5000 *Toll Free Tel:* 800-665-3000
(CN); 800-387-3030 (US)
E-mail: hollywoodedge@sound-ideas.com
Web Site: www.sound-ideas.com; www.
hollywoodedge.com
Key Personnel
Pres: Brian Nimens
Ultimate Hollywood sound effect library collec-
tion.
Catalog(s) available

Hollywood Lights Inc
5251 SE McLoughlin Blvd, Portland, OR 97202-
4836
Tel: 503-232-9001; 503-232-8855
Toll Free Tel: 800-826-9881 *Fax:* 503-517-8686
E-mail: portland@hollywoodlights.biz
Web Site: www.hollywoodlights.biz
Key Personnel
Pres: Frank Locke *E-mail:* frank@
hollywoodlights.biz
AV Servs Mgr: Jason Phair *E-mail:* jasonp@
hollywoodlights.biz
Electrical Servs Mgr: Nai Saechao *E-mail:* nai@
hollywoodlights.biz
Electrical Servs Mgr (Seattle): Star Moser
E-mail: star@hollywoodlights.biz
Lighting Prodn Mgr: Greg Eggen *E-mail:* greg@
hollywoodlights.biz
Lighting Prodn Mgr (Seattle): Kerrigan O'Neill
E-mail: kerrigan@hollywoodlights.biz
Rentals Mgr: Gavin Christian *E-mail:* gavin@
hollywoodlights.biz
Rentals Mgr (Seattle): Scott Rode *E-mail:* scott@
hollywoodlights.biz
Sales Mgr/System Sales & Design: Clay Miller
E-mail: clay@hollywoodlights.biz
Sales Mgr (Seattle): Kevin Fuller *E-mail:* kevin@
hollywoodlights.biz

Systems Sales & Design Mgr (Seattle): Jim Graham *E-mail:* jimg@hollywoodlights.biz
Founded: 1948
Full service stage & event lighting design, production, rentals & sales.
Online catalog(s) available
Branch Office(s)
660 S Dakota St, Seattle, WA 98108-5226
Tel: 206-292-2353 *Toll Free Tel:* 800-547-2353 *Fax:* 206-215-9370 *E-mail:* seattle@hollywoodlights.biz
Membership(s): CIC-APEX; International Live Events Association; Meeting Professionals International; Professional Lighting & Sound Association; Trade Show Exhibitions Association; USITT

Hollywood Sound Systems
4209 Vanowen Place, Burbank, CA 91505
Tel: 323-466-2416 *Fax:* 323-460-2676
Web Site: www.hollywoodsound.com
Key Personnel
Pres: Les Harrison *E-mail:* l.harrison@hollywoodsound.com
VP, Admin: Shelley Harrison *E-mail:* shelley@hollywoodsound.com
VP, Opers: Jon Leblanc *E-mail:* j.leblanc@hollywoodsound.com
Mgr, Sales: John Conard *E-mail:* j.conard@hollywoodsound.com
Professional audio equipment rentals & sales. Full range of production services.

Hollywood Theatre Equipment Inc
1941 N 66 Ave, Hollywood, FL 33024
Tel: 954-920-2832 *Fax:* 954-986-6914
E-mail: hwdtheatre@aol.com
Key Personnel
Owner & Pres: Don Gallagher
Founded: 1979
Sale of motion picture theatre equipment.
Branch Office(s)
231 Steeple Chase Trail, Dallas, GA 30132, Contact: Don Gallagher, Jr
Membership(s): Theatre Equipment Association

Hollywood Vaults Inc
742 N Seward St, Hollywood, CA 90038
Tel: 323-461-6464 *Toll Free Tel:* 800-569-5336
Fax: 323-461-6479
E-mail: vault@hollywoodvaults.com
Web Site: www.hollywoodvaults.com
Key Personnel
Owner & Founder: David Wexler *E-mail:* david@hollywoodvaults.com; Julie Wexler *E-mail:* juliewexler@mac.com
Opers Mgr: Raymond Barber *E-mail:* raymond@hollywoodvaults.com
Founded: 1985
Preservation-quality storage of film, tape & digital media.
Online catalog(s) available
Membership(s): ASIS; Association of Moving Image Archivists; SMPTE®; SPARS

Holo-Spectra Inc
7742B Gloria Ave, Van Nuys, CA 91406
Tel: 818-994-9577 *Fax:* 818-994-4709
E-mail: info@lasershs.com
Web Site: www.lasershs.com
Key Personnel
Pres: William Arkin *E-mail:* bill@lasershs.com
VP, Engg: Robert Arkin
Founded: 1974
Laser & display projection equipment, laser shows, IP network based transport of audio & video sources.
Catalog(s) available

HOME Inc
566 Columbus Ave, Boston, MA 02118

Tel: 617-427-4663 *Fax:* 617-427-4664
Web Site: homeinc.org
Key Personnel
Co-Founder & Pres: Alan Michel *E-mail:* alanmichel@homeinc.org
Catalog(s) available

Homespun Video
Division of Homespun Tapes Ltd
1610 Rte 212, Saugerties, NY 12477
Mailing Address: PO Box 340, Woodstock, NY 12498-0340
Tel: 845-246-2550 *Toll Free Tel:* 800-338-2737 (orders-US & CN)
E-mail: info@homespun.com
Web Site: www.homespun.com
Key Personnel
Co-Founder & Pres: Happy Traum
Co-Founder & VP: Jane Traum
Founded: 1967
Distribute & produce music video, instructional.
Online catalog(s) available

Hoodman Corp
20445 Gramercy Place, Suite 201, Torrence, CA 90501
Tel: 310-222-8608 *Toll Free Tel:* 800-818-3946
E-mail: sales@hoodmanusa.com
Web Site: www.hoodmanusa.com
Key Personnel
VP, Mktg: Lou Schmidt *E-mail:* lou@hoodmanusa.com
Founded: 1986
Manufacture flash memory cards, i.e. CF, SD, SxS adapters, monitor hoods.
Online catalog(s) available
Membership(s): NAB

Hooper Camera & Imaging
Division of GKM Enterprises Inc
21902 Devonshire St, Chatsworth, CA 91311-2907
Tel: 818-709-0014 *Fax:* 818-709-0130
E-mail: sales@hoopercamera.com
Web Site: hoopercamera.com
Key Personnel
Opers Mgr: Dean Lawrence *Tel:* 818-292-5532 *E-mail:* mgr@hoopercamera.com
Founded: 1951
Digital photo supplies & photo finishing. Rent, repair & sell digital cameras.
Branch Office(s)
616 E Thousand Oaks Blvd, Thousand Oaks, CA 91360 *Tel:* 805-494-3080 *Fax:* 805-494-3159

Tom Hopkins International Inc
465 E Chilton Dr, Suite 4, Chandler, AZ 85225
Tel: 480-949-0786 *Toll Free Tel:* 800-528-0446 *Fax:* 480-949-1590
E-mail: info@tomhopkins.com
Web Site: www.tomhopkins.com
Key Personnel
CEO: Tom O Hopkins
Pres: Laura Oien
Founded: 1976
Seminars, CDs & DVDs on selling & selling skills.

Horita Co Inc
34192 Camino Capistrano, Capistrano Beach, CA 92624
Tel: 949-489-0240
E-mail: sales@horita.com; horita@horita.com
Web Site: horita.com
Founded: 1986
Time code & video equipment provider.
Online catalog(s) available

Horizon Film + Video Productions
3903 S Congress Ave, Suite 40186, Austin, TX 78704

Tel: 512-459-3100
Web Site: www.horizonvideo.com
Key Personnel
Owner & Ed, Motion Graphics: Chris Westerman *E-mail:* cw@horizonvideo.com
Dir, Photog & Ed: Paul Murski *E-mail:* pm@horizonvideo.com
Founded: 1982
Full service video production company. Provides script to screen services as well as duplication.
Catalog(s) available

Horizon Films & Media LLC
PO Box 1087, Shelbyville, KY 40066
Tel: 502-647-9966 *Fax:* 502-647-9968
E-mail: horizonfilms@insightbb.com
Web Site: www.horizon-films.com
Key Personnel
Owner, Cinematographer & Prodr: Sandy Mortimer
Educational videos.
Online catalog(s) available

Horizon Video Productions Inc
6114 Fayetteville St, Suite 106, Durham, NC 27713
Tel: 919-941-0901 *Toll Free Tel:* 800-768-3776 *Fax:* 919-941-1939
E-mail: info@horizonvp.com
Web Site: www.horizonvp.com
Key Personnel
Founder & Pres: Donna Mitchell
Dir, Multimedia: Jason Cooper *E-mail:* jason@horizonvp.com
Prodn Mgr: Jen Moreland *E-mail:* jen@horizonvp.com
Off Mgr: Brenda Dejewski *E-mail:* brenda@horizonvp.com
Founded: 1982
Full service agency providing turnkey video, film & multimedia production.

Horizon Worldwide
1765 Stebbins Dr, Houston, TX 77043
Tel: 713-647-7400 *Fax:* 713-647-6664
E-mail: info@horizonworldwide.com
Web Site: horizonworldwide.com
Key Personnel
Owner & Pres: Gary M Seline *Tel:* 713-647-7400 ext 101 *E-mail:* gary.seline@horizonworldwide.com
Founded: 1979
Full service advertising, marketing, communication & imaging group. Specialize in direct response advertising, promotions & retail product marketing.

Susan Hormuth, Visual Resource Consultant
3356 Pennsylvania Ave SE, Washington, DC 20020
Tel: 202-584-3994
E-mail: susanhormuth@verizon.net
Founded: 1990
Still picture & footage research, specializing in historical images & public domain sources.

Hosa Technology Inc
6650 Caballero Blvd, Buena Park, CA 90620
Tel: 714-522-8878 *Toll Free Tel:* 800-255-7527 *Fax:* 714-522-4540
E-mail: info@hosatech.com; sales@hosatech.com; orders@hosatech.com
Web Site: hosatech.com
Key Personnel
Opers Mgr: Jennifer Paquette
Founded: 1984
Supplier of analog & digital connectivity solutions to the musical instrument & professional AV industries.
Online catalog(s) available

Hot Buttered Content, see HB-Content

Hot House Professional Audio
275 Martin Ave, Highland, NY 12528
Tel: 845-691-6077
E-mail: info@hothousepro.com
Web Site: www.hothousepro.com
Key Personnel
Owner: Richard Rose
Design & install high-end studio monitor systems.

HOThead
56 W 45 St, 17th fl, New York, NY 10036
Tel: 212-575-5566
E-mail: info@hothead.tv
Web Site: hothead.tv
Key Personnel
Owner & Creative Dir: Jim Stauffer
Audio post-production facility.

Hotronic Inc
1875 S Winchester Blvd, Campbell, CA 95008
Tel: 408-378-3883
E-mail: sales@hotronics.com
Web Site: hotronics.com
Founded: 1982
Catalog(s) available

Hottrax Records
1957 Kilburn Dr, Atlanta, GA 30324-4852
Mailing Address: PO Box 13584, Atlanta, GA
 30324-0584
Tel: 770-662-6661
E-mail: hotwax@hottrax.com
Web Site: www.hottrax.com
Key Personnel
CEO: Aleck Janoulis
Founded: 1975
Catalog(s) available

House of Cinemagraphics
4802 Quail Ave N, Minneapolis, MN 55429
Tel: 612-339-7803; 763-458-8244
 Toll Free Tel: 888-813-0413
E-mail: film@visi.com
Web Site: www.houseofcinemagraphics.com
Key Personnel
Owner: Bill Felker
Founded: 1975
Motion picture services & rentals.

House of Grace, see Sound*Light

House of Moves
5419 McConnell Ave, Los Angeles, CA 90066-
 7027
Tel: 310-306-6131
E-mail: info@moves.com
Web Site: www.moves.com
Key Personnel
CEO: Brian Rausch *E-mail:* rausch@moves.com
Busn Devt Mgr: Jimmy Corvan *E-mail:* jimmy@
 moves.com
Founded: 1997
Motion capture studio.

The House Studios
325 Second Ave W, Seattle, WA 98119
Tel: 206-724-6639
E-mail: book@thehousestudios.com
Web Site: thehousestudios.com
Key Personnel
Founder & Owner: Emily Goodnight
 E-mail: emily@thehousestudios.com
Commercial photography & visual media studio.
 Equipment & prop rentals & on-site production
 team.

Houston Photo Imaging
5250 Gulfton, Suite 3-B, Houston, TX 77081
Tel: 713-666-0282 *Toll Free Tel:* 800-664-0282
 Fax: 713-667-9625

E-mail: info@hpihouston.com
Web Site: hpihouston.com
Key Personnel
Pres: Steve Hogan
Founded: 1976
Outdoor, large format printer.
Catalog(s) available
Membership(s): The Imaging Alliance

Hover-Views Unlimited
PO Box 1164, Syosset, NY 11791
Tel: 516-496-2946 *Fax:* 516-496-8029
Web Site: www.hoverviews.com
Key Personnel
Owner: Al Cerullo *Tel:* 516-315-8063
Aerial cinematography for feature films, televi-
 sion, commercials, documentaries & specials,
 print ads & music videos.

HSA Inc
1717 E Sixth St, Mishawaka, IN 46544
Tel: 574-255-6100 *Fax:* 574-255-8131
E-mail: hsainfo@hsarolltops.com
Web Site: www.hsarolltops.com
Key Personnel
CEO & Pres: Richard Johnson
Sales: Alan Oglesby
Manufacture a line of oak rolltop desks & 19
 inch equipment racks for the AV industry.

Hubbard Supply Co
901 W Second St, Flint, MI 48503
Tel: 810-234-8681 *Toll Free Tel:* 800-875-4811
 Fax: 810-234-6142
E-mail: information@hubbardsupply.com
Web Site: www.hubbardsupply.com
Key Personnel
CEO: Jeff Bigelow
COO: Tim Brooks
Cust Serv Mgr: Jane Knapp *E-mail:* jknapp@
 hubbardsupply.com
Founded: 1865
Closed channel TV for security purposes.
Catalog(s) available
Online catalog(s) available
Branch Office(s)
4560 W Dickman Rd, Battle Creek, MI 49037
 Tel: 269-965-2211 *Toll Free Tel:* 800-632-9606
 Fax: 269-965-3164
3900 E Washington Rd, Saginaw, MI 48601
 Tel: 989-753-2453 *Toll Free Tel:* 800-875-4812
 Fax: 989-753-3266

Hubbell Wiring Device-Kellems
Division of Hubbell Inc
40 Waterview Dr, Shelton, CT 06484
Tel: 475-882-4800 (sales & mktg)
 Toll Free Tel: 800-288-6000 (cust serv)
 Fax: 475-882-4849 (sales & mktg)
 Toll Free Tel: 800-255-1031 (cust serv)
E-mail: techserv@hubbell.com
Web Site: www.hubbell-wiring.com
Key Personnel
Dir, Intl Sales: Steve Consolo *E-mail:* sconsolo@
 hubbell.com
Online catalog(s) available

Hughie's Event Production Services
1260 E 38 St, Cleveland, OH 44114
Tel: 216-361-4600 *Toll Free Tel:* 800-449-4115
 Fax: 216-361-2570
Web Site: www.hughies.com
Key Personnel
Pres: David M Wheeler *E-mail:* dwheeler@
 hughies.com
Founded: 1953
Event production service & professional industry
 equipment in the Ohio & Western Pennsylvania
 region.
Catalog(s) available

Branch Office(s)
7034 Worthington-Galena Rd, Worthington, OH
 43805 *Tel:* 614-436-5273 *Toll Free Tel:* 800-
 643-2959 *Fax:* 614-436-5290 *E-mail:* cbsales@
 hughies.com
26 39 St, Pittsburgh, PA 15201 *Tel:* 412-621-1220
 Fax: 412-621-7260 *E-mail:* pasales@hughies.
 com
Membership(s): Audiovisual and Integrated Experience Association

Charles A Hulcher Co Inc
909 "G" St, Hampton, VA 23661
Tel: 757-245-6190 *Fax:* 757-245-2882
Key Personnel
Pres: Betty H Giles
VP: Gary Beasley
Founded: 1952
Manufacturer of sequence & panoramic cameras.
Catalog(s) available

Human Circuit
9346 Gaither Rd, Gaithersburg, MD 20877
Tel: 240-864-4000
Web Site: www.humancircuit.com
Key Personnel
Pres & CEO: Bruce Kaufmann *Tel:* 240-864-4000
 ext 4058
CTO: Jim Hatcher
Founded: 1966
Technology system design.
Membership(s): Audiovisual and Integrated Expe-
 rience Association; SMPTE®

Human Relations Media
41 Kensico Dr, Mount Kisco, NY 10549
Tel: 914-666-9151 *Toll Free Tel:* 800-431-2050
 (cust serv) *Fax:* 914-666-9506
E-mail: service@hrmvideo.com; orders@
 hrmvideo.com; help@hrmvideo.com; letters@
 hrmvideo.com
Web Site: www.hrmvideo.com
Key Personnel
CEO & Pres: Anson W Schloat
Founded: 1976
Videos on substance abuse prevention, health edu-
 cation, career education, math & science.
Catalog(s) available

Hunt's Photo & Video
100 Main St, Melrose, MA 02176-6104
Tel: 781-662-8822 (retail sales)
 Toll Free Tel: 800-924-8682 (retail sales); 800-
 221-1830 (ext 2340, corp sales) *Fax:* 781-662-
 6524
E-mail: ecommerce@wbhunt.com (retail online
 sales)
Web Site: www.huntsphotoandvideo.com
Key Personnel
Pres: Scott Farber
Corp Sales Mgr: Marty Weiskoff *Tel:* 781-462-
 2339 *E-mail:* mweiskoff@wbhunt.com
Photography retailer.
Online catalog(s) available

Hurst Digital
4472 Spring Valley Rd, Dallas, TX 75244
Tel: 469-644-1390
Web Site: hurstdigital.net
Key Personnel
Creative Dir: Josh Hurst
Video production company. Core focus is corpo-
 rate video solutions, branded visual content &
 animation used for education or innovation.

Frank D Hurst Corp, see Pechman Imaging

Editions Hurtubise HMH Ltee
1815 Avenue De Lorimier, Montreal, QC H2K
 3W6, Canada

Tel: 514-523-1523 *Toll Free Tel:* 800-361-1664
   Fax: 514-523-9969
Web Site: www.distributionhmh.com
Key Personnel
Pres: Herve Foulon
VP, Opers: Arnaud Foulon *E-mail:* arnaud.
   foulon@editionshurtubise.com
Admin Dir: Johanne Livernoche *E-mail:* johanne.
   livernoche@distributionhmh.com
Prodn Mgr: Dominique Thuillot
   E-mail: dominique.thuillot@editionshurtubise.
   com
Founded: 1960
Catalog(s) available
Membership(s): Association nationale des editeurs
   de livres; UELF

Hybrid Studios
3021 S Shannon St, Santa Ana, CA 92704
Tel: 714-850-1499
E-mail: info@hybridstudiosca.com
Web Site: www.hybridstudiosca.com
Key Personnel
Founder & Co-Owner: Patrick Akhamlich
   E-mail: patrick@hybridstudiosca.com; Bill
   Klein *E-mail:* billy@hybridstudiosca.com
Studio Opers Supv: Mike Miller *E-mail:* mike@
   hybridstudiosca.com
Founded: 2012
Multimedia production facility with digital & ana-
   log recording studio, soundstage, gear & staff.

Hydrogen Whiskey Studios
Subsidiary of Dragonlight Productions Inc
12327 Santa Monica Blvd, Suite 202, Los Ange-
   les, CA 90025
Tel: 310-394-8130 *Fax:* 310-820-0401
Key Personnel
Chief Creative Offr: Ron Franco *E-mail:* ron@
   hwhiskey.com
Exec Prodr: Krissie King *E-mail:* krissie@
   hwhiskey.com
Founded: 1992
Full service 3D animation & audio production.

Hyperspective Studios Inc
2800 Woodlawn Dr, Suite 253, Honolulu, HI
   96822
Tel: 808-353-3618 *Toll Free Tel:* 800-353-3618
E-mail: info@hyperspective.com
Web Site: hyperspective.com
Key Personnel
Pres & CEO: Todd J Robertson *Tel:* 808-741-
   1292 *E-mail:* todd@hyperspective.com
COO: Charisse Lindsey *Tel:* 808-386-7172
Founded: 1996
Visual production services, multimedia, video FX,
   graphics illustration. 3D & 2D animation, video
   production & special effects.

I M P A C T Publishing Inc
3409 47 Ave E, Bradenton, FL 34203
Mailing Address: PO Box 10058, Bradenton, FL
   34282-0058
Tel: 941-739-2611 *Toll Free Tel:* 800-221-6121;
   800-426-3963
E-mail: potentialsunlimitedcs@gmail.com
Web Site: www.potentialsunlimited.com
Key Personnel
Pres: Stephanie Banfill *E-mail:* skonicov@
   potentialsunlimited.com
Exclusive licensee of Potentials Unlimited sub-
   liminal persuasion & self-hypnosis audio &
   video products.
Catalog(s) available, free

I-25 Studios
9201 Pan American Fwy NE, Albuquerque, NM
   87113
Tel: 505-822-7115
E-mail: info@i-25studios.com

Web Site: i-25studios.com
Key Personnel
CEO: Rick Clemente *Tel:* 505-688-4148 (cell)
   E-mail: rick@i-25studios.com
Mng Dir: Drew Dolan
Full service motion picture production facility.

IAC Acoustics
Division of Sound Seal
401 Airport Rd, North Aurora, IL 60542
Tel: 630-270-1790
E-mail: iacacoustics@soundseal.com
Web Site: www.iac-noisecontrol.com/us; www.
   iacacoustics.com
Founded: 1949
Metal acoustical & noise control products & solu-
   tions serving the industrial, architectural, com-
   mercial & construction industries.
Online catalog(s) available

IAI Records & Video
Division of Improvising Artists International
PO Box 4, Cherry Valley, NY 13320-0004
Tel: 646-696-5645
E-mail: iai@improvart.com
Web Site: www.improvart.com
Key Personnel
Prodr & Dir: Carol Goss
Mktg: A I Goss-Bley
Founded: 1974
Produce & distribute jazz & video art, long play
   music video, documentary & educational pro-
   grams for the home video, educational & cable
   markets & Internet.
Catalog(s) available

IAMP Professional Audio
218 Reindollar Ave, Unit 6-A, Marina, CA 93933
Tel: 831-884-9558 *Fax:* 831-643-2131
E-mail: iamp-pro-audio@comcast.net
Web Site: www.iampproaudio.com
Key Personnel
Owner: Anthony Nocita *Tel:* 831-224-2201 (cell)
Sound system consultant, design & installation.
   35 years experience in professional audio. Spe-
   cialize in houses of worship, schools & the-
   aters. Live sound expertise in music production
   & triathlons, marathons & extreme sports.
Membership(s): AES; NAMM, the National Asso-
   ciation of Music Merchants

IAPC Inc, see Imageworks

IBM Collaboration Solutions
One New Orchard Rd, Armonk, NY 10504-1722
Toll Free Tel: 800-426-4968; 877-426-3774
Web Site: www-01.ibm.com/software/lotus
Enterprise social software.

IBM SPSS
200 W Madison Ave, 23rd fl, Chicago, IL 60606
Toll Free Tel: 800-543-2185 *Toll Free Fax:* 800-
   841-0064
E-mail: salesbox@us.ibm.com
Web Site: www-01.ibm.com/software/analytics/
   spss
Global provider of predictive analytics software &
   solutions.

Icarus Films Inc
32 Court St, 21st fl, Brooklyn, NY 11201
Tel: 718-488-8900 *Toll Free Tel:* 800-876-1710
   Fax: 718-488-8642
E-mail: mail@icarusfilms.com
Web Site: www.icarusfilms.com
Key Personnel
Pres: Jonathan Miller
Founded: 1978

Catalog(s) available
Membership(s): The Alliance for Media Arts and
   Culture; Consortium of College & University
   Media Centers

ICL Imaging Inc
51 Mellen St, Framingham, MA 01702
Tel: 508-872-3280 *Toll Free Tel:* 800-660-3280
   Fax: 508-872-7364
E-mail: csr@icl-imaging.com
Web Site: www.icl-imaging.com
Key Personnel
Pres: Larry Capodilupo, III
Dir, Sales & Mktg: Bill Smith
Prodn Mgr: Jim Lyon
Founded: 1956

Icom Multimedia
2498 Danders Ct, Columbus, OH 43220
Tel: 614-207-4400 *Fax:* 614-457-8050
Web Site: www.icommultimedia.com
Key Personnel
Pres: Phil Yoder *E-mail:* phil@icommultimedia.
   com
Webcasting meeting products.
Catalog(s) available

Icontent
122 W 26 St, New York, NY 10001
Tel: 212-462-0022
E-mail: info@icontent.tv
Web Site: www.icontent.tv
Key Personnel
Dir: Douglas Sloan
Documentary filmmaker & commercial produc-
   tion.
Catalog(s) available

iCorpTv
PO Box 461172, Los Angeles, CA 90046
Tel: 818-492-4623
E-mail: icorptv@gmail.com
Web Site: icorptv.com
Key Personnel
Dir & Prodr: Gregory McDonald
Founded: 1996
Scriptwriting, video & film production & post-
   production, DVD/CD & flash authoring.

iCrossing Inc, a Hearst Company
300 W 57 St, New York, NY 10019
Tel: 212-649-3900 *Toll Free Tel:* 866-620-3780
E-mail: general@icrossing.com
Web Site: www.icrossing.com
Key Personnel
CEO: Nick Brien
Pres, West Reg: Mike Parker
Mng Dir, NY Off: Emma Armstrong
Founded: 1998
Global digital marketing agency.
Branch Office(s)
15169 N Scottsdale Rd, Suite C-400, Scottsdale,
   AZ 85254 *Tel:* 480-505-5800
550 Kearny St, 4th fl, San Francisco, CA 94108
   Tel: 415-869-1120
333 Wacker Dr, Suite 950, Chicago, IL 60606
   Tel: 312-277-4700
2828 Routh St, Suite 777, Dallas, TX 75201
   Tel: 214-210-6800
1902 Campus Commons, Suite 200, Reston, VA
   20191 *Tel:* 703-262-3200
Foreign Office(s): Malabia 1720, Area tres,
   Palermo, Buenos Aires, Argentina *Tel:* (011)
   5984 3037
Santa Maria 2880, Off 303, Providencia, Santiago, Chile *Tel:* (02) 26161300
Parkview Green Fangcaodi, Rm 1001-1006,
   Tower B, 9 Dongdaqiao Rd, Chaoyang District, Beijing PWC 100020, China *Tel:* (010)
   85676688

Tal 11, 80331 Munich, Germany *Tel:* (089) 24 20 53-0

Cybage Towers, Survey No 13A/1+2+3/1, Vadgaon Sheri, Pune 411 014, India *Tel:* (020) 66041700

Campeche 300, Col Hipodromo Condesa, 06100 Mexico, DF, Mexico *Tel:* (0155) 6798278

516 Ave Dos de Mayo, Off 603, Miraflores, Lima, Peru *Tel:* (01) 7052215

275 Gongdeok-dong, Mapo-gu, Seoul 121-721, South Korea *Tel:* (02) 3782 6813

Calle Lezama 16, 28034 Madrid, Spain *Tel:* 917288751

13 Black Lion St, Brighton, East Sussex BN1 1ND, United Kingdom *Tel:* (01273) 827700 *Web Site:* icrossing.co.uk

22 Chapter St, 2nd fl, London SW1P 4NP, United Kingdom *Tel:* (020) 7821 2300 *Web Site:* icrossing.co.uk

Stamford House, Northenden Rd, Sale, Cheshire M33 2DH, United Kingdom *Tel:* (01614) 510822 *Web Site:* icrossing.co.uk

Idaho Camera Inc
1310 N Orchard Ave, Boise, ID 83706
Tel: 208-377-3686 (corp) *Toll Free Tel:* 877-323-8734
E-mail: info@idahocamera.com; orchard@idahocamera.com; sales@idahocamera.com
Web Site: www.idahocamera.com
Key Personnel
Pres: Patrick F Nagel
Compt: Dennis Nagel
Founded: 1946
Full service camera retailer.
Online catalog(s) available

IDC, see International Datacasting

Ideascape Inc
PO Box 1966, Lake Oswego, OR 97035
Tel: 503-246-2439
E-mail: info@ideascapeinc.com
Web Site: www.ideascapeinc.com
Key Personnel
VP: Douglas Freeman *E-mail:* dfreeman@ideascapeinc.com
Prodr & Prodn Asst: MacKenzie Freeman *E-mail:* mfreeman@ideascapeinc.com
Founded: 1997
Media scripting & production services.
Membership(s): Oregon Media Production Association

IDenticard Systems Inc
Division of Brady Corp
148 E Stiegel St, Manheim, PA 17545
Tel: 717-569-5797 *Toll Free Tel:* 800-233-0298 *Fax:* 717-427-1654
E-mail: identicard.info@identicard.com
Web Site: www.identicard.com
Key Personnel
Gen Mgr: Jeff Bill
Founded: 1970
Digital imaging systems, Security 10, Access Control Systems, Smart Card, Biometrics.
Catalog(s) available

Idle Minds Productions Inc
3405 Pepperhill Rd, Lexington, KY 40502
Tel: 859-268-8500 *Fax:* 859-268-8500
E-mail: idleminds@twc.com
Key Personnel
Pres & Owner: Timothy Asher
Membership(s): Collegiate Sports Video Association; Kentucky Film & Video Professionals

IDX System Technology Inc
19001 Harborgate Way, Suite 105, Torrance, CA 90501
Tel: 310-328-2850 *Fax:* 310-328-8202

E-mail: idx.usa@idx.tv
Web Site: www.idx.tv
Key Personnel
Western Regl Sales Mgr: Tomo Nishikawa *E-mail:* tomo@idx.tv
Eastern Regl Sales Mgr: Don Mainardi *E-mail:* donm@idx.tv
Founded: 1989
Manufacturer & distributor of batteries, chargers & power supplies.
Foreign Office(s): IDX Co Ltd (Japan), 6-28-11 Shukugawara, Tama-ku Kawasaki-shi, Kanagawa-ken 214-0021, Japan *Tel:* (044) 850 8801 *Fax:* (044) 850 8838 *E-mail:* idx.japan@idx.tv
IDX Technology Europe (UK), Langley Park, Unit 9, Waterside Dr, Langley, Berks SL3 6AD, United Kingdom *Tel:* (01753) 547 692 *Fax:* (01753) 546 660 *E-mail:* idx.europe@idx.tv
Membership(s): NAB

IEEE Computer Society Press
10662 Los Vaqueros Circle, Los Alamitos, CA 90720-1314
Tel: 714-821-8380 *Toll Free Tel:* 800-272-6657 (cust serv) *Fax:* 714-821-4010
E-mail: help@computer.org
Web Site: www.computer.org
Key Personnel
Mktg Communs Mgr: Katherine Mansfield *E-mail:* k.mansfield@computer.org
Sr Mgr, Edit Servs: Robin Baldwin *E-mail:* rbaldwin@computer.org
Catalog(s) available

IFM World Releasing Inc
1328 E Palmer Ave, Glendale, CA 91205
Tel: 818-243-4976 *Fax:* 818-550-9728
E-mail: contact@ifmfilm.com
Web Site: www.ifmfilm.com
Key Personnel
Pres: Antony I Ginnane
EVP: Anthony J Lyons
VP, Intl: David Makhlout
Founded: 1995
International film & TV distribution. Executive production, theatrical, video, TV, feature film, TV movies & factual.
Foreign Office(s): 25 Second St, Unit 2, Clayton, Victoria 3169, Australia *Tel:* (03) 9515 9249 *Fax:* (03) 9515 9248

Ikegami Electronics (USA) Inc
37 Brook Ave, Maywood, NJ 07607
Tel: 201-368-9171 *Fax:* 201-569-1626
E-mail: sales@ikegami.com; service@ikegami.com
Web Site: www.ikegami.com
Key Personnel
CEO & Pres (US): Akira Harada
Pres (Japan): Masaki Matsubara
VP & Dir, Engg: Alan Keil
Catalog(s) available
Branch Office(s)
2633 Manhattan Beach Blvd, Redondo Beach, CA 90278, Contact: Tom Carr *Tel:* 310-297-1900 *Fax:* 310-536-9550 *E-mail:* tcarr@ikegami.com
710 E Hillsboro Blvd, Suite 100, Deerfield Beach, FL 33441, Contact: Bill Munoz *Tel:* 954-571-7177 *Fax:* 954-571-7760 *E-mail:* gmunoz@ikegami.com
16206 Hunter Ct, Orland Hills, IL 60487, Contact: James Daniel *Tel:* 708-460-1451 *E-mail:* jdaniels@ikegami.com
773 Bearden, Waxahachie, TX 75167, Contact: John Webb *Tel:* 972-869-2363 *Fax:* 972-556-1057 *E-mail:* jwebb@ikegami.com
Membership(s): NAB; SMPTE®

ILIO Enterprises LLC
5356 Sterling Center Dr, Westlake Village, CA 91361
Tel: 818-707-7222; 818-707-3655
Toll Free Tel: 800-747-4546
E-mail: info@ilio.com
Web Site: www.ilio.com
Key Personnel
Mgr: Mark Hiskey
Founded: 1994
Sound effects libraries, virtual instruments, plug-ins & tools for music production.
Online catalog(s) available

Illuminart Lighting
7320 Griffin Rd, Suite 111, Davie, FL 33314
Tel: 954-327-0564
E-mail: lightisart@aol.com
Key Personnel
Owner: Marco Rose *Tel:* 954-529-3720 (cell) *E-mail:* marcolight@aol.com
Catalog(s) available

Illuminate Post/Digital Finishing
10900 Ventura Blvd, Studio City, CA 91604
Tel: 323-969-8822 *Fax:* 323-969-8860
E-mail: info@illuminatehollywood.com
Web Site: illuminatehollywood.com
Key Personnel
CEO: Jim Hardy
EVP, Sales: Steve Tannen
Post-production facility offering digital finishing for independent films & television.

Illuminate Studios
10900 Ventura Blvd, Studio City, CA 90068
Tel: 818-769-4500 *Fax:* 818-769-7150
E-mail: info@illuminatehollywood.com
Web Site: illuminatehollywood.com
Key Personnel
CEO: Jim Hardy
EVP & Gen Mgr: Sandy Crawford
EVP, Sales: Steve Tannen
Opers Mgr: Manuel Garcia
Fully equipped stage rentals with satellite broadcasting capabilities. Multiple HD camera shoots for live & taped productions. RED cameras available for rent.

Illusion Television Productions, see ITV Productions

Image Associates Inc
5475 Rumley Rd, Suite 102, Durham, NC 27703
Tel: 919-876-6400 *Fax:* 919-876-6400
E-mail: info@imageassociates.com
Web Site: www.imageassociates.com
Key Personnel
Pres & CEO: Carla Davenport
Multimedia Prodr: John Maruca
Founded: 1964
Catalog(s) available
Membership(s): Special Interest Group on Computer Graphics

Image Audiovisuals
2130 S Dahlia St, Denver, CO 80222
Tel: 303-758-1818 *Toll Free Tel:* 800-818-1857 *Fax:* 303-758-5722
Web Site: www.imageav.com
Key Personnel
CEO: Diana Mueller *E-mail:* diana@imageav.com
Pres: David Mueller *E-mail:* dmueller@imageav.com
Dir, Opers: David Kreutz
Natl Sales Mgr: Levi Bulkley
Designs, engineers & installs AV systems for corporate, healthcare, government & educational clients.

Image Craft LLC
3401 E Broadway Rd, Phoenix, AZ 85040

Tel: 602-276-2082 *Toll Free Tel:* 800-274-2422
  Fax: 602-232-0719
E-mail: designgroup@imcraft.com
Web Site: www.imcraft.com
Key Personnel
Owner: Doug Olson
Founded: 1979
Digital imaging, large format printing & photo-
  graphic imaging.
Catalog(s) available
Branch Office(s)
12503 E Euclid Dr, Suite 10, Centennial, CO
  80111 *Tel:* 303-274-1011 *Fax:* 303-274-7605
Membership(s): Arizona Industrial Photographers;
  ASMP; The Imaging Alliance

Image Entertainment
Subsidiary of RLJ Entertainment Inc
6320 Canoga Ave, Suite 800, Woodland Hills,
  CA 91367
Tel: 818-407-9100 *Toll Free Tel:* 800-473-3475
E-mail: inquiries@rljentertainment.com
Independent films, music, documentaries, stand-
  up comedy, stage plays, classic TV/movies &
  African-American movies in theaters, on TV,
  on DVD, digital streaming & digital down-
  loads.
Catalog(s) available

The Image Generators
18156 Darnell Dr, Olney, MD 20832
Tel: 301-924-5700 *Fax:* 240-363-0062
E-mail: info@imagegenerators.com
Web Site: www.imagegenerators.com
Key Personnel
Pres & CEO: Michael J Weiner *E-mail:* mike@
  imagegenerators.com
Founded: 1985
Voice-over services with ISDN.
Membership(s): SAG-AFTRA; Women in Film &
  Video

Image Integration
2619 Benvenue Ave, No A, Berkeley, CA 94704
Tel: 510-504-2605 *Fax:* 510-841-8524
Key Personnel
Pres: Vincent Casalaina *Tel:* 510-504-2605 (cell)
  E-mail: vincesail@aol.com
Founded: 1973
Documentary production of sailing events.
Membership(s): DGA; Television Academy

Image Logic Corp
6807 Brennon Lane, Chevy Chase, MD 20815-
  3255
Tel: 202-223-2888
E-mail: info@imagelogic.com
Web Site: www.imagelogic.com
Key Personnel
Mktg Dir: Rick Hofmann
Manufacture & distribute captioning systems.

Image Management Systems Inc
239 W 15 St, New York, NY 10011
Tel: 212-741-8765
E-mail: info@imagemgt.com
Web Site: www.imagemgt.com
Key Personnel
Pres: Jack Berry
Founded: 1980
System solutions for information capture, storage,
  access & communication. Satellite phone sales
  & rentals. Satellite video phone systems. DVD
  equipment & jukes. Electronic imaging.
Membership(s): SMPTE®

Image Marketing Corp
1636 N 24 St, Mesa, AZ 85213
Tel: 480-969-7032 *Fax:* 480-969-0939
E-mail: info@image4u.com
Web Site: www.image4u.com

Key Personnel
Owner: Rik W Beimfohr
Founded: 1979
Distribute magnifiers.
Online catalog(s) available

Image Technologies Corp, see ITC

Image Up Studio
295 Pierson Ave, Suite 103, Edison, NJ 08837
Tel: 732-549-1845
Web Site: www.imageup.com
Key Personnel
Pres: David Glasofer *E-mail:* david@imageup.
  com
Founded: 1978

Image Video
Division of 1077541 Ontario Ltd
1620 Midland Ave, Scarborough, ON M1P 3C2,
  Canada
Tel: 416-750-8872 *Fax:* 416-750-8015
E-mail: sales@imagevideo.com
Web Site: www.imagevideo.com
Key Personnel
VP: David Russell
Founded: 1974
Manufacture & distribute tally systems, alarm
  systems & multi-image display systems.
Catalog(s) available
Membership(s): NAB; SMPTE®

Image Video Services & Productions
1210 Southview Dr, Sudbury, ON P3E 2L6,
  Canada
Tel: 705-698-1212 *Fax:* 705-805-0110
E-mail: info@ivsproductions.ca
Web Site: www.ivsproductions.ca
Key Personnel
Media Prodr: Daniel Thomson
Ed: Susan Thomson
Founded: 1998
Video production for live event, corporate, in-
  structional & marketing purposes.
Sample(s) available, free, DVD samples

Image Video Teleproductions Inc
6755 Freedom Ave NW, North Canton, OH
  44720
Tel: 330-494-9303 *Fax:* 330-966-1792
E-mail: info@image-video.com
Web Site: www.image-video.com
Key Personnel
Pres: Michael A Tonges
Gen Mgr: Dean Marini *E-mail:* dmarini@image-
  video.com
Sales & Mktg: Mike Simon
Rent 2 GHZ portable microwave transmitters &
  receivers. Also remote production.
Catalog(s) available

Image Zone Inc
11 W 69 St, Suite 10A, New York, NY 10023
Tel: 212-924-8804
Web Site: www.imagezone.com
Key Personnel
Mng Dir: Douglas Ehrlich *E-mail:* dehrlich@
  imagezone.com
Creative Dir: Peter Smallman
Founded: 1987
Provide full service interactive & multimedia
  products.

Imagecraft Productions
3318 Burton Ave, Burbank, CA 91504
Tel: 818-954-0187 *Fax:* 818-954-0189
Web Site: www.imagecraftproductions.com
Key Personnel
Founder & Dir, Photog: Robin Hirsch
  E-mail: robin@imagecraftproductions.com
Pres: Jason Been

Rentals Mgr: Ben Fuller *E-mail:* ben@
  imagecraftproductions.com
Sales & Mktg Mgr: Gene Duggan *E-mail:* gene@
  imagecraftproductions.com
Founded: 1984
Full service production rental house; cameras,
  video/engineering, audio, grip, electric, gear,
  services, crewing.

imageReal Pictures LLC
4 Lighthouse St, No 8, Marina del Rey, CA
  90292
E-mail: info@imagereal.com
Web Site: www.imagereal.com
Key Personnel
Founder & Exec Prodr: Katie Cadigan
Founded: 1997
Documentary film & video production.
Membership(s): IDA

Imagers
1575 Northside Dr, Bldg 400, Suite 490, Atlanta,
  GA 30318-5411
Tel: 404-351-5800 *Toll Free Tel:* 800-232-5411
  Fax: 404-351-9020
E-mail: imagers@imagers.com
Web Site: www.imagers.com
Key Personnel
CEO: Joe Edwards
Founded: 1947
Provide printing, prepress, color laser & photo
  print services.
Catalog(s) available
Membership(s): The Imaging Alliance

Images in Motion Media Inc
720 Ladera Dr, Sonoma, CA 95476
Tel: 707-996-9474
E-mail: images@vom.com
Web Site: www.imagesmedia.com
Key Personnel
Co-Owner & Prodr: Lee Armstrong
Co-Owner & Prodn Designer: Kamela Portuges
TV/film production using live action, puppets &
  animation. Complete video production studio
  rental & 3D printing.

Images II Inc
1700 "O" St, Lincoln, NE 68508
Tel: 402-475-4000 *Toll Free Tel:* 800-669-4001
  Fax: 402-475-8063
E-mail: graphics@images2.com
Web Site: www.images2.com
Key Personnel
Gen Mgr: Redge Johnson
Founded: 1974
Design of imaging technology equipment.
Membership(s): The Imaging Alliance

Imageworks
1039 Meade Ave, San Diego, CA 92116-1038
Tel: 619-512-3348
E-mail: info@imageworks.tv
Web Site: www.imageworks.tv
Key Personnel
Prodr/Dir/Writer: Craig Bentley
Founded: 1986
Video production company.

ImageWorks Communications
10155 High Point Lane, Suite 100, Salt Lake
  City, UT 84092
Tel: 801-231-7234 (cell) *Toll Free Tel:* 888-810-
  0100
Web Site: imageworkscommunications.com
Key Personnel
Owner & CEO: Walt Winters *E-mail:* walt@
  imageworkscommunications.com
Founded: 2005
Video production & post-production services,
  conference & event staging, web site design.
Membership(s): NABET-CWA

Imagine Communications Corp
3001 Dallas Pkwy, Suite 300, Frisco, TX 75034
Tel: 469-803-4900 *Toll Free Tel:* 866-4-IMAGINE
(446-2446) *Fax:* 469-803-4899
E-mail: insidesales@imaginecommunications.com
Web Site: www.imaginecommunications.com
Key Personnel
CEO: Charlie Vogt
CFO: Terry Hungle
CTO: Steve Reynolds
Chief Legal Offr: Chuck Gilbert
Chief Mktg Offr: Glodina Connan-Lostanlen
Media software & video infrastructure solutions
serving broadcast, multichannel video program-
ming distributor, government & enterprise cus-
tomers.
Company formed from the rebranding of Har-
ris Broadcast which split into two companies,
Imagine Communications & GatesAir.
Branch Office(s)
3400 W Olive Ave, Suite 220, Burbank, CA
91505 *Tel:* 818-717-6800 *Fax:* 818-842-8945
101 W Colfax Ave, Suite 600, Denver, CO 80202
Tel: 303-476-5000 *Fax:* 303-568-4715
CALA Regional Ctr, 703 Waterford Way, Suite
810, Miami, FL 33126 *Tel:* 786-437-1960
Fax: 305-267-4154
1160 US Hwy 22, Bridgewater, NJ 08807-2931
One Penn Plaza, 39th fl, Suite 3915, New York,
NY 10119 *Tel:* 212-303-4200 *Fax:* 212-303-
4205
25 Dyas Rd, North York, ON M3B 1V7, Canada
Tel: 416-445-9640 *Fax:* 416-445-0595
26 Peppler St, Waterloo, ON N2J 3C2, Canada
Tel: 519-570-9111 *Fax:* 519-570-9140

Imagivations
11314 Sheldon St, Sun Valley, CA 91352
Tel: 818-767-6767 *Fax:* 818-767-3637
E-mail: info@imagivations.com
Web Site: www.imagivations.com
Key Personnel
Owner: Michael Fuller; Andrew Menschik
Founded: 1996
Entertainment - custom fabrication; custom, con-
struction, scenic & design.
Online catalog(s) available

IMAX Corp
2525 Speakman Dr, Mississauga, ON L5K 1B1,
Canada
Tel: 905-403-6500 *Fax:* 905-403-6450
E-mail: info@imax.com
Web Site: www.imax.com
Key Personnel
Chmn: Bradley J Wechsler
CEO: Richard L Gefond
EVP & CFO: Patrick McClymont
Chief Mktg Offr: Eileen Campbell
SVP: Greg Foster

IME, see INTER-Media Electronics

Imig Audio/Video Inc
2611 Fairbanks St, Suite 100, Anchorage, AK
99503
Tel: 907-274-2161 *Fax:* 907-279-0219
E-mail: information@imigav.com
Web Site: www.imigav.com
Key Personnel
Pres: Charles Imig
Commercial AV Equip & Design Consultant: Eric
Imig *E-mail:* eric@imigav.com
Founded: 1971
Events & staging, AV installation & equipment
rentals, media production.

Immersion Corp
50 Rio Robles, San Jose, CA 95134
Tel: 408-467-1900 *Fax:* 408-467-1901
Web Site: www.immersion.com

Key Personnel
Pres & CEO: Victor Viegas
CFO: Paul Norris
SVP, Sales & Mktg: Dennis Sheehan
VP, Engg: Rob Lacroix
VP, HR: Janice Passarello
Catalog(s) available
Branch Office(s)
4200 Blvd Sainte-Laurent, Suite 1105, Montreal,
QC H2W 2R2, Canada *Tel:* 514-987-9800
Fax: 514-987-9808
Foreign Office(s): Tallberginkatu 2B, 00180
Helsinki, Finland
Level 20, Marunouchi Trust Tower - Main, 1-8-
3 Marunouchi, Chiyoda-ku, Tokyo 100-0005,
Japan *Tel:* (03) 6269-3430
ERW Bldg, 5th fl, 1330-8 Seocho-dong, Seocho-
gu, Seoul 137-85, South Korea *Tel:* (02) 3472
3141 *Fax:* (02) 3472 3145
12F-3 No 866, ZhongZheng Rd, ZhongHe City,
Taipei County 235, Taiwan *Tel:* (02) 32345467

**IMP Digital Studios, A PharmaSphere
Company**
120 Rte 17N, Paramus, NJ 07652
Tel: 201-261-3959
E-mail: info@impdigital.us
Web Site: impdigital.us; www.facebook.com/
impdigital
Key Personnel
Chief Audio Engr & Prodr: Mike Goldberg
Founded: 2012
Video production services from concept develop-
ment through post-production. Audio recording
facility & production services. App & web site
development.

Impact Christian Books Inc
332 Leffingwell Ave, Suite 101, Kirkwood, MO
63122
Tel: 314-822-3309
E-mail: info@impactchristianbooks.com
Web Site: www.impactchristianbooks.com
Key Personnel
Pres: Stephen Banks
Founded: 1971
Catalog(s) available

Impact Group, see Impact Technology Group
LLC

Impact Technology Group LLC
One Cardinal Rd, Unit 5, Hilton Head Island, SC
29926
Toll Free Tel: 800-675-2200 *Toll Free Fax:* 800-
500-2565
E-mail: sales@impact-group.com
Web Site: impact-group.com
Key Personnel
Pres: Fred W Gerhart
Leading provider of business communications
technology, offering complete turnkey solutions
for productions, concerts, corporate events,
business offices, tradeshows & multimedia
needs.
Branch Office(s)
100 Pine St, Suite 1250, San Francisco, CA
94111

Imtronics Industries Inc
11930 31 Ct N, St Petersburg, FL 33716
Tel: 727-572-9010 *Fax:* 727-572-9012
E-mail: imtronics@imtronics.com
Web Site: imtronics.com
Founded: 1972
Manufacture electronic parts & testing equipment.
Catalog(s) available

In Concert Production Inc (ICP)
680 Wharton Circle SW, Suite C, Atlanta, GA
30336

Tel: 404-355-7943 *Fax:* 404-350-9045
Web Site: icpatlanta.com
Key Personnel
Pres: Jay Rabbitt
Sound, lighting & stage production.

In the Wild Productions
PO Box 1443, Provincetown, MA 02657-5443
Tel: 508-241-5990
E-mail: info@inthewildproductions.com
Web Site: www.inthewildproductions.com
Key Personnel
Exec Dir & Prodr: Christopher P Hamilton
Tel: 508-487-2887 (cell) *E-mail:* chris@
inthewildproductions.com
Founded: 1999
Supplier of wildlife stock footage, particularly
whales & dolphins.

InCharge Systems, see Applied Integration Corp

Increase Video/Silver Mine Video
Division of Silver Mine Inc
5776 D Lindero Canyon Rd, Westlake Village,
CA 91362
Tel: 805-480-0303
Key Personnel
Pres: Howard Silvers
Mgr, Mktg: Stefan Silvers
Catalog(s) available
Membership(s): Entertainment Merchants Associ-
ation; Music Business Association

Independent Audio Inc
43 Deerfield Rd, Portland, ME 04101
Tel: 207-773-2424 *Fax:* 207-773-2422
E-mail: info@independentaudio.com
Web Site: www.independentaudio.com
Key Personnel
Co-Owner & Pres: Fraser Jones
Co-Owner & Treas: Jean Todd *E-mail:* jean@
independentaudio.com
Founded: 1993
Brochure(s) available, free

The Independent Production Fund
Division of Alvin H Perlmutter Inc
200 Central Park S, Suite 12F, New York, NY
10019
Tel: 212-221-6310 *Fax:* 212-302-1854
Web Site: www.ipfmedia.org/vetc.htm
Key Personnel
Dir: Alvin H Perlmutter *Tel:* 212-221-6310 ext
200 *E-mail:* ahp@ipfmedia.org
VP, Prodn & Opers: Joseph Schroeder *Tel:* 212-
221-6310 ext 201 *E-mail:* joe@ipfmedia.org
Production company.

Indian House
PO Box 472, Taos, NM 87571-0472
Tel: 575-776-2953 *Toll Free Tel:* 800-748-0522
Fax: 575-776-2804
E-mail: music@indianhouse.com
Web Site: www.indianhouse.com
Key Personnel
Prop: Tony Isaacs
Founded: 1966
Traditional American Indian music.
Online catalog(s) available

Indiana University Press
Off of Scholarly Publg, Herman B Wells Library
350, 1320 E Tenth St, Bloomington, IN 47405-
3907
Tel: 812-855-8817 *Toll Free Tel:* 800-842-6796
Fax: 812-855-8507
E-mail: iupress@indiana.edu
Web Site: www.iupress.indiana.edu
Key Personnel
Dir, IU Press & Digital Publg: Gary Dunham
Tel: 812-855-4773 *E-mail:* dunhamg@indiana.
edu

Founded: 1950
Online catalog(s) available
Shipping Address: 1320 E Tenth St, Bloomington, IN 47405 *Tel:* 812-855-4362
Membership(s): Association of University Presses

Indie Aerials
16425 Hart St, Van Nuys, CA 91406
Tel: 818-988-9382
E-mail: info@indieaerials.com
Web Site: indieaerials.com
Aerial production company serving the film industry.

Indigo Productions
313 Kensington Ave, Buffalo, NY 14214
Tel: 716-836-2930 *Fax:* 716-836-6830
E-mail: indigo@indigoproductions.net
Web Site: www.indigoproductions.net
Concert grade professional audio equipment.
Catalog(s) available

Induro
Division of MAC Group
75 Virginia Rd, North White Plains, NY 10603
Tel: 914-347-3300 *Fax:* 914-347-3309
E-mail: info@indurogear.com
Web Site: www.indurogear.com
Key Personnel
Pres, MAC Group: Jan Lederman
Photographic tripods, monopods, heads & photographic support gear.

Indus International Inc
340 S Oak St, West Salem, WI 54669
Mailing Address: PO Box 890, West Salem, WI 54669
Tel: 608-786-0300 *Toll Free Tel:* 800-843-9377
Fax: 608-786-0786
Web Site: www.indususa.com
Key Personnel
Pres: Ameen Ayoob
Founded: 1985
Book scanners, micrographic products, jackets, electronic document management system.

Industrial Light & Magic (ILM)
Division of Lucasfilm Ltd Co
1110 Gorgas St, San Francisco, CA 94129
Tel: 415-746-3000 *Fax:* 415-746-3015
E-mail: contact-sf@ilm.com
Web Site: www.ilm.com
Key Personnel
Dir, PR & Communs: Greg Grusby
Gen Mgr, Lucasfilm Ltd Co: Lynwen Brennan
Founded: 1975
Visual effects.

Industrial Strength Inc
3232 44 Ave N, St Petersburg, FL 33714
Tel: 727-528-2877 *Toll Free Fax:* 888-804-7680
E-mail: sales@industrialstrengthstaging.com
Web Site: www.isstaging.com
Full service, audio, video, lighting & production/staging source.
Catalog(s) available
Membership(s): Audiovisual and Integrated Experience Association

Industrial Timer Co
30 Industrial Park Rd, Centerbrook, CT 06409
Tel: 860-767-7130 *Toll Free Tel:* 800-394-7130
Fax: 860-767-9137 *Toll Free Fax:* 800-767-9137
E-mail: sales@epg-inc.com
Web Site: www.industrialtimercompany.com
Key Personnel
Pres: Peter Griffin
Founded: 1938
Manufacture timers for industrial use.
Catalog(s) available

Inferno Film Productions LLC
PO Box 151048, Lakewood, CO 80215-9048
Tel: 303-587-9792
E-mail: sales@infernofilm.com
Web Site: www.infernofilm.com
Key Personnel
Owner: Darlene Cypser; Mark Steven Grove; Trygve Lode
Develops & produces its own movies in-house.

Inferno Films
3404 Guadalupe St, Austin, TX 78705
Tel: 512-302-9009 *Fax:* 512-302-9022
Web Site: www.infernofilms.com
Key Personnel
Dir: Layton Blaylock *E-mail:* lblaylock@infernofilms.com
Exec Prodr: Jeff Hastings; Quincy Lowman
Founded: 1999
Full service commercial film & video production company. Three edit suites equipped with Avid & Final Cut systems, Sony FS7 camera package.
Membership(s): American Advertising Federation

Inferno Motion Pictures, see Inferno Film Productions LLC

InFocus Corp
13190 SW 68 Pkwy, Suite 200, Portland, OR 97223-8368
Tel: 503-207-4700 *Toll Free Tel:* 877-388-8385
E-mail: sales@infocus.com
Web Site: www.infocus.com
Key Personnel
Pres: Raymond Yu
Founded: 1986
Catalog(s) available
Foreign Office(s): InFocus International, 4 Teck Lim Rd, Singapore 088382, Singapore *Tel:* 6513 9600 *Fax:* 6238 0535
E-mail: asiapacific@infocus.com

Infosat Communications Inc
3130 114 Ave SE, Calgary, AB T2Z 3V6, Canada
Tel: 403-543-8188 *Toll Free Tel:* 888-524-3038
Fax: 403-289-8133
E-mail: info@infosat.com
Web Site: infosat.com
Key Personnel
VP, Opers: Bryan Hetlinger
Dir, Fin: Neil MacIntosh
Dir, Network Servs: Chad Teer
Opers Mgr: David Storrier
Founded: 1986
Provider of remote communication needs.
Catalog(s) available
Branch Office(s)
Able Infosat Communications, 5906 Broadway St, Pearland, TX 77581, Gen Mgr: Michelle Williamson *Tel:* 281-485-8800 *Fax:* 281-485-8230 *Web Site:* www.ableinfosat.com
Membership(s): Audiovisual and Integrated Experience Association

Ingenuity Films LLC
8075 Livorna Way, Fair Oaks, CA 95628
Mailing Address: PO Box 770, Fair Oaks, CA 95628
Toll Free Tel: 844-411-FILM (411-3456)
E-mail: support@ingenuityfilms.com
Web Site: www.ingenuityfilms.com
Key Personnel
Owner: Brent Miller
Production company featuring documentary films.

Ingram Content Group LLC
One Ingram Blvd, La Vergne, TN 37086-1986
Tel: 615-793-5000 *Toll Free Tel:* 800-937-8000 (retailers); 800-937-5300 (ext 1, libs)
E-mail: customerservice@ingramcontent.com

Web Site: www.ingramcontent.com
Key Personnel
Chmn: John Ingram
Pres & CEO: Shawn Morin
Chief Commercial Offr: Shawn Everson
Chief Content Offr: Phil Ollila
CFO: Brian Dauphin
Chief HR Offr: Wayne Keegan
CIO: Steve Marshall
Chief Legal Offr: Kelly Arnold
Chief Logistics Offr: John Secrest
Chief Strategy & Devt Offr: Kent Freeman
Chief Venture Capital Offr: David Roland
VP, Application Servs: Lori Dunbar
VP, Community Rel: Emily Weiss
VP, Content Acq: Kelly Gallagher
VP, Credit: Roger Lee
VP, HR: Jacqueline Letson
VP, Mdsg: George Tattersfield
VP, Retail Sales: Donald Roseman
Dir, Academic Servs: Kurt Hettler
Dir, Application Servs: Robert Barnard
Dir, Digital Servs: Margaret Harrison
Dir, Mass Merchandisers Sales: Lisa Tomasello
Dir, Natl Accts: Michael Bell
Sales Dir: Sharon Swados
Sr Mgr, Mktg Servs: Ann Zangri
Sr Mgr, PR & Communs: Kris Wiese
Lib Sales & Servs Mgr: Tricia Racke Bengel
Mgr, Client Rel: Louisa Brody
Prod Mktg Mgr: Catherine Robinson
Proj Mgr, Integration & Outsource: Sterling Crawford
Specialty Retail Mgr: Megan Smith
Sales & Support Rep, Mass Mdse Group: Tori Cushman
Founded: 1964
Comprehensive publishing industry services company that offers numerous solutions, including physical book distribution, print-on-demand & digital services. Ingram works closely with publishers, retailers, libraries & schools around the world to provide them with the right products & services to help them succeed in the dynamic & increasingly complex world of content publishing. Ingram's operating units are Ingram Book Group LLC, Lightning Source LLC, VitalSource Technologies LLC, Ingram International Inc, Ingram Library Services LLC, Spring Arbor Distributors Inc, Ingram Publisher Services LLC & Tennessee Book Co LLC.
Catalog(s) available
Branch Office(s)
6050 Dana Way, Antioch, TN 37013
7315 Innovation Blvd, Fort Wayne, IN 46818
4260 Port Union Rd, Fairfield, OH 45011
201 Ingram Dr, Roseberg, OR 97470
860 Nestle Way, Breinigsville, PA 18031
1200 Ingram Dr, Chambersburg, PA 17202
Membership(s): Audio Publishers Association

Ingram Entertainment Inc
2 Ingram Blvd, La Vergne, TN 37089
Tel: 615-287-4000 (corp) *Toll Free Tel:* 800-621-1333 (sales & cust serv)
Web Site: www.ingramentertainment.com
Key Personnel
Chmn: David Ingram
VChmn: W Donnie Daniel
Pres & CEO: Robert Webb
EVP, Sales & Mktg: Robert A Geistman
Founded: 1980
National distributor of entertainment software & hardware, including Blu-ray, DVD, audiobooks, games & music players.
Online catalog(s) available
Branch Office(s)
1130 Iron Point Rd, Suite 288, Folsom, CA

95630 *Tel:* 916-605-1500 *Toll Free Tel:* 800-366-2111 *Fax:* 916-605-1760; 916-605-2383
Membership(s): Entertainment Merchants Association

Ingram Micro
3351 Michelson Dr, Suite 100, Irvine, CA 92612
Mailing Address: PO Box 25125, Santa Ana, CA 92799
Tel: 714-566-1000
Web Site: www.ingrammicro.com
Key Personnel
CEO: Alain Monie
Founded: 1979
Distribute & market a large variety of technology & mobility products.
Branch Office(s)
1759 Wehrle Dr, Williamsville, NY 14221
  Tel: 716-633-3600 (east coast corp off)
Shipping Address: 415 E Lies Rd, Carol Stream, IL 60188 *Tel:* 630-668-0106; 80 Micro Dr, Jonestown, PA 17038 *Tel:* 717-865-0800; 3820 Micro Dr, Millington, TN 38053 *Tel:* 901-873-7000; 1809 W Frankford, Suite 100, Carrollton, TX 75007 *Tel:* 972-512-2700
Membership(s): Global Technology Distribution Council

InJoy Birth & Parenting Education
7107 La Vista Place, Longmont, CO 80503
Tel: 303-447-2082 (ext 2) *Toll Free Tel:* 800-326-2082 (ext 2) *Fax:* 303-449-8788
E-mail: custserv@injoyvideos.com
Web Site: www.injoyvideos.com
Key Personnel
Pres: Charlie Stein
Founded: 1988
Producers of prenatal, labor & delivery & postpartum curriculum. Offers DVDs, parent guides, PowerPoint programs & online education.
Online catalog(s) available
Catalog(s) available

Inland Audio Visual Co
1414 N Fiske St, Suite E, Spokane, WA 99202
Tel: 509-328-0706 *Fax:* 509-328-0730
E-mail: inland@inlandav.com
Web Site: www.inlandav.com
Key Personnel
Owner: Tracy Cahalan
Founded: 1946
AV rentals, set-up & production work.
Membership(s): IABC

Inland Audio Visual Ltd
422 Lucas Ave, Box 102, Group 200, RR 2, Winnipeg, MB R3C 2E6, Canada
Tel: 204-786-6521 *Toll Free Tel:* 800-933-6006
  Fax: 204-783-6281
E-mail: winnipeg@inlandav.ca
Web Site: www.inlandav.ca
Key Personnel
Owner, CEO & Pres: Kim E Werbowski
  E-mail: kwerbowski@inlandav.ca
Founded: 1937
Full service AV company.
Online catalog(s) available
Branch Office(s)
700 58 Ave SE, Bay 1, Calgary, AB T2H 2E2, Canada *Tel:* 403-252-7726 *Toll Free Tel:* 800-495-6006 *Fax:* 403-253-1716 *E-mail:* calgary@inlandav.ca
17893 106-A Ave, No 100, Edmonton, AB T5S 1V8, Canada, Mgr: Ben Mejia *Tel:* 780-423-4833 *Toll Free Tel:* 800-587-4004 *Fax:* 780-423-1671 *E-mail:* edmonton@inlandav.ca
2501 Seventh Ave, Regina, SK S4R 1C7, Canada, Mgr: Tim Wiest *Tel:* 306-525-8726 *Toll Free Tel:* 800-743-8008 *Fax:* 306-525-0690 *E-mail:* regina@inlandav.ca

21-1738 Quebec Ave, Saskatoon, SK S7K 1V9, Canada, Mgr: Ralph Niekamp *Tel:* 306-664-8622 *Toll Free Tel:* 800-925-6006 *Fax:* 306-664-2809 *E-mail:* saskatoon@inlandav.ca
Membership(s): Audiovisual and Integrated Experience Association

Inner Traditions International
One Park St, Rochester, VT 05767
Mailing Address: PO Box 388, Rochester, VT 05767-0388
Tel: 802-767-3174 *Toll Free Tel:* 800-246-8648
  Fax: 802-767-3726
E-mail: customerservice@innertraditions.com
Web Site: www.innertraditions.com
Key Personnel
Pres: Ehud Sperling
Dir, Sales & Mktg: John Hays
Sales & Mktg Assoc: Jessica Arsenault
  Tel: 802-767-3174 ext 118 *E-mail:* jessa@innertraditions.com
Publicity: Manzanita Carpenter
Catalog(s) available, free
Online catalog(s) available

Innocinema
1351 Oakbrook Dr, Suite 160, Norcross, GA 30093
Tel: 770-857-3435
E-mail: info@innocinema.com; rentals@innocinema.com; support@innocinema.com
Web Site: www.innocinema.com
Key Personnel
Founder & Partner: Justin Goff
Founded: 2010
Equipment & accessories for professionals working in large-scale movie & video production.

Innovision Media Group
100 Mill Rd, Suite 2, Clifton Heights, PA 19018
Tel: 484-688-1200 *Fax:* 484-688-0148
E-mail: sales@innovision.net
Web Site: www.thecrewstore.com
Key Personnel
Pres: Dan Fried *Tel:* 610-662-2688 (cell)
Founded: 1990
Full service production & media company. Also provide production management for event projects.

Innovision Optics
1834 Broadway, Santa Monica, CA 90404
Tel: 310-453-4866 *Fax:* 310-453-4677
Web Site: www.innovision-optics.com
Key Personnel
Pres: Mark Centkowski *E-mail:* mark@innovisionoptics.com
Founded: 1987
Specialize in the sale & rental of special lenses, motion control camera tracking systems & unique camera support equipment. Provide specialized lenses & camera accessories for broadcast quality, camera systems to the film & TV industry, corporations, the government, theatrical & sporting events. With this, the areas of optics, motion control & camera support were combined into specialized equipment for productions worldwide.
Online catalog(s) available

Inspired Image Picture Co (IIPC)
1090 E Georgia St, Vancouver, BC V6A 2A7, Canada
Tel: 604-874-7513 *Toll Free Tel:* 800-352-1454 (prodn rentals); 800-567-0037 (equip rentals) *Fax:* 604-874-7516
E-mail: info@inspiredimage.ca
Web Site: inspiredimage.ca
Key Personnel
Pres, CEO & Exec Prodr: Roger Williams
CFO: Carole Walkinshaw

Natl Opers Mgr: Anthony Sacco
Cinema Opers Mgr: Richard Metzker
Post-Prodn Mgr: Kevin Jacques
Ed: Fraser Amyott
Television production & rental facility for broadcasting & HD equipment.
Branch Office(s)
310 Judson St, Unit 5, Toronto, ON M8Z 5T6, Canada *Tel:* 416-405-9977
Membership(s): International Alliance of Theatrical Stage Employees

Instant Music Now
Formerly "PBTM" Music
1160 W 26 Ave, Eugene, OR 97405
Tel: 541-345-8117
E-mail: info@instantmusicnow.com
Web Site: www.instantmusicnow.com
Key Personnel
Owner: Michael Brewer
Founded: 1988
Royalty free music library.
Online catalog(s) available

Institute for Teaching & Learning Excellence (ITLE)
Division of Oklahoma State University
100 ITLE, Oklahoma State University, Stillwater, OK 74078
Tel: 405-744-1000 *Fax:* 405-744-8563
E-mail: itle@okstate.edu
Web Site: itle.okstate.edu
Key Personnel
Prodr/Dir: Wade A Pearson *Tel:* 405-744-3936
  E-mail: wade.pearson@okstate.edu
Provide resources through quality video production, multimedia creation & broad distribution services for OSU & its students.

The Institute Inc
787 East Ave, Brockport, NY 14420
Tel: 585-637-6531
Web Site: www.the-institute-ny.com
Key Personnel
Pres: Jack Rollwagen *E-mail:* jrollwag@the-institute-ny.com
Founded: 1972
Film production.

Institute of Precision Muscle Balancing
6035 Vantage Ave, North Hollywood, CA 91616-4637
Tel: 818-766-8555 *Fax:* 818-766-8645
Web Site: www.dralexander.com
Key Personnel
Owner: Dr Ric D Alexander
  E-mail: ricalexander@dralexander.com
Distribute unique self-treatment videos.

Institute of Texan Cultures
Division of University of Texas at San Antonio
UTSA HemisFair Park Campus, 801 E Cesar E Chavez Blvd, San Antonio, TX 78205-3296
Tel: 210-458-2300 *Toll Free Tel:* 800-776-7651
  Fax: 210-458-2205
Web Site: www.texancultures.com
Key Personnel
Sr Admin Assoc: Eva Trevino *Tel:* 210-458-2233
  E-mail: eva.trevino@utsa.edu
Founded: 1968
History & diverse cultures of Texas.
Catalog(s) available, biennial

Institute on Religious Life Inc
PO Box 7500, Libertyville, IL 60048-7500
Tel: 847-573-8975 *Fax:* 847-573-8960
Web Site: www.religiouslife.com
Key Personnel
Exec Dir: Michael Wick *E-mail:* mike@religiouslife.com

Dir, Opers: Anne Tschanz *E-mail:* anne@
religiouslife.com
Founded: 1974
Distribute audio & CD-ROM material on voca-
tions to the religious life.
Brochure(s) available

**Instructional Materials & Equipment
Distributors (I-Med)**
1520 Cotner Ave, Los Angeles, CA 90025
Tel: 323-879-0377; 310-473-5558 *Fax:* 310-473-
5558
Web Site: www.i-med-inc.com
Key Personnel
Pres: Donald H Parson, Jr
Distribute school & church AV equipment & sup-
plies.
Catalog(s) available

IntegraColor
3210 Innovative Way, Mesquite, TX 75149
Tel: 972-289-0705 *Toll Free Tel:* 800-933-9511
Fax: 972-285-4881
E-mail: salesinfo@integracolor.com
Web Site: www.integracolor.com
Key Personnel
CEO: Larry C King
Pres: Adam Geerts
Founded: 1972
Creative & design service, film scanning, volume-
film scanning, scanning for web, digital asset
management, digital file access-ordering sys-
tems, digital procurement systems, trade show
graphics, 4-color printing-sales collateral.
Online catalog(s) available

Integrated Event Management
1239 Vista Leaf Dr, Decatur, GA 30033
Tel: 404-633-8541 *Fax:* 404-633-8691
Web Site: integratedevents.com
Key Personnel
Pres: Thomas Kann *E-mail:* kann@
integratedevents.com
Founded: 1999
Full service creative & technical event production.
Branch Office(s)
Orlando, FL, Dir, Mktg & Prodn Servs: Nancy
McFarland *Tel:* 407-353-4513 *Fax:* 407-622-
8851 *E-mail:* mcfarland@integratedevents.com
Membership(s): ASAE; Audiovisual and Inte-
grated Experience Association; International
Association of Speakers Bureaus

Integrated Solutions Group
Division of The Camera Company
858 Boston Providence Tpke, Norwood, MA
02062
Tel: 781-769-7810 *Toll Free Tel:* 866-769-0210
E-mail: info@isgboston.com
Web Site: isgboston.com
Key Personnel
Pres: David Katz *E-mail:* dkatz@isgboston.com
VP: Martin Feldman *E-mail:* mfeldman@
isgboston.com
Sales Mgr/Lighting Specialist: Jonathan Lipsy
E-mail: jlipsy@isgboston.com
Acct Exec & Mgr, Engg Dept: Gary Pink
E-mail: gpink@isgboston.com
Prod Specialist & Lead Installer: Michael Goul-
ston *E-mail:* mgoulston@isgboston.com
Mgr, Retail Showroom: Gene Katz
E-mail: gkatz@isgboston.com
Founded: 2014
Broadcast & professional video, audio & lighting
equipment sales, studio design & install.
Online catalog(s) available
Membership(s): SMPTE®

Integrated Systems Support Group, see Axxis
Leasing Inc

Intelite Inc, see MeshTel

Intellidyne LLC
2677 Prosperity Ave, Suite 301, Fairfax, VA
22031
Tel: 703-575-9715 *Fax:* 703-575-9718
Web Site: www.intellidyne-llc.com
Key Personnel
Founder & Pres: Robert L Grey
CEO: Tony Crescenzo
COO: Ed Abner
Gen Coun: Fern Ward
SVP, Technol: Ric Sears
Founded: 1998

INTER-Media Electronics
11 Gerald Rd, Milton, MA 02186
Tel: 617-698-8315 *Fax:* 617-698-8315
E-mail: intermedia.ex@verizon.net
Web Site: www.intermedia-electronics.com
Key Personnel
Pres: Tad Walkowiak
Imaging hardware replacement.

Inter Video
2000 N Lincoln St, Burbank, CA 91504
Tel: 818-843-3624 *Toll Free Tel:* 866-204-0340
(sales) *Fax:* 818-843-6884
E-mail: rentals@intervideo24.com
Web Site: www.intervideo24.com
3D & 2D video services & AV support for the
motion picture & television industry.

Interactive Products
Division of Numonics Corp
101 Commerce Dr, Montgomeryville, PA 18936
Tel: 215-362-2766 *Toll Free Tel:* 800-523-6716
Fax: 215-361-0167
E-mail: numonics@numonics.com; orders@
numonics.com
Web Site: www.numonics.com
Key Personnel
Mgr, Sales Admin: Phyllis Ulrich
Manufacture interactive whiteboards.
Catalog(s) available

InterAmerica Stage Inc
5401 Benchmark Lane, Sanford, FL 32773
Tel: 407-302-0881 *Toll Free Tel:* 877-302-4274
Fax: 407-302-0882
E-mail: info@iastage.com
Web Site: www.iastage.com
Key Personnel
Sales Mgr: Jeffrey Craycraft
Founded: 1989
Designers & manufacturers of custom rigging
systems. Speaker hoist & installation, format
projection screens, frames & rigging.
Membership(s): Audiovisual and Integrated Ex-
perience Association; Entertainment Technician
Certification Program; International Associa-
tion of Music Ministries; NAB; Professional
Lighting & Sound Association; USITT

Intercollegiate Studies Institute Inc (ISI)
3901 Centerville Rd, Wilmington, DE 19807
Tel: 302-652-4600 *Toll Free Tel:* 800-526-7022
Fax: 302-652-1760
E-mail: info@isi.org
Web Site: www.isi.org
Key Personnel
Contact: Charley Copeland
Founded: 1953
Nonprofit, tax exempt educational organization
with online lectures that can be downloaded.
Online catalog(s) available

Intercon 1
Division of Nortech Systems Inc
12136 Crystal Lake Rd, Merrifield, MN 56465
Tel: 218-828-3157 *Toll Free Tel:* 800-237-9576
Fax: 218-828-1096
E-mail: intercon@nortechsys.com
Web Site: www.intercon-1.com
Key Personnel
Busn Mgr: Ron Folkeringa *E-mail:* rfolkeringa@
nortechsys.com
Founded: 1978
Manufacture AV cables.
Online catalog(s) available

Interface Media Group
1233 20 St NW, Washington, DC 20036
Tel: 202-861-0500
E-mail: info@interfacemedia.com
Web Site: interfacemedia.com
Key Personnel
Pres & CEO: Jeff Weingarten
EVP, Strategic Partnerships: Adam Hurst
E-mail: ahurst@interfacemedia.com
Founded: 1977
Full service production/post-production facility.
Catalog(s) available
Membership(s): Promax

Interlink Technologies
139 W Indiana Ave, Suite 203, Perrysburg, OH
43552
Mailing Address: PO Box 970, Perrysburg, OH
43552
Tel: 419-893-9011 *Toll Free Tel:* 800-655-5465
Fax: 419-893-7280
E-mail: info@thinkinterlink.com
Web Site: thinkinterlink.com
Key Personnel
Pres & CEO: Jessie Miller
Founded: 1986
Warehouse management software solutions for the
supply chain industry.
Membership(s): Association for Supply Chain
Management; Council of Supply Chain Man-
agement Professionals; International Warehouse
Logistics Association; Material Handling In-
dustry of America; Warehousing Education and
Research Council

Intermark Industries Inc
2980 NW 74 Ave, Miami, FL 33122
Tel: 305-591-8930 *Fax:* 305-593-1091
E-mail: info@intermarkindustries.com
Web Site: www.intermarkindustries.com
Key Personnel
EVP: Dan Kremen *Tel:* 305-591-8930 ext 108
E-mail: dan@intermarkindustries.com
Manufacturing & Pro-audio DJ wholesale distri-
bution of electronic equipment.
Catalog(s) available

Intermedia Inc
3703 S Edmunds St, Suite 203, Seattle, WA
98118
Tel: 206-284-2995 *Toll Free Tel:* 800-553-8336
Toll Free Fax: 800-553-1655
E-mail: info@intermedia-inc.com
Web Site: www.intermedia-inc.com
Key Personnel
Pres: Rob Williams *E-mail:* rob@intermedia-inc.
com
Producer & distributor of social interest educa-
tional programs.
Online catalog(s) available

Intermedia Technologies, see Techkno
Integration & Design Services LLC

InterNation Inc
299 Broadway, Suite 918, New York, NY 10007
Tel: 212-619-5545 *Toll Free Tel:* 800-222-8799
Fax: 212-619-5887
E-mail: info@internation.com
Web Site: www.internation.com

Key Personnel
Pres: Erick Derkatsch
Founded: 1990
Foreign language translations, voice-over recording, subtitling & web localization.

International Audio Visual Inc
622 Rte 10, Unit 21, Whippany, NJ 07981
Tel: 973-887-7744 *Toll Free Tel:* 888-887-7749
E-mail: iav@iavnj.com
Web Site: www.iavnj.com
Key Personnel
Pres: Martin Dalakian
Founded: 1986
Full service AV company.
Online catalog(s) available
Membership(s): Audiovisual and Integrated Experience Association

International Cellulose Corp
12315 Robin Blvd, Houston, TX 77045
Tel: 713-433-6701 *Toll Free Tel:* 800-444-1252
 Fax: 713-433-2029
E-mail: icc@spray-on.com
Web Site: www.spray-on.com
Key Personnel
Regl Sales Mgr: Joey Dickey
Develop & manufacture cellulose spray-applied thermal insulation & acoustical finishes.
Online catalog(s) available

International Contact Inc
2820 Adeline St, Suite 1, Berkeley, CA 94703
Tel: 510-836-1180 *Fax:* 510-835-1314
E-mail: sales@intlcontact.com
Web Site: www.intlcontact.com
Key Personnel
Chmn & Creative Dir: Norma Armon
 E-mail: norma@intlcontact.com
Pres: Carla Itzkowich *E-mail:* carla@intlcontact.com
Founded: 1982
Translation services.
Membership(s): ATA; IABC; Visual Media Alliance

International Datacasting
50 Frank Nighbor Place, Kanata, ON K2V 1B9, Canada
Tel: 613-596-4120 *Fax:* 613-596-4863
E-mail: marketing@datacast.com
Web Site: www.datacast.com
Key Personnel
Pres & CFO: Steven Archambault
VP, Busn Devt & Prods: Gary Carter
VP, Corp Mktg & Sales: Diana Cantu
Founded: 1984
Manufacture & distribute satellite data broadcasting equipment.
Brochure(s) available

International Digital Centre
216 E 45 St, 7th fl, New York, NY 10017
Tel: 212-581-3940 *Fax:* 212-581-3979
E-mail: info@idcdigital.com
Web Site: www.idcdigital.com
Key Personnel
Pres & CEO: Marcy Gilbert *E-mail:* marcy@idcdigital.com
Prodr, VP, Opers & Scheduling: Scott Caroll
 E-mail: scott@idcdigital.com
Founded: 1988
Multi-format, audio-video duplication, standards conversion, digital video compression, HD transfers & DVD authoring. Digital delivery via Smart Jog.

International Display & Exhibit Corp (IDEC)
60 Shawmut St, Suite 5, Canton, MA 02021
Tel: 617-527-7878 *Toll Free Tel:* 800-533-7878
Fax: 617-964-5099

E-mail: sales@idec-displays.com
Web Site: www.idecdisplays.com
Key Personnel
Pres: Steve Levin *E-mail:* slevin@idec-displays.com
Founded: 1967
Manufacturer of all types of flip-chart easels & flip-chart pads: plain, graph & ruled. Also manufacture all types of display stands & equipment. Trade show exhibits & booths, folding screens, drapes all types.
Catalog(s) available

International E-Z UP Inc
1900 Second St, Norco, CA 92860
Tel: 951-279-0999 *Toll Free Tel:* 800-45SHADE (457-4233) *Fax:* 951-279-0888
Web Site: www.ezup.com
Founded: 1983
Instant shelters, shelter accessories, flags, directors chairs, tables, table covers & banner displays.
Catalog(s) available
Sales Office(s): E-Z UP Europe BV, Ringveste 7, 3992 DD Houten, Netherlands *Tel:* (030) 635 4100 *Fax:* (030) 634 1767 *E-mail:* euinfo@ezup.com *Web Site:* www.ezup.nl (European sales)

International Electro-Magnetics Inc
1033A S Noel Ave, Wheeling, IL 60090
Tel: 847-358-4622 *Fax:* 847-947-8239
E-mail: information@iemmag.com; service@iemmag.com; sales@iemmag.com
Web Site: www.iemmag.com
Key Personnel
Pres: Anthony Pretto
Founded: 1976

International Historic Films Inc
3533 S Archer Ave, Chicago, IL 60609
Mailing Address: PO Box 5796, Chicago, IL 60680
Tel: 773-927-2900; 773-927-9091 (cust serv)
 Fax: 773-927-9211
E-mail: intrvdeo@ix.netcom.com
Web Site: ihffilm.com
Key Personnel
Pres: Peter Bernotas
Catalog(s) available
Online catalog(s) available

International Light Technologies Inc
10 Technology Dr, Peabody, MA 01960
Tel: 978-818-6180 *Fax:* 978-818-6181
E-mail: ilsales@intl-lighttech.com
Web Site: www.intl-lighttech.com
Key Personnel
Sales Mgr: Jill Fowler
Founded: 1965
Produce light measurement systems, specialty light sources, LED modules for use in illuminated signs & commercial LED lighting fixtures.
Catalog(s) available

International Marketing Group
1900 Elm Hill Pike, Nashville, TN 37210
Tel: 615-889-8000 *Fax:* 615-871-4817
Key Personnel
CEO: Moe Lytle
Distributes music on CDs.

International Robotics Inc
2001 Palmer Ave, Suite LL-1, Larchmont, NY 10538
Tel: 914-630-1060
E-mail: info@internationalrobotics.com
Web Site: internationalrobotics.com

Key Personnel
Pres & CEO: Robert Doornick
 E-mail: doornickr@internationalrobotics.com
VP: Jason Doornick *E-mail:* jadoornick@internationalrobotics.com
Social robots for marketing & communication, television, movies & technology consulting.

The International Society of Automation (ISA)
67 T W Alexander Dr, Research Triangle Park, NC 27709
Mailing Address: PO Box 12277, Research Triangle Park, NC 27709-2277
Tel: 919-549-8411 *Fax:* 919-549-8288
E-mail: info@isa.org
Web Site: www.isa.org
Key Personnel
Exec Dir: Patrick Gouhin *Tel:* 919-990-9240
 E-mail: pgouhin@isa.org
Exec Off Mgr: Debbie Eby *Tel:* 919-990-9241
 E-mail: deby@isa.org
Founded: 1945
Membership society for automation professionals.
Catalog(s) available

International Tae Kwon Do Association (ITA Institute)
PO Box 281, Grand Blanc, MI 48480
Tel: 810-232-6482
E-mail: hq@itatkd.com
Web Site: www.itatkd.com
Key Personnel
Founder & Pres: James S Benko
Founded: 1973
DVDs & CDs on the art of Tae Kwon Do & other Korean martial arts.
Online catalog(s) available

Interscope, Geffen, A&M Records
Member of Universal Music Group
2220 Colorado Ave, Santa Monica, CA 90404
Tel: 310-865-4500
Web Site: www.interscope.com
Founded: 1999
Music label.

Intersil Americas LLC
1001 Murphy Ranch Rd, Milpitas, CA 95035
Tel: 408-432-8888 *Toll Free Tel:* 888-INTERSIL (468-3774) *Fax:* 408-434-5351
Web Site: www.intersil.com
Key Personnel
Pres, CEO & Dir: Necip Sayiner
SVP & CFO: Rick Crowley
Founded: 1967
Analog circuit, semi-conductors.
Branch Office(s)
1650 Robert J Conlan Blvd NE, Palm Bay, FL 32905 *Tel:* 321-724-7000 *Fax:* 321-729-7320
Foreign Office(s): Unit 1509-11, One ICC, Shanghai ICC, 999 Middle Huaihai Rd, Shanghai 200031, China *Tel:* (021) 6335-1198 *Fax:* (021) 6335-1958
Han Tang Bldg, Suite 701, Overseas Chinese Town, Shenzhen 518053, China *Tel:* (0755) 8246-5118 *Fax:* (0755) 8246-1718
Oskar-Messter-Str 29, 85737 Ismaning, Germany *Tel:* (089) 46263-0 *Fax:* (089) 46263-148
6F, Mita Nitto Daibiru, 3-11-36, Mita, Minato-ku, Tokyo 108-0073, Japan *Tel:* (03) 5439-2311 *Fax:* (03) 5439-2300
Hampshire Place Off, Suite A-13-1, 157 Hampshire, No 1, Jl Mayang Sari, 50450 Kuala Lumpur, Malaysia *Tel:* (03) 2180 7888 *Fax:* (03) 2180 7840
Warwick House, Roydon Rd, Harlow, Essex CM19 5DY, United Kingdom *Tel:* (01279) 630900 *Fax:* (01279) 630938

Interstate Connecting Components
Division of Heilind Mil-Aero LLC
120 Mount Holly Bypass, Lumberton, NJ 08048-1112

Tel: 856-722-5535 *Toll Free Tel:* 888-881-5420
Fax: 856-813-5419
E-mail: info@connecticc.com
Web Site: www.connecticc.com
Key Personnel
Pres: Scott Jacobs *Tel:* 856-722-5535 ext 102
E-mail: scott@connecticc.com
Sales Mgr: Tracey Renshaw *E-mail:* tracey.
renshaw@connecticc.com
Founded: 1985
Distribution of audio connectors & custom cable assemblies.
Catalog(s) available
Branch Office(s)
5055 E Washington St, Suite 120, Phoenix, AZ 85034 *Toll Free Tel:* 844-201-2451 *Fax:* 856-505-1054
6701 Katella Ave, Suite 200, Cypress, CA 90630 *Toll Free Tel:* 888-913-3509 *Toll Free Fax:* 888-913-3578

Intervideo Duplication Services
Division of International Historic Films Inc
3533 S Archer Ave, Chicago, IL 60609
Tel: 773-927-9091 *Fax:* 773-927-9211
E-mail: info@intervideoduplication.com
Web Site: www.intervideoduplication.com
Key Personnel
Pres: Peter Bernotas
DVD & CD duplication. Film to video transfers. Format conversions & archival tape transfers.

InterVision Media
44 W Broadway, Suite 426, Eugene, OR 97401
Tel: 541-343-7993; 547-345-5951
E-mail: info@intervisionmedia.com
Web Site: www.intervisionmedia.com
Key Personnel
CEO: Steve Christiansen
Sr Software Engr & CFO: Toan Tran
Pres: Tom Jacobs
Founded: 1983
Full service design & development for web, interactive media & video.
Online catalog(s) available
Membership(s): Mid-Oregon Production Arts Network

Iowa State University-Information Technology Services
192 Parks Library, Ames, IA 50011
Tel: 515-294-8026; 515-294-4000
E-mail: solution@iastate.edu
Web Site: www.it.iastate.edu
Services to support classroom equipment & event & media production. Collaborates to create & implement online tools that advance learning & teaching.

Ipitek Inc
2461 Impala Dr, Carlsbad, CA 92010
Tel: 760-438-1010 *Toll Free Tel:* 888-4-IPITEK (447-4835, US only) *Fax:* 760-438-2412
E-mail: sales@ipitek.com
Web Site: www.ipitek.com
Key Personnel
Founder, Chmn of the Bd & CEO: Michael Salour *E-mail:* msalour@ipitek.com
SVP, Corp Devt: William J Moore
E-mail: wmoore@ipitek.com
Founded: 1980
Fiber optic broadband technology.
CD-ROM catalog(s) available, free
Catalog(s) available, free
Membership(s): SCTE; Video Services Forum

iProbe Multilingual Solutions Inc
20 Jay St, Suite 638, New York, NY 11201
Tel: 212-489-6035 *Toll Free Tel:* 888-489-6035
Fax: 212-202-4790
E-mail: info@iprobesolutions.com

Web Site: iprobesolutions.com
Key Personnel
Founder & CEO: Julie H Setbon
E-mail: setbon@iprobesolutions.com
Founded: 2001
Facilitate language accessibility for AV content. Live event services, AV rentals & sales, TV/film production support. Authorized dealer for leading brands of AV & language distribution.

Ironbound Film & Television Studios LLC
169 Malvern St, Newark, NJ 07105
Tel: 201-456-4754
Web Site: www.ironboundfilmstudios.com
Key Personnel
Contact: Peter Meister *E-mail:* peter.meister@ironboundfilmstudios.com; Mary Beth O'Connor *Tel:* 917-842-9571 (cell)
E-mail: mb@luckyviii.com
Offers facilities for television, motion picture & digital media productions.

Ironik Design & Post
56 E Main St, Suite 203, Avon, CT 06001
Tel: 860-404-2386 *Fax:* 860-404-2735
E-mail: info@ironikdesign.com
Web Site: www.ironikdesign.com
Key Personnel
Pres: Sean E Stall *E-mail:* sean@ironikdesign.com
Prodn & Facility Mgr: Angela Pace-Stall
E-mail: angela@ironikdesign.com
Graphic design & post-production company specializing in editorial & finishing processes of standard definition & HD content. Avid Media Composer, Avid DS, Discreet Combustion, DVD authoring, Avid Xpress Pro & Adobe Suite.

Ironstone Technologies Inc
534 Berry St, Winnipeg, MB R3H 0R9, Canada
Tel: 204-697-0159 *Toll Free Tel:* 800-665-4766
Fax: 204-694-9355
E-mail: info@ironstone.ca
Web Site: www.ironstone.ca
Key Personnel
Pres: Joel Remis *E-mail:* jremis@ironstone.ca
Founded: 1992
CD & DVD duplication service bureau & DVD authoring. Manufacture digital storage solutions.

ISCAN Inc
21 Cabot Rd, Woburn, MA 01801
Tel: 781-932-1199 *Fax:* 781-932-1155
E-mail: info@iscaninc.com
Web Site: www.iscaninc.com
Key Personnel
Pres: Rikki Razdan
Founded: 1980
Video based eye & target tracking equipment manufacturer.

Ishtar Films
12400 Moorpark St, Suite 2, Studio City, CA 91604
Toll Free Tel: 800-428-7136 *Fax:* 818-985-0567
E-mail: ishtarfilms2@sbcglobal.net
Web Site: www.ishtarfilms.com
Key Personnel
Owner & Pres: Martha Wheelock
Founded: 1976
Produce & distribute documentary films on women & women's history.
Catalog(s) available
Membership(s): Alliance of Women Directors; International Documentary Association

ITA Audio Visual Solutions
2162 Dana Ave & I-71, Cincinnati, OH 45207-1341
Tel: 513-631-7000 *Toll Free Tel:* 800-899-8877
Fax: 513-631-3290
E-mail: csr@ita.com
Web Site: www.ita.com
Key Personnel
Pres: Mark Greene
Regl Mgr, Rental Opers: Dennis Segrist
Founded: 1982
AV equipment rental, sales & service; creative & convention services & video production.
Online catalog(s) available
Branch Office(s)
1076 Rarig Ave, Columbus, OH 43219 *Tel:* 614-258-2900
2309 Dryden Rd, Dayton, OH 45439 *Tel:* 937-298-8880
Membership(s): Audiovisual and Integrated Experience Association; NSCA

ITC
523 Hanley Industrial Ct, St Louis, MO 63144
Tel: 314-646-1800 *Toll Free Tel:* 800-962-2344
Fax: 314-646-1818
Web Site: www.itcjourneys.com
Key Personnel
Founder & CEO: Tom Kuntz *E-mail:* tkuntz@itcjourneys.com
Pres: Scott Fehr *E-mail:* sfehr@itcjourneys.com
VP & Exec Creative Dir: Annie Castellano
E-mail: acastellano@itcjourneys.com
VP, Tech Opers: Dave Boser *E-mail:* dboser@itcjourneys.com
Dir, Opers: Sam Hanna *E-mail:* shanna@itcjourneys.com
Founded: 1994
Concept, design & create live, full-sensory experiences for meeting, trade shows & special events.
Brochure(s) available
Branch Office(s)
3100 Terrace St, Kansas City, MO 64111
Tel: 816-221-7663
Membership(s): HSMAI; MPI

ITC Learning LLC
330 Himmarshee St, Suite 108, Fort Lauderdale, FL 33312
Toll Free Tel: 800-638-3757
E-mail: sales@itclearning.com
Web Site: www.itclearning.com
Key Personnel
Co-Founder & Consultant: Bill Walton
E-mail: bwalton@itclearning.com
SVP, Opers: Jack Lynn
Founded: 1977
Industrial skills training courseware.
Catalog(s) available

ITEC Entertainment Corp
8544 Commodity Circle, Orlando, FL 32819
Tel: 407-226-0200 *Fax:* 407-226-0201
E-mail: productionsinfo@itec.com
Web Site: www.itec.com
Key Personnel
Owner: Bill Coan
Theme park engineering, including strategic planning, creative design & content development, entertainment technology, project development & pre-visualization.
Membership(s): International Association of Amusement Parks and Attractions

ITT Veam LLC
Division of ITT Industries
100 New Wood Rd, Watertown, CT 06795
Tel: 860-274-9681 *Fax:* 860-274-4963
Web Site: www.ittcannon.com
Manufacture electrical connectors.
Catalog(s) available

ITV Productions
1649 S Robertson Blvd, Los Angeles, CA 90035
Tel: 310-204-1234
E-mail: itvproductions1@gmail.com
Web Site: www.itvproductions.com
Key Personnel
Owner & Pres: Cid Hunter
Founded: 1971

IV Media Resources
910 Redwing Dr, Geneva, IL 60134
Tel: 630-389-0000
E-mail: info@infinitevideo.com
Web Site: www.infinitevideo.com
Key Personnel
Owner: Nancy Ellen Temple
Founded: 1982
Corporate/industrial video production, multimedia
DVD duplication & related services. Transfer
slides & film to DVD.

iVideo Technologies
6779 Engle Rd, Suite G, Middleburg Heights, OH
44130
Toll Free Tel: 800-352-6150
E-mail: info@ivideo.com
Web Site: www.ivideo.com
Key Personnel
Pres: Timothy Czyzak
Serv Dir: Tony Farace
Regl Sales Mgr: David Walters
Founded: 1968
Supplier of products & services for the audio,
video & broadcast industries.
Online catalog(s) available
Branch Office(s)
659 Lakeview Plaza, Suite C, Columbus, OH
43085 *Tel:* 614-509-2360 *Fax:* 614-825-1003
Sales Office(s): 8190 A Beechmont Ave, Suite
279, Cincinnati, OH 45237 *Tel:* 513-624-8666
Fax: 513-624-6407
Membership(s): ITVG; National Foundation
of Independent Businesses; NSCA; SBE;
SMPTE®

Ivie Technologies Inc
1195 Spring Creek Place, Suite B, Springville,
UT 84663
Tel: 801-489-8703 *Toll Free Fax:* 877-829-6567
E-mail: ivie@ivie.com
Web Site: www.ivie.com
Key Personnel
Pres & CEO: Scott Merrell
CFO: Don Merrell
Dir, Mktg: Bill Raventos
Founded: 1965
Manufacturers of acoustic instrumentation & au-
dio electronics.
Foreign Office(s): Ivie Europe, Milan, Piazza
Bonaparte 22/E, 20030 Bovisio M MI, Italy
Tel: (0362) 571116 *Fax:* (0362) 596220
E-mail: info@audionetwork.it

Ivory Productions
529 Plymouth Rd, Gwynedd Valley, PA 19437
Tel: 215-591-9900
Web Site: www.ivoryproductions.com; www.
facebook.com/davidivoryproductions
Key Personnel
Owner: David Ivory *E-mail:* david@
ivoryproductions.com
Musical production & engineering.
Membership(s): The Recording Academy

IVS Imaging
Division of Costar Video Systems LLC
101 Wrangler Dr, Suite 201, Coppell, TX 75019
Toll Free Tel: 888-446-1301 *Fax:* 469-635-6800
E-mail: info@ivsimaging.com
Web Site: www.ivsimaging.com

Key Personnel
Div Mgr: J Fields
Video parts distributor. Machine/industrial camera
& accessories distributor.
Catalog(s) available
Membership(s): Automated Imaging Association

J & R Film Co
Division of Moviola
1135 N Mansfield Ave, Hollywood, CA 90038
Tel: 323-467-1116 *Toll Free Tel:* 877-668-4652
Web Site: moviola.com
Key Personnel
CEO: Joe Paskal
Pres: Randy Paskal
SVP: Michael Mostin *E-mail:* mmostin@moviola.
com
Founded: 1924
Total solutions provider for production, post-
production editing & education.
Online catalog(s) available
Branch Office(s)
545 W 45 St, 4th fl, New York, NY 10036
Tel: 212-247-8722 *Fax:* 212-265-0972
Membership(s): Audiovisual and Integrated Expe-
rience Association; SMPTE®

J K Audio Inc
1311 E Sixth St, Sandwich, IL 60548
Tel: 815-786-2929 *Toll Free Tel:* 800-552-8346
Fax: 815-786-8502
E-mail: info@jkaudio.com
Web Site: www.jkaudio.com
Key Personnel
Founder & Owner: Joseph Klinger
Founded: 1992
Manufacture telephone audio interface products.
Catalog(s) available

Jack's Camera Shop
300 E Main St, Muncie, IN 47305
Tel: 765-282-0204 *Fax:* 765-284-6405
E-mail: info@jackscamera.com
Web Site: jackscamera.com
Founded: 1948
Sells & rents photographic & video equipment &
supplies.

JaffeHolden
114-A Washington St, Norwalk, CT 06854
Tel: 203-838-4167 *Fax:* 203-838-4168
Web Site: www.jaffeholden.com
Key Personnel
Chmn: Mark Holden
Pres: Russell Cooper *Tel:* 203-838-4167 ext 113
E-mail: rcooper@jaffeholden.com
Principal, Acoustics: Mark Reber
Founded: 1968
Offer consulting services including the AV indus-
try with state-of-the-art acoustical equipment.
Catalog(s) available

Jaguar Distribution Corp
12711 Ventura Blvd, Suite 300, Studio City, CA
91604
Tel: 818-508-3377 *Fax:* 818-508-3340
Web Site: www.jaguardc.com
Key Personnel
Pres: Jeff Klein
VP, Acq & Publicity: Mona Kwan
VP, Sales: France Capor
Founded: 1982
Distributor of independent films to the worldwide
in-flight marketplace.

Jai Inc
6800 Santa Teresa Blvd, Suite 175, San Jose, CA
95119
Tel: 408-383-0300 *Toll Free Tel:* 800-445-5444
Fax: 408-383-0301
E-mail: camerasales.americas@jai.com

Web Site: www.jai.com
Key Personnel
Mgr, Mktg Communs: Rich Dickerson
E-mail: rdi@jai.com
Video camera equipment manufacturer.
Foreign Office(s): JAI Technology (Beijing) Co
Ltd, 1235-1236, Bldg 2 Jinrongjie (Chang'an)
Ctr, Shijingshan District, Beijing, China
Tel: (010) 5397-4049 *E-mail:* camerasales.
apac@jai.com
JAI A/S, Valby Torvegade 17, 1st fl, 2500 Valby,
Copenhagen, Denmark, Mgr, Mktg Communs:
Gregers Potts *Tel:* 44578888 *Fax:* 44913252
E-mail: camerasales.emea@jai.com (global
headquarters)
JAI A/S, Industriering 7, 63868 Grosswallstadt,
Germany *Tel:* (06022) 26 1500 *Fax:* (06022)
26 1504 *E-mail:* camerasales.emea@jai.com
JAI Ltd, 10-35 Sakae-cho, Kanagawa-ku, Yoko-
homa City, Kanagawa, Japan, Global Mktg
Mgr: Nick Hazama *Tel:* (045) 440-0154
Fax: (045) 440-0166 *E-mail:* camerasales.
apac@jai.com
JAI Manufacturing, 2960-14 Uenojo Nishikata,
Kushima City, Miyazaki, Japan *Tel:* (0987) 71-
1077 *Fax:* (0987) 71-1139

Jai Pulnix, see Jai Inc

Jalbert Productions International
230 New York Ave, Huntington, NY 11743
Tel: 631-351-5878 *Fax:* 631-351-5875
E-mail: jalbert@jalbertfilm.com
Web Site: jalbertfilm.com
Key Personnel
VP, Syndication Sales: Carol Randel
Founded: 1971
Producer of sports videos & sports TV program-
ming.
Online catalog(s) available
Branch Office(s)
1201 Broadway, Suite 407, New York, NY 10001
Tel: 212-596-7001

JAM Industries Ltd
21000 Trans-Canadienne, Baie D'Urfe, QC H9X
4B7, Canada
Tel: 514-457-2555 *Fax:* 514-457-0055
E-mail: info@jamindustries.com
Web Site: jamindustries.com
Key Personnel
VP, Erikson Audio: Jeff Carman
Founded: 1972
Music, sound & audio distribution.

Jameco Electronics
1355 Shoreway Rd, Belmont, CA 94002
Tel: 650-592-8097 *Toll Free Tel:* 800-831-4242
(orders); 800-536-4316 (cust serv) *Fax:* 650-
592-2503 *Toll Free Fax:* 800-237-6948
E-mail: info@jameco.com; sales@jameco.com
Web Site: www.jameco.com
Key Personnel
CEO: James Farrey
VP, Mktg & Sales: Greg Harris
Dir, IT: Matt Smith
Mktg Dir: Angela Avanzino *Tel:* 650-592-8097
ext 507 *E-mail:* aavanzino@jameco.com
Founded: 1974
Distributing electronic components.
Catalog(s) available, free, quarterly

James Agee Film Project
PO Box 73, Riverdale, MD 20738-0073
Tel: 301-277-3880
E-mail: jagee@cstone.net
Web Site: www.ageefilms.org
Key Personnel
Prodr: Ross Spears
Founded: 1974
Production & distribution of documentary films.

Catalog(s) available
Branch Office(s)
913 Althea St, Johnson City, TN 37601

Jams Productions Inc
Production Trailer No 1, 206 Holt Rd, Bow-
manville, ON L1C 3K7, Canada
Tel: 647-273-4844
E-mail: info@jamsproductions.ca
Web Site: www.jamsproductions.ca
Key Personnel
Prodr: Alan J Schwarz *E-mail:* alan@
jamsproductions.ca; Susan Schwarz
E-mail: susan@jamsproductions.ca
Founded: 1990
Independent TV production company.

JamSync
Music Row, 1232 17 Ave S, Nashville, TN 37212
Mailing Address: PO Box 120969, Nashville, TN
37212
Tel: 615-320-5050
E-mail: info@jamsync.com
Web Site: www.jamsync.com
Key Personnel
Pres & Chief Engr: K K Proffitt *E-mail:* kk@
jamsync.com
Founded: 1997
Full service AV production.
Membership(s): AES

Jan-Al Cases
3339 Union Pacific Ave, Los Angeles, CA 90023
Mailing Address: PO Box 23337, Los Angeles,
CA 90023
Tel: 323-260-7212 *Toll Free Tel:* 800-735-2625
Fax: 323-260-4696
Web Site: www.janalcase.com
Key Personnel
Owner & Corp Sales: Jan M Alejandro *Tel:* 323-
260-7212 ext 140 *E-mail:* jan@janalcase.com
Pres: Miriam (Muffie) Alejandro *Tel:* 323-260-
7212 ext 120 *E-mail:* muffie@janalcase.com
Founded: 1983
Manufacture ATA 300 CAT 1 custom cases & de-
sign solutions for any trade show. Thousands of
designs on file.
Membership(s): Institute of Packaging Profession-
als; NAMM, the National Association of Music
Merchants

J&D Laboratories Inc
27 E 21 St, 4th fl, New York, NY 10010
Tel: 212-982-3330 *Fax:* 212-982-3332
E-mail: jdvideolab@aol.com; sales@jdvideolab.
com
Web Site: www.jdvideolab.com
Key Personnel
Pres: Joseph David *E-mail:* joe@jdvideolab.com
VP: Patricia David
Founded: 1966
Video duplication & editing, CD & DVD replica-
tion.
Catalog(s) available

J&S Audio Visual Inc, see JSAV

Janson Industries
1200 Garfield Ave SW, Canton, OH 44706
Tel: 330-455-7029 *Toll Free Tel:* 800-548-8982
Fax: 330-455-5919
Web Site: www.jansonindustries.com
Key Personnel
Owner & Mktg Mgr: Eric Janson
Founded: 1936
Manufacture, installation & design of stage equip-
ment.

Janson Media Inc
The Cunningham House, 118 Main St, Tappan,
NY 10983

Tel: 845-359-8488
E-mail: info@janson.com
Web Site: www.janson.com
Key Personnel
Pres: Stephen Janson *E-mail:* stephen.janson@
janson.com
VP: Zara Janson *E-mail:* zara.janson@janson.com
Mktg Dir: Betsy Van Ost *E-mail:* betsy.vanost@
janson.com
Founded: 1989
Distribute videos, DVDs & films.
Online catalog(s) available
Membership(s): NATPE

Janus Films Inc
215 Park Ave S, 5th fl, New York, NY 10003
Tel: 212-756-8822 *Fax:* 212-756-8850
E-mail: booking@janusfilms.com
Web Site: www.criterion.com; www.janusfilms.
com
Key Personnel
Mng Dir: Jon Mulvaney *E-mail:* mulvaney@
criterion.com
Distribute contemporary & classical film.
Online catalog(s) available

Jazzology
Division of George H Buck Junior Jazz Founda-
tion
61 French Market Place, New Orleans, LA 70116
Tel: 504-525-5000 *Fax:* 504-525-1776
E-mail: geobuck@jazzology.com
Web Site: www.jazzology.com
Key Personnel
VP: Lars Edegran
Parent of GHB, Audiophile, Circle, Southland,
Progressive, Black Swan Records & Solo Art
& American Music.
Online catalog(s) available

JBL Professional
Division of Harman Professional Solutions
8500 Balboa Blvd, Northridge, CA 91329
Tel: 818-894-8850 *Fax:* 818-830-7865 (mktg);
818-894-3479; 818-830-7801 (sales)
E-mail: info@jblpro.com
Web Site: www.jblpro.com; www.harman.com
Key Personnel
Harman Entertainment Mktg Specialist: Becky
Barabas *Tel:* 818-895-3498
Manufacture & design professional loud speakers.
Online catalog(s) available
Catalog(s) available
Membership(s): AES; ASA; International Back-
ground Music Association; NAB; NSCA

JCS Video Productions
Division of Vosburgh Ventures
4617 Sequoia Park Ave, Las Vegas, NV 89139
Tel: 702-596-9291 (cell); 702-546-0150
Toll Free Tel: 800-791-8671 *Fax:* 702-546-0150
Web Site: www.jcsvideo.com
Key Personnel
Owner & Pres: Jack M Vosburgh
E-mail: vosburghj@gmail.com
Founded: 1987
Video production business, Betacam SP, DV, 36
inch media 100xR NLE, multimedia, commer-
cials, local & cable TV programming.

JD Audio Visual Inc
77 N Altadena Dr, Pasadena, CA 91107
Tel: 626-792-6682 *Toll Free Tel:* 800-532-8346
Fax: 626-796-6635
E-mail: sales@jdav.com; rentals@jdav.com
Web Site: jdav.com
Key Personnel
Owner: Kenneth L Dymmel
Founded: 1959
Full service AV equipment company offering
sales & rentals.

Online catalog(s) available
Membership(s): Audiovisual and Integrated Ex-
perience Association; NAMM, the National
Association of Music Merchants; NSCA

JDC Wilmington Camera Services
905 N 23 St, Wilmington, NC 28405
Tel: 910-343-1089 *Fax:* 910-343-0247
E-mail: info@wilmingtoncameraservices.com
Key Personnel
Owner: Joe Dunton
Rental Mgr: Channing Duke
Founded: 1991
Motion picture camera rental & anamorphic lens
specialists.

JDS Video & Media Productions Inc
28069 Diaz Rd, Suite D & E, Temecula, CA
92590
Tel: 951-296-6715 *Toll Free Fax:* 866-737-2239
E-mail: info@jds-productions.com
Web Site: jds-productions.com
Key Personnel
Owner & Pres: Diane Strand
Full service video production company. HD pro-
duction & post-production.

Jeep Jazz Media Solutions
8 Graham Terr, Montclair, NJ 07042
Tel: 973-222-5737
E-mail: jeepjazz@hotmail.com
Web Site: www.jeepjazz.com
Key Personnel
Pres: Shane Faber
Producer of jazz music tapes & CDs.

JENSEN Tools + Supply
335 Willow St, North Andover, MA 01845-5995
Tel: 978-682-9844 *Toll Free Tel:* 800-225-5370
(sales) *Toll Free Fax:* 800-743-8141
E-mail: sales@sbdinc.com
Web Site: www.jensentools.com
Key Personnel
Multimedia Mgr: Julie Giordano
Supplier of products & services for assembling,
repairing & testing electronic equipment.
Catalog(s) available

Jensen Transformers Inc
9304 Deering Ave, Chatsworth, CA 91311
Tel: 818-374-5857 *Toll Free Tel:* 866-476-6291
Fax: 818-374-5856
E-mail: sales@jensen-transformers.com; info@
jensen-transformers.com
Web Site: www.jensen-transformers.com
Key Personnel
Pres: Bill Whitlock
VP, Opers & Gen Mgr: Dave Hill
Founded: 1974
Manufacture audio equipment.
Online catalog(s) available
Membership(s): AES; Audiovisual and Integrated
Experience Association; Custom Electronic De-
sign & Installation Association; IEEE

Jeppesen
Division of Boeing Co
55 Inverness Dr E, Englewood, CO 80112
Tel: 303-799-9090 *Toll Free Tel:* 800-621-5377;
800-353-2107 *Fax:* 303-328-4153
Web Site: www.jeppesen.com
Key Personnel
CEO & VP, Digital Aviation: Kevin Crowley
Founded: 1934
Producing private pilot training kits.

Jereco Studios Inc
627 E Peach St, Suite E, Bozeman, MT 59715
Tel: 406-586-5262
Web Site: www.jerecostudios.com

Key Personnel
Pres, Prodr & Sound Engr: Jeremiah Slovarp
E-mail: jeremiah@jerecostudios.com
Prodr & Engr: Luke Flansburg *E-mail:* luke@
jerecostudios.com
Founded: 2002
Film & post-production with in-studio recording.

Jeron Electronic Systems Inc
7501 N Natchez Ave, Niles, IL 60714
Tel: 773-275-1900 *Toll Free Tel:* 800-621-1903
Fax: 773-275-0283
E-mail: sales@jeron.com
Web Site: www.jeron.com
Key Personnel
VP, Mktg: Ericka C Baran *E-mail:* ebaran@jeron.com
Founded: 1965
Design & manufacture communication solutions.

JFA Studio
3062 N Lima St, Burbank, CA 91504
Tel: 818-861-9090
E-mail: info@jfastudio.com
Web Site: www.jfastudio.com
Studio facility for the film & TV industry.
Equipment rental & full production & post-production services.

JFB Communications
3 Haig Ave, Toronto, ON M1N 2W2, Canada
Tel: 416-691-5001; 416-526-9400 (cell)
E-mail: jfb@jfb.ca
Web Site: www.jfb.ca
Key Personnel
Pres: John Fulford-Brown
Founded: 1991
Corporate communications, film & television production.

JFW Industries Inc
5134 Commerce Square Dr, Indianapolis, IN 46237
Tel: 317-887-1340 *Toll Free Tel:* 877-887-4539
Fax: 317-881-6790
E-mail: sales@jfwindustries.com; jfwengr@jfwindustries.com
Web Site: www.jfwindustries.com
Key Personnel
Pres: Fred Walker
VP: Jim Leach
Mktg: Connie Ventress
Founded: 1979
Manufacturer of attenuation & RF switching products.
Online catalog(s) available
Brochure(s) available
Foreign Office(s): 7 Albion Rd, South Benfleet, Essex SS7 5PU, United Kingdom *Tel:* (07768) 662666 *E-mail:* simon@jfwindustries.com

JIB Shots Equipment Inc
1828 Lorraine Ave, Ottawa, ON K1H 6Z8, Canada
Tel: 613-293-3318
Web Site: www.jibshots.com
Key Personnel
Owner: Graham Dunnell *E-mail:* graham.dunnell@sympatico.ca
Founded: 1999
Rentals & operation of specialized camera support (jibs, galaxy crane, golf carts).

The Jim Henson Co
1416 N La Brea Ave, Hollywood, CA 90028
Tel: 323-802-1500 *Fax:* 323-802-1825
Web Site: www.henson.com
Key Personnel
Chmn: Brian Henson
CEO: Lisa Henson, Esq
EVP & CFO: Laurie Don

EVP, Children's Entertainment: Halle Stanford
EVP, Global Dist & Intl Consumer Prods: Richard Goldsmith
EVP, Worldwide Admin: Joe Henderson
SVP, Mktg & Publicity: Nicole Goldman *E-mail:* ngoldman@henson.com
VP, Busn Opers & Global Dist: Karen Lee Arbeeny
VP, Busn Devt-JHCS: Jeremy Nocon
VP, Digital Devt & Interactive Media: Celine Willard
VP, Feature Film Prodn: Blanca Lista
VP, US Admin: Howard Sharp
Creative Supv, JHCS: Peter Brooke
Soundstage & post-production facilities. Home to Jim Henson's Creature Shop™ & Henson Recording Studios.
Branch Office(s)
37-18 Northern Blvd, Suite 400, Long Island City, NY 11101 *Tel:* 212-794-2400 *Fax:* 212-439-7452

Jin Records
Division of Swallow Publications Inc
700 S Chataignier, Ville Platte, LA 70586
Mailing Address: PO Drawer 10, Ville Platte, LA 70586-0010
Tel: 337-363-2177 *Toll Free Tel:* 800-738-8668 (orders) *Fax:* 337-363-2094
E-mail: info@flattownmusic.com
Web Site: www.flattownmusic.com
Key Personnel
Pres: Floyd Soileau
Founded: 1957
Catalog(s) available

JIST Publishing
Division of EMC Publishing LLC
875 Montreal Way, St Paul, MN 55102
Toll Free Tel: 800-328-1452 *Toll Free Fax:* 800-328-4564
E-mail: educate@emcp.com
Web Site: jist.emcp.com
Key Personnel
Sr Acct Mgr: Bob Grilliot *Tel:* 855-213-0737
Founded: 1981
Career & job search print & digital resources, including assessments, workbooks, reference books, trade books, videos, posters, games & online workshops.
Online catalog(s) available

JL Recording Studios
270 Adelaide St W, Suite 202, Toronto, ON M5H 1X6, Canada
Tel: 416-598-7979
Web Site: www.jlstudios.ca; www.facebook.com/jlrecordingstudios; twitter.com/JLStudios
Key Personnel
Owner: Jeffrey LeClair
Proj Engr: Lorne Mower
Founded: 1994
Professional audio recording, editing & sound mixing studio.

JLCooper Electronics
142 Arena St, El Segundo, CA 90245
Tel: 310-322-9990 *Fax:* 310-335-0110
E-mail: sales@jlcooper.com; service@jlcooper.com
Web Site: www.jlcooper.com
Key Personnel
VP & Gen Mgr: Chuck Thompson
Founded: 1979
Offer a complete range of branded products for the professional audio, video & multimedia markets.
Online catalog(s) available
Membership(s): AES; IBC; NAB; NAMM, the National Association of Music Merchants

JMC Photo & Digital Services Inc
10 Westport Ct, Bloomington, IL 61704-8233
Tel: 309-663-4677
E-mail: jmcpds@jmcpds.com
Web Site: www.jmcpds.com
Key Personnel
Owner: Ann Charback
Photofinishing, film processing & large format printing & studio shooting.
Brochure(s) available

JoeAudio
10850 John Galt Blvd, Omaha, NE 68137
Tel: 402-341-9153 *Toll Free Tel:* 866-JOE-AUDIO (563-2834)
Web Site: www.joeaudioproductions.com
Key Personnel
Pres & Prodr: Joe Wolf *E-mail:* joe@joeaudioproductions.com
Founded: 1992
Recording studio services for voice-over & audio post; ISDN, ProTools.

John McLean Media
802 Newton, Penthouse 3, Seattle, WA 98109
Tel: 206-285-2603
E-mail: info@johnmcleanmedia.com
Web Site: www.johnmcleanmedia.com
Key Personnel
Founder & Pres: John McLean
Founded: 1999
Video program distribution.

Alan Johnson Recording
5763 Park Plaza Ct, Indianapolis, IN 46220
Tel: 317-439-6521
E-mail: alan@alanjohnsonrecording.com
Web Site: www.alanjohnsonrecording.com
Key Personnel
Contact: Alan Johnson

Johnson Systems Inc (JSI)
1923 Highfield Crescent SE, Calgary, AB T2G 5M1, Canada
Tel: 403-287-8003 *Fax:* 403-287-9003
E-mail: info@johnsonsystems.com
Web Site: www.johnsonsystems.com
Key Personnel
Pres: Shaun Johnson
Founded: 1987
Manufactures lighting systems, lighting control products & equipment.
Catalog(s) available

Pamela Johnston Voice Talent
249 Eighth Ave, Cramerton, NC 28032
Tel: 703-371-7341 *Fax:* 703-997-8971
Web Site: www.pjvoicetalent.com
Key Personnel
Voice Talent: Pamela Johnston *E-mail:* pamela@pjvoicetalent.com
Founded: 1995
Voice talent, providing narrations & voice-overs for educational, e-learning, IVR, film, video, web, radio, TV & audiobook projects in English, Spanish & German.
Membership(s): Women in Film & Video; Women in Film/Atlanta

Jointure for Community Adult Education Inc
Centre at Raritan, Suite B-11, 1124 US Hwy 202 S, Raritan, NJ 08869
Tel: 908-722-0233 *Fax:* 908-722-0388
E-mail: info@jointure.org
Web Site: www.jointure.org
Key Personnel
Exec Dir: Erica Condon
Dir, Opers: Dianne Lewis *Tel:* 908-722-0233 ext 10
Founded: 1914
Adult education courses.
Catalog(s) available

JoLida Inc
21310 Ridgecroft Dr, Brookeville, MD 20833
Tel: 301-953-2014 *Fax:* 301-498-0554
E-mail: jolidacorp@msn.com
Web Site: www.jolida.com
Key Personnel
CEO: Mike Allen
Founded: 1983
Catalog(s) available

Jordan Klein Film & Video (JKFV)
10197 SE 144 Place, Summerfield, FL 34491
Tel: 352-288-3999
Web Site: www.jordy.com
Key Personnel
Owner & Pres: Jordan Klein, Jr *Tel:* 352-427-2560 (cell) *E-mail:* jordy@jordy.com
Film & video production.
Catalog(s) available

Joseph Electronics
6633 W Howard St, Niles, IL 60714
Tel: 847-588-3800 *Toll Free Tel:* 800-323-5925
  Fax: 847-588-3300 *Toll Free Fax:* 800-446-8366
E-mail: sales@josephelectronics.com
Web Site: www.josephelectronics.com
Key Personnel
Pres & CEO: Yohay Hahamy
Mktg Mgr: Chris Annella *E-mail:* chrisa@josephelectronics.com
Founded: 2001
Distributor of broadcast products & value added services.
Catalog(s) available
Branch Office(s)
Joseph Electronics West, 3045 Teagarden St, San Leandro, CA 94577 *Tel:* 510-352-7500 *Fax:* 510-352-7510
Membership(s): NAB; SBE; Sports Video Group; Texas Association of Broadcasters; Wisconsin Broadcasters Association

Harry Joseph & Associates Inc
PO Box 20993, New York, NY 10025
Tel: 212-244-5900
E-mail: harry@hja.com
Web Site: www.hja.com
Key Personnel
CEO: Harry Joseph
Founded: 1974
Membership(s): SMPTE®

Josephson Engineering Inc
329-A Ingalls St, Santa Cruz, CA 95060
Tel: 831-420-0888 *Fax:* 831-420-0890
E-mail: info@josephson.com
Web Site: www.josephson.com
Key Personnel
CEO & Dir: David Josephson
Founded: 1988
Design & manufacture microphones for sound recording in studios, live & stage environments & for accoustical measurement.
Catalog(s) available

Joyce Media Inc
3413 Soledad Canyon Rd, Acton, CA 93510
Mailing Address: PO Box 57, Acton, CA 93510-0057
Tel: 661-269-1169 *Fax:* 661-269-2139
E-mail: help@joycemediainc.com
Web Site: www.joycemediainc.com
Key Personnel
CEO: John Joyce
Pres: Gayle Joyce
Founded: 1969
Educational DVDs including sign language songs & stories.
Online catalog(s) available, updated weekly

JPL
471 JPL Wick Dr, Harrisburg, PA 17111-2504
Tel: 717-558-8048 *Fax:* 717-558-8349
E-mail: jpl@jplcreative.com
Web Site: www.jplcreative.com; www.facebook.com/jplcreative
Key Personnel
Dir, Communs: Susan Cort *E-mail:* scort@jplcreative.com
Founded: 1989
Strategic integrated communications. Video & media production.
Branch Office(s)
3355 Keswick Rd, Suite 300, Baltimore, MD 21211 *Tel:* 410-630-8440

JRF Magnetic Sciences Inc
249 Kennedy Rd, Greendell, NJ 07839
Mailing Address: PO Box 309, Greendell, NJ 07839-0309
Tel: 973-579-5773 *Fax:* 973-579-6021
E-mail: jrf@jrfmagnetics.com
Web Site: www.jrfmagnetics.com
Key Personnel
Pres: John French
Secy & Treas: Cookie French
Founded: 1979
Distribution & repair of magnetic recording equipment.
Catalog(s) available
Membership(s): AES; The Recording Academy

JSAV
9150 N Royal Lane, Suite 150, Irving, TX 75063
Tel: 972-241-5444 *Toll Free Tel:* 800-852-8771
  Fax: 972-247-2590
E-mail: info@jsav.com
Web Site: www.jsav.com
Key Personnel
CEO: Chuck Bauman
Pres: Kevin Jost *E-mail:* kevinj@jsav.com
SVP, Opers: Conor Donahue
Dir, Corp Opers: Kris Gutz
Founded: 1986
Provide an integrated suite of AV & event production services.
Online catalog(s) available
Branch Office(s)
448 Garden Oaks Blvd, Houston, TX 77018
  Tel: 713-957-4567 *Fax:* 713-957-4622
1107 AT&T Center Pkwy, Suite 111, San Antonio, TX 78219 *Tel:* 210-572-1551
1301 S Jason St, Unit A, Denver, CO 80223, Gen Mgr: Chris Brennan *Tel:* 303-792-5588 *Toll Free Tel:* 800-835-7966 *Fax:* 303-792-5599
455 N Tenth St, Omaha, NE 68102 *Tel:* 402-599-6492

JSC Wire & Cable
Division of Seminole Wire & Cable
7861 Airport Hwy, Pennsauken, NJ 08109
Tel: 856-324-2929 *Toll Free Tel:* 800-572-9473
E-mail: sales@jscwire.com
Web Site: www.jscwire.com
Key Personnel
Pres: Michael Genzel
Founded: 1942
Manufacturer of wire & cable for the audio & video market.
Printed material(s) available, free

JT Communications
579 NE 44 Ave, Ocala, FL 34470-1421
Tel: 352-236-0744 *Fax:* 352-236-5130
E-mail: general_info@jtcomms.com
Web Site: www.jtcomms.com
Key Personnel
Owner: Jim Trapani
Founded: 1990
Manufacture & repair of audio & communications equipment.
Catalog(s) available

Juice Goose
7320 Ashcroft, Suite 104, Houston, TX 77081
Tel: 713-772-1404 *Fax:* 713-772-7360
E-mail: info@juicegoose.com
Web Site: www.juicegoose.com
Key Personnel
VP: Peter M Cook *E-mail:* pcook@juicegoose.com
Manufacturer & distributor of electric power distribution, conditioning & control equipment.
Online catalog(s) available
Membership(s): Audiovisual and Integrated Experience Association

Juice Studios
1648 Tenth St, Santa Monica, CA 90404
Tel: 310-460-7830 *Fax:* 310-460-7845
Web Site: www.facebook.com/juicestudiosla; www.juicestudios.tv
Founded: 1985
Audio recording & mixing facility.

JungleTV
571 NW Mercantile Place, Port St Lucie, FL 34986
Mailing Address: PO Box 881122, Port St Lucie, FL 34988-1122
Tel: 772-370-0043
E-mail: info@jungletv.com
Web Site: www.jungletv.com
Key Personnel
Dir & Exec Prodr: Michael Stankoski
Dir, Photog: Jon Schellenger
Founded: 1998
Offers a comprehensive suite of video & visual arts services that includes video production, post-production, commercial photography, file conversion services & video transfers/duplication.

Jupiter Moon Productions
219 36 St, No 3A, Brooklyn, NY 11232
Tel: 631-553-9750
Key Personnel
Owner: Laura Serpico
Videography, producing & editing.

Jupiter Systems
31015 Huntwood Ave, Hayward, CA 94544
Tel: 510-675-1000 *Fax:* 510-675-1001
E-mail: sales@jupiter.com
Web Site: www.jupiter.com
Key Personnel
Co-Founder & Pres: Eric Wogsberg
Co-Founder & VP: Jack Klingelhofer
CFO: Bob Worthington
SVP, Worldwide Sales: Daniel LeCour
VP, Mktg & Strategic Alliances: Brady O Bruce
Founded: 1982
Worldwide supplier of visualization & collaboration solutions for video walls, PCs & mobile devices.
Foreign Office(s): Jupiter Systems China (Shenzhen) Ltd, Rm D501-503, 5th fl, Shenzhen Tech-Innovation Intl Bldg, 10 Kejinan Rd, Nashan, Shenzhen, China, Gen Mgr: Guomin Zhang *Tel:* (0755) 2672-7856 *E-mail:* gzhang@jupiter.com

Just Bulbs - The Light Bulb Store
222 E 58 St, New York, NY 10022
Tel: 212-888-5707 *Fax:* 212-888-5704
E-mail: sales@justbulbsnyc.com
Web Site: www.justbulbsnyc.com
Key Personnel
Pres: David Brooks *E-mail:* dbrooks@justbulbsnyc.com
Founded: 1980
Light bulbs of every description.

JVC Professional Products Co
Division of JVC Americas Corp
1700 Valley Rd, Wayne, NJ 07470
Tel: 973-317-5000 *Toll Free Tel:* 800-582-5825;
800-247-3608; 800-252-5722 *Fax:* 973-317-
5030 *Toll Free Fax:* 800-582-5825 (option 2)
E-mail: proinfo@jvc.com
Web Site: www.jvc.com
Key Personnel
Asst VP, Mktg: David Walton *E-mail:* dwalton@
us.jvckenwood.com
Distribute a complete line of broadcast, profes-
sional & presentation equipment.
Online catalog(s) available
Membership(s): AES; Content Delivery & Stor-
age Association; NAB; NCTA - The Internet &
Television Association; PPA; SBE; SMPTE®;
SPARS

JWP Inc
PO Box 14867, Fort Worth, TX 76117
Tel: 817-233-6462
Web Site: www.jwproductions.org
Key Personnel
Owner & Exec Prodr: Jeff Watts
E-mail: jeffwatts@jwproductions.org
Full service production company. Equipment in-
cludes HD camera.

Ka Io Productions Inc
PO Box 5150, Hilo, HI 96720-1150
Tel: 808-959-3885 *Toll Free Tel:* 888-458-7538
Fax: 808-959-3885
E-mail: lava@volcanovideo.com
Web Site: www.volcanovideo.com
Key Personnel
Pres: Cheryl Gansecki
VP: Jenda Johnson
Founded: 1987
Produce & distribute educational & scientific
videos on DVD & Blu-ray; production of stock
footage, particularly of volcanic eruptions.

Kaboom Productions
2169 Folsom St, Suite 201-M, San Francisco, CA
94110
Tel: 415-434-2666 *Fax:* 415-874-9324
E-mail: hello@kaboomproductions.com
Web Site: kaboomproductions.com
Key Personnel
Dir: Michele Atkins; Carolyn Corben; Brandon
Dickerson; Erik Moe; Doug Werby
Exec Prodr: Lauren Schwartz *E-mail:* lauren@
kaboomproductions.com
Head, Prodn: Steven Sills
Founded: 1996
Full service television, music video, feature film
& commercial production company.
Branch Office(s)
13045 Pacific Promenade, Loft 320, Los Angeles,
CA 90094 *Tel:* 310-478-1620

KAE Corp
955 E 500 S, Salt Lake City, UT 84102
Tel: 801-238-2300
E-mail: kaecorp@xmission.com
Web Site: www.kaecorp.com
Key Personnel
Pres: Ed Scott
Founded: 1998
Rack accessory products.
Catalog(s) available
Membership(s): NAB

KAKE-TV
Subsidiary of Lockwood Broadcast Group
1500 N West St, Wichita, KS 67203-1323
Tel: 316-943-4221; 316-946-1363 (sales)
Fax: 316-943-5493 (sales)
E-mail: sales@kake.com; news@kake.com
Web Site: kake.com

Key Personnel
News Dir: Anthony Maisel *E-mail:* amaisel@
kake.com
Gen Mgr: Mike Rajewski *E-mail:* mrajewski@
kake.com
Founded: 1954
Locally produced news coverage.

Kaleidosound
936 Dewing Ave, Suite I, Lafayette, CA 94549
Tel: 925-283-9901 *Fax:* 925-283-9902
Web Site: www.k-sound.com
Key Personnel
Owner & Creative Consultant: Forrest G Patten
E-mail: forrest@k-sound.com
Founded: 1978
Music production & sound effects.
Membership(s): ASCAP; NATAS

Kalglo Electronics Co Inc
5911 Colony Dr, Bethlehem, PA 18017-9348
Tel: 610-837-0700 *Fax:* 610-837-7978
E-mail: kalglo@kalglo.com
Web Site: www.kalglo.com
Key Personnel
Pres: R Bruce MacDougall
Founded: 1969
Manufacture surge protectors, voltage & power
line protectors.

K&R All Media Productions LLC
28533 Greenfield Rd, Southfield, MI 48076
Tel: 248-557-8276
Web Site: www.knr.net
Key Personnel
Pres: Ken Glaza *E-mail:* ken@kandrforensic.com
Prodr & Engr: Dan Hanley
Founded: 1973
Recording studio with forensic expertise.
Online catalog(s) available

K&R PhotoDigital
538 Terry Lane, Fort Mitchell, KY 41017
Tel: 859-341-6998; 859-341-6986 (orders)
Fax: 859-341-6987
E-mail: photodigitalpro@mac.com; wilmakr@aol.
com
Web Site: www.krphotodigital.com
Key Personnel
Owner: Rob Kumler *E-mail:* rob@krphotodigital.
com
Founded: 1975
High-end digital professional photographic sup-
plier.
Membership(s): The Imaging Alliance

K&R's Recording Studios Inc
28533 Greenfield, Southfield, MI 48076
Tel: 248-557-8276; 248-569-5422
Web Site: www.knr.net; www.kandrforensic.com
Key Personnel
Owner & Pres: Kenneth Glaza *E-mail:* ken@knr.
net
Recording studio providing forensic qualifications
& services.
Online catalog(s) available

Kangaroo Cases
4027 Main St, Dallas, TX 75226
Tel: 214-823-5264 *Toll Free Tel:* 800-890-1073
Fax: 214-824-1179
E-mail: info@kangaroocases.com
Web Site: www.kangaroocases.com
Key Personnel
Pres & CEO: David Chandler
Case manufacturing.
Catalog(s) available, upon request

Kantola Productions LLC
55 Sunnyside Ave, Mill Valley, CA 94941

Tel: 415-381-9363 *Toll Free Tel:* 800-280-1180
Fax: 415-381-9801
E-mail: kantola@kantola.com
Web Site: www.kantola.com
Key Personnel
Pres: Steve Kantola
Founded: 1985
Business training videos.
Catalog(s) available

Richard Kaplan Productions
455 N End Ave, Apt 1114, New York, NY
10282-1139
Tel: 212-787-0258 *Fax:* 212-787-0268
E-mail: richardkaplan33@gmail.com
Web Site: richardkaplanproductions.com
Key Personnel
Pres: Richard Kaplan
Distribution of Richard Kaplan films.

Kappa Map Group LLC
112 E New York Ave, Deland, FL 32724
Tel: 386-873-3010 *Toll Free Tel:* 800-829-6277
(cust serv) *Fax:* 386-873-3011
E-mail: info@kappamapgroup.com; sales@
kappamapgroup.com
Web Site: kappamapgroup.com
Key Personnel
Dir, Specialty Sales: Sharon Edwards
Founded: 2011
Branch Office(s)
Kappa Publishing Group Inc, 6198 Butler Pike,
Suite 200, Blue Bell, PA 19422 (corp off)
Membership(s): Education Market Association;
International Map Dealers Association

Kappa optronics Inc
Subsidiary of Kappa optronics GmbH
825 S Primrose Ave, Suite I, Monrovia, CA
91016
Tel: 626-256-4343
E-mail: contact@kappa-optronics.com
Web Site: www.kappa-optronics.com
Key Personnel
Dir, Sales: Christian Koziol
Develop & manufacture application-specific cam-
eras.

Karst Productions Inc
5779 NE County Rd 340, High Springs, FL
32643
Tel: 386-454-3556 *Fax:* 386-454-3749
E-mail: support@karstproductions.com
Web Site: www.karstproductions.com

Kart-A-Bag Manufacturing Inc
Division of Remin Laboratories Inc
510 Manhattan Rd, Joliet, IL 60433
Tel: 815-723-1940 *Toll Free Tel:* 800-423-9328
Fax: 815-723-2495
E-mail: sales@kart-a-bag.com
Web Site: www.kart-a-bag.com
Key Personnel
Pres: Eugene Kazmark, Jr
Treas: Mary Kazmark-Bruskotter
Founded: 1967
Manufacture heavy duty telescoping carts & hand
trucks.
Catalog(s) available
Membership(s): The Imaging Alliance; LLGMA;
NAB

KAS Music & Sound
Subsidiary of Kaufman Astoria Studios
34-12 36 St, Astoria, NY 11106
Tel: 718-786-3400 *Fax:* 718-729-3007
Web Site: www.kasmusic.com
Key Personnel
Exec Creative Dir: Joe Castellon *E-mail:* joe@
kasmusic.com
Membership(s): AES; American Federation of
Musicians; The Recording Academy; SPARS

Kavanagh Productions Inc
32 Broadway, Suite 1711-12, New York, NY 10004
Tel: 212-480-0065 *Fax:* 212-480-0149
E-mail: create@kavanaghproductions.com
Web Site: kavanaghproductions.com
Key Personnel
Dir & Prodr: Bill Kavanagh
Ed: Sylke Froechtenigt
Production company & post-production house that specializes in documentary, live event video & corporate projects. Avid media composer, final cut pro. Field & multicamera production.
Membership(s): Film Video Arts

Kavich Reynolds Productions Inc
3151 Cahuenga Blvd, Suite 101, Los Angeles, CA 90068
Tel: 323-851-2490
E-mail: info@kavichreynolds.com
Web Site: www.kavichreynolds.com
Key Personnel
Pres: John Reynolds *E-mail:* johnreynolds@ kavichreynolds.com
Full service production company that handles all phases of creative development, scriptwriting, production & post-production.

Kay Industries Inc
PO Box 1323, South Bend, IN 46624
Tel: 574-236-6220 *Toll Free Tel:* 800-348-5257
Fax: 574-289-5932
E-mail: techsupport@kayind.com; info@kayind. com
Web Site: www.kayind.com
Manufacture rotary phase converters for broadcasting.
Online catalog(s) available
Branch Office(s)
Power Solutions, 4127 Bay St, Suite 6, Fremont, CA 94538, Contact: Larry Katz *Tel:* 510-656-8766 *Fax:* 510-657-7283

KCFW Television
401 First Ave E, Kalispell, MT 59901
Mailing Address: PO Box 857, Kalispell, MT 59903
Tel: 406-755-5239 *Fax:* 406-752-8002
E-mail: news@kcfw.com
Web Site: www.nbcmontana.com/news/kcfw
Key Personnel
Asst News Dir: Cyndy Koures *E-mail:* ckoures@ sbgtv.com
Founded: 1968

KD Kanopy Inc
1921 E 68 Ave, Denver, CO 80229
Tel: 303-650-1310 *Toll Free Tel:* 800-432-4435
Fax: 303-650-5211
E-mail: sales@kdkanopy.com
Web Site: www.kdkanopy.com
Key Personnel
Pres & CEO: Matt Kayser
Founded: 1984
Manufacture canopies & tents used for remotes, concerts & on-location shoots, etc.
Catalog(s) available
Online catalog(s) available
Membership(s): GSA

KDM Electronics Inc
55 Mills Rd, Unit 3, Ajax, ON L1S 2H2, Canada
Tel: 416-439-7158 *Toll Free Tel:* 800-567-6282
Fax: 416-439-7232
E-mail: kdm@octasound.com
Web Site: www.octasound.com
Key Personnel
Pres: Martin Bull *E-mail:* martin@octasound.com
Mktg & Inside Sales: Kevin Bull *E-mail:* kevin@ octasound.com

Founded: 1976
Audio & video equipment manufacturing.

KEF Media
1161 Concord Rd SE, Smyrna, GA 30080
Tel: 404-605-0009
E-mail: info@kefmedia.com
Web Site: kefmedia.com
Key Personnel
Founder & CEO: Kevin Foley
COO: Yvonne Goforth-Hanak
Co-Pres: Linda Buckley
SVP, Asst Gen Mgr & Exec Prodr: Audrey Kelsey
Founded: 1986
Corporate video production, video news releases. Integrates digital & social media services into traditional & radio broadcast services.
Catalog(s) available

Kelmscott Communications
1665 Mallette Rd, Aurora, IL 60505-1354
Tel: 630-898-0800 *Fax:* 630-898-2183
Web Site: kelmscottcommunications.com
Key Personnel
Pres & CEO: Scott Voris
VP, Mktg: Jason Tews *E-mail:* jtews@kelmscott. com
Founded: 1982
CD audio, CD-ROM replication/CD-R duplication services.

Ken-A-Vision Manufacturing Co Inc
5615 Raytown Rd, Kansas City, MO 64133
Tel: 816-353-4787 *Toll Free Tel:* 800-501-7366; 800-627-1953 (cust serv) *Fax:* 816-358-5072
E-mail: info@ken-a-vision.com
Web Site: www.ken-a-vision.com
Key Personnel
Pres: Steven M Dunn
Founded: 1954
Manufacture microscopes & flexible document cameras for science education.
Catalog(s) available
Online catalog(s) available
Membership(s): Audiovisual and Integrated Experience Association

Ken-Del Productions Inc
1500 First State Blvd, Wilmington, DE 19804-3596
Tel: 302-999-1111; 302-999-1110; 302-999-1164 *Toll Free Tel:* 800-249-1110 *Fax:* 302-999-1656
E-mail: info@ken-del.com
Web Site: www.ken-del.com
Key Personnel
Pres & Gen Mgr: William Burgess, III
Dir, Sales: Rose Burke
Prodr/Engr: Paul Janocha *E-mail:* paul@ken-del. com
Founded: 1950
AV & staging facilities installation & rental, productions, vault storage, shrink wrapping, printing, graphic design & fulfillment. Rent 16mm, 8mm, S8mm, 35mm projectors, equipment & facility lights.
Membership(s): AES; ASA; Delaware Media Association; SMPTE®; SPARS

Ken-Del Studios
Division of Ken-Del Productions Inc
1500 First State Blvd, Wilmington, DE 19804-3596
Tel: 302-999-1111 *Toll Free Tel:* 800-249-1110 *Fax:* 302-999-1656
E-mail: info@ken-del.com
Web Site: www.ken-del.com
Key Personnel
Pres & Gen Mgr: William Burgess, III
Prodr & Engr: Paul Janocha *E-mail:* paul@ken-del.com

Sales: Rose Burke
Founded: 1950
All allied services, CD replication & recording studios, control rooms, duplication equipment & music libraries. Graphic design & printing.
Catalog(s) available
Membership(s): AES; ASA; ASC; SMPTE®; SPARS

Kendall Hunt Publishing Co
4050 Westmark Dr, Dubuque, IA 52002
Mailing Address: PO Box 1840, Dubuque, IA 52004-1840
Tel: 563-589-1000 *Toll Free Tel:* 800-228-0810 *Fax:* 563-589-1237 *Toll Free Fax:* 800-772-9165
E-mail: orders@kendallhunt.com; corpinfo@ kendallhunt.com
Web Site: www.kendallhunt.com
Key Personnel
VP, Higher Educ: David Tart *Tel:* 563-589-1000 ext 1195
Sr Opers Asst: Kristy Kelly *Tel:* 563-589-1128 *E-mail:* kkelly@kendallhunt.com
Founded: 1994
Textbook publishing with CD supplements.
Online catalog(s) available

Keng Seng Enterprises Inc
4000 Rue St Ambroise, Suite 103, Montreal, QC H4C 2C7, Canada
Tel: 514-939-3971
E-mail: canada@kengseng.com
Web Site: www.kengseng.com
Key Personnel
Pres & Prod Mgr: David Chen
VP: Charles Cheng
Dir: Virginia Poon
Graphic art book & color reference guide book distributor. Also X-Rite distributor.
Foreign Office(s)
Rua Do General Rodrigues, Suite 11-A, R/C, Macau, Macau *Tel:* 522813 *Fax:* 522812 *E-mail:* macau@kengseng.com

Kenko Tokina USA
7642 Woodwind Dr, Huntington Beach, CA 92647
Tel: 714-849-5700 *Toll Free Tel:* 800-421-1141 *Fax:* 714-849-5677
E-mail: support@kenkotokinausa.com
Web Site: kenkotokinausa.com
Key Personnel
Pres: Yasu Suga

Kensington Falls Animation
1680 Hillsdale Ave, Ambridge, PA 15003
Tel: 724-266-0329
E-mail: kensingtonfalls@aol.com
Web Site: kensingtonfalls.com
Key Personnel
Prodr & Dir: Michael C Schwab
Founded: 1979
Full service animation production.

Kensington Technology Group
Division of ACCO Brands Corp
1500 Fashion Island Blvd, 3rd fl, San Mateo, CA 94404
Tel: 650-572-2700 *Toll Free Tel:* 800-535-4242 (tech support); 800-235-6708 (cust serv)
E-mail: sales@kensington.com
Web Site: www.kensington.com
Key Personnel
Dir, Mktg: Rob Humphrey
Founded: 1981
Computer accesssory products.
Branch Office(s)
ACCO Brands Inc, 5 Precidio Ct, Brampton, ON, Canada *Toll Free Tel:* 800-266-3447 *Toll Free Fax:* 800-263-1063

Norman Kent Productions
PO Box 1749, Flagler Beach, FL 32136
Tel: 386-446-0505
Web Site: www.normankent.com
Key Personnel
Owner: Norman Kent *E-mail:* norman@
normankent.com
Aerial cinematography & photography for feature
films, television, commercials, sports events &
printed media.

Kentucky Grip & Lighting
Subsidiary of Cabin Hill Communications Inc
10005 Bunsen Way, Louisville, KY 40299
Tel: 502-548-5833
Web Site: www.kentuckygrip.com
Key Personnel
Owner: Steve Staley *E-mail:* steve@kentuckygrip.
com
Founded: 1987
Freelance cameraman (owner operator), grip &
lighting trucks.

Kenyon Laboratories LLC
12 Scovil Rd, Higganum, CT 06441
Tel: 860-345-2097 *Toll Free Tel:* 800-253-4681
Fax: 860-345-8652
E-mail: kenyonlabs@comcast.net; info@
kenyongyro.com
Web Site: www.ken-lab.com
Key Personnel
Owner: Ron Denman
Manufacture, rent, sell & repair gyro stabilizers.
Online catalog(s) available

Kerrigan Productions Inc
3877 Draper Ave, Montreal, QC H4A 2N9,
Canada
Tel: 514-486-8456
Web Site: www.kerrigan.ca
Key Personnel
Dir, Photog & Camera Operator: Bill Kerrigan
Tel: 514-238-9775 (cell)
Founded: 1986
Film & video production company.

Keslow Camera Inc
5900 Blackwelder St, Culver City, CA 90232
Tel: 310-636-4600 *Fax:* 310-915-5335
E-mail: info@keslowcamera.com
Web Site: www.keslowcamera.com
Key Personnel
CEO: Robert Keslow
CFO: Denny Taing
COO: Dennis McDonald
Film & digital camera rentals. Offices in Miami,
FL, Chicago, IL & New Orleans, LA.

KET The Kentucky Network
600 Cooper Dr, Lexington, KY 40502
Tel: 859-258-7000 *Toll Free Tel:* 800-432-0951
Fax: 859-258-7396
E-mail: adulted@ket.org
Web Site: www.ket.org
Key Personnel
CEO & Exec Dir: Shae Hopkins *Tel:* 859-258-
7220 *E-mail:* shopkins@ket.org
Dir, Enterprise Div: Ron Griffin *Tel:* 859-258-
7218 *E-mail:* rgriffin@ket.org
Adult education video-based learning material:
GED preparation, pre-GED, workplace skills,
life skills & ESL. Video, workbooks & online.
Catalog(s) available

Ketchum Change, see Ketchum Inc

Ketchum Inc
1285 Avenue of the Americas, 4th fl, New York,
NY 10019
Tel: 646-935-3900
Web Site: www.ketchum.com

Key Personnel
Partner, Chmn & CEO: Rob Flaherty *E-mail:* rob.
flaherty@ketchum.com
Partner & Pres: Barri Freidman Rafferty
E-mail: barri.rafferty@ketchum.com
Partner & Chief Engagement Offr: Stephen
Waddington *E-mail:* stephen.waddington@
ketchum.com
Chief Communs Offr: Mindy Rubinstein
E-mail: mindy.rubinstein@ketchum.com
Pres, Ketchum Digital: Debra Forman
E-mail: debra.forman@ketchum.com
Regl Pres, North America: Mike Doyle
E-mail: mike.doyle@ketchum.com
EVP, Media & Content Strategy: Lori Beecher
E-mail: lori.beecher@ketchum.com
Media & public relations consulting company.
Branch Office(s)
12777 W Jefferson Blvd, Bldg C, Los Angeles,
CA 90066, Partner & Dir, Ketchum West:
Melissa Kinch *Tel:* 310-437-2600 *Fax:* 310-
437-2599 *E-mail:* melissa.kinch@ketchum.com
1050 Battery St, San Francisco, CA 94111, Part-
ner & Dir, Ketchum West: Melissa Kinch
Tel: 415-984-6100 *E-mail:* melissa.kinch@
ketchum.com
1615 "L" St NW, Suite 500, Washington, DC
20036, Mng Dir: Jerry Olszewski *Tel:* 202-835-
8800 *E-mail:* jerry.olszewski@ketchum.com
3500 Lenox Rd, Suite 1900, Atlanta, GA 30326,
Dir: Diana Gaarza Ciarlante *Tel:* 404-879-9071
E-mail: diana.ciarlante@ketchum.com
200 E Randolph, 36th fl, Chicago, IL 60601,
Partner & Dir, Ketchum Midwest: Bill
Zucker *Tel:* 312-228-6800 *Fax:* 312-228-6868
E-mail: bill.zucker@ketchum.com
290 Congress St, 7th fl, Boston, MA 02210,
EVP: Shawn McBride *Tel:* 781-436-5214
E-mail: shawn.mcbride@ketchum.com
1201 Edwards Mill Rd, Suite 400, Raleigh,
NC 27607, Partner & Dir, Ketchum South:
James Peters *Tel:* 214-259-3444 *E-mail:* james.
peters@ketchum.com
912 Fort Duquesne Blvd, Suite 330, Pittsburgh,
PA 15222-5488, Partner & Dir, Ketchum
Midwest: Bill Zucker *Tel:* 412-456-3500
E-mail: bill.zucker@ketchum.com
Harwood Ctr, 1999 Bryan St, Suite 2500, Dal-
las, TX 75201, Dir, Ketchum South: James
Peters *Tel:* 214-259-3400 *Fax:* 214-259-3450
E-mail: james.peters@ketchum.com
33 Bloor St E, Suite 1607, Toronto, ON M4W
3H1, Canada, Dir, Gen Mgr, Ketchum Toronto:
Emma Capombassis *Tel:* 416-355-7400
E-mail: emma.capombassis@ketchum.com

Key Digital Systems
521 E Third St, Mount Vernon, NY 10553
Tel: 914-667-9700 *Toll Free Tel:* 855-539-3448
Fax: 914-668-8666
E-mail: info@keydigital.com; marketing@
keydigital.com
Web Site: www.keydigital.com
Key Personnel
Founder & Pres: Mike Tsinberg
VP, Mktg: Masha Lakhter *Tel:* 914-667-9700 ext
211
VP, Sales: Michael Lakhter *Tel:* 914-667-9700 ext
210 *E-mail:* michael@keydigital.com
Manufacture technology solutions for virtually all
applications where high-end video & control
are important.

Key Pix Productions Inc, see Air Bud
Entertainment

The Keyboard Workshop
PO Box 700, Medford, OR 97501
Tel: 541-664-7052
Web Site: www.playpiano.com; www.facebook.
com/pianochords

Key Personnel
Owner: Duane Shinn *E-mail:* duaneshinn1@
gmail.com
Founded: 1965
Sale of educational audio & video programs on
piano playing techniques & chords.
Online catalog(s) available

Keymark Inc
105 Tech Lane, Liberty, SC 29657
Tel: 864-343-0500 *Toll Free Tel:* 800-446-2826
E-mail: support@keymarkinc.com
Web Site: www.keymarkinc.com
Key Personnel
Sales Coord: Kami Turner *E-mail:* kami.turner@
keymarkinc.com
Capture, storage, retrieval, distribution & conver-
sion of documents, data & microforms.
Branch Office(s)
275 Grandview Ave, Suite 104, Camp Hill, PA
17011 *Tel:* 717-364-3700
Shipping Address: IMR Digital Business Process
Outsourcing Center, Valmont Industrial Park,
20 Unico Dr, Hazleton, PA 18202 *Toll Free
Tel:* 800-582-6319
Membership(s): AIIM; ARMA; Custom Elec-
tronic Design & Installation Association

Keystone View
2200 Dickerson Rd, Reno, NV 89503
Tel: 775-324-2799; 510-931-7747 *Fax:* 775-324-
5375
E-mail: sales@keystoneview.com
Web Site: www.keystoneview.com
Manufacture vision screeners for testing visionary
functions.
Catalog(s) available

Keywest Technology Inc
14563 W 96 Terr, Lenexa, KS 66215
Tel: 913-492-4666 *Toll Free Tel:* 800-331-2019
Fax: 913-322-1864
E-mail: sales@keywesttechnology.com
Web Site: www.keywesttechnology.com
Key Personnel
Pres: Koytt O Nichols
Engg Dir: John Macan
Sales Dir: West Dixon
Sales: Matt Weiss
Founded: 1999
Digital signage.
Catalog(s) available
Membership(s): Audiovisual and Integrated Expe-
rience Association; Digital Signage Federation

KFOR-TV
Subsidiary of Local TV LLC
444 E Britton Rd, Oklahoma City, OK 73114
Tel: 405-424-4444 *Fax:* 405-478-6228
Web Site: www.kfor.com
Key Personnel
Pres & Gen Mgr: Wes Milbourn
Promos: Todd Rich

KHNL/KGMB
Affiliate of Raycom Media Inc
420 Waiakamilo Rd, Suite 205, Honolulu, HI
96817
Tel: 808-847-3246 *Fax:* 808-845-3616
E-mail: info8@khnl.com; news@hawaiinewsnow.
com
Web Site: www.hawaiinewsnow.com
Key Personnel
Gen Mgr: Rick Blangiardi *E-mail:* rblangiardi@
hawaiinewsnow.com

Killer Tracks
Unit of Universal Music Publishing Group
2110 Colorado Ave, Suite 110, Santa Monica, CA
90404

Tel: 310-865-4455 *Toll Free Tel:* 800-4-KILLER (454-5537)
E-mail: info@killertracks.com
Web Site: www.killertracks.com
Key Personnel
VP/Head, Music Prodn: Carl Peel *E-mail:* cpeel@killertracks.com
VP/Head, Music Licensing: Anna Maria Hall *E-mail:* ahall@killertracks.com
Founded: 1989
Music licensing for film, television & interactive media.

Kimbo Educational
Division of United Sound Arts Inc
One Industrial Way, Bldg D, Suite E, Eatontown, NJ 07724
Mailing Address: PO Box 477, Long Branch, NJ 07740-0477
Tel: 732-229-4949 *Toll Free Tel:* 800-631-2187 *Fax:* 732-870-3340
E-mail: kimboed@aol.com; service@kimboed.com
Web Site: www.kimboed.com
Key Personnel
CEO: Gertrude S Kimble
Pres: James A Kimble
Sales & Mktg: Elaine Murphy
Catalog Ed: Amy Laufer
Founded: 1954
CDs & DVDs for children; educational market.
Catalog(s) available
Sales Office(s): 504 Via Ventana Dr, Mesquite, NV 89027, Contact: Elaine Murphy *Toll Free Tel:* 800-848-6099
Membership(s): Education Market Association

Kinetic Arts
306 Gold St, No 5-I, Brooklyn, NY 11201
Tel: 917-439-4008
E-mail: info@kineticarts.tv
Web Site: www.kineticarts.tv
Key Personnel
Partner: Alex Twersky
Founded: 1997
Film production & development.

Kinetic Corp
200 Distillery Commons, Suite 200, Louisville, KY 40206-1990
Tel: 502-719-9500 *Fax:* 502-719-9509
Web Site: kinetictms.com
Key Personnel
Founder & CEO: G Raymond Schuhmann
Cont: Ron Hess
Dir, Digital Servs: Tim Pitts
Visual communications for business.
Membership(s): APGU; The Imaging Alliance

Kineticvideo.com
4839 Noble Lane, Battersea, ON K0H 1H0, Canada
Tel: 416-538-6613 *Toll Free Tel:* 800-263-6910 (CN only) *Fax:* 416-538-9984
E-mail: info@kineticvideo.com
Web Site: www.kineticvideo.com
Key Personnel
Pres: Frances M Broome *E-mail:* fmb@kineticvideo.com
VP, Sales & Cust Serv: Gary Malloy *E-mail:* gmt@kineticvideo.com
Acctg: Michael Phillips *E-mail:* mp@kineticvideo.com
Founded: 1976
Catalog(s) available
Branch Office(s)
255 Great Arrow Ave, Buffalo, NY 14207 *Toll Free Tel:* 800-466-7631 *Fax:* 716-856-7838
Membership(s): Educational Media Producers & Distributors Association of Canada

Kinetronics Corp
1459 Tallevast Rd, Sarasota, FL 34243
Tel: 941-951-2432 *Toll Free Tel:* 800-624-3204 (US & CN) *Fax:* 941-955-5992
E-mail: info@kinetronics.com; order@kinetronics.com
Web Site: www.kinetronics.com
Key Personnel
Off Mgr: Sally Robbins
Founded: 1973
Products to serve the AV & photographic industries.
Online catalog(s) available
Membership(s): The Imaging Alliance

Kingsway Motion Picture Inc
200 Evans Ave, Unit 4, Toronto, ON M8Z 1J7, Canada
Tel: 416-463-4345
E-mail: info@kingswaycanada.com
Web Site: kingswaycanada.com
Key Personnel
Pres: Doug Macaulay
New & used equipment sales & rentals for film & television production.

Kingswood Productions
Division of United Methodist Communications
810 12 Ave S, Nashville, TN 37203
Tel: 615-742-5779
Web Site: www.kingswoodproductions.com
Key Personnel
Dir, Prodns: Harry Leake *Tel:* 615-742-5477
Mgr: Debbie Wamsley *Tel:* 615-742-5779 *E-mail:* dwamsley@kingswoodproductions.com
Audio & video production, post-production, live event production, live streaming & equipment rentals.

Kino Flo Lighting Systems
2840 N Hollywood Way, Burbank, CA 91505
Tel: 818-767-6528 *Fax:* 818-252-0290 (rental); 818-767-7517 (sales)
E-mail: sales@kinoflo.com
Web Site: www.kinoflo.com
Key Personnel
Pres & Founder: Frieder Hochheim *E-mail:* fhochheim@kinoflo.com
Gen Mgr: Ray Goitiandia *E-mail:* rgoitiandia@kinoflo.com
Founded: 1987
Lighting systems for HD cinema, television & digital imaging.
Catalog(s) available
Membership(s): ASC; NAB; Professional Lighting & Sound Association; SMPTE®

Kino International Corp
333 W 39 St, Suite 503, New York, NY 10018
Tel: 212-629-6880 *Toll Free Tel:* 800-562-3330 *Fax:* 212-714-0871
E-mail: contact@kinolorber.com
Web Site: www.kinolorber.com
Key Personnel
Pres: Richard Lorber
Founded: 1977
Catalog(s) available
Membership(s): Entertainment Merchants Association

Kino Mountain Productions LLC
2004 Production Dr, Apex, NC 27539
Tel: 919-355-2725
E-mail: info@kinomountain.com
Web Site: www.kinomountain.com
Key Personnel
Owner: Greg Winters
Founded: 2010

KION-TV
1550 Moffett St, Salinas, CA 93905

Tel: 831-784-6500; 831-422-3500 *Fax:* 831-784-6502
Web Site: www.kion546.com
Key Personnel
Sales: Kristy Santiago *E-mail:* kristy.santiago@kionrightnow.com

Kipp Visual Systems Inc
3920 Vero Rd, Suite C, Baltimore, MD 21227
Tel: 410-235-9900 *Toll Free Tel:* 800-278-6912 *Fax:* 410-235-7122
Web Site: kippvisual.com
Key Personnel
Pres: Ryan Lessans *E-mail:* ryan.lessans@kippvisual.com
Catalog(s) available
Membership(s): Audiovisual and Integrated Experience Association

Kirkwood Community College
Linn Hall, Rm 102, 6301 Kirkwood Blvd SW, Cedar Rapids, IA 52406
Tel: 319-398-5517 *Toll Free Tel:* 800-363-2220 *Fax:* 319-398-5413
E-mail: info@kirkwood.edu
Web Site: www.kirkwood.edu
Certificate & training programs.

The Kitchen
Division of TM Systems
265 NE 24 St, Suite 401, Miami, FL 33137
Tel: 305-415-6200
E-mail: info@thekitchen.tv
Web Site: www.thekitchen.tv
Key Personnel
Pres & CEO: Ken Lorber *E-mail:* ken@thekitchen.tv
Chmn & CFO: Don Denkhaus *E-mail:* don@thekitchen.tv
EVP: Deeny Kaplan *Tel:* 818-306-5300 *E-mail:* deeny@thekitchen.tv
VP, Engg & Facilities: Tim Fox *E-mail:* tim@thekitchen.tv
VP, Intl Sales: Alexis Cardenas *E-mail:* alexis@thekitchen.tv
Gen Mgr: Maritza Alvarado *E-mail:* maritza@thekitchen.tv
Founded: 2001
Emmy-Award® winning language translation, dubbing, subtitling & media services facility.
Membership(s): NAB; NATPE; SMPTE®; Television Academy

KJfilms LLC
33 Serra Dr, Middletown, CT 06457
Tel: 860-873-2419; 860-995-5106 (cell)
E-mail: info@kjfilms.com
Web Site: www.kjfilms.com
Key Personnel
Dir, Photog/Lighting: Jeff Hoyt *E-mail:* jeff@kjfilms.com
Founded: 1998
Lighting & grip equipment rentals.

KK Office Solutions Inc
3910 N Bridgeport Circle, Wichita, KS 67219
Tel: 316-944-5464 *Toll Free Tel:* 800-362-1317 *Fax:* 316-944-0605 *Toll Free Fax:* 888-319-9600
E-mail: info@kkofficesolutions.com
Web Site: kkosinc.com
Key Personnel
CEO: Matthew Brandt
Founded: 1994
Educational supplier of AV needs.

Klipsch Group Inc
Subsidiary of Audiovox Corp
3502 Woodview Trace, Suite 200, Indianapolis, IN 46268
Tel: 317-860-8100 *Toll Free Tel:* 800-544-1482
Web Site: www.klipsch.com

Key Personnel
Pres & CEO: Paul Jacobs
Treas & CFO: Fred Farrar
Founded: 1946
Shipping Address: 3700 Hwy 32 N, Hope, AR 71801 *Fax:* 870-777-3376
Membership(s): Consumer Technology Association™

Klutz
Division of Scholastic Inc
568 Broadway, Suite 503, New York, NY 10012
Tel: 212-343-6360 *Toll Free Tel:* 800-737-4123
 Fax: 212-343-6366
E-mail: orders@klutz.com
Web Site: www.scholastic.com/books/klutz
Founded: 1977
Activity products for kids.
Online catalog(s) available

Knowledge Unlimited Inc
2320 Pleasant View, Middleton, WI 53562
Mailing Address: PO Box 52, Madison, WI 53701
Tel: 608-836-6660 *Toll Free Tel:* 800-356-2303
 Fax: 608-836-6684 *Toll Free Fax:* 800-618-1570
E-mail: csis@newscurrents.com
Web Site: www.knowledgeunlimited.com
Key Personnel
Founder & Pres: Judith Laitman
Founded: 1983
Writing, editing & video production of educational materials for social studies, science, language arts & current events.
Online catalog(s) available
Membership(s): National Council for the Social Studies

Knowles Video Inc (KVI)
5450 Buck Lake Rd, Tallahassee, FL 32317
Mailing Address: PO Box 12127, Tallahassee, FL 32317-2127
Tel: 850-878-2298 *Fax:* 850-656-0119
E-mail: info@knowlesvideo.com
Web Site: www.knowlesvideo.com
Key Personnel
Pres: Karl Knowles
Full service production company specializing in the creation of video & multimedia programs & materials.
Membership(s): Florida Motion Picture & Television Association

KO Creative
465 S Beverly Dr, 3rd fl, Beverly Hills, CA 90212
Tel: 310-288-3820
Web Site: www.ko-creative.com
Key Personnel
CEO: Kristi Kilday *E-mail:* kristi@ko-creative.com
Founded: 1993
Full service creative agency specializing in trailers, posters, interactive web sites, production & post-production of TV series & feature films.

Kodak Graphic Communications Canada Co
Subsidiary of Eastman Kodak Co
4225 Kincaid Ave, Burnaby, BC V5G 4P5, Canada
Tel: 604-551-2700 *Toll Free Tel:* 800-465-6325
 Fax: 604-570-3501
Web Site: graphics.kodak.com
Founded: 1899

Koerner Camera Systems
2828 SE 14 Ave, Portland, OR 97202
Tel: 503-274-6533 *Toll Free Tel:* 800-377-1132
E-mail: michael@koernercamera.com
Web Site: www.koernercamera.com
Founded: 1996

Digital cinema camera rental house.
Branch Office(s)
101 Nickerson, Suite B500, Seattle, WA 98109
 Tel: 206-285-7334 *Toll Free Tel:* 855-285-7334
 E-mail: seattle@koernercamera.com

Kofax Inc
15211 Laguna Canyon Rd, Irvine, CA 92618-3146
Tel: 949-727-1733 *Fax:* 949-727-3144
E-mail: info@kofax.com
Web Site: www.kofax.com
Key Personnel
CEO: Reynolds Bish
Chief Strategy Offr: Chris Huff
Founded: 1985
A leading supplier of Intelligent Automation software to digitally transform end-to-end business operations.
Catalog(s) available
Branch Office(s)
Kofax-E-Signature Solutions Support, 2520 Wrangle Hill Rd, Suite 210, Bear, DE 19701 *Tel:* 302-504-0606
36 Cosby Dr, Bedford, MA 01730 *Tel:* 781-743-1900 *Fax:* 781-743-2200
Altosoft, A Kofax Company, 1400 N Providence Rd, Suite 3005, Media, PA 19063 *Tel:* 484-423-6100 *E-mail:* info@altosoft.com
11044 Research Blvd, Suite C-120, Austin, TX 78759 *Tel:* 512-241-3400
Foreign Office(s): Kofax Australia Pty Ltd, Norwich House, Level 7, 6 O'Connell St, Sydney, NSW 2000, Australia *Tel:* (02) 8916 0200 *Fax:* (02) 8916 0299 *E-mail:* mailbox.au@ kofax.com
Kofax Australia Pty Ltd, One Queens Rd, Suite 246-248, Level 2, Melbourne, Victoria 3004, Australia *Tel:* (03) 8807 9924 *Fax:* (03) 8807 9928 *E-mail:* mailbox.au@kofax.com
Kofax Austria GmbH, Talpagasse 1, 1230 Vienna, Austria *Tel:* (01) 86645-55000 *Fax:* (01) 86645-58000 *E-mail:* mailbox.at@kofax.com
Kofax Benelux NV/SA, Mechelen Campus, Schalienhoevedreef 20 E, 2800 Mechelen, Belgium *Tel:* (015) 444 900 *Fax:* (015) 444 901 *E-mail:* mailbox.be@kofax.com
Kofax Produtos de Imagem do Brasil Ltda, Rua Vila Olimpia do Rocio 430, 04552-906 Sao Paulo-SP, Brazil *Tel:* (011) 3047 4000 *E-mail:* kofax.brasil@kofax.com
Kofax Singapore Pte Ltd, 8/F, Yueda 889 Ctr, No 1111, Chang Shou Rd, Jing'an District, Shanghai 200042, China *Tel:* (021) 2230 1729 *E-mail:* mailbox.asia@kofax.com
Kofax Danmark, Dr Neergaards Vej 5A, 2970 Horsholm, Denmark *Tel:* 4342-4150 *Fax:* 4342-4180
Kofax France, 18 rue Gustave Flourens, 92150 Suresnes, France *Tel:* 01 46 67 41 03 *Fax:* 01 46 67 41 07 *E-mail:* mailbox.fr@kofax.com
Kofax Deutschland AG, Unterschweinstiege 8 (Main Airport Ctr), 60549 Frankfurt am Main, Germany *Tel:* (0761) 45269-0 *Fax:* (0761) 45269-90 *E-mail:* mailbox.de@kofax.com
Kofax Deutschland AG, Wilhelmstr 34, 71034 Boeblingen, Germany *Tel:* (030) 230 48754 *Fax:* (07031) 6606 66 *E-mail:* e-signaturesolutions@kofax.com
Kofax Asia Holdings Pte Ltd, 2/F Shui On Ctr, 6-8 Harbour Rd, Rm 275C, Wan Chai, Hong Kong *Tel:* 9368 6795 *E-mail:* mailbox.asia@ kofax.com
Kofax India Pvt Ltd, The V, Auriga Bldg, 2nd fl, B-Wing, Plot No 17, Software Units Layout, Madhapur, Hyderabad 500 081, India *Tel:* (040) 4545 9949 *Fax:* (040) 4545 9922 *E-mail:* mailbox.asia@kofax.com
Kofax Asia Holdings Pte Ltd, Sahid Sudirman Ctr, 11th fl, Suite A, Jl Jend Sudirman 86, Jakarta 10220, Indonesia *Tel:* (021) 80 631 612 *Fax:* (021) 80 631 614 *E-mail:* mailbox.asia@ kofax.com

Kofax Italia SRL, Viale Monza, 270, 20128 Milan MI, Italy *Tel:* (02) 252051 *Fax:* (02) 2570534 *E-mail:* mailbox.it@kofax.com
Kofax Japan Co Ltd, 9F Soc Takanawa Bldg, 3-19-26 Takanawa, Minato-ku, Tokyo 108-0074, Japan *Tel:* (03) 6853 0001 *Fax:* (03) 6853 0002 *E-mail:* mailbox.jp@kofax.com
Kofax Malaysia Sdn Bhd, The Gardens South Tower, Suite 13.06, Level 13, Mid Valley City, Lingkaran Syed Putra, 59200 Kuala Lumpur, Malaysia *Tel:* (03) 2092 0202 *Fax:* (03) 2092 0211 *E-mail:* mailbox.asia@kofax.com
Ave Presidente Masaryk 111-1, Col Chapultepec Morales, 11560 Mexico, DF, Mexico *Tel:* (0155) 33 00 58 86
Kofax Netherlands, Kerkenbos 10-129, 6546 BJ Nijmegen, Netherlands *Tel:* (024) 3710230 *Fax:* (024) 3710231
Kofax Benelux NV/SA, Papendorpseweg 99, 5th fl, 3528 BJ Utrecht, Netherlands *Tel:* (030) 264 3030 *Fax:* (030) 264 3048 *E-mail:* mailbox. nl@kofax.com
Kofax Portugal SA, Av Clotilde, Edificio Centro Congressos do Estoril, 4°A, 2765-211 Estoril, Portugal *Tel:* 214646190 *Fax:* 214646191 *E-mail:* mailbox.pt@kofax.com
Kofax Singapore Pte Ltd, Republic Plaza I, No 53-01, 9 Raffles Place, Singapore 048619, Singapore *Tel:* 6278 7662 *Fax:* 6278 4345 *E-mail:* mailbox.asia@kofax.com
Kofax South Africa Ltd, Gillooly's View Off Park, Block C, 1st fl, One Osborne Lane, Bedfordview 2007, South Africa *Tel:* (011) 417 8629 *E-mail:* mailbox.za@kofax.com
Kofax Software Iberica SAU, Torre Mapfre, C/ de la Marina 16-18, 11-B, 08005 Barcelona, Spain *Tel:* 934 09 20 63 *Fax:* 934 09 20 64 *E-mail:* mailbox.es@kofax.com
Kofax Software Iberica SAU, Via de las dos Castillas 33, Edificio Atica 6, 2° Planta, 2-D, Pozuelo de Alarcon, 28224 Madrid, Spain *Tel:* 91 789 84 07 *Fax:* 91 567 12 71 *E-mail:* mailbox.es@kofax.com
Kofax Sverige AB, Energigatan 11, 43437 Kungsbacka, Sweden *Tel:* (08) 544 404 80 *E-mail:* mailbox.se@kofax.com
Kofax Sverige AB, Frosundaviks Alle 15, 169 70 Solna, Sweden *Tel:* (08) 5444 0480 *E-mail:* mailbox.se@kofax.com
Kofax Schweiz AG, Business Bldg Forren W, Grundstr 14, 6343 Rotkreuz, Switzerland *Tel:* (041) 799 82 82 *Fax:* (041) 799 82 95 *E-mail:* mailbox.ch@kofax.com
Kofax ME FZE, Dubai Airport Free Zone & Busn Park, E Wing 3E Off 216, PO Box 54574, Dubai, United Arab Emirates *Tel:* (04) 2306 800 *Fax:* (04) 2306 899 *E-mail:* mailbox. ae@kofax.com
Kofax UK Ltd, One Cedarwood, Chineham Business Park, Basingstoke, Hants RG24 8WD, United Kingdom *Tel:* (0870) 777 3767 *Fax:* (0870) 777 3768 *E-mail:* mailbox.uk@ kofax.com
Kofax Northern Ireland Ltd, 26 Linenhall St, Belfast BT2 8BG, United Kingdom *Tel:* (028) 9072 7000 *Fax:* (028) 9072 7038
Kofax Northern Ireland Ltd, 113-118 Duncreggan Rd, Derry BT48 0AA, United Kingdom *Tel:* (028) 7126 7767 *Fax:* (028) 7126 8085
Kofax UK-London, Leaf A, Level 1, Tower 42, 25 Old Broad St, London EC2N 1HQ, United Kingdom *Tel:* (020) 7496 1760 *Fax:* (020) 7256 8151
Kofax UK-Essex, Cumberland House, 3rd fl, 24-28 Baxter Ave, Southend-on-Sea, Essex SS2 6HZ, United Kingdom *Tel:* (0870) 7773767 *Fax:* (01256) 374695
Kofax Vietnam Co Ltd, RESCO Bldg, A Tower, 11th fl, 521 Kim Ma St, Ba Dinh District, Hanoi, Vietnam *Tel:* (04) 3771 2546; (04) 3771 2547 *Fax:* (04) 3771 2543 *E-mail:* mailbox. asia@kofax.com

KOH Design Inc
540 Barnum Ave, Bridgeport, CT 06608
Tel: 203-336-1334 *Fax:* 203-335-9361
E-mail: info@kohdesign.com
Web Site: www.kohdesign.com
Key Personnel
Mktg Dir: Karl Hasselrot
Engineering designs geared for corporate & industrial training facilities & teaching environments.

Konica Minolta Business Solutions
100 Williams Dr, Ramsey, NJ 07446
Tel: 201-825-4000
Web Site: kmbs.konicaminolta.us
Key Personnel
CEO: Tom Taiko
Mgr, PR: Kristina Marchitto *Tel:* 201-236-4399
E-mail: kmarchitto@kmbs.konicaminolta.us
Catalog(s) available
Branch Office(s)
Konica Minolta Business Solutions-West Region, 1900 S State College Blvd, Suite 600, Anaheim, CA 94404 *Tel:* 714-630-7780
Konica Minolta Business Innovation Center, 1051 E Hillside Blvd, Foster City, CA 94404 *Web Site:* bic.konicaminolta.us
Konica Minolta Business Solutions-South Region, 9799 International Court N, St Petersburg, FL 33716 *Tel:* 727-622-4343
Konica Minolta Business-Central Region, 500 W Madison St, Suite 2680, Chicago, IL 60601 *Tel:* 312-726-9100
Konica Minolta Business-East Region, 485 Lexington Ave, 19th fl, New York, NY 10017 *Tel:* 212-294-6200

Kontron America
14118 Stowe Dr, Poway, CA 92064-7147
Tel: 858-677-0877 *Toll Free Tel:* 888-294-4558; 800-480-0044 (cust serv & tech support) *Fax:* 858-677-0898
E-mail: sales@us.kontron.com
Web Site: www.kontron.com
Key Personnel
EVP, Busn Unit Avionics, Transportation & Defense & Gen Mgr, Americas: Kevin Rhoads
Online catalog(s) available
Branch Office(s)
6505 Dumbarton Circle, Fremont, CA 94538 *Tel:* 510-284-1100 *Toll Free Tel:* 800-995-7579 *Fax:* 510-284-1111
4555 Rue Ambroise-Lafortune, Boisbriand, QC J7H 0A4, Canada *Tel:* 450-437-5682 *Toll Free Tel:* 800-387-4222 *Fax:* 450-437-8053
Membership(s): PICMG

KOOL-FM Radio
Division of Entercom Communications Corp
840 N Central Ave, Phoenix, AZ 85004
Tel: 602-452-1000; 602-260-9494 (studio) *Fax:* 602-440-6530
Web Site: kool.radio.com
Key Personnel
Prog Dir: Tim Richards *E-mail:* tim@kmle1079.com

Kool Music
9 Hector Ave, Toronto, ON M6G 3G2, Canada
Tel: 416-533-3520
E-mail: host@koolmusic.com
Web Site: www.koolmusic.com
Key Personnel
Pres: Al Kussin
Founded: 1999
Production music library.
Online catalog(s) available, royalty free production music, $39 full length tracks
Membership(s): The Society of Composers, Authors and Music Publishers of Canada

Kopp Glass
2108 Palmer St, Pittsburgh, PA 15218
Tel: 412-271-0190 *Fax:* 412-271-4103
E-mail: sales@koppglass.com
Web Site: www.koppglass.com
Key Personnel
Dir, Tech Servs: Jim Forish
Founded: 1926
Manufacturer of specialty & technical glass including clear & colored borosilicate glass.

Korg USA Inc
Subsidiary of Korg Inc Japan
316 S Service Rd, Melville, NY 11747
Tel: 631-390-6500; 631-390-6800 (cust serv)
E-mail: sales@korgusa.com; customerservice@korgusa.com
Web Site: www.korgusa.com
Key Personnel
Pres: Joseph Castronovo
Mktg Rel Mgr: Jennifer Lewis *Tel:* 631-390-6864
E-mail: jenniferl@korgusa.com
Founded: 1963
Distribute recorders, converters, players & amplifiers.
Catalog(s) available

Koss Corp
4129 N Port Washington Ave, Milwaukee, WI 53212
Tel: 414-964-5000 *Toll Free Tel:* 800-USA-KOSS (872-5677)
E-mail: customersupport@koss.com
Web Site: www.koss.com
Key Personnel
Pres & CEO: Michael Koss
VP, Sales: John Koss, Jr
Founded: 1958
Catalog(s) available

Kostov Productions
Division of CP Production Inc
Whispering Wind Ranch, 16320 High Bridge Rd, Monroe, WA 98272
Tel: 206-755-0050
E-mail: info@kostov.com
Web Site: www.kostov.com
Key Personnel
Pres: Michael Kostov
Founded: 1981
Independent film & video company.
Membership(s): CIA

Kozmic Lazer Show LLC
PO Box 140197, Nashville, TN 37214-0197
Tel: 615-391-3226 *Toll Free Tel:* 800-MRLASER (675-2737) *Fax:* 615-391-3265
E-mail: mrlaser800@aol.com
Web Site: www.kozmiclazershow.com
Key Personnel
Pres: Patrick Sittnick
Provider of laser light show & pyrotechnic systems.
Online catalog(s) available
Membership(s): National Fire Protection Association

KPBS Public Broadcasting
5200 Campanille Dr, San Diego, CA 92182
Tel: 619-594-1515; 619-265-6438 (newsroom) *Toll Free Tel:* 888-399-5727 *Fax:* 619-594-3812
Web Site: www.kpbs.org
Key Personnel
Gen Mgr: Tom Karlo *E-mail:* tkarlo@kpbs.org
Television, radio & digital media.
Membership(s): IMCCA; NAB; NATPE; Promax

KPDX-TV Production Center
Division of Meredith Corp
14975 NW Greenbrier Pkwy, Beaverton, OR 97006-5731

Tel: 503-906-1249 *Fax:* 503-548-6920
E-mail: ezone@kpdx.com; fox12news@kptv.com
Web Site: www.kptv.com; www.kpdx.com
Key Personnel
EVP & Gen Mgr: Adrienne Roark
Dir, Sales Content: Linda Johns
Gen Sales Mgr: Mike Simpson *E-mail:* mike.simpson@kptv.com

KPHO-TV CBS 5
Subsidiary of Meredith Corp
5555 N Seventh Ave, Phoenix, AZ 85013
Tel: 602-207-3333
E-mail: cbs5gm@cbs5az.com
Web Site: www.cbs5az.com

KPLR-TV
Affiliate of CW Television Network
2250 Ball Dr, St Louis, MO 63146
Tel: 314-213-2222; 314-213-7831 (newsroom)
E-mail: kplradmin@tribune.com
Web Site: kplr11.com
Key Personnel
Pres & Gen Mgr: Spencer Koch
Founded: 1959

Kramer Communications Video Production
12504 Quarterhorse Dr, Bowie, MD 20720
Tel: 301-352-3042
E-mail: kcam@his.com
Web Site: kcommproductions.com
Key Personnel
Exec Prodr: Jeffrey T Kramer
Script writing & video production. Editing DVDs, CDs & web streaming.
Membership(s): IBEW; NATAS; Television, Internet & Video Association of DC Inc

Kramer Electronics USA Inc
Subsidiary of Kramer Electronics Ltd
6 Rte 173 W, Clinton, NJ 08809
Tel: 908-735-0018 *Toll Free Tel:* 888-275-6311 *Fax:* 908-735-0515
E-mail: info@kramerus.com
Web Site: www.kramerav.com
Key Personnel
Founder & CEO: Dr Joseph Kramer
COO: Clint Hoffman
Founded: 1981
Electronic parts supplier.
Catalog(s) available
Membership(s): Audiovisual and Integrated Experience Association; Custom Electronic Design & Installation Association; NAB; NSCA

Joan Kramer & Associates Inc
10490 Wilshire Blvd, Suite 1701, Los Angeles, CA 90024
Tel: 310-446-1866 *Fax:* 310-446-1856
E-mail: ekeeeek@earthlink.net
Key Personnel
Pres: Joan Kramer

Kris Stevens Enterprises
22362 Dardenne St, Calabasas, CA 91302
Tel: 818-225-7585
E-mail: inquiry@kriserikstevens.com
Web Site: www.kriserikstevens.com
Key Personnel
CEO, Pres: Kris Erik Stevens *E-mail:* kris@kriserikstevens.com
Admin: Lauren Parrent
Founded: 1975
Audio recording & mix, voice-over talent, ISDN worldwide connection & sound recording studios.
Membership(s): Promax; SAG-AFTRA

Krishnamurti Foundation of America
1070 McAndrew Rd, Ojai, CA 93023
Mailing Address: PO Box 1560, Ojai, CA 93024
Tel: 805-646-2726 (ext 10) *Fax:* 805-646-6674

E-mail: kfa@kfa.org
Web Site: www.kfa.org
Key Personnel
Exec Dir: Jaap Sluijter
Dir, K Pubns: Cory Fisher
Founded: 1969
Produce & distribute Krishnamurti's work.
Catalog(s) available, free, biannual
Foreign Office(s): Krishnamurti Foundation
Trust Ltd, Brockwood Park, Bramdean, Hants
SO24 0LQ, United Kingdom *Tel:* (01962) 771
525 *Fax:* (01962) 771 159 *Web Site:* www.
kfoundation.org

KRK Systems
Division of Gibson Pro Audio
c/o Gibson Pro Audio, 309 Plus Park Blvd,
Nashville, TN 37217
Toll Free Tel: 800-4GIBSON (444-2766)
E-mail: service@gibson.com (cust serv)
Web Site: www.krksys.com
Founded: 1986
Provider of monitors & control room solutions.
Catalog(s) available

KTHV-TV
Subsidiary of TEGNA Media
720 Izard St, Little Rock, AR 72201
Tel: 501-376-1111 *Fax:* 501-376-9928 (sales);
501-376-3324 (admin); 501-376-1645 (news)
Web Site: www.thv11.com
Key Personnel
Pres & Gen Mgr: Michael Caplan

KTVA Productions
9818 SE 17 Ave, Suite B, Milwaukie, OR 97222
Mailing Address: PO Box 22911, Portland, OR
97269
Tel: 503-659-4417
E-mail: mail@ktvavideo.com
Web Site: www.ktvavideo.com
Key Personnel
Owner: Rick Phillips
Founded: 1987
Video production services.
Membership(s): Oregon Media Production Asso-
ciation

KTVB-TV
Subsidiary of TEGNA Media
5407 W Fairview Ave, Boise, ID 83706
Mailing Address: PO Box 7, Boise, ID 83707
Tel: 208-375-7277 *Toll Free Tel:* 800-559-7277
Fax: 208-378-5642; 208-375-7770 (news fax)
E-mail: info@ktvb.com; ktvbnews@ktvb.com
Web Site: www.ktvb.com
Key Personnel
Gen Mgr: Doug Armstrong
Community Serv Dir: Traci Liew

KTVU-Retail Services
Subsidiary of Fox Broadcasting
2 Jack London Sq, Oakland, CA 94607
Tel: 510-834-1212
Web Site: www.ktvu.com
Catalog(s) available

K2 Productions
2303 Walters St, Greensboro, NC 27408
Tel: 336-664-8036
E-mail: info@k2production.com
Web Site: www.k2production.com
Key Personnel
Exec Prodr: April Eller
Prodr & Dir: Kevin Eller
Film & video production company, from pre- to
post-production.

K2B2 Records
1748 Roosevelt Ave, Los Angeles, CA 90006
Web Site: k2b2.com

Key Personnel
Pres: Marty Krystall *Tel:* 213-705-1248 (cell)
E-mail: marty@k2b2.com
Founded: 1979
On-site mastering, production, editing, jazz record
label.
Online catalog(s) available
Membership(s): American Federation of Musi-
cians; ASCAP; Recording Musicians of Amer-
ica

Kuhn Productions LLC
4423 44 Place, Des Moines, IA 50310
Tel: 515-244-1618
Key Personnel
Owner: Bill Kuhn *E-mail:* bill@kuhnproductions.
com
Photography & video services.

Kultur International Films Ltd Inc
PO Box 755, Forked River, NJ 08731
Tel: 732-784-6470 *Toll Free Tel:* 888-329-2580
Toll Free Fax: 866-205-2744
E-mail: support@kultur.com
Web Site: www.kulturvideo.com
Key Personnel
Chmn: Dennis M Hedlund
DVD & Blu-ray programming.
Online catalog(s) available
Membership(s): Entertainment Merchants Associ-
ation

KUSM TV
Visual Communications Bldg 183, Montana State
University, Bozeman, MT 59717
Tel: 406-994-3437 *Toll Free Tel:* 866-832-0829
Fax: 406-994-6545
E-mail: kusm@montanapbs.org
Web Site: www.montanapbs.org

KVAL
Affiliate of Sinclair Broadcasting
4575 Blanton Rd, Eugene, OR 97405
Tel: 541-342-4961 *Fax:* 541-342-2635
E-mail: kvalnews@kval.com
Web Site: kval.com
Key Personnel
VP & Gen Mgr: J R Jackson *E-mail:* jrjackson@
kval.com
Gen Sales Mgr: Jane Chase *E-mail:* chase@kval.
com

KVIE-Channel 6
2030 W El Camino Ave, Sacramento, CA 95833
Tel: 916-929-5843 *Toll Free Tel:* 800-347-5843
Fax: 916-929-7215
E-mail: member@kvie.org
Web Site: www.kvie.org
Key Personnel
Pres & Gen Mgr: David Lowe

KVL Audio Visual Services Inc
200 Corporate Blvd S, Yonkers, NY 10701
Tel: 914-479-3300 *Toll Free Tel:* 800-862-3210
Fax: 914-965-1423
E-mail: info@kvlav.com
Web Site: www.kvlav.com
Key Personnel
Pres & CEO: Les Lieberman *Tel:* 914-479-3300
ext 333
Founded: 1976
Branch Office(s)
500 W 37 St, New York, NY 10018 *Tel:* 212-
643-0040 *Fax:* 212-582-6409 *E-mail:* info@
avworkshop.com

L A Bruell Inc
120 W 70 St, No 3-B, New York, NY 10023
Tel: 646-336-5977
Web Site: labruell.com

Key Personnel
Pres, Dir & Prodr: Lucy Bruell *E-mail:* lucy@
labruell.com
Founded: 1986
Video production, multimedia & interactive design & development. Healthcare communications, continuing medical education, training &
educational programs.

L A Management Co LLC
8131 Bay Pointe Dr, Denver, NC 28037
Tel: 704-560-6274 *Toll Free Tel:* 800-651-7818
Fax: 704-973-7968
E-mail: info@lamanagementco.com
Web Site: lamanagementco.com
Key Personnel
Pres: Lou Amico
VP: Joe Zammit
Video Prodr: Steven Huff
Video production services, including script writ-
ing, narration, music, graphics, animation &
editing.

L-Acoustics Inc
2645 Townsgate Rd, Suite 600, Westlake Village,
CA 91361
Tel: 805-604-0577 *Fax:* 805-556-4846
E-mail: info.us@l-acoustics.com
Web Site: www.l-acoustics.com
Founded: 1984
Loudspeaker manufacturer.
Catalog(s) available

L'AIR International
117 Vacek St, Fort Worth, TX 76107
Tel: 817-237-9390 *Toll Free Tel:* 844-243-8574
E-mail: info@lairfloors.com
Web Site: www.lairfloors.com
Key Personnel
Pres: Kenneth Snipes
Busn Mgr: Serena West-Snipes
E-mail: serenawest@lairfloors.com
Founded: 1989
Manufacturer of suspended dance flooring.
Catalog(s) available
Membership(s): ISPA; USITT

L R Light & Sound
5317 54 St, Drayton Valley, AB T7A 1R6,
Canada
Mailing Address: Box 6067, Drayton Valley, AB
T7A 1R6, Canada
Tel: 780-542-4242; 780-542-9363 *Fax:* 780-542-
4283
E-mail: lrlightandsound@yahoo.ca
Web Site: www.lrlightandsound.ca
Key Personnel
Owner: Lonnie Ross

L-3 ESSCO
Division of L-3 Technologies Inc
90 Nemco Way, Ayer, MA 01432
Tel: 978-568-5100 *Fax:* 978-772-7555
E-mail: info.essco@l3t.com
Web Site: www2.l3t.com/essco
Key Personnel
Pres: Thomas Casale
VP, Engg & CTO: Anatol Kwartler
VP, Busn Devt: Eric Rossol
VP, Fin & Admin: Gary P Boyer
VP, Opers & Prod Engg: Andrew Rusnock
Mgr, Quality Assurance: John T Hall
Producer of radomes & high-precision antenna
reflectors. Second plant location in Europe.

L-3 Global Communications Solutions (GCS),
see L3Harris Technologies Inc

L-3 WESCAM
Division of L-3 Technologies Inc
649 N Service Rd W, Burlington, ON L7P 5B9,
Canada

Tel: 905-633-4000; 905-633-4175 (cust serv)
Toll Free Tel: 888-593-7226 *Fax:* 905-633-4100
E-mail: sales.wescam@l-3com.com
Web Site: www.wescam.com
Key Personnel
Pres: Mike Richi
VP & CFO: Pat McKay
CTO: Steve Tritchew
SVP, Opers: Mario Grande
VP, Cust Serv: Rod Till
VP, Engg: Duane Heslinga
VP, Gen Coun & Secy: Bruce Latimer
VP, Govt Sales & New Busn Devt: Cameron McKenzie
VP, HR: Roman Turchyn
Electro-optic/infrared laser imaging & targeting sensor sytems to the defense/military, homeland security & airborne law enforcement agencies.
BSI Division supplies wireless on-board camera systems for live television/broadcast sports.
Branch Office(s)
Applied Physics Specialties (APS), 17 Prince Andrew Place, Toronto, ON M3C 2H2, Canada
Tel: 416-445-1870 *Fax:* 416-445-7977

LA Castle Studios
154 S Victory Blvd, Burbank, CA 91502
Tel: 818-861-7317
Web Site: lacastlestudios.com
Key Personnel
Owner/Prodr: Tim Pipher
Founded: 2012
HDTV & feature film studios. Full studio configuration. 3D virtual studio system.

La Paloma Films
Division of Stillman Productions Ltd
PO Box 269, Gilbertsville, NY 13776
Tel: 607-376-4300
E-mail: lapalomafilms@yahoo.com
Web Site: www.lapalomafilms.com
Key Personnel
Pres & CEO: Joseph C Stillman
Founded: 1974
Full service motion picture/video production company.

LA Sound Co
9001 Canoga Ave, Canoga Park, CA 91304
Tel: 818-772-9200 *Fax:* 818-772-9977
E-mail: rentals@lasoundco.com; sales@lasoundco.com
Key Personnel
Pres: Richard Ralke *E-mail:* richard@lasoundco.com
Founded: 1977
Supply production sound systems to the event & entertainment industry. Offer turnkey system design, installation & operation.

Laboratories Inc
Subsidiary of Pioneer Electronics (USA) Inc
1925 E Dominguez St, Long Beach, CA 90810
Toll Free Tel: 800-745-3271
E-mail: info@tad-labs.com
Web Site: technicalaudiodevices.com
Foreign Office(s): Haven 1087, Keet Berglaan 1, 9120 Melsele, Belgium *Tel:* (03) 570-0511
25-1 Yamada, Kawagoe-shi, Saitama 350-8555, Japan
4-15-3 Nishi-Shinjuku, Shinjuku-ku, Tokyo 160-0023, Japan (headquarters)

Labrecque Creative Sound
2825 Main St, Becket, MA 01223
Tel: 520-240-6001
Key Personnel
Owner & Prodr: David Labrecque
Tel: 520-240-6001 (cell) *E-mail:* dave@labrecquecreativesound.com

Founded: 1993
Radio commercial production, film/video/audio post-production, voice-overs, live sound reinforcement & recording.

Lacquer-Mat Inc
13030 Wayne Rd, Livonia, MI 48150
Toll Free Tel: 800-942-2223 (cust serv) *Fax:* 734-422-4205 (orders)
Web Site: www.lacquer-mat.com
Key Personnel
Pres: Ben Tyndell
Membership(s): The Imaging Alliance; PPA

Ladyslipper Music
PO Box 14, Cedar Grove, NC 27231
Tel: 919-245-3737
E-mail: info@ladyslipper.org
Web Site: www.ladyslipper.org
Key Personnel
Dir: Laurie Fuchs
Founded: 1976
Audio & DVD recordings featuring the achievements of women in music.
Catalog(s) available, free

Lagoon Video
Division of Circle Associates Ltd
3323 Marble Front Rd, Caldwell, ID 83605
Tel: 208-455-3457
E-mail: kapsm@aol.com
Key Personnel
Pres: Mike Kaplan *E-mail:* mike@circlelagoon.com
Founded: 1987

Laird Digital Cinema
Division of Tower Products Inc
One Tower Dr, Saugerties, NY 12477
Mailing Address: PO Box 720, Mount Marion, NY 12456
Tel: 845-339-9555 *Toll Free Tel:* 800-898-0759
Fax: 845-339-0231
E-mail: info@lairddigitalcinema.com; sales@lairddigitalcinema.com
Web Site: www.lairddigitalcinema.com
Founded: 1971

Lakeshore Productions, see Lakeshore Public Media

Lakeshore Public Media
8625 Indiana Place, Merriville, IN 46410
Tel: 219-756-5656 *Toll Free Tel:* 888-694-5253
Fax: 219-755-4312
E-mail: info@lakeshorepublicmedia.org
Web Site: lakeshorepublicmedia.org
Mobile production, satellite uplink, production management.

Lamb & Lion Ministries
PO Box 919, McKinney, TX 75070
Tel: 972-736-3567
E-mail: lamblion@lamblion.com
Web Site: christinprophecy.org
Key Personnel
Founder & Dir: Dr David R Reagan
Founded: 1980
Produce Christian ministry audiotapes.
Catalog(s) available
Shipping Address: 2067 County Rd 463, Princeton, TX 75407
Membership(s): ECFA; NRB

L&S Video Inc
875 Fifth Ave, New York, NY 10065
Tel: 914-238-9366
E-mail: videopaint2@msn.com
Web Site: www.landsvideo.com

Key Personnel
Principal: Linda Freeman
Founded: 1987
Produce artists' documentaries. DVDs are free at the Metropolitan Museum Library in New York City.
Online catalog(s) available
Membership(s): CAA; NAEA

Langie Audio Visual Systems
Piano Works Mall, 349 W Commercial St, East Rochester, NY 14445
Tel: 585-385-4880 *Fax:* 585-385-4882
E-mail: info@langieav.com; sales@langieav.com; rental@langieav.com
Web Site: www.langieav.com
Key Personnel
Pres: Ed Ali
Founded: 1970
Catalog(s) available
Membership(s): Audiovisual and Integrated Experience Association; Greater Rochester Chamber of Commerce; MPI

LANGUAGE/30™
Division of MPS Multimedia Inc
708 Elm Ct, Unit B, Paso Robles, CA 93446
Tel: 559-462-0153 *Fax:* 805-296-3889
Web Site: www.lang30.com
Founded: 1948
Publish LANGUAGE/30™ self-teaching audio CD & MP3 language courses.

Lank/Beach Productions Inc
362 Brock St, Winnipeg, MB R3N 0Y9, Canada
Tel: 204-452-9422
E-mail: info@lankbeach.com
Web Site: www.lankbeach.com
Key Personnel
Pres & Dir: Barry Lank
Prodr: Luanne Lank
Founded: 1983
Independent production company dedicated to producing high quality documentaries, television series, television commercials & corporate work.
Membership(s): Canadian Society of Cinematographers; Documentary Organization of Canada; Manitoba Motion Picture Industry Association/Manitoba Film Producers' Association

Lannan Foundation
313 Read St, Santa Fe, NM 87501-2628
Tel: 505-986-8160 *Fax:* 505-986-8195
E-mail: info@lannan.org
Web Site: www.lannan.org
Key Personnel
Pres: J Patrick Lannan, Jr
VP & Dir, Opers: Frank C Lawler
The Foundation supports its mission by making grants to nonprofit organizations in the areas of contemporary visual art, literature, indigenous communities & cultural freedom. Audio & video recordings from live events & interviews spanning a period of 15 years available online.
Catalog(s) available, annual

Larrabee Sound Studio
4162 Lankershim Blvd, North Hollywood, CA 91602
Tel: 818-753-0717 *Fax:* 818-753-8046
E-mail: info@larrabeestudios.com
Web Site: www.larrabeestudios.com
Key Personnel
Owner: Kevin Mills
Studio Mgr: Amy Butt *E-mail:* amyb@larrabeestudios.com
Recording & mixing studio.

Laser Fantasy/HECK Industries/Photon Manufacturing
4228 159 Ave SE, Bellevue, WA 98006
Tel: 425-890-6026 (software & creative support);
425-214-0777 (hardware & tech support)
Toll Free Fax: 866-299-6849
E-mail: info@heckindustries.com
Web Site: www.laserfantasy.com
Key Personnel
Owner & Creative Dir, HECK Industries: Jay
Heck *E-mail:* jay@laserfantasy.com
Founded: 1977
Laser entertainment, manufacturing & engineering.
Membership(s): International Association of
Amusement Parks and Attractions; LDI

Laser Magic Productions
722 N Orlando Ave, No 207, Los Angeles, CA
90069
Tel: 818-590-5899
Web Site: www.laser-magic.com
Key Personnel
CEO: Gene Baum *E-mail:* gbaum@laser-magic.
com
Founded: 1981

Laser Rentals Inc
1953 S County Lane 282, Joplin, MO 64804
Tel: 417-782-8484
E-mail: laserwam@swbell.net
Web Site: www.laserrentalsinc.com
Key Personnel
Pres: Walter Meador
Laser lighting shows.
Catalog(s) available
Online catalog(s) available

Laser Spectacles Inc
PO Box 1535, San Marcos, TX 78667
Tel: 512-392-4600 *Fax:* 512-392-4601
E-mail: laserinfo@laserspectacles.com
Web Site: www.laserspectacles.com
Key Personnel
Pres: Timothy Walsh
Founded: 1985
Producer of laser light shows.
Membership(s): IFEA; International Laser Display Association; Texas Association of Fairs &
Events; Texas Chamber of Commerce Executives

Laser Video Corp
401 Germantown Pike, Lafayette Hill, PA 19444
Tel: 610-825-2500 *Toll Free Tel:* 800-448-8772
Fax: 610-941-9989
E-mail: customerservice@laservideousa.com
Web Site: www.lvconline.com
Key Personnel
Pres: Ken O'Neill; Trudie O'Neill
Founded: 1985
Digital ad delivery, broadcast tape duplication,
video customization, Nielsen SIGMA watermarking, closed captioning, digital archiving,
CD/DVD/Blu-ray services, DVD/Blu-ray authoring, packaging & fulfillment.

Lasergraphics Inc
20 Ada, Irvine, CA 92618
Tel: 949-753-8282 *Fax:* 949-727-9282
E-mail: info@lasergraphics.com
Web Site: www.lasergraphics.com
Key Personnel
CEO: Dr Stefan Demetrescu
VP & CFO: David T Boyd
Founded: 1981
Film imaging system technology.

Laserium®
84777 Charlottes Way, Eugene, OR 97405
Tel: 541-687-1414

Web Site: www.laserium.com
Key Personnel
Creative Dir: Cory Simpson
Tech Dir: Tim Ziegenbein
Busn Dev: Scott Anderson
Founded: 1973
Full service laser show production for all worldwide industries & sales & service of laser
projection systems. Exclusive agents for
Laserium® productions.
Online catalog(s) available

The LAST Factory
Subsidiary of Gamma Omega Associates Inc
2011 Research Dr, Livermore, CA 94550-3803
Tel: 925-449-9449 *Fax:* 925-447-0662
E-mail: thelastfactory@gmail.com
Web Site: thelastfactory.com
Key Personnel
Owner: Walter Davies *E-mail:* wdavies@
lastfactory.com
Founded: 1979
Audio mag tape preservation treatment & tape
head treatment, record preservative for vinyl
records, stylus cleaner & treatment, CD/DVD
cleaner & treatment, CD/DVD shields. Our
goal is to provide quality cleaners & treatments
for all commercial media & to help maintain
media whether it be a personal collection or an
archive for a museum or library.
Catalog(s) available, free, annual
Online catalog(s) available
Membership(s): ARSC

Latham Foundation Publications
1320 Harbor Bay Pkwy, Suite 200, Alameda, CA
94502
Tel: 510-521-0920 *Fax:* 510-521-9861
E-mail: info@latham.org
Web Site: www.latham.org
Key Personnel
Pres: Hugh Tebault, III
Admin Asst: Sue Spiersch
Founded: 1918
Produce & distribute DVD educational programs.

Launch Media
804 Main St, Baton Rouge, LA 70802
Tel: 225-612-2112
E-mail: contactus@launchmedia.tv
Web Site: www.launchmedia.tv
Key Personnel
Partner & Coordinating Prodr: Michael Trufant
Pres & Exec Prodr: John E Jackson *Tel:* 225-612-
2112 ext 1
Dir, Prodn Servs: Wes Kennison *Tel:* 225-612-
2112 ext 2
Multimedia production company. Specialize in
developing & producing strategies & communication tools through customized video & experiential event production.

Laurel Canyon Stages
9337 Laurel Canyon Blvd, Arleta, CA 91331-
4315
Tel: 818-768-8935 *Fax:* 818-768-6852
E-mail: mary@lcstages.com
Web Site: www.lcstages.com
Facility, grip, lighting & electrical equipment
rentals.

Laurel Hill Press
PO Box 16516, Chapel Hill, NC 27516-6516
Toll Free Tel: 800-942-6516 *Fax:* 919-942-9533
E-mail: plantsforus@gmail.com
Web Site: www.laurelhillpress.com
Key Personnel
Owner: Anne H Lindsey
Publisher of colorful & informative natural history books & DVDs.
Catalog(s) available

Laurel Video Productions
1999 E Rte 70, Cherry Hill, NJ 08003
Tel: 856-424-3300
E-mail: inquiries@laurelvideo.net
Web Site: www.laurelvideo.net
Key Personnel
Founder & Owner: Steven Tadzynski
Videotape transfers to DVD & DV files. Videocassette repair & camcorder DVD recovery.
Membership(s): SBE; SMPTE®

Lavine Production Group
189 Dean St, Brooklyn, NY 11217
Tel: 917-804-1870
Web Site: www.lavinegroup.com
Key Personnel
Pres & Exec Prodr: Miriam Lewin
E-mail: miriamlewin@lavinegroup.com
Producer of audio & video documentary programs. Specialize in arts, education & Jewish
topics.

Donna Lawrence Productions
624 Baxter Ave, Louisville, KY 40204
Tel: 502-589-9617
E-mail: dlp@dlproductions.com
Web Site: www.dlproductions.com
Key Personnel
Principal: Donna Lawrence
Admin: Carol Mooney *Tel:* 502-589-9617 ext 225
Full service production company.

Lawrence Productions Inc
6146 W Main St, Suite A, Kalamazoo, MI 49009
Tel: 269-903-2395
E-mail: sales@lpi.com
Web Site: www.lpi.com
Key Personnel
VP: Curtis Cunningham *Tel:* 269-903-2395 ext 28
E-mail: ccunningham@lpi.com
Film & video production company.
Membership(s): American Marketing Association

LBA Technology Inc
Division of LBA Group Inc
3400 Tupper Dr, Greenville, NC 27834
Tel: 252-757-0279 *Toll Free Tel:* 800-522-4464
Fax: 252-752-9155
E-mail: lbagrp@lbagroup.com
Web Site: www.lbagroup.com
Key Personnel
CEO, LBA Group: Lawrence Behr
E-mail: lbwireless@lbagroup.com
COO & VP, Sales: Mike Britner *E-mail:* mike.
britner@lbagroup.com
Mktg Dir: Carolyn Linton *E-mail:* carolyn.
linton@lbagroup.com
Founded: 1963
Manufacturer & integrator of radio frequency systems, lightning protection & EMC equipment
for broadcast, industrial & government users
worldwide.

LEA International
Member of Smiths Power Protection Technology
Group
10701 Airport Rd, Hayden, ID 83835
Tel: 208-762-6121; 208-772-8515
Toll Free Tel: 800-882-9110 *Fax:* 208-762-6117
Founded: 1971
Surge suppressor manufacturer.
Catalog(s) available
Membership(s): NAB; SBE

LEAD Technologies Inc
1927 S Tryon St, Suite 200, Charlotte, NC 28203
Tel: 704-332-5532 *Toll Free Tel:* 800-637-4699
Fax: 704-372-8161
E-mail: sales@leadtools.com
Web Site: www.leadtools.com

Key Personnel
Pres: Richard Little
Founded: 1990
Our primary focus is providing digital imaging & compression technology to programmers.

Leader Instruments Corp
Subsidiary of Leader Electronics Corp
1501 E Orangethorpe Ave, Suite 140, Fullerton, CA 92831
Tel: 714-527-9300 *Toll Free Tel:* 800-645-5104
Fax: 714-527-7490
E-mail: info@leaderamerica.com
Web Site: www.leaderamerica.com
Key Personnel
Dir, Sales: Pete Anderson *Tel:* 714-527-9300 ext 106 *E-mail:* anderson@leaderamerica.com
Monitoring system manufacturer.
Catalog(s) available

Learn Quickly
PO Box 4464, Palm Springs, CA 92263-4464
Toll Free Tel: 888-LRN-FAST (576-3278)
Toll Free Fax: 888-LRN-FAST (576-3278)
Web Site: www.learnquickly.com
Key Personnel
Owner & Creator: Janet Scarpone *E-mail:* janet@learnquickly.com
Founded: 1996
Produce & distribute educational books & DVDs in math, communication, writing, & grammar. Online format available.
Brochure(s) available

Learning Ally
20 Roszel Rd, Princeton, NJ 08540
Toll Free Tel: 800-221-4792
E-mail: custserv@learningally.org; media@learningally.org
Web Site: www.learningally.org
Key Personnel
Dir, Media Rel: Doug Sprei *Tel:* 800-221-4792 ext 5
Online library of more than 80,000 accessible human-narrated audio textbooks & literature titles. Along with audiobooks, it provides support to people with a wide range of reading disabilities, including blindness, visual impairment, dyslexia & other learning differences.
Online catalog(s) available
Branch Office(s)
431 Burgess Dr, Suite 120, Menlo Park, CA 94025 *Tel:* 650-493-3717
1355 S Colorado Blvd, Bldg C, Suite 801, Denver, CO 80222 *Tel:* 303-757-0787
5225 Wisconsin Ave NW, Suite 312, Washington, DC 20015 *Tel:* 202-244-8990
320 S Hull St, Athens, GA 30605 *Tel:* 706-549-1313
14600 S Ravinia Ave, Orland Park, IL 60462 *Tel:* 708-349-9356
545 Fifth Ave, Suite 1005, New York, NY 10017 *Tel:* 212-557-5720
1314 W 45 St, Austin, TX 78756 *Tel:* 512-323-9390

The Learning House Inc
427 S Fourth St, Suite 300, Louisville, KY 40202
Tel: 502-589-9878 *Fax:* 502-589-9825
E-mail: sales@learninghouse.com; info@learninghouse.com
Web Site: www.learninghouse.com
Key Personnel
Chmn: David T Richardson
Pres & CEO: Todd Zipper
CFO: Jim Lintner
Chief Academic Offr: Dave Clinefelter
SVP, Client Mgmt & Busn Devt: John Anderson
VP, Busn Devt & Gen Coun: Jay Hatcher
VP, Curriculum Devt: Krysia Lazarewicz
VP, Enrollment: Julie Delich
VP, HR: Kelly Sweasy

VP, Mktg: Wendy Parrish
VP, Strategic Initiatives: Jeremy Walsh
VP, Strategic Opers: Cindy Sadler
VP, Technol: Justin Klutka
VP of Opers, Software Guild: Rachel McGalliard
Founded: 2001
Course development, learning management systems.
Catalog(s) available

Learning Seed
208 S Jefferson St, Suite 402, Chicago, IL 60661
Toll Free Tel: 800-634-4941 *Toll Free Fax:* 800-998-0854
E-mail: info@learningseed.com
Web Site: www.learningseed.com
Key Personnel
Pres: Christine Schrank
Educational programming.
Catalog(s) available

Learning Strategies Corp
2000 Plymouth Rd, Minnetonka, MN 55305-2335
Tel: 952-767-9800 *Toll Free Tel:* 888-800-2688 (cust serv); 866-292-1861 (24 hour order line)
Fax: 952-475-2373
E-mail: info@learningstrategies.com
Web Site: www.learningstrategies.com
Key Personnel
Pres: Peter Bissonette
Founded: 1981
Provider of self-improvement, education & health programs. Live online events.
Catalog(s) available

Learning Technology Services
Affiliate of University of Wisconsin-Stout
301 Millennium Hall, Menomonie, WI 54751
Tel: 715-232-5002
E-mail: helpdesk@uwstout.edu
Web Site: www.uwstout.edu/academics/academic-services/learning-and-information-technology

Lectrosonics Inc
581 Laser Rd NE, Rio Rancho, NM 87124
Mailing Address: PO Box 15900, Rio Rancho, NM 87174
Tel: 505-892-4501 *Toll Free Tel:* 800-821-1121
Fax: 505-892-6243
E-mail: sales@lectrosonics.com
Web Site: www.lectrosonics.com
Key Personnel
Pres: Gordon Moore
VP, Engg: Bob Cunnings
VP, Mfg: Wes Herron
VP, Mktg: Bruce Jones
VP, Sales: Karl Winkler
Mktg Coord: Kathy Baca
Founded: 1971
Wireless technology for the film, broadcast, music & theater technical communities.
Catalog(s) available, annual
Branch Office(s)
720 Spadina Ave, Suite 600, Toronto, ON M5S 2T9, Canada *Tel:* 416-596-2202 *Toll Free Tel:* 877-7LECTRO (753-2876) *Fax:* 416-596-6648
Membership(s): Audiovisual and Integrated Experience Association; NAB; NAMM, the National Association of Music Merchants; NSCA

LEDtronics Inc
23105 Kashiva Ct, Torrance, CA 90505
Tel: 310-534-1505 *Toll Free Tel:* 800-579-4875
Fax: 310-534-1424
E-mail: info@ledtronics.com
Web Site: www.ledtronics.com
Founded: 1983
Manufacturer of LED bulbs & LED lamps.
Catalog(s) available

Lee Co Inc
27 S 12 St, Terre Haute, IN 47807
Tel: 812-235-8155 *Fax:* 812-235-3587
E-mail: leeco@leecompanyinc.com; sales@leecompanyinc.com
Web Site: www.leecompanyinc.com
Key Personnel
Pres: Ken Senseman
Founded: 1932
Catalog(s) available

Lee Dan® Communications Inc
155 Adams Ave, Hauppauge, NY 11788-3699
Tel: 631-231-1414 *Toll Free Tel:* 800-231-1414
Fax: 631-231-1498
E-mail: info@leedan.com
Web Site: www.leedan.com
Key Personnel
Pres: Larry Goldberg
VP: David H Goldberg
Founded: 1955
Intercom manufacturer.
Catalog(s) available

LEE Filters
Division of Panavision
2237 N Hollywood Way, Burbank, CA 91505
Tel: 818-238-1220 *Toll Free Tel:* 800-576-5055
Fax: 818-238-1228
E-mail: mail@leefiltersusa.com
Web Site: www.leefilters.com
Key Personnel
VP & Gen Mgr: Jessie Friend
Precision products for photographers, cinematographers, lighting designers & architects.
Catalog(s) available

Lee Hartman & Sons Inc
3236 Cove Rd NW, Roanoke, VA 24017
Tel: 540-366-3493 *Toll Free Tel:* 800-344-1832
Fax: 540-362-4659
E-mail: info@leehartman.com; roanokeva@leehartman.com
Web Site: www.leehartman.com
Key Personnel
Pres: Steve M Hartman
VP: Rob Hartman
Mktg Dir: Ashton Williams *Tel:* 540-366-3493 ext 1123 *E-mail:* awilliams@leehartman.com
Founded: 1936
Retail/wholesale AV products. Consultation services, delivery, installation & rental department. Education, government, religious & business specialists.
Catalog(s) available, free, annual
Branch Office(s)
610 Prosperity Way, Chesapeake, VA 23320, Contact: Cindy Smith *Tel:* 757-873-4944 *Fax:* 757-382-4801 *E-mail:* chesapeakeva@leehartman.com
16063 Continental Blvd, South Chesterfield, VA 23834 *Tel:* 804-477-8676 *Fax:* 804-477-8683 *E-mail:* richmondva@leehartman.com
8839 Kelso St, Suite M, Baltimore, MD 21221, Contact: Quentin Mills *Tel:* 410-686-6975 *Fax:* 410-686-5170 *E-mail:* qmills@leehartman.com
10993 Ocean Hwy, Suite 507, Pawleys Island, SC 29585 *Tel:* 843-235-8580 *Fax:* 804-477-8683 *E-mail:* myrtlebeachsc@leehartman.com
3 Davis Ct, Hurricane, WV 25526, Contact: Larry Cox *Tel:* 304-397-4100 *Fax:* 304-397-4101 *E-mail:* lcox@leehartman.com
Membership(s): Audiovisual and Integrated Experience Association; Chamber of Commerce; Custom Electronic Design & Installation Association

Leedal Inc
3453 Commercial Ave, Northbrook, IL 60062
Tel: 847-498-0111 *Fax:* 847-498-0198
E-mail: sink@leedal.com
Web Site: www.leedal.com

Key Personnel
VP: A J Levin
Founded: 1946
Membership(s): Audiovisual and Integrated Experience Association; The Imaging Alliance

Lefco Video Services Inc
600 W Sunset Rd, Suite 103, Henderson, NV 89011
Tel: 702-566-1770 *Fax:* 702-566-1798
E-mail: info1@lefco.com
Web Site: www.lefco.com
Key Personnel
Pres & Gen Mgr: Michael Minkoff
On-site multi camera video production.
Catalog(s) available

Legendary Entertainment
160 Torrance Woods, Brampton, ON L6Y 4K2, Canada
Tel: 416-712-9994
E-mail: legendary_ent@rogers.com
Web Site: legendaryentertainment.com
Record label & media company.

Legendary Pictures
Division of Legendary Entertainment
2900 W Alameda Ave, 15th fl, Burbank, CA 91505
Tel: 818-688-7003
E-mail: info@legendary.com
Web Site: www.legendary.com
Key Personnel
Founder & CEO: Thomas Tull
Pres & Chief Creative Offr: Jon Jashni
Founded: 2000
Film production company. Co-production & co-financing of films with Legendary Entertainment's Legendary Television & Digital Media division.

Legion Lighting Co Inc
221 Glenmore Ave, Brooklyn, NY 11207
Tel: 718-498-1770 *Fax:* 718-498-0128
Toll Free Fax: 800-4-LEGION (453-4466)
E-mail: sales@legionlighting.com
Web Site: www.legionlighting.com
Key Personnel
Pres: Michael Bellovin *E-mail:* mbellovin@legionlighting.com
Founded: 1946
Manufacture energy efficient fluorescent lighting fixtures & exit lighting.
Catalog(s) available

Lehigh Electric Products Co
6265 Hamilton Blvd, Allentown, PA 18106
Tel: 610-395-3386 *Fax:* 610-395-7735
E-mail: sales@lehighdim.com
Web Site: www.lehighdim.com
Key Personnel
Pres: Lloyd H Jones
Founded: 1961
Theatrical & architectural lighting systems manufacturer.
Catalog(s) available
Membership(s): USITT

Leica Camera Inc
Subsidiary of Leica Camera Group (Germany)
One Pearl Ct, Unit A, Allendale, NJ 07401
Toll Free Tel: 800-222-0118 *Fax:* 201-995-1686
Web Site: en.leica-camera.com
Key Personnel
VP, Mktg: Roland Wolfe
Manufacturer & distributor of camera equipment.
Catalog(s) available

Leightronix Inc
1125 N Cedar Rd, Mason, MI 48854

Tel: 517-694-8000 *Toll Free Tel:* 800-243-5589
Fax: 517-694-1600
E-mail: support@leightronix.com; sales@leightronix.com; info@leightronix.com
Web Site: www.leightronix.com
Key Personnel
Inside Sales Mgr: Sara Mason
Founded: 1981
Manufacture IPTV System Solutions & hardware & software (middleware).

Leisure Video
Division of GCI Inc
747 Magazine St, New Orleans, LA 70130
Tel: 504-299-9000 *Toll Free Tel:* 800-432-3853
E-mail: info@dukesofdixieland.com
Web Site: www.dukesofdixieland.com; www.leisurejazz.com
Key Personnel
Pres: John Shoup
Jazz music videos.
Membership(s): Entertainment Merchants Association; NATPE

LEMO USA Inc
Subsidiary of LEMO SA (Switzerland)
635 Park Ct, Rohnert Park, CA 94928
Mailing Address: PO Box 2408, Rohnert Park, CA 94927-2408
Tel: 707-578-8811 *Toll Free Tel:* 800-444-LEMO (444-5366) *Fax:* 707-578-0869
E-mail: info-us@lemo.com
Web Site: www.lemo.com
Key Personnel
Mktg Mgr: Julie Carlson *Tel:* 707-206-3776 *E-mail:* jcarlson@lemo.com
Founded: 1946
Electronic connectors for headsets, microphones & professional cameras.
Catalog(s) available

Lenel Systems International Inc
Subsidiary of United Technologies Corp
1212 Pittsford-Victor Rd, Pittsford, NY 14534-3820
Tel: 585-248-9720 *Toll Free Tel:* 866-788-5095
Fax: 585-248-9185
E-mail: insidesales@lenel.com
Web Site: www.lenel.com
Founded: 1991
Advanced security systems.

Lensless Camera Manufacturing Co
809 Lark Dr, Fernley, NV 89408
Mailing Address: PO Box 261, Fernley, NV 89408-0261
Tel: 775-575-5189
E-mail: info@pinholecamera.com
Web Site: www.pinholecamera.com
Key Personnel
Owner: Charles Levy
Single shot lensless camera made available in 4x5, 5x7, 8x10 & 11x14 formats. These cameras take film holders & Polaroid backs.

Leprecon®
Division of CAE Inc
10087 Industrial Dr, Hamburg, MI 48139
Mailing Address: PO Box 218, Hamburg, MI 48139-0218
Tel: 810-852-4300 *Toll Free Tel:* 888-422-3537
Fax: 810-231-1631
E-mail: sales@leprecon.com
Web Site: www.leprecon.com
Key Personnel
Pres: James Fackert
Sales: Peter Stewart *E-mail:* pstewart@leprecon.com
Off Mgr: Lois Riske
Membership(s): Professional Lighting & Sound Association; USITT

The Lerro Corp
905 Madison Ave, Norristown, PA 19403
Tel: 610-650-4100 *Fax:* 610-650-4110
E-mail: lerrocorp@lerro.com
Web Site: www.lerro.com
Key Personnel
Pres: Matthew E Murphy *E-mail:* mattm@lerro.com
Secy & Treas: Marion E Murphy *Tel:* 610-650-4100 ext 217 *E-mail:* marionm@lerro.com
Founded: 1949
Integrator of multi-format, broadcast quality video technology.
Branch Office(s)
3510 Margo Rd, Camp Hill, PA 17011, Patrick Bucher *Tel:* 717-763-1580 *E-mail:* patb@lerro.com
400 Penn Center Blvd, Suite 721, Pittsburgh, PA 15235, Joe SeNay *Tel:* 412-824-5222 *Fax:* 412-824-5190 *E-mail:* joes@lerro.com

Leucos USA Inc
Subsidiary of Leucos SRL SU
11 Mayfield Ave, Edison, NJ 08837
Tel: 732-225-0010 *Toll Free Tel:* 800-832-3360
Fax: 732-225-0250
E-mail: info@leucosusa.com
Web Site: www.leucos.com
Key Personnel
Pres: Josie A Anthony
Founded: 1991
Distributor of contemporary glass lighting.
Catalog(s) available
Foreign Office(s): Leucos SRL SU, Via delle industrie 16/b, 30030 Scorze VE, Italy *Tel:* (041) 574 1111 *Fax:* (041) 574 1321 *E-mail:* info@leucos.com

Level 3 Communications Inc
1025 Eldorado Blvd, Broomfield, CO 80021
Tel: 720-888-1000 *Toll Free Tel:* 877-2LEVEL3 (253-8357)
Web Site: www.level3.com
Key Personnel
Pres & CEO: Jeff Storey
CIO: Atilla Tinic
Chief Mktg Offr: Anthony Christie
CTO: Andrew Dugan
EVP & CFO: Sunit Patel
EVP, Chief Legal Offr & Secy: John Ryan
Regl Pres, North America & Asia Pacific: Laurinda Pang
Provider of global communication services to enterprise, government & carrier customers.

Leviton LES (Lighting & Energy Solutions)
Division of Leviton Manufacturing Co Inc
20497 SW Teton Ave, Tualatin, OR 97062
Toll Free Tel: 800-736-6682 *Fax:* 503-404-5594
Web Site: www.leviton.com
Founded: 1906
Advanced architectural lighting control systems.
Online catalog(s) available

C H Levy & Co, see Lensless Camera Manufacturing Co

Levy NYC Design & Production
356 Devoe St, Brooklyn, NY 11211
Tel: 212-925-4640 *Fax:* 212-925-4216
E-mail: info@levynyc.net
Web Site: www.levylighting.com
Key Personnel
Creative Dir: Ira Levy
Dir, Busn Devt: Helene Safdie *E-mail:* hsafdie@levynyc.net
Dir, Prodn: Diane Bayne *E-mail:* dbayne@levynyc.net

Dir, Sales & Mktg: Flora Zaretskaya
E-mail: flora@levynyc.net
Full service design & production company focused on lighting, sound & video for events, architecture & architainment.

Lex Products Corp
15 Progress Dr, Shelton, CT 06484
Tel: 203-363-3738 *Toll Free Tel:* 800-643-4460
Fax: 203-363-3742
E-mail: info@lexproducts.com; orders@
lexproducts.com; customerservice@lexproducts.
com
Web Site: www.lexproducts.com
Key Personnel
VP, Sales: Leonard Miller *Tel:* 203-892-5434
E-mail: lmiller@lexproducts.com
Founded: 1989
Manufacturer & distributor of portable & permanent power distribution & lighting systems.
Online catalog(s) available
Branch Office(s)
12701 Van Nuys Blvd, Suite Q, Pacoima, CA
91331 *Tel:* 818-768-4474 *Fax:* 818-768-4040
15751 SW 41 St, Suite 300, Davie, FL 33331
Tel: 954-888-1024 *Fax:* 954-888-1026
Membership(s): ARA; Association of the United States Army; Canadian Institute for Theatre Technology; Electrical Generating Systems Association; Entertainment Services and Technology Association; National Association of Electrical Distributors; National Defense Industrial Association; USITT

LHV Audio Services
3417 Lake Breeze Rd, Orlando, FL 32808
Tel: 407-295-3565
E-mail: service@lhvaudio.com
Web Site: www.lhvaudio.com
Key Personnel
Owner, Pres & Chief Engr: Laurence Vexler
Founded: 1990
Sound design & audio production services.
Membership(s): AES; The Recording Academy

Liberty AV Solutions
Division of WESCO Distribution Inc
11675 Ridgeline Dr, Colorado Springs, CO 80921
Tel: 719-260-0061 *Toll Free Tel:* 800-530-8998
Fax: 719-260-0075
E-mail: orders@libav.com
Web Site: secure.libertycable.com
Key Personnel
Pres: Ed Jankowski
VP, Mktg: Becky McWilliams
Supplier of wire & cable, plates & panels, digital solutions & networked media systems.
Online catalog(s) available

Liberty Uplink
2547 Yellow Springs Rd, Malvern, PA 19355
Tel: 215-964-5222; 917-254-0155
E-mail: info@libertyuplink.com
Web Site: www.libertyuplink.com
Key Personnel
Founder & Partner: Adam Sirkin
Partner: Chuck Ranney
Founded: 1999
Pre-production scouting services, satellite time booking, production coordination, camera crews & transmission services.

Library of Congress, Motion Picture, Broadcasting & Recorded Sound Division
Division of Library of Congress
James Madison Bldg, LM 336, 101 Independence Ave SE, Washington, DC 20540-1000
Tel: 202-707-8572 *Fax:* 202-707-2371
Web Site: www.loc.gov/rr/mopic

Key Personnel
Admin Offr: David Critics *Tel:* 202-707-2678
E-mail: dcri@loc.gov
Catalog(s) available, for sound recordings only; includes folk music & poetry readings

Library Video Company
7 E Wynnewood Rd, Wynnewood, PA 19096
Tel: 610-645-4000 *Toll Free Tel:* 800-843-3620
Fax: 610-645-4040
E-mail: sales@libraryvideo.com; comments@
libraryvideo.com
Web Site: www.libraryvideo.com
Key Personnel
CEO: Andrew Schlessinger
Founded: 1985
Leading publisher of educational media to schools & libraries.
Catalog(s) available, free, 5 times/yr, educational media
Membership(s): ALA; Entertainment Merchants Association

Lieberman Productions
455 Ninth St, San Francisco, CA 94103-4410
Tel: 415-955-0855 *Fax:* 415-955-0822
E-mail: lpinfo@lieberman.com
Web Site: www.lieberman.com
Key Personnel
Pres: Lenny Lieberman
Full service production company. Specialize in infomercials.

Life Cycle Books Ltd
1085 Bellamy Rd N, Unit 20, Toronto, ON M1H 1H7, Canada
Tel: 416-690-5860 *Toll Free Tel:* 866-880-5860
Fax: 416-690-8532 *Toll Free Fax:* 866-690-8532
E-mail: support@lifecyclebooks.com; billing@
lifecyclebooks.com; orders@lifecyclebooks.com
Web Site: www.lifecyclebooks.com
Key Personnel
Founder & Pres: Paul Broughton *E-mail:* paulb@
lifecyclebooks.com
Catalog(s) available
Branch Office(s)
PO Box 799, Fort Collins, CO 80522 *Toll Free
Tel:* 800-214-5849 *Toll Free Fax:* 888-690-8532

Life House Productions LLC
PO Box 4007, Manchester, CT 06045-4007
Tel: 860-432-9177
Web Site: www.lifehouseproductions.com
Key Personnel
Partner & Pres: William Matthews *E-mail:* bill@
lifehouseproductions.com
Partner: Dena Matthews *E-mail:* dena@
lifehouseproductions.com
Founded: 1998
Medical & scientific 3D computer animation & graphics.

Lifetime Television®
Unit of Lifetime Entertainment Services LLC
235 E 45 St, New York, NY 10017
Tel: 212-424-7000
Web Site: www.mylifetime.com
Key Personnel
EVP & Gen Mgr: Rob Sharenow
Founded: 1984
TV programming.
Branch Office(s)
2049 Century Park E, Suite 840, Los Angeles, CA 90067 *Tel:* 310-556-7500
444 N Michigan Ave, Suite 3270, Chicago, IL 60611 *Tel:* 312-464-1991

Light Impressions
Division of FDM Brands

2340 Brighton Henrietta Townline Rd, Rochester, NY 14623
Toll Free Tel: 844-656-4876 *Toll Free Fax:* 866-592-8642
E-mail: help@fdmbrands.com
Web Site: www.lightimpressionsdirect.com
Founded: 1969
Manufacturer & distributor of archival supplies.
Online catalog(s) available
Catalog(s) available

The Light Source
3935 Westinghouse Blvd, Charlotte, NC 28273
Tel: 704-504-8399 *Fax:* 704-588-4693 (acctg); 704-588-4637 (orders)
E-mail: mail@thelightsource.com; sales@
thelightsource.com
Web Site: www.thelightsource.com
Key Personnel
Owner: Eric Von Fange *E-mail:* ericvf@
thelightsource.com
Manufacture lighting clamps.
Catalog(s) available
Membership(s): Professional Lighting & Sound Association

LightBox-NY
841 Barretto St, Bronx, NY 10474
Tel: 718-759-6419
E-mail: lightboxny@gmail.com
Web Site: www.lightbox-ny.com
Daylight studio rental for film, photography, music videos, parties & events.

LightHouse Films
225 W 39 St, Suite 600, New York, NY 10018
Tel: 646-649-3600 *Fax:* 646-398-7122
E-mail: contact@lhfny.com; rent@lhfny.com
Web Site: www.light-house-films.com
Key Personnel
Founder & Partner: Camille De Galbert
Partner & Exec Prodr: Thibaut Estellon
Dir: Antoine Pai; Anthony Pellino
Founded: 2008
Commercial, corporate & music video production services. Camera & accessories rental.

Lighthouse Photo & Video Productions
1100 Chicago Ave, Suite 7C, Goshen, IN 46528
Tel: 574-533-1400 (off); 574-202-5502 (studio)
E-mail: lighthousevideo@gmail.com
Web Site: www.lighthousephotoandvideo.com
Key Personnel
Owner & Pres: William Landow
Photography & videography for family & corporate events. Film & video transfer service. Documentary production for promotion, training or TV broadcast.

Lighting & Production Equipment Inc
590 Travis St, Atlanta, GA 30318
Tel: 404-352-0464 *Toll Free Tel:* 800-275-3721
Fax: 404-351-4399
Web Site: www.lpe.com
Key Personnel
Founder & CEO: W Bruce Harlan *Tel:* 404-924-7600 *E-mail:* bharlan@lpe.com
Founded: 1976
Catalog(s) available
Online catalog(s) available
Membership(s): AICP; NABET-CWA; NATAS

The Lighting Design Alliance
2830 Temple Ave, Long Beach, CA 90806-2213
Tel: 562-989-3843 *Fax:* 562-989-3847
E-mail: info@lightingdesignalliance.com
Web Site: www.lightingdesignalliance.com
Key Personnel
Pres: Chip Israel *E-mail:* cisrael@
lightingdesignalliance.com

Founded: 1992
Lighting designers.

Lighting Design Group
49 W 27 St, Suite 920, New York, NY 10001
Tel: 212-685-4940 *Fax:* 212-685-4927
E-mail: lighting@ldg.com
Web Site: www.ldg.com
Key Personnel
EVP, Design: Dennis M Size
Founded: 1989
Lighting design & lighting production service
company.
Online catalog(s) available
Membership(s): IALD; Illuminating Engineer-
ing Society; International Alliance of Theatri-
cal Stage Employees; NABET-CWA; NATAS;
SMPTE®; United Scenic Artists; USITT

Lighting Industry Resource Council
Affiliate of The International Association of
Lighting Designers (IALD)
440 N Wells St, Suite 210, Chicago, IL 60654
Tel: 312-527-3677 *Fax:* 312-527-3680
E-mail: iald@iald.org
Web Site: www.iald.org/council
Key Personnel
CEO: Marsha L Turner *Tel:* 312-527-3677 ext
106 *E-mail:* marsha@iald.org
Membership Mgr: Ashley Robbins
E-mail: ashley@iald.org
Founded: 1996
Manufacturer of lighting equipment.

Lighting Sales Connection Inc
757 SE 17 St, No 254, Fort Lauderdale, FL
33316
Tel: 954-655-9074 *Fax:* 954-764-7013
E-mail: info@lightingsales.com
Web Site: www.lightingsales.com
Key Personnel
Pres: Richard J Blanco
Wholesale marine, solar, LED fiber optics & sig-
nage products.
Online catalog(s) available

Lighting Services Inc
2 Holt Dr, Stony Point, NY 10980
Tel: 845-942-2800 *Toll Free Tel:* 800-999-9574
(US & CN) *Fax:* 845-942-2177
E-mail: applications@maillsi.com; sales@maillsi.
com
Web Site: www.lightingservicesinc.com
Key Personnel
Mktg Specialist: Kerri Galgano *E-mail:* k.
galgano@maillsi.com
Founded: 1958
Manufacture track lighting, accent lighting, dis-
play lighting & LED lighting systems.
Online catalog(s) available

Lightning Eliminators & Consultants Inc
6687 Arapahoe Rd, Boulder, CO 80303
Tel: 303-447-2828 *Toll Free Tel:* 800-521-6101
Fax: 303-447-8122
E-mail: info@lecglobal.com
Web Site: www.lightningprotection.com
Key Personnel
Pres: Matt Napier
EVP & Dir, Applied Engg: Peter A Carpenter
E-mail: peterc@lecglobal.com
VP, Sales & Engg: Joe Lanzoni *Tel:* 303-951-
3156 *E-mail:* jlanzoni@lecglobal.com
Dir, Engg: Kirk S Chynoweth *E-mail:* kirkc@
lecglobal.com
Mktg Mgr: Shawn McTigue *Tel:* 303-951-3158
E-mail: smctigue@lecglobal.com
Founded: 1971
Lightning prevention systems & products, appli-
cation engineering, consulting & educational
services.

Lightning Master Corp
2100-A Palmetto St, Clearwater, FL 33765
Tel: 727-447-6800 *Toll Free Tel:* 877-334-8006
Fax: 727-499-0138
E-mail: info@lightningmaster.com
Web Site: www.lightningmaster.com
Key Personnel
Pres: Bruce Kaiser
Founded: 1984
Manufacturer of full spectrum static solutions &
lightning & transient protection systems, serv-
ing the oil, gas & chemical industries.
Online catalog(s) available
Membership(s): American Petroleum Institute;
IEEE; National Fire Protection Association

Lightning Media
1415 Cahuenga Blvd, Hollywood, CA 90028
Tel: 323-957-9255
E-mail: info@lightningmedia.com
Web Site: www.lightningmedia.com
Post-production services to media & entertain-
ment clients.

Lightronics Inc
509 Central Dr, Virginia Beach, VA 23454
Tel: 757-486-3588 *Toll Free Tel:* 800-472-8541
Fax: 757-486-3391
Web Site: www.lightronics.com
Key Personnel
Natl Dir, Sales: Dennis Degen *Tel:* 301-788-3667
Sales & Mktg Mgr: Chris Pease
Manufacture lighting control equipment.
Membership(s): Illuminating Engineering Society;
Lighting Controls Association; Professional
Lighting & Sound Association

Lights On
1720 Merriam Lane, Kansas City, KS 66106
Tel: 913-362-6940 *Toll Free Tel:* 800-229-5876
Fax: 913-362-6958
E-mail: kansascity@lightson.com
Web Site: www.lightson.com
Rental & sales of film & video production sup-
plies.

Lights On Nebraska
7520 Burlington St, Omaha, NE 68127
Tel: 402-331-4340 *Fax:* 402-331-4556
E-mail: ne@lightsonrentals.com
Web Site: www.lightsonrentals.com
Founded: 1992
Lighting/grip rental house, full studio soundstage
& production office.

LightSpace Studios
1115 Flushing Ave, Brooklyn, NY 11237
Tel: 212-202-0372
E-mail: reserve@lightspace.tv
Web Site: www.lightspace.tv
Full service photo & film production facility. Of-
fers large inventory of lighting, grip, camera,
digital capture & crew roster.

Lightspeed Technologies Inc
11509 SW Herman Rd, Tualatin, OR 97062
Tel: 503-684-5538 *Toll Free Tel:* 800-732-8999
Fax: 503-684-3197
E-mail: info@lightspeed-tek.com
Web Site: www.lightspeed-tek.com
Key Personnel
EVP, Sales & Mktg: David Solomon
Founded: 1990
Classroom audio technology, a low volume am-
plification system providing clarity of speech &
even sound distribution throughout the learning
environment.
Online catalog(s) available, educational

LightTech Group Inc
PO Box 300642, Jamaica, NY 11430

Tel: 718-525-2900
Web Site: www.lighttech.com
Key Personnel
Pres: Leon R Saddler *E-mail:* levon.saddler@
gmail.com
VP: Jacques F Pardovany *E-mail:* jacques@
lighttech.com
Founded: 1992
Professional television lighting production ser-
vices. Specialize in television studio & church
lighting design & installation.

Lightware Inc
1329 W Byers Place, Denver, CO 80223-1723
Tel: 303-744-0202 *Fax:* 303-722-4545
E-mail: info@lightwareinc.com
Web Site: www.lightwareinc.com; www.
lightwaredirect.com
Key Personnel
Pres: Paul Peregrine
Lightweight airline shippable equipment cases for
the still & video photographer. Film or digital
still photography - studio & location; cases for
computers & monitors.
Online catalog(s) available
Membership(s): ASMP; The Imaging Alliance;
National Press Photographers Association

Lightworks Audio & Video Inc
PO Box 661593, Los Angeles, CA 90066
Tel: 310-398-4949
E-mail: sales1@lightworksav.com; edmedia@
lightworksav.com
Web Site: www.lightworksav.com
Key Personnel
Pres & CEO: Harry DeLigter
Founded: 1992
Distribution of enlightening media.

Lightyear Entertainment
4011 Alcove Ave, Studio City, CA 91604
Tel: 818-855-1318 *Fax:* 818-855-1320
Web Site: lightyear.com
Key Personnel
Owner: Arnie Holland *E-mail:* arnie@lightyear.
com
Founded: 1987
Producer & distributor of entertainment software
products.
Online catalog(s) available

Ligos Corporation
6001 Chatham Ctr Dr, Suite 300, Savannah, GA
31405
Mailing Address: PO Box 15387, Savannah, GA
31416
Tel: 912-236-8993 *Fax:* 912-234-1366
Web Site: www.ligos.com
Founded: 1997
MPEG encoder systems.

Limbo Films
2223 NE Martin Luther King Jr Blvd, Portland,
OR 97212
E-mail: info@limbofilms.com
Web Site: www.limbofilms.com
Key Personnel
Owner & Dir: Gary Nolton *E-mail:* gary@
limbofilms.com
Dir: Guy Baker; Padraic O'Meara
Exec Prodr: Judy Kettler *E-mail:* judy@
limbofilms.com
Founded: 1992
Full service production company.
Membership(s): AICP

Limelight Communications Inc
2812 Roesh Way, Vienna, VA 22181
Tel: 703-242-4596
E-mail: moreinfo@limelightdc.com
Web Site: www.limelightdc.com

Key Personnel
Pres & Exec Prodr: Kenny Reff
Founded: 1985
Video production & digital media solutions.
Membership(s): International Television Video Association; Television, Internet & Video Association of DC Inc

Limelight Production® Inc
471 Pleasant St, Lee, MA 01238-9322
Tel: 413-243-4950 *Toll Free Tel:* 800-243-4950 *Fax:* 413-243-4993 *Toll Free Fax:* 800-243-4951
E-mail: info@limelightproductions.com; sales@limelightproductions.com
Web Site: www.limelightproductions.com
Key Personnel
Pres: William Beautyman *Tel:* 413-243-4950 ext 1200 *E-mail:* wbeautyman@limelightproductions.com
Rentals Mgr/Inside Sales Assoc: Jean Kalin *Tel:* 413-243-4950 ext 1100 *E-mail:* jkalin@limelightproductions.com
Curtain Fabrication: Ginny Bentley *Tel:* 413-243-4950 ext 5000 *E-mail:* gbentley@limelightproductions.com
Electronics Technician: Greg Mitchell *Tel:* 413-243-4950 ext 2100 *E-mail:* gmitchell@limelightproductions.com
Founded: 1972
Provide equipment, supplies & service for stage, film, video & event productions.
Catalog(s) available
Membership(s): Entertainment Services and Technology Association; International Alliance of Theatrical Stage Employees; Professional Lighting & Sound Association; USITT

Lineco
Division of University Products Inc
517 Main St, Holyoke, MA 01040-2604
Toll Free Tel: 800-322-7775 *Fax:* 413-532-9281 (sales) *Toll Free Fax:* 800-298-7815
E-mail: info@lineco.com
Web Site: www.lineco.com
Key Personnel
Pres & COO: Scott Magoon
Manufactures a broad line of bookbinding items such as repair tapes, book binding boards, spine tapes, pH neutral adhesives, along with many tools & associated supplies. Also known for its Books-By-Hand line of bookbinding materials & easy to assemble kits available as scrapbooks, boxes, journals & accordion photo albums.
Online catalog(s) available
Membership(s): The Imaging Alliance

Linguistic Systems Inc
260 Franklin St, Suite 230, Boston, MA 02110
Toll Free Tel: 800-654-5006
E-mail: clientservice@linguist.com
Web Site: linguist.com
Founded: 1967
Create foreign language versions of AV.
Catalog(s) available

Linguist's Software Inc
844 Adler St, Edmonds, WA 98020-3301
Tel: 425-775-1130
E-mail: fonts@linguistsoftware.com
Web Site: www.linguistsoftware.com
Key Personnel
Pres: Philip B Payne *E-mail:* phil@linguistsoftware.com
Founded: 1984
Create & sell foreign language fonts (Unicode & ASCII) & input software for over 2,600 languages.
Catalog(s) available, free

Linhoff Photo & Digital Imaging
4400 France Ave S, Edina, MN 55410
Tel: 952-927-7333
E-mail: info@linhoff.com
Web Site: linhoff.com
Key Personnel
Owner: John Linhoff
Founded: 1954
Photo prints, film services, custom photo products, photo restoration, digital archiving, large format printing, film & video to DVD, DVD duplication, studio portraits.
Catalog(s) available
Membership(s): The Imaging Alliance; Minnesota Commercial Industrial Photographers Association

Link Electronics Inc
2360 N High St, Suite 10, Jackson, MO 63755
Tel: 573-334-4433 *Toll Free Tel:* 800-776-4411 *Fax:* 573-204-4554
E-mail: sales@linkelectronics.com
Web Site: www.linkelectronics.com
Key Personnel
Founder: Jim Timberlake
Pres: David Kendall
Founded: 1989
Electronic products manufacturer.
Catalog(s) available
Membership(s): NAB

Linkabit
Division of L-3 Technologies Inc
9890 Towne Centre Dr, San Diego, CA 92121
Tel: 858-552-9500 *Toll Free Tel:* 800-331-9401
E-mail: linkabitproducts@l3t.com
Web Site: www2.l-3com.com/linkabit
Founded: 1968
Video exploitation & management systems. Reconfigurable video/image processing technologies.
Branch Office(s)
1200 S Woody Burke Dr, Melbourne, FL 32901
Tel: 321-727-0660
613 Global Way, Linthicum Heights, MD 21090
One Federal St, Camden, NJ 08103
Membership(s): AFCEA

Linker Systems Inc
13612 Onkayha Circle, Irvine, CA 92620
Tel: 949-552-1904 *Toll Free Tel:* 800-315-1174
Web Site: linkersystems.com
Key Personnel
Owner & Pres: Toni Poper
VP & CTO: Sheldon Linker *E-mail:* sol@linker.com
Manufacture animation systems & special effects generators. Custom software developer & consultant.
Online catalog(s) available

Lion & Fox Recording Studios
9517 Baltimore Ave, College Park, MD 20740
Tel: 301-982-4431
E-mail: mail@lionfox.com
Web Site: www.lionfox.com
Key Personnel
Gen Mgr, Prodr & Engr: Greg Hartman *E-mail:* greg@lionfox.com
Prodr & Engr: Rob Buhrman *E-mail:* rob.buhrman@lionfox.com; Jim Fox
Mastering Engr: Mike Caplan *E-mail:* mike@lionfox.com
Founded: 1979
Post-production recording studio. Edit, mix, master, voice-over, ADR, surround sound mixing.
Membership(s): AES; The Recording Academy

Lions Gate Entertainment Corp
2700 Colorado Ave, Santa Monica, CA 90404
Tel: 310-449-9200 *Fax:* 310-255-3870
E-mail: generalinquiries@lionsgate.com
Web Site: www.lionsgate.com; corporate.lionsgate.com
Key Personnel
SVP, Investor Rel & Exec Communs: Peter Wilkes *Tel:* 310-255-3998
Motion picture production & distribution, television programming & syndication, home entertainment, family entertainment, digital distribution, new channel platforms & international distribution & sales.
Membership(s): Entertainment Merchants Association

Lippincott Williams & Wilkins
Unit of Wolters Kluwer Health
Two Commerce Sq, 2001 Market St, Philadelphia, PA 19103
Tel: 215-521-8300; 301-223-2300 (cust serv)
Toll Free Tel: 800-638-3030 (cust serv)
Fax: 215-521-8902
Web Site: www.lww.com
Founded: 1998
Catalog(s) available
Branch Office(s)
351 W Camden St, Baltimore, MD 21201
Tel: 410-528-4000
Foreign Office(s): Wolters Kluwer/Lippincott Williams & Wilkins Pty Ltd, 101 Waterloo Rd, Level 2, North Ryde, NSW 2113, Australia *Tel:* (02) 9857 1313 *Fax:* (02) 9857 1304
Lippincott Williams & Wilkins Asia Ltd, 15F W Sq, 314-324 Hennessy Rd, Wan Chai, Hong Kong *Tel:* 2610 7000 *Fax:* 2610 7098

Lipsner-Smith Co
Subsidiary of Research Technology International (RTI)
4700 Chase Ave, Lincolnwood, IL 60712-1689
Tel: 847-677-3000 *Toll Free Tel:* 800-323-7520 *Fax:* 847-677-1311 *Toll Free Fax:* 800-784-6733
E-mail: sales@lipsner.com; sales@rtico.com
Web Site: www.lipsner.com; lipsner-smith.com
Key Personnel
Pres, RTI Film Group: Jonathan A Banks
Sales & Ad: Sherwin Berger
Founded: 1958
Film cleaning systems, negative & print laboratory equipment.
Catalog(s) available
Membership(s): AECT; AIIM; ALA; Audiovisual and Integrated Experience Association; British Kinematograph Sound & Television Society; Consortium of College & University Media Centers; ICVM; NAB; National Association of Media & Technology Centers; SMPTE®

A Liss & Co
51-55 59 Place, Woodside, NY 11377-7408
Tel: 718-728-0600 *Toll Free Tel:* 800-221-0938 *Fax:* 718-728-1227
E-mail: sales@alissco.com
Web Site: alissco.com
Key Personnel
Pres: Jeffery Liss
Founded: 1936
Materials handling company.
Online catalog(s) available

Listen & Live Audio Inc
1700 Manhattan Ave, Union City, NJ 07068
Tel: 201-558-9000 *Toll Free Tel:* 800-653-9400 (orders) *Fax:* 201-558-9800
Web Site: www.listenandlive.com
Key Personnel
Pres: Alfred C Martino *E-mail:* alfred@listenandlive.com
Publr: Alisa S Weberman
Founded: 1993
Publish audiobooks in all genres.

Listen Technologies Corp
14912 Heritage Crest Way, Bluffdale, UT 84065-4818
Tel: 801-233-8992 *Toll Free Tel:* 800-330-0891
Fax: 801-233-8995
E-mail: info@listentech.com
Web Site: www.listentech.com
Key Personnel
Chmn, Pres & CEO: Russell Gentner
Assistive listening solutions to bring clear, focused & personalized audio to performance venues & public spaces. Audio over WiFi systems to enrich video wall environments.

Listening Library
Division of Penguin Random House Audio Publishing
1745 Broadway, New York, NY 10019
Tel: 212-782-9000 *Toll Free Tel:* 800-733-3000 (cust serv)
E-mail: audio@penguinrandomhouse.com
Web Site: www.penguinrandomhouseaudio.com/kids-and-teens
Founded: 1955
Unabridged audiobooks for children & young adults.
Catalog(s) available
Membership(s): American Booksellers for Children

LITE-IT Grip Truck Rentals
450 Saint Andrews Ct, West Chicago, IL 60185
Tel: 630-231-1671 *Fax:* 630-231-1672
E-mail: liteit1@sbcglobal.net
Web Site: www.liteit1.com
Key Personnel
Owner: Tom Scott *Tel:* 630-292-1671 (cell)
Founded: 1980
Lighting & grip rentals. Grip Trix camera cart rentals.

Little Big Bang Design Inc
33 Moya Loop, Santa Fe, NM 87508
Tel: 786-218-0713
E-mail: hello@littlebigbangstudios.com
Web Site: www.littlebigbangdesign.com
Specialize in motion graphics & animation.

Little Mammoth Media
Division of VanDerKloot Film & Television Inc
750 Ralph McGill Blvd NE, Atlanta, GA 30312
Toll Free Tel: 800-KIDVIDEO (543-8433)
E-mail: bv@vanderkloot.com; service@littlemammoth.com
Web Site: littlemammoth.com
Children's educational videos.
Online catalog(s) available

Littlite LLC
Division of CAE Inc
PO Box 430, Hamburg, MI 48139-0430
Tel: 810-852-4242 *Fax:* 810-231-1631
E-mail: sales@littlite.com
Web Site: www.littlite.com
Key Personnel
Pres: James H Fackert *E-mail:* jfackert@littlite.com
Ad Dir: Barbara Burns *Tel:* 810-852-4242 ext 214
E-mail: bburns@littlite.com
Spec Prods Mgr: Donn Deniston *Tel:* 810-852-4242 ext 212 *E-mail:* ddeniston@littlite.com
Manufacture LED task lamps & accessories.
Catalog(s) available
Membership(s): NAMM, the National Association of Music Merchants; NSCA; Professional Lighting & Sound Association; USITT

Liturgy Training Publications
Division of Archdiocese of Chicago
3949 S Racine Ave, Chicago, IL 60609-2523

Tel: 773-579-4900 *Toll Free Tel:* 800-933-1800 (orders) *Fax:* 773-579-4929
E-mail: orders@ltp.org; info@ltp.org
Web Site: www.ltp.org
Key Personnel
Acting Dir: Deanna M Keefe *Tel:* 773-579-4900 ext 3570
HR Mgr & Facilities Admin: Brian Wells *Tel:* 775-579-4900 ext 3533
Mktg & Sales Mgr: Kathleen Sommers Garcia *Tel:* 773-579-4900 ext 3535
E-mail: ksommers@ltp.org
Prodn Mgr: Jeanne Troxel *Tel:* 773-579-4900 ext 3555
Religious education programs.
Catalog(s) available
Membership(s): Association of Catholic Publishers Inc

Live Oak Media
PO Box 652, Pine Plains, NY 12567
Toll Free Tel: 800-788-1121 *Toll Free Fax:* 866-398-1070
E-mail: info@liveoakmedia.com
Web Site: www.liveoakmedia.com
Key Personnel
Owner & Pres: Arnold M Cardillo
Owner & Publr: Debra Cardillo
Produce audiobooks.
Catalog(s) available
Membership(s): ALA; Audio Publishers Association

Live Spark Inc
700 Raymond Ave, Suite 100, St Paul, MN 55114
Tel: 651-289-7375
E-mail: info@live-spark.com
Web Site: www.live-spark.com
Key Personnel
CEO: Daniel Yaman
Live event design, custom interactive games, Ani-Mates (real-time computer-generated characters that can interact live with presenters & attendees).

Live Wire Media
2355 Westwood Blvd, No 312, Los Angeles, CA 90064
Tel: 415-564-9500 *Toll Free Tel:* 800-359-KIDS (359-5437) *Fax:* 415-552-4087
E-mail: sales@livewiremedia.com
Web Site: www.livewiremedia.com
Key Personnel
Co-Founder: David Elkind; Freddy Sweet, PhD
Character education videos for grades K-12.
Online catalog(s) available

Live'N'Loud
PO Box 557, Mena, AR 71953
Tel: 479-216-6727
Web Site: nahteboy.tripod.com
Key Personnel
Owner, Dir, Ed & Writer: Ethan Nahte
E-mail: nahteboy@livenloud.net
Founded: 1992
Production/post-production services for broadcast & internal use. Provide voice-over talent & actors. Produce press kits, writing talent, web design & photography.

LKG Industries Inc
3660 Publishers Dr, Rockford, IL 61109
Tel: 815-874-2301 *Toll Free Tel:* 800-645-2262
Fax: 815-874-2896 *Toll Free Fax:* 800-554-0795
E-mail: sales-lkgindustries@t6b.com
Web Site: www.philmore-datak.com
Key Personnel
Pres: Katheryn Granath
Admin Asst: Gail Wheaton
Manufacturer of electronic products.

Catalog(s) available
Online catalog(s) available

C V Lloyde
702 W Killarney St, Urbana, IL 61801
Tel: 217-352-7031 *Toll Free Tel:* 800-779-7031
E-mail: sales@cvlloyde.com
Web Site: www.cvlloyde.com
Key Personnel
Pres: Stephen Morris
Catalog(s) available
Membership(s): Audiovisual and Integrated Experience Association; NAMM, the National Association of Music Merchants; NSCA

LM Cases/LM Engineering Inc
2720 Intertech Dr, Youngstown, OH 44509
Tel: 330-270-2400 *Toll Free Tel:* 800-874-8326
Fax: 330-270-2424
E-mail: info@lmcases.com
Web Site: www.lmcases.com
Key Personnel
CEO: William La Guardia
Pres & CFO: Jo Ann La Guardia
E-mail: jlaguard@lmengineering.com
Founded: 1985
Custom case manufacturer.
Online catalog(s) available

Location Camera Ltd
300 Pennsylvania Ave, Oreland, PA 19075
Tel: 215-576-5600 *Fax:* 215-576-6022
E-mail: mail@locationcamera.com
Web Site: www.locationcamera.com
Key Personnel
Owner & Pres: Brad Shapiro
Owner & VP: Tom Greco
Founded: 1998
Rental of cameras & accessories including Canon C300 MII & 5D.

The Location Connection Inc
1600 Rosecrans Ave, Manhattan Beach, CA 90266
Tel: 310-376-9797
E-mail: lconnect@aol.com
Web Site: www.locationconnection.com
Key Personnel
Pres & Creator: Darian Mathias *Tel:* 818-422-8127 (cell)
Founded: 1991
Offer privately owned mansions & unique homes for film shoots, weddings & other special events.

Location Lighting Ltd
300 Pennsylvania Ave, Oreland, PA 19075
Tel: 215-576-5600 *Fax:* 215-576-6022
E-mail: mail@locationlighting.com; rentals@locationlighting.com
Web Site: www.locationlighting.com
Key Personnel
Owner & Pres: Brad Shapiro *Tel:* 215-353-0543
E-mail: brad@locationlighting.com
Rental Mgr: Allison Ruff *Tel:* 215-200-5083
Founded: 1998
Lighting & grip equipment rental & sales for film & video production. Dealer for many leading manufacturers.

Location Sound Corp
10639 Riverside Dr, North Hollywood, CA 91602
Tel: 818-980-9891 *Toll Free Tel:* 800-228-4429
Fax: 818-980-9911; 818-980-7932 (rentals)
E-mail: information@locationsound.com
Web Site: www.locationsound.com
Key Personnel
Sales Mgr: Steve Joachim *Tel:* 818-980-9891 ext 302
Rental Mgr: Robert Noone *Tel:* 818-980-9891 ext 315 *E-mail:* rnoone@locationsound.com
Founded: 1977

Pro audio equipment sales, rental & service.
Membership(s): AES; NAB; SMPTE®

Location 05 Studios
450 W 31 St, 7th fl, New York, NY 10001
Tel: 212-219-2144
E-mail: info@location05.com
Web Site: location05.com
Founded: 1991
Photo studio, location rental & meeting venue.
Provides photography needs for film & video
production & provides event space.

Loft 19
21618 N Ninth Ave, Suite A, Phoenix, AZ 85027
Tel: 623-434-3791 *Fax:* 623-434-5003
E-mail: info@loft19.com
Web Site: loft19.com
Key Personnel
Owner: Floyd Bannister
Founded: 2003
Sound studios equipped with lights & grip for
film & video production.

Logan Productions Inc
8035 N Port Washington Rd, Milwaukee, WI
53217
Tel: 414-352-9691 *Fax:* 414-352-4993
E-mail: info@loganproductions.com
Web Site: www.loganproductions.com
Key Personnel
CEO: Beth Logan *E-mail:* beth@
loganproductions.com
Pres: Jim Logan
Busn Mgr: Jenny Schubert *E-mail:* jenny@
loganproductions.com
Founded: 1978
Full service rentals, live events, multilingual web
broadcasting, video production company.

Logitech
7700 Gateway Blvd, Newark, CA 94560
Tel: 510-795-8500 *Toll Free Tel:* 866-291-1505
Web Site: www.logitech.com
Key Personnel
Chmn of the Bd: Guerrino De Luca
Pres & CEO: Bracken Darrell
CFO: Vincent Pilette
SVP, Consumer Computing Platforms Busn
Group: Marcel Stolk
SVP, Worldwide Opers: L Joseph Sullivan
Founded: 1981
Catalog(s) available
Branch Office(s)
Logitech Audio Group, 4700 NW Camas Mead-
ows Dr, Camas, WA 98607 *Tel:* 360-817-1200
(busn off)
Foreign Office(s): Logitech Europe SA, EPFL-
Quartier de l'Innovation, Daniel Borel Innova-
tion Ctr, 1015 Lausanne, Switzerland *Tel:* (021)
863 55 11 *Fax:* (021) 863 55 12

Logitek Electronic Systems Inc
5622 Edgemoor Dr, Houston, TX 77081
Tel: 713-664-4470 *Toll Free Tel:* 800-231-
5870 (sales); 877-231-5870 (tech support)
Fax: 713-664-4479
E-mail: northamericansales@logitekaudio.com
Web Site: www.logitekaudio.com
Key Personnel
Pres: Tag Borland
VP: Susan Borland
Sales Dir: Frank Grundstein
Founded: 1979
Manufacture digital audio equipment, audio
routers & consoles.
Online catalog(s) available
Membership(s): AES; NAB

Loma Scientific International (LSI)
Subsidiary of JP Associates Inc

3115 Kashiwa St, Torrance, CA 90505
Tel: 310-539-8655 *Fax:* 310-539-8634
E-mail: info@lomasci.com; sales@lomasci.com
Web Site: www.lomasci.com
Key Personnel
Founder, Pres & Sales Mgr: Patrick Loughboro
VP, Engg & Opers: Jeff Loughboro
Founded: 1957
Broadband wireless access MMDS transmitter
manufacturer & systems company.
Online catalog(s) available
Membership(s): NAB

Long Island University Media Arts Dept
One University Plaza, Brooklyn, NY 11201-8423
Tel: 718-488-1052 *Fax:* 718-780-4578
E-mail: mediart@brooklyn.liu.edu
Web Site: www.liu.edu/brooklyn.aspx
Key Personnel
Dept Chmn: Larry Banks *Tel:* 718-488-1343
E-mail: larry.banks@liu.edu
Academic media department.

Long Island Video Enterprises Live Inc
110 Pratt Oval, Glen Cove, NY 11542
Tel: 516-759-5483 *Fax:* 516-671-5874
E-mail: info@longislandvideo.com
Web Site: www.longislandvideo.com
Key Personnel
Pres: Peter L Warzer
VP, Sales: Lori Di Giacomo
Founded: 1982
Video & audio sales, rentals, design & installation
services.
Flyer(s) available
Membership(s): Audiovisual and Integrated Expe-
rience Association; Long Island Association

Long-Term Success Publishing
766 Ninth Ave N, Suite 1, Fort Dodge, IA 50501
Tel: 515-571-8880
E-mail: judypayne@judypayne.com
Web Site: judypayne.com
Key Personnel
Owner: Judy Payne *E-mail:* judypayne@mchsi.
com
Online catalog(s) available

Loopmedia Inc
26 Duncan St, Toronto, ON M5V 2B9, Canada
Tel: 416-595-6496
E-mail: info@loopmedia.com
Web Site: loopmedia.com
Key Personnel
VP: William Morassutti *E-mail:* william@
loopmedia.com
Founded: 1995
Animation, live action, design & commercial
production studio specializing in end-to-end
brand solutions for all platforms geared to-
wards broadcasters, advertising agencies &
entertainment companies.

Los Angeles Center Studios
450 S Bixel St, Los Angeles, CA 90017
Mailing Address: 1201 W Fifth St, Suite T-110,
Los Angeles, CA 90017
Tel: 213-534-3000
E-mail: productionservices@lacenterstudios.com
Web Site: lacenterstudios.com
Key Personnel
Pres: Sam Nicassio *E-mail:* snicassio@
lacenterstudios.com
Dir, Mktg: Dolly Wyatt *Tel:* 213-534-2334
E-mail: dwyatt@lacenterstudios.com
Prodn Servs Mgr: Bobby Hunt *Tel:* 213-534-2370
E-mail: bhunt@lacenterstudios.com
Full service studio for TV, film & commercial
production.

Los Angeles Post Music Inc
4340 E Kentucky Ave, Suite 308, Glendale, CO
80246
Tel: 310-896-5176
Web Site: www.lapostmusic.com
Key Personnel
Agent: Vel Lewis *E-mail:* hammondjammin@aol.
com
Founded: 1995
Nationally & internationally recognized music
provider. Production music & original composi-
tion.

The Lot (Skye Partners)
1041 N Formosa Ave, West Hollywood, CA
90046
Tel: 323-850-3180 *Fax:* 323-850-3189
E-mail: info@thelotstudios.com; stages@
thelotstudios.com
Web Site: www.thelotstudios.com
Key Personnel
Dir, Stage Opers: Tricia Bodak-Smith *Tel:* 323-
850-3184
Full service studio for TV, film & commercial
production. Soundstage & equipment rentals.

LOUD Technologies Inc
16220 Wood-Red Rd NE, Woodinville, WA
98072
Tel: 425-487-4333; 415-892-6500
Toll Free Tel: 866-858-LTEC (858-5832)
Fax: 425-487-4337
Web Site: www.mackie.com; www.loudtechinc.
com
Key Personnel
Chmn of the Bd & CEO: Mark Graham
CFO: Case Kuehn
Professional audio & music products.
Catalog(s) available
Branch Office(s)
One Main St, Whitinsville, MA 01588 *Tel:* 508-
234-6158 *Fax:* 508-234-8251
560 Johnson St, Suite 320, Victoria, BC V8W
3C6, Canada *Tel:* 425-892-6500 *Fax:* 250-382-
7737
Foreign Office(s): 8 Eu Tong Sen St, No 14-93,
The Central, Singapore 059818, Singapore
Loud Technologies PLC, Cressex Business
Park, Unit 2, Century Point, Halifax Rd, High
Wycombe, Bucks HP12 3SL, United Kingdom
Tel: (01494) 557398 *Fax:* (01494) 557396

**Louisiana State University Division of Strategic
Communications**
Video Services Dept, 3960 W Lakeshore Dr, Ba-
ton Rouge, LA 70808
Tel: 225-578-8654 *Fax:* 225-578-3860
E-mail: stratcomm@lsu.edu
Web Site: www.lsu.edu/stratcomm/resources/
video-services.php
Media services to support the LSU community.
Services provided are: video production, ra-
dio production, on-hold message production,
LSU YouTube channel management, radio in-
terviews, television broadcast uplink facility,
archival footage storage-University beauty
shots, third-party video & radio production
contract review/approval.

James Loupas Associates Inc
134 Carrington Dr, Coppell, TX 75019
Tel: 972-304-0455
Web Site: jimloupas.com
Key Personnel
Pres: James Loupas *E-mail:* jim@jimloupas.com
Founded: 1976
Audio & technology consulting - psychoacoustic
services.

Love Shack Recording Studios
Division of EMG LLC
909 18 Ave S, Nashville, TN 37212
Tel: 615-843-0019

E-mail: book@loveshackstudios.com
Web Site: loveshackstudios.com
Key Personnel
CEO & COO: Andrew Kautz
Contact: Doug Rich; Chris Rowe
Editing, broadcast production, music/recording
studio.

Lowell Manufacturing
100 Integram Dr, Pacific, MO 63069-3476
Tel: 636-257-3400 *Toll Free Tel:* 800-325-9660
Fax: 636-257-6606 *Toll Free Fax:* 888-456-
9355
E-mail: sales@lowellmfg.com
Web Site: www.lowellmfg.com
Key Personnel
Pres & CEO: John Lowell
Eastern Sales Mgr: Jeff Garstick
E-mail: jgarstick@lowellmfg.com
Founded: 1947
Designs & manufactures audio, rack & power
products for professional systems integration.

Lowing Light & Grip Inc
1500 Whiting St SW, Wyoming, MI 49509-1056
Tel: 616-530-7440 *Toll Free Tel:* 888-530-7440
Fax: 616-249-8947
Web Site: www.lowinglight.com
Key Personnel
Owner & Pres: David R Lowing *E-mail:* dave@
lowinglight.com
Founded: 1985
Grip, electric, camera support, staff, gear & ex-
pendables for the filmed entertainment industry.
Online catalog(s) available
Membership(s): International Alliance of Theatri-
cal Stage Employees

Lowrance Sound Co Inc
2132 Nailling Dr, Union City, TN 38261
Tel: 731-885-4504 *Toll Free Tel:* 800-852-5418
E-mail: info@lowrancesoundcompany.com
Web Site: www.lowrancesoundcompany.com
Key Personnel
Pres: Mark Lowrance *E-mail:* mark@
lowrancesoundcompany.com
Founded: 1975
AV design, sales & installation.
Membership(s): Audiovisual and Integrated Expe-
rience Association; NSCA

Loyal Studios
3513 W Pacific Ave, Burbank, CA 91505
Tel: 818-845-5123 (studio); 818-399-9499
Web Site: www.loyalstudios.tv
Key Personnel
Prodr: Bob Bekian *E-mail:* bob@loyalstudios.tv
Studio with control room & edit bay. Specialize
in greenscreen commercials, interviews & web
content.

LT Sound Inc
7980 LT Pkwy, Lithonia, GA 30058
Tel: 770-482-4836
Web Site: www.ltsound.com
Key Personnel
Pres: Lacy Thompson, Jr *E-mail:* lacy@ltsound.
com
Founded: 1976
Distribute audio-digital signal processing & pro-
fessional audio equipment.
Online catalog(s) available

L3Harris Technologies Inc
1025 W NASA Blvd, Melbourne, FL 32919
E-mail: info@l3harris.com
Web Site: www.l3harris.com
Key Personnel
Dir, Global PR: Jim Burke *Tel:* 321-727-9131
E-mail: jim.burke@l3harris.com
Founded: 1995

Global aerospace & defense technology innovator.
Provides advanced defense & commercial technologies across air, land, sea, space & cyber
domains.

LTM Corp of America
25520 Ave Stanford, Valencia, CA 91355
Tel: 818-780-9828 *Toll Free Tel:* 800-762-4291
E-mail: info@ltmlighting.us
Key Personnel
EVP: Richard Espinoza *E-mail:* richarde@ltm-
lighting.com
Founded: 1976
Broad selection of HML lights.
Catalog(s) available
Membership(s): American Society of Cinematog-
raphers; NAB; SMPTE®

Lubbock Audio Visual Inc
2120 Ave "Q", Lubbock, TX 79405
Mailing Address: PO Box 1935, Lubbock, TX
79408-1935
Tel: 806-744-2559 *Toll Free Tel:* 800-850-2559
Fax: 806-747-6939
E-mail: sales@lav.com
Web Site: www.lav.com
Key Personnel
Pres: Stan Wagnon *E-mail:* swagnon@lav.com
Founded: 1978
Authorized for over 300 manufacturers of pro-
fessional video, audio & telecommunications
products.
Catalog(s) available
Branch Office(s)
2505 Lakeview Dr, Suite 209, Amarillo, TX
79109, Acct Mgr: Dennis Smith *Tel:* 806-358-
0795 *Fax:* 806-351-2800
1030 Andrews Hwy, Suite 202, Midland, TX
79701 *Tel:* 432-218-9829 *Fax:* 432-218-9830
Membership(s): Audiovisual and Integrated Experience Association; NSCA; Professional Systems Network International; Texas Association
of Broadcasters; Western Texas Association of
General Contractors

Lubell Labs Inc
21 N Stanwood Rd, Columbus, OH 43209
Tel: 614-235-6740
E-mail: lubell_labs@wowway.com
Web Site: www.lubell.com
Key Personnel
Pres: Alan H Lubell
Speaker manufacturer.

David Lubman Acoustics, see DL Acoustics

Ludlow Media
Division of Brevidia
15501 San Pablo Ave, Suite G-320, San Pablo,
CA 94806
Tel: 415-927-1300
E-mail: info@ludlowmedia.com
Web Site: www.ludlowmedia.com
Key Personnel
Founder & Sr Prodr: Rhys Ludlow *E-mail:* rhys@
ludlowmedia.com
Content Ed & Prodr: Alec Oyung *E-mail:* alec@
ludlowmedia.com
Founded: 1997

Lumalaser
84777 Charlottes Way, Eugene, OR 97405
Tel: 541-687-1414 *Toll Free Tel:* 800-606-2597
Fax: 541-687-1438
E-mail: info@lumalaser.com
Web Site: www.lumalaser.com
Key Personnel
Pres: Tim Ziegerbein *E-mail:* tim@lumalaser.com
Proj Mgr: Nicole Poisson
Quality laser projectors.
Catalog(s) available

Lumedyne Inc
6010 Wall St, Port Richey, FL 34668
Tel: 727-847-2777; 727-847-5394
Toll Free Tel: 800-586-3396 *Fax:* 727-841-0000
E-mail: info@lumedyne.com; sales@lumedyne.
com; service@lumedyne.com
Web Site: www.lumedyne.com
Key Personnel
Sales Mgr: D J La Dez *E-mail:* dj@lumedyne.
com
Founded: 1972
Manufacture & distribute portable flash equip-
ment for photographers.
Catalog(s) available

Lumeni Productions Inc
1632 Flower St, Glendale, CA 91201
Tel: 818-956-2200 *Fax:* 818-956-3298
E-mail: info@lumeni.com
Web Site: www.lumeni.com
Key Personnel
Pres & Creative Dir: Tony Valdez
VP & Chief Tech Dir: Gilbert Yablon
Catalog(s) available
Sample(s) available

Luminaud Inc
8688 Tyler Blvd, Mentor, OH 44060
Tel: 440-255-9082 *Toll Free Tel:* 800-255-3408
Fax: 440-255-2250
E-mail: info@luminaud.com
Web Site: www.luminaud.com
Key Personnel
Pres: Thomas Lennox
Founded: 1972
Manufacture & distribute battery powered,
portable systems.
Catalog(s) available

Luminys Systems Corp
11961 Sherman Rd, North Hollywood, CA 91605
Tel: 818-827-3941 *Toll Free Tel:* 800-321-3644
E-mail: info@luminyscorp.com
Web Site: www.luminyscorp.com
Key Personnel
Chmn & CTO: David Pringle *E-mail:* dpringle@
luminyscorp.com
Premier provider of lighting fixtures.
Catalog(s) available

Lumisphere™ USA
9429 Everett Ct, Spotsylvania, VA 22553
Tel: 540-582-7897 *Fax:* 540-582-5233
Web Site: www.lumisphereusa.com
Key Personnel
Pres: John Bernard *E-mail:* jrbent@rcn.com
Low-voltage festoon lighting.
Online catalog(s) available

G T Luscombe Co Inc
106 Kansas St, Frankfort, IL 60423
Mailing Address: PO Box 722, Frankfort, IL
60423-0722
Tel: 815-469-2478 *Toll Free Tel:* 800-435-7855
Fax: 815-469-5429 *Toll Free Fax:* 888-469-
5429
E-mail: info@gtluscombe.com
Web Site: www.gtluscombe.com
Key Personnel
Founder: George Luscombe
Pres & CEO: John Luscombe *E-mail:* john@
gtluscombe.com
Founded: 1974
AV wholesale distribution.
Catalog(s) available
Membership(s): Evangelical Christian Publishers
Association

Luxor
Subsidiary of EBSCO Industries
2245 Delany Rd, Waukegan, IL 60087

Tel: 847-244-1800 *Toll Free Tel:* 800-323-4656
Fax: 847-244-1818 *Toll Free Fax:* 800-327-
1698
E-mail: info@luxorfurn.com; customerservice@
luxorfurn.com; sales@luxorfurn.com
Web Site: www.luxorfurn.com
Key Personnel
Div Gen Mgr: Steve Hill *Tel:* 847-244-1800 ext
128 *E-mail:* shill@luxorfurn.com
Founded: 1946
Design & distribution of specialty carts & fur-
niture for offices, schools, libraries & more.
Products include mobile equipment tables,
computer workstations, video production cen-
ters, LCD mounting systems, presentation
easels, overhead projector tables & AV storage
cabinets.
Online catalog(s) available
Membership(s): Audiovisual and Integrated Expe-
rience Association; Education Market Association; Material Handling Industry of America;
NSCA

LuXout Stage Curtains
Division of The Specialty Group Ltd
1221 Admiral St, Richmond, VA 23220
Tel: 804-264-3000; 804-264-3700
Toll Free Tel: 800-817-1204
Toll Free Fax: 888-227-8064
E-mail: luxoutinfo@luxout.com
Web Site: www.luxout.com
Key Personnel
Pres: Tony Lovette
VP, Sales: Ned Dunford
Founded: 1948
Manufacturer of staging products; stage curtains,
TV studio curtains & photo backdrop curtains.
Catalog(s) available

Luzerne County Community College
1333 S Prospect St, Nanticoke, PA 18634-3899
Tel: 570-740-0200 *Toll Free Tel:* 800-377-5222
Fax: 570-740-0250
Web Site: www.luzerne.edu/index.jsp
Key Personnel
HR: Kim Hogan *Tel:* 800-377-5222 ext 7363
E-mail: khogan@luzerne.edu
Distance Educ/Off Campus Coord: Ann Saxton
Tel: 800-377-5222 ext 7393 *E-mail:* asaxton@
luzerne.edu
Founded: 1967
Online educational programs.
Online catalog(s) available

Lylofilm Productions
Division of Graphissimo Entertainment
503 Beech St, New Hyde Park, NY 11040
Tel: 516-587-0567
E-mail: lylofilm@gmail.com
Web Site: www.lylofilm.com; www.graphissimo.
com
Key Personnel
Owner & Dir: Simona Lyriti *E-mail:* simona@
graphissimo.com
Prodr: Stanley Lozowski *E-mail:* stanley@
graphissimo.com
Founded: 2001
Production for film, animation, motion graphic
design & publishing.

Lynch Communications
525 Loma Vista Terr, Pacifica, CA 94044
Tel: 678-939-1212 *Fax:* 480-287-9401
Web Site: www.lynchcommunications.com
Key Personnel
Pres: Paul Lynch *E-mail:* paul@
lynchcommunications.com
Founded: 1980
Multimedia & live event technical production.
Membership(s): MPI

Lynx Broadband
12219 Wood Lake Dr, Burnsville, MN 55337
Tel: 952-894-9590 *Fax:* 952-894-9380
E-mail: info@lynxbroadband.com
Web Site: www.lynxbroadband.com
Key Personnel
Natl Sales & Mktg Mgr: Ray Fugitt
Founded: 1967
Manufacture products that distribute television
(RF) on Cat 6 cable.

Lynx Studio Technology Inc
190 McCormick Ave, Costa Mesa, CA 92626-
3307
Tel: 714-545-4700 *Fax:* 714-545-4777
E-mail: sales@lynxstudio.com
Web Site: www.lynxstudio.com
Founded: 1998
Manufacture high-end audio PCI cards & convert-
ers.
Online catalog(s) available
Branch Office(s)
PCI Express, 2900 Government Way, Suite 42,
Coeur d'Alene, ID 83815-3751

Lyon Video Inc
2091 Arlingate Lane, Columbus, OH 43228
Tel: 614-297-0001
E-mail: info@lyonvideo.com
Web Site: www.lyonvideo.com
Key Personnel
COO: Chad Snyder
Pres: Chad Snyder *E-mail:* chad@lyonvideo.com
Opers Mgr: Stacia Fritchie
Founded: 1986
Mobile television production facilities, full ser-
vice video & film production, post-production
& DVD authoring.

Lyon Workspace Products LLC
420 N Main St, Montgomery, IL 60538
Mailing Address: PO Box 671, Aurora, IL 60507-
0671
Tel: 630-892-8941 *Toll Free Tel:* 800-433-8488
Fax: 630-892-8966 *Toll Free Fax:* 800-367-
6681
E-mail: lyon@lyonworkspace.com
Web Site: www.lyonworkspace.com
Key Personnel
Dir, Mktg: Bryce Hiner
Founded: 1901
Storage solutions company.
Catalog(s) available
Online catalog(s) available

LYRASIS
1438 W Peachtree NW, Suite 150, Atlanta, GA
30309
Mailing Address: PO Box 116179, Atlanta, GA
30368
Tel: 404-892-0943 *Toll Free Tel:* 800-999-8558
Fax: 404-892-7879
Web Site: www.lyrasis.org
Key Personnel
CEO: Robert Miller
CFO: Vern Ritter
Founded: 2009
Membership association for libraries formed by
the merger of PALINET, SOLINET & NE-
LINET.

Lyrichord, see Multicultural Media Inc

Lyrichord/Multicultural Media
27 Main St, Suite 6, Montpelier, VT 05602
Tel: 802-839-0371
E-mail: info@lyrichord.com
Web Site: www.lyrichord.com
Key Personnel
Pres: Stephen McArthur *E-mail:* stephen@
multiculturalmedia.com

Founded: 1950
Producers of CDs & DVDs of classical, early &
world music.
Online catalog(s) available

M-Audio
Subsidiary of inMusic Brands Inc
2000 Scenic View Dr, Cumberland, RI 02864
Tel: 401-658-5765 (support)
E-mail: info@m-audio.com
Web Site: m-audio.com
Founded: 1988
Music & computer interface & studio integration
solutions, keyboard & controller products &
essential musical hardware.
Online catalog(s) available
Membership(s): NAMM, the National Association
of Music Merchants

M Works Mastering Studio
60 Hampshire St, Cambridge, MA 02139
Tel: 617-577-0089
E-mail: studio@m-works.com; info@m-works.
com
Web Site: www.m-works.com
Key Personnel
Pres & Chief Engr: Jonathan Wyner
Engr: Nick Dragoni
Mastering services, restoration, location record-
ing, duplication, DVD audio authoring & en-
coding.
Membership(s): AES

MAC Group
75 Virginia Rd, North White Plains, NY 10603
Tel: 914-347-3300 *Fax:* 914-347-3309
E-mail: info@macgroupus.com
Web Site: www.macgroupus.com
Key Personnel
Chief Mktg, Inspiration & Elation Offr:
Alan Shapiro *Tel:* 914-347-3300 ext 264
E-mail: alans@macgroupus.com
VP, Sales: Barry Burstein *Tel:* 914-643-2033
E-mail: barryb@macgroupus.com
Exec Prodr & Creative Dir: Ab Sesay *Tel:* 914-
347-3300 ext 664 *E-mail:* abs@macgroupus.
com
Dir, Mktg Servs: Sara Roberts *Tel:* 914-347-3300
ext 668 *E-mail:* sarar@macgroupus.com
Digital Mktg & Media Specialist: Colleen
Carlisle-Nicholas *Tel:* 914-347-3300 ext 678
E-mail: colleenc@macgroupus.com
Sales & marketing company supplying profes-
sional photographers, filmmakers, educators &
students with the world's finest image-making
tools.
Represent the following photo & video brands:
4V, Benro, Elinchrom, Gepe, Heliopan, Il-
ford, Induro, Kaiser, Kupo, Light & Motion,
MeFOTO, Novoflex, PhotoVideoEDU, Phottix,
Rotatrim, Sekonic, Tenba, Toyo-View, Vu.

MAC Production Group
3500 Aloma Ave, Winter Park, FL 32792
Tel: 407-234-8898 *Fax:* 407-671-5360
E-mail: info@macproav.com
Web Site: macproav.com
Audio, lighting, video, design, pre- & post-
production services for event presentation
needs.

MacGillivray Freeman Films Inc
PO Box 205, Laguna Beach, CA 92652-0205
Tel: 949-494-1055 *Fax:* 949-494-2079
E-mail: info@macfreefilms.com
Web Site: www.macfreefilms.com
High resolution digital cinema source.
Shipping Address: 2470 S Coast Hwy, Unit F,
Laguna Beach, CA 92651

Mach 1 Productions
1101 N Himes Ave, Tampa, FL 33607

Tel: 813-873-7700 *Fax:* 813-875-6633
E-mail: info@mach1pro.com
Web Site: www.mach1pro.com
Key Personnel
Pres: Darren Howard
Gen Mgr: Dan Mockensturm
Audio recording & production, sound design, music composition, scoring, arranging, audio post & mix-to-picture in stereo or multiple surround formats.

Mackenzie Laboratories Inc
1163 Nicole Ct, Glendora, CA 91740
Tel: 909-394-9007 *Fax:* 909-394-9411
E-mail: info@macklabs.com
Web Site: www.macklabs.com
Key Personnel
Pres: Nagy Khattar
Natl Sales Mgr: Joe Vitale *E-mail:* jvitale@macklabs.com
Founded: 1954
Manufacture digital audio messaging equipment. Applications served include Message-On-Hold, Storecasting, Overhead Paging, Public Address Announcement, Exhibit/Kiosk Announcements, Intercom & transit communications.
Catalog(s) available
Membership(s): AES; APTA; National Fire Protection Association; NSCA

Macmillan Audio
Division of Macmillan
120 Broadway, 22nd fl, New York, NY 10271
Tel: 646-600-7856; 646-307-5472
Toll Free Tel: 888-330-8477; 800-221-7945 *Toll Free Fax:* 800-672-7703 (orders)
E-mail: macmillan.audio@macmillanusa.com
Web Site: www.macmillanaudio.com
Key Personnel
Pres & Publr: Mary Beth Roche
E-mail: marybeth.roche@macmillan.com
Pres, Sales Div: Alison Lazarus
Assoc Publr: Robert Allen
Dir, Prodn: Laura Wilson
Assoc Mktg Mgr: Emily Dyer
Prodr: Becky Celestina; Tom Mis
Ad Opers Specialist: Michelle Margulis
Founded: 1987
Publisher of audiobooks of general interest in fiction & nonfiction for adults & children. Produce digital downloads.
Catalog(s) available, 3 times/yr
Membership(s): Audio Publishers Association

Macrosystem US Inc
4282 Arnie Rd, Blaine, WA 98230
Tel: 360-371-4942 *Toll Free Tel:* 877-554-2846
Toll Free Fax: 855-269-6999
E-mail: info@macrosystem.us
Web Site: www.macrosystem.us
Key Personnel
Owner: Gary McNally *E-mail:* gary@macrosystem.us
Founded: 1990
Design, manufacture & distribute stand-alone digital video editors & HDV storage devices & security products.

Madison Square Garden
Division of MSG Sports & Entertainment LLC
2 Pennsylvania Plaza, New York, NY 10121-0091
Tel: 212-465-6741
E-mail: msgnetpr@msgnetwork.com
Web Site: www.thegarden.com; themadisonsquaregardencompany.com
Key Personnel
Exec Chmn: James L Dolan
VChmn: Gregg Seibert
Pres & CEO: David O'Connor
CIO: David Michael
EVP & Chief Admin Offr: Sandra Kapell
EVP & Chief Communs Offr: Barry Watkins

EVP & CFO: Donna M Coleman
EVP & Chief Mktg Offr: Sharon Otterman
EVP, Gen Coun & Secy: Lawrence Burian
EVP, Mktg Parnerships: Ron Skotarczak
EVP, Marquee Events & Opers: Joel Fisher
EVP, MSG Productions: Colin Ingram
EVP, MSG Sports: Jordan Solomon
Live sports & entertainment production.

Madisound Speaker Components Inc
8608 University Green, Suite 10, Middleton, WI 53562
Tel: 608-831-3433 *Toll Free Tel:* 866-883-1488 (orders) *Fax:* 608-831-3771
E-mail: info@madisound.com
Web Site: www.madisound.com
Key Personnel
Mgr: Brian Kane
Founded: 1972
Provide loudspeaker parts to manufacturers, audio customers & autosound installers.

Madonna University Information Technology
36600 Schoolcraft Rd, Livonia, MI 48150-1173
Tel: 734-432-5800 *Toll Free Tel:* 800-852-4951
Web Site: www.madonna.edu
Key Personnel
TV Opers & Prodn Mgr: Sue Boyd *Tel:* 734-432-5578 *E-mail:* sboyd@madonna.edu
Systs Engr: Dan Boyd *Tel:* 734-432-5575
E-mail: dboyd@madonna.edu
Membership(s): NATAS; SMPTE®

Magic Gadgets™
12986 Mapleleaf Ct NE, Aurora, OR 97002-8418
Tel: 503-678-6236; 818-655-5465 (rentals)
E-mail: info@magicgadgets.com
Web Site: www.magicgadgets.com
Key Personnel
Contact: David Martin Del Campo
Online catalog(s) available

Magic Teleprompting Inc
1390 Waller St, San Francisco, CA 94117
Tel: 415-626-5283 *Toll Free Tel:* 800-646-6244
Fax: 415-626-2762
E-mail: info@magicscroll.com; sales@magicscroll.com
Web Site: www.magicscroll.com
Key Personnel
Founder & CEO: Japji Khalsa
Founded: 1989
Teleprompting service company.

Magick Lantern
750 Ralph McGill Blvd, Atlanta, GA 30312
Tel: 404-688-3348 *Fax:* 404-584-5247
E-mail: info@magicklantern.com
Web Site: magicklantern.com
Key Personnel
CEO: Chris Fogg
VP & Creative Dir: Jim Bowhann *E-mail:* jim@magicklantern.com
Stage Mgr: Joe Spenneberg *E-mail:* joe@magicklantern.com
Founded: 1990
Video production & post-production services, including editorial, design, motion graphics, audio, Blu-ray authoring & studio services.

Magna-Tech Electronic Co Inc
1998 NE 150 St, North Miami, FL 33181
Tel: 305-573-7339 *Fax:* 305-573-8101
E-mail: sales@iceco.com; digital@myiceco.com
Web Site: www.magna-tech.com
Key Personnel
Founder & Pres: Steven H Krams
VP, 21st Century Cinemas: Barney L Kaufman
Founded: 1975

Online catalog(s) available
Membership(s): Audiovisual and Integrated Experience Association; NAB; SMPTE®

Magna Visual Inc
9400 Watson Rd, St Louis, MO 63126-1596
Tel: 314-843-9000 *Toll Free Tel:* 800-843-3399
Fax: 314-843-0000
E-mail: magna@magnavisual.com
Web Site: www.magnavisual.com
Key Personnel
VP, Sales & Mktg: Frank Venturella
Founded: 1961
Manufacture white boards & magnetic accessories.
Catalog(s) available, free, annual

Magnanimous Media
600 W Cermak, Chicago, IL 60616
Tel: 312-465-2366
E-mail: rentals@magnanimous.biz
Web Site: www.magnanimous.biz
Offers professional HD video production assistance. Rents cameras, accessories & equipment.

Magnepan Inc
1645 Ninth St, White Bear Lake, MN 55110
Tel: 651-426-1645 *Toll Free Tel:* 800-474-1646
Fax: 651-426-0441
Web Site: www.magnepan.com
Key Personnel
Pres: Mark Winey
Mktg Mgr: Wendell Diller
Founded: 1969
Speaker manufacturer.
Online catalog(s) available

Magnet Sales & Manufacturing Inc
Division of The Integrated Technologies Corp
11248 Playa Ct, Culver City, CA 90230
Tel: 310-391-7213 *Toll Free Tel:* 800-421-6692
Fax: 310-391-7463
E-mail: info@magnetsales.com
Web Site: www.magnetsales.com; www.magnetshop.com
Key Personnel
Pres: Anil Nanji
Founded: 1955
Engineering assistance, stock & custom magnets & complete magnetic sub-assemblies in prototype to production quantities.
Online catalog(s) available

Magnetek Inc
N49 W13650 Campbell Dr, Menomonee Falls, WI 53051
Tel: 262-783-3500 *Toll Free Tel:* 800-288-8178
Toll Free Fax: 800-298-3503
E-mail: sales@magnetek.com
Web Site: www.magnetek.com
Key Personnel
Pres & CEO: Peter M McCormick
VP & CFO: Marty J Schwenner
Dir, Communs: Lynn Bostrom *Tel:* 262-252-2903
E-mail: lbostrom@magnetek.com
Founded: 1984
Manufacture digital power & motion control systems.
Online catalog(s) available

Magnetic Music Publishing Co
155 W 68 St, Suite 22-D, New York, NY 10023-5834
Tel: 212-255-8527 *Fax:* 212-595-2067
E-mail: info@magneticmusic.ws
Web Site: magneticmusic.ws
Key Personnel
Composer & Prodr: Reynold Weidenaar *Tel:* 212-769-1514
Music producer.
Catalog(s) available

Magnetic Post Production
4 Marshall Rd, Wappingers Falls, NY 12590-4105
Tel: 212-598-3000
Web Site: www.magneticimage.com
Key Personnel
Owner & Ed: Harry Douglas *E-mail:* harry@magneticimage.com
Founded: 1990
Production & post-production services.

Magnetic Reference Laboratory Inc
165 Wyandotte Dr, San Jose, CA 95123
Tel: 408-227-8631 *Fax:* 408-227-8631
E-mail: mrltapes@comcast.net
Web Site: www.mrltapes.com
Key Personnel
Pres: Jay McKnight
Founded: 1972
Manufacture & sell open reel calibration tapes for analog audio tape recorders.
Online catalog(s) available
Membership(s): AES

Magnetic Shield Corp
740 N Thomas Dr, Bensenville, IL 60106
Tel: 630-766-7800 *Toll Free Tel:* 888-766-7800
Fax: 630-766-2813
E-mail: shields@magnetic-shield.com
Web Site: www.magnetic-shield.com
Key Personnel
Chief Engr: Don Lammersfeld
E-mail: dlammersfeld@magnetic-shield.com
Busn Devt Mgr: Brad Friestedt
E-mail: bfriestedt@magnetic-shield.com
Eastern Regl Mgr: Terrence Lannon
E-mail: tlannon@magnetic-shield.com
Western Regl Mgr: Robert Dasso
E-mail: rdasso@magnetic-shield.com
Founded: 1941
Manufacture magnetic shielding products & materials used in electrical/electronic wiring applications.
Catalog(s) available

Magnicon Media/Image d'Or
5050 Williamson St, Dearborn, MI 48126
Tel: 313-846-8694; 313-574-3546 (cell)
Key Personnel
Tech Prodr: Peter Herb *E-mail:* peterpahl8@gmail.com
Founded: 1983
Field production services, film/video, camera & lighting equipment & crew services, AV technician services.

Magno Sound & Video, see Magno Sound Inc

Magno Sound Inc
729 Seventh Ave, New York, NY 10019
Tel: 212-302-2505 *Fax:* 212-819-1282
E-mail: staff@magnosound.com
Web Site: magnoscreening.com
Key Personnel
EVP: David Friedman
Founded: 1950
Full service production company. Television & film post-production & screening theaters.

MAGNUM Companies Ltd
205 Armour Dr NE, Atlanta, GA 30324
Tel: 404-872-0553 *Toll Free Tel:* 800-255-1774
Fax: 404-875-5629
E-mail: rent@magnumco.com; design@magnumco.com; production@magnumco.com; buy@magnumco.com
Web Site: www.magnumco.com
Key Personnel
Pres & Gen Mgr: Todd Finch *E-mail:* tfinch@magnumco.com

Mktg Mgr: Jake Ellwood *E-mail:* jellwood@magnumco.com
Founded: 1980
Lighting design & technical production company.
Online catalog(s) available
Membership(s): International Live Events Association; MPI; Professional Lighting & Sound Association

Magnum Towers Inc
9370 Elder Creek Rd, Sacramento, CA 95829
Tel: 916-381-5053 *Fax:* 916-381-2144
E-mail: office@magnumtowers.com
Web Site: www.magnumtowers.com
Key Personnel
Pres: Ronald Kardokus
Off Mgr: Lori Morris
Tower manufacturer for broadcast, microwave, cellular, railroad, wind & other industries.

Mailing Avenue Stageworks
1144 Mailing Ave, Atlanta, GA 30315
Tel: 404-601-9500 (ext 11)
Web Site: www.mailingavenuestageworks.com
Key Personnel
Owner: Tyler Edgarton; John Raulet *Tel:* 404-353-1118 (cell) *E-mail:* john@raulet.com; Paul Raulet
Motion picture & television production facility.

Main Point Productions
295 Lobachsville Rd, Oley, PA 19547
Tel: 610-987-9320; 610-987-9163
E-mail: mainpoint301@gmail.com
Web Site: www.mainpoint.com
Key Personnel
Writer & Prodr: William Stanton
E-mail: wrstanton3@gmail.com
Full service production company.

Main Street Media Inc
185 Pier Ave, Suite 105, Santa Monica, CA 90405
Tel: 310-450-1846
E-mail: info@mainstreetmediainc.com
Web Site: www.mainstreetmediainc.com
Key Personnel
Owner & CEO: Robert Newell *E-mail:* robn60@gmail.com
Owner & Pres: Christopher Blakely
E-mail: chris@mainstreetmediainc.com
Founded: 1982
Motion picture production, services & equipment.

Maine Imaging
PO Box 753, Wiscasset, ME 04578
Tel: 207-380-6343
Web Site: www.maineimaging.com
Key Personnel
Owner: Dave Cleaveland *E-mail:* dave@maineimaging.com
Full service custom aerial photography in Maine & New England.

MainSail Production Services Inc
521 Byers Rd, Suite 109, Miamisburg, OH 45342
Tel: 937-866-7800 *Toll Free Tel:* 800-877-0093
Fax: 937-866-8088
E-mail: discover@mainsailproductions.com
Web Site: www.mainsailproductions.com
Key Personnel
Pres: Mark D Morgan
Video production services.

Maison de Soul Records
Subsidiary of Flat Town Music Co
PO Drawer 10, Ville Platte, LA 70586-0010
Tel: 337-363-2177 *Toll Free Tel:* 800-738-8668
Fax: 337-363-2094
E-mail: info@flattownmusic.com; info@floydsrecordshop.com

Web Site: www.flattownmusic.com
Key Personnel
Founder & Pres: Floyd Soileau
VP: Chris Soileau
Online catalog(s) available

Major Media Inc
PO Box 209, Deerfield, IL 60015
Tel: 847-433-1682
E-mail: dmchistory@aol.com
Web Site: www.major-media.com
Key Personnel
Pres: Jay Steinberg *E-mail:* jay@major-media.com
Duplication services.
Brochure(s) available

Major Media Productions Inc
PO Box 209, Deerfield, IL 60015
Tel: 847-433-1682
E-mail: dmchistory@aol.com
Web Site: www.major-media.com
Key Personnel
Pres: Jay Steinberg *E-mail:* jay@major-media.com
Production services.

Major Reproductions Equipment Co
PO Box 209, Deerfield, IL 60015
Tel: 847-433-1682
E-mail: dmchistory@aol.com
Web Site: www.major-media.com
Key Personnel
Pres: Jay Steinberg *E-mail:* jay@major-media.com
Audio & video equipment & supplies.

Majortech Inc
8464 Ninth Line RR-1, Norval, ON L0P 1K0, Canada
Tel: 905-873-0778 *Fax:* 905-873-1244
Key Personnel
Pres: Ken Stelmakowich *Tel:* 905-873-0778 ext 24 *E-mail:* kens@majortech.com
Sales Mgr, Broadcast: Mike Sandwell *Tel:* 905-873-0778 ext 28 *E-mail:* michaels@majortech.com
Broadcast, production & post-production, system design, consultation & installation.
Membership(s): SMPTE®; WABE

MakeMusic® Inc
7007 Winchester Circle, Suite 140, Boulder, CO 80301
Tel: 952-937-9611 *Toll Free Tel:* 800-843-2066 (cust serv) *Fax:* 720-465-6419
Web Site: www.makemusic.com
Key Personnel
CEO: Gear Fisher
Music software for notation & performance.

Mamiya
Division of MAC Group
75 Virginia Rd, Suite 1, North White Plains, NY 10603
Tel: 914-347-3300 *Fax:* 914-347-3309
E-mail: info@mamiya-usa.com
Web Site: www.mamiyaleaf.com
Key Personnel
Pres, MAC Group: Mr Jan Lederman
Medium format cameras & lenses.

Mammoth HD
PO Box 2064, Evergreen, CO 80437
Tel: 303-670-7973
E-mail: mammothhd@me.com; info@mammothhd.com
Web Site: www.mammothhd.com
Key Personnel
Creative Dir & CEO: Clark Dunbar
E-mail: clark@mammothhd.com
Gen Mgr: Andy Klingelhoefer

Original HD & RED stock footage, 3D animation & motion graphics for broadcast film, advertising, corporate, educational videos & digital screen signage/display.
Membership(s): Global Society for Asset Management; Hollywood Professional Association; NAB

Manchester Music Library Inc
6857 Colton Blvd, Oakland, CA 94611
Tel: 413-369-4331
Web Site: www.manchestermusiclibrary.com
Key Personnel
Pres: John Manchester
   E-mail: johnkmanchester@gmail.com
Founded: 1994
Catalog(s) available
Membership(s): ASCAP

Manfrotto Distribution Inc
Subsidiary of Vitec Group
10 Mountainview Rd, Suite 320 S, Upper Saddle River, NJ 07458
Tel: 201-818-9500
E-mail: info@manfrottodistribution.us
Web Site: www.manfrottodistribution.us; www.manfrotto.us
Design, manufacture & marketing of camera & lighting support equipment for the professional photographic, film, theater, live entertainment & video markets.
Online catalog(s) available

Manhattan Center Studios Inc
311 W 34 St, New York, NY 10001
Tel: 212-279-7740 *Fax:* 212-564-1072
E-mail: info@mcstudios.com
Web Site: www.mcstudios.com
Key Personnel
EVP: Marcus Karr
Gen Coun: Peter D Ross *Tel:* 212-279-7740 ext 300
Dir, Audio & Television: Obie O'Brien *Tel:* 212-695-6600 ext 212 *E-mail:* oobrien@mcstudios.com
Dir, Video Engg & Opers: Marvin Williams *Tel:* 212-695-6600 ext 312 *E-mail:* marvin@mcstudios.com
Sales & Mktg: Crystal Longo *Tel:* 212-279-7740 ext 219 *E-mail:* crystal@mcstudios.com
Founded: 1986
Full service production & post-production facility.
Brochure(s) available

Manhattan Production Music Inc
Division of Chesky Productions Inc
1650 Broadway, Suite 900, New York, NY 10019
Tel: 212-333-5766 *Fax:* 212-262-0814
E-mail: info@mpmmusic.com
Web Site: www.mpmmusic.com
Key Personnel
Pres: Norman Chesky
VP, Mktg & Sales: Ron Goldberg
Catalog(s) available, free

Maniac Productions
3888 Viewpoint Way, Lafayette, CO 80026
Tel: 303-661-0920
E-mail: mpcl@aol.com; info@maniacproductions.com
Web Site: maniacproductions.com
Key Personnel
Founder: Mani Boniek *E-mail:* mani@maniacproductions.com; Patrisha Boniek *E-mail:* patrisha@maniacproductions.com
Complete service AV production company.

Maniglia Media LLC
7925 Jones Branch Dr, Suite LL-110, Tysons, VA 22102
Tel: 703-283-8532 (cell); 703-942-8011 (studio)

Web Site: www.manigliamedia.com
Key Personnel
Pres & CEO: Frank Maniglia, Jr *E-mail:* frank@manigliamedia.com
Media production services including 4K, 2K & HD digital media.
Brochure(s) available
Price list(s) available

Manios Digital & Film
Division of Ste-Man Inc
10663 Burbank Blvd, North Hollywood, CA 91601
Tel: 818-760-8290 *Toll Free Tel:* 800-845-6619
   Fax: 818-760-8805
E-mail: sales@maniosdigital.com
Web Site: www.maniosdigital.com
Key Personnel
Pres: Steven Manios, Jr *E-mail:* steve@maniosdigital.com
Natl Sales Mgr: David Butler *E-mail:* david@maniosdigital.com
Founded: 1991
Camera equipment.

Manitoba Film & Music
410-93 Lombard Ave, Suite 410, Winnipeg, MB R3B 3B1, Canada
Tel: 204-947-2040 *Fax:* 204-956-5261
E-mail: info@mbfilmmusic.ca
Web Site: www.mbfilmmusic.ca
Key Personnel
CEO & Film Commissioner: Carole Vivier *E-mail:* carole@mbfilmmusic.ca
Commns & Mktg Dir: Ginny Collins *Tel:* 204-947-2040 ext 16 *E-mail:* ginny@mbfilmmusic.ca
Mgr, Fin & Opers: Kevin Gabriel *Tel:* 204-947-2040 ext 15 *E-mail:* kevin@mbfilmmusic.ca
Founded: 1998
Provincial funding agency & film commission. Produce & market film, television, video & music recording projects.
Membership(s): Association of Film Commissioners International

Manley Laboratories Inc
13880 Magnolia Ave, Chino, CA 91710
Tel: 909-627-4256 *Fax:* 909-628-2482
Web Site: www.manley.com
Key Personnel
Owner & Pres: EveAnna Manley
   E-mail: emanley@manleylabs.com
Founded: 1993
Manufacturer of professional audio equipment.
Online catalog(s) available
Membership(s): NAMM, the National Association of Music Merchants

Manning Productions
115 N Morgan St, Chicago, IL 60607
Tel: 312-756-1100 *Fax:* 312-756-1200
E-mail: info@manningproductions.com
Web Site: www.manningproductions.com
Key Personnel
Pres & Exec Prodr: Douglas Manning
VP: Char Manning
Founded: 1985
Web site design & development; iPad development.
Membership(s): DGA

Map Resources
50 S Union St, Lambertville, NJ 08530
Mailing Address: PO Box 334, Lambertville, NJ 08530
Tel: 609-397-1611 *Toll Free Tel:* 800-334-4291
   Fax: 609-751-9378
E-mail: info@mapresources.com; sales@mapresources.com
Web Site: www.mapresources.com

Key Personnel
Mktg Dir: Barbara Fordyce
Founded: 1984
Maps for graphic design applications.

MAPS Production House
212 Collins Ave, Miami Beach, FL 33139
Tel: 305-532-7880; 786-245-2491 (equip rentals)
   Fax: 305-532-7673
E-mail: info@mapsproduction.com; equipment@mapsproduction.com
Web Site: mapsproduction.com
Founded: 1991
Studios available for photo shoots, film & commercial shoots as well as private events. Equipment rental.
Branch Office(s)
350 NW 24 St, Wynwood, FL 33127 (backlot-events & photo shoots)

MarathonNorco Aerospace Inc
8301 Imperial Dr, Waco, TX 76712-6588
Tel: 254-776-0650 *Fax:* 254-776-6558
E-mail: marathon@mptc.com
Web Site: www.mnaerospace.com
Key Personnel
CEO: Sergio Rodriguez *Tel:* 254-776-0650 ext 409
Busn Unit Mgr, Power Prods: Graham Cook *Tel:* 254-741-5437 *E-mail:* gcook@mptc.com
Founded: 2003
Aircraft batteries, Christie chargers & mechanical products.
Catalog(s) available
Membership(s): NAB; SMPTE®

Marblemedia
74 Fraser Ave, Suite 100, Toronto, ON M6K 3E1, Canada
Tel: 416-646-2711
E-mail: connect@marblemedia.com
Web Site: www.marblemedia.com
Key Personnel
Co-CEO & Exec Prodr: Mark Bishop; Matt Hornburg
Exec Asst: Kerri Grasser
Founded: 1998
Television, film & new media production. Specialize children's, music, documentary, drama & new media production.
Membership(s): Academy of Canadian Cinema & Television; Canadian Film & Television Production Association

March Manufacturing Inc
1819 Pickwick Ave, Glenview, IL 60026
Tel: 847-729-5300 *Fax:* 847-729-7062
E-mail: sales@marchpump.com
Web Site: www.marchpump.com
Key Personnel
Mktg Mgr: Otto Zimmermann *Tel:* 847-729-5300 ext 40 *E-mail:* ozimmermann@marchpump.com
Founded: 1954
Online catalog(s) available

March of Dimes Foundation
1275 Mamaroneck Ave, White Plains, NY 10605
Tel: 914-997-4488 *Toll Free Tel:* 888-663-4637
Web Site: www.marchofdimes.org/video
Key Personnel
Pres: Stacey Stewart
Founded: 1939
Educational video producer & distributor.
Online catalog(s) available

Marco Inc
451 Carson Rd N, Birmingham, AL 35215
Tel: 205-856-1110 *Toll Free Tel:* 888-465-2514
   Fax: 205-856-1136
E-mail: marco@marcoconsoles.com
Web Site: www.marcoconsoles.com

Key Personnel
Pres: John Matthews *E-mail:* john@
marcoconsoles.com
Founded: 1973
Technical furniture design & manufacturer.
Online catalog(s) available

Mardi Gras Costume Shop
5895 N Granite Reef Rd, Scottsdale, AZ 85250
Tel: 480-948-4030 *Fax:* 480-948-0754
E-mail: info@mardigrascostumeshop.com
Web Site: mardigrascostumeshop.com
Key Personnel
Owner: Oscar Gibson
Founded: 1974
Sales & rentals.
Membership(s): National Costumers Association

Marengo Films
27206 Waterfall Hill Pkwy, Spicewood, TX 78669
Tel: 972-365-0406 *Fax:* 830-693-0949
E-mail: cosgray@outlook.com
Web Site: www.marengofilms.com
Key Personnel
Pres: Craig Cosgray
Founded: 1996
Manufacture & distribute movies on DVD to retail markets.
Catalog(s) available, $9.98

Marinco Electrical Group
N85 W12545 Westbrook Crossing, Menomonee Falls, WI 53051-3330
Tel: 262-293-0600
E-mail: marincopowerprod.sales@powerprodllc.com
Web Site: www.marincopowerproducts.com
Key Personnel
Gen Mgr: John Nethery
Electrical components for the marine, mobile & industrial markets including battery chargers, inverters, power distribution & circuit protection. Brands include Ancor, BEP, Blue Sea Systems, Guest, Marinco, Marinco Power Products, Mastervolt, Park Power, Promariner & Progressive Industries.
Catalog(s) available

Maritime Mobile Communications LLC, see Digital Video Systems

Mark Custom Recording Service Inc
10815 Bodine Rd, Clarence, NY 14031-2252
Mailing Address: PO Box 406, Clarence, NY 14031-0406
Tel: 716-759-2600 *Fax:* 716-759-2329
E-mail: info@markcustom.com
Web Site: www.markcustom.com
Key Personnel
Owner & Pres: Mark J Morette
Owner: Cecilia M Morette
Founded: 1962
Online catalog(s) available
Membership(s): American Band Masters Association; American School Band Directors Association; Association of Concert Bands ; Florida Music Educators Association; Grammy Foundation; Illinois Music Educators Association; Kentucky Music Educators Association; NBA; New York State Band Directors Association; New York State School Music Association; Texas Bandmasters Association; Texas Choral Directors Association; Texas Music Educators Association; Women Band Directors International

Mark Sonder Productions & Entertainment Agency
2479 Freezeland Rd, Linden, VA 22642
Tel: 540-636-1640

E-mail: inquiry@marksonderproductions.com
Web Site: mspentertainmentagency.com
Key Personnel
CEO: Mark Sonder *E-mail:* msonder@
marksonderproductions.com
Founded: 1985
Complete entertainment packages to corporations, associations, facilities, casinos, concerts & special events worldwide.
Membership(s): American Independent Business Alliance; Association of Entertainment Professionals Worldwide; IFEA; International Association of Venue Managers; International Entertainment Buyers Association; International Institute for Sustainable Tourism; Meeting Professionals International; North Carolina Presenters Consortium

Mark X Productions Inc
300 E 40 St, New York, NY 10016
Key Personnel
Pres: Mark Druck
Founded: 1969

Markertek Video Supply
Division of Tower Products Inc
One Tower Dr, Saugerties, NY 12477
Mailing Address: PO Box 397, Saugerties, NY 12477-0397
Tel: 845-246-3036 *Toll Free Tel:* 800-522-2025
Fax: 845-246-1757
E-mail: sales@markertek.com
Web Site: www.markertek.com
Key Personnel
Natl Sales Mgr: Wesley Brewer *E-mail:* wesley@markertek.com
Broadcast AV supply company.
Catalog(s) available
Online catalog(s) available
Membership(s): AES; NAB; NSCA; SBE

The Market Place
PO Box 4126, Rockford, IL 61110-0626
Tel: 815-877-1514
Web Site: www.maxbooks.9k.com
Key Personnel
Pres: Max Anderson *E-mail:* mander8813@aol.com
Children's programming.

Marketec
Division of Rack Innovations Inc
419 S Flower St, Burbank, CA 91502
Tel: 818-847-0200 *Toll Free Tel:* 800-557-8861
Toll Free Fax: 888-262-1726
E-mail: info@marketec.com
Web Site: www.marketec.com
Key Personnel
Pres: Penny Russell
Founded: 1998
AV chairs. Distributor of technical furniture & electronics.

Marketron Broadcast Solutions
101 Empty Saddle Trail, Hailey, ID 83333
Tel: 208-788-6800 *Toll Free Tel:* 800-476-7226
Fax: 208-788-6273
E-mail: sales@marketron.com
Web Site: www.marketron.com
Key Personnel
CEO: Jim Howard
CFO: Matt Wellner
SVP, Prod: Jimshade Chaudhari
SVP, Engg: Mike Jackson
SVP, Sales: Todd Kalman
SVP, Client Servs: Jeff London
Founded: 1969
Broadcast & radio software solutions.
Branch Office(s)
508 S Seventh St, Opelika, AL 36801-4910

2935 Larimer St, Denver, CO 80205
Membership(s): NAB; National Religious Broadcasters; SBE

Marlboro Productions
1076 Moss Hollow Rd, Marlboro, VT 05344
Tel: 802-257-0743
E-mail: mfilmpro@sover.net
Web Site: marlboroproductions.com
Key Personnel
Owner & Pres: Alan Dater
Video production services.

Marsand Inc
6100 S IH-35W, Alvarado, TX 76009
Mailing Address: PO Box 485, Alvarado, TX 76009-0485
Tel: 817-783-5566 *Fax:* 817-783-5577
Web Site: www.marsand.com
Key Personnel
Pres: Matthew A Sanderford, Jr
E-mail: tvcowboy@marsand.com
VP: David Sanderford *E-mail:* david@marsand.com
Broadcasting engineering consulting firm.
Membership(s): AFCCE; IEEE; NAB; PBE; SBE; Texas Association of Broadcasters

Marsh Media
200 Avila Circle, Kansas City, MO 64114
Mailing Address: PO Box 8082, Shawnee Mission, KS 66208-0082
Tel: 816-523-1059 *Toll Free Tel:* 800-821-3303
Fax: 816-333-7421 *Toll Free Fax:* 866-333-7421
E-mail: info@marshmedia.com
Web Site: www.marshmedia.com
Key Personnel
VP: Dan Witcher
Mgr: Brenna Witcher
Founded: 1969
Specialize in the production & distribution of health education programs primarily sold to schools, health departments, etc throughout the US.
Catalog(s) available, free, annual
Membership(s): The Imaging Alliance

Marshad Technology Group
99 Hudson St, 5th fl, New York, NY 10013
Tel: 917-209-3467
E-mail: info@marshad.com
Web Site: www.marshad.com
Key Personnel
Founder & Pres: Neal Marshad
Providers of proprietary & third party software.

Marshall Electronics Inc
20608 Madrona Ave, Torrance, CA 90503
Tel: 310-333-0606 *Toll Free Tel:* 800-800-6608
Fax: 310-333-0688
E-mail: support@marshall-usa.com
Web Site: www.mars-cam.com; www.marshall-usa.com
Key Personnel
Opers: David Quinlan
Manufacturer of broadcast & professional AV multimedia products.
Catalog(s) available, by request
Online catalog(s) available
Membership(s): AES; NAB

Marshall Furniture Inc
999 Anita Ave, Antioch, IL 60002
Tel: 847-395-9350 *Fax:* 847-395-9351
E-mail: sales@marshallfurniture.com
Web Site: www.marshallfurniture.com
Key Personnel
Pres: Colleen Maatta
Mng Partner, Sales & Mktg: Michelle Wille
Founded: 1986

Custom multimedia lecterns, workstations & conference tables, collaboration & video conferencing tables, ADA furniture, rack cabinets & credenzas, monitor carts & cabinets, kiosks, digital signage & confidence monitor furniture.
Catalog(s) available
Online catalog(s) available, PDF download
Membership(s): Architectural Woodworking Institute; Audiovisual and Integrated Experience Association

Martel Electronics Sales Inc
Yorba Linda Hills Business Park, 23221 E La Palma Ave, Yorba Linda, CA 92887
Tel: 714-692-6690 *Toll Free Tel:* 800-553-5536 *Fax:* 714-692-1835 *Toll Free Fax:* 800-553-6954
Web Site: www.martelelectronics.com
Key Personnel
Pres: Ron Smith
Founded: 1957
Dictation & recording company.
Online catalog(s) available

C F Martin & Co Inc, see The Martin Guitar Co

The Martin Guitar Co
510 Sycamore St, Nazareth, PA 18064
Mailing Address: PO Box 329, Nazareth, PA 18064-0329
Tel: 610-759-2837 *Toll Free Tel:* 800-633-2060; 888-433-9177 *Fax:* 610-759-5757
Web Site: www.martinguitar.com
Key Personnel
Chmn & CEO: Christian Frederick Martin, IV
VP, HR: Debra Karlowitch
Founded: 1833
Producer of acoustic instruments & recording equipment.
Catalog(s) available

Martin Professional Inc
Division of Harman Professional Solutions
3300 Corporate Ave, Suite 108, Weston, FL 33331
Tel: 954-858-1800 *Toll Free Tel:* 888-832-4180 *Fax:* 954-858-1811
E-mail: support@martinpro.com
Web Site: www.martin.com
Lighting company.
Online catalog(s) available
Branch Office(s)
1718 W Mishawaka Rd, Elkhart, IN 46517
Sales Office(s): 3001 San Fernando Blvd, Burbank, CA 91504 *Toll Free Tel:* 888-287-4776
Membership(s): Illuminating Engineering Society; Professional Lighting & Sound Association; USITT

Martinsound Inc
1151 W Valley Blvd, Alhambra, CA 91803
Tel: 626-281-3555 *Toll Free Tel:* 800-582-3555 *Fax:* 626-284-3092
E-mail: info@martinsound.com
Web Site: www.martinsound.com
Key Personnel
Pres: Joe Martinson
Founded: 1980
Audio equipment manufacturers.
Catalog(s) available
Membership(s): AES; NAMM, the National Association of Music Merchants

Marvel Photo Inc
1720 N Sheridan Rd, Tulsa, OK 74115
Tel: 918-836-0741 *Toll Free Tel:* 800-806-3616 *Fax:* 918-836-0949
Key Personnel
CEO: Anthony Perrault

Manufacturer of identification equipment.
Catalog(s) available

Marvell Semiconductor Inc
Division of Marvell Technology Group Ltd
5488 Marvell Lane, Santa Clara, CA 95054
Tel: 408-222-2500 *Toll Free Tel:* 855-MARVELL (627-8355) *Fax:* 408-988-8279
E-mail: info@marvell.com
Web Site: www.marvell.com
Key Personnel
Pres & CEO: Matt Murphy
Founded: 1995
Online catalog(s) available
Branch Office(s)
30 Enterprise, Suite 200, Aliso Viejo, CA 92656 *Tel:* 949-614-7700
890 Glenn Dr, Folsom, CA 95630 *Tel:* 916-605-3700
1750 E Northrop Blvd, Suite 100, Chandler, AZ 85286 *Tel:* 480-612-8700
1921 Corporate Center Circle, Suite 3-A, Longmont, CO 80501 *Tel:* 303-651-5800 *Fax:* 303-684-9248
6074 N Discovery Way, Boise, ID 83713
700 Commerce Dr, 5th fl, Oak Brook, IL 60523 *Tel:* 630-341-4023
293 Boston Post Rd W, Suite 120, Marlborough, MA 01752 *Tel:* 508-573-3292
7825 Washington Ave S, Suite 720, Bloomington, MN 55439 *Tel:* 952-852-4000
4238 SW Research Way, Corvallis, OR 97333 *Tel:* 541-768-3800 *Fax:* 541-768-3855
20333 State Hwy 249, Suite 200, Houston, TX 77070 *Tel:* 281-378-1536
10545 Willows Rd NE, Suite 100, Redmond, WA 98052
Foreign Office(s): Marvell Technology Group Ltd, Canon's Ct, 22 Victoria St, Hamilton HM 12, Bermuda *Tel:* (441) 296-6395 *Fax:* (441) 295-3328 (corp headquarters)
Marvell Technology (Beijing) Ltd, Unit 407, Vision International Ctr, Tsinghua Science Park Bldg 9, No 1, Zhongguancun E Rd, Haidian District, Beijing 100084, China *Tel:* (010) 8215 1511 *Fax:* (010) 8215 1121 *E-mail:* sunw@marvell.com
Marvell Technology (Beijing) Ltd, 26F, Bldg C, Tianhui Mansion, No 569 Huizhou Ave, Hefei 230001, China
Marvell Technology (Nanjing) Ltd, 4th fl, 28 Ningshuang Rd, Yuhuatai District, Nanjing, China
Marvell Technology (Shanghai) Ltd, 4F, Bldg 2, 399 Keyuan Rd, Pudong District, Shanghai 201203, China *Tel:* (021) 6109 2800 *Fax:* (021) 5080 9769
Marvell Technology (Beijing) Ltd, Bldg 4, 399 Keyuan Rd, Pudong District, Shanghai 201203, China
Marvell Technology (Beijing) Ltd, 2nd fl, Block 1, China Merchants Tower, No 1166 Wanghai Rd, She Kou Nan Shan District, Shenzhen 518057, China *Tel:* (0755) 21629408
Marvell Technology (Chengdu) Ltd, Fl 25, Bldg 10, Area C, Tianfu Software Park, Chengdu Hi-Tech Industrial Devt Zone, No 219 Tianhua Second St, Sichuan Province 610041, China
Marvell Tehnology Denmark ApS, Agern Alle 24, 2970 Horsholm, Denmark
Marvell UK, 15, Ave de Norvege, BP 116, 91140 Villebon-sur-Yvette, France *Tel:* 01 60 92 41 41 *Fax:* 01 69 29 09 19
Marvell Semiconductor Germany GmbH, Siemenstr 23, 76275 Ettlingen, Germany *Tel:* (07243) 502 100 *Fax:* (07243) 502 593
Marvell Hong Kong Ltd, Units 89 & 91, 10th fl, Kowloonbay Intl Trade & Exhibition Ctr, One Trademart Dr, Kowloon Bay, Hong Kong *Tel:* 2628 3216 *Fax:* 2628 3215
Marvell India Pvt Ltd, RMZ Ecoworld, 3rd fl, East Wing, Bldg 8A, Marathahalli, Sarjapur

Outer Ring Rd, Bangalore, Karnataka 560 103, India *Tel:* (080) 4664-6000
Marvell India Pvt Ltd, Pioneer Towers, 6th fl, Software Units Layout No 16, Madhapur, Hyderabad 500 081, India *Tel:* (040) 6612-6900 *Fax:* (040) 6612-6901
Marvell India Pvt Ltd, Muttha Towers, 1st fl, Don Bosco Marg (off Airport Rd), Pune 411 006, India *Tel:* (020) 4013-0000 *Fax:* (020) 4013-0101
PT Marvell Technology Indonesia, Pondok Indah Off Tower 3, 5th fl, Suite 503, Jl Sultan Iskandar Muda Kav V-TA, Pondok Pinang, Kebayoran Lama, Jakarta 12310, Indonesia
Marvell Israel (MISL) Ltd, 94 Em Hamoshavot way, Azorim Park, PO Box 10097, 49527 Petah Tikva, Israel *Tel:* (04) 909-1500 *Fax:* (03) 970-4999
Marvell Israel (MISL) Ltd, Mordot HaCarmel Industrial Park, 6 Hamada St, 20692 Yokneam, Israel *Tel:* (04) 909-1500 *Fax:* (04) 909-1501
Marvell Italia SRL, Viale Della Republica 38, 27100 Pavia, Italy *Tel:* (0382) 3755300 *Fax:* (0382) 20502
Marvell Japan KK, Hiratsuka Off, Hiratsuka MN, Bldg 9F, 3-1 Takara-cho, Hiratsuka, Kenagawa-ken 254-0034, Japan *Tel:* (03) 5324-0355
Marvell Japan KK, 2nd fl, Sakaisuji Hon machi Ctr Bldg, 2-1-6, Hon machi, Chuo-ku, Osaka 541-0053, Japan *Tel:* (03) 5324-0355
Marvell Japan KK/Marvell Technology Japan YK, Shinjuku Ctr Bldg, 44F, 1-25-1, Nishi-Shinjuku, Shinjuku-ku, Tokyo 163-0644, Japan *Tel:* (03) 5324-0355 *Fax:* (03) 5324-0354
Marvell Semiconductor Sdn Bhd, Plot 10, Bayan Lepas Technoplex, Phase IV, Bayan Lepas Indus Zone, 11900 Penang, Malaysia *Tel:* (04) 615 8899 *Fax:* (04) 615 8877
Marvell Netherlands BV, Laan van Diepenvoorde 4, 5582 LA Waalre, Netherlands *Tel:* (040) 236 6690
Marvell Asia Pte Ltd, 8 Tai Seng Link, Singapore 534158, Singapore *Tel:* 6756 1600 *Fax:* 6756 7600
Marvell Semiconductor Korea Ltd, 15F Prudential Tower, 298 (838 Youksam-1 Dong), Gangnam-daero, Gengnam-gu, Seoul 06253, South Korea *Tel:* (02) 560-6700 *Fax:* (02) 560-6788
Marvell Hispania SL, Europark Bldg C / Narcis Monturiol 1 Estarriol 11D, Parque Tecnologico, 46980 Paterna, Spain *Tel:* 961 366 004
Marvell Switzerland Sarl, Rte de Pallatex 17, 1163 Etoy, Switzerland
Marvell Taiwan Ltd, 5F-3, No 120, Section 2, Gongdaowu Rd, Hsinchu City 300, Taiwan *Tel:* (03) 516-5098 *Fax:* (03) 573-9907
Marvell Taiwan Ltd, 2nd fl, No 1, Alley 20, Lane 407, Sec 2, Ti-Ding Blvd, Nei Hu District, Taipei 114, Taiwan *Tel:* (02) 8177-7071 *Fax:* (02) 8752-5707

MarVista Entertainment Inc
10877 Wilshire Blvd, 10th fl, Los Angeles, CA 90024
Tel: 424-274-3000 *Fax:* 424-274-3050
E-mail: info@marvista.net
Web Site: www.marvista.net
Key Personnel
Partner: George Port *E-mail:* gport@marvista.net; Joseph Szew *E-mail:* jszew@marvista.net
CEO: Fernando Szew *E-mail:* fszew@marvista.net
Founded: 2003
International distribution for video, television & merchandising rights.
Catalog(s) available
Membership(s): Independent Film & Television Alliance®; NATPE

Marx InDigital
7921 Skylake Dr, Fort Worth, TX 76179
Tel: 414-351-5060
Web Site: www.marxindigital.com

Key Personnel
Pres: David Marx
Founded: 1920
Strategic marketing & production specialists.
Membership(s): AICP; NAB; SBE

Maryland Sound International Holding Co LLC
4900 Wetheredsville Rd, Baltimore, MD 21207
Tel: 410-448-1400 *Toll Free Tel:* 800-76SOUND
(767-6863) *Fax:* 410-448-1467
E-mail: martha@msihc.com
Web Site: www.marylandsound.com
Key Personnel
Pres: Robert Goldstein
Founded: 1968
Special event production. Concert touring systems & services. System analysis & consultation, equipment sales & rentals, system design.

Mason Video
9632 N 34 St, Omaha, NE 68112
Tel: 402-455-9422
E-mail: mason.video@mac.com
Web Site: www.masonvideo.com
Key Personnel
Owner: Mele Mason *Tel:* 402-680-5802 (cell)
Founded: 1987
HD, XD & SD video production.

massAV
3 Radcliffe Rd, Pewksbury, MA 01876
Tel: 978-670-0027 *Toll Free Tel:* 800-423-7830
Fax: 978-640-9900
E-mail: info@massav.com
Web Site: www.massav.com
Key Personnel
Pres: Patricia Basteri
VP: Jeffrey Robinson
Founded: 1975
A premier event production firm.
Online catalog(s) available
Membership(s): Audiovisual and Integrated Experience Association; International Live Events Association; MPI; NACE

MastCom
807 Broadway St NE, Suite 210, Minneapolis, MN 55413
Tel: 612-397-9637
E-mail: info@mastcom.com
Web Site: www.mastcom.com
Key Personnel
Pres & CEO: Tim Lewis *E-mail:* tlewis@mastcom.com
Founded: 1977
Video production services.

Mastech Digital
1305 Cherrington Pkwy, Bldg 210, Suite 400, Moon Township, PA 15108
Tel: 412-787-2100 *Toll Free Tel:* 800-627-8323
Fax: 412-494-9272
E-mail: experience@mastechdigital.com
Web Site: www.mastechdigital.com
Key Personnel
Pres & CEO: Vivek Gupta
CFO: Jack Cronin
Head, HR: Vishwanath Shetty
Founded: 1986
Fully integrated technology & operations firm. Digital transformation & learning services.
Branch Office(s)
39465 Paseo Padre Pkwy, Suite 1200, Fremont, CA 94538 *Tel:* 510-713-8283
6312 S Fiddlers Green Circle, Suite 300-E, Greenwood Village, CO 80111 *Tel:* 720-443-2799
3504 Lake Lynda Dr, Suite 380, Orlando, FL 32817 *Tel:* 407-393-6700

Towers at West Shore, 1408 N West Shore Blvd, Suite 305, Tampa, FL 33607 *Tel:* 813-559-1234
111 W Washington, Suite 1420, Chicago, IL 60602 *Tel:* 312-795-4211
330 Bear Hill Rd, Suite 301, Waltham, MA 02451 *Tel:* 781-902-6083
14643 Dallas Pkwy, Suite 670, Dallas, TX 75254 *Tel:* 214-615-3701
Foreign Office(s): 8th fl, B-07, Sector-132, Noida 201 301, India *Tel:* (0120) 6494025

Master Bond
154 Hobart St, Hackensack, NJ 07601
Tel: 201-343-8983 *Fax:* 201-343-2132
E-mail: main@masterbond.com
Web Site: www.masterbond.com
Founded: 1976

Master Books®
Division of New Leaf Publishing Group Inc
3142 Hwy 103 N, Green Forest, AR 72638
Mailing Address: PO Box 726, Green Forest, AR 72638
Tel: 870-438-5288 *Toll Free Tel:* 800-999-3777
Fax: 870-438-5120
E-mail: info@nlpg.com
Web Site: www.nlpg.com
Key Personnel
Pres, New Leaf Publishing Group: Tim Dudley
E-mail: tim@newleafpress.net
Ed-in-Chief: Laura Welch *E-mail:* laura@newleafpress.net
Founded: 1975
Christian audio books & videos.
Catalog(s) available, free, 2 times/yr

Master Duplicating Corp, see Master Video Disc & Design

Master Video Disc & Design
7349 N Via Paseo del Sur, Suite 515-455, Scottsdale, AZ 85258
Tel: 480-948-0305
Web Site: www.mastervdd.com
Key Personnel
CEO: Janita Cooper *E-mail:* janita@mastervdd.com
Founded: 1987
Full in-house AV studio complete with green screen & stage performance capacity. Full media production including video service/product demos, book, product & event trailers, training videos & web site video productions, product package & design.

Masterclock Inc
2484 W Clay St, St Charles, MO 63301-2548
Tel: 636-724-3666 *Toll Free Tel:* 800-940-2248
Fax: 636-724-3776
E-mail: sales@masterclock.com; support@masterclock.com
Web Site: www.masterclock.com
Key Personnel
Pres & CEO: John Clark
Founded: 1994
Complete time synchronization solutions.

Masterdisk Corp
8 John Walsh Blvd, Suite 411, Peekskill, NY 10566
Tel: 212-541-5022
Web Site: www.masterdisk.com
Key Personnel
Owner & Pres: Scott Hull *E-mail:* scott@masterdisk.com
Founded: 1973
Specialize in music mastering for CD, vinyl, surround, download & M4iT (mastered for iTunes).

Mastervision Inc
490 Seventh St, Brooklyn, NY 11215
Tel: 347-725-0545
Web Site: www.mastervision.com
Key Personnel
Pres: Peter Kreutzer *E-mail:* peter@mastervision.com
Video & DVD producers & distributors.
Online catalog(s) available

Mastery Technologies Inc
41214 Bridge St, Novi, MI 48375
Tel: 972-943-9214 *Toll Free Tel:* 800-258-3837
Fax: 248-888-8424
E-mail: sales@masterytech.com
Web Site: www.mastery.com
Key Personnel
Pres: William Marker
Founded: 1974
Interactive training systems.

Mathmadeeasy.com
Subsidiary of Multi Media Tutorial Services Inc
PO Box 190846, Brooklyn, NY 11219
Toll Free Tel: 866-599-MATH (599-6284)
Web Site: www.mathmadeeasy.com
Key Personnel
CEO: Barry Reichman
Multimedia tutorial review programs for elementary through high school & college math.

MathMastery, see Systems Impact Inc

Matrix Video Communications Corp (MVCC)
103, 1626 115 Ave NE, Calgary, AB T3K 5Y8, Canada
Tel: 403-640-4490 *Fax:* 403-640-9012
Web Site: www.matrixvideocom.com
Key Personnel
Pres & Gen Mgr: Glenn Burgess
E-mail: glennburgess@matrixvideocom.com
VP & CFO: Shelly Burgess
E-mail: shellyburgess@matrixvideocom.com
VP & Acct Mgr: Dave Campbell
E-mail: dcampbell@mvcc.ca
VP, Sales: Robert Wojtas *E-mail:* robertwojtas@matrixvideocom.com
Mktg Mgr & Communs Technologies Prod Mgr: Marielle Crisanti *E-mail:* mariellecrisanti@matrixvideocom.com
Founded: 1994
Consultation, design, integration & installation of audio, video & multimedia solutions in the education, corporate, healthcare, government, broadcast & post-production markets.
Branch Office(s)
11775 156 St, Edmonton, AB T5M 3N4, Canada *Tel:* 780-489-8787 *Fax:* 780-489-4496
106-8678 Greenall Ave, Burnaby, BC V5J 3M6, Canada *Tel:* 604-436-4492 *Fax:* 604-436-4482
PO Box 8321, Victoria, BC V8W 3R9, Canada *Tel:* 250-360-7480
320 Gardiner Park Ct, Regina, SK S4V 1R9, Canada *Tel:* 306-757-5902 *Fax:* 306-761-2620
515 45 St W, Saskatoon, SK S7L 5X5, Canada *Tel:* 306-652-5033 *Fax:* 306-652-5037

Matrox Video Products Group
Division of Matrox Electronic Systems Ltd
1055 Saint Regis Blvd, Dorval, QC H9P 2T4, Canada
Tel: 514-822-6000 *Toll Free Tel:* 800-361-4903
Fax: 514-685-2853
Web Site: www.matrox.com/video
Key Personnel
Worldwide Sales Mgr: Albert Cieri
Media Rel: Myles Carter
Founded: 1976
Technology market leader in the field of 4K, HD & SD digital video hardware & software for accelerated H.264 encoding, realtime editing,

audio/video input/output, streaming, AV signal conversion, capture/playout servers, channel-in-a-box systems & CGs. Matrox's Emmy award-winning technology powers a full range of multi-screen content creation & delivery platforms used by broadcasters, telcos, cable operators, post-production facilities, live event producers, videographers & AV professionals worldwide.
Member of the ASPEN (Adaptive Sample Picture Encapsulation) community.
Online catalog(s) available
Foreign Office(s): 1602, 38-A Zhongguancun Rd, Beijing 100086, China *Tel:* (010) 6256-4853 *Fax:* (010) 6253-6251 *E-mail:* asiapacific@matrox.com
Chaplin House, Moorhall Rd, Harefield, Middx UB9 6NS, United Kingdom *Tel:* (01895) 827220 *Fax:* (01895) 827239 *E-mail:* video.info.emea@matrox.com
Membership(s): Advanced Media Workflow Association Inc; Alliance for IP Media Solutions; IABM; NAB; SMPTE®; Video Services Forum

Matson Creative, see Matson Multi-Media

Matson Multi-Media
403 E Ramsey Rd, Suite 202, San Antonio, TX 78216
Tel: 210-349-3674
E-mail: sales@matsonmultimedia.com
Web Site: www.matsonmultimedia.com; www.matsoncreative.com
Key Personnel
Pres: James Berg *E-mail:* jim@matsoncreative.com
Full AV production & equipment.

Matthews Studio Equipment Inc
4520 W Valerio St, Burbank, CA 91505
Tel: 818-843-6715 *Fax:* 818-480-5808
E-mail: info@msegrip.com
Web Site: www.msegrip.com
Key Personnel
Owner & Pres: Ed Phillips *E-mail:* info@msegrip.com
Founded: 1970
Manufacture equipment for the film, television, theatrical & still photographic industries.
Catalog(s) available, free, 2 times/yr
Membership(s): Audiovisual and Integrated Experience Association; NAB; Production Equipment Rental Association

MAVCO
77 S Main St, Newtown, CT 06470
Tel: 203-270-8292 *Fax:* 203-270-8292
Key Personnel
Pres: Chris M Helland
AV equipment distributor.
Catalog(s) available

Maverick Video Productions
121 Interpark, Suite 601, San Antonio, TX 78216
Tel: 210-495-1111 *Fax:* 210-495-8033
Web Site: www.maverickstudio.com
Key Personnel
CFO: Patricia Iverson *E-mail:* pat@maverickstudio.com
Pres: Glenn Duchaine
Founded: 1992
Full service film/video production.

Max Films Inc
5333, rue Casgrain, Suite 406, Montreal, QC H2T 1X3, Canada
Tel: 514-282-8444
Web Site: www.maxfilms.ca
Key Personnel
Pres & Prodr: Roger Frappier *Tel:* 514-282-8444 ext 222

Founded: 1990
Develop & produce feature films.

Maxell Corp of America
Subsidiary of Hitachi Maxell Ltd (Japan)
3 Garret Mountain Plaza, Suite 300, Woodland Park, NJ 07424-3352
Tel: 973-653-2400 *Toll Free Tel:* 800-533-2836; 800-377-5887 (tech support) *Fax:* 201-796-8790
E-mail: techsupp@maxell.com
Web Site: www.maxell-usa.com
Founded: 1969
Producer of optical magnetic memory media.
Online catalog(s) available
Branch Office(s)
Maxell Canada, 10 Parr Blvd, Unit 106, Bolton, ON L7E 4E9, Canada *Tel:* 905-669-8107 *Toll Free Tel:* 800-661-9500 *Fax:* 905-669-8108 *E-mail:* support@maxellcanada.com
Foreign Office(s): Hitachi Maxell Ltd, Beijing Fortune Bldg 12F, Rm 1203, 5-Dong San Huan Bei Lu, Beijing 100004, China *Tel:* (010) 6501-4318 *Fax:* (010) 6501-4319 (all Asian countries not listed elsewhere)
Maxell AB, Ennekuja 4, 02270 Espoo, Finland *Tel:* (09) 804 2055 *Fax:* (09) 804 2066
Maxell SA, 14 Rue de Petit Albi, BP 8269, 95801 Cergy Pontoise Cedex, France *Tel:* 01 34 24 88 11 *Fax:* 01 30 73 56 77
Maxell Europe GmbH, Mollsfeld 2, 40670 Meerbusch, Germany *Tel:* (02159) 913-0 *Fax:* (02159) 913-150 (Germany, Austria, Czech Republic, Hungary & Switzerland)
Maxell Asia Ltd, 506 World Commerce Ctr, Harbour City, Phase 1, Canton Rd, Kowloon, Hong Kong *Tel:* 2730 9243 *Fax:* 2735 6250 *E-mail:* maxell@maxell.com.hk *Web Site:* www.maxell.com.hk (Hong Kong, China & Vietnam)
Hitachi Maxell Ltd, Totate-Nagai Bldg, 2-18-2 Iidabashi, Chiyada-ku, Tokyo 102-8521, Japan *Tel:* (03) 3515-8211 *Fax:* (03) 3515-8314 *Web Site:* www.maxell.co.jp
Maxell Mexico, Blvd Manuel Avila Camacho, No 32, Piso 2, Col Lomas de Chapultepec, 11000 Mexico, DF, Mexico *Tel:* (0155) 91787991 *E-mail:* cgongalez@maxmelmx.com (consumer prods)
Maxell BV, Wamberg 37, 1083 CW Amsterdam, Netherlands *Tel:* (020) 6460346 *Fax:* (020) 6426685
Maxell Latin America SA, Calle 50, Edificio P H Universal, Piso 2, PO Box 0831-0222, Paitilla, Panama City, Panama *Tel:* 269-6291 *Fax:* 263-4413 *E-mail:* maxell@ciabtesh.com *Web Site:* www.maxell-latin.com
Maxell Asia Pte Ltd, 10 Anson Rd, 25-06 International Plaza, Singapore 079 903, Singapore *Tel:* 6220 9291 *Fax:* 6220 6070 *E-mail:* sales@maxell.com.sg *Web Site:* www.maxell.com.sg (Singapore, India, Indonesia, Malaysia & Myanmar)
Maxell Scandinavia AB, Archimedesvaegen 6, Box 20094, 161 02 Bromma, Sweden *Tel:* (08) 445 22 00 *Fax:* (08) 981080 *E-mail:* msa@maxell.se
Maxell Europe Ltd, 3A High St, Rickmansworth, Herts WD3 1HR, United Kingdom *Tel:* (01923) 77-7171 *Fax:* (01923) 77-7710 *Web Site:* www.maxell.eu.com (Belgium, Denmark, Italy, Norway, Portugal & Spain)
Membership(s): Content Delivery & Storage Association; Entertainment Merchants Association; NAB; SBE; SMPTE®

Maximus Media Inc
2727 N Grove Industrial Dr, Suite 111, Fresno, CA 93727
Tel: 559-255-1688 *Toll Free Tel:* 800-2THEMAX (284-3629) *Fax:* 559-255-0323
Web Site: www.tothemax.com

Key Personnel
Pres: Jeff Hall *E-mail:* jeff@maximusmedia.net
Opers Mgr: Raymond Settle
Founded: 1985
Audio & video production & creative services, network & custom scoring.
Membership(s): AAF; AES; The Recording Academy

MAXON Computer Inc
2640 Lavery Ct, Suite A, Newbury Park, CA 91320
Tel: 805-376-3333 *Fax:* 805-376-3331
E-mail: info_us@maxon.net
Web Site: www.maxon.net
Key Personnel
CEO: Paul Babb
VP, Opers: Rick Barrett
Founded: 1986
Develops professional 3D modeling, painting, animation & rendering solutions. Maxon's Cinema 4D & Body Paint 3D are used in entertainment, science, architecture & other industries.
Foreign Office(s): MAXON Computer GmbH, Max-Planckstr 20, 61381 Friedrichsdorf, Germany *Tel:* (01672) 59 06 0 *Fax:* (01672) 59 06 30 *E-mail:* info@maxon.de (headquarters)

MB Productions
450 Fairfield Place, West Caldwell, NJ 07006
Tel: 973-439-0044 *Toll Free Tel:* 800-622-2224 *Fax:* 973-439-9844
E-mail: mbp@mbvideo.com
Web Site: www.mbvideo.com
Key Personnel
Pres: Brian Brooks *Tel:* 973-439-0044 ext 101 *E-mail:* brian@mbvideo.com
Founded: 1979
Video staging services, supplying video projection, camera packages & flat panel displays for the special events & television industries.

McAlister Electronics
926 E Fremont Ave, Sunnyvale, CA 94087
Tel: 408-739-2605 *Fax:* 408-733-2895
E-mail: mcalelect@aol.com
Web Site: www.werepairallbrands.com
Key Personnel
Pres & Mktg Mgr: William McAlister
Founded: 1967
Membership(s): NESDA; Photographic Society of America

McBain Camera Ltd
10805 107 Ave, Edmonton, AB T5H 0W9, Canada
Tel: 780-420-0404 *Toll Free Tel:* 800-661-6980 *Fax:* 780-421-1188
Web Site: www.mcbaincamera.com
Key Personnel
Store Mgr: Brian Young
Founded: 1949
AV equipment sales.
Online catalog(s) available
Membership(s): Audiovisual and Integrated Experience Association

MCCOM Inc
383 Rte 206, Chester, NJ 07930
Tel: 908-879-9590 *Fax:* 908-879-9679
Web Site: www.mccom.tv
Key Personnel
Owner: Michael Mehalko
COO: Scott Trupp *E-mail:* scott@mccom.tv
Buy, sell & trade new & used video equipment. Panasonic, Hitachi & Fujinon dealer.

Robert McConnell Productions
4303 67 Ave NW, Gig Harbor, WA 98335

Tel: 253-265-3184 *Toll Free Tel:* 800-532-4017 *Fax:* 253-265-1550 *Toll Free Fax:* 800-948-8463
E-mail: info@parli.com
Web Site: parli.com
Key Personnel
Pres: Robert McConnell
Educational training videos & books. Production services include transfers from film or VHS to DVD.
Catalog(s) available

McCune Audio-Video-Lighting
101 Utah Ave, South San Francisco, CA 94080
Tel: 650-873-1111 *Toll Free Tel:* 800-899-7686
Fax: 650-246-6702
E-mail: info@mccune.com
Web Site: www.mccune.com
Key Personnel
Pres: Allan McCune *E-mail:* aamccune@mccune.com
VP: David Molnar *E-mail:* dmolnar@mccune.com
Founded: 1932
Full service equipment rental, production & staging company.
Branch Office(s)
168 E Liberty Ave, Anaheim, CA 92801, Regl Mgr: Hugh O'Donovan *Tel:* 714-578-1900 *Toll Free Tel:* 800-486-7686 *Fax:* 714-525-6022
222 Ramona Ave, No 1, Monterey, CA 93940, Regl Mgr: Pete Bender *Tel:* 831-372-6038 *Toll Free Tel:* 800-372-3611 *Fax:* 831-372-0513
Membership(s): Audiovisual and Integrated Experience Association

McGraw-Hill School Education Group
Division of McGraw-Hill Education
8787 Orion Place, Columbus, OH 43240-4027
Mailing Address: PO Box 182605, Columbus, OH 43218
Tel: 614-430-4000 *Toll Free Tel:* 800-334-7734
Fax: 614-755-5682
Web Site: mheonline.com; www.mheducation.com
Key Personnel
Pres & CEO: David Levin
SVP & Gen Coun: David Stafford *E-mail:* david.stafford@mheducation.com
Founded: 1971
Educational materials for elementary, middle school & high school.
Online catalog(s) available
Branch Office(s)
2 Penn Plaza, New York, NY 10121 *Tel:* 212-904-2000 (headquarters)

McGuane Studio Inc
36 Horatio St, Suite 5-B, New York, NY 10014-1691
Tel: 212-463-7259
Key Personnel
Dir, Spec Effects: James P McGuane
Founded: 1972
Television production studio.
Membership(s): AICP

McIntyre Media Inc
203-75 First St, Orangeville, ON L9W 5B6, Canada
Tel: 519-942-9640 *Toll Free Tel:* 800-565-3036
Fax: 519-942-8489
E-mail: info@mcintyre.ca
Web Site: www.mcintyre.ca
Key Personnel
Pres: Peter Whyte *E-mail:* peter@mcintyre.ca
Founded: 1965
Children's programming distribution, DVD & digital streaming.
Catalog(s) available

McKay Conant Hoover Inc
5655 Lindero Canyon Rd, Suite 325, Westlake Village, CA 91362

Tel: 818-991-9300 *Fax:* 818-991-2324
E-mail: info@mchinc.com
Web Site: www.mchinc.com
Key Personnel
Principal: David Conant
Founded: 1987
Consulting services in all areas of building acoustics & AV systems.
Branch Office(s)
3961 N 75 St, Scottsdale, AZ 85251, Supervisory Consultant: Randal B Willis *Tel:* 480-947-3335 *Fax:* 480-947-3416
Membership(s): AES; Audiovisual and Integrated Experience Association; NSCA

Lloyd F McKinney Associates Inc
25350 Cypress Ave, Hayward, CA 94544
Tel: 510-783-8043 *Fax:* 510-783-2130
E-mail: info@mckinneyassoc.com
Web Site: www.mckinneyassoc.com
Key Personnel
Pres: Sherri Stanley *E-mail:* sherri.stanley@mckinneyassoc.com
VP, CTS: Ty McKinney *E-mail:* ty.mckinney@mckinneyassoc.com
Engg Mgr: Frits Groenhuizen *E-mail:* fritsg@mckinneyassoc.com
Founded: 1961
Full range of audio video services including planning, design, integration & installation.
Membership(s): AES; Audiovisual and Integrated Experience Association; IEEE; National Institute for Certification in Engineering Technologies; NSCA

McNabb & Connolly
60 Briarwood Ave, Mississauga, ON L5G 3N6, Canada
Tel: 905-278-0566 *Toll Free Tel:* 866-722-1522
Fax: 905-278-2801 *Toll Free Fax:* 866-722-1822
E-mail: info@mcnabbconnolly.ca
Web Site: www.mcnabbconnolly.ca
Key Personnel
Pres: Steve Connolly
Natl Sales Mgr: Bea Morton
Acqs & Mktg: Anne Connolly
Admin & Orders: Janice Hadfield
Founded: 1986
Educational programming for K-12 schools, post secondary institutions & public libraries on DVD, streaming or digital file.
Online catalog(s) available

McNee Productions Inc
3301 W Alabama St, Houston, TX 77098
Tel: 713-526-5333 *Fax:* 713-526-4634
E-mail: mcnee@mcnee.com
Web Site: www.mcnee.com
Key Personnel
Pres: Doug McNee
Acctg: Sheryl McNee
Founded: 1970
Full service production company.

MCS Recording Studios
550 Queen St E, Suite G-100, Toronto, ON M5A 1V2, Canada
Tel: 416-361-1688 *Toll Free Tel:* 866-322-8555
Fax: 416-361-5088
E-mail: info@mcsrecording.com
Web Site: www.mcsrecording.com
Key Personnel
Pres & Studio Mgr: Bill Walker *E-mail:* bwalker@mcsrecording.com
Founded: 1969
Recording studio, ISDN patch for audio.

Medcom Inc
6060 Phyllis Dr, Cypress, CA 90630-5243

Mailing Address: PO Box 6003, Cypress, CA 90630-0003
Tel: 714-891-1443 *Toll Free Tel:* 800-541-0253; 800-877-1443 *Fax:* 714-891-3140
E-mail: customerservice@medcominc.com
Web Site: www.medcominc.com
Key Personnel
Pres: Mike Zoradi
Mktg Mgr: Lisa Hammonds
Medical training programs.
Catalog(s) available

Media Bridge Gamekids
3281 Waikomo Rd, Koloa, HI 96756
Mailing Address: PO Box 1724, Koloa, HI 96756
Tel: 808-280-9591
E-mail: gkkauai@gamekids.com
Web Site: www.gamekids.com
Key Personnel
Publr & Prodr: Rennie Mau
Founded: 2001
Musical production company.
Online catalog(s) available
Membership(s): Multicultural Publishing & Educational Council

The Media Collaboratory
215 E High St, Lexington, KY 40507
Tel: 859-255-9049 *Fax:* 859-281-6537
E-mail: info@mediacollaboratory.com
Web Site: mediacollaboratory.com
Key Personnel
Owner & Sr Dir: Arthur Rouse
Full service production company.

Media-Comm
9700 S Pine Blvd, Charlotte, NC 28273
Tel: 704-527-8853
Web Site: www.media-comm.com
Key Personnel
Pres: Mark A Kramer *Tel:* 803-578-1409 *E-mail:* mkramer@media-comm.com
VP, Opers: Brack Rogers *Tel:* 704-507-4332 *E-mail:* brogers@media-comm.com
Provides rental of facilities for audio, video production, post-production & captioning.

Media Control Systems LLC
1050 Pioneer Way, Suite Q, El Cajon, CA 92020
Tel: 619-599-1050 *Fax:* 619-599-1051
Web Site: www.mediacontrolsystems.com
Key Personnel
CEO & Mktg Dir: Thomas Walsh *E-mail:* twalsh@mediacontrolsystems.com
COO: Tracy Cummins *E-mail:* tcummins@mediacontrolsystems.com
Founded: 2000
Manufacturer & television systems integrator.

Media Cybernetics Inc
Subsidiary of Roper Technologies Inc
401 N Washington St, Suite 350, Rockville, MD 20850
Tel: 301-495-3305 *Fax:* 240-328-6193
E-mail: info@mediacy.com
Web Site: www.mediacy.com
Key Personnel
Pres: Nick Beavers
Mktg & Communs Mgr: Stephen Hart *E-mail:* sahart@mediacy.com
Founded: 1981
Software creator; scientific imaging analysis.

Media Dimensions LLC
2212 Autumn Glow Ct, Bel Air, MD 21015
Tel: 410-561-4550
E-mail: info@mediadimensions.com
Web Site: www.mediadimensions.com
Key Personnel
Pres: Thomas Topscher
Founded: 1984
Full service production company.

Media Distributors
4514 W Vanowen St, Burbank, CA 91505
Tel: 818-980-9916 *Toll Free Tel:* 800-851-3113
  Fax: 818-566-8989
E-mail: la@mediadistributors.com
Web Site: www.mediadistributors.com
Key Personnel
Sales Mgr: Ken Kist *Tel:* 415-321-5939
Founded: 1998
New & evaluated blank tape sales & other media
  products.
Catalog(s) available

Media Elite Productions
Affiliate of Company Care Associates/DSRK
  LLC
11900 NE First St, Suite 300, Bellevue, WA
  98005
Tel: 425-336-3707 *Toll Free Fax:* 877-391-3778
E-mail: mediaeliteproductions@yahoo.com
Web Site: mediaeliteproductions.com
Multimedia, aviation & business consulting.

Media Event Concepts Inc
2036 Centimeter Circle, Austin, TX 78758
Tel: 512-832-1142 *Toll Free Tel:* 800-299-1142
  Fax: 512-832-0236
E-mail: info@mecteam.com
Web Site: www.mecteam.com
Key Personnel
VP: Deb Kobelan
Founded: 1988
Event planners.

Media Fabricators Inc
8509 Washington Blvd, Culver City, CA 90232
Tel: 323-937-3344 *Fax:* 323-937-1142
E-mail: mfi@mediafab.com
Web Site: www.mediafab.com
Key Personnel
Pres: Barry Fluster *Tel:* 323-937-3344 ext 15
Founded: 1971
Sales & rentals of AV, video & computer equip-
  ment for presenters & presentation profession-
  als.
Catalog(s) available

Media Inc
PO Box 496, Media, PA 19063
Tel: 610-565-2844 *Toll Free Tel:* 800-523-0118
  Fax: 610-565-3614
Web Site: www.mediaincorporated.com
Producer & distributor of educational & chil-
  dren's programs.

Media Loft Inc
615 First Ave NE, Suite 100, Minneapolis, MN
  55413
Tel: 612-375-1086 *Fax:* 612-375-0913
E-mail: info@medialoft.com
Web Site: www.medialoft.com
Key Personnel
CEO: Gene Di Lorenzo
Pres: David Kelsey
Full service production company.
Membership(s): National Professional Photogra-
  phers Association

Media Magic
11 Tanzanite, Rancho Santa Margarita, CA 92688
Tel: 949-713-9696
E-mail: request@mediamagic.tv
Web Site: www.mediamagic.tv
Key Personnel
Owner: Bill Ennis *Tel:* 949-257-8871 (cell)
  E-mail: bill@mediamagic.tv
Founded: 1984
Independent video production from concept to
  completion. Specialize in HD video production,
  Final Cut Pro editing, YouTube & Facebook

video creation & optimization, video consulting
  for B to C, B to B & nonprofits.
Membership(s): Association of Fundraising Professionals

Media Productions
3241 S University Dr, Fargo, ND 58104
Tel: 701-237-6863 *Toll Free Tel:* 800-480-6863
  Fax: 701-280-1226
E-mail: info@mediaproductions.com
Web Site: www.mediaproductions.com
Key Personnel
Pres & Exec Prodr: Lee Massey *Tel:* 701-237-
  6863 ext 6981
Founded: 1975
Full service audio, video, film & event production
  company.

The Media Staff Inc
8425 W Third St, Suite 401, Los Angeles, CA
  90048
Tel: 323-658-8996
E-mail: info@themediastaff.com
Web Site: www.themediastaff.com
Key Personnel
Founder & Pres: Jerry Maybrook *Tel:* 323-541-
  5900 (cell) *E-mail:* jerry@themediastaff.com
Founded: 1974
Full service production company.

Media Supply Inc
611 Jeffers Circle, Exton, PA 19341
Tel: 610-884-4400 *Toll Free Tel:* 800-944-4237
  Fax: 610-884-4500
E-mail: info@mediasupply.com
Web Site: www.mediasupply.com
Key Personnel
Sales: Pat McBride *Tel:* 610-884-4400 ext 110
Founded: 1986
CD-R, DVD, CD business cards, diskette dupli-
  cation, fulfillment, order tracking & packaging
  services, media & supplies.
Catalog(s) available

Media Systems Design Group
4253 Stewart Ave, Los Angeles, CA 90066
Mailing Address: PO Box 66337, Los Angeles,
  CA 90066-0337
Tel: 310-398-0281
Web Site: msd-group.com
Key Personnel
Principal: Timothy S Hart *E-mail:* thart@msd-
  group.com
Founded: 2000
Consulting & design services for AV, media pre-
  sentation systems & telecommunications ca-
  bling infrastructure.
Membership(s): Audiovisual and Integrated Expe-
  rience Association; NSCA

Media 3 Ltd
535 Fifth Ave, 13th fl, New York, NY 10017
Tel: 212-983-5200 *Fax:* 212-983-5200
E-mail: media3@liveshots.com
Web Site: liveshots.com
Live broadcast facility to accommodate live shots,
  satellite media tours, webcasts & other produc-
  tions.

Media Vision USA
1078 60 St, Oakland, CA 94608
Tel: 415-391-9090 *Toll Free Tel:* 877-746-8375
  Fax: 415-391-9192
E-mail: info@media-vision.com
Web Site: www.media-vision.com/en/north-
  america/usa
Key Personnel
VP, Sales: Curtiss Singleton
Founded: 2002
Provider of professional wired & wireless con-
  ferencing solutions for multipurpose meeting

rooms, VTC boardrooms, training centers,
  council chambers & auditoriums.
Branch Office(s)
7008 Virginia Manor Rd, Beltsville, MD 20705
  Tel: 202-688-3588
462 Seventh Ave, 9th fl, New York, NY 10018
  Tel: 917-746-4605
Foreign Office(s): Media Vision SARL, Chemin
  J-Ph de Sauvage 37, 1219 Chatelain, Switzerland *Tel:* (022) 518 16 17 *Fax:* (022) 594 80
  56

Mediaforce Productions
6328 Yorkdale Dr, Plano, TX 75093
Tel: 972-473-6888
Web Site: www.mediaforcepro.com
Key Personnel
Owner: Dr Terri Howard-Hughes *Tel:* 972-897-
  3345 (cell) *E-mail:* terri@mediaforcepro.com
Founded: 2001
Video, multimedia & web.
Membership(s): Dallas Producers Association;
  Video Association of Dallas; Women in Film

MediaFX
10445 SW Canyon Rd, Suite 220, Beaverton, OR
  97005
Tel: 503-646-9884
Web Site: www.mediafxvideo.com
Key Personnel
Owner: Lisa Sherman *E-mail:* lisa@
  mediafxvideo.com
Dir & Prodr: Erik Mayne *E-mail:* erik@
  mediafxvideo.com
Founded: 1994
Specialize in commercial, marketing, training &
  custom videos from pre- to post-production &
  content delivery.

Mediaimage Communications Group
10 Sacks Ave, Grimsby, ON L3M 4Y4, Canada
Tel: 905-309-5554 *Fax:* 905-309-0999
Key Personnel
Pres: Brian E Purdy *E-mail:* brianpurdy@
  sympatico.ca
Founded: 1966
Production & directing.
Catalog(s) available

MediaMation Inc
23410 Garnier St, Torrance, CA 90505
Tel: 310-320-0696 *Fax:* 310-320-0699
E-mail: sales@mediamation.com
Web Site: www.mediamation.com
Key Personnel
CEO: Dan Jamele
Founded: 1991
CD-ROM catalog(s) available
Membership(s): American Alliance of Museums;
  AZA; International Association of Amusement
  Parks and Attractions; International Cinema
  Technology Association; NAMM, the National
  Association of Music Merchants

MediaMix Inc
4 Pearl Ct, Allendale, NJ 07401
Tel: 201-262-3700 (day); 201-378-3035 (nights/
  weekends) *Fax:* 201-262-3798
E-mail: info@mmix.net
Web Site: www.mediamix.tv
Key Personnel
Pres: Joe Vargas *Tel:* 201-262-3700 ext 103
  E-mail: joevargas@mmix.net
Full service video & film production facility.

MediaNow Inc
One Maple Ave, 1-E, Netcong, NJ 07857
Tel: 973-347-2155 *Toll Free Tel:* 888-515-2255
  Fax: 973-215-2121
E-mail: info@medianow.com
Web Site: www.usa.medianow.com

Key Personnel
Pres: Marty Pisano
Founded: 1997
Management, delivery & display of digital media. Studio, consulting & design, content creation, sourcing, procurement, support & maintenance.
Branch Office(s)
4214 Third Ave, Brooklyn, NY 11232

MediaOne Studios
950 Battery St, 2nd fl, San Francisco, CA 94111
Tel: 415-262-4222
E-mail: hi@mediaonestudios.com
Web Site: mediaonestudios.com
Key Personnel
Dir, Venue Opers: Michael Ciabattari
  E-mail: michael@mediaonestudios.com
Gen Mgr & Dir, Prodn: Danny Skarka
  E-mail: danny@m1sf.com
Studio Opers: Drew Norris *E-mail:* drew@m1sf.com
Founded: 1987
Live-to-air studios, video production, webcasting, remote shoots & transmission for TV & Internet applications.

MediaPOINTE
3952 Camino Ranchero, Camarillo, CA 93012
Tel: 805-480-3700 *Fax:* 805-480-3770
E-mail: info@mediapointe.com; sales@mediapointe.com
Web Site: www.mediapointe.com
Key Personnel
Pres & CEO: Stephen Villoria
Founded: 1979
Membership(s): ACA; AES; American Institute of Architects; Audiovisual and Integrated Experience Association; IEEE; INCE; NSCA; USITT

Medical Media Systems
2916 NW Bucklin Hill Rd, No 481, Silverdale, WA 98383
Tel: 360-516-6110 *Fax:* 360-516-6113
Web Site: medicalmediasystems.com
Key Personnel
Founder & Pres: Dr Donald W Novey
  E-mail: dnovey@medicalmediasystems.com
Founded: 1984
Online catalog(s) available

Medical Visual Creations (MVC)
1700 California St, Suite 350, San Francisco, CA 94109
Tel: 415-928-1623 *Fax:* 415-928-4642
E-mail: info@lifestyleinmotion.com
Web Site: www.mvcvideodvd.com
Key Personnel
Owner: Dobri Dobrev Kiprov

Medifecta Healthcare Training
Division of Institute for Professional Care Education (IPCed)
5109 NE 82 Ave, Suite 201, Vancouver, WA 98662
Toll Free Tel: 833-974-1437
E-mail: medifectasupport@relias.com
Web Site: medifecta.com
Founded: 1995
Offer DVDs, textbooks, workbooks & online content to train professional & family caregivers.
Catalog(s) available

Medina Software Inc
PO Box 952440, Lake Mary, FL 32795-2440
Web Site: www.medinasoft.com
Key Personnel
Pres: Carmen Medina
CFO: Jorge Medina *E-mail:* jm@medinasoft.com
Founded: 1985

Assists high-tech companies in the production of Spanish language versions of their products.
Catalog(s) available

Meeting Services Inc, see MSI Production Services

Meetinghouse Event Design & Production
Division of SBR Events Group
781 N Church Rd, Elmhurst, IL 60126-1413
Tel: 630-941-0600 *Fax:* 630-941-7777
E-mail: info@sbrevents.com
Web Site: www.sbrevents.com
Key Personnel
Pres & CEO: Deborah Borsum
Founded: 1981
In-house services include production management, event design, decor, floral & event technology.
Membership(s): ARA; International Live Events Association

Megatrax
7629 Fulton Ave, North Hollywood, CA 91605
Tel: 818-255-7100 *Toll Free Tel:* 888-MEGA-555 (634-2555) *Fax:* 818-255-7199
E-mail: info@megatrax.com
Web Site: www.megatrax.com
Key Personnel
Pres & CEO: Ron Mendelsohn
Chief Communs Offr & Exec Prodr: J C Dwyer
Mktg Mgr: Marcia Kellogg
Founded: 1991
Quality production music, scoring, recording & music editing.
Catalog(s) available
Membership(s): Production Music Association

Megavideo LLC
22 Cedar St, No 2, Garfield, NJ 07026
Tel: 973-478-1921
E-mail: megamail@megadv.com
Web Site: www.megadv.com
Key Personnel
Owner & Pres: Jack Falzarano
Founded: 1983
Full service production company.

Melmat Inc
5333 Industrial Dr, Huntington Beach, CA 92649
Tel: 714-379-4555 *Toll Free Tel:* 800-635-6289 *Fax:* 714-379-4554
E-mail: info@melmat.com
Web Site: www.melmat.com
Key Personnel
Pres: John Mellott *E-mail:* john@melmat.com
Founded: 1971
Manufacturer & distributor of custom & stock carrying cases, plastic containers & packaging. Products include metal edge cases as well as Pelican, SKB & Flambeau cases.
Catalog(s) available
Online catalog(s) available
Membership(s): Society of Plastics Engineers

Meltzer Media Productions
49 Nassau St, 3rd fl, New York, NY 10038
Tel: 212-868-4600
E-mail: contact@meltzermedia.com
Web Site: www.meltzermedia.com
Key Personnel
Owner: Jeff Meltzer
Full service production.

Memphis Communications Corp
4771 Summer Ave, Memphis, TN 38122
Tel: 901-725-9271 *Toll Free Tel:* 866-805-5893 *Fax:* 901-272-3577
Web Site: memphiscommunications.net
Key Personnel
Chmn: Shane Berry

VP, Sales: Scot Berry
Founded: 1972
AV system design & installation, sound systems, rentals, presentation & producer services.
Branch Office(s)
MCC Mississippi, 114 W Jackson St, Suite B, Ridgeland, MS 39157 *Tel:* 601-228-1800
MCC Jackson, 1926 Emporium Dr, Jackson, TN 38305 *Tel:* 731-300-4500
MCC Nashville, 5217 Linbar Dr, No 306, Nashville, TN 37211 *Tel:* 615-370-4211
Membership(s): Audiovisual and Integrated Experience Association; Business Technology Association

Merck & Hill Consultants Inc
1995 N Park Place, Suite 450, Atlanta, GA 30339
Tel: 770-937-0185 *Fax:* 770-937-0919
E-mail: info@merckhill.com
Web Site: www.merckhill.com
Key Personnel
Principal: Harold Merck
Founded: 1985
Independent acoustics, AV, production lighting, design & consulting services.
Membership(s): ASA; National Council of Acoustical Consultants

Merestone
Division of Unique Inc
7232 E First St, Scottsdale, AZ 85251
Tel: 480-945-4631 *Fax:* 480-945-0590
Web Site: www.merestone.com
Key Personnel
Pres: Camille Hill *E-mail:* camillehill@merestone.com
VP: Rob Hill
Exec Dir: Nancy Waller-Stults
Sr Animator/IT: David Derosier
Founded: 1974
Support & creative services for anyone needing AV, videography, editing, production & scripting. Advanced meeting & event services.

Meridia ARS
1646 West Chester Pike, Suite 15, West Chester, PA 19382
Tel: 610-260-6800 *Fax:* 610-260-6810
E-mail: rsvp@meridiaars.com
Web Site: www.meridiaars.com
Key Personnel
Owner & CEO: Rick Baker
Pres: Keith Reiner
Manufacturer & distributor of audience response systems.
Catalog(s) available
Membership(s): Audiovisual and Integrated Experience Association; Meeting Planners International

Meridian Education Corp
Division of Films Media Group
c/o Films Media Group, 132 W 31 St, 16th fl, New York, NY 10001
Toll Free Tel: 800-257-5126; 800-322-8755 *Toll Free Fax:* 800-678-3633
E-mail: custserv@films.com
Web Site: meridian.films.com
Founded: 1959
Meridian-brand products are ideal for career & technical education instructors who want to teach & reinforce job & employability skills through a multimodal approach to learning. As a leader in educational media for students preparing to enter the workforce, Meridian offers a library of products covering topics such as allied health, culinary arts & child care. Meridian's skills-based, up-to-date educational media thoroughly addresses specific career/job-related skills & prepares students to enter the workforce. Meridian is a trademark of Films Media Group, an award-winning source of over

13,000 titles & exclusive US distributor for BBC Educational Collections, the Bill Moyers Collection, PBS & HBO, as well as many offerings from ABC & NBC News.
Online catalog(s) available

Meridian Studios
1020 Highland Park Rd, Neenah, WI 54956
Tel: 920-720-4200
Key Personnel
Partner: Julie Mata *E-mail:* julie@meridianstudiosusa.com; Tony Mata
Founded: 2004
Complete film, video & stage (large venue) production. Full avid media composer 1000XL Editing Suite & digital EFP package plus on-site studio. Specialize in planning, pre-production, field/studio production & post-production, final cut professional HD system & still photography.

Merrimack Films
530 Concord Ave, Belmont, MA 02478
Tel: 617-489-4729
E-mail: henrysuebass@gmail.com
Web Site: www.merrimack-films.com
Founded: 1983
Produces & distributes educational videos on labor relations.
Online catalog(s) available
Membership(s): IDA

MeshTel
PO Box 774, Genoa, NV 89411
Tel: 775-267-5959 *Fax:* 775-267-5958
E-mail: info@meshtel.com
Web Site: laserinfo.com
Key Personnel
Pres: Michael Eshaghnia
Founded: 1990
Manufacturer & supplier of electro-optics, communications & laser related products.
Catalog(s) available

MessageMakers
1217 Turner St, Lansing, MI 48906
Tel: 517-482-3333 *Toll Free Tel:* 888-482-6688
E-mail: info@messagemakers.com
Web Site: www.messagemakers.com
Key Personnel
Founder, Pres & CEO: Terry N Terry
    E-mail: terry@messagemakers.com
Sr Video Prodr: Tom Lietz *E-mail:* lietz@messagemakers.com
Founded: 1977
Full service production company specializing in live events, HD video production & learning programs.
Catalog(s) available
Membership(s): ATD; International Live Events Association; International Society for Performance and Instruction; Lansing Chamber of Commerce

Metalworks Recording Studios Inc
3611 Mavis Rd, Mississauga, ON L5C 1T7, Canada
Tel: 905-279-4000 *Fax:* 905-279-4006
Web Site: www.metalworksstudios.com
Key Personnel
Studio Mgr: Giancarlo Gallo *E-mail:* giancarlo@metalworksstudios.com
Founded: 1978
Recording studios.

Method Studios
Division of Deluxe Entertainment Services Group Inc
3401 Exposition Blvd, Santa Monica, CA 90404
Tel: 310-434-6000
Web Site: www.methodstudios.com

Key Personnel
COO: Eric Combrie
Pres & Gen Mgr: Ed Ulbrich
EVP, Global Features VFX: Erika Burton
SVP, Busn Devt, Method EXP: Sinjin Bain
SVP, Global Features VFX, Busn Devt: Deborah Giarratana; Marc Sadeghi
SVP, Global Integration: Carsten Sorensen
VP & Exec Prodr, Features VFX, Busn Devt: Heather Jennings
VP, Global Prodn Opers: Tom Wild
Head, R&D, Method EXP: Peter Shipkov
Head, Technol: Craig Zerouni
Dir, Digital Studio: Jeff Werner
Sr Exec Prodr & VP, Commercials VFX: Stephanie Gilgar
Sr Exec Prodr, Busn Devt: Alaina Zanotti
Exec Prodr, Method EXP: Meg Crowel
VFX, digital & design studios providing a full range of services for the film, TV & advertising industries.
Branch Office(s)
160 Pacific Ave, Suite 204, San Francisco, CA 94111 *Tel:* 514-600-0399
3399 Peachtree Rd NE, Suite 200, Atlanta, GA 30326 *Tel:* 404-732-1001
218 W 18 St, New York, NY 10011, Exec Prodr, Design: Adrienne Mitchell *Tel:* 212-907-1200
50 W Second Ave, Vancouver, BC V5Y 1B3, Canada, Head, Studio: Steve Garrad *Tel:* 604-874-8700
2050 Rue de Bleury, 8th fl, Montreal, QC H3A 2J5, Canada, Head, Studio: Carl Walters *Tel:* 514-600-0399
Foreign Office(s): 476 St Kilda Rd, Level 4, Melbourne, Victoria 3004, Australia, Exec VFX Prodr: Ineke Majoor *Tel:* (03) 9251 1888
Cluster E, 7th fl, Wing-2, SEZ EON, Kharadi Infrastructure Pvt Ltd, MIDC, Kharadi Knowledge Park, Pune 411 014, India, Mng Dir: Akhauri P Sinha *Tel:* (020) 4660 0999

Metro Productions
8570 Magellan Pkwy, Suite 400, Richmond, VA 23227
Tel: 804-261-1172 *Toll Free Tel:* 877-669-4687
    Fax: 804-261-1885
E-mail: contactmetro@metro-productions.com
Web Site: www.metro-productions.com
Key Personnel
Pres & CEO: Ray Walsh
Dir, Devt: Jim Miller *Tel:* 804-261-1172 ext 211
    E-mail: jmiller@metro-productions.com
Founded: 1981
Full service video, film, multimedia & animation production.
Branch Office(s)
1000 Cameron St, Alexandria, VA 22314
    Tel: 571-257-7349
27 W Queen's Way, Hampton, VA 23669
    Tel: 757-726-0877 *Fax:* 757-726-0876

Metro Teleproductions Inc (MTI)
2500 Virginia Ave NW, 416-S, Washington, DC 20037
Tel: 301-608-9077 *Fax:* 301-608-9078
Web Site: www.mtitv.com
Key Personnel
Owner & Pres: Dave Lilling *Tel:* 301-370-5898 (cell) *E-mail:* dave@mtitv.com
Founded: 1989
Video production, crews & webcasting.

Metro Video Systems Inc
1220 E Imperial Ave, El Segundo, CA 90245
Tel: 310-640-9250 *Fax:* 310-640-9347
E-mail: sales@metrovideosystems.com
Web Site: www.metrovideosystems.com
Key Personnel
Owner: Robert L Weir
Founded: 1969
CCTV distribute & repair.

Metromotion Productions LLC
450 W 31 St, 8th fl, New York, NY 10001
Tel: 212-967-2000 *Fax:* 212-967-1988
E-mail: info@metromotion.com; pr@metromotion.com
Web Site: www.metromotion.com
Key Personnel
Owner: Marc Chanti
Founded: 1990
Production services for the international commercial photography industry.

Metropolitan Acoustics LLC
8 Penn Ctr, Suite 1902, 1628 John F Kennedy Blvd, Philadelphia, PA 19103
Tel: 215-248-4352
E-mail: info@metro-acoustics.com
Web Site: www.metro-acoustics.com
Key Personnel
Founder & Principal Consultant: Felicia Doggett *E-mail:* f.doggett@metro-acoustics.com
Founded: 1990
Acoustical & AV consulting.
Membership(s): American Institute of Architects; ASA; Audiovisual and Integrated Experience Association; INCE; National Council of Acoustical Consultants; NSCA

Metropolitan Audio Visual Co LLC
22923 Quicksilver Dr, Suite 117, Dulles, VA 20166
Mailing Address: PO Box 1843, Herndon, VA 20172
Tel: 703-834-0004 *Fax:* 703-834-0866
E-mail: sales@metroav.com
Web Site: www.metroav.com
Key Personnel
Pres: John Elstrodt
VP: David Wilkins
Founded: 1967
Full service AV dealer.
Membership(s): Audiovisual and Integrated Experience Association; Virginia Educational Vendors Association

Metropolitan Audio-Visual Inc
35333 N 27 Lane, Phoenix, AZ 85086
Tel: 480-948-9008
Key Personnel
Pres: James A Smidt
VP: Jeanette E Smidt
AV sales & rentals.

Metropolitan Opera Guild Inc
Samuel B & David Rose Bldg, 70 Lincoln Center Plaza, 6th fl, New York, NY 10023-6593
Tel: 212-769-7000
E-mail: info@metguild.org
Web Site: www.metguild.org
Key Personnel
Mng Dir: Thomas M Martin
Founded: 1935
Shipping Address: 165 W 65 St, New York, NY 10023-6593
Membership(s): Opera Guild International

MetroSonic Recording Studio
143 Roebling St, 3rd fl, Brooklyn, NY 11211
Tel: 718-782-1872
E-mail: manager@metrosonic.net
Web Site: www.metrosonic.net
Key Personnel
Owner: Pete Mignola
Studio & Mktg Mgr: Ryan Impey
Audio Engr: Teruhisa Uchiyama
Founded: 1991
Full service studio & music production facility.

Meyer Sound Laboratories Inc
2832 San Pablo Ave, Berkeley, CA 94702

Tel: 510-486-1166 *Toll Free Tel:* 855-641-3288 (US & CN) *Fax:* 510-486-8356
E-mail: sales@meyersound.com; techsupport@meyersound.com; service@meyersound.com
Web Site: www.meyersound.com
Key Personnel
CEO: John Meyer
Dir, Mktg: Amy Huson *E-mail:* ahuson@meyersound.com
Mktg Mgr: Eve Bryggman *E-mail:* eveb@meyersound.com
Founded: 1979
Speaker manufacturer.
Catalog(s) available
Branch Office(s)
Meyer Sound Canada, 100 Kalamalka Lake Rd, No 23, Vernon, BC V1T 9G1, Canada *Tel:* 250-549-2588 *Fax:* 250-549-2668 *E-mail:* canada@meyersound.com (R&D only)
Foreign Office(s): Meyer Sound China, C203-16, Beijing Lufthansa Centre Off Bldg, 50 Liang-maqiao Rd, Chaoyang District, Beijing 100125, China *Tel:* (010) 6410 5336 *E-mail:* china@meyersound.com (tech support only)
Meyer Sound Lab Germany GmbH, Horresser Berg 4a, 56410 Montabaur, Germany *Tel:* (02602) 99908-0 *Fax:* (02602) 99908-99 *E-mail:* germany@meyersound.com *Web Site:* www.meyersound.de
Meyer Sound Mexico S de RL de CV, Ave Toluca 373-4B, Col Olivar de los Padres, Delegacion Alvaro Obregon, 01780 Mexico, DF, Mexico *Tel:* (0155) 5631 8137 *Fax:* (0155) 5630 5391 *E-mail:* mexico@meyersound.com
Meyer Sound Middle East, Shatha Tower, Suite 3018, PO Box 72280, Dubai Media City, Dubai, United Arab Emirates *Tel:* (055) 643 1283 *E-mail:* middleeast@meyersound.com
Shipping Address: 1080 Heinz Ave, Berkeley, CA 94710

MFJ Enterprises Inc
300 Industrial Park Rd, Starkville, MS 39759-3992
Mailing Address: PO Box 494, Mississippi State, MS 39762-0494
Tel: 662-323-5869 *Toll Free Tel:* 800-647-1800 *Fax:* 662-323-6551
E-mail: mfjcustserv@mfjenterprises.com
Web Site: www.mfjenterprises.com
Key Personnel
Pres: Martin F Jue
VP: Steven Pan
Founded: 1972
Ham radio communications company.
Catalog(s) available
Online catalog(s) available

MG Electronics
32 Ranick Rd, Hauppauge, NY 11788
Tel: 631-582-3400 *Fax:* 631-582-3229
E-mail: info@mgelectronics.com
Web Site: www.mgelectronics.com
Key Personnel
Owner: Elliott Maltz
Founded: 1961
OEM supplier of electrical components & products to manufacturers & distributors.
Membership(s): IPMA; NSCA

MG Studio
6625 S Valley View Blvd, Suite C-304, Las Vegas, NV 89118
Tel: 702-836-3686
E-mail: office@mgstudio.com
Web Site: mgstudio.com
Key Personnel
Dir: Michael Gaskell *Tel:* 818-681-0808 *E-mail:* michaelg@mgstudio.com
Production company. Provides rental of studio, stages, cameras, lighting & grip.

MGM Home Entertainment
Division of MGM Studios Inc
245 N Beverly Dr, Beverly Hills, CA 90210
Tel: 310-449-3000
Web Site: www.mgm.com

MHS-TV
Mamaroneck High School, 1000 W Boston Post Rd, Mamaroneck, NY 10543
Tel: 914-220-3100 *Fax:* 914-220-3115
Web Site: www.mamkschools.org; www.mhstv.org
School television broadcasting & documentary production.

Mia Mind Music
254 Sixth St, Suite 2, Hoboken, NJ 07030-6916
Toll Free Tel: 800-843-8575
E-mail: info@miamindmusic.com
Web Site: www.miamindmusic.com
Key Personnel
Owner: Stevie B
Founded: 1984
Entertainment promotion & marketing company for musicians & labels.
Membership(s): ASCAP

Miami Daylight Studios
1819 West Ave, Bay 5, Miami Beach, FL 33139
Tel: 305-763-8490
E-mail: info@miamidaylightstudios.com
Web Site: miamidaylightstudios.com
Still & motion equipment rental for professional productions. Offers photographic services, equipment rentals, studio space, transportation & production support, digital tech & creative services.

Miami Stagecraft Inc
2855 E 11 Ave, Hialeah, FL 33013
Tel: 305-836-9356 *Fax:* 305-696-3322
E-mail: info@miamistagecraft.com
Web Site: www.miamistagecraft.com
Key Personnel
Mgr: Andrew Martin *Tel:* 305-836-9356 ext 1
Stage lighting distributor.

MiB MediaWorks
85 Main St, Little Falls, NJ 07424
Tel: 973-403-1133 *Fax:* 973-638-1699
E-mail: info@mibmediaworks.com
Web Site: www.mibmediaworks.com
Key Personnel
Pres & Dir, Films: Mark Brodie *Tel:* 917-416-4840 (cell) *E-mail:* mark@mibmediaworks.com
Founded: 1986
Video production, marketing, web services & media consulting.

Michigan Office Solutions (MOS), A Xerox Company
2859 Walkent Dr NW, Grand Rapids, MI 49544
Toll Free Tel: 800-442-9070
E-mail: info@mos-xerox.com
Web Site: www.mos-xerox.com
Key Personnel
Pres: Ralph Slider
EVP, Sales: Bill Orr
VP, HR: Kathy Richter
VP, Serv, Eastern Michigan: Bill Mickey
VP, Serv, Western Michigan: Drew Westcott
Regl VP, Eastern Michigan: Walter Reynolds
Regl VP, Western Michigan: Keith Stewart
Dir, Contract Admin: Stacey Reed
Dir, Finance & Corp Cont: Claire McFadden
Dir, IT: Brian Dudek
Dir, Mktg: Shelly Bernecker
Dir, Opers: Will Richert
Founded: 1957
Office equipment & technology supplier.
Catalog(s) available

Branch Office(s)
1223 S State St, Suite D, Alpena, MI 49707 *Tel:* 989-356-9500
1001 Woodward Ave, Suite 800, Detroit, MI 48226 *Tel:* 313-324-7362
WMU Business Technology & Research Park, 4664 Campus Dr, Suite 105, Kalamazoo, MI 49008 *Tel:* 269-381-0805
MSU Corporate Research Park, 3101 Technology Blvd, Suite J, Lansing, MI 48910 *Tel:* 517-332-2153
40000 Grand River Ave, Suite 500, Novi, MI 48375 *Tel:* 248-919-3333
4177 Fashion Square Blvd, Suite 2, Saginaw, MI 48603
3281 Racquet Club Dr, Suite B, Traverse City, MI 49686

Michigan Recording Arts Institute & Technologies
Division of K&R All Media Productions LLC
28533 Greenfield, Southfield, MI 48076
Tel: 248-569-5422
Web Site: mirecordingarts.com
Key Personnel
Professor: Kenneth Glaza *Tel:* 248-557-8276 *E-mail:* ken@mirecordingarts.com
Founded: 1984
School, institute.
Online catalog(s) available

Micor Analytics
7538 Saint Louis Ave, Skokie, IL 60076
Tel: 847-329-8590 *Fax:* 847-329-8599
Web Site: www.micoranalytics.com
Key Personnel
Principal Analyst & Founder: James Minchella *Tel:* 847-329-8590 ext 214 *E-mail:* jim.minchella@micoranalytics.com
Principal Consultant: Valentine Christian
Mng Analyst: Chris Minchella *E-mail:* chris.minchella@micoranalytics.com
Field Mgr: Myriam Banks; Seid Grebovic
Founded: 1985
Industry & technology consulting for the media, high tech manufacturing, telecommunications & computing industries.
Catalog(s) available
Membership(s): American Society of Appraisers; American Society of Mechanical Engineers; Association for Computing Machinery; SMPTE®

Micro Express
8 Hammond, Suite 105, Irvine, CA 92618-1601
Tel: 949-460-9911 *Toll Free Tel:* 800-989-9900 *Fax:* 949-269-3070
E-mail: info@microexpress.net
Web Site: www.microexpress.net
Founded: 1986
Manufacture gaming, laptop & desktop computers & accessories.

Micro Focus
1800 S Novell Place, Bldgs G & H, Provo, UT 84606
Tel: 801-861-7000 *Toll Free Tel:* 877-686-9637
E-mail: media.relations@microfocus.com
Web Site: www.microfocus.com
Key Personnel
VP, Prod Mktg: Eric Varness
Global software company.
Branch Office(s)
575 Anton Blvd, Suite 510, Costa Mesa, CA 92626-7666 *Tel:* 714-445-4400 *Fax:* 714-445-4404
6701 Koll Center Pkwy, Suite 300, Pleasanton, CA 94566
4555 Great America Pkwy, Suite 400, Santa Clara, CA 95054 *Tel:* 650-258-6827 (US headquarters)

3420 E Harmony Rd, Bldg 5, Fort Collins, CO
80528-9544

900 North Point Pkwy, Alpharetta, GA 30005

One Irvington Ctr, 700 King Farm Blvd, Suite
125, Rockville, MD 20850-5736 *Tel:* 301-838-
5000 *Fax:* 301-838-5025

30 Corporate Dr, Suite 130, Burlington, MA
01803-4252 *Tel:* 978-341-5300 *Fax:* 978-341-
5307

150 Cambridgepark Dr, Suite 800, Cambridge,
MA 02140

50 W Big Beaver Rd, Suite 500, Troy, MI 48084
Tel: 248-824-1661 *Fax:* 248-824-1662

One Penn Plaza, 36th fl, New York, NY 10019

424 Wards Corner Rd, Suite 100, Loveland, OH
45140

1415 Argonne Blvd, Suite B, South Euclid, OH
44121-2920

2345 NW Amberbrook Dr, Suite 200, Hillsboro,
OR 97006

One Allegheny Sq, Suite 204, Pittsburgh, PA
15212

14231 Tandem Blvd, Austin, TX 78738

515 Post Oak Blvd, Suite 1200, Houston, TX
77027 *Tel:* 713-548-1700

5400 Legacy, Plano, TX 75024

8609 Westwood Center Dr, Suite 700, Vienna,
VA 22182 *Tel:* 703-663-5500 (govt solutions
headquarters)

2925 Roeder Ave, Suite 300, Bellingham, WA
98225 *Tel:* 360-715-1170

705 Fifth Ave S, Suite 1000, Seattle, WA 98104
Tel: 206-217-7500

Foreign Office(s): The Lawn, 22-30 Old Bath Rd,
Newbury, Berks RG14 1QN, United Kingdom
Tel: (01635) 565-200 (UK headquarters)

Micro Technology Unlimited Inc
PO Box 5, Rolesville, NC 27571
Tel: 919-870-0344
E-mail: sales@mtu.com
Web Site: www.mtu.com
Key Personnel
Pres: David B Cox
Founded: 1977
Manufacture & distribute digital audio worksta-
tions (DAW), digital audio editing software,
software to remove vocals & karaoke software.
Catalog(s) available

Microboards Technology LLC
8150 Mallory Ct, Chanhassen, MN 55317
Tel: 952-556-1600 *Toll Free Tel:* 800-646-8881;
800-290-9012 *Fax:* 952-556-1620
E-mail: sales@microboards.com
Web Site: www.microboards.com
Key Personnel
Sales Mgr: Brian Towey *E-mail:* briant@
microboards.com
Founded: 1989
AV equipment distributor.
Foreign Office(s): Microboards Technology Inc,
Kuroto-machi Yachiyo Bldg 20F, Kabutocho
Nihonbashi 4F, Chuo-ku, Toyko 103-0026,
Japan *Tel:* (03) 3561-2266 *Fax:* (03) 3663-0115
Web Site: www.microboards.co.jp
Microboards Technology, 7 Harriott Dr, Heathcote
Industrial Estate, Warwick CV34 6TJ, United
Kingdom *Tel:* (0845) 230 7800 *Fax:* (0845)
230 7900 *E-mail:* sales@microboards.co.uk
Web Site: www.microboards.co.uk

Microdolly Hollywood
135 N Victory Blvd, Burbank, CA 91502
Tel: 818-845-8383
E-mail: microdolly@microdolly.com
Web Site: www.microdolly.com
Key Personnel
Owner & CEO: Jerry Johnson
Founded: 1996
Manufacture jibs, dollies, mounts & remote
heads.

Catalog(s) available
Membership(s): NAB

MicroImage Video Systems
PO Box 331, Boyertown, PA 19512-0331
Tel: 610-754-6800 *Fax:* 610-754-9766
Web Site: www.mivs.com
Key Personnel
Pres: John Taylor *E-mail:* jataylor@mivs.com
Founded: 1983
Online catalog(s) available
Shipping Address: 625 Hoffmansville Rd, Bech-
telsville, PA 19505

MicrophoneRentals.com
75-3050 Edgemont Blvd, North Vancouver, BC
V7R 4X1, Canada
Tel: 604-980-5703
E-mail: info@microphonerentals.com
Web Site: www.microphonerentals.com
Key Personnel
Owner: Larry Hennessey
Founded: 1997
Providing vintage microphones & vintage period
electronics to the movie & entertainment indus-
try. As seen in *The Watchmen, Chronicles of
Riddick, The Interview & Birth of the Dragon.*

Microsemi Corp
One Enterprise, Aliso Viejo, CA 92656
Tel: 949-380-6100 *Toll Free Tel:* 800-713-4113
Fax: 949-215-4996
Web Site: www.microsemi.com
Key Personnel
Pres & CEO: James J Peterson
EVP, Secy & Treas: John Hohener
EVP & Chief Strategy Offr: Steven Litchfield
Online catalog(s) available
Branch Office(s)
4721 Calle Carga, Camarillo, CA 93012
11861 Western Ave, Garden Grove, CA 92841
101 Creekside Ridge Ct, Roseville, CA 95678
Microsemi Semiconductor (US) Inc, 15822
Bernardo Center Dr, Unit B, San Diego, CA
92127
3870 N First St, San Jose, CA 95134
Microsemi Corp-RF Power Products, 3000 Oak-
mead Village Dr, Santa Clara, CA 95051
3843 Brickway Blvd, Santa Rosa, CA 95403
1380 Bordeaux Dr, Sunnyvale, CA 94089
1711 Holt Rd NE, Tuscaloosa, AL 35404
4775 Walnut St, Suite 1B, Boulder, CO 80301
Microsemi Corp-Analog Mixed Signal Group,
250 Scientific Dr, Suite 350, Norcross, Atlanta,
GA 30092
Microsemi Corp-Analog Mixed Signal Group,
3875 Johns Creek Pkwy, Suite B, Off No 3,
Suwanee, GA 30024
Chatham Executive Suites, 1901 N Roselle Rd,
Suite 826, Schaumburg, IL 60195
123 Brimbal Ave, Beverly, MA 01915
34 Tozer Rd, Beverly, MA 01915
6 Lake St, Lawrence, MA 01841
75 Technology Dr, Lowell, MA 01851
Microsemi Frequency & Time Corp, 48 Abby Rd,
Manchester, NH 03103
61 Spit Brook Rd, Nashua, NH 03060
Microsemi Corp-Analog Mixed Signal Group,
535 Broad Hollow Rd, Suite B-45, Melville,
NY 11747
Microsemi Corp-Power Products Group, 307/405
SW Columbia St, Bend, OR 97702
10220 SW Greenburg Rd, Suite 245, Portland,
OR 97223
5100 Tilghman St, Suite 120 & 155, Allentown,
PA 18104
Microsemi Semiconductor (US) Inc, 2136 N 13
St, Reading, PA 19604
Microsemi Semiconductor (US) Inc, 4006 Belt
Line Rd, Suite 205, Addison, TX 75001
Microsemi Semiconductor (US) Inc, 4509 Frei-
drich Lane, Austin, TX 78744

900 S Capital of Texas Hwy, Suite 300, Austin,
TX 78746
11450 Compaq Center Dr W, Houston, TX 77070
Microsemi SOC Corp, 2805 N Dallas Tollway,
Plano, TX 75093
8555 Baxter Place, Burnaby, BC V5A 4V7,
Canada
Microsemi SOC Corp, 101 Frederick St, Suite
1000, Kitchener, ON N2H 6R2, Canada
Microsemi Semiconductor ULC, 400 March Rd,
Ottawa, ON K2K 3H4, Canada
3333 Graham Blvd, Suite 110, Montreal, QC
H3R 3L5, Canada
510 Cope Way, No 230, Saskatoon, SK S7T 0G3,
Canada

Microspace Communications Corp
Subsidiary of Capitol Broadcasting Co Inc
3100 Highwoods Blvd, Suite 120, Raleigh, NC
27604
Tel: 919-850-4500 *Fax:* 919-850-4518
Web Site: www.microspace.com
Key Personnel
VP: Joseph L Amor, III
Mgr, Video Servs: Greg Hurt *E-mail:* ghurt@
microspace.com
Live shot studio. Branch offices in Charlotte &
Wilmington, NC.
Online catalog(s) available

Microtran Manufacturing, see Tamura
Corporation of America

Microwave Filter Co Inc
6743 Kinne St, East Syracuse, NY 13057
Tel: 315-438-4700 *Toll Free Tel:* 800-448-1666
Fax: 315-463-1467 *Toll Free Fax:* 888-411-
8860
E-mail: mfcsales@microwavefilter.com
Web Site: www.microwavefilter.com
Key Personnel
Dir, Sales: Scott Parsell *Tel:* 315-438-4720
E-mail: scott-p@microwavefilter.com
Cust Rel Mgr: Sandy Nelepovitz *Tel:* 315-438-
4745 *E-mail:* sandy-n@microwavefilter.com
Founded: 1967
Passive electronic filter design & manufacture.
Catalog(s) available
Membership(s): NAB; National Satellite Program-
ming Network; SCTE; Wireless Communica-
tions Association International

Mid-South Color Labs Inc
496 Emmett St, Jackson, TN 38301
Tel: 731-422-6691 *Toll Free Tel:* 800-221-3920
Fax: 731-424-1902
E-mail: info@midsouthcolor.com
Web Site: www.midsouthcolor.com
Key Personnel
Pres: Brooks Clayton *E-mail:* bclayton@
midsouthcolor.com
Founded: 1957
Photographic & digital imaging.
Online catalog(s) available
Membership(s): The Imaging Alliance; PPA

MidCanada Production Services Inc (MidCan)
509 Century St, Winnipeg, MB R3H 0L8, Canada
Tel: 204-772-0368 *Fax:* 204-772-0360
E-mail: info@midcan.com
Web Site: www.midcan.com
Key Personnel
Pres & CEO: Wayne Sheldon *Tel:* 204-480-0999
E-mail: wayne@midcan.com
Founded: 1977
AV rental & production company. Specialize in
film, commercial TV & video production.

Middle Atlantic Products, a Legrand AV Inc
brand
300 Fairfield Rd, Fairfield, NJ 07004

Tel: 973-839-1011 *Fax:* 973-839-1976
E-mail: info@middleatlantic.com
Web Site: www.middleatlantic.com
Founded: 1979
Manufacture equipment rack enclosures & related rack accessories.
Catalog(s) available
Branch Office(s)
Middle Atlantic Canada Inc, 113 Iber Rd, Ottawa, ON K2S 1E7, Canada *Tel:* 613-836-2501 *Toll Free Tel:* 888-766-9770 *Fax:* 613-836-2690 *Toll Free Fax:* 888-599-5009 *E-mail:* customerservicecanada@middleatlantic.ca *Web Site:* ca.middleatlantic.com
Membership(s): AES; BICSI; Consumer Technology Association™; Custom Electronic Design & Installation Association; NAMM, the National Association of Music Merchants; NSCA

Midland Video Productions Inc
3315 N 124 St, Brookfield, WI 53005
Tel: 414-276-8300
E-mail: request@midlandvideo.com
Web Site: midlandvideo.com
Key Personnel
Pres: Joe Liberatore *E-mail:* joe@midlandvideo.com
Writer: Deanne Haines
Ed: Matt Mueller
Graphics: Josh Rasmussen
Founded: 1980
Full service production company.

Midnight Media Group Inc
45 E Willow St, Millburn, NJ 07041-1416
Tel: 973-379-5959
E-mail: info@mmgi.tv
Web Site: mmgi.tv
Key Personnel
Partner & Prodr: Dave Emmerling *E-mail:* dave@mmgi.tv
Partner: Robert Camitta; Walter Schoeknecht
Founded: 1981
Production & post-production services for business & television media.

Midtown Video Inc
4824 SW 74 Ct, Miami, FL 33155
Tel: 305-669-1117 *Fax:* 305-662-2860
E-mail: info@midtownvideo.com
Web Site: midtownvideo.com
Key Personnel
Pres & CEO: Kenneth J Miller *E-mail:* kmiller@midtownvideo.com
EVP & CFO: Debra Miller *E-mail:* dmiller@midtownvideo.com
CTO: Jesse Miller *Tel:* 305-669-1117 ext 105 *E-mail:* jmiller@midtownvideo.com
VP, Opers & Sales Engr: Fernando Iglesias *Tel:* 305-669-1117 ext 114 *E-mail:* figlesias@midtownvideo.com
Dir, Tech Servs: Virge Castillo *Tel:* 305-669-1117 ext 107
Founded: 1984
Sales, rental & integration of AV systems.
Online catalog(s) available, sales & rental
Branch Office(s)
4320 Deerwood Lakes Pkwy, Suite 101-255, Jacksonville, FL 32216 *Tel:* 904-472-3347 *E-mail:* carl@midtownvideo.com
Membership(s): AICP; Audiovisual and Integrated Experience Association; Production Equipment Rental Association

Midwest Digital Corp
PO Box 204, Palos Park, IL 60464-0204
Tel: 708-790-4040
E-mail: sales@midwestdig.com; midwestdig@gmail.com
Web Site: www.midwestdigitalcorp.com
Key Personnel
Founder: Brian J Falatovich

Founded: 1996
New & pre-owned equipment. Sell AKG audio products, broadcast video/audio equipment (Sony, Panasonic, JVC, Grass Valley, Atomos, Soliton, Manfrotto, Swit).

Midwest Photo Exchange
2887 Silver Dr, Columbus, OH 43211
Tel: 614-261-1264 *Toll Free Tel:* 866-940-3686
E-mail: mpx@mpex.com; orders@mpex.com
Web Site: mpex.com
Key Personnel
Pres: Moshie Appelbaum *Tel:* 614-827-9824 *E-mail:* moshie@mpex.com
Opers Mgr: Andrew Clark *Tel:* 614-827-9832 *E-mail:* andrew@mpex.com
Sales Mgr: Ken Lewis *Tel:* 614-827-9826 *E-mail:* ken@mpex.com
Sells photo, lighting & video equipment.

Midwest Uplink Inc
911 N East St, Indianapolis, IN 46202
Tel: 317-423-8684 *Toll Free Tel:* 866-886-6247
Web Site: midwestuplink.com
Key Personnel
Co-Owner: Paul Mpistolarides *Tel:* 317-714-1095 *E-mail:* paulpistol@aol.com; Tony Williams *Tel:* 317-250-4687 *E-mail:* twilliams003@mac.com
Founded: 2002
Fully integrated supplier of television & broadcast logistics & transmission services. Uplink studios & 3 satellite trucks.

Mightybytes Inc
4001 N Ravenswood Ave, Suite 404, Chicago, IL 60613
Tel: 773-561-7529
E-mail: info@mightybytes.com
Web Site: www.mightybytes.com
Key Personnel
CEO: Tim Frick *E-mail:* tim@mightybytes.com
Opers Mgr: Jeff Yurkanin
Prod Mgr: Ethan Spotts
Prod Mgr & Busn Devt Lead: Keith McGorisk
Founded: 1998
Full service design & digital media communications firm.

Mike's Camera
2500 Pearl St, Boulder, CO 80302
Tel: 303-444-1257; 303-443-1715 (ext 132)
E-mail: store1@mikescamera.com
Web Site: www.mikescamera.com
Key Personnel
Image Processing Mgr: David Lindquist *E-mail:* davidl@mikescamera.com
Founded: 1967
Full service photographic retailer & complete imaging & output source. Camera & video rentals/repair. Video services, transfers, duplication & editing.

Milbrodt/Music & Sound Design
1835 US Hwy 9, Howell, NJ 07731
Tel: 848-459-4965
E-mail: info@ideasinmedia.com
Web Site: www.ideasinmedia.com
Key Personnel
Owner: Bill Milbrodt
Picture, music & sound services.

Milestone Film & Video Inc
PO Box 128, Harrington Park, NJ 07640-0128
Tel: 201-767-3117 *Toll Free Tel:* 800-603-1104 *Fax:* 201-767-3035
E-mail: milefilms@gmail.com
Web Site: www.milestonefilms.com
Key Personnel
Owner & Pres: Amy Heller *E-mail:* amy@milestonefilms.com

Owner: Dennis Doros
Founded: 1990
Film distribution company.
Online catalog(s) available

Milgrom Productions
50 Kent Rd, Glen Rock, NJ 07452
Tel: 201-444-8838
E-mail: info@milgromproductions.com
Web Site: milgrom.adcstudio.com

Milky Way Press
317 Ridge Run Dr, Georgetown, TX 78628
Tel: 512-863-7278; 512-677-0861
Key Personnel
Owner: Beverly Morgan *E-mail:* bev@bmorgan.com
Publisher of audiobooks on breastfeeding.

Millennia Media, FPC
6411 Capitol Ave, Diamond Springs, CA 95619
Tel: 530-647-0750 *Toll Free Tel:* 866-MIC-PREAMP (642-7732) *Fax:* 530-647-9921
E-mail: sales@mil-media.com; tech@mil-media.com (tech support)
Web Site: www.mil-media.com
Key Personnel
Founder & Pres: John La Grou
Audio equipment manufacturer.
Membership(s): AES; IEEE; NAMM, the National Association of Music Merchants; The Recording Academy

Miller Camera Support LLC
216 Little Falls Rd, Unit 15 & 16, Cedar Grove, NJ 07009-1276
Tel: 973-857-8300 *Fax:* 973-857-8188
E-mail: service@millertripods.us
Web Site: www.millertripods.com
Key Personnel
Sales Mgr: Gus Harilaou *E-mail:* gus@millertripods.us
Founded: 1954
Design professional fluid heads & tripods for the film & television industry.
Catalog(s) available
Foreign Office(s): Miller Camera Support Equipment, 30 Hotham Parade, Artarmon, NSW 2064, Australia *Tel:* (02) 9439 6377 *Fax:* (02) 9438 2819 *E-mail:* daniel.sissons@miller.com.au
Miller Fluid Heads Europe, Shepperton Business Park, Unit 12A, Govett Ave, Shepperton, Middx TW17 8BA, United Kingdom *Tel:* (01932) 222 888 *Fax:* (01932) 222 211 *E-mail:* sales@millertripods-europe.com
Membership(s): NAB; SMPTE®

Earl Miller Productions Inc
1702 W Koenig Lane, Austin, TX 78756
Tel: 512-458-4343 *Fax:* 512-458-4485
E-mail: info@earlmillerproductions.com
Web Site: www.earlmillerproductions.com
Key Personnel
Gen Mgr: Mike Miller
Founded: 1975
Full service production company.

Robin Miller, Filmaker Inc, see Filmaker Technology

Barney Miller's Inc
232 E Main St, Lexington, KY 40507-1310
Tel: 859-252-2216 *Toll Free Tel:* 800-755-6799
Web Site: www.barneymillers.com
Key Personnel
Pres: Barney Miller *E-mail:* bmiller@barneymillers.com
Founded: 1922

Home entertainment systems.
Membership(s): Home Technology Specialists of America

Mills James Productions
3545 Fishinger Blvd, Columbus, OH 43026-9489
Tel: 614-777-9933
E-mail: info@mjp.com
Web Site: www.millsjames.com
Key Personnel
VP, Sales & Mktg: Mike Yearling
 E-mail: myearling@mjp.com
Mktg Coord: Richelle Antczak McCuen
 E-mail: rantczak@mjp.com
Founded: 1984
Full service production company.
Branch Office(s)
Mills James Experience Group (MJx), 2250 Westbelt Dr, Columbus, OH 43228 *Tel:* 614-777-9933
Mills James Cleveland, 1220 W Sixth St, Cleveland, OH 44113 *Tel:* 216-443-0468
Mills James Cincinnati, 120 W Pike St, Covington, KY 41011 *Tel:* 513-407-5593
Membership(s): International Live Events Association; Meeting Planners International

Milner-Fenwick Inc
119 Lakefront Dr, Hunt Valley, MD 21030-2216
Tel: 410-252-1700 *Toll Free Tel:* 800-432-8433
 Fax: 410-252-6316
E-mail: mail@milner-fenwick.com
Web Site: www.milner-fenwick.com
Key Personnel
CEO: Richard Milner
Pres: David Milner *Tel:* 410-252-1700 ext 266
VP, Sales: John Pollara
Catalog(s) available

Mimi Productions
4343 N Western Ave, No 1N, Chicago, IL 60618
Tel: 773-293-7292
E-mail: info@mimiproductions.com
Web Site: www.mimiproductions.com
Key Personnel
Pres & CEO: Michelle De Long
Founded: 1997
Television & video production company, including industrial & training films, corporate & marketing videos, TV commercials & television series. WOSB & WBE certified.
Membership(s): NATAS

Mind Resources Inc
130 Shoemaker St, Unit 1, Kitchener, ON N2E 3G4, Canada
Tel: 519-895-0330 *Toll Free Tel:* 877-414-6463
E-mail: sales@mindresources.com
Web Site: www.mindresources.com
Key Personnel
Pres: Barry Kahl
Founded: 1976
Distribution of educational resources.

MindPlay
Division of Methods & Solutions Inc
4400 E Broadway Blvd, Suite 400, Tucson, AZ 85711
Tel: 520-888-1800 *Toll Free Tel:* 800-221-7911
E-mail: mail@mindplay.com
Web Site: www.mindplay.com
Key Personnel
CEO: Judith Bliss *Tel:* 520-888-1800 ext 104
 E-mail: judith@mindplay.com
Founded: 1986
Distribute & produce AV interactive programs focused on literacy.
Online catalog(s) available

Saul Mineroff Electronics Inc (SME)
574 Meacham Ave, Elmont, NY 11003

Tel: 516-775-1370 *Fax:* 516-775-1371
E-mail: tapenixon@aol.com
Web Site: www.mineroff.com
Key Personnel
Owner & Pres: Saul Mineroff
Founded: 1970
Focuses on sales, service, custom design & engineering of audio & video equipment.
Online catalog(s) available

Mirror 34 Productions
Formerly ProVideo
2302 W Badger Rd, Madison, WI 53713-2322
Tel: 608-271-1226 *Toll Free Tel:* 800-569-6810
E-mail: human@mirror34.com
Web Site: www.mirror34.com
Key Personnel
Exec Prodr: Jonas Dolkart; Jim Stiener
Prodn Mgr: Britta Thostrup
Founded: 1986
Full service production company.
Branch Office(s)
9663 Santa Monica Blvd, Beverly Hills, CA 90210
Membership(s): Madison Ad Federation

MISCO
2637 32 Ave S, Minneapolis, MN 55406-1641
Tel: 612-825-1010 *Toll Free Tel:* 800-276-9955
 Fax: 612-825-7010
E-mail: info@miscospeakers.com
Web Site: www.miscospeakers.com
Key Personnel
Owner: Dan Digre
Opers Mgr: Dave Wilson
Founded: 1949
Catalog(s) available

Mr Mark's Used Musical, Stereo & Studio Equipment Store
109 Grizzard Ave, Nashville, TN 37207-4413
Tel: 615-596-6094
E-mail: mrmarksmusic@aol.com
Key Personnel
Owner: Mark Stephan Hughes
Founded: 1980
Recording & production studio for audio. World's largest trader of used & vintage musical, stereo & recording equipment parts & manuals. Also, country music collectables, CDs, cassettes, posters & other paper products.
Catalog(s) available

Mitchell Acoustics Research
2005B Industrial Blvd, Rockwall, TX 75087
Tel: 214-741-7136 *Toll Free Fax:* 866-492-2470
E-mail: info@frazierspeakers.com
Web Site: www.frazierspeakers.com
Key Personnel
Pres: J E Mitchell
Speaker manufacturing.
Catalog(s) available
Membership(s): AES; NSCA

MKE Production Rental
159 N Broadway, Suite 202, Milwaukee, WI 53202
Tel: 414-939-3653
E-mail: rent1@mkeproductionrental.com
Web Site: www.mkeproductionrental.com
Key Personnel
Owner: Jon Kline
Founded: 2013
Cameras, lighting & grip rental for photo & video production & events in Milwaukee.

MMI Marketing
2950 Wyman Pkwy, Baltimore, MD 21211-2802
Tel: 410-366-1222 *Fax:* 410-366-1222
E-mail: mail@mmi-marketing.com
Web Site: www.mmi-marketing.com

Key Personnel
Dir: Ralph C Levy
Founded: 1973
AV planetarium (portable & permanent) observatory domes, AV astronomy & earth science.
Online catalog(s) available
Membership(s): International Planetarium Society

Mobile Arts Production Services, see MAPS Production House

Mobile Stage Rentals Inc
2331 N State Rd 7, Suite 221, Fort Lauderdale, FL 33313
Toll Free Tel: 877-882-8889 *Toll Free Fax:* 866-704-1194
E-mail: info@mobilestagerentals.com
Web Site: www.mobilestagerentals.com
Mobile hydrolic stage rentals.
Branch Office(s)
827 L'Ange Gardien Blvd, L'Assomption, QC J5W 1T3, Canada

Mobile-Video Productions Inc
7315 Wisconsin Ave, Suite 1300 W, Bethesda, MD 20814
Tel: 301-656-2525 *Fax:* 301-656-4343
E-mail: mobilevp@verizon.net
Web Site: www.mobilevideoproductions.tv
Key Personnel
Pres: Stephen King
Founded: 1977
Video production services.

Modern Communications Inc
1231 Horan Dr, Fenton, MO 63026
Tel: 636-343-0800 *Toll Free Tel:* 800-428-2442
 Fax: 636-343-0906
Web Site: www.modcomm.com
Key Personnel
VP, Broadcast & Prof Video Sales: Bill Johnson
 E-mail: bjohnson@modcomm.com
Founded: 1978
Video & audio systems dealer.

Modernage Photographic Services Inc
Division of Modernage
555 Eighth Ave, New York, NY 10018
Tel: 212-997-1800
Web Site: www.modernage.com
Key Personnel
Pres: Kenneth Troiano *E-mail:* ktroiano@modernage.com
Direct digital printing in color & on fiber base B&W paper, color & B&W ink-jet printing & large murals on paper or vinyl. Digital imaging, retouching, film output & giclee printing.
Catalog(s) available
Membership(s): ASMP; DIMA; The Imaging Alliance; NYPP

modprop.com
1044 Madison Ave, New York, NY 10021
Tel: 212-628-7582
E-mail: info@modprop.com
Web Site: modprop.com
Key Personnel
Pres & CEO: Stephen Wallis
Founded: 2001
Online modern furniture prop rental company.

Moe AV LLC
133 Deerfield Rd, Sayreville, NJ 08872-1618
Tel: 732-257-3760
Web Site: www.moeco.net
Key Personnel
Owner & Pres: Michael "Moe" Mosakowski
 E-mail: mike@moeco.net
Founded: 1981
Sound systems, AV, corporate meetings, consulting.
Membership(s): Synergetic Audio Concepts

Mohawk
Division of Belden CDT Networking Inc
324 Clark St, Worcester, MA 01606
Tel: 978-537-9961 *Toll Free Tel:* 800-422-9961
Fax: 978-537-4358
E-mail: o@mohawk-cable.com
Web Site: www.mohawk-cable.com
Founded: 1952
Manufactures high-end camera cables & assemblies.
Online catalog(s) available
Membership(s): NAB

Mole-Richardson Co
12154 Montague St, Pacoima, CA 91331
Tel: 323-851-0111 *Fax:* 323-851-5593
E-mail: info@mole.com
Web Site: www.mole.com
Key Personnel
CEO: Michael Parker
VP, Admin Opers: Andrea Setterstrom
VP, Sales: Glenn Weiner
Founded: 1927
Manufacturer of entertainment lighting equipment.
Catalog(s) available
Membership(s): American Cinematographers Society; Canadian Society of Cinematographers; NAB; SMPTE®; University Film & Video Association

Monaco LLC
145 Grassy Plain St, Bethel, CT 06801-2806
Mailing Address: PO Box 40, Bethel, CT 06801-0040
Tel: 203-744-3398 *Toll Free Tel:* 800-448-4877
Fax: 203-744-3228
E-mail: monaco@hangupbags.com
Web Site: www.hangupbags.com
Key Personnel
CEO: Mindy Capecelatro *E-mail:* mindy@hangupbags.com
Manufacture & distribute storage systems, filing bags & hang-up storage bags & pharmacy bags.
Online catalog(s) available

Monad Trainer's Aide Inc
163-60 22 Ave, Whitestone, NY 11357
Tel: 718-352-2314 *Toll Free Tel:* 800-344-6088
Fax: 718-352-8276
Web Site: www.monadtrainersaide.com
Key Personnel
CEO & VP: Eugene Richman *E-mail:* gene@monadtrainersaide.com
Pres: Carol Richman *E-mail:* carol@monadtrainersaide.com
Founded: 1973
Distribute self-development & group HR/training programs online & on DVD.
Catalog(s) available
Online catalog(s) available

Monadnock Media Inc
59 North St, Hatfield, MA 01038
Tel: 413-247-6447 *Fax:* 413-247-6448
E-mail: info@monadnock.org
Web Site: www.monadnock.org
Key Personnel
Exec Dir: Steven H Bressler *E-mail:* steve@monadnock.org
Opers Mgr: Laura T Varney *E-mail:* laura@monadnock.org
Sr Prodr: Claudia Levin *E-mail:* claudia@monadnock.org; Tracy Litwin *E-mail:* tracy@monadnock.org
Founded: 1980
Non-profit organization that designs, produces, & supports multimedia exhibits for museums. Commercial work not accepted.
Membership(s): American Alliance of Museums

Monarch Instrument
Division of Monarch International Inc
15 Columbia Dr, Amherst, NH 03031-2305
Tel: 603-883-3390 *Toll Free Tel:* 800-999-3390
Fax: 603-886-3300
E-mail: sales@monarchinstrument.com
Web Site: www.monarchinstrument.com
Key Personnel
CEO & Pres: Kenneth Grabeau
Sales & Mktg Mgr: Timothy French
Founded: 1982
Manufacture tachometers, vibration meters, stroboscopes, paperless recorders, data acquisition systems & other meters, as well as diagnostic inspection.
Catalog(s) available

Monotype Imaging Inc
600 Unicorn Park Dr, Woburn, MA 01801
Tel: 781-970-6000 *Toll Free Tel:* 800-424-8973
Fax: 781-970-6001; 781-970-6002 (gen questions)
E-mail: info@monotype.com
Web Site: www.monotype.com
Key Personnel
Pres & CEO: Scott Landers
EVP & CFO: Tony Callini
EVP & Chief Innovation Offr: Steve Martin
EVP, Gen Coun & Secy: Janet Dunlap
EVP, Sales & Mkt Strategy: Ben Semmes
Catalog(s) available
Branch Office(s)
127 Second St, Suite 2, Los Altos, CA 94022
Tel: 650-905-2900
25 Northwest Point Blvd, Suite 525, Elk Grove Village, IL 60007 *Tel:* 847-718-0400 *Fax:* 847-718-0500
260 Fifth Ave, 7th fl, New York, NY 10001
Tel: 212-389-6255
Foreign Office(s): Monotype Shanghai Representative Office, Rm 922, 9/F, Tower 12, KIC III, No 333 Song Hu Rd, Yangpu District, Shanghai 200433, China *Tel:* (021) 2510 1551
Monotype GmbH, Werner-Reimers-Str 2-4, 61352 Bad Homburg, Germany *Tel:* (06172) 484 418 *Fax:* (06172) 484 429
Monotype GmbH, Bergmannstr 102, 10961 Berlin, Germany *Tel:* (030) 69596 415
Monotype Hong Kong Ltd, 7A Yardley Commercial Bldg, 3 Connaught Rd W, Sheung Wan, Hong Kong *Tel:* 2575 6789 *Fax:* 2591 9232
Monotype Solutions India Pvt Ltd, Tower B, 4th fl, GYS Universal Plot A-3, 4 & 5, Sector-125, Noida, Uttar Pradesh 201 301, India *Tel:* (0120) 4524974
Monotype Ltd, Alexander House, 17a Ormeau Ave, Belfast BT2 8HD, Ireland
Monotype KK, MG Ichigaya Bldg, 5th fl, 1-9 Gobancho, Chiyoda-ku, Tokyo 102-0076, Japan *Tel:* (03) 5275 6251 *Fax:* (03) 5275 6252
Monotype Korea, No 805, Seongji Heights 3-Cha Bldg, Yeoksam-dong, Gangnam-gu, Seoul 135-717, South Korea *Tel:* (02) 2051-9900 *Fax:* (02) 6919-2044
141-143 Shoreditch High St, London E1 6JE, United Kingdom
Monotype Ltd, Unit 2, Perrywood Business Park, Salfords, Redhill, Surrey RH1 5DZ, United Kingdom *Tel:* (01737) 765959 *Fax:* (01737) 769243
Membership(s): ABCD; MicroComputer Industry Association

Monroe Electronics Inc
100 Housel Ave, Lyndonville, NY 14098
Mailing Address: PO Box 535, Lyndonville, NY 14098
Tel: 585-765-2254 *Fax:* 585-765-9330
Web Site: www.monroe-electronics.com
Key Personnel
COO: Jim Heminway *E-mail:* jfheminway@monroe-electronics.com
Pres: William E Vosteen

Founded: 1954
Catalog(s) available

Monster Cable Products Inc
455 Valley Dr, Brisbane, CA 94005-1209
Tel: 415-840-2000 *Toll Free Tel:* 877-800-8989 (cust serv)
Web Site: www.monsterproducts.com
Key Personnel
Owner: Noel Lee
Founded: 1979
Manufacture high performance cables that connect AV components for home, car & professional use as well as computers & computer games.
Online catalog(s) available
Membership(s): AES; AHFA; Custom Electronic Design & Installation Association; Music Business Association; NAMM, the National Association of Music Merchants

Monster Tracks
Division of Baker Sound Studios Inc
1821 Ranstead St, Philadelphia, PA 19103
Tel: 215-567-0400 *Toll Free Tel:* 800-369-1280
Fax: 215-567-0350
Web Site: www.monstertracks.com
Key Personnel
Music Dir: Chuck Butler *E-mail:* chuck@monstertracks.com
Gen Mgr: Ellen Kancher
Founded: 1987
Original music production for film, television, advertising & corporate.

monterey media inc
125 Auburn Ct, Suite 220, Westlake Village, CA 91360
Tel: 805-494-7199 *Fax:* 805-496-6061
E-mail: customerservice@montereymedia.com; publicity@montereymedia.com
Web Site: www.montereymedia.com
Key Personnel
CEO & Mng Partner: Scott Mansfield
CFO & Mng Partner: Jere Rae-Mansfield
Publicity Dir: Jennifer Manocchio
Mktg Mgr: Darrell Rae
Founded: 1979
Privately owned entertainment company specializing in the creation, acquisition, distribution & sale of motion pictures.
Membership(s): American Publishers Association; Coalition for Quality Children's Media; Entertainment Merchants Association

monterey video
Division of monterey media inc
125 Auburn Ct, Suite 220, Westlake Village, CA 91362
Tel: 805-494-7199 *Fax:* 805-496-6061
E-mail: customerservice@montereymedia.com; publicity@montereymedia.com
Web Site: www.montereymedia.com
Key Personnel
CEO & Mng Partner: Scott Mansfield
CFO & Mng Partner: Jere Rae-Mansfield
Publicity Dir: Jennifer Manocchio
Mktg Mgr: Darrell Rae
Privately owned entertainment company specializing in the creation, acquisition, distribution & sale of motion pictures.
Online catalog(s) available
Membership(s): American Publishers Association; Entertainment Merchants Association

Mood Creations Ltd
3541 Main St, Shruboak, NY 10588
E-mail: info@moodcreations.com
Web Site: www.moodcreations.com
Key Personnel
Pres: Scott Cohen *Tel:* 914-643-3031
Full audio & video production.

Moodtapes, see Ron Roy Productions/Moodtapes

Moog Inc
400 Jamison Rd, Elma, NY 14059
Tel: 716-652-2000
E-mail: info@moog.com
Web Site: www.moog.com
Key Personnel
Mktg Mgr: Amy Garrett *Tel:* 716-687-7157
    E-mail: agarrett@moog.com
Founded: 1951
Design & manufacture motion control products &
    systems. For the entertainment industry, simu-
    lation motion bases & solutions for Dark Rides
    & 4D theaters.
Online catalog(s) available
Brochure(s) available, PDF

Moog Music Inc
160 Broadway St, Asheville, NC 28801
Tel: 828-251-0090 *Toll Free Tel:* 800-948-1990
    Fax: 828-254-6233
E-mail: info@moogmusic.com
Web Site: www.moogmusic.com
Key Personnel
Pres: Mike Adams
Sr Sales Mgr: Linda Lafferty
Opers Mgr: Dean Cavanaugh
Prod Mktg Mgr: Trent Thompson
Founded: 1953
Manufacture & distribute electronic musical in-
    struments.
Catalog(s) available
Membership(s): MMA; NAMM, the National As-
    sociation of Music Merchants

Moore Creative Talent Inc
3130 Excelsior Blvd, Minneapolis, MN 55416
Tel: 612-827-3823
Web Site: www.mooretalent.com
Key Personnel
Pres: Andrea M Hjelm
Founded: 1958

MooreCo Inc
2885 Lorraine Ave, Temple, TX 76501
Toll Free Tel: 800-749-2258 *Toll Free Fax:* 866-
    888-7483
Web Site: moorecoinc.com; mooreco360.com
Key Personnel
Pres & CEO: Greg Moore
Founded: 1985
Visual communication products, technology sup-
    port equipment & office furniture for educa-
    tional & commercial markets.
Online catalog(s) available
Branch Office(s)
4930 S Congress, Austin, TX 78745 (showroom)
Membership(s): Audiovisual and Integrated Expe-
    rience Association; Education Market Associa-
    tion

Moose School Productions
Box 960, Topanga, CA 90290-0960
Tel: 310-455-2318 *Toll Free Tel:* 800-676-5480
    Fax: 310-455-4192
Web Site: www.peteralsop.com
Key Personnel
CEO: Peter Alsop *E-mail:* peter@peteralsop.com
Founded: 1975
Educational materials on child abuse prevention,
    chemical abuse & co-dependency, loss & grief
    for children & families. Video production ser-
    vices.
Online catalog(s) available
Shipping Address: 21418 Entrada, Topanga, CA
    90290
Membership(s): American Federation of Musi-
    cians

Morefield Communications Inc
35 N 35 St, Camp Hill, PA 17011-2707
Tel: 717-761-6170 *Toll Free Tel:* 800-382-1266
E-mail: info@morefield.com
Web Site: www.morefield.com
Key Personnel
Pres: John D Morefield
VP: Nicholas F Spallone
VP, Multimedia & Security Technologies: Jay R
    Dissinger
VP, Sales & Mktg: John M George, Sr
VP, Servs: Wesley W Kelly
Founded: 1945
Designs, installs & supports a wide array of in-
    formation technology solutions. Specialize in
    networking, IP telephone systems, IT support
    services, managed services, premise security &
    audio/video.
Branch Office(s)
801 S Kettle St, Altoona, PA 16602-5521
    Tel: 814-944-3344
Membership(s): NSCA

Morning Music Ltd
5200 Dixie Rd, Suite 203, Mississauga, ON L4W
    1E4, Canada
Tel: 905-625-2676 *Fax:* 905-625-2092
E-mail: info@morningmusic.ca
Web Site: www.morningmusic.ca
Key Personnel
Pres: Mark Altman *E-mail:* mark@morningmusic.
    ca
Founded: 1971
Online catalog(s) available
Membership(s): ASCAP; National Music Publish-
    ers' Association; The Society of Composers,
    Authors and Music Publishers of Canada

MorphoTrust USA, A Safran Company
296 Concord Rd, Suite 300, Billerica, MA 01821
Tel: 978-215-2400 *Fax:* 978-215-2500
E-mail: info@morphotrust.com; prmorphotrust@
    morphotrust.com
Web Site: www.morphotrust.com
Key Personnel
CEO: Robert Eckel
Founded: 2011
Identity solutions & services through the use of
    advanced biometric technology.
Branch Office(s)
1255 23 St NW, Suite 800, Washington, DC
    20037 *Tel:* 202-688-4800 *Fax:* 202-688-4801
3051 Hollis Dr, Suite 310, Springfield, IL 62704
    Tel: 217-793-2080
3400 E Coliseum Blvd, Suite 150, Ft Wayne, IN
    46805 *Tel:* 260-496-7500
1700 Dixon St, Suite 3, Des Moines, IA 50316
    Tel: 515-261-5400
5705 W Old Shakopee Rd, Suite 100, Blooming-
    ton, MN 55437 *Tel:* 952-932-0888 *Toll Free
    Tel:* 800-932-0890
6840 Carothers Pkwy, Suite 601, Franklin, TN
    37067 *Tel:* 615-871-0522 *Toll Free Tel:* 888-
    245-1114 *Fax:* 615-871-0845

Rex Morris Productions
5521 S Firethorn Place, Boise, ID 83716
Tel: 208-344-9878 *Fax:* 208-344-9878
Web Site: rexmorrisproductions.com
Key Personnel
Owner & Pres: Rex Morris *Tel:* 208-866-2143
    (cell) *E-mail:* rex142@juno.com
Founded: 1981

Morrisound Recording
PO Box 49004, Tampa, FL 33647
Tel: 813-989-2108
E-mail: info@morrisound.com
Web Site: morrisound.com
Key Personnel
Pres & Studio Mgr: Tom Morris *E-mail:* tom@
    morrisound.com

Founded: 1981
Full audio production services.

Jack Morton Worldwide
Member of The Interpublic Group of Companies
    Inc
909 Third Ave, New York, NY 10022
Tel: 212-401-7000; 212-401-7212
E-mail: experience@jackmorton.com
Web Site: www.jackmorton.com
Key Personnel
Chmn & CEO: Josh McCall
VChmn & Pres, Intl: Julian Pullan
COO & CFO: Bill Davies *E-mail:* bill_davies@
    jackmorton.com
EVP: Craig Millon
Chief Creative Offr: Bruce Henderson
SVP, Worldwide HR: Cara Antonacci
VP, Brand Mktg: Peter Sun *E-mail:* peter_sun@
    jackmorton.com
Founded: 1939
Catalog(s) available
Branch Office(s)
600 Battery St, 2nd fl, San Francisco, CA 94111,
    SVP & Mng Dir: Edward Scott *Tel:* 415-318-
    4300 *E-mail:* edward_scott@jackmorton.com
8687 Melrose Ave, Suite G700, West Hollywood,
    CA 90069, SVP & Mng Dir: Edward Scott
    Tel: 310-967-2400 *E-mail:* edward_scott@
    jackmorton.com
875 N Michigan Ave, 27th fl, Chicago, IL 60611,
    SVP & Mng Dir: Matt Pensinger *Tel:* 312-274-
    6060 *E-mail:* matt_pensinger@jackmorton.com
142 Berkeley St, Boston, MA 02116, EVP &
    Mng Dir: Steve Mooney *Tel:* 617-585-7000
    E-mail: steve_mooney@jackmorton.com
2000 Brush St, Suite 301, Detroit, MI 48226,
    EVP & Mng Dir: John Howard *Tel:* 313-596-
    9100 *E-mail:* john_howard@jackmorton.com
10 Applegate Dr, Robbinsville, NJ 08691, SVP
    & Mng Dir: Cyndi Davis *Tel:* 609-259-0500
    E-mail: cyndi_davis@jackmorton.com (ex-
    hibits)
Foreign Office(s): 114 Flinders St, Level 2, Mel-
    bourne, Victoria 3000, Australia, SVP & Mng
    Dir: Helen Graney *Tel:* (03) 8644 2100; (02)
    8231 4500 *E-mail:* helen.graney@jackmorton.
    com.au
Royal Naval House, 32 Grosvenor St, The
    Rocks, Sydney, NSW 2000, Australia, SVP
    & Mng Dir: Helen Graney *Tel:* (02) 8231 4500
    E-mail: helen.graney@jackmorton.com.au
Av Antonio Joaquim de Moura, Andrade,
    425, Vila Nova Conceicao, 04507-000
    Sao Paulo-SP, Brazil, Contact: Bill Davies
    E-mail: bill_davies@jackmorton.com
17/F China Life Tower, 16 Chao Wai Ave,
    Chaoyong District, Beijing 100020, China,
    SVP & Mng Dir: Evie Loo *Tel:* (021) 2411
    0060 *E-mail:* evie_loo@jackmorton.com.cn
16/F, Huai Hai Plaza, 1045 Huaihai Zhong
    Rd, Shanghai 200031, China, SVP &
    Mng Dir: Evie Loo *Tel:* (021) 2411-0058
    E-mail: evie_loo@jackmorton.com.cn
Kasernenstr 1, 40213 Dusseldorf, Germany, SVP
    & Mng Dir: Jens Oliver Mayer *Tel:* (0211)
    49554 504 *E-mail:* jens_mayer@jackmorton.
    com
Karlstr 68, 80335 Munich, Germany, SVP &
    Mng Dir: Jens Oliver *E-mail:* jens_mayer@
    jackmorton.com
10/F Oxford House, TaiKoo Place, Quarry
    Bay, Hong Kong, SVP & Mng Dir:
    Natalie Ackerman *Tel:* 2805 1767
    E-mail: natalie_ackerman@jackmorton.com.hk
MacDonald House, No 07-01, 40-A Orchard
    Rd, Singapore 238838, Singapore, SVP &
    Mng Dir: Charles Robinson *Tel:* 6499 8800
    E-mail: charles_robinson@jackmorton.com.sg
Dae-gong Bldg, 4/F, 126, Teheran-ro, Gangnam-
    gu, Seoul, South Korea, SVP & Mng
    Dir: Mike Kunheim *Tel:* (0208) 735 2000
    E-mail: mike_kunheim@jackmorton.co.uk

1st fl, MCN Hive, TECOM Section C, PO Box 6834, Dubai, United Arab Emirates, SVP & Mng Dir: Rebecca Amey *Tel:* (04) 559 1500
E-mail: rebecca.amey@jackmorton.com
16-18 Acton Park Estate, London W3 7QE, United Kingdom, SVP & Mng Dir: Mike Kunheim *Tel:* (020) 8735 2000
E-mail: mike_kunheim@jackmorton.co.uk

Mosby Inc
Division of Elsevier, Health Sciences Division
3251 Riverport Lane, Maryland Heights, MO 63043
Tel: 314-872-8370 *Toll Free Tel:* 800-325-4177
Fax: 314-432-1380
Web Site: www.us.elsevierhealth.com
Founded: 1906
Catalog(s) available

Mother Basilea Films
Affiliate of Evangelical Sisterhood of Mary
9849 N 40 St, Phoenix, AZ 85028-4099
Tel: 602-996-4040 *Fax:* 602-953-1303
Web Site: www.canaaninthedesert.com
Catalog(s) available

The Mother Co
1504 Fourth St, No 216, Santa Monica, CA 90401
Tel: 310-826-2400 *Fax:* 310-826-0024
E-mail: hello@themotherco.com
Web Site: www.themotherco.com
Key Personnel
Founder & CEO: Abbie Schiller
Pres: Samantha Kurtzman-Counter
Family-focused media company. Producer of the children's TV series "Ruby's Studio".

Mother West
187 Devoe St, Brooklyn, NY 11211
E-mail: info@motherwest.com
Web Site: www.motherwest.com
Key Personnel
Prodr: Charles Newman *E-mail:* charles@motherwest.com
Founded: 1990

Motion & Graphic Image Corp Inc (MAGIC)
25 McPhillips Ave, Mobile, AL 36604
Web Site: magichd.com
Key Personnel
Pres: Chris Meztista
Founded: 1989
HD acquisition & post-production.

Motion Picture Enterprises Inc
432 W 45 St, New York, NY 10036
Mailing Address: PO Box 276, Tarrytown, NY 10591-0276
Tel: 212-245-0969 *Toll Free Tel:* 800-673-3348
Fax: 212-245-0974
E-mail: sales@mpenyc.com
Web Site: www.mpenyc.com
Founded: 1948
Supplier of post production rental equipment & film supplies.
Publisher of the *Motion Picture TV & Theatre Directory.*
Catalog(s) available
Branch Office(s)
11222 Satellite Blvd, Orlando, FL 32837
Tel: 407-704-7859

Motion Picture Licensing Corp (MPLC)
5455 Centinela Ave, Los Angeles, CA 90066
Tel: 310-822-8855 (intl calls) *Toll Free Tel:* 800-462-8855 *Fax:* 310-822-4440
Web Site: www.mplc.org
Key Personnel
Pres, Licensing: Sal Laudicina *Tel:* 310-822-8855 ext 3007

VP, Licensing: Y Julian Eftekar
Opers Mgr: Stephanie Collins
Independent copyright licensing service exclusively authorized by motion picture studios to grant the Umbrella License.
Catalog(s) available

Motion Picture Marine
578 Washington Blvd, Suite 866, Marina del Rey, CA 90292
Tel: 310-951-1110
Web Site: perfect-horizon.com
Key Personnel
Pres: David Grober *E-mail:* davidgrober1@gmail.com
Camera stabilization equipment rentals.

Motion Picture Services
7542 Savannah Dr, Ooltewah, TN 37363
Tel: 423-238-7000
E-mail: info@motionpictureservices.net
Web Site: www.motionpictureservices.net
Key Personnel
Pres: Daniel R Johnson *Tel:* 423-238-7000
E-mail: dan@motionpictureservices.net
Founded: 1980
Motion picture film production serving network TV & motion picture film industry.

MotionArt Studios
27 Common St, Boston, MA 02129
Tel: 617-242-2228
Web Site: www.motionart.org; www.linestorm.com
Key Personnel
Founder & Dir: Pell Osborn *E-mail:* posborn@motionart.org
Founded: 1982
Media & design, animation education & production curriculum. Producers of public service announcements, videowalls & exhibit videos.
Brochure(s) available
Membership(s): Listen Up! National Youth Media Network; Mass Media Alliance; Massachusetts Cultural Council

MotionMasters
2288 Roxalana Rd, Dunbar, WV 25064
Tel: 304-345-8800 *Fax:* 304-345-8809
E-mail: storytellers@motionmasters.com
Web Site: motionmasters.com
Key Personnel
CEO: Diana Sole Walko *E-mail:* dsole@motionmasters.com
Sr Prodr: Diane Dimoff *Tel:* 304-345-8806
E-mail: ddimoff@motionmasters.com
Proj Mgr & Prodr: Richard Granberry *Tel:* 304-345-8804 *E-mail:* rgranberry@motionmasters.com
Videographer/Ed: Wesley Poole *E-mail:* wpoole@motionmasters.com
Founded: 1987
Award-winning corporate video production & design studio for TV, video, web or DVD.

Motor Racing Network
Subsidiary of International Speedway Corp
555 MRN Dr, Concord, NC 28027
Tel: 704-262-6700 *Fax:* 704-262-6801
E-mail: sales@motorracingnetwork.com
Web Site: www.motorracingnetwork.com
Key Personnel
Pres: David Hyatt
Founded: 1970
Voice of NASCAR.

Motown®
Member of Capitol Music Group
c/o Capitol Music Group, Capitol Records Bldg, 1750 N Vine St, Hollywood, CA 90028
Tel: 212-841-8000; 212-373-0750

Web Site: www.motownrecords.com
Founded: 1959

Mountainair Films Inc
PO Box 4097, Santa Fe, NM 87502-4097
Tel: 505-471-9293 *Fax:* 505-438-0294
E-mail: produce@mountainairfilms.com
Web Site: mountainairfilms.com
Key Personnel
Owner & Prodr: Alton Walpole *E-mail:* alton@mountainairfilms.com
Founded: 1989
Motion picture, documentary, commercial, feature film & video production services.
Membership(s): DGA

Mouser Electronics Inc - A TTI Berkshire Hathaway Company
1000 N Main St, Mansfield, TX 76063-1514
Tel: 817-804-3888 *Toll Free Tel:* 800-346-6873
Fax: 817-804-3899
E-mail: sales@mouser.com
Web Site: www.mouser.com
Key Personnel
Pres & CEO: Glenn Smith
VP, Busn Devt: Todd S McAtee *Tel:* 817-804-3672
Founded: 1964
Capacitors, resistors, inductors, potentiometers, switches, interconnects, fans, transformers (audio), tranducers, LED knobs, panel meters & switches.
Line card(s) available

Moviecraft Inc
PO Box 438, Orland Park, IL 60462-0438
Tel: 708-460-9082 *Fax:* 708-460-9099
E-mail: stock@moviecraft.com
Web Site: www.moviecraft.com
Key Personnel
Pres: Larry Urbanski
Founded: 1985
Stock footage archive. Online lists available.
Membership(s): Association of Moving Image Archivists

Movies Unlimited
Division of DirectToU
740 Hilltop Dr, Itasca, IL 60143
Toll Free Tel: 800-466-8437
E-mail: movies@moviesunlimited.com; info@moviefanfare; askmff@moviefanfare.com
Web Site: www.moviesunlimited.com
Key Personnel
Pres: Jeff Walker
Gen Mgr: Tim Hinsley
Founded: 1978
Catalog(s) available, annual

Moving Art by Louie Schwartzberg
3371 Cahuenga Blvd W, Los Angeles, CA 90068
Tel: 323-436-2229 *Fax:* 323-436-2230
E-mail: team@movingart.com
Web Site: www.movingart.com
Key Personnel
Founder & Dir: Louis Schwartzberg
Founded: 1997
Catalog(s) available
Membership(s): AMPAS; DGA

Moving Picture
748 N Victoria Park Rd, Fort Lauderdale, FL 33304
Tel: 954-522-1361 *Toll Free Tel:* 800-800-1361
Fax: 954-523-1361
E-mail: info@movingpicture.com
Web Site: www.movingpicture.com
Key Personnel
Pres: David Wells *E-mail:* davidwells@movingpicture.com
Post-Prodn: Monica Glaysher *E-mail:* monica@movingpicture.com

Founded: 1987

Specialized film & video equipment rentals, including cameras, lenses, lighting, grip equipment, camcorders, photographic equipment & supplies.

Branch Office(s)

400 NW 26 St, Suite 100, Miami, FL 33127 *Tel:* 205-522-1361

139 Fulton St, No 921, New York, NY 10038 *Tel:* 212-203-0218

Moving Pictures

Division of Innovative Video Services Inc

2820 Selwyn Ave, Suite 789, Charlotte, NC 28209

Tel: 704-676-0868

E-mail: info@mpicts.com

Web Site: www.mpicts.com

Key Personnel

Pres & Dir: Christopher Wilson

Founded: 1983

Brochure(s) available

Price list(s) available

Demo disk(s) available

Membership(s): Charlotte Film & Video Association

Moving Pictures

Unit of gener8or communications

PO Box 64, Chester, CT 06412

Tel: 860-704-6900

Web Site: www.gener8or.com

Film, video, multimedia & graphics.

Moviola

Subsidiary of J&R Film Co Inc

1135 N Mansfield Ave, Hollywood, CA 90038

Tel: 323-467-3107; 818-487-5000

> *Toll Free Tel:* 877-MOVIOLA (668-4652)
> *Fax:* 323-464-1518

Web Site: www.moviola.com

Key Personnel

Pres: Randy Paskal

SVP: Michael Mostin *E-mail:* mmostin@moviola.com

SVP, Opers: Jenna Andrews

VP, Data Media: Jerry Pierucci *E-mail:* jpierucci@moviola.com

VP, Sales: Jeff Buchignani; Dan Gillett

Principal Instructor/Training Opers Mgr: Jim Turner *E-mail:* jturner@moviola.com

Media Sales: Michelle Frazier *E-mail:* mfrazier@moviola.com

Founded: 1919

Catalog(s) available

Branch Office(s)

1015 N Hollywood Way, Burbank, CA 91505

4000 W Alameda Ave, Suite 220, Burbank, CA 91505

Moxie Media

1301 Dealers Ave, New Orleans, LA 70123

Tel: 504-733-6907 *Toll Free Tel:* 800-346-6943 *Fax:* 504-733-9493

E-mail: info@moxiemedia.com

Web Site: www.moxietraining.com; www.moxiemedia.com

Key Personnel

Pres & Exec Prodr: Martin Glenday

Mktg Dir: Parker Hillery

Busn Mgr: Lucy Glenday

Gen Mgr: Bob Stout

Sales Rep: Kim Gallup

Founded: 1985

Video & digital media production servicing. Produce & distribute safety & training programs for offshore oil & gas & maritime, marine & general industry. Distribute for other producers.

Catalog(s) available

MPLC, see Motion Picture Licensing Corp (MPLC)

MQ Power Corp

Division of Multiquip Inc

1800 Waters Ridge Dr, Suite 500, Lewisville, TX 75057

Toll Free Tel: 800-883-2551; 800-427-1244 (parts); 800-426-1244 (sales) *Fax:* 972-315-1847

E-mail: mqpowersales@multiquip.com

Web Site: www.multiquip.com

Key Personnel

Chmn & COO: Tom Yasuda

Pres & COO: Bob Graydon *E-mail:* bgraydon@multiquip.com

SVP, Opers: Mike Howlett

Founded: 1973

Manufacturer of generators for studios, special events, construction, telecommunications, military & emergency standby.

Catalog(s) available

Online catalog(s) available

MRM//McCANN

Member of McCann Worldgroup

622 Third Ave, New York, NY 10017

Tel: 646-865-6230

E-mail: gbc@mrm-mccann.com

Web Site: www.mrm-mccann.com

Key Personnel

Global COO, Mng Dir-US East: Kate MacNevin *E-mail:* kate.macnevin@mrm-mccann.com

Global CTO: Neal Prescott *E-mail:* neal.prescott@mrm-mccann.com

Pres, North America: Lori Feld

EVP & Chief Creative Offr: Sung Chang

EVP, Mktg Transformation & Performance: Pedro LaBoy *E-mail:* pedro.laboy@mrm-mccann.com

Dir, Communs: Nicole Dowswell *E-mail:* nicole.dowswell@mrm-mccann.com

Branch Office(s)

600 Battery St, San Francisco, CA 94111 *Tel:* 415-262-5600

360 W Maple Rd, Birmingham, MI 48009 *Tel:* 248-203-8000

105 Carnegie Ctr, Princeton, NJ 08540 *Tel:* 609-895-0200

60 E South Temple, Suite 1400, Salt Lake City, UT 84111 *Tel:* 801-257-7700

200 Wellington St W, Suite 1300, Toronto, ON M5V 0N6, Canada *Tel:* 416-594-6000

Foreign Office(s): Nicaragua 5468 Palermo, C1414BWB Buenos Aires, Argentina *Tel:* (011) 5550 0500

574 St Kilda Rd, Level 7, Melbourne, Victoria 3000, Australia *Tel:* (03) 9994 4177 *E-mail:* brent.clarke@mrm-mccann.com

32 Grosvenor St Sydney, Sydney, NSW 2000, Australia *Tel:* (02) 9994 4177 *E-mail:* brent.clarke@mrm-mccann.com

Heitor Penteado, 1.420, 5th fl, 05438-100 Sao Paulo-SP, Brazil *Tel:* (011) 3032 3339

Andres Bello 2711, 7550611 Santiago, Chile *Tel:* (02) 337 6991 *E-mail:* galvarino.ponce@mrm.cl *Web Site:* mrm.cl

Zhaowei Bldg, 9th fl, No 14 Jiuxianqiao Rd, Chaoyang District, Beijing 100000, China *Tel:* (010) 5804 0000

Huaihai International Plaza, 18F, 1045 Middle Huaihai Rd, Shanghai 200031, China *Tel:* (021) 2411 1121

69 Blvd du General Leclerc, 92583 Clichy Cedex, Paris, France *Tel:* 01 47 59 42 57 *Web Site:* www.mrm-mccann.fr

Grosser Hasenpfad 44-46, 60598 Frankfurt, Germany *Tel:* (069) 60 50 70 *Web Site:* www.mrm.de

30/F, Hysan Place, 500 Hennessy Rd, Causeway Bay, Hong Kong *Tel:* 2808 7888

Divyasree Chambers, Suites 11 & 15, 2nd fl, Wing A, 11 O'Shaugnessy Rd, Langford Town, Bangalore 560 025, India

F-Block, Voltas House, TB Kadam Marg, Chinchpokli (East), Mumbai 400 033, India *Tel:* (022) 6668 7777 *E-mail:* india@mrmworldwide.com

8 Balaji Estate Guru, Ravidass Marg, Kalkaji, New Delhi 110 019, India *Tel:* (011) 4903 5400

Via Valtelina 15/17, 20159 Milan, Italy *Tel:* (02) 85421

Shin-Aoyama Bldg E, 1-1-1 Minami-Aoyama, Minato-ku, Tokyo 107-0062, Japan *Tel:* (03) 3746 8900

Palo Santo 22, 11950 Lomas Altas, Mexico *Tel:* (055) 5258 5900

Jr Tripoli 102, Miraflores, Lima, Peru *Tel:* (01) 6108135 *E-mail:* miguelg.bulnes@mrm-mccann.com

18 Jules Michelet St, 010463 Bucharest, Romania *Tel:* (021) 23 200

40A Orchard Rd, No 05-01 The MacDonald House, Singapore 238838, Singapore *Tel:* 6737 9911

W Bldg 7th fl, 813-4 Yeoksam-dong, Kangnam-gu, Seoul 135-010, South Korea *Tel:* (02) 2186 9700

Josep Irla i Bosch 1-3, 08034 Barcelona, Spain *Tel:* 932 525 500

Enrique Jardiel Poncela, 6, 28016 Madrid, Spain *Tel:* 914 360 138

Grev Turegatan 11A, Box 5379, 102 49 Stockholm, Sweden *Tel:* (08) 506 500 60

98 Sathorn Square Office Tower, 25th & 26th fl, North Sathorn Rd Silom, Bangrak Bangkok 10500, Thailand *Tel:* (02) 343 6000

MCN Hive, Tecom, Section C, PO Box 6834, Dubai, United Arab Emirates *Tel:* (04) 445 4360

Bankside Studios, 76-80 Southwark St, London SE1 0PN, United Kingdom *Tel:* (020) 7153-8000

MRY

299 W Houston St, 14th fl, New York, NY 10014

Tel: 917-292-9429

E-mail: info@mry.com

Web Site: mry.com; www.facebook.com/MRY

Founded: 1987

Creative & technology agency.

Branch Office(s)

30 Hotaling Place, Suite 200, San Francisco, CA 94111, Mgr: Kingsley Taylor *Tel:* 415-293-2111 *Toll Free Fax:* 888-666-9741

Foreign Office(s): 146 Brick Lane, London E1 6RU, United Kingdom *Tel:* (020) 7063 6465 *Fax:* (020) 7063 6001

Membership(s): AIGA, the professional association for design

MSE Media Solutions

6013 Scott Way, Los Angeles, CA 90040

Tel: 323-721-1656 *Toll Free Tel:* 800-626-1955 *Fax:* 323-721-1506

E-mail: info@msemedia.com

Web Site: www.msemedia.com

Key Personnel

Owner: Fernando Ruballos *E-mail:* fernando@msemedia.com

Founded: 1986

Video tape restoration.

Catalog(s) available

Membership(s): NAB

MSI Production Services

10895 Thornmint Rd, Suite A, San Diego, CA 92127

Tel: 858-348-0100

Web Site: www.msiprod.com

Key Personnel

Owner, Partner & Pres: John Brinkman

Owner, Partner & Dir, Opers: Ray Lucy

Owner, Partner & Dir, Sales: Ed LaFever

Owner, Partner & Tech Dir: Tom Bollard

Founded: 1946

AV equipment sales & rentals, event production.

Catalog(s) available
Membership(s): ASAE; Audiovisual and Integrated Experience Association; HMA; HSMA; NAEM

MSR, see Mobile Stage Rentals Inc

MSU Technologies
325 E Grand River, Suite 350, East Lansing, MI 48823
Tel: 517-355-2186 *Fax:* 517-432-3880
E-mail: msut@msu.edu
Web Site: www.technologies.msu.edu
Key Personnel
Off Mgr: Tana Boehn *Tel:* 517-884-0287
Distribute & produce faculty produced materials in subjects such as veterinary medicine.
Online catalog(s) available

MTI Home Video
14216 SW 136 St, Miami, FL 33186
Tel: 305-255-8684 *Fax:* 305-233-6943
Web Site: www.mtivideo.com
Key Personnel
CEO & Pres: Larry Brahms *E-mail:* lbrahms@mtivideo.com
VP: Claudia Brahms *E-mail:* cbrahms@mtivideo.com
VP, Sales & Acqs: Jay Grossman
  E-mail: jgrossman@mtivideo.com
Founded: 1984

MTV
Subsidiary of ViacomCBS Domestic Media Networks
c/o MTV Studios, 1515 Broadway, New York, NY 10036
Tel: 212-258-8000
Web Site: www.mtv.com; www.mtvpress.com
Key Personnel
EVP, Communs: Jeannie Kedas *Tel:* 212-846-4629 *E-mail:* jeannie.kedas@mtvstaff.com
Founded: 1981
Branch Office(s)
1540 Broadway, New York, NY 10036
1575 N Gower St, Hollywood, CA 90028

M2 Communications
235 Bellefontaine St, Pasadena, CA 91105
Tel: 626-441-2024 *Toll Free Tel:* 800-423-8273
  Fax: 626-441-2694
E-mail: m2com@aol.com
Web Site: www.m2com.com
Key Personnel
Pres: Michael McKinney *E-mail:* mckinney@m2com.com
Founded: 1980
Membership(s): National Speakers Association

MTX Audio
Unit of MiTek Consumer Electronics Group
4545 E Baseline Rd, Phoenix, AZ 85042
Tel: 602-438-4545 *Toll Free Tel:* 800-225-5689
  Fax: 602-438-8692
E-mail: mtx@mtx.com
Web Site: www.mtx.com
Founded: 1983
Catalog(s) available
Membership(s): NAMM, the National Association of Music Merchants

Muderick Media
101 Earlington Rd, Havertown, PA 19083
Tel: 610-449-6970
Key Personnel
Owner: Michael Muderick *E-mail:* michael@muderick.com
Founded: 1984
Digital voice over narration.
Membership(s): IABC; SMPTE®

Michael Mueller Video Productions
211 Exchange St, Hot Springs, AR 71901
Tel: 501-282-4107
Web Site: muellervideo.com
Key Personnel
Owner & Operator: Michael Mueller
  E-mail: michael@muellervideo.com
Founded: 2000
Professional videography & video services (production, transfers & duplication). HD cameras, digital editing suite, transfers & duplications units.
Membership(s): WEVA

Ray Mueller Productions
5 E Waterloo Rd, Stanhope, NJ 07874
Tel: 973-691-2088; 973-801-6004
Web Site: www.muellerproductions.com
Key Personnel
Owner & Prodr: Ray Mueller *E-mail:* ray.mueller@verizon.net
Founded: 1996
Production & editing of videos, streaming video & DVD authoring for religious & nonprofit organizations. Avid video editing facilities.

Muller Entertainment LLC
Subsidiary of Muller Holdings International LLC
540 Commerce St, Southlake, TX 76092
Tel: 214-317-0800
E-mail: info@mullerentertainment.com
Web Site: www.mullerentertainment.com
Key Personnel
Pres & CEO: Justin K Muller *E-mail:* justin@mullerentertainment.com
VP & CFO: Alan Medellin *E-mail:* alan@mullerentertainment.com
Founded: 2002
Film/video production service company.
Membership(s): DPA; Texas Association of Motion Media Professionals

Mullikin Agency
1391 Plaza Place, Suite A, Springdale, AR 72764-5225
Tel: 479-750-0871 *Toll Free Tel:* 800-750-0871
  Fax: 479-750-2685
Web Site: www.mullikinad.com
Key Personnel
Pres: Randy Mullikin *E-mail:* randy@mullikinad.com
VP: Julie Magnuson *E-mail:* julie@mullikinad.com
Founded: 1994

Multicom Inc
1076 Florida Central Pkwy, Longwood, FL 32750
Tel: 407-331-7779 *Toll Free Tel:* 800-423-2594
  Fax: 407-339-0204
E-mail: multicom@multicominc.com
Web Site: www.multicominc.com
Key Personnel
Founder & Pres: Sherman G Miller
Dir, Sales & Mktg: Ray Shedden
Mktg & Technol Mgr: Matt Conrad
  E-mail: matt@multicominc.com
Sales Mgr: Scott Brietz
Founded: 1982
Manufacturer & full-line stocking distributor for end-to-end integration of communication solutions. Multicom stocks over 13,000 products from more than 270 of the world's major manufacturers. These products are used to acquire, process & distribute television, data, voice, security & traffic control signals over fiber optic, copper & coax cable.
CD-ROM catalog(s) available, free, distributed upon request

Printed material(s) available, free, distributed upon request, product specification sheets, product flyers, manuals
Membership(s): Audiovisual and Integrated Experience Association; NSCA; SCTE

Multicultural Media Inc
27 Main St, Suite 6, Montpelier, VT 05602
Tel: 802-839-0371
E-mail: support@worldmusicstore.com
Web Site: www.worldmusicstore.com; www.multiculturalmedia.com; www.lyrichord.com
Key Personnel
Pres & CEO: Stephen McArthur
  E-mail: stephen@multiculturalmedia.com
Founded: 1993
Producer of CDs & DVDs of classical, early & world music.
Online catalog(s) available

MultiDyne Video & Fiber Optics Systems
10 Newton Place, Hauppauge, NY 11788
Tel: 516-671-7278 *Toll Free Tel:* 877-MULTIDYNE (685-8439) *Fax:* 516-671-3362
E-mail: sales@multidyne.com
Web Site: www.multidyne.com
Key Personnel
Pres: Frank Jachetta
Sales: Matt Watkins
Founded: 1977
Manufacturer of fiber optic transport for video, audio, data, LAN, Elhbernet, Firewire, SDI & HD-SDI.
Online catalog(s) available
Membership(s): NAB; SMPTE®

Multimedia Audio Visual Inc
2640 S Raritan Circle, Denver, CO 80110
Tel: 303-623-2324 *Toll Free Tel:* 800-756-6118
  Fax: 303-623-0829
E-mail: info@multimedia-av.com
Web Site: www.multimedia-av.com
Key Personnel
Owner & Pres: Neal Cohen *E-mail:* ncohen@multimedia-av.com
Founded: 1992
Stage & event production, rentals.
Online catalog(s) available

Multimedia LED
4225 Prado Rd, Suite 108, Corona, CA 92880
Tel: 951-280-7500 *Toll Free Tel:* 888-98-MMLED (986-6533, sales); 800-888-3007 (cust serv)
  Fax: 951-335-8152
E-mail: info@multimedialed.com
Web Site: www.multimedialed.com
Brochure(s) available
Branch Office(s)
1359 Broadway, Suite 1108, New York, NY 10018 *Tel:* 212-404-7671

Multimedia Marketing Group
6048 Broadcast Pkwy, Loves Park, IL 61111
Tel: 779-774-3188 *Fax:* 779-423-0090
E-mail: info@mmg-1.com
Web Site: mmg-1.com
Key Personnel
Pres & Dir: Joseph Arco
Prodr: Susan Arco
Founded: 1984
Full service video production studio. Produce broadcast quality HD programs.

Multivision Video & Film
3031 SW 28 Lane, Miami, FL 33133
Tel: 305-662-6011
E-mail: info@multivisionvideo.com
Web Site: www.multivisionvideo.com
Key Personnel
Pres: Robert Berkowitz *E-mail:* bob@multivisionvideo.com

Founded: 1977
Video production.

Munday & Collins AV
2122 Zanker Rd, San Jose, CA 95131-2108
Tel: 408-451-9155 *Toll Free Tel:* 800-834-5551
    Fax: 408-451-9192
E-mail: info@avevents.com
Web Site: www.avevents.com
Key Personnel
Pres: Robert Munday *E-mail:* rmunday@avevents.
    com
Founded: 1944
Online catalog(s) available

Musco Lighting
100 First Ave W, Oskaloosa, IA 52577
Mailing Address: PO Box 808, Oskaloosa, IA
    52577-0808
Tel: 641-673-0411 *Toll Free Tel:* 800-825-6030
    Fax: 641-673-4852
E-mail: lighting@musco.com
Web Site: www.musco.com
Key Personnel
Mobile Sales Coord: Robyn Anderson
Founded: 1976
Membership(s): NAB

Muse Entertainment Enterprises
3451 Rue Saint Jacques, Montreal, QC H4C 1H1,
    Canada
Tel: 514-866-6873 *Fax:* 514-876-3911
E-mail: bpalik@muse.ca
Web Site: www.muse.ca
Key Personnel
Pres & CEO: Michael Prupas
Pres, Prodn: Irene Litinsky *E-mail:* ilitinsky@
    muse.ca
VP, Devt: Jesse Prupas *E-mail:* jprupas@muse.ca
Founded: 1998
Produces & sells TV series, movies, documen-
    taries, miniseries & feature films & interna-
    tional co-productions. Also supplies production
    services for international clients & press kits &
    "making-of" behind-the-scenes videos.
Brochure(s) available, free, annual
Branch Office(s)
Muse Entertainment Ontario, 2 Pardee Ave, Suite
    102, Toronto, ON M6K 3H5, Canada, Gen
    Mgr: Jonas Prupas *Tel:* 416-306-6473; 647-
    919-4711 *E-mail:* jonasprupas@muse.ca
Muse Entertainment USA, 4400 Coldwater
    Canyon Ave, Suite 355, Studio City, CA
    91605, Pres: Joel S Rice *Tel:* 818-358-3615
    Fax: 818-474-7700 *E-mail:* jrice@muse.ca
Membership(s): Academy of Canadian Cinema &
    Television; Canadian Film & Television Pro-
    duction Association; Television Academy

Muse Presentation Technologies
3510 S Susan St, Santa Ana, CA 92704
Tel: 714-850-1008 *Toll Free Tel:* 800-950-4955
    Fax: 714-850-1018
Web Site: www.museprestech.com
Key Personnel
CEO: Jim Muse *Tel:* 714-850-1008 ext 201
    E-mail: jimmuse@museprestech.com
Off Mgr: Nicole Pizzuto *Tel:* 714-850-1008 ext
    200 *E-mail:* nicole@museprestech.com
AV equipment rental/staging/sales.
Membership(s): Audiovisual and Integrated Expe-
    rience Association; Exhibition Approved Con-
    tractors Association; Healthcare Convention &
    Exhibitors Association; IAA-VC

Museum of the City of New York
1220 Fifth Ave, New York, NY 10029
Tel: 212-534-1672 *Fax:* 212-423-0758
E-mail: info@mcny.org
Web Site: www.mcny.org

Key Personnel
COO: Jerry Gallagher
Dir & Pres: Whitney Donhauser
Dir, Event Sales: Francesca Bertolino
Communs Mgr: Justyna Zajac
Costume & Textiles Curator: Phyllis Magidson;
    Elizabeth Farran Tozer
Founded: 1923

The Music Bakery
7522 Campbell Rd, Suite 113, Dallas, TX 75248
Tel: 214-636-5887
E-mail: helpnow@musicbakery.com
Web Site: www.musicbakery.com
Key Personnel
Pres & Exec Prodr: Jack Waldenmaier
Original music for films, videography, commer-
    cials, etc.
Online catalog(s) available
Membership(s): BMI

Music Group Commercial Ltd
335 Gage Ave, Suite 1, Kitchener, ON N2M 5E1,
    Canada
Tel: 519-745-1158 *Fax:* 519-745-2364
E-mail: musicinfoca@music-group.com
Web Site: www.music-group.com
A leading innovator of premium audio solutions
    utilizing cutting edge acoustic, electronic &
    digital expertise.
Catalog(s) available

MUSIC Group Services Nevada
Unit of MUSIC Group IP Ltd
5270 Procyon St, Las Vegas, NV 89118
Tel: 702-800-8290
E-mail: careente@music-group.com
Web Site: www.music-group.com
Founded: 1970
AV repair & service center.

Music Hall LLC
108 Station Rd, Great Neck, NY 11023
Tel: 516-487-3663 *Fax:* 516-773-3891
E-mail: info@musichallaudio.com
Web Site: musichallaudio.com
Key Personnel
Owner & Pres: Roy Hall
VP, Sales & Mktg: Leland Leard *E-mail:* leland@
    musichallaudio.com
Founded: 1985
Distributor & manufacturer of speciality audio
    equipment.
Online catalog(s) available
Membership(s): Consumer Technology Associa-
    tion™

The Music Kitchen Inc
12400 Connery Way, Bakersfield, CA 93312
Tel: 661-338-4749
Web Site: www.themusickitchen.com
Key Personnel
Pres: Michael Benghiat *E-mail:* michael@
    themusickitchen.com
Founded: 1991
Music production, production music library, Au-
    dio Addiction Music (6,500 tracks).

Music Lab Inc
500 E Saint Elmo Rd, Austin, TX 78745
Tel: 512-707-0560 (ext 2) *Fax:* 512-707-2946
E-mail: info@musiclab.net
Web Site: musiclabaustin.com
Key Personnel
Pres: Daniel Cabela
Rentals: David Nordyke
Founded: 1992
Retail, rehearsal spaces & rental gear.

Branch Office(s)
1306 W Oltorf St, Austin, TX 78704 *Tel:* 512-
    326-3816 ext 1
Membership(s): NAMM, the National Association
    of Music Merchants

The Music People Inc
154 Woodlawn Rd, Suite C, Berlin, CT 06037-
    1500
Tel: 860-829-9229 *Toll Free Tel:* 800-289-8889
    Fax: 860-828-1353
E-mail: support@musicpeopleinc.com
Web Site: www.musicpeopleinc.com
Key Personnel
Owner & SVP, Sales: Sharon Hennessey
Co-Pres/Owner & VP, Opers: John Hennessey
Co-Pres & Dir, R&D: James R Hennessey
Founded: 1979
Distributor of audio/video equipment & products.
Catalog(s) available
Membership(s): AES; NAMM, the National Asso-
    ciation of Music Merchants; NSCA

The Music Place
844 Rte 73, West Berlin, NJ 08091
Tel: 856-768-2226 *Fax:* 856-768-7135
E-mail: zeronemusic@aol.com
Key Personnel
Owner: Tim Zerone
Provide a full line of musical instrument needs
    including band instrument rentals.
Membership(s): Better Business Bureau; NAMM,
    the National Association of Music Merchants

Music Rhapsody
1603 Aviation Blvd, Redondo Beach, CA 90278
Tel: 310-376-8646 *Toll Free Tel:* 888-TRY-
    MUSIC (879-6874) *Fax:* 310-376-8490
E-mail: info@musicrhapsody.com
Web Site: musicrhapsody.com
Key Personnel
Owner & Pres: Lynn Kleiner *E-mail:* lynn@
    musicrhapsody.com
Founded: 1983
Music classes for babies & young children & re-
    tail stores.
Catalog(s) available

Music Sales Corp
180 Madison Ave, 24th fl, New York, NY 10016
Tel: 212-254-2100 *Fax:* 212-254-2013
E-mail: info@musicsales.com
Web Site: www.musicsales.com
Key Personnel
Pres: Tomas Wise
Founded: 1935
Publisher of books with music related DVDs &
    CDs.
Catalog(s) available
Branch Office(s)
1247 Sixth St, Santa Monica, CA 90401 *Tel:* 310-
    393-9900 *Fax:* 310-393-9925
Shipping Address: 2 Old State Rte 17, Chester,
    NY 10918 *Tel:* 845-469-4699 *Fax:* 845-469-
    7544 (dist)

Music World/Vocal Power School
9826 Columbus Ave, North Hills, CA 91343
Tel: 818-895-7464 *Toll Free Tel:* 800-929-7464
E-mail: MusicMan@music-world.com;
    provoice777@icloud.com
Web Site: www.BornToSing.com; www.music-
    world.com
Key Personnel
CEO: Howard Austin
Founded: 1981
Products & services for vocal performance.
Catalog(s) available
Membership(s): AEA; NAMM, the National As-
    sociation of Music Merchants; NATS; SAG-
    AFTRA

MusicMaster Inc
8330 LBJ Fwy, Suite B1050, Dallas, TX 75243
Tel: 469-717-0100
E-mail: info@musicmaster.com; sales@
  musicmaster.com
Web Site: www.musicmaster.com
Key Personnel
Pres: Joe Knapp *E-mail:* joe@musicmaster.com
Sell & manufacture music scheduling software for
  use by radio stations, video channels & Inter-
  net music providers. Also background music
  providers (non-broadcast).

Musicol Recording
780 Oakland Park Ave, Columbus, OH 43224
Tel: 614-267-3133 *Toll Free Tel:* 800-240-5963
  Fax: 614-267-3135
E-mail: info@musicolrecording.com
Web Site: www.musicolrecording.com
Key Personnel
Pres: John W Hull
VP: Charlene Hull
Opers Mgr: Warren J Hull *E-mail:* warren1@
  musicolrecording.com
Founded: 1964

Musikvergnuegen
1800 S Grand Blvd, Suite 114, Glendale, CA
  91204
Tel: 323-856-5900 *Fax:* 323-856-5917
E-mail: info@musikv.com
Web Site: www.musikvergnuegen.com
Key Personnel
Off Mgr: Adriana Wilbur *E-mail:* adriana@
  musikv.com

Musivision Inc
8 Deepwood Rd, Weston, CT 06883
Tel: 203-227-1017
E-mail: info@musivision.com
Web Site: musivision.com
Key Personnel
Pres: Fred Kessler *E-mail:* fred@musivision.com
Exec Prodr: Alisa Cohen
Production services company. Digital content,
  commercials, branding videos, corporate com-
  munications & more.

Mutoh America Inc
Subsidiary of Mutoh Industries Ltd
2602 S 47 St, Phoenix, AZ 85034-7401
Tel: 480-968-7772 *Toll Free Tel:* 800-99-MUTOH
  (996-8864) *Fax:* 480-968-7990
E-mail: sales@mutoh.com; support@mutoh.com
Web Site: www.mutoh.com
Key Personnel
Pres: Brian Phipps
Commns & Events Mgr: Michelle Johnson
Founded: 1963
Manufacture large format digital printers.
Catalog(s) available
Sales Office(s): 2291 W 205 St, Suite 105, Tor-
  rance, CA 90501 *Tel:* 310-783-0281 *Fax:* 310-
  783-0299
5950 Shiloh Rd E, Suite T, Alpharette, GA 30005
  Tel: 678-771-5890
5410 Newport Dr, Suite 32, Rolling Meadows, IL
  60008 *Tel:* 847-483-9107 *Fax:* 847-483-9108
99 Rosewood Dr, Suite 148, Danvers, MA 01923
  Tel: 978-739-1576
Membership(s): International Reprographic Association; International Sign Association; Specialty Graphic Imaging Association

Mutual Hardware
Subsidiary of Mutual Sales Corp
36-27 Vernon Blvd, Long Island City, NY 11106
Toll Free Tel: 866-361-2480 *Fax:* 718-786-9591
E-mail: info@mutualhardware.com
Web Site: www.mutualhardware.com

Key Personnel
Pres: Mary Stewart
Gen Mgr: Sal Trentacosti *E-mail:* sal@
  mutualhardware.com
Founded: 1935
Product distributor to the television & film indus-
  try.
Catalog(s) available
Online catalog(s) available
Membership(s): USITT

MVD Entertainment Group
203 Windsor Rd, Pottstown, PA 19464
Tel: 610-650-8200 *Toll Free Tel:* 800-888-0486
  Fax: 610-650-9102 *Toll Free Fax:* 888-536-
  7998
Web Site: mvdb2b.com
Key Personnel
CEO: Tom Seaman
Dir, Publicity, Mktg & Mdse Devt: Clint Weiler
  Tel: 610-650-8200 ext 115 *E-mail:* clint@
  mvdb2b.com
Founded: 1986
Catalog(s) available
Membership(s): Entertainment Merchants Associ-
  ation; Music Business Association

MVI - MultiVision Inc
120 McLevin Ave, Unit 3, Toronto, ON M1B
  3E9, Canada
Tel: 416-449-1080 *Toll Free Tel:* 800-563-5902
  (ext 228) *Fax:* 416-449-5131
E-mail: business@mvidisplay.com
Web Site: www.mvidisplay.com
Key Personnel
Owner & Chmn: Peter Penkala *E-mail:* penkala@
  mvidisplay.com
Pres: Christopher Parry *E-mail:* parry@
  mvidisplay.com
Founded: 1974
Full service AV support. Specialize in LED video
  displays.
Membership(s): Audiovisual and Integrated Expe-
  rience Association; SMPTE®; TESA

MVP International Inc
518 S Nevada Ave, Suite 2, Colorado Springs,
  CO 80903
Tel: 713-771-1132 *Toll Free Tel:* 800-432-0687
E-mail: info@mvp-av.com
Web Site: www.mvp-av.com
Key Personnel
VP: Charles Petering
Online AV training.
Membership(s): Audiovisual and Integrated Expe-
  rience Association

Myriad Productions
415 Barlow Ct, Johns Creek, GA 30022
Tel: 678-417-0043 *Fax:* 678-417-0043
Key Personnel
Pres: Ed Harris

Mystery Electronics LLC
6438 Morton Rd, Greenbrier, TN 37073
Tel: 615-643-8460 *Toll Free Tel:* 800-798-2256
  Fax: 615-643-8464
E-mail: sales@mysteryelectronics.com
Web Site: www.mysteryelectronics.com
Founded: 1979
Manufacturer of EasyMix DSP Remote Control
  Surface, floor boxes, wall boxes, wall plates &
  connection enclosures for AV & data systems.
Catalog(s) available
Membership(s): Audiovisual and Integrated Expe-
  rience Association

Mystic Seaport (Film & Video Archives)
75 Greenmanville Ave, Mystic, CT 06355
Tel: 860-572-0711; 860-572-5365
  Toll Free Tel: 888-973-2767

E-mail: permissions@mysticseaport.org;
  info@mysticseaport.org; advancement@
  mysticseaport.org (donations)
Web Site: www.mysticseaport.org
Key Personnel
Pres: Stephen C White
VP, Collections & Res: Paul O'Pecko *Tel:* 860-
  572-5366
Founded: 1929
Catalog(s) available, featuring maritime videos

Myton Industries Inc
1981 S Park Rd, Pembroke Park, FL 33009
Tel: 954-989-0113 *Toll Free Tel:* 800-544-2406
  Fax: 954-989-1488
E-mail: myton@msn.com; sales@
  mytonindustries.com
Web Site: www.mytonindustries.com
Key Personnel
Pres: Raymond Leone
Founded: 1974
Catalog(s) available

Nady Systems Inc
Division of PromarkBRANDS Inc
3341 Vincent Rd, Pleasant Hill, CA 94523
Tel: 510-652-2411 *Fax:* 510-652-5075
E-mail: ussales@nady.com; support@nady.com
Web Site: www.nady.com
Key Personnel
Sales Mgr: Ed Van Waes *E-mail:* ed@nady.com
Founded: 1976
Manufacture professional audio & AV equipment.
Catalog(s) available, free
Membership(s): AES; NAB

Nalpak Inc
1267 Vernon Way, El Cajon, CA 92020
Tel: 619-258-1200 *Toll Free Tel:* 888-488-3372
  (help desk) *Fax:* 619-258-0925
E-mail: service@nalpak.com
Web Site: www.nalpak.com
Key Personnel
Pres: Debra Kaplan
Pelican computer cases & Tuffpak cases for the
  television & motion picture industries.
Online catalog(s) available
Membership(s): NAB

Nandar Entertainment Pictures
Division of Nandar Group LLC
Lucy Bungalow, No 101, 5555 Melrose Ave, Los
  Angeles, CA 90038
Toll Free Tel: 800-969-6022
E-mail: mail@nandarentertainment.com
Web Site: nandarentertainment.com
Full service movie/television production & post-
  production company.

N&N Productions Ltd
5540 High Rock Way, Sparks, NV 89431
Tel: 775-355-9080
E-mail: sales@brassgobos.com
Web Site: www.brassgobos.com
Key Personnel
Owner: Ann Norris
Founded: 1982
Manufacture custom gobos for all theatrical light-
  ing instruments. Manufacture custom stencils at
  a stencilboard & plastic stencils as large as 12
  x 24 inches. Female owned.

NASCAR Productions LLC
550 S Caldwell St, Suite 2000, Charlotte, NC
  28202
Tel: 704-348-7100
E-mail: productions@nascar.com
Web Site: productions.nascar.com
Key Personnel
Dir, Busn Devt: Abbey Grahovac *Tel:* 704-348-
  7131 *E-mail:* agrahovac@nascar.com

Full service video & digital production company.
Membership(s): BMA; BPAA; IABC

Nashville Production Rentals (NPR)
125 Commerce Dr, Hendersonville, TN 37075
Tel: 615-431-5822
E-mail: mail@takeone.tv
Web Site: www.takeone.tv
Professional & broadcast HD equipment rentals.

National Association of Elementary School Principals (NAESP)
1615 Duke St, Alexandria, VA 22314
Tel: 703-684-3345 *Toll Free Tel:* 800-386-2377
   Fax: 703-549-5568 *Toll Free Fax:* 800-396-2377
E-mail: naesp@naesp.org
Web Site: www.naesp.org
Key Personnel
Asst Exec Dir, Conferences & Exhibits: Deborah Young *Tel:* 703-684-3345 ext 296
   E-mail: dyoung@naesp.org
Founded: 1921
Serving all elementary & middle school principals. Production of instructional videos.
Online catalog(s) available

National Audiovisual Center (NAC)
Division of National Technical Information Service (NTIS), US Department of Commerce
5301 Shawnee Rd, Alexandria, VA 22312
E-mail: info@ntis.gov; customerservice@ntis.gov
Web Site: classic.ntis.gov/products/nac
Key Personnel
Dir, NTIS: Avi Bender
Deputy Dir, NTIS: Greg Capella
Prog Mgr: John Hounsell
Distributor of videos, audiocassettes, multimedia kits & CD-ROMs. Provides access to AV/multimedia products from government organizations.
Catalog(s) available

National Boston
115 Dummer St, Brookline, MA 02446
Tel: 617-734-4800 *Fax:* 617-734-6323
E-mail: info@nationalboston.com
Web Site: www.nationalboston.com
Key Personnel
Client Servs Dir: Roger Bayley *Tel:* 617-734-4800 ext 134
Founded: 1992
Film & video services including HD.

National Council of Churches
110 Maryland Ave NE, Suite 108, Washington, DC 20002
Tel: 202-544-2350
E-mail: info@nationalcouncilofchurches.us
Web Site: nationalcouncilofchurches.us
Key Personnel
COO: Dr Leslie Copeland
CFO: Debra A Shaw
Pres & Gen Secy: Jim Winkler
Dir, Communs & Devt: Reverend Steven D Martin
Founded: 1950

National Education Association (NEA)
1201 16 St NW, Washington, DC 20036-3290
Tel: 202-833-4000 *Fax:* 202-822-7974
Web Site: www.nea.org
Key Personnel
Pres: Lily Eskelsen Garcia
VP: Rebecca S "Becky" Pringle
Secy-Treas: Princess R Moss
Exec Dir: Kim A Anderson
Founded: 1857
Educational video programs & PowerPoint teaching resources.
Catalog(s) available

National Event Marketing Inc, see Sky-View Search Lights & Promotions

National Film Board of Canada/Office National du Film du Canada
Ilot Balmoral, 1501 de Bleury St, Montreal, QC H3A 0H3, Canada
Mailing Address: PO Box 6100, Centre-ville Sta, Montreal, QC H3A 2H7, Canada
Tel: 514-287-9000; 514-261-1650 (animation studio) *Toll Free Tel:* 800-267-7710 (CN only); 800-542-2164 (US only) *Fax:* 514-841-3500
Web Site: www.nfb.ca; onf-nfb.gc.ca
Key Personnel
Commissioner: Claude Joli-Coeur *E-mail:* c.joli-coeur@nfb.ca
Founded: 1939
Canada's public producer of award-winning creative documentaries, auteur animation, interactive stories & participatory experiences. NFB producers are embedded in communities across the country, from St John's to Vancouver, working with talented creators on innovative & socially relevant projects. The NFB is a leader in gender equity in film & digital media production & is working to strengthen indigenous-led production, guided by the recommendations of Canada's Truth & Reconciliation Commission.
Online catalog(s) available
Branch Office(s)
9700 Jasper Ave, No 142, Edmonton, AB T5J 4C3, Canada *Fax:* 780-495-6412
   E-mail: northwest@nfb.ca
250-351 Abbott St, Vancouver, BC V6B 0G6, Canada
145 McDermot Ave, Winnipeg, MB R3B 0R9, Canada *Fax:* 204-983-0742
11045 Main St, 1st fl, Moncton, NB E1C 1H1, Canada
200-354 Water St, St John's, NL A1C 5W8, Canada
Bond Bldg, 201-5475 Spring Garden Rd, Halifax, NS B3J 3T2, Canada
145 Wellington St W, Suite 1000, Toronto, ON M5J 1H8, Canada *Tel:* 416-453-7452
   E-mail: ontarioinfo@nfb.ca

National Fire Protection Association (NFPA)
One Batterymarch Park, Quincy, MA 02169-7471
Tel: 617-770-3000 *Toll Free Tel:* 800-344-3555 (US & CN); 855-274-8525 (US & CN)
   Fax: 508-895-8301 *Toll Free Fax:* 800-593-NFPA (593-6372, US & CN)
E-mail: custserv@nfpa.org
Web Site: www.nfpa.org
Key Personnel
Pres & CEO: Jim Pauley
EVP: Bruce Mullen
Exec Asst: Melinda Collins
Founded: 1896
Video & online training.
Catalog(s) available

National Geographic Learning
Unit of Cengage Learning
10650 Toebben Dr, Independence, KY 41051
Tel: 859-525-2230 *Toll Free Tel:* 888-915-3276
Web Site: ngl.cengage.com
Founded: 1980
Publisher of preK-12 language & literary educational materials; Spanish & English.
Online catalog(s) available
Membership(s): Association of American Publishers

National Institute for Trial Advocacy (NITA)
1685 38 St, Suite 200, Boulder, CO 80301-2735
Tel: 720-890-4860 *Toll Free Tel:* 800-225-6482
   Fax: 720-890-7069
E-mail: customerservice@nita.org
Web Site: www.nita.org

Key Personnel
Dir, Mktg: Amy Shapiro *E-mail:* ashapiro@nita.org
Founded: 1971
Advocacy training programs that give attorneys the opportunity to learn & practice skills such as taking despositions, making opening & closing arguments, examining witnesses & more.
Online catalog(s) available

National Instruments Corp
11500 N Mopac Expwy, Austin, TX 78759-3504
Tel: 512-683-0100 *Toll Free Tel:* 888-280-7645 (sales); 877-388-1952 *Fax:* 512-683-8411; 512-683-5794 (sales)
Web Site: www.ni.com
Key Personnel
Co-Founder & Busn & Technol Fellow: Jeff Kodosky
CEO: Alex Davern
Pres & COO: Eric Starkloff
Treas & CFO: Karen Rapp
Chief Mktg Offr: Carla Pineyro Sublett
SVP & Gen Mgr, Electronics, Electrical Machinery & Energy Busn: Ajit Gokhale
SVP & Gen Mgr, Semiconductor Busn: Ritu Favre
SVP, Busn Devt: Pete Zogas
SVP, Global Sales, Support, Servs & Opers: Jason Green
SVP, Prod R&D: Scott Rust
VP, Gen Coun & Secy: R Eddie Dixon, Jr
VP & Gen Mgr, Aerospace, Defense & Govt Busn: Luke Schreier
VP & Gen Mgr, Transportation Busn: Chad Chesney
VP, Corp Strategy: Kevin Ilcisin
VP, Global HR: Cate Prescott
VP, Mfg: Rob Porterfield
VP, Prod Planning: Stefanie Breyer
Founded: 1976
Develops high performance automated test & automated measurement systems.
Online catalog(s) available

National Media Services Inc
613 N Commerce Ave, Front Royal, VA 22630
Tel: 540-635-4181 *Fax:* 540-636-4240
Web Site: nationalmediaservices.com
Key Personnel
Pres: Michael D McCool *Tel:* 540-635-4181 ext 246 *E-mail:* mike@nationalmediaservices.com
Prodn Coord: Susan Clark *Tel:* 540-635-4181 ext 223 *E-mail:* susan@nationalmediaservices.com
CD & DVD manufacturing & custom packaging.
Catalog(s) available

National Safety Council (NSC)
1121 Spring Lake Dr, Itasca, IL 60143-3201
Tel: 630-285-1121 *Toll Free Tel:* 800-621-7615; 800-621-7619 (cust serv) *Fax:* 630-285-1434 (cust serv); 630-285-1315
E-mail: customerservice@nsc.org
Web Site: www.nsc.org
Key Personnel
Pres & CEO: Lorraine Martin
COO: Nicholas Smith
CFO: John Udelhofen
Founded: 1913
Making our world safer. Occupational safety information & resources including online training & instructional videos.
Online catalog(s) available
Branch Office(s)
317 Massachusetts Ave NE, Suite 300, Washington, DC 20002 *Tel:* 202-602-1020 (govt aff)

National School Products
1523 Old Niles Ferry Rd, Maryville, TN 37803

Tel: 865-984-3960 *Toll Free Tel:* 800-627-9393
Fax: 865-983-9355 *Toll Free Fax:* 800-289-3960
E-mail: customerservice@nationalschoolproducts.com
Web Site: nationalschoolproducts.com
Key Personnel
Owner: John Nowell *E-mail:* nowell@nationalschoolproducts.com
Founded: 1974
Provide teachers with quality educational materials & supplies. Products include AV equipment, CD-ROM software, electronic learning aids, music & audio, videos & DVDs.
Online catalog(s) available

National Teaching Aids Inc, see American Educational Products LLC

National Teleproductions Inc
PO Box 1804, West Palm Beach, FL 33402-1804
Tel: 561-689-9271 *Fax:* 561-640-4677
E-mail: ntp@ntpworldwide.com
Key Personnel
Pres: Robert M Peterson
Founded: 1980

Nationwide Audio Visual Co
4100-B Sladeview Crescent, Units 1 & 2, Mississauga, ON L5L 5Z3, Canada
Tel: 905-608-8899 *Fax:* 905-608-8890
E-mail: sales@nationwideav.com
Web Site: www.nationwideav.com
Key Personnel
Pres: Shawn Quinlan
Founded: 1962
Online catalog(s) available
Membership(s): Audiovisual and Integrated Experience Association

NatureVision Stock Footage Library
4407 67 Ave Circle E, Sarasota, FL 34243
Tel: 856-873-6546 *Toll Free Tel:* 877-327-3207
Web Site: www.naturevisiontv.com
Key Personnel
Owner & Prodr: Jon Gorchow
E-mail: jgorchow@naturevisiontv.com
Searchable stock footage database. Royalty free footage collections & HD footage & production.
Catalog(s) available

NatureVision TV
4407 67 Ave Circle E, Sarasota, FL 34243
Tel: 856-873-6546 *Toll Free Tel:* 877-327-3207
Web Site: www.naturevisiontv.com
Key Personnel
CEO: Jon Gorchow *E-mail:* jgorchow@naturevisiontv.com
Founded: 2014
Distribution & production, broadcasting & streaming.

Nautilus Entertainment Design Inc (NED)
1010 Turquoise St, Suite 215, San Diego, CA 92109
Tel: 858-456-6395
E-mail: info@n-e-d.com
Web Site: www.n-e-d.com
Key Personnel
Pres, Principal Consultant & Lighting Designer: W James Tetlow *Tel:* 858-456-6395 ext 18
E-mail: jimtetlow@n-e-d.com
Founded: 1990
California certified consultants (analysis, design, specification, commission systems, drafting).
Membership(s): Entertainment Services and Technology Association

Navigator Systems Ltd
1312 W Main St, Suite E, Lebanon, TN 37087

Tel: 615-547-1895 *Fax:* 615-547-1897
Web Site: www.hiretracknx.com
Key Personnel
Sales & Training Mgr: Greg Smith
E-mail: greg@navigator.co.uk
Rental management software.
Foreign Office(s): Old Mills Industrial Estate, Unit 12, Paulton, Bristol BS39 7SU, United Kingdom *Tel:* (020) 7183 0011 *Fax:* (01225) 464984 *E-mail:* sales@navigator.co.uk *Web Site:* www.navigator.co.uk

Navitar Inc
200 Commerce Dr, Rochester, NY 14623
Tel: 585-359-4000 *Toll Free Tel:* 800-828-6778
Fax: 585-359-4999
E-mail: info@navitar.com
Web Site: www.navitar.com
Key Personnel
Pres: Jeremy Goldstein; Julian Goldstein
COO: Thomas McCune
Founded: 1946
Manufacture lighting & inspection equipment.
Online catalog(s) available
Branch Office(s)
Special Optics Division, 315 Richard Mine Rd, Wharton, NJ 07885, Gen Mgr: Steve Morales *Tel:* 973-366-7289 *Fax:* 973-366-7407 *E-mail:* sales@specialoptics.com *Web Site:* www.specialoptics.com
Membership(s): ACIA

Nazdar®
Subsidiary of Thrall Enterprises
8501 Hedge Lane Terr, Shawnee, KS 66227-3290
Tel: 913-422-1888 *Toll Free Tel:* 800-767-9942 (cust serv) *Fax:* 913-422-2296
E-mail: custserv@nazdar.com
Web Site: www.nazdar.com
Key Personnel
Pres: Mike Fox
VP, Global Sales & Mktg: Phil McGugan
Founded: 1922
Catalog(s) available
Foreign Office(s): Nazdar Asia, 10, Changi South St 3, No 04-04, Singapore 486147, Singapore
Nazdar Ltd, Battersea Rd, Heaton Mersey, Stockport SK4 3EA, United Kingdom *Tel:* (0161) 442 2111 *Fax:* (0161) 442 2001
Membership(s): SPAI

NBA Entertainment Inc
Subsidiary of NBA Properties Inc
450 Harmon Meadow Blvd, Secaucus, NJ 07094
Tel: 201-865-1500 *Fax:* 201-865-2626
Web Site: www.nba.com
Key Personnel
Pres, Global Media Dist: William S Koenig
EVP, Opers & Technol: Stephen M Hellmuth
Founded: 1982

NBC-5
4805 Amon Carter Blvd, Fort Worth, TX 76155
Tel: 817-429-5555 *Fax:* 817-654-6325
Web Site: www.nbcdfw.com
Key Personnel
VP, Digital Media Prodn & Res: Brian Hocker
Producer of TV commercials (taped).

NBC News Archives
Division of NBC News
30 Rockefeller Plaza, New York, NY 10112
Tel: 212-664-5015 *Toll Free Tel:* 855-NBC-VIDEO (622-8433) *Fax:* 212-703-8558
E-mail: nbcnewsarchives@nbcuni.com
Web Site: www.nbcnewsarchivesxpress.com
Footage licensing division of NBC News offering digital access to over 70 years of content from NBC, MSNBC & more.

NBC Production Facilities
Affiliate of NBC Broadcast & Entertainment Operations
30 Rockefeller Plaza, New York, NY 10112
Tel: 212-664-4444 *Fax:* 212-664-5056
Web Site: www.nbc.com
Catalog(s) available
Branch Office(s)
3000 W Alameda Ave, Burbank, CA 91523

NBCUniversal Archives, see NBC News Archives

NDS Surgical Imaging LLC
5750 Hellyer Ave, San Jose, CA 95138
Tel: 408-776-0085 *Toll Free Tel:* 866-637-5237
E-mail: info@ndssi.com
Web Site: www.ndssi.com
Key Personnel
Pres & Gen Mgr: Karim Khadr
VP, Engg: Rainer Scholl
Sr Dir, Global Opers: Mike Nguyen
Sr Dir, Quality Assurance & Regulatory Aff: Shala Famil
Design & manufacture surgical visualization, video processing & wireless imaging systems.
Online catalog(s) available
Foreign Office(s): Oriental Media Ctr, Suite 2302, Tower C, No 4 Guang Hua Rd, Chao Yang District, Beijing 100026, China *Tel:* (010) 8559 7859 *Fax:* (010) 8559 7853 *E-mail:* info@ndssi.com.cn *Web Site:* www.ndssi.com.cn
Bldg A - Engineering, Londynske nam 1/853, 639 00 Brno, Czechia *Tel:* 530 511 900 *E-mail:* customercare-emea@ndssi.com (technol ctr)
Novanta Europe GmbH, Parkring 57-59, 85748 Garching, Germany *Tel:* (089) 31 707 100 *E-mail:* info.novanta-europe@novanta.com (sales)
Novanta Japan, East Square Omori, 6-20-14 Minamioi, Shinagawa-ku, Tokyo 140-0013, Japan *Tel:* (03) 5753-2466 *Fax:* (03) 5753-2467

NEA, see National Education Association (NEA)

Malcolm Neal Productions
111 Everest Dr, Thomaston, GA 30286-4603
Tel: 706-646-2749; 706-647-5372
E-mail: nealritz@charter.net
Key Personnel
Owner & Prodr: Malcolm Neal
Founded: 1980
Foreign Office(s): 200 Longfellow Rd, Coventry CV2 5HH, United Kingdom, Contact: Pamela Reeve
Membership(s): ACTT

NEC Display Solutions of America
Subsidiary of NEC Corp
500 Park Blvd, Suite 1100, Itasca, IL 60143
Tel: 630-467-3000
Web Site: www.necdisplay.com
Key Personnel
Pres & CEO: Todd Bowman
SVP, Sales: Clark Brown
VP, Channel Sales: Betsy Larson
VP, Mktg: Jennifer Cheh
Catalog(s) available

NED, see Nautilus Entertainment Design Inc (NED)

Nelson Education Ltd
1120 Birchmount Rd, Scarborough, ON M1K 5G4, Canada
Tel: 416-752-9100 *Toll Free Tel:* 800-268-2222 (cust support) *Fax:* 416-752-8101
Toll Free Fax: 800-430-4445
E-mail: inquire@nelson.com
Web Site: www.nelson.com

Key Personnel
Pres: Greg Nordal
Provider of educational resources.

Nelson Enterprises Theatrical Supply Co
1014 Rte 173 E, Bloomsbury, NJ 08804
Tel: 908-479-6902 *Fax:* 908-479-6903
E-mail: sales@nelson-enterprises.com; rentals@
nelson-enterprises.com
Web Site: www.nelson-enterprises.com
Key Personnel
Owner/CEO: William A Nelson, III
E-mail: billnelson@nelson-enterprises.com
Rentals Mgr: Randy Werd
Founded: 1985
Online catalog(s) available

L E Nelson Sales Corp
Division of L E Nelson Corp
6050 S Valley View Blvd, Las Vegas, NV 89118
Tel: 702-367-3656 *Fax:* 702-367-7058
Key Personnel
Pres: Heidi Nelson-Dowd *E-mail:* hdowd@
lenelsonsales.com
Catalog(s) available
Branch Office(s)
915 Secaucus Rd, Secaucus, NJ 07094, Mgr: Dan
Imfeld *Tel:* 201-794-6700 *Fax:* 201-758-4363
E-mail: dimfeld@lenelsonsales.com
Membership(s): NAB; SMPTE®; USITT

Scott Nelson HD Productions Inc
PO Box 1198, Bend, OR 97709-1198
Tel: 541-410-8680
E-mail: snp@bendcable.com
Web Site: vimeo.com/scottnelson
Key Personnel
Owner & Pres: Scott Nelson
Founded: 1988
Video production services worldwide. Shoots HD
video with 240fps Sony FS5700, stills with
Canon 7D HDSLR.

Nelson White Systems Inc
8725-A Loch Raven Blvd, Baltimore, MD 21286
Tel: 410-668-9628 *Toll Free Tel:* 800-296-7555
Fax: 410-668-9629
E-mail: sales@nelsonwhite.com; service@
nelsonwhite.com; rentals@nelsonwhite.com
Web Site: www.nelsonwhite.com
Key Personnel
Pres: Thomas Wilder *E-mail:* twilder@
nelsonwhite.com
Founded: 1955
Systems integrator & AV equipment reseller.
Catalog(s) available
Membership(s): Audiovisual and Integrated Expe-
rience Association

Nemal Electronics International Inc
12240 NE 14 Ave, North Miami, FL 33161
Tel: 305-899-0900 *Toll Free Tel:* 800-522-2253
Fax: 305-895-8178
E-mail: info@nemal.com
Web Site: www.nemal.com
Key Personnel
Pres & CEO: Benjamin L Nemser
E-mail: bnemser@nemal.com
Founded: 1977
Manufacturer of electronic cable, connectors, as-
semblies & panels.
Catalog(s) available
Online catalog(s) available
Foreign Office(s): Nemal do Brasil Ltda, Av Mo-
rumbi 7948, 04703-001 Sao Paulo-SP, Brazil,
Contact: Carlos Heckmann, Jr *Tel:* (011) 5533-
4452; (011) 5535-2368 *Fax:* (011) 5049-
0378 *E-mail:* nemalbrasil@nemal.com.br *Web
Site:* www.nemal.com.br
Membership(s): NAB; SMPTE®

Otto Nemenz International Inc
870 N Vine St, Los Angeles, CA 90038
Tel: 323-469-2774 *Fax:* 323-469-1217
E-mail: info@ottonemenz.com
Web Site: www.ottonemenz.com
Key Personnel
Founder & CEO: Otto Nemenz
Gen Mgr: Alex Weingert
Opers Mgr: Marc Gordon
Founded: 1979
Rental & maintenance of motion picture & digital
cinema cameras, lenses & accessories.

NeoSoft Corp
PO Box 5667, Bend, OR 97708-5667
Tel: 541-389-5489 *Fax:* 541-388-8221
E-mail: sales@neosoftware.com
Web Site: www.neosoftware.com
Key Personnel
Owner/Pres: David Riley
Founded: 1990
Catalog(s) available
Membership(s): Association of Shareware Profes-
sionals

NEP Group Inc
2 Beta Dr, Pittsburgh, PA 15238
Tel: 412-826-1414 *Toll Free Tel:* 800-444-0054
E-mail: info@nepinc.com
Web Site: www.nepgroup.com
Key Personnel
Founder & Exec Chmn: Deb Honkus
CEO: Kevin Rabbitt
CFO: Gerry Delon
Pres, US: Glen Levine
Chief Strategy Offr: Carrie Galvin
SVP, HR: Lynda Wilkes
SVP, IT: John Gierl
VP, Systems Integration, US Mobile Units: Joe
Signorino
Pres, NEP Broadcast Servs: Mike Werteen
Pres, NEP Broadcast Solutions: Saeed Izadi
SVP & Gen Mgr, NEP Studios: Barry Katz
VP, Entertainment Mobile Units: Kevin Hayes
Chief Engr, NEP US Mobile Units: Dan Turk

Neptune Photo Inc
130 Seventh St, Garden City, NY 11530
Tel: 516-741-4484 *Toll Free Tel:* 800-955-1110
E-mail: sales@neptunephoto.com
Web Site: www.neptunephoto.com
Key Personnel
Pres: Robert K Jacobs
Catalog(s) available
Membership(s): Audiovisual and Integrated Expe-
rience Association

Nesbit Systems Inc
243 N Union St, Suite 112, Lambertville, NJ
08530
Tel: 609-397-7720
E-mail: info@nesbit.com
Web Site: www.nesbit.com
Key Personnel
Pres: Irene S Nesbit *E-mail:* irene@nesbit.com
EVP: Ken Michielsen
Providers of media asset tracking software & con-
sulting services.
Sales Office(s): PO Box 106, New York, NY
10021 *Tel:* 212-268-2717

NetWell Noise Control
18525 37 Ave N, Minneapolis, MN 55446-2855
Tel: 763-694-8908 *Toll Free Tel:* 800-638-9355
Fax: 763-694-8909
E-mail: help@controlnoise.com
Web Site: www.controlnoise.com
Key Personnel
Pres: Mark Rustad
Founded: 1991

Manufacture & distribute noise reduction products.
Online catalog(s) available

Network Entertainment Inc
1488 Frances St, Vancouver, BC V5L 1Y9,
Canada
Tel: 604-739-8825 *Fax:* 604-739-8835
E-mail: info@networkentertainment.ca
Web Site: www.networkentertainment.ca
Key Personnel
Founder/CEO: Derik Murray
Pres & COO: Paul Gertz
Founded: 1999
Television, feature film production & production
service company.
Membership(s): Canadian Film & Television Pro-
duction Association

Network Technologies Inc
1275 Danner Dr, Aurora, OH 44202
Tel: 330-562-7070 *Toll Free Tel:* 800-742-8324
Fax: 330-562-1999
E-mail: sales@ntigo.com
Web Site: www.networktechinc.com
Key Personnel
Sr Acct Exec: Tammy Kuhn *E-mail:* tammy.
kuhn@ntigo.com
Catalog(s) available
Online catalog(s) available

Neumann USA
Member of The Sennheiser Group
One Enterprise Dr, Old Lyme, CT 06371
Tel: 860-434-9190 *Fax:* 860-434-1759
E-mail: neumann-help@neumannusa.com
Web Site: www.neumannusa.com
Catalog(s) available
Membership(s): AES

Neutrik® USA Inc
4115 Taggart Creek Rd, Charlotte, NC 28208
Tel: 704-972-3050 *Fax:* 704-438-9202
Toll Free Fax: 877-220-4089
E-mail: info@neutrik.us
Web Site: www.neutrik.us
Key Personnel
Pres: Pete Milbery *E-mail:* pmilbery@neutrikusa.
com
Prod Dir: Fred Morgenstern
E-mail: fmorgenstern@neutrikusa.com
Applications Mgr: Mark Boyadjian
E-mail: mboyadjian@neutrikusa.com
Founded: 1975
Solder or IDC XLR connectors; 1/4 inch
jacks/plugs; Combo; EasyPatch TT/TB pro-
grammable patchbays; patchcords; PatchLink
SPL® or RPM 1/4 inch balanced patchpanels;
circular DIN; RCA jacks/plugs; 3.5mm plugs;
BNC connectors; full accessory line including
DMX adapters. Ethercon® ruggedized RJ45
series, Speakon® SPX & STX, Powercon®.
REAN plastic knobs, sliders, buttons; TT/TB
quad cords.
Online catalog(s) available

Nevion USA Inc
Subsidiary of Nevion AS
400 W Ventura Blvd, Suite 155, Camarillo, CA
93010
Tel: 805-247-8560
E-mail: ussales@nevion.com
Web Site: nevion.com
Develops, produces, markets & sells hardware &
software & complete solutions for the transport
of broadcast quality audio & video.
Foreign Office(s): Suite 713, Henderson Ctr, No
18 Jianguomennei Ave, Beijing 100005, China
E-mail: asiasales@nevion.com
Nevion AS, Lysaker Torg 5, 1366 Lysaker, Nor-
way *Tel:* 22 88 97 50 *E-mail:* sales@nevion.
com (headquarters)

Nordre Kullerod 1, 3241 Sandefjord, Norway
Tel: 33 48 99 99 99 *E-mail:* sales@nevion.com
Ul Trakt Sw Wojciecha 237, 80-017 Gdansk,
Poland *Tel:* (58) 3191085
No 05-01 Parkview Sq, 600 North Bridge Rd,
Singapore 188778, Singapore *Tel:* 6678 6581
E-mail: asiasales@nevion.com
Dubai Media City, Bldg 8, Media Busn Ctr, Off
60, PO Box 502199, Dubai, United Arab Emi-
rates *Tel:* (04) 390 1018 *E-mail:* middle-east@
nevion.com
Unit 11 Brewery Ct, High St, Theale, Reading,
Berks RG7 5AJ, United Kingdom *Tel:* (0118)
973 5831 *E-mail:* uksales@nevion.com
N2-02 Columba House, Adastral Park, Martle-
sham Heath, Ipswich, Suffolk IP5 3RE, United
Kingdom *Tel:* (01473) 617 370
Membership(s): SMPTE®

New & Unique Videos™
Subsidiary of Crystal Pyramid Productions™
7323 Rondel Ct, San Diego, CA 92119-1530
Tel: 619-644-3000
E-mail: video@newuniquevideos.com
Web Site: www.newuniquevideos.com
Key Personnel
CEO: Mark Schulze
CFO & COO: Patty Mooney
Acqs: Candace Love
Online catalog(s) available
Membership(s): NATAS; SDMediaPros; Televi-
sion Academy

New Circuit Films LLC
421 Canyon Dr, Glendale, CA 91206
Tel: 818-378-0033
Web Site: www.newcircuit.com
Key Personnel
Mgr: Roy Kurtluyan *E-mail:* roy@newcircuit.com
Full service film & video production company.
Camera crews for entertainment, TV & corpo-
rations. Rental of 4K, 2K, HD & XDCAM film
cameras.

New Cyberian Systems Inc
1919 O'Toole Way, San Jose, CA 95131
Tel: 408-922-0682 *Toll Free Tel:* 877-423-4383
Fax: 408-884-2257
E-mail: sales@newcyberian.com
Web Site: www.newcyberian.com
Key Personnel
Pres: Isaac Cheung
Founded: 2000
CD/DVD/Blu-ray replication & duplication with
facilities worldwide.
Brochure(s) available, free, quarterly

New Day Films
190 Rte 17 M, Suite D, Harriman, NY 10926
Toll Free Tel: 888-367-9154 *Fax:* 845-774-2945
E-mail: orders@newday.com; curator@newday.
com
Web Site: www.newday.com
Founded: 1971
Collective of independent filmmaker run distribu-
tion company with company members selecting
the films that are made available.
Catalog(s) available
Online catalog(s) available

New Deal Studios
15392 Cobalt St, Los Angeles, CA 91342
Tel: 310-578-9929
E-mail: info@newdealstudios.com
Web Site: www.newdealstudios.com
Key Personnel
Co-Founder & CEO: Shannon Blake Gans
Co-Founder & Creative Dir: Ian Hunter; Matthew
Gratzner
Creative Dir: Dave Asling
Digital FX Supv & CTO: Jeffrey Jasper

Head, Prodn: David Sanger
Founded: 1995
Design, previsualization, fabrication, photography,
production, compositing, 3D animation & post-
production services. Visual effects for feature
films. Produces features, shorts & commercial
spots.

New England Keyboard Inc
One Princeton Rd, Fitchburg, MA 01420
Tel: 978-345-8332 *Fax:* 978-345-4329
E-mail: info@newenglandkeyboard.com
Web Site: www.newenglandkeyboard.com
Key Personnel
Gen Mgr: Mark Yates
Manufacture computer input devices.
Catalog(s) available

New England Technology Group Inc (NETG)
One Davenport St, Cambridge, MA 02140
Tel: 617-864-5551 *Fax:* 520-844-5551
E-mail: teamnetg@netgworld.com
Web Site: netgworld.com
Key Personnel
Pres: Steven Gregory
Founded: 1981
Specialize in design & production of interactive
multimedia systems for a wide variety of appli-
cations.

New Era Media, see Ark Media Group Ltd

The New Film Company Inc
7 Scott St, Cambridge, MA 02138
Tel: 617-520-5005 *Fax:* 617-491-9201
E-mail: newfilmco@aol.com
Web Site: www.newfilmco.com
Key Personnel
Pres: Christopher Knight
Sales Mgr: Joyce A Zinno
Founded: 1969
Online catalog(s) available

New Harbinger Publications
5674 Shattuck Ave, Oakland, CA 94609
Tel: 510-652-0215 *Toll Free Tel:* 800-748-6273
Fax: 510-652-5472
E-mail: customerservice@newharbinger.com
Web Site: www.newharbinger.com
Key Personnel
CFO: Kirk Johnson
Pres & Publr: Matthew McKay, PhD
Sales & Mktg Dir: Julie Bennett
Founded: 1973
The best in self-help psychology & health books
& CDs.
Catalog(s) available, free on request
Online catalog(s) available

New Horizon Studios
202 E 42 St, New York, NY 10017
Tel: 212-490-0355
Key Personnel
Pres: Joe Bevilacqua
Membership(s): ASMP

New Horizons Computer Learning Centers Inc
100 Four Falls Corporate Ctr, Suite 408, Con-
shohocken, PA 19428-4132
Tel: 484-567-3000 *Toll Free Tel:* 888-236-3625
Web Site: www.newhorizons.com
Key Personnel
CEO: Earle Pratt
Independent IT training company with 300 cen-
ters in 70 countries.
Online catalog(s) available
Branch Office(s)
1900 S State College Blvd, Suite 450, Anaheim,
CA 92806-6135 (corp off)

Foreign Office(s): One Maritime Sq, No 10-24/25,
Lobby B, Harbourfront Ctr, Singapore 099253,
Singapore *Tel:* 6822 8282 *E-mail:* info@
newhorizons.com.sg

New Leaf Distributing Co
Subsidiary of Shakti LLC
401 Thornton Rd, Lithia Springs, GA 30122-1557
Tel: 770-948-7845 *Toll Free Tel:* 800-326-2665
(orders) *Fax:* 770-944-2313 *Toll Free Fax:* 800-
326-1066
E-mail: customerservice@newleaf-dist.com
Web Site: newleaf-dist.com
Key Personnel
Pres: Santosh Krinsky
VP, Opers: Karen Price
Founded: 1975
Catalog(s) available, monthly

New Letters on the Air
c/o University of Missouri, Kansas City, 5101
Rockhill Rd, Kansas City, MO 64110
Tel: 816-235-1159; 816-235-1168 *Fax:* 816-235-
2611
E-mail: radio@newletters.org
Web Site: www.newletters.org
Key Personnel
Prodr/Host: Angela Elam
Asst Prodr: Jamie Walsh *Tel:* 816-235-5182
E-mail: walshjm@umkc.edu
Founded: 1977
Half-hour radio show produced by & audio com-
panion to *New Letters* quarterly literary maga-
zine. Distributed via the Public Radio Satellite
System & the Public Radio Exchange (PRX).
Online catalog(s) available, updated weekly

New Life Communications Inc
905 Hwy 71 NE, Willmar, MN 56201-2654
Mailing Address: PO Box 1075, Willmar, MN
56201-1075
Tel: 320-235-6404 *Toll Free Tel:* 800-233-6470
Fax: 320-235-6418
E-mail: nlc@newlifecomm.com
Web Site: www.newlifecomm.com
Key Personnel
Owner & Engr: Ron Huisinga
Sales: David Honken
Founded: 1973
AV contractor.
Membership(s): NSCA

New Line Cinema
Division of Warner Bros Entertainment Inc
116 N Robertson Blvd, Suite 200, Los Angeles,
CA 90048
Tel: 310-854-5811 *Fax:* 310-854-1824
Web Site: www.warnerbros.com/studio/divisions/
new-line-cinema
Key Personnel
Chairman: Toby Emmerich
Founded: 1967
Catalog(s) available
Branch Office(s)
4000 Warner Blvd, Burbank, CA 91522 *Tel:* 818-
954-6000 (headquarters)
New Line Productions, 888 Seventh Ave, 20th fl,
New York, NY 10106-2599 *Tel:* 212-649-4900
Fax: 212-649-4966

New London Media
78 Washington St, New London, CT 06320
Tel: 860-961-6300
Web Site: www.andrewclydebell.com
Key Personnel
Owner: Andrew Bell *E-mail:* andrew@
newlondonmedia.com

New Wave Entertainment
2660 W Olive Ave, Burbank, CA 91505
Tel: 818-295-5000

E-mail: biz@nwe.com
Web Site: nwe.com
Key Personnel
CEO: Paul Apel
COO: Rick Nowak
EVP & CFO: Greg Woertz
SVP, Post Prodn: Shawn Stoner
SVP, Opers: Kit Chambers
VP, Tech Opers: Michael Clow
Production, creative marketing & talent management company.
Branch Office(s)
35 W 36 St, 10th fl, New York, NY 10018

New World Records
20 Jay St, Suite 1001, Brooklyn, NY 11201
Tel: 212-290-1680 *Fax:* 646-224-9638
E-mail: info@newworldrecords.org
Web Site: www.newworldrecords.org
Key Personnel
Pres & CFO: Lisa Kahlden *Tel:* 646-442-7929
  E-mail: lkahlden@dramonline.org
Founded: 1975
Like the university press, New World preserves neglected treasures of the past & nurtures the creative future of American music. In an industry obsessed with million-unit sales & immediate profits, New World chooses artistic merit as its indicator of success.
Catalog(s) available
Online catalog(s) available

New York Audio Productions
344 W 38 St, 6th fl, New York, NY 10018
Tel: 212-244-1114 *Fax:* 212-243-7210
E-mail: info@nyaudio.com
Web Site: www.nyaudio.com
Producing audio books.
Catalog(s) available

New York Camera & Video
1139 Street Rd, Southampton, PA 18966
Tel: 215-357-6222
E-mail: rentals@nycv.com
Web Site: www.nycv.com
Founded: 1978
Sells & rents new & used photographic & video equipment & supplies. Video & film to DVD transfer, audio transfer, equipment rental, restoration, video editing.

The New York Historical Society
170 Central Park W, New York, NY 10024
Tel: 212-873-3400 *Fax:* 212-787-9474
Web Site: www.nyhistory.org
Key Personnel
Pres & CEO: Louise Mirrer *E-mail:* lmirrer@
  nyhistory.org
Founded: 1804

New York Sound Inc
166 Fifth Ave, No 6, New York, NY 10010
Tel: 917-523-0770
E-mail: nysnd@mac.com
Web Site: www.newyorksound.net
Key Personnel
Pres: Joe Cunningham
Audio pre- & post-production for film, video, radio & TV.

The New York Times Photo Archive
Division of NYT Licensing
The New York Times Co, 620 Eighth Ave, New York, NY 10018
E-mail: nytlg-sales@nytimes.com
Web Site: nytlicensing.com
Photo licensing. Access to over 4,000 historic photographs.

The Newhouse Media Group
13710 Antler Point Dr, Tampa, FL 33626

Tel: 813-625-2326
Web Site: www.newhousemediagroup.com
Key Personnel
Owner, Pres & Chief Creative Offr: Zack Koczanski *E-mail:* zack@newhousemediagroup.com
VP, Mktg: Kathi Koczanski
Founded: 1985
Video infomercials. Creating the video that matches your message.

NEWIST/CESA 7
595 Baeten Rd, Green Bay, WI 54304
Tel: 920-617-5614 *Fax:* 920-492-5964
E-mail: contactus@cesa7.org
Web Site: www.cesa7.org/o/CESA%207/page/
  communications-video
Key Personnel
Off Mgr: Pam Racine
Founded: 1967
Produces award-winning documentaries on today's social issues.
Catalog(s) available, free

Julye Newlin Productions Inc
129 E 13 St, Houston, TX 77008
Tel: 713-869-3609; 832-689-3609 (cell) *Fax:* 713-862-6505
E-mail: julye@julyenewlin.com
Web Site: www.julyenewlin.com
Key Personnel
Owner: Julye Newlin
Founded: 1992
Video production company; crew, camera, editorial & full production.
Online catalog(s) available
Membership(s): International Alliance of Theatrical Stage Employees; Society of Camera Operators; Texas Association of Motion Media Professionals

News Broadcast Network Inc
75 Broad St, 15th fl, New York, NY 10004
Web Site: newsbroadcastnetwork.com
Key Personnel
Pres: Michael Hill
Founded: 1968
Producer & media distributor of broadcast public relations & branded news programming for TV, radio & online outlets.

News Corp
1211 Avenue of the Americas, New York, NY 10036
Tel: 212-416-3400
E-mail: media@newscorp.com
Web Site: newscorp.com
Key Personnel
Exec Chmn: Rupert Murdoch
Co-Chmn: Lachlan Murdoch
Chief Exec: Robert Thomson
CFO: Susan Panuccio
Chief Comms Offr: Jim Kennedy
Chief HR Offr: Dana Ritzcovan
Chief Strategy Offr: Anoushka Healy
CTO: Marc Frons
Gen Coun: David Pitofsky
Global Head, Govt Aff: Antoinette Bush
Founded: 1923
Media & information services company.

NewsBank Inc
5801 Pelican Bay Blvd, Suite 600, Naples, FL 34108
Tel: 802-875-2910 *Toll Free Tel:* 800-762-8182
Fax: 802-875-2904
E-mail: sales@newsbank.com; custservice@
  newsbank.com
Web Site: www.newsbank.com
Key Personnel
SVP: John McDowell
Founded: 1972

Information resources to meet the research needs of public libraries, colleges & universities, schools, military & government libraries & professionals worldwide.
Online catalog(s) available
Branch Office(s)
215 E Yandell Dr, El Paso, TX 79902 *Toll Free Tel:* 800-243-7694 (microfilm prodn facility)
PO Box 219, Chester, VT 05143-0219 *Toll Free Tel:* 800-243-7694 (opers & prodn facility)

Newtec America Inc
1055 Washington Blvd, Stamford, CT 06901
Tel: 203-323-0042 *Fax:* 203-323-8406
E-mail: sales@newtec.eu; customersupport@
  newtec.eu
Web Site: www.newtec.eu
Key Personnel
VP, North America: Slava Frayter
Satellite communications company.
Online catalog(s) available
Foreign Office(s): ST Engineering iDirect (Europe) CY NV, Hoogkamerstr 42, 9100 Sint-Niklaas, Belgium *Tel:* (03) 780 65 00 *Fax:* (03) 780 65 49 (tech & sales support)
ST Engineering iDirect (Europe) CY NV, Laarstr 5, 9100 Sint-Niklaas, Belgium *Tel:* (03) 780 65 00 *Fax:* (03) 780 65 49 (tech & sales support)
Newtec America do Sul Eq e Sol, Praca Silvio Romero, 55 sala 105, 03323-000 Sao Paulo-SP, Brazil *Tel:* (011) 2092 6220 *Fax:* (011) 2093 3756
Beijing Sunflower Tower, No 37, Rm 2020, Maizidian St, Chaoyang District, Beijing 100125, China *Tel:* (010) 82318730 *Fax:* (010) 82318731
Newtec Communications GmbH, Berliner Str 26, 13507 Berlin, Germany *Tel:* (030) 43095 550 *Fax:* (030) 43095 579
Newtec Asia Pacific Pte Ltd, Cintech III Bldg, Science Park I, 77 Science Park Dr, No 03-08, Singapore 118256, Singapore *Tel:* 6911 4920 *Fax:* 6911 4939
Dubai Internet City, Aurora Tower, Off 1203-1203A, PO Box 502388, Dubai, United Arab Emirates *Tel:* (04) 443 60 58 *Fax:* (04) 443 61 92

Newton Instrument Co Inc
111 E "A" St, Butner, NC 27509-2426
Tel: 919-575-6426 *Fax:* 919-575-4708
E-mail: info@enewton.com
Web Site: www.enewton.com
Key Personnel
Natl Acct Mgr: Leslie Brunson *Tel:* 919-575-5506
  E-mail: lesb@enewton.com
Founded: 1949
Domestic supplier of hardware solutions to the telecommunications market.
Online catalog(s) available
Brochure(s) available, online

Newtown Psychological Center
660 Newtown Yardley Rd, Suite 102, Newtown, PA 18940
Tel: 215-968-5378
Key Personnel
Exec Dir: Dr James T Richard
Catalog(s) available

Nexsan Inc
900 E Hamilton Ave, Suite 230, Campbell, CA 95008
Tel: 408-724-9809
E-mail: sales@nexsan.com
Web Site: www.nexsan.com
Key Personnel
CEO: Robert Fernander
Chief Mktg Offr: Victoria Grey
CTO: Geoff Barrall
SVP, Engg: Mark Herbert
SVP, Sales: Tony Craythorne
VP, Cust Serv: Doug O'Shaughnessy

VP, Global Opers: Stewart Gallacher
Cost-effective storage for IT professionals. For the media & entertainment industries, Nexsan Unity provides high density storage & global file sharing across the media lifecycle, from video ingest through post-production editing & archiving.
Branch Office(s)
302 Enterprise St, Suite A, Escondido, CA 92029
1445 Lawrence Dr, Thousand Oaks, CA 91320
1405 Trans Canada Hwy, Dorval, QC H9P 2V9, Canada
Foreign Office(s): Parker Ctr, Units 33-35, Mansfield Rd, Derby DE21 4SZ, United Kingdom

Next Arts
1300 25 St, Unit C, San Francisco, CA 94107
Mailing Address: PO Box 880418, San Francisco, CA 94188
Tel: 415-970-9005
E-mail: mail@nextarts.org
Web Site: www.nextarts.org
Founded: 1998
Full service event production. Items also for rent on a will call basis.
Branch Office(s)
221 Jana Way, American Canyon, CA 94503
Tel: 707-812-3170

NFL Films Inc
One Sabol Way, Mount Laurel, NJ 08054
Tel: 856-222-3500
E-mail: licensing@nfl.com
Web Site: www.nfl.com/films; www.facebook.com/NFLFilms
Key Personnel
VP, Prodn Mgmt & Budgets: Kelly Viseltear
Dir, Team & Media Servs: Dan Haessler
Founded: 1962
Produces television programs, feature films & documentaries for & about the National Football League.
Online catalog(s) available

NFL Films Music Library
Division of NFL Films Inc
One Sabol Way, Mount Laurel, NJ 08054
Tel: 856-222-3500
Web Site: nflfilms.nfl.com; apmmusic.com/libraries/nfl-films-music-library-nfl
Key Personnel
Mgr, Music Admin: Christine Black
Online catalog(s) available

Nickelodeon
Subsidiary of ViacomCBS Domestic Media Networks
1515 Broadway, 38th fl, New York, NY 10036
Tel: 212-258-8000 (Viacom)
Web Site: www.nick.com
Key Personnel
Pres: Brian Robbins
EVP, Corp Communs: David Bittler
    E-mail: david.bittler@nick.com
VP, Studio Busn Devt: Eddie Gamarra
Children's entertainment brand, including television programming & production plus consumer products, digital, recreation, books & feature films.

Joseph Nicoletti Consulting-Promotion
PO Box 386, Laguna Beach, CA 92652
Tel: 949-632-3338
E-mail: music-film@att.net
Key Personnel
Owner & CEO: Joseph Nicoletti, Jr
Founded: 1976
Offices in England & NSW, Australia.
Membership(s): ASCAP; BMI; ISA; National Music Publishers' Association

Nightingale-Conant Corp
1400 S Wolf Rd, Bldg 300, Suite 103, Wheeling, IL 60090
Toll Free Tel: 800-557-1660 (sales); 800-560-6081 (cust serv)
Web Site: www.nightingale.com
Key Personnel
Chmn: Vic Conant
Founded: 1960
Educational & self-improvement audio & video programs.
Online catalog(s) available

Nightingale Music Productions Inc
5460 Yonge St, Suite 1611, Toronto, ON M2N 6K7, Canada
Tel: 416-221-2393 *Fax:* 416-221-2676
E-mail: admin@nightingalemusic.com
Web Site: www.nightingalemusic.com
Key Personnel
Founder & Pres: Caron Nightingale
Founded: 1988
Award winning music & SFX for film, television & multimedia.

Nikon Inc
1300 Walt Whitman Rd, Melville, NY 11747-3064
Toll Free Tel: 800-NIKONUS (645-6687 - tech & serv support)
Web Site: www.nikonusa.com
Online catalog(s) available

Nilfisk Inc
Indus Vacuum Div, 740 Hemlock Rd, Suite 100, Morgantown, PA 19543
Toll Free Tel: 800-NILFISK (645-3475) *Fax:* 610-286-7350
E-mail: questions@nilfisk.com
Web Site: www.nilfiskcfm.com
Key Personnel
Div Cont: Gabe DiGiacomo
Catalog(s) available

Nilgiri Press
Division of Blue Mountain Center of Meditation
PO Box 256, Tomales, CA 94971-0256
Tel: 707-878-2369 *Toll Free Tel:* 800-475-2369
    Fax: 707-878-2375
E-mail: info@bmcm.org
Web Site: www.bmcm.org
Practical resources for leading the spiritual life.
Online catalog(s) available
Shipping Address: 3600 Tomales Rd, Tomales, CA 94971

NIMCO Inc
102 Hwy 81 N, Calhoun, KY 42327
Tel: 270-273-5000 *Toll Free Tel:* 800-962-6662
    Fax: 270-273-5844
Web Site: www.nimcoinc.com
Anatomy & physiology DVDs & CD-ROMs, prevention resources.
Catalog(s) available
Online catalog(s) available

Nineteen87
1024 Harding Ave, Suite 201, Venice Beach, CA 90291
Tel: 310-577-5009 *Fax:* 310-577-1960
E-mail: info@1-9-8-7.com
Web Site: www.1-9-8-7.com
Key Personnel
Dir: Rick Bieber; Martina Buckley; L Lonnie Peralta; Eric Alan Donaldson
Founded: 1997
Creative direction, production & post-production services for ad agencies, record labels, TV networks & media corporations.
Membership(s): Music Video Production Association

NKK Switches of America Inc
Subsidiary of Nihon Switches Co Ltd
7850 E Gelding Dr, Scottsdale, AZ 85260
Tel: 480-991-0942 *Toll Free Tel:* 877-228-9655
    Fax: 480-998-1435
E-mail: sales@nkkswitches.com
Web Site: www.nkkswitches.com
Key Personnel
Mktg Mgr: Jessica Reimann
Founded: 1981
Manufacturer of electronic components (switches). Electro-mechanical switches (pushbuttons, toggles, slide, rotary, rocker, keylock, tactile).
Catalog(s) available, free, 18-24 months
Brochure(s) available, Smartswitch pushbutton
Foreign Office(s): NK Switches Co Ltd, 715-1 Unane, Takatsu-ku, Kawasaki-shi, Japan *Tel:* (044) 813-8001 *Web Site:* www.nkkswitches.co.jp (corp headquarters)
Membership(s): Electronic Components Industry Association

Nolte Media
2540 Eastmoor Dr, Santa Rosa, CA 95405
Tel: 707-483-1536
Web Site: www.noltemedia.com
Key Personnel
Owner: Ron Schilling *E-mail:* ron@noltemedia.com
Video production & web design.
Brochure(s) available
Demo video(s) available

Noontide Press
Subsidiary of Legion for the Survival of Freedom Inc
PO Box 2719, Newport Beach, CA 92759
Tel: 714-593-9725
E-mail: orders@noontidepress.com
Web Site: www.noontidepress.com
Key Personnel
Dir: Mark Weber
Offers important & often hard-to-find books & recordings from a dissident "politically incorrect" perspective.

NOR-COM Inc
2126 Petersburg Rd, Hebron, KY 41048
Tel: 859-689-7451 *Toll Free Tel:* 800-689-6889
    Fax: 859-689-7483
E-mail: hello@nor-com.com
Web Site: nor-com.com
Key Personnel
CEO: Dan Van Meter
Pres: Tony Wiggins
Founded: 1971
Provider of AV, security/surveillance, digital media, IT & performance sound technologies.
Branch Office(s)
3600 Chamberlain Lane, Suite 232, Louisville, KY 40241 *Tel:* 502-386-3608

Noramco Wire & Cable
70 Glacier St, Coquitlam, BC V3K 5Y9, Canada
Tel: 604-472-6980 *Toll Free Tel:* 800-663-8434
    Fax: 604-472-6981
E-mail: norcorp@noramco.ca
Web Site: www.noramco.ca
Key Personnel
VP & Gen Mgr: Gary McNeil
    E-mail: gary_mcneil@ncsintl.com
Electrical, electronic, wire & cable distributor, Data Comm Products.
Branch Office(s)
3529 12 St NE, Suite 1, Calgary, AB T2E 6P4, Canada *Tel:* 403-291-2955 *Toll Free Tel:* 800-661-8530 *Fax:* 403-291-2995 *E-mail:* norcgy@noramco.ca
4328 55 Ave, Edmonton, AB T6B 3S2, Canada *Tel:* 780-468-5678 *Toll Free Tel:* 800-232-7390

Fax: 780-465-5614 *E-mail:* noredm@noramco. ca

1266 Border St, Winnipeg, MB R3H 0M6, Canada *Tel:* 204-661-8302 *Toll Free Tel:* 800-706-9519 *Fax:* 204-663-3898 *E-mail:* norwpg@noramco.ca

1031 Hubrey Rd, Unit 8, London, ON N6N 1B4, Canada *Tel:* 519-649-1636 *Toll Free Tel:* 866-387-2564 *Fax:* 519-649-1575 *E-mail:* norldn@ noramco.ca

7635 Tranmere Dr, Mississauga, ON L5S 1L4, Canada *Tel:* 905-673-3570 *Toll Free Tel:* 800-387-7622 *Fax:* 905-676-9825 *E-mail:* nortor@ noramco.ca

1100 S Service Rd, Unit 104, Stoney Creek, ON L8E 0C5, Canada *Tel:* 905-643-9188 *Toll Free Tel:* 866-566-2166 *Fax:* 905-643-9177 *E-mail:* norham@noramco.ca

3490 Griffith St, Ste-Laurent, QC H4T 1A7, Canada *Tel:* 514-595-9595 *Toll Free Tel:* 800-567-9595 *Fax:* 514-595-9599 *E-mail:* normtl@ noramco.ca

3703 Millar Ave, Unit 7, Saskatoon, SK S7P 0B3, Canada *Tel:* 855-249-6886 *Toll Free Tel:* 855-249-6886 *Fax:* 306-249-6895

Norcostco Inc
825 Rhode Island Ave S, Minneapolis, MN 55426-1611
Tel: 763-544-0601 *Toll Free Tel:* 800-220-6920 *Fax:* 763-525-8676
E-mail: theatretechmn@norcostco.com; costumesmn@norcostco.com; makeupmn@ norcostco.com
Web Site: www.norcostco.com
Founded: 1884
Theatrical supplies & costumes.
Online catalog(s) available
Branch Office(s)
4395 Broadway, Denver, CO 80216-3549, Sales: Ian Floyd *Tel:* 303-620-9734 *Toll Free Tel:* 800-220-6928 *Fax:* 303-615-9115 *E-mail:* denver@norcostco.com
2089 Monroe Dr NE, Atlanta, GA 30324 *Tel:* 404-874-7511 *Toll Free Tel:* 800-241-5356 *Fax:* 404-873-3524 *E-mail:* theatretechatl@ norcostco.com
333-A Rte 46 W, Fairfield, NJ 07004-2427, Sales: Steve Schweer *Tel:* 973-575-3503 *Toll Free Tel:* 800-220-6940 *Fax:* 973-575-2563 *E-mail:* newjersey@norcostco.com
1231 Wycliff Ave, Suite 300, Dallas, TX 75207-6205, Sales: Larry Danforth *Tel:* 214-630-4048 *Toll Free Tel:* 800-657-1887 *Fax:* 214-630-4474 *E-mail:* theatretechtx@norcostco.com

Noritsu America Corp
6900 Noritsu Ave, Buena Park, CA 90620
Tel: 714-521-9040 *Toll Free Tel:* 800-521-3686; 888-435-7448 (tech support)
E-mail: sales@noritsu.com
Web Site: www.noritsu.com
Key Personnel
Pres & CEO: Go Yoshii
Founded: 1978
Digital photo imaging equipment, service & support.
Online catalog(s) available
Branch Office(s)
Noritsu Canada Ltd, 102-17750 56 Ave, Suite 501, Cloverdale, BC V3S 1K4, Canada *Tel:* 647-689-2140

Norlake Manufacturing Co
39301 Taylor Pkwy, Elyria, OH 44036
Mailing Address: PO Box 215, Elyria, OH 44036-0215
Tel: 440-353-3200 *Fax:* 440-353-3232
E-mail: info@norlakemfg.com
Web Site: www.norlakemfg.com
Key Personnel
Pres: James Markus

Founded: 1963
Electrical transformers.

Norsat International Inc
Subsidiary of Hytera Communications Co Ltd
110-4020 Viking Way, Richmond, BC V6V 2L4, Canada
Tel: 604-821-2800 *Toll Free Tel:* 800-644-4562
E-mail: support@norsat.com
Web Site: www.norsat.com
Key Personnel
Pres & CEO: Dr Amiee Chan
CFO: Arthur Chin
Founded: 1977
Provider of innovative communication solutions that enable the transmission of data, audio & video for challenging applications & environments. Norsat's products & services include fly-away satellite terminals, M2M Solutions, antennas, Radio Frequency (RF) conditioning products, microwave components, maritime based satellite terminals & remote network connectivity solutions. Additionally, through its Norsat Power Solutions segment, Norsat is a provider of power conversion & energy storage solutions for the communications, transportation & resource sectors.
Catalog(s) available

Nortek Security & Control LLC
Subsidiary of Nortek Inc
5919 Sea Otter Place, Carlsbad, CA 92010
Tel: 760-438-7000 *Toll Free Tel:* 800-421-1587 *Fax:* 760-683-6385 *Toll Free Fax:* 800-468-1340
Web Site: www.nortekcontrol.com
Founded: 1961
Wired & wireless products serving the security & access control markets as well as health & wellness & home technology needs.
Online catalog(s) available

North-by-Northwest - A Digital Studio
903 W Broadway Ave, Spokane, WA 99201
Tel: 509-324-2949 *Fax:* 509-324-2959
E-mail: spokane@nxnw.net
Web Site: www.nxnw.net
Key Personnel
Prodr & CEO: Kara Rowe *E-mail:* krowe@nxnw. net
Partner & Prodr: Matt Jaime *E-mail:* mjaime@ nxnw.net; Randy Kron *E-mail:* rkron@nxnw. net; Dave Tanner *E-mail:* dtanner@nxnw.net
Founded: 1990
Full service digital studio focusing on video production, custom photography & creating integrated digital solutions.
Online catalog(s) available
Branch Office(s)
710 W Franklin St, Boise, ID 83702, Dir: Jeff Noble *Tel:* 208-345-7870 *E-mail:* boise@nxnw. net

North Coast Studios Inc
29181 Calahan Rd, Roseville, MI 48066
Tel: 586-359-6630 *Toll Free Tel:* 888-866-0652 *Fax:* 586-359-6638
E-mail: sales@northcoaststudiosinc.com
Key Personnel
Pres: Steven J Burns
Theatre & stage equipment, projection screens, curtains, tracks & rigging.

North County Media Center
1130 N Melrose Dr, Suite 404, Vista, CA 92083
Toll Free Tel: 888-393-0580
E-mail: info@northcountymediacenter.com
Web Site: northcountymediacenter.com
Key Personnel
Exec Prodr: Joel Fieri
Prodr: Jefferson Drexler

Mktg, Sales & Consulting: Bill Ludwig
Video & audio production studio.

North Star Satellite Communications Inc
2547 Yellow Springs Rd, Malvern, PA 19355
Tel: 610-407-9290
Key Personnel
Pres: John Loudis
Founded: 1981

Northeast Video Productions Inc
Box 8425, Sleepy Hollow, NY 10591
Tel: 914-714-0703
Key Personnel
Dir & Prodr: Henry Steiner *E-mail:* nevsteiner@ aol.com
VP: John Herbert; Lucie Rohan
Founded: 1979
Script-to-screen production.
Rate card(s) available
Membership(s): Industrial Television Society; SMPTE®

Northeastern Digital Recording Inc
2750 14 St NW, No 402, Washington, DC 20009
Tel: 508-330-9069
Web Site: www.northeasterndigital.com
Key Personnel
Pres: Toby Mountain *E-mail:* tm@ northeasterndigital.com
Founded: 1985
Mastering for all media: music, soundtracks for film/video & archival materials.
Online catalog(s) available
Membership(s): AES

Northern Light Productions (NLP)
300 Western Ave, 2nd fl, Boston, MA 02134
Tel: 617-789-4344 *Fax:* 617-789-4744
E-mail: info@nlprod.com
Web Site: www.nlprod.com
Key Personnel
Founder & Sr Prodr: Bestor Cram *Tel:* 617-789-4344 ext 210 *E-mail:* bcram@nlprod.com
Principal: Andrew Kukura *Tel:* 617-789-4344 ext 202 *E-mail:* akukura@nlprod.com; Tim Lay *Tel:* 617-789-4344 ext 212 *E-mail:* tlay@ nlprod.com
Dir, Broadcast: Susan Gray *Tel:* 617-789-4344 ext 214 *E-mail:* sgray@nlprod.com
Lead Mktg Assoc: Daniela Moya *Tel:* 617-789-4344 ext 208 *E-mail:* dmoya@nlprod.com
Founded: 1982
Creates distinctive media including immersive environments, interactive installations & documentary films.
Online catalog(s) available

Northern Lights & Pro Audio
19720 44 Ave W, Suite F, Lynnwood, WA 98036
Tel: 425-774-1905 (off); 425-772-6021 (cell)
Web Site: loud.net
Key Personnel
Owner & Pres: Douglas Jones *E-mail:* doug@ loud.net
Founded: 1978
Stage lighting & pro sound.
Online catalog(s) available

Northport Records, see Sparrow Sound Design

Northwest Film Center
934 SW Salmon St, Portland, OR 97205
Tel: 503-221-1156
E-mail: info@nwfilm.org
Web Site: www.nwfilm.org
Key Personnel
Educ Dir: Ellen Thomas *E-mail:* ellen@nwfilm. org
Devt Mgr: Rachel Record *Tel:* 503-276-4254 *E-mail:* rachel@nwfilm.org

Exhibition Prog Mgr & Programmer: Morgen Ruff *Tel:* 503-276-4223 *E-mail:* morgen@nwfilm.org
Filmmaker Servs Mgr & Programmer: Ben Popp *Tel:* 503-276-4222 *E-mail:* ben@nwfilm.org
Founded: 1971
Regional media arts resource & service organization. Provides a variety of film & video exhibition, education & information programs primarily directed to the residents of Oregon, Washington, Idaho, Montana & Alaska.

Nostalgia Family Video Inc
PO Box 606, Baker City, OR 97814
Key Personnel
Owner & Pres: Jeremy Brunner
Founded: 1989
Membership(s): Entertainment Merchants Association

Nova Electric
Division of Technology Dynamics Inc
100 School St, Bergenfield, NJ 07621-2915
Tel: 201-385-0500 *Fax:* 201-385-0702
E-mail: novasales@theallpower.com; info@novaelectric.com
Web Site: www.novaelectric.com
Key Personnel
VP, Mktg: Howard Schrier *Tel:* 201-385-0500 ext 128 *E-mail:* howard@novaelectric.com
Founded: 1966
Power conversion equipment including UPS systems inverters & power supplies.
Online catalog(s) available

Novalis
Division of Bayard Canada
One Eglinton Ave E, Suite 800, Toronto, ON M4P 3A1, Canada
Tel: 416-363-3303 *Toll Free Tel:* 877-702-7773 (CN & US only); 800-387-7164 (cust serv, CN & US only) *Fax:* 416-363-9409 *Toll Free Fax:* 877-702-7775 (CN & US only); 855-393-1555 (cust serv)
E-mail: books@novalis.ca; resources@novalis.ca
Web Site: www.novalis.ca
Key Personnel
Publg Dir: Joseph Sinasac *E-mail:* joseph.sinasac@novalis.ca
Mktg Dir: Nancy Lauzon *E-mail:* nancy.lauzon@novalis.ca
Founded: 1936
Bilingual religious publisher of books, digital books, CDs, DVDs & gift items.
Online catalog(s) available
Membership(s): Association of Catholic Publishers Inc

Noventri
Division of Specialized Communications Corp
20940 Twin Springs Dr, Smithsburg, MD 21783-1510
Tel: 301-790-0103 *Fax:* 301-790-0173
E-mail: sale@noventri.com
Web Site: www.noventri.com
Key Personnel
Pres: David Linetsky
VP: Andrew Hoffman *E-mail:* andrewh@spec-comm.com
Sales Mgr: Robb Mullen *E-mail:* robertm@noventri.com
Mktg & PR: Judy Hoffman *E-mail:* judyh@noventri.com
Founded: 1985
Broadcast & multimedia video equipment, engineering, maintenance & sales & digital signage manufacturer & provider.
Online catalog(s) available
Membership(s): NAB; SBE

NPR Distribution Services
Formerly NPR Satellite Services

Division of National Public Radio
1111 N Capitol St NE, Washington, DC 20002
Tel: 202-513-2624 *Fax:* 202-513-3035
E-mail: linkup@npr.org
Web Site: nprds.org
Founded: 1979
Provides comprehensive satellite communications solutions including space segment, system design, engineering support, equipment, uplink services & 24/7 customer support to commercial radio & television programmers, broadcasters, network operators & other businesses who need a reliable, always on platform for distributing their video, audio or data content.

NPR Satellite Services, see NPR Distribution Services

NPRDS, see NPR Distribution Services

NRD Static Control LLC
2937 Alt Blvd, Grand Island, NY 14072-1285
Mailing Address: PO Box 310, Grand Island, NY 14072-0310
Tel: 716-773-7634 *Toll Free Tel:* 800-525-8076 (US only)
E-mail: sales@nrdllc.com
Web Site: www.nrdstaticcontrol.com
Key Personnel
Dir, Engg & Sales: Greg Gumkowski
Dir, Sales, Mktg & Prod Mgmt: John Glynn, II
Founded: 1969
Provider of advanced static control solutions.
Brochure(s) available
Data sheet(s) available
Foreign Office(s): NRD Asia Pte Ltd, 114 Lavender St, No 08-90 CT Hub 2, Singapore 338729, Singapore *Tel:* 6679 1707

NTi Americas Inc, see NTi Audio Inc

NTi Audio Inc
Subsidiary of NTi Audio AG
7405 SW Tech Center Dr, Suite 130, Tigard, OR 97223
Tel: 503-684-7050
E-mail: americas@nti-audio.com
Web Site: www.nti-audio.com
Key Personnel
Sales & Support: Brian MacMillan
Manufacturer of test & measurement solutions for acoustics, audio & vibration applications.
Online catalog(s) available
Foreign Office(s): NTi China, Lisheng Mansion, Ganglong, Rm 701, No 60 Suli Rd, Wuzhong District, Suzhou, China *Tel:* (0512) 6802 0075 *Fax:* (0512) 6802 0097 *E-mail:* china@nti-audio.com
NTi Audio Praha, Lublanska 9, 120 00 Prague 2, Czechia *Tel:* 220 999 992 *E-mail:* czech@nti-audio.com
NTi Audio GmbH, Frielingsdorfweg 4, 45239 Essen, Germany *Tel:* (0201) 6470 1900 *Fax:* (0201) 6470 1999 *E-mail:* de@nti-audio.com
NTi Japan, Ryogokusakamoto Bldg, 1-8-4 Ryogoku, Sumida-ku, Tokyo 130-0026, Japan *Tel:* (03) 3634-6110 *Fax:* (03) 3634-6160 *E-mail:* japan@nti-audio.com
NTi Audio AG, Im alten Riet 102, 9494 Schaan, Liechtenstein *Tel:* 239 60 60 *E-mail:* info@nti-audio.com
NTi Korea, Dangsandong 6-ga, 3-4, 2nd fl, Bldg 10, Dangsan-ro 50ga-gil, Yeongdeungpo-gu, Seoul 07223, South Korea *Tel:* (010) 3230 4978 *Fax:* (02) 6407 4978 *E-mail:* korea@nti-audio.com
NTi Audio UK Ltd, Julians Rd, Off 33C, Stevenage, Herts SG1 3ES, United Kingdom *Tel:* (01438) 870632 *E-mail:* uk@nti-audio.com

NTS ProMedia
Division of WTSmedia
1033 Elm Hill Pike, Nashville, TN 37210
Tel: 615-254-8178 *Toll Free Tel:* 800-591-4804
E-mail: sales@ntspromedia.com
Web Site: www.ntspromedia.com
Distributor of analog reel to reel tape, professional grade hard drives & recording supplies. CD & DVD manufacturer with price competitive replication & duplication services.

Nuance Communications Inc
One Wayside Rd, Burlington, MA 01803
Tel: 781-565-5000 *Toll Free Tel:* 800-654-1187 (cust serv) *Fax:* 781-565-5001
Web Site: www.nuance.com
Key Personnel
CEO: Mark Benjamin
EVP & CFO: Dan Tempesta
EVP & CTO: Joe Petro
Founded: 1992
Conversational AI innovations that bring intelligence to everyday work & life. The company delivers solutions that understand, analyze & respond to people—amplifying human intelligence to increase productivity & security. Nuance works with organizations globally across healthcare, financial services, telecommunications, government & retail to create stronger relationships & better experiences for their customers & workforce.
Online catalog(s) available

Numark Industries LP
Subsidiary of inMusic Brands Inc
200 Scenic View Dr, Cumberland, RI 02864
Tel: 401-658-3131
E-mail: info@numark.com
Web Site: www.numark.com
Founded: 1971
Manufacture DJ equipment.
Online catalog(s) available
Branch Office(s)
4200 Blvd Matte, Unit C, Brossard, QC J4Y 3J5, Canada *Toll Free Tel:* 833-466-9165
Foreign Office(s): Numark Japan Corp, 6F, 3-19-23, Minami Azabu, Minato-ku, Tokyo 106-0047, Japan *Tel:* (03) 6277 2230; (03) 6277 2231 (support) *Fax:* (03) 6277 0025 *Web Site:* numark.co.jp
No 165, Nanking East Rd, 7th fl, Section 4, Taipei 105, Taiwan *Tel:* (02) 2717 2389 *Fax:* (02) 2717 2734
Numark Alesis Europe Ltd, Unit 3, Nexus Park, Lysons Ave, Ash Vale, Hants GU12 5QE, United Kingdom *Tel:* (01252) 896040
Membership(s): LDI; NAMM, the National Association of Music Merchants

NuMynd Studios
915 Twin Elms Ct, Nashville, TN 37210
Tel: 615-259-1143 *Fax:* 615-259-1141
E-mail: hello@numyndstudios.com
Web Site: www.numyndstudios.com
Key Personnel
CEO: Greg Page
Prodn Mgr: Charity Spencer
Studio Mgr: Nick Eagles
Rental of soundstages with lighting, grip & electric included, equipment rental & personnel. Editing & compositing, voice-over & tracking.

NVerzion Inc
296 E 3900 S, Salt Lake City, UT 84107-1531
Tel: 801-293-8420
E-mail: sales@nverzion.com
Web Site: www.nverzion.com
Key Personnel
Pres & CEO: Scott Murphy
TV station automation, broadcast video servers.
Online catalog(s) available
Membership(s): NAB

Nystrom Education
Division of Social Studies School Service
10200 Jefferson Blvd, Culver City, CA 90232
Tel: 310-839-2436 *Toll Free Tel:* 800-421-4246
   Fax: 310-839-2249 *Toll Free Fax:* 800-944-
   5432
E-mail: customerservice@nystromeducation.com;
   access@nystromeducation.com
Web Site: www.nystromeducation.com
Key Personnel
Natl Sales Dir: Jennifer Carlson
   E-mail: jcarlson@nystromeducation.com
Digital maps & atlases, ebooks, professional
   learning (including product-specific training,
   webinars & online courses).
Catalog(s) available

OAP Audio Products
Division of Loeber-Hickey Enterprises Inc
1000 Peachtree Industrial Blvd, Suite 6-132,
   Suwanee, GA 30024
Tel: 770-945-1033 *Fax:* 678-765-7198
E-mail: sales@oapaudio.com
Web Site: oapaudio.com
Key Personnel
Pres & CEO: Ted Hickey, Sr *E-mail:* tedsr@
   oapaudio.com
VP, Opers: Ted Hickey, Jr
VP, Sales: Kevin Patterson *E-mail:* kevin@
   oapaudio.com
Founded: 1974
Online catalog(s) available
Branch Office(s)
Chicago, IL *Tel:* 847-226-9461

Oasic CD Manufacturing, see Oasis Disc
   Manufacturing

Oasis Disc Manufacturing
Formerly Oasic CD Manufacturing
7905 N Crescent Blvd, Delair, NJ 08110
Toll Free Tel: 888-296-2747 *Fax:* 856-661-3450
   Toll Free Fax: 866-929-8402
E-mail: info@oasiscd.com
Web Site: www.oasiscd.com
Founded: 1987
CD/DVD/Blu-ray duplication & replication,
   record pressing, audio mastering, DVD/Blu-ray
   authoring & package design.
Catalog(s) available, free, by request
Membership(s): ASCAP; NATAS; The Recording
   Academy

O'Connor Engineering Labs
Division of The Vitec Group PLC
2701 N Ontario St, Burbank, CA 91504
Tel: 818-847-8666 *Fax:* 818-847-1205
E-mail: usasales@ocon.com; info@ocon.com
Web Site: www.ocon.com
Key Personnel
Accts Mgr: Bob Low *E-mail:* bob.low@
   vitecgroup.com
Founded: 1949
Catalog(s) available
Branch Office(s)
16 Progress Dr, Shelton, CT 06484 *Tel:* 203-929-
   1100 *Fax:* 203-925-2684
Foreign Office(s): Derun Bldg, YongAn
   Dongli A No 8, Rm 706, Jianwai Ave,
   Chaoyang District, Beijing 100022, China
   Tel: (010) 8528 8748 *Fax:* (010) 8528 8749
   E-mail: apac_sales@ocon.com
171 Ave des Gresillons, 92635 Gennevillers
   Cedex, France *Tel:* 08 20 82 13 36 *Fax:* 08
   25 82 61 81
Planigerstr 34 (Gebaeude 16), 55543 Bad
   Kreuznach, Germany *Tel:* (0671) 483 43-30
   Fax: (0671) 483 43-40
Erfurterstr 16, 85386 Eching, Germany *Tel:* (089)
   321 58 200 *Fax:* (089) 321 58 227

PA Bldg 5F, 3-12-6 Aobadai, Meguro-ku, Tokyo
   153-0042, Japan *Tel:* (03) 5457 1381 *Fax:* (03)
   5457 1382
No 02-02 Hoe Huat Industrial Bldg, 6 New In-
   dustrial Rd, Singapore 536199, Singapore
   Tel: 6297 5776 *Fax:* 6297 5778
William Vinten Bldg, Western Way, Bury St Ed-
   munds, Suffolk IP33 3TB, United Kingdom
   Tel: (01284) 752121 *Fax:* (01284) 750560
   E-mail: emea_sales@ocon.com
Membership(s): NAB; Production Equipment
   Rental Association; SMPTE®

Oddball Film + Video, see Oddball Films Inc

Oddball Films Inc
Formerly Oddball Film + Video
275 Capp St, San Francisco, CA 94110
Tel: 415-558-8112
E-mail: info@oddballfilms.com
Web Site: www.oddballfilms.com
Key Personnel
Dir & CEO: Tara Lee Ford
Founded: 1984
An eclectic stock footage company featuring a
   comprehensive collection of historical & con-
   temporary footage in all genres.
Online catalog(s) available
Membership(s): Association of Moving Image
   Archivists

Odyssey Productions Inc
2800 NW Thurman St, Portland, OR 97210
Tel: 503-223-3480 *Fax:* 503-223-3493
E-mail: info@odysseypro.com
Web Site: www.odysseypro.com
Key Personnel
Pres & Dir: Steve Heiser
Exec Prodr & Proj Mgr: Carolyn Zelle
Writer & Prodr: Adam Heiser
Founded: 1973
Full service film/video & interactive multime-
   dia production company, specializing in mu-
   seum & visitor center programs. Documentary
   film/video productions from concept to comple-
   tion.
Membership(s): Oregon Media Production Asso-
   ciation

OECA, see TVO/Ontario Educational
   Communications Authority (OECA)

OGM Production Music
Subsidiary of OGM Inc
6464 Sunset Blvd, Suite 920, Hollywood, CA
   90028
Tel: 323-461-2701 *Toll Free Tel:* 800-421-4163
   (sales) *Fax:* 323-461-1543
E-mail: ogmmusic@gmail.com
Web Site: www.olegeorgmusic.com
Key Personnel
Pres: Ole Georg
Production music library.
Online catalog(s) available
Membership(s): LEVA; NAB

Ohio HD Video
350 W Johnstown Rd, Gahanna, OH 43230
Tel: 614-656-1162 *Fax:* 614-656-4343
E-mail: info@ohiohdvideo.com
Web Site: ohiohdvideo.com
Key Personnel
Owner & Dir, Photog: Scott Handel
Broadcast & documentary crews. Camera, lens,
   electronics & grip rentals.

O'Keefe Communications Inc
4301 Connecticut Ave NW, Suite 200, Washington, DC 20008-2304
Tel: 202-363-2101
E-mail: info@okeefecom.com

Web Site: www.okeefecom.com
Key Personnel
CEO: Kevin O'Keefe
Founded: 1979
A video, multimedia & event production company
   serving associations, businesses, government &
   nonprofits.
Membership(s): ASAE; Professional Convention
   Management Association; Women in Film &
   Video; Women's Business Enterprise National
   Council

Oklahoma Sound Corp
149 Entin Rd, Clifton, NJ 07014
Tel: 973-594-9000 *Toll Free Tel:* 800-261-4112
   Fax: 973-594-9339
Web Site: www.nationalpublicseating.com
Founded: 1981
Manufacture lecterns, multimedia carts, micro-
   phones & PA systems.
Catalog(s) available, annual
Online catalog(s) available
Membership(s): Audiovisual and Integrated Expe-
   rience Association; Education Market Associa-
   tion

Old Army Press (OAP)
218 Alabaster Way, Johnstown, CO 80534
Mailing Address: PO Box 1650, Johnstown, CO
   80534-1650
Tel: 970-587-9530; 970-420-8193 (cell)
E-mail: oldarmypress@msn.com
Web Site: oldarmypress.com
Key Personnel
Pres: Mike Koury
VP: Dee Koury
Founded: 1968
Pioneered western military history to videotapes
   & DVDs.
Catalog(s) available, free

The Old Rhinebeck Aerodome®
9 Norton Rd, Red Hook, NY 12571
Mailing Address: PO Box 229, Rhinebeck, NY
   12572
Tel: 845-752-3200 *Fax:* 845-758-6481
E-mail: info@oldrhinebeck.org
Web Site: www.oldrhinebeck.org
Key Personnel
Pres: Michael DiGiacomio
Founded: 1959
Gift shop sells "Cole Palen's Flying Circus" on
   DVD.
Online catalog(s) available

Old School Cameras
5625 Melrose Ave, Hollywood, CA 90038
Tel: 818-397-1555
E-mail: sdrentals@oldschoolcameras.com
Web Site: www.oldschoolcameras.com
Key Personnel
Owner: Jesse MacDonald
Founded: 2006
Offers digital motion cinema camera & lens
   rentals as well as educational workshops. Pro-
   vide services around the country & globally.
   ARRI ALEXA MINI, RED Weapon Helium
   8K, RED EPIC Helium W 8K, Canon C300
   MK2, ARRI 416, SR3 Hi Speed, Bolex, Digi-
   tal Bolex, Kodak Digital 8mm & much more.
   Specialize in rare lenses & primes sets. ARRI
   Master Primes, LEICA Summicron C, Cooke
   Speed Panchro, Super Baltars, Kowa Cine
   Prominar, Canon K35, Zeiss Super Speeds Un-
   coated, Zeiss Standard Speeds Uncoated, Lomo
   Spherical & Anamorphic Cooke, Kowa, Cineo-
   vision, Ultrascope, LOMO & more.
Branch Office(s)
302 Oceanside Blvd, Oceanside, CA 92054
   Tel: 760-309-2302

Olden Camera & Lens Co Inc
1263 Broadway, 4th fl, New York, NY 10001-3593
Tel: 212-226-3727
Key Personnel
Pres: Robert Olden
New & used cameras.

Olden Lighting
2008 Alexander Ave, Austin, TX 78722
Tel: 512-416-8080 *Fax:* 512-416-8096
E-mail: rental@oldenlighting.com; sales@oldenlighting.com
Web Site: www.oldenlighting.com
Key Personnel
Owner: Walter L Olden
Founded: 1985
Sales & rental of lighting equipment & supplies.

Jim Olive Photography, see Stockyard Photos/Jim Olive Photography

Olsen Audio Group Inc
7845 E Evans Rd, Scottsdale, AZ 85260-2919
Tel: 480-998-7140 *Fax:* 480-998-7192
E-mail: web-info2@olsenaudio.com
Web Site: www.phototech.tv
Founded: 1976
Professional audio manufacturing & distribution.
Catalog(s) available
Membership(s): NAMM, the National Association of Music Merchants

Olson Visual Inc
13000 Weber Way, Hawthorne, CA 90250
Tel: 310-355-1681 *Toll Free Tel:* 800-480-6643
   Fax: 310-263-6980
E-mail: info@olsonvisual.com
Web Site: olsonvisual.com
Key Personnel
Pres: Rick Olson
VP: Dan Olson
Founded: 1954
Full service large format digital graphics provider for the entertainment, museum, retail & event markets.
Membership(s): EDPA; The Imaging Alliance

Olympic Case Co
9110 King Palm Dr, Suite 101, Tampa, FL 33619
Tel: 813-246-5525 *Toll Free Tel:* 888-246-5525
   Fax: 813-246-4748
E-mail: info@olycase.com
Web Site: www.olycase.com
Key Personnel
Natl Sales Mgr: Josh Schneidmiller
   E-mail: josh@olycase.com
Founded: 1996
Provider of ATA & custom cases.

Olympusat
477 S Rosemary Ave, Suite 306, West Palm Beach, FL 33401
Tel: 561-472-2859
E-mail: info@olympusat.com
Web Site: www.olympusat.com
Complete film, TV & commercial production.

Omega Broadcast Group
817 W Howard Lane, Austin, TX 78753
Tel: 512-251-7778 *Fax:* 512-251-8633
E-mail: rental@omegabroadcast.com; sales@omegabroadcast.com
Web Site: www.omegabroadcast.com
Key Personnel
Pres: Pam Fry
VP: David Fry
Dir, Mktg: Brooke Vernon
Dir, Sales: Ross Grasse
Prodn Mgr: Enrique Garcia

Rental Mgr: Troy Marx
Professional video sales, rentals & services.

Omega Media Group Inc
PO Box 924499, Peachtree Corners, GA 30010
Web Site: www.omegamediagroup.com
Key Personnel
Dir: Stephen Keown *Tel:* 678-232-7637
   E-mail: stephen@omegamediagroup.com
Prodr: Heather Durden *Tel:* 770-826-8433
   E-mail: heather@omegamediagroup.com
Founded: 1985
Full video production facility, pre- & post-production, full in-house studio. Also produces video conferences & live events.

Omega Productions
456 Commerce St, Palacios, TX 77465
Tel: 214-891-9585
E-mail: getinfo@omegalive.com
Web Site: www.omegalive.com
Key Personnel
Pres: Paul A Christensen
Founded: 1973
Specialize in live concert HD, DVD & CD recording services as well as live entertainment & event management.
Membership(s): NATAS; The Recording Academy; SPARS

Omega Recording Studios
12712 Rock Creek Mill Rd, Suite 14A, Rockville, MD 20852
Tel: 301-230-9100 *Fax:* 301-230-9103
Web Site: omegastudios.com
Key Personnel
Studio Mgr: Shannon Follin *E-mail:* shannon@omegastudios.com
Full service recording studios.

OmegaBrandess Distribution
626 Hanover Pike, Suite 102, Hampstead, MD 21074-2036
Tel: 410-374-3250 *Fax:* 410-374-3184
E-mail: customerservice@omegabrandess.com
Web Site: www.omegabrandess.com
Key Personnel
Cont: Dana Zacharias
Pres: Cindy Wesolowski
Dir, Sales & Serv: Jeff Seidel
Opers Mgr: Kim Russo
Manufacture & distribute photographic equipment.
Online catalog(s) available
Membership(s): The Imaging Alliance

Omni Intercommunications Inc
2825 Wilcrest Dr, Suite 400, Houston, TX 77042
Tel: 713-781-2188 *Toll Free Tel:* 800-777-2304
   Fax: 713-781-2315
E-mail: info@omni-inter.com
Web Site: www.omni-inter.com
Key Personnel
Pres: Herve F Chain *E-mail:* hchain@omni-inter.com
Founded: 1978
Provide high quality foreign language services.
Membership(s): ATA; ATD; DSA

Omni International Inc
4928 Crosshill Lane, Northport, AL 35473
Key Personnel
Pres: James L Riley
Dir, Support Opers: Donald R Myres
Founded: 1957
Design, manufacture, market & sell contract/commercial furniture to include office, residential life (institutional) & library products.

OMNI Productions
Division of The Omni Corp
PO Box 302, Carmel, IN 46082-0302
Tel: 317-846-2345 *Fax:* 317-846-6664
E-mail: omni@omniproductions.com
Web Site: www.omniproductions.com
Key Personnel
Owner & Gen Mgr: W H Long *Tel:* 317-846-2345 ext 111
VP: S M Long
Prodn Mgr: J A Mullet
Founded: 1976
Full service digital media production company, including windows media streaming services provider.
Membership(s): AECT; NAB

Omnia Audio
Division of The Telos Alliance
1241 Superior Ave E, Cleveland, OH 44114
Tel: 216-241-7225 *Fax:* 216-241-4103
E-mail: social@telosalliance.com
Web Site: www.telosalliance.com/omnia
Key Personnel
Founder & Exec Chmn, Telos Alliance: Frank Foti
VP, Busn Devt, TV Solutions Group: Martin Dyster
VP, Prod Devt, Radio: Derek Pilkington
Founded: 1988
Audio processing, processing/encoding for streaming audio, voice processing, analysis tools & studio audio processing.
Membership(s): AES

OmniMount Systems
4409 E Baseline Rd, Suite 130, Phoenix, AZ 85042
Tel: 480-829-8000 *Toll Free Tel:* 800-MOUNT-IT (668-6848) *Fax:* 480-756-9000
E-mail: info@omnimount.com
Web Site: www.omnimount.com
Key Personnel
Pres: Geoff Miller
SVP, Sales: John Deutsch
VP, Sales Opers: Scott Ashbaugh
Founded: 1978
Manufacturer of audio & video mounts & furniture.

Omnirax Furniture Co
PO Box 1792, Sausalito, CA 94966-1792
Tel: 415-332-3392 *Toll Free Tel:* 800-332-3393
E-mail: info@omnirax.com
Web Site: omnirax.com
Key Personnel
Pres: Philip Zittell
VP, Design: David Holland
Opers Mgr & CFO: Sara Dawson
Prodn Mgr: David Fuentes
Prod Specialist: Jonathan Hilton
Founded: 1985
Multimedia workstation designer & manufacturer.
Membership(s): NAB; NAMM, the National Association of Music Merchants; National Association for Music Education; NSCA

OMNISound Recording Studio
Division of Sounds Perfect LLC
1806 Division St, Nashville, TN 37203
Tel: 615-482-1151 *Fax:* 615-321-5528
Web Site: www.omnisoundstudios.com
Key Personnel
Gen Mgr: Chris Holloway *E-mail:* chris@omnisoundstudios.com
Recording studio.

On-Line Productions
2515 Hawthorne Dr, Atlanta, GA 30345
Tel: 404-634-5572
E-mail: esptv@mindspring.com

Web Site: on-lineproductions.com
Key Personnel
Prodr & Dir: Steven Panayioto
Founded: 2007
Video production & post-production services; provide on location, HD & 4K quality services as well as editing services for corporate, cable, broadcast & web sites. 3D services also available.
Online catalog(s) available
Membership(s): Atlanta Stereoscopic Association; Georgia Production Partnership; NATAS

On Location North Carolina
502 S West St, No 104, Raleigh, NC 27601
Tel: 919-755-9488; 919-349-GRIP (349-4747, cell) *Toll Free Tel:* 888-469-GRIP (469-4747)
E-mail: info@onlocation-nc.com
Web Site: www.onlocation-nc.com
Key Personnel
Prodn Coord: John Piner
Founded: 1982
Production, lighting, grip, sound, camera equipment & crew in the Carolinas & Southern Virginia.

ON Services, a GES Company
6779 Crescent Dr, Norcross, GA 30071
Tel: 770-457-0966 *Toll Free Tel:* 800-967-2419
    Fax: 770-451-7925
E-mail: service@oneventservices.com; atlanta@oneventservices.com
Web Site: www.oneventservices.com
Key Personnel
Pres: Stan Milner *E-mail:* smilner@oneventservices.com
Founded: 1985
AV rental & staging, sales & installation.
Branch Office(s)
1327 Northbrook Pkwy, Suwanee, GA 30024
    Fax: 770-409-0277
700 Monroe St, Huntsville, AL 35801 *Tel:* 256-348-8592 *E-mail:* huntsville@oneventservices.com
567 Ocoee Business Pkwy, Ocoee, FL 34761
    Fax: 407-654-5826
3655 E Patrick Lane, Suite 1000, Las Vegas, NV 89120 *Fax:* 702-252-8201
4209 Stuart Andrew Blvd, Suite 1, Charlotte, NC 28217 *Fax:* 704-940-4047
4238 Piedmont Pkwy, Greensboro, NC 27410
    Fax: 336-854-5282
100 Southcenter Ct, Suite 400, Morrisville, NC 27560 *Fax:* 919-462-0166
3085 Directors Row, Memphis, TN 38131
    Tel: 901-969-0255 *Fax:* 901-969-0256
    E-mail: memphis@oneventservices.com
1443 Donelson Pike, Nashville, TN 37217
    Tel: 615-301-6740 *Fax:* 615-780-2681
    E-mail: nashville@oneventservices.com
3720 Dacoma St, Houston, TX 77092 *Fax:* 713-688-5840
212 S Henry St, Suite 200, Alexandria, VA 22314
Membership(s): Audiovisual and Integrated Experience Association; HSMAI; International Live Events Association; MPI; MPPA; NACE

On Site Video
Subsidiary of Producers Video LLC
PO Box 1865, Palatine, IL 60078-1865
Tel: 847-980-9808 *Fax:* 847-358-8697
E-mail: producersvideo@hotmail.com
Key Personnel
Owner & Pres: Jerry Skora
Founded: 1980
HD video production & post-production.
Catalog(s) available
Membership(s): Digital Cinema Society; IEEE; SBE; SMPTE®

On-Site Video
Subsidiary of Video Security Inc

325 E Southern Ave, Suite 110, Tempe, AZ 85282
Tel: 480-967-5062
Web Site: www.on-sitevideo.com
Key Personnel
Owner: Betsy Gruber *E-mail:* betsy_gruber@yahoo.com
Founded: 1979
Full service video production services.

On Stage Audio, see OSA International Inc

On Stage Visuals
420 Baker St, Lansing, MI 48910-1543
Tel: 517-393-7800 *Toll Free Tel:* 800-373-LIVE (373-5483) *Fax:* 517-481-2482
E-mail: support@onstagevisuals.com
Web Site: www.onstagevisuals.com
Founded: 1985
Retail, rental, installations of lighting, pro audio & video equipment.

On-Trax Inc
3052 Vine St, Riverside, CA 92507
Tel: 951-786-3921 *Fax:* 951-786-3922
Web Site: www.on-trax.com
Key Personnel
Owner & Pres: Bradford Williams
    E-mail: bradford@on-trax.com
Founded: 1980
Full service AV production company.
Catalog(s) available, free

Oncourt Offcourt Ltd
7011 Gaston Pkwy, Dallas, TX 75214
Tel: 214-823-3078 *Toll Free Tel:* 888-TENNIS-11 (366-4711) *Fax:* 214-823-3082
E-mail: info@oncourtoffcourt.com
Web Site: www.oncourtoffcourt.com
Key Personnel
Founder & Pres: Joe Dinoffer *E-mail:* joe@oncourtoffcourt.com
Founded: 1994
Distribute sports training equipment, books & speaking.
Catalog(s) available

One Stop CD Shop LLC
3149 S State St, Salt Lake City, UT 84115
Tel: 801-303-6100 *Fax:* 801-303-6129
E-mail: info@1stopcdshop.com
Web Site: 1stopcdshop.com
Key Personnel
Owner: Ken Rasmussen
Founded: 1986
CD, DVD & Blu-ray duplication & replication.
Membership(s): UITA

One Touch Systems Inc
2528 Qume Dr, Unit 14, San Jose, CA 95131
Tel: 408-436-4643
E-mail: info@onetouchsys.com
Web Site: www.onetouchsys.com
Key Personnel
Pres & CEO: Larry Speckels
VP & CFO: Bob Wilkinson
VP, Enterprise Sales: Michael Schenk
VP, Software Engg: Gopinath Rebala
Founded: 1989
Manufacturer & distributor of audience response systems.
Branch Office(s)
655 Engineering Dr, Norcross, GA 30092
    Tel: 404-246-0555 *Fax:* 404-246-0051
Membership(s): USDLA

Onkyo USA Corp
Subsidiary of Onkyo Corp
18 Park Way, Upper Saddle River, NJ 07458
Tel: 201-785-2600 *Toll Free Tel:* 800-229-1687
Web Site: www.onkyousa.com

Key Personnel
Retail Natl Sales Mgr: Mike Criscitiello
Audio component manufacturer & distributor.
Online catalog(s) available

OnLine Power Inc
14000 S Broadway, Los Angeles, CA 90061
Tel: 323-721-5017 *Toll Free Tel:* 800-227-8899
    Fax: 323-721-3929
E-mail: sales@onlinepower.com
Web Site: www.onlinepower.com
Founded: 1975
Manufacturer of medical power products & top switching regulators.
Catalog(s) available
Membership(s): IMSA; ITE

ONstage
Division of ON Services, a GES Company
567 Ocoee Business Pkwy, Ocoee, FL 34761
Tel: 407-654-5822 *Fax:* 407-654-5826
E-mail: orlando@oneventservices.com
Web Site: www.oneventservices.com
Founded: 1991
Stage equipment sales & rentals.
Membership(s): Audiovisual and Integrated Experience Association

Onstage Systems
8721 Forney Rd, Dallas, TX 75227
Tel: 972-686-4488 *Fax:* 972-686-7732
E-mail: info@onstagesystems.com
Web Site: www.onstagesystems.com
Key Personnel
Pres: Hyacinth Belcher *E-mail:* hyacinth@onstagesystems.com
Founded: 1978
Audio equipment rentals.
Membership(s): International Entertainment Buyers Association

ooLite Media LLC
3300 Graf St, Unit 4, Bozeman, MT 59715
Tel: 406-570-6474
E-mail: info@oolitemedia.com
Web Site: oolitemedia.com
Key Personnel
Pres & CEO: Daniel J Smith *E-mail:* dan@oolitemedia.com
Founded: 1990
Multimedia development firm. Specialize in web site development & digital video production.

Opamp Labs Inc
1033 N Sycamore Ave, Los Angeles, CA 90038
Tel: 323-934-3566 *Fax:* 323-462-6490
E-mail: opamplabs@gmail.com
Web Site: www.opamplabs.com
Key Personnel
Pres: Bel Losmandy
Sales Mgr: I Losmandy
Founded: 1965
Manufacture amplifiers, switchers, press boxes, audio transformers, oscillators & power supplies.
Online catalog(s) available

Open Media Foundation
700 Kalamath St, Denver, CO 80204
Tel: 720-222-0159 *Fax:* 303-534-5098
E-mail: info@openmediafoundation.org
Web Site: openmediafoundation.org; denveropenmedia.org
Key Personnel
Founder & Exec Dir: Tony Shawcross

OpenText Corp
275 Frank Tompa Dr, Waterloo, ON N2L 0A1, Canada
Tel: 519-888-7111 *Toll Free Tel:* 800-499-6544
    Fax: 519-888-0677

Web Site: www.opentext.com
Key Personnel
Vice Chair, CEO & CTO: Mark J Barrenechea
EVP & CFO: Madhu Ranganathan
EVP & Chief Prod Offr: Muhi Majzoub
EVP, Chief Legal Offr & Corp Devt: Gordon A Davies
EVP, Cust Opers: James McGourlay
EVP, Worldwide Sales: Simon "Ted" Harrison
SVP & CIO: David Jamieson
SVP & Chief Mktg Offr: Patricia E Nagle
SVP, Corp Devt: Douglas M Parker
SVP, Portfolio Group: Prentiss Donohue
SVP, Revenue Opers: Paul Duggan
Founded: 1991
Provider of enterprise content management solutions.
Online catalog(s) available

Oppenheimer Camera Products
7400 Third Ave S, Seattle, WA 98108-4143
Tel: 206-467-8666 *Toll Free Tel:* 877-467-8666
Fax: 206-467-9165
Web Site: oppenheimercameraproducts.com
Key Personnel
Pres: Marty Oppenheimer *E-mail:* marty@oppcam.com
Founded: 1979
Film & video equipment rental, sales & service.

Opterna, a Belden brand
44901 Falcon Place, Suite 116, Sterling, VA 20166-9531
Tel: 703-653-1100 *Toll Free Tel:* 800-248-9004
Fax: 703-803-8313
Web Site: www.opterna.com
Founded: 1992
Opto-electronic product company.
Online catalog(s) available
Branch Office(s)
8045 Leesburg Pike, Suite 503, Vienna, VA 22182
Foreign Office(s): 69 Rue Crozatier, 75012 Paris, France *Tel:* 01 53 02 90 92
1/1 Kalyana Mantapa Rd, Vintage Bldg, Jakkasandara, Koramangala, Bangalore 560 034, India *Tel:* (080) 25506808; (080) 25500982
No 8-1-199/2/P 1st fl, High Mark Chambers, Gachibowli Rd, Hyderabad 500 028, India *Tel:* (040) 6463 3340
Plot 43A, Cochin Special Economic Zone (CSEZ), Kakkanad, Kochi 682 037, India *Tel:* (0484) 2413394
Tatweer Tower, Bldg 3, 8th fl, Unit 5, King Fahd Rd, Riyadh 12361, Saudi Arabia
Dubai Airport Free Zone, PO Box 293862 B-14, Dubai, United Arab Emirates *Tel:* (04) 2997676 *Fax:* (04) 2991767
5 Vermont Place, Michigan Dr, Tongwell, Milton Keynes MK15 8JA, United Kingdom *Tel:* (02031) 301 700
Membership(s): PCTA; SCTE

Opti-Case Inc
1175 CR 481 W, Henderson, TX 75654
Tel: 903-657-5666 *Toll Free Tel:* 800-637-6635
Fax: 903-657-6030
E-mail: sales@opti-case.net
Web Site: www.opti-case.net
Key Personnel
Contact: Charlotte Thrasher
Founded: 1978
ATA shipping cases.

Opticomm-EMCORE
2015 Chestnut St, Alhambra, CA 91803
Tel: 626-293-3400; 626-293-3670 (west coast team); 540-626-3381 (east coast team)
Toll Free Tel: 800-8OPTICOMM (867-8426)
Fax: 626-293-3427
E-mail: video-sales@emcore.com

Web Site: www.opticomm.com
Key Personnel
Dir, Busn Devt: Henok Tafese
Founded: 1986
Fiber optic video/audio/data/RGB/sdi communications products.
Catalog(s) available
Branch Office(s)
EMCORE Corp, 10420 Research Rd SE, Albuquerque, NM 87123 *Tel:* 505-332-5000 *Fax:* 505-332-5100 (headquarters)
Foreign Office(s): Camino del tomillaron 59-T8, 28231 Madrid, Spain *Tel:* 916378101
Membership(s): Audiovisual and Integrated Experience Association; IEEE Computer Society; International Technology and Engineering Educators Association; NAB; OFC; OSA; SBE; SPIE

Optics 1 Inc
Subsidiary of Vectronix AG
2 Cooper Lane, Bedford, NH 03110
Tel: 603-296-0469 *Fax:* 603-296-0473
E-mail: info@optics1.com
Web Site: www.optics1.com
Founded: 1987
Designers of optical systems & sub-assemblies.
Catalog(s) available

Optikinetics Ltd - The Americas
11211 Air Park Rd, Suite 1, Ashland, VA 23005
Tel: 804-752-2570 *Toll Free Tel:* 800-575-6784
Fax: 804-752-2888
E-mail: optius@optikinetics.com
Web Site: www.optikinetics.com
Key Personnel
CEO: Rob Stitcher
Sales Coord: Jennifer Caler *E-mail:* jennifer@optikinetics.com
Manufacturer & distributor of GoBo & solar projection products & aluminum trussing.
Catalog(s) available, free
Online catalog(s) available
Branch Office(s)
2470 Ramsay Conc, No 8, Almonte, ON K0A 1A0, Canada, Mgr: Ray Turner *Toll Free Tel:* 877-298-5164 *Fax:* 613-256-6290 *E-mail:* sales@optikinetics.ca
Foreign Office(s): Optikinetics Ltd, 38 Cromwell Rd, Luton, Beds LU3 1DN, United Kingdom, Sales Mgr: Idunn Rodziewicz *Tel:* (01582) 411413 *Fax:* (01582) 400613 *E-mail:* optiuk@optikinetics.com *Web Site:* www.optikinetics.co.uk (headquarters)

The Optikon Corp
Affiliate of PCO AG
1099 Guelph St, Kitchener, ON N2B 2E4, Canada
Tel: 519-745-4115 *Fax:* 519-745-6922
E-mail: info@optikon.ca
Web Site: www.optikon.ca
Key Personnel
Opers Mgr: Barry Brandon *Tel:* 519-745-4115 ext 226
Founded: 1974
Sales of photonic products including light instrumentation: lightmeters, colormeters, spotmeters & scientific cameras.

Optimus
161 E Grand Ave, Chicago, IL 60611
Tel: 312-321-0880
Web Site: www.optimus.com
Key Personnel
Pres: Tom Duff
Exec Prodr & Mng Dir: Brian Hrastar *Tel:* 312-276-2444 *E-mail:* brian@optimus.com
Exec Prodr: Jon Desir *Tel:* 312-276-2283 *E-mail:* jon@optimus.com; Tracy Spera *Tel:* 312-276-2447 *E-mail:* tracy@optimus.com
Full service film & video production company.

Catalog(s) available
Membership(s): AICP; IAA-VC; NAB; SMPTE®

Optisonics Productions
311 South Pkwy, Clifton, NJ 07014
Tel: 973-458-0951
E-mail: optisonics@aol.com
Web Site: www.optisonics.com
Key Personnel
Pres: Jim Brown *E-mail:* jimbrown@optisonics.com
Graphic & multimedia production & audio recording.
Brochure(s) available

Optronics®
Division of Karl Storz Imaging
175 Cremona Dr, Goleta, CA 93117
Tel: 805-968-3568 *Toll Free Tel:* 800-796-8909
Fax: 805-968-0933
E-mail: oeinfo@optronics.com; sales@optronics.com
Web Site: www.optronics.com
Key Personnel
Dir, Busn Devt: Richard Crandall *E-mail:* rcrandall@optronics.com
Manufacturer & distributor of video & digital cameras.
Catalog(s) available

Opulen Studios
1309 S Flower St, Los Angeles, CA 90015
Tel: 310-867-5023; 310-902-6996
E-mail: info@opulenstudios.com
Web Site: opulenstudios.com
Photography studio, film location & event venue.

Oral Tradition Sound & Music
PO Box 51155, Pacific Grove, CA 93950-6155
Tel: 831-372-0352 *Toll Free Tel:* 800-779-1116 (orders)
Key Personnel
Owner: Richard Chelew *E-mail:* rickchelew@gmail.com
Founded: 1990
Location sound recording.

Orange County Sound Stage
17518 Von Karman Ave, Irvine, CA 92614
Tel: 714-598-6557
E-mail: sm@ocsoundstage.com
Web Site: orangecountysoundstage.com
Video production studio.

Orban
Division of JBL Professionals
7209 Browning Rd, Pennsauken, NJ 08109
Tel: 856-719-9900
E-mail: info@orban.com; sales@orban.com
Web Site: www.orban.com
Key Personnel
Dir, Sales & Mktg: David Rusch
Professional broadcast technology manufacturer.
Catalog(s) available
Branch Office(s)
Orban Northern California Design Center Group, 14798 Wicks Blvd, San Leandro, CA 94577 *Tel:* 510-351-3500 *Fax:* 510-297-2701

Orevox USA Corp
240 N Puente Ave, City of Industry, CA 91746-2303
Mailing Address: PO Box 2207, La Puente, CA 91746
Tel: 626-336-0516 *Fax:* 626-336-3748
Web Site: www.dynavox.com
Key Personnel
Pres: Dan Wu

OEM of home theater sound systems, DJ & PA sound systems, sirens & alarms, parts & accessories.
Catalog(s) available, annual

Oriental Records Inc
PO Box 387, Williston Park, NY 11596-0387
Tel: 516-746-0140 *Fax:* 516-747-4285
E-mail: info@orientalrecords.com; orientalcd@aol.com
Web Site: www.orientalrecords.com
Key Personnel
Pres: Mr Rangasami Parthasarthy
Founded: 1977
Classical & devotional Indian music & CDs for learning Indian language.

Origin Instruments Corp
854 Greenview Dr, Grand Prairie, TX 75050-2438
Tel: 972-606-8740 *Fax:* 972-606-8741
E-mail: support@orin.com; marketing@orin.com
Web Site: www.orin.com
Key Personnel
VP: Mel Dashner
Founded: 1990
Develops & manufactures advanced electro-optical instruments & software.
Catalog(s) available

Original Cast Records
PO Box 496, Georgetown, CT 06829-0496
Tel: 203-544-8288 *Fax:* 203-544-8288
E-mail: originalcast@aol.com
Web Site: www.originalcastrecords.com; footlight.com
Key Personnel
Owner & Pres: Bruce Yeko
Record distributor.
Catalog(s) available
Shipping Address: 33 Irmgard, Wilton, CT 06897
Membership(s): The Recording Academy

Orion Software
6000 Cote-des-Neiges, Suite 240, Montreal, QC H3S 1Z8, Canada
Tel: 514-484-9661 *Toll Free Tel:* 877-755-2012
Fax: 514-484-1339
E-mail: info@orion-soft.com
Web Site: www.orion-soft.com
Key Personnel
Pres: Patrice Boivin *E-mail:* pboivin@orion-soft.com
Sales Mgr: Gary Kappel *E-mail:* gkappel@orion-soft.com
Computer software, rental software.

Orlando Special Effects
14222 Lake Mary Jane Rd, Orlando, FL 32832
Tel: 407-648-1867
Web Site: www.orlandospfx.com
Key Personnel
Pres: Andrew Nicholls *E-mail:* andy@orlandospfx.com
Founded: 1989
SPFX equipment.
Membership(s): Hollywood Foreign Press Association; International Alliance of Theatrical Stage Employees; International Association of Amusement Parks and Attractions; Pyrotechnics Guild International

Rob Orr Productions Ltd
1336 Pine St, Glenview, IL 60025
Tel: 847-724-5228
E-mail: rob@roborrproductions.com
Web Site: www.roborrproductions.com
Key Personnel
Prodr & Dir: Rob Orr *Tel:* 847-400-4694 (cell)
Founded: 1982
Video production services.

Orvac Electronics
1645 E Orangethorpe Ave, Fullerton, CA 92831
Tel: 714-871-1020
E-mail: myorvac@orvac.com
Web Site: www.orvac.com
Key Personnel
Pres & CEO: L J Vaccher
Founded: 1958
Family owned electronics distributor. Stocks a wide variety of products including electronic components, relays & switches, data & networking products, video security, structured cabling, commercial sound equipment, wire & cable, audio & video accessories & test equipment.

OSA International Inc
Formerly On Stage Audio
537 N Edgewood Ave, Wood Dale, IL 60191
Tel: 630-227-1008 *Toll Free Tel:* 877-OSA-INTL (672-4685) *Toll Free Fax:* 866-OSA-FAX2 (672-3292)
E-mail: connect@osacorp.com
Web Site: www.osacorp.com
Key Personnel
Pres & CEO: Mario C Educate
E-mail: meducate@osacorp.com
VP: Paul Driggs *E-mail:* pdriggs@osacorp.com
Founded: 1985
Global technical services provider for live events & entertainment.
Branch Office(s)
6275 S Sandhill Rd, Suite 500, Las Vegas, NV 89120 *Tel:* 702-458-0445
100 Northfork Lane, Goodlettsville, TN 37072
Tel: 615-829-8494

Osho Viha Information Center & Book Distributors
PO Box 352, Mill Valley, CA 94942-0352
Tel: 415-472-5381 *Toll Free Tel:* 866-856-7019
E-mail: oshoviha@oshoviha.org
Web Site: www.oshoviha.org
Key Personnel
Pres: Swami Prabodh Dhanyam
Founded: 1986
Catalog(s) available

Osorio Media, see Video Ideas Productions

Osram Sylvania Inc
200 Ballardvale St, Wilmington, MA 01887
Tel: 978-570-3000 *Toll Free Tel:* 800-842-7010
Web Site: www.sylvania.com
Manufacturer & distributor of lighting fixtures & equipment.
Catalog(s) available
Branch Office(s)
71 Cherry Hill Dr, Beverly, MA 01915 *Tel:* 978-777-1900
54 Cherry Hill Dr, Danvers, MA 01923
800 Church St, Lake Zurich, IL 60047 *Tel:* 847-726-6200
Valeo Sylvania, 1231 A Ave N, Seymour, IN 47274 *Tel:* 812-523-5200 *Fax:* 812-524-5316 (joint venture with Valeo)
1000 Tyrone Pike, Versailles, KY 40383 *Tel:* 859-873-7351
435 E Washington St, Winchester, KY 40391
Tel: 859-744-3464
131 Portsmouth Ave, Exeter, NH 03833 *Tel:* 603-772-4331
275 W Main St, Hillsboro, NH 03244 *Tel:* 603-464-5533
655 S Willow St, Manchester, NH 03103
Tel: 603-669-5350
835 Washington Rd, St Marys, PA 15857
Tel: 814-834-1800
One Jackson St, Wellsboro, PA 16901 *Tel:* 570-724-8200
Osram Sylvania Ltd/LTEE, 2001 Drew Rd, Mississauga, ON L5S 1S4, Canada, Con-

tact: Steven Duff *Tel:* 905-673-6171 *Toll Free Tel:* 800-LIGHTBULB (544-4828) *Fax:* 905-671-5584 (Canadian headquarters)
Sales Office(s): 18725 N Union St, Westfield, IN 46074 *Tel:* 317-867-6000 *Toll Free Tel:* 800-LIGHTBULB (544-4828) (also cust serv)

Osram Sylvania Ltd/Ltee
2001 Drew Rd, Mississauga, ON L5S 1S4, Canada
Tel: 905-673-6171 *Toll Free Tel:* 800-LIGHTBULB (544-4828) *Fax:* 905-671-5584
Web Site: www.sylvania.com
Founded: 1801
Manufacturer & distributor of lighting fixtures & equipment.
Catalog(s) available
Branch Office(s)
One Sylvan St, Drummondville, QC J2C 2S8, Canada *Tel:* 819-478-6500
Osram Sylvania Inc, 200 Ballardvale St, Wilmington, MA 01887, Sales Mgr: Howard Ames *Tel:* 978-777-1900 *Toll Free Tel:* 800-842-7010 *Fax:* 978-750-2152 (US headquarters)
Membership(s): Canadian Institute for Theatre Technology; CSG; Society of Television Lighting and Design

Ostergaard Acoustical Associates
200 Executive Dr, Suite 350, West Orange, NJ 07052
Tel: 973-731-7002 *Fax:* 973-731-6680
E-mail: info@acousticalconsultant.com
Web Site: www.acousticalconsultant.com
Key Personnel
Principal: Edward M Clark *E-mail:* emclark@acousticalconsultant.com
Sr Consultant: Joe Keefe *E-mail:* jkeefe@acousticalconsultant.com
Founded: 1972
Acoustical engineering.
Membership(s): American Council of Engineering Companies; National Council of Acoustical Consultants

Osum Event Rentals
730 Andover Park E, Tukwila, WA 98188
Tel: 206-575-5055
E-mail: info@osumeventrentals.com
Web Site: osumeventrentals.com
Key Personnel
Owner: Chad Anderson
Event gear & decor rentals.

OSV Studios
29605 Lorain Rd, North Olmsted, OH 44070
Tel: 440-779-1900
Web Site: www.osvstudios.com
Key Personnel
Pres: Craig Smith *E-mail:* csmith@osvstudios.com
Busn Mgr: Kelly Smith *E-mail:* ksmith@osvstudios.com
Consumer Prodn Mgr: Michele Schneider
E-mail: mschneider@osvstudios.com
Video production facility, including editing & graphics, studio space, audio recording, grip truck & equipment rentals.

OTR Studios
PO Box 874, Belmont, CA 94002
Tel: 650-595-8475
E-mail: info@otrstudios.com
Web Site: www.otrstudios.com
Key Personnel
Owner: Cookie Marenco *E-mail:* cookie@otrstudios.com
Gen Mgr: Patrick O'Connor *Tel:* 650-759-1357
E-mail: patrick@otrstudios.com
Analog & digital recording for studio, home & location audio.

Our Sunday Visitor Inc
200 Noll Plaza, Huntington, IN 46750
Tel: 260-356-8400 *Toll Free Tel:* 800-348-2440
  Fax: 260-356-8472
E-mail: osvsales@osv.com
Web Site: www.osv.com
Key Personnel
Sales Mgr: Valerie Vogel
Distributor of Catholic books & videos.
Catalog(s) available
Membership(s): Catholic Press Association

Out of the BLUE Media
1413 Brenda Lane, Allen, TX 75002
Tel: 469-853-9015
Web Site: www.outofthebluemedia.com
Key Personnel
Prodr: Chuck Andrle *E-mail:* chuck@
outofthebluemedia.com

Outland Technology Inc
38190 Commercial Ct, Slidell, LA 70458
Tel: 985-847-1104 *Fax:* 985-847-1106
E-mail: sales@outlandtech.com
Web Site: www.outlandtech.com
Key Personnel
Owner: Buddy Mayfield
Design Engr: Charles Daussin
Founded: 1984
Underwater video systems.

Outside The Box Interactive LLC
150 Bay St, Suite 706, Jersey City, NJ 07302
Tel: 201-610-0625
E-mail: office@outboxin.com
Web Site: www.outboxin.com
Key Personnel
Founder & Mng Partner: Frank DeMarco
Partner & Creative Dir: Lauren Schwartz
Founded: 1995
Interactive digital design & online marketing firm.

Outwater Plastics Industries Inc
Affiliate of Architectural Products by Outwater
  LLC
24 River Rd, Bogota, NJ 07603
Mailing Address: PO Box 500, Bogota, NJ
  07603-0500
Tel: 201-498-8750 *Toll Free Tel:* 800-631-8375
  Toll Free Fax: 800-888-3315
E-mail: info@outwaterplastics.com;
  customerservice@outwaterplastics.com
Web Site: www.outwater.com
Founded: 1972
Stocking more than 65,000 standard & innovative
  component product essentials which include ex-
  trusions, injection molded parts, casters, store
  fixture components, lighting & lighting acces-
  sories, engineering plastics, millwork & hard-
  ware.
Catalog(s) available
Online catalog(s) available
Sales Office(s): 4720 W Van Buren, PO Box
  18190, Phoenix, AZ 85043 *Toll Free Tel:* 800-
  248-2067

Oval Window Audio
33 Wildflower Ct, Nederland, CO 80466
Tel: 303-447-3607 *Fax:* 303-447-3607
E-mail: info@ovalwindowaudio.com
Web Site: www.ovalwindowaudio.com
Key Personnel
Dir, R&D: Norman Lederman *E-mail:* norman@
ovalwindowaudio.com
Educ Dir: Paula Hendricks *E-mail:* paula@
ovalwindowaudio.com
Founded: 1984
Hearing assistance systems compatible with hear-
ing aids, multisensory sound systems for edu-
cational & therapeutic applications.

Catalog(s) available
Online catalog(s) available

OWI Inc
17141 Kingsview Ave, Carson, CA 90746
Tel: 310-515-1900 *Toll Free Tel:* 800-638-1694
  Fax: 310-515-1606
E-mail: info@owi-inc.com
Web Site: www.owi-inc.com
Key Personnel
VP, Sales: Joe Martinez *Tel:* 310-515-1900 ext
  208 *E-mail:* joe@owi-inc.com
Regl Sales Mgr: Pierre Louis *Tel:* 310-515-1900
  ext 201 *E-mail:* pierre@owi-inc.com
Founded: 1978
Products include self-amplified in-ceiling & trum-
  pet speakers, 70 volt in-wall amps, compact
  in-wall mounted control system modules &
  wall-mounted infrared wireless microphone
  systems for classrooms, boardrooms, training
  rooms & meeting rooms. The newest offering is the three source integratable amplified
  speaker models with bluetooth features.
Online catalog(s) available

Ozam Productions Inc
1516 Equestrian Rd, Ozark, MO 65721
Tel: 417-866-3232
Web Site: ozam.com
Key Personnel
Owner & Prodr: Dale DeToni
Founded: 1978
Audio & video production services.

Pace Systems
301 Hickory Ave, Harahan, LA 70123
Tel: 504-837-4224 *Toll Free Tel:* 800-722-3797
  Fax: 504-837-4307
E-mail: info@pacesys.com
Key Personnel
Pres: Peter Schulman
VP: Patricia Schulman
Founded: 1976
Technical stage production company.

PACE Worldwide
346 Grant Rd, Vass, NC 28394
Tel: 910-695-7223 *Toll Free Tel:* 877-882-7223
  Fax: 910-695-1594
E-mail: support@paceworldwide.com; sales@
  paceworldwide.com
Web Site: www.paceworldwide.com
Electronic design assembly & productivity solu-
tions company.
Foreign Office(s): PACE Europe Ltd, 11 Holdom
  Ave, Bletchley, Milton Keyes, Bucks MK1
  1QU, United Kingdom *Tel:* (01908) 277666

Pacific Grip & Lighting Inc
6550 NE Portland Hwy, Portland, OR 97218
Tel: 503-233-4747 *Fax:* 503-233-5830
Web Site: www.pacific-grip.com
Key Personnel
Mgr: Doug Boss
Lighting fixture & equipment distribution &
  rentals.
Online catalog(s) available, rentals
Branch Office(s)
10401 Martin Luther King Jr Way S, Seattle, WA
  98178, Mgr: Ray Hammond *Tel:* 206-622-8540
  Fax: 206-292-2919
Membership(s): Oregon Media Production Asso-
ciation

Pacific Light Studios
265 Caspian Dr, Sunnyvale, CA 94089
Tel: 408-541-1800
E-mail: info1@pacificlightstudios.com
Web Site: www.pacificlightstudios.com
Key Personnel
Owner: Philip Goldworth

Photog: Mel Lindstrom
Founded: 2009
Commercial photo & video agency providing
  video production assistance, cameras, lenses
  & lighting.

Pacific Media
PO Box 9489, Canoga Park, CA 91309
Tel: 805-418-7552
E-mail: info@pac-media.com
Web Site: www.pac-media.com
Key Personnel
Pres: Scott S Brastow *E-mail:* scott@pac-media.
  com
Founded: 1993

Pacifica Multimedia Inc
4917 Seaview Way, Everett, WA 98203
Tel: 425-347-4110 *Toll Free Tel:* 888-373-8273
Web Site: www.pacmultimedia.com
Key Personnel
Pres: Jim Campbell *E-mail:* jim@pacmultimedia.
  com
Audiovisual production company.

Pacific Northwest Theatre Associates, see
PNTA

Pacific Radio Electronics
3031 Thornton Ave, Burbank, CA 91504
Tel: 818-556-4177 *Toll Free Tel:* 800-634-9476
  Fax: 818-556-4185
E-mail: sales@pacrad.com
Web Site: www.pacrad.com
Key Personnel
Gen Mgr: Dan Gutierrez
Founded: 1932
Specialize in serving the needs of film, TV, ra-
  dio, multimedia, recording, post-production,
  networking, home integration & live entertain-
  ment.
Catalog(s) available
Online catalog(s) available
Membership(s): NAB

Pacific Video Image
9065 E Rosecrans Ave, Bellflower, CA 90706
Tel: 562-634-4200 *Fax:* 562-634-4700
Web Site: www.pvideo.com
Key Personnel
Owner: Brad Coker
Ed: David Lopez *E-mail:* david@pvideo.com
Founded: 1986
Video concept design, writing, production & post-
  production.

Pacific Video Products Inc
14312 Franklin Ave, Suite 100, Tustin, CA 92780
Tel: 714-508-2750 *Toll Free Tel:* 800-576-0060
  Fax: 714-508-2136
E-mail: tvink@pacvideo.com
Web Site: www.pacvideo.com
Founded: 1975
Professional distributor of video equipment.
Catalog(s) available
Membership(s): Professional Systems Network
International

Pacifica Radio Archives
Division of Pacifica Foundation
3729 Cahuenga Blvd W, North Hollywood, CA
  91604
Tel: 818-506-1077 *Toll Free Tel:* 800-735-0230
  Fax: 818-506-1084
E-mail: pacarchive@aol.com
Web Site: www.pacificaradioarchives.org
Key Personnel
Sr Prodr/Opers Dir: Mark Torres *Tel:* 800-
  735-0230 ext 266 *E-mail:* mark@
pacificaradioarchives.org

Busn Mgr, Acctg: Mariana Berkovich *Tel:* 800-735-0230 ext 260 *E-mail:* mariana@pacificaradioarchives.org
Prodn Coord: Edgar Toledo *Tel:* 800-735-0230 ext 268 *E-mail:* edgar@pacificaradioarchives.org
Archivist: Jolene Beiser *Tel:* 800-735-0230 ext 265 *E-mail:* jolene@pacificaradioarchives.org
Off Admin: Shawn Dellis *Tel:* 800-735-0230 ext 261 *E-mail:* shawn@pacificaradioarchives.org
Radio/audio archives.
Online catalog(s) available
Membership(s): National Federation of Community Broadcasters

Pal Productions Inc
13751 Lake City Way, Suite 208, Seattle, WA 98125
Tel: 206-361-9366
Web Site: www.paladventurevideos.com
Key Personnel
Pres: Laszlo Pal *Tel:* 206-459-6801 (cell)
  E-mail: lazpal123@gmail.com
Founded: 1969
Producer of award-winning outdoor adventure videos.
Membership(s): Director's Guild of Canada; NATAS

Palace Costume & Prop Co
835 N Fairfax Ave, Hollywood, CA 90046
Tel: 323-651-5458 *Fax:* 323-658-7133
E-mail: rentals@palacecostume.com
Web Site: www.palacecostume.com
Key Personnel
Pres: Melody Barnett
Mgr: Valerie Speaks
Founded: 1970
Rent authentic 1850-1990 costumes & props - jewelry & fashion accessories.

Palace Production Center
29 N Main St, South Norwalk, CT 06854
Tel: 203-853-1740 *Fax:* 203-855-9608
Web Site: www.palaceproductioncenter.com
Key Personnel
CEO: Chris Campbell
Full service video post-production center.
Rate card(s) available

Palace Productions MediaVision
Subsidiary of Connecticut Public Broadcasting Network
29 N Main St, Norwalk, CT 06854
Tel: 203-523-0602; 203-523-0604
Web Site: cpbn.org/palace-productions-media-vision
Key Personnel
VP: Maureen Connelly Barone
Sr Design Dir: Dan Chau
Script to screen services for corporate, commercial & digital content.
Branch Office(s)
1049 Asylum Ave, Hartford, CT 06105

Palardo Productions
Subsidiary of Palardo Studios
1807 Taft Ave, Suite 4, Hollywood, CA 90028
Tel: 323-469-8991
E-mail: palardo2@msn.com
Key Personnel
Prodr & Dir: Paul Ardolino
Casting Dir: Sandy Sanchez Wright
Dir, Devt: Tommy Ardolino
Dir, Photog: Russell Carpenter
Music Dir: Bjorn Englen
Prodn Mgr: Chip Clements
Chief Audio Engr: Paul Mittenberg
Chief Audio Mixer: Max Cherkassakah
Cust Rel: Deanna Palfrey
Prodn Designer & Modeler: Dr Alan Friedler

Special Effects: Michael Jittlov
Cable Boy: Todd Skelton
Founded: 1971
Full service production company featuring television & music videos.
Membership(s): DGA; PGA; SMPTE®; Writers Guild of America, West

The Palmer Group
PO Box 1455, New York, NY 10156-1455
Tel: 212-532-3880
E-mail: info@shellypalmer.com
Web Site: www.shellypalmer.com
Key Personnel
CEO: Mr Shelly Palmer
Founded: 1982
AV company focusing on digital solutions, television production, advertising & advanced media.
Demo reel(s) available

Panamax
Subsidiary of Core Brands LLC
1800 S McDowell Blvd, 2nd fl, Petaluma, CA 94954
Tel: 707-283-5900 (intl) *Toll Free Tel:* 800-472-5555 (US & CN) *Fax:* 707-283-5901
E-mail: custrelations@panamax.com
Web Site: www.panamax.com
Key Personnel
Pres: Joe Roberts
Founded: 1975
Manufactures high-end power protection/filtration products for custom AV installations; power filters, line conditioners, surge protection.
Product sheet(s) available, online
Shipping Address: 1730 Corporate Circle, Petaluma, CA 94954

Panasonic Consumer Electronics Co
Division of Panasonic Corporation of North America
2 Riverfront Plaza, Newark, NJ 07012
Tel: 201-348-7066
Web Site: www.panasonic.com
Products include ultra HD TVs, Blu-ray disc players, LUMIX digital cameras, camcorders, home audio, cordless phones, home appliances, wellness, beauty, personal care products & more.
Catalog(s) available

Panasonic Corporation of North America
Subsidiary of Panasonic Corporation
2 Riverfront Plaza, Newark, NJ 07012
Tel: 201-348-7000 *Toll Free Tel:* 800-211-7262; 888-275-2595 *Fax:* 201-348-7807
Web Site: www.panasonic.com
Key Personnel
Chmn & CEO: Joseph Taylor
Pres: Thomas Gebhardt
Founded: 1959

Panasonic Industrial Devices Sales Company of America
Division of Panasonic Corporation of North America
2 Riverfront Plaza, Newark, NJ 07012
Toll Free Tel: 800-344-2112
E-mail: industrial@us.panasonic.com
Web Site: na.industrial.panasonic.com
Industrial electronic components, energy solutions & industrial automation.

Panavid
210 West Pkwy, Unit 5, Pompton Plains, NJ 07444
Tel: 973-831-5655
E-mail: info@panavid.com; support@panavid.com
Web Site: www.panavid.com

Key Personnel
CEO: Rob Loehr
CFO: Gail Loehr
Dir of Design & Integration: Michael Turro
Proj Mgr, Integration: Ken Marechek
Proj Mgr, Prodn: Mark Miller
Busn Devt: Brent Brito
Client Rel Exec: Guy Nadeau *E-mail:* gnadeau@panavid.com
Natl Sales Mgr: Rob Allen
Lead Audio Engr: Stephen Turro
Lead Technician: Mike Cirrito
Audio Engr & Tech Servs: Joe Rumeau
Technician: Greg Gilkes
Logistics Mgr: Bryan Yurcik
Acct Mgr: Oliver Urrego
Mktg: Matt Carpenter
Founded: 1979
Specialize in AV production services & comprehensive AV technology solutions, including professional video, lighting & staging, for corporate meetings & other live events.
Membership(s): Audiovisual and Integrated Experience Association

Panavideo Inc
347 Marie de l'Incarnation, Quebec, QC G1N 3G9, Canada
Tel: 418-687-3150 *Toll Free Tel:* 800-463-5076 *Fax:* 418-687-0366
E-mail: info@panavideo.ca
Web Site: www.panavideo.ca
Key Personnel
Mktg Mgr: Norman Fiset
Founded: 1957
Full service AV equipment distributor.
Catalog(s) available
Branch Office(s)
3777 Blvd du Tricentenaire, Montreal, QC H1B 5W3, Canada *Tel:* 514-354-3152 *Fax:* 514-354-1728

Panavision
6101 Variel Ave, Woodland Hills, CA 91367
Tel: 818-316-2100
E-mail: panastore@panavision.com
Web Site: www.panavision.com
Founded: 1954
Film equipment rentals.
Branch Office(s)
6735 Selma Ave, Hollywood, CA 90028
1250 Menlo Dr NW, Suite A, Atlanta, GA 30318
Bldg 2004, Suite 103, 500 Sandy Creek Rd, Fayetteville, GA 30214
2226 W Walnut St, Chicago, IL 60612
837 Distributors Row, New Orleans, LA 70123
3521 Bryn Mawr NE, Albuquerque, NM 87107
150 Varick St, 2nd fl, New York, NY 10013
8000 Jetstar Dr, Irving, TX 75063, Gen Mgr: John Schrimpf *Tel:* 972-929-8585 *Toll Free Tel:* 800-260-1846 *Fax:* 972-929-8686 *E-mail:* john.schrimpf@panavision.com
2880 107 Ave SE, Unit 118, Calgary, AB T2Z 3R7, Canada
5560 Trapp Ave, Burnaby, BC V3N 5G4, Canada
192 Joseph Zatzman Dr, Suite 5, Dartmouth, NS B3B 1N4, Canada
900A Don Mills Rd, Toronto, ON M3C 1V6, Canada

P&H Crystalite LLC
800 Belle Terre Pkwy, Palm Coast, FL 32164
Toll Free Tel: 800-468-8673
E-mail: phcrystalite@gmail.com
Web Site: phcled.com
Key Personnel
Pres & CEO: Antoinette V Rubin
Founded: 1980
LED lighting products.
Online catalog(s) available

Pandisc Music Corp
936 SW First Ave, Suite 349, Miami, FL 33130
Tel: 305-557-1914 *Toll Free Fax:* 888-493-7778
Key Personnel
Pres: Bo Crane *Tel:* 305-557-1914 ext 101
  E-mail: bocrane@pandisc.com
Founded: 1982
Catalog(s) available

P&P Studios Inc
110 Lenox Ave, Suite 210, Stamford, CT 06906
Tel: 203-359-9292 *Toll Free Tel:* 888-WEPRODUCE (937-7638)
E-mail: ppstudios@weproduce.com; info@weproduce.com
Web Site: www.weproduce.com
Key Personnel
Pres: John R Fishback
VP, Admin: Abbie Wilson
VP, Mktg: Layne Rodney
Founded: 1970
Full range of AV & multimedia production services.

Pangolin Laser Systems Inc
9501 Satellite Blvd, Suite 109, Orlando, FL 32837
Tel: 407-299-2088 *Toll Free Tel:* 800-PAN-GOLIN (726-4654) *Fax:* 407-299-6066
E-mail: contact@pangolin.com
Web Site: www.pangolin.com
Key Personnel
Pres & CTO: William R Benner
COO: Justin Perry *E-mail:* justin@pangolin.com
Founded: 1986
Professional laser show projects. Control software/hardware & safety system manufacturer.
Online catalog(s) available
Membership(s): ELA; International Association of Amusement Parks and Attractions; International Laser Display Association

Panta Rhei Media Inc
565 Brown Ave, Turtle Creek, PA 15145
Tel: 412-824-8858
E-mail: info@panta-rhei.com
Web Site: panta-rhei.com
Key Personnel
Pres: Martha O'Grady
Founded: 1983
Multimedia, communication design, DVD & Internet, production, consultation & training for business, industry & healthcare.

PAR Inc
16204 N Florida Ave, Lutz, FL 33549
Tel: 813-449-4065 *Toll Free Tel:* 800-331-8378
  Fax: 813-961-2196 *Toll Free Fax:* 800-727-9329
E-mail: cs@parinc.com
Web Site: www.parinc.com
Key Personnel
Founder & Exec Chmn: R Bob Smith, III
CEO: Kristin Greco
Pres & COO: Travis White, PhD
EVP & CIO: Jim Eddy
EVP & CFO: Donna Drackett
VP, Dist: Greg Presson
VP, Mktg: Eric Jessen
Dir, Cust Support: Daniel McFadden
Dir, HR Assessments: Craig Dawson, PhD
Dir, Prod Devt: Melissa A Messer
Dir, Sales: David Houser
Prodn Mgr: Erika Thompson
Founded: 1978
Leading publisher of psychological assessment tools.
Online catalog(s) available
Shipping Address: 16130 N Florida Ave, Lutz, FL 33549
Membership(s): Association of Test Publishers

Paradigm Marketing & Creative
89 N Cooper St, Memphis, TN 38104
Tel: 901-685-7703
E-mail: info@2dimes.com
Web Site: www.2dimes.com
Key Personnel
Principal & Pres: Charles T Gaushell
Founded: 1992
Marketing, illustration, 3D computer graphics, special effects, animation & interactive multimedia firm serving the real estate, architectural, developer, institutional, aviation & medical professions.

Paradise Show & Design Inc
4653 35 St, Orlando, FL 32811
Tel: 407-649-7220 *Fax:* 407-649-7225
Web Site: www.paradiseshow.com
Key Personnel
Founder & Pres: Larry Epstein
Production services company specializing in staging, technical design & support.
Membership(s): NSCA

Paradise Video & Film
10148 NW 47 St, Sunrise, FL 33351
Tel: 954-747-1118 *Fax:* 954-747-3380
E-mail: info@paradisevideo.com
Web Site: www.paradisevideo.com
Key Personnel
Prodn Mgr: Sabra Karanian *E-mail:* sabra@paradisevideo.com
Founded: 1984
Membership(s): NATAS

Paradoxal Inc
103 E Broadway, New York, NY 10012
Tel: 212-366-5526; 917-400-4507 (cell)
E-mail: contact@paradoxal.net
Web Site: www.paradoxal.net
Key Personnel
Owner: Gaetan Rousseau *E-mail:* gaetan@paradoxal.net
Full service production company offering production services all over the US for foreign production companies when they have a project to shoot in the US. Expertise in producing TV programs, TV series, documentaries, music videos, commercials & feature films.

Paramount Motion Pictures Group
Division of Paramount Pictures Corporation
1515 Broadway, 3rd fl, New York, NY 10019
Tel: 212-258-6000 *Fax:* 212-846-4315
Web Site: www.paramountpictures.com
Filmmaker & distributor.

Paramount Pictures Corporation
5555 Melrose Ave, Los Angeles, CA 90038
Tel: 323-956-8398
Web Site: www.paramount.com
Key Personnel
Chmn & CEO: Jim Ginopulos
CFO & EVP: Mark Badagliacca
Pres, Consumer Prods & EVP, Worldwide Mktg Partnerships: LeeAnne Stables
Pres, Dom Dist, Motion Pictures Group: Don Harris
Pres, Dom Mktg & Dist: Megan Colligan
Pres, Home Media Dist: Hal Richardson
Pres, Worldwide Home Media Dist: Dennis Maguire
EVP, Worldwide HR: Catherine Houser
Feature film production & distribution, video & DVD worldwide distribution & production of programs for television broadcast & syndication.

Paramount Studios, see The Studios at Paramount

Parasound Products Inc
2250 McKinnon Ave, San Francisco, CA 94124
Tel: 415-397-7100 *Fax:* 415-397-0144
E-mail: sales@parasound.com; service@parasound.com
Web Site: www.parasound.com
Key Personnel
Pres: Richard Schram *E-mail:* richard@parasound.com
Founded: 1981
Manufacture & distribute audio equipment.
Online catalog(s) available
Membership(s): Consumer Technology Association™; Custom Electronic Design & Installation Association

Parlights Inc
1662 Bowmans Farm Rd, Suite 111, Frederick, MD 21701
Tel: 301-698-9242 *Fax:* 301-846-0369
E-mail: sales@parlights.com
Web Site: www.parlights.com
Key Personnel
CEO: Cary Levitt *E-mail:* cary.levitt@parlights.com
Pres & COO: Walt Dowling *E-mail:* walt.dowling@parlights.com
Gen Mgr: Lesley Vandever *E-mail:* lesley.vandever@parlights.com
Mktg Coord: Suzanne Levitt *E-mail:* suzanne.levitt@parlights.com
Founded: 1978
Licensed stage equipment contractor & supplier. Specialize in the design & installation of theatrical lighting & rigging systems throughout the Mid-Atlantic region.
Membership(s): Entertainment Services and Technology Association; International Association of Amusement Parks and Attractions; Virginia Theatre Association

Partech Lighting Systems Inc
8711 Reading Rd, Cincinnati, OH 45215
Tel: 513-761-5678 *Toll Free Tel:* 800-701-9551
  Fax: 513-679-8282
E-mail: info@partechlighting.com
Web Site: www.partechlighting.com
Key Personnel
Pres: David Groh
VP: Tina Groh
Founded: 1988
Full entertainment lighting services.
Membership(s): Professional Lighting & Sound Association

Parts Express
725 Pleasant Valley Dr, Springboro, OH 45066-1158
Tel: 937-743-3000 *Toll Free Tel:* 866-366-4909; 800-338-0531 (cust serv & tech support)
  Fax: 937-743-1677 *Toll Free Fax:* 866-755-7557
E-mail: sales@parts-express.com
Web Site: www.parts-express.com
Founded: 1986
Leading suppliers of speakers & AV products in the country. Wholesale program available.
Flyer(s) available, free, monthly, print & e-mail
Membership(s): Consumer Technology Association™; Custom Electronic Design & Installation Association

PASCO
224 48 St, Brooklyn, NY 11220
Tel: 718-833-9100
E-mail: pasco2@aol.com
Key Personnel
Pres: Joseph Anastasi
Photographic lab design & fabrication company.

Jim Passin Productions
1900 W Berwyn Ave, Chicago, IL 60640
Tel: 773-334-0408
Media production company.

Pat Kogan Productions Inc
4121 42 St, Sunnyside, NY 11104
Tel: 914-661-0049
E-mail: pkpmedia4142@gmail.com
Web Site: www.pkpmedia.com
Key Personnel
Pres: Patricia Kogan
Production company. Business development. Produces & directs videos.

PatchAmp
20 E Kennedy St, Hackensack, NJ 07601
Tel: 201-457-1504 *Fax:* 201-457-1507
E-mail: sales@patchamp.com
Web Site: www.patchamp.com
Key Personnel
Pres: James Tronolone
Leader in innovative, high quality, cost-effective patching & distribution solutions.
Online catalog(s) available
Membership(s): NAB; SBE; SMPTE®

Pathway Connectivity
Member of Acuity Brands Lighting Canada
103-1439 17 Ave SE, Calgary, AB T2G 1J9, Canada
Tel: 403-243-8110 *Fax:* 403-287-1281
E-mail: orders@pathwayconnect.com
Web Site: www.pathwayconnect.com
Key Personnel
Dir, Prod Innovation: Robert Bell *E-mail:* rbell@pathwayconnect.com
Mktg Mgr: Kerri Pitts *E-mail:* kpitts@pathwayconnect.com
Mgr, Engg: Kevin Loewen *E-mail:* kloewen@pathwayconnect.com
Mgr, Prodn: Ron Fisher *E-mail:* rfisher@pathwayconnect.com
Mgr, Purch: Neil James *E-mail:* njames@pathwayconnect.com
Cust Care & Inside Sales Assoc: Bernie Rooke *E-mail:* brooke@pathwayconnect.com
Founded: 1985
Full service DMX products manufacturing company.
Membership(s): Canadian Institute for Theatre Technology; Professional Lighting & Sound Association; USITT

Pauline Books & Media
50 St Paul's Ave, Boston, MA 02130
Tel: 617-522-8911 *Toll Free Tel:* 800-876-4463 (orders); 800-836-9723 (cust serv) *Fax:* 617-541-9805
E-mail: daughtersofstpaulusa@gmail.com
Web Site: www.pauline.org
Key Personnel
Publr: Sister Mary Mark Wickenhiser
Publisher of church documents, children's books, books on the theology of the body & marriage preparation program.
Online catalog(s) available

Paulist Press
997 Macarthur Blvd, Mahwah, NJ 07430-9990
Tel: 201-825-7300 *Toll Free Tel:* 800-218-1903 (orders) *Fax:* 201-825-6921
E-mail: info@paulistpress.com
Web Site: www.paulistpress.com
Key Personnel
Pres & Publr: Mark-David Janus, PhD
Dir, Mktg & Sales: Bob Byrns *E-mail:* bbyrns@paulistpress.com
Mng Ed: Donna Crilly
Founded: 1865

Distributor of religious books, videos & audios, as well as CDs & DVDs.
Online catalog(s) available
Shipping Address: 39 Ramapo Valley Rd, Mahwah, NJ 07430

Paulist Productions
6430 W Sunset Blvd, Suite 1220, Los Angeles, CA 90028
Tel: 310-454-0688
E-mail: paulistmail@paulistproductions.org
Web Site: www.paulistproductions.org
Key Personnel
Pres: Reverend Chris Donahue
VP: Marybeth Sprows
Exec Asst: Alicia Cordova
Founded: 1960
Religious film & TV program producers.
Catalog(s) available
Membership(s): DGA; SAG-AFTRA; Writers Guild of America

PBS Video
Division of Public Broadcasting Service
2100 Crystal Dr, Arlington, VA 22202
Tel: 703-739-5000
Web Site: shop.pbs.org; www.pbs.org/video
Key Personnel
Chief Programming Exec & Gen Mgr, Gen Audience Programming: Perry Simon
VP, Children's Programming: Linda Simensky
VP, Programming & Devt: Bill Gardner
Founded: 1969
Producers of children's & educational programs & DVDs.
Catalog(s) available, by request
Online catalog(s) available

"PBTM" Music, see Instant Music Now

PC&E
2235 DeFoor Hills Rd, Atlanta, GA 30318
Tel: 404-609-9001 *Toll Free Tel:* 800-537-4021 *Fax:* 404-609-9926
E-mail: marketing@pce-atlanta.com
Web Site: pce-atlanta.com
Key Personnel
Camera Mgr: Paul O'Daniel *E-mail:* paul@pce-atlanta.com
Rental Mgr: Jon Omps *E-mail:* jon@pce-atlanta.com
Camera equipment distributor, lighting, stages & studio for TV commercials.

PCO-TECH Inc
6930 Metroplex Dr, Romulus, MI 48174
Tel: 248-276-8820 *Fax:* 248-276-8825
E-mail: info@pco-tech.com; service@pco-tech.com
Web Site: www.pco-tech.com
Key Personnel
Pres: Thomas Bauersachs
Opers Mgr: Barry Brandon
Founded: 1986
Scientific cameras, high speed, high performance sCMOS & CCD, photonic instrumentation & complete systems manufacturer.
Online catalog(s) available
Membership(s): SPIE

PDC Productions
3217 N Flood Ave, Norman, OK 73069
Tel: 405-360-5130 *Fax:* 405-360-0524
E-mail: info@pdcproductions.com
Web Site: www.pdcproductions.com
Key Personnel
Owner: Patrick M Boylan
Pres: Jane Anderson *Tel:* 405-360-5130 ext 659
Specializes in live event production.

Peak Performance Publishing
Subsidiary of Peak Performance Consultants Inc
14728 Shirley St, Omaha, NE 68144
Tel: 402-334-1676 *Toll Free Tel:* 800-293-1676 *Fax:* 402-334-4437
Web Site: www.peakperformanceconsult.com
Key Personnel
Pres: Stephen J Brennan, PhD *E-mail:* brennan160@cox.net
DVD resources for corporate health, wellness & sports psychology.
Online catalog(s) available

Pearson Education Canada
Division of Pearson Canada Inc
26 Prince Andrew Place, North York, ON M3C 2H4, Canada
Tel: 416-447-5101 *Toll Free Tel:* 800-361-6128 *Fax:* 416-447-2551 *Toll Free Fax:* 800-563-9196
E-mail: school_inquiries@pearsoned.com
Web Site: www.pearson.com/ca; www.pearsoncanadaschool.com
Produce educational programs.

Peavey Electronics Corp
5022 Hartley Peavey Dr, Meridian, MS 39305
Tel: 601-483-5365 *Fax:* 601-486-1278
Web Site: peavey.com
Key Personnel
Founder & CEO: Hartley D Peavey
COO: Courtland Gray
Pres: Mary Peavey
Founded: 1965
Manufacturer of audio equipment.
Catalog(s) available
Foreign Office(s): Peavey Electronics Ltd, Great Folds Rd, Oakley Hay, Corby, Northants NN18 9ET, United Kingdom *Tel:* (01536) 461234 *Fax:* (01536) 747222 *E-mail:* info@peavey-eu.com

Pechman Imaging
106 E Second St, Kaukauna, WI 54130
Tel: 920-766-6160 *Toll Free Tel:* 800-777-0221 *Fax:* 920-766-6161
E-mail: customerservice@pechmanimaging.com
Web Site: www.pechmanimaging.com
Key Personnel
Pres: Frank Hurst
Providers of innovative digital & optical printing.
Catalog(s) available
Membership(s): The Imaging Alliance

Peckham Productions Inc
65 S Broadway, Tarrytown, NY 10591-4003
Web Site: www.peckhampix.com
Key Personnel
Exec Prodr, Dir & Cinematographer: Russell Peckham *Tel:* 914-329-8758 *E-mail:* russell@peckhampix.com
Prodr: Yola Kupniewska *Tel:* 914-584-3904 *E-mail:* yola@peckhampix.com
Founded: 1958

Peckhampix LLC, see Peckham Productions Inc

Peerbolte Creative LLC
182 NW 361, Warrensburg, MO 64093
Mailing Address: PO Box 754, Warrensburg, MO 64093
Tel: 660-429-1383
E-mail: solutions@peerbolte.com
Web Site: www.peerbolte.com
Key Personnel
Principal: Carl Hutcherson *E-mail:* carl@peerbolte.com
Founded: 1994
Theatre rigging, lighting consultation & design.
Branch Office(s)
PO Box 571, Cedar Falls, IA 50613 *Tel:* 319-296-5927

Peerless Industries
2300 White Oak Circle, Aurora, IL 60502
Tel: 630-375-5100 *Toll Free Tel:* 800-865-2112
Fax: 630-820-8537 *Toll Free Fax:* 800-359-
6500
E-mail: info@peerless-av.com
Web Site: www.peerless-av.com
Key Personnel
Pres: John Potts
Manufacturer of mounting accessories for AV
equipment.
Catalog(s) available
Membership(s): Audiovisual and Integrated Ex-
perience Association; Consumer Technology
Association™; Custom Electronic Design &
Installation Association; Digital Screenmedia
Association; Digital Signage Federation

Pelco
3500 Pelco Way, Clovis, CA 93612
Tel: 559-292-1981 (intl) *Toll Free Tel:* 800-289-
9100 (US & CN) *Fax:* 559-348-1120 (intl)
Toll Free Fax: 800-289-9150 (US & CN)
Web Site: www.pelco.com
Key Personnel
CEO: Sharad Shekhar
Manufacture digital CCTV systems.
Online catalog(s) available
Membership(s): Automated Imaging Association;
SIA

Pelican Products Inc
147 N Main St, South Deerfield, MA 01373
Mailing Address: PO Box 201, South Deerfield,
MA 01373-0201
Tel: 413-665-2163 *Toll Free Tel:* 800-542-7344
Fax: 413-665-8330
Web Site: www.pelican.com
Key Personnel
Dir Prod Mgmt, Commercial: John Luna
E-mail: john.luna@pelican.com
Founded: 1954
Manufacturer of shipping & storage containers for
sensitive electronics.
Catalog(s) available, free
Sales Office(s): 23215 Early Ave, Torrance, CA
90505 *Tel:* 310-326-4700 *Toll Free Tel:* 800-
473-5422 *Fax:* 310-326-3311
Membership(s): NAB

Pelican Publishing Co
1000 Burmaster St, Gretna, LA 70053-2246
Tel: 504-368-1175 *Toll Free Tel:* 800-843-1724;
888-PELICAN (735-4226 - cust serv); 888-
5PELICAN (888-573-5422) *Fax:* 504-368-1195
E-mail: sales@pelicanpub.com
Web Site: www.pelicanpub.com
Key Personnel
Sales Mgr: Don Anderson *Tel:* 504-368-1175 ext
335 *E-mail:* danderson@pelicanpub.com
Founded: 1926
Distributing books, videos & audio programs.
Catalog(s) available
Online catalog(s) available

Pendle Hill Bookstore
338 Plush Mill Rd, Wallingford, PA 19086
Tel: 610-566-4507 *Toll Free Tel:* 800-742-3150;
800-966-4556 *Fax:* 610-566-3679
E-mail: bookstore@fgc.quaker.org
Web Site: pendlehill.org
Distribute religious books & programs.
Catalog(s) available, free, annual

Pendulum Entertainment
444 Dufferin St, Studio 1, Toronto, ON M6K
2A3, Canada
Tel: 416-721-7593
E-mail: info@pendulumentertainment.com
Web Site: www.pendulumentertainment.com

Key Personnel
Creative Dir: Jacob Troy Miller
Founded: 2001
Boutique production company that produces all
forms of broadcast media.

Penfield Productions Ltd
35 Springfield St, Agawam, MA 01001
Tel: 413-786-4454
Web Site: www.penfieldprod.com
Key Personnel
Pres & Gen Mgr: John Shanahan *E-mail:* john@
penfieldprod.com
Founded: 1943
Full service HD, Ultra HD, 4K video & interac-
tive media production company.
Catalog(s) available

Penguin Random House Audio Publishing
Division of Penguin Random House Inc
1745 Broadway, New York, NY 10019
E-mail: audio@penguinrandomhouse.com
Web Site: www.penguinrandomhouseaudio.com
Key Personnel
Pres & Publr: Amanda D'Acierno
SVP, Assoc Publr & Edit Dir: Amy Metsch
SVP, Content Prodn: Dan Zitt
SVP, Mktg & Publicity: Donna Passannante
SVP, Opers: Sue Daulton
VP, Audio Fin & Strategy: Len Wiggins
VP, Mktg: Heather Dalton
VP, Publicity: Katie Punia
Dir, Audio Prodn: Karen Dzienkonski
Dir, Post-Prodn & Technol: Ok Hee Kolwitz
Assoc Dir, Creative Mktg: Jennifer Rubins
Assoc Dir, Digital Prods: Dennis Tyrrell
Assoc Dir, Mktg Strategy: Victoria Tomao
Assoc Dir, Strategic Mktg: Taraneh Djangi
Asst Dir, Acqs & Edit Opers: Catherine Bucaria
Exec Prodr: Sarah Jaffe; Linda Korn
Prodr: Nick Martorelli
Mng Ed: Kelly Atkinson
Ed: Jennifer Donovan
Sr Mgr, Creative Partnership Devt: Kelly Gildea
Sr Mgr, Digital Prodn Platforms: Julie Wilson
Sr Mgr, Mktg Strategy: Robert Guzman
Sr Publicity Mgr: Nicole Morano
Sr Soc Media Mgr: Juliette Koronkiewicz
Assoc Mgr, Post-Prodn: Simon Katz
Asst Mgr, Rts & Perms: Tara Hart
Assoc Publicist: Heather Job
Proj Mgmt Coord: Ruby Liu
Fiction & nonfiction audiobooks.
Online catalog(s) available

Penguin Random House Canada
Division of Penguin Random House Inc
320 Front St W, Suite 1400, Toronto, ON M5V
3B6, Canada
Tel: 416-364-4449 *Toll Free Tel:* 888-523-9292
(cust serv) *Fax:* 416-598-7764
E-mail: customerservicescanada@
penguinrandomhouse.com
Web Site: www.penguinrandomhouse.ca
Key Personnel
CEO: Kristin Cochrane
CFO: Barry Gallant
COO: Robert Wheaton
Exec Publr & EVP: Louise Dennys
SVP & Dir, Prodn: Janine Laporte
VP & Deputy Publr: Marion Garner
VP & Publr, Appetite by Random House: Robert
McCullough
VP, PRHC & Publr, Penguin Canada: Nicole
Winstanley
VP, Mktg & Communs: Beth Lockley
VP, Sales: Charidy Johnston
Dir, Communs: Katie Saunoris
Prodn Dir: Carla Kean
Publicity Dir: Josh Glover
Prodr, Audiobooks: Ann Jansen

Penn Elcom Inc
Subsidiary of Penn Elcom Ltd
7465 Lampson Ave, Garden Grove, CA 92841
Tel: 714-230-6200 *Toll Free Tel:* 800-228-9122
(US orders) *Fax:* 714-230-6222
E-mail: california@penn-elcom.com
Web Site: www.penn-elcom.com
Flight case & speaker cabinet solutions.
Online catalog(s) available
Branch Office(s)
232 W Parkway, Pompton Plains, NJ 07444
Tel: 973-839-7777 *Toll Free Tel:* 800-
446-7174 (US orders) *Fax:* 973-839-2277
E-mail: new_jersey@penn-elcom.com
Penn Elcom Online, 8204 N Lamar, Suite B15,
Austin, TX 78753 *Tel:* 512-992-0383 *Toll Free
Tel:* 844-407-5188 *E-mail:* onlineusa@penn-
elcom.com *Web Site:* www.pennelcomonline.
com
5609 Campbell Rd, Houston, TX 77041 *Tel:* 281-
855-9772 *Toll Free Tel:* 800-503-8999 (US or-
ders) *Fax:* 281-855-4856 *E-mail:* texas@penn-
elcom.com
2020 Halford Dr, Windsor, ON N9A 6J3,
Canada *Tel:* 519-737-9494 *Toll Free Tel:* 888-
736-6322 (CN orders) *Fax:* 519-737-9499
E-mail: canada@penn-elcom.com
Foreign Office(s): Penn Elcom SRL, Calle 12
de Octubre, 743, Ciudad de Avellaneda,
Buenos Aires, Argentina *Tel:* (011) 4201 5790
E-mail: argentina@penn-elcom.com
Penn Elcom, 15 Silicon Place, Tullamarine,
Victoria 3043, Australia *Tel:* (03) 9335 6455
E-mail: australia@penn-elcom.com
Spectrus BH, Av Olegafrio Maciel, 256, Centro,
Belo Horizonte-MG, Brazil *Tel:* (031) 3212
1999 *E-mail:* spectrusbh@penn-elcom.com.br
Spectrus BH, Rua Alba, 1872, Jabaquara, 04360-
000 Sao Paulo-SP, Brazil *Tel:* (011) 5678 2000
Fax: (011) 5678 2000 *E-mail:* spectrusbh@
penn-elcom.com.br *Web Site:* www.
spectrusbrasil.com.br
Comercial e Importadora Penn Elcom Ltda, Co-
tapos No 1387-A, Independencia, Santiago,
Chile *Tel:* (02) 27320212 *Fax:* (02) 27322370
E-mail: chile@penn-elcom.com
Penn Elcom (Dongguan), Yuquan Industrial Area,
Fenggang Town, Dongguan City, Guangdong
Province 523681, China *Tel:* (0769) 86803388
Fax: (0769) 86803366 *E-mail:* sales@penn-
elcom.cn
Penn Elcom Tianjin, Huang Zhuang Industrial
Area, West Side of 104 Rd, Wuqing Dis-
trict, Tianjin City, China *Tel:* (022) 22145132
Fax: (022) 22145133 *E-mail:* sales@penn-
elcom.cn
Penn Elcom de Colombia SAS, Av Carrera 106,
No 15A-25, Bodega 4, Manzana 4, Carrera
3A, Lote 11, Zona Franca Bogota, Bogota,
Colombia *Tel:* (01) 7438617; (01) 7438620
E-mail: colombia@penn-elcom.com
Penn Elcom GmbH, Groenlandstr 2, 46446
Emmerich-Elten, Germany *Tel:* (02828)
3130100 *Fax:* (02828) 3130900 *E-mail:* post.
eu@penn-elcom.com
Penn Elcom HK Ltd, Ming Sang Industrial
Bldg, Rm 17, 7/F, 21 Hing Yip St, Kwun
Tong, Kowloon, Hong Kong *Tel:* 2790 8009
Fax: 2343 2656 *E-mail:* info@penn-elcom.hk
Penn Elcom Hardware Pvt Ltd, U5/4 Green In-
dustrial Park, Dongripada, Kaman Bhiwandi
Rd, Poman, Vasai E, Maharashtra 401 208, In-
dia *Tel:* 9869119110 (cell); 9920119110 (cell)
E-mail: india@penn-elcom.com
Penn Elcom Ireland Ltd, Johnstown Lane, Unit
A, Dun Laoghaire, Co Dublin A96 H6Y6, Ire-
land *Tel:* (01) 5558698 *E-mail:* ireland@penn-
elcom.com
Penn Fabrication (Japan), 128-2 Chome, Fuji-
hashi, OME-SH1, Tokyo 198-0022, Japan
Tel: (0428) 32-5690 *Fax:* (0428) 32-5691
E-mail: info@penn-fab.jp *Web Site:* www.penn-
fab.jp

Penn Elcom Sdn Bhd, No 15, Jl Meranti Puchong, D25 Meranti Puchong, 47120 Puchong, Selangor, Malaysia *Tel:* (03) 8052 7967
Fax: (03) 8066 7967 *E-mail:* sales@penn-
elcom.my

Diamant Group World Audio SA de CV, El
Huerto No 63, Colonia Centro, 44100 Guadala-
jara, JAL, Mexico *Tel:* (0133) 36 13 87 96
E-mail: ventas.gdl@diamant.com.mx *Web
Site:* www.diamant.com.mx

Sesamee Mexicana SA de CV, Circuito de la
Industria Norte 71, Parque Industrial Lerma,
52000 Lerma, MEX, Mexico *Tel:* (01728) 282
18 78; (01728) 282 28 87; (01728) 282 18 87
Fax: (01728) 282 18 78; (01728) 282 28 87;
(01728) 282 18 87 *E-mail:* direccion.sancher@
sesamee.com.mx *Web Site:* www.sesamee.com.
mx

Diamant Group World Audio SA de CV, Calle
Meave 21-A, Colonia Centro, Delegacion
Cuauhtemoc, 06080 Mexico, CDMX, Mexico *Tel:* (0155) 55126321; (0155) 55127762
Toll Free Tel: 800 633 83 31 *Fax:* (0155)
55126321; (0155) 55127762 *E-mail:* contacto@
diamant.com.mx *Web Site:* www.diamant.com.
mx

Live Sound Manufacturing Ltd, 34-C Crummer
Rd, PO Box 68216, Grey Lynn, Auckland,
New Zealand *Tel:* (09) 378-0542 *Fax:* (09)
378-9863 *E-mail:* john@livesound.co.nz *Web
Site:* www.livesound.co.nz

P A Systems A/S, Normannsgata 25, 0655
Oslo, Norway *Tel:* 22679313 *Fax:* 22682101
E-mail: pasystem@online.no *Web Site:* www.
pasystem.no

Penn Elcom SAC, Calle Solidaridad MZ D2 LT
18 II Parcella, Villa El Salvador, Lima, Peru
Tel: (01) 287-6850 *E-mail:* peru@penn-elcom.
com

Joa Beslag AB, Grabo Industrivag 3, 443 40
Grabo, Sweden *Tel:* (0302) 45300 *Fax:* (0302)
40066 *E-mail:* info@joabeslag.se *Web
Site:* www.joabeslag.se

Holmberg Cases Sweden AB, Foretagsvagen 1,
953 33 Haparanda, Sweden *Tel:* (0922) 14640
Fax: (0922) 14690 *E-mail:* info@hbc.se *Web
Site:* www.hbc.se

UMKA-1 Ltd, Ap 3, 37 Yrkovskaya, Kiev 04080,
Ukraine *Tel:* (044) 517530 *Fax:* (044) 824496
E-mail: pennelcom.kiev@gmail.com

Penn Elcom Ltd, Philips House, Drury Lane,
Ponswood Industrial Estate, St Leonards-on-
Sea, East Sussex TN38 9BA, United Kingdom
Tel: (01424) 718576; (01424) 722944 (sales)
Fax: (01424) 718572 *E-mail:* info@penn-
elcom.com

Penn Elcom Ltd, Parsons Industrial Estate, 9-10
Parsons Rd, Tyne & Wear NE37 1HB, United
Kingdom *Tel:* (0191) 416 1717 *Fax:* (0191)
419 3715 *E-mail:* info@penn-elcom.com

Membership(s): NAMM, the National Association
of Music Merchants

Pennebaker Hegedus Films Inc
262 W 91 St, New York, NY 10024
Tel: 212-496-9195 *Fax:* 212-496-8195
E-mail: info@phfilms.com
Web Site: phfilms.com
Key Personnel
Prodr: Chris Hegedus; D A Pennebaker; Frazer
Pennebaker *E-mail:* frazer@phfilms.com
Documentary filmmakers.

Penrose Productions
2310 Homestead Rd, Suite C1-No 211, Los Al-
tos, CA 94024
Tel: 650-969-8273
E-mail: info@penroseproductions.com
Web Site: www.penroseproductions.com
Key Personnel
Owner & Pres: Jim Penrose *E-mail:* jim@
penroseproductions.com

Founded: 1981
Video production & web marketing.

PentaVision Communications Inc
712 N Niles Ave, South Bend, IN 46617
Tel: 574-272-8365
E-mail: hello@pentavision.net
Web Site: pentavision.net
Key Personnel
Co-Owner, Dir of Photog & Prodn Mgr: Bob
Richthammer *E-mail:* bob@pentavision.net
Founded: 2002
Professional full service media production com-
pany. Outdoor & indoor studio facilities.

Pentrex Media Group LLC
2652 E Walnut St, Pasadena, CA 91107-3723
Mailing Address: PO Box 94911, Pasadena, CA
91109-4911
Tel: 626-793-3400 *Toll Free Tel:* 800-950-9333
Fax: 626-793-3797
E-mail: pentrex@pentrex.com
Web Site: www.pentrex.com
Key Personnel
Pres: Michael Clayton
Founded: 1984
Producer of railroad videos.
Catalog(s) available, free

People Productions
1737 15 St, Suite 200, Boulder, CO 80302
Tel: 303-449-6086 *Fax:* 303-449-9526
E-mail: info@peopleproductions.com
Web Site: peopleproductions.com
Key Personnel
Pres: Brad Gilbert
Founded: 1984
Video & digital media production company. We-
binars & eLearning, motion graphics, 2D & 3D
video animation.

People Skills International
720 Gateway Center Dr, Bldg A, San Diego, CA
92102
Tel: 619-262-9951
Web Site: www.journeytolovingyourself.com
Key Personnel
Pres: Ida Greene, PhD *E-mail:* idagreene@
idagreene.com
Founded: 1985
Author of 22 books *Light the Fire Within You;
Self Esteem: The Essence of You; Soft Power
Negotiation Skills; How to Be a Success in
Business; How to Improve Self Esteem in
Any Child; How to Improve Self Esteem in
the African American Child; Money, How to
Get It, Keep It; Say Goodbye to Your Small-
ness, Hello to Your Greatness; Are You Ready
for Success?; Anger Management Skills for
Children-Elementary; Anger Management Skills
for Children-Middle School; Anger Manage-
ment Skills for Teenagers; Anger Management
Skills for Women; Anger Management Skills for
Men; Stirring up the African American Spirit;
Secret of Success; Angels Among Us; Earth
Angels; Looking for Love in All the Wrong
Places; How to Be Alone Without Feeling
Lonely; Understanding Relationships and How
to Improve Them; Soft Power Skills, Women
and Negotiation.*
Online catalog(s) available

PeopleVisionFX
311 E First Ave, Bldg A, Roselle, NJ 07203
Tel: 973-509-2056
Web Site: peoplevisionfx.com
Key Personnel
Pres: Wayne Sullivant *E-mail:* waynesullivant@
peoplevisionfx.com

Pepper Group
220 N Smith St, Suite 406, Palatine, IL 60067
Tel: 847-963-0333 *Fax:* 847-963-0888
E-mail: pepper@peppergroup.com
Web Site: www.peppergroup.com
Key Personnel
Founder & CEO: Tim Padgett
CFO: Denise O'Neill
Pres: George Couris
VP & Creative Dir: Cindy Wojdyla
Founded: 1994
Multimedia production; full service marketing
provider.

Peppers Ghost HD®
Subsidiary of Bob Thomas Productions Inc
c/o Bob Thomas Productions Inc, 2 Franklin Ct,
Montville, NJ 07045
Tel: 973-335-9100
Web Site: www.peppersghosthd.com
Key Personnel
Pres: Robert Thomas *E-mail:* bobthomas@
bobthomas.net

Perennial Pictures Film Corp
2102 E 52 St, Indianapolis, IN 46205
Tel: 317-253-1519
E-mail: mail@perennialpictures.com
Web Site: www.perennialpictures.com
Key Personnel
Pres: G Brian Reynolds *E-mail:* brian.reynolds@
perennialpictures.com
SVP: Russell Harris *E-mail:* russ.harris@
perennialpictures.com
VP: Michael Ruggiero *E-mail:* mike.ruggiero@
perennialpictures.com
Founded: 1979
Producers of animated web site logos, television
commercials, television specials & limited se-
ries for home video.
Membership(s): ASIFA-Hollywood

Perfection Learning Corp
1000 N Second Ave, Logan, IA 51546
Mailing Address: PO Box 500, Logan, IA 51546-
0500
Tel: 712-644-2831 *Toll Free Tel:* 800-831-4190
(US & CN) *Toll Free Fax:* 800-543-2745
E-mail: orders@perfectionlearning.com
Web Site: www.perfectionlearning.com
Founded: 1926
Distribute educational programs.
Online catalog(s) available
Membership(s): International Literacy Association

Performance Audio LLC
2456 S West Temple St, Salt Lake City, UT
84115
Tel: 801-466-3196 *Toll Free Tel:* 800-771-8330
Fax: 801-484-1538
E-mail: sales@performanceaudio.com; rental@
performanceaudio.com
Web Site: www.performanceaudio.com
Key Personnel
Owner: Chris Fillmore *Tel:* 801-466-3196
E-mail: chris@performanceaudio.com; Darrin
Porter *E-mail:* darrin@performanceaudio.com
Founded: 1977
Distribute audio systems & equipment.
Branch Office(s)
1050 S Academy Blvd, Suite 124, Colorado
Springs, CO 80910 *Tel:* 719-323-6100

Personal Achievement Institute
One Speaking Success Rd, Kingman, AZ 86402
Tel: 928-753-5315
Web Site: burtdubin-blog.com
Key Personnel
Pres: Burt Dubin
Founded: 1978
Speaking Business Success system.
Membership(s): National Speakers Association

PESA
103 Quality Circle, Suite 210, Huntsville, AL 35806
Tel: 256-726-9200 *Toll Free Tel:* 800-323-7372
E-mail: sales@pesa.com
Web Site: www.pesa.com
Key Personnel
Exec Chmn: Howard G Sutton
CFO: Ricky Ng
CTO: Scott Barella
Sales & Busn Dev: Chuck D Tillett
Mgr, Cust Serv: Doug Sotherland
Founded: 1973
Design & manufacture routing switchers & distribution equipment.
Online catalog(s) available
Branch Office(s)
90 Allstate Pkwy, Suite 404, Markham, ON L3R 6H3, Canada *Tel:* 905-752-3700
Foreign Office(s): Rm 1308, A Tower, Jingonghongyang Plaza, No 25 of Rd Nanbinhe, Xicheng District, Beijing 100055, China, Mgr: Lou Libin *Tel:* (01380) 126 2787 *E-mail:* libin@pesa.com
Membership(s): Alliance for IP Media Solutions; NAB; ONVIF®; SMPTE®; VESA

Peterson's Video Transfer Services
5693 S Jones Blvd, Suite 110, Las Vegas, NV 89118
Toll Free Tel: 800-888-0426
E-mail: contact@petersonsvideotransfer.com
Web Site: www.petersonsvideotransfer.com
Key Personnel
Pres: Jeff Peterson
Video transfer.
Online catalog(s) available
Membership(s): The Imaging Alliance; IPI - Member Network; SMPTE®

PetroSkills | RDC Solutions
25403 Katy Mills Pkwy, Katy, TX 77494
Toll Free Tel: 800-360-7222
E-mail: solutions@petroskills.com
Web Site: www.resourcedev.com; www.petroskills.com
Key Personnel
Mktg Specialist: Lori Koran
Web-based learning modules for the oil & gas industry.
Catalog(s) available

PGi
3280 Peachtree Rd NE, Suite 1000, Atlanta, GA 30305
Tel: 404-262-8400 *Toll Free Tel:* 866-755-4878
Web Site: www.pgi.com
Key Personnel
Pres & CEO: Theodore P Schrafft
Chief Admin Offr: Sean P O'Brien
CFO: Kevin McAdams
CIO & EVP, Global Opers & Cust Care: Warren Neuburger
CTO: David M Guthrie
EVP & Mng Dir, PGi International: John D Stone
EVP, Cust Care: Michele Dobnikar
EVP, Global Sales, Mktg & Field Opers: J Scott Tapp
EVP, Legal, Gen Coun & Secy: Michele Nelson
EVP, Strategy & Busn Devt: Michael W Dickerson
SVP, HR: Alison Sheehan
Founded: 1991
Collaboration software & services.
Branch Office(s)
2300 Lakeview Pkwy, Suite 225/275/300, Alpharetta, GA 30004, Facilities Mgr: Bob Snopek *Toll Free Tel:* 866-962-8400
15 Corporate Park, No 200, Irvine, CA 92606
87 N Raymond Ave, 6th fl, Pasadena, CA 91103

44 Montgomery St, Suite 1300, San Francisco, CA 94104, Contact: Mark Lopez *Tel:* 415-343-8226
2424 Garden of the Gods, Colorado Springs, CO 80919, Contact: Penny Gibson *Tel:* 719-578-0700
222 N LaSalle St, Suite 900, Chicago, IL 60601, Off Mgr: Tom Parker *Tel:* 312-794-6706 *Toll Free Fax:* 866-642-0163
18103 W 106 St, Olathe, KS 66061, Exec Asst: Angie Jones *Tel:* 913-661-0700
100 William St, Suite 800, New York, NY 10038, Acct Exec: John Fallon *Tel:* 212-915-2812
300 Hapel Harbor Dr, Suite 100, Pittsburgh, PA 15238
612 W Fourth St, Austin, TX 78701, Contact: Tony Wrubel *Tel:* 512-697-2093
2150 S 1300 E, Suite 500, Salt Lake City, UT 84106, SVP, Conference: Angela Beitia
12020 Sunrise Valley Dr, Suite 100, Reston, VA 20191, Contact: Anita Peterson

Phase One Media Group, see Phase One Studios

Phase One Studios
1121 Bellamy Rd N, Unit 5, Scarborough, ON M1H 3B9, Canada
Tel: 416-291-9553
Web Site: www.phaseonestudios.com; www.facebook.com/phaseonestudio
Key Personnel
Studio Mgr: Jen D Fabico *E-mail:* jen@phaseonestudios.com
Founded: 1974
Membership(s): Canadian Independent Record Production Association

Phase Technology
Subsidiary of MSE Audio
6400 Youngerman Circle, Jacksonville, FL 32244
Tel: 913-663-5600 *Toll Free Tel:* 855-663-5600 *Fax:* 913-663-3200
E-mail: sales@mseaudio.com
Web Site: phasetech.mseaudio.com
Key Personnel
Acct Specialist: Cheryl Susser *E-mail:* csusser@unitedspeaker.com
Founded: 1981

Phat Planet Recording Studios
3473 Parkway Center Ct, Orlando, FL 32808
Tel: 407-295-7270 *Toll Free Tel:* 800-667-4893 *Fax:* 321-549-6229
E-mail: info@phatplanetstudios.com
Web Site: www.phatplanetstudios.com
Key Personnel
Pres & Studio Mgr: Ed Krout *E-mail:* edkrout@phatplanetstudios.com
Founded: 1996
Recording studio offering voice-over sessions, live recording, mixing, production & mastering as well as archiving solutions & audio format transfers; producers on staff in all genres.

Philips Entertainment Lighting
Subsidiary of Philips Lighting Business Unit-Professional Luminaires North America
10911 Petal St, Dallas, TX 75238
Tel: 214-647-7880 *Toll Free Tel:* 877-VARILITE (877-827-4548) *Fax:* 214-647-8038
E-mail: entertainment.service@philips.com
Web Site: www.vari-lite.com
Key Personnel
Cust Serv Mgr: David Garcia *E-mail:* david.a.garcia@philips.com
Founded: 1981
Designer, manufacturer & distributor of automated lighting products, systems & related products.

Online catalog(s) available
Membership(s): Professional Lighting & Sound Association; Texas Association of Broadcasters; USITT

Philips Lighting Controls
Subsidiary of Philips Lighting Business Unit-Professional Luminaires North America
10911 Petal St, Dallas, TX 75238
Toll Free Tel: 800-555-0050
E-mail: controls.support@philips.com
Web Site: www.usa.lighting.philips.com/products/lighting-controls; www.lightingproducts.philips.com
Innovative & energy efficient lighting technology for indoor, outdoor, commercial, architectural & entertainment applications.
Online catalog(s) available

Philips Lightolier
Division of Signify
200 Franklin Square Dr, Somerset, NJ 08873
Toll Free Tel: 800-555-0050; 855-486-2216
Web Site: www.lightingproducts.philips.com
LED lighting solutions.
Online catalog(s) available

Philips Stonco
Division of Signify
200 Franklin Square Dr, Somerset, NJ 08873
Toll Free Tel: 800-555-0050; 855-486-2216
Web Site: www.lightingproducts.philips.com
Outdoor lighting manufacturer.
Online catalog(s) available

Phillips Media Source
750 N St Paul, Suite 1000, Dallas, TX 75201
Tel: 214-741-1300 *Toll Free Tel:* 800-TEXAS13 (839-2713) *Fax:* 214-741-3942
Web Site: phillipsmediasource.com
Key Personnel
Owner: Bob Phillips
CFO: Kelli Phillips
Film & HD video production for TV, radio, web, laptop, table & mobile screens.

PHL17, see WPHL-TV

Phoebus Manufacturing
Division of The Phoebus Co Inc
2800 Third St, San Francisco, CA 94107
Tel: 415-550-1177
Key Personnel
Pres: John Tedesco
Founded: 1976
Lighting fixtures & equipment.
Catalog(s) available
Membership(s): AICP; Professional Lighting & Sound Association; USITT

Phoenix Aerial Photography Inc
PO Box 68432, Nashville, TN 37206
Tel: 615-255-2000; 615-975-4226 (cell)
E-mail: info@phoenixaerialphoto.com
Web Site: www.phoenixaerialphoto.com
Key Personnel
Owner: Paul Cardel
Founded: 1985
Gyros & gyro stabilized video platform.
Membership(s): PPA; Professional Aerial Photography Association

The Phoenix Learning Group Inc
1990 E Lohman Ave, Suite 102, Las Cruces, NM 88001
Toll Free Tel: 800-221-1274
E-mail: customerservice@phoenixlearninggroup.com; orders@phoenixlearninggroup.com
Web Site: phoenixlearninggroup.com

Key Personnel
EVP: Bryan Sullivan
Founded: 1993
Educational DVD film & video producer & distributor.
Online catalog(s) available
Membership(s): AECT; National Media Market

Phoenix Society for Burn Survivors Inc
525 Ottawa Ave NW, Front, Grand Rapids, MI 49503
Tel: 616-458-2773 *Toll Free Tel:* 800-888-BURN (888-2876) *Fax:* 616-458-2831
E-mail: info@phoenix-society.org
Web Site: www.phoenix-society.org
Key Personnel
COO: Steve Lieberman
Exec Dir: Amy Acton
Prog Dir: Pam Peterson
Off Mgr: Kerri Hanson
Founded: 1977
Produce & distribute medical programs.
Catalog(s) available

Phonic Ear Inc, see FrontRow

Photo Film Stage
820 Thompson Ave, Suite 34, Glendale, CA 91201
Tel: 213-304-5608
E-mail: photofilmstage@yahoo.com
Web Site: photofilmstage.com
Photography & film studio.

Photo Finish
Auburn Mall, 550 Center St, No 9007, Auburn, ME 04210
Tel: 207-783-3354
Web Site: www.mainephotofinish.com
Key Personnel
Exec Dir: Francis Gagnon
Founded: 1989
Film & video production company. Weddings & dance videography, film & video transfers, video projector rentals.

Photo-Sonics Inc
9131 Independence Ave, Chatsworth, CA 91311
Tel: 818-842-2141 *Fax:* 818-842-2610
E-mail: mail@photosonics.com
Web Site: www.photosonics.com
Key Personnel
CFO: Kate Treesuwan *Tel:* 818-531-3246
    E-mail: kate@photosonics.com
Pres: Philip Kiel *Tel:* 818-531-3219
    E-mail: pkiel@photosonics.com
Founded: 1952
Design, manufacture & distribute photo-optical instrumentation.
Online catalog(s) available
Membership(s): SPIE

Photo Tech Inc
910 Fifth Ave, Suite 101, Baldwin, WI 54002
Tel: 651-702-6717 (support) *Toll Free Tel:* 800-525-6486
E-mail: rollie@phototechinc.com
Web Site: www.phototechinc.com
Founded: 1953
Photographic equipment & accessories.
Online catalog(s) available

Photodyne Technologies
8531 Alcott St, Suite 201, Los Angeles, CA 90035
Tel: 310-497-0968 *Toll Free Tel:* 800-660-2147
E-mail: info@photodyne.com
Web Site: www.photodyne.com
Key Personnel
Owner & Pres: Henry Corech

Founded: 1983
Manufacturer of computerized macro photography systems & industrial light tables & stands.

Photoflex Inc
Division of PromarkBRANDS Inc
1268 Humbracht Circle, Bartlett, IL 60103-1631
Tel: 831-786-1370 *Toll Free Tel:* 800-486-2674
E-mail: sales@photoflex.com; techsupport@photoflex.com
Web Site: www.photoflex.com
Founded: 1978
Lighting products for the photo, film & video industries worldwide.
Online catalog(s) available

Photogenic Professional Lighting
1268 Humbracht Circle, Bartlett, IL 60103-1631
Tel: 630-830-2500 *Toll Free Tel:* 800-682-7668
    Fax: 630-830-2525
E-mail: sales@photogenic.com
Web Site: www.photogenic.com
Key Personnel
Sales Mgr: Jim Fennig
Founded: 1903
Manufacturer of photographic lighting equipment & accessories.
Online catalog(s) available

Photographers' Formulary Inc
7079 Hwy 83 N, Condon, MT 59826
Mailing Address: PO Box 950, Condon, MT 59826-0950
Tel: 406-754-2891 *Toll Free Tel:* 800-922-5255
    Fax: 406-754-2896
E-mail: formulary@blackfoot.net
Web Site: www.photoformulary.com
Key Personnel
Co-Owner & Pres: William "Bud" G Wilson
Co-Owner & Workshops Prog Dir: Lynn Wilson
    E-mail: lynnw@blackfoot.net
Manufacture & distribute photographic chemicals & supplies.
Catalog(s) available, free
Online catalog(s) available

Photographic Apparatus Systems Co, see PASCO

Photographic Rental Service Inc (PRS)
1109 S La Brea Ave, Los Angeles, CA 90019
Tel: 323-965-9900 *Fax:* 323-965-9901
E-mail: prsrental@gmail.com
Web Site: prsla.com
Key Personnel
Rental Specialist: Geoffrey Ford
Digital & analog camera repair, sensor cleaning, strobe repair, pocket wizard repair; camera, grip & lighting rentals.

Photographic Solutions Inc, see Photosol Inc

Photogroup Studios
321 W Ben White, Suite 106A & 107, Austin, TX 78704
Tel: 512-373-8547
E-mail: photogroup@photogroupaustin.com
Web Site: www.photogroupaustin.com
Founded: 2011
Rental facility for photographers & videographers. Equipment & grip rental as well as full production services available.

Photomart Cine-Video LLC, see AudioVideoElectric

Photosol Inc
Formerly Photographic Solutions Inc
318 Seaboard Ave, Venice, FL 34285
Tel: 941-445-2231

E-mail: orders4photosol@gmail.com
Web Site: www.photosol.com
Key Personnel
Pres: David M Stone
Founded: 1983
Global distributor of digital camera cleaning products as well as film & negative cleaning solutions.
Catalog(s) available

Photosound of Orlando Inc
7055 University Blvd, Winter Park, FL 32792
Tel: 407-898-8841 *Toll Free Tel:* 800-552-8776
E-mail: info@photosoundav.com
Web Site: www.photosoundav.com
Key Personnel
Owner: Evan Hoffman
Founded: 1955
AV rentals & sales, in-house production department for editing & composing presentation-related videos, film & tape to DVD transfers.

Physical Optics Corp (POC)
1845 E 205 St, Torrance, CA 90501-1510
Tel: 310-320-3088
E-mail: info@poc.com
Web Site: www.poc.com
Key Personnel
Co-Founder, Chmn & Chief Value Offr: Joanna Jannson, PhD
VChmn & Chief Strategic Offr: Rick Shie
    E-mail: rshie@poc.com
Pres & CEO: Kevin Walter, PhD
COO: Gajendra Savant, PhD
CFO: Yun Kim
Chief Admin Offr: Keith Baker
Chief Busn Devt Offr: Robert Waldo, PhD
CTO: Andrew Kostrzewski, PhD
Busn Devt & Mktg Communs Dir: Nydia Aizpuru *E-mail:* nyaizpuru@poc.com
Founded: 1985
Systems integrator of advanced technology serving military & defense, homeland security & select commercial markets. Products include HD data & video recorders, 3D imagery presentation systems & automated target recognition.
Brochure(s) available

Pico Digital, see ATX Networks

Picture This Production Services
2223 NE Oregon St, Portland, OR 97232
Tel: 503-235-3456 *Fax:* 503-236-2302
E-mail: info@pixthis.com
Web Site: pixthis.com
Specialize in commercial/cable broadcast television, web content & high-end corporate events & services. Also provide full post-production services.

Picturestart
817 Hilldale Ave, West Hollywood, CA 90069
Tel: 310-422-3280
E-mail: info@picturestart.com
Web Site: www.picturestart.com
Key Personnel
Founder & CEO: Erik Feig
Chief of Staff: Teri Koral
EVP, Prodn: Lucy Kitada; Ryan Lindenberg
VP, Prodn: Jessica Switch
Creative Dir & Head, Mktg: Martina Lund
Founded: 2018
Media company that makes Discovery of Voice content for worldwide engagement across all platforms.

Pignose-Gorilla
570 W Cheyenne Ave, Suite 80, North Las Vegas, NV 89030
Tel: 702-648-2444 *Toll Free Tel:* 800-9-PIGNOSE (974-4667) *Fax:* 702-648-2440

E-mail: sales@pignoseamps.com
Web Site: www.pignoseamps.com
Key Personnel
Pres: Howard Chatt *E-mail:* hchatt@aol.com
Manufacturer & distributor of amplifiers, PA systems & accessories.
Catalog(s) available
Membership(s): NAMM, the National Association of Music Merchants

Pinewood Sound
555 Brooksbank Ave, Bldg S, North Vancouver, BC V7J 3S5, Canada
Tel: 604-669-6900; 604-983-5200 *Fax:* 604-983-5204
E-mail: info@pinewoodsound.com; sales@pinewoodsound.com
Web Site: www.pinewoodsound.com
Key Personnel
Opers Mgr: Jean Turner *E-mail:* jean@pinewoodsound.com
Full service audio post-production services for film & television.

pinta acoustic inc
Division of pinta elements GmbH
2601 49 Ave N, Suite 400, Minneapolis, MN 55430
Tel: 612-355-4200 *Toll Free Tel:* 800-662-0032
Fax: 612-355-4299
E-mail: sales@pinta-acoustic.com; info@pinta-acoustic.com
Web Site: www.pinta-acoustic.com
Key Personnel
Regl Sales Mgr (East): Eric Johnson *Tel:* 800-438-0685 *E-mail:* ejohnson@pinta-acoustic.com
Regl Sales Mgr (West): Bob Donohue *Tel:* 866-205-8707 *E-mail:* bdonohue@pinta-acoustic.com
Manufacturer of acoustic wall panels & ceiling tiles.
Catalog(s) available
Membership(s): NAB; NAMM, the National Association of Music Merchants; NSCA

Pioneer Electronics (USA) Inc
Subsidiary of Pioneer Corp (Japan)
2050 W 190 St, Suite 100, Torrance, CA 90504
Tel: 310-952-2000 *Toll Free Tel:* 800-421-1404 (cust serv, car, marine & computer prods); 800-228-7221 (parts dept); 844-679-5350 (cust serv, home prods)
Web Site: www.pioneerelectronics.com
Founded: 1938
Develops & manufactures innovative & high-tech entertainment & electronic products.
Catalog(s) available

Pioneer Research Inc
97 Foster Rd, Suite 5, Moorestown, NJ 08057
Tel: 856-866-9191 *Toll Free Tel:* 800-257-7742
Fax: 856-866-8615
E-mail: info@pioneer-research.com
Web Site: www.pioneer-research.com
Key Personnel
VP: Bjorn Harms *E-mail:* bjorn@pioneer-research.com; Sven E Harms *E-mail:* sven@pioneer-research.com
Manufacture & distribute underwater photographic equipment.
Online catalog(s) available

PipelineFX LLC
500 Ala Moana Blvd, Tower 7, Suite 400, Honolulu, HI 96813
Tel: 808-685-7823 *Toll Free Tel:* 855-685-7823
Fax: 808-685-7800
E-mail: sales@pipelinefx.com
Web Site: www.pipelinefx.com

Key Personnel
CEO: Richard Lewis *E-mail:* richard@pipelinefx.com
Dir, Mktg & Sales Opers: Michelle Ray
Founded: 2002
Producer of Qube!, the leading render farm management software for digital media creation.

Piper Media Services Inc
904 W Kenosha St, Broken Arrow, OK 74012
Tel: 918-251-0477
E-mail: info@piper.media
Web Site: www.piper.media
Key Personnel
Pres: Daniel B Piper
Conference services, conference recording, media editing, media duplications, series duplications, flash drives & transfer services.
Online catalog(s) available

Nicholas P Pipino Associates Inc
10545 Guilford Rd, Suite 108, Jessup, MD 20794
Tel: 301-596-3397; 410-995-0041
Toll Free Tel: 888-596-0014 *Fax:* 410-964-1191
Web Site: pipinoinc.com
Key Personnel
Pres & CEO: Stephen J Pipino *E-mail:* spipino@pipinoinc.com
Founded: 1969
Sales & service of state-of-the-art AV products.

Pixar Animation Studios
Subsidiary of The Walt Disney Co
1200 Park Ave, Emeryville, CA 94608
Tel: 510-922-3000 *Fax:* 510-922-3151
Web Site: www.pixar.com
Key Personnel
Chief Creative Offr: Pete Docter
Pres: Jim Morris
SVP, Busn Aff & Chief Legal Coun: James M Kennedy
SVP, Prodn: Jonas Rivera
SVP, Prodn Strategy: Thomas Porter
SVP, Talent: Katherine Sarafian
SVP, Worldwide Mktg & Franchise: Jonathan Garson
VP & CTO: Steve May
VP, Cont & Facility Opers: Mark Joseph
VP, Busn Aff & Legal Coun: Jody Weinberg
VP, Creative: Dan Scanlon; Andrew Stanton
VP, Devt: Lindsey Collins
VP, Fin & Strategy: Chris Kaiser
VP, HR: Reema Batnagar
VP, Inclusion Strategies: Britta M Wilson
VP, Renderman: Oliver Meiseberg
VP, Software R&D: Guido Quaroni
VP, Systems: John Kirkman
VP, Worldwide Publicity: Michael Agulnek
Founded: 1986
Animation studio.

PixeLINK
1900 City Park Dr, Suite 410, Ottawa, ON K1J 1A3, Canada
Tel: 613-247-1211 *Fax:* 613-247-2001
E-mail: sales@pixelink.com
Web Site: www.pixelink.com
Key Personnel
CEO: Lisanne Glavin
Founded: 1992
Manufacture digital cameras & video converters for scientific/industrial & professional markets.

PixMix Video Services
395 Western Ave, Suite 112 & 113, Boston, MA 02134
Tel: 617-923-0102; 617-254-0590 *Fax:* 617-923-0105
E-mail: info@pixmix.net
Web Site: www.pixmix.net

Key Personnel
Principal Proj Mgr: Ray Boyer *Tel:* 617-901-7157 (cell) *E-mail:* ray@pixmix.net
Founded: 1998
Video production, single camera ENG production & multi-camera production.
Branch Office(s)
7 Cliff Rd, Suite 201, Bellingham, MA 02019
Tel: 508-966-3648 (busn off)

piXvfm Inc
1805 E Dyer Rd, Suite 107, Santa Ana, CA 92705
Tel: 949-419-2563 *Fax:* 949-419-3485
Web Site: pixvfm.com
Key Personnel
Pres: Ridgie Barton
VP, Prodn: Rick Stewart
Video & interactive solutions for sales, marketing, e-learning, mobile learning & education.
Branch Office(s)
Napa, CA 94558 *Tel:* 707-927-4114
Membership(s): ATD; IAA-VC

PK Productions
313 E Broadway, No 1205, Glendale, CA 91209
E-mail: info@pkproductions.com
Web Site: pkproductions.com
Key Personnel
Owner, Prodr & Dir: Phil Kubel
Founded: 1986
Full service digital production agency. Services include digital & social media production, web site design & marketing, film & video production, corporate videos & promotions, event coverage & streaming.

Planet Dallas Recording Studios
Division of Planet Dallas Inc
PO Box 110995, Carrollton, TX 75011
Tel: 214-521-2216; 214-893-1130 (cell)
E-mail: planetd@ix.netcom.com
Web Site: planetdallas.com
Key Personnel
Pres: Rick Rooney
Founded: 1984
Recording studio.
Membership(s): ASCAP; Austin Songwriters Group; BMI; Dallas Songwriters Association; The Recording Academy

Plank Road Publishing Inc
11111 W Plank Ct, Wauwatosa, WI 53226
Mailing Address: PO Box 26627, Wauwatosa, WI 53226
Tel: 262-790-5210 *Toll Free Tel:* 800-437-0832
Fax: 414-771-7672 *Toll Free Fax:* 888-272-0212
E-mail: contact-us@musick8.com
Web Site: www.musick8.com
Key Personnel
Asst Mgr, Opers: Lynn Crowell *E-mail:* lynn@musick8.com
Founded: 1990
Publishers of quality music & vendor of music-related products for elementary & middle school teachers. Audio programming on CD, MP3 & MP4. Shipping via UPS or USPS, rates based on subtotal.
Affiliated with Music K-8 Marketplace, World Music Press, Golden Rule Music & Recorder Classroom.
Catalog(s) available, annual, interactive +/or downloadable on web site
Membership(s): National Association for Music Education

plan9films
9 Willingdon Place, Saskatoon, SK S7L 1C2, Canada
Tel: 306-955-NINE (955-6463)
E-mail: info@plan9films.com
Web Site: www.plan9films.com

Key Personnel
Prodr & Dir: Darryl Kesslar *E-mail:* dkesslar@
plan9films.com
Production management, cinematography, post-
production, editing & visual effects.

Plantronics Inc, see Poly

Platt Cases, see Platt Luggage Inc

Platt Luggage Inc
4051 W 51 St, Chicago, IL 60632
Tel: 773-838-2000 *Toll Free Tel:* 800-222-1555
Fax: 773-838-2010
E-mail: info@plattcases.com
Web Site: www.plattcases.com
Founded: 1921
Manufacture professional cases for business &
industry, including AV & computer cases.
Online catalog(s) available

Playback Now Inc
3139 Campus Dr, Suite 700, Norcross, GA
30071-1402
Tel: 770-447-0616 *Toll Free Tel:* 800-241-7785
(prod support)
E-mail: info@playbacknow.com
Web Site: www.playbacknow.com
Key Personnel
Owner & CEO: Jonathan Galucki
E-mail: jonathan.galucki@playbacknow.com
Founded: 1978
Captures & delivers conference content.

Playback Recording Studio
400 E Gutierrez, Santa Barbara, CA 93101
Tel: 917-331-0429
Web Site: www.playbackrecording.com
Key Personnel
Owner & Head Engr: Tucker Bodine *Tel:* 917-
331-0429
Sound recording studio & post-production house
for the entertainment industry.

Playboy Entertainment Group Inc
Division of Playboy Enterprises Inc
9346 Civic Center Dr, Suite 200, Beverly Hills,
CA 90210
Tel: 310-424-1800
Web Site: www.playboy.com

PLS Staging
371 Little Falls Rd, Cedar Grove, NJ 07009
Tel: 973-857-7242
E-mail: rfp@plsstaging.com
Web Site: plsstaging.com
Key Personnel
Owner & Pres: Jim Koziol
Founded: 1979
AV production company. Design, construct &
produce a wide variety of conferences, corpo-
rate events, meetings & technical projects while
offering audio, video, lighting, scenic & stag-
ing production support along with quality AV
rental services.
Membership(s): AV Alliance; Healthcare Con-
vention & Exhibitors Association; International
Live Events Association; MPI

Plume Ltd
888 Main St, Silver Plume, CO 80476
Mailing Address: PO Box 9, Silver Plume, CO
80476-0009
Tel: 303-569-3236; 303-888-8099 *Fax:* 303-569-
2932
Web Site: www.plumeltd.com
Key Personnel
Pres: Gary Regester *E-mail:* garyregester@gmail.
com
Founded: 1985

Lighting equipment for digital, cine & still photographers.
Online catalog(s) available

PLUS Corp of America
9655 SW Sunshine Ct, Suite 300, Beaverton, OR
97005
Tel: 503-748-8700 *Toll Free Tel:* 800-211-9001
E-mail: sales@plus-america.com; info@plus-
america.com
Web Site: www.plus-america.com
Key Personnel
Pres: Tsutomu (Tom) Oishi
Natl Sales Mgr: Dave Billhimer
Founded: 1995
Manufacture electronic copyboards & interactive
panels.
Foreign Office(s): 1033-1 Oshitate, Inagi-shi,
Tokyo 206-0811, Japan

PM Productions
5882 Bowcroft St, Suite 2, Los Angeles, CA
90016
Tel: 310-559-3127 *Fax:* 310-559-3168
Web Site: pmproductionsvideos.com
Key Personnel
Owner: Odell Mack *E-mail:* odellmack@hotmail.
com
Founded: 1985
Full service video production.

PME Audio/Video
2003 S El Camino Real, Suite 108, Oceanside,
CA 92054
Tel: 760-439-0281
E-mail: solutions@pmevideo.com
Web Site: www.pmevideo.com
Founded: 1998
Analog to digital conversion.
Online catalog(s) available
Membership(s): Content Delivery & Storage As-
sociation

PMP Marketing Inc
337 Grant St, Redlands, CA 92373
Tel: 909-557-8685
Web Site: www.pmpmarketing.com
Key Personnel
Pres & CEO: Art Schindele *E-mail:* art@
pmpmarketing.com
Sales Support Coord: Laura Schindele
E-mail: laura@pmpmarketing.com
Commercial manufacturers representation firm.
Membership(s): Audiovisual and Integrated Expe-
rience Association; NSCA

PMTV, see Producers Management Television
(PMTV)

PNTA
2414 SW Andover St, Suite C100, Seattle, WA
98106
Tel: 206-622-7850 *Toll Free Tel:* 800-622-7850
Fax: 206-267-1789
E-mail: sales@pnta.com; events@pnta.com
Web Site: www.pnta.com
Key Personnel
Pres & CEO: Richard Carlson
Founded: 1975
Distribution & rental of audio, lighting, video,
staging, special effects & drapery needs.
Online catalog(s) available
Membership(s): Professional Lighting & Sound
Association; USITT

Pogo Pictures
114 E Ponce de Leon Ave, Suite B, Decatur, GA
30030
Tel: 404-892-9490
Web Site: www.pogopictures.com

Key Personnel
Pres & Dir: Steve Colby *E-mail:* colby@
pogopictures.com
Exec Prodr: Ruth Agee *E-mail:* ruth@
pogopictures.com
Full service creative content provider.

Point of View Productions
2477 Folsom St, San Francisco, CA 94110
Fax: 415-821-0434
Key Personnel
Pres: Karil Daniels *Tel:* 415-602-0435 (cell)
E-mail: karil@karildaniels.com
Catalog(s) available
Membership(s): Bay Area Video Coalition; Bay
Area Women in Film & Media; NATAS;
Women in Multimedia

Point Source Audio
1304 Southpoint Blvd, No 260, Petaluma, CA
94954
Tel: 415-226-1122 *Fax:* 415-520-2110
E-mail: info@point-sourceaudio.com; sales@
point-sourceaudio.com
Web Site: www.point-sourceaudio.com
Key Personnel
Pres: James Lamb *E-mail:* jlamb@point-
sourceaudio.com
VP, Sales & Mktg: Yvonne Ho *E-mail:* yho@
point-sourceaudio.com
Design, engineer & manufacture earmount, head-
set & earset microphones & accessories.
Online catalog(s) available

Point.360
2701 Media Center Dr, Los Angeles, CA 90065
Tel: 323-987-9400 *Fax:* 818-847-2503
E-mail: sales@point360.com
Web Site: www.point360.com
Key Personnel
Pres & CEO: Haig Bagerdjian
VP & Cont: John Schweizer *E-mail:* jschweizer@
point360.com
Full service entertainment media company offer-
ing episodic & feature picture finishing, con-
tent management, audio, localization, quality
control, film scanning & restoration & media
storage services.
Catalog(s) available
Branch Office(s)
1133 N Hollywood Way, Burbank, CA 91505
Tel: 818-556-5700 *Fax:* 818-556-5753
Membership(s): International Teleproduction Soci-
ety

Pointward
400 First Ave N, Suite 100, Minneapolis, MN
55401
Tel: 651-646-2442
Web Site: www.pointward.com
Key Personnel
CEO: Peter Hager
Chief People Offr: Marlene Nelson
VP, Client Engagement: Jeff Gravagna
Experience in marketing communications, creative
services, web & interactive technology, multi-
media, print & technology solutions.
Catalog(s) available

Polarity Post Production
69 Green St, San Francisco, CA 94111
Tel: 415-421-6622 *Fax:* 415-391-4995
E-mail: info@polaritypost.com
Web Site: www.polaritypost.com
Key Personnel
Pres: Patrick Fitzgerald
Founded: 2003
Full service audio post house.
Catalog(s) available
Membership(s): AES; Bay Area Video Coalition;
Northern California Production Community;
The Recording Academy; San Francisco Film
& Tape Council; SMPTE®

Polestar Films & Associated Arts Ltd
Subsidiary of Polestar Animation
PO Box 20104, New York, NY 10014-0708
Tel: 212-352-1375
Key Personnel
Pres & Creative Dir: Irra Verbitsky
Founded: 1976
Animation studio.

Polhemus
40 Hercules Dr, Colchester, VT 05446-5835
Tel: 802-655-3159 *Toll Free Tel:* 800-357-4777
(US & CN)
E-mail: sales@polhemus.com
Web Site: polhemus.com
Key Personnel
Pres & Co-Owner: Skip Rodgers
Founded: 1969
Motion tracking technology serving the healthcare, military & research & technology markets.
Catalog(s) available

Pollstar
4697 W Jacquelyn Ave, Fresno, CA 93722-6413
Tel: 559-271-7900 *Fax:* 559-271-7979
E-mail: info@pollstar.com
Web Site: www.pollstarpro.com; www.pollstar.com
Key Personnel
News Ed: Joe Reinartz
Founded: 1981
Concert industry trade publication & database.
Foreign Office(s): Pollstar UK, Leroy House, 436
Essex Rd, Suite 4M, London N1 3QP, United
Kingdom, Contact: Brij Gosai *Tel:* (020) 7359
1110 *Fax:* (020) 7359 1131
Membership(s): Academy of Country Music;
Country Music Association; IAFE; International Association of Assembly Managers; International Entertainment Buyers Association;
NACA

Pollution Studios
3239 Union Pacific Ave, Los Angeles, CA 90023
Mailing Address: 1539 S Grande Vista Ave, Los
Angeles, CA 90023
Tel: 323-981-1520
E-mail: info@pollutionstudios.com
Web Site: pollutionstudios.com
Full service studio & equipment rental facilty.

Gabriel Polonsky Studio
33 Harvard Rd, Suite 2, Belmont, MA 02478
Tel: 617-515-5642
E-mail: gp-studio@verizon.net
Web Site: www.facebook.com/GPstudioarts
Key Personnel
Founder & Creative Dir: Gabriel Polonsky
Founded: 1992
Full service animation, illustration, video, design
& creative ideas company.

Poly
345 Encinal St, Santa Cruz, CA 95060
Tel: 831-426-5858 *Toll Free Tel:* 800-544-4660
Fax: 831-426-6098
Web Site: www.poly.com
Key Personnel
Pres & CEO: Joe Burton
EVP & CFO: Chuck Boynton
EVP & Chief HR Offr: Anja Hamilton
EVP & Chief Legal & Compliance Offr: Mary
Huser
EVP & Chief Mktg Offr: Amy Barzdukas
EVP & Chief Strategy Offr: Darrius Jones
EVP & Pres, Global Opers: Alex Bustamante
EVP & Gen Mgr, Prods: Tom Puorro
EVP, Global Servs: Navin Mehta
SVP & Chief of Staff to Off of CEO: Phil Sherburne

VP & CIO: Paul Johnson
Founded: 1961
Global communications company.
Branch Office(s)
1470 Exposition Way, San Diego, CA 92154
6001 America Center Dr, 1st-6th fl, San Jose, CA
95002 *Tel:* 408-586-3837 *Toll Free Tel:* 800-
765-9266
1765 W 121 Ave, Bldg B, 100B, Westminster,
CO 80234-2301 *Tel:* 303-223-5003
2475 NorthWinds Pkwy, Suite 200, Off 244A,
Alpharetta, GA 30009 *Tel:* 770-350-4147
600 Federal St, 1st & 2nd fl, Andover, MA 01810
Tel: 978-292-5000
10 Burlington Mall Rd, 1st fl, Burlington, MA
01803-4121 *Tel:* 781-270-0144
One Penn Plaza, Suite 4800, New York, NY
10119-0002 *Tel:* 212-372-6997
7700 W Parmer Lane, Bldg C, 1st fl, Austin, TX
78729-8101 *Tel:* 512-372-7000
13650 Dulles Technology Dr, 5th fl, Herndon, VA
20171-6158 *Tel:* 703-793-2080

Polyline LLC
1400 W Burbank Blvd, Burbank, CA 91506
Tel: 630-993-2700 *Toll Free Tel:* 800-701-7689
E-mail: sales@polylinecorp.com
Web Site: www.polylinecorp.com
Founded: 1972
Distributor of CD-ROM, DVD-R & Blu-ray media, media packaging products, ink, disc publishing equipment & more.
Online catalog(s) available
Shipping Address: 4514 W Vanowen St, Burbank,
CA 91505-1135 *Tel:* 747-400-3777 (warehouse)

PolyScience
Division of Preston Industries Inc
6600 W Touhy Ave, Niles, IL 60714-4516
Tel: 847-647-0611 *Toll Free Tel:* 800-229-7569
Fax: 847-647-1155
E-mail: sales@polyscience.com
Web Site: www.polyscience.com
Key Personnel
Pres: Philip Preston
Sales Mgr: Sue Gibbons
Founded: 1963
Manufacturer of temperature control equipment.
Online catalog(s) available

PolyVision Corporation
Subsidiary of Steelcase Inc
10700 Abbotts Bridge Rd, Suite 100, Johns
Creek, GA 30097
Tel: 678-542-3100 *Toll Free Tel:* 888-325-6351
Fax: 678-542-3200
E-mail: info@polyvision.com; customerservice@
polyvision.com
Web Site: polyvision.com
Founded: 1954
Manufacturer of CeramicSteel surfaces for use
in multiple applications including chalkboards
& marker boards for education & commercial
markets as well as CeramicSteel panels for architecture & infrastructure.
Catalog(s) available, free, annual
Branch Office(s)
4301 North Wood Dr, Okmulgee, OK 74447
Tel: 918-756-7392 *Fax:* 918-756-6818 (mfg
plant)
Sales Office(s): 200 Varick St, 8th fl, New York,
NY 10014 *Tel:* 212-886-8108
Zuiderring 56, 3600 Genk, Belgium *Tel:* (089)
3231 30 *Fax:* (089) 3231 31 (also mfg plant)
Kinwick Centre, 15th fl, 32 Hollywood Rd, Central District, Hong Kong *Tel:* 2520 0160
One Horizon Ctr, 11th fl, DLF City 5, Sector 43,
DLF Golf Course Rd, Gurgaon, Haryana 122
003, India *Tel:* 9910044108 (cell)

Membership(s): Audiovisual and Integrated Experience Association; Education Market Association; International Multimedia & Collaborative
Communications

Pook Diemont & Ohl Inc
Division of Texas Scenic Co Inc
701 E 132 St, Bronx, NY 10454
Tel: 718-402-2677 *Fax:* 718-402-2859
E-mail: info@texasscenic.com
Web Site: www.texasscenic.com
Key Personnel
Dir, Engg & Prodn: Tony Diemont
Dir, Prog Mgmt: Barbara Pook
Founded: 1982
Stage machinery manufacturing contractor for
theaters, auditoriums, broadcast studios, entertainment facilities, corporate & retail installations.
Online catalog(s) available

Porta-Jib
Division of Hollywood General Machining Inc
416 N Varney St, Burbank, CA 91502
Tel: 747-283-1077 *Fax:* 747-283-1078
Web Site: www.porta-jib.com
Key Personnel
Owner: Scott Losmandy
Sales Mgr: Mark Schweickart *E-mail:* mark@
porta-jib.com
Manufacturer of lightweight dollies & jib arms
for the film & video camera market.
Online catalog(s) available

PortaBrace Inc
160 Benmont Ave, Suite 100, North Bennington,
VT 05201
Tel: 802-442-8171 *Fax:* 802-442-9118
E-mail: info@portabrace.com
Web Site: www.portabrace.com
Key Personnel
Pres: Gregg Haythorn
Global Sales Mgr: Mike D'Angelo
Founded: 1972
Manufacture high quality professional camera
cases & covers.
Online catalog(s) available
Membership(s): NAB

James Porter Photography
211 E Columbine Ave, Suite A-1, Santa Ana, CA
92707
Tel: 714-546-4148
E-mail: info@jamesporterphotography.com
Web Site: www.jamesporterphotography.com
Key Personnel
Owner: James Porter *E-mail:* jim@
jamesporterphotography.com
Founded: 1975
Digital photography in studio & on location. Specializing in food, product & people. Full service studio with commercial kitchen.

Porter Productions
211 E Columbine Ave, Suite B, Santa Ana, CA
92707
Tel: 714-546-4148
E-mail: studio@porterproductions.info
Web Site: www.porterproductions.info
Key Personnel
Owner: James Porter
Photo studio rental, grip equipment, digital equipment, photo crew, full kitchen & prep area for
food photography.

Post Production Services, see The PPS Group

Posthorn Recordings
142 W 26 St, 10th fl, New York, NY 10001-6814
Tel: 212-242-3737 *Fax:* 212-924-1243
Web Site: www.posthorn.com

Key Personnel
Pres & CEO: Jerry Bruck *E-mail:* jbruck@
posthorn.com
Mgr: Louise A Bloomfield
Founded: 1964
Catalog(s) available
Price list(s) available
Membership(s): AES

PostWorks
110 Leroy St, New York, NY 10014
Tel: 212-609-9400 *Fax:* 212-609-9450
E-mail: inquiry@technicolorpwny.com
Web Site: www.postworks.com
Key Personnel
COO: Rob DeMartin
VP, Broadcast: Dan Porcelli
VP, Post-Prodn Servs: Anthony Caputo
Founded: 1995
Full service post-production services to motion
picture studios, broadcasters, television produc-
ers & independent filmmakers.
Branch Office(s)
345 Hudson St, New York, NY 10014
609 Greenwich St, New York, NY 10014

Potentials Unlimited
Division of I M P A C T Publishing Inc
3409 47 Ave E, Bradenton, FL 34203-3974
Mailing Address: PO Box 10058, Bradenton, FL
34282-0058
Tel: 941-739-2611 *Toll Free Tel:* 800-221-6121;
800-426-3963 *Fax:* 941-756-0315
Web Site: www.potentialsunlimited.com
Key Personnel
Pres: Stephanie Konicov-Banfill
Producer of Subliminal Persuasion™ guided med-
itation MP3s, CDs, tapes & videos.
Catalog(s) available, free
Online catalog(s) available

Potomac Instruments Inc
7309 Grove Rd, Unit D, Frederick, MD 21704
Tel: 301-696-5550 *Fax:* 301-696-5553
E-mail: sales@pi-usa.com; service@pi-usa.com
Web Site: www.pi-usa.com
Key Personnel
Pres: Zachary Babendreier
Founded: 1968
Precision measurement & control equipment for
the broadcast industry.
Online catalog(s) available
Brochure(s) available, online

Pounds Photographic Labs Inc
901 Regal Row, Dallas, TX 75247
Tel: 214-688-1425 *Toll Free Tel:* 800-350-5671
Fax: 214-688-1429
E-mail: custsvc@poundslabs.com
Web Site: www.poundslabs.com
Founded: 1976
Photofinishing lab providing workflow solutions.

Power & Light
1313 Mound St, Alameda, CA 94501
Tel: 510-205-4101 (cell)
Web Site: www.powerlight.net
Key Personnel
Founder & Gaffer: Mike Van Dine
E-mail: mike@powerlight.net
Founded: 1994
Lighting & grip trucks in northern California.

Power & Telephone Supply Co
44 Hull St, Suite 2, Randolph, VT 05060
Toll Free Tel: 800-451-4381 *Fax:* 802-234-5006
E-mail: cablesales@ptsupply.com
Web Site: www.ptsupply.com
National distributor of wire, cable, fiber optics,
tools & test equipment.
Catalog(s) available, free

Power Factory Productions
4344 Gessner Rd, Houston, TX 77041
Tel: 281-630-6900
E-mail: info@powerfactorypro.com
Web Site: www.powerfactoryproductions.com
Founded: 1995
Professional sound & lighting production. Spe-
cialize in concert & touring production, as well
as corporate events, AV services, festivals, spe-
cial events, sales & installation.

Power Integrity Corporation
2109 Patterson St, Greensboro, NC 27407
Mailing Address: PO Box 9682, Greensboro, NC
27429
Tel: 336-379-9773 *Toll Free Tel:* 800-237-6260
(tech support)
Web Site: powerintegritycorp.com
Key Personnel
Pres: James T Fesmire *E-mail:* j.fesmire@
powerintegritycorp.com
VP: Debbie Wilson *E-mail:* d.wilson@
powerintegritycorp.com
VP, Busn Devt: Craig Jones *E-mail:* c.jones@
powerintegritycorp.com
Sales Coord: Lynn Moudy *E-mail:* l.moudy@
powerintegritycorp.com
Founded: 1980
Electrical power distribution systems.
Catalog(s) available
Membership(s): PEI

Power Sonic Corp
365 Cabela Dr, Suite 300, Reno, NV 89523
Tel: 619-661-2020 *Fax:* 619-661-3650
Web Site: www.power-sonic.com
Key Personnel
CEO: Jim Mannenbach
Pres, Battery Div: Brian Crowe
EVP, Busn Devt: JD Johnson
COO & CFO: Jeff Kyle
Sales Dir, Indus Dist, Battery Div: Peter J Mur-
phy
Dir, Strategic Accts, Battery Div: Jeff Shelby
Dir, Fin, Battery Div: Karen Costa
Commercial Dir, Utilities & Infrastructure, Bat-
tery Div: Robert Hamilton
Founded: 1970
Design, manufacture & market rechargeable bat-
teries & chargers.
Catalog(s) available
Foreign Office(s): 5-7 Ave du General De Gaulle,
60300 Senlis, France *Tel:* 03 44 32 18 17
Fax: 03 44 32 18 18
Smitspol 4, 3861 RS Nijkerk, Netherlands
Tel: (033) 7410 700 (EMEA headquarters)
3 Buckingham Sq, Hurricane Way, Wickford, Es-
sex SS11 8YQ, United Kingdom *Tel:* (01268)
560686 *Fax:* (01268) 560902

PowerPhysics Inc
877 Production Place, Newport Beach, CA
92663-2809
Tel: 949-371-6202 *Fax:* 815-572-8936
E-mail: contact@powerphysics.com
Web Site: powerphysics.com
Key Personnel
Pres: Gordon Wanlass
Founded: 1998
Amplifier & power supply design & manufacture.

Powerstation Events
Division of Powerstation LLC
1718 Highland Ave, Cheshire, CT 06410
Tel: 203-250-8500 *Toll Free Tel:* 800-423-7835
Fax: 203-250-8575
E-mail: info@powerstationevents.com
Web Site: www.powerstationevents.com
Key Personnel
Founder, Pres & CEO: Alfred Vagnini
Tel: 800-423-7835 ext 221 *E-mail:* al@
powerstationevents.com

VP, Opers: Jim Manger
Sr Dir, Event Sales: Rich Gumpert *Tel:* 800-
423-7835 ext 225 *E-mail:* richg@
powerstationevents.com
Founded: 1983
Commercial, corporate & event video production.

PPS, see Precision Projection Systems Inc

The PPS Group
424 Scott St, Covington, KY 41011
Tel: 859-291-5100 *Toll Free Tel:* 800-978-3445
Fax: 859-291-5150
E-mail: info@theppsgroup.com
Web Site: www.pps-inc.com; www.theppsgroup.
com
Key Personnel
CEO: Bob Gerding
Pres: Jim Bird
VP: Dave Dittgen
Also offers HDTV production & editing,
Boomerang interactive & DVD authoring. Film
& videotape archiving.

Practising Law Institute
1177 Avenue of the Americas, 2nd fl, New York,
NY 10036
Tel: 212-824-5710 (cust serv) *Toll Free Tel:* 800-
260-4PLI (260-4754, cust serv)
Toll Free Fax: 800-321-0093 (cust serv)
E-mail: info@pli.edu; cs@pli.edu (cust serv)
Web Site: www.pli.edu
Key Personnel
Chief Busn Offr: Alan G Cohen *Tel:* 212-824-
5795 *E-mail:* acohen@pli.edu
Treas & CFO: Frank DeVivo *Tel:* 212-824-5709
E-mail: fdevivo@pli.edu
CIO: Christopher Rousseau *Tel:* 212-824-5878
E-mail: crousseau@pli.edu
Pres: Anita C Shapiro *Tel:* 212-824-5701
E-mail: ashapiro@pli.edu
VP, HR: Joan Sternberg *Tel:* 212-824-5764
E-mail: jsternberg@pli.edu
VP, Mktg & Communs: David Smith *Tel:* 212-
590-8838 *E-mail:* dsmith@pli.edu
VP, Membership: Craig Miller *Tel:* 212-590-8839
E-mail: cmiller@pli.edu
VP, Print & Digital Publg: Ellen Siegel *Tel:* 212-
824-5761 *E-mail:* esiegel@pli.edu
VP, Progs: Kara L O'Brien, Esq *Tel:* 212-824-
5852 *E-mail:* kobrien@pli.edu
Founded: 1933
Nonprofit continuing legal education & profes-
sional business training organization.
Brochure(s) available
Branch Office(s)
685 Market St, Suite 100, San Francisco, CA
94105 *Tel:* 415-498-2800

Prairie Pictures Film & Video
690 E Lamar Blvd, Arlington, TX 76011
Mailing Address: PO Box 122020, Arlington, TX
76012-8020
Tel: 817-276-9500
E-mail: info@prairiepictures.com
Web Site: prairiepictures.com
Key Personnel
Founder, Prodr & Dir: Martin Lisius
E-mail: lisius@prairiepictures.com
Founded: 1986
Full service video & film production company.
Founded Stormstock in 1993, recognized as
the world's premier storm footage library
(www.stormstock.com).
Membership(s): Dallas Producers Association;
Royal Photographic Society; The Society of
Aerial Cinematography; Texas Association of
Motion Media Professionals; Texas Film Com-
mission

Prakken Publications Inc
251 Jackson Plaza, Suite A, Ann Arbor, MI
48103-1955
Mailing Address: PO Box 8623, Ann Arbor, MI
48107-8623
Tel: 734-975-2800 *Toll Free Tel:* 800-530-9673
Fax: 734-975-2787
E-mail: matt@techdirections.com
Web Site: www.techdirections.com
Key Personnel
Mng Ed: Vanessa Revelli *Tel:* 734-975-2800 ext
306 *E-mail:* vanessa@techdirections.com
Founded: 1935
Technology & career technical education publi-
cations, books, video, software, CD-ROM &
posters.
Membership(s): EdPress

PRC Digital Media, see Gemstone Media Inc

Precision Camera & Video
2438 W Anderson Lane, Suite B-4, Austin, TX
78757
Tel: 512-467-7676 *Toll Free Tel:* 800-677-1023
Fax: 512-467-0607
Web Site: www.precision-camera.com
Key Personnel
Founder & CEO: Jerry Sullivan
Gen Mgr: Gregg Burger *E-mail:* gburger@
precision-camera.com
Sales Mgr: Mike Luxenberg
E-mail: mluxenberg@precision-camera.com
Founded: 1976
New & used photographic & video equipment for
sale & rent. Equipment repair, classes & work-
shops.

Precision Camera & Video Repair Inc
7 Anngina Dr, Enfield, CT 06082
Tel: 860-749-7380; 860-272-2100
Toll Free Tel: 800-665-6515 (cust serv)
E-mail: info@precisioncamera.com
Web Site: www.precisioncamera.com
Key Personnel
Pres & CEO: John Malinosky
VP, Opers: Steven Moloney
Founded: 1948
Factory authorized repair for all major brands.
Membership(s): The Imaging Alliance; NESDA;
Photographic Society of America; SPT

Precision Electronics Inc
Division of Grommes
1331 Estes Ave, Gurnee, IL 60031
Tel: 847-599-1799 *Toll Free Tel:* 800-SINCE-46
(746-2346) *Fax:* 847-599-6178
E-mail: info@grommesprecision.com; sales@
grommesprecision.com
Web Site: www.grommesprecision.com
Key Personnel
Gen Mgr: J W Franzen
Founded: 1946
Design & manufacture audio & electronic equip-
ment.
Catalog(s) available

Precision Microproducts of America
One Comac Loop, Unit 13, Ronkonkoma, NY
11779
Tel: 631-580-3456 *Toll Free Tel:* 800-932-9215
Fax: 631-580-3003
E-mail: sales@p-m-a.com
Web Site: www.p-m-a.com
Key Personnel
Pres: Carlos Fernandes
Microfilm supplies, equipment & parts; document
scanners, supplies & parts.
Catalog(s) available
Membership(s): The Imaging Alliance

Precision Projection Systems Inc
17508 Studebaker Rd, Cerritos, CA 90703
Tel: 562-865-8552 *Fax:* 562-924-7133
E-mail: info@ppsfx.com
Web Site: www.ppsfx.com
Key Personnel
Pres: Carl Hannigan *E-mail:* carl@ppsfx.com
Founded: 1983
Manufacturer of laser display equipment, LED,
fiber optic, specialty lighting fixtures & custom
illumination systems for entertainment, display
& industrial applications.
Online catalog(s) available

Prelinger Archives
PO Box 590622, San Francisco, CA 94159-0622
Tel: 415-750-0445
E-mail: footage@panix.com
Web Site: www.prelinger.com
Key Personnel
Pres: Richard Prelinger *E-mail:* rick@archive.org
Founded: 1983
Access to over 8,000 films. License stock
footage available through Getty Images
(www.gettyimages.com).
Online catalog(s) available
Membership(s): Association of Moving Image
Archivists

Premier Lighting & Production Co
12023 Victory Blvd, North Hollywood, CA 91606
Tel: 818-762-0884 *Toll Free Tel:* 800-770-0884
Fax: 818-762-0896
E-mail: premier@premier-lighting.com; rentals@
premier-lighting.com
Web Site: www.premier-lighting.com
Key Personnel
Prodn: Wynn Zucchero *E-mail:* wynn@premier-
lighting.com
Rentals: Jorge Mendoza
Sales & Serv: Amy Rivera *E-mail:* amy@
premier-lighting.com
Founded: 1977
Full service entertainment company. Sales, rentals
& production for stage, studio & special
events.
Online catalog(s) available
Membership(s): Professional Lighting & Sound
Association; USITT

Pres-On Corp
2600 E 107 St, Bolingbrook, IL 60440
Toll Free Tel: 800-323-7467 *Fax:* 630-628-8025
E-mail: sales@preson.com
Web Site: www.preson.com
Key Personnel
CEO: Henry J Gianatasio
Founded: 1949
Manufacture custom adhesive coatings, gaskets &
laminations for a wide range of major indus-
trial markets.
Catalog(s) available

Presagis
4700 de la Savane, Suite 300, Montreal, QC H4P
1T7, Canada
Tel: 514-341-3874 *Toll Free Tel:* 800-361-6424
Fax: 514-341-8018
E-mail: info@presagis.com
Web Site: www.presagis.com
Key Personnel
Pres: Jean-Michel Briere
Mktg & Commns Mgr: Andre Demers
E-mail: andre.demers@presagis.com
Founded: 2007
Global provider of software for the development
of modeling, simulation, visualization & em-
bedded display applications.
Data sheet(s) available
Branch Office(s)
Presagis USA, 12424 Research Pkwy, Suite

390, Orlando, FL 32826 *Tel:* 407-380-7229
Fax: 407-380-7243
Foreign Office(s): Presagis Europe SAS, 44 ter
blvd St-Antoine, 78150 Le Chesnay, France
Tel: 01 30 70 50 00
Presagis Italy, Via Vincenzo Monti 8, 20123 Mi-
lan MI, Italy *Tel:* (02) 46712 231 *Fax:* (02)
48013 233
Presagis UK, Windmill Hill Business Park,
Whitehill Way, Swindon, Wilts SN5 6QR,
United Kingdom *Tel:* (01793) 441447
Fax: (01793) 441574

Prescolite
Division of Hubbell Lighting Inc
701 Millennium Blvd, Greenville, SC 29607
Tel: 864-678-1000 *Fax:* 864-678-1740
Web Site: www.hubbell.com/prescolite
Key Personnel
Dir, Mktg: Paige Malouche
Founded: 1944
Lighting fixture manufacturer.
Online catalog(s) available

Presence Records
Subsidiary of Presence Productions
67 Candace Lane, Chatham Township, NJ 07928-
1115
Tel: 973-701-0707
Web Site: www.paulpayton.com; www.
presenceproductions.com
Key Personnel
Owner & Pres: Paul Payton *E-mail:* paul@
paulpayton.com
Founded: 1985
CD & record production & services.
Online catalog(s) available
Membership(s): CineTech Media Professionals

Presence Studios
80 Wells Hill Rd, Suite 100, Weston, CT 06883
Tel: 203-221-8061
E-mail: info@presencestudios.com
Web Site: www.presencestudios.com
Key Personnel
Owner: Jon Russell
Studio Mgr: Kathleen Lombard *E-mail:* kathy@
presencestudios.com
Founded: 1980
Audio recording, mixing, ADR, post-production,
video & editing.

Presentation Products Inc
171 Madison Ave, 12th fl, New York, NY 10016
Tel: 212-736-6350 *Toll Free Tel:* 877-774-4523
Fax: 212-736-6353
E-mail: customerservice@pproducts.com
Web Site: www.presentationproducts.com
Key Personnel
Pres & CEO: Orin Knopp
Principal: Kyle Balkcom; Barclay Bulleit
Founded: 1996
AV systems integrator.

Preston Cinema Systems
1659 11 St, Suite 100, Santa Monica, CA 90404
Tel: 310-453-1852 *Fax:* 310-453-5672
E-mail: sales@prestoncinema.com
Web Site: www.prestoncinema.com
Key Personnel
Pres: Howard Preston
Camera support system services.

Preston Productions Inc
128 Bartlett St, Marlborough, MA 01752
Toll Free Tel: 800-822-2299
E-mail: ideas@prestonevents.com
Web Site: www.prestonproductions.com; www.
prestonevents.com
Key Personnel
CEO: Rick Preston

CFO: Susan Preston
Dir, Digital Media: Hannah Fullam
Dir, Prodn: Wayne Jackson
Founded: 1983
Full service event communication & production firm.
Brochure(s) available
Catalog(s) available, on request
Online catalog(s) available
Membership(s): Meeting Planners International

Prevention Products & Services Inc, see The Bureau for At-Risk Youth

PRG, see Production Resource Group LLC (PRG)

PRI Productions
1819 Kings Ave, Jacksonville, FL 32207
Tel: 904-398-8179
E-mail: info@priproductions.com
Web Site: www.priproductions.com
Key Personnel
Pres & Owner: Randy Goodwin
Founded: 1994
Event production company of corporate videos, image transfers, photography, audio duplication & computer graphics.

Primacoustic
1588 Kebet Way, Port Coquitlam, BC V3C 5M5, Canada
Tel: 604-942-1001 *Fax:* 604-942-1010
E-mail: info@primacoustic.com
Web Site: www.primacoustic.com
Key Personnel
Busn Devt: Steve Dickson
Busn Devt, CN: James Wright
Acoustic treatment products.
Catalog(s) available, hard copy or PDF
Membership(s): AES; NAMM, the National Association of Music Merchants

PrimaLux Video Inc
30 W 26 St, 7th fl, New York, NY 10010
Tel: 212-206-1402
Web Site: www.primalux.com
Key Personnel
Pres: Jeff Schwartz
Prodn Coord: Judy Cashman
Founded: 1982
Full service video production company. Full camera crews available.
Online catalog(s) available
Membership(s): International Alliance of Theatrical Stage Employees

Prime Cut Productions
1224 Orange Grove Ave, South Pasadena, CA 91030
Key Personnel
Pres: John Refoua

Prime Image Inc
200 Highpoint Dr, Suite 215, Chalfont, PA 18914
Tel: 215-822-1561
E-mail: info@primeimage.com; sales@primeimage.com
Web Site: www.primeimage.com
Founded: 1985
Programmatic data analysis, multiplatform delivery & analytics, activation & monetization.

PrimeArray Systems Inc
1500 District Ave, Burlington, MA 01803
Tel: 978-455-9488 *Toll Free Tel:* 800-433-5133
E-mail: info@primearray.com; sales@primearray.com
Web Site: www.primearray.com
CD manufacturer.

PrimeLight Productions Inc
750 Kappock St, Suite 805, Riverdale, NY 10463
Tel: 718-543-3991
E-mail: info@primelight.net
Web Site: www.primelight.net
Key Personnel
Owner & Dir: Don Forschmidt *Tel:* 917-680-5780
    E-mail: don@primelight.net
Founded: 1990
Corporate video production; creative development, studio & location production, post-production, video & DVD.

Princeton Book Company, Publishers
15 W Front St, 3rd fl, Trenton, NJ 08608
Tel: 609-426-0602 *Toll Free Tel:* 800-220-7149
    Fax: 609-426-1344
E-mail: pbc@dancehorizons.com
Web Site: www.dancehorizons.com
Key Personnel
Pres: Charles H Woodford
Publish & distribute dance books & videos.
Online catalog(s) available

Print File Inc
1846 S Orange Blossom Trail, Apopka, FL 32703
Tel: 407-886-3100 *Toll Free Tel:* 800-508-8539
    Fax: 407-886-0008 *Toll Free Fax:* 800-546-4145
E-mail: support@printfile.com
Web Site: printfile.com
Key Personnel
Pres: Mark Amat
High quality archival photographic storage & presentation products.
Catalog(s) available
Online catalog(s) available
Membership(s): The Imaging Alliance; PPA

Prior Scientific Inc
80 Reservoir Park Dr, Rockland, MA 02370
Tel: 781-878-8442 *Toll Free Tel:* 800-877-2234
    Fax: 781-878-8736
E-mail: info@prior.com; techsupportus@prior.com
Web Site: www.prior.com
Key Personnel
CEO: Thomas Freda
CFO: Simon Smith
CTO: Stuart Jarvis
VP, Fin & Admin: Mark Cherwek
VP, Sales: Dennis Doherty
Sr Prod Mktg Mgr: James Hunt
Founded: 1919
Design & manufacture precision optical & electro-mechanical equipment & instrumentation.
Foreign Office(s): Prior Scientific Instruments (Suzhou) Ltd, 509 Tayun Plaza, 188 Tayun Rd, Suzhou 215000, China *Tel:* (0512) 6617 5866
    E-mail: info-china@prior.com
Prior Scientific Instruments GmbH, Hans-Knoell-Str 6, 07745 Jena, Germany, Country Mgr: Heiko Roehler *Tel:* (03641) 675 650
    Fax: (03641) 675 651 *E-mail:* jena@prior.com
Kayabacho 3rd Nagaoka Bldg 10F, 2-7-10, Nihonbashi Kayabacho, Chuo-ku, Tokyo 103-0025, Japan, Country Mgr: Tatsuro Ohmura
    Tel: (03) 5652-8831 *E-mail:* info-japan@prior.com
Prior Scientific Instruments Ltd, 3-4 Fielding Industrial Estate, Wilbraham Rd, Fulbourn, Cambridge CB21 5ET, United Kingdom, Sales Mgr: Colin Duncan *Tel:* (01223) 881711
    Fax: (01223) 881710 *E-mail:* inquiries@prior.com

Pristine Systems Inc
PO Box 6482, San Pedro, CA 90734
Tel: 310-831-2234
Web Site: www.pristinesys.com

Key Personnel
Pres: Kevin Loper *E-mail:* kevin@pristinesys.com
Founded: 1983
Digital storage & delivery systems featuring live assist, digital automation, satellite automation, remote control access & live web site content.
Membership(s): NAB

Private Island Audio Inc
1882 S Cochran Ave, Los Angeles, CA 90019
Tel: 323-856-8729
Web Site: www.privateislandaudio.net
Key Personnel
Owner & CEO: Robyn Whitney
Music Prodr & Chief Engr: Michael McDonald
Full service audio post, professional recording & mixing.

Private Island Trax, see Private Island Audio Inc

Pro AV Systems
275 Billerica Rd, Suite 3, Chelmsford, MA 01824
Tel: 978-692-5111 *Fax:* 978-692-5252
E-mail: info@proavsi.com
Web Site: proavsi.com
Key Personnel
Owner & CFO: Les Bishop
Owner & Pres: Kim Bishop
Dir, Engg: Mark Woods
Dir, Mktg & Spec Events: Adrienne Blasioli
Dir, Sales: David Bishop
Founded: 1999
Full service AV integrator.
Branch Office(s)
17 Patrick Dr, Suite 1, Westbrook, ME 04092
    Tel: 207-370-6050
Installation & Service Office, Merrimack, NH
    Tel: 603-913-9658
74 Cotton Mill Hill, Suite 303, Brattleboro, VT 05301 *Tel:* 802-246-7166

Pro Camera Repair
8250 Vickers Ave, San Diego, CA 92111
Tel: 858-277-3700
E-mail: info@procamerarepair.com
Web Site: www.procamerarepair.com
Key Personnel
Gen Mgr: Kelly Chong
Founded: 1975
Professional photographic repair company.
Membership(s): The Imaging Alliance; National Foundation of Independent Businesses

Pro Cuts Editing Services
2138 Priest Bridge Ct, Suite 1, Crofton, MD 21114
Tel: 301-464-5067; 443-274-6115
E-mail: info@procutsediting.com
Web Site: www.procutsediting.com
Key Personnel
Dir, Post-Prodn: Kenneth G Davis *E-mail:* kgd@procutsediting.com
Founded: 2002
Post-production including video editing, DVD & Blu-ray authoring, streaming video, web design consulting, DVD & Blu-ray replication & duplication, digital storage solutions. Editing suites available. Music & sound effects libraries available upon request.
Membership(s): Baltimore Videographers Association; Professional Videographers of Greater Washington DC

Pro8mm
Division of Small Format Film & Video Inc
2805 W Magnolia Blvd, Burbank, CA 91505
Tel: 818-848-5522 *Fax:* 818-848-5956
E-mail: sales@pro8mm.com; info@pro8mm.com
Web Site: www.pro8mm.com
Key Personnel
Pres: Philip Vigeant
VP, Mktg: Rhonda Vigeant

Founded: 1971
AV equipment sales, archival work & compression & decompression service.
Online catalog(s) available
Membership(s): Association of Moving Image Archivists; Association of Personal Photo Organizers; UFVA

Pro HD Rentals
2201 N Hollywood Way, Suite 1, Burbank, CA 91505
Tel: 818-450-1115 *Fax:* 818-450-1115
E-mail: sales@prohdrentals.com
Web Site: www.prohdrentals.com
Key Personnel
Pres: Dan Toomey
Mgr: Frankie George
Full service production equipment rentals including cameras, lenses, lighting & grip.
Membership(s): Production Equipment Rental Group

Pro Media Productions
2593 Hamline Ave N, Roseville, MN 55113
Tel: 651-631-3681 *Fax:* 651-631-1606
E-mail: info@promediahd.com
Web Site: www.promediaproductions.com
Full service video production, including training videos, product promotion, corporate overviews, employee communications, trade show presentations & television commercials.

Pro Power Products Inc
913 S Victory Blvd, Burbank, CA 91502
Tel: 818-558-6222; 818-558-6740
Toll Free Tel: 800-395-8466 *Fax:* 818-558-3999
Web Site: propowerproducts.com
Key Personnel
VP, Sales: Jim Tessmar *E-mail:* jim@propowerproducts.com
Provide custom battery solutions for customers with high power applications.
Online catalog(s) available
Membership(s): NAB; SMPTE®

Pro-Tape & Specialities Inc
621 Rte 1 S, Suite B, North Brunswick, NJ 08902
Tel: 732-346-0900 *Toll Free Tel:* 800-345-0234
Fax: 732-729-7373
Web Site: www.protapes.com
Key Personnel
COO: Barry Hart
Mktg Mgr: Dennis Mirabella *Tel:* 732-346-0900 ext 115 *E-mail:* dennism@protapes.com
Founded: 1977
Pressure sensitive tapes.
Catalog(s) available

Pro Video
600 First Ave NW, Cedar Rapids, IA 52405
Tel: 319-368-7779 *Toll Free Tel:* 800-234-7680
E-mail: service@provideoweb.com
Web Site: www.provideoweb.com
Specialize in film to DVD transfer as well as other media (VHS tape, Mini DV, 8mm cassette, audio recordings, etc) onto DVD & external hard drive. Also videography & video equipment & accessories rentals.

Pro Video & Film Equipment Co Inc
11425 Mathis Ave, Studio 404, Dallas, TX 75234
Tel: 972-869-9990 *Toll Free Tel:* 888-869-9998
E-mail: providfilm@aol.com
Web Site: www.provideofilm.com; www.usedequipmentnewsletter.com
Key Personnel
Founder & Pres: Bill Reiter
Ad Mgr: Stephanie Fox
Founded: 1987

Used equipment dealer. Specialize in film, video, audio, lighting & production equipment.
Online catalog(s) available
Membership(s): Chamber of Commerce; NAB

PROCAM
13624 Black Elk Trail, Prescott, AZ 86305
Tel: 928-708-9901
E-mail: bolexusa@yahoo.com
Key Personnel
Owner: Dieter Schaefer
Founded: 1983

Producers Group Ltd
713 S Pacific Coast Hwy, Suite B, Redondo Beach, CA 90277-4233
Tel: 310-316-0481
Web Site: www.producers-group.tv
Key Personnel
Pres & Exec Prodr: Lee W Gluckman, Jr
E-mail: lee.gluckman@producers-group.tv
Founded: 1967
Full service production company. Chief negotiator of SAG-AFTRA National Board ratified 3-year agreement to the new National Code of Fair Practice for Corporate/Educational & Non-Broadcast Recorded Material. The agreement with the Producers Group brings together 2 legacy SAG & AFTRA contracts for corporate, non-broadcast & educational work.
Membership(s): IQ; SMPTE®

Producers Library
10832 Chandler Blvd, North Hollywood, CA 91601
Tel: 818-752-9097
E-mail: research@producerslibrary.com
Web Site: www.producerslibrary.com
Key Personnel
Pres: Jeff Goodman *E-mail:* jeff@producerslibrary.com
Founded: 1957
Stock footage & still photos.
Online catalog(s) available

The Producer's Loft
2773 Folsom St, Suite 101, San Francisco, CA 94110
Tel: 415-334-4700
Web Site: theproducersloft.com
Key Personnel
Prodr: Vic Ferrer
Founded: 2006
Full service rental studio, stage & workplace for photography, film & video production.

Producers Management Television (PMTV)
681 Moore Rd, Suite 100, King of Prussia, PA 19406
Tel: 610-768-1770 *Fax:* 610-768-1773
E-mail: info@pmtv.com
Web Site: www.pmtv.com
Key Personnel
Pres: Brian Powers *Tel:* 484-690-9180
E-mail: bpowers@pmtv.com
SVP: Rob Schmoll *Tel:* 484-690-9182
E-mail: rschmoll@pmtv.com
Opers Mgr: Danna Doo *Tel:* 484-690-9185
E-mail: ddoo@pmtv.com
Founded: 1989
TV production trucks, satellite uplink trucks & crewing services.
Membership(s): NATPE

Producers Video
3700 Malden Ave, Baltimore, MD 21211
Tel: 410-523-7520 *Fax:* 410-669-3347
E-mail: info@producers.tv
Web Site: producers.tv
Key Personnel
VP & CFO: Ray Hare

Pres & Dir: Rip Lambert
Founded: 1982
Production & rental company.
Catalog(s) available

Product Productions
1850 W Hubbard St, Chicago, IL 60622
Tel: 312-421-9030
E-mail: info@productproductions.com
Web Site: www.productproductions.com
Production services, location services & production vehicles. Rent video & audio equipment & accessories.

Production Advantage Inc
PO Box 1700, Williston, VT 05495
Tel: 802-651-6915 (sales, option 1)
Toll Free Tel: 800-424-9991 *Fax:* 802-651-6914
Toll Free Fax: 877-424-9991
E-mail: sales@proadv.com; orders@proadv.com
Web Site: proadv.com
Key Personnel
Gen Mgr: Ron Kline *Tel:* 802-651-6915 ext 201
Theatrical supplies & equipment.
Membership(s): Professional Lighting & Sound Association

Production Central
873 Broadway, Suite 205, New York, NY 10003
Tel: 212-631-0435
E-mail: info@prodcentral.com
Web Site: www.prodcentral.com

Production Consultants & Equipment, see PC&E

Production Craft Inc
1937 W Walnut St, Chicago, IL 60612
Tel: 312-829-0272 *Fax:* 312-829-8936
E-mail: info@productioncraft.com
Web Site: www.productioncraft.com
Key Personnel
Pres: Dawn Arnold *E-mail:* dawn@productioncraft.com
Founded: 1984
Professional video production company offering comprehensive services including custom corporate video programs, video production crews & equipment & broadcast systems integration.
Catalog(s) available

Production Garden Music
Division of Taylor Media Productions Inc
13423 Blanco Rd, No 147, San Antonio, TX 78216
Tel: 210-530-5200 *Toll Free Tel:* 800-247-5317
Fax: 210-530-5230
E-mail: info@productiongarden.com
Web Site: www.productiongarden.com
Key Personnel
Pres & Owner: Mel Taylor
Founded: 1990
Production music library.
Online catalog(s) available

Production Gear Rentals (PGR)
16140 Runnymede St, Van Nuys, CA 91406
Tel: 818-989-8640 *Fax:* 818-989-8644
E-mail: oscar@pgr.tv
Web Site: pgr.tv
Video & audio production & post-production equipment rentals.

The Production Group Studios
1626 N Wilcox Ave, Suite 281, Hollywood, CA 90028
Tel: 323-469-8111 *Fax:* 323-962-2182
E-mail: info@productiongroup.tv
Web Site: productiongroup.tv
Key Personnel
VP & Gen Mgr: Carol Noorigian *E-mail:* carol@productiongroup.tv

VP, Opers: Mark Biase
Founded: 1981
Full service production stages.

The Production House, see Educational Technology & Media Services

Production Masters Inc (PMI)
204 Fifth Ave, Pittsburgh, PA 15222
Tel: 412-281-8500
E-mail: info@pmi.tv
Web Site: pmi.tv
Key Personnel
Pres & CEO: David Case *E-mail:* dcase@pmidigital.com
Founded: 1985
TV production.
Catalog(s) available
Membership(s): NAB; NATPE; SMPTE®

Production Outfitters
1833 San Mateo Blvd NE, Albuquerque, NM 87110
Tel: 505-237-0770
E-mail: info@productionoutfitters.com
Web Site: www.productionoutfitters.com
Key Personnel
Pres & Dir, Photog: Gary Marsh *E-mail:* gary@productionoutfitters.com
Founded: 1995
TV & AV crew services. HD crews, producers, sound packages & lighting. Live single & multicam HDTV & 4D productions. Video equipment rentals.

Production Partners Media
520 Enterprise Dr, Suite C, Lewis Center, OH 43035
Tel: 614-888-4888
Web Site: productionpartnersmedia.com
Key Personnel
Dir & Prodr: Scott Spears *E-mail:* scott@productionpartnersmedia.com
Prodr & Ed: Peter John Ross
Video production, CD/DVD duplication, commercial production, multimedia, corporate video, equipment rental, audio production & feature film production.

Production Resource Group LLC (PRG)
200 Business Park Dr, Suite 109, Armonk, NY 10504
Tel: 212-589-5400 *Toll Free Tel:* 877-774-7088
E-mail: info@prg.com
Web Site: www.prg.com
Key Personnel
Chmn & CEO: Jere Harris
CEO, APAC (Australia): John Swain
CEO, Central Europe & VP, Global Sports & Spec Events (Belgium): Tom Van Hemelryck
CEO, Global Theatre: Darren DeVerna
Chief Asset Offr (New Windsor, NY): Scott Hansen
CFO (New Windsor, NY): Joseph Cirillo
EVP & Chief Admin Offr: Nicole Scano-Schwiebert
EVP & Gen Coun: Robert Manners
Founded: 1995
Provider of entertainment & event technology solutions providing turnkey design & production services for concert touring, TV/film, corporate clients, special events, trade shows, expositions, themed environments & theater.
Branch Office(s)
539 Temple Hill Rd, New Windsor, NY 12553-5533 *Tel:* 845-567-5700 *Fax:* 845-567-5800
630 Ninth Ave, Suite 610, New York, NY 10036-3748 *Tel:* 212-589-5400 *Fax:* 212-589-5425
1245 Aviation Place, San Fernando, CA 91340
Tel: 818-252-2600 *Fax:* 818-252-2620

8063 Beacon Lake Dr, Suite 100, Orlando, FL 32809 *Tel:* 407-855-8060 *Fax:* 407-855-8059
1053 Willingham Dr, Atlanta, GA 30344
Tel: 404-214-4800 *Fax:* 404-214-4801
200 Hastings Dr, Buffalo Grove, IL 60089
Tel: 847-227-5171 *Fax:* 847-557-9033
9590 Lynn Buff Ct, Suite 16, Laurel, MD 20723
Tel: 240-568-4000 *Fax:* 240-568-4007
360 N Main St, Royal Oak, MI 48067 *Tel:* 248-824-1080 *Fax:* 248-824-1070
6050 S Valley View Blvd, Las Vegas, NV 89118-3123 *Tel:* 702-942-4774 *Fax:* 702-942-4772
915 Secaucus Rd, Secaucus, NJ 07094 *Tel:* 201-758-4000 *Fax:* 201-758-4312
8617 Ambassador Row, Suite 120, Dallas, TX 75247-4639 *Tel:* 214-819-3100 *Fax:* 214-630-5867
137 Horner Ave, Unit 4, Toronto, ON M8Z 4Y1, Canada *Tel:* 905-366-6900 *Fax:* 905-270-2590
Foreign Office(s): Debenedetti 3895 Olivos, B1636EJW Buenos Aires, Argentina *Tel:* (011) 4794-1600 *Fax:* (011) 4799-5200
342 Chisholm Rd, Auburn, NSW 2144, Australia *Tel:* (02) 8568 4400 *Fax:* (02) 8568 4401
E-mail: info.au@prg.com
88 Nathan Rd, Dandenong South, Victoria 3175, Australia *Tel:* (03) 8710 2555 *Fax:* (03) 8710 2599 *E-mail:* info.au@prg.com
Getreidemarkt 11/9, 1060 Vienna, Austria
Tel: (0699) 143 30 063 *E-mail:* rrarrel@prg.com
Blvd du Souverain, 100, 1170 Brussels, Belgium *Tel:* (02) 663 21 80 *Fax:* (02) 663 01 60
E-mail: belgium@prg.com
Industriezone Hambos, Vaartdijk, 6, 3150 Tildonk, Belgium *Tel:* (016) 61 53 00
Fax: (016) 60 88 61 *E-mail:* belgium@prg.com
Suite 16A, No 918, Middle Huaihai Rd, Huang Pu District, Shanghai 200020, China *Tel:* (021) 3356-6706 *Fax:* (021) 3356-6708 *E-mail:* info@cn.prg.com
16, Blvd Gallieni, 92230 Gennevilliers, France
Tel: 01 40 86 49 39 *Fax:* 01 40 86 49 38
E-mail: france@prg.com
Sophie-Charlotten-Str 4c, 14059 Berlin, Germany *Tel:* (030) 364 345 3 0 *Fax:* (030) 364 345 3 30 *E-mail:* berlin@prg.com
Am Coloneum 1/Gebaeude D3, 50829 Cologne, Germany *Tel:* (0221) 870 74-0 *Fax:* (0221) 870 74-41 *E-mail:* koeln@prg.com
Hanauer Landstr 289, 60314 Frankfurt, Germany *Tel:* (069) 944 392 0 *Fax:* (069) 499 00-33 *E-mail:* frankfurt@prg.com
Bredowstr 34, 22113 Hamburg, Germany
Tel: (040) 670 886 0 *Fax:* (040) 670 886-300 *E-mail:* hamburg@prg.com
Balanstr 73, Haus 21a, 81541 Munich, Germany
Tel: (089) 958 462 0 *Fax:* (089) 958 462-22 *E-mail:* muenchen@prg.com
Schlosserstr 8, 72622 Nuertingen, Germany
Tel: (07022) 242 38 50 *Fax:* (07022) 242 38 59
PRG Co Ltd, DS Coast Bldg 6F, 2-2-6 Kaigan, Minato-ku, Tokyo 105-0022, Japan *Tel:* (03) 6414-8600 *Fax:* (03) 6414-8605 *E-mail:* infojapan@prg.com
Ontariodreef, 10, 3565 BD Utrecht, Netherlands
Tel: (030) 263 20 40 *E-mail:* utrecht@prg.com
C/ Violeta N°26 Pol Ind El Lomo, Humanes de Madrid, 28970 Madrid, Spain *Tel:* 914920461
Industriestr 23, 8196 Wil ZH, Switzerland
Tel: (043) 233 40 10 *Fax:* (043) 233 40 11
E-mail: zuerich@prg.com
Dubai Investment Park 1, PO Box 53407, Dubai, United Arab Emirates *Tel:* (04) 8850541 *Fax:* (04) 8850542 *E-mail:* dubai@prg.com
The Cofton Ctr, Groveley Lane, Longbridge, Birmingham B31 4PT, United Kingdom
Tel: (0845) 470 6400
Ockham Dr, Unit 21, Greenford, London UB6 0FD, United Kingdom *Tel:* (0345) 470 6400

77 St Martin's Lane, 1st fl, Covent Garden, London WC2N 4AA, United Kingdom *Tel:* (0345) 470 6400
Membership(s): Production Equipment Rental Association; Professional Lighting & Sound Association

Production Solutions Inc
PO Box 49431, Dayton, OH 45449
Tel: 937-866-2028 *Fax:* 253-423-8997
E-mail: proso@att.net
Web Site: www.psiohio.com
Key Personnel
Pres: Louis Todd Knopp
Founded: 2001
Sound reinforcement. Sound systems & audio equipment rental & leasing services.

Production Support Services Inc
827 Koeln Ave, St Louis, MO 63111
Tel: 314-535-8548 *Toll Free Tel:* 800-394-1257 *Fax:* 314-236-0735
E-mail: info@productionsupportservices.com
Web Site: www.productionsupportservices.com
Key Personnel
Owner: Robin Nunn *E-mail:* robinnunn@productionsupportservices.com
Founded: 1985
Produces lighting, sounds, staging & special effects for live events, as well as equipment rentals, sales & installation.

Production West
Division of R2C Group Inc
207 NW Park Ave, Portland, OR 97209
Tel: 503-222-0025 *Fax:* 503-573-1941
E-mail: info@r2cgroup.com
Web Site: www.r2cgroup.com
Key Personnel
Dir, Post-Prodn: Brad Grove
Founded: 1987
Award winning production facility.

Productions Grand Nord Quebec Inc
5141 Notre Dam de Grace, Montreal, QC H4A 1K4, Canada
Tel: 514-521-7433 *Fax:* 514-522-3013
Key Personnel
Pres: Ian McLaren *E-mail:* imclaren@grandnord.ca
Educational programming.

Les Productions Via Le Monde (Daniel Bertolino) Inc
758, rue Halpern, Dorval, QC H9P 1G6, Canada
Tel: 514-636-6633 *Fax:* 514-636-9633
E-mail: distribution@vialemonde.com; info@vialemonde.com
Web Site: www.vialemonde.com
Key Personnel
Pres: Daniel Bertolino *Tel:* 514-636-6633 ext 222 *E-mail:* daniel.bertolino@vialemonde.qc.ca
VP: Catherine Viau *Tel:* 514-636-6633 ext 223 *E-mail:* catherine.viau@vialemonde.qc.ca
Prodr: Gregoire Viau *Tel:* 514-636-6633 ext 302 *E-mail:* gregoire.viau@vialemonde.qc.ca
Full service production company.
Catalog(s) available
Membership(s): Academy of Canadian Cinema & Television; L'Association quebecoise de la production mediatique

Professional Advancement Enterprises (PAE)
2182 Saginaw SE, Grand Rapids, MI 49506
Tel: 616-956-9443 *Fax:* 616-956-7973
E-mail: paeworld@comcast.net
Web Site: www.paeworld.com
Key Personnel
Founder & Pres: Jorge W Garcia, PhD

Founded: 1981
Translations & DTP in all foreign languages.
Voice-overs & subtitling.

Professional Audio Design Inc
90 Corporate Park Dr, Suite 1420, Pembroke, MA 02359
Tel: 781-982-2600 *Toll Free Tel:* 877-223-8858
 Fax: 781-982-2610
E-mail: info@proaudiodesign.com
Web Site: www.proaudiodesign.com
Key Personnel
Pres: Dave Malekpour *E-mail:* davem@proaudiodesign.com
Audio equipment sales & service.

Professional Education Institute (PEI)
7020 High Grove Blvd, Burr Ridge, IL 60527
Tel: 312-521-8002 *Toll Free Tel:* 800-320-7517
Web Site: thepei.com
Key Personnel
Chief Revenue Offr: Roger Sinnes
Pres: Michael E Hussey
Founded: 1983
Build interactive education programs that focus on self-improvement.
Membership(s): Association of National Advertisers Inc; Electronic Retailing Association; International Association for Continuing Education & Training

Professional Label Inc
7726 N King Hwy, Myrtle Beach, SC 29572
Mailing Address: PO Box 70913, Myrtle Beach, SC 29572
Tel: 301-570-0774 *Fax:* 301-570-0776
E-mail: info@professionallabel.com
Web Site: professionallabel.com; prolabel.com
Key Personnel
Owner & Pres: Rick Fry
Founded: 1985
Print & ship labels for CDs & DVDs.
Online catalog(s) available

Professional Marketing Services Inc
105 S Southgate Dr, Chandler, AZ 85226
Mailing Address: 4802 E Ray Rd, No 2328, Phoenix, AZ 85044
Tel: 480-940-5400 *Toll Free Tel:* 800-201-2160
 Fax: 480-603-1048
E-mail: pmsi@promarketinc.com
Web Site: www.promarketinc.com
Key Personnel
Pres: Ted C Williams
Founded: 1987
Pro digital imaging products & supplies.
Online catalog(s) available

Professional Sound Corp
28085 Smyth Dr, Valencia, CA 91355
Tel: 661-295-9395 *Fax:* 661-295-8398
E-mail: sales@professionalsound.com; service@professionalsound.com
Web Site: www.professionalsound.com
Key Personnel
Pres: Ron Meyer
Founded: 1986
Online catalog(s) available
Membership(s): AES; AFI; NAB

Proforma Good Wood Marketing
3839 E 17 St, Spokane, WA 99223
Tel: 509-534-7477 *Fax:* 509-534-9703
Web Site: proformagwm.espwebsite.com
Key Personnel
Pres: Lori Humphrey *E-mail:* lori.humphrey@proforma.com
Brand management, including printing, promotional products & related graphic products & solutions.
Online catalog(s) available

The Program Source International
2494 Loch Creek Way, Bloomfield Hills, MI 48304
Mailing Address: PO Box 444, Bloomfield Hills, MI 48303-0444
Tel: 248-333-2010
E-mail: info@program-source.com
Web Site: www.program-source.com
Key Personnel
Pres: David A Eicher
Founded: 1983
Television production, post-production service & multimedia production. Location & studio shooting. HD cameras with new editing suite including 3D editing. Also aerial videography.
Catalog(s) available, product list

Progressive AE
1811 Four Mile Rd NE, Grand Rapids, MI 49525
Tel: 616-361-2664 *Fax:* 616-361-1493
E-mail: info@progressiveae.com
Web Site: www.progressiveae.com
Key Personnel
CEO & Pres: Brad Thomas
Founded: 1987
Design centered, research guided, architectural & engineering firm.
Catalog(s) available

Projection
Formerly Projection Presentation Technology
5803 Rolling Rd, Suite 200, Springfield, VA 22152
Tel: 301-459-9011 *Fax:* 301-575-3101
E-mail: info@projection.com
Web Site: www.projection.com
Key Personnel
Founder & CEO: David Campbell
Founded: 1970
Specialties include convention services, meetings & events, AV production & rental services. In-house AV provider for major venues located in Mobile, AL; Long Beach, Ontario & San Francisco, CA; Washington, DC; Honolulu, HI; Baltimore, MD; Boston, MA.
Membership(s): Audiovisual and Integrated Experience Association; IAEM; Meeting Planners International

Projection Presentation Technology, see Projection

Projector SuperStore LLC
17350 N Hartford Dr, Scottsdale, AZ 85255
Tel: 480-922-9420 *Toll Free Tel:* 888-525-6696
 Fax: 480-348-0273
Web Site: www.projectorsuperstore.com
Key Personnel
Gen Mgr: Jeff Phillips *Tel:* 480-922-9420 ext 236
 E-mail: jeff@projectorsuperstore.com
Founded: 1996
Online direct source for presentation technology equipment. Serve the corporate, education & nonprofit markets.

Projects in Knowledge Inc
290 W Mount Pleasant Ave, Suite 2350, Livingston, NJ 07039
Tel: 973-890-8988 *Toll Free Tel:* 800-772-8277
Web Site: www.projectsinknowledge.com
Key Personnel
Pres & CEO: Robert Stern
CIO: David Setiadi, PhD
SVP, Educ Planning Mgmt: Patricia Peterson
SVP, Joint Opers: Michele Fallon Ingram
VP, Chief Content Offr & Mng Ed: Elaine Rudell
Founded: 1980
Medical programming producer for healthcare education.

Online catalog(s) available
Membership(s): ASAE; The Imaging Alliance; International Association of Speakers Bureaus; MPI; SCMP

ProLine Digital
Division of AMI Corp
PO Box 27682, Denver, CO 80227-0682
Tel: 303-761-3999 *Toll Free Tel:* 800-325-0853
 Fax: 303-761-1818
E-mail: info@prolinedigital.com
Web Site: www.prolinedigital.com
Key Personnel
Pres: Tony Marcon *E-mail:* tony@prolinedigital.com
Founded: 1993
Technology accessories & produce digital signage. Foreign office in Australia.
Online catalog(s) available

Promax Systems
2850 S Fairview St, Santa Ana, CA 92704
Tel: 949-861-2700 *Toll Free Tel:* 800-977-6629
E-mail: sales@promax.com
Web Site: www.promax.com
Key Personnel
CEO: Jess Hartmann *E-mail:* jess.hartmann@promax.com
Founded: 1994
Video storage systems.
Catalog(s) available
Membership(s): NAB

Promedia Digital, see Central Ohio Audio Video

Prominent Video, see Deja View Video

Prop Closet LLC, see Theatre Effects

Propeller Music & Sound Design Inc
62 W 45 St, 10th fl, New York, NY 10036
Tel: 917-922-3289
E-mail: info@propellermusic.com
Web Site: www.propellermusic.com
Key Personnel
Creative Dir, Exec Prodr & Composer: Doug Hall
Music, composing, arranging & sound design.

ProPhotonix Ltd
13 Red Roof Lane, Suite 200, Salem, NH 03079
Tel: 603-893-8778
E-mail: sales@prophotonix.com; info@prophotonix.com
Web Site: www.prophotonix.com
Key Personnel
Pres & CEO: Tim Losik
Dir, Technol: Simon Stanley
Founded: 1951
Design & manufacture LED illumination solutions, produce laser modules & distribute laser diodes.
Data sheet(s) available
Foreign Office(s): 3020 Euro Business Park, Little Island, Cork T45 X211, Ireland *Tel:* (021) 500-1300 (LED solutions/R&D ctr)
Pierce Williams, Sparrow Lane, Hatfield Broad Oak, Herts CM22 7BA, United Kingdom, Mng Dir: Jeremy Lane *Tel:* (01279) 717170 (laser solutions/EMEA & Asian sales)
Membership(s): Archeological Institute of America

Prositions Inc
6200 Aurora Ave, Suite 400W, Urbandale, IA 50322
Tel: 515-864-7200 *Toll Free Tel:* 877-244-8848
E-mail: info@prositions.com
Web Site: prositions.com
Key Personnel
CEO: Frank Russell
CFO: Sam Gill
Pres: Robin Salsberry

VP, Busn Devt: Lloyd Singer
VP, Sales & Mktg: Jill Dillenburg
Dir, Career Solutions: Tommy Russell
Dir, Mktg: Ellen Linkenhoker
Dir, Talent Devt Solutions: Craig Robbins
Talent consulting firm. Micro-video learning (audio & video learning bites on a mobile-first application).

Prosper Media Group Inc
348 E Main St, Lexington, KY 40507
Tel: 859-400-0136 *Toll Free Tel:* 888-528-1999
E-mail: producer@prosperproductions.com
Web Site: prospermg.com
Key Personnel
Exec Prodr & CEO: Kyle M Lake
Founded: 1998
Delivers affordable professional multimedia video production services to any business of any size.
Membership(s): NATAS

Protech Audio Corp
192 Cedar River Rd, Indian Lake, NY 12842
Mailing Address: PO Box 597, Indian Lake, NY 12842-0597
Tel: 518-648-6410 *Fax:* 518-648-6395
E-mail: proinfo@protechaudio.com; prosales@protechaudio.com
Web Site: www.protechaudio.com
Key Personnel
Pres: William Murphy
Founded: 1979
Audio equipment manufacturer.
Online catalog(s) available
Data sheet(s) available

Protocol Telecommunications Inc
16844 Saticoy St, Van Nuys, CA 91406
Tel: 818-782-5705 *Toll Free Tel:* 800-400-5705
    Fax: 818-782-5817
E-mail: orders@walkietalkie.com
Web Site: www.walkietalkie.com
Key Personnel
CEO: Keith Merrill Hanson
Walkie talkie rental & service.

Provident Distribution
Division of Sony Music Entertainment
741 Cool Springs Blvd, Franklin, TN 37067
Tel: 615-261-6500 *Toll Free Tel:* 800-333-9000
    Fax: 615-261-5904 *Toll Free Fax:* 800-333-9408
E-mail: info@pmgsonymusic.com
Web Site: www.thep.com
Spiritual music distributor.
Online catalog(s) available

ProVideo, see Mirror 34 Productions

PSAV® Presentation Services
111 W Ocean Blvd, Suite 1110, Long Beach, CA 90802-4688
Tel: 562-366-0620; 562-366-0621
    Toll Free Tel: 877-430-7728 *Fax:* 562-366-0628
Web Site: www.psav.com
Key Personnel
Pres: J Michael McIlwain
COO: Sky Cunningham
CFO: Ben Erwin
CIO & SVP: Cathie Kozik
SVP & Gen Mgr: Arthur A Clyne, Jr
Founded: 1967
Full service event technology provider.
Branch Office(s)
16320 Arthur St, Cerritos, CA 90703, Br Dir: Jeff Symes *Tel:* 562-991-6050 *Web Site:* www.psav.com/losangeles
1725 Corporate Dr, Suite 300, Norcross, GA 30093, Br Dir: Peter Graves *Tel:* 404-352-1418 *Web Site:* www.psav.com/atlanta

2826 Ualena St, Honolulu, HI 96819, Regl VP: Steven C Osborne *Tel:* 808-877-9400 *Web Site:* www.psav.com/hawaii
50 Rawls Rd, Des Plaines, IL 60018, Dir, Sales: Nick Vitogiannes *Tel:* 847-759-8321 *Web Site:* www.psav.com/chicago
5100 River Rd, Schiller Park, IL 60176
45 Fourth Ave, Needham, MA 02494, Dir, Sales & Opers: Scott Queipo *Tel:* 339-225-3199 *Web Site:* www.psav.com/boston
99 Fifth Ave NW, Suite 500, New Brighton, MN 55112, Br Dir: Nick Madsen *Tel:* 847-759-8321 *Web Site:* www.psav.com/minneapolis
4375 S Valley View, Suite D, Las Vegas, NV 89103, Dir, Sales: Jay Jurgensen *Tel:* 702-891-0953 *Web Site:* www.psav.com/vegas
409 Elk Park Dr, Asheville, NC 28804, Contact: Jay Kirk *Tel:* 828-236-0924 *Web Site:* www.psav.com/asheville
3421 St Vardell Lane, Suite G, Charlotte, NC 28217, Dir, Sales & Opers: Scott Stinson *Tel:* 704-525-2380 ext 204 *Web Site:* www.psav.com/charlotte
1341 N Delaware Ave, Suite 103, Philadelphia, PA 19125, Br Dir: Bonnie Santanna *Tel:* 215-425-5206 *Web Site:* partner.psav.com/philadelphia
517 Meeting St, Charleston, SC 29403, Br Dir: Frank Richardson *Tel:* 843-577-9185 *Web Site:* www.psav.com/charleston
18 Hunter Rd, Hilton Head, SC 29926, Br Dir: David A Delaney *Tel:* 843-681-2034 *Web Site:* partner.psav.com/hiltonheadisland
925 Freeport Pkwy, Suite 100, Coppell, TX 75019, Br Dir: B J Hammer *Tel:* 214-210-8061 *Web Site:* www.psav.com/dallas
2055 Silber Rd, Suite 130, Houston, TX 77055, Br Dir: Dexter Oliver *Tel:* 713-680-8360 *Web Site:* www.psav.com/houston
600 Hemisphere Park, Bldg 277, Suite 113-B, San Antonio, TX 78202, Contact: Ray Ramirez *Tel:* 210-308-0182 *Web Site:* www.psav.com/sanantonio
Membership(s): ASAE; Audiovisual and Integrated Experience Association; MPI; NACE; Professional Convention Management Association

PSAV® Presentation Services (Hotel Services Division)
5100 N River Rd, Suite 300, Schiller Park, IL 60176
Tel: 847-222-9800 *Toll Free Tel:* 866-716-9691
E-mail: psavglobal@gmail.com
Web Site: www.psav.com
Key Personnel
CEO: Mike McIlwain
Chief Commercial Offr: Michael Leone
Pres: Ben Erwin
SVP, Mktg: Cathy Schlosberg
Exec Asst: Glenda Van Jaarsveld
AV presentation professionals.
Catalog(s) available
Membership(s): Audiovisual and Integrated Experience Association; NAPTE

PSB Speakers International
Member of The Lenbrook Group of Companies
633 Granite Ct, Pickering, ON L1W 3K1, Canada
Tel: 905-831-6555 *Fax:* 905-831-6936
Web Site: www.psbspeakers.com
Key Personnel
Founder & Chief Designer: Paul Barton
Founded: 1972
Design & engineer loudspeakers for music & home cinema applications.
Online catalog(s) available

PSI Inc
16755 Von Karman Ave, Suite 200, Irvine, CA 92606
Tel: 949-261-6119

Web Site: www.psivideoinc.com
Key Personnel
Pres, Meeting & Event Prodr, Videographer/Ed: Timothy Loftus *E-mail:* tim@psivideoinc.com
Founded: 1972
Video production & event staging for corporate audiences.

PSSI Global Services LLC
7030 Hayvenhurst Ave, Van Nuys, CA 91406
Tel: 310-575-4400 *Toll Free Tel:* 800-SAT-LINK (728-5465); 800-634-6530 (teleport inquiries)
E-mail: info@pssiglobal.com
Web Site: www.pssiglobal.com
Key Personnel
CEO: Robert C Lamb *E-mail:* rlamb@pssiglobal.com
Pres, Strategic Television: Matt Bridges *E-mail:* mbridges@pssiglobal.com
EVP, Global Servs: Brian Nelles *E-mail:* bnelles@pssiglobal.com
VP & Gen Mgr, PSSI International Teleport: William Sciolla
VP, SatCom Div: AJ Miceli
VP, Strategic Television: Jason Land
Dir, Broadcast Sports: Rick Ball
Dir, Proj Engg: Tracy Michaels
Gen Mgr: Clint Bergeson *E-mail:* cbergeson@pssiglobal.com
Founded: 1979
Full service provider of satellite transmission, event management & engineering solutions for live broadcasters.
Brochure(s) available
Branch Office(s)
5644 Commerce Dr, Unit G, Edgewood, FL 32839
786 Hartford Tpke, Shrewsbury, MA 01545
4415 Wagon Trail Ave, Las Vegas, NV 89118
PSSI International Teleport, 320 Fort Duquesne Blvd, Pittsburgh, PA 15222 *Tel:* 412-565-3471
PSSI Pittsburgh Videotech Center, 320 Fort Duquesne Blvd, Pittsburgh, PA 15222 *Tel:* 412-565-3471
Membership(s): NAB; SSPI

Psychological Assessment Resources Inc, see PAR Inc

Psychsoft Inc
PO Box 232, North Quincy, MA 02171
Tel: 617-471-8733
E-mail: sales@psychsoftpc.com
Web Site: www.psychsoftpc.com
Founded: 1987
Computer & workstation manufacturer.

Publishers Group West (PGW), an Ingram brand
Division of Ingram Content Group LLC
1700 Fourth St, Berkeley, CA 94710
Tel: 510-809-3700 *Toll Free Tel:* 866-400-5351 (cust serv) *Fax:* 510-809-3777
E-mail: info@pgw.com
Web Site: www.pgw.com
Key Personnel
VP, Busn Devt: Kevin Votel *E-mail:* kevin.votel@ingramcontent.com
VP, Field Sales: Elise Cannon *E-mail:* elise.cannon@pgw.com
Founded: 1976
Educational programming.
Catalog(s) available
Branch Office(s)
154 W 14 St, 12th fl, New York, NY 10011 (natl accts off)

Purdue University Digital Education
Stewart Ctr, Rm G59, 128 Memorial Mall, West Lafayette, IN 47907

Tel: 765-494-8619 *Toll Free Tel:* 800-830-0269
Fax: 765-496-2484
E-mail: distancelearning@purdue.edu
Web Site: www.digitaleducation.purdue.edu
Key Personnel
Exec Dir: Jon Harbor *E-mail:* jharbor@purdue.
edu
Dir: Mike Eddy *Tel:* 765-494-4654
E-mail: mmeddy@purdue.edu
Assoc Dir, Degree & Prof Progs: Robin Cunningham *Tel:* 765-494-2975 *E-mail:* rec@purdue.
edu
Continuing education, professional development,
workforce training & self-directed learning programs.
Catalog(s) available

Purefire Communications Inc, see Silver Creek
Media Inc

Pyramid Media
Division of Pyramid Films Corp
3200 Airport Ave, No 19, Santa Monica, CA
90405
Tel: 310-398-6149 *Toll Free Tel:* 800-421-2304
Fax: 310-398-7869
E-mail: sales@pyramidmedia.com
Web Site: www.pyramidmedia.com
Key Personnel
Mgr: Denise Adams
Founded: 1960
Educational media distributor.
Online catalog(s) available

Pyramind Studios
Subsidiary of Music Production & Sound Design
Training & Services
2727 Mariposa St, Suite 200, San Francisco, CA
94110
Tel: 415-896-9800 (ext 200)
Web Site: www.pyramind.com
Key Personnel
Founder & CEO: Gregory Gordon *E-mail:* greg@
pyramind.com
Founded: 1997
Music production & training facility.
Online catalog(s) available
Membership(s): The Game Audio Network Guild;
The Recording Academy

Pyro Spectaculars Inc
3196 N Locust Ave, Rialto, CA 92377
Mailing Address: PO Box 2329, Rialto, CA
92377-2329
Tel: 909-355-8120 *Toll Free Tel:* 888-477-PYRO
(477-7976)
E-mail: information@pyrospec.com
Web Site: www.pyrospec.com
Key Personnel
Pres & CEO: James Souza
Show Prodr: Jeff Martin *E-mail:* jmartin@
pyrospec.com
Founded: 1979
Fireworks & special effects for film & television,
student & local events.
Membership(s): American Pyrotechnics Association

Pyrotek Special Effects Inc
201 Whitehall Dr, Suite 6, Markham, ON L3R
9Y3, Canada
Tel: 905-479-9991 *Toll Free Tel:* 800-481-9910
E-mail: info@pyrotekfx.com
Web Site: pyrotekfx.com
Key Personnel
Pres & CEO: Scott Dunlop *Tel:* 416-727-0628
E-mail: sdunlop@pyrotekfx.com
VP, Client Experience & CFO: Anthony Nehme
Tel: 416-727-9283 *E-mail:* anehme@pyrotekfx.
com

VP, Opers: Brian McDavid *Tel:* 416-317-4147
E-mail: bmcdavid@pyrotekfx.com
Catalog(s) available
Branch Office(s)
6120 N Hollywood Blvd, Suite 105, Las Vegas,
NV 89115, Proj Mgr: Elise Luquette *Tel:* 702-
450-7976 *E-mail:* eluquette@pyrotekfx.com
70 N Industry Ct, Deer Park, NY 11729, Sr Busn
Devt Mgr: Mike Merle *Tel:* 631-242-6206
E-mail: mmerle@pyrotekfx.com
201 Rock Lititz Blvd, Suite 42, Lititz, PA
17543, Prod & Tech Support Mgr: Brian Panther *Tel:* 717-484-9777 *E-mail:* bpanther@
pyrotekfx.com
601 Cowan St, Nashville, TN 37207, Proj
Mgr: Josh Hedge *Tel:* 615-840-6901
E-mail: jhedge@pyrotekfx.com

Pyxis Industries Inc
25695 Jefferson Ave, Suite 8, Murrieta, CA
92562
Tel: 951-526-1999 *Toll Free Tel:* 888-PYXISAN
(799-4728) *Fax:* 951-253-9290
Web Site: pyxisindustries.com
Key Personnel
Owner & Pres: Chad Costanzo *Tel:* 951-526-1999
ext 1201 *E-mail:* chad@pyxisindustries.com
Mgr: Kelly Costanzo *Tel:* 951-526-1999 ext 1205
E-mail: kelly@pyxisindustries.com
Prodn Servs: R J Givens *Tel:* 951-526-1999 ext
1208 *E-mail:* rj@pyxisindustries.com
Full service audio, lighting & video event production & sales company.

Q-Prompt Inc
5356 Vail Ct, Mississauga, ON L5M 6G9,
Canada
Tel: 416-908-5886 *Toll Free Tel:* 866-578-8852
E-mail: scripts@qprompt.com
Web Site: www.qprompt.com
Key Personnel
Owner: Christian Quilliam
Founded: 1994
Teleprompting services including support for live
meetings, video & film shoots.

QCA
2832 Spring Grove Ave, Cincinnati, OH 45225
Tel: 513-681-8400 *Toll Free Tel:* 800-859-8401
E-mail: info@go-qca.com
Web Site: www.go-qca.com
Key Personnel
CFO: Andrea Winterhalter *Tel:* 513-681-8400 ext
103 *E-mail:* andrea@go-qca.com
Pres: Jim Bosken *Tel:* 513-681-8400 ext 102
E-mail: jim@go-qca.com
Catalog(s) available
Online catalog(s) available

Qioptiq, An Excelitas Technologies Company
44370 Christy St, Fremont, CA 94538-3180
Tel: 510-979-6500 *Toll Free Tel:* 800-429-0257
Fax: 510-687-1140
E-mail: generalinquiries.na@excelitas.com
Web Site: www.qioptiq.com; www.excelitas.com
Supply industrial lenses & accessories for OEM
applications. Standard & custom products include photo/electronic imaging optics, laser
optics & medical/bio-imaging lenses.
Online catalog(s) available
Foreign Office(s): Qioptiq Photonics GmbH & Co
KG, Industriestr 10, 35614 Asslar, Germany
Tel: (06441) 9896-0 *Fax:* (06441) 9896-33
Qioptiq Photonics GmbH & Co KG, Koenigsallee
23, 37081 Goettingen, Germany *Tel:* (0551)
6935-0 *Fax:* (0551) 6935-166
Qioptiq Photonics GmbH & Co KG, Hans-Riedl-
Str 9, Feldkirchen, 85622 Munich, Germany
Tel: (089) 255 458-0 *Fax:* (089) 255 458-111
Qioptiq Photonics GmbH & Co KG, Strassfeld 2,
94209 Regen, Germany *Tel:* (09921) 97006-0

Qioptiq Singapore Pte Ltd, 8 Tractor Rd, Singapore 627969, Singapore *Tel:* 6304 4260 (lighting/detection); 6499 7777 (optics) *Fax:* 6265
1479
Qioptiq Space Technology, Unit 2, Kimmel
Park, Bodelwyddan, Rhyl, Denbighshire LL18
5TY, United Kingdom *Tel:* (01745) 589800
Fax: (01745) 584208
Qioptiq Ltd, Glascoed Rd, St Asaph, Denbighshire LL17 0LL, United Kingdom
Tel: (01745) 588000 *Fax:* (01745) 584258
Qioptiq Photonics Ltd, Mitchell Point, Ensign
Way, Hamble, Hants SO31 4RF, United Kingdom *Tel:* (02380) 744 500 *Fax:* (02380) 744
501

QRS Software Services
11879 Woodbury Rd, Garden Grove, CA 92843
Tel: 714-537-5100 *Toll Free Tel:* 800-228-9699
Fax: 714-539-9448
E-mail: qrs@qrssoftware.com; sales@qrssoftware.
com
Web Site: www.qrssoftware.com
Key Personnel
VP, Sales & Mktg: Kelly Joseph *Tel:* 714-537-
5100 ext 223 *E-mail:* joseph@qrssoftware.com
Founded: 1994
Software manufacturer & distributor.
Catalog(s) available

QSC Audio Products LLC
1675 MacArthur Blvd, Costa Mesa, CA 92626
Tel: 714-754-6161 *Toll Free Tel:* 800-772-2834
(US only) *Fax:* 714-754-6173
E-mail: info@qscaudio.com
Web Site: www.qsc.com
Key Personnel
Pres & CEO: Joe Pham
EVP & COO: Jatan Shah
Founded: 1968
Professional audio sound system manufacturer.
Catalog(s) available
Foreign Office(s): Hoi Shing Rd, No 9, Unit 7A,
28th fl, Tsuen Wan New Territories, Hong
Kong *Tel:* 3752 8300
Membership(s): AES; International Technology and Engineering Educators Association;
NAMM, the National Association of Music
Merchants; NSCA

Quabbin Wire & Cable Co Inc
10 Maple St, Ware, MA 01082-1597
Tel: 413-967-6281 *Toll Free Tel:* 800-368-3311
Fax: 413-967-7564
E-mail: sales@quabbin.com
Web Site: www.quabbin.com
Key Personnel
Pres: Paul Engel
Sr Mktg Coord: Jacqui Jamieson *Tel:* 413-967-
6281 ext 343 *E-mail:* jacquij@quabbin.com
Founded: 1975
Manufacture wire & cable.
Catalog(s) available, free
Online catalog(s) available

Quality Audio Visual Service Inc
6938 Boulevard 26, Fort Worth, TX 76180-8808
Tel: 817-284-3192 *Toll Free Tel:* 800-371-6741
Fax: 817-595-2942
E-mail: info@qualityaudiovisual.com
Web Site: www.qualityaudiovisual.com
Key Personnel
Pres: John W Pierce *E-mail:* john@
qualityaudiovisual.com
Founded: 1980
AV equipment sales, service & rental.
Catalog(s) available

Quality Clones
3940 Laurel Canyon Blvd, Suite 405, Studio City,
CA 91604

Tel: 323-464-5853
E-mail: info@qualityclones.com
Web Site: www.qualityclones.com
Key Personnel
Pres: Jerry Zampas
CD, DVD, web site & video services.

Quality Digest
290 Airpark Blvd, Chico, CA 95973
Tel: 530-893-4095 *Fax:* 530-893-0395
E-mail: comments@qualitydigest.com
Web Site: www.qualitydigest.com
Key Personnel
Pres: Jeff Dewar
Founded: 1978
Training videos.
Catalog(s) available
Membership(s): American Society for Quality;
Association for Quality & Participation

Quality Film & Video
3321 Main St, Suite B-1, Manchester, MD 21102
Tel: 410-785-1920
E-mail: quality3321@comcast.net
Web Site: www.qualityfilmvideo.com
Key Personnel
Pres: Peter A Garey
VP: Guy G Garey
Founded: 1958
Production services, video to DVD transfers,
home movies to DVD.
Catalog(s) available

Quantum Data Inc
Division of Teledyne LeCroy
2111 Big Timber Rd, Elgin, IL 60123-1100
Tel: 847-888-0450 *Toll Free Tel:* 888-252-
6133 (tech support); 800-909-7211 (sales)
Fax: 847-888-2802
E-mail: qd.sales@teledyne.com
Web Site: www.quantumdata.com
Key Personnel
Founder & Pres: Allen Jorgensen
VP, Sales: Chuck Evans *Tel:* 630-234-8750
E-mail: chuck.evans@teledyne.com
Founded: 1979
Video signal generator manufacturing.
Catalog(s) available
Membership(s): SID; VESA

Quantum Instruments Inc
Division of PromarkBRANDS Inc
1268 Humbracht Circle, Bartlett, IL 60103-1631
Toll Free Tel: 800-989-0505 *Fax:* 630-830-2525
E-mail: quantumhelp@qtm.com; quantsales@qtm.
com
Web Site: www.qtm.com
Founded: 1975
Design & manufacture professional photo equip-
ment.
Online catalog(s) available

Quatrefoil Associates Inc
29 "C" St, Laurel, MD 20707
Tel: 301-470-4748 *Fax:* 301-470-4749
E-mail: info@quatrefoil.com
Web Site: www.quatrefoil.com
Key Personnel
Founding Partner & VP: Paula Schuman
COO: Paul De Camp
Design Dir: Michael Burns; Abbie Chessler
E-mail: abbie@quatrefoil.com
Technol Dir: Ernie Falcone
Museum exhibit design & fabrication.

Questar Corp
6204 Ingham Rd, New Hope, PA 18938
Tel: 215-862-5277 *Toll Free Tel:* 800-247-9607
Fax: 215-862-0512
E-mail: questar@erols.com
Web Site: www.questarcorporation.com

Key Personnel
VP, Opers: James A Perkins
Founded: 1950
Design & manufacture a series of microscopes,
accessories & integrated systems.
Online catalog(s) available
Membership(s): The Optical Society

Questar Entertainment Inc
307 N Michigan Ave, 5th fl, Chicago, IL 60601-
5305
Tel: 312-266-9400 *Toll Free Tel:* 800-544-8422
(cust serv)
E-mail: info@questarentertainment.com
Web Site: www.questarentertainment.com
Key Personnel
Pres & CEO: Jonathan Plowman
Dir, Acqs & Digital Content, Cow Lamp Films &
Questar: Josh da Silva
Dir, Acqs & Sales: Bess Butler
Prodr & Video Ed: William Mallek
Questar Direct Mgr: Ryan Nahigian
TV & Film Mktg Mgr: Amanda Elliott
Fin & Opers: Terry Gomez
Multimedia Designer & Digital Delivery Special-
ist: Marissa Harrington
Technol: Craig Patno
Founded: 1985
Video production, acquisition & distribution com-
pany for the consumer, educational & institu-
tional markets.
Membership(s): Entertainment Merchants Associ-
ation

Quickbeam Systems Inc (QSI)
4411 McLeod Rd NE, Suite E, Albuquerque, NM
87109
Tel: 505-345-9230
E-mail: sales@quickbeam.com
Web Site: www.quickbeam.com
Key Personnel
Co-Founder: Kurt Jaeckel *Tel:* 505-345-9230 ext
17 *E-mail:* kurtj@quickbeam.com; Gary Math-
ews *Tel:* 505-345-9230 ext 15 *E-mail:* garym@
quickbeam.com
Founded: 1977
Stage lighting, video, audio.

Quiet Planet LLC
PO Box 900, Indianola, WA 98342
Tel: 360-477-9588
Web Site: www.quietplanet.com
Key Personnel
Founder & Publr: Gordon W Hempton
E-mail: gordon@soundtracker.com
Nature sound library for independent producers.

Quilt in a Day
1955 Diamond St, San Marcos, CA 92078
Tel: 760-591-0082 *Toll Free Tel:* 800-777-4852
Fax: 760-591-4424
E-mail: customerservice@quiltinaday.com
Web Site: www.quiltinaday.com
Key Personnel
Owner: Eleanor Burns
Gen Mgr: Orion Burns
Founded: 1978
Quilting videos.
Catalog(s) available

Quince Imaging Inc
2810 Towerview Rd, Herndon, VA 20171-3206
Tel: 703-742-7520 *Toll Free Tel:* 888-252-4960
Fax: 703-742-7586
E-mail: info@quinceimaging.com; sales@
quinceimaging.com; operations@
quinceimaging.com
Web Site: www.quinceimaging.com
Key Personnel
CEO: Ron Currier

CFO: Scott Williams *E-mail:* scott@
quinceimaging.com
Founded: 1997
Staging equipment sales & rentals.
Catalog(s) available

Quintessence Audio Ltd
5701 W Dempster St, Morton Grove, IL 60053
Tel: 847-966-4434
Web Site: www.quintessenceaudio.com
Key Personnel
Owner: Mick Survance *E-mail:* mick@
quintessenceaudio.com
Founded: 1977
High-end audio dealer, including home delivery &
installation.

R & R Cases & Cabinets
Division of R & R Holdings Inc
1217 Rand Rd, Des Plaines, IL 60016
Tel: 847-299-8100 *Fax:* 847-299-8110
E-mail: sales@rrcases.com
Web Site: www.rrcases.com
Key Personnel
VP, Sales & Mktg: Mike Krutsch *Tel:* 847-299-
8100 ext 12 *E-mail:* mike@rrcases.com
Sales Mgr: Jim Price *Tel:* 847-299-8100 ext 15
E-mail: jim@rrcases.com
Founded: 1974
Manufacturer of carrying cases.
Online catalog(s) available

R/GA
450 W 33 St, 12th fl, New York, NY 10001
Tel: 212-946-4000
E-mail: web@rga.com
Web Site: www.rga.com
Key Personnel
CEO: Bob Greenberg
SVP, Mng Dir, Busn Devt: Dave Edwards
Tel: 212-946-4263 *E-mail:* dave.edwards@rga.
com
Founded: 1977
Creative design.
Catalog(s) available
Branch Office(s)
12777 W Jefferson Blvd, Los Angeles, CA 90066
Tel: 310-882-2680
35 S Park St, San Francisco, CA 94107 *Tel:* 415-
624-2000
217 N Jefferson, 5th fl, Chicago, IL 60661
Tel: 312-276-5300
420 NW 14 Ave, Portland, OR 97209 *Tel:* 503-
734-2320
405 N Lamar Blvd, Suite 300, Austin, TX 78703
Tel: 512-774-3600
Foreign Office(s): Uriarte 1572, C1414DAP
Buenos Aires, Argentina *Tel:* (011) 5984 0500
32 Grosvenor St, Sydney, NSW 2000, Australia
Tel: (02) 9994 4193
Rua Estados Unidos 136, 01427-000 Sao Paulo-
SP, Brazil *Tel:* (011) 3958-0900
No 322 Anfu Rd, 2F, Bldg 6, Shanghai 200031,
China
Str Buzesti 50-52, Et 2, Sector 1, 011015
Bucharest, Romania *Tel:* (021) 302 16 14
The MacDonald House, No 05-01, 40-A Orchard
Rd, Singapore 238838, Singapore *Tel:* 6737
7472
Oxtorgsgrand 2-4, 111 57 Stockholm, Sweden
Tel: (08) 509 0723 0
Mesrutiyet Cd No 74 Beyoglu, 34430 Istanbul,
Turkey *Tel:* (0532) 2102484
151 Rosebery Ave, London EC1R 4AB, United
Kingdom *Tel:* (020) 7071 3300
Membership(s): AICP; AIGA, the professional
association for design; AMPAS; SMPTE®

Radial Engineering Ltd
1588 Kebet Way, Port Coquitlam, BC V3C 5M5,
Canada

Tel: 604-942-1001 *Toll Free Tel:* 800-939-1001
(orders) *Fax:* 604-942-1010
E-mail: info@radialeng.com
Web Site: www.radialeng.com
Key Personnel
Pres & CEO: Peter Janis *Tel:* 604-942-1001 ext
250 *E-mail:* peterj@radialeng.com
Founded: 1991
Professional audio interface equipment.
Catalog(s) available
Membership(s): AES; NSCA

Radian Audio Engineering Inc
600 N Batavia St, Orange, CA 92868
Tel: 714-288-8900 *Fax:* 714-288-1133
E-mail: sales@radianaudio.com
Web Site: www.radianaudio.com
Founded: 1988
High performance audio systems.
Online catalog(s) available

Radiant Images
2702 Media Center Dr, Los Angeles, CA 90065
Tel: 323-737-1314 *Fax:* 310-861-0163
E-mail: info@radiantimages.com
Web Site: www.radiantimages.com
Key Personnel
Founder: Michael Mansouri; Gianna Wolfe
Head, Virtual Reality Prodn: Amanda Shelby
Tel: 323-642-1341 *E-mail:* amanda@
radiantimages.com
Gen Mgr: Syrous Nabatian
Client Servs: Tony Ferriter *Tel:* 323-642-1351
E-mail: tony@radiantimages.com
Rental Agent: Angel Jimenez *Tel:* 323-642-1360
E-mail: angel@radiantimages.com
Founded: 2005
Provides 2D & 3D digital cinema solutions, sup-
port & high-end cameras & equipment to the
film & entertainment industry.

Radio Design Labs (RDL)
659 N Sixth St, Prescott, AZ 86301
Tel: 928-443-9391 (sales); 928-778-3554 (cust
serv) *Toll Free Tel:* 800-281-2683 (sales); 800-
933-1780 (cust serv) *Fax:* 928-778-3506 (cust
serv); 928-443-9392 (sales) *Toll Free Fax:* 800-
289-7338 (sales)
E-mail: sales@rdlnet.com; service@rdlnet.com;
exportsales@rdlnet.com (Latin America &
Asia/Pacific sales)
Web Site: www.rdlnet.com
Manufacture professional audio, video & control
modules & equipment.
Catalog(s) available
Online catalog(s) available
Foreign Office(s): RDL Europe, BV, Gebouw Y-
Tech, Van Diemenstr 36, 1013 NH Amsterdam,
Netherlands *Tel:* (020) 6238 983 *Fax:* (020)
6225 287 *E-mail:* eurosale@rdlnet.com
Membership(s): AES; Audiovisual and Integrated
Experience Association; Custom Electronic De-
sign & Installation Association; NAB; NSCA

Radio Systems Inc
601 Heron Dr, Logan Township, NJ 08085
Tel: 856-467-8000 *Fax:* 856-467-3044
E-mail: sales@radiosystems.com; tech@
radiosystems.com
Web Site: www.radiosystems.com
Key Personnel
Founder & Pres: Dan Braverman *E-mail:* dan@
radiosystems.com
Sales Mgr, US: Katie McDowell *E-mail:* katie@
radiosystems.com
Founded: 1976
Audio equipment manufacturer.
Online catalog(s) available
Membership(s): NAB

Radio Vision Inc
531 W Main St, Denison, TX 75020

Tel: 903-337-4200 *Toll Free Tel:* 800-326-3198
Fax: 903-337-4296
E-mail: info@radiovisioninc.com
Web Site: www.radiovisioninc.com
Founded: 2005
Radio & TV commercial production facility.

Radio Visions
PO Box 4732, Toms River, NJ 08754-4732
Tel: 732-240-3119
E-mail: sales@radiovisions.com
Web Site: www.radiovisions.com
Key Personnel
Founder & Owner: Walt Gradzki
Founded: 1994
A full range of broadcast & non-broadcast techni-
cal services.

RadioArt/Bob & Ray CDs & MP3 Files
Division of Radio Foundation Inc
PO Box 519, Plantarium Sta, New York, NY
10024-0519
Tel: 212-595-1837
Web Site: www.bobandray.com
Key Personnel
Pres: Larry Josephson *E-mail:* larryjo@radioart.
org
Not-for-profit radio production company.
Online catalog(s) available
Membership(s): Association of Independents in
Radio Inc

Radiotechniques Engineering LLC
Affiliate of Radiotechniques Manufacturing LLC
402 Tenth Ave, Haddon Heights, NJ 08035-1838
Mailing Address: PO Box 367, Haddon Heights,
NJ 08035-0367
Tel: 856-546-8008 *Fax:* 856-546-1841
E-mail: sales@radiotechniques.com
Web Site: www.radiotechniques.com
Key Personnel
Pres & Engr: Edward A Schober *Tel:* 856-546-
8008 ext 111
Founded: 1979
Primarily provide design services for radio sta-
tions.
Membership(s): Association of Federal Communi-
cations Consulting Engineers; IEEE; SBE

Radius® Display Products Inc
800 Fabric Xpress Way, Dallas, TX 75234
Tel: 972-406-1221 *Toll Free Tel:* 800-FABRIC-
X (322-7429); 866-966-4066 (sales); 866-
966-8266 (hospitality) *Fax:* 972-406-1321
Toll Free Fax: 888-322-7429
Web Site: www.radiusdp.com
Key Personnel
Pres: Tim Lightfoot
VP & Client Servs: Ross Trayler
Graphic Mktg Designer: Zach Jobin
Sales & Mktg: Geoffrey Duncan
Founded: 1977
AV draping for projection screens, tripod screens
& AV carts.
Online catalog(s) available
Membership(s): Audiovisual and Integrated Expe-
rience Association; EDPA; Promotional Prod-
ucts Association International

RADMAR Inc
PO Box 425, Northbrook, IL 60065-0425
Tel: 847-298-7980
E-mail: radmarinc@gmail.com
Web Site: www.radmarinc.com
Key Personnel
Pres: Richard M Davidson
Founded: 1971
Perform CD, DVD & flash drive duplication.
Also publish print & digital books.
Catalog(s) available, see web site or send e-mail
inquiry

Rafik
817 Broadway, 2nd fl, Suite 11, New York, NY
10003
Tel: 646-480-5729
E-mail: info@rafikvideo.com; sales@rafikvideo.
com
Web Site: www.rafikvideo.com
Key Personnel
Dir & CEO: Mindy Wyatt *E-mail:* mindy@
rafikvideo.com
Digital multimedia production & vintage.

Rahlic Publishing Co
301 Keithwood Rd, Wynnewood, PA 19096
Tel: 610-649-0982
Key Personnel
Owner & Pres: Alicia M Boyd
Brochure(s) available

Rainbow International Inc
Division of Rainbow Productions Inc
1103 Canyon Rd, Santa Fe, NM 87501
Tel: 773-505-6264
Web Site: www.rainbowplace.com;
greatplainspress.com
Key Personnel
Dir & Writer: Dirk Wales *E-mail:* dirk@
rainbowplace.com
Prodr: Stacey Evenson
Media & communications consulting & children's
book publisher (Great Plains Press).
Membership(s): CAPA

Rainbow Media Taos
27 Valencia Rd, Taos, NM 87571
Mailing Address: PO Box 472, Taos, NM 87571-
0472
Tel: 575-776-2268 *Toll Free Tel:* 800-748-1540
Fax: 575-776-2804
Key Personnel
Pres: Tony Isaacs

Rainbow Video Productions Inc
23803 S 162 St, Adams, NE 68301
Tel: 402-430-7343
Web Site: www.rainbowvideo.com
Key Personnel
Pres: Phil Troupe *E-mail:* ptroupe@rainbowvideo.
com
Industrial video & multimedia productions.

Raincoast Books
Division of Raincoast Book Distribution Ltd
2440 Viking Way, Richmond, BC V6V 1N2,
Canada
Tel: 604-448-7100 *Toll Free Tel:* 800-663-5714
(cust serv & book orders) *Fax:* 604-270-7161
Toll Free Fax: 800-565-3770 (cust serv & book
orders)
E-mail: info@raincoast.com; customerservice@
raincoast.com
Web Site: www.raincoast.com
Key Personnel
CEO: John Sawyer *E-mail:* johns@raincoast.com
EVP, Sales & Mktg: Paddy Laidley
E-mail: paddy@raincoast.com
Founded: 1979
Publisher, distributor & wholesaler.
Online catalog(s) available

RAM® Mounts
Unit of National Products Inc
8410 Dallas Ave S, Seattle, WA 98108
Tel: 206-763-8361 *Toll Free Tel:* 800-497-7479
Fax: 206-763-9615
E-mail: sales@rammount.com
Web Site: www.rammount.com
Key Personnel
Pres & CEO: Jeff Carnevali
COO: Chad Remmers

CFO: Mike Turner
Corp Cont: Bill Yun
Dir, Busn Devt: Jake Parker
Dir, Electrical Engg: Scott Anderson
Dir, HR: Dave Johnson
Dir, IT: Chris Lasswell
Dir, Mfg: Cliff Lucas
Dir, Mktg: Andrew DeDonker
Dir, Mechanical Engg: Stefan Gottschalk
Dir, Opers: Pory Chhun
Dir, Planning: Jack Kropp
Busn Devt Mgr: David Brinn; Kyle Lonzak
Field Mktg Mgr: Ashley Swearingen
Inventory Audit Mgr: Janetta Knight
Mktg Mgr, Content & Soc Media: Bryden Mc-
Grath
Prod Devt Mgr: Jessica Nawar
Prod Mktg Mgr: Rick Phillips
Proj Mgr, IT & Mktg: Cheryl Valentine Tran
Founded: 1995
Manufacturer of rugged & versatile mounting so-
lutions for applications & devices, including
phones, tablets, cameras, GPS systems, laptops,
marine electronics, printers & radios.
Online catalog(s) available

RAMSA Professional Audio Systems
Division of Panasonic Corporation of North
America
2 Riverfront Plaza, Newark, NJ 07012
Tel: 201-348-7000
Web Site: panasonic.net/pss/ramsa
Founded: 1979
State-of-the-art technology to create better audio
spaces.
Catalog(s) available
Membership(s): AES; NAMM, the National Asso-
ciation of Music Merchants; NSCA

Rand McNally Education
9855 Woods Dr, Skokie, IL 60077
Mailing Address: 75 Remittance Dr, Suite 3043,
Chicago, IL 60675-3043
Toll Free Tel: 800-333-0136
Web Site: www.randmcnally.com; education.
randmcnally.com
Key Personnel
VP, Publg: Joan Sharpe *E-mail:* jsharp@
randmcnally.com
Teacher resources.
Online catalog(s) available

Randall House Publications
114 Bush Rd, Nashville, TN 37217
Mailing Address: PO Box 17306, Nashville, TN
37217
Tel: 615-361-1221 *Toll Free Tel:* 800-877-7030
Fax: 615-367-0535
E-mail: info@randallhouse.com
Web Site: www.randallhouse.com
Key Personnel
CEO & Exec Dir: Ron Hunter
Christian publications.
Catalog(s) available

R&B Communications Inc
2397 Somrack Dr, Willoughby, OH 44094
Tel: 440-946-9511
Web Site: www.rbcommunications.net
Key Personnel
Owner & Pres: Robert Matzen *Tel:* 440-479-8771
(cell) *E-mail:* bob@rbcommunications.net
Founded: 1982
Full service media production from script to
screen. Extensive location production equip-
ment for broadcast quality video. Full post-
production facilities, editing, graphics & audio.
Complete script to screen video & audio pro-
duction services.
Membership(s): IABC; NATAS

Randolf Productions Inc
7271 Garden Grove Blvd, Suite F, Garden Grove,
CA 92841
Tel: 949-794-9109 *Toll Free Tel:* 800-266-7741
Fax: 949-794-9117
E-mail: sales@go2rpi.com
Web Site: www.go2rpi.com; christianmovieshop.
com
Key Personnel
Pres: Dick Hong
Opers Mgr: David Duncan
Founded: 1984
Christian music & video products & books.
Online catalog(s) available

Random House Children's Books
Division of Penguin Random House Inc
1745 Broadway, 10th fl, New York, NY 10019
Tel: 212-782-9000
Web Site: www.randomhousekids.com
Key Personnel
Pres & Publr: Barbara Marcus
Literature for pre-school aged children through
young adult readers in all formats.
Catalog(s) available
Membership(s): Association of American Publish-
ers

Rane
200 Scenic View Dr, Cumberland, RI 02864
Tel: 401-658-3131; 401-659-8192 *Fax:* 401-658-
3640
E-mail: info@rane.com
Web Site: www.rane.com
Key Personnel
Mgr, Cust Serv: Rob Griffith
Founded: 1981
Catalog(s) available
Membership(s): AES; Audiovisual and Integrated
Experience Association; NAMM, the National
Association of Music Merchants; NSCA; Syn-
ergetic Audio Concepts

The RapcoHorizon Co
3581 Larch Lane, Jackson, MO 63755
Toll Free Tel: 800-253-7360; 800-467-2726
Fax: 269-388-9681
E-mail: info@rhcholdings.net; customerservice@
rhcholdings.net; sales@rhcholdings.net
Web Site: www.rapcohorizon.com
Key Personnel
Pres: Lisa Williams
Manufacturer of guitar, microphone & speaker
cables as well as custom audio device boxes.
Online catalog(s) available

David Rapkin Audio Production
473 West End Ave, Unit 6A, New York, NY
10024
Tel: 212-362-7236
E-mail: drapco@aol.com
Key Personnel
Owner & Prodr: David Rapkin
Direct & produce audiobooks.

Rauland-Borg Corp
1802 W Central Rd, Mount Prospect, IL 60056
Tel: 847-590-7100 *Toll Free Tel:* 800-752-7725
Web Site: www.rauland.com
Key Personnel
Pres & CEO: Norman Kidder *Tel:* 847-590-7100
ext 252 *E-mail:* norm.kidder@rauland.com
VP & CFO: Mike Peipert *Tel:* 847-590-7100 ext
202 *E-mail:* mike.peipert@rauland.com
VP, Sales & Mktg: Maureen Pajerski *Tel:* 847-
590-7100 ext 220 *E-mail:* maureen.pajerski@
rauland.com
Founded: 1949
Manufacturer of life-safety equipment.
Catalog(s) available

RAVA Films
67 West St, Suite 604, Brooklyn, NY 11222
E-mail: info@ravafilms.com
Web Site: www.ravafilms.com
Key Personnel
Dir & Prodr: Ava Wiland *E-mail:* ava@ravafilms.
com
Dir & Ed: Rafael Salazar *E-mail:* rafa@ravafilms.
com
Founded: 2011
Create documentaries, films & branded content.

Raven Rental
2617 Peach St, Erie, PA 16508
Tel: 814-456-0331
Web Site: www.ravensound.com
Key Personnel
Owner: Phil Papotnik *E-mail:* phil@ravensound.
com
Founded: 1971
Professional sound & lighting, sales & rental.

Raven Screen Corp
PO Box 691, Harriman, NY 10926
Tel: 845-782-1844 *Toll Free Tel:* 800-847-6906
Fax: 845-782-1840
E-mail: info@ravenscreen.com
Web Site: www.ravenscreen.com
Key Personnel
Pres: Martin Soss
Projection screens visual display boards &
mount/lift accessories.

Ray Audio Video, see Ray Supply Inc

Ray Supply Inc
9 Pine St, Glens Falls, NY 12801
Tel: 518-792-5848 *Toll Free Tel:* 800-347-5851
(orders) *Fax:* 518-792-1727
E-mail: sales@raysupply.com
Web Site: www.raysupply.com
Key Personnel
Pres: Keith Zoll
Founded: 1937
AV equipment sales, rentals & repair.
Catalog(s) available

RB Productions
3-4191 Longmoor Dr, Burlington, ON L7L 5J9,
Canada
Tel: 905-633-7474
E-mail: sales@radicalbob.com
Web Site: www.rbproductionz.com
Key Personnel
Creative Dir & Media Prodr: Robert Diltz
E-mail: rob@radicalbob.com
Founded: 1999
Full service media facility for video production,
multimedia animation, web application con-
struction & graphic design.

RBR Productions
1926 Greenview Rd, Northbrook, IL 60062
Tel: 847-362-4060
Web Site: www.rbrproductions.com
Key Personnel
Pres: Rick Johnson
Multimedia production studio. Audio & video
conversions to digital media, CD-ROM du-
plication & replication, web development &
packaging design.
Catalog(s) available

RC Communications
Division of Rent Com Inc
131 Garlisch Dr, Elk Grove Village, IL 60007
Tel: 847-678-7000 *Fax:* 847-678-9378
E-mail: rccsales@rentcom.com; rent@rentcom.
com
Web Site: www.rentcom.com; www.rc-
communications.com

Key Personnel
Owner: Glen Steinberg
Founded: 1971
Audio video systems for corporate communications. Provides complete AV system design.
Catalog(s) available
Membership(s): Audiovisual and Integrated Experience Association

RCA Records
Division of Sony Music Entertainment
25 Madison Ave, New York, NY 10010
Tel: 212-833-8000
E-mail: publicity@rcarecords.com
Web Site: www.rcarecords.com; www.sonymusic.com
Key Personnel
SVP, Publicity: Sarah Weinstein Dennison
Founded: 1929

RCI Custom Products
801 N East St, Suite 2-A, Frederick, MD 21701
Tel: 301-620-9130 *Toll Free Tel:* 800-546-4724
Fax: 301-620-9103 *Toll Free Fax:* 800-546-6175
E-mail: info@rcicustom.com
Web Site: www.rcicustom.com
Key Personnel
Pres: Doug Macuch *Tel:* 301-620-9130 ext 221
E-mail: dmacuch@rcicustom.com
Off Mgr: Nancy Cox *Tel:* 301-620-9130 ext 222
E-mail: nancyc@rcicustom.com
Leading manufacturer of premium quality audio & video control & connector plates, rack panels & custom devices.
Catalog(s) available
Membership(s): Audiovisual and Integrated Experience Association; NAB; NSCA

RCS Enterprises
Division of RCS Inc
445 Hamilton Ave, 7th fl, White Plains, NY 10601
Tel: 914-428-4600 *Fax:* 914-428-5922
E-mail: info@rcsworks.com
Web Site: www.rcsworks.com
Key Personnel
VP, Sales: Neal Perchuk
Founded: 1979
Provides broadcast software, develops real-time audio recognition technology & creates strategic audio programming content for Internet, corporate sites & broadcast sites.
Branch Office(s)
RCS West, 220 Roslyn St, Denver, CO 80230, Contact: Bob Adler *Toll Free Tel:* 877-774-1018
RCS Latin America, 1720 Melrose Ave, Unit 7, Chula Vista, FL 91911, Contact: Horacio Gonzales *Tel:* 619-428-7729 *Fax:* 619-428-7729
Web Site: www.rcslatinamerica.com
RCS Southeast, 5046 Highpoint Dr, PO Box 9208, Pensacola, FL 32505, Contact: Jim Colley *Toll Free Tel:* 877-774-1008 *Toll Free Fax:* 877-774-1009
RCS Midwest, 214 N Spruce St, PO Box 887, Ogallala, NE 69153, Contact: Carolyn Bell *Toll Free Tel:* 877-774-1038 *Toll Free Fax:* 877-774-1092
Foreign Office(s): 19/21 Ave George V, 75008 Paris, France, Mgr: Lionel Guiffante *Tel:* 01 53 27 36 36 *Fax:* 01 53 27 36 30

RDC Solutions, see PetroSkills | RDC Solutions

Reading Plus®, see Taylor Associates

Real Cool Productions
800 S Main St, Suite 203, Mansfield, MA 02048
Tel: 508-337-8520
E-mail: info@rcplearning.com

Web Site: www.realcoolproductions.com
Key Personnel
CEO: James Ringrose
COO & VP, Sales: Pia Proal
Prodn Mgr: Tom Ribeiro
Founded: 2009
Video & animation training contract development.

Real to Reel Studios Inc
4141 Office Pkwy, Dallas, TX 75204
Mailing Address: 10639 Aledo Dr, Dallas, TX 75228
Tel: 214-528-4242
Web Site: www.rtrstudios.com
Key Personnel
Owner: David Buell *E-mail:* david@rtrstudios.com
Mgr: Mickey Buell
Founded: 1975
Specialize in commercial digital recording, editing, file format conversions, audio for radio/TV, industrials, audio books, phone prompts & Internet web sites. Also offer phone patch, music/sound FX libraries & Internet audio delivery.

Reality Check Systems
726 S Flower St, Burbank, CA 91502
Tel: 323-465-3900 *Fax:* 323-465-3600
E-mail: info@realitychecksystems.com
Web Site: www.realityx.com
Key Personnel
Partner: Andrew Heimbold *E-mail:* a.heimbold@realitychecksystems.com; Steven Heimbold *E-mail:* s.heimbold@realitychecksystems.com
Founded: 1997
Animation & computer graphics for broadcast & film.

Really Good Stuff
448 Pepper St, Monroe, CT 06468
Tel: 203-261-1920 *Toll Free Tel:* 800-366-1920 (orders); 877-867-1920 (cust serv) *Fax:* 203-268-1796
Web Site: www.reallygoodstuff.com
Key Personnel
Opers & Gen Mgr: Tim Kochuba
Founded: 1992
Fun & creative teaching tools for today's classroom.
Catalog(s) available

RealNetworks Inc
1501 First Ave S, Suite 600, Seattle, WA 98134
Mailing Address: PO Box 91123, Seattle, WA 98111-9223
Tel: 206-674-2700 *Toll Free Tel:* 800-444-8011
Fax: 206-674-2696
Web Site: www.real.com; www.realnetworks.com
Founded: 1995
Delivers digital entertainment to consumers directly & indirectly through business relationships with mobile operators & other businesses around the world.
Branch Office(s)
470 Seventh Ave, 11th fl, New York, NY 10018 *Tel:* 212-391-6668 *Fax:* 212-391-9566
11600 Sunrise Valley Dr, Suite 200, Reston, VA 20191 *Tel:* 703-437-4422 *Fax:* 703-437-6515
Foreign Office(s): RealNetworks Australia Pty Ltd, Suite 310, Level 3, 60 City Rd, Southbank, Victoria 3006, Australia *Tel:* (03) 9939 4730
RealNetworks GmbH, Sonystr 18, 5081 Anif, Salzburg, Austria *Tel:* (06246) 77007 1700 *Fax:* (06246) 77007 1719
RealNetworks Latin America, Rua Samuel Morse, 74, sala 183, Cidade Moncoes, 04576-060 Sao Paulo-SP, Brazil
2116, Tower A, Pacific Century Place, 2A Gong Ti Bei Lu, Chaoyang District, Beijing 100027,

China *Tel:* (010) 5954 2700 *Fax:* (010) 8565 6477
RealNetworks India Pvt Ltd, Unit No 110, 1st fl, BPTP Park Centra,, Village-Shilokhera, Sector-30, Gurgaon 122 002, India *Tel:* (0124) 6623800 *Fax:* (0124) 6623826
PT RealNetworks Indonesia, Menara Global 20th fl, Suite A, Jl Jend Gatot Subroto kav 27, Jakarta Selatan 12950, Indonesia *Tel:* (021) 2951 7007 *Fax:* (021) 2951 7006
RealNetworks KK, Shinjuku Eastside Sq 3F, 6-27-30 Shinjuku, Shinjuku-ku, Tokyo 160-0022, Japan *Tel:* (03) 6233 1301 *Fax:* (03) 5285 6500
Web Site: www.jp.realnetworks.com
RealNetworks Asia Pacific Philippines, Unit 901, Picadilly Star Bldg, Fourth Ave, Corner 27 St, Fort Bonifacio Global City, Taguig City, Metro Manila, Philippines *Tel:* (02) 856 3967 *Fax:* (02) 856 7032
RealNetworks GmbH, Av D Joao II, n 16, 1°Dto, 1990-091 Lisbon, Portugal *Tel:* 218 937 010 *Fax:* 218 937 019
RealNetworks Asia Pacific Co Ltd, 14th fl, K1 REIT Bldg, 463, Chungjeong-ro 3-ga, Seodaemun-gu, Seoul 120-709, South Korea *Tel:* (02) 2014 5114 *Fax:* (02) 2014 5017
RealNetworks Ltd, Off 2.08, 31 Southampton Row, London WC1B 5HJ, United Kingdom *Tel:* (020) 7748 3767

Rebel Records
PO Box 7405, Charlottesville, VA 22906-7405
Tel: 434-973-5151
E-mail: questions@rebelrecords.com
Web Site: rebelrecords.com
Key Personnel
Owner: David Freeman *E-mail:* dfreeman@rebelrecords.com
Pres: Mark Freeman *E-mail:* mfreeman@rebelrecords.com
Founded: 1959
Produce & distribute bluegrass recordings.
Catalog(s) available
Membership(s): IBMA

Rebirth Inc
81 Chandler St, Detroit, MI 48202
Tel: 313-875-0289
E-mail: wenhajazz@aol.com
Web Site: www.rebirthjazz.org
Key Personnel
Exec Dir: Pamela Wise
Artistic Dir: Wendell Harrison
Proj Dir: John Roberts
Jazz AV recordings.

Record Plant Remote
1170 Greenwood Lake Tpke, Ringwood, NJ 07456
Tel: 973-728-8114 *Fax:* 973-728-8761
E-mail: info@recordplantremote.com
Web Site: www.recordplantremote.com
Key Personnel
Owner & Chief, Engg: Robert "Kooster" McAllister *E-mail:* kooster@recordplantremote.com
Established as the industry leader in remote audio over 20 years ago, the legendary Record Plant Remote Truck has forged the direction of live music as we know it today. Live album projects, handling audio for live broadcasts & recording in secluded locations.

Recorded Books Inc, an RBmedia company
270 Skipjack Rd, Prince Frederick, MD 20678
Tel: 410-535-5590 *Toll Free Tel:* 800-638-1304
Fax: 410-535-5499
E-mail: customerservice@recordedbooks.com
Web Site: www.recordedbooks.com
Key Personnel
Pres & CEO: Tom MacIsaac
COO: Edward Longo *E-mail:* elongo@recordedbooks.com
Chief Content Offr: Troy Juliar

CFO: Neil Tress *E-mail:* ntress@recordedbooks.
com
CIO & CTO: Mike Pyland
Founded: 1979
Audiobook publisher, educational & library re-
sources.
Catalog(s) available

Recordex USA Inc
10-50 46 Ave, Long Island City, NY 11101
Tel: 718-392-5380 *Fax:* 718-392-5485
E-mail: sales@recordexusa.com; support@
recordexusa.com
Web Site: www.recordexusa.com
Founded: 1969
Digital CD & DVD duplicators.
Catalog(s) available

Recording Media & Equipment Inc (RM&E)
3736 SW 30 Ave, Fort Lauderdale, FL 33312
Tel: 954-791-9797 *Toll Free Tel:* 800-541-9797
Fax: 954-791-6662
Web Site: www.rmeinc.com
Key Personnel
Pres: Lutz Meyer
VP & Treas: Mary Meyer
Founded: 1985
Online catalog(s) available

Recortec Inc
3329 Kifer Rd, Santa Clara, CA 95051-0719
Tel: 408-928-1480 *Toll Free Tel:* 800-729-7654
Fax: 408-928-1489
E-mail: info@recortec.com; support@recortec.
com; sales@recortec.com
Web Site: www.recortec.com
Key Personnel
CEO & Pres: Dr Lester Lee
VP: George Wussow
Founded: 1969
Quality rack mount products.

The Recruiters Library
Subsidiary of The Best College Recruiter
14728 Shirley St, Omaha, NE 68144
Tel: 402-334-1676 *Toll Free Tel:* 800-293-1676
Fax: 402-334-4437
Web Site: www.thebestcollegerecruiter.com
Key Personnel
Pres: Stephen J Brennan, PhD
E-mail: brennan160@cox.net
DVD, CD, audio & video resources for college
athletic recruiters.
Online catalog(s) available

Red Hill Corp
1540 Biglerville Rd, Gettysburg, PA 17325
Mailing Address: PO Box 4234, Gettysburg, PA
17325-4234
Tel: 717-337-3038 *Toll Free Tel:* 800-822-4003
Fax: 717-337-0732
E-mail: customerservice@supergrit.com
Web Site: www.supergrit.com
Key Personnel
Pres: Arturo M Ottolenghi
Founded: 1978
Mail order abrasives & refinishing products.
Online catalog(s) available

Red Sky Studios
184 Everett St, Allston, MA 02134
Tel: 617-903-3373
E-mail: mail@redsky-studios.com
Web Site: redsky-studios.com
Key Personnel
CFO: Dave Cambria
Pres: Frans Weterrings
Studio Prodn Mgr: Ruben Alves
Soundstage & equipment rental, short-term office
pre-production & production office rental, event
hosting.

RED Studios Hollywood
846 N Cahuenga Blvd, Los Angeles, CA 90038
Tel: 323-463-0808
Web Site: www.redstudio.com
Founded: 2007
Working studio lot with 8 soundstages, host to
television, motion picture, music video & com-
mercial filming. Home & headquarters for RED
Digital Cinema.

Redco Audio Inc
1701 Stratford Ave, Stratford, CT 06615
Tel: 203-502-7600 *Toll Free Tel:* 800-572-7280
Fax: 203-502-7610
E-mail: orders@redco.com
Web Site: www.redco.com
Key Personnel
Sales Mgr: Chris Stubbs *E-mail:* chris@redco.
com
Manufacture panels & patch bay.
Catalog(s) available
Membership(s): AES; NAMM, the National Asso-
ciation of Music Merchants

Redman Movies & Stories
1075 S 700 W, Salt Lake City, UT 84104
Tel: 801-978-9292 *Fax:* 801-978-2299
E-mail: info@redmanmovies.com
Web Site: www.redmanmovies.com
Key Personnel
Pres: Bryan Clifton
Grip/electric, camera, still photography equipment
rental.

Redwood Audiobooks
10375 Nichols Lane, Mendocino, CA 95460
Mailing Address: PO Box 1456, Mendocino, CA
95460-1456
Tel: 707-937-1225
E-mail: audiobks@mcn.org
Web Site: www.universitypressaudiobooks.com
Key Personnel
Pres & COO: Margy Bauman
Founded: 1990
Catalog(s) available

Reed Presentations Inc (RPI)
17 Water St, Lebanon, NJ 08833
Tel: 908-753-8800 *Fax:* 908-753-8823
E-mail: info@reedpresentations.com
Web Site: www.reedpresentations.com
Key Personnel
Founder, CEO & Pres: Barry A Reed *Tel:* 908-
753-8800 ext 101 *E-mail:* barryreed@
reedpresentations.com
VP, Fin: Alene Reed
Founded: 1990
Catalog(s) available
Membership(s): AGC; ATD; The New Jersey
Communications, Advertising and Marketing
Association; NJPMA

Reef Photo & Video
2303 N Andrews Ave, Fort Lauderdale, FL 33311
Tel: 954-537-0644 *Toll Free Tel:* 877-453-8927
Fax: 954-537-0645
Web Site: reefphoto.com
Offers underwater photography & videography
cameras & equipment.

Reel Men Rentals Inc
3902 E Broadway Rd, Phoenix, AZ 85040
Tel: 602-286-6800 *Fax:* 602-286-0080
E-mail: rentals@reelmen.com
Web Site: www.reelmen.com
Full service provider of rental equipment to the
film, video & still photography industry.

Reel One International Ltd
Unit of Premiere Bobine Inc

486 Ste-Catherine W, Suite 100, Montreal, QC
H3B 1A6, Canada
E-mail: sales@reeloneent.com
Web Site: reeloneent.com
Key Personnel
CEO: Tom Berry
VP & Head, Dist: Sebastian Battro
VP & Head, Intl Dist: Louisa Cadywould
Founded: 2001
Develops, finances, produces & distributes com-
mercial scripted programming for a worldwide
audience.
Branch Office(s)
1112 W Pender St, Suite 407, Vancouver, BC
V6E 2S1, Canada
1801 Century Park E, Suite 1820, Los Angeles,
CA 90067
Foreign Office(s): Shakespeare House, 168 Laven-
der Hill, London SW11 5TG, United Kingdom

Reel Picture
5330 Eastgate Mall, San Diego, CA 92121
Tel: 858-587-0301 *Toll Free Tel:* 866-502-3472
(US & CN) *Fax:* 858-587-8838
Web Site: www.reelpicture.com
Key Personnel
VP, Sales & Mktg: Keith Wright *Tel:* 858-888-
7999 *E-mail:* keith@reelpicture.com
Founded: 1983
Full service video/DVD/CD duplicator & replica-
tor & authoring lab.

Reelsound Recording Co
701 Southern Dr, Buda, TX 78610
Tel: 512-312-1610; 512-422-7098 (cell)
Web Site: www.reelsound-usa.com
Key Personnel
Owner & Pres: Malcolm H Harper, Jr
E-mail: malcolmharper@mac.com
Founded: 1969
Mobile audio production truck studio.
Membership(s): AES; Latin Recording Academy;
The Recording Academy

Rees
Rees Plaza at East Wharf, Suite 300, 9211 Lake
Hefner Pkwy, Oklahoma City, OK 73120
Tel: 405-942-7337 *Fax:* 405-948-1261
E-mail: rees@rees.com
Web Site: www.rees.com
Key Personnel
CEO: Allen R Parr
VP & Dir, Opers OK: Jay W Tullis
VP & Client Devt Leader: Stephen E Lawson
Founded: 1975
Architecture, planning & interiors firm that serves
broadcast facilities.
Branch Office(s)
1025 N Stemmons Fwy, Suite 737, Dallas, TX
75207 *Tel:* 214-522-7337
800 Town & Country Blvd, Suite 300, Houston,
TX 77024 *Tel:* 713-988-7337
Foreign Office(s): Kelvin 10 5to Piso, 11590
Colonia Anzures, Mexico *Tel:* (0155) 5250-
5354

Reference Recordings
PO Box 77225, San Francisco, CA 94107
Tel: 650-355-1845 *Toll Free Tel:* 800-336-8866
Fax: 650-355-1949
E-mail: referencerecordings@gmail.com
Web Site: www.referencerecordings.com
Key Personnel
Partner, Chief Engr & Tech Dir: Keith O Johnson
Exec Dir: Marcia Martin
Sales & Mktg: Janice Mancuso
Founded: 1976
Classics, jazz & blues record label. Reference
Recordings selects its own artists & is not a
for-hire production company.
Catalog(s) available
Membership(s): The Recording Academy

Regal Photo Products Inc/Arkay Corp
2769 S 34 St, Milwaukee, WI 53215-3541
Tel: 414-645-2050 *Toll Free Tel:* 800-695-2055
(sales) *Fax:* 414-645-9515
Key Personnel
Off Mgr: Donna Swanson
Catalog(s) available
Membership(s): The Imaging Alliance

Regent Press Publishers & Printers
2747 Regent St, Berkeley, CA 94705
Tel: 510-845-1196
E-mail: regentpress@mindspring.com
Web Site: www.regentpress.net
Key Personnel
Owner, Publr & Mng Ed: Mark Weiman
Publishers of books, videos & audio.
Online catalog(s) available

Register Data Systems
Subsidiary of Register Communications Inc
1691 Forsyth St, Macon, GA 31201
Tel: 478-745-5858
Manufactures & sells custom computer systems
to radio & television stations. Products include
the RDS Phantom digital audio system.
Membership(s): Georgia Association of Broadcasters; NAB

REI - Radio Engineering Industries
6534 "L" St, Omaha, NE 68117
Tel: 402-339-2200 *Toll Free Tel:* 800-228-
9275 (sales); 877-726-4617 (tech support)
Fax: 402-339-1704
E-mail: info@radioeng.com; orderdesk@radioeng.
com
Web Site: www.radioeng.com
Key Personnel
CFO: Kevin Hermann *E-mail:* khermann@
radioeng.com
Pres: Scott Hays *E-mail:* shays@radioeng.com
Founded: 1938
Design & manufacture AV products for the com-
mercial vehicle market (radios, speakers, moni-
tors, amps, PAs, microphones).

**Allan Reider Photography & Video
Productions**
2174 Morris Ave, Union, NJ 07083
Tel: 908-688-8808
E-mail: info@njphotographer.com
Web Site: www.njphotographer.com
Key Personnel
Owner: Allan Reider *E-mail:* allanreider@aol.com
Photography, video, guest portraits & large screen
montages.

Richard Reiter Productions Inc
36 Catherine Ct, Cedar Grove, NJ 07009
Tel: 973-857-2557 *Fax:* 973-857-2935
E-mail: reiterjazz@gmail.com; reiterjazz@yahoo.
com; reiterjazz@optonline.net
Web Site: www.richardreiter.com
Key Personnel
Pres: Richard Reiter
Founded: 1978
Original music for films, TV, radio, commercials,
theater & dance.

Dick Reizner Film & Video
801 Atherton Dr, Suite 120, Manteca, CA 95337
Tel: 209-665-7166
Web Site: www.reizner.com
Key Personnel
Owner: Dick Reizner *Tel:* 408-828-3555 (cell)
E-mail: dick@reizner.com
Founded: 1972
Membership(s): American Society of Lighting
Designers; LEVA; NFVA; SMPTE®

Remote Audio Products
220 Great Circle Rd, Suite 114, Nashville, TN
37228-1737
Tel: 615-256-3513 *Fax:* 615-634-2277
E-mail: info@remoteaudio.com
Web Site: www.remoteaudio.com

Renaissance Albums
21 Grace Church St, Port Chester, NY 10573
Tel: 914-939-6878 *Toll Free Tel:* 800-961-6710
Fax: 914-939-8047
E-mail: info@renaissancealbums.com
Web Site: www.renaissancealbums.com
Key Personnel
Pres: Terry Huang
Founded: 1988
Design, printing & binding services for photo al-
bums.
Online catalog(s) available

Renaissance Media
909 Logan St, Suite 11F, Denver, CO 80203
Tel: 303-892-1415
Web Site: www.renaissancemedia.com
Key Personnel
Founder & Pres: Tom Dudzinski *E-mail:* tomd@
renaissancemedia.com
Produce HD broadcast television & streaming
media.

Renaissance Unity
11200 E 11 Mile Rd, Warren, MI 48089
Tel: 586-353-2300 *Fax:* 586-758-1159
E-mail: info@renaissanceunity.org
Web Site: www.renaissanceunity.org;
mastermindjournal.org (catalog)
Key Personnel
Dir, Opers: Mary Hanser *Tel:* 586-353-2300 ext
2311 *E-mail:* mhanser@renaissanceunity.org
Religious programming.
Online catalog(s) available

Renegade Animation Inc
111 E Broadway, Suite 208, Glendale, CA 91205
Tel: 818-551-2351 *Fax:* 818-551-2350
Web Site: www.renegadeanimation.com
Key Personnel
Supervising Dir: Darrell Van Citters
Exec Prodr: Ashley Postlewaite
Dir, Opers: Heidi Ewart *E-mail:* heidi.ewart@
renegadeanimation.com
Founded: 1992
Animation production & post-production services.

Renkus-Heinz Inc
19201 Cook St, Foothill Ranch, CA 92610-3501
Tel: 949-588-9997 *Fax:* 949-588-9514
E-mail: sales@renkus-heinz.com
Web Site: www.renkus-heinz.com
Key Personnel
Pres & CEO: Harro K Heinz *E-mail:* harro@
renkus-heinz.com
CTO: Ralph Heinz *E-mail:* ralph@renkus-heinz.
com
COO: Monika Smetona *Tel:* 949-588-9997 ext
112 *E-mail:* monika@renkus-heinz.com
VP, Intl Sales: Karl Brunvol *E-mail:* karl@
renkus-heinz.com
Dir, Mktg: Margie Kirby *Tel:* 949-588-9997 ext
149 *E-mail:* margie@renkus-heinz.com
North American Sales Mgr: Ladd Temple
E-mail: ladd@renkus-heinz.com
Prodn Mgr: Alex Aguilar
Tech Sales Mgr: Jim Mobley *E-mail:* jim@
renkus-heinz.com
Engineers & manufactures integrated sound rein-
forcement systems, loud speakers, power am-
plifiers, signal processors & control networks.
Catalog(s) available
Membership(s): NAMM, the National Association
of Music Merchants; NSCA

RentACamera.com
Division of The Video Co
2605 Westwood Dr, Nashville, TN 37204
Tel: 615-320-3200 *Toll Free Tel:* 855-588-2882
E-mail: info@tvcnashville.com
Web Site: www.rentacamera.com
Key Personnel
Owner: Adam Rector
Rents professional, state-of-the-art, broadcast,
prosumer & industrial quality video, photogra-
phy, audio, support, grip, lighting equipment,
as well as crewing to the professional photo,
video, television & film production industries.

Replicopy Digital Media Center
1120 Jupiter Rd, Suite 190, Plano, TX 75074
Tel: 972-702-8388 *Toll Free Tel:* 800-628-1124
E-mail: replicopy@replicopy.com
Web Site: www.replicopy.com
Key Personnel
Owner & Pres: Daniel L Redd *E-mail:* dlr@
replicopy.com
VP & Gen Mgr: Jason Ross
Dir: Robert Redd
Cust Serv: Meagan Holley
Founded: 1984
Offer full line of services including CD, DVD &
Blu-ray duplication or replication, mini CDs &
DVDs, CD mastering, DVD authoring, video
production & video editing.
Membership(s): American Independent Media
Manufacturers Association; International Disc
Duplicating Association

Reprise Records
Subsidiary of Warner Bros Records
3300 Warner Blvd, Burbank, CA 91505
Tel: 818-846-9090
Web Site: www.warnerbrosrecords.com

**Research for Advanced Music Sound &
Acoustics,** see RAMSA Professional Audio
Systems

Research Press
2612 N Mattis Ave, Champaign, IL 61822
Mailing Address: PO Box 7886, Champaign, IL
61826
Tel: 217-352-3273 *Toll Free Tel:* 800-519-2707
Fax: 217-352-1221
E-mail: orders@researchpress.com
Web Site: www.researchpress.com
Key Personnel
Pres & CEO: Judy Parkinson
E-mail: jparkinson@researchpress.com
Founded: 1968
Independent publishing business focusing in the
educational field.
Online catalog(s) available
Catalog(s) available

Research Technology International (RTI)
4700 Chase Ave, Lincolnwood, IL 60712-1689
Tel: 847-677-3000 *Toll Free Tel:* 800-323-7520
Fax: 847-677-1311 *Toll Free Fax:* 800-784-
6733
E-mail: sales@rtico.com
Web Site: rtico.com
Key Personnel
Founder: Ray Short *E-mail:* jshort@rtico.com
Pres & CEO: Jonathan Banks *E-mail:* jbanks@
rtico.com
CFO: Matthew Malone *E-mail:* mmalone@rtico.
com
VP, Sales: Bill Wolavka *E-mail:* bwolavka@rtico.
com
Founded: 1970
Distribute & manufacture CD, DVD & videotape
test & cleaning equipment.
Online catalog(s) available
Branch Office(s)
RTI Canada, 17665 66A Ave, No 107, Surrey,

BC V3S 2A7, Canada *Tel:* 604-542-1170 *Toll Free Tel:* 866-237-3724 *Fax:* 604-542-1185
E-mail: info@discgotech.com
Foreign Office(s): RTI-UK Ltd, 6 Swan Wharf, Waterloo Rd, Uxbridge UB8 2RA, United Kingdom *Tel:* (01895) 252191 *Fax:* (01895) 274692 *E-mail:* rti-inbox@rtiuk.co.uk
Membership(s): AECT; AIIM; Audiovisual and Integrated Experience Association; British Kinematograph Sound & Television Society; Consortium of College & University Media Centers; ICVM; NAB; National Association of Media & Technology Centers; SMPTE®

Resolution Productions Group
2226 W Walnut St, Chicago, IL 60612
Tel: 312-243-8230
E-mail: info@resolutionproductionsgroup.com
Web Site: www.resolutionproductionsgroup.com
Key Personnel
CEO: Lee Facklis
COO: Jeff Facklis
Founded: 1983
Meeting & event staging, audio, video, lighting, scenic & show management.
Catalog(s) available
Membership(s): Audiovisual and Integrated Experience Association; MPI; Professional Lighting & Sound Association

RetinaVision Productions
19 Barker Ave, Fairfax, CA 94930
Tel: 415-459-3926
Key Personnel
Pres: Clark Higgins
Founded: 1975
Video assisted film production systems, production engineering, aerial photography & video.
Membership(s): AES; International Alliance of Theatrical Stage Employees; SMPTE®

Rev UP Tech
20929 Ventura Blvd, Suite 47-212, Woodland Hills, CA 91364
Tel: 818-995-1719 *Toll Free Tel:* 877-372-0005 *Fax:* 818-979-9599
Web Site: revuptech.com
Key Personnel
Co-Owner & CEO: Diana Weynand
Co-Owner: Shirley Craig *E-mail:* shirley@revuptech.com
Authorized Apple training center, final cut pro & shake after effects. HD cameras & videotape theory.
Catalog(s) available

Revelli
PO Box 150098, San Rafael, CA 94915
Tel: 415-460-9898 *Fax:* 415-460-9897
E-mail: colorstyledesign@aol.com
Key Personnel
Owner: Clare Revelli
Catalog(s) available

Revels Records
Division of Revels Inc
80 Mount Auburn St, Watertown, MA 02472
Tel: 617-972-8300 *Fax:* 617-972-8400
E-mail: info@revels.org
Web Site: www.revels.org
Key Personnel
Dir, Mktg & PR: Alan Casso *Tel:* 617-972-8300 ext 22 *E-mail:* acasso@revels.org
Founded: 1971
Producer of music CDs, songbooks & educational material focusing on traditional music, dance, customs & rituals from around the world.
Catalog(s) available, free, semiannual
Online catalog(s) available

Revolution Lighting Technologies Inc
177 Broad St, 12th fl, Stamford, CT 06901
Tel: 203-504-1111 *Toll Free Tel:* 877-578-2536
E-mail: support@rvlti.com; info@rvlti.com
Web Site: www.rvlti.com
Key Personnel
Chmn, CEO & Pres: Robert V La Penta
CFO: James A De Palma
SVP, Sales & Mktg: Brian L Daley
Founded: 1993
LED & fiber optic lighting manufacturer.
Online catalog(s) available
Branch Office(s)
Lumificient Corp, 1795 N Lapeer Rd, Oxford, MI 48371 *Tel:* 248-969-3800 *Fax:* 248-969-3803; 248-969-3804 (signage lighting div)

REX
610 SW 17 Ave, Portland, OR 97205
Tel: 503-238-4525
E-mail: info@rexpost.com
Web Site: www.rexpost.com
Key Personnel
Gen Mgr & Chief Audio Engr: Russell Gorsline
5.1 surround sound, audio, video & design for production & post-production. Experience in consumer & marketing communications segments.
Membership(s): Oregon Media Production Association

RF Industries
7610 Miramar Rd, San Diego, CA 92126
Tel: 858-549-6340 *Toll Free Tel:* 800-233-1728 *Fax:* 858-549-6345
E-mail: rfi@rfindustries.com; tech@rfindustries.org; invest@rfindustries.org
Web Site: www.rfindustries.com
Key Personnel
Interim CEO & Pres: Howard Hill
VP, Mktg: Manny Gutsche
Founded: 1979
Design, manufacture & distribute coaxial connectors, cable assemblies, kits & crimp tools as well as signal processing equipment.
Catalog(s) available, free, biennial

RF Specialties of Texas LLC
PO Box 1010, Newark, TX 76071-1010
Tel: 214-697-3477 (cell); 817-489-2730 *Toll Free Tel:* 800-537-1801 (Newark)
E-mail: rfstx@swbell.net
Web Site: www.rfspecialties.com
Key Personnel
Gen Mgr: Dan Sessler
Off Mgr: Nicole Shephard
Distribute everything to do with radio & TV products.
Catalog(s) available
Branch Office(s)
3528 Fairfax Ave, Forth Worth, TX 76119, Sales Engr: Wray Reed *Tel:* 817-535-0784 *Toll Free Tel:* 888-839-7373 *Fax:* 817-535-1979 *E-mail:* rfstxftw@charter.net

RGB Spectrum
950 Marina Village Pkwy, Alameda, CA 94501
Tel: 510-814-7000 *Fax:* 510-814-7026
Web Site: www.rgb.com
Key Personnel
Pres & CEO: Robert Marcus
CFO: Iana Zemniakova
COO: Scott Norder
VP, Busn Devt: Bob Ehler
VP, Engg: Lynton Auld
VP, Intl Sales: Jason Tirado
VP, Mktg: Andy Thompson
VP, Worldwide Sales: Denis Carle
Founded: 1987
Manufacturer of multiview processors, videowall processors, scan converters, fiber optic cables, digital video routers & transmission equip-

ment. Additional offices in Los Angeles, CA; Hartford, CT; Washington, DC; Atlanta, GA; Cincinnati, OH; Dallas, TX.
Foreign Office(s): Utown Intl Off Bldg No 7, fl 17-1557, Block B, Sanfengbei Lane, Chaowai St, Chaoyang District, Beijing, China *Tel:* (010) 5780 3068
Yes Business Ctr, Suite 302, Al Barsha 1, Dubai, United Arab Emirates *Tel:* (04) 513 4783
Membership(s): Audiovisual and Integrated Experience Association; Custom Electronic Design & Installation Association

RGB Technology Inc
Subsidiary of KLC Network Services Inc
590 Herndon Pkwy, Suite 500, Herndon, VA 20170-5267
Tel: 703-834-1500 *Fax:* 703-834-1506
E-mail: solutions@rgbtec.com
Web Site: www.rgbtec.com
Key Personnel
Pres & CEO: SL "Shaun" Huang
EVP & COO: S David Warman
EVP, Admin & CFO: David W Chen
Prog Dir: Darlene Holseth; Ronaldo A C Serrano; David Vitter
Founded: 1987
Systems integration of data, network, audio & video products & services.
Membership(s): Audiovisual and Integrated Experience Association

Rhythm & Hues Studios Inc
5890 W Jefferson Blvd, Suite Q, Los Angeles, CA 90016
Tel: 310-448-7500 *Fax:* 310-448-7600
E-mail: info-la@rhythm.com
Web Site: rhythm.com
Key Personnel
Founder & VP, Devt: Pauline Ts'o *E-mail:* tso@rhythm.com
Pres: Kristin Dornig
SVP, Prodn: Henrik Fett
Founded: 1987
Character animation & visual effects for entertainment & advertising.

Rhythmic Medicine
10425 W 177 Terr, Overland Park, KS 66221
Tel: 913-851-5100
E-mail: music@rhythmicmedicine.com
Web Site: www.rhythmicmedicine.com
Key Personnel
Founder & Owner: Janalea Hoffman
Dir: Marilyn Miller
Therapeutic music on CD & DVD.
Online catalog(s) available

Rhythms Productions (Tom Thumb Music)
PO Box 786, Malibu, CA 90265-0786
Tel: 310-836-4678
E-mail: tomthumbkids@gmail.com
Web Site: www.tomthumbkids.com
Key Personnel
Pres: Lotte Cherin
Founded: 1955
Interactive DVDs, books, vinyl, cassettes, CDs & kits.
Catalog(s) available
Online catalog(s) available
Membership(s): AES; American Federation of Musicians; ASCAP

RIA Corp
1615 W 2200 S, Suite B, Salt Lake City, UT 84119
Tel: 801-486-8822 *Fax:* 801-486-2741
E-mail: sales@riacorp.com
Web Site: www.riacorp.com
Key Personnel
Pres: Mike Hodges
VP, Sales: Jeff Wade

Founded: 1973
Line sheet(s) available

Rich-Heape Films Inc
5952 Royal Lane, Suite 254, Dallas, TX 75230
Tel: 214-696-6916 *Toll Free Tel:* 888-600-2922
Web Site: www.richheape.com
Key Personnel
Pres & Exec Prodr: Steven R Heape
    E-mail: heape@richheape.com
Dir: Chip Richie *E-mail:* chip@richheape.com
Founded: 1994
Specializes in film, video, HD & multi-media
    production.

Lynda Richardson Photography
7239 Lookout Dr, Richmond, VA 23225
Tel: 804-347-9668
E-mail: lynda@lyndarichardson.com
Web Site: lyndarichardson.com
Key Personnel
Owner: Lynda Richardson
Photographic services.
Stock list(s) available
Membership(s): North American Nature Photography Association

Richie Media Productions LLC
2035 Royal Lane, Suite 203, Dallas, TX 75229
Tel: 214-696-9040
Web Site: www.richiemedia.com
Key Personnel
Prodr & Dir: Chip Richie *E-mail:* chip@
    richiemedia.com
Founded: 1939
Turnkey production, Premiere Pro suite, stock
    footage, HD cameras. Independent producer.
Membership(s): Dallas Producers Association

Richmond Sound Design Ltd
5264 Ross St, Vancouver, BC V5W 3K7, Canada
Web Site: www.richmondsounddesign.com
Key Personnel
Pres: Charlie Richmond *E-mail:* charlie.rsd@
    gmail.com
Proj Mgr: Marilyn Williams *E-mail:* marilyn.
    rsd@gmail.com
Founded: 1972
Theatre sound design, show control & virtual
    sound system software.
Online catalog(s) available

Richter Productions Inc
521 E 14 St, Suite 4F, New York, NY 10009
Tel: 917-608-7427
E-mail: rrprod@aol.com; richter330@aol.com
Web Site: www.richtervideos.com
Key Personnel
Pres & Prodr: Robert Richter
Founded: 1968
Produce & distribute documentaries.
Online catalog(s) available, updated regularly
Membership(s): New Day Film Distribution Cooperative

Richter Studios
1143 W Rundell Place, Chicago, IL 60607
Tel: 312-861-9999 *Fax:* 312-997-2387
E-mail: info@richterstudios.com
Web Site: www.richterstudios.com
Key Personnel
Co-Founder & CEO: Jeremy Richter
VP, New Busn Devt: Eric Schmidt
Founded: 1997
Video & professional photography.

Right Coast Recording Inc
341 Chestnut St, Columbia, PA 17512
Tel: 717-681-9801 *Fax:* 717-681-9801
E-mail: rightcoastrecording@gmail.com; studio@
    rightcoastrecording.com

Web Site: www.rightcoastrecording.com
Key Personnel
Co-Owner, Engr & Prodr: Dave Natale
Co-Owner, Chief Engr & Boffin: Dave Wilkerson
Engr & Prodr: Bob Gentilo
Founded: 1990
State of the art vintage recording equipment.

Right Stuf Inc
512 NE Main St, Grimes, IA 50111-2188
Tel: 515-986-1028 *Toll Free Tel:* 800-338-6827
    Fax: 515-986-1129
E-mail: info@rightstuf.com
Web Site: www.rightstufanime.com
Key Personnel
Pres & CEO: Shawne Kleckner
VP: Christine Morgan
Founded: 1987
Anime publisher, distributor & retailer.
Catalog(s) available, $4

RingSide Creative
13320 Northend, Suite 3000, Oak Park, MI 48237
Tel: 248-548-2500
E-mail: info@ringsidecreative.com; newbiz@
    ringsidecreative.com
Web Site: www.ringsidecreative.com
Key Personnel
Founder: Doug Cheek
CEO: Steve Wild
CFO: Brian Efrusy
VP, Opers: John Mroz
Exec Prodr: Robin Tracey
Proj Mgr: Sara Smith
Integrated media studio.
Catalog(s) available

Rink Rat Productions Inc
2 Monk Lane, St John's, NL A1E 1M8, Canada
Mailing Address: 3 Monk Lane, St John's, NL
    A1E 1M8, Canada
Tel: 709-739-9055 *Fax:* 709-739-9065
E-mail: info@rinkratproductions.com
Web Site: www.rinkratproductions.com
Key Personnel
Prodr: Mary Sexton *E-mail:* msexton@
    rinkratproductions.com
Founded: 1994
TV & film production.

The Rip-Tie Co
883 San Leandro Blvd, San Leandro, CA 94577
Mailing Address: PO Box 549, San Leandro, CA
    94577-0549
Tel: 510-577-0200 *Toll Free Tel:* 800-7-RIPTIE
    (774-7843) *Fax:* 510-553-0160
E-mail: info@riptie.com
Web Site: www.riptie.com
Key Personnel
Pres: Michael Paul Fennell
Manufacture cable management straps & sell bulk
    velcro.
Brochure(s) available

Risk International & Associates Inc
c/o Global Health & Safety Network, 8803 W
    Ontario Ave, Littleton, CO 80128
Tel: 720-922-0707 *Fax:* 720-922-0707
Web Site: www.globalhealthandsafety.net
Key Personnel
Founder & Pres: Dr Randall W A Davidson
    E-mail: rdavidson@globalhealthandsafety.net
Risk management, health, safety & environmental
    programs/audits, publications & master classes.

Ritz Camera & Image
114 Tived Lane E, Edison, NJ 08837
Toll Free Tel: 855-622-RITZ (622-7489)
E-mail: customerservice@ritzcamera.com
Web Site: www.ritzcamera.com
Founded: 1918

Online catalog(s) available
Membership(s): The Imaging Alliance

RJ Video Productions
15585 Tilden St, San Leandro, CA 94579-2316
Tel: 510-357-6535
Key Personnel
Owner & Prodr: Robert J Smart
Founded: 1987
Price list(s) available, folder
Video(s) available, folder

RJS Productions
Division of Gilro Associates Inc
PO Box 739, Westminster, MD 21158
Tel: 410-876-6300 *Fax:* 410-857-0608
Key Personnel
Exec Prodr: Richard J Slechter, Sr
    E-mail: slechter@qis.net
Full production facility for industrial/commercial
    videos, TV, promotionals, commercials & full-
    length programs. Post on media 100-XS facil-
    ity. Full service from scripting to final product.

RKO Pictures Inc
11301 W Olympic Blvd, Suite 510, Los Angeles,
    CA 90064
Tel: 310-277-0707 *Fax:* 310-566-8940
E-mail: info@rko.com
Web Site: rko.com
Key Personnel
Chmn & CEO: Ted Hartley
VChmn: Dina Merrill
EVP, Prodn & Devt: Mary Beth O'Connor
Founded: 1929
Branch Office(s)
750 Lexington Ave, Suite 2200, New York, NY
    10022 *Tel:* 212-644-0600 *Fax:* 212-644-0384
Membership(s): Independent Film & Television
    Alliance®

RLJ Entertainment Inc
Subsidiary of AMC Networks Inc
8515 Georgia Ave, Suite 650, Silver Spring, MD
    20910
Tel: 301-608-2115 *Toll Free Tel:* 800-999-0212
E-mail: inquiries@rljentertainment.com
Web Site: www.us.rljentertainment.com
Key Personnel
Chmn of the Bd: Robert L Johnson
CEO: Miguel Penella
Chief Acctg Offr: Mark Nunis
Chief Acqs Offr, Feature Film Div: Mark Ward
Chief Content Offr, Acorn Brands: Mark Stevens
Chief Digital Offr & EVP, Opers: Titus Bicknell
Chief Mktg Offr: Sylvia George
Pres, US Dist: Mike Pears
Mng Dir, RLJE Intl: Stuart Shaw
Catalog(s) available
Branch Office(s)
6320 Canoga Ave, 8th fl, Woodland Hills, CA
    91367 *Tel:* 818-407-9100
Foreign Office(s): The Studio 203, 4-14 Buck-
    ingham St, Surry Hills, NSW 2010, Australia
    Tel: (02) 9310 7333
Acorn Media UK Ltd, 16 Welmar Mews Ivy
    Works, 154 Clapham Park Rd, London SW4
    7DD, United Kingdom, Mng Dir: Paul Holland
    Tel: (020) 7627 7200 *Fax:* (020) 7627 2501
    E-mail: info@acornmediauk.com
Strand Bridge House, 138-142 Strand, 2nd
    fl, London WC2R 1HH, United Kingdom
    Tel: (020) 3734 8706
Membership(s): Entertainment Merchants Asso-
    ciation; Reading Recovery Council of North
    America

RNJ Electronics
202 New Hwy, Amityville, NY 11701
Mailing Address: PO Box 667, Amityville, NY
    11701-0667

Tel: 631-226-2700 *Toll Free Tel:* 800-645-5833
Fax: 631-226-2700 *Toll Free Fax:* 800-765-3291
E-mail: sales@rnjelectronics.com
Web Site: www.rnjelectronics.com
Key Personnel
Pres: Jeff Mutterperl *E-mail:* jeff@rnjelectronics.com
Founded: 1981
Distribute security, commercial & pro sound, datacom, home theater, tools & educational supplies.
Catalog(s) available

Road Cases USA Inc
1121-20 Lincoln Ave, Holbrook, NY 11741
Tel: 631-557-0000
E-mail: sales@roadcases.com
Web Site: www.roadcases.com
Founded: 1976
Manufacture & distribute shipping cases.
Catalog(s) available, by request
Online catalog(s) available

Road Pictures
212 W Tenth St, Suite B-100, Indianapolis, IN 46202
Tel: 317-267-9590 *Fax:* 317-267-9677
Web Site: www.roadpictures.com
Key Personnel
Owner & Pres: Greg Malone *E-mail:* gmalone@roadpictures.com
Exec Prodr & Sales: Kim Cline *E-mail:* kcline@roadpictures.com
Founded: 1994
Film & video production company. Television commercials, Internet films & corporate films. Final cut pro-edit suite. Production management for out-of-town & foreign producers.
Membership(s): AICP

Roadside Attractions
7920 Sunset Blvd, No 402, Los Angeles, CA 90046
Tel: 323-882-8490
E-mail: roadsideflix@gmail.com
Web Site: roadsideattractions.com
Key Personnel
Co-Pres: Howard Cohen; Eric d'Arbeloff
SVP, Acqs, Co-Productions & Devt: Jennifer Berman
Founded: 2003
Production company & film distributor.

Robbins Media Inc
450 North End Ave, Suite 14E, New York, NY 10282
Tel: 212-661-7670
E-mail: info@robbinsmedia.com
Web Site: www.robbinsmedia.com
Key Personnel
Exec Prodr & Creative Dir: Shawn Robbins
E-mail: sr@robbinsmedia.com
Founded: 2001
Production company.

Robertson Worldwide
4700 137 St, Crestwood, IL 60445
Tel: 708-388-2315 *Toll Free Tel:* 800-323-5633
Fax: 708-388-2420 *Toll Free Fax:* 877-388-2420
E-mail: info@robertsonlighting.com
Web Site: www.robertsondirect.com
Key Personnel
Pres: Sandy Bryant
VP, Sales & Mktg: Robert Pelino
Founded: 1950
Manufacturer of electronic & magnetic ballasts & transformers for fluorescent HID & low-voltage lamps.
Catalog(s) available, product family specific

Robertstock.com, see
ClassicStock.com/Robertstock.com

Rocking Horse Studio
1380 Upper City Rd, Pittsfield, NH 03263
Tel: 603-512-5347
E-mail: info@rockinghorsestudio.com
Web Site: www.rockinghorsestudio.com
Key Personnel
Prodr & Engr: Brian Coombes
Founded: 2008
Commercial recording studio for hire.

Rockland Colloid LLC
PO Box 3120, Oregon City, OR 97045-0306
Tel: 503-655-4152 (sales) *Toll Free Fax:* 866-737-0174
E-mail: orders@rockaloid.com
Web Site: www.rockaloid.com
Key Personnel
Owner & Gen Mgr: Robert Cone
Founded: 1965
Manufacture photographic emulsions, toners, etc.
Online catalog(s) available

Rocktown Media
1361 Lincolnshire Dr, Harrisonburg, VA 22802
Tel: 540-433-7700 *Toll Free Tel:* 888-433-8700
E-mail: info@rocktown.tv
Web Site: www.rocktown.tv
Key Personnel
Owner & Prodr: Richard Hiett
Founded: 1996
Complete production service company.
Membership(s): CCM

Rockwell Communications Inc
321 Burnham St, East Hartford, CT 06108
Tel: 860-528-9091 *Toll Free Tel:* 800-566-6681
Fax: 860-289-2334
E-mail: rockwellservice@aol.com
Web Site: www.rockwellcommunications.com
Key Personnel
Pres: Richard D Carlson *E-mail:* rdc@rockwellcommunications.com
Off Mgr: Barbara Petersen *E-mail:* petersen@rockwellcommunications.com
Serv Mgr: Ray Nunez *E-mail:* r.nunez@rockwellcommunications.com
Founded: 1947
Catalog(s) available
Membership(s): Audiovisual and Integrated Experience Association

Rocky Mountain Audio/Video Productions Inc
7950 S Lincoln St, B-100, Littleton, CO 80122
Tel: 303-730-1100 *Toll Free Tel:* 877-856-4644
Web Site: www.rmavp.com
Key Personnel
Pres: Terry Talley *E-mail:* terryt@rmavp.com
Founded: 1982
Full service audio video production company.
Catalog(s) available

Rodeo Video Inc
412 S Main, Snowflake, AZ 85937
Tel: 928-536-7111 *Toll Free Tel:* 800-331-1269
Fax: 928-536-7120
E-mail: info@rodeovideo.com
Web Site: www.rodeovideo.com
Key Personnel
Owner & Pres: Keith Flake *E-mail:* kflake@rodeovideo.com
Rodeo videotapes-from bloopers to training & events.
Catalog(s) available

Fred Rogers Productions
2100 Wharton St, Suite 700, Pittsburgh, PA 15203
Tel: 412-687-2990 *Toll Free Tel:* 877-677-6437
E-mail: info@fredrogers.org
Web Site: www.fredrogers.org
Key Personnel
Pres & CEO: Paul Siefken
COO: Christopher Arnold
CFO: Lisa Moss
Dir, Busn & Legal Aff: Matthew Shiels
Dir, Devt: Alan Friedman *E-mail:* friedman@fredrogers.org
Dir, Licensing: Micah Southwood
Dir, Mktg & Communs: Suzanne Masri
Prodn Exec: Ellen Doherty
Digital Prodr: Shannon Case
Prodr: Chris Loggins
Founded: 1971
Educational children's media producer. Programs are based on the *Mister Rogers' Neighborhood* TV series. Children's programs: *Daniel Tiger's Neighborhood*, *Peg + Cat* & *Odd Squad* (seen on PBS KIDS) & *Through the Woods* (with Curious Media).
Online catalog(s) available

Rohde & Schwarz USA Inc
Subsidiary of Rohde & Schwarz GmbH & Co KG
6821 Benjamin Franklin Dr, Columbia, MD 21046
Tel: 410-910-7800 *Toll Free Tel:* 888-837-8772
Fax: 410-910-7801
E-mail: info@rsa.rohde-schwarz.com
Web Site: www.rohde-schwarz.us
Manufacture test & measurement equipment for mobile radios & radio communications.
Catalog(s) available, free
Branch Office(s)
2255 N Ontario St, Suite 150, Burbank, CA 91504 *Tel:* 818-846-3600 *Fax:* 818-846-3648
7700 Irvine Center Dr, Suite 100, Irvine, CA 92618 *Tel:* 949-885-7000 *Fax:* 949-885-7001
409 Dixon Landing Rd, Milpitas, CA 95035
9255 SW Nimbus Ave, Beaverton, OR 97008 *Tel:* 503-403-4700 *Fax:* 503-403-4701
1500 Lakeside Pkwy, Suite 100, Flower Mound, TX 75028 *Tel:* 469-713-5300 *Fax:* 469-713-5301
Rohde & Schwarz Canada Inc, One Hines Rd, Suite 100, Ottawa, ON K2K 3C7, Canada *Tel:* 613-592-8000 *Toll Free Tel:* 877-438-2880 *Fax:* 613-592-8009 *E-mail:* sales.rsc@rohde-schwarz.com *Web Site:* www.rohde-schwarz.ca

Roland Corp US
5100 S Eastern Ave, Los Angeles, CA 90040-2938
Tel: 323-890-3700; 323-890-3771 (parts & serv); 323-890-3740 (prod support) *Fax:* 323-721-4875
Web Site: www.rolandus.com/us
Key Personnel
VP & Busn Devt: Brian Alli
Mktg Communs Mgr: Rebecca Eaddy *Tel:* 323-890-3718 *E-mail:* rebecca.eaddy@rolandus.com
Founded: 1972
Manufacturer & distributor of electronic musical instruments, digital recording equipment & audio processing devices.
Catalog(s) available

Glenn Roland Films
PO Box 24035, Los Angeles, CA 90024
Tel: 310-475-0937 *Fax:* 310-475-0939
Key Personnel
Dir, Dir of Photog & Exec Prodr: Glenn Roland
Motion picture & television production, cinematography & production services, lighting & grip equipment, dolly with track packages, studio, director +/or director of photography services, mobile production unit, Super 35mm HD cinematography.

Rollin Studios
259 Green St, 2nd fl, Brooklyn, NY 11222
Toll Free Tel: 844-576-5546
E-mail: more@rollin-studios.com
Web Site: www.rollin-studios.com
Key Personnel
Asst Dir & Prodn Mgr: Satti Ombao
Prodr: Anthony Argento
Founded: 2010
Movie, music & media production services. Location & equipment rentals. Film & TV production services, narrative & commercial.

Rolls Corp
5968 S 350 W, Murray, UT 84107
Tel: 801-263-9053 *Fax:* 801-263-9068
E-mail: info@rolls.com
Web Site: www.rolls.com
Founded: 1989
Audio electronics manufacturing.
Online catalog(s) available
Membership(s): Audiovisual and Integrated Experience Association; NAMM, the National Association of Music Merchants; NSCA

Romar Learning Solutions LLC
6700 Woodlands Pkwy, Suite 230-292, Woodlands, TX 77382
Tel: 281-292-5508 *Fax:* 281-363-2309
E-mail: info@romarlearning.com
Web Site: romarlearning.com
Key Personnel
Owner & Pres: David A Davis *E-mail:* ddavis@romarlearning.com
VP: Kaye Leavelle *E-mail:* kleavelle@romarlearning.com
Tech Dir: Theresa Teltschik *E-mail:* tteltschik@romarlearning.com
Founded: 1986
Specialize in designing custom management, leadership & relationship development solutions that broaden leadership skills, enhance productivity & faster business growth.
Membership(s): ASTO; HeSCA

Rosco Laboratories Inc
52 Harbor View, Stamford, CT 06902
Tel: 203-708-8900 *Toll Free Tel:* 800-ROSCO NY (767-2669) *Fax:* 203-708-8919
E-mail: info@rosco.com
Web Site: us.rosco.com
Key Personnel
Chmn of the Bd: Stan Miller *E-mail:* stan.miller@rosco.com
CEO: Mark Engel *E-mail:* mark.engel@rosco.com
CFO & COO: Rich Luce
Pres, EMEA: Kees Frijters *E-mail:* kees.frijters@rosco.com
Pres, North America: Ed Donohue *E-mail:* ed.donohue@rosco.com
VP, EMEA: Cristian Arroyo
Sr Dir, Prods: Tracey Cosgrove *E-mail:* tracey.cosgrove@rosco.com
Creative Dir: Donna Nicol *E-mail:* donna.nicol@rosco.com
Mktg Dir: Lauren Proud *E-mail:* lauren.proud@rosco.com
Founded: 1910
Filters for entertainment lighting, gobos, fog & haze machines, dance floors, scenic paint & paint drops & lighting equipment products.
Catalog(s) available
Branch Office(s)
9420 Chivers Ave, Sun Valley, CA 91352, Dir, Intl Busn Devt: Jim Meyer *Tel:* 818-543-6700 *Toll Free Tel:* 800-ROSCO LA (767-2652) *Fax:* 818-662-9470 *E-mail:* jim.meyer@rosco.com
1600 Chisholm Trail, Round Rock, TX, Gen Mgr: John Hunter *Tel:* 512-388-5299 *Toll Free Tel:* 866-228-2256 *Fax:* 512-388-0196 *E-mail:* john.hunter@rosco.com
Rosco Canada, 1241 Denison St, No 44, Markham, ON L3R 4B4, Canada, Busn Mgr: Angela Cumbers *Tel:* 905-475-1400 *Toll Free Tel:* 888-ROSCO TO (767-2686) *Fax:* 905-475-3351 (Canadian head off)
Foreign Office(s): Rosco Australia Pty Ltd, 42 Sawyer Lane, Artarmon, NSW 2064, Australia, Dir, Busn Devt: Tom Swartz *Tel:* (02) 9906 6262 *Fax:* (02) 9906 3430 *E-mail:* info.australia@rosco.com
Rosco EMEA, Fabriekstr 38/9, 2547 Lint, Belgium *Tel:* (03) 455 4987 *E-mail:* info.belgium@rosco.com
Rosco de Brasil, Rua Visconde de Itaborai, 141, Tatuape, 03308-050 Sao Paulo-SP, Brazil *Tel:* (011) 2098 2865 *E-mail:* vendas@roscobrasil.com.br *Web Site:* roscobrasil.com.br
Gobos Factory Sarl, 2 rue de Vienne, 75008 Paris, France *Tel:* 08 10 51 05 01 *E-mail:* info.france@rosco.com
Rosco EMEA, Gorlitzer Str 2, 33758 Schloss Holte-Stukenbrock, Germany *Tel:* (05207) 995989 *E-mail:* info.germany@rosco.com
Estudios Churubusco Azteca, Edificio Luis Bunuel, 304 A, Atletas, 2 Col Country Club, Del Coyoacan, 04220 Mexico, DF, Mexico, Acct Mgr, Latin America: Ricardo Ortiz *Tel:* (0155) 5544 3440 *E-mail:* rortiz@rosco.com
Rosco EMEA, Horst ten Daallaan 1, 2181 GP Hillegom, Netherlands *Tel:* (023) 5288 257 *E-mail:* info.netherlands@rosco.com
Rosco EMEA, Krasnaormeyskaya Str 2 bldg 4, Off 211, Moscow, Russia *Tel:* (985) 991 56 85 *E-mail:* info.russia@rosco.com
Rosco Iberica SA, C/Oro, 76 Poligono Industrial Sur, 28870 Colmenar Viejo, Madrid, Spain, Busn Mgr: Jose Cerrillo *Tel:* 918 473 900 *Fax:* 918 463 634 *E-mail:* info.spain@rosco.com
Roscolab EMEA, Kangley Bridge Rd, Sydenham, London SE26 5AQ, United Kingdom, Dir, Opers: Gordon Tomkins *Tel:* (020) 8659 2300 *Fax:* (020) 8659 3153 *E-mail:* gordon.tomkins@rosco.com
Rosco EMEA, Blvd Plaza Tower 1, Level 14, Sheikh Mohammed Bin Rashid Blvd, PO Box 336868, Dubai, United Arab Emirates *Tel:* (04) 439 4205 *Fax:* (04) 455 8556 *E-mail:* info.uae@rosco.com

Rose Brand
4 Emerson Lane, Secaucus, NJ 07094
Tel: 201-809-1730 *Toll Free Tel:* 800-223-1624 *Fax:* 201-809-1851
E-mail: info@rosebrand.com
Web Site: www.rosebrand.com
Key Personnel
VP, Outside Sales: Roger Claman *Tel:* 201-809-1730 ext 125
Founded: 1921
Theatrical fabric & fabrication company.
Catalog(s) available
Branch Office(s)
11440 Sheldon St, Sun Valley, CA 91352, Gen Mgr: Tina Wright *Tel:* 818-505-6290 *Toll Free Tel:* 800-360-5056 *Fax:* 818-505-6293
Membership(s): USITT

Rose City Sound
4811 SE 16 Ave, Portland, OR 97202
Tel: 503-238-6330 *Toll Free Tel:* 877-503-7673 *Fax:* 503-238-9872
E-mail: sales@rosecitysound.com
Web Site: www.rosecitysound.com
Key Personnel
AV Sales: Eric Iverson *E-mail:* eric@rosecitysound.com
Founded: 1938
Sound, lighting & AV sales, rentals, production, design & installation.
Membership(s): Audiovisual and Integrated Experience Association

Rose Packaging & Design Inc
4000 Sopris Mountain Rd, Basalt, CO 81621-9179
Mailing Address: PO Box 3316, Basalt, CO 81621-3316
Tel: 970-927-6515 *Toll Free Tel:* 800-308-1003 *Fax:* 303-557-6366
E-mail: sales@rosepkg.com
Web Site: www.rosepkg.com
Key Personnel
Owner, VP & Mktg Mgr: Robert Rose *E-mail:* robrose@rosepkg.com
Media & presentation packaging products, full service printing, media replication & fulfillment services.
Online catalog(s) available

Judson Rosebush Co Inc
630 Ninth Ave, Suite 507, New York, NY 10036
Tel: 212-581-3000
E-mail: judson@rosebush.com
Web Site: www.rosebush.com
Key Personnel
Owner & Prodr: Judson Rosebush
Creates interactive multimedia Internet products from start to finish. Expert witness in litigation for film, video & digital issues.
Catalog(s) available

Peter Rosen Productions Inc
c/o Du Art, 245 W 55 St, Suite 308, New York, NY 10019
Tel: 212-535-8927 *Fax:* 212-517-5337
E-mail: rosenprod@aol.com
Web Site: www.peterrosenproductions.com
Key Personnel
Pres & Prodr: Peter Rosen
Founded: 1970
Film & television production.
Membership(s): BAFTA; DGA; NATAS; Television Academy

The Rosenthal Group
10625 Cohasset St, Sun Valley, CA 91352
Tel: 818-252-1010 *Fax:* 818-252-1070
Web Site: www.therosenthalgroup.com
Key Personnel
Owner: Jim Rosenthal *E-mail:* jim@therosenthalgroup.com
Motion picture & video lighting, rental & design.
Online catalog(s) available

Mary Riepma Ross Media Arts Center
University of Nebraska-Lincoln, 313 N 13 St, Lincoln, NE 68588
Mailing Address: PO Box 880253, Lincoln, NE 68588-0253
Tel: 402-472-9100 *Fax:* 402-472-2576
E-mail: info@theross.org
Web Site: www.theross.org
Key Personnel
Dir: Danny Lee Ladely
Busn Mgr: Kassandra Hill
Film-video exhibition programs.
Membership(s): The Alliance for Media Arts and Culture

Ross Video Ltd
8 John St, Iroquois, ON K0E 1K0, Canada
Mailing Address: PO Box 220, Iroquois, ON K0E 1K0, Canada
Tel: 613-652-4886 *Fax:* 613-652-4425
E-mail: solutions@rossvideo.com
Web Site: www.rossvideo.com
Key Personnel
CEO: David Ross *E-mail:* dross@rossvideo.com

CFO: George Angus
CTO: Troy English
EVP & Chief Mktg Offr: Jeff Moore *Tel:* 613-228-0688 *E-mail:* jmoore@rossvideo.com
SVP, Mfg & Servs: Jeff Poapst
SVP, Worldwide Sales: Darren Budrow
E-mail: dbudrow@rossvideo.com
VP, Sales (US & CN): Jared Schatz
Dir, Creative Servs: Jim Doyle
Dir, Mktg Communs: Jan Mills *E-mail:* jmills@rossvideo.com
Dir, Sales (CN): Julian Frasier
Dir, Sales (US): Peter DeBenny
Dir, Sales Opers: Sheldon Speers
Dir, Spec Projs: Steve Romain
Founded: 1974
Designs, markets, manufactures & supports innovative products for use in broadcast, distribution, live event & production applications.
Branch Office(s)
62 Auriga Dr, Ottawa, ON K2E 7W6, Canada *Tel:* 613-228-0688 *Fax:* 613-228-0464
Ross Video Inc, PO Box 880, Ogdensburg, NY 13669-0880
Foreign Office(s): Ross Video Australia-Sydney, 15-21 Doody St, B4, Alexandria, NSW 2015, Australia *Tel:* (02) 8020 5844
Ross Video Australia Pty, 42-50 Stud Rd, Unit 5, Bayswater, Victoria 3153, Australia *Tel:* (03) 9721 3200
Ross Video (Singapore) Pte Ltd, 3 Ang Mo Kio St 62, Link@AMK, No 01-63, Singapore 569139, Singapore
Ross Video EMEA, Pinewood Studios, Pinewood Rd, Iver Health, Buckinghamshire SL0 0NH, United Kingdom

Rough House
550 Bryant St, San Francisco, CA 94107-1217
Tel: 415-561-4544 *Fax:* 415-543-8370
E-mail: info@roughhouse.com
Web Site: www.roughhouse.com
Key Personnel
Exec Prodr: Michael Tickman-Thoon
Prodn Coord: Karen Stillwell
Founded: 1988
HD digital production & post-production.

Round Hill Music LLC
400 Madison Ave, 18th fl, New York, NY 10017
Tel: 212-380-0080 *Fax:* 212-380-0081
E-mail: info@roundhillmusic.com
Web Site: roundhillmusic.com
Key Personnel
Chmn & CEO: Josh Gruss
VChmn: Richard Rowe
COO: Michael Lau
CFO: Jennifer Scher
Pres: Neil Gillis
Sr Dir & Head, Admin: John Sadocha
Dir, Artist Rel, Mktg & PR: Amy Birnbaum
Founded: 2014
Full service creative music company with a core focus on music publishing & rights management.
Branch Office(s)
520 Broadway, 2nd fl, Santa Monica, CA 90403, Gen Mgr: Tami Lester *Tel:* 310-428-0859
1802 Grand Ave, Nashville, TN 37212, Gen Mgr: Mark Brown *Tel:* 615-292-5100

Roundabout Entertainment Inc
217 S Lake St, Burbank, CA 91502
Tel: 818-842-9300 *Fax:* 818-842-9301
E-mail: info@roundabout.com
Web Site: www.roundabout.com
Key Personnel
CEO: Craig Clark
Founded: 1992
Comprehensive post solutions for television & film.

Rounder Records
Member of Concord Music Group Inc
1209 Pine St, Suite 100, Nashville, TN 37203
Web Site: www.rounder.com
Key Personnel
Founder: Ken Irwin; Marian Leighton-Levy; Bill Nowlin
Pres: John Virant
Founded: 1970

Ron Roy Productions/Moodtapes
4835 Pradera St, Sparks, NV 89436
E-mail: info@moodtapes.com
Web Site: www.moodtapes.com
Key Personnel
Pres: Ron Roy *E-mail:* ronroy@moodtapes.com
Founded: 1986
Series of nature/relaxation audio collectibles & videos.

RSS Distributors
7930 Old Auction Rd, Manheim, PA 17545
Tel: 717-892-6743 *Toll Free Tel:* 800-233-0175
Fax: 717-892-5981
E-mail: orders@rssd.com
Web Site: www.rssd.com
Key Personnel
Owner: Jim Miller
Distributes AV equipment for the special events industry.
Catalog(s) available
Online catalog(s) available

RSVP, see Russ Sturgeon Productions/RSVP

RTS Inc
40 Burt Dr, Suite 11, Deer Park, NY 11729
Tel: 631-242-6801 *Fax:* 631-242-6808
E-mail: rtsinc@rcn.com
Web Site: www.rtsphoto.com
Key Personnel
Mktg Dir: Mike Stango
Distributes Billingham camera bags, Rotolight LED lighting, EWA-marine underwater camera housings, Cullmann tripods, Graf/Studio ball, Hahnel battery, charger & camera remotes.
Catalog(s) available
Membership(s): NAB

RTZ Audio Visual
6725 Santa Barbara Ct, Suite 103, Elkridge, MD 21075
Tel: 443-757-0480 *Toll Free Tel:* 800-543-0582
Fax: 443-757-0487
E-mail: sales@rtzav.com
Web Site: www.rtzav.com
Key Personnel
Owner: Gary Lunsford
Founded: 1988
Catalog(s) available

Rucinski Write!Now LLC
2155 Terrebonne Dr, Mosinee, WI 54455
Tel: 715-241-7316; 715-212-6241 (cell) *Fax:* 715-355-4274
Web Site: www.rucinskiwritenow.com
Key Personnel
Owner & Prodr: Pamela Rucinski *E-mail:* pam@rucinskiwritenow.com
Copywriting, video script writing, producing, graphic/web design.

Ben Rudnick and Friends
Subsidiary of Bartlett Ave Productions Inc
PO Box 1426, Arlington, MA 02474
Tel: 781-643-5137
Web Site: www.benrudnick.com
Key Personnel
CEO: Ben Rudnick *E-mail:* ben@benrudnick.com
Founded: 2000

Creative multiple award-winning musical recordings targeted to the family audience. Live band specializing in adventurously played family music to audiences small to very large. Recordings have won every Parenting Award including seven Parents Choice Awards. Videos are available for many of the band's songs. Most recent recording "A Frog named Sam: A Musical for Children" (2016), includes playbook, soundtrack CD, showtracks CD & transcriptions.
Membership(s): BMI

RuffHouse LLC
2823 Lariat Trail, Austin, TX 78734
Tel: 512-965-2957
E-mail: info@ruffhousin.com
Web Site: www.ruffhousin.com
Key Personnel
Dir, Prodr & Writer: Charles Wiedman
E-mail: charlie@ruffhousin.com
Prodr: Katherine Willis *E-mail:* katherine@ruffhousin.com
Founded: 2003

Rule Boston Camera
1284 Soldier's Field Rd, Boston, MA 02135
Tel: 617-277-2200 *Toll Free Tel:* 800-785-3266
Fax: 617-277-6800
E-mail: answers@rule.com
Web Site: www.rule.com
Key Personnel
Pres: John Rule *Tel:* 617-277-2200 ext 101
E-mail: j.rule@rule.com
Gen Mgr: Brian Malcolm *Tel:* 617-277-2200 ext 102 *E-mail:* malcolm@rule.com
Founded: 1978
Distribute AV equipment & professional video equipment.
Online catalog(s) available
Line card(s) available, online with links
Membership(s): Audiovisual and Integrated Experience Association; MAB; Northern New England Broadcasters Association; SBE; WEVA

Rum Jungle Media
5295 Eden Rd, Mound, MN 55364
Tel: 952-472-5525
E-mail: rumjungle@rumjungle.com
Web Site: www.rumjungle.com
Key Personnel
Prodn Mgr: Lee Houghtaling *E-mail:* lee@rumjungle.com
Founded: 1991
Television production. Services include camera crews, satellite truck, live event production, HD video production, web streaming, web casts, ENG camera crews, EFP camera crews, satellite services, Ku digital transmissions, location sound, video & lighting, live broadcasts, satellite uplinks & downlinks, tape feeds & fiber.

Running Pony Productions LLC
1770 Kirby Pkwy, Suite 118, Memphis, TN 38138
Tel: 901-683-6693 *Toll Free Tel:* 877-891-7669
Fax: 901-683-3093
E-mail: info@runningpony.com
Web Site: www.runningpony.com
Key Personnel
Principal: Rod Starns *E-mail:* rstarns@runningpony.com
Membership(s): NATAS

Russ Bassett Corp
8189 Byron Rd, Whittier, CA 90606-2615
Tel: 562-945-2445 *Toll Free Tel:* 800-350-2445
Fax: 562-698-8972
E-mail: info@russbassett.com
Web Site: www.russbassett.com
Key Personnel
Pres & CEO: Mike Dressendorfer
Founded: 1960

Tape & media storage.
Catalog(s) available

Russ InVision Co/AbridgeClub.com
3219 Conquista Ave, Long Beach, CA 90808
Tel: 562-421-1836 *Toll Free Tel:* 888-421-7488
E-mail: info@abridgeclub.com
Web Site: abridgeclub.com
Key Personnel
Owner: Angela Russ-Ayon
Music, books & movement for young children.

Russell Industries Inc
40 Horton Ave, Lynbrook, NY 11563
Tel: 516-536-5000 *Toll Free Tel:* 800-645-2202
    Fax: 516-764-5747 *Toll Free Fax:* 800-645-
    2200
E-mail: sales@russellind.com
Web Site: www.russellind.com
Key Personnel
Pres: Adam Russell
Sales Mgr: Neil Eiger
Distributor of rubber belts, phono needles &
    cartridges, fuses, bumpers & grommets, heat
    shrink tubing, velcro wire ties, cable clamps,
    split loom tubing & flyback transformers.
Online catalog(s) available

Russound
One Forbes Rd, Newmarket, NH 03857
Tel: 603-659-5170 *Toll Free Tel:* 800-638-8055
    (US) *Fax:* 603-659-5388
E-mail: sales@russound.com; tech@russound.com
Web Site: www.russound.com
Key Personnel
Owner: Maureen Baldwin
CEO: Charlie Porritt
Intl Acct Mgr: Steve Dube *E-mail:* steved@
    russound.com
Founded: 1967
Membership(s): Consumer Technology Associa-
    tion™; Custom Electronic Design & Installa-
    tion Association

RWD Productions Inc, see Video Advantage

S I Video Sales Group
1318 S Carlisle St, Philadelphia, PA 19146
Tel: 267-519-2222
Web Site: www.sivideo.com; www.capclassics.
    com; takinglasvegas.com
Key Personnel
Pres: Stan Nicotera *E-mail:* stann@sivideo.com
Produce & distribute educational programs as
    well as captioned classic movies, children's &
    sports programs.
Catalog(s) available
Membership(s): Music Business Association;
    NATPE

Saah Video
12221 Parklawn Dr, Rockville, MD 20852
Tel: 301-770-6699 *Fax:* 301-770-3250
Web Site: www.saahvideo.com
Key Personnel
Owner: Ron Saah *E-mail:* ron@saahvideo.com
Catalog(s) available

Sacramento Theatrical Lighting Ltd (STL)
950 Richards Blvd, Sacramento, CA 95811
Tel: 916-447-3258 *Toll Free Tel:* 800-283-2785
    Fax: 916-447-5012
E-mail: info@stlltd.com
Web Site: www.stlltd.com
Key Personnel
Pres: John Cox
Sr Projs Mgr: Steve Odehnal *E-mail:* steveo@
    stlltd.com
Rentals: Marcus Daniel

Catalog(s) available
Membership(s): MPI; Professional Lighting &
    Sound Association; USITT

SADiE Inc
Division of Prism Media Products Inc
45 Pine St, Rockaway, NJ 07866
Tel: 973-983-9577 *Fax:* 973-983-9588
E-mail: sales@prismmpi.com
Web Site: www.sadie.com; www.prismsound.com
Key Personnel
US Sales Mgr: Janice Norton *E-mail:* janice@
    prismmpi.com
CD mastering & digital audio workstations.
Membership(s): AES; NAB

Safe Harbor Computers
530 W Oklahoma Ave, Suite 500, Milwaukee, WI
    53207
Tel: 414-615-4560 *Toll Free Tel:* 800-544-6599
    Fax: 414-615-4567
E-mail: sales@sharbor.com
Web Site: www.sharbor.com
Key Personnel
Mktg Coord: Marc Leitner *E-mail:* marc@
    sharbor.com
Founded: 1987
Computer hardware & software for video editing,
    post-production & animation. Custom Tsunami
    workstations. Authorized reseller for major
    brands including Avid, Adobe, AJA, Sony &
    more.

Sagebrush Video Productions
2304 County Rd 370, Otis, KS 67565
Tel: 785-222-3313
Web Site: www.sagebrushvideo.com
Key Personnel
Owner: Rachel Harmon *E-mail:* rachel@
    sagebrushvideo.com
Founded: 1992

**Sahara Records & Filmworks Entertainment
Co**
Division of The Edward De Miles Co
10573 W Pico Blvd, Suite 352, Los Angeles, CA
    90064-2348
Tel: 310-948-9652
E-mail: info@edmsahara.com
Key Personnel
Pres & CEO: Edward De Miles
Founded: 1984
Entertainment productions & services for film,
    television, radio & recording.

Saint Elmo Soundstage
415 E Saint Elmo, Austin, TX 78745
Tel: 512-535-5113
E-mail: contact@saintelmo.info
Web Site: saintelmo.info
Soundstage for film, video, photography & music
    production.

Salesmaker Carts
403 Roberts Ave, Louisville, KY 40214
Toll Free Tel: 800-281-2278 *Toll Free Fax:* 800-
    418-2525
Web Site: www.salesmakercarts.com
Key Personnel
CEO: Nathan McKay *E-mail:* nathanm@
    salesmakercarts.com
Manufacture carts allowing one person to trans-
    port heavy or bulky equipment by vehicle.
Catalog(s) available

Salter, Charles M, Associates Inc, see Charles
    M Salter Associates Inc

Steven Samler Music & Sound
2830 Vogay Lane, Northbrook, IL 60062

Tel: 847-400-5080
Web Site: www.stevensamler.com
Key Personnel
Owner & Pres: Steven Samler *E-mail:* steve@
    stevensamler.com
Founded: 1972
Customization of music libraries & sound design.

Samson Technologies Corp
278-B Duffy Ave, Hicksville, NY 11801
Tel: 516-870-7200 *Fax:* 516-938-1696
E-mail: info@samsontech.com
Web Site: www.samsontech.com
Key Personnel
Pres: Jack Knight
Dir, Mktg: Sean Meagher
Mktg Coord: Evan Hay
Founded: 1980
Online catalog(s) available

Samsung Electronics America
Subsidiary of Samsung Electronics Co Ltd
85 Challenger Rd, Ridgefield Park, NJ 07660
Toll Free Tel: 800-SAMSUNG (726-7864)
Web Site: www.samsung.com
Founded: 1969

The Samuels Co
Box 770874, Houston, TX 77215-0874
Tel: 281-564-1055 *Fax:* 530-420-4631
Web Site: www.thesamuelsco.com
Key Personnel
Pres: Ron Samuels *E-mail:* ron@samuels.net
Founded: 1985

Samy's Camera
431 S Fairfax Ave, Los Angeles, CA 90036
Tel: 323-938-2420 *Toll Free Tel:* 800-321-4726
    Fax: 323-937-2919
E-mail: lacamera@samys.com; info@samys.com;
    locations@samys.com
Web Site: www.samys.com
Key Personnel
Owner & Pres: Samy Kamienowicz
Ad Mktg Mgr: David Dimont
Sales Mgr: Fernando Del Vaglio
Founded: 1976
Online catalog(s) available
Catalog(s) available
Branch Office(s)
12636 Beatrice St, Los Angeles, CA 90066
    Tel: 310-450-7062 *E-mail:* info@samysdv.com
    Web Site: www.samysdv.com (returns)
Samy's Cinema Works, 148 S Victory Blvd,
    Burbank, CA 91502 *Tel:* 818-562-1960 *Web
    Site:* samyscinemaworks.com
4411 Sepulveda Blvd, Culver City, CA 90230
    Tel: 310-450-4551 *Fax:* 310-450-8590
    E-mail: infocc@samys.com
1759 E Colorado Blvd, Pasadena, CA 91106
    Tel: 626-796-3300 *Fax:* 626-432-6731
    E-mail: pasadena@samys.com
1090 Bryant St, San Francisco, CA 94103
    Tel: 415-621-8400; 415-621-7400 (rentals)
    E-mail: sfinfo@samys.com
3309-B S Bristol St, Santa Ana, CA 92704
    Tel: 714-557-9400 *E-mail:* infosa@samys.com
530 State St, Santa Barbara, CA 93101 *Tel:* 805-
    963-7269 *Fax:* 805-963-4100 *E-mail:* infosb@
    samys.com
2800 Wilshire Blvd, Santa Monica, CA 90403
    Tel: 310-264-0197
Membership(s): AICP

San Diego Stage & Lighting Supply Inc
2203 Verus St, San Diego, CA 92154
Tel: 619-299-2300 *Fax:* 619-299-0058
E-mail: info@sdstagelighting.com
Web Site: www.sdstagelighting.com
Key Personnel
Pres: Denise DeMent *E-mail:* denise@
    sdstagelighting.com

Gen Mgr: Charlene Doll *E-mail:* charlene@
sdstagelighting.com
Rentals: Daniel Doll *E-mail:* rentals@
sdstagelighting.com
Sales: Valerie Clemons *E-mail:* valerie@
sdstagelighting.com
Founded: 1974

**San Juan School District Heritage Language
Resource Center**
28 W 200 N, Blanding, UT 84511
Tel: 435-678-1230 *Fax:* 435-678-1283
Web Site: media.sjsd.org
Key Personnel
Media Center Coord: Rebecca Stoneman
E-mail: rstoneman@sjsd.org
Sell Navajo & Ute language & culture curriculum
materials.
Catalog(s) available

Sanako Inc
300 Spectrum Center Dr, Irvine, CA 92618
Toll Free Tel: 888-611-4785 *Toll Free Fax:* 888-
611-4785
E-mail: info-us@sanako.com
Web Site: www.sanako.com
Key Personnel
Busn Mgr: Ron Rehbein *E-mail:* ron@sanako.
com
Multimedia labs, web-based language labs &
web-based online learning.
Catalog(s) available
Membership(s): AECT; AES; Audiovisual and
Integrated Experience Association; NAB

Sand Box Studio
555 Minnesota St, San Francisco, CA 94107
Tel: 415-550-8732
E-mail: inquiries@sandboxstudio.com
Web Site: www.sandboxstudio.com
Key Personnel
CEO: Myles Peacock
COO: Kaly Minh-Nguyen Girot
Mng Partner: Matt Kwan; Charlie Maier; Tom
Strollo
Founded: 1992
Facility rentals for photo or video production,
consulting & post-production services.
Branch Office(s)
10016 Pioneer Blvd, No 106, Santa Fe Springs,
CA 90670 *Tel:* 562-345-5335
55 Water St, New York, NY 10041 *Tel:* 212-924-
4410
1710 SE Brooklyn St, Portland, OR 97202
Tel: 503-501-5870

S&P Global Marketing Intelligence
Division of S&P Global Inc
55 Water St, New York, NY 10041
Toll Free Tel: 877-863-1306
E-mail: questions@spcapitaliq.com
Web Site: marketingintelligence.spglobal.com
Key Personnel
CEO & Pres: Mike Chinn
Chief Commercial Offr: Will Pappas
COO: Nick Cafferillo
CFO: Hywel Thomas
Chief Legal Offr: Nancy Gardner
Head, Global Risk Servs: Martina Cheung
Head, HR: Anna Sharkey
Founded: 1969
Worldwide analyses of the media & communica-
tions industry sectors, including Broadcast, TV
Networks, Wireless & Wireline, US Multichan-
nel, Global Multichannel, TV Programming,
Filmed Entertainment & Internet Media.
Catalog(s) available
Foreign Office(s): Unit 01, Level 69, International
Commerce Ctr, One Austin Rd W, Kowloon,

Hong Kong *Tel:* 2533 3565 (Asia-Pacific headquarters)
20 Canada Sq, Canary Wharf, London E14 5LH,
United Kingdom *Tel:* (020) 7176 1234 (EMEA
headquarters)

Sandusky Lee Corp
PO Box 6, Littlestown, PA 17340
Tel: 717-359-4111 *Toll Free Tel:* 800-233-7076
Fax: 717-359-4414
E-mail: customerserv@sanduskycabinets.
com; help@sanduskycabinets.com; sales@
sanduskycabinets.com
Web Site: www.sanduskycabinets.com
Key Personnel
VP, Sales: Ron Nickle
Founded: 2003
Manufacturer & supplier of steel storage solutions
including cabinetry, AV carts & shelving.
Catalog(s) available
Online catalog(s) available
Branch Office(s)
PO Box 517, Arvin, CA 93203 *Tel:* 661-854-
5551 *Toll Free Tel:* 800-336-0674 *Fax:* 661-
854-2003
PO Box 125, Millington, TN 38053 *Tel:* 901-872-
0188 *Toll Free Tel:* 800-264-3453 *Fax:* 901-
873-1239
Sales Office(s): PO Box 1040, Sandusky, OH
44870 *Tel:* 419-626-5465 *Toll Free Tel:* 800-
336-0671 *Fax:* 419-626-3308 *E-mail:* sales@
sanduskycabinets.com

Sano Videos
Columbia Plaza, 2450 Virginia Ave NW, Suite E
322, Washington, DC 20037
Tel: 202-293-0454
Key Personnel
Owner: Louise Bedichek *E-mail:* lbedichek@
gmail.com
Founded: 1991
Cultural exchange consultants.
Membership(s): American Foreign Service Asso-
ciation

Santa Barbara Location Services
100 Miramar Ave, Suite C, Santa Barbara, CA
93108
Tel: 805-403-4620
E-mail: geoff@sblocationservices.com
Web Site: www.santabarbaralocations.com
Key Personnel
Owner: Geoff Alexander *E-mail:* geoff@
sblocationservices.com
Founded: 1983
One stop pre-production services: scouting, man-
agement, permits, crew, locations, casting, pro-
duction vans, catering & more.

Santa Clarita Studios
25135 Anza Dr, Santa Clarita, CA 91355
Tel: 661-294-2000 *Fax:* 661-294-2020
E-mail: mike@sc-studios.com
Web Site: www.santaclaritastudios.com
Full service independent studio with 10 sound
stages.

SAPSIS Rigging Inc
3883 Ridge Ave, Philadelphia, PA 19132
Tel: 215-228-0888 *Toll Free Tel:* 800-SAPSIS-1
(727-7471) *Fax:* 215-228-1786
E-mail: sales@sapsis-rigging.com
Web Site: www.sapsis-rigging.com
Key Personnel
Owner & Pres: Bill Sapsis *E-mail:* bill@sapsis-
rigging.com
Catalog(s) available
Membership(s): ABTT; ETA; League of Historic
American Theatres; Opera America; Profes-
sional Lighting & Sound Association; USITT

Sargent Welch
Division of VWR International LLC
5100 W Henrietta Rd, West Henrietta, NY 14586
Mailing Address: PO Box 92912, Rochester, NY
14692-9012
Toll Free Tel: 800-727-4368 *Toll Free Fax:* 800-
676-2540
E-mail: sargentwelchcs@vwr.com
Web Site: www.sargentwelch.com
Supplier of laboratory equipment, furniture &
supplies for science education.
Catalog(s) available
Online catalog(s) available

SAS Institute Inc
100 SAS Campus Dr, Cary, NC 27513-2414
Tel: 919-677-8000 *Toll Free Tel:* 800-727-0025
Fax: 919-677-4444
Web Site: www.sas.com
Key Personnel
Co-Founder & CEO: Jim Goodnight
Co-Founder & EVP: John Sall
EVP & CFO: Don Parker
EVP & CIO: Keith Collins
EVP & CTO: Oliver Schabenberger
EVP & Chief Cust Offr: Fritz Lehman
EVP & Chief HR Offr: Jenn Mann
EVP & Chief Legal Offr: John Boswell
EVP & Chief Mktg Offr: Randy Guard
EVP & Chief Revenue Offr: Carl Farrell
Founded: 1976
International offices throughout Africa,
Asia/Pacific, Europe, Latin America, the
Caribbean & the Middle East.
Branch Office(s)
Interstate Tower, Suite 2200, 121 W Trade St,
Charlotte, NC 28202-5399 *Tel:* 704-831-5595
Fax: 704-831-5594
Jamboree Ctr, Suite 900, 5 Park Plaza, Irvine, CA
92614 *Tel:* 949-852-8550 *Fax:* 949-852-5277
(serves CA & OR)
Esquire Plaza, 1215 "K" St, Suite 1100, Sacra-
mento, CA 95814-3945 *Tel:* 916-737-4900
Seaview Corporate Ctr, Suite 200, 10188 Telesis
Ct, San Diego, CA 92121 *Tel:* 858-526-1502
Fax: 858-526-1579 (serves San Diego county)
Post Montgomery Ctr, 34th fl, One Montgomery
St, San Francisco, CA 94104 *Tel:* 415-421-
2227 *Fax:* 415-421-1213 (bldg entrance 120
Kearny St, serves northern CA)
15300 Ventura Blvd, Suite 523, Sherman Oaks,
CA 91403-5845 *Tel:* 818-906-7638 *Fax:* 818-
907-6012
95 Glastonbury Blvd, Suite 301, Glastonbury, CT
06033-4453 *Tel:* 860-633-4119 *Fax:* 860-633-
4064
Atlanta Plaza, Suite 3200, 950 E Paces Ferry Rd
NE, Atlanta, GA 30326 *Tel:* 404-814-2560
Fax: 404-814-2566 (serves GA)
2 Prudential Plaza, Suite 1600, 180 N Stetson
St, Chicago, IL 60601 *Tel:* 312-819-6800
Fax: 312-240-0342 (serves IL, IN, IA & WI)
111 Rockville Pike, Suite 1100, Rockville, MD
20850 *Tel:* 301-838-7030
Prudential Tower, Suite 2200, 800 Boylston
St, Boston, MA 02199 *Tel:* 617-262-4201
Fax: 617-262-4253
IDeaS, a SAS company, 8500 Normandale Lake
Blvd, Suite 1200, Bloomington, MN 55437
Tel: 952-698-4200 *Fax:* 952-698-4299
US Bancorp Ctr, Suite 2800, 800 Nicollet Mall,
Minneapolis, MN 55402 *Tel:* 612-349-9023
Fax: 612-349-9349
787 Seventh Ave, 47th fl, New York, NY 10019
Tel: 212-757-3826 *Fax:* 212-757-4086
1550 Liberty Ridge Dr, Suite 110, Chesterbrook,
PA 19087 *Tel:* 610-640-0940 *Fax:* 610-640-
1488
One PPG Place, Suite 2950, Pittsburgh, PA 15222
Tel: 412-227-6446 *Fax:* 412-227-6596
Millennium I, 15455 N Dallas Pkwy, Suite
1300, Addison, TX 75001 *Tel:* 214-977-3916
Fax: 214-977-3921

11920 Wilson Parke Ave, Austin, TX 78726
Tel: 512-258-5171 *Fax:* 512-258-3906 (serves
TX, LA, NM & OK)
1330 Post Oak Blvd, Post Oak Place, Suite 2900,
Houston, TX 77056 *Tel:* 713-325-9800
1530 Wilson Blvd, Suite 800-900, Arlington, VA
22209 *Tel:* 571-227-7000 *Fax:* 571-227-7010
517 –Tenth Ave SW, Suite 850, Calgary, AB T2R
0A8, Canada *Tel:* 403-265-5177 *Fax:* 403-265-
5410
666 Burrard St, Suite 500, Vancouver, BC V6C
3P6, Canada *Tel:* 604-639-3177 *Fax:* 604-682-
1347
Ottawa Constitution Sq, 360 Albert St, Suite
1600, Ottawa, ON K1R 7X7, Canada *Tel:* 613-
231-8503 *Fax:* 613-231-8526
SAS Institute (Canada) Inc, 280 King St E, Suite
500, Toronto, ON M5A 1K7, Canada *Tel:* 416-
363-4424 *Fax:* 416-363-5399 (CN headquarters)
2001 McGill College Ave, Suite 1800, Montreal, QC H3A 1G1, Canada *Tel:* 514-395-8922
Fax: 514-395-8962
70, rue Saint-Pierre, Quebec, QC G1K 3Z9,
Canada *Tel:* 418-380-8791 *Fax:* 418-694-0643

Satellite Center
2535 Williams Blvd, Kenner, LA 70062
Tel: 504-466-3474 *Toll Free Tel:* 800-256-4010
E-mail: info@satctr.com
Web Site: satctr.com
Key Personnel
Pres: Dan Teachworth
Video Prodn: Tom Fitzgerald
Founded: 1984
Specialize in satellite reception systems for TV &
radio stations.

Satellite Digital Teleproductions (SDTV)
4004 La Salle St, San Diego, CA 92110-5124
Tel: 619-293-7777 *Toll Free Tel:* 800-SKY-PROD
(759-7763 US) *Fax:* 619-223-3626
E-mail: info@sdtv.com
Web Site: www.sdtv.com
Key Personnel
Pres: Mark Yancey

Satellite Media Production
8379 Inspiration Ave, Walkersville, MD 21793
Tel: 301-845-2737 *Toll Free Tel:* 800-747-0856
Web Site: www.satellitemediaproduction.com;
www.oldietv.com
Key Personnel
Owner: Ellen Berney
Owner/Video Prodr: Fred Berney
E-mail: fsberney@verizon.net
Founded: 1956
Video post-production. Reel-to-reel decks, DAT
recorders, 16 inch turntable for transcription
transfers, mini disc, CD, location recording,
microphones & mixers, film, video & slide
transfer to DVD, DVD duplicating, reel-to-reel
tapes & audiocassette transfers to CD, digital
recording.

Satellite Technology Systems Inc
4702 State Rte 176, Unit F, Crystal Lake, IL
60014
Tel: 815-482-0224 *Toll Free Tel:* 800-838-1472
Fax: 815-568-8478
E-mail: sts@mc.net
Web Site: www.satellitetechsys.com
Key Personnel
Owner: Charles Spoto *Tel:* 815-482-0224 (cell)
Founded: 1988
Satellite media tours, video production, global
video conferencing, video news releases, uplink
trucks, event photos.

Saturn Studios
Subsidiary of Rock Dog Records

PO Box 3687, Hollywood, CA 90078-3687
Tel: 323-871-4134
Web Site: rollingplanet.com
Key Personnel
CEO: Patt Connolly *E-mail:* mrpatt2@yahoo.com
VP & Prodn Mgr: Gerald North Cannizzaro
E-mail: gerry.cannizzaro@att.net
Founded: 1986
Audio & video recording, editing & mastering,
CD-R & DVD-R recording & mastering equip-
ment.
Online catalog(s) available
Branch Office(s)
Rock Dog Records/Saturn Studios East Coast Div,
PO Box 884, Syosset, NY 11791-0884, Con-
tact: Maria Cuccia *Tel:* 631-544-9596
Membership(s): Network of Alternatives for Pub-
lishers, Retailers & Artists Inc

Alwin Sauers Audio Productions (ASAP)
10 Wisteria Way, Ventura, CA 93004-1435
Tel: 206-484-6144
E-mail: alwinaudio@yahoo.com
Key Personnel
Owner & Engr: Alwin Sauers

Savage Universal Corp
2050 S Stearman Dr, Chandler, AZ 85286
Tel: 480-632-1320 *Toll Free Tel:* 800-624-8891
Fax: 480-632-1322
E-mail: info486@savagepaper.com
Web Site: savageuniversal.com
Key Personnel
COO: Rich Reiser
Pres: Sylvester Hank
VP, Sales: Rich Memoli
Founded: 1937
Catalog(s) available
Online catalog(s) available
Membership(s): The Imaging Alliance

Savant Systems LLC
45 Perseverance Way, Hyannis, MA 02601
Tel: 508-683-2500 *Fax:* 508-683-2600
Web Site: www.savant.com
Manufacture residential & commercial lighting
control & automation systems.

Save the Children Federation Inc
501 Kings Hwy E, Suite 400, Fairfield, CT 06825
Tel: 203-221-4000 *Toll Free Tel:* 800-728-3843;
800-999-2445
E-mail: supportercare@savechildren.org;
twebster@savechildren.org
Web Site: www.savethechildren.org
Catalog(s) available
Branch Office(s)
899 N Capitol St, Suite 900, Washington, DC
20002 *Tel:* 202-794-1500

SC Media Canada
2100 Onesime-Gagnon, Lachine, QC H8T 3M8,
Canada
Tel: 514-780-0808 *Toll Free Tel:* 888-595-3966
Fax: 514-780-1604 *Toll Free Fax:* 800-790-
2000
E-mail: information@scmediacanada.com
Web Site: www.scmediacanada.com
Key Personnel
Natl Sales Mgr: Rahim Nathu
Founded: 1983
Distributor of professional audio, lighting &
video products.

Scala Inc
7 Great Valley Pkwy, Suite 300, Malvern, PA
19355
Tel: 610-363-3350 *Toll Free Tel:* 888-SCALA-96
(722-5296) *Fax:* 610-363-4010
E-mail: team@scala.com
Web Site: scala.com

Key Personnel
Chmn & CEO: Chris Riegel
COO: Joe Sullivan
VP, Global Mktg: Harry Horn
Founded: 1987
Manufacture multimedia software.
Branch Office(s)
5850 Canoga Ave, 4th fl, Woodland Hills, CA
91367
Foreign Office(s): Scala Digital Signage Services
India Pvt Ltd, 16 Museum Rd, Suite G02,
Phoenix Towers, Bangalore, Karnataka 560
001, India
Scala KK, Gotanda Alpha Bldg, 10th fl, 2-29-
9 Nishi-Gotanda, Shinagawa-ku, Tokyo 141-
0031, Japan *Tel:* (03) 6417 9645 *Fax:* (03)
6417 9646
Bergerweg 170, 6135 KD Sittard, Netherlands
Tel: (046) 8080 151 *Fax:* (046) 8080 152 *Web
Site:* scala.nl
Scala Nordic AS, Vollsveien 13C, 1366 Lysaker,
Norway *Tel:* 23 13 30 90 *Web Site:* scala.com/
no
Membership(s): Audiovisual and Integrated Expe-
rience Association; NSCA

Sceno Plus
5423 ave de Lorimier, Montreal, QC H2H 2C3,
Canada
Tel: 514-529-4364 *Fax:* 514-529-9164
E-mail: mailinfo@scenoplus.com
Web Site: www.sceno-plus.com
Key Personnel
COO: Lorraine Berthiaume
Pres: Patrick Berge
Founded: 1985
Performing arts & entertainment venue designer.
Integration of specialized equipments & other
scenic technology such as lighting & rigging
design.
Membership(s): Canadian Institute for Theatre
Technology; Professional Lighting & Sound
Association; USITT

Scheimpflug Digital
546 W 48 St, New York, NY 10036
Tel: 212-244-8300 *Fax:* 212-244-8769
Web Site: www.scheimpflug.com
Founded: 2004
Equipment rentals, digital services & trucks for
independent filmmakers, commercials & still
photographers.

Schiller's Audio-Visual
9240 Manchester Rd, St Louis, MO 63144-2636
Tel: 314-968-3650 *Toll Free Tel:* 800-366-7244
Fax: 314-968-1184
E-mail: sales@schillers.com; av@schillers.com
Web Site: www.schillers.com
Key Personnel
Presentation Sales Mgr: David Wyne *Tel:* 314-
968-3650 ext 110 *E-mail:* dwyne@schillers.
com
Membership(s): Audiovisual and Integrated Expe-
rience Association; The Imaging Alliance

Schlessinger Media
Division of Library Video Co
PO Box 680, Conshohocken, PA 19428
Tel: 610-645-4000 *Toll Free Tel:* 800-843-3620
Fax: 610-645-4040
E-mail: cs@schlessingermedia.com
Web Site: www.libraryvideocompany.com
Key Personnel
Founder & CEO: Andrew Schlessinger
Founded: 1985
Online catalog(s) available
Membership(s): ALA; Entertainment Merchants
Association

Schneider Optics Inc
Subsidiary of Schneider-Kreuznach
285 Oser Ave, Hauppauge, NY 11788

Tel: 631-761-5000 *Toll Free Tel:* 800-645-7239
Fax: 631-761-5090
E-mail: info@schneideroptics.com
Web Site: www.schneideroptics.com
Key Personnel
CEO: Dwight Lindsey
Sales Admin: Henry Greese *E-mail:* hgreese@
schneideroptics.com
Founded: 1972
Manufacturer of high quality film lenses, video
lenses & filters.
Catalog(s) available, price list
Branch Office(s)
7701 Haskill Ave, Van Nuys, CA 91406-1906
Tel: 818-766-3715 *Toll Free Tel:* 800-228-1254
Fax: 818-505-9865
Membership(s): NAB; SMPTE®

Schoeps, see Posthorn Recordings

Scholastic Canada Ltd
Subsidiary of Scholastic Inc
175 Hillmount Rd, Markham, ON L6C 1Z7,
Canada
Tel: 905-887-7323 *Toll Free Tel:* 800-268-3860
Fax: 905-887-1131 *Toll Free Fax:* 800-387-
4944
E-mail: custserv@scholastic.ca
Web Site: www.scholastic.ca
Founded: 1957
Catalog(s) available

Scholastic Library Publishing
Division of Scholastic Inc
90 Old Sherman Tpke, Danbury, CT 06816
Toll Free Tel: 800-621-1115 (cust serv)
Toll Free Fax: 866-783-4361
Web Site: scholasticlibrary.digital.scholastic.com
Key Personnel
Pres, Scholastic Classroom & Community Group:
Greg Worrell
VP, Digital Initiatives: Evan St Lifer
Publishers of children's nonfiction & reference
materials in print & online.
Catalog(s) available
Online catalog(s) available

Scholastic Media
Division of Scholastic Inc
557 Broadway, New York, NY 10012
Toll Free Tel: 800-724-6527
Web Site: www.scholastic.com/aboutscholastic/
librarypublishing.htm
Founded: 1995
Catalog(s) available

School Media Associates LLC
5815 Live Oak Pkwy, Suite 2-B, Norcross, GA
30093-1700
Tel: 770-441-0600 *Toll Free Tel:* 800-451-5226
(orders) *Fax:* 770-441-8529
E-mail: info@smavideo.net; orders@smavideo.net
Web Site: www.smavideo.net
Key Personnel
Pres: Randy Kenworthy *E-mail:* rkenworthy@
smavideo.net
Distributor of multimedia educational program-
ming.
Catalog(s) available

School Specialty Inc
W6316 Design Dr, Greenville, WI 54942
Mailing Address: PO Box 1579, Appleton, WI
54912-1579
Tel: 419-589-1425 *Toll Free Tel:* 888-388-3224
Fax: 419-589-1600 *Toll Free Fax:* 888-388-
6344
E-mail: internationalorders@schoolspecialty.com
Web Site: www.schoolspecialty.com
Distributor of educational AV needs.

Catalog(s) available
Membership(s): Audiovisual and Integrated Experience Association; Education Market Association

Schroder Music Co
PO Box 2067, Berkeley, CA 94702-0067
Tel: 510-843-0533 *Fax:* 510-834-5201
Web Site: www.sisterschoice.com
Key Personnel
Mgr: Ruth Pohlman
Contact: Nancy Schimmel *E-mail:* nancy@
sisterschoice.com
Permission to use songs by Maluina Reynolds, as
well as sell recorded music & songbooks.
Online catalog(s) available
Membership(s): ASCAP

M Schwartz & Gettinger Feather Inc
45 Hoffman Ave, Hauppauge, NY 11788
Tel: 631-234-7722 *Fax:* 631-234-7817
E-mail: info@msgfeather.com
Web Site: www.msgfeather.com
Key Personnel
Co-Owner: Daniel Gettinger; Michael Schwartz
Founded: 1910
Wholesale feathers, plumes, fans & boas.
Catalog(s) available, free

SCI Television & Creative Media LLC
160 E Grand Ave, 5th fl, Chicago, IL 60611
Tel: 312-643-2080
E-mail: info@scitvproductions.com
Web Site: www.scitvproductions.com
Key Personnel
Exec Prodr & Dir: Mark Traverso *Tel:* 312-399-
0131 *E-mail:* markt@scitvproductions.com
Prodn Coord: Valerie Kennedy
Founded: 1988
Full-service media production services, including
remote ENG crews & live production studio.
Membership(s): NATAS; NATPE

Science First/STARLAB™
86475 Gene Lasserre Blvd, Yulee, FL 32097
Tel: 904-225-5558 *Toll Free Tel:* 800-875-3214
Fax: 904-225-2228
E-mail: starlab@starlab.com; info@starlab.com
Web Site: starlab.com
Founded: 2008
Portable planetariums.
Catalog(s) available
Membership(s): Association of Science-
Technology Centers; IPS; MAPS; National
Science Teachers Association

Science Museum of Minnesota
120 W Kellogg Blvd, St Paul, MN 55102
Tel: 651-221-9444 *Toll Free Tel:* 800-221-9444
Fax: 651-221-4533
E-mail: info@smm.org; science@smm.org
Web Site: www.smm.org
Key Personnel
Pres & CEO: Alison Brown
VP, HR: Juliette Francis
Founded: 1907
Producers & distributors of educational programs.

Science Television Co, see SciMedTv

Scientifics Direct Inc
532 Main St, Tonawanda, NY 14150
Toll Free Tel: 800-728-6999; 800-818-4955
Toll Free Fax: 800-828-3299
E-mail: support@scientificsdirect.com
Web Site: www.scientificsonline.com
Key Personnel
Dir: Tim Burns *E-mail:* tim.burns@
scientificsdirect.com
Catalog(s) available
Online catalog(s) available

SciMedTv
Formerly Science Television Co
460 W 24 St, Unit 3A, New York, NY 10011
Tel: 917-593-2537
E-mail: SciMedTV@gmail.com
Web Site: www.scimedtv.com
Key Personnel
Pres: Gary Welz *E-mail:* gary.welz@scimed.tv
Produce & distribute educational science videos.
Online catalog(s) available

Score Productions Inc
219 E 49 St, New York, NY 10017
Tel: 212-751-2510 *Fax:* 212-754-6305
E-mail: score@scoreproductions.com
Key Personnel
Pres: Robert Israel
Founded: 1963
Musical scoring company.

Scott Resources Inc
Division of American Educational Products LLC
401 Hickory St, Fort Collins, CO 80524-1125
Mailing Address: PO Box 2121, Fort Collins, CO
80522-2121
Tel: 970-484-7445 *Toll Free Tel:* 800-289-9299
Fax: 970-484-1198
E-mail: custserv@amep.com
Web Site: amep.com
Key Personnel
Pres: Michael Warring
Natl Sales & Mktg Mgr: Candace Coffman
Sales Mgr: Katie Dugan
Producers of educational mathematics programs.
Catalog(s) available

Ron Scott
2020 Colquitt St, Houston, TX 77098
E-mail: ron@ronscott.com
Web Site: www.ronscott.com
Photography & digital images for sale or license
for stock use.

Screen Door Entertainment Inc
5709 Fairview Place, Agoura Hills, CA 91301
Mailing Address: PO Box 1002, Agoura Hills,
CA 91376
Key Personnel
Pres & Exec Prodr: Joel Rizor
Founded: 2001
TV & video production company. Full service
production & post-production with all broad-
cast & non-broadcast video production.

The Screen Works®
2226 W Walnut St, Chicago, IL 60612
Tel: 312-243-8265 *Toll Free Tel:* 800-294-8111
Fax: 312-243-8290
E-mail: screens@thescreenworks.com
Web Site: www.thescreenworks.com
Key Personnel
Sales Mgr: David Hull *E-mail:* dhull@
thescreenworks.com
Founded: 1959
Manufactures, sells & rents E-Z Fold® portable
projection screens in single-tube & 6-inch truss
frames in 16:9, 16:10 & wide screen formats
in front or rear projection. Manufacture & rent
lace & grommet surfaces up to 120 feet wide.
The Screen Works® specializes in custom,
made-to-order screens. Available accessories
include pipe & drape, trim kits, tech surrounds
& equipment towers. Service includes screen
surface cleaning & frame repair to our screens
& competitive models.
Online catalog(s) available
Membership(s): Audiovisual and Integrated Experience Association

Scripps Networks
Division of Scripps Networks Interactive

9721 Sherrill Blvd, Knoxville, TN 37932
Tel: 865-694-2700
Web Site: www.scrippsnetworks.com
Key Personnel
Pub Aff Mgr: Stephanie Halouma
   E-mail: publicaffairs@scrippsnetwork.com
Television production company.

Roger Scruggs Films
PO Box 321054, Cocoa Beach, FL 32932-1054
Tel: 321-783-6545 (off); 321-795-6545 (cell)
Web Site: www.tvphotog.com
Key Personnel
Owner: Roger Scruggs *E-mail:* scruggs@
   tvphotog.com
Videography, photography & cinematography services.
Belongs to both the Brevard Aviation Association & the Experimental Aircrafts Association.
Brochure(s) available
Online catalog(s) available

SDI Technologies Inc
1299 Main St, Rahway, NJ 07065-5024
Tel: 732-574-9000 *Toll Free Tel:* 800-333-3092;
   800-888-4491 (cust serv) *Fax:* 732-382-2954
E-mail: customerservice@sditech.com
Web Site: www.sditechnologies.com; www.
   ihomeaudio.com
Key Personnel
Mgr, Mktg: Nisan Davydov
Founded: 1956
Designs, manufactures & markets a broad range of consumer electronics. Key product lines include alarm clocks, clock radios, portable speakers, bluetooth vanity mirrors, sleep therapy devices & bluetooth water bottles. SDI markets these products under the iHome & Timex brands .

Sea Studios Foundation
PO Box 267, Carmel Valley, CA 93924
E-mail: info@seastudios.org; jefe@seastudios.org
Web Site: www.seastudios.org
Key Personnel
Exec Prodr: Mark Shelley
Developers of educational television programs.

SeaChange International Inc
50 Nagog Park, Acton, MA 01720
Tel: 978-897-0100 *Fax:* 978-897-0132
E-mail: globalsalesoperations@schange.com
Web Site: www.schange.com
Key Personnel
CEO & Dir: Ed Terino
CFO: Peter Faubert
COO: Jon Rider
SVP, Sales & Mktg: Paul Crann
Digital multimedia distributing & manufacturing.
Catalog(s) available
Branch Office(s)
1075 Virginia Dr, Suite 300, Fort Washington, PA 19034
Membership(s): Interactive Multimedia Association

Seagate Technology LLC
10200 S De Anza Blvd, Cupertino, CA 95014
Toll Free Tel: 800-SEAGATE (732-4283)
Web Site: www.seagate.com
Key Personnel
CEO: Dr Dave Mosley
CIO: Ravi Naik
SVP & CTO: Dr Mark Re
SVP, Chief Legal Offr & Corp Secy: Kate Schuelke
EVP, Worldwide Sales & Mktg: James J Murphy
SVP, Global Sales & Sales Opers: Mr B S Teh
Founded: 1979
Invents, designs & delivers storage solutions for the world to access & share digital content.
Online catalog(s) available

Sear Sound
353 W 48 St, 6th fl, New York, NY 10036
Tel: 212-582-5380 *Fax:* 212-581-2731
E-mail: waltersear@aol.com
Web Site: www.searsound.com
Key Personnel
Mgr: Roberta Findlay
Chief Engr: Chris Allen *E-mail:* chris@
   searsound.com
Engr: Ted Tuthill
Founded: 1963
Recording studios - digital & analog. Garritan sound library.
Online catalog(s) available
Membership(s): AES

2nd Cine Inc
637 Frazier Ave, Suite 2, Elgin, IL 60123
Tel: 773-455-5808
E-mail: info@2ndcine.com
Web Site: www.2ndcine.com
Key Personnel
Owner: Thomas S Ciciura
Chicago's filmmaking microbrewery. Specialize in providing crew, camera, dollies, lighting & production services for video productions for movies, TV or web.

Second Line Stages
800 Richard St, New Orleans, LA 70130
Tel: 504-528-3050
E-mail: info@secondlinestages.com
Web Site: secondlinestages.com
Founded: 2009
Rental of soundstages where operations are designed to enable cleaner, smarter, more responsible physical production practices. Built to comply with the US Green Building Council's LEED Silver Certification standard.

See Factor Industry Inc
37-11 30 St, Long Island City, NY 11101
Tel: 718-784-4200 *Fax:* 718-784-0617
Web Site: www.seefactor.com
Key Personnel
Founder: Bob See *E-mail:* bobsee@seefactor.com
Pres & CEO: Annmarie See *E-mail:* asee@
   seefactor.com
EVP & Mng Partner: Mark Friedman
   E-mail: mfriedman@seefactor.com
Lighting, sound & production company.

See Production Services
3330 Cobb Pkwy, Suite 17-327, Acworth, GA 30101
Tel: 404-474-4416
E-mail: info@seeproductionservices.com
Web Site: seeproductionservices.com
Key Personnel
Owner: Eason Duncan *E-mail:* eason@
   seeproductionservices.com
Offers full service teleprompting, video assist & camera equipment rental.

Sekonic
Division of MAC Group
75 Virginia Rd, North White Plains, NY 10603
Tel: 914-347-3300 *Fax:* 914-347-3309
E-mail: info@macgroupus.com
Web Site: www.macgroupus.com; www.sekonic.com
Key Personnel
Pres: Mr Jan Lederman *E-mail:* janl@
   macgroupus.com
Professional exposure, color, light measuring instruments.
Online catalog(s) available

Selco Products Co
Division of Sel Sales Inc
8780 Technology Way, Reno, NV 89521-5908

Tel: 775-674-5100 *Toll Free Tel:* 800-257-3526
   Fax: 775-674-5111
E-mail: sales@selcoproducts.com
Web Site: www.selcoproducts.com
Key Personnel
CEO: Timothy Wilkinson
Pres & COO: James Reed
Founded: 1958
Catalog(s) available

Selden Associates
150 S Mountain Ave, Montclair, NJ 07042
Tel: 973-493-9039 (cell); 650-327-1972 (CA location)
Key Personnel
CEO: Charles J Selden *E-mail:* charles.selden@
   mac.com
Freelance writing & scripting services.

Semiconductor Services
2269 Chestnut St, No 735, San Francisco, CA 94123
Tel: 650-369-7890 *Fax:* 415-346-8099
E-mail: moreinfo@semiconductorservices.com
Founded: 1981
Training resource company.
Online catalog(s) available

Semtech
Division of Semtech Corp
4281 Harvester Rd, Burlington, ON L7L 5M4, Canada
Tel: 905-632-2996 *Fax:* 905-632-2055
Web Site: www.semtech.com
Founded: 1960
Design analog, optical & mixed signal semiconductors for use with video broadcasts, data communications & consumer connecting products.
Catalog(s) available
Branch Office(s)
Snowbush IP, 70 University Ave, Suite 1100, Toronto, ON M5J 2M4, Canada *Tel:* 416-925-5643 *E-mail:* sales@snowbush.com *Web Site:* www.snowbush.com
Foreign Office(s): Semtech Advanced Systems India Pte Ltd, Module No A, 6th fl, Fortune Towers, Chandrasek Harpur, Bhubaneswar, Odisha 751 023, India *Tel:* (0674) 398 1400 *Fax:* (0674) 398 1443
Semtech Switzerland GmbH, A-Place Gotanda 5F, 2-27-3 Nishigotanda, Shinagawa-ku, Tokyo 141-0031, Japan *Tel:* (03) 5719-7560 *Fax:* (03) 5179-7561
2 West Point Ct, Great Park Rd, Bradley Stoke, Bristol BS32 4PY, United Kingdom *Tel:* (01454) 462200 *Fax:* (01454) 462201
Shipping Address: 3150 Harvester Rd, Burlington, ON L7L 5M4, Canada
Membership(s): NAB; SMPTE®

Sencore Inc
3200 W Sencore Dr, Sioux Falls, SD 57107
Tel: 605-978-4600 *Fax:* 605-335-6379
Web Site: www.sencore.com
Key Personnel
Pres: Jeff Zhu
VP, Engg: Jeff Briden
VP, North American Sales: David Jockheck
VP, Opers: Dana Nachreiner
Founded: 1951
Designers & manufacturers of innovative electronic test equipment.
Online catalog(s) available
Membership(s): ATSC; Custom Electronic Design & Installation Association; NAB; NESDA; SCTE

The Mack Sennett Studios
1215 Bates Ave, Los Angeles, CA 90029

Tel: 323-660-8466
E-mail: info@macksennettstudios.net
Web Site: www.macksennettstudios.net
Key Personnel
Pres & Prodr: Jesse Rogg *E-mail:* jesse@
  macksennettstudios.net
Dir, Busn Devt: Ryan Harvie
Creative Dir: Brandon Fuller
Dir, Opers: Erin Gray
Admin Asst: Mariah Flores
Founded: 1916

Sennheiser (Canada) Inc
Division of Sennheiser electronic GmbH & Co
  KG
221 Labrosse Ave, Pointe-Claire, QC H9R 1A3,
  Canada
Tel: 514-426-3014 (serv/repair); 952-649-3618
  (orders)
E-mail: sennheiser.en.cs@digitalriver.com
Web Site: en-ca.sennheiser.com
Key Personnel
Mktg Dir: Roseline Boire
Founded: 1945

Sennheiser Electronic Corp
Division of Sennheiser electronic GmbH & Co
  KG
 One Enterprise Dr, Old Lyme, CT 06371
Tel: 860-434-9190 *Toll Free Tel:* 877-
  SENNHEISER (736-6434)
Web Site: en-us.sennheiser.com
Founded: 1945
Distribute microphones, headphones, recording
  media, loudspeakers, conferencing systems, as-
  sisted listening devices, audio-tour equipment
  & software.
Catalog(s) available

Sensaphone
901 Tryens Rd, Aston, PA 19014
Tel: 610-558-2700 *Toll Free Tel:* 877-373-2700
  Fax: 610-558-0222
E-mail: sales@sensaphone.com
Web Site: www.sensaphone.com
Catalog(s) available

Sensormatic®
Division of Johnson Controls
6600 Congress Ave, Boca Raton, FL 33487
Tel: 561-912-6000
E-mail: tycocommunications@tyco.com
Web Site: www.tyco.com; www.sensormatic.com
Key Personnel
Off Mgr: Cheryl Madison
Design, manufacture & service electronic article
  surveillance systems.
Catalog(s) available
Online catalog(s) available
Membership(s): American Society for Industrial
  Security

Sensory Technologies LLC
Division of Markey's Audio Visual
6951 Corporate Circle, Indianapolis, IN 46278
Tel: 317-347-5252 *Toll Free Tel:* 800-488-4336
  (help desk)
E-mail: csc@sensorytechnologies.com
Web Site: sensorytechnologies.com
Key Personnel
Mng Principal: Anne Sellers *E-mail:* aesellers@
  sensorytechnologies.com
Principal: Kevin Markey *E-mail:* kmarkey@
  sensorytechnologies.com; Derek Paquin
  E-mail: dpaquin@sensorytechnologies.
  com; Andrew Sellers *E-mail:* asellers@
  sensorytechnologies.com
Founded: 2006
AV & videoconference solutions provider. Design,
  sales, installation & support of AV systems.
Online catalog(s) available

Branch Office(s)
301 W Jefferson Blvd, Suite 108, Ft Wayne, IN
  46802 *Tel:* 260-483-3023 *Fax:* 260-484-4679
201 Hansen Ct, Suite 109, Wood Dale, IL 60191
  Tel: 847-258-4165
6800 Old Collamer Rd, Suite 5, East Syracuse,
  NY 13057 *Tel:* 315-414-1414
150 Metro Park, Rochester, NY 14623 *Toll Free*
  Tel: 800-724-2480
100 Colvin Woods Pkwy, Suite 100, Tonawanda,
  NY 14150 *Tel:* 716-362-6300
5335 Springboro Pike, Suite E, Dayton, OH
  45439 *Tel:* 937-746-4670 *Fax:* 317-347-5265
Membership(s): Audiovisual and Integrated Experience Association; NSCA

Sentai Filmworks LLC
5373 W Alabama St, Suite 640, Houston, TX
  77056
Tel: 713-490-7638 *Fax:* 713-647-0535
E-mail: info@sentaifilmworks.com
Web Site: www.sentaifilmworks.com
Anime & genre entertainment across traditional
  & digital media platforms. Offers industry-
  leading expertise in all facets of production,
  development, localization, licensing, marketing
  & distribution.

Sentry Industries Inc
One Bridge St, Hillburn, NY 10931-0885
Mailing Address: PO Box 885, Hillburn, NY
  10931-0885
Tel: 845-753-2910 *Fax:* 845-753-2920
E-mail: techsupport@sentryindustries.com
Web Site: www.sentryindustries.com
Key Personnel
Owner: Daniel Rosen
Sales Mgr: James Staropoli *E-mail:* jstaropoli@
  sentryindustries.com
Founded: 1963
Manufacturer & distributor of audio equipment.
Catalog(s) available

Serendipity Recordings
511 Slab City Rd, Lincolnville, ME 04849
Tel: 207-763-3677
Key Personnel
Owner: Michael Paul Lund *E-mail:* mplund@
  tidewater.net
Founded: 1972
Nostalgia of all kinds in CD, record & DVD for-
  mats. Voice-overs for radio/TV. Service radio &
  television stations as well as general public.
Catalog(s) available

Service Quality Institute
9201 E Bloomington Fwy, Minneapolis, MN
  55420-3437
Tel: 952-884-3311 *Toll Free Tel:* 800-548-0538
  Fax: 952-884-8901
E-mail: quality@servicequality.com
Web Site: www.customer-service.com
Key Personnel
Pres: John Tschohl
Founded: 1972
Design & produce customer service video training
  programs.
Catalog(s) available
Membership(s): NSA

Servoreeler Systems
Unit of Xedit Corp
218-31 97 Ave, Queens Village, NY 11429
Tel: 718-464-9400 *Toll Free Tel:* 800-431-8900
  Fax: 718-464-9435
E-mail: srsystems@servoreelers.com
Web Site: www.servoreelers.com
Key Personnel
Pres: Claude M Karczmer
Dir, Sales: Eileen Karczmer
Founded: 1972

Manufacture & distribute professional microphone
  retraction systems.
Online catalog(s) available

SES SA
4 Research Way, Princeton, NJ 08540-6684
Tel: 609-987-4000
E-mail: info@ses.com
Web Site: www.ses.com
Key Personnel
Pres & CEO: Karim Michel Sabbagh
CFO: Padraig McCarthy
CTO: Martin Halliwell
Chief Commercial Offr: Ferdinand Kayser
Chief Devt Offr: Christophe De Hauwer
VP, Corp Communs: Markus Payer
  E-mail: markus.payer@ses.com
Founded: 1985
The world-leading satellite operator & the first to
  deliver a differentiated & scaleable GEO-MEO
  offering worldwide, with more than 50 satel-
  lites in Geostationary Earth Orbit (GEO) & 12
  in Medium Earth Orbit (MEO). SES focuses
  on value-added, end-to-end solutions in 4 key
  market verticals (Video, Enterprise, Mobility
  & Government). It provides satellite communications services to broadcasters, content &
  internet service providers, mobile & fixed network operators, governments & institutions &
  business worldwide.
Branch Office(s)
1129 20 St NW, Suite 1000, Washington, DC
  20036 *Tel:* 202-478-7100
SES Government Solutions, 11790 Sunrise Valley
  Dr, Suite 300, Reston, VA 20191 *Tel:* 703-610-
  1000
Foreign Office(s): Chateau de Betzdorf, Betzdorf
  6815, Luxembourg *Tel:* 710-725-1 (headquarters)
Membership(s): NAB; World Teleport Association

Sescom Inc
Division of Tower Product Inc
PO Box 720, Mount Marion, NY 12456
Tel: 845-246-1915 *Fax:* 845-246-0626
E-mail: info@sescom.com
Web Site: www.sescom.com
Key Personnel
Dir: Jon Fitzer *E-mail:* jon@sescom.com
Founded: 1975
Manufacturer of high quality audio products &
  enclosures.

The Set Shop
Subsidiary of Lidderdale Enterprises Inc
428 Colyton St, Los Angeles, CA 90013
Tel: 213-680-1668 *Fax:* 213-680-4269
Key Personnel
Owner: William Lidderdale *Tel:* 310-486-1741
  (cell) *E-mail:* wlidderdale@gmail.com
Founded: 1997
Entertainment construction (sets & props), art de-
  partment, installation, filming location/studio.

Set To Go Studios
86 Lackawana Ave, Suite 235, Woodland Park,
  NJ 07424
Tel: 973-638-1646
Web Site: www.settogostudio.com
Key Personnel
Pres: Dale Kolarek *E-mail:* dale@settogostudio.
  com
Professional shooting stage with 30+ beautifully
  furnished, ready-to-shoot sets for video, film &
  still photography.

Setcom Corp™
3019 Alvin De Vane Blvd, Suite 560, Austin, TX
  78741
Tel: 650-965-8020 *Fax:* 650-965-1193
E-mail: info@setcomcorp.com; sales@
  setcomcorp.com
Web Site: www.setcomcorp.com

Founded: 1970
Manufacturer of headphones, headsets & radio equipment.
Catalog(s) available

7seas Productions
970 Ninth St, Boulder, CO 80302
Tel: 303-818-5771
E-mail: mermaid7seas@gmail.com
Web Site: moondancefilmfestival.com/7seas-productions
Key Personnel
Owner: Elizabeth English
Founded: 1999
Script & film consulting.

The Sextant Group Inc
11301 W Olympic Blvd, Suite 348, Los Angeles, CA 90064
Tel: 213-402-0991
Web Site: www.thesextantgroup.com
Key Personnel
Contact: Norman Russell *E-mail:* nrussell@thesextantgroup.com
Founded: 1978
Lighting consultation & design, fixtures & control equipment.

SF Global Sourcing
3450 Sacramento St, Suite 353, San Francisco, CA 94118
Tel: 415-288-9400 *Toll Free Tel:* 800-545-5865
Web Site: www.sfglobalsourcing.com
Key Personnel
CEO: Michael Brandon *E-mail:* michael@sfglobalsourcing.com
Sr Acct Mgr: Tracey Harbo *E-mail:* tracey@sfglobalsourcing.com
Founded: 1990
Product sourcing experts committed to creating the greatest perceived value with the lowest cost of goods. Specialize in large volume DVD, CD & Blu-ray replication, media replication printing, packaging & fulfillment as well as the ability to source all ancillary products to round out an offer. Global manufacturing capabilities include the US, China & Europe.
Foreign Office(s): 668 Huai An Rd, Suite 5E, Shanghai 200041, China
Membership(s): Electronic Retailing Association; Northern California Production Community

SGW Teleprompter Solutions Inc
844 Eighth Ave, La Grange, IL 60525-2949
Tel: 773-402-0105 *Fax:* 708-482-9159
E-mail: teleprompter@sbcglobal.net
Web Site: telepromptersolutions.com
Key Personnel
Pres: Sean Graham-White
Teleprompter rental. Camera mount & executive speech teleprompters. Exclusive Stroll & Scroll teleprompter for handheld camera & steadicam use. Interatron.
Membership(s): International Alliance of Theatrical Stage Employees

Shadow Play Records & Video
Division of Educational Graphics Press Inc
PO Box 180476, Austin, TX 78718-0476
Tel: 512-349-9962
Web Site: www.hellojoe.com
Key Personnel
Pres: Peter Markham *E-mail:* pete@hellojoe.com
Online catalog(s) available

Shaker Microphones & Promotions Inc
701 W Newman Ave, Harrison, AR 72601
Tel: 870-204-6152
E-mail: shakermicrophone@shakermicrophone.net
Web Site: www.shakermicrophone.net

Key Personnel
Owner: Joe Harless
Founded: 1992
Build microphones for harmonica players (dynamic & crystal types) as well as recording microphones for resonator guitars.

Shakticom
Division of Satchidananda Ashram-Yogaville
108 Yogaville Way, Buckingham, VA 23921
Tel: 434-969-1347 *Toll Free Tel:* 800-476-1347 (orders)
E-mail: sales@shakticom.org
Web Site: www.shakticom.org
Key Personnel
Owner: Satchidananda Ashram
Yoga AV production.
Catalog(s) available
Online catalog(s) available

Shambhala Publications
4720 Walnut St, Suite 106, Boulder, CO 80301
Tel: 720-799-8228 (cust serv); 303-222-9598; 720-799-8242 (course support)
Toll Free Tel: 888-424-2329 (orders & cust serv) *Fax:* 617-236-1563
E-mail: customercare@shambhala.com; course-support@shambhala.com
Web Site: www.shambhala.com
Key Personnel
Off Mgr: Lindsay Michko *E-mail:* lmichko@shambhala.com
Founded: 1969
Premier publisher of books on Buddhism & classics of the wisdom traditions.

Shamrock Communications
106 Apple St, Suite 202, Tinton Falls, NJ 07724
Tel: 732-686-1140
E-mail: info@shamrockcommunications.com
Web Site: www.shamrockcommunications.com
Key Personnel
Pres: Mr Pat Scanlon
Dir, Fin: Jamye Scanlon
Prodn Coord & Staff Ed: Janet Malik Dorgan
Video production studio rental. Web site, business & corporate video production services.

Shanachie Entertainment Corp
37 E Clinton St, Newton, NJ 07860
Tel: 973-579-7763
Web Site: shanachie.com
Key Personnel
Founder & Pres: Richard Nevins
VP, Publicity: Monifa Brown
Gen Mgr: Randall Grass
Prodn Mgr: Linda Cilurso
Founded: 1975
Music label production company.
Catalog(s) available
Membership(s): Entertainment Merchants Association; Music Business Association; SNA

Shanix Inc
40 Worthington Rd, Cranston, RI 02920
Tel: 401-941-4222 *Toll Free Tel:* 800-783-2067
Fax: 401-941-4333
E-mail: info@shanix.com
Web Site: www.shanix.com
Key Personnel
VP: Mustapha Gharaee
Proj Mgr: Jeff Budzinski
AV systems integrators.

Shapeshifter
3405 Cahuenga Blvd W, Los Angeles, CA 90068
Tel: 323-876-3444 *Fax:* 323-876-1444
E-mail: sales@shapeshifterpost.com
Web Site: www.shapeshifterpost.com
Key Personnel
Pres: Mark Knell

Founded: 1999
Post-production for TV, DVDs & films. HD & audio mixing.

Steve Shapiro Music
7777 Skyline Blvd, Oakland, CA 94611
Tel: 510-339-9930
Web Site: www.stevemusic.com
Key Personnel
Owner: Steve Shapiro *E-mail:* steve@stevemusic.com
Founded: 1980

Sharp Electronics Corp, Professional Display Division
Subsidiary of Sharp Corp (Osaka, Japan)
100 Paragon Dr, Montvale, NJ 07645
Tel: 201-529-8200 *Toll Free Tel:* 800-BE-SHARP (237-4277) *Fax:* 201-529-8425
Web Site: www.sharpusa.com
Key Personnel
Dir, B2B Channel Mktg & CRM: Dan Wynne
Assoc VP, Document: Shane Coffey
Founded: 1962
Catalog(s) available
Membership(s): Audiovisual and Integrated Experience Association

Brad Shaw Productions Inc
9950 W Roan Meadows Dr, Boise, ID 83709
Tel: 208-362-5500
Web Site: bradshawproductions.com
Key Personnel
Pres: Brad W Shaw *E-mail:* brad@bradshawproductions.com
Founded: 1993
Film & video production & live event services to promote, train & inform.
Membership(s): Idaho Film & Video Association

The Fulton J Sheen Co Inc
73 State St, Rochester, NY 14614
Tel: 585-232-1150
E-mail: info@bishopsheen.com
Web Site: www.bishopsheen.com
Offers DVD & VHS episodes of Archbishop Fulton J Sheen's TV series "Life Is Worth Living".
Online catalog(s) available

Sheffield Audio/Video Productions
Subsidiary of The Sheffield Institute for the Recording Arts
13816 Sunnybrook Rd, Phoenix, MD 21131
Tel: 410-628-7260 *Toll Free Tel:* 800-355-6613
Fax: 410-628-1977
E-mail: info@sheffieldav.com
Web Site: www.sheffieldav.com/production
Key Personnel
Owner: John Ariosa *E-mail:* john@sheffieldav.com
Pres: Richard "Vance" Van Horne
E-mail: vance@sheffieldav.com
Founded: 1968
Full service AV production company.

Shelburne Films
54545 SR 681, Reedsville, OH 45772
Mailing Address: PO Box 6, Reedsville, OH 45772-0006
Tel: 740-378-6297
E-mail: info@shelburnefilms.com
Web Site: www.shelburnefilms.com
Key Personnel
Pres: David Shelburne
VP & Mktg Dir: Ellen Shelburne *E-mail:* ellen@shelburnefilms.com
Film & video producers & distributors.
Online catalog(s) available

Shen Milsom & Wilke LLC
417 Fifth Ave, New York, NY 10016

Tel: 212-725-6800 *Fax:* 212-725-0864
E-mail: semspak@smwllc.com
Web Site: www.smwllc.com
Key Personnel
Partner, NY: Steve Emspak
Pres & CEO, NY: Thomas Shen
Global Dir, Mktg, NY: Meredith Lovejoy
Founded: 1986
Acoustical & technology consulting firm.
Branch Office(s)
33 New Montgomery St, 10th fl, San Francisco,
  CA 94105, Dir: Steve Shea *Tel:* 415-391-7610
  Fax: 415-391-0171 *E-mail:* sshea@smwllc.com
1822 Blacke St, Suite 2A, Denver, CO 80202,
  Dir: Jerome Smith *Tel:* 720-482-0770
  Fax: 720-482-0450 *E-mail:* jsmith@smwllc.
  com
2 N Riverside Plaza, Suite 1460, Chicago, IL
  60606, Dir: Randy Tritz *Tel:* 312-559-4585
  Fax: 312-559-5393 *E-mail:* rtritz@smwllc.com
44 Princeton Highstown Rd, Princeton Junction,
  NJ 08550, Dir: James Merrill *Tel:* 609-716-
  1900 *Fax:* 609-716-6464 *E-mail:* jmerrill@
  smwllc.com
531 Plymouth Rd, Suite 527, Plymouth Meeting,
  PA 19462, Dir: Kevin Klasic *Tel:* 610-940-
  4310 *E-mail:* kklasic@smwllc.com
712 Main St, Suite 730, Houston, TX 77002, Dir:
  Tyson Leonard *Tel:* 713-278-8228 *Fax:* 713-
  278-8235 *E-mail:* tleonard@smwllc.com
1220 N Fillmore St, Suite 360, Arlington, VA
  22201, Dir: Jeffrey Tonero *Tel:* 703-243-6301
  Fax: 703-243-6304 *E-mail:* jtonero@smwllc.
  com
Foreign Office(s): Rm F, 19th fl, Bldg D, Oriental Kenzo, No 48 Dongzhimenwai Ave,
  Dongcheng District, Beijing 100027, China,
  Dir: Kevin Chen *Tel:* (021) 6208 3337
  E-mail: kchen@smwhk.com
Rm 304, Bldg A, Soho, Zhongshan Plaza No
  1055 W Zhongshan Rd, Changing District,
  Shanghai 200052, China, Dir: Kevin Chen
  Tel: (021) 6208 3337 *E-mail:* kchen@smwhk.
  com
16 Greenwich Ctr, 260 King's Rd, North Point,
  Hong Kong, Dir: Zane Au *Tel:* 2851 1086
  E-mail: zau@smwhk.com
291 Beach Rd, Suite 02-01, Singapore 199553,
  Singapore, Dir: Ralph Stefanelli *Tel:* 6292 4101
  Fax: 6292 3868 *E-mail:* rstefanelli@smwhk.
  com
HDS Tower, Off 3110, Jumeirah Lake Towers,
  PO Box 336359, Dubai, United Arab Emirates,
  Dir: Russell Wood *Tel:* (04) 3902476 *Fax:* (04)
  3908246 *E-mail:* rwood@smwllc.com
Abbey House, 3rd fl, 74-76 Saint John St, London EC1M 4DZ, United Kingdom, Dir: James
  Quinton *Tel:* (020) 7014 1441 *Fax:* (020) 7014
  1444 *E-mail:* jquinton@smwllc.com
Membership(s): AES; American Institute of Architects; ASA; Audiovisual and Integrated Experience Association; IACC; National Council
  of Acoustical Consultants; NSCA

Sherwood America Inc
4325 Executive Dr, Suite 300, Southaven, MS
  38672
Toll Free Tel: 866-916-4667 *Toll Free Fax:* 877-
  457-2588
E-mail: info@americanaudiovideo.com
Web Site: www.sherwoodamerica.com
Founded: 1953
Audio systems.
Catalog(s) available
Membership(s): Canadian Export Association;
  Consumer Technology Association™

ShiftFocus Productions
5126 N Ravenswood Ave, Chicago, IL 60640
Tel: 773-231-2000
Web Site: www.shiftfocusproductions.com

Video production & motion graphics services.
  Production facility include soundstages, audio
  production suite, editing, client services & production offices.

Shokus Video
PO Box 3125, Chatsworth, CA 91313-3125
Tel: 818-538-9985 *Toll Free Tel:* 800-SHOKUS-1
  (746-5871 - orders) *Fax:* 818-701-0560
E-mail: info@shokus.com
Web Site: www.shokus.com
Key Personnel
Pres & Owner: Stuart Shostak *E-mail:* stuart@
  shokus.com
Catalog(s) available, $3

Stan Sholik Photography
1946 E Blair Ave, Santa Ana, CA 92705
Tel: 949-250-9275 *Fax:* 949-756-2623
E-mail: stan@stansholik.com
Web Site: www.stansholik.com
Key Personnel
Founder & CEO: Stan Sholik
Founded: 1973
Commercial & advertising photo studio.

Shook Mobile Technology LP
7451 FM 3009, Schertz, TX 78154
Tel: 210-651-5700 *Toll Free Tel:* 888-651-5775
  Fax: 210-651-5220
E-mail: shook@shook-usa.com
Web Site: www.shook-usa.com
Key Personnel
Pres & CEO: John P Heaney *Tel:* 210-651-5700
  ext 219 *E-mail:* jpheaney@shook-usa.com
VP, Sales: Ron Laurence *Tel:* 210-651-5700 ext
  204 *E-mail:* rlaurence@shook-usa.com
Founded: 1977
Manufacturer of high-tech mobile vehicles.
Catalog(s) available
Foreign Office(s): c/o De Keijzer Nipius A Co,
  Passheuvelweg 16, Postbus 22866, 1100 DJ
  Amsterdam ZO, Netherlands, Mng Dir: Efi
  Jaegermann *Tel:* (077) 4477799 *Fax:* (0577)
  977203 *E-mail:* shookeurope@shook-usa.com
Sanam Tech, Bldg 104, 201/301, 438 Changjeon-
  Dong Mapo-Gu, Seoul 121-8822, South Korea,
  Contact: J S Oh *Tel:* (02) 711-4090 *Fax:* (02)
  711-4095 *E-mail:* sanamtek@unitel.co.kr
Membership(s): NAB; RTDNA; SBE; SMPTE®

Shooting Star Video
256 Shearwater Isle, Foster City, CA 94404
Tel: 650-345-0919
E-mail: rent@ssv.com
Web Site: www.ssv.com
Key Personnel
Owner: Jeff Regan
Video equipment rentals & service. Single &
  multi-camera packages & expert consultation
  for broadcast, cable, corporate & independent
  productions.

Shooting Stars Post Inc
3106 W North "A" St, Tampa, FL 33609
Tel: 813-873-0100
E-mail: ssp@sspmedia.com
Web Site: www.sspmedia.com
Key Personnel
Owner & Pres: John Samaha
Founded: 1987
Full service multimedia company. Digital non-
  linear & linear edit suites - graphic suites,
  4,000 sq ft studio with corner cyc, film &
  video production.

Shopware
Division of Infobase Learning
c/o Films Media Group, 132 W 31 St, 16th fl,
  New York, NY 10001

Toll Free Tel: 800-322-8755 *Toll Free Fax:* 800-
  678-3633
E-mail: custserv@films.com
Web Site: shopware.films.com
Key Personnel
CEO & Pres, Infobase Learning: Mark McDonnell
Founded: 1959
Provider of skills-based, technology driven educational media. Develop content that thoroughly
  addresses specific vocational & technical skills
  such as building trades, vehicle maintenance
  & technology. Assist educators in preparing
  students to enter the workforce & facilitate professional development programs with videos,
  interactive media & posters.
Catalog(s) available, free, weekly, over 100
  unique catalogs mailed throughout the year
Online catalog(s) available

Shore Manufacturing Co
222 Beade St, Plymouth, PA 18651
Mailing Address: PO Box 214, Manasquan, NJ
  08736-0214
Tel: 570-779-4042 *Toll Free Tel:* 800-321-5153
  (orders) *Fax:* 570-779-7607 *Toll Free Fax:* 800-
  272-4334
E-mail: shoremfg@att.net
Web Site: shoremfg.com
Key Personnel
VP, Opers: William Loughran, Jr
Manufacturer of special effects generators.

Shot Glass Films
2210 W Olive Ave, Suite 300, Burbank, CA
  91506
Tel: 323-464-5111
E-mail: information@shotglassfilms.com
Web Site: www.shotglassfilms.com
Key Personnel
Partner, CEO, Pres & Exec Prodr: Jessica Manherz *E-mail:* jessica@shotglassfilms.com
Partner & Sr Dir: Eric Jackson *E-mail:* eric@
  shotglassfilms.com
Founded: 1985
Los Angeles based full-service video production
  company, specializing in commercials, online
  content & high end corporate video. We work
  with Fortune 500 companies, brands, creative
  agencies & local/federal government.

Shoulder High Productions
50 Elsie St, San Francisco, CA 94110
Tel: 415-235-1984
E-mail: info@shoulderhigh.com
Web Site: shoulderhigh.com
Founded: 1998
Full service media production company.

Show Canada Industries Inc
5555 Maurice-Cullen, Laval, QC H7C 2T8,
  Canada
Tel: 450-664-5155 *Toll Free Tel:* 888-329-5556
  Fax: 450-664-0852
E-mail: info@show-canada.ca
Web Site: www.show-canada.com
Key Personnel
Pres & CEO: Jean Labadie
HR Mgr: Nicole Gagnon
Founded: 1999
Manufacturer of stage lift & winch.
Foreign Office(s): 7 Xingguang St, Xihongmen,
  Daxing District, Beijing 100162, China
PO Box 6201, Al Mamoura, Doha, Qatar
  Tel: 5528 2179 (cell)
304 Business Ctr "Arbat", 81, Krasnayastr,
  Krasnodar 350000, Russia
Membership(s): American Society for Testing
  Materials; International Association of Amuse-
  ment Parks and Attractions

Show-Me Audio-Visual
Corporate Ridge, 4501 Blue Ridge Cutoff, Kansas City, MO 64133
Tel: 816-358-8700 *Toll Free Tel:* 800-2-SHOWME (274-6963) *Fax:* 816-358-8701
E-mail: info@showmeav.com
Web Site: www.showmeav.com
Key Personnel
Owner & Pres: Ron Dake
Rental Mgr: Nick Baker
AV equipment rentals.

ShowBiz Studios
15521 Lanark St, Van Nuys, CA 91406
Tel: 818-989-7007 *Fax:* 818-989-8272
Web Site: www.showbizstudios.com
Key Personnel
Owner: Scott Webley
Stage rentals for commercials, films, music videos & television.

Showman Fabricators Inc
148 E Fifth St, Bayonne, NJ 07002
Tel: 718-935-9899
E-mail: info@showfab.com
Web Site: www.showfab.com
Key Personnel
Pres: Bob Usdin *Tel:* 718-935-9899 ext 304
  E-mail: rusdin@showfab.com
VP: Mark Viola *Tel:* 718-935-9899 ext 335
  E-mail: mviola@showfab.com
Sr Proj Mgr: Chris Hayes *Tel:* 718-935-9899 ext 334 *E-mail:* chayes@showfab.com;
  Justin Kurtz *Tel:* 718-935-9899 ext 302
  E-mail: jkurtz@showfab.com
Founded: 1986
Manufacturer & distributor of props, drapes & blinds.
Catalog(s) available

Showorks Audio Visual Inc
730 Philadelphia Pike, Wilmington, DE 19809
Tel: 302-798-7999
E-mail: info@showorksav.com
Web Site: showorksav.com
Key Personnel
Pres: Jesse Logan
Founded: 1988
Catalog(s) available
Membership(s): Audiovisual and Integrated Experience Association

Showreel International Inc, see Shot Glass Films

Showtime Networks Inc
Subsidiary of ViacomCBS Inc
1633 Broadway, New York, NY 10019
Tel: 212-708-1600 *Fax:* 212-708-1217
Web Site: www.sho.com
Key Personnel
Chmn: Matthew C Blank
Pres & CEO: David Nevins
Owns & operates premium television networks Showtime®, The Movie Channel™, FLIX® & more.

SHP Electronics
1225 Hulman St, Terre Haute, IN 47802
Tel: 812-232-1003 *Fax:* 812-232-3170
Web Site: www.shpelectronics.com
Key Personnel
Pres: George S Petit *E-mail:* george@shpelectronics.com
Founded: 1978
Electronics systems design, installation, integration & service.

Shure Inc
5800 W Touhy Ave, Niles, IL 60714-4608
Tel: 847-600-2000; 847-600-8440 (tech support); 847-600-8699 (cust serv) *Toll Free Tel:* 800-25-SHURE (257-4873); 800-516-2525 (cust serv) *Fax:* 847-600-1212; 847-600-8444 (tech support); 847-600-8686 (cust serv); 847-600-8688 (parts)
E-mail: info@shure.com
Web Site: www.shure.com
Key Personnel
Pres & CEO: Chris Schyvinck
VP & CFO: Bruce Skof
Founded: 1925
Designers & manufacturer of professional audio products-microphones, wireless systems, earphones & headphones.
Catalog(s) available
Foreign Office(s): Suzhou Shure Trading Co Ltd, 18/A E Ocean Ctr, 618 Yan An Rd E, Shanghai 200001, China *E-mail:* info@shure.com.cn
Shure Europe GmbH, Jakob-Dieffenbacherstr 12, 75031 Eppingen, Germany *Tel:* (07262) 9249-107 *Fax:* (07262) 9249-114 *E-mail:* info@shure.de
Shure Asia Ltd, 22/F, 625 King's Rd, North Point, Island East, Hong Kong *Tel:* 2893 4290 *Fax:* 2393 4055 *E-mail:* info@shure.com.hk
Shure Japan Ltd, 16F NBF Hibiya Bldg, 1-1-7 Uchisaiwaicho, Chiyoda-ku, Tokyo 100-0011, Japan *E-mail:* info@shure.co.jp

Shure Manufacturing Corp
1901 W Main St, Washington, MO 63090
Tel: 636-390-7100 *Toll Free Tel:* 800-227-4873 *Fax:* 636-390-7171
E-mail: sales@shureusa.com
Web Site: www.shureusa.com
Key Personnel
CEO: Andrew T Richardson
Mktg Mgr: Brad E Smith
Manufacturers of storage cabinets.
Catalog(s) available

Side Door Studio Inc
69 Albe Dr, Newark, DE 19702
Tel: 302-420-6211 *Fax:* 302-731-7601
E-mail: sdseng@sidedoorstudioinc.net
Web Site: www.sidedoorstudioinc.net; www.facebook.com/sidedoorstudioinc
Key Personnel
Chief Engr: Glenn Miller
Founded: 1995
Recording studio.

Side 3 Studios
725 Mariposa St, Denver, CO 80204
Tel: 720-515-2649
E-mail: info@side3.com
Web Site: www.side3.com
Key Personnel
CEO: Adelio Lombardi
Studio Mgr: Jon Bonus
Recording studio & multimedia facility. Offers both audio recording/engineering & full service video production for broadcast television & original programming.

Sierra Automated Systems
2821 Burton Ave, Burbank, CA 91504
Tel: 818-840-6749 *Fax:* 818-840-6751
E-mail: sales@sasaudio.com; marketing@sasaudio.com
Web Site: www.sasaudio.com
Key Personnel
Pres: Ed Fritz *E-mail:* ed@sasaudio.com
VP: Al Salci *E-mail:* al@sasaudio.com
Sales Support: Emilio Gomez *E-mail:* emilio@sasaudio.com
Founded: 1988
Digital audio network routing, mixing, console control & integrated intercom & talkback systems.

Catalog(s) available
Membership(s): AES; IEEE; SMPTE®

Sight & Sound Production Services Inc
1143 Boland Place, St Louis, MO 63117-1411
Tel: 314-647-0665
Web Site: www.sspsinc.com
Key Personnel
Owner: David Houlle *Tel:* 314-374-4314 (cell)
  E-mail: sspshoulle@sbcglobal.net
Founded: 1983
Rental of grip electrical lighting equipment, 3- & 5-ton grip electrical & lighting trucks.

Sight & Sound Productions
11193 Saint Johns Industrial Pkwy N, Jacksonville, FL 32246
Tel: 904-645-7880 *Toll Free Tel:* 800-339-0846 *Fax:* 904-645-7787
E-mail: info@ssav.net
Web Site: www.ssav.net
Key Personnel
Owner & CEO: Jon Davis *Tel:* 904-361-3300
  E-mail: jdavis@ssav.net
VP, Sales: Alfredo Garcia *Tel:* 904-361-3315
  E-mail: agarcia@ssav.net
Mktg Dir: Victoria Staszewski *Tel:* 904-361-3309
  E-mail: vstaszewski@ssav.net
Founded: 1987
Event & production company.
Catalog(s) available
Membership(s): Audiovisual and Integrated Experience Association; MPI

Sight & Sound Studios
66 Queen St, Suite 1705, Honolulu, HI 96813
Tel: 808-599-7600 *Fax:* 808-599-7601
Web Site: www.sightandsoundhawaii.com
Key Personnel
Owner & Pres: William Maheras *Tel:* 808-754-0080 *E-mail:* bill@sightandsoundhawaii.com
Catalog(s) available
Membership(s): International Alliance of Theatrical Stage Employees

Sigma Corp of America
Subsidiary of Sigma Corp
15 Fleetwood Ct, Ronkonkoma, NY 11779
Tel: 631-585-1144 *Toll Free Tel:* 800-896-6858 (cust serv) *Fax:* 631-585-1895
E-mail: info@sigmaphoto.com
Web Site: www.sigmaphoto.com
Key Personnel
Pres: Mark Amir-Hamzeh
Dir, Mktg: Rick Booth *Tel:* 631-227-2017
Founded: 1985
Import sales, wholesale distribution & service of Sigma products.
Catalog(s) available
Membership(s): The Imaging Alliance

Sign Media Inc
4020 Blackburn Lane, Burtonsville, MD 20866-1167
Tel: 301-421-0268 *Toll Free Tel:* 800-475-4756 *Fax:* 301-421-0270
E-mail: info@signmedia.com
Web Site: www.signmedia.com
Key Personnel
Owner: Verden A Ness
Founded: 1979
Producers of videotaped text material on American Sign Language.
Online catalog(s) available

Signal Transport
Division of SigT Inc
PO Box 1028, Lake Forest, CA 92609-1028
Tel: 714-641-5665 *Fax:* 714-641-5664
E-mail: sales@sigt.com
Web Site: sigt.com

Key Personnel
Sales Mgr: Jorgen Ravn
Founded: 1998
Source for connector interfaces & control panels.

Signature Entertainment
8306 Wilshire Blvd, Suite 791, Beverly Hills, CA 90211
Tel: 310-498-1805 *Fax:* 310-276-2521
Key Personnel
Owner: Kelly Andrea Rubin
    E-mail: kellyarubin@signature-ent.com
Film producer, line producer & production company.

Signs.com
1550 S Gladiola St, Salt Lake City, UT 84104
Tel: 801-441-3400 *Toll Free Tel:* 888-222-4929
E-mail: support@signs.com
Web Site: www.signs.com
Key Personnel
Co-Founder: Nelson James
Cust Experience Offr: Madison Page
Busn Devt: Bo Steed
Mktg: Dustin Heap
Founded: 2012
E-commerce signage. Specialty & photo prints.
Online catalog(s) available

Sihl Inc
Member of Diatec Group
538 Main St, Fiskeville, RI 02823
Tel: 401-821-1000 *Toll Free Tel:* 800-556-6866; 800-366-7393 (ext 1, cust serv)
Web Site: www.sihlinc.com
Key Personnel
CFO: Stephanie Provost
Mng Dir: Chris McInerney *E-mail:* cmcinerney@sihlinc.com
Sr Prod Mgr: Melissa Jendzejec-Blanchard *Tel:* 401-821-1000 ext 3420
    E-mail: mjendzejec@sihlinc.com
Prod & Mktg Communs: Tyler Pacheco *Tel:* 401-821-1000 ext 3308 *E-mail:* tpacheco@sihlinc.com
Founded: 1802
Produce films, papers & specialty materials for inkjet, solvent, UV curable, latex & toner-receptive wide format plotter, printers & presses.
Online catalog(s) available
Membership(s): AECT; ATD; Audiovisual and Integrated Experience Association; Education Market Association; NOPA

Silent Source
58 Nonotuck St, Northampton, MA 01062
Tel: 413-584-7944 *Toll Free Tel:* 800-583-7174 (orders) *Fax:* 413-584-2377
E-mail: info@silentsource.com
Web Site: www.silentsource.com
Key Personnel
Pres: W Ridabock
Founded: 1992
Interior acoustical products. Silent source is your one-stop-shop for interior acoustic treatment & soundproofing needs.
Catalog(s) available

Silver Creek Media Inc
Formerly Purefire Communications Inc
3-1750 The Queensway, 221, Toronto, ON M9C 5H5, Canada
Tel: 416-503-2323
E-mail: info@silvercreekmedia.com
Web Site: www.silvercreekmedia.com
Key Personnel
Mng Dir: Tony Patafio
Founded: 2001
Web design, graphic design, video production, online marketing & digital media services.

Silvestri California
8125 Beach St, Los Angeles, CA 90001
Tel: 323-277-4420 *Toll Free Tel:* 800-647-8874
Fax: 323-585-0791
E-mail: info@silvestricalifornia.com
Web Site: www.silvestricalifornia.com
Key Personnel
VP, Mktg & Design: Fidel Argomaniz
    E-mail: fidel@silvestricalifornia.com
Founded: 1934
Manufacturer of props & products fabricated in fiberglass, urethane, wood & metal.
Catalog(s) available

SIM Digital
Member of SIM Group
One Atlantic Ave, Suite 110, Toronto, ON M6K 3E7, Canada
Tel: 416-979-9958 *Fax:* 416-979-7770
E-mail: info.toronto@simdigital.com
Web Site: www.simdigital.com
Key Personnel
Pres: Rob Sim
Rentals: Craig Milne *E-mail:* craigmilne@simdigital.com
Founded: 1982
Provides film & broadcast producers with the latest in video equipment rentals.
Branch Office(s)
5258 Lougheed Hwy, Burnaby, BC V5B 2Z8, Canada *Tel:* 604-298-5258 *Fax:* 604-298-4336
1017 N Las Palmas Ave, Hollywood, CA 90038 *Tel:* 323-978-9000 *Fax:* 323-978-9018
1379 Chattahoochee Ave NW, Atlanta, GA 30318 *Tel:* 404-355-8000 *Fax:* 404-355-8005
Foreign Office(s): Baijiazhuang Xiezilou, Bldg C, Suite 101, Baijiazhuang Rd 3, Chaoyang District, Beijing 100020, China *Tel:* (010) 65928900 *Fax:* (010) 65928930

Sima Products Corp
Division of Arista Enterprises Inc
125 Commerce Dr, Hauppauge, NY 11788
Tel: 631-435-0200 *Toll Free Tel:* 800-274-7824
Fax: 631-435-4545 *Toll Free Fax:* 800-274-7828
E-mail: customerservice@simaproducts.com
Web Site: www.simaproducts.com
Key Personnel
Pres: Richard Leifert
VP, Ad & Mktg: Michael Fedonchik
Manufactures consumer electronic accessories in the US in the categories of video, power, digital imaging, first alert systems & home theaters.
Online catalog(s) available
Membership(s): Consumer Technology Association™; Custom Electronic Design & Installation Association; The Imaging Alliance

Simco-Ion
Division of Illinois Tool Works
2257 N Penn Rd, Hatfield, PA 19440
Tel: 215-822-6401 *Toll Free Tel:* 800-203-3419
Fax: 215-822-3795
E-mail: customerservice@simco-ion.com
Web Site: www.simco-ion.com
Key Personnel
US Indus Busn Unit Mgr: Jay Perry
Mktg Mgr: Kim West
Founded: 1936
Manufacturer of static bar systems, static charging systems, web & sheet cleaning systems.
Online catalog(s) available
Branch Office(s)
Simco-Ion, Technology Group, 1601 Harbor Bay Pkwy, Suite 150, Alameda, CA 94502 *Tel:* 510-217-0600 *Toll Free Tel:* 800-367-2452
Foreign Office(s): Simco-Ion China, 2/F, Bldg 11, Heng Ming Zhu Tech Park, Xiang Xing Rd, Sha Jing, Bao An, Shenzhen, Guangdong 518104, China

Simco-Ion Japan Inc, 1-2-4, Minatojima Naka-machi, Chuo-ku, Kobe City 650-0046, Japan
Simco-Ion Europe, Postbus 71, Lochem 7240 AB, Netherlands

Simon & Schuster, Inc
Division of ViacomCBS Inc
1230 Avenue of the Americas, New York, NY 10020
Tel: 212-698-7000; 212-698-7126
Toll Free Tel: 800-223-2348 (cust serv)
Fax: 212-698-7664 *Toll Free Fax:* 800-943-9831
E-mail: audiopublicity@simonandschuster.com
Web Site: www.simonandschuster.net; www.simonandschuster.biz; www.simonandschuster.com
Key Personnel
Pres & CEO: Carolyn K Reidy
EVP & Gen Coun: Hazel-Ann Mayers
EVP & Chief Mktg Offr: Liz Perl
EVP, Opers & CFO: Dennis Eulau
EVP, Sales & Mktg: Michael Selleck
Pres & Publr, Simon & Schuster Audio: Chris Lynch
VP & Gen Mgr, Adult, Children's & Audio: Craig Mandeville
Asst Dir, Mktg & Publicity: Lauren Pires
Founded: 1924
Resources of school or library, grades kindergarten through college.
Catalog(s) available
Shipping Address: Riverside Distribution Center, 100 Front St, Riverside, NJ 08075 *Tel:* 856-461-6500 *Fax:* 856-824-2402

D S Simon Productions
229 W 36 St, 9th fl, New York, NY 10018
Tel: 212-736-2727 *Toll Free Tel:* 800-377-4666
Fax: 212-736-7040
E-mail: news@dssimon.com
Web Site: dssimon.com
Key Personnel
Pres & CEO: Douglas Simon *E-mail:* doug@dssimon.com
Media & business communications. Specialize in satellite media tours, Internet media tours, B-roll production & distribution, corporate & web video, video players, ground tours, co-op tours & radio tours.

Simon - Kaloi Engineering Ltd
31192 La Baya Dr, Unit G, Westlake Village, CA 91362
Tel: 818-707-8400 *Fax:* 818-707-8401
E-mail: sales@skeng.com
Web Site: www.skeng.com
Key Personnel
CFO: Richard A Simon
Pres: Dennis Kaloi *Tel:* 818-707-8402
    E-mail: dennis@skeng.com
Manufacture products including integrated sound, lighting & motion controllers, digital message repeaters, show control equipment & professional audio products. Electronic consulting services.
Online catalog(s) available

Simplex Grinnell LP
Division of Tyco
50 Technology Dr, Westminster, MA 01441
Tel: 978-731-2500 *Toll Free Tel:* 800-746-7539
Web Site: www.tycosimplexgrinnell.com
Sales & design of professional audio systems for performance applications & sound masking.
Branch Office(s)
2400 Skymark Ave, Mississauga, ON L4W 5K5, Canada *Tel:* 905-212-4600
Membership(s): AES; Audiovisual and Integrated Experience Association; NSCA; The Recording Academy

SimpliPhi Power Inc
420 Bryant Circle, Bldg B, Ojai, CA 93023
Tel: 805-640-6700
E-mail: info@simpliphipower.com
Web Site: www.simpliphipower.com
Key Personnel
Pres & CEO: Catherine Von Burg
Founded: 2010
Design & manufacture new technology battery
belts, blocks & energy storage systems.

Simply Audiobooks
935 Sheldon Ct, Burlington, ON L7L 5K6,
Canada
Toll Free Tel: 877-554-4332
E-mail: customerservice@simplyaudiobooks.com;
help@simplyaudiobooks.com
Web Site: www.simplyaudiobooks.com
Key Personnel
Cust Serv Mgr: Colin Sword
Founded: 2003
Unlimited audiobooks delivered to your door.
Branch Office(s)
2225 Kenmore Ave, Suite 122, Buffalo, NY
14207-1359

Simpson Electric Co
520 Simpson Ave, Lac du Flambeau, WI 54538-
0099
Mailing Address: PO Box 99, Lac du Flambeau,
WI 54538-0099
Tel: 715-588-3947 (cust serv); 715-588-3311
Fax: 715-588-1248 (cust serv); 715-588-3326
E-mail: cservice@simpsonelectric.com; support@
simpsonelectric.com
Web Site: www.simpsonelectric.com
Key Personnel
CEO: Jon Schmitz
Sales Mgr: Krista Covey
HR: Kathy Marose *E-mail:* kmarose@
simpsonelectric.com
Cust Serv: Patricia Hickman
Founded: 1927
Manufacturer of panel instrumentation & test
equipment.
Catalog(s) available

Sinauer Associates
Division of Oxford University Press
23 Plumtree Rd, Sunderland, MA 01375
Mailing Address: PO Box 407, Sunderland, MA
01375-0407
Tel: 413-549-4300 *Fax:* 413-549-1118
E-mail: orders@sinauer.com (orders); publish@
sinauer.com (gen edit correspondence);
custserv@sinauer.com (cust serv)
Web Site: www.sinauer.com
Key Personnel
Pres & Ed: Andrew D Sinauer
VP & Mktg Dir: Dean H Scudder
Media & Supplements Mgr: Jason Dirks
Founded: 1969
Publisher of college-level textbooks & educational
multimedia products.

Sinclair Institute
402 Millstone Dr, Hillsborough, NC 27278
Tel: 919-732-6005 *Toll Free Tel:* 888-736-2247
Fax: 919-732-6146
E-mail: sales@sinclairwholesale.com
Web Site: www.sinclairwholesale.com; www.
bettersex.com
Key Personnel
Chmn & Media Mgr: Bruce Cabral
Founded: 1991
Producer & distributor of educational & medical
programs.
Catalog(s) available

The Singing Machine Co Inc
6301 NW Fifth Way, Suite 2900, Fort Lauderdale,
FL 33309

Tel: 954-596-1000 *Toll Free Tel:* 866-670-6888
(cust serv) *Fax:* 954-596-2000
E-mail: sales@singingmachine.com;
customerservice@singingmachine.com
Web Site: singingmachine.com
Key Personnel
CEO: Gary Atkinson
CFO: Lionel Marquis
VP, Global Sales & Mktg: Bernardo Melo
Media Contact: Radelys Comas
    E-mail: radelyscomas@singingmachine.com
Founded: 1982
Distribute a full line of consumer-oriented
karaoke systems, youth electronics & ac-
cessories under The Singing Machine®,
SoundX®, Home™ & SMDigital™ brand
names.
Foreign Office(s): 5/F Shing Dao Industrial
Bldg, 232 Aberdeen Main Rd, Hong Kong,
Hong Kong *Tel:* 3471 1313 *Fax:* 3580 0189
    E-mail: info@singingmachine-hk.com
Comercial Offshore de Macau Ltda, No 371
Edificio Comercial "KengOu," 11 andar "C",
Macau, Macau *Tel:* 2871 7000 *Fax:* 2871 7003
    E-mail: info@smc-macau.com

SintecMedia
135 E 57 St, 12th fl, New York, NY 10022
Tel: 646-745-3900 *Fax:* 646-745-3901
E-mail: sales@sintecmedia.com
Web Site: www.sintecmedia.com
Key Personnel
Pres: Chanan Weiss
EVP, Enterprise Sales: Amir Lavi
Founded: 2000
Broadcast management systems, air time sales &
traffic.
Branch Office(s)
1580 Lincoln St, Suite 560, Denver, CO 80203
    Tel: 303-830-0600 *Fax:* 303-830-0601
The Fountains at Piedmont Ctr, Bldg 11, 3495
Piedmont Rd NE, Suite 360, Atlanta, GA
30305, COO: Eric Levitan *Tel:* 404-869-4575
    Fax: 404-844-9009
1000 Monroe Ave NW, Grand Rapids, MI 49503
    Tel: 616-454-4400 *Fax:* 616-454-4410
1355 W Towne Square Rd, Mequon, WI 53092,
CTO: Toufic Moubarak *Tel:* 262-241-9005
    Fax: 262-241-9036
Foreign Office(s): 21 Nahum Hafzadi St, POB
34406, 9134302 Jerusalem, Israel, CEO: Amotz
Yarden *Tel:* (02) 651 5122 *Fax:* (02) 651 5133
(headquarters)

Siqura Inc
Formerly TKH Security Solutions USA Inc
Member of TKH Group NV
12920 Cloverleaf Center Dr, Germantown, MD
20874
Tel: 301-444-2200 *Toll Free Tel:* 800-BY-
FIBER (293-4237) *Fax:* 301-444-2299
Toll Free Fax: 800-293-4237
E-mail: sales.us@siqura.com
Web Site: www.siqura.com
Founded: 1972
Catalog(s) available
Foreign Office(s): Siqura BV, Meridiaan 32, 2801
DA Gouda, Netherlands *Tel:* (0182) 592 333
    E-mail: info@siqura.com (headquarters)
Siqura BV, KOP Bldg, No 05-01, 25 Tai Seng
Ave, Singapore 534104, Singapore *Tel:* 6264
7501 *E-mail:* sales@sigura.com
Siqura SL, Edificio Fiteni, Calle Anabel Segura,
10, 3° plta, 28108 Alcobendas (Madrid), Spain
    Tel: 91 676 81 64 *Fax:* sales@siqura.com
Siqura BV, Off F-509, DSOA HQ Bldg, Dubai
Silicon Oasis, Dubai, United Arab Emirates
    Tel: (050) 458 0507 *E-mail:* sales.ae@siqura.
com
Siqura Ltd, Century Business Centre, Manvers
Way, Rotherham S63 5DA, United Kingdom
    Tel: (0845) 528 0004 *E-mail:* sales@siqura.
com

Sirius Images Corp, see WaveGuide Studios

SirsiDynix
3300 N Ashton Blvd, Suite 500, Lehi, UT 84043
Tel: 801-223-5200; 0800 016 3147
    Toll Free Tel: 800-288-8020 *Fax:* 801-331-7770
Web Site: www.sirsidynix.com
Key Personnel
CEO: Bill Davison
CFO: Christie Kent
Chief, Mktg & Strategic Alliances: Eric Keith
SVP, Opers: Scott Wheelhouse
VP, Sales Americas: Chris Harris
Integrated library automation package for K-12
school libraries combining functionality, sup-
port & flexibility cloud-based special library
software.
Branch Office(s)
EOS, 1902 Wright Place, 2nd fl, Carlsbad, CA
92008-7208 *Toll Free Tel:* 800-876-5484
    Fax: 801-765-6200
55 King St W, 7th fl, Kitchener, ON N2G 4W1,
Canada *Fax:* 801-223-5202
Foreign Office(s): Level 11, 535 Bourke St, Melbourne, Victoria 3000, Australia *Tel:* (03) 8688
0500 *Fax:* (03) 8688 0518
10/F, Central Plaza, Rm 1013, 381 Huai Hai
Zhong Rd, Shanghai 200020, China *Tel:* (021)
63915210 *Fax:* (021) 63915970
13, rue Camille Desmoulins, 92441 Paris Cedex,
France *Tel:* 0800 906 580 *Fax:* 01 58 04 23 81
Calle Lopez de Hoyos, 35 - 1°, 28002 Madrid,
Spain *Tel:* 900 971 850 *Fax:* 91 745 99 995
22 F-3, 91, Section 2, Roosevelt Rd, Taipei, Taiwan *Tel:* (02) 2369 0072
54 Clarendon Rd, Watford WD17 1DU, United
Kingdom *Tel:* (01923) 202900; 0800 016 3147
    Fax: (01923) 431847

Sisters' Choice Press
PO Box 2067, Berkeley, CA 94702-0067
Tel: 510-843-0533 *Fax:* 510-834-5201
Web Site: www.sisterschoice.com
Key Personnel
Mgr: Ruth Pohlman
Contact: Nancy Schimmel *E-mail:* nancy@
sisterschoice.com
Creates books & recordings of storytelling &
songs for children & adults.
Online catalog(s) available
Membership(s): The Association of Publishers
for Special Sales; Independent Book Publishers
Association

SISU Home Entertainment Inc
2219 41 Ave, Suite 509, Long Island City, NY
11101
Tel: 212-947-7888 *Toll Free Tel:* 800-223-7478
    Fax: 212-947-8388 *Toll Free Fax:* 888-221-
7478
E-mail: sisu@sisuent.com
Web Site: www.sisuent.com
Key Personnel
Pres: Haim Scheininger
Founded: 1988
Distributor, producer & co-producer of DVDs,
videos, films, TV programs & CDs.
Online catalog(s) available
Membership(s): Entertainment Merchants Asso-
ciation; Music Business Association; National
Media Market; NATPE

Frank Siteman Photography
136 Pond St, Winchester, MA 01890
Tel: 781-729-3747 *Fax:* 781-729-2549
Web Site: www.franksiteman.com
Key Personnel
Pres: Frank Siteman *E-mail:* frank@franksiteman.
com

Photography for print company.
Membership(s): American Society of Picture Professionals; ASMP

Sitler's Supplies Inc
111 Westview Dr, Washington, IA 52353
Tel: 319-653-2123 *Toll Free Tel:* 800-426-3938
Fax: 319-653-3198
E-mail: renfred@sitlersupplies.com
Web Site: sitlersupplies.com
Key Personnel
Pres: Jason Prochaska *E-mail:* jason@
sitlersupplies.com
Off Mgr: Nancy Flynn *E-mail:* nancy@
sitlersupplies.com
Founded: 1978
Distributor of projectors, stage lights & related equipment.
Online catalog(s) available
Branch Office(s)
305 Second Ave SE, Suite 206, Cedar Rapids, IA 52401
5550 Wild Rose Lane, Suite 4050, West Des Moines, IA 50266

63588 Manitoba Ltd, see Big Deal Custom Casings

16 x 9 Inc
28314 Constellation Rd, Valencia, CA 91355
Tel: 661-295-3313 *Toll Free Tel:* 866-800-1699
Fax: 661-295-3314
E-mail: info@16x9inc.com
Web Site: www.16x9inc.com
Key Personnel
Mktg Mgr: John Diaz *E-mail:* john.diaz@
16x9inc.com
Tech Support Mgr, Sales: James Lee
E-mail: james@16x9inc.com
Founded: 2000

SKC Communication Products Inc
8320 Hedge Lane Terr, Shawnee Mission, KS 66227
Mailing Address: 3958 Solutions Ctr, Chicago, IL 60677-3009
Tel: 913-422-4222 *Toll Free Tel:* 800-882-7779
Toll Free Fax: 800-454-4752
E-mail: contact.us@skccom.com
Web Site: www.skccom.com
Key Personnel
CEO & Pres: Tray Vedock
CFO: Jennifer Lowe
Chief Mktg Offr: Jill Phillips
CTO: Jeff Holton
VP, Opers: Mark Linton
Founded: 1986
Voice, AV & video conferencing products, solutions & services.
Branch Office(s)
1201 Wiley Rd, Schaumburg, IL 60173
112 N First Ave, Winterset, IA 50273
8710 "F" St, Suite 112, Omaha, NE 68127
1000 Connell Pkwy, Suite 200, Oklahoma City, OK 73108
274 Museum Rd, Rock Hill, SC 29732
1910 Firman Dr, Suite 120, Richardson, TX 75081
11370 Theo Trecker Way, Milwaukee, WI 53214

Skjonberg Controls Inc
1363 Donlon St, Suite 6, Ventura, CA 93003
Tel: 805-650-0877 *Fax:* 805-650-0360
Toll Free Fax: 800-650-0360
E-mail: sales@skjonberg.com
Web Site: www.skjonberg.com
Key Personnel
Pres: Knut Skjonberg *Tel:* 805-650-0877 ext 104
Acctg & Mktg Dir: Carolyn Meyer *Tel:* 805-650-0877 ext 103
Prodn Mgr: Jorge Diaz

Sales, Gen Admin & Coord: Monica Skjonberg
Sr Techician: Ivan Campos
Founded: 1983
Manufacturer & distributor of control systems.

Skotel Corp
2645 Croissant Moreau, Brossard, QC J4Y 1P7, Canada
Tel: 514-806-2340
Key Personnel
Pres: Stephen Scott
Founded: 1975
Catalog(s) available
Membership(s): SMPTE®

Sky City Audio
1819 Willow Creek Rd, Prescott, AZ 86301
Tel: 928-830-2313
Web Site: skycityaudio.com
Key Personnel
Owner: Justin Ames *E-mail:* justin@skycityaudio.com
Founded: 2012
Full service professional recording studio.

Sky-View Co, see Sky-View Search Lights & Promotions

Sky-View Search Lights & Promotions
702 Spring Cypress Rd, Spring, TX 77373
Tel: 210-845-7622 *Toll Free Tel:* 800-562-8439 (US & CN); 888-396-6653
E-mail: sales@sky-view.com
Web Site: sky-view.com
Key Personnel
Pres: Chris Purtee
Founded: 1983
Manufacture, distribute & rent advertising balloons & search lights.
Online catalog(s) available

Skyfire Video
PO Box 2266, Sparks, NV 89432
Tel: 775-323-0965 *Toll Free Tel:* 800-852-2330
Web Site: www.skyfirevideo.com
Key Personnel
CEO/Prodr: Jim Mitchell
Video production company.

Skyhoundz
Subsidiary of PRB & Associates Inc
660 Hembree Pkwy, Suite 110, Roswell, GA 30076
Tel: 770-751-3882 *Fax:* 770-740-1665
E-mail: info@skyhoundz.com
Web Site: www.skyhoundz.com
Key Personnel
Dir: Peter Bloeme
Founded: 1998
Disc Dog videos, books & apparel distribution.
Catalog(s) available

Skystorm Productions
103 Commerce St, Suite 100, Lake Mary, FL 32746
Tel: 407-328-4747 *Toll Free Tel:* 800-783-8508
Fax: 407-328-4479
E-mail: info@skystorm.com
Web Site: www.skystorm.com
Key Personnel
CEO/Pres: John Haslam
Dir: Alex Sivers
Exec Prodr: Rob Mica
Prodn Mgr: Eleonora Belyaeva
Founded: 1998
Video production company. HD mobile production vehicle.

Skyviews Survey Inc
32 Highline Trail, Stamford, CT 06902

Tel: 203-359-3754
Web Site: www.skyviewsurvey.com
Key Personnel
Pres: David Margolis *Tel:* 203-352-2500 (cell)
E-mail: david@skyviewsurvey.com
Founded: 1946
Aerial photography/videography production service company. Manufacture & rent stabilization platforms for aerial video.

Slim Goodbody Corp
161 Narrows Rd, Lincolnville, ME 04850
Mailing Address: PO Box 242, Lincolnville Center, ME 04850
Tel: 207-831-2607
E-mail: info@slimgoodbody.com
Web Site: www.slimgoodbody.com
Key Personnel
Founder & Pres: John Burstein
Founded: 1975
Live performances, TV broadcasting & teaching resources on topics including health, fitness, math, reading, science & other core curriculums.
Catalog(s) available

SLR Enterprises LLC
PO Box 1111, Orleans, MA 02653
Tel: 508-737-7788 *Fax:* 508-240-6878
E-mail: stephenroth@c4.net
Key Personnel
Pres: Stephen Roth
Founded: 1998
Broker & distributor of wire, cable, fiber optics, assemblies & hardware, velcro, screws & IRF connection cable ties.

SmackDab Media
252 Glenhaven Dr, Amherst, NY 14228
Tel: 615-957-6618
Web Site: smackdabmedia.us
Key Personnel
Owner: John Fucile *E-mail:* johnafucile@gmail.com
Post Prodn Supv: Lisa DeAngelo
Prodn Coord: Liz Taylor
Film & video stage/studio for rehearsal & shooting. Full production & post-production services.

Small Business File Inc, see Ludlow Media

Small Planet Communications Inc
15 Union St, Lawrence, MA 01840
Tel: 978-794-2201
E-mail: planet@smplanet.com
Web Site: www.smplanet.com
Key Personnel
Pres: Joe Buschini
Dir, New Busn Devt: Lisa Lyons
Develop print & multimedia materials.

Small World Productions Inc
140 Lakeside Ave, Suite 200, Seattle, WA 98122
Mailing Address: PO Box 28369, Seattle, WA 98118-8369
Tel: 206-329-7167 *Toll Free Tel:* 800-866-7425 (orders); 800-325-7111 (cust serv) *Fax:* 206-329-0269 (credit card orders)
E-mail: info@travelsmallworld.com; customercare@smarttravels.tv
Web Site: www.smarttravels.tv
Key Personnel
Exec Prodr & CEO: John Givens
Partner: Patricia Larsen; Sandra Nisbet
Off Mgr: Ann Conroy *E-mail:* annconroy@travelsmallworld.com
Travel video producers.
Catalog(s) available
Membership(s): NATAS

SMART Technologies ULC
3636 Research Rd NW, Calgary, AB T2L 1Y1, Canada
Tel: 403-245-0333 *Toll Free Tel:* 888-42-SMART (427-6278, CN & US); 800-260-9408 (sales) *Fax:* 403-228-2500
Web Site: home.smarttech.com
Key Personnel
Pres & CEO: John Hui
CTO: Warren Barkley
VP, Mktg: Jeff Lowe *Tel:* 403-407-5330
    E-mail: jefflowe@smarttech.com
VP, Opers: Nicholas Svensson
Founded: 1987
Manufacturer & distributor of AV equipment.
Branch Office(s)
SMART Technologies Corp, 200 Lexington Ave, Suite 1115, New York, NY 10016 *Tel:* 212-696-9762 *E-mail:* ny.info@smarttech.com
SMART Technologies Corp, 1655 N Fort Myer Dr, Suite 1120, Arlington, VA 22209 *Tel:* 571-227-7392 *E-mail:* dc.info@smarttech.com
SMART Technologies (Seattle) Inc, 1505 West-lake Ave N, Suite 700, Seattle, WA 98109
Foreign Office(s): Collins Street Tower, Level 3, 480 Collins St, Melbourne, Victoria 8000, Australia *Tel:* (013) 0016 5312 (Australia); (09) 8896806 (New Zealand) *E-mail:* anzenquiries@smarttech.com
SMART Technologies (China) Inc, Rm 807, 107 Zunyi Rd, Changning District, Shanghai 200051, China *Tel:* (021) 6288 6000 *E-mail:* chinatraining@smarttech.com
SMART Technologies (France) SAS, 35 Rue de Rome, 75008 Paris, France *E-mail:* franceinfo@smarttech.com
SMART Technologies (Germany) GmbH, Gustav-Heinemann-Ufer 72c, 50968 Cologne, Germany *Tel:* (0221) 846166-0 *Fax:* (0221) 846166-35 *E-mail:* info@germany.smarttech.com
SMART Technologies (Singapore) Pvt Ltd, 3791 Jl Bukit Merah, Singapore 159741, Singapore *Tel:* 6697 5650
SMART Technologies (Middle East) FZE, 4th fl, Jafza View 19, PO Box 263017, Jebel Ali, Dubai, United Arab Emirates *Tel:* (04) 8857794 *Fax:* (04) 8857791 *E-mail:* meinfo@smarttech.com
SMART Technologies (GB) Ltd, 8 The Square, Stockley Park, Uxbridge UB11 1FW, United Kingdom

SmartSource Computer & AV Rentals
265 Oser Ave, Hauppauge, NY 11788
Tel: 631-273-8888 *Toll Free Tel:* 844-313-8833 *Fax:* 631-273-8889
E-mail: info@smartsourcerentals.com
Web Site: www.smartsourcerentals.com
Key Personnel
Mktg Coord: Debbie Church *E-mail:* dchurch@smartsourcerentals.com
Founded: 1984
AV, IT & interactive technology rentals.
Sales Office(s): 1430 W 12 Place, Tempe, AZ 85281
4828 W Rosecrans Ave, Hawthorne, CA 90250
9240 Trade Place, Suite 300, San Diego, CA 92126
408 N Canal St, Suite D, South San Francisco, CA 94080
3402 SW 26 Terr, Suite B-1, Fort Lauderdale, FL 33312
9401 Southridge Part Ct, Suite 600, Orlando, FL 32819
1850 MacArthur Blvd NW, Suite A, Atlanta, GA 30318
2025 Glen Ellyn Rd, Glendale Heights, IL 60139
575 University Ave, Suite 5, Norwood, MA 02062
6425 S Jones Blvd, Suite 103, Las Vegas, NV 89118
490 S Dean St, Englewood, NJ 07631

2101 Midway Rd, Suite 100, Carrollton, TX 75006
7664 Fullerton Rd, Suite K, Springfield, VA 22153
8635 154 Ave NE, Suite 140, Redmond, WA 98052
Membership(s): International Technology Rental Association

SMI® Inc
4567 Lake Shore Dr, Waco, TX 76710
Tel: 254-776-2060 *Toll Free Tel:* 800-568-1241 *Fax:* 254-772-9588
E-mail: dmcminn@lmi-inc.com; info@lmi-inc.com; info@success-motivation.com
Web Site: www.lmi-world.com/smi
Key Personnel
Pres & CEO: Randy Slechta
EVP: Ian G Dawson *E-mail:* idawson@lmi-inc.com; Merlyn Beeman *Tel:* 254-776-2060 ext 205
Organizational & leadership materials & tools.

Smith-Victor Corp
Division of PromarkBRANDS Inc
1268 Humbracht Circle, Bartlett, IL 60103-1631
Tel: 630-830-9200 *Toll Free Tel:* 800-348-9862 *Fax:* 630-830-9201 *Toll Free Fax:* 800-352-0490
E-mail: sales@smithvictor.com
Web Site: www.promarkbrands.com
Key Personnel
Pres: Kenneth Orlando
Founded: 1874
Online catalog(s) available
Membership(s): Audiovisual and Integrated Experience Association; Education Market Association; The Imaging Alliance

Smithsonian Folkways Recordings
Division of Smithsonian Institution
600 Maryland Ave SW, Suite 2001, Washington, DC 20024
Mailing Address: PO Box 37012, MRC 520, CG 2001, Washington, DC 20013-7012
Tel: 202-633-6450 *Toll Free Tel:* 888-FOLKWAYS (365-5929) *Fax:* 202-633-6477
E-mail: smithsonianfolkways@si.edu
Web Site: folkways.si.edu
Key Personnel
Dir, Busn Aff & Royalties: Cecille Chen
Assoc Dir, Opers: John Smith
Licensing Mgr: William Griffith
Mktg Mgr: Jonathan Williger
Prodn Mgr: Mary Monseur
Audio Recording Specialist: Ronnie Simpkins
Founded: 1948
Produce traditional music from around the world. Physical goods, digital downloads, streaming audio & licensing.
Online catalog(s) available

Smithsonian National Museum of the American Indian
Affiliate of Film & Video Center for the Smithsonian Institution
Fourth St & Independence Ave SW, Washington, DC 20560
Tel: 202-633-1000
E-mail: nmai-info@si.edu; nmai-grouppreservations@si.edu (DC group tours); nmaitours@si.edu (NY group tours)
Web Site: americanindian.si.edu
Key Personnel
Dir: Kevin Gover
Founded: 1979
Film & video library.
Branch Office(s)
Alexander Hamilton US Custom House, One Bowling Green, New York, NY 10004-1415, Asst Curator: Millie Seubert *Tel:* 212-514-3700 *Fax:* 212-514-3725

Smolian Sound Studios
One Worman's Mill Ct, Frederick, MD 21701
Tel: 301-694-5134
E-mail: smolians@erols.com
Web Site: www.soundsaver.com
Key Personnel
Owner: Steven Smolian
Founded: 1962
Audio preservation for reel-to-reel tapes, audio cassette tapes, acetate discs, dictation formats. Sound restoration & preservation suites.
Online catalog(s) available
Membership(s): Association for Recorded Sound Collections; Music Library Association

SMP Digital Graphics
163 W 22 St, New York, NY 10011
Tel: 212-691-6766
E-mail: info@smpdigitalgraphics.com
Web Site: smpdigitalgraphics.com
Key Personnel
Pres: Stuart Penny
Full service graphics company.
Catalog(s) available

SMPTE, see Society of Motion Picture & Television Engineers® (SMPTE®)

SNAP
18653 Ventura, Suite 295, Tarzana, CA 91356
Tel: 818-340-0283
E-mail: hdcine@gmail.com
Web Site: www.facebook.com/barry.seybert
Key Personnel
Owner: Barry Seybert
Founded: 1979
Complete production & post-production company & equipment supplier.
Membership(s): Digital Cinema Society; STE

So Smart Productions
701 Sharpley Rd, Wilmington, DE 19803
Tel: 484-753-1520
Web Site: www.sosmart.com
Key Personnel
Founder, CEO & Pres: Scott Tornek *E-mail:* scott@sosmart.com
Founded: 1997
Producers of award winning "So Smart!" & "King Otis" learning videos & music for babies, toddlers & preschoolers. Distribute & produce DVDs, video/CD-ROMs, computer multimedia & DVD interactive.
Catalog(s) available

Social Studies School Service
10200 Jefferson Blvd, PO Box 802, Culver City, CA 90232
Tel: 310-839-2436 *Toll Free Tel:* 800-421-4246 *Fax:* 310-839-2249 *Toll Free Fax:* 800-944-5432 (US & CN)
E-mail: access@socialstudies.com
Web Site: www.socialstudies.com
Key Personnel
CEO: David Weiner
Chief Learning Offr: Aaron Willis
Founded: 1965
Educational resources-supplementary learning materials including books, CD-ROMs, videos, DVDs, software, charts, posters, maps, globes & atlases.
Divisions: Nystom Education; The Center for Learning; MindSparks; The Writing Co; Interact; Good Year Books; School Counselor Resources; Classroom Science Resources; Classroom Health Resources.
Catalog(s) available

Society of Manufacturing Engineers (SME)
One SME Dr, Dearborn, MI 48128
Tel: 313-425-3000 *Toll Free Tel:* 800-733-4763 *Fax:* 313-425-3400

E-mail: service@sme.org (cust care)
Web Site: www.sme.org
Key Personnel
CEO: Jeffrey M Krause
Pres: Dean L Bartles
Founded: 1932
Professional society supporting lifelong manufacturing education.
Online catalog(s) available
Branch Office(s)
7100 Woodbine Ave, Suite 312, Markham, ON L3R 5J2, Canada *Tel:* 905-752-4415 *Toll Free Tel:* 888-322-7333 *Fax:* 905-479-0113
E-mail: canadasales@sme.org

Society of Motion Picture & Television Engineers® (SMPTE®)
White Plains Plaza, 445 Hamilton Ave, Suite 601, White Plains, NY 10601-1827
Tel: 914-761-1100 *Fax:* 914-206-4216
E-mail: marketing@smpte.org
Web Site: www.smpte.org
Key Personnel
Exec Dir: Barbara H Lange *Tel:* 914-205-2370
Dir, Events & Governance Liaison: Sally-Ann D'Amato *Tel:* 914-205-2375 *E-mail:* sdamato@smpte.org
Mktg & Commun: Aimee Ricca *Tel:* 914-205-2381 *E-mail:* aimeericca@smpte.org
Founded: 1916
Technical society for the motion imaging industry - advance engineering & technical aspects of movies, television, arts & sciences.

Sodanceabit
11372 Kelly Lane, Los Alamitos, CA 90720
Tel: 562-799-4340 *Toll Free Tel:* 800-64-DANCE (643-2623)
E-mail: sodanceabit@live.com
Web Site: www.sodanceabit.com
Key Personnel
Owner: Phil Martin
Produce & distribute audios & videos on how to dance & keep fit.
Catalog(s) available, free

Sofradir EC
373 Rte 46 W, Fairfield, NJ 07004-2442
Tel: 973-882-0211 *Fax:* 973-882-0997
E-mail: info@sofradir-ec.com
Web Site: www.sofradir-ec.com
Founded: 1969
Manufacture night vision modules for ENG cameras, digital & film cameras & camcorders.
Catalog(s) available

Elliot Sokolov Music
Division of User Friendly Music (BMI)
One Hillside Ave, Goldens Bridge, NY 10526
Tel: 917-690-5487
E-mail: elliotsounds@gmail.com
Web Site: www.elliotsokolov.com
Key Personnel
Owner & Prodr: Elliot Sokolov
Music producer, including MP3. User friendly music library.
Membership(s): BMI

Solar Studios
1601 S Central Ave, Glendale, CA 91204
Tel: 818-240-1893 *Fax:* 818-240-4187
Web Site: www.solarstudios.com
Key Personnel
Contact: Peter Cohn *E-mail:* peter@solarstudios.com
Studio & soundstage rental for filming, commercial shoots, green screen work, music video, still photo shoots & special events.

Solid Sound Recording Studio
2400 Hassell Rd, Suite 430, Hoffman Estates, IL 60169
Tel: 847-490-2101
E-mail: solidsoundchicago@icloud.com
Key Personnel
Studio Mgr: John Towner
Founded: 1979

Solid State Logic Inc
320 W 46 St, 2nd fl, New York, NY 10036-8398
Tel: 212-315-1111
E-mail: sales@solidstatelogic.com; nysales@solidstatelogic.com
Web Site: www.solidstatelogic.com
Key Personnel
SVP: Don Wershba
Founded: 1976
Designer of audio mixing consoles.
Catalog(s) available
Brochure(s) available
Membership(s): AES; Florida Motion Picture & Television Association; NAB; SMPTE®; SPARS

Solutek Corp
94 Shirley St, Boston, MA 02119
Tel: 617-445-5335 *Toll Free Tel:* 800-403-0770 *Fax:* 617-445-9623
Web Site: www.solutekphotochemicals.com
Key Personnel
Pres: M A Sigal
Catalog(s) available

Solution Tree
555 N Morton St, Bloomington, IN 47404-3730
Tel: 812-336-7700 *Toll Free Tel:* 800-733-6786 *Fax:* 812-336-7790
E-mail: info@solutiontree.com
Web Site: www.solutiontree.com
Key Personnel
CEO: Jeff Jones
Founded: 1998
Delivers comprehensive professional development to schools & districts through a wide range of services & products including educator conferences, customized district solutions for long-term professional development, books, videos & online courses.
Foreign Office(s): 2/47 Wangara Rd, Cheltenham, Victoria 3192, Australia *Tel:* (03) 8558 2456 *Fax:* (03) 8558 2400 *E-mail:* pd@solution-tree.com.au

SOM Publishing Co
Division of School of Metaphysics
163 Moon Valley Rd, Windyville, MO 65783
Tel: 417-345-8411
E-mail: som@som.org
Web Site: www.som.org
Key Personnel
CEO & Dir, Prodn: Barbara O'Guinn Condron
Pres: Dr Christine Spretnjak
Secy: Linda Pecaut
Asst Dir, Prodn & Intl Secy: Karen Mosby
Master Prodn Engr: Terry Martin
Online catalog(s) available, printable

Sonalysts Media
215 Parkway N, Waterford, CT 06385
Mailing Address: PO Box 280, Waterford, CT 06385
Tel: 860-442-4355 *Toll Free Tel:* 800-526-8091 (ext 3848)
E-mail: production@sonalysts.com; media@sonalysts.com; exhibits@sonalysts.com
Web Site: www.sonalystsmedia.com
Key Personnel
VP, Events & Exhibits: Don Venditto *Tel:* 860-326-3600

VP, Film & Broadcast: Eric Toriello *Tel:* 860-326-3821
Soundstage rentals. Offers a full suite of integrated media services. Provides services in the areas of animation, audio production, exhibits & events, graphic communications, video production & post-production, web site development, new media & social media marketing.

Sonance
Division of Dana Innovations
212 Avenida Fabricante, San Clemente, CA 92672-7531
Tel: 949-492-7777 *Toll Free Tel:* 800-582-0772 (tech support); 800-582-7777
E-mail: customerservice@sonance.com
Web Site: www.sonance.com
Key Personnel
Founder: Geoff Spencer; Scott Struthers
Founded: 1983
Manufacture sound systems.
Catalog(s) available
Membership(s): American Society of Interior Designers; CES; Custom Electronic Design & Installation Association; NSCA

Sonar Radio Corp
761-6 Coco Plum Circle, Plantation, FL 33324
Tel: 954-981-8800
Key Personnel
Chmn: Bernard E Klein
Engineering & licensing company distributing video recording accessories.
Catalog(s) available

Sonic Gravy
2515 Laurel Pass, Los Angeles, CA 90046
Tel: 323-650-2751
E-mail: info@sonicgravy.com
Web Site: www.johnswihart.com
Key Personnel
Composer: John Swihart *E-mail:* john@sonicgravy.com
Mgr: Susan Swihart
Original music.

Sonic IT Communications
79 Denlow Blvd, Toronto, ON M3B 1P8, Canada
Tel: 416-383-0260 *Toll Free Tel:* 800-267-6642 *Fax:* 416-383-0261
E-mail: sales@sonicscience.com
Web Site: www.sonicscience.com
Key Personnel
Pres: Martin Yale *E-mail:* martin@sonicscience.com
Founded: 1980
Developer of sound retrieval & media mangement systems.

SonicPool
6860 Lexington Ave, Hollywood, CA 90038
Tel: 323-460-4649 *Toll Free Tel:* 866-203-7213 *Fax:* 323-460-6063
E-mail: production@sonicpool.com
Web Site: www.sonicpool.com
Key Personnel
Founder & Pres: Patrick Bird
Founder: John Frost
Founded: 2001
Post-production picture & sound, VFX, titles, deliverables, DVD/Blu-ray creation, authoring & rental. 20,000 sq ft secure access facility.

SoNo Studios
18 Leonard St, Norwalk, CT 06850
Tel: 203-354-4002
E-mail: info@sonostudios.com
Web Site: www.sonostudios.com
Key Personnel
Owner/Feature Film & Commerical Dir: Bret Stern

Full service soundstage rental. SoNo Studios houses a 4,000 sq ft soundproof sound stage with drive-in door for vehicle access & a wide selection of grip & electric equipment available on hand daily.

Sonora Recorders
3222 Los Feliz Blvd, Los Angeles, CA 90039
Tel: 213-841-0712
E-mail: ductape@aol.com
Web Site: www.sonorarecorders.com
Key Personnel
Owner & Engr: Richard Barron
Founded: 1992
Audio recording & mixing.

Sonoton Music Library
Division of Associated Production Music LLC
6255 Sunset Blvd, Suite 900, Hollywood, CA 90028
Tel: 323-461-3211 *Toll Free Tel:* 800-543-4276
Fax: 323-461-9102
Web Site: www.apmmusic.com
Key Personnel
US Mktg Dir: Elisabeth Oei *Tel:* 818-888-6523
Catalog(s) available

Sony Broadcast & Business Solutions Co, see Sony Pro Audio

Sony Electronics Inc
Division of Sony Corp of America
16530 Via Esprillo, San Diego, CA 92127
Tel: 858-942-2400
Web Site: www.sony.com
Key Personnel
VP, Corp Communs: John Dolak *Tel:* 858-942-2905 *E-mail:* john.dolak@am.sony.com
Manufacture electronics.
Catalog(s) available

Sony Music Commercial Music Group
Division of Sony Music Entertainment
550 Madison Ave, New York, NY 10022
Tel: 212-833-8000
Web Site: www.sonymusic.com
Key Personnel
Pres: Richard Story
EVP, Busn & Legal Aff: Gil Aronow
SVP, Sales: Scott van Horn
VP, Busn & Legal Aff: Jennifer Goodman
Mgr, Busn Aff Admin, Sony Music Entertainment: Aneil Sahota
Music production.

Sony Music Entertainment
Division of Sony Music
25 Madison Ave, New York, NY 10010
Tel: 212-833-8000
Web Site: www.sonymusic.com
Key Personnel
CFO: Kevin Kelleher
Membership(s): AES; The Recording Academy; RIAA; SPARS

Sony Pictures Entertainment Inc
Subsidiary of Sony Corp of America
10202 W Washington Blvd, Culver City, CA 90232
Tel: 310-244-4000
Web Site: www.sonypictures.com
Key Personnel
CEO: Michael Lynton
Sr EVP & CFO: Philip Rowley
EVP & Chief Communs Mgr: Robert Lawson
Founded: 1918
Film & video producer & distributor.

Sony Pictures Home Entertainment
10202 W Washington Blvd, Culver City, CA 90232-3119
Tel: 310-244-4000 *Fax:* 310-244-2485
Web Site: www.sonypictures.com
Key Personnel
SVP, Worldwide Publicity: Fritz Friedman
Catalog(s) available
Membership(s): Entertainment Merchants Association

Sony Pro Audio
Division of Sony Electronics Inc
One Sony Dr, Park Ridge, NJ 07656
Tel: 201-930-1000
Web Site: pro.sony.com/bbsc/ssr/home.do
Manufacture electronics such as digital recorders & players, cameras, professional audio equipment & accessories.
Catalog(s) available
Membership(s): AES; NAMM, the National Association of Music Merchants; NSCA; Professional Audio Manufacturers Alliance

SOS Film Works (Space Ordnance Systems)
Subsidiary of Agua Dulce Movie Ranch Inc
34855 Petersen Rd, Agua Dulce, CA 91390
Tel: 661-251-2365 *Fax:* 661-268-7680
Web Site: www.sosfilmworks.com
Key Personnel
Pres: William Fix *E-mail:* williamfix@sosfilmworks.com
Founded: 1991
Location(s) for feature film, television, commercials & music videos.

SOTA Sales & Service Center
436 E Locust St, DeKalb, IL 60115
Tel: 608-538-3500 *Toll Free Tel:* 800-772-7682
Fax: 608-538-3502
E-mail: sales@sotaturntables.com
Web Site: www.sotaturntables.com
Key Personnel
Founder: Donna Bodinet; Kirk Bodinet
Founded: 1997
Manufacture & service turntables & turntable accessories.
Online catalog(s) available

Soularium Recording Studios
702 S Alpine Hwy, Alpine, UT 84004
Tel: 801-492-0505
E-mail: info@soulariumstudios.com
Web Site: www.soulariumstudios.com
Key Personnel
Owner & Mng Partner: Kenny Amacher
Assoc Engr: Jordan Turner
Founded: 1996
Music recording/mixing & all audio post-production.

Sound & Images Inc
1211 Virginia St, Columbia, SC 29201
Tel: 803-791-3925
E-mail: marketing@s-and-i.com
Web Site: www.s-and-i.com
Key Personnel
Founder & CEO: Eddie Wright *E-mail:* ceo@s-and-i.com
Dir, Mktg & Events: Rob Nelson
Founded: 1981
Corporate audio, video & lighting company that rents, sells & installs.

Sound & Vision Communications Inc
4100 W Kennedy Blvd, Suite 208, Tampa, FL 33609-2244
Tel: 813-289-4297
Web Site: www.gosvc.com
Key Personnel
Pres: Ian Cuthbertson *E-mail:* ian@gosvc.com

Founded: 1982
Full service meeting, event & video production.

Sound & Vision Media
372 Squire Rd, Revere, MA 02151
Tel: 781-284-9707
E-mail: info@soundandvisionmedia.com
Web Site: www.soundandvisionmedia.com
Key Personnel
Mng Partner: Mark Helms
Gen Mgr: Charles Vitale
Founded: 1972
In-house corporate & commercial video, radio & web production.

Sound Arts Recording Studio
8377 Westview Dr, Houston, TX 77055-5737
Tel: 713-464-4653
Web Site: www.soundartsrecording.com
Key Personnel
Engr, Mixer & Prodr: Brian Baker
    E-mail: brianbaker@soundartsrecording.com
Music recording studio.
Brochure(s) available
Membership(s): ASCAP; BMI

Sound Associates Inc
424 W 45 St, New York, NY 10036
Tel: 212-757-5679 *Toll Free Tel:* 888-772-7686
Fax: 212-265-1250
E-mail: newyork@soundassociates.com
Web Site: www.soundassociates.com
Key Personnel
CEO: Richard Fitzgerald *Tel:* 914-963-3452
Founded: 1946
Manufacturer & distributor of hearing assistance systems as well as professional audio & video systems.
Branch Office(s)
979 Saw Mill River Rd, Yonkers, NY 10710
    Tel: 914-963-3452 *Fax:* 914-963-4236
    E-mail: info@soundassociates.com
560-F Amsterdam Ave NE, Atlanta, GA 30306,
    Acct Mgr: Amy Edelkind *Tel:* 404-724-9050 *Fax:* 404-724-9891 *E-mail:* atlanta@soundassociates.com (prodn servs)

Sound by Fitch
Division of Fitch Electronics Inc
1134 Ridge Rd, Pottstown, PA 19465
Tel: 610-469-6082 *Fax:* 610-469-0559
Key Personnel
Pres: William Fitch
Audio equipment distributor.
Membership(s): AES; ARCA

Sound by Singer Ltd
242 W 27 St, 2nd fl, New York, NY 10001
Tel: 212-924-8600 *Fax:* 212-366-6351
E-mail: info@soundbysinger.com
Web Site: www.soundbysinger.com
Key Personnel
Pres: Andrew Singer
Full service AV dealer.

Sound Control Technologies Inc
28 Knight St, Norwalk, CT 06851
Tel: 203-854-5701 *Fax:* 203-854-5702
E-mail: sales@soundcontrol.net
Web Site: www.soundcontrol.net
Key Personnel
Co-Founder & Pres: David Neaderland
    E-mail: dneaderland@soundcontrol.net
Founded: 1987
Manufacturer of electronic components for conference & training rooms.
Catalog(s) available
Membership(s): Audiovisual and Integrated Experience Association; IMFA; NSCA

Sound-Craft Systems Inc
1584 Petit Jean Mountain Rd, Morrilton, AR 72110
Tel: 501-727-5476 *Toll Free Tel:* 800-643-8747
    Fax: 501-727-5402
E-mail: sales@sound-craft.com
Web Site: www.sound-craft.com
Key Personnel
Sales Mgr: Jeffery Zimmerman *E-mail:* jeffz@
    sound-craft.com
Founded: 1947
Manufacturer of presentation equipment & furniture.
Catalog(s) available
Membership(s): ARA; Audiovisual and Integrated
    Experience Association

Sound Feelings Records
18375 Ventura Blvd, No 8000, Tarzana, CA 91356
Tel: 818-757-0600
Web Site: www.soundfeelings.com
Key Personnel
Pres: Howard Richman
Founded: 1984
Music for transformation including MP3.
Catalog(s) available

Sound-FX-Design
Subsidiary of Shortwave Recording Co Inc
PO Box 3541, Newport, RI 02840
Tel: 401-952-1186
E-mail: info@sound-fx-design.com
Web Site: www.sound-fx-design.com
Key Personnel
Owner & Pres: Steve Cerilli
Founded: 2000
Sound design, audio & video post-production for
    3D animation & TV, production sound & location sound for film & commercials.

Sound Ideas
105 W Beaver Creek Rd, Suite 4, Richmond Hill,
    ON L4B 1C6, Canada
Tel: 905-886-5000 *Toll Free Tel:* 800-387-3030;
    800-665-3000 (CN) *Fax:* 905-886-6800
E-mail: info@sound-ideas.com; contact@sound-
    ideas.com; wbc105@sound-ideas.com
Web Site: www.sound-ideas.com
Key Personnel
Pres & CEO: Brian Nimens
Founded: 1978
Sound effects & production music for broadcast,
    film & multimedia.
Catalog(s) available
Foreign Office(s): DeWolfe Ltd, Shropshire
    House, 2nd fl East, 11/20 Capper St, London
    WC1E 6JA, United Kingdom *Tel:* (020) 7631
    3600 *Fax:* (020) 7631 3700
Membership(s): AES; NAB; SMPTE®

The Sound Lab Inc
3355 Bee Cave Rd, Bldg 7, Suite 705, Austin,
    TX 78746
Tel: 512-476-2122 *Fax:* 512-476-2127
E-mail: info@thesoundlabinc.com
Web Site: www.thesoundlabinc.com
Key Personnel
Owner: Steve Metz *E-mail:* steve@
    thesoundlabinc.com
Owner & Pres: Phil Mezzetti *E-mail:* phil@
    thesoundlabinc.com
Founded: 2002
Recording studio; pro tools digital editing, ISDN
    digital phone patch, ADR, large cutting room;
    music & sound effects libraries. Radio & TV
    audio production, audio for film, animation &
    gaming.

Sound*Light
5438 Tennessee Ave, New Port Richey, FL 34652
Tel: 727-842-6788 *Fax:* 727-842-6788
Web Site: www.awakening-healing.com; www.
    soundlight.org
Key Personnel
Master of Light: Keth Luke *E-mail:* keth@
    soundlight.org
Astrologer Consultant: Jan Carter
Founded: 1974
Light photographic, AV services & support.
Brochure(s) available
Membership(s): NATAS

Sound of Birmingham Productions
3625 Fifth Ave S, Birmingham, AL 35222
Tel: 205-595-8497 *Fax:* 205-595-5220
Web Site: www.soundofbirmingham.com
Key Personnel
Owner: Don Mosley *E-mail:* don@
    soundofbirmingham.com
Founded: 1975
All types of audio recording. Three studios with
    DeWolfe, AMC & Custom music libraries.

Sound Service Co
6630 Morella Ave, North Hollywood, CA 91606-
    1651
Tel: 818-503-4440
Key Personnel
Owner & Sr Systems Engr: Joel Thames
    E-mail: jetames@sbcglobal.net

Sound Sound
843 Hiawatha Place S, Unit 304, Seattle, WA
    98144-2823
Tel: 206-330-6438
Web Site: www.soundsound.com; www.
    undisclosedlocation.us
Key Personnel
Owner & CEO: Tom Fallat *E-mail:* tom@
    soundsound.com
Founded: 1990
Audio recording & production facility.
Catalog(s) available

Sound Strations Audio Productions Inc
3120 South Ave, La Crosse, WI 54601
Tel: 608-787-8133 *Fax:* 608-787-0012
Web Site: soundstrations.com
Key Personnel
Founder: Brett Huus *E-mail:* bhuus@
    soundstrations.com
Founded: 1993
Full service digital recording studio for market-
    ing, communication & music professionals.

The Sound Tracker®, see Quiet Planet LLC

Sound Venture Productions
441 MacLaren St, Suite 401, Ottawa, ON K2P
    2H3, Canada
Tel: 613-241-5111 *Fax:* 613-241-5010
E-mail: info@soundventure.com
Web Site: www.soundventure.com
Key Personnel
Pres: Tim Joyce *Tel:* 613-241-5111 ext 248
    E-mail: tim@soundventure.com
Founded: 1980
Produce performing arts, documentary, cultural
    & children's programming. Film & TV drama
    production. Audio, video & graphic design ser-
    vices.

Sound/Video Impressions Inc
110 S River Rd, Des Plaines, IL 60016
Tel: 847-297-4360 *Fax:* 847-297-6870
E-mail: info@soundvideoimpressions.com
Web Site: www.soundvideoimpressions.com
Key Personnel
Owner & VP, Opers: Paul Snead
Studio Mgr: Kathy Dunaj
Sales: Jerry Jacobs *E-mail:* jerry@
    soundvideoimpressions.com
Video & audio production & post-production,
    interactive programming for web, CD-ROM,
    DVD, video web casts & web sites.
Catalog(s) available

Sound Works
7110 Gary St, Houston, TX 77055
Tel: 713-960-8222
Web Site: www.soundworks.com
Key Personnel
Founder & Owner: Dwight Cook
    E-mail: dcook@soundworks.com
Premier media production company.
Membership(s): AAF; SPARS

SoundByte Productions Inc
636 E Sixth St, New York, NY 10009
Tel: 212-675-0600 *Fax:* 212-675-3724
E-mail: info@soundbyte.com
Web Site: www.soundbyte.com
Key Personnel
Owner: Nelson Wong
Owner & Chief Engr: Paul Zinman
Founded: 1994
Independent audio services company offering pro-
    duction, post-production & location recording
    services.
Catalog(s) available

Soundcraft
Division of Harman Professional Solutions
8500 Balboa Blvd, North Ridge, CA 91329
Toll Free Tel: 800-622-6983
E-mail: support@soundcraft.com
Web Site: www.soundcraft.com
Key Personnel
Sales: Tom Der *E-mail:* tder@harman.com
Founded: 1973
Design & manufacture professional audio mixing
    consoles.
Catalog(s) available
Membership(s): AES; NSCA

Soundfold Inc
9200 N State Rte 48, Centerville, OH 45458
Tel: 937-885-5100 *Toll Free Tel:* 800-782-8018
    Fax: 937-885-5115
E-mail: info@soundfold.com
Web Site: soundfold.com
Key Personnel
Pres: Tony Sickels *E-mail:* tsickels@soundfold.
    com
EVP: Mike Sickels *E-mail:* msickels@soundfold.
    com
VP: Chad Pierson *E-mail:* cpierson@soundfold.
    com; Kelli Pierson *E-mail:* kpierson@
    soundfold.com
Founded: 1967
Manufacturer of acoustical wall coverings, wall
    carpets & surround mounts.
Online catalog(s) available

Soundmaster Group
89 Barford Rd, Toronto, ON M9W 4H8, Canada
Tel: 416-741-7057 *Fax:* 416-477-2496
E-mail: mail@soundmaster.com
Web Site: www.soundmaster.com
Key Personnel
Chmn & CEO: Robert Predovich
Developer of the award-winning ION® Operating
    Environment.

Sounds Interesting Studio
112 Fuller St, Middleboro, MA 02346
Mailing Address: PO Box 465, Middleboro, MA
    02346-0465
Tel: 508-947-7387
Web Site: www.soundsinterestingstudio.com

Key Personnel
Owner & Pres: Erik Lindgren *E-mail:* erik@
arfarfrecords.com
Engr: Brian Cass *Tel:* 508-264-7727
E-mail: brian@overclockinc.com
Acoustically designed professional recording studio.

Sounds Unique
1721-A Little Orchard St, San Jose, CA 95125
Tel: 408-287-3002
Web Site: www.soundsunique.com
Key Personnel
Owner: Michael Steiner *E-mail:* micky@
soundsunique.com
Founded: 1972
High-end speaker systems, electronics & media products wholesale to the public.

SoundSpace Inc
845 Dayton St, Yellow Springs, OH 45387
Tel: 937-767-7353
E-mail: soundspace@sbcglobal.net
Web Site: soundspaceinc.com
Key Personnel
Pres: Chris Hertzler
Audio production service company & video editing.
Catalog(s) available

Soundsphere
Division of Sonic Systems Inc
10 Research Dr, Stratford, CT 06615
Tel: 203-386-9200 *Fax:* 203-386-0773
E-mail: info@soundsphere.com
Web Site: www.soundsphere.com
Key Personnel
Pres: Peter Hamilton
Sales Mgr: Scott Gronsbell
Founded: 1976
Manufacture Soundsphere omnidirectional loudspeakers.
Catalog(s) available
Membership(s): Audiovisual and Integrated Experience Association

Soundtrack Group
162 Columbus Ave, Boston, MA 02116
Tel: 617-303-7500 *Fax:* 617-303-7555
Web Site: www.soundtrackgroup.com
Key Personnel
COO: Amy Blankenship *E-mail:* ablankenship@
soundtrackgroup.com
Production & post-production space & services.
Branch Office(s)
936 Broadway, New York, NY 10010, Dir of Opers: Lori Shinn *Tel:* 212-420-6010 *Fax:* 212-777-6403 *E-mail:* lori.shinn@soundtrackgroup.com
128 W 22 St, New York, NY 10010 *Tel:* 212-420-6010

Soundtracks Production Services LLC
22 N Central Ave, Sicklerville, NJ 08081
Tel: 856-728-8112 *Fax:* 856-728-8075
E-mail: info@soundtracksnj.com
Web Site: www.soundtracksnj.com
Key Personnel
Founder & Pres: Robert J Sallade
Founded: 1985
Production equipment rentals, including speakers, amplifiers, signal processing equipment, microphones, lighting fixtures, special effects generators, projectors, screens & stages.

Soundtrax Inc
8116 Brucar Ct, Gaithersburg, MD 20877
Tel: 240-401-9555
Key Personnel
Owner & Pres: Leonard Schmitz

Founded: 1982
Audio equipment rental & location sound recording. Optical sound recording for documentaries, commercials, feature films, corporate, & radio.

SoundTube Entertainment Inc
Subsidiary of MSE Audio
10661 Rene St, Lenexa, KS 66215
Tel: 913-663-5600 *Toll Free Tel:* 855-663-5600
Fax: 913-663-3200
E-mail: sales@mseaudio.com
Web Site: www.soundtube.com
Key Personnel
VP, Sales-US, Commercial & Residential:
Michael Sipe *E-mail:* mtsipe@mseaudio.com
Sales Dir, Northeast US: Jonathan Duran
E-mail: jdduran@mseaudio.com
World leader in speaker innovation.
Membership(s): Audiovisual and Integrated Experience Association

SoundView Services Inc
One Phillips Dr NW, Leesburg, VA 20176
Tel: 703-777-9570 *Toll Free Tel:* 866-680-8189
E-mail: info@soundviewservices.com
Web Site: www.soundviewservices.com
Key Personnel
Prodr: David Mercado *E-mail:* david@
soundviewservices.com
Founded: 2001
Special event staging coast to coast, video editing, script writing, AV services, video & audio production.

Source Film Studio
1111 N Beachwood Dr, Hollywood, CA 90038
Tel: 323-463-5555
E-mail: info@sourcefilmstudio.com
Web Site: www.sourcefilmstudio.com
Key Personnel
Contact: Juan Hernandez *Tel:* 323-463-5555
ext 3 *E-mail:* juan@sourcefilmstudio.com;
Bobby Naidu *Tel:* 323-463-5555 ext 4
E-mail: bobby@sourcefilmstudio.com
Studio rentals with an extensive inventory of lighting equipment, grip equipment & production supplies.

Source School of Tantra Yoga Inc
PO Box 368, Kahului, HI 96733
Toll Free Tel: 888-6-TANTRA (682-6872)
E-mail: school@sourcetantra.com
Web Site: sourcetantra.com
Key Personnel
Founder: Charles Muir *E-mail:* charles@
sourcetantra.com
Founded: 1978
Workshops, appearances, books & products on Tantra Yoga.
Catalog(s) available

The Source Stock Footage Library Inc
Subsidiary of The Source Films
140 S Camino Seco, Suite 308, Tucson, AZ 85710
Tel: 520-298-4810 *Fax:* 520-290-4376
E-mail: requests@sourcefootage.com
Web Site: www.sourcefootage.com
Key Personnel
Pres: Rick De Croix *Tel:* 212-925-2547
Lib Mgr: Don E French
Founded: 1982
Stock footage library, assorted film & video originated images transferred to video.
Demo reel(s) available, VHS demo copy available, no charge to video professionals
Online catalog(s) available
Membership(s): IQ

South Coast Film & Video
5234 Elm St, Houston, TX 77081

Tel: 713-661-3550 *Toll Free Tel:* 800-229-3550
Fax: 713-661-4357
E-mail: info@scfilmvideo.com
Web Site: www.southcoastfilmvideo.com
Key Personnel
Pres & Dir: Everett Gorel
Prod Mgr & Audio Engr: Michael Bell
Sr Ed: Marco DuBose
Founded: 1980
Full service production & post-production company.
Online catalog(s) available
Membership(s): NABET-CWA; Texas Association of Motion Media Professionals

South Florida Rehearsal Studios
1885 NE 149 St, Suite 100, North Miami, FL 33181
Tel: 305-949-5303; 786-238-1890 *Fax:* 305-947-3030
E-mail: sfrsmusic@gmail.com; info@sfrs.net
Web Site: www.sfrs.net
Founded: 1996
Full service production recording facility with 5 acoustically designed rehearsal studios equipped with professional rehearsal equipment & audio gear.

South Trunk Studios
825 S Trunk Ave, Dallas, TX 75210
Tel: 214-826-2513
E-mail: southtrunk@sbcglobal.net
Web Site: www.southtrunk.com
Key Personnel
Owner: Randy Murphy
Photography, studio & location; specialty props.

Southern California Sound Image Inc
2425 Auto Park Way, Escondido, CA 92029-1222
Tel: 760-737-3900 *Fax:* 760-737-3929
Web Site: www.sound-image.com
Key Personnel
Pres: Dave Shadoan
Sr Estimator: Jason Schmidlapp
E-mail: jschmidlapp@sound-image.com
Founded: 1971
Audio, video & control integration.
Branch Office(s)
1545 W University Dr, Tempe, AZ 85281
Tel: 480-483-6422 *Fax:* 480-483-6428
7127 Cockrill Bend Blvd, Nashville, TN 37209
Tel: 615-256-0528 *Fax:* 615-256-9945

Southern Illinois University
Ctr for Teaching Excellence, Morris Library Rm 180, 605 Agriculture Dr, Mailcode 6510, Carbondale, IL 62901
Tel: 618-453-2258 *Fax:* 618-453-3010
E-mail: teach@siu.edu
Web Site: cte.siu.edu/video-and-image-production
Key Personnel
Dir: Karla Berry *Tel:* 618-453-5493 *E-mail:* k.
berry@siu.edu
Digital Imaging: Priscilla Pimentel *Tel:* 618-453-2946 *E-mail:* ppimente@siu.edu
Video & imaging services to enrich instruction & class presentations.
Catalog(s) available

Southport Records, see Sparrow Sound Design

Southwest Audio-Visual Inc
3058 E Cairo, Springfield, MO 65802
Tel: 417-887-4900 *Fax:* 417-866-6500
E-mail: info@southwestav.com
Web Site: www.southwestav.com
Key Personnel
Pres: Kevin Lines
Founded: 1996
Full service AV provider.

Southwest Binding & Laminating
109 Millwell Ct, Maryland Heights, MO 63043-2509
Mailing Address: PO Box 150, Maryland Heights, MO 63043-9150
Tel: 314-739-4400 *Toll Free Tel:* 800-325-3628
Toll Free Fax: 800-942-2010
E-mail: sales@swbindinglaminating.com
Web Site: swbindinglaminating.com
Key Personnel
Pres: Mark Mercer
Founded: 1966
Binding, laminating & presentation supplies & equipment.
Membership(s): VAC

SouthWest Organizing Project (SWOP)
211 Tenth St SW, Albuquerque, NM 87102-2919
Tel: 505-247-8832 *Fax:* 505-247-9972
E-mail: swop@swop.net
Web Site: www.swop.net
Key Personnel
Off Mgr: Robert Roibal *E-mail:* roberto@swop.net
Founded: 1980
A statewide multi-racial, community based membership organization that produces & distributes educational materials.

Southwest Sound Solutions
2323 Loop 410 NW, San Antonio, TX 78230-5348
Tel: 210-341-4411 *Fax:* 210-349-8300
E-mail: info@swsoundsolutions.com
Web Site: www.swsoundsolutions.com
Key Personnel
CEO: Curtis Bobsin
Pres: Dillon Boyd
Commercial sound, professional audio contractor.
Membership(s): Audiovisual and Integrated Experience Association; NSCA

Sovfoto/Eastfoto Inc
263 W 20 St, Suite 3, New York, NY 10011
Tel: 212-727-8170
E-mail: info@sovfoto.com
Web Site: www.sovfoto.com
Key Personnel
Dir: Mr Vanya Edwards
Founded: 1932
Historical photo archive dealing with photography from the Soviet era including all the satellite countries of the time.
Brochure(s) available

SpaceCam
31240 La Baya Dr, Westlake Village, CA 91362
Tel: 818-889-6060 *Fax:* 818-889-6062
E-mail: rentals@spacecam.com
Web Site: spacecam.com
Key Personnel
Pres & CEO: Ron Goodman
VP, Mktg: Sandra Crawford *E-mail:* sandy@spacecam.com
Camera system rentals for aerial film production.

Sparkfactor
943 W Randolph St, Suite 2E, Chicago, IL 60607
Tel: 773-292-8000
E-mail: info@sparkfactor.com
Web Site: www.sparkfactor.com
Key Personnel
Pres: George F Lowe
Founded: 2000
Full service digital agency.

Sparkworks Media
1818 E Yesler Way, Seattle, WA 98122
Tel: 206-284-5500
E-mail: info@sparkworksmedia.com
Web Site: sparkworksmedia.com

Key Personnel
Owner & Pres: Michel Hansmire
E-mail: michel@sparkworksmedia.com
Founded: 2004
Video production & motion media agency.
Online catalog(s) available

Sparrow Sound Design
3501 N Southport, 2nd fl, Chicago, IL 60657-1435
Tel: 773-281-8510 *Fax:* 773-472-1632
E-mail: southport@chicagosound.com
Web Site: www.chicagosound.com
Key Personnel
Owner & Engr: Bradley Parker-Sparrow
E-mail: sparrow@chicagosound.com; Joanie Pallatto *E-mail:* joanie@chicagosound.com
Engr: Sal Vito; Todd Carter; Hillary Bryan
Founded: 1977
Recording studio & CD production company.
Online catalog(s) available

SPEAK HOUSE Audio™
Division of A Jim-N-I Recording LLC
1844 E Montecito Ave, Phoenix, AZ 85016
Tel: 602-279-0900 *Fax:* 602-279-0980
Web Site: www.speakhouseaudio.com
Key Personnel
Owner: Susan Bolin *E-mail:* susan@speakhouseaudio.com
Owner & Pres: Jim Sherry *E-mail:* jim@speakhouseaudio.com
Founded: 1977
Audio production & duplication.

Speakeasy™ Productions Inc
9 Westminster Shopping Center, No 152, Westminster, MD 21157
Tel: 410-889-0374
Web Site: www.voiceover.com
Key Personnel
Pres: Kurt Kolb
Founded: 1994
Audio production, voice-overs & audio post. ISDN, Source Connect Pro, in-house FTP, phone patch.

Speakers Unlimited
7532 Courtyard Place, Cary, NC 27519
Tel: 919-466-7676 *Toll Free Tel:* 888-333-6676
E-mail: prospeak@aol.com
Web Site: www.speakersunlimited.com
Key Personnel
Owner: Mike Frank
Founded: 1971
Full service speaker bureau.
Catalog(s) available
Online catalog(s) available
Membership(s): National Speakers Association

Special Archives Division, Motion Picture Branch
Affiliate of National Archives & Records Administration
8601 Adelphi Rd, College Park, MD 20740-6001
Tel: 301-837-2000 *Toll Free Tel:* 866-272-6272
(86-NARA-NARA, cust serv) *Fax:* 301-837-0483
E-mail: mopix@nara.gov
Web Site: www.archives.gov
Key Personnel
Dir & Chief, Motion Pictures: Daniel Rooney
Tel: 301-837-1995 *E-mail:* daniel.rooney@nara.gov
Distribution center for documentaries & government programs.
Branch Office(s)
National Archives Foundation, 700 Pennsylvania Ave NW, Washington, DC 20408-0001 *E-mail:* info@archivesfoundation.org

Special Effects Systems Inc
6160 Edgewater Dr, Suite F, Orlando, FL 32810
Tel: 407-297-6520
Web Site: www.confetticannonstore.com
Founded: 1996
Distributor of confetti launchers & products.
Online catalog(s) available

Special Effects Unlimited Inc
1005 N Lillian Way, Hollywood, CA 90038
Tel: 323-466-3361 *Fax:* 323-466-5712
E-mail: seuefx@aol.com
Web Site: www.specialefxunltd.com
Key Personnel
Special Effects Coord: Allen Hall
Prodn Mgr: Pam Elliott
Founded: 1962
Supplier of specialized rental equipment & materials to the film industry as well as special effects service supplier to the commercial & music industries.

Special Event Services
3135 Indiana Ave, Winston-Salem, NC 27105
Tel: 336-725-7799 *Toll Free Tel:* 800-423-3996
Fax: 336-725-0019
Web Site: www.specialeventservices.com
Key Personnel
Pres: Jim Brammer *E-mail:* jbrammer@specialeventservices.com
Full service technical production company.

Specialized Audio-Visual Inc
14 Solar Dr, Clifton Park, NY 12065
Tel: 518-383-6501 *Fax:* 518-383-6506
E-mail: info@saviusa.com; sales@saviusa.com
Web Site: www.saviusa.com
Key Personnel
Pres: Michael Cusick
Founded: 1986
AV equipment rentals.
Catalog(s) available
Membership(s): AES; Audiovisual and Integrated Experience Association

Specialized Products Co
1100 S Kimball Ave, Southlake, TX 76092
Tel: 817-329-6647 *Toll Free Tel:* 800-866-5353
Toll Free Fax: 800-234-8286
E-mail: customerservice@specialized.net; spcintl@specialized.net
Web Site: www.specialized.net
Key Personnel
Pres: Pete Smith
Govt Sales Mgr: Steve Lynes *E-mail:* slynes@specialized.net
Founded: 1965
Tool kits, cases & test equipment.
Catalog(s) available, 400+ pages
Membership(s): Audiovisual and Integrated Experience Association; Consumer Technology Association™

Specialty Bulb Co Inc
80 Orville Dr, Suite 101, Bohemia, NY 11716
Mailing Address: PO Box 231, Bohemia, NY 11716-0231
Tel: 631-589-3393 *Toll Free Tel:* 800-331-BULB
(331-2852) *Fax:* 631-563-3089
Web Site: www.bulbspecialists.com
Key Personnel
Pres: Caden Zollo *E-mail:* caden@bulbspecialists.com
Sales Rep: LuAnn Buckholz *E-mail:* luann@bulbspecialists.com
Founded: 1984
Distributor of lamps.

Specialty Bulb Products Inc
20010-100A Ave, Unit 2, Langley, BC V1M 3G4, Canada

Tel: 604-513-8500 *Toll Free Tel:* 800-663-1120
Fax: 604-513-8200
E-mail: info@specialtybulb.com; bulbexpert@
specialtybulb.com
Web Site: specialtybulb.com
Key Personnel
Pres: Peter Janzen
Acct Mgr: Herb Ens *E-mail:* herbens@
specialtybulb.com
Founded: 1985
Distributor of projection & photographic equipment.
Online catalog(s) available
Membership(s): IPPD

Specialty Tapes Manfacturing Inc
4221 Courtney Rd, Franksville, WI 53126
Tel: 262-835-0748 *Toll Free Tel:* 800-545-8273
Fax: 262-835-0749
E-mail: sales@specialtytapes.net
Web Site: www.specialtytapes.net
Key Personnel
Mkt Specialist: Tammy Rainer
Founded: 1977
Manufacture pressure sensitive tapes used to
hold cables, wires & cords in place. Used for
photo, motion pictures, TV studios, convention halls & AU applications; dry mounting &
laminating equipment & supplies & slide bindings/mounting supplies.
Online catalog(s) available

Spectra Cine Inc
3607 W Magnolia Blvd, Burbank, CA 91505
Tel: 818-954-9222 *Fax:* 818-954-0016
E-mail: info@spectracine.com
Web Site: www.spectracine.com
Key Personnel
Pres: Nasir Zaidi
VP, Sales: Bernadette Perez

Spectra Film & Video
5626 Vineland Ave, North Hollywood, CA 91601
Tel: 818-762-4545 *Fax:* 818-762-5454
E-mail: sales@spectrafilmandvideo.com
Web Site: www.spectrafilmandvideo.com
Key Personnel
Pres: Douglas Thomas
VP: Gerry Luca
Film processing & telecine services.
Catalog(s) available
Online catalog(s) available
Price list(s) available
Membership(s): The Imaging Alliance; PPA

Spectra Sonics LLC
860 W Riverdale Rd, Suite D-6, Riverdale, UT
84405
Tel: 801-593-9813 (repair)
E-mail: info@spectra-sonics.com
Web Site: spectra-sonics.squarespace.com
Key Personnel
Pres: Bill Cheney *E-mail:* billcheney@spectra-
sonics.com
Founded: 1964
Recording equipment sales & manufacturer; vintage.
Catalog(s) available

Spectra Video Productions Ltd
380 Montrose St, Winnipeg, MB R3M 3M8,
Canada
Tel: 204-452-9832
Web Site: www.spectra-productions.com
Key Personnel
Owner & Pres: Byrnes Benoit *Tel:* 204-781-0079
E-mail: byrnes@spectra-productions.com
Founded: 1979
Video production company.

Spectrum
Division of Charter Communications
400 Atlantic St, 10th fl, Stamford, CT 06901
Tel: 203-905-7800
Web Site: www.spectrum.com; www.facebook.
com/Spectrum
TV, Internet & voice services to residential &
business customers.

Spectrum Audio Visual Services
351 W 45 Ave, Denver, CO 80216
Tel: 303-477-4456 *Toll Free Tel:* 800-477-4752
Fax: 303-477-0114
E-mail: info@spectrumav.com
Web Site: www.spectrumav.com
Key Personnel
SVP & Gen Mgr: Bill MacDonald
E-mail: bmacdonald@spectrumav.com
Dir, Sales-Hotel Div: Pete Yurish
E-mail: pyurish@spectrumav.com
Natl Sales Mgr, Rental & Staging: Gail Brienza
E-mail: gbrienza@spectrumav.com
Full service AV distributor.
Catalog(s) available
Membership(s): SMPTE®

Spectrum Engineers
324 S State St, Suite 400, Salt Lake City, UT
84111
Tel: 801-328-5151 *Toll Free Tel:* 800-678-7077
Fax: 801-328-5155
E-mail: info@spectrum-engineers.com
Web Site: www.spectrum-engineers.com
Key Personnel
Principal & Corp Communs Dir: Jackie McGill
E-mail: jxm@spectrum-engineers.com
Founded: 1982
AV systems design, acoustical engineering &
lighting design.
Branch Office(s)
1501 W Fountainhead Pkwy, Suite 330, Tempe,
AZ 85282 *Tel:* 480-621-3444
9520 Berger Rd, Suite 212, Columbia, MD 21046
Tel: 410-381-8010
Membership(s): AES; ASA; IALD; Illuminating
Engineering Society; INCE; National Council
on Qualifications for the Lighting Professions;
Synergetic Audio Concepts; USITT

Spectrum Enterprise
401 Park Ave S, New York, NY 10016
Tel: 212-379-5826
Web Site: enterprise.spectrum.com
Key Personnel
Mktg Mgr: David A Fitts *E-mail:* david.fitts1@
charter.com
Catalog(s) available

Spectrum Industries Inc
925 First Ave, Chippewa Falls, WI 54729
Mailing Address: PO Box 400, Chippewa Falls,
WI 54729
Tel: 715-723-6750 *Toll Free Tel:* 800-235-1262
Fax: 715-738-2309 *Toll Free Fax:* 800-335-
0473
E-mail: info@spectrumfurniture.com
Web Site: www.spectrumfurniture.com
Key Personnel
Pres & CEO: Dave Hancock
EVP, Sales & Mktg: Scott Dorn
VP, Sales: Robert Kensinger
Mktg & PR: Tony Nelson
Founded: 1968
Manufacturer of computer, training, laptop &
multimedia furniture as well as integrated technology lecterns & instructional stations.
Catalog(s) available
Membership(s): Audiovisual and Integrated Experience Association; NSCA

Spectrum Productions
565 Pinedale Dr, Annapolis, MD 21401

Web Site: www.markgoldberg.com
Key Personnel
Pres: Mark Goldberg *Tel:* 410-212-6879 (cell)
E-mail: mark@markgoldberg.com
Founded: 1978
Video production & photography.
Membership(s): WEVA

Spectrum Sound Inc
1040 Acorn Dr, Suite C, Nashville, TN 37210
Tel: 615-391-3700
Web Site: www.spectrumsound.net
Key Personnel
Founder, CEO & Pres: Ken Porter
Retail Sales Mgr: Barry Sanders *E-mail:* barry@
spectrumsound.net
System Integration Sales Mgr: Ken DeBelius
E-mail: kendeb@spectrumsound.net
Live Sound Acct Rep: Bobby George
Founded: 1979
Professional audio equipment & services.

Speedotron Corp
Division of PromarkBRANDS Inc
1268 Humbracht Circle, Bartlett, IL 60103-1631
Tel: 630-246-5001 *Fax:* 630-830-2525
E-mail: support@speedotron.com
Web Site: www.speedotron.com
Key Personnel
Pres: Ken Orlando *E-mail:* ken.orlando@
promarkbrands.com
Founded: 1939
Professional lighting systems for still photography.
Catalog(s) available

Spence-Thomas Audio Post
70 Richmond St E, Suite 300, Toronto, ON M5C
1N8, Canada
Tel: 416-361-6383 *Toll Free Tel:* 866-547-2617
Fax: 416-361-2970
E-mail: info@spence-thomas.com; bookings@
spence-thomas.com
Web Site: www.spence-thomas.com
Key Personnel
Gen Mgr & Chief Engr: Richard Spence-Thomas
E-mail: richard@spence-thomas.com
Off Mgr: Marilyn A Serr
Founded: 1967
Sound recordings & video production.

Spider Support Systems
11654 Plaza America Dr, Suite 180, Reston, VA
20190
Tel: 703-758-0699
E-mail: service@spidersupport.com
Web Site: www.spidersupport.com
Support equipment for the professional video &
photography industry.

Spirig Advanced Technologies Inc (SAT)
Subsidiary of Spirig Ernest Dipl Ing
144 Oakland St, Springfield, MA 01108
Tel: 413-788-6191 *Toll Free Tel:* 866-977-4744
Fax: 413-788-0490
E-mail: sat@spirig.com
Web Site: www.spirig.com
Key Personnel
Gen Mgr: Lori Topjian
Founded: 1979
Catalog(s) available
Foreign Office(s): Hohlweg 1, PO Box 1140,
8640 Rapperswil, Switzerland *Tel:* (055) 222
6900 *Fax:* (055) 222 6969 *E-mail:* info@spirig.
com

Spirit Media
12042 SE Sunnyside Rd, Suite 700, Happy Valley, OR 97015
Tel: 503-698-5540 *Fax:* 503-698-8408
E-mail: info@spiritmedia.com
Web Site: www.spiritmedia.com

Key Personnel
Pres & Creative Dir: Bill Dolan
Creative Servs Dir: Anne DeRock
Mktg Coord: Suzanne Shelley
Prodn & Events Coord: Zee Farrouge
Founded: 1989
Media production company specializing in video & Webinar production, live & web event services & marketing/messaging.
Membership(s): American Marketing Association; NATAS; NRB

Spizzirri Press Inc
PO Box 9397, Rapid City, SD 57709-9397
Tel: 605-348-2749 *Toll Free Tel:* 800-325-9819
Fax: 605-348-6251 *Toll Free Fax:* 800-322-9819
E-mail: spizzpub@aol.com
Web Site: www.spizzirri.com
Key Personnel
Co-Founder & Partner: Linda Spizzirri; Peter Spizzirri
Children's programming.
Catalog(s) available
Online catalog(s) available
Shipping Address: 15 E Chicago St, Rapid City, SD 57701

Split Image Productions
4134 243 St, Flushing, NY 11363-1658
Tel: 718-428-1438 *Fax:* 718-428-1438
Key Personnel
Pres: Stuart Hersh
Small production company.
Membership(s): AFI; Audiovisual and Integrated Experience Association; NATAS

Spoken Arts Inc
195 S White Rock Rd, Holmes, NY 12531
Tel: 845-878-9600 *Toll Free Tel:* 800-326-4090
Fax: 845-878-9009
E-mail: sales@spokenartsmedia.com
Web Site: www.spokenartsmedia.com
Key Personnel
Owner: Daniel M Welsh
Cust Serv: Susan Welsh
Founded: 1956
Producing audio & video for K-6 school & library market.
Online catalog(s) available
Membership(s): ALA; Audio Publishers Association

Sports Cinematography Group
Division of Sonic Films Inc
715 Pier Ave, Santa Monica, CA 90405
Tel: 310-962-2200
E-mail: sportscinema@earthlink.net
Web Site: www.sportscinematographygroup.com
Key Personnel
Pres & Exec Prodr: David Stoltz
Founded: 1987
HD sports stock footage & full service production company.
Catalog(s) available

Sportsmen on Film Inc
231 Earl Garrett, Suite 300, Kerrville, TX 78028
Tel: 830-792-4200 *Toll Free Tel:* 800-910-HUNT
(910-4868) *Fax:* 830-792-4224
Web Site: www.sportsmenonfilm.com
Key Personnel
Pres & Video Prodr: Ken Wilson
E-mail: kwilson@sportsmenonfilm.com
Hunting, "how to" video production & sales.
Catalog(s) available

Spot Media Production Group
2745 Locust St, St Louis, MO 63103
Tel: 314-667-5915
E-mail: info@spotmpg.com

Web Site: www.spotmpg.com
Key Personnel
Partner: Lynn Hensel; Rick Hensel; Don Rockwell
Exec Prodr: Aleta Harris
Busn Mgr: Mary Smith
Founded: 2003
Video production, post-production, satellite uplink & live streaming.

Sprayway Inc
2651 Warrenville Rd, Downers Grove, IL 60515
Tel: 630-628-3000 *Toll Free Tel:* 800-332-9000
Fax: 630-543-7797
E-mail: info@spraywayinc.com
Web Site: www.spraywayinc.com
Key Personnel
Mktg Dir: Stacey Incavo
Founded: 1947
Manufacturer of aerosol products.
Catalog(s) available

Spring Arbor Distributors Inc
Unit of Ingram Content Group LLC
One Ingram Blvd, La Vergne, TN 37086-1986
Toll Free Tel: 800-395-4340 *Toll Free Fax:* 800-876-0186
E-mail: customerservice@ingramcontent.com
Web Site: www.ingramcontent.com
Key Personnel
Sales Rep: Mary Lou Alexander *Tel:* 615-213-3319 *E-mail:* marylou.alexander@ingramcontent.com
Founded: 1978
Distribution services for Christian booksellers.
Branch Office(s)
Indiana Distribution Center, 7315 Innovation Blvd, Fort Wayne, IN 46818-1371
Oregon Distribution Center, 201 Ingram Dr, Roseburg, OR 97471
Chambersburg Distribution Center, 1240 Ingram Dr, Chambersburg, PA 17202
Membership(s): Entertainment Merchants Association; ICVM

Sprocket Digital
PO Box 1420, Claremont, CA 91711
Tel: 909-946-2364 *Fax:* 909-946-2631
E-mail: sdsales@sprocketdigital.com
Web Site: www.sprocketdigital.com
Key Personnel
Pres: Jeff Des Combes
Manufactures professional audio & video equipment & provides design services for the film & television production & post-production industries.

SSL Industries Inc
4935 Anne Louise Lane, Suite 2, Placerville, CA 95667
Mailing Address: PO Box 3113, Diamond Springs, CA 95619-3113
Tel: 530-644-0233
E-mail: ssl@sllinc.net
Web Site: www.sslinc.net
Key Personnel
Pres: John C Russ
Catalog(s) available
Branch Office(s)
PO Box 190, Scotts Mills, OR 97375 *Tel:* 503-873-7127
Membership(s): AES; SMPTE®

SST/SRS, see Synthesizer Rental Service

ST Productions
Division of Sarkes Tarzian Inc
900 Whitehall Rd, Chattanooga, TN 37405
Tel: 423-267-5412 *Fax:* 423-267-6840
E-mail: stps@wrcbtv.com
Web Site: www.wrcbtv.com

Key Personnel
Prodn Mgr: Doug Loveridge *E-mail:* dlove@wrcbtv.com
Television programming.

Staco Energy Products Co
301 Gaddis Blvd, Dayton, OH 45403
Tel: 937-253-1191 *Toll Free Tel:* 866-261-1191
Fax: 937-253-1723
E-mail: sales@stacoenergy.com; service@stacoenergy.com
Web Site: www.stacoenergy.com
Key Personnel
Busn Devt Mgr: Paul Heiligenberg *Tel:* 937-253-1191 ext 128 *E-mail:* heiligenbergp@stacoenergy.com
Founded: 1937
Manufacture power quality & voltage control equipment.
Catalog(s) available

Staedtler-Mars Ltd
850 Matteson Blvd W, Unit 4, Mississauga, ON L5V 0B4, Canada
Tel: 905-501-9008 *Toll Free Tel:* 800-776-5544 (US); 800-387-5872 (US) *Fax:* 905-501-9117
Toll Free Fax: 800-675-8249 (US)
E-mail: info@staedtler.ca
Web Site: www.staedtler.ca
Key Personnel
Pres: Axel Huelsmann
Mktg: Diane S Brasil
OHP marker manufacturer (Lumocolor®).
Catalog(s) available
Branch Office(s)
4664 Lougheed Hwy, Suite 177, Burnaby, BC V5C 5T5, Canada *Tel:* 604-299-1001 *Toll Free Tel:* 800-661-6144 (US) *Fax:* 604-291-8884
Toll Free Fax: 877-318-6502 (US)
204 boul de Montarville, bureau 130, Boucherville, QC J4B 6S2, Canada *Tel:* 450-449-7460 *Fax:* 450-449-2865

Stage America LLC
2300 N Atlantic Ave, Suite 1002, Daytona Beach, FL 32811
Tel: 702-879-8177
E-mail: info@stageamerica.com
Web Site: www.stageamerica.com
Key Personnel
Pres & Prodn Dir: Raymond W Franklin
E-mail: rfranklin@stageamerica.com
Prodn Mgr: Mike Benson *E-mail:* mbenson@stageamerica.com
Founded: 1982
Production management for corporate & special events.
Membership(s): Meeting Professionals International; RTDNA; SMPTE®

Stage Crew Audiovisual Inc
PO Box 6097, San Juan, PR 00914-6097
Tel: 787-723-6398 *Fax:* 787-721-1410
Key Personnel
Pres: Hamid Azize *E-mail:* hamid.azize@gmail.com

Stage Directions
8311 Hempstead Rd, Houston, TX 77008
Tel: 713-863-7469 *Fax:* 713-863-9418
E-mail: sales@stagedirections.com
Web Site: www.stagedirections.com
Key Personnel
Owner & Pres: Richard Hoggatt, Jr
E-mail: richard@stagedirections.com
Founded: 1987
Media production services, staging services, AV equipment rentals & sales, studio & lighting facilities.

Stage Equipment & Lighting Inc
4600 SW 36 St, Orlando, FL 32811

Tel: 407-425-2010 *Fax:* 407-648-2604
E-mail: mail@seal-fla.com
Web Site: www.seal-fla.com
Key Personnel
Br Mgr & Tech Consultant, Sales: Curt Contrata
  E-mail: ccontrata@seal-fla.com
Lighting production equipment for rentals & production services.
Catalog(s) available
Branch Office(s)
12250 NE 13 Ct, Miami, FL 33161 *Tel:* 305-891-2010 *Fax:* 305-893-2828

Stage Front Presentation Systems
6 Southern Oaks Dr, Savannah, GA 31405
Tel: 912-236-1345 *Toll Free Tel:* 800-736-9242
  Fax: 912-233-5350
Web Site: www.sfps.net; www.
  stagefrontproductions.com
Founded: 1978
Performance & presentation systems.
Catalog(s) available
Branch Office(s)
11460 Maxwell Rd, Suite C, Alpharetta, GA
  30009 (sales & serv)
2060 Northbrook Dr, North Charleston, SC 29406
  Tel: 843-329-0562 (event prodn)
Membership(s): Audiovisual and Integrated Experience Association

Stage Post
255 French Landing Dr, Nashville, TN 37228
Tel: 615-248-1978 *Toll Free Tel:* 877-250-1839
  Fax: 615-242-8861
E-mail: mail@stagepost.com
Web Site: www.stagepost.com
Key Personnel
Owner & Pres: Lynn Bennett *E-mail:* l.bennett@
  stagepost.com
Video production company.

Stage 3 Productions
27500 Donald Ct, Warren, MI 48092
Tel: 586-576-0625 *Toll Free Tel:* 888-330-5179
Web Site: www.stage3.com
Key Personnel
Agent: Andre LaRoche *Tel:* 248-755-0964
  E-mail: andre@stage3.com
Provides photography, computer generated imagery, graphic design, retouching, video, print & broadcast production services.

Stageline Mobile Stage Inc
700 Marsolais St, L'Assomption, QC J5W 2G9,
  Canada
Tel: 450-589-1063 *Toll Free Tel:* 800-26-STAGE
  (267-8243) *Fax:* 450-589-1711
E-mail: info@stageline.com
Web Site: www.stageline.com
Key Personnel
Mktg & Communs Coord: Alexis Delage
Founded: 1987
Distributor & manufacturer of mobile hydraulic stages.
Branch Office(s)
827 L'Ange-Gardien Blvd, L'Assomption, QC
  J5W 1T3, Canada
Membership(s): IFEA

Stageright Corp, a Rogers Group brand
495 Pioneer Pkwy, Clare, MI 48617
Tel: 989-386-7393 (Intl Sales) *Toll Free Tel:* 800-438-4499
E-mail: info@stageright.com
Web Site: www.stageright.com
Key Personnel
VP & Gen Mgr: Jeff Schultz
Founded: 1984
Manufacturer of portable staging & equipment.

Stages Video Productions
514 29 Ave N, Myrtle Beach, SC 29577
Tel: 843-626-7466
E-mail: info@stagesvideo.com
Web Site: www.stagesvideo.com
Key Personnel
Founder: Chuck Stokes *E-mail:* chuck@
  stagesvideo.com; Diane De Vaughn-Stokes
  E-mail: diane@stagesvideo.com
Founded: 1989
Full service video production company. Specialize in marketing/training videos & television commercial production.

StageSound
2240 Shenandoah Ave NW, Roanoke, VA 24017
Tel: 540-342-2040 *Toll Free Tel:* 800-778-9839
  Fax: 540-345-5158
Web Site: stagesound.com
Key Personnel
Gen Mgr & VP, Sales: Jeff Moore *Tel:* 540-342-2040 ext 120
Sales of pro audio, lighting & video products. Design & installation of commercial sound, lighting & video systems. Audio, lighting & video production services for corporate & concert events. Pro audio & lighting electronic repair services.

Stagestep Inc
4701 Bath St, No 46, Philadelphia, PA 19137
Tel: 215-636-9000 *Toll Free Tel:* 800-523-0960
  (US & CN) *Fax:* 267-672-2912
E-mail: stagestep@stagestep.com; info@
  stagestep.com
Web Site: www.stagestep.com
Key Personnel
Founder & Pres: Randy Swartz *Tel:* 215-636-9000
  ext 105 *E-mail:* randy@stagestep.com
Founded: 1979
Manufacture stage flooring & studio flooring for dances, theatre, health & fitness. Books, CDs, videos & gifts.
Online catalog(s) available

Staging Concepts
8400 Wyoming Ave N, Suite 100, Minneapolis,
  MN 55445
Tel: 763-533-2094 *Toll Free Tel:* 800-337-5339
E-mail: info@stagingconcepts.com
Web Site: www.stagingconcepts.com
Key Personnel
CEO: John Lewis
Founded: 1990
Manufacturer of portable staging equipment.
Catalog(s) available, free
Online catalog(s) available

Staging Directions Inc
1327 Northbrook Pkwy, Suite 440, Suwanee, GA
  30024
Tel: 770-409-9909 *Toll Free Tel:* 800-782-4322
  Fax: 770-409-0277
E-mail: sales@teamsdi.net
Web Site: www.stagingdirections.com
Key Personnel
CEO & Pres: Nick D'Allen *E-mail:* nick.allen@
  teamsdi.net
VP: Kevin Miller *E-mail:* kevin.miller@teamsdi.
  net
VP, Opers: Richard Palm *E-mail:* richard.palm@
  teamsdi.net
VP, Sales & Mktg: Kevin McGarty *E-mail:* kevin.
  mcgarty@teamsdi.net
Stage equipment rentals.

Staging Resources Inc
257 E Helen Rd, Palatine, IL 60067
Tel: 847-963-6600 *Toll Free Tel:* 877-963-6600
  Fax: 847-963-6601
E-mail: info@stagingresources.com

Web Site: www.stagingresources.com
Key Personnel
Pres: Jeff Thommes *E-mail:* jt@stagingresources.
  com
Founded: 1987
Provides rental of soundstages, audio equipment, lighting, cameras & projectors.

Stampede Presentation Products Inc
55 Woodridge Dr, Amherst, NY 14228
Tel: 716-635-9474 *Toll Free Tel:* 800-398-5652
  Fax: 716-635-9484 (sales); 716-691-0854
E-mail: stampedenews@stampedeglobal.com
Web Site: www.stampedeglobal.com
Key Personnel
Owner, COO & Pres: Kevin Kelly
Worldwide distributor of presentation & home theatre productions.
Branch Office(s)
165 Matheson Blvd E, Unit 11 & 12, Mississauga, ON L4Z 3K2, Canada *Tel:* 905-602-0888 *Toll Free Tel:* 888-459-8181
Membership(s): Audiovisual and Integrated Experience Association; Consumer Technology Association™; Custom Electronic Design & Installation Association; NSCA

Stanco Sales LLC
1529 S Terry St, Longmont, CO 80501
Tel: 303-776-3770
Key Personnel
Pres: Burton Moquist
AV equipment manufacturer & distributor.
Catalog(s) available

James Stanfield Co Inc
129 S Quarantina St, Santa Barbara, CA 93103
Mailing Address: PO Box 41058, Santa Barbara,
  CA 93140
Tel: 805-897-1185 *Toll Free Tel:* 800-421-6534
  Fax: 805-897-1187
E-mail: maindesk@stanfield.com
Web Site: www.stanfield.com
Key Personnel
Founder: James Stanfield, EdD
Founded: 1976
Special education & school to life transitions, educational videos, slides & curriculum.
Catalog(s) available, free

Stanford Research Systems Inc
1290-D Reamwood Ave, Sunnyvale, CA 94089
Tel: 408-744-9040 *Fax:* 408-744-9049
E-mail: info@thinksrs.com
Web Site: www.thinksrs.com
Key Personnel
Sales & Mktg Mgr: David Ames
Founded: 1980
Catalog(s) available

Stanislaus AV Inc
Division of EKC Enterprises Inc
1431 Kansas Ave, Modesto, CA 95351
Tel: 209-529-2700; 559-438-0330 (EKC)
  Fax: 559-438-0333 (efax)
Web Site: www.stanav.com; ekccorp.com
Founded: 1972
Full service provider & integrator of AV, sound, video, audio & video conference systems.

Jay S Stanley & Associates Inc
5313 McClanahan Dr, Suite G-5, North Little
  Rock, AR 72116
Tel: 501-758-8029 *Toll Free Tel:* 888-758-4728
  Fax: 501-758-8037
E-mail: info@jaystanley.com
Web Site: www.jaystanley.com
Key Personnel
Pres: Jay S Stanley *E-mail:* jay.stanley@
  jaystanley.com
Founded: 1935
AV systems integrator.

Stanton DJ, see Stanton Magnetics

Stanton Magnetics
Division of Gibson Pro Audio
c/o Gibson Pro Audio, 309 Plus Park Blvd, Nashville, TN 37217
Toll Free Tel: 800-4GIBSON (444-2766)
E-mail: service@gibson.com (cust serv)
Web Site: stantondj.com
Founded: 1946
Makers of the SCS (Stanton Control System), professional DJ equipment & accessories.
Catalog(s) available

Star Case Manufacturing Co Inc
648 Superior Ave, Munster, IN 46321
Tel: 219-922-4440 *Toll Free Tel:* 800-822-STAR (822-7827); 800-782-CASE (782-2273)
Fax: 219-922-4442
E-mail: star@starcase.com
Web Site: www.starcase.com
Key Personnel
Pres: Darren Eason
VP, Sales & Mktg: Ralph Hoopes
Founded: 1975
Manufacturer of custom cases.
Catalog(s) available
Membership(s): AES; Audiovisual and Integrated Experience Association; NAB; NAMM, the National Association of Music Merchants; NSCA; SMPTE®

Star Video Duplicating
7100 Mockingbird Lane, Paradise Valley, AZ 85253
Tel: 602-437-0646
Web Site: www.starvideo.com
Key Personnel
Owner & Pres: Paul Brown *E-mail:* paul@starvideo.com
Full duplicating & editing services.

Starburns Industries
1700 W Burbank Blvd, Burbank, CA 91506
Tel: 818-433-3300 *Fax:* 818-433-3383
E-mail: contact@starburnsind.com
Web Site: www.starburnsindustries.com
Key Personnel
CEO & Exec Prodr: Joe Russo, II
Exec Prodr: James A Fino; Dan Harmon; Dino Stamatopoulos
Founded: 2010
Provides services for stop-motion animation, 2D animation, post-production & audio recording.
Branch Office(s)
1101 W Isabel St, Burbank, CA 91506 *Tel:* 818-955-8977

Starline Costumes
1286 Bandera Rd, San Antonio, TX 78228
Tel: 210-435-3535 *Fax:* 210-435-9425
Web Site: starlinecostumes.com
Key Personnel
Gen Mgr: Julie Moore Kech *E-mail:* julie@starlinecostumes.com
Costume & prop distributor & rental company.
Membership(s): National Costumers Association

Starlite
Subsidiary of Starlite Productions International Inc
9 Whittendale Dr, Moorestown, NJ 08057
Tel: 856-780-8000 *Toll Free Tel:* 800-738-7400
Fax: 856-780-8001
E-mail: info@starlite.com
Web Site: www.starlite.com
Key Personnel
Pres & CEO: Dean Danowitz *Tel:* 856-780-8000 ext 8021 *E-mail:* deand@starlite.com
VP, Opers: Joe Masciangelo *E-mail:* joem@starlite.com

VP, Event Technol: Jason Danowitz *Tel:* 856-780-8000 ext 8033 *E-mail:* jasond@starlite.com
Lighting Sales Mgr: Bob Wolfe *Tel:* 856-780-8000 ext 8031 *E-mail:* bobw@starlite.com
Founded: 1983
Design & consultations, 53,000 sq ft corporate office plus wholesale audio, lighting, video & special effects equipment. Retail & wholesale sales, system integration plus installation complete show production services, long & short term rentals, factory authorized repair service.
Membership(s): Audiovisual and Integrated Experience Association; NSCA; Professional Lighting & Sound Association

StarTrak Studios Inc
36 Vermont Ave, Unit 1, Warwick, RI 02888
Tel: 401-732-1880
E-mail: info@startrakstudios.com
Web Site: www.startrakstudios.com
Key Personnel
Pres: Jack Rametta
Founded: 1981
ADR, sound design for radio & TV, ISDN casting, corporate & web creative & production services.

Starwest Productions
8760 W 68 Place, Arvada, CO 80004
Tel: 303-295-2222
E-mail: info@estarwest.com
Web Site: www.estarwest.com
Key Personnel
Pres: Steven Pettit
Full service production company.

State of the Art Acoustik Inc
43-1010 Polytek St, Ottawa, ON K1J 9J3, Canada
Tel: 613-745-2003 *Fax:* 613-745-9687
E-mail: sota@sota.ca
Web Site: www.sota.ca
Key Personnel
Principal: Dr Claude Fortier *E-mail:* cfortier@sota.ca
Pres: Kathryn Savage *E-mail:* ksavage@sota.ca
Founded: 1987
Acoustic design & testing services for performance spaces.
Catalog(s) available
Membership(s): ASA; CAA; INCE; NCAC

Staylor-Made Communications Inc
11835 Carmel Mountain Rd, Suite 1304-365, San Diego, CA 92128-4609
Toll Free Tel: 800-711-6699
E-mail: info@staylor-made.com
Web Site: staylor-made.com
Key Personnel
Pres & Exec Prodr: Jim Staylor *E-mail:* jim@staylor-made.com
VP: Anne Farrell Staylor *E-mail:* anne@staylor-made.com
Creative Dir: Dennis McNabb *E-mail:* dennis@staylor-made.com
Founded: 1992
Video production & communication services for training, marketing & entertainment.

Stedman Corp
9625 E "D" Ave, Richland, MI 49083
Tel: 269-629-5930 *Toll Free Tel:* 888-629-5960
E-mail: info@stedmancorp.com
Web Site: www.stedmancorp.com
Key Personnel
Owner: William "Bill" Hannapel
Founded: 1992
Manufacturer of the Proscreen™ XL, PS101 & PS100 metal pop filters, SHH Studio Headphone Hanger™ & PC-1 Proclip™ sheet music holder.
Catalog(s) available

Steeldeck® Inc
3339 Exposition Place, Los Angeles, CA 90018-4034
Tel: 323-290-2100 *Toll Free Tel:* 800-50STAGE (507-8243) *Fax:* 323-290-9600
E-mail: sales@steeldeck.com; rentals@steeldeck.com
Web Site: www.steeldeck.com
Key Personnel
VP: Adrian Funnell *E-mail:* adrian@steeldeck.com
Founded: 1993
Manufacture, sales & rentals of platforms & risers, steeldeck, stagebase, nivoflex, ultralight, mirage & platform design.

Steiner Studios
15 Washington Ave, Brooklyn Navy Yard, Brooklyn, NY 11205
Tel: 718-858-1600
Web Site: www.steinerstudios.com
Founded: 2004
Hollywood-style production & support facility equipped for start-to-finish production of major motion pictures, independent films, television, broadcast commercials, photo shoots & music videos.

Stereo Sales Inc
1530 S Monroe St, Tallahassee, FL 32301
Tel: 850-224-2635
E-mail: sales@stereosales.net
Web Site: www.stereosales.org; www.stereosales.net
Key Personnel
Pres: Richard W Menasco
Mgr: Travis Vinson
Founded: 1966
Car & professional stereo equipment sales.
Branch Office(s)
700 N Monroe, Tallahassee, FL 32303 *Tel:* 850-536-6900
Membership(s): AES

Bret Stern Productions
c/o SoNo Studios, 18 Leonard St, Norwalk, CT 06850
Tel: 203-354-4002
E-mail: info@bretsternproductions.com
Web Site: bretsternproductions.com
Key Personnel
Owner/Feature Film & Commericial Dir: Bret Stern
Full service video production company providing production, editing & post-production services for commercials, web videos, documentaries & more. Also offers animation & still photography.

Stevens Design & Animation LLC
PO Box 90612, Albuquerque, NM 87199
Tel: 505-200-2042
Web Site: stevensanimation.com
Key Personnel
Directing Animator: Tim Stevens *E-mail:* tstevens@stevensanimation.com
Full service animation & production house specializing in all things character.

Stewart Acoustical Consultants
7330 Chapel Hill Rd, Suite 201, Raleigh, NC 27607
Tel: 919-858-0899 *Fax:* 919-858-0899
Web Site: www.sacnc.com
Key Personnel
Pres & Principal Consultant: Noral D Stewart, PhD *Tel:* 919-858-0899 ext 1 *E-mail:* noral@sacnc.com
Founded: 1979
Provide professional acoustical consulting services including noise control primarily for the

architectural, environmental & industrial work-place markets.
Membership(s): National Council of Acoustical Consultants

Stewart Audio
14435 Cuesta Ct, Suite C, Sonora, CA 95370
Tel: 209-588-8111 *Fax:* 209-588-8113
E-mail: sales@stewartaudio.com; support@stewartaudio.com
Web Site: www.stewartaudio.com
Key Personnel
Chief Mktg Offr: Brian McCormick
Gen Mgr: Kevin Stone
Founded: 1982
Manufacturer of audio power amplifiers.

Stewart Filmscreen Corp
1161 Sepulveda Blvd, Torrance, CA 90502-2754
Tel: 310-784-5300 *Toll Free Tel:* 800-762-4999 (North America only) *Fax:* 310-326-6870
E-mail: request@stewartfilmscreen.com
Web Site: www.stewartfilmscreen.com
Key Personnel
Pres: Grant Stewart
Founded: 1947
Catalog(s) available
Branch Office(s)
3919 Bach-Buxton Rd, Amelia, OH 45102-1013
Tel: 513-753-0800 *Fax:* 513-753-0854
Foreign Office(s): Mileparken 29, 2730 Herlev, Denmark *Tel:* 3648 2204 *Fax:* 3648 2299 *E-mail:* info@stewartfilm-europe.com
No 07-02 Midland House, 112 Middle Rd, Singapore 188970, Singapore *Tel:* 6747 0555 *Fax:* 6747 2221 *E-mail:* stewart@stewartfilm.com.sg
Membership(s): SMPTE®

STIL Casing Solution
76 Saint Paul, Suite 103, Quebec City, QC G1K 3V9, Canada
Tel: 418-694-0449 (ext 10); 418-694-0449 (ext 11, sales & cust serv); 418-694-0449 (ext 12, admin) *Toll Free Tel:* 888-414-0449 (CN & US) *Fax:* 418-694-1621
E-mail: info@stilcasing.com; sales@stilcasing.com; admin@stilcasing.com
Web Site: www.stilcasing.com
Key Personnel
CEO: Frederic Lapointe *E-mail:* frederic.lapointe@stilcasing.com
Sales Asst: Melanie Simard *Tel:* 418-694-0449 ext 11 *E-mail:* melanie.simard@stilcasing.com
Founded: 1997
Manufactures, markets & distributes film containers made of plastic to archivists, museums, film laboratories, studios & any other private or public enterprises involved in film conservation or transport may use our products.

Still N' Motion
1727 Little Orchard St, Suite A, San Jose, CA 95125
Tel: 408-292-9982
E-mail: info1@stillnmotion.com
Web Site: stillnmotion.com
Founded: 1982
Full service creative media design studio. Specialize in video & motion graphics for corporate, documentary & independent productions. Services include conceptualization, design, script writing, studio & location videography & photography, custom soundtracks, HD video editing with advanced effects, 2D & 3D animation, photography, graphic design, interactive authoring, video streaming & web 2.0 programming.

Stockfootage.com
231 S Mountain Way Dr, Orem, UT 84058
Tel: 801-221-9570; 801-361-0012 (cell)
E-mail: sales@stockfootage.com
Web Site: www.stockfootage.com
Key Personnel
Owner & CEO: John Farr
Royalty free stock motion footage.

StockMusic.com
Division of Sound Ideas
105 W Beaver Creek Rd, Suite 4, Richmond Hill, ON L4B 1C6, Canada
Tel: 905-886-0077 *Fax:* 905-886-6800
E-mail: info@stockmusic.com
Web Site: www.stockmusic.com
Key Personnel
CEO: Brian Nimens
Exec Coord: Martha Lonsdale *E-mail:* martha@stockmusic.com
Production music & sound effects via online downloads.
Catalog(s) available

Stockyard Photos/Jim Olive Photography
Division of Photolive Inc
1520 Center St, Studio 2, Houston, TX 77007
Tel: 281-802-3597
Web Site: stockyard.com
Key Personnel
Owner & Photog: James "Jim" Lee Olive *E-mail:* jim@stockyard.com
Photography & stock photography.
Online catalog(s) available
Membership(s): North American Nature Photography Association

Story Teller Effects Group LLC
333 River Rd, Jefferson, LA 70121
Tel: 504-832-9800 *Fax:* 504-832-9955
E-mail: storytellerfx@gmail.com; sales@storytellerfx.com
Web Site: www.riggspfx.com
Key Personnel
Owner/Coord: John Baker *Tel:* 310-994-6983 (cell) *E-mail:* baker@storytellerfx.com; Robert Riggs *Tel:* 360-239-8218 *E-mail:* bob@storytellerfx.com
Founded: 2010
Provides special effects rental equipment & expendables along with full shop capabilities for design & fabrication. Stocking distributors for ULTRATEC, LOOK, CITC & more.
Branch Office(s)
240 Industrial Way, Fayetteville, GA 30215

StoryTrack
3224 Locust St, Suite 301, St Louis, MO 63103
Tel: 314-725-3003
Web Site: www.storytrack.com
Key Personnel
Exec Prodr: Lori Dowd *E-mail:* lori@storytrack.com
Video production & digital marketing services.
Branch Office(s)
2320 N Damen Ave, Suite 2B, Chicago, IL 60647
Tel: 847-754-7550

Stouffer Graphic Arts
922 S Cleveland St, Mishawaka, IN 46544
Tel: 574-252-5772 *Fax:* 574-252-5776
E-mail: info@stouffer.net
Web Site: www.stouffer.net
Founded: 1929
Quality control devices for photosensitive systems.
Brochure(s) available
Price list(s) available

Stouffer Industries Inc, see Stouffer Graphic Arts

Straight Shoot'r Cranes Inc
18434 Oxnard St, Unit H, Tarzana, CA 91356
Tel: 818-609-8310 *Fax:* 818-609-8311
Web Site: www.straightshootr.com
Key Personnel
Owner: Andy Coradeschi *E-mail:* andy@straightshootr.com
Founded: 1993
Equipment rental-motion picture crane/jib-arm combined with a proprietary linear sliding camera mount.

Straight Wire Inc
2032 Scott St, Hollywood, FL 33020
Tel: 954-925-2470 *Toll Free Tel:* 800-683-4434 *Fax:* 954-925-7253
E-mail: info@straightwire.com
Web Site: www.straightwire.com
Key Personnel
Owner & Pres: Steven Hill
Founded: 1985
Distribute & manufacture audio cables, interconnects & speaker cables.
Catalog(s) available

Strand Lighting Inc
Division of Philips Entertainment Group
10911 Petal St, Dallas, TX 75238
Tel: 214-647-7880 *Fax:* 214-647-8031
E-mail: sales@strandlighting.com
Web Site: www.strandlighting.com
Founded: 1914
Television, motion picture, stage & architectural lighting services. Serving North America, Europe, Middle East, Africa & the Asia/Pacific region.
Catalog(s) available
Foreign Office(s): Philips Entertainment Asia Ltd, Roxy Industrial Ctr, Unit C, 14/F, 41-49 Kwai Cheung Rd, Kwai Chung, NT, Hong Kong *Tel:* 2796 9786 *Fax:* 2798 6545
Rondweg zuid 85, Winterswijk 7102 JD, Netherlands *Tel:* (0543) 542513 *E-mail:* entertainment.europe@philips.com
Philips-Selecon Lighting, 19-21 Kawana St, Auckland 0627, New Zealand *Tel:* (09) 481 0100 *Fax:* (09) 481 0101 *Web Site:* www.seleconlight.com
Membership(s): American Society of Lighting Directors; LDI; NAB; Professional Film & Video Equipment Association; SMPTE®; USITT

Strata™
3013 Santa Clara Dr, Santa Clara, UT 84765
Tel: 435-628-5218 *Toll Free Tel:* 800-STRATA-3D (787-2823); 800-6-STRATA (678-7282) *Fax:* 435-628-9756
E-mail: sales@strata.com
Web Site: www.strata.com
Key Personnel
Off Mgr: Rebecca Taylor *E-mail:* rebeccat@strata.com
Founded: 1988
Computer software package; 3D modeling, rendering & animation & digital video software.

Strategic Connections
3000 Spring Forest Rd, Raleigh, NC 27616
Tel: 919-878-0550 *Toll Free Tel:* 800-255-5664 *Fax:* 919-875-8712
Web Site: www.strategicconnections.net
Key Personnel
Pres: Scott McLaughlin
VP: Tom Rause *E-mail:* tom.rause@strategicmail.net
Founded: 1998
Technology systems integrator-structured cabling, AV, commercial security, fire alarm, fire protection, telephone & power supply.
Branch Office(s)
1464 Center Park Dr, Charlotte, NC 28217
961 Burke St, Winston-Salem, NC 27101

1335 Enterprise Ave, Suite A, Myrtle Beach, SC 29577
Membership(s): Audiovisual and Integrated Experience Association

Stray Angel Films
11318 Santa Monica Blvd, Los Angeles, CA 90025
Tel: 310-277-6900 *Fax:* 801-438-5009
E-mail: rentals@strayangel.com
Web Site: www.strayangel.com
Key Personnel
Founder & CEO: Suren M Seron *E-mail:* suren@strayangel.com
COO: Josh Burrows *E-mail:* josh@strayangel.com
Chief Rental Offr: Billy Civitella *E-mail:* billy@strayangel.com
Exec Dir: Howard Asher *E-mail:* howard@strayangel.com
Founded: 2003
Digital motion picture rental, production & production services company.

Stretching Inc
PO Box 767, Palmer Lake, CO 80133-0767
Tel: 719-481-3928 *Toll Free Tel:* 800-333-1307
Fax: 719-481-9058
E-mail: office@stretching.com
Web Site: www.stretching.com
Key Personnel
Founder: Bob Anderson; Jean E Anderson
Mail-order & publishing. Produce & distribute videos, DVDs, books, software & posters; fitness related.
Online catalog(s) available, updated as needed

Strong Cinema Products
Division of Ballantyne Strong Inc
11422 Miracle Hills Dr, Suite 300, Omaha, NE 68154
Tel: 402-453-4444 *Toll Free Tel:* 800-424-1215
Fax: 402-453-7238
E-mail: info@btn-inc.com
Web Site: ballantynestrong.com
Key Personnel
Pres: Ray F Boegner
Cinema Prods Mgr: Troy James *E-mail:* troy.james@btn-inc.com
Manufacture & distribute digital projection systems & entertainment lighting products.
Membership(s): International Cinema Technology Association

Strong Screen Systems
Division of Ballantyne Strong Inc
1440 Raoul-Charrette, Joliette, QC J6E 8S7, Canada
Tel: 450-755-3795 *Toll Free Tel:* 877-755-3795
Fax: 450-755-3122
E-mail: sales@strongmdi.com
Web Site: strongmdi.com
Key Personnel
Gen Mgr: Francois Barrette *E-mail:* francois.barrette@strongmdi.com
Founded: 1968
Manufacturer of screen systems.
Brochure(s) available
Membership(s): Custom Electronic Design & Installation Association; Theatre Equipment Association

Joseph Struhl Company Inc
195 Atlantic Ave, Garden City Park, NY 11040
Mailing Address: PO Box N, Garden City Park, NY 11040
Tel: 516-741-3660 *Toll Free Tel:* 800-552-0023
Fax: 516-742-3617
E-mail: info@magicmaster.com; orders@magicmaster.com
Web Site: www.magicmaster.com
Founded: 1948

Manufacturer of display equipment.
Catalog(s) available

Studio B Mastering
821 Louise Ave, Charlotte, NC 28204
Tel: 704-372-9661
Web Site: www.studiobmastering.com
Key Personnel
Owner & Chief Mastering Engr: Dave Harris *E-mail:* dave@studiobmastering.com
Founded: 1990
Full service mastering.
Membership(s): AES; The Recording Academy

Studio Center Corp
161 Business Park Dr, Virginia Beach, VA 23462
Tel: 757-286-3080 (24 hour cell)
    Toll Free Tel: 866-515-2111 *Fax:* 757-622-0583 (acctg)
Web Site: www.studiocenter.com
Key Personnel
Owner & CEO: William "Woody" Prettyman *E-mail:* william@studiocenter.com
Founded: 1966
Creator, recorder & producer of commercial media for television & radio.
Catalog(s) available
Branch Office(s)
1707 Summit Ave, Richmond, VA 23230
    Tel: 804-359-2111
315 Madison Ave, 11th fl, New York, NY 10017
    Tel: 212-986-1929

Studio Charleston
620 Dobbin Rd, Charleston, SC 29414
Tel: 843-376-1190 *Fax:* 843-737-4282
E-mail: info@studiocharleston.com
Web Site: www.facebook.com/studiocharleston/
Film/TV productions, music video productions, commercial video & photo shoots. Services include studio space rental, production services, production design, set construction, equipment rental & supplies, craft services & catering.

Studio Circle Recordings
863 Woodside Way, San Mateo, CA 94401
Tel: 650-328-8338
E-mail: info@studiocirclerecordings.com
Web Site: www.studiocirclerecordings.com
Key Personnel
Founder, Prodr & Engr: Jermaine Hamilton *E-mail:* jermaine@studiocirclerecordings.com
Founded: 2013
Media services, production management services, music recording/album production, audio for multimedia technologies & marketing, audio format transfers.

Studio Consulting & Construction Inc
2805 Oakview Dr, Dryden, MI 48428-9740
Tel: 810-796-3235; 248-496-9000 (cell)
E-mail: scc@hdakers.com
Web Site: www.hdakers.com
Key Personnel
Pres: Harry D Akers *E-mail:* hdakers@hdakers.com
Consult on & build studio facilities for motion pictures, video recording, audio recording & still photographers.
Video(s) available

Studio Dynamics
7245 Alondra Blvd, Paramount, CA 90723
Tel: 562-531-6700 *Toll Free Tel:* 800-595-4273
E-mail: sales@studiodynamics.com
Web Site: www.studiodynamics.com
Key Personnel
Founder & Pres: Robert Potier *E-mail:* bob@studiodynamics.com
VP: Thomas O'Hare *E-mail:* thomas@studiodynamics.com

Founded: 1984
Backdrops.
Catalog(s) available

Studio 1444
1444 N Highland Ave, Hollywood, CA 90028
Tel: 323-482-1004
E-mail: info@studio1444.com
Key Personnel
Owner: Alen Lin
Founded: 2008
Photo, film & video production facility. Provider of grip & lighting equipment.

Studio Instrument Rentals (SIR)
475 Tenth Ave, 2nd fl, New York, NY 10018
Tel: 212-627-4900
E-mail: nyinfo@sir-usa.com
Web Site: www.sir-usa.com
Key Personnel
Prodn Mgr: Ralph Petrosino *E-mail:* ralph@sir-usa.com
Audio Prodn Coord: Baker Lee *E-mail:* baker@sir-usa.com
Founded: 1967
Musical equipment rentals, sound systems & rehearsal studios.
Branch Office(s)
3541 E Broadway Rd, Phoenix, AZ 85040
    Tel: 480-966-7800 *Fax:* 480-966-7801
    E-mail: azinfo@sir-usa.com
68703 Perez Rd, Unit A-16, Cathedral City, CA 92234 *Tel:* 706-620-5625 *Fax:* 858-274-1906
    E-mail: psinfo@sir-usa.com
6465 Sunset Blvd, Los Angeles, CA 90028
    Tel: 323-957-5460 *Fax:* 323-957-5472
    E-mail: lainfo@sir-usa.com
4620 Santa Fe St, San Diego, CA 92109
    Tel: 858-274-1384 *Fax:* 858-274-1906
    E-mail: sdinfo@sir-usa.com
1215 Fairfax Ave, San Francisco, CA 94124
    Tel: 415-957-9400 *Fax:* 415-957-9470
    E-mail: sfinfo@sir-usa.com
12200 NE 14th Ave, North Miami, FL 33161
    Tel: 305-891-3350 *Fax:* 305-891-3530
    E-mail: miinfo@sir-usa.com
2835 N Kedzie Ave, Chicago, IL 60618, Gen Mgr: Joey Duchscher *Tel:* 773-478-8500
    Fax: 773-478-8555 *E-mail:* chinfo@sir-usa.com
4545 Cameron St, Bldg A, Las Vegas, NV 89103 *Tel:* 702-382-9147 *Fax:* 702-384-5638
    E-mail: lvinfo@sir-usa.com
1432 SE 34 Ave, Portland, OR 97214 *Tel:* 503-282-5583 *E-mail:* orinfo@sir-usa.com
1101 Cherry Ave, Nashville, TN 37203 *Tel:* 615-255-4500 *Fax:* 615-255-4511 *E-mail:* tninfo@sir-usa.com
3631 Interlake Ave N, Seattle, WA 98103
    Tel: 206-782-6800 *E-mail:* wainfo@sir-usa.com
Shipping Address: 501 W 36 St, 2nd fl, New York, NY 10018-1100

Studio 1 Productions™ Inc
5312 Peach Blossom Blvd, Port Orange, FL 32128
Tel: 386-788-6075
E-mail: studio1@studio1productions.com
Web Site: www.studio1productions.com
Key Personnel
Owner & Pres: David Knarr
Founded: 1993
Provide royalty free animation, music & stock footage to the video & film industries.
Online catalog(s) available

Studio 132
6802 Gunn Dr, Oakland, CA 94611-1443
Tel: 510-338-1240
E-mail: info@studio132.com
Web Site: www.studio132.com
Key Personnel
Founder & Owner: B Z Lewis
Founded: 1996

Commercial recording studio. Protools HDX, drum room, vocal booth & control room. Winner of six Emmy Awards.
Membership(s): ASCAP; NATAS; The Recording Academy

Studio 637
637 Cypress Ave, Hermosa Beach, CA 90254
Tel: 310-372-8218
Web Site: studio-637.com
Key Personnel
Owner & Prodr: Kevin Yamada *E-mail:* kevin@studio-637.com
Founded: 2013
Full service audio & video production house & live streaming.

Studio South
4912 Old Pineville Rd, Charlotte, NC 28217
Tel: 704-525-0296
E-mail: service@studiosouthmedia.com
Web Site: www.studiosouthmedia.com
Key Personnel
Owner & Pres: William J Schinman
Video production company providing location video, film transfer, standards conversions & more.

Studio Space Atlanta
3080 McCall Dr, Suite 2, Atlanta, GA 30340
Tel: 404-630-0508
E-mail: info@studiospaceatl.com
Web Site: www.studiospaceatl.com
Key Personnel
Owner: Daniel Minchew
Video, film, photography & production rental studio. Production equipment rentals.

Studio Technologies Inc
7440 Frontage Rd, Skokie, IL 60077-3202
Tel: 847-676-9177
E-mail: stisales-2018@studio-tech.com
Web Site: www.studio-tech.com
Key Personnel
Owner & Pres: Gordon Kapes
Commns Mgr: Carrie Gage *Tel:* 847-676-9177 ext 239
Founded: 1978
Manufacture microphone mixers, intercom & IFB products, loud speaker monitoring management systems & fiber optic transport systems.
Catalog(s) available
Membership(s): NAB

Studio Thirteen11
1311 Chemical St, Dallas, TX 75207
Tel: 214-377-8606
Web Site: www.studiothirteen11.com
Key Personnel
Owner & Gen Mgr: Miguel Pardo
  E-mail: miguel@studiothirteen11.info
Photography equipment rental house & studio.

Studio Worx Inc
218 Country Creek Ct, Ballwin, MO 63011
Tel: 314-968-2626 *Fax:* 314-968-9866
E-mail: bret.s@stlswi.com
Web Site: www.studioworxinc.com
Founded: 1986
Full video production services: in-studio, on location, broadcast & production crews. Audio services: recording, editing, mastering & restoration. CD & DVD services: duplication, replication, conversion, authoring & packaging.

The Studios at Paramount
5555 Melrose Ave, Hollywood, CA 90038
Tel: 323-956-5000
Web Site: www.paramountstudios.com
Key Personnel
Pres, Paramount Studio Group: Randall Baumberger

Stunt Wings Adventure Sports Talent & Equipment
Division of Windsports International Inc
12623 Gridley St, Sylmar, CA 91342
Tel: 818-367-2430; 818-353-5580 (home); 818-266-0874 (cell)
E-mail: stuntwings@me.com
Web Site: www.stuntwings.com
Key Personnel
Pres: Joe Greblo
Founded: 1974
Sports talent equipment rentals for production needs.
Catalog(s) available
Membership(s): SAG-AFTRA

Russ Sturgeon Productions/RSVP
916 Third Ave S, Nashville, TN 37210
Tel: 615-255-7787
Web Site: www.rsvpnashville.com
Key Personnel
Owner: Russ Sturgeon *E-mail:* russrsvp@bellsouth.net
Founded: 1972
Full service production company.

Style-City Music Inc
PO Box 40403, St Petersburg, FL 33743
Tel: 727-520-2336
E-mail: stylecitymusic@yahoo.com
Web Site: stylecitymusicinc.wordpress.com
Key Personnel
Owner: Steven Barry
Founded: 1991
Corporate AV rentals & event services.

Subject Matter
1201 New York Ave NW, Suite 900, Washington, DC 20005
Tel: 202-544-8400
Web Site: teamsubjectmatter.com
Key Personnel
Opers Mgr: Vaniah Holtz
Full service, fully integrated strategic communications agency.

Success Motivation® International Inc, see SMI® Inc

Suede Interactive
693 Main St, Hackensack, NJ 07601-4713
Tel: 201-646-0416
E-mail: suede@suede.tv
Web Site: www.suede.tv
Key Personnel
Owner: Bob Suede
Founded: 1971
Video editing & recording studios.
Catalog(s) available

Sugar Mountain PR
5505 SW Illinois St, Portland, OR 97221-1643
Tel: 503-293-9498
E-mail: sugarmountainnews@msn.com
Web Site: www.sugarmountainpr.com
Key Personnel
Founder: Beth Blenz-Clucas *E-mail:* beth@sugarmountainpr.com
Founded: 2001
Public relations company specializing in children's & family-friendly music & other media.
Membership(s): Coalition for Quality Children's Media; The Recording Academy

Suggs Media Productions Inc
156 W 44 St, 7th fl, New York, NY 10036
Tel: 212-398-4200 *Fax:* 212-382-0922
Key Personnel
Pres: Jeanne Suggs *E-mail:* jeanne@suggsmedia.com
Full service production company.

Sullivan Home Entertainment
110 Davenport Rd, Toronto, ON M5R 3R3, Canada
Tel: 416-921-7177 *Fax:* 416-921-7538
E-mail: inquire@sullivan-ent.com
Web Site: sullivanmovies.com
Key Personnel
Pres & Exec Prodr: Trudy Grant *E-mail:* tgrant@sullivan-ent.com
Pres, Dir & Exec Prodr: Kevin Sullivan *E-mail:* ksullivan@sullivan-ent.com
Founded: 1981
Educational programming distributor.
Catalog(s) available

Sumiko Inc
Subsidiary of Fine Sounds Group
2431 Fifth St, Berkeley, CA 94710
Tel: 510-843-4500 *Fax:* 510-843-7120
E-mail: mail@sumikoaudio.com
Web Site: www.sumikoaudio.net
Manufacturer & distributor of audio equipment.

Summit Audio Inc
Unit of Blue Microphones
2685 Dow Ave, Suite A-1, Tustin, CA 92780
Tel: 714-730-3010; 714-730-2086 *Fax:* 714-730-2087
E-mail: sound@summitaudio.com
Web Site: www.summitaudio.com
Founded: 1979
Manufacture pre-amplifiers.

Summit Electronics Corp
4260 NW First Ave, Suite 50, Boca Raton, FL 33431
Tel: 561-226-8500 *Toll Free Tel:* 800-226-6960 *Fax:* 561-226-8523
E-mail: sales@summitelectronics.com
Web Site: www.summitelectronics.com; www.partsprocurement.com; bocasemi.com
Key Personnel
CEO: Richard Rosenstein *E-mail:* richard@summitelectronics.com
Pres: Scott Rosenstein
Gen Mgr: Sam Rosenstein *E-mail:* sam@summitelectronics.com
Founded: 1961
Sell semiconductors & hard-to-find electronic component parts.
Catalog(s) available
Line card(s) available

Sun Entertainment Corp
3106 Belmont Blvd, Nashville, TN 37212
Tel: 615-385-1960
E-mail: info@sunrecords.com
Web Site: www.sunrecords.com
Key Personnel
Pres & Dir: John A Singleton *E-mail:* john@sunrecords.com
SVP: Sidney S Singleton
Founded: 1952
Leasing record masters to other companies.
Online catalog(s) available

Sunburst Digital Inc
1501 N Michael Dr, Wood Dale, IL 60191
Toll Free Tel: 800-321-7511 *Toll Free Fax:* 888-800-3028
E-mail: service@sunburst.com; sales@sunburst.com
Web Site: www.sunburst.com

Founded: 1972

Connects educators with instructional technology & digital content solutions for keyboarding, STEM, math, science, social studies, dual language & professional development.

Online catalog(s) available

Sunburst Recording
4174 Madison Ave, Culver City, CA 90232
Tel: 310-204-2222
Key Personnel
Dir & Archive Specialist: Robert C Wayne
 E-mail: bob@sunburstrecording.com
Founded: 1977
Audio restoration services.
Catalog(s) available
Membership(s): The Recording Academy

Sundance Systems, Fibox Products Division
Subsidiary of Sundance Systems
7411 Hines Place, Suite 123, Dallas, TX 75235
Mailing Address: PO Box 459, Rio Vista, TX 76093
Tel: 214-920-9190 *Toll Free Tel:* 800-525-3443
Fax: 214-920-9339
Web Site: www.sundancesys.com
Key Personnel
SVP: Hamilton Johnson *E-mail:* hsjohnson@sundancesys.com
Manufacturing of 24 bit audio, video & data fiber optic transmission systems.
Catalog(s) available, PDF

Sunfire Communications Inc
6965 Piazza Grande Ave, Suite 214, Orlando, FL 32835
Tel: 407-226-8226 *Fax:* 407-226-1660
E-mail: info@sunfirecommunications.com
Web Site: www.sunfirecommunications.com
Key Personnel
Pres & Prodr: Ron Gehring *E-mail:* ron@sunfirecommunications.com
Prodn Mgr: Paula Scillipoti *E-mail:* paula@sunfirecommunications.com
Founded: 1994
AV production in English & Spanish including translations.
Brochure(s) available, free, with DVD demo, upon request

Sunnex Inc
8001 Tower Point Dr, Charlotte, NC 28227
Toll Free Tel: 800-445-7869 *Toll Free Fax:* 888-668-1920
E-mail: sunnex@sunnex.com; info@sunnex.com
Web Site: www.sunnexonline.com
Lighting manufacturer.
Catalog(s) available

Sunny Day Productions Inc, see REX

Sunnyside Communications Inc
348 W 38 St, Suite 12-B, New York, NY 10018
Tel: 212-564-4606 *Fax:* 212-967-2968
Web Site: www.sunnysiderecords.com
Key Personnel
Founder & Pres: Francois Zalacain
 E-mail: francois@sunnysiderecords.com
Founded: 1982
CD producers.

Sunrise Packaging Inc
1214 98 Ave NE, Blaine, MN 55434
Tel: 763-785-2505 *Toll Free Tel:* 800-634-8160
 Fax: 763-785-2210
E-mail: customerservice@sunpack.com
Web Site: www.sunpack.com
Founded: 1982
Catalog(s) available

Sunrise Studios
6412 N University Dr, Suite 107, Tamarac, FL 33321
Mailing Address: 5461 NW 90 Ave, Sunrise, FL 33351
Tel: 954-653-8480
E-mail: info@sunrisestudios.tv
Web Site: www.sunrisestudios.tv
Key Personnel
Owner: Robert Pianka *E-mail:* bob@sunrisestudios.tv
Founded: 1999
Full service video production company.

Sunset Bronson Studios
5800 W Sunset Blvd, Hollywood, CA 90028
Tel: 323-460-5858 *Fax:* 323-460-3844
E-mail: reception@sunsetbronson.com
Web Site: sgsandsbs.com
Key Personnel
Dir, Opers: Jericho Gilmore *Tel:* 323-491-2112
 E-mail: jgilmore@hudsonppi.com
Sales Coord: Eric Alonso *Tel:* 323-491-2239
 E-mail: ealonso@hppsandsgower.com
Ten stages available for television & film productions in addition to office & support space.

Sunset Gower Studios
1438 N Gower St, Hollywood, CA 90028
Tel: 323-467-1001 *Fax:* 323-467-2717
E-mail: reception@sunsetgower.com
Web Site: sunsetgowerstudios.com
Key Personnel
Opers Mgr: Tammy McCann *Tel:* 323-447-8388
 E-mail: tmccann@sunsetgower.com
Dir, Sales & Mktg: Mike Mosallam
 E-mail: mmosallam@sunsetgower.com
Office, support, stage space, practical locations, sound-editing facilities & post-production facility for television series, features & commercials.

Sunset Las Palmas Studios
1040 N Las Palmas Ave, Los Angeles, CA 90038
Tel: 323-860-0000
E-mail: reception@sunsetlaspalmas.com
Web Site: www.sunsetlaspalmas.com
Key Personnel
VP, Prodn: Pat Mahoney *E-mail:* pmahoney@sunsetlaspalmas.com
Sales & Client Servs: Caitlyn Hardy *Tel:* 323-860-3356 *E-mail:* chardy@sunsetlaspalmas.com
Dir, Opers: Carl Geller *Tel:* 323-860-3360
 E-mail: cgeller@sunsetlaspalmas.com
Opers Mgr: Brian Luce *Tel:* 323-860-3357
 E-mail: bluce@sunsetlaspalmas.com
Founded: 1919
Provides grip, lighting & production facilities for film, television & commercial shoots.

Supercircuits
11000 N Mopac Expwy, Bldg 300, Austin, TX 78759
Toll Free Tel: 877-995-2288
E-mail: operations@supercircuits.com; customercare@supercircuits.com
Web Site: www.supercircuits.com
Key Personnel
Pres & CEO: Brian Wood
VP, Mktg: George Farley
VP, Sales: Mike Compton
Founded: 1989
Micro video cameras, transmitters & VCRs/CCTV.
Catalog(s) available
Membership(s): National Retail Federation; Retail Industry Leaders Association

SuperDigital Ltd
1150 NW 17 Ave, Portland, OR 97209-2403

Tel: 503-228-2222 *Toll Free Tel:* 888-79AUDIO (792-8346)
E-mail: audiosales@superdigital.com
Web Site: www.superdigital.com
Key Personnel
Owner: Rick McMillen
Founded: 1987
Audio equipment distributor & duplication services.

Supergrit® Abrasives, see Red Hill Corp

Superior Electric
Division of Dynapar Corp
One Cowles Rd, Plainville, CT 06062
Tel: 860-507-2025 *Toll Free Tel:* 800-787-3532
 Fax: 860-507-2050 *Toll Free Fax:* 800-821-1369
E-mail: customer.service@superiorelectric.com
Web Site: www.superiorelectric.com
Key Personnel
Dir, Sales: Mike Miga *E-mail:* mike.miga@superiorelectric.com
Manufacturer of voltage control components & power quality solutions.
Online catalog(s) available
Membership(s): NAB; SBE

Superscope LLC
1508 Batavia Ave, Geneva, IL 60134-3302
Tel: 630-232-8900 *Toll Free Tel:* 800-374-4118
 Fax: 630-232-8905
Web Site: www.superscopetechnologies.com
Key Personnel
Sales & Mktg Coord: Jeff Anderson
Founded: 1993
Manufacturer of audio equipment.
Catalog(s) available

SuperStock Inc
Division of RGB Ventures LLC
6620 Southpoint Dr S, Suite 501, Jacksonville, FL 32216
Tel: 904-565-0066 *Toll Free Tel:* 800-828-4545
 Fax: 904-565-1620
E-mail: info@superstock.com; yourfriends@superstock.com
Web Site: www.superstock.com
Key Personnel
Gen Mgr: Carolyn Nolte *E-mail:* carolyn@superstock.com
Contemporary photography, fine art & vintage images.
Catalog(s) available
CD-ROM catalog(s) available
Membership(s): Digital Media Licensing Association

Supertack® Hot Melt Glue Sticks & Glue Guns, see Red Hill Corp

SuperVision
Division of Sunrise Communications Inc
Pacific Design Ctr, Suite B-120, 8687 Melrose Ave, Los Angeles, CA 90069
Tel: 310-652-9510 *Toll Free Tel:* 877-287-9783
 Fax: 310-652-9516
E-mail: mail@supervisionav.com
Web Site: www.supervisionav.com
Key Personnel
Pres: Greg Pass
Founded: 1977
Audio equipment distributor.
Membership(s): Custom Electronic Design & Installation Association

SurgeX
Division of Electronic Systems Protection Inc (ESP)
8001 Knightdale Blvd, Suite 121, Knightdale, NC 27545

Toll Free Tel: 800-645-9721 (tech & cust support)
E-mail: order.desk@ametek.com
Web Site: espsurgex.com/surgex/
Key Personnel
Pres & CEO: Stephen F Galloway
Dir & CFO: Rob Wood
Dir & Busn Mgr: Dave Perrotta
Dir, Mktg: Tanya Flores
Dir, Sales: David D'Agostino *Tel:* 518-210-4488
   E-mail: dave.dagostino@ametek.com
Founded: 1995
Manufacturer of premium AC power conditioning products for the professional & residential audio, video & multimedia marketplace.

SVAT Electronics
4080 Montrose Rd, Niagara Falls, ON L2H 1J9, Canada
Fax: 905-353-1701 *Toll Free Fax:* 888-771-1701
E-mail: marketing@svat.com
Web Site: www.svat.com
Key Personnel
Pres: Raj Jain
Develop, manufacture & market do-it-yourself video surveillance & lifestyle improving consumer electronics.
Branch Office(s)
840 Aero Dr, Cheektowaga, NY 14225
Membership(s): Consumer Technology Association™; Juvenile Products Manufacturers Association

SVS Inc
2513 Jenks Ave, Panama City, FL 32405
Tel: 850-522-4747 *Fax:* 850-522-4739
E-mail: sales@svslifts.com
Web Site: www.svslifts.com
Key Personnel
Sales & Mktg Mgr: Patricia Palmer
   E-mail: patriciap@svslifts.com
Founded: 1989
Manufacture projector lifts & accessories.
Online catalog(s) available
Membership(s): National Foundation of Independent Businesses

Swallow
Division of Swallow Publications Inc
700 S Chataignier St, Drawer 10, Ville Platte, LA 70586
Tel: 337-363-2177 *Fax:* 337-363-2094
E-mail: info@flattownmusic.com
Web Site: www.flattownmusic.com
Key Personnel
Pres: Floyd Soileau
Founded: 1957
Catalog(s) available

Sweetsong Productions
193 Meadsville Rd, Parkersburg, WV 26104
Tel: 304-428-7773
E-mail: sweetsongproductions@yahoo.com
Web Site: www.sweetsong.com
Key Personnel
Owner: Roger Hoover
Founded: 1976

Sweetwater Sound Inc
5501 US Hwy 30 W, Fort Wayne, IN 46818
Tel: 260-432-8176 *Toll Free Tel:* 800-222-4700
   Fax: 260-432-1758
Web Site: www.sweetwater.com
Key Personnel
Founder & Pres: Chuck Surack
Edit Dir: Mitch Gallagher
Founded: 1979
Retailer of music technology & music instruments.
Catalog(s) available, free, 3 issues/yr, industry standard

Online catalog(s) available
Membership(s): NAMM, the National Association of Music Merchants

Switch
6600 Manchester Ave, St Louis, MO 63139
Tel: 314-206-7700
E-mail: info@switch.us
Web Site: www.switch.us
Key Personnel
Pres: John Nickel
VP, Corp Busn Dev: Chris Jobst *E-mail:* chrisj@
   switch.us
Founded: 1980
Integrated marketing firm.

Switchcraft® Inc
Division of HEICO Corp
5555 N Elston Ave, Chicago, IL 60630
Tel: 773-792-2700 *Fax:* 773-792-2129
E-mail: sales@switchcraft.com
Web Site: www.switchcraft.com
Key Personnel
Pres & CEO: Keith A Bandolik
EVP: Dave Dunmead
Sales: Wendy Charak *E-mail:* wcharak@
   switchcraft.com
Founded: 1946
Switchcraft offers a wide variety of connectors, adapters, audio & video jacks, plugs, audio & video patchbays & patch cords.
Catalog(s) available
Branch Office(s)
c/o Conxall, 601 E Wildwood, Villa Park, IL
   60181 *Tel:* 630-834-7504 *Fax:* 630-834-8540
   E-mail: sales@conxall.com
Foreign Office(s): Switchcraft Korea, South Korea *Tel:* (032) 578-1201 *Fax:* (032) 578-1205
   E-mail: sales@switchcraft.co.kr
Membership(s): Electronic Components Industry Association; NAB; NAMM, the National Association of Music Merchants; NSCA

Swivelier
600 Bradley Hill Rd, Blauvelt, NY 10913
Tel: 845-353-1455 *Fax:* 845-353-1512
E-mail: info@swivelier.com
Web Site: www.swivelier.com
Key Personnel
Pres: Michael Schwartz *Tel:* 845-353-1455 ext 231
Founded: 1947
Manufacture adjustable lighting fixtures, display equipment & accessories for stores, exhibits, convention centers, malls & specialty applications.

Symbolic Sound Corp
206 N Randolph St, Suite 520, Champaign, IL 61820
Tel: 217-355-6273
E-mail: info-kyma@symbolicsound.com
Web Site: kyma.symbolicsound.com
Key Personnel
Pres: Carla Scaletti
VP: Kurt Hebel
Founded: 1990
Designs, manufactures & markets hardware & software for computer-based digital audio. Creators of the Kyma sound design workstation.
Catalog(s) available
Membership(s): AES; Association for Computing Machinery; ICMA; IEEE; The Society for Electro-Acoustic Music in the United States

SYMCO Inc
29 Poplar Dr, Stirling, NJ 07980
Tel: 908-647-6262 *Fax:* 908-647-4904
E-mail: orders@symcoinc.com
Web Site: www.symcoinc.com

Key Personnel
Pres: Frank Michael Culotta *E-mail:* fmculotta@
   symcoinc.com
Acct Mgr: Ruth Walter *E-mail:* rwalter@
   symcoinc.com
Audio & Technol Specialist: Jim Zagryn
   E-mail: jzagryn@symcoinc.com
Mktg & Cust Support Specialist: Daniel Pilar
   E-mail: dpilar@symcoinc.com
New Busn Dev, IT Channel: Doug Cook
   E-mail: dcook@symcoinc.com
Founded: 1972
AV equipment distributor. Field offices located in Middletown, CT, Columbus, MD, Mahwah & Ridgefield Park, NJ, Duncannon, PA, Coventry, RI.
Membership(s): ASIS; Audiovisual and Integrated Experience Association; Computer Technology Industry Association; Consumer Technology Association™; NSCA

Symetrix Inc
6408 216 St SW, Mountlake Terrace, WA 98043-2093
Tel: 425-778-7728
E-mail: support@symetrix.co; sales@symetrix.co
Web Site: www.symetrix.co
Key Personnel
Founder & CEO: Dane Butcher
Western Regl Sales Mgr: Tim Murray *Tel:* 310-433-1348 *E-mail:* tmurray@symetrix.co
Manufacturer of amplifiers.
Catalog(s) available

Synaptic Digital
79 Fifth Ave, 14th fl, New York, NY 10003
Tel: 212-682-8300 *Fax:* 212-201-4207
E-mail: learnmore@synapticdigital.com
Web Site: www.synapticdigital.com
Key Personnel
CEO: Jeff Katz
SVP, Busn Dev: Laura Pair
SVP, Prods & Servs: Dan Schwartzberg
VP, Head of Prodn: Rick Vasta
VP, Client Solutions: Rich Quigley
Global leader in providing turnkey video & media distribution solutions.
Branch Office(s)
Los Angeles, CA *Tel:* 323-936-6390
Washington, DC *Tel:* 202-662-8937
Atlanta, GA *Tel:* 404-870-0323

SynAudCon
8780 Rufing Rd, Greenville, IN 47124
Tel: 812-923-0174 *Toll Free Fax:* 866-547-0298
Web Site: www.synaudcon.com
Key Personnel
Owner & Corp Secy: Brenda Brown
   E-mail: bbrown@synaudcon.com
Founded: 1973
Programming by type (audio) & also produce educational seminars, both online & in person training.

Synergem
2323 Randolph Ave, Avenel, NJ 07001
Tel: 732-225-0001
E-mail: sales@synergem.com
Web Site: synergem.com
Key Personnel
Chmn: Thomas De Maeyer
Pres: Amy Silverman
Dir of Opers: Jennifer Love
Founded: 1985
Packaging & media content delivery. Duplication & manufacturing of USBs.
Catalog(s) available
Membership(s): American Independent Media Manufacturers Association

Synergetic Audio Concepts Inc, see SynAudCon

Synergistic Batteries Inc
5975 Providence Lane, Cumming, GA 30040
Tel: 770-886-6621 *Toll Free Tel:* 800-634-6000
E-mail: sbicheri@synbat.com
Web Site: www.synergisticbatteries.com
Key Personnel
CEO: W B Caspari
Founded: 1975
Custom battery assembler.

Synergy Group Inc
Affiliate of Jeff Cooper Architects/Synergy Inc
23930 Craftsman Rd, Calabasas, CA 91302-1437
Tel: 818-223-9009 *Fax:* 818-223-8999
Web Site: www.jeffcooper.com
Key Personnel
Owner: Jeff Cooper *E-mail:* jeff@jeffcooper.com
Design, build & equip post-production facilities, theatres, home theatres & recording studios.

Synthesizer Rental Service
10907 W Magnolia Blvd, North Hollywood, CA 91601
Tel: 323-660-4065; 818-907-7780; 615-327-3515 (Nashville dispatch)
E-mail: sst.shop@yahoo.com; sstmusiccity@gmail.com
Web Site: sstsynths.com
Key Personnel
Owner & Pres: Michael Boddicker
Founded: 1988
Rent synthesizers & Pro Tools™ Systems.
Catalog(s) available

Synthesizer Systems Technologies Inc (SST), see Synthesizer Rental Service

Syracuse Scenery & Stage Lighting Co Inc
101 Monarch Dr, Liverpool, NY 13088-4915
Tel: 315-453-8096 *Toll Free Tel:* 800-453-7775
Fax: 315-453-7897
E-mail: info@syracusescenery.com
Web Site: www.syracusescenery.com
Key Personnel
Sales & Rentals: Steven Le Porte
E-mail: sleporte@syracusescenery.com
Founded: 1922
Provide & install theatrical equipment.
Catalog(s) available, free, annual
Membership(s): Professional Lighting & Sound Association; USITT

Systems Impact Inc
3515 Woodley Rd NW, Washington, DC 20016
Toll Free Tel: 888-568-6284
E-mail: support@mathmastery.com
Web Site: mathmastery.com
Educational online math courses.

T & M Digital Services LLC
54 Flint Ridge Rd, Monroe, CT 06468
Mailing Address: PO Box 873, Monroe, CT 06468-0873
Tel: 203-268-5290 *Fax:* 203-268-5290
Key Personnel
Mng Partner: Richard Kraus

T-stop Inc
957 Cole Ave, Hollywood, CA 90038
Tel: 323-544-1000 *Fax:* 323-544-4970
E-mail: info@t-stopinc.com
Web Site: www.t-stopinc.com
Founded: 2004
High-end film equipment rentals, including cutting-edge digital cameras, lenses & support.

TAD Laboratories, see Laboratories Inc

TADL, see Laboratories Inc

TAI Audio
5828 Old Winter Garden Rd, Orlando, FL 32835
Tel: 407-296-9959 *Toll Free Tel:* 800-486-6444
Fax: 407-648-1352
E-mail: sales@taiaudio.com
Web Site: www.taiaudio.com
Key Personnel
Pres: Joseph Guzzi
Founded: 1988
Production audio equipment distributor.
Online catalog(s) available

Take One Film & Video
125 Commerce Ave, Hendersonville, TN 37075
Tel: 615-431-5822
E-mail: mail@takeone.tv
Web Site: www.takeone.tv
Key Personnel
Pres: Chad Hall
AV & broadcast system design & integration.

Take 1 Media Services
31335 Center Ridge Rd, Cleveland, OH 44145
Tel: 440-899-0101
Web Site: www.take1media.com
Key Personnel
Pres: Jeff Kassouf *E-mail:* jeffk@take1media.com
Founded: 1983
Award winning video, film & multimedia productions.

Take One Productions Ltd
11010 Lake Grove Blvd, Suite 100-317, Morrisville, NC 27560
Key Personnel
Pres: James C Cando, Jr
Treas: Laura Cando
Founded: 1972

Talas
Division of Technical Library Service Inc
330 Morgan Ave, Brooklyn, NY 11211
Tel: 212-219-0770 *Fax:* 212-219-0735
E-mail: info@talasonline.com
Web Site: www.talasonline.com
Key Personnel
Pres: Marjorie Salik
VP: Jake Salik
Founded: 1962
Archival & conservation supply company.
Catalog(s) available, free
Membership(s): AIC; ALA; IIC; SLA

Talk-A-Phone Co
7530 N Natchez Ave, Niles, IL 60714
Tel: 773-539-1100 *Fax:* 773-539-1241
E-mail: info@talkaphone.com
Web Site: www.talkaphone.com
Key Personnel
VP, Sales: Bob Shanes *E-mail:* rshanes@talkaphone.com
Eastern Regl Sales Mgr: Erez Sharoni *Tel:* 773-633-5980 *E-mail:* esharoni@talkaphone.com
Founded: 1937
Manufacturer of intercom systems.
Catalog(s) available

Tallahassee Audio Visual
900 Capital Circle SE, Suite 4, Tallahassee, FL 32301
Tel: 850-877-1154
Web Site: talcam.com
Key Personnel
Pres & Mgr: Mike Fraser *E-mail:* mfraser@talcam.com
AV systems integration, digital signage, home theater installation, AV rental & home automation.

Tallahassee Photo & Frame
900 Capital Circle SE, Suite 3, Tallahassee, FL 32301
Tel: 850-877-1152
E-mail: mgr@talcam.com
Web Site: talcam.com
Key Personnel
Mgr: Brendan Fraser
Photo printing, video transfer & custom framing.

Tally Display Corp
19 Gardner Rd, Fairfield, NJ 07004
Tel: 973-777-7760 *Toll Free Tel:* 800-758-2559
Fax: 973-777-6220
E-mail: info@tallydisplay.com
Web Site: www.tallydisplay.com
Key Personnel
Pres & CEO: Steven Rose
Founded: 1991
Electronic signage. Full color, indoor/outdoor, LED signs, displays, tickers & custom.
Membership(s): International Sign Association; NAB; NSA; United States Sign Council

Tam Communications Inc
5610 Scotts Valley Dr, Suite B-552, Scotts Valley, CA 95066
Tel: 831-439-1500 *Toll Free Fax:* 866-390-1218
E-mail: info@tamcom.com
Web Site: www.tamcom.com
Key Personnel
Co-Founder & Pres: Susan O'Connor Fraser
Co-Founder: Tam O'Connor Fraser
Founded: 1979
Full service production company.

Tamrac® Inc
2036 Lincoln Ave, Suite 104, Ogden, UT 84401
Tel: 385-405-2700 *Fax:* 385-405-2682
E-mail: info@tamrac.com
Web Site: www.tamrac.com
Founded: 1977
Manufacture camera bags & accessories.
Online catalog(s) available
Membership(s): The Imaging Alliance

Tamron USA Inc
Subsidiary of Tamron Co Ltd
10 Austin Blvd, Commack, NY 11725
Tel: 631-858-8400 *Toll Free Tel:* 800-827-8880
Fax: 631-543-5666; 631-858-8462 (cust serv)
E-mail: custserv@tamron.com
Web Site: www.tamron-usa.com
Key Personnel
Pres & CEO: Greg Maniaci
SVP: Hidekazu Suzuki
VP, Mktg & Communs: Stacie Errera
E-mail: errera@tamron.com
Founded: 1979
Manufacture optical equipment.
Catalog(s) available
Online catalog(s) available
Foreign Office(s): Tamron Co Ltd, 1385, Hasunuma, Minuma-ku, Saitama-shi, Saitama 337-8556, Japan, Pres & CEO: Morio Ono *Tel:* (048) 684-9111 *Fax:* (048) 683-8289 *Web Site:* www.tamron.co.jp (headquarters)

Tamura Corporation of America
1040 S Andreasen Dr, Suite 100, Escondido, CA 92029
Tel: 951-699-1270 *Toll Free Tel:* 800-472-6624
Fax: 951-676-9482
Web Site: www.tamuracorp.com
Key Personnel
Sr Field Sales Rep: Craig Simpson *Tel:* 951-699-1270 ext 105 *E-mail:* simpsonc@tamuracorp.com
Manufacture Microtran power/telecom transformers for PCBs. Also manufacture large transformers, inductors & reactors for the renewable energy industry. Tamura has standard catalog hall effect current sensors, DC/DC power mod-

ules, gate drivers for IGBT & SiC power modules.
Catalog(s) available
Membership(s): Power Sources Manufacturers Association

Tanglewood Productions
125 Brinkby Ave, Reno, NV 89509
Tel: 775-688-6282 *Toll Free Tel:* 877-671-8933
E-mail: info@tanglewoodproductions.com
Web Site: www.tanglewoodproductions.com
Key Personnel
Founder & Pres: Michael Eardley
Founded: 1983
Produce award winning audios & have a talent pool of top voice talents from all over the globe. Very efficient studios & producers make sure your project is completed on time & within budget. Preview any of our talent's demos on our web site. If you need a particular talent to do a test read on a script, that's no problem. We'll cut the sample & drop it right onto your desktop as an MP3 file. We offer a downloads page on our web site. When it's time for delivery of your spot, we post it on our web site & you or any of your radio or TV stations can download the file with no additional charges.

Tantor Media Inc
6 Business Park Rd, Old Saybrook, CT 06475
Tel: 860-395-1155 *Toll Free Tel:* 877-7-TANTOR (782-6867) *Toll Free Fax:* 888-782-7821
E-mail: service@tantor.com
Web Site: www.tantor.com
Key Personnel
Co-Founder/Partner: Laura Colebank
CEO: Kevin Colebank
Founded: 2000
Audiobooks.
Online catalog(s) available

Taperwire
Division of Fuller Manufacturing
c/o Fuller Manufacturing, 523 S Flower St, Burbank, CA 91502
Tel: 818-238-9911 *Fax:* 818-238-9959
E-mail: taperwire@taperwire.com
Web Site: www.taperwire.com
Key Personnel
Engg Mgr: Ronald Fuller
Founded: 1991
Manufacture flat cable suitable for under carpeting.
Catalog(s) available

TAPPI
15 Technology Pkwy S, Norcross, GA 30092
Tel: 770-446-1400 *Toll Free Tel:* 800-332-8686 (US); 800-446-9431 (CN) *Fax:* 240-396-5973
E-mail: memberconnection@tappi.org
Web Site: www.tappi.org
Key Personnel
Pres & CEO: Larry N Montague
  E-mail: lmontague@tappi.org
Cont: Dennis Thompson *Tel:* 770-209-7245
  E-mail: dthompson@tappi.org
VP, Opers: Eric Fletty *Tel:* 770-209-7535
  E-mail: efletty@tappi.org
Dir, Mktg: Simona Marcellus *Tel:* 770-209-7293
  E-mail: smarcellus@tappi.org
Founded: 1915
Leading technical association for the pulp, paper & converting industry.
Catalog(s) available

TARA Labs
716 Rossanley Dr, Medford, OR 97501
Tel: 541-488-6465 *Fax:* 541-245-9119
E-mail: sales@taralabs.com
Web Site: www.taralabs.com

Key Personnel
Pres: M J Bergs
Founded: 1986
Manufacturer & distributor of AV cables.

Tarpley Media Systems
Subsidiary of Tarpley Music Co Inc
3737 50 St, Lubbock, TX 79413
Tel: 806-797-5833 *Toll Free Tel:* 800-600-5833
  Fax: 806-797-5139
E-mail: tms@tarpleymedia.com
Web Site: www.tarpleymedia.com
Key Personnel
VP: David Tarpley
Mgr & Consultant: Jonathan Smither
Sr Consultant: Casey McGrew
Founded: 1927
AV integrator.
Membership(s): AES; Audiovisual and Integrated Experience Association; NAMM, the National Association of Music Merchants

TASCAM
Division of TEAC America Inc
1834 Gage Rd, Montebello, CA 90640
Tel: 323-726-0303 (ext 617)
Web Site: www.tascam.com
Key Personnel
Dir, Prod Mktg: Jeff Laity
Founded: 1953
Audio equipment manufacturer.

Tasman Group Pacific Rim
15304 Spring Ave, Sante Fe Springs, CA 90670
Tel: 562-566-1330 *Toll Free Tel:* 888-355-8889
  Fax: 562-404-0716
Web Site: www.tasmangrouppr.com
Key Personnel
Acct Mgr: Christine Martinez
Manufacturing displays & store equipment.
Online catalog(s) available

Tatum Video
Division of Tatum Communications Inc
103 S Davis St, Telluride, CO 81435
Mailing Address: PO Box 944, Telluride, CO 81435-0944
Tel: 213-999-5970 (cell); 970-728-4892
E-mail: utemtn@aol.com
Key Personnel
Pres & Prodr: Tom Tatum
Prodn Coord: Kathryn Vinson
Asst to Prodr: Robin Streichler
Dist: Jim Rokas Tomwil *Tel:* 818-769-0883
Founded: 1981
Video & film production company specializing in outdoor extreme sports adventure programs.
Catalog(s) available
Branch Office(s)
87 Vista del Ocaso, Ranchos de Taos, NM 87557

Tatung Co of America Inc
Subsidiary of Tatung Co
2850 El Presidio St, Long Beach, CA 90810
Tel: 310-637-2105 *Toll Free Tel:* 800-827-2850
E-mail: tus@tatungusa.com
Web Site: www.tatungusa.com
Founded: 1972
Worldwide provider of technologically advanced products, customer solutions & manufacturing services.

Carl Tatz Design
6666 Brookmont Terr, Suite 1109, Nashville, TN 37205
Tel: 615-354-6242
E-mail: carl@carltatzdesign.com
Web Site: www.carltatzdesign.com
Key Personnel
Pres: Carl Tatz *Tel:* 615-400-5479 (cell)
Acoustic design, analysis & implementation.

The Taunton Press Inc
63 S Main St, Newtown, CT 06470
Mailing Address: PO Box 5506, Newtown, CT 06470-5506
Tel: 203-426-8171 *Toll Free Tel:* 800-926-8776 (ext 3893 - PR); 800-888-8286 (orders)
  Fax: 203-426-3434
Web Site: www.taunton.com
Key Personnel
Pres & CEO: Dan McCarthy
Dir, HR: Carol Marotti
Catalog(s) available

Taylor Associates
110 W Canal St, Suite 301, Winooski, VT 05404
Tel: 802-735-1942 *Toll Free Tel:* 800-READ-PLUS (732-3758) *Fax:* 802-419-4786
E-mail: info@readingplus.com
Web Site: www.readingplus.com
Key Personnel
Owner & CEO: Mark Taylor
COO: Kelly Scanell
Chief Academic Offr: Karen Feller
CIO: Rick Cusick
Dir, Res: Alexandra Spichtig
Nat Sales Dir: Joel Brown
Educational computer software publisher (reading). Visigraph (hardware & software) & other products available online only.
Membership(s): International Literacy Association

Chip Taylor Communications LLC
2 East View Dr, Derry, NH 03038
Tel: 603-434-9262 *Toll Free Tel:* 800-876-CHIP (876-2447) *Fax:* 603-432-2723
E-mail: chip.taylor@chiptaylor.com
Web Site: www.chiptaylor.com
Key Personnel
Pres: Chip Taylor
Founded: 1985
Produce & distribute over 4,000 programs for broadcast, streaming & DVD markets.
Catalog(s) available
Membership(s): ACA; AECT; AIME; ALA; ASCO; Consortium of College & University Media Centers; Music Business Association; National Association of Media & Technology Centers; PAECT

TBC Consoles Inc
170 Rodeo Dr, Edgewood, NY 11717
Tel: 631-293-4068 *Toll Free Tel:* 888-CONSOLE (266-7653) *Fax:* 631-293-4075
E-mail: info@tbcconsoles.com; sales@tbcconsoles.com; support@tbcconsoles.com
Web Site: www.tbcconsoles.com
Key Personnel
CFO: Diana Lukasik *Tel:* 631-293-4068 ext 103
  E-mail: dlukasik@tbcconsoles.com
CTO: Peter Pedisich *Tel:* 631-293-4068 ext 111
  E-mail: ppedisich@tbcconsoles.com
Pres: Jerry Hahn *Tel:* 631-293-4068 ext 102
  E-mail: jhahn@tbcconsoles.com
Sr Acct Mgr: Steve Struhs *Tel:* 631-293-4068 ext 104 *E-mail:* sstruhs@tbcconsoles.com
Opers Mgr: Jansen Hahn *Tel:* 631-293-4068 ext 121 *E-mail:* jansen@tbcconsoles.com
Founded: 1988
Design & manufacture video production consoles & equipment cabinetry.
Catalog(s) available
Membership(s): ACCP; The Business Council of New York State Inc; NAB; SMPTE®

TBC Studios
10201 W Appleton Ave, Milwaukee, WI 53225
Tel: 414-536-7337
E-mail: info@tbcstudios.com
Web Site: www.tbcstudios.com
HD video production & digital audio recording facility.

TEA, see Television Equipment Associates Inc (TEA)

Teaberry
770 W Landoran Lane, Tucson, AZ 85737
Tel: 520-429-7952 *Fax:* 520-742-0652
E-mail: info@tellens.com
Web Site: www.tellens.com
Key Personnel
Pres: Pat Barey *E-mail:* pbarey@aol.com
Founded: 1994
Media production.

TEAC America Inc
Subsidiary of TEAC Corp
1834 Gage Rd, Montebello, CA 90640
Tel: 323-726-0303
E-mail: custser@teac.com
Web Site: www.teac.com
Founded: 1953
Manufacturer of data recording equipment.

Teach America Corp
121 N Love St, Quincy, FL 32351-2440
Tel: 850-528-6056 (cell)
Web Site: teachamerica.com; www.accessmanagement.info
Key Personnel
Pres: Frank Broen *E-mail:* fbroen@teachamerica.com
Founded: 1979
Explaining transportation planning issues. Produces interactive visualizations, video/flash programs & multimedia communications.
Catalog(s) available
Membership(s): ATD; Transportation Research Board

TeachLogic Inc
1688 Ord Way, Oceanside, CA 92056
Tel: 760-631-7800 *Toll Free Tel:* 800-588-0018
Fax: 760-631-1283
E-mail: sales@teachlogic.com; info@teachlogic.com
Web Site: www.teachlogic.com
Key Personnel
Pres: Brian Van Waay *E-mail:* bvanwaay@teachlogic.com
VP, Sales & Mktg: Jerry Hogerson
E-mail: jhogerson@teachlogic.com
Founded: 1992
Manufacture sound field systems & wireless microphones.

Teatown Communications Group
1560 Broadway, New York, NY 10036
Tel: 212-302-0722
E-mail: info@teatown.tv
Key Personnel
Pres: Marlen Hecht
Founded: 1980
Editing services/post-production.
Catalog(s) available
Membership(s): AFI; IFP

TEC/West USA Inc
3050 E Victoria St, Rancho Dominguez, CA 90221
Tel: 310-961-3491 *Toll Free Tel:* 800-421-7215
Fax: 310-464-9210
E-mail: info@tecwest.com
Web Site: www.tecwest.com
Key Personnel
Natl Sales: Frances Doiuchi
Founded: 1973
Catalog(s) available

Tech 21 USA Inc
790 Bloomfield Ave, Clifton, NJ 07012
Tel: 973-777-6996 *Fax:* 973-777-9899
E-mail: info@tech21nyc.com

Web Site: www.tech21nyc.com
Key Personnel
Pres: B Andrew Barta
VP: Dale Krevens *E-mail:* dale@tech21nyc.com
Dir, Sales: Tyme Rogers *E-mail:* tyme@tech21nyc.com
Founded: 1989
Manufacture signal processing equipment, bass & guitar amplifiers & effects.

Techflex Inc
Division of Dermody Associates Inc
104 Demarest Rd, Sparta, NJ 07871
Tel: 973-300-9242 *Toll Free Tel:* 800-323-5140
Fax: 973-300-9409
E-mail: techflex@techflex.com
Web Site: www.techflex.com
Key Personnel
Pres: William Dermody, III
Founded: 1965
Sleeving for wires & cables, bundling & protection, Flexo Brand.
Catalog(s) available
Membership(s): NAB

Techkno Integration & Design Services LLC
1720 Kaliste Saloom, Bldg 2, Suite B-2, Lafayette, LA 70508
Tel: 337-406-9428 *Fax:* 337-406-9482
Key Personnel
Pres & CEO: Bobby Cobb
Cont: Carol Bourque
Mgr: Kelly Cobb
Founded: 2001
Design & installation of multimedia presentation systems, projectors, conferencing, white boards & all AV & professional audio equipment.
Membership(s): Audiovisual and Integrated Experience Association

Technet® Systems Group
Division of Steve Vanni Associates Inc
2600 Lake Shore Rd, Unit 157, Gilford, NH 03249
Tel: 603-483-5365 *Toll Free Tel:* 888-TECHNET (832-4638)
E-mail: info@technetsystems.com
Web Site: www.technetsystems.com
Key Personnel
Pres: Steve Vanni
Founded: 1982
Broadcast equipment & systems sales & service.

Techni-Lux Inc
10900 Palmbay Dr, Orlando, FL 32824
Tel: 407-857-8770 *Fax:* 407-857-8771
E-mail: sales@techni-lux.com
Web Site: www.techni-lux.com
Key Personnel
VP: Alex Gonzalez
Sales Exec: Felix Gallardo
Founded: 1991
Online catalog(s) available

Techni-Tool, a TestEquity LLC company
1547 N Trooper Rd, Worcester, PA 19490
Mailing Address: PO Box 1117, Worcester, PA 19490-1117
Tel: 610-941-2400 *Toll Free Tel:* 800-832-4866
Fax: 610-828-5623 *Toll Free Fax:* 800-854-8665
E-mail: sales@techni-tool.com; support@techni-tool.com (tech support)
Web Site: www.techni-tool.com
Key Personnel
VP: Kevin McNamee
Dir, Procurement & Prod Mgmt: Don Zebrauskas
Founded: 1959
Electronic repair & production tools.
Catalog(s) available, quarterly
Online catalog(s) available

Technical Exhibits Corp
Subsidiary of Model Builders Inc
6155 S Oak Park Ave, Chicago, IL 60638
Tel: 773-586-3377 *Fax:* 773-586-6575
Web Site: www.technicalexhibits.net
Key Personnel
Pres: Hal Chaffee *E-mail:* hchaffee@sbcglobal.net
Founded: 1960
Exhibit products including telephone handsets & the "Hearphone" handheld exhibit speaker.

Technical Services
10567 Oak Creek Dr, Lakeside, CA 92040
Tel: 619-561-4410
Web Site: www.widcoinc.com
Key Personnel
CEO: Michael D Bell

Technical Services
2750 Northaven Rd, Suite 206, Dallas, TX 75229
Tel: 972-421-4230 *Fax:* 972-421-4231
Web Site: www.tecserv.biz
Key Personnel
Mgr: John Eldridge *E-mail:* john@tecserv.biz

Technical Support Systems LLC
2232 Central Ave, Memphis, TN 38104
Tel: 901-398-5908 *Fax:* 901-398-5914
Web Site: www.techsupportsys.com
Key Personnel
Owner: Chip Benson *E-mail:* chip@techsupportsys.com
Founded: 1984
Membership(s): Audiovisual and Integrated Experience Association; NSCA

Technicolor - PostWorks, see PostWorks

Technicolor USA Inc
Subsidiary of Technicolor SA
6040 Sunset Blvd, Hollywood, CA 90028
Tel: 323-817-6600
E-mail: info@technicolor.com
Web Site: www.technicolor.com
Key Personnel
CEO: Frederic Rose
Deputy CEO & Pres, Connected Home: Michel Rahier
Deputy CEO & Pres, Prodn Servs: Tim Sarnoff
COO, Prodn Servs: Nathan Wappet
CFO: Esther Gaide
Chief Mktg Offr: Sandra Carvalho
CTO & Head, Res & Innovation: Cristina Gomila
Pres, Connected Home North America: Luis Martinez-Amago
Pres, Home Entertainment Servs: Quentin Lilly
EVP, Intl Opers, Home Entertainment Servs: Simon Hibbins
EVP, HR & Corp Soc Responsibility: Fabienne Brunet
SVP, Corp Devt & Technol: Vince Pizzica
VP, Corp Communs: Lane Cooper
Founded: 1915
Branch Office(s)
861 N Seward St, Hollywood, CA 90038
Tel: 323-960-2140
5555 Melrose Ave, Hollywood, CA 90038, Sales: Mark Kaplan *Tel:* 323-956-7010 *E-mail:* mark.kaplan@technicolor.com
2233 N Ontario St, Burbank, CA 91504-4503
Tel: 818-260-3700
1223 W Olympic Blvd, Los Angeles, CA 90064
Tel: 424-298-2250
470 E Paces Ferry Rd NE, Suite 380, Atlanta, GA 30305 *Tel:* 678-506-8545
935 Gravier St, New Orleans, LA 70112
Tel: 504-322-4182
100 Avenue of the Americas, 10th fl, New York, NY 10013 *Tel:* 212-894-4000
110 Leroy St, New York, NY 10014 *Tel:* 212-609-9400

609 Greenwich St, New York, NY 10014
Tel: 212-399-6342
15 E Fourth Ave, 2nd fl, Burnaby, BC V5T 1E9,
Canada, Dir, Sales: Lindsay Elizabeth Donovan
Tel: 604-689-1090 *E-mail:* lindsay.donovan@
technicolor.com
555 Brooksbank Ave, North Vancouver, BC V7J
3S5, Canada *Tel:* 604-689-1090
49 Ontario St, Toronto, ON M5A 2V1, Canada
Tel: 416-585-9995
2101 St Catherine St W, Suite 300, Montreal, QC
H3H 1M6, Canada *Tel:* 514-939-5060
Foreign Office(s): 221 bis bd Jean-Jaures, 92100
Boulogne Billancourt, France *Tel:* 01 41 04 31
00
28-32 Lexington St Soho, London W1F 0LF,
United Kingdom, Dir, Sales: Matt Adams
Tel: (020) 7319 4900 *E-mail:* matt.adams@
technicolor.com

Technics
Division of Panasonic Corporation of North
America
2 Riverfront Plaza, 828 McCarter Hwy, Newark,
NJ 07102
Tel: 201-348-7000 *Toll Free Tel:* 800-405-0652
(orders)
E-mail: technicssupport@us.panasonic.com
Web Site: www.panasonic.com; www.technics.
com
Manufacturer of audio components.

Technomad™ Inc
PO Box 273, South Deerfield, MA 01373
Tel: 617-275-8898 *Toll Free Tel:* 800-464-7757
Fax: 617-535-9712
E-mail: sales@technomad.com; customercare@
technomad.com
Web Site: www.technomad.com
Founded: 1994
Speaker manufacturer.
Catalog(s) available
Shipping Address: No 5 Tina Dr, South Deerfield,
MA 01373
Membership(s): Audiovisual and Integrated Expe-
rience Association; NSCA

Technomedia Solutions
4545 36 St, Orlando, FL 32811
Tel: 407-351-0909 *Fax:* 407-248-9484
E-mail: sales@gotechnomedia.com
Web Site: www.gotechnomedia.com
Key Personnel
EVP & CEO: Joni McElwee
Pres: John Miceli
Dir, Engg: Jason Ford
Programmer: John Stancil
Founded: 2001
AV system design & integration blended with
custom media creative services for a turnkey
entertainment solutions offering.
Branch Office(s)
1756 Flower St, Glendale, CA 91201 *Tel:* 818-
937-9351
132 Nassau St, Suite 310, New York, NY 10038
Tel: 212-452-1100
Membership(s): AES; International Association
of Amusement Parks and Attractions; NSCA;
SMPTE®; Themed Entertainment Association

Technovision® Interactive Inc
529 Mountain Ash Dr, Pickering, ON L1W 3Z8,
Canada
Tel: 905-509-9482
E-mail: sales@technovision.com
Web Site: www.technovision.com
Manufacturer, integrator & supplier of a
full range of interfaces, control devices &
computer-based systems for a multitude of applications. More than 45,000 of our proprietary
laserdisc, DVD & other controllers, merchandising solutions, music samplers & computer-

based applications have been placed around the
world.
Catalog(s) available

TecNec Distributing
Division of Tower Products Inc
812 Kings Hwy, Saugerties, NY 12477
Mailing Address: PO Box 397, Saugerties, NY
12477
Tel: 845-246-0428 *Toll Free Tel:* 800-543-0909
Fax: 845-246-0626
E-mail: sales@tecnec.com
Web Site: www.tecnec.com
Key Personnel
VP, Sales: Andy Barth *Tel:* 845-246-0428 ext
7311
Pro AV, broadcast & pro audio products distribu-
tor.
Catalog(s) available

Tecplot Inc
3535 Factoria Blvd SE, Suite 550, Bellevue, WA
98006
Mailing Address: PO Box 52708, Bellevue, WA
98015-2708
Tel: 425-653-1200; 425-653-9393 (tech support)
Toll Free Tel: 800-763-7005 (orders)
E-mail: info@tecplot.com; support@tecplot.com
Web Site: www.tecplot.com
Key Personnel
CTO: Dr Scott Imlay
Pres: Tom Chan
VP, Cust Devt: Alan Klug
VP, Software Devt: Dan Delapp
Mktg Mgr: Margaret Connelly
Prod Mgr: Scott Fowler
Founded: 1981
Software solutions for scientists & engineers to
discover, analyze & communicate results.

Tectonics Industries LLC
Division of Quantum Digital Group LLC
1681 Harmon Rd, Auburn Hills, MI 48326
Tel: 248-597-1600 *Toll Free Tel:* 888-408-3199
E-mail: info@tectonics.com
Web Site: tectonics.com
Key Personnel
CEO: Lee Skandalaris
Founded: 1933
Full service graphics & digital imaging company
serving the tradeshow, event, exhibit, live enter-
tainment & other markets.
Online catalog(s) available
Branch Office(s)
213 Thornton Rd, Suite 100, Lithia Springs, GA
30122 *Tel:* 404-892-1688
2628 E Lone Mountain Rd, Suite A, North Las
Vegas, NV 89081 *Tel:* 702-389-3997

Tek Data Systems Co
1111 W Park Ave, Libertyville, IL 60048
Tel: 847-367-8800 *Fax:* 847-367-0235
E-mail: tekdata@tekdata.com; sales@tekdata.com
Web Site: www.tekdata.com
Key Personnel
Sales Mgr: Randy Kick
Proprietary computer software & media manage-
ment systems.
Literature available
Membership(s): AECT; ALA; Consortium of Col-
lege & University Media Centers; National As-
sociation of Media & Technology Centers

Tek Gear
938 Corydon Ave, Winnipeg, MB R3M 0Y5,
Canada
Tel: 204-988-3001 *Fax:* 204-988-3050
E-mail: sales@tekgear.com
Web Site: tekgear.com
Key Personnel
Pres: Tony Havelka *E-mail:* tonyh@tekgear.com

Sales Mgr: Eric Austman *E-mail:* eric@tekgear.
com
Founded: 1993

TEK Media Group
711 S Victory Blvd, Burbank, CA 91502
Tel: 818-244-4440; 818-255-5045
Toll Free Tel: 800-255-5045 (support)
Fax: 818-855-8762
E-mail: as@tekmg.com
Web Site: www.tekmg.com
Key Personnel
Serv Mgr: Michael Shank *E-mail:* mshank@
tekmg.com
Professional AV broadcast equipment & industrial
electronics repair.

Tekskil Industries Inc
102-998 Harbourside Dr, North Vancouver, BC
V7P 3T2, Canada
Tel: 604-985-2250 *Toll Free Tel:* 877-835-7545
Toll Free Fax: 877-576-8361
E-mail: team@tekskil.com
Web Site: www.tekskil.com
Key Personnel
Pres: John Veenstra
Opers & Tech Support: Rick Anselmo
E-mail: rick@tekskil.com
Founded: 1981

Tel-Air Interests Inc
4104 Grant St, Hollywood, FL 33021
Tel: 954-924-4949 *Fax:* 954-924-4980
E-mail: telair@aol.com
Web Site: www.telairint.com
Key Personnel
Pres: Grant H Gravitt, Jr
Prodr: Mary Lou Gravitt
Founded: 1960
Full service production company.

TEL Systems LLC
7235 Jackson Rd, Ann Arbor, MI 48103
Tel: 734-761-4506 *Toll Free Tel:* 800-686-7235
Fax: 734-761-9776
E-mail: sales@thalner.com
Web Site: www.thalner.com
Key Personnel
Pres: Timothy Boggs *E-mail:* tboggs@
telsystemsusa.com
VP: Paul Eiswerth *E-mail:* peiswerth@
telsystemsusa.com
Dir & Secy/Treas: Richard Schoenfeldt
Founded: 1965
Design, installation, training, service & mainte-
nance of educational, industrial & broadcast
audio & video systems.
Membership(s): Audiovisual and Integrated Expe-
rience Association

Tel-Test
Division of Corporate One Hundred Inc
605 NW 53 Ave, Suite A-17, Gainesville, FL
32609
Tel: 352-335-0901 *Fax:* 352-376-3260
Key Personnel
Pres: Zeke Zetien *E-mail:* zekezetien@aol.com
Catalog(s) available
Membership(s): NAB

Telarc International Corp
Division of Concord Music Group Inc
100 N Crescent Dr, Garden Level, Beverly Hills,
CA 90210
Tel: 310-385-4455
E-mail: submissions@concordmusicgroup.com
Web Site: www.concordmusicgroup.com/labels/
telarc
Key Personnel
CEO, Concord Music Group: Glen Barros
Founded: 1977

Classical music recording company.
Newsletter(s) available, electronic, monthly

Tele-Measurements Inc
145 Main Ave, Clifton, NJ 07014
Mailing Address: PO Box 1078, Clifton, NJ
07014-1078
Tel: 973-473-8822 *Toll Free Tel:* 800-223-0052
(ext 207) *Fax:* 973-473-0521
E-mail: contact@tele-measurements.com
Web Site: www.tele-measurements.com
Key Personnel
Pres: W Chris Endres
VP, Sales: Gary Gorski *Tel:* 973-473-8822 ext
207 *E-mail:* ggorski@tele-measurements.com
Founded: 1959
Catalog(s) available

Tele-Time Systems
313 Parkway Dr, Cary, IL 60013
Tel: 847-640-1420
E-mail: teletimesystems@netzero.com
Key Personnel
Owner & Mgr: Curtis A Bendell
Catalog(s) available

Telect Inc
22425 E Appleway Ave, Liberty Lake, WA 99019
Tel: 509-926-6000 *Toll Free Tel:* 800-551-4567
E-mail: getinfo@telect.com
Web Site: www.telect.com
Key Personnel
Pres & CEO: Wayne E Williams
Dir, Fin: Cameron Headley

Teledyne DALSA Inc
Subsidiary of Teledyne Technologies
605 McMurray Rd, Waterloo, ON N2V 2E9,
Canada
Tel: 519-886-6000 *Fax:* 519-886-8023
Web Site: www.teledynedalsa.com
Key Personnel
EVP, Fin: Silvio Favrin
Founded: 1980
Manufacture, design, research & development
of high performance solid-state image sensors
& modular expandable cameras; large format
sensor & camera technology; line scan & area
scan technology; Time Delay & Integration
(TDI) line scan technology for high sensitiv-
ity & low noise operation under low light level
conditions.
Catalog(s) available

Teledyne Energy Systems Inc
Subsidiary of Teledyne Technologies Inc
10707 Gilroy Rd, Hunt Valley, MD 21031
Tel: 410-771-8600 *Fax:* 410-771-8620
Web Site: www.teledynees.com
Catalog(s) available

**Telemanagement Resources International Inc
(TRI)**
83 Harvey Cedar Way, Waretown, NJ 08758
Tel: 609-597-6334
Web Site: www.triinc.com
Key Personnel
Pres: Dr S Ann Earon *E-mail:* annearon@aol.com
Opers Mgr: Shirley Gerwin
Sr Consultant: Spencer Freund
Founded: 1982
Catalog(s) available
Membership(s): IMCCA

Telemetrics Inc
75 Commerce Dr, Allendale, NJ 07401
Tel: 201-848-9818 *Fax:* 201-848-9819
E-mail: info@telemetricsinc.com
Web Site: www.telemetricsinc.com

Key Personnel
Pres: Anthony E Cuomo *E-mail:* aec@
telemetricsinc.com
Founded: 1973
Camera robotics & control systems for broadcast,
industrial, educational & military applications.
Online catalog(s) available
Membership(s): NAB; SMPTE®

Telemotions LLC
405 E 54 St, Suite 3-N, New York, NY 10022
Tel: 212-486-3010
Web Site: www.telemotions.net
Key Personnel
Exec Prodr: Tom Hayes *E-mail:* tomhay972@aol.
com
Sr Prodr: Sabine Beckert
Full service production company for TV & film
projects.

Teleometrics International
Division of Leadership Management Inc
4567 Lake Shore Dr, Waco, TX 76710
Mailing Address: PO Box 9126, Waco, TX
76714-9126
Tel: 254-776-2060 *Toll Free Tel:* 800-876-2389
E-mail: teleocsrv@teleometrics.com
Web Site: www.teleometrics.com
Founded: 1967
Producer of training materials.
Catalog(s) available
Membership(s): ATD

Telepro Video Inc
2650 Rd 32, Linwood, NE 68036
Tel: 402-593-0999
E-mail: tmtelepro@aol.com
Key Personnel
Pres: Theo Mercer
Founded: 1984
AV production facility.
Catalog(s) available

Telequest Inc
174 Nassau St, Suite 383, Princeton, NJ 08542
Tel: 609-430-3004
E-mail: contact@telequestinc.com
Web Site: www.telequestinc.com
Key Personnel
Pres: Dan Preston
Founded: 1978
Independent production company providing
script-to-screen services for nonprofit, educa-
tional & corporate clients.

Telescript International
55 Walnut St, Norwood, NJ 07648
Tel: 201-767-6733 *Fax:* 201-660-7804
E-mail: info@telescript.com
Web Site: telescript.com
Key Personnel
Mng Dir: Chris O'Brien *E-mail:* chris@telescript.
com
Professional teleprompting solutions.
Catalog(s) available
Membership(s): NAB; NAMM, the National As-
sociation of Music Merchants

Telestream Inc
848 Gold Flat Rd, Nevada City, CA 95959
Tel: 530-470-1300 *Toll Free Tel:* 877-257-6245
Fax: 530-470-1301
E-mail: info@telestream.net
Web Site: www.telestream.net
Key Personnel
Pres & CEO: Dan Castles
CFO: Neal Peterson
CTO: Shawn Carnahan
VP, Desktop Busn & Corp Mktg: Scott Murray
VP, Engg: Steve Tilly
Mktg Commns Mgr: Rose Sponder

Founded: 1998
Video/audio encoding & transcoding workflow
automation software & hardware supplier.
Branch Office(s)
2020 Milvia St, Suite 500, Berkeley, CA 94704-
1298
21351 Ridgetop Circle, Suite 120, Sterling, VA
20166
Foreign Office(s): Telestream GmbH, Dietkirchen-
str 30, 53111 Bonn, Germany
Telestream UK Ltd, The Crescent Ctr, Suite 1C,
Temple Back, Bristol BS1 6EZ, United Kingdom
Membership(s): IABM

TeleTime Productions
7 Willow Rd, Lynbrook, NY 11563
Tel: 516-255-8383
Web Site: www.teletimevideo.com
Key Personnel
Co-Founder & Pres: Nan Givner-Klein
Co-Founder: Harold Klein
Founded: 1976

TeleVideos
1566 Dola St, Eugene, OR 97402
Toll Free Tel: 800-2-VIDEOS (284-3367)
E-mail: televideos@msn.com
Web Site: televideos.com
Key Personnel
Owner: Barry Hood
Brochure(s) available

Television Equipment Associates Inc (TEA)
16 Mount Ebo Rd S, Suite 6, Brewster, NY
10509
Mailing Address: PO Box 404, Brewster, NY
10509-0404
Tel: 845-278-0960 *Fax:* 845-278-0964
E-mail: sales@teaheadsets.com
Web Site: www.teaheadsets.com
Key Personnel
Pres: Jeff Norment
Founded: 1969
Catalog(s) available
Membership(s): NAB; SMPTE®

Tellabs Inc
18583 North Dallas Pkwy, Suite 200, Dallas, TX
75287
Tel: 972-588-7000 *Toll Free Fax:* 866-665-8280
Web Site: www.tellabs.com
Branch Office(s)
1415 W Diehl Rd, Naperville, IL 60563 *Toll Free
Tel:* 800-690-2324
9711 Washingtonian Blvd, Suite 550, Gaithersburg, MD 20878 *Tel:* 301-978-3007

The Telos Alliance
1241 Superior Ave E, Cleveland, OH 44114
Tel: 216-241-7225 *Fax:* 216-241-4103
E-mail: inquiry@telosalliance.com
Web Site: www.telosalliance.com
Audio technology for the radio & television in-
dustries. Six brands: Telos® Systems, Omnia®
Audio, Axia® Audio, Linear Acoustic®, 25-
Seven® Systems & Minnetonka™ Audio.
Catalog(s) available
Foreign Office(s): General-von-Nagelstr 21,
85354 Freising, Germany *Tel:* (08161) 424-
67 *Fax:* (08161) 424-02 *E-mail:* europe-info@
telos-systems.com
Membership(s): Alliance for IP Media Solutions;
IABM; Media Networking Alliance; NAB;
Open Control Architecture Alliance

Tempe Camera
606 W University, Tempe, AZ 85281
Tel: 480-966-6954 *Toll Free Tel:* 800-836-7374
E-mail: rent@tempecamera.com; sales@
tempecamera.biz

Web Site: www.tempecamera.biz
Key Personnel
Founder & Owner: Joe Wojcich
Founded: 1972
New & used equipment sales including cameras, lenses, lighting, supplies & darkroom gear. Rent lenses, digital & film cameras & accessories, computer projectors, lighting & grip equipment. Repair services for all items sold.

Tempe Tape & Disc
722 W Raven Dr, Chandler, AZ 85286
Tel: 602-453-9663
Web Site: www.tempetape.com
Key Personnel
Owner: Andy Baade *E-mail:* andy@tempetape. com
Founded: 1984
CD & DVD replication & duplication services.

Temple Hill Entertainment
9255 W Sunset Blvd, West Hollywood, CA 90069
Tel: 310-270-4383 *Fax:* 310-270-4395
Web Site: twitter.com/TempleHillEnt
Key Personnel
Founder: Marty Bowen; Wyck Godfrey
Founded: 2006
Production company behind The Twilight Saga & Revenge.

1013 Integrated
1013 Kawaiahao St, Honolulu, HI 96814
Tel: 808-593-8848
E-mail: info@1013integrated.com
Web Site: www.facebook.com/1013integrated; 1013integrated.com
Key Personnel
Owner & Founding Partner: Dennis Burns
Founded: 1976
Fully integrated branding & production company.

Tenba
Division of MAC Group
75 Virginia Rd, North White Plains, NY 10603
Tel: 914-347-3300 *Fax:* 914-347-3309
E-mail: info@tenba.com
Web Site: www.tenba.com
Key Personnel
Pres, MAC Group: Mr Jan Lederman
Manufactures shipping & carrying cases for LCD projector cases, photo & computer equipment.
Catalog(s) available

Tennessee Prompters
Division of MediaMan® Productions
727 Wildview Dr, Nashville, TN 37211-1142
Tel: 615-834-9655
E-mail: info@tennesseeprompters.com
Web Site: www.tennesseeprompters.com
Key Personnel
Owner: Will Reynolds *Tel:* 615-202-7626 (cell)
Founded: 1991
Complete teleprompter equipment & service company. Podium, stage & through-the-lens prompter systems & operators.

Tepco Corp
2603 Bridgeview Dr, Rapid City, SD 57701-5801
Tel: 605-343-7200 *Fax:* 605-343-7240
Key Personnel
Pres: Don Le Fever
FM translators.
Catalog(s) available

Terra Nova Films Inc
9848 S Winchester Ave, Chicago, IL 60643
Tel: 773-881-8491 *Toll Free Tel:* 800-779-8491
Fax: 773-881-3368
E-mail: tnf@terranova.org
Web Site: www.terranova.org

Key Personnel
Exec Dir: James Vanden Bosch
Off Mgr: Ginny Priestman *E-mail:* ginny@terranova.org
Founded: 1981
Producer & distributor of videos dealing with aging.
Online catalog(s) available

Test Equipment Connection
30 Skyline Dr, Lake Mary, FL 32746
Tel: 407-804-1299 *Toll Free Tel:* 800-615-8378
Fax: 407-804-1277
E-mail: sales@testequipmentconnection.com
Web Site: www.testequipmentconnection.com
Global supplier of new & refurbished electronic test & measurement equipment & IT networking equipment.

TestEquity LLC, see JENSEN Tools + Supply

Tetrahedron LLC
5348 Las Vegas Dr, Suite 353, Las Vegas, NV 89108
Tel: 208-265-8065 *Toll Free Tel:* 888-923-9936
E-mail: tetra@tetrahedron.org
Web Site: www.tetrahedron.org; www. healthyworldstore.com
Key Personnel
Founder & Pres: Dr Leonard G Horowitz
Founded: 1978
Educational programming.
Catalog(s) available, free, 3 times/yr

Texas Heart Institute Visual Communication Services
Denton A Cooley Bldg, Suite C-530, 6770 Bertner Ave, Houston, TX 77030
Tel: 832-355-9558 *Fax:* 832-355-9511
Web Site: www.texasheart.org
Key Personnel
Off Mgr: Jackie Berry *Tel:* 832-355-6737
E-mail: jberry@texasheart.org
Catalog(s) available

Texas Rebel Radio Network
c/o Hill Country Broadcasting, 210 Woodcrest, Fredericksburg, TX 78624
Mailing Address: c/o Hill Country Broadcasting, PO Box 311, Fredericksburg, TX 78624-0311
Tel: 830-997-2197 *Fax:* 830-997-2198
E-mail: hillcountrybroadcasting@gmail.com
Web Site: www.texasrebelradio.com
Key Personnel
Gen Mgr: Jayson Fritz
Radio station & production & programming services.

Texas Scenic Co Inc
8053 Potranco Rd, San Antonio, TX 78251
Tel: 210-684-0091 *Toll Free Tel:* 800-292-7490
Fax: 210-684-4557
E-mail: info@texasscenic.com
Web Site: www.texasscenic.com
Key Personnel
Gen Mgr & COO: Stephen G Surratt
CFO: Ron Fairchild
Pres: Richard Mecke
Founded: 1936
Designs, manufactures & installs theatrical stage equipment. Provides counterweight & motorized stage rigging, lighting, dimming & control equipment, stage & acoustical curtains, orchestra pit lifts & shells & other custom stage equipment. Brands include stage equipment contractor Pook Diemont & Ohl Inc & variable acoustic banner manufacturer acouStaCorp LLC.

Online catalog(s) available
Branch Office(s)
701 E 132 St, Bronx, NY 10454 *Tel:* 718-402-2677 *Fax:* 718-402-2859

Texcam Inc
1323 N First St, Bellaire, TX 77401
Tel: 713-524-2774 *Toll Free Tel:* 800-735-2774
Fax: 713-524-2779
E-mail: info@texcam.com
Web Site: www.texcam.com
Key Personnel
Off Mgr: Sherry Kasprzak
Founded: 1985
Motion picture & video equipment rental.
Membership(s): Production Equipment Rental Association; SMPTE®; Texas Association of Motion Media Professionals

TGA Recording Co
295 Urbandale Ave, Benton Harbor, MI 49022
Tel: 269-926-7581
E-mail: tgarecording@sbcglobal.net
Web Site: www.tgarecording.com
Key Personnel
Owner: Thomas Alti
Pres: Larry Coyle
Founded: 1970
Services include webcasting & RC aerial video.

Thales Angenieux, see Angenieux

Thalner Electronic Laboratories Inc, see TEL Systems LLC

The Studio of David Inocencio
41 Fairlawn Ave, Daly City, CA 94015
Tel: 415-716-2791 *Fax:* 415-716-2796
Key Personnel
Partner: David Inocencio *E-mail:* david@sbcglobal.net
Multimedia production studio. Services also include: digital production (video, PowerPoint, Keynote), web site art direction & production, photography (corporate portraits & events) & AV technical direction of events.
Catalog(s) available

Theatre Arts Video Library
174 Andrew Ave, Leucadia, CA 92024
Tel: 760-547-6039 *Fax:* 760-632-6859
E-mail: admin@theatreartsvideo.com
Web Site: www.theatreartsvideo.com
Key Personnel
Owner: Ron Ranson
Founded: 1988
Video programs for theatre training.
Catalog(s) available, annual

Theatre Effects
1810 Airport Exchange Blvd, Suite 400, Erlanger, KY 41018-3184
Tel: 859-647-8844 *Toll Free Tel:* 800-791-7646
Fax: 859-647-0075
E-mail: service@theatrefx.com
Web Site: www.theatrefx.com
Key Personnel
Owner: Doug Weber *E-mail:* doug@theatrefx.com
Sales Mgr: Chris Wyllie *E-mail:* chris@theatrefx. com
Founded: 1976
Online catalog(s) available
Spec sheet(s) available
Membership(s): Professional Lighting & Sound Association

Theatre House Inc
400 W Third St, Covington, KY 41011-1306
Tel: 859-431-2414 *Toll Free Tel:* 800-827-2414
Fax: 859-431-1837

E-mail: info@theatrehouse.com
Web Site: www.theatrehouse.com
Key Personnel
Mgr: Rick Gaukel
Founded: 1955
Theatrical equipment sales.

Theatre Service & Supply Corp
10004-F Pulaski Hwy, Baltimore, MD 21220
Tel: 410-686-1398 *Fax:* 410-574-2417
E-mail: sales@stage-n-studio.com
Web Site: www.stage-n-studio.com
Key Personnel
Owner: Jacauelin Keleman
Catalog(s) available
Membership(s): Entertainment Services and Technology Association

Theatrical Services & Supplies Inc
3340 Veterans Memorial Hwy, Bohemia, NY 11716
Tel: 631-873-4790 *Fax:* 631-873-4795
E-mail: sales@gotheatrical.com
Web Site: www.gotheatrical.com
Key Personnel
Owner: Robert F Bayer
Founded: 1969
Theatre system integrator - AV, lighting, rigging, dimming.

Theatrical Services Inc
128 S Washington St, Wichita, KS 67202
Tel: 316-263-4415 *Toll Free Tel:* 888-874-2649
Fax: 316-263-9927
Web Site: www.theatricalservices.com
Key Personnel
Pres: Steve Wolf
VP: Tom Johnson
Sales & Rental Mgmt: Josh Jones
Sales: Sean Roberson
Founded: 1976
Catalog(s) available
Membership(s): Professional Lighting & Sound Association

Theatrical Technicians Inc (TTI)
2700 Connecticut Ave NW, Suite 109, Washington, DC 20008-5308
E-mail: info@perfect-pickup.com
Key Personnel
Owner, Pres & CEO: Bert Morris
Founded: 1980
Manufactures the Perfect-Pickup Followspot Sight, the world's first patented followspot sight. Also publisher of the IATSE union craft text "Getting the Most from Your Followspot - An Operator's Handbook" & the official IATSE craft "Followspot Training Program".
Catalog(s) available
Membership(s): ECTC; International Alliance of Theatrical Stage Employees; USITT

Theosophical Publishing House
Division of The Theosophical Society in America
306 W Geneva Rd, Wheaton, IL 60187
Mailing Address: PO Box 270, Wheaton, IL 60189-0270
Tel: 630-665-0130 *Toll Free Tel:* 800-669-9425
Fax: 630-665-8791
E-mail: customerservice@questbooks.net; marketing@questbooks.net
Web Site: questbooks.com
Key Personnel
Dir, Opers: Pat Griebeler *Tel:* 630-668-1571 ext 307
Dir, Mktg & Publicity: Jessica Salasek *Tel:* 630-668-1571 ext 358
Publg Mgr: Sharron Dorr *E-mail:* sdorr@theosophical.org
Founded: 1875
Religious, educational video producer.

Catalog(s) available
Membership(s): Network of Alternatives for Publishers, Retailers & Artists Inc; Reading Recovery Council of North America

Thermodyne Cases
1841 Business Pkwy, Ontario, CA 91761
Tel: 909-923-9945 *Fax:* 909-923-7505
E-mail: sales@thermodyne.com
Web Site: www.thermodyne.com
Key Personnel
Pres: Gary S Ackerman
Founded: 1958
Catalog(s) available
CD-ROM catalog(s) available, free

Thin-Lite Corp
530 Constitution Ave, Camarillo, CA 93012
Tel: 805-987-5021 *Fax:* 805-388-0921
E-mail: sales@thinlite.com
Web Site: www.thinlite.com
Founded: 1969
Manufacturer of low volt light fixtures & ballasts.

Think 3-D.com
180 Cross Hwy, Westport, CT 06880
Tel: 646-873-0050
Web Site: www.think3-d.com
Key Personnel
Owner & Pres: Mark Yurkiw *E-mail:* mark@think3-d.com
3D art & special effects for film & video.

Thinking Allowed Productions
5966 Zinn Dr, Oakland, CA 94611
Tel: 510-339-8004 *Toll Free Tel:* 800-999-4415
E-mail: thinking@thinkingallowed.com
Web Site: www.thinkingallowed.com
Key Personnel
Pres: Arthur Bloch
Founded: 1986
Independent public television series "Thinking Allowed" DVD collection.
Catalog(s) available

Thinking Maps Inc
401 Cascade Pointe Lane, Cary, NC 27513-5780
Tel: 919-678-8778 *Toll Free Tel:* 800-243-9169
Fax: 919-678-8782
E-mail: office@thinkingmaps.com
Web Site: thinkingmaps.com
Key Personnel
Pres: Sherwin Suddreth
Distribute educational programs.
Brochure(s) available

Third Ear Sound Co
30965 San Benito St, Hayward, CA 94544
Tel: 510-429-1000 *Toll Free Tel:* 800-587-1115
Fax: 510-429-1001
E-mail: raul@thirdearsound.com
Web Site: www.thirdearsound.com
Key Personnel
Partner: Don Albonico
Mktg Dir: Raul Suarez
Audio equipment rentals.

Third World Newsreel/Camera News Inc
545 Eighth Ave, Suite 550, New York, NY 10018
Tel: 212-947-9277 *Fax:* 212-594-6417
E-mail: twn@twn.org
Web Site: www.twn.org
Key Personnel
Exec Dir: J T Takagi
Dist & Mktg Dir: Roselly Torres Rojas
Founded: 1968
Educational social issue media.
Catalog(s) available

31st Street Studios
77 31 St, Pittsburgh, PA 15201
Tel: 412-228-0231
E-mail: info@31ststreetstudios.com
Web Site: www.31ststreetstudios.com
Key Personnel
Owner: Chris Breakwell
Production services, studio development & management.

30 Second Street Ltd
1209 Mountain Road Place NE, Suite B, Albuquerque, NM 87110
Tel: 505-265-0224
E-mail: info@30sst.com
Web Site: www.thirtysecst.com
Key Personnel
Gen Mgr: Colleen Burns
Creative Dir: Kelly Lujan
Sr Ed: Clark Morris
Opers Coord: Jade Norris
Video post-production service company.

Thomas & Betts Power Solutions LLC
5900 Eastport Blvd, Bldg V, Richmond, VA 23231-4453
Tel: 804-236-3300 *Toll Free Tel:* 800-238-5000; 800-CYBEREX (292-3739) *Fax:* 804-236-4040; 804-236-4841
Web Site: www.tnbpowersolutions.com
Key Personnel
Mktg Communs Mgr: Susan Hughson
Uninterrupted power sources.
Catalog(s) available

Thomas Printworks
600 N Central Expwy, Richardson, TX 75080
Tel: 972-231-7161 *Toll Free Tel:* 800-877-3776
Fax: 972-644-6308
E-mail: richardson@thomasprintworks.com
Web Site: thomasprintworks.com
Key Personnel
Pres & CEO, Dallas/Fort Worth Area: Bryan Thomas
District Mgr, Dallas/Fort Worth Area: Kent Long
Mktg Dir: Brianna Thomas Long
Founded: 1956
Digital printing.
Online catalog(s) available
Branch Office(s)
15125 Quorum Dr, Addison, TX 75001, Store Mgr: Johnny Milstead *Tel:* 972-726-8991 *E-mail:* addison@thomasprintworks.com
304 E Third St, Austin, TX 78701, Store Mgr: Jill Fletcher *Tel:* 512-302-4664 *Fax:* 512-302-4666 *E-mail:* austinaec@thomasprintworks.com
3610 Oak Lawn Ave, Dallas, TX 75219, Store Mgr: Jon Sauve *Tel:* 214-880-0022 *Fax:* 214-880-0006 *E-mail:* uptownaec@thomasprintworks.com
4718 Greenville Ave, Dallas, TX 75206, Store Mgr: Nancy Riddell *Tel:* 214-363-6561 *Fax:* 214-363-6564 *E-mail:* greenvilleave@thomasprintworks.com
2518 W Forest Lane, Dallas, TX 75234, Store Mgr: Larry Phillips *Tel:* 972-620-1861 *Fax:* 972-620-1862 *E-mail:* forestlane@thomasprintworks.com
805 Lamar St, Fort Worth, TX 76102, Store Mgr: Shawn Smith *Tel:* 817-336-0565 *Fax:* 817-336-1902 *E-mail:* fortworth@thomasprintworks.com
4235 Richmond Ave, Houston, TX 77027, Store Mgr: Chad Lang *Tel:* 713-621-0022 *Fax:* 713-621-2537 *E-mail:* richmondaec@thomasprintworks.com
707 West Rd, Houston, TX 77038, Commercial Print & Mail Servs Mgr: Don Lawler *Tel:* 832-201-2000 *Fax:* 832-201-2001
10606 Hempstead Rd, Houston, TX 77092, Store Mgr: Jamitta Honore *Tel:* 713-690-5636 *Fax:* 713-690-7565 *E-mail:* hempstead@thomasprintworks.com

3232 Chimney Rock Rd, Houston, TX 77056,
Store Mgr: Glynn Donnelly *Tel:* 713-977-6363
Fax: 713-977-4619 *E-mail:* chimneyrock@
thomasprintworks.com
982 N Garden Ridge Blvd, Suite 150, Lewisville,
TX 75067, Store Mgr: David Zaviska
Tel: 972-353-0059 *Fax:* 972-353-9460
E-mail: lewisville@thomasprintworks.com
1223 Arion Pkwy, Suite 108, San Antonio, TX 78216, Store Mgr: Christi Dock-
ery *Tel:* 210-829-7000 *Fax:* 210-824-6717
E-mail: sanantonioaec@thomasprintworks.com
817 E Indian School Rd, Phoenix, AZ 85014,
Store Mgr: Peter O'Rourke *Tel:* 602-264-
6871 *Fax:* 602-264-4399 *E-mail:* phoenixaec@
thomasprintworks.com
15685 N Greenway-Hayden Loop, Suite 100C,
Scottsdale, AZ 85260, Store Mgr: Edward
Hamm *Tel:* 480-342-8860 *Fax:* 480-515-5961
E-mail: northscottsdale@thomasprintworks.com
8100 E Indian School Rd, Suite 101, Scottsdale, AZ 85251, Store Mgr: Johnnie Bethel
Tel: 480-994-5520 *Fax:* 480-994-5862
E-mail: scottsdale@thomasprintworks.com
1775 W University Dr, Suite 125, Tempe, AZ
85281, Store Mgr: Allison Earl *Tel:* 480-967-
1400 *Fax:* 480-968-3011 *E-mail:* tempe@
thomasprintworks.com
275 University Dr, Coral Gables, FL 33134,
Store Mgr: Andres Taborda *Tel:* 305-461-
3540 *Fax:* 305-461-3575 *E-mail:* coralgables@
thomasprintworks.com
801 N Andrews Ave, Fort Lauderdale, FL 33311,
Store Mgr: Alex Montoto *Tel:* 954-525-0157
Fax: 954-525-0387 *E-mail:* ftlauderdale@
thomasprintworks.com
160 Candace Dr, Maitland, FL 32751, Store
Mgr: Tommy Luong *Tel:* 407-647-3034
Fax: 407-647-3312 *E-mail:* orlandocolor@
thomasprintworks.com
100 Candace Dr, Suite 108, Maitland,
FL 32751, Store Mgr: Tommy Luong
E-mail: orlandoaec@thomasprintworks.com
(AEC servs)
5000 SW 75 Ave, Suite 114, Miami, FL 33155,
Store Mgr: Santiago Ceron *Tel:* 305-667-
4149 *Fax:* 305-669-9331 *E-mail:* miamiaec@
thomasprintworks.com
1335 Okeechobee Rd, West Palm Beach,
FL 33401, Store Mgr: Kenny Lipnicki
Tel: 561-802-3599 *Fax:* 561-651-1104
E-mail: westpalm@thomasprintworks.com
801 Second Ave N, Minneapolis, MN
55405, Store Mgr: Ahmed Aboujouda
Tel: 612-374-1120 *Fax:* 612-374-1129
E-mail: minneapolisaec@thomasprintworks.
com
8025 Glen Lane, Eden Prairie, MN 55344,
Store Mgr: Dave Butler *Tel:* 952-835-2141
Fax: 952-835-2383 *E-mail:* edenprairie@
thomasprintworks.com
3345 W Saint Germain St, St Cloud, MN
56301, Store Mgr: Jake Hoeft *Tel:* 320-656-
1300 *Fax:* 320-656-1302 *E-mail:* stcloud@
thomasprintworks.com
Membership(s): International Reprographic Association

Thomega Entertainment Inc
North Star Business Centre, 210-820 51 St E,
Saskatoon, SK S7K 0X8, Canada
Mailing Address: PO Box 25104, RPO River
Heights, Saskatoon, SK S7K 8B7, Canada
Tel: 306-280-4982 *Fax:* 306-242-5845
E-mail: thomega@sasktel.net
Web Site: www.thomega.com
Key Personnel
Pres: Anthony J Towstego
Founded: 1988
Film & TV production.
Membership(s): Saskatchewan Chamber of Com-
merce; Saskatchewan Film & Television Pro-
ducers Association

**Thompson Rivers University Marketing &
Communications Dept**
805 TRU Way, Kamloops, BC V2C 0C8, Canada
Tel: 250-852-7000
Web Site: www.tru.ca/marcom
Key Personnel
Assoc VP, Mktg & Communs: Lucille
Gnanasihamany *Tel:* 778-471-8389
E-mail: lgnanasihamany@tru.ca
Dir, Mktg & Brand: Jennifer Read *Tel:* 250-852-
6837 *E-mail:* jread@tru.ca
Dir, Media Rels & Communs: Diana Skoglund
Tel: 250-371-5897 *E-mail:* dskoglund@tru.ca
Communs & Digital Media Mgr: Lindsey Norris
Tel: 250-371-5933 *E-mail:* lnorris@tru.ca
Creative Mgr: Linda Komori *Tel:* 250-852-7148
E-mail: lkomori@tru.ca
Mktg Mgr: Corey Wiwchar *Tel:* 250-852-6845
E-mail: cwiwchar@tru.ca
Mgr, Web Strategy: Matthew Tarzwell *Tel:* 250-
852-6256 *E-mail:* mtarzwell@tru.ca
Distance learning audio & video programs.
Catalog(s) available

Thorburn Associates (TA)
20880 Baker Rd, Castro Valley, CA 94546
Mailing Address: PO Box 20399, Castro Valley,
CA 94546-8399
Tel: 510-886-7826 *Fax:* 510-886-7828
E-mail: ta@ta-inc.com
Web Site: www.ta-inc.com
Key Personnel
Founding Principal & Pres: Lisa A Thorburn
Principal: Steven J Thorburn
Acoustics, AV, telecom & lighting design.
Brochure(s) available
Branch Office(s)
1317 N San Fernando Blvd, Suite 212, Burbank,
CA 91504 *Tel:* 818-569-0234 *Fax:* 818-569-
0233
7780 Chapelhill Dr, MS 100, Orlando, FL 32819
Tel: 407-898-5645
401 N Tryon St, 10th fl, Charlotte, NC 28202
Tel: 704-334-1040
2500 Gateway Centre Blvd, Suite 800, Mor-
risville, NC 27560 *Tel:* 919-463-9995
Fax: 919-463-9973
Membership(s): AES; ASA; Audiovisual and In-
tegrated Experience Association; IEEE; NSPE

Thread Marketing Group
4635 W Alexis Rd, Toledo, OH 43623-1005
Tel: 419-887-6801 *Fax:* 419-887-6802
E-mail: info@threadgroup.com
Web Site: www.threadgroup.com
Key Personnel
CEO: Judy McFarland *Tel:* 419-887-6820
E-mail: judy@threadgroup.com
COO: Joe Sharp *Tel:* 419-887-6820 *E-mail:* joe@
threadgroup.com
EVP: Holly Goldstein *Tel:* 419-887-6803
E-mail: holly@threadgroup.com
SVP: Michael Dempsey *Tel:* 419-887-6810
Creative Dir: David Proudfoot *Tel:* 419-887-6809
Founded: 1986
Integrated multimedia solutions.

Three D Graphics Inc
11340 W Olympic Blvd, Suite 352, Los Angeles,
CA 90064-1613
Tel: 310-231-3330 *Toll Free Tel:* 800-913-0008
Fax: 310-231-3303
E-mail: info@threedgraphics.com
Web Site: www.threedgraphics.com
Key Personnel
Pres: Elmer Easton
Founded: 1986

Three Pillars Media
140 N Eighth St, Suite 220, Lincoln, NE 68508
Tel: 402-937-0984
E-mail: contact@threepillarsmedia.com

Web Site: www.threepillarsmedia.com
Key Personnel
Owner: Ryan Cole
Pres: Matt Sherman
Founded: 2003
Video production & photography studio.

Three Rivers Publishing Co
Subsidiary of Kurt House Enterprises Inc
2330 Buroak Ridge, San Antonio, TX 78248
Tel: 210-490-2433
E-mail: cowboyhous@aol.com
Web Site: www.kurthouse.com
Key Personnel
Pres: Kurt D House
Founded: 1980
Publishing books & videos on western col-
lectibles & electric fans.
Flyer(s) available, 1 page

360 Systems
3281 Grande Vista Dr, Newbury Park, CA 91320-
1193
Tel: 818-991-0360 *Fax:* 818-991-1360
E-mail: sales@360systems.com
Web Site: www.360systems.com
Key Personnel
CEO: Alan Jermagian
Dir, Global Sales: John Hall *E-mail:* john.hall@
360systems.com
Sales Mgr, Prof Video Prods: Robert Nilo
Tel: 617-823-2051 *E-mail:* robert.nilo@
360systems.com
Sales Admin, Prof Audio Prods: Roxanna Veltze
E-mail: roxanna.veltze@360systems.com
Founded: 1972
Online catalog(s) available

3008
3008 Ross Ave, Suite 100, Dallas, TX 75204
Tel: 214-922-9232 *Fax:* 214-922-8861
Web Site: www.3008.com
Key Personnel
Partner & Pres: Brent Harrington *E-mail:* brent@
3008.com
Exec Prodr: Brian Hwang *E-mail:* brian@3008.
com
Production & post-production services for film &
video.

3M Touch Systems
3M Center, St Paul, MN 55144-1000
Toll Free Tel: 888-3M-HELPS (364-3577)
Toll Free Fax: 800-603-7758
Web Site: www.3m.com/touch
Touchscreen systems & displays engineered for
commercial applications.
Online catalog(s) available

THV11, A TEGNA Company, see KTHV-TV

Leo Ticheli Productions
2801 University Blvd, Suite 101, Birmingham,
AL 35233
Tel: 205-930-0500 *Fax:* 205-930-0505
E-mail: hello@ltpro.com
Web Site: www.ltpro.com
Key Personnel
Pres: Don McNutt
Audio Engr: Clint Jones
Full service production company.

Tickets.com
555 Anton Blvd, Costa Mesa, CA 92626
Tel: 714-327-5400 *Toll Free Tel:* 800-352-0212
(cust serv) *Fax:* 714-327-5410
E-mail: sales@tickets.com
Web Site: www.tickets.com
Ticket sellers.

Tierney Brothers Inc
1771 Energy Park Dr, Suite 100, St Paul, MN
55108
Tel: 612-331-5500 *Toll Free Tel:* 866-557-6062
 Fax: 612-331-3424
E-mail: contactform@tierneybrothers.com
Web Site: www.tierneybrothers.com
Key Personnel
Chmn: Tom Tierney
CEO: Rob Gag
Pres: Jim Tierney
Founded: 1977
Provider of LCD projectors, systems integration,
large format printers, graphic & engineering
supplies & audio & visual communication solu-
tions. Also design & install conference, training
& boardrooms. Offers 24/7 technical service,
along with complete rental & image depart-
ments.
Branch Office(s)
405 Forest St, Oconomowoc, WI 53066

The Tiffen Co LLC
90 Oser Ave, Hauppauge, NY 11788-3886
Tel: 631-273-2500 *Toll Free Tel:* 800-645-2522
 Fax: 631-273-2557
E-mail: techsupport@tiffen.com
Web Site: www.tiffen.com
Key Personnel
Pres & CEO: Steven Tiffen
Dir, Prod Mktg: Andrew Tiffen *Tel:* 631-273-
2500 ext 3116 *E-mail:* andrew@tiffen.com
Founded: 1938
Manufacture imaging accessories for the con-
sumer/professional imaging & motion picture
& broadcast television industries, including:
Tiffen optical photographic filters & lens acces-
sories; Steadicam camera stabilizing systems;
Lowel location lighting equipment; Domke
camera bags & Zing camera covers; Dfx dig-
ital effects software; Listec teleprompters;
Davis & Sanford tripods & support systems;
Stroboframe flash brackets.
Online catalog(s) available
Branch Office(s)
Tiffen-Steadicam, 2815 Winona Ave, Burbank,
CA 91504 *Tel:* 818-843-4600 *Fax:* 818-843-
8321
Foreign Office(s): Tiffen International Ltd,
Pinewood Rd, Iver Heath SL0 0NH, United
Kingdom *Tel:* (0870) 00 1220 *Fax:* (01869) 32
1766
Membership(s): ASMP; National Press Photogra-
phers Association

Tight Line Productions
1902 Oak St, Melbourne, FL 32901
Tel: 321-725-4668 *Fax:* 321-768-6528
E-mail: info@tightlinetv.com
Web Site: www.tightlineproductions.com
Key Personnel
Pres: Mark Lewis *E-mail:* mlewis@tightlinetv.
com
Founded: 1995

Tiki Recording Studios Inc
30-A Glen St, Suite 204, Glen Cove, NY 11542
Tel: 516-671-4300 (ext 101) *Fax:* 516-671-8754
Web Site: www.tikirecording.com
Key Personnel
Owner & Engr: Fred Guarino *Tel:* 516-924-3296
(cell) *E-mail:* fred@tikirecording.com
Founded: 1978
Recording studio.
Membership(s): The Recording Academy; SPARS

TIMECODE Post Production
12340 Santa Monica Blvd, Suite 230, West Los
Angeles, CA 90025
Tel: 310-826-9199
E-mail: info@timecodemedia.com
Web Site: www.timecodepost.com

Key Personnel
Pres: Stuart Ferreyra
Founded: 1999
Post-production & digital media services.

Timed Exposures Films
122 Old Rd, Germantown, NY 12526-6014
Tel: 518-537-2012
E-mail: info@timedexposures.com
Web Site: www.timedexposures.com
Key Personnel
Pres, Prodr & Dir: Ralph Arlyck *E-mail:* ralph@
timedexposures.com
Film & video production.
Online catalog(s) available

Timeless Books
Division of Association for the Development of
Human Potential
Box 9, Kootenay Bay, BC V0B 1X0, Canada
Tel: 250-227-9224 *Toll Free Tel:* 800-661-8711
 Fax: 250-227-9494
E-mail: bookstore@timeless.org
Web Site: www.timeless.org
Key Personnel
Gen Mgr: Maya Skalinska
Founded: 1978
Catalog(s) available
Branch Office(s)
PO Box 3543, Spokane, WA 99220-3543 *Toll
Free Tel:* 800-251-9273 *Fax:* 509-838-8652
 E-mail: timelessorders@comcast.net

Timeless Productions
5050 Traverse Creek Rd, Garden Valley, CA
95633
Tel: 530-333-1335 *Toll Free Tel:* 800-729-1325
E-mail: 4info@timelessproductions.com
Web Site: www.timelessproductions.com
Key Personnel
Owner: David Blonski
Music production.
Catalog(s) available

TimeLogic Corp
Division of Active Motif Inc
1914 Palomar Oaks Way, Suite 150, Carlsbad,
CA 92008
Tel: 760-431-1263 *Toll Free Tel:* 877-222-9543
 Fax: 760-431-1351
Web Site: www.timelogic.com
Key Personnel
Dir, IT & Bioinformatics: Steve Stelman
 Tel: 877-222-9543 ext 348 *E-mail:* stelman@
activemotif.com
Brochure(s) available

Times-Square Fantasy Theatre
Subsidiary of Cude & Pickens Productions
519 N Halifax Ave, Daytona Beach, FL 32118
Tel: 386-252-0381 *Fax:* 386-252-0381
E-mail: timessquare@bellsouth.net
Web Site: www.timessquarefantasytheatre.com;
www.broadwaymusicdownload.com
Key Personnel
Owner & CEO: Bobby Lee Cude
Online catalog(s) available
Membership(s): Alliance of Artists & Recording
Companies; BMI; National Music Publishers'
Association; The Recording Academy

TimeSteps Productions Inc
2 Glenside Dr, West Orange, NJ 07052
Tel: 973-669-1930
E-mail: info@timesteps.com
Web Site: timesteps.com
Key Personnel
Partner: Rob Lieberman; Marilyn Petrokubi
Founded: 1987

Live-action & animated video, digital post-
production, 4K video & soundtrack design.
Membership(s): New York Women in Film &
Television

Timestream Video
11821 N Circle Dr, Whittier, CA 90601-2338
Tel: 562-699-8797 *Fax:* 562-695-0252
Web Site: www.timestreamvideo.com
Key Personnel
Owner & Prodr: Larry Scher *E-mail:* lscher.tv@
verizon.net
Designer: J F Podevin
Founded: 1978
Membership(s): SMPTE®

Rik Tinory Productions
180 Pond St, Cohasset, MA 02025
Mailing Address: PO Box 311, Cohasset, MA
02025-0311
Tel: 781-383-9494

Tisch School of the Arts
Division of New York University
721 Broadway, 10th & 11th fl, New York, NY
10003
Tel: 212-998-1700; 212-998-1780 *Fax:* 212-995-
4062; 212-995-4063
Web Site: www.tisch.nyu.edu
Key Personnel
Sr Assoc Dean, Strategic Initiatives: Sheril Anto-
nio
Assoc Dean, Karbar Film & Television: Michael
Burke *E-mail:* michael.burke@nyu.edu
Catalog(s) available
Membership(s): Consortium of College & Univer-
sity Media Centers

Titus Technological Laboratories (TTL)
77 Kreiger Lane, Glastonbury, CT 06033
Tel: 860-633-5472 *Toll Free Tel:* 800-806-TTL1
(806-8851) *Fax:* 860-633-8244
E-mail: sales1@tituslabs.com
Web Site: www.tituslabs.com
Key Personnel
Owner & Pres: Lawrence Titus
Founded: 1971
Manufacturer of radio, television & satellite
broadcast equipment.
Catalog(s) available

TiVo Corp
2 Circle Star Way, San Carlos, CA 94070
Tel: 408-562-8400 *Toll Free Tel:* 877-367-8486
(cust support); 877-289-8486 (sales support)
 Fax: 408-567-1800
Web Site: business.tivo.com; www.tivo.com
Key Personnel
CEO & Pres: Thomas Carson
CFO: Peter Halt
EVP & COO: Pete Thompson
Chief Admin & Internal Opers Offr: Dustin Finer
EVP, Gen Counsel & Chief Compliance Offr:
Pamela Sergeeff
EVP, Integration: Bill Corry
EVP, Intellectual Property & Licensing: Samir
Armaly
EVP, Strategy & Corp Devt: Sean Matthews
SVP & Gen Mgr, IP Licensing: Matt Milne
Digital rights management, electronic program
guide software & metadata.
Literature available
Branch Office(s)
2233 N Ontario St, Burbank, CA 91504 *Tel:* 818-
295-6650 *Fax:* 818-295-6797
2160 Gold St, San Jose, CA 95002 *Tel:* 408-519-
9100 *Fax:* 408-941-9739
DigitalSmiths, 1860 Blake St, Suite 210, Denver,
CO 80202 *Tel:* 919-695-9109
500 Golden Ridge Rd, Suite 100, Golden, CO
80401-9552 *Tel:* 303-273-7800 *Fax:* 303-273-
7880

300 A St, Suite 500, Boston, MA 02210-1620
Tel: 408-562-8400 *Fax:* 408-567-1800
100 Phoenix Dr, Suite 201, Ann Arbor, MI
48108-2202 *Fax:* 734-975-9177
TiVo Research & Analytics, 150 E 52 St, Suite
6000, New York, NY 10022 *Tel:* 212-286-7810
DigitalSmiths, 320 Blackwell St, Suite 200,
Durham, NC 27701 *Tel:* 919-695-9109
7140 S Lewis Ave, Tulsa, OK 74136-5422
Tel: 918-488-4000 *Fax:* 915-488-4860
550 E Swedesford Rd, Suite 350, Wayne, PA
19087-1601 *Tel:* 610-293-8500 *Fax:* 610-687-
2640
5800 Tennyson Pkwy, Suite 330, Plano, TX
75024-3993 *Tel:* 408-562-8400 *Fax:* 408-567-
1800
Foreign Office(s): 5th fl, Augusta Bldg, Embassy
Golf Links Business Park, Challaghatta Village, Varthur Hobli, Bangalore 560 071, India
Tel: (080) 4661 2200
2F, Marunouchi Trust Tower Main, 1-8-3
Marunouchi, Chiyoda-ku, Tokyo 100-0005,
Japan *Tel:* (03) 4577 1500 *Fax:* (03) 3212 0680
42-44 Ave de la Gare, 1610 Luxembourg, Luxembourg
Cubiware Sp z oo, a TiVo Co, 8th fl, Equator II
Bldg, Al Jerozolimskie 96, 00-807 Warsaw,
Poland *Tel:* (22) 207 29 41
8F, Taewoo Bldg, 285 Gangnamdae-ro, Seocho-
gu, Seoul 06729, South Korea *Tel:* (02) 6948
5700 *Fax:* (02) 6948 5701
Woolyard, 52 Bermondsey St, London SE1 3UD,
United Kingdom *Fax:* (020) 7407 4950
3rd fl, Braywick Gate, Braywick Rd, Maidenhead,
Berks SL6 1DA, United Kingdom *Tel:* (01628)
677300 *Fax:* (01628) 677392
Membership(s): Content Delivery & Storage Association; Entertainment Merchants Association

TKH Security Solutions USA Inc, see Siqura
Inc

TM Studios Inc
Subsidiary of Triton Medial/Dial-Global
2002 Academy Lane, Suite 110, Dallas, TX
75234
Tel: 972-406-6800 *Fax:* 972-406-6890
E-mail: info@tmstudios.com;
tmcustomerservice@tmstudios.com
Web Site: www.tmstudios.com
Key Personnel
VP & Gen Mgr: Greg Clancy *Tel:* 972-406-6847
E-mail: clancy@tmstudios.com
Dir, Mktg & Web Devt: Ryan Lambert *Tel:* 972-
406-6869 *E-mail:* rlambert@tmstudios.com
Acctg: Leticia Black *Tel:* 972-406-6859
E-mail: lblack@tmstudios.com
Catalog(s) available
Membership(s): NAB; Texas Association of
Broadcasters

TMW Media Group
2321 Abbot Kinney Blvd, Suite 101, Venice, CA
90291
Tel: 310-577-8581 *Toll Free Tel:* 800-262-8862
Fax: 310-574-0886
E-mail: sale@tmwmedia.com
Web Site: www.tmwmedia.com
Key Personnel
Pres: Michael Bennett
VP, Sales: Leslie Collins
Dir, Mktg: Elaine Dochard
Founded: 1989
K-12 educational programming.
Catalog(s) available

TOA Electronics Inc
Subsidiary of TOA Corp (Japan)
400 Oyster Point Blvd, Suite 301, South San
Francisco, CA 94080

Tel: 650-452-1200 *Toll Free Tel:* 800-733-
7088 (cust serv) *Fax:* 650-452-1250
Toll Free Fax: 800-733-9766
E-mail: info@toaelectronics.com; orders@
toaelectronics.com
Web Site: www.toaelectronics.com
Online catalog(s) available
Branch Office(s)
One Harmon Plaza, Suite 602, Secaucus, NJ
07094
Foreign Office(s): 7-2-1 Minatojima-Nakamachi,
Chuo-ku, Kobe 650-0046, Japan *Tel:* (078) 303
5620 *Fax:* (078) 303 4634 *Web Site:* www.toa.
co.jp
Membership(s): AES; IBMA; IPMA; NAMM,
the National Association of Music Merchants;
NSCA

Tobias Associates Inc
50 Industrial Dr, Ivyland, PA 18974-1433
Mailing Address: PO Box 2699, Ivyland, PA
18974-0347
Tel: 215-322-1500 *Toll Free Tel:* 800-877-3367
Fax: 215-322-1504
E-mail: sales@tobiasinc.com; service@tobiasinc.
com; repair@tobiasinc.com
Web Site: www.densitometers.net
Key Personnel
Pres: Eric M Tobias
Dir, Sales: William Bender
Founded: 1959
Catalog(s) available

Tobins Lake Sales
3313 Yellowstone Dr, Ann Arbor, MI 48105
Fax: 734-449-9812
Web Site: www.tobinslakesales.com
Key Personnel
Owner & Pres: William Ebeling *Tel:* 810-813-
4691 (cell) *E-mail:* bill@tobinslakesales.com
Catalog(s) available
Membership(s): Professional Lighting & Sound
Association; USITT

ToCad America Inc
53 Green Pond Rd, Suite 5, Rockaway, NJ 07866
Tel: 973-627-9600 *Toll Free Tel:* 800-886-2236
Fax: 973-664-2438
E-mail: info@tocad.com
Web Site: www.tocad.com
Key Personnel
Pres: Richard Darrow *Tel:* 972-627-9600 ext 103
VP, Sales: Nick Cheremsak
Photographic equipment manufacturer.
Catalog(s) available

Dorothy Tod Films
41 Hazel Brown Rd, Warren, VT 05674
Tel: 802-496-5280 *Fax:* 802-496-5280
Key Personnel
Pres: Dorothy Tod *E-mail:* dorothy.tod@gmail.
com
Catalog(s) available

Todd-AO Studios
4712 Admiralty Way, No 497, Marina del Rey,
CA 90292
Tel: 310-399-4557 *Toll Free Tel:* 877-315-3647
E-mail: info@todd-ao.com
Web Site: www.todd-ao.com
Founded: 1953
Recording studio.
Catalog(s) available
Branch Office(s)
2428 Third St, Santa Monica, CA 90405
Tel: 310-613-7138
Membership(s): SMPTE®

Toko America Inc
Subsidiary of Toko Inc
1250 Feehanville Dr, Mount Prospect, IL 60056

Tel: 847-297-0070 *Toll Free Tel:* 800-PIK-TOKO
(745-8656) *Fax:* 847-699-7864
E-mail: info@tokoam.com
Web Site: www.tokoam.com
Founded: 1955
Manufacturer of leading edge electronic compo-
nents.
Membership(s): GSA

Tom Thumb Music, see Rhythms Productions
(Tom Thumb Music)

TOMCAT USA Inc
5427 N National Dr, Knoxville, TN 37914
Mailing Address: PO Box 9187, Knoxville, TX
37940
Tel: 865-219-3700 *Fax:* 865-673-5818
E-mail: info@tomcatusa.com; sales@tomcatusa.
com
Web Site: www.tomcatglobal.com
Key Personnel
Pres & CEO: Scott Johnson *Tel:* 865-219-3720
Prodn Mgr: Adam Gross
Fabrication of aluminum structural components
for the entertainment & leisure industries, as
well as providing related products such as the-
atrical chain hoists, custom electric assemblies,
lighting products & rigging hardware.
Catalog(s) available
Membership(s): Professional Lighting & Sound
Association

Tommy Boy Entertainment LLC
220 E 23 St, New York, NY 10010
Tel: 212-388-8300
E-mail: info@tommyboy.com
Web Site: www.tommyboy.com
Key Personnel
Pres: Rosie Lopez
Founded: 1981
Hip hop & electronic label.
Online catalog(s) available

Tone Zone Recording
939 W Wilson Ave, Chicago, IL 60640
Mailing Address: 920 W Wilson Ave, Chicago,
IL 60640
Tel: 312-664-5353 *Fax:* 312-664-6560
E-mail: tonezonerecording@sbcglobal.net
Key Personnel
Mgr: Roger Heiss

Topbulb, a Semmer Lighting Company
1051 Clinton Ave, Buffalo, NY 14206
Toll Free Tel: 800-TOP-BULB (867-2852)
Toll Free Fax: 877-329-2852
E-mail: sales@topbulb.com
Web Site: www.topbulb.com
Founded: 1930
Distributor of light bulbs, lighting products & ac-
cessories.
Catalog(s) available, free

TopCat Records LLC
PO Box 670234, Dallas, TX 75367-0234
Tel: 972-484-4141 *Fax:* 972-620-8333
E-mail: info@topcatrecords.com
Web Site: www.topcatrecords.com
Key Personnel
Owner & CEO: Richard Chalk
Founded: 1992
Production & distribution of blues, jazz & out-
law country music CDs, DVDs & record label.
Branch office in Rio de Janeiro, Brazil.
Online catalog(s) available

Torpey Time
Subsidiary of Dixon Systems
132 Commerce Park Dr, Suite 255, Barrie, ON
L4N 0Z7, Canada
Tel: 705-487-2915

Web Site: ram68.com
Founded: 1975
Flyer(s) available
Branch Office(s)
6411 Roundup Rd, McHenry, IL 60050

Toshiba America Information Systems Inc
Subsidiary of Toshiba Corp
9740 Irvine Blvd, Irvine, CA 92618
Tel: 949-583-3000
Web Site: www.toshiba.com

Tosoh USA Inc
Subsidiary of Tosoh Corp
3600 Gantz Rd, Grove City, OH 43123
Tel: 614-277-4348 *Fax:* 614-875-8086
E-mail: info.tusa@tosoh.com
Web Site: www.tosohusa.com
Founded: 1964
Branch Office(s)
Tosoh Bioscience Inc, 6000 Shoreline Ct,
    Suite 101, South San Francisco, CA 94080
    Tel: 650-615-4970 *Toll Free Tel:* 800-248-
    6764 *Fax:* 650-615-0415 *E-mail:* info.diag.
    am@tosohbioscience.com *Web Site:* www.
    diagnostics.us.tosohbioscience.com
Tosoh Quartz Inc, 14380 NW Science Park
    Dr, Portland, OR 97229 *Tel:* 503-605-5600
    Fax: 503-605-5688 *E-mail:* info@tosohquartz.
    com *Web Site:* www.tosohquartz.com

Total AV Systems
9301 Georgia Ave, Silver Spring, MD 20910
Tel: 301-589-3337 *Toll Free Tel:* 800-447-7632
    Fax: 301-494-4770
E-mail: info@total-av.com
Web Site: total-av.com
Key Personnel
Pres: Han S Jan
VP: Josephine Jan
Systems Integrator: Kenneth Jan
Founded: 1978
Professional AV equipment sales, design-
    integration, service, engineering & installation.
Catalog(s) available
Branch Office(s)
1009 W Barre St, Baltimore, MD 21230 *Tel:* 410-
    625-4700 *Fax:* 410-625-4704

Total Concept Sales
2505 Foothill Blvd, Suite G, La Crescentia, CA
    91214
Tel: 818-236-3966 *Toll Free Tel:* 800-488-0589
    Fax: 818-236-3969
Web Site: www.totalups.com
Key Personnel
Data Mgr: Alfred Derohanessian *E-mail:* alfred@
    totalups.com
Catalog(s) available

Total Creative
432 N Canal St, Suite 12, South San Francisco,
    CA 94080
Tel: 650-583-8236 *Fax:* 650-583-4708
E-mail: info@totalcreative.com
Web Site: totalcreative.com
Key Personnel
Pres: Megan McKenna
Founded: 1979
Total Creative produces the entire experience. Of-
    fers everything from creative strategy to the
    AV equipment, crews, producers & visuals on
    stage. Also offers services a la carte.
Brochure(s) available
Membership(s): Bay Area Video Coalition; North-
    ern California Production Community

Total Impact Multimedia Group Ltd
1475 Pea Pond Rd, North Bellmore, NY 11710
Tel: 516-783-8800
E-mail: info@totalimpactltd.com

Web Site: totalimpactltd.com
Key Personnel
Owner & Pres: Kenneth Book
3D rendering & animation, 4D presentations, pro-
    posal support, brochures & print advertising,
    photography, video production & web develop-
    ment.

Total Media Inc
681 Lawlins Rd, Unit 10, Wyckoff, NJ 07481
Tel: 201-848-1100 *Toll Free Tel:* 800-355-4400
    Fax: 201-840-0300
E-mail: info@totalmedia.com
Web Site: www.totalmedia.com
Founded: 1989
Supplier of professional & commercial blank
    recording media, AV & computer media &
    printing supplies.

Total Video Products Inc
414 Southgate Ct, Mickleton, NJ 08056
Tel: 856-423-7400 *Toll Free Tel:* 800-447-0920
    Fax: 856-423-4747
E-mail: info@totalvideoproducts.com
Web Site: www.totalvideoproducts.com
Key Personnel
Pres: Larry Gallner *E-mail:* lgallner@
    totalvideoproducts.com
Dir, Sales: Lux Marx *E-mail:* lmarx@
    totalvideoproducts.com
Founded: 1976
AV & digital media integrator.
Catalog(s) available, free, annual
Membership(s): American Institute of Architects;
    Audiovisual and Integrated Experience Asso-
    ciation; Consortium of College & University
    Media Centers; CSI; International Facilities
    Management Association; NSCA; Philadelphia
    Advertising Club

ToteVision
3257 17 Ave W, Bldg 1, Suite 201, Seattle, WA
    98119
Tel: 206-623-6000; 206-623-6000 (ext 200, sales);
    206-623-6000 (ext 202, tech support & re-
    pairs); 206-623-6000 (ext 209, cust care); 206-
    623-6000 (ext 211, returns) *Fax:* 206-623-6609
E-mail: info@totevision.com
Web Site: totevision.com
Key Personnel
VP: Mark Lakefish *E-mail:* mlakefish@totevision.
    com
Founded: 1981
Manufacture LCD color monitors. Also provide
    customized packages of commercial grade
    monitors to the education & training, govern-
    ment, hospitality, pro AV, digital signage &
    broadcasting industries.

Touchstone Center Publications
Subsidiary of The Touchstone Center for Children
    Inc
141 E 88 St, Apt 3E, New York, NY 10128
Tel: 212-831-7717
Web Site: touchstonecenter.net
Key Personnel
Dir: Richard Lewis *E-mail:* rlewis212@aol.com
Founded: 1969
A series of videos by Geoffry Jones & others
    interpreting recent books by Richard Lewis. In-
    cluding: *The Bird of Imagining*; *Each Sky Has
    Its Words*, *Cave & Evocation of the Beginnings
    of Art*; as well as a variety of documentary
    tapes on the work of The Touchstone Center
    in schools & classrooms encouraging the use of
    the imaginative & poetic process in learning.
Catalog(s) available

Towards 2000 Inc
215 W Palm Ave, Suite 101, Burbank, CA 91502
Tel: 818-557-0903 *Toll Free Fax:* 866-836-5725

E-mail: info@t2k.com
Web Site: www.t2k.com
Key Personnel
Pres: Mark Rowlands *E-mail:* mark@t2k.com
Founded: 1978
Catalog(s) available

Toys From The Attic
27 Holland Ave, White Plains, NY 10603
Tel: 914-421-0069
E-mail: tftamail@gmail.com
Web Site: tftaus.com
Key Personnel
Owner & Pres: Mario A Campa
Founded: 1995
Retail & custom electronic installations. High-end
    AV retail & installation, vintage & collectible
    guitars & basses, mechanical watches & acces-
    sories.

TPR Enterprises Ltd
644 Fayette Ave, Mamaroneck, NY 10543
Tel: 914-698-1141 *Fax:* 914-698-9419
E-mail: info@tprlights.com
Web Site: www.tprlights.com
Key Personnel
Pres: Thomas Fay *E-mail:* tfay@tprlights.com
Commercial Sales Mgr: Paul Benton *Tel:* 320-
    266-8996 *E-mail:* pbenton@tprlights.com
Off Mgr: Lisa MacFadden *E-mail:* lmacfadden@
    tprlights.com
Founded: 1980
Lighting fixture, control equipment, fiber optic
    lighting & LED lighting.

TR Productions
Charlstown Navy Yard, Captains Quarters Bldg, 2
    13 St, 3rd fl, Charlestown, MA 02129
Tel: 617-241-5500
E-mail: info@trprod.com
Web Site: trprod.com
Key Personnel
Pres, Sr Creative Dir & Prodr: Cary M Benjamin
Admin & Sr Writer: Ross Benjamin
Founded: 1947
Business communications & production company.
    Specialize in the production of video presenta-
    tions, interactive CDs, webcasts, web presen-
    tations, business meetings, collateral & web
    design & multimedia screen shows.

Trac Recording Studio
Affiliate of Sellwood Publishing
180 E Warner Ave, Fresno, CA 93710
Tel: 559-903-0701
E-mail: tracrecording@pmicp.com
Web Site: tracrecordingstudio.com
Key Personnel
Owner: Stan Anderson
Founded: 1972
Recording studio, record label, publishing & artist
    development of original audio works for multi-
    ple genres. Equipment includes MCI console &
    tape recorder 24 track.

Trac Records, see Trac Recording Studio

Trafalgar Square Books
388 Howe Hill Rd, North Pomfret, VT 05053
Mailing Address: PO Box 257, North Pomfret,
    VT 05053-0257
Tel: 802-457-1911 *Toll Free Tel:* 800-423-4525
    Fax: 802-457-1913
E-mail: contact@trafalgarbooks.com; cs@
    trafalgarbooks.com (cust serv)
Web Site: www.horseandriderbooks.com; www.
    trafalgarbooks.com
Key Personnel
Publr: Caroline Robbins
Mng Dir: Martha Cook *E-mail:* mcook@
    trafalgarbooks.com

Mktg Dir & Craft Ed: Kim Cook
E-mail: kcook@trafalgarbooks.com
Mng Ed & Graphic Designer: Rebecca Didier
E-mail: rdidier@trafalgarbooks.com
Founded: 1972
Publish craft & equestrian books & DVDs.
Catalog(s) available, free, biannual

Trailblazer Studios®
1610 Midtown Place, Raleigh, NC 27609
Tel: 919-645-6600 *Fax:* 919-645-6601
E-mail: info@trailblazerstudios.com
Web Site: www.trailblazerstudios.com
Key Personnel
CEO: Tom Waring
VP, Original Programming: Jeff Lanter *Tel:* 919-645-6633 *E-mail:* jeff@trailblazerstudios.com
Exec Prodr, Music & Sound: Eric Johnson *Tel:* 919-645-6622 *E-mail:* eric@trailblazerstudios.com
Exec Prodr, Post Prodn: Leah Welsh *Tel:* 919-645-6657 *E-mail:* leah@trailblazerstudios.com
Exec Prodr, Prodn: Katye Rone *Tel:* 919-645-6615 *E-mail:* katye@trailblazerstudios.com
Catalog(s) available

Trans-Lux Multimedia Corp
Subsidiary of Trans-Lux Corp
445 Park Ave, Suite 2001, New York, NY 10022
Tel: 203-853-4321 *Toll Free Tel:* 800-243-5544; 800-462-2716
E-mail: sales@trans-lux.com
Web Site: www.trans-lux.com
Key Personnel
Pres & CEO: Jean-Marc L Allain
VP, CFO & Compt: Todd Dupree
Designers of real-time programmable display systems.
Brochure(s) available

The Transfer Zone®
4301 Orchard Lake Rd, Suite 180-191, West Bloomfield, MI 48323
Tel: 248-225-0477
Key Personnel
Mktg Dir: Roxane B Newhouse *E-mail:* rpida1@yahoo.com
Founded: 1976
Video post-production facility.
Membership(s): The Adcraft Club of Detroit

Transformational Education Initiatives
PO Box 344, Phoenicia, NY 12464
Tel: 310-795-4910
E-mail: lioneltv@aol.com
Web Site: transformationaledu.org
Key Personnel
Chmn: David Lionel
Founded: 1977
Educational DVD production & editing.

Transistor Devices Inc, see Astrodyne TDI

Transparent Office Products LLC
2550 Haddonfield Rd, Pennsauken, NJ 08110
Tel: 856-488-5455 *Fax:* 856-488-5411
E-mail: sales@transoffprod.biz
Web Site: www.transoffprod.biz
Key Personnel
Opers Mgr: Rick Brown
Archival storage pages.
Catalog(s) available

Transtar Entertainment Co Inc
11776 E Evans Ave, Aurora, CO 80014
Tel: 303-489-1450
Web Site: www.transtarfilm.com
Key Personnel
Pres, Exec Prodr, Dir & Ed: Doug Hanes
E-mail: doug@transtarfilm.com
Prodr & Dir: Nick Connell

Prodr: Mark Miller
Founded: 1982
Full service production company.
Catalog(s) available
Membership(s): DAF

Transtector Systems Inc
10701 N Airport Dr, Hayden, ID 83835
Tel: 208-772-8515 *Toll Free Tel:* 800-882-9110
Fax: 208-762-6133
E-mail: sales@transtector.com
Web Site: www.transtector.com
Key Personnel
Dir, Engg: Christine Blair
Dir, Sales: Mark Norrie
Manufactures surge suppression equipment.
Catalog(s) available

Transvideo International
130 E Prospect Ave, Burbank, CA 91502
Tel: 818-985-4903 *Fax:* 818-985-4921
Web Site: www.transvideointl.com
Key Personnel
Owner & Pres: Marianne Exbrayat
E-mail: marianne@transvideointl.com
Founded: 1999
Design & manufacture professional flat panel monitors, HD & SD wireless video systems & other film & video accessories. Manufacture, sell & repair monitors, format converters, frameline generators, electronic horizon & lightweight prompters.
Membership(s): NAB

TRC Interactive Inc
4200 Crums Mill Rd, Harrisburg, PA 17112
Mailing Address: PO Box 6685, Harrisburg, PA 17112
Tel: 717-652-3100 *Toll Free Tel:* 800-222-9909
E-mail: customerservicetrc01@trcinteractive.com; info@trcinteractive.com
Web Site: www.trcinteractive.com
Key Personnel
Pres & CEO: Jay B Bowden
Founded: 1973
Interactive training systems.
Catalog(s) available

Trebas Institute
550 Sherbrooke St W, Suite 600, Montreal, QC H3A 1B9, Canada
Tel: 514-845-4141 *Toll Free Tel:* 866-5TREBAS (587-3227) *Fax:* 514-845-2581
E-mail: infomtl@trebas.com
Web Site: www.trebas.com
Key Personnel
Pres & CEO: David P Leonard
Founded: 1979
Career training in audio engineering & music production, film & television production, entertainment management, event & venue management.
Membership(s): AES; Canadian Academy of Recording Arts & Sciences; Music & Entertainment Industry Educators Association; National Association of Career Colleges; The Recording Academy; SMPTE®

Trebas Institute
2340 Dundas St W, 2nd fl, Toronto, ON M6P 4A9, Canada
Tel: 416-966-3066
E-mail: info@trebas.com
Web Site: www.trebas.com
Key Personnel
Pres & CEO: David P Leonard
Founded: 1979
Career training in audio engineering & music production, film & television production, entertainment management, event & venue management.
Membership(s): AES; Canadian Academy of Recording Arts & Sciences; Music & En-

tertainment Industry Educators Association; National Association of Career Colleges; The Recording Academy; SMPTE®

Treehaus Communications Inc
906 W Loveland Ave, Loveland, OH 45140-2150
Mailing Address: PO Box 249, Loveland, OH 45140-0249
Tel: 513-683-5716 *Toll Free Tel:* 800-638-4287
Fax: 513-683-2882
E-mail: info@mammothhd.com
Web Site: www.treehaus1.com
Key Personnel
Publr/Owner: Gerard A Pottebaum
Catalog(s) available

Tremetrics Inc Industrial Instruments Division
Division of Diagnostic Group LLC
10393 W 70 St, Eden Prairie, MN 55344
Toll Free Tel: 800-825-0121 *Fax:* 952-903-4100
E-mail: info@tremetrics.com
Web Site: www.tremetrics.com
Key Personnel
Prod Line Mgr: Shaun Kelly *Tel:* 800-825-0121 ext 4403 *E-mail:* stkt@tremetrics.com
Test equipment manufacturer.
Catalog(s) available

Trendy Studio LLC
64 NW 54 St, Miami, FL 33127
Mailing Address: 260 Crandon Blvd, Suite 32 No 84, Key Biscayne, FL 33149
Tel: 305-438-4244 *Fax:* 305-438-4243
Web Site: www.trendystudio.com
Full service production company managing productions either in studio or on location. Services include: still & video production coordination; budget management; equipment rental; location scouting; studio rental; casting & talent booking; creative crew booking; wardrobe & styling; props & set building; travel arrangements; permits & insurance; security; local transportation & production vehicles; catering & behind the scenes.

Trew Audio Inc
220 Great Circle Rd, Suite 116, Nashville, TN 37228
Tel: 615-256-3542 *Toll Free Tel:* 800-241-8994
Fax: 615-259-2699
E-mail: info@trewaudio.com; sales@trewaudio.com
Web Site: www.trewaudio.com
Key Personnel
EVP & CFO: Richard Rosing *E-mail:* richard@trewaudio.com
Founded: 1994
Sales, rentals & service of audio & communications equipment for film & TV production.
Catalog(s) available
Branch Office(s)
Coffey Sound: A Trew Audio Co, 2243 N Hollywood Way, Burbank, CA 91505 *Tel:* 323-876-7525 *Toll Free Tel:* 888-293-3030 *Fax:* 747-477-1558
1706 Defoor Place NW, Atlanta, GA 30318 *Tel:* 404-947-2160 *Fax:* 404-902-8870
3737 Napier St, Burnaby, BC V5C 3E4, Canada *Tel:* 604-299-9122 *Toll Free Tel:* 877-333-9122 *Fax:* 604-299-9127
17 Carlaw Ave, Unit 4, Toronto, ON M4M 2R6, Canada *Tel:* 416-778-0656 *Toll Free Tel:* 866-778-8739 *Fax:* 416-778-4511
Membership(s): CAS

TRF Production Music Libraries
Subsidiary of TRF Music Inc
106 Apple St, Tinton Falls, NJ 07724
Tel: 201-335-0005 *Toll Free Tel:* 800-899-MUSIC (899-6874) *Fax:* 201-335-0004
E-mail: info@trfmusic.com
Web Site: www.trfmusic.com

Key Personnel
Pres & CEO: Michael Nurko
Creative Dir: Eric Nurko
Promos Mgr: Anne Marie Russo
    E-mail: annemarie@trfmusic.com
Largest collection of contemporary, retro & traditional production music. Every category available including all types of ethnic & specialty music. Well-known TRF libraries include Arcadia, Bravo, Pyramid, Cobra library & the authentic international ethnic library, PAN.
Catalog(s) available, free
Membership(s): ASCAP; BMI; National Music Publishers' Association; Production Music Association

Tri-Ed Distribution Inc
Subsidiary of Anixter International Inc
135 Crossways Park Dr, Suite 101, Woodbury, NY 11797
Tel: 516-941-2800 *Toll Free Tel:* 888-874-3336 (US); 800-398-7282 (CN); 800-366-4472 (tech sales)
E-mail: info@tri-ed.com; sales@tri-ed.com; marketing@tri-ed.com
Web Site: www.tri-ed.com
Key Personnel
Pres & CEO: Pat Comunale
Chief Mktg Offr: James Rothstein
Founded: 1982
Distributor of CCTV, IP video, access control, fire, intrusion, sound, communications, structured cabling & home automation products.
Online catalog(s) available

Tri-State Audio Visual Co
2901 Glendora Ave, Cincinnati, OH 45219
Tel: 513-281-7500 *Toll Free Tel:* 800-348-8728
    Fax: 513-281-7539
E-mail: sales@tristateav.com
Web Site: www.tristateav.com
Key Personnel
Pres: Bruce A Bock *E-mail:* bruce.bock@tristateav.com
Founded: 1984
Sell, install, repair video & sound systems.
Catalog(s) available, free, annual
Membership(s): Audiovisual and Integrated Experience Association

Tri-State Loudspeaker
650 Franklin Ave, Aliquippa, PA 15001
Key Personnel
Owner: Dante Maruca
Founded: 1987
Speaker reconing & refoaming services.
Catalog(s) available, wholesale & retail; factory authorized all brands
Price list(s) available, wholesale & retail
Membership(s): AES; ETA; IEEE

Tri-State Visual Products Inc
885 Ohio Pike, Suite C, Cincinnati, OH 45245
Tel: 513-471-7111 *Toll Free Tel:* 800-473-4474
E-mail: info@trivisual.com
Web Site: www.trivisual.com
Key Personnel
Pres: Greg Games
Founded: 1990
AV equipment supplier. Projection systems, video conferencing systems, digital displays, teleconferencing equipment, broadcast & recording equipment & interactive electronic whiteboards.

Triad Communications Ltd
2751 Oxford St, Vancouver, BC V5K 1N5, Canada
Tel: 604-253-3990
E-mail: triadc@comwave.com
Web Site: www.triadcommunications.ca

Key Personnel
Owner: Roland Loughhead; Gay Ludlow
Founded: 1973

Tributestone
709 N Sixth St, Kansas City, KS 66101
Tel: 913-321-3978
Web Site: www.tributestone.com
Key Personnel
Pres: Jaren Higginbotham
Mktg Dir: Shelly Higginbotham *E-mail:* shelly@tributestone.com
Manufacturer of projection audio device, used indoors or outdoors, with narration, music & sound effects.
Catalog(s) available

Tricycle Studios
1905 E Seventh Ave, Tampa, FL 33605
Tel: 813-258-6867 *Fax:* 813-258-8595
E-mail: hi@tricyclestudios.com
Web Site: www.tricyclestudios.com
Key Personnel
Co-owner: Tona Bell; Randy Rosenthal
Founded: 1995
Tricyle Studios is a marketing communications company that uses technology based media to achieve high impact results.

Trinity Recording Studio
3406 Brawner Pkwy, Corpus Christi, TX 78411
Tel: 361-854-7464
E-mail: info@trinitystudio.com
Web Site: www.trinitystudio.com
Key Personnel
Owner: Jim Wilken; Rachel Whitefield Wilken
Founded: 1988
Full service recording studio. Spirit Digital 328 Mixer, Sonar Platinum, Adobe Audition, Pro Tools 11, many plug-ins.
Membership(s): Coastal Bend Gospel Music Association; Texas Country Music Association Inc

Tripp Lite
1111 W 35 St, Chicago, IL 60609
Tel: 773-869-1234 (support); 773-869-1111; 773-869-1773 (sales) *Fax:* 773-869-1329
E-mail: international@tripplite.com
Web Site: www.tripplite.com
Key Personnel
Media & PR Mgr: Andrew Hattaway *Tel:* 773-869-1229 *E-mail:* andrew_hattaway@tripplite.com
Founded: 1922
Catalog(s) available

Tritech Communications
625 Locust St, Suite 300, Garden City, NY 11530
Tel: 631-254-4500 *Fax:* 631-254-4499
E-mail: sales@tritechcomm.com
Web Site: www.tritechcomm.com
Key Personnel
Chmn & CEO: Matthew P O'Reilly
Pres A/V Div: Joseph Melfa
Pres, Communs & Security Div: Edward Dougherty
VP, Fin & Admin: Christian Schachinger
VP, Sales & Mktg: Cliff Alberti
Founded: 2002
AV solutions provider: systems integration, service & maintenance.
Branch Office(s)
4200 Forbes Blvd, Suite 105, Lanham, MD 20706 *Tel:* 301-577-7610 *Fax:* 301-459-3194
225 Franklin St, 26th fl, Boston, MA 02110
    Tel: 617-217-2540 *Fax:* 617-217-2001
555 Eighth Ave, Suite 202, New York, NY 10018
    Tel: 212-292-1500 *Fax:* 212-292-1505
Membership(s): Audiovisual and Integrated Experience Association; NSCA

Triumph Learning LLC
Affiliate of School Specialty Inc
136 Madison Ave, 7th fl, New York, NY 10016
Toll Free Tel: 800-338-6519 *Toll Free Fax:* 866-805-5723
E-mail: customerservice@triumphlearning.com
Web Site: www.triumphlearning.com
Educational programming.
Catalog(s) available

Triune Arts
1804 Bedell Rd, RR 5, Kemptville, ON K0G 1J0, Canada
Web Site: triune.ca
Founded: 1981
Develop film, video, multimedia, music & theatre related projects & developing communications skills for professionals.

Tropical Visions Video Inc
13-3435 Kupono St, Pahoa, HI 96778
Tel: 808-895-0077
E-mail: redhotlava@hawaii.rr.com
Web Site: www.tropicalvisions.com
Key Personnel
Pres & Mgr: Mick Kalber
Treas & Secy: Ann Kalber *E-mail:* annthen@hawaii.rr.com
Stock footage & programming/production. HD DVD/Cable/Broadcast TV.
Catalog(s) available, free, periodically
Membership(s): Film & Video Association at Hawaii

Tropikal Productions
137 Sequoia Rd, Rockwall, TX 75032
Tel: 972-771-3797 *Fax:* 972-771-0853
E-mail: tropikalproductions@gmail.com
Web Site: www.tropikalproductions.com
Key Personnel
Owner & Prodr: Jimi Towry *Tel:* 469-338-9237 (cell)
Engr: Arik Miles
Founded: 1990
Music production, recording, sequencing, arranging, label & booking agency. 24 tracks ADAT, Mac running Opcode Vision. Office in Jaco, Costa Rica.
CD-ROM catalog(s) available, price varies
Membership(s): BMI; Raggae Ambassadors Worldwide

The Troupe
Subsidiary of Orth-Tec Corp
3 Industrial Dr, Windham, NH 03087
Tel: 603-893-4554
E-mail: info@thetroupe.com
Web Site: www.thetroupe.com
Key Personnel
COO: John Connors *E-mail:* john@thetroupe.com
Gen Mgr: Fred Connors, Jr *E-mail:* fred@thetroupe.com
Full service production facility.
Catalog(s) available

Troxell-CDI
Formerly Troxell Communications Inc
4675 E Cotton Center Blvd, Suite 155, Phoenix, AZ 85040
Tel: 602-437-7240 *Toll Free Tel:* 855-TROXELL (876-9355) *Fax:* 602-752-1299
    Toll Free Fax: 800-752-1299
E-mail: csg@trox.com
Web Site: www.troxellsolutions.com
Key Personnel
CEO: Erez Pikar
CFO: Naipaul Sheosankar
COO: Sarah Kydd
SVP, Sales: Mark Barber
VP, Busn Systems: Craig Schramm
VP, Sales: Michael McKean
VP, Busn Devt: James Drohan
VP, Purchasing: Fred Hastings

VP, Mktg: Raigan Irwin-McCabe
Regl VP, Southeast: Michael Logan
Regl VP, Northeast & Central: Jerry Scacchitti
Dir, HR: Dorri Carpenter
Founded: 1946
Large AV equipment distributor.
Catalog(s) available, free, annual, 4-color
Online catalog(s) available

Troxell Communications Inc, see Troxell-CDI

True Audio
387 Duncan Lane, Andersonville, TN 37705
Tel: 865-494-3388 *Toll Free Tel:* 800-621-4411
   Fax: 865-494-3388
E-mail: sales@trueaudio.com
Web Site: www.trueaudio.com
Key Personnel
Mktg Dir: Sharon Alsup *E-mail:* sharon.alsup@
   trueaudio.com
Founded: 1990
Software publisher, audio products.

TRUMATCH Inc
PO Box 501, Water Mill, NY 11976-0501
Tel: 631-204-9100 *Toll Free Tel:* 800-TRU-9100
   (878-9100) *Fax:* 631-204-0002
E-mail: info@trumatch.com
Web Site: www.trumatch.com
Key Personnel
Pres: Steve Abramson
Founded: 1990
Established the digital 4-color standard (palette)
   for desktop publishing that makes selecting &
   matching colors easy & accurate. The TRU-
   MATCH® System was developed for design &
   illustration software & for output, exclusively,
   by electronic imagesetters, printers & copiers.
Catalog(s) available, $85, TRUMATCH Col-
   orfinder Coated Paper (fanguide)
Catalog(s) available, $85, TRUMATCH Col-
   orfinder Uncoated Paper (fanguide)
Membership(s): Printing Industries of America

Truth Consciousness Publications
Subsidiary of Truth Consciousness Inc
Desert Ashram, 3403 W Sweetwater Dr, Tucson,
   AZ 85745-9301
Tel: 520-743-8821
E-mail: info@truthconsciousness.org
Web Site: truthconsciousness.org
Founded: 1974
Spiritual publications including audio Satsangs of
   Swami Amar Jyoti.
Online catalog(s) available

TSG Publishing Foundation Inc USA
28641 N 63 Place, Cave Creek, AZ 85331
Mailing Address: PO Box 7068, Cave Creek, AZ
   85327-7068
Tel: 480-502-1909 *Fax:* 480-502-0713
E-mail: info@tsgfoundation.org
Web Site: www.tsgfoundation.org
Key Personnel
Pres: Gita Saraydarian
Catalog(s) available, by request
Online catalog(s) available

TSR/Baja/Damabi Records
18653 Ventura Blvd, Suite 513, Tarzana, CA
   91356
Tel: 818-702-9902
Key Personnel
Pres: Tom Hayden

**Turner Broadcasting System Inc, A Time
   Warner Company**
One CNN Ctr, Atlanta, GA 30303
Tel: 404-827-1700
E-mail: turner.info@turner.com
Web Site: www.turner.com

Key Personnel
Chmn & CEO: John Martin
Pres: David Levy
Pres, CNN Worldwide: Jeff Zucker
Pres, Turner Intl: Gerhard Zeiler
Exec VP & CFO: Pascal Desroches
EVP & Chief Strategy Off: Doug Shapiro
EVP & Global Chief HR Off: Angela Santone

Turner Engineering Inc
14 Morris Ave, Mountain Lakes, NJ 07046-1433
Tel: 973-263-1000 *Fax:* 973-334-1620
E-mail: info@turnereng.com
Web Site: www.turnereng.com
Key Personnel
Principal & Owner: John Turner
Founded: 1967
Veteran provider of technical design & build ser-
   vices to broadcast, telecom & commercial AV
   users.
Membership(s): AES; IEEE; NAB; SBE;
   SMPTE®

Turning Technologies LLC
255 W Federal St, Youngstown, OH 44503
Tel: 330-746-3015 *Toll Free Tel:* 866-746-3015
E-mail: info@turningtechnologies.com; support@
   turningtechnologies.com
Web Site: www.turningtechnologies.com
Key Personnel
CEO: Kenneth Frank
CFO: Richard Vareha
CTO: Fares Bouchedid
VP, Client Success: Kevin Herrholtz
VP, K12, Corp & Govt Sales: Chuck Reigrut
VP, Software Engg & DevOps: John Sofko
Sr Dir, Higher Educ & Publr Sales: Barry Gro-
   mada
Dir, Mktg: Morgan Tondo Cretella
Founded: 2002
Learning engagement & assessment services,
   polling software, interactive whiteboards &
   learning tools.
Foreign Office(s): The Innovative Centre, Queens
   Rd, Queen's Island, Belfast BT3 9DT, United
   Kingdom, VP: Gary Morrison *Tel:* (028) 9008
   0188 *Web Site:* www.turningtechnologies.eu
   (intl headquarters)

TV One Multimedia Solutions
621 B Wilmer Ave, Cincinnati, OH 45226
Tel: 513-666-4210 *Toll Free Tel:* 800-721-4044
   Fax: 513-666-4220 (tech)
E-mail: sales@tvone.com; info@tvone.com
Web Site: www.tvone.com
Key Personnel
VP, Sales & Mktg: Andy Fliss
Manufacturer of video components.
Catalog(s) available
Foreign Office(s): Continental Approach, West-
   wood Industrial Estate, Margate, Kent CT9
   4JG, United Kingdom *Tel:* (01843) 873300
   E-mail: sales.europe@tvone.com
Membership(s): Audiovisual and Integrated Expe-
   rience Association; NAB

TV Pro Gear
1630 Flower St, Glendale, CA 91201
Tel: 818-246-7100 *Fax:* 818-246-1945
Web Site: www.tvprogear.com
Key Personnel
Pres & CEO: Andrew Maisner *E-mail:* andy@
   tvprogear.com
Founded: 1998
Build TV & production studios & video trucks.
   Sell professional TV equipment.

TV Specialists Inc
180 E 2100 S, Salt Lake City, UT 84115
Tel: 801-486-5757 *Toll Free Tel:* 888-486-5757
   Fax: 801-486-7566

E-mail: info@tvspecialists.com
Web Site: www.tvspecialists.com
Key Personnel
VP, Sales: Ted Bollinger *E-mail:* tedb@
   tvspecialists.com
Founded: 1953
Sales, rentals & service of professional produc-
   tion video & display technology including
   Sony, Canon & Panasonic broadcast products.
Catalog(s) available

TVA Media Group
3950 Vantage Ave, Studio City, CA 91604
Tel: 818-505-8300 *Toll Free Tel:* 888-322-4296
E-mail: info@tvamediagroup.com
Web Site: www.tvamediagroup.com
Key Personnel
Founder & CEO: Jeffery Goddard
Partner & CFO: Laura Tu
Sr Dir & Ed: Mark Mannschreck
Founded: 1987
Video production, post-production & studio
   rental.
Membership(s): Television Academy

TVN-The Video Network
31 Cutler Dr, Ashland, MA 01721-1210
Tel: 508-881-1800
E-mail: info@tvnvideo.com
Web Site: www.tvnvideo.com
Key Personnel
CEO: Gregg C McAllister
Founded: 1987
Full service production.
Catalog(s) available

**TVO/Ontario Educational Communications
   Authority (OECA)**
2180 Yonge St, Toronto, ON M4S 2B9, Canada
Mailing Address: Box 200, Sta Q, Toronto, ON
   M4T 2T1, Canada
Tel: 416-484-2600; 416-484-2665 (cust rel)
Toll Free Tel: 800-613-0513; 800-INFO-TVO
   (463-6886)
E-mail: asktvo@tvo.org
Web Site: tvo.org
Key Personnel
CEO: Lisa de Wilde
CFO & VP, Busn Devt: Paul Dancy
CTO: Todd Slivinskas
VP, Talent & Engagement: Jennifer Hinshelwood
Dir, Mktg: Shannon O'Rourke
Digital media organization specializing in educa-
   tional media.
Catalog(s) available

Twentieth Century Fox Film Corp
Subsidiary of 21st Century Fox
10201 W Pico Blvd, Bldg 88, Rm 311, Los An-
   geles, CA 90035
Mailing Address: PO Box 900, Beverly Hills, CA
   90213
Tel: 310-369-1000 *Toll Free Tel:* 888-223-4369
   (cust care) *Fax:* 310-369-8825
E-mail: support@foxcustomercare.com (cust care)
Web Site: www.foxmovies.com
Key Personnel
EVP, Corp Communs: Dan Berger *Tel:* 310-369-
   1181
Founded: 1935
One of the world's largest producers & distribu-
   tors of motion picture entertainment.

21st Century Video Productions
890 S Higley Rd, Pahrump, NV 89048
Mailing Address: PO Box 2075, Pahrump, NV
   89041
Tel: 775-727-9400 *Fax:* 775-727-8750
Web Site: www.kpvm.tv
Key Personnel
Pres & CEO: Vernon Van Winkle
   E-mail: videovern@kpvm.tv

Founded: 1986
Television station & production house.

24 Frames Film & Video
Division of Super Suite Digital Post & Transfer
15 Fourth Ave E, Vancouver, BC V5T 1E9,
 Canada
Tel: 604-877-2299
E-mail: info@24frames.ca
Web Site: www.24frames.ca
Key Personnel
CEO: Andy Nathani

20/20 Communications Inc
10112 Voss Rd, Marengo, IL 60152
Tel: 847-364-7666
Web Site: www.2020communications.com
Key Personnel
Opers Mgr: Leona Haba *E-mail:* leona@
 2020communications.com
Founded: 1988
Full service video production & commercial pho-
 tography studio. Specialize in content for web
 sites, trade shows & sales videos.

20k
709 rue de Saint-Vallier Est, Quebec, QC G1K
 3P9, Canada
Tel: 418-694-2220 *Toll Free Tel:* 855-933-2220
E-mail: info@20k.ca
Web Site: www.20k.ca
Consulting specialists in the field of arts & enter-
 tainment.

Twin Peaks Creative
445 W Seventh St, San Pedro, CA 90731
Tel: 310-832-3303
E-mail: postmaster@bestmedia.com
Web Site: www.twinpeakscreative.com
Key Personnel
Owner: Mary Jo Masters; Robert Masters
 E-mail: robert@bestmedia.com
Founded: 1983
Branch office in Maui, HI (Tel: 808-878-1020).

Twin Sisters® Digital Media™
1653 Merriman Rd, Suite L1, Akron, OH 44313
Tel: 330-730-9558
E-mail: twinsisters@twinsisters.com
Web Site: www.twinsisters.com
Key Personnel
CEO: Karen Mitzo Hilderbrand
Pres: Kim Mitzo Thompson
Founded: 1987
Children's educational company. Digital audio-
 books, ebooks & music.
Catalog(s) available, annual, wholesale

TWIST Integration Solutions Technology
3915-F Dacoma, Houston, TX 77092
Tel: 713-688-0696
E-mail: info@twistIST.com
Web Site: www.twistist.com
Key Personnel
Contact: Curt Hall
Founded: 1997
Distributor & integrator of professional AV equip-
 ment, media & supplies.

TWIST IST, see TWIST Integration Solutions
Technology

Twisted Media Inc
2100 Hollyvista Ave, Los Angeles, CA 90027
Tel: 773-972-2972
Web Site: www.twistedmedia.com
Key Personnel
Pres: Derek Frederickson *E-mail:* derek@
 twistedmedia.com
Founded: 2000

Playback graphics.
Membership(s): ASCAP; BMI; International Alliance of Theatrical Stage Employees

Twistedtracks.com, see Twisted Media Inc

Two Animators LLP
PO Box 3174, Mercerville, NJ 08619
Tel: 609-532-6138
E-mail: cartoons@twoanimators.com
Web Site: www.twoanimators.com
Key Personnel
Creative Dir & Partner: Tom Costantini
Animation Dir & Partner: Joe Costantini
Founded: 2001
Full service animation production & development
 studio.

2BruceStudio
2 Wall St, Suite 119, Asheville, NC 28801
Tel: 828-255-2700
E-mail: info@2brucestudio.com
Web Site: 2brucestudio.com
Key Personnel
Owner: Bruce Sales
Founded: 2007
Twenty years of New York experience in the me-
 dia & entertainment industries, specializing in
 original music composition, sound design &
 audio post for film, TV & all media.
Membership(s): ASCAP

Two Door Productions LLC
416 N Harper Ave, Los Angeles, CA 90048
E-mail: shoot@usphotograph.com
Web Site: www.twodoorfx.com
Key Personnel
Dir & Prodr: Diego Torroija *Tel:* 310-936-6194
 (cell) *E-mail:* diego@twodoorfx.com
Writer/Prodr: Holly Payberg-Torroija
Founded: 2002
Digital production company specializing in find-
 ing high-tech visual solutions to suit all bud-
 getary needs. Our goal is to offer creative op-
 tions to communicate "your story" in an un-
 compromised way.
Branch Office(s)
220 E Central Pkwy, Suite 3040, Altamonte
 Springs, FL 32701, Contact: Tracy Stuck

Tyler Camera Systems
14218 Aetna St, Van Nuys, CA 91401
Tel: 818-989-4420 *Toll Free Tel:* 800-390-6070
 Fax: 818-989-0423
E-mail: info@tylermount.com
Web Site: www.tylermount.com
Key Personnel
Owner: Liz Ziegler
Photography equipment.
Catalog(s) available

U-Direct Productions Inc
10 White St, 1st fl, New York, NY 10013
Tel: 212-647-9200 *Fax:* 212-625-9400
E-mail: udirect@udirect.nyc
Web Site: udirect.nyc
Key Personnel
Founder & Dir: Daniel Miller *E-mail:* daniel@
 udirect.nyc
Founded: 1993
Independent film/video production company. Spe-
 cialize Media 100, Digj-Beta, Beta, After Ef-
 fects. Pre-production through post-production,
 on-air commercials & industrials.

U-Edit Video
1002 N Central Expwy, Suite 555, Richardson,
 TX 75080
Tel: 972-690-EDIT (690-3348)
E-mail: info@ueditvideo.com
Web Site: www.ueditvideo.com

Key Personnel
Pres: Owen Benatar *E-mail:* owen@ueditvideo.
 com
Founded: 1973
Turnkey production from recording or mastering
 to final packaging. Archive services.

UConn Health Multimedia Services
Division of UConn Health
263 Farmington Ave, Farmington, CT 06030-2910
Tel: 860-679-2000
E-mail: multimedia@uchc.edu
Web Site: multimedia.uchc.edu
Production & support services for the UConn
 Health community, including graphic design &
 printing, event coordination, internally-focused
 communications, photography, video & web
 site production.

Ultimate Presentation Systems Inc
901 S Hohokam Dr, Tempe, AZ 85281
Tel: 480-966-2000 *Toll Free Tel:* 800-866-4066
 Fax: 480-968-3009
E-mail: sales@ult.com
Web Site: www.ult.com
Key Personnel
Pres: Diane Reese
VP: Michael Reese *E-mail:* mreese@ult.com
Professional AV sales & systems integration.
Catalog(s) available

Ultimate Support Systems Inc
5836 Wright Dr, Loveland, CO 80538
Tel: 970-776-1920 *Toll Free Tel:* 800-525-5628
 Fax: 970-776-1941
E-mail: info@ultimatesupport.com
Web Site: www.ultimatesupport.com
Founded: 1977
Invent, design & manufacture support solutions &
 music accessories for the music industry.
Online catalog(s) available

Ultralife Corporation
2000 Technology Pkwy, Newark, NY 14513
Tel: 315-332-7100 *Toll Free Tel:* 800-332-5000
 (US & CN) *Fax:* 315-331-7800
E-mail: orders@ulbi.com
Web Site: ultralifecorporation.com
Founded: 1991
The Battery & Energy Products Unit provides a
 wide range of high-energy non-rechargeable
 & rechargeable power & charging systems for
 both defense & commercial applications.
The Communications Systems Unit provides a
 single source for tactical communications solutions that support the warfighter & homeland
 security, from RF amplifiers, to power supplies,
 to antennas & accessory products for mission
 requirements.
Catalog(s) available

Ulysses Travel Guides Inc
4176 Rue Saint-Denis, Montreal, QC H2W 2M5,
 Canada
Tel: 514-843-9882 *Fax:* 514-843-9448
E-mail: info@ulysses.ca; st-denis@ulysse.ca
Web Site: www.ulysse.ca (French); www.
 ulyssesguides.com (English)
Key Personnel
Dir, Mktg & Sales: Olivier Gougeon
Founded: 1980
Travel guides in print & digital format.
Online catalog(s) available
Foreign Office(s): Le Guides de Voyage Ulysses
 Sarl, 127 Rue Amelot, 75011 Paris, France
Tel: 01 43 38 89 50 *Fax:* 01 43 38 89 52
E-mail: voyage@ulysse.ca

UM Productions, see United Methodist
Productions

Umbra of Newburgh LLC
9 Scobie Dr, Newburgh, NY 12550
Tel: 845-670-7493
E-mail: umbrastages@choicefilms.com
Web Site: www.umbranewburgh.com
Key Personnel
Founder & Owner: Ted Doering
Founded: 2011
Film production facility.

Uncharted Country Publishing
PO Box 756, Taos, NM 87571
Tel: 575-776-3470 *Toll Free Tel:* 800-488-4940
E-mail: ucp@taichihealth.com
Web Site: taichihealth.com
Key Personnel
Owner & Dir: Tricia Yu *E-mail:* tyu@
taichihealth.com
Founded: 1999
Mind, body & health resources; Tai Chi & ROM
Dance.

UND Television Center
Subsidiary of University of North Dakota
4300 James Ray Dr, Stop 7307, Grand Forks, ND
58202
Tel: 701-777-4346 *Toll Free Tel:* 800-CALL-UND
(225-5863) *Fax:* 701-777-4342
E-mail: tv@und.edu
Web Site: www.und.edu/television-center
Key Personnel
Dir, TV: Barry S Brode *E-mail:* barry.brode@und.
edu

Ungar Video & Film
2407 Grovewood Ave, Cleveland, OH 44134
Tel: 216-661-5090
Key Personnel
Pres: Donald Ungar

Uniconn Productions
8485 Valley Circle Blvd, Suite 203, West Hills,
CA 91304
Tel: 818-887-9108 *Fax:* 818-348-6544
E-mail: measeburl@aol.com
Web Site: www.uniconnproductions.com
Key Personnel
Owner: Michael P Connelly
Founded: 1988
Stop-motion & CGI animation production com-
pany that provides animation for the TV, film
& music video industries.

Unified Packaging Inc (UPI)
1187 E 68 Ave, Denver, CO 80229
Tel: 303-733-1000; 469-272-9000 (TX off)
Toll Free Tel: 866-715-1700 *Fax:* 303-733-
6789; 469-272-9300 (TX off)
E-mail: contact@unifiedbinders.com
Web Site: www.unifiedbinders.com
Founded: 1952
Manufacture media packaging solutions for the
distribution of media products. Satellite office
in Cedar Hill, TX.
Catalog(s) available, free
Membership(s): Binding Industries Association;
Entertainment Merchants Association; Printing
Industries of America

Unilux Inc
59 N Fifth St, Saddle Brook, NJ 07663
Tel: 201-712-1266 *Toll Free Tel:* 800-522-0801
(US only) *Fax:* 201-712-1366
Web Site: www.unilux.com
Key Personnel
Mgr: Earl Wallace *E-mail:* earl.wallace@unilux.
com
Founded: 1962
Stroboscopic lighting equipment for film & video
production.

Foreign Office(s): Unilux China, 1081-1089
Pudong Ave, Apt 10-B, Shanghai 200135,
China, Contact: Joe Zhao *Tel:* (021) 68552511
Fax: (021) 68552511 *E-mail:* joezhao@unilux.
com
Unilux EMEA, Seeweg 20, 40627 Duessel-
dorf, Germany, Contact: Volker Schlevoigt
Tel: (0211) 28071171 *Fax:* (0211) 28071177
E-mail: vschlevoigt@unilux.com
Unilux Asia, 179/177 Sualai Place, Sukhumvit
Soi 39, Bangkok 10110, Thailand, Contact:
Kirk Nell *Tel:* (06) 977-1303 *Fax:* (02) 662-
0022 *E-mail:* kirk@unilux.com

Union Connector Co Inc
8182 Baymeadow Way W, Jacksonville, FL
32256
Tel: 631-753-9550 *Fax:* 631-753-9560
E-mail: sales@unionconnector.com
Web Site: www.unionconnector.com
Key Personnel
Pres: Raymond Wolpert
Membership(s): International Association of As-
sembly Managers; International Independent
Showman's Federation; Professional Lighting
& Sound Association; USITT

Unique Business Systems
1100 Colorado Ave, Suite B, Santa Monica, CA
90401
Tel: 310-396-3929 *Toll Free Tel:* 800-669-4827
Fax: 310-396-6114
E-mail: info@unibiz.com
Web Site: www.unibiz.com
Key Personnel
Dir, Busn Devt: Vikran Khosla
Founded: 1982

Unique Communications Ltd
2232 Pegasus Way NE, Calgary, AB T2E 8M5,
Canada
Tel: 403-250-3763 *Toll Free Tel:* 800-661-8575
Fax: 403-250-2604
Web Site: www.uniquecommunications.ca
Key Personnel
Pres: Dave Ruff *E-mail:* daver@
uniquecommunications.ca
Founded: 1981
Membership(s): AES; Audiovisual and Integrated
Experience Association; NSCA

UniSat, see Universal Satellite Communications
Inc

Uniset LLC
449 Avenue "A", Rochester, NY 14621
Tel: 585-544-3820 *Fax:* 585-544-1110
E-mail: info@unisetcorp.com
Web Site: www.unisetcorp.com
Key Personnel
Co-Owner: Angelo Casciani; Bobby McLain
Founded: 1966
Manufacture studio settings/cycloramas/new set-
tings.
Online catalog(s) available
Membership(s): Alliance for Community Media;
Broadcast Education Association; NAB

United Audio Video Inc
6855 Vineland Ave, North Hollywood, CA 91605
Tel: 818-980-6700 *Toll Free Tel:* 800-247-8606
Fax: 818-508-8273
Web Site: www.unitedavg.com
Key Personnel
Gen Mgr: Larry Schwartz
Founded: 1972
DVD replications, authoring, editing & transfers.
Catalog(s) available
Membership(s): AES

United Methodist Productions
Subsidiary of United Methodist Communications
810 12 Ave S, Nashville, TN 37203
Mailing Address: PO Box 320, Nashville, TN
37202-0320
Tel: 615-742-5400
E-mail: umcom@umcom.org
Web Site: www.umcom.org
Key Personnel
Dir, Prodns: Harry Leake *Tel:* 615-742-5477
E-mail: hleake@umcom.org
Sr Mgr, Prodns: Debbie Wamsley *Tel:* 615-742-
5779
Full service video, audio & post-production com-
pany. Production facility with professional ex-
pertise in motion, graphics & sound production.

**United Nations Department of Public
Information-News & Media Division**
405 E 42 St, Rm IN-913B, New York, NY 10017
Tel: 917-367-5007
E-mail: mediapartnerships@un.org
Web Site: www.un.org
Key Personnel
Chief, Partnerships Unit: Ms Fang Chen
AV library holds a unique collection of raw audio
& video footage which is used by film & video
producers who wish to produce documentaries
on the work of the United Nations.
Brochure(s) available

United Nations Multimedia Resources Unit
c/o Audio Library, UN Dept of Public Informa-
tion, Rm S-1046 & S-1083, New York, NY
10017
Tel: 212-963-9268; 212-963-0656
E-mail: avlibrary@un.org
Web Site: www.unmultimedia.org
Key Personnel
Chief: Antonio Carlos da Silva
International organization, produce & promote
their own radio & TV programs to broadcasters
worldwide.
Catalog(s) available

United Sound & Electronics
525 E Main St, Bridgeport, WV 26330
Tel: 304-842-6030
E-mail: questions@unitedsound.net
Web Site: www.unitedsound.net
Key Personnel
CEO: Rob Harold *E-mail:* rob@unitedsound.net
Event Prodn: Jeremy Harold *E-mail:* jeremy@
unitedsound.net
Founded: 1934
Concerts, production stages, lighting & full
sound.

United Way Worldwide
701 N Fairfax St, Alexandria, VA 22314-2045
Tel: 703-836-7112
Web Site: www.unitedway.org
Key Personnel
Pres & CEO: Brian A Gallagher
Catalog(s) available

Unitron Ltd
73 Mall Dr, Commack, NY 11725
Tel: 631-543-2000 *Fax:* 631-589-6975
E-mail: info@unitronusa.com
Web Site: www.unitronusa.com
Key Personnel
Sales: Peter Indrigo *E-mail:* peterd@unitronusa.
com
Mktg Support: Jeane P Miller *E-mail:* jeane@
unitronusa.com
Founded: 1952
Online catalog(s) available

Univenture Inc
4266 Tuller Rd, Dublin, OH 43017

Tel: 937-645-4600 *Toll Free Tel:* 877-831-9428
  Fax: 937-645-4700
E-mail: sales@univenture.com
Web Site: www.univenture.com
Key Personnel
Founder & CEO: Ross O Youngs
Pres: Michele Cole
Dir, IT & E-Commerce: Mike Rader
Founded: 1988
Design & manufacture media packaging for lead-
  ing companies in the entertainment, software &
  publishing industries.
Catalog(s) available, free, Information Manage-
  ment Specialties (IMS)
Catalog(s) available, free, FlexPak
Catalog(s) available, free, Resource Guide
Online catalog(s) available
Branch Office(s)
16710 Square Dr, Marysville, OH 43040

Universal Audio Inc
4585 Scotts Valley Dr, Scotts Valley, CA 95066
Tel: 831-440-1176 *Toll Free Tel:* 877-698-2834
  (cust serv)
E-mail: sales@uaudio.com
Web Site: www.uaudio.com
Key Personnel
E-Commerce Mgr: Dan Fulop
Founded: 1958
Catalog(s) available
Membership(s): AES; NAMM, the National Asso-
  ciation of Music Merchants

Universal Music Group
2220 Colorado Ave, Santa Monica, CA 90404
Tel: 310-865-5000
Web Site: www.universalmusic.com
Key Personnel
Chmn & CEO: Sir Lucian Grainge
CFO & EVP: Boyd Muir
EVP: Michele Anthony
EVP, Communs: Will Tanous
EVP, Mktg: Andrew Kronfeld
Recorded music, music publishing & merchandis-
  ing.
Branch Office(s)
1755 Broadway, New York, NY 10019 *Tel:* 212-
  841-8000 *Fax:* 212-840-9390

Universal Pictures Home Entertainment
Division of NBCUniversal
10 Universal City Plaza, Universal City, CA
  91608
Web Site: www.uphe.com
Catalog(s) available
Membership(s): Content Delivery & Storage As-
  sociation; Entertainment Merchants Associa-
  tion; Motion Picture Association of America;
  RIAA

Universal Radio Inc
6830 Americana Pkwy, Reynoldsburg, OH 43068
Tel: 614-866-4267 *Toll Free Tel:* 800-431-3939
  (orders) *Fax:* 614-866-2339
E-mail: dx@universal-radio.com
Web Site: www.universal-radio.com
Key Personnel
Mgr: Eric Scheibeck *E-mail:* eric@universal-
  radio.com
Founded: 1942
Catalog(s) available, annual
Online catalog(s) available

Universal Satellite Communications Inc
1530 Nandina Ave, Perris, CA 92571
Tel: 562-483-4800; 951-943-4420 (corp off)
  Toll Free Tel: 888-867-6620 *Fax:* 954-943-0263
Web Site: www.unisatmobile.com
Key Personnel
Pres: Juan Renteria *E-mail:* juan@unisatmobile.
  com

EVP: Anne Komarovsk *E-mail:* anne@
  unisatmobile.com
Mktg & Client Servs: Julie C Ragozzino
  E-mail: julie@unisatmobile.com
Fully integrated supplier of television logistics,
  production & transmission services, including
  satellite uplinks, downlinks, fiber, microwave,
  digital provisions, full production, editing,
  ENG packages & logistical planning.
Branch Office(s)
13426 Rosecrans Ave, Unit C, Norwalk, CA
  90650

Universal Studios
100 Universal City Plaza, Universal City, CA
  91608-1002
Toll Free Tel: 800-892-1979 *Fax:* 818-866-0293
E-mail: studio.operations2@nbcuni.com
Web Site: www.nbcuni.com; universalstudioslot.
  com
Key Personnel
Pres, Studio Opers: Michael Moore
SVP, Mktg & Publicity: Jeanne Cordova
Founded: 1912
Production & post-production services for film,
  television & commercials.

Universal Studios Canada Inc
2450 Victoria Park Ave, Toronto, ON M2J 4A2,
  Canada
Tel: 416-491-3000
E-mail: uniadvertising@nbcuni.com
Web Site: www.universalpictures.ca
Key Personnel
EVP: Ron Suter
Founded: 2009
Creates & distributes theatrical & non-theatrical
  filmed entertainment, direct-to-DVD titles, con-
  sumer products & specialty motion pictures.
Catalog(s) available

Universal Studios Florida® Production Group
1000 Universal Studios Plaza, Bldg 22A, Or-
  lando, FL 32819
Tel: 407-363-8400 *Toll Free Tel:* 877-612-3737
  (outside FL) *Fax:* 407-363-8869
E-mail: productiongroup@universalorlando.com
Web Site: studio.florida.universalstudios.com
Key Personnel
VP & Gen Mgr: Pamela Tuscany
Sr Mgr, Prodn: Chris Silveira
Sr Mgr, Studio Facilities: Michael Hetchler
Client Servs Mgr: Katrinka VanDeventer
Mgr, Prodn, Scheduling & Fulfillment: Jennifer
  Lenhart-Belawski
Prodn Mgr: Bernadette Everlof
Exec Asst & Mktg Coord: Julie Gibson
Founded: 1988
Premier production facility that features state-
  of-the-art sound stages, backlot locations &
  support facilities.

Universe Kogaku America Inc
116 Audrey Ave, Oyster Bay, NY 11771
Tel: 516-624-2444 *Fax:* 516-624-3109
E-mail: info@universeoptics.com
Web Site: universeoptics.com
Key Personnel
Pres: Mike Ohtsuki
Founded: 1949
UV quartz lenses & lens design for electronic,
  optics, medical & precision industrial applica-
  tions.
Catalog(s) available
Foreign Office(s): Universe Optical Industries
  Co Ltd, 2729 Inatomi, Tatsuno-Machi, Kami-
  ina, Nagano 399-0428, Japan *Tel:* (0266) 41-
  0262 *Fax:* (0266) 41-2084 *Web Site:* www.
  universekk.com
Membership(s): AIIM; The Imaging Alliance;
  SPIE

University Media Services
University of Delaware, 85 E Delaware Ave,
  Newark, DE 19716
Tel: 302-831-3546
Web Site: sites.udel.edu/it-ums/
Key Personnel
Mgr: Jason Atkinson
University AV equipment rental for the campus,
  provides creative technical design, production
  & support for professional video production &
  audio services, campus performances & events,
  classroom technology & media engineering.
Catalog(s) available
Membership(s): AMCEE; AMS; National Associ-
  ation for Music Education; NVTN

University of Florida, Warrington College of
Business Information Technology Support
Programs
Bryan Hall 300D, 1384 Union Rd, Gainesville,
  FL 32611
Mailing Address: PO Box 117158, Gainesville,
  FL 32611-7158
Tel: 352-273-1616 *Fax:* 352-392-6250
E-mail: itsp@warrington.ufl.edu
Web Site: warrington.ufl.edu/itsp
Key Personnel
Dir: Eric Olson *Tel:* 352-273-1615 *E-mail:* eric.
  olson@warrington.ufl.edu
Prodn Mgr: Christopher Smith *Tel:* 352-294-7804
  E-mail: christopher.smith@warrington.ufl.edu
AV systems monitoring & maintenance, AV
  project consultation, design, installation &
  management. Studio lecture & interview
  recording, marketing or informational video
  production, guest speaker/classroom recording,
  video editing, digital file conversion, VHS or
  DVD to file conversion & YouTube video creation.

University of Idaho Engineering Outreach
875 Perimeter Dr MS 1014, Moscow, ID 83844-
  1014
Tel: 208-885-6373 *Toll Free Tel:* 800-824-2889
  Fax: 208-885-9249
E-mail: outreach@uidaho.edu
Web Site: eo.uidaho.edu
Key Personnel
Assoc Dean, Outreach: Dr Barry Willis
State university (accredited). Provides online
  courses for Master's degrees in engineering,
  statistical science & teaching mathematics.
Catalog(s) available
Online catalog(s) available

University of Maine Media Services
19 Shibles Hall, Orono, ME 04469
Tel: 207-581-2500; 207-581-2516
Web Site: umaine.edu
Key Personnel
Mgr: Cliff Fletcher *E-mail:* clifton.fletcher@
  maine.edu
Media Servs Technician: Nick Robbins
  E-mail: nicolas.robbins@maine.edu
Classroom technology & AV equipment.
Membership(s): Consortium of College & Univer-
  sity Media Centers

University of Memphis, Music Industry
Division
Music Bldg, Rm 123, 3775 Central Ave, Mem-
  phis, TN 38152-3160
Tel: 901-678-2559; 901-678-2541
E-mail: music@memphis.edu
Web Site: www.memphis.edu/music
Key Personnel
Div Head: Jeff Cline *E-mail:* jwcline@memphis.
  edu
Online catalog(s) available
Membership(s): AES; Music & Entertainment
  Industry Educators Association; SPARS

University of Michigan, Center for Middle Eastern & North African Studies
500 Church St, Suite 500, Ann Arbor, MI 48109-1042
Tel: 734-647-4143 *Fax:* 734-936-0996
E-mail: cmenas@umich.edu
Web Site: www.ii.umich.edu/cmenas
Key Personnel
Dir: Samer Mandy Ali *E-mail:* samerali@umich.edu
Prof: Juan Cole *E-mail:* jrcole@umich.edu

University of Missouri-Columbia
Film & Video Library, 505 E Stewart Rd, Columbia, MO 65211-2040
Tel: 573-882-3608
E-mail: asc@missouri.edu
Web Site: asc.missouri.edu
Key Personnel
Dir: Sue Hollingsworth *Tel:* 573-882-2801
Promotion & improvement of teaching, research & service through educational communication technologies.

University of Missouri-Kansas City School of Dentistry
650 E 25 St, Kansas City, MO 64108
Tel: 816-235-2100 *Fax:* 816-235-5001
E-mail: dentistry@umkc.edu
Web Site: dentistry.umkc.edu
Oral healthcare education institution.

University of South Carolina Press
1600 Hampton St, Suite 544, Columbia, SC 29208
Tel: 803-777-5243 *Toll Free Tel:* 800-768-2500
Toll Free Fax: 800-868-0740
Web Site: www.sc.edu/uscpress
Key Personnel
Dir: Richard Brown *Tel:* 803-777-2243
Asst to Dir: Vicki Bates *Tel:* 803-777-5245
E-mail: batesvc@mailbox.sc.edu
Founded: 1944
University press & scholarly publisher, including ebooks & audiobooks.
Catalog(s) available
Shipping Address: 718 Devine St, Columbia, SC 29208

University of Texas at Austin - Petroleum Extension Service
J J Pickle Research Campus, 10100 Burnet Rd, Bldg 2, Austin, TX 78758-4445
Tel: 512-471-5940 *Toll Free Tel:* 800-687-4132
Fax: 512-471-9410 *Toll Free Fax:* 800-687-7839
E-mail: info@petex.utexas.edu
Web Site: www.utexas.edu/ce/petex
Key Personnel
Dir: Coy Wilcox
Training for industry professionals in new technologies, cutting-edge equipment & current industry standards through the use of traditional instructor-led classroom & online courses.
Catalog(s) available
Branch Office(s)
University of Texas, 4702 N Sam Houston Pkwy W, Suite 800, Houston, TX 77086 *Tel:* 281-397-2440

University of Toronto, Classroom Technology Support
Saint George Campus, McMurrich Bldg, 4th fl, 12 Queen's Park Crescent W, Toronto, ON M5S 1S8, Canada
Tel: 416-978-6544 *Fax:* 416-978-4802
E-mail: avrequest@utoronto.ca
Web Site: www.ace.utoronto.ca
Key Personnel
AV Coord: David Carinci
Providing AV support for classroom teaching.

University of Vermont, Instructional Television Dept
Affiliate of Department of Continuing & Distance Education
538 Main St, Burlington, VT 05405
Tel: 802-656-2927
E-mail: video@uvm.edu
Web Site: www.uvm.edu; www.uvm.edu/~video
Key Personnel
Dir: Elizabeth Hayward *E-mail:* ehayward@uvm.edu
Videographer: Eric Melton *E-mail:* emelton@uvm.edu
Broadcast Engr: Foster Nye *Tel:* 802-656-2927 ext 60565 *E-mail:* fnye@uvm.edu
Professional broadcast video production facility.

University of Wisconsin-Oshkosh Radio-TV-Film Dept
Arts & Communications Bldg, W-112, 800 Algoma Blvd, Oshkosh, WI 54901
Tel: 920-424-3131
E-mail: rtf@uwosh.edu
Web Site: rtf.uwosh.edu
Key Personnel
Dir, Radio Servs: Randall Davidson *E-mail:* davidsor@uwosh.edu
Dir, TV Servs: Justine Stokes *Tel:* 920-424-3133 *E-mail:* stokesj@uwosh.edu
Founded: 1964
Program developed to provide students with professional media curriculum featuring critical media analysis & hands on experience.
Membership(s): National Broadcasting Society

University Products Inc
517 Main St, Holyoke, MA 01040-0073
Mailing Address: PO Box 101, Holyoke, MA 01041-0101
Tel: 413-532-3372 *Toll Free Tel:* 800-628-1912
Fax: 413-532-9281 *Toll Free Fax:* 800-532-9281
E-mail: custserv@universityproducts.com; info@universityproducts.com
Web Site: www.universityproducts.com
Key Personnel
Owner & CEO: Scott E Magoon
VP & Gen Mgr: John A Dunphy
Founded: 1968
Museum quality products & archival materials. Electronic media storage, photo products, lighting & magnification.
Catalog(s) available
Online catalog(s) available
Membership(s): ALA

UPN 20 WDCA-TV
Division of Fox Television Stations LLC
5151 Wisconsin Ave NW, Washington, DC 20016
Tel: 202-244-5151
Web Site: www.fox5dc.com/my20dc
Key Personnel
VP & Gen Mgr: Patrick Paolini *E-mail:* patrick.paolini@foxtv.com
Catalog(s) available
Membership(s): Independent Media Producers Association; Independent TV Association

Upstage Video
201 Rock Lititz Blvd, Suite 20, Lititz, PA 17543
Tel: 717-240-2400 *Toll Free Tel:* 877-484-3887
E-mail: info@upstagevideo.com
Web Site: www.upstagevideo.com
Key Personnel
Pres: Doug Murray
VP, Busn Devt: Jason Cataldi
Founded: 2001
Rent LED video screens.
Branch Office(s)
9420 Telfair Ave, Sun Valley, CA 91352 *Tel:* 818-651-2000 *E-mail:* ed@upstagevideo.com

Urbanski Film
PO Box 438, Orland Park, IL 60462-0438
Tel: 708-460-9082 *Fax:* 708-460-9099
E-mail: info@urbanskifilm.com
Web Site: www.urbanskifilm.com
Key Personnel
Pres: Larry Urbanski
Online lists available.

US Case Corp
6301 J Richard Dr, Raleigh, NC 27617
Tel: 919-783-6166 *Toll Free Tel:* 800-648-8474
Fax: 919-783-0740
E-mail: customersupport@uscase.com
Web Site: www.uscase.com
Key Personnel
Owner & Pres: Jeff Hines *E-mail:* jeffhines@uscase.com
VP: Brad Blumeyer *E-mail:* bradblumeyer@uscase.com
Founded: 1988
Custom casing for AV, sound, music, computers & more.

US Holocaust Memorial Museum
100 Raoul Wallenberg Place SW, Washington, DC 20024-2126
Tel: 202-488-0400
E-mail: membership@ushmm.org
Web Site: www.ushmm.org
Key Personnel
New Audience Engagement & Membership Dir: Dana Weinstein
Films on the subject of Genocide & the Holocaust available as teacher resources.
Catalog(s) available

US Music Corp
Division of Jam Industries USA LLC
1649 Barclay Blvd, Buffalo Grove, IL 60089
Toll Free Tel: 800-877-6863
E-mail: sales.support@usmusiccorp.com
Web Site: www.usmusiccorp.com
Manufacture & distribute guitars, musical instruments & amplifiers.

USA Studios
253 W 35 St, New York, NY 10001
Tel: 212-398-6400 *Toll Free Tel:* 800-872-3821
Fax: 212-398-4145
E-mail: sales@usastudios.tv; marketing@usastudios.tv
Web Site: www.usastudios.tv
Key Personnel
CEO: Kenny Khan
Founded: 1988
TV post-production & distribution company.

USAV Group Inc
584 W 18768 Enterprise Dr, Muskego, WI 53150
Tel: 262-814-2000 *Toll Free Tel:* 800-596-USAV (596-8728) *Fax:* 262-814-2006
Web Site: www.usavgroup.com
Key Personnel
Acct Mgr: Liam Connelly *E-mail:* lconnelly@usavgroup.com
Event staging & video production.

USCCB Publishing
Division of United States Conference of Catholic Bishops
3211 Fourth St NE, Washington, DC 20017
Tel: 202-541-3000 *Toll Free Tel:* 800-235-8722 (cust serv) *Fax:* 202-722-8709 (cust serv)
E-mail: publications@usccb.org
Web Site: www.usccbpublishing.org
Key Personnel
Dir, Creative Servs: David Felber
Assoc Dir, Perms: Mary E Sperry

Official publisher of the US bishops. Subject areas in print & AV media are catechesis, social justice, priestly life & documents from the Vatican.
Online catalog(s) available

USDA/FSA Aerial Photography Field Office
2222 W 2300 S, Salt Lake City, UT 84119-2020
Tel: 801-844-2922 *Toll Free Fax:* 855-415-2014
E-mail: apfo.sales@slc.usda.gov
Web Site: www.fsa.usda.gov/programs-and-services/aerial-photography
Key Personnel
Busn Mgmt Offr: Lori Uhlhorn *E-mail:* lori.uhlhorn@slc.usda.gov
Aerial imagery.

Ushio America Inc
Subsidiary of Ushio Inc (Japan)
5440 Cerritos Ave, Cypress, CA 90630-4567
Tel: 714-236-8600 *Toll Free Tel:* 800-838-7446 (cust serv) *Fax:* 714-229-3180
Toll Free Fax: 800-776-3641 (cust serv)
E-mail: customerservice@ushio.com
Web Site: www.ushio.com
Key Personnel
Pres & CEO: William F MacKenzie
Founded: 1967
Catalog(s) available
Membership(s): Entertainment Services and Technology Association; International Cinema Technology Association; International Ultraviolet Association; Laser Illuminated Projector Association; RadTech International North America

USI Inc
98 Fort Path Rd, Suite A, Madison, CT 06443
Tel: 203-245-8586 *Toll Free Tel:* 800-282-9290
Fax: 203-245-8619
E-mail: customers@usi-corp.com
Web Site: www.usi-laminate.com
Key Personnel
Pres & CEO: Peter Gianacoplos
Founded: 1975
Marketer of roll & pouch laminating machines, films, binding equipment, supplies, mounting & display boards & photo ID systems.
Catalog(s) available

Utah Scientific Inc
4750 Wiley Post Way, Suite 150, Salt Lake City, UT 84116
Tel: 801-575-8801 *Toll Free Tel:* 800-453-8782
Fax: 801-537-3099
E-mail: info@utahscientific.com
Web Site: utahscientific.com
Key Personnel
Pres & CEO: Tom Harmon
CTO: Scott Barella
Founded: 1977

Utopia Films
1976 S La Cienega Blvd, No 130, Los Angeles, CA 90034
Tel: 310-338-0580 *Fax:* 313-557-0580
E-mail: reception@utopiafilms.com; production@utopiafilms.com (reels)
Web Site: utopiafilms.com
Key Personnel
Exec Prodr: Justin Bird *Tel:* 877-784-2739
E-mail: jbird@utopiafilms.com
Exec Prodr/Intl Rep: Howard Cohen
E-mail: hcohen@utopiafilms.com
Intl Prodr: Daniel Araujo *E-mail:* daraujo@utopiafilms.com
Assoc Prodr: Luis Valderrama
E-mail: lvalderrama@utopiafilms.com
Asst Prodr: Daniel Araujo *E-mail:* daraujo@utopiafilms.com
Founded: 1997

Production company providing competitive cost options for international producers filming in Brazil & Venezuela, as well as leading still photographers & ad agencies.
Foreign Office(s): Av Princesa Isabel 150, Suite 903, 22011-010 Rio de Janeiro-RJ, Brazil
Tel: (021) 2244 2271 *Fax:* (021) 2244 3841
Calle El Servicio Parque Res, Valle Arriba, Santa Fe-Sur Edificio, Campomanes, Suite 2E, Caracas 1060, Venezuela *Tel:* (0212) 720 2197

Vaddio
131 Cheshire Lane, Suite 500, Minnetonka, MN 55305
Tel: 763-971-4400 *Toll Free Tel:* 800-572-2011
Fax: 763-971-4464
E-mail: info@vaddio.com
Web Site: www.vaddio.com
Founded: 2005
Leading designer & OEM distributor of specialty PTZ cameras & high-end camera control systems used in the broadcasting, AV & videoconferencing industries. Headquartered in a suburb of Minneapolis, MN, we also have operations throughout the Americas as well as sales & support partners throughout the world.
Online catalog(s) available
Membership(s): Audiovisual and Integrated Experience Association; IABM; NAB; NSCA

Valencia Studios
26030 Avenue Hall, Studio 5, Valencia, CA 91355
Tel: 661-702-9102
E-mail: info@valenciastudios.com
Web Site: www.valenciastudios.com
Key Personnel
Stage Mgr: Suzanne Burr
Full service independent TV & film production facility offering soundstages & attached production offices.

Valiant National AV Supply, see AlltecPro

Valley Media
421 Roanoke Dr, Martinez, CA 94553-6240
Tel: 925-937-5207; 510-612-5215 (cell)
Web Site: www.valleymedia.com
Key Personnel
Prodr & Dir: Bob Briggs *E-mail:* bobriggs@valleymedia.com
Founded: 1979
Producer & director of videos.

Valley of the Sun Publishing Co
Division of The Sutphen Center
PO Box 2053, Sedona, AZ 86339
Tel: 928-554-1333
E-mail: info@dicksutphen.com
Web Site: www.dicksutphen.com
Key Personnel
Owner: Richard Sutphen
Online publisher of spiritual & human-potential self-help meditation & hypnosis programming ebooks, MP3s, CDs & DVDs.
Online catalog(s) available
Membership(s): International Hypnosis Federation

Jack Van Impe Ministries International
1718 Northfield Dr, Rochester Hills, MI 48309-3818
Mailing Address: PO Box 7004, Troy, MI 48007-7004
Tel: 248-852-2244; 248-852-5225 (orders)
Fax: 248-852-2692
E-mail: jvimi@jvim.com
Web Site: www.jvim.com

Key Personnel
Pres: Dr Jack Van Impe
Branch Office(s)
PO Box 1717, Postal Sta A, Windsor, ON N9A 6Y1, Canada

Vancouver Film Studios Ltd
Division of The McLean Group
3500 Cornett Rd, Vancouver, BC V5M 2H5, Canada
Tel: 604-453-5000 *Fax:* 604-453-5045
E-mail: info@vancouverfilmstudios.com
Web Site: www.vancouverfilmstudios.com
Key Personnel
Pres & COO: Pete Mitchell
VP, Opers: Natasha Dickson
VP, Prodn Servs: Gerry Rutherford
VP, Sales & Mktg: Jennifer Roe Emery
Production facilities for film & television production, including soundstages & production offices.

Vanguard Documentaries
PO Box 26635, Brooklyn, NY 11202
Tel: 347-725-1677
Web Site: www.vanguarddocumentaries.com
Key Personnel
Founder & Exec Prodr: Charles Hobson
E-mail: charleshobson@gmail.com
Film development & production company. Specialize in arts, cultural affairs & political documentaries.

Vanner Inc
4282 Reynolds Dr, Hilliard, OH 43026
Tel: 614-771-2718 *Toll Free Tel:* 800-ACPOWER (227-6937) *Fax:* 614-771-4904
E-mail: info@vanner.com; pwrsales@vanner.com
Web Site: www.vanner.com
Key Personnel
VP, Sales & Mktg: Bruce Beegle *Tel:* 704-489-9793 *E-mail:* bruceb@vanner.com
Cust Care Mgr: Darlene Dowell
Online catalog(s) available

Vantage Controls, a Legrand AV Inc brand
2168 W Grove Pkwy, Suite 300, Pleasant Grove, UT 84062
Tel: 801-229-2800 *Toll Free Tel:* 800-555-9891
Fax: 801-224-0355
E-mail: vantage.info@vantagecontrols.com
Web Site: www.vantagecontrols.com
Founded: 1984
Designer & manufacturer of home control systems for luxury residences.
Catalog(s) available
Membership(s): American Society of Interior Designers; Consumer Technology Association™; Continental Automated Buildings Association; Custom Electronic Design & Installation Association; ISO; US Green Building Council

Vantage Point Products Corp
PO Box 2485, Santa Fe Springs, CA 90670
Tel: 562-946-1718 *Fax:* 562-946-3898
Web Site: www.thinkvp.com
Key Personnel
Opers Mgr: John Silva
Founded: 1988
Manufacturer of stylish, well designed AV support products: TV mounts, LCD mounts, speaker stands, furniture, iPad stands & mounts.

Varese Sarabande Records Inc
9100 Wilshire Blvd, Suite 455E, Beverly Hills, CA 90212
Tel: 310-853-5400
E-mail: info@varesesarabande.com; orders@varesesarabande.com

Web Site: www.varesesarabande.com
Key Personnel
Sales Mgr: Jeff Safran

Vari-Lite, see Philips Entertainment Lighting

VariQuest Visual Learning Tools, see
Varitronics LLC

Varitronics LLC
7200 93 Ave N, Suite 120, Brooklyn, MN 55445
Tel: 763-536-6400 *Toll Free Tel:* 800-328-0585
E-mail: customerservice@variquest.com;
tech_support@variquest.com; variquest@
variquest.com
Web Site: www.variquest.com
Key Personnel
Pres & CEO: David Grey
Founded: 1983
Provides education technology solutions & visual
support to improve academic progress & class-
room engagement.

VARTA Microbattery Inc
Subsidiary of VARTA Microbattery GmbH
555 Theodore Fremd Ave, Suite C-304, Rye, NY
10580
Tel: 914-592-2500 *Toll Free Tel:* 800-468-2782
Fax: 914-345-0488
Web Site: www.varta-microbattery.com; www.
varta-microbattery.com/contact/?lang=en
Key Personnel
CEO: Herbert Schein
CFO: James Bremner
Research, development, production & sales of
high quality batteries & battery packs for elec-
tronic devices.
Catalog(s) available
Foreign Office(s): VARTA Microbattery (Shang-
hai) Co Ltd, Block 3, Shanghai Pudong Chuan-
sha Industrial Park, No 6999 Chuansha Rd,
Pudong New Area, Shanghai 201202, China
Tel: (021) 58 59 83 85 *Fax:* (021) 58 59 33 13
VARTA Microbattery GmbH, 12/14 rue Raymond
Ridel, 92250 La Garenne Colombes, France
Tel: 01 47 84 84 54 *Fax:* 01 47 84 28 32 *Web
Site:* www.varta-microbattery.fr
VARTA Microbattery GmbH, Daimlerstr 1,
73479 Ellwangen, Germany *Tel:* (07961) 921
0 *Fax:* (07961) 921 553
VARTA Storage GmbH, Nuremberg, Germany
Tel: (07961) 921 752 *Fax:* (07961) 921 73462
Web Site: www.varta-storage.com
VARTA Microbattery Pte Ltd, 1702-317/F
Fullerton Ctr, 19 Hung To Rd, Kwun Tong,
Kowloon, Hong Kong *Tel:* 2898 8373
Fax: 2897 7609
VARTA Microbattery Indonesia, Jl Gaharu, Lot
23, Batamindo Industrial Park, Mukakuning,
Batam, Kepri 29433, Indonesia *Tel:* (077) 0611
099 *Fax:* (077) 0611 966
VARTA Microbattery Pte Ltd, Kyobashi Y'SUS
Bldg, 3F, 1-6-12 Kyobashi, Chuo-ku, Tokyo
104-0031, Japan *Tel:* (03) 356 781 71
Fax: (03) 356 781 75 *Web Site:* www.varta-
microbattery.co.jp
VARTA Microbattery SRL, Blvd Grivita 1,
500177 Brasov, Romania *Tel:* (021) 2030077
VARTA Microbattery SRL, Blvd Grivitei 1X,
500177 Brasov, Romania (factory)
VARTA Microbattery Pte Ltd, 300, Tampines Ave
5, No 05-01, Tampines Junction, Singapore
529653, Singapore *Tel:* 6260 5801 *Fax:* 6260
5812 *Web Site:* www.varta-microbattery.sg
VARTA Microbattery Pte Ltd, 11F-4, No 130,
Section 2, Chung Hsiao East Rd, Taipei 10053,
Taiwan *Tel:* (02) 339 315 57 *Fax:* (02) 339 315
56 *Web Site:* www.varta-microbattery.com.tw

Varto Technologies
195 Hackensack St, East Rutherford, NJ 07073

Toll Free Tel: 888-656-6233 *Fax:* 201-604-2661
E-mail: sales@vartotechnologies.com
Web Site: www.vartotechnologies.com
Founded: 1984
Design & integrate reliable, cost-effective audio,
video, digital media & live broadcast solutions.

Mike Vasilinda Productions Inc
310 N Monroe St, Tallahassee, FL 32301
Mailing Address: PO Box 10004, Tallahassee, FL
32302-2004
Tel: 850-224-5420
Web Site: mvptv.tv
Key Personnel
SVP & Opers Mgr: Andy Bundschuh
E-mail: andy@mvptv.tv
Television production & television news service.

VCI Entertainment
Division of Blair & Associates Ltd
11333 E 60 Place, Tulsa, OK 74146-6828
Tel: 918-254-6337 *Toll Free Tel:* 800-331-4077
E-mail: vci@vcientertainment.com
Web Site: www.vcientertainment.com; www.
vcient.com
Key Personnel
Pres: Robert A Blair *E-mail:* rablair@
vcientertainment.com
VP: Don Blair
Founded: 1976
Producer & distributor of motion pictures.
Online catalog(s) available
Membership(s): Entertainment Merchants Associ-
ation

Vcom IMC
80 Little Falls Rd, Fairfield, NJ 07004
Toll Free Tel: 800-572-6373
E-mail: info@vcomimc.com
Web Site: www.vcomimc.com
Key Personnel
Pres & CEO: Sheldon "Shelly" Goldstein
Founded: 1969
Services including AV products, classroom elec-
tronics, cables, connectors, converters & digital
signage.

Vcom International Multimedia Corp, see
Vcom IMC

VCSvideo
2807 Hunterdon Dr, Cinnaminson, NJ 08077
Tel: 856-273-8800 *Toll Free Tel:* 877-VCS-
VIDEO (827-8433)
Web Site: www.vcsvideo.com
Key Personnel
Principal & Prodr/Dir/Writer: David Fox
Principal & Prodr/Dir: Frank Siegel
Founded: 1979
Membership(s): NATAS; NATPE

VDO Lab Inc
520 White Plains Rd, Suite 500, Tarrytown, NY
10591
Tel: 914-467-7860; 914-374-8727
E-mail: info@vdolab.net; vdolabinc@gmail.com
Web Site: vdolab.net
Key Personnel
Pres: Jeff Hass
Founded: 1984
Film & video transfer, DVD-CD duplicating &
printing & packaging.
Online catalog(s) available

Vedanta Press & Catalog
Division of Vedanta Society of Southern California
1946 Vedanta Place, Hollywood, CA 90068
Tel: 323-960-1727 (bookstores); 323-960-1736
(outside US) *Toll Free Tel:* 800-816-2242
E-mail: info@vedanta.com

Web Site: www.vedanta.com
Key Personnel
Mgr: Robert Adjemian *Tel:* 323-960-1728
E-mail: bob@vedanta.org
Founded: 1934

Vedanta Society of St Louis
205 S Skinker Blvd, St Louis, MO 63105
Tel: 314-721-5118
Web Site: vedantastl.org
Key Personnel
Contact: Swami Chetanananda
Publish materials on Vedanta & comparative reli-
gion.
Flyer(s) available

Veetronix Inc
1311 W Pacific St, Lexington, NE 68850
Mailing Address: PO Box 480, Lexington, NE
68850-0480
Tel: 308-324-6661 *Toll Free Tel:* 800-445-0007
Fax: 308-324-4985
E-mail: sales@veetronix.com
Web Site: www.veetronix.com
Key Personnel
Pres: Roger Teeters
Manufacture push-button switches, key caps &
communication products.
Online catalog(s) available

Vela Research
5576 Rio Vista Dr, Clearwater, FL 33760-3107
Tel: 727-507-5301
E-mail: sales@vela.com
Web Site: www.vela.com
Founded: 1992
Provider of MPEG video encoding & decoding
technology & products.
Online catalog(s) available, available for down-
load
Membership(s): NAB; SCTE; SMPTE®

Velodyne LiDAR Inc
5521 Hellyer Ave, San Jose, CA 95738
Tel: 408-465-2800 *Fax:* 408-779-9208 (cust serv);
408-779-9377 (orders)
E-mail: lidar@velodyne.com
Web Site: velodynelidar.com
Key Personnel
Founder & CEO: David Hall
Pres & CEO: Mike Jellen
COO: Marty Neese
CFO: Bob Brown
CTO: Anand Gopalan
Cont: Houshang Vala
Pres, Busn Devt: Marta Thoma Hall
VP, Opers & Supply Chains: Frank Blohm
Gen Coun: Alex Korzh
Founded: 1983
Universally recognized as the leading manufac-
turer of high performance, low distortion pow-
ered subwoofers at all price levels.
Data sheet(s) available

Venice Media Group
101 W Venice Ave, Suite 6, Venice, FL 34285
Tel: 941-485-0699
E-mail: info@venicemediagroup.com
Web Site: www.venicemediagroup.com
Key Personnel
Owner: Ed Vinson
Video production services, TV commercials, web
advertising, music videos, conversion & dupli-
cation services, photography, graphic design,
audio recording studio.

Venture Media
902 Harvest Pointe Dr, Fort Mill, SC 29708
Tel: 803-547-3878
E-mail: info@venturemedia.tv
Web Site: www.venturemedia.tv

Key Personnel
CEO & Prodr: Kris Duffy
Pres & Dir: Jim Duffy *E-mail:* jim@
venturemedia.tv
Founded: 1979
Provide creative development, writing, film &
video production & multimedia services.
Online catalog(s) available

VER
Member of Production Resource Group LLC
(PRG)
757 W California Ave, Bldg 4, Glendale, CA
91203
Tel: 818-956-1444 *Toll Free Tel:* 800-794-1407
Fax: 818-546-1040
Web Site: www.ver.com
Key Personnel
CEO: Bob Krakauer
Founded: 1982
Equipment rental company with vast inventory of
AV, audio, broadcast & computer equipment,
creative LED & lighting.
Online catalog(s) available
Branch Office(s)
6170 Valley View, Buena Park, CA 90620
Tel: 714-978-8811
9516 Chesapeake Dr, Suite 404, San Diego, CA
92123 *Tel:* 619-299-8336 *Fax:* 858-560-0564
410 E Grand Ave, South San Francisco, CA
94080 *Tel:* 650-837-9480 *Fax:* 650-837-9488
4625 S 32 St, Phoenix, AZ 85040 *Tel:* 602-268-
8000 *Fax:* 602-268-8014
5000 Dahlia St, Suite D, Denver, CO 80216
Tel: 303-355-5001 *Toll Free Tel:* 844-924-8285
Fax: 303-355-5015
3300 Davie Rd, Suite 101, Davie, FL 33314
Tel: 954-723-2828 *Fax:* 954-723-2833
8063 Beacon Lake Dr, Orlando, FL 32809
Tel: 407-582-0350
1053 Willingham Dr, Atlanta, GA 30344
Tel: 770-300-0401
8401 W 47 St, Suite D, McCook, IL 60525
Tel: 847-671-4966
3000 Lausat St, Metairie, LA 70001 *Tel:* 504-
831-6966
9590 Lynn Buff Ct, Suite 16, Laurel, MD 20723
Tel: 301-731-9560 *Fax:* 301-731-9570
175 New Boston St, Suite A, Woburn, MA 01801
Tel: 781-937-7612 *Fax:* 781-937-0682
4155 W Russell Rd, Suite E-H, Las Vegas, NV
89118 *Tel:* 702-895-9777 *Fax:* 702-895-7377
75A Twinbridge Dr, Pennsauken, NJ 08110
Tel: 856-312-3850
50 Meadowlands Pkwy, Bldg A, Secaucus, NJ
07094 *Tel:* 201-392-0145 *Fax:* 201-864-1397
147 41 St, 3rd fl, Suite A, Brooklyn, NY 11232
Tel: 212-206-3730 *Fax:* 212-206-9154
12630 Old Hickory Blvd, Antioch, TN 37013
Tel: 615-280-2255 *Fax:* 615-280-2181
3110 Roy Orr Blvd, Suite 200, Grand Prairie, TX
75050 *Tel:* 214-260-1295 *Fax:* 214-591-0304
8251 Kempwood Dr, Houston, TX 77055
Tel: 713-691-1332 *Fax:* 713-691-1378
12610 Interurban Ave S, Suite 110, Tukwila, WA
98168 *Tel:* 206-242-3860 *Fax:* 206-242-3859
6741 Cariboo Rd, Unit 301, Burnaby, BC V3N
4A3, Canada *Tel:* 604-420-3440 *Fax:* 604-420-
3446
137 Horner Ave, Unit 4, Toronto, ON M8Z 4Y1,
Canada *Tel:* 905-795-8008 *Fax:* 905-795-2769

Ver Sales Inc
2509 N Naomi St, Burbank, CA 91504
Tel: 818-567-3000 *Toll Free Tel:* 800-229-
0518; 800-300-WIRE (300-9479, CA only)
Fax: 818-567-3018
E-mail: sales@versales.com
Web Site: www.versales.com
Key Personnel
VP, Opers: Craig Ryan
VP, Sales: Paul Ryan
Inside Sales: Vince Yanes

Founded: 1972
Lighting rental & fall protection safety, rigging &
hardware.

Verbatim Americas LLC
Subsidiary of Mitsubishi Chemical Corp
8210 University Executive Park Dr, Suite 300,
Charlotte, NC 28262
Toll Free Tel: 800-538-8589
Web Site: www.verbatim.com
Key Personnel
Dir, Mktg & Communs: Becky Morrison
E-mail: becky.morrison@verbatim.com
Founded: 1969
Data storage company.

Verilux® - The Healthy Lighting Co
340 Mad River Park, Suite 1, Waitsfield, VT
05673
Tel: 802-496-3101 *Toll Free Tel:* 888-544-
4865 (cust support); 800-454-4408 (orders)
Fax: 802-496-3105 (orders)
E-mail: info@verilux.com
Web Site: www.verilux.com
Key Personnel
Pres: Nicholas Harmon
Sr Sales Acct Mgr: Dawn Tudor *Tel:* 802-496-
3101 ext 112 *E-mail:* dtudor@verilux.com
Founded: 1956
Originator of the HappyLight®.

Versatech Industries Inc
14750 S Grant St, Bixby, OK 74008
Tel: 918-366-7400
Key Personnel
Owner: Gene B Randall, Jr
Remote surveillance, closed-circuit TV.
Catalog(s) available

Versatruss
Division of 1859936 Ontario Inc
5028 Hwy 43, Perth, ON K7H 3C7, Canada
Tel: 613-264-0074 *Toll Free Tel:* 888-430-7613
Fax: 613-264-0889
E-mail: info@versatruss.com
Web Site: www.versatruss.com
Key Personnel
Acct Exec: Gordon O'Connor
Manufacture aluminum truss systems.
Online catalog(s) available

Vertiv
Formerly Emerson Network Power
1050 Dearborn Dr, Columbus, OH 43085
Tel: 614-888-0246
Web Site: www.vertiv.com
Key Personnel
CEO: Rob Johnson
CFO: David Fallon
COO & EVP, Infrastructure & Solutions: Jason
Forcier
Chief Organizational Devt & HR Offr: Andrew
Cole
Chief Strategy & Devt Offr: Gary Niederpruem
Pres, Americas: John Hewitt
Gen Coun: Colin Flannery
EVP, IT & Edge Infrastructure: Pat Johnson
EVP, Servs: Steve Lalla
Media Rel: Tracy Krawczyk *Tel:* 614-841-6962
Digital continuity solutions with a portfolio of
power, thermal & infrastructure management
solutions.
Online catalog(s) available

Verve Label Group
Member of Universal Music Group
1755 Broadway, New York, NY 10019
Tel: 212-841-8000
Web Site: www.vervelabelgroup.com; www.
universalmusic.com

Key Personnel
Pres & CEO: Danny Bennett
Pres, US Classical Labels: Graham Parker
Founded: 1956
Comprised of jazz imprint Impulse plus Universal
Music Group's US classical holdings which in-
clude Deutsche Grammophon, Decca, Mercury
Classics & distributed label ECM.

Vexcel Corp
Subsidiary of Microsoft
5775 Flatiron Pkwy, Suite 220, Boulder, CO
80301
Tel: 303-415-6000 *Fax:* 303-442-2956
E-mail: vexcel@microsoft.com
Web Site: www.vexcel.com
Founded: 1985
The company offers a range of aerial mapping &
remote sensing products & services to government & commercial markets. Areas of special-
ization include:
i) photogrammetry & mapping hardware & software
ii) GIS products & system solutions
iii) SAR research, exploitation software & services
iv) remote sensing ground systems.

La Vezzi Precision Inc
250 Madsen Dr, Bloomingdale, IL 60108-2637
Tel: 630-582-1230 *Toll Free Tel:* 800-323-1772
(outside IL) *Fax:* 630-582-1238 (orders)
E-mail: lpi@lavezzi.com
Web Site: www.lavezzi.com
Key Personnel
Sales & Mktg Mgr: Stephanie La Vezzi
E-mail: stephlav@lavezzi.com
Founded: 1908
Precision machined components manufacturer.
Online catalog(s) available
Membership(s): SMPTE®

VFGadgets Inc
22 Elmer Ave, Toronto, ON M4L 3R7, Canada
Tel: 416-686-1452
E-mail: sales@vfgadgets.com; customerservice@
vfgadgets.com
Web Site: www.vfgadgets.com
Key Personnel
Prod Devt: David O'Keefe *E-mail:* djokeefe@
vfgadgets.com
Founded: 2001
Sells equipment solutions for video & film pro-
duction.

Via Verde Productions
22631 Pacific Coast Hwy, Suite 480, Malibu, CA
90265-5036
Tel: 310-458-3778 *Fax:* 310-496-2992
E-mail: info@viaverdedigital.com
Web Site: www.viaverdedigital.com
Key Personnel
Founder & Dir: Melissa Landini
Full service film & digital production company &
post-production studio.
Membership(s): IDA

Vicon Industries Inc
135 Fell Ct, Hauppauge, NY 11788-4351
Tel: 631-952-2288 *Toll Free Tel:* 800-645-9116
Fax: 631-951-2288
E-mail: sales@vicon-security.com
Web Site: www.vicon-security.com
Key Personnel
CEO/CFO: John Badke
SVP, Sales & Mktg: Bret McGowan
VP, Opers: Peter Horn
Founded: 1967
Design, manufacture & market a broad line of
products used in integrated video surveillance
systems. Vicon's marketing & development ef-
forts focus on today's leading edge security
technologies, including digital recording & IP

video solutions, access control, matrix controls, cameras, monitors, mounting accessories, remote positioning devices & fiber optic equipment. Our products are used in a variety of surveillance, security, safety & control applications, in banks, gaming casinos, traffic control, hospitals, retailing, multiple commercial & industrial installations, etc.
Catalog(s) available
Foreign Office(s): Vicon Industries Ltd, Brunel Way, Fareham PO15 5TX, United Kingdom *Tel:* (01489) 566300 *Fax:* (01489) 566322
Membership(s): ASIS; Closed Circuit Television Manufacturers Association; SIA

Victory Studios
2247 15 Ave W, Seattle, WA 98119
Tel: 206-282-1776 *Toll Free Tel:* 888-282-1776
Fax: 206-282-3535
E-mail: info@victorystudios.com
Web Site: www.victorystudios.com
Key Personnel
Owner & CEO: Conrad W Denke
E-mail: conrad@victorystudios.com
Founded: 1978
Branch Office(s)
10911 Riverside Dr, Suite 200, North Hollywood, CA 91602 *Tel:* 818-769-1776 *Toll Free Fax:* 888-785-9563
Membership(s): AICP; NATAS; NATPE; Producers Guild of America

VidCAD LLC
2010 E Lohman Ave, Suite 2, Las Cruces, NM 88001
Tel: 575-522-0003 *Toll Free Tel:* 800-VIDCAD-6 (843-2236 sales) *Fax:* 575-522-0009
E-mail: sales@vidcad.com
Web Site: www.vidcad.com
Key Personnel
CEO: Janine Sotelo
Manufacturer of software that automates the design & documentation of television, radio, AV & telecommunications systems. VidCAD ESP (Enterprise-wide in scope), VidCAD Engineer, VidCAD Designer & VidCAD TecXpert.

VidCan Media Solutions
24133 Del Monte Dr, Unit 204, Valencia, CA 91355
Tel: 818-312-5128
Web Site: www.vidcan.com
Key Personnel
Owner: Graham Jones *E-mail:* gjones@vidcan.com
Award winning production & full service post-production & gear rentals.

Vidcraft Productions Ltd
425 Curling St, Corner Brook, NL A2H 3K4, Canada
Tel: 709-785-1157
E-mail: info@vidcraft.com
Web Site: www.vidcraft.com
Key Personnel
Pres: Ron O'Connell *E-mail:* ron@vidcraft.com
Founded: 1991
Professional multimedia/broadcast video production.

Video Accessory Corp
1243 Sherman Dr, Suite 8, Longmont, CO 80501
Tel: 303-443-1319 *Toll Free Tel:* 800-821-0426
Fax: 303-440-8878
E-mail: sales@vac-brick.net
Web Site: www.vac-brick.com
Manufactures video & audio distribution amplifiers, switches, breakouts, black burst generators & other products for video & audio professionals.
Online catalog(s) available

Video Advantage
90 Houseman Crescent, Richmond Hill, ON L4C 7S6, Canada
Tel: 905-883-5332
E-mail: info@videoadvantage.ca
Web Site: www.videoadvantage.ca
Key Personnel
Principal & Exec Prodr: Rick Davis
Creative Dir: Michael O'Brien
Founded: 1998
HD video production, from concept to post-production, TV commercials & PSAs, corporate & web video production, TV series & documentaries.

Video Aided Instruction Inc
PO Box 740023, Boyton Beach, FL 33474-0023
Toll Free Tel: 800-238-1512 *Toll Free Fax:* 800-588-1419
E-mail: info@videoaidedinstruction.com
Web Site: www.videoaidedinstruction.com
Key Personnel
Pres: Peter Lanzer
VP: Mona E Lanzer
Founded: 1983
Publish multimedia products for the educational market. Provide DVDs to the institutional & consumer markets.
Online catalog(s) available

Video Artists International & VAI Audio
109 Wheeler Ave, Pleasantville, NY 10570
Tel: 914-769-3691 *Toll Free Tel:* 800-477-7146
Fax: 914-769-5407
E-mail: orders@vaimusic.com
Web Site: www.vaimusic.com
Key Personnel
Owner: Edward Cardona
Prodn Coord: Allan Altman
Founded: 1983
Production & distribution of own label, also distribute other related classical labels. Music video, classical, opera, ballet & jazz.
Catalog(s) available

Video Associates Labs Inc
2201 Denton Dr, Suite 109 B, Austin, TX 78758-3231
Tel: 512-491-7091 *Toll Free Tel:* 800-331-0547
Fax: 512-491-7619
E-mail: sales@val.com
Web Site: www.val.com
Key Personnel
Pres: Randy Feingersh
CFO: Nancy Nawrocki
Manufacture USB cameras for photo ID applications.

Video Caption Corp
88 Hunns Lake Rd, Stanfordville, NY 12581
Tel: 845-868-1200 *Toll Free Tel:* 800-705-1203
Fax: 845-868-1188 *Toll Free Fax:* 800-705-1207
E-mail: mail@vicaps.com
Web Site: www.vicaps.com
Key Personnel
VP, Sales & Mktg: Tiffany Thomas
E-mail: tsthomas@vicaps.com
Founded: 1997
Transcription, captioning, post-production work & translation to video.
Branch Office(s)
300 E Magnolia Blvd, Suite 506, Burbank, CA 91502 *Tel:* 818-736-5446

Video Catalogue Co Inc
105 E 34 St, Suite 105, New York, NY 10016
Toll Free Tel: 866-843-2282
E-mail: info@vidcat.com
Web Site: www.vidcat.com

Key Personnel
Pres & Exec Prodr: Janet Pytowski
E-mail: janet@vidcat.com
Fashion show videos, DVDs, footage & fashion TV.
Catalog(s) available

Video Communication Services, see VCSvideo

Video Copy Services Inc
3980 Dekalb Technology Pkwy, Suite 670, Atlanta, GA 30340
Tel: 404-321-6933 *Toll Free Tel:* 800-553-3616
E-mail: info@video-copy.com
Web Site: www.video-copy.com
Key Personnel
Owner & Pres: George Helms *E-mail:* george@video-copy.com
Dir, Opers: Bob Chirum
Founded: 1984
CD & DVD duplication.
Membership(s): Women in Film

Video Corporation of America (VCA)
7 Veronica Ave, Somerset, NJ 08873
Mailing Address: PO Box 5480, Somerset, NJ 08875-5480
Tel: 732-545-8000 *Fax:* 732-545-5101
Web Site: www.vcaglobal.com
Key Personnel
Pres: David M Berlin
VP, Sales: Tom Bigliani *E-mail:* tom@vcaglobal.com
Founded: 1972
AV systems integrator & reseller of professional audio & digital video equipment & AV presentation systems.
Branch Office(s)
5 Concourse Pkwy, Suite 3000, Atlanta, GA 30328 *Tel:* 770-392-3368
370 Seventh Ave, Suite 550, New York, NY 10001 *Tel:* 212-967-4400 *Fax:* 212-967-1585
2 Logan Sq, 100 N 18 St, Suite 300, Philadelphia, PA 19103 *Tel:* 267-207-3551
Membership(s): Audiovisual and Integrated Experience Association; NAB; PSNI

Video Dimensions Inc
545 W 45 St, New York, NY 10036
Tel: 212-262-5453
Web Site: videodimensions.net
Key Personnel
Pres: Steve Liebowitz
Sr Prodr/Ed: Drew Smith
Sr Prodn Coord: Kelly O'Neill
Equip Mgr: Sam Parsons
Prodn Servs Mgr: Jim Coble
Busn Aff: Kim Liebowitz
Founded: 2005
Full service production & post-production, on location or in studio.

Video Editing Services Inc, see The Media Collaboratory

Video Equipment Rentals, see VER

Video Excellence Productions
94 Breckonwood Crescent, Thornhill, ON L3T 5E8, Canada
Tel: 905-731-4355
Web Site: www.videoexcellence.com
Key Personnel
Owner & Pres: Brian Korson *E-mail:* brian@videoexcellence.com
Founded: 1983
Filming & editing of industrial, promotional & training programs with output to tape, CD, DVD & Internet. Multi-camera filming of events & streaming of video content.
Membership(s): PEO

Video Express
88 Black Falcon Ave, Suite 220, Boston, MA 02210
Tel: 617-267-7900 *Fax:* 617-267-6306
E-mail: operations@evideoexpress.com
Web Site: www.evideoexpress.com
Key Personnel
Pres: Bill Taylor, Jr
Founded: 1982
Media distribution, processing & production services.

Video/Film Associates
413 N Seventh St, Philadelphia, PA 19123-3900
Tel: 215-922-3333
Key Personnel
Owner: Ron Kanter *E-mail:* ronkanter@gmail.com
Produce documentary based programs for broadcast, industry & the medical community.

Video I-D Teleproductions Inc
105 Muller Rd, Washington, IL 61571
Tel: 309-444-4323 *Fax:* 309-444-4333
E-mail: videoid@videoid.com
Web Site: www.videoid.com
Key Personnel
Owner & Pres: Sam B Wagner
Founded: 1977
Production services include DVD Interactive.

Video Ideas Productions
1501 64 St, North Bergen, NJ 07047
Tel: 201-951-3798 *Fax:* 201-662-4846
E-mail: osoriomedia@yahoo.com
Web Site: osoriomedia.com
Key Personnel
Pres: William Osorio
Fully equipped professional video production & post-production house.

Video Impressions
1946 Fays Lane, Sugar Grove, IL 60554
Tel: 630-851-1663
E-mail: info@video-impressions.com
Web Site: www.video-impressions.com
Key Personnel
Founder: Mark W Hislop *E-mail:* mark@video-impressions.com
Founded: 1981
Full service video production. HD & UHD post, HD & Ultra HD recording, single & multiple camera recording, motion graphics, 3D animation, scriptwriting & consultation.

Video Learning Library
15838 N 62 St, Scottsdale, AZ 85254-1988
Tel: 480-596-9970 *Toll Free Tel:* 800-383-8811 (orders)
E-mail: videos@videolearning.com
Web Site: www.videolearning.com
Key Personnel
Pres: James R Spencer
Founded: 1987
Rental & sales of how-to, special interest & educational videos.
Online catalog(s) available
Membership(s): Entertainment Merchants Association

Video Memories LLC, see Sunrise Studios

The Video Messenger Co
862 Judson Place, Stratford, CT 06615
Tel: 203-358-8842 *Toll Free Tel:* 800-800-7128
Fax: 203-547-6216
E-mail: vmc@videomessenger.com
Web Site: www.videomessenger.com
Key Personnel
Pres: Charles P Corsello
Sales: Peter Murphy

Founded: 1989
Also manufacture & distribute networkable video message system, digital signs.
Catalog(s) available

Video Mount Products (VMP)
345 Log Canoe Circle, Stevensville, MD 21666
Tel: 410-643-6390 *Toll Free Tel:* 877-281-2169
Fax: 410-643-6615
E-mail: contact@videomount.com
Web Site: www.videomount.com
Key Personnel
Pres: Keith Fulmer
Founded: 1994
Mounting solutions for AV communications & security.
Online catalog(s) available

Video Movie Magic
26941 Cabot Rd, Suite 127, Laguna Hills, CA 92653
Tel: 949-582-8596 *Fax:* 949-582-8223
E-mail: sales@videomoviemagic.com
Web Site: www.videomoviemagic.com
Key Personnel
Owner: R Mike Jones
Mgr: Rick Jones
Founded: 1982

Video Out Distribution
Affiliate of VIVO Media Arts Centre
2625 Kaslo St, Vancouver, BC V5M 3G9, Canada
Tel: 604-872-8337 *Fax:* 604-876-1185
E-mail: info@vivomediaarts.com; info@videoout.ca
Web Site: vivomediaarts.com; www.videoout.ca
Key Personnel
Gen Mgr, VIVO Media Arts Centre: Julia Aoki
Tel: 604-872-8337 ext 4
Founded: 1980
Nonprofit, non-exclusive distributor of media art on video to galleries, festivals, educational institution collections & broadcasters nationally & internationally.
Catalog(s) available
Membership(s): Canadian Museums Association; Independent Film & Video Alliance

Video Perspective
1410 Hutchins St, Houston, TX 77003
Tel: 281-996-7974 *Toll Free Tel:* 888-996-7974
E-mail: vp@vidper.com
Web Site: www.videoperspective.com
Founded: 1990
Full service video production company.

Video Production Associates Inc
525 Bridgeport Ave, Shelton, CT 06484-1397
Tel: 203-929-8869
Web Site: www.vpa-inc.com
Key Personnel
Pres: Joseph Sullivano *E-mail:* joe-vpa@snet.net
Founded: 1978
Full service HD video production & CD-ROM/DVD duplication facility.

The Video Project
145 Ninth St, Suite 102, San Francisco, CA 94103
Tel: 415-981-9710 *Toll Free Tel:* 800-475-2638
Fax: 415-692-6223
E-mail: orders@videoproject.com; support@videoproject.com
Web Site: www.videoproject.com
Key Personnel
COO: Kathy Douglas
Pres: Steve Michelson
Dir, Busn Aff: Craig Malina
Dir, Opers: Arlin Golden
Mktg Consultant: Steve Ladd
Acctg: Salman Ali

Graphic Designer: Bernadette McVerry
Founded: 1983
Distribute documentary film to educational institutions on the topics of the environment, science & social sciences.
Online catalog(s) available

Video Resources Inc
1809 E Dyer Rd, Suite 307, Santa Ana, CA 92705
Tel: 949-261-7266
E-mail: info@videoresources.com
Web Site: www.videoresources.com
Key Personnel
Gen Mgr: Patrick Kelly
Video production, animation, staging, equipment rentals & event production.
Branch Office(s)
110 Campus Dr, Marlborough, MA 01752
Tel: 508-485-8100 *E-mail:* dane@videoresources.com

Video Resources Software
11767 S Dixie Hwy, Suite 222, Miami, FL 33156
Toll Free Tel: 888-223-6284 *Fax:* 305-256-0467
E-mail: mailroom@tutorace.com
Web Site: www.tutorace.com
Instructional videos & software providing tutorial help in grammar, ESL, math, business & other studies.
Online catalog(s) available

Video Service of America Inc, see VSA Inc

Video Solutions
2121 Eisenhower Ave, Suite 103, Alexandria, VA 22314
Tel: 703-683-5305; 703-628-0702 (cell)
E-mail: inquiries@thevideosolution.com
Web Site: www.thevideosolution.com
Key Personnel
Owner & Pres: Clark Bavin
Founded: 1991
Your DC area video solution. Deliver imaginative, compelling, award-winning results through our creative talent & technical capabilities. Complete HD video & multimedia production. Two HD video edit suites & narration booth, insert studio & amenities. We put ideas into motion.

The Video Store Shopper
Division of The Shopper Inc
3987 Heritage Oak Ct, Simi Valley, CA 93063
Tel: 805-583-8500 *Toll Free Tel:* 800-429-4900
Fax: 805-583-8546 *Toll Free Fax:* 800-947-2060
E-mail: sales@shopperinc.com; customerservice@shopperinc.com
Web Site: www.thevideostoreshopper.com; www.tsisupplies.com
Key Personnel
Pres: Bill Bieda
Founded: 1983
Catalog(s) available
Membership(s): Entertainment Merchants Association

Video Techniques Inc
1731 First St E, Bradenton, FL 34208
Mailing Address: PO Box 9649, Bradenton, FL 34206-9649
Tel: 941-758-3077 *Fax:* 941-758-4896
E-mail: vti-web@videotechniques.com
Web Site: videotechniques.com
Key Personnel
Pres & Exec Prodr: Bob Lorentzen
E-mail: bobl@videotechniques.com
Founded: 1979
Preserving memories: films, slides, photos, video, audiotapes, CD, DVD & Blu-ray. Duplication, image enhancement & preservation into digital formats.

Video Technology Services Inc
5 Ariel Way, Suite 300, Syosset, NY 11791
Tel: 516-937-9700
E-mail: info@vts.global
Web Site: www.vts.global
Key Personnel
Pres: Andres Sierra
Founded: 1986
Manufacture audio, video & communication equipment for system installation on any type of aircraft configuration including individual, overhead & AVOD (Audio Video On Demand) via seat integrated entertainment systems.
Online catalog(s) available

Video Visions Inc
Division of Milanese Associates Inc
3600 Boundbrook Ave, Trevose, PA 19053
Tel: 215-942-6642 *Fax:* 267-684-6819
E-mail: sales@video-visions.com
Web Site: www.video-visions.com
Key Personnel
Pres: Mary Ellen Milanese-DiStasio
    E-mail: memilanesedistasio@video-visions.com
VP: Vincent DiStasio
Dir, Sales & Systems Engg: Ted Manahan
Chief Systems Engr: Jeffrey Pasternak
Gen Mgr: Vince Faville
Founded: 1991
Specialize in video wall displays & large screen display products, sales & service.
Online catalog(s) available
Branch Office(s)
1015 N Bumby Ave, Orlando, FL 32803, Dir, Strategic Accts: Joe McConahy *Tel:* 407-249-8500 *Fax:* 407-249-1900
Membership(s): Audiovisual and Integrated Experience Association; NAB; Women's Business Enterprise National Council

Video West Inc
1050 N 52 St, Phoenix, AZ 85008
Tel: 480-222-3180 *Toll Free Tel:* 800-659-0880
    Fax: 480-222-3190
E-mail: info@videowestinc.com
Web Site: www.videowestinc.com
Key Personnel
Pres: Jack Waitkus
Mktg/Show Acct Mgmt: Becky Spooner
    E-mail: beckyspooner@videowestinc.com
Founded: 1982
Provides broadcast & professional quality video, audio & lighting equipment for the industrial, corporate, entertainment & live events marketplace.
Online catalog(s) available

Video Wisconsin Inc
18110 W Bluemound Rd, Brookfield, WI 53045
Tel: 262-785-1110 *Fax:* 262-785-9827
Web Site: www.videowisconsin.tv
Key Personnel
VP, Opers: Colleen S Hartley
Video, multimedia production & post-production.

Videobotics
220 N Palisade Dr, Santa Maria, CA 93454
Tel: 805-349-1104
E-mail: videobotics@megagem.com; sales@videobotics.com
Web Site: www.videobotics.com; camrobot.com
Key Personnel
Owner: Daniel Wolf
Founded: 1999
Create computer software to control video equipment (PTZ cameras, video switchers/mixers, DVDs), direct from PC or through network or Internet. Applications: TV production, remote observation, multimedia presentation, film production, military, churches, city government, industrial & education. Android tablets & phone apps to control video equipment.

Online catalog(s) available
Membership(s): AAAS

Videofashion Network
611 Broadway, Suite 307, New York, NY 10012
Tel: 212-274-1600 *Fax:* 212-219-1969
E-mail: info@videofashion.com; licensing@videofashion.com
Web Site: videofashion.com
Key Personnel
Exec Chmn & Edit Dir: Nicolas H Charney, PhD
Pres & Mng Ed: Anne V Adami *Tel:* 212-274-1600 ext 25 *E-mail:* aadami@videofashion.com
Founded: 1976
Online catalog(s) available
Foreign Office(s): Videofashion Asia Pacific LLC, Block 28 Kallang Place, No 04-01/02/03/04/05 Kallang Place, Singapore 339158, Singapore, Contact: Michael Tan *Tel:* 6475 6996 *Fax:* 6336 6929 *E-mail:* michael@videofashion.com.sg
Membership(s): NATPE

Videofax
1750 Cesar Chavez St, Unit G, San Francisco, CA 94124
Tel: 415-641-0100
E-mail: rentals@videofax.com
Web Site: www.videofax.com
Key Personnel
Mng Partner: Leigh Blicher *E-mail:* leigh@videofax.com
Partner: Jim Rolin; Tomas Tucker
Rental Mgr: Mona Marks *E-mail:* mona@videofax.com
Founded: 1987
Rents video equipment & accessories to serve the commercial & motion picture industries as well as corporate, documentary, television & the online media community.

Videofilm Systems Inc
7 Islandbrook Ave, Unit D-1, Bridgeport, CT 06606
Tel: 203-870-6013
E-mail: info@videofilmsystems.com
Key Personnel
Owner: Justin Cihi *Tel:* 203-823-1606 (cell)
SVP, Prodn: Giselle Vogel
Founded: 1979
Systems integration & design. Sales & rentals, digital signage & projection.

Videograf
144 W 27 St, 12th fl, New York, NY 10001
Tel: 212-242-7871
E-mail: videograf@verizon.net
Web Site: vgraflive.org
Key Personnel
Pres: Michael Frenchman
General video production & webcasting.

Videografix LLC
2530 Berryessa Rd, Suite 314, San Jose, CA 95132-2903
Tel: 408-499-1280
E-mail: info@videografix.com
Web Site: www.videografix.com
Key Personnel
Sr Prodr: Steve Young
Creative Dir: Bill Rice
Dir, Photog: Dan Agulian
Mktg Dir: Dylis Watts
Founded: 1989
Teleprompting & green screen.
Online catalog(s) available

Videography Productions
PO Box 653, Amagansett, NY 11930-0653
Tel: 520-907-1900
Web Site: www.dickfisher.net

Key Personnel
Owner & Pres: Dick Fisher *E-mail:* fisherdp@yahoo.com
Founded: 1982
Video production services; on location.
Membership(s): Society of Camera Operators

Videoguys
10-12 Charles St, Glen Cove, NY 11542
Tel: 516-759-1611 *Toll Free Tel:* 800-323-2325
    Fax: 516-671-3092
E-mail: sales@videoguys.com
Web Site: www.videoguys.com
Key Personnel
Pres: Gary Bettan
Full range of video editing software & hardware.

The Videohouse Inc
975 Greentree Rd, Pittsburgh, PA 15220
Tel: 412-921-7577 *Fax:* 412-921-5535
E-mail: info@thevideohouse.com
Web Site: www.thevideohouse.com
Key Personnel
Founder & Pres: Ron Bruno
Prodn Coord: Dawn Azua *E-mail:* dawn@thevideohouse.com
Founded: 1985
Full range of broadcast quality video production services including shooting, editing, 3-D animation & duplication.

VideoLink Inc, an AVI-SPL company
1230 Washington St, West Newton, MA 02465
Tel: 617-340-4100 *Toll Free Tel:* 800-452-5565
    Fax: 617-340-4101
E-mail: sales@videolinktv.com
Web Site: www.videolinktv.com
Key Personnel
Pres & CEO: Richard G Silton
SVP, Sales & Mktg: Lloyd Bunting
VP, Prodn: Gregg Bevan
VP, Engg: Leigh Willis
VP, Fin & Admin: Kristen Mobilia
Gen Mgr, ReadyCam: Mark Pantridge
Founded: 1992
ReadyCam®, HD live insert studio, HD transmission satellite trucks. Creative services, webcasting, general video production.
Branch Office(s)
1400 Terra Bella Ave, Suite M, Mountain View, CA 94043 *Tel:* 650-968-1540
3401 S Congress Ave, Boynton Beach, FL 33426 *Tel:* 561-737-8000
10 N Calvert St, Baltimore, MD 21202 *Tel:* 443-524-8000 *Toll Free Tel:* 800-741-7913 *Fax:* 443-524-1958
10 Liberty Sq, Boston, MA 02109 *Tel:* 617-340-4290
360 Woods Hole Rd, Woods Hole, MA 02543 *Tel:* 617-340-4300 *Fax:* 508-457-2180
11 Saint Anselm Dr, Manchester, NH 03102
1524 Delancey St, Philadelphia, PA 19102 *Tel:* 215-940-3000 *Toll Free Tel:* 800-990-4995 *Fax:* 215-940-3026
Membership(s): CMAA; IABC; SMEI

Videomagnetics
3970 Clearview Frontage Rd, Colorado Springs, CO 80911
Tel: 719-390-1313 *Toll Free Tel:* 800-432-3887
    Fax: 719-390-1316
E-mail: vmi@csprings.com
Web Site: www.videomagnetics.com
Key Personnel
Pres: Tony Korte
Cont: Jane Pennie
Full video equipment service & repair facility.
Online catalog(s) available
Membership(s): NAB

Videosmith Inc
200 Spring Garden St, Suite C, Philadelphia, PA 19123
Tel: 215-238-5070 *Fax:* 215-238-5075
E-mail: info@videosmith.com
Web Site: videosmith.com
Key Personnel
Pres: Steven T Smith
Gen Mgr: Chris Cerasoli
Full service broadcast video equipment rental company.
Online catalog(s) available
Membership(s): NATAS

Videotex Systems Inc
10255 Miller Rd, Dallas, TX 75238
Tel: 972-231-9200 *Toll Free Tel:* 800-88-VIDEO (888-4336) *Fax:* 972-231-2420
E-mail: info@videotexsystems.com
Web Site: www.videotexsystems.com
Key Personnel
Pres: Bob Gillman *Tel:* 972-231-9200 ext 102
  E-mail: gillman@videotexsystems.com
Founded: 1984
AV equipment provider. Specialize in AV integration for schools, churches, corporations & government organizations.
Online catalog(s) available

Videowerks
3434-135 Kildaire Farm Rd, No 181, Cary, NC 27518
Tel: 310-780-4156 (cell)
Web Site: www.videowerkseast.com
Key Personnel
Owner: David M Werk *E-mail:* david@videowerkseast.com
Founded: 1981
Professional video production services.

Videssence
10768 Lower Azusa Rd, El Monte, CA 91731
Tel: 626-579-0943 *Fax:* 626-579-6803
E-mail: contact@videssence.tv
Web Site: www.videssence.tv
Key Personnel
Pres: Lauri Maines
Intl Sales Mgr: Amanda McGinnis
  E-mail: mmcginnis@videssence.tv
Natl Sales Mgr: Gary Thomas *E-mail:* gthomas@videssence.tv
Prod Mgr: Stan Wong *E-mail:* swong@videssence.tv
Founded: 1980
Sell LED studio lighting fixtures for broadcast & production.
Catalog(s) available

Vidicom Inc
520 Eighth Ave, Suite 2206, New York, NY 10018
Tel: 212-895-8300
E-mail: sales@vidicom.com
Web Site: vidicom.com
Key Personnel
SVP, Sales: David Weiss
Branded video content, digital distribution & interactive live programming.

Vidox Motion Imagery
204 Winchester Dr, Lafayette, LA 70506
Tel: 337-237-1700 *Fax:* 337-237-1712
Web Site: www.vidox.com
Key Personnel
Owner: Chris Allain *E-mail:* chris@vidox.com
Prodr: Scott Rachal
Founded: 1982
Full service video production company offering HD cinematography & post-production. In addition to turnkey projects, the company regularly tackles complex animation & visual effects, like lip-synced characters or 3D industrial illustrations. In-house music composition & sound design round out the list of creative & technical services.
Membership(s): Open Studio Association

VIEW Inc (Video International Entertainment World Inc)
11 Reservoir Rd, Saugerties, NY 12477
Mailing Address: PO Box 77, Saugerties, NY 12477
Tel: 845-246-9955 *Toll Free Tel:* 800-843-9843
  Fax: 845-246-9966
E-mail: viewvid@aol.com
Key Personnel
Pres: Bob Karcy
Mgr: Tom Hoose
Off Mgr: Emily Roberts-Negron
Founded: 1983
International home video production & distribution, licensing & TV syndication of special interest programs in areas of art, jazz, pop music, opera, dance, children's interactive sports & modern lifestyle programs.
Catalog(s) available
Membership(s): Entertainment Merchants Association; IAJE; Music Business Association; NAMM, the National Association of Music Merchants; NATAS; NATPE; The Recording Academy

Viewpoint Production Services Inc
419 Mount Nebo Rd, Pittsburgh, PA 15237
Tel: 412-369-7171 *Toll Free Tel:* 800-820-0402
E-mail: contact@viewpoint.tv
Web Site: viewpoint.tv
Founded: 1982
Serving the broadcast & video production community. Equipment rental, ENG/EFP shoots, crewing, mobile units, production management, studio facilities & turnkey production.

ViewSonic
10 Pointe Dr, 2nd fl, Brea, CA 92821
Tel: 909-444-8888 *Toll Free Tel:* 800-688-6688 (cust serv); 800-888-8583
E-mail: customerservice@viewsonic.com
Web Site: www.viewsonic.com
Founded: 1987
Manufacture desktop virtualization, monitors, projectors & large format displays.

Vincent Associates
803 Linden Ave, Rochester, NY 14625
Tel: 585-385-5930 *Toll Free Tel:* 800-828-6972
  Fax: 585-385-6004
E-mail: info@uniblitz.com
Web Site: www.uniblitz.com
Key Personnel
Sales Mgr: Stephanie Schaffer *E-mail:* sschaffer@uniblitz.com
Founded: 1969
Manufacture & distribute Uniblitz® electronic shutter systems.
Catalog(s) available

Vincent Lighting Systems
6161 Cochran Rd, Suite D, Solon, OH 44139
Tel: 216-475-7600 *Toll Free Tel:* 800-922-5356
  Fax: 216-475-6376
E-mail: info@vls.com
Web Site: www.vls.com
Key Personnel
Pres: Paul Vincent
Mktg Dir: Kim Craigie *E-mail:* kcraigie@vincentlighting.com
Founded: 1978
Branch Office(s)
1420 Jamike Ave, Suite 1, Erlanger, KY 41018
  Tel: 859-525-2000 *Fax:* 859-525-2050

36500 Ford Rd, Suite 173, Westland, MI 48185-2211, Contact: Drew Franklin *Tel:* 734-660-8959 *Fax:* 734-722-6079
920 Vista Park Dr, Pittsburgh, PA 15205 *Tel:* 412-788-5250 *Fax:* 412-788-6115
Membership(s): Professional Lighting & Sound Association; USITT

Vineyard Video & Photography
4193 Concord Ave, Santa Rosa, CA 95407
Tel: 707-591-9999; 707-591-1927 (cell)
Web Site: www.vineyardvideo.com
Key Personnel
Dir, Photog: Stuart Kiehl *E-mail:* stuart@vineyardvideo.com

VirtualMix
701 S Carson St, Suite 200-2914, Carson City, NV 89701
Tel: 818-209-6176
E-mail: virtualmixpost@gmail.com
Web Site: www.virtualmix.com
Key Personnel
Sound Designer & Location Sounds: Patrick Giraudi
Founded: 2001
Audio post-production for film, television & multimedia.
Branch Office(s)
2607 W Magnolia Blvd, Burbank, CA 91505

Vision Identics Systems Inc
110 Villa Ave, Mamaroneck, NY 10543
Mailing Address: PO Box 193, Mamaroneck, NY 10543
Tel: 914-381-2625
E-mail: visionid@prodigy.net
Key Personnel
Pres: George Kiriazides
Founded: 1990
Distributors of machine vision components.
Catalog(s) available

Vision Maker Media
1800 N 33 St, Lincoln, NE 68503-1409
Tel: 402-472-3522 *Fax:* 402-472-8675
E-mail: visionmaker@unl.edu
Web Site: www.visionmakermedia.org
Key Personnel
Exec Dir: Shirley Sneve *Tel:* 402-472-0208
Asst Dir: Rebekka Schlichting
Dir of Fin & Admin: Matt Nehe *Tel:* 402-472-0940
Dir of Mktg & Devt: Dawn Amory *Tel:* 402-472-3113
Mktg & Communs Specialist: Alyssa Ranard *Tel:* 402-472-8607
Proj Coord: Alana Stone *Tel:* 402-472-3222
Founded: 1977
Nonprofit 501(c)(3) formed to support the creation, promotion & distribution of Native American media.
Catalog(s) available

Vision Quest Productions Inc
PO Box 1896, Wayne, NJ 07470-1896
Tel: 973-686-9400 *Fax:* 973-694-8314
Web Site: vqpi.yolasite.com; visionquestproductions.com
Key Personnel
Pres: James Benson *E-mail:* bensonj@earthlink.net
Founded: 1996
Full service provider of television production services.

Vision Video
2030 Wentz Church Rd, Lansdale, PA 19446
Mailing Address: PO Box 540, Worcester, PA 19490-0540

Tel: 610-584-3500 *Toll Free Tel:* 800-523-0226
 Fax: 610-584-6643
E-mail: support@visionvideo.com
Web Site: www.visionvideo.com
Key Personnel
Gen Mgr: Bill Curtis *E-mail:* bill@visionvideo.com
Mail order video & DVD distribution.
Catalog(s) available
Online catalog(s) available
Membership(s): ICVM

Visionary Solutions Inc
2060 Alameda Padre Serra, Suite 100, Santa Barbara, CA 93103
Tel: 805-845-8900 *Fax:* 805-845-8889
E-mail: sales@vsicam.com
Web Site: www.vsicam.com
Key Personnel
Pres: Jordan Christoff
Founded: 1995
Manufacturer & supplier of IPTV & AV over IP equipment.

Visioneering International Inc
659 Auburn Ave NE, Suite 267, Atlanta, GA 30312
Tel: 404-681-9028 *Fax:* 404-681-5947
E-mail: design@visioneering.com
Web Site: www.visioneering.com
Key Personnel
Pres & CEO: Robert Foah
VP & Creative Dir: Honora Foah
Dir, Fin: H R Fraval
Dir, Lighting & Set Design: Gregg Aukerman
Production & communications company including inventions, product launches, annual meetings & public relations events.

Visions Plus
200 Valley Dr, Suite 5, Brisbane, CA 94005
Tel: 415-467-3300
E-mail: web_inquiry@visionsplus.com
Web Site: visionsplus.com
Key Personnel
Pres: Steven Dung
Founded: 1986
Video production services for businesses & non-profit organizations in the San Francisco Bay Area.

Visionworks Design Services Inc
204 Peach Way, Suite H, Columbia, MO 65203
Tel: 573-449-8567
E-mail: info@visionworksgroup.com
Web Site: visionworksgroup.com
Key Personnel
Pres: Lili Vianello

Visix™ Inc
230 Scientific Dr, Suite 800, Norcross, GA 30092
Tel: 770-446-1416 *Toll Free Tel:* 800-572-4935
 Fax: 770-448-5724
E-mail: info@visix.com
Web Site: www.visix.com
Key Personnel
Pres & CEO: Sean Matthews
CFO: Christy Gear
Chief Sales Offr: Trey Hicks
Mktg Communs Mgr: Debbie DeWitt
Founded: 1980
Online catalog(s) available

Vista Color Imaging Inc
4770 Van Epps Rd, Unit 101, Brooklyn Heights, OH 44113
Tel: 216-651-2830 *Fax:* 216-651-5004
E-mail: info@vistacolorimaging.com
Web Site: vistacolorimaging.com
Key Personnel
Owner & Pres: Kevin Vesely

Founded: 1929
Produce interpretive exhibit & museum graphics. Supplier of digital imaging solutions.
Online catalog(s) available
Membership(s): Specialty Graphic Imaging Association

Vista Group International Inc
25 Van Zant St, Unit 8-D, Norwalk, CT 06855
Tel: 203-852-5557 *Toll Free Tel:* 800-866-2113
 Fax: 203-852-5559
E-mail: info@vistagroupinternational.com
Web Site: www.vistagroupinternational.com
Key Personnel
Pres: Martha Yaney *E-mail:* martha.yaney@vistagroupinternational.com
Designs, manufactures & markets SoundStik® audio handsets for museums, trade shows & tourist attractions. The SoundStik® personal listening device is used with video kiosks & exhibits to deliver clear, crisp sound while maintaining a quiet ambiance. Vista Group also offers custom outdoor listening stations, audio tour systems & services, FM tour guide systems & related products. Interactives & applications.
Catalog(s) available
Membership(s): American Alliance of Museums; NAME

Vistacom Inc
1902 Vultee St, Allentown, PA 18103-2998
Tel: 610-791-9081 *Toll Free Tel:* 800-747-0459
 Fax: 610-791-9510
E-mail: info@vistacominc.com
Web Site: www.vistacominc.com
Key Personnel
Pres: James Ferlino
COO: Angela Nolan
Founded: 1954
Commercial AV integration firm.
Membership(s): AES; Audiovisual and Integrated Experience Association; NSCA

Vistamax Productions
9705 Little Pond Way, Tampa, FL 33647
Tel: 813-907-1010 *Fax:* 813-907-1991
E-mail: info@vistamax.com; sales@vistamax.com
Web Site: www.vistamax.com
Key Personnel
Exec Prodr: Steve Farkas
Creative Dir: Jeff Morgan
Founded: 1997
Full service video production company.

Visual Communications - Southern California Asian American Studies Central Inc
120 Judge John Aiso St, Basement Level, Los Angeles, CA 90012
Tel: 213-680-4462 *Fax:* 213-687-4848
E-mail: info@vconline.org
Web Site: www.vconline.org
Key Personnel
Interim Exec Dir: Francis Cullado *Tel:* 213-680-4462 ext 22 *E-mail:* francis@vconline.org
Opers Dir: Dorothy Xiao *Tel:* 213-680-4462 ext 38 *E-mail:* dorothy@vconline.org
Tech Dir: Mark Mangoba *E-mail:* mark@vconline.org
Founded: 1970
Asian Pacific American media arts center. Training & education workshops in film, video & new media.
Membership(s): The Alliance for Media Arts and Culture

Visual Departures Ltd
48 Sheffield Business Park, Ashley Falls, MA 01222
Tel: 413-229-2272 *Toll Free Tel:* 800-628-2003
 Fax: 413-229-2274

E-mail: sales@visualdepartures.com
Web Site: www.visualdepartures.com
Key Personnel
Pres: Allen Green
Founded: 1982
Distributes film, photography & theatre products worldwide.
Catalog(s) available

Visual Instrumentation Corp
1110 West Ave L-12, Unit 2, Lancaster, CA 93534-7039
Tel: 661-945-7999 *Fax:* 661-723-5667
E-mail: visinst@earthlink.net
Web Site: www.visinst.com
Key Personnel
Pres: Robert Lewis
Founded: 1970
Manufacturer & distributor of precision accessory products for high-speed digital & film camera applications.
Membership(s): Audiovisual and Integrated Experience Association; SPIE

Visual Products Inc
790 Shiloh Ave, Wellington, OH 44090
Tel: 440-647-4999 *Fax:* 440-647-4998
E-mail: sales@visualproducts.com
Web Site: www.visualproducts.com
Key Personnel
Owner & Pres: Jim Budzilek
Reseller of used motion picture equipment.

Visual Sound Inc
485 Park Way, Broomall, PA 19008
Tel: 610-544-8700 *Toll Free Tel:* 800-523-7525
 Fax: 610-544-3385
Web Site: www.visualsound.com
Key Personnel
Pres: Karen Bogosian
VP, Educ Sales: Ann Pfister
VP, Sales: Richard Hopkins
Founded: 1967
Provides AV system design, installation, service & product sales to corporate, education, healthcare, government & houses of worship. Systems include: Integrated AV control, unified collaboration, presentation, command & control video walls, interactive flat panels, digital signage & more. For customers planning special events or meetings, Visual Sound's Event Technology Division is available to provide on-site production services or as-needed equipment rentals. Certified WBE.
Catalog(s) available
Branch Office(s)
4706 Westport Dr, Suite 1500, Mechanicsburg, PA 17055
1642 Sulphur Springs Rd, Baltimore, MD 21227
Membership(s): Audiovisual and Integrated Experience Association; NSCA

The Visual Studies Workshop (VSW)
31 Prince St, Rochester, NY 14607
Tel: 585-442-8676 *Fax:* 585-442-1992
E-mail: info@vsw.org
Web Site: www.vsw.org
Key Personnel
Exec Dir: Tate Shaw *Tel:* 585-442-8676 ext 21 *E-mail:* tateshaw@vsw.org
Asst Dir: Jessica Johnston *Tel:* 585-442-8676 ext 24 *E-mail:* jessica.johnston@vsw.org
Founded: 1969
Center for media studies, including photography, visual books, digital imaging, film & video.
Online catalog(s) available

Visual Systems
845 Encino Place, Santa Paula, CA 93060
Tel: 805-933-8044 *Fax:* 805-933-9744

E-mail: info@visualsystemsonline.com
New & used digital & analog video equipment, broadcast video equipment & motion picture equipment.

Visual Technologies Corp
Subsidiary of VTC Specialties Inc
1620 Burnet Ave, Syracuse, NY 13206
Tel: 315-423-2000 *Toll Free Tel:* 888-423-0004
E-mail: contact@visualtec.com
Web Site: visualtec.businesscatalyst.com
Key Personnel
Pres: David J Foor *E-mail:* dfoor@visualtec.com
VP, Opers: Andrew Reichel *E-mail:* areichel@visualtec.com
Sales Coord: Michelle Fontaine
  E-mail: mfontaine@visualtec.com
Founded: 1954
AV equipment & services including staging, rentals, sales & installation, video production & video conferencing.
Membership(s): ATD; Audiovisual and Integrated Experience Association

Visual Word Systems Inc
35 W 36 St, 8th fl, New York, NY 10018
Tel: 212-629-8383 *Fax:* 212-629-8333
Web Site: www.visualword.com
Key Personnel
Pres: Ike Eckstein *E-mail:* ike@visualword.com
Founded: 1981
Sales, rental & staging of AV equipment.
Membership(s): Audiovisual and Integrated Experience Association

VITAC
8300 E Maplewood Ave, Suite 310, Greenwood Village, CO 80111
Toll Free Tel: 800-278-4822 (sales); 800-775-7838
E-mail: info@vitac.com
Web Site: www.vitac.com
Key Personnel
CEO: P Kevin Kilroy
COO & Gen Mgr: Chuck Karlovits
Chief Busn Devt Offr: Doug Karlovits
CFO: Lindsay Wynter
CIO: Joe Antonio
CTO: Ted Collins
Founded: 1986
Captioning services for TV, OTT, web video, stadiums, conference calls & audio description for TV, museums & online video platforms.
Branch Office(s)
101 Hillpointe Dr, Canonsburg, PA 15317
  Tel: 724-514-4077 (sales)

Vital Learning LLC
3001 Brighton Blvd, Suite 2765, Denver, CO 80216
Toll Free Tel: 800-243-5858
E-mail: support@vital-learning.com; info@vital-learning.com
Web Site: www.vital-learning.com
Key Personnel
Pres & CEO: Todd Macey
Dir, Affiliate Opers: Dominique Giroux
Produce & distribute training & development courses for businesses & organizations.
Online catalog(s) available
Membership(s): ATD

VITEC Multimedia
931 Benecia Ave, Sunnyvale, CA 94085
Tel: 650-230-2400 *Toll Free Tel:* 800-451-5101
E-mail: info@vitec.com
Web Site: www.vitec.com
Key Personnel
Dir, US Opers: Lionel Zajde
VP, Prod Mgmt: Eli Garten
Founded: 1988

Worldwide leading provider of powerful digital video products that support end-to-end media solutions for broadcast, corporate, education, government, industrial, medical, military & Telco customers. By integrating world famous brands including Optibase, Focus, Como & Stradis, VITEC Multimedia now controls the complete video chain with professional-grade products for acquisition, encoding, processing, management & delivery. With over 100 R&D engineers specializing in digital video, we offer innovative & effective hardware & software, advanced technology research & custom product designs for world-class OEMs. VITEC Multimedia is headquartered in Paris, France, with worldwide R&D Sales & System Integration offices.
Branch Office(s)
99, rue Pierre Semard, 92324 Chatillon Cedex, France *Tel:* 01 46 73 06 06 *Fax:* 09 59 85 99 92 (headquarters)

Vitec Videocom Inc
Division of The Vitec Group
14 Progress Dr, Shelton, CT 06484
Tel: 203-929-1100 *Fax:* 203-925-2684
E-mail: info@vitecgroup.com
Web Site: www.vitecgroup.com; www.vitecvideocom.com
Key Personnel
SVP, Americas Servs: Halid Hatic
SVP, Sales & Mktg: Martin Vann
SVP, Technol: Nicol Verheem
Inside Sales Coord: Mara-Lynne Brenner
  Tel: 203-402-7988
Founded: 1983
Camera support equipment.
Online catalog(s) available
Branch Office(s)
20600 Plummer St, Chatsworth, CA 91311 *Toll Free Tel:* 800-541-1667
Foreign Office(s): Vitec Videocom SARL, 171, Ave des Gresillons, 92635 Gennevilliers Cedex, France *Tel:* 01 41 32 30 42
Vitec Videocom GmbH, Parkring 29, 85748 Garching, Germany *Tel:* (089) 321 58200 *Fax:* (089) 321 58227
Vitec Videocom KK, Shibakoen 3-chrome, Bldg 1F, 3-1-38 Shibakoen, Minato-ku, Tokyo 105-0011, Japan *Tel:* (03) 5777 8040 *Fax:* (03) 5777 8041
Vitec Videocom Pte Ltd, 6 New Industrial Rd, No 02-02, New Century 536199, Singapore *Tel:* 6297 5776
Vitec Videocom Ltd, Western Way, Bury St Edmunds, Suffolk IP33 3TB, United Kingdom *Tel:* (01284) 776700 *Fax:* (01284) 750560
Membership(s): NAB; SBE; SMPTE®

Vitruvian Entertainment
4712 Admirality Way, Unit 417, Marina del Rey, CA 90292
Tel: 818-720-3250 (cell)
Web Site: vitruvianent.com
Key Personnel
Pres: Irfan Merchant *E-mail:* merchant@vitruvianent.com
Founded: 2011
Virtual production, motion capture, 3D animation, stereo, event, live & post-production services. Specialize in television, commercials, promos, YouTube content & corporate productions.

ViVi Co
PO Box 750, Glendale, CA 91209
Tel: 818-500-8889; 818-500-8084 *Fax:* 818-507-6600
E-mail: zibreathe@aol.com
Web Site: www.theartofbreathing.com
Key Personnel
Pres: Nancy Zi

Founded: 1993
Shipping Address: 222 Monterey Rd, Suite 1006, Glendale, CA 91206 *Tel:* 818-500-8084

VMI Inc
211 E Weddell Dr, Sunnyvale, CA 94089
Tel: 408-745-1700; 415-362-1330
Web Site: www.vmivideo.com
Key Personnel
VP: Jennifer Dorsa
Founded: 1975
Broadcast, production, presentation, security, streaming & video conferencing products for every application.
Online catalog(s) available
Branch Office(s)
VMI Inc Broadcast & Professional Video, 11258 Monarch St, Unit A, Garden Grove, CA 92481
  Tel: 714-894-6100

VMS Inc
02400 37 1/2 St, Gobles, MI 49055
Tel: 269-377-0234
E-mail: vms.texts@gmail.com
Web Site: www.vms-online.com
Key Personnel
Pres: Michael S Walsh
Founded: 1986
Distributor of occupational training books, videos & software to schools.
Online catalog(s) available, 2 issues/yr, 3,000 titles in 6 major catalogs
Membership(s): Educational Exhibitor's Association

The Vocal Point/Profile Communications Ltd
1196 Habgood St, White Rock, BC V4B 4W9, Canada
Tel: 604-531-6908
Web Site: www.profilecomm.com
Key Personnel
Owner & Pres: Steve Herringer *E-mail:* steve@profilecomm.com
Founded: 1985
Audio, video & film voice-overs.

Voice & Video Rentals
4909 Ruffner St, San Diego, CA 92111
Tel: 858-560-5000 *Fax:* 858-560-9900
Web Site: www.voiceandvideo.com
Key Personnel
Co-Owner: David Schuety; Jim Kotyk
Founded: 1973
Audio, video rentals & AV event productions.

Volcano Video Productions, see Ka Io Productions Inc

VO2 Mix Audio Post
116 Spadina Ave, Suite 208, Toronto, ON M5V 2K6, Canada
Tel: 416-603-3954 *Fax:* 416-603-3957
E-mail: info@vo2mix.ca
Web Site: www.vo2mix.ca
Key Personnel
Founder: Euan Hunter *E-mail:* ehunter@vo2mix.ca; Terry Wedel *E-mail:* twedel@vo2mix.ca
Founded: 1999
Audio post facility.

Voyager Recordings & Publications
424 35 Ave, Seattle, WA 98122
Tel: 206-323-1112
E-mail: info@voyagerrecords.com
Web Site: www.voyagerrecords.com
Key Personnel
Founder & Owner: Vivian T Williams
Founded: 1967
Independent record label & book publishing company focusing on traditional fiddle & string

band music from the Pacific Northwest & throughout North America.
Catalog(s) available

Voyetra Turtle Beach
100 Summit Lake Dr, Suite 100, Valhalla, NY 10595
Tel: 914-345-2255 *Fax:* 914-345-2266
E-mail: sales@turtlebeach.com
Web Site: www.turtlebeach.com
Key Personnel
VP, Opers: Scott Rankin
Designs & markets award-winning gaming headsets.

VRSim Inc
222 Pitkin St, Suite 119, East Hartford, CT 06108-3220
Tel: 860-893-0080
E-mail: info@vrsim.net
Web Site: www.vrsim.net
Key Personnel
Pres & CEO: Matthew Wallace
Opers Mgr: David Zboray
Off Mgr: Lisa Sawicki
Founded: 2001
Virtual reality systems for industrial training & technical education.

VSA Inc
6929 Seward Ave, Lincoln, NE 68507
Toll Free Tel: 800-888-2140 (orders) *Fax:* 402-325-8033
E-mail: sales@vsa1.com
Web Site: www.vsa1.com
Key Personnel
Pres: Allen L Dayton
Founded: 1976
Suppliers of broadcast & professional video equipment, pro audio equipment & accessories.
Online catalog(s) available
Branch Office(s)
1110 W Lake Cook Rd, Suite 353, Buffalo Grove, IL 60089 *Toll Free Tel:* 855-376-7164
Toll Free Fax: 866-480-6510 *E-mail:* info@vsa1.com

VSG Digital Media Solutions
11126 Lindbergh Business Ct, St Louis, MO 63123
Tel: 314-487-8045 *Toll Free Tel:* 800-737-8045
Fax: 314-487-9387
E-mail: info@vsginc.net
Web Site: www.vsginc.net
Key Personnel
Owner: Chris Ramsey *Tel:* 314-487-8045 ext 103; Barry Romine *Tel:* 314-487-8045 ext 104
Pres: Patrick Reagan *Tel:* 314-487-8045 ext 117
Dir, Sales: Mike Gallagher *Tel:* 314-487-8045 ext 123
Founded: 1981
Full service media manufacturing.
Branch Office(s)
1033 Elm Hill Pike, Nashville, TN 37210, Regl Sales Mgr: Greg Shriner *Tel:* 615-248-1010
Toll Free Tel: 800-251-1009
1870 Crown Dr, Suite 1505, Farmers Branch, TX 75234, Regl Sales Mgr: Patrick Spellman *Tel:* 972-830-9400

VTP Inc
1309 S Flower St, Burbank, CA 91502
Tel: 818-566-9898 *Toll Free Tel:* 800-422-2444
E-mail: sales@vtpcorp.com
Web Site: www.myvtp.com
Key Personnel
Pres & CEO: John L Palazzola
VP, Sales: Randy Marzec
Founded: 1979
Full line video & audio hardware distributors.
Online catalog(s) available

Branch Office(s)
41210 Bridge St, Novi, MI 48375 *Toll Free Tel:* 800-422-2444 ext 300
Membership(s): SMPTE®

Vutec Corp
11711 W Sample Rd, Coral Springs, FL 33065-3155
Tel: 954-545-9000 *Toll Free Tel:* 800-770-4700
E-mail: info@vutec.com; sales@vutec.com
Web Site: vutec.com
Key Personnel
Founder & CEO: Howard L Sinkoff
Founded: 1977
Manufacturer of video projection screens, accessories & AV presentation tools.
Online catalog(s) available
Membership(s): Audiovisual and Integrated Experience Association; Consumer Technology Association™; Custom Electronic Design & Installation Association; Imaging Science Foundation

VWR International LLC
Radnor Corporate Ctr, Bldg 1, 100 Matsonford Rd, Suite 200, Radnor, PA 19087-8660
Mailing Address: PO Box 6660, Radnor, PA 19087-8660
Tel: 610-431-1700 (corp off) *Toll Free Tel:* 800-932-5000 (cust serv)
Web Site: www.vwr.com; us.vwr.com
Key Personnel
Pres & CEO: Manuel A.H Brocke-Benz
SVP & CFO: Gregory L Cowan
Dir, Corp Communs: Valerie Collado *Tel:* 484-885-9338 *E-mail:* valerie_collado@vwr.com
Founded: 1852
Online catalog(s) available

WAC Lighting Co
44 Harbor Park Dr, Port Washington, NY 11050
Tel: 516-515-5000 *Toll Free Tel:* 800-526-2588
Fax: 516-515-5050 *Toll Free Fax:* 800-526-2585
E-mail: sales@waclighting.com
Web Site: www.waclighting.com
Key Personnel
CEO: Tony Wang
VP, Mktg: Sean Tham
Lighting fixture company.
Branch Office(s)
1750 Archibald Ave, Ontario, CA 91761
1600 Distribution Ct, Lithia Springs, GA 30122

Wacom Technology Corp
Affiliate of Wacom Co Ltd (Japan)
1458 NW Irving St, Portland, OR 97209
Toll Free Tel: 855-MY-WACOM (699-2266)
Web Site: www.wacom.com
Key Personnel
Pres: Masahiko Yamada
Manufacturer of pen tablets, interactive pen displays & digital interface solutions.

Waldom Electronics Corp
1801 Morgan St, Rockford, IL 61102-2690
Tel: 815-968-9661 *Toll Free Tel:* 800-435-2931 (cust serv) *Fax:* 815-968-9029
E-mail: sales@waldom.com
Web Site: www.waldom.com
Key Personnel
Tech Specialist: Shawn Seeverson
Distribute audio equipment.

Wallace Creative LLC
1705 NW 25 Ave, Portland, OR 97210
Tel: 503-224-9660
E-mail: info@wallyhood.com
Web Site: www.wallyhood.com
Key Personnel
Pres & Creative Dir: Donald Wallace

Animation & design studio. Animation, illustration, cartoons & design art of all kinds for both traditional & digital applications .
Membership(s): Oregon Media Production Association

Wallace Film Studios
258 Wallace Ave, Toronto, ON M6P 3N9, Canada
Tel: 416-538-3535
E-mail: info@wallacefilmstudios.ca
Web Site: wallacefilmstudios.ca
Three studios available with in-house lighting & grip availability for film, video or photographic production.

Walltalkers
Division of Koroseal Interior Products Group
3875 Embassy Pkwy, Fairlawn, OH 44333
Tel: 330-668-7600 *Fax:* 330-668-7703
E-mail: customerservice@koroseal.com
Web Site: www.walltalkers.com
Key Personnel
Mgr, Cust Serv: Andrea Repine
Manufacture dry erase presentation wallcoverings.
Membership(s): ATD; Audiovisual and Integrated Experience Association

Walters-Storyk Design Group Inc (WSDG)
262 Martin Ave, Highland, NY 12528
Tel: 845-691-9300 *Fax:* 845-691-9361
E-mail: info@wsdg.com
Web Site: www.wsdg.com
Key Personnel
Principal & Designer: John Storyk
Principal & Interior Designer: Beth Walters
Full service architectural design & acoustical consulting firm specializing in media facility planning & technical commercial architecture, acoustics, mechanical noise control, sound system design, AV system design.

Walterscheid Productions
PO Box 995, Wichita, KS 67201
Tel: 316-258-1152
E-mail: bobwalter1@aol.com
Web Site: www.wponline.com
Founded: 1968
Create TV commercials & infomercials & business videos.

WAM, see Whalley-Abbey Media Holdings Inc

Wanted! Sound + Picture
409 King St W, Suite 300, Toronto, ON M5V 1K1, Canada
Tel: 416-596-1101 *Fax:* 416-596-0690
E-mail: info@wantedsp.com; bookings@wantedsp.com
Web Site: www.wantedsp.com
Key Personnel
Pres & CEO: John deNottbeck *E-mail:* john@wantedsp.com
Exec Prodr: Augusta Brook *E-mail:* augusta@wantedsp.com
Dir, Sales & Mktg/New Busn Devt: Bob Johnston *E-mail:* bob@wantedsp.com
Voice & Music Dir: Earl Torno *E-mail:* earl@retrieversound.com
Founded: 1970
Creative development & production services for digital media production/radio & television advertising. Original music & audio/video postproduction for commercials, animation/dubbing, games, reality TV, documentaries, corporate & live action content.

Ward-Beck Systems Ltd
945 Middlefield Rd, Unit 9, Toronto, ON M1V 5E1, Canada
Tel: 416-335-5999 *Toll Free Tel:* 800-771-2556
Fax: 416-335-5202
E-mail: sales@ward-beck.com

Web Site: www.ward-beck.com
Key Personnel
Pres: Kevin Lyver *E-mail:* kevinlyver@ward-beck.com
Mng Dir: Eugene L Johnson
  E-mail: eugenejohnson@ward-beck.com
Founded: 1967
Design & manufacture analog & digital broadcast equipment.
Online catalog(s) available
Membership(s): AES; NAB; SMPTE®

Warner Bros Animation
Division of Warner Bros
4000 Warner Blvd, Burbank, CA 91522
Tel: 818-954-6000
Web Site: www.warnerbros.com
Key Personnel
Pres: Sam Register
All facets of animation as well as programming.

Warner Bros Entertainment Inc
Division of Time Warner Inc
4000 Warner Blvd, Burbank, CA 91522
E-mail: wbsf@warnerbros.com
Web Site: www.warnerbros.com/studio; studiofacilities.warnerbros.com
Key Personnel
EVP & CFO: Kim Williams
Chief Digital Offr & EVP, Strategy & Busn Devt: Thomas Gewecke
EVP & Gen Coun: John Rogovin
EVP, Intl: Reg Harpur
EVP, Worldwide Corp Communs & Pub Aff: Dee Dee Myers
EVP, Worldwide HR: Kiko Washington
Founded: 1923
Fully integrated, broad-based entertainment company. Feature films to television, home entertainment/DVD, animation, product & brand licensing & interactive entertainment.
Online catalog(s) available

Warner Bros Production Sound & Video Services
Division of Time Warner Inc
4000 Warner Blvd, Burbank, CA 91522
Tel: 818-954-2511; 818-954-2310 (rentals)
  Fax: 818-954-2901
E-mail: wbsf@warnerbros.com; wbsfproductionsound@warnerbros.com
Web Site: www.wbsf.com; www.wbsoundandvideo.com
Founded: 1955
Supplier of audio & video equipment for single & multi-camera productions, corporate presentations, meetings & special events.
Catalog(s) available

Warner Chappell Production Music
Division of Warner Chappell Music
1030 16 Ave S, Nashville, TN 37212
Toll Free Tel: 888-615-8729 *Fax:* 615-242-2455
E-mail: info@warnerchappellpm.com
Web Site: www.warnerchappellpm.com
Key Personnel
SVP, Prodn: Aaron Gant *Tel:* 615-244-6515
  E-mail: aaron.gant@warnerchappellpm.com
Founded: 1984
Production music library & custom music production.
Branch Office(s)
777 Santa Fe Ave, Los Angeles, CA 90021, Dir, Licensing, Trailers: David Epstein *Tel:* 310-441-8722 *E-mail:* david@nonstopmusic.com
1633 Broadway, 9th fl, New York, NY 10019
915 W 100 S, Salt Lake City, UT 84104 *Toll Free Tel:* 800-554-6462 *Toll Free Fax:* 800-531-0346
Membership(s): Production Music Association

Warner Home Video Inc
Subsidiary of Warner Bros Entertainment Inc
4000 Warner Blvd, Bldg 160, Burbank, CA 91522
Tel: 818-954-6000 *Fax:* 818-954-6480
Web Site: www.warnerbros.com
Key Personnel
Pres: Jim Wuthrich
SVP, New Media Applications: Lewis Ostrover
EVP, Sales: Mike Takac
VP, Dom Sales: Darlene Walters
Sales Dir: Joe Bakala
BP Sales Communs, Events: Amy Beth Chamberlin
Founded: 1980
Online catalog(s) available
Branch Office(s)
3903 W Olive Ave, Suite 3139, Burbank, CA 91505, VP, Sales Communs: Christine Martinez
  Tel: 818-954-7300
3400 W Riverside Dr, Burbank, CA 91505
Shipping Address: 3903 W Olive Ave, Suite 3139, Burbank, CA 91505
Membership(s): Entertainment Merchants Association

WARPed Pictures
2447 Benedict Canyon Dr, Beverly Hills, CA 90210
Tel: 310-777-8828; 310-999-1219 (cell) *Fax:* 310-777-8805
E-mail: info@warpedpictures.com
Web Site: www.warpedpictures.com
Key Personnel
Pres: Volker Fleck *E-mail:* v@warpedpictures.com
Founded: 1996
Production service & representation company.

Washington State University College of Nursing
103 E Spokane Falls Blvd, Spokane, WA 99202
Mailing Address: 412 E Spokane Falls Blvd, Spokane, WA 99202-2131
Tel: 509-324-7360 *Toll Free Tel:* 800-281-2589 *Fax:* 509-324-7341
Web Site: nursing.wsu.edu
Key Personnel
Electronic Media Prodr: Mike Lynch
  E-mail: michael.lynch@wsu.edu
Media production, photography, DVD authoring, duplication & label design.
Membership(s): AAN; STT

Waterworks Acoustics Design Inc
6465 Sierra Lane, Dublin, CA 94568
Key Personnel
Pres: Thomas A George
Founded: 1986
High-end audio, indoor/outdoor weatherproof speakers.
Catalog(s) available

WATL-TV Inc
Subsidiary of TEGNA Media
One Monroe Place NE, Atlanta, GA 30324
Tel: 404-881-3600
Web Site: www.myatltv.com
Key Personnel
Pres & Gen Mgr: John Deushane
Busn Mgr: Lillian Ryan
TV station.

Watson Desking
26246 Twelve Trees Lane NW, Poulsbo, WA 98370
Tel: 360-394-1300 *Fax:* 360-394-1322
E-mail: marketing@watsondesking.com
Web Site: www.watsonfurniture.com
Key Personnel
CEO: Clif McKenzie

Natl Sales Mgr: Anje Ard *E-mail:* aard@watsonfg.com; Mike Hanson
Mktg Admin: Lisa Hope *E-mail:* lhope@watsonfg.com
Manufacture ergonomic furniture/media storage.
Online catalog(s) available

Watts Communications Inc
149 N 120 St, Wauwatosa, WI 53226
Tel: 414-727-9505 *Fax:* 414-727-9506
E-mail: sales@wattscom.com
Web Site: www.wattscom.com
Key Personnel
Founder & CEO: Keith Watts
Pres & Prodr: Jeff Watts *E-mail:* jeffw@wattscom.com
Founded: 1991
Full service production company specializing in promotional & training videos, television programming, web site design, digital photography - from concept to completion.
Membership(s): NATAS

WAVE Inc, see AudioVideoElectric

WaveGuide Studios
2062 Weems Rd, Tucker, GA 30084
Tel: 770-939-2004 *Toll Free Tel:* 800-578-2004
E-mail: info@waveguidestudios.com
Web Site: www.waveguidestudios.com
Key Personnel
Pres: Marshall Peterson
Gen Mgr: Stephanie Phillips
Film production services.

Wavemaker Media Design
PO Box 226, Duncans Mills, CA 95430
Tel: 707-788-6040 *Fax:* 707-788-6040
E-mail: sales@wavemakermediadesign.com
Web Site: www.wavemakermediadesign.com
Key Personnel
Owner & Prodr: Steve Witte
Founded: 1996
Full service logo, print, web, video design & production company.

WaxWorks VideoWorks
Subsidiary of WaxWorks Inc
325 E Third St, Owensboro, KY 42303
Tel: 270-926-0008 *Toll Free Tel:* 800-825-8558 *Fax:* 270-663-0737
Web Site: www.waxworksonline.com
Key Personnel
Pres: Terry Woodward
Mktg Mgr: Jessica Stone
Wholesale entertainment distributor.
Catalog(s) available

Wayne State University Media Services
Division of Wayne State University Libraries
Purdy/Kresge Library, 5244 Gullen Mall, Detroit, MI 48202
Tel: 313-577-1980 *Fax:* 313-577-6777
E-mail: mediaservices@wayne.edu
Web Site: library.wayne.edu
Key Personnel
Assoc Dir: Alan Bartlett *Tel:* 313-993-4321
  E-mail: ab2475@wayne.edu
University media library.
Catalog(s) available
Membership(s): AECT; Consortium of College & University Media Centers; Michigan Association for Media in Education

WCJB TV20
Subsidiary of Gray Television Inc
6220 NW 43 St, Gainesville, FL 32653
Tel: 352-416-0623 *Fax:* 352-373-6516
E-mail: comments@wcbj.com
Web Site: wcjb.com
Key Personnel
Prodn Mgr: Ron Bates

Founded: 1971
Studios, grip lighting truck, camera crew, digital editing, public service programs & commercial programs.

The Weather Company, An IBM Business
400 Minuteman Rd, Andover, MA 01810
Tel: 978-983-6300 *Fax:* 978-983-6400
Web Site: business.weather.com
Key Personnel
VP & Head, Busn Solutions: Mark Gildersleeve
VP, Global Media Sales: Steve Ward
Head, Global Mktg: Michelle Boockoff-Bajdek
Head, Media Solutions: Bill Dow
Corp Communs Mgr: Lea Armstrong *E-mail:* lea. armstrong@weather.com
Mktg Mgr: Kerry McCord-Morelli
World's leading source of professional on-air weather related graphic systems & forecasting tools for television; turning mountains of meteorological information into the country's most popular real-time weather data & forecasting services.
Branch Office(s)
401 Charmany Dr, Suite 200, Madison, WI 53719 (Midwest headquarters)
Foreign Office(s): 76178 Upper Grand, South Bank, London SE1 9PZ, United Kingdom
Tel: (0121) 233 7600 (Europe, Middle East & Africa headquarters)
Membership(s): NAB; RTDNA

Webb Audio Visual
3020 S West Temple, Salt Lake City, UT 84115
Tel: 801-484-8567 (installation)
Toll Free Tel: 877-909-8567 *Fax:* 801-484-8589
E-mail: info@wearewebb.com
Web Site: www.wearewebb.com
Key Personnel
Owner & Pres: Steven M Webb
Owner & VP: Scott T Webb
Founded: 1955
Full service AV company.
Membership(s): Audiovisual and Integrated Experience Association

Webster Communications
6323 Repton St, Los Angeles, CA 90042
Tel: 323-258-6741
E-mail: info@vanwebster.com
Web Site: vanwebster.com
Key Personnel
Founder & Pres: Van Webster
Independent creative presentation company.
Online catalog(s) available
Membership(s): AES; The Recording Academy; SMPTE®

WEEK TV
Division of Quincy Media Inc
2907 Springfield Rd, East Peoria, IL 61611
Tel: 309-698-2525
Web Site: www.week.com
Key Personnel
Pres & Gen Mgr: Mark DeSantis *Tel:* 309-698-3850 *E-mail:* mdesantis@week.com
Television station.

Wegener Communications Inc
Subsidiary of Wegener, a Novra Group company
Technology Park, 11350 Technology Circle, Johns Creek, GA 30097
Tel: 770-814-4000; 770-814-4036 (sales); 770-814-4057 (cust serv) *Fax:* 770-623-0698
E-mail: info@wegener.com
Web Site: www.wegener.com
Key Personnel
CEO/CFO: C Troy Woodbury, Jr
Founded: 1978
Full range of customized media distribution solutions.
Online catalog(s) available

Weigl Publishers Inc
350 Fifth Ave, 59th fl, New York, NY 10118
Toll Free Tel: 866-649-3445 *Toll Free Fax:* 866-449-3445
Web Site: www.weigl.com
Key Personnel
Pres & Publr: Linda A Weigl *E-mail:* linda@ weigl.com
Founded: 1992
Educational programming producer.
Catalog(s) available

Alan Weiss Productions
1243 California Rd, Suite 2R, East Chester, NY 10709
Tel: 212-974-0606
E-mail: awpinfo@awptv.com
Web Site: www.awptv.com
Key Personnel
Pres & Exec Prodr: Alan Weiss
VP & Proj Mgr: Marilou Yacoub *Tel:* 212-974-0606 ext 313 *E-mail:* myacoub@awptv.com
Full service production company.

Welk Music Group
Division of The Welk Group Inc
11400 W Olympic Blvd, Suite 760, Los Angeles, CA 90064
Tel: 310-829-9355 *Fax:* 310-264-9875
Key Personnel
Pres: Kevin Welk
Music distributors.
Online catalog(s) available

The Well-Tempered Music Library
PO Box 465, Middleboro, MA 02346-0465
Tel: 508-947-7387 *Fax:* 508-947-7387
E-mail: info@arfarfrecords.com; page@ arfarfrecords.com
Web Site: www.arfarfrecords.com; www. arfarfrecords.com/wtml/home.html
Key Personnel
Pres: Erik Lindgren *E-mail:* erik@arfarfrecords. com
Buy-out music library consisting of 427 tracks on 7 CDs.
Online catalog(s) available

Wells-Gardner Electronics Corp, see Wells-Gardner Technologies Inc

Wells-Gardner Technologies Inc
Subsidiary of HT Precision Technologies Inc
3078 E Sunset Rd, Suite 1, Las Vegas, NV 89120
Tel: 702-330-0330 *Toll Free Tel:* 800-336-6630
Web Site: www.wellsgardner.com
Key Personnel
Gen Mgr: Wally Sa'd *E-mail:* wsad@ wellsgardner.com
Inside Sales: Lauren Nowosad *E-mail:* lnowosad@wellsgardner.com
Founded: 1925
Manufacturer & integrator of LCD panels, touch screens, audio speakers & accessories.
Catalog(s) available, free, call to order
Membership(s): Association of Gaming Equipment Manufacturers

Welocalize
241 E Fourth St, Suite 207, Frederick, MD 21701
Tel: 301-668-0330 *Toll Free Tel:* 800-370-9515
Fax: 301-668-0335
E-mail: info@welocalize.com
Web Site: www.welocalize.com
Key Personnel
Co-Founder & CEO: Smith Yewell
Co-Founder: Julia Yewell
CFO: Jeff Ash
Chief Cust Offr: Erin Wynn
Chief Innovation Offr: Chris Grebisz
Founded: 1997

Translating & dubbing videos, AV, film & audio-tapes into foreign languages.
Membership(s): Association of Language Companies; ATA; European Language Industry Association; Translation Automation User Society

WEP LLC
Subsidiary of Koplar Communications Inc
50 Maryland Plaza, Suite 300, St Louis, MO 63108
Tel: 314-345-1000
E-mail: wep@wep.com
Web Site: www.wep.com
Key Personnel
Mng Dir: Tiffany Ilardi *E-mail:* tiffany@koplar. com
Founded: 1980
Producer of innovative & cutting edge children's entertainment.

WESCAM, see L-3 WESCAM

Wespen Audio Visual Co
101 Riverside Dr, Hawthorn, PA 16230
Key Personnel
Pres: J Richard George
Founded: 1944
AV equipment supplier.
Membership(s): Audiovisual and Integrated Experience Association

West Coast Projections Inc
12463 Rancho Bernardo Rd, No 149, San Diego, CA 92128-2143
Tel: 858-674-7334
E-mail: wcpinfo@westcoastprojections.com
Web Site: westcoastprojections.com
Key Personnel
Pres: David Gibbs
Founded: 1980
Full service production company.

West Eagle Films Inc
800 Lower Ganges Rd, Salt Spring Island, BC V8K 2N5, Canada
Tel: 250-538-1780
Web Site: www.westeaglefilms.com
Key Personnel
Writer, Dir & Cinematographer: David Douglas
Prodr: Diane Roberts *E-mail:* droberts@ westeaglefilms.com
Full service production company. Specialize in large format film production, innovative digital film design & multimedia communication exhibits for science centers & museums.

West Penn Wire
Unit of Belden Inc
2833 W Chestnut St, Washington, PA 15301
Tel: 724-222-7060 *Toll Free Tel:* 800-245-4964
Fax: 724-222-6420
E-mail: info@westpennwire.com; sales@ westpennwire.com
Web Site: www.westpenn-wpw.com
Key Personnel
Pres: Scott Harden
VP, Sales: Andy Oswald
Dir, Engg: Mark Sams
Dir, Mktg: Aaron Reighard
Dir, Sales-Eastern Region: Ron Leone
Sr Prod Mgr: Todd Hirt
Founded: 1971
Manufacturer of fiber optics, low voltage wire & cable for AV, security & networking applications.
Online catalog(s) available
Branch Office(s)
4641 Pell Dr, No 4, Sacramento, CA 95838
4606 Elk Ridge Ct, Suite F, Flowery Branch, GA 30542

Westar Music
105 W Beaver Creek Rd, Suite 4, Richmond Hill, ON L4B 1C6, Canada
Tel: 905-886-3100 *Toll Free Tel:* 866-463-0100
Fax: 905-886-6800
E-mail: info@westarmusic.com
Web Site: www.westarmusic.com
Key Personnel
Pres: Brian Nimens
Sales Mgr: Peter Alexander
Stock music library/production music.

Westbury National Show Systems Ltd
772 Warden Ave, Toronto, ON M1L 4T7, Canada
Tel: 416-752-1371 *Toll Free Tel:* 855-752-1372
Fax: 416-752-1382
E-mail: info@westbury.com
Web Site: www.westbury.com
Key Personnel
CFO: Isaac Osiel
Pres: Frank Gerstein
VP: Rob Sandolowich
Founded: 1971
Professional audio, AV, lighting & staging company. With more than a hundred full time employees at our Toronto headquarters, Westbury offers equipment rentals & production services as well as sound reinforcement, system sales, design, installation & repair services.
Branch Office(s)
28 Capital Dr, Ottawa, ON K2G 0E9, Canada
Tel: 613-723-1371
Membership(s): AES; Audiovisual and Integrated Experience Association; NSCA

Westcoast Video Productions Inc
14141 Covello St, Suite 9-A, Van Nuys, CA 91405
Tel: 818-785-8033
Web Site: www.wvpinc.com
Key Personnel
Pres & CTO: Larry Chong *E-mail:* larry@wvpinc.com
Founded: 1986
Full broadcast video facility that specializes in renting video & audio equipment.
Catalog(s) available

Western Digital Corp
5601 Great Oaks Pkwy, San Jose, CA 95119
Tel: 408-717-6000 *Toll Free Tel:* 800-275-4932 (tech support)
Web Site: www.wdc.com
Key Personnel
Pres & CEO: Steve Milligan
Founded: 1970
Manufacturer of network systems.
Sales Office(s): 44100 Osgood Rd, Fremont, CA 94539 *Tel:* 510-683-6100
3355 Michelson Dr, Suite 100, Irvine, CA 92612 *Tel:* 949-672-7000 *Toll Free Tel:* 888-935-8893 *Fax:* 949-672-5408
401 Corbett St, Suite 250A, Belleair, FL 33756 *Tel:* 727-449-2878 *Fax:* 727-449-2904
One Park Place, Executive Suite 240, 621 NW 53 St, Boca Raton, FL 33487 *Tel:* 561-995-1494 *Fax:* 561-995-1496
PO Box 1051, Pasadena, MD 21122 *Tel:* 410-439-9968 *Fax:* 410-439-0718
North Suburban Business Center, 23 Walkers Brook Dr, Suite 11, Reading, MA 01867 *Tel:* 781-942-4460 *Fax:* 781-942-4462
206 Military Rd, North Sioux City, SD 57049 *Tel:* 605-232-3545 *Fax:* 605-232-3543
3600 W Palmer Lane, Suite 160, Austin, TX 78727 *Tel:* 512-835-9898 *Fax:* 512-835-5801
20445 State Hwy 249, Suite 275, Houston, TX 77070 *Tel:* 281-257-9722 *Fax:* 281-251-9986
Redmond Storage Center, 2331 130 Ave NE, Suite 110, Bellevue, WA 98005 *Tel:* 425-755-1000 *Fax:* 425-636-1411

Westlake Recording Studios
7265 Santa Monica Blvd, Los Angeles, CA 90046
Tel: 323-851-9800
E-mail: bookings@westlakestudios.com; info@westlakestudios.com
Web Site: www.westlakestudios.com
Key Personnel
Owner & CEO: Al Machera
Owner & Pres: Steve Burdick
Studio Mgr: Sara Clark
Asst Studio Mgr: Alex Burdick
Recording studio for music, film, TV & commercials.

Weston Woods Canada
Division of McNabb & Connolly
60 Briarwood Ave, Mississauga, ON L5G 3N6, Canada
Tel: 905-278-0566 *Toll Free Tel:* 866-722-1522 *Toll Free Fax:* 866-722-1822
E-mail: info@mcnabbconnolly.ca
Web Site: www.mcnabbconnolly.ca
Key Personnel
Founder: Steve Connolly
Founded: 1986
Canadian supplier of quality educational programming for K-12 schools, post secondary institutions & public libraries.

Weston Woods Studios Inc
Division of Scholastic Inc
90 Old Sherman Tpke, Danbury, CT 06816
Tel: 203-797-3520 *Toll Free Tel:* 800-243-5020 *Fax:* 203-797-3541
E-mail: westonwoodsquestions@scholastic.com
Web Site: www.scholastic.com/westonwoods
Key Personnel
Pres: Lori Benton *E-mail:* lbenton@scholastic.com
Prodr/Acqs: Melissa Reilly Ellard *Tel:* 800-243-5020 ext 3522 *E-mail:* mreillyellard@scholastic.com
Founded: 1953
Produces public performance DVDs & audios based on outstanding children's books.
Catalog(s) available, biannual
Membership(s): AECT; ALA

Westworks Studios
4100 E Dry Creek Rd, Littleton, CO 80122
Toll Free Tel: 800-491-1947
E-mail: info@westworksstudios.com
Web Site: westworksstudios.com
Key Personnel
Dir, Prodn Opers: Todd Smoots
Mgr, Prodn Engg: Robert Baker
Prodn Coord: Jennifer Jefferson
Full service provider for HD studio production & post-production.

WETA Production Center
Subsidiary of WETA-Channel 26 (PBS)
3620 S 27 St, Arlington, VA 22206
Tel: 703-998-2054
Web Site: www.weta.org/tv
Key Personnel
Mgr: Jim Snyder
Video programming, videoconferencing, webcasts, teleconferencing, producer of local programming for the Washington DC area & local PBS station. Also produced & broadcast the Muscular Dystrophy Telethon.
Membership(s): NAB

David Wexler & Co
7807 E Greenway Rd, Suite 8, Scottsdale, AZ 85260-1717
Tel: 480-675-8888 *Fax:* 480-675-8900
E-mail: wexlermusic@aol.com

Web Site: www.wexlermusic.com
Founded: 1920

Wexler Music, see David Wexler & Co

WFRV-TV 5 CBS
1181 E Mason St, Green Bay, WI 54301
Tel: 920-437-5411 *Fax:* 920-437-4576
E-mail: tips@wearegreenbay.com
Web Site: www.wearegreenbay.com
Key Personnel
VP & Gen Mgr: Mike Smith
Mktg Dir: Dan Beckwith
Assignment Ed: Ed Walters
Television station.
Membership(s): NAB; Wisconsin Broadcasters Association

WGBH Production Group
Division of WGBH Educational Foundation
One Guest St, Boston, MA 02135
Tel: 617-300-2000
E-mail: productiongroup@wgbh.org; studios@wgbh.org; outpost@wgbh.org
Web Site: productiongroup.wgbh.org
Key Personnel
Sr Dir, Prodn Technol: Tim Mangini
Sr Opers Mgr, Studio & EFP: Terry Quinn *Tel:* 617-300-2349 *E-mail:* terry.quinn@wgbh.org
Post-Prodn Systems Engr: Stepehn Barker
Post-Prodn Opers Mgr: Beth Godlin Lillis
Asst Dir, Post-Prodn: Deb Holland
Prodn Mgr, Studios: Margaret Heffernan
TV Opers Mgr: Chloe Ferrarone *Tel:* 617-300-3426
Sr Tech Dir: Bill Francis
Award-winning studios, production, post-production & tape playouts.

WGBH Stock Sales
Division of WGBH Educational Foundation
One Guest St, Boston, MA 02135
Tel: 617-300-3939 *Fax:* 617-300-1056
E-mail: stock_sales@wgbh.org
Web Site: www.wgbhstocksales.org
Key Personnel
Lead Sales Supv: James Auclair *Tel:* 617-300-3901 *E-mail:* james_auclair@wgbh.org
Stock footage from PBS's largest producer: NOVA, Antiques Roadshow, Frontline & American Experience.
Membership(s): Association of Commercial Stock Image Licensors

WGME-TV
Division of Sinclair Broadcast Group Inc
81 Northport Dr, Portland, ME 04103
Tel: 207-797-1313 *Fax:* 207-878-7482
E-mail: tvmail@wgme.com
Web Site: wgme.com
Key Personnel
Gen Mgr: Tom Humpage *Tel:* 207-228-7700 *E-mail:* thumpage@sbgtv.com
Television station.
Membership(s): NAB; NATPE

WGVU TV
Division of Grand Valley State University
301 Fulton St W, Grand Rapids, MI 49504-6492
Tel: 616-331-6666 *Toll Free Tel:* 800-442-2771
Web Site: www.wgvu.org
Key Personnel
Gen Mgr: Michael T Walenta
Prog Mgr: Ed Spier
Founded: 1972
Post-production services.
Membership(s): PBS

The Whale Video Co
225 Indian Creek Dr, Mechanicsburg, PA 17050

Tel: 717-763-9507
Web Site: www.whalevideo.com
Key Personnel
Founder & Pres: A Daniel Knaub
E-mail: danknaub@comcast.net
Founded: 1988
Produce & distribute DVDs & videotapes of
whales for education & entertainment.
Membership(s): CSI

Whalley-Abbey Media Holdings Inc
3800 Rue St Patrick, Suite 100, Montreal, QC
H4E 1A4, Canada
Tel: 514-846-1940
E-mail: info@wamgrp.com
Web Site: wamgrp.com
Key Personnel
Co-Founder & Exec Prodr: Hans Rosenstein;
Debbie Travis
Exec Prodr & Mng Partner: Petro Duszara; Scott
Bailey
Founded: 1991
Full service production company.

Wheatstone Corp
600 Industrial Dr, New Bern, NC 28562
Tel: 252-638-7000 *Fax:* 252-635-1285
E-mail: sales@wheatstone.com
Web Site: www.wheatstone.com
Key Personnel
Dir, Sales: Jay Tyler *E-mail:* jay@wheatstone.
com
Manufactures digital audio network infrastruc-
tures, digital audio control surfaces, audio net-
work systems, audio network routers & signal
processors.
Online catalog(s) available

Whirlwind Music Distributors Inc
99 Ling Rd, Greece, NY 14612
Tel: 585-663-8820 *Toll Free Tel:* 800-733-9473
(US only) *Fax:* 585-865-8930
E-mail: sales@whirlwindusa.com; techsupport@
whirlwindusa.com; darylg@whirlwindusa.com
(CN inquiries)
Web Site: whirlwindusa.com
Key Personnel
Pres: Michael Laiacona *Tel:* 800-733-9473 ext
147 *E-mail:* michael@whirlwindusa.com
Gen Mgr: Joe Barnes *Tel:* 800-733-9473 ext 137
E-mail: joeb@whirlwindusa.com
Mktg Dir/Artist Rel: Will Young *Tel:* 800-733-
9473 ext 169 *E-mail:* willy@whirlwindusa.com
Chief Engr: Carl Cornell *Tel:* 800-733-9473 ext
130 *E-mail:* carlc@whirlwindusa.com
Prodn Mgr: Debbie Noble *Tel:* 800-733-9473 ext
142 *E-mail:* debbien@whirlwindusa.com
Manufacturers & distributes audio interface, fiber
optics & AC power solution accessories.
Online catalog(s) available
Membership(s): AES; NAB; NAMM, the Na-
tional Association of Music Merchants; NSCA

WhisperRoom™ Inc
109 S Northshore Dr, Suite 303, Knoxville, TN
37919
Tel: 865-558-5364 *Toll Free Tel:* 800-200-8168
Fax: 865-558-5370
E-mail: info@whisperroom.com
Web Site: www.whisperroom.com
Key Personnel
Dir, Busn Devt: Chet Burgess
Mktg Mgr: Benton White *E-mail:* bentonwhite@
whisperroom.com
Sales Mgr: Debbie Sweany
Founded: 1990
Manufacturer of sound isolation enclosures.
Catalog(s) available
Membership(s): NAB; NAMM, the National As-
sociation of Music Merchants

White Diamond Productions LLC
605 Hwy 62 65 N, No 359, Harrison, AR 72601
Key Personnel
Projs Mgr: Marty Roberts
Award winning production company.

White Dog Studios
1986 Mercer Rd, Smyrna, GA 30080
Tel: 404-355-2200
Web Site: www.whitedogstudios.net
Key Personnel
Founder & Pres: Curt Bush *E-mail:* curt@
whitedogstudios.net
Audio post-production facility.

White Rain Films Ltd
2009 Dexter Ave N, Seattle, WA 98109
Tel: 206-682-5417 *Fax:* 206-682-3038
E-mail: info@whiterainfilms.com
Web Site: www.whiterainfilms.com
Key Personnel
Owner & Prodr: Bill Phillips
Dir & Ed: Brad Bolling
Founded: 1991
Digital cinema company.

White Swan Music Inc
6395 Gunpark Dr, Suite A, Boulder, CO 80301
Tel: 303-527-0770 *Toll Free Tel:* 800-825-86J6
Fax: 303-527-0771
E-mail: info@whiteswanmusic.com
Web Site: whiteswanmusic.com
Key Personnel
Owner: Parmita Pushman *E-mail:* parmita@
whiteswanmusic.com
Distributes a diverse catalog of yoga & world
music.
Catalog(s) available
Membership(s): Museum Store Association; Net-
work of Alternatives for Publishers, Retailers &
Artists Inc

William F White International Inc
Member of Comweb Group
800 Islington Ave, Toronto, ON M8Z 6A1,
Canada
Tel: 416-239-5050 *Toll Free Tel:* 800-465-0160
(CN only)
Web Site: www.whites.com
Key Personnel
Chmn & CEO: Paul Bronfman
EVP & CFO: Munir Noorbhai
EVP & COO: Paul Roscorla
Asst COO: Garin Josey
VP, Busn Devt: Rick Perotto
VP, Indus/Govt Rel & Sustainability: David
Hardy
Dir, Fin & Admin: Michael Yee
Dir, HR: Allison Spicer
Gen Mgr: Michael Drabot
Founded: 1963
Motion picture, television & theatrical equipment
supply.
Branch Office(s)
828 Beatrice Crescent, Sudbury, ON P3A 3E5,
Canada *Tel:* 705-885-1242
Calgary Film Ctr, 5750 76 Ave SE, Unit 50, Cal-
gary, AB T2C 5N5, Canada *Tel:* 403-279-2693
8363 Lougheed Hwy, Unit 100, Burnaby, BC
V5A 1X3, Canada *Tel:* 604-253-5050
Whites Specialty Equipment-Western Canada,
3555 Bainbridge Ave, Burnaby, BC V5A 2T3,
Canada *Tel:* 604-428-2144
11-2073 Logan Ave, Winnipeg, MB R2R 0J1,
Canada *Tel:* 204-774-7903
180 Thornhill Dr, Unit 2, Dartmouth, NS B3B
1V3, Canada *Tel:* 902-450-1284

The Whitlock Group
12820 West Creek Pkwy, Richmond, VA 23238

Tel: 804-273-9100 *Toll Free Tel:* 800-726-9843
Fax: 804-273-9380
E-mail: information@whitlock.com; marketing@
whitlock.com
Web Site: www.whitlock.com
Key Personnel
Founder & Chmn: John Whitlock
CEO: Doug Hall *E-mail:* halld@whitlock.com
COO: Roger Patrick
CFO: Mark Baker
EVP: Julian Phillips; John Steinhauer
VP, IT & Serv Delivery: Chris Jamison
VP, Technol: John Bailey
Regl VP, East: Ewan Smith
Regl VP, West: John Bagnell
Dir, Mktg & Communs: Cheryl Cox
Broadcast & presentation solutions.
Online catalog(s) available
Branch Office(s)
20099 Ashbrook Place, Suite 105, Ashburn, VA
20147, Contact: Lonnie Essex *Tel:* 703-297-
8561 *E-mail:* essexl@whitlock.com
230 Clearfield Ave, Suite 103, Virginia
Beach, VA 23462, Contact: Doug Onhaizer
Tel: 757-671-7478 *Fax:* 757-671-7481
E-mail: onhaizerd@whitlock.com
47400 Seabridge Dr, Fremont, CA 95483,
Contact: Justin Shong *Tel:* 510-344-5618
E-mail: shongj@whitlock.com
6555 S Kenton St, Suite 303, Centennial, CO
80112, Contact: Jeff Lindvall *Tel:* 303-799-
1480 *Fax:* 303-799-8539 *E-mail:* lindvallj@
whitlock.com
1075 Florida Central Pkwy, Suite 2150, Longwood, FL 32750, Contact: Reid Holden
Tel: 813-902-2013 *E-mail:* holdenr@whitlock.
com
5607 N Hiatus Rd, Suite 300, Tamarac, FL
33321, Contact: Reid Holden *Tel:* 954-384-
4286 *Fax:* 954-473-0205 *E-mail:* holdenr@
whitlock.com
5910 Breckenridge Pkwy, Suite H, Tampa, FL
33610, Contact: Reid Holden *Tel:* 813-886-
5252 *Fax:* 813-884-4145 *E-mail:* holdenr@
whitlock.com
1075 Windward Ridge Pkwy, Suite 180, Atlanta,
GA 30005, Contact: Reid Holden *Tel:* 770-993-
1001 *Fax:* 770-992-8175 *E-mail:* holdenr@
whitlock.com
2171 Executive Dr, Suite 250, Addison, IL
60101, Contact: Tony Karigan *Tel:* 847-380-
1007 *E-mail:* karigana@whitlock.com
One North Ave, Suite D, Burlington, MA 01803,
Contact: Simon Davis *Tel:* 781-328-0048
E-mail: simon.davis@whitlock.com
380 North St, Teterboro, NJ 07608, Contact: John
Cerone *Tel:* 201-365-4706 *Fax:* 201-426-3592
E-mail: ceronej@whitlock.com
1001 Avenue of the Americas, 11th fl, New York,
NY 10018, Contact: John Cerone *Tel:* 212-719-
7555 *Fax:* 212-719-7554 *E-mail:* ceronej@
whitlock.com
8200 Arrowridge Blvd, Suite D, Charlotte, NC
28273, Contact: Felix Lopez *Tel:* 704-494-3500
E-mail: lopezf@whitlock.com
4018 Patriot Dr, Suite 150, Durham, NC 27703,
Contact: Felix Lopez *Tel:* 919-806-1009
Fax: 919-806-1016 *E-mail:* lopezf@whitlock.
com
10671 William Penn Hwy, Huntingdon, PA
16652, Contact: Kathy Porter *Tel:* 814-542-
2588 *Fax:* 814-542-9299 *E-mail:* porterk@
whitlock.com
273 Great Valley Pkwy, Malvern, PA 19355, Contact: John Cerone *Tel:* 610-296-0100 *Fax:* 610-
296-2583 *E-mail:* ceronej@whitlock.com
100 Purity Rd, Pittsburgh, PA 15235, Contact:
John Cerone *Tel:* 412-564-1250 *Fax:* 610-296-
2583 *E-mail:* ceronej@whitlock.com
11100 Metric Blvd, Suite 200E, Austin, TX
78758, Contact: Alyson Horn *Tel:* 512-280-
3710 *Fax:* 512-933-0291 *E-mail:* horna@
whitlock.com

1201 Lakeside Pkwy, Suite 160, Flower Mound, TX 75028, Contact: Alyson Horn *Tel:* 972-465-8888 *Fax:* 972-360-7398 *E-mail:* horna@whitlock.com

9101 Jameel Rd, Suite 160, Houston, TX 77040, Contact: Alex Guajardo *Tel:* 713-796-0700 *Fax:* 713-796-0701 *E-mail:* guajardoa@whitlock.com

15207 NE 95 St, Redmond, WA 98052, Contact: Ken Bayern *Tel:* 425-861-3484 *Fax:* 425-861-3481 *E-mail:* bayernk@whitlock.com

Membership(s): Audiovisual and Integrated Experience Association

Whole Person Associates Inc
101 W Second St, Suite 203, Duluth, MN 55802-5004
Tel: 218-727-0500 *Toll Free Tel:* 800-247-6789
Fax: 218-727-0505
E-mail: books@wholeperson.com
Web Site: www.wholeperson.com
Key Personnel
Publr: Carlene Sippola
Founded: 1980
Distribute & produce AV programs on stress management & wellness promotion.
Online catalog(s) available

WHYY Inc
Independence Mall West, 150 N Sixth St, Philadelphia, PA 19106
Tel: 215-351-1200 *Fax:* 215-351-0398
E-mail: talkback@whyy.org
Web Site: www.whyy.org
Key Personnel
Pres & CEO: William J Marrazzo
E-mail: wmarrazzo@whyy.org
EVP & COO: Kyra G McGrath
E-mail: kmcgrath@whyy.org
EVP & CFO: A William Dana *E-mail:* bdana@whyy.org
VP, Communs & Memb Rel: Art Ellis
E-mail: aellis@whyy.org
Public media organization, television, radio & online.
Branch Office(s)
625 Orange St, Wilmington, DE 19801 *Tel:* 302-516-7506

Wide Eye Productions
1018 W Hays St, Boise, ID 83702
Tel: 208-336-0391 *Fax:* 208-336-6644
E-mail: info@wideeye.tv
Web Site: wideeye.tv
Key Personnel
Dir & Photog: Tom Hadzor *Tel:* 208-861-1184 (cell)
Writer & Prodr: Jennifer Isenhart *Tel:* 208-861-6824 (cell)
Founded: 1996
Full service professional & broadcast video production utilizing top of the line Sony 4K, Super 35x3, sound, lighting & non-linear editing gear. ENG/EFP. Branch office in Seattle, WA.
Membership(s): NATAS

WIFR-TV
Division of Gray Television Inc
2523 N Meridian Rd, Rockford, IL 61101
Tel: 815-987-5300 *Fax:* 815-965-0981
E-mail: talkto23@wifr.com
Web Site: www.wifr.com
Key Personnel
Gen Mgr: Tim Myers *E-mail:* tim.myers@wifr.com
Opers Mgr: Jeff Clark *E-mail:* jeff.clark@wifr.com
Television programming.

Wild Plum
23371 Mulholland Dr, Suite 409, Woodland Hills, CA 91364

Tel: 310-823-7445
Web Site: www.wildplum.tv
Key Personnel
Partner & CFO: Alisa Allen *Tel:* 818-802-8886
E-mail: alisa@wildplum.tv
Partner & Exec Prodr: Shelby Sexton *Tel:* 310-962-9340 *E-mail:* shelby@wildplum.tv
Creative Dir: Ben Ross *Tel:* 310-923-8159
E-mail: ben@wildplum.tv
Founded: 2007

Wild Visions Inc
PO Box 42194, Phoenix, AZ 85080
Tel: 623-512-9810
Web Site: www.wildvisions.net
Key Personnel
Pres: Mike Pellegatti *Tel:* 623-516-1975
E-mail: mike@wildvisions.net
TV & video productions using HD, DVCAM & Beta SP cameras. Final cut & PCO editing.

WildBrain™
5657 Spring Garden Rd, Suite 505, Halifax, NS B3J 3R4, Canada
Tel: 902-423-0260 *Fax:* 902-422-0752
E-mail: info@wildbrain.com; halifax@wildbrain.com; sales@wildbrain.com
Web Site: www.wildbrain.com
Key Personnel
Vice Chair & CEO: Eric Ellenbogen
CFO: Aaron Ames
Chief Commercial Offr: Anne Loi
Pres: Josh Scherba
EVP & Mng Dir, WildBrain CPLG: Maarten Weck
EVP & Gen Mgr, WildBrain Television: Joe Tedesco
EVP, Content & Current Series: Stephanie Betts
EVP, Global Talent: Tara Talbot
EVP, Fin & Chief Acctg Offr: Danielle Neath
EVP, Peanuts Worldwide: Roz Nowicki
Mng Dir, WildBrain Spark: Jon Gisby
Founded: 2006
Global children's content & brands company. Home to such brands as Peanuts, Teletubbies, Strawberry Shortcake, Caillou, Inspector Gadget & Degrassi.
Branch Office(s)
WildBrain Studios, 380 W Fifth Ave, Vancouver, BC V5Y 1J5, Canada *Tel:* 604-684-2363 *Fax:* 604-602-0208 *E-mail:* studios@wildbrain.com
Queen's Quay Terminal, 207 Queens Quay W, Suite 550, Toronto, ON M5J 1A7, Canada *Tel:* 416-363-8034 *Fax:* 416-363-8919 *E-mail:* toronto.reception@wildbrain.com
Peanuts Worldwide, 370 Seventh Ave, 7 Penn Plaza, Suite 1701, New York, NY 10001 *Tel:* 212-293-8555 *Fax:* 212-967-0692 *E-mail:* info@peanuts.com
Foreign Office(s): WildBrain CPLG, One Queen Caroline St, 2nd fl, London W6 9YD, United Kingdom *Tel:* (020) 8563 6400 *Fax:* (020) 8563 6465 *E-mail:* cplginfo@cplg.com
WildBrain Spark, 183 Eversholt St, London NW1 1BU, United Kingdom *Tel:* (020) 7631 3931 *E-mail:* contact@wildbrain.com

Wilderness Video
1110 Barrington Circle, Ashland, OR 97520
Tel: 541-488-9363
Web Site: www.wildernessvideo.com
Key Personnel
Owner: Robert Glusic *Tel:* 541-951-0111 (cell)
E-mail: bob@wildernessvideo.com
Founded: 1980
Vast collection of wilderness footage in 4K & 8K stock. Footage includes time lapse, aerial, nature & city.

Wildfire Lighting & Visual Effects
2908 Oregon Ct, Suite G-1, Torrance, CA 90503

Tel: 310-755-6780 *Toll Free Tel:* 800-937-8065
Fax: 310-755-6781
E-mail: sales@wildfirelighting.com
Web Site: www.wildfirefx.com
Key Personnel
Founder & Chmn: Laurence Friedman
Pres & CEO: John Berardi
Founded: 1989
Manufacturer of long-throw UV (blacklight) fixtures, UV fluorescent paints & materials & scenic art.
Online catalog(s) available
Membership(s): International Association of Amusement Parks and Attractions; Themed Entertainment Association

John Wiley & Sons Inc
111 River St, Hoboken, NJ 07030-5774
Tel: 201-748-6000 *Toll Free Tel:* 800-225-5945 (cust serv) *Fax:* 201-748-6088
Web Site: www.wiley.com
Key Personnel
Chmn: Jesse C Wiley
Pres & CEO: Brian Napack
EVP & Group Exec: Matthew S Kissner
CFO & EVP, Technol & Opers: John Kritzmacher
Chief People Offr: Danielle McMahan
Chief Prod Offr, Res Busn: Jay Flynn
Corp Secy: Joanna Jia
EVP & Chief HR Offr: Archana Singh
EVP & Chief Mktg Offr: Clay Stobaugh
EVP & Chief Strategy Offr: Taneli Ruda
EVP & Gen Coun: Gary M Rinck
EVP & Gen Mgr, Res: Judy Verses
EVP, Knowledge & Learning: Ella Balagula
SVP & Corp Cont: Christopher Caridi
SVP & Treas: Vincent Marzano
Sr Acqs Ed: Zachary Schisgal
Sr Advisor: Mark Allin
Founded: 1807
Branch Office(s)
One Montgomery St, Suite 1000, San Francisco, CA 94104 *Tel:* 415-433-1740 *Fax:* 415-433-0499
Union Sta, 1550 Wewatta St, Denver, CO 80202
851 Trafalgar Ct, Suite 420, Maitland, FL 32751
1415 W 22 St, Suite 800, Oak Brook, IL 60523 *Tel:* 630-366-2900 *Fax:* 630-528-3101
10475 Crosspoint Blvd, Indianapolis, IN 46256 *Tel:* 317-572-3000; 317-572-3994 (consumer tech support) *Fax:* 317-572-4000 (cust care ctr/consumer accts)
101 Station Landing, Suite 300, Medford, MA 02155 *Tel:* 781-388-8200 *Fax:* 781-388-8210
400 Hwy 169, Suite 300, Minneapolis, MN 55426 *Tel:* 763-765-2222 *Fax:* 763-765-2276
One Wiley Dr, Somerset, NJ 08875-1272 *Tel:* 732-302-2300 (US cust care opers/trade & wholesale)
5205 Lake Shore Dr, Waco, TX 76710 *Tel:* 254-751-1644
90 Eglington Ave E, Suite 300, Toronto, ON M4P 2Y3, Canada *Tel:* 416-236-4433 *Toll Free Tel:* 800-567-4797 *Fax:* 416-236-8743 *Toll Free Fax:* 800-565-6802 *E-mail:* canada@wiley.com

The Will-Burt Co
169 S Main St, Orrville, OH 44667
Tel: 330-682-7015; 330-684-4000 (cust serv)
E-mail: contact_us@willburt.com
Web Site: www.willburt.com
Manufacture telescoping masts & portable towers for the broadcast & entertainment industries.
Sales Office(s): One Fullerton Rd, No 02-01, Singapore 049213, Singapore *Tel:* 6832 5689 *Fax:* 6722 0664 *E-mail:* xfwu@willburt.com
Unit 5B, Station Approach, Four Marks, Alton, Hants G434 5HN, United Kingdom *Tel:* (01403) 265532 *Fax:* (01403) 259072 *E-mail:* kbrigham@willburt.com

Williams AV LLC
10300 Valley View Rd, Eden Prairie, MN 55344-3446
Tel: 952-943-2252 *Toll Free Tel:* 800-328-6190
Fax: 952-943-2174
E-mail: info@williamsav.com
Web Site: www.williamsav.com
Key Personnel
Pres & CEO: Rob Sheeley
EVP, Sales & Mktg: Tom Mingo
VP, North American Sales: Anthony Braun
Dir, Intl Sales: Per Persson
VP, Engg & CTO: Gregg Abram
Founded: 1976
Manufacturer of large area FM, infrared, loop & digital wireless communication assistive listening devices, wireless intercom, tour guide, language interpretation.
Online catalog(s) available
Membership(s): International Technology and Engineering Educators Association; NSCA

Williams Sound LLC, see Williams AV LLC

Willoughby's® Camera
298 Fifth Ave, New York, NY 10001
Tel: 212-564-1600 *Toll Free Tel:* 800-378-1898
E-mail: customersupport@willoughbys.com
Web Site: www.willoughbys.com
Key Personnel
Chmn & CEO: Joseph Douek
Founded: 1898
Distributes cameras & photo equipment, camcorders & binoculars.
Online catalog(s) available
Membership(s): Audiovisual and Integrated Experience Association

Willow Mixed Media Inc
25 Lennox Ave, Glenford, NY 12433
Mailing Address: PO Box 194, Glenford, NY 12433-0194
Tel: 845-657-2914
E-mail: video@hvc.rr.com
Web Site: www.willowmixedmedia.org; www.documentaryworld.com
Key Personnel
Pres: Tobe Carey
Edit DVDs & documentary production (DVD & streaming from Vimeo on Demand).
Online catalog(s) available

Wilson Case Inc
113 Road 3168, Hastings, NE 68901-9418
Tel: 402-463-5040 *Toll Free Tel:* 800-322-5493
Fax: 402-463-5276
E-mail: sales@wilsoncase.com
Web Site: www.wilsoncase.com
Founded: 1976
Custom manufacturer of ATA300 (cat 1) protective cases.
Catalog(s) available, free
Online catalog(s) available

Wilson McLeran Inc
41 Corey Hill Rd, Saxtons River, VT 05154
Mailing Address: PO Box 744, Saxtons River, VT 05154-0744
Tel: 802-869-3111 *Toll Free Tel:* 800-562-9646
Fax: 802-869-3111
Web Site: www.robertfwilson.net
Key Personnel
Pres: Robert F Wilson *E-mail:* robertfwilson@gmail.com
VP & Secy: Martha Buchanan
Founded: 1988
Online catalog(s) available
Membership(s): American Association of Journalists & Authors; The Authors Guild

Wiltronix Inc
5504 Waterway Terr, Rockville, MD 20853
Key Personnel
Pres: Dwight Wilcox
Founded: 1970
Distribute scan converters & Internet to HDTV equipment.
Membership(s): IEEE Computer Society; SBE; SMPTE®

Win Media Inc
317 N Dodge St, Burlington, WI 53105
Tel: 262-763-6397
E-mail: info@winmediainc.com
Web Site: www.winmediainc.com
Key Personnel
Pres: Shad Branen *Tel:* 262-763-6397 ext 11
E-mail: shad@winmediainc.com
Multimedia development services.

Winchester Electronics Corp
68 Water St, Norwalk, CT 06854
Tel: 203-741-5400
E-mail: info@winchesterelectronics.com
Web Site: www.winchesterelectronics.com
Key Personnel
Pres & CEO: Kevin Perhamus
Inside Sales Busn Mgr: Beth Beadle
Tel: 203-741-5481 *E-mail:* beth_beadle@winchesterelectronics.com
Founded: 1941
Manufacturer of connectors & cable assemblies.
Catalog(s) available
Membership(s): EDS; NAB; SMPTE®

Wind River Broadcast Center
117 E 11 St, Loveland, CO 80537
Tel: 970-669-3442
Web Site: www.windriverbroadcast.com
Key Personnel
Owner: Jim McDonald *E-mail:* jim@windriverbroadcast.com
Broadcast services.
Product sheet(s) available

Windel International/Weyel
Division of ICA Corp
3714 Illinois Ave, St Charles, IL 60174-2421
Toll Free Tel: 800-395-7093 *Fax:* 630-587-2833
Web Site: www.windel.com
Online catalog(s) available
Membership(s): ASTO; CSI

WindTech™ Microphone Windscreens & Accessories
Division of Olsen Audio Group Inc
7845 E Evans Rd, Scottsdale, AZ 85260-2919
Tel: 480-998-7140
E-mail: information@olsenaudio.com; web-info3@olsenaudio.com
Web Site: www.olsenaudio.com; www.windtech.tv
Key Personnel
Pres: Craig N Olsen
Founded: 1976
Online catalog(s) available
Membership(s): AES; NAMM, the National Association of Music Merchants

The Wine Appreciation Guild Ltd
450 Taraval St, No 201, San Francisco, CA 94116
Tel: 650-866-3020 *Toll Free Tel:* 800-231-9463
Fax: 650-866-3513
E-mail: info@wineappreciation.com
Web Site: www.wineappreciation.com
Key Personnel
Pres: Donna Bottrell *E-mail:* donna@wineappreciation.com
Founded: 1939

Publisher & distributor of wine education materials: audiotapes, videotapes, DVDs, CD-ROMs & multimedia packages.
Catalog(s) available, annual
Membership(s): American Wine Society; The Wine Institute

Winegard Co
2736 Mount Pleasant St, Suite 140, Burlington, IA 52601
Tel: 319-754-0600 *Toll Free Tel:* 800-288-8094
E-mail: chat@winegard.com
Web Site: www.winegard.com
Key Personnel
CEO: Randy Winegard
Pres: Grant Whipple
Dir, Sales: Keith Larson *Tel:* 319-754-0628
E-mail: klars@winegard.com
Natl Sales Mgr: Brad Larson *Tel:* 319-754-0721
E-mail: blars@winegard.com
Manufacture TV antenna & satellite television products.
Online catalog(s) available
Branch Office(s)
3000 Kirkwood St, Burlington, IA 52601

Wings Wildlife Production, see Birds & Animals Unlimited

Babe Winkelman Productions Inc
PO Box 407, Brainerd, MN 56401
Tel: 218-821-6866 *Toll Free Tel:* 800-333-0471
Web Site: www.winkelman.com
Key Personnel
Pres & CEO: Babe Winkelman *E-mail:* babe@winkelman.com
Dir, Custom Prodn: Ray Eng *Tel:* 218-232-1403
E-mail: reng@winkelman.com
Founded: 1965
Full service television & production company with a staff of producers, videographers, editors, graphic designers, musicians & voice talent.

Winsted Corp
10901 Hampshire Ave S, Minneapolis, MN 55438
Tel: 952-944-9050 *Toll Free Tel:* 800-447-2257
Fax: 952-944-1546 *Toll Free Fax:* 800-421-3839
E-mail: info@winsted.com
Web Site: www.winsted.com
Key Personnel
Pres: Randy Smith
Founded: 1963
Manufacture control room consoles, furniture & vertical racks.
Catalog(s) available, annual
Branch Office(s)
1750 Breckinridge Pkwy, Suite 100, Duluth, GA 30096 *Tel:* 770-840-0880 *Toll Free Tel:* 800-237-5606 *Fax:* 770-840-9685 *E-mail:* custom@winsted.com *Web Site:* winstedcustom.com
Foreign Office(s): Winsted Europe-Middle East, Unit D1, Sapphire Ct, Isidore Rd, Bromsgrove Enterprise Park, Bromsgrove B60 3FL, United Kingdom *Tel:* (01527) 833 714 *E-mail:* info@winsted.co.uk
Membership(s): NAB

Winter Productions
10625 S Hoyne, Chicago, IL 60643
Tel: 773-238-1656
E-mail: winterpr@aol.com
Web Site: www.winterproductions.com
Key Personnel
Pres: Don Winter *Tel:* 773-405-3899 (cell)
Full service production company.

Wintergreen Learning Materials
3075 Line 8, RR2, Bradford, ON L3Z 3R5, Canada

Tel: 905-778-8584 *Toll Free Tel:* 800-268-1268
Toll Free Fax: 800-567-8054
E-mail: info@wintergreen.ca; sales@wintergreen.
ca; custserv@wintergreen.ca
Web Site: www.wintergreen.ca
Key Personnel
CFO: Joe Hayward
Pres: Michael Hayward
Founded: 1977
Educational software & technology products, fur-
niture, curriculum materials & resources.

Winterland Studios
5417 Boone Ave N, New Hope, MN 55428
Tel: 763-971-8943 *Fax:* 763-971-8952
E-mail: studio@winterlandstudios.com
Web Site: www.winterlandstudios.com
Key Personnel
Prodr & Engr: Todd Fitzgerald
Worldclass recording studio.

Wire X 17 LLC
1840 County Line Rd, Suite 301, Huntingdon
Valley, PA 19006
Tel: 215-322-4600 *Toll Free Tel:* 800-233-0013
Fax: 215-322-1385
E-mail: sales@wirexgroup.com
Web Site: wirex17.com
Key Personnel
Opers Mgr: Daniel Kenderdine *Tel:* 800-233-0013
ext 1404 *E-mail:* dankenderdine@wirex17.com
Sales Mgr: Mike Derricks *Tel:* 800-233-0013 ext
1126 *E-mail:* mderricks@wirex17.com
Computer, battery, automotive & wireless acces-
sory distributor.

Wired 4 Sound Inc
PO Box 683, Clifton, NJ 07012-0683
Tel: 973-773-2565
E-mail: info@wired4sound.com
Web Site: www.wired4sound.com
Key Personnel
Pres & CEO: Andre Grandinetti
    E-mail: agrandinetti@wired4sound.com
Founded: 1987
AV systems design, engineering, consulting, in-
stallation & integration services.
Catalog(s) available
Shipping Address: 17 Frances Ct, Cedar Grove,
NJ 07009
Membership(s): Custom Electronic Design & In-
stallation Association; NSCA

Wireworks Corp
380 Hillside Ave, Hillside, NJ 07205
Tel: 908-686-7400 *Toll Free Tel:* 800-642-9473
    Fax: 908-686-0483 (sales); 908-686-0680
E-mail: sales@wireworks.com; info@wireworks.
com
Web Site: www.wireworks.com
Key Personnel
Pres: Gerald J Krulewicz *E-mail:* krulewicz@
wireworks.com
CFO: Larry J Williams *E-mail:* williams@
wireworks.com
Sr Prod Specialist: Richard Chilvers
Founded: 1974
Manufacturer of audio & video cable assemblies.
Online catalog(s) available
Membership(s): AES; Audiovisual and Integrated
Experience Association; NAB; NSCA

Wisconsin Public Television
Division of University of Wisconsin Extension-
Wisconsin Education Communications Board
821 University Ave, Madison, WI 53706
Tel: 608-263-2121 *Toll Free Tel:* 800-422-9707
    Fax: 608-263-9763
E-mail: comments@wpt.org
Web Site: www.wpt.org

Key Personnel
COO, Assoc Dir & Dir, Prodn: Kathy Bissen
    Tel: 608-263-8496 *E-mail:* kathy.bissen@wpt.
    org
Dir, Communs & Community Collabora-
    tion: Michael Harryman *Tel:* 608-265-3855
    E-mail: michael.harryman@wpt.org
Dir, Educ: Alyssa Tsagong
Dir, Programming: Garry Denny *Tel:* 608-262-
    6834 *E-mail:* garry.denny@wpt.org
Dir, Television: Jon Miskowski *Tel:* 608-263-0299
    E-mail: jon.miskowski@wpt.org
Chief Engr: Chad Myers *Tel:* 608-263-4097
    E-mail: chad.myers@wpt.org
Fin Mgr: Deborah Allen Schultz *Tel:* 608-262-
    5260 *E-mail:* deb.allenschultz@wpt.org
Online catalog(s) available

**Wisconsin Technical College System
    Foundation Inc**
6602 Normandy Lane, Madison, WI 53719-1081
Tel: 608-841-1800 *Toll Free Tel:* 800-821-6313
    Fax: 608-841-1806
E-mail: foundation@wtcsf.tec.wi.us
Web Site: www.wtcsf.tec.wi.us
Key Personnel
Pres: Edward Chin
VP: Robert Sorensen
Secy: Paul Nelson
Treas: Daniel Clancy
Exec Dir: Paul Gabriel *E-mail:* pgabriel@wtcsf.
com
Opers Mgr: Diane Sutton *E-mail:* dsutton@wtcsf.
com
Founded: 1977
Owns & operates WIDS (curriculum develop-
ment, management software & consulting ser-
vices) & ModuMath (basic math & algebra
courses for adult student success).

Wise Audio Video
PO Box 105523, Jefferson City, MO 65110
Tel: 573-761-7888 *Toll Free Tel:* 877-775-7888
Web Site: www.wiseaudiovideo.com
Key Personnel
Owner & Pres: John Hickey *Tel:* 573-353-3885
    E-mail: johnhickey@wiseaudiovideo.com
Founded: 1999
Specialize in audio, video, lighting, acoustical
treatment, teleconferencing, digital signage &
security systems.

Witcher Productions, see Marsh Media

WKMG-TV News 6
Subsidiary of Graham Media Group
4466 N John Young Pkwy, Orlando, FL 32804
Tel: 407-521-1200 *Fax:* 407-521-1204
Web Site: www.clickorlando.com
Key Personnel
Creative Servs Dir: Kym Peoples
    E-mail: kpeoples@wkmg.com
Television station.

WKYT-TV
Subsidiary of Gray Television Inc
2851 Winchester Rd, Lexington, KY 40509
Tel: 859-299-0411; 859-299-2727 (newsroom)
Web Site: www.wkyt.com
Key Personnel
Gen Mgr: Chris Mossman *E-mail:* chris.
mossman@gray.tv
Opers Mgr: Mike Kanarek *E-mail:* mike.
kanarek@wkyt.com
Broadcast & media production company.
Membership(s): NAB

WMAR-TV
Member of Scripps TV Station Group
6400 York Rd, Baltimore, MD 21212
Tel: 410-377-2222

E-mail: newsroom@wmar.com
Web Site: www.abc2news.com
Key Personnel
VP & Gen Mgr: Bill Hooper
News Dir: Kelly Groft
Television station.

WMS Media Inc
189 W Santa Clara St, San Jose, CA 95110
Tel: 510-825-7402
E-mail: info@wmsmedia.com
Web Site: www.wmsmedia.com
Key Personnel
Chmn: Thomas A Wohlmut *E-mail:* tom@
wmsmedia.com
Dir, Photog/Ed: Jake Heindel
Prodr/Writer: Laura Monczynski
Founded: 1978
Video, web sites, multimedia & print.
Membership(s): ATD

WNET/New York Public Media
825 Eighth Ave, New York, NY 10019
Tel: 212-560-1313 *Fax:* 212-560-1314
E-mail: programming@thirteen.org
Web Site: www.thirteen.org; www.wnet.org
Key Personnel
Pres & CEO: Neal Shapiro
Chief Digital Offr: Daniel Greenberg
Chief Mktg & Engagement Offr: Kellie Castrutta
    Specter
CTO: Peter Brickman
VP, CFO & Treas: Caroline C Croen
VP, Gen Coun & Secy: Robert A Feinberg
VP, HR: Charlene Shapiro
VP, Media & Broadcast Opers: Roslyn Davis
VP, Programming: Stephen Segaller
VP, Subs Stations: John Servidio
Gen Mgr, Creative News Group: Scott Davis
Television programming.

Wohler Technologies Inc
31055 Huntwood Ave, Hayward, CA 94544
Tel: 510-870-0810 *Toll Free Tel:* 888-5-WOHLER
    (596-4537)
E-mail: sales@wohler.com
Web Site: www.wohler.com
Founded: 1983
Audio & video equipment manufacturer.
Online catalog(s) available
Foreign Office(s): Wohler APAC, 45/F The
    Lee Gardens, 33 Hysan Ave, Causeway Bay,
    Hong Kong *Tel:* 8199 9659 *Fax:* 3180 2299
    E-mail: salesasia@wohler.com
Wolher Europe, Medaxon House, Suite 3, Mill
    Mead, Staines TW18 4UQ, United Kingdom
    Tel: (020) 7193 7066 *E-mail:* salesemea@
    wohler.com
Membership(s): SMPTE®

WolfVision Inc
Subsidiary of WolfVision Austria
2055 Sugarloaf Circle, Suite 125, Duluth, GA
    30097
Tel: 770-931-6802 *Toll Free Tel:* 877-873-WOLF
    (873-9653) *Fax:* 770-931-6906
E-mail: sales@wolfvision.us; support@
    wolfvision.us; orders@wolfvision.us
Web Site: wolfvision.com
Key Personnel
Pres & CEO: Arthur Jenni
VP & Regional Sales Mgr: Andrea Mayer
    E-mail: andrea.mayer@wolfvision.us
Founded: 1995
Manufacturer of top quality portable, profes-
sional & ceiling visualizers used for display-
ing material in presentations, training, educa-
tion/teaching, video-conferencing, 3D scanning,
telemedicine & broadcasting. Designed to eas-
ily & accurately capture any kind of material
to be displayed, whether it be written material

on paper or transparency, x-rays, 3D objects & even items or people in a room.
Online catalog(s) available
Branch Office(s)
WolfVision Canada Inc, 500-1101 Polyteck St, Ottawa, ON K1J 0B3, Canada, Intl Sales Mgr: Jon Ivar Husby *Tel:* 613-741-9898 *Toll Free Tel:* 888-294-9889 *Fax:* 613-741-3747 *Toll Free Fax:* 888-294-2160 *E-mail:* wolfvision. canada@wolfvision.com
Foreign Office(s): WolfVision GmbH, Oberes Ried 14, 6833 Klaus, Austria, Mng Dir: Michael Lisch *Tel:* (05523) 52250 *Fax:* (05523) 52249 *E-mail:* wolfvision@wolfvision.com (headquarters)
WolfVision Co Ltd, 9F, 1-30-15 Takadanobaba, Shinjuku, Tokyo 169-0075, Japan, Sales Mgr: Akihiko Natori *Tel:* (03) 6233 9465 *Fax:* (03) 6233 9466 *E-mail:* wolfvision. japan@wolfvision.com
WolfMusic Nordic, Selma Ellefsens vei 6, 0581 Oslo, Norway *E-mail:* wolfvision.nordic@ wolfvision.com
WolfVision Pte Ltd, 7030 Ang Mo Kio Ave 5, No 01-15, Singapore 569880, Singapore, Gen Mgr: Adrian Yaw *Tel:* 6636 1268 *Fax:* 6636 1269 *E-mail:* wolfvision.asia@wolfvision.net
WolfVision Middle East, Off 104, Technohub-2, PO Box 341290, Dubai Silicon Oasis, Dubai, United Arab Emirates, Sales Mgr: Hazem Mahdy *Tel:* (04) 354 2233 *Fax:* (04) 354 2244 *E-mail:* wolfvision.mideast@wolfvision.com
WolfVision UK Ltd, Jubilee House, Third Ave, Marlow SL7 1EY, United Kingdom, Sales Mgr: Stuart Dockerill *Tel:* (01628) 509067 *Fax:* (01628) 509100 *E-mail:* wolfvision.uk@ wolfvision.com
Membership(s): Audiovisual and Integrated Experience Association

Women Make Movies Inc
115 W 29 St, Suite 1200, New York, NY 10001
Tel: 212-925-0606 *Fax:* 212-925-2052
E-mail: info@wmm.com
Web Site: www.wmm.com
Key Personnel
Exec Dir: Debra Zimmerman *E-mail:* dz@wmm. com
Dir, Acqs & Exhibition: Kristen Fitzpatrick *E-mail:* kf@wmm.com
Founded: 1972
Video distributor.
Catalog(s) available

Wonderwomen™ Enterprises
485 Rugby Rd, Brooklyn, NY 11226
Tel: 646-456-3266; 718-693-4322
E-mail: info@wonderwomen.com
Key Personnel
Pres & CEO: Harriet Rita Semegram
Founded: 1961
Documentary film production, education, child bearing, Alexander technique.

WoodenBoat Publications
41 WoodenBoat Lane, Brooklin, ME 04616
Mailing Address: PO Box 78, Brooklin, ME 04616-0078
Tel: 207-359-4651 *Toll Free Tel:* 800-877-5284 (subns) *Fax:* 207-359-8920
E-mail: woodenboat@woodenboat.com
Web Site: www.woodenboat.com
Key Personnel
Chmn: Jon Wilson
Pres & Gen Mgr: James E Miller
Edit: Matt Murphy *E-mail:* matt@woodenboat. com
Founded: 1974
Boat design, construction & repair videos.
Online catalog(s) available
Membership(s): SIVA

Woodside Avenue Music Productions Inc
2906 Central St, No 117, Evanston, IL 60201
Tel: 847-864-6655
E-mail: music@woodsideavenue.com
Web Site: www.woodsideavenue.com
Key Personnel
Prodr: Steve Rashid
Dir: Bea Rashid
Full service production company.

Mark Woollen & Associates
207 Ashland Ave, Santa Monica, CA 90405
Tel: 310-399-2690
E-mail: info@markwoollen.com
Web Site: www.markwoollen.com
Key Personnel
Prodr: Scott Mitsui *E-mail:* scott@markwoollen. com
Motion picture advertising.

Word Label Group
Division of Word Entertainment LLC
25 Music Sq W, Nashville, TN 37203
Tel: 615-251-0600
E-mail: wordtech@wbr.com
Web Site: www.wordlabelgroup.com; www. wordentertainment.com
Key Personnel
Pres & CEO: Rod Riley
Christian recording & music publications.
Online catalog(s) available

World Beat Studio
137 Sequoia Rd, Rockwall, TX 75032
Tel: 972-771-3797 *Fax:* 972-771-0853
E-mail: tropikalproductions@gmail.com
Web Site: www.tropikalproductions.com; www. tropikalproductions.com/studio.html
Key Personnel
Owner & Prodr: Jimi Towry *Tel:* 469-338-9237 (cell)
Engr: Arik Miles
Founded: 1990
Recording/music production studio. Digital recording-MAC with Apple Logic Pro, MIDI keyboards, drums, percussion, bass amp, guitar amp, piano. Office in Playa Bejuco, Costa Rica.
Membership(s): BMI

World Beatnik Records, see World Beat Studio

World Class Learning Materials Inc
PO Box 639, Candler, NC 28715
Toll Free Tel: 800-638-6470 *Toll Free Fax:* 800-638-6499
E-mail: info@wclm.com
Web Site: www.wclm.com
Key Personnel
Owner: Bruce Brown *E-mail:* bbrown@wclm.com
Manufacturer & publisher of supplemental learning materials.
Online catalog(s) available
Membership(s): Education Market Association

World Media Group Inc
7373 Dogwood Park, Richland Hills, TX 76118
Toll Free Tel: 800-400-4964 *Fax:* 817-885-8859
E-mail: getstarted@worldmediagroup.com; information@worldmediagroup.com
Web Site: www.worldmediagroup.com
Key Personnel
Pres & CEO: Jeff Mellentine *Tel:* 317-275-1042 *E-mail:* jeffm@worldmediagroup.com
VP, Busn Devt: Michael Cantor *Tel:* 917-821-7223 *E-mail:* michaelc@worldmediagroup.com
VP, Opers: Josh Mellentine *Tel:* 317-275-1058 *E-mail:* joshm@worldmediagroup.com
VP, Sales: Holly Viering *Tel:* 317-275-1041 *E-mail:* hollyv@worldmediagroup.com

Graphic design & custom printing on plastic cards, digital mastering & manufacturing of USB flash drives & DVDs.
Online catalog(s) available
Membership(s): Audio Publishers Association

World Wide Pictures Inc
Subsidiary of Billy Graham Evangelistic Association
One Billy Graham Pkwy, Charlotte, NC 28266-8029
Mailing Address: PO Box 668029, Charlotte, NC 28266-8029
Tel: 704-401-2432 *Toll Free Tel:* 877-247-2426 *Fax:* 704-401-3045
Web Site: www.wwp.org; www.billgraham. org/wwp
Key Personnel
Video & Film Archives Mgr: David Eades
Christian films from the Billy Graham Evangelistic Association.
Online catalog(s) available

WorldStage
259 W 30 St, 12th fl, New York, NY 10001-2863
Tel: 212-582-2345 *Fax:* 718-610-1750
E-mail: info@worldstage.com
Web Site: www.worldstage.com
Key Personnel
CEO: Gary Standard
CFO: Stan Jacobs
Pres: Josh Weisberg
AV & lighting equipment, LED lighting & video.

Worldview Entertainment Holdings Inc
1384 Broadway, 25th fl, New York, NY 10018
Tel: 212-431-3090
E-mail: info@worldviewent.com
Web Site: www.worldviewent.com
Founded: 2007
Motion picture investment & production company focused on well-crafted high production value filmed entertainment.
Catalog(s) available

WorldView Software
11 Barby Lane, Plainview, NY 11803
Tel: 516-681-1773
E-mail: history@worldviewsoftware.com
Web Site: www.worldviewsoftware.com
Key Personnel
Pres: Jerry Kleinstein
VP: Arnold Kleinstein
Founded: 1990
Produce & distribute educational/social studies software programs for grades 7-12.
Online catalog(s) available

Worldwide Entertainment Corp
135 S McCarty Dr, Suite 101, Beverly Hills, CA 90212
Tel: 310-858-1272 *Fax:* 310-858-3774
Key Personnel
VP: Judith Parker Harris *E-mail:* jph@ healthesteem.com
Founded: 1974
Producing & distribution of classic sci-fi & exploitation films, including *The Blob.*
Catalog(s) available
Brochure(s) available

Worthwhile Films
317 Winona St, Northfield, MN 55057
Tel: 507-645-6868 *Toll Free Tel:* 877-507-5077
Web Site: worthwhilefilms.org
Key Personnel
Prodr: Steve Braker *E-mail:* braker@ worthwhilefilms.org
Founded: 1985
Narration-free documentary production with & for virtuous nonprofit organizations, benign government agencies & other worthwhile causes.

Rate sheet(s) available, on request, call or write for a detailed proposal
Membership(s): IDA

WOUB Public Media
35 S College St, Athens, OH 45701
Tel: 740-593-1771 *Toll Free Tel:* 800-456-2044
E-mail: woub@woub.org
Web Site: woub.org
Key Personnel
CTO: Steve Skidmore *E-mail:* skidmore@ohio.edu
Dir: Thomas Hodson *E-mail:* hodson@ohio.edu
Gen Mgr: Mark Brewer *E-mail:* brewer@ohio.edu
Public television, radio station, distance learning & production services.

WPA Film Library
Division of MPI Media Group
16101 S 108 Ave, Orland Park, IL 60467
Tel: 708-460-0555 *Toll Free Tel:* 800-323-0442
Fax: 708-460-0187
E-mail: sales@wpafilmlibrary.com
Web Site: www.wpafilmlibrary.com
Key Personnel
Gen Mgr: Nicola Goelzhauser
Founded: 1987
License stock footage.
Foreign Office(s): Library Media Solutions Ltd, Liberty House, 222 Regent St, London W1B 5TR, United Kingdom, Contact: Patrick Smith *Tel:* (020) 3755 3177 *Fax:* (020) 7183 2360 *E-mail:* patrick@librarymediasolutions.com
Membership(s): Association of Moving Image Archivists; Entertainment Merchants Association; The Federation of Commercial Audiovisual Libraries Ltd

WPGH-TV
Subsidiary of Sinclair Broadcast Group Inc
750 Ivory Ave, Pittsburgh, PA 15214
Tel: 412-931-5300; 412-931-8020 (sales)
Fax: 412-931-4284
Web Site: www.sbgi.net; www.wpgh53.com
Key Personnel
Gen Mgr: Jim Lapiana
Station Admin & Dir, HR: Julie Dallas
TV broadcasting.

WPHL-TV
5001 Wynnefield Ave, Philadelphia, PA 19131
Tel: 215-878-1700
E-mail: feedback@phl17.com
Web Site: www.phl17.com
Key Personnel
SVP & Gen Mgr: Vincent Giannini
Creative Servs Dir: Travis Brower
Dir, Sales & Gen Sales Mgr: Dave Yost
Founded: 1965
Local television station.

WQED-Multimedia
4802 Fifth Ave, Pittsburgh, PA 15213
Tel: 412-622-1300; 412-622-1370
Web Site: www.wqed.org
Key Personnel
Pres & CEO: Deborah L Acklin *Tel:* 412-622-1314 *E-mail:* dacklin@wqed.org
VP, Content: Darryl Ford-Williams *Tel:* 412-622-1393 *E-mail:* dfwillia@wqed.org
VP, Devt & Membership: Lilli Mosco *Tel:* 412-622-1371 *E-mail:* lmosco@wqed.org
Founded: 1954
HD studio & field production, HD non-linear editing, VYUX connectivity (HD), fiber connectivity to Pittsburgh Teleport (HD). Studios available to rent: 35' x 35', 40' x 60' & 80' x 80'. Omni music, studio cutz & sound ideas music libraries.

Writer's AudioShop/Davenport Productions
1316 Overland Stage Rd, Dripping Springs, TX 78620
Tel: 512-476-1616 (edit); 512-264-7067 (sales)
E-mail: wrtaudshop@aol.com
Web Site: www.writersaudio.com
Key Personnel
Owner & Publr: Elaine Davenport
Founded: 1985
Publishes live seminars on how to write - workshops from America's top writers, teaching the ABCs (art, business & craft) of writing. Also, folklore & Texana recordings.
Membership(s): Audio Publishers Association

The Writing Co
Division of Social Studies School Service
10200 Jefferson Blvd, Culver City, CA 90232
Mailing Address: PO Box 802, Culver City, CA 90232-0802
Tel: 310-839-2436 *Toll Free Tel:* 800-421-4246 *Fax:* 310-839-2249 *Toll Free Fax:* 800-944-5432
E-mail: access@writingco.com; customerservice@writingco.com
Web Site: www.socialstudies.com
Key Personnel
Pres: Sanford Weiner
Supplementary curriculum material.
Catalog(s) available

WSAZ-TV NewsChannel 3
Division of Gray Television Inc
645 Fifth Ave, Huntington, WV 25701
Tel: 304-697-4780 *Fax:* 304-690-3065 (newsroom); 304-690-3061 (sales)
E-mail: news@wsaz.com
Web Site: www.wsaz.com
Key Personnel
Gen Mgr: Matt Moran *E-mail:* matt.moran@wsaz.com
Satellite uplink facility KU band. Produce & edit short form/long form commercials.
Branch Office(s)
111 Columbia Ave, Charleston, WV 25302, Opers Mgr: Jeff Sadler *Tel:* 304-344-3521 *Fax:* 304-340-4649 (newsroom) *E-mail:* jeff.sadler@wsaz.com

WSI, see The Weather Company, An IBM Business

WTL Productions
345 E 52 St, Suite 1, New York, NY 10022
Tel: 212-355-1893
E-mail: wtlvideo@aol.com
Key Personnel
Prodr: William Whitlock
Small, independent production company.

WTMJ-TV
Member of Scripps TV Station Group
720 E Capitol Dr, Milwaukee, WI 53212
Tel: 414-332-9611 *Fax:* 414-967-5378
E-mail: tmj4feedback@scripps.com
Web Site: www.tmj4.com
Key Personnel
VP & Gen Mgr: Joe Poss *E-mail:* joe.poss@tmj4.com
Mgr, Opers: Tony Lucas *E-mail:* tony.lucas@scripps.com
Programming: Oneda Walker *E-mail:* oneda.walker@scripps.com
TV broadcasting.

WTSmedia
2841 Hickory Valley, Chattanooga, TN 37421
Tel: 423-894-9427 *Toll Free Tel:* 888-987-6334; 800-251-7228 *Fax:* 423-894-7281 *Toll Free Fax:* 800-591-4809
E-mail: sales@wtsmedia.com

Web Site: www.wtsduplication.com
Key Personnel
CEO: Diane Salley Frady
Pres: Michael Salley
Founded: 1977
CD, DVD & Blu-ray replication.
Branch Office(s)
526 E Iris Dr, Nashville, TN 37204 *Tel:* 615-457-2519

WTVS, Detroit Public Television
Riley Broadcast Ctr, One Clover Ct, Wixom, MI 48393-2247
Tel: 248-305-DPTV (305-3788); 313-872-7500
E-mail: email@dptv.org
Web Site: www.dptv.org
Key Personnel
Pres & CEO: Rich Homberg *E-mail:* rhomberg@dptv.org
COO: Tom Szczepanski *E-mail:* tomsz@dptv.org
Acting CFO: John Wenzel *E-mail:* jwenzel@dptv.org
Dir, Communs: Martin Fischhoff *Tel:* 248-305-3770 *E-mail:* mfischhoff@dptv.org
Opers Mgr: Laura Hinojasa *Tel:* 248-305-3759 *E-mail:* lhinojasa@dptv.org
Busn Devt: Jamie Westrick *E-mail:* jwestrick@dptv.org
Content & Community Engagement: Georgeann Herbert *E-mail:* gherbert@dptv.org
Prodn: Fred Nahhat *E-mail:* fnahhat@dptv.org
TV, Radio & Digital Communs: Dave Devereaux *E-mail:* devereaux@dptv.org
Founded: 1955
Studio, field & post-production services with transmission & HD mobile production truck.
Rate card(s) available
Membership(s): DGA; IBEW; Michigan Association of Public Broadcasters; PBS

WVLA-TV
Subsidiary of White Knight Broadcasting
10,000 Perkins Rd, Baton Rouge, LA 70810
Tel: 225-766-3233 *Fax:* 225-768-9293
Web Site: www.brproud.com
Key Personnel
Dir of Opers: Devin Womack *E-mail:* dwomack@brproud.com
Gen Mgr, Sales: Trista Henson
Commercial & industrial production & studio rental.
Membership(s): AAF

WVP Boston
50 Hunt St, Watertown, MA 02472
Tel: 617-926-2089
Web Site: wvpboston.com
Key Personnel
Prodr & Prodn Mgr: Andy Jablon *E-mail:* andy@wvpboston.com
Dir, Photog: Jim Petit *E-mail:* jim@wvpboston.com
Full service video production.

The Wyland Group
Division of Faith for Today
11291 Pierce St, Riverside, CA 92505
Tel: 805-955-7681 *Fax:* 805-522-1082
Key Personnel
Acct Exec: Chauncey Smith
Founded: 1955

X-Rite
4300 44 St SE, Grand Rapids, MI 49512
Tel: 616-803-2100 *Toll Free Tel:* 800-248-9748; 888-800-9580
Web Site: www.xrite.com
Key Personnel
CFO: Jeffrey McKee
EVP & CTO: Dr Francis Lamy
Founded: 1958
Color systems & software.
Online catalog(s) available

Branch Office(s)
2 Highwood Dr, Suite 102, Tewksbury, MA 01876 *Fax:* 978-851-6697
Foreign Office(s): X-Rite Beijing, Rm 1201, Block C Wangjing Fangheng Bldg, No 6 Futong East St, Chaoyang District, Beijing 100101, China *Tel:* (010) 8478 5490 *Fax:* (010) 8478 5491 *E-mail:* info_beijing@xrite.com
2510 Tower B China International Ctr, Guangzhou 101125, China *Tel:* (020) 8375-2900 *Fax:* (020) 8375-2911 *E-mail:* info_guangzhou@xrite.com
X-Rite (Shanghai) Color Management Co Ltd, 6/F, Bldg 1, IBP Phase 2, 518 Fuquan North Rd, Changning District, Shanghai, China *Tel:* (021) 3279 6666 *Fax:* (021) 3279 6649 *E-mail:* info_shanghai@xrite.com
Palanek 374/1a, 2nd fl, 682 01 Vyskov, Czechia *Tel:* 517 332 331 *E-mail:* xritecz@infos.cz
X-Rite Mediterranee, Parc d'Activites du Moulin, 43, rue du Saule Trapu, 91300 Massy, France, *Off Mgr:* Marie-Helene Boucher *Tel:* 01 69 53 66 20 *Fax:* 01 69 53 00 52
Fraunhoferstr 14, 82152 Martinsried, Germany *Tel:* (089) 85 707-0 *Fax:* (089) 85 707-222 *E-mail:* info@erx50.com
Siemensstr 12b, 63263 Neu-Isenburg, Germany *Tel:* (061) 0279 57-0 *Fax:* (061) 0279 5757
X-Rite Asia Pacific Ltd, Suite 2801, 28th fl, AXA Tower, Landmark E, 100 How Ming St, Kwun Tong, Kowloon, Hong Kong *Tel:* 2568 6283 *Fax:* 2885 8610 *E-mail:* info_ap@xrite.com
X-Rite India Pvt Ltd, Esteem Tower, No 71, Railway Parallel Rd, Kumara Park W, Bangalore 560 020, India *Tel:* (080) 4352 0214; 8884901319 (cell) *E-mail:* rajendrannarayan@xrite.com
X-Rite Italy SRL, Via Braille, 69/69A, 59100 Prato PO, Italy, *Sales Dir:* Andrea Vannacci *Tel:* (0574) 527755 ext 210 *Fax:* (0574) 527671
6/F Telecom Ctr, 2-5-10 Aomi, Koto-ku, Tokyo 135-0064, Japan *Tel:* (03) 5579-6545 *Fax:* (03) 5579-6547
X-Rite Europe GmbH, Gostinichnyy proezd, 4A, Bldg 1, 127106 Moscow, Russia, *Sales Dir:* Andrey Kotik *Tel:* (495) 988-4552; (915) 074-9930 (cell) *Fax:* (499) 976-3710
8 Changi Business Park Ave 1, No 07-51, UE BizHub East (S Tower) S486018, Singapore, Singapore *Tel:* 6420 0411 *E-mail:* info. seasiapacific@xrite.com
13F, Pantech Bldg, 179 Seongam-ro, Mapo-gu, Seoul 03929, South Korea, Contact: Mr Sae Hoon Lee *Tel:* (070) 4279-9119 *E-mail:* saehoonlee@xrite.com
X-Rite Iberica, Torre Realia-BCN Plaza Europa 41-43, 4° Planta, L'Hospitalet de Llobregat, 08908 Barcelona, Spain, *Sales Dir:* Nacho Benito *Tel:* 935473709; 935473741 (tech support) *E-mail:* x-riteiberica@xrite.com
X-Rite Europe GmbH, Althardstr 70, 8105 Regensdorf, Switzerland *Toll Free Tel:* 800 700 300 01 *Fax:* (044) 842 22 22
The Acumen Centre, First Ave, Poynton, Cheshire SK12 1FJ, United Kingdom, *Mng Dir:* Mike Smyth *Tel:* (01625) 871100 *Fax:* (01625) 871444
Membership(s): American Manufacturers Association; American Society for Testing Materials

Xantech LLC
Subsidiary of Core Brands LLC
1800 S McDowell Blvd, Petaluma, CA 94954
Tel: 707-283-5900 *Toll Free Tel:* 800-472-5555
Fax: 707-283-5901
E-mail: info@corebrands.com
Web Site: www.xantech.com
Founded: 1969
Manufacturer & marketer of consumer electronics components & AV entertainment systems.

Catalog(s) available
Membership(s): Consumer Technology Association™; Custom Electronic Design & Installation Association; NSCA

Xenon Pictures Inc
Division of Xenon Entertainment Group
3521 Jack Northrop Ave, Hawthorne, CA 90250
Tel: 310-451-5510 *Fax:* 310-395-4058
E-mail: info@xenonpictures.com
Web Site: xenonpictures.com
Key Personnel
Founder, Pres & CEO: S Leigh Savidge
EVP & COO: Steve Housden
Cont: Joey Hipolito
Dir, Opers: Thad Simpson
Natl Sales Dir: Haydee Rios *E-mail:* haydee@xenonpictures.com
Prodr: Jeff Scheftel
Opers Mgr: James Renn
Consultant: Kent Little
PR: Susan Self *E-mail:* susan@xenonpictures.com
Founded: 1986
Film production & distribution company.
Online catalog(s) available
Membership(s): Entertainment Merchants Association

Xintekvideo Inc
56 W Broad St, Stamford, CT 06902
Tel: 203-348-9229
Web Site: www.xintekvideo.com
Key Personnel
Pres: John Rossi *E-mail:* jrossi@xintekvideo.com
Founded: 1986
Manufacture video processing equipment for picture enhancement & video quality restoration.
Brochure(s) available
Membership(s): NAB

XTA Electronics Ltd
Division of Group One Ltd
70 Sea Lane, Farmingdale, NY 11735
Tel: 631-396-0195 (audio div); 631-396-0184 (lighting div) *Fax:* 631-396-0190
E-mail: sales@g1limited.com
Web Site: www.g1limited.com
Key Personnel
Pres: Jack Kelly *Tel:* 516-249-1399 ext 102 *E-mail:* jackk@g1limited.com
Membership(s): AES; NAB; NSCA

Xtech Systems Inc
241 Rock Creek Lane, Scarsdale, NY 10583
Mailing Address: PO Box 147, Scarsdale, NY 10583-0147
Tel: 718-543-1222 *Fax:* 914-472-2111
Toll Free Tel: 888-528-6511
E-mail: info@xtechsystems.com
Web Site: www.xtechsystems.com
Key Personnel
Pres: Richard Woolf
Wireless systems infrastructure specialists.
Catalog(s) available
Membership(s): ARA; ASAE

Xytech Systems Corp
15451 San Fernando Mission Blvd, Suite 400, Mission Hills, CA 91345
Tel: 818-698-4900 *Fax:* 818-698-4901
E-mail: sales@xytechsystems.com
Web Site: www.xytechsystems.com
Key Personnel
Pres & CEO: Richard Gallagher
COO: Greg Dolan
SVP, Fin & Admin: Susie Nemeti
SVP, R&D: Ken Shook
VP, Prof Servs: Tanmay Goel
Dir, Mktg: Alexandra Kuipers *E-mail:* akuipers@xytechsystems.com
Founded: 1998

Delivers one-stop shopping for any size facility, from a single user to hundreds of interactive users, with the support infrastructure of consulting, technical assistance, training & systems integration. Installs facilities management systems in commercial teleproduction & corporate industrial facilities, satellite broadcasting corporations & Fortune 500 companies around the globe.
Foreign Office(s): Xytech Systems UK Ltd, 28 Margaret St, 3rd fl, London W1W 8RZ, United Kingdom, Gen Mgr: Daniel Lynch *Tel:* (020) 3478 1450 *Fax:* (020) 3478 1441

Yada/Levine Video Productions
3129 S Hacienda Blvd, No 423, Hacienda Heights, CA 91745
Tel: 323-461-1616 *Fax:* 323-461-2288
E-mail: video@yadalevine.com
Web Site: www.yadalevine.com
Key Personnel
Pres: Michael Yada
Founded: 1983
Video production.

Yale Film & Video
Affiliate of Yale Laboratory Inc
25640 Avenue Stanford, Valencia, CA 91355
Tel: 661-295-7170; 661-295-7160
E-mail: info@yalefilmandvideo.com; yalefilmandvideo@gmail.com
Web Site: www.yalefilmandvideo.com
Founded: 1946
Motion picture processing & film to video transfers. Transfer film to DVD/hard drive & film processing. Offering HD, 2K & 4K scanning for super 8, regular 8, 16, S16 & 35mm.
Price list(s) available

Yamaha Electronics Corp
Subsidiary of Yamaha Corporation of America
6660 Orangethorpe Ave, Buena Park, CA 90620
Tel: 714-522-9105 *Toll Free Tel:* 800-292-2982 (cust support)
Web Site: usa.yamaha.com/products/audio_visual/index.html
Founded: 1960
Home audio components & systems.
Online catalog(s) available
Membership(s): Consumer Technology Association™

Yanchar Design & Consulting Group
26741 Portola Pkwy, Suite 1E, Foothill Ranch, CA 92610-1763
Tel: 949-770-6601 *Fax:* 949-770-6575
E-mail: info@yanchardesign.com
Web Site: www.yanchardesign.com
Key Personnel
Pres: Carl J Yanchar
Design/build firm for recording, video, motion picture & broadcast facilities.
Membership(s): AES; American Institute of Architects; ASA; SMPTE®

YAP Films
233 Broadview Ave, Toronto, ON M4M 2G3, Canada
Tel: 416-504-3662 *Fax:* 416-504-3667
E-mail: thedog@yapfilms.com
Web Site: www.yapfilms.com
Key Personnel
Exec Prodr & Dir: Elliot Halpern
Exec Prodr & Dir, Devt: Elizabeth Trojian
Busn Aff Mgr: Robin Gleadall
In-House Prodn Mgr: Anja Sobkowska
Independent production company.

Yarn Barn of Kansas
930 Massachusetts St, Lawrence, KS 66044
Tel: 785-842-4333 *Toll Free Tel:* 800-468-0035

E-mail: info@yarnbarn-ks.com
Web Site: www.yarnbarn-ks.com
Key Personnel
Pres: Susan Bateman
Founded: 1971
Online catalog(s) available

Yellow Cat Productions Inc
505 11 St SE, Washington, DC 20003
Tel: 202-543-2221
E-mail: yellowcat@yellowcat.com
Web Site: www.yellowcat.com
Key Personnel
Pres/Prodr/Dir/Writer/Dir, Photog: Michael Ford
Prodr/Writer/Ed/Animator: Katie Gates
Writer/Prodr/Prog Developer: Lou Linden
Founded: 1980
Full service video production.
Online catalog(s) available
Membership(s): NABET-CWA; Women in Film & Video

Yellow Moon Press
29 Josephine Ave, Somerville, MA 02144
Mailing Address: PO Box 381316, Cambridge, MA 02238-1316
Tel: 617-776-2230 *Toll Free Tel:* 800-497-4385
E-mail: story@yellowmoon.com
Web Site: www.yellowmoon.com
Key Personnel
Pres: Robert Smyth
Founded: 1978
Publish material from the various arts of the oral tradition as it pertains to storytelling, poetry & music. It is our goal to make available material that both explores the history of the oral tradition & breathes new life into it.
Online catalog(s) available

Yellowknife Films Inc
5021 53 St, Yellowknife, NT X1A 1V5, Canada
Tel: 867-873-8610
E-mail: ykf@theedge.ca
Web Site: www.ykfilms.ca
Key Personnel
Owner: Alan Booth
HD video production, editing videography & arctic specialists.
Online catalog(s) available

YES Productions
Subsidiary of WYES-TV
916 Navarre Ave, New Orleans, LA 70124
Tel: 504-840-4891 *Toll Free Tel:* 800-736-8812
Fax: 504-840-4895
Web Site: www.yesproductions.com
Key Personnel
VP & Gen Mgr: Jim Moriarty *Tel:* 504-616-3999 (cell) *E-mail:* jim@yesproductions.com
Complete television production facility.
Online catalog(s) available

Yessian
137 Fifth Ave, 3rd fl, New York, NY 10010
Tel: 212-533-3443
E-mail: info-ny@yessian.com
Web Site: www.yessian.com
Key Personnel
Partner & Chief Commercial Offr: Brian Yessian
    E-mail: brian@yessian.com
Partner & Head, Prodn: Michael Yessian
    E-mail: michael@yessian.com
Mng Dir & Exec Prodr: Marlene Bartos
    E-mail: marlene@yessian.com
Founded: 1971
Full service studio facility. Specialize in original music, sound design, audio engineering & TV & film scores.
Branch Office(s)
1275 Electric Ave, Venice, CA 90291 *Tel:* 310-844-1184 *E-mail:* info-la@yessian.com

33117 Hamilton Ct, Farmington Hills, MI 48334 *Tel:* 248-553-4044 *E-mail:* info-detroit@yessian.com
Foreign Office(s): Schulterblatt 58, 20357 Hamburg, Germany *Tel:* (040) 40185159 *E-mail:* info-germany@yessian.com

The Yesterday USA Radio Networks
2001 Plymouth Rock Dr, Richardson, TX 75081-3946
Tel: 972-889-9872 *Fax:* 972-889-2329
Web Site: www.yesterdayusa.com
Key Personnel
Founder: Bill Bragg *E-mail:* bb@yesterdayusa.com
Founded: 1983
Broadcasting old time radio shows & vintage music.

YMAA Publication Center Inc
51 Mill St, Wolfeboro, NH 03894
Mailing Address: PO Box 480, Wolfeboro, NH 03894
Tel: 603-569-7988 *Toll Free Tel:* 800-669-8892
    Fax: 603-569-1889
E-mail: info@ymaa.com
Web Site: www.ymaa.com
Key Personnel
Pres & Publr: David Ripianzi *E-mail:* publisher@ymaa.com
Founded: 1982
Production & distribution of martial arts instructional videos, books & DVDs.
Online catalog(s) available
Membership(s): ABA; Independent Book Publishers Association

Yorktel
81 Corbett Way, Eatontown, NJ 07724
Tel: 732-413-6000 *Toll Free Tel:* 866-836-8463
    Fax: 732-413-6060
E-mail: knowmore@yorktel.com
Web Site: yorktel.com
Key Personnel
Founder & Chmn of the Bd: Vork Wang, PhD
CEO: Ron Gaboury
CTO: Bin Guan
CIO: Dr Joe-E Hu
EVP, Corp Servs & CFO: Judi Pulig
EVP, Busn Mgmt: Karen Paglia
EVP, Media Servs: Mark Maxey
EVP, Opers: Frankie Escribano
EVP, Sales & Mktg: Greg Douglas
SVP, Healthcare: Peter McLain
SVP, Mktg: Samantha Osowski
SVP, Prod Mgmt: John Vitale
SVP, Prof Servs: Vishal Brown
VP, Busn Devt Asia Pacific: Aaron Wentzel
Founded: 1985
AV & presentation products.
Catalog(s) available
Branch Office(s)
857 Elkridge Landing Rd, Suite 600, Linthicom, MD 21090 *Tel:* 240-898-2400 ext 2227 (fed off)
33 Upton Dr, Wilmington, MA 01887 *Tel:* 978-658-5150 *Toll Free Tel:* 800-868-5150
    Fax: 978-753-4777
4140 Sheridan Dr, Suite 4, Williamsville, NY 14221 *Tel:* 716-810-9550 *Fax:* 716-810-9553
1930 Camden Rd, Suite 100, Charlotte, NC 28203 *Tel:* 980-430-3828
342 Victory Dr, Herndon, VA 20170 *Tel:* 571-612-8991
Foreign Office(s): Yorktel France SAS, 53 Ave Hoche, 75008 Paris, France *Tel:* 05 82 88 14 80 *E-mail:* france.eu@yorktel.com
98 Lower Baggot St, Dublin 2, Ireland
    E-mail: eu.ireland@yorktel.com
Membership(s): Audiovisual and Integrated Experience Association; PSNI

Yorkville Sound Inc
550 Granite Ct, Pickering, ON L1W 3Y8, Canada
Tel: 905-837-8481 *Fax:* 905-839-5776
E-mail: canada@yorkville.com; orders@yorkville.com
Web Site: www.yorkville.com
Designs, manufactures & distributes professional PA products.
Online catalog(s) available
Branch Office(s)
4625 Witmer Industrial Estate, Niagara Falls, NY 14305 *Tel:* 716-297-2920 *Fax:* 716-297-3689
    E-mail: usa@yorkville.com
Membership(s): AES; LDI; NAMM, the National Association of Music Merchants; NSCA

Young Chang America
Subsidiary of Hyundai Development Co (HDC)
6000 Phyllis Dr, Cypress, CA 90630
Tel: 657-200-3470 *Fax:* 657-200-3477
E-mail: marketing@ycapiano.com (sales & mktg); info@ycapiano.com
Web Site: www.youngchang.com
Founded: 1982
Specialize in pianos & Kurzweil® brand music systems/synthesizers.
Membership(s): NAMM, the National Association of Music Merchants

Z-Axis Corp
4600 S Ulster St, Suite 270, Denver, CO 80237
Tel: 303-713-0200 *Toll Free Tel:* 800-827-2947
E-mail: info@zaxis.com
Web Site: www.zaxis.com
Key Personnel
CEO: Alan Treibitz
Pres: Stephanie Kelso
Visual Strategy Consultant/Sr Prodr: Gary Freed
Natl Accts Mgr: Raymond Hauschel
Founded: 1983
Strategic consulting, visual production services, technology & on-site presentation support for court cases in the US & abroad.
Online catalog(s) available

Z-Systems Audio Engineering
1325 NW 53 Ave, Suite B, Gainesville, FL 32609
Tel: 352-371-0990
E-mail: z-sys@z-sys.com
Web Site: www.z-sys.com
Key Personnel
Pres: Glenn Zelnikel
VP, Opers: Richard Auerbach
Founded: 1993
Manufacture professional digital audio equipment. R&D for customer concepts using DSP.

Z-Ville Productions
34710 Lancaster Rd, Gorman, CA 93536
Mailing Address: PO Box 42, Gorman, CA 93243
Tel: 310-422-9590
E-mail: info@zvpro.com
Web Site: www.z-ville.com
Key Personnel
Owner: Zander Villayne
Full service production company for the independent filmmaker/producer.

Zachry Associates Inc
500 Chestnut St, Suite 2000, Abilene, TX 79602
Tel: 325-677-1342
E-mail: info@zachryinc.com
Web Site: zachryinc.com
Key Personnel
Founder & Chmn: H C Zachry
Pres: Paul Fulham *Tel:* 325-677-1342 ext 108
    E-mail: pfulham@zachryinc.com
VP: Bob Nutt *Tel:* 325-677-1342 ext 123
    E-mail: bnutt@zachryinc.com
Founded: 1970

Services in marketing/advertising, research, fundraising & new media.
Branch Office(s)
6301 Gaston Ave, Dallas, TX 75214 *Tel:* 325-829-1671

Zack Electronics Inc
1075 Hamilton Rd, Duarte, CA 91010
Tel: 626-303-0655 *Toll Free Tel:* 800-466-0449
    Fax: 626-303-8694
E-mail: info@zackelectronics.com
Web Site: www.zackelectronics.com
Key Personnel
Pres: Dennis Awad *E-mail:* dawad@zackelectronics.com
Founded: 1931
Specialize in wire, cable, connectors & installation solutions for audio, video, broadcast & datacom professionals.
Catalog(s) available
Membership(s): NAB; SBE; SMPTE®

Zacuto
401 W Ontario Ave, Chicago, IL 60654
Tel: 312-863-3453 (rentals); 312-863-3456
    Toll Free Tel: 888-294-3456 *Fax:* 312-863-3455
E-mail: rentals@zacuto.com
Web Site: www.zacuto.com
Key Personnel
VP, Sales & Mktg: Mandy Rogers
    E-mail: mandy@zacuto.com
Mktg Mgr: Rachel Kenton *E-mail:* kenton@zacuto.com
Founded: 2000
Creates, sells & rents filmmaking accessories & creates original content for the web.

Zamacona Productions
2600 Tenth St, Suite 302, Berkeley, CA 94710
Tel: 510-704-4011 *Fax:* 510-704-4013
E-mail: admin@zamacona-productions.com
Web Site: www.zamacona-productions.com
Key Personnel
Dir & Prodr: Frank Zamacona
Founded: 1983
Director & producer services with emphasis on live & live-on-tape productions.
Membership(s): DGA; NATAS

ZBS Foundation
174 N River Rd, Fort Edward, NY 12828-9713
Tel: 518-695-6406 *Toll Free Tel:* 800-662-3345
    Fax: 518-695-4041
E-mail: custserv@zbs.org
Web Site: www.zbs.org
Key Personnel
Pres: Thomas Lopez
Founded: 1970
Radio/audio story producers.
Online catalog(s) available

Zebedee Productions
231 SW Fifth Ct, Pompano Beach, FL 33060
Tel: 954-942-0044
E-mail: info@zbd.us
Web Site: zebedeeproductions.com
Key Personnel
Owner: Andrea Arnold; Sandy Arnold
Services include AV rental & production, sound, lighting, video & staging. Specialize in design, fabrication, sales & installation services for complete AV systems, theatrical curtains & acoustical treatments.

Zeitgeist Films Ltd
333 W 39 St, New York, NY 10018
Tel: 212-274-1989 *Fax:* 212-714-0871

E-mail: mail@zeitgeistfilms.com
Web Site: www.zeitgeistfilms.com
Key Personnel
Co-Pres: Nancy Gerstman *E-mail:* nancy@zeitgeistfilms.com; Emily Russo
    E-mail: emily@zeitgeistfilms.com
Founded: 1988
Acquires & distributes quality foreign & independent feature films & documentaries.
Online catalog(s) available

Zelman Studios Ltd
623 Cortelyou Rd, Brooklyn, NY 11218
Key Personnel
Pres: Sidney M Zelman
Video design, production & presentation.

Zelo Productions Inc
3 S Newton St, Denver, CO 80220
Tel: 303-936-8995; 303-898-0911 (cell)
E-mail: zelo@zeloproductions.com
Web Site: www.zeloproductions.com
Key Personnel
Pres: V Zorba
Founded: 1990
Film & video production & post-production.

Zenith Electronics LLC
Subsidiary of LG Electronics USA
2000 Millbrook Dr, Lincolnshire, IL 60069
Tel: 847-941-8000 *Toll Free Tel:* 800-243-0000
    (cust serv)
Web Site: www.zenith.com
Key Personnel
Broadcasting Standards & Technol: Wayne Luplow *E-mail:* wayne.luplow@zenith.com
Licensing: Jack Kail *E-mail:* jack.kail@zenith.com
Media/Press: John Taylor *E-mail:* john.taylor@zenith.com
Founded: 1918
Plasma TV, HDTV.

ZERO Manufacturing Inc
500 W 200 N, North Salt Lake, UT 84054
Tel: 801-298-5900 *Toll Free Tel:* 800-959-5050
    Fax: 801-299-7389
E-mail: orders@zerocases.com; quote@zerocases.com; sales@zerocases.com
Web Site: www.zerocases.com
Founded: 1952
Aluminum & molded plastic cases & enclosures.
Catalog(s) available
Membership(s): AFCEA; The National Institute of Packaging, Handling & Logistics Engineers; SPHE

ZGC Inc
264 Morris Ave, Mountain Lakes, NJ 07046
Tel: 973-335-4460 *Fax:* 973-335-4560
E-mail: sales@zgc.com
Web Site: www.zgc.com
Key Personnel
Pres & Head, Prod Sales: Les Zellan *Tel:* 973-335-4460 ext 10 *E-mail:* les@zgc.com
Tech Dir: Guy Genin *Tel:* 973-335-4460 ext 15
    E-mail: guy@zgc.com
Mktg Coord, Webmaster & Engr: Patti Greene
    Tel: 973-335-4460 ext 21 *E-mail:* patti@zgc.com
Founded: 1986
Online catalog(s) available

Zion Music Group
Subsidiary of Nashville Teleproductions Co
306 Monticello Rd, Franklin, TN 37064
Tel: 615-559-2108 *Fax:* 615-591-5102

Web Site: www.zionmusic.com
Key Personnel
Pres: Kevin T McManus
VP: Beverly Cohron McManus
Dir, Natl Promos: Jennifer Brewer
Asst Engr: Tyson Pardee
Recording engineering & production.

Zippertubing® Co
7150 W Erie St, Chandler, AZ 85226
Tel: 480-285-3990 *Toll Free Tel:* 855-289-1874
    Fax: 480-285-3997
E-mail: info@zippertubing.com; sales@zippertubing.com; customer.service@zippertubing.com
Web Site: www.zippertubing.com
Founded: 1957
Cable management solutions, wire protection.
Catalog(s) available

Zondervan
Division of HarperCollins Christian Publishing
3900 Sparks Dr, Grand Rapids, MI 49546
Tel: 616-698-6900 *Toll Free Tel:* 800-226-1122;
    800-727-1309 (retail orders)
Web Site: www.zondervan.com
Key Personnel
Pres & CEO: Mark Schoenwald
SVP & Group Publr, HarperCollins: Annette Bourland
SVP & Publr: Stanley N Gundry
SVP, Sales: Tom Knight
Assoc Publr: Stephanie Smith
HR Mgr: Anna Elzinga
Founded: 1931
Religious programming distributor.
Online catalog(s) available
Membership(s): ABA; Association of American Publishers; Audio Publishers Association; Better Business Bureau; Book Industry Study Group; Chamber of Commerce; Evangelical Christian Publishers Association; Evangelical Press Association; ICVM; Society of Bible Literature; Society of Children's Book Writers & Illustrators; Software & Information Industry Association

ZTV Broadcast Services Inc
1670 Enterprise Rd, Mississauga, ON L4W 4L4, Canada
Tel: 905-290-4430 *Fax:* 905-290-3370
Web Site: ztvbroadcast.com
Key Personnel
Pres: Steve Zajaczkiwsky *E-mail:* steve@ztvbroadcast.com
Rentals & Tech Support: Henry Pinnock
    E-mail: henry@ztvbroadcast.com
Founded: 1992
Professional video equipment rentals.

Zygote Media Group Inc
1045 S 500 E, Suite 200, American Fork, UT 84003
Tel: 801-765-4141 *Fax:* 801-705-2234
E-mail: service@zygote.com
Web Site: www.zygote.com
Key Personnel
Pres: Roger Clarke
VP, Busn Devt: Dave Dunston
Founded: 1994
3D animation studio specializing in characters & biomedical content as well as vehicles & electronic products. Catalogue of licensable content. Services include modeling, texture mapping, animation, compositing, motion graphics & effects utilizing Maya, XS1, 305Max, after effects & combustion.

Associations

AV trade associations, as well as selected media-related organizations and educational and library groups with an AV interest, are listed in this section.

AAM, see American Alliance of Museums (AAM)

AAP, see Association of American Publishers (AAP)

AASA, The School Superintendents Association
1615 Duke St, Alexandria, VA 22314
Tel: 703-528-0700 *Fax:* 703-841-1543
E-mail: info@aasa.org
Web Site: www.aasa.org
Key Personnel
Exec Dir: Daniel A Domenech *Tel:* 703-875-0722
  E-mail: ddomenech@aasa.org
Founded: 1865
International organization for school superintendents.
Number of Members: 13,000
2021 Conference(s): AASA National Conference on Education, New Orleans, LA, Feb 18-20, 2021
2022 Conference(s): ASA National Conference on Education, Nashville, TN, Feb 17-19, 2022
Publication(s): *The School Administrator* (11 issues/yr, $10/issue membs; $11/issue non-membs)

AAUW, see American Association of University Women (AAUW)

AAVIM, see American Association for Vocational Instructional Materials (AAVIM)

Academy of Motion Picture Arts and Sciences (AMPAS)
8949 Wilshire Blvd, Beverly Hills, CA 90211
Tel: 310-247-3000 *Fax:* 310-859-9619
E-mail: awardsoffice@oscars.org
Web Site: www.oscars.org
Key Personnel
CEO: Dawn Hudson
Mng Dir, Memb Rel & Awards: Lorenza Munoz
  Tel: 310-247-3000 ext 1127 *E-mail:* lmunoz@oscars.org
Founded: 1927
Advance the arts & sciences of motion pictures.
Number of Members: 8,000

Academy of Science Fiction, Fantasy & Horror Films
334 W 54 St, Los Angeles, CA 90037
Tel: 323-752-5811
E-mail: saturn.awards@ca.rr.com
Web Site: www.saturnawards.org
Key Personnel
Pres, CEO & Awards Mgr: Robert Holguin
VP: Roger Fenton
Dir, Opers: Michael Laster
Founded: 1972
Nonprofit organization to honor, promote & recognize genre entertainment. Sponsor of the annual Saturn Awards.
Number of Members: 3,000
Publication(s): *The Saturn Rings*

Academy of Television Arts & Sciences, see Television Academy

Acoustical Society of America (ASA)
1305 Walt Whitman Rd, Suite 300, Melville, NY 11747-4300
Tel: 516-576-2360 *Fax:* 631-923-2875
E-mail: asa@acousticalsociety.org
Web Site: www.acousticalsociety.org
Key Personnel
Exec Dir: Susan E Fox
Founded: 1929
Increase & diffuse the knowledge of acoustics & promote its practical applications.
Number of Members: 7,500
2020 Conference(s): 179th Meeting, Chicago, IL, May 11-15, 2020
Publication(s): *The Journal of the Acoustical Society of America* (monthly)

AFI, see American Film Institute (AFI)

AHIMA, see American Health Information Management Association (AHIMA)

AIGA, the professional association for design
233 Broadway, Suite 1740, New York, NY 10279
Tel: 212-807-1990 *Toll Free Tel:* 800-548-1634
E-mail: general@aiga.org
Web Site: www.aiga.org
Key Personnel
Chief of Staff: Amy Chapman *Tel:* 212-710-3137
Dir, Mktg: David Trier *Tel:* 212-710-3149
Dir, Membership: Lauren Schultz *Tel:* 212-710-3136
Dir, Progs & Events: Kathleen Budny *Tel:* 212-710-3144
Dir, Technol: Tiia Schurig *Tel:* 212-710-3134
Founded: 1914
Organization for graphic artists involved in book design, illustration, advertising, corporate graphics, promotion & exhibitions.
Number of Members: 25,000

AIIM, see Association for Information and Image Management (AIIM)

AIME, see Association for Information Media & Equipment

ALA, see American Library Association (ALA)

Alliance for Community Media (ACM)
4248 Park Glen Rd, Minneapolis, MN 55416
Tel: 952-928-4643
E-mail: info@allcommunitymedia.org
Web Site: www.allcommunitymedia.org
Key Personnel
Pres & CEO: Mike Wassenaar
Conference Mgr: Katie Benson
  E-mail: kbenson@allcommunitymedia.org
Mktg & Communs Coord: Angie Newgren
Founded: 1976
Provide services to people working in community programming & cultivate citizen participation in community access TV.
Number of Members: 413
2020 Conference(s): ACM Annual Conference, Fairmont Chicago Millennium Park, 200 N Columbus Dr, Chicago, IL, June 30-July 2, 2020

Alliance for IP Media Solutions (AIMS)
23117 39 Ave SE, Bothell, WA 98021
Tel: 425-870-6574
E-mail: info@aimsalliance.org
Web Site: aimsalliance.org
Key Personnel
Admin: Tina Lipscomb *E-mail:* tina@aimsalliance.org
Nonprofit trade organization founded by leading companies to foster the adoption of industry standards for the broadcast & media industry as it transitions from SDI to IP.
Publication(s): *AIMS Connect* (newsletter, monthly)

Alliance for Women in Media/Alliance for Women in Media Foundation
2365 Harrodsburg Rd, A-325, Lexington, KY 40504
Tel: 202-750-3664 *Fax:* 202-750-3664
Web Site: www.allwomeninmedia.org
Key Personnel
Exec Dir: Becky Brooks *E-mail:* becky.brooks@allwomeninmedia.org
Events Dir: Lisa Stephenson *E-mail:* lisa.stephenson@allwomeninmedia.org
Opers Mgr: LaTonya Jackson *E-mail:* latonya.jackson@allwomeninmedia.org
Founded: 1951 (as American Women in Radio & Television)
Works to improve the quality of the media. Promotes the entry, development & advancement of women in the media & allied fields.
Publication(s): *Fast Forward* (ezine, weekly, free)

Alliance of Motion Picture & Television Producers (AMPTP)
15301 Ventura Blvd, Bldg E, Sherman Oaks, CA 91403
Tel: 818-995-3600 *Fax:* 818-285-4450
Web Site: www.amptp.org
Key Personnel
Communs Dir: Jarryd Gonzales
Founded: 1982
Trade organization; handle collective bargaining negotiation for the entertainment industry.

alliance quebecoise des techniciens et techniciennes de l'image et du son (AQTIS)
1001, blvd De Maisonneuve E, bureau 900, Montreal, QC H2L 4P9, Canada
Tel: 514-844-2113 (ext 285) *Fax:* 514-844-3540
E-mail: info@aqtis.qc.ca
Web Site: www.aqtis.qc.ca
Key Personnel
Gen Mgr: Jean-Claude Rocheleau
  E-mail: jcrocheleau@aqtis.qc.ca
Mgr, Labor Rel: Charles Paradis
  E-mail: cparadis@aqtis.qc.ca
Quebec's film, TV & creative technicians' union.
Number of Members: 3,500

ALMA International
39962 W Thornberry Lane, Maricopa, AZ 85138
Tel: 602-388-8669
E-mail: management@almainternational.org
Web Site: almaint.org
Key Personnel
Exec Dir: Barry Vogel
Founded: 1961
Not-for-profit trade association of loudspeaker & electro-acoustics professionals.

Number of Members: 1,200
Publication(s): *ALMAGrams* (monthly)

AMA, see American Management Association®
(AMA)

American Alliance of Museums (AAM)
2451 Crystal Dr, Suite 1005, Arlington, VA
22202
Tel: 202-289-1818 *Fax:* 202-289-6578
Web Site: www.aam-us.org
Key Personnel
Pres & CEO: Laura Lott *Tel:* 202-289-9112
E-mail: llott@aam-us.org
Sr Dir, Leadership Progs: Dean Phelus *Tel:* 202-
218-2674 *E-mail:* dphelus@aam-us.org
Founded: 1906
Promote the welfare of museums & museum pro-
fessionals.
Number of Members: 26,000
2020 Conference(s): Annual Meeting & Museum-
Expo, San Francisco, CA, May 17-20, 2020
2021 Conference(s): Annual Meeting & Museum-
Expo, Chicago, IL, May 9-12, 2021
Publication(s): *Aviso* (ezine, monthly, free to
membs; $40/yr nonmembs); *Museum* (maga-
zine, 6 issues/yr, free to membs; $38/yr non-
membs)

**American Association for Vocational
Instructional Materials (AAVIM)**
220 Smithonia Rd, Winterville, GA 30683
Tel: 706-742-5355 *Toll Free Tel:* 800-228-4689
Fax: 706-742-7005
E-mail: sales@aavim.com
Web Site: www.aavim.com
Key Personnel
Dir: Gary Farmer
Founded: 1949
Develop, produce & distribute training materials
for vocational education.
Membership(s): National Association of Agricul-
ture Educators

**American Association of School Librarians
(AASL)**
Division of The American Library Association
(ALA)
50 E Huron St, Chicago, IL 60611
Tel: 312-280-4382 *Toll Free Tel:* 800-545-2433
(ext 4382) *Fax:* 312-280-5276
E-mail: aasl@ala.org
Web Site: www.ala.org
Key Personnel
Exec Dir: Sylvia Norton *Tel:* 800-545-2433 ext
4388 *E-mail:* snorton@ala.org
Founded: 1951
Advocate excellence, facilitate change & develop
leaders in the school library media field.
Number of Members: 7,537
2021 Conference(s): AASL National Conference
& Exhibition (biennial), Salt Lake City, UT,
Oct 21-23, 2021
2023 Conference(s): AASL National Conference
& Exhibition (biennial), Tampa, FL, Oct 19-21,
2023
2025 Conference(s): AASL National Conference
& Exhibition (biennial), St Louis, MO, Oct 16-
18, 2025
Publication(s): *Knowledge Quest* (journal); *KQ
Express* (enewsletter, monthly); *School Library
Research* (journal)

**American Association of University Women
(AAUW)**
1310 "L" St, Suite 1000, Washington, DC 20005
Tel: 202-785-7700 *Toll Free Tel:* 800-326-AAUW
(326-2289) *Fax:* 202-872-1425
E-mail: helpline@aauw.org; connect@aauw.org
Web Site: www.aauw.org

Key Personnel
CEO: Kimberly Churches
Founded: 1881
Promote education & equity for women & girls.
Number of Members: 100,000
Publication(s): *AAUW Outlook* (ezine, 3 issues/yr,
free to membs)

American Cinema Editors Inc (ACE)
Max Bros Bldg, Rm 108, 5555 Melrose Ave, Los
Angeles, CA 90038
Tel: 323-956-2900
E-mail: admin@americancinemaeditors.com
Web Site: americancinemaeditors.org
Key Personnel
Pres: Stephen Rivkin
VP: Alan Heim
Founded: 1950
To advance the art & science of the editing pro-
fession in motion pictures & television. To
bring into close alliance those editors who de-
sire to advance the prestige & dignity of the
editing profession. It is an honorary profes-
sional society apart from the editors guild.
Number of Members: 1,000
Publication(s): *Cinemaeditor Magazine* (maga-
zine, quarterly, $39/yr)

**American Educational Research Association
(AERA)**
1430 "K" St NW, Suite 1200, Washington, DC
20005
Tel: 202-238-3200 *Fax:* 202-238-3250
E-mail: communications@aera.net; members@
aera.net
Web Site: www.aera.net
Key Personnel
Exec Dir & Ethics Offr: Felice J Levine, PhD
Tel: 202-238-3200 ext 201 *E-mail:* flevine@
aera.net
Assoc Exec Dir, Progs & Policy Res & Res Sci-
entist: Lori Diane Hill, PhD *Tel:* 202-238-3200
ext 229 *E-mail:* lhill@aera.net
Dir, Communs: Tony Pals *Tel:* 202-238-3200 ext
235 *E-mail:* tpals@aera.net
Dir, Fin & Admin: Norman Tenorio *Tel:* 202-238-
3200 ext 245 *E-mail:* ntenorio@aera.net
Dir, Govt Rel: Juliane Baron *Tel:* 202-238-3200
ext 222 *E-mail:* jbaron@aera.net
Dir, Prof Devt & Diversity Offr: George Wim-
berly, PhD *Tel:* 202-238-3200 ext 225
E-mail: gwimberly@aera.net
Dir, Pubns: John Neikirk *Tel:* 202-238-3200 ext
238 *E-mail:* jneikirk@aera.net
Founded: 1916
Support & disseminate educational research.
Number of Members: 25,000
2020 Conference(s): Annual Meeting, San Francisco, CA, April 17-21, 2020
2021 Conference(s): Annual Meeting, Orlando,
FL, April 9-12, 2021
2022 Conference(s): Annual Meeting, San Diego,
CA, April 22-25, 2022
2023 Conference(s): Annual Meeting, Chicago,
IL, April 13-16, 2023
Publication(s): *AERA Open* (journal, online, free);
American Educational Research Journal (journal, 6 issues/yr, print & online, $83); *Educa-
tional Evaluation & Policy Analysis* (journal,
quarterly, print & online, $72); *Educational Re-
searcher* (journal, 9 issues/yr, print & online,
$72); *Journal of Educational & Behavioral
Statistics* (6 issues/yr, print & online, $84);
Review of Educational Research (journal, 6
issues/yr, print & online, $72); *Review of Re-
search in Education* (journal, annual, print &
online, $72)

**American Federation of Musicians of the
United States & Canada (AFM)**
1501 Broadway, 9th fl, New York, NY 10036

Tel: 212-869-1330 *Toll Free Tel:* 800-762-3444
Fax: 212-764-6134
Web Site: www.afm.org
Key Personnel
Intl Pres: Ray Hair *E-mail:* presoffice@afm.org
Intl VP: Bruce Fife *E-mail:* bfife@afm99.org
Founded: 1896
Labor union for musicians.
Number of Members: 80,000
Branch Office(s)
3220 Winona Ave, Burbank, CA 91504 *Tel:* 818-
565-3400
5335 Wisconsin Ave NW, Suite 440, Washington,
DC 20015 *Tel:* 202-274-4756 (legislative ofc)
150 Ferrand Dr, Suite 202, Toronto, ON M3C
3E5, Canada *Tel:* 416-391-5161
Conference(s): AFM Convention
Publication(s): *International Musician* (monthly,
$43.90/yr nonmembs US; $59.90/yr nonmembs
CN & foreign)

American Film Institute (AFI)
Attn: Facilities Off, 2021 N Western Ave, Los
Angeles, CA 90027-1657
Tel: 323-856-7600 *Toll Free Tel:* 800-774-4AFI
(774-4234 membership) *Fax:* 323-462-4049
E-mail: information@afi.com
Web Site: www.afi.com
Key Personnel
Pres & CEO: Bob Gazzale
COO: Nancy Harris
Founded: 1967
AFI is a national institute providing leadership in
screen education & the recognition & celebra-
tion of excellence in the art of film, television
& digital media.
Number of Members: 12,000

American Foundation for the Blind (AFB)
2 Penn Plaza, Suite 1102, New York, NY 10121
Tel: 212-502-7600 *Toll Free Tel:* 800-232-5463
Fax: 212-502-7777 *Toll Free Fax:* 888-545-
8331
E-mail: info@afb.org
Web Site: www.afb.org
Key Personnel
Pres & CEO: Kirk Adams
Chief Busn Offr: Kelly Bleach
Chief Community Engagement Offr: Adrianna
Montague
Founded: 1921
A national nonprofit that expands possibilities
for people with vision loss. Priorities include
broadening access to technology; elevating the
quality of information & tools for the profes-
sionals who serve people with vision loss; &
promoting independent & healthy living for
people with vision loss by providing them &
their families with relevant & timely resources.
In addition, AFB's web site serves as a gateway to a wealth of vision loss information &
services. Houses the Helen Keller Archives &
honors the over forty years that Helen Keller
worked tirelessly with AFB. For more information, visit www.afb.org.
Branch Office(s)
AFB Public Policy Center, 1401 S Clark St, Suite
730, Arlington, VA 22202 *Tel:* 202-469-6831
Fax: 646-478-9260 *E-mail:* afbgov@afb.net
739 W Peachtree St NW, Suite 250, Atlanta, GA
30308 *Tel:* 404-525-2303 *Fax:* 646-478-9260
E-mail: literacy@afb.net
AFB Center on Vision Loss, 11030 Ables Lane,
Dallas, TX 75229 *Tel:* 214-352-7222 *Fax:* 646-
478-9260 *E-mail:* dallas@afb.net
1108 Third Ave, Suite 200, Huntington, WV
25701 *Tel:* 304-523-8651 *Fax:* 646-478-9260
Publication(s): *AccessWorld* (magazine, monthly);
Journal of Visual Impairment & Blindness (6
issues/yr)

American Health Information Management Association (AHIMA)

233 N Michigan Ave, 21st fl, Chicago, IL 60601-5809
Tel: 312-233-1100 *Toll Free Tel:* 800-335-5535
Fax: 312-233-1090; 312-233-1500 (orders)
E-mail: info@ahima.org
Web Site: www.ahima.org
Key Personnel
CEO: Wylecia Wiggs Harris, PhD
Founded: 1928
Promote the art & science of medical records administration; aim to improve the quality of comprehensive health information services for the public welfare.
Number of Members: 71,000
2020 Conference(s): AHIMA Convention & Exhibit, Atlanta, GA, Oct 13-17, 2020
2021 Conference(s): AHIMA Convention & Exhibit, Houston, TX, Sept 18-22, 2021
Publication(s): *Journal of AHIMA* (journal, 11 issues/yr, free to membs; $100/yr US, $110/yr CN, $120/yr other, nonmembs)

American Library Association (ALA)

50 E Huron St, Chicago, IL 60611-2795
Tel: 312-944-6780 *Toll Free Tel:* 800-545-2433
Fax: 312-440-9374
E-mail: ala@ala.org
Web Site: www.ala.org
Key Personnel
Exec Dir: Mary Ghikas *Tel:* 800-545-2433 ext 1392 *E-mail:* mghikas@ala.org
Dir, Communs & Mktg: Stephanie Hlywak *Tel:* 800-545-2433 ext 5042 *E-mail:* shlywak@ala.org
Founded: 1876
Promote & improve library & information services & the profession of librarianship.
Number of Members: 60,000
2020 Conference(s): Annual Conference, Chicago, IL, June 25-30, 2020
2021 Conference(s): Midwinter Meeting, Indianapolis, IN, Jan 22-26, 2021; Annual Conference, Chicago, IL, June 24-29, 2021
2022 Conference(s): Annual Conference, Washington, DC, June 23-28, 2022
2023 Conference(s): Annual Conference, Chicago, IL, June 22-27, 2023
2024 Conference(s): Annual Conference, San Diego, CA, June 27-July 2, 2024
Publication(s): *American Libraries* (6 issues/yr, free to membs; $70/yr US, CN & Mexico; $80/yr elsewhere); *Booklist* (22 issues/yr, $147.50/yr membs)

American Management Association® (AMA)

1601 Broadway, New York, NY 10019
Tel: 212-586-8100 *Toll Free Tel:* 877-566-9441 (cust serv) *Fax:* 212-903-8168; 518-891-0368 (cust serv)
E-mail: customerservice@amanet.org
Web Site: www.amanet.org
Key Personnel
Pres & CEO: Edward T Reilly
PR Mgr: Roger Kelleher
Founded: 1923
With over 85 years of experience delivering 140+ training seminars throughout the country, AMA has refined their training programs to meet today's challenges. AMA promotes the goals of individuals & organizations through a comprehensive range of solutions, including business seminars, blended learning, webcasts & podcasts, conferences, books, whitepapers, articles & more.
Number of Members: 100,000

American Optometric Association (AOA)

243 N Lindbergh Blvd, 1st fl, St Louis, MO 63141-7881
Tel: 314-991-4100 *Toll Free Tel:* 800-365-2219
Fax: 314-991-4101
Web Site: www.aoa.org
Key Personnel
Exec Dir: Jon Hymes
Founded: 1898
A federation of state, student & armed forces, optometric associations serving members consisting of optometrists, students of optometry, paraoptometric assistants & technicians.
Number of Members: 39,000
Branch Office(s)
1505 Prince St, Suite 300, Alexandria, VA 22314
Tel: 703-739-9200 ext 1372 *Fax:* 703-739-9497
2020 Conference(s): Optometry's Meeting®, Gaylord National Resort & Convention Center, National Harbor, MD, June 24-28, 2020
2021 Conference(s): Optometry's Meeting®, Anaheim Convention Center, Anaheim, CA, June 23-27, 2021
2022 Conference(s): Optometry's Meeting®, McCormick Place Convention Center, Chicago, IL, June 15-19, 2022
2023 Conference(s): Optometry's Meeting®, Walter E Washington Convention Center, Washington, DC, June 21-25, 2023
Publication(s): *AOA Focus* (9 issues/yr, free to membs)

American Society for Photogrammetry and Remote Sensing (ASPRS)

425 Barlow Place, Suite 210, Bethesda, MD 20814-2160
Tel: 301-493-0290 *Fax:* 301-493-0208
E-mail: asprs@asprs.org
Web Site: www.asprs.org
Key Personnel
Prog Mgr & Acting Exec Dir: Jessie Winch *Tel:* 301-493-0290 ext 101 *E-mail:* jwinch@asprs.org
Founded: 1934
Nonprofit scientific society. Disseminate information on photogrammetry, remote sensing, geographic information systems & supporting technology.
Number of Members: 7,000
Conference(s): Imaging & Geospatial Technology Forum (IGTF)
Publication(s): *Photogrammetric Engineering & Remote Sensing* (monthly)

American Society of Cinematographers (ASC)

1782 N Orange Dr, Los Angeles, CA 90028
Mailing Address: PO Box 2230, Los Angeles, CA 90078
Tel: 323-969-4333 *Toll Free Tel:* 800-448-0145 (US only) *Fax:* 323-882-6391
E-mail: office@theasc.com; customerservice@theasc.com
Web Site: theasc.com
Key Personnel
Pres: Kees van Oostrum
Founded: 1919
Private association of motion picture cameramen. Membership is by invitation only.
Number of Members: 500
Publication(s): *American Cinematographer* (magazine, monthly)

American Society of Media Photographers Inc (ASMP)

PO Box 31207, Bethesda, MD 20824
Toll Free Tel: 877-771-2767
E-mail: info@asmp.org
Web Site: asmp.org
Key Personnel
Exec Dir: Tom Kennedy *E-mail:* kennedy@asmp.org
Founded: 1944
Protect & promote the interests of professional photographers whose photographs are primarily for publication; maintain & promote high professional standards & ethics in photography; cultivate friendship & mutual understanding among professional photographers.
Number of Members: 7,000
Publication(s): *ASMP Bulletin* (quarterly); *Professional Business Practices in Photography* (free to membs; $35 nonmembs plus shipping & handling. Available at amazon.com for discount)

American Society of Photographers (ASP)

3120 N Argonne Dr, Milwaukee, WI 53222
Tel: 414-871-6600
Web Site: asofp.com
Key Personnel
Exec Dir: Jon Allyn *E-mail:* jonallyn@aol.com
Founded: 1937
Professional photographers organization promoting the ideas of photography as an art & science.
Number of Members: 850
Publication(s): *ASP Magazine* (quarterly)

American Society of Safety Professionals (ASSP)

520 N Northwest Hwy, Park Ridge, IL 60068
Tel: 847-699-2929 (cust serv) *Fax:* 847-768-3434
E-mail: customerservice@assp.org
Web Site: www.assp.org
Key Personnel
Exec Dir: Jennifer McNelly *E-mail:* Executive@assp.org
Dir, Fin/Cont: Bruce Sufranski *Tel:* 847-768-3401
Ed, Professional Safety Journal: Tina Angley *Tel:* 847-768-3438 *E-mail:* tangley@assp.org
Founded: 1911
A nonprofit individual membership society of safety professionals in industry, insurance, government, education & private consulting.
Number of Members: 38,000
2020 Conference(s): Safety 2020, Orange County Convention Center, Orlando, FL, June 23-25, 2020
Publication(s): *Professional Safety Journal* (monthly, free to membs)

American Sportscasters Association Inc (ASA)

Affiliate of American Sportscasters Hall of Fame Trust
225 Broadway, Suite 2030, New York, NY 10007
Tel: 212-227-8080 *Fax:* 212-571-0556
Web Site: www.americansportscastersonline.com
Key Personnel
Chmn of the Bd: Dick Enberg
Pres: Louis O Schwartz *E-mail:* lschwa8918@aol.com
Founded: 1979
Advance the profession of sportscasting, voting for Sportscaster of the Year, Sports Personality, Hall of Fame inductee, Graham McNamee Award, Sports Legend Award, International Sportscaster of the Year.
Number of Members: 500
Publication(s): *Insiders Sports Letter* (quarterly)

America's Public Television Stations (APTS)

2100 Crystal Dr, Suite 700, Arlington, VA 22202
Tel: 202-654-4200 *Fax:* 202-654-4236
Web Site: apts.org
Key Personnel
Pres & CEO: Patrick Butler
EVP, COO & Gen Coun: Lonna Thompson *Tel:* 202-654-4215 *E-mail:* lonna@apts.org
VP, Fin, Admin & Membership: Emil Mara *Tel:* 202-654-4201 *E-mail:* emara@apts.org
VP, Govt & Pub Aff: Kate Riley *Tel:* 202-654-4206 *E-mail:* kriley@apts.org
Dir, Communs: Stacey Karp *Tel:* 202-654-4222 *E-mail:* skarp@apts.org
Founded: 1979
Trade association; deals with congressional lobbying & research on behalf of America's public broadcasting stations.

AMPAS, see Academy of Motion Picture Arts and Sciences (AMPAS)

Amusement & Music Operators Association (AMOA)
380 Terra Cotta Rd, Suite F, Crystal Lake, IL 60012
Tel: 847-428-7699 *Toll Free Tel:* 800-YES-AMOA (937-2662) *Fax:* 847-428-7719
E-mail: amoa@amoa.com
Web Site: www.amoa.com
Key Personnel
EVP: Lori Schneider
Founded: 1948
Trade association representing music, amusement & vending industries & coin-operated amusement devices.
Number of Members: 1,400
2021 Conference(s): Amusement Expo International, Westgate Las Vegas Resort & Casino, Las Vegas, NV, March 16-18, 2021

AQTIS, see alliance quebecoise des techniciens et techniciennes de l'image et du son (AQTIS)

Arizona Production Association
6615 N Scottsdale Rd, Suite 101, Scottsdale, AZ 85250
Tel: 480-345-6464 *Toll Free Tel:* 866-345-6469 *Fax:* 480-941-2557
E-mail: info@azproduction.com; sales@azproduction.com
Web Site: www.azproduction.com
Key Personnel
Admin Dir: Julie Lee *E-mail:* julie@azproduction.com
Nonprofit trade organization of film, theatre & television professionals.
Number of Members: 350
Publication(s): *Arizona Production Guide (online only)*; *On the Arizona Set* (newsletter, 2-3 issues/yr, $12)

Art Directors Guild (ADG)
11969 Ventura Blvd, 2nd fl, Studio City, CA 91604
Tel: 818-762-9995 *Fax:* 818-762-9997
Web Site: www.adg.org
Key Personnel
Exec Dir: Chuck Parker *E-mail:* chuck@artdirectors.org
Dir, Opers: Lydia Zimmer Prescott *E-mail:* lydia@artdirectors.org
Opers Mgr: Cynthia Paskos *E-mail:* cynthia@artdirectors.org
International union representing employees in the entertainment industry, including art directors, graphic artists, illustrators, matte artists, model makers, scenic artists, set designers & title artists.
Number of Members: 2,000

ASCD®
1703 N Beauregard St, Alexandria, VA 22311-1714
Tel: 703-578-9600 *Toll Free Tel:* 800-933-ASCD (933-2723) *Fax:* 703-575-5400
E-mail: exhibits@ascd.org
Web Site: www.ascd.org
Key Personnel
Interim CEO & Exec Dir: Ronn Nozoe *E-mail:* ronn.nozoe@ascd.org
Founded: 1943
ASCD is a membership organization that develops programs, products & services essential to the way educators learn, teach & lead. Advertising opportunities on the web site as well.
Number of Members: 114,000

2021 Conference(s): ASCD Empower: The Conference for Learning, Teaching & Leading Together, Washington, DC, March 27-29, 2021
Publication(s): *Educational Leadership* (9 issues/yr, 8 print & digital, 1 digital only, free to membs)

ASMP, see American Society of Media Photographers Inc (ASMP)

ASPRS: The Imaging & Geospatial Information Society, see American Society for Photogrammetry and Remote Sensing (ASPRS)

Association for Educational Communications and Technology (AECT)
320 W Eighth St, Suite 101, Bloomington, IN 47404-3745
Tel: 812-335-7675 *Toll Free Tel:* 877-677-AECT (677-2328) *Fax:* 812-335-7678
E-mail: aect@aect.org
Web Site: www.aect.org
Key Personnel
Exec Dir: Dr Phillip Harris *E-mail:* pharris@aect.org
Dir, Electronic Servs: Larry Vernon *E-mail:* lvernon@aect.org
Convention Coord: Lois Freeland
HR & Admin Servs: Terri Lawson
Founded: 1923
Represents professionals in a broad range of occupations who have an interest in improving learning through the use of media & technology.
Number of Members: 5,000
Publication(s): *Educational Technology Research & Development* (journal, 6 issues/yr); *TechTrends* (journal, 6 issues/yr)

Association for Information and Image Management (AIIM)
1100 Wayne Ave, Suite 1100, Silver Spring, MD 20910
Tel: 301-587-8202 *Toll Free Tel:* 800-477-2446 *Fax:* 301-587-2711
E-mail: aiim@aiim.org
Web Site: www.aiim.org
Key Personnel
Pres & CEO: Peggy Winton
CFO: Felicia Dillard
SVP, Busn Devt, EMEA: Atle Skjekkeland
VP, Mktg: Anthony Paille
VP, Mkt Intelligence: Bob Larrivee
VP, Sales: Amy Michalski
VP, Events: Georgina Clelland
Founded: 1943
Trade association & professional society representing the document management industry.
Number of Members: 6,800
Branch Office(s)
Broomhall Business Centre, Lower Broomhall Farm, Broomhall Lane, Worcester WR5 TNT, United Kingdom *Tel:* (01905) 727600 *Fax:* (01905) 727609

Association for Information Media & Equipment
PO Box 378, West Milton, PA 17866
Tel: 570-701-4202
Web Site: www.aime.org
Key Personnel
Exec Dir: Geoff Craven *Tel:* 570-701-4202 ext 2
Founded: 1986
Promote copyright awareness & education for informational motion media.
Number of Members: 150
Publication(s): *AIME News* (quarterly, $35/yr; free to membs)

Association for Print Technologies (APTech)
1896 Preston White Dr, Reston, VA 20191

Tel: 703-264-7200 *Fax:* 703-620-0994
E-mail: aptech@aptech.org
Web Site: www.printtechnologies.org
Key Personnel
Pres: Thayer Long *E-mail:* tlong@aptech.org
Dir, Membership & Devt: Carol Lee Hawkins *E-mail:* clhawkins@aptech.org
Dir, Mktg & Communs: Jane Pratt *E-mail:* jpratt@aptech.org
Founded: 1933 (as the National Printing Equipment Association)
US trade association representing more than 650 companies that manufacture & distribute equipment, software & supplies used across the workflow of printing, publishing & converting processes.
Number of Members: 650
2020 Conference(s): Brand Print Americas, Donald E Stephens Convention Center, Rosemont, IL, Sept 15-17, 2020
Publication(s): *APTech* (newsletter, monthly)

Association for Recorded Sound Collections (ARSC)
1299 University of Oregon, Eugene, OR 97403-1299
Web Site: www.arsc-audio.org
Key Personnel
Exec Dir: Nathan Georgitis *E-mail:* execdir@arsc-audio.org
Founded: 1966
Performs research & studies, publication & information exchange covering all aspects of recordings, recorded sound & audio archives.
Number of Members: 1,000
2020 Conference(s): ARSC Annual Conference, Hotel Delta Montreal, 475 President Kennedy Ave, Montreal, QC, CN, May 20-23, 2020
Publication(s): *ARSC Blog*; *ARSC Journal* (semi-annual); *ARSC Newsletter* (3 issues/yr)

Association for Talent Development (ATD)
1640 King St, Alexandria, VA 22314-2743
Tel: 703-683-8100 *Toll Free Tel:* 800-628-2783 *Fax:* 703-299-8723
E-mail: customercare@td.org
Web Site: www.td.org
Key Personnel
Pres & CEO: Tony Bingham *E-mail:* tony@td.org
VP, Community & Branding: Jennifer Homer *E-mail:* jhomer@td.org
Founded: 1943
Mission: Provides leadership to individual organizations & society. Achieve work related competence & fulfillment. Empower professionals to develop knowledge & skills successfully.
Number of Members: 36,000
2020 Conference(s): ATD International Conference & Exposition, Colorado Convention Center, 700 14 St, Denver, CO, May 17-20, 2020
2021 Conference(s): ATD International Conference & Exposition, Los Angeles, CA, May 23-26, 2021
2022 Conference(s): ATD International Conference & Exposition, Orlando, FL, May 15-18, 2022
Publication(s): *TD at Work* (monthly, $119 membs, all access print & digital; $99 membs, all access digital; $69 membs, digital only); *TD Magazine* (monthly, free to membs)

The Association for Women in Communications (AWC)
1717 E Republic Rd, Suite A, Springfield, MO 65804
Tel: 417-886-8606 *Fax:* 417-886-3685
E-mail: info@womcom.org
Web Site: www.womcom.org
Founded: 1909
Champions the advancement of women across all communications disciplines by recognizing ex-

cellence, promoting leadership & positioning its members at the forefront of the evolving communications era communication. More than 90 professional & campus chapters worldwide provide the membership with the opportunity for local networking, education & support.
Number of Members: 3,000
Conference(s): AWC National Conference

Association of American Publishers (AAP)
455 Massachusetts Ave NW, Suite 700, Washington, DC 20001-2777
Tel: 202-347-3375 *Fax:* 202-347-3690
E-mail: info@publishers.org
Web Site: publishers.org
Key Personnel
Pres & CEO: Maria Pallante
EVP & Gen Coun: Allan R Adler
Asst Gen Coun: Sofia Castillo
SVP, Communs: John McKay
VP, Admin & Bd Liaison: Syreeta N Swann
VP, Communs: Cara Duckworth; Susanna Hinds
VP, Fin & Strategic Planning: Karen McInnis
VP, Global Policy: M Lui Simpson
VP, Public Policy: Matthew Barblan
Sr Dir, Educ Policy & Progs: Kelly L Denson
Mng Dir, Meetings & Progs: Sara Pinto
Policy Specialist: Amanda Straub
Founded: 1970
Monitor & promote the USA publishing industry. Members: those actively engaged in the creation, publication & production of books, journals, electronic media, testing materials & a range of educational materials.
Number of Members: 450
Publication(s): *AAP Export Sales Report* (annual); *AAP StatShot* (monthly)

Association of Catholic TV & Radio Syndicators
518 S Alandele Ave, Los Angeles, CA 90036
Tel: 323-938-4861
Key Personnel
VP: Mary Jane Hopkins
Discuss TV & radio syndication.
Number of Members: 60
Publication(s): *Newsletter* (annual)

Association of Federal Communications Consulting Engineers (AFCCE)
PO Box 19333, Washington, DC 20036-0333
E-mail: secretary@afcce.org
Web Site: afcce.org
Key Personnel
Pres: John Lyons
VP: Chris Horne
Secy: John Gorge
Treas: Bob Weller
Founded: 1948
Registered professional consulting engineers who practice before the FCC.
Number of Members: 242

Association of Independent Commercial Producers (AICP)
3 W 18 St, 5th fl, New York, NY 10011
Tel: 212-929-3000 *Fax:* 212-929-3359
E-mail: info@aicp.com
Web Site: www.aicp.com
Key Personnel
Natl Pres & CEO: Matt Miller *E-mail:* mattm@aicp.com
Chief of Staff/VP, Opers: Kristin Wilcha *E-mail:* kristinw@aicp.com
VP, Post & Digital Prodn: Danny Rosenbloom *E-mail:* dannyr@aicp.com
Dir, Relationship Mktg & Devt: Neal Lattner *E-mail:* neall@aicp.com
Natl Events Prodr: Aurora Warfield *E-mail:* auroraw@aicp.com
Sr Communs Mgr: Brian Doherty *E-mail:* briand@aicp.com

Mgr, East & Natl Events: Katie Mulligan *E-mail:* katiem@aicp.com
Mgr, Membership Info & Systems: David Stewart *E-mail:* davids@aicp.com
Off Mgr: Laurie R Nichtern *E-mail:* laurier@aicp.com
Events Coord: Nick Duvarney *E-mail:* nickd@aicp.com
Founded: 1972
Represents, exclusively, the interests of companies that specialize in the production & post-production of commercials in various media (film, video & digital) for advertisers & agencies. The association, with national offices in New York & Los Angeles as well as regional chapters across the country, serves as a strong collective voice for this $5 billion-plus industry. Assists its members by: disseminating information; representing production & post-production companies within the advertising community in business circles, in labor negotiations & dealing with employment issues & before governmental officials; developing industry standards & tools; providing professional development; marketing American production & post-production via events & awards shows.
Number of Members: 500
Branch Office(s)
Raleigh Studios, 650 N Bronson Ave, Suite 223B, Los Angeles, CA 90004, VP, Busn Aff & Media Issues: Denise Gilmartin *Tel:* 323-960-4763 *E-mail:* deniseg@aicp.com
2020 Conference(s): AICP Week, MoMA, New York, NY, June 9-11, 2020

Association of Loudspeaker Manufacturing & Acoustics International, see ALMA International

Association of National Advertisers Inc (ANA)
10 Grand Central, 155 E 44 St, New York, NY 10017
Tel: 212-697-5950 *Fax:* 212-687-7310
E-mail: info@ana.net
Web Site: www.ana.net
Key Personnel
CEO: Bob Liodice *Tel:* 212-455-8050 *E-mail:* bliodice@ana.net
Pres & COO: Christine Manna *Tel:* 212-455-8060 *E-mail:* cmanna@ana.net
Group EVP & CIO: Robert Rothe *Tel:* 212-455-8029 *E-mail:* rrothe@ana.net
EVP & Chief Mktg Offr: Duke Fanelli *Tel:* 212-455-8030 *E-mail:* dfanelli@ana.net
SVP: Andrea Kislan *Tel:* 212-455-8071 *E-mail:* akislan@ana.net
VP: Barbara Markfield *Tel:* 212-455-8077 *E-mail:* bmarkfield@ana.net
Founded: 1910
Advertising trade association, conduct educational seminars, conferences, forums for member companies & others.
Number of Members: 2,000
Branch Office(s)
2020 "K" St NW, Suite 660, Washington, DC 20006 *Tel:* 202-296-1883 *Fax:* 202-296-1430
2020 Conference(s): ANA Masters of Marketing Conference, Rosen Shingle Creek, 9939 Universal Blvd, Orlando, FL, Oct 20-23, 2020
Publication(s): *ANA Magazine*; *B-to-B Marketer* (magazine); *Forward* (newsletter)

Association of Progressive Rental Organizations (APRO)
500 E Whitestone Blvd, Suite 4189, Cedar Park, TX 78613
Tel: 512-794-0095 *Toll Free Tel:* 800-204-2776 *Fax:* 512-794-0097
E-mail: info@rtohq.org
Web Site: www.rtohq.org
Key Personnel
Pres: Louis Garcia

Exec Dir: Jill McClure
Founded: 1980
National trade association for the rent-to-own industry.
Number of Members: 2,752
2020 Conference(s): RTO World National Convention & Trade Show, Tampa, FL, Aug 17-19, 2020
Publication(s): *RTOHQ: The Magazine*

ASSP, see American Society of Safety Professionals (ASSP)

ATD, see Association for Talent Development (ATD)

Audio Engineering Society (AES)
551 Fifth Ave, Suite 1225, New York, NY 10176
Tel: 212-661-8528
Web Site: www.aes.org
Key Personnel
Pres: David W Scheirman
Exec Dir: Colleen Harper
Dir, Communs: Frank Wells
Dir, Opers: Chris Plunkett
Founded: 1948
Uniting persons performing professional services in the audio engineering field & its allied arts. Collecting, collating & disseminating scientific knowledge in the field of audio engineering & its allied arts. Advancing such science in both theoretical & practical applications & preparing, publishing & distributing literature & periodicals relative to the foregoing purposes & policies.
Number of Members: 12,000
2020 Conference(s): AES Convention, Jacob K Javits Convention Center, 655 W 34 St, New York, NY, Oct 21-24, 2020
Publication(s): *Journal of the AES* (10 issues/yr, $75/yr print, online free membs; $310/yr print, $565 online (access to archive), $715/yr print & online nonmembs)

Audiovisual and Integrated Experience Association (AVIXA)
11242 Waples Mill Rd, Suite 200, Fairfax, VA 22030
Tel: 703-273-7200 *Toll Free Tel:* 800-659-7469
E-mail: membership@avixa.org
Web Site: www.avixa.org
Key Personnel
Exec Dir & CEO: David Labuskes
SVP, Mktg & Communs: Dan Goldstein
SVP, Memb Servs: Betsy Jaffe
Founded: 1939
The trade association for the professional AV & information communications industries worldwide & founder of InfoComm, the largest exhibition & conference for AV professionals.
Number of Members: 5,000
2020 Conference(s): InfoComm, Las Vegas Convention Center, Las Vegas, NV, June 13-19, 2020

Austin Film Society (AFS)
1901 E 51 St, Austin, TX 78723
Tel: 512-322-0145
E-mail: afs@austinfilm.org
Web Site: www.austinfilm.org
Key Personnel
CEO: Rebecca Campbell
COO: Sarah Ann Mockbee *Tel:* 512-322-0145 ext 3211 *E-mail:* sarahann@austinfilm.org
Chief Devt Offr: Jesse Greendyk *E-mail:* jesse@austinfilm.org
Cinema & Event Dir: Laura Fleischauer *E-mail:* laura@austinfilm.org
Dir, Mktg: Christine Lee *Tel:* 512-322-0145 ext 3213 *E-mail:* christine@austinfilm.org
Dir, Opers: Ayleen Perez *Tel:* 512-322-0145 ext 3226 *E-mail:* ayleen@austinfilm.org

Dir, Progs: Erica Deiparine-Sugars *Tel:* 512-478-8600 *E-mail:* erica@austinfilm.org
Event Coord: Victoria Pollock *E-mail:* victoria@austinfilm.org
Founded: 1985
Nonprofit media arts organization & production studio.
Number of Members: 1,900

BEA, see Broadcast Education Association (BEA)

BFF (Black Filmmaker Foundation)
200 Broadway, New York, NY 10038
Key Personnel
Founder & Pres: Warrington Hudlin
  E-mail: hudlin@dvrepublic.org
Founded: 1978
Develops the awareness of Black independent film & video as an important artistic movement. Supports emerging filmmakers & builds audiences for their work with a wide variety of programs & services. Created video series "Pass the Torch," about prominent entertainer-activists such as Harry Belafonte, Katherine Dunham, James Mtume & Pam Grier.

Black Filmmaker Foundation, see BFF (Black Filmmaker Foundation)

Broadcast Education Association (BEA)
Affiliate of National Association of Broadcasters (NAB) (in partnership with)
1771 "N" St NW, Washington, DC 20036-2891
Tel: 202-602-0587 *Fax:* 202-609-9940
E-mail: help@beaweb.org
Web Site: www.beaweb.org
Key Personnel
Exec Dir: Heather Birks *Tel:* 202-602-0584
  E-mail: heather@beaweb.org
Founded: 1955
Professional development association of professors, students, broadcasters or any individuals interested in electronic communication.
Number of Members: 1,530
2020 Conference(s): BEA2020, Westgate Las Vegas Resort & Casino, 3000 Paradise Rd, Las Vegas, NV, April 18-21, 2020
Publication(s): *Journal of Broadcasting & Electronic Media (JoBEM)* (quarterly); *Journal of Media Education (JoME)* (quarterly); *Journal of Radio & Audio Media (JRAM)* (semiannual)

Broadcasters Foundation of America
125 W 55 St, 4th fl, New York, NY 10019-5366
Tel: 212-373-8250 *Fax:* 212-373-8254
E-mail: info@thebfoa.org
Web Site: www.thebfoa.org;
  broadcastersfoundation.org
Key Personnel
Pres: James B Thompson *E-mail:* jim@thebfoa.org
VP: Peter M Doyle *E-mail:* peter@thebfoa.org
VP, Busn Aff: Frank Pesce *E-mail:* frank@thebfoa.org
Off & Grant Mgr: Emily Barratt *E-mail:* emily@thebfoa.org
Founded: 1946
Assisting radio & television broadcasters in personal financial need; awards & distinguished notices given.
Number of Members: 5,000
Publication(s): *On The Air* (magazine, 3 issues/yr, free to membs)

Business Technology Association (BTA)
12411 Wornall Rd, Suite 200, Kansas City, MO 64145
Tel: 816-941-3100 *Toll Free Tel:* 800-826-6159; 800-505-2821 (memb servs) *Fax:* 816-941-4843 *Toll Free Fax:* 800-941-2829

E-mail: info@bta.org
Web Site: www.bta.org
Key Personnel
Exec Dir: Brent Hoskins *Tel:* 816-303-4040
  Fax: 816-303-4056 *E-mail:* brent@bta.org
Mktg Dir: Valerie Briseno *Tel:* 816-303-4082
  Fax: 816-941-4838 *E-mail:* valerie@bta.org
Founded: 1926
International not-for-profit trade association serving independent dealers, value-added resellers, systems integrators, manufacturers & distributors in the office technology industry. BTA provides a wide variety of services to its members including free legal advice & guidance; business benchmarking studies & reports; information on the latest news, trends & products in the industry; strong educational offerings; industry-specific publications.
2020 Conference(s): BTA National Conference, Chicago, IL, June 11-12, 2020
Publication(s): *BTA Hotline* (enewsletter, weekly, free); *Office Technology* (magazine, monthly, free to membs; $100/yr US, $115/yr elsewhere, nonmembs)

Cable & Telecommunications Association for Marketing (CTAM)
120 Waterfront St, Suite 200, National Harbor, MD 20745
Tel: 301-485-8900 *Fax:* 301-560-4964
E-mail: info@ctam.com
Web Site: www.ctam.com
Key Personnel
CEO & Pres: Vicki Lins *E-mail:* vicki@ctam.com
Nonprofit professional association dedicated to helping the cable industry grow.
Number of Members: 3,000
Publication(s): *CTAM SmartBrief*

Canadian Academy of Recording Arts & Sciences (CARAS)
219 Dufferin St, Suite 211C, Toronto, ON M6K 3J1, Canada
Tel: 416-485-3135 (CN only) *Toll Free Tel:* 888-501-3135 *Fax:* 416-485-4978
E-mail: submissions@junoawards.ca; info@carasonline.ca
Web Site: carasonline.ca; junoawards.ca
Key Personnel
Pres & CEO: Allan Reid *E-mail:* allan@junoawards.ca
COO: Jackie Dean *E-mail:* jackie@junoawards.ca
Mgr, Communs & Soc Media: Elyssa Macri
  E-mail: elyssa@junoawards.ca
Founded: 1975
Not-for-profit organization promoting & celebrating Canadian music & artists.
Number of Members: 1,600
Publication(s): *CARAS News* (quarterly)

Canadian Broadcast Standards Council (CBSC)
PO Box 3265, Sta D, Ottawa, ON K1P 6H8, Canada
Tel: 613-233-4607 *Toll Free Tel:* 866-696-4718 (CN only) *Fax:* 613-233-4826
E-mail: info@cbsc.ca
Web Site: www.cbsc.ca
Key Personnel
Chair: Sylvie Courtemanche
  E-mail: scourtemanche@cbsc.ca
Exec Dir: John MacNab *Tel:* 613-233-4607 ext 111 *E-mail:* jmacnab@cbsc.ca
Founded: 1990
Number of Members: 790

Catholic Library Association (CLA)
8550 United Plaza Blvd, Suite 1001, Baton Rouge, LA 70809
Tel: 225-408-4417
E-mail: cla2@cathla.org
Web Site: www.cathla.org

Key Personnel
Pres: N Curt LeMay *E-mail:* nclemay@stthomas.edu
VP & Treas: Jack Fritts *E-mail:* jfritts@ben.edu
Exec Dir: Bland O'Connor
Association Coord: Madison Petty
Gen Ed: Sigrid Kelsey
Founded: 1921
Fostering advancement of library services & improvement of library resources through Catholic, ecumenical & interreligious collaboration, publication, education & information.
Publication(s): *Catholic Library World* (journal, 3 issues/yr, $55/yr membs; $100/yr nonmembs US; $125/yr nonmembs foreign)

CBSC, see Canadian Broadcast Standards Council (CBSC)

CCUMC, see Consortium of College & University Media Centers (CCUMC)

CEDIA IPRO Affinity Group
8475 Nightfall Lane, Fishers, IN 46037
Tel: 317-328-4336 *Toll Free Tel:* 800-669-5329
E-mail: info@cedia.org
Web Site: cedia.net
Key Personnel
Global Pres & CEO: Tabatha O'Connor *Tel:* 800-669-5329 ext 113
SVP, Indus Engagement: Giles Sutton *Tel:* 800-669-5329 ext 157
VP, Educ & Training: Samantha Ventura
  Tel: 800-669-5329 ext 122
VP, Mktg & Indus Rel: Christine Haley Pyle
  Tel: 800-669-5329 ext 119
VP, Technol Application & Workforce: Ian Bryant
  Tel: 800-669-5329 ext 141
Sr Dir, Fin: Kory Dickerson *Tel:* 800-669-5329 ext 142
Sr Dir, Opers: Leslie Lowes *Tel:* 800-669-5329 ext 140
Sr Dir, Sales, Sponsorships & Partnerships: Robert Keeler
Sr Dir, Technol & Standards: Walt Zerbe
  Tel: 800-669-5329 ext 117
Content Dir: Ed Wenck *Tel:* 800-669-5329 ext 131
Dir, Busn Devt & Sales: Jody Larsen *Tel:* 800-669-5329 ext 153
Dir, Certification: David Whitney *Tel:* 800-669-5329 ext 176
Dir, Curriculum: Derick Abshire *Tel:* 800-669-5329 ext 165
Dir, Govt Aff: Darren Reaman *Tel:* 800-669-5329 ext 144
Dir, HR: Eileen Mullany *Tel:* 800-669-5329 ext 173
Dir, Mktg: Desiree Friedman *Tel:* 800-669-5329 ext 154
Dir, Meetings & Events: Jennifer Roth *Tel:* 800-669-5329 ext 139
Dir, PR & Indus Rel: Olivia Sellke *Tel:* 800-669-5329 ext 130
Dir, Tech Training: Steven Rissi *Tel:* 800-669-5329 ext 112
Dir, Workforce Devt: Tommy Tabor *Tel:* 800-669-5329 ext 134
Founded: 1989
International trade association of companies that specialize in designing & installing electronic systems for the home.
Number of Members: 3,700
2020 Conference(s): CEDIA Expo, Denver, CO, Sept 8-12, 2020
Publication(s): *CEDIA Communicates* (newsletter, quarterly)

Center for Asian American Media (CAAM)
145 Ninth St, Suite 350, San Francisco, CA 94103
Tel: 415-863-0814 *Fax:* 415-863-7428
E-mail: publicity@caamedia.org

Web Site: caamedia.org
Key Personnel
Exec Dir: Stephen Gong *Tel:* 415-863-0814 ext 103 *E-mail:* sgong@caamedia.org
Dir, Devt: Frances Pomperada *Tel:* 415-863-0814 ext 104 *E-mail:* fpomperada@caamedia.org
Dir, Progs: Donald Young *Tel:* 415-863-0814 ext 105 *E-mail:* don@caamedia.org
Festival & Exhibitions Dir: Masashi Niwano *Tel:* 415-863-0814 ext 109 *E-mail:* mniwano@caamedia.org
Fin & Admin Dir: James Ott *Tel:* 415-863-0814 ext 119 *E-mail:* jott@caamedia.org
Membership & Devt Mgr: Jennifer Chu *Tel:* 415-863-0814 ext 102 *E-mail:* jchu@caamedia.org
A nonprofit, educational organization. Support high quality film, video & digital media works produced by & about Asian Americans, encourage greater multi-cultural understanding of the Asian-American experience & promote artistic quality & merit in Asian-American productions.
Number of Members: 600
2020 Conference(s): CAAMFest, San Francisco & Oakland, CA, May 14-24, 2020

Centre for Art Tapes (CFAT)
2238 Maitland St, Halifax, NS B3K 2Z9, Canada
Tel: 902-422-6822
E-mail: info@cfat.ca
Web Site: cfat.ca
Key Personnel
Prodn Dir: Thomas Elliott *E-mail:* tom@cfat.ca
Founded: 1979
Supports artists working with media technologies by providing subsidized public access to professional equipment, facilities, technical expertise, educational resources, mentorship & other forms of professional & creative support.

Chicago Film Critics Association
155 E Algonquin Rd, Arlington Heights, IL 60006
Mailing Address: PO Box 280, Arlington Heights, IL 60006
Tel: 847-427-4530 *Fax:* 847-427-1301
Web Site: www.chicagofilmcritics.org
Key Personnel
Pres: Dann Gire
VP: Brian Tallerico
Exec Secy: Erik Childress
Treas: Alejandro Riera
Founded: 1990
Critics views at annual awards show; critics roundtable at colleges; critic membership & representation such as issuing statements on artists rights & media issues. Membership fees $75/yr.
Number of Members: 49

CineTech Media Professionals
PO Box 34, Olivebridge, NY 12461
Web Site: cinetechmediapros.org
Key Personnel
Pres: Ken White *E-mail:* kawhite1@email.com
VP: Dave Landau *E-mail:* davidlandau5@gmail.com
Secy & Membership: Judie Luszcz *E-mail:* judie@sugarshockmedia.com
Treas & Webmaster: Liz de Nesnera *E-mail:* liz@hireliz.com
Organization for professionals working in the digital moving image industry, from TV & corporate video to commercials, infomercials, music videos, sales videos, instructional videos, Internet content & independent digital feature films & news.
Conference(s): CineTech Expo, Hennessy Hall Mansion, Fairleigh Dickinson University, Madison, NJ
Publication(s): *Newsletter* (newsletter, monthly)

City of Boston Office of Broadband & Cable
43 Hawkins St, Suite 1B, Boston, MA 02114
Tel: 617-635-3112
E-mail: cable@boston.gov
Web Site: www.cityofboston.gov/cable
Key Personnel
Dir: Mike Lynch *E-mail:* mike.lynch@boston.gov
Air & produce news, athletic events, educational shows & other programming. Also work with cable franchises & broadband companies to advocate for residents.

Communications Media Management Association (CMMA)
1604 Glendale Hills Dr NE, Suite B25, Rochester, MN 55906-8376
Tel: 507-271-4307
Web Site: cmma.org
Key Personnel
Exec Dir: Marv Mitchell *E-mail:* executive.director@cmma.org
Founded: 1946
Dedicated to professional growth of corporate, education & government communications managers.
2020 Conference(s): National Conference, Milwaukee, WI, Oct 4-6, 2020
Publication(s): *e-visions* (3 issues/yr by e-mail to membs, can view past issues on web site)

Consortium of College & University Media Centers (CCUMC)
c/o Indiana University, 306 N Union St, Bloomington, IN 47405-3888
Tel: 812-855-6049
E-mail: ccumc@ccumc.org
Web Site: www.ccumc.org
Key Personnel
Exec Dir: Aileen Scales
Membership & Mktg: Kirsten Phillips
Founded: 1971
To provide leadership & a forum for information exchange to the providers of media content, academic technology & support for quality teaching & learning at institutions of higher education.
Number of Members: 800
2020 Conference(s): Annual Conference, Crowne Plaza Indianapolis-Downtown Union Station, Indianapolis, IN, Nov 4-7, 2020

Consumer Technology Association (CTA)
1919 S Eads St, Arlington, VA 22202
Tel: 703-907-7600 *Toll Free Tel:* 866-858-1555 *Fax:* 703-907-7675 *Toll Free Fax:* 866-858-2555
E-mail: cta@cta.tech
Web Site: www.cta.tech
Key Personnel
Pres & CEO: Gary Shapiro
Represents all facets of electronics manufacturing, including US manufacturers of audio, video, accessories, mobile electronics, communications equipment, information products & multimedia products.
Number of Members: 2,000
2021 Conference(s): International CES (Consumer Electronics Show), Las Vegas Convention Center, 3150 Paradise Rd, Las Vegas, NV, Jan 6-9, 2021
2022 Conference(s): International CES (Consumer Electronics Show), Las Vegas Convention Center, 3150 Paradise Rd, Las Vegas, NV, Jan 5-8, 2022
2023 Conference(s): International CES (Consumer Electronics Show), Las Vegas Convention Center, 3150 Paradise Rd, Las Vegas, NV, Jan 5-8, 2023
2024 Conference(s): International CES (Consumer Electronics Show), Las Vegas Convention Center, 3150 Paradise Rd, Las Vegas, NV, Jan 9-12, 2024
Publication(s): *Vision Magazine*

Corporation for Public Broadcasting (CPB)
401 Ninth St NW, Washington, DC 20004-2129
Tel: 202-879-9600 *Toll Free Tel:* 800-272-2190 *Fax:* 202-879-9700
E-mail: press@cpb.org
Web Site: www.cpb.org
Key Personnel
Pres & CEO: Patricia de Stacy Harrison
EVP & COO: Michael Levy
Treas & CFO: William P Tayman, Jr
EVP & Chief Policy & Busn Aff Offr: Steven J Altman
SVP, Corp Secy & Chief of Staff: Teresa Safon
SVP & Gen Coun: Westwood Smithers, Jr
Founded: 1967
Private nonprofit corporation providing funding for public radio, television & related online & mobile services. Its mission is to ensure universal access to non-commercial, high quality content & telecommunications services.

CPB, see Corporation for Public Broadcasting (CPB)

CTA, see Consumer Technology Association (CTA)

CTAM, see Cable & Telecommunications Association for Marketing (CTAM)

Data & Marketing Association (DMA)
Division of Association of National Advertisers Inc (ANA)
225 Reinekers Lane, Suite 325, Alexandria, VA 22314
Tel: 212-768-7277; 212-790-1500
Web Site: thedma.org
Key Personnel
CEO: Thomas J Benton
PR & Memb Communs Mgr: Michael Uehlein *E-mail:* muehlein@thedma.org
Founded: 1917
Champions deeper consumer engagement & business value through the innovative & responsible use of data-driven marketing. Hosts the International ECHO Awards & the DMA Innovation Awards.
Number of Members: 4,500

Denver Film Society
1510 York St, 3rd fl, Denver, CO 80206
Tel: 303-595-3456
E-mail: info@denverfilm.org
Web Site: www.denverfilm.org
Key Personnel
Exec Dir: Andrew Rodgers *E-mail:* andrew@denverfilm.org
Artistic Dir: Brit Withey *E-mail:* brit@denverfilm.org
Dir, Devt: Holly Porterfield *E-mail:* holly@denverfilm.org
Dir, Opers: Gina Cuomo *E-mail:* gina@denverfilm.org
Festival Dir: Britta Erickson *E-mail:* britta@denverfilm.org
Mktg Dir: Kevin Smith *E-mail:* kevins@denverfilm.org
Founded: 1978
Nonprofit arts organization, producers of the Denver Film Festival & Film on the Rocks. Year-round operators of the Sie Film Center.
Number of Members: 2,000

DGA, see Directors Guild of America (DGA)

Digital Signage Federation (DSF)
11 Main St, Suite D, Warrenton, VA 20186
Mailing Address: PO Box 3363, Warrenton, VA 20188
Tel: 540-551-5500 *Fax:* 202-962-3939
Web Site: www.digitalsignagefederation.org
Key Personnel
Exec Dir: Brian Gorg *E-mail:* bgorg@digitalsignagefederation.org
Founded: 2010
Education, networking & advocacy to continue moving the growth of the digital signage industry.
2020 Conference(s): Digital Signage Expo, Las Vegas Convention Center, 3150 Paradise Rd, Las Vegas, NV, March 31-April 3, 2020

Directors Guild of America (DGA)
7920 Sunset Blvd, Los Angeles, CA 90046
Tel: 310-289-2000 *Toll Free Tel:* 800-421-4173
Web Site: www.dga.org
Founded: 1936
Guild & labor union.
Number of Members: 15,000
Branch Office(s)
110 W 57 St, New York, NY 10019 *Tel:* 212-258-0800 *Toll Free Tel:* 800-356-3754
Publication(s): *DGA Monthly* (free to membs); *DGA Quarterly* (free to membs; $32/yr nonmembs)

DMA, see Data & Marketing Association (DMA)

Documentary Organization of Canada
Centre for Social Innovation, 215 Spadina Ave, Suite 126, Toronto, ON M5T 2C7, Canada
Tel: 416-599-3844 *Toll Free Tel:* 877-467-4485
E-mail: info@docorg.ca
Web Site: docorg.ca
Key Personnel
Exec Dir: Judy Gladstone *Tel:* 416-599-3844 ext 1 *E-mail:* judy@docorg.ca
Communs & Outreach Dir: Danielle Couture *Tel:* 416-599-3844 ext 2 *E-mail:* danielle@docorg.ca
Premier organization for Canadian documentary advocacy. Offers professional development & networking opportunities through workshops, master classes, mentorship programs, services & benefits.

The Electronic Document Systems Association®, see Xplor® International

Electronic Service Dealers Association (ESDA)
PO Box 391, LaPorte, IN 46352-0391
Tel: 847-798-6520 *Fax:* 219-324-3384
E-mail: esdaweb@gmail.com
Web Site: www.esdaweb.org
Key Personnel
Exec Dir: David Kliss
Founded: 1989
Promote independent electronic service dealers in the Midwest.
Number of Members: 100

Electronics Representatives Association (ERA)
1325 S Arlington Heights Rd, Suite 204, Elk Grove Village, IL 60007
Tel: 312-419-1432 *Fax:* 312-419-1660
E-mail: info@era.org
Web Site: www.era.org
Key Personnel
CEO: Walter Tobin *E-mail:* wtobin@era.org
Communs Dir: Neda Simeonova *E-mail:* nsimeonova@era.org
Events Coord: Erin Collins
Admin Asst: Karin Derkacz *E-mail:* kderkacz@era.org
Founded: 1935

To advance & support the professional outsourced field sales function in the global electronics industry.
Number of Members: 562
Publication(s): *ERA Quick Connections* (enewsletter, monthly); *The Representor* (magazine, quarterly)
Membership(s): Manufacturers' Representatives Educational Research Foundation; Small Business Legislative Council

Electronics Technicians Association International Inc
5 Depot St, Greencastle, IN 46135
Tel: 765-653-8262 *Toll Free Tel:* 800-288-3824 *Fax:* 765-653-4287
E-mail: eta@eta-i.org
Web Site: www.eta-i.org
Key Personnel
Pres: Teresa Maher *E-mail:* tmaher@eta-i.org
Founded: 1978
Education, information, certification of electronics technicians, FCC exams; membership nonprofit professional association; fiber optics certification; telecommunication, industrial, consumer, biomedical electronics, wireless communications, cyber security, smart technology systems, customer service & more.
Number of Members: 5,000
2020 Conference(s): Education Forum (in conjunction with the International Wireless Communications Expo), Las Vegas, NV, March 30-April 3, 2020
Publication(s): *The High Tech News* (magazine, 6 issues/yr, free to membs; $20 nonmembs)

EMA, see The Entertainment Merchants Association (EMA)

The Entertainment Merchants Association (EMA)
PO Box 6339, North Hollywood, CA 91603
Tel: 818-385-1500
E-mail: info@entmerch.org
Web Site: www.entmerch.org
Key Personnel
Pres & CEO: Mark Fisher *E-mail:* mfisher@entmerch.org
SVP, Pub Aff: Sean Bersell *E-mail:* sbersell@entmerch.org
VP, Indus Leadership: Eric Hanson *E-mail:* ehanson@entmerch.org
VP, Indus Sales: Steven Apple *E-mail:* sapple@entmerch.org
VP, Mktg & Events: Jennifer Lane Burnell *E-mail:* jlane@entmerch.org
Founded: 2006
Not-for-profit international trade association dedicated to advancing the interests of the home entertainment industry. Represents retailers & distributors of DVDs, computer & console video games & digital versions of these products.
Number of Members: 4,200

Entertainment Services and Technology Association (ESTA)
630 Ninth Ave, Suite 609, New York, NY 10036
Tel: 212-244-1505 *Fax:* 212-244-1502
E-mail: info@esta.org; membership@esta.org
Web Site: www.esta.org
Key Personnel
Exec Dir: Erin Grabe *Tel:* 212-244-1505 ext 606 *E-mail:* erin.grabe@esta.org
ETCP Certification Mgr: Meredith Moseley-Bennett *Tel:* 212-244-1505 ext 705 *E-mail:* etcp@esta.org
Membership Mgr: Frances Thompson *Tel:* 212-244-1505 ext 630 *E-mail:* frances.thompson@esta.org
PERG Mgr: Harry Box *Tel:* 323-541-3200 *E-mail:* harry.box@esta.org

Tech Standards Mgr: Karl G Ruling *Tel:* 212-244-1505 ext 703 *E-mail:* standards@esta.org
Nonprofit trade association whose members have created industry programs including the Technical Standards Program, Entertainment Technician Certification Program & Rental Guard.

ETA® International, see Electronics Technicians Association International Inc

Exhibitor Appointed Contractor Association (EACA)
2214 NW Fifth St, Bend, OR 97703
Tel: 541-317-8768
E-mail: info@eaca.com
Web Site: eaca.com
Key Personnel
Exec Dir: Jim Wurm *E-mail:* jimwurm@eaca.com
Tradeshow industry association representing & supporting the interests of exhibitor appointed contractors & other exhibit services organizations that service customers on the trade show floor.
Number of Members: 200

Film Florida
2516 Quail Park Terr, Kissimmee, FL 34743
Tel: 407-494-6195
E-mail: info@filmflorida.org
Web Site: www.filmflorida.org
Key Personnel
Pres: Bonnie King
Exec Dir: John Lux
Entertainment production association representing the film, television, production & digital media/tech industry in Florida.

Film Liaisons In California Statewide (FLICS)
c/o Humboldt-Del Norte Film Commission, 520 "E" St, Eureka, CA 95501
E-mail: info@filmcalifornia.com
Web Site: www.filmcalifornia.com
Key Personnel
Pres: Cassandra Hesseltine *Tel:* 707-443-4488
Founded: 2005
Professional association of film commissioners throughout California.
Number of Members: 41
Conference(s): The Film in California Conference, Los Angeles, CA, Annually in May; California On Location Awards (COLA), Los Angeles, CA, Annually in Dec

Film Society KC
601 E 63 St, Suite 400, Kansas City, MO 64110
E-mail: filmsocietykc@gmail.com
Web Site: www.filmsocietykc.org
Founded: 2014 (result of Film Commission of Greater Kansas City merger with the Film Society)
Promote & support local filmmakers & theaters by providing educational programs & events to its members. Administers the Robert Altman Emerging Filmmakers Fund.

FilmL.A., Inc
6255 W Sunset Blvd, 12th fl, Los Angeles, CA 90028
Tel: 213-977-8600 *Fax:* 213-977-8601 (permits)
E-mail: info@filmla.com
Web Site: www.filmla.com
Key Personnel
Pres: Paul Audley
Founded: 1995 (as Entertainment Industry Development Corp)
Nonprofit film office serving the greater Los Angeles area. Film permits & programs to minimize filming impact on local community.
Membership(s): Association of Film Commissioners International

Filmmakers Alliance (FA)
1317 N San Fernando Blvd, Unit 366, Burbank,
CA 91504
Tel: 310-568-0633
E-mail: info@filmmakersalliance.org
Web Site: filmmakersalliance.org
Key Personnel
Co-Founder: Diane Gaidry
Co-Founder & Pres: Jacques Thelemaque
Founded: 1993
Nonprofit organization of film artists dedicated
to the advancement of true independent film
through community action.

Foundation for Economic Education (FEE)
1819 Peachtree Rd NE, Suite 300, Atlanta, GA
30309
Tel: 404-554-9980 *Toll Free Tel:* 800-960-4333
E-mail: editor@fee.org; info@fee.org
Web Site: fee.org
Key Personnel
Pres: Lawrence W Reed *E-mail:* lreed@fee.org
Founded: 1946
Tax-exempt educational organization. FEE also
conducts seminars & conferences. FEE's mis-
sion is to inspire, educate & connect young
adults with the economic, ethical & legal prin-
ciples of a free society.
Number of Members: 14,000

Giant Screen Cinema Association (GSCA)
624 Holly Springs Rd, Suite 243, Holly Springs,
NC 27540
Tel: 919-346-1123 *Fax:* 919-573-9100
E-mail: info@giantscreencinema.com
Web Site: www.giantscreencinema.com
Key Personnel
Exec Dir: Tammy Seldon *E-mail:* tammy@
giantscreencinema.com
Communs & Membership Dir: Kelly Ger-
main *Tel:* 651-917-1080 *E-mail:* kelly@
giantscreencinema.com
Founded: 2006 (with the unification of the Large
Format Cinema Association & the Giant Screen
Theater Association)
To advance the business of producing & present-
ing educational giant screen & immersive cin-
ema experiences globally.
Membership fees: $250 (indiv), $850 (corp), $75
(student - proof of college or univ enrollment
required)
Number of Members: 260

Graphic Artists Guild Inc
31 W 34 St, 8th fl, New York, NY 10001
Tel: 212-791-3400
E-mail: admin@graphicartistsguild.org;
membership@graphicartistsguild.org
Web Site: graphicartistsguild.org
Key Personnel
Admin Dir: Paula Hinkle
National advocacy organization representing pro-
fessional graphic & interactive designers, illus-
trators, animators, web programmers & devel-
opers.
Number of Members: 3,000
Publication(s): *Graphic Artists Guild Handbook:
Pricing & Ethical Guidelines* (biennial, free to
membs, $44.99 nonmembs)

Graphic Arts Technical Foundation, see
Printing Industries of America

GSCA, see Giant Screen Cinema Association
(GSCA)

Guild of Italian American Actors (GIAA)
Subsidiary of Associated Actors & Artists of
America
1026A Shetland Dr, Lakewood, NJ 08701
Tel: 201-344-3411

E-mail: info@giaa.us
Web Site: www.giaa.us
Key Personnel
Pres: Carlo Fiorletta *E-mail:* carlofiorletta@giaa.
us
1st VP: Carson Ferri-Grant
2nd VP: Debbie Klaar
Secy/Treas: Mara Lesemann *Tel:* 551-200-8112
E-mail: maralesemann@yahoo.com
Founded: 1937
Acting union representing actors in Italian lan-
guage theatre in the US & Canada.
Number of Members: 150

Hollywood Post Alliance, see Hollywood
Professional Association (HPA)

Hollywood Professional Association (HPA)
Formerly Hollywood Post Alliance
2501 W Burbank Blvd, No 207, Burbank, CA
91505
Tel: 818-273-1482
Web Site: hpaonline.com
Key Personnel
Exec Dir: Barbara Lange
Busn Devt Mgr: Joyce Cataldo
Digital Projs Coord: Max Ma *Tel:* 818-273-1484
Awards & Events Admin: Mimi Rossi *Tel:* 818-
273-1505
Event Planner/Opers: Alicia Rock *Tel:* 818-273-
1508
Ad Sales Rep: Jeff Victor
Founded: 2001
Trade association for business & professionals in
post-production.
Number of Members: 400
Conference(s): HPA Tech Retreat, Annually in
Feb
Publication(s): *HPA Newsline* (newsletter,
monthly)

**IAA-VC (International Association of Audio
Visual Communicators)**
PO Box 270779, Flower Mound, TX 75027-0779
Tel: 469-464-4180 *Fax:* 469-464-4170
E-mail: cindy@cindys.com
Web Site: cindys.com
Key Personnel
Exec Dir: Phillip N Shuey *E-mail:* phillip@
cindys.com
Founded: 1957
Promote excellence within digital media produc-
tion industries. Two international & 14 regional
CINDY Awards events annually.
Number of Members: 5,900
Publication(s): *The Communicator* (enewsletter)

IABC, see International Association of Business
Communicators (IABC)

IATSE
207 W 25 St, 4th fl, New York, NY 10001
Tel: 212-730-1770 *Fax:* 212-730-7809
Web Site: www.iatse-intl.org; iatse.net
Key Personnel
Intl Pres: Matthew D Loeb
Gen Secy & Treas: James B Wood
Founded: 1893
Nonprofit union for theatrical & commercial
film/tape craft employees.
Number of Members: 120,000
Publication(s): *Official Bulletin* (quarterly)

IATSE Local 600, see International
Cinematographers Guild (ICG)

IES, see Illuminating Engineering Society (IES)

IFP, see The Independent Filmmaker Project
(IFP)

IISE, see Institute of Industrial & Systems
Engineers (IISE)

Illuminating Engineering Society (IES)
120 Wall St, 17th fl, New York, NY 10005-4026
Tel: 212-248-5000
E-mail: ies@ies.org
Web Site: ies.org
Key Personnel
Exec Dir: Timothy Licitra *Tel:* 212-248-5000 ext
2001 *E-mail:* tlicitra@ies.org
Dir, Devt: Shayna Bramley *Tel:* 212-248-5000 ext
5001 *E-mail:* sbramley@ies.org
Dir, Educ: Tom Butters *Tel:* 647-649-6660
E-mail: tbutters@ies.org
Dir, Memb Servs: Jennifer Marotta Collin
Tel: 212-248-5000 ext 4001 *E-mail:* jmarotta-
collin@ies.org
Events Coord: Klara Steupert *Tel:* 212-248-5000
ext 4006 *E-mail:* ksteupert@ies.org
Founded: 1906
Technical authority for the illumination field; in-
formation on all aspects of lighting practice
for individual members, industry & consumers
through a variety of programs, publications &
services.
Number of Members: 8,000
2020 Conference(s): IES Annual Conference,
Hilton New Orleans Riverside, 2 Poydras St,
New Orleans, LA, Aug 6-8, 2020; IES Street
& Area Lighting Conference, Dallas, TX, Oct
18-21, 2020
Publication(s): *IES Lighting Handbook* ($350/yr
membs; $595/yr nonmembs); *LEUKOS, The
Journal of the Illuminating Engineering Society of North America* (quarterly online, end
of yr print compilation, free to membs; end of
yr print $25); *Lighting Design + Application
(LD+A)* (monthly, free to membs; $48/yr non-
membs)

The Imaging Alliance
7600 Jericho Tpke, Suite 301, Woodbury, NY
11797
Tel: 516-802-0895 *Fax:* 516-364-0140
E-mail: info@theimagingalliance.com
Web Site: www.theimagingalliance.com
Key Personnel
Exec Dir: Jerry Grossman
Prog Dir: Michelle Tramantano
E-mail: michelle@theimagingalliance.com
Founded: 2016 (as a result of the merger of
PMDA & PMAI)
Promotes the welfare of the imaging industry
through its support of products & services that
lead to innovation in capturing, printing, shar-
ing, experiencing, enhancing, storing & dis-
tributing visual communication.

IMCCA, see Interactive Multimedia &
Collaborative Communications Alliance
(IMCCA)

In-Plant Printing & Mailing Association
103 N Jefferson St, Kearney, MO 64060
Tel: 816-919-1691 *Fax:* 816-945-4505
E-mail: ipmainfo@ipma.org
Web Site: ipma.org
Key Personnel
Exec Dir: Mike Loyd *E-mail:* mloyd@ipma.org
Founded: 1964
Membership association for in-house print & mail
professionals. Provides opportunities for educa-
tion & further managerial advancement.
Number of Members: 700
2020 Conference(s): IPMA Annual Conference,
The Hyatt Coconut Point, Fort Myers, FL, June
7-11, 2020

The Independent Book Publishers Association (IBPA)

1020 Manhattan Beach Blvd, Suite 204, Manhattan Beach, CA 90266
Tel: 310-546-1818 *Fax:* 310-546-3939
E-mail: info@ibpa-online.org
Web Site: www.ibpa-online.org
Key Personnel
CEO: Angela Bole *E-mail:* angela@ibpa-online.org
COO: Terry Nathan *E-mail:* terry@ibpa-online.org
Founded: 1983
Cooperative marketing & education for independent book publishers.
Number of Members: 3,000
Publication(s): *Independent* (newsletter, monthly, $40/yr membs; $65/yr nonmembs)

Independent Film & Television Alliance® (IFTA)

10850 Wilshire Blvd, 9th fl, Los Angeles, CA 90024-4311
Tel: 310-446-1000 *Fax:* 310-446-1600
E-mail: info@ifta-online.org
Web Site: www.ifta-online.org
Key Personnel
Pres & CEO: Jean M Prewitt *Tel:* 310-446-1001
   E-mail: jprewitt@ifta-online.org
EVP & Mng Dir, American Film Market:
   Jonathan Wolf *E-mail:* jwolf@ifta-online.org
Founded: 1980
Trade association for independent motion picture & TV distributors.
Number of Members: 170
2020 Conference(s): American Film Market, Santa Monica, CA, Nov 4-11, 2020
2021 Conference(s): American Film Market, Santa Monica, CA, Nov 3-10, 2021
2022 Conference(s): American Film Market, Santa Monica, CA, Nov 2-9, 2022
2023 Conference(s): American Film Market, Santa Monica, CA, Nov 1-8, 2023
2024 Conference(s): American Film Market, Santa Monica, CA, Nov 6-13, 2024

The Independent Filmmaker Project (IFP)

c/o Made in NY Media Ctr by IFP, 30 John St, Ground fl, Brooklyn, NY 11201
Tel: 212-465-8200
Web Site: www.ifp.org
Key Personnel
Dir, Busn Devt: Colin Whitlow
   E-mail: cwhitlow@nymediacenter.com
Deputy Dir & Head, Programming: Amy Dotson
   E-mail: adotson@ifp.org
Deputy Dir, Fin & Opers: Mitch Mitchell
   E-mail: businessoffice@ifp.org
Sr Dir, Programming: Milton Tabbot
   E-mail: mtabbot@ifp.org
Assoc Dir, Devt: Steven Pfeiffer
   E-mail: spfeiffer@ifp.org
Mgr & Prodr, Intl & Episodic: Gabriele Capolino
   E-mail: gcapolino@ifp.org
Prog Mgr & Prodr: Zach Mandinach
   E-mail: zmandinach@ifp.org
Ed-in-Chief, Filmmaker Magazine: Scott Macaulay *E-mail:* scott@filmmakermagazine.com
Founded: 1979
Represents a network of over 30,000 filmmakers, film industry representatives & film enthusiasts. Supports independent film & the independent filmmaker through education, advocacy, outreach & community.
Branch Office(s)
7000 E Mayo Blvd, Suite 1059, Phoenix, AZ 85054, Exec Dir: Jason Carney *Tel:* 602-955-6444 *E-mail:* jason@phxfilm.com *Web Site:* ifpphx.org
Publication(s): *Filmmaker Magazine* (quarterly, $10/yr digital only; $18/yr print & digital)

Institute of Industrial & Systems Engineers (IISE)

3577 Parkway Lane, Suite 200, Norcross, GA 30092
Tel: 770-449-0460 *Toll Free Tel:* 800-494-0460
   Fax: 770-441-3295
E-mail: executiveoffices@iise.org
Web Site: www.iise.org
Key Personnel
CEO: Don Greene
COO: Donna Calvert
Dir, Communs: Karen Barnett
Dir, Membership: Bill Boyd *E-mail:* bboyd@iise.org
Mgr, Sales & Mktg: Michael Hughes
   E-mail: mhughes@iise.org
Founded: 1948
International nonprofit association that provides leadership for the application, education, training, research & development of industrial engineering.
Number of Members: 30,000
2020 Conference(s): IISE Annual Conference & Expo, Hyatt Regency New Orleans, 601 Loyola Ave, New Orleans, LA, May 30-June 2, 2020
Publication(s): *ISE Magazine* (monthly, $248/yr US; $307/yr outside US; $110 additional fee for non-US subscribers choosing delivery via airmail; free to membs)

Interactive Multimedia & Collaborative Communications Alliance (IMCCA)

PO Box 756, Syosset, NY 11791
Tel: 516-818-8184
Web Site: www.imcca.org
Key Personnel
Chpn: Michael Brandofino
Exec Dir: Carol Zelkin *E-mail:* czelkin@imcca.org
Founded: 1998
Resolved to grow the overall conferencing & collaboration market by providing impartial information & education about people-to-people, environmentally friendly communication & collaboration technology & applications.
Number of Members: 2,500

International Alliance of Theatrical Stage Employees, see IATSE

International Association of Audio Visual Communicators, see IAA-VC (International Association of Audio Visual Communicators)

International Association of Business Communicators (IABC)

649 Mission St, 5th fl, San Francisco, CA 94105
Tel: 415-544-4700 *Toll Free Tel:* 800-776-4222
   Fax: 415-544-4747
E-mail: member_relations@iabc.com
Web Site: www.iabc.com
Founded: 1970
Help communicators & organizations worldwide improve their communication with all audiences via publications, conferences & local chapters.
Number of Members: 12,000
2020 Conference(s): IABC World Conference, Hyatt Regency Chicago, Chicago, IL, June 14-17, 2020

International Cinema Technology Association (ICTA)

311 W 43 St, Suite 301, New York, NY 10036
Tel: 212-493-4097; 212-493-4058 *Fax:* 212-257-6428
Web Site: www.internationalcinematechnologyassociation.com
Key Personnel
Exec Dir: Robert H Sunshine
Founded: 1971
Trade organization that represents companies involved in cinema technology, including leading cinema equipment manufacturers, dealers & service companies from around the world.

International Cinematographers Guild (ICG)

7755 Sunset Blvd, Hollywood, CA 90046
Tel: 323-876-0160 *Fax:* 323-876-6383 (exec off)
Web Site: www.icg600.com
Key Personnel
Natl Exec Dir: Rebecca Rhine *E-mail:* rrhine@icg600.com
Founded: 1946
Represents camera professionals & publicists nationwide.
Branch Office(s)
1355 Peachtree St NE, Suite 1060, Atlanta, GA 30309 *Tel:* 404-888-0600 *Fax:* 404-888-6593
901 W Jackson Blvd, Suite 201, Chicago, IL 60607 *Tel:* 312-243-3841 *Fax:* 312-243-4275
New Orleans, LA *Tel:* 501-708-4224; 352-409-2129 (cell) *Fax:* 504-324-0727
80 Eighth Ave, 14th fl, New York, NY 10011 *Tel:* 212-647-7300 *Fax:* 212-647-7317

International Documentary Association

3470 Wilshire Blvd, Suite 980, Los Angeles, CA 90010
Tel: 213-232-1660 *Fax:* 213-232-1669
E-mail: info@documentary.org
Web Site: www.documentary.org
Key Personnel
Exec Dir: Simon Kilmurry
Deputy Dir: Amy Halpin
Public Progs & Events Mgr: Cassidy Dimon
Founded: 1982
Nonprofit membership organization that promotes nonfiction filmmakers & is dedicated to increasing public awareness for the documentary genre.
Number of Members: 2,735
Publication(s): *Documentary* (magazine, quarterly, free to membs); *Membership Directory* (online)

International Radio & Television Society Foundation, see IRTS Foundation

International Society for Performance Improvement® (ISPI)

PO Box 13035, Silver Spring, MD 20910
Tel: 301-587-8570 *Fax:* 301-587-8573
E-mail: info@ispi.org
Web Site: www.ispi.org
Key Personnel
Exec Dir: Courtney Brooks Kamin
   E-mail: courtneyb@ispi.org
Founded: 1962
Dedicated to increasing productivity & competence in the workplace through the application of performance & instructional technologies.
Number of Members: 30,000
2020 Conference(s): ISPI Annual Conference, Loews Ventana Canyon Resort, Tucson, AZ, April 29-May 4, 2020
Publication(s): *Performance Digest* (weekly, electronic); *Performance Improvement Journal (PIJ)* (10 issues/yr, free to membs; $109 nonmembs online or print only; $121 nonmembs print & online); *Performance Improvement Quarterly (PIQ)* (journal, $62 membs; $76 nonmembs); *PerformanceXpress* (newsletter, free to membs)

International Storytelling Center

116 W Main St, Jonesborough, TN 37659
Tel: 423-753-2171 *Toll Free Tel:* 800-952-8392
   Fax: 423-913-8219
E-mail: customerservice@storytellingcenter.net
Web Site: www.storytellingcenter.net
Key Personnel
Pres: Kiran Singh Sirah *E-mail:* kiran@storytellingcenter.net

Dir, Progs: Susan O'Connor *Tel:* 423-913-8217
E-mail: susan@storytellingcenter.net
Nonprofit association open to anyone interested
in the preservation & promotion of the storytelling tradition as an educational tool & pre-
server of folkloric history & its perpetuation
as a major art form. Maintain a video & audio archive, produce the National Storytelling
Festival & Teller-in-Residence program.
Conference(s): Teller-in-Residence Series, Jonesborough, TN, May-Oct; National Storytelling
Festival, Jonesborough, TN, Annually in Oct

**International Ticketing Association Inc
(INTIX)**
5868 E 71 St, Suite E 367, Indianapolis, IN
46220
Tel: 212-629-4036 *Fax:* 212-629-4036
E-mail: info@intix.org; media@intix.org
Web Site: www.intix.org
Key Personnel
Pres: Maureen Andersen *E-mail:* manderson@
intix.org
Mktg Mgr: Christine Payne
Busn Devt: Dorothea Heck
Membership Assoc: Tiffany Kelham
Founded: 1980
Leading forum for the entertainment ticketing in-
dustry.
Number of Members: 1,100
Conference(s): INTIX Annual Conference & Ex-
hibition
Publication(s): *INTIX Way* (enewsletter, membs
only, free)

**Iowa Cable & Telecommunications Association
(ICTA)**
3737 Westown Pkwy, Suite C, West Des Moines,
IA 50266
Tel: 515-697-6646
E-mail: info@iacable.com
Web Site: www.iacable.com
Key Personnel
Pres: Ed Pardini
EVP: William F Peard
Number of Members: 215
Publication(s): *Iowa Cable News* (monthly, online
only)
Membership(s): Association of Cable Television
Operators

IPI - Member Network™
2518 Anthem Village Dr, Suite 104, Henderson,
NV 89052
Tel: 702-617-1141 *Fax:* 702-617-1181
E-mail: info@ipiphoto.com
Web Site: www.ipiphoto.com
Key Personnel
Exec Dir: Ron Mohney *Tel:* 702-465-0339
E-mail: ron@ipiphoto.com
VP, Mktg: Erin von Holdt *Tel:* 702-739-4515
E-mail: erin@ipiphoto.com
VP, Memb Success: Brenda DiVincenzo *Tel:* 702-
524-1415 *E-mail:* brenda@ipiphoto.com
IPI Engagement Mgr: Whitney Solomon *Tel:* 702-
617-1141 ext 202 *E-mail:* whitney@ipiphoto.
com
Mktg Coord: Natalie Gunn *E-mail:* natalie@
ipiphoto.com
Founded: 1982
Marketing team, educator, purchasing co-op, net-
working hub & business consultant for the
world of digital, print, photo, signage, graphics & art.
2020 Conference(s): International Print & Imaging Conference (IPIC), Red Rock Casino Resort & Spa, 11011 W Charleston Blvd, Las
Vegas, NV, July 12-16, 2020

IPMA, see In-Plant Printing & Mailing
Association

IPRO, see CEDIA IPRO Affinity Group

IRTS Foundation
1697 Broadway, Suite 404, New York, NY 10019
Tel: 212-867-6650
E-mail: info@irts.org
Web Site: irtsfoundation.org
Key Personnel
Pres & CEO: Joyce M Tudryn *Tel:* 212-867-6650
ext 11 *E-mail:* joyce.tudryn@irts.org
Founded: 1939
Train & educate future media & communication
professions through educational programs &
diversity initiatives.
Number of Members: 1,000

Kentucky Film Association
2365 Harrodsburg Rd, Suite B-325, Lexington,
KY 40591
Tel: 859-317-9789
Web Site: ky.film
Works in Frankfort & Washington to protect film
incentives & advocate for the industry.

**Library & Information Technology Association
(LITA)**
Division of American Library Association (ALA)
c/o American Library Association, 50 E Huron
St, Chicago, IL 60611-2795
Toll Free Tel: 800-545-2433 (ext 4270) *Fax:* 312-
280-3257
E-mail: lita@ala.org
Web Site: www.ala.org/lita
Key Personnel
Exec Dir: Jenny Levine *Tel:* 312-280-4267
E-mail: jlevine@ala.org
Membership & Mktg Mgr: Chrishelle Thomas
Tel: 312-280-4268 *E-mail:* cthomas@ala.org
Founded: 1966
Provides the library & information science com-
munity a forum for discussion, an environment
for learning & a program for actions on the
design, development & implementation of auto-
mated & technological systems in the library &
information science field.
Number of Members: 2,100
Publication(s): *Information Technology & Li-
braries (ITAL)* (journal, quarterly)

LITA, see Library & Information Technology
Association (LITA)

**Location Managers Guild International
(LMGI)**
8033 Sunset Blvd, Suite 1017, Los Angeles, CA
90046
Tel: 310-967-2007 *Fax:* 310-967-2013
E-mail: contact@locationmanagers.org
Web Site: locationmanagers.org
Key Personnel
Admin Dir: Kiki Akinrele
Founded: 2003
Organization of experienced location profession-
als in the motion picture, television, commer-
cial & print production industries.
Publication(s): *LMGI Compass* (magazine, quar-
terly)

Media Alliance
2830 20 St, Suite 102, San Francisco, CA 94110
Tel: 415-746-9475
E-mail: information@media-alliance.org
Web Site: www.media-alliance.org
Key Personnel
Exec Dir: Tracy Rosenberg *Tel:* 510-684-6853
(cell) *E-mail:* tracy@media-alliance.org
Founded: 1976
Membership driven policy advocate for demo-
cratic communications focusing on legacy
broadcast & digital platform regulation & me-
dia justice issues.

Number of Members: 800
Publication(s): *How-to Media Guidebook* ($15
membs; $20 nonmembs); *Media Directory* ($50
Northern CA); *Media News* (enewsletter, free
to subscribers)

**Media Financial Management Association
(MFM)**
550 W Frontage Rd, Suite 3600, Northfield, IL
60093
Tel: 847-716-7000 *Fax:* 847-716-7004
E-mail: info@mediafinance.org
Web Site: www.mediafinance.org
Key Personnel
MFM/BCCA Pres & CEO: Mary M Collins
E-mail: mary.collins@mediafinance.org
Dir of Opers, MFM/BCCA: Jamie L Grande
Founded: 1961
Professional membership organization for finan-
cial executives, business managers, credit pro-
fessionals & related fields for the media indus-
try.
Number of Members: 1,200
2020 Conference(s): Media Finance Focus 2020
(MFM & BCCA Annual Conference), Loews
Hollywood Hotel, 1755 N Highland Ave, Los
Angeles, CA, May 18-20, 2020
Publication(s): *The Financial Manager (TFM)* (6
issues/yr, $69)

Media Networking Alliance (MNA)
23117 39 Ave SE, Bothell, WA 98021
Tel: 425-870-6574
Web Site: medianetworkingalliance.com
Key Personnel
Chmn: Rich Zwiebel
Secy: Terry Holton
Fin Offr: Marty Sacks
Admin: Tina Lipscomb *E-mail:* tina@
medianetworkingalliance.com
Trade association to promote adoption & sup-
port adopters of the newly ratified AES67-2013
standard through a program of education, mar-
keting & ongoing technical support.

MEIEA, see Music & Entertainment Industry
Educators Association (MEIEA)

**Motion Picture Association of America
(MPAA)**
15301 Ventura Blvd, Bldg E, Sherman Oaks, CA
91403-5885
Tel: 818-995-6600 *Fax:* 818-285-4403
E-mail: contactus@mpaa.org
Web Site: www.mpaa.org
Key Personnel
Chmn & CEO: Charles H Rivkin
Founded: 1922
Serves as the voice & advocate of the American
motion picture & television industry.
Branch Office(s)
1301 "K" St NW, Suite 900 E, Washington, DC
20005 *Tel:* 202-293-1966 *Fax:* 202-785-3026
12650 N Beach St, Suite 114-No 6, Fort Worth,
TX 76244 *Tel:* 817-205-6330
55 Saint Clair Ave W, Suite 210, Toronto,
ON M4V 2Y7, Canada *Tel:* 416-961-1888
Fax: 416-968-1016 *Web Site:* www.mpa-
canada.org
3470 NW 82 Ave, Suite 680, Doral, FL 33122
Tel: 786-999-1359

Motion Picture Editors Guild Local 700
Affiliate of IATSE
7715 Sunset Blvd, Suite 200, Hollywood, CA
90046
Tel: 323-876-4770 *Toll Free Tel:* 800-705-8700
Fax: 323-876-0861
E-mail: mail@editorsguild.com
Web Site: www.editorsguild.com

Key Personnel
Natl Exec Dir: Catherine A Repola
  E-mail: crepola@editorsguild.com
Western Exec Dir: Scott M George
  E-mail: sgeorge@editorsguild.com
Dir, Membership Servs: Shanda Zuniga *Tel:* 323-978-1081 *E-mail:* szuniga@editorsguild.com
Membership Coord: Shawn Marchetti *Tel:* 323-978-1085 *E-mail:* smarchetti@editorsguild.com
Number of Members: 7,000
Branch Office(s)
145 Hudson St, Suite 201, New York, NY 10013, Eastern Exec Dir: Paul Moore *Tel:* 212-302-0700 *Fax:* 212-302-1091 *E-mail:* pmoore@editorsguild.com
Publication(s): *CineMontage Magazine* (quarterly)

Music & Entertainment Industry Educators Association (MEIEA)
1900 Belmont Blvd, Nashville, TN 37212-3758
Tel: 615-460-6946
E-mail: office@meiea.org; membership@meiea.org
Web Site: www.meiea.org
Key Personnel
Pres: Storm Gloor *E-mail:* president@meiea.org
VP: Armen Shaomian *E-mail:* vicepresident@meiea.org
Treas: Clyde Rolston *E-mail:* treasurer@meiea.org
Secy: Scott LeGere *E-mail:* secretary@meiea.org
Dir, Membership: Darren Walters
Admin Asst: Angela Breedon
Founded: 1979
Establish & maintain standards of music industry education; encourage & facilitate interaction between the education community & the music industry.
Number of Members: 650
Publication(s): *MEIEA Journal* (annual, free to membs; $25/issue for past issues)

Music Business Association (Music Biz)
106 E Center Blvd, Marlton, NJ 08053
Tel: 856-596-2221
Web Site: musicbiz.org
Key Personnel
Pres: James Donio *E-mail:* james.donio@musicbiz.org
Founded: 1958
Advance & promote music commerce.
Number of Members: 350
2020 Conference(s): Music Biz 2020, JW Marriott, Nashville, TN, May 11-14, 2020

NAB, see National Association of Broadcasters (NAB)

NABA, see North American Broadcasters Association (NABA)

NABJ, see National Association of Black Journalists (NABJ)

NAMM, the National Association of Music Merchants
5790 Armada Dr, Carlsbad, CA 92008
Tel: 760-438-8001 *Toll Free Tel:* 800-767-6266 (memb hotline) *Fax:* 760-438-7327
E-mail: info@namm.org
Web Site: www.namm.org
Key Personnel
Pres & CEO: Joe Lamond
CFO: Larry Manley
Exec Dir, Museum of Making Music: Carolyn Grant
Dir, HR & Admin: Dana Hofseth
Dir, Intl Aff: Betty Heywood
Dir, Mktg & Communs: Andy Tompkins
  E-mail: andyt@namm.org
Dir, Membership: Causby Challacombe

Dir, Prof Devt: Zach Phillips
Dir, Pub Aff & Govt Rel: Mary Luehrsen
Dir, PR & Soc Media: Chalise Zolezzi
  E-mail: chalisez@namm.org
Dir, Technol: Dan Kessler
Dir, Trade Show Opers: Cindy Sample
Dir, Trade Show Sales: Dan Moylan
Founded: 1901
To unify, lead & strengthen the global music products industry & to increase active participation in music.
Number of Members: 9,000
2020 Conference(s): Summer NAMM, Nashville Music City Center, 700 Korean Veterans Blvd, Nashville, TN, July 9-11, 2020
2021 Conference(s): The NAMM Show, Anaheim Convention Center, 800 W Katella Ave, Anaheim, CA, Jan 21-24, 2021; Summer NAMM, Nashville Music City Center, 700 Korean Veterans Blvd, Nashville, TN, July 15-17, 2021
2022 Conference(s): The NAMM Show, Anaheim Convention Center, 800 W Katella Ave, Anaheim, CA, Jan 20-23, 2022

NARAS, see The Recording Academy

NARIP, see National Association of Record Industry Professionals (NARIP)

NATAS, see The National Academy of Television Arts & Sciences (NATAS)

National Academy of Recording Arts & Sciences Inc, see The Recording Academy

The National Academy of Television Arts & Sciences (NATAS)
1697 Broadway, Suite 404, New York, NY 10019
Tel: 212-586-8424 *Fax:* 212-246-8129
Web Site: emmyonline.tv
Key Personnel
SVP, Communs: Paul Pillitteri
  E-mail: ppillitteri@emmyonline.tv
Founded: 1955
Encourage excellence in television.
Number of Members: 12,000

National Association for Music Education (NAfME)
1806 Robert Fulton Dr, Reston, VA 20191
Tel: 703-860-4000 *Toll Free Tel:* 800-336-3768 *Fax:* 703-860-1531 *Toll Free Fax:* 888-275-6362
E-mail: memberservices@nafme.org
Web Site: nafme.org
Key Personnel
Exec Dir & CEO: Mike Blakeslee
  E-mail: mikeb@nafme.org
COO: Christopher Woodside *E-mail:* chrisw@nafme.org
CFO: Paul Baker *E-mail:* paulb@nafme.org
Dir, Acctg & Fin: Linda Hair *E-mail:* lindah@nafme.org
Dir, Devt, Strategic Initiatives & Student Progs: Kristen Rencher *E-mail:* kristenr@nafme.org
Dir, IT: Byron Smith *E-mail:* byrons@nafme.org
Dir, Membership & Mktg Communs: Elizabeth Lasko *E-mail:* elizabethl@nafme.org
Dir, Public Policy, Res & Prof Devt: Lynn M Tuttle *E-mail:* lynnt@nafme.org
Dir, Strategic Governance Engagement: Adriane Darvishian *E-mail:* adrianed@nafme.org
Arts education organization that addresses all aspects of music education. Provides resources for teachers, parents & administrators.
Number of Members: 60,000
2020 Conference(s): NAfME Music Research and Teacher Education (MRTE) Conference, Gaylord Palms Resort, Orlando, FL, Nov 4-8, 2020
Publication(s): *General Music Today* (3 issues/yr, online only, free to membs); *Journal of Mu-*

sic Teacher Education (3 issues/yr, online only, free to membs); *Journal of Research in Music Education* (quarterly); *Music Educators Journal* (quarterly, $20 print ed); *Teaching Music* (quarterly); *UPDATE: Applications of Research in Music Education* (3 issues/yr, online only, free to membs)

National Association of Biology Teachers (NABT)
PO Box 3363, Warrenton, VA 20188
Tel: 703-264-9696 *Toll Free Tel:* 888-501-NABT (501-6228)
E-mail: office@nabt.org
Web Site: www.nabt.org
Key Personnel
Exec Dir: Jaclyn Reeves-Pepin *Tel:* 719-596-9782
  E-mail: jreevespepin@nabt.org
Founded: 1938
Professional education association for life science & biology teachers at all levels.
Number of Members: 8,000
2020 Conference(s): NABT Professional Development Conference, Baltimore Marriott Waterfront, Baltimore, MD, Nov 5-8, 2020
2021 Conference(s): NABT Professional Development Conference, Atlanta Marriott Marquis, Atlanta, GA, Nov 11-14, 2021
Publication(s): *American Biology Teacher* (9 issues/yr); *News & Views* (enewsletter, 2 issues/mo)

National Association of Black Journalists (NABJ)
1100 Knight Hall, Suite 3100, College Park, MD 20742
Tel: 301-405-0248 *Fax:* 301-314-1714
Web Site: www.nabj.org
Key Personnel
Exec Dir: Drew Berry *E-mail:* dberry@nabj.org
Membership Mgr: Veronique Dodson *Tel:* 301-405-0554 *E-mail:* vdodson@nabj.org
Prog & Devt Coord: Vanessa Evans *Tel:* 301-405-2592 *E-mail:* vevans@nabj.org
Founded: 1975
An organization of journalists, students & media-related professionals that provide quality programs & services & advocates on behalf of Black journalists worldwide.
Number of Members: 3,000
2020 Conference(s): NABJ Annual Convention & Career Fair, Washington, DC, July 8-12, 2020
2021 Conference(s): NABJ Annual Convention & Career Fair, Houston, TX, Aug 4-8, 2021
Publication(s): *NABJ Journal* (3 issues/yr)

National Association of Broadcasters (NAB)
1771 "N" St NW, Washington, DC 20036
Tel: 202-429-5300
E-mail: nab@nab.org; membership@nab.org
Web Site: www.nab.org
Key Personnel
Pres & CEO: Gordon H Smith
EVP, Conventions & Busn Opers: Mr Chris Brown *Tel:* 202-429-5335
EVP, Mktg: Michelle Lehman
  E-mail: mlehman@nab.org
Founded: 1922
Trade association that advocates on behalf of free, local radio & television stations & also broadcast networks before Congress, the Federal Communications Commissions & the Courts.
2020 Conference(s): NAB Show®, Las Vegas Convention Center, Las Vegas, NV, April 18-22, 2020; Radio Show (co-produced with Radio Advertising Bureau), Omni Nashville, Nashville, TN, Sept 13-16, 2020; Nab Show® New York, Jacob K Javits Convention Center, 655 W 34 St, New York, NY, Oct 21-22, 2020

National Association of Record Industry Professionals (NARIP)
PO Box 2446, Toluca Lake, CA 91610-2446

Tel: 818-769-7007
E-mail: info@narip.com
Web Site: www.narip.com
Key Personnel
Pres: Tess Taylor
Founded: 1998
Created to promote career advancement, education & good will in the record industry & related music fields. Provides access to resources, career development & new business relationships.
Publication(s): *Electronic bulletin* (weekly)

National Association of Theatre Owners (NATO)
1705 "N" St NW, Washington, DC 20036
Tel: 202-962-0054
E-mail: nato@natodc.com
Web Site: www.natoonline.org
Key Personnel
Pres & CEO: John Fithian
VP & COO: Kathy Conroy
Dir, Govt Rel: Esther Baruh
Dir, Membership: David Binet
Data & Res Mgr: Phil Contrino
Trade organization to advance & protect the motion picture exhibition industry.
Branch Office(s)
4605 Lankershim Blvd, Suite 180, North Hollywood, CA 91602, VP & Chief Communs Offr: Patrick Corcoran *Tel:* 818-506-1778
2020 Conference(s): CinemaCon, Caesars Palace, Las Vegas, NV, March 30-April 2, 2020
2021 Conference(s): CinemaCon, Caesars Palace, Las Vegas, NV, April 26-29, 2021

National Board of Review (of Motion Pictures)
40 W 37 St, Suite 501, New York, NY 10018
Tel: 212-465-9166 *Fax:* 212-465-9168
E-mail: nbr@nbrmp.org
Web Site: www.nationalboardofreview.org
Key Personnel
Mng Dir: Orson Robbins-Pianka *E-mail:* orson@nbrmp.org
Creative Dir: Wendy Smith
Founded: 1909
Dedicates its efforts to the support of film, domestic & foreign, as both art & entertainment. The NBR is a nonprofit, membership organization which promotes commentary on all aspects of film production & history of film with panels, seminars & Q&As at screenings held throughout the year.
Number of Members: 150
Conference(s): NBR Annual Awards Gala, New York, NY, Jan

National Council of Acoustical Consultants (NCAC)
9100 Purdue Rd, Suite 200, Indianapolis, IN 46268
Tel: 317-328-0642 *Fax:* 317-328-4629
E-mail: info@ncac.com
Web Site: ncac.com
Key Personnel
Exec Dir: Kim Paugh *E-mail:* kpaugh@ncac.com
Founded: 1962
Dedicated to management & related concerns of professional acoustical consulting firms & to the interests of the clients & public which they serve.
Number of Members: 130
2020 Conference(s): NCAC Annual Meeting, Sheraton Portsmouth Harborside Hotel, 250 Market St, Portsmouth, NH, Aug 28-30, 2020
Publication(s): *NCAC Newsletter* (newsletter, quarterly, print & online, free to membs)

National Council of Teachers of English (NCTE)
1111 W Kenyon Rd, Urbana, IL 61801-1096

Tel: 217-328-3870 *Toll Free Tel:* 877-369-6283
Fax: 217-328-9645
Web Site: www.ncte.org
Key Personnel
Exec Dir: Emily Kirkpatrick
Founded: 1911
Improve the quality of instruction in English at all education levels; encourage research, experimentation & investigation in teaching English.
Number of Members: 35,000
2020 Conference(s): NCTE Annual Convention, Denver, CO, Nov 19-22, 2020
2021 Conference(s): NCTE Annual Convention, Louisville, KY, Nov 18-21, 2021
Publication(s): *College Composition & Communication* (quarterly); *College English* (6 issues/yr); *The Council Chronicle Magazine* (quarterly); *English Education* (quarterly); *English Journal* (6 issues/yr); *English Leadership Quarterly*; *Inbox Newsletter* (weekly e-mail); *Language Arts* (6 issues/yr); *Research in the Teaching of English* (quarterly); *Talking Points* (semiannual); *Teaching English in the Two-Year College* (quarterly); *Voices From the Middle* (quarterly)

National Freedom of Information Coalition (NFOIC)
University of Florida College of Journalism, 3208 Weimer Hall, 1885 Stadium Rd, Gainesville, FL 32611
Mailing Address: PO Box 118400, Gainesville, FL 32611-8400
Tel: 352-294-7082
E-mail: nfoic@nfoic.org
Web Site: www.nfoic.org
Key Personnel
Off Admin: Maggy Stansly
An affiliation of member state FOI groups, academic centers & interested individuals.
2020 Conference(s): FOI Summit, TheFontaine Hotel, Kansas City, MO, Sept 24-26, 2020
Publication(s): *FOI InSight* (enewsletter)

National Press Photographers Association (NPPA)
120 Hooper St, Athens, GA 30602-3018
Tel: 706-542-2506
E-mail: info@nppa.org; director@nppa.org
Web Site: nppa.org
Key Personnel
Gen Coun: Mickey Osterreicher
Exec Dir: Akili Ramsess *E-mail:* aramsess@nppa.org
Prof Servs Dir: Thomas Kenniff *Tel:* 919-237-1782 *E-mail:* tkenniff@nppa.org
Founded: 1946
Educational advancement of visual journalism.
Number of Members: 9,000
Conference(s): News Video Workshop, Gaylord College of Journalism & Mass Communications, University of Oklahoma, Norman, OK, Annually in March
Publication(s): *News Photographer* (magazine, 10 issues/yr)

National Public Radio (NPR)
1111 N Capitol St NE, Washington, DC 20002
Tel: 202-513-2000
Web Site: www.npr.org
Key Personnel
Treas & CFO: Deborah A Cowan
Chief Devt Offr: Stephanie Witte
Chief Digital Offr: Thomas Hjelm
Chief Legal Offr & Gen Coun: Jonathan Hart
Chief Mktg Offr: Meg Goldthwaite
Pres, Opers: Loren Mayor
SVP, Programming & Audience Devt: Anya Grundmann
VP, Brand & Mktg: Matt Myers
VP, Busn Devt: Michael Lutzky
VP, Corp Communs: Emily Littleton

VP, Dist: Michael F Beach
VP, Opers: Stacey Foxwell
Multimedia news organization & radio program producer. Leading membership & representation organization for public radio.

National Religious Broadcasters (NRB)
600 N Capitol St NW, Suite 210, Washington, DC 20001
Tel: 202-543-0073 *Fax:* 202-543-2649
E-mail: info@nrb.org; press@nrb.org
Web Site: nrb.org
Key Personnel
Pres & CEO: Dr Jerry A Johnson
EVP & COO: Troy Miller
SVP, Communs & Gen Coun: Kenneth Chan
Founded: 1944
Number of Members: 1,600
2021 Conference(s): NRB International Christian Media Convention, Gaylord Texan Resort & Convention Center, Grapevine, TX, March 16-19, 2021
Publication(s): *NRB Today* (newsletter, weekly)

National School Boards Association (NSBA)
1680 Duke St, 2nd fl, Alexandria, VA 22314-3493
Tel: 703-838-6722 *Fax:* 703-683-7590
E-mail: info@nsba.org
Web Site: www.nsba.org
Key Personnel
Exec Dir: Thomas Gentzel *Tel:* 703-838-6730 *E-mail:* tgentzel@nsba.org
Founded: 1940
Represents state school boards associations & local school board members.
Number of Members: 90,000
2020 Conference(s): Annual Conference & Exposition, Chicago, IL, April 4-6, 2020

National Systems Contractors Association (NSCA)
3950 River Ridge Dr NE, Cedar Rapids, IA 52402
Tel: 319-366-6722 *Toll Free Tel:* 800-446-6722
Fax: 319-366-4164
E-mail: nsca@nsca.org
Web Site: www.nsca.org
Key Personnel
Exec Dir: Chuck Wilson *E-mail:* cwilson@nsca.org
Association of low voltage systems integrators. Represents more than 1,250 companies worldwide & is a leading advocate for the commercial electronic systems industry. The services offered by the NSCA are an invaluable resource for systems integrators, design firms, large & small contracting companies & others in the electronic systems industry from around the globe.
Number of Members: 1,250
Publication(s): *Building Connections* (6 issues/yr, free to membs)

National Telemedia Council Inc
1922 University Ave, Madison, WI 53726
Tel: 608-218-1182
E-mail: ntelemedia@aol.com
Web Site: www.nationaltelemediacouncil.org
Key Personnel
Exec Dir & Ed: Marieli Rowe
Founded: 1953
Work toward a mediawise society by developing media literacy & critical viewing skills, work with educators, parents & the broadcast industry.
Number of Members: 350
Publication(s): *The Journal of Media Literacy* (up to 3 issues/yr, free to membs)

NCAC, see National Council of Acoustical Consultants (NCAC)

NCTE, see National Council of Teachers of English (NCTE)

Nevada Broadcasters Association
3900 Paradise Rd, Suite 279, Las Vegas, NV 89169
Tel: 702-794-4994 *Fax:* 702-794-4997
Web Site: www.nevadabroadcasters.org
Key Personnel
Busn Mgr: Melanie Mueller *E-mail:* melanie@nevadabroadcasters.org
Information resource for Nevada's broadcast radio & television stations. Assists in workforce development.

New York Film/Video Council (NYFVC)
PO Box 2092, New York, NY 10021
E-mail: nyfvcrsvp@gmail.com
Web Site: www.nyfvc.org
Founded: 1946
Nonprofit cultural membership organization of people involved in the production, distribution & study of documentary, industrial & non-theatrical films. Annual schedule of ten monthly meetings/programs on broad range of subjects of interest to members. Events held monthly exc July & Aug.
Number of Members: 250

New York Production Alliance (NYPA)
PO Box 383, Village Station, NY 10014
E-mail: info@nypa.org
Web Site: www.nypa.org
Founded: 1998
Nonprofit organization engaged in government lobbying & independent advocacy for job creation, retention & community organization within New York State's film & television industry.
Number of Members: 65

North American Broadcasters Association (NABA)
Canadian Broadcasting Centre, 25 John St, Suite 9C200, Toronto, ON M5V 3G7, Canada
Tel: 416-205-3363 *Fax:* 416-205-2901
E-mail: contact@nabanet.com
Web Site: nabanet.com
Key Personnel
Dir Gen: Michael McEwen
Dir, Admin: Anh Ngo
Sr Coord: Jenn Hadfield
Founded: 1972
Number of Members: 34
Conference(s): Annual Meeting & Conference
Membership(s): World Broadcasting Unions

Northeast Conference on the Teaching of Foreign Languages (NECTFL)
c/o NYSAFLT, 2400 Main St, Buffalo, NY 14214
Tel: 716-777-1798
E-mail: info@nectfl.org
Web Site: www.nectfl.org
Key Personnel
Exec Dir: John D Carlino
Founded: 1954
World language education & professional development for teachers at all levels, in both public & private settings.
Number of Members: 150
Conference(s): Annual Conference, Feb
Publication(s): *The NECTFL Review* (journal, semiannual)

NPR, see National Public Radio (NPR)

NSCA, see National Systems Contractors Association (NSCA)

NYFVC, see New York Film/Video Council (NYFVC)

Open Control Architecture Alliance (OCA Alliance)
23117 39 Ave SE, Bothell, WA 98021
Tel: 425-870-6574
Web Site: ocaalliance.com
Key Personnel
Admin: Tina Lipscomb *E-mail:* tina.lipscomb@oca-alliance.com
Founded: 2011
Nonprofit corporation formed to secure the standardization of the Open Control Architecture (OCA) as a media networking system control standard for professional applications.

Photographic Society of America® (PSA®)
8241 S Walker Ave, Suite 104, Oklahoma City, OK 73139
Tel: 405-843-1437 *Toll Free Tel:* 855-PSA-INFO (772-4636)
E-mail: hq@psa-photo.org
Web Site: www.psa-photo.org
Key Personnel
Off Mgr: Twila Bourlon
Founded: 1934
Deals with photographic material & its techniques.
Number of Members: 5,500
2020 Conference(s): PSA Annual Conference, Colorado Springs, CO, Sept 29-Oct 3, 2020
Publication(s): *PSA Journal* (monthly)

PRIMIR, see Print Industries Market Information and Research Organization (PRIMIR)

Print Industries Market Information and Research Organization (PRIMIR)
Unit of Association for Print Technologies (APTech)
1899 Preston White Dr, Reston, VA 20191
Tel: 703-264-7200 *Fax:* 703-620-0994
Web Site: www.primir.org
Key Personnel
Sr Dir, Mkt Res: Rekha Ratnam
   E-mail: rratnam@aptech.org
Dir, Mkt Data & Res: Jason Goodwin
   E-mail: jgoodwin@aptech.org
Global source of data, analysis & trend information about print & related communications industries through research, initiated by the industry, for the industry. Any firm, corporation, division or separate business unit of a corporation, engaged in printing or converting by any & all processes, within the US or globally, or in the manufacture or distribution of equipment, software, materials or supplies to the graphic communications or converting industry, is eligible for PRIMIR membership. Membership is open to manufacturers, suppliers, printers, converters or brand owners.

Printing Industries of America
301 Brush Creek Rd, Warrendale, PA 15086-7529
Tel: 412-741-6860 *Toll Free Tel:* 800-910-4283
   Fax: 412-741-2311
E-mail: printing@printing.org
Web Site: www.printing.org
Key Personnel
Pres & CEO: Michael F Makin
CFO: Nicholas G Stratigos
Printing Industries of America, along with its affiliates, delivers products & services that enhance the growth, efficiency & profitability of its members & the industry through advocacy, education, research & technical information.
Number of Members: 10,900
Branch Office(s)
1325 "G" St NW, Suite 500, Washington, DC 20005 *Tel:* 202-627-6924

2020 Conference(s): Continuous Improvement Conference, Renaissance Columbus Downtown Hotel, 50 N Third St, Columbus, OH, April 5-8, 2020
Publication(s): *Printing Industries of America: The Magazine* (10 issues/yr)

Producers Guild of America Inc (PGA)
8530 Wilshire Blvd, Suite 400, Beverly Hills, CA 90211
Tel: 310-358-9020
E-mail: info@producersguild.org
Web Site: www.producersguild.org
Key Personnel
Natl Exec Dir & COO: Vance Van Petten
Assoc Natl Exec Dir & COO: Susan Sprung
Dir, Memb Servs: Kyle Katz *E-mail:* kyle@producersguild.org
Dir, Membership: Bryce Averitt *E-mail:* bryce@producersguild.org
Dir, Opers: Jo-Ann West *E-mail:* joann@producersguild.org
Mgr, Digital Opers & Mktg: Andrew Mahlmann
   E-mail: andrew@producersguild.org
Supv, Communs: Chris Green *E-mail:* chris@producersguild.org
Founded: 1950
Nonprofit trade group that represents, protects & promotes the interests of all members of the producing team in the film, television & new media.
Number of Members: 7,000
Branch Office(s)
PGA East, 116 W 23 St, 5th fl, New York, NY 10011
Conference(s): Produced By Conference, Annually in Summer
Publication(s): *Produced By* (magazine, 6 issues/yr, $48/yr; free to membs)

Production Equipment Rental Group (PERG)
c/o ESTA, 630 Ninth Ave, Suite 609, New York, NY 10036
Tel: 212-244-1505 *Fax:* 212-244-1502
E-mail: info@esta.org; membership@esta.org
Web Site: www.esta.org/perg
Key Personnel
Exec Dir: Erin Grabe *Tel:* 212-244-1505 ext 606
   E-mail: erin.grabe@esta.org
Mgr: Harry Box *Tel:* 323-541-3200 *E-mail:* harry.box@esta.org
Membership Mgr: Frances Thompson *Tel:* 212-244-1505 ext 630 *E-mail:* frances.thompson@esta.org
Serves the film & digital community within ESTA (Entertainment Services & Technology Association). Main focus is rental companies that offer cameras, grip & lighting equipment to the motion picture, television & commercial production market.

Professional Photographers of America (PPA)
229 Peachtree St NE, Suite 2200, Atlanta, GA 30303
Tel: 404-522-8600 *Toll Free Tel:* 800-786-6277
   Fax: 404-614-6400
E-mail: csc@ppa.com
Web Site: www.ppa.com
Key Personnel
CEO: David Trust *E-mail:* trustd@ppa.com
CFO/COO: Scott Kurkian *E-mail:* skurkian@ppa.com
Pres: Stephen Thetford *E-mail:* sthetford@ppa.com
Art Dir: Debbie Todd *E-mail:* dtodd@ppa.com
Certification Dir: Julia Boyd *E-mail:* jboyd@ppa.com
Dir, Educ: Angela Kurkian *E-mail:* akurkian@ppa.com
Dir, Events: Fiona Corbett *E-mail:* fcorbett@ppa.com
Dir, HR: Wilda Oken *E-mail:* woken@ppa.com

Dir, IT & Admin: Scott Morgan
E-mail: smorgan@ppa.com
Dir, Mktg/Communs: Carla Plouin
E-mail: cplouin@ppa.com
Dir, Pubns: Jane Gaboury *E-mail:* jgaboury@ppa.com
Dir, Sales & Strategic Alliances: Wayne Jones
E-mail: wjones@ppa.com
Founded: 1869
Advance the art & science of professional photography & help professional photographers in their careers.
Number of Members: 30,000
2021 Conference(s): Imaging USA, Gaylord Texan Resort & Convention Center, Grapevine, TX, Jan 17-19, 2021
Publication(s): *Professional Photographer* (monthly, $19.95/yr digital US & CN; $19.95/yr print or digital US; $35.95/yr print only CN; $45.95/yr print & digital CN; free to membs)

Professional Women Photographers (PWP)
119 W 72 St, Suite 223, New York, NY 10023
E-mail: pwp@pwponline.org
Web Site: www.pwponline.org
Key Personnel
Pres: Fredda Gordon
Founded: 1975
To educate the public & support women photographers; monthly meetings every first Wednesday exc July & Aug.
Number of Members: 200
Publication(s): *IMPRINTS* (magazine)

Promax
Formerly PromaxBDA
5700 Wilshire Blvd, Suite 275, Los Angeles, CA 90036
Tel: 310-788-7600 *Fax:* 310-788-7616
Web Site: www.promax.org
Key Personnel
Pres & CEO: Steve Kazanjian
SVP & CFO: Randy Smith
CIO: Lucian Cojescu
SVP, Global Awards Devt & Exec Prodr, Conference Prodn & Experience: Stacy La Cotera *Tel:* 310-789-1503 *E-mail:* stacy@promaxbda.org
Head, Mktg & Brand: Jennifer Ball *Tel:* 310-789-1521 *E-mail:* jennifer.ball@promaxbda.org
Edit Dir: Paige Albiniak *E-mail:* paige@promaxbda.org
Mgr, Memb Servs: Anush Payaslyan *Tel:* 310-789-1509 *E-mail:* anush@promaxbda.org
Mktg Mgr: Max Follmer *Tel:* 310-789-1583 *E-mail:* max@promaxbda.org
Mktg Proj Mgr: Noura Chehade *Tel:* 310-789-1508 *E-mail:* noura.chehade@promaxbda.org
Event Coord: Esther Choi *Tel:* 310-789-1513 *E-mail:* esther.choi@promaxbda.org
Founded: 1956
Global association for the entertainment marketing industry.
2020 Conference(s): Promax Conference, JW Marriott Los Angeles LA Live, Los Angeles, CA, June 16-18, 2020

PromaxBDA, see Promax

PSA®, see Photographic Society of America® (PSA®)

PSNI (Professional Systems Network Intl)
1831 E 71 St, Tulsa, OK 74136
Tel: 918-388-1343
Web Site: www.psni.org
Key Personnel
Exec Dir: Chris Miller *E-mail:* cmiller@psni.org
Dir, Mktg: Hailey Klein *E-mail:* hklein@psni.org
Founded: 1986
Network of independent AV & broadcast communications systems integrators.

Quickdraw Animation Society
2011 Tenth Ave SW, Calgary, AB T3C 0K4, Canada
Tel: 403-261-5767
E-mail: info@quickdrawanimation.ca; production@quickdrawanimation.ca; programming@quickdrawanimation.ca
Web Site: quickdrawanimation.ca; www.giraffest.ca
Key Personnel
Exec Dir: Peter Hemminger *E-mail:* peter@quickdrawanimation.ca
Prodn Dir: Tyler Klein Longmire
Prog Dir: Ryan Von Hagen
Founded: 1984
Fosters connection, innovation, creativity & artistic excellence through animation production, education & appreciation.
Conference(s): GIRAF (Giant Incandescent Resonating Animation Festival), Plaza Theatre, Calgary, AB, CN, Annually in Nov

RAB, see Radio Advertising Bureau (RAB)

Radio Advertising Bureau (RAB)
125 W 55 St, 5th fl, New York, NY 10019
Tel: 212-681-7200 *Toll Free Tel:* 800-252-7234 *Fax:* 212-681-7223
E-mail: memberresponse@rab.com
Web Site: www.rab.com
Key Personnel
CEO & Pres: Erica Farber *E-mail:* efarber@rab.com
CFO & EVP: Van Allen *E-mail:* vallen@rab.com
SVP/Mktg & Communs: Leah Kamon *E-mail:* lkamon@rab.com
Sales & marketing arm for radio industry; provide sales tools & services to radio stations.
Number of Members: 7,000
Branch Office(s)
400 E Las Colinas Blvd, Suite 350, Irving, TX 75039 *Toll Free Tel:* 800-232-3131
2020 Conference(s): Radio Show (co-produced with National Association of Broadcasters), Nashville, TN, Sept 13-16, 2020

Radio Television Digital News Association (RTDNA)
The National Press Bldg, 529 14 St NW, Suite 1240, Washington, DC 20045
Tel: 202-662-7254 *Fax:* 202-223-4007
Web Site: www.rtdna.org; www.excellenceinjournalism.org
Key Personnel
Exec Dir: Dan Shelley *Tel:* 212-246-0398 *E-mail:* dans@rtdna.org
Dir, Membership, Mktg & Communs: Karen Hansen *Tel:* 202-662-7257 *E-mail:* karenh@rtdna.org
To foster professionalism in electronic journalism.
Number of Members: 1,200
2020 Conference(s): Excellence in Journalism Conference (co-hosted by SPJ, RTDNA & NAHJ), Washington Hilton, 1919 Connecticut Ave NW, Washington, DC, Sept 10-12, 2020
Publication(s): *Communicator* (newsletter, online, free)

The Recording Academy
3030 Olympic Blvd, Santa Monica, CA 90404
Tel: 310-392-3777 *Fax:* 310-392-2306
E-mail: losangeles@grammy.com
Web Site: www.grammy.org/recording-academy
Key Personnel
Pres/CEO: Neil Portnow
VP: Phil Soussan
Nonprofit Grammy Award association.
Number of Members: 21,000
Publication(s): *GRAMMY Magazine*

Recording Industry Association of America® (RIAA)
1025 "F" St NW, 10th fl, Washington, DC 20004
Tel: 202-775-0101
Web Site: www.riaa.com
Key Personnel
Chmn & CEO: Cary Sherman
Pres: Mitch Glazier
Nonprofit trade association for US record companies.

RIAA, see Recording Industry Association of America® (RIAA)

SAG-AFTRA, see Screen Actors Guild - American Federation of Television & Radio Artists (SAG-AFTRA)

Satellite Broadcasting & Communications Association (SBCA)
1100 17 St NW, Suite 1150, Washington, DC 20036
Tel: 202-349-3620 *Toll Free Tel:* 800-541-5981 *Fax:* 202-349-3621
E-mail: info@sbca.org
Web Site: www.sbca.com
Key Personnel
Pres: Steven Hill *Tel:* 202-349-3620
Founded: 1986
Represent satellite broadcasting communication industry.
Number of Members: 350

Screen Actors Guild - American Federation of Television & Radio Artists (SAG-AFTRA)
5757 Wilshire Blvd, 7th fl, Los Angeles, CA 90036-3600
Tel: 323-954-1600 (former SAG); 323-634-8100 (former AFTRA) *Toll Free Tel:* 855-SAG-AFTRA (724-2387) *Fax:* 323-549-6654 (communs & mktg)
E-mail: info@sagaftra.org
Web Site: www.sagaftra.org
Key Personnel
COO & Gen Coun: Duncan Crabtree-Ireland
CFO: Arianna Ozzanto
Chief Broadcast Offr: Mary Cavallaro
Chief Communs & Mktg Offr: Pamela Greenwalt
Chief Contracts Offr: Ray Rodriguez
Chief Economist: David Viviano
Chief Technol & Innovation Offr: Daniel Inukai
Natl Exec Dir: David P White
Assoc Natl Exec Dir: Mathis Dunn
Founded: 2012
Performers labor union.
Number of Members: 160,000
Branch Office(s)
1900 Broadway, 5th fl, New York, NY 10023 *Tel:* 212-944-1030 *E-mail:* newyork@sagaftra.org
Publication(s): *SAG-AFTRA Magazine* (quarterly)

SCTE, see Society of Cable Telecommunications Engineers Inc (SCTE)

SDMediaPros (SDMP)
5205 Kearny Villa Way, No 100, San Diego, CA 92123
Tel: 619-672-1000
E-mail: membership@sdmediapros.org; marketing@sdmediapros.org; programs@sdmediapros.org
Web Site: sdmediapros.org
Key Personnel
Pres: Tom Kihneman *E-mail:* president@sdmediapros.org
VP: Mike Towe *E-mail:* vp@sdmediapros.org
CFO/Treas: Mark Maisonneuve *E-mail:* cfo@sdmediapros.org
Secy: Augie Augusto

Meeting Coord: Bob Unger
E-mail: meetingcoordinator@sdmediapros.org
Mktg: Jane Hare
Membership/Volunteers: Marianne Bates
Progs: Keith Methven
Community of & for professional media communications experts.
Conference(s): SDMediaPRos Annual Showcase, Nov

SESAC Inc
35 Music Sq E, Nashville, TN 37203
Tel: 615-320-0055
Web Site: www.sesac.com
Key Personnel
Chmn & CEO: John Josephson
VChmn & Sr Advisor: Pat Collins
Chief Mktg Offr: Samantha Saturn
EVP, Opers & Corp Devt/CFO: Kelli Turner
SVP & CIO: Stephen Rollins
SVP & Gen Coun: Christos P Badavas
SVP, Creative Opers: Sam Kling
Founded: 1930
Performing rights organization.
Branch Office(s)
2150 Colorado Ave, Suite 150, Santa Monica, CA 90404 *Tel:* 424-291-4750
152 W 57 St, 57th fl, New York, NY 10019
Tel: 212-586-3450
40 Wall St, 6th fl, New York, NY 10005
Hohenstaufenstr 1, 80801 Munich, Germany
One Primrose St, London EC2A 2EX, United Kingdom *Tel:* (020) 7616 9284

Sesame Workshop
1900 Broadway, 4th fl, New York, NY 10023
Tel: 212-595-3456
Web Site: www.sesameworkshop.org
Key Personnel
Pres & CEO: Gary Knell
Founded: 1968 (as the Children's Television Workshop)
Nonprofit educational organization which develops educational content for TV, radio, books, magazines, interactive media & outreach.
Number of Members: 300
Publication(s): *Sesame Street Magazine*

Set Decorators Society of America (SDSA)
7100 Tujunga Ave, Suite A, North Hollywood, CA 91605
Tel: 818-255-2425 *Fax:* 818-982-8597
E-mail: sdsa@setdecorators.org
Web Site: www.setdecorators.org
Key Personnel
Pres: Shirley Starks
VP: Regina O'Brien; David Smith
Treas: Jennifer Gentile
Recording Secy: Natalie Contreras
Exec Dir: Gene Cane
Founded: 1993
Number of Members: 550
Publication(s): *Set Decor* (magazine, online)

SIIA, see Software & Information Industry Association (SIIA)

SMPTE, see Society of Motion Picture & Television Engineers® (SMPTE®)

Societe de developpement des enterprises culturelles, see SODEC

Society for Imaging Science and Technology (IS&T)
7003 Kilworth Lane, Springfield, VA 22151
Tel: 703-642-9090 *Fax:* 703-642-9094
E-mail: info@imaging.org
Web Site: imaging.org

Key Personnel
Pres: Steven J Simske *E-mail:* ssimske@imaging.org
Exec Dir: Suzanne E Grinnan *E-mail:* sgrinnan@imaging.org
Conference Prog Mgr: Marion S Zoretich
E-mail: mzoretich@imaging.org
Exec Asst: Donna Smith *E-mail:* dsmith@imaging.org
Founded: 1947
Disseminate information in the field of imaging science: digital printing, electronic imaging, color science, image preservation, photofinishing, prepress technologies, hybrid imaging systems & silver halide research.
Number of Members: 1,500
Conference(s): Electronic Imaging; Printing for Fabrication
2020 Conference(s): Archiving 2020, National Archives and Records Administration, College Park, MD, May 18-21, 2020
Publication(s): *IS&T Reporter* (6 issues/yr); *Journal of Electronic Imaging (JEI)* (print & online, $75); *Journal of Imaging Science & Technology (JIST)* (6 issues/yr, print & online, $75 US & foreign; $45 additional online subn; free to membs)

Society for Information Display (SID)
1475 S Bascom Ave, Suite 114, Campbell, CA 95008-4006
Tel: 408-879-3901 *Fax:* 408-879-3833
E-mail: office@sid.org
Web Site: www.sid.org
Key Personnel
Pres: Yong-Seog Kim
Secy: Achin Bhowmik
Treas: Takatoshi Tsujiumura
Dir, Opers: Tony Caldwell *E-mail:* tcaldwell@sid.org
Founded: 1962
Committed to the presentation, exchange & preservation of the ideas & technologies of information display.
Number of Members: 5,000
2020 Conference(s): Display Week, San Francisco Moscone Center, San Francisco, CA, June 7-12, 2020
Publication(s): *Information Display Magazine* (monthly); *SID International Symposium Digest of Technical Papers* (annual, online)

Society for Photographic Education (SPE)
PO Box 6653, Cleveland, OH 44101
Tel: 216-622-2733 *Fax:* 216-622-2733
E-mail: admin@spenational.org; info@spenational.org
Web Site: www.spenational.org
Key Personnel
Events Mgr & Chapter Liaison: Ginenne Clark
Exhibits & Design Mgr: Nina Barcellona Kidd
Fosters understanding of photography in all its forms & related media.
Number of Members: 1,800
Conference(s): SPE Annual Conference, March
Publication(s): *Exposure* (journal, digital)

Society of Broadcast Engineers Inc (SBE)
9102 N Meridian St, Suite 150, Indianapolis, IN 46260
Tel: 317-846-9000
Web Site: www.sbe.org
Key Personnel
Exec Dir: John Poray *E-mail:* jporay@sbe.org
Certification Dir: Megan Clappe
E-mail: mclappe@sbe.org
Founded: 1964
Society for television & radio broadcast engineers, membership services, education, certification.
Number of Members: 5,000
Publication(s): *The Signal* (newsletter, 6 issues/yr)

Society of Cable Telecommunications Engineers Inc (SCTE)
140 Philips Rd, Exton, PA 19341-1318
Tel: 610-363-6888 *Toll Free Tel:* 800-542-5040
Fax: 610-884-7237
E-mail: info@scte.org
Web Site: www.scte.org
Key Personnel
Pres & CEO: Mark Dzuban *Tel:* 610-594-7309
Founded: 1969
A nonprofit professional association that provides technical leadership for the telecommunications industry & serves its members through professional development, standards, certification & information. The society serves its diverse membership & the industry by offering a wide variety of educational programs & services.
Number of Members: 25,000
2020 Conference(s): SCTE Cable-Tec Expo®, Denver, CO, Oct 13-16, 2020

Society of Camera Operators
PO Box 2006, Toluca Lake, CA 91610-0006
Tel: 818-563-9110 *Fax:* 818-563-9117
E-mail: sooffice@soc.org
Web Site: www.soc.org
Key Personnel
Pres: George Billinger
Treas: Bill McClelland
Founded: 1979
Publication(s): *Camera Operator* (magazine, quarterly, $25/yr US; $35/yr intl)

Society of Motion Picture & Television Engineers® (SMPTE®)
White Plains Plaza, 445 Hamilton Ave, Suite 601, White Plains, NY 10601-1827
Tel: 914-761-1100 *Fax:* 914-206-4216
E-mail: membership@smpte.org
Web Site: www.smpte.org
Key Personnel
Exec Dir: Barbara H Lange *Tel:* 914-205-2370
Dir, Events & Governance Liaison: Sally-Ann D'Amato *Tel:* 914-205-2375 *E-mail:* sdamato@smpte.org
Dir, Membership: Roberta Gorman *Tel:* 914-205-2376 *E-mail:* rgorman@smpte.org
Founded: 1916
Advance engineering & technical aspects of motion picture, television, the allied arts & sciences.
Number of Members: 7,000
2020 Conference(s): SMPTE® Annual Technical Conference & Exhibition, Westin Bonaventure, Los Angeles, CA, Oct 19-22, 2020
Publication(s): *SMPTE Motion Imaging Journal* (8 issues/yr)

SODEC
215 rue Saint-Jacques St, Rm 800, Montreal, QC H2Y 1M6, Canada
Tel: 514-841-2200 *Toll Free Tel:* 800-363-0401 (CN only) *Fax:* 514-841-8606
E-mail: info@sodec.gouv.qc.ca
Web Site: www.sodec.gouv.qc.ca
Key Personnel
CEO & Pres: Suzie Bouchard
Film, television, books, records, theater, dance, etc; SODEC is a government agency.

Software & Information Industry Association (SIIA)
1090 Vermont Ave NW, 6th fl, Washington, DC 20005-4095
Tel: 202-289-7442 *Fax:* 202-289-7097
Web Site: www.siia.net
Key Personnel
Pres: Ken Wasch *Tel:* 202-789-4440
VP, Membership: Eric Fredell *Tel:* 202-789-4464
Mktg Mgr: Nevena Jovanovic *Tel:* 202-789-4461

Represent corporations interested in the business opportunities associated with the generation, distribution & use of information.
Number of Members: 950

SPIE
PO Box 10, Bellingham, WA 98227-0010
Tel: 360-676-3290 *Toll Free Tel:* 888-504-8171
Fax: 360-647-1445
E-mail: customerservice@spie.org
Web Site: www.spie.org
Key Personnel
AV Mgr: Ben Lockwood
Founded: 1955
Not-for-profit international society dedicated to advancing optics & photonics; organize worldwide science conferences & publish the proceedings.
Publication(s): *Optical Engineering Journal* (monthly)

Television Academy
5220 Lankershim Blvd, North Hollywood, CA 91601-3109
Tel: 818-754-2800
Web Site: www.emmys.com
Key Personnel
Pres & COO: Maury McIntyre
CFO & EVP, Busn Opers: Heather Cochran
SVP, Awards: Dr John Leverence
SVP, Media & Brand Mktg: Susan Spence
VP, Awards: Julie Shore
VP, Mktg: Laurel Whitcomb
Founded: 1946
To further the telecommunications arts & sciences.
Number of Members: 25,000
Publication(s): *Emmy Magazine* ($5.95/issue US, $7.95/issue CN, $37/yr nonmembs)

Television Bureau of Advertising Inc (TVB)
120 Wall St, 15th fl, New York, NY 10005-3908
Tel: 212-486-1111 *Fax:* 212-935-5631
E-mail: info@tvb.org
Web Site: www.tvb.org
Key Personnel
CEO & Pres: Steve Lanzano
EVP & Chief Commsuns Offr: Abby Auerbach
Marketing trade association for TV industry; represent TV stations, networks, national spot sales representatives & program producer syndicators.
Number of Members: 800

Texas Association of Motion Media Professionals (TAMMP)
9629 Carnegie Dr, Dallas, TX 75228
Tel: 214-613-7601
E-mail: info@tammp.com
Web Site: www.tammp.com
Key Personnel
Pres: Brent Turman
Founded: 1976
Nonprofit association dedicated to promoting Texas crews & vendors to industry professionals in the film, television, video & gaming professions worldwide.
Number of Members: 950

Texas Motion Picture Alliance (TXMPA)
815-A Brazos St, Austin, TX 78701
Tel: 512-489-6723
E-mail: admin@txmpa.org; communications@txmpa.org
Web Site: www.txmpa.org
Key Personnel
Exec Dir: Paul Jensen *E-mail:* executivedirector@txmpa.org
Communs Dir: Mindy Raymond
Founded: 2006

Serves the film, video, interactive & digital media production industry, representing professionals seeking economic & creative incentives for media work in Texas.

United Scenic Artists Local 829
29 W 38 St, 15th fl, New York, NY 10018
Tel: 212-581-0300 *Toll Free Tel:* 877-728-5635
Fax: 212-977-2011
E-mail: vfxinfo@usa829.org
Web Site: www.usa829.org; vfx.usa829.org
Key Personnel
Natl Busn Agent: Cecilia Friederichs
E-mail: ceciliaf@usa829.org
Pres: Beverly Miller *E-mail:* bev@usa829.org
Busn Rep: Mike Smith *E-mail:* mikes@usa829.org
Founded: 1897
Labor union representing art directors, scenic, costume, lighting, sound & projection designers & scenic & computer artists in motion pictures, television & live performance.
Number of Members: 3,800

United States Institute for Theatre Technology Inc, see USITT

University Film & Video Association (UFVA)
c/o University of Illinois Press, 1325 S Oak St, Champaign, IL 61820-6975
Toll Free Tel: 866-647-8382
E-mail: ufvahome@gmail.com
Web Site: www.ufva.org
Key Personnel
Pres: Laura Vazquez *E-mail:* lvazquez@niu.edu
Treas: Tom Sanny *E-mail:* tsanny@me.com
Founded: 1947
Foster the development, improvement of film & video studies & production in educational institutions. Serves as liaison with the industry.
Number of Members: 800
2020 Conference(s): UFVA Conference, Florida State University, Tallahassee, FL, July 27-30, 2020
Publication(s): *The Journal of Film & Video* (quarterly); *UFVA Digest* (enewsletter, monthly)

USITT
290 Elwood Davis Rd, Suite 100, Liverpool, NY 13088
Tel: 315-463-6463 *Toll Free Tel:* 800-938-7488
Toll Free Fax: 866-398-7488
E-mail: info@usitt.org
Web Site: www.usitt.org
Key Personnel
Exec Dir: David Grindle *E-mail:* david@usitt.org
Dir, Educ & Training: Christine Troscher
E-mail: christine@usitt.org
Dir, Engagement: Mark Blackmon
E-mail: mark@usitt.org
Dir, Fin & HR: Carol Carrigan *E-mail:* carol@usitt.org
Founded: 1960
USITT is an association for performing arts & entertainment professionals. Its mission is to advance the knowledge & skills of its members who are design, production & technology professionals in the performing arts & live entertainment industry.
Number of Members: 4,000
2020 Conference(s): Annual Conference & Stage Expo, Houston, TX, April 1-4, 2020
2021 Conference(s): Annual Conference & Stage Expo, Columbus, OH, March 10-13, 2021
Publication(s): *Sightlines* (newsletter, monthly); *Theatre Design & Technology* (journal, 5 issues/yr)

Virginia Theatre Association (VTA)
1111 Church St, Lynchburg, VA 24504

Mailing Address: PO Box 1160, Lynchburg, VA 24505
Tel: 434-845-7529
E-mail: executivedirector@vtasite.org
Web Site: www.virginiatheatre.org
Key Personnel
Exec Dir: Chelsea Miller
Works with other fine & performing arts organizations throughout Virginia to assure the inclusion of theatre arts in education & supports theatre in all communities of the state by advocating for fair & adequate arts funding.
Conference(s): Annual Conference, late Oct
Membership(s): American Alliance for Theatre & Education; American Association of Community Theatre; Southeastern Theatre Conference Inc; Virginians for the Arts

WIA - The Wireless Infrastructure Association
2111 Wilson Blvd, Suite 210, Arlington, VA 22201
Tel: 703-739-0300 *Toll Free Tel:* 800-759-0300
Fax: 703-836-1608
Web Site: wia.org
Key Personnel
Pres & CEO: Jonathan S Adelstein
EVP: Tim House *Tel:* 703-535-7409
VP, Fin & Admin: Marta Sokol *Tel:* 703-535-7447
VP, Govt Aff: D Zachary Champ
VP, Spectrum Mgmt: Don Andrew *Tel:* 703-535-7502
Exec Dir, Memb Servs: Tracy Ford *Tel:* 703-535-7459
Dir, Meetings & Events: Nancy Touhill *Tel:* 703-535-7411 *E-mail:* nancy.touhill@wia.org
Dir, Workforce Devt: Kimberly Curley
Founded: 1924
Trade group for the wireless infrastructure industry.
2020 Conference(s): Connectivity Expo, Miami Beach Convention Center, Miami, FL, May 18-21, 2020

Women In Film
4221 Wilshire Blvd, Suite 130, Los Angeles, CA 90010
Tel: 323-935-2211
E-mail: info@wif.org
Web Site: womeninfilm.org
Key Personnel
Exec Dir: Kirsten Schaffer
Founded: 1973
Advocates for & advances the careers of women working in the screen industries to achieve gender parity & transform culture.
Number of Members: 2,000

Women in Film & Television-Florida (WIFT-FL)
PO Box 533541, Orlando, FL 32853-3541
E-mail: info@womeninfilmfl.org
Web Site: womeninfilmfl.org
Key Personnel
Pres: Nancy McBride
Founded: 1989
Promotes women's roles in film industry.
Number of Members: 10,000

Writers Guild of America, West (WGAW)
7000 W Third St, Los Angeles, CA 90048
Tel: 323-951-4000 *Toll Free Tel:* 800-548-4532
Web Site: www.wga.org
Key Personnel
Pres: David A Goodman
VP: Marjorie David
Secy & Treas: Aaron Mendelsohn
Union for writers in TV, screen & radio, film broadcasting & cable industry including writers of entertainment, news, documentaries & informational programming.

Number of Members: 12,000
Publication(s): *Written By: The Magazine of the Writers Guild of America, West* (6 issues/yr, $40)

Xplor® International
24156 State Rd 54, Suite 4, Lutz, FL 33559
Tel: 813-949-6170

E-mail: info@xplor.org
Web Site: www.xplor.org
Key Personnel
Pres & CEO: Skip Henk *Tel:* 813-949-6171
  E-mail: skip@xplor.org
Mktg Coord: Chad Henk *Tel:* 813-949-6171
  E-mail: chad@xplor.org
Prog Coord: Jennifer J Smith *Tel:* 813-949-6171
  E-mail: jennifer@xplor.org

Founded: 1981
Provides organizations & individuals with learning & networking opportunities which enhance the effective use of digital document technology to achieve business objectives.
Number of Members: 3,500
2020 Conference(s): XPLOR20, Tradewinds Island Grand Resort, 5500 Gulf Blvd, St Pete Beach, FL, April 14-16, 2020

Film & Television Commissions

Listed here are state, county and city agencies that are responsible for providing information and services (location scouting, local casting, permits, shelter, etc.) to prospective film, TV and commercial producers. The listings in this section are sorted geographically by state, then city.

ALABAMA

Mobile Film Office
Affiliate of City of Mobile
164 Saint Emanuel St, Mobile, AL 36602
Tel: 251-438-7102 *Fax:* 251-438-7104
Web Site: www.mobilefilmoffice.com
Key Personnel
Dir: Eva H Golson *E-mail:* golson@cityofmobile. org
Film Off & Location Coord: Diane Hall *Tel:* 251-438-7100 *E-mail:* diane.hall@cityofmobile.org
Assisting in finding locations, scouting & permits.

Alabama Film Office
Alabama Ctr for Commerce, 401 Adams Ave, Suite 170, Montgomery, AL 36104
Tel: 334-242-4195 *Fax:* 334-242-2077
Web Site: www.alabamafilm.org
Key Personnel
Mgr: Kathy Faulk *Tel:* 334-242-7127
  E-mail: kathy.faulk@film.alabama.gov
Community Liaison: Courtney Murphy *Tel:* 334-242-3989 *E-mail:* courtney.murphy@film. alabama.gov
Assist all legitimate motion picture production companies; location scouting available.
Membership(s): Association of Film Commissioners International

ALASKA

Alaska Department of Commerce, Community & Economic Development
Affiliate of State of Alaska Division of Economic Development
550 W Seventh Ave, Suite 1770, Anchorage, AK 99501-3569
Tel: 907-269-4048
Web Site: www.commerce.alaska.gov
Key Personnel
Mgr: Ethan Tyler *E-mail:* ethan.tyler@alaska.gov
Film promotion.

Alaska Film Services Inc
11050 Cange St, Anchorage, AK 99516
Tel: 907-230-8839
E-mail: filmservices@alaska.net
Web Site: www.alaskafilmservices.com
Key Personnel
Owner: Deborah Schildt
Founded: 1994
Pre-production services including bidding/budgets, location scouting & management, casting & permitting; Production services, fixers & crew; Post-production services & shipping.

ARIZONA

Apache Junction Chamber of Commerce
567 W Apache Trail, Apache Junction, AZ 85120
Mailing Address: PO Box 1747, Apache Junction, AZ 85117-1747
Tel: 480-982-3141 *Fax:* 480-982-3234
E-mail: admin@ajchamber.com
Web Site: www.ajchamber.com
Key Personnel
Off Mgr: Karyn Burwell

Flagstaff Convention & Visitors Bureau
211 W Aspen Ave, Flagstaff, AZ 86001
Tel: 928-213-2924 *Toll Free Tel:* 800-842-7293
  Fax: 928-556-1305
Web Site: www.flagstaffarizona.org
Key Personnel
Communs Specialist: Meg Roederer
  E-mail: mroederer@flagstaffaz.gov
Assists with location, scouting & permits for film, TV companies & still photography.

Globe-Miami Film Commission
Division of Globe-Miami Chamber of Commerce
1360 N Broad St, US 60, Globe, AZ 85501
Tel: 928-425-4495 *Toll Free Tel:* 800-804-5623
  Fax: 928-425-3410
E-mail: visitorinfo@globemiamichamber.com
Web Site: globemiamichamber.com
Key Personnel
Exec Dir: Cami Lucero
Provide films on Globe-Miami area culture & history.

Parker Area Chamber of Commerce
1217 California Ave, Parker, AZ 85344
Tel: 928-669-2174 *Fax:* 928-669-6304
E-mail: info@parkeraz.org
Web Site: www.parkeraz.org
Key Personnel
Exec Dir: Mary Hamilton *E-mail:* director@ parkeraz.org
Offer tourism, business & economic development services.

City of Phoenix Film Office
200 W Washington St, 20th fl, Phoenix, AZ 85003
Tel: 602-262-4850
E-mail: filmphx@phoenix.gov
Web Site: www.phoenix.gov/econdev/filming
Key Personnel
Film Commissioner: Philip Bradstock
Founded: 1974
Promote Phoenix as the site for filming of motion pictures, feature films, commercials, industrial & educational productions to the film & tape industry.
Membership(s): Association of Film Commissioners International

City of Prescott Film Office
201 S Cortez St, Prescott, AZ 86303
Tel: 928-777-1204 *Fax:* 928-777-1255
Web Site: www.prescott-az.gov
Key Personnel
Economic Devt Coord: Wendy Bridges
  E-mail: wendy.bridges@prescott-az.gov
Offers a variety of locations for filming.
Membership(s): Association of Film Commissioners International

Sedona Film Office
Division of Sedona Chamber of Commerce & Tourism Bureau
45 Sunset Dr, Sedona, AZ 86336
Tel: 928-204-1123 (ext 170) *Fax:* 928-204-1064
E-mail: pr@sedonachamber.com
Web Site: visitsedona.com/about-us/film-office

Key Personnel
Dir, Communs: Kegn Marissa Moorcroft
  E-mail: kmoorcroft@sedonachamber.com
Film liaison, permits, location assistance.

Cochise County Tourism & Economic Council
1011 N Coronado Dr, Sierra Vista, AZ 85635
Tel: 520-432-2209 *Fax:* 520-458-0584
E-mail: info@explorecochise.com
Web Site: www.explorecochise.com
Key Personnel
Mktg Coord: Kate Cox
Promote & develop tourism & economic development in Cochise County through cooperative leadership of major communities in the county. The Council seeks to present a unified voice in the marketplace that captures & communicates the unique assets of each community.

Film Tucson
Division of Visit Tucson
100 S Church Ave, Tucson, AZ 85701
Tel: 520-770-2151 *Fax:* 520-629-0160
Web Site: www.filmtucson.com
Key Personnel
Dir: Shelli Hall *E-mail:* shall@visittucson.org
Prodn Coord: Peter Catalanotte
  E-mail: pcatalanotte@visittucson.org
Scouting; assist with government agencies, clearances & on-site; work with television, film, commercial & still shots. Publish production manual.

Wickenburg Film Commission
216 N Frontier St, Wickenburg, AZ 85390
Tel: 928-684-5479; 928-684-0977
  Toll Free Tel: 800-942-5242 *Fax:* 928-684-5470
E-mail: info@wickenburgchamber.com
Web Site: www.wickenburgchamber.com/film-commission
Key Personnel
Exec Dir: Julie Brooks
Chmn, Film Commission: Kristi Henson
Local film services, photo library of area & location assistance.
Membership(s): Association of Film Commissioners International

Yuma Film Commission
Division of Yuma Visitors Bureau
180 W First St, Suite D, Yuma, AZ 85364
Tel: 928-376-0100 *Fax:* 928-373-0133
Web Site: www.filmyuma.com
Key Personnel
Exec Dir, Yuma Visitors Bureau: Linda Morgan
  E-mail: linda@visityuma.com
Mktg Dir: Dustin Mylius *E-mail:* dustin@ visityuma.com

ARKANSAS

Eureka Springs Advertising & Promotions Commission
PO Box 522, Eureka Springs, AR 72632-0522
Tel: 479-253-7333 *Fax:* 479-363-9380
E-mail: admin@eurekasprings.org
Web Site: www.eurekasprings.org
Key Personnel
Exec Dir: Mike Maloney *Tel:* 479-253-7333 ext 13 *E-mail:* director@eurekasprings.org

Founded: 1972
Filming accepted only for advertising purposes for the city of Eureka Springs.

Arkansas Film Commission
900 W Capitol Ave, Suite 400, Little Rock, AR 72201
Tel: 501-682-7676
Web Site: www.arkansasproduction.com
Key Personnel
Film Commissioner: Christopher Crane
E-mail: ccrane@arkansasedc.com
Founded: 1979
Promote location filming in Arkansas.

CALIFORNIA

Calaveras Film Commission
Calaveras Visitors Bureau, 1192 S Main St, Angels Camp, CA 95222
Mailing Address: PO Box 637, Angels Camp, CA 95222
Tel: 209-736-0049 *Toll Free Tel:* 800-225-3764
Web Site: filmcalaveras.org
Key Personnel
Film Commissioner/Exec Dir: Lisa Boulton
Assist film, TV & other media in completing location shoots.

Placer-Lake Tahoe Film Office
Division of Placer County Office of Economic Development
145 Fulweiler Ave, Auburn, CA 95603
Mailing Address: 175 Fulweiler Ave, Auburn, CA 95603
Tel: 530-889-4091 *Toll Free Tel:* 877-228-3456
Fax: 530-889-4095
Web Site: www.placer.ca.gov/films
Key Personnel
Dir: Beverly Lewis *E-mail:* blewis@placer.ca.gov
Founded: 1998
Film commission, location assistance (photo library, maps, etc); facilitates county film permits.
Membership(s): Film Liaisons in California Statewide

Catalina Island Film Commission
One Green Pleasure Pier, Avalon, CA 90704
Mailing Address: PO Box 217, Avalon, CA 90704
Tel: 310-510-7649; 310-510-7643 *Fax:* 310-510-7607
Web Site: www.catalinachamber.com/catalina-filming-information
Key Personnel
CEO & Film Liaison: Jim Luttjohann
E-mail: jluttjohann@catalinachamber.com
Information & coordination for all shooting on Catalina Island.
Membership(s): California Film Commission; Film Liaisons in California Statewide

Kern County Film Commission
1115 Truxtun Ave, Bakersfield, CA 93301
Tel: 661-868-7097 *Toll Free Tel:* 800-500-KERN (500-5376) *Fax:* 661-861-2017
E-mail: kerninfo@kerncounty.com
Web Site: www.filmkern.com
Coordinate film location sites & permits. Film location directory available.

Berkeley Film Office
2030 Addison St, Suite 102, Berkeley, CA 94704
Tel: 510-549-7040 *Toll Free Tel:* 800-847-4823
Fax: 510-644-2052
E-mail: film@visitberkeley.com
Web Site: www.filmberkeley.com
Key Personnel
CEO & Film Commissioner: Barbara Hillman

Founded: 1994
Assist with location referrals & coordination of commercial filming within the city of Berkeley.
Membership(s): Film Liaisons in California Statewide

Bishop Area Chamber of Commerce & Visitors Bureau
690 N Main St, Bishop, CA 93514
Tel: 760-873-8405
Web Site: www.bishopvisitor.com
Key Personnel
Exec Dir: Tawni Thomson *E-mail:* execdir@bishopvisitor.com
Founded: 1913
Promote business, tourism & greater Bishop.
Number of Members: 300

San Mateo County Film Commission
Division of San Mateo County/Silicon Valley Convention & Visitors Bureau
111 Anza Blvd, Suite 410, Burlingame, CA 94010
Tel: 650-348-7600 *Toll Free Tel:* 800-288-4748
Fax: 650-348-7687
E-mail: info@smccvb.com
Web Site: www.smccvb.com/film
Key Personnel
Film Commissioner: Marie Ivich *E-mail:* marie@smccvb.com
Covers 20 cities surrounding San Francisco International Airport, north of Santa Clara County, south of San Francisco.
Membership(s): Association of Film Commissioners International; Bay Area Women in Film & Media; California Film Commission; Film Liaisons in California Statewide

Chico Chamber of Commerce/Butte County Film Commission
180 Fourth St, Suite 120, Chico, CA 95928
Mailing Address: PO Box 3300, Chico, CA 95927-3300
Tel: 530-891-5556 *Toll Free Tel:* 800-852-8570
Fax: 530-891-3613
E-mail: info@chicochamber.com
Web Site: chicochamber.com
Key Personnel
Pres & CEO: Kelsey Torner *Tel:* 530-891-5556 ext 303 *E-mail:* kelsey@chicochamber.com
Memb Servs & Events Mgr: Heather Ugie *Tel:* 530-891-5556 ext 314 *E-mail:* heather@chicochamber.com
Opers & Communs Mgr: Jennifer Horn *Tel:* 530-891-5556 ext 306 *E-mail:* jennifer@chicochamber.com
Provide free location & production assistance.

Humboldt-Del Norte Film Commission
520 "E" St, Eureka, CA 95501
Tel: 707-443-4488
E-mail: info@filmhumboldtdelnorte.org
Web Site: www.filmhumboldtdelnorte.org
Key Personnel
Film Commissioner: Cassandra Hesseltine *Tel:* 707-502-0018 (cell)
Locations for movie making in the majestic redwoods & source of permits.

Fresno County Film Commission
2220 Tulare St, Suite 800, Fresno, CA 93721
Tel: 559-600-4271 *Fax:* 559-600-4573
E-mail: tourism@fresnocountyca.gov
Web Site: www.filmfresno.com
Key Personnel
Film Commissioner: Kristi Johnson
E-mail: kristigjohnson@fresnocountyca.gov
Location & production services for filming throughout Fresno County, CA.
Membership(s): Association of Film Commissioners International; California Film Commission; Film Liaisons in California Statewide

Greater Grass Valley Chamber of Commerce
128 E Main St, Grass Valley, CA 95945
Tel: 530-273-4667 *Fax:* 530-272-5440
Web Site: www.grassvalleychamber.com
Key Personnel
Exec Dir & CEO: Robin Galvan-Davies
E-mail: rdavies@grassvalleychamber.com
Provide information for filming in the area, assist with permits & location services. Film permits are necessary when photographing or filming at Empire Mine State Park & permits for filming that requires street closure or any pedestrian impediment within the cities of Grass Valley & Nevada City.

California Film Commission (CFC)
7080 Hollywood Blvd, Suite 900, Hollywood, CA 90028-6936
Tel: 323-860-2960 (24-hour serv)
Toll Free Tel: 800-858-4749 *Fax:* 323-860-2972
E-mail: filmca@film.ca.gov
Web Site: www.film.ca.gov
Key Personnel
Exec Dir: Amy Lemisch *Tel:* 323-860-2960 ext 102 *E-mail:* alemisch@film.ca.gov
Deputy Dir: Eve Honthaner *Tel:* 323-860-2960 ext 102 *E-mail:* ehonthaner@film.ca.gov
Write permits to film on state-owned & operated property. Location resource library & mediator services. Administers California film & TV tax credit program.
Membership(s): Association of Film Commissioners International

Orange County Film Commission
53 La Costa Ct, Laguna Beach, CA 92651
Tel: 949-246-9704
Web Site: www.filmorangecounty.org
Key Personnel
Film Commissioner: Janice Arrington
E-mail: jarrington@filmorangecounty.org
Locations scouting; assistance in obtaining permits, negotiating fees, finding local cast & crew members, products & services.

Antelope Valley Film Office/North Los Angeles County
42035 12 St W, Suite 103, Lancaster, CA 93534
Tel: 661-510-4231
Web Site: www.avfilm.com
Key Personnel
Film Liaison: Pauline East *E-mail:* pauline@filmantelopevalley.org
Provide location & local support services referrals for the entertainment industry (film, television & still production companies).

FilmL.A., Inc
6255 W Sunset Blvd, 12th fl, Los Angeles, CA 90028
Tel: 213-977-8600 *Fax:* 213-977-8601 (permits)
E-mail: info@filmla.com
Web Site: www.filmla.com
Key Personnel
Pres: Paul Audley
Founded: 1995 (as Entertainment Industry Development Corp)
Nonprofit corporation issuing permits & providing assistance for filming in the county of Los Angeles.

Mammoth Location Services
10001 Minaret Rd, Mammoth Lakes, CA 93546
Mailing Address: PO Box 24, Mammoth Lakes, CA 93546-0024
Tel: 760-934-2571 (ext 3628)
Web Site: www.mammothmountain.com/winter/home/film-locations

Key Personnel
Film & Entertainment Mgr: Steve Morrison
  E-mail: smorrison@mammothresorts.com
Location scouting & coordination; local casting &
  crew; equipment rentals.

Merced Film Commission
California Welcome Ctr, 710 W 16 St, Merced,
  CA 95340
Tel: 209-724-8104 *Toll Free Tel:* 800-446-5353
E-mail: info@visitmerced.travel
Web Site: visitmerced.travel
Key Personnel
Exec Dir & Film Commissioner: Karen Baker
  E-mail: bakerk@cityofmerced.org
Assist filmmakers with scouting & securing loca-
  tions for filming & can act as a liaison for city
  services.

Modesto Convention & Visitors Bureau
1150 Ninth St, Suite C, Modesto, CA 95354
Tel: 209-526-5588 *Toll Free Tel:* 888-640-8467
  Fax: 209-526-5586
E-mail: films@visitmodesto.com; info@
  visitmodesto.com
Web Site: www.visitmodesto.com
Key Personnel
CEO & Exec Dir: Jennifer Mullen
  E-mail: jennifer@visitmodesto.com
Free preliminary location scouting services, pho-
  tos & production information available to loca-
  tion scouts & managers upon request.
Membership(s): Association of Film Commission-
  ers International

Modesto/Stanislaus County Film Commission,
  see Modesto Convention & Visitors Bureau

Monterey County Film Commission
801 Lighthouse Ave, Suite 104, Monterey, CA
  93940
Mailing Address: PO Box 111, Monterey, CA
  93942-0111
Tel: 831-646-0910 *Fax:* 831-655-9250
E-mail: info@filmmonterey.org
Web Site: www.filmmonterey.org
Key Personnel
Dir, Mktg & Film Prodn: Karen Nordstrand
  E-mail: karen@filmmonterey.org
Off Admin: Moira LaMountain *E-mail:* moira@
  filmmonterey.org
Founded: 1987
Provide assistance & information on locations,
  permits, crew & other production services.
Membership(s): Association of Film Commission-
  ers International

Madera County Film Commission Inc
Division of Eastern Madera County Economic
  Development Coalition
PO Box 3690, Oakhurst, CA 93644
Tel: 559-760-1143 *Fax:* 559-658-2851
E-mail: filmcommissioner@filmmadera.com
Web Site: www.yosemite-sierra.com
Key Personnel
Film Commissioner: Dave Wolin
  E-mail: davewolin@earthlink.net
Location scouting, permits, security, lodging.
Membership(s): Film Liaisons in California
  Statewide

Yosemite/Madera County Film Commission,
  see Madera County Film Commission Inc

Oakland Film Office
One Frank H Ogawa Plaza, 9th fl, Oakland, CA
  94612
Tel: 510-238-4734
E-mail: filmoakland@filmoakland.com
Web Site: www.filmoakland.com

Key Personnel
Film Coord: Jim MacIlvaine
Act as a liaison between film companies & city;
  provide assistance with locations & approval
  processes.

City of Ojai, City Manager's Office
401 S Ventura St, Ojai, CA 93023
Tel: 805-646-5581 *Fax:* 805-646-1980
Web Site: ojaicity.org/film-permit
Key Personnel
Asst City Mgr: James Vega *Tel:* 805-646-5581 ext
  102 *E-mail:* vega@ojaicity.org
Film permits for the city of Ojai.

Palmdale Chamber of Commerce
817 E Avenue Q-9, Palmdale, CA 93550
Tel: 661-273-3232 *Fax:* 661-273-8508
E-mail: pcc@palmdalechamber.org
Web Site: www.palmdalechamber.org
Key Personnel
CEO: Jeanna Huerta
Founded: 1941
To promote, develop & service business, industry
  & community.
Number of Members: 420

El Dorado Lake Tahoe Film & Media Office
Division of The El Dorado County Chamber of
  Commerce
542 Main St, Placerville, CA 95667
Tel: 530-626-4400 *Toll Free Tel:* 800-457-6279
  Fax: 530-642-1624
E-mail: film@eldoradocounty.org
Web Site: filmtahoe.com
Key Personnel
Exec Dir: Kathleen Dodge
Free maps, scouting, location photo library, per-
  mits, crew & service referrals; key locations:
  South Lake Tahoe, Placerville, Apple Hill,
  Wineries, The American River.
Membership(s): Association of Film Commission-
  ers International; California Film Commission;
  Film Liaisons in California Statewide

Film Shasta, see Shasta County Film
  Commission

Shasta County Film Commission
Subsidiary of Redding Convention & Visitors Bu-
  reau
1448 Pine St, Redding, CA 96001
Tel: 530-710-7784 *Fax:* 530-225-4354
E-mail: info@filmshasta.com
Web Site: www.visitredding.com/film; filmshasta.
  com; www.facebook.com/filmshasta
Key Personnel
Film Commissioner: Sabrina Jurisich *Tel:* 530-
  225-4103 *E-mail:* sabrina@visitredding.com
Founded: 1986
Location scout-resource files & permits.
Membership(s): Association of Film Commission-
  ers International; California Film Commission;
  Film Liaisons in California Statewide

Ridgecrest Regional Film Commission
643 N China Lake Blvd, Ridgecrest, CA 93555
Mailing Address: PO Box 1838, Ridgecrest, CA
  93556
Tel: 760-375-8202 *Toll Free Tel:* 800-847-4830
  Fax: 760-375-9850
E-mail: permits@filmridgecrest.com
Web Site: www.filmridgecrest.com
Key Personnel
Film Commissioner: Doug Lueck
Founded: 1992
Facilitation of film locations; specialize in deserts,
  small towns, unique geological formations &
  360 degrees unobstructed panoramas.
Membership(s): Film Liaisons in California
  Statewide

Sacramento Film Commission
1608 "I" St, Sacramento, CA 95814-2042
Tel: 916-808-7777 *Toll Free Tel:* 800-292-2334
Web Site: www.visitsacramento.com/film
Key Personnel
Arts Admin: Lucy Steffens *Tel:* 916-808-5553
  E-mail: lsteffens@cityofsacramento.org
Membership(s): Association of Film Commission-
  ers International; Film Liaisons in California
  Statewide

San Francisco Film Commission
City Hall, Rm 473, One Dr Carlton B Goodlett
  Place, San Francisco, CA 94102
Tel: 415-554-6241 *Fax:* 415-554-6503
E-mail: film@sfgov.org
Web Site: www.filmsf.org/film-commission; www.
  facebook.com/FilmSF
Key Personnel
Pres: Villy Wang
VP: Matt Striker
Exec Dir: Susannah Greason Robbins
Film SF Mgr: Manijeh Fata
Sr Film Coord: Janet Austin
Arrange permits for filming on city streets; pro-
  vide information for local film industry; loca-
  tion photo file.

San Jose Film & Video Commission
Division of San Jose Convention & Visitors Bu-
  reau
c/o San Jose Convention & Visitors Bureau, 408
  Almaden Blvd, San Jose, CA 95110
Tel: 408-295-9600 *Toll Free Tel:* 800-SAN-JOSE
  (726-5673)
E-mail: eventservices@sanjose.org
Web Site: www.sanjose.org/media/film-office
Key Personnel
CEO: Karolyn Kirchgesler *Tel:* 408-792-4107
  E-mail: kkirchgesler@sanjose.org
Dir, Event Opers: Valerie Collins
  E-mail: vcollins@sanjose.org
Location assistance for production companies, in-
  formation on permits & services for production
  in the San Jose/Silicon Valley area.

San Luis Obispo County Film Commission
811 El Capitan Way, Suite 200, San Luis Obispo,
  CA 93401
Tel: 805-541-8000 *Toll Free Tel:* 800-634-1414
Web Site: www.slocal.com
Serve as liaison between film & TV companies &
  the county.

SLO County Film Commission, see San Luis
  Obispo County Film Commission

Santa Barbara County Film Commission
500 E Montecito St, Santa Barbara, CA 93103
Tel: 805-966-9222 *Toll Free Tel:* 800-676-1266
  Fax: 805-966-1728
E-mail: film@santabarbaraca.com
Web Site: santabarbaraca.com/film-commission
Promotions & referrals to assist film companies
  filming in the county.

Santa Clarita Film Office
Division of City of Santa Clarita Economic De-
  velopment Division
23920 Valencia Blvd, Suite 100, Santa Clarita,
  CA 91355
Tel: 661-284-1425 *Fax:* 661-286-4001
E-mail: film@santa-clarita.com
Web Site: filmsantaclarita.com
Key Personnel
Film Prog Specialist: Matthew Curran
Film Permit Technician: Jennifer Jzyk
Film Proj Technician: Kelli Lajer
Economic Devt Assoc: Evan Thomason
Film permits, location inquiries & scouting.

Sonoma County Film Office
Division of Sonoma County Economic Development Board
141 Stony Circle, Suite 110, Santa Rosa, CA 95401-4154
Tel: 707-565-7170 *Fax:* 707-565-7231
E-mail: film@sonoma-county.org
Web Site: www.sonoma-county.org/film
Key Personnel
Dir, Sonoma County Economic Development Board: Ben Stone
Film Liaison: Colette Thomas
Founded: 1974
Free & prompt film services, including location information, permits, accommodations, recommendations & local industry personnel referrals.
Membership(s): Film Liaisons in California Statewide

Tuolumne County Film Commission
193 S Washington St, Sonora, CA 95370
Tel: 209-533-4420 *Toll Free Tel:* 800-446-1333
E-mail: film@gotuolumne.com
Web Site: www.filmtuolumne.org
Key Personnel
Exec Dir: Lisa Mayo *E-mail:* lisa@gotuolumne.com
Founded: 1991
Film information & services to the film & television industry; scout locations, film permits.
Membership(s): Association of Film Commissioners International; FLIC

Stockton & San Joaquin Film Commission
Division of Visit Stockton
125 Bridge Place, 2nd fl, Stockton, CA 95202
Mailing Address: PO Box 2336, Stockton, CA 95201
Tel: 209-938-1555 *Toll Free Tel:* 877-778-6258
E-mail: visitorinfo@visitstockton.org
Web Site: www.visitstockton.org/about-us/film-commission
Key Personnel
Film Liaison: Wes Rhea *Tel:* 209-938-1551
E-mail: wes@visitstockton.org
Location scouting, logistics & casting services offered to film, television & commercial industry.

Santa Monica Mountains National Recreation Area
Office of Special Park Uses, 401 W Hillcrest Dr, Thousand Oaks, CA 91360
Tel: 805-370-2308
E-mail: samo_permits@nps.gov
Web Site: www.nps.gov/samo
Key Personnel
Spec Park Uses Coord: Catharine Beverly-Bishop *Tel:* 805-370-2325 *E-mail:* catharine_beverly-bishop@nps.gov
Founded: 1978
Film permits, locations.

Vallejo/Solano County Film Commission
289 Mare Island Way, Vallejo, CA 94590
Tel: 707-642-3653 *Toll Free Tel:* 800-4-VALLEJO (482-5535) *Fax:* 707-644-2206
Web Site: www.visitvallejo.com/film-office
Key Personnel
Film Liaison: Jim Reikowsky *E-mail:* jim@visitvallejo.com
Founded: 1996
Maintain photo library, assist location managers facilitate photo shoots (movies, commercials, still) & facilitate permit issuing.
Membership(s): Association of Film Commissioners International; Film Liaisons in California Statewide

City of West Hollywood Film Office
8300 Santa Monica Blvd, West Hollywood, CA 90069

Tel: 323-848-6489
E-mail: wehofilm@weho.org
Web Site: www.weho.org/film
Key Personnel
Film Coord: Eddie Robinson *E-mail:* erobinson@weho.org
Founded: 1984
Film location permitting for the City of West Hollywood.
Membership(s): Film Liaisons in California Statewide

COLORADO

Boulder County Film Commission
Affiliate of Colorado Film Commission
2440 Pearl St, Boulder, CO 80302
Tel: 303-442-2911 *Toll Free Tel:* 800-444-0447 *Fax:* 303-938-2098
E-mail: visitor@bouldercvb.com
Web Site: www.bouldercoloradousa.com/film-commission
Key Personnel
Film Commissioner: Emiliano Lake-Herrera *E-mail:* emiliano.lake-herrera@bouldercvb.com
A resource & referral organization for filming in Boulder County & assistance with production companies in finding locations & permits.
Membership(s): Association of Film Commissioners International

Fremont/Custer County Film Commission
403 Royal Gorge Blvd, Canon City, CO 81212
Tel: 719-275-2331 *Toll Free Tel:* 800-876-7922
E-mail: chamber@canoncity.com
Web Site: www.canoncity.com
Key Personnel
Exec Dir: Kristina Wedd
Provide local scouting & production assistance.

Colorado Springs Film Commission
515 S Cascade Ave, Colorado Springs, CO 80903
Tel: 719-685-7630 *Toll Free Tel:* 800-888-4748 (ext 130) *Fax:* 719-635-4968
E-mail: film@visitcos.com
Web Site: www.visitcos.com/film
Key Personnel
Chief Innovation Offr: Amy Long *E-mail:* amy@visitcos.com
Founded: 1989
Permit info & assistance, crew referrals, location scouting referrals, HD video b-roll.

Colorado Office of Film, Television & Media
Division of Colorado Office of Economic Development & International Trade
1600 Broadway, Suite 2500, Denver, CO 80202
Tel: 303-892-3840 *Fax:* 303-892-3848
E-mail: info@coloradofilm.org
Web Site: coloradofilm.org
Key Personnel
State Film Commissioner: Donald Zuckerman *E-mail:* donald.zuckerman@state.co.us
Full service film commission.

Greeley/Weld Film Commission
902 Seventh Ave, Greeley, CO 80631
Tel: 970-352-3566 *Toll Free Tel:* 800-449-3866 *Fax:* 970-352-3572
E-mail: info@greeleycvb.com
Web Site: www.greeleychamber.com; www.visitgreeley.org
Key Personnel
Visit Greeley Dir: Amy Dugan *E-mail:* amy@greeleychamber.com
Respond to inquiries about film production in the Greeley area.

Steamboat Springs Film Committee
125 Anglers Dr, Steamboat Springs, CO 80487

Mailing Address: PO Box 774408, Steamboat Springs, CO 80477
Tel: 970-879-0880
E-mail: info@steamboatchamber.com
Web Site: www.steamboatchamber.com/media/steamboat-springs-film-committee
Key Personnel
Mktg Dir: Laura Soard *E-mail:* laura@steamboatchamber.com
Assistance with film locations & support services in Northwest Colorado.

CONNECTICUT

Connecticut Office of Film, Television & Digital Media
c/o Dept of Economic & Community Development, 480 Columbus Blvd, Suite 5, Hartford, CT 06103
Tel: 860-500-2300
Web Site: www.ct.gov
Key Personnel
Dir: George Norfleet *E-mail:* george.norfleet@ct.gov
Prodn & Location Servs: Mark Dixon *Tel:* 860-500-2318 *E-mail:* mark.dixon@ct.gov
Film Tax Credit Admin: Ed Ruggiero *Tel:* 860-500-2411 *E-mail:* ed.ruggiero@ct.gov
Statewide contact for motion picture, television & digital media production & serves as a liaison between production companies, state agencies, municipalities, production facilities, local crew & vendors. Administers the tax credit programs designed to incentivize the development of the industry in Connecticut.
Membership(s): Association of Film Commissioners International

Western Connecticut Convention & Visitors Bureau
PO Box 968, Litchfield, CT 06759-0968
Tel: 860-567-4506 *Toll Free Tel:* 800-663-1273 *Fax:* 860-567-5214
E-mail: info@litchfieldhills.com
Web Site: www.visitwesternct.com; www.litchfieldhills.com; www.visitfairfieldcountyct.com
Key Personnel
Co-Exec Dir: Janet Serra *E-mail:* lhcvbnwct@aol.com; Jim Whitney *E-mail:* jim@northwestct.com
Assist with locations in 63 towns of northwest Connecticut.
Number of Members: 600

City of Stamford
888 Washington Blvd, Stamford, CT 06901
Tel: 203-977-5858
Web Site: www.stamfordct.gov
Key Personnel
Supv: Frank Fedeli
All city services, including film permits.

DELAWARE

Delaware Tourism Office
99 Kings Hwy, Dover, DE 19901
Tel: 302-739-4271 *Toll Free Tel:* 866-284-7483
E-mail: visit.delaware@state.de.us
Web Site: www.visitdelaware.com
Services arranged on an individual basis. Film services information available.

DISTRICT OF COLUMBIA

Office of Cable Television, Film, Music & Entertainment (OCTFME)
Brentwood Broadcast Ctr, 1899 Nine St NE, Washington, DC 20018
Tel: 202-727-6608 *Fax:* 202-727-3246

E-mail: film@dc.gov
Web Site: www.film.dc.gov
Key Personnel
Dir: Angie M Gates
The goal of the OCTFME is to initiate, implement & manage the operations & logistics of programs aimed at generating revenue & stimulating employment & business opportunities in the District through the production of film, television, video, photography & other multimedia projects.
Number of Members: 50

FLORIDA

Central Florida Visitors & Convention Bureau
2701 Lake Myrtle Park Rd, Auburndale, FL 33823
Tel: 863-551-4750 *Toll Free Tel:* 800-828-7655 *Fax:* 863-551-4740
Web Site: visitcentralflorida.org
Key Personnel
Client Servs Coord: Elisabeth Lineberger
Tel: 863-551-4710 *E-mail:* elizabeth@ visitcentralflorida.org
Provide one-stop permitting, preliminary scouting & liaison services.

Polk County Film Office, see Central Florida Visitors & Convention Bureau

Space Coast Film Commission
430 Brevard Ave, Suite 150, Cocoa Village, FL 32922
Tel: 321-433-4470 *Toll Free Tel:* 877-57-BEACH (572-3224) *Fax:* 321-433-4476
Web Site: www.visitspacecoast.com/film
Key Personnel
Film Commissioner: Bonnie King *E-mail:* bonnie. king@visitspacecoast.com
Provide varied locations: beaches, wildlife refuge, unique architecture, lakes & the Kennedy Space Center; Port Canaveral cruise ships.

Team Volusia Economic Development Corp
International Motorsports Ctr, One Daytona Blvd, Daytona Beach, FL 32114
Tel: 386-265-6332
Web Site: www.teamvolusiaedc.com
Key Personnel
Exec Asst/Off Mgr: Debbie Ott *E-mail:* dott@ tvedc.com
Conduit for film & motion picture inquiries.

Greater Fort Lauderdale/Broward Office of Film, Music, Fashion & Create
Division of Greater Fort Lauderdale Convention & Visitors Bureau (GFLCVB)
101 NE Third Ave, Suite 100, Fort Lauderdale, FL 33301
Tel: 954-767-2467 *Fax:* 954-767-4681
E-mail: film@broward.org
Web Site: www.sunny.org/film
Key Personnel
VP, Film, Music & Entertainment: Noelle P Stevenson *Tel:* 954-767-2440
E-mail: nstevenson@broward.org
Film Permit Asst: Kristen Norona *Tel:* 954-767-2472 *E-mail:* knorona@broward.org
Encourage companies to work in the Broward County/Fort Lauderdale area & serve as resource & liaison between production companies & the community.

Emerald Coast Film Commission
Division of Okaloosa County Tourist Development Council
1540 Miracle Strip Pkwy, Fort Walton Beach, FL 32548
Tel: 850-651-7644 *Fax:* 850-651-7149

E-mail: emeraldfilm@co.okaloosa.fl.us
Web Site: filmemeraldcoast.com
Key Personnel
Film Commissioner: Gail Morgan
Founded: 1996
Pre-scouting, on location support, production guide & talent, casting assistance & location library.
Membership(s): Association of Film Commissioners International; Film Florida

Jacksonville Office of Economic Development, Film & Television Office
117 W Duval St, Suite 280, Jacksonville, FL 32202
Tel: 904-630-2522
Web Site: www.coj.net
Key Personnel
Dir: Todd Roobin *E-mail:* troobin@coj.net
Site location scouting assistance. Liaison between community & production companies. Assistance coordinating permits.

Florida Keys & Key West Film Commission
Division of Monroe County Tourist Development Council
1201 White St, Suite 102, Key West, FL 33040
Tel: 305-293-1800 *Toll Free Tel:* 800-FILM-KEYS (345-6539) *Fax:* 305-296-0788
Web Site: www.filmkeys.com
Key Personnel
Film Commissioner: Chad Newman
E-mail: chad@filmkeys.com
Provide location scouting, permits, assistance in accomodations & any other services that would assist in film production in Monroe County.

St Petersburg/Clearwater Film Commission
Division of St Petersburg/Clearwater Area Convention & Visitors Bureau
8200 Bryan Dairy Rd, Suite 200, Largo, FL 33777
Tel: 727-464-7241 *Toll Free Tel:* 877-352-3224
E-mail: info@filmspc.com
Web Site: www.filmstpeteclearwater.com
Key Personnel
Film Commissioner: Tony Armer *Tel:* 727-464-7240 *E-mail:* tony@filmspc.com
Film Commission Mgr: Lisa Dozois
E-mail: lisa@filmspc.com
Digital Creative Dir: J Declan Flynn *Tel:* 727-464-7211 *E-mail:* declan@filmspc.com
Serves Pinellas County, FL, supporting & working to bring commercials, TV shows, feature films & digital media projects to the area.
Membership(s): Association of Film Commissioners International; Film Florida; Media Professionals of Florida Inc; Women in Film & TV-FL

Miami-Dade Office of Film & Entertainment
111 NW First St, 12th fl, Miami, FL 33128
Tel: 305-375-3288
E-mail: film@miamidade.gov
Web Site: www.filmiami.org
Key Personnel
Film Commissioner: Sandy Lighterman
E-mail: sandyl@miamidade.gov
Film/Photo Permit Coord: Jeanie Lisenby
E-mail: lisenby@miamidade.gov
Permit Coord & Digital Info Specialist: Dee Belz
E-mail: dbelz@miamidade.gov
Issue permits for filming or photography. Coordinate use of public properties for film, video, photo use. Provide information on personnel, goods & services available.

The Paradise Coast Film Commission
755 Eighth Ave S, Naples, FL 34102
Tel: 239-659-FILM (659-3456)
Web Site: film.paradisecoast.com

Key Personnel
Film Commission Dir: Maggie McCarty
E-mail: maggie@shootinparadise.com
Full service film commission for Southwest Florida's Naples, Marco Island & the Everglades. Scouting assistance, permits, itinerary planning, production resources, film incentives.
Membership(s): Association of Film Commissioners International

Ocala/Marion County Visitors & Convention Bureau
109 W Silver Springs Blvd, Ocala, FL 34475
Tel: 352-438-2800 *Toll Free Tel:* 888-FL-OCALA (356-2252) *Fax:* 352-438-2801
E-mail: exploreocalamarion@marioncountyfl.org
Web Site: www.ocalamarion.com
Key Personnel
Tourism Dir: Loretta Shaffer *Tel:* 352-438-2804
E-mail: loretta.shaffer@marioncountyfl.org
Mktg & Communs Coord: Ashley Dobbs
Tel: 352-438-2806 *E-mail:* ashley.dobbs@ marioncountyfl.org
Film permits for the city of Ocala & Marion County.

Orlando Film Commission
Division of Orlando Economic Development Commission
301 E Pine St, Suite 900, Orlando, FL 32801
Tel: 407-422-7159 *Fax:* 407-425-6428
E-mail: info@filmorlando.com
Web Site: www.filmorlando.com
Key Personnel
Film Commissioner: Sheena Fowler
E-mail: sheena@filmorlando.com
Assoc Dir: Lindsey Sandrin *E-mail:* lindsey@ filmorlando.com
Media: Laureen Martinez *E-mail:* laureen. martinez@orlandoedc.com
Full service film commission; film permitting; location assistance.

The Bradenton Area Film Commission
One Haben Blvd, Palmetto, FL 34221
Tel: 941-729-9177 *Fax:* 941-729-1820
Web Site: www.bradentongulfislands.com/film
Key Personnel
Film Commissioner: Sean Walter *Tel:* 941-729-9177 ext 3951 *E-mail:* sean.walter@bacvb.com
Film Liaison: Monica Luff *Tel:* 941-729-9177 ext 3944 *E-mail:* monica.luff@bacvb.com

Film Liaison of Escambia County
Division of Pensacola Area Chamber of Commerce
1401 E Gregory St, Pensacola, FL 32501
Tel: 850-390-3974 *Toll Free Tel:* 800-874-1234
E-mail: info@filmnorthflorida.com
Web Site: filmnorthflorida.com
Key Personnel
Film Liaison: Tom Roush *E-mail:* tom@ filmnorthflorida.com
Founded: 1983
Marketing organization for Pensacola, Pensacola Beach, Perdido Key & Gulf Breeze.
Number of Members: 204

City of Port St Lucie Community Relations/Communications Dept
121 SW Port St Lucie Blvd, Bldg A, 1st fl, Rm 145, Port St Lucie, FL 34984
Tel: 772-871-5219 *Fax:* 772-344-4111
E-mail: info@cityofpsl.com
Web Site: www.cityofpsl.com
Key Personnel
Communs Dir: Kristina Ciuperger

Sarasota County Film & Entertainment Office
Division of Economic Development Corp of Sarasota County

1680 Fruitville Rd, Suite 402, Sarasota, FL 34236
Tel: 941-309-1200 (ext 104) *Fax:* 941-309-1209
E-mail: info@filmsarasota.com
Web Site: www.filmsarasota.com
Key Personnel
Dir: Jeanne Corcoran *E-mail:* jeanne@
filmsarasota.com
Prodn Coord: Kimmi Heath-Carrico
Liaison between production companies & the
community; assist with locations, permitting,
talent & technical support; resource guide is
available at no cost to production companies.

**St Augustine, Ponte Vedra & The Beaches
Visitors and Convention Bureau**
29 Old Mission Ave, St Augustine, FL 32084
Tel: 904-829-1711 *Toll Free Tel:* 800-653-2489
Web Site: www.floridashistoriccoast.com
Key Personnel
Communs Dir: Kathryn Catron *Tel:* 904-209-4424
E-mail: kcatron@floridashistoriccoast.com
Communs Mgr: Barbara Golden *Tel:* 904-209-
4425 *E-mail:* bgolden@floridashistoriccoast.
com
Founded: 1996
Film liaison office, assists with location & scout-
ing.

The Florida Office of Film & Entertainment
Division of Florida Department of Economic Opportunity
107 E Madison St, MSC 80, Tallahassee, FL
32399
Tel: 850-717-8990 *Toll Free Tel:* 877-FLA-FILM
(352-3456)
E-mail: floridaofe@deo.myflorida.com
Web Site: www.filminflorida.com
Key Personnel
Film Commissioner: Niki Welge *E-mail:* niki.
welge@deo.myflorida.com
Prodn Mgr: Susan Simms *E-mail:* susan.simms@
deo.myflorida.com
State of Florida's economic development program for the advancement & expansion of the
motion picture, digital media & entertainment
industry sectors.

Film Tampa Bay, see Tampa Hillsborough Film
& Digital Media Commission

**Tampa Hillsborough Film & Digital Media
Commission**
Division of Visit Tampa Bay
One Tampa City Ctr, 201 N Franklin St, Suite
2900, Tampa, FL 33602
Web Site: filmtampabay.com
Key Personnel
Exec Dir/Film Commissioner: Tyler Martinolich
Tel: 813-218-3302 *E-mail:* tmartinolich@
visittampabay.com
Mktg/PR Mgr & Prodn Coord: Jesse Brock
Tel: 813-218-3303 *E-mail:* jbrock@
visittampabay.com
Prodn Mgr: Hilary Webber
Founded: 2013
Location assistance, crews, accommodations &
vendors to assist feature, television, or commer-
cial production.
Membership(s): Film Florida

**Palm Beach County Film & Television
Commission**
1555 Palm Beach Lakes Blvd, Suite 900, West
Palm Beach, FL 33401
Tel: 561-233-1000 *Toll Free Tel:* 800-745-FILM
(745-3456) *Fax:* 561-233-3113
Web Site: www.pbfilm.com
Key Personnel
Film Commissioner: Chuck Elderd
E-mail: celderd@pbfilm.com

Deputy Film Commissioner: Michelle Hillery
E-mail: mhillery@pbfilm.com
Founded: 1989
Palm Beach County offers an all-inclusive invitation to film in a world-class destination that
features a film-friendly community, year-round
warm weather, diverse locations & free production space. Take advantage of uncharted
hot spots, ambitious crews & a film commission that will go the distance to guarantee your
satisfaction. Go beyond your set & explore all
that Palm Beach County has to offer.

GEORGIA

Georgia Film Office
75 Fifth St W, Suite 1200, Atlanta, GA 30308
Tel: 404-962-4052 *Toll Free Tel:* 877-SHOOTGA
(746-6842) *Fax:* 404-962-4053
E-mail: film@georgia.org
Web Site: www.georgia.org/film
Key Personnel
Deputy Commissioner: Lee Thomas *Tel:* 404-962-
4048 *E-mail:* lthomas@georgia.org
Mktg & Budget Proj Mgr: Alison Fibben
Tel: 404-962-4050 *E-mail:* afibben@georgia.org
Founded: 1973
Location scouting, pre-production & production
assistance.
Membership(s): Association of Film Commission-
ers International

City of Savannah Film Office
One Waring Dr, Savannah, GA 31404
Mailing Address: PO Box 1027, Savannah, GA
31402
Tel: 912-651-2360 *Fax:* 912-651-0982
Web Site: filmsavannah.org
Key Personnel
Film Servs Dir: Susan Broker *E-mail:* sbroker@
savannahga.org
Founded: 1994
Full service, professionally staffed & certified
film commission. We promote & enable all
types of media production in the Savannah
area, including permitting, location assistance
& assistance in coordinating with local crew
& services. The Savannah area boasts a wealth
of locations including the nation's largest historical district, an evergreen urban forest &
unique coastal & rural settings. The commission will assist those wanting to utilize the natural beauty of Savannah in their next project.

HAWAII

Hawaii Island Film Office
Division of County of Hawaii Department of Re-
search & Development
25 Aupuni St, Rm 1301, Hilo, HI 96720
Tel: 808-961-8369; 808-961-8366 *Fax:* 808-935-
1205
Web Site: hawaiiislandfilm.com
Key Personnel
Film Commissioner: Justin Finestone *Tel:* 808-
936-9426 (cell) *E-mail:* justin.finestone@
hawaiicounty.gov
Founded: 1995
Business commission.

Honolulu Film Office
530 S King St, Suite 306, Honolulu, HI 96813
Tel: 808-768-6108 *Fax:* 808-768-6102
E-mail: info@filmhonolulu.com
Web Site: www.filmhonolulu.com
Key Personnel
Film Commissioner: Walea L Constantinau
Location photographs-free of charge; permit in-
formation; islandwide resources information;

liaison to city & county agencies including fire
department, police department, parks, streets &
others in Honolulu & on Oahu.

State of Hawaii Film Office
Division of Department of Business, Economic
Development & Tourism
250 S Hotel St, Suite 510-A, Honolulu, HI 96813
Mailing Address: PO Box 2359, Honolulu, HI
96804
Tel: 808-586-2570 *Fax:* 808-586-2572
E-mail: info@hawaiifilmoffice.com
Web Site: filmoffice.hawaii.gov
Key Personnel
Chief Offr, Creative Industries Div: Georja Skin-
ner
State Film Commissioner: Donne Dawson
Founded: 1978
Coordinate film permits for filmmakers seeking to
use state property; promote local film industry;
refer production resources & provide general
project assistance to filmmakers.

Maui County Film Office
Division of Office of Economic Development
2200 S Main St, Suite 305, Wailuku, HI 96793
Tel: 808-270-8237 *Fax:* 808-270-7995
Web Site: www.filmmaui.com
Key Personnel
Film Commissioner: Mr Tracy Bennett
E-mail: tracy.bennett@mauicounty.gov
Founded: 1993
Permitting, location scouting, production services
& accommodations.
Membership(s): Association of Film Commission-
ers International; International Cinematogra-
phers Guild

IDAHO

Idaho Film Office
Affiliate of Idaho Department of Commerce
700 W State St, Boise, ID 83702
Mailing Address: PO Box 83720, Boise, ID
83720-0093
Tel: 208-334-2470 *Toll Free Tel:* 800-842-5858
Fax: 208-334-2631
Web Site: www.filmidaho.com
Key Personnel
Dir: Bobbi-Jo Meuleman
Film Mgr: Amy Alpers *E-mail:* amy.alpers@
tourism.idaho.gov
Mgr, Tourism: Diane Norton *E-mail:* diane.
norton@tourism.idaho.gov
Provide assistance for location scouting, pre-
production & production assistance.

ILLINOIS

Chicago Film Office
Division of City of Chicago Department of Cul-
tural Affairs & Special Events
Chicago Cultural Ctr, 78 E Washington, Rm 108,
Chicago, IL 60602
Tel: 312-744-6415 *Fax:* 312-744-1378
E-mail: filmoffice@cityofchicago.org
Web Site: www.cityofchicago.org/city/en/depts/
dca/provdrs/chicago_film_office.html
Key Personnel
Dir: Richard Moskal *E-mail:* rmoskal@
cityofchicago.org
Deputy Dir: Betsey Grais
Proj Coord: Yolanda Arias
Founded: 1980
Coordinates all production for film making in the
city; agents & liaisons.

Illinois Film Office
Affiliate of Department of Commerce & Economic Opportunity

James R Thompson Ctr, Suite 3-400, 100 W Randolph, Chicago, IL 60601
Tel: 312-814-3600 *Fax:* 312-814-8874
E-mail: film@illinois.gov
Web Site: www.film.illinois.gov
Key Personnel
Dir: Christine Dudley
Administers the Illinois Film Production Tax Credit Program, provides assistance with navigation of state government services, location scouting, production directory.
Membership(s): Association of Film Commissioners International

INDIANA

Film Indiana
Affiliate of Indiana Office of Tourism Development (IOTD)
One N Capitol, Suite 600, Indianapolis, IN 46204-2288
Toll Free Tel: 800-677-9800
E-mail: filmindiana@visitindiana.com
Web Site: www.filmindiana.com
Key Personnel
Dir: Amy Howell
Scout film locations; establish liaison with film companies & the communities in which they work; help contact local crew & production companies.
Membership(s): Association of Film Commissioners International

IOWA

Quad Cities First
Affiliate of Quad Cities Chamber of Commerce
331 W Third St, Davenport, IA 52801
Tel: 563-326-1005
Web Site: www.quadcitiesfirst.com
Founded: 2009 (successor to Quad City Development Group)
Film coalition group, location information, liaisons.

Dubuque Area Convention & Visitors Bureau
300 Main St, Suite 120, Dubuque, IA 52001
Tel: 563-845-7698
Web Site: www.traveldubuque.com
Key Personnel
Pres & CEO: Keith Rahe
VP, Sales: Julie Kronlage
VP, Opers: Sara Hanten
Dir of Mktg: Taylor Cummings
Dir of Sports & Events: Tyler Daugherty
Develop & implement plans to promote the Dubuque area as a convention & tourist destination.
Branch Office(s)
280 Main St, Dubuque, IA 52001, Welcome Ctr
Mgr: Becky Carkeek *Toll Free Tel:* 800-798-8844 *E-mail:* welcomectr@traveldubuque.com
Web Site: www.facebook.com/traveldubuque (welcome ctr)

KANSAS

Explore Lawrence
PO Box 526, Lawrence, KS 66044
Tel: 785-856-3040; 785-856-5282 (mktg)
Fax: 785-856-5303
E-mail: visinfo@explorelawrence.com
Web Site: www.explorelawrence.com
Key Personnel
Exec Dir: Michael Davidson
Dir, Mktg: Andrea Johnson
Mgr: Debbie McCarthy

Asst Mgr: Keith Manies
Marketing service for convention, convention sales & group tours, help visiting production companies find proper locations.

Manhattan Film Commission
Affiliate of Manhattan CVB
501 Poyntz Ave, Manhattan, KS 66502
Tel: 785-776-8829 *Toll Free Tel:* 800-759-0134
Fax: 785-776-0679
E-mail: cvb@manhattan.org
Web Site: visitmanhattanks.org
Key Personnel
Manhattan CVB Dir: Karen Hibbard
E-mail: karen@manhattan.org
Assistance with location & scouting.

Kansas Creative Arts Industries Commission
Affiliate of Kansas Department of Commerce
1000 SW Jackson St, Suite 100, Topeka, KS 66612-1354
Tel: 785-296-2178 *Fax:* 785-296-3490
Web Site: www.kansascommerce.gov/caic
Key Personnel
Dir: Peter Jasso *E-mail:* peter.jasso@ks.gov
Offer location scouting assistance, liaison between communities & production companies as well as pre-production & production assistance. Publish *Kansas Production Guide*, listing Kansas crews, companies & important information regarding filming in Kansas.

Visit Topeka Inc
618 S Kansas Ave, Topeka, KS 66603
Tel: 785-234-1030 *Toll Free Tel:* 800-235-1030
Fax: 785-234-8282
E-mail: info@visittopeka.com
Web Site: www.visittopeka.com
Key Personnel
Pres & CEO: Brett Oetting
Dir, Mktg: Michaela Saunders
Coordinates with the Kansas Film Commission, film companies & hotels; provides service directory, cast, crews & materials; assists with permits within the city.

Greater Wichita Convention & Visitors Bureau/Wichita Film Commission
515 S Main St, Suite 115, Wichita, KS 67202
Tel: 316-265-2800 *Toll Free Tel:* 800-288-9424
Fax: 316-265-0162
E-mail: wfc@visitwichita.com
Web Site: www.visitwichita.com
Key Personnel
Pres & CEO: Susie Santo *E-mail:* ssanto@visitwichita.com
VP, Strategic Devt: Maureen Hofrenning
E-mail: mhofrenning@visitwichita.com
Assists in all areas of film location & production, what to do, where to go, scouting, etc.

Wichita Film Commission, see Greater Wichita Convention & Visitors Bureau/Wichita Film Commission

KENTUCKY

Kentucky Film Office
Affiliate of Kentucky Cabinet of Tourism, Arts & Heritage
100 Airport Rd, Suite 200, Frankfort, KY 40601
Tel: 502-564-3456 *Toll Free Tel:* 800-345-6591
Fax: 502-564-5695
E-mail: email@kyfilm.com
Web Site: kyfilmoffice.com
Key Personnel
Dir: Jay Hall *Tel:* 502-229-4290 (cell)
E-mail: jay.hall@ky.gov

Administer tax credit to film & national TV producers. Database of location scouts available via web site for use by production companies.
Membership(s): Association of Film Commissioners International; Kentucky Film Association

LOUISIANA

Louisiana Entertainment
Division of Louisiana Economic Development
617 N Third St, Baton Rouge, LA 70802
Mailing Address: PO Box 94185, Baton Rouge, LA 70804-9185
Tel: 225-342-5403 *Fax:* 225-342-5554
E-mail: led-entertainment@la.gov
Web Site: louisianaentertainment.gov
Key Personnel
Exec Dir: Christopher Stelly *E-mail:* chris.stelly@la.gov
Film Dir: Stephen Hamner *E-mail:* stephen.hamner@la.gov
Administers Louisiana's motion picture incentive program & facilitates filming in our state's communities.
Membership(s): Association of Film Commissioners International; The Broadway League

Jeff Davis Parish Film Commission
100 Rue de l'Acadie, Jennings, LA 70546
Tel: 337-821-5521 *Toll Free Tel:* 800-264-5521
Fax: 337-821-5536
E-mail: info@jeffdavis.org
Web Site: jeffdavis.org/film-commission
Key Personnel
Exec Asst/Off Mgr: Tracie Fontentnot
E-mail: tracie@jeffdavis.org
Graphics/Communs Coord: Jamie Lee
E-mail: jamie@jeffdavis.org
Scouting & location work.

Monroe-West Monroe Convention & Visitors Bureau
601 Constitution Dr, West Monroe, LA 71292
Mailing Address: PO Box 1436, West Monroe, LA 71294-1436
Tel: 318-387-5691 *Toll Free Tel:* 800-843-1872
Fax: 318-324-1752
Web Site: nelafilm.com
Key Personnel
Communs Dir: Sheila M Snow *E-mail:* ssnow@monroe-westmonroe.org
Responds to requests on film locations.

Northeast Louisiana Film Commission
601 Constitution Dr, West Monroe, LA 71292
Mailing Address: PO Box 1436, West Monroe, LA 71294
Toll Free Tel: 800-843-1872
Web Site: nelafilm.com
Key Personnel
Chmn: Sheila Snow *E-mail:* ssnow@monroe-westmonroe.org
Secy: Sarita Daniel
Founded: 2005
Aims to develop Northeast Louisiana as a film, video & television production center. Markets its locations, resources & personnel to motion picture & television production companies.

MAINE

Maine Film Office
Division of Maine Department of Economic & Community Development
59 State House Sta, Augusta, ME 04333
Tel: 207-624-9828 *Fax:* 207-287-8070
E-mail: film@maine.gov
Web Site: www.filminmaine.com

Key Personnel
Dir: Karen Carberry Warhola *E-mail:* karen.
carberrywarhola@maine.gov
Founded: 1987
Promote & assist location filming.
Membership(s): Association of Film Commissioners International

MARYLAND

Baltimore Film Office
Division of Baltimore Office of Promotion & the Arts
10 E Baltimore St, 10th fl, Baltimore, MD 21202
Tel: 410-752-8632 *Fax:* 410-385-0361
Web Site: www.baltimorefilm.com
Key Personnel
Dir: Debbie Donaldson Dorsey *Tel:* 443-807-2220 (cell) *E-mail:* ddorsey@promotionandarts.org
Logistics Coord: Fran Carmen *Tel:* 443-807-7190 (cell) *E-mail:* fcarmen@promotionandarts.org
Assist production teams in finding locations; act as liaison between city agencies & film companies.

Maryland Film Office
Division of Maryland Commerce Department
401 E Pratt St, 14th fl, Baltimore, MD 21202
Tel: 410-767-6343 *Toll Free Tel:* 800-333-6632 *Fax:* 410-333-0044
E-mail: filminfo@marylandfilm.org
Web Site: www.marylandfilm.org
Key Personnel
Dir, Film & Digital Media: Jack Gerbes *Tel:* 410-767-6343
Deputy Dir: Catherine Batavick *Tel:* 410-767-6342
Scout locations, offer information on caterers, hotels, equipment rentals; provide liaison with police, fire, medical, security; arrange 24-hour dailies & technical staff & talent for film, TV, commercial productions & features.

MASSACHUSETTS

Boston Film Bureau
One City Hall Sq, Rm 802, Boston, MA 02201-2029
Tel: 617-635-3911 *Fax:* 617-635-4428
E-mail: filmbureau@cityofboston.gov
Web Site: www.cityofboston.gov/arts/film
Key Personnel
Film Dir: Amy Yandle *Tel:* 617-635-3962
Permits, film locations & assistance.

MICHIGAN

Detroit Film Office
Coleman A Young Municipal Ctr, 2 Woodward Ave, Suite 333, Detroit, MI 48226
Tel: 313-224-3876; 313-224-1606
E-mail: dfo@detroitmi.gov
Web Site: detroitmi.gov/departments/detroit-film-office
Film permits.

Michigan Film & Digital Media Office
Affiliate of Michigan Economic Development Corp
300 N Washington Sq, 4th fl, Lansing, MI 48913
Tel: 517-241-6757 *Toll Free Tel:* 800-477-FILM (477-3456) *Fax:* 517-241-3689
E-mail: mfo@michigan.org
Web Site: www.michiganbusiness.org/industries/mfdmo
Key Personnel
Prog Mgr: Lynn McNamara *E-mail:* mcnamaral@michigan.org

PR Mgr: Frank Provenzano
E-mail: provenzanof@michigan.org
Promotional Agent: Tony Garcia
E-mail: garciat3@michigan.org
Dept Technician: Erika Murdey
E-mail: murdeye1@michigan.org
Founded: 1979
Assist & attract incoming production companies; promote the growth of indigenous industry. Services include film tourism, production directory, cast & crew calls, permitting & location scouting.
Membership(s): Association of Film Commissioners International

City of Traverse City
400 Boardman Ave, Traverse City, MI 49684
Tel: 231-922-4480
E-mail: tcclerk@traversecitymi.gov
Web Site: www.traversecitymi.gov
Key Personnel
Licensing & Election Specialist: Kim Lautner *E-mail:* klautner@traversecitymi.gov
Film production permits.

MINNESOTA

Minneapolis Licenses & Consumer Services
350 S Fifth St, Rm 1, Minneapolis, MN 55415-1391
Tel: 612-673-2080 *Fax:* 612-673-3399
Web Site: www.minneapolismn.gov/licensing
Key Personnel
Film & Video Coord: Craig Eliason *Tel:* 612-673-3370 *E-mail:* craig.eliason@minneapolismn.gov
Permits, information & referrals for filming in the city of Minneapolis.

Minnesota Film & TV
401 N Third St, Suite 245, Minneapolis, MN 55401
Tel: 612-767-0095
E-mail: info@mnfilmtv.org
Web Site: mnfilmtv.org
Key Personnel
Exec Dir: Melodie Bahan *E-mail:* melodie@mnfilmtv.org
Dir, Opers: Jade Orth *E-mail:* jade@mnfilmtv.org
Incentives Specialist: Jill Johansen *E-mail:* jill@mnfilmtv.org
Founded: 1983
Snowbate incentive program to attract production to Minnesota; market talent, crew & production infrastructure in the *Minnesota Production Directory*; maintain extensive statewide digital location photo database; develop & sustain relationships with independent producers & executives at major studios & networks nationwide; facilitate production with location & scouting services & crew, equipment & permitting referrals.
Membership(s): Association of Film Commissioners International

MISSISSIPPI

Columbus Film Commission
117 Third St S, Columbus, MS 39701
Mailing Address: PO Box 789, Columbus, MS 39703
Tel: 662-329-1191 *Toll Free Tel:* 800-327-2686; 800-920-3533 *Fax:* 662-329-8969
E-mail: marketing@visitcolumbusms.org
Web Site: visitcolumbusms.org
Key Personnel
Exec Dir: Nancy Carpenter *Tel:* 662-574-2036 (cell) *E-mail:* nancy@visitcolumbusms.org
Liaison for city, county & government; provides clearance & location assistance.

Greenwood Convention & Visitors Bureau & Film Commission
225 Howard St, Greenwood, MS 38935
Mailing Address: PO Drawer 739, Greenwood, MS 38935-0739
Tel: 662-453-9197
Web Site: www.visitgreenwood.com
Key Personnel
Exec Dir: Danielle Morgan *E-mail:* danielle@visitgreenwood.com
Busn Coord: Ashley Farmer
Sales Coord: Forrest Hodge
Founded: 1989
Location assistance, government liaison.

Mississippi Film Office
501 N West St, 5th fl, Jackson, MS 39201
Mailing Address: PO Box 849, Jackson, MS 39205
Tel: 601-359-3297 *Fax:* 601-359-5048
Web Site: www.filmmississippi.org
Key Personnel
Assoc Mgr: Nina Parikh
Off Coord: Betty Black
Founded: 1973
Location scouting & pre-production services, coordination of local casting. Acts as liaison between production & local/state government. New incentive program.
Membership(s): Association of Film Commissioners International

Visit Natchez & Natchez Convention Promotion Commission
640 S Canal St, Box C, Natchez, MS 39120
Tel: 601-446-6345 *Toll Free Tel:* 800-647-6724
E-mail: info@visitnatchez.org
Web Site: www.visitnatchez.org/p/media/film
Key Personnel
Exec Dir: Jennifer Ogden Combs
E-mail: jennifer@visitnatchez.org
Assists filmmakers in Mississippi: location scouting & research; pre-production help with casting, extras, crew, equipment; trouble-shooting during production & wrap.

Oxford Film Commission
1013 Jackson Ave E, Oxford, MS 38655
Tel: 662-232-2477 *Toll Free Tel:* 800-758-9177
E-mail: tourism@visitoxfordms.com
Web Site: visitoxfordms.com
Key Personnel
Dir: Mary Allyn Hedges *E-mail:* maryallyn@visitoxfordms.com
Deputy Dir: Kinney Ferris *E-mail:* kinney@visitoxfordms.com
Founded: 1988

MISSOURI

Cape Girardeau Convention & Visitors Bureau
220 N Fountain St, Cape Girardeau, MO 63701
Tel: 573-335-1631 *Toll Free Tel:* 800-777-0068 *Fax:* 573-334-6702
E-mail: info@visitcape.com
Web Site: visitcape.com
Key Personnel
PR Dir: Brenda Newbern *E-mail:* bnewbern@visitcape.com
Sales Dir: Alyssa Phares *E-mail:* aphares@visitcape.com
Admin Asst: Betty Roth *E-mail:* broth@visitcape.com
Founded: 1984
Help obtain permits needed to film on public property, to close streets +/or traffic control; secure accommodations for scouting & location personnel; provide pre-scouting for any necessary photos & related material; provide help to

the production company in the event problems arise during their stay.
Membership(s): Missouri Association of Convention & Visitors Bureaus; Missouri Travel Council

Missouri Film Office
Division of Department of Tourism & Economic Development
301 W High St, Suite 290, Jefferson City, MO 65101
Tel: 573-526-3566
E-mail: mofilm@ded.mo.gov
Web Site: www.mofilm.org
Key Personnel
Film Commissioner: Andrea Sporcic Klund
  E-mail: andrea.sporcic@ded.mo.gov
Founded: 1983
Works to develop, coordinate & market the film industry & film-related activities in Missouri. Serves as the official central point of contact for all state-wide inquiries: film, TV shows, segments, commercials, web content & digital media.
Membership(s): Association of Film Commissioners International

Kansas City Film Office
Division of VisitKC
1321 Baltimore Ave, Kansas City, MO 64105
Tel: 816-691-3800 *Toll Free Tel:* 800-767-7700
E-mail: film@visitkc.com
Web Site: www.kcfilmoffice.com
Key Personnel
Film Commissioner: Steph Scupham *Tel:* 816-691-3842 *E-mail:* sscupham@visitkc.com
Film Coord: Rachel Kephart *Tel:* 816-691-3845
  E-mail: rkephart@visitkc.com
Location assistance, permits, crew & support services. Local film incentive rebate program, up to 10% rebate on qualified spend in KMCO - film, television, commercial, music video & corporate video productions can qualify.
Membership(s): Association of Film Commissioners International; Missouri Motion Media Association

MONTANA

Visit Billings
815 S 27 St, Billings, MT 59101
Mailing Address: PO Box 31177, Billings, MT 59107-1177
Tel: 406-245-4111 *Fax:* 406-245-7333
E-mail: info@visitbillings.com
Web Site: www.visitbillings.com
Key Personnel
Exec Dir: Alex Tyson *E-mail:* alex@visitbillings.com
Work with & advocate for film projects. Answers questions regarding the region's offering, offers financial & directional assistance with site selection & can work directly with the Montana Film Office when/if they cannot be in town or on site to work with a client or potential client.

Butte Montana Chamber of Commerce
1000 George St, Butte, MT 59701
Tel: 406-723-3177 *Toll Free Tel:* 800-735-6814
  Fax: 406-723-1215
E-mail: marketing@buttechamber.org
Web Site: www.buttechambersite.org; www.visitbutte.com
Key Personnel
Exec Dir: Stephanie Sorini
Assist with filming & scouting when possible (especially arrangements prior to filming), permissions, accommodations, etc.

Montana Film Office
Division of Montana Department of Commerce

301 S Park Ave, Helena, MT 59620
Tel: 406-841-2879
E-mail: montanafilm@mt.gov
Web Site: www.montanafilm.com
Key Personnel
Locations Coord: J D Jacoby *Tel:* 406-841-2880
Founded: 1974
State film commission for Montana. Provide location services & assistance with permits, online production guide with searchable location database, extensive photo library, administers film production incentives & Montana Big Sky Film Grant program.
Membership(s): Association of Film Commissioners International

NEBRASKA

Eastern Nebraska Film Office
302 S Woodland Ct, Fremont, NE 68025
Tel: 402-968-4280
E-mail: filminnebraska@gmail.com
Web Site: www.facebook.com/easternebraskafilmoffice
Key Personnel
Commissioner: Stacy Heatherly
Full service film commission.

Nebraska Film Office
Affiliate of Nebraska Department of Economic Development
PO Box 98907, Lincoln, NE 68509-8907
Tel: 402-471-3746 *Toll Free Tel:* 800-426-6505
Web Site: film.nebraska.gov; opportunity.nebraska.gov/ded-partners
Key Personnel
Film Offr: Laurie Richards *Tel:* 402-202-1905
  E-mail: lrichards2@neb.rr.com
State liaison with film & video industry; site location; crews.

NEVADA

Nevada Film Office
Division of State of Nevada, Governor's Office of Economic Development
6655 W Sahara, Suite C-106, Las Vegas, NV 89146
Tel: 702-486-2711 *Toll Free Tel:* 877-638-3456
  Fax: 702-486-2712
E-mail: lvnfo@nevadafilm.com
Web Site: www.nevadafilm.com
Key Personnel
Dir: Eric Preiss *E-mail:* epreiss@nevadafilm.com
Resources Coord: Danette Tull *E-mail:* dtull@nevadafilm.com
Film & television production coordination.
Membership(s): Association of Film Commissioners International

Lake Tahoe Visitors Authority (LTVA)
169 Hwy 50, Stateline, NV 89449
Mailing Address: PO Box 5878, Stateline, NV 89449
Tel: 775-588-5900 *Toll Free Tel:* 800-288-2463
  (reservations) *Fax:* 775-588-1941
E-mail: info@ltva.org
Web Site: ltva.org
Key Personnel
Exec Dir: Carol Chaplin *Tel:* 775-588-5900 ext 302 *E-mail:* carol@ltva.org
Deputy Dir: Sue Barton *Tel:* 530-544-5050 ext 224 *E-mail:* sue@ltva.org
Founded: 1986
Provide information for filming in the area, assist with permits & location services.
Membership(s): National Tour Association; US Travel Association

NEW HAMPSHIRE

New Hampshire Film Bureau
One Eagle Sq, Suite 100, Concord, NH 03301
Tel: 603-271-2220
E-mail: film@livefree.nh.gov
Web Site: www.visitnh.gov/film
Key Personnel
Bureau Chief: Matthew W Newton
  E-mail: matthew.newton@livefree.nh.gov
Founded: 1998
Markets the state of New Hampshire as a filming location & supports New Hampshire filmmakers.
Membership(s): Association of Film Commissioners International

NEW JERSEY

New Jersey Motion Picture & Television Commission
153 Halsey St, 5th fl, Newark, NJ 07102-2807
Mailing Address: PO Box 47023, Newark, NJ 07101-8004
Tel: 973-648-6279 *Fax:* 973-648-7350
E-mail: njfilm@sos.nj.gov
Web Site: www.film.nj.gov
Key Personnel
Exec Dir: Steven Gorelick
Assoc Dir: David W Schoner, Jr
Opers & Creative Dir: Charles Ricciardi
Prodn Coord: Joseph Marra
Spec Projs: John Borelli
Location assistance/liaison with state, county & municipal governments.

NEW MEXICO

Albuquerque Film Office
Economic Development Dept, One Civic Plaza NW, Albuquerque, NM 87102
Mailing Address: PO Box 1293, Albuquerque, NM 87103
Tel: 505-768-3283
Web Site: www.cabq.gov/film
Key Personnel
Film Liaison: Ann Lerner *E-mail:* alerner@cabq.gov
Coordination & permit assistance. Serves as a clearing house of information for the public concerning projects currently in the area.
Membership(s): Association of Film Commissioners International

Film Las Cruces
1300-G El Paseo, Suite 174, Las Cruces, NM 88001
Tel: 575-805-3456
Web Site: www.filmlascruces.com
Key Personnel
Film Liaison: Scott Murray *E-mail:* scott@filmlascruces.com
Founded: 2015
Location assistance, permitting for city, marketing assistance.
Membership(s): Association of Film Commissioners International

New Mexico Film Office
Division of New Mexico Economic Development Dept
Joseph M Montoya Bldg, 1st fl, 1100 St Francis Dr, Suite 1213, Santa Fe, NM 87505
Tel: 505-476-5600 *Fax:* 505-476-5601
E-mail: info@nmfilm.com
Web Site: www.nmfilm.com
New Mexico continues to offer one of the most competitive incentive packages, which includes a 25% refundable tax credit, film investment loan program & film crew advancement Pro-

gram. Post-production services rendered in New Mexico also qualify for the 25% Refundable Tax Credit.

NEW YORK

Suffolk County Film Commission
H Lee Dennison Bldg, 11th fl, 100 Veterans Memorial Hwy, Hauppauge, NY 11788
Tel: 631-853-4800 *Fax:* 631-853-4767
Web Site: www.suffolkcountyfilmcommission.com
Key Personnel
Chair: Diana Cherryholmes
  E-mail: dianacherryholmes@suffolkcountyny.gov
To encourage, participate & assist in the making, promotion, distribution & exhibition of the Suffolk County film community. Staff is available for location & facility information & provides complete production services by coordinating activities between production companies, communities & government agencies.
Membership(s): Association of Film Commissioners International; New York Production Alliance; New York Women in Film & Television

Nassau County Film Office
Affiliate of Long Island Film/TV Foundation
Executive Bldg, One West St, Mineola, NY 11501
Tel: 516-571-3168 *Fax:* 516-571-6195
Web Site: www.longislandfilm.com
Key Personnel
Dir: Debra Markowitz *E-mail:* dmarkowitz@nassaucountyny.gov
Founded: 1989
Assist in site location, permits & police assistance, film support service brochure, location brochure, photo file. Long Island International Film Expo.
Membership(s): Association of Film Commissioners International

Cayman Islands Department of Tourism
Empire State Bldg, 350 Fifth Ave, Suite 2720, New York, NY 10018
Tel: 212-889-9009
E-mail: film@caymanislands.ky; usareception@caymanislands.ky
Web Site: www.visitcaymanislands.com
Key Personnel
Northeast Mktg Rep: Veronica Torra *Tel:* 732-789-5122
Facilitates productions with permitting & licensing, as well as providing creative input from development & pre-production through post-production.

New York City Mayor's Office of Film, Theatre & Broadcasting
Division of The Mayor's Office of Media & Entertainment (MOME)
Ed Sullivan Theatre Bldg, 6th fl, 1697 Broadway, New York, NY 10019
Tel: 212-489-6710 *Fax:* 212-307-6237
Web Site: www.nyc.gov/mome
Key Personnel
Commissioner: Julie Menin
Provide shooting permits, police assistance, production assistance, project development assistance, promotion & economic development services.

New York State Governor's Office for Motion Picture & Television Development (MPTV)
633 Third Ave, 37th fl, New York, NY 10017
Tel: 212-803-2330
E-mail: nyfilm@esd.ny.gov
Web Site: esd.ny.gov/industries/tv-and-film

Key Personnel
Exec Dir: Gigi Semone
Helps productions navigate the landscape, serving as a liaison between production companies & city & local governments, state agencies, a network of statewide contacts, local film offices & professional location scouts & managers. MPTV offers film, television & commercial production & post-production tax credits for qualified expenditures in New York State.

Saint Vincent & The Grenadines Tourist Office
801 Second Ave, 4th fl, New York, NY 10017
Tel: 212-687-4981 *Toll Free Tel:* 800-729-1726
  Fax: 212-949-5946
E-mail: svgtony@aol.com
Web Site: www.discoversvg.com
Key Personnel
Asst Sales Dir: Eleen Ackie

Rochester/Finger Lakes Film Commission
45 East Ave, Suite 400, Rochester, NY 14604-2294
Tel: 585-279-8308 *Fax:* 585-232-4822
Web Site: www.filmrochester.org
Key Personnel
Exec Dir: Nora Brown *E-mail:* nbrown@visitrochester.com
Deputy Dir: Karl Goldsmith
  E-mail: kgoldsmith@visitrochester.com
Founded: 1990
Location scouting assistance, information & extensive film production resources & services.
Membership(s): Association of Film Commissioners International

Film Upstate NY
28 Clinton St, Saratoga Springs, NY 12866
Tel: 518-584-3255 *Fax:* 518-587-0318
E-mail: info@filmupstateny.com
Web Site: filmupstateny.com
Key Personnel
VP, Tourism: Annamaria Bellantoni
Founded: 1980 (expanded 2004)
Offers staff, community & business support for the film & television production companies in the Northeast. Film tax credits available.

NORTH CAROLINA

North Carolina Film Office
15000 Weston Pkwy, Cary, NC 27513
Tel: 919-447-7800 *Fax:* 919-447-7780
Web Site: www.filmnc.com
Key Personnel
Dir: Guy Gaster *E-mail:* guy@filmnc.com
Promote film & television work.

Charlotte Regional Film Commission
500 S College St, Suite 300, Charlotte, NC 28202
Tel: 704-331-2723 *Toll Free Tel:* 800-722-1994
  Fax: 704-342-3972
Web Site: www.charlottefilm.com
Key Personnel
Dir, Film Div: Beth Petty *E-mail:* bpetty@charlottefilm.com
Serving the film industry extending to commercial, television & features.

Triangle Regional Film Commission
PO Box 13041, Research Triangle Park, NC 27709-3041
Tel: 919-544-5501
E-mail: triangleregionalfilm@gmail.com
Web Site: www.trianglencfilm.com
Key Personnel
Exec Dir: Rob Shoaf
Founded: 2011

Location scouting services for film productions, housing, catering & liaison with Research Triangle Park community service providers.
Membership(s): Association of Film Commissioners International

Wilmington Regional Film Commission Inc
1223 N 23 St, Wilmington, NC 28405
Tel: 910-343-3456 *Fax:* 910-343-3457
E-mail: commish@wilmingtonfilm.com
Web Site: www.wilmingtonfilm.com
Key Personnel
Dir: Johnny Griffin
Founded: 1999
Full service regional film commission. Location scouting, location library, annual production guide, crew/equipment/service information & production clearinghouse.
Membership(s): Association of Film Commissioners International

North Carolina's Piedmont Triad Film Commission
717 S Marshall St, Suite 105-F, Winston-Salem, NC 27101
Tel: 336-393-0001
E-mail: info@piedmontfilm.com
Web Site: www.piedmontfilm.com
Key Personnel
Exec Dir: Rebecca Clark *E-mail:* rebecca@piedmontfilm.com
Founded: 1993
Extensive photographic library, location scouting, pre-production & production assistance.
Membership(s): Association of Film Commissioners International

Piedmont Triad Film Commission, see North Carolina's Piedmont Triad Film Commission

NORTH DAKOTA

North Dakota Tourism Division
Century Ctr, 1600 E Century Ave, Suite 2, Bismarck, ND 58502-2057
Mailing Address: PO Box 2057, Bismarck, ND 58502-2057
Tel: 701-328-2525 *Toll Free Tel:* 800-435-5663
  Fax: 701-328-4878
E-mail: tourism@nd.gov
Web Site: www.ndtourism.com
Key Personnel
Dir, Tourism Div: Sara Otte Coleman
  E-mail: socoleman@nd.gov
Mktg Mgr: Heather LeMoine *E-mail:* hlemoine@nd.gov
Outdoor Promos Mgr: Mike Jensen
  E-mail: mjjensen@nd.gov
Coordinate economic development & promotion for North Dakota. In-kind support for film projects.

OHIO

Greater Cincinnati & Northern Kentucky Film Commission
1106 Race St, Cincinnati, OH 45202
Tel: 513-784-1744
Web Site: www.filmcincinnati.com
Key Personnel
Exec Dir: Kristen Schlotman *E-mail:* kristen@filmcincinnati.com
Provide assistance with location scouting, permits, talent, supplies, vehicles, hotels, traffic & props.

Film Columbus
100 E Broad St, Suite 2250, Columbus, OH 43215
Tel: 614-221-8648

E-mail: info@filmcolumbus.com
Web Site: filmcolumbus.com
Key Personnel
Exec Dir: John Daugherty *E-mail:* john@
  filmcolumbus.com
Founded: 2006
Location searching & resource for film & video
  production companies when shooting in Central
  Ohio.
Membership(s): Association of Film Commission-
  ers International

Greater Columbus Film Commission, see Film
  Columbus

OKLAHOMA

Oklahoma Film & Music Office
900 N Stiles Ave, Oklahoma City, OK 73104
Tel: 405-230-8440 *Toll Free Tel:* 800-766-3456
  Fax: 405-201-4561
Web Site: okfilmmusic.org
Key Personnel
Dir: Tava Sofsky *E-mail:* tava.sofsky@travelok.
  com
Deputy Dir: Jeanette Stanton *E-mail:* jeanette.
  stanton@travelok.com
Founded: 1979
Provide liaison with state, county & local gov-
  ernments; assistance with hotel accomodations,
  props, set dressing & equipment rental; produc-
  tion files available. Free location scouting & set
  assistance. Few permits required.

OREGON

**Eugene, Cascades & Coast-Travel Lane
  County**
754 Olive St, Eugene, OR 97401
Mailing Address: PO Box 10286, Eugene, OR
  97440-2286
Tel: 541-484-5307 *Toll Free Tel:* 800-547-5445
Web Site: www.eugenecascadescoast.org
Key Personnel
VP, Tourism Mktg: Natalie Inouye *Tel:* 541-743-
  8754 *E-mail:* natalie@eugenecascadescoast.org
Tourism Sales Mgr: Meg Trendler *Tel:* 541-743-
  8759 *E-mail:* meg@eugenecascadescoast.org
Liaison to Oregon Film Commission; advice on
  permits & scouting.

Travel Lane County, see Eugene, Cascades &
  Coast-Travel Lane County

Oregon Film & Video Office
123 NE Third Ave, Suite 210, Portland, OR
  97232
Tel: 971-254-4020
E-mail: shoot@oregonfilm.org
Web Site: www.oregonfilm.org
Key Personnel
Exec Dir: Tim Williams *E-mail:* tim@oregonfilm.
  org
Sr Proj Mgr: Bob Schmaling *E-mail:* bob@
  oregonfilm.org
IT & Creative Mgr: Nathan Cherrington
  E-mail: nathan@oregonfilm.org
Mktg Communs & Spec Events Mgr: Jane Ridley
  E-mail: jane@oregonfilm.org
Founded: 1968
Film commission, logistics & location scouting.

Portland Film Office
Division of Portland Development Commission
222 NW Fifth Ave, Portland, OR 97209-3859
Tel: 503-823-3326
E-mail: filmoffice@pdc.us
Web Site: www.portlandfilmoffice.com

Key Personnel
Contact: Brian Lord
Permit coordination.

PENNSYLVANIA

Pennsylvania Film Office
Affiliate of Department of Community & Eco-
  nomic Development
Commonwealth Keystone Bldg, 4th fl, 400 North
  St, Harrisburg, PA 17120-0225
Tel: 717-783-3456
E-mail: info@filminpa.com
Web Site: www.filminpa.com
Key Personnel
Locations Mgr & Admin Offr: Maryann P Mar-
  sico
Film Tax Credit Mgr: Janice Collier
Founded: 1977
Work to attract feature films, TV movies & se-
  ries, commercials & documentaries to Pennsyl-
  vania.

Greater Philadelphia Film Office
One Parkway Bldg, 11th fl, 1515 Arch St,
  Philadelphia, PA 19102
Tel: 215-686-2668 *Fax:* 215-686-3659
E-mail: mail@film.org
Web Site: www.film.org
Key Personnel
Exec Dir: Sharon Pinkenson *E-mail:* sharon@
  film.org
Dir, Greater Philadelphia Filmmakers & Program-
  ming: Joan Bressler *E-mail:* joan@film.org
Dir, Mktg & Multicultural Aff: Amira Smith
  E-mail: amira@film.org
Dir, Opers & Govt Aff: Nicole Shiner
  E-mail: nicole@film.org
Prodn Coord: Erin Jackson Wagner
  E-mail: erin@film.org
Off Mgr: Nicole Hornbeck *E-mail:* nicoleh@film.
  org
Founded: 1992
Markets Southeastern Pennsylvania area as loca-
  tion to feature film, television, video, commer-
  cial, production companies etc. Provides liaison
  services with city departments. Maintains lo-
  cation photo files & sends out informational
  packets including *Greater Philadelphia Film &
  Video Guide*.

Pittsburgh Film Office
The Oliver Bldg, 535 Smithfield St, Suite 500,
  Pittsburgh, PA 15222
Tel: 412-261-2744
E-mail: info@pghfilm.org
Web Site: www.pghfilm.org
Key Personnel
Dir: Dawn M Keezer
Deputy Dir: Heather Bolton
Off & Soc Media Coord: Katie Fahringer
Founded: 1990
Pittsburgh/Western Pennsylvania office for infor-
  mation regarding production locations, crew &
  resources. Will also assist with location permits
  & clearances.

RHODE ISLAND

Rhode Island Film & Television Office
Division of Rhode Island State Council on the
  Arts
One Capitol Hill, 3rd fl, Providence, RI 02908
Tel: 401-222-3456; 401-222-6666 (hotline)
  Fax: 401-222-3018
Web Site: www.film.ri.gov
Key Personnel
Exec Dir: Steven Feinberg *E-mail:* steven.
  feinberg@arts.ri.gov

One-stop permit office, free location scouting assistance with travel, hotel & catering arrangements; assist with pre-production, on-location
  & post-production requirements for successful
  filmmaking. Aggressive tax incentives.
Membership(s): Association of Film Commissioners International

SOUTH CAROLINA

South Carolina Film Commission
Division of South Carolina Department of Parks,
  Recreation & Tourism
1205 Pendleton St, Rm 225, Columbia, SC 29201
Tel: 803-737-0490 *Fax:* 803-734-1163
E-mail: filmsc@scprt.com
Web Site: www.filmsc.com
Key Personnel
Dir: Tom Clark *Tel:* 803-737-0498
  E-mail: tclark@scprt.com
Sr Proj Mgr: Dan Rogers *Tel:* 803-737-0496
  E-mail: danrogers@scprt.com
Production incentives are wage & supplier cash
  rebates. Free location scouting services for
  qualified prospects; liaison assistance between
  local communities & the production company;
  contacts with state & local officials; assistance
  with accommodations & contacts with local
  crew & casting assistance.
Membership(s): Association of Film Commissioners International

SOUTH DAKOTA

South Dakota Film Office
Division of South Dakota Department of Tourism
711 E Wells Ave, Pierre, SD 57501
Tel: 605-773-3301 *Toll Free Tel:* 800-952-3625
  Fax: 605-773-5977
E-mail: filmsd@state.sd.us
Web Site: filmsd.com
Key Personnel
Deputy Dir: Rebecca Cruse *E-mail:* rebecca.
  cruse@state.sd.us
Founded: 1989
Location scouting, lodging, catering, production
  assistance, hosting.

Sioux Falls Convention & Visitors Bureau
200 N Phillips Ave, Suite 102, Sioux Falls, SD
  57104
Tel: 605-275-6060 *Toll Free Tel:* 800-333-2072
  Fax: 605-338-0682
E-mail: sfcvb@siouxfalls.com
Web Site: visitsiouxfalls.com
Key Personnel
Exec Dir: Teri Schmidt
Founded: 1973
Full service convention & visitors bureau.

TENNESSEE

**The Memphis & Shelby County Film & TV
  Commission**
496 S Main St, Suite 101, Memphis, TN 38103
Tel: 901-527-8300 *Fax:* 901-527-8326
E-mail: hello@filmmemphis.org
Web Site: www.filmmemphis.org
Key Personnel
Film Commissioner: Linn Sitler *E-mail:* linn@
  filmmemphis.org
Deputy Film Commissioner & Contact: Sharon
  Fox O'Guin *E-mail:* sharon@filmmemphis.org
Founded: 1985
Location scouting & services; free production di-
  rectory; crew equipment; scout West Tennessee,
  Eastern Arkansas & Northern Mississippi.
Membership(s): Association of Film Commission-
  ers International

Mayor's Office of Economic & Community Development

One Public Sq, Suite 100, Nashville, TN 37201
Tel: 615-862-6000
Web Site: www.nashville.gov
Key Personnel
Exec Dir: Justine Avila
Dir: Matthew Wiltshire
Mgr: Audra Ladd

Tennessee Entertainment Commission

Tennessee Tower, 27th fl, 312 Rosa L Parks Ave, Nashville, TN 37243
Tel: 615-741-FILM (741-3456)
    Toll Free Tel: 877-818-FILM (818-3456)
E-mail: tn.film@tn.gov
Web Site: www.tnentertainment.com
Key Personnel
Exec Dir: Bob Raines *Tel:* 615-337-3838
    E-mail: bob.raines@tn.gov
Proj Mgr: Gisela Moore
Proj Mgr, Digital Content: Corey R Johns
Liaison & assistance to production companies working on location.
Membership(s): Association of Film Commissioners International

TEXAS

Amarillo Film Commission

Division of Amarillo Convention & Visitors Council
1000 S Polk St, Amarillo, TX 79101
Tel: 806-342-2016 *Toll Free Tel:* 800-692-1338
Fax: 806-373-3909
Web Site: www.amarillofilm.org; www.visitamarillo.com
Business referral/liaison to the private sector & city government; limited location scouting. Provide free production directory & some location pictures.
Membership(s): Texas Association of Film Commissions; Texas Motion Picture Alliance

Austin Film Commission

111 Congress Ave, Suite 700, Austin, TX 78701
Tel: 512-583-7230 *Toll Free Tel:* 800-926-2282
    (ext 7230) *Fax:* 512-583-7282
Web Site: www.austintexas.org/film-commission
Key Personnel
Dir: Brian Gannon *E-mail:* bgannon@austintexas.org
Location, crew, permits, studio space & equipment suppliers.
Membership(s): Association of Film Commissioners International; Texas Association of Film Commissions

Texas Film Commission

Division of State of Texas Governor's Office
1100 San Jacinto, Suite 3.410, Austin, TX 78701
Mailing Address: PO Box 12428, Austin, TX 78711
Tel: 512-463-9200 *Fax:* 512-463-4114
Web Site: gov.texas.gov/film
Key Personnel
Dir: Stephanie Whallon
Deputy Dir: Lindsey Ashley
Mktg Specialist: Katie Kelly
Founded: 1971
Resources that serve the film, television, commercial, animation, visual effects, video game & extended reality industries of Texas. Competitive production incentive program.
Membership(s): Association of Film Commissioners International

Corpus Christi Convention & Visitors Bureau

101 N Shoreline Blvd, Suite 430, Corpus Christi, TX 78401
Toll Free Tel: 800-678-6232
Web Site: www.visitcorpuschristitx.org

El Paso Film Commission

Affiliate of El Paso Convention & Visitors Bureau
One Civic Center Plaza, El Paso, TX 79901
Tel: 915-534-0600 *Fax:* 915-534-0687
E-mail: film@destinationelpaso.com
Web Site: visitelpaso.com/film
Key Personnel
Film Commissioner: Drew Mayer-Oakes
Location scouting, liaison in obtaining permits.
Membership(s): Association of Film Commissioners International; Texas Association of Film Commissions

Houston Film Commission

Division of Houston First Corp
701 Avenida de las Americas, Houston, TX 77010
Tel: 713-853-8959; 713-853-8100
    Toll Free Tel: 800-446-8786 *Fax:* 713-853-8341
E-mail: jmontgomery@houstonfilmcommission.com
Web Site: www.houstonfilmcommission.com
Key Personnel
VP & Exec Dir: Rick Ferguson *Tel:* 713-853-8956
Founded: 1987
Free location scouting; script breakdown; conduct location survey for production crew, assist as a liaison with city, county & state agencies.
Membership(s): Association of Film Commissioners International

Kerrville Convention & Visitors Bureau

2108 Sidney Baker St, Kerrville, TX 78028
Tel: 830-792-3535 *Toll Free Tel:* 800-221-7958
E-mail: info@kerrvilletexascvb.com
Web Site: www.kerrvilletexascvb.com
Key Personnel
Exec Dir: Charlie McIlvain
Videos & books about Texas.

San Antonio Film Commission

Division of Department for Culture & Creative Development
115 Plaza de Armas, Suite 102, San Antonio, TX 78205
Tel: 210-207-6777; 210-207-6730
    Toll Free Tel: 800-447-3372 *Fax:* 210-207-4526
E-mail: filmsa@filmsanantonio.com
Web Site: www.filmsanantonio.com; www.getcreativesanantonio.com/film-commission
Key Personnel
Film Commissioner: Galia Farber *E-mail:* galia.farber@sanantonio.gov
Location Coord: Janet Vasquez *E-mail:* janetv@filmsanantonio.com
Founded: 1985
Location scouting, liaison services, permitting, crew & resource information.
Membership(s): Association of Film Commissioners International; Texas Association of Film Commissions

UTAH

Kanab/Kane County Film Commission

Kane County Utah Off of Tourism, 78 S 100 E, Kanab, UT 84741
Tel: 435-644-5033 *Toll Free Tel:* 800-SEE-KANE (733-5263)
E-mail: kanetrav@kaneutah.com
Web Site: visitsouthernutah.com
Key Personnel
Exec Dir: Ken Gotzen-Berg
    E-mail: kgotzenberg@visitsouthernutah.com
Membership(s): Association of Film Commissioners International

Moab to Monument Valley Film Commission

111 E 100 N, Moab, UT 84532
Tel: 435-259-4341 *Fax:* 435-259-4135
Web Site: moabcity.org; film.utah.gov (Utah Film Commission)
Key Personnel
Dir: Virginia Pearce
Founded: 1949
Location scouting services; liaison for permitting & services.
Membership(s): Association of Film Commissioners International

Park City Film Commission

1850 Sidewinder Dr, No 320, Park City, UT 84060
Mailing Address: PO Box 1630, Park City, UT 84060-1630
Tel: 435-649-6100 *Toll Free Tel:* 800-453-1360
    Fax: 435-649-4132
Web Site: www.visitparkcity.com/film
Key Personnel
Film Commissioner: Sue Kapis
Assist crews, provide locating services.

Utah Valley Film Commission

220 W Center St, Suite 100, Provo, UT 84601
Tel: 801-851-2100 *Toll Free Tel:* 800-222-UTAH (222-8824)
E-mail: visitors@utahvalley.com
Web Site: www.utahvalley.com/film
Key Personnel
Dir, Sales: Lee Adamson *Tel:* 801-851-2110
    E-mail: lee@utahvalley.com
Lodging options, location presentations, film permit assistance & community liaison services.
Membership(s): Association of Film Commissioners International

Utah Film Commission

Subsidiary of Utah Governor's Office of Economic Development
Council Hall/Capitol Hill, 300 N State St, Salt Lake City, UT 84114
Tel: 801-538-8740 *Toll Free Tel:* 800-453-8824
Web Site: www.film.utah.gov
Key Personnel
Film Commissioner: Virginia Pearce
Founded: 1974
Provide location scouting, photographs of the area, help secure permits, provide information & resource materials, script breakdown. Serves as a liaison between video & filmmakers & all government agencies as well as private industry & local residents.
Membership(s): Association of Film Commissioners International

VIRGINIA

Virginia Film Office

Division of Virginia Tourism Corp
901 E Cary St, Richmond, VA 23219-4048
Tel: 804-545-5530 *Toll Free Tel:* 800-854-6233
    Fax: 804-545-5531
E-mail: vafilm@virginia.org
Web Site: www.film.virginia.org
Key Personnel
Dir: Andy Edmunds *Tel:* 804-545-5534
    E-mail: aedmunds@virginia.org
Commun Mgr: Margaret Finucane *Tel:* 804-545-5530 *E-mail:* mfinucane@virginia.org
Founded: 1980
Assistance in finding locations for film, television, video & still shoots. Extensive online location library. Custom location packages overnight or by e-mail. Staff will arrange for location scouts with key production personnel. Comprehensive Production Services Directory available. Provide research assistance. Facilitate use of government facilities & services for filming. Virginia has a broad sales & use tax exemption

for filmmakers. Call for additional incentive information.

Membership(s): Association of Film Commissioners International; Location Managers Guild International; Virginia Production Alliance; Women in Film & Video

WASHINGTON

Seattle Office of Film + Music
700 Fifth Ave, Suite 5752, Seattle, WA 98104
Mailing Address: PO Box 94708, Seattle, WA 98124-4708
Tel: 206-684-8993 *Fax:* 206-684-0379
E-mail: filmoffice@seattle.gov
Web Site: www.seattle.gov/filmandmusic
Key Personnel
Film & Special Events Prog Mgr: Christopher Swenson *Tel:* 206-733-9245 *Fax:* 206-684-7025
E-mail: christopher.swenson@seattle.gov
Permits, location scouting services & film liaison.

Washington Filmworks
1411 Fourth Ave, Suite 420, Seattle, WA 98101
Tel: 206-264-0667 *Fax:* 206-382-4343
E-mail: info@washingtonfilmworks.org
Web Site: washingtonfilmworks.org
Key Personnel
Exec Dir: Amy Lillard
Dir, Fin & Opers: Julie Daman
Prodn Servs Coord: Krys Karns
Communs Coord: Andrew Espe
Manages Washington State's film & production incentive programs. Free assistance for all pre-production needs, location scouting & support service referral. Free location photos, permitting contact & resources. Resource manual available.

Tacoma-Regional Film Commission
1516 Commerce St, Tacoma, WA 98402
Tel: 253-627-2836 *Fax:* 253-627-8783
Web Site: www.traveltacoma.com
Key Personnel
VP, Mktg: Jaime Vogt *E-mail:* jaime@traveltacoma.com
Film resources & permits.

WEST VIRGINIA

West Virginia Film Office
Unit of West Virginia Department of Commerce
90 MacCorkle Ave SW, South Charleston, WV 25303
Toll Free Tel: 866-6WV-FILM (698-3456)
Fax: 304-558-1662
E-mail: wvfilm@wv.gov
Web Site: wvfilm.com
Key Personnel
Dir: Pam Haynes *Tel:* 304-957-9382
E-mail: pamela.j.haynes@wv.gov
Acts as liaison between production companies & state agencies, municipalities & the private sector to expedite motion picture, television & commercial productions. Provides scouting assistance in securing locations. Offers a production directory containing a comprehensive listing of in-state personnel & production services; assists with facilitating introductions for the use of locations.
Membership(s): Association of Film Commissioners International; Location Managers Guild International

WISCONSIN

Milwaukee Film Office
648 N Plankinton Ave, Suite 425, Milwaukee, WI 53203-2917

Tel: 414-273-3950 *Toll Free Tel:* 800-554-1448
Fax: 414-273-5596
E-mail: info@milwaukee.org
Web Site: www.visitmilwaukee.org
Key Personnel
Dir, Communs: Kristin Settle *Tel:* 414-287-6230
E-mail: ksettle@milwaukee.org
Locations, permits, accommodations, production services, personnel, facilities.

VISIT Milwaukee, see Milwaukee Film Office

Film Wisconsin Inc
PO Box 93, Waunakee, WI 53597
Tel: 920-360-8827
E-mail: info@filmwisconsin.net
Web Site: www.filmwisconsin.net
Key Personnel
Pres: Jay Schillinger
Mng Dir: Lisa Ledford-Kerr
Founded: 1987
Public/private film office partnership featuring state incentives program & location & logistical services.
Membership(s): Association of Film Commissioners International

WYOMING

Wyoming Office of Tourism
5611 High Plains Rd, Cheyenne, WY 82007
Tel: 307-777-7777 *Fax:* 307-777-2877
E-mail: info@filmwyoming.com
Web Site: www.travelwyoming.com/film
Provides location scouting & liaison services to the motion picture industry interested in production in Wyoming.
Membership(s): Association of Film Commissioners International

Jackson Hole Film Commission
260A Broadway Ave, Jackson, WY 83001
Mailing Address: PO Box 550, Jackson, WY 83001-0550
Tel: 307-733-3316 *Fax:* 307-733-5585
Web Site: www.jacksonholechamber.com
Key Personnel
Dir, Destination Global Sales: Kent Elliott *Tel:* 307-733-3316 ext 106 *E-mail:* kent@jacksonholechamber.com
Communs Mgr: Cecilie Davila *Tel:* 307-201-2304
E-mail: cecilie@jacksonholechamber.com
Founded: 1946
Resource reference center for companies wanting to film in Jackson.
Number of Members: 1,000
Membership(s): Destination Marketing Association International

PUERTO RICO

Puerto Rico Film Commission
Affiliate of Department of Economic Development & Commerce
355 FD Roosevelt Ave, Suite 101, Hato Rey, PR 00918
Mailing Address: PO Box 362350, San Juan, PR 00936-2350
Tel: 787-754-6444 *Fax:* 787-756-5706
E-mail: info@puertoricofilm.pr.gov
Web Site: www.puertoricofilm.org
Key Personnel
Tax Credit Prog Mgr: Carla Cardona *Tel:* 787-758-4747 ext 5106 *E-mail:* carla.cardona@puertoricofilm.pr.gov
Founded: 1980
Provide assistance to production companies by researching & pre-scouting locations; liaison between local, state & federal authorities; secures permits & clearances & arranges accom-

modations & itineraries for scouting & location stays. Also process applications for tax credits (40% local residents & 20% actors, producers, directors, screenwriters & qualified personnel).
Membership(s): Association of Film Commissioners International

VIRGIN ISLANDS

US Virgin Islands Film Promotion Office
Affiliate of US Virgin Islands Dept of Tourism
PO Box 6400, St Thomas, VI 00804-6400
Tel: 340-775-1444 (ext 2243) *Fax:* 340-774-4390
E-mail: info@filmusvi.com
Web Site: www.filmusvi.com
Key Personnel
Dir: Luana Wheatley *E-mail:* lawheatley@usvitourism.vi
Founded: 1973
Free color location manual, location pictures, maps & videos, scouting assistance, liaison with government agencies & with the private sector, introduction to local production services.
Membership(s): Association of Film Commissioners International; Location Managers Guild International

ALBERTA

City of Calgary Film Commission
Division of Calgary Economic Development
731 First St SE, Calgary, AB T2G 2G9, Canada
Tel: 403-221-7886 *Toll Free Tel:* 888-222-5855
Fax: 403-221-7828
Web Site: www.calgaryeconomicdevelopment.com
Key Personnel
Commissioner, Film, TV & Creative Industries: Luke Azevedo
Tel: 403-221-7868 *E-mail:* lazevedo@calgaryeconomicdevelopment.com
Logistics Coord, Film, TV & Creative Industries: Lissa Craig *Tel:* 403-221-7829 *E-mail:* lissa@calgaryeconomicdevelopment.com
Development of film industry in Calgary city & Southern Alberta area, including locations & liaisons with city, media & film industry.
Membership(s): Association of Film Commissioners International

Alberta Film
140 Whitemud Crossing, 4211-106 St, Edmonton, AB T6J 6L7, Canada
Tel: 780-422-8584 *Toll Free Tel:* 888-813-1738
E-mail: info@albertafilm.ca
Web Site: www.albertafilm.ca
Key Personnel
Film Commissioner: Mark Ham *Tel:* 780-422-8581 *E-mail:* mark.ham@gov.ab.ca
Founded: 2002
Develops & implements marketing plans & associated activities that attract film, television & digital media production to the province. Provides location services that support production within the province. Consults with industry & makes recommendations on funding policies & strategic initiatives to grow the industry.
Branch Office(s)
Standard Life Bldg, 3rd fl, 639 Fifth Ave SW, Calgary, AB T2P 0M9, Canada, Contact: Marla Touw *Tel:* 403-592-4190 *E-mail:* marla.touw@gov.ab.ca
Membership(s): AMPIA; Association of Film Commissioners International

BRITISH COLUMBIA

Burnaby Film Office
6450 Deerlake Ave, Burnaby, BC V5G 2J3, Canada
Tel: 604-294-7314 *Fax:* 604-205-3001

E-mail: filming@burnaby.ca
Web Site: www.burnaby.ca
Key Personnel
Film Coord: TC Brotherston *E-mail:* tc.
brotherston@burnaby.ca
Film liaison & permits (approvals).
Membership(s): Motion Picture Production Indus-
try Association of British Columbia

Thompson-Nicola Film Commission
300-465 Victoria St, Kamloops, BC V2C 2A9,
Canada
Tel: 250-377-8673 *Toll Free Tel:* 877-377-8673
(BC only) *Fax:* 250-372-5048
E-mail: tnfc@tnrd.ca
Web Site: www.filmthompsonnicola.com
Key Personnel
Film Commissioner: Victoria (Vicci) Weller
Tel: 250-377-8673 ext 7058 *E-mail:* vweller@
tnrd.ca
Full service film commission, scouting, script
breakdown services plus location library & di-
rectory of services.
Membership(s): Association of Film Commission-
ers International

Okanagan Film Commission
1450 KLO Rd, Kelowna, BC V1W 3Z4, Canada
Tel: 250-717-0087 *Fax:* 250-868-0512
E-mail: info@okanaganfilm.com
Web Site: www.okanaganfilm.com
Key Personnel
Film Commissioner: Jon Summerland
Founded: 1990
To generate a positive economic impact by
enabling the growth of the Okanagan-
Similkameen-Boundary region as a film centre.
The Okanagan Film Commission will continue
to attract & build the film industry in this re-
gion through infrastructure development, strate-
gic partnering, marketing & promotion.

Creative BC (CrBC)
7 W Sixth Ave, Vancouver, BC V5Y 1K2,
Canada
Tel: 604-730-2732 *Fax:* 604-736-7290
E-mail: info@creativebc.com; media@creativebc.
com
Web Site: www.creativebc.com
Key Personnel
VP: Robert Wong *Tel:* 604-730-2236
E-mail: bwong@creativebc.com
Dir, Busn Opers: Karin Watson *Tel:* 604-730-
2250 *E-mail:* kwatson@creativebc.com
BC Film Commissioner & Dir, Prodn Servs:
Marnie Orr *Tel:* 604-730-2247 *E-mail:* morr@
creativebc.com
Mgr, Prodn Servs: Julie Bernard *Tel:* 604-730-
2244 *E-mail:* jbernard@creativebc.com
Assoc Mgr, Motion Picture Indus & Commu-
nity Aff: Katharine Pavoni *Tel:* 604-730-2248
E-mail: kpavoni@creativebc.com; Julie Stangeland *Tel:* 604-730-2245 *E-mail:* jstangeland@
creativebc.com
Founded: 1978
Worldwide promotion of British Columbia within
the film industry as a prime location for film,
TV & commercial production. Initial scouting,
photographs, maps, budget & production information supplied. Provide information on the
availability of local crews, technical facilities
& other support services. Acts as a liaison between production companies & other interested
parties during & after the production crews
work.

Vancouver Film & Special Events Office
Division of City of Vancouver
126 Keefer St, Vancouver, BC V6A 1X4, Canada
Tel: 604-257-8840 *Fax:* 604-257-8859
E-mail: film.office@vancouver.ca

Web Site: vancouver.ca/doing-business/film-
permits.aspx
Key Personnel
Sr Mgr: Sandi Swanigan
Opers Mgr: Cael Hopwood *Tel:* 604-257-8848
E-mail: cael.hopwood@vancouver.ca
Founded: 1978
Act as liaison with film production companies;
coordinate use of city services; authorize use of
city streets by film production companies; issue
permits as required.

Greater Victoria Film Commission, see
Vancouver Island South Film & Media
Commission

**Vancouver Island South Film & Media
Commission**
Affiliate of British Columbia Film Commission
514 Government St, 2nd fl, Victoria, BC V8V
2L7, Canada
Mailing Address: PO Box 38034 Fort St, Victo-
ria, BC V8W 3N2, Canada
Tel: 250-386-3976 *Toll Free Tel:* 888-537-3456
E-mail: admin@filmvictoria.com
Web Site: www.filmvictoria.com
Key Personnel
Film Commissioner: Kathleen Gilbert
Founded: 1976
Facilitate the growth of the film industry within
the greater Victoria region.
Number of Members: 120
Membership(s): Association of Film Commission-
ers International

MANITOBA

Manitoba Film & Music
410-93 Lombard Ave, Suite 410, Winnipeg, MB
R3B 3B1, Canada
Tel: 204-947-2040 *Fax:* 204-956-5261
E-mail: info@mbfilmmusic.ca
Web Site: www.mbfilmmusic.ca
Key Personnel
CEO & Film Commissioner: Carole Vivier
E-mail: carole@mbfilmmusic.ca
Mgr, Film Progs & Location Servs: Louise
O'Brien-Moran *Tel:* 204-947-2040 ext 17
E-mail: louise@mbfilmmusic.ca
Founded: 1998
Provide a variety of location services supported
by an extensive photo library, full location
scouting, script & budget breakdowns, assis-
tance regarding local crews & resources & liaison with all levels of government & private
business. On-going production assistance & a
comprehensive production guide that lists local
production personnel & services & contains a
photo survey of Manitoba locations. Also administers the Manitoba Film & Video Production Tax Credit which is a tax credit of up to
55% (base rate = 45%, plus eligible bonuses).
A statutory corporation funded by the Province
of Manitoba through the Department of Culture, Heritage & Tourism.
Membership(s): Association of Film Commissioners International

NEW BRUNSWICK

**Government of New Brunswick Department of
Tourism, Heritage & Culture**
Marysville Place, 20 McGloin St, 4th fl, Frederic-
ton, NB E3A 5T8, Canada
Mailing Address: PO Box 6000, Fredericton, NB
E3B 5H1, Canada
Tel: 506-453-3115 *Fax:* 506-444-5760
E-mail: thctpcinfo@gnb.ca
Web Site: www2.gnb.ca

Key Personnel
Dir, Communs: Stephanie Bilodeau *Tel:* 506-444-
3659 *E-mail:* stephanie.bilodeau@gnb.ca
Promotional travel assistance & short film venture
programs. Development & production incentive
programs for the film & television industry.

NEWFOUNDLAND AND LABRADOR

**Newfoundland and Labrador Film
Development Corp**
12 King's Bridge Rd, St John's, NL A1C 3K3,
Canada
Tel: 709-738-3456 *Toll Free Tel:* 877-738-3456
(CN) *Fax:* 709-739-1680
E-mail: info@nlfdc.ca
Web Site: www.nlfdc.ca
Key Personnel
Exec Dir & Film Commissioner: Dorian Rowe
E-mail: dorian@nlfdc.ca
Promote the local capabilities & infrastructure
that is currently available to the film & video
industry in Newfoundland and Labrador.

NORTHWEST TERRITORIES

Northwest Territories Film Commission
Division of Government of the Northwest Territo-
ries
PO Box 1320, Yellowknife, NT X1A 2L9,
Canada
Tel: 867-920-8793 *Toll Free Tel:* 844-NWT-FILM
(698-3456) *Fax:* 867-873-0101
E-mail: nwtfilm@gov.nt.ca
Web Site: www.nwtfilm.com
Key Personnel
Film Commissioner: Camilla MacEachern
Affiliated with a local industry of experienced
& established northern professionals to act as
your liaison through every phase of production.
Membership(s): Association of Film Commis-
sioners International; Association of Provincial
Funding Agencies.

NWT Film Commission, see Northwest
Territories Film Commission

ONTARIO

Ontario Creates
South Tower, Suite 501, 175 Bloor St E, Toronto,
ON M4W 3R8, Canada
Tel: 416-314-6858 *Fax:* 416-314-6876
E-mail: reception@ontariocreates.ca
Web Site: www.ontariocreates.ca
Key Personnel
Pres & CEO: Karen Thorne-Stone *Tel:* 416-642-
6612 *E-mail:* kthorne-stone@ontariocreates.ca
Communs Offr: Sharon Wilson *Tel:* 416-642-6616
E-mail: swilson@ontariocreates.ca
Mktg Consultant, Film: Janice Reid Johnston
Tel: 416-642-6629 *E-mail:* jreidjohnston@
ontariocreates.ca
Encourage producers to make films by offering
tax credits, skills development & marketing ini-
tiatives, funding specific programs & locations
library with photos.

**Toronto Film, Television & Digital Media
Office**
Toronto City Hall, Main fl, Rotunda N, 100
Queen St W, Toronto, ON M5H 2N2, Canada
Tel: 416-338-FILM (338-3456) *Fax:* 416-392-
0675
E-mail: filmtoronto@toronto.ca
Web Site: www.toronto.ca/tfto
Key Personnel
Film Commissioner & Dir, Entertainment Indus-
tries: Marguerite Pigott
Free location filming permits & assistance.

University of Toronto Academic & Campus Events
St George Campus, McMurrich Bldg, 4th fl, 12 Queen's Park Crescent W, Toronto, ON M5S 1S8, Canada
Tel: 416-978-2187; 416-978-8613 (film & photo shoot permits) *Fax:* 416-978-4802
E-mail: ace.team@utoronto.ca
Web Site: www.ace.utoronto.ca
Key Personnel
Dir: Steven Bailey

QUEBEC

Montreal Film & TV Commission
Duke Pavilion, 5th fl, 801 Brennan St, Montreal, QC H3C 0G4, Canada
Tel: 514-872-2883 *Fax:* 514-872-3409
E-mail: film.tv@ville.montreal.qc.ca
Web Site: www.montrealfilm.com
Key Personnel
Dir: Daniel Bissonnette *E-mail:* dbissonnette_2@ ville.montreal.qc.ca
Team Leader, Logistics & Permits:
    Josee Rochefort *Tel:* 514-872-1164
    E-mail: jrochefort@ville.montreal.qc.ca

Liaison Agent, Location & Resources: Yan Ethier *Tel:* 514-872-1503 *E-mail:* yanethier@ville. montreal.qc.ca
Liaison Agent, Logistics & Permits: Valerie Martel *Tel:* 514-872-1023 *E-mail:* valerie.martel@ ville.montreal.qc.ca
Liaison Agent, Info & Resources: Sylvie Lacelle *Tel:* 514-872-1162 *E-mail:* slacelle@ville. montreal.qc.ca
Clerk: Josee Rochon *Tel:* 514-872-4261
    E-mail: jrochon@ville.montreal.qc.ca
Founded: 1979
One-stop shop to help filmmakers & producers to shoot in Montreal. Offers access to relevant services offered by the City of Montreal, such as permits & authorizations, locations & troubleshooting.

YUKON

Yukon Film & Sound Commission (YFSC)
Division of Yukon Department of Economic Development
Box 2703, Whitehorse, YT Y1A 2C6, Canada

Tel: 867-667-5400; 867-661-0408 (ext 5400, no charge for calls from within Yukon)
    Fax: 867-393-6228
E-mail: info@reelyukon.com
Web Site: www.reelyukon.com
Key Personnel
Mgr, Film & Media: Iris Merritt *Tel:* 867-667-5678 *E-mail:* iris.merritt@gov.yk.ca
Film Offr: Kevin Hannam *Tel:* 867-667-8285
    E-mail: kevin.hannam@gov.yk.ca
Founded: 1998
Assists producers who are filming or are contemplating filming in Canada's Yukon Territory. May provide ground transportation & qualified personnel for location scouting. Clearing agency services & communications with all other levels of government. Assistance in obtaining permits & licenses where required. Still photography & location videos of prospective locations; incentive programs available.
Membership(s): Association of Film Commissioners International

Awards & Festivals

Included in this section are selected AV awards and festivals open to professional, student, educational and/or industrial media producers.

AAAS Kavli Science Journalism Awards
The American Association for the Advancement of Science (AAAS)
1200 New York Ave NW, Washington, DC 20005
Tel: 202-326-6431; 202-326-6440
E-mail: media@aaas.org
Web Site: www.aaas.org
Key Personnel
Exec Dir: Earl Lane *E-mail:* elane@aaas.org
Established: 1945
Encourage & recognize outstanding reporting for general audience on science & engineering & its application in a large newspaper, small newspaper, general circulation magazines, TV, radio, online & science news for children.
Other Sponsor(s): The Kavli Foundation
Categories: Print: Large newspaper, small newspaper, magazine; Television: Spot news/feature reporting (20 minutes or less), in-depth reporting (more than 20 minutes); Audio; Online; Children's Science News
Award: $5,000 (Gold Award), $3,500 (Silver Award) plus travel & hotel expenses to awards ceremony
Closing Date: Submitted on or before midnight, Aug 1
Entry Fee: None

Academy Awards®
Academy of Motion Picture Arts and Sciences (AMPAS)
8949 Wilshire Blvd, Beverly Hills, CA 90211
Tel: 310-247-3000; 310-247-3090 (publicity)
Fax: 310-859-9619
E-mail: awardsoffice@oscars.org; publicity@oscars.org
Web Site: www.oscars.org
Key Personnel
CEO: Dawn Hudson
Mng Dir, Memb Rel & Awards: Lorenza Munoz
Tel: 310-247-3000 ext 1127 *E-mail:* lmunoz@oscars.org
Established: 1929
Categories: Film features, documentaries & shorts
Award: Gold statuettes
Presented: Dolby Theatre, Hollywood, CA, Annually in Feb

AFI FEST
American Film Institute (AFI)
2021 N Western Ave, Los Angeles, CA 90027-1657
Tel: 323-856-7600 *Toll Free Tel:* 866-AFI-FEST (234-3378) *Fax:* 323-462-4049
E-mail: afifest@afi.com; festpublicity@afi.com
Web Site: www.afi.com/afifest
Key Personnel
Dir, Festival & Opers: Jacqueline Lyanga
E-mail: jlyanga@afi.com
Dir, Progamming: Lane Kneedler
Established: 1971
International, documentary & shorts.
Other Sponsor(s): Audi
Media: Submissions: Secure online screener; Exhibition: Shorts-DCP (NTSC), digital media file, 35mm; Features-DCP (NTSC), 35mm
Categories: Shorts, American narrative features, American documentary features, international narrative features, international documentary features
Award: Cash, trophy
Closing Date: April (early), May (regular), July (final), see web site for exact dates

Entry Fee: Shorts: $35 early, $45 regular, $55 final deadline; Features (over 30 minutes): $55 early, $65 regular, $75 final deadline
Presented: Nov

aGLIFF-The Austin Gay & Lesbian International Film Festival
aGLIFF
1216 E 51 St, Austin, TX 78723
Tel: 512-302-9889
E-mail: info@agliff.org
Web Site: agliff.org
Key Personnel
Prog Dir: Jim Brunzell, III
Established: 1987
Award: Program with over 100 films relevant to the lives of LGBTQ+ identified people
Presented: Austin, TX, Sept

Alabama State Council on the Arts Fellowships & Grants
Alabama State Council on the Arts (ASCA)
RSA Tower, Suite 110, 201 Monroe St, Montgomery, AL 36130-1800
Tel: 334-242-4076 *Fax:* 334-240-3269
E-mail: staff@arts.alabama.gov
Web Site: www.arts.alabama.gov
Key Personnel
Prog Mgr, Visual Arts: Elliot Knight, PhD
Two-year residency required.
Award: $5,000
Closing Date: Annually, March 1
Presented: Quarterly Meeting, Montgomery, AL, Annually in June

American Legion Fourth Estate Award
The American Legion National Headquarters
Media & Communs Div, 700 N Pennsylvania St, Indianapolis, IN 46204
Tel: 317-630-1253 *Fax:* 317-630-1368
E-mail: pr@legion.org
Web Site: www.legion.org
Key Personnel
PR: Debra Murrell *Tel:* 317-630-1253 ext 253
Media & Communs: John Raughter *Tel:* 317-630-1350 *E-mail:* jraughter@legion.org
Established: 1958
Presented annually to a publication, broadcast organization & online (Internet-based) media for outstanding achievement in the field of journalism.
Categories: Print, broadcast, online (Internet-based)
Award: 15 inch pylon trophy, miniature trophy, $2,000 stipend
Closing Date: March 1
Entry Fee: None
Presented: National Convention, Aug

The David A Andelman & Pamela Title Award
Overseas Press Club of America
40 W 45 St, New York, NY 10036
Tel: 212-626-9220 *Fax:* 212-626-9210
E-mail: info@opcofamerica.org
Web Site: www.opcofamerica.org
Key Personnel
Exec Dir: Patricia Kranz
Best international reporting in the broadcast media showing a concern for the human condition.
Other Sponsor(s): David A Andelman & Pamela Title
Award: Certificate & $1,000 check

Closing Date: Annually in late Jan
Entry Fee: $200
Presented: Hotel Mandarin-Oriental, New York, NY, Annually in April

Ann Arbor Film Festival
230 Collingwood Dr, Suite 160B, Ann Arbor, MI 48103
Mailing Address: PO Box 8232, Ann Arbor, MI 48107
Tel: 734-995-5356 *Fax:* 734-995-5396
E-mail: info@aafilmfest.org
Web Site: www.aafilmfest.org
Key Personnel
Exec Dir: Leslie Raymond *E-mail:* leslie@aafilmfest.org
Prog Dir: David Dinnell
Tech Dir: Tom Bray
Assoc Dir, Progs: Katie G McGowan
E-mail: katie@aafilmfest.org
Opers Mgr: Allison Buck *E-mail:* allison@aafilmfest.org
Established: 1963
Submissions open July 1.
Media: Internet link (URL) & 16mm
Categories: Experimental, animation, documentary, narrative, music video
Award: $20,000 in cash prizes
Closing Date: Aug 1 (early), Sept 1 (regular), Oct 1 (late), Oct 15 (extended)
Entry Fee: Shorts: $30 early, $45 regular, $60 late & extended; Features: $40 early, $55 regular, $70 late & extended
Presented: The Historic Michigan Theater & various other locations in Ann Arbor, MI, Annually in March

Arkansas Arts Council Fellowships & Grants Program
Arkansas Arts Council (AAC)
1100 North St, Little Rock, AR 72201-2606
Tel: 501-324-9766 *Fax:* 501-324-9207
E-mail: info@arkansasarts.org
Web Site: www.arkansasarts.org
Key Personnel
Artist Servs Prog Mgr: Robin McClea
Categories: Rotating categories of fellowships; Arkansas residents only
Closing Date: Annually in April
Entry Fee: None
Presented: Annually in Oct

ARSC Awards for Excellence
Association for Recorded Sound Collections (ARSC)
1299 University of Oregon, Eugene, OR 97403-1299
Tel: 541-346-1852
Web Site: www.arsc-audio.org
Key Personnel
Exec Dir: Nathan Georgitis *E-mail:* execdir@arsc-audio.org
Established: 1991
Presented to authors & publishers of books, articles, or recording liner notes, to recognize outstanding published research in the field of recorded sound.
Categories: Best history, best discography
Award: Certificate, plaque
Closing Date: Annually, Dec 31
Presented: ARSC Annual Conference, Annually in May (awards announced in Autumn)

Artadia James D Phelan Award in the Visual Arts
The San Francisco Foundation (TSFF)
One Embarcadero Ctr, Suite 1400, San Francisco, CA 94111
Tel: 415-733-8500 *Fax:* 415-477-2783
E-mail: artsinfo@sff.org; info@sff.org
Web Site: www.sff.org
Key Personnel
VP, Progs: Judith Bell
Artists may apply through the Artadia web site (artadia.org/awards).
Other Sponsor(s): Artadia
Award: $15,000
Closing Date: Aug 1
Entry Fee: None

Artist Fellowships
North Carolina Arts Council
Division of North Carolina Department of Natural & Cultural Resources
109 E Jones St, Raleigh, NC 27601
Mailing Address: Dept of Natural & Cultural Resources, c/o Mail Serv Ctr 4632, Raleigh, NC 27699-4632
Tel: 919-807-6500 *Fax:* 919-807-6532
E-mail: ncarts@ncdcr.gov
Web Site: www.ncarts.org
Key Personnel
Sr Prog Dir: Jeff Pettus *Tel:* 919-807-6513
    E-mail: jeff.pettus@ncdcr.gov
Established: 1980
Program operates on a two-year cycle. Songwriters, composers & writers are eligible to apply in even-numbered years. Choreographers & visual, craft & film/video artists are eligible to apply in odd-numbered years. Artists residing in NC for at least one year prior to the deadline & at least 18 years old are eligible. Must be US citizen or holder of permanent resident alien status & must remain NC resident & be physically present in the state during the grant period. Artists who received the fellowship grant in the past 5 years or are enrolled in an academic or degree-granting program at the time of application or during the grant period are not eligible. Apply online via web site.
Award: $10,000
Closing Date: Nov 1

Artist Initiative Grant Program
Minnesota State Arts Board
Park Square Ct, Suite 200, 400 Sibley St, St Paul, MN 55101-1928
Tel: 651-215-1600 *Toll Free Tel:* 800-866-2787
    Fax: 651-215-1602
E-mail: msab@arts.state.mn.us
Web Site: www.arts.state.mn.us
Key Personnel
Prog Offr: Sherrie Fernandez-Williams *Tel:* 651-215-1626 *E-mail:* sherrie.fernandez-williams@arts.state.mn.us
Established: 2003
Annual grant. Must be current Minnesota resident, professional artist, 18 years of age or older & a US citizen or permanent resident. Applicants must use WebGrants system & submit all materials electronically.
Media: JPG for images, MP3 for audio, PDF with Vimeo URL for videos
Categories: Dance, media arts, music, photography, poetry, prose, theater, 2D & 3D visual arts
Award: $2,000-$10,000
Closing Date: Literary & performing arts: June, Visual arts: Aug
Entry Fee: None

Artist Research & Development Grants
Arizona Commission on the Arts
417 W Roosevelt St, Phoenix, AZ 85003-1326
Tel: 602-771-6501 *Fax:* 602-256-0282
E-mail: info@azarts.gov

Web Site: www.azarts.gov
Key Personnel
Exec Dir: Jamie Dempsey *Tel:* 602-771-6520
    E-mail: jdempsey@azarts.gov
Deputy Dir: Alex Nelson *Tel:* 602-771-6521
    E-mail: anelson@azarts.gov
Artist Progs Mgr: Gabriela Munoz *Tel:* 602-771-6530 *E-mail:* gmunoz@azarts.gov
Grants awarded to individual artists from all disciplines. Applicants must be 18 years of age or older, not enrolled for more than 3 credit hours at a college or university & a resident of Arizona.
Award: $3,000-$5,000 in funding
Closing Date: Annually in Nov

Artist Residency Program
Ragdale Foundation
1260 N Green Bay Rd, Lake Forest, IL 60045
Tel: 847-234-1063
E-mail: info@ragdale.org
Web Site: www.ragdale.org
Key Personnel
Exec Dir: Jeffrey Meeuwsen *Tel:* 847-234-1063 ext 22
Dir, Residencies & Fellowships: Regin Igloria
    E-mail: reginigloria@gmail.com
Established: 1976
Nonprofit artists' community offering annual residencies to creative professionals. Applications are juried annually by the Ragdale Curatorial Board.
Award: 18 to 25-day residency
Closing Date: Jan 15 (residencies June-1st week of Sept), May 15 (residencies for Sept-Dec), Sept 15 (residencies Jan-May)
Entry Fee: Application fee: $40; $35/day residency fee if accepted

Asian American International Film Festival (AAIFF)
Asian CineVision Inc (ACV)
c/o Made in NY Media Ctr by IFP, 30 John St, Brooklyn, NY 11201
Tel: 212-989-1422 *Fax:* 212-727-3584
E-mail: submissions@asiancinevision.org; info@asiancinevision.org
Web Site: aaiff.org; www.asiancinevision.org
Key Personnel
Exec Dir: John C Woo *E-mail:* john@asiancinevision.org
Festival Dir: Judy Lei *E-mail:* judy@asiancinevision.org
Prog Mgr: Haisong Li *E-mail:* programs@asiancinevision.org
Established: 1978
Accepts completed film & video submissions produced, written, directed by media makers of Asian descent from any nationality, or about the Asian community.
Media: Submissions: Secure online screener, DVD (NTSC Region 0 or 1). Various exhibition formats-see FilmFreeway for details
Categories: Shorts, features, music videos, for youth by youth, works-in-progress, screenplay
Closing Date: Jan (early), Feb (regular), March (late), April (work-in-progress final)
Presented: Various locations throughout New York, NY, Mid-Summer

Atlanta Film Festival (ATLFF)
Atlanta Film Society
25 Park Place NE, Suite 800, Atlanta, GA 30303
Mailing Address: PO Box 5060, Atlanta, GA 30302-5060
Tel: 678-929-8103
E-mail: info@atlantafilmfestival.com; submit@atlantafilmfestival.com
Web Site: www.atlantafilmfestival.com
Key Personnel
Exec Dir: Christopher Escobar

Assoc Dir: Cameron McAllister
    E-mail: cameron@atlantafilmsociety.org
Opers Dir: Kimberly Kabel *E-mail:* kimberly@atlantafilmsociety.org
Programming Dir: Alyssa Armand
    E-mail: alyssa@atlantafilmsociety.org
Established: 1976
Now in its 4th decade, the Atlanta Film Festival is an Academy Award qualifying festival & one of the region's largest & longest-running pre-eminent celebrations of cinema in the Southeast US. Over 28,000 festival attendees enjoy independent, animated, documentary & short films each year, selected from over 8,400 submissions from all over the world.
Categories: Feature film, short film, episodic, experimental short, puppetry short, music video, virtual reality film, Georgia film, food film
Award: Jury awards & audience awards
Closing Date: June 6 (hella early), July 11 (early), Sept 26 (regular), Oct 24 (late), Nov 14 (extended)
Entry Fee: Features: $45 hella early, $50 early, $60 regular, $75 late, $100 extended; Shorts & food films: $30 hella early, $35 early, $45 regular, $60 late, $85 extended; GA film: $25, $50 (extended); All other categories: $5 hella early, $10 early, $20 regular, $35 late, $55 extended
Presented: Plaza Theatre, 7 Stages Theatre, Rialto Center for the Arts, High Museum, Atlanta, GA, April 30-May 10, 2020

Austin Film Festival
1801 Salina St, Austin, TX 78702
Tel: 512-478-4795 *Toll Free Tel:* 800-310-FEST (310-3378) *Fax:* 512-478-6205
E-mail: info@austinfilmfestival.com; programming@austinfilmfestival.com; marketing@austinfilmfestival.com
Web Site: www.austinfilmfestival.com
Key Personnel
Founder & Exec Dir: Barbara Morgan
    E-mail: barb@austinfilmfestival.com
Sr Film Prog Dir: Liz Mims *E-mail:* liz@austinfilmfestival.com
Conference Dir: Colin Hyer *E-mail:* colin@austinfilmfestival.com
Dir, Script Competitions: Matt Dy *E-mail:* matt@austinfilmfestival.com
Dir, Strategic Parnerships & Devt: Katy Daly
    E-mail: katy@austinfilmfestival.com
Film Competition Dir: Harrison Glaser
    E-mail: harrison@austinfilmfestival.com
Mktg Dir: Samantha Levine
Established: 1993
Media: Submissions: Secure online screener, DVD (NTSC or PAL); Exhibition: Digital files only
Categories: Narrative feature, narrative short, narrative student short, documentary feature, documentary short, comedy vanguard feature, dark matters feature, animated short
Closing Date: March (early), May (regular), June (late), July (extended)
Entry Fee: $50 early; $60 regular; $75 late; $85 extended
Presented: Movie theaters throughout downtown Austin, TX & the surrounding area, Annually in Oct

Austin Gay & Lesbian International Film Festival, see aGLIFF-The Austin Gay & Lesbian International Film Festival

Avatar Award
Media Financial Management Association (MFM)
550 W Frontage Rd, Suite 3600, Northfield, IL 60093
Tel: 847-716-7000 *Fax:* 847-716-7004
E-mail: info@mediafinance.org
Web Site: www.mediafinance.org

Key Personnel
MFM/BCCA Pres & CEO: Mary M Collins
    E-mail: mary.collins@mediafinance.org
Dir of Opers, MFM/BCCA: Jamie L Grande
Categories: Broadcast/Cable industry
Closing Date: Dec 31
Presented: Annual Conference, May

Banff Mountain Film & Book Festival
The Banff Centre
107 Tunnel Mountain Dr, Banff, AB T1L 1H5, Canada
Mailing Address: PO Box 1020, Sta 43, Banff, AB T1L 1H5, Canada
Tel: 403-762-6347; 403-762-6369
    Toll Free Tel: 800-298-1229 *Fax:* 403-762-6277
E-mail: banffmountainfestival@banffcentre.ca;
    banffmountainfilms@banffcentre.ca
Web Site: www.banffcentre.ca/banff-mountain-film-and-book-festival
Key Personnel
Festival Dir: Deb Smythe
Mktg Offr: Nicky Lynch *Tel:* 403-762-6496
    E-mail: nicky_lynch@banffcentre.ca
Film Coord: Christie Pashby *Tel:* 403-762-6441
Established: 1976
Festival is presented over 9 days each fall. Film entries can be of any duration in either narrative, story, animated or experimental-art form. Submissions accepted by professional or amateur filmmakers.
Media: Submissions: Low resolution pre-screener file, H.264 in either .mov or .mp4 format; Finalist masters: Avid DNxHD or Apple ProRes 422 at 1920x1080i/p or 1280x720p, in .mov or .mfx wrapper
Categories: Climbing, mountain sports, snow sports, mountain culture, exploration & adventure, mountain environment & natural history
Award: Film Competition: Cash Award $2,000; Grand Prize $4,000
Closing Date: Aug 3
Entry Fee: $60
Presented: Fall

Banff World Media Festival
Brunico Communications Ltd
100-366 Adelaide St W, Toronto, ON M5V 1R9, Canada
Tel: 416-408-2300 *Toll Free Tel:* 888-287-2279
    Fax: 416-408-0870
E-mail: info@achillesmedia.com
Web Site: banffmediafestival.com
Key Personnel
Dir, Busn Devt: Joel Fecht *E-mail:* jfecht@brunico.com
Dir, Mktg: Scott Benzie *E-mail:* sbenzie@brunico.com
Established: 1979
World's largest gathering of entertainment & digital media executives dedicated to media content production, broadcast & distribution.
Media: International television media programs, interactive media
Presented: The Fairmont Banff Springs Hotel, 405 Spray Ave, Banff, AB, CN, June 14-17, 2020

The Whitman Bassow Award
Overseas Press Club of America
40 W 45 St, New York, NY 10036
Tel: 212-626-9220 *Fax:* 212-626-9210
E-mail: info@opcofamerica.org
Web Site: www.opcofamerica.org
Key Personnel
Exec Dir: Patricia Kranz
Best reporting in any medium on international environmental issues. All entries are submitted online.
Other Sponsor(s): Citi
Award: Certificate & $1,000 check
Closing Date: Annually in late Jan

Entry Fee: $200 per category
Presented: Hotel Mandarin-Oriental, New York, NY, Annually in April

BEA National Scholarships in Broadcasting
Broadcast Education Association (BEA)
Affiliate of National Association of Broadcasters (NAB) (in partnership with)
1771 "N" St NW, Washington, DC 20036-2891
Tel: 202-602-0587 *Fax:* 202-609-9940
E-mail: help@beaweb.org
Web Site: www.beaweb.org
Key Personnel
Exec Dir: Heather Birks *Tel:* 202-602-0584
    E-mail: heather@beaweb.org
Award: Scholarships
Closing Date: Oct

The Robert Spiers Benjamin Award
Overseas Press Club of America
40 W 45 St, New York, NY 10036
Tel: 212-626-9220 *Fax:* 212-626-9210
E-mail: info@opcofamerica.org
Web Site: www.opcofamerica.org
Key Personnel
Exec Dir: Patricia Kranz
Best reporting in any medium on Latin America. All entries are submitted online.
Other Sponsor(s): Didi Hunter
Award: Certificate & $1,000 check
Closing Date: Annually in late Jan
Entry Fee: $200
Presented: Hotel Mandarin-Oriental, New York, NY, Annually in April

Berkeley Video & Film Festival
East Bay Media Center
1939 Addison St, Berkeley, CA 94704
Tel: 510-843-3699
E-mail: maketv@aol.com
Web Site: www.berkeleyvideofilmfest.org
Key Personnel
Festival Dir: Mel Vapour
Established: 1990
Media: DVD or Blu-ray, NTSC format
Categories: Student films, documentaries, features, shorts, animation & experimental
Closing Date: Aug 1
Entry Fee: $40
Presented: East Bay Media Center Performance Space, 1939 Addison St, Berkeley CA, Oct

Best Digital Reporting on International Affairs
Overseas Press Club of America
40 W 45 St, New York, NY 10036
Tel: 212-626-9220 *Fax:* 212-626-9210
E-mail: info@opcofamerica.org
Web Site: www.opcofamerica.org
Key Personnel
Exec Dir: Patricia Kranz
Best story or series of stories using creative & dynamic digital storytelling techniques.
Award: Certificate & $1,000 check
Closing Date: Annually in late Jan
Entry Fee: $200
Presented: Hotel Mandarin-Oriental, New York, NY, Annually in April

The Best of Photojournalism (BOP)
National Press Photographers Association (NPPA)
120 Hooper St, Athens, GA 30602-3018
Tel: 706-542-2506
E-mail: info@nppa.org
Web Site: nppa.org
Key Personnel
Exec Dir: Akili Ramsess *E-mail:* aramsess@nppa.org
Prof Servs Dir: Thomas Kenniff *Tel:* 919-237-1782 *E-mail:* tkenniff@nppa.org
Established: 1947

World's leading annual photojournalism contest. Open to professional photographers, editors & online photojournalists. No entry fee. NPPA membership is not required, but encouraged, in order to enter. See web site for entry rules & procedures.
Categories: Still, picture editing, multimedia & video
Award: Certificates & plaques
Closing Date: Jan (video div), Feb (still, photo editing & multimedia div)
Presented: Annual Summit, June

Big Muddy Film Festival
Southern Illinois University at Carbondale, Department of Cinema & Photography
1100 Lincoln Dr, Rm 1101, Carbondale, IL 62901-6610
Tel: 618-453-8301
E-mail: info@bigmuddyfilm.com
Web Site: www.bigmuddyfilm.com
Key Personnel
Chair & Dir: Caleb Bunn
Exec Dir: Hassan Pitts
Established: 1978
The festival showcases all independent films & while it emphasizes the experimental & documentary filmmaker, the festival also includes narrative & feature length works. The festival provides an opportunity for filmmakers to compete & gain recognition for their work. Among the monetary awards is the newly established John Michaels Memorial Film Award, presented to the best work entered in the Big Muddy Film Festival that promotes human rights, peace & justice topics or environmental issues.
Other Sponsor(s): Illinois Arts Council
Media: Submissions: DVD/Blu-ray, .MOV Quicktime or online screener; Screening: DVD/Blu-ray or .MOV Quicktime
Categories: Animation, documentary, experimental, narrative
Award: $4,000 cash & certificate
Closing Date: Aug (early), Sept (regular), Oct (late)
Entry Fee: $20-$45
Presented: Feb

Black Maria Film Festival
Thomas A Edison Media Arts Consortium Inc
c/o New Jersey City University, Dept of Media Arts, 2039 Kennedy Blvd, Jersey City, NJ 07305
Tel: 201-200-2043 *Fax:* 201-200-3490
E-mail: info@blackmariafilmfestival.org
Web Site: www.blackmariafilmfestival.org
Key Personnel
Exec Dir: Jane Steuerwald *E-mail:* jane@blackmariafilmfestival.org
Established: 1981
International juried film competition with a focus on short films. The festival's touring collection addresses topics such as the environment, public health, climate change, substance abuse, gun violence, sustainability, immigration, people with disabilities & LGBTQ issues.
Other Sponsor(s): New Jersey City University; New Jersey State Council on the Arts; The Edison Foundations; The Hudson County Office of Cultural Affairs & Tourism
Media: MOV or MP4 file, download link, or USB thumb drive (if mailed)
Categories: Animation, documentary, experimental, narrative
Award: Cash & certificate
Closing Date: July (early), Oct (late)
Entry Fee: $40 early; $50 late
Presented: Festival tours nationally

Blue Ocean Film Festival & Conservation Summit
646 Second Ave S, St Petersburg, FL 33701

Tel: 727-388-6682
E-mail: info@blueoceanfilmfestival.org; entries@
blueoceanfilmfestival.org
Web Site: www.blueoceanfilmfestival.org
Key Personnel
Co-Founder & CEO: Deborah Kinder
Co-Founder & COO: Charles Kinder
Seven-day event honoring the best in ocean filmmaking. Over 100 finalist films are screened
& recognized for achieving excellence in more
than 20 award categories.
See web site for film entry form for competition.
Categories: Broadcast program, broadcast series,
children's program, cinematography, documentary feature program, educational non-broadcast
program, emerging filmmaker program, marine animal behavior program, marine sciences
program, marine history, archaeology & anthropological perspectives, music, narrative feature
program, ocean exploration & adventure program, ocean sports, ocean issues, people & the
sea & cultural connections program, short program, student program
Closing Date: May (early), June (regular), July
(late), Aug (extended)
Entry Fee: Student: $10 (early), $15 (regular),
$20 (late), $30 (extended); Shorts: $30 (early),
$40 (regular), $60 (late), $75 (extended); Stan-
dard: $65 (early), $80 (regular), $100 (late),
$105 (extended)
Presented: Biennially in Nov, even-numbered
years

The Brainwash Movie Festival

1675 Seventh St, No 23302, Oakland, CA 94623-
6009
Tel: 510-836-3210
E-mail: brainwash.movies@gmail.com
Web Site: www.brainwashm.com
Key Personnel
Festival Founder & Contact: Shelby Toland
E-mail: shelbytoland@yahoo.com
Festival Dir: Dave Krzysik
Established: 1995
Shorts are under 13 minutes, features are under
130 minutes. Movies 13-59 minutes are shorts
& 60-129 minutes are features.
Other Sponsor(s): InkTip; Jungle Software
Media: Region 1 or 0 DVD, MP4
Award: Gorilla Software, Story-O & prize pack-
age from InkTip (3 winners)
Closing Date: Jan 15 (extra early), March 15
(early), May 1 (regular), May 11 (late), May
21 (extended)
Entry Fee: Shorts $20, Features $40 (extra early);
Shorts $25, Features $50 (early); Shorts $30,
Features $65 (regular); Shorts $40, Features
$90 (late); Shorts $50, Features $100 (ex-
tended)
Presented: Nimby, 8410 Amelia St, Oakland, CA,
Annually in July

Bronze Anvil Awards

The Public Relations Society of America Inc
(PRSA)
120 Wall St, 21st fl, New York, NY 10005-4024
Tel: 212-460-1438
E-mail: awards@prsa.org
Web Site: www.prsa.org; anvils.prsa.org
Key Personnel
VP, Spec Events & Progs: Karla Voth
E-mail: karla.voth@prsa.org
Recognize the best in public relations tactics—
the use of social media, video, blogs, podcasts,
annual reports, digital newsletters, web sites—
that contribute to the success of overall pro-
grams or campaigns. See web site for list of 32
categories. Winner recognized in *Strategies and
Tactics.*
Award: Trophy
Closing Date: March
Entry Fee: $225 membs, $325 nonmembs (early);
$325 membs, $425 nonmembs (final/late)

Brooklyn Film Festival (BFF)

Brooklyn Film Society
180 S Fourth St, Suite 2-S, Brooklyn, NY 11211
Tel: 718-388-4306 *Fax:* 718-599-5039
E-mail: festival@wbff.org
Web Site: www.brooklynfilmfestival.org
Key Personnel
Exec Dir: Marco Ursino *E-mail:* marco@wbff.org
Dir, Devt: Susan E Mackell *E-mail:* susan@wbff.
org
Established: 1998
Best in each category, best of festival & others.
Media: Secure online screener or DVD
Categories: Narrative feature, documentary fea-
ture, narrative short, documentary short, experi-
mental & animation
Award: $50,000 in services, products & cash
Closing Date: Nov 30 (early), Jan 27 (regular),
Feb 17 (late), March 10 (extended)
Entry Fee: $60 early; $75 regular; $80 late; $95
extended
Presented: Brooklyn, NY, May 29-June 7, 2020

Heywood Broun Award

The NewsGuild - CWA
501 Third St NW, 6th fl, Washington, DC 20001-
2797
Tel: 202-434-7177
E-mail: guild@cwa-union.org
Web Site: www.newsguild.org
Annual competition to encourage & recognize
individual journalistic achievement by members of the working media, particularly if it
helps right a wrong or correct an injustice. No
application. Faxed & e-mailed entries are not
accepted. See web site for eligibility & requirements.
Categories: Professional journalism
Award: $5,000 plus 2 awards of $1,000 for entries of substantial distinction
Closing Date: Jan
Entry Fee: None

James W Brown Publication Award

Association for Educational Communications and
Technology (AECT)
320 W Eighth St, Suite 101, Bloomington, IN
47404-3745
Tel: 812-335-7675 *Toll Free Tel:* 877-677-AECT
(677-2328) *Fax:* 812-335-7678
E-mail: aect@aect.org
Web Site: www.aect.org
Key Personnel
Exec Dir: Dr Phillip Harris *E-mail:* pharris@aect.
org
Nominations are restricted to published books,
including ebooks, in the field of educational
technology bearing a publication date no later
than 5 years prior to the year of the award.
Categories: Educational technology
Award: $100 & plaque
Closing Date: Aug 15
Entry Fee: None
Presented: AECT Annual Convention, Oct/Nov

Buffalo Niagara International Film Festival (BNIFF)

3840 E Robinson Rd, Suite 166, Amherst, NY
14228
Tel: 716-693-0912
E-mail: info@bniff.com
Web Site: thebnff.com
Key Personnel
Founder & Press: Bill Cowell *E-mail:* bcowell@
thebnff.com
Dir, Programming: Alex Chionetti
Tech Dir: Rob Imbs *E-mail:* robi@
buffaloniagarafilmfestival.com;
Charles Quinniey *E-mail:* charlesq@
buffaloniagarafilmfestival.com
Established: 2007

A filmmaker's festival. Hosted by filmmakers &
screenwriters for filmmakers & screenwriters. Film entries are accepted in short (under
45 minutes) & feature length (45 minutes or
longer).
Media: DVD (NTSC), 35mm, Blu-ray
Categories: Experimental, animation, documentary, narrative, music video
Award: Trophies & cash
Closing Date: Nov 15 (early), Dec 15 (regular),
Jan 15 (late), Feb 15 (extended), March15 (final)
Entry Fee: $45 early; $50 regular; $55 late; $60
extended; $100 final
Presented: Buffalo, NY/Niagara Falls, NY, June

Calgary International Film Festival

Calgary International Film Festival (CIFF)
214 11 Ave SE, Unit 207, Calgary, AB T2G 0X8,
Canada
Tel: 403-283-1490
E-mail: info@calgaryfilm.com
Web Site: www.calgaryfilm.com
Key Personnel
Exec Dir: Steve Schroeder
Established: 1999
Audience Awards presented include Best Docu-
mentary Feature, Best First Documentary Fea-
ture (Discovery Award), Best Narrative Fea-
ture, Best First Narrative Feature (Discovery
Award), Best Documentary Short Film, Best
Narrative Short Film. Juried Awards include:
Best Overall Short, Best Documentary Short,
Alberta Spirit Short, Youth By Youth Cinema
(4 awards for students).
Media: Online links
Categories: Genres include animation, art-house,
Asian, Black, comedy, documentary, drama, experimental, gay & lesbian, historical, humor,
independent, Jewish, music video, national, religious, romance, science fiction, short, silent,
student, thriller & women. Series: Galas, head-
liners, Canadian, new American, world, documentaries, music on screen, late shows, shorts
Closing Date: June
Entry Fee: Feature films (60 minutes & over):
$40 early, $55 regular, $70 late; Short films (30
minutes & under): $25 early, $35 regular, $50
late; fees waived for AB filmmakers; USD only
for FilmFreeway
Presented: Calgary, AB, CN, Annually end of
Sept for 12 days

California Independent Film Festival (CAIFF)

CAIFF Association
350 Park St, Moraga, CA 94566
Tel: 925-388-0752
E-mail: info@caiff.org
Web Site: caiff.org
Key Personnel
Pres & Founder: Derek Zemrak *E-mail:* derek@
caiff.org
Exec Dir: Leonard Pirkle *E-mail:* leonard@caiff.
org
VP: Joanne Foy *E-mail:* joanne@caiff.org
Festival Dir: Lindsay Pirkle
Established: 1997
Annual festival & premier showcase for inde-
pendent, foreign & mainstream films. Includes
Slate Award, screenplay competition & Iron
Filmmaker contest.
Presented: Multiple theatres

Canadian Screen Awards

Academy of Canadian Cinema & Television
(ACCT)
49 Ontario St, Suite 501, Toronto, ON M5A 2V1,
Canada
Tel: 416-366-2227 *Toll Free Tel:* 800-644-5194
Fax: 416-366-8454
E-mail: awards@academy.ca; info@academy.ca
Web Site: www.academy.ca/canadian-screen-
awards

Key Personnel
CEO: Beth Janson *Tel:* 416-366-2227 ext 240
  E-mail: beth@academy.ca
Dir, Awards & Spec Events: Louis Calabro
  Tel: 416-366-2227 ext 234 *E-mail:* louis@
  academy.ca
Sr Programming Coord: Marko Balaban *Tel:* 416-
  366-2227 ext 246 *E-mail:* marko@academy.ca
Recognize excellence in Canadian film, television
  & digital media.
Media: Streaming video & DVDs
Award: Statuette
Closing Date: Aug (TV & digital media), Sept
  (news/sports), Oct (film)
Entry Fee: See web site for complete entry fee
  information
Presented: March

Canadian Student Film Festival
Montreal World Film Festival
1432 de Bleury St, Montreal, QC H3A 2J1,
  Canada
Tel: 514-848-3883 *Fax:* 514-848-3886
E-mail: program@ffm-montreal.org; info@ffm-
  montreal.org
Web Site: www.ffm-montreal.org
Key Personnel
Contact: Ubavka Ferzanovic
Norman McLaren Award (Best Film) $10,000,
  Jury Award (Best New Director), honorable
  mentions.
Media: Submissions: Blu-ray, DVD or link with
  password; Screening: ProRes422, DCP, Blu-ray
  zone free, DVD
Categories: Fiction, documentary, animation, ex-
  perimental
Award: Cash, certificate
Closing Date: June 10
Entry Fee: $50 per film
Presented: Montreal, QC, CN, Aug

The Robert Capa Gold Medal Award
Overseas Press Club of America
40 W 45 St, New York, NY 10036
Tel: 212-626-9220 *Fax:* 212-626-9210
E-mail: info@opcofamerica.org
Web Site: www.opcofamerica.org
Key Personnel
Exec Dir: Patricia Kranz
Best published photographic reporting from
  abroad requiring exceptional courage & en-
  terprise.
Other Sponsor(s): Time Magazine
Award: Certificate & $1,000 check
Closing Date: Annually in late Jan
Entry Fee: $200
Presented: Hotel Mandarin-Oriental, New York,
  NY, Annually in April

Capacity Building Grant Program
Arts & Cultural Council for Greater Rochester
31 Prince St, Rochester, NY 14607
Tel: 585-473-4000 *Fax:* 585-473-4051
E-mail: communications@artsrochester.org
Web Site: artsrochester.org
Key Personnel
Grants Coord: Ann C Salter *Tel:* 585-473-4000
  ext 2 *E-mail:* asalter@artsrochester.org
Funds nonprofit arts & cultural organizations with
  annual operating budgets at or below $500,000
  located in Genesee, Livingston, Monroe, On-
  tario, Orleans, Seneca, Wayne & Yates coun-
  ties.
Other Sponsor(s): Rochester Area Community
  Foundation
Award: $500-$4,000
Closing Date: Jan 15

Chester F Carlson Award
Society for Imaging Science and Technology
  (IS&T)
7003 Kilworth Lane, Springfield, VA 22151

Tel: 703-642-9090 *Fax:* 703-642-9094
E-mail: info@imaging.org
Web Site: imaging.org
Key Personnel
Exec Dir: Suzanne E Grinnan *E-mail:* sgrinnan@
  imaging.org
Exec Asst: Donna Smith *E-mail:* dsmith@
  imaging.org
Established: 1985
Recognizes outstanding technical work that ad-
  vances the state of the art in electrophoto-
  graphic printing.
Other Sponsor(s): Xerox Corp
Award: $1,000 & engraved plaque
Closing Date: Annually, Oct 1

Celebration of Service to America Awards
National Association of Broadcasters Education
  Foundation (NABEF)
1771 "N" St NW, Washington, DC 20036-2891
Tel: 202-421-3191
E-mail: nabef@nab.org
Web Site: www.nabef.org
Key Personnel
Mktg & Events Mgr: Michelle Abanez
  E-mail: mabanez@nab.org
Established: 1999
Annual awards to honor the outstanding public
  service commitment of local television & radio
  broadcasters.
Media: Radio & television
Categories: Service to Community Award for
  Television: Ownership group, large market,
  medium market & small market; Service to
  Community Award for Radio: Major market,
  medium market, small market
Award: Eagle trophy
Closing Date: March
Presented: Washington, DC, June

Chicago International Children's Film Festival
Facets Multi-Media Inc
1517 W Fullerton Ave, Chicago, IL 60614
Tel: 773-281-9075 (ext 3011) *Fax:* 773-929-0266
E-mail: filmreg@facets.org; press@facets.org
Web Site: festival.facets.org
Key Personnel
Founder: Milos Stehlik
Educ Dir: Kathleen Beckman *Tel:* 773-281-9075
  ext 109 *E-mail:* kids@facets.org
Festival Dir: Ann Vikstrom *Tel:* 773-281-9075 ext
  102 *E-mail:* annv@facets.org
Mktg Dir: Paul Gonter *Tel:* 773-281-9075 ext 106
  E-mail: paul@facets.org
Festival Registrar: Sophie Gordon
Established: 1984
Represents the very best in international chil-
  dren's video, film & television programs.
Media: Submissions: DVD or Blu-ray (NTSC Re-
  gion 0 or 1), media files; Exhibition: DVD or
  Blu-ray (NTSC Region 0 or 1), DCP, media
  files
Categories: Animated feature, animated short, an-
  imated TV, documentary feature, documentary
  short, live-action feature, live-action short, live-
  action TV
Award: Plaque, certificate & cash
Closing Date: May 1 (early), May 31 (late)
Entry Fee: $40 shorts (under 40 minutes); $80
  features (40 minutes or longer); $60 shorts,
  $100 features (late entries)
Presented: Facets Multi-Media & other Chicago
  venues, Chicago, IL, Oct/Nov

Chicago International Film Festival
Cinema/Chicago
212 W Van Buren St, Suite 400, Chicago, IL
  60607
Tel: 312-683-0121 *Fax:* 312-683-0122
E-mail: info@chicagofilmfestival.com; entries@
  chicagofilmfestival.com
Web Site: www.chicagofilmfestival.com

Key Personnel
Mng Dir: Vivian Teng *E-mail:* vteng@
  chicagofilmfestival.com
Artistic Dir: Mimi Plauche
Competitions Coord: Sam Flancher
Established: 1964
Media: Submissions: Online screener, DVD or
  Blu-ray (features); DVD, Blu-ray or online
  video link (shorts)
Categories: Feature length narratives, feature
  length documentaries, short subjects (under
  40 minutes)
Award: Gold & silver "Hugos," gold & silver
  plaques, certificates of merit
Closing Date: Annually in April (early), June
  (regular), July (late)
Entry Fee: Feature narrative $90 early, $100 regular, $200 late; Feature documentary $70 early,
  $80 regular, $150 late; Short subjects $40 early,
  $50 regular, $70 late; Student film feature $40
  early, $50 regular, $80 late; Student film short
  $20 early, $30 regular, $50 late
Presented: Annually in Oct

**Chicago International REEL Shorts Film
Festival**
Project Chicago
2700 W Grand Ave, Chicago, IL 60612
E-mail: info@projectchicago.com
Web Site: www.projectchicago.com
Key Personnel
Co-Dir: Nels Dahlquist *E-mail:* nels@
  projectchicago.com; Scott Rudolph
  E-mail: scott@projectchicago.com
Dir, Submissions: Dan Christofano *E-mail:* dc@
  projectchicago.com
Established: 2003
Media: Submissions: DVD (NTSC); Exhibition:
  MP4
Categories: Short film narrative (any genre), short
  film documentary (any subject), short film
  youth, music video, TV pilot/web series/ film-
  TV trailer
Closing Date: March 31 (early), May 31 (regu-
  lar), July 31 (late), Sept 30 (extended)
Entry Fee: $20 early; $30 regular; $40 late; $50
  extended
Presented: Chicago, IL, Annually in Autumn

Chicago Irish Film Festival (CIFF)
c/o Society for Arts, 1112 N Milwaukee Ave,
  Chicago, IL 60642
Tel: 773-486-9612 *Fax:* 773-486-9613
Web Site: www.chicagoirishfilmfestival.com
Key Personnel
Festival Dir: Jude Blackburn *E-mail:* jude@
  chicagoirishfilmfestival.com
Established: 2000
Entries must be submitted online or on DVD. See
  web site for details.
Other Sponsor(s): Consulate General of Ireland;
  Film Ireland; IFTN; Irish American News; Irish
  Film Board; Irish Film Institute; Network Ire-
  land Television; Northern Ireland Screen
Media: Blu-ray Region Free, DCP, Digital Betz
  NTSC. HDCAM
Categories: Features, shorts, animation, documen-
  taries, Indie, experimental
Entry Fee: None
Presented: Annually in March

Chicago Latino Film Festival
The International Latino Cultural Center
55 W Van Buren St, Suite 310, Chicago, IL
  60605
Tel: 312-431-1330
E-mail: info@latinoculturalcenter.org
Web Site: www.chicagolatinofilmfestival.org
Key Personnel
Founder & Exec Dir: Pepe Vargas
Dir, Devt & Mktg: Lourdes Resto
Opers Mgr: Maria Lopez

Established: 1985
Media: Submissions: Online
Closing Date: Annually in Dec
Entry Fee: $50 feature; $30 short
Presented: Chicago, IL, Annually in April

Chicago South Asian Film Festival (CSAFF)
Chicago South Asian Arts Council Inc
2909 N Sheridan Rd, Unit 1902, Chicago, IL
60657
Tel: 773-669-8348
E-mail: info@csaff.org; programming@csaff.org
Web Site: www.csaff.org
Key Personnel
Festival Dir: Archana Jain
Festival Coord: Monika Sharma
Established: 2010
Categories: Features, shorts, midwest filmmakers,
student filmmakers, Chicago student filmmak-
ers
Closing Date: July (early), Aug (regular), Sept
(late)
Entry Fee: $50 feature, $35 other (regular); $70
feature, $50 other (late)
Presented: Downtown Chicago, IL, Oct

Chicago Underground Film Festival (CUFF)
IFP Chicago
2558 W 16 St, Stage 18, Chicago, IL 60608
Tel: 773-998-1082
E-mail: info@cuff.org; publicity@cuff.org
Web Site: cuff.org
Key Personnel
Artistic Dir: Bryan Wendorf *E-mail:* bryan@cuff.
org
Commus Dir: Kristi Kucera
Festival Coord: JC Farris *E-mail:* coordinator@
ifpchicago.org
Established: 1993
Annual event showcasing independent, experi-
mental & documentary films from around the
world.
Media: Submissions: Secure online screener; Ex-
hibition: DCP
Categories: Narrative feature, narrative short, doc-
umentary feature, documentary short, music
video, experimental/avant garde short, anima-
tion short, experimental/avant garde feature,
animation feature
Closing Date: Oct (early), Dec (regular), Jan
(late)
Entry Fee: Early: Features $35 (students $25);
Shorts $30 (students $20). Regular: Features
$45 (students $35); Shorts $35 (students $25).
Late: Features $55 (students $45); Shorts $40
(students $30)
Presented: Annually in June

CINDY Awards
IAA-VC (International Association of Audio Vi-
sual Communicators)
3824 Trogdon Ct, Flower Mound, TX 75022-
5326
Mailing Address: PO Box 270779, Flower
Mound, TX 75027-0779
Tel: 469-464-4180 *Fax:* 469-464-4170
Web Site: cindys.com
Key Personnel
Exec Dir: Phillip N Shuey *E-mail:* phillip@
cindys.com
Established: 1959
Two international & 12 regional awards events
presented annually recognizing digital media
producers & their work. A wide variety of me-
dia formats, content applications & categories
are represented.
Media: Web sites, video, audio, webinars, apps,
live events & others
Categories: Documentaries, educational, commer-
cials, training, student, public relations & more
Award: Certificates & plaques

Closing Date: 12 regional: April-Nov; 2 intl:
March 31 & Sept 30
Entry Fee: AV: $90 membs, $130 nonmembs; Au-
dio only: $70 membs, $100 nonmembs; Tech-
nical & artistic: $80 membs, $110 nonmembs
Presented: Trade show events

Cine Las Americas International Film Festival (CLAIFF)
Cine Las Americas
1104 W 34 St, No 625, Austin, TX 78705
Tel: 512-535-0765
E-mail: cine@cinelasamericas.org; entries@
cinelasamericas.org
Web Site: cinelasamericas.org; www.facebook.
com/cinelasamericasaustin
Key Personnel
Festival Dir: Jean Anne Lauer
Tech Dir: Francisco Garcia
Film Prog Assoc: Elena Bessire
Membership & Community Outreach Coord: Julia
McMahan
Film Prog Asst: Rebecca Morelo Jackson
Established: 1998
Other Sponsor(s): American Airlines; City of
Austin; LatinWorks; Texas Commission on the
Arts
Media: Submissions: DVD or Blu-ray (NTSC Re-
gion 1 or 0)
Categories: First or second dramatic feature, doc-
umentary feature, dramatic short, documentary
short, panorama (non-competitive), youth film,
original music video
Closing Date: Jan 13 (regular), Feb 1 (late &
youth films)
Entry Fee: $35 regular; $75 late; no fee for youth
films; Students/NALIP membs: $25 regular,
$50 late
Presented: Austin, TX, Annually in May

Cine-World Film Festival
Sarasota Film Society Inc (SFS)
10715 Rodeo Dr, Suite 8, Lakewood Ranch, FL
34202
Tel: 941-364-8478 *Fax:* 941-364-8478
E-mail: mail@filmsociety.org
Web Site: www.filmsociety.org
Key Personnel
Exec Dir: Barbara Caras *Tel:* 941-364-8662 ext
2011 *E-mail:* barbara@filmsociety.org
Mng Dir: Nick Caras *Tel:* 941-364-8662 ext 2006
E-mail: nick@filmsociety.org
Mktg Dir: Joshua Goodnough
Established: 2006
Media: DVD, DCP
Presented: Burns Court Cinemas, Sarasota, FL,
Nov

Cinema in Industry Awards, see CINDY
Awards

Cinequest Film & VR Festival (CQFF)
Cinequest
PO Box 720040, San Jose, CA 95172-0040
Tel: 408-295-FEST (295-3378); 408-995-5033
(off) *Fax:* 408-995-5713
E-mail: contact@cinequest.org
Web Site: www.cinequest.org
Key Personnel
Pres & Co-Founder: Kathleen Powell
Dir, CEO & Co-Founder: Halfdan Hussey
Programming Dir: Mike Rabehl
Media: Submission: Secure online screener, DVD,
Blu-ray; Exhibition: Blu-ray, DCP
Categories: Narrative feature film (dramatic, new
visions & global landscapes), documentary fea-
ture film, short film, high school film, college
short film, virtual reality
Entry Fee: Varies
Presented: San Jose, CA, Annually in Feb/March

The Citation of Outstanding Service to the Society Award
Society of Motion Picture & Television Engi-
neers® (SMPTE®)
White Plains Plaza, 445 Hamilton Ave, Suite 601,
White Plains, NY 10601-1827
Tel: 914-761-1100 *Fax:* 914-206-4216
E-mail: marketing@smpte.org
Web Site: www.smpte.org
Key Personnel
Exec Dir: Barbara H Lange *Tel:* 914-205-2370
Dir, Events & Governance Liaison: Sally-Ann
D'Amato *Tel:* 914-205-2375 *E-mail:* sdamato@
smpte.org
Mktg & Commun: Aimee Ricca *Tel:* 914-205-
2381 *E-mail:* aimeericca@smpte.org
Exec Asst: June Marie Sobrito *Tel:* 914-205-2384
E-mail: jsobrito@smpte.org
Recognizes dedicated service to the society over a
sustained period of time.
Closing Date: Annually in April
Presented: SMPTE® Annual Technical Confer-
ence & Exhibition, Loews Hollywood Hotel,
Hollywood, CA, Annually in Oct

Clarion Awards
The Association for Women in Communications
(AWC)
1717 E Republic Rd, Suite A, Springfield, MO
65804
Tel: 417-886-8606 *Fax:* 417-886-3685
E-mail: clarion@womcom.org
Web Site: www.womcom.org
Established: 1972
Honors excellence in more than 100 categories
across all communications disciplines.
Categories: Advertising & marketing; books,
brochures, custom & special publications; edu-
cation; fund development; magazines; newslet-
ters; newspapers; online media; photography &
graphics; public relations; radio; special events;
student; television
Award: Crystal awards
Closing Date: Feb (early), April (regular)
Entry Fee: Early: $70 membs, $30 student
membs, $90 nonmembs; Regular: $85 membs,
$30 student membs, $120 nonmembs; discounts
for multiple entries
Presented: National Conference, Annually in Fall

Cleveland International Film Festival
Cleveland Film Society
2510 Market Ave, Cleveland, OH 44113-3434
Tel: 216-623-3456 *Fax:* 216-623-0103
E-mail: cfs@clevelandfilm.org; submissions@
clevelandfilm.org
Web Site: www.clevelandfilm.org
Key Personnel
Exec Dir: Marcie Goodman *E-mail:* marcie@
clevelandfilm.org
Artistic Dir: Bill Guentzler *E-mail:* bill@
clevelandfilm.org
Dir, Programming & Projection: Mallory Martin
E-mail: mallory@clevelandfilm.org
Mktg & Media Dir: Debby Samples
E-mail: debby@clevelandfilm.org
Membership Dir & Opers Mgr: Debbie Marshall
E-mail: marshall@clevelandfilm.org
Spec Progs Dir: Beth Steele Radisek
E-mail: beth@clevelandfilm.org
Assoc Dir: Patrick Shepherd *E-mail:* patrick@
clevelandfilm.org
Devt Mgr: Allie Freeman *E-mail:* allie@
clevelandfilm.org
Established: 1977
Annual festival promoting artistically & cultur-
ally significant film arts through education &
exhibition to enrich the life of the community.
Media: Online screener only
Award: $1,000-$15,000
Closing Date: July 31 (early), Dec (final)

Entry Fee: Features: $70-$125; Shorts, music videos & web series: $50-$105; New Media: Free
Presented: Tower City Cinemas, Cleveland, OH, March 25-April 5, 2020

The Clio Awards
Clio Awards LLC
825 Eighth Ave, 29th fl, New York, NY 10019
Tel: 212-683-4300
E-mail: event@clioawards.com
Web Site: clios.com
Key Personnel
Pres: Nicole Purcell
VP, Mktg: Brooke Levy
Exec Dir, Prog Mgmt & Devt: Emily Seal
Sr Dir, Opers: Marissa Piper
Assoc Dir, Mktg: Catherine Amelio
Assoc Dir, Prog Mgmt & Devt: Ashley Falls
Established: 1959
Celebrates creative excellence & innovation in advertising, design & communications.
Media: JPEG, mp4, PDF, mp3 & URL. No CDs or DVDs are accepted
Categories: Audio, audio technique, brand design, branded content, branded entertainment, digital/mobile, digital/mobile & social media technique, direct, events/experiential, film, film technique, innovation, integrated campaign, out of home, partnerships & collaborations, print, print & out of home technique, product design, public relations, social media, student work
Award: Gold, silver & bronze statues
Closing Date: Late June
Entry Fee: $5-$1,150. See web site for breakdown of fees & charges
Presented: Annual Clio Awards Festival, Sept

Columbus International Film + Video Festival
Columbus College of Art & Design
60 Cleveland Ave, Columbus, OH 43215
Tel: 614-222-6185
E-mail: info@columbusfilmfestival.org
Web Site: www.ccad.edu/experience-art/columbus-international-film-festival
Key Personnel
Exec Dir: Jeremy Henthorn
Festival Programmer: John Beattie
Established: 1952
Showcases independent student & professional films.
Other Sponsor(s): Ohio Arts Council
Media: Secure online screener or secure Vimeo or Youtube link preferred. Also accept DVD (Region 0 or 1)
Categories: Student, animation, narrative feature, promotional/industrial, documentary feature, documentary short, new media/experimental, narrative short
Closing Date: Oct 30 (early), Nov 17 (regular), Dec 17 (late), Jan 8 (extended)
Entry Fee: $25-$80, varies by category & deadline
Presented: April

Communication Arts Visual Communications Competition
Communication Arts Magazine
Affiliate of Coyne & Blanchard Inc
110 Constitution Dr, Menlo Park, CA 94025
Tel: 650-326-6040 *Fax:* 650-326-1648
E-mail: competition@commarts.com
Web Site: www.commarts.com
Key Personnel
Competition Coord: Lauren Coyne
Established: 1960
Media: Digital images: RGB or JPG format; Video & motion/animation entries: MOV, MP4 or MPG format; Audio entries: MP3, WAVE or AIFF files; Web-based entries: Common web browser; Downloadable apps: Apple App Store or Google Play URL only

Categories: Illustration, photography, design, advertising, interactive, typography
Award: Winners will be published in one of our annuals, as well as receiving an Award of Excellence trophy
Closing Date: Varies by category
Entry Fee: Varies by category

Creative Arts Film Festival (CAFF)
PO Box 823, Malvern, PA 19355
Tel: 610-889-4928
E-mail: creativeartsfilmfestival@gmail.com
Web Site: www.creativeartsfilmfestival.com
Key Personnel
Festival Dir: Connie Spielberg
Established: 2011
Online international short film festival that promotes filmmakers.
Media: Online link or DVD (NTSC Region 0 or 1), 60 minutes maximum
Categories: Action adventure, animated, documentary, dramatic, experimental, fantasy, horror, science fiction, thriller
Award: Perfect Spirit Film Awards, free promotional listings & cash prizes
Closing Date: April 15 (early), June 15 (regular), July 31 (late), Aug 31 (filmmaker hospitality), Sept 15 (filmmaker appreciation), Sept 30 (extended)
Entry Fee: $35 early; $45 regular; $55 late; $60 filmmaker hospitality; $65 filmmaker appreciation; $115 extended
Presented: Annually the entire month of Dec

Creative Impulse Awards (Impies)
Creative Impulse Group
c/o RIIFF, 36 Rhode Island Ave, Newport, RI 02840
Mailing Address: c/o RIIFF, PO Box 162, Newport, RI 02840-0002
Tel: 401-861-4445 *Fax:* 401-490-6735
E-mail: info@film-festival.org
Web Site: www.film-festival.org/CreativeIM.php
Key Personnel
Exec Dir/CEO: George T Marshall
E-mail: georget@film-festival.org
Prog Dir: Shawn Quirk *E-mail:* quirk@film-festival.org
Foil stamped certificate.
Media: Video/Film materials: DVD NTSC; Print materials: no specific requirements, except that an English translation must accompany foreign language entries; Audio entries: CD or DAT; Web site entries: CD or provide URL
Award: Silver & Gold
Closing Date: Annually in May
Entry Fee: $35
Presented: Rhode Island International Film Festival (RIIFF)

CSC Awards
Canadian Society of Cinematographers (CSC)
131-3007 Kingston Rd, Toronto, ON M1M 1P1, Canada
Tel: 416-266-0591 *Fax:* 416-266-3996
E-mail: admin@csc.ca
Web Site: www.csc.ca
Key Personnel
Exec Offr: Susan Saranchuk
Awards Chair: Alwyn Kumst
Established: 1957
Cinematography competition in 15 categories.
Media: 35mm, DCP, QuickTime/ProRes
Closing Date: Jan 31
Entry Fee: $101.70-$113 membs; $135.60-$146.90 nonmembs; $28.25 student; no fee for camera assistant category
Presented: CSC Awards Gala, Toronto, ON, CN, Annually in Spring

Cucalorus Film Festival
Jengo's Playhouse, 815 Princess St, Wilmington, NC 28401
Tel: 910-343-5995
E-mail: programming@cucalorus.org; press@cucalorus.org; comm@cucalorus.org
Web Site: www.cucalorus.org
Key Personnel
Dir: Dan Brawley
Commans Dir: Becca Ederer
Programming Dir: Rachel Taylor
Established: 1994
Non-competitive.
Media: Online screener
Categories: Documentary features, narrative features, shorts, shorts blocks
Closing Date: Annually in May (early), June (regular), July (late), Aug (extended)
Entry Fee: $25 early; $35 regular; $45 late; $55 extended
Presented: Wilmington, NC, Annually in Nov

Dailey & Vincent LandFest in the Mountains
Springer Mountain Farms
1311 Music Hall Rd, Hiawassee, GA 30546
Tel: 706-896-4191
Web Site: www.daileyvincentfest.com
Music festival featuring a lineup of country, bluegrass & gospel music.
Presented: Georgia Mountain Fairgrounds, Hiawassee, GA

Dallas VideoFest Alternative Fiction
Video Association of Dallas (VAD)
1405 Woodlawn Ave, Dallas, TX 75208
Tel: 214-207-7696
E-mail: info@videofest.org
Web Site: www.videofest.org
Key Personnel
Founder & CEO, VAD: Bart Weiss *E-mail:* bart@videofest.org
Mng Dir: Raquel Chapa *E-mail:* raquel@videofest.org
Open to professional & nonprofessional filmmakers working in all genres: documentary, narrative, animation & experimental. All video entries must have been originally produced within the last 2 years +/or post-produced in video or some electronic form. Features are over 25 minutes, shorts are under 25 minutes.
Media: Submissions: Vimeo link; Screening: DCP
Categories: Narrative feature, narrative short, Texas Show, Big D Mobile Phone Fest, television
Award: Trophy & laurel for Best Short, Best Narrative Feature; Audience award for Best of the Texas Show; $150 cash prize for Texas Show
Closing Date: July (early), Aug (regular), Nov (late)
Entry Fee: Narrative feature: $30 early, $35 regular, $55 late; Narrative short & Texas Show: $25 early, $30 regular, $45 late; Big D Mobile Phone Fest & television: $20 early, $28 regular, $30 late
Presented: Annually in Feb

Dallas VideoFest DocuFest
Video Association of Dallas (VAD)
1405 Woodlawn Ave, Dallas, TX 75208
Tel: 214-207-7696
E-mail: info@videofest.org
Web Site: www.videofest.org
Key Personnel
Founder & CEO, VAD: Bart Weiss *E-mail:* bart@videofest.org
Mng Dir: Raquel Chapa *E-mail:* raquel@videofest.org
Media: Vimeo link
Categories: Documentary feature, documentary short

Closing Date: April 27 (early), July 1 (regular), Aug 16 (late)
Entry Fee: $15 standard, $12 student early; $25 standard, $20 student regular; $35 standard, $30 student late

Dance on Camera Festival
Dance Films Association Inc
252 Java St, Suite 333, Brooklyn, NY 11222
Tel: 347-505-8649
E-mail: info@dancefilms.org; festival@dancefilms.org
Web Site: www.dancefilms.org
Key Personnel
Prog Dir: Brighid Greene *E-mail:* brighid@dancefilms.org
Festival Co-Curator: Liz Wolff *E-mail:* liz@dancefilms.org
Established: 1971
Other Sponsor(s): Film Society of Lincoln Center; National Endowment for the Arts (NEA); NY State Council on the Arts; NYC Dept of Cultural Affairs
Media: Online submission
Categories: Documentary, experimental, narrative, short & feature
Closing Date: Annually in Oct
Presented: Film Society of Lincoln Center, New York, NY, Annually in Feb

Dances With Films
Formosa Bldg, 2nd fl, 1041 N Formosa Ave, West Hollywood, CA 90046
Tel: 323-854-8176
E-mail: info@danceswithfilms.com; submissions@danceswithfilms.com
Web Site: www.danceswithfilms.com
Key Personnel
Founder: Leslee Scallon; Michael Trent
Established: 1998
Media: Submissions: Secure online screener, DVD (NTSC) or Blu-ray; Screening: DCP, .MOV
Categories: Narrative feature, documentary feature, narrative short, documentary short, music video, TV pilot-half hour, TV pilot-1 hour, web series pilot
Closing Date: Nov (early), Feb (regular), March (late)
Entry Fee: Feature-length narratives & documentaries over 40 minutes: $55 early, $70 regular, $95 late; Short narratives & documentaries under 40 minutes: $40 early, $50 regular, $75 late; TV pilots & web series pilots: $35 early, $50 regular, $65 late; Music videos: $25
Presented: Hollywood, CA, Annually in June

DC Asian Pacific American Film Festival
Asian Pacific American Film Inc
2515 Virginia Ave NW, No 58205, Washington, DC 20037
Tel: 202-796-9680; 202-792-6393
E-mail: info@apafilm.org; admin@apafilm.org
Web Site: www.apafilm.org
Key Personnel
Exec Dir: Christian Oh *E-mail:* christian@apafilm.org
Assoc Dir: Zhibo Lai *E-mail:* zhibo@apafilm.org
Creative Dir: Andrew Bittan *E-mail:* andrew@apafilm.org
Festival Dir: Paul Marengo *E-mail:* pmarengo@apafilm.org
Filmmaker Hospitality Dir: Judy Go Wong *E-mail:* judy@apafilm.org
Fin Dir: Rong Wang *E-mail:* rong@apafilm.org
Programming Liaison: Rhonda Mendoza
Established: 2000
Feature film, short film, or video productions by Asian Americans & Asian International filmmakers, or with subject matter concerning Asian issues.

Media: Submissions: Secure online screener or digital file; Exhibition: DVD, Blu-ray & digital file
Categories: Narrative/documentary feature, narrative/documentary short
Closing Date: Dec 1 (early), Feb 1 (regular), Feb 15 (late)
Entry Fee: Narrative/documentary feature: $25 early, $35 regular & late; Narrative/documentary short: $15 early, $25 regular & late
Presented: Annually in May

DEC Grants
Arts Mid-Hudson Inc
696 Dutchess Tpke, Suite F, Poughkeepsie, NY 12603
Tel: 845-454-3222
E-mail: info@artsmidhudson.org
Web Site: www.artsmidhudson.org
Key Personnel
Exec Dir: Linda Marston-Reid *E-mail:* lmr@artsmidhudson.org
Dir, Admin: Lisa Fiorese
Dir, Folk Arts Prog: Elinor Levy
Dir, Progs & Art Servs: Merritt Minnemeyer
Grants Assoc: Lilia Perez
Annual award. Some residential restrictions apply. Please see web site for details.
Award: Cash
Entry Fee: None

Denver Film Festival
Denver Film Society
1510 York St, 3rd fl, Denver, CO 80206
Tel: 303-595-3456
E-mail: dff@denverfilm.org
Web Site: denverfilmfestival.denverfilm.org
Key Personnel
Exec Dir: Andrew Rodgers *E-mail:* andrew@denverfilm.org
Artistic Dir: Brit Withey *E-mail:* brit@denverfilm.org
Dir, Devt: Holly Porterfield *E-mail:* holly@denverfilm.org
Dir, Opers: Gina Cuomo *E-mail:* gina@denverfilm.org
Festival Dir: Britta Erickson *E-mail:* britta@denverfilm.org
Mktg Dir: Kevin Smith *E-mail:* kevins@denverfilm.org
Film Programmer: Matthew Campbell *E-mail:* matt@denverfilm.org
Established: 1978
Media: Submissions: DVD screener; Screening: 35mm, Blu-ray, digital file & DCP
Categories: Shorts, contemporary world cinema, documentary, First Look Student Program, screenwriting, music video
Closing Date: April (early), July (regular, late & extended)
Entry Fee: $25-$95
Presented: Sie Film Center, 2510 E Colfax, Denver, CO, Nov

DGA Awards
Directors Guild of America (DGA)
7920 Sunset Blvd, Los Angeles, CA 90046
Tel: 310-289-2038 *Fax:* 310-289-5398
E-mail: awards@dga.org
Web Site: www.dga.org
Key Personnel
Assoc Exec Dir: Sahar Moridani *Tel:* 310-289-5334 *E-mail:* sahar.moridani@dga.org
Awards Admin: Elisabeth Jones
Established: 1948
To recognize leadership in the film & TV industry.
Other Sponsor(s): BMW
Categories: Feature film, first-time feature film, documentary, comedy series, dramatic series, variety/talk/news/sports-specials, movies for

television/miniseries, reality programs, children's programs, commercials
Award: Medallion
Closing Date: Dec 2
Entry Fee: None
Presented: The Beverly Hilton Hotel International Ballroom, Beverly Hills, CA, Feb 4

Dollar Bank Three Rivers Arts Festival
Pittsburgh Cultural Trust
803 Liberty Ave, Pittsburgh, PA 15222
Tel: 412-456-6666
Web Site: traf.trustarts.org
Established: 1960
Annual 10-day festival of visual & performing arts.
Other Sponsor(s): Dollar Bank
Closing Date: Jan
Presented: Downtown Pittsburgh, Pittsburgh, PA, June 5-14, 2020

Doyle Lawson & Quicksilver's Bluegrass Festival
Denton FarmPark
1072 Cranford Rd, Denton, NC 27239-7930
Tel: 336-859-2755 *Fax:* 336-859-2567
Web Site: www.farmpark.com
Established: 1981
Presented: Denton FarmPark, 1072 Cranford Rd, Denton, NC, Annually in May, 3 days preceding Mother's Day

DV Awards
6300 N Sagewood Dr, Suite H-383, Park City, UT 84098
E-mail: info@dvawards.com
Web Site: www.dvawards.com
Key Personnel
Pres & Awards Admin: Martin Rhodes
Established: 2003
Recognizing outstanding creative & technical achievement in digital video production.
Categories: 44 total
Award: Acrylic sculpture
Closing Date: May 1 & Nov 1 (2 sessions)
Presented: Twice annually, Spring & Fall

East Lansing Film Festival (ELFF)
210 Abbot Rd, Suite 48, East Lansing, MI 48823
Tel: 517-980-5802
Web Site: elff.com
Key Personnel
Dir: Susan W Woods *E-mail:* susanw.woods@gmail.com
LMFC Dir: Karl Millisor *Tel:* 517-325-3017 *E-mail:* kjm.lmfcdirector.elff@gmail.com
Established: 1997
The Lake Michigan Film Competition (LMFC), consisting of films from the Lake Michigan region, takes place during the festival.
Media: Submissions: DVD; Exhibition: 35mm, Blu-ray, DVD & digital files
Categories: Features, documentaries & shorts
Closing Date: March 31 (early), May 15 (regular), June 15 (late), July 1 (extended)
Presented: East Lansing, MI, Nov

ELFF, see East Lansing Film Festival (ELFF)

Emmy Awards (Primetime)
Television Academy
5220 Lankershim Blvd, North Hollywood, CA 91601-3109
Tel: 818-754-2800 *Fax:* 818-761-3814
E-mail: emmyawards@televisionacademy.com
Web Site: www.emmys.com
Key Personnel
SVP, Awards: Dr John Leverence
VP, Awards: Julie Shore
Established: 1949

Presented annually for program, commercial & individual achievement.
Award: Statuettes
Closing Date: May 31
Entry Fee: $425 program categories; $225 individual achievement entries; $275 commercial category
Presented: Los Angeles, CA, Sept

Feature Photography Award
Overseas Press Club of America
40 W 45 St, New York, NY 10036
Tel: 212-626-9220 *Fax:* 212-626-9210
E-mail: info@opcofamerica.org
Web Site: www.opcofamerica.org
Key Personnel
Exec Dir: Patricia Kranz
Annual award for best feature photography published in any medium on an international theme.
Other Sponsor(s): Cyma Rubin - Business of Entertainment
Award: Certificate & $1,000 check
Closing Date: Late Jan
Entry Fee: $200
Presented: Hotel Mandarin-Oriental, New York, NY, April

Federico Fellini Award
Tiburon International Film Festival (TIFF)
6 Beach Rd, 544, Tiburon, CA 94920
Tel: 415-251-8433 *Fax:* 253-663-1250
E-mail: info@tiburonfilmfestival.com
Web Site: www.tiburonfilmfestival.com
Annual award given to a first time international filmmaker.
Media: Submissions: Secure online screener, DVD (NTSC Region 0 or 1, PAL Region 0); Exhibition: DVD or Blu-ray (NTSC Region 0)
Categories: Fiction, documentary, animation, student, children, comedy, experimental, music video, sports
Award: Trophy & certificate
Closing Date: Dec 1 (regular), Jan 15 (late)
Entry Fee: Feature films (over 50 minutes): $45 regular, $50 late; Short films (50 minutes & under): $35 regular, $45 late; Student films $30 regular, $35 late
Presented: Tiburon, CA, April

Festival du cinema international en Abitibi-Temiscamingue, see International Film Festival in Abitibi-Teiscamingue

Festival du Nouveau Cinema de Montreal
3805 Blvd Saint-Laurent, Montreal, QC H2W 1X9, Canada
Tel: 514-282-0004 *Fax:* 514-282-6664
E-mail: info@nouveaucinema.ca; soumissions@nouveaucinema.ca
Web Site: www.nouveaucinema.ca
Key Personnel
Founder & Dir, Programming: Claude Chamberlan *E-mail:* chamberlan@nouveaucinema.ca
Founder & Feature Films Programmer: Dimitri Eipides *E-mail:* deipides@nouveaucinema.ca
Exec Dir: Nicolas Girard Deltruc *E-mail:* ngirard@nouveaucinema.ca
Communs & Mktg Dir: Thomas Giboudeaux *E-mail:* tgiboudeaux@nouveaucinema.ca
Opers Dir: Alice Renucci *E-mail:* arenucci@nouveaucinema.ca
Established: 1971
International competition.
Media: Submissions: Secure online screener; DVD or Blu-ray (NTSC or PAL), .MOV; Exhibition: Blu-ray (NTSC or PAL, Region 0), DigiBeta, HDCAM, DCP, BetaSP, .MOV, 16mm, 35mm
Categories: Feature, short, interactive
Award: Cash prizes & post-production services

Entry Fee: Shorts & interactive works: $35 early, $40 regular, $45 late; Features: $40 early, $45 regular, $55 late
Presented: Montreal, QC, CN, Mid-Oct

Festival International du Film sur l'Art, see International Festival of Films on Art (FIFA)

Film, Video & Digital Production Grants
Jerome Foundation
550 Vandalia St, Suite 109, St Paul, MN 55114
Tel: 651-224-9431
E-mail: info@jeromefdn.org
Web Site: www.jeromefdn.org/film-video-production-grants
Key Personnel
Prog Dir: Eleanor Savage *Tel:* 651-925-5613 *E-mail:* esavage@jeromefdn.org
Prog Offr: Lann Briel *Tel:* 651-925-5614 *E-mail:* lbriel@jeromefdn.org
Grants Admin: Andrea Brown *Tel:* 651-925-5615 *E-mail:* abrown@jeromefdn.org
Film, video & digital production grant program to emerging film directors who reside in Minnesota or New York City & who have already completed & released at least 2 works with a combined significant length. Application open in January.
Media: Film, Video & Digital
Categories: Documentary, narrative, experimental, animation
Award: Up to $30,000

Robert Flaherty Film Seminar
International Film Seminars Inc
6 E 39 St, 12th fl, New York, NY 10016
Tel: 212-448-0457 *Fax:* 212-448-0458
E-mail: ifs@flahertyseminar.org
Web Site: flahertyseminar.org
Key Personnel
Exec Dir: Jon-Sesrie Goff
Prog Mgr: Sarie Horowitz
Established: 1955
Annual film/video seminar featuring independent moving-image making. Takes place one week every summer. Open to all interested in pursuing the art of cinema & video. Registration fee & guest filmmakers.
Presented: Colgate University, Hamilton, NY, June

Flickers' Rhode Island International Film Festival™ (RIIFF)
Flickers Art Collaborative
83 Park St, Suite 5, Providence, RI 02903
Mailing Address: PO Box 162, Newport, RI 02840-0002
Tel: 401-861-4445 *Fax:* 401-490-6735
E-mail: info@film-festival.org
Web Site: film-festival.org
Key Personnel
Exec Dir/CEO: George T Marshall *E-mail:* georget@film-festival.org
Prog Dir: Shawn Quirk *E-mail:* quirk@film-festival.org
Established: 1997
Media: Submissions: Secure online screener; Exhibition: Digital H264 files & Blu-ray back-up if requested
Categories: Feature film, short narrative film, documentary short, documentary feature, animated, children's/family, screenplay, LGBTQ, sci-fi/fantasy, horror, Jewish, Canadian, French, Japanese, Chinese, video games, high school, music videos, New England, webisodes, TV/cable/Internet pilot, experimental film, African-American
Award: Trophies, prizes
Closing Date: Jan 15 (early), May 15 (regular), June 1 (late), June 15 (extended)

Entry Fee: $50 early; $55 regular; $75 late; $80 extended
Presented: Venues throughout RI, Aug 4-9, 2020

Florida Film Festival
c/o Enzian Theater, 1300 S Orlando Ave, Maitland, FL 32751
Tel: 407-629-1088 *Fax:* 407-629-6870
E-mail: entries@enzian.org; marketing@enzian.org; events@enzian.org
Web Site: www.floridafilmfestival.com
Key Personnel
Exec Dir: David Schillhammer
Programming Dir: Matthew Curtis
Devt Mgr: McKenzi Vanderberg
Mktg Mgr: Valerie Cisneros *Tel:* 407-629-1088 ext 302
Events Coord: Katie Countryman
Programming Coord: Tim Anderson
Established: 1992
Jury & audience awards. Hosted by the historic Enzian Theater.
Other Sponsor(s): Full Sail University
Media: Submissions: Secure online screener, DVD (NTSC or PAL Region 0 or 1); Exhibition: MOV or AVI
Categories: Narrative features, documentary features, short films, international shorts, international features, animation, documentary shorts
Award: Trophies
Closing Date: Shorts: Oct (early), Nov (late); Features: Nov (early), Dec (late)
Entry Fee: Features: $50 regular, $70 late, $90 extended; Shorts: $30 regular, $50 late, $70 extended
Presented: Enzian Theater, Orlando, FL, April

Frameline Completion Fund
Frameline
145 Ninth St, Suite 300, San Francisco, CA 94103
Tel: 415-703-8650 *Fax:* 415-861-1404
E-mail: info@frameline.org; programming@frameline.org
Web Site: www.frameline.org
Key Personnel
Exec Dir: Frances Wallace *Tel:* 415-703-8650 ext 310 *E-mail:* fwallace@frameline.org
Dir, Exhibition & Programming: Paul Struthers *Tel:* 415-703-8650 ext 313 *E-mail:* pstruthers@frameline.org
Established: 1990
Grants to emerging & established filmmakers for the completion of films that represent & reflect LGBTQ+ life in all its complexity & richness.
Categories: Documentary, narrative, experimental, animated, episodic
Award: Up to $5,000 grant
Closing Date: Annually in Oct
Entry Fee: None
Presented: Annually in Jan

Freedoms Foundation National Awards
Freedoms Foundation at Valley Forge
1601 Valley Forge Rd, Valley Forge, PA 19481
Mailing Address: PO Box 67, Valley Forge, PA 19481-0067
Tel: 610-933-8825 *Fax:* 610-935-0522
E-mail: info@ffvf.org
Web Site: www.freedomsfoundation.org
Key Personnel
Pres & CEO: David Harmer *Tel:* 610-933-8825 ext 240 *E-mail:* dharmer@ffvf.org
EVP: Jason Raia *Tel:* 610-933-8825 ext 233 *E-mail:* jraia@ffvf.org
VP, Educ: Eugene J Halus, Jr *Tel:* 610-933-8825 ext 242 *E-mail:* ehalus@ffvf.org
Sr Dir, Devt: Maureen Troutman *Tel:* 610-933-8825 ext 210 *E-mail:* mtroutman@ffvf.org
Sr Dir, Educ Progs: Carolyn Santangelo *Tel:* 610-933-8825 ext 234 *E-mail:* csantangelo@ffvf.org

Assoc Dir, Devt: Shannon Sisson *Tel:* 610-933-8825 ext 232 *E-mail:* ssisson@ffvf.org
Assoc Dir, Educ: Eileen Cornish *Tel:* 610-933-8825 ext 230 *E-mail:* ecornish@ffvf.org;
Kim DeBlase *Tel:* 610-933-8825 ext 292 *E-mail:* kdeblase@ffvf.org
Established: 1949
To publicly honor & recognize exceptional efforts of individuals, corporations, schools & organizations who promote through words & deeds an understanding of responsible citizenship & the benefits of a free society. Entries should focus on the themes of patriotism, responsible citizenship & community involvement. Entries should consist of a 1-page summary & no more than 10 supporting documents.
Award: George Washington honor medal
Closing Date: Annually, Oct 1
Entry Fee: None
Presented: Recipients are notified in Dec, presentations in Feb

Fresh Film Northwest (FFNW)
Northwest Film Center
934 SW Salmon St, Portland, OR 97205
Mailing Address: 1219 SW Park Ave, Portland, OR 97205
Tel: 503-221-1156 *Fax:* 503-294-0874
E-mail: info@nwfilm.org
Web Site: www.nwfilm.org
Key Personnel
Educ Dir: Ellen Thomas *E-mail:* ellen@nwfilm.org
Educ Progs Mgr: Mia Ferm *Tel:* 503-276-4239 *E-mail:* mia@nwfilm.org
Juried survey of work by teen filmmakers (age 13-19) living in AK, BC, ID, MT, OR & WA.
Award: Certificate
Closing Date: Annually, Aug 1
Entry Fee: None
Presented: Northwest Film Center, Annually in Aug

Gabriel Awards
Catholic Press Association of the United States & Canada
205 W Monroe St, Suite 470, Chicago, IL 60606
Tel: 312-380-6789 *Fax:* 312-361-0256
E-mail: cpaawards@catholicpress.org
Web Site: www.catholicpress.org/page/gabrielawards
Key Personnel
Exec Dir: Timothy M Walter *E-mail:* twalter@catholicpress.org
Proj Coord: Kathleen Holloway *E-mail:* kholloway@catholicpress.org
Established: 1965
Annual awards honoring works of excellence in film, broadcast & cross-platform media productions released in the US & Canada.
Other Sponsor(s): SIGNIS North America
Categories: Film, radio, television, social media, general excellence hot topic
Award: Gabriel statuette
Closing Date: Jan 27 (early), Feb 3 (late)
Entry Fee: $125 radio; $150 television & social media; $200 film & general excellence hot topic; add $25 for late entries

Gemini Awards, see Prix Gemeaux (French language TV)

Gettysburg Bluegrass Festival
3340 Fairfield Rd, Gettysburg, PA 17325
Tel: 717-642-8749
E-mail: bluegrass@granitehillcampingresort.com
Web Site: www.gettysburgbluegrass.com
Key Personnel
Contact: Rich Winkelmann
Established: 1979
Presented: Granite Hill Camping Resort, Gettysburg, PA, Twice annually in May & Aug

The Global Awards®
New York Festivals®
260 W 39 St, 10th fl, New York, NY 10018
Tel: 212-643-4800 *Fax:* 212-643-0170
E-mail: info@newyorkfestivals.com
Web Site: www.theglobalawards.com
Key Personnel
Pres & Exec Dir: Michael Demetriades *E-mail:* mdemetriades@newyorkfestivals.com
Established: 1994
Healthcare & wellness advertising awards.
Media: MP3, JPEG, PDF, MOV
Categories: Health & Wellness: Animal health; devices, diagnostics, products & services (HWB); health awareness & advocacy (HWC); health services & corporate communications; lifestyle & personal technology; over-the-counter (OTC) medicine, nutraceuticals & applications. Pharma (RX): Devices, diagnostics, products & services; direct-to-consumer; direct-to-professional; health awareness & advocacy; veterinary
Award: Finalist certificates are also awarded
Closing Date: Annually in Sept
Entry Fee: $425 single entry; $695 campaign single media; $795 campaign (integrated) mixed media. Add $40 for Aug deadline & $65 for Sept final deadline
Presented: Annually in Nov

Global Peace Film Festival (GPFF)
PO Box 3310, Winter Park, FL 32790-3310
Tel: 407-582-6018
E-mail: info@peacefilmfest.org
Web Site: www.peacefilmfest.org
Key Personnel
Exec Dir: Nina Streich *E-mail:* nina@peacefilmfest.org
Artistic Dir: Kelly DeVine
Tech Dir: Penny Stout
Established: 2003
Uses creative media as a catalyst to strengthen community bonds, encourage direct engagement with vital issues & reshape divisive narratives using film & the arts toward a more respectful & peaceful world.
Media: DVD, Blu-ray, HD link
Categories: Features & shorts, documentary, narrative & animation
Closing Date: April (early/regular), May (late/final)
Entry Fee: Features: $25 early, $35 regular, $45 late, $55 final; Shorts: $20 early, $30 regular, $40 late, $50 final
Presented: Various locations in Orlando, Winter Park & Maitland, FL, Annually in Sept

Golden Gate Awards
San Francisco International Film Festival
Division of San Francisco Film Society
c/o San Francisco Film Society, The Presidio, Suite 110, 39 Mesa St, San Francisco, CA 94129-1025
Tel: 415-561-5000 *Fax:* 415-440-1760
E-mail: info@sffilm.org; gga@sffilm.org
Web Site: sffilm.org/sffilm-festival/
Key Personnel
Dir, Commun: Bill Proctor *Tel:* 415-561-5024 *E-mail:* bproctor@sffilm.org
Dir, Programming: Rachel Rosen *Tel:* 415-561-5010 *E-mail:* rrosen@sffilm.org
Established: 1957
Media: All formats
Categories: Documentary features, animated short, documentary short, family films, narrative short, new visions, youth works
Award: Cash
Closing Date: Sept (early), Oct (primary), Nov (final)
Entry Fee: $25-$100
Presented: April/May

Golden Globe Awards
Hollywood Foreign Press Association
646 N Robertson Blvd, West Hollywood, CA 90069
Tel: 310-657-1731 *Fax:* 310-657-5576
E-mail: awards@goldenglobes.com
Web Site: www.goldenglobes.com
Key Personnel
Gen Coun & COO: Gregory Goeckner *Tel:* 818-633-5190 *E-mail:* ggoeckner@hfpa.org
Pres: Meher Tatna
Established: 1945
Motion picture eligibility: Must be feature-length (70 minutes or longer) & have been both released & screened for the active membership in the greater Los Angeles area during the qualifying year (Jan 1-Dec 31). Television eligibility: Includes broadcast, basic & premium cable & digital delivery. Only programs aired during the qualifying calendar year in prime time (Mon-Sat 8-11pm & Sun 7-11pm) are eligible.
Categories: Motion pictures/television
Award: Golden Globe statuettes
Closing Date: Oct 31 for submission of entry forms
Presented: Beverly Hilton, Beverly Hills, CA, Annually in Jan

Golden Mike Award
Broadcasters Foundation of America
125 W 55 St, 4th fl, New York, NY 10019-5366
Tel: 212-373-8250 *Fax:* 212-373-8254
E-mail: info@thebfoa.org
Web Site: www.thebfoa.org; broadcastersfoundation.org
Key Personnel
Pres: James B Thompson *E-mail:* jim@thebfoa.org
VP: Peter M Doyle *E-mail:* peter@thebfoa.org
VP, Busn Aff: Frank Pesce *E-mail:* frank@thebfoa.org
Off & Grant Mgr: Emily Barratt *E-mail:* emily@thebfoa.org
Awarded annually to individuals for distinguished service in the broadcast area.
Presented: Feb

Golden Reel Awards
Tiburon International Film Festival (TIFF)
6 Beach Rd, 544, Tiburon, CA 94920
Tel: 415-251-8433 *Fax:* 253-663-1250
E-mail: info@tiburonfilmfestival.com
Web Site: www.tiburonfilmfestival.com
Established: 2002
Media: Submissions: Secure online screener, DVD (NTSC Region 0 or 1, PAL Region 0); Exhibition: DVD or Blu-ray (NTSC Region 0)
Categories: Fiction, documentary, animation, student, children, comedy, experimental, music video, sports
Award: Trophy & certificate
Closing Date: Annually, Dec 1 (regular), Jan 15 (late)
Entry Fee: Feature films (over 50 minutes): $45 regular, $50 late; Short films (50 minutes & under): $35 regular, $45 late; Student films $30 regular, $35 late
Presented: Tiburon, CA, Annually in April

Golden Reel Awards
Motion Picture Sound Editors
10061 Riverside Dr, PMB 751, Toluca Lake, CA 91602-2550
Tel: 818-506-7731 *Fax:* 818-506-7732
E-mail: office@mpse.org
Web Site: www.mpse.org
Key Personnel
Pres: Thomas McCarthy
VP: Mark Lanza
Established: 1953
Awarded for excellence in sound editing. See web site for application & presentation information.

Media: Film, television & computer entertainment
Categories: Dialogue, ADR, sound effects, sound design, music & Foley artistry
Award: Golden Reel Award trophies
Presented: Feb

Golden Sheaf Awards

Yorkton Film Festival (YFF)
49 Smith St E, Yorkton, SK S3N 0H4, Canada
Tel: 306-782-7077 *Fax:* 306-782-1550
E-mail: info@yorktonfilm.com
Web Site: yorktonfilm.com/golden-sheaf-awards/
Key Personnel
Exec Dir: Ms Randy Goulden
Prog Mgr: Mr Blair Yacishyn
Festival Coord: Scott Stelmaschuk
Outreach Coord: Kathy Morrell
Established: 1956
Media: DVD
Categories: Animation, children/youth productions, comedy, community television productions, drama, experimental, lifestyle & reality, multicultural, performing arts & entertainment, short subject-fiction, short subject-nonfiction, student productions, documentary arts/culture, documentary history & biography, documentary POV (point of view), documentary science/nature/technology, documentary series, documentary social/political
Award: Plaques, cash, bronze statuette
Closing Date: Nov 18 (super early), Dec 21 (early), Jan 31 (regular)
Entry Fee: $50 super early; $70 early; students free up to Dec 21; $95 regular; $20 students regular
Presented: Yorkton Film Festival, Yorkton, SK, CN, Annually in May

Golden Space Needle Awards

Seattle International Film Festival (SIFF)
305 Harrison St, Seattle, WA 98109
Tel: 206-464-5830 *Fax:* 206-264-7919
E-mail: info@siff.net; entries@siff.net
Web Site: www.siff.net
Key Personnel
Exec Dir: Andrew L Haines
Artistic Dir: Beth Barrett
Dir, Mktg & Communs: Elizabeth Rossi *Tel:* 206-315-0673 *E-mail:* elizabeth.rossi@siff.net
Cinema Opers Mgr: Andrew Niece
Festival Opers Mgr: Carley Callahan
Mktg Mgr: Leah Anderson *Tel:* 206-315-0685 *E-mail:* leah.anderson@siff.net
Audience voted awards include best narrative film, actor, actress, director, best short film & best documentary. Juried awards include Official Competition, New Directors Competition, New American Cinema Competition, Ibero-American Cinema Competition, Documentary Film Competition, Shorts & FutureWave.
Media: Submissions: Online screener or digital media file; Exhibition: 35mm film or DCP (NTSC or PAL)
Award: Cash prizes for juried awards
Closing Date: Oct 4 (early), Dec 13 (regular), Jan 31 (final), Feb 28 (FutureWave)
Entry Fee: Features: $70 early, $100 regular, $125 final; Shorts/Episodics: $40 early, $70 regular, $90 final; FutureWave: $20 early & regular, $30 final
Presented: Seattle, WA

The Gracies®

Alliance for Women in Media/Alliance for Women in Media Foundation
2365 Harrodsburg Rd, A-325, Lexington, KY 40504
Tel: 202-750-3664 *Fax:* 202-750-3664
E-mail: gracies@allwomeninmedia.org
Web Site: allwomeninmedia.org/gracies

Key Personnel
Exec Dir: Becky Brooks *E-mail:* becky.brooks@allwomeninmedia.org
Events Dir: Lisa Stephenson *E-mail:* lisa.stephenson@allwomeninmedia.org
Opers Mgr: LaTonya Jackson *E-mail:* latonya.jackson@allwomeninmedia.org
Established: 1975
Awarded annually, the national winners are honored at the Gracies Gala in CA. Awards for excellence in local, online, public & student markets presented in NY.
Media: CD, DVD, digital media online
Categories: TV, radio, interactive media; many sub-categories
Award: Statue
Closing Date: Dec (early), Jan (final)
Entry Fee: National/Syndicated: $230 early, $280 regular; Local: $170 early, $220 regular; Student: $50 early, $75 regular
Presented: Gracies Gala (national), Gracies Luncheon (local), June

Grammy Awards

The Recording Academy
3030 Olympic Blvd, Santa Monica, CA 90404
Tel: 310-392-3777
E-mail: communications@grammy.com
Web Site: www.grammy.org; www.grammy.com
Key Personnel
Pres/CEO: Deborah Dugan
Established: 1959
Awarded annually by The Recording Academy's voting membership to honor excellence in the recording arts & sciences.
Award: Statuette
Presented: Staples Center, Los Angeles, CA, Winter

Grants for Arts & Cultural Activities, see DEC Grants

Beatrice E Griggs Elementary Administrator's Award

New York Library Association/Section of School Librarians (NYLA/SSL)
6021 State Farm Rd, Guilderland, NY 12084
Tel: 518-432-6952 *Toll Free Tel:* 800-252-6952
Fax: 518-427-1697
E-mail: info@nyla.org
Web Site: www.nyla.org
Key Personnel
Exec Dir, NYLA: Jeremy Johannesen *Tel:* 518-432-6952 ext 101 *E-mail:* director@nyla.org
Awards Chair: Dawn Pressimone *E-mail:* dpressimone@waynecsd.org
To recognize an elementary or district administrator who has been responsible for initiation, maintenance +/or the improvement of an elementary school library program in a New York State school district during the past 3-5 years. Nominations accepted from current NYLA/SSL members.
Award: Plaque
Closing Date: Annually in Dec
Presented: SSL Spring Conference

The Hamptons International Film Festival

47 Newtown Lane, East Hampton, NY 11937
Tel: 631-324-4600 *Fax:* 631-324-1558
E-mail: info@hamptonsfilmfest.org; programming@hamptonsfilmfest.org (submissions)
Web Site: hamptonsfilmfest.org
Key Personnel
Exec Dir: Anne Chaisson
Deputy Dir: Lily Singer
Artistic Dir: David Nugent
Digital Content & Pubns Dir: Kristin McCracken
Devt Mgr: Vanessa Greaves
Programmer & Prog Mgr: Megan Costello
Established: 1993

Forum for independent filmmakers from around the world.
Categories: Independent film - long, short, fiction & documentary
Award: Best Narrative Feature Film: $3,000 & $100,000 film production package; Best Documentary Feature Film: $3,000 & $30,000 & film production package; Best Narrative & Documentary Short Films each receive $500 & qualify for consideration at the Academy Awards®. Additional awards include: Brizzolara Family Foundation Award for Films of Conflict & Resolution: $5,000; Vimeo Staff Pick Award & Suffolk County Next Exposure Grant: $3,000 each; Zelda Penzel Giving Voice to the Voiceless Award: $2,500; Victor Rabinowitz & Joanne Grant Award for Social Justice: $1,500; University Film Awards: $500
Presented: Annually 5 days in mid-Oct

Havana Film Festival New York (HFFNY)

American Friends of the Ludwig Federation of Cuba
4 W 43 St, Suite 304, New York, NY 10036
Tel: 212-687-2146 *Fax:* 212-681-8037
E-mail: info@hffny.com; info@aflfc.org; press@hffny.com
Web Site: www.hffny.com
Key Personnel
Pres, AFLFC: Carole Rosenberg *E-mail:* cr@aflfc.org
Artistic Dir: Diana Vargas *E-mail:* vargasher@gmail.com
Festival Coord: Samantha Choos
Prodn & Hospitality Coord: Gabriela Vazquez
Established: 2000
Annual festival showcasing the latest award-winning films & classics from & about Latin America, the Caribbean & the US Latino community.
Presented: Seven venues in New York City, the Bronx & Queens, April

Hawaii International Film Festival

680 Iwilei Rd, Suite 100, Honolulu, HI 96817
Tel: 808-792-1577 (ext 7) *Fax:* 808-792-1583
Toll Free Fax: 877-749-7783
E-mail: info@hiff.org; entries@hiff.org
Web Site: www.hiff.org
Key Personnel
Exec Dir: Beckie Stocchetti *E-mail:* beckie@hiff.org
Artistic Dir: Anderson Le
Dir, Programming: Anna Page
Festival Mgr: Joshua Nye *E-mail:* josh@hiff.org
Sponsorship & Mktg Mgr: Gianni Minga
Programming Coord & Exec Asst: Nancy McDonald *E-mail:* nancy@hiff.org
Established: 1981
Other Sponsor(s): Halekulani; Hawaii Tourism Authority; Hawaiian Airlines; Middle Management; Regal Entertainment Group
Media: Submissions: Secure online screener, DVD or Blu-ray (NTSC Region 0 or 1), MOV; Exhibition: Blu-ray (NTSC Region 0 or 1), DCP, HDCAM (features), DCP, MOV (shorts)
Categories: Narrative feature/short, documentary feature/short, student under 18, Pacific showcase feature/short, Hawaii feature/short
Award: Jury Award, Audience Award & NETPAC Award
Entry Fee: Features: $45 early, $55 regular, $65 late/extended; Shorts: $35 early, $45 regular, $60 late/extended; Pacific Islander Showcase: $35; Made in Hawaii: $20; Student Under 18: Free
Presented: Nov

Heartland International Film Festival

Heartland Film Inc
1043 Virginia Ave, Suite 2, Indianapolis, IN 46203

Tel: 317-464-9405
E-mail: submissions@heartlandfilm.org
Web Site: heartlandfilm.org/festival
Key Personnel
Pres: Craig Prater
VP, Devt: Michael Ault
Dir, Opers: Adam Howell
Dir, Film Programming: Greg Sorvig
Devt Mgr: Edward Fry
Events Mgr: Christiana Beasley
Mktg Mgr: Emily Darr
Film Programming Coord: Julia Ricci
Established: 1991
Categories: Narrative & documentary feature
  films
Award: $25,000 grand prize each for best narra-
  tive & best documentary features; $1,000 each
  to 4 finalists in the 2 categories
Closing Date: March (early), May (regular), June
  (late/extended)
Entry Fee: $50 early, $65 regular, $85 late, $105
  extended; Students: $30 early, $40 regular, $55
  late, $75 extended
Presented: Indianapolis, IN, Annually 10 days in
  Oct

Hillman Prizes
The Sidney Hillman Foundation
330 W 42 St, Suite 900, New York, NY 10036
Tel: 646-448-6413
Web Site: hillmanfoundation.org
Key Personnel
Exec Dir: Alexandra Lescaze *Tel:* 917-696-2494
  E-mail: alex@hillmanfoundation.org
Established: 1950
Presented annually to honor investigative journal-
  ism & commentary in service of the common
  good. Winners exemplify reportorial excellence,
  storytelling skill & social justice impact.
Media: Book, broadcast, magazine, newspaper,
  opinion & analysis, web. Produced, published,
  or broadcast material only
Award: $5,000 & certificate
Closing Date: Jan 30
Entry Fee: None
Presented: TheTimesCenter, New York, NY, May

Hot Springs Documentary Film Festival
Hot Springs Documentary Film Institute
659 Ouchita Ave, Hot Springs, AR 71901
Tel: 501-538-0452
E-mail: hsdfi@hsdfi.org
Web Site: www.hsdfi.org
Key Personnel
Exec Dir: Jennifer Gerber
Mng Dir: Annie Gerber
Assoc Dir: Sheryl Santacruz
Dir, Educ & Outreach: Sophie Finkelstein
Established: 1991
Other Sponsor(s): Arkansas Arts Council; Hot
  Springs National Park; Morris Foundation; Na-
  tional Endowment for the Arts; The Arlington
  Resort Hotel & Spa; TLI Print
Media: Submissions: Secure online screener,
  MOV; Exhibition: MOV
Categories: Documentary shorts, documentary
  features, Spa City sports series, virtual reality
  projects, episodic content
Entry Fee: Shorts: $40 early, $50 regular, $60
  late, $75 extended; Features & Spa City shorts
  series: $50 early, $60 regular, $70 late, $80 extended; Virtual reality series: $30 early, $35
  regular, $45 late, $60 extended; Episodic content: $45 early, $55 regular, $75 late, $80 extended
Presented: Annually in Oct

Houston International Film Festival, see
  WorldFest-Houston International Film Festival

Humboldt International Film Festival
Humboldt State University

Dept of Theatre, Film & Dance, One Harpst St,
  Arcata, CA 95521
Tel: 707-826-4113 *Fax:* 707-826-4112
E-mail: filmfest@humboldt.edu
Web Site: hsufilmfestival.com
Key Personnel
Faculty Advisor: Susan M Abbey *E-mail:* sa45@
  humboldt.edu
Established: 1967
Oldest continuous student-run film festival in the
  world. Works must be 30 minutes or less, com-
  pleted after January 2015, include English sub-
  titles (if film is in another language) & brief
  synopsis.
Other Sponsor(s): Associated Students at HSU
Media: DVD/Blu-ray
Categories: Narrative, documentary, experimental,
  animation
Award: $250 juried & specialty awards; $500
  Best of the Fest
Closing Date: Feb 17 (regular), March 9 (late)
Entry Fee: $25 regular, $15 student; $50 late, $30
  student
Presented: Minor Theatre, Arcata, CA, April 24-
  28, 2020

IDA Documentary Awards
International Documentary Association
3470 Wilshire Blvd, Suite 980, Los Angeles, CA
  90010
Tel: 213-232-1660 *Fax:* 213-232-1669
E-mail: info@documentary.org
Web Site: www.documentary.org
Key Personnel
Exec Dir: Simon Kilmurry
Deputy Dir: Amy Halpin
Public Progs & Events Mgr: Cassidy Dimon
Open submission. Membership organization for
  documentary filmmakers & friends of the doc-
  umentary. Promotion of documentary production, exhibition & distribution around the
  world. Winners are screened at IDA's Docu-
  Day. David L Wolper Student Documentary
  Awards open to university level students. ABC
  News VideoSource Award for best use of news
  footage as an integral component in a documentary. Pare Lorentz Award for a film demonstrating concern for the appropriate use of natural environment, justice for all & illumination
  of pressing social problems. Creative Recognition Awards for cinematography, editing, writing & music.
Media: DVD (NTSC Region 1 or 0), streaming
  video link
Categories: Documentary-feature, short, curated
  series, limited series, episodic series, short
  form series
Award: Statuette for IDA Awards; $1,000 cash
  prize for David L Wolper Student Awards competition
Closing Date: June (early), July (regular)
Presented: Dec

IES Medal
Illuminating Engineering Society (IES)
120 Wall St, 17th fl, New York, NY 10005-4026
Tel: 212-248-5000
E-mail: ies@ies.org
Web Site: ies.org
Key Personnel
Events Mgr: Ilana Orlansky *Tel:* 212-248-5000
  ext 4002
For technical achievement that has furthered the
  profession, art or knowledge of illuminating
  engineering. Candidates need not be IES mem-
  bers.
Categories: Engineering, design, applied illumina-
  tion, optics, ophthalmology, lighting, research,
  education
Award: Medal & framed certificate
Presented: IES Annual Conference

IFP Gotham Awards™
The Independent Filmmaker Project (IFP)
c/o Made in NY Media Ctr by IFP, 30 John St,
  Ground fl, Brooklyn, NY 11201
Tel: 212-465-8200 (ext 224)
E-mail: gothamawards@ifp.org
Web Site: gotham.ifp.org
Key Personnel
Deputy Dir & Head, Programming: Amy Dotson
  E-mail: adotson@ifp.org
Sr Dir, Programming: Milton Tabbot
  E-mail: mtabbot@ifp.org
Eight competitive awards for feature-length films:
  Best Feature, Best Documentary, Best Actress,
  Breakthrough Actor, Best Screenplay, Bing-
  ham Ray Breakthrough Director Award & IFP
  Gotham Audience Award.
Other Sponsor(s): The New York Times
Closing Date: Annually in Sept
Presented: Annually in Nov

IFP Week
The Independent Filmmaker Project (IFP)
c/o Made in NY Media Ctr by IFP, 30 John St,
  Ground fl, Brooklyn, NY 11201
Tel: 212-465-8200
Web Site: www.ifp.org
Key Personnel
Deputy Dir & Head, Programming: Amy Dotson
  E-mail: adotson@ifp.org
Sr Dir, Programming: Milton Tabbot
  E-mail: mtabbot@ifp.org
Six-day program including: Screen Forward
  Talks, What's Now Talks, Meet the Decision
  Makers (film, audio & series) & Direct Access
  (financing, streaming, audio & series).
Other Sponsor(s): Amazon Studios; HBO
Categories: Emerging Storytellers, No Borders In-
  ternational Co-production Market, Independent
  Filmmaker Labs, Spotlight on Documentaries
Closing Date: March-May
Presented: New York, NY, Annually in Sept

Independent Film Week, see IFP Week

Indianapolis International Film Festival
125 W South St, No 1930, Indianapolis, IN
  46206
Tel: 317-560-4433
E-mail: info@indyfilmfest.org; submissions@
  indyfilmfest.org
Web Site: indyfilmfest.org
Key Personnel
Exec Dir: Dan Moore
Assoc Dir: Brandon Peters
Artistic Dir: Craig Mince
Mktg Dir: Jason Roemer
Established: 2004
Media: Submissions: Secure online screener,
  DVD or Blu-ray (NTSC Region 0 or 1), MPG,
  MOV; Exhibition: DVD or Blu-ray (NTSC Re-
  gion 0 or 1), MPG, MOV
Categories: American spectrum features, Amer-
  ican spectrum shorts, world cinema features,
  world cinema shorts, documentary features,
  documentary shorts
Award: $5,000 split amongst winning filmmakers
Closing Date: Oct 1 (early), Dec 31 (regular), Feb
  2 (late), Feb 22 (extended)
Entry Fee: Features & shorts: $15 early, $25 reg-
  ular, $35 late, $75 extended
Presented: Annually in May

Individual Artist Fellowship
Delaware Division of the Arts
Carvel State Off Bldg, 4th fl, 820 N French St,
  Wilmington, DE 19801
Tel: 302-577-8278 *Fax:* 302-577-6561
E-mail: delarts@state.de.us
Web Site: www.artsdel.org
Key Personnel
Dir: Paul Weagraff *E-mail:* paul.weagraff@state.
  de.us

Deputy Dir: Kristin Pleasanton *Tel:* 302-577-8284
E-mail: kristin.pleasanton@state.de.us
Prog Offr, Artist Progs & Servs: Roxanne Stanulis *Tel:* 302-577-8283 *E-mail:* roxanne.
stanulis@state.de.us
Provides funding to Delaware creative artists working in the visual, performing, media, folk & literary arts. A Master's Fellowship is available to artists who meet specific criteria in different disciplines on a rotating basis every 3 years. Applicants must be Delaware residents 18 years of age or older. See web site for complete details.
Other Sponsor(s): Delaware State Legislature; National Endowment for the Arts (NEA)
Media: Digital file, MP4
Categories: Dance: choreography; Folk Art: music, oral literature, visual arts; Jazz: composition, performance; Literature: creative nonfiction, fiction, playwriting, poetry; Media arts: video/film; Music: composition, solo recital; Visual arts: crafts, painting, photography, sculpture, works on paper
Award: $3,000 emerging professionals, $6,000 established professionals, $10,000 master
Closing Date: Aug
Presented: Annually in Jan

Indy Film Fest, see Indianapolis International Film Festival

Indy Shorts, see Indy Shorts International Film Fest

Indy Shorts International Film Fest
Heartland Film Inc
1043 Virginia Ave, Suite 2, Indianapolis, IN 46203
Tel: 317-464-9405
E-mail: submissions@heartlandfilm.org
Web Site: heartlandfilm.org
Key Personnel
Pres: Craig Prater
VP, Devt: Michael Ault
Dir, Film Programming: Greg Sorvig
Dir, Opers: Adam Howell
Devt Mgr: Edward Fry
Events Mgr: Christiana Beasley
Mktg Mgr: Emily Darr
Film Programming Coord: Julia Ricci
Exclusively showcases the best in international short films (runtime 40 minutes or less).
Categories: Narrative short, documentary short, animated short, high school film, Indiana spotlight
Award: $5,000 each narrative, documentary & animated shorts, $500 each to 4 finalists; $2,500 Indiana spotlight; $2,000 high school film, $500 each to 4 category winners
Closing Date: February (early), March (regular/late), April (extended)
Entry Fee: Narrative, documentary & animated shorts: $30 early, $45 regular, $65 late, $85 extended; Student shorts: $20 early, $35 regular, $55 late, $75 extended; High school film: Free early, $10 regular, $15 late, $30 extended
Presented: Indianapolis, IN, Annually in July

International Emmy® Awards
The International Academy of Television Arts & Sciences
25 W 52 St, New York, NY 10019
Tel: 212-489-6969 *Fax:* 212-489-6557
E-mail: iemmys@iemmys.tv; awardsdept@
iemmys.tv
Web Site: www.iemmys.tv
Key Personnel
SVP & Exec Dir: Camille Bidermann-Roizen
Events & Partnership Mgr: Yesima Sherrod
E-mail: yesima.sherrod@iemmys.tv
Established: 1969

Best television programs produced & initially aired outside the US.
Categories: Arts Programming; Best Performance by an Actor; Best Performance by an Actress; Comedy; Documentary; Drama Series; Non-Scripted Entertainment; Kids: Series; Kids: TV Movie/Miniseries; News; Non-Scripted Entertainment; Telenovela; TV Movie/Miniseries; Non-English Language US Primetime Program
Award: Statuette
Closing Date: Annually in Feb
Entry Fee: $350 (non-English); $400 (English)
Presented: Annually in Nov

International Festival of Films on Art (FIFA)
International Festival of Films on Art (FIFA)/Festival International du Film sur l'Art
5333 Ave Casgrain, Suite 403, Montreal, QC H2T 1X3, Canada
Tel: 514-874-1637
E-mail: info@artfifa.com
Web Site: www.lefifa.org
Key Personnel
Founder: Rene Rozon
Established: 1981
Nonprofit organization devoted to the worldwide promotion & presentation of films on art, media art & new narratives on art. Its principal activity is an annual 11-day festival held in Montreal.
Media: Preselection process: Vimeo; Festival screening: .Mov Apple pro res 422/444
Categories: FIFA Competition, FIFA Grand Panorama, FIFA Experimental, FIFA Nouvelles Ecritures
Award: 5 honorary awards, some with cash grants, public prize
Closing Date: Oct
Entry Fee: $55 per film or video; $12 for short films; $40 if submitted no later than early Sept
Presented: Montreal, QC, CN, March

International Film Festival in Abitibi-Teiscamingue
International Film Festival in Abitibi-Teiscamingue/Festival du cinema international en Abitibi-Temiscamingue
215 Ave Mercier, Rouyn-Noranda, QC J9X 5W8, Canada
Tel: 819-762-6212 *Fax:* 819-762-6762
E-mail: info@festivalcinema.ca
Web Site: festivalcinema.ca
Key Personnel
Gen Dir: Emilie Villeneuve *E-mail:* direction@
festivalcinema.ca
Activities: France Gaudreault
Commun: Virgil Heroux-Laferte
Graphic Designer: Stephanie Cloutier
Logistics: Louise Marcotte
Partnerships & Mktg: Cedric Poirier
Shipping: Christian Beauchemin
Ticketing: Sarah Gelineau-Paradis
Established: 1982
Media: DCP
Categories: Short film, medium-length film, feature film
Award: $1,000 grant (3 of the 6 awards)
Closing Date: June (short & medium-length), Aug (feature)
Entry Fee: None
Presented: Rouyn-Noranda, QC, CN, Last Sat in Oct through the following Thurs (6 days)

International Short Film & Video Competition
USA Film Festival
6116 N Central Expwy, Suite 105, Dallas, TX 75206
Tel: 214-821-6300; 214-821-FILM (821-3456)
Fax: 214-821-6364
E-mail: usafilmfest@aol.com
Web Site: www.usafilmfestival.com

Key Personnel
Mng Dir: Ann Alexander
Prog Coord: Tori Collatos
Established: 1979
Media: Submissions: DVD screener; Finished formats: 16mm, 35mm & 70mm film, IMAX, HDCAM, DVCAM, DCI, BetaSP, DigiBeta, Blu-ray, DCP, DVD
Categories: Fiction, nonfiction, experimental, animated, student, Texas-produced
Award: $1,000
Closing Date: Dec 15 (early), Jan 1 (regular), Feb 15 (final)
Entry Fee: $50 early; $55 regular; $65 final
Presented: Annually, late April

International Wildlife Film Festival
International Wildlife Media Center & Film Festival
Roxy Theater, 718 S Higgins Ave, Missoula, MT 59801
Tel: 406-728-9380 *Fax:* 406-728-2881
E-mail: iwff@wildlifefilms.org
Web Site: www.wildlifefilms.org
Key Personnel
Coord: Chris Sand *E-mail:* coordinator@
wildlifefilms.org
Established: 1977
Multiple glass engraved awards for best of categories & special jury prize.
Other Sponsor(s): Animal Planet; BBC; Center for Environmental Filmmaking; Discovery; Montana Film Office; Montana State University Graduate Program in Science & Natural History Filmmaking; National Geographic; Nature; Panasonic; University of Montana
Award: Engraved glass & certificates
Closing Date: Nov 18 (early), Jan 6 (regular), Jan 20 (late)
Entry Fee: Contingent on categories
Presented: Missoula, MT, Annually in April

IRE Annual Awards for Investigative Reporting
Investigative Reporters & Editors (IRE)
Missouri School of Journalism, 141 Neff Annex, Columbia, MO 65211
Tel: 573-882-2042 *Fax:* 573-882-5431
E-mail: info@ire.org; rescntr@ire.org
Web Site: www.ire.org/awards
Key Personnel
Resource Ctr Dir: Lauren Grandestaff *Tel:* 573-882-6668 *E-mail:* lauren@ire.org
Recognizes top investigative work in print, broadcast & online media.
Media: Print, audio, video & online
Categories: Print/online-large, medium, small; broadcast/video-large, medium, small; innovation in investigative journalism-large, medium, small; radio/audio-all sizes; book-all sizes; student-large, small; special categories: Tom Renner Award, IRE FOI Award, Investigations Triggered by Breaking News
Award: Plaque, certificate, cash
Closing Date: Beginning of Jan
Entry Fee: $55 per entry (IRE membs); $125 per entry (nonmembs); $25 per entry (nonmemb students)
Presented: April

Israel Film Festival
IsraFest Foundation Inc
324 S Beverly Dr, No 424, Beverly Hills, CA 90212
Tel: 310-247-1800
E-mail: info@israelfilmfestival.org
Web Site: www.israelfilmfestival.com
Key Personnel
Founder & Exec Dir: Meir Fenigstein
E-mail: meir@israelfilmfestival.org
Established: 1982

Audience Choice awards presented for best feature film & best documentary.
Media: DVD
Categories: Feature films, documentaries, student shorts
Presented: Los Angeles, CA

The Peter Jennings Award
Overseas Press Club of America
40 W 45 St, New York, NY 10036
Tel: 212-626-9220 *Fax:* 212-626-9210
E-mail: info@opcofamerica.org
Web Site: www.opcofamerica.org
Key Personnel
Exec Dir: Patricia Kranz
Award for the best TV, video or documentary about international affairs over 30 minutes. Work must be published or broadcast in the US or be accessible to an American audience for the first time during the year prior to the award with reporting primarily outside the US.
Award: Certificate & $1,000 check
Closing Date: Jan 30
Entry Fee: $200
Presented: April 27

Juno Awards
Canadian Academy of Recording Arts & Sciences (CARAS)
219 Dufferin St, Suite 211C, Toronto, ON M6K 3J1, Canada
Tel: 416-485-3135 (CN only) *Toll Free Tel:* 888-501-3135 *Fax:* 416-485-4978
E-mail: info@carasonline.ca; submissions@junoawards.ca
Web Site: junoawards.ca; www.facebook.com/theJunoAwards
Key Personnel
Pres & CEO: Allan Reid *E-mail:* allan@junoawards.ca
Dir, Events: Chris Topping *E-mail:* chris@junoawards.ca
Sr Mgr, Awards & Spec Events: Laura Kirk *E-mail:* laura@junoawards.ca
Mgr, Communs & Soc Media: Elyssa Macri *E-mail:* elyssa@junoawards.ca
Promotes & celebrates Canadian music & artists.
Categories: 42 categories for professionals from "Album of the Year" to "Recording Engineer of the Year"
Award: Statuette
Closing Date: Jan 5
Entry Fee: $40-$95 per submission
Presented: Annually during Juno Week

Kansas City FilmFest International (KCFFI)
4741 Central, Suite 306, Kansas City, MO 64112
Tel: 816-286-4777
E-mail: info@kcfilmfest.org
Web Site: kcfilmfest.org
Key Personnel
Founder: Fred G Andrews
Exec Dir: Veronica Elliott Loncar
Established: 1996
Media: Secure online screener, digital media, DVD & Blu-ray (NTSC Region 0 or 1)
Categories: Narrative short, narrative feature, documentary feature, documentary short, Heartland student short
Award: $250-$1,000
Closing Date: Sept (early), Oct (regular), Nov (late), Dec (extended)
Entry Fee: $30 early, $40 regular, $50 late, $65 extended
Presented: Festival Awards Gala, Annually in April

The David Kaplan Award
Overseas Press Club of America
40 W 45 St, New York, NY 10036
Tel: 212-626-9220 *Fax:* 212-626-9210
E-mail: info@opcofamerica.org

Web Site: www.opcofamerica.org
Key Personnel
Exec Dir: Patricia Kranz
Best TV or spot news reporting from abroad. All entries are submitted online.
Other Sponsor(s): Ben & Karen Sherwood
Award: Certificate & $1,000 check
Closing Date: Annually in late Jan
Entry Fee: $200 per category
Presented: Hotel Mandarin-Oriental, New York, NY, Annually in April

KC FilmFest International, see Kansas City FilmFest International (KCFFI)

Robert F Kennedy Journalism Awards
Robert F Kennedy Center for Justice & Human Rights
1300 19 St NW, Suite 750, Washington, DC 20036
Tel: 646-553-4750
E-mail: info@rfkhumanrights.org; communications@rfkhumanrights.org
Web Site: rfkhumanrights.org/awards
Key Personnel
Pres: Kerry Kennedy
Sr Advisor & Exec Dir: Lynn Delaney
Established: 1968
Honors outstanding reporting on issues that reflect Robert Kennedy's concerns, including human rights, social justice & the power of individual action in the US & around the world.
Categories: Print, television, radio, photography, editorial cartoon, new media
Award: $1,000 & bust of Robert F Kennedy
Closing Date: Annually in Feb
Entry Fee: $75
Presented: Washington, DC, Annually in May

KidFilm®
USA Film Festival
6116 N Central Expwy, Suite 105, Dallas, TX 75206
Tel: 214-821-6300; 214-821-FILM (821-3456) *Fax:* 214-821-6364
E-mail: usafilmfest@aol.com
Web Site: www.usafilmfestival.com
Key Personnel
Mng Dir: Ann Alexander
Prog Coord: Tori Collatos
Established: 1985
Oldest & largest children's film festival in the US. Submissions accepted year-round via filmfreeway.com & festhome.com.
Media: Submissions: Online or DVD screener (NTSC); Finished formats: 16mm & 35mm film, DVD, BetaSP, DigiBeta & Blu-ray (NTSC)
Categories: Shorts & feature length
Closing Date: Nov 15 (regular), Nov 30 (late)
Entry Fee: $10 regular; $20 late
Presented: Angelika Film Center (in Mockingbird Station), 5321 E Mockingbird Lane, Dallas, TX, Annually in Jan

KidsEye™ International Film Festival
Flickers Art Collaborative
83 Park St, Suite 5, Providence, RI 02903
Mailing Address: PO Box 162, Newport, RI 02840-0002
Tel: 401-861-4445 *Fax:* 401-490-6735
E-mail: info@film-festival.org
Web Site: film-festival.org
Key Personnel
Exec Dir/CEO: George T Marshall *E-mail:* georget@film-festival.org
Educ Prog Dir: Reshad Kulenovic
Prog Dir: Shawn Quirk *E-mail:* quirk@film-festival.org
Prizes given for best children's animation & best children's live action. Official sidebar of the Flickers' Rhode Island International Film Fes-

tival™ with children/family films. All films accepted & featured come from the entry pool of the Rhode Island International Film Festival & are featured during the same week as part of the larger festival.

LA Femme International Film Festival
Subsidiary of La Femme Inc
324 S Beverly Dr, Suite 436, Beverly Hills, CA 90212
Tel: 310-441-1645 *Fax:* 310-475-8213
Web Site: www.lafemme.org
Key Personnel
Pres & Festival Dir: Leslie LaPage *E-mail:* llapage@lafemme.org
Established: 2005
Focus on women filmmakers platforming their commercial films for the worldwide audience.
Other Sponsor(s): SAG; WGA
Media: Submissions: Secure online screener, DVD (NTSC Region 0 or 1), Blu-ray (NTSC Region 0); Exhibition: DVD (NTSC Region 0 or 1), Blu-ray (NTSC Region 0)
Categories: Screenplay, feature, documentary, short, music video/commercial, mid-length film, mobisode, webisode, game, animation short, animation feature, special documentary of focus, TV pilot script
Award: Each winner receives a crystal award, gifts & prizes valued up to $3,000
Closing Date: May (early), June (regular), July (late), Aug (extended)
Entry Fee: $35-$115 depending on entry date
Presented: LA LIVE Regal Theatre Stadium 14, Los Angeles, CA, Annually in Oct

The Livingston Awards for Young Journalists
University of Michigan
Wallace House, 620 Oxford Rd, Ann Arbor, MI 48104
Tel: 734-998-7575 *Fax:* 734-998-7979
E-mail: livawards@umich.edu
Web Site: wallacehouse.umich.edu/livingston-awards
Key Personnel
Dir: Lynette Clemetson
Prog Admin: Melissa Riley
Established: 1981
Annual award recognizing an exceptional professional under the age of 35 for their excellence in print, online or broadcast journalism.
Other Sponsor(s): Knight Foundation
Media: Print, online, broadcast
Categories: Local, national & international reporting
Award: $10,000
Closing Date: Feb 1
Entry Fee: None
Presented: New York, NY, June

The Los Angeles Asian Pacific Film Festival
Visual Communications
120 Judge John Aiso St, Basement Level, Los Angeles, CA 90012-3805
Tel: 213-680-4462
E-mail: festival@vconline.org
Web Site: asianfilmfestla.org; www.vconline.org/festival
Key Personnel
Dir, Exhibitions: Abraham Ferrer *Tel:* 213-680-4462 ext 25 *E-mail:* abe@vconline.org
Festival Co-Dir: David Magdael *Tel:* 213-624-7827 *E-mail:* dmagdael@tcdm-associates.com
Established: 1983
Grand Jury Awards (narrative feature; documentary feature); Festival Golden Reel Award (excellence in short film); Linda Mabalot New Directors/New Visions Award (innovation in short film); Festival Audience Award (favorite narrative feature; favorite documentary feature).
Media: D Cinema, DCP, 35mm
Categories: Experimental, documentary, narrative, graphic/animation

Award: Cash, certificate, product
Closing Date: Nov (early), Dec (final)
Entry Fee: $25 early; $35 final
Presented: Multiple venues throughout Los Angeles, CA

Los Angeles Film Festival

Film Independent
5670 Wilshire Blvd, 9th fl, Los Angeles, CA 90036
Tel: 323-556-9300 *Toll Free Tel:* 866-345-6337
Fax: 323-556-9303
E-mail: lafilmfest@filmindependent.org;
programming@filmindependent.org
Web Site: www.filmindependent.org/la-film-festival
Key Personnel
Festival Dir: Jennifer Cochis *E-mail:* jcochis@filmindependent.org
Dir, Event Prodn: Shawn Davis *E-mail:* sdavis@filmindependent.org
Dir, Opers: Rachel Bleemer *E-mail:* rbleemer@filmindependent.org
Sr Events Prodr: Danielle Federico
E-mail: dfederico@filmindependent.org
Established: 1995
Juried & audience awards.
Media: Submissions: Online screener; Exhibition: DCP (must be DCI compliant)
Closing Date: Feb (early), April (regular), May (late)
Entry Fee: Feature (membs): $40 early, $65 regular, $90 late; Feature (nonmembs): $50 early, $75 regular, $100 late; Short (membs): $25 early, $40 regular, $55 late; Short (nonmembs): $30 early, $45 regular, $60 late
Presented: Annually in Sept

Love Your Shorts Film Festival

608 S Elm Ave, Sanford, FL 32771
E-mail: contact@loveyourshorts.com
Web Site: www.loveyourshorts.com
Key Personnel
Festival & Programming Dir: Nelson D Beverly
Grants Dir: Debra Martin
Sponsorships Dir & Media Rel: Rachel Delinski; Gene Kruckemyer
Established: 2010
Welcomes short films (30 minutes or less) in all genres. Open to amateur & professional filmmakers in all categories.
Other Sponsor(s): Florida Division of Cultural Affairs; Sanford Community Redevelopment Agency; Seminole Cultural Arts Council; United Arts of Central Florida
Categories: Drama, documentary, animation, Florida flavor, sci-fi/horror, comedy & family friendly
Award: Monroe Award: Metal artwork designed by Julie Kessler; $400 cash each competition block, $1,500 Best of the Fest
Closing Date: June 30 (early), Sept 15 (regular), Oct 15 (late), Oct 31 (extended)
Entry Fee: $15 early; $20 regular; $25 late; $35 extended
Presented: Wayne Densch Performing Arts Center, Sanford, FL, Annually in Feb

Maine Artist Fellowship Program

Maine Arts Commission
193 State St, 25 State House Sta, Augusta, ME 04330-0025
Tel: 207-287-2724 *Fax:* 207-287-2725
E-mail: mainearts.info@maine.org
Web Site: mainearts.maine.gov/Pages/Funding/Individual-Artist-Fellowships
Key Personnel
Exec Dir: Julie Richard *Tel:* 207-287-2710
E-mail: julie.richard@maine.gov
Established: 1988

Award to honor artistic excellence in all artistic disciplines for current work (within past 3 years). Maine artists only.
Media: Text files are preferred in PDF, but DOC or RTF files allowed. Work samples should be submitted as follows - Mss: PDF or WORD; Images: JPEG or PDF; Audio: MP3, WAV or AIFF; Video: MPEG-4, MOV or AVI; Web: URL address in PDF or WORD
Categories: Functional craft, literary arts, performing/media arts, traditional arts, visual arts
Award: $5,000 grant (maximum)
Closing Date: Spring for all genres
Entry Fee: None
Presented: Fall

Maine Student Film & Video Festival

c/o Maine Film Ctr, 76 Main St, Waterville, ME 04901
Tel: 207-861-8138
E-mail: msfvf@mainefilmcenter.org
Web Site: www.msfvf.com
Annual awards for Maine residents & students 19 years of age or younger. Films are judged on the basis of originality, content, style & technique.
Other Sponsor(s): Adobe® Creative Cloud™; Maine Film Center; Maine Public Broadcasting Network
Media: All video formats & DVD
Categories: Narrative, documentary, creative: preteen grades (K-6), junior (grades 7-8), senior (grades 9-12)
Award: Certificate of merit. Prizes vary
Closing Date: June
Entry Fee: None
Presented: Maine International Film Festival, Waterville Opera House, Waterville, ME, July

The Martha's Vineyard Film Festival (MVFF)

9 State Rd, Chilmark, MA 02535
Mailing Address: PO Box 592, Chilmark, MA 02535
Tel: 508-645-9599
Web Site: www.tmvff.org
Key Personnel
Founder, Prodr & Creative Dir: Thomas Bena
Mng Dir: Brian Ditchfield
Established: 2001
Presented: Chilmark Community Center, 520 South Rd, Chilmark, MA, Annually 4 days, 3rd week in March

Martha's Vineyard International Film Festival

Martha's Vineyard Film Society Inc
PO Box 4423, Vineyard Haven, MA 02568
Tel: 508-696-9369
E-mail: info@mvfilmsociety.com
Web Site: mvfilmsociety.com
Key Personnel
Founder/Exec Dir: Richard Paradise
E-mail: rich@mvfilmsociety.com
Established: 2006
Laid back beach style 6-day festival presenting a selection of films from around the globe by international filmmakers.
Award: $1,000 cash prize for winning short film-jury competition
Presented: Martha's Vineyard Film Center, Capawock Movie Theater, Vineyard Haven, MA & Strand Theater, Oak Bluffs, MA, Annually in Sept

Maverick Awards

Woodstock Film Festival
13 Rock City Rd, Woodstock, NY 12498
Mailing Address: PO Box 1406, Woodstock, NY 12498-8406
Tel: 845-679-4265; 845-810-0131 *Fax:* 509-479-5414
E-mail: info@woodstockfilmfestival.com
Web Site: www.woodstockfilmfestival.com

Key Personnel
Co-Founder & Festival Dir: Meira Blaustein
E-mail: meira@woodstockfilmfestival.com
Co-Founder & Dir, Devt: Laurent Rejto
E-mail: laurent@woodstockfilmfestival.com
Established: 2000
Cash, prizes +/or services are given out in most categories. Audience awards are also presented for best feature & best documentary.
Categories: Narrative, documentary, short narrative, short animation, short documentary, short teen, short music video, short student
Closing Date: June
Entry Fee: $15-$50
Presented: Woodstock, NY, Oct

Lowry Mays Excellence in Broadcasting Award

Broadcasters Foundation of America
125 W 55 St, 4th fl, New York, NY 10019-5366
Tel: 212-373-8250 *Fax:* 212-373-8254
E-mail: info@thebfoa.org
Web Site: www.thebfoa.org;
broadcastersfoundation.org
Key Personnel
Pres: James B Thompson *E-mail:* jim@thebfoa.org
VP: Peter M Doyle *E-mail:* peter@thebfoa.org
VP, Busn Aff: Frank Pesce *E-mail:* frank@thebfoa.org
Off & Grant Mgr: Emily Barratt *E-mail:* emily@thebfoa.org
Awarded annually to an individual in broadcasting whose work exemplifies innovation, community service, advocacy & entrepreneurship.
Other Sponsor(s): The Mays Family Foundation
Presented: April

Melbourne Independent Filmmakers Festival (MIFF)

3 Boys Productions
1399 S Harbor City Blvd, Melbourne, FL 32901
Tel: 321-726-1711 *Fax:* 321-726-1715
Web Site: www.3boysproductions.com
Key Personnel
Prog Chmn: Terry Cronin *E-mail:* tcronin2@aol.com
Established: 1999
Audience Award, Peer Award.
Categories: Features, shorts, documentaries, animation, horror, science fiction, drama, comedy
Closing Date: May 1
Entry Fee: None; $10 after deadline

MerleFest

Wilkes Community College Foundation
PO Box 120, Wilkesboro, NC 28697
Toll Free Tel: 800-343-7857
E-mail: merlefest@wilkescc.edu
Web Site: merlefest.org
Established: 1988
Music festival founded in memory of Eddy Merle Watson as a fundraiser for Wilkes Community College.
Other Sponsor(s): Window World
Presented: Wilkes Community College, Wilkesboro, NC, April 23-26, 2020

Miami Film Festival

Miami Dade College
300 NE Second Ave, Miami, FL 33132
Tel: 305-237-FILM (237-3456)
E-mail: info@miamifilmfestival.com
Web Site: miamifilmfestival.com
Key Personnel
Exec Dir & Dir, Programming: Jaie Laplante
Established: 1984
Showcases emerging & established international & Ibero-American filmmakers.
Media: Submissions: Secure online screener; Screening: DCP
Categories: Knight Competition, Knight Documentary Achievement Award, Lexus Compe-

tition, Jordan Ressler Award, Shorts Competition, Shorts out of Competition, Cinema 360º, Reel Music, Florida Focus, MIFFecito (KIDS), Encuentros, CineSlam
Award: Cash totalling more than $60,000
Closing Date: June (early), July (regular), Aug (late), Sept (extended)
Entry Fee: $45 early; $55 regular; $65 late; $100 extended
Presented: Annually in March

Miami short Film Festival (MsFF)
247 SW Eighth St, Suite 44, Miami, FL 33130
E-mail: info@miamishortfilmfestival.com
Web Site: www.miamishortfilmfestival.com
Key Personnel
Exec Dir/Founder: William Vela
Dir, Mktg & Devt: Krystle Carrara
Tech Dir/Webmaster: Esteban Prieto
Established: 2002
Short films of 20 minutes or less. See web site for full list of eligibility requirements.
Other Sponsor(s): WOW MKTG
Media: 35mm, 16mm, 8mm, HD
Categories: Narrative, music video, documentary, experimental, animation, web/new media, environmental
Closing Date: Dec 15 (early), Feb 15 (regular), April 15 (late), Sept 1 (extended)
Entry Fee: Varies, see web site for complete fee information
Presented: Silverspot Cinema, 300 SE Third St, No 100, Miami, FL, Annually in Nov

MIFF, see Melbourne Independent Filmmakers Festival (MIFF)

Mill Valley Film Festival
California Film Institute
Affiliate of Christopher B Smith Rafael Film Center
1001 Lootens Place, Suite 220, San Rafael, CA 94901
Tel: 415-383-5256 *Fax:* 415-383-8606
E-mail: mvff@cafilm.org; info@cafilm.org
Web Site: www.mvff.com; www.cafilm.org
Key Personnel
Founder/Dir: Mark Fishkin *E-mail:* director@cafilm.org
Dir, Mktg & Publicity: Shelley Spicer
Dir, Programming: Zoe Elton
Opers Dir: Jeromy Zajonc *E-mail:* jzajonc@cafilm.org
Established: 1977
Non-competitive, invitational festival; call for entry & institute requests.
Media: Submissions: Online screener; Exhibition: 35mm & DCP
Categories: Animated, narrative, features & shorts, documentary, experimental, children/family, youth produced
Award: Bronze sculpture
Closing Date: May 18 (early); June 15 (regular); June 29 (late)
Entry Fee: Shorts (under 30 minutes): $30 early, $40 regular, $55 final; Mid-length (30-49 minutes): $35 early, $45 regular, $55 final; Features (50 minutes & over): $45 early, $55 regular, $70 final
Presented: Christopher B Smith Rafael Film Center, San Rafael, CA, 1st Thursday in Oct, 11-day festival

Minneapolis St Paul International Film Festival (MSPIFF)
The Film Society of Minneapolis St Paul
125 SE Main St, Suite 341, Minneapolis, MN 55414
Tel: 612-331-7563
E-mail: info@mspfilm.org; submissions@mspfilm.org
Web Site: mspfilm.org/festivals/mspiff

Established: 1981
Emerging Filmmaker, Best Documentary, Minnesota Made, Audience Choice.
Media: Submissions: Online screener (Vimeo preferred); Screening: DCP
Categories: Narrative feature, documentary feature, narrative short, documentary short, emerging filmmaker, Minnesota made
Award: $500 & $2,500 cash prizes
Closing Date: Aug (early), Oct (regular), Nov (late), Dec (extended)
Entry Fee: Features: $45 early, $60 regular, $75 late, $90 extended; Shorts: $30 early, $45 regular, $60 late, $75 extended; NextWave: Free; Minnesota Made: Free before late deadline, 50% discount can be requested if after late deadline
Presented: April 9-30, 2020

Missouri Honor Medal for Distinguished Service in Journalism
Missouri School of Journalism
School of Journalism, 120 Neff Hall, 309 S Ninth St, Columbia, MO 65211-1200
Tel: 573-882-4821 *Fax:* 573-884-5400
E-mail: journalism@missouri.edu
Web Site: journalism.missouri.edu
Key Personnel
Exec Dir, Advancement: Colin Kilpatrick
Tel: 573-884-4803 *E-mail:* kilpatrickc@missouri.edu
Established: 1930
Award: Certificate & medal
Presented: Columbia, MO

The Mobius® Awards
713 S Pacific Coast Hwy, Suite A, Redondo Beach, CA 90277-4233
Tel: 310-540-0959 *Fax:* 310-316-8905
E-mail: mobiusinfo@mobiusawards.com; mediarelations@mobiusawards.com
Web Site: mobiusawards.com
Key Personnel
Chmn: Lee W Gluckman, Jr
E-mail: leegluckman@mobiusawards.com
Creative Dir & Digital Coord: David Chan
E-mail: davidchan@mobiusawards.com
Mgr, Entrant Rel & Opers: Kristen Szabo
E-mail: kristenszabo@mobiusawards.com
Mgr, Press & Media Rel: Sandra Kelly
Established: 1971
Categories: Brand identity, branded content/entertainment, brochure/book, cinema/in-flight, digital-mobile, digital-online, direct, guerilla/ambush marketing, integrated campaign, online commercials, outdoor/out-of-home, package design & redesign, point-of-purchase, print, radio, social media marketing, spec advertising, television
Award: Mobius statuettes, certificates & special industry sponsored awards
Closing Date: Oct 1
Entry Fee: Varies. See web site for single & campaign fees
Presented: Los Angeles, CA, Annually in March

Moondance International Film Festival
7seas Productions
970 Ninth St, Boulder, CO 80302
Tel: 303-818-5771
Web Site: moondancefilmfestival.com
Key Personnel
Founder & Exec Dir: Elizabeth English
E-mail: director@moondancefilmfestival.com
Established: 1999
Awards: Spirit of Moondance (women), Seahorse (men), Dolphin (18 years & under), Neptune (75 years & over), Sand Castle (male-female team), Calypso (environmental protection), Gaia (inspirational), Columbine (non-violent conflict resolution), Atlantis (foreign), Starfish (comedy), Angel (men & women), Cinema

Pioneer (men & women), Abyss (meaningful thriller, horror & supernatural), Colorado Ocean (CO residents), Seven Seas (promote cross-cultural knowledge & awareness), Mermaid's Pearl (contributing women in film industry), Legacy (women who helped others achieve success in film), Better World (important contribution about vital humanitarian or environmental issues), Chambered Nautilus (vital & generous financial support), Seagull (short film drone cinematography)
Media: Films: DVD (NTSC or PAL Region 0 or 1) or digital; Written works: on paper or digital; Music: CD or DVD (NTSC or PAL Region 0 or 1), digital
Closing Date: May 31 (regular), June 30 (late), July 15 (extended)
Entry Fee: Films: $55 regular; $80 late; $105 extended; Written works: $50 regular, $75 late, $100 extended; Film Scores & Original Music: $80 regular & late, $85 extended

Mountainfilm in Telluride
109 E Colorado Ave, Suite 1, Telluride, CO 81435
Mailing Address: PO Box 1088, Telluride, CO 81435-1088
Tel: 970-728-4123
E-mail: entries@mountainfilm.org
Web Site: www.mountainfilm.org
Key Personnel
Exec Dir: Sage Martin
Festival Dir: David Holbrooke
Festival Prodr: Stash Wislocki
Established: 1979
Media: Submissions: Online screener (preferred) or 2 DVDs; Screening: DCP, HDCAM
Categories: Norman Vaughan Indomitable Spirit Award, Moving Mountains Prize, Student Award, Audience Choice Award, Charlie Fowler Award, Cinematography Award, Festival Director's Award
Award: $3,000 (grand prize)
Closing Date: Dec (early), Jan (regular), Feb (late)
Entry Fee: Early: $60 features, $30 shorts; Regular: $80 features, $40 shorts; Late: $100 features, $50 shorts
Presented: Telluride, CO, May

The Edward R Murrow Award
Overseas Press Club of America
40 W 45 St, New York, NY 10036
Tel: 212-626-9220 *Fax:* 212-626-9210
E-mail: info@opcofamerica.org
Web Site: www.opcofamerica.org
Key Personnel
Exec Dir: Patricia Kranz
Best TV, video, or documentary interpretation on international affairs up to 30 minutes. All entries are submitted online.
Other Sponsor(s): CBS
Award: Certificate & $1,000 check
Closing Date: Annually in late Jan
Entry Fee: $200 per category
Presented: Hotel Mandarin-Oriental, New York, NY, Annually in April

Edward R Murrow Award
Corporation for Public Broadcasting (CPB)
401 Ninth St NW, Washington, DC 20004-2129
Tel: 202-879-9600 *Toll Free Tel:* 800-272-2190
E-mail: press@cpb.org
Web Site: www.cpb.org
Key Personnel
SVP & Chief Content Offr: Joseph Tovares
VP, Radio: Erika Pulley-Hayes
Established: 1977
Honors individuals whose work has contributed to the growth, quality & positive image of public radio.
Media: Radio

Award: Plaque
Closing Date: Varies
Entry Fee: None
Presented: Public Radio Program Conference

NAB Distinguished Service Award
National Association of Broadcasters (NAB)
1771 "N" St NW, Washington, DC 20036
Tel: 202-429-5300
E-mail: nab@nab.org
Web Site: www.nab.org
Key Personnel
SVP, Event Opers & Planning: Justin McVaney
Established: 1953
Awarded annually to a distinguished member of
the broadcast industry.
Award: Sculpture
Presented: The NAB Show, Las Vegas, NV, April

Nantucket Film Festival (NFF)
68 Jay St, Suite 319, Brooklyn, NY 11201
Mailing Address: 228 Park Ave S, No 83799,
New York, NY 10003
Tel: 646-480-1900 *Fax:* 646-365-3367
E-mail: info@nantucketfilmfestival.org;
submissions@nantucketfilmfestival.org
Web Site: nantucketfilmfestival.org
Key Personnel
Exec Dir: Mystelle Brabbee *E-mail:* mystelle@
nantucketfilmfestival.org
Devt Dir: Megan Inaba
Digital Outreach Dir: Allyson Morgan
Film Prog Dir: Basil Tsiokos
Mktg Dir: Jaclyn Rose Wohl
Opers Dir: Molly Martin
Signature Progs Prodr: Beth Emelson
Assoc Programmer: Opal H Bennett
Established: 1996
Media: Submission: Vimeo link (preferred) or se-
cure online screener; Exhibition: DCP
Categories: Narrative feature, documentary fea-
ture, animation feature, narrative short, docu-
mentary short, animation short, feature screen-
play, episodic screenplay (30 minutes), script
analysis (feature screenplay), episodic screen-
play (60 minutes), short screenplay
Closing Date: Oct (early), Jan (regular), March
(final)
Entry Fee: $25-$75 films; $30-$80 screenplays
Presented: Various venues, Nantucket, MA, June
23-29, 2020

The Thomas Nast Award
Overseas Press Club of America
40 W 45 St, New York, NY 10036
Tel: 212-626-9220 *Fax:* 212-626-9210
E-mail: info@opcofamerica.org
Web Site: www.opcofamerica.org
Key Personnel
Exec Dir: Patricia Kranz
Annual award for best cartoons on international
affairs.
Award: Certificate & 1,000 check
Closing Date: Late Jan
Entry Fee: $200
Presented: Hotel Mandarin-Oriental, New York,
NY, April

National Headliner Awards
Press Club of Atlantic City
PO Box 128, Somers Point, NJ 08244
Tel: 609-927-1850; 609-350-3099
E-mail: info@headlinerawards.org
Web Site: www.headlinerawards.org
Key Personnel
Prog Chmn: Mark Melhorn
Exec Dir: Diane D'Amico
Contest Admin: Erika Melhorn
Established: 1934
Annual contest recognizing journalistic merit in
the communications industry. All entries must
be submitted online.

Categories: Newspapers, magazines, news syndi-
cates, TV, radio, online
Award: Plaques & certificates, $1,500 for each
division of grand award
Closing Date: Feb
Entry Fee: $75 per entry

National Storytelling Festival
International Storytelling Center
Affiliate of Smithsonian Institution
116 W Main St, Jonesborough, TN 37659
Tel: 423-753-2171 *Toll Free Tel:* 800-952-8392
Fax: 423-913-8219
E-mail: customerservice@storytellingcenter.net
Web Site: www.storytellingcenter.net/festival
Key Personnel
Pres: Kiran Singh Sirah *E-mail:* kiran@
storytellingcenter.net
Dir, Progs: Susan O'Connor *Tel:* 423-913-8217
E-mail: susan@storytellingcenter.net
Prog Admin: Becky Brunson *E-mail:* becky@
storytellingcenter.net
Communs Coord: Rachel Stiltner
E-mail: rachel@storytellingcenter.net
Festival Registration Coord: Marianne Huff
E-mail: marianne@storytellingcenter.net
Established: 1973
Premier storytelling event.
Presented: Jonesborough, TN, Annually, first full
weekend in Oct

National Student Production Awards
College Broadcasters Inc (CBI)
Hershey Square Ctr, 1152 Mae St, Hummelstown,
PA 17036
Toll Free Tel: 855-ASK-4CBI (275-4224)
Web Site: www.askcbi.org
Key Personnel
Awards Coord: Steven Hames *Tel:* 706-368-6963
E-mail: shames@berry.edu
Presented annually for excellence in student tele-
vision & radio production.
Media: Audio: MP3; Video: MP4 or MOV
Categories: Student media, station imaging, so-
cial media presence, documentary/public af-
fairs, sportscast, sports reporting, sports PBP,
newscast, news reporting, promo, PSA, special
broadcast, vodcast, podcast, comedy, DJ, regu-
larly scheduled program, general entertainment
program
Award: Certificate & trophy
Closing Date: May
Entry Fee: Free for CBI memb stations; $65 non-
membs
Presented: Oct

National Undergraduate Student Electronic Media Competition
National Broadcasting Society-Alpha Epsilon Rho
(NBS-AERho)
PO Box 4206, Chesterfield, MO 63006
Tel: 314-628-1196
Web Site: www.nbs-aerho.org
Key Personnel
Exec Dir: Jim Wilson *E-mail:* jim.wilson@nbs-
aerho.org
Established: 1962
Annual award presented to reward students for
accomplishments in audio, video, scriptwrit-
ing, web development, academic research &
writing.
Categories: 56 media categories
Award: Certificate & trophy
Closing Date: Nov (early), Dec (regular)
Entry Fee: Membs: $25 early, $35 regular; Non-
membs: $50 early, $60 regular
Presented: NBS-AERho Annual National Conven-
tion, March

New Jersey Film Festival
Rutgers Film Co-op/New Jersey Media Arts Center Inc

Rutgers University, 018 Loree Hall, 72 Lipman
Dr, New Brunswick, NJ 08901-1414
Mailing Address: Rutgers University, 4170
Academic Bldg, 15 Seminary Place, New
Brunswick, NJ 08901-8525
Tel: 848-932-8482 *Fax:* 732-932-1935
E-mail: njmac@aol.com; njmac12@gmail.com
Web Site: www.njfilmfest.com
Key Personnel
Exec Dir & Curator: Albert Gabriel Nigrin
Established: 1982
Competition open to US & international entries.
Maximum film age is 24 months.
Other Sponsor(s): Jimmy Johns; Johnson & John-
son; Jungle Software; Middlesex County Cul-
tural & Heritage Commission; New Brunswick
City Market; New Jersey State Council on the
Arts/Department of State; Rutgers University
Program in Cinema Studies
Media: DVD or Blu-ray
Categories: Animation, documentary, experimen-
tal, short narrative, feature, music video & stu-
dent filmmaker
Award: Varies
Closing Date: On-going spring/fall seasons
Entry Fee: $45 works up to 20 minutes; $55
works 20-50 minutes; $75 works over 50 min-
utes
Presented: Rutgers University, New Brunswick,
NJ, Spring: Jan-March; Fall: Sept-Nov

New Orleans Film Festival
New Orleans Film Society
1215 Prytania St, Suite 423, New Orleans, LA
70130
Tel: 504-309-6633
E-mail: noff@neworleansfilmsociety.org
Web Site: neworleansfilmsociety.org/festival
Key Personnel
Exec Dir: Fallon Young *E-mail:* fallon@
neworleansfilmsociety.org
Artistic Dir: Clint Bowie *E-mail:* clint@
neworleansfilmsociety.org
Devt Dir: Jennifer Samani *E-mail:* jennifer@
neworleansfilmsociety.org
Opers Dir: Monika Baudoin *E-mail:* monika@
neworleansfilmsociety.org
Tech Dir: Sergio Lobo-Navia *E-mail:* sergio@
neworleansfilmsociety.org
Busn Mgr: Hector Cassini *E-mail:* hector@
neworleansfilmsociety.org
Mktg & Communs Mgr: Zaf Yumru
E-mail: zaf@neworleansfilmsociety.org
Established: 1989
Media: Submissions: Secure online screener; Ex-
hibition: DCP, MOV; Screenplays: PDF
Categories: Narrative feature, narrative short,
animation, experimental, documentary fea-
ture, documentary short, Louisiana feature,
Louisiana short, music video, episodic, virtual
reality, screenplay feature, screenplay short,
screenplay episodic, screenplay Louisiana
Closing Date: Jan (early), March (regular), May
(late), June (extended)
Entry Fee: $20-$75
Presented: Annually in Oct

New York Emmy® Awards
New York Chapter, The National Academy of
Television Arts & Sciences (NY/NATAS)
Division of The National Academy of Television
Arts & Sciences
450 Seventh Ave, Suite 808, New York, NY
10123
Tel: 212-459-3630
E-mail: awards@nyemmys.org
Web Site: www.nyemmys.org
Key Personnel
Dir, Awards & Communs: Sean Schenk
Established: 1955
Honoring outstanding achievement in local televi-
sion.
Media: Video upload

Categories: News programming, news gathering, news & program specialty, programming, spot announcements, crafts achievement
Award: Statuette
Closing Date: Oct
Entry Fee: $125 membs; $255 nonmembs
Presented: New York, NY, April

New York Festivals® International Advertising Awards

New York Festivals®
260 W 39 St, 10th fl, New York, NY 10018
Tel: 212-643-4800 *Fax:* 212-643-0170
E-mail: info@newyorkfestivals.com
Web Site: advertising.newyorkfestivals.com; www. newyorkfestivals.com
Key Personnel
Pres & Exec Dir: Michael Demetriades
E-mail: mdemetriades@newyorkfestivals.com
Honors advertising excellence through 19 competitions in all media. All entries require brief synopsis (200 word maximum). Entries not in English must provide translation or detailed synopsis.
Media: All media
Categories: Activation & engagement, avant-garde/innovative, branded entertainment, creative marketing effectiveness, design, digital, direct & collateral, film, film craft, integrated, media, mobile, outdoor, package & product design, print, public & media relations, public service announcements, audio, student
Award: First, Second, Third Prize, Grand Awards for Best of Show. Finalists in public service advertising categories are eligible for the United Nations Department of Public Information (UNDPI) Awards for advertising that best exemplifies the aims & ideals of the United Nations
Closing Date: Jan 31
Entry Fee: Varies
Presented: Frederick P Rose Hall, Jazz at Lincoln Center, New York, NY, Official notification in May

New York Festivals® International Radio Program Awards

New York Festivals®
260 W 39 St, 10th fl, New York, NY 10018
Tel: 212-643-4800 *Fax:* 212-643-0170
E-mail: info@newyorkfestivals.com
Web Site: radio.newyorkfestivals.com; www. newyorkfestivals.com/radio
Key Personnel
Pres & Exec Dir: Michael Demetriades
E-mail: mdemetriades@newyorkfestivals.com
All professional radio programs, features, audio books & spots first broadcast after Jan 1 the year prior to the presentation. Productions not in English must provide a translation of at least the first 10 minutes & last 10 minutes.
Media: MP3 upload, URL for online radio or audio podcast, audio CD
Categories: News programs, news reports/features, information/documentary, entertainment programs & specials, talk programs, on-air talent, programming format, morning drive time programming, promotions, program opens & station IDs, online, satellite, podcasts, student, audiobooks & craft
Award: Gold, Silver & Bronze World Medals & Grand Awards for Best of Show will be presented to the winning entries. Finalist certificates also awarded. Finalists are eligible for the United Nations Department of Public Information (UNDPI) Awards
Closing Date: March
Entry Fee: Varies
Presented: New York, NY, Annually in June

New York Festivals® International TV & Film Awards

New York Festivals®
260 W 39 St, 10th fl, New York, NY 10018
Tel: 212-643-4800 *Fax:* 212-643-0170
E-mail: info@newyorkfestivals.com
Web Site: tvfilm.newyorkfestivals.com; www. newyorkfestivals.com/tvfilm
Key Personnel
Pres & Exec Dir: Michael Demetriades
E-mail: mdemetriades@newyorkfestivals.com
Feature & corporate films, all TV programs including news, documentary, entertainment, sports, promotions spots & station IDs. Entries in language other than English must have either subtitles or overdubbing in English (preferred) or detailed synopsis & translation of first & last 10 minutes. Campaign entries should feature no more than 3 spots.
Media: H.264.mov files
Categories: Distributed/transmitted group: News programs, news reports/features, entertainment programs, entertainment specials, promotions/station IDs & opens, documentaries, music videos, online programs, student productions/Webisodes, video art & experimental films, on-air performers & categories for crafts; Exhibited/screened group: Feature films, documentary films, short films, movie trailers, industrial productions, corporate presentations, network upfronts, business theater, event venue productions, education/information/entertainment productions/for-purchase-videos & categories for crafts
Award: Gold, Silver & Bronze World Medals & Grand Awards for Best of Show; finalist certificates also awarded; special presentations are made of the United Nations Department of Information (UNDPI) Awards for programming that best exemplifies the aims & ideals of the United Nations
Closing Date: Nov
Entry Fee: $395 single; $745 series; $75 student
Presented: NAB Show, Las Vegas, NV, April 21, 2020

New York Film Festival

Film at Lincoln Center
70 Lincoln Center Plaza, New York, NY 10023-6595
Tel: 212-875-5610; 212-875-5367 (cust serv)
Web Site: www.filmlinc.org
Key Personnel
Dir: Kent Jones
Established: 1963
Categories: Documentary, retrospective, revivals, projections, convergence & shorts
Presented: Walter Reade Theater & Elinor Bunin Munroe Film Center, Lincoln Center, New York, NY, Sept 25-Oct 11, 2020

Newark Black Film Festival (NBFF)

Newark Museum
49 Washington St, Newark, NJ 07102-3176
Tel: 973-596-6550
E-mail: nbff@newarkmuseum.org
Web Site: www.newarkmuseum.org/nbff
Key Personnel
NBFF Coord: Patricia Faison *Tel:* 973-596-6635
E-mail: pfaison@newarkmuseum.org
Established: 1974
Other Sponsor(s): Bank of America
Categories: Films related to the African-American experience
Closing Date: Jan 1
Presented: Newark, NJ, Summer

Nicholl Fellowships in Screenwriting

Academy of Motion Picture Arts and Sciences (AMPAS)
8949 Wilshire Blvd, Beverly Hills, CA 90211
Tel: 310-247-3010
E-mail: nicholl@oscars.org
Web Site: www.oscars.org/nicholl

Key Personnel
Mng Dir, Memb Rel & Awards: Lorenza Munoz
Tel: 310-247-3000 ext 1127 *E-mail:* lmunoz@oscars.org
Established: 1986
Categories: Original feature film screenplays, unproduced screenwriters
Award: $35,000 fellowship (up to 5)
Closing Date: March (early), April (regular), May (late)
Entry Fee: $45 early; $60 regular; $85 late

Nikon Small World

Nikon Instruments Inc
1300 Walt Whitman Rd, Melville, NY 11747-3064
Tel: 631-547-8500 *Toll Free Tel:* 800-52-NIKON (526-4566, US only) *Fax:* 631-547-0306
E-mail: info@nikonsmallworld.com
Web Site: www.nikonsmallworld.com; www. nikoninstruments.com
Key Personnel
Communs Mgr: Eric Flem *Tel:* 631-547-8532
Fax: 631-547-4033 *E-mail:* eflem@nikon.net
Established: 1975
Photomicography & digital video competitions. Any subject & technique employing a light microscope.
Media: Digital files
Award: $3,000 (first prize), $2,000 (2nd prize), $1,000 (3rd prize)
Closing Date: April 30
Presented: New York, NY, Early Oct

Northwest Filmmakers' Festival

Northwest Film Center
934 SW Salmon St, Portland, OR 97205
Mailing Address: 1219 SW Park Ave, Portland, OR 97205
Tel: 503-221-1156 *Fax:* 503-294-0874
E-mail: info@nwfilm.org; nwfest@nwfilm.org
Web Site: www.nwfilm.org
Key Personnel
Exhibition Prog Mgr & Programmer: Morgen Ruff *Tel:* 503-276-4223 *E-mail:* morgen@nwfilm.org
Filmmaker Servs Mgr & Programmer: Ben Popp *Tel:* 503-276-4222 *E-mail:* ben@nwfilm.org
Publicity & Promos Mgr: Nick Bruno *Tel:* 503-276-4209 *E-mail:* nick@nwfilm.org
Established: 1973
Juried showcase of new work by regional artists. Any length or genre released since Jan 1, two years prior & not previously entered in the festival. Open to permanent residents of AK, BC, ID, MT, OR & WA. Student entries (college & university only) must be from a school located in the Northwest.
Categories: Feature, short, long short
Award: Audience & judge's awards. Selected works will be assembled for the Best of Northwest Touring Program that will circulate throughout the region in the following year
Closing Date: Annually in Aug
Entry Fee: None
Presented: Northwest Film Center, Annually in Nov

NWT Arts Council

Department of Education, Culture & Employment Community Programs Office, PO Box 1320, Yellowknife, NT X1A 2L9, Canada
Tel: 867-767-9347 (ext 71474) *Toll Free Tel:* 877-445-2787 *Fax:* 867-873-0205
Web Site: www.nwtartscouncil.ca
Key Personnel
Mgr, Community Cultural Devt: Boris Atamanenko *E-mail:* boris_atamanenko@gov.nt.ca
Established: 1985
Grants & contributions open to residents & organizations of the Northwest Territories only.

Categories: Audio recording, performing arts, visual arts & crafts, film & media, writing & publishing, mentorship
Closing Date: Annually, Feb 28 & Oct 31

NYFF, see New York Film Festival

NYSCA/NYFA Artist Fellowships
New York Foundation for the Arts
20 Jay St, 7th fl, Suite 740, Brooklyn, NY 11201
Tel: 212-366-6900 *Fax:* 212-366-1778
E-mail: fellowships@nyfa.org
Web Site: www.nyfa.org
Key Personnel
Exec Dir: Michael L Royce
Sr Communs Offr: Amy Aronoff
Sr Offr, Indiv Giving & Spec Events: Barbara Toy
Established: 1985
Submissions accepted in 15 different disciplines, with 5 disciplines reviewed each year on a rotating 3-year cycle. Only NY state residents age 25 or over are eligible.
Other Sponsor(s): New York State Council on the Arts
Categories: Architecture/environmental structures/design, choreography, music/sound, photography, playwriting/screenwriting
Award: $7,000 fellowship
Closing Date: Jan
Entry Fee: None
Presented: July

OIAF, see Ottawa International Animation Festival

168 Film Festival
168 Film Project
PO Box 6184, Burbank, CA 91510
Tel: 818-557-8507 *Fax:* 818-942-6076
E-mail: info@168project.com
Web Site: www.168film.com/festival
Key Personnel
Founder & Dir: John David Ware
Established: 2003
Original short films based on a Bible verse.
Closing Date: Annually in May
Entry Fee: $168-$398
Presented: Annually in Aug

Ottawa International Animation Festival
Canadian Film Institute
2 Daly Ave, Suite 120, Ottawa, ON K1N 6E2, Canada
Tel: 613-232-8769 *Fax:* 613-232-6315
E-mail: info@animationfestival.ca; entries@animationfestival.ca
Web Site: www.animationfestival.ca
Key Personnel
Mng Dir: Kelly Neall *E-mail:* kelly@animationfestival.ca
Artistic Dir: Chris Robinson *E-mail:* chris@animationfestival.ca
Dir, Film Opers: Keltie Duncan *E-mail:* keltie@animationfestival.ca
Dir, Indus Programming: Azarin Sohrabkani *E-mail:* azarin@animationfestival.ca
Established: 1976
Media: Submissions: Streamable URL link; Exhibition: DCP & MOV
Categories: Feature film, independent short film, student animation, commissioned films, films/videos for young audiences, virtual reality
Closing Date: May
Entry Fee: None
Presented: Multiple venues throughout Ottawa, ON, CN, Annually in Sept

Outfest Los Angeles LGBT Film Festival
Outfest

3470 Wilshire Blvd, Suite 935, Los Angeles, CA 90010
Tel: 213-480-7088 *Fax:* 213-480-7099
E-mail: outfest@outfest.org
Web Site: www.outfest.org
Key Personnel
Exec Dir: Christopher Racster
Sr Dir, External Aff: Kerri Stoughton-Jackson *E-mail:* kerri@outfest.org
Dir, Programming: Lucy Mukerjee
Communs Mgr: Andrae Vigil-Romero *E-mail:* andrae@outfest.org
Established: 1982
Other Sponsor(s): HBO
Media: Submissions: Secure online screener, MOV; Exhibition: MOV
Categories: Narrative, documentary & experimental features & shorts, web & TV series, virtual reality & multimedia installations
Closing Date: Jan (early), Feb (regular), March (late/extended)
Entry Fee: Features: $30 early, $50 regular, $60 late, $90 extended; Shorts, web & TV series, virtual reality & multimedia installations: $20 early, $40 regular, $50 late, $75 extended
Presented: Venues include Directors Guild of America, Orpheum Theatre & REDCAT: Roy & Edna Disney/Calarts Theatre at Walt Disney Concert Hall, Downtown Los Angeles, CA, Annually in July

Palm Springs International Film Festival
Palm Springs International Film Society
1700 E Tahquitz Canyon Way, Suite 3, Palm Springs, CA 92262
Tel: 760-322-2930 *Toll Free Tel:* 800-898-7256
Fax: 760-322-4087
E-mail: info@psfilmfest.org
Web Site: www.psfilmfest.org
Key Personnel
Mng Dir: Rhea A Lewis-Woodson
Artistic Dir: Michael Lerman
Dir, Programming: Liliana Rodriguez
Film Awards Dir, Opers: Christine Sasse
Opers Mgr: Lauren Tutzauer
Established: 1990
Black Tie Gala film awards.
Media: Submission: Digital screener (Vimeo preferred); Exhibition: DCP
Categories: Feature, documentary feature
Closing Date: Aug 1 (regular), Sept 1 (late)
Entry Fee: $75 regular; $95 late
Presented: Palm Springs Convention Center, Palm Springs, CA, Annually in Jan

Pan African Film & Arts Festival
Pan African Film Festival (PAFF)
6820 La Tijera Blvd, Suite 200, Los Angeles, CA 90045
Tel: 310-337-4737 *Fax:* 310-337-4736
E-mail: info@paff.org; submissions@paff.org
Web Site: www.paff.org
Key Personnel
Exec Dir: Ayuko Babu *E-mail:* babu@paff.org
Publicity Dir: Candace Ledbetter *E-mail:* candace@paff.org
Prodn Designer, Art Show: Allohn Agbenya
Established: 1992
Exhibits films made by +/or about people of African descent made in the US, Africa, Europe, the Caribbean, the South Pacific, Latin America, Canada & Asia. Films of any genre are accepted. All submissions must be in English or have English subtitles. Official competition & audience awards, as well as programmer's & special festival awards.
Media: Submission: Online screener (Vimeo or YouTube preferred) or DVD screener (with prior approval only); Exhibition: DCP, HD resolution or greater online link & Blu-ray
Categories: Features, shorts, narratives, documentaries

Closing Date: July (early), Sept (regular), Oct (late), Nov (extended late)
Entry Fee: Features: $40 early, $55 regular, $75 late, $115 extended late; Shorts: $20 early, $30 regular, $50 late, $90 extended late
Presented: Annually in Feb

George Foster Peabody Awards
Grady College of Journalism & Mass Communication
c/o University of Georgia, 120 Hooper St, Athens, GA 30602-3018
Tel: 706-542-3787
E-mail: peabody@uga.edu
Web Site: www.peabodyawards.com
Key Personnel
Chief Mktg Offr: Christine Drayer
Dir: Dr Jeffrey P Jones *E-mail:* jpjones7@uga.edu
Communs Dir: Margaret Blanchard
Assoc Dir, Strategy & Opers: Lynh Tran
Events & Sponsorship Coord: Molly Williams
Established: 1940
Entry formats: Radio/Podcast, Television/Video, Interactive/Web.
Other Sponsor(s): The Coca Cola Co USA; Variety
Categories: News, entertainment, documentary, children's programming, public service
Award: Statuette
Closing Date: Dec (early), Jan (final)
Entry Fee: Radio/podcast: $225 early, $300 final; TV/digital: $350 early, $425 final
Presented: New York, NY, Annually in late May or early June

Philadelphia Film Festival
Philadelphia Film Society
1412 Chestnut St, Philadelphia, PA 19102
Tel: 267-239-2941
E-mail: info@filmadelphia.org
Web Site: filmadelphia.org/festival
Key Personnel
Exec Dir: J Andrew Greenblatt *E-mail:* agreenblatt@filmadelphia.org
Artistic Dir: Michael Lerman *E-mail:* mlerman@filmadelphia.org
Festival & Events Dir: Alex Gibson *E-mail:* agibson@filmadelphia.org
Established: 1992
Media: Submissions: Secure online screener or DVD NTSC; Exhibition: Blu-ray NTSC, DCP & 35mm
Categories: Feature, documentary, short, local
Closing Date: Annually in May (early), June (regular), July (late), Aug (extended)
Entry Fee: Features & documentaries: $40 early, $50 regular, $60 late, $75 extended; Local: $35 early, $45 regular, $55 late, $75 extended; Shorts: $30 early, $35 regular, $45 late, $55 extended
Presented: Philadelphia, PA, Annually in Oct

Philadelphia International Film Festival & Market
International Association of Motion Picture & Television Producers Inc
PO Box 48134, Philadelphia, PA 19144
Tel: 215-849-2716 (festival) *Toll Free Tel:* 877-347-FILM (347-3456)
E-mail: info@philafilm.org
Web Site: www.philafilm.org
Key Personnel
Festival Dir: Larry Smallwood, Jr *E-mail:* lsmall1@yahoo.com
Established: 1977
Other Sponsor(s): African-American Museum in Philadelphia; Ink Tip Inc; Philadelphia Corporation for Aging; UBC Network Inc; WPVI-TV 6, Philadelphia, PA
Media: 35mm, 16mm, DVD

Categories: Professional & independent film/television producers, directors, writers
Award: Trophies, certificates & product prizes
Closing Date: April 15
Entry Fee: $20-$100 (based upon entry category)
Presented: Varied Center City locales, Philadelphia, PA

PhilaFilm, see Philadelphia International Film Festival & Market

George Polk Awards in Journalism
Long Island University
Journalism Dept, One University Plaza, Brooklyn, NY 11201-5372
Tel: 718-488-1009
Web Site: www.liu.edu/polk
Key Personnel
Curator: John Darnton *E-mail:* john.darnton@gmail.com
Faculty Coord: Ralph Engelman *E-mail:* ralph.engelman@liu.edu
Established: 1949
Investigative journalism (print & electronic).
Media: Audio, video or digital recordings, DVD
Categories: Media
Award: Plaque & monetary award
Closing Date: Jan
Entry Fee: $25
Presented: New York, NY, April

Premio Mesquite
San Antonio CineFestival
Subsidiary of Guadalupe Cultural Arts Center
723 S Brazos St, San Antonio, TX 78207
Tel: 210-271-3151 *Fax:* 210-271-3480
E-mail: cine@guadalupeculturalarts.org
Web Site: www.guadalupeculturalarts.org
Key Personnel
CineFestival Dir: Jim Mendiola
Recognizes excellence in Chicano/Latino film & video production.
Media: 35mm film, HDCAM, Blu-ray, DVD, Digi-Beta; English subtitles strongly recommended
Categories: Feature, documentary, short, emerging artist/first film, special jury award
Closing Date: Oct (early), Nov (late)
Entry Fee: Early: $25, $15 student; Late: $35, $25 student
Presented: San Antonio, TX, Feb

The Presidential Proclamation
Society of Motion Picture & Television Engineers® (SMPTE®)
White Plains Plaza, 445 Hamilton Ave, Suite 601, White Plains, NY 10601-1827
Tel: 914-761-1100 *Fax:* 914-206-4216
E-mail: marketing@smpte.org
Web Site: www.smpte.org
Key Personnel
Exec Dir: Barbara H Lange *Tel:* 914-205-2370
Dir, Events & Governance Liaison: Sally-Ann D'Amato *Tel:* 914-205-2375 *E-mail:* sdamato@smpte.org
Mktg & Commun: Aimee Ricca *Tel:* 914-205-2381 *E-mail:* aimeericca@smpte.org
Exec Asst: June Marie Sobrito *Tel:* 914-205-2384 *E-mail:* jsobrito@smpte.org
Annually recognizes an individual of established & outstanding status & reputation in the motion picture & television industry worldwide.
Closing Date: April
Presented: SMPTE® Annual Technical Conference & Exhibition, Loews Hollywood Hotel, Hollywood, CA, Oct

Prix Gemeaux (French language TV)
Academy of Canadian Cinema & Television (ACCT)
225 rue Roy E, bureau 106, Montreal, QC H2W 1M5, Canada
Tel: 514-849-7448 *Fax:* 514-849-5069
E-mail: academie@acct.ca
Web Site: www.acct.ca/prixgemeaux; www.acct.ca; www.academy.ca
Key Personnel
Exec Dir: Patrice Lachance *Tel:* 514-849-7448 ext 21 *E-mail:* plachance@acct.ca
Award Coord: Samuel Belisle *Tel:* 514-849-7448 ext 28 *E-mail:* sbelisle@acct.ca
Media: Online streaming
Categories: TV & digital media
Award: Statuette
Presented: Montreal, QC, CN, Annually in Fall

PromaxBDA Promotion, Marketing and Design North America Awards
Promax
5700 Wilshire Blvd, Suite 275, Los Angeles, CA 90036
Tel: 310-788-7600 *Fax:* 310-788-7616
E-mail: awards@promaxbda.org
Web Site: www.promax.org/awards
Key Personnel
SVP, Global Awards Devt & Exec Prodr, Conference Prodn & Experience: Stacy La Cotera *Tel:* 310-789-1503 *E-mail:* stacy@promaxbda.org
Mgr, Global Awards & Competitions: Paul Lee *Tel:* 310-789-1585 *E-mail:* paul.lee@promaxbda.org
Coord, Global Awards & Competitions: Sam Jae *Tel:* 310-789-1515 *E-mail:* sam.jae@promaxbda.org
Television promotion, marketing & design work from any company or individual, broadcast, published or released in the US & Canadian markets during the previous calendar year is eligible.
Award: Gold & silver statues
Closing Date: Annually in Jan (1st price), Feb (2nd price), March (final)
Entry Fee: Single entry (Jan deadline) $275 membs, $375 nonmembs, campaign $375 membs, $475 nonmembs; Single entry (Feb deadline) $350 membs, $450 nonmembs, campaign $450 membs, $550 nonmembs; Single entry (final March deadline) $425 membs, $525 nonmembs, campaign $525 membs, $625 nonmembs
Presented: Annually in June

Providence Underground Film Festival
Flickers Art Collaborative
83 Park St, Suite 5, Providence, RI 02903
Mailing Address: PO Box 162, Newport, RI 02840-0002
Tel: 401-861-4445 *Fax:* 401-490-6735
E-mail: info@film-festival.org
Web Site: www.film-festival.org
Key Personnel
Exec Dir/CEO: George T Marshall *E-mail:* georget@film-festival.org
Prog Dir: Shawn Quirk *E-mail:* quirk@film-festival.org
Established: 1998
Annual event showcasing radically independent experimental, narrative & documentary films. Official sidebar of the Flickers' Rhode Island International Film Festival™ with films by local Rhode Island & New England filmmakers. All films accepted & featured come from the entry pool of the Rhode Island International Film Festival & are featured during the same week as part of the larger festival.
Award: Trophies

PXL This Video Festival
2427 1/2 Glyndon Ave, Venice, CA 90291
Tel: 310-306-7330
E-mail: pfsuzy@aol.com

Web Site: laughtears.com
Key Personnel
Dir & Curator: Gerry Fialka
Established: 1991
Toy camera film festival featuring Pixelvision films made with the Fisher-Price PXL-2000 camcorder celebrating creative filmmaking by everyone from kids to professionals.
Categories: All categories accepted
Closing Date: Annually in Oct
Entry Fee: None
Presented: Publicly in Los Angeles, CA & tours in US, Annually in Nov & May

Ward L Quaal Leadership Awards
Broadcasters Foundation of America
125 W 55 St, 4th fl, New York, NY 10019-5366
Tel: 212-373-8250 *Fax:* 212-373-8254
E-mail: info@thebfoa.org
Web Site: www.thebfoa.org; broadcastersfoundation.org
Key Personnel
Pres: James B Thompson *E-mail:* jim@thebfoa.org
VP: Peter M Doyle *E-mail:* peter@thebfoa.org
VP, Busn Aff: Frank Pesce *E-mail:* frank@thebfoa.org
Off & Grant Mgr: Emily Barratt *E-mail:* emily@thebfoa.org
Awarded annually in recognition of individuals' career contributions to the broadcast industry & the community-at-large.
Presented: April

Radio & Television Engineering Achievement Awards
National Association of Broadcasters (NAB)
1771 "N" St NW, Washington, DC 20036
Tel: 202-429-5300
E-mail: nab@nab.org; techawards@nab.org (nominations)
Web Site: www.nab.org
Key Personnel
VP, Technol Opers: Janet Elliott
Established: 1959
Recognized annually on basis of single significant contribution or contributions made over a period of time, which significantly advance the state of the art of broadcast engineering.
Award: Plaque
Presented: NAB: We Are Broadcasters Celebration, Las Vegas Convention Center, Las Vegas, NV

Real to Reel International Film Festival
Subsidiary of Cleveland County Arts Council
111 S Washington St, Shelby, NC 28150
Tel: 704-484-2787 *Fax:* 704-481-1822
Web Site: www.ccartscouncil.org/realtoreel
Key Personnel
Mktg Dir: Violet Arth *E-mail:* violet.arth@ccartscouncil.org
Established: 2000
Showcase thought-provoking films.
Media: Original formats can be shot on all formats of video as well as all formats digital & computer multimedia. All formats must be on DVD or Blu-ray
Categories: Feature short, documentary, animation, by children 14 & under, for children
Award: Cash award for top winners, $300-$1,000
Closing Date: Feb (early bird), March (regular), April (late)
Entry Fee: Professional: $40 early bird, $50 regular, $55 late; Student/amateur: $20 early bird, $25 regular, $30 late
Presented: Joy Performance Theater, Kings Mountain, NC, July

The Olivier Rebbot Award
Overseas Press Club of America
40 W 45 St, New York, NY 10036

Tel: 212-626-9220 Fax: 212-626-9210
E-mail: info@opcofamerica.org
Web Site: www.opcofamerica.org
Key Personnel
Exec Dir: Patricia Kranz
Best photographic reporting from abroad in any
media.
Award: Certificate & $1,000 check
Closing Date: Annually in late Jan
Entry Fee: $200
Presented: Hotel Mandarin-Oriental, New York,
NY, Annually in April

Reelout Queer Film + Video Festival
Reelout Arts Project Inc
82 Sydenham St, Kingston, ON K7L 3H4,
Canada
Tel: 613-549-REEL (549-7335)
Web Site: www.reelout.com
Key Personnel
Festival Dir: Matt Salton E-mail: director@
reelout.com
Established: 1999
Showcase for independent GLBTT films &
videos. Audience awards for Best Feature, Best
Documentary, Best Canadian Short Film.
Categories: Film, Video
Closing Date: Annually, Sept 30
Entry Fee: None

ReelWorld Film Festival
ReelWorld Foundation
50 Carroll St, Suite 200, Toronto, ON M4M 3G3,
Canada
Tel: 416-598-7933
E-mail: info@reelworld.ca; contact@reelworld.ca
Web Site: www.reelworld.ca
Key Personnel
Founder & Pres: Tonya Williams E-mail: tonya@
reelworld.ca
Exec Dir: Gave Lindo
Prog Dir: Sherien Barsoum
Fin Mgr: Rodrigo Diaz Varela
Established: 2001
Not-for-profit & charity organizations that create
year-round screenings, speakers & educational
opportunities for racially & culturally diverse
artists with an emphasis on social impact me-
dia.

Regional Artist Project Grants Program
Arts & Science Council Charlotte/Mecklenburg
227 W Trade St, Suite 250, Charlotte, NC 28202
Tel: 704-333-2272 Fax: 704-333-2720
E-mail: asc@artsandscience.org
Web Site: www.artsandscience.org
Key Personnel
VP, Cultural & Community Investment: Ryan
Deal
Grant awarded to all disciplines. Recipients noti-
fied by mail/e-mail.
Other Sponsor(s): Cabarrus Arts Council; Cleve-
land Arts Council; Gaston Arts Council; Iredell
Arts Council; North Carolina Arts Council;
Rowan Arts Council; Rutherford Arts Council;
Union County Arts Council; York (SC) Arts
Council
Categories: All disciplines
Award: Up to $2,000 cash grant
Closing Date: Annually in Sept

Residency Fellowship
Virginia Center for the Creative Arts (VCCA)
154 San Angelo Dr, Amherst, VA 24521
Tel: 434-946-7236 Fax: 434-946-7239
E-mail: vcca@vcca.com
Web Site: www.vcca.com
Key Personnel
Exec Dir: Joy Peterson Heyrman
Artists Serv Dir: Sheila Gulley Pleasants
E-mail: spleasants@vcca.com

Dir, Communs & Grants Mgmt: Sarah Sargent
E-mail: ssargent@vcca.com
Off Mgr: Beatrice Booker E-mail: bbooker@vcca.
com
Established: 1971
Residential fellowships for writers, visual artists
& composers.
Media: Digital images & videos, PDF
Closing Date: Annually, Jan 15, May 15 & Sept
15
Entry Fee: $40 application fee. Artists are ac-
cepted to VCCA without regard for their finan-
cial situation. Fellows are asked to contribute
according to their ability

Rhode Island International Film Festival™
(RIIFF), see Flickers' Rhode Island
International Film Festival™ (RIIFF)

Rhode Island State Council on the Arts
Fellowships & Grants Program
Division of The State of Rhode Island
One Capitol Hill, 3rd fl, Providence, RI 02908
Tel: 401-222-3880 Fax: 401-222-3018
E-mail: info@arts.ri.gov
Web Site: www.arts.ri.gov
Key Personnel
Dir, Grants: Adrienne Adeyemi Tel: 401-222-
3882 E-mail: adrienne.adeyemi@arts.ri.gov
Established: 1967
Grants for Rhode Island resident artists, nonprofit
organizations, schools & arts educators.
Other Sponsor(s): National Endowment for the
Arts
Categories: April 1st deadline for fellowships in
fiction, poetry, playwriting/screenwriting, crafts,
film & video, folk art, photography & 3D art;
Oct 1st deadline for choreography, drawing &
printmaking, music composition, new genres &
painting. Project grants accepted from individ-
uals & organizations also on these deadlines in
all disciplines
Award: Cash
Closing Date: Annually, April 1 & Oct 1
Entry Fee: None
Presented: Annually, 4 months after closing date

The RIAA® Gold® & Platinum® Awards
Recording Industry Association of America®
(RIAA)
1025 "F" St NW, 10th fl, Washington, DC 20004
Tel: 202-775-0101
Web Site: www.riaa.com/gold-platinum
Key Personnel
Chmn & CEO: Cary Sherman
Pres: Mitch Glazier
EVP, Communs & Mktg: Jonathan Lamy
Established: 1958
Gold® award for the sale of 500,000 units.
Platinum® award for the sale of 1,000,000
units. Multi-Platinum™ award for the sale of
2,000,000 units. Diamond® award for the sale
of 10,000,000 units.
Media: On-demand audio/video song streams,
digital tracks, digital albums, ringtones
Categories: Record industry
Award: Plaque containing RIAA® holographic
seal

The Bart Richards Award for Media Criticism
Penn State College of Communications
302 James Bldg, University Park, PA 16801
Tel: 814-865-8801 Fax: 814-863-6134
Web Site: comm.psu.edu/bart
Key Personnel
Dir, Strategic Communs: Steve Sampsell
E-mail: steves@psu.edu
Established: 1994
Improving print & broadcast journalism through
responsible evaluation or critical evaluation.
Media: DVD (with final script or summaries)
Award: $1,000

Closing Date: Jan 31
Entry Fee: None
Presented: New York, NY, Annually in May

The Ridenhour Documentary Film Prize
The Nation Institute
116 E 16 St, 8th fl, New York, NY 10003
Tel: 212-822-0257 Fax: 212-253-5356
E-mail: ridenhour@nationinstitute.org
Web Site: www.ridenhour.org
Key Personnel
Exec Dir & CEO: Taya Kitman Tel: 212-822-
0252 E-mail: taya@nationinstitute.org
Ridenhour Coord: Kristine Bruch Tel: 212-822-
0263 E-mail: kristine@nationinstitute.org
Given to a documentary film that in the view
of the judges best reflects the legacy of Ron
Ridenhour-journalist, whistleblower, truth-teller
& social activist. The prize seeks to recognize
a documentary that defends the public interest,
advances or promotes social justice, or illumi-
nates a more just vision of society.
Other Sponsor(s): The Fertel Foundation
Media: Secure online screener (preferred), DVD
(NTSC Region 1)
Award: $10,000 stipend
Closing Date: Dec 1

Paul Robeson Awards
Newark Museum
49 Washington St, Newark, NJ 07102-3176
Tel: 973-596-6550
E-mail: nbff@newarkmuseum.org
Web Site: www.newarkmuseum.org/nbff
Key Personnel
NBFF Coord: Patricia Faison Tel: 973-596-6635
E-mail: pfaison@newarkmuseum.org
Established: 1985
Biennial film competition featured during the
Newark Black Film Festival in even-numbered
years.
Other Sponsor(s): Bank of America
Media: Vimeo or DVD (NTSC) format only
Categories: Films related to the African-American
experience
Award: Cash
Closing Date: Feb
Entry Fee: $40
Presented: Newark, NJ, Summer

Rochester International Film Festival
Movies on a Shoestring Inc
PO Box 17746, Rochester, NY 14617
Tel: 585-234-7411 (voice mail)
E-mail: president@rochesterfilmfest.org
(use MOAS on subject); submissions@
rochesterfilmfest.org
Web Site: www.rochesterfilmfest.org
Key Personnel
Pres: Al Figler
Established: 1959
Media: Submissions: DVD (Region 1 or Region
free) format; Screening: Quicktime (.MOV),
16mm, 35mm
Categories: Shorts under 30 minutes, all genre
Award: Trophy
Closing Date: Feb 1
Entry Fee: $50; $35 before Dec 1
Presented: Dryden Theatre, George Eastman
House, 900 East Ave, Rochester, NY, Annually
in Spring

Rockie Awards Program Competition
Brunico Communications Ltd
100-366 Adelaide St W, Toronto, ON M5V 1R9,
Canada
Tel: 416-408-2300 Toll Free Tel: 888-287-2279
Fax: 416-408-0870
E-mail: info@achillesmedia.com
Web Site: banffmediafestival.com; rockies.
playbackonline.ca

Key Personnel

Prodr, Content: Zoe Sherwood *Tel:* 416-408-2300 ext 237 *E-mail:* zsherwood@brunico.com

Celebrates excellence in television & digital content.

Categories: Documentary & Factual Stream: crime & investigative; environment & wildlife; history & biography; science & technology; social & current affairs; web nonfiction; Children & Youth Stream: children & youth-animation; children & youth-fiction; children & youth-nonfiction; children & youth-interactive content; preschool; Arts & Entertainment Stream: animation program-other; interactive content; lifestyle; arts & music; comedy & variety; reality-docusoap & docuseries; reality-competition series & game shows; comedy series-English language; comedy series-non-English language; drama series-English language; drama series-non-English language; limited series; sci-fi & genre-based; television movie; web fiction; Podcast of the Year; Rogers Prize for Excellence in Canadian Content; Rockies Francophone Prize

Award: Trophy

Closing Date: Dec 6 (early), Feb 7 (final)

Entry Fee: $300 early; $400 final

Presented: Banff World Media Festival, The Fairmont Banff Springs Hotel, 405 Spray Ave, Banff, AB, CN, June 14-17, 2020

The Madeline Dane Ross Award

Overseas Press Club of America

40 W 45 St, New York, NY 10036

Tel: 212-626-9220 *Fax:* 212-626-9210

E-mail: info@opcofamerica.org

Web Site: www.opcofamerica.org

Key Personnel

Exec Dir: Patricia Kranz

Given to a correspondent in print medium or digital for the best international reporting showing a concern for the human condition. All entries are submitted online.

Other Sponsor(s): Linda Fasulo

Media: Print & online

Award: Certificate & $1,000 check

Closing Date: Annually in late Jan

Entry Fee: $200

Presented: Hotel Mandarin-Oriental, New York, NY, Annually in April

Roving Eye International Film Festival

Flickers Art Collaborative

83 Park St, Suite 5, Providence, RI 02903

Mailing Address: PO Box 162, Newport, RI 02840-0002

Tel: 401-861-4445 *Fax:* 401-490-6735

E-mail: info@film-festival.org

Web Site: film-festival.org

Key Personnel

Exec Dir/CEO: George T Marshall
E-mail: georget@film-festival.org

Prog Dir: Shawn Quirk *E-mail:* quirk@film-festival.org

Official sidebar of the Flickers' Rhode Island International Film Festival™. All films accepted & featured come from the entry pool of the Rhode Island International Film Festival.

Presented: Annually in April

Royal Starr Film Festival (RSFF)

Royal Starr Arts Institute

880 S Old Woodward Ave, Birmingham, MI 48009

Tel: 248-825-3110

E-mail: info@royalstarr.org

Web Site: www.royalstarr.org; filmfreeway.com/RoyalStarrFilmFestival (submissions)

Established: 2015

International film festival which screens short, feature & documentary films. All submissions must have been completed on or after October 1, 2017 & must be available by June 15, 2020 for inclusion in the festival.

Categories: Narrative feature, documentary feature, international narrative feature, international documentary feature, narrative short, documentary short, international narrative short, international documentary short, animated feature, animated short, family friendly feature, Michigan feature, Michigan short, music video

Closing Date: Dec 31 (super early), Feb 15 (early), March 15 (regular), April 15 (late), May 31 (extended)

Entry Fee: Shorts: $10-$45; Features: $10-$50

Presented: Emagine Royal Oak Theater, 200 N Main St, Royal Oak, MI, Sept 11-Sept 20, 2020

RTDNA Edward R Murrow Awards

Radio Television Digital News Association (RTDNA)

The National Press Bldg, 529 14 St NW, Suite 1240, Washington, DC 20045

Tel: 202-662-7254 *Fax:* 202-223-4007

E-mail: awards@rtdna.org

Web Site: www.rtdna.org

Key Personnel

Exec Dir: Dan Shelley *Tel:* 212-246-0398
E-mail: dans@rtdna.org

Dir, Events & Awards: Kate Switchenko

Established: 1971

Outstanding achievements in electronic journalism.

Categories: Radio & television stations only

Award: National Murrow winner receives a crystal trophy. All others receive a plaque

Closing Date: Feb

Entry Fee: $80-$260; see web site for rates per category

Presented: RTDNA Awards Dinner, Gotham Hall, New York, NY, Columbus Day

St Barth Film Festival

c/o Cobblestone Films, 140 Riverside Dr, No 5D, New York, NY 10024

Tel: 212-989-8004 *Fax:* 212-727-1774

E-mail: staff@stbarthff.org

Web Site: www.stbarthff.org

Key Personnel

Dir: Joshua Harrison *E-mail:* jharrison@stbarthff.org; Ellen Lampert-Greaux *E-mail:* elgreaux@wanadoo.fr

Established: 1996

Media: 35mm, DVD, Blu-ray

Categories: Feature/Documentary

Closing Date: Annually, March 1

Entry Fee: Sliding scale

Presented: L'Orient, St Barth, Annually in April

St John's International Women's Film Festival

28 Cochrane St, Suite 101, St John's, NL A1C 3L3, Canada

Mailing Address: PO Box 984, Sta C, St John's, NL A1C 5M3, Canada

Tel: 709-754-3141 *Fax:* 709-754-0049

E-mail: info@womensfilmfestival.com

Web Site: www.womensfilmfestival.com

Key Personnel

Exec Dir: Jenn Brown *E-mail:* jenn@womensfilmfestival.com

Tech Dir: Victoria Wells *E-mail:* victoria@womensfilmfestival.com

Asst Festival Dir: Chantal Lovell
E-mail: chantal@womensfilmfestival.com

Communs Coord: Katie Thompson

Progs Coord: Nicole Boggan

Established: 1989

Non-competitive.

Other Sponsor(s): ArtsNL; Canada Council for the Arts; Canadian Heritage; CBC; Government of Newfoundland and Labrador; Telefilm Canada

Media: Submissions: High Resolution QuickTime MOV or other digital screener; Exhibition: DCP (gala screenings only), QuickTime MOV, HDCAM, XDCAM-HD

Categories: Shorts & features: Drama (including comedy), documentary, animation, experimental

Closing Date: March 23 (early), April 20 (regular), May 25 (late), June 8 (extended shorts), June 22 (extended features)

Entry Fee: Features: $35 all deadlines; Shorts: $20 early, $30 regular, $45 late, $65 extended

Presented: LSPU Hall, The Rooms, Rocket Bakery, Scotiabank Theatre, NIFCO & Alt Hotel, Oct 14-18, 2020

Sally Mountain Park Bluegrass Festival

Sally Mountain Show

703-A N Marion St, Greentop, MO 63546

Tel: 660-949-2345

E-mail: festival@marktwain.net

Web Site: www.sallymountainshow.com

Key Personnel

Contact: Carolyn Vincent

Presented: Queen City, MO, July 1-5, 2020

San Antonio Film Festival

8452 Fredericksburg Rd, PMB 264, San Antonio, TX 78229

Tel: 210-885-5888

E-mail: safilm@gmail.com; hello@safilm.com

Web Site: www.safilm.com

Key Personnel

Festival Dir: Adam Rocha *E-mail:* adam@safilm.com

Festival Prodr: Susan Ranjel *E-mail:* susan@safilm.com

Communs Dir: Angela Covo *E-mail:* angela@safilm.com

Established: 1994

Media: Submissions: Online screener or DVD; Screening: DVD or Blu-ray (NTSC)

Categories: Feature length films, short films, college films, high school films, films made in San Antonio, screenplay, short script

Closing Date: Annually in Aug

Entry Fee: Feature, short, college & San Antonio: $25 early, $35 regular, $75 late, $90 extended; High school: $5 early, $10 regular, $35 late, $90 extended; Screenplay: $55 early, $60 regular, $65 late, $70 extended; Short script: $35 early, $40 regular, $50 late, $60 extended

Presented: San Antonio, TX, Annually in June

San Diego Film Festival

San Diego Film Foundation

2683 Via de la Valle, Suite G-210, Del Mar, CA 92014

Tel: 619-818-2221

E-mail: info@sdfilmfest.com

Web Site: www.sdfilmfest.com

Key Personnel

Exec Dir & Founder: Tonya Montooth

Established: 2001

Closing Date: June 15 (regular), July 10 (late)

Presented: Annually in Sept

San Francisco Black Film Festival

PO Box 15490, San Francisco, CA 94115

Tel: 770-369-3776

E-mail: sfbff@sfbff.org

Web Site: www.sfbff.org

Key Personnel

Co-Dir & Festival Registrar: Katera Crossley
E-mail: katera@sfbff.org

Co-Dir: Kali O'Ray

Established: 1998

Other Sponsor(s): San Francisco Arts Commission

Media: Submissions: Secure online screener, DVD or Blu-ray

Categories: Animation, feature, student, shorts, documentary, narrative, French, foreign, African, youth (5-12), youth (12+)
Closing Date: Sept (early), March (regular), April (late)
Entry Fee: $30-$75
Presented: June

San Francisco International Film Festival
Division of San Francisco Film Society
39 Mesa St, Suite 110, The Presidio, San Francisco, CA 94129-1025
Tel: 415-561-5000 *Fax:* 415-440-1760
E-mail: info@sffilm.org
Web Site: sffilm.org/sffilm-festival/
Key Personnel
Dir, Communs: Bill Proctor *Tel:* 415-561-5024
E-mail: bproctor@sffilm.org
Dir, Programming: Rachel Rosen *Tel:* 415-561-5010 *E-mail:* rrosen@sffilm.org
Established: 1957
The festival highlights current trends in international film & video production with an emphasis on work that has not yet secured US distribution. Also invites recent feature length narratives & documentaries & archival presentations from around the globe, special awards & tributes recognizing individual achievement.
Closing Date: Oct-Dec for following year's festival
Entry Fee: Varies
Presented: Annually in April/May

San Francisco International LGBTQ Film Festival
Frameline
145 Ninth St, Suite 300, San Francisco, CA 94103
Tel: 415-703-8650 *Fax:* 415-861-1404
E-mail: info@frameline.org
Web Site: www.frameline.org/festival
Key Personnel
Exec Dir: Frances Wallace *Tel:* 415-703-8650 ext 310 *E-mail:* fwallace@frameline.org
Established: 1977
Media: Submissions: Secure online screener; Exhibition: DCP
Categories: Narrative features, documentary features, shorts, episodic
Award: Cash prizes for filmmakers: $7,500 First Feature Award; $1,000 Festival Audience Award
Closing Date: Dec (early), Jan (regular), Feb (late/extended)
Entry Fee: $20-$75
Presented: Annually in June

San Francisco Jewish Film Festival
145 Ninth St, Suite 200, San Francisco, CA 94103
Tel: 415-621-0556 *Fax:* 415-621-0568
E-mail: jewishfilm@sfjff.org; programming@jfi.org
Web Site: www.sfjff.org; jfi.org
Key Personnel
Exec Dir: Lexi Leban *E-mail:* lleban@jfi.org
Prog Dir: Jay Rosenblatt *Tel:* 415-621-0556 ext 203 *E-mail:* jrosenblatt@jfi.org
Mktg & Communs Mgr: Nate Gellman
E-mail: ngellman@jfi.org
Established: 1980
Annually presents best of independent Jewish-themed film. All genres & subject matter welcome.
Media: Submissions: Online screener or DVD (NTSC preferred), PAL & non-region 1 permitted; Exhibition: DCP, ProRes, Blu-ray & 35mm
Categories: Feature, documentary, narrative short, documentary short
Closing Date: Feb

Entry Fee: $25 shorts (under 50 minutes); $35 features (over 50 minutes)
Presented: Five Bay Area cities, CA, Summer

Santa Barbara International Film Festival
1528 Chapala St, Suite 203, Santa Barbara, CA 93101
Tel: 805-963-0023 *Fax:* 805-962-2524
E-mail: contactus@sbiff.org
Web Site: sbiff.org
Key Personnel
Exec Dir: Roger Durling
Devt Dir: Benjamin Goedert
Mng Dir: Sean Pratt
Established: 1985
Media: Submissions: DVD (NTSC Region 0 or 1); Exhibition: 35mm, HDCAM 23.98P & 60i(59.94) (stereo), DigitBeta 29.97fps (stereo), DCP
Categories: Independent features, documentaries, live action shorts, animated shorts, world cinema, local films
Award: Certificate, plaque & cash prizes
Closing Date: Annually in Sept, late entries by special request. Specific dates online
Entry Fee: Varies by date submitted
Presented: Santa Barbara, CA

Saturn Awards
Academy of Science Fiction, Fantasy & Horror Films
334 W 54 St, Los Angeles, CA 90037
Tel: 323-752-5811
E-mail: saturn.awards@ca.rr.com
Web Site: www.saturnawards.org
Key Personnel
Pres, CEO & Awards Mgr: Robert Holguin
Exec Admin: David Bilbrey
Dir, Opers: Michael Laster
Prodr: Aaron Griffin
Publicity: John Singh
Established: 1972
Categories: Film, television, home entertainment & live stage production
Award: Saturn gold color award statue
Presented: Annually in June

Screamfest® Horror Film Festival & Screenplay Competition
8840 Wilshire Blvd, Beverly Hills, CA 90211
Tel: 310-358-3273
E-mail: info@screamfestla.com
Web Site: www.screamfestla.com
Key Personnel
Founder & Festival Dir: Rachel Belofsky
Established: 2001
Eligible films must have been completed after Jan of the year prior to the festival & not have been released on DVD. Feature film script length should be at least 75 pages & not over 130.
Media: Submissions: Secured online screeners
Categories: Feature, shorts, super shorts, documentary, animation, student horror film
Award: Cash, software, statue, film
Closing Date: Film: April 15 (early), July 15 (regular), Aug 1 (final); Screenplay: Jan 15 (early), March 15 (regular), June 2 (final)
Entry Fee: Feature: $52 early, $57 regular, $67 final; Short: $37 early, $42 regular, $52 final; Super short: $32 early, $37 regular, $47 final; Screenplay: $37 early, $52 regular, $62 final, $77 extended
Presented: Los Angeles, CA, Oct

Seattle International Film Festival (SIFF)
305 Harrison St, Seattle, WA 98109
Tel: 206-464-5830 *Fax:* 206-264-7919
E-mail: info@siff.net; entries@siff.net
Web Site: www.siff.net
Key Personnel
Exec Dir: Andrew L Haines

Dir, Mktg & Communs: Elizabeth Rossi *Tel:* 206-315-0673 *E-mail:* elizabeth.rossi@siff.net
Artistic Dir: Beth Barrett
Cinema Opers Mgr: Andrew Niece
Festival Opers Mgr: Carley Callahan
Mktg Mgr: Leah Anderson *Tel:* 206-315-0685
E-mail: leah.anderson@siff.net
Established: 1976
Media: Submissions: Online screener or digital media file; Exhibition: 35mm film or DCP (NTSC or PAL)
Categories: Feature film, short film, documentary short film, FutureWave, SIFF Catalyst Screenplay Competition
Closing Date: Oct 4 (early), Dec 13 (regular), Jan 31 (final), Feb 28 (FutureWave)
Entry Fee: Features: $70 early, $100 regular, $125 final; Shorts/Episodics: $40 early, $70 regular, $90 final; FutureWave: $20 early & regular, $30 final
Presented: Seattle, WA, May 14-June 7, 2020

Seattle Jewish Film Festival (SJFF)
Stroum Jewish Community Center
3801 E Mercer Way, Mercer Island, WA 98040
Tel: 206-388-0833; 206-232-7115 (SJCC)
E-mail: sjff@sjcc.org
Web Site: www.seattlejewishfilmfestival.org; sjcc.org/arts-ideas/seattle-jewish-film-festival
Key Personnel
Festival Dir: Pamela Lavitt *Tel:* 206-388-0832
E-mail: pamelal@sjcc.org
Established: 1995
Audience Choice Award for best narrative, documentary & short films. Also REEL Difference Award for extraordinary human rights, civil rights or profound impact on the community.
American Jewish Committee (AJC) is a founding partner of this 11-day annual event.
Other Sponsor(s): Martin Selig & Catherine Mayer; Xfinity
Media: Submissions: Secure online screener, 2 DVD screeners (preferably NTSC Region 0 or 1); Exhibition: DCP, Blu-ray, HDCAM
Categories: Animated, documentary feature, documentary short, narrative feature, narrative short
Closing Date: Nov 1
Entry Fee: Features: $30, $25 student; Shorts: $20, $15 student, no fee for student films under 10 minutes; Animated: $30 over 40 minutes, $20 under 40 minutes, students $25 over 40 minutes, $15 under 40 minutes, no fee for student animated films under 10 minutes
Presented: Venues in downtown Seattle, WA & the Stroum Jewish Community Center, Mercer Island, WA, March/April

Sigma Delta Chi Awards in Journalism
Society of Professional Journalists
Eugene S Pulliam National Journalism Ctr, 3909 N Meridian St, Indianapolis, IN 46208
Tel: 317-927-8000 *Fax:* 317-920-4789
E-mail: awards@spj.org
Web Site: www.spj.org
Key Personnel
Exec Dir: Joe Skeel *Tel:* 317-927-8000 ext 216
E-mail: jskeel@spj.org
Assoc Exec Dir: Chris Vachon *Tel:* 317-927-8000 ext 207 *E-mail:* cvachon@spj.org
Awards Coord: Abbi Martzall *Tel:* 317-927-8000 ext 210 *E-mail:* amartzall@hq.spj.org
Established: 1932
Recognize the best in professional journalism in categories covering print, radio, television, newsletters, art/graphics, online & research.
Media: PDF or URL
Categories: Various journalism
Award: Plaque with medallion
Closing Date: Annually in Feb
Entry Fee: $60 membs, $85 after deadline; $100 nonmembs, $120 after deadline
Presented: SPJ National Press Club, Washington, DC, Annually in June

Silver Anvil Awards

The Public Relations Society of America Inc
(PRSA)
120 Wall St, 21st fl, New York, NY 10005-4024
Tel: 212-460-1438
E-mail: awards@prsa.org
Web Site: www.prsa.org
Key Personnel
VP, Spec Events & Progs: Karla Voth
E-mail: karla.voth@prsa.org
Established: 1945
Recognizes oustanding strategic public relations
programs. Awarded in 18 categories & various
subcategories.
Award: Trophy
Closing Date: Feb
Entry Fee: $325 membs, $425 nonmembs (early);
$525 membs, $625 nonmembs (final/late)
Presented: June

Silver Gavel Awards for Media & the Arts

American Bar Association
Div for Public Education, 321 N Clark St,
Chicago, IL 60654-7598
Tel: 312-988-5733 *Toll Free Tel:* 800-285-2221
Fax: 312-988-5494 (Attn: Gavel Awards)
E-mail: publiceducation@americanbar.org
Web Site: www.americanbar.org
Key Personnel
Div Dir: Mabel McKinney-Browning *Tel:* 312-
988-5731 *E-mail:* mabel.mckinneybrowning@
americanbar.org
Awards Chair: Stephen Edds
Assoc Dir, Admin/Progs: Howard Kaplan
Tel: 312-988-5738 *E-mail:* howard.kaplan@
americanbar.org
To recognize work in media & the arts published
or presented during the preceding year that
have been exemplary in helping to foster the
American public's understanding of law & the
legal system.
Media: CDs, DVDs, uploaded digital file or
linked URLs
Categories: Books, magazines, newspapers, com-
mentary, drama & literature, documentaries,
TV, radio & other media
Award: Silver gavel & wooden plaques for honor-
able mentions
Closing Date: Annually in Jan
Entry Fee: $75 per entry
Presented: National Press Club, Washington, DC,
July

Slamdance Film Festival

5634 Melrose Ave, Los Angeles, CA 90038
Tel: 323-466-1786 *Fax:* 323-466-1784
E-mail: submissions@slamdance.com
Web Site: www.slamdance.com
Key Personnel
Founder & Pres: Peter Baxter
Founder: Jon Fitzgerald; Shane Kuhn; Dan
Mirvish; Paul Rothman
Established: 1995
Independent filmmakers festival.
Media: Film & video
Categories: New filmmakers, special screenings
Award: $90,000 in goods & services
Closing Date: Oct
Entry Fee: $40-$70 short; $50-$110 feature (de-
pending on date submitted)
Presented: Park City, UT, Jan

SMPTE® Journal Award & SMPTE® Journal Certificate of Merit

Society of Motion Picture & Television Engi-
neers® (SMPTE®)
White Plains Plaza, 445 Hamilton Ave, Suite 601,
White Plains, NY 10601-1827
Tel: 914-761-1100 *Fax:* 914-206-4216
E-mail: marketing@smpte.org
Web Site: www.smpte.org
Key Personnel
Exec Dir: Barbara H Lange *Tel:* 914-205-2370
Dir, Events & Governance Liaison: Sally-Ann
D'Amato *Tel:* 914-205-2375 *E-mail:* sdamato@
smpte.org
Mktg & Commun: Aimee Ricca *Tel:* 914-205-
2381 *E-mail:* aimeericca@smpte.org
Exec Asst: June Marie Sobrito *Tel:* 914-205-2384
E-mail: jsobrito@smpte.org
The Journal Award recognizes the outstanding pa-
per originally published in the journal of the
society during preceding calendar year, either
in the field of motion pictures or in the field
of television. SMPTE Journal Certificate of
Merit: presented to the authors of the paper(s)
receiving the next highest score (up to 2 may
be presented).
Closing Date: Annually in April
Presented: SMPTE® Annual Technical Conference & Exhibition, Loews Hollywood Hotel,
Hollywood, CA, Annually in Oct

SMPTE® Progress Medal Award

Society of Motion Picture & Television Engi-
neers® (SMPTE®)
White Plains Plaza, 445 Hamilton Ave, Suite 601,
White Plains, NY 10601-1827
Tel: 914-761-1100 *Fax:* 914-206-4216
E-mail: marketing@smpte.org
Web Site: www.smpte.org
Key Personnel
Exec Dir: Barbara H Lange *Tel:* 914-205-2370
Dir, Events & Governance Liaison: Sally-Ann
D'Amato *Tel:* 914-205-2375 *E-mail:* sdamato@
smpte.org
Mktg & Commun: Aimee Ricca *Tel:* 914-205-
2381 *E-mail:* aimeericca@smpte.org
Exec Asst: June Marie Sobrito *Tel:* 914-205-2384
E-mail: jsobrito@smpte.org
Recognizes outstanding technical contributions
to the progress of engineering phases of the
motion picture, television or motion imaging
industries.
Closing Date: Annually in April
Presented: SMPTE® Annual Technical Confer-
ence & Exhibition, Loews Hollywood Hotel,
Hollywood, CA, Annually in Oct

Stanley Film Festival

The Stanley Hotel, 333 Wonderview Ave, Estes
Park, CO 80517
Tel: 970-577-4112
Web Site: www.stanleyfilmfest.com
Key Personnel
Exec Dir: Frederic Lahey *E-mail:* flahey@
stanleyfilmfest.com
Established: 2013
Showcases classic & contemporary independent
horror cinema.
Media: Submissions: Online screener; Screening:
Blu-ray, digital file, DCP
Categories: Features, shorts, Stanley Dean's Cup
student competition
Closing Date: Oct 30 (early), Dec 30 (regular),
Jan 30 (late)
Entry Fee: Features: $30/$25 student early,
$45/$40 student regular, $60/$55 student late;
Shorts: $30 early, $45 regular, $60 late; Stanley
Dean's Cup student competition: $15 early, $20
regular, $30 late
Presented: The Stanley Hotel, Estes Park, CO,
April

Student Academy Awards Competition

Academy of Motion Picture Arts and Sciences
(AMPAS)
8949 Wilshire Blvd, Beverly Hills, CA 90211
Tel: 310-247-3000 *Fax:* 310-859-9619
E-mail: saa@oscars.org
Web Site: www.oscars.org/saa
Key Personnel
CEO: Dawn Hudson

Prog Admin: Shawn Guthrie *Tel:* 310-247-3000
ext 3306 *E-mail:* sguthrie@oscars.org
Prog Asst: Tracy Dillon
Established: 1972
To recognize & honor student filmmakers who
demonstrate excellence in the creation of mo-
tion pictures.
Media: Submissions: digital upload; Screening:
16mm, 35mm, DCP, ProRes digital file
Categories: Animation, documentary, narrative,
alternative
Award: Trophy, cash: $5,000 (gold), $3,000 (sil-
ver) & $2,000 (bronze)
Closing Date: June 1
Entry Fee: None
Presented: Academy's Samuel Goldwyn Theater,
8949 Wilshire Blvd, Beverly Hills, CA, Sept

Sundance Film Festival

Sundance Institute
1825 Three Kings Dr, Park City, UT 84060
Mailing Address: PO Box 684429, Park City, UT
84068
Tel: 435-658-3456 *Fax:* 435-658-3457
E-mail: customerservice@sundance.org; press@
sundance.org; institute@sundance.org
Web Site: www.sundance.org/festival
Key Personnel
Dir: John Cooper
Co-Mng Dir, Opers & Utah Community Rel:
Sarah Pearce
Dir, Mktg & Communs: Jared Hendler
Dir, Programming: Trevor Groth
Mgr, Festival Opers: Meredith Potter
Established: 1985
Other Sponsor(s): Acura; Canada Goose; Chase
Sapphire; Sundance TV
Presented: Park City, UT, Annually in Jan

Technicolor-Herbert T Kalmus Medal Award

Society of Motion Picture & Television Engi-
neers® (SMPTE®)
White Plains Plaza, 445 Hamilton Ave, Suite 601,
White Plains, NY 10601-1827
Tel: 914-761-1100 *Fax:* 914-206-4216
E-mail: marketing@smpte.org
Web Site: www.smpte.org
Key Personnel
Exec Dir: Barbara H Lange *Tel:* 914-205-2370
Dir, Events & Governance Liaison: Sally-Ann
D'Amato *Tel:* 914-205-2375 *E-mail:* sdamato@
smpte.org
Mktg & Commun: Aimee Ricca *Tel:* 914-205-
2381 *E-mail:* aimeericca@smpte.org
Exec Asst: June Marie Sobrito *Tel:* 914-205-2384
E-mail: jsobrito@smpte.org
Honors an individual who has made outstanding
contributions that reflect a commitment to the
highest standards of quality & innovation in
motion picture post-production & distribution
services.
Closing Date: Annually in April
Presented: SMPTE® Annual Technical Confer-
ence & Exhibition, Loews Hollywood Hotel,
Hollywood, CA, Annually in Oct

Technology and Engineering Emmy® Awards

The National Academy of Television Arts & Sci-
ences (NATAS)
1697 Broadway, Suite 404, New York, NY 10019
Tel: 212-586-8424 *Fax:* 212-246-8129
E-mail: techemmys@emmyonline.tv
Web Site: emmyonline.com/tech
Key Personnel
SVP, Communs: Paul Pillitteri
E-mail: ppillitteri@emmyonline.tv
Exec Dir: Robert P Seidel
Established: 1948
Honors development & innovation in broadcast
technology & recognizes companies, organiza-
tions & individuals for breakthroughs in tech-

nology that have a significant effect on television engineering.
Media: TV
Award: Gold statuette
Presented: Las Vegas, NV, Annually in April

Telluride Film Festival
National Film Preserve Ltd
800 Jones St, Berkeley, CA 94710
Tel: 510-665-9494 *Fax:* 510-665-9589
E-mail: mail@telluridefilmfestival.org; press@
telluridefilmfestival.org
Web Site: www.telluridefilmfestival.org
Media: Submissions: DVD & URL link; Screening: 35mm & DCP
Closing Date: Annually in July
Presented: Telluride, CO, Sept 4-7, 2020

The Lowell Thomas Award
Overseas Press Club of America
40 W 45 St, New York, NY 10036
Tel: 212-626-9220 *Fax:* 212-626-9210
E-mail: info@opcofamerica.org
Web Site: www.opcofamerica.org
Key Personnel
Exec Dir: Patricia Kranz
Best radio, audio or podcast news or interpretation of international affairs. All entries are submitted online.
Award: Certificate & $1,000 check
Closing Date: Annually in late Jan
Entry Fee: $200 per category
Presented: Hotel Mandarin-Oriental, New York, NY, Annually in April

Three Rivers Arts Festival, see Dollar Bank Three Rivers Arts Festival

Tiburon International Film Festival (TIFF)
6 Beach Rd, 544, Tiburon, CA 94920
Tel: 415-251-8433 *Fax:* 253-663-1250
E-mail: info@tiburonfilmfestival.com
Web Site: www.tiburonfilmfestival.com
Established: 2002
Annual event showcasing independent feature & short films from around the world & a platform for the independent filmmakers from any nation.
Media: Submissions: Secure online screener, DVD (NTSC Region 0 or 1, PAL Region 0); Exhibition: DVD or Blu-ray (NTSC Region 0)
Categories: Fiction, documentary, animation, student, children, comedy, experimental, music video, sports
Award: Certificate of Excellence
Closing Date: Dec 1 (regular), Jan 15 (late)
Entry Fee: Feature films (over 50 minutes): $45 regular, $50 late; Short films (50 minutes & under): $35 regular, $45 late; Student films $30 regular, $35 late
Presented: Tiburon, CA, April

Toronto Reel Asian International Film Festival
401 Richmond St W, Suite 309, Toronto, ON M5V 3A8, Canada
Tel: 416-703-9333 *Fax:* 416-703-9986
E-mail: info@reelasian.com; programming@
reelasian.com
Web Site: www.reelasian.com
Key Personnel
Exec Dir: Louanne Chan *E-mail:* louanne@
reelasian.org
Head, Programming: Kristine Estorninos
Festival & Opers Mgr: Chris Chin *E-mail:* chris@
reelasian.com
Established: 1997
Encourage submissions that are independently produced with an East/South/Southeast Asian/Asian North American & Asian diaspora artist in a key creative role (behind the camera +/or on screen). Welcome films & videos of all

genres including but not limited to: narrative, documentary, short, animation, experimental, etc.
Other Sponsor(s): National Bank
Media: Submissions: Online screener (preferred) or DVD (NTSC Region 0 or 1)
Categories: Feature film, short film
Closing Date: April (early), June (regular), July (final)
Entry Fee: Features: Free up to early deadline, $25 (regular), $45 (final); Shorts: Free up to early deadline, $15 (regular), $30 (final)
Presented: Toronto, ON, CN, Annually in Nov

Town of Bel Air Film Festival
37 N Main St, Bel Air, MD 21014
Tel: 410-838-0584
Web Site: www.townofbelairfilmfestival.com
Key Personnel
Exec Prodr: Trish Heidenreich
Festival Dir: Rebecca Jessop
Tech Dir: John Heidenreich
Established: 2009
Other Sponsor(s): Bel Air Cultural Arts Commission; Cultural Arts Board; Maryland Film Office; Maryland State Arts Council through the Harford County; Town of Bel Air; Visit Hartford!
Presented: Bel Air Reckord Armory, Annually in Oct

Tribeca Film Festival
Tribeca Enterprises
Communications Dept, 375 Greenwich St, New York, NY 10013
Tel: 212-941-2400 *Fax:* 212-941-3939
E-mail: festival@tribecafilmfestival.org; entries@tribecafilmfestival.org; press@
tribecafilmfestival.org
Web Site: www.tribecafilm.com/festival
Key Personnel
COO: Pete Torres
EVP, Communs & Programming: Tammie Rosen
E-mail: trosen@tribecaenterprises.com
Established: 2001
Annual diverse international film festival.
Other Sponsor(s): AT&T; Squarespace
Categories: Narrative & documentary features; narrative, documentary, animated & experimental film shorts; broadcast television +/or streaming; new online work (web series, online shorts, online episodic); immersive (virtual reality, 360 films, apps, etc); X Award (scripted & documentary work for film, TV, digital, social & VR/AR, both feature or short length)
Closing Date: Sept 25 (early), Oct 30 (regular), Dec 2 (late); X Award: Oct 30 (early), Dec 2 (regular), Jan 15 (late)
Entry Fee: Features: $65 early, $85 regular, $110 late; TV, Immersive & New Online Work: $40 early, $60 regular, $80 late; X Award: $325 early, $425 regular, $525 late
Presented: New York, NY, April 15-26, 2020

United States Super 8mm Film & Digital Video Festival
Rutgers Film Co-op/New Jersey Media Arts Center Inc
Rutgers University, 018 Loree Hall, 72 Lipman Dr, New Brunswick, NJ 08901-1414
Mailing Address: Rutgers University, 4170 Academic Bldg, 15 Seminary Place, New Brunswick, NJ 08901-8525
Tel: 848-932-8482 *Fax:* 732-932-1935
E-mail: njmac@aol.com; njmac12@gmail.com
Web Site: www.njfilmfest.com
Key Personnel
Exec Dir & Curator: Albert Gabriel Nigrin
Other Sponsor(s): Jungle Software; Middlesex County Cultural & Heritage Commission; NAMAC & NEA; New Jersey Media Arts; New

Jersey State Council on the Arts Center; Pro 8mm; Rutgers University
Media: DVD or Blu-ray; must have originally been shot predominantly on Super 8/8mm film or digital/Hi 8/8mm video
Categories: Animation, documentary, experimental, short narrative & feature
Award: $3,000-$5,000
Closing Date: Annually in Jan
Entry Fee: $45 works under 20 minutes; $55 works 20-50 minutes; $75 works over 50 minutes
Presented: Rutgers University, New Brunswick, NJ, Annually in Feb

US International Film & Video Festival
713 S Pacific Coast Hwy, Suite A, Redondo Beach, CA 90277-4233
Tel: 310-540-0959 *Fax:* 310-316-8905
E-mail: filmfestinfo@filmfestawards.com; mediarelations@filmfestawards.com
Web Site: www.filmfestawards.com
Key Personnel
Chmn: Lee W Gluckman, Jr
E-mail: leegluckman@filmfestawards.com
Creative Dir & Digital Coord: David Chan
E-mail: davidchan@filmfestawards.com
Mgr, Entrant Rel & Opers: Kristen Szabo
E-mail: kristenszabo@filmfestawards.com
Mgr, Press & Media Rel: Sandra Kelly
Established: 1967
For productions produced or released within the 18 months preceding the entry deadline. Offer categories covering all subjects & production techniques.
Media: MP4, URL (Vimeo, YouTube, etc), DVD (PAL or NTSC)
Categories: Corporate, education, entertainment, documentary, student
Award: Gold Camera Statuette (1st place), Silver Screen Statuette (2nd place), Certificate for Creative Excellence (3rd place), Student Award Certificate, Best of Festival (Grand Prix) Awards, One World Award
Closing Date: Annually, March 15
Presented: Los Angeles, CA, Annually in June

USA Film Festival
6116 N Central Expwy, Suite 105, Dallas, TX 75206
Tel: 214-821-6300; 214-821-FILM (821-3456)
Fax: 214-821-6364
E-mail: usafilmfest@aol.com
Web Site: www.usafilmfestival.com
Key Personnel
Mng Dir: Ann Alexander
Prog Coord: Tori Collatos
Established: 1971
Other Sponsor(s): City of Dallas Office of Cultural Affairs; National Endowment for the Arts; Texas Commission on the Arts
Media: Submissions: Secure online screener, DVD (NTSC Region 0 or 1), .MOV (Quicktime); Exhibition: DVD or Blu-ray (NTSC Region 0 or 1, .MOV (Quicktime), DCP, 16mm, 35mm
Categories: International short film & video, feature
Closing Date: Dec 15 (early), Jan 15 (regular), Feb 15 (late)
Entry Fee: Short film & video: $50 early, $55 regular, $65 late; No fee for features
Presented: April

Vancouver International Film Festival (VIFF)
The Greater Vancouver International Film Festival Society
Vancouver International Film Ctr, 1181 Seymour St, Vancouver, BC V6B 3M7, Canada
Tel: 604-685-0260 *Fax:* 604-688-8221
E-mail: info@viff.org; submissions@viff.org
Web Site: www.viff.org

Key Personnel
Exec Dir: Jacqueline Dupuis
Dir, Intl Programming: Alan Franey
Dir, Mktg: Laine Slater
Festival Exhibitions Mgr: Sean Wilson
Prog Mgr & Sr Programmer: PoChu AuYeung
Spec Projs & Communs Mgr: Lauren Stasila
Established: 1982
One of the largest film festivals in North America, VIFF features approximately 370 films from over 70 countries to an expected audience of 140,000. VIFF is officially "non-competitive" but does offer several adjudicated cash prizes & audience awards.
Media: Submissions: Secure online screener, DVD (NTSC or Region 1); Exhibition: DCP, HDCam, 35mm, 16mm
Categories: International narrative features, international nonfiction features, international shorts, Canadian features/documentaries, Canadian shorts
Award: Over $85,000 in cash prizes plus $25 in services & prize packs
Closing Date: CN: May 13 (early), June 10 (regular), June 24 (extended); Intl: April 29 (early), June 10 (regular), June 24 (extended)
Entry Fee: CN features/documentaries: $40 early, $50 regular, $60 extended; CN shorts: $20 early, $25 regular, $30 extended; Intl narrative/nonfiction features: $65 early, $80 regular, $95 extended; Intl shorts: $50 early, $55 regular, $60 extended
Presented: Vancouver, BC, CN, Sept-Oct

VC Filmfest, see The Los Angeles Asian Pacific Film Festival

Vermont International Film Festival
PO Box 483, Burlington, VT 05402-0483
Tel: 802-660-2600
E-mail: info@vtiff.org
Web Site: www.vtiff.org
Key Personnel
Pres: Lorna-Kay Peal
Exec Dir: Orly Yadin
Established: 1985
International festival of independent films.
Media: Blu-ray
Categories: Independent films of all genres
Award: Cash, plaque & certificate
Presented: Several locations in Burlington, VT, Oct

The Virginia Film Festival
University of Virginia
617 W Main St, 2nd fl, Charlottesville, VA 22903
Mailing Address: PO Box 400869, Charlottesville, VA 22904
Tel: 434-982-5277 *Fax:* 434-924-3374
E-mail: info@virginiafilmfestival.org;
vffsubmissions@virginia.edu
Web Site: virginiafilmfestival.org
Key Personnel
Dir: Jody Kielbasa *E-mail:* jkielbasa@virginia.edu
Mng Dir: Jenny Mays *E-mail:* jmays@virginia.edu
Opers Mgr: Sarah Cain *E-mail:* sarahcain@virginia.edu
Busn Mgr & Outreach Coord: Erica Barnes *E-mail:* eb4va@virginia.edu
Prodn Coord: Rebecca Malaret
Programmer: Wesley Harris *E-mail:* wrh3n@virginia.edu
Media: Submissions: DVD (NTSC Region 0 or 1) or online screener; Exhibition: 35mm, Blu-ray, DCP, MOV
Categories: Narrative feature, narrative short, documentary feature, documentary short, animated feature, animated short, experimental feature, experimental short, Virginia narrative feature, Virginia documentary feature, Virginia documentary short, Virginia

animated feature, Virginia animated short, Virginia experimental feature, Virginia experimental short, virtual reality
Closing Date: June (regular), July (extended)
Entry Fee: Features (50 minutes & above): $35 regular, $50 extended; Shorts (under 50 minutes): $15 regular, $25 extended. Free for VA residents & students at VA schools
Presented: Annually in Autumn

Visions Film Festival & Conference
University of North Carolina Wilmington Film Studies Dept
601 S College Rd, Wilmington, NC 28403
Tel: 919-607-0031
E-mail: visions7programming@gmail.com;
visions7development@gmail.com
Web Site: www.visionsffc.org
Key Personnel
Mng Dir: Mariah Smallwood
Asst Mng Dir & Programming Dir: Carly Dawson
Asst Mng Dir: Kelsey Davis
Art Dir: Jake Hart
Devt Dir: Maggie Auzenne
Festival Dir: Shannon Silva
Hospitality Dir: Hannah Hearn
Mktg Dir: Isaac Dunn
Opers Dir: Chance Saller
Established: 2006
International event that unites a community of undergraduates & provides a supportive environment to showcase their work. Short films of all genres, as well as scholarly articles related to film & media studies, are encouraged for submission.
Presented: Annually in Spring

Voice of Democracy Scholarship Program
Veterans of Foreign Wars of the United States
406 W 34 St, Kansas City, MO 64111
Tel: 816-968-1117 *Fax:* 816-968-1149
Web Site: www.vfw.org
Key Personnel
Prog Coord: Kris Harmer *E-mail:* kharmer@vfw.org
Established: 1947
National audio essay competition for high school students in grades 9-12; one contestant from each state who voices their opinion on their responsibility to our country via CD & DVD. Information about the winners can be found on our web site www.vfw.org/VOD.
Media: Audio CD, DVD
Categories: Audio essay
Award: $30,000 scholarship (1st place); $153,000 in national awards; state winners receive an all-expense paid trip to Washington, DC
Closing Date: Nov 1
Entry Fee: None
Presented: National Finals, Washington, DC, March

Vortex Sci-Fi, Fantasy & Horror Film Festival
Flickers Art Collaborative
83 Park St, Suite 5, Providence, RI 02903
Mailing Address: PO Box 162, Newport, RI 02840-0002
Tel: 401-861-4445 *Fax:* 401-490-6735
E-mail: info@film-festival.org
Web Site: www.film-festival.org
Key Personnel
Exec Dir/CEO: George T Marshall *E-mail:* georget@film-festival.org
Prog Dir: Shawn Quirk *E-mail:* quirk@film-festival.org
Official sidebar of the Flickers' Rhode Island International Film Festival™ with films in the sci-fi, fantasy & horror genres. All films accepted & featured come from the entry pool of the Rhode Island International Film Festival.
Presented: Annually in Oct

The Samuel L Warner Memorial Medal Award
Society of Motion Picture & Television Engineers® (SMPTE®)
White Plains Plaza, 445 Hamilton Ave, Suite 601, White Plains, NY 10601-1827
Tel: 914-761-1100 *Fax:* 914-206-4216
E-mail: marketing@smpte.org
Web Site: www.smpte.org
Key Personnel
Exec Dir: Barbara H Lange *Tel:* 914-205-2370
Dir, Events & Governance Liaison: Sally-Ann D'Amato *Tel:* 914-205-2375 *E-mail:* sdamato@smpte.org
Mktg & Commun: Aimee Ricca *Tel:* 914-205-2381 *E-mail:* aimeericca@smpte.org
Exec Asst: June Marie Sobrito *Tel:* 914-205-2384 *E-mail:* jsobrito@smpte.org
Honors an individual who has made outstanding contributions to the design & development of new & improved methods +/or apparatus for motion picture sound including any step in the process.
Closing Date: Annually in April
Presented: SMPTE® Annual Technical Conference & Exhibition, Loews Hollywood Hotel, Hollywood, CA, Annually in Oct

Washington DC International Film Festival
PO Box 21396, Washington, DC 20009-0896
Tel: 202-274-5782 *Fax:* 202-274-6690
E-mail: filmfestdc@filmfestdc.org
Web Site: www.filmfestdc.org
Key Personnel
Dir: Anthony Gittens
Deputy Dir: Shirin Ghareeb
Awards presented: Audience Award, Circle Award, Justice Matters Award, First Feature Award & Signis Award.
Media: DCP, HDCam, Blu-ray, Beta (SP/digital/NTSC/PAL)
Closing Date: Jan 31
Entry Fee: $15 under 30 minutes; $30 over 30 minutes
Presented: April

Waterfront Film Festival (WFF)
479 Columbia Ave, Holland, MI 49423
Tel: 269-767-8765
E-mail: info@waterfrontfilm.org
Web Site: www.waterfrontfilm.org
Key Personnel
Founder: Dana DePree-Minter; Dori DePree; Hopwood DePree; Kori Eldean; Judy Smith
Established: 1999
Media: Online screener or DVD
Categories: Films (any genre)
Closing Date: Feb 15
Presented: Multiple venues throughout MI

Orson Welles Award
Tiburon International Film Festival (TIFF)
6 Beach Rd, 544, Tiburon, CA 94920
Tel: 415-251-8433 *Fax:* 253-663-1250
E-mail: info@tiburonfilmfestival.com
Web Site: www.tiburonfilmfestival.com
Annual award given to a first time American filmmaker.
Media: Submissions: Secure online screener, DVD (NTSC Region 0 or 1, PAL Region 0); Exhibition: DVD or Blu-ray (NTSC Region 0)
Categories: Fiction, documentary, animation, student, children, comedy, experimental, music video, sports
Award: Trophy & certificate
Closing Date: Dec 1 (regular), Jan 15 (late)
Entry Fee: Feature films (over 50 minutes): $45 regular, $50 late; Short films (50 minutes & under): $35 regular, $45 late; Student films $30 regular, $35 late
Presented: Tiburon, CA, April

Western Heritage Awards

National Cowboy & Western Heritage Museum
1700 NE 63 St, Oklahoma City, OK 73111
Tel: 405-478-2250
Web Site: nationalcowboymuseum.org
Key Personnel
Events Coord: Kaylia McCracken *Tel:* 405-478-2250 ext 218 *E-mail:* kmccracken@nationalcowboymuseum.org
Established: 1961
Application online.
Media: DVD, CD, Books
Categories: All western genre: music new artist, music original composition, traditional music album. theatrical motion picture, television feature film, docudrama, documentary, fictional drama, lifestyle, novel, nonfiction book, photography or art book, juvenile book, magazine or journal, article, poetry book
Award: "The Wrangler" - bronze sculpture of a cowboy on horseback
Closing Date: Nov 30 (literature), Dec 31 (film & music)
Entry Fee: $50 per entry per category
Presented: National Cowboy & Western Heritage Museum, Oklahoma City, OK, Annually in April

Williamsburg International Film Festival, see WILLiFEST

WILLiFEST

Brooklyn Films
PO Box 20412, New York, NY 10021-0066
E-mail: inquiries@willifest.com; programming@willifest.com; screenplays@willifest.com
Web Site: www.willifest.com
Key Personnel
Founder & Exec Dir: Michael Helman *E-mail:* michael.helman@brooklynfilms.com
Admin Dir: Stella McGovern
In addition to 6 film categories, there are screenplay, commercial, soundtrack, TV/Web episode & trailer competitions.
Other Sponsor(s): Brooklyn Design Studio; Crowdzu
Media: Online screener only via FilmFreeway. No DVD submissions or any physical media
Categories: Narrative feature films, documentary feature films, narrative short films, documentary short films, animated films, music videos
Closing Date: March 18 (early), April 29 (regular), May 27 (late), June 17 (extended)
Entry Fee: $30-$85 depending on category
Presented: Annually in Sept

Winter Film Awards Indie Film Festival

Winter Film Awards (WFA)
31 W 34 St, New York, NY 10001
Tel: 646-355-4371
E-mail: info@winterfilmawards.com; submissions@winterfilmawards.com
Web Site: winterfilmawards.com
Key Personnel
Chmn & Founder: George Isaacs
Treas & CFO: Lesley Sigall

Exec Dir: Steffanie L Finn
Media: Submissions: Online screener; Screening: MP4, MOV, AVI, WMA, MKV format
Categories: Narrative (non-horror) fiction feature film, nonfiction/documentary film, narrative (non-horror) fiction short film, animated film, music video, Winter FEAR Awards-horror film, web series
Award: Crystal icicle statue & various prizes
Closing Date: Sept (early), Oct (regular), Nov (late)
Entry Fee: $25 early; $40 regular; $60 late; $100 extended
Presented: Annually in Feb/March

Women in Film Finishing Fund

Women in Film Foundation
6100 Wilshire Blvd, Suite 710, Los Angeles, CA 90048
Tel: 323-935-2211 *Fax:* 323-935-2212
E-mail: info@wif.org
Web Site: www.wif.org
Key Personnel
Exec Dir: Gayle Nachlis *E-mail:* gnachlis@wif.org
Foundation Coord: Lauren Byrd *E-mail:* lbyrd@wif.org
Established: 1985
Awarded for films made by, for, or about women. The number of grants given vary from year to year. Student projects are not eligible.
Media: DVD (NTSC Region 1 or 0), Blu-ray
Categories: Narrative, documentary, educational, animated & experimental (long or short format)
Award: Cash & in-kind services
Closing Date: See web site
Entry Fee: $75

World Film Festival/Festival des Films du Monde/Montreal

Montreal World Film Festival
1432 de Bleury St, Montreal, QC H3A 2J1, Canada
Tel: 514-848-3883 *Fax:* 514-848-3886
E-mail: program@ffm-montreal.org
Web Site: www.ffm-montreal.org
Key Personnel
Chmn: Serge Losique
Established: 1976
Media: DCP, 3D
Categories: World Competition, First Films World Competition, World Greats, Focus on World Cinema (Americas, Europe, Asia, Africa, Oceania), Documentaries of the World, Tributes, Our Cinema, Cinema Under the Stars, Student Film Festival
Closing Date: July features (60 minutes or longer); June short & medium (59 minutes or less)
Entry Fee: $120 features; $50 shorts
Presented: Multiple locations in Montreal, QC, CN, Annually in Aug/Sept

WorldFest-Houston International Film Festival

The Houston Film Society
9898 Bissonnet St, Suite 650, Houston, TX 77036

Mailing Address: PO Box 56566, Houston, TX 77256-6566
Tel: 713-965-9955 *Fax:* 713-965-9960
E-mail: mail@worldfest.org; entry@worldfest.org
Web Site: www.worldfest.org
Key Personnel
Chmn & Founding Dir: Hunter Todd
Prog & Artistic Dir: Kathleen Haney
Entry Dir: Lauren Calderon
Established: 1968
Premieres approximately 100 new feature films & 130 new short films annually, screened on AMC Theater screens. More than 1,000 international filmmakers attend each year. Major category winners streamed online after each festival.
Other Sponsor(s): AMC Theaters; Boxer Property®; City of Houston, TX; Eastman Kodak; Houston Arts Alliance
Media: DVD, Blu-ray, online streaming, jump drive
Categories: Short, documentary, feature, experimental, interactive, TV, student, music video, new media & screenplays
Award: Remi Statuette, Special Jury Award, Platinum, Gold, Silver & Bronze Awards, Gold Lone Star, Cash Grants (winners are part of the WorldFest "Discovery Program" & are entered into more than 200 top international film festivals)
Closing Date: Dec 15 (regular), Jan 15 (final)
Entry Fee: $40-$150, depending on length
Presented: Houston, TX, Annually in April

Yorkton Film Festival (YFF)

49 Smith St E, Yorkton, SK S3N 0H4, Canada
Tel: 306-782-7077 *Fax:* 306-782-1550
E-mail: info@yorktonfilm.com
Web Site: yorktonfilm.com
Key Personnel
Exec Dir: Ms Randy Goulden
Prog Mgr: Mr Blair Yacishyn
Festival Coord: Scott Stelmaschuk
Outreach Coord: Kathy Morrell
Established: 1950
Best in Canadian short media content (productions 60 minutes or under). Emerging Filmmaker Award, Indigenous Award, Golden Sheaf Award & Kathleen Shannon Award also presented during the festival.
Categories: Animation, children's/youth productions, comedy, community television productions, digital media, drama, experimental, lifestyle & reality, performing arts & entertainment, short subject-fiction, short subject-nonfiction, student productions, documentary arts/culture, documentary history & biography, documentary POV (point of view), documentary science/nature/technology, documentary series, documentary social/political
Closing Date: Nov 16 (super early), Dec 19 (early), Jan 31 (regular); Students: Nov 16 (early), Dec 20 (regular)
Entry Fee: $55 super early; $75 early; $95 regular; $10 student super early; $20 student regular
Presented: Yorkton, SK, CN, May 21-24, 2020

Calendar of Events—Alphabetical Index of Sponsors

Calendar of Events—Alphabetical Index of Events

Calendar of Events

AV-related trade shows, meetings and conventions scheduled (at press time) from early 2020 through 2024 are listed chronologically by year and month, and then alphabetically by the event name. Preceding this section are two indexes: the Sponsor Index is an alphabetical list of event sponsors and includes the names and dates of the events they sponsor; the Event Index is an alphabetical list of events along with the dates on which they are held.

2020

MARCH

Computers in Libraries (CIL)
Sponsored by Information Today, Inc
143 Old Marlton Pike, Medford, NJ 08055-8750
Tel: 609-654-6266 *Toll Free Tel:* 800-300-9868
   (cust serv) *Fax:* 609-654-4309
E-mail: custserv@infotoday.com
Web Site: www.facebook.com/
   ComputersInLibraries; www.infotoday.com
Key Personnel
Pres & CEO: Thomas H Hogan
Dir, Meeting Planning: Stacey Hogan
Conference & exhibition focusing on all aspects
   of library & information delivery technology.
Location: Hyatt Regency Crystal City, 2799 Jef-
   ferson Davis Hwy, Arlington, VA
March 31-April 2, 2020

APRIL

AERA Annual Meeting
Sponsored by American Educational Research
   Association (AERA)
1430 "K" St NW, Suite 1200, Washington, DC
   20005
Tel: 202-238-3200 *Fax:* 202-238-3250
E-mail: annualmtg@aera.net
Web Site: www.aera.net
Key Personnel
Meeting Dir: Robert Smith *Tel:* 202-238-3200 ext
   210 *E-mail:* rsmith@aera.net
Asst Dir: Mary Piper Waters *Tel:* 202-238-3200
   ext 213 *E-mail:* mpiperwaters@aera.net
Meeting Mgr: Kendra McGee *Tel:* 202-238-3200
   ext 212 *E-mail:* kmcgee@aera.net
Location: San Francisco, CA
April 17-21, 2020

BEA2020
Sponsored by Broadcast Education Association
   (BEA)
Affiliate of National Association of Broadcasters
   (NAB) (in partnership with)
1771 "N" St NW, Washington, DC 20036-2891
Fax: 202-609-9940
E-mail: help@beaweb.org
Web Site: www.beaweb.org
Key Personnel
Exec Dir: Heather Birks *Tel:* 202-602-0584
   E-mail: heather@beaweb.org
Dir of Mktg & Sales: J-D Boyle *Tel:* 202-602-
   0586 *E-mail:* jd@beaweb.org
Mgr, Busn Opers: Traci Bailey *Tel:* 202-602-0587
   E-mail: traci@beaweb.org
Co-located with NAB Show each April in Las
   Vegas.
Location: Westgate Las Vegas Resort & Casino,
   3000 Paradise Rd, Las Vegas, NV
April 18-21, 2020

ISPI Annual Conference
Sponsored by International Society for Performance Improvement® (ISPI)

PO Box 13035, Silver Spring, MD 20910
Tel: 301-587-8570 *Fax:* 301-587-8573
E-mail: conference@ispi.org; info@ispi.org
Web Site: www.ispi.org
Key Personnel
Exec Dir: Courtney Brooks Kamin
   E-mail: courtneyb@ispi.org
Pre-conference workshops held April 29-May 2,
   2020.
Location: Loews Ventana Canyon Resort, Tucson,
   AZ
April 29-May 4, 2020

NAB Show®
Sponsored by National Association of Broadcast-
   ers (NAB)
1771 "N" St NW, Washington, DC 20036
Tel: 202-429-5300 *Toll Free Tel:* 888-740-4622
   (registration); 800-NAB-EXPO (622-3976, ex-
   hibit sales)
E-mail: nab@nab.org
Web Site: www.nabshow.com; www.facebook.
   com/pages/NAB-Show/195269533220/; twitter.
   com/NABShow; www.nab.org
Key Personnel
Pres & CEO: Gordon H Smith
EVP, Conventions & Busn Opers: Mr Chris
   Brown *Tel:* 202-429-5335
SVP, Communs: Ann Marie Cumming *Tel:* 202-
   429-5307 *E-mail:* amcumming@nab.org
Mgr, Communs: Jamie Enright *Tel:* 202-429-5359
   E-mail: jenright@nab.org
The NAB Show® delivers the most comprehen-
   sive showcase of digital communications tech-
   nologies including every element of television
   & radio broadcasting, film/video production &
   post-production, audio production, multimedia,
   the Internet, satellite & telecommunications.
Location: Las Vegas Convention Center, Las Vegas, NV
April 18-22, 2020

NCEA Convention & Expo
Sponsored by National Catholic Educational As-
   sociation (NCEA)
1005 N Glebe Rd, Suite 525, Arlington, VA
   22201
Tel: 571-257-0010 *Toll Free Tel:* 800-711-NCEA
   (711-6232) *Fax:* 703-243-0025
E-mail: info@ncea.org
Web Site: www.ncea.org/convention; www.ncea.
   org
Key Personnel
Dir of Events: Amy Durkin *E-mail:* adurkin@
   ncea.org
Annual meeting for all working in Catholic edu-
   cation, Pre-K through college.
Location: Baltimore Convention Center, Balti-
   more, MD
April 16-20, 2020

NSBA Annual Conference & Exposition
Sponsored by National School Boards Association
   (NSBA)
1680 Duke St, 2nd fl, Alexandria, VA 22314-
   3493
Tel: 703-838-6722 *Fax:* 703-683-7590
E-mail: registration@nsba.org; info@nsba.org
Web Site: www.nsba.org/conference; www.nsba.
   org

Key Personnel
Dir, Conferences & Meetings: John Cesaretti
Mng Dir, Conferences & Meetings: Kanisha
   Williams
Location: Chicago, IL
April 4-6, 2020

USITT Annual Conference & Stage Expo
Sponsored by USITT
290 Elwood Davis Rd, Suite 100, Liverpool, NY
   13088
Toll Free Tel: 800-938-7488 *Toll Free Fax:* 866-
   398-7488
E-mail: info@usitt.org
Web Site: www.usitt.org
Key Personnel
Meeting Planner: Jody Harris *E-mail:* jody@usitt.
   org
Location: Houston, TX
April 1-4, 2020

MAY

AAM Annual Meeting & MuseumExpo
Sponsored by American Alliance of Museums
   (AAM)
2451 Crystal Dr, Suite 1005, Arlington, VA
   22202
Tel: 202-289-1818 *Fax:* 202-289-6578
Web Site: www.aam-us.org
Key Personnel
Dir, Meetings & Events: Veronica Mooney
   Tel: 202-218-7678 *E-mail:* vmooney@aam-
   us.org
Meetings & Events Mgr: Clara Allen *Tel:* 202-
   218-7708 *E-mail:* callen@aam-us.org
Location: San Francisco, CA
May 17-20, 2020

Archiving 2020
Sponsored by Society for Imaging Science and
   Technology (IS&T)
7003 Kilworth Lane, Springfield, VA 22151
Tel: 703-642-9090 *Fax:* 703-642-9094
E-mail: info@imaging.com
Web Site: imaging.org
Key Personnel
Exec Dir: Suzanne E Grinnan *E-mail:* sgrinnan@
   imaging.org
Exec Asst: Donna Smith *E-mail:* dsmith@
   imaging.org
Conference Prog Mgr: Marion S Zoretich
   E-mail: mzoretich@imaging.org
Digital preservation & stewardship of hard copy,
   audio & video is the focus.
Location: National Archives and Records Admin-
   istration, College Park, MD
May 18-21, 2020

ATD International Conference & Exposition
Sponsored by Association for Talent Development
   (ATD)
1640 King St, Alexandria, VA 22314-2743
Tel: 703-683-8100 *Toll Free Tel:* 800-628-2783
   Fax: 703-299-8723
E-mail: customercare@td.org

Web Site: www.atdconference.org; www.td.org
Location: Colorado Convention Center, 700 14 St, Denver, CO
May 17-20, 2020

BookExpo

Sponsored by ReedPOP
Division of Reed Exhibitions USA
383 Main Ave, Norwalk, CT 06851
Tel: 203-840-4800 *Toll Free Tel:* 800-840-5614 (cust serv)
E-mail: inquiry@bookexpoamerica.com (cust serv)
Web Site: www.bookexpoamerica.com; www.reedpop.com
Key Personnel
Event Dir: Brien McDonald *Tel:* 203-840-5483
  E-mail: brien@reedpop.com
Event Mgr: Jenny Martin *E-mail:* jenny@reedpop.com
Produced & managed by ReedPOP, BookExpo is sponsored by the American Booksellers Association (ABA), the Association of American Publishers Inc (AAP) & the Association of Authors' Representatives Inc (AAR).
Location: Jacob K Javits Convention Center, 655 W 43 St, New York, NY
May 27-29, 2020

Connectivity Expo

Formerly Wireless Infrastructure Show
Sponsored by WIA - The Wireless Infrastructure Association
2111 Wilson Blvd, Suite 210, Arlington, VA 22201
Tel: 703-739-0300 *Toll Free Tel:* 800-759-0300
  Fax: 703-836-1608
Web Site: wia.org
Key Personnel
Dir, Meetings & Events: Nancy Touhill *Tel:* 703-535-7411 *E-mail:* nancy.touhill@wia.org
Location: Miami Beach Convention Center, Miami, FL
May 18-21, 2020

Data Summit

Sponsored by Information Today, Inc
143 Old Marlton Pike, Medford, NJ 08055-8750
Tel: 609-654-6266 *Toll Free Tel:* 800-300-9868 (cust serv) *Fax:* 609-654-4309
E-mail: custserv@infotoday.com
Web Site: www.dbta.com/DataSummit/2020; www.infotoday.com
Key Personnel
Pres & CEO: Thomas H Hogan
Dir, Meeting Planning: Stacey Hogan
Data Summit is a two-day comprehensive educational experience that brings together IT managers, data architects, application developers, data analysts, project managers & business managers for an intense immersion into the key technologies & strategies for becoming a data-informed business. Data Summit also features two co-located events: Hadoop Day & Virtualization Day. Additionally, pre-conference workshops take place on May 18.
Location: Hyatt Regency Boston, One Avenue de Lafayette, Boston, MA
May 19-20, 2020

Media Finance Focus 2020

Sponsored by Media Financial Management Association (MFM)
550 W Frontage Rd, Suite 3600, Northfield, IL 60093
Tel: 847-716-7000 *Fax:* 847-716-7004
E-mail: info@mediafinance.org
Web Site: www.mediafinance.org
Key Personnel
Dir of Opers, MFM/BCCA: Jamie L Grande
Fin Consultant & Conference Prog Dir, MFM/BCCA: Charlie Warner

Co-sponsored by the Broadcast Cable Credit Association (BCCA).
Location: Loews Hollywood Hotel, Los Angeles, CA
May 18-21, 2020

PMBA Annual Conference

Sponsored by Public Media Business Association (PMBA)
1330 Piccard Dr, Suite LL 14, Rockville, MD 20850
Tel: 240-844-3600 *Fax:* 301-990-9771
E-mail: info@pmbaonline.com
Web Site: www.pmbaonline.org/; www.pbma.org
Key Personnel
Meeting Planner: Lynette Randazzo
  E-mail: lrandazzo@msp-amc.com
Location: MGM National Harbor, Oxon Hill, MD
May 26-29, 2020

JUNE

ACM Annual Conference

Sponsored by Alliance for Community Media (ACM)
4248 Park Glen Rd, Minneapolis, MN 55416
Tel: 952-928-4643
E-mail: info@allcommunitymedia.org
Web Site: www.allcommunitymedia.org
Key Personnel
Conference Mgr: Katie Benson
  E-mail: kbenson@allcommunitymedia.org
Location: Fairmont Chicago Millennium Park, 200 N Columbus Dr, Chicago, IL
June 30-July 2, 2020

AICP Week

Sponsored by Association of Independent Commercial Producers (AICP)
3 W 18 St, 5th fl, New York, NY 10011
Tel: 212-929-3000 *Fax:* 212-929-3359
E-mail: info@aicp.com
Web Site: www.aicp.com
Key Personnel
Natl Pres & CEO: Matt Miller *E-mail:* mattm@aicp.com
Natl Events Prodr: Aurora Warfield
  E-mail: auroraw@aicp.com
The show is produced in partnership with MoMA & the work that will be honored by inclusion in the show is given further tribute by becoming part of the film collection of MoMA's Department of Film.
In the months following the main event, the show travels to several locations around the country.
Location: MoMA, New York, NY
June 9-11, 2020

ALA Annual Conference

Sponsored by American Library Association (ALA)
50 E Huron St, Chicago, IL 60611-2795
Tel: 312-944-6780 *Toll Free Tel:* 800-545-2433 (ext 3223, conference servs) *Fax:* 312-440-9374
E-mail: ala@ala.org
Web Site: www.ala.org
Key Personnel
Conference Dir: Paul Graller *Tel:* 800-545-2433 ext 3219 *E-mail:* pgraller@ala.org
Registration & Housing Mgr: Alicia Hamann
  Tel: 800-545-2433 ext 3229 *E-mail:* ahamann@ala.org
Meeting Mgr: Yvonne McLean *Tel:* 800-545-2433 ext 3222 *E-mail:* ymclean@ala.org
Meeting Coord: Megan Kaiko *Tel:* 800-545-2433 ext 3220 *E-mail:* mkaiko@ala.org

Location: Chicago, IL
June 25-30, 2020

Display Week

Sponsored by Society for Information Display (SID)
1475 S Bascom Ave, Suite 114, Campbell, CA 95008-4006
Tel: 408-879-3901 *Fax:* 408-879-3833
E-mail: office@sid.org
Web Site: www.displayweek.org; www.sid.org
Key Personnel
Conference Coord: Samantha Tola *Tel:* 212-460-8090 ext 203 *E-mail:* stola@pcm411.com
Premier showcase of the electronic display industry.
Location: San Francisco Moscone Center, San Francisco, CA
June 7-12, 2020

EastPack®

Sponsored by Informa Markets
2901 28 St, Suite 100, Santa Monica, CA 90405
Tel: 310-445-4200
E-mail: clientservices@ubm.com
Web Site: informamarkets.com
Location: Jacob K Javits Convention Center, 655 W 34 St, New York, NY
June 9-11, 2020

IABC World Conference

Sponsored by International Association of Business Communicators (IABC)
649 Mission St, 5th fl, San Francisco, CA 94105
Tel: 415-544-4700 *Toll Free Tel:* 800-776-4222
  Fax: 415-544-4747
E-mail: conference@iabc.com
Web Site: wc.iabc.com; www.iabc.com
Key Personnel
Sponsorships & Ad Mgr: Pamela Strother
  Tel: 202-486-5990 *E-mail:* pstrother@iabc.com
Location: Hyatt Regency Chicago, Chicago, IL
June 14-17, 2020

InfoComm

Sponsored by Audiovisual and Integrated Experience Association (AVIXA)
11242 Waples Mill Rd, Suite 200, Fairfax, VA 22030
Tel: 703-273-7200 *Toll Free Tel:* 800-659-7469
  Fax: 703-273-5924
Web Site: www.infocommshow.org; www.avixa.org
Key Personnel
Exec Dir & CEO: David Labuskes
Exposition Servs Mgr: Randi Cavitt *Tel:* 703-279-9921 *E-mail:* rcavitt@avixa.org
Exposition Servs Coord: Willie Wolfman
  Tel: 703-279-9933 *E-mail:* wwolfman@avixa.org
Location: Las Vegas Convention Center, Las Vegas, NV
June 13-19, 2020

ISTE® 2020

Sponsored by International Society for Technology in Education (ISTE®)
621 SW Morrison St, Suite 800, Portland, OR 97205
Toll Free Tel: 800-336-5191 (US & CN)
  Fax: 503-882-0813
E-mail: iste@iste.org; conf-program@iste.org
Web Site: www.isteconference.org; www.iste.org
Key Personnel
Chief Events Offr, Conference Servs: Jennifer Ragan-Fore
Prog Dir: Camilla Gagliolo
Location: Anaheim Convention Center, Anaheim, CA
June 28-July 1, 2020

Optometry's Meeting®
Sponsored by American Optometric Association (AOA)
243 N Lindbergh Blvd, 1st fl, St Louis, MO 63141-7881
Tel: 314-991-4100 *Toll Free Tel:* 800-386-6825 (meetings hotline) *Fax:* 314-991-4101
E-mail: optometrysmeeting@aoa.org
Web Site: www.optometrysmeeting.org; www.exhibitsom.org; www.aoa.org
Key Personnel
Exhibits & Sponsorship Mgr: Kellie Rodrigue
 Tel: 314-983-4255 *E-mail:* kerodrigue@aoa.org
Annual meeting of the American Optometric Association & the American Optometric Student Association.
Location: Gaylord National Resort & Convention Center, National Harbor, MD
June 24-28, 2020

Promax Conference
Sponsored by Promax
5700 Wilshire Blvd, Suite 275, Los Angeles, CA 90036
Tel: 310-788-7600 *Fax:* 310-788-7616
E-mail: conference@promax.org
Web Site: www.promax.org
Location: JW Marriott Los Angeles LA Live, Los Angeles, CA
June 16-18, 2020

Safety 2020
Sponsored by American Society of Safety Professionals (ASSP)
520 N Northwest Hwy, Park Ridge, IL 60068
Tel: 847-699-2929 (cust serv) *Fax:* 847-768-3434
E-mail: customerservice@assp.org
Web Site: safety.assp.org; www.assp.org
Key Personnel
Sr Mgr, Conferences & Meetings: Stephanie Rennie-Sanchez *E-mail:* srennie-sanchez@assp.org
Mgr, Conferences & Meetings: Bonnie Lipinski *E-mail:* blipinski@assp.org
Professional development conference & exposition.
Location: Orange County Convention Center, Orlando, FL
June 23-25, 2020

SLA Annual Conference & INFO-EXPO
Sponsored by Special Libraries Association (SLA)
7918 Jones Branch Dr, Suite 300, McLean, VA 22102
Tel: 703-647-4900 *Fax:* 703-506-3266
E-mail: learning@sla.org
Web Site: www.sla.org
Key Personnel
Dir, Learning & Success: Diana Schapiro
 E-mail: dschapiro@sla.org
Location: Charlotte Convention Center, Charlotte, NC
June 6-9, 2020

Streaming Media East
Sponsored by Information Today, Inc
143 Old Marlton Pike, Medford, NJ 08055-8750
Tel: 609-654-6266 *Toll Free Tel:* 800-300-9868 (cust serv) *Fax:* 609-654-4309
E-mail: custserv@infotoday.com
Web Site: www.streamingmedia.com; www.infotoday.com
Key Personnel
Pres & CEO: Thomas H Hogan
Dir, Meeting Planning: Stacey Hogan
Streaming Media conferences & expos are the only events dedicated entirely to the business, technology, & content of online video. At Streaming Media East in New York City, you'll learn from online video experts, try out new products on the expo floor & most impor-

tantly, have fun while learning new things & networking with your peers. You can expect to leave with actionable advice & new strategies for moving your business forward. Additionally, pre-conference workshops take place on June 1.
Location: The Westin Copley Place, 10 Huntington Ave, Boston, MA
June 2-3, 2020

UPAA Annual Symposium
Sponsored by University Photographers' Association of America (UPAA)
PO Box 433, Califon, NJ 07830-0433
Tel: 908-335-0157
Web Site: www.upaa.org
Key Personnel
Pres: Glenn Carpenter *E-mail:* carpenter@morainevalley.edu
Co-hosted by Utah Valley University & Brigham Young University.
Location: Provo Marriott, Provo, UT
June 15-19, 2020

VidCon
1515 Broadway, New York, NY 10036
E-mail: info@vidcon.com
Web Site: www.vidcon.com; www.facebook.com/vidcon
Key Personnel
Co-Founder & Chairman: Hank Green
Co-Founder: John Green
Annual multi-genre online video conference.
Location: Anaheim Convention Center, Anaheim, CA
June 17-20, 2020

JULY

Design Automation Conference (DAC)
Sponsored by MP Associates Inc
1721 Boxelder St, Suite 107, Louisville, CO 80027
Tel: 303-530-4333; 303-530-4562
 Toll Free Tel: 800-321-4573 *Fax:* 303-530-4334
E-mail: info@dac.com
Web Site: www.dac.com; www.mpassociates.com
Key Personnel
Dir of Exhibit Opers: Susie Horn *Tel:* 303-530-4562 ext 125 *E-mail:* susie@mpassociates.com
Exhibit Servs Mgr: Candi Wooldridge *Tel:* 303-530-4562 ext 222
Exhibit Coord: Annette Crider *Tel:* 303-530-4562 ext 129
Conference Mgr: Sophia Sun *Tel:* 303-530-4562 ext 130 *E-mail:* sophia@dac.com
Events Coord: Callie Koble *Tel:* 303-530-4562 ext 223
Event for the design of electronic circuits & systems, embedded systems & software & electronic design automation.
Sponsored by the Association for Computing Machinery (ACM) & the Institute of Electrical & Electronics Engineers (IEEE), & is supported by ACM's Special Interest Group on Design Automation (SIGDA).
Location: Moscone Center West, San Francisco, CA
July 19-23, 2020

NAESP PreK-8 Principals Conference
Sponsored by National Association of Elementary School Principals (NAESP)
1615 Duke St, Alexandria, VA 22314
Tel: 703-684-3345 *Toll Free Tel:* 800-386-2377
 Fax: 703-549-5568 *Toll Free Fax:* 800-396-2377
E-mail: conference@naesp.org; naesp@naesp.org

Web Site: www.naesp.org
Key Personnel
Asst Exec Dir, Conferences & Exhibits: Deborah Young *Tel:* 703-684-3345 ext 296
 E-mail: dyoung@naesp.org
Location: Kentucky International Convention Center, Louisville, KY
July 12-14, 2020

SIGGRAPH 2020
Sponsored by ACM SIGGRAPH
1601 Broadway, 10th fl, New York, NY 10019-7434
Tel: 212-626-0500 *Toll Free Tel:* 800-342-6626 (US & CN) *Fax:* 212-944-1318
E-mail: confadmin@siggraph.org (conference info); acmhelp@acm.org (memb servs)
Web Site: s2020.siggraph.org; www.siggraph.org; www.acm.org
Key Personnel
Asst Dir, Off of SIG Servs: Ashley Cozzi
 Tel: 212-626-0614 *E-mail:* acozzi@hq.acm.org
Prog Coord, SIG Conference Opers: April Mosqus *Tel:* 212-626-0602 *E-mail:* mosqus@hq.acm.org
International conference & exhibition on computer graphics & interactive techniques.
Location: Walter E Washington Convention Center, 801 Mount Vernon Place NW, Washington, DC
July 19-23, 2020

Summer NAMM
Sponsored by NAMM, the National Association of Music Merchants
5790 Armada Dr, Carlsbad, CA 92008
Tel: 760-438-8001 *Toll Free Tel:* 800-767-6266 (memb hotline) *Fax:* 760-438-7327
E-mail: info@namm.org
Web Site: www.namm.org
Key Personnel
Dir, Trade Show Sales: Dan Moylan
Location: Nashville Music City Center, 700 Korean Veterans Blvd, Nashville, TN
July 9-11, 2020

VenueConnect Annual Conference & Trade Show
Sponsored by International Association of Venue Managers (IAVM)
635 Fritz Dr, Suite 100, Coppell, TX 75019-4442
Tel: 972-906-7441 *Toll Free Tel:* 800-935-4226
 Fax: 972-906-7418
E-mail: meetings@iavm.org
Web Site: www.iavm.org
Key Personnel
Dir of Meetings: Tonya Farmer *Tel:* 972-538-1019 *E-mail:* tonya.farmer@iavm.org
Meetings Mgr: Kristyn Popp *Tel:* 972-538-1020
 E-mail: kristyn.popp@iavm.org
Meetings & Certification Coord: Hillary Goodfellow *Tel:* 972-538-1027 *E-mail:* hillary.goodfellow@iavm.org
Location: Long Beach, CA
July 26-29, 2020

AUGUST

IES Annual Conference
Sponsored by Illuminating Engineering Society (IES)
120 Wall St, 17th fl, New York, NY 10005-4026
Tel: 212-248-5000
E-mail: annualconference@ies.org; ies@ies.org
Web Site: ies.org
Key Personnel
Events Coord: Klara Steupert *Tel:* 212-248-5000 ext 4006 *E-mail:* ksteupert@ies.org

Location: Hilton New Orleans Riverside, 2 Poydras St, New Orleans, LA
Aug 6-8, 2020

MAB Advocacy Conference & Annual Meeting
Sponsored by Michigan Association of Broadcasters (MAB)
820 N Capitol Ave, Lansing, MI 48906
Tel: 517-484-7444 *Toll Free Tel:* 800-YOUR-MAB (968-7622) *Fax:* 517-484-5810
E-mail: mab@michmab.com
Web Site: www.michmab.com
Key Personnel
MABF Mgr & Devt Dir: Jacquelen Timm
Sponsored jointly with MAB Foundation.
Location: MGM Grand Detroit, Detroit, MI
Aug 3-4, 2020

SEPTEMBER

Brand Print Americas
Sponsored by Association for Print Technologies (APTech)
1896 Preston White Dr, Reston, VA 20191
Tel: 703-264-7200 *Fax:* 703-620-0994
E-mail: aptech@aptech.org
Web Site: www.printtechnologies.org
Key Personnel
Sr Dir, Meetings: Deedee (Diana) Tinkham
   E-mail: dtinkham@aptech.org
Technologies & solutions for print. Co-located with Labelexpo Americas.
Location: Donald E Stephens Convention Center, Rosemont, IL
Sept 15-17, 2020

FiO/LS®
Sponsored by The Optical Society (OSA)
2010 Massachusetts Ave NW, Washington, DC 20036
Tel: 202-223-8130; 202-416-1907 (cust serv)
   Fax: 202-416-6140 (cust serv)
E-mail: exhibits@osa.org; custserv@osa.org; info@osa.org
Web Site: www.frontiersinoptics.com; www.osa.org
Co-sponsored by American Physical Society/Division of Laser Science.
Location: Marriott Wardman Park, Washington, DC
Sept 13-17, 2020

Interop
Formerly Interop ITX
Sponsored by Informa Tech
Suite 900, 9th fl, South Tower, 303 Second St, San Francisco, CA 94107
Tel: 415-947-6916 (registration dept)
   Toll Free Tel: 866-535-8992 (registration dept)
E-mail: interopregistration@ubm.com; interoplv@ubm.com (exhibitor servs)
Web Site: www.interop.com; tech.informa.com
Key Personnel
Gen Mgr, Interop: Meghan Reilly
   E-mail: meghan.reilly@ubm.com
Cloud, Data & Analytics, DevOps, Emerging Tech, Infrastructure, IT Strategy, Professional Development & Security Content for IT organizations.
Location: Austin Convention Center, Austin, TX
Sept 21-24, 2020

Radio Show
Sponsored by National Association of Broadcasters (NAB)
1771 "N" St NW, Washington, DC 20036

Tel: 202-429-5300 *Toll Free Tel:* 888-740-4622 (registration); 800-NAB-EXPO (622-3976, exhibit sales)
E-mail: nab@nab.org
Web Site: www.radioshowweb.com; www.facebook.com/radioshowweb; twitter.com/RadioShowWeb; www.nab.org
Key Personnel
Pres & CEO: Gordon H Smith
EVP, Conventions & Busn Opers: Mr Chris Brown *Tel:* 202-429-5335
SVP, Communs: Ann Marie Cumming *Tel:* 202-429-5307 *E-mail:* amcumming@nab.org
Mgr, Communs: Jamie Enright *Tel:* 202-429-5359 *E-mail:* jenright@nab.org
Co-produced with Radio Advertising Bureau (RAB).
Location: Omni Nashville, Nashville, TN
Sept 13-16, 2020

OCTOBER

AES Convention
Sponsored by Audio Engineering Society (AES)
551 Fifth Ave, Suite 1225, New York, NY 10176
Tel: 212-661-8528
Web Site: www.aes.org
Key Personnel
Exec Dir: Colleen Harper
Location: Jacob K Javits Convention Center, 655 W 34 St, New York, NY
Oct 21-24, 2020

ANA Masters of Marketing Conference
Sponsored by Association of National Advertisers Inc (ANA)
10 Grand Central, 155 E 44 St, New York, NY 10017
Tel: 212-697-5950 *Fax:* 212-687-7310
E-mail: info@ana.net
Web Site: www.ana.net
Key Personnel
Sr VP, Conferences: Kristen McDonough
   Tel: 212-455-8056 *E-mail:* kmcdonough@ana.net
Coord, Conferences: Kathleen Kresse *Tel:* 212-455-8065 *E-mail:* kkresse@ana.net
Location: Rosen Shingle Creek, 9939 Universal Blvd, Orlando, FL
Oct 20-23, 2020

ASTC Annual Conference
Sponsored by Association of Science-Technology Centers (ASTC)
818 Connecticut Ave NW, 7th fl, Washington, DC 20006-2734
Tel: 202-783-7200 *Fax:* 202-783-7207
E-mail: conference@astc.org; info@astc.org
Web Site: www.astc.org/conference; www.astc.org
Key Personnel
Conference Mgr: Nina Humes *Tel:* 202-783-7200 ext 133
Location: Carnegie Science Center, Pittsburgh, PA
Oct 17-20, 2020

CMMA National Conference
Sponsored by Communications Media Management Association (CMMA)
1604 Glendale Hills Dr NE, Suite B25, Rochester, MN 55906-8376
Tel: 507-271-4307
Web Site: cmma.org
Key Personnel
Exec Dir: Marv Mitchell *E-mail:* executive.director@cmma.org
Annual event that blends critical leadership education, information sharing, networking, emerg-

ing technical issues relevant to media managers & social opportunities.
Location: Milwaukee, WI
Oct 4-6, 2020

IES Street & Area Lighting Conference
Sponsored by Illuminating Engineering Society (IES)
120 Wall St, 17th fl, New York, NY 10005-4026
Tel: 212-248-5000
E-mail: salc@ies.org; ies@ies.org
Web Site: ies.org
Key Personnel
Events Coord: Klara Steupert *Tel:* 212-248-5000 ext 4006 *E-mail:* ksteupert@ies.org
Location: Dallas, TX
Oct 18-21, 2020

Live Design International (LDI)
Sponsored by Informa Markets
605 Third Ave, New York, NY 10158
Tel: 212-204-4200
Web Site: www.ldishow.com; www.livedesignonline.com
Key Personnel
Creative Dir/LDI Conference Dir: Ellen Lampert-Greaux *Tel:* 917-725-5043 *E-mail:* elgreaux@livedesignonline.com
Location: Las Vegas Convention Center, Central Halls, Las Vegas, NV
Oct 19-25, 2020

NAB Show® New York
Sponsored by National Association of Broadcasters (NAB)
1771 "N" St NW, Washington, DC 20036
Tel: 202-429-5300
E-mail: nab@nab.org
Web Site: www.nabshowny.com; twitter.com/NABShow; www.nab.org
Key Personnel
Pres & CEO: Gordon H Smith
EVP, Conventions & Busn Opers: Mr Chris Brown *Tel:* 202-429-5335
SVP, Communs: Ann Marie Cumming *Tel:* 202-429-5307 *E-mail:* amcumming@nab.org
Mgr, Communs: Jamie Enright *Tel:* 202-429-5359 *E-mail:* jenright@nab.org
Showcases technology for media, entertainment & telecom professionals with conferences & workshops focused on television, film, satellite, online video, live events, corporate AV production & post-production. Co-located with Audio Engineering Society Convention.
Location: Jacob K Javits Convention Center, 655 W 34 St, New York, NY
Oct 21-22, 2020

PDN PhotoPlus International Conference + Expo
Sponsored by Emerald Expositions LLC
100 Broadway, 14th fl, New York, NY 10005
Tel: 949-226-5700
E-mail: info@emeraldexpo.com
Web Site: www.photoplusexpo.com; www.emeraldexpositions.com
Key Personnel
Sr Conference Mgr: Laura Caskey *E-mail:* laura.caskey@emeraldexpo.com
Annual photo & imaging show first held in 1983.
Location: Jacob K Javits Convention Center, 655 W 34 St, New York, NY
Oct 22-24, 2020

SCTE Cable-Tec Expo®
Sponsored by Society of Cable Telecommunications Engineers Inc (SCTE)
140 Philips Rd, Exton, PA 19341-1318
Tel: 610-363-6888 *Toll Free Tel:* 800-542-5040
   Fax: 610-884-7237
E-mail: expo@scte.org

Web Site: expo.scte.org; www.scte.org

SCTE's Cable-Tec Expo® - the industry's engineering show of the year - hosts thousands of annual attendees & provides the opportunity to discover & learn first-hand about the latest in cable telecommunications technology, products & services in one cost-effective setting.

Location: Denver, CO
Oct 13-16, 2020

SMPTE® Annual Technical Conference & Exhibition

Sponsored by Society of Motion Picture & Television Engineers® (SMPTE®)
White Plains Plaza, 445 Hamilton Ave, Suite 601, White Plains, NY 10601-1827
Tel: 914-761-1100 *Fax:* 914-206-4216
Web Site: www.smpte.org
Key Personnel
Dir, Events & Governance Liaison: Sally-Ann D'Amato *Tel:* 914-205-2375 *E-mail:* sdamato@smpte.org
Location: Westin Bonaventure, Los Angeles, CA
Oct 19-22, 2020

TechNet Indo-Pacific

Formerly TechNet Asia-Pacific
Sponsored by AFCEA International
4114 Legato Rd, Suite 1000, Fairfax, VA 22033
Tel: 703-631-6158 (events) *Toll Free Tel:* 800-336-4583 *Fax:* 703-631-6169
E-mail: events@afcea.org
Web Site: www.afcea.org
Key Personnel
Sr Dir, Events: Tammy Goehring *Tel:* 703-631-6119
Mgr, Events: Terry Rogers *Tel:* 703-631-6238
Co-sponsored by AFCEA Hawaii & managed by J Spargo & Associates Inc.
Location: Hilton Hawaiian Village, Honolulu, HI
Oct 27-29, 2020

NOVEMBER

American Film Market® & Conferences

Sponsored by Independent Film & Television Alliance® (IFTA)
10850 Wilshire Blvd, 9th fl, Los Angeles, CA 90024-4311
Tel: 310-446-1000 *Fax:* 310-446-1600
E-mail: afm@ifta-online.org
Web Site: americanfilmmarket.com; www.ifta-online.org
Key Personnel
EVP & Mng Dir, American Film Market: Jonathan Wolf *E-mail:* jwolf@ifta-online.org
VP, Mktg & Membership: Robin Burt *E-mail:* rburt@ifta-online.org
Dir, AFM Attendee Servs: Wendy Arroyo *E-mail:* warroyo@ifta-online.org
Dir, AFM Exhibitor Servs: Holly Sortomme *E-mail:* hsortomme@ifta-online.org
Event offering producers & distributors the opportunity to license films. Screenings take place at theaters throughout Santa Monica, CA. Conferences are held at the Fairmont Miramar Hotel in Santa Monica, CA.
Location: Santa Monica, CA
Nov 4-11, 2020

CCUMC Annual Conference

Sponsored by Consortium of College & University Media Centers (CCUMC)
c/o Indiana University, 306 N Union St, Bloomington, IN 47405-3888
Tel: 812-855-6049
E-mail: ccumc@ccumc.org
Web Site: www.ccumc.org

Key Personnel
Exec Dir: Aileen Scales
Membership & Mktg: Kirsten Phillips
Location: Crowne Plaza Indianapolis-Downtown Union Station, Indianapolis, IN
Nov 4-7, 2020

KMWorld

Sponsored by Information Today, Inc
143 Old Marlton Pike, Medford, NJ 08055-8750
Tel: 609-654-6266 *Toll Free Tel:* 800-300-9868 (cust serv) *Fax:* 609-654-4309
E-mail: custserv@infotoday.com
Web Site: www.kmworld.com; www.facebook.com/KMWorldConference; www.infotoday.com
Key Personnel
Pres & CEO: Thomas H Hogan
Dir, Meeting Planning: Stacey Hogan
Enterprise Search & Discovery; SharePoint Symposium & Taxonomy Boot Camp held in conjunction with KMWorld. Additionally, pre-conference workshops take place on Nov 16.
Location: JW Marriott Washington DC, 1331 Pennsylvania Ave NW, Washington, DC
Nov 16-19, 2020

NABT Professional Development Conference

Sponsored by National Association of Biology Teachers (NABT)
PO Box 3363, Warrenton, VA 20188
Tel: 703-264-9696 *Toll Free Tel:* 888-501-NABT (501-6228) *Fax:* 202-962-3939
E-mail: conference@nabt.org; office@nabt.org
Web Site: www.nabt.org
Key Personnel
Exec Dir: Jaclyn Reeves-Pepin *Tel:* 719-596-9782 *E-mail:* jreevespepin@nabt.org
Location: Baltimore Marriott Waterfront, Baltimore, MD
Nov 5-8, 2020

NAfME Music Research and Teacher Education (MRTE) Conference

Sponsored by National Association for Music Education (NAfME)
1806 Robert Fulton Dr, Reston, VA 20191
Tel: 703-860-4000 *Toll Free Tel:* 800-336-3768 *Toll Free Fax:* 888-275-6362
E-mail: memberservices@nafme.org; nafme@nafme.org
Web Site: nafme.org
Key Personnel
Exec Dir & CEO: Mike Blakeslee *E-mail:* mikeb@nafme.org
Held in conjunction with the NAfME National Conference.
Location: Gaylord Palms Resort, Orlando, FL
Nov 4-8, 2020

NCTE Annual Convention

Sponsored by National Council of Teachers of English (NCTE)
1111 W Kenyon Rd, Urbana, IL 61801-1096
Tel: 217-328-3870 *Toll Free Tel:* 877-369-6283 *Fax:* 217-328-9645
E-mail: conventionquestions@ncte.org
Web Site: www.ncte.org; www.facebook.com/ncte.org
Location: Denver, CO
Nov 19-22, 2020

2021

JANUARY

Imaging USA

Sponsored by Professional Photographers of America (PPA)

229 Peachtree St NE, Suite 2200, Atlanta, GA 30303
Tel: 404-522-8600 *Toll Free Tel:* 800-786-6277 *Fax:* 404-614-6400
E-mail: info@imagingusa.org
Web Site: imagingusa.org; www.ppa.com
Key Personnel
Dir, Events: Fiona Corbett *E-mail:* fcorbett@ppa.com
Events Mgr: Sharon Palmer *E-mail:* spalmer@ppa.com
Location: Gaylord Texan Resort & Convention Center, Grapevine, TX
Jan 17-19, 2021

International CES

Sponsored by Consumer Technology Association (CTA)
1919 S Eads St, Arlington, VA 22202
Tel: 703-907-7600 *Toll Free Tel:* 866-858-1555 (cust serv) *Toll Free Fax:* 866-858-2555
E-mail: cta@cta.tech
Web Site: www.ces.tech; www.cta.tech
Key Personnel
VP, Strategic Partnerships & Conferences: Kara Dickerson
Dir of Mktg, Events: Nicole Vidovich
Sr Dir, CES Conferences: Amanda Whipkey McMaster
Location: Las Vegas Convention Center, 3150 Paradise Rd, Las Vegas, NV
Jan 6-9, 2021

The NAMM Show

Sponsored by NAMM, the National Association of Music Merchants
5790 Armada Dr, Carlsbad, CA 92008
Tel: 760-438-8001 *Toll Free Tel:* 800-767-6266 (memb hotline) *Fax:* 760-438-7327
E-mail: info@namm.org
Web Site: www.namm.org; www.facebook.com/nammshow; twitter.com/nammshow
Key Personnel
Dir, Trade Show Sales: Dan Moylan
Location: Anaheim Convention Center, 800 W Katella Ave, Anaheim, CA
Jan 21-24, 2021

PTC Conference

Sponsored by Pacific Telecommunications Council (PTC)
914 Coolidge St, Honolulu, HI 96826-3085
Tel: 808-941-3789 *Fax:* 808-944-4874
E-mail: info@ptc.org
Web Site: www.ptc.org
Key Personnel
Lead Conference & HR Coord: Lori Takeuchi *Tel:* 808-941-3789 ext 111 *E-mail:* lori@ptc.org
Conference Coord: Jamie Wan-Lopaz *Tel:* 808-941-3789 ext 124 *E-mail:* jamie@ptc.org
Location: Hilton Hawaiian Village Waikiki, 2005 Kalia Rd, Honolulu, HI
Jan 2021

FEBRUARY

AACTE Annual Meeting

Sponsored by American Association of Colleges for Teacher Education (AACTE)
1307 New York Ave NW, Suite 300, Washington, DC 20005
Tel: 202-293-2450 *Fax:* 202-457-8095
E-mail: events@aacte.org; aacte@aacte.org
Web Site: www.aacte.org
Key Personnel
VP, Memb Servs & Events: Matthew Wales *Tel:* 202-478-4597 *E-mail:* mwales@aacte.org

Location: Washington State Convention Center, Seattle, WA
Feb 26-28, 2021

National Conference on Education
Sponsored by AASA, The School Superintendents Association
1615 Duke St, Alexandria, VA 22314
Tel: 703-528-0700 *Fax:* 703-841-1543
E-mail: info@aasa.org
Web Site: nce.aasa.org; www.aasa.org
Key Personnel
Exec Dir, Meetings: Chris Daw *Tel:* 703-875-0713 *E-mail:* cdaw@aasa.org
Dir, Meetings: Jennifer Rooney *Tel:* 703-875-0778 *E-mail:* jrooney@aasa.org
Location: New Orleans, LA
Feb 18-20, 2021

MARCH

American Council on Education Annual Meeting
Sponsored by American Council on Education (ACE)
One Dupont Circle NW, Washington, DC 20036
Tel: 202-939-9300
E-mail: annualmeeting@acenet.edu
Web Site: www.aceannualmeeting.org; www.acenet.edu
Key Personnel
Pres: Ted Mitchell
Location: Washington Marriott Wardman Park, Washington, DC
March 20-23, 2021

Amusement Expo International
Sponsored by Amusement & Music Operators Association (AMOA)
380 Terra Cotta Rd, Suite F, Crystal Lake, IL 60012
Tel: 815-893-6010 *Fax:* 815-893-6248
E-mail: info@amusementexpo.com
Web Site: www.amusementexpo.org; www.amoa.com
Key Personnel
EVP: Lori Schneider
Sponsored jointly by American Amusement Machine Association (AAMA) & Amusement & Music Operators Association (AMOA). Co-located with NBVA (National Bulk Vendors Association) Conference & Tradeshow & The Laser Tag Convention.
Location: Westgate Las Vegas Resort & Casino, Las Vegas, NV
March 16-18, 2021

ASCD Empower: The Conference for Learning, Teaching & Leading Together
Sponsored by ASCD®
1703 N Beauregard St, Alexandria, VA 22311-1714
Tel: 703-578-9600 *Toll Free Tel:* 800-933-ASCD (933-2723) *Fax:* 703-575-5400
Web Site: annualconference.ascd.org; www.ascd.org
Location: Washington, DC
March 27-29, 2021

ITEEA Annual Conference
Sponsored by International Technology and Engineering Educators Association (ITEEA)
1914 Association Dr, Suite 201, Reston, VA 20191-1539
Tel: 703-860-2100 *Fax:* 703-860-0353
E-mail: iteea@iteea.org
Web Site: www.iteea.org

Key Personnel
Exec Dir: Steven A Barbato *E-mail:* sbarbato@iteea.org
Location: Denver, CO
March 24-27, 2021

NRB International Christian Media Convention
Sponsored by National Religious Broadcasters (NRB)
600 N Capitol St NW, Suite 210, Washington, DC 20001
Tel: 202-543-0073 *Fax:* 202-543-2649
E-mail: info@nrb.org
Web Site: www.nrbconvention.org; nrb.org; facebook.com/nrbconvention; twitter.com/nrbconvention
Key Personnel
Dir, Events: Beth Wakefield *E-mail:* bwakefield@nrb.org
Location: Gaylord Texan Resort & Convention Center, Grapevine, TX
March 16-19, 2021

USITT Annual Conference & Stage Expo
Sponsored by USITT
290 Elwood Davis Rd, Suite 100, Liverpool, NY 13088
Toll Free Tel: 800-938-7488 *Toll Free Fax:* 866-398-7488
E-mail: info@usitt.org
Web Site: www.usitt.org
Key Personnel
Meeting Planner: Jody Harris *E-mail:* jody@usitt.org
Location: Columbus, OH
March 10-13, 2021

APRIL

AERA Annual Meeting
Sponsored by American Educational Research Association (AERA)
1430 "K" St NW, Suite 1200, Washington, DC 20005
Tel: 202-238-3200 *Fax:* 202-238-3250
E-mail: annualmtg@aera.net
Web Site: www.aera.net
Key Personnel
Meeting Dir: Robert Smith *Tel:* 202-238-3200 ext 210 *E-mail:* rsmith@aera.net
Asst Dir: Mary Piper Waters *Tel:* 202-238-3200 ext 213 *E-mail:* mpiperwaters@aera.net
Meeting Mgr: Kendra McGee *Tel:* 202-238-3200 ext 212 *E-mail:* kmcgee@aera.net
Location: Orlando, FL
April 9-12, 2021

NCEA Convention & Expo
Sponsored by National Catholic Educational Association (NCEA)
1005 N Glebe Rd, Suite 525, Arlington, VA 22201
Tel: 571-257-0010 *Toll Free Tel:* 800-711-NCEA (711-6232) *Fax:* 703-243-0025
E-mail: info@ncea.org
Web Site: www.ncea.org/convention; www.ncea.org
Key Personnel
Dir of Events: Amy Durkin *E-mail:* adurkin@ncea.org
Annual meeting for all working in Catholic education, Pre-K through college.
Location: Los Angeles, CA
April 6-8, 2021

MAY

AAM Annual Meeting & MuseumExpo
Sponsored by American Alliance of Museums (AAM)
2451 Crystal Dr, Suite 1005, Arlington, VA 22202
Tel: 202-289-1818 *Fax:* 202-289-6578
Web Site: www.aam-us.org
Key Personnel
Dir, Meetings & Events: Veronica Mooney *Tel:* 202-218-7678 *E-mail:* vmooney@aam-us.org
Meetings & Events Mgr: Clara Allen *Tel:* 202-218-7708 *E-mail:* callen@aam-us.org
Location: Chicago, IL
May 9-12, 2021

ATD International Conference & Exposition
Sponsored by Association for Talent Development (ATD)
1640 King St, Alexandria, VA 22314-2743
Tel: 703-683-8100 *Toll Free Tel:* 800-628-2783 *Fax:* 703-299-8723
E-mail: customercare@td.org
Web Site: www.atdconference.org; www.td.org
Location: Los Angeles, CA
May 23-26, 2021

JUNE

ALA Annual Conference
Sponsored by American Library Association (ALA)
50 E Huron St, Chicago, IL 60611-2795
Tel: 312-944-6780 *Toll Free Tel:* 800-545-2433 (ext 3223, conference servs) *Fax:* 312-440-9374
E-mail: ala@ala.org
Web Site: www.ala.org
Key Personnel
Conference Dir: Paul Graller *Tel:* 800-545-2433 ext 3219 *E-mail:* pgraller@ala.org
Registration & Housing Mgr: Alicia Hamann *Tel:* 800-545-2433 ext 3229 *E-mail:* ahamann@ala.org
Meeting Mgr: Yvonne McLean *Tel:* 800-545-2433 ext 3222 *E-mail:* ymclean@ala.org
Meeting Coord: Megan Kaiko *Tel:* 800-545-2433 ext 3220 *E-mail:* mkaiko@ala.org
Location: Chicago, IL
June 24-29, 2021

Optometry's Meeting®
Sponsored by American Optometric Association (AOA)
243 N Lindbergh Blvd, 1st fl, St Louis, MO 63141-7881
Tel: 314-991-4100 *Toll Free Tel:* 800-386-6825 (meetings hotline) *Fax:* 314-991-4101
E-mail: optometrysmeeting@aoa.org
Web Site: www.optometrysmeeting.org; www.exhibitsom.org; www.aoa.org
Key Personnel
Exhibits & Sponsorship Mgr: Kellie Rodrigue *Tel:* 314-983-4255 *E-mail:* kerodrigue@aoa.org
Annual meeting of the American Optometric Association & the American Optometric Student Association.
Location: Anaheim Convention Center, Anaheim, CA
June 23-27, 2021

JULY

NAESP PreK-8 Principals Conference
Sponsored by National Association of Elementary
  School Principals (NAESP)
1615 Duke St, Alexandria, VA 22314
Tel: 703-684-3345 *Toll Free Tel:* 800-386-2377
  Fax: 703-549-5568 *Toll Free Fax:* 800-396-
  2377
E-mail: conference@naesp.org; naesp@naesp.org
Web Site: www.naesp.org
Key Personnel
Asst Exec Dir, Conferences & Exhibits: Deb-
  orah Young *Tel:* 703-684-3345 ext 296
  E-mail: dyoung@naesp.org
Location: Hyatt Regency Chicago, Chicago, IL
July 8-10, 2021

Summer NAMM
Sponsored by NAMM, the National Association
  of Music Merchants
5790 Armada Dr, Carlsbad, CA 92008
Tel: 760-438-8001 *Toll Free Tel:* 800-767-6266
  (memb hotline) *Fax:* 760-438-7327
E-mail: info@namm.org
Web Site: www.namm.org
Key Personnel
Dir, Trade Show Sales: Dan Moylan
Location: Nashville Music City Center, 700 Ko-
  rean Veterans Blvd, Nashville, TN
July 15-17, 2021

OCTOBER

Advanced Manufacturing Canada Conference
Sponsored by Society of Manufacturing Engineers
  Canada (SME Canada)
7100 Woodbine Ave, Suite 312, Markham, ON
  L3R 5J2, Canada
Tel: 905-752-4415 *Toll Free Tel:* 888-322-7333
  Fax: 905-479-0113
E-mail: exposales@sme.org
Web Site: www.sme.org/smecanada; www.
  advancedmfg.ca
Advanced manufacturing technologies including
  automation & robotics, additive manufactur-
  ing/3D printing, materials & software.
Location: The International Centre, Mississauga,
  ON, CN
Oct 4-7, 2021

NOVEMBER

American Film Market® & Conferences
Sponsored by Independent Film & Television Al-
  liance® (IFTA)
10850 Wilshire Blvd, 9th fl, Los Angeles, CA
  90024-4311
Tel: 310-446-1000 *Fax:* 310-446-1600
E-mail: afm@ifta-online.org
Web Site: americanfilmmarket.com; www.ifta-
  online.org
Key Personnel
EVP & Mng Dir, American Film Market:
  Jonathan Wolf *E-mail:* jwolf@ifta-online.org
VP, Mktg & Membership: Robin Burt
  E-mail: rburt@ifta-online.org
Dir, AFM Attendee Servs: Wendy Arroyo
  E-mail: warroyo@ifta-online.org
Dir, AFM Exhibitor Servs: Holly Sortomme
  E-mail: hsortomme@ifta-online.org
Event offering producers & distributors the oppor-
  tunity to license films. Screenings take place at
  theaters throughout Santa Monica, CA. Confer-

ences are held at the Fairmont Miramar Hotel
in Santa Monica, CA.
Location: Santa Monica, CA
Nov 3-10, 2021

NABT Professional Development Conference
Sponsored by National Association of Biology
  Teachers (NABT)
PO Box 3363, Warrenton, VA 20188
Tel: 703-264-9696 *Toll Free Tel:* 888-501-NABT
  (501-6228) *Fax:* 202-962-3939
E-mail: conference@nabt.org; office@nabt.org
Web Site: www.nabt.org
Key Personnel
Exec Dir: Jaclyn Reeves-Pepin *Tel:* 719-596-9782
  E-mail: jreevespepin@nabt.org
Location: Atlanta Marriott Marquis, Atlanta, GA
Nov 11-14, 2021

NCTE Annual Convention
Sponsored by National Council of Teachers of
  English (NCTE)
1111 W Kenyon Rd, Urbana, IL 61801-1096
Tel: 217-328-3870 *Toll Free Tel:* 877-369-6283
  Fax: 217-328-9645
E-mail: conventionquestions@ncte.org
Web Site: www.ncte.org; www.facebook.com/ncte.
  org
Location: Louisville, KY
Nov 18-21, 2021

TechNet Indo-Pacific
Formerly TechNet Asia-Pacific
Sponsored by AFCEA International
4114 Legato Rd, Suite 1000, Fairfax, VA 22033
Tel: 703-631-6158 (events) *Toll Free Tel:* 800-
  336-4583 *Fax:* 703-631-6169
E-mail: events@afcea.org
Web Site: www.afcea.org
Key Personnel
Sr Dir, Events: Tammy Goehring *Tel:* 703-631-
  6119
Mgr, Events: Terry Rogers *Tel:* 703-631-6238
Co-sponsored by AFCEA Hawaii & managed by
  J Spargo & Associates Inc.
Location: Hilton Hawaiian Village, Honolulu, HI
Nov 9-11, 2021

2022

JANUARY

International CES
Sponsored by Consumer Technology Association
  (CTA)
1919 S Eads St, Arlington, VA 22202
Tel: 703-907-7600 *Toll Free Tel:* 866-858-1555
  (cust serv) *Toll Free Fax:* 866-858-2555
E-mail: cta@cta.tech
Web Site: www.ces.tech; www.cta.tech
Key Personnel
VP, Strategic Partnerships & Conferences: Kara
  Dickerson
Dir of Mktg, Events: Nicole Vidovich
Sr Dir, CES Conferences: Amanda Whipkey Mc-
  Master
Location: Las Vegas Convention Center, 3150
  Paradise Rd, Las Vegas, NV
Jan 5-8, 2022

The NAMM Show
Sponsored by NAMM, the National Association
  of Music Merchants
5790 Armada Dr, Carlsbad, CA 92008
Tel: 760-438-8001 *Toll Free Tel:* 800-767-6266
  (memb hotline) *Fax:* 760-438-7327
E-mail: info@namm.org

Web Site: www.namm.org; www.facebook.
  com/nammshow; twitter.com/nammshow
Key Personnel
Dir, Trade Show Sales: Dan Moylan
Location: Anaheim Convention Center, 800 W
  Katella Ave, Anaheim, CA
Jan 20-23, 2022

FEBRUARY

National Conference on Education
Sponsored by AASA, The School Superintendents
  Association
1615 Duke St, Alexandria, VA 22314
Tel: 703-528-0700 *Fax:* 703-841-1543
E-mail: info@aasa.org
Web Site: nce.aasa.org; www.aasa.org
Key Personnel
Exec Dir, Meetings: Chris Daw *Tel:* 703-875-
  0713 *E-mail:* cdaw@aasa.org
Dir, Meetings: Jennifer Rooney *Tel:* 703-875-
  0778 *E-mail:* jrooney@aasa.org
Location: Nashville, TN
Feb 17-19, 2022

MARCH

AACTE Annual Meeting
Sponsored by American Association of Colleges
  for Teacher Education (AACTE)
1307 New York Ave NW, Suite 300, Washington,
  DC 20005
Tel: 202-293-2450 *Fax:* 202-457-8095
E-mail: events@aacte.org; aacte@aacte.org
Web Site: www.aacte.org
Key Personnel
VP, Memb Servs & Events: Matthew Wales
  Tel: 202-478-4597 *E-mail:* mwales@aacte.org
Location: New Orleans Marriott, New Orleans,
  LA
March 4-6, 2022

**American Council on Education Annual
  Meeting**
Sponsored by American Council on Education
  (ACE)
One Dupont Circle NW, Washington, DC 20036
Tel: 202-939-9300
E-mail: annualmeeting@acenet.edu
Web Site: www.aceannualmeeting.org; www.
  acenet.edu
Key Personnel
Pres: Ted Mitchell
Location: Marriott Marquis San Diego Marina,
  San Diego, CA
March 5-8, 2022

ITEEA Annual Conference
Sponsored by International Technology and Engi-
  neering Educators Association (ITEEA)
1914 Association Dr, Suite 201, Reston, VA
  20191-1539
Tel: 703-860-2100 *Fax:* 703-860-0353
E-mail: iteea@iteea.org
Web Site: www.iteea.org
Key Personnel
Exec Dir: Steven A Barbato *E-mail:* sbarbato@
  iteea.org
Location: Orlando, FL
March 9-12.2022

APRIL

AERA Annual Meeting
Sponsored by American Educational Research
Association (AERA)
1430 "K" St NW, Suite 1200, Washington, DC
20005
Tel: 202-238-3200 *Fax:* 202-238-3250
E-mail: annualmtg@aera.net
Web Site: www.aera.net
Key Personnel
Meeting Dir: Robert Smith *Tel:* 202-238-3200 ext
210 *E-mail:* rsmith@aera.net
Asst Dir: Mary Piper Waters *Tel:* 202-238-3200
ext 213 *E-mail:* mpiperwaters@aera.net
Meeting Mgr: Kendra McGee *Tel:* 202-238-3200
ext 212 *E-mail:* kmcgee@aera.net
Location: San Diego, CA
April 22-25, 2022

MAY

ATD International Conference & Exposition
Sponsored by Association for Talent Development
(ATD)
1640 King St, Alexandria, VA 22314-2743
Tel: 703-683-8100 *Toll Free Tel:* 800-628-2783
Fax: 703-299-8723
E-mail: customercare@td.org
Web Site: www.atdconference.org; www.td.org
Location: Orlando, FL
May 15-18, 2022

JUNE

ALA Annual Conference
Sponsored by American Library Association
(ALA)
50 E Huron St, Chicago, IL 60611-2795
Tel: 312-944-6780 *Toll Free Tel:* 800-545-2433
(ext 3223, conference servs) *Fax:* 312-440-
9374
E-mail: ala@ala.org
Web Site: www.ala.org
Key Personnel
Conference Dir: Paul Graller *Tel:* 800-545-2433
ext 3219 *E-mail:* pgraller@ala.org
Registration & Housing Mgr: Alicia Hamann
Tel: 800-545-2433 ext 3229 *E-mail:* ahamann@
ala.org
Meeting Mgr: Yvonne McLean *Tel:* 800-545-2433
ext 3222 *E-mail:* ymclean@ala.org
Meeting Coord: Megan Kaiko *Tel:* 800-545-2433
ext 3220 *E-mail:* mkaiko@ala.org
Location: Washington, DC
June 23-28, 2022

Optometry's Meeting®
Sponsored by American Optometric Association
(AOA)
243 N Lindbergh Blvd, 1st fl, St Louis, MO
63141-7881
Tel: 314-991-4100 *Toll Free Tel:* 800-386-6825
(meetings hotline) *Fax:* 314-991-4101
E-mail: optometrysmeeting@aoa.org
Web Site: www.optometrysmeeting.org; www.
exhibitsom.org; www.aoa.org
Key Personnel
Exhibits & Sponsorship Mgr: Kellie Rodrigue
Tel: 314-983-4255 *E-mail:* kerodrigue@aoa.org
Annual meeting of the American Optometric As-
sociation & the American Optometric Student
Association.

Location: McCormick Place Convention Center,
Chicago, IL
June 15-19, 2022

NOVEMBER

American Film Market® & Conferences
Sponsored by Independent Film & Television Al-
liance® (IFTA)
10850 Wilshire Blvd, 9th fl, Los Angeles, CA
90024-4311
Tel: 310-446-1000 *Fax:* 310-446-1600
E-mail: afm@ifta-online.org
Web Site: americanfilmmarket.com; www.ifta-
online.org
Key Personnel
EVP & Mng Dir, American Film Market:
Jonathan Wolf *E-mail:* jwolf@ifta-online.org
VP, Mktg & Membership: Robin Burt
E-mail: rburt@ifta-online.org
Dir, AFM Attendee Servs: Wendy Arroyo
E-mail: warroyo@ifta-online.org
Dir, AFM Exhibitor Servs: Holly Sortomme
E-mail: hsortomme@ifta-online.org
Event offering producers & distributors the oppor-
tunity to license films. Screenings take place at
theaters throughout Santa Monica, CA. Confer-
ences are held at the Fairmont Miramar Hotel
in Santa Monica, CA.
Location: Santa Monica, CA
Nov 2-9, 2022

2023

JANUARY

International CES
Sponsored by Consumer Technology Association
(CTA)
1919 S Eads St, Arlington, VA 22202
Tel: 703-907-7600 *Toll Free Tel:* 866-858-1555
(cust serv) *Toll Free Fax:* 866-858-2555
E-mail: cta@cta.tech
Web Site: www.ces.tech; www.cta.tech
Key Personnel
VP, Strategic Partnerships & Conferences: Kara
Dickerson
Dir of Mktg, Events: Nicole Vidovich
Sr Dir, CES Conferences: Amanda Whipkey Mc-
Master
Location: Las Vegas Convention Center, 3150
Paradise Rd, Las Vegas, NV
Jan 5-8, 2023

FEBRUARY

AACTE Annual Meeting
Sponsored by American Association of Colleges
for Teacher Education (AACTE)
1307 New York Ave NW, Suite 300, Washington,
DC 20005
Tel: 202-293-2450 *Fax:* 202-457-8095
E-mail: events@aacte.org; aacte@aacte.org
Web Site: www.aacte.org
Key Personnel
VP, Memb Servs & Events: Matthew Wales
Tel: 202-478-4597 *E-mail:* mwales@aacte.org
Location: JW Marriott Indianapolis, Indianapolis,
IN
Feb 25-27, 2023

MARCH

**American Council on Education Annual
Meeting**
Sponsored by American Council on Education
(ACE)
One Dupont Circle NW, Washington, DC 20036
Tel: 202-939-9300
E-mail: annualmeeting@acenet.edu
Web Site: www.aceannualmeeting.org; www.
acenet.edu
Key Personnel
Pres: Ted Mitchell
Location: Washington Marriott Wardman Park,
Washington, DC
March 11-14, 2023

APRIL

AERA Annual Meeting
Sponsored by American Educational Research
Association (AERA)
1430 "K" St NW, Suite 1200, Washington, DC
20005
Tel: 202-238-3200 *Fax:* 202-238-3250
E-mail: annualmtg@aera.net
Web Site: www.aera.net
Key Personnel
Meeting Dir: Robert Smith *Tel:* 202-238-3200 ext
210 *E-mail:* rsmith@aera.net
Asst Dir: Mary Piper Waters *Tel:* 202-238-3200
ext 213 *E-mail:* mpiperwaters@aera.net
Meeting Mgr: Kendra McGee *Tel:* 202-238-3200
ext 212 *E-mail:* kmcgee@aera.net
Location: Chicago, IL
April 13-16, 2023

ITEEA Annual Conference
Sponsored by International Technology and Engi-
neering Educators Association (ITEEA)
1914 Association Dr, Suite 201, Reston, VA
20191-1539
Tel: 703-860-2100 *Fax:* 703-860-0353
E-mail: iteea@iteea.org
Web Site: www.iteea.org
Key Personnel
Exec Dir: Steven A Barbato *E-mail:* sbarbato@
iteea.org
Location: Minneapolis, MN
April 12-15, 2023

JUNE

ALA Annual Conference
Sponsored by American Library Association
(ALA)
50 E Huron St, Chicago, IL 60611-2795
Tel: 312-944-6780 *Toll Free Tel:* 800-545-2433
(ext 3223, conference servs) *Fax:* 312-440-
9374
E-mail: ala@ala.org
Web Site: www.ala.org
Key Personnel
Conference Dir: Paul Graller *Tel:* 800-545-2433
ext 3219 *E-mail:* pgraller@ala.org
Registration & Housing Mgr: Alicia Hamann
Tel: 800-545-2433 ext 3229 *E-mail:* ahamann@
ala.org
Meeting Mgr: Yvonne McLean *Tel:* 800-545-2433
ext 3222 *E-mail:* ymclean@ala.org
Meeting Coord: Megan Kaiko *Tel:* 800-545-2433
ext 3220 *E-mail:* mkaiko@ala.org

Location: Chicago, IL
June 22-27, 2023

Optometry's Meeting®
Sponsored by American Optometric Association
(AOA)
243 N Lindbergh Blvd, 1st fl, St Louis, MO
63141-7881
Tel: 314-991-4100 *Toll Free Tel:* 800-386-6825
(meetings hotline) *Fax:* 314-991-4101
E-mail: optometrysmeeting@aoa.org
Web Site: www.optometrysmeeting.org; www.
exhibitsom.org; www.aoa.org
Key Personnel
Exhibits & Sponsorship Mgr: Kellie Rodrigue
Tel: 314-983-4255 *E-mail:* kerodrigue@aoa.org
Annual meeting of the American Optometric As-
sociation & the American Optometric Student
Association.
Location: Walter E Washington Convention Cen-
ter, Washington, DC
June 21-25, 2023

NOVEMBER

American Film Market® & Conferences
Sponsored by Independent Film & Television Al-
liance® (IFTA)
10850 Wilshire Blvd, 9th fl, Los Angeles, CA
90024-4311
Tel: 310-446-1000 *Fax:* 310-446-1600
E-mail: afm@ifta-online.org
Web Site: americanfilmmarket.com; www.ifta-
online.org
Key Personnel
EVP & Mng Dir, American Film Market:
Jonathan Wolf *E-mail:* jwolf@ifta-online.org
VP, Mktg & Membership: Robin Burt
E-mail: rburt@ifta-online.org
Dir, AFM Attendee Servs: Wendy Arroyo
E-mail: warroyo@ifta-online.org
Dir, AFM Exhibitor Servs: Holly Sortomme
E-mail: hsortomme@ifta-online.org

Event offering producers & distributors the opportunity to license films. Screenings take place at
theaters throughout Santa Monica, CA. Conferences are held at the Fairmont Miramar Hotel
in Santa Monica, CA.
Location: Santa Monica, CA
Nov 1-8, 2023

2024

JANUARY

International CES
Sponsored by Consumer Technology Association
(CTA)
1919 S Eads St, Arlington, VA 22202
Tel: 703-907-7600 *Toll Free Tel:* 866-858-1555
(cust serv) *Toll Free Fax:* 866-858-2555
E-mail: cta@cta.tech
Web Site: www.ces.tech; www.cta.tech
Key Personnel
VP, Strategic Partnerships & Conferences: Kara
Dickerson
Dir of Mktg, Events: Nicole Vidovich
Sr Dir, CES Conferences: Amanda Whipkey Mc-
Master
Location: Las Vegas Convention Center, 3150
Paradise Rd, Las Vegas, NV
Jan 9-12, 2024

JUNE

ALA Annual Conference
Sponsored by American Library Association
(ALA)
50 E Huron St, Chicago, IL 60611-2795
Tel: 312-944-6780 *Toll Free Tel:* 800-545-2433
(ext 3223, conference servs) *Fax:* 312-440-
9374

E-mail: ala@ala.org
Web Site: www.ala.org
Key Personnel
Conference Dir: Paul Graller *Tel:* 800-545-2433
ext 3219 *E-mail:* pgraller@ala.org
Registration & Housing Mgr: Alicia Hamann
Tel: 800-545-2433 ext 3229 *E-mail:* ahamann@
ala.org
Meeting Mgr: Yvonne McLean *Tel:* 800-545-2433
ext 3222 *E-mail:* ymclean@ala.org
Meeting Coord: Megan Kaiko *Tel:* 800-545-2433
ext 3220 *E-mail:* mkaiko@ala.org
Location: San Diego, CA
June 27-July 2, 2024

NOVEMBER

American Film Market® & Conferences
Sponsored by Independent Film & Television Al-
liance® (IFTA)
10850 Wilshire Blvd, 9th fl, Los Angeles, CA
90024-4311
Tel: 310-446-1000 *Fax:* 310-446-1600
E-mail: afm@ifta-online.org
Web Site: americanfilmmarket.com; www.ifta-
online.org
Key Personnel
EVP & Mng Dir, American Film Market:
Jonathan Wolf *E-mail:* jwolf@ifta-online.org
VP, Mktg & Membership: Robin Burt
E-mail: rburt@ifta-online.org
Dir, AFM Attendee Servs: Wendy Arroyo
E-mail: warroyo@ifta-online.org
Dir, AFM Exhibitor Servs: Holly Sortomme
E-mail: hsortomme@ifta-online.org
Event offering producers & distributors the oppor-
tunity to license films. Screenings take place at
theaters throughout Santa Monica, CA. Confer-
ences are held at the Fairmont Miramar Hotel
in Santa Monica, CA.
Location: Santa Monica, CA
Nov 6-13, 2024

Periodicals for the Trade

The majority of the publications listed in this section are specifically media-oriented. Others have been included because they contain important AV-related information, such as software reviews, equipment appraisals or guidelines on AV instruction.

Ad Age
Formerly Advertising Age
Published by Crain Communications Inc
685 Third Ave, New York, NY 10017-4024
Tel: 212-210-0100 *Toll Free Tel:* 877-320-1721
    Fax: 212-210-0200
E-mail: adageeditor@adage.com; info@adage.
    com; customerservice@adage.com
Web Site: adage.com
Key Personnel
Pres & Publr: Josh Golden *E-mail:* jgolden@
    adage.com
Assoc Publr, Gen Mgr, Mktg & Brand: Heidi
    Waldusky *E-mail:* hwaldusky@adage.com
Exec Ed: Judann Pollack *E-mail:* jpollack@adage.
    com
Ed: Brian Braiker *E-mail:* bbraiker@adage.com
Covers advertising in business, media, trade
    newspapers & magazines. Print & digital.
First published 1930
Media Reviewed: Advertising, Commercials
Frequency: 24 issues/yr
Circulation: 58,000
$109/yr (All Access), $279/yr (Insider), $1,199/yr
    (Editor's Circle)
ISSN: 0001-8899 (print); 1557-7414 (online)
Trim Size: 10 x 13
Ad Rates: B&W page (1-5x) $27,060, 4-color
    page (1-5x) $35,190

Advertising Age, see Ad Age

AES-Journal of the Audio Engineering Society
Published by Audio Engineering Society (AES)
551 Fifth Ave, Suite 1225, New York, NY 10176
Tel: 212-661-8528
Web Site: www.aes.org/journal
Key Personnel
Ed-in-Chief: Bozena Kostek
Mng Ed: William T McQuaide *E-mail:* wtm@aes.
    org
Sr Ed: Mary Ellen Ilich
Peer-reviewed journal devoted exclusively to au-
    dio technology.
First published 1953
Media Reviewed: Books
Frequency: 10 issues/yr
$75/yr print, online free membs, $310/yr print,
    $565 online (includes archived), $715/yr print
    & online nonmembs
ISSN: 1549-4950
Trim Size: 8 1/4 x 11
Ad Rates: $1,150 page, $958 2/3 page, $863 1/2
    page island, $767 1/2 page, $671 1/3 page
    island, $575 1/3 page, $345 1/6 page, bleed
    charge $95 per page, $500 extra/standard color,
    $550 extra/matched color, $1,850 extra/page or
    fraction

**Afterimage: The Journal of Media Arts and
Cultural Criticism**
Published by University of California Press
155 Grand Ave, Suite 400, Oakland, CA 94612-
3758
Tel: 510-883-8232
Web Site: www.ucpress.edu/journals
Key Personnel
Ed: Karen vanMeenen *E-mail:* afterimageeditor@
    ucpress.edu
Feature articles, conference & festival reports,
    books & exhibition reviews, essay & news

about the visual arts, photography, indepen-
    dent film & video, new media & alternative
    publishing. Online only.
Media Reviewed: Alternative Publishing, Artists
    Books, Books, Hypermedia, Independent Films,
    Mixed Media, Photography, Videotapes
Frequency: Quarterly
Indivs: $20/issue, $45/yr; Instns: $99/issue, $399/
    yr
ISSN: 2578-8531 (online)

AI Update
Published by Worldwide Videotex
68 Russell St, North Andover, MA 01845
Tel: 781-439-5505
Web Site: wvpubs.com/publications
Providing the latest news & information on all
    products & news in the artificial intelligence
    industry.
First published 1981
Frequency: Monthly
$185/yr, $200/yr foreign, $165 e-file
ISSN: 1045-5795

American Cinematographer
Published by American Society of Cinematogra-
phers (ASC)
1782 N Orange Dr, Los Angeles, CA 90028
Mailing Address: PO Box 2230, Los Angeles, CA
90078
Tel: 323-969-4333 *Toll Free Tel:* 800-448-0145
    (US only) *Fax:* 323-876-4973
E-mail: publisher@ascmag.com (edit);
    customerservice@theasc.com
Web Site: theasc.com; ascmag.com
Key Personnel
Ed-in-Chief & Publr: Stephen Pizzello
    E-mail: publisher@ascmag.com
Mng Ed: Jon Witmer
International journal on motion-imaging tech-
    niques.
First published 1920
Media Reviewed: Books, Commercials, Films,
    TV
Frequency: Monthly
Circulation: 30,000 print
$34.95/yr print, $59.95/2 yrs print, $29.95/yr digi-
    tal
ISSN: 0002-7928
Trim Size: 8 1/8 x 10 1/2
Ad Closing Date(s): 3rd week of 2nd month pre-
    ceding cover date

American Libraries
Published by American Library Association
(ALA)
50 E Huron St, Chicago, IL 60611-2795
Tel: 312-944-6780 *Toll Free Tel:* 800-545-2433
    (ext 4216) *Fax:* 312-440-9374
E-mail: americanlibraries@ala.org
Web Site: www.americanlibrariesmagazine.org
Key Personnel
Publr & Ed: Sanhita SinhaRoy *Tel:* 800-545-2433
    ext 4219 *E-mail:* ssinharoy@ala.org
Mng Ed: Terra Dankowski *Tel:* 800-545-2433 ext
    5282 *E-mail:* tdankowski@ala.org
Sr Ed, Online Media: Amy Carlton *Tel:* 800-545-
    2433 ext 5105 *E-mail:* acarlton@ala.org
News & trends for the library community.
First published 1907

Media Reviewed: CD-ROMs, DVDs, Library
    Software
Frequency: 6 issues/yr
Circulation: 58,000
$74/yr North American & Mexican, $84/yr for-
    eign instns
ISSN: 0002-9769
Trim Size: 7 7/8 x 10 1/2
Ad Rates: 4-color page $5,310
Ad Closing Date(s): Approximately 4 weeks prior
    to cover date. See media kit for additional info

American Record Guide
Published by Record Guide Productions
4412 Braddock St, Cincinnati, OH 45204
Tel: 513-941-1116
E-mail: subs@americanrecordguide.com
Web Site: www.americanrecordguide.com
Key Personnel
Ed: Donald R Vroon *E-mail:* don@
    americanrecordguide.com
Art & Circ: Ray Hassard
Classical music reviews. No unsol mss, query
    first.
First published 1935
Media Reviewed: CDs, Concerts, DVDs, Operas
Frequency: 6 issues/yr
Circulation: 2,200
$48/yr US, $75/yr foreign
ISSN: 0003-0716
Trim Size: 6 x 9
Ad Rates: B&W page $1,000, 1/2 page $550,
    1/3 page $375, 1/4 page $280; 4-color cover
    $1,500
Ad Closing Date(s): 6 weeks before issue date

The AMSAT Journal
Published by Radio Amateur Satellite Corp (AM-
SAT)
10605 Concord St, No 304, Kensington, MD
20895-2526
Tel: 301-822-4376 *Toll Free Tel:* 888-322-6728
    (US only) *Fax:* 301-822-4371
Web Site: www.amsat.org
Key Personnel
Ed-in-Chief: Joe Kornowski *E-mail:* kb6igk@
    gmail.com
First published 1989
Frequency: 6 issues/yr
Free to membs
ISSN: 1047-3076

Animation Magazine
Published by Animation Magazine Inc
26500 W Agoura Rd, Suite 102-651, Calabasas,
CA 91302
Tel: 818-883-2884 *Fax:* 818-883-3773
E-mail: info@animationmagazine.net;
    sales@animationmagazine.net; edit@
    animationmagazine.net
Web Site: www.animationmagazine.net
Key Personnel
Pres & Publr: Jean Thoren *E-mail:* jthoren@
    animationmagazine.net
Ed-in-Chief: Ramin Zahed *E-mail:* ramin@
    animationmagazine.net
Assoc Ed: Mercedes Milligan *E-mail:* mercedes@
    animationmagazine.net
Sales: Sheri Shelton *Tel:* 818-665-2050
    E-mail: sshelton@animationmagazine.net

Publication dedicated to the business, technology & art of animation & VFX.
First published 1987
Media Reviewed: Records
Frequency: 10 issues/yr (plus supplements), calendar, school guide & show guides
Circulation: 20,824
Print only: $60/yr US, $75/yr CN & Mexico, $90/yr intl; Digital only: $36/yr; Digital & print: $78/yr US, $93/yr CN & Mexico, $108/yr intl
ISSN: 1041-617X
Trim Size: 8 3/8 x 10 7/8

ARSC Journal
Published by Association for Recorded Sound Collections (ARSC)
1299 University of Oregon, Eugene, OR 97403-1299
Tel: 541-346-1852
Web Site: www.arsc-audio.org/journal.html
Key Personnel
Exec Dir: Nathan Georgitis *E-mail:* execdir@arsc-audio.org
Ed: Sarah Bryan *E-mail:* sarah@culturesouth.org
Ad Ed: David Lewis *E-mail:* dlewis@gmail.com
Book Reviews Ed: Jim Farrington
   E-mail: jfarrington@esm.rochester.edu
Sound Recording Reviews Ed: John H Haley
   E-mail: jhaleyesq@gmail.com
Peer reviewed publication that serves to document the history of sound recording & includes original articles on many aspects of research & preservation: biography; cataloging; copyright law; current research; discography; technical aspects of sound restoration, etc. Selected ARSC conference papers are a regular feature. The journal also includes book, CD-ROM & sound recording reviews & publishes a running bibliography of articles appearing in other specialist publications & of related interest.
First published 1967
Media Reviewed: Books, CD-ROMs
Frequency: Semiannual
Circulation: 1,100
$75 membership fee for instns includes 1 yr subn, $45 indiv membership fee includes 1 yr subn, foreign postage extra (Mexico & CN $15, $30 foreign), $18 full-time students
ISSN: 0004-5438
Trim Size: 6 x 9
Ad Rates: Covers (not newsletter) $350, full page $200, 1/2 page vertical or horizontal $150, 1/4 page $100
Ad Closing Date(s): Feb 1 for Spring issue, Sept 1 for Fall issue

Arts & Activities
Published by Publishers Development Corp
12345 World Trade Dr, San Diego, CA 92128
Tel: 858-605-0242 (edit); 858-605-0251 (subns)
   Toll Free Tel: 888-651-7567 *Fax:* 858-605-0205
E-mail: subs@artsandactivities.com
Web Site: artsandactivities.com
Key Personnel
Ed & Publr: Maryellen Bridge *E-mail:* ed@artsandactivities.com
Ad Mgr: Amy Tanguay *E-mail:* amy.tanguay@artsandactivities.com
Art education & instruction for teachers at all levels, K-12.
First published 1932
Media Reviewed: CD-ROMs, DVDs, Software
Frequency: Monthly (exc July & Aug)
Number of pages: 52
Circulation: 18,000
$3/issue, $40/yr US, $90/yr foreign
ISSN: 0004-3931
Trim Size: 8 x 10 7/8
Ad Rates: B&W page $2,324, 2-color page $2,578, 4-color page $2,979
Ad Closing Date(s): 1st or 2nd week of the month, 1 month prior to cover date

ATM Telecommunications Newsletter
Published by Information Gatekeepers Inc (IGI)
Division of IGI Group Inc
PO Box 606, Winchester, MA 01890
Tel: 617-782-5033 *Fax:* 617-507-8338
E-mail: info@igigroup.com
Web Site: www.igigroup.com
Key Personnel
Chief Analyst & Ed-in-Chief: Dr Hui Pan
   E-mail: hpan@igigroup.com
Mng Ed: Bev Wilson *E-mail:* editor@igigroup.com
Technology, markets, industry events & international developments. Submissions accepted by e-mail.
First published 1989
Frequency: Monthly
Number of pages: 16
Circulation: 1,000
$695/yr US & CN, $745/yr other print, $695 PDF (1 user), multi-user licenses available
ISSN: 1051-1903
Trim Size: 8 1/2 x 11

AudioFile® Magazine
Published by AudioFile® Publications Inc
37 Silver St, Portland, ME 04101
Mailing Address: PO Box 109, Portland, ME 04112-0109
Tel: 207-774-7563 *Toll Free Tel:* 800-506-1212
   Fax: 207-775-3744
E-mail: info@audiofilemagazine.com
Web Site: www.audiofilemagazine.com
Key Personnel
Publr: Michele L Cobb
Art Dir: Jennifer Steele
Mng Ed: Jennifer M Dowell
Review Ed: Elizabeth K Dodge
Ed: Robin F Whitten *E-mail:* robin@audiofilemagazine.com
Audiobook & spoken audio reviews & articles.
First published 1992
Media Reviewed: Audiobooks
Frequency: 6 issues/yr
Circulation: 15,000 print, 120,000 digital
$36/yr print & digital; $2.95/mo digital; AudioFile PLUS: $60/yr print & digital, also includes Archive of Reviews, Audiobook Reference Guide, RealTime Reviews & Library Listeners
ISSN: 1063-0244
Trim Size: 8 3/8 x 10 7/8
Ad Rates: 4-color page $3,250
Ad Closing Date(s): 8 weeks prior to cover date

Billboard: The International Newsweekly of Music, Video & Home Entertainment
Published by Prometheus Global Media LLC
340 Madison Ave, 6th fl, New York, NY 10173
Tel: 212-493-4100
E-mail: subscriptions@billboard.com
Web Site: www.billboard.com/biz; www.billboard.com (online ed)
Key Personnel
Edit Dir: Denise Warner *E-mail:* denise.warner@billboard.com
Deputy Ed: Isabel Gonzalez-Whitaker
Print & online magazine covering retailing & programming news for the music & home entertainment industries.
Bureaus in Los Angeles, Miami & London with editorial correspondents worldwide.
First published 1894
Media Reviewed: CDs, Home Video, Records, Video Games
Frequency: Weekly
Circulation: 20,568
$9.99/mo print US, $12.99/mo digital, $19.99/mo print & digital; $24.99/mo print foreign, $12.99/mo digital only, $29.99/mo print & digital; all include iPad ed access
ISSN: 0006-2510
Trim Size: 10 x 13

BMI: MusicWorld®
Published by Broadcast Music Inc
7 World Trade Center, 250 Greenwich St, New York, NY 10007-0030
Tel: 212-220-3000
E-mail: newyork@bmi.com
Web Site: www.bmi.com/musicworld
Key Personnel
Pres & CEO: Michael O'Neill
Exec Dir: Deirdre Chadwick
Online publication that features advice & career strategies for songwriters, awards show coverage & more.
Frequency: Monthly
Free

Booklist
Published by American Library Association (ALA)
50 E Huron St, Chicago, IL 60611-2795
Tel: 312-944-6780 *Toll Free Tel:* 800-545-2433
   Fax: 312-440-9374
E-mail: info@booklistonline.com
Web Site: www.booklistonline.com
Key Personnel
Publr & Ed: Bill Ott *Tel:* 800-545-2433 ext 5717
   E-mail: bott@ala.org
Exec Ed: Keir Graff *Tel:* 800-545-2433 ext 5728
   E-mail: kgraff@ala.org
Mktg Dir: Melissa Carr *Tel:* 800-545-2433 ext 5713 *E-mail:* mcarr@ala.org
Sr Ed, Collection Mgmt & Lib Outreach: Susan Maguire *Tel:* 800-545-2433 ext 5720
   E-mail: smaguire@ala.org
Audio Ed: Heather Booth *E-mail:* hbooth@ala.org
Ed, Adult Books: Donna Seaman *Tel:* 800-545-2433 ext 5754 *E-mail:* dseaman@ala.org
Ed, Books for Youth: Sarah Hunter *Tel:* 800-545-2433 ext 5711 *E-mail:* shunter@ala.org
Reviews of adult fiction & nonfiction; children's & young adult books; multivolume encyclopedias, dictionaries & atlases; foreign language materials; AV materials.
First published 1905
Media Reviewed: Audiobooks, CD-ROMs, Children's Recordings
Frequency: 22 issues/yr (semimonthly Sept-June, monthly July-Aug)
Circulation: 11,000
$165.50/yr
ISSN: 0006-7385
Trim Size: 7 7/8 x 10 1/2
Ad Rates: B&W page $6,545, 4-color page $9,045
Ad Closing Date(s): Approximately 5-6 weeks prior to cover date. See media kit for additional info

BoxOffice® Pro
Published by Boxoffice® Media LLC
63 Copps Hill Rd, Ridgefield, CT 06877
Tel: 203-438-8389; 818-286-3108 (subns)
E-mail: help@boxoffice.com; bxpcs@magserv.com
Web Site: proboxoffice.com
Key Personnel
Publr & CEO: Julien Marcel *E-mail:* julien@boxoffice.com
VP, Ad: Susan Uhrlass *Tel:* 310-876-9090
   E-mail: susan@boxoffice.com
VP, Content Strategy & Edit Dir: Daniel Loria
   E-mail: daniel.loria@boxoffice.com
Creative Dir: Kenneth James Bacon
   E-mail: ken@boxoffice.com
Leading resource on exhibitor data services & business intelligence. Box office news, tracking, forecast & analysis. Official publication of all Film Expo Group shows.
First published 1920

Media Reviewed: Books (film related), DVDs (on web site only), Films, Software (movie theatre industry related), Trailers
Frequency: Monthly
$59.95/yr, $89.95/2 yrs, $109.95/3 yrs US, $74.95/yr CN, $135/yr intl
ISSN: 0006-8527
Trim Size: 8 1/4 x 10 7/8
Ad Rates: Full page $4,567, 1/2 page $3,197

Broadband Newsletter
Published by Information Gatekeepers Inc (IGI)
Division of IGI Group Inc
PO Box 606, Winchester, MA 01890
Tel: 617-782-5033 *Fax:* 617-507-8338
E-mail: info@igigroup.com
Web Site: www.igigroup.com
Key Personnel
Chief Analyst & Ed-in-Chief: Dr Hui Pan
  E-mail: hpan@igigroup.com
Mng Ed: Bev Wilson *E-mail:* editor@igigroup.com
Provides information on technology, applications & products for broadband. International development. Submissions accepted by e-mail.
Frequency: Monthly
Number of pages: 16
Circulation: 1,000
$695/yr PDF (1 user), multi-user licenses available
ISSN: 1078-1005
Trim Size: 8 1/2 x 11

Broadcasting & Cable
Published by Future US Inc
11 W 42 St, 15th fl, New York, NY 10036
Tel: 212-378-0448
Web Site: www.broadcastingcable.com
Key Personnel
Mng Dir, Content: Mark Robichaux *Tel:* 917-281-4750 *E-mail:* mark.robichaux@futurenet.com
Content Dir: Kent Gibbons *Tel:* 917-281-4722
  E-mail: kent.gibbons@futurenet.com
Content Mgr: Michael Demenchuk *Tel:* 917-281-4712 *E-mail:* michael.demenchuk@futurenet.com
Content Engagement Mgr: Jessika Walsten
  Tel: 650-238-0352 *E-mail:* jessika.walsten@futurenet.com
Television industry publication serving the broadcast, cable & program syndication communities.
First published 1931
Frequency: 45 issues/yr
$249/yr print & digital
ISSN: 1068-6827
Trim Size: 9 x 10 7/8

CableFAX: The Magazine
Published by Access Intelligence LLC
9211 Corporate Blvd, 4th fl, Rockville, MD 20850-4024
Tel: 301-354-2000 *Fax:* 301-738-8453
E-mail: clientservices@accessintel.com
Web Site: www.cablefax.com
Key Personnel
Publr: Michael Grebb *Tel:* 323-380-6263
  E-mail: mgrebb@accessintel.com
Edit Dir: Amy Maclean *Tel:* 301-354-1760
  E-mail: amaclean@accessintel.com
Assoc Ed: Sara Winegardner
Magazine highlighting the people, programs, companies & technologies in the cable television industry.
First published 1989
Frequency: Quarterly
Circulation: 48,000 print & e-media
Trim Size: 7 7/8 x 10 3/4

Camera Obscura: Feminism, Culture, and Media Studies
Published by Duke University Press

905 W Main St, Suite 18B, Durham, NC 27701
SAN: 201-3436
Tel: 919-688-5134 *Toll Free Tel:* 888-651-0122 (US) *Fax:* 919-688-2615 *Toll Free Fax:* 888-651-0124
E-mail: orders@dukeupress.edu; cameraobscura@filmandmedia.ucsb.edu
Web Site: read.dukeupress.edu/camera-obscura
Key Personnel
Journals Dir: Rob Dilworth
Mng Ed: Chip Badley
Journals Acqs Ed: Erich Staib *Tel:* 919-687-3664
  E-mail: erich.staib@dukeupress.edu
Provides a forum for scholarship & debate on feminism, culture & media studies. Encourages contributions in areas such as the conjuctions of gender, race, class & sexuality with AV culture; new histories & theories of film, television, video & digital media & politically engaged approaches to a range of media practices.
First published 1976
Frequency: 3 issues/yr
Circulation: 630
$30/yr indivs, $20/yr students, $247/yr instns print, $201/yr instns online, $267/yr instns print & online
ISSN: 0270-5346 (print); 1529-1510 (online)
Trim Size: Full page 3 3/4 x 6 3/4, 1/2 page 3 3/4 x 3 3/8
Ad Rates: Full page $300, 1/2 page $225, digital ads $250
Ad Closing Date(s): Feb (May issue), July (Sept issue), Oct (Dec issue)

Canadian Journal of Communication
c/o Simon Fraser University at Harbour Centre, 3576-515 W Hastings St, Vancouver, BC V6B 5K3, Canada
Tel: 250-653-0066; 604-897-5240 (subns)
E-mail: subscriptions@cjc-online.ca
Web Site: www.cjc-online.ca
Key Personnel
Publr: Rowland Lorimer
Mng Ed: Marilyn Bittman
  E-mail: managing_editor@cjc-online.ca
Ed: Michael Dorland *E-mail:* editor@cjc-online.ca
Asst Ed: Simon Vodrey *E-mail:* assistant_editor@cjc-online.ca
A journal for academics, media practitioners & government personnel about communications & journalism research.
First published 1974
Media Reviewed: Cable TV, CD-ROMs, Films, Radio, TV
Frequency: Quarterly
Circulation: 325
Indivs: $30 online, $60 print & online, $25 student online, $35 student print & online; Instns: $110 online, $160 print, $180 print & online
ISSN: 0705-3657 (print); 1499-6642 (online)
Trim Size: 4 1/2 x 7
Ad Rates: $250 full page, $100 1/2 page, $300 back cover

CHOICE
Published by Association of College & Research Libraries (ACRL)
Division of The American Library Association (ALA)
575 Main St, Suite 300, Middletown, CT 06457
Tel: 860-347-6933 *Fax:* 860-346-8586
E-mail: support@acrlchoice.freshdesk.com; submissions@ala-choice.org
Web Site: www.choice360.org; www.ala.org/acrl/choice
Subscription Address: PO Box 15995, North Hollywood, CA 91615 *Tel:* 818-487-4555 *Toll Free Tel:* 844-291-0455 *Fax:* 818-487-4550
E-mail: acrlsubscriptions@pubservice.com

Key Personnel
Publr & Ed: Mark Cummings *Tel:* 860-347-6933 ext 119 *E-mail:* mcummings@ala-choice.org
Ad Sales Mgr: Pamela Marino *E-mail:* pmarino@ala-choice.org
Premier review journal of new academic titles.
First published 1963
Media Reviewed: Books, CD-ROMs, Microcomputer Software, Online Databases, Web Sites
Frequency: Monthly
Circulation: 887
$41/issue, $513/yr, $551/yr CN & Mexico, $660/yr intl
ISSN: 0009-4978
Trim Size: 8 1/2 x 11
Ad Rates: B&W page $2,650, 4-color page $3,825
Ad Closing Date(s): 8 weeks prior to issue date

Cineaste
Published by Cineaste Publishers Inc
708 Third Ave, 5th fl, New York, NY 10017-4201
Tel: 212-209-3856
E-mail: cineaste@cineaste.com
Web Site: www.cineaste.com
Subscription Address: PO Box 180, New York, NY 10009-9998
Key Personnel
Founder & Ed-in-Chief: Gary Crowdus
Ad Rep: Barbara Saltz
Offers a social, political & esthetic perspective on cinema. Accept unsol mss.
First published 1967
Media Reviewed: DVDs, Films, Home Video
Frequency: Quarterly
Circulation: 15,000
$24/yr US, $30/yr CN & Mexico, $44/yr foreign
ISSN: 0009-7004
Trim Size: 8 1/4 x 10 7/8
Ad Rates: Full page $850, 1/2 page $600, 1/4 page $375
Ad Closing Date(s): Approximately 3 weeks prior to publication

Cinematic Codes Review (CCR)
Published by Anaphora Literary Press
1108 W Third St, Quanah, TX 79252
Tel: 470-289-6395
Web Site: anaphoraliterary.com
Key Personnel
Dir: Dr Anna Faktorovich *E-mail:* director@anaphoraliterary.com
Features works in all visual genres, especially those with moving pictures, such as music videos, feature films, documentaries, photography, or just about any other mode or genre of art not considered "literature". E-mail your submission with a bio & an abstract (for researched projects) to director@anaphoraliterary.com.
First published 2016
Frequency: 3 issues/yr
Number of pages: 200
Circulation: 1,000
$45/yr (e-mail subn request to director@anaphoraliterary.com with your payment preference)
ISSN: 2473-3385 (print); 2473-3377 (online)
Trim Size: 6 x 9
Ad Rates: $50 full page or free ad exchange

CineVue
Published by Asian CineVision Inc (ACV)
c/o Made in NY Media Ctr by IFP, 30 John St, Brooklyn, NY 11201
Tel: 212-989-1422 *Fax:* 212-727-3584
E-mail: cinevue@asiancinevision.org; info@asiancinevision.org
Web Site: www.asiancinevision.org/cinevue
Key Personnel
Festival Dir: Judy Lei *E-mail:* judy@asiancinevision.org

Online journal that showcases media content produced by, for & about the Asian Pacific American experience including profiles, features, interviews, critiques, essays, commentary & original content.
First published 1986
ISSN: 0895-805X

Classic Images
Published by Muscatine Journal
Subsidiary of Lee Enterprises Inc
301 E Third St, Muscatine, IA 52761
Tel: 563-262-0537 *Fax:* 563-262-8042
E-mail: classicimages@classicimages.com
Web Site: www.classicimages.com
Key Personnel
Gen Mgr & Ed: Bob King *Tel:* 563-262-0538
Articles, features & reviews of classic films & movies. Film history & film-related products.
First published 1962
Media Reviewed: DVDs, VHS Tapes, Videotapes
Frequency: Monthly
Subn rates vary depending on location & delivery preference. See web site for details
ISSN: 0275-8423
Trim Size: 9 1/2 x 9 8/10
Ad Rates: Camera ready: Full page $220, 1/2 page $118, 1/4 page $70, 1/8 page $40; Non-camera ready: Full page $256, 1/2 page $144, 1/4 page $88, 1/8 page $54; Color charges: $85 1 color & black, $160 2 colors & black, $240 full color
Ad Closing Date(s): 10th of the month prior to issue

Communication Abstracts
Published by EBSCOhost®
10 Estes St, Ipswich, MA 01938
Tel: 978-356-6500 *Toll Free Tel:* 800-653-2726 (US & CN) *Fax:* 978-356-6565
E-mail: information@ebsco.com
Web Site: www.ebsco.com
Subscription Address: PO Box 1943, Birmingham, AL 35201 *Tel:* 205-991-6600 *Toll Free Tel:* 800-633-4604 (US & CN) *Web Site:* journals.ebsco.com
Online database providing cover-to-cover indexing & abstracts for major journals in communication, mass media & other closely-related fields of study.
First published 1978
Media Reviewed: Journals

Communication Arts
Published by Coyne & Blanchard Inc
110 Constitution Dr, Menlo Park, CA 94025
Tel: 650-326-6040 *Fax:* 650-326-1648
E-mail: editorial@commarts.com; commarts@commarts.com
Web Site: www.commarts.com
Key Personnel
Ed & Designer: Patrick S Coyne
Exec Ed: Jean A Coyne
Print & online magazine that covers creativity in design & advertising. Features six juried competitions that cover the entire field of visual communications.
First published 1959
Frequency: 6 issues/yr
Circulation: 25,000 paid
$30/yr digital; Print & digital: $53/yr, $99/2 yrs US; $70/yr, $129/2 yrs CN; $110/yr, $199/2 yrs intl
ISSN: 0010-3519
Trim Size: 8 5/8 x 10 7/8
Ad Rates: 4-color page $5,405, 1/2 page $2,930, 1/4 page $1,495
Ad Closing Date(s): Approximately 2 months prior to cover date. See media kit for additional info

Communication Research
Published by SAGE Publishing
2455 Teller Rd, Thousand Oaks, CA 91320
Tel: 805-499-9774 *Toll Free Tel:* 800-818-7243
Toll Free Fax: 800-583-2665
E-mail: journals@sagepub.com; orders@sagepub.com
Web Site: journals.sagepub.com/home/crx
Key Personnel
Ed: Jennifer Gibbs; Silvia Knobloch-Westerwick
Publishes articles that explore the processes, antecedents & consequences of communication in a broad range of societal systems. Although most of the published articles are empirical, we also consider overview/review articles. These include the following: mass media, interpersonal, health, political, entertainment, advertising/persuasive communication, new technology, online, computer-mediated & mobile communication, organizational, intercultural, group & family. Serves as the international forum aimed at the academic or professional interested in current research in communication & its related fields.
First published 1974
Frequency: 8 issues/yr
Number of pages: 158
Circulation: 510
$204 indiv print only, $1,589 instl e-access only, $1,731 print only, $1,766 print & e-access; single print issue $33 indiv, $283 instl
ISSN: 0093-6502 (print); 1552-3810 (online)
Trim Size: 6 x 9
Ad Rates: B&W page $800, 4-color page $1,000 per image
Ad Closing Date(s): 1st of the month, 2 months prior to publication month

Communications Daily
Published by Warren Communications News Inc
2115 Ward Ct NW, Washington, DC 20037
Tel: 202-872-9200 *Toll Free Tel:* 800-771-9202 (cust serv)
E-mail: info@warren-news.com
Web Site: www.communicationsdaily.com; www.warren-news.com
Key Personnel
Chmn & Publr: Paul Warren *E-mail:* pwarrendc@warren-news.com
Pres & Ed: Daniel Warren *E-mail:* dwarrendc@warren-news.com
Exec Sr Ed: Howard Buskirk *E-mail:* hbuskirkdc@warren-news.com
Mng Ed: Jonathan Make *E-mail:* jmakedc@warren-news.com
Dir, Sales: William R Benton *E-mail:* wbentondc@warren-news.com
Covers electronic communications including broadcasting, cable, telephone & data communications, electronic information distribution, satellites, electronic mail, consumer electronics, home video & mobile radio. No unsol mss. Online only.
First published 1981
Frequency: Daily (weekdays)
Ad Rates: See www.communicationsdaily.com/advertise
Ad Closing Date(s): By 2 pm 2 business days prior to publication

Creative
Published by Magazines/Creative Inc
31 Merrick Ave, Merrick, NY 11566
Tel: 516-378-0800
E-mail: info@creativemag.com
Web Site: www.creativemag.com
Key Personnel
Publr & Ed: Larry Flasterstein
AV & marketing news & ideas for advertising, sales promotion & marketing managers.
First published 1966
Frequency: 6 issues/yr
Circulation: 15,000

$4/issue, $30/yr, $50/yr foreign, $20 annual illustrated guide
ISSN: 0737-5883
Trim Size: 8 1/4 x 11 1/4
Ad Rates: B&W page $1,960, 4-color page $2,560

Creative Planet Network
Published by Future US Inc
11 W 42 St, 15th fl, New York, NY 10036
Tel: 212-378-0448
Web Site: www.creativeplanetnetwork.com
Daily resource for content creators to keep informed about issues & advances that impact video production, post-production & delivery.
First published 2011
Frequency: Monthly
ISSN: 2164-0963
Trim Size: 9 x 10 7/8

District Administration
Published by LRP Media Group
35 Nutmeg Dr, Trumbull, CT 06611
Tel: 203-663-0100 *Fax:* 203-663-0149
Web Site: www.districtadministration.com
Key Personnel
Publr: Robert M Avossa
Art Dir: Rebecca Eller *E-mail:* reller@lrp.com
Edit Dir: JD Solomon *E-mail:* jdsolomon@lrp.com
Sr Mng Ed: Melissa Ezarik *E-mail:* mezarik@lrp.com
Sr Ed: Tim Goral *E-mail:* tgoral@lrp.com
Sr Assoc Ed: Matt Zalaznick
E-mail: mzalaznick@lrp.com
Deputy Ed: Ray Bendici *E-mail:* rbendici@lrp.com
Assoc Ed: Stephen Blackburn
E-mail: sblackburn@lrp.com; Emily Ann Brown *E-mail:* ebrown@lrp.com
Includes descriptions of new products; for school administrators & personnel at district level, administrators K-12.
First published 1986
Media Reviewed: Educational Media
Frequency: Monthly
Circulation: 242,341 print & digital
Free
Trim Size: 7 3/4 x 10 1/2
Ad Closing Date(s): Approximately 4-5 weeks prior to issue month

Documentary
Published by International Documentary Association
3470 Wilshire Blvd, Suite 980, Los Angeles, CA 90010
Tel: 213-232-1660 *Fax:* 213-232-1669
E-mail: info@documentary.org; magazine@documentary.org
Web Site: www.documentary.org
Key Personnel
Exec Dir: Simon Kilmurry
Deputy Dir: Amy Halpin
Ed: Tom White *Tel:* 213-232-1600 ext 214 *E-mail:* tom@documentary.org
US publication dedicated to documentaries. The magazine has an international readership that includes over 20,000 filmmakers, producers, distributors, network, cable & OTT outlets, educators & students & fans of nonfiction. Circulation includes the 2,000 members of IDA; over 200 university, institution & public libraries; newsstand sales in Los Angeles, New York & major cities throughout the US & Canada; selected festivals & markets around the world.
First published 1982
Media Reviewed: Books
Frequency: Quarterly
Circulation: 5,500

$5.50/issue indiv, $6/issue instns; $45/yr US, $55/yr intl (libs/instns only); free to membs
ISSN: 1559-1034
Trim Size: 8 3/8 x 10 7/8
Ad Closing Date(s): Jan 10 (Spring), June 9 (Summer), Aug 18 (Fall), Nov 16 (Winter)

Educational Dealer
Published by Fahy-Williams Publishing Inc
171 Reed St, Geneva, NY 14456
Mailing Address: PO Box 1080, Geneva, NY 14456
Tel: 315-789-0458 *Toll Free Tel:* 800-344-0559
Fax: 315-789-4263
Web Site: fwpi.com; educationaldealermagazine. com
Key Personnel
Publr: J Kevin Fahy *E-mail:* kfahy@fwpi.com
Edit Dir: Tina Manzer *E-mail:* tmanzer@fwpi. com
Dir, Ad: Tim Braden *E-mail:* tbraden@fwpi.com
Mktg Dir: Amy Colburn *E-mail:* amy@fwpi.com
Prodn Mgr: Mark Stash *E-mail:* mstash@fwpi. com
Interviews, news, retailing tips, reports on industry trends & helpful display ideas for dealers & producers of educational materials.
First published 1976
Frequency: 5 issues/yr
Circulation: 8,435
Free
ISSN: 0193-1067
Trim Size: 8 3/8 x 10 7/8
Ad Rates: B&W page $1,185, 2-color page $1,345, 4-color page $1,580 (1x rates)

Educational Technology Research & Development (ETR&D)
Published by Association for Educational Communications and Technology (AECT)
320 W Eighth St, Suite 101, Bloomington, IN 47404-3745
Tel: 812-335-7675 *Toll Free Tel:* 877-677-AECT (677-2328) *Fax:* 812-335-7678
E-mail: aect@aect.org
Web Site: www.aect.org
Key Personnel
Exec Dir: Dr Phillip Harris *E-mail:* pharris@aect. org
Co-Ed-in-Chief: Tristan Johnson; Lin Lin
E-mail: lin.lin@unt.edu
Offers controversial, well-documented articles on research & applied theory in educational technology & development.
First published 1953
Media Reviewed: CD-ROMs, Software
Frequency: 6 issues/yr
Circulation: 7,500
$35/yr membs
ISSN: 1042-1629

Electronic Musician
Published by Future US Inc
11 W 42 St, 15th fl, New York, NY 10036
Tel: 212-378-0448
Web Site: www.emusician.com
Project recording & sound techniques for the professional audio market. Digital version also available.
First published 1990
Frequency: Monthly
$23.97/yr US, $30/yr CN, $50/yr intl print only; $19.99 digital only
ISSN: 1050-7868
Trim Size: 9 x 10 7/8

ETR&D, see Educational Technology Research & Development (ETR&D)

Exposure
Published by Society for Photographic Education (SPE)

2530 Superior Ave, Suite 407, Cleveland, OH 44114
Tel: 216-622-2733 *Fax:* 216-622-2712
E-mail: exposure@spenational.org
Web Site: www.spenational.org/exposure; medium.com/exposure-magazine
Contemporary photographic discourse. Digital platform.
First published 1970
Media Reviewed: CDs, DVDs, Films, Photography
$17/issue

Fiber Optics Weekly Update
Published by Information Gatekeepers Inc (IGI)
Division of IGI Group Inc
PO Box 606, Winchester, MA 01890
Tel: 617-782-5033 *Fax:* 617-507-8338
E-mail: info@igigroup.com
Web Site: www.igigroup.com
Key Personnel
Chief Analyst & Ed-in-Chief: Dr Hui Pan
E-mail: hpan@igigroup.com
Mng Ed: Bev Wilson *E-mail:* editor@igigroup. com
Provides information on technology, markets, applications & products for fiber optics. Submissions accepted by e-mail.
First published 1978
Frequency: Weekly
Number of pages: 16
Circulation: 800
$695/yr US & CN, $745/yr other print, $695/yr PDF (1 user), multi-user licenses available at a discount
ISSN: 1051-189X
Trim Size: 8 1/2 x 11

Film & History: An Interdisciplinary Journal
Published by Center for the Study of Film & History
Lawrence University, Memorial Hall B-5, 711 E Boldt Way, Appleton, WI 54911
Tel: 920-832-6649
E-mail: center@filmandhistory.org; subscriptions@filmandhistory.org
Web Site: www.filmandhistory.org
Key Personnel
Ed-in-Chief: Loren PQ Baybrook *E-mail:* editor@ filmandhistory.org
Book Reviews Ed: Paul M Cohen *E-mail:* book. reviews.editor@filmandhistory.org
Film Reviews Ed: Cynthia J Miller *E-mail:* film. reviews.editor@filmandhistory.org
Articles by scholars in multiple disciplines, researching the exchanges between culture/history & the moving-image arts. Accepts article-length mss of 4,000-7,000 words (see web site for topics).
First published 1971
Media Reviewed: Books, Films
Frequency: Semiannual
Circulation: 3,500
$55/yr indiv, $90/yr instn
ISSN: 0360-3695
Trim Size: 8 1/2 x 11
Ad Rates: $200/issue ad or insert
Ad Closing Date(s): May 1 Spring issue, Nov 1 Winter issue

Film Comment
Published by Film Society of Lincoln Center
70 Lincoln Center Plaza, New York, NY 10023
Tel: 212-875-5610 *Toll Free Tel:* 888-313-6085
E-mail: editor@filmlinc.org; custsvc_fc@fulcoinc. com
Web Site: www.filmlinc.org; www.filmcomment. com
Key Personnel
Dir, Ad: Jeryll Adler *E-mail:* jadler@filmlinc.org
Dir, Mktg & Sales: David Goldberg
E-mail: dgoldberg@filmlinc.org

Ed-in-Chief: Nicolas Rapold
Mng Ed: Laura Kern
Prodn Mgr: Vicki Robinson *E-mail:* vrobinson@ filmlinc.org
Feature reviews & analysis of mainstream, arthouse & avant-garde filmmaking from around the world.
First published 1962
Media Reviewed: Books, Films, TV
Frequency: 6 issues/yr
Circulation: 15,000 paid
$5.95/issue, $29.95/yr, $40/yr Mexico & CN, $60/yr elsewhere
ISSN: 0015-119X
Trim Size: 8 3/16 x 10 7/8
Ad Rates: B&W page $3,699, 4-color page $4,347

Film Quarterly
Published by University of California Press, Journals Division
155 Grand Ave, Suite 400, Oakland, CA 94612-3758
Tel: 510-643-7154 (cust serv) *Fax:* 510-642-9917
E-mail: editorial@filmquarterly.org; customerservice@ucpress.edu
Web Site: www.ucpress.edu/journals; filmquarterly.org
Key Personnel
Ed: B Ruby Rich
Assoc Ed: Rebecca Prime
Asst Ed: Marc Francis
Book Review Ed: Noah Isenberg
E-mail: isenbern@newschool.edu
Scholarly film criticism, theory & history.
First published 1958
Media Reviewed: Films
Frequency: Quarterly
Circulation: 2,500
Indiv: $22/issue, $46/yr online only, $60/yr print & online; Instl: $73/issue, $251/yr online only, $343/yr print & online; Student/retired: $26/yr online only
ISSN: 0015-1386 (print); 1533-8630 (online)
Trim Size: 8 1/2 x 11
Ad Rates: B&W page $660, 1/2 page $465
Ad Closing Date(s): Jan 15, April 15, July 15, Oct 15

Filmmaker: The Magazine of Independent Film
Published by The Independent Filmmaker Project (IFP)
c/o Made in NY Media Ctr by IFP, 30 John St, Ground fl, Brooklyn, NY 11201
Tel: 212-465-8200 (ext 206) *Fax:* 212-465-8525
E-mail: subscriptions@filmmakermagazine.com
Web Site: filmmakermagazine.com; www.ifp.org
Key Personnel
Ed-in-Chief: Scott Macaulay *E-mail:* scott@ filmmakermagazine.com
Mng Ed: Vadim Rizov *E-mail:* vadim@ filmmakermagazine.com
Consulting Dir, Ad: Jeryll Adler *E-mail:* jadler@ ifp.org
First published 1992
Frequency: Quarterly
Circulation: 11,500 paid
$10/yr digital, $18/yr US, $20/yr CN, $80/yr foreign, $40/yr dom instn, $60 foreign instn
ISSN: 1063-8954
Trim Size: 8 3/8 x 10 7/8
Ad Rates: 4-color page $4,000, 1/2 page $2,555
Ad Closing Date(s): Approximately 5 weeks prior to issue date

Government Video
Published by Future US Inc
5285 Shawnee Rd, Suite 525, Alexandria, VA 22312-2334
Tel: 703-852-4600
Web Site: www.governmentvideo.com

Resource for media production, AV & surveillance news for public sector professionals.
First published 1989
Frequency: 10 issues/yr
ISSN: 1087-917X
Trim Size: 8 x 10 3/4

ICG Magazine

Published by International Cinematographers Guild (ICG)
7755 Sunset Blvd, Hollywood, CA 90046
Tel: 323-876-0160
E-mail: info@icgmagazine.com
Web Site: icgmagazine.com; www.cameraguild.com
Key Personnel
Publr: Teresa M Munoz *Tel:* 323-969-2714
    Fax: 323-878-1180 *E-mail:* teresa@icgmagazine.com
Exec Ed: David Geffner *Tel:* 323-969-2715
    E-mail: davidgeffner@icgmagazine.com
Professional film & video/digital techniques magazine.
First published 1929
Frequency: Monthly
Number of pages: 75
Circulation: 12,000
$48/yr, $36/yr student, $82/yr foreign (surface mail), $117/yr foreign (air mail)
ISSN: 0020-8299
Trim Size: 8 1/2 x 11
Ad Rates: B&W page $2,275, 4-color page $3,435
Ad Closing Date(s): Approximately 5-6 wks prior to cover date

IEEE Journal on Selected Areas in Communications

Published by Institute of Electrical and Electronics Engineers Inc (IEEE)
3 Park Ave, 17th fl, New York, NY 10016
Tel: 732-981-0060 (orders) *Toll Free Tel:* 800-678-4333 (contact ctr) *Fax:* 732-981-0624 (pubns)
E-mail: trans@ieee.org; customer-service@ieee.org
Web Site: www.ieee.org; ieeexplore.ieee.org; www.comsoc.org/jsac
Key Personnel
Sr Dir, Publg Opers: Dawn Melley *Tel:* 732-562-3902 *Fax:* 732-981-1855 *E-mail:* d.melley@ieee.org
Mng Dir, Pubns: Michael Forster *Tel:* 732-562-3998 *E-mail:* m.b.forster@ieee.org
Ed-in-Chief: Raouf Boutaba *E-mail:* rboutaba@uwaterloo.ca
Each issue is devoted to a specific technical topic spanning the entire field of communications & networking.
First published 1983
Frequency: Monthly
ISSN: 0733-8716
Trim Size: 8 1/2 x 11

IEEE Spectrum Magazine

Published by Institute of Electrical and Electronics Engineers Inc (IEEE)
3 Park Ave, 17th fl, New York, NY 10016
Tel: 212-419-7555 *Fax:* 212-419-7570
E-mail: spectrum@ieee.org
Web Site: spectrum.ieee.org
Key Personnel
Ed-in-Chief: Susan Hassler *E-mail:* s.hassler@ieee.org
Exec Ed: Glenn Zorpette *E-mail:* g.zorpette@ieee.org
Mng Ed: Elizabeth A Bretz *E-mail:* e.bretz@ieee.org
First published 1964
Frequency: Monthly
Circulation: 394,540
Print subn free to membs, $19.95 digital

ISSN: 0018-9235
Trim Size: 7 7/8 x 10 1/2
Ad Rates: $18,000 full page (North America ed), $16,000 full page (non-North America ed)
Ad Closing Date(s): Space reservations 1st of month preceding issue date

IEEE Transactions on Broadcasting

Published by Institute of Electrical and Electronics Engineers Inc (IEEE)
445 Hoes Lane, Piscataway, NJ 08854-4141
Tel: 732-562-6061 *Toll Free Tel:* 800-678-4333 (contact ctr)
E-mail: bts@ieee.org; bt-pubs@ieee.org
Web Site: bts.ieee.org; www.ieee.org
Key Personnel
Ed-in-Chief: Yiyan Wu *Tel:* 613-998-2870
    E-mail: yiyan.wu@crc.ca
Pubns Coord: Jennifer Barbato *Tel:* 732-562-3905
    E-mail: j.barbato@ieee.org
Contains information on broadcast transmission systems engineering, including the design & utilization of broadcast equipment. No advertising included.
First published 1955
Frequency: Quarterly
Circulation: 3,800
ISSN: 0018-9316
Trim Size: 8 1/2 x 11

IEEE Transactions on Communications

Published by Institute of Electrical and Electronics Engineers Inc (IEEE)
3 Park Ave, 17th fl, New York, NY 10016
Tel: 732-981-0060 (orders) *Toll Free Tel:* 800-678-4333 (contact ctr) *Fax:* 732-981-0624 (pubns)
E-mail: trans@ieee.org; customer-service@ieee.org
Web Site: www.ieee.org; ieeexplore.ieee.org; www.comsoc.org/tc
Key Personnel
Sr Dir, Publg Opers: Dawn Melley *Tel:* 732-562-3902 *Fax:* 732-981-1855 *E-mail:* d.melley@ieee.org
Mng Dir, Pubns: Michael Forster *Tel:* 732-562-3998 *E-mail:* m.b.forster@ieee.org
Ed-in-Chief: Naofal Al-Dhahir *E-mail:* eictcom@utdallas.edu
Publishes high quality papers reporting theoretical & experimental advances in the general area of communications.
First published 1953
Frequency: Monthly
ISSN: 0090-6778
Trim Size: 8 1/2 x 11

Information Technology and Libraries

Published by Library & Information Technology Association (LITA)
Division of American Library Association (ALA)
c/o American Library Association, 50 E Huron St, Chicago, IL 60611-2795
Toll Free Tel: 800-545-2433 (ext 4270) *Fax:* 312-280-3257
E-mail: lita@ala.org
Web Site: www.ala.org/lita
Key Personnel
Exec Dir: Jenny Levine *Tel:* 312-280-4267
    E-mail: jlevine@ala.org
Ed: Ken Varnum *E-mail:* varnum@umich.edu
Covers digital libraries, general library & information technology, electronic publishing & library automation. Available online only.
First published 1968
Media Reviewed: Books, Periodicals, Software
Frequency: Quarterly
ISSN: 2163-5226

Information Today

Published by Information Today, Inc
143 Old Marlton Pike, Medford, NJ 08055-8750

Tel: 609-654-6266 *Toll Free Tel:* 800-300-9868 (cust serv) *Fax:* 609-654-4309
E-mail: custserv@infotoday.com
Web Site: www.infotoday.com/IT/default.asp
Key Personnel
Publr/Pres & CEO: Thomas H Hogan
Ed: Brandi Scardilli *E-mail:* bscardilli@infotoday.com
Electronic information delivery for users & providers of information services. Includes editorial focus on news: new services, databases, information companies, technology trends, controversial issues. Also includes information about events that impact the industry.
First published 1983
Frequency: 9 issues/yr
Number of pages: 32
Circulation: 8,000
Print: $99.95/yr, $188/2 yrs, $288/3 yrs US; $128/yr CN & Mexico; $143/yr other; Digital/PDF: $99.95/yr, $188/2 yrs, $288/3 yrs; Print & Digital/PDF: $124.95/yr, $234/2 yrs, $360/3 yrs US; $160/yr CN & Mexico; $179/yr other
ISSN: 8755-6286
Trim Size: 8 1/2 x 11
Ad Rates: See web site for complete details

Journal of Applied Communication Research

Published by Routledge Journals
Member of Taylor & Francis Group, an Informa Business
711 Third Ave, New York, NY 10017
Tel: 212-216-7800 *Toll Free Tel:* 800-354-1420
    Fax: 212-564-7854
Web Site: www.routledge.com; www.tandfonline.com
Key Personnel
Ed: Debbie S Dougherty *E-mail:* doughertyd@missouri.edu
For applied communication practitioners & scholars.
First published 1973
Frequency: 6 issues/yr
Circulation: 2,000
$194 indiv print
ISSN: 0090-9882 (print); 1479-5752 (online)

Journal of Broadcasting & Electronic Media (JOBEM)

Published by Broadcast Education Association (BEA)
1771 "N" St NW, Washington, DC 20036-2891
Tel: 202-602-0587 *Fax:* 202-609-9940
E-mail: help@beaweb.org
Web Site: www.beaweb.org
Key Personnel
Exec Dir: Heather Birks *Tel:* 202-602-0584
    E-mail: heather@beaweb.org
Ed: Carolyn Lin *Tel:* 860-486-3984
    E-mail: carolyn.lin@uconn.edu
Considered one of the leading publications in the communication field, this scholarly journal contains timely articles about new developments, trends & research in electronic media written by academicians, researchers & other electronic media professionals.
Accepts unsol mss. See www.beaweb.org/wp/?page_id=2289 for details.
First published 1956
Frequency: Quarterly
Circulation: 2,400
Free to membs
ISSN: 0883-8151
Trim Size: 6 x 9

Journal of Cinema & Media Studies

Published by Society for Cinema & Media Studies
Affiliate of University of Texas Press
3001 Lake Austin Blvd, Austin, TX 78703
Mailing Address: Journals Div, PO Box 7819, Austin, TX 78713-7819

Tel: 512-232-7621; 512-471-7233 *Fax:* 512-232-7178
E-mail: journals@utpress.utexas.edu; editors@cinemajournal.org
Web Site: utpress.utexas.edu/journals/cinema-journal; www.cmstudies.org/page/jcms
Key Personnel
Ed: Caetlin Benson-Allott
Book Review Ed: Laura Isabel Serna
Prodn Ed: Scott Richmond
Assoc Ed: Jeff Menne
Assoc Online Ed: Julia Himberg
Mktg Coord: Sheila Scoville *E-mail:* sscoville@utpress.utexas.edu
Publishes outstanding scholarship in all areas of media studies including film, television, radio, comics, video games & digital media. Accepts unsol mss from current SCMS members only (8,000-12,000 words including notes).
First published 1961
Frequency: Quarterly
$264/yr instns, $72/issue instns, $60/yr indivs, $22/issue indivs
ISSN: 2578-4900 (print); 2578-4919 (online)
Trim Size: 6 x 9
Ad Rates: Full page $500, 1/2 page horizontal $400
Ad Closing Date(s): March 1, June 1, Sept 1, Dec 1

Journal of Communication
Published by Oxford University Press USA
198 Madison Ave, New York, NY 10016
SAN: 202-5892
Toll Free Tel: 800-445-9714 (cust serv) *Fax:* 919-677-1303
E-mail: custserv.us@oup.com
Web Site: global.oup.com
Key Personnel
Journals Publg Dir: Alison Denby *E-mail:* alison.denby@oup.com
Covers communication theory, research, history, policy & practice. Published on behalf of the International Communications Association. Book reviews available online only.
First published 1951
Media Reviewed: Books
Circulation: 290 print
$92/yr student (print & online), $135/yr indivs (print & online)
ISSN: 0021-9916 (print); 1460-2466 (online)
Trim Size: 7 x 10
Ad Rates: Full page $855, 1/2 page $685

Journal of Educational Technology Systems
Published by SAGE Publishing
2455 Teller Rd, Thousand Oaks, CA 91320
Tel: 805-583-9774 *Toll Free Tel:* 800-818-7243
Toll Free Fax: 800-583-2665
E-mail: journals@sagepub.com; orders@sagepub.com
Web Site: www.sagepub.com
Key Personnel
Ed-in-Chief: Dr Thomas T Liao; Dr Lori L Scarlatos
Deals with systems in which technology & education interface & is designed to inform educators who are interested in making optimum use of technology. More importantly, the journal focuses on techniques & curriculum that utilize technology in all types of educational systems. Description of actual classroom practice & experimentation with the educational use of technology is an equally important aspect of the journal.
First published 1972
Frequency: Quarterly
Indiv: $51/issue, $156/yr print & online; Instl: $182/issue, $607/yr online, $661/yr print, $674/yr print & online
ISSN: 0047-2395 (print); 1541-3810 (online)
Trim Size: 6 x 9

Journal of Film and Video
Published by University Film & Video Association (UFVA)
c/o University of Illinois Press, 1325 S Oak St, Champaign, IL 61820-6975
Tel: 217-333-0950 *Fax:* 217-244-8082
E-mail: journaloffilmandvideo@gmail.com
Web Site: ufva.site-ym.com/page/journal; www.press.uillinois.edu/journals/jfv.html
Key Personnel
Pres: Laura Vazquez *E-mail:* lvazquez@niu.edu
Journals Mktg Mgr: Alexa Colella *Tel:* 217-244-5619 *E-mail:* acolella@uillinois.edu
Ed: Stephen Tropiano
Scholarly articles on film & video production, history, theory, criticism & aesthetics.
First published 1947
Media Reviewed: Books, Films, Videotapes
Frequency: Quarterly
Circulation: 1,300
$20 single issue, $75/yr print or electronic, $95/yr print & electronic; $10 non-US postage (CN & Mexico), $35 (other non-US locations)
ISSN: 0742-4671 (print); 1934-6018 (online)
Trim Size: Full page 4 3/8 x 7 1/4, half page 4 3/8 x 3 5/8
Ad Rates: Full page $250, 1/2 page $185
Ad Closing Date(s): March 1, June 1, Sept 1, Dec 1

Journal of Imaging Science & Technology (JIST)
Published by Society for Imaging Science and Technology (IS&T)
7003 Kilworth Lane, Springfield, VA 22151
Tel: 703-642-9090 *Fax:* 703-642-9094
E-mail: info@imaging.org; subscriptions@imaging.org
Web Site: imaging.org
Key Personnel
Ed-in-Chief: Chunghui Kuo
Prodn Mgr: Donna Smith *E-mail:* dsmith@imaging.org
Imaging applications for scientists & engineers. Typical issues include research papers & comprehensive reviews, as well as technical information concerning hardware & engineering applications associated with acquisition, evaluation & use of image data.
First published 1990
Frequency: 6 issues/yr
Instns: hard copy $215 US, $245 foreign, online only $485, hard copy & online $695 US, $725 foreign; Indivs: Free online subn with membership, add hard copy $75, add online $45
ISSN: 1062-3701
Trim Size: 8 1/2 x 10 7/8
Ad Rates: Full page interior $650 (1x), $585 (3x), $500 (6x); 1/2 page $352 (1x), $300 (3x), $275 (6x); 1/4 page $225 (1x), $200 (3x), $175 (6x)
Ad Closing Date(s): 1st of month preceding publication

Jump Cut: A Review of Contemporary Media
Published by Jump Cut Associates
3480 Mill St, Eugene, OR 97405
Web Site: www.ejumpcut.org
Key Personnel
Ed: Julia Lesage *E-mail:* jlesage@uoregon.edu
Progressive political perspective. Online reviews & articles on all aspects of film, video, TV & new media.
First published 1974
Media Reviewed: Films, Multimedia, TV, Videotapes
Frequency: Annual
Free

Library Journal
Published by Media Source Inc
123 William St, Suite 802, New York, NY 10038

Tel: 646-380-0700 *Toll Free Tel:* 800-588-1030
Fax: 646-380-0756
E-mail: ljinfo@mediasourceinc.com
Web Site: www.libraryjournal.com
Key Personnel
Ed-in-Chief: Rebecca T Miller *Tel:* 646-380-0738 *E-mail:* rmiller@mediasourceinc.com
Exec Ed: Meredith Schwartz *Tel:* 646-380-0745 *E-mail:* mschwartz@mediasourceinc.com
Mng Ed: Bette-Lee Fox *Tel:* 646-380-0717 *E-mail:* blfox@mediasourceinc.com
News; features; book, magazine, AV & CD-ROM reviews; new product information for academic, public & special librarians. Also available online.
First published 1876
Media Reviewed: Audiobooks, Books (& ebooks), DVDs, Videotapes, Web Sites (& databases/systems)
Frequency: Semimonthly (exc monthly during Jan, July, Aug & Dec)
Number of pages: 104
Circulation: 12,000
$157.99/yr US, $199.99/yr CN & Mexico, $219.99/yr foreign
ISSN: 0363-0277
Trim Size: 10 1/2 x 7 7/8

Lightwave
Published by PennWell Corp
61 Spit Brook Rd, 5th fl, Nashua, NH 03060
Tel: 603-891-0123 *Toll Free Tel:* 800-225-0556
Fax: 603-891-9294
Web Site: www.lightwaveonline.com
Key Personnel
Group Publr: Alan Bergstein *Tel:* 603-891-9178 *E-mail:* alanb@pennwell.com
Edit Dir & Assoc Publr: Stephen Hardy *Tel:* 603-891-9454 *E-mail:* stephenh@pennwell.com
Media Sales Mgr: Kris Collins *Tel:* 603-910-9876 *E-mail:* kristinec@pennwell.com
Technical, application & business insights to senior-level decision makers for optical communications worldwide. Online only.
First published 1984
Ad Rates: See web site for regional sales contact

Literature/Film Quarterly
Published by Salisbury University
1101 Camden Ave, Salisbury, MD 21801-6860
Tel: 410-677-5329
E-mail: litfilmquart@salisbury.edu
Web Site: lfq.salisbury.edu
Key Personnel
Ed-in-Chief: Elsie Walker
Copy Ed: Bonni Miller
Consulting Ed: David T Johnson
International journal devoted to the study of adaptation. Serves as a forum for scholars & writers to discuss, debate & articulate various ways of conceptualizing adaptation, whether in the more traditional considerations of transforming fiction & drama into film or in the more recent reflections on intertextuality, adaptation theory & other related concerns.
First published 1973
Frequency: Quarterly
ISSN: 2573-7597

Markee 2.0
Published by Markee Publishing
PO Box 250, San Luis Rey, CA 92068-0250
Tel: 760-622-3500
E-mail: submissions@markeemagazine.com
Web Site: markeemagazine.com
Key Personnel
Owner: Tom Inglesby *Tel:* 760-390-1661 *E-mail:* tom@markeemagazine.com
Digital magazine for movie & video production crews & producers/directors.
First published 1985
Frequency: 6 issues/yr

Number of pages: 32
Free
ISSN: 1073-8924
Trim Size: 8 3/8 x 10 7/8

Media Play News
Published by JCH Media Inc
3988 Monroe St, Carlsbad, CA 92008
E-mail: admin@mediaplaynews.com
Web Site: www.mediaplaynews.com
Key Personnel
Publr & Edit Dir: Thomas K Arnold
Assoc Publr & Ad Dir: John Boezinger *Tel:* 949-413-9311 *E-mail:* jboezinger@mediaplaynews.com
Assoc Publr & Ed-in-Chief: Stephanie Prange *Tel:* 714-307-3228 *E-mail:* sprange@mediaplaynews.com
Exec Ed: John Latchem
Sr Ed: Erik Gruenwedel
Delivers news, analysis, market research & product reviews to studio & digital executives, retailers, distributors, technology providers & marketers.
Media Reviewed: DVDs
Frequency: Monthly
Circulation: 16,482
Trim Size: 10 1/4 x 13

Mix Magazine
Published by Future US Inc
11 W 42 St, 15th fl, New York, NY 10036
Tel: 212-378-0448
Web Site: www.mixonline.com
Key Personnel
EVP & Group Publg Dir: Adam Goldstein *Tel:* 212-378-0465 *E-mail:* adam.goldstein@futurenet.com
Assoc Publr: Tara Preston *Tel:* 917-331-8904
Ed: Thomas Kenny *Tel:* 650-238-0345
E-mail: thomas.kenny@futurenet.com
Prodn Mgr: Beatrice Weir *Tel:* 650-238-0265
E-mail: beatrice.weir@futurenet.com
Leading industry magazine covering the full spectrum of professional audio & music production, including AV post-production & live performance. Available in print & digital.
First published 1977
Media Reviewed: Concerts, Music
Frequency: Monthly
$23.97/yr US, $40/yr CN, $50/yr intl print only; $35.97/yr US, $46/yr CN, $56/yr intl print & digital; $23.96/yr, $35.96/yr CN & intl digital only
ISSN: 0164-9957
Trim Size: 9 x 10 7/8

Motion Picture TV & Theatre Directory
Published by Motion Picture Enterprises Publications Inc
Division of Motion Picture Enterprises Inc
PO Box 276, Tarrytown, NY 10591-0276
Tel: 212-245-0969 *Fax:* 212-245-0974
E-mail: publications@mpe.net
Web Site: www.mpe.net
Key Personnel
Publr: Neal R Pilzer
Classified directory listing companies in the motion picture, television & video industry for products & services. Also available online.
First published 1960
Frequency: Semiannual
Number of pages: 264
Circulation: 82,500
$22.53/issue within NY, $20.79/issue outside NY
ISSN: 0580-0412
Trim Size: 4 x 8 1/2
Ad Rates: Single line $116.40, B&W 1/3 page $809, 1/2 page $1,198.60, full page $2,061.10
Ad Closing Date(s): Jan 20 for March issue, July 26 for Sept issue

Multichannel News
Published by Future US Inc
11 W 42 St, 15th fl, New York, NY 10036
Tel: 212-378-0448
Web Site: www.multichannel.com
Key Personnel
Mng Dir, Content: Mark Robichaux *Tel:* 917-281-4750 *E-mail:* mark.robichaux@futurenet.com
Content Dir: Kent Gibbons *Tel:* 917-281-4722
E-mail: kent.gibbons@futurenet.com
Content Mgr: Michael Demenchuk *Tel:* 917-281-4712 *E-mail:* michael.demenchuk@futurenet.com
Programming, advertising, marketing, finance, technology, broadband & government activities for the worldwide multichannel industries.
First published 1980
Media Reviewed: Cable TV
Frequency: 47 issues/yr
$249/yr print & digital
ISSN: 0276-8593
Trim Size: 10 1/2 x 13 1/2

Multimedia Publisher
Published by Worldwide Videotex
68 Russell St, North Andover, MA 01845
Tel: 781-439-5505
Web Site: wvpubs.com/publications
Provides news & information on the multimedia publishing industry. Explores the trends & latest developments & marketing strategies of the vendors & publishers of information & entertainment products.
First published 1990
Frequency: Monthly
$185/yr, $200/yr foreign, $165 e-file

The Music & Sound Retailer
Published by Testa Communications
25 Willowdale Ave, Port Washington, NY 11050-3779
Tel: 516-767-2500 *Toll Free Tel:* 800-937-7678
Web Site: www.testa.com; www.msretailer.com
Key Personnel
Pres & Publr: Vincent P Testa
Prodn Mgr: Steve Thorakos *E-mail:* sthorakos@testa.com
Ed: Brian Berk *Tel:* 516-767-2500 ext 710
E-mail: bberk@testa.com
Trade magazine serving musical instrument dealers & professional audio shops.
First published 1983
Frequency: Monthly
$18/yr, free to qualified industry professionals
Trim Size: 9 1/2 x 12

Music Connection Magazine
3441 Ocean View Blvd, Glendale, CA 91208
Tel: 818-995-0101 *Fax:* 818-638-8015
E-mail: contactmc@musicconnection.com
Web Site: musicconnection.com
Key Personnel
Publr & Ad Dir: Eric Bettelli *E-mail:* ericb@musicconnection.com
Assoc Publr & Sr Ed: Mark Nardone
E-mail: markn@musicconnection.com
Busn Devt Mgr: Steve Sattler *E-mail:* steves@musicconnection.com
Mktg & Ad Mgr: Hillorie Rudolph
E-mail: hillorier@musicconnection.com
Opers Mgr & Directories Ed: Denise Coso
E-mail: denisec@musicconnection.com
Music industry trade publication.
First published 1977
Frequency: Monthly
Number of pages: 80
Circulation: 110,000
$3.95/issue, $35/yr US, $60 foreign
ISSN: 1091-9791
Trim Size: 8 3/8 x 10 7/8

Ad Rates: B&W full page $1,980, 4-color full page $2,700
Ad Closing Date(s): Approximately 2-3 weeks prior to cover date

Optical Networks/WDM Newsletter
Published by Information Gatekeepers Inc (IGI)
Division of IGI Group Inc
PO Box 606, Winchester, MA 01890
Tel: 617-782-5033 *Fax:* 617-507-8338
E-mail: info@igigroup.com
Web Site: www.igigroup.com
Key Personnel
Chief Analyst & Ed-in-Chief: Dr Hui Pan
E-mail: hpan@igigroup.com
Mng Ed: Bev Wilson *E-mail:* editor@igigroup.com
Technology, international developments & market trends. Submissions accepted by e-mail, any length.
First published 1990
Frequency: Monthly
Number of pages: 20
Circulation: 1,000
$695/yr US & CN, $745/yr other print, $695 PDF (1 user), multi-user licenses available at a discount
ISSN: 1097-8275
Trim Size: 8 1/2 x 11

Photo Life Magazine
Published by Apex Publications (2017) Inc
171 rue Saint Paul, Suite 102, Quebec, QC G1K 3W2, Canada
Tel: 418-692-2110 *Toll Free Tel:* 800-905-7468
Fax: 418-692-3392
E-mail: art@photolife.com; write@photolife.com
Web Site: www.photolife.com
Key Personnel
Publr & Mktg Dir: Valerie Racine
E-mail: vracine@photolife.com
Art Dir & Ed-in-Chief: Guy Langevin
E-mail: glangevin@photolife.com
Business-to-consumer photography magazine.
First published 1976
Frequency: 6 issues/yr
Number of pages: 68
Circulation: 15,000
$24.95/yr CN, plus $10 postage US, plus $90 postage elsewhere, includes back issues in digital
ISSN: 0700-3021
Trim Size: 8 1/4 x 10 7/8
Ad Rates: 4-color page $3,500 (1x rate)
Ad Closing Date(s): 60 days before publication date

Photo Solution Magazine
Published by Apex Publications (2017) Inc
171 rue Saint Paul, Suite 102, Quebec, QC G1K 3W2, Canada
Tel: 418-692-2110 *Toll Free Tel:* 800-905-7468
Fax: 418-692-3392
E-mail: art@photosolution.ca; redaction@photosolution.ca
Web Site: www.photosolution.ca
Key Personnel
Publr & Mktg Dir: Valerie Racine
E-mail: vracine@photosolution.ca
Art Dir & Ed-in-Chief: Guy Langevin
E-mail: glangevin@photosolution.ca
Business to consumer photography magazine.
First published 1981
Media Reviewed: CDs, Photography Equipment
Frequency: 6 issues/yr
Number of pages: 52
Circulation: 7,700
$24.95/yr CN, plus $10 postage US, plus $90 postage elsewhere, includes back issues in digital
ISSN: 1916-100X
Trim Size: 8 1/4 x 10 7/8

Ad Rates: 4-color page $1,800 (1x rate)
Ad Closing Date(s): 60 days before publication date

Playback
Published by Brunico Communications Ltd
100-366 Adelaide St W, Toronto, ON M5V 1R9, Canada
Tel: 416-408-2300 *Toll Free Tel:* 888-BRUNICO (278-6426) *Fax:* 416-408-0870
E-mail: customersupport-playback@brunico.com
Web Site: playbackonline.ca; www.brunico.com
Key Personnel
Pres & CEO: Russell Goldstein
    E-mail: rgoldstein@brunico.com
VP & Edit Dir: Mary Maddever
    E-mail: mmaddever@brunico.com
Assoc Publr: Jenn Kuzmyk *Tel:* 416-408-2300 ext 320 *E-mail:* jkuzmyk@brunico.com
Ed-in-Chief: Liza Sardi *Tel:* 416-408-2300 ext 380 *E-mail:* lsardi@brunico.com
Assoc Ed: Jordan Pinto *Tel:* 416-408-2300 ext 227 *E-mail:* jp.pinto@brunico.com
Print & online publication dealing with production, broadcasting & interactive media in Canada.
First published 1986
Frequency: Quarterly
$12.95/mo, $129.95/yr
ISSN: 0836-2114
Trim Size: 9 x 10 7/8
Ad Rates: Full page $4,395

Post Magazine
Published by COP Communications Inc
620 W Elk Ave, Glendale, CA 91204
Tel: 818-291-1100 (subns) *Fax:* 818-547-4607
Web Site: www.postmagazine.com
Key Personnel
Dir, Sales: Mari Kohn *Tel:* 818-291-1153
    E-mail: mkohn@postmagazine.com
Mng Ed: Linda Romanello *Tel:* 516-931-0730
    E-mail: lromanello@postmagazine.com
Sr Ed: Marc Loftus *Tel:* 516-376-1087
    E-mail: mloftus@postmagazine.com
Focus on all aspects of post-production for TV, feature films, commercials, etc. News & features on creative technology in audio, video & films.
First published 1986
Media Reviewed: DVDs
Frequency: 6 issues/yr
Circulation: 26,000
Print +/or digital free for qualified subscribers, intl free digital only
Trim Size: 10 x 12
Ad Rates: 4-color page $8,630

Pro Sound News
Published by Future US Inc
11 W 42 St, 15th fl, New York, NY 10036
Tel: 212-378-0448
Web Site: www.prosoundnetwork.com
Key Personnel
Content Dir: Clive Young *E-mail:* clive.young@futurenet.com
Professional sound production industry. Digital edition available.
First published 1978
Frequency: Monthly
Circulation: 31,032
$59/yr US, $109/yr CN, $169/yr intl, free to qualified US residents
ISSN: 0164-6338
Trim Size: 8 x 10 3/4

Professional Photographer
Published by PPA Publications & Events Inc
229 Peachtree St NE, Suite 2300, Atlanta, GA 30303
Tel: 404-522-8600 *Toll Free Tel:* 800-786-6277; 800-742-7468 (subns)

E-mail: csc@ppa.com; editors@ppa.com; subscriptions@ppa.com
Web Site: ppmag.com
Key Personnel
Art Dir: Debbie Todd *E-mail:* dtodd@ppa.com
Sr Ed: Joan Sherwood
Helps readers advance a career in photography by containing cutting-edge lessons in the artistic, business & technological aspects of professional photography.
First published 1907
Media Reviewed: Books
Frequency: Monthly
US: $19.95/yr print or digital, $29.95/yr print & digital; CN: $19.95/yr digital only, $35.95/yr print only, $45.95 print & digital
ISSN: 1528-5286
Trim Size: 8 7/8 x 10 7/8

PSA Journal
Published by Photographic Society of America Inc
8241 S Walker Ave, Suite 104, Oklahoma City, OK 73139
Tel: 405-843-1437 *Toll Free Tel:* 855-772-4636
E-mail: hq@psa-photo.org
Web Site: www.psa-photo.org
Key Personnel
Ed: Donna Brennan *E-mail:* editor@psa-photo.org
Monthly magazine for PSA members containing how-to articles for advanced amateur photographers. Also available online.
First published 1934
Media Reviewed: Photography Books, Photography Equipment, Software
Frequency: Monthly
Circulation: 5,600
$60/yr US membs, CN & Mexico, $100/yr other
ISSN: 0030-8277
Trim Size: 7 1/2 x 10
Ad Rates: Color page $1,336 (1x), $1,247 (3x)
Ad Closing Date(s): 1st day of month, 2 months prior to issue month

Publishers Weekly
Published by PWxyz LLC
71 W 23 St, Suite 1608, New York, NY 10010
Tel: 212-377-5500 *Fax:* 212-377-2733
Web Site: www.publishersweekly.com
Key Personnel
Pres: George Slowik, Jr *E-mail:* george@publishersweekly.com
Publr: Cevin Bryerman *Tel:* 212-377-5703
    E-mail: cbryerman@publishersweekly.com
VP, Busn Devt: Carl Pritzkat *E-mail:* cpritzkat@publishersweekly.com
VP, Opers: Patrick Turner *E-mail:* patrick@publishersweekly.com
Adult Book Dir: Louisa Ermelino
    E-mail: lermelino@publishersweekly.com
Art Dir: Clive Chiu *E-mail:* cchiu@publishersweekly.com
Edit Dir: Jim Milliot *Tel:* 212-377-5705
    E-mail: jmilliot@publishersweekly.com
Dir, Digital Opers: Craig Teicher
    E-mail: cteicher@publishersweekly.com
News Dir: Rachel Deahl *E-mail:* rdeahl@publishersweekly.com
Exec Ed: Jonathan Segura *E-mail:* jsegura@publishersweekly.com
Mng Ed: Dan Berchenko *E-mail:* dberchenko@publishersweekly.com
Sr Ed: Mark Rotella *E-mail:* mrotella@publishersweekly.com
Sr News Ed: Calvin Reid *E-mail:* creid@publishersweekly.com
Sr Religion Ed: Lynn Garrett *E-mail:* lgarrett@publishersweekly.com
Sr Reviews Ed: Peter Cannon; Rose Fox
BookLife Ed: Adam Boretz *E-mail:* aboretz@publishersweekly.com
Bookselling & Intl News Ed: Ed Nawotka
    E-mail: enawotka@publishersweekly.com

Children's Book Ed: Diane Roback
    E-mail: roback@publishersweekly.com
Fiction Reviews Ed: David Varno
Assoc Ed, Children's Books: Emma Kantor
    E-mail: ekantor@publishersweekly.com
Assoc Reviews Ed: Phoebe Cramer
Asst Ed, Children's Books: Matia Burnett
    E-mail: mburnett@publishersweekly.com
Copy Ed: Hannah Kushnick *E-mail:* hkushnick@publishersweekly.com
Digital Ed & Assoc News Ed: John Maher
    E-mail: jmaher@publishersweekly.com
Features Ed: Carolyn Juris *E-mail:* cjuris@publishersweekly.com
Religion News Ed: Emma Koonse
    E-mail: ekoonse@publishersweekly.com
Religion Reviews Ed: Seth Satterlee
    E-mail: ssatterlee@publishersweekly.com
Reviews Ed: Alex Crowley; Annie Coreno; Everett Jones
Sr Writer: Andrew R Albanese
    E-mail: aalbanese@publishersweekly.com
Mktg/Licensing Mgr: Christi Cassidy
    E-mail: ccassidy@publishersweekly.com
International news magazine of book publishing & bookselling.
First published 1872
Frequency: 51 issues/yr
Number of pages: 112
Circulation: 68,000 print; 1,000,000 online
Print, digital & online: $289.99/yr US, $339.99/yr CN; Digital & online: $229.99/yr US & CN
ISSN: 0000-0019 (print); 2150-4000 (digital)
Books Reviewed: 9,000/yr
Trim Size: 7 7/8 x 10 1/2

Radio Ink
Published by Streamline Publishing Inc
331 SE Mizner Blvd, Boca Raton, FL 33432
Tel: 561-655-8778
Web Site: radioink.com
Key Personnel
CEO: B Eric Rhoads *E-mail:* bericrhoads@gmail.com
Publr: Deborah Parenti *Tel:* 610-321-0281
    E-mail: parenti@aol.com
Art Dir: Ken Whitney *E-mail:* kenneth.whitney@gmail.com
Ed-in-Chief: Ed Ryan *E-mail:* edryantheeditor@gmail.com
Mng Ed: Brida Connolly *E-mail:* bridaconnolly@gmail.com
Ad Rep: Tracey Homberg
    E-mail: tracey4radioink@gmail.com; Carl Marcucci *E-mail:* cmarcucci66@gmail.com; George Wymer *E-mail:* george.wymer@gmail.com
Premier radio management, marketing & business magazine for the radio broadcasting industry.
First published 1986
Frequency: 14 issues/yr
$199/yr US, $249/yr intl, $49/yr digital

Rangefinder (Rf)
Published by Emerald Expositions LLC
100 Broadway, 14th fl, New York, NY 10005
Tel: 646-668-3700
Web Site: www.rangefinderonline.com
Subscription Address: Creative Data Services, 440 Quadrangle Dr, Suite E, Bollingbrook, IL 60440 *Tel:* 603-739-0900
    E-mail: subscriptions@cds1976.com (subns & cust serv)
Key Personnel
SVP: Johanna Morse *E-mail:* johanna.morse@emeraldexpo.com
Group Mktg Dir: Mike Pehel *E-mail:* mike.pehel@emeraldexpo.com
Group Prodn Dir: Daniel Ryan *E-mail:* daniel.ryan@emeraldexpo.com
Art Dir: Lisa Realmuto-Walsh
Ed-in-Chief: Jacqueline Tobin *E-mail:* jacqueline.tobin@emeraldexpo.com

Sr Ed: Libby Peterson *E-mail:* libby.peterson@
emeraldexpo.com
Sr Technol Ed: David Alexander Willis
E-mail: david.willis@emeraldexpo.com
Mktg Mgr: Shanna Allen *E-mail:* shanna.allen@
emeraldexpo.com
Prodn Mgr: Gennie Kiuchi *E-mail:* gennie.
kiuchi@emeraldexpo.com
Premier magazine for international wedding &
portrait photographers. Official publication of
the annual WPPI Conference & Expo. Fea-
tures creative & innovative work in wedding,
boudoir, maternity, newborn, high school senior
& school sports portraiture, as well as in-depth
information on business, marketing & emerging
technology.
First published 1952
Media Reviewed: New Products, Photography,
Photography Equipment, Software
Frequency: 11 issues/yr
Circulation: 33,200 print, 62,000 digital
Free in the US, contact cust serv outside the US
ISSN: 0033-9202
Trim Size: 9 x 10 7/8
Ad Rates: 2-page spread $15,000, full page
$7,500, 2/3 page $5,000, 1/2 page $3,500, 1/3
page $2,800, 1/6 page $1,200, see web site for
digital ad pricing
Ad Closing Date(s): Approximately 4-6 weeks
prior to issue month

Recording
Published by Music Maker Publications Inc
5408 Idylwild Trail, Boulder, CO 80301
Tel: 303-516-9118 *Toll Free Tel:* 800-783-4903
(subns)
E-mail: info@recordingmag.com
Web Site: www.recordingmag.com
Key Personnel
Pres & Publr: Tom Hawley *E-mail:* tom@
recordingmag.com
VP & Assoc Publr: Brent Heintz *E-mail:* brent@
recordingmag.com
Ed: Mike Metlay, PhD *E-mail:* mike@
recordingmag.com
Recording musicians - geared toward use with
music equipment.
First published 1987
Media Reviewed: Recording Equipment
Frequency: Monthly
Number of pages: 112
Circulation: 24,000
$5.99/issue, $19.95/yr US, $34.95/yr CN & Mex-
ico, $64.95/yr other
ISSN: 1078-8352

The Reel Directory
739 Ladera Dr, Sonoma, CA 95476
Tel: 415-531-9760
E-mail: ivisual@aol.com
Web Site: www.reeldirectory.com
Key Personnel
Publr: Lynetta Freeman
Art Dir: Keith Marsalis *E-mail:* keith@
reeldirectory.com
Resource guide for film, video & multimedia in
Northern California. Also offer iVisual, The
Art Dawgs Guide, a supplement printed & dis-
tributed along with the Reel Directory.
Frequency: Annual
Circulation: 3,000
$30
Trim Size: 8 1/2 x 11
Ad Rates: B&W page $1,500 ($1,350 if received
by Feb 1), 4-color page $2,200 ($2,050 if re-
ceived by Feb 1)
Ad Closing Date(s): March 15

Rf, see Rangefinder (Rf)

SB&F, see Science Books & Films

Science Books & Films
Published by American Association for the Advancement of Science
1200 New York Ave NW, Washington, DC 20005
Tel: 202-326-6417 (orders); 202-326-6454 (edit
ctr) *Toll Free Tel:* 866-434-2227 *Fax:* 202-842-
1065 (orders)
E-mail: sbf.editors@gmail.com
Web Site: www.aaas.org; www.sbfonline.com
Key Personnel
Ed-in-Chief: Suzanne Thurston *E-mail:* sthurs@
aaas.org
Online publication including short reviews of
books, AV materials & software in all the sci-
ences for all ages; for librarians, media special-
ists, educators.
First published 1965
Media Reviewed: Books, DVDs, Microcomputer
Software
Frequency: Monthly
Circulation: 2,000
$45/yr

SHOOT
Published by DCA Business Media LLC
606 Post Rd E, No 650, Westport, CT 06880
Tel: 203-227-1699 *Fax:* 203-571-3355
E-mail: info@shootonline.com
Web Site: www.shootonline.com
Key Personnel
Publr & Edit Dir: Roberta Griefer *Tel:* 203-227-
1699 ext 701 *E-mail:* rgriefer@shootonline.com
Ed: Robert Goldrich *Tel:* 323-445-6818
E-mail: rgoldrich@shootonline.com
Print & online publication for professionals in the
commercial production industry.
First published 1960
Frequency: 6 issues/yr
Circulation: 13,000
Free for industry personnel, $75/yr US, $115/yr
CN, $145/yr other
ISSN: 1055-9825
Trim Size: 9 x 10 7/8
Ad Rates: B&W page $2,500, 4-color page
$3,800
Ad Closing Date(s): 10 days prior to issue date

SMPTE® Motion Imaging Journal
Published by Society of Motion Picture & Televi-
sion Engineers® (SMPTE®)
White Plains Plaza, 445 Hamilton Ave, Suite 601,
White Plains, NY 10601-1827
Tel: 914-761-1100 *Fax:* 914-206-4216
E-mail: smpte@allenpress.com
Web Site: www.smpte.org/publications/journal
Subscription Address: PO Box 7065, Lawrence,
KS 66044-7065
Key Personnel
Exec Dir: Barbara H Lange *Tel:* 914-205-2370
Dir, Educ: Joel Welch
Chair, Bd of Eds: John Belton
Mng Ed: Dianne Purrier *Tel:* 914-205-2377
E-mail: dpurrier@smpte.org
Offers readers a view into the technical world of
motion-imaging science.
First published 1916
Media Reviewed: Technical Books, Television
Systems
Frequency: 10 issues/yr (9 print/online, 1 online
only)
Circulation: 7,000
$750; free to membs
ISSN: 1545-0279 (print); 2160-2492 (online)
Trim Size: 7 7/8 x 10 3/4
Ad Rates: Full page $4,800 (3x), $4,500 (6x),
$3,900 (9x); 1/2 page $3,200 (3x), $3,000 (6x),
$2,500 (9x)

Sound & Communications
Published by Testa Communications
25 Willowdale Ave, Port Washington, NY 11050-
3779

Tel: 516-767-2500
Web Site: www.soundandcommunications.com
Key Personnel
Pres & Publr: Vincent P Testa
Assoc Publr: John Carr *Tel:* 516-767-2500 ext
509 *E-mail:* jcarr@testa.com
Ed: Dan Ferrisi *Tel:* 516-767-2500 ext 704
E-mail: dferrisi@testa.com
Business, product & technical journal for pro-
fessionals who design, specify & integrate
commercial AV & communication systems
in venues across many verticals. Unsol mss
that are brand-agnostic & educational will
be considered for publication; e-mail to dfer-
risi@testa.com for consideration. Press releases
should be provided in the e-mail body, text or
Word format & should include an image file.
First published 1955
Media Reviewed: AV Products (commercial),
Books, Engineered Sound Products, Test
Equipment
Frequency: Monthly
Number of pages: 120
Circulation: 28,100
Free to qualified recipients in the US, digital edi-
tion free worldwide
ISSN: 0038-1845
Trim Size: 8 1/2 x 10 7/8
Ad Rates: 4-color full page $6,610
Ad Closing Date(s): 16th of the month prior to
cover date

Sound & Video Contractor
Published by Future US Inc
11 W 42 St, 15th fl, New York, NY 10036
Tel: 212-378-0448
Web Site: www.svconline.com
Key Personnel
Ed: Cynthia Wisehart
Provides in-depth applications & technology-
related information covering the spectrum
of the professional AV industry: commercial
sound, security, home theater, automation, con-
trol systems & video presentation.
First published 1983
Media Reviewed: Books
Frequency: Monthly
$39/yr US, $59/yr CN, $79/yr intl, free to quali-
fied US residents
ISSN: 0741-1715
Trim Size: 9 x 10 7/8

Sound & Vision
Published by AVTech Media Americas Inc
260 Madison Ave, 8th fl, New York, NY 10016
Toll Free Tel: 800-264-9872 (subn)
Web Site: www.soundandvision.com
Key Personnel
Publr: Keith Pray *Tel:* 914-469-0042
E-mail: kpray@avtechmediausa.com
Assoc Publr: Ed DiBenedetto *Tel:* 917-662-6936
E-mail: edibenedetto@avtechmediausa.com
Sales/Digital Mgr: Rosemarie Torcivia *Tel:* 917-
353-7774 *E-mail:* rtorcivia@avtechmediausa.
com
In-depth coverage of home theater developments
in HDTV, DVD & more, previews of hot new
products, objective product reviews & compar-
isons, DVD reviews & more.
First published 1958
Media Reviewed: DVDs
Frequency: 10 issues/yr with Feb/March & July/
Aug being combined issues
Circulation: 90,000
$14.99/yr digital only; Print only: $22.99/yr US,
$34.99/yr CN, $46.99/yr intl; Print & digital:
$24.99/yr US, $36.99/yr CN, $48.99/yr intl
ISSN: 1537-5838
Trim Size: 8 1/4 x 10 7/8
Ad Rates: 4-color page $18,360 (1x), $16,520
(3x), $15,600 (6x), $14,695 (10x); 4-color 1/2

page $13,225 (1x), $11,910 (3-6x), $10,585 (10x)
Ad Closing Date(s): 7 weeks prior to issue date

strategy™
Published by Brunico Communications Ltd
100-366 Adelaide St W, Toronto, ON M5V 1R9, Canada
Tel: 416-408-2300 *Toll Free Tel:* 888-BRUNICO (278-6426) *Fax:* 416-408-0870
E-mail: strategycustomercare@brunico.com; strategysales@brunico.com
Web Site: strategyonline.ca; www.brunico.com
Key Personnel
Pres & CEO: Russell Goldstein
    E-mail: rgoldstein@brunico.com
SVP & Edit Dir: Mary Maddever
    E-mail: mmaddever@brunico.com
Assoc Publr: Jenn Kuzmyk *Tel:* 416-408-2300 ext 320 *E-mail:* jkuzmyk@brunico.com
Art Dir: Tim Davin *E-mail:* tdavin@brunico.com
Ed: Jennifer Horn *E-mail:* jhorn@brunico.com
Print & online magazine about marketing & advertising in Canada.
First published 1989
Frequency: 6 issues/yr
Circulation: 13,875
$80/yr, $144/2 yrs CN; $108/yr, $194/2 yrs US; $214/yr, $385/2 yrs intl
Ad Rates: Full page $5,675

StudioDaily
Published by Access Intelligence LLC
40 Wall St, 50th fl, New York, NY 10005
Tel: 212-621-4900
E-mail: clientservices@accessintel.com
Web Site: www.studiodaily.com
Key Personnel
SVP & Group Publr: Diane Schwartz *Tel:* 212-621-4964 *E-mail:* dschwartz@accessintel.com
EVP, HR & Corp Communs: Mary Fecto
    Tel: 301-354-1550 *E-mail:* mfecto@accessintel.com
Assoc Publr & Edit Dir: Bryant Frazer *Tel:* 914-361-9699 *E-mail:* bfrazer@accessintel.com
Dir, Strategic Partnerships: Jonathan Toback *Tel:* 973-557-6915 *E-mail:* jtoback@accessintel.com
Contrib Ed: Beth Marchant
    E-mail: bmarchant05@gmail.com
Online publication for news, features, tips & techniques, applications, software & equipment reviews of products & services used in the production of video, audio, 3D/animation, digital video & interactive media. Audience includes producers & managers of professional video productions, media managers & independent producers.
First published 1996
Frequency: Online 24/7; part of StudioDaily.com online network of sites
ISSN: 1554-3412

Systems Contractor News
Published by Future US Inc
11 W 42 St, 15th fl, New York, NY 10036
Tel: 212-378-0448
Web Site: www.avnetwork.com/systems-contractor-news
Key Personnel
VP/Mkt Expert: Adam Goldstein *E-mail:* adam.goldstein@futurenet.com
Content Dir: Megan A Dutta *E-mail:* megan.dutta@futurenet.com
Serves the AV integration industry with thorough news analysis, trend reports & the latest product & technology information.
First published 1994
Frequency: Monthly + 2 special issues & 1 product guide
Circulation: 25,000

$59/yr US, $109/yr CN, $169/yr other, free to qualified US residents
ISSN: 1078-4993
Trim Size: 10 3/8 x 14 1/4

TechTrends: For Leaders in Education & Training
Published by Association for Educational Communications and Technology (AECT)
320 W Eighth St, Suite 101, Bloomington, IN 47404-3745
Tel: 812-335-7675 *Toll Free Tel:* 877-677-AECT (677-2328) *Fax:* 812-335-7678
E-mail: aect@aect.org
Web Site: www.aect.org
Key Personnel
Exec Dir: Dr Phillip Harris *E-mail:* pharris@aect.org
Ed-in-Chief: Chuck Hodges
Designed for educators who use technology to enhance the learning process.
First published 1956
Media Reviewed: Books, CD-ROMs, Computer Hardware, Educational Media, Software
Frequency: 6 issues/yr
Circulation: 3,000
$20/yr membs
ISSN: 8756-3894 (print); 1559-7075 (electronic)
Trim Size: 8 1/2 x 11
Ad Rates: B&W page $1,300, 4-color page $2,100
Ad Closing Date(s): 15th of month, 2 months prior to publication date

The Music & Sound Retailer
Published by Retailer Publishing Inc
25 Willowdale Ave, Port Washington, NY 11050-3779
Tel: 516-767-2500 *Fax:* 516-767-9335
E-mail: msreditor@testa.com
Web Site: msretailer.com
Key Personnel
Pres & Publr: Vincent P Testa
Ad Dir: Robert L Iraggi *E-mail:* riraggi@testa.com
Art Dir: Janice Pupelis
Opers Mgr: Robin Hazan *E-mail:* rhazan@testa.com
Prodn Mgr: Steve Thorakos
Ed: Brian Berk *E-mail:* bberk@testa.com
Assoc Ed: Anthony Vargas *E-mail:* avargas@testa.com
Asst Ed: Matt Van Dyke *E-mail:* mvandyke@testa.com
News magazine for the music products market.
Frequency: Monthly
Non-qualified residents: $18/yr US, $28/yr CN & Mexico, $58/yr other countries
ISSN: 0894-1238

TV Guide Magazine
Published by NTVB Media Inc
50 Rockefeller Plaza, 14th fl, New York, NY 10020
Toll Free Tel: 800-866-1400 (cust serv)
Web Site: www.tvguidemagazine.com
Key Personnel
SVP, Sales & Mktg: David Jackson *Tel:* 212-852-7322 *E-mail:* david.jackson@tvgm.com
VP, Brand Partnerships: Gary Kleinman *Tel:* 212-852-7528 *E-mail:* gary.kleinman@tvgm.com
Sr Acct Dir: Gail Dorfman *Tel:* 212-852-7531 *E-mail:* gail.dorfman@tvgm.com
Acct Dir, Entertainment: Marielle Riordan *Tel:* 212-852-7540 *E-mail:* marielle.riordan@tvgm.com
Mktg Dir: Mike Ankener *Tel:* 212-852-7330 *E-mail:* mike.ankener@tvgm.com
Sr Mktg Mgr: Sai Saha *Tel:* 212-852-7337 *E-mail:* sai.saha@tvgm.com
Helps viewers navigate genres, networks & sources of programming.

First published 1953
Media Reviewed: Books, Films, TV, Video Games
Frequency: 26 issues/yr
Circulation: 13,000,000
$4.99 newsstand, $20/yr subn
ISSN: 0039-8543
Trim Size: 7 x 10
Ad Rates: B&W page $110,000, 4-color page $134,100
Ad Closing Date(s): 18 days prior to issue date

TV Technology
Published by Future US Inc
5285 Shawnee Rd, Suite 525, Alexandria, VA 22312-2334
Tel: 703-852-4600
E-mail: tvtechnology@futurenet.com
Web Site: www.tvtechnology.com
Key Personnel
Content Dir: Tom Butts
Serving the professional video industry as a source of news analysis, trend reports & the latest product & technology information for the broadcast, cable, production, post-production, corporate & new media markets.
First published 1983
Media Reviewed: Publications
Frequency: Monthly
Circulation: 30,000
$39.95/yr, $74.95/2 yrs US; $125/yr, $250/2 yrs foreign; free to qualified US residents
ISSN: 0887-1701
Trim Size: 10 5/8 x 13

TVyVideo + Radio
Published by Latin Press
2455 SW 27 Ave, Suite 200, Miami, FL 33145
Tel: 305-285-3133 *Fax:* 305-285-3134
E-mail: editorial@tvyvideo.com
Web Site: www.tvyvideo.com
Key Personnel
Proj Mgr, Latin Press: Adriana Ramirez *Tel:* 305-285-3133 ext 75
Proj Dir, AV/Security Systems: Sandra Camacho
Ed: Richard Santa
A multimedia publication dedicated to serving the information needs of over 10,000 television industry & video professionals throughout all of Latin America, with BPA-qualified subscribers. Directed to engineering & management in TV stations, cable companies, satellite operators, pre- & post-production agencies & other companies engaged in the production or broadcasting of television. Also, features product & industry news & technical articles dealing with all facets of the TV production process. Text in Spanish, Portuguese & English.
First published 1994
Frequency: 6 issues/yr
Circulation: 10,250
ISSN: 0121-9235

2.5-4G Newsletter
Published by Information Gatekeepers Inc (IGI)
Division of IGI Group Inc
PO Box 606, Winchester, MA 01890
Tel: 617-782-5033 *Fax:* 617-507-8338
E-mail: info@igigroup.com
Web Site: www.igigroup.com
Key Personnel
Chief Analyst & Ed-in-Chief: Dr Hui Pan
    E-mail: hpan@igigroup.com
Mng Ed: Bev Wilson *E-mail:* editor@igigroup.com
Technology, markets & industry activities. Submissions accepted by e-mail.
Frequency: Monthly
Number of pages: 16
Circulation: 1,000

$695/yr US & CN, $745/yr other print, $695/yr PDF (1 user), multi-user licenses available at a discount
ISSN: 1058-6725
Trim Size: 8 1/2 x 11

Variety
Published by Penske Media Corp
11175 Santa Monica Blvd, Los Angeles, CA 90025
Tel: 323-617-9100 *Toll Free Tel:* 800-552-3632
E-mail: news@variety.com; variety@pubservice.com
Web Site: www.variety.com
Key Personnel
Chief Mktg Offr: Dea Lawrence
Group Publr & Chief Revenue Offr: Michelle Sobrino-Sterns
SVP: Timothy M Gray
VP & Exec Ed: Steven Gaydos
Assoc Publr: Donna Pennestri
Mng Ed: Joe Bel Bruno
Co Ed-in-Chief: Claudia Eller; Andrew Wallenstein
Mng Ed, Television: Cynthia Littleton
B2B publication for the entertainment industry.
First published 1905
Media Reviewed: Concerts, Films, Music, Nightclubs, TV, Videotapes
Frequency: 48 issues/yr
Circulation: 40,000
$109/yr print, $129 yr print +/or digital US, $299/yr print & digital CN, $129/yr digital only CN & intl, $349/yr print & digital intl
ISSN: 0042-2738
Trim Size: 10 1/2 x 13 1/2
Ad Closing Date(s): 6 days prior to issue

Video Librarian
9479 Bayshore Dr NW, Suite 203, Silverdale, WA 98383
Tel: 360-626-1259 *Toll Free Tel:* 800-265-7965 (ad sales); 800-692-2270 (subns) *Fax:* 360-626-1260
E-mail: vidlib@videolibrarian.com
Web Site: www.videolibrarian.com
Key Personnel
Publr & Ed: Randy Pitman
Assoc Ed: Jazza Williams-Wood *E-mail:* jazza@videolibrarian.com

Mktg Dir: Anne Williams *E-mail:* anne@videolibrarian.com
Over 200 critical reviews per issue alerting readers to upcoming new releases of documentaries, children's titles, movies, TV series, Japanese anime & musical performances.
First published 1986
Media Reviewed: DVDs
Frequency: 6 issues/yr
Circulation: 2,000
$11/issue, $64/yr dom, $69/yr CN, $86/yr elsewhere (print only), $99/yr dom, $104/yr CN, $121/yr elsewhere (print & online)
ISSN: 0887-6851
Trim Size: 8 1/2 x 11
Ad Rates: B&W full page $950, 4-color full page $1,300
Ad Closing Date(s): Approximately 1 month prior to publication

Videomaker
Published by York Publishing
645 Mangrove Ave, Chico, CA 95926-3946
Tel: 530-891-8410 *Toll Free Tel:* 800-284-3226 *Fax:* 530-891-8443
E-mail: customerservice@videomaker.com; editor@videomaker.com; sales@videomaker.com
Web Site: www.videomaker.com
Key Personnel
Publr: Matt York
Assoc Publr: Patrice York
Art Dir: Susan Schmierer
Dir, Busn Devt: Lindsay Steinberg
Dir, Sales: Terra York *E-mail:* tyork@videomaker.com
Ed-in-Chief: Mike Wilhelm
Mng Ed: Nicole LaJeunesse
Multimedia Ed: Chris Monlux
Coverage of video production tools, tips & techniques information for hobbyists & professionals involved with video production as a hobby, in business, or in education; "how-to" source for video production products & services, trends & potentials. Includes thorough coverage of computer-based video editing systems. No unsol mss, query first.
First published 1985
Media Reviewed: Books (video production related only), DVDs (video production related only)
Frequency: Monthly
Circulation: 50,000 paid

$5.99/issue, $19.97/yr
ISSN: 0889-4973
Trim Size: 7 3/4 x 10 1/2
Ad Rates: B&W page $5,234, 4-color page $6,647 (1x rates)

WiFi/WLAN Monthly Newsletter
Published by Information Gatekeepers Inc (IGI)
Division of IGI Group Inc
PO Box 606, Winchester, MA 01890
Tel: 617-782-5033 *Fax:* 617-507-8338
E-mail: info@igigroup.com
Web Site: www.igigroup.com
Key Personnel
Chief Analyst & Ed-in-Chief: Dr Hui Pan *E-mail:* hpan@igigroup.com
Mng Ed: Bev Wilson *E-mail:* editor@igigroup.com
Technology, market trends & international developments. Submissions accepted by e-mail.
First published 1991
Frequency: Monthly
Number of pages: 16
Circulation: 1,000
$695/yr US & CN, $745/yr other print, $695/yr PDF (1 user), multi-user licenses available
ISSN: 1057-5391
Trim Size: 8 1/2 x 11

Wireless Satellite & Broadcasting Newsletter
Published by Information Gatekeepers Inc (IGI)
Division of IGI Group Inc
PO Box 606, Winchester, MA 01890
Tel: 617-782-5033 *Fax:* 617-507-8338
E-mail: info@igigroup.com
Web Site: www.igigroup.com
Key Personnel
Chief Analyst & Ed-in-Chief: Dr Hui Pan *E-mail:* hpan@igigroup.com
Mng Ed: Bev Wilson *E-mail:* editor@igigroup.com
Markets, technology, applications, standard regulatory & systematical. Submissions accepted by e-mail.
First published 1991
Frequency: Monthly
Number of pages: 16
Circulation: 1,000
$695/yr US & CN, $745/yr other print, $695 PDF (1 user), multi-user licenses available
ISSN: 1058-6695
Trim Size: 8 1/2 x 11

Reference Books for the Trade

The books listed below represent a selected list of major audio visual reference materials that deal with such topics as AV production techniques, multimedia education and AV hardware, software and review sources.

A Short History of the Movies
Published by Pearson Higher Education
330 Hudson St, New York, NY 10013
Tel: 201-236-7000 (orders) *Toll Free Tel:* 800-922-0579 (cust serv)
Web Site: www.mypearsonstore.com
Key Personnel
Author: Bruce F Kawin; Gerald Mast
Cinema's evolution from its earliest beginnings to the digital age.
11th abridged ed, 2011: 480 pp, $110.60
ISBN(s): 978-0-205-21062-6

Advanced Techniques in Multimedia Watermarking: Image, Video and Audio Applications
Published by IGI Global
701 E Chocolate Ave, Hershey, PA 17033
Tel: 717-533-8845 (ext 100) *Toll Free Tel:* 866-342-6657 *Fax:* 717-533-8661; 717-533-7115
E-mail: cust@igi-global.com
Web Site: www.igi-global.com
Covers new advancements in digital image watermarking to prevent illegal & malicious copying & distribution of digital media. Individual chapters available for purchase online.
2010: 566 pp, $180 list price hardcover or ebook; $215 list price hardcover & ebook
ISBN(s): 978-1-61520-903-3; 978-1-61520-904-0 (ebook)

Art of Digital Audio
Published by Focal Press
Member of Taylor & Francis Group, an Informa Business
711 Third Ave, New York, NY 10017
Tel: 212-216-7800 *Toll Free Tel:* 800-634-7064 (cust serv & orders) *Fax:* 212-564-7854
Toll Free Fax: 800-248-4724 (cust serv & orders)
E-mail: orders@taylorandfrancis.com
Web Site: www.routledge.com/focalpress
Key Personnel
Author: John Watkinson
Basic concepts, theory, advanced topics & practical implementation of digital audio.
3rd ed, Dec 2000; ebook April 2013: 768 pp, $250 hardcover, $83.95 paper or ebook
ISBN(s): 978-0-240-51587-8 (hardcover); 978-0-240-52277-7 (paper); 978-1-136-11710-7 (ebook)

ASMP Professional Business Practices in Photography
Published by American Society of Media Photographers Inc (ASMP)
PO Box 31207, Bethesda, MD 20824
Toll Free Tel: 877-771-2767
E-mail: info@asmp.org
Web Site: asmp.org
Key Personnel
Exec Dir: Tom Kennedy *E-mail:* kennedy@asmp.org
Key business practices, industry standards & resources. Coverage includes digital asset management; metadata standards; the role of Internet, FTP & e-mail technologies; the impact of media consolidation on assignment & stock photography & more. Covers the full range of business & legal questions that photographers might have, with comprehensive advice from

the ASMP. Industry experts explore pricing & negotiating, ethics, rights in traditional & electronic media, publishing. Includes business & legal forms, checklists & extensive cross-media bibliography.
7th ed, 2008: 480 pp, $23.21 nonmembs
ISBN(s): 978-1-58115-497-9

Audio Post Production for Television and Film: An Introduction to Technology and Techniques
Published by Focal Press
Member of Taylor & Francis Group, an Informa Business
711 Third Ave, New York, NY 10017
Tel: 212-216-7800 *Toll Free Tel:* 800-634-7064 (cust serv & orders) *Fax:* 212-564-7854
Toll Free Fax: 800-248-4724 (cust serv & orders)
E-mail: orders@taylorandfrancis.com
Web Site: www.routledge.com/focalpress
Key Personnel
Author: Tim Amyes; Hilary Wyatt
Step-by-step guide to professional techniques used to shape a soundtrack through the production process.
3rd ed, Oct 2004: 302 pp, $195 hardcover, $57.95 paper or ebook
ISBN(s): 978-0-240-51947-0 (paper); 978-1-136-12006-0 (ebook); 978-1-138-45977-1 (hardcover)

Audio-Tutorial System
Published by Educational Technology Publications Inc
PO Box 1564, Englewood Cliffs, NJ 07632
Tel: 201-871-4007 *Fax:* 201-871-4009
E-mail: edtecpubs@aol.com
Web Site: bookstoread.com/etp
Key Personnel
Author: James D Russell
Ed: Danny G Langdon
Vol 3 in the Instructional Design Library.
1978: 80 pp, $27.95
ISBN(s): 978-0-87778-107-3

Audio-Visual Aide
Published by National Learning Corporation®
212 Michael Dr, Syosset, NY 11791
Tel: 516-921-8888 *Toll Free Tel:* 800-645-6337 (outside NY); 800-632-8888 *Fax:* 516-921-8743
E-mail: info@passbooks.com
Web Site: www.passbooks.com
Key Personnel
Author: Jack Rudman
Study guide.
$39.95 paper
ISBN(s): 978-0-8373-2903-1 (paper)

Audio-Visual Aide Technician
Published by National Learning Corporation®
212 Michael Dr, Syosset, NY 11791
Tel: 516-921-8888 *Toll Free Tel:* 800-645-6337 (outside NY); 800-632-8888 *Fax:* 516-921-8743
E-mail: info@passbooks.com
Web Site: www.passbooks.com
Key Personnel
Author: Jack Rudman
Study guide.

$39.95 paper
ISBN(s): 978-0-8373-0058-0 (paper)

Audio-Visual Programs Specialist
Published by National Learning Corporation®
212 Michael Dr, Syosset, NY 11791
Tel: 516-921-8888 *Toll Free Tel:* 800-645-6337 (outside NY); 800-632-8888 *Fax:* 516-921-8743
E-mail: info@passbooks.com
Web Site: www.passbooks.com
Key Personnel
Author: Jack Rudman
Study guide.
$39.95 paper
ISBN(s): 978-0-8373-3209-3 (paper)

Audio-Visual Specialist
Published by National Learning Corporation®
212 Michael Dr, Syosset, NY 11791
Tel: 516-921-8888 *Toll Free Tel:* 800-645-6337 (outside NY); 800-632-8888 *Fax:* 516-921-8743
E-mail: info@passbooks.com
Web Site: www.passbooks.com
Key Personnel
Author: Jack Rudman
Study guide.
$39.95 paper
ISBN(s): 978-0-8373-1826-4 (paper)

Audio-Visual Technician
Published by National Learning Corporation®
212 Michael Dr, Syosset, NY 11791
Tel: 516-921-8888 *Toll Free Tel:* 800-645-6337 (outside NY); 800-632-8888 *Fax:* 516-921-8743
E-mail: info@passbooks.com
Web Site: www.passbooks.com
Key Personnel
Author: Jack Rudman
Study guide.
$39.95 paper
ISBN(s): 978-0-8373-1894-3 (paper)

Audio-Visual Training Modules
Published by Educational Technology Publications Inc
PO Box 1564, Englewood Cliffs, NJ 07632
Tel: 201-871-4007 *Fax:* 201-871-4009
E-mail: edtecpubs@aol.com
Web Site: bookstoread.com/etp
Key Personnel
Author: Harold D Stolovitch
Ed: Danny G Langdon
Vol 4 in the Instructional Design Library.
1978: 104 pp, $27.95
ISBN(s): 978-0-87778-108-0

Audio-Workbook
Published by Educational Technology Publications Inc
PO Box 1564, Englewood Cliffs, NJ 07632
Tel: 201-871-4007 *Fax:* 201-871-4009
E-mail: edtecpubs@aol.com
Web Site: bookstoread.com/etp
Key Personnel
Ed & Author: Danny G Langdon
Vol 5 in the Instructional Design Library.

1978: 80 pp, $27.95
ISBN(s): 978-0-87778-109-7

AV Market Place (AVMP)
Published by Information Today, Inc
121 Chanlon Rd, Suite G-20, New Providence, NJ 07974-2195
Tel: 908-795-3755 *Toll Free Tel:* 800-409-4929 (press 3); 800-300-9868 (cust serv)
E-mail: custserv@infotoday.com
Web Site: www.infotoday.com
A complete directory of the AV Market, listing the activities of almost 4,200 manufacturers, distributors & production service companies. Heavily indexed. Also contains information on related associations, state & local film & TV commissions, awards & festivals, periodicals, reference books & AV oriented conferences & exhibits.
Annual (Feb).
48th ed, 2020: 1,306 pp, $389.50 paper
ISBN(s): 978-1-57387-560-8

The Avid Handbook: Advanced Techniques, Strategies and Survival Information for Avid Editing Systems
Published by Focal Press
Member of Taylor & Francis Group, an Informa Business
711 Third Ave, New York, NY 10017
Tel: 212-216-7800 *Toll Free Tel:* 800-634-7064 (cust serv & orders) *Fax:* 212-564-7854
Toll Free Fax: 800-248-4724 (cust serv & orders)
E-mail: orders@taylorandfrancis.com
Web Site: www.routledge.com/focalpress
Key Personnel
Author: Steve Bayes; Greg Staten
Workflow efficiencies for the experienced editor. Emphasizes time-saving techniques, shortcuts & workflow procedures.
5th ed, Sept 2008 paper; ebook Aug 2012; hardcover July 2017: 378 pp, $195 hardcover, $54.95 paper or ebook
ISBN(s): 978-0-08-092813-5 (VitalSource ebook); 978-0-240-81081-2 (paper); 978-1-136-13270-4 (Taylor & Francis ebook for librarians); 978-1-138-41937-7 (hardcover)

Basics of the Video Production Diary
Published by Focal Press
Member of Taylor & Francis Group, an Informa Business
711 Third Ave, New York, NY 10017
Tel: 212-216-7800 *Toll Free Tel:* 800-634-7064 (cust serv & orders) *Fax:* 212-564-7854
Toll Free Fax: 800-248-4724 (cust serv & orders)
E-mail: orders@taylorandfrancis.com
Web Site: www.routledge.com/focalpress
Key Personnel
Author: Des Lyver
Guide to learning all aspects of planning & documenting a video production, from conceptualization to final screening.
July 2001: 224 pp, $165 hardcover, $41.95 paper or ebook
ISBN(s): 978-0-240-51658-5 (paper); 978-1-136-05474-7 (ebook); 978-1-138-16461-1 (hardcover)

Basics of Video Lighting
Published by Focal Press
Member of Taylor & Francis Group, an Informa Business
711 Third Ave, New York, NY 10017
Tel: 212-216-7800 *Toll Free Tel:* 800-634-7064 (cust serv & orders) *Fax:* 212-564-7854
Toll Free Fax: 800-248-4724 (cust serv & orders)
E-mail: orders@taylorandfrancis.com
Web Site: www.routledge.com/focalpress

Key Personnel
Author: Des Lyver; Graham Swainson
What you need to know about the planning, selecting & positioning of lights. Covers the fundamentals of lighting, including comprehensive details on various types of equipment.
2nd ed, May 1999 paper; ebook Jan 2013; hardcover May 2016: 158 pp, $175 hardcover, $39.95 paper or ebook
ISBN(s): 978-0-240-51559-5 (paper); 978-1-136-05642-0 (Taylor & Francis ebook for librarians); 978-1-138-14627-3 (hardcover)

Broadband and Cable Industry Law
Published by Practising Law Institute
1177 Avenue of the Americas, 2nd fl, New York, NY 10036
Tel: 212-824-5700 (message ctr); 212-824-5710 (cust serv) *Toll Free Tel:* 800-260-4PLI (260-4754, cust serv) *Toll Free Fax:* 800-321-0093 (cust serv)
E-mail: info@pli.edu; cs@pli.edu (cust serv)
Web Site: www.pli.edu
Key Personnel
VP, Mktg & Communs: David Smith *Tel:* 212-590-8838 *E-mail:* dsmith@pli.edu
Course handbook.
Annual.
2020: 301 pp, $230

The Broadcast Century and Beyond: A Biography of American Broadcasting
Published by Focal Press
Member of Taylor & Francis Group, an Informa Business
711 Third Ave, New York, NY 10017
Tel: 212-216-7800 *Toll Free Tel:* 800-634-7064 (cust serv & orders) *Fax:* 212-564-7854
Toll Free Fax: 800-248-4724 (cust serv & orders)
E-mail: orders@taylorandfrancis.com
Web Site: www.routledge.com/focalpress
Key Personnel
Author: Robert L Hilliard, PhD; Michael C Keith, PhD
The story of broadcasting told in a direct & informal style, blending personal insight & authoritative scholarship to fully capture the many facets of this dynamic industry.
5th ed, Feb 2010; ebook Oct 2012; hardcover Aug 2015: 378 pp, $180 hardcover, $62.95 paper or ebook
ISBN(s): 971-1-136-02738-3 (ebook); 978-0-240-81236-6 (paper); 978-1-138-17096-8 (hardcover)

The Broadcast Communications Dictionary
Published by ABC-CLIO/Greenwood
Division of ABC-CLIO
130 Cremona Dr, Santa Barbara, CA 93117
Mailing Address: PO Box 1911, Santa Barbara, CA 93116-1911
Tel: 805-968-1911 *Toll Free Tel:* 800-368-6868 *Fax:* 805-685-9685 *Toll Free Fax:* 866-270-3856
E-mail: customerservice@abc-clio.com
Web Site: www.abc-clio.com
Key Personnel
Ed-in-Chief: Lincoln Diamant
Dictionary of technical, common & slang language used in the field of broadcasting.
3rd ed, 1989: 266 pp, $64 hardcover
ISBN(s): 978-0-313-26502-0

CAI Author-Instructor: An Introduction and Guide to the Independent Preparation of Computer-Assisted Instruction Materials
Published by Educational Technology Publications Inc
PO Box 1564, Englewood Cliffs, NJ 07632
Tel: 201-871-4007 *Fax:* 201-871-4009
E-mail: edtecpubs@aol.com

Web Site: bookstoread.com/etp
Key Personnel
Author: Joseph C Meredith
How to design instruction programs for the computer.
1971: 144 pp, $29.95 hardcover
ISBN(s): 978-0-87778-014-4

Career Opportunities in the Film Industry
Published by Ferguson Publishing
Division of Infobase Learning
132 W 31 St, 16th fl, New York, NY 10001
Tel: 212-967-8800 *Toll Free Tel:* 800-322-8755
Toll Free Fax: 800-678-3633
E-mail: custserv@factsonfile.com
Web Site: www.infobasepublishing.com
Key Personnel
Author: Fred Yager; Jan Yager
Edit Dir, Facts on File: Laurie Likoff
A complete guide to career opportunities in the film industry. Includes career profiles & career ladders for more than 80 specific job titles in areas of development, financing, cinematography, sound, editing, casting, distribution & marketing. Also contains listings of degree & non-degree programs, unions, associations & important publications.
2nd ed: 296 pp, $18.95 paper
ISBN(s): 978-0-8160-7353-5 (paper)

Cataloging Sound Recordings: A Manual With Examples
Published by Routledge
Member of Taylor & Francis Group, an Informa Business
711 Third Ave, New York, NY 10017
SAN: 213-196X
Tel: 212-216-7800 *Toll Free Tel:* 800-634-7064 (order enquiries, cust serv) *Toll Free Fax:* 800-248-4724 (order enquiries, cust serv)
E-mail: orders@taylorandfrancis.com
Web Site: www.routledge.com; taylorandfrancis.com
Key Personnel
Author: Deanne Holzberlein; Ruth C Carter
A manual that takes the chore out of cataloging sound recordings. The author clarifies the AACR2 rules in the thought process used in cataloging a sound recording. All the examples of catalog cards presented range from 20th century music to spoken records & compact discs. The appendixes include order & content of cataloging notes, order of parts in a uniform title, a glossary of musical terms & acronyms, a list of basic reference books & thematic indexes, a complete set of catalog cards & the Library of Congress rule interpretations for sound recordings.
1st ed, 1988: 300 pp, $140 hardcover
ISBN(s): 978-0-86656-790-9

Cision® Media Database
Published by Cision US Inc
Subsidiary of Cision Ltd
130 E Randolph St, 7th fl, Chicago, IL 60601
Tel: 312-922-2400 *Toll Free Tel:* 877-922-2400; 866-639-5087; 800-588-3827 (client support & servs)
E-mail: cisionpr@cision.com
Web Site: www.cision.com/us/
Database containing traditional & social media contacts. Inquire about pricing & subscription options through web site. Continually updated, this database contains over 1.6 million records.

Collection Development Policies & Procedures
Published by ABC-CLIO/Greenwood
Division of ABC-CLIO
130 Cremona Dr, Santa Barbara, CA 93117
Mailing Address: PO Box 1911, Santa Barbara, CA 93116-1911

Tel: 805-968-1911 *Toll Free Tel:* 800-368-6868
Fax: 805-685-9685 *Toll Free Fax:* 866-270-3856
E-mail: customerservice@abc-clio.com
Web Site: www.abc-clio.com
Key Personnel
Author: Elizabeth Futas
Helps to acquire & manage a strong collection for your library in the most cost-effective manner.
3rd ed, 1994: 360 pp, $57.95 hardcover
ISBN(s): 978-0-313-38762-3 (ebook); 978-0-89774-797-4 (hardcover)

Communication Technology Update and Fundamentals
Published by Focal Press
Member of Taylor & Francis Group, an Informa Business
711 Third Ave, New York, NY 10017
Tel: 212-216-7800 *Toll Free Tel:* 800-634-7064 (cust serv & orders) *Fax:* 212-564-7854
Toll Free Fax: 800-248-4724 (cust serv & orders)
E-mail: orders@taylorandfrancis.com
Web Site: www.routledge.com/focalpress
Key Personnel
Ed: August E Grant; Jennifer H Meadows
Latest developments in mass media, computers, consumer electronics, networking & telephony.
Biennial.
16th ed, 2018: 338 pp, $200 hardcover, $59.95 paper or ebook
ISBN(s): 978-0-203-70287-1 (ebook); 978-1-138-57133-4 (hardcover); 978-1-138-57136-5 (paper)

Communications Law in the Digital Age
Published by Practising Law Institute
1177 Avenue of the Americas, 2nd fl, New York, NY 10036
Tel: 212-824-5700 (message ctr); 212-824-5710 (cust serv) *Toll Free Tel:* 800-260-4PLI (260-4754, cust serv) *Toll Free Fax:* 800-321-0093 (cust serv)
E-mail: info@pli.edu; cs@pli.edu (cust serv)
Web Site: www.pli.edu
Key Personnel
VP, Mktg & Communs: David Smith *Tel:* 212-590-8838 *E-mail:* dsmith@pli.edu
Course handbook.
Annual.
Nov 2019: 1,092 pp, $220
ISBN(s): 978-1-4024-3512-6

Complete Video Directory™
Published by Grey House Publishing Inc™
4919 Rte 22, Amenia, NY 12501
Mailing Address: PO Box 56, Amenia, NY 12501-0056
Tel: 518-789-8700 *Toll Free Tel:* 800-562-2139
Fax: 518-789-0556
E-mail: books@greyhouse.com
Web Site: greyhouse.com
Complete bibliographic information on video options available for public, community & academic libraries across the nation. Provides details on over 72,000 feature films & filmed performing arts/other entertainment events, as well as over 90,000 documentaries, religious videos & other videos directed toward specialized audiences.
Annual.
March 2020: 7,900 pp, $1055/4 vol set
ISBN(s): 978-1-64265-518-6 (4 vol set)

Computer-Based Integrated Learning Systems
Published by Educational Technology Publications Inc
PO Box 1564, Englewood Cliffs, NJ 07632
Tel: 201-871-4007 *Fax:* 201-871-4009
E-mail: edtecpubs@aol.com
Web Site: bookstoread.com/etp

Key Personnel
Ed: Gerald D Bailey
1993: 184 pp, $34.95
ISBN(s): 978-0-87778-256-8

Computer Managed Instruction: Theory and Practice
Published by Educational Technology Publications Inc
PO Box 1564, Englewood Cliffs, NJ 07632
Tel: 201-871-4007 *Fax:* 201-871-4009
E-mail: edtecpubs@aol.com
Web Site: bookstoread.com/etp
Key Personnel
Author: Frank B Baker
Describes & shows detailed examples of how to manage instruction using a computer.
1978: 440 pp, $44.95
ISBN(s): 978-0-87778-099-1

Copywriting for the Electronic Media: A Practical Guide
Published by Cengage Learning
20 Channel Center St, Boston, MA 02210
Tel: 617-289-7700 *Toll Free Tel:* 800-354-9706
Fax: 617-289-7844
Web Site: www.cengage.com
Key Personnel
Author: Milan D Meeske
Offers basic principles & techniques for writing effective copy for all types of electronic media, with an emphasis on commercial writing.
6th ed, 2009: 336 pp, $199.95
Shipping Address: Cengage Learning Distribution Center, 10650 Toebben Dr, Independence, KY 41051 *Tel:* 859-525-2230
ISBN(s): 978-0-495-41117-8

Creating Special Effects for TV and Video
Published by Focal Press
Member of Taylor & Francis Group, an Informa Business
711 Third Ave, New York, NY 10017
Tel: 212-216-7800 *Toll Free Tel:* 800-634-7064 (cust serv & orders) *Fax:* 212-564-7854
Toll Free Fax: 800-248-4724 (cust serv & orders)
E-mail: orders@taylorandfrancis.com
Web Site: www.routledge.com/focalpress
Key Personnel
Author: Bernard Wilkie
Concise & practical introduction to the techniques used in television production.
3rd ed, Nov 1996 paper & ebook; hardcover June 2017: 188 pp, $195 hardcover, $60.95 paper or ebook
ISBN(s): 978-0-08-050333-2 (VitalSource ebook); 978-0-240-51474-1 (paper); 978-1-136-04970-5 (Taylor & Francis ebook for librarians); 978-1-138-42601-6 (hardcover)

Criteria for the Selection and Use of Visuals for Instruction
Published by Educational Technology Publications Inc
PO Box 1564, Englewood Cliffs, NJ 07632
Tel: 201-871-4007 *Fax:* 201-871-4009
E-mail: edtecpubs@aol.com
Web Site: bookstoread.com/etp
Key Personnel
Author: George L Gropper
How to select visuals to achieve specific instructional objectives. Includes workbook.
1971: 971 pp, $59.95 paper
ISBN(s): 978-0-87778-021-2

Digital Audio Technology: A Guide to CD, MiniDisc, SACD, DVD(A), MP3 & DAT
Published by Focal Press
Member of Taylor & Francis Group, an Informa Business

711 Third Ave, New York, NY 10017
Tel: 212-216-7800 *Toll Free Tel:* 800-634-7064 (cust serv & orders) *Fax:* 212-564-7854
Toll Free Fax: 800-248-4724 (cust serv & orders)
E-mail: orders@taylorandfrancis.com
Web Site: www.routledge.com/focalpress
Key Personnel
Ed: Jan Maes; Marc Vercammen
An expert team from SONY Europe explains the technology behind today's major digital audio consumer products, including the Compact Disc, MiniDisc, Super Audio CD, DVD-Audio, MP3 & Digital Audio Tape.
4th ed, 2001: 356 pp, $195 hardcover, $88.95 paper or ebook
ISBN(s): 978-0-240-51654-7 (paper); 978-1-136-11862-3 (ebook); 978-1-138-41271-2 (hardcover)

Digital Moviemaking
Published by Cengage Learning
20 Channel Center St, Boston, MA 02210
Tel: 617-289-7700 *Toll Free Tel:* 800-354-9706
Fax: 617-289-7844
Web Site: www.cengage.com
Key Personnel
Author: Lynne S Gross
Emphasizes the use of single-camera video equipment, in conjunction with traditional film techniques, to produce narratives & documentaries. Offers both technical information & aesthetic guidance.
7th ed, 2009: 304 pp, $124.95
Shipping Address: Cengage Learning Distribution Center, 10650 Toebben Dr, Independence, KY 41051 *Tel:* 859-525-2230
ISBN(s): 978-0-495-57050-9

Digital TV Over Broadband: Harvesting Bandwidth
Published by Focal Press
Member of Taylor & Francis Group, an Informa Business
711 Third Ave, New York, NY 10017
Tel: 212-216-7800 *Toll Free Tel:* 800-634-7064 (cust serv & orders) *Fax:* 212-564-7854
Toll Free Fax: 800-248-4724 (cust serv & orders)
E-mail: orders@taylorandfrancis.com
Web Site: www.routledge.com/focalpress
Key Personnel
Author: Joan Van Tassel
Examines the recent industry toward a combination of digital services, including the use of the new bandwidth for additional channels of programming, as well as some HDTV.
2nd ed, Jan 2001: 608 pp, $195 hardcover, $78.95 paper
ISBN(s): 978-0-240-80357-9 (paper); 978-1-138-41274-3 (hardcover)

Directing the Documentary
Published by Focal Press
Member of Taylor & Francis Group, an Informa Business
711 Third Ave, New York, NY 10017
Tel: 212-216-7800 *Toll Free Tel:* 800-634-7064 (cust serv & orders) *Fax:* 212-564-7854
Toll Free Fax: 800-248-4724 (cust serv & orders)
E-mail: orders@taylorandfrancis.com
Web Site: www.routledge.com/focalpress
Key Personnel
Author: Michael Rabiger
Definitive guide to making a documentary, with in-depth lessons & insider perspectives on every aspect of pre-production, production & post-production.

6th ed, Aug 2014: 536 pp, $175 hardcover,
$65.95 paper or ebook
ISBN(s): 978-0-415-71930-8 (paper); 978-1-
138-12768-5 (hardcover); 978-1-315-86750-2
(ebook)

Educational Computing: Principals and Applications
Published by Educational Technology Publications Inc
PO Box 1564, Englewood Cliffs, NJ 07632
Tel: 201-871-4007 *Fax:* 201-871-4009
E-mail: edtecpubs@aol.com
Web Site: bookstoread.com/etp
Key Personnel
Author: Reza Azarmsa
1991: 230 pp, $24.95 paper
ISBN(s): 978-0-87778-222-3

Educational Media and Technology Yearbook
Published by Libraries Unlimited
147 Castilian Dr, Santa Barbara, CA 93117
Mailing Address: PO Box 1911, Santa Barbara,
CA 93116-1911
Tel: 805-968-1911 *Toll Free Tel:* 800-368-6868
Toll Free Fax: 866-270-3856
E-mail: customerservice@abc-clio.com
Web Site: www.abc-clio.com
Up-to-date source of significant information about
educational media & instructional technology.
Vol 33, April 2008: 368 pp, $80 hardcover
ISBN(s): 978-0-313-36374-0 (ebook); 978-1-
59158-647-0

Educational Technology: Leadership Perspectives
Published by Educational Technology Publications Inc
PO Box 1564, Englewood Cliffs, NJ 07632
Tel: 201-871-4007 *Fax:* 201-871-4009
E-mail: edtecpubs@aol.com
Web Site: bookstoread.com/etp
Key Personnel
Ed: Greg Kearsley; William Lynch
1994: 218 pp, $34.95 cloth
ISBN(s): 978-0-87778-265-0

Educational Technology Telecommunications Dictionary with Acronyms
Published by Educational Technology Publications Inc
PO Box 1564, Englewood Cliffs, NJ 07632
Tel: 201-871-4007 *Fax:* 201-871-4009
E-mail: edtecpubs@aol.com
Web Site: bookstoread.com/etp
Key Personnel
Author: Douglas E Hansen
1991: 55 pp, $24.95 paper
ISBN(s): 978-0-87778-232-2

Effective TV Production
Published by Focal Press
Member of Taylor & Francis Group, an Informa
Business
711 Third Ave, New York, NY 10017
Tel: 212-216-7800 *Toll Free Tel:* 800-634-7064
(cust serv & orders) *Fax:* 212-564-7854
Toll Free Fax: 800-248-4724 (cust serv & orders)
E-mail: orders@taylorandfrancis.com
Web Site: www.routledge.com/focalpress
Key Personnel
Author: Gerald Millerson
Thorough overview of the production process.
3rd ed, April 1994: 224 pp, $160 hardcover,
$55.95 paper or ebook
ISBN(s): 978-0-08-050512-1 (ebook); 978-0-240-
51324-9 (paper); 978-1-138-14032-5 (hardcover)

Electronic Text: Learning to Write, Read, and Reason with Computers
Published by Educational Technology Publications Inc
PO Box 1564, Englewood Cliffs, NJ 07632
Tel: 201-871-4007 *Fax:* 201-871-4009
E-mail: edtecpubs@aol.com
Web Site: bookstoread.com/etp
Key Personnel
Author: William V Costanzo
1989: 320 pp, $39.95 cloth
ISBN(s): 978-0-87778-208-7

Empowering Networks: Computer Conferencing in Education
Published by Educational Technology Publications Inc
PO Box 1564, Englewood Cliffs, NJ 07632
Tel: 201-871-4007 *Fax:* 201-871-4009
E-mail: edtecpubs@aol.com
Web Site: bookstoread.com/etp
Key Personnel
Ed: Michael D Waggoner
1992: 263 pp, $39.95 cloth
ISBN(s): 978-0-87778-238-4

Exploring Multimodal Composition and Digital Writing
Published by IGI Global
701 E Chocolate Ave, Hershey, PA 17033
Tel: 717-533-8845 (ext 100) *Toll Free Tel:* 866-
342-6657 *Fax:* 717-533-8661; 717-533-7115
E-mail: cust@igi-global.com
Web Site: www.igi-global.com
Investigates the use of digital technologies to create
multimedia documents that utilize video,
audio & web-based elements to further written
communication. Individual chapters available
for purchase online.
2014: 352 pp, $175 list price hardcover or ebook;
$210 list price hardcover & ebook
ISBN(s): 978-1-4666-4345-1; 978-1-4666-4346-8
(ebook)

Film Plots: Scene-by-Scene Narrative Outlines for Feature Film Study
Published by Pierian Press
3196 Maple Dr, Ypsilanti, MI 48197
Tel: 734-434-4074
Web Site: www.pierianpress.com
Key Personnel
Author: Leonard J Leff
Contact: Mary Ellen Wall *E-mail:* mew_42strat@
yahoo.com
Provides scene-by-scene analysis of classic &
modern films.
Vol 1: 1983 (67 films, 402 pp), Vol 2: 1988 (50
films, 483 pp), $65/vol hardcover plus $6 shipping for both vols
ISBN(s): 978-0-87650-149-8 (vol 1); 978-0-
87650-241-9 (vol 2)

Filmstrips
Published by Educational Technology Publications Inc
PO Box 1564, Englewood Cliffs, NJ 07632
Tel: 201-871-4007 *Fax:* 201-871-4009
E-mail: edtecpubs@aol.com
Web Site: bookstoread.com/etp
Key Personnel
Author: LaMond F Beatty
Ed: James E Duane
Vol 4 in the Instructional Media Library.
1981: 104 pp, $27.95 hardcover
ISBN(s): 978-0-87778-164-6

The Focal Encyclopedia of Photography
Published by Focal Press
Member of Taylor & Francis Group, an Informa
Business
711 Third Ave, New York, NY 10017

Tel: 212-216-7800 *Toll Free Tel:* 800-634-7064
(cust serv & orders) *Fax:* 212-564-7854
Toll Free Fax: 800-248-4724 (cust serv & orders)
E-mail: orders@taylorandfrancis.com
Web Site: www.routledge.com/focalpress
Key Personnel
Ed-in-Chief: Michael Peres
Features the history & historical processes of
photography, contemporary applications & new
& evolving digital technologies.
4th ed: 846 pp, $150 hardcover, $99.95 paper or
ebook
ISBN(s): 978-0-08-047784-8 (VitalSource ebook);
978-1-136-10614-9 (Taylor & Francis ebook
for librarians); 978-1-138-29857-6 (paper);
978-1-138-65658-1 (hardcover)

Guide to Reference Materials for School Library Media Centers
Published by Libraries Unlimited
147 Castilian Dr, Santa Barbara, CA 93117
Mailing Address: PO Box 1911, Santa Barbara,
CA 93116-1911
Tel: 805-968-1911 *Toll Free Tel:* 800-368-6868
Toll Free Fax: 866-270-3856
E-mail: customerservice@abc-clio.com
Web Site: www.abc-clio.com
Key Personnel
Author: Barbara Ripp Safford
Suggests reference materials in all formats recommended for elementary & secondary school
media centers.
6th ed, 2010: 236 pp, $60 hardcover
ISBN(s): 978-1-59158-277-9

Haven't I Seen You Somewhere Before? Remakes, Sequels & Series in Motion Pictures, Videos, and Television, 1896-1990
Published by Pierian Press
3196 Maple Dr, Ypsilanti, MI 48197
Tel: 734-434-4074
Web Site: www.pierianpress.com
Key Personnel
Author: James L Limbacher
Contact: Mary Ellen Wall *E-mail:* mew_42strat@
yahoo.com
Covers film remakes (including those remade for
television), film sequels & film series. Contains
information on producer, year of production,
original source & pertinent notes.
2nd ed, 1991: 440 pp, $65 hardcover plus $5
shipping
ISBN(s): 978-0-87650-244-3

Hawaii Production Index
Published by Media Index Publishing Group
14240 Interurban Ave S, Suite 190, Tukwila, WA
98168
Mailing Address: PO Box 24365, Seattle, WA
98124-0365
Tel: 206-382-9220 *Toll Free Tel:* 800-332-1736
Fax: 206-382-9437
E-mail: media@media-inc.com
Web Site: hawaiifilm.com; www.
mediaindexpublishing.com
Key Personnel
Pres: James Baker *E-mail:* jbaker@media-inc.com
Assoc Ed/Res Dir: Katie Sauro *E-mail:* ksauro@
media-inc.com
Sales Mgr: Katie Higgins *E-mail:* khiggins@
media-inc.com
Production resource companies in Hawaii. Available online.

Human-Computer Interaction: A Design Guide
Published by Educational Technology Publications Inc
PO Box 1564, Englewood Cliffs, NJ 07632
Tel: 201-871-4007 *Fax:* 201-871-4009
E-mail: edtecpubs@aol.com
Web Site: bookstoread.com/etp

Key Personnel
Author: Mark K Jones
1989: 160 pp, $24.95 paper
ISBN(s): 978-0-87778-207-0

Impact of Technology on Resource Sharing: Experimentation & Maturity
Published by CRC Press
Subsidiary of Taylor & Francis Group, an Informa Business
6000 Broken Sound Pkwy NW, Suite 300, Boca Raton, FL 33487
Toll Free Tel: 800-272-7737 (orders) *Fax:* 561-989-9732 (intl orders) *Toll Free Fax:* 800-374-3401 (orders)
E-mail: orders@taylorandfrancis.com
Web Site: www.crcpress.com
Key Personnel
CEO: Annie Callahan
Author: Thomas C Wilson
Critical analysis of the impact groundbreaking technologies, new & established, have had on resource sharing in the information industry.
1993: 196 pp, $105 hardcover
ISBN(s): 978-1-56024-391-5

Institute on Telecommunications Policy & Regulation
Published by Practising Law Institute
1177 Avenue of the Americas, 2nd fl, New York, NY 10036
Tel: 212-824-5700 (message ctr); 212-824-5710 (cust serv) *Toll Free Tel:* 800-260-4PLI (260-4754, cust serv) *Toll Free Fax:* 800-321-0093 (cust serv)
E-mail: info@pli.edu; cs@pli.edu (cust serv)
Web Site: www.pli.edu
Key Personnel
VP, Mktg & Communs: David Smith *Tel:* 212-590-8838 *E-mail:* dsmith@pli.edu
Course handbook.
Annual.
37th ed, Dec 2019: 778 pp, $220
ISBN(s): 978-1-4024-3524-9

Instructional Materials Centers
Published by Educational Technology Publications Inc
PO Box 1564, Englewood Cliffs, NJ 07632
Tel: 201-871-4007 *Fax:* 201-871-4009
E-mail: edtecpubs@aol.com
Web Site: bookstoread.com/etp
Key Personnel
Author: LaMond F Beatty
Ed: James E Duane
Vol 5 in the Instructional Media Library.
1981: 104 pp, $27.95 hardcover
ISBN(s): 978-0-87778-165-3

Instructional Systems Development in Large Organizations
Published by Educational Technology Publications Inc
PO Box 1564, Englewood Cliffs, NJ 07632
Tel: 201-871-4007 *Fax:* 201-871-4009
E-mail: edtecpubs@aol.com
Web Site: bookstoread.com/etp
Key Personnel
Author: Wallace J Hannum; Carol Hansen
1989: 328 pp, $44.95 cloth
ISBN(s): 978-0-87778-204-9

Interactive Multimedia Instruction
Published by Educational Technology Publications Inc
PO Box 1564, Englewood Cliffs, NJ 07632
Tel: 201-871-4007 *Fax:* 201-871-4009
E-mail: edtecpubs@aol.com
Web Site: bookstoread.com/etp
Key Personnel
Author: Richard A Schwier; Earl R Misanchuk

1993: 392 pp, $44.95 cloth
ISBN(s): 978-0-87778-251-3

Interactive Television and Instruction: A Guide to Technology, Technique, Facilities Design, and Classroom Management
Published by Educational Technology Publications Inc
PO Box 1564, Englewood Cliffs, NJ 07632
Tel: 201-871-4007 *Fax:* 201-871-4009
E-mail: edtecpubs@aol.com
Web Site: bookstoread.com/etp
Key Personnel
Author: Robert H Lochte
1993: 160 pp, $32.95 cloth
ISBN(s): 978-0-87778-252-0

Interactive Video
Published by Educational Technology Publications Inc
PO Box 1564, Englewood Cliffs, NJ 07632
Tel: 201-871-4007 *Fax:* 201-871-4009
E-mail: edtecpubs@aol.com
Web Site: bookstoread.com/etp
Key Personnel
Publr & Sr Ed: Lawrence Lipsitz
Author: Richard A Schwier
Computer assisted instruction.
1987: 202 pp, $39.95 cloth
ISBN(s): 978-0-87778-206-7

Interactive Video Management and Production
Published by Educational Technology Publications Inc
PO Box 1564, Englewood Cliffs, NJ 07632
Tel: 201-871-4007 *Fax:* 201-871-4009
E-mail: edtecpubs@aol.com
Web Site: bookstoread.com/etp
Key Personnel
Author: Steven Imke
1991: 176 pp, $24.95 paper
ISBN(s): 978-0-87778-233-9

Library Media Specialist, see Media Specialist—Library & Audio-Visual Services

Lighting for Television and Film
Published by Focal Press
Member of Taylor & Francis Group, an Informa Business
711 Third Ave, New York, NY 10017
Tel: 212-216-7800 *Toll Free Tel:* 800-634-7064 (cust serv & orders) *Fax:* 212-564-7854
Toll Free Fax: 800-248-4724 (cust serv & orders)
E-mail: orders@taylorandfrancis.com
Web Site: www.routledge.com/focalpress
Key Personnel
Author: Gerald Millerson
Fundamental principles of lighting in studios, on location & display, as well as single-camera, small unit production, improvised & economy lighting & working with limited facilities. Emphasis is also placed on the safety aspects of working with lighting equipment.
3rd ed, June 1999: 470 pp, $175 hardcover, $93.95 paper or ebook
ISBN(s): 978-0-080-57349-6 (VitalSource ebook); 978-0-240-51582-3 (paper); 978-1-136-05522-5 (Taylor & Francis ebook); 978-1-138-13012-8 (hardcover)

Lighting for Video
Published by Focal Press
Member of Taylor & Francis Group, an Informa Business
711 Third Ave, New York, NY 10017
Tel: 212-216-7800 *Toll Free Tel:* 800-634-7064 (cust serv & orders) *Fax:* 212-564-7854
Toll Free Fax: 800-248-4724 (cust serv & orders)

E-mail: orders@taylorandfrancis.com
Web Site: www.routledge.com/focalpress
Key Personnel
Author: Gerald Millerson
A practical guide to lighting for anyone using a video camera.
3rd ed, July 1991: 154 pp, $175 hardcover, $46.95 paper
ISBN(s): 978-0-240-51303-4 (paper); 978-1-138-17379-8 (hardcover)

Loudspeaker and Headphone Handbook
Published by Focal Press
Member of Taylor & Francis Group, an Informa Business
711 Third Ave, New York, NY 10017
Tel: 212-216-7800 *Toll Free Tel:* 800-634-7064 (cust serv & orders) *Fax:* 212-564-7854
Toll Free Fax: 800-248-4724 (cust serv & orders)
E-mail: orders@taylorandfrancis.com
Web Site: www.routledge.com/focalpress
Key Personnel
Ed: John Borwick
Provides a detailed technical reference of all aspects of loudspeakers & headphones.
3rd ed, March 2001: 736 pp, $235 all formats
ISBN(s): 978-0-240-51578-6 (hardcover); 978-0-240-52276-0 (paper); 978-1-136-12086-2 (ebook)

Managing Interactive Video/Multimedia Projects
Published by Educational Technology Publications Inc
PO Box 1564, Englewood Cliffs, NJ 07632
Tel: 201-871-4007 *Fax:* 201-871-4009
E-mail: edtecpubs@aol.com
Web Site: bookstoread.com/etp
Key Personnel
Author: Robert E Bergman; Thomas V Moore
1990: 240 pp, $44.95 paper
ISBN(s): 978-0-87778-209-4

Mass Media Research: An Introduction
Published by Cengage Learning
20 Channel Center St, Boston, MA 02210
Tel: 617-289-7700 *Toll Free Tel:* 800-354-9706 *Fax:* 617-289-7844
Web Site: www.cengage.com
Key Personnel
Author: Roger D Wimmer; Joseph R Dominick
Comprehensive overview of mass communication research & a thorough exploration of each major approach, including qualitative research, content analysis, survey research, longitudinal research & experimental research. Also available as ebook.
10th ed, 2014: 496 pp, $199.95
Shipping Address: Cengage Learning Distribution Center, 10650 Toebben Dr, Independence, KY 41051 *Tel:* 859-525-2230
ISBN(s): 978-1-133-30733-4

Media About Media: An Annotated Listing of Media Software
Published by Educational Technology Publications Inc
PO Box 1564, Englewood Cliffs, NJ 07632
Tel: 201-871-4007 *Fax:* 201-871-4009
E-mail: edtecpubs@aol.com
Web Site: bookstoread.com/etp
Key Personnel
Author: James E Duane
Vol 6 of the Instructional Media Library.
1981: 232 pp, $34.95 hardcover
ISBN(s): 978-0-87778-166-0

Media and You: An Elementary Media Literacy Curriculum
Published by Educational Technology Publications Inc
PO Box 1564, Englewood Cliffs, NJ 07632

Tel: 201-871-4007 *Fax:* 201-871-4009
E-mail: edtecpubs@aol.com
Web Site: bookstoread.com/etp
Key Personnel
Author: Donna Lloyd-Kolkin; Kathleen R Tyner
1991: 170 pp, $34.95 paper
ISBN(s): 978-0-87778-226-1

Media Law for Producers
Published by Focal Press
Member of Taylor & Francis Group, an Informa
Business
711 Third Ave, New York, NY 10017
Tel: 212-216-7800 *Toll Free Tel:* 800-634-7064
(cust serv & orders) *Fax:* 212-564-7854
Toll Free Fax: 800-248-4724 (cust serv & orders)
E-mail: orders@taylorandfrancis.com
Web Site: www.routledge.com/focalpress
Key Personnel
Author: Philip Miller
Helps the media producer recognize legal questions that can arise during production, including contracts, permits, defamation, patents, releases & insurance, libel, royalties & residuals, as well as protecting the finished production.
4th ed, Oct 2003: 422 pp, $175 hardcover, $61.95 paper or ebook
ISBN(s): 978-0-240-80478-1 (paper); 978-1-136-04602-5 (ebook); 978-1-138-13045-6 (hardcover)

Media Programming: Strategies and Practices
Published by Cengage Learning
20 Channel Center St, Boston, MA 02210
Tel: 617-289-7700 *Toll Free Tel:* 800-354-9706
Fax: 617-289-7844
Web Site: www.cengage.com
Key Personnel
Author: Susan Tyler Eastman; Douglas A Ferguson
Treats decision making in broadcast programming, both day-to-day & long range strategies. Also available as ebook.
9th ed, 2013: 496 pp, $124.95
Shipping Address: Cengage Learning Distribution Center, 10650 Toebben Dr, Independence, KY 41051 *Tel:* 859-525-2230
ISBN(s): 978-1-111-34447-4

Media Specialist—Library & Audio-Visual Services
Published by National Learning Corporation®
212 Michael Dr, Syosset, NY 11791
Tel: 516-921-8888 *Toll Free Tel:* 800-645-6337
(outside NY); 800-632-8888 *Fax:* 516-921-8743
E-mail: info@passbooks.com
Web Site: www.passbooks.com
Key Personnel
Author: Jack Rudman
Study guide.
$49.95 paper
ISBN(s): 978-0-8373-8439-9

Memphis & Shelby County Production Directory
Published by The Memphis & Shelby County Film & TV Commission
496 S Main St, Suite 101, Memphis, TN 38103
Tel: 901-527-8300 *Fax:* 901-527-8326
E-mail: hello@filmmemphis.org
Web Site: www.filmmemphis.org
Key Personnel
Film Commissioner: Linn Sitler *E-mail:* linn@filmmemphis.org
Deputy Film Commissioner & Contact: Sharon Fox O'Guin *E-mail:* sharon@filmmemphis.org
Production directory in digital format of Memphis area services; location scouting services; free

production directory; crew/equipment information; scout West Tennessee, Eastern Arkansas & Northern Mississippi.

Messages That Work: A Guide to Communication Design
Published by Educational Technology Publications Inc
PO Box 1564, Englewood Cliffs, NJ 07632
Tel: 201-871-4007 *Fax:* 201-871-4009
E-mail: edtecpubs@aol.com
Web Site: bookstoread.com/etp
Key Personnel
Author: Patrick O Marsh
1983: 460 pp, $49.95 hardcover
ISBN(s): 978-0-87778-184-4

Microcomputer/Audio-Visual Repair Supervisor
Published by National Learning Corporation®
212 Michael Dr, Syosset, NY 11791
Tel: 516-921-8888 *Toll Free Tel:* 800-645-6337
(outside NY); 800-632-8888 *Fax:* 516-921-8743
E-mail: info@passbooks.com
Web Site: www.passbooks.com
Key Personnel
Author: Jack Rudman
Study guide.
$49.95 paper
ISBN(s): 978-0-8373-3732-6

The MIDI Manual: A Practical Guide to MIDI in the Project Studio
Published by Focal Press
Member of Taylor & Francis Group, an Informa
Business
711 Third Ave, New York, NY 10017
Tel: 212-216-7800 *Toll Free Tel:* 800-634-7064
(cust serv & orders) *Fax:* 212-564-7854
Toll Free Fax: 800-248-4724 (cust serv & orders)
E-mail: orders@taylorandfrancis.com
Web Site: www.routledge.com/focalpress
Key Personnel
Author: David Miles Huber
Comprehensive guide to the musical instrument digital interface. Provides a clear explanation of what MIDI is, how to use electronic instruments & an explanation of sequencers & how to use them.
3rd ed, March 2007: 378 pp, $195 hardcover, $38.95 paper or ebook
ISBN(s): 978-0-08-047946-0 (ebook); 978-0-240-80798-0 (paper); 978-1-138-45224-4 (hardcover)

Modern Radio and Audio Production: Programming and Performance
Published by Cengage Learning
20 Channel Center St, Boston, MA 02210
Tel: 617-289-7700 *Toll Free Tel:* 800-354-9706
Fax: 617-289-7844
Web Site: www.cengage.com
Overview of radio production & programming as well as coverage of cutting-edge technologies along with traditional equipment & real-world practices. New for the 10th edition are chapters on ethics & mobile radio. Also available as ebook.
10th ed, 2016: 464 pp, $124.95
Shipping Address: Cengage Learning Distribution Center, 10650 Toebben Dr, Independence, KY 41051 *Tel:* 859-525-2230
ISBN(s): 978-1-305-07749-2

Modern Recording Techniques
Published by Focal Press
Member of Taylor & Francis Group, an Informa
Business
711 Third Ave, New York, NY 10017

Tel: 212-216-7800 *Toll Free Tel:* 800-634-7064
(cust serv & orders) *Fax:* 212-564-7854
Toll Free Fax: 800-248-4724 (cust serv & orders)
E-mail: orders@taylorandfrancis.com
Web Site: www.routledge.com/focalpress
Key Personnel
Author: David Miles Huber; Robert E Runstein
Authoritative guide on the art & technologies of music production. Presents the latest production technologies & includes an in-depth coverage of the DAW, networked audio, MIDI, signal processing & more.
9th ed, Nov 2017: 616 pp, $150 hardcover, $59.95 paper or ebook
ISBN(s): 978-1-138-20367-9 (hardcover); 978-1-138-95437-3 (paper); 978-1-315-66695-2 (ebook)

Motion Picture Operator
Published by National Learning Corporation®
212 Michael Dr, Syosset, NY 11791
Tel: 516-921-8888 *Toll Free Tel:* 800-645-6337
(outside NY); 800-632-8888 *Fax:* 516-921-8743
E-mail: info@passbooks.com
Web Site: www.passbooks.com
Key Personnel
Author: Jack Rudman
Study guide.
$34.95 paper
ISBN(s): 978-0-8373-0501-1

Movies Unlimited DVD & Blu-ray Catalog
Published by Movies Unlimited
740 Hilltop Dr, Itasca, IL 60143
Toll Free Tel: 800-466-8437
E-mail: movies@moviesunlimited.com; info@moviefanfare.com; askmff@moviefanfare.com
Web Site: www.moviefanfare.com/?p=50028; www.moviesunlimited.com/musite/catalog; www.moviesunlimited.com
Pre-recorded DVD & Blu-ray titles.
Annual.
2019: 400 pp, $5.95

MPEG Handbook
Published by Focal Press
Member of Taylor & Francis Group, an Informa
Business
711 Third Ave, New York, NY 10017
Tel: 212-216-7800 *Toll Free Tel:* 800-634-7064
(cust serv & orders) *Fax:* 212-564-7854
Toll Free Fax: 800-248-4724 (cust serv & orders)
E-mail: orders@taylorandfrancis.com
Web Site: www.routledge.com/focalpress
Key Personnel
Author: John Watkinson
Professional resource on all aspects of audio & video compression using MPEG technology, including the MPEG-4 standard & H-264.
2nd ed, Sept 2004: 448 pp, $93.95 hardcover, $57.95 ebook
ISBN(s): 978-0-240-80578-8 (hardcover); 978-1-136-02898-4 (ebook)

Multimedia for Learning: Development, Application, Evaluation
Published by Educational Technology Publications Inc
PO Box 1564, Englewood Cliffs, NJ 07632
Tel: 201-871-4007 *Fax:* 201-871-4009
E-mail: edtecpubs@aol.com
Web Site: bookstoread.com/etp
Key Personnel
Ed: Diane M Gayeski
1993: 184 pp, $34.95 hardcover
ISBN(s): 978-0-87778-250-6

Northwest Production Index
Published by Media Index Publishing Group

14240 Interurban Ave S, Suite 190, Tukwila, WA 98168
Mailing Address: PO Box 24365, Seattle, WA 98124-0365
Tel: 206-382-9220 *Toll Free Tel:* 800-332-1736 *Fax:* 206-382-9437
E-mail: media@media-inc.com
Web Site: nwfilm.com; www.mediaindexpublishing.com
Key Personnel
Pres: James Baker *E-mail:* jbaker@media-inc.com
Assoc Ed/Res Dir: Katie Sauro *E-mail:* ksauro@media-inc.com
Sales Mgr: Katie Higgins *E-mail:* khiggins@media-inc.com
Comprehensive guide to production services in the greater Seattle & Portland areas, from video editing services to feature film production. Available online.

Orion Blue Book: Audio Equipment
Published by UsedPrice.com
1776 N Scottsdale Rd, No 1543, Scottsdale, AZ 85252
E-mail: sales@usedprice.com; support@usedprice.com
Web Site: www.usedprice.com
Key Personnel
Owner: Mark Rohrs; Rob Rohrs
Audio equipment used prices.
$150/yr online only

Orion Blue Book: Video & Television
Published by UsedPrice.com
1776 N Scottsdale Rd, No 1543, Scottsdale, AZ 85252
E-mail: sales@usedprice.com; support@usedprice.com
Web Site: www.usedprice.com
Key Personnel
Owner: Mark Rohrs; Rob Rohrs
Used television prices & video equipment values.
$130/yr online only

Photography
Published by Educational Technology Publications Inc
PO Box 1564, Englewood Cliffs, NJ 07632
Tel: 201-871-4007 *Fax:* 201-871-4009
E-mail: edtecpubs@aol.com
Web Site: bookstoread.com/etp
Key Personnel
Author: Robert V Bullough
Ed: James E Duane
Vol 11 in the Instructional Media Library.
1981: 104 pp, $27.95 hardcover
ISBN(s): 978-0-87778-171-4

Placing Shadows: Lighting Techniques for Video Production
Published by Focal Press
Member of Taylor & Francis Group, an Informa Business
711 Third Ave, New York, NY 10017
Tel: 212-216-7800 *Toll Free Tel:* 800-634-7064 (cust serv & orders) *Fax:* 212-564-7854
Toll Free Fax: 800-248-4724 (cust serv & orders)
E-mail: orders@taylorandfrancis.com
Web Site: www.routledge.com/focalpress
Key Personnel
Author: Chuck Gloman; Tom Le Tourneau
Instructs the student & professional in the physical properties of light & the selection of proper instruments for the best possible effect.
3rd ed, Feb 2005: 310 pp, $175 hardcover, $52.95 paper or ebook
ISBN(s): 978-0-240-80661-7 (paper); 978-1-136-04170-9 (ebook); 978-1-138-16958-6 (hardcover)

Portable Video: News and Field Production
Published by Focal Press
Member of Taylor & Francis Group, an Informa Business
711 Third Ave, New York, NY 10017
Tel: 212-216-7800 *Toll Free Tel:* 800-634-7064 (cust serv & orders) *Fax:* 212-564-7854
Toll Free Fax: 800-248-4724 (cust serv & orders)
E-mail: orders@taylorandfrancis.com
Web Site: www.routledge.com/focalpress
Key Personnel
Author: Edward J Fink; Norman Medoff
Presents students with the techniques & technology of single camera electronic news gathering & electronic field production. Covering everything from creative & technical recording & editing techniques to budgets & copyright issues. Updates feature the latest advances in techniques & equipment. New coverage includes digital workflow techniques, digital cameras (including DSLRs), lighting, audio & mobile.
6th ed, March 2012: 400 pp, $175 hardcover, $60.95 paper or ebook
ISBN(s): 978-0-240-81499-5 (paper); 978-0-240-81500-8 (ebook); 978-1-138-12998-6 (hardcover)

Preparing Instructional Text: Document Design Using Desktop Publishing
Published by Educational Technology Publications Inc
PO Box 1564, Englewood Cliffs, NJ 07632
Tel: 201-871-4007 *Fax:* 201-871-4009
E-mail: edtecpubs@aol.com
Web Site: bookstoread.com/etp
Key Personnel
Author: Earl R Misanchuk
1992: 327 pp, $39.95 paper
ISBN(s): 978-0-87778-241-4

Real Objects and Models
Published by Educational Technology Publications Inc
PO Box 1564, Englewood Cliffs, NJ 07632
Tel: 201-871-4007 *Fax:* 201-871-4009
E-mail: edtecpubs@aol.com
Web Site: bookstoread.com/etp
Key Personnel
Author: J Steven Soulier
Ed: James E Duane
Vol 12 in the Instructional Media Library.
1981: 96 pp, $27.95 hardcover
ISBN(s): 978-0-87778-172-1

School District Instructional Computer-Use Evaluation Manual
Published by Educational Technology Publications Inc
PO Box 1564, Englewood Cliffs, NJ 07632
Tel: 201-871-4007 *Fax:* 201-871-4009
E-mail: edtecpubs@aol.com
Web Site: bookstoread.com/etp
Key Personnel
Author: Chris Morton; Don Beverly
1989: 61 pp, $24.95 paper
ISBN(s): 978-0-87778-214-8

Senior Audio-Visual Aid Technician
Published by National Learning Corporation®
212 Michael Dr, Syosset, NY 11791
Tel: 516-921-8888 *Toll Free Tel:* 800-645-6337 (outside NY); 800-632-8888 *Fax:* 516-921-8743
E-mail: info@passbooks.com
Web Site: www.passbooks.com
Key Personnel
Author: Jack Rudman
Study guide.
$34.95 paper
ISBN(s): 978-0-8373-1471-6

Sight, Sound, Motion: Applied Media Aesthetics
Published by Cengage Learning
20 Channel Center St, Boston, MA 02210
Tel: 617-289-7700 *Toll Free Tel:* 800-354-9706 *Fax:* 617-289-7844
Web Site: www.cengage.com
Key Personnel
Author: Herbert Zettl
Analyzes television & film in terms of light, space, time-motion & sound & demonstrates how to apply these to create clarity & impact. Also available as ebook.
Triennial.
8th ed, 2017: 464 pp, $124.95
Shipping Address: Cengage Learning Distribution Center, 10650 Toebben Dr, Independence, KY 41051 *Tel:* 859-525-2230
ISBN(s): 978-1-305-57890-6

Slides
Published by Educational Technology Publications Inc
PO Box 1564, Englewood Cliffs, NJ 07632
Tel: 201-871-4007 *Fax:* 201-871-4009
E-mail: edtecpubs@aol.com
Web Site: bookstoread.com/etp
Key Personnel
Author: Roger A Kueter; Janeen Miller
Ed: James E Duane
Vol 13 in the Instructional Media Library.
1981: 112 pp, $27.95 hardcover
ISBN(s): 978-0-87778-173-8

Sound and Recording: Applications and Theory
Published by Focal Press
Member of Taylor & Francis Group, an Informa Business
711 Third Ave, New York, NY 10017
Tel: 212-216-7800 *Toll Free Tel:* 800-634-7064 (cust serv & orders) *Fax:* 212-564-7854
Toll Free Fax: 800-248-4724 (cust serv & orders)
E-mail: orders@taylorandfrancis.com
Web Site: www.routledge.com/focalpress
Key Personnel
Author: Tim McCormick; Francis Rumsey
Provides vital reading for audio students & trainee engineers in both theory & industry practices in audio, sound & recording.
7th ed, March 2014: 660 pp, $215 hardcover, $81.95 paper or ebook
ISBN(s): 978-0-203-75623-2 (ebook); 978-0-415-84337-9 (paper); 978-0-415-84340-9 (hardcover)

Sound Studio: Audio Techniques for Radio, Television, Film and Recording
Published by Focal Press
Member of Taylor & Francis Group, an Informa Business
711 Third Ave, New York, NY 10017
Tel: 212-216-7800 *Toll Free Tel:* 800-634-7064 (cust serv & orders) *Fax:* 212-564-7854
Toll Free Fax: 800-248-4724 (cust serv & orders)
E-mail: orders@taylorandfrancis.com
Web Site: www.routledge.com/focalpress
Key Personnel
Author: Alec Nisbett
Reference work on audio techniques encompassing the rapidly expanding range of possibilities offered by today's digital equipment. Now covering the virtual studio; 5.1 surround sound; hard drive mixers & multichannel recorders; DVD & CD-RW.
7th ed, July 2003: 400 pp, $195 hardcover, $82.95 paper or ebook
ISBN(s): 978-0-240-51911-1 (paper); 978-1-136-11686-5 (ebook); 978-1-138-41265-1 (hardcover)

Still Pictures
Published by Educational Technology Publications Inc
PO Box 1564, Englewood Cliffs, NJ 07632
Tel: 201-871-4007 *Fax:* 201-871-4009
E-mail: edtecpubs@aol.com
Web Site: bookstoread.com/etp
Key Personnel
Author: LaMond F Beatty
Ed: James E Duane
Vol 14 in the Instructional Media Library.
1981: 112 pp, $27.95 hardcover
ISBN(s): 978-0-87778-174-5

Subject Access to Visual Resources Collections: A Model for the Computer Construction of Thematic Catalogs
Published by ABC-CLIO/Greenwood
Division of ABC-CLIO
130 Cremona Dr, Santa Barbara, CA 93117
Mailing Address: PO Box 1911, Santa Barbara, CA 93116-1911
Tel: 805-968-1911 *Toll Free Tel:* 800-368-6868
Fax: 805-685-9685 *Toll Free Fax:* 866-270-3856
E-mail: customerservice@abc-clio.com
Web Site: www.abc-clio.com
Key Personnel
Author: Karen Markey
Offers a step-by-step method of describing subject content in visual images.
1986: 209 pp, $112.95 hardcover
ISBN(s): 978-0-313-24031-7

Taxonomy of Communication Media
Published by Educational Technology Publications Inc
PO Box 1564, Englewood Cliffs, NJ 07632
Tel: 201-871-4007 *Fax:* 201-871-4009
E-mail: edtecpubs@aol.com
Web Site: bookstoread.com/etp
Key Personnel
Author: Rudy Bretz
Description of the various categories of AV media.
1971: 192 pp, $34.95 hardcover
ISBN(s): 978-0-87778-012-0

Techniques and Principles in Three-Dimensional Imaging: An Introductory Approach
Published by IGI Global
701 E Chocolate Ave, Hershey, PA 17033
Tel: 717-533-8845 (ext 100) *Toll Free Tel:* 866-342-6657 *Fax:* 717-533-8661; 717-533-7115
E-mail: cust@igi-global.com
Web Site: www.igi-global.com
Provides the reader with a concrete understanding of basic principles & pitfalls for 3D capturing. Individual chapters available for purchase online.
2014: 324 pp, $200 list price hardcover or ebook; $240 list price hardcover & ebook
ISBN(s): 978-1-4666-4932-3; 978-1-4666-4933-0 (ebook)

Technologies for Education: A Practical Guide
Published by Libraries Unlimited
147 Castilian Dr, Santa Barbara, CA 93117
Mailing Address: PO Box 1911, Santa Barbara, CA 93116-1911
Tel: 805-968-1911 *Toll Free Tel:* 800-368-6868
Toll Free Fax: 866-270-3856
E-mail: customerservice@abc-clio.com
Web Site: www.abc-clio.com
Key Personnel
Author: Ann E Barron; Karen S Ivers; Nick Lilavois; Julie A Wells
Designed for all educators who are interested in the instructional applications of technology, it provides an overview of teaching with technology; computer graphics; advanced computer

graphics: animation, 3D graphics & virtual reality; digital audio; digital video; telecommunications; distance learning & assistive technologies in the classroom. The advantages, disadvantages & educational applications of each technology are presented, along with detailed graphics & glossaries. Each chapter also provides a scenario to illustrate implementation techniques, a copy-ready brochure for in-service training workshops & abundant resource information.
5th ed, July 2006: 204 pp, $55 paper
First published 1997
ISBN(s): 978-1-59158-250-2

Telecommunications for Learning
Published by Educational Technology Publications Inc
PO Box 1564, Englewood Cliffs, NJ 07632
Tel: 201-871-4007 *Fax:* 201-871-4009
E-mail: edtecpubs@aol.com
Web Site: bookstoread.com/etp
Vol 3 of the Educational Technology Anthology Series.
1991: 202 pp, $34.95
ISBN(s): 978-0-87778-225-4

Television Production
Published by Educational Technology Publications Inc
PO Box 1564, Englewood Cliffs, NJ 07632
Tel: 201-871-4007 *Fax:* 201-871-4009
E-mail: edtecpubs@aol.com
Web Site: bookstoread.com/etp
Key Personnel
Author: Dan Baker; Bill Weisgerber
Ed: James E Duane
Volume 15 in the Instructional Media Library.
1981: 112 pp, $27.95 hardcover
ISBN(s): 978-0-87778-175-2

Television Production
Published by Focal Press
Member of Taylor & Francis Group, an Informa Business
711 Third Ave, New York, NY 10017
Tel: 212-216-7800 *Toll Free Tel:* 800-634-7064 (cust serv & orders) *Fax:* 212-564-7854
Toll Free Fax: 800-248-4724 (cust serv & orders)
E-mail: orders@taylorandfrancis.com
Web Site: www.routledge.com/focalpress
Key Personnel
Author: Gerald Millerson; Jim Owens
Details the major features of television production, including camerawork, lighting techniques, sound treatment, scenic design & video editing.
16th ed, Dec 2015: 450 pp, $215 hardcover, $75.95 paper or ebook
ISBN(s): 978-1-138-84166-6 (paper); 978-1-138-93534-1 (hardcover); 978-1-315-73202-2 (VitalSource ebook); 978-1-317-55374-8 (Taylor & Francis ebook)

Television Production: A Classroom Approach
Published by Libraries Unlimited
147 Castilian Dr, Santa Barbara, CA 93117
Mailing Address: PO Box 1911, Santa Barbara, CA 93116-1911
Tel: 805-968-1911 *Toll Free Tel:* 800-368-6868
Toll Free Fax: 866-270-3856
E-mail: customerservice@abc-clio.com
Web Site: www.abc-clio.com
Key Personnel
Author: Christopher Curchy; Keith Kyker
Hands on approach offers students the opportunity to learn about topics ranging from TV studio design, scripting & camera work to creating a dramatic video production. Grades 7-12.

2nd ed, Sept 2004: 256 pp, $55 paper
ISBN(s): 978-0-89789-967-3 (ebook); 978-1-56308-774-5

Television Production Handbook
Published by Cengage Learning
20 Channel Center St, Boston, MA 02210
Tel: 617-289-7700 *Toll Free Tel:* 800-354-9706
Fax: 617-289-7844
Web Site: www.cengage.com
Key Personnel
Author: Herbert Zettl
Practical guide to major elements & techniques of TV production. Also available as ebook.
12th ed, 2015: 528 pp, $124.95
Shipping Address: Cengage Learning Distribution Center, 10650 Toebben Dr, Independence, KY 41051 *Tel:* 859-525-2230
ISBN(s): 978-1-285-05267-0

TV Scenic Design
Published by Focal Press
Member of Taylor & Francis Group, an Informa Business
711 Third Ave, New York, NY 10017
Tel: 212-216-7800 *Toll Free Tel:* 800-634-7064 (cust serv & orders) *Fax:* 212-564-7854
Toll Free Fax: 800-248-4724 (cust serv & orders)
E-mail: orders@taylorandfrancis.com
Web Site: www.routledge.com/focalpress
Key Personnel
Author: Gerald Millerson
2nd ed, Aug 1997 paper; ebook Aug 2013; hardcover July 2016: 282 pp, $175 hardcover, $87.95 paper or ebook
ISBN(s): 978-0-080-51981-4 (VitalSource ebook); 978-0-240-51493-2 (paper); 978-1-136-04450-7 (Taylor & Francis ebook for librarians); 978-1-138-17246-3 (hardcover)

Using Video: Interactive and Linear Designs
Published by Educational Technology Publications Inc
PO Box 1564, Englewood Cliffs, NJ 07632
Tel: 201-871-4007 *Fax:* 201-871-4009
E-mail: edtecpubs@aol.com
Web Site: bookstoread.com/etp
Key Personnel
Author: Joseph W Arwady; Diane M Gayeski
Part of the Techniques in Training & Performance Development Series.
1989: 190 pp, $39.95 cloth
ISBN(s): 978-0-87778-199-8

Video Camera Techniques
Published by Focal Press
Member of Taylor & Francis Group, an Informa Business
711 Third Ave, New York, NY 10017
Tel: 212-216-7800 *Toll Free Tel:* 800-634-7064 (cust serv & orders) *Fax:* 212-564-7854
Toll Free Fax: 800-248-4724 (cust serv & orders)
E-mail: orders@taylorandfrancis.com
Web Site: www.routledge.com/focalpress
Key Personnel
Author: Gerald Millerson
Covers the latest types of video camera & gives guidance on camera handling & picture making from basic to advanced techniques.
2nd ed, Aug 1994: 160 pp, $175 hardcover, $49.95 paper or ebook
ISBN(s): 978-0-240-51376-8 (paper); 978-1-136-04994-1 (ebook); 978-1-138-13092-0 (hardcover)

Video Production Handbook
Published by Focal Press
Member of Taylor & Francis Group, an Informa Business

711 Third Ave, New York, NY 10017
Tel: 212-216-7800 *Toll Free Tel:* 800-634-7064 (cust serv & orders) *Fax:* 212-564-7854
Toll Free Fax: 800-248-4724 (cust serv & orders)
E-mail: orders@taylorandfrancis.com
Web Site: www.routledge.com/focalpress
Key Personnel
Author: Gerald Millerson; Jim Owens
Guide to the full video production process, from inception of idea to final distribution. Concentrates on techniques & concepts behind the latest equipment, demonstrating the fundamental principles needed to create good video content on any budget. Companion web site.
6th ed, March 2017: 306 pp, $160 hardcover, $62.95 paper or ebook
ISBN(s): 978-1-138-69348-7 (hardcover); 978-1-138-69349-4 (paper); 978-1-315-53057-4 (ebook)

The Video Source Book
Published by Gale
Division of Cengage Learning
27500 Drake Rd, Farmington Hills, MI 48331-3535
Mailing Address: PO Box 9187, Farmington Hills, MI 48333-9187
Toll Free Tel: 800-877-4253 *Toll Free Fax:* 877-363-4253
E-mail: galeord@cengage.com; gale.customerservice@cengage.com
Web Site: www.cengage.com
Comprehensive coverage of more than 170,000 programs on video, encompassing such categories as movies & entertainment, instructional, business & vocational training, fine arts & children's/educational videos. All listings are arranged alphabetically by title. Each entry provides a description of the program & information on obtaining the title. Six indexes.
59th ed, 2017: 5,513 pp, $1,100/9 vol set paper
ISBN(s): 978-1-4103-2499-3 (9 vol set)

Video Surveillance Techniques and Technologies
Published by IGI Global
701 E Chocolate Ave, Hershey, PA 17033
Tel: 717-533-8845 (ext 100) *Toll Free Tel:* 866-342-6657 *Fax:* 717-533-8661; 717-533-7115
E-mail: cust@igi-global.com
Web Site: www.igi-global.com
Presents empirical research & acquired experience on the original solutions & mathematical algorithms for motion detection & object identification problems. Individual chapters available for purchase online.

2014: 369 pp, $215 list price hardcover or ebook; $260 list price hardcover & ebook
ISBN(s): 978-1-4666-4896-8; 978-1-4666-4897-5 (ebook)

Videocassette Technology in American Education
Published by Educational Technology Publications Inc
PO Box 1564, Englewood Cliffs, NJ 07632
Tel: 201-871-4007 *Fax:* 201-871-4009
E-mail: edtecpubs@aol.com
Web Site: bookstoread.com/etp
Key Personnel
Author: George N Gordon; Irving A Falk
Analysis of potential uses for videocassettes in the nation's schools.
1972: 176 pp, $34.95 hardcover
ISBN(s): 978-0-87778-035-9

Videodisc/Microcomputer Courseware Design
Published by Educational Technology Publications Inc
PO Box 1564, Englewood Cliffs, NJ 07632
Tel: 201-871-4007 *Fax:* 201-871-4009
E-mail: edtecpubs@aol.com
Web Site: bookstoread.com/etp
Key Personnel
Ed: Michael L DeBloois
Describes how-to design materials for videodisc/microcomputer presentations.
1982: 192 pp, $37.95 hardcover
ISBN(s): 978-0-87778-183-7

Videodiscs
Published by Educational Technology Publications Inc
PO Box 1564, Englewood Cliffs, NJ 07632
Tel: 201-871-4007 *Fax:* 201-871-4009
E-mail: edtecpubs@aol.com
Web Site: bookstoread.com/etp
Key Personnel
Author: Edward W Schneider; Junius L Bennion
Ed: James E Duane
Vol 16 in the Instructional Media Library.
1981: 128 pp, $27.95 cloth
ISBN(s): 978-0-87778-176-9

Visual Communicating
Published by Educational Technology Publications Inc
PO Box 1564, Englewood Cliffs, NJ 07632
Tel: 201-871-4007 *Fax:* 201-871-4009
E-mail: edtecpubs@aol.com
Web Site: bookstoread.com/etp
Key Personnel
Author: Ralph E Wileman

1993: 160 pp, $37.95
ISBN(s): 978-0-87778-248-3

Visual Information
Published by Educational Technology Publications Inc
PO Box 1564, Englewood Cliffs, NJ 07632
Tel: 201-871-4007 *Fax:* 201-871-4009
E-mail: edtecpubs@aol.com
Web Site: bookstoread.com/etp
Key Personnel
Author: Rune Pettersson
2nd ed, 1993: 400 pp, $59.95
ISBN(s): 978-0-87778-262-9

When Words Collide: A Media Writer's Guide to Grammar and Style
Published by Cengage Learning
20 Channel Center St, Boston, MA 02210
Tel: 617-289-7700 *Toll Free Tel:* 800-354-9706 *Fax:* 617-289-7844
Web Site: www.cengage.com
Key Personnel
Author: Lauren Kessler; Duncan McDonald
Grammar & writing guidelines for both beginning & continuing media writers. Provides concise, clear explanations & examples, as well as quick & accurate answers to common grammar & usage questions. Also available as ebook.
Quadrennial.
9th ed, 2016: 224 pp, $99.95
Shipping Address: Cengage Learning Distribution Center, 10650 Toebben Dr, Independence, KY 41051 *Tel:* 859-525-2230
ISBN(s): 978-0-285-05247-2

Writing for Television, Radio, and New Media
Published by Cengage Learning
20 Channel Center St, Boston, MA 02210
Tel: 617-289-7700 *Toll Free Tel:* 800-354-9706 *Fax:* 617-289-7844
Web Site: www.cengage.com
Key Personnel
Author: Robert L Hilliard
Concepts, approaches & techniques concentrating on the key media formats of commercials; news & sports; documentaries; reality programs; talk shows; interviews; music programs; corporate, educational & children's formats; drama & sitcoms. Also available online & as ebook.
11th ed, 2015: 528 pp, $124.95
Shipping Address: Cengage Learning Distribution Center, 10650 Toebben Dr, Independence, KY 41051 *Tel:* 859-525-2230
ISBN(s): 978-1-285-46507-4

Company Index

Included in this index are the names, addresses, telecommunication numbers and electronic addresses of the organizations included in *AVMP*. Entries also include the page number(s) on which the listings appear.

Sections not represented in this index are **Calendar of Events; Periodicals for the Trade** and **Reference Books for the Trade.**

acouStaCorp, 701 E 132 St, Bronx, NY 10454 *Tel:* 718-402-2677 *Fax:* 718-402-2859 *E-mail:* info@texasscenic.com *Web Site:* acoustacorp.texasscenic.com, pg 674

Acoustical Society of America (ASA), 1305 Walt Whitman Rd, Suite 300, Melville, NY 11747-4300 *Tel:* 516-576-2360 *Fax:* 631-923-2875 *E-mail:* asa@acousticalsociety.org *Web Site:* www.acousticalsociety.org, pg 947

Acoustical Solutions LLC, 2420 Grenoble Rd, Richmond, VA 23294 *Tel:* 804-346-8350 *Toll Free:* 800-782-5742 *Fax:* 804-346-8808 *E-mail:* info@acousticalsolutions.com *Web Site:* www.acousticalsolutions.com, pg 674

Acoustics First Corp, 2247 Tomlyn St, Richmond, VA 23230-3334 *Tel:* 804-342-2900 *Toll Free Tel:* 888-765-2900 *Fax:* 804-342-1107 *E-mail:* info@acousticsfirst.com *Web Site:* www.acousticsfirst.com, pg 674

Acoustone Corp, 140 58 St, Suite W, Brooklyn, NY 11220 *Tel:* 718-782-5560 *Toll Free Tel:* 800-782-5742 *Fax:* 718-782-7367 *E-mail:* acoustone@newcastlefabrics.com; info@acousticalsolutions.com *Web Site:* www.acoustonegrillecloth.com, pg 674

ACS Technologies, 180 Dunbarton Dr, Florence, SC 29501 *Tel:* 843-662-1681 *Toll Free Tel:* 800-736-7425 (sales); 800-669-2309 (support) *Fax:* 843-669-7513 *E-mail:* info@acstechnologies.com *Web Site:* www.acstechnologies.com, pg 674

ACT Productions, 407 Lincoln Rd, Suite 302, Miami Beach, FL 33139 *Tel:* 305-538-3809 *Fax:* 305-538-3814 *E-mail:* info@actproductions.com *Web Site:* www.actproductions.com, pg 675

ACTA Publications, 4848 N Clark St, Chicago, IL 60640 *Tel:* 773-271-1030 *Toll Free Tel:* 800-397-2282 *Fax:* 773-271-7399 *Toll Free Fax:* 800-397-0079 *E-mail:* actapublications@actapublications.com *Web Site:* www.actapublications.com, pg 675

Action Audio & Visual, 5907 Yarmouth Ave, Encino, CA 91316 *Tel:* 818-760-2585 *E-mail:* info@actionaudioandvisual.com *Web Site:* www.actionaudioandvisual.com, pg 675

Action Photo Digital Graphics, 1741 Clayton Rd, Concord, CA 94520 *Tel:* 925-676-7777 *E-mail:* actionps@sbcglobal.net *Web Site:* www.actionphotoservice.com, pg 675

Action Sports/All Stock, PO Box 301, Malibu, CA 90265-0301 *Tel:* 310-459-2526 *E-mail:* info@actionsportsstockfootage.com *Web Site:* www.actionsportsstockfootage.com; www.allstockfootage.com, pg 675

Action Video, 2373 Walnut Blvd, Walnut Creek, CA 94597 *Tel:* 925-934-4366 *E-mail:* actvid@aol.com *Web Site:* actionvideo.biz, pg 675

Activu Corp, 301 Roundhill Dr, Rockaway, NJ 07866 *Tel:* 973-366-5550 *Toll Free Tel:* 888-ACTIVU1 (228-4881) *Fax:* 973-625-7775 *E-mail:* facebook@activu.com *Web Site:* activu.com, pg 675

Actors Attic, 540 Otis Dr, Dover, DE 19901 *Tel:* 302-734-8214 *Fax:* 302-734-8207 *E-mail:* sales@actorsattic.com *Web Site:* www.actorsattic.com, pg 675

Acuity Brands Lighting Inc, One Lithonia Way, Conyers, GA 30012 *Tel:* 770-922-9000 *E-mail:* info@acuitybrands.com *Web Site:* www.acuitybrands.com, pg 675

ADAM Inc, One Ebix Way, Johns Creek, GA 30097 *Tel:* 770-625-3450 *Toll Free Tel:* 800-755-ADAM (755-2326) *E-mail:* aod-info@ebix.com *Web Site:* www.adam.com, pg 675

Adams Creative & Production Services, PO Box 98636, Des Moines, WA 98198-0636 *Tel:* 206-300-1094 (cell) *Fax:* 206-824-7036, pg 675

D L Adams Associates Inc, 1536 Ogden St, Denver, CO 80218 *Tel:* 303-455-1900 *E-mail:* infodenver@dlaa.com *Web Site:* www.dlaa.com, pg 675

D L Adams Associates Ltd, 970 N Kalaheo Ave, Suite A-311, Kailua, HI 96734 *Tel:* 808-254-3318 *E-mail:* infohawaii@dlaa.com *Web Site:* www.dlaa.com, pg 675

Adams Evidence Grade Technology Inc, 4123 N Little Creek Rd, Utopia, TX 78884 *Tel:* 830-966-4210 *Toll Free Tel:* 877-643-4900 *Fax:* 830-966-4214 *E-mail:* info1@evidencegrade.com; customerservice@evidencegrade.com *Web Site:* www.evidencegrade.com, pg 675

Adaptive Technologies Group Inc, 1635 E Burnett St, Signal Hill, CA 90755 *Tel:* 562-424-1100 *E-mail:* sales@adaptivetechnologiesgroup.com *Web Site:* www.adaptivetechnologiesgroup.com, pg 675

Adcis Inc, PO Box 6473, Monroe Township, NJ 08831-6473 *Tel:* 609-944-8855 *Toll Free Tel:* 877-664-8772 *E-mail:* info@adcis.net *Web Site:* www.adcis.net, pg 675

ADD Plus, 488 Glacier Way S, Monmouth, OR 97361 *Toll Free Tel:* 800-847-1233 *Fax:* 503-838-1608 *Web Site:* www.add-plus.com, pg 676

Adelphi Records Inc, PO Box 7688, Silver Spring, MD 20907-7688 *Tel:* 301-434-6958 *Fax:* 301-434-3056 *E-mail:* adelphi@adelphirecords.com *Web Site:* www.adelphirecords.com, pg 676

ADI Global Distribution, 263 Old Country Rd, Melville, NY 11747 *Toll Free Tel:* 800-233-6261 (sales/serv); 800-234-7971 (prod/systems) *E-mail:* awebadmin@adi-dist.com *Web Site:* adiglobal.us, pg 676

Adobe Systems Inc, 345 Park Ave, San Jose, CA 95110-2704 *Tel:* 408-536-6000 *Fax:* 408-537-6000 *Web Site:* www.adobe.com, pg 676

Adorama Rental Co, 50 W 17 St, Ground fl, New York, NY 10011 *Tel:* 212-627-8487 *Fax:* 212-929-9013 *E-mail:* rent@adorama.com *Web Site:* www.adoramarentals.com, pg 676

Adrenaline Films, 5224 S Orange Ave, Orlando, FL 32809 *Tel:* 407-850-0711 *Fax:* 407-859-6527 *E-mail:* contact@adrenalinefilms.com *Web Site:* www.adrenalinefilms.com, pg 676

Adrienne Electronics Corp (AEC), HC 65 Box 254, 1008 York Ranch Rd, Pie Town, NM 87827 *Tel:* 575-772-2572 *Toll Free Tel:* 800-782-2321 *Fax:* 575-772-2575 *E-mail:* info@adrielec.com; orders@adrielec.com; support@adrielec.com *Web Site:* www.adrielec.com, pg 676

The ADS Group, 2155 Niagara Lane N, Suite 120, Plymouth, MN 55447 *Tel:* 763-449-5500 *Toll Free Tel:* 800-759-0992 *Fax:* 763-449-5555 *E-mail:* sales@theadsgroup.com *Web Site:* theadsgroup.com, pg 676

ADS Media, 620 Trinity Church Rd, Hamilton, ON L0R 1P0, Canada *Tel:* 905-692-2960 *Fax:* 905-692-2961 *E-mail:* info@adsmedia.ca *Web Site:* www.adsmedia.ca, pg 677

Adtec Digital Inc, 408 Russell St, Nashville, TN 37206 *Tel:* 615-256-6619 *Fax:* 615-256-6593 *E-mail:* sales@adtecinc.com *Web Site:* www.adtecinc.com, pg 677

Advance Audiovisual Presentation Ltd, 5 Rothschild Ct, Gaithersburg, MD 20878 *Tel:* 301-937-0900 *Fax:* 301-330-2937 *E-mail:* aaplav@outlook.com *Web Site:* aaplav.com, pg 677

Advance Concepts Inc, 8453 Tyco Rd, Suite N, Vienna, VA 22182-2623 *Tel:* 703-448-0445 *Fax:* 703-893-8049 *Web Site:* www.advanceconcepts.com, pg 677

Advance Pro, 62 Sucurfield Blvd, Unit 12 & 14, Winnipeg, MB R3Y 1M5, Canada *Tel:* 204-772-0386 *Toll Free Tel:* 800-392-1295 *Fax:* 204-783-2177 *E-mail:* ap@advance.mb.ca *Web Site:* advance-pro.com, pg 677

Advanced Audio Technology, 200 Easy St, Carol Stream, IL 60188 *Tel:* 630-665-3344 *Fax:* 630-665-3347 *E-mail:* aat@ameritech.net *Web Site:* www.advancedaudio.net, pg 677

Advanced AV LLC, 208 Carter Dr, Suite 7, West Chester, PA 19382 *Toll Free Tel:* 877-696-7700 *Fax:* 610-692-8421 *E-mail:* sales@advancedav.com *Web Site:* www.advancedav.com, pg 677

Advanced Battery Systems Inc, 516 Bedford St, East Bridgewater, MA 02333 *Tel:* 508-378-2284 *E-mail:* abs@batteryprice.com *Web Site:* www.batteryprice.com, pg 677

Advanced Designs Corp, 1169 W Second St, Bloomington, IN 47403 *Tel:* 812-333-1922 *Fax:* 812-333-2030 *E-mail:* service@doprad.com *Web Site:* www.doprad.com, pg 677

Advanced Digital Design, 6429 Independence Ave, Woodland Hills, CA 91367 *Web Site:* advanced-digital-design.com, pg 677

Advanced Imaging Concepts Inc, 301 N Harrison St, No 9F 266, Princeton, NJ 08540 *Tel:* 609-921-3629; 609-529-9200 *Fax:* 609-924-3010 *E-mail:* info@aic-imagecentral.com; sales@aic-imagecentral.com *Web Site:* www.aic-imagecentral.com, pg 677

Advanced Lighting & Production Services Inc (ALPS), 125 Shamut Rd, Canton, MA 02021 *Tel:* 781-961-3066 *Toll Free Tel:* 866-961-3066 *Fax:* 781-961-3256 *E-mail:* info@alpsweb.com *Web Site:* www.alpsweb.com, pg 677

Advanced Media Integration, 2300 Meyer Rd, Fort Wayne, IN 46805 *Tel:* 260-428-2698 *Toll Free Tel:* 877-428-2610 *E-mail:* info@amifw.com *Web Site:* amifw.com, pg 677

Advanced Media LLC, 369 N Fairfax Ave, Suite A, Los Angeles, CA 90036 *Tel:* 323-658-6102 *E-mail:* info@advancedmediallc.com *Web Site:* www.advancedmediallc.com; www.gomemoriesforever.com, pg 677

Advanced Sound, 4611 Central Ave Pike, Suite F, Knoxville, TN 37912 *Tel:* 865-661-5961 *Web Site:* www.advancedsound.com, pg 677

Advanced Systems Group LLC, 1226 Powell St, Emeryville, CA 94608-2618 *Tel:* 510-654-8300 *Fax:* 510-654-8370 *Web Site:* www.asgllc.com, pg 677

Advent Media Inc, 5629 Fraley Ct, Columbus, OH 43235 *Tel:* 614-538-1622 *Toll Free Tel:* 877-538-1622 *Fax:* 614-538-1621 *Web Site:* www.adventmediainc.com, pg 677

AdventSource, 5120 Prescott Ave, Lincoln, NE 68506 *Tel:* 402-486-8800 *Toll Free Tel:* 800-328-0525 *Fax:* 402-486-8819 *E-mail:* service@adventsource.org *Web Site:* www.adventsource.org, pg 678

Adventure Productions LLC, 5910 York Rd, Lower Level, Baltimore, MD 21212 *Tel:* 410-878-1261; 410-961-5942 (cell) *Fax:* 410-878-1263 *Web Site:* adventureproductions.com, pg 678

Adwar Video, 125 Gazza Blvd, Farmingdale, NY 11735 *Tel:* 631-777-7070 *Toll Free Tel:* 877-GOADWAR (462-3927) *Fax:* 631-777-7011 *E-mail:* sales@adwarvideo.com *Web Site:* adwarvideo.com, pg 678

AEMC Instruments, 200 Foxborough Blvd, Foxborough, MA 02035 *Tel:* 508-698-2115 *Toll Free Tel:* 800-343-1391 *Fax:* 508-698-2118 *E-mail:* sales@aemc.com *Web Site:* www.aemc.com, pg 678

Aerial Imaging Productions, 4258 Tennyson St, Unit 101, Denver, CO 80212 *Tel:* 720-255-1195 *E-mail:* info@aerialimagingproductions.com *Web Site:* www.aerialimagingproductions.com, pg 678

Aerial Video Systems, 3200 W Valhalla Dr, Burbank, CA 91505 *Tel:* 818-954-8842 *Fax:* 818-954-8842 *E-mail:* info@aerialvideo.com *Web Site:* aerialvideo.com, pg 678

Affton Graphics Inc, 400 E 85 St, Unit 3F, New York, NY 10028 *Tel:* 718-401-4040 *Toll Free Tel:* 800-777-0539 *E-mail:* amproducts@aol.com *Web Site:* amgraphics-classe.com, pg 678

AFI FEST, 2021 W Western Ave, Los Angeles, CA 90027-1657 *Tel:* 323-856-7600 *Toll Free Tel:* 866-AFI-FEST (234-3378) *Fax:* 323-462-4049 *E-mail:* afifest@afi.com; festpublicity@afi.com *Web Site:* www.afi.com/afifest, pg 981

African American Images Inc, PO Box 1799, Sauk Village, IL 60412 *Tel:* 708-672-4909 *Toll Free Tel:* 800-552-1991 *Fax:* 708-672-0466 *E-mail:* customer@africanamericanimages.com *Web Site:* africanamericanimages.com, pg 678

AGF Media Services, 21522 Osborne St, Canoga Park, CA 91304 *Tel:* 818-780-7400 *Fax:* 818-904-9905 *E-mail:* info@agfmedia.com *Web Site:* www.agfmedia.com, pg 678

Agfa Graphics, 611 River Dr, Ctr 3, Elmwood Park, NJ 07407 *Tel:* 201-440-2500 *Toll Free Tel:* 800-540-2432; 888-274-8626 (cust serv) *E-mail:* graphics@agfa.com *Web Site:* www.agfa.com; www.agfagraphics.com, pg 678

aGLIFF-The Austin Gay & Lesbian International Film Festival, 1216 E 51 St, Austin, TX 78723 *Tel:* 512-302-9889 *E-mail:* info@agliff.org *Web Site:* agliff.org, pg 981

Agrama Film Enterprises Inc, 7655 Sunset Blvd, Los Angeles, CA 90046 *Tel:* 323-851-4900 *Fax:* 323-851-5599 *E-mail:* sales@harmonygold.com *Web Site:* harmonygold.com, pg 678

Ahead Stereo Inc, 7428 Beverly Blvd, Los Angeles, CA 90036 *Tel:* 323-931-8873 *E-mail:* sales@aheadstereo.com *Web Site:* www.aheadstereo.com, pg 678

AheadTeK, 6410 Via Del Oro, San Jose, CA 95119 *Tel:* 408-226-9800; 408-226-9991 *Toll Free Tel:* 800-971-9191 *Fax:* 408-226-9195 *Web Site:* www.aheadtek.com, pg 678

AIGA, the professional association for design, 233 Broadway, Suite 1740, New York, NY 10279 *Tel:* 212-807-1990 *Toll Free Tel:* 800-548-1634 *E-mail:* general@aiga.org *Web Site:* www.aiga.org, pg 947

Aiphone Corp, 6670 185 Ave NE, Redmond, WA 98052 *Tel:* 425-455-0510 *Toll Free Tel:* 800-692-0200 *Fax:* 425-455-0071 *Toll Free Fax:* 800-525-3372 (cust serv) *E-mail:* info@aiphone.com; cs@aiphone.com *Web Site:* www.aiphone.com/home, pg 678

Air Bud Entertainment, 22525 Pacific Coast Hwy, Malibu, CA 90265 *Tel:* 310-317-4883 *Web Site:* www.airbud.com, pg 678

Air Philosophy Inc, 1933 S Broadway, Suite 1107B, Los Angeles, CA 90007 *Tel:* 310-980-3902 *E-mail:* info@airphilosophy.com *Web Site:* airphilosophy.com, pg 678

Air Sea Land Productions Inc (ASL), 19-69 Steinway St, Astoria, NY 11105-1108 *Tel:* 718-626-2646 *Toll Free Tel:* 888-ASL-LENS (275-5367) *E-mail:* info@airsealand.com *Web Site:* www.airsealand.com, pg 678

AirBrands Event & Marketing Group, 6470 Wyoming St, Suite 2024, Dearborn, MI 48126 *Tel:* 519-254-9563 *Toll Free Tel:* 800-411-6200 (ext 26) *Fax:* 519-735-5446 *Web Site:* www.airbrandsmarketing.com; famousinflatables.com, pg 679

AirCraft Production Libraries, 162 Columbus Ave, Boston, MA 02116-5222 *Tel:* 617-303-7600 *Toll Free Tel:* 800-343-2514 *Fax:* 617-303-7555 *E-mail:* info@aircraftmusiclibrary.com; acsales@aircraftmusiclibrary.com *Web Site:* www.aircraftmusiclibrary.com, pg 679

Airwave Recording Studio, 5176 Hollow Log Lane, Birmingham, AL 35244 *Tel:* 205-427-4675, pg 679

Airways Digital Media, 4055 W Peterson Ave, Chicago, IL 60646 *Tel:* 773-539-8400 *E-mail:* info@airwaysdigital.com *Web Site:* www.airwaysdigital.com, pg 679

AITech International, 1973 O'Toole Way, San Jose, CA 95131 *Tel:* 408-991-9699 *Fax:* 408-991-9691 *E-mail:* sales@aitech.com *Web Site:* www.aitech.com, pg 679

AJA Video Systems Inc, 180 Litton Dr, Grass Valley, CA 95945 *Tel:* 530-274-2048 *Fax:* 530-274-9442 *E-mail:* sales@aja.com *Web Site:* www.aja.com, pg 679

AJS Events, 317 Forsgate Dr, Unit C, Monroe Township, NJ 08831 *Tel:* 732-382-2333 *Web Site:* www.alljerseystudios.com, pg 679

Akai Professional, 200 Scenic View Dr, Cumberland, RI 02864 *Tel:* 401-658-3131 *E-mail:* pressrelations@akaipro.com *Web Site:* www.akaipro.com, pg 679

AKG Acoustics US, 8500 Balboa Blvd, Northridge, CA 91329 *Tel:* 818-920-3212 *Toll Free Tel:* 888-452-4254 *Web Site:* www.akg.com/pro, pg 679

Alabama Film Office, Alabama Ctr for Commerce, 401 Adams Ave, Suite 170, Montgomery, AL 36104 *Tel:* 334-242-4195 *Fax:* 334-242-2077 *Web Site:* www.alabamafilm.org, pg 965

Alabama State Council on the Arts Fellowships & Grants, RSA Tower, Suite 110, 201 Monroe St, Montgomery, AL 36130-1800 *Tel:* 334-242-4076 *Fax:* 334-240-3269 *E-mail:* staff@arts.alabama.gov *Web Site:* www.arts.alabama.gov, pg 981

Alarmco Intelligent Message Repeaters, One Bailey Dr, Guilford, CT 06437 *Tel:* 203-458-2646 *Toll Free Tel:* 800-824-5006 *E-mail:* info@messagerepeaters.com *Web Site:* www.messagerepeaters.com, pg 679

Alaska Department of Commerce, Community & Economic Development, 550 W Seventh Ave, Suite 1770, Anchorage, AK 99501-3569 *Tel:* 907-269-4048 *Web Site:* www.commerce.alaska.gov, pg 965

Alaska Film Services Inc, 11050 Cange St, Anchorage, AK 99516 *Tel:* 907-230-8839 *E-mail:* filmservices@alaska.net *Web Site:* www.alaskafilmservices.com, pg 965

Alaska Media Pros LLC, 11050 Cange St, Anchorage, AK 99516 *Tel:* 907-230-8839 *E-mail:* ifilm@alaska.net *Web Site:* www.alaskamediapros.com, pg 679

Alaska Video Postcards Inc, 11405 Discovery Park Dr, Anchorage, AK 99515 *Tel:* 907-349-8002 *Toll Free Tel:* 800-248-2624, pg 679

Albany Theatre Supply Co Inc, 445 N Pearl St, Albany, NY 12204 *Tel:* 518-229-7899 *E-mail:* sales@albanytheatresupply.com *Web Site:* www.albanytheatresupply.com, pg 679

Alberta Film, 140 Whitemud Crossing, 4211-106 St, Edmonton, AB T6J 6L7, Canada *Tel:* 780-422-8584 *Toll Free Tel:* 888-813-1738 *E-mail:* info@albertafilm.ca *Web Site:* www.albertafilm.ca, pg 977

Albuquerque Film Office, Economic Development Dept, One Civic Plaza NW, Albuquerque, NM 87102 *Tel:* 505-768-3283 *Web Site:* www.cabq.gov/film, pg 973

Alcorn McBride Inc, 3300 S Hiawassee Rd, Bldg 105, Orlando, FL 32835 *Tel:* 407-296-5800 *Fax:* 407-296-5801 *E-mail:* info@alcorn.com; sales@alcorn.com *Web Site:* www.alcorn.com, pg 679

Alden Films, PO Box 449, Clarksburg, NJ 08510-0449 *Tel:* 732-462-3522 *Toll Free Tel:* 800-832-0980 *Fax:* 732-294-0330 *E-mail:* info@aldenfilms.com *Web Site:* www.aldenfilms.com, pg 679

Alegra House Publishers, PO Box 1443, Warren, OH 44482-1443 *Tel:* 330-372-2951 *Fax:* 330-399-1619, pg 679

Alexander Media Productions, 1901 Diamond Ridge Dr, Carrollton, TX 75010 *Tel:* 214-274-3456 *Web Site:* www.heatheralexander.net, pg 679

Alexander Street, a ProQuest Company, 99 Canal Center Plaza, Suite 200, Alexandria, VA 22314 *Tel:* 703-212-8520 *Toll Free Tel:* 800-889-5937 *E-mail:* sales@alexanderstreet.com; marketing@alexanderstreet.com; info@alexanderstreet.com *Web Site:* alexanderstreet.com; academicvideostore.com, pg 679

Alford Media Services, 296 Freeport Pkwy, Coppell, TX 75019 *Tel:* 972-538-9400 *Toll Free Tel:* 800-554-9144 *E-mail:* info@alfordmedia.com; sales@alfordmedia.com *Web Site:* www.alfordmedia.com, pg 680

Alien Skin Software LLC, 1111 Haynes St, Suite 113, Raleigh, NC 27604 *Tel:* 919-832-4124 *Toll Free Tel:* 888-921-7546 *Fax:* 919-832-4065 *E-mail:* sales@alienskin.com *Web Site:* www.alienskin.com, pg 680

Aliso Creek Productions Inc, 4106 W Burbank Blvd, Burbank, CA 91510 *Tel:* 818-954-9931 *Web Site:* www.alisocreek.net, pg 680

All Access Staging & Productions, 1320 Storm Pkwy, Torrance, CA 90501 *Tel:* 310-784-2464 *Toll Free Tel:* 877-784-2464 *Fax:* 310-517-0899 *E-mail:* sales@allaccessinc.com *Web Site:* www.allaccessinc.com, pg 680

All Comm Rentals Inc (ALLCOMM), 1402 SW 13 Ct, Pompano Beach, FL 33069 *Tel:* 954-788-9555 *Web Site:* www.allcommrentals.com, pg 680

All Mobile Video Inc, 221 W 26 St, New York, NY 10001 *Tel:* 212-727-1234 *Fax:* 212-255-6644 *E-mail:* contact@amvchelsea.com *Web Site:* allmobilevideo.com, pg 680

All Pro Media Inc, 422 S Spring St, Burlington, NC 27215 *Tel:* 336-229-7700 *Toll Free Tel:* 800-270-2207 *Fax:* 336-229-7778 *Web Site:* www.allpromedia.com, pg 680

All Service Musical Electronics Repair, 33470 SW Chinook Plaza, PMB 154, Scapoose, OR 97056 *Tel:* 503-231-6552 *E-mail:* service@asmusic.org *Web Site:* www.all-service-musical.com, pg 680

All Terrain Power Co Inc, 3055 49 St, Astoria, NY 11103 *Tel:* 718-852-4922 *Fax:* 718-267-0002 *Web Site:* www.allterrainpower.com, pg 680

All Video Productions, 726 Santa Monica Blvd, Suite 212, Santa Monica, CA 90401 *Tel:* 310-656-1155 *Fax:* 310-656-1155 *E-mail:* info@allvideoproductions.com *Web Site:* www.allvideoproductions.com, pg 680

Allegro Productions Inc, 347 Main St, Chester, NJ 07930 *Tel:* 908-879-0428 *Toll Free Tel:* 800-232-2133 *Web Site:* www.allegrovideo.com, pg 680

Allen Avionics Inc, 255 E Second St, Mineola, NY 11501 *Tel:* 516-248-8080 *Fax:* 516-747-6724 *E-mail:* info@allenavionics.com *Web Site:* www.allenavionics.com, pg 680

John E Allen Inc, PO Box 452, Newfoundland, PA 18445 *Tel:* 570-676-4152 *Fax:* 570-676-9194 *E-mail:* jeainc@gmail.com *Web Site:* www.allenarchive.com/wordpress, pg 680

Allen Visual Systems Inc, 1405 Busch Pkwy, Buffalo Grove, IL 60089 *Tel:* 847-520-4960 *Fax:* 847-520-7370 *E-mail:* sales@allenvisual.com *Web Site:* www.allenvisual.com, pg 680

Alliance Entertainment Corp (AEC) LLC, 1401 NW 136 Ave, Suite 100, Sunrise, FL 33323 *Toll Free Tel:* 800-329-7664 *Web Site:* www.aent.com, pg 680

The Alliance for Christian Media, 2715 Peachtree Rd NE, Atlanta, GA 30305 *Toll Free Tel:* 888-411-DAY-1 (411-3291) *E-mail:* info@day1.org *Web Site:* day1.org, pg 680

Alliance for Community Media (ACM), 4248 Park Glen Rd, Minneapolis, MN 55416 *Tel:* 952-928-4643 *E-mail:* info@allcommunitymedia.org *Web Site:* www.allcommunitymedia.org, pg 947

Alliance for IP Media Solutions (AIMS), 23117 39 Ave SE, Bothell, WA 98021 *Tel:* 425-870-6574 *E-mail:* info@aimsalliance.org *Web Site:* aimsalliance.org, pg 947

Alliance for Women in Media/Alliance for Women in Media Foundation, 2365 Harrodsburg Rd, A-325, Lexington, KY 40504 *Tel:* 202-750-3664 *Fax:* 202-750-3664 *Web Site:* www.allwomeninmedia.org, pg 947

Alliance of Motion Picture & Television Producers (AMPTP), 15301 Ventura Blvd, Bldg E, Sherman Oaks, CA 91403 *Tel:* 818-995-3600 *Fax:* 818-285-4450 *Web Site:* www.amptp.org, pg 947

alliance quebecoise des techniciens et techniciennes de l'image et du son (AQTIS), 1001, blvd De Maisonneuve E, bureau 900, Montreal, QC H2L 4P9, Canada *Tel:* 514-844-2113 (ext 285) *Fax:* 514-844-3540 *E-mail:* info@aqtis.qc.ca *Web Site:* www.aqtis.qc.ca, pg 947

Alliant Event Services, 196 University Pkwy, Pomona, CA 91768 *Tel:* 909-622-3306 *Toll Free Tel:* 800-851-5415 *Fax:* 909-622-3917 *E-mail:* marketing@alliantevents.com *Web Site:* www.alliantevents.com, pg 681

Allied Artists International Inc, Production Services Ctr, 15810 E Gale Ave, Suite 133, Hacienda Heights, CA 91745 *Tel:* 626-330-0600 *Fax:* 626-961-0411, pg 681

Allied Media Corp, 5252 Cherokee Ave, Suite 200, Alexandria, VA 22312 *Tel:* 703-333-2008 *Fax:* 703-997-7539 *E-mail:* info@allied-media.com; contact@allied-media.com *Web Site:* www.allied-media.com, pg 681

Allied Photocolor Co, 3728 Market St, Suite 100, St Louis, MO 63110 *Tel:* 314-652-4000 *Fax:* 314-652-8203 *E-mail:* aimaging@alliedphotocolor.com *Web Site:* alliedphotocolor.com, pg 681

Alligator Records & Artist Management Inc, 1441 W Devon Ave, Chicago, IL 60660 *Tel:* 773-973-7736 *E-mail:* info@allig.com; publicity@allig.com *Web Site:* www.alligator.com, pg 681

Allsop Inc, PO Box 23, Bellingham, WA 98227-0023 *Tel:* 360-734-9090 *Toll Free Tel:* 800-426-4303 *Fax:* 360-734-9858 *E-mail:* info@allsop.com *Web Site:* www.allsop.com, pg 681

Allstar Audio Systems Inc, 750 Cowan St, Nashville, TN 37017 *Tel:* 615-804-7800 *Web Site:* allstaraudio.com, pg 681

Allstar Show Industries Inc, 10331 176 St, Edmonton, AB T5S 2E4, Canada *Tel:* 780-486-4000 *Toll Free Tel:* 800-663-4063 (CN & US) *E-mail:* info@allstar-show.com *Web Site:* www.allstar-show.com, pg 681

Alltec Stores, a Vcom IMC Company, 80 Little Falls Rd, Fairfield, NJ 07004 *Tel:* 800-637-3181 *Toll Free Fax:* 800-965-7836 *E-mail:* sales@alltecstores.com *Web Site:* www.alltecstores.com, pg 681

AlltecPro, 80 Little Falls Rd, Fairfield, NJ 07004 *Toll Free Tel:* 800-243-2518 *E-mail:* sales@alltecpro.com *Web Site:* www.alltecpro.com, pg 681

Allusion Studios & Pure Wave Audio, 248 W Elm St, Tucson, AZ 85705 *Tel:* 520-622-3895 *E-mail:* contact@allusionstudios.com *Web Site:* www.allusionstudios.com; www.purewaveaudio.com, pg 681

ALMA International, 39962 W Thornberry Lane, Maricopa, AZ 85138 *Tel:* 602-388-8669 *E-mail:* management@almainternational.org *Web Site:* almaint.org, pg 947

ALOM Technologies Corp, 48105 Warm Springs Blvd, Fremont, CA 94539-7498 *Tel:* 510-360-3600 *Toll Free Tel:* 800-500-9991 *Fax:* 510-226-7617 *E-mail:* customerservice@alom.com *Web Site:* www.alom.com, pg 681

Alpec®, 3098 Kenneth St, Santa Clara, CA 95054 *Tel:* 408-735-6180 *Toll Free Tel:* 800-854-6686 *Fax:* 408-735-6190 *E-mail:* info@alpec.com *Web Site:* www.alpec.com, pg 681

Alpha Source Inc, 6619 W Calumet Rd, Milwaukee, WI 53223-4186 *Tel:* 414-760-2222 *Toll Free Tel:* 800-654-9845 *E-mail:* customer.service@alphasource.com; info@alphasource.com *Web Site:* www.alphasource.com, pg 681

Alpha Technologies Inc, 3767 Alpha Way, Bellingham, WA 98226 *Tel:* 360-647-2360 *Toll Free Tel:* 800-322-5742 *E-mail:* alpha@alpha.com *Web Site:* www.alpha.com, pg 681

Alpha Video & Audio Inc, 7690 Golden Triangle Dr, Eden Prairie, MN 55344 *Tel:* 952-896-9898 *Toll Free Tel:* 800-388-0008 *Fax:* 952-896-9899 *E-mail:* info@alphavideo.com *Web Site:* www.alphavideo.com, pg 682

Alpha Video Productions, 441 Biscay Dr, Garland, TX 75043 *Tel:* 972-497-9959 *E-mail:* alphaghb@sbcglobal.net *Web Site:* www.alphavideo.net, pg 682

Alpha Wire Co, 711 Lidgerwood Ave, Elizabeth, NJ 07207-0711 *Tel:* 908-925-8000 *Toll Free Tel:* 800-52-ALPHA (522-5742) *Fax:* 908-925-6923 *E-mail:* info@alphawire.com *Web Site:* www.alphawire.com, pg 682

AlphaDogs Inc, 1612 W Olive Ave, Suite 200, Burbank, CA 91506-2462 *Tel:* 818-729-9262 *Fax:* 818-729-8537 *Web Site:* www.alphadogs.tv, pg 682

Alpine Optics Inc, 14 Helping Hands Way, Pisgah Forest, NC 28768 *Tel:* 828-884-5822 *E-mail:* info@alpine-optics.com *Web Site:* www.alpine-optics.com, pg 682

Altel Systems Group Inc, 2856 Broadway Center Blvd, Brandon, FL 33510 *Tel:* 813-628-6100 *Fax:* 813-628-8949 *Web Site:* www.asg-av.com, pg 682

Alternative Rentals, 5805 W Jefferson Blvd, Los Angeles, CA 90016 *Tel:* 310-204-3388 *Fax:* 310-204-3384 *E-mail:* info@alternativerentals.com *Web Site:* www.alternativerentals.com, pg 682

ALTINEX Inc, 592 Apollo St, Brea, CA 92821 *Tel:* 714-990-2300 *Toll Free Tel:* 800-ALTINEX (258-4639) *Fax:* 714-990-3303 *E-mail:* sales@altinex.com *Web Site:* www.altinex.com, pg 682

Altruist Media LLC, 2601A Wilson Blvd, Arlington, VA 22201 *Tel:* 703-812-8813, pg 682

AM Stock-Cameo Film Library, 12340 Santa Monica Blvd, Suite 212, Los Angeles, CA 90025 *Tel:* 310-479-4800 *Fax:* 310-933-6979 *E-mail:* researcher@amstockcameo.com *Web Site:* www.amstockcameo.com, pg 682

AMA Nystrom Printing/Finishing, 920 N Valley Mills Dr, Waco, TX 76710 *Tel:* 254-776-8860 *Toll Free Tel:* 800-369-9226 *Fax:* 254-751-2127 *E-mail:* info@amanystrom.com *Web Site:* www.amanystrom.com, pg 682

Amarillo Film Commission, 1000 S Polk St, Amarillo, TX 79101 *Tel:* 806-342-2016 *Toll Free Tel:* 800-692-1338 *Fax:* 806-373-3909 *Web Site:* www.amarillofilm.org; www.visitamarillo.com, pg 976

Ambrose Video Publishing Inc, 1202 Lexington Ave, Suite 171, New York, NY 10028 *Tel:* 212-768-7373 *Toll Free Tel:* 800-526-4663 *Fax:* 212-768-9282 *E-mail:* customerservice@ambrosevideo.com *Web Site:* www.ambrosevideo.com, pg 682

America By Air LLC, 5390 Venetia Ct, Unit D, Boynton Beach, FL 33437 *Tel:* 386-663-4567 *E-mail:* footage@americabyair.com *Web Site:* www.americabyair.com, pg 682

American Alliance of Museums (AAM), 2451 Crystal Dr, Suite 1005, Arlington, VA 22202 *Tel:* 202-289-1818 *Fax:* 202-289-6578 *Web Site:* www.aam-us.org, pg 948

American Artist Studio, 1114 W 26 St, Erie, PA 16508-1518 *Tel:* 814-455-4796 *Toll Free Tel:* 888-462-7813 *Web Site:* americanartiststudio.com, pg 682

American Artists Representatives Inc, One Chatsworth Ave, No 518, Larchmont, NY 10538 *Tel:* 646-286-5633 (cell); 212-682-2462 *E-mail:* info@aareps.com *Web Site:* www.aareps.com, pg 682

American Association for Vocational Instructional Materials (AAVIM), 220 Smithonia Rd, Winterville, GA 30683 *Tel:* 706-742-5355 *Fax:* 706-742-7005 *E-mail:* sales@aavim.com *Web Site:* www.aavim.com, pg 682

American Association for Vocational Instructional Materials (AAVIM), 220 Smithonia Rd, Winterville, GA 30683 *Tel:* 706-742-5355 *Toll Free Tel:* 800-228-4689 *Fax:* 706-742-7005 *E-mail:* sales@aavim.com *Web Site:* www.aavim.com, pg 948

American Association of School Librarians (AASL), 50 E Huron St, Chicago, IL 60611 *Tel:* 312-280-4382 *Toll Free Tel:* 800-545-2433 (ext 4382) *Fax:* 312-280-5276 *E-mail:* aasl@ala.org *Web Site:* www.ala.org, pg 948

American Association of University Women (AAUW), 1310 "L" St, Suite 1000, Washington, DC 20005 *Tel:* 202-785-7700 *Toll Free Tel:* 800-326-AAUW (326-2289) *Fax:* 202-872-1425 *E-mail:* helpline@aauw.org; connect@aauw.org *Web Site:* www.aauw.org, pg 948

American AV, 8005 Haute Ct, Springfield, VA 22150 *Tel:* 703-573-6910 *Fax:* 703-573-3539 *E-mail:* sales@aavevents.com *Web Site:* www.aavevents.com, pg 682

American Blackguard Inc, PO Box 680686, Franklin, TN 37068-0686 *Tel:* 615-599-4032 *E-mail:* contact@americanblackguard.com *Web Site:* www.americanblackguard.com, pg 683

American Chemical Society (ACS), Dept of Professional Education, 1155 16 St NW, Washington, DC 20036 *Tel:* 202-872-4508 *Toll Free Tel:* 800-ACS-5558 (227-5558 ext 4508) *Fax:* 202-872-6336 *E-mail:* proed@acs.org *Web Site:* proed.acs.org, pg 683

American Choral Catalog Ltd, 205 S Water St, Northfield, MN 55057 *Tel:* 507-645-4695 *Fax:* 507-645-2474 *E-mail:* info@americanchoral.com *Web Site:* www.americanchoral.com, pg 683

American Cinema Editors Inc (ACE), Max Bros Bldg, Rm 108, 5555 Melrose Ave, Los Angeles, CA 90038 *Tel:* 323-956-2900 *E-mail:* admin@americancinemaeditors.com *Web Site:* americancinemaeditors.org, pg 948

The American Classical League, 860 NW Washington Blvd, Suite A, Hamilton, OH 45013 *Tel:* 513-529-7741 *Fax:* 513-529-7742 *E-mail:* info@aclclassics.org *Web Site:* www.aclclassics.org, pg 683

American Color Imaging (ACI), 715 E 18 St, Cedar Falls, IA 50613 *Tel:* 319-277-3655 *Toll Free Tel:* 800-728-2722 *Fax:* 319-277-6522 *E-mail:* sales@acilab.com *Web Site:* www.acilab.com, pg 683

American Counseling Association, 6101 Stevenson Ave, Suite 600, Alexandria, VA 22304 *Tel:* 703-823-9800 (ext 222) *Toll Free Tel:* 800-347-6647 (ext 222) *Fax:* 703-823-0252 *E-mail:* membership@counseling.org *Web Site:* www.counseling.org, pg 683

American Educational Products LLC, 401 Hickory St, Fort Collins, CO 80524 *Tel:* 970-484-7445 *Toll Free Tel:* 800-289-9299 *Fax:* 970-484-1198 *E-mail:* custserv@amep.com *Web Site:* www.amep.com, pg 683

American Educational Research Association (AERA), 1430 "K" St NW, Suite 1200, Washington, DC 20005 *Tel:* 202-238-3200 *Fax:* 202-238-3250 *E-mail:* communications@aera.net; members@aera.net *Web Site:* www.aera.net, pg 948

American Federation of Musicians of the United States & Canada (AFM), 1501 Broadway, 9th fl, New York, NY 10036 *Tel:* 212-869-1330 *Toll Free Tel:* 800-762-3444 *Fax:* 212-764-6134 *Web Site:* www.afm.org, pg 948

American Fibertek Inc, 120 Belmont Dr, Somerset, NJ 08873-4243 *Tel:* 732-302-0660 *Toll Free Tel:* 877-234-7200 *Fax:* 732-302-0667 *E-mail:* websales@americanfibertek.com *Web Site:* www.americanfibertek.com, pg 683

American Film Institute (AFI), Attn: Facilities Off, 2021 N Western Ave, Los Angeles, CA 90027-1657 *Tel:* 323-856-7600 *Toll Free Tel:* 800-774-4AFI (774-4234 membership) *Fax:* 323-462-4049 *E-mail:* information@afi.com *Web Site:* www.afi.com, pg 948

American Foundation for the Blind (AFB), 2 Penn Plaza, Suite 1102, New York, NY 10121 *Tel:* 212-502-7600 *Toll Free Tel:* 800-232-5463 *Fax:* 212-502-7777 *Toll Free Fax:* 888-545-8331 *E-mail:* info@afb.org *Web Site:* www.afb.org, pg 948

American Harlequin Corp, 1531 Glen Ave, Moorestown, NJ 08057 *Tel:* 856-234-5505 *Toll Free Tel:* 800-642-6440 *Fax:* 856-231-4403 *E-mail:* dance@harlequinfloors.com; contact@harlequinfloors.com *Web Site:* us.harlequinfloors.com, pg 683

American Health Information Management Association (AHIMA), 233 N Michigan Ave, 21st fl, Chicago, IL 60601-5809 *Tel:* 312-233-1100 *Toll Free Tel:* 800-335-5535 *Fax:* 312-233-1090; 312-233-1500 (orders) *E-mail:* info@ahima.org *Web Site:* www.ahima.org, pg 949

American History Workshop (NY) Inc, 588 Seventh St, Brooklyn, NY 11215-3707 *Tel:* 718-499-6500 *E-mail:* info@americanhistoryworkshop.com *Web Site:* www.americanhistoryworkshop.com, pg 683

American Hospital Association, 155 N Wacker Dr, Suite 400, Chicago, IL 60606-1725 *Tel:* 312-422-3000 *Fax:* 312-422-4700 *Web Site:* www.aha.org, pg 683

American Law Institute Continuing Legal Education (ALI CLE), 4025 Chestnut St, Philadelphia, PA 19104-3099 *Toll Free Tel:* 800-CLE-NEWS (253-6397) *Fax:* 215-243-1664 *E-mail:* custserv@ali-cle.org *Web Site:* www.ali-cle.org, pg 683

American Legion Fourth Estate Award, Media & Communs Div, 700 N Pennsylvania St, Indianapolis, IN 46204 *Tel:* 317-630-1253 *Fax:* 317-630-1368 *E-mail:* pr@legion.org *Web Site:* www.legion.org, pg 981

American Library Association (ALA), 50 E Huron St, Chicago, IL 60611-2795 *Tel:* 312-944-6780 *Toll Free Tel:* 800-545-2433 *Fax:* 312-440-9374 *E-mail:* ala@ala.org *Web Site:* www.ala.org, pg 949

American Management Association® (AMA), 1601 Broadway, New York, NY 10019 *Tel:* 212-586-8100 *Toll Free Tel:* 877-566-9441 (cust serv) *Fax:* 212-903-8168; 518-891-0368 (cust serv) *E-mail:* customerservice@amanet.org *Web Site:* www.amanet.org, pg 683, 949

American Melody, PO Box 270, Guilford, CT 06437-0270 *Tel:* 203-457-0881 *E-mail:* studio@americanmelody.com *Web Site:* www.americanmelody.com, pg 683

American Montage Inc, PO Box 1042, New York, NY 10003 *Tel:* 212-334-8283 *Web Site:* americanmontage.com, pg 683

American Museum of Natural History (AMNH), c/o Special Collections, Library Services Dept, Central Park W & 79 St, New York, NY 10024-5192 *Tel:* 212-769-5420 *Fax:* 212-769-5009 *E-mail:* speccol@amnh.org *Web Site:* www.amnh.org, pg 683

American Music & Sound (AM&S), 925 Broadbeck Dr, No 220, Newbury Park, CA 91320 *Toll Free Tel:* 800-431-2609 *Toll Free Fax:* 866-707-0717 *E-mail:* info@americanmusicandsound.com *Web Site:* www.americanmusicandsound.com, pg 684

American Music Environments Inc (AME), 1133 W Long Lake Rd, Suite 200, Bloomfield Hills, MI 48302 *Tel:* 248-646-2020 *Toll Free Tel:* 888-AME-5005 (263-5005) *Toll Free Fax:* 888-AME-6006 (263-6006) *E-mail:* info@amemusic.com *Web Site:* www.amemusic.com, pg 684

American Optometric Association (AOA), 243 N Lindberg Blvd, 1st fl, St Louis, MO 63141-7881 *Tel:* 314-991-4100 *Toll Free Tel:* 800-365-2219 *Fax:* 314-991-4101 *Web Site:* www.aoa.org, pg 684, 949

American Playback Images, 27748 Caraway Lane, Santa Clarita, CA 91350 *Tel:* 818-427-8292 *Fax:* 661-263-2387 *E-mail:* americanplayback@aol.com *Web Site:* americanplayback.com, pg 684

American Production Services LLC, 1763 Earl Dr, Fort Mill, SC 29715 *Tel:* 803-548-2290 *Fax:* 803-548-3406 *Web Site:* www.apsvideo.com, pg 684

American Recordable Media, 110 Dewey Dr, Suite A, Nicholasville, KY 40356 *Tel:* 859-881-1036 *Toll Free Tel:* 800-598-8273 *Fax:* 859-881-1035 *E-mail:* info@americanrecordablemedia.com *Web Site:* www.americanrecordablemedia.com, pg 684

American Society for Photogrammetry and Remote Sensing (ASPRS), 425 Barlow Place, Suite 210, Bethesda, MD 20814-2160 *Tel:* 301-493-0290 *Fax:* 301-493-0208 *E-mail:* asprs@asprs.org *Web Site:* www.asprs.org, pg 949

American Society of Cinematographers (ASC), 1782 N Orange Dr, Los Angeles, CA 90028 *Tel:* 323-969-4333 *Toll Free Tel:* 800-448-0145 (US only) *Fax:* 323-882-6391 *E-mail:* office@theasc.com; customerservice@theasc.com *Web Site:* theasc.com, pg 949

American Society of Media Photographers Inc (ASMP), PO Box 31207, Bethesda, MD 20824 *Toll Free Tel:* 877-771-2767 *E-mail:* info@asmp.org *Web Site:* asmp.org, pg 949

American Society of Photographers (ASP), 3120 N Argonne Dr, Milwaukee, WI 53222 *Tel:* 414-871-6600 *Web Site:* asofp.com, pg 949

American Society of Safety Professionals (ASSP), 520 N Northwest Hwy, Park Ridge, IL 60068 *Tel:* 847-699-2929 (cust serv) *Fax:* 847-768-3434 *E-mail:* customerservice@assp.org *Web Site:* www.assp.org, pg 949

American Sportscasters Association Inc (ASA), 225 Broadway, Suite 2030, New York, NY 10007 *Tel:* 212-227-8080 *Fax:* 212-571-0556 *Web Site:* www.americansportscastersonline.com, pg 949

The American University, Dept of Performing Arts, 4400 Massachusetts Ave NW, Washington, DC 20016-8053 *Tel:* 202-885-3420 *Fax:* 202-885-1092 *Web Site:* www.american.edu, pg 949

American Video Inc, 780 Third Ave, 5th fl, New York, NY 10017-2024 *Tel:* 212-527-9000 *E-mail:* sales@accnewyork.com, pg 684

American Visions, One Deerfield Lane, Cedar Rapids, IA 52403 *Tel:* 319-360-3211 *Web Site:* www.americanvisions.org, pg 684

America's Public Television Stations (APTS), 2100 Crystal Dr, Suite 700, Arlington, VA 22202 *Tel:* 202-654-4200 *Fax:* 202-654-4236 *Web Site:* apts.org, pg 949

Ametek Programmable Power Inc, 9250 Brown Deer Rd, San Diego, CA 92121 *Tel:* 858-450-0085; 858-458-0223 *Toll Free Tel:* 888-608-0992 *Fax:* 858-458-0267 *E-mail:* sales.ppd@ametek.com *Web Site:* programmablepower.com, pg 684

Ametron Audio/Video, 1546 N Argyle Ave, Hollywood, CA 90028-6410 *Tel:* 323-466-4321 *Fax:* 323-871-0127 *E-mail:* info@ametron.com *Web Site:* www.ametron.com, pg 684

AMG Studios (Los Angeles), 2225 E 28 St, Suite 511, Signal Hill, CA 90755 *Tel:* 562-424-0824 *Web Site:* www.amgstudiosla.com, pg 684

AMP Services Inc, 3111 Fortune Way, Suite B-18, West Palm Beach, FL 33414 *Tel:* 561-333-0335 *Fax:* 561-333-0370 *Web Site:* www.audiomagnetics.com, pg 684

Ampex Data Systems Corp, 26460 Corporate Ave, Hayward, CA 94545 *Tel:* 650-367-2011 *E-mail:* info@ampex.com *Web Site:* www.ampex.com, pg 684

Amplifier Technologies Inc (ATI), 1749 Chapin Rd, Montebello, CA 90640 *Tel:* 323-278-0001 *Fax:* 323-278-0083 *E-mail:* sales@ati-amp.com *Web Site:* www.ati-amp.com, pg 684

AmpliVox Portable Sound Systems, 650 Anthony Trail, Suite D, Northbrook, IL 60062-2512 *Tel:* 847-498-9000 *Toll Free Tel:* 800-267-5486 *Toll Free Fax:* 800-267-5489 *E-mail:* info@ampli.com *Web Site:* www.ampli.com, pg 684

AMPLUS Productions, 1484 Liveoak Dr, Mississauga, ON L5E 2X1, Canada *Tel:* 416-889-7664 *Fax:* 905-274-7687 *Web Site:* www.amplusproductions.com, pg 684

AMS Pictures, 16986 N Dallas Pkwy, Dallas, TX 75248 *Tel:* 972-818-7400 *Toll Free Tel:* 866-691-3660 *Fax:* 972-818-1257 *Web Site:* amspictures.com, pg 684

Amusement & Music Operators Association (AMOA), 380 Terra Cotta Rd, Suite F, Crystal Lake, IL 60012 *Tel:* 847-428-7699 *Toll Free Tel:* 800-YES-AMOA (937-2662) *Fax:* 847-428-7719 *E-mail:* amoa@amoa.com *Web Site:* www.amoa.com, pg 950

AMV/Unitel Studios, 515 W 57 St, New York, NY 10019 *Tel:* 212-265-3600 (studios); 212-586-8616 (sales) *Fax:* 212-246-5059 *E-mail:* hdsales@allmobilevideo.com *Web Site:* www.allmobilevideo.com, pg 685

AMX® by Harman, 8500 Balboa Blvd, Northridge, CA 91329 *Toll Free Tel:* 800-222-0193 (cust care); 844-776-4899 (tech support) *E-mail:* hprotechsupportusa@harman.com *Web Site:* www.amx.com, pg 685

Analog Man Recording Studio, PO Box 70245, Nashville, TN 37207 *Tel:* 615-596-6094 *E-mail:* mrmarksmusic@gmail.com, pg 685

Analog Way Inc, 3047 Summer Oak Place, Buford, GA 30518 *Tel:* 212-269-1902 *Fax:* 212-269-1943 *E-mail:* salesusa@analogway.com *Web Site:* www.analogway.com, pg 685

Anaphora Literary Press, 1108 W Third St, Quanah, TX 79252 *Tel:* 470-289-6395 *Web Site:* anaphoraliterary.com, pg 685

Anchor Audio Inc, 5931 Darwin Ct, Carlsbad, CA 92008 *Tel:* 760-827-7100 *Toll Free Tel:* 800-262-4671 *Fax:* 760-827-7105 *E-mail:* sales@anchoraudio.com *Web Site:* www.anchoraudio.com, pg 685

Anchor Distributors, 1030 Hunt Valley Circle, New Kensington, PA 15068 *Tel:* 724-334-7000 *Toll Free Tel:* 800-444-4484 *Fax:* 724-334-1200 *Toll Free Fax:* 800-765-1960 *E-mail:* customercare@anchordistributors.com; marketing@anchordistributors.com *Web Site:* www.whitakerhouse.com; www.anchordistributors.com, pg 685

Ancient Future, PO Box 264, Kentfield, CA 94914-0264 *Tel:* 415-459-1892 *E-mail:* info@ancient-future.com *Web Site:* www.ancient-future.com, pg 685

The David A Andelman & Pamela Title Award, 40 W 45 St, New York, NY 10036 *Tel:* 212-626-9220 *Fax:* 212-626-9210 *E-mail:* info@opcofamerica.org *Web Site:* www.opcofamerica.org, pg 981

Olson Anderson Co, 3124 Kochville Rd, Suite 121, Saginaw, MI 48604-9305 *Tel:* 989-399-3024 *E-mail:* oac100@aol.com *Web Site:* www.olsonanderson.com, pg 685

Angenieux, 140 Centennial Ave, Piscataway, NJ 08854 *Tel:* 973-812-3858 *E-mail:* angenieux@tccus.com *Web Site:* www.angenieux.com, pg 685

Angstrom Lighting, 12224 Montague St, Pacoima, CA 91331 *Tel:* 323-462-4246 *E-mail:* info@angstromlighting.com *Web Site:* www.angstromlighting.com, pg 685

Animated Software Co, PO Box 1936, Carlsbad, CA 92018-1936 *Tel:* 760-720-7261 *Toll Free Tel:* 800-551-2726 *Web Site:* www.animatedsoftware.com, pg 685

Animotion Inc, 501 W Fayette St, Syracuse, NY 13204 *Tel:* 315-471-3533 *E-mail:* info@animotioninc.com *Web Site:* animotioninc.com, pg 685

Anixter Inc, 2301 Patriot Blvd, Glenview, IL 60026 *Tel:* 224-521-8000 *Toll Free Tel:* 800-323-8167 *Fax:* 224-521-8100 *Web Site:* www.anixter.com, pg 685

Ann Arbor Film Festival, 230 Collingwood Dr, Suite 160B, Ann Arbor, MI 48103 *Tel:* 734-995-5356 *Fax:* 734-995-5396 *E-mail:* info@aafilmfest.org *Web Site:* www.aafilmfest.org, pg 981

Annenberg Learner, PO Box 26983, St Louis, MO 63118 *Tel:* 202-783-0500 (outside US) *Toll Free Tel:* 800-LEARNER (532-7637) *Fax:* 202-783-0333 *E-mail:* order@learner.org *Web Site:* www.learner.org, pg 685

R B Annis Instruments Inc, 117 W Franklin St, Greencastle, IN 46135-1223 *Tel:* 765-848-1621 *Fax:* 765-848-1625 *E-mail:* info@rbannis.com *Web Site:* www.rbannis.com, pg 685

Anode Inc, 926 Main St, Nashville, TN 37206 *Tel:* 615-742-1490 *Fax:* 615-742-1487 *E-mail:* inquiry@anode.com *Web Site:* www.anode.com, pg 686

Anonymous Content, 3532 Hayden Ave, Culver City, CA 90232 *Tel:* 310-558-6000 *Fax:* 310-558-2724 *E-mail:* filmtv@anonymouscontent.com *Web Site:* www.anonymouscontent.com, pg 686

Ansonia Prompting Inc, 39 W 29 St, Suite 305, New York, NY 10001 *Tel:* 212-594-0500 *Fax:* 212-202-4925 *E-mail:* info@ansoniaprompting.com *Web Site:* www.ansoniaprompting.com, pg 686

AnswersMedia, 30 N Racine Ave, Suite 300, Chicago, IL 60607 *Tel:* 312-421-0113 *E-mail:* contactus@answersmediainc.com *Web Site:* www.answersmediainc.com, pg 686

Antelope Valley Film Office/North Los Angeles County, 42035 12 St W, Suite 103, Lancaster, CA 93534 *Tel:* 661-510-4231 *Web Site:* www.avfilm.com, pg 966

Antelope Valley Locations & Production Services, 42848 150 St E, Lancaster, CA 93535 *Tel:* 661-946-1515 *Fax:* 661-946-0454 *E-mail:* clubed@avlocations.com *Web Site:* www.avlocations.com, pg 686

Antenna International, 383 Main Ave, Norwalk, CT 06851 *Tel:* 203-523-0320 *E-mail:* inquiry@ antennainternational.com; marketing@ antennainternational.com *Web Site:* www. antennainternational.com, pg 686

Anton/Bauer®, 14 Progress Dr, Shelton, CT 06484 *Tel:* 203-929-1100 *Toll Free Tel:* 800-422-3473 *Fax:* 203-929-9935 *E-mail:* salessupport_USA@ vitecgroup.com *Web Site:* www.antonbauer.com, pg 686

Antronics Inc, 25 Summer Ave, Waltham, MA 02452-5634 *Tel:* 781-891-7525 *Fax:* 781-647-3667 *E-mail:* info@antronics.net *Web Site:* www.antronics. net, pg 686

Anvil Cases, 1242 E Edna Place, Covina, CA 91724 *Tel:* 626-968-4100 *Toll Free Tel:* 800-FLYANVIL (359-2684) *Fax:* 626-968-1703 *E-mail:* web.sales@ anvilcase.com *Web Site:* www.calzoneandanvil.com, pg 686

Aon Hewitt, 1100 Reynolds Blvd, Winston-Salem, NC 27105-3400 *Tel:* 336-748-1120 *Fax:* 847-953-4854 *Web Site:* www.aon.com, pg 686

AP Images, 200 Liberty St, New York, NY 10281 *Tel:* 212-621-1930 *Fax:* 212-621-1955 *Web Site:* www. apimages.com; apimagesblog.com, pg 686

Apache Junction Chamber of Commerce, 567 W Apache Trail, Apache Junction, AZ 85120 *Tel:* 480-982-3141 *Fax:* 480-982-3234 *E-mail:* admin@ajchamber.com *Web Site:* www.ajchamber.com, pg 965

APC by Schneider Electric, 132 Fairgrounds Rd, West Kingston, RI 02892 *Tel:* 401-789-5735 *Toll Free Tel:* 800-800-4272 *Fax:* 401-789-3710 *Web Site:* www. apc.com, pg 686

Apertura, 535 Main St, Orford, NH 03777 *Tel:* 603-353-9067 *Web Site:* www.apertura.org, pg 686

Aperture Studios Miami, 385 NE 59 St, Miami, FL 33137 *Tel:* 305-759-4327 *Fax:* 305-757-1198 *E-mail:* rental@aperturepro.com *Web Site:* aperturepro. com, pg 687

Apex Jr, 1450 W 228 St, Unit 4, Torrance, CA 90501 *Tel:* 818-248-0416 *Toll Free Tel:* 866-4-ApexJr (427-3957) *Fax:* 424-263-4614 *E-mail:* steve.apexjr@ prodigy.net *Web Site:* www.apexjr.com, pg 687

Apex Machine Co Inc, 3000 NE 12 Terr, Fort Lauderdale, FL 33334 *Tel:* 954-566-1572 *Fax:* 954-563-2844 *E-mail:* email@apexmachine.com *Web Site:* www.apexmachine.com, pg 687

Aphex, PO Box 91028, Long Beach, CA 90809-1028 *Tel:* 562-364-7400 *Toll Free Fax:* 888-412-4664 *E-mail:* info@aphex.com *Web Site:* www.aphex.com, pg 687

API, 8301 Patuxent Range Rd, Jessup, MD 20794 *Tel:* 301-776-7879 *Fax:* 301-776-8117 *E-mail:* service@apiaudio.com *Web Site:* www. apiaudio.com, pg 687

Apogee Communications Group, 159 Alpine Way, Boulder, CO 80304 *Tel:* 303-443-8473 *Toll Free Tel:* 800-210-5700 *Fax:* 303-443-0500 *E-mail:* sales@apogeevideo.com; contact@ apogeecommunicationsgroup.com *Web Site:* www. apogeevideo.com; apogeecommunicationsgroup.com, pg 687

Apogee Electronics Corp, 1715 Berkeley St, Santa Monica, CA 90404 *Tel:* 310-584-9394 *Fax:* 310-584-9385 *E-mail:* info@apogeedigital.com *Web Site:* www. apogeedigital.com, pg 687

Apogee Sound International LLC, 1200 MacArthur Blvd, Suite 304, Mahwah, NJ 07430-2331 *Tel:* 800-443-3979 *Toll Free Fax:* 800-999-9016 *E-mail:* info@apogee-sound.com *Web Site:* www. apogee-sound.com, pg 687

Apollo Design Technology Inc, 4130 Fourier Dr, Fort Wayne, IN 46818 *Tel:* 260-497-9191 *Fax:* 260-497-9192 *E-mail:* sales@apollodesign.net *Web Site:* apollodesign.net, pg 687

Applause Learning Resources, 85 Fernwood Lane, Roslyn, NY 11576 *Tel:* 516-625-1145 *Toll Free Tel:* 800-277-5287 *Toll Free Fax:* 877-365-7484 *E-mail:* info@applauselearning.com *Web Site:* www. applauselearning.com, pg 687

Applause Productions & Publications, PO Box 820024, Dallas, TX 75382-0024 *Tel:* 214-652-4300 *E-mail:* info@applauseproductions.com *Web Site:* applauseproductions.com, pg 687

Apple Inc, One Infinite Loop, Cupertino, CA 95014 *Tel:* 408-996-1010 *Web Site:* www.apple.com, pg 687

Applebox Studio, 379 53 Circle, Vero Beach, FL 32968 *Tel:* 203-803-9115 *Web Site:* www.appleboxstudio. com, pg 687

Pat Appleson Studios Inc, 2359 Hwy 70 SE, Suite 102, Hickory, NC 28602 *Tel:* 828-461-3003 (cell); 828-994-4361 *Web Site:* www.appleson.com, pg 687

Applied Electronics, 722 Blue Crab Rd, Newport News, VA 23606 *Tel:* 757-591-9371 *Toll Free Tel:* 800-883-0008 *Fax:* 757-591-9514 *E-mail:* sales@appliednn. com *Web Site:* www.appliednn.com, pg 687

Applied Electronics Ltd, 1260 Kamato Rd, Mississauga, ON L4W 1Y1, Canada *Tel:* 905-625-4321 *Fax:* 905-625-4333 *E-mail:* ael.toronto@appliedelectronics.com *Web Site:* www.appliedelectronics.com, pg 687

Applied Integration Corp, 3930 W New York Dr, Tucson, AZ 85745 *Tel:* 520-743-3095 *E-mail:* info@ appliedi.com *Web Site:* www.appliedi.com, pg 687

Applied Voice & Speech Technologies Inc (AVST), 27042 Towne Centre Dr, Suite 200, Foothill Ranch, CA 92610-2810 *Tel:* 949-699-2300 *Toll Free Tel:* 866-368-0400 *Fax:* 949-699-2301 *E-mail:* info@avst.com; sales@avst.com *Web Site:* www.avst.com, pg 688

APS Lighting-Sound-AV, 901 Columbia Circle, Merrimack, NH 03054 *Tel:* 603-424-9198 *Toll Free Tel:* 800-837-0005 *Fax:* 603-423-9816 *E-mail:* info@ apslightingnh.com *Web Site:* www.apslightingnh.com, pg 688

Arbor Oakland Group, 4303 Normandy Ct, Royal Oak, MI 48073-2266 *Tel:* 248-549-0150 *Toll Free Tel:* 800-886-5661 *Fax:* 248-549-5270 *E-mail:* info@ arboroakland.com *Web Site:* www.arboroakland.com, pg 688

ARC Document Solutions, 1981 N Broadway, Suite 385, Walnut Creek, CA 94596 *Tel:* 925-949-5100 *Toll Free Tel:* 855-500-0660 *E-mail:* contact@e-arc.com *Web Site:* www.e-arc.com, pg 688

Arc Light Efx Inc, 9338 San Fernando Rd, Sun Valley, CA 91352 *Tel:* 818-394-6330 *Fax:* 818-252-3486 *E-mail:* gaslights@arclightefx.com *Web Site:* www. arclightefx.com, pg 688

Archai Media, 31E Patrick St, Frederick, MD 21701 *Tel:* 301-401-8117 *E-mail:* rentals@archaimedia.com *Web Site:* archaimedia.com, pg 688

Arcor Electronics Co, 5689 W Howard St, Niles, IL 60714 *Tel:* 847-588-0088 *Fax:* 847-588-0080 *E-mail:* sales@arcorelectronics.com *Web Site:* www. arcorelectronics.com, pg 688

Arcube Multimedia Inc, 1845 Summit Ave, Suite 407, Plano, TX 75074 *Tel:* 972-267-1800 *Toll Free Tel:* 877-677-9582 *Fax:* 972-267-1922 *E-mail:* sales@ arcube.com *Web Site:* www.arcube.com, pg 688

Ardent Music LLC, 2000 Madison Ave, Memphis, TN 38104 *Tel:* 901-725-0855 *Fax:* 901-725-7011 *E-mail:* info@ardentmusic.com *Web Site:* www. ardentmusic.com, pg 688

Ardent Studios Inc, 2000 Madison Ave, Memphis, TN 38104 *Tel:* 901-725-0855 *Fax:* 901-725-7011 *E-mail:* info@ardentstudios.com *Web Site:* www. ardentstudios.com, pg 688

ARF! ARF!, PO Box 465, Middleboro, MA 02346-0465 *Tel:* 508-947-7387 *Fax:* 508-947-7387 *E-mail:* page@ arfarfrecords.com *Web Site:* www.arfarfrecords.com, pg 688

Argentine Productions Inc, 111 Mayfair Dr, Pittsburgh, PA 15228 *Tel:* 412-341-6448 *E-mail:* engage@argentineproductions.com *Web Site:* argentineproductions.com, pg 688

Argraph Corp, 111 Asia Place, Carlstadt, NJ 07072 *Tel:* 201-939-7722 *Toll Free Tel:* 800-526-6290 *Fax:* 201-939-7782 *E-mail:* info@argraph.com; sales@ argraph.com *Web Site:* www.argraph.com, pg 688

Aries Productions Inc, 1110 Avenue "H" E, Suite 200, Arlington, TX 76011 *Tel:* 817-640-9955; 817-300-5255 (cell) *Web Site:* www.aries-prods.com, pg 688

Arizona Cine Equipment, 2125 E 20 St, Tucson, AZ 85719 *Tel:* 520-623-8268 *Fax:* 520-623-1092 *Web Site:* www.azcine.com, pg 688

Arizona Production Association, 6615 N Scottsdale Rd, Suite 101, Scottsdale, AZ 85250 *Tel:* 480-345-6464 *Toll Free Tel:* 866-345-6469 *Fax:* 480-941-2557 *E-mail:* info@azproduction.com; sales@azproduction. com *Web Site:* www.azproduction.com, pg 950

Arizona Public Media, 1423 E University, MLB67, Rm 223, Tucson, AZ 85719 *Tel:* 520-621-5828; 520-621-5836 (sales) *Fax:* 520-621-3360 *Web Site:* www.azpm. org, pg 688

Arizona Studios, 4614 E McDowell Rd, Phoenix, AZ 85008 *Tel:* 602-275-9100 *E-mail:* info@ arizonastudios.com *Web Site:* arizonastudios.com, pg 688

Ariztical Entertainment Inc, 12400 Ventura Blvd, Suite 686, Studio City, CA 91604-2406 *Tel:* 818-760-3740 *Fax:* 818-760-3581 *E-mail:* info@ariztical.com; customerservice@ariztical.com; sales@ariztical.com *Web Site:* www.ariztical.com, pg 689

Ark Media Group Ltd, PO Box 410685, San Francisco, CA 94141-0685 *Tel:* 415-863-7200; 415-863-3555 *Fax:* 415-864-5437 *E-mail:* sales@arkmedia.com *Web Site:* www.arkmedia.com, pg 689

Arkansas Arts Council Fellowships & Grants Program, 1100 North St, Little Rock, AR 72201-2606 *Tel:* 501-324-9766 *Fax:* 501-324-9207 *E-mail:* info@ arkansasarts.org *Web Site:* www.arkansasarts.org, pg 981

Arkansas Film Commission, 900 W Capitol Ave, Suite 400, Little Rock, AR 72201 *Tel:* 501-682-7676 *Web Site:* www.arkansasproduction.com, pg 966

Arkon Resources Inc, 20 La Porte St, Arcadia, CA 91006 *Tel:* 626-254-9005 *Toll Free Tel:* 800-841-0884 *Fax:* 626-254-9266 *E-mail:* arkon8@arkon.com *Web Site:* www.arkon.com, pg 689

Arrakis Systems, 6604 Powell St, Loveland, CO 80538 *Tel:* 970-461-0730 *E-mail:* sales@arrakis-systems.com *Web Site:* www.arrakis-systems.com, pg 689

ARRI Inc, 600 N Victory Blvd, Burbank, CA 91502-1639 *Tel:* 818-841-7070 *Fax:* 818-848-4028 *E-mail:* info@arri.com *Web Site:* www.arri.com, pg 689

ARRIS Group Inc, 3871 Lakefield Dr, Suwanee, GA 30024 *Tel:* 678-473-2907 *Toll Free Tel:* 866-36-ARRIS (362-7747); 877-466-8646 (tech) *Fax:* 678-473-8470 *E-mail:* marketing@arris.com *Web Site:* www.arris.com, pg 689

ARS Electronics, 7110 DeCelis Place, Van Nuys, CA 91406 *Tel:* 818-997-6279 *Fax:* 818-997-6158 *E-mail:* info@arselectronics.com *Web Site:* www. arselectronics.com, pg 690

ARSC Awards for Excellence, 1299 University of Oregon, Eugene, OR 97403-1299 *Tel:* 541-346-1852 *Web Site:* www.arsc-audio.org, pg 981

ART (Applied Research & Technology Inc), 4625 Witmer Industrial Estate, Niagara Falls, NY 14305 *Tel:* 716-297-2920 *Fax:* 716-297-3689 *E-mail:* usa@ yorkville.com *Web Site:* www.artproaudio.com; www. yorkville.com, pg 690

Art Directors Guild (ADG), 11969 Ventura Blvd, 2nd fl, Studio City, CA 91604 *Tel:* 818-762-9995 *Fax:* 818-762-9997 *Web Site:* www.adg.org, pg 950

Art Gallery of Ontario, 317 Dundas St W, Toronto, ON M5T 1G4, Canada *Tel:* 416-979-6648 *Toll Free Tel:* 877-225-4246 *Web Site:* ago.ca, pg 690

Attainment Co Inc, 504 Commerce Pkwy, Verona, WI 53593 *Tel:* 608-845-7880 *Toll Free Tel:* 800-327-4269 *Fax:* 608-845-8040 *Toll Free Fax:* 800-942-3865 *E-mail:* customerservice@attainmentcompany.com; international@attainmentcompany.com *Web Site:* www.attainmentcompany.com, pg 692

ATTO Technology Inc, 155 CrossPoint Pkwy, Amherst, NY 14068 *Tel:* 716-691-1999 *Fax:* 716-691-9353 *Web Site:* www.atto.com, pg 692

ATV Research Inc, 1301 Broadway, Dakota City, NE 68731 *Tel:* 402-987-3771 *Toll Free Tel:* 800-392-3922 *Fax:* 402-987-3709 *E-mail:* sales@atvresearch.com *Web Site:* www.atvresearch.com, pg 692

ATV Video Center Inc, 2424 Glendale Lane, Sacramento, CA 95825 *Tel:* 916-973-9100 *Toll Free Tel:* 800-635-1266 *E-mail:* info@atv.net *Web Site:* www.atv.net, pg 692

A2D Solutions Inc, 20200 NW Second Ave, Suite 403, Miami Gardens, FL 33169 *Tel:* 305-895-5888 *Toll Free Tel:* 866-223-7253 *E-mail:* sales@a2dsolutions.com *Web Site:* a2dsolutions.com, pg 692

ATX Networks, 8-1602 Tricont Ave, Whitby, ON L1N 7C3, Canada *Tel:* 289-204-7800 *Toll Free Tel:* 866-968-7289 *E-mail:* info@atx.com *Web Site:* atx.com, pg 692

Audacity Recording Studios, 2734 Polk St, Suite B, Hollywood, FL 33020 *Tel:* 954-920-4418 *Web Site:* www.audacityrecordingstudios.com, pg 693

Audience Response Systems Inc, 5611-C E Morgan Ave, Evansville, IN 47715 *Tel:* 812-479-7507 *Toll Free Tel:* 800-INVOLVE (468-6583) *Fax:* 812-479-1057 *E-mail:* arsales@audienceresponse.com *Web Site:* www.audienceresponse.com, pg 693

Audio Accessories Inc, 25 Mill St, Marlow, NH 03456 *Tel:* 603-446-3335 *Fax:* 603-446-7543 *E-mail:* audioacc@patchbays.com *Web Site:* www.patchbays.com, pg 693

Audio & Light, 2209 Randleman Rd, Greensboro, NC 27406 *Tel:* 336-274-1234 *Fax:* 336-274-4022 *E-mail:* info@audio-light.com *Web Site:* www.audio-light.com, pg 693

Audio Art, 124 Forsythe Dr, Chapel Hill, NC 27517 *Tel:* 919-260-1507, pg 693

Audio Book Contractors LLC, PO Box 96, Riverdale, MD 20738-0096 *Tel:* 301-439-5830 *Fax:* 301-439-5830 *E-mail:* info@audiobookcontractors.com; audiobookcontractors@verizon.net *Web Site:* www.audiobookcontractors.com, pg 693

Audio Consultant Services Inc, 4020 S Spruce St, Denver, CO 80237 *Tel:* 303-437-0308 *Web Site:* www.audio-consultants.com, pg 693

The Audio Department Inc, 324 Mills Place, Wycloff, NJ 07481 *Tel:* 212-586-3503 *Fax:* 212-245-1675 *E-mail:* scheduling@theaudiodepartment.com *Web Site:* www.theaudiodepartment.com, pg 693

Audio Editions Books-On-Cassette & CD, 131 E Placer St, Auburn, CA 95603 *Tel:* 530-888-7801 *Toll Free Tel:* 800-231-4261 *Toll Free Fax:* 800-882-1840 *E-mail:* info@audioeditions.com *Web Site:* audioeditions.com; audioeditionslibrary.com, pg 693

Audio Engineering Society (AES), 551 Fifth Ave, Suite 1225, New York, NY 10176 *Tel:* 212-661-8528 *Web Site:* www.aes.org, pg 951

Audio Graphic Services, 1516 Ferris Ave, Royal Oak, MI 48067 *Tel:* 248-544-1793 *E-mail:* netmail@audiographicservices.com *Web Site:* www.audiographicservices.com, pg 693

Audio Images Corp, 701 Bryant St, 2nd fl, San Francisco, CA 94107 *Tel:* 415-957-9131 *Fax:* 415-957-1531 *Web Site:* www.facebook.com/Audio-Images-Corporation-262409103085/, pg 693

Audio Mechanics, 1200 W Magnolia Blvd, Burbank, CA 91506 *Tel:* 818-846-5525 *Fax:* 818-846-5501 *E-mail:* info@audiomechanics.com *Web Site:* audiomechanics.com, pg 693

Audio Media Productions, 6739 Kirby Trace Cove, Memphis, TN 38119 *Tel:* 901-751-2363 *E-mail:* ampman@aol.com *Web Site:* www.audiomediaproductions.net, pg 693

Audio Network US Inc, 48 W 25 St, 10th fl, New York, NY 10010 *Tel:* 646-688-4320 *E-mail:* nyoffice@audionetwork.com *Web Site:* us.audionetwork.com, pg 693

Audio Precision, 5750 SW Arctic Dr, Beaverton, OR 97005 *Tel:* 503-627-0832 *Toll Free Tel:* 800-231-7350 *E-mail:* message@ap.com *Web Site:* www.ap.com, pg 693

Audio Rents, 4209 E Vanowen Pl, Burbank, CA 91505 *Tel:* 323-874-1000 *Fax:* 323-460-2676 *E-mail:* info@audiorents.com *Web Site:* www.audiorents.com, pg 693

Audio-Technica US Inc, 1221 Commerce Dr, Stow, OH 44224 *Tel:* 330-686-2600 *Fax:* 330-686-0719 *E-mail:* pro@atus.com *Web Site:* www.audio-technica.com, pg 693

Audio Upgrades, 6982 Mimosa Dr, Carlsbad, CA 92011 *Tel:* 818-780-1222 *Web Site:* www.audioupgrades.com, pg 694

Audio-Video Corp, 213 Broadway, Albany, NY 12204 *Tel:* 518-449-7213 *Fax:* 518-449-1205 *E-mail:* info@audiovideocorp.com; sales@audiovideocorp.com; service@audiovideocorp.com *Web Site:* www.audiovideocorp.com, pg 694

Audio-Video Resources Inc, 1043 Adams Ave, Montgomery, AL 36104 *Tel:* 334-262-4806 *Fax:* 334-240-0000 *E-mail:* avrinc@bellsouth.net, pg 694

Audio/Video Supply Inc, 4575 Ruffner St, San Diego, CA 92111 *Tel:* 858-565-1101 *Toll Free Tel:* 800-284-2288 *Fax:* 858-565-7845 *E-mail:* sales@avsupply.com *Web Site:* www.avsupply.com, pg 694

Audio-VideoGraphics Inc, 17501 E 40 Hwy, Suite 219, Independence, MO 64055 *Tel:* 816-350-0800 *Toll Free Tel:* 800-322-2832 *Fax:* 816-350-0804 *Web Site:* www.avginc.com, pg 694

Audio Visions Inc, 1501 N George St, York, PA 17404 *Tel:* 717-747-1898, pg 694

Audio Vistas LLC, 170 N Woods Dr, South Orange, NJ 07079 *Tel:* 212-586-2177 *E-mail:* info@audiovistas.com *Web Site:* www.audiovistas.com, pg 694

Audio Visual Actions Inc (AVA), 5641-C General Washington Dr, Alexandria, VA 22312 *Tel:* 703-750-0950 *Toll Free Tel:* 866-893-5382 *Fax:* 703-750-0954 *E-mail:* info@avactions.com *Web Site:* avactions.com, pg 694

Audio Visual Associates, One Stewart Ct, Denville, NJ 07834 *Toll Free Tel:* 888-435-6678 *Fax:* 973-442-0888 *E-mail:* sales@avaonline.com; info@avaonline.com *Web Site:* www.avaonline.com, pg 694

Audio Visual Communications Inc, 1336 Cherry St, Boothwyn, PA 19061 *Tel:* 610-272-8500 *E-mail:* audiovc@verizon.net *Web Site:* www.audiovc.com, pg 694

The Audio Visual Co (AVCO), 98-810 Moanalua Rd, Aiea, HI 96701 *Tel:* 808-485-3200 *Fax:* 808-487-0733 *Web Site:* www.theavco.com, pg 694

Audio Visual Concepts Inc, Rd 1, Km 29.3, Rio Canas, Caguas, PR 00725 *Tel:* 787-753-7700 *Fax:* 787-766-4578 *Web Site:* www.mig-avc.com, pg 694

Audio Visual Consultants, 3207 Lakeshore Ave, 2nd fl, Oakland, CA 94610 *Tel:* 510-839-2020 *E-mail:* info@avconsultants.com *Web Site:* www.avconsultants.com, pg 694

Audio Visual Dynamics, 2360 23 Ave, Lachine, QC H8T 0A3, Canada *Tel:* 514-332-6440 *Fax:* 514-332-2009 *E-mail:* service@avd.ca *Web Site:* www.avd.ca, pg 694

Audio Visual Dynamics®, 424 Sand Shore Rd, Hackettstown, NJ 07840 *Tel:* 973-993-8500 *Fax:* 973-984-0644 *Web Site:* www.avdusa.com, pg 694

Audio Visual Imagineering Inc, 6565 Hazeltine National Dr, Suite 2, Orlando, FL 32822 *Tel:* 407-859-8166 *Fax:* 407-859-8254 *Web Site:* www.av-imagineering.com, pg 694

Audio Visual Media, 1141 Lexington Ave, Mansfield, OH 44907 *Tel:* 419-756-2698 *E-mail:* avm2698@aol.com *Web Site:* audiovisualmedia.net, pg 694

Audio Visual of Milwaukee Inc, 285 N Janacek Rd, Brookfield, WI 53045 *Tel:* 262-432-1077 *Toll Free Tel:* 800-236-6909 *Fax:* 262-432-1078 *E-mail:* avm@avmonline.com *Web Site:* www.avmonline.com, pg 694

Audio Visual Resources Inc, 3932 Ogeechee Rd, Savannah, GA 31405 *Tel:* 912-447-5656 *E-mail:* aaavr@aol.com *Web Site:* www.avrsav.com, pg 695

Audio Visual Sales & Service Inc, 2601 Curry Rd, Schenectady, NY 12303 *Tel:* 518-688-0640 *Fax:* 518-688-0634 *E-mail:* info@avssi.com, pg 695

Audio Visual Techniques Inc, 905 Georgetown St, Lexington, KY 40511 *Tel:* 859-254-8954 *Fax:* 859-233-4754 *E-mail:* info@avtav.com *Web Site:* avtav.com, pg 695

Audio Visual Technologies Group (AVTG), 12502 Exchange Dr, Suite 404, Stafford, TX 77477 *Tel:* 281-240-2329 *Toll Free Tel:* 800-522-3687 *E-mail:* info@avtg.com *Web Site:* www.avtg.com, pg 695

Audioarts Engineering, 600 Industrial Dr, New Bern, NC 28562 *Tel:* 252-638-7000 *Fax:* 252-635-4857 (sales); 252-637-1285 *E-mail:* sales@wheatstone.com *Web Site:* www.wheatstone.com, pg 695

Audiobook Department, 6429 N Talman Ave, Chicago, IL 60645 *Tel:* 773-338-8813 *Fax:* 773-338-8813 *Web Site:* www.judithwest.com, pg 695

AudioControl® Inc, 22410 70 Ave W, Mountlake Terrace, WA 98043 *Tel:* 425-775-8461 *Fax:* 425-778-3166 *E-mail:* sound.great@audiocontrol.com *Web Site:* www.audiocontrol.com, pg 695

AudioImage Recording, 110 N Jefferson St, Richmond, VA 23220-5022 *Tel:* 804-644-7700 *Fax:* 804-644-8801 *E-mail:* info@audioimagerecording.com *Web Site:* www.audioimagerecording.com, pg 695

Audiomoxie®, PO Box 304, Georgetown, TX 78627 *E-mail:* info@audiomoxie.com *Web Site:* www.audiomoxie.com, pg 695

AudioSolutionz LLC, 2222 Sedwick Rd, Durham, NC 27713 *Toll Free Tel:* 800-223-8720 *Fax:* 919-287-2643 *E-mail:* support@audiosolutionz.com *Web Site:* www.audiosolutionz.com, pg 695

AudioVideoElectric, 3907 Peppervine Dr, Orlando, FL 32828 *Toll Free Tel:* 888-792-9283 *Fax:* 407-381-5610 *E-mail:* sales@audiovideoelectric.com *Web Site:* www.audiovideoelectric.com, pg 695

Audiovisual and Integrated Experience Association (AVIXA), 11242 Waples Mill Rd, Suite 200, Fairfax, VA 22030 *Tel:* 703-273-7200 *Toll Free Tel:* 800-659-7469 *E-mail:* membership@avixa.org *Web Site:* www.avixa.org, pg 951

Audiovox®, 180 Marcus Blvd, Hauppauge, NY 11788 *Tel:* 631-231-7750 *Toll Free Tel:* 800-645-4994 *Web Site:* www.voxxelectronics.com; www.voxxintl.com, pg 695

Audix Microphones, 9400 SW Barber St, Wilsonville, OR 97070 *Tel:* 503-682-6933 *Toll Free Tel:* 800-966-8261 *Fax:* 503-682-7114 *E-mail:* info@audixusa.com *Web Site:* audixusa.com, pg 695

Augsburg Fortress, 510 Marquette Ave, Suite 800, Minneapolis, MN 55402 *Tel:* 612-330-3300 *Toll Free Tel:* 800-328-4648 *Toll Free Fax:* 800-722-7766 *E-mail:* customercare@augsburgfortress.org; salesandservice@augsburgfortress.org *Web Site:* www.augsburgfortress.org, pg 695

August House Audio, 3500 Piedmont Rd NE, Suite 310, Atlanta, GA 30305 *Tel:* 404-442-4420 *Toll Free Tel:* 800-284-8784 *Fax:* 404-442-4435 *E-mail:* ahinfo@augusthouse.com *Web Site:* augusthouse.com, pg 695

Aura Sonic Ltd (ASL), PO Box 520791, Flushing, NY 11352-0791 *Tel:* 718-886-6500 *E-mail:* somebody@ aurasonic.com *Web Site:* www.aurasonicltd.com, pg 695

Aural Gratification Inc, 32 Nissen Lane, West Hurley, NY 12491-5903 *Tel:* 845-679-5674 *E-mail:* auralg@ gmail.com, pg 695

Auralex Acoustics Inc, 9955 Westpoint Dr, Suite 101, Indianapolis, IN 46256 *Tel:* 317-842-2600 *Toll Free Tel:* 800-95-WEDGE (959-3343, orders) *Fax:* 317-842-2760 *E-mail:* info@auralex.com *Web Site:* www. auralex.com, pg 696

Auriga Productions Ltd, 2856 rue du Comtois, Ste-Lazare, QC J7T 0E7, Canada *Tel:* 514-984-4202 *E-mail:* aurigapix@gmail.com *Web Site:* www. aurigapix.com, pg 696

Aurora Films, 324 E Dowling Rd, Suite 4, Anchorage, AK 99518 *Tel:* 907-258-4686 *E-mail:* aurorafilms@ gci.net, pg 696

aurora productions, 315 Walt Whitman Rd, Suite 210, Huntington Station, NY 11746-4112 *Tel:* 631-549-8933 *E-mail:* info@auroraproductions.tv *Web Site:* www.auroraproductions.tv, pg 696

Austin Film Commission, 111 Congress Ave, Suite 700, Austin, TX 78701 *Tel:* 512-583-7230 *Toll Free Tel:* 800-926-2282 (ext 7230) *Fax:* 512-583-7282 *Web Site:* www.austintexas.org/film-commission, pg 976

Austin Film Festival, 1801 Salina St, Austin, TX 78702 *Tel:* 512-478-4795 *Toll Free Tel:* 800-310-FEST (310-3378) *Fax:* 512-478-6205 *E-mail:* info@austinfilmfestival.com; programming@ austinfilmfestival.com; marketing@austinfilmfestival. com *Web Site:* www.austinfilmfestival.com, pg 982

Austin Film Society (AFS), 1901 E 51 St, Austin, TX 78723 *Tel:* 512-322-0145 *E-mail:* afs@austinfilm.org *Web Site:* www.austinfilm.org, pg 951

Autocue, 14 Progress Dr, Shelton, CT 06484 *Tel:* 212-929-7755 *Fax:* 212-929-2105 *Web Site:* www.autocue. com/teleprompter, pg 696

Autodesk Inc, 111 McInnis Pkwy, San Rafael, CA 94903 *Tel:* 415-507-5000 *Fax:* 415-507-5100 *Web Site:* www. autodesk.com, pg 696

AutoDesSys Inc, 3518 Riverside Dr, Suite 206, Columbus, OH 43221 *Tel:* 614-488-8838 *Fax:* 614-488-0848 *E-mail:* sales@formz.com; marketing@ formz.com *Web Site:* www.formz.com, pg 696

Autogram/CRL, 920 Edison Ave, Benton, AR 72015 *Tel:* 501-794-6994 *Fax:* 501-776-0357 *E-mail:* support@autogram.net *Web Site:* www. autogram.net, pg 696

Automated Entertainment, PO Box 1079, Littlerock, CA 95343-1079 *Tel:* 661-944-2299 *Toll Free Tel:* 800-880-6567 (orders) *E-mail:* questions@automatedhd.com *Web Site:* www.automatedhd.com, pg 696

Automatic Devices Co (ADC), 2121 S 12 St, Allentown, PA 18103 *Tel:* 610-797-6000 *Toll Free Tel:* 800-360-2321 *Fax:* 610-797-4088 *E-mail:* info@automaticdevices.com *Web Site:* www. automaticdevices.com, pg 696

Automobile Film Club of America Inc, 10 Cross St, Staten Island, NY 10304 *Tel:* 718-447-2255 *E-mail:* contact@autofilmclub.com *Web Site:* www. autofilmclub.com, pg 696

Auton Motorized Systems, 24856 Avenue Rockefeller, Valencia, CA 91355 *Tel:* 661-257-9282 *Fax:* 661-295-5638 *E-mail:* info@auton.com *Web Site:* auton.com, pg 696

AV Bluebook, 80 Little Falls Rd, Fairfield, NJ 07004 *Toll Free Tel:* 800-631-7791 *Toll Free Fax:* 800-332-5871 *E-mail:* info@avbluebook.com; sales@ avbluebook.com *Web Site:* www.avbluebook.com, pg 696

AV Chicago Inc, 619 W Taylor St, Chicago, IL 60607 *Tel:* 312-229-4100 *Toll Free Tel:* 888-709-9599 *Fax:* 312-229-5642 *Web Site:* avchicago.com, pg 696

AV Concepts Inc, 1917 W First St, Tempe, AZ 85281 *Tel:* 480-557-6000; 480-646-4216 (sales & serv) *Toll Free Tel:* 866-927-7590 *E-mail:* exhibitorservices@ avconcepts.com *Web Site:* www.avconcepts.com, pg 696

AV Conferencing LLC (AVC), PO Box 21606, Concord, CA 94521 *Tel:* 925-216-6319 *Fax:* 801-382-5573 *E-mail:* sales@avconferencing.com *Web Site:* www. avconferencing.com, pg 697

AV Connections Inc, 245 Executive Park Blvd, Winston-Salem, NC 27103 *Tel:* 336-768-5454 *Fax:* 336-768-5054 *E-mail:* avrentals@avconnectionsusa.com *Web Site:* avconnectionsusa.com, pg 697

A/V Davey, 71 Clifton Place, Bridgeport, CT 06606 *Tel:* 203-372-3286 *Fax:* 203-372-3307 *Web Site:* avdavey.com, pg 697

AV Guys, 1641 Pacific Rim Ct, Suite A, San Diego, CA 92154 *Tel:* 619-474-5050 *Fax:* 619-474-5454 *Web Site:* www.avguys.com, pg 697

AV Metro Inc, 5401 Etta Burke Ct, Raleigh, NC 27606 *Tel:* 919-233-1901 *Fax:* 919-233-1804 *E-mail:* info@ avmetro.com *Web Site:* www.avmetro.com, pg 697

A/V Presentations Inc, 104 Otis St, Suite 30, Northborough, MA 01532 *Tel:* 508-393-9767 *Toll Free Tel:* 800-648-7176 *Fax:* 508-393-6698 *E-mail:* staff@ avpresentations.com *Web Site:* www.avpresentations. com, pg 697

AV Toolbox, 621 Wilmer Ave, Cincinnati, OH 45226 *Tel:* 859-282-7303 *Toll Free Tel:* 800-235-3280; 800-721-4044 *E-mail:* sales@avtoolbox.com *Web Site:* www.avtoolbox.com, pg 697

AV Workshop, 500 W 37 St, 3rd fl, New York, NY 10018 *Tel:* 212-643-0040 *Fax:* 212-564-5277 *E-mail:* sales@avworkshop.com *Web Site:* avworkshop.com, pg 697

Available Light, 29-20 37 Ave, Long Island City, NY 11101 *Tel:* 718-707-9670; 718-707-9671 *Fax:* 718-707-9693 *E-mail:* contactus@alny.net *Web Site:* www. alny.net, pg 697

Available Light, 5251 Dixon Rd, Oceanside, CA 92056-2319 *Tel:* 760-505-1605 *E-mail:* availablelight@cox. net *Web Site:* www.availablelightandgrip.com, pg 697

Available Lighting & Motion Picture Services Inc, 826 Jefferson Hwy, New Orleans, LA 70121 *Tel:* 504-831-5214 *Fax:* 504-831-5361 *E-mail:* avlight@bellsouth. net *Web Site:* www.availablelighting.com, pg 697

Avalon Acoustics, 2800 Wilderness Place, Boulder, CO 80301 *Tel:* 303-440-0422 *Web Site:* avalonacoustics. com, pg 697

Avast! Recording Co, 601 NW 80 St, Seattle, WA 98117 *Fax:* 206-789-7569 *E-mail:* avast@comcast.net *Web Site:* www.avastrecording.com, pg 697

Avatar Award, 550 W Frontage Rd, Suite 3600, Northfield, IL 60093 *Tel:* 847-716-7000 *Fax:* 847-716-7004 *E-mail:* info@mediafinance.org *Web Site:* www. mediafinance.org, pg 982

Avatar Studios, 2675 Scott Ave, Suite G, St Louis, MO 63103 *Tel:* 314-533-2242 *Fax:* 314-533-3349 *E-mail:* info@avatar-studios.com *Web Site:* avatar-studios.com, pg 697

Avaya Inc, 4655 Great American Pkwy, Santa Clara, CA 95054 *Tel:* 908-953-6000 *Toll Free Tel:* 866-GO-AVAYA (462-8292 US & CN) *Web Site:* www.avaya. com, pg 697

Avekta Productions Inc, One Rock Place, Yonkers, NY 10705 *Tel:* 914-378-8000 *Web Site:* avekta.com, pg 697

AVerMedia Technologies Inc, 47358 Fremont Blvd, Fremont, CA 94538 *Tel:* 510-403-0006 *Fax:* 510-403-0022 *E-mail:* avtsales.usa@avermedia.com *Web Site:* www.avermedia.com, pg 697

AVES Audio Visual Systems Inc, PO Box 500, Sugar Land, TX 77487-0500 *Tel:* 281-295-1300 *Toll Free Tel:* 800-365-AVES (365-2837) *Fax:* 281-295-1311 *E-mail:* sales@avesav.com *Web Site:* www.avesav.com, pg 698

AVFX Inc, 96 Holton St, Boston, MA 02135 *Tel:* 617-254-0770 *Toll Free Tel:* 888-254-0770 *E-mail:* info@ avfx.com *Web Site:* www.avfx.com, pg 698

AVI-SPL, 6301 Benjamin Rd, Suite 101, Tampa, FL 33634 *Tel:* 813-884-7168 *Toll Free Tel:* 866-708-5034; 866-925-8298 (cust serv); 866-559-8197 (sales) *E-mail:* contact@avispl.com; sales@avispl.com; customerservice@avispl.com *Web Site:* www.avispl. com, pg 698

AVI Systems, 9675 W 76 St, Suite 130, Eden Prairie, MN 55344 *Tel:* 952-949-3700 *Toll Free Tel:* 800-488-4954 (support); 855-521-0050 *Fax:* 952-949-6000 *E-mail:* info@avisystems.com *Web Site:* www. avisystems.com, pg 698

Avid Technology Inc, 65-75 Network Dr, Burlington, MA 01830 *Tel:* 978-640-6789 *Web Site:* www.avid. com, pg 698

Avidex Inc, 13555 Bel-Red Rd, Suite 226, Bellevue, WA 98005 *Tel:* 425-643-0330 *Toll Free Tel:* 800-798-0330 *Fax:* 425-274-7091 *E-mail:* info@avidexav.com *Web Site:* www.avidexav.com, pg 699

Aviom Inc, 1157 Phoenixville Pike, Suite 201, West Chester, PA 19380-4254 *Tel:* 610-738-9005 *Fax:* 610-738-9950 *E-mail:* info@aviom.com *Web Site:* www. aviom.com, pg 699

Avitecture Inc, One Export Dr, Sterling, VA 20164-4421 *Tel:* 703-404-8900 *Fax:* 703-404-8940 *E-mail:* info@ avitecture.com *Web Site:* www.avitecture.com, pg 699

AVL Systems Design LLC, 14901 Bristol Park Blvd, Edmond, OK 73013 *Tel:* 405-749-1866 *Fax:* 405-749-1851 *E-mail:* dnix@avl1.com *Web Site:* www.avl1. com, pg 699

AVP Mfg & Supply Inc, 2288-B7 Dumfries Rd, RR2, Cambridge, ON N1R 5S3, Canada *Tel:* 519-740-7966 *Toll Free Tel:* 800-481-2493 *Fax:* 519-740-0131 *E-mail:* sales@jackfields.com *Web Site:* www. jackfields.com, pg 699

AVS Group, 3120 South Ave, Suite 133, La Crosse, WI 54601 *Tel:* 608-780-7019 *Fax:* 608-787-0012 *E-mail:* info@avsgroup.com *Web Site:* www.avsgroup. com, pg 699

AVS Media Group, 11193 Old Hwy 31, Suite 1, Spanish Fort, AL 36527 *Tel:* 251-621-1200 *E-mail:* info@ avsmediagroup.com *Web Site:* www.avsmediagroup. com, pg 699

Avtech Systems Inc, 7-1 Bellair Ave, Fair Lawn, NJ 07410 *Tel:* 201-833-8777, pg 699

Award Productions Inc, 164 Great Rd, Acton, MA 01720 *Tel:* 978-635-8000 *E-mail:* web@awardprod.com *Web Site:* www.awardproductions.com, pg 699

Axis Films, 3138 Cumberland Rd, Berkley, MI 48072 *Tel:* 248-722-1734 *Web Site:* www.axisfilms.tv, pg 700

Axxis Leasing Inc, 845 S Ninth St, Louisville, KY 40203 *Tel:* 502-568-6030 *Fax:* 502-568-6204 *E-mail:* info@axxisinc.com *Web Site:* www.axxisinc. com, pg 700

Aydin Displays, a Sparton Company, One Riga Lane, Birdsboro, PA 19508 *Tel:* 610-404-7400 *Toll Free Tel:* 866-367-2934 *Fax:* 610-404-8190 *E-mail:* sales@ spartonre.com *Web Site:* www.spartonre.com, pg 700

Aylmer Press, PO Box 2302, Madison, WI 53701-2302 *Tel:* 608-441-5277 *Fax:* 608-251-0890 *Web Site:* www. signit2.com, pg 700

AZ Spectrum, 53-53 62 St, Maspeth, NY 11378 *Tel:* 718-779-1892 *Fax:* 718-779-1892 *E-mail:* az@az-spectrum.com; azspectrum@aol.com *Web Site:* www. az-spectrum.com, pg 700

Aztec Video Productions, 2967 Montana Ave, Cincinnati, OH 45211 *Tel:* 513-481-5004 *E-mail:* aztec@fuse.net *Web Site:* www.aztecvideo.com, pg 700

Aztech Productions LLC, 6 Hillcrest Ave, Erdenheim, PA 19038 *Tel:* 215-836-5490 *Web Site:* aztechproductions.com, pg 700

Aztek Inc, 13765-F Alton Pkwy, Irvine, CA 92618 *Tel:* 949-770-8787 *Toll Free Tel:* 800-GRAPH-55 (472-7455) *Fax:* 949-770-4986 *E-mail:* mail@aztek. com *Web Site:* www.aztek.com, pg 700

B & B Video Productions Inc, 233 N Main St, West Point, NE 68788 *Tel:* 402-380-9042 *Web Site:* www. bandbvideo.com, pg 700

B-K Lighting, 40429 Brickyard Dr, Madera, CA 93636 *Tel:* 559-438-5800 *Fax:* 559-438-5900 *E-mail:* info@ bklighting.com *Web Site:* www.bklighting.com, pg 700

Back to the Bible, 6400 Cornhusker Hwy, Suite 100, Lincoln, NE 68507 *Tel:* 402-464-7200 *Toll Free Tel:* 800-759-6655 *Fax:* 402-464-7474 *E-mail:* info@ backtothebible.org *Web Site:* www.backtothebible.org, pg 700

Backdrop Outlet, 3540 Seagate Way, Oceanside, CA 92056 *Tel:* 760-547-2900 *Toll Free Tel:* 800-466-1755 *Fax:* 760-547-2899 *E-mail:* cs@backdropoutlet.com *Web Site:* backdropoutlet.com, pg 700

Backstage Equipment Inc, 8052 Lankershim Blvd, North Hollywood, CA 91605 *Tel:* 818-504-6026 *Toll Free Tel:* 800-692-2787 *Fax:* 818-504-6180 *E-mail:* info@ backstageweb.com *Web Site:* www.backstageweb.com, pg 700

Backstage Pass Entertainment Inc, 7438 Shoshone Ave, Lake Balboa, CA 91406-2340 *Tel:* 818-881-9888 *Toll Free Tel:* 800-664-6555 *Fax:* 818-881-0555 *E-mail:* blowinsmokeband@ktb.net, pg 700

Backstar Creative Media Inc, 70 W Hubbard St, Suite 203, Chicago, IL 60654 *Tel:* 312-467-0425 *Toll Free Tel:* 800-955-8900 *E-mail:* solutions@backstar.com *Web Site:* www.backstar.com, pg 700

Badiyan Inc, 720 W 94 St, Bloomington, MN 55420 *Tel:* 952-888-5507 *Fax:* 952-888-0360 *E-mail:* info@ badiyan.com *Web Site:* www.badiyan.com, pg 700

Bag End Loudspeakers, 1201 Armstrong St, Algonquin, IL 60102 *Tel:* 847-658-8888 *Fax:* 847-658-5008 *Web Site:* www.bagend.com, pg 700

Baha'i Distribution Service (BDS), 401 Greenleaf Ave, Wilmette, IL 60091 *Tel:* 847-425-7950; 847-853-7899 *Toll Free Tel:* 800-999-9019 *E-mail:* bds@usbnc.org *Web Site:* www.bahaibookstore.com, pg 700

Baker Audio Visual, 2195 N Norcross Tucker Rd, Norcross, GA 30071 *Tel:* 770-441-2000 *Toll Free Tel:* 800-847-3523 *Fax:* 770-449-7719 *E-mail:* support@bakeraudiovisual.com *Web Site:* www.bakeraudiovisual.com, pg 700

Baldwin Productions Services Inc, 160 Tioga Lane, Greenbrae, CA 94904 *Tel:* 415-699-0729 *Web Site:* www.baldwinproductionsinc.com, pg 701

Ballantyne Strong Inc, 11422 Miracle Hills Dr, Suite 300, Omaha, NE 68154 *Tel:* 402-453-4444 *Toll Free Tel:* 800-424-1215; 800-722-0046 *E-mail:* customerservice@btn-inc.com *Web Site:* ballantynestrong.com, pg 701

Baltimore Film Office, 10 E Baltimore St, 10th fl, Baltimore, MD 21202 *Tel:* 410-752-8632 *Fax:* 410-385-0361 *Web Site:* www.baltimorefilm.com, pg 972

Band Pro Film & Digital Inc, 3403 W Pacific Ave, Burbank, CA 91505 *Tel:* 818-841-9655 *Toll Free Tel:* 888-BANDPRO (226-3776) *Fax:* 818-841-7649 *E-mail:* info@bandpro.com; customercare@bandpro. com *Web Site:* www.bandpro.com, pg 701

B+B SmartWorx, 707 Dayton Rd, Ottawa, IL 61350 *Tel:* 815-433-5100 *Toll Free Tel:* 800-346-3119 *Fax:* 815-433-5109 *E-mail:* info@advantech-bb.com; orders@advantech-bb.com *Web Site:* advantech-bb. com, pg 701

B&H Photo Video, 420 Ninth Ave, New York, NY 10001 *Tel:* 212-444-5000; 212-444-6615 *Toll Free Tel:* 800-606-6969 *Fax:* 212-239-7770 *Toll Free Fax:* 800-947-7008 *Web Site:* www.bhphotovideo.com, pg 701

B&H Publishing Group, One LifeWay Plaza, Nashville, TN 37234 *Tel:* 615-251-2520 *Fax:* 615-251-5004 *Web Site:* www.bhpublishinggroup.com, pg 701

B&K AV Ltd, 140-12031 Horsheshoe Way, Richmond, BC V7A 4V4, Canada *Tel:* 604-274-7711 (intl) *Toll Free Tel:* 800-949-3344 (US) *Fax:* 323-278-0083 *E-mail:* info@bandkav.com *Web Site:* www.bandkav. com, pg 701

Banff Mountain Film & Book Festival, 107 Tunnel Mountain Dr, Banff, AB T1L 1H5, Canada *Tel:* 403-762-6347; 403-762-6369 *Toll Free Tel:* 800-298-1229 *Fax:* 403-762-6277 *E-mail:* banffmountainfestival@ banffcentre.ca; banffmountainfilms@banffcentre.ca *Web Site:* www.banffcentre.ca/banff-mountain-film-and-book-festival, pg 983

Banff World Media Festival, 100-366 Adelaide St W, Toronto, ON M5V 1R9, Canada *Tel:* 416-408-2300 *Toll Free Tel:* 888-287-2279 *Fax:* 416-408-0870 *E-mail:* info@achillesmedia.com *Web Site:* banffmediafestival.com, pg 983

Bang! Pictures Inc, 78 Graterford Rd, Schwenksville, PA 19473 *Tel:* 610-357-1015 *Web Site:* www.bangpictures. com, pg 701

The Banquet Sound Studios, 5870 McFarland Rd, Sebastopol, CA 95472 *Tel:* 707-823-3500 *E-mail:* main@banquetstudios.com *Web Site:* www. banquetstudios.com, pg 701

Barber Tech Video Products, 5111 Via Corona St, East Los Angeles, CA 90022 *Tel:* 818-982-7775 *E-mail:* info@barbertvp.com; info@barbertech.com, pg 701

Barbizon Electric Co Inc, 456 W 55 St, New York, NY 10019-4403 *Tel:* 212-586-1620 *Toll Free Tel:* 800-582-9941 *Fax:* 212-247-8818 *E-mail:* benysales@barbizon. com *Web Site:* www.barbizon.com, pg 701

Barco Inc, 3059 Premiere Pkwy, Suite 400, Duluth, GA 30097 *Tel:* 916-859-2500; 678-475-8000 *Toll Free Tel:* 888-414-7226 *E-mail:* sales.events.us@barco.com *Web Site:* www.barco.com, pg 701

Bardes Products Inc, 5245 W Clinton Ave, Milwaukee, WI 53223 *Tel:* 414-354-9000 *Toll Free Tel:* 800-223-1357 *Fax:* 414-354-1921 *E-mail:* sales@bardes.com *Web Site:* www.bardes.com, pg 702

Barger-Lite, 12023 Victory Blvd, Los Angeles, CA 91606 *Tel:* 310-401-0633 *E-mail:* sales@bargerlite. com *Web Site:* www.bargerlite.com, pg 702

Bill Barnes Video Productions LLC, 14238 Honeysuckle Ridge, Matthews, NC 28105-6403 *Tel:* 704-847-8685 *E-mail:* bill@bbvp.tv *Web Site:* www.bbvp.tv, pg 702

Baron Stage Curtain & Equipment Co Inc, 1910 Light St, Baltimore, MD 21230 *Tel:* 410-327-6962 *Toll Free Tel:* 800-249-6464 *E-mail:* curtains@baronstage.com *Web Site:* www.baronstage.com, pg 702

Carl Barth Images, PO Box 5325, Santa Barbara, CA 93150-5325 *Tel:* 805-637-0881 *E-mail:* carlbarthimages@cox.net, pg 702

Bartha, 600 N Cassady Ave, Columbus, OH 43219 *Tel:* 614-252-7455 *Toll Free Tel:* 800-363-2698 *Fax:* 614-252-7641 *E-mail:* info@bartha.com *Web Site:* www.bartha.com, pg 702

The Whitman Bassow Award, 40 W 45 St, New York, NY 10036 *Tel:* 212-626-9220 *Fax:* 212-626-9210 *E-mail:* info@opcofamerica.org *Web Site:* www. opcofamerica.org, pg 983

Bay Photo Lab, 920 Disc Dr, Scotts Valley, CA 95066 *Tel:* 831-475-6686 *Toll Free Tel:* 800-435-6686 *Fax:* 831-475-5275 *E-mail:* support@bayphoto.com (cust serv); sales@bayphoto.com *Web Site:* www. bayphoto.com, pg 702

Bay Records, 3365 S Lucille Lane, Lafayette, CA 94549 *Tel:* 925-284-7797 *Web Site:* www.bayrec.com, pg 702

Bay Stage Lighting Co Inc, 4008 W Alva St, Tampa, FL 33614 *Tel:* 813-877-1089 *Fax:* 813-875-8837 *Web Site:* www.baystagelive.com, pg 702

BBC Worldwide Canada Ltd, 401-409 King St W, 5th fl, Toronto, ON M5V 1K1, Canada *Tel:* 416-204-0500 *E-mail:* canada.sales@bbc.com (sales) *Web Site:* www. bbcworldwide.com, pg 702

BBC Worldwide Learning, 1120 Avenue of the Americas, 5th fl, New York, NY 10036 *Tel:* 212-339-1700 *E-mail:* bbcwlearningamericas@bbc.com *Web Site:* www.bbcworldwidelearning.com, pg 702

BBE Sound Inc, 2548 Fender Ave, Fullerton, CA 92831 *Tel:* 714-897-6766 *Toll Free Tel:* 800-233-8346 *Fax:* 714-895-6728 *Web Site:* www.bbesound.com, pg 702

BC Studio, 152 W 25 St, 2nd fl, New York, NY 10001 *Tel:* 212-242-4065 *Fax:* 212-242-4190 *E-mail:* info@bcvideo.com *Web Site:* www. greenscreenproductionnyc.com, pg 702

BCD Associates Inc, 2800 NW 36 St, Suite 220, Oklahoma City, OK 73112 *Tel:* 405-702-6888 *Toll Free Tel:* 800-223-6734 *E-mail:* salesweb@bcdusa. com; sales@bcdusa.com *Web Site:* www.bcdusa.com, pg 702

The BD Co, PO Box 2048, Chandler, AZ 85225-2048 *Tel:* 480-632-1160 *Toll Free Tel:* 800-704-3072 *Fax:* 480-632-1163 *Web Site:* bdbackgrounds.com, pg 702

Be Media, 9729 Lurline Ave, Chatsworth, CA 91311 *Tel:* 310-725-8500 *Toll Free Tel:* 877-210-7664 *Fax:* 310-725-9500 *Web Site:* www.bemedia.com, pg 702

BEA National Scholarships in Broadcasting, 1771 "N" St NW, Washington, DC 20036-2891 *Tel:* 202-602-0587 *Fax:* 202-609-9940 *E-mail:* help@beaweb.org *Web Site:* www.beaweb.org, pg 983

BeachTek Inc, 480 Osprey Ave, Kelowna, BC V1Y 5A5, Canada *Tel:* 778-478-9872 *E-mail:* info@beachtek. com *Web Site:* www.beachtek.com, pg 702

Beachwood Productions, 1500 Mill Creek Ct SW, Marietta, GA 30008 *Tel:* 770-432-6563; 404-324-7271 (cell) *Web Site:* www.beachwoodproductions.com, pg 702

Bear Creek Studio & Music Production Inc, 6313 Maltby Rd, Woodinville, WA 98072 *Tel:* 425-481-4100 *Fax:* 425-486-2718 *E-mail:* bearcreek@seanet. com *Web Site:* bearcreekstudio.com, pg 702

Beast Atlanta, 3399 Peachtree Rd NE, Suite 200, Atlanta, GA 30326-1149 *Tel:* 404-237-9977 *Fax:* 404-237-3923 *Web Site:* www.beast.tv, pg 703

Beatty TeleVisual Productions, 1287 Wabash Ave, Springfield, IL 62704 *Tel:* 217-787-4747 *Fax:* 217-787-4857 *Web Site:* www.beattytelevisual.com, pg 703

Russ Beckner Pictures, 2100 Heatherwood Ct, Middletown, OH 45042 *Tel:* 513-422-9552 *E-mail:* rdbvideo@gmail.com *Web Site:* russbeckner. com, pg 703

Beekman Books Inc, 300 Old All Angels Hill Rd, Wappingers Falls, NY 12590 *Tel:* 845-297-2690 *Fax:* 845-297-1002 *E-mail:* beekmanbooks@yahoo. com, pg 703

Beholder Productions Inc, 1769 Old York Rd, Abington, PA 19001 *Toll Free Tel:* 844-BEHOLD-R (234-6537) *E-mail:* info@beholderproductions.com *Web Site:* www.beholderagency.com, pg 703

Lawrence Behr Associates Inc, 3400 Tupper Dr, Greenville, NC 27834 *Tel:* 252-757-0279 *Toll Free Tel:* 800-522-4464 *Fax:* 252-752-9155 *E-mail:* lbagrp@lbagroup.com *Web Site:* www. lbagroup.com/associates, pg 703

Bel Fuse Inc, 299 Johnson Ave, Suite 100, Waseca, MN 56093 *Tel:* 507-833-8822 *Fax:* 507-833-6287 *E-mail:* ccsorders@us.cinch.com *Web Site:* cinch.com, pg 703

Belar Electronics Laboratory Inc, 1140 McDermott Dr, Suite 105, West Chester, PA 19380-4043 *Tel:* 610-687-5550 *Fax:* 610-687-2686 *E-mail:* sales@belar.com *Web Site:* www.belar.com, pg 703

Belden Inc, 401 Pennsylvania Pkwy, Suite 200, Indianapolis, IN 46280 *Tel:* 317-818-6300 *Toll Free Tel:* 800-235-3362; 800-BELDEN-1 (235-3361) *Fax:* 317-818-6365 *E-mail:* info@belden. com *Web Site:* www.belden.com, pg 703

Belew Enterprises, 524 Vance Dr, Bristol, TN 37620 *Tel:* 423-764-4116 *E-mail:* bsv@tricon.net, pg 703

Bell and Howell LLC, 3791 S Alston Ave, Durham, NC 27713 *Toll Free Tel:* 800-220-3030; 800-792-4782 (cust care) *E-mail:* info@bhemail.com *Web Site:* www. bellhowell.net, pg 703

Bella Faccia Inc, 5137 Lawrence Place, Hyattsville, MD 20781 *Tel:* 202-291-1932 *E-mail:* contact@bellafaccia. net *Web Site:* www.bellafaccia.net, pg 703

Bellin Productions, 109 Mosher Rd, Glenmont, NY 12077 *Tel:* 518-472-0037; 914-980-6322 (cell) *Toll Free Tel:* 888-834-5520 *E-mail:* info@ bellinproductions.com *Web Site:* www. bellinproductions.com, pg 703

Ben Nye Makeup, 3655 Lenawee Ave, Los Angeles, CA 90016 *Tel:* 310-839-1984 *Fax:* 310-839-2640 *Web Site:* www.bennye.com, pg 703

Benchmark Media Systems Inc, 203 E Hampton Place, Suite 2, Syracuse, NY 13206 *Tel:* 315-437-6300 *Toll Free Tel:* 800-262-4675 *Fax:* 315-437-8119 *E-mail:* sales@benchmarkmedia.com *Web Site:* www. benchmarkmedia.com, pg 703

Benedetto Guitars, 10 Mall Terr, Suite A, Savannah, GA 31406 *Tel:* 912-692-1400 *Fax:* 912-692-1403 *Web Site:* www.benedettoguitars.com, pg 703

The Robert Spiers Benjamin Award, 40 W 45 St, New York, NY 10036 *Tel:* 212-626-9220 *Fax:* 212-626-9210 *E-mail:* info@opcofamerica.org *Web Site:* www. opcofamerica.org, pg 983

Bennett-Watt HD Productions Inc, 13021 244 Ave SE, Issaquah, WA 98027 *Tel:* 425-392-3935 *Toll Free Tel:* 800-327-2893 *Fax:* 425-526-5851 *E-mail:* info@ bennett-watt.com *Web Site:* www.bennett-watt.com, pg 703

Benro, 75 Virginia Rd, Suite 1, North White Plains, NY 10603 *Tel:* 914-347-3300 *Fax:* 914-347-3309 *E-mail:* info@benrousa.com *Web Site:* www.benrousa. com, pg 704

The Bergman Collection of Medical/Technical/Scientific Stock Images, 134 Leabrook Lane, Princeton, NJ 08540-3622 *Tel:* 609-921-0749 *E-mail:* information@ pmiprinceton.com *Web Site:* pmiprinceton.com, pg 704

Bergwall Productions Inc, 120 N Church St, Suite 106, West Chester, PA 19380 *E-mail:* info@bergwall.com *Web Site:* www.bergwall.com, pg 704

Berke Creative Inc, 50 Mendell St, Suite 11, San Francisco, CA 94124 *Tel:* 415-312-2476 *Web Site:* www.berkecreative.com, pg 704

Berkeley Film Office, 2030 Addison St, Suite 102, Berkeley, CA 94704 *Tel:* 510-549-7040 *Toll Free Tel:* 847-4823 *Fax:* 510-644-2052 *E-mail:* film@ visitberkeley.com *Web Site:* www.filmberkeley.com, pg 966

Berkeley Sound Artists Inc, 2600 Tenth St, Suite 312, Berkeley, CA 94710 *Tel:* 510-486-2290 *E-mail:* info@ berkeleysoundartists.com *Web Site:* www. berkeleysoundartists.com, pg 704

Berkeley Video & Film Festival, 1939 Addison St, Berkeley, CA 94704 *Tel:* 510-843-3699 *E-mail:* maketv@aol.com *Web Site:* www. berkeleyvideofilmfest.org, pg 983

Bernie's Photo Center, 525 E Ohio St, Pittsburgh, PA 15212 *Tel:* 412-231-1717 *Toll Free Tel:* 800-346-8884 *Fax:* 412-231-1217 *E-mail:* berniesphotocenter.info@ gmail.com *Web Site:* www.berniesphoto.com, pg 704

Berry & Homer, 2035 Richmond St, Philadelphia, PA 19125 *Tel:* 215-425-0888 *Web Site:* www. berryandhomer.com, pg 704

BES Studios, 5711 Old Osbourne Tpke, Henrico, VA 23231 *Tel:* 804-276-0806 *Toll Free Tel:* 800-995-2371 *E-mail:* info@besstudios.com *Web Site:* www. besstudios.com, pg 704

Beseler Photo, 2018 W Main St, Stroudsburg, PA 18360 *Toll Free Tel:* 800-237-3537 *Toll Free Fax:* 800-966-4515 *Web Site:* www.beselerphoto.com, pg 704

Best Digital Reporting on International Affairs, 40 W 45 St, New York, NY 10036 *Tel:* 212-626-9220 *Fax:* 212-626-9210 *E-mail:* info@opcofamerica.org *Web Site:* www.opcofamerica.org, pg 983

Best Film & Video, 3913 Fall Wheat Dr, Plano, TX 75075 *Tel:* 214-395-4070 *Web Site:* www. bestfilmandvideo.com, pg 704

The Best of Photojournalism (BOP), 120 Hooper St, Athens, GA 30602-3018 *Tel:* 706-542-2506 *E-mail:* info@nppa.org *Web Site:* nppa.org, pg 983

Bestek Lighting & Staging, 98 Mahan St, West Babylon, NY 11704 *Tel:* 631-643-0707 *Fax:* 631-643-0764 *E-mail:* production@bestek.com *Web Site:* www. bestek.com, pg 704

Bestwell Optical Instrument Corp, 46 Henry St, Merrick, NY 11566 *Tel:* 516-889-1178 *Fax:* 516-706-1744 *Web Site:* www.bestwelloptical.com, pg 704

Beta Electronics Inc, 318 Bronze, Irvine, CA 92618 *Tel:* 614-538-8207 *Toll Free Tel:* 800-546-2382 *Fax:* 614-358-9945 *Toll Free Fax:* 888-329-2382 *E-mail:* sales@betalaser.com *Web Site:* www.betalaser. com, pg 704

Bethesda Softworks LLC, 1370 Piccard Dr, Suite 120, Rockville, MD 20850 *Tel:* 301-926-8300 *E-mail:* info@bethsoft.com; press@bethsoft.com *Web Site:* bethesda.net, pg 704

Bevilacqua Studios, 202 E 42 St, New York, NY 10017 *Tel:* 212-490-0355 *Fax:* 212-490-0355, pg 704

Bexel, an NEP Broadcast Services Company, 2701 N Ontario St, Burbank, CA 91504 *Tel:* 818-565-4322 *Toll Free Tel:* 800-225-6185 (tech support) *E-mail:* services@bexel.com *Web Site:* bexel.com, pg 704

Bext Inc, 1045 Tenth Ave, San Diego, CA 92101 *Tel:* 619-BEXTINC (239-8462) *Toll Free Tel:* 888-BEXTINC (239-8462) *Fax:* 619-239-8474 *E-mail:* bext@bext.com *Web Site:* www.bext.com, pg 704

beyerdynamic Inc, 56 Central Ave, Farmingdale, NY 11735 *Tel:* 631-293-3200 *Fax:* 631-293-3288 *E-mail:* info@beyerdynamic-usa.com *Web Site:* north-america.beyerdynamic.com, pg 704

BeyerSound & Essay Audio, PO Box 120442, St Paul, MN 55112-0018 *Tel:* 651-633-3933 *E-mail:* info@ essayaudio.com *Web Site:* www.essayaudio.com, pg 705

BFF (Black Filmmaker Foundation), 200 Broadway, New York, NY 10038, pg 952

BIAMP Systems, 9300 SW Gemini Dr, Beaverton, OR 97008 *Tel:* 503-641-7287 *Toll Free Tel:* 800-826-1457 (US & CN) *E-mail:* biampinfo@biamp.com *Web Site:* www.biamp.com, pg 705

Bias Studios, 5400 Carolina Place, Springfield, VA 22151 *Tel:* 703-941-3333 *E-mail:* info@biasstudios. com *Web Site:* www.biasstudios.com, pg 705

Biblical Archaeology Society (BAS), 4710 41 St NW, Washington, DC 20016 *Tel:* 202-364-3300 *Toll Free Tel:* 800-221-4644 *Fax:* 202-364-2636 *E-mail:* bas@bib-arch.org; merchandise@bib-arch.org *Web Site:* www.biblicalarchaeology.org, pg 705

Big Apple Films, 636 W 28 St, New York, NY 10001 *E-mail:* info@bigapplefilms.com *Web Site:* www. bigapplefilms.com, pg 705

Big Deal Custom Casings, 100 Durand Rd, Winnipeg, MB R2J 3T2, Canada *Tel:* 204-663-4870 *Toll Free Tel:* 800-337-3325 *Fax:* 204-668-7404 *E-mail:* info@ bigdealcases.com *Web Site:* bigdealcases.ca, pg 705

Big Door, 114 Sheldon St, El Segundo, CA 90245 *Tel:* 310-546-6100 *Fax:* 310-906-4585 *E-mail:* sales@ bigdoor.tv *Web Site:* www.bigdoor.tv; www. bigdoorstudio.tv, pg 705

Big Event Productions LLC, 77 13 Ave NE, Studio 101, Minneapolis, MN 55413 *Tel:* 612-623-7800 *Web Site:* www.bigeventpros.com, pg 705

Big Film Design, 375 South End Ave, Suite 3H, New York, NY 10280 *Tel:* 212-627-3430 *E-mail:* info@ bigfilmdesign.com *Web Site:* www.bigfilmdesign.com, pg 705

Big Fish Production US, PO Box 782, Bronx, NY 10462-0782 *Tel:* 347-526-5211 *E-mail:* bigfishproductionus@gmail.com *Web Site:* www.bigfishproductionus.com, pg 705

Big Foot Productions Inc, 37-09 36 Ave, Long Island City, NY 11101 *Tel:* 718-729-1900 *E-mail:* info@ bigfootnyc.com *Web Site:* www.bigfootnyc.com, pg 705

The Big House Group, 17 Waller Ave, Ossining, NY 10562 *Tel:* 914-944-4011 *Fax:* 914-944-8044 *Web Site:* www.bighousetv.com, pg 705

Big House Sound Inc, 4001 Drossett Dr, Austin, TX 78744 *Tel:* 512-443-0019 *Fax:* 512-443-0916 *Web Site:* www.bighousesound.com, pg 705

Big Muddy Film Festival, 1100 Lincoln Dr, Rm 1101, Carbondale, IL 62901-6610 *Tel:* 618-453-8301 *E-mail:* info@bigmuddyfilm.com *Web Site:* www. bigmuddyfilm.com, pg 983

Big Shoulders Digital Video Productions, 875 N Michigan Ave, Suite 3750, Chicago, IL 60611 *Tel:* 312-540-5400 *E-mail:* info@bigshoulders.com; sales@bigshoulders.com *Web Site:* www.bigshoulders. com, pg 705

BigFoot Mobile Systems, 4015 Blackthorn Dr, Vacaville, CA 95688 *Tel:* 707-602-5548 *Fax:* 707-602-5549 *E-mail:* info@bigfootmobilecarts.com *Web Site:* www. bigfootmobilecarts.com, pg 705

Bil-Jax Inc, 125 Taylor Pkwy, Archbold, OH 43502 *Tel:* 419-445-8915 *Toll Free Tel:* 800-537-0540 *Fax:* 419-445-0367 *E-mail:* sales@biljax.com *Web Site:* www.biljax.com, pg 705

Bill Bachmann Studios, PO Box 950833, Lake Mary, FL 32795 *Tel:* 407-333-9988 *Web Site:* www. billbachmann.com, pg 705

BingoLewis, 5828 N Lombard St, Portland, OR 97203 *Tel:* 503-223-2224 *E-mail:* info@bingolewis.com *Web Site:* www.bingolewis.com, pg 706

Biomorph Desks, 11 Broadway, Rm 905, New York, NY 10004 *Tel:* 212-809-4323 *Toll Free Tel:* 888-302-DESK (302-3375) *Toll Free Fax:* 888-652-7137 *E-mail:* info@biomorphdesk.com *Web Site:* www. biomorphdesk.com, pg 706

Birds & Animals Unlimited, 34145 Pacific Coast Hwy, No 761, Dana Point, CA 92629 *Tel:* 661-269-0148 *Toll Free Tel:* 877-542-1355 *Toll Free Fax:* 866-212-7899 *E-mail:* california@birdsandanimals.com *Web Site:* www.birdsandanimals.com, pg 706

Birns & Sawyer Inc, 3039 Roswell St, Los Angeles, CA 90065 *Tel:* 323-466-8211 *E-mail:* info@ birnsandsawyer.com *Web Site:* www.birnsandsawyer. com, pg 706

Bishop Area Chamber of Commerce & Visitors Bureau, 690 N Main St, Bishop, CA 93514 *Tel:* 760-873-8405 *Web Site:* www.bishopvisitor.com, pg 966

Bisk Education, 9417 Princess Palm Ave, Tampa, FL 33619 *Toll Free Tel:* 800-280-9718 *E-mail:* media@ bisk.com *Web Site:* www.bisk.com, pg 706

Bismeaux Studios, PO Box 463, Austin, TX 78767-0463 *Tel:* 512-444-9885 *Web Site:* www.bismeauxstudios. com, pg 706

Bitcentral Inc, 4340 Von Karman Ave, Suite 400, Newport Beach, CA 92660 *Tel:* 949-253-9000 *Toll Free Tel:* 800-272-4004 (support) *E-mail:* sales@bitcentral.com; support@bitcentral.com *Web Site:* www.bitcentral.com, pg 706

BitFlow Inc, 400 W Cummings Park, Suite 5050, Woburn, MA 01801 *Tel:* 781-932-2900 *Fax:* 781-933-9965 *E-mail:* sales@bitflow.com *Web Site:* www. bitflow.com, pg 706

Biway Media, 5803 Sovereign, Suite 204, Houston, TX 77036 *Tel:* 713-271-4036 *Toll Free Tel:* 877-BIWAY DV (249-2938) *E-mail:* info@biwaymedia.com; sales@biwaymedia.com *Web Site:* www.biwaymedia. com, pg 706

BJU Press, 1430 Wade Hampton Blvd, Greenville, SC 29609 *Tel:* 864-770-1317 *Toll Free Tel:* 800-845-5731 *Fax:* 864-271-8151 *Toll Free Fax:* 800-525-8398 *E-mail:* bjupinfo@bjupress.com *Web Site:* www.bjupress.com; www.bjupresshomeschool.com, pg 706

The Black Academy of Arts & Letters Inc, Dallas Convention Ctr Theater Complex, 1309 Canton St, Dallas, TX 75201 *Tel:* 214-743-2440 *Fax:* 214-743-2451 *E-mail:* info@tbaal.org *Web Site:* www.tbaal.org, pg 706

Black Film Center/Archive, Indiana University, Wells Library, Rm 044, 1320 E Tenth St, Bloomington, IN 47405 *Tel:* 812-855-6041 *Fax:* 812-856-5832 *E-mail:* bfca@indiana.edu *Web Site:* www.indiana.edu/~bfca, pg 706

Black Maria Film Festival, c/o New Jersey City University, Dept of Media Arts, 2039 Kennedy Blvd, Jersey City, NJ 07305 *Tel:* 201-200-2043 *Fax:* 201-200-3490 *E-mail:* info@blackmariafilmfestival.org *Web Site:* www.blackmariafilmfestival.org, pg 983

Black Media Works, 534 21 Ave SW, Calgary, AB T2S 0H1, Canada *Tel:* 403-802-0010 *E-mail:* info@blackmediaworks.com *Web Site:* www.blackmediaworks.com, pg 706

Black Star Publishing Co Inc, 333 Mamaroneck Ave, No 175, White Plains, NY 10605 *Tel:* 212-679-3288 *Fax:* 212-889-2052 *Web Site:* www.blackstar.com, pg 706

Blackburst Entertainment LLC, 1011 E Colonial Dr, No 304, Orlando, FL 32803 *Tel:* 321-439-2844 *E-mail:* contact@blackburstentertainment.com *Web Site:* blackburstentertainment.com, pg 706

Blackmagic Design Pty Ltd, 2875 Bayview Dr, Fremont, CA 94538 *Tel:* 408-954-0500 *Fax:* 408-954-0508 *E-mail:* info-usa@blackmagicdesign.com *Web Site:* www.blackmagicdesign.com, pg 707

Blackstone Audio Inc, 31 Mistletoe Rd, Ashland, OR 97520 *Toll Free Tel:* 800-621-0182 *Toll Free Fax:* 877-492-0793 *E-mail:* libraryservices@blackstoneaudio.com *Web Site:* www.blackstoneaudio.com; www.blackstonelibrary.com, pg 707

Blackwater Video Productions, PO Box 909, Morgantown, WV 26507 *Tel:* 304-296-4048 *E-mail:* blackwatervideo@hotmail.com *Web Site:* www.blackwatervideo.com, pg 707

Michael Blackwood Productions Inc, 6 W 18 St, Suite 2B, New York, NY 10011 *Tel:* 212-242-1805 *Fax:* 212-242-1671 *E-mail:* blackwoodfilm@aol.com *Web Site:* www.michaelblackwoodproductions.com, pg 707

Blair Inc, 7001 Loisdale Rd, Springfield, VA 22150 *Tel:* 703-922-0200 *Fax:* 703-924-0765 *E-mail:* info@blairinc.com *Web Site:* www.blairinc.com, pg 707

Les Blank Films Inc, 10341 San Pablo Ave, El Cerrito, CA 94530-3123 *Tel:* 510-525-0942 *E-mail:* lesblankfilmsinc@gmail.com *Web Site:* lesblank.com, pg 707

Blind™, 1702 Olympic Blvd, Santa Monica, CA 90404 *Tel:* 310-314-1618 *Fax:* 310-314-1718 *Web Site:* www.blind.com, pg 707

Blonder Tongue Laboratories Inc, One Jake Brown Rd, Old Bridge, NJ 08857 *Tel:* 732-679-4000 *Toll Free Tel:* 800-523-6049 *Fax:* 732-679-4353 *E-mail:* custsvc@blondertongue.com; btglobalsales@blondertongue.com (outside US & CN); information@blondertongue.com *Web Site:* www.blondertongue.com, pg 707

Blood-Horse Publications, 3101 Beaumont Centre Circle, Lexington, KY 40513 *Toll Free Tel:* 800-866-2361; 800-582-5604 *E-mail:* advertise@bloodhorse.com; customerservice@bloodhorse.com *Web Site:* www.bloodhorse.com, pg 707

Blue Barn Pictures Inc, 68 Jay St, Suite 311, Brooklyn, NY 11201 *Web Site:* www.bluebarnpictures.com, pg 707

Blue Earth Pictures, 5532 Code Ave, Minneapolis, MN 55436 *Tel:* 612-619-5909 *E-mail:* missioncontrol@blueearthpictures.com *Web Site:* www.blueearthpictures.com, pg 707

Blue Lotus Temple Studio, PO Box 888, Boulder Creek, CA 95006 *Tel:* 831-338-2544 *E-mail:* info@bluelotustemple.com *Web Site:* www.bluelotustemple.com, pg 707

Blue Media Supply Inc, 3511 Church St, Suite F, Atlanta, GA 30021 *Tel:* 404-622-6709 *Toll Free Tel:* 866-717-6334 *Fax:* 404-622-1008 *E-mail:* sales@bluemediasupply.com *Web Site:* www.bluemediasupply.com, pg 707

Blue Mouse Studio, 26829 37 St, Gobles, MI 49055 *Tel:* 269-628-5160 *E-mail:* frogville@earthlink.net; mwivi@earthlink.net, pg 707

Blue Ocean Film Festival & Conservation Summit, 646 Second Ave S, St Petersburg, FL 33701 *Tel:* 727-388-6682 *E-mail:* info@blueoceanfilmfestival.org; entries@blueoceanfilmfestival.org *Web Site:* www.blueoceanfilmfestival.org, pg 983

Blue Onion Media, 940 Wadsworth Blvd, 3rd fl, Lakewood, CO 80214 *Tel:* 303-597-9661 *Fax:* 303-232-2241 *Web Site:* www.blueonionmedia.com, pg 708

Blue River Productions, PO Box 1535, Breckenridge, CO 80424-1535 *Tel:* 970-390-8568 *E-mail:* filmbreckenridge@gmail.com, pg 708

Blue Room Post, MBS Raleigh Studios, Bldg 5-A, Suite 100, 1600 Rosecrans Ave, Manhattan Beach, CA 90266 *Tel:* 310-727-2600 *Web Site:* www.blueroompost.com, pg 708

Blue Sky Stock Footage, PO Box 177, Santa Fe, NM 87504-0177 *Tel:* 310-859-4709 *E-mail:* sales@blueskyfootage.com *Web Site:* www.blueskyfootage.com, pg 708

Blue Wave Records, 3221 Perryville Rd, Baldwinsville, NY 13027 *Tel:* 315-638-4286 *E-mail:* bluewave@localnet.com *Web Site:* www.bluewaverecords.com, pg 708

Blueeyed Pictures Inc, 8950 W Olympic Blvd, Suite 324, Beverly Hills, CA 90211 *Tel:* 310-295-0848 *E-mail:* la@blueyedpictures.com *Web Site:* www.blueyedpictures.com, pg 708

BMI Supply, 571 Queensbury Ave, Queensbury, NY 12804 *Tel:* 518-793-6706 *Toll Free Tel:* 800-836-0524 *Fax:* 518-793-6181 *E-mail:* bminy@bmisupply.com *Web Site:* www.bmisupply.com, pg 708

Boeckeler Instruments Inc, 4650 S Butterfield Dr, Tucson, AZ 85714 *Tel:* 520-745-0001 *Toll Free Tel:* 800-552-2262 *Fax:* 520-745-0004 *E-mail:* info@boeckeler.com *Web Site:* www.boeckeler.com, pg 708

Bogen Communications Inc, 1200 MacArthur Blvd, Suite 304, Mahwah, NJ 07430 *Tel:* 201-934-8500 *Toll Free Tel:* 800-999-2809 *E-mail:* info@bogen.com; customerservice@bogen.com *Web Site:* www.bogen.com, pg 708

Boitnott Visual Communications Corp (BVC), 14201 Justice Rd, Midlothian, VA 23113 *Tel:* 804-379-9400 *Fax:* 804-379-9413 *Web Site:* www.boitnottvisual.com, pg 708

Boland Communications Inc, 16 Rancho Circle, Lake Forest, CA 92630 *Tel:* 949-465-9911 *Toll Free Tel:* 800-918-9090 *E-mail:* sales@bolandcom.com *Web Site:* www.bolandcom.com, pg 708

Bolchazy - Carducci Publishers Inc, 1570 Baskin Rd, Mundelein, IL 60060 *Tel:* 847-526-4344 *Fax:* 847-526-2867 *E-mail:* info@bolchazy.com *Web Site:* www.bolchazy.com, pg 708

Bond Street Studio, 235 Bond St, Brooklyn, NY 11217 *Tel:* 718-858-2238 *E-mail:* info@bondstreetstudio.com *Web Site:* www.bondstreetstudio.com, pg 708

Bonnin Electronics Inc, 619 Hipodromo St, San Juan, PR 00909 *Tel:* 787-725-4765 *Fax:* 787-725-0840 *E-mail:* sales@bonninelectronics.com *Web Site:* www.bonninelectronics.com, pg 708

Book Marketing Works LLC, 50 Lovely St, Avon, CT 06001 *Tel:* 860-675-1344 *Web Site:* www.bookmarketingworks.com, pg 708

Books In Motion, 9922 E Montgomery Dr, Suite 31, Spokane Valley, WA 99206 *Tel:* 509-922-1646 *Toll Free Tel:* 800-752-3199 *Fax:* 509-922-1445 *E-mail:* sales@booksinmotion.com *Web Site:* www.booksinmotion.com, pg 708

Books on Tape™, c/o Library & School Servs, 400 Hahn Rd, Westminster, MD 21157 *Toll Free Tel:* 800-733-3000 *Toll Free Fax:* 800-940-7046 *E-mail:* csbot@penguinrandomhouse.com *Web Site:* www.booksontape.com, pg 708

Boonton Electronics, 25 Eastmans Rd, Parsippany, NJ 07054 *Tel:* 973-386-9696 *Fax:* 973-386-9191 *E-mail:* info@boonton.com *Web Site:* www.boonton.com, pg 709

Bosch Security Systems Inc, 12000 Portland Ave S, Burnsville, MN 35337 *Toll Free Tel:* 800-289-0096 *E-mail:* buv.orders@us.bosch.com *Web Site:* us.boschsecurity.com, pg 709

Bose Corp, The Mountain, MS 2C3, Framingham, MA 01701-8863 *Tel:* 508-879-7330; 508-766-6885 (sales outside US) *Toll Free Tel:* 800-999-2673; 800-379-2073 (sales) *E-mail:* support@bose.com *Web Site:* www.bose.com, pg 709

Boston Acoustics, One Viper Way, Suite C, Vista, CA 92081 *Toll Free Tel:* 877-924-5817 (tech/prod support) *Web Site:* www.bostonacoustics.com, pg 709

The Boston Connection Inc, 7 High St, Cotuit, MA 02635 *Tel:* 617-908-6258 *Fax:* 508-428-2036 *E-mail:* bconnect@cutfilm.com *Web Site:* www.cutfilm.com, pg 709

Boston Film Bureau, One City Hall Sq, Rm 802, Boston, MA 02201-2029 *Tel:* 617-635-3911 *Fax:* 617-635-4428 *E-mail:* filmbureau@cityofboston.gov *Web Site:* www.cityofboston.gov/arts/film, pg 972

Boston Light & Sound Inc, 290 N Beacon St, Boston, MA 02135-1990 *Tel:* 617-787-3131 *Fax:* 617-787-4257 *E-mail:* info@blsi.com *Web Site:* www.blsi.com, pg 709

Boston Productions Inc (BPI), 290 Vanderbilt Ave, Suite 1, Norwood, MA 02062 *Tel:* 781-255-1555; 720-233-1250 (sales) *E-mail:* info@bostonproductions.com *Web Site:* www.bostonproductions.com, pg 709

Boulder County Film Commission, 2440 Pearl St, Boulder, CO 80302 *Tel:* 303-442-2911 *Toll Free Tel:* 800-444-0447 *Fax:* 303-938-2098 *E-mail:* visitor@bouldercvb.com *Web Site:* www.bouldercoloradousa.com/film-commission, pg 968

Bowens USA, 75 Virginia Rd, North White Plains, NY 10603 *Tel:* 914-347-3300 *Fax:* 914-347-3309, pg 709

Bowie Audio Visual Enterprises Inc, 290 Highpoint Dr, Ridgeland, MS 39157 *Tel:* 601-957-6566 *Toll Free Tel:* 800-748-9030 *Fax:* 601-957-7042 *Toll Free Fax:* 800-748-3401 *E-mail:* sales@bowieav.com; info@bowieav.com *Web Site:* www.bowieav.com, pg 709

Boxlight Inc, 1045 Progress Circle, Lawrenceville, GA 30043 *Toll Free Tel:* 866-972-1549 *E-mail:* service@boxlight.com; marketing@boxlight.com *Web Site:* mimio.boxlight.com, pg 709

Boyce Nemec Designs, PO Box 566, Norfolk, CT 06058-0566 *Tel:* 860-542-5937 *Web Site:* www.boycenemec.com, pg 709

The Bradenton Area Film Commission, One Haben Blvd, Palmetto, FL 34221 *Tel:* 941-729-9177 *Fax:* 941-729-1820 *Web Site:* www.bradentongulfislands.com/film, pg 969

Bradley Broadcast & Pro Audio, PO Box 756, New Market, MD 21774 *Tel:* 301-682-8700 *Toll Free Tel:* 800-732-7665 *Fax:* 301-263-7042 *E-mail:* beburg@bradleybroadcast.com *Web Site:* www.bradleybroadcast.com, pg 709

Brady Corp, 6555 W Good Hope Rd, Milwaukee, WI 53201-0571 *Tel:* 414-358-6600 *Toll Free Tel:* 888-250-3082 *E-mail:* bradyusa@bradycorp.com (cust serv & sales) *Web Site:* www.bradyid.com, pg 709

The Brainwash Movie Festival, 1675 Seventh St, No 23302, Oakland, CA 94623-6009 *Tel:* 510-836-3210 *E-mail:* brainwash.movies@gmail.com *Web Site:* www.brainwashm.com, pg 984

Branam Enterprises Inc, 9152 Independence Ave, Chatsworth, CA 91311 *Tel:* 818-885-6474 *Toll Free Tel:* 877-295-3390 *Fax:* 818-885-6475 *E-mail:* info@branament.com *Web Site:* www.branament.com, pg 709

Brantley Sound Associates Inc, 115 Duluth Ave, Nashville, TN 37209-1207 *Tel:* 615-256-6260 *Web Site:* www.brantleysound.com, pg 709

Bravo Studios, 40 W 27 St, 2nd fl, New York, NY 10001 *Tel:* 212-563-0054 *E-mail:* info@newyorkgreenscreen.com *Web Site:* www.newyorkgreenscreen.com, pg 709

BRB Audiovisual Productions, 135 Punkup Rd, Oxford, CT 06478-1747 *Tel:* 203-881-3577 *Toll Free Tel:* 800-587-7521 *Fax:* 203-828-0732 *E-mail:* services@brbaudiovisual.com *Web Site:* www.brbaudiovisual.com, pg 709

Breeze Productions Inc, 1660 Edgewood Rd, Highland Park, IL 60035 *Web Site:* www.breezeprod.com, pg 710

Bretford Manufacturing Inc, 11000 Seymour Ave, Franklin Park, IL 60131 *Tel:* 847-678-2545 *Toll Free Tel:* 800-521-9614 *Fax:* 847-678-0852 *Toll Free Fax:* 800-343-1779 *E-mail:* customerservice@bretford.com *Web Site:* www.bretford.com, pg 710

Brian Film Productions LLC, 254 W 25 St, Suite 6-A, New York, NY 10001-7325 *Tel:* 212-645-8795, pg 710

Bridge Publications Inc, 5600 E Olympic Blvd, Los Angeles, CA 90022 *Tel:* 323-888-6200 *Toll Free Tel:* 800-722-1733 *Fax:* 323-888-6202 *E-mail:* info@bridgepub.com *Web Site:* www.bridgepub.com, pg 710

Bridge Records Inc, 200 Clinton Ave, New Rochelle, NY 10801 *Tel:* 914-654-9270 *Web Site:* www.bridgerecords.com, pg 710

Bridger Productions Inc, 4150 Glory View Lane, Jackson, WY 83001 *Tel:* 307-733-7871 *E-mail:* bridgerproductions@gmail.com *Web Site:* www.bridgerproductions.com, pg 710

Bright Ideas Creative Services, 107 W Maple St, Suite 206, Jeffersonville, IN 47130 *Tel:* 812-282-9900; 502-693-9900 (cell) *Toll Free Tel:* 866-593-5753 *Web Site:* www.brightideascreative.com, pg 710

Bright Star Productions Inc, 2420 Center St, Houston, TX 77007 *Tel:* 713-529-2757 *Fax:* 713-529-2329 *Web Site:* www.brightstarproductions.com, pg 710

Brightline LP, 580 Mayer St, Bldg 7, Bridgeville, PA 15017 *Tel:* 412-206-0106 *Fax:* 412-206-0146 *E-mail:* information@brightlines.com *Web Site:* www.brightlines.com, pg 710

Brilliance Audio, 1704 Eaton Dr, Grand Haven, MI 49417 *Tel:* 616-846-5256 *Toll Free Tel:* 800-648-2312 (orders) *Fax:* 616-846-0630 *E-mail:* help@audiobookstand.com *Web Site:* www.brillianceaudio.com, pg 710

Brim Electronics, 120 Home Place, Lodi, NJ 07644 *Tel:* 201-796-2886 *Fax:* 973-778-2792 *E-mail:* info@brimelectronics.com *Web Site:* www.brimelectronics.com, pg 710

Britannica Digital Learning, 325 N La Salle St, Suite 200, Chicago, IL 60654 *Tel:* 800-621-3900 *Toll Free Fax:* 800-344-9624 *E-mail:* contact@eb.com; bdlpress@eb.com *Web Site:* britannicalearn.com, pg 710

Broadcast Center Studios, 700 Millbridge Gardens, Clementon, NJ 08021 *Tel:* 856-751-3500, pg 710

Broadcast Devices Inc, Westchester Industrial Complex, 3199 Albany Post Rd, Suite 122, Buchanan, NY 10511-1639 *Tel:* 914-737-5032 *Fax:* 914-736-6916 *E-mail:* sales@broadcast-devices.com; customer.service@broadcast-devices.com *Web Site:* www.broadcast-devices.com, pg 710

Broadcast Education Association (BEA), 1771 "N" St NW, Washington, DC 20036-2891 *Tel:* 202-602-0587 *Fax:* 202-609-9940 *E-mail:* help@beaweb.org *Web Site:* www.beaweb.org, pg 952

Broadcast Electronics, 4100 N 24 St, Quincy, IL 62305 *Tel:* 217-224-9600 *Fax:* 217-224-9607 *E-mail:* bdcast@bdcast.com *Web Site:* www.bdcast.com, pg 710

Broadcast Management Group, 718 Seventh St NW, Washington, DC 20001 *Tel:* 202-609-7757 *E-mail:* info@broadcastmgmt.com *Web Site:* www.broadcastmgmt.com, pg 710

Broadcast Microwave Services Inc (BMS), a StoneCalibre company, 12305 Crosthwaite Circle, Poway, CA 92064 *Tel:* 858-391-3050 *Toll Free Tel:* 800-669-9667 (US) *Fax:* 858-391-3049 *E-mail:* sales@bms-inc.com *Web Site:* www.bms-inc.com, pg 711

Broadcast Rentals, 2343 W University Dr, Suite 101, Tempe, AZ 85281 *Tel:* 480-894-1456 *Toll Free Tel:* 888-686-7368 *Fax:* 480-894-1023 *E-mail:* rent@broadcastrentals.com *Web Site:* www.broadcastrentals.com, pg 711

Broadcast Supply World Wide, 2237 S 19 St, Tacoma, WA 98405 *Tel:* 253-565-2301 (intl) *Toll Free Tel:* 800-426-8434 *Fax:* 253-565-8114 (intl) *Toll Free Fax:* 800-231-7055 *E-mail:* sales@bswusa.com; info@bswusa.com; customersupport@bswusa.com *Web Site:* www.bswusa.com, pg 711

Broadcasters Foundation of America, 125 W 55 St, 4th fl, New York, NY 10019-5366 *Tel:* 212-373-8250 *Fax:* 212-373-8254 *E-mail:* info@thebfoa.org *Web Site:* www.thebfoa.org; broadcastersfoundation.org, pg 952

Broadcasters General Store Inc, 2480 SE 52 St, Ocala, FL 34480 *Tel:* 352-622-7700 *Fax:* 352-629-7000 *E-mail:* sales@bgs.cc (orders) *Web Site:* www.bgs.cc, pg 711

BroadcastStore.com, 9420 Lurline Ave, Unit C, Chatsworth, CA 91311 *Tel:* 818-998-9100 *Fax:* 818-998-9106 *E-mail:* sales@broadcaststore.com *Web Site:* www.broadcaststore.com, pg 711

Broadstreet Productions LLC, 242 W 30 St, 2nd fl, New York, NY 10001 *Tel:* 212-780-5700 *E-mail:* newyork@broadstreet.com; admin@broadstreet.com *Web Site:* www.broadstreet.com, pg 711

Broadview Software Inc, 110 Adelaide St E, Toronto, ON M5C 1K9, Canada *Tel:* 647-255-3500 *Fax:* 416-778-0648 *E-mail:* sales@broadviewsoftware.com *Web Site:* www.broadviewsoftware.com, pg 711

Broadway Costumes Inc, 1100 W Cermak Rd, 2nd fl, Chicago, IL 60608 *Tel:* 312-829-6400 *Fax:* 312-829-8621 *E-mail:* rentals@broadwaycostumes.com *Web Site:* www.broadwaycostumes.com, pg 711

Broadway Digital, 1014 E Broadway, Louisville, KY 40204 *Tel:* 502-540-5301 *Fax:* 502-540-5565 *E-mail:* msworkscm@mindspring.com *Web Site:* www.broadwaydigital.us, pg 711

Brodart Co, 500 Arch St, Williamsport, PA 17701 *Tel:* 570-326-2461 *Toll Free Tel:* 888-820-4377 *Toll Free Fax:* 800-283-6087 *E-mail:* supplies.customerservice@brodart.com *Web Site:* www.shopbrodart.com, pg 711

Bronze Anvil Awards, 120 Wall St, 21st fl, New York, NY 10005-4024 *Tel:* 212-460-1438 *E-mail:* awards@prsa.org *Web Site:* www.prsa.org; anvils.prsa.org, pg 984

Paul H Brookes Publishing Co, PO Box 10624, Baltimore, MD 21285-0624 *Tel:* 410-337-9580 *Toll Free Tel:* 800-638-3775 (cust serv) *Fax:* 410-337-8539 *E-mail:* custserv@brookespublishing.com *Web Site:* www.brookespublishing.com, pg 711

Brookline Books, 8 Trumbull Rd, Suite B-001, Northampton, MA 01060 *Tel:* 413-584-0184; 603-669-7032 (orders) *Toll Free Tel:* 800-666-BOOK (666-2665 cust serv) *Fax:* 413-584-6184 *E-mail:* brbooks@yahoo.com *Web Site:* www.brooklinebks.com, pg 711

Brooklyn Botanic Garden, 1000 Washington Ave, Brooklyn, NY 11225 *Tel:* 718-623-7200 *E-mail:* feedback@bbg.org *Web Site:* www.bbg.org, pg 711

Brooklyn College Television Center, Whitehead Hall, Rm 018, 2900 Bedford Ave, Brooklyn, NY 11210 *Tel:* 718-951-5585 *E-mail:* tvcenter@brooklyn.cuny.edu *Web Site:* www.bctvcenter.org, pg 711

Brooklyn Film Festival (BFF), 180 S Fourth St, Suite 2-S, Brooklyn, NY 11211 *Tel:* 718-388-4306 *Fax:* 718-599-5039 *E-mail:* festival@wbff.org *Web Site:* www.brooklynfilmfestival.org, pg 984

Brooklyn Films, PO Box 20412, New York, NY 10021-0066 *E-mail:* connect@brooklynfilms.com *Web Site:* www.brooklynfilms.com, pg 711

Brooklyn Fire Proof, 119 Ingraham St, Brooklyn, NY 11237 *Tel:* 718-456-7570 *E-mail:* hello@brooklynfireproof.com *Web Site:* www.brooklynfireproof.com, pg 711

Brooklyn Studios, 8-16 43 Ave, Long Island City, NY 11101 *Tel:* 718-392-1007 *Fax:* 718-392-1008 *E-mail:* info@brooklynstudios.net *Web Site:* www.brooklynstudios.net, pg 711

The Brookwood Studio Inc, 6870 N Territorial Rd, Plymouth, MI 48170 *Tel:* 734-358-6071 *E-mail:* info@brookwoodstudio.com *Web Site:* www.brookwoodstudio.com, pg 711

Broughton's Church Supplies, Religious Books & Gifts, 322 Consumers Rd, North York, ON M2J 1P8, Canada *Tel:* 416-690-4777 *Toll Free Tel:* 800-268-4449 *Fax:* 416-690-5357 *E-mail:* sales@bbroughton.com *Web Site:* www.bbroughton.com, pg 711

Heywood Broun Award, 501 Third St NW, 6th fl, Washington, DC 20001-2797 *Tel:* 202-434-7177 *E-mail:* guild@cwa-union.org *Web Site:* www.newsguild.org, pg 984

James W Brown Publication Award, 320 W Eighth St, Suite 101, Bloomington, IN 47404-3745 *Tel:* 812-335-7675 *Toll Free Tel:* 877-677-AECT (677-2328) *Fax:* 812-335-7678 *E-mail:* aect@aect.org *Web Site:* www.aect.org, pg 984

Brown United Inc, PO Box 1700, Monrovia, CA 91017-5700 *Tel:* 626-357-1161 *Toll Free Tel:* 800-44-BROWN (442-7696) *Fax:* 626-358-3064 *Web Site:* www.brownunited.com, pg 711

Bryston Ltd, 677 Neal Dr, Peterborough, ON K9J 6X7, Canada *Tel:* 705-742-5325 *Toll Free Tel:* 800-632-8217 *Fax:* 705-742-0882 *Web Site:* www.bryston.com, pg 712

BTX Technologies, 5 Skyline Dr, Hawthorne, NY 10532 *Tel:* 914-592-1800 *Toll Free Tel:* 800-666-0996 *Toll Free Fax:* 800-569-4244 *E-mail:* info@btx.com *Web Site:* www.btx.com, pg 712

Bud Industries, 4605 E 355 St, Willoughby, OH 44094 *Tel:* 440-946-3200 *Fax:* 440-951-4015 *E-mail:* saleseast@budind.com *Web Site:* www.budind.com, pg 712

Billy Budd Films Inc, 235 E 57 St, New York, NY 10022 *Tel:* 212-755-3968 *E-mail:* info@billybuddfilms.com *Web Site:* www.billybuddfilms.com, pg 712

Budget Films Stock Footage Inc, 706 N Vendome St, Suite 6, Los Angeles, CA 90026 *Tel:* 323-660-0187 *Fax:* 323-660-5571 *E-mail:* filmclip@aol.com; info@budgetfilms.com *Web Site:* www.budgetfilms.com, pg 712

Budget Video Rentals, 1825 NE 149 St, Miami, FL 33181 *Tel:* 305-945-8888 *Toll Free Tel:* 800-772-1111 *Fax:* 305-945-0300 *E-mail:* rentals@budgetvideo.com *Web Site:* budgetvideo.com, pg 712

BUF Technology, 12335 World Trade Dr, Suite 11, San Diego, CA 92128 *Tel:* 858-451-1350 *Fax:* 858-451-6589 *E-mail:* info@buftek.com *Web Site:* www.buftek.com, pg 712

Buffalo Niagara International Film Festival (BNIFF), 3840 E Robinson Rd, Suite 166, Amherst, NY 14228 *Tel:* 716-693-0912 *E-mail:* info@bniff.com *Web Site:* thebnff.com, pg 984

Buffalo Video Production, 233 Fillmore Ave, Suite 8, Tonawanda, NY 14150 *Tel:* 716-807-1510 *Web Site:* www.buffalovideoproduction.com, pg 712

Bulbman Inc, 630 Sunshine Lane, Reno, NV 89502 *Tel:* 775-788-5661 *Toll Free Tel:* 800-648-1163 *Fax:* 775-329-6599 *Toll Free Fax:* 800-548-6216 *E-mail:* service@bulbman.com *Web Site:* www. bulbman.com, pg 712

Bulbtronics Inc, 45 Banfi Plaza N, Farmingdale, NY 11735 *Tel:* 631-249-2272 *Toll Free Tel:* 800-654-8542 (sales); 800-588-2852 *E-mail:* sftv@bulbtronics.com *Web Site:* www.bulbtronics.com, pg 712

Bullfrog Films Inc, 372 Dautrich Rd, Reading, PA 19606 *Tel:* 610-779-8226 *Toll Free Tel:* 800-543-3764 *Fax:* 610-370-1978 *E-mail:* info@bullfrogfilms. com; video@bullfrogfilms.com *Web Site:* www. bullfrogfilms.com, pg 712

Richard W Burden Associates, 20944 Sherman Way, Canoga Park, CA 91303 *Tel:* 818-340-4590, pg 712

The Bureau for At-Risk Youth, 40 Aero Rd, Suite 2, Bohemia, NY 11716 *Toll Free Tel:* 800-99-YOUTH (999-6884) *Fax:* 631-389-2511 *Toll Free Fax:* 800-262-1886 *Web Site:* www.guidance-group.com; www. at-risk.com, pg 712

Burk Technology Inc, 7 Beaver Brook Rd, Littleton, MA 01460 *Tel:* 978-486-0086 *Fax:* 978-486-0081 *E-mail:* sales@burk.com; orders@burk.com; support@ burk.com *Web Site:* www.burk.com, pg 712

Burlington A/V Recording Media, 106 Mott St, Oceanside, NY 11572 *Tel:* 516-678-4414 *Fax:* 516-678-8959 *E-mail:* shopping@recordingstore.com *Web Site:* www.recordingstore.com, pg 712

Burnaby Film Office, 6450 Deerlake Ave, Burnaby, BC V5G 2J3, Canada *Tel:* 604-294-7314 *Fax:* 604-205-3001 *E-mail:* filming@burnaby.ca *Web Site:* www. burnaby.ca, pg 977

Burrud Productions Inc, 468 N Camden Dr, 2nd fl, Beverly Hills, CA 90210, pg 713

Burst Electronics Inc, PO Box 820, Edgewood, NM 87015 *Tel:* 505-898-1455 *E-mail:* sales@ burstelectronics.com *Web Site:* www.burstelectronics. com, pg 713

Burst Video/Film Inc, 1104 Alta Ave NE, Atlanta, GA 30307, pg 713

Business & Legal Reports Inc, 141 Mill Rock Rd E, Old Saybrook, CT 06475 *Tel:* 860-510-0100 *Toll Free Tel:* 800-727-5257 *Toll Free Fax:* 800-785-9212 *E-mail:* service@blr.com *Web Site:* www.blr.com, pg 713

Business Education Films, PO Box 449, Clarksburg, NJ 08510-0449 *Tel:* 732-462-3522 *Fax:* 732-294-0330 *E-mail:* info@aldenfilms.com *Web Site:* www. aldenfilms.com, pg 713

Business Technology Association (BTA), 12411 Wornall Rd, Suite 200, Kansas City, MO 64145 *Tel:* 816-941-3100 *Toll Free Tel:* 800-826-6159; 800-505-2821 (memb servs) *Fax:* 816-941-4843 *Toll Free Fax:* 800-941-2829 *E-mail:* info@bta.org *Web Site:* www.bta. org, pg 952

Butkowski Digital Imaging (BDI), 2229 Roosevelt Rd, St Cloud, MN 56301 *Tel:* 320-333-1520 *E-mail:* info@ bdiphoto.com *Web Site:* www.bdiphoto.com, pg 713

Butte Montana Chamber of Commerce, 1000 George St, Butte, MT 59701 *Tel:* 406-723-3177 *Toll Free Tel:* 800-735-6814 *Fax:* 406-723-1215 *E-mail:* marketing@buttechamber.org *Web Site:* www. buttechambersite.org; www.visitbutte.com, pg 973

Butter Tree Studios, 32 Merry Lane, East Hanover, NJ 07936 *Tel:* 973-585-7632 *Fax:* 973-585-7633 *Web Site:* www.buttertreestudios.com, pg 713

Buttercup Pictures, 206 N Bundy Dr, Los Angeles, CA 90049 *Tel:* 310-869-9405 *Web Site:* cargocollective. com/buttercup, pg 713

Buzzco Associates Inc, 33 Bleecker St, New York, NY 10012 *Tel:* 212-473-8800 *Fax:* 212-473-8891 *E-mail:* info@buzzco.com *Web Site:* www.buzzzco. com, pg 713

BZ/Rights & Permissions Inc, 145 W 86 St, New York, NY 10024 *Tel:* 212-924-3000 *Fax:* 212-924-2525 *E-mail:* info@bzrights.com; www.thepublicdomainsite. com, pg 713

C & M Publishing Co, 1076 Torrey Pines Rd, Chula Vista, CA 91915 *Tel:* 619-656-6462, pg 713

C-Ducer/C T Audio, 54 Old Lakeside Rd S, Hewitt, NJ 07421 *Tel:* 973-728-1743 *Toll Free Tel:* 800-282-8346 *E-mail:* meow54@rocketmail.com *Web Site:* www.c-ducer.com, pg 713

C Vision Productions, 5533 144 Ave NW, Ramsey, MN 55303-5646 *Tel:* 763-577-1358 *Toll Free Tel:* 888-827-3287 *E-mail:* laskovideo@yahoo.com *Web Site:* www. cvisionproductions.com, pg 713

Cabbage Cases Inc, 1166-C Steelwood Rd, Columbus, OH 43212-1356 *Tel:* 614-486-2495 *Toll Free Tel:* 800-888-2495 *Fax:* 614-486-2788 *E-mail:* sales@ cabbagecases.com *Web Site:* www.cabbagecases.com, pg 713

Cable & Telecommunications Association for Marketing (CTAM), 120 Waterfront St, Suite 200, National Harbor, MD 20745 *Tel:* 301-485-8900 *Fax:* 301-560-4964 *E-mail:* info@ctam.com *Web Site:* www.ctam. com, pg 952

CACI Integrated Communications, 14370 Newbrook Dr, Chantilly, VA 20151 *Tel:* 703-679-4221 *Fax:* 703-679-3434 *E-mail:* cicinfo@caci.com *Web Site:* www.caci. com/cic, pg 713

CAD Audio, 6573 Cochran Rd, Bldg I, Solon, OH 44139 *Tel:* 440-349-4900 *Fax:* 440-248-4904 *E-mail:* info@cadaudio.com *Web Site:* cadaudio.com, pg 713

Cadence Jazz Records, Cadence Bldg, Redwood, NY 13679 *Tel:* 315-287-2852 *Fax:* 315-287-2860 *E-mail:* cjr@cadencebuilding.com; cadence@ cadencebuilding.com; orders@cadencebuilding.com *Web Site:* www.cadencejazzworld.com, pg 713

Cadex Electronics Inc, 22000 Fraserwood Way, Richmond, BC V6W 1J6, Canada *Tel:* 604-231-7777 *Toll Free Tel:* 800-565-5228 *Fax:* 604-231-7755 *E-mail:* info@cadex.com *Web Site:* www.cadex.com, pg 713

CADint, 5719 Mallardview Way, Elk Grove, CA 95757 *Tel:* 209-606-0660 *Toll Free Tel:* 800-553-1177 (sales) *E-mail:* support@cadint.com; sales@cadint.com *Web Site:* www.cadint.com, pg 713

Cahokia Mounds Museum Society, 30 Ramey Dr, Collinsville, IL 62234 *Tel:* 618-344-7316 *Fax:* 618-346-5162 *E-mail:* museumsociety@cahokiamounds.org *Web Site:* www.cahokiamounds.org, pg 713

Calaveras Film Commission, Calaveras Visitors Bureau, 1192 S Main St, Angels Camp, CA 95222 *Tel:* 209-736-0049 *Toll Free Tel:* 800-225-3764 *Web Site:* filmcalaveras.org, pg 966

Calbor Enterprises Two Inc, 10646 Chiquita St, Toluca Lake, CA 91602 *Tel:* 818-760-3222, pg 713

Calculated Industries Inc, 4840 Hytech Dr, Carson City, NV 89706 *Tel:* 775-885-4900 *Toll Free Tel:* 800-854-8075 *Fax:* 775-885-4949 *E-mail:* info@calculated.com *Web Site:* www.calculated.com, pg 714

Calgary International Film Festival, 214 11 Ave SE, Unit 207, Calgary, AB T2G 0X8, Canada *Tel:* 403-283-1490 *E-mail:* info@calgaryfilm.com *Web Site:* www. calgaryfilm.com, pg 984

Calger Lighting Inc, 200 Lexington Ave, Suite 434, New York, NY 10016 *Tel:* 212-689-9511 *Fax:* 212-779-0721 *E-mail:* sales@calgerlighting.com *Web Site:* www.calgerlighting.com, pg 714

Califone International Inc, 9135 Alabama Ave, Suite B, Chatsworth, CA 91311 *Tel:* 818-407-2400 *Toll Free Tel:* 800-722-0500 *Fax:* 818-407-2405 *Toll Free Fax:* 877-402-2248 *Web Site:* www.califone, pg 714

California Film Commission (CFC), 7080 Hollywood Blvd, Suite 900, Hollywood, CA 90028-6936 *Tel:* 323-860-2960 (24-hour serv) *Toll Free Tel:* 800-858-4749 *Fax:* 323-860-2972 *E-mail:* filmca@film.ca. gov *Web Site:* www.film.ca.gov, pg 966

California Independent Film Festival (CAIFF), 350 Park St, Moraga, CA 94566 *Tel:* 925-388-0752 *E-mail:* info@caiff.org *Web Site:* caiff.org, pg 984

California Language Laboratories, 6170 Palmero Circle, Cameron Park, CA 95682 *Tel:* 530-350-8072 *E-mail:* info@esltapes.com *Web Site:* www.esltapes.com, pg 714

California Newsreel, 44 Gough St, Suite 303, San Francisco, CA 94103 *Tel:* 415-284-7800 *Fax:* 415-284-7801 *E-mail:* contact@newsreel.org *Web Site:* www.newsreel.org, pg 714

California Stainless Manufacturing Inc, 32 N Wood Rd, Camarillo, CA 93010 *Tel:* 805-484-1038 *Toll Free Tel:* 888-712-7035 *Fax:* 805-484-1030 *E-mail:* calstainless@aol.com *Web Site:* www. calstainless.com, pg 714

California Tape Products Inc, PO Box 177, Forest Falls, CA 92339-0177 *Tel:* 909-794-6524 *E-mail:* info@ caltape.com *Web Site:* www.caltape.com, pg 714

California Teleprompter, PO Box 13024, La Jolla, CA 92039-3024 *Tel:* 858-945-2076 *E-mail:* caprompter@ aol.com *Web Site:* www.sandiegoteleprompter.com, pg 714

Callen Photo Mount Corp, 185 Sixth Ave, Paterson, NJ 07524 *Tel:* 973-925-2390 *Toll Free Tel:* 800-225-5360 *Fax:* 973-925-9615, pg 714

Calrad Electronics, 819 N Highland Ave, Los Angeles, CA 90038 *Tel:* 323-465-2131 *Fax:* 323-465-3504 *E-mail:* sales@calrad.com *Web Site:* www.calrad.com, pg 714

Calumet Carton Co, 16920 State St, South Holland, IL 60473 *Tel:* 708-333-6521 *E-mail:* info@calumetcarton. com *Web Site:* www.calumetcarton.com, pg 714

Calzone Case Co, 225 Black Rock Ave, Bridgeport, CT 06605 *Toll Free Tel:* 800-243-5152 *Fax:* 203-336-4406 *Web Site:* www.calzoneandanvil.com, pg 714

CAM Audio Inc, 2210 Executive Dr, Garland, TX 75041 *Tel:* 972-271-2800 *Toll Free Tel:* 800-527-3458 *Fax:* 972-271-1555 *E-mail:* sales@camaudio.com *Web Site:* www.camaudio.com, pg 714

Camart, 6 W 20 St, New York, NY 10011 *Tel:* 212-691-8840 *E-mail:* rentals@camart.com *Web Site:* www. camart.com, pg 714

Cambridge Documentary Films Inc, 3099 Hidden Valley Lane, Santa Barbara, CA 93108 *Tel:* 617-484-3993 *E-mail:* info@cambridgedocumentaryfilms.org; mail@ cambridgedocumentaryfilms.org *Web Site:* www. cambridgedocumentaryfilms.org, pg 714

Cambridge University Press, One Liberty Plaza, 20th fl, New York, NY 10006 *Tel:* 212-337-5000 *Toll Free Tel:* 800-221-4512; 800-872-7423 *E-mail:* information@cambridge.org; customer_service@cambridge.org *Web Site:* www. cambridge.org, pg 715

Camcor Inc, 2273 S Church St, Burlington, NC 27215 *Tel:* 336-228-0251 *Toll Free Tel:* 800-868-2462 *Fax:* 336-222-8011 *Toll Free Fax:* 800-298-1181 *E-mail:* info@camcor.com *Web Site:* www.camcor. com, pg 715

Camera Corner Connecting Point, PO Box 248, Green Bay, WI 54305-0248 *Tel:* 920-435-5353 *Toll Free Tel:* 800-236-4950 (orders) *Fax:* 920-438-0389 *E-mail:* salessupport@cccp.com; contactus@cccp.com *Web Site:* www.cccp.com, pg 715

The Camera Division, 7351 Fulton Ave, North Hollywood, CA 91605 *Tel:* 323-465-7700 *Fax:* 818-997-3802 *E-mail:* rentals@thecameradivision.com *Web Site:* thecameradivision.com, pg 715

Camera Essentials, 91 N Daisy Ave, Pasadena, CA 91107-3705 *Tel:* 626-844-3722 *Fax:* 323-686-5230 *E-mail:* info@cameraessentials.com *Web Site:* www. cameraessentials.com, pg 715

CamMate Systems, 425 E Comstock, Chandler, AZ 85225 *Tel:* 480-813-9500 *Fax:* 480-813-9292 *Web Site:* www.cammate.com, pg 715

The Campbell Agency, Hidden Grove Bldg, 12404 Park Central Dr, Suite 222 S, Dallas, TX 75251 *Tel:* 214-522-8991 *Fax:* 214-522-8997 *Web Site:* www. thecampbellagency.com, pg 715

Campus Productions, 42 Oak Ave, Tuckahoe, NY 10707 *Tel:* 914-395-1010 *Fax:* 914-395-1095 *E-mail:* sales@ campusgroup.com *Web Site:* www.campusgroup.com, pg 715

CamTec Motion Picture Cameras, 4221 W Magnolia Blvd, Burbank, CA 91505 *Tel:* 818-841-8700 *Fax:* 818-841-8777 *Web Site:* www.camtec.tv, pg 715

Can-Am Merchandising Systems, 70 Shields Ct, Markham, ON L3R 9T5, Canada *Tel:* 905-475-6622 *Toll Free Tel:* 800-387-9790 *Fax:* 905-475-1154 *E-mail:* mail@can-am.ca *Web Site:* www.can-am.ca, pg 715

Canadian Academy of Recording Arts & Sciences (CARAS), 219 Dufferin St, Suite 211C, Toronto, ON M6K 3J1, Canada *Tel:* 416-485-3135 (CN only) *Toll Free Tel:* 888-501-3135 *Fax:* 416-485-4978 *E-mail:* submissions@junoawards.ca; info@ carasonline.ca *Web Site:* carasonline.ca; junoawards.ca, pg 952

Canadian American Records, PO Box 808, Lititz, PA 17543-0538 *Tel:* 717-627-4800 *E-mail:* canadianamerican@dejazzd.com *Web Site:* www.canadianamericanrecords.net; www. canadianamericanrecordcompany.com, pg 715

Canadian Broadcast Standards Council (CBSC), PO Box 3265, Sta D, Ottawa, ON K1P 6H8, Canada *Tel:* 613-233-4607 *Toll Free Tel:* 866-696-4718 (CN only) *Fax:* 613-233-4826 *E-mail:* info@cbsc.ca *Web Site:* www.cbsc.ca, pg 952

Canadian Filmmakers Distribution Center (CFMDC), 401 Richmond St W, Toronto, ON M5V 3A8, Canada *Tel:* 416-588-0725 *E-mail:* info@cfmdc.org *Web Site:* www.cfmdc.org, pg 715

Canadian Learning Co Inc, 95 Vansittart Ave, Woodstock, ON N4S 6E3, Canada *Tel:* 519-537-2360 *Toll Free Tel:* 800-267-2977 (CN) *Fax:* 519-537-1035 *Web Site:* www.canlearn.com, pg 715

Canadian Screen Awards, 49 Ontario St, Suite 501, Toronto, ON M5A 2V1, Canada *Tel:* 416-366-2227 *Toll Free Tel:* 800-644-5194 *Fax:* 416-366-8454 *E-mail:* awards@academy.ca; info@academy.ca *Web Site:* www.academy.ca/canadian-screen-awards, pg 984

Canadian Student Film Festival, 1432 de Bleury St, Montreal, QC H3A 2J1, Canada *Tel:* 514-848-3883 *Fax:* 514-848-3886 *E-mail:* program@ffm-montreal. org; info@ffm-montreal.org *Web Site:* www.ffm-montreal.org, pg 985

Canamedia Inc, 1540 Cornwall Rd, Suite 216, Oakville, ON L6J 7W5, Canada *Tel:* 416-363-6765 *Toll Free Tel:* 866-999-5292 *Fax:* 416-363-7834 *Web Site:* www. canamedia.com, pg 715

Canare Corporation of America, 45 Commerce Way, Unit C, Totowa, NJ 07512 *Tel:* 973-837-0070 *Fax:* 973-837-0080 *E-mail:* sales@canare.com *Web Site:* www.canare.com, pg 716

Canavan Scenic & Light LLC, 2440 Dinneen Ave, Orlando, FL 32804 *Tel:* 407-888-8002 *Web Site:* www. csandl.com, pg 716

Candee Productions Inc, 301 W Deer Valley Rd, Suite 7, Phoenix, AZ 85027 *Tel:* 623-266-3070 *Web Site:* candeeproductionsinc.wordpress.com, pg 716

C&I An Idea Agency, 541 NW First Ave, Fort Lauderdale, FL 33301 *Tel:* 954-357-3934 *E-mail:* contact@c-istudios.com *Web Site:* www.c-istudios.com, pg 716

Cannon Stage Lighting Inc, 7110 Ambassador Rd, Windsor Mill, MD 21244 *Tel:* 410-298-0636 *Fax:* 410-298-7950 *E-mail:* cannonstage@gmail.com *Web Site:* www.cannonstage.com, pg 716

Canon USA Inc, One Canon Park, Melville, NY 11747 *Toll Free Tel:* 800-652-2666 *E-mail:* pr@cusa.canon. com *Web Site:* www.usa.canon.com, pg 716

Cantrax Recorders, 2119 Fidler Ave, Long Beach, CA 90815 *Tel:* 562-498-6492 *E-mail:* cantrax@verizon. net, pg 716

Canvys™, 40W267 Keslinger Rd, LaFox, IL 60147-0393 *Tel:* 508-460-5400 *Toll Free Tel:* 800-291-1344 *Fax:* 508-460-5470 *Web Site:* www.canvys.com, pg 716

Canyon Cinema Inc, 1777 Yosemite Ave, Suite 210, San Francisco, CA 94124 *Tel:* 415-626-2255 *E-mail:* info@canyoncinema.com *Web Site:* www.canyoncinema.com, pg 716

The Robert Capa Gold Medal Award, 40 W 45 St, New York, NY 10036 *Tel:* 212-626-9220 *Fax:* 212-626-9210 *E-mail:* info@opcofamerica.org *Web Site:* www. opcofamerica.org, pg 985

Capacity Building Grant Program, 31 Prince St, Rochester, NY 14607 *Tel:* 585-473-4000 *Fax:* 585-473-4051 *E-mail:* communications@artsrochester.org *Web Site:* artsrochester.org, pg 985

Cape Girardeau Convention & Visitors Bureau, 220 N Fountain St, Cape Girardeau, MO 63701 *Tel:* 573-335-1631 *Toll Free Tel:* 800-777-0068 *Fax:* 573-334-6702 *E-mail:* info@visitcape.com *Web Site:* visitcape.com, pg 972

Capitol Christian Music Group, 101 Winners Circle, Brentwood, TN 37027 *Tel:* 615-371-4300 *Toll Free Tel:* 800-877-4443 (sales) *Fax:* 615-371-6980 (sales) *E-mail:* ccmgdistribution@umusic.com (sales) *Web Site:* www.capitolchristianmusicgroup.com, pg 716

Capitol Records, 1750 N Vine St, Hollywood, CA 90028 *Tel:* 323-871-5001 *Web Site:* www.capitolrecords.com, pg 716

Caprock Developments Inc, 475 Speedwell, Morris Plains, NJ 07950 *Tel:* 973-267-9292 *Toll Free Tel:* 800-222-0325 *Fax:* 973-292-0614 *E-mail:* info@ caprockdev.com *Web Site:* www.caprockdev.com, pg 716

Capron Lighting & Sound Co Inc, 278 West St, Needham, MA 02494 *Tel:* 781-444-8850 *E-mail:* info@capron.net *Web Site:* www.capron.net, pg 716

Captain Fiddle Music & Publications, 94 Wiswall Rd, Lee, NH 03861 *Tel:* 603-659-2658 *E-mail:* cfiddle@ tiac.net *Web Site:* captainfiddle.com, pg 716

CaptionMax, 2438 27 Ave S, Minneapolis, MN 55406 *Tel:* 612-341-3566 *Web Site:* www.captionmax.com, pg 716

Captions & Subtitle Services Ltd, 5113 S Harper, Suite 2C, Chicago, IL 60615 *Tel:* 872-222-9057 *E-mail:* quote@capsubservices.com *Web Site:* www. capsubservices.com, pg 716

Cardinal Sound & Video, 7510 Rickenbacker Dr, Gaithersburg, MD 20879 *Tel:* 301-589-3700 *Fax:* 301-740-7820 *E-mail:* info@cardinalsound.us *Web Site:* www.cardinalsoundvideo.com, pg 717

Chester F Carlson Award, 7003 Kilworth Lane, Springfield, VA 22151 *Tel:* 703-642-9090 *Fax:* 703-642-9094 *E-mail:* info@imaging.org *Web Site:* imaging.org, pg 985

Carlton-Bates Co, 3600 W 69 St, Little Rock, AR 72209 *Tel:* 501-562-9100 *Toll Free Tel:* 866-600-6040 *E-mail:* customerservicecb@carltonbates.com; sales@ carltonbates.com *Web Site:* www.carltonbates.com, pg 717

Carolina Biological Supply Co, 2700 York Rd, Burlington, NC 27215-3398 *Tel:* 336-586-4399 (intl sales) *Toll Free Tel:* 800-334-5551 *Toll Free Fax:* 800-222-7112 (intl sales) *E-mail:* customer_service@carolina.com; internationalsales@carolina.com *Web Site:* www. carolina.com, pg 717

Carpel Video Inc, 429 E Patrick St, Frederick, MD 21701 *Tel:* 301-694-3500 *Toll Free Tel:* 800-238-4300 *Fax:* 301-694-9510 *Web Site:* www.carpelvideoonline. com, pg 717

Carr McLean Ltd, 461 Horner Ave, Toronto, ON M8W 4X2, Canada *Tel:* 416-252-3371 *Toll Free Tel:* 800-268-2123 (CN) *Fax:* 416-252-9203 *Toll Free Fax:* 800-871-2397 *E-mail:* sales@carrmclean.ca *Web Site:* www.carrmclean.ca, pg 717

Carvin Amps & Audio, 16262 W Bernardo Dr, San Diego, CA 92127 *Tel:* 858-751-4884 *Web Site:* carvinaudio.com, pg 717

CAS Video Productions, 820 White Marsh Ct, Huntingtown, MD 20639 *Tel:* 301-674-2000 (cell) *E-mail:* info@casvideo.com *Web Site:* www.casvideo. com, pg 717

Case Design Corp, 333 School Lane, Telford, PA 18969 *Tel:* 215-703-0130 *Toll Free Tel:* 800-847-4176 *Fax:* 215-703-0139 *E-mail:* sales@casedesigncorp.com *Web Site:* www.casedesigncorp.com, pg 717

Case Logic Inc, 6303 Dry Creek Pkwy, Longmont, CO 80503 *Tel:* 303-652-1000 *Toll Free Tel:* 800-925-8111 *E-mail:* help.na@caselogic.com *Web Site:* www. caselogic.com, pg 717

Casio America Inc, 570 Mount Pleasant Ave, Dover, NJ 07801 *Tel:* 973-361-5400 *Web Site:* www. casioprojector.com, pg 717

Castillo Theatre, 543 W 42 St, New York, NY 10036 *Tel:* 212-941-5800 *Toll Free Tel:* 800-435-7453 *Web Site:* www.castillo.org, pg 717

Castleview Productions, 1100 W 41 St, Austin, TX 78756 *Tel:* 512-442-9944 *Fax:* 512-442-8823 *E-mail:* contact@castleviewproductions.com *Web Site:* castleviewproductions.com, pg 717

Catalina Island Film Commission, One Green Pleasure Pier, Avalon, CA 90704 *Tel:* 310-510-7649; 310-510-7643 *Fax:* 310-510-7607 *Web Site:* www. catalinachamber.com/catalina-filming-information, pg 966

Catapult Films Inc, 832 Third St, Suite 303, Santa Monica, CA 90403 *Tel:* 310-395-1470, pg 717

Catholic Books & Tapes, PO Box 350333, Fort Lauderdale, FL 33335-0333 *Tel:* 954-583-5108 *Fax:* 954-583-5108 *E-mail:* mascmen7@yahoo.com *Web Site:* www.catholicbook.com, pg 717

Catholic Library Association (CLA), 8550 United Plaza Blvd, Suite 1001, Baton Rouge, LA 70809 *Tel:* 225-408-4417 *E-mail:* cla2@cathla.org *Web Site:* www. cathla.org, pg 952

Cavalcade Productions Inc, PO Box 2480, Nevada City, CA 95959-1948 *Tel:* 530-477-0701 (outside US & CN) *Toll Free Tel:* 800-345-5530 *Fax:* 530-477-0701 (outside US & CN) *Toll Free Fax:* 800-345-5530 *E-mail:* info@cavalcadeproductions.com *Web Site:* www.cavalcadeproductions.com, pg 717

Cavanaugh Tocci Associates Inc, 327F Boston Post Rd, Sudbury, MA 01776 *Tel:* 978-443-7871 *E-mail:* cta@ cavtocci.com *Web Site:* www.cavtocci.com, pg 717

Cavision Enterprises Ltd, 2323 Boundary Rd, Suite 210, Vancouver, BC V5M 4V8, Canada *Tel:* 604-298-9053 *E-mail:* info@cavision.com *Web Site:* www.cavision. com, pg 717

Cayman Islands Department of Tourism, Empire State Bldg, 350 Fifth Ave, Suite 2720, New York, NY 10018 *Tel:* 212-889-9009 *E-mail:* film@ caymanislands.ky; usareception@caymanislands.ky *Web Site:* www.visitcaymanislands.com, pg 974

CBC/Radio-Canada, 181 Queen St, Ottawa, ON K1P 1K9, Canada *Tel:* 613-288-6000; 613-288-6445 (newsroom) *Toll Free Tel:* 866-306-4636 (CN only) *E-mail:* cbcnewsottawa@cbc.ca *Web Site:* cbc.radio-canada.ca, pg 717

CBM Ltd, High Point Business Park, 8750 Holgate Cresent, Milton, ON L9T 0K3, Canada *Tel:* 905-878-0648 *Toll Free Tel:* 800-387-4834 *Fax:* 905-878-6748 *Toll Free Fax:* 888-554-5501 *E-mail:* sales@cbmmetal. com *Web Site:* www.cbmmetal.com, pg 718

CCH Continuing Education, 2700 Lake Cook Rd, Riverwoods, IL 60015 Tel: 773-866-3648 Toll Free Tel: 800-248-3248 Fax: 773-866-3084 Web Site: www. cch.com, pg 718

CCH Inc, A Wolters Kluwer business, 2700 Lake Cook Rd, Riverwoods, IL 60015 Tel: 847-267-7000 Toll Free Tel: 888-224-7377 E-mail: press@wolterskluwer. com Web Site: www.cch.com; taxna.wolterskluwer. com, pg 718

CCI Communications Inc, 643 Swedesford Rd, Malvern, PA 19355 Tel: 610-296-7233 Fax: 610-296-7358 E-mail: info@ccivideo.com Web Site: www.ccivideo. com, pg 718

CCI Digital, a DVS Company, 2921 W Alameda Ave, Burbank, CA 91505 Tel: 818-562-6300 E-mail: info@ ccidigital.com Web Site: www.ccidigital.com, pg 718

CCI Entertainment Ltd, 210 St Clair Ave W, 4th fl, Toronto, ON M4V 1R2, Canada Tel: 416-964-8750 E-mail: info@ccientertainment.com Web Site: www. ccientertainment.com, pg 718

CCI Solutions, 1342 88 Ave SE, Olympia, WA 98501 Tel: 360-943-5378 Toll Free Tel: 800-562-6006 Fax: 360-754-1566 E-mail: info@ccisolutions.com Web Site: www.ccisolutions.com, pg 718

CCore Media Inc, 1421 Lowe Dr, Algonquin, IL 60102 Tel: 815-219-0424 Web Site: www.creativecore.com, pg 718

CD Meyer Inc, 15 Oak Rd, No 202, Fairfield, NJ 07004 E-mail: info@cdmeyer.com Web Site: www.cdmeyer. com; www.point2explore.com; museumdigitalsignage. com, pg 718

The CD Recycling Center of America, 68 E Stiles Rd, Salem, NH 03079 Tel: 603-894-5553 Fax: 603-898-4319 E-mail: info@cdrecyclingcenter.com Web Site: www.cdrecyclingcenter.com, pg 718

CD ROM™ Inc, 3131 E Riverside Dr, Fort Myers, FL 33916 Toll Free Tel: 866-662-3766 (orders) Fax: 239-332-2808 E-mail: sales@cdrominc.com Web Site: www.cdrominc.com, pg 718

CDR Communications Inc, 9310B/9302C Old Keene Mill Rd, Burke, VA 22015 Tel: 703-569-3400 Toll Free Tel: 800-729-2237 Fax: 703-569-3448 E-mail: info@cdrcommunications.com Web Site: www.cdrcommunications.com, pg 719

Ceavco Audio Visual Company Inc, 6240 W 54 Ave, Arvada, CO 80002 Tel: 303-539-3500 E-mail: solutions@ceavco.com Web Site: ceavco.com, pg 719

CEDIA IPRO Affinity Group, 8475 Nightfall Lane, Fishers, IN 46037 Tel: 317-328-4336 Toll Free Tel: 800-669-5329 E-mail: info@cedia.org Web Site: cedia.net, pg 952

CELCO, 14 Industrial Ave, Mahwah, NJ 07430 Web Site: www.celco.com, pg 719

Celebration of Service to America Awards, 1771 "N" St NW, Washington, DC 20036-2891 Tel: 202-421-3191 E-mail: nabef@nab.org Web Site: www.nabef.org, pg 985

Celebrity Helicopters Inc, 961 W Alondra Blvd, Compton, CA 90220 Tel: 310-618-1155 Toll Free Tel: 877-999-2099 Fax: 424-785-8768 Toll Free Fax: 877-999-2099 Web Site: www.celebheli.com, pg 719

Celestial Harmonies/Fortuna Records/Kuckuck Schallplatten/Black Sun Music/MonteVideo, 1951 N Wilmot Rd, Bldg 2, Unit 7, Tucson, AZ 85712-8000 Tel: 520-326-4400 Fax: 520-326-3333 E-mail: celestial@harmonies.com Web Site: www. harmonies.com, pg 719

Centaur Records Inc, 136 Saint Joseph St, Baton Rouge, LA 70802 Tel: 225-336-4877 Fax: 225-336-9678 E-mail: info@centaurrecords.com Web Site: www. centaurrecords.com, pg 719

Center City Film & Video Inc, 1501-1503 Walnut St, Philadelphia, PA 19102 Tel: 215-568-4134 Fax: 215-568-6011 E-mail: info@ccfv.com; sales@ccfv.com Web Site: www.ccfv.com, pg 719

Center for Asian American Media (CAAM), 145 Ninth St, Suite 350, San Francisco, CA 94103 Tel: 415-863-0814 Fax: 415-863-7428 E-mail: publicity@caamedia. org Web Site: caamedia.org, pg 952

Center for Southern Folklore Inc, 119 S Main St, Memphis, TN 38103 Tel: 901-525-3655 Fax: 901-544-9965 E-mail: info@southernfolklore.com Web Site: www.southernfolklore.com, pg 719

Center for the Collaborative Classroom, 1001 Marina Village Pkwy, Suite 110, Alameda, CA 94501-1042 Tel: 510-533-0213 Toll Free Tel: 800-666-7270 Fax: 510-464-3670 E-mail: info@ collaborativeclassroom.org Web Site: www. collaborativeclassroom.org, pg 719

Center for Touch Drawing, PO Box 1595, Langley, WA 98260 Tel: 360-221-5745 E-mail: center@ touchdrawing.com Web Site: www.touchdrawing.com, pg 719

CenterStaging LLC, 3407 Winona Ave, Burbank, CA 91504 Tel: 818-559-4333 Fax: 818-848-4016 E-mail: info@centerstaging.com Web Site: centerstaging.com, pg 719

Central Audio-Visual Equipment Inc, 375 Roma Jean Pkwy, Streamwood, IL 60107 Tel: 630-372-8100 Toll Free Tel: 800-323-4239 Fax: 630-372-9281 Web Site: www.cavinc.com, pg 719

Central Florida Visitors & Convention Bureau, 2701 Lake Myrtle Park Rd, Auburndale, FL 33823 Tel: 863-551-4750 Toll Free Tel: 800-828-7655 Fax: 863-551-4740 Web Site: visitcentralflorida.org, pg 969

Central Lighting & Equipment Inc (CLE), 4103 E 16 St, Des Moines, IA 50313 Tel: 515-277-4190 Toll Free Tel: 877-977-4190 Fax: 515-277-2295 E-mail: info@ cleproductions.com Web Site: cleproductions.com, pg 719

Central Ohio Audio Video, 6650 Busch Rd, Columbus, OH 43229 Toll Free Tel: 877-432-8273 Web Site: www.centralohav.com, pg 719

Central Texas College KNCT-Radio FM, PO Box 1800, Killeen, TX 76540-1800 Tel: 254-526-1176 E-mail: knct@knct.org Web Site: www.knct.org, pg 719

Centralite Systems Inc, 1701 Industrial Park Dr, Mobile, AL 36693 Tel: 251-607-9119 Toll Free Tel: 877-466-5483 Fax: 251-607-9117 E-mail: info@centralite.com Web Site: centralite.com, pg 719

Centre Communications Inc, 75 Manhattan Dr, Suite 200, Boulder, CO 80303 Tel: 303-444-1166 E-mail: centre@ecentral.com Web Site: www. centrecommunicationinc.com; www.centredm.com, pg 720

Centre for Art Tapes (CFAT), 2238 Maitland St, Halifax, NS B3K 2Z9, Canada Tel: 902-422-6822 E-mail: info@cfat.ca Web Site: cfat.ca, pg 953

Century Business Solutions, 100 Carlson Rd, Rochester, NY 14610 Toll Free Tel: 844-656-3476 Toll Free Fax: 866-592-8642 (orders) E-mail: info@ centurybusinesssolutions.com; help@fdmbrands.com Web Site: www.centurybusinesssolutions.com, pg 720

Century Color Labs Inc, 494 School St, East Hartford, CT 06108 Tel: 860-289-9501 Toll Free Tel: 800-242-9501 Fax: 860-291-9098 E-mail: production@ centurycolor.com Web Site: www.centurycolor.com, pg 720

Cerutti Productions Inc, 18211 Bulverde Rd, Suite 10202, San Antonio, TX 78259-3625 Tel: 210-403-0800 Web Site: www.cerutti.org, pg 720

Cerwin-Vega! Inc, c/o Gibson Pro Audio, 309 Park Plus Blvd, Nashville, TN 37217 Toll Free Tel: 800-4GIBSON (444-2766) E-mail: service@gibson.com (cust serv) Web Site: www.cerwinvega.com, pg 720

CET, 1223 Central Pkwy, Cincinnati, OH 45214 Tel: 513-381-4033 E-mail: comments@cetconnect.org Web Site: www.cetconnect.org, pg 720

CEV Multimedia Ltd, 1020 SE Loop 289, Lubbock, TX 79404 Toll Free Tel: 877-610-5017 Toll Free Fax: 800-243-6398 E-mail: customersupport@ cevmultimedia.com Web Site: www.cevmultimedia. com, pg 720

CFP Video Productions Inc, 149 Meriden Rd, Boonton, NJ 07005 Tel: 973-226-2481 Web Site: cfpvideo.com, pg 720

Chace Audio by Deluxe, 900 Seward St, Hollywood, CA 90038 Toll Free Tel: 800-842-8346 Web Site: www. bydeluxe.com, pg 720

Chalk Dust Co, 16107 Kensington Dr, PMB 256, Sugar Land, TX 77479-4401 Tel: 281-265-2495 Toll Free Tel: 800-588-7564 Fax: 281-265-3197 E-mail: sales@ chalkdust.com Web Site: www.chalkdust.com, pg 720

Challenge Productions/Challenge Aerial Imaging, 400 E George St, Marion, OH 43302 Tel: 740-531-3077 E-mail: info@challenge-pro.com Web Site: challenge-pro.com, pg 720

Championship Productions Inc, Ames Community Development Park, 2730 Graham St, Ames, IA 50010 Tel: 515-232-3687 Toll Free Tel: 800-873-2730 Fax: 515-232-3739 E-mail: info@ championshipproductions.com Web Site: www. championshipproductions.com, pg 720

Steve Chandler, 798 W 26 St, San Bernardino, CA 92405 Tel: 909-882-1621 E-mail: stevevldy@aol.com, pg 720

Channell One Video, PO Box 399, Epping, NH 03042-0399 Tel: 603-679-6796 E-mail: racevid@earthlink. net, pg 720

Chapman/Leonard Studio Equipment Inc, 12950 Raymer St, North Hollywood, CA 91605 Tel: 818-764-6726 Toll Free Tel: 888-883-6559 Fax: 818-764-6730 E-mail: marketing@chapman-leonard.com Web Site: www.chapman-leonard.com, pg 720

Charles Beseler Co, 2018 W Main St, Stroudsburg, PA 18360 Toll Free Tel: 800-237-3537 Toll Free Fax: 800-966-4515 Web Site: www.beselerphoto.com, pg 721

Charles M Salter Associates Inc, 130 Sutter St, 5th fl, San Francisco, CA 94104 Tel: 415-397-0442 Fax: 415-397-0454 E-mail: info@cmsalter.com Web Site: www.cmsalter.com, pg 721

Charlex Inc, 2 W 45 St, 7th fl, New York, NY 10036 Tel: 212-719-4600 E-mail: info@chrlx.com Web Site: www.chrlx.com, pg 721

Charlotte Regional Film Commission, 500 S College St, Suite 300, Charlotte, NC 28202 Tel: 704-331-2723 Toll Free Tel: 800-722-1994 Fax: 704-342-3972 Web Site: www.charlottefilm.com, pg 974

Chartpak Inc, One River Rd, Leeds, MA 01053 Tel: 413-584-5446 Toll Free Tel: 800-628-1910 E-mail: info@ chartpak.com Web Site: www.chartpak.com, pg 721

Chater Camera Inc, 1336 Ninth St, Berkeley, CA 94710 Tel: 510-525-5400 Fax: 510-295-2478 E-mail: rentals@chatercamera.com Web Site: www. chatercamera.com, pg 721

Chatterbox Productions Inc, 5305 Johnson St, Hollywood, FL 33021-5721 Tel: 754-816-5432 Web Site: www.facebook.com/chatterboxproductions, pg 721

Chauvet Lighting, 5200 NW 108 Ave, Sunrise, FL 33351-8040 Tel: 954-577-4455 Toll Free Tel: 800-762-1084 Fax: 954-929-5560 Toll Free Fax: 800-544-4898 E-mail: marketing@chauvetlighting.com Web Site: www.chauvetlighting.com, pg 721

Checkers Safety Group, 620 Compton St, Broomfield, CO 80020 Toll Free Tel: 800-438-9336; 877-384-6103 E-mail: sales@checkers-safety.com Web Site: www. checkers-safety.com, pg 721

Chelsea Decorative Metal Co, 8212 Braewick Dr, Dept AV, Houston, TX 77074 Tel: 713-721-9200 Fax: 713-776-8661 E-mail: tinman83@earthlink.net Web Site: www.tinman.com, pg 721

Chelsea Green Publishing Co, 85 N Main St, Suite 120, White River Junction, VT 05001 Tel: 802-295-6300 Toll Free Tel: 800-639-4099 (orders) Fax: 802-295-6444 E-mail: customerservice@chelseagreen.com Web Site: www.chelseagreen.com, pg 721

Cheng & Tsui Co, 25 West St, 2nd fl, Boston, MA 02111-1213 *Tel:* 617-988-2400 *Toll Free Tel:* 800-554-1963 (orders) *Fax:* 617-426-3669 *E-mail:* orders@cheng-tsui.com *Web Site:* www.cheng-tsui.com, pg 721

Cherry Multimedia, 2129 Colorado Blvd, Los Angeles, CA 90041 *Toll Free Tel:* 800-378-7598 *E-mail:* info@cherrymultimedia.com *Web Site:* cherrymultimedia.com, pg 721

Cheuvront Studios, 4607 NW Sixth St Ext, Studio I, Gainesville, FL 32609 *Tel:* 352-378-4671 *Fax:* 352-338-9215 *E-mail:* allen@cheuvront.com *Web Site:* www.cheuvront.com, pg 721

Chicago Film Critics Association, 155 E Algonquin Rd, Arlington Heights, IL 60006 *Tel:* 847-427-4530 *Fax:* 847-427-1301 *Web Site:* www.chicagofilmcritics.org, pg 953

Chicago Film Office, Chicago Cultural Ctr, 78 E Washington, Rm 108, Chicago, IL 60602 *Tel:* 312-744-6415 *Fax:* 312-744-1378 *E-mail:* filmoffice@cityofchicago.org *Web Site:* www.cityofchicago.org/city/en/depts/dca/provdrs/chicago_film_office.html, pg 970

Chicago International Children's Film Festival, 1517 W Fullerton Ave, Chicago, IL 60614 *Tel:* 773-281-9075 (ext 3011) *Fax:* 773-929-0266 *E-mail:* filmreg@facets.org; press@facets.org *Web Site:* festival.facets.org, pg 985

Chicago International Film Festival, 212 W Van Buren St, Suite 400, Chicago, IL 60607 *Tel:* 312-683-0121 *Fax:* 312-683-0122 *E-mail:* info@chicagofilmfestival.com; entries@chicagofilmfestival.com *Web Site:* www.chicagofilmfestival.com, pg 985

Chicago International REEL Shorts Film Festival, 2700 W Grand Ave, Chicago, IL 60612 *E-mail:* info@projectchicago.com *Web Site:* www.projectchicago.com, pg 985

Chicago Irish Film Festival (CIFF), c/o Society for Arts, 1112 N Milwaukee Ave, Chicago, IL 60642 *Tel:* 773-486-9612 *Fax:* 773-486-9613 *Web Site:* www.chicagoirishfilmfestival.com, pg 985

Chicago Latino Film Festival, 55 W Van Buren St, Suite 310, Chicago, IL 60605 *Tel:* 312-431-1330 *E-mail:* info@latinoculturalcenter.org *Web Site:* www.chicagolatinofilmfestival.org, pg 985

The Chicago Production Center, 5400 N Saint Louis Ave, Chicago, IL 60625-4698 *Tel:* 773-509-5571 *Fax:* 773-509-5303 *Web Site:* www.wttw.com, pg 721

Chicago Scenic Studios Inc, 955 W Cermak Rd, Chicago, IL 60608 *Tel:* 312-274-9900 *Fax:* 312-274-9901 *E-mail:* info@chicagoscenic.com *Web Site:* www.chicagoscenic.com, pg 721

Chicago South Asian Film Festival (CSAFF), 2909 N Sheridan Rd, Unit 1902, Chicago, IL 60657 *Tel:* 773-669-8348 *E-mail:* info@csaff.org; programming@csaff.org *Web Site:* www.csaff.org, pg 986

Chicago Spotlight Inc, 3418 N Knox Ave, Chicago, IL 60641 *Tel:* 312-455-1171 *Web Site:* www.grandstage.com, pg 721

Chicago Underground Film Festival (CUFF), 2558 W 16 St, Stage 18, Chicago, IL 60608 *Tel:* 773-998-1082 *E-mail:* info@cuff.org; publicity@cuff.org *Web Site:* cuff.org, pg 986

Chick Russell Communications, 490 Castano Ave, Pasadena, CA 91107 *E-mail:* info@chickrussell.com *Web Site:* www.chickrussell.com, pg 721

Chico Chamber of Commerce/Butte County Film Commission, 180 Fourth St, Suite 120, Chico, CA 95928 *Tel:* 530-891-5556 *Toll Free Tel:* 800-852-8570 *Fax:* 530-891-3613 *E-mail:* info@chicochamber.com *Web Site:* chicochamber.com, pg 966

Chief, a Legrand AV Inc brand, 6436 City West Pkwy, Eden Prairie, MN 55344 *Tel:* 952-894-6280 *Toll Free Tel:* 866-977-3901 *Toll Free Fax:* 877-894-6918 *E-mail:* av.chief.support@legrand.com *Web Site:* www.legrandav.com/products/chief, pg 722

Children of Mary, PO Box 350333, Fort Lauderdale, FL 33335-0333 *Tel:* 954-583-5108 *Fax:* 954-583-5108 *E-mail:* mascmen7@yahoo.com *Web Site:* www.catholicbook.com, pg 722

The Children's Book Store Distribution (CBSD), 23 Griffin St, Waterdown, ON L0R 2H0, Canada *Tel:* 905-690-9397 (ext 237) *Toll Free Tel:* 800-757-8372 (cust serv, CN & US) *Fax:* 905-690-3419 *E-mail:* info@childrensgroup.com; sales@idla.ca *Web Site:* www.childrensgroup.com, pg 722

Chimera®, 1067 Telleen Ave, Erie, CO 80516 *Tel:* 303-444-8000 *Toll Free Tel:* 888-444-1812 *Fax:* 303-444-8303 *E-mail:* info@chimeralighting.com *Web Site:* chimeralighting.com, pg 722

Chinmaya Publications, 560 Bridgetown Pike, Langhorne, PA 19053-7210 *Tel:* 215-396-0390 *Toll Free Tel:* 888-CMW-READ (269-7323) *Fax:* 215-396-9710 *E-mail:* publications@chinmayamission.org *Web Site:* www.chinmayamission.org; www.chinmayapublications.org, pg 722

Richard Chisolm Cinematography, 311 Somerset Rd, Baltimore, MD 21210 *Tel:* 410-340-5308 *E-mail:* chisolmcamera@gmail.com *Web Site:* www.richardchisolm.com, pg 722

CHK Electronics Ltd, 836B Southampton Rd, No 260, Benicia, CA 94510 *Tel:* 707-750-8446 *Fax:* 707-361-0230 *E-mail:* sales@chk-electronics.com *Web Site:* www.chk-electronics.com, pg 722

Christian Media Network, PO Box 728, Garberville, CA 95542-8728 *Tel:* 541-899-8888 *Web Site:* www.christianmedianetwork.com, pg 722

Christie Digital Systems USA Inc, 10550 Camden Dr, Cypress, CA 90630 *Tel:* 714-236-8610 *Toll Free Tel:* 866-880-4462 (cust serv) *Fax:* 714-503-3375 *E-mail:* sales-us@christiedigital.com; orders@christiedigital.com *Web Site:* www.christiedigital.com, pg 722

Christie Lites, 6990 Lake Ellenor Dr, Orlando, FL 32809 *Tel:* 407-856-0016 *Fax:* 407-856-0765 *Web Site:* www.christielites.com, pg 722

Christopher Gray Post Production, 3918 Michael Ave, Los Angeles, CA 90066 *Tel:* 310-395-9845 *E-mail:* cgray@cgpost.com *Web Site:* www.cgpost.com, pg 722

The Christophers, 5 Hanover Sq, 22nd fl, New York, NY 10004 *Tel:* 212-759-4050 *Toll Free Tel:* 888-298-4050 (orders) *Fax:* 212-838-5073 *E-mail:* mail@christophers.org *Web Site:* www.christophers.org, pg 722

Christy's Editorial, 3625 W Pacific Ave, Burbank, CA 91505 *Tel:* 818-845-1755 *Toll Free Tel:* 800-468-6391; 800-556-5706 (CA) *Fax:* 818-845-1756 *E-mail:* info@christys.net *Web Site:* www.christys.net, pg 723

Chromavision Corp, The Radio Wave Bldg, Suite 900, 49 W 27 St, New York, NY 10001 *Tel:* 212-686-7366 *E-mail:* info@chromavision.net *Web Site:* www.chromavision.net, pg 723

ChronTrol Corp, 7525-K Mission Gorge Rd, San Diego, CA 92120 *Tel:* 619-282-8686 *Toll Free Tel:* 800-854-1999 *Fax:* 619-563-6563 *E-mail:* info@chrontrol.com *Web Site:* www.chrontrol.com, pg 723

ChyronHego Corp, 5 Hub Dr, Melville, NY 11747 *Tel:* 631-845-2000 *E-mail:* info@chyronhego.com; sales@chryronhego.com *Web Site:* chyronhego.com, pg 723

Cibola Systems, 180 S Cypress St, Orange, CA 92866 *Tel:* 714-480-0272 *Fax:* 714-480-0768 *E-mail:* info@cibolasystems.com *Web Site:* cibolasystems.com, pg 723

CINDY Awards, 3824 Trogdon Ct, Flower Mound, TX 75022-5326 *Tel:* 469-464-4180 *Fax:* 469-464-4170 *Web Site:* cindys.com, pg 986

Cine Audio Visual Sales & Service Ltd, 10251 106 St NW, Edmonton, AB T5J 1H5, Canada *Tel:* 780-423-5081 *Toll Free Tel:* 877-423-5081 *Fax:* 780-424-0309 *E-mail:* cineav@cineav.com; sales@cineav.com; info@cineav.com *Web Site:* www.cineav.com, pg 723

Cine Las Americas International Film Festival (CLAIFF), 1104 W 34 St, No 625, Austin, TX 78705 *Tel:* 512-535-0765 *E-mail:* cine@cinelasamericas.org; entries@cinelasamericas.org *Web Site:* cinelasamericas.org; www.facebook.com/cinelasamericasaustin, pg 986

Cine-Med Inc, 127 Main St N, Woodbury, CT 06798 *Tel:* 203-263-0006 *Toll Free Tel:* 800-253-7657 *Fax:* 203-263-4839 *E-mail:* support@cine-med.net *Web Site:* www.cine-med.com, pg 723

Cine 60 Inc, 630 Ninth Ave, New York, NY 10036 *Tel:* 347-673-3240 *E-mail:* cine60nyc@gmail.com *Web Site:* cine60.jimdo.com, pg 723

Cine-World Film Festival, 10715 Rodeo Dr, Suite 8, Lakewood Ranch, FL 34202 *Tel:* 941-364-8478 *Fax:* 941-364-8478 *E-mail:* mail@filmsociety.org *Web Site:* www.filmsociety.org, pg 986

CineBags Inc, 825 Western Ave, Suite 17, Glendale, CA 91201 *Tel:* 818-662-0605 *E-mail:* sales@cinebags.com *Web Site:* www.cinebags.com, pg 723

Cinebar Productions Inc, 10 San Jose Dr, Suite 4-C, Newport News, VA 23606 *Tel:* 757-873-3232 *E-mail:* cinebar@cinebarproductions.com, pg 723

Cinecraft Productions Inc, 2515 Franklin Blvd, Cleveland, OH 44113 *Tel:* 216-781-2300 *Toll Free Tel:* 800-959-2463 *Fax:* 216-781-1067 *E-mail:* info@cinecraft.com *Web Site:* cinecraft.com, pg 723

Cinema Antiques, 11425 Mathis Ave, Studio 404, Dallas, TX 75234 *Tel:* 972-869-0011 *E-mail:* gallery@cinemaantiques.com *Web Site:* www.cinemaantiques.com, pg 723

Cinema Camera Rentals, 4700 W Jefferson Blvd, Suite 102, Los Angeles, CA 90016 *Tel:* 323-795-0300 *E-mail:* info@cinemacamerarentals.com *Web Site:* www.cinemacamerarentals.com, pg 723

Cinema Concepts, 2030 Powers Ferry Rd, Suite 214, Atlanta, GA 30339 *Tel:* 770-956-7460 *Toll Free Tel:* 800-SHOWADS (746-9237) *Fax:* 770-956-8358 *E-mail:* info@cinemaconcepts.com *Web Site:* cinemaconcepts.com, pg 724

Cinema Equipment & Supplies Inc, 12457 SW 130 St, Miami, FL 33186 *Tel:* 305-232-8182 *E-mail:* sales@cinemaequip.com *Web Site:* www.cinemaequip.com, pg 724

Cinema Equipment Sales of California Inc, 31858 Castaic Rd, No 326, Castaic, CA 91384 *Tel:* 949-470-0298 *Fax:* 949-470-0835 *E-mail:* cinemadealer@cinemadealer.com, pg 724

The Cinema Guild Inc, 2803 Ocean Ave, Brooklyn, NY 11229 *Tel:* 212-685-6242 *Toll Free Tel:* 800-723-5522 *E-mail:* info@cinemaguild.com *Web Site:* www.cinemaguild.com, pg 724

Cinema Rentals Inc, 25876 The Old Rd, Suite 174, Stevenson Ranch, CA 91381 *Tel:* 661-222-7342 *E-mail:* ocxinc@gmail.com *Web Site:* www.cinemarentals.com, pg 724

Cinema Stage Inc, 110 Saunders Rd, Unit 4, Barrie, ON L4N 9A8, Canada *Tel:* 705-733-8740 *Toll Free Tel:* 800-387-6205 *Fax:* 705-733-8742 *E-mail:* info@cinemastage.ca *Web Site:* www.cinemastage.ca, pg 724

Cinema-Vision, 424 W 33 St, Suite 370, New York, NY 10001 *Tel:* 212-620-8191 *Fax:* 212-620-8198 *E-mail:* info@motionpicturerentals.com *Web Site:* www.motionpicturerentals.com, pg 724

Cinema Xenon International Inc, 261 Valley Vista Dr, Camarillo, CA 93010-1655 *Tel:* 805-383-5548 *Toll Free Tel:* 888-669-7271 *Fax:* 805-389-9611 *E-mail:* info@cxilamps.com *Web Site:* www.cxilamps.com, pg 724

CinemaGear.com, 14737 Arminta St, Unit B, Panorama City, CA 91402 *Tel:* 818-780-5404 *Fax:* 818-780-5405 *E-mail:* cinemagear@cinemagear.com *Web Site:* www.cinemagear.com, pg 724

Cinemarr Entertainment, 711 Dolly Parton Pkwy, Box 5941, Sevierville, TN 37864 *E-mail:* cinemarrstudios@aol.com *Web Site:* cinemarrstudios.com, pg 724

Cinemat Inc, 2520 NW 112 Ave, Doral, FL 33172 *Tel:* 305-887-7726 *E-mail:* info@cinematusa.com *Web Site:* cinematusa.com, pg 724

Cinematography Electronics Inc, 5321 Derry Ave, Suite G, Agoura Hills, CA 91301 *Tel:* 818-706-3334 *Fax:* 818-706-3335 *E-mail:* info@cinemaelec.com *Web Site:* cinemaelec.com, pg 724

Cinemills Corp, 2021 N Lincoln St, Burbank, CA 91504 *Tel:* 818-843-4560 *Toll Free Tel:* 877-CMC-HMIS (262-4647) *Fax:* 818-843-7834 *E-mail:* sales@cinemills.com *Web Site:* www.cinemills.com, pg 724

Cinequest Film & VR Festival (CQFF), PO Box 720040, San Jose, CA 95172-0040 *Tel:* 408-295-FEST (295-3378); 408-995-5033 (off) *Fax:* 408-995-5713 *E-mail:* contact@cinequest.org *Web Site:* www.cinequest.org, pg 986

Cinequipt Inc, 2601 49 Ave N, Suite 500, Minneapolis, MN 55430 *Tel:* 612-627-9080 *Toll Free Tel:* 800-809-9080 *Fax:* 612-627-9789 *Web Site:* www.cinequipt.com, pg 724

Cinestate, 4100 Swiss Ave, Dallas, TX 75204 *E-mail:* info@cinestate.com *Web Site:* cinestate.com, pg 724

CineTech Media Professionals, PO Box 34, Olivebridge, NY 12461 *Web Site:* cinetechmediapros.org, pg 953

CineTel Films Inc, 8484 Wilshire Blvd, Suite 850C, Beverly Hills, CA 90211 *Tel:* 323-654-4000 *Fax:* 323-650-6400 *E-mail:* info@cinetelfilms.com *Web Site:* cinetelfilms.com, pg 724

CineVantage LLC, 8560 W Sunset Blvd, 5th fl, West Hollywood, CA 90069 *Tel:* 323-904-9363 *Toll Free Tel:* 888-518-7571 *Web Site:* cinevantage.com, pg 724

Cinevest, PO Box 261112, Encino, CA 91426 *Tel:* 310-913-0284 *Web Site:* www.cinevest.com, pg 725

CineVideotech Inc, 14458 Commerce Way, Miami Lakes, FL 33016 *Tel:* 305-754-2611 *Fax:* 305-573-5587 *Web Site:* www.cinevideotech.com, pg 725

Cinevision Corp, 3300 Northeast Expwy NE, Bldg 2, Suite A, Atlanta, GA 30341 *Tel:* 770-455-8988 *Fax:* 770-455-4066 *Web Site:* www.cinevisionatlanta.com, pg 725

Cintrex Audio Visual, 101 Weldon Pkwy, Maryland Heights, MO 63043 *Toll Free Tel:* 800-325-9541 *E-mail:* websales@cintrexav.com *Web Site:* www.cintrexav.com, pg 725

CircuitWerkes Inc, 2805 NW Sixth St, Gainesville, FL 32609 *Tel:* 352-335-6555 *Fax:* 352-380-0230 *E-mail:* sales@circuitwerkes.com *Web Site:* www.broadcastboxes.com; www.circuitwerkes.com, pg 725

Circulating Film & Video Library, 11 W 53 St, New York, NY 10019-5401 *Tel:* 212-708-9530 *Fax:* 212-708-9531 *E-mail:* circfilm@moma.org *Web Site:* www.moma.org, pg 725

Tim Cissell Music, 10732 W 107 Circle, Westminster, CO 80021 *Tel:* 303-955-4436 *E-mail:* tim@cissellmusic.com *Web Site:* www.cissellmusic.com, pg 725

The Citation of Outstanding Service to the Society Award, White Plains Plaza, 445 Hamilton Ave, Suite 601, White Plains, NY 10601-1827 *Tel:* 914-761-1100 *Fax:* 914-206-4216 *E-mail:* marketing@smpte.org *Web Site:* www.smpte.org, pg 986

Citizens Systems America Corp, 363 Van Ness Way, Suite 404, Torrance, CA 90501 *Tel:* 310-781-1460 *Toll Free Tel:* 800-421-6516 *Fax:* 310-781-9152 *Web Site:* www.citizen-systems.com, pg 725

City Events Group, 57 Park Dr, Troy, MI 48083-2724 *Tel:* 248-589-0600 *Toll Free Tel:* 800-872-8295 *Fax:* 248-589-2020 *E-mail:* info@cityeventsgroup.com *Web Site:* www.cityeventsgroup.com, pg 725

City of Boston Office of Broadband & Cable, 43 Hawkins St, Suite 1B, Boston, MA 02114 *Tel:* 617-635-3112 *E-mail:* cable@boston.gov *Web Site:* www.cityofboston.gov/cable, pg 953

City of Calgary Film Commission, 731 First St SE, Calgary, AB T2G 2G9, Canada *Tel:* 403-221-7886 *Toll Free Tel:* 888-222-5855 *Fax:* 403-221-7828 *Web Site:* www.calgaryeconomicdevelopment.com, pg 977

City of Ojai, City Manager's Office, 401 S Ventura St, Ojai, CA 93023 *Tel:* 805-646-5581 *Fax:* 805-646-1980 *Web Site:* ojaicity.org/film-permit, pg 967

City of Phoenix Film Office, 200 W Washington St, 20th fl, Phoenix, AZ 85003 *Tel:* 602-262-4850 *E-mail:* filmphx@phoenix.gov *Web Site:* www.phoenix.gov/econdev/filming, pg 965

City of Port St Lucie Community Relations/Communications Dept, 121 SW Port St Lucie Blvd, Bldg A, 1st fl, Rm 145, Port St Lucie, FL 34984 *Tel:* 772-871-5219 *Fax:* 772-344-4111 *E-mail:* info@cityofpsl.com *Web Site:* www.cityofpsl.com, pg 969

City of Prescott Film Office, 201 S Cortez St, Prescott, AZ 86303 *Tel:* 928-777-1204 *Fax:* 928-777-1255 *Web Site:* www.prescott-az.gov, pg 965

City of Savannah Film Office, One Waring Dr, Savannah, GA 31404 *Tel:* 912-651-2360 *Fax:* 912-651-0982 *Web Site:* filmsavannah.org, pg 970

City of Stamford, 888 Washington Blvd, Stamford, CT 06901 *Tel:* 203-977-5858 *Web Site:* www.stamfordct.gov, pg 968

City of Traverse City, 400 Boardman Ave, Traverse City, MI 49684 *Tel:* 231-922-4480 *E-mail:* tcclerk@traversecitymi.gov *Web Site:* www.traversecitymi.gov, pg 972

City of West Hollywood Film Office, 8300 Santa Monica Blvd, West Hollywood, CA 90069 *Tel:* 323-848-6489 *E-mail:* wehofilm@weho.org *Web Site:* www.weho.org/film, pg 968

Civins Productions Inc, 5881 NW 122 Dr, Coral Springs, FL 33076 *Tel:* 954-938-8600 *E-mail:* info@civins.com *Web Site:* www.civins.com, pg 725

Clair Companies, One Clair Blvd, Manheim, PA 17545 *Tel:* 717-665-4000 *Fax:* 717-665-8000 *E-mail:* contact@clairbrothers.com; sales@clairbrothers.com *Web Site:* www.claircompanies.com; www.clairbrothers.com; www.clairsolutions.com, pg 725

Clarion Awards, 1717 E Republic Rd, Suite A, Springfield, MO 65804 *Tel:* 417-886-8606 *Fax:* 417-886-3685 *E-mail:* clarion@womcom.org *Web Site:* www.womcom.org, pg 986

Clarity Media Group, 166 Fifth Ave, 6th & 7th fl, New York, NY 10010 *Tel:* 212-262-7015 *E-mail:* info@claritymediagroup.com *Web Site:* www.claritymediagroup.com, pg 725

Clarity Sound & Light, 14618 Tyler Foote Rd, Nevada City, CA 95959 *Tel:* 530-478-7600 *Toll Free Tel:* 800-424-1055 *E-mail:* seva@crystalclarity.com *Web Site:* www.crystalclarity.com, pg 725

Clark, 1225 Old Alpharetta Rd, Suite 295, Alpharetta, GA 30005 *Tel:* 770-888-5088 *Toll Free Tel:* 888-621-8841 *E-mail:* info@clark.is *Web Site:* www.clark.is, pg 725

Clark Services Audio Visual & Exhibit Inc, 113 Board Rd, Lafayette, LA 70508 *Tel:* 337-234-5653 *Fax:* 337-232-0243 *E-mail:* clarkservices@bellsouth.net, pg 725

Clark Wire & Cable, 408 Washington Blvd, Mundelein, IL 60060-3102 *Tel:* 847-949-9944 *Toll Free Tel:* 800-222-5348 *Fax:* 847-949-9595 *E-mail:* sales@clarkwire.com *Web Site:* www.clarkwire.com, pg 725

Clark's Audio Visual Services Ltd, 1615 Venables St, Vancouver, BC V5L 2H1, Canada *Tel:* 604-877-8558 *Toll Free Tel:* 800-667-1819 *Fax:* 604-879-2993 *Toll Free Fax:* 800-665-2932 *E-mail:* info@clarksav.com *Web Site:* www.clarksav.com, pg 725

Clarkson Studio, 401 N Hoback St, Helena, MT 59601 *Web Site:* www.clarksonstudio.com, pg 726

Classic Images Stock Footage LLC, 469 1/2 S Bedford Dr, Beverly Hills, CA 90212 *Tel:* 310-277-0400 *Toll Free Tel:* 800-949-CLIP (949-2547) *Fax:* 310-277-0412 *E-mail:* sales@classicimg.com *Web Site:* www.classicimg.com, pg 726

ClassicStock.com/Robertstock.com, 4203 Locust St, Philadelphia, PA 19104 *Tel:* 215-386-6300 *Toll Free Tel:* 800-786-6300 *Toll Free Fax:* 800-786-1920

E-mail: info@robertstock.com; info@classicstock.com *Web Site:* www.robertstock.com; www.classicstock.com, pg 726

Clayton-Davis & Associates, 4 Warridge Dr, St Louis, MO 63124 *Tel:* 314-862-7800, pg 726

Clean Slate Video, 3070 Kerner Blvd, Unit O, San Rafael, CA 94901 *Tel:* 415-485-0727 *E-mail:* info@cleanslatevideo.com *Web Site:* www.cleanslatevideo.com, pg 726

Clear Choice Creative Corp, 260 Monroe St, NW, Warren, OH 44483 *Tel:* 330-469-9542; 330-469-9524 *E-mail:* info@clearchoicecreative.com *Web Site:* www.clearchoicecreative.com, pg 726

Clear-Com® LLC, 1301 Marina Village Pkwy, Suite 105, Alameda, CA 94501 *Tel:* 510-337-6600 *Toll Free Tel:* 800-462-HELP (462-4357) *Fax:* 510-337-6699 *E-mail:* salessupportus@clearcom.com *Web Site:* www.clearcom.com, pg 726

Clear Focus Media LLC, 6402 Creel Dr, Weston, WI 54476 *Tel:* 715-212-6239 *Web Site:* www.clearfocus.media, pg 726

ClearOne Inc, Edgewater Corporate Park, South Tower, Suite 500, 5225 Wiley Post Way, Salt Lake City, UT 84116 *Tel:* 801-975-7200 *Fax:* 801-303-5711 *E-mail:* contact@clearone.com; marketing@clearone.com *Web Site:* www.clearone.com, pg 726

Wally Cleaver's Recording Service, 2200 Airport Ave, Fredericksburg, VA 22401-7220 *Tel:* 540-846-6382 *E-mail:* wallycleavers@mac.com *Web Site:* www.facebook.com/wallycleavers, pg 726

Cleveland Costume & Display Corp, 1271 Pearl Rd, Brunswick, OH 44212 *Tel:* 440-846-9292, pg 726

Cleveland International Film Festival, 2510 Market Ave, Cleveland, OH 44113-3434 *Tel:* 216-623-3456 *Fax:* 216-623-0103 *E-mail:* cfs@clevelandfilm.org; submissions@clevelandfilm.org *Web Site:* www.clevelandfilm.org, pg 986

Clever Cleaver Productions, 7050 E Sunrise Dr, Suite 2101, Tucson, AZ 85750 *Tel:* 520-333-8403, pg 726

Clever Devices Ltd, 300 Crossways Park Dr, Woodbury, NY 11797 *Tel:* 516-433-6100 *Toll Free Tel:* 800-872-6129 *Web Site:* www.cleverdevices.com, pg 726

The Clio Awards, 825 Eighth Ave, 29th fl, New York, NY 10019 *Tel:* 212-683-4300 *E-mail:* event@clioawards.com *Web Site:* clios.com, pg 987

Close Up Foundation, 1330 Braddock Place, Suite 400, Alexandria, VA 22314 *Tel:* 703-706-3300 *Toll Free Tel:* 800-CLOSEUP (256-7387) *E-mail:* info@closeup.org *Web Site:* www.closeup.org, pg 726

CMD Agency, 1631 NW Thurman St, Portland, OR 97209 *Tel:* 503-223-6794 *E-mail:* info@cmdagency.com *Web Site:* www.cmdagency.com, pg 726

CMEinfo™, 2 Perimeter Park S, Suite 160E, Birmingham, AL 35243 *Toll Free Tel:* 800-633-4743 *E-mail:* oakstoneservice@ebix.com *Web Site:* www.cmeinfo.com, pg 727

CMI, 612 Hampton Dr, Venice, CA 90291 *Tel:* 310-392-8771 *E-mail:* cmi@cmifilms.com *Web Site:* www.cmifilms.com, pg 727

CMI Communications, 400 Mile Crossing Blvd, Rochester, NY 14624 *Tel:* 585-424-1900 *Toll Free Tel:* 888-736-8264 *Fax:* 585-424-1913 *E-mail:* info@cmiav.com *Web Site:* www.cmiav.com, pg 727

CMI Media Management, 9 W Broad St, Stamford, CT 06902 *Tel:* 203-989-9955 *Toll Free Tel:* 800-431-1102 *Fax:* 203-316-8353 *Web Site:* www.cminyla.com, pg 727

CNS Productions Inc, 897 Royal Ave, Suite A, Medford, OR 97504 *Tel:* 541-779-3361 *Toll Free Tel:* 800-888-0617 *Fax:* 541-773-5905 *E-mail:* info@cnsproductions.com *Web Site:* www.cnsproductions.com, pg 727

Coast Learning Systems, 11460 Warner Ave, Fountain Valley, CA 92708 *Tel:* 714-241-6109 *Toll Free Tel:* 800-547-4748 *E-mail:* coastlearning@coastline.edu *Web Site:* www.coastlearning.org, pg 727

Coastal Training Technologies Corp, 500 Studio Dr, Virginia Beach, VA 23452 *Tel:* 757-498-9014 *Toll Free Tel:* 877-262-7825 *Fax:* 757-498-3657 *E-mail:* support@training.consultdss.com *Web Site:* www.coastalflix.com, pg 727

Coastline Productions, 2647 Gateway Rd, No 105-355, Carlsbad, CA 92009 *Tel:* 760-598-1860 *Toll Free Tel:* 888-781-5714 *E-mail:* productions@coastlinevideo.com *Web Site:* www.coastlinevideo.com, pg 727

Cobalt Studios Inc, 134 Royce Rd, White Lake, NY 12786 *Tel:* 845-583-7025 *Fax:* 845-583-7025 *E-mail:* mail@cobaltstudios.net *Web Site:* www.cobaltstudios.net, pg 727

Cochise County Tourism & Economic Council, 1011 N Coronado Dr, Sierra Vista, AZ 85635 *Tel:* 520-432-2290 *Fax:* 520-458-0584 *E-mail:* info@explorecochise.com *Web Site:* www.explorecochise.com, pg 965

Steven Cohen Motion Picture Production, 1182 Coral Club Dr, Coral Springs, FL 33071 *Tel:* 954-346-7370 *Fax:* 954-346-7370, pg 727

Cohn Creative Group LLC, 630 Ninth Ave, Suite 806, New York, NY 10036 *Tel:* 212-333-3241 *Fax:* 212-246-5727 *E-mail:* info@cohncreative.com *Web Site:* cohncreative.com, pg 727

CohuHD Costar LLC, 7330 Trade St, San Diego, CA 92121 *Tel:* 858-391-1800 *E-mail:* info@cohuhd.com *Web Site:* www.cohuhd.com, pg 727

Cokesbury, 2222 Rosa Parks Blvd, Nashville, TN 37228 *Tel:* 615-749-6000 (UMPH) *Toll Free Tel:* 800-672-1789; 844-381-2708 (cust care) *Fax:* 615-749-6578 *Toll Free Fax:* 800-445-8189 *E-mail:* cokes_serv@cokesbury.com; customerhelp@cokesbury.com *Web Site:* www.cokesbury.com, pg 727

Cole Wire & Cable Co Inc, 620 Margate Dr, Lincolnshire, IL 60069-4247 *Toll Free Tel:* 800-323-1403 *Fax:* 847-634-4988; 847-634-4300 *E-mail:* sales@colewire.com *Web Site:* www.colewire.com, pg 727

Collective Systems LLC, 76 Progress Dr, Suite 270, Stamford, CT 06902 *Tel:* 203-973-7011 *Fax:* 203-323-8078 *E-mail:* sales@collectivesys.com *Web Site:* www.cs-av.com, pg 727

Colonial Williamsburg Foundation, PO Box 1776, Williamsburg, VA 23187-1776 *Tel:* 757-229-1000 *Toll Free Tel:* 888-974-7926 *E-mail:* social@cwf.org *Web Site:* www.colonialwilliamsburg.org; www.history.org/foundation, pg 727

Color Leasing Studios, 330 Rte 46 E, Fairfield, NJ 07004 *Tel:* 973-575-1118 *Fax:* 973-575-1170 *Web Site:* www.colorleasingstudios.com, pg 727

Colorado Office of Film, Television & Media, 1600 Broadway, Suite 2500, Denver, CO 80202 *Tel:* 303-892-3840 *Fax:* 303-892-3848 *E-mail:* info@coloradofilm.org *Web Site:* coloradofilm.org, pg 968

Colorado Sound Recording LLC, 3100 W 71 Ave, Westminster, CO 80030 *Tel:* 303-430-8811 *E-mail:* colosnd@coloradosound.com *Web Site:* www.coloradosound.com, pg 728

Colorado Springs Film Commission, 515 S Cascade Ave, Colorado Springs, CO 80903 *Tel:* 719-685-7630 *Toll Free Tel:* 800-888-4748 (ext 130) *Fax:* 719-635-4968 *E-mail:* film@visitcos.com *Web Site:* www.visitcos.com/film, pg 968

Colorado Studios, 8455 Highfield Pkwy, Englewood, CO 80112 *Fax:* 303-388-9600 *E-mail:* info@coloradostudios.com *Web Site:* coloradostudios.info, pg 728

Colorado Time Systems LLC, 1551 E 11 St, Loveland, CO 80537 *Tel:* 970-667-1000; 970-612-3573 (intl sales) *Toll Free Tel:* 800-279-0111 *Fax:* 970-667-5876; 970-667-1788 (intl sales) *E-mail:* info@coloradotime.com *Web Site:* www.coloradotime.com, pg 728

Colorado Video Inc, PO Box 952, Longmont, CO 80502 *Tel:* 303-530-9580 *Fax:* 303-530-9569 *E-mail:* sales@colorado-video.com *Web Site:* www.colorado-video.com, pg 728

Coloredge Inc, 1919 W Empire Ave, Burbank, CA 91504 *Tel:* 818-842-1121 *Toll Free Tel:* 800-321-8864 *E-mail:* lainfo@coloredge.com *Web Site:* coloredge.com, pg 728

Colortek of Boston, 727 Atlantic Ave, Boston, MA 02111 *Tel:* 617-451-0894 *E-mail:* info@colortekofboston.com *Web Site:* www.colortekofboston.com, pg 728

Colortone Audio Visual, 181 Westchester Ave, Suite 408B, Port Chester, NY 10573 *Tel:* 914-592-4151 *Fax:* 914-592-2833 *Web Site:* www.colortone-av.com, pg 728

Columbia Lighting, 701 Millennium Blvd, Greenville, SC 29607 *Tel:* 864-678-1000; 864-678-1664 (cust support) *Toll Free Fax:* 866-898-0131 *Web Site:* www.columbialighting.com, pg 728

Columbia Pictures Inc, 10202 W Washington Blvd, Culver City, CA 90232 *Tel:* 310-244-4000 *Web Site:* www.sonypictures.com, pg 728

Columbus Film Commission, 117 Third St S, Columbus, MS 39701 *Tel:* 662-329-1191 *Toll Free Tel:* 800-327-2686; 800-920-3533 *Fax:* 662-329-8969 *E-mail:* marketing@visitcolumbusms.org *Web Site:* visitcolumbusms.org, pg 972

Columbus International Film + Video Festival, 60 Cleveland Ave, Columbus, OH 43215 *Tel:* 614-222-6185 *E-mail:* info@columbusfilmfestival.org *Web Site:* www.ccad.edu/experience-art/columbus-international-film-festival, pg 987

Comex Systems Inc, 101 Pleasant Hill Rd, Chester, NJ 07930 *Tel:* 908-881-6301 (cell) *E-mail:* mail@comexsystems.com *Web Site:* www.comexsystems.com, pg 728

Comm-Arts Inc, 2512 E 71 St, Suite A, Tulsa, OK 74136 *Tel:* 918-493-5700 *E-mail:* marketing@comm-arts.com *Web Site:* www.comm-arts.com, pg 728

CommCreative, 75 Fountain St, Framingham, MA 01702 *Tel:* 508-620-6664 *Toll Free Tel:* 877-620-6664 *Fax:* 508-620-0592 *E-mail:* info@commcreative.com *Web Site:* www.commcreative.com, pg 728

Commercial Electronics Ltd, 1565 W Seventh St, Vancouver, BC V6J 1S1, Canada *Tel:* 604-669-5525 *E-mail:* info@commercialelectronics.ca *Web Site:* commercialelectronics.ca, pg 728

Commonwealth Films Inc, 223 Commonwealth Ave, Boston, MA 02116 *Tel:* 617-262-5634 *E-mail:* info@commonwealthfilms.com *Web Site:* www.commonwealthfilms.com, pg 728

CommScope Inc, 1100 CommScope Place SE, Hickory, NC 28602 *Tel:* 828-324-2200 *Toll Free Tel:* 800-982-1708 *E-mail:* publicrelations@commscope.com *Web Site:* www.commscope.com, pg 728

Communication Arts Multimedia Inc, 1618 Williams Dr, No 5, Georgetown, TX 78628 *Tel:* 512-868-0548 *Fax:* 512-868-0548 *E-mail:* mail@commartsmultimedia.com *Web Site:* www.commartsmultimedia.com, pg 728

Communication Arts Visual Communications Competition, 110 Constitution Dr, Menlo Park, CA 94025 *Tel:* 650-326-6040 *Fax:* 650-326-1648 *E-mail:* competition@commarts.com *Web Site:* www.commarts.com, pg 987

Communication Ministries, PO Box 1986, Indianapolis, IN 46206-1986 *Tel:* 317-713-2492 *Web Site:* disciples.org/dns, pg 728

Communications & Power Industries (CPI), Satcom & Medical Products Division, 45 River Dr, Georgetown, ON L7G 2J4, Canada *Tel:* 905-877-0161 *Fax:* 905-877-5327 *E-mail:* satcommarketing@cpii.com *Web Site:* www.cpii.com, pg 728

Communications Concepts Inc (CCI), 7980 N Atlantic Ave, Suite 101, Cape Canaveral, FL 32920 *Tel:* 321-783-5232 *Web Site:* cci321.com, pg 729

Communications Design Associates, 437 Turnpike St, Canton, MA 02021 *Tel:* 339-502-6551 *Web Site:* www.cdaconsultants.com, pg 729

The Communications Group Inc, 502 S West St, Raleigh, NC 27601 *Tel:* 919-828-4086 *Toll Free Tel:* 800-595-2937 *E-mail:* info@cgfilm.com *Web Site:* cgroupfilm.tv, pg 729

Communications Media Management Association (CMMA), 1604 Glendale Hills Dr NE, Suite B25, Rochester, MN 55906-8376 *Tel:* 507-271-4307 *Web Site:* cmma.org, pg 953

Communilux Productions, 4001 East Side Ave, Dallas, TX 75226 *Tel:* 214-821-8706 *Toll Free Tel:* 877-323-5189 *Fax:* 214-827-6306 *E-mail:* info@communilux.com *Web Site:* www.communilux.com, pg 729

Communitronics Corp, 970 Bolger Ct, Fenton, MO 63026 *Tel:* 314-771-7160 *Fax:* 314-771-9144 *E-mail:* info@communitronics.com *Web Site:* www.communitronics.com, pg 729

Community Professional Loudspeakers, 333 E Fifth St, Chester, PA 19013-4511 *Tel:* 610-876-3400 *Toll Free Tel:* 800-523-4934 *Fax:* 610-874-0190 *Toll Free Fax:* 800-220-3661 (orders) *E-mail:* info@communitypro.com; sales@communitypro.com *Web Site:* www.communitypro.com, pg 729

Compact Storage Systems Inc, 9757 Reseda Blvd, Suite 68, Northridge, CA 91324 *Tel:* 818-772-0996 *E-mail:* info@halfthespace.com *Web Site:* www.halfthespace.com, pg 729

Compass Records, 916 19 Ave S, Nashville, TN 37212 *Tel:* 615-320-7672 *Fax:* 615-320-7378 *E-mail:* info@compassrecords.com *Web Site:* www.compassrecords.com, pg 729

Compix Media Inc, 5151 California Ave, Suite 100, Irvine, CA 92617 *Tel:* 949-585-0055 *E-mail:* info@compix.tv *Web Site:* www.compix.tv, pg 729

Composer Louis Anthony deLise, 83 Park Dr, Cherry Hill, NJ 08002-3002 *Tel:* 856-616-2867 *E-mail:* louis@bocagemusic.com *Web Site:* www.louisanthonydelise.com, pg 729

Comprehensive Cable & Connectivity Co, 80 Little Falls Rd, Fairfield, NJ 07004 *Toll Free Tel:* 800-526-0242 *Fax:* 201-814-0510 *E-mail:* sales@comprehensiveco.com; customerservice@comprehensiveco.com *Web Site:* www.comprehensiveco.com, pg 729

Comprehensive Technical Group, 2030 Powers Ferry Rd SE, Suite 130, Atlanta, GA 30339 *Tel:* 404-352-3000 *Toll Free Tel:* 888-557-4284 *Fax:* 404-352-2962 *E-mail:* info@ctgatlanta.com *Web Site:* www.ctgatlanta.com, pg 729

Comprompter Inc, 1601 Caledonia St, Suite E, La Crosse, WI 54601 *Tel:* 608-785-7766 *E-mail:* sales@comprompter.com *Web Site:* www.comprompter.com, pg 729

Computer Dynamics, 3030 Whitehall Park Dr, Charlotte, NC 28273 *Tel:* 704-227-4600 *Toll Free Tel:* 866-599-6512 *Fax:* 704-583-9671 *Web Site:* www.cdynamics.com, pg 729

The Computer Language Co Inc, 5521 State Park Rd, Point Pleasant, PA 18950 *Tel:* 215-297-8082 *E-mail:* sales@computerlanguage.com; comments@computerlanguage.com *Web Site:* www.computerlanguage.com, pg 729

Computer Modules Inc, 11409 W Bernardo Ct, San Diego, CA 92127 *Tel:* 858-613-1818 *Fax:* 858-613-1815 *E-mail:* info@dveo.com *Web Site:* www.dveo.com, pg 729

Compuvideo Sales USA Ltd, 7255 Brunswick Circle, Boynton Beach, FL 33472 *Tel:* 561-733-4780 *E-mail:* sales@compuvideo.com; customerservice@compuvideo.com *Web Site:* www.compuvideo.com, pg 729

CompuWeather Inc, 2566 Rte 52, Hopewell Junction, NY 12533 *Tel:* 845-227-8500 *Toll Free Tel:* 800-825-4445 *Fax:* 845-227-8400 *Toll Free Fax:* 800-825-4441 *E-mail:* info@compuweather.com *Web Site:* www.compuweather.com, pg 729

Comrex Corp, 19 Pine Rd, Devens, MA 01434 *Tel:* 978-784-1776 (intl) *Toll Free Tel:* 800-237-1776 *Fax:* 978-784-1717 *E-mail:* info@comrex.com *Web Site:* www.comrex.com, pg 730

Comtek Communications Technology Inc, 357 W 2700 S, Salt Lake City, UT 84115 *Tel:* 801-466-3463 *Toll Free Tel:* 800-496-3463 *Fax:* 801-484-6906 *E-mail:* sales@comtek.com *Web Site:* www.comtek.com, pg 730

Comtel Inc, 14901 NE 20 Ave, North Miami, FL 33181 *Tel:* 305-424-4160 (facility servs); 305-424-4178 (local inquiries); 516-816-5152 (natl inquiries) *Web Site:* www.comtelinc.com; www.facebook.com/comtelinc/, pg 730

Concept Associates Inc, 5371 Punta Alta, Unit 1E, Laguna Woods, CA 92637, pg 730

Concept Productions Inc, 7878 Big Sky Dr, Madison, WI 53719 *Tel:* 608-833-8273 *E-mail:* info@conceptpro.biz *Web Site:* www.conceptpro.biz, pg 730

Concepts TV Productions Inc, 53 Indian Lane E, Towaco, NJ 07082 *Tel:* 973-331-1500 *Fax:* 973-331-1550 *E-mail:* sales@conceptstv.com *Web Site:* conceptstv.com, pg 730

Concoction Lab, 520 Frederick St, No 8, San Francisco, CA 94117 *Tel:* 415-997-9649 *Fax:* 415-294-2178 *E-mail:* info@concoctionlab.com *Web Site:* www.concoctionlab.com, pg 730

Concord Jazz, 5750 Wilshire Blvd, Suite 450, Los Angeles, CA 90036 *Tel:* 310-385-4455 *Web Site:* concord.com/labels/concord-jazz, pg 730

Concord Records, 5750 Wilshire Blvd, Suite 450, Los Angeles, CA 90036 *Tel:* 310-385-4455 *Web Site:* concord.com/labels/concord-records, pg 730

Concrete Images, 1301 Main St, Venice, CA 90291 *Tel:* 310-452-9655 *Fax:* 310-452-9866 *E-mail:* office@concreteimages.com *Web Site:* www.concreteimages.com, pg 730

Conex Electro Systems Inc, 789 W Smith Rd, Bellingham, WA 98226-9613 *Tel:* 360-734-4323 *Toll Free Tel:* 800-645-1061 *Fax:* 360-676-4822 *E-mail:* sales@conex-electro.com *Web Site:* www.conex-electro.com, pg 730

Conference Technologies Inc, 11653 Adie Rd, Maryland Heights, MO 63043 *Tel:* 314-993-1400 *Toll Free Tel:* 800-743-6051 *Toll Free Fax:* 855-329-2844 *E-mail:* info@conferencetech.com *Web Site:* www.conferencetech.com, pg 730

Conly Productions, 1563 Oneida St, Denver, CO 80220 *Tel:* 303-393-6240 *Fax:* 303-393-6240, pg 730

Connecticut Audio & Theatrical Supply, 125-F Old Iron Ore Rd, Bloomfield, CT 06002 *Tel:* 860-206-9555 *Fax:* 860-206-0485 *Web Site:* www.ctaudio.com, pg 731

Connecticut Office of Film, Television & Digital Media, c/o Dept of Economic & Community Development, 480 Columbus Blvd, Suite 5, Hartford, CT 06103 *Tel:* 860-500-2300 *Web Site:* www.ct.gov, pg 968

Connections Film & Video Inc, PO Box 110929, Anchorage, AK 99511 *Tel:* 907-561-6450 *Web Site:* www.filmalaska.com, pg 731

Conquest Sound Co Inc, 209 Cypress Dr, Manteno, IL 60950 *Tel:* 708-534-0390 *Toll Free Tel:* 800-323-7671 *Fax:* 708-534-0398 *E-mail:* info@conquestsound.com *Web Site:* www.conquestsound.com, pg 731

Consolidated Communications Consultants, 1837 SE Harold St, Portland, OR 97202-4932 *Tel:* 503-232-9787 *Toll Free Tel:* 800-929-5119 *Fax:* 503-232-9787 *Toll Free Fax:* 800-929-5119 *E-mail:* acmrl@myexcel.com *Web Site:* www.acmusicresearch.com, pg 731

Consolidated Display Co Inc, 1210 US Hwy 34, Oswego, IL 60543 *Tel:* 630-851-8666 *Toll Free Tel:* 888-851-7669 *Fax:* 630-851-8756 *E-mail:* info@letitsnow.com *Web Site:* www.letitsnow.com, pg 731

Consortium of College & University Media Centers (CCUMC), c/o Indiana University, 306 N Union St, Bloomington, IN 47405-3888 *Tel:* 812-855-6049 *E-mail:* ccumc@ccumc.org *Web Site:* www.ccumc.org, pg 953

Consumer Technology Association (CTA), 1919 S Eads St, Arlington, VA 22202 *Tel:* 703-907-7600 *Toll Free Tel:* 866-858-1555 *Fax:* 703-907-7675 *Toll Free Fax:* 866-858-2555 *E-mail:* cta@cta.tech *Web Site:* www.cta.tech, pg 953

Contemporary Research, 4355 Excel Pkwy, Suite 600, Addison, TX 75001 *Tel:* 972-931-2728 *Toll Free Tel:* 888-972-2728 *E-mail:* contact@crwww.com *Web Site:* contemporaryresearch.com, pg 731

Continental Film, 1466 Riverside Dr, Suite E, Chattanooga, TN 37406 *Tel:* 423-622-1193 *Toll Free Tel:* 888-909-3456 *Fax:* 423-629-0853 *E-mail:* info@continentalfilm.com *Web Site:* www.continentalfilm.com, pg 731

Continental Recordings Inc, 23 Mirimichi St, Plainville, MA 02762 *Tel:* 508-699-0003 *Toll Free Tel:* 888-729-3130 *Fax:* 508-699-0004, pg 731

Convenience, 3012 N Long Ave, Chicago, IL 60641-4930 *Tel:* 773-545-3073, pg 731

Convergent Media Systems, 190 Bluegrass Valley Pkwy, Alpharetta, GA 30005-2204 *Tel:* 770-369-9000 *Fax:* 770-369-9100 *Web Site:* www.convergent.com, pg 731

Cooking by the Book, 13475 N Applegate Rd, Grants Pass, OR 97527 *Tel:* 541-846-0654 *Toll Free Tel:* 800-655-9071 *Fax:* 541-846-0654 *Web Site:* www.atasteofnature.org, pg 731

Cool-Lux, 1268 Humbracht Circle, Bartlett, IL 60103 *Toll Free Tel:* 800-ACDC-LUX (223-2589) *Fax:* 630-830-2525 *Web Site:* www.cool-lux.com, pg 731

Copp Integrated Systems, 123 S Keowee St, Dayton, OH 45402 *Tel:* 937-228-4188 *Toll Free Tel:* 877-450-2677 *Fax:* 937-228-2901 *Web Site:* www.copp.com, pg 731

CopShopMiami.com, 160 E 35 St, Hialeah, FL 33013 *Tel:* 305-333-5791 *E-mail:* omar@copshopmiami.com *Web Site:* www.copshopmiami.com, pg 731

Corel Corp, 1600 Carling Ave, Ottawa, ON K1Z 8R7, Canada *Toll Free Tel:* 877-582-6735 *Web Site:* www.corel.com, pg 731

Corinth Films Inc, 3117 Bursonville Rd, Riegelsville, PA 18077 *E-mail:* john@corinthfilms.com *Web Site:* www.corinthreleasing.com; www.corinthfilms.com, pg 731

Cornell Laboratory of Ornithology, Cornell University, 159 Sapsucker Woods Rd, Ithaca, NY 14850 *Toll Free Tel:* 866-989-BIRD (989-2473) *Web Site:* www.birds.cornell.edu, pg 731

Cornerstone Media Productions Inc, 306 W Market St, Georgetown, DE 19947 *Tel:* 302-855-9380 *Web Site:* www.cornerstonemedia.com, pg 731

Corporate Color Graphics Inc, 3525 Lousma Dr SE, Grand Rapids, MI 49548 *Tel:* 616-774-9583 *Toll Free Tel:* 800-776-9583 *E-mail:* production@corpcolor.com *Web Site:* www.corpcolor.com, pg 732

Corporation for Public Broadcasting (CPB), 401 Ninth St NW, Washington, DC 20004-2129 *Tel:* 202-879-9600 *Toll Free Tel:* 800-272-2190 *Fax:* 202-879-9700 *E-mail:* press@cpb.org *Web Site:* www.cpb.org, pg 953

Corpus Christi Convention & Visitors Bureau, 101 N Shoreline Blvd, Suite 430, Corpus Christi, TX 78401 *Toll Free Tel:* 800-678-6232 *Web Site:* www.visitcorpuschristitx.org, pg 976

CORTRON Media LLC, 320 Fort Duquesne Blvd, Suite 100, Pittsburgh, PA 15222-1146 *Tel:* 412-565-3471 (ext 3) *Web Site:* cortronmedia.com, pg 732

Cosumnes River College, 8401 Center Pkwy, Sacramento, CA 95823 *Tel:* 916-691-7474 *Web Site:* www.crc.losrios.edu, pg 732

Council on Foundations, 2121 Crystal Dr, Suite 700, Arlington, VA 22202 *Toll Free Tel:* 800-673-9036 *E-mail:* membership@cof.org *Web Site:* www.cof.org, pg 732

Countdown Productions Inc, PO Box 180220, Dallas, TX 75218 *Tel:* 214-321-3233; 214-808-9988 (cell) *E-mail:* info@countdownproductions.com *Web Site:* www.countdownproductions.com, pg 732

Countryman Associates Inc, 195 Constitution Dr, Menlo Park, CA 94025 *Tel:* 650-364-9988 *Toll Free Tel:* 800-669-1422 *Fax:* 650-364-2794 *E-mail:* sales@countryman.com *Web Site:* www.countryman.com, pg 732

County Sales, 117A W Main St, Floyd, VA 24091 *Tel:* 540-745-2001 *Fax:* 540-745-2008 *E-mail:* info@countysales.com *Web Site:* www.countysales.com, pg 732

Courter Films LLC, 1145 N Stoney Point, Crystal River, FL 34429 *Tel:* 352-563-7888 (cell) *E-mail:* info@courterfilms.com *Web Site:* www.courterfilms.com, pg 732

Coustic, 4545 E Baseline Rd, Phoenix, AZ 85042 *Toll Free Tel:* 800-225-5689; 800-372-3029 (orders) *E-mail:* mtx@mtx.com; orders@mtx.com *Web Site:* www.coustic.com, pg 732

Covid Inc, 1723 W Fourth St, Tempe, AZ 85281 *Tel:* 480-966-2221 *Toll Free Tel:* 800-638-6104 *Fax:* 480-966-6728 *E-mail:* sales@covid.com *Web Site:* www.covid.com, pg 732

Cox Creative Studios, 17602 N Black Canyon Hwy, Phoenix, AZ 85053 *Tel:* 623-328-4778 *Web Site:* www.coxcreativestudios.com, pg 732

Cox Media, 6205 Peachtree Dunwoody Rd, No B17, Atlanta, GA 30328 *Toll Free Tel:* 855-755-2691 *Web Site:* www.coxmedia.com, pg 732

Coyote Cowboy Co, PO Box 2190, Benson, AZ 85602-2190 *Tel:* 520-586-1077 *Toll Free Tel:* 800-654-2550 *Web Site:* baxterblack.com, pg 732

CP Communications, 15 Ninnie Dr, Wappingers Falls, NY 12590 *Tel:* 914-345-9292 *Toll Free Tel:* 800-762-4254 *Fax:* 914-345-9222 *E-mail:* info@cpcomms.com; sales@cpcomms.com *Web Site:* www.cpcomms.com, pg 732

CP Digital, 102 Madison Ave, New York, NY 10016 *Tel:* 212-686-9570 *Web Site:* www.cpdigital.com, pg 732

CPI Malibu, 3760-A Calle Tecate, Camarillo, CA 93012-5060 *Tel:* 805-383-1829 *Fax:* 805-383-1859 *E-mail:* malibu.sales@cpii.com *Web Site:* www.cpii.com/division.cfm/10, pg 732

CPR MultiMedia Solutions, 7812 Cessna Ave, Gaithersburg, MD 20879 *Tel:* 301-590-9400 *Fax:* 301-590-9402 *E-mail:* info@cprmms.com *Web Site:* www.cprmms.com, pg 732

CPT Rental Inc, 36-01A 48 Ave, Long Island City, NY 11101 *Tel:* 718-424-1600 *E-mail:* rental@cptrental.com *Web Site:* www.cptrental.com, pg 732

Craig Recording Studios, 2381 Philmont Ave, Suite 112, Huntingdon Valley, PA 19006 *Tel:* 215-947-8900 *Web Site:* www.craigrecording.com; www.craigrecordingstudios.com, pg 732

Cramer, 425 University Ave, Norwood, MA 02062 *Tel:* 781-278-2300 *E-mail:* theteam@cramer.com *Web Site:* cramer.com, pg 732

Crash Video Productions, 713 N Mansfield Ave, Los Angeles, CA 90038 *Tel:* 310-489-6848 *E-mail:* crash@crashproductions.com *Web Site:* www.crashproductions.com, pg 733

Thomas Craven Film Corp, 5 W 19 St, 3rd fl, New York, NY 10011-4216 *Tel:* 212-463-7190 *Fax:* 212-627-4761 *E-mail:* info@cravenfilms.com *Web Site:* cravenfilms.com, pg 733

Crawford Media Services Inc, 6 W Druid Hills Dr NE, Atlanta, GA 30329 *Tel:* 404-876-0333 *Toll Free Tel:* 800-831-8029 *E-mail:* bookit@crawford.com *Web Site:* audio.crawford.com; www.facebook.com/crawfordmediaservices, pg 733

Creation Technologies Inc, 8999 Fraserton Ct, Burnaby, BC V5J 5H8, Canada *Tel:* 604-430-4336 *Toll Free Tel:* 800-736-1271 *E-mail:* info@creationtech.com; sales@creationtech.com *Web Site:* www.creationtech.com, pg 733

Creative Artists Agency LLC, 2000 Avenue of the Stars, Los Angeles, CA 90067 Tel: 424-288-2000 Fax: 424-288-2900 E-mail: info@caa.com Web Site: www.caa.com, pg 733

Creative Arts Film Festival (CAFF), PO Box 823, Malvern, PA 19355 Tel: 610-889-4928 E-mail: creativeartsfilmfestival@gmail.com Web Site: www.creativeartsfilmfestival.com, pg 987

Creative Arts Television, PO Box 739, Kent, CT 06757-0739 E-mail: info@catarchive.com Web Site: www.catarchive.com, pg 733

Creative Backstage, 4829 S 36 St, Suite 1, Phoenix, AZ 85040 Tel: 480-580-2222 E-mail: sales@creativebackstage.com Web Site: www.creativebackstage.com, pg 733

Creative BC (CrBC), 7 W Sixth Ave, Vancouver, BC V5Y 1K2, Canada Tel: 604-730-2732 Fax: 604-736-7290 E-mail: info@creativebc.com; media@creativebc.com Web Site: www.creativebc.com, pg 978

Creative Impulse Awards (Impies), c/o RIIFF, 36 Rhode Island Ave, Newport, RI 02840 Tel: 401-861-4445 Fax: 401-490-6735 E-mail: info@film-festival.org Web Site: www.film-festival.org/CreativeIM.php, pg 987

Creative Media Recording, 11105 Knott Ave, Suite G, Cypress, CA 90630 Tel: 714-892-9469 E-mail: info@creativemediarecording.com Web Site: www.creativemediarecording.com, pg 733

Creative Realities Inc (CRI), 13100 Magisterial Dr, Suite 100, Louisville, KY 40223 Tel: 502-791-8800 Web Site: cri.com, pg 733

Creative Sound Corp, 5515 Medea Valley Dr, Agoura Hills, CA 91301 Tel: 818-707-8986 E-mail: info@csoundcorp.com Web Site: www.csoundcorp.com, pg 733

Creative Stage Lighting Co Inc, 149 Rte 28 N, North Creek, NY 12853 Tel: 518-251-3302 Fax: 518-251-2908 E-mail: info@creativestagelighting.com Web Site: www.creativestagelighting.com, pg 733

Creative Support Services/CSS Music, 1948 Riverside Dr, Los Angeles, CA 90039 Tel: 323-666-7968 Toll Free Tel: 800-468-6874 Fax: 323-660-2070 E-mail: info@cssmusic.com Web Site: www.cssmusic.com, pg 733

Creative Technology, 222 Front St, 2nd fl, San Francisco, CA 94111 Tel: 415-513-5918 E-mail: studio@ct-sf.com Web Site: www.ct-sf.com, pg 733

Creative Technology (CT), 2200 S Mount Prospect Rd, Unit A, Des Plaines, IL 60018 Tel: 847-671-9670 E-mail: info@ctus.com Web Site: www.ct-group.com, pg 733

Creative Video, 26 Colonial Ave, Woodbury, NJ 08096 Tel: 856-848-0046 Fax: 856-848-8905 E-mail: contact@creativevideo.org Web Site: www.creativevideo.org, pg 734

Cre-a-tv Studios, 1393 Progress Way, Eldersburg, MD 21784 Toll Free Tel: 800-628-0112 E-mail: production@cre-a-tv.com Web Site: cre-a-tv.com, pg 734

Credo Interactive Inc, 4612 Strathcona Rd, North Vancouver, BC V7O 1G3, Canada E-mail: info@charactermotion.com Web Site: www.charactermotion.com, pg 734

Crescendo Designs Inc, 641 County Rd 39-A, Southampton, NY 11968 Tel: 631-283-2133 Fax: 631-204-1066 E-mail: sales@crescendodesigns.com; service@crescendodesigns.com Web Site: www.crescendodesigns.com, pg 734

Crest Audio Inc, 5022 Hwy 493, Meridian, MS 39305 Toll Free Tel: 866-812-7378 Fax: 601-486-1380 E-mail: webmaster@peavey.com Web Site: www.peaveycommercialaudio.com, pg 734

Crest Electronics Inc, 3703 Alliance Dr, Suite A, Greensboro, NC 27407 Tel: 336-855-6422 Toll Free Tel: 888-502-7378 Fax: 336-855-6676 Web Site: www.crestelectronics.com, pg 734

Cresta Creative, 1050 N State St, Chicago, IL 60610 Tel: 312-944-4700 Fax: 312-944-1582 E-mail: info@crestagroup.com Web Site: www.crestacreative.com, pg 734

Crestron Electronics Inc, 15 Volvo Dr, Rockleigh, NJ 07647 Tel: 201-767-3400 (sales & support); 201-750-7004 (admin) Toll Free Tel: 800-237-2041; 855-791-5322 Fax: 201-767-1903 (sales & support); 201-767-8872 (admin) E-mail: inquiries@crestron.com Web Site: www.crestron.com, pg 734

Crew West Inc, 1515 W Deer Valley Rd, Suite C-109, Phoenix, AZ 85027 Tel: 480-367-6888 Toll Free Tel: 888-444-2739 Fax: 480-367-6888 E-mail: tvcrews@crewwestinc.com Web Site: www.crewwestinc.com, pg 734

Crispin Corp, 600 Wade Ave, Raleigh, NC 27605 Tel: 919-845-7744 Fax: 919-845-7766 E-mail: welisten@crispincorp.com; support@crispincorp.com Web Site: www.crispincorp.com, pg 734

Criterion Collection, 215 Park Ave S, 5th fl, New York, NY 10003 Tel: 212-756-8822 E-mail: orders@criterion.com; press@criterion.com Web Site: www.criterion.com, pg 735

Cross-Cultural Communications, 239 Wynsum Ave, Merrick, NY 11566-4725 Tel: 516-868-5635 Fax: 516-379-1901 E-mail: info@cross-culturalcommunications.com Web Site: www.cross-culturalcommunications.com, pg 735

Crossroads Audio Inc, 2623 Myrtle Springs Ave, Dallas, TX 75220 Tel: 214-358-2623 Toll Free Tel: 800-287-0436 Fax: 214-358-0185 E-mail: mail@crossroadsaudio.com Web Site: www.crossroadsaudio.com, pg 735

Crown Ministries International, PO Box 26479, Colorado Springs, CO 80936-6479 Toll Free Tel: 800-433-4685 E-mail: crownmin@intlcom.org Web Site: www.crownmin.org, pg 735

CRT Custom Products Inc, 7532 Hickory Hills Ct, Whites Creek, TN 37189 Tel: 615-876-5490 Toll Free Tel: 800-453-2533 Fax: 615-876-0096 E-mail: sales@crtcustomproducts.com Web Site: www.crtcustomproducts.com, pg 735

Crystal Clear Media Group, 7370 Dogwood Park, Richland Hills, TX 76118 Toll Free Tel: 800-880-0073 E-mail: information@crystalclearcds.com Web Site: www.crystalclearcds.com, pg 735

Crystal Pictures Inc, 2000 Riverside Dr, Asheville, NC 28804 Tel: 828-285-9995 Toll Free Tel: 800-669-4057 Fax: 828-285-9997 E-mail: cryspic@aol.com Web Site: ivyvideo.com, pg 735

Crystal Productions, 401 Hickory St, Fort Collins, CO 80524 Toll Free Tel: 800-289-9299 E-mail: custserv@crystalproductions.com Web Site: www.crystalproductions.com, pg 735

Crystal Pyramid Productions™, 7323 Rondel Ct, San Diego, CA 92119-1530 Tel: 619-644-3000 E-mail: info@crystalpyramid.com Web Site: sandiegovideoproduction.com, pg 735

Crystal Records Inc, 28818 NE Hancock Rd, Camas, WA 98607 Tel: 360-834-7022 Fax: 360-834-9680 E-mail: info@crystalrecords.com Web Site: www.crystalrecords.com, pg 735

CSC Awards, 131-3007 Kingston Rd, Toronto, ON M1M 1P1, Canada Tel: 416-266-0591 Fax: 416-266-3996 E-mail: admin@csc.ca Web Site: www.csc.ca, pg 987

CSI Film & Video LLC, 1913 Sonora St, Fort Collins, CO 80525 Tel: 970-310-9039 Web Site: csifilms.com, pg 735

CSI/Orion, 1709 Utica Sq, Tulsa, OK 74114 Tel: 918-743-7881 Toll Free Tel: 888-579-1850 Web Site: www.csihealthcarecommunications.com; www.csiorion.com, pg 735

CSI Rentals, 133 W 19 St, Ground Level, New York, NY 10011 Tel: 212-243-7368 Fax: 212-243-2102 E-mail: orders@csirentals.com Web Site: www.csirentals.com, pg 735

CSPI, 175 Cabot St, Suite 210, Lowell, MA 01854 Tel: 978-937-7598; 978-954-5038 Toll Free Tel: 800-325-3110 E-mail: hello@cspi.com Web Site: www.cspi.com, pg 735

CSPMedia.com, 9411 Gumtree Park St, Capitol Heights, MD 20743 Tel: 301-350-3181 Web Site: www.soundstore.com; www.cspmedia.com, pg 735

CTGaudio, 2100 Constitution Blvd, Sarasota, FL 34231 Tel: 941-922-2322 Toll Free Tel: 866-871-6874 E-mail: orders@ctgaudio.com; info@ctgaudio.com Web Site: ctgaudio.com, pg 735

C2 Imaging, 2 Harborside, 200 Hudson St, Suite 201, Jersey City, NJ 07311 Tel: 646-557-6300 Web Site: www.c2spark.com, pg 735

Cucalorus Film Festival, Jengo's Playhouse, 815 Princess St, Wilmington, NC 28401 Tel: 910-343-5995 E-mail: programming@cucalorus.org; press@cucalorus.org; comm@cucalorus.org Web Site: www.cucalorus.org, pg 987

Cue Tech Teleprompting Inc, 5527 Satsuma Ave, North Hollywood, CA 91601 Tel: 818-487-2700 Fax: 818-487-2750 E-mail: info@cue-tech.com Web Site: www.cue-tech.com, pg 736

Curb Entertainment International Corp, 3907 W Alameda Ave, Burbank, CA 91505 Tel: 818-843-8580 Fax: 818-566-1719 Web Site: www.curbentertainment.com, pg 736

Curtis Company, 886 Plantation Way, Montgomery, AL 36117 Tel: 334-279-7127 Toll Free Tel: 800-228-5937 Fax: 334-270-8787 Toll Free Fax: 800-325-6341 Web Site: www.curtisav.com, pg 736

Curtis Inc, 1105 Western Ave, Cincinnati, OH 45203 Tel: 513-621-8895 Toll Free Tel: 800-733-2878 Fax: 513-621-0942 E-mail: info@curtisinc.com Web Site: www.curtisinc.com, pg 736

Custom Color Corp, 14320 W 101 Terr, Lenexa, KS 66215 Tel: 913-730-3100 Fax: 913-730-3101 E-mail: info@customcolor.com Web Site: customcolor.com, pg 736

Custom Computer Specialists Inc, 70 Suffolk Ct, Hauppauge, NY 11788 Tel: 631-864-6699 Toll Free Tel: 800-589-8989 Fax: 401-765-6440 Toll Free Fax: 800-986-5518 E-mail: info@customtech.com; support@customtech.com Web Site: www.customonline.com, pg 736

Custom Video Productions Inc, 707 Torrance Blvd, Suite 105, Redondo Beach, CA 90277 Tel: 310-543-4901 E-mail: info@customvideo.tv Web Site: www.customvideo.tv, pg 736

Custom Video Productions Inc, 15 Lake Shore Dr, Red Bank, NJ 07701 Tel: 732-936-1001 E-mail: info@cvpnj.com Web Site: www.cvpnj.com, pg 736

The Cutting Corporation, GraphicAudio® & Archival Sound Lab, 7520 Standish Place, Suite 100, Rockville, MD 20855 Tel: 301-654-CUTS (654-2887) Fax: 301-444-4519 E-mail: sales@graphicaudio.net Web Site: cuttingcorporation.com; www.graphicaudio.net, pg 736

Cutting Edge Productions, 22904 Lockness Ave, Torrance, CA 90501 Tel: 310-326-4500; 818-503-0400 E-mail: info@cuttingedgeproductions.tv Web Site: www.cuttingedgeproductions.tv, pg 736

Cuyahoga Community College Student Production Office (SPO), Metro Campus Media Ctr, 2900 Community College Ave, Cleveland, OH 44115 Tel: 216-987-6000 Web Site: www.tri-c.edu, pg 736

CVW Event Productions, 470 Spring Park Place, Suite 900, Herndon, VA 20170 Tel: 703-891-2620 Fax: 703-891-2625 E-mail: info@cvwevents.com Web Site: cvwevents.com, pg 736

CyberIconics International, 1752 N 74 Place, Mesa, AZ 85207-2932 Tel: 480-396-8731, pg 736

Cybernetics, 111 Cybernetics Way, Yorktown, VA 23693 Tel: 757-833-9000 Fax: 757-833-9300 E-mail: techsales@cybernetics.com;

customer_service@cybernetics.com; media@
cybernetics.com *Web Site:* www.cybernetics.com,
pg 736

CyberOptics Corp, 5900 Golden Hills Dr, Minneapolis,
MN 55416 *Tel:* 763-542-5000 *Fax:* 763-542-5100
E-mail: info@cyberoptics.com *Web Site:* cyberoptics.
com, pg 736

Czar Productions Inc, 809 New Britain Ave, Hartford,
CT 06106 *Tel:* 860-953-0809 *E-mail:* czar.
productions@snet.net, pg 737

D A S Audio of America Inc, 6900 NW 52 St, Miami,
FL 33166 *Tel:* 305-436-0521 *Fax:* 305-436-0528
E-mail: infousa@dasaudio.com *Web Site:* www.
dasaudio.com, pg 737

D A Sound, 12932 SE Kent Kangley Rd, Box 460, Kent,
WA 98030 *Tel:* 206-632-7773 *Toll Free Tel:* 855-
DASOUND (327-6863) *E-mail:* info@dasound.biz
Web Site: www.dasound.biz, pg 737

Da-Lite, a Legrand AV Inc brand, 3100 N Detroit
St, Warsaw, IN 46582 *Tel:* 574-267-8101 *Toll Free
Tel:* 866-977-3901 *E-mail:* av.da-lite.support@legrand.
com *Web Site:* www.legrandav.com/products/da-lite,
pg 737

Daburn Electronics & Cable Corp, 44 Richboynton Rd,
Dover, NJ 07801 *Tel:* 973-328-3200 *Fax:* 973-328-
3130 *E-mail:* daburn@daburn.com *Web Site:* www.
daburn.com, pg 737

DACAPO Productions Inc, 516 Hargrave St, Winnipeg,
MB R3A 0X8, Canada *Tel:* 204-956-2867 *Fax:* 204-
956-2869 *Web Site:* www.dacapo.ca, pg 737

Dadco, 11078 Fleetwood St, Sun Valley, CA
91352 *Tel:* 818-768-8886 *Web Site:* www.
dadcopowerandlights.com, pg 737

Dage-MTI, 701 N Roeske Ave, Michigan City, IN 46360
Tel: 219-872-5514 *Fax:* 219-872-5559 *E-mail:* info@
dagemti.com *Web Site:* dagemti.com, pg 737

Dailey & Vincent LandFest in the Mountains, 1311
Music Hall Rd, Hiawassee, GA 30546 *Tel:* 706-896-
4191 *Web Site:* www.daileyvincentfest.com, pg 987

Daily Electronics Corp, PO Box 822437, Vancouver, WA
98682-0053 *Tel:* 360-896-8856 *Toll Free Tel:* 800-
346-6667 *Fax:* 360-896-5476 *E-mail:* daily@
worldaccessnet.com *Web Site:* dailyelectronics.net,
pg 737

Dake Publishing Inc, 764 Martins Chapel Rd,
Lawrenceville, GA 30046 *Toll Free Tel:* 800-241-1239
E-mail: info@dake.com *Web Site:* www.dake.com,
pg 737

Dalet Digital Media Systems, 88 Pine St, 8th fl, New
York, NY 10005 *Tel:* 212-269-6700 *E-mail:* ddms@
dalet.com *Web Site:* www.dalet.com, pg 737

Dallas Prompter, PO Box 571233, Dallas, TX 75357
Tel: 214-275-9000 *Web Site:* www.dallasprompter.com,
pg 737

Dallas VideoFest Alternative Fiction, 1405 Woodlawn
Ave, Dallas, TX 75208 *Tel:* 214-207-7696
E-mail: info@videofest.org *Web Site:* www.videofest.
org, pg 987

Dallas VideoFest DocuFest, 1405 Woodlawn Ave, Dallas,
TX 75208 *Tel:* 214-207-7696 *E-mail:* info@videofest.
org *Web Site:* www.videofest.org, pg 987

Dance Horizons Video, 15 W Front St, 3rd fl, Trenton,
NJ 08608 *Tel:* 609-426-0602 *Toll Free Tel:* 800-220-
7149 *Fax:* 609-426-1344 *E-mail:* pbc@dancehorizons.
com *Web Site:* www.dancehorizons.com, pg 737

Dance on Camera Festival, 252 Java St, Suite
333, Brooklyn, NY 11222 *Tel:* 347-505-8649
E-mail: info@dancefilms.org; festival@dancefilms.org
Web Site: www.dancefilms.org, pg 988

Dances With Films, Formosa Bldg, 2nd fl, 1041 N
Formosa Ave, West Hollywood, CA 90046 *Tel:* 323-
854-8176 *E-mail:* info@danceswithfilms.com;
submissions@danceswithfilms.com *Web Site:* www.
danceswithfilms.com, pg 988

Dark Star Lighting & Production, 102 Commerce St,
Hinesburg, VT 05461 *Tel:* 802-482-4802 *Toll Free
Tel:* 877-375-7827 *E-mail:* sales@darkstarlighting.com
Web Site: www.darkstarlighting.com, pg 737

DASAN Zhone Solutions (DZS) Inc, 7195 Oakport
St, Oakland, CA 94621 *Tel:* 510-777-7000 *Toll Free
Tel:* 877-ZHONE-20 (946-6320, US & CN) *Fax:* 510-
777-7001 *Web Site:* dasanzhone.com, pg 737

Data & Marketing Association (DMA), 225 Reinekers
Lane, Suite 325, Alexandria, VA 22314 *Tel:* 212-768-
7277; 212-790-1500 *Web Site:* thedma.org, pg 953

Data Projections Inc, 3700 W Sam Houston Pkwy S,
Suite 525, Houston, TX 77042 *Tel:* 713-781-1999
Toll Free Tel: 866-225-5374 *Fax:* 713-781-3338
E-mail: dpiweb@dataprojections.com *Web Site:* www.
dataprojections.com, pg 738

Data Security Inc, 300 S Seventh St, Lincoln, NE
68508 *Tel:* 402-434-5959 *Toll Free Tel:* 800-225-7554
Fax: 402-434-3291 *E-mail:* sales@telesis-inc.com
Web Site: www.datasecurityinc.com, pg 738

Data Translation, 10 Commerce Way, Norton, MA
02766 *Tel:* 508-946-5100 *Toll Free Tel:* 800-234-
4232 *Fax:* 508-946-9500 *E-mail:* info@mccdaq.com
Web Site: www.mccdaq.com/data-translation, pg 738

DataDirect Networks, 9351 Deering Ave, Chatsworth,
CA 91311 *Tel:* 818-700-4000 *Toll Free Tel:* 800-
TERABYTE (837-2298) *E-mail:* info@ddn.com;
sales@ddn.com *Web Site:* www.ddn.com, pg 738

Dav Tronics Ltd, 1543 Venables St, Suite 200,
Vancouver, BC V5L 2G8, Canada *Tel:* 604-255-2200
Web Site: www.broadcasttechnical.com, pg 738

Davenport Music Library, PO Box 690536, Charlotte,
NC 28227-7009 *Web Site:* www.davenportmusic.com,
pg 738

David Clark Co Inc, 360 Franklin St, Worcester, MA
01604 *Tel:* 508-751-5800 *Toll Free Tel:* 800-900-3434
Fax: 508-753-5827 *E-mail:* sales@davidclark.com
Web Site: www.davidclark.com, pg 738

Davidson Productions, 1180 Vista Del Lago, San Luis
Obispo, CA 93405 *Tel:* 415-886-7540 *E-mail:* dfi@
davidsonfilms.com *Web Site:* davidsonfilms.com,
pg 738

Davies Publishing Inc, 32 S Raymond Ave, Suites
4-5, Pasadena, CA 91105 *Tel:* 626-792-3046 *Toll
Free Tel:* 877-792-0005 (US only) *Fax:* 626-
792-5308 *E-mail:* info@daviespublishing.com
Web Site: www.daviespublishing.com, pg 738

Davis Art Images, 50 Portland St, Worcester, MA
01608 *Tel:* 508-754-7201 *Toll Free Tel:* 800-533-
2847 *Fax:* 508-753-3834 *E-mail:* contactus@davisart.
com; das@davisart.com *Web Site:* www.davisart.com,
pg 738

John J Davis & Associates Consulting Engineers, PO
Box 128, Sierra Madre, CA 91025-0128 *Tel:* 626-355-
6909, pg 739

DaviSound, PO Box 521, Newberry, SC 29108-0521
Tel: 803-944-7972 (messages only) *Web Site:* www.
davisound.com, pg 739

DAWNco, 7111 Dixie Hwy, Suite 118, Clarkston, MI
48346 *Tel:* 248-391-9200; 248-391-9207 *Toll Free
Tel:* 800-866-6969 *Fax:* 248-391-9206 *E-mail:* sales@
dawnco.com *Web Site:* www.dawnco.com, pg 739

DawnSignPress, 6130 Nancy Ridge Dr, San Diego, CA
92121-3223 *Tel:* 858-625-0600 *Toll Free Tel:* 800-
549-5350 *Fax:* 858-625-2336 *E-mail:* contactus@
dawnsign.com *Web Site:* www.dawnsign.com, pg 739

Daylight Productions & Rentals, 4700 Sterling Dr,
Suite I, Boulder, CO 80301 *Tel:* 303-440-3334
E-mail: info@daylightav.com *Web Site:* www.
daylightav.com, pg 739

Dazian LLC, 18 Central Blvd, South Hackensack, NJ
07606 *Toll Free Tel:* 877-232-9426 *Fax:* 201-641-
2728; 201-549-1055 (efax) *E-mail:* info@dazian.com
Web Site: www.dazian.com, pg 739

Dazor Lighting Technology LLC, 2360 Chaffee Dr,
St Louis, MO 63146 *Tel:* 314-652-2400 *Toll Free
Tel:* 800-345-9103 *Fax:* 314-652-2069 *E-mail:* info@
dazor.com *Web Site:* www.dazor.com, pg 739

db electronics, 4611G Central Ave Pike, Knoxville,
TN 37912 *Tel:* 865-588-9532 *E-mail:* service@
dbelectronics.com *Web Site:* www.dbelectronics.com, pg 739

db interactive Inc, PO Box 302064, Austin, TX 78703
Tel: 512-436-8586 *E-mail:* info@dbinteractive.com
Web Site: dbinteractive.com, pg 739

dbF a Media Company, 9683 Charles St, La Plata,
MD 20646 *Tel:* 301-645-6110 *Fax:* 301-392-6111
E-mail: service@dbfmedia.com *Web Site:* www.
dbfmedia.com, pg 739

DBM Communications Inc, 606 Baltimore Ave, Suite
200, Towson, MD 21204 *Tel:* 410-825-7400 *Fax:* 443-
269-0213 *Web Site:* www.dbmcommunications.com,
pg 739

DC Asian Pacific American Film Festival, 2515 Virginia
Ave NW, No 58205, Washington, DC 20037 *Tel:* 202-
796-9680; 202-792-6393 *E-mail:* info@apafilm.org;
admin@apafilm.org *Web Site:* www.apafilm.org,
pg 988

DD Audio, 4025 NW 36 St, Oklahoma City, OK
73112 *Tel:* 405-239-2800 *Fax:* 405-239-7100
E-mail: service@ddaudio.com *Web Site:* ddaudio.com,
pg 739

De Nonno Productions Inc (DPI), 7119 Shore Rd,
Suite 6-F, Brooklyn, NY 11209 *Tel:* 917-304-
6610 *Web Site:* www.denonnoprod.com; www.
denonnoscelebrityphotos.com, pg 739

De Sisti Lighting/I-Light Corp USA, 1011 Rte 22 E,
Unit D, Mountainside, NJ 07092 *Tel:* 908-317-0020
Fax: 908-317-0021 *Web Site:* www.desisti.it, pg 739

de Wolfe Music USA, 37 W 17 St, 7th fl, Suite E, New
York, NY 10011 *Tel:* 212-259-0524 *E-mail:* info@
dewolfemusicusa.com *Web Site:* dewolfemusic.com,
pg 739

Debbie Regan Locations Ltd, PO Box 353, Old
Westbury, NY 11568 *Tel:* 516-626-1928; 212-591-
1313 *Fax:* 516-626-2337 *E-mail:* DRLNYC@gmail.
com *Web Site:* www.debbiereganlocations.com, pg 739

DebsVoice, 19 Park Trail, Midhurst, ON L0L 1X0,
Canada *Tel:* 604-459-5559 (cell) *Web Site:* www.
debsvoice.com; www.voiceactortraining.com, pg 739

DEC Grants, 696 Dutchess Tpke, Suite F, Poughkeepsie,
NY 12603 *Tel:* 845-454-3222 *E-mail:* info@
artsmidhudson.org *Web Site:* www.artsmidhudson.org,
pg 988

DecisionOne Corp, 640 Lee Rd, 3rd fl, Wayne, PA
19087 *Tel:* 610-296-6000 *Toll Free Tel:* 800-767-2876;
800-777-8800 (cust serv); 888-287-9202 (sales); 800-
554-5179 (CN) *Fax:* 610-296-2910 *E-mail:* sales@
decisionone.com *Web Site:* www.decisionone.com,
pg 740

Deck Hand Inc, 1905 S Victory Blvd, Suite 8, Glendale,
CA 91201 *Tel:* 818-557-8403 *Fax:* 818-557-8406
E-mail: info@deckhand.com *Web Site:* www.
deckhand.com, pg 740

Dedotec USA Inc, 48 Sheffield Business Park, Ashley
Falls, MA 01222 *Tel:* 413-229-2550 *E-mail:* info@
dedolight.com *Web Site:* www.dedolight.com, pg 740

Deerfield Laboratory Inc, 7 Millbrae Ave, San Anselmo,
CA 94960 *Tel:* 650-632-4090 *Web Site:* www.
deerfieldlab.com, pg 740

Definitive Technology LLP, One Viper Way, Vista, CA
92081 *Tel:* 410-363-7148 *Toll Free Tel:* 800-228-
7148 *E-mail:* info@definitivetech.com *Web Site:* www.
definitivetech.com, pg 740

Deja View Video, 417 S Eldorado St, San Mateo, CA
94402-1374 *Tel:* 650-343-8899 *Web Site:* www.
dejaview.com, pg 740

deKramer Productions Inc, 515 Western Ave, Petaluma,
CA 94952 *Tel:* 707-765-0888 *E-mail:* dekramer@
sonic.net *Web Site:* www.dekramerproductions.com,
pg 740

Delaware Tourism Office, 99 Kings Hwy, Dover, DE
19901 *Tel:* 302-739-4271 *Toll Free Tel:* 866-284-7483
E-mail: visit.delaware@state.de.us *Web Site:* www.
visitdelaware.com, pg 968

Delmark Records, 4121 N Rockwell, Chicago, IL 60618 *Tel:* 773-539-5001 *Fax:* 773-539-5004 *E-mail:* info@delmark.com *Web Site:* www.delmark.com, pg 740

Delta Electronics Inc, 5730 General Washington Dr, Alexandria, VA 22312 *Tel:* 703-354-3350 *Toll Free Tel:* 800-8-DELTA-8 (833-5828) *Fax:* 703-354-0216 *E-mail:* sales@deltaelectronics.com *Web Site:* www.deltaelectronics.com, pg 740

Deluxe Entertainment Services Group Inc, 2400 W Empire Ave, 2nd fl, Burbank, CA 91504 *Tel:* 818-260-7005; 818-526-3700 *Toll Free Tel:* 800-99-FILMS (993-4567) *E-mail:* ddchelp@bydeluxe.com; pr@bydeluxe.com *Web Site:* www.bydeluxe.com, pg 740

Demco Inc, 4810 Forest Run Rd, Madison, WI 53704 *Tel:* 608-241-1201 *Toll Free Tel:* 800-962-4463; 800-279-1586 *Toll Free Fax:* 800-245-1329 *Web Site:* www.demco.com, pg 740

Denecke Inc, 25209 Ave Tibbitts, Valencia, CA 91355 *Tel:* 661-607-0206 *Fax:* 661-257-2236 *E-mail:* info@denecke.com *Web Site:* www.denecke.com, pg 740

Denver Film Festival, 1510 York St, 3rd fl, Denver, CO 80206 *Tel:* 303-595-3456 *E-mail:* dff@denverfilm.org *Web Site:* denverfilmfestival.denverfilm.org, pg 988

Denver Film Society, 1510 York St, 3rd fl, Denver, CO 80206 *Tel:* 303-595-3456 *E-mail:* info@denverfilm.org *Web Site:* www.denverfilm.org, pg 953

Denver Media Center, 2601 Lemay, Suite 7, PMB 227, Fort Collins, CO 80525 *Tel:* 720-255-1640 (ext 101) *Web Site:* denvermediacenter.com, pg 740

Department of Education Resources, 2000B S Club Dr, Landover, MD 20785 *Tel:* 202-842-6706 *Fax:* 202-842-6937 *E-mail:* edresources@nga.gov *Web Site:* www.nga.gov/education.html, pg 740

Department of VSA & Accessibility at the John F Kennedy Center for the Performing Arts, 2700 "F" St NW, Washington, DC 20566 *E-mail:* vsainfo@kennedy-center.org *Web Site:* education.kennedy-center.org/education/vsa, pg 740

Derksen (USA) Inc, 4934 Pathway Ct, Fair Oaks, CA 95628 *Tel:* 916-903-7515 *Fax:* 916-903-7022 *E-mail:* info@derksen.com *Web Site:* www.derksen.com, pg 740

Design & Production Inc, 7110 Rainwater Place, Lorton, VA 22079 *Tel:* 703-550-8640 *Fax:* 703-339-0296 *E-mail:* email@d-and-p.com *Web Site:* www.d-and-p.com, pg 740

Design Audio Visual Inc, 195-A Central Ave, Farmingdale, NY 11735 *Tel:* 631-694-3334 *Toll Free Tel:* 800-886-1328 *Fax:* 631-694-3549 *Web Site:* www.design-av.com, pg 741

Design Media, 650 Alabama St, Suite 203, San Francisco, CA 94110-2038 *Tel:* 415-641-4848 *Fax:* 415-641-5245 *E-mail:* info@designmedia.com *Web Site:* www.designmedia.com, pg 741

Designomotion, 67 E 11 St, Suite 324, New York, NY 10003 *Tel:* 917-532-0738 *E-mail:* info@designomotion.com *Web Site:* designomotion.com, pg 741

Desktop Video Systems, 9052 Parkhill, Lenexa, KS 66215 *Tel:* 913-782-8888, pg 741

Detroit Film Office, Coleman A Young Municipal Ctr, 2 Woodward Ave, Suite 333, Detroit, MI 48226 *Tel:* 313-224-3876; 313-224-1600 *E-mail:* dfo@detroitmi.gov *Web Site:* detroitmi.gov/departments/detroit-film-office, pg 972

DGA Awards, 7920 Sunset Blvd, Los Angeles, CA 90046 *Tel:* 310-289-2038 *Fax:* 310-289-5398 *E-mail:* awards@dga.org *Web Site:* www.dga.org, pg 988

DGI-Invisuals LLC, 101 Billerica Ave, Bldg 6, North Billerica, MA 01862 *Toll Free Tel:* 800-344-0432 *Fax:* 781-270-3663 *E-mail:* sales@dgi-invisuals.com *Web Site:* www.dgi-invisuals.com, pg 741

DH Satellite, 600 N Marquette Rd, Prairie du Chien, WI 53821 *Tel:* 608-326-8406 *Toll Free Tel:* 800-627-9443 *Fax:* 608-326-4233 *E-mail:* dhsat@mhtc.net; sales@dhsatellite.com *Web Site:* www.dhsatellite.com, pg 741

Dialect Accent Specialists Inc, 7048 Timberrose Way, Roseville, CA 95747 *Toll Free Tel:* 800-753-1016 *E-mail:* dasinc@kingcon.com; info@dialectaccentspecialists.com *Web Site:* www.dialectaccentspecialists.com; www.learnaccent.com, pg 741

Diamond Dreams Music Productions, North Ocean County, Carbon Canyon, Chino Hills, CA 91709 *Tel:* 909-393-6120 *Fax:* 909-606-5779 *E-mail:* diamonddreamsmusic@yahoo.com *Web Site:* www.diamonddreamsmusic.com, pg 741

Diamond Studios, Woods Point 1, 1855 Data Dr, Suite 255, Hoover, AL 35244 *Tel:* 205-987-2121 *Fax:* 205-987-2128 *Web Site:* www.tvstuff.com, pg 741

Diaquest, 5808 Vallejo St, Emeryville, CA 94608 *Tel:* 510-547-4544 *Fax:* 510-654-8370 *E-mail:* sales@diaquest.com; support@diaquest.com *Web Site:* www.diaquest.com, pg 741

Dickensheets Design Associates, 10919 Conchos Trail, Suite 100, Austin, TX 78726-1431 *Tel:* 512-331-8977 *Web Site:* www.dickensheets.com, pg 741

DiCon Fiberoptics Inc, 1689 Regatta Blvd, Richmond, CA 94804 *Tel:* 510-620-5000; 510-620-5200 (sales) *Fax:* 510-620-4100; 510-620-4102 (sales) *E-mail:* sales@diconfiberoptics.com *Web Site:* www.diconfiberoptics.com, pg 741

Dielectric, 22 Tower Rd, Raymond, ME 04071 *Tel:* 207-655-4555 *Toll Free Tel:* 800-341-9678 *Fax:* 207-655-8173 *E-mail:* PF-dielec-sales@sbgtv.com *Web Site:* www.dielectric.com, pg 741

Diemer Amp & Keyboard Repair, 12814 Landale St, Studio City, CA 91604-1351 *Tel:* 818-762-0804 *Web Site:* bustedgear.com, pg 741

Different Fur Recording Ltd, 3470 19 St, San Francisco, CA 94110 *Tel:* 415-828-4060 (bookings) *Web Site:* differentfurstudios.com, pg 741

Digi Sign Design LLC, 28533 Greenfield Rd, Southfield, MI 48076 *Web Site:* www.digisigndesign.com, pg 741

Digimation, 1515 International Pkwy, Suite 2013, Lake Mary, FL 32746 *Tel:* 407-833-0600 *E-mail:* sales@digimation.com *Web Site:* digimation.com, pg 741

Digital Art Video Inc, 8506 60 Ave, 3rd fl, Middle Village, NY 11379-5430 *Tel:* 718-457-5388 *E-mail:* production@digitalartvideo.com *Web Site:* www.digitalartvideo.com, pg 741

Digital Arts NY, 130 W 29 St, New York, NY 10001 *Tel:* 212-460-9600 *Fax:* 212-660-3600 *Web Site:* digitalartsny.com, pg 742

Digital Audio Labs, 1266 Park Rd, Chanhassen, MN 55317 *Tel:* 952-401-7700 *Fax:* 952-401-7725 *E-mail:* sales@digitalaudio.com; contact@digitalaudio.com *Web Site:* www.digitalaudio.com, pg 742

Digital Comm Link Inc, 10450 W State Rd 84, Davie, FL 33324-4206 *Tel:* 954-236-2993 *Toll Free Tel:* 877-532-5438 *Fax:* 954-236-3633 *E-mail:* bookings@dclinc.net *Web Site:* www.dclinc.net, pg 742

Digital Display Solutions Inc, 2840, 12223 San Pedro Ave, San Antonio, TX 78216 *Tel:* 210-404-1233 *Fax:* 210-979-6585 *E-mail:* info@ddsav.com *Web Site:* ddsav.com, pg 742

Digital Film Studios LLC, 11800 Sheldon St, Unit C/D, Sun Valley, CA 91352 *Tel:* 818-771-0019 *Web Site:* www.digitalfilmstudios.com, pg 742

Digital Force Ltd, 248 W 35 St, 14th fl, New York, NY 10001 *Tel:* 212-252-9300 *Toll Free Tel:* 877-DISC-USA (347-2872) *Fax:* 212-252-7377 *E-mail:* frontdesk@digitalforce.com *Web Site:* digitalforce.com, pg 742

Digital FX Inc, 6010 Perkins Rd, Suite B, Baton Rouge, LA 70808 *Tel:* 225-763-6010 *Toll Free Tel:* 888-898-6010 *E-mail:* info@digitalfx.tv; rentals@digitalfx.tv *Web Site:* www.digitalfx.tv, pg 742

Digital Image Studios LLC, 22915 Commerce Dr, Farmington Hills, MI 48335 *Tel:* 248-477-5600 *Toll Free Tel:* 888-434-7839 *Fax:* 248-477-4322 *Web Site:* www.dimage.com, pg 742

Digital Jungle, 28348 Constellation Rd, Suite 880, Santa Clara, CA 91355 *Tel:* 323-962-0867 *Fax:* 323-962-9960 *E-mail:* info@digijungle.com *Web Site:* www.digijungle.com, pg 742

Digital Lighting Systems Inc, 12302 SW 128 Ct, Suite 105, Miami, FL 33186 *Tel:* 305-969-8442 *Fax:* 305-969-8675 *E-mail:* info@digitallighting.com; sales@digitallighting.com *Web Site:* www.digitallighting.com, pg 742

Digital Music Corp, 3165 Coffey Lane, Santa Rosa, CA 95403 *Tel:* 707-545-0600 *Fax:* 707-545-9777 *E-mail:* info@voodoolab.com *Web Site:* www.voodoolab.com, pg 742

digital OutPost, 2772 Loker Ave W, Carlsbad, CA 92010 *Tel:* 760-431-3575 *Toll Free Tel:* 800-464-6434 *E-mail:* sales@dop.com *Web Site:* www.dop.com, pg 742

Digital Projection, 55 Chastain Rd, Suite 115, Kennesaw, GA 30144 *Tel:* 770-420-1350 *Fax:* 770-420-1360 *E-mail:* contact@digitalprojection.com *Web Site:* www.digitalprojection.com, pg 742

Digital Rain LLC, 253 Lagoda Dr, Locust, NC 28097 *Tel:* 980-354-1209 *Web Site:* www.digitalrainllc.com, pg 742

Digital Services Recording Studios, 1601 S Cherry St, Tomball, TX 77375 *Tel:* 832-463-5781 *E-mail:* studio@dsrecordings.com *Web Site:* www.dsrecordings.com, pg 742

Digital Signage Federation (DSF), 11 Main St, Suite D, Warrenton, VA 20186 *Tel:* 540-551-5500 *Fax:* 202-962-3939 *Web Site:* www.digitalsignagefederation.org, pg 954

Digital Video Productions, 257 Federal Rd, Brookfield, CT 06804 *Tel:* 203-743-7663 *Fax:* 203-743-1658 *E-mail:* info@dvpllc.com *Web Site:* dvpllc.com, pg 742

Digital Video Systems, 3270 Executive Way, Miramar, FL 33025 *Tel:* 954-239-4410 *Fax:* 954-239-4486 *E-mail:* info@digitalvideosystems.net *Web Site:* digitalvideosystems.net, pg 742

Digital Zoetrope Productions, 1902 Oak St, Melbourne, FL 32901 *Tel:* 321-821-7404 *Fax:* 321-821-2287 *Web Site:* digitalzoetrope.com, pg 742

DigiTech, 8500 Balboa Blvd, Northridge, CA 91329 *Toll Free Tel:* 800-222-0193 (cust care); 844-776-4899 (tech support) *E-mail:* hprotechsupportusa@harman.com *Web Site:* digitech.com, pg 742

Digitron Electronics, 7801 E Telegraph Rd, Montebello, CA 90640 *Tel:* 323-629-4518 *Fax:* 323-887-0891 *E-mail:* repairs@digitronelectronics.com *Web Site:* digitronelectronics.com, pg 743

DimcoGray Co, 900 Dimco Way, Centerville, OH 45458 *Tel:* 937-433-7600 *Fax:* 937-433-0520 *E-mail:* dgsales@dimcogray.com *Web Site:* www.dimcogray.com, pg 743

Direct Cinema Ltd Inc, PO Box 10003, Santa Monica, CA 90410-1003 *Tel:* 310-636-8200 *Fax:* 310-636-8228 *E-mail:* dclvideo@aol.com *Web Site:* www.directcinema.com, pg 743

Direct Current Video Productions, 1928 E Highland Ave, Suite F104-448, Phoenix, AZ 85016 *Tel:* 602-263-7717 *Web Site:* www.directcurrentproductions.com, pg 743

Direct Images Interactive Inc, 1933 Davis St, Suite 308, San Leandro, CA 94577 *Tel:* 510-613-8299 *E-mail:* info@directimages.com *Web Site:* www.directimages.com, pg 743

Directed Electronics, One Viper Way, Suite A, Vista, CA 92081 *Tel:* 760-598-6200 *Toll Free Tel:* 800-876-0800 *E-mail:* pr@directed.com *Web Site:* www.directed.com, pg 743

Directors Guild of America (DGA), 7920 Sunset Blvd, Los Angeles, CA 90046 *Tel:* 310-289-2000 *Toll Free Tel:* 800-421-4173 *Web Site:* www.dga.org, pg 954

Disc Makers, 7905 N Crescent Blvd, Pennsauken, NJ 08110-1402 Tel: 856-663-9030 Toll Free Tel: 800-468-9353 Fax: 856-661-3450 E-mail: info@discmakers.com Web Site: www.discmakers.com, pg 743

Discovery Education - Chicago, 111 E Wacker Dr, Suite 3000, Chicago, IL 60601-4803 Web Site: www.discoveryeducation.com, pg 743

Discovery Education Inc, 230 Park Ave S, New York, NY 10003 Toll Free Tel: 800-323-9084 Toll Free Fax: 855-495-6542 E-mail: education_info@discoveryed.com Web Site: www.discoveryeducation.com, pg 743

Discovery Education - Los Angeles, 10100 Santa Monica Blvd, Suite 1500, Los Angeles, CA 90067 Tel: 310-551-1611 Fax: 310-551-1684 Web Site: www.discoveryeducation.com, pg 743

Discovery Education - South Burlington, 700 Indian Springs Dr, Lancaster, PA 17601 Toll Free Tel: 888-892-3484 Toll Free Fax: 877-324-6830 E-mail: education_info@discovery.com Web Site: store.discoveryeducation.com, pg 743

Disk Productions Inc, 1100 Perkins Rd, Baton Rouge, LA 70802 Tel: 225-343-5438 E-mail: disk_productions@yahoo.com, pg 743

DiskFactory, 1145 Polk St, Suite DF, San Francisco, CA 94109 Toll Free Tel: 855-273-4263 E-mail: customercare@diskfaktory.com Web Site: diskfaktory.com, pg 743

Disney Consumer Products & Interactive Media (DCPI), 1201 Flower St, Glendale, AZ 91201 Tel: 818-544-0000 Web Site: dcpi.disney.com, pg 743

The Walt Disney Co, 500 S Buena Vista St, Burbank, CA 91521 Tel: 818-560-1000 Web Site: disney.com; thewaltdisneycompany.com, pg 743

The Walt Disney Studios, 500 S Buena Vista St, Burbank, CA 91521 Tel: 818-560-1000 Web Site: studioservices.go.com; waltdisneystudios.com, pg 743

Display Devices Inc, 21075 Westgate Rd, Golden, CO 80403 Tel: 303-412-0399 E-mail: sales@displaydevices.com; tech@displaydevices.com Web Site: www.displaydevices.com, pg 743

Display Systems International, 2214 Hanselman Ave, Saskatoon, SK S7L 6A4, Canada Tel: 306-934-6884 Toll Free Tel: 877-934-6884 Fax: 306-934-6447 Toll Free Fax: 800-410-4419 E-mail: sales@displaysystemsintl.com Web Site: www.displaysystemsintl.com, pg 743

Diversified, 37 Market St, Kenilworth, NJ 07033 Tel: 908-245-4833 Fax: 908-245-0011 E-mail: customerservice@diversifiedus.com; info@diversifiedus.com Web Site: diversifiedus.com, pg 744

DL Acoustics, 14301 Middletown Lane, Westminster, CA 92683 Tel: 714-373-3050 Fax: 714-373-3050 Web Site: www.dlacoustics.biz, pg 744

DL Sound & Lighting Productions Ltd, 450 Banga Place, Victoria, BC V8Z 6X5, Canada Tel: 250-216-7898 Web Site: www.dlsound.net, pg 744

DME Studios, 1025 Greenwood Blvd, Suite 191, Lake Mary, FL 32746 Tel: 407-585-7500 E-mail: creativeteam@dmestudios.com Web Site: www.dmestudios.com, pg 744

DNASTAR Inc, 3801 Regent St, Madison, WI 53705-5204 Tel: 608-258-7420 Toll Free Tel: 866-511-5090 Fax: 608-258-7439 E-mail: info@dnastar.com Web Site: www.dnastar.com, pg 744

DNP Imagingcomm America Corp (DNP IAM), 4524 Enterprise Dr NW, Concord, NC 28027 Tel: 704-784-8100 Toll Free Tel: 800-814-4672 Fax: 704-784-7196 E-mail: sales_marketing@dnp.imgcomm.com Web Site: www.dnpimagingcomm.com; www.dnpphoto.com, pg 744

Docter Optics Inc, 1425 W Elliot Rd, Suite A-105, Gilbert, AZ 85233 Tel: 480-844-7585 Fax: 480-844-7826 E-mail: doi@docteroptics.com Web Site: www.docteroptics.com, pg 744

Documentary Educational Resources Inc, 108 Water St, Suite 5A, Watertown, MA 02472 Tel: 617-926-0491 Toll Free Tel: 800-569-6621 Fax: 617-926-9519 E-mail: info@der.org Web Site: www.der.org, pg 744

Documentary Organization of Canada, Centre for Social Innovation, 215 Spadina Ave, Suite 126, Toronto, ON M5T 2C7, Canada Tel: 416-599-3844 Toll Free Tel: 877-467-4485 E-mail: info@docorg.ca Web Site: docorg.ca, pg 954

DocuWare Corp, 4 Crotty Lane, Suite 200, New Windsor, NY 12553 Tel: 845-563-9045 Toll Free Tel: 888-565-5907 Fax: 845-563-9046 E-mail: info@docuware.com; dwsales@docuware.com Web Site: www.docuware.com, pg 744

Dog & Pony Productions Inc, 8928 "L" St, Omaha, NE 68127 Tel: 402-391-7691 Fax: 402-341-2751 E-mail: dognponyinc@aol.com Web Site: www.dogandponyinc.com, pg 744

Dogwood Productions Inc, 757 Government St, Mobile, AL 36602 Tel: 251-476-0858 Toll Free Tel: 800-254-9903 Fax: 251-479-0364 E-mail: info@dogwoodproductions.com Web Site: www.dogwoodproductions.com, pg 745

Dolby Laboratories Inc, 1275 Market St, San Francisco, CA 94103-1410 Tel: 415-558-0200 Fax: 415-645-4000 Web Site: www.dolby.com, pg 745

Dollar Bank Three Rivers Arts Festival, 803 Liberty Ave, Pittsburgh, PA 15222 Tel: 412-456-6666 Web Site: traf.trustarts.org, pg 988

Dolphin MultiMedia Inc, 1660 Belleville Way, Sunnyvale, CA 94087 Tel: 650-354-0800 Fax: 408-737-8404 Web Site: dolphinmm.com, pg 745

Domo Tactical Communications (DTC) Ltd, 3845 Gateway Centre Blvd, Suite 360, Pinellas Park, FL 33782 Tel: 727-741-6900 Toll Free Tel: 800-665-4648 E-mail: tampa@domotactical.com Web Site: domotactical.com, pg 745

Donnelly Sound Inc, 59 Hylan Blvd, Apt 1C, Staten Island, NY 10305 Tel: 917-496-7752 E-mail: donnellysound@gmail.com Web Site: billdonnelly.com, pg 745

Doomsday Studios Limited, 212 James St, Ottawa, ON K1R 5M7, Canada Tel: 613-230-9769 Fax: 613-230-6004 E-mail: info@doomsdaystudios.com, pg 745

Dorfman Museum Figures Inc, 6224 Holabird Ave, Baltimore, MD 21224 Tel: 410-284-3248 Toll Free Tel: 800-634-4873 Fax: 410-284-3249 E-mail: info@museumfigures.com Web Site: www.museumfigures.com, pg 745

Dorian Color, 100 Main St, Melrose, MA 02176 Tel: 781-648-8040 E-mail: images@doriancolor.com Web Site: www.doriancolor.com, pg 745

Dorrough Electronics Inc, 5221 Collier Place, Woodland Hills, CA 91364 Tel: 818-998-2824 E-mail: dorroughel@aol.com Web Site: www.dorrough.com, pg 746

Dorst MediaWorks Inc, 1219 Blagden Alley NW, 2nd fl, Washington, DC 20001 Tel: 202-258-9612 Web Site: dorstmediaworks.com, pg 746

Dot C Software Inc, 117 Waihili Place, Honolulu, HI 96825 E-mail: info@dotcsw.com Web Site: www.dotcsw.com, pg 746

Dotronix Technology Inc, 160 First St SE, New Brighton, MN 55112 Tel: 651-633-1742 E-mail: service@dotronix.com; sales@dotronix.com Web Site: www.dotronix.com, pg 746

Douglas House Inc, 275 Kings Hwy, Orangeburg, NY 10962 Tel: 845-359-1477 Fax: 845-359-2945 E-mail: thedouglashouse@earthlink.net Web Site: www.thedouglashouse.com, pg 746

Dover Publications Inc, 31 E Second St, Mineola, NY 11501 Tel: 516-294-7000 Fax: 516-742-5049 (wholesale orders); 516-742-6953 (cust care) Web Site: store.doverpublications.com, pg 746

Dow-Key Microwave Corp, 4822 McGrath St, Ventura, CA 93003 Tel: 805-650-0260 Toll Free Tel: 800-266-3695 Fax: 805-650-1734 E-mail: askdk@dowkey.com Web Site: www.dowkey.com, pg 746

Downpour.com, 31 Mistletoe Rd, Ashland, OR 97520 Toll Free Tel: 855-369-6768 Toll Free Fax: 800-482-9294 E-mail: customercare@downpour.com Web Site: www.downpour.com, pg 746

Downtown Community Television Center (DCTV), 87 Lafayette St, New York, NY 10013 Tel: 212-966-4510 Fax: 212-226-3053 E-mail: info@dctvny.org Web Site: www.dctvny.org, pg 746

Doyle Lawson & Quicksilver's Bluegrass Festival, 1072 Cranford Rd, Denton, NC 27239-7930 Tel: 336-859-2755 Fax: 336-859-2567 Web Site: www.farmpark.com, pg 988

R L Drake Co, 710 Pleasant Valley Dr, Springboro, OH 45066 Tel: 937-746-4556 Fax: 937-806-1510 E-mail: salesgroup@rldrake.net Web Site: www.rldrake.com, pg 746

DR&A Inc, 45 Willow St, Nashville, TN 37210 Tel: 615-256-6200 Fax: 615-256-6236 Web Site: www.griptruck.com, pg 746

Draper Inc, 411 S Pearl St, Spiceland, IN 47385 Tel: 765-987-7999 Toll Free Tel: 800-238-7999 Fax: 765-987-7142 E-mail: av@draperinc.com Web Site: www.draperinc.com; blog.draperinc.com, pg 746

Drastic Technologies Ltd, 523 The Queensway, Suite 102, Toronto, ON M8Y 1J7, Canada Tel: 416-255-5636 Fax: 416-255-8780 E-mail: sales@drastictech.com Web Site: www.drastic.tv, pg 746

Dreambox Media Inc, PO Box 8132, Philadelphia, PA 19101-8132 E-mail: mail@dreamboxmedia.com Web Site: www.dreamboxmedia.com, pg 746

The Dreaming Tree, 1112 Chestnut St, Unit B, Burbank, CA 91506 Tel: 818-845-3230 E-mail: info@dreamingtreeproductions.com Web Site: www.dreamingtreeproductions.com, pg 746

Dreamscape Lighting Mfg Inc, 5521 W Washington Blvd, Los Angeles, CA 90016 Tel: 323-933-5760 Fax: 323-933-3607 E-mail: info@dreamscapelighting.com Web Site: dreamscapelighting.com, pg 746

Dreamscape Media LLC, 1417 Timberwolf Dr, Holland, OH 43528 Tel: 419-867-6965 Toll Free Tel: 877-983-7326 E-mail: info@dreamscapeab.com Web Site: www.dreamscapeab.com, pg 746

DRM: sir reel sound, 2952 Cohoba Dr, Austin, TX 78748 Tel: 469-360-1443 (studio) E-mail: drmuzik@mac.com Web Site: drm-sirreelsound.com, pg 746

Drumbeat Indian Arts Inc, 4143 N 16 St, Phoenix, AZ 85016 Tel: 602-266-4823 Toll Free Tel: 800-895-4859 Fax: 602-265-2402 E-mail: info@drumbeatindianarts.com Web Site: drumbeatindianarts.com, pg 747

Drytac Corp, 5601 Eastport Blvd, Richmond, VA 23231 Tel: 804-222-3094 Toll Free Tel: 800-280-6013 E-mail: customerservice@drytac.com Web Site: www.drytac.com, pg 747

DSan Corp, 142 Mineola Ave, Roslyn Heights, NY 11577 Tel: 516-625-5608 Fax: 516-625-0878 E-mail: sales@dsan.com Web Site: www.dsan.com, pg 747

DSI RF Systems Inc, 249 Homestead Rd, Hillsborough, NJ 08844 Tel: 732-563-1144 Fax: 732-563-1818 E-mail: sales@dsirf.com; info@dsirf.com Web Site: www.dsirf.com, pg 747

DSR Computer Technology Specialists Inc, 961-M Mercantile Dr, Hanover, MD 21076 Tel: 410-579-4508 Toll Free Tel: 800-875-0037 Fax: 410-579-8412 E-mail: dsr@dsr-inc.com Web Site: www.dsr-inc.com, pg 747

DTC Lighting & Grip, 1280 65 St, Emeryville, CA 94608 Tel: 510-595-0770 Fax: 510-595-0772 E-mail: sales@dtcgrip.com; rentals@dtcgrip.com Web Site: www.dtcgrip.com, pg 747

DuArt Media Services, 245 W 55 St, New York, NY 10019 Tel: 212-757-4580 Fax: 212-977-5609 E-mail: info@duart.com Web Site: www.duart.com, pg 747

Dub King, 8133 Callaghan Rd, San Antonio, TX 78230 *Tel:* 210-979-8779 *E-mail:* dubking@dubking.com *Web Site:* www.dubking.com, pg 747

Dubuque Area Convention & Visitors Bureau, 300 Main St, Suite 120, Dubuque, IA 52001 *Tel:* 563-845-7698 *Web Site:* www.traveldubuque.com, pg 971

Dan Dugan Sound Design Inc, 290 Napoleon St, Suite E, San Francisco, CA 94124 *Tel:* 415-821-9776 *Fax:* 415-826-7699 *Web Site:* www.dandugan.com, pg 747

Duggal Visual Solutions Inc, Brooklyn Navy Yard, 63 Flushing Ave, Bldg 25, Brooklyn, NY 11205 *Tel:* 212-924-8100 (prodn); 212-242-7000 (corp) *Fax:* 212-486-1399 *E-mail:* info@duggal.com *Web Site:* duggal.com, pg 747

Dukane Corp, Audio Visual Products Division, 2900 Dukane Dr, St Charles, IL 60174 *Tel:* 630-762-4040 *Toll Free Tel:* 888-245-1966 *Fax:* 630-584-5156 *E-mail:* avsales@dukane.com *Web Site:* dukaneav.com, pg 747

Duke Media Services, 0052 Bryan Ctr, Durham, NC 27708 *Tel:* 919-660-1740 *Fax:* 919-660-1719 *E-mail:* dms-info@duke.edu *Web Site:* sites.duke.edu/mediaservices, pg 747

Dunning Photo Equipment Inc, 605 W Needles St, Bixby, OK 74008 *Tel:* 918-366-4917 *Fax:* 918-366-4918 *Web Site:* www.dunningphoto.com, pg 747

Duplication Depot Inc, 7 Plane Tree Lane, St James, NY 11780 *Tel:* 631-752-0608 *E-mail:* copymydisc@gmail.com *Web Site:* www.duplicationdepot.com, pg 748

Duplication Media, 8126 Douglas Ave, Urbandale, IA 50322 *Tel:* 515-334-DUPS (334-3877) *E-mail:* info@duplicationmedia.com *Web Site:* www.duplicationmedia.com, pg 748

Duplication Specialists Inc, 843 Merrick Rd, Baldwin, NY 11510 *Tel:* 516-867-7300 *E-mail:* sales@dupespec.com *Web Site:* dupespec.com, pg 748

Duray Lighting, 500 E Touhy Ave, Suite F, Des Plaines, IL 60018 *Tel:* 773-271-2800 *Fax:* 773-271-4410 *E-mail:* info@duraylighting.com; sales@duraylighting.com *Web Site:* www.duraylighting.com, pg 748

Durrin Productions Inc, 6443 Wynkoop St, Los Angeles, CA 90045 *Tel:* 202-413-8971 *Web Site:* www.durrinproductions.com, pg 748

Duxbury Systems Inc, 270 Littleton Rd, Unit 6, Westford, MA 01886-3523 *Tel:* 978-692-3000 *Fax:* 978-692-7912 *E-mail:* info@duxsys.com *Web Site:* www.duxburysystems.com, pg 748

DV Awards, 6300 N Sagewood Dr, Suite H-383, Park City, UT 84098 *E-mail:* info@dvawards.com *Web Site:* www.dvawards.com, pg 988

DV Post, 505 N Tustin Ave, Suite 220, Santa Ana, CA 92705 *Tel:* 714-550-0925 *Web Site:* www.dvpostvideo.com, pg 748

DVDs4Less, 6519 Jamon Dr, Sparks, NV 89436-9142 *Tel:* 775-323-0965 *Toll Free Tel:* 800-852-2330 *Fax:* 775-323-1055 *E-mail:* info@dvds4less.net *Web Site:* www.dvds4less.net, pg 748

The DVI Group, 1486 Mecaslin St NW, Atlanta, GA 30309 *Tel:* 404-873-6283 *Toll Free Tel:* 888-736-7384 *E-mail:* makeitbetter@thedvigroup.com *Web Site:* www.thedvigroup.com, pg 748

DVS InteleStream, 2600 W Olive Ave, Burbank, CA 91505 *Tel:* 818-566-4151 *E-mail:* info@dvs.tv *Web Site:* www.dvs.tv, pg 748

DW Electrochemicals Ltd, 3-97 Newkirk Rd N, Richmond Hill, ON L4C 3G4, Canada *Tel:* 905-508-7500 *Fax:* 905-508-7502 *E-mail:* dwel@stabilant.com *Web Site:* www.stabilant.com, pg 748

DWD Theatre Design & Consulting, Suite 485, 425 Carrall St, Vancouver, BC V6B 6E3, Canada *Tel:* 604-874-0552 *E-mail:* info@d-w-d.com *Web Site:* www.d-w-d.com, pg 748

DXC Technology Co, 1775 Tysons Blvd, Tysons, VA 22102 *Tel:* 317-331-1197 *Web Site:* www.dxc.technology, pg 748

Dyer-Bennet Records, 792 Columbus Ave, Rm 16-0, New York, NY 10025 *Tel:* 212-866-3675, pg 748

Dykeman Associates Inc, 4115 Rawlins St, Dallas, TX 75219 *E-mail:* info@dykemanassociates.com *Web Site:* www.dykemanassociates.com, pg 748

Dyna-Lite Inc, 1050 Commerce Ave, Union, NJ 07083 *Tel:* 908-687-8800 *Toll Free Tel:* 800-722-6638 *E-mail:* flash@dynalite.com *Web Site:* www.dynalite.com, pg 748

Dystopian Studios, 651 Clover St, Bldg 1, Los Angeles, CA 90031 *Tel:* 310-503-2365 *Web Site:* dystopianstudios.com, pg 748

E Video Productions LLC, 17 Washington St, Toms River, NJ 08753 *Tel:* 732-349-4762 *Toll Free Tel:* 877-384-3365 *E-mail:* info@evideoproductions.net *Web Site:* www.evideoproductions.net, pg 749

Eagle Camera Support Systems Ltd, 2787 Norland Ave, Burnaby, BC V5B 3A9, Canada *Tel:* 604-649-6350 *E-mail:* info@eaglecss.com *Web Site:* eaglecss.com, pg 749

Eagle Films, 2806 Cameron Rd, Falls Church, VA 22042-2004 *Tel:* 703-237-8160 *Web Site:* www.eaglefilms.com, pg 749

Eagle Photographics & Digital Imaging Inc, 3612 W Swann Ave, Tampa, FL 33609 *Tel:* 813-870-2495 *Web Site:* www.eaglefineartimaging.com, pg 749

EAR Professional Audio/Video, 2641 E McDowell Rd, Phoenix, AZ 85008 *Tel:* 602-267-0600 *Toll Free Tel:* 800-473-6914 *Fax:* 602-275-3277 *E-mail:* info@ear.net *Web Site:* ear.net, pg 749

Earl Girls Inc, 1648 White Horse Pike, Egg Harbor City, NJ 08215 *Tel:* 609-965-6900 *Web Site:* earlgirlsinc.com, pg 749

Early Films, 9 Richter St, Randolph, NJ 07869-3309 *Tel:* 973-361-5817 *E-mail:* info@earlyfilms.net *Web Site:* www.earlyfilms.net, pg 749

Earth Mother Productions Inc™, PO Box 43204, Tucson, AZ 85733-3204 *Tel:* 520-365-3608 *E-mail:* art4wall@aol.com *Web Site:* www.earthmotherproductions.com, pg 749

EarthDesign Inc, 9 Riverfront Dr, Venice, FL 34293 *Tel:* 941-276-8689 *Toll Free Tel:* 800-327-8433 *E-mail:* gp@jamilin.com *Web Site:* jamilin.com, pg 749

Earthworks Inc, 37 Wilton Rd, Suite 1, Milford, NH 03055 *Tel:* 603-654-1512 (sales); 603-654-2433 *Fax:* 603-654-6107 *E-mail:* info@earthworksaudio.com *Web Site:* www.earthworksaudio.com, pg 749

Earwax Productions Inc, 916 Kearny St, San Francisco, CA 94133 *Tel:* 415-860-9403 (cell) *Web Site:* www.earwaxproductions.com, pg 749

Earwig Music Co Inc, 2054 W Farwell Ave, Unit G, Chicago, IL 60645 *Tel:* 773-262-0278 *E-mail:* orders@earwigmusic.com *Web Site:* www.earwigmusic.com, pg 749

EASI, 21477 Orchid Ave, Mason City, IA 50401 *Tel:* 641-424-5079 *Toll Free Tel:* 888-327-4797 *Fax:* 641-424-8869 *Web Site:* easisat.com, pg 749

East Arizona Good Luck Enterprises Inc, PO Box 579, Clarkdale, AZ 86324 *Tel:* 928-204-2597 *Fax:* 928-204-2568 *E-mail:* hier_bosch@yahoo.com, pg 749

East Lansing Film Festival (ELFF), 210 Abbot Rd, Suite 48, East Lansing, MI 48823 *Tel:* 517-980-5802 *Web Site:* elff.com, pg 988

East of Hollywood NY, 140 53 St, Brooklyn, NY 11232 *Tel:* 718-492-7400 *Fax:* 718-439-3930 *Web Site:* www.eastofhollywoodny.com, pg 749

Eastern Acoustic Works Inc (EAW), One Main St, Bldg 13, Whitinsville, MA 01588-2238 *Tel:* 508-234-6158 *Toll Free Tel:* 800-992-5013 *Toll Free Fax:* 800-322-8251 *Web Site:* www.eaw.com, pg 749

Eastern Effects Inc, 99 Ninth St, Brooklyn, NY 11215 *Tel:* 718-855-1197 *Toll Free Fax:* 888-566-6547 *Web Site:* easterneffects.com, pg 749

Eastern Nebraska Film Office, 302 S Woodland Ct, Fremont, NE 68025 *Tel:* 402-968-4280 *E-mail:* filminnebraska@gmail.com *Web Site:* www.facebook.com/easternebraskafilmoffice, pg 973

Eastman Corp, 7447 Via de Fortuna, Carlsbad, CA 92009 *Tel:* 760-603-8646 *Web Site:* www.kbwfoundation.com, pg 749

Eastman Kodak Co, 343 State St, Rochester, NY 14650 *Toll Free Tel:* 800-698-3324 *Web Site:* www.kodak.com, pg 750

Easy Edit Video Inc, 8431 Baymeadows Way, Jacksonville, FL 32256 *Tel:* 904-730-9999 *Web Site:* www.easyeditvideo.com, pg 750

Easy Street Productions LLC, 118 Redhaven Ct, Thurmont, MD 21788 *Tel:* 301-471-8058 *E-mail:* info@publicdomainfootage.com *Web Site:* www.publicdomainfootage.com, pg 750

Eaton Corp, 8609 Six Forks Rd, Raleigh, NC 27615 *Tel:* 919-872-3020 *Toll Free Tel:* 800-356-5794 *Web Site:* powerquality.eaton.com, pg 750

ECG Productions, 120 Interstate N Pkwy SE, Suite 435, Atlanta, GA 30339 *Tel:* 678-855-5169 *Toll Free Tel:* 855-787-4487 *E-mail:* info@ecgprod.com *Web Site:* www.ecgprod.com, pg 750

ECONEWS (Environmental Television Series) & (Environmental Directions Radio Series), PO Box 351419, Los Angeles, CA 90035-9119 *Tel:* 310-559-9160 *E-mail:* ecnp@aol.com *Web Site:* www.ecoprojects.org, pg 750

Edgenuity Inc, 8860 E Chaparral Rd, Scottsdale, AZ 85250 *Toll Free Tel:* 877-725-4257 (sales) *E-mail:* customersupport@edgenuity.com; solutions@edgenuity.com (sales) *Web Site:* www.edgenuity.com, pg 750

Edgewood Studios, One Scale Ave, Suite 90, Unit 309, Bldg 3, Rutland, VT 05701 *Tel:* 802-773-0510 *E-mail:* flicks@edgewoodstudios.com *Web Site:* www.edgewoodstudios.com, pg 750

Edison Price Lighting Inc, 41-50 22 St, Long Island City, NY 11101 *Tel:* 718-685-0700 *E-mail:* orders@epl.com; info@epl.com *Web Site:* www.epl.com, pg 750

Edit House Chicago, 5325 W Berenice Ave, Chicago, IL 60641 *Tel:* 773-725-1525 *E-mail:* info@edithousechicago.com *Web Site:* www.edithousechicago.com, pg 750

The Editing Co, 7030 Empire Central Dr, Houston, TX 77040 *Tel:* 713-783-2655 *Fax:* 713-783-8642 *Web Site:* www.editingco.com, pg 750

Les Editions CEC Inc, 9001 Louis-H-La Fontaine Blvd, Anjou, QC H1J 2C5, Canada *Tel:* 514-351-6010 *Toll Free Tel:* 800-363-0494 *Fax:* 514-351-3534 *Toll Free Fax:* 877-913-5920 *E-mail:* sac@editionscec.com *Web Site:* www.editionscec.com, pg 750

Education Development Center Inc (EDC), 43 Foundry Ave, Waltham, MA 02453-8313 *Tel:* 617-969-7100 *Fax:* 617-969-5979 *E-mail:* contact@edc.org *Web Site:* www.edc.org, pg 750

Educational Activities Inc, PO Box 87, Baldwin, NY 11510-0087 *Tel:* 516-223-4666 *Toll Free Tel:* 800-797-3223 *Fax:* 516-623-9282 *Web Site:* edact.com, pg 750

Educational Insights, 152 W Walnut St, Suite 201, Gardena, CA 90248 *Toll Free Tel:* 800-995-4436 *Toll Free Fax:* 888-498-8670 *E-mail:* sales@educationalinsights.com *Web Site:* www.educationalinsights.com, pg 750

Educational Technology & Media Services, University of Northern Iowa, Inno Teaching & Technol Ctr 101, Cedar Falls, IA 50614-0301 *Web Site:* it.uni.edu/educational-technology-media-services, pg 751

Educational Technology Services (ETS), Medical Sciences, Rm SB-43, 513 Parnassus Ave, San Francisco, CA 94143-0702 *Tel:* 415-476-4310 *Fax:* 415-514-3735 *E-mail:* edtech@ucsf.edu *Web Site:* edtech.ucsf.edu, pg 751

Educational Video Group Inc, 291 Southwind Way, Greenwood, IN 46142-9190 *Tel:* 317-889-8253 *Fax:* 317-888-5857 *E-mail:* service@evgonline.com *Web Site:* www.evgonline.com, pg 751

Educational Video Network, 1401 19 St, Huntsville, TX 77340 *Tel:* 936-295-5767 *Toll Free Tel:* 800-762-0060 *Fax:* 936-294-0233 *Web Site:* www.evndirect.com, pg 751

EduMedia of Sugar Land, Texas, PO Box 2428, Sugar Land, TX 77487-2428 *Tel:* 281-756-7510 *E-mail:* service@history2u.com *Web Site:* www.history2u.com, pg 751

EEG Enterprises Inc, 586 Main St, Farmingdale, NY 11735 *Tel:* 516-293-7472 *Fax:* 516-293-7417 *E-mail:* sales@eegent.com *Web Site:* www.eegent.com, pg 751

Effective Engineering Inc, 2805 W Empire Ave, Burbank, CA 91504 *Tel:* 818-841-4437 *Fax:* 818-841-4389 *E-mail:* info@effeng.com *Web Site:* www.effeng.com, pg 751

Effective Learning Systems LLC, PO Box 366666, Bonita Springs, FL 34136 *Tel:* 612-513-0760 *Web Site:* www.effectivelearning.com, pg 751

eFootage LLC, 530 S Lake Ave, Suite 450, Pasadena, CA 91101 *Tel:* 626-395-9593 *Fax:* 626-792-5394 *E-mail:* info@efootage.com *Web Site:* www.efootage.com, pg 751

EFX Media, 2300 S Ninth St, Suite 136, Arlington, VA 22204 *Tel:* 703-486-2303 *E-mail:* info@efxmedia.com; sales@efxmedia.com *Web Site:* www.efxmedia.com, pg 751

Egan Visual Inc/Egan TeamBoard Inc, 300 Hanlan Rd, Woodbridge, ON L4L 3P6, Canada *Tel:* 905-851-2826 *Toll Free Tel:* 800-263-2387 (CN & US) *Toll Free Fax:* 888-609-8886 *E-mail:* sales@teamboard.com *Web Site:* www.egan.com, pg 751

Eggplant Pictures & Sound, 157 Princess St, Toronto, ON M5A 4M4, Canada *Tel:* 416-214-9911 *Fax:* 416-214-9912 *Web Site:* www.eggplantps.com, pg 751

Egripment USA, 2009 O'Neil Rd, Hudson, WI 54016 *Tel:* 715-386-0777 *E-mail:* egripment@egripment.com *Web Site:* www.egripment.com, pg 751

18 Label Studios, 18 Label St, Montclair, NJ 07042 *Tel:* 973-744-7382 *E-mail:* info@18label.com *Web Site:* 18label.com, pg 751

Eiki International Inc, 30251 Esperanza, Rancho Santa Margarita, CA 92688-2132 *Tel:* 949-457-0200 *Toll Free Tel:* 800-242-3454 *Fax:* 949-457-7878 *Toll Free Fax:* 800-457-3454 *E-mail:* usa@eiki.com; orders-usa@eiki.com *Web Site:* www.eiki.com, pg 751

EiKO Global LLC, 23220 W 84 St, Shawnee, KS 66227 *Toll Free Tel:* 800-852-2217 *Fax:* 913-441-6679 *E-mail:* orders@eiko.com; info@eikom.com *Web Site:* www.eiko.com, pg 752

EKU Media, 102 Perkins Bldg, 521 Lancaster Ave, Richmond, KY 40475 *Tel:* 859-622-6671 *Web Site:* video.eku.edu, pg 752

El Dorado Lake Tahoe Film & Media Office, 542 Main St, Placerville, CA 95667 *Tel:* 530-626-4400 *Toll Free Tel:* 800-457-6279 *Fax:* 530-642-1624 *E-mail:* film@eldoradocounty.org *Web Site:* filmtahoe.com, pg 967

El Mar Plastics Inc, 833 E Walnut St, Carson, CA 90746 *Tel:* 310-436-6444 *Toll Free Tel:* 800-255-5210 *Fax:* 310-436-6445 *E-mail:* sales@elmarplastics.com *Web Site:* www.elmarplastics.com, pg 752

El Paso Film Commission, One Civic Center Plaza, El Paso, TX 79901 *Tel:* 915-534-0600 *Fax:* 915-534-0687 *E-mail:* film@destinationelpaso.com *Web Site:* visitelpaso.com/film, pg 976

ELC Sales & Service Inc, 3100 S Congress Ave, Suite 6, Boynton Beach, FL 33426 *Tel:* 561-756-2210 *E-mail:* tvman@gate.net, pg 752

Electric Lady Studios, 52 W Eighth St, New York, NY 10011 *Tel:* 212-677-4700 *Web Site:* electricladystudios.com, pg 752

Electriduct Inc, 1650 NW 18 St, Unit 801, Pompano Beach, FL 33069 *Tel:* 954-867-9100 *Toll Free Tel:* 866-673-9590 *Fax:* 954-206-0799 *E-mail:* sales@electriduct.com *Web Site:* www.electriduct.com, pg 752

Electro Impulse Laboratory Inc, 1805 Rte 33, Neptune, NJ 07754 *Tel:* 732-776-5800 *Fax:* 732-776-6793 *E-mail:* sales@electroimpulse.com *Web Site:* www.electroimpulse.com, pg 752

Electron Microscopy Sciences (EMS), 1560 Industry Rd, Hatfield, PA 19440 *Tel:* 215-412-8400 *Toll Free Tel:* 800-523-5874 *Fax:* 215-412-8450 *E-mail:* info@emsdiasum.com *Web Site:* www.emsdiasum.com/microscopy, pg 752

Electronic Arts Inc, 209 Redwood Shores Pkwy, Redwood City, CA 94065 *Tel:* 650-628-1500 *Web Site:* www.ea.com, pg 752

Electronic Design Solutions Inc, 41785 Elm St, Suite 201, Murrieta, CA 92562 *Tel:* 951-304-3879 *Toll Free Tel:* 888-611-1741 *Fax:* 951-304-0608 *E-mail:* sales@myedsinc.com *Web Site:* www.gmfsound.com; www.myedsinc.com, pg 752

Electronic Service Dealers Association (ESDA), PO Box 391, LaPorte, IN 46352-0391 *Tel:* 847-798-6520 *Fax:* 219-324-3384 *E-mail:* esdaweb@gmail.com *Web Site:* www.esdaweb.org, pg 954

Electronics Representatives Association (ERA), 1325 S Arlington Heights Rd, Suite 204, Elk Grove Village, IL 60007 *Tel:* 312-419-1432 *Fax:* 312-419-1660 *E-mail:* info@era.org *Web Site:* www.era.org, pg 954

Electronics Technicians Association International Inc, 5 Depot St, Greencastle, IN 46135 *Tel:* 765-653-8262 *Toll Free Tel:* 800-288-3824 *Fax:* 765-653-4287 *E-mail:* eta@eta-i.org *Web Site:* www.eta-i.org, pg 954

Electrosonic Inc, 3320 N San Fernando Blvd, Burbank, CA 91504 *Tel:* 818-333-3600 *Toll Free Tel:* 888-343-3604 (sales) *E-mail:* contactus@electrosonic.com *Web Site:* www.electrosonic.com, pg 752

Elegant Packaging, 5253 W Roosevelt Rd, Cicero, IL 60804 *Tel:* 708-652-3400 *Toll Free Tel:* 800-367-5493 *Fax:* 708-652-6444 *E-mail:* info@elegantpackaging.com *Web Site:* www.elegantpackaging.com, pg 752

Elektrashock, 1320 Main St, Venice, CA 90291 *Tel:* 310-399-4985 *E-mail:* info@elektrashock.com *Web Site:* www.elektrashock.com, pg 753

Elite Video Inc, 209 E Emerson Rd, Lexington, MA 02420 *Tel:* 781-862-6606, pg 753

Albert Ellis Institute (AEI), 145 E 32 St, 9th fl, New York, NY 10016 *Tel:* 212-535-0822 *Fax:* 212-249-3582 *E-mail:* info@albertellis.org *Web Site:* albertellis.org, pg 753

ELMO USA Corp, 1478 Old Country Rd, Plainview, NY 11803 *Tel:* 516-501-1400 *Toll Free Tel:* 800-947-3566 *Fax:* 516-501-0429 *E-mail:* elmo@elmousa.com *Web Site:* www.elmousa.com, pg 753

Elo TouchSystems, 670 N McCarthy Blvd, Milpitas, CA 95035 *Toll Free Tel:* 800-356-8682; 800-557-1458 *Fax:* 650-361-4722 *E-mail:* eloinfo@elotouch.com; customerservice@elotouch.com *Web Site:* www.elotouch.com, pg 753

ELS Productions Inc, 627 W Olympic Lane, Elk Ridge, UT 84651 *Tel:* 801-676-0807 *Toll Free Tel:* 800-927-3472 *Web Site:* www.elsproductions.com, pg 753

Em Gee Film Library, 13502 Erwin St, Van Nuys, CA 91401 *Tel:* 818-997-0410, pg 753

eMagin Corp, 700 South Dr, Suite 201, Hopewell Junction, NY 12533 *Tel:* 845-838-7900 *Fax:* 845-838-7901 *E-mail:* info@emagin.com; sales@emagin.com; customersupport@emagin.com *Web Site:* www.emagin.com, pg 753

EMC Publishing LLC, 875 Montreal Way, St Paul, MN 55102 *Tel:* 651-290-2800 (corp) *Toll Free Tel:* 888-851-7094 *E-mail:* info@carnegielearning.com *Web Site:* www.emcp.com, pg 753

Emcor Enclosures-Crenlo, 1600 Fourth Ave NW, Rochester, MN 55901 *Tel:* 507-289-3371; 507-216-9245 (cust serv) *Fax:* 507-287-3405 *Web Site:* www.crenlo.com/emcor, pg 753

Emerald Coast Film Commission, 1540 Miracle Strip Pkwy, Fort Walton Beach, FL 32548 *Tel:* 850-651-7644 *Fax:* 850-651-7149 *E-mail:* emeraldfilm@co.okaloosa.fl.us *Web Site:* filmemeraldcoast.com, pg 969

Emergency Film Group, 1811 Bering Dr, Suite 430, Houston, TX 77057 *Tel:* 713-621-1100 (cust support); 713-952-1156 (direct sales) *Toll Free Tel:* 866-427-2467 *Fax:* 713-621-7500 *E-mail:* info@efilmgroup.com *Web Site:* www.efilmgroup.com, pg 753

Emerson Radio Corp, 3 University Plaza, Suite 405, Hackensack, NJ 07601 *Tel:* 973-884-5800 *Toll Free Tel:* 800-909-1240 (cust serv) *Fax:* 973-428-2067 *E-mail:* internet@emersonradio.com *Web Site:* www.emersonradio.com, pg 753

Emery-Pratt Co, 1966 W M 21, Owosso, MI 48867-9317 *Tel:* 989-723-5291 *Toll Free Tel:* 800-248-3887 *Fax:* 989-723-4677 *Toll Free Fax:* 800-523-6379 *Web Site:* www.emery-pratt.com, pg 753

Emlight Design, 1179 N Eastman Ave, Suite 1, Los Angeles, CA 90063 *Tel:* 323-261-5162 *Toll Free Fax:* 866-728-9164 *E-mail:* service@dimmer.com; service@emlightdesign.com *Web Site:* www.dimmer.com; www.emlightdesign.com, pg 753

Emmy Awards (Primetime), 5220 Lankershim Blvd, North Hollywood, CA 91601-3109 *Tel:* 818-754-2800 *Fax:* 818-761-3814 *E-mail:* emmyawards@televisionacademy.com *Web Site:* www.emmys.com, pg 988

eMotion Studios, 85 Liberty Ship Way, Suite 110, Sausalito, CA 94965 *Tel:* 415-331-6975 *E-mail:* info@emotionstudios.com *Web Site:* www.emotionstudios.com, pg 753

Empire Pro, 5675 Mansfield Way, Bell, CA 90201 *Tel:* 213-748-5200 *Toll Free Tel:* 866-748-5200 *Fax:* 213-748-5505 *E-mail:* sales@empirepro.com *Web Site:* www.empirepro.com, pg 753

ENCO Systems Inc, 29444 Northwestern Hwy, Southfield, MI 48034 *Tel:* 248-827-4440 *Toll Free Tel:* 800-362-6797 (sales) *Fax:* 248-827-4441 *E-mail:* sales@enco.com; support@enco.com *Web Site:* www.enco.com, pg 754

Encore A & S Case Co, 8818 Lankershim Blvd, Sun Valley, CA 91352 *Tel:* 818-768-8803 *E-mail:* info@encorecases.com *Web Site:* www.encorecases.com, pg 754

Encore Broadcast Solutions, 2104 W Kennedy Blvd, Tampa, FL 33606 *Tel:* 813-253-2774 *Toll Free Tel:* 800-780-8857 *Fax:* 813-254-5907 *Web Site:* www.encorebroadcast.com, pg 754

Encore Event Technologies LLC, 8850 W Sunset Rd, 3rd fl, Las Vegas, NV 89148 *Tel:* 702-739-8803 *Fax:* 702-739-8831 *Web Site:* www.encoreglobal.com/us, pg 754

Encore Video Productions, 811 Main St, Myrtle Beach, SC 29577 *Tel:* 843-448-9900 *Web Site:* www.encorevideo.biz, pg 754

Encounter Video Inc, 1761 N Jantzen Ave, Portland, OR 97217 *Web Site:* www.encountervideo.com, pg 754

Encyclomedia, 1526 Dekalb Ave, Atlanta, GA 30307 *Tel:* 404-527-3600 *Fax:* 404-584-5171 *E-mail:* info@encyclomedia.net *Web Site:* www.encyclomedia.net, pg 754

Encyclopaedia Britannica Inc, 325 N La Salle St, Suite 200, Chicago, IL 60654 *Tel:* 312-347-7000 (all other countries) *Toll Free Tel:* 800-323-1229 (US & CN) *Fax:* 312-294-2104 *Web Site:* www.britannica.com, pg 754

Endtime Ministries Inc, PO Box 940729, Plano, TX 75094-0729 *Tel:* 972-422-0857 *Toll Free Tel:* 833-563-6063; 800-363-8463 (cust serv) *E-mail:* endtime@endtime.com *Web Site:* www.endtime.com, pg 754

Enhanced View Services Inc, 12360 SW 132 Ct, Suite 114, Miami, FL 33186 *Tel:* 305-971-2916 *Toll Free Tel:* 877-873-3843, pg 754

Ensemble Designs Inc, 870 Gold Flat Rd, Nevada City, CA 95959 *Tel:* 530-478-1830 *Fax:* 530-478-1832 *E-mail:* info@ensembledesigns.com; service@ensembledesigns.com *Web Site:* www.ensembledesigns.com, pg 754

Entel Systems Inc, 230 W Parkway, Pompton Plains, NJ 07444 *Tel:* 201-447-2000 *Toll Free Tel:* 888-914-7100 *Fax:* 201-447-2880 *E-mail:* service@entelsystems.com *Web Site:* www.entelsystems.com, pg 754

Enterprise Media LLC, 91 Harvey St, Cambridge, MA 02140 *Tel:* 617-354-0017 *Toll Free Tel:* 800-423-6021 *Fax:* 617-354-1637 *E-mail:* info@enterprisemedia.com *Web Site:* www.enterprisemedia.com, pg 754

The Entertainment Merchants Association (EMA), PO Box 6339, North Hollywood, CA 91603 *Tel:* 818-385-1500 *E-mail:* info@entmerch.org *Web Site:* www.entmerch.org, pg 954

Entertainment One Distribution, 70 Driver Rd, Unit 1, Brampton, ON L6T 5V2, Canada *Tel:* 905-624-7337 *Toll Free Tel:* 800-387-0184 *Fax:* 905-624-7310 *Web Site:* entertainmentone.com, pg 754

Entertainment One US, 10 Harbor Park Dr, Port Washington, NY 11050 *Tel:* 516-484-1000 *Web Site:* entertainmentone.com, pg 754

Entertainment Services and Technology Association (ESTA), 630 Ninth Ave, Suite 609, New York, NY 10036 *Tel:* 212-244-1505 *Fax:* 212-244-1502 *E-mail:* info@esta.org; membership@esta.org *Web Site:* www.esta.org, pg 954

Envision Communications Inc, 2002 N 204 St, Elkhorn, NE 68022 *Tel:* 402-289-2220, pg 755

EON247 Inc, 1245 Champa St, Basement, Denver, CO 80204 *Tel:* 720-935-7497 *E-mail:* info@eon247.com *Web Site:* www.eon247.com, pg 755

Epic Software Group Inc, 701 Sawdust Rd, The Woodlands, TX 77380 *Tel:* 281-363-3742 *E-mail:* epic@epicsoftware.com *Web Site:* www.epicsoftware.com, pg 755

EPIX Inc, 381 Lexington Dr, Buffalo Grove, IL 60089 *Tel:* 847-465-1818 *Fax:* 847-465-1919 *E-mail:* epix@epixinc.com; orders@epixinc.com *Web Site:* epixinc.com, pg 755

Kat Epple Music Productions, PO Box 3156, North Fort Myers, FL 33918-3156 *Tel:* 239-997-0323 *E-mail:* music@katepple.com *Web Site:* www.katepple.com, pg 755

Equi=Tech Corp, PO Box 249, Selma, OR 97538-0249 *Tel:* 541-218-6900 (tech support, cust serv); 541-291-9253 *Toll Free Tel:* 877-EQUITECH (378-4832) *Fax:* 541-787-8740 *E-mail:* sales@equitech.com; customerservice@equitech.com; marketing@equitech.com *Web Site:* www.equitech.com, pg 755

ERA Learning, PO Box 3428, Hillsboro, OR 97123 *Tel:* 503-228-6345 *Toll Free Tel:* 800-827-2499 (orders) *Fax:* 810-885-5811 *E-mail:* info@eralearning.com; customerservice@eralearning.com; sales@eralearning.com *Web Site:* www.eralearning.com, pg 755

Ergo Media Inc, 668 American Legion Dr, Teaneck, NJ 07666 *Tel:* 201-692-0404 *Fax:* 201-692-0663 *E-mail:* info@jewishvideo.com *Web Site:* www.jewishvideo.com, pg 755

ESE, 142 Sierra St, El Segundo, CA 90245 *Tel:* 310-322-2136 *Fax:* 310-322-8127 *E-mail:* ese@ese-web.com *Web Site:* www.ese-web.com, pg 755

ESECO Speedmaster, 730 E Eseco Rd, Cushing, OK 74023-5505 *Tel:* 918-225-1266 *Toll Free Tel:* 800-331-5904 (US & CN) *E-mail:* info@eseco-speedmaster.com *Web Site:* www.eseco-speedmaster.com, pg 755

ESL Power Systems, 2800 Palisades Dr, Corona, CA 92880-9427 *Tel:* 951-739-7000 *Toll Free Tel:* 800-922-4188 *Fax:* 951-739-7048 *E-mail:* sales@eslpwr.com; info@eslpwr.com *Web Site:* eslpwr.com, pg 755

Esoteric Sound, 1608 Hemstock Ave, Wheaton, IL 60189 *Tel:* 630-933-9801 *Fax:* 630-933-9801 *E-mail:* esoterictt@aol.com *Web Site:* www.esotericsound.com, pg 755

ESPN Inc, ESPN Plaza, 545 Middle St, Bristol, CT 06010 *Tel:* 860-766-2000 *Web Site:* www.espn.com, pg 755

Essex Television Group Inc, 7 Vista Dr, Old Lyme, CT 06371 *Tel:* 860-434-7200 *Fax:* 860-434-7210 *E-mail:* contact@essextelevision.com *Web Site:* www.essextelevision.com, pg 755

Estiluz Inc, 330 W 38 St, Suite 710, New York, NY 10018 *Tel:* 201-641-1997; 646-454-1285 *Fax:* 201-641-2092; 646-454-1799 *E-mail:* info@estiluzusa.com *Web Site:* www.estiluzusa.com, pg 755

ETA Systems, 1601 Jack McKay Blvd, Ennis, TX 75119 *Toll Free Tel:* 800-321-6699 *Toll Free Fax:* 800-996-3821, pg 756

ETC, 3031 Pleasant View Rd, Middleton, WI 53562-4809 *Tel:* 608-831-4116 *Toll Free Tel:* 800-688-4116 *Fax:* 608-836-1736 *Web Site:* www.etcconnect.com, pg 756

Eternal Word Television Network (EWTN), 5817 Old Leeds Rd, Irondale, AL 35210-2164 *Tel:* 205-271-2900 *Fax:* 205-271-2920 *E-mail:* viewer@ewtn.com *Web Site:* www.ewtn.com, pg 756

ETR, 100 Enterprise Way, Suite G 300, Scotts Valley, CA 95066 *Toll Free Tel:* 800-620-8884 *Fax:* 831-438-4284 *E-mail:* customerservice@etr.org, pg 756

ETS-Lindgren, 1301 Arrow Point Dr, Cedar Park, TX 78613 *Tel:* 512-531-6400; 512-531-2609 (serv) *Fax:* 512-531-6500 *E-mail:* sales@ets-lindgren.com *Web Site:* www.ets-lindgren.com, pg 756

EUE/Screen Gems Studios, 1223 N 23 St, Wilmington, NC 28405 *Tel:* 910-343-3500 *Fax:* 910-343-3574 *Web Site:* euescreengems.com, pg 756

Eugene, Cascades & Coast-Travel Lane County, 754 Olive St, Eugene, OR 97401 *Tel:* 541-484-5307 *Toll Free Tel:* 800-547-5445 *Web Site:* www.eugenecascadescoast.org, pg 975

Eureka Springs Advertising & Promotions Commission, PO Box 522, Eureka Springs, AR 72632-0522 *Tel:* 479-253-7333 *Fax:* 479-363-9380 *E-mail:* admin@eurekasprings.org *Web Site:* www.eurekasprings.org, pg 965

Euro-Pacific Film & Video Productions Inc, 101 Crawfords Corner Rd, Suite 4-101R, Holmdel, NJ 07733 *Tel:* 732-530-4451 *Toll Free Tel:* 800-387-6776 *E-mail:* info@euro-pacific.com *Web Site:* www.euro-pacific.com, pg 756

Event Essentials, 6485 Blanchar's Crossing, Windsor, WI 53598 *Tel:* 608-846-5004 *Toll Free Tel:* 800-220-4991 *Fax:* 608-222-5063 *Web Site:* www.eventessentials.com, pg 756

Event Tech, 7601 Brandon Woods Blvd, Baltimore, MD 21226 *Tel:* 410-360-5006 *Toll Free Tel:* 866-950-8343 *E-mail:* info@eventtech.com *Web Site:* www.eventtech.com, pg 756

Eventide Inc, One Alsan Way, Little Ferry, NJ 07643 *Tel:* 201-641-1200 *Fax:* 201-641-1640 *E-mail:* audio@eventide.com; support@eventide.com *Web Site:* www.eventide.com, pg 756

Ever-Ready Media Packaging, 8192 Gatherly Circle, Easton, MD 21601 *Tel:* 973-566-9333 *E-mail:* packages@erpack.com *Web Site:* www.erpack.com, pg 757

Everlast Productions, 59 SW 12 Ave, Unit 110, Dania Beach, FL 33004 *Tel:* 954-456-7167 *Fax:* 954-456-1243 *E-mail:* info@everlastproductions.com *Web Site:* everlastproductions.com, pg 757

Evertz Microsystems Ltd, 5292 John Lucas Dr, Burlington, ON L7L 5Z9, Canada *Tel:* 905-335-3700 *Toll Free Tel:* 877-995-3700 *Fax:* 905-335-3573 *E-mail:* sales@evertz.com *Web Site:* www.evertz.com, pg 757

Evia, 8424 154 Ave NE, Redmond, WA 98052 *Tel:* 425-284-3888 *Toll Free Tel:* 800-206-2547 *Fax:* 425-883-3887 *E-mail:* hello@evia.events *Web Site:* www.tri-digital.com, pg 757

Evolution AV, 129, 2312-52 Ave SE, Calgary, AB T2C 0A3, Canada *Tel:* 403-259-3793 *Toll Free Tel:* 800-561-9820 *Fax:* 403-259-2374 *Toll Free Fax:* 800-561-9820 *Web Site:* www.evolutionav.ca, pg 757

Evolve Inc, 1210 E Arlington Blvd, Greenville, NC 27858 *Tel:* 252-754-2957 *Fax:* 252-754-2832 *Web Site:* www.evolveinc.com, pg 757

Jasper Ewing & Sons Inc, PO Box 12853, Jackson, MS 39236 *Tel:* 601-942-3325 *E-mail:* info@jasperewing.com *Web Site:* jasperewing.com, pg 757

Excel Duplication Services, 1219 N Cass St, Milwaukee, WI 53202 *Tel:* 414-225-9235, pg 757

Executive Development Systems Inc, 3818 Vinecrest Dr, Dallas, TX 75229 *Tel:* 214-351-0055 *Toll Free Tel:* 800-955-7353 *Web Site:* www.edforeman.com, pg 757

Exeltech, 7317 Jack Newell Blvd N, Fort Worth, TX 76118 *Tel:* 817-595-4969 *Toll Free Tel:* 800-886-4683 *Fax:* 817-595-1290 *Web Site:* www.exeltech.com, pg 757

Exhibitor Appointed Contractor Association (EACA), 2214 NW Fifth St, Bend, OR 97703 *Tel:* 541-317-8768 *E-mail:* info@eaca.com *Web Site:* eaca.com, pg 954

Explore, 311 W Superior St, Suite 218, Chicago, IL 60610 *Tel:* 312-818-2101 *E-mail:* info@explore-media.com *Web Site:* www.explore-media.com, pg 757

Explore Lawrence, PO Box 526, Lawrence, KS 66044 *Tel:* 785-856-3040; 785-856-5282 (mktg) *Fax:* 785-856-5303 *E-mail:* visinfo@explorelawrence.com *Web Site:* www.explorelawrence.com, pg 971

ExpoDisplays, 3401 Mary Taylor Rd, Birmingham, AL 35235 *Toll Free Tel:* 800-747-3976 *E-mail:* info@expodisplays.com *Web Site:* www.expodisplays.com, pg 757

Express Media Inc, 2225 Palou Ave, San Francisco, CA 94124 *Tel:* 415-255-9883 *Fax:* 415-255-0139 *Web Site:* expressmedia.tv, pg 757

Express Video Supply Inc, 1819 Victory Blvd, Glendale, CA 91201 *Tel:* 818-552-4590 *Toll Free Tel:* 800-238-8480 *Fax:* 818-552-4591 *E-mail:* rentals@evsonline.com; sales@evsonline.com; studios@evsonline.com *Web Site:* www.evsonline.com, pg 757

Extraordinary Demos/Videos, 2131 Yellowstar Lane, Naperville, IL 60564-5330 *Tel:* 630-904-3636 *Web Site:* www.extraordinaryvideos.com, pg 757

Extreme Reach Inc, 75 Second Ave, Suite 720, Needham, MA 02494 *Tel:* 781-577-2016 *Toll Free Tel:* 877-769-9382 *E-mail:* sales@extremereach.com; support@extremereach.com *Web Site:* extremereach.com, pg 757

Extron Electronics, 1025 E Ball Rd, Suite 100, Anaheim, CA 92805-5957 *Tel:* 714-491-1500 *Toll Free Tel:* 800-633-9876 (sales & tech support); 800-633-9873 (order support) *Fax:* 714-491-1517 *E-mail:* sales-usa@extron.com *Web Site:* www.extron.com, pg 758

Eye & I Productions, 1250 Kay Lane, Oakley, CA 94561 *Tel:* 925-625-7888 *Toll Free Tel:* 800-720-9014 *E-mail:* contact@voicecrystal.com *Web Site:* www.voicecrystal.com, pg 758

Eye on Dance, 70 E Tenth St, Suite 19-D, New York, NY 10003 *Tel:* 212-206-6492 *E-mail:* info@eyeondance.org *Web Site:* www.eyeondance.org, pg 758

Eyecon Video Productions, 1865 Summit Ave, Suite 605, Plano, TX 75074 *Tel:* 972-881-3200 *Toll Free Tel:* 877-704-1517 *E-mail:* info@eyeconvideo.com *Web Site:* www.eyeconvideo.com, pg 758

Eyeline Teleprompting, 1313 Mound St, Alameda, CA 94501 *Tel:* 510-205-6762 *E-mail:* info@eyeline.tv *Web Site:* www.eyeline.tv, pg 758

EZ FX Inc, 324 Maguire Rd, Ocoee, FL 34761 *Tel:* 407-877-2335 *Toll Free Tel:* 800-541-5706 *E-mail:* sales@ezfx.com *Web Site:* ezfx.com, pg 758

EZ Scenic, 834 NW 1911 Rd, Lone Jack, MO 64070 *Tel:* 816-861-4200 *Web Site:* www.ezscenic.com, pg 758

Fabled Films LLC, 200 Park Ave S, 15th fl, New York, NY 10003 *Tel:* 212-220-5804 *E-mail:* info@fabledfilms.com *Web Site:* www.fabledfilms.com, pg 758

FACE Foundation, 972 Fifth Ave, New York, NY 10075 *Tel:* 212-439-1439 *E-mail:* info@face-foundation.org *Web Site:* www.face-foundation.org, pg 758

Facet Media, 408 NE Sixth St, Fort Lauderdale, FL 33304 *Tel:* 954-593-0411 *E-mail:* info@facetmedia.com *Web Site:* www.facetmedia.com, pg 758

Facets Multi-Media Inc, 1517 W Fullerton Ave, Chicago, IL 60614 *Tel:* 773-281-9075 *Fax:* 773-929-5437 *E-mail:* sales@facets.org; press@facets.org *Web Site:* www.facets.org, pg 758

Falcon Safety Products Inc, 25 Imclone Dr, Branchburg, NJ 08876 *Tel:* 908-707-4900 *Toll Free Tel:* 800-332-5266 (ext 220, cust serv) *Fax:* 908-707-8855 *Web Site:* www.falconsafety.com; www.shopfalcon.com, pg 758

Family Health Media, PO Box 5832, Charlottesville, VA 22905-5832 *Tel:* 434-566-0123 *Toll Free Tel:* 800-366-3641 *Toll Free Fax:* 888-234-2579 *E-mail:* support@familyhealthmedia.com *Web Site:* www.familyhealthmedia.com, pg 758

F&F Productions LLC, 14333 Myerlake Circle, Clearwater, FL 33760 *Tel:* 727-530-5000 *Fax:* 727-535-6547 *E-mail:* info@fandfhd.tv *Web Site:* www.fandfhd.tv, pg 759

Fanlight Productions, c/o Icarus Films, 32 Court St, Brooklyn, NY 11201 *Tel:* 718-488-8900 *Fax:* 781-488-8642 *E-mail:* info@fanlight.com; sales@icarusfilms.com; rentals@icarusfilms.com *Web Site:* www.fanlight.com; www.icarusfilms.com, pg 759

Fantasee Lighting, 14857 Martinsville Rd, Belleville, MI 48111 *Tel:* 734-699-7200 *Fax:* 734-699-7400 *E-mail:* info@fantaseelighting.com *Web Site:* fantaseelighting.com, pg 759

Fantasy Creations FX, 2060 E McDaniel St, Springfield, MO 65802 *Tel:* 417-619-1138 *E-mail:* fcfxmike@yahoo.com *Web Site:* www.fantasycreationsfx.com, pg 759

Far West Media Services Inc, 904 Silver Spur Rd, No 804, Rolling Hills Estates, CA 90274 *Tel:* 562-496-3342 *Fax:* 562-496-4329 *Web Site:* www.farwestmedia.com, pg 759

Fastlane Productions LLC, 7 Riverdale Rd, Billerica, MA 01821 *Tel:* 978-667-8399 *Fax:* 978-667-8398 *E-mail:* info@fastlaneproductions.net *Web Site:* www.fastlaneproductions.net, pg 759

Fax Animation Co, 5625 Melrose Ave, Hollywood, CA 90038 *Tel:* 323-466-3561 *Fax:* 323-871-2193 *E-mail:* contactus@alangordon.com *Web Site:* www.alangordon.com, pg 759

D W Fearn, 124 Tartan Terr, Chalfont, PA 18914 *Tel:* 567-DWFEARN (393-3276) *E-mail:* support@hazelriggindustries.com *Web Site:* www.dwfearn.com, pg 759

Feature Photography Award, 40 W 45 St, New York, NY 10036 *Tel:* 212-626-9220 *Fax:* 212-626-9210 *E-mail:* info@opcofamerica.org *Web Site:* www.opcofamerica.org, pg 989

Feldenkrais® Resources, 3680 Sixth Ave, San Diego, CA 92103 *Tel:* 619-220-8776 *Toll Free Tel:* 800-765-1907 *Fax:* 619-330-4993 *E-mail:* info@feldenkraisresources.com *Web Site:* feldenkraisresources.com, pg 759

Federico Fellini Award, 6 Beach Rd, 544, Tiburon, CA 94920 *Tel:* 415-251-8433 *Fax:* 253-663-1250 *E-mail:* info@tiburonfilmfestival.com *Web Site:* www.tiburonfilmfestival.com, pg 989

Fender Musical Instruments Corp, 17600 N Perimeter Dr, Suite 100, Scottsdale, AZ 85255 *Tel:* 480-596-9690 *Toll Free Tel:* 800-856-9801 (consumer rel) *E-mail:* consumerrelations@fender.com *Web Site:* www.fender.com, pg 759

Ferrari Productions, 13323 Deer Canyon Place, San Diego, CA 92129 *Tel:* 858-354-8888 *E-mail:* info@ferrariproductions.com; sales@ferrariproductions.com *Web Site:* www.ferrariproductions.com, pg 759

Festival du Nouveau Cinema de Montreal, 3805 Blvd Saint-Laurent, Montreal, QC H2W 1X9, Canada *Tel:* 514-282-0004 *Fax:* 514-282-6664 *E-mail:* info@nouveaucinema.ca; soumissions@nouveaucinema.ca *Web Site:* www.nouveaucinema.ca, pg 989

Festival Films, 6115 Chestnut Terr, Shorewood, MN 55331 *Tel:* 952-470-2172 *E-mail:* fesfilms@aol.com *Web Site:* www.fesfilms.com, pg 759

Fiber Optic Cable Shop, 136 S Second St, Richmond, CA 94804 *Tel:* 510-234-9090 *Toll Free Tel:* 800-777-6269 *Fax:* 510-233-8888 *E-mail:* sales@fibermailbox.com *Web Site:* www.fiberopticcableshop.com, pg 759

Fiber Optic Systems Inc (FOSI), 2 Railroad Ave, Whitehouse Station, NJ 08889 *Tel:* 908-534-5500 *Toll Free Tel:* 800-809-3674 *Fax:* 908-534-2272 *E-mail:* info@fosi.com *Web Site:* www.fosi.com, pg 759

Fiddler Films, 1111 Fifth Ave S, Naples, FL 34102 *Tel:* 239-435-1818 *E-mail:* lou@fiddlerfilms.com *Web Site:* www.fiddlerfilms.com, pg 759

FIDM Productions, 919 S Grand Ave, Los Angeles, CA 90015-1421 *Tel:* 213-624-1201 *Toll Free Tel:* 800-624-1200 *Fax:* 213-624-4799 *Web Site:* fidm.edu, pg 759

5th Floor Recording Co, 316 N Milwaukee St, Suite 501, Milwaukee, WI 53202 *Tel:* 414-276-1919 *Fax:* 414-271-6621 *Web Site:* www.5thfloorrecording.com, pg 760

FILM Archives Inc, 35 W 35 St, Suite 904, New York, NY 10001-2238 *Tel:* 212-696-2616 *Fax:* 503-210-9927 *E-mail:* info@filmarchivesonline.com *Web Site:* www.filmarchivesonline.com, pg 760

Film Columbus, 100 E Broad St, Suite 2250, Columbus, OH 43215 *Tel:* 614-221-8648 *E-mail:* info@filmcolumbus.com *Web Site:* filmcolumbus.com, pg 974

Film Creations Ltd, 4349 E Fifth St, Tucson, AZ 85711 *Tel:* 520-624-4444 *Toll Free Tel:* 888-877-2490 *Fax:* 520-624-9659 *E-mail:* info@filmcreations.com *Web Site:* www.filmcreations.com, pg 760

Film Emporium, 1890 Palmer Ave, Suite 403, Larchmont, NY 10538 *Tel:* 914-833-2433 *Toll Free Tel:* 800-371-2555 *Fax:* 914-833-2430 *E-mail:* info@filmemporium.com *Web Site:* www.filmemporium.com, pg 760

Film Florida, 2516 Quail Park Terr, Kissimmee, FL 34743 *Tel:* 407-494-6195 *E-mail:* info@filmflorida.org *Web Site:* www.filmflorida.org, pg 954

Film House Inc, 810 Dominican Dr, Nashville, TN 37228 *Tel:* 615-255-4000 *Fax:* 615-255-4111 *E-mail:* results@filmhouse.com *Web Site:* www.filmhouse.com, pg 760

Film Ideas Inc, 308 N Wolf Rd, Wheeling, IL 60090 *Tel:* 847-419-0255 *Toll Free Tel:* 800-475-3456 (US only) *Fax:* 847-419-8933 *E-mail:* info@filmideas.com; orders@filmideas.com (cust serv) *Web Site:* www.filmideas.com, pg 760

Film Indiana, One N Capitol, Suite 600, Indianapolis, IN 46204-2288 *Toll Free Tel:* 800-677-9800 *E-mail:* filmindiana@visitindiana.com *Web Site:* www.filmindiana.com, pg 971

Film Las Cruces, 1300-G El Paseo, Suite 174, Las Cruces, NM 88001 *Tel:* 575-805-3456 *Web Site:* www.filmlascruces.com, pg 973

Film Liaison of Escambia County, 1401 E Gregory St, Pensacola, FL 32501 *Tel:* 850-390-3974 *Toll Free Tel:* 800-874-1234 *E-mail:* info@filmnorthflorida.com *Web Site:* filmnorthflorida.com, pg 969

Film Liaisons In California Statewide (FLICS), c/o Humboldt-Del Norte Film Commission, 520 "E" St, Eureka, CA 95501 *Tel:* 707-445-7500 *E-mail:* info@filmcalifornia.com *Web Site:* www.filmcalifornia.com, pg 954

The Film-Makers' Cooperative, 475 Park Ave S, 6th fl, New York, NY 10016 *Tel:* 212-267-5665 *E-mail:* filmmakerscoop@gmail.com; info@filmmakerscoop.com *Web Site:* film-makerscoop.com, pg 760

Film Marketing Services Inc, 4640 Admiralty Way, Suite 500, Marina del Rey, CA 90292 *E-mail:* info@filmmarketingservices.com *Web Site:* filmmarketingservices.com, pg 760

Film Police, 2558 W 16 St, Chicago, IL 60608 *Tel:* 773-463-4010 *E-mail:* info@filmpolice.com *Web Site:* www.filmpolice.com, pg 760

Film Society KC, 601 E 63 St, Suite 400, Kansas City, MO 64110 *E-mail:* filmsocietykc@gmail.com *Web Site:* www.filmsocietykc.com, pg 954

Film Tucson, 100 S Church Ave, Tucson, AZ 85701 *Tel:* 520-770-2151 *Fax:* 520-629-0160 *Web Site:* www.filmtucson.com, pg 965

Film TV Sound, PO Box 950207, Mission Hills, CA 91395-0207 *Tel:* 818-231-1038 *Fax:* 818-892-9236 *E-mail:* editorial@filmtvsound.com; eqe-media@filmtvsound.com *Web Site:* www.filmtvsound.com, pg 760

Film Upstate NY, 28 Clinton St, Saratoga Springs, NY 12866 *Tel:* 518-584-3255 *Fax:* 518-587-0318 *E-mail:* info@filmupstateny.com *Web Site:* filmupstateny.com, pg 974

Film, Video & Digital Production Grants, 550 Vandalia St, Suite 109, St Paul, MN 55114 *Tel:* 651-224-9431 *E-mail:* info@jeromefdn.org *Web Site:* www.jeromefdn.org/film-video-production-grants, pg 989

Film Wisconsin Inc, PO Box 93, Waunakee, WI 53597 *Tel:* 920-360-8827 *E-mail:* info@filmwisconsin.net *Web Site:* www.filmwisconsin.net, pg 977

Filmaker Technology, 606 W Broad St, Bethlehem, PA 18018 *Tel:* 610-691-0900 *Fax:* 610-691-0952 *E-mail:* enquire@filmaker.com *Web Site:* www.filmaker.com, pg 760

Filmakers Library, 3212 Duke St, Alexandria, VA 22314 *Tel:* 703-212-8520 *E-mail:* sales@alexanderstreet.com; orders@alexanderstreet.com; info@alexanderstreet.com *Web Site:* www.academicvideostore.com; www.academicvideostore.com/filmakers, pg 760

FilmL.A., Inc, 6255 W Sunset Blvd, 12th fl, Los Angeles, CA 90028 *Tel:* 213-977-8600 *Fax:* 213-977-8601 (permits) *E-mail:* info@filmla.com *Web Site:* www.filmla.com, pg 954, 966

Filmlites Montana, 6465 River Rd, Bozeman, MT 59718 *Tel:* 406-587-0226 *Fax:* 406-551-4555 *E-mail:* info@filmlitesmt.com *Web Site:* www.filmlitesmt.com, pg 760

Filmmakers Alliance (FA), 1317 N San Fernando Blvd, Unit 366, Burbank, CA 91504 *Tel:* 310-568-0633 *E-mail:* info@filmmakersalliance.org *Web Site:* filmmakersalliance.org, pg 955

FilmNation Entertainment, 150 W 22 St, 9th fl, New York, NY 10011 *Web Site:* www.filmnation.com, pg 760

Films by Huey, 103 Montrose Ave, Portland, ME 04103 *Tel:* 207-773-1130 *E-mail:* huey@filmsbyhuey.com *Web Site:* www.filmsbyhuey.com, pg 760

Films Media Group, 132 W 31 St, 16th fl, New York, NY 10001 *Toll Free Tel:* 800-322-8755 *Toll Free Fax:* 800-678-3633 *E-mail:* custserv@films.com *Web Site:* www.films.com, pg 760

Filmtools®, 1400 W Burbank Blvd, Burbank, CA 91506 *Tel:* 818-845-8066 *Toll Free Tel:* 888-807-1900 *Fax:* 818-845-4237 *E-mail:* sales@filmtools.com; customerservice@filmtools.com *Web Site:* www.filmtools.com, pg 761

FilmWorks Pacific, PO Box 61281, Honolulu, HI 96839-1281 *Tel:* 808-221-2255 *E-mail:* studio@filmworkspacific.com *Web Site:* filmworkspacific.com, pg 761

Final Draft, A Cast & Crew Company, 2300 Empire Ave, Burbank, CA 91504 *Tel:* 818-995-8995; 818-906-8930 (tech support) *Toll Free Tel:* 800-231-4055 *E-mail:* info@finaldraft.com *Web Site:* www.finaldraft.com, pg 761

Fingerpaint, 13 Walker Way, Albany, NY 12205 *Tel:* 518-869-1968 *Web Site:* fingerpaintmarketing.com, pg 761

Stuart Finley Films, 3428 Mansfield Rd, Falls Church, VA 22041 *Tel:* 703-820-7700, pg 761

Fire Power Music LLC, 3400 S Mill Ave, No 29, Tempe, AZ 85282 *Tel:* 602-463-2988, pg 761

Fire Station Studios, 224 N Guadalupe St, San Marcos, TX 78666 *Tel:* 512-396-1144 *Fax:* 512-396-1169 *E-mail:* info@firestationstudios.com *Web Site:* www.firestationstudios.com, pg 761

Firehouse Studios, 1545 W Rosemont Ave, Chicago, IL 60660 *Tel:* 773-271-3100 *E-mail:* folks@firehousestudios.com *Web Site:* firehousestudios.com, pg 761

First Camera, 2472 Third St, San Francisco, CA 94107 *Tel:* 415-647-3400 *Fax:* 415-647-3410 *E-mail:* sfvideo@firstcamera.com *Web Site:* www.firstcamera.com, pg 761

First Cut Communications LLC, 301 W Broome St, Suite 100, LaGrange, GA 30240 *Tel:* 706-882-5581 *Fax:* 706-407-4528 *E-mail:* info@firstcutcommunications.com *Web Site:* www.firstcutcommunications.com, pg 761

1st Financial Training Services Inc, 1515 E Woodfield Rd, Suite 345, Schaumburg, IL 60173 *Tel:* 847-969-0900 *Toll Free Tel:* 800-442-8662 *Fax:* 847-969-0521 *E-mail:* info@1stfinancialtraining.com *Web Site:* www.1stfinancialtraining.com, pg 761

First Person Inc, 550 Bryant St, San Francisco, CA 94107 *Tel:* 415-495-5595 *E-mail:* hi@firstperson.is *Web Site:* firstperson.is, pg 761

First Run Features, The Film Center Bldg, Suite 1213, 630 Ninth Ave, New York, NY 10036-3708 *Tel:* 212-243-0600 *Fax:* 212-989-7649 *E-mail:* info@firstrunfeatures.com *Web Site:* www.firstrunfeatures.com, pg 761

1st Wave Productions, 2017 Pacific Ave, Venice, CA 90291 *Tel:* 310-279-7059 *Web Site:* www.1stwaveproductions.com, pg 761

FirstCom Music, 14860 Montfort Dr, Suite 260, Dallas, TX 75254 *Tel:* 972-446-8742 *Toll Free Tel:* 800-858-8880 *E-mail:* info@firstcom.com; musicsearch@firstcom.com *Web Site:* www.firstcom.com, pg 761

FirstGeneration Audio/Visual Services, 410 Allentown Dr, Allentown, PA 18109 *Tel:* 610-437-4300 *Fax:* 610-437-3200 *E-mail:* information@firstgencom.com; contact@firstgencom.com *Web Site:* www.firstgencom.com, pg 761

Fish Films Footage World, 4548 Van Noord Ave, Studio City, CA 91604 *Tel:* 818-905-1071 *E-mail:* footageworld@aol.com *Web Site:* www.footageworld.com, pg 761

FitzCo Sound Inc, 4300 W Wall St, Bldg B, Midland, TX 79703 *Tel:* 432-684-0861 *Fax:* 432-682-9978 *Web Site:* www.fitzcosound.com, pg 761

5 Alarm Music, 3500 W Olive Ave, Suite 810, Burbank, CA 91505 *Tel:* 626-304-1698 *Toll Free Tel:* 800-322-7879 *Fax:* 626-795-2058 *E-mail:* info@5alarmmusic.com *Web Site:* www.5alarmmusic.com, pg 762

FJ Productions Inc, 14900 Ventura Blvd, Suite 350, Sherman Oaks, CA 91403-3465 *Tel:* 818-788-0153 *E-mail:* contact@fjproductions.com *Web Site:* www.fjproductions.com, pg 762

FJW Optical Systems Inc, 322 N Woodwork Lane, Palatine, IL 60067-4933 *Tel:* 847-358-2500 *Toll Free Tel:* 800-535-4FJW (355-4359) *Fax:* 847-358-2533 *E-mail:* irsales@findrscope.com *Web Site:* www.findrscope.com, pg 762

FlagHouse, 601 Flaghouse Dr, Hasbrouck Heights, NJ 07604-3116 *Tel:* 201-288-7600 *Toll Free Tel:* 800-793-7900 *Fax:* 201-288-7887 *Toll Free Fax:* 800-793-7922 *E-mail:* sales@flaghouse.com; info@flaghouse.com *Web Site:* www.flaghouse.com, pg 762

Flagstaff Convention & Visitors Bureau, 211 W Aspen Ave, Flagstaff, AZ 86001 *Tel:* 928-213-2924 *Toll Free Tel:* 800-842-7293 *Fax:* 928-556-1305 *Web Site:* www.flagstaffarizona.org, pg 965

Robert Flaherty Film Seminar, 6 E 39 St, 12th fl, New York, NY 10016 *Tel:* 212-448-0457 *Fax:* 212-448-0458 *E-mail:* ifs@flahertyseminar.org *Web Site:* flahertyseminar.org, pg 989

Flash Electronics Inc, Brooklyn Army Terminal, Suite 1-A, Mail Box 3, 140 58 St, Brooklyn, NY 11220 *Tel:* 718-492-4040 *Toll Free Tel:* 800-831-3127 *Fax:* 718-492-4590 *E-mail:* customercare@flashdistributors.com *Web Site:* www.flashdistributors.com, pg 762

Flashback Media Productions, 1172 Lombardi St, Erie, CO 80516 *Tel:* 303-545-9955 *E-mail:* info@flashbackmedia.tv *Web Site:* www.flashbackmedia.tv, pg 762

Flashback Stage Lighting (FBSL), 1124 Bay Blvd, Suite A, Chula Vista, CA 91911-7155 *Tel:* 619-697-2729 *Fax:* 619-697-2782 *E-mail:* mail@flashbackstagelighting.com *Web Site:* flashbackstagelighting.com, pg 762

Flat Town Music Co, 700 S Chataignier St, Ville Platte, LA 70586 *Tel:* 337-363-2177 *Toll Free Tel:* 800-738-8668 *Fax:* 337-363-2094 *E-mail:* info@flattownmusic.com; order@flattownmusic.com *Web Site:* www.flattownmusic.com, pg 762

Doug Fleenor Design Inc, 396 Corbett Canyon Rd, Arroyo Grande, CA 93420 *Tel:* 805-481-9599 *Toll Free Tel:* 888-436-9512 *Fax:* 805-481-9599 *E-mail:* info@dfd.com *Web Site:* www.dfd.com, pg 762

Fleetwood Group Inc, 11832 James St, Holland, MI 49424 *Tel:* 616-396-1142 *Toll Free Tel:* 800-257-6390 *Fax:* 616-820-8300 *Web Site:* www.fleetwoodgroup.com; www.fleetwoodelectronics.com; www.fleetwoodfurniture.com, pg 762

Flickers' Rhode Island International Film Festival™ (RIIFF), 83 Park St, Suite 5, Providence, RI 02903 *Tel:* 401-861-4445 *Fax:* 401-490-6735 *E-mail:* info@film-festival.org *Web Site:* film-festival.org, pg 989

Flight Form Cases Inc, 6543 S Laramie Ave, Bedford Park, IL 60638 *Tel:* 708-458-8989 *Toll Free Tel:* 800-334-4884 *Fax:* 708-458-9023, pg 762

Flip 2 Media Inc, 1067 Serpentine Lane, Pleasanton, CA 94566-4759 *Tel:* 925-417-1420 *E-mail:* info@flip2media.com *Web Site:* www.flip2media.com, pg 762

FLIR Systems Inc, 27700 SW Parkway Ave, Wilsonville, OR 97070 *Tel:* 503-498-3547 *Toll Free Tel:* 800-322-3731 *Fax:* 503-498-3904 *Web Site:* www.flir.com, pg 762

Florentine Films, 136 E 56 St, Suite 4-B, New York, NY 10022 *Tel:* 212-980-5966 *Fax:* 212-980-5944 *E-mail:* Sherman.Pictures@florentinefilms.com *Web Site:* www.florentinefilms.com/sherman, pg 762

Florical Systems Inc, 4500 NW 27 Ave, Bldg B-1, Gainesville, FL 32606 *Tel:* 352-372-8326 *Fax:* 352-375-0859 *E-mail:* sales@florical.com *Web Site:* www.florical.com, pg 762

Florida Digital Studios, 6677 13 Ave N, Suite 3C, St Petersburg, FL 33710 *Tel:* 727-546-7900 *Web Site:* www.floridadigitalstudios.com, pg 762

Florida Film & Tape, 3417 Lake Breeze Rd, Orlando, FL 32808 *Tel:* 407-297-0091 *E-mail:* info@ffandt.com *Web Site:* ffandt.com, pg 763

Florida Film & Video, 4461 38 Way S, St Petersburg, FL 33711 *Tel:* 727-369-0732 *E-mail:* info@flhd.tv *Web Site:* www.flhd.tv, pg 763

Florida Film Festival, c/o Enzian Theater, 1300 S Orlando Ave, Maitland, FL 32751 *Tel:* 407-629-1088 *Fax:* 407-629-6870 *E-mail:* entries@enzian.org; marketing@enzian.org; events@enzian.org *Web Site:* www.floridafilmfestival.com, pg 989

Florida Keys & Key West Film Commission, 1201 White St, Suite 102, Key West, FL 33040 *Tel:* 305-293-1800 *Toll Free Tel:* 800-FILM-KEYS (345-6539) *Fax:* 305-296-0788 *Web Site:* www.filmkeys.com, pg 969

The Florida Office of Film & Entertainment, 107 E Madison St, MSC 80, Tallahassee, FL 32399 *Tel:* 850-717-8990 *Toll Free Tel:* 877-FLA-FILM (352-3456) *E-mail:* floridaofe@deo.myflorida.com *Web Site:* www.filminflorida.com, pg 970

Fluke Corp, 6920 Seaway Blvd, Everett, WA 98203 *Tel:* 425-347-6100 *Toll Free Tel:* 800-443-5853 *Fax:* 425-446-5116 *E-mail:* fluke-info@fluke.com *Web Site:* www.fluke.com, pg 763

The Fluorescent Co Inc, c/o Red*D*Mix Rentals Inc, 388 Carlaw Ave, Suite 116, Toronto, ON M4M 2T4, Canada *Tel:* 416-879-3761 *Fax:* 905-681-8520 *E-mail:* reddmix@cogeco.ca *Web Site:* www.flo-co.com, pg 763

Flying Colors Broadcasts, 2000 "M" St NW, Suite 345, Washington, DC 20036 *Tel:* 202-293-5300 *E-mail:* info@fc-tv.com *Web Site:* www.fc-tv.com, pg 763

FM Systems Inc, 3877 S Main St, Santa Ana, CA 92707 *Tel:* 714-979-3355 *Toll Free Tel:* 800-235-6960 *Fax:* 714-979-0913 *E-mail:* fmsystemsinc@sbcglobal.net *Web Site:* www.fmsystems-inc.com, pg 763

FMP Media Solutions Inc, 3600 Horizon Dr, Suite 180, King of Prussia, PA 19406 *Tel:* 610-825-4000 *Toll Free Tel:* 800-346-5071 *Fax:* 610-825-4430 *E-mail:* info@fmpmedia.com *Web Site:* www.fmpmedia.com, pg 763

Focus Features, 100 Universal City Plaza, Bldg 2160, Suite 7-C, Los Angeles, CA 90068 *Web Site:* www.focusfeatures.com, pg 763

Focus on Animals, PO Box 340, Charles Town, WV 25414-0340 *Tel:* 304-725-0506 *Fax:* 304-725-1523 *E-mail:* information@nhes.org; education@nhes.org *Web Site:* www.nhes.org, pg 763

Follett School Solutions Inc, 1340 Ridgeview Dr, McHenry, IL 60050 *Tel:* 815-759-1700 *Toll Free Tel:* 888-511-5114 (cust serv); 877-899-8550 (sales) *Fax:* 815-759-9831 *Toll Free Fax:* 800-852-5458 *E-mail:* info@follettlearning.com; customerservice@follett.com *Web Site:* www.follettlearning.com; www.follett.com/prek12; www.titlewave.com, pg 763

The Food & Beverage Institute, 1946 Campus Dr, Hyde Park, NY 12538 *Tel:* 845-452-9600 *Toll Free Tel:* 800-888-7850 *Fax:* 845-451-1078 *E-mail:* ciaprochef@culinary.edu *Web Site:* www.ciachef.edu; www.ciaprochef.com, pg 763

FootageBank HD, 13470 Washington Blvd, Suite 210, Marina del Rey, CA 90292 *Tel:* 310-822-1400 *Fax:* 310-822-4100 *E-mail:* info@footagebank.com *Web Site:* www.footagebank.com, pg 763

Foothill Digital Inc, 217 Storer Ave, New Rochelle, NY 10801 *Tel:* 914-235-5670 *E-mail:* info@foothilldigital.com *Web Site:* www.foothilldigital.com; www.tuckersound.com, pg 763

For-A Corp of America, 11155 Knott Ave, Suite G & H, Cypress, CA 90630 *Tel:* 714-894-3311 *Fax:* 714-894-5399 *E-mail:* info@for-a.com *Web Site:* www.for-a.com, pg 763

Ford AV, 4800 W Interstate 40, Oklahoma City, OK 73128 *Tel:* 405-946-9966 *Toll Free Tel:* 800-654-6744 *Web Site:* www.fordav.com, pg 763

Forensic Video Deposition Service, 11111 N Scottsdale Rd, Suite 205, Scottsdale, AZ 85254 *Tel:* 480-840-1222 *Fax:* 480-360-1421 *E-mail:* office@forensicvideo.net *Web Site:* forensicvideo.net, pg 764

Foresight Imaging, One Executive Dr, Suite 202, Chelmsford, MA 01824 *Tel:* 978-458-4624 *Fax:* 978-458-5488 *E-mail:* info@fi-llc.com *Web Site:* www.fi-llc.com, pg 764

Forge Recording LLC, 100 Mill Rd, Oreland, PA 19075 *Tel:* 215-885-7000 *Fax:* 215-887-3501 *E-mail:* info@ forgerecording.com *Web Site:* www.forgerecording. com, pg 764

Forte Productions, PO Box 17, San Geronimo, CA 94963-0325 *Tel:* 415-488-9446 *Fax:* 415-488-9446 *Web Site:* www.pianovideos.com, pg 764

48 Windows, 1661 N Lincoln Blvd, Suite 220, Santa Monica, CA 90404 *Tel:* 310-392-9545 *Fax:* 310-392-9445 *E-mail:* ziv@48windows.com *Web Site:* www. 48windows.com, pg 764

J E Foss Co, 3328-B Industrial Blvd, Bethel Park, PA 15102 *Tel:* 412-564-5644 *Toll Free Tel:* 800-245-6240 *Fax:* 412-564-5646 *E-mail:* jefoss@earthlink.net *Web Site:* www.jefoss.com, pg 764

FotoKem, 2801 W Alameda Ave, Burbank, CA 91505 *Tel:* 818-846-3101 *Toll Free Tel:* 800-FOTOKEM (368-6536) *E-mail:* info@fotokem.com *Web Site:* www.fotokem.com, pg 764

FOTON Hawaii, 98-021 Kamehameha Hwy, Aiea, HI 96701 *Tel:* 808-206-5244 *E-mail:* rentals@ fotonhawaii.com *Web Site:* www.fotonhawaii.com, pg 764

Fotosearch Stock Photography, 21155 Watertown Rd, Waukesha, WI 53186 *Tel:* 262-717-0740 *Toll Free Tel:* 800-827-3920 *Fax:* 262-717-0745 *E-mail:* fotosearch@fotosearch.com *Web Site:* www. fotosearch.com, pg 764

Foundation for Economic Education (FEE), 1819 Peachtree Rd NE, Suite 300, Atlanta, GA 30309 *Tel:* 404-554-9980 *Toll Free Tel:* 800-960-4333 *E-mail:* editor@fee.org; info@fee.org *Web Site:* fee. org, pg 955

Four Corners Productions, 101 W 90 St, No 6J, New York, NY 10024 *Tel:* 212-228-6492 *Fax:* 212-228-6492 *Web Site:* www.operatitles.net; www. gracepaleyvideo.com, pg 764

4-D Creative Media, 16 W 46 St, 12th fl, New York, NY 10036 *Tel:* 646-483-7768 *Web Site:* www.4-dcreative. com, pg 764

411 Video Information, PO Box 1223, Pebble Beach, CA 93953-1223 *Tel:* 408-671-2859 (cell) *Web Site:* www.411videoinfo.com, pg 764

4 Wall Entertainment, 3165 W Sunset Rd, Suite 100, Las Vegas, NV 89118 *Tel:* 702-263-3858 *Toll Free Tel:* 877-789-8167 (Western US) *Fax:* 702-263-3863 *E-mail:* info@4wall.com; info@usedlighting.com *Web Site:* www.4wall.com; www.usedlighting.com, pg 764

4th Street Recording, 1211 Fourth St, Santa Monica, CA 90401 *Tel:* 310-395-9114 *E-mail:* info@ 4thstreetrecording.com *Web Site:* www. 4thstreetrecording.com, pg 764

Fox 40 KTXL TV, 4655 Fruitridge Rd, Sacramento, CA 95820 *Tel:* 916-454-4422 *Fax:* 916-739-1079 *E-mail:* foxprogramming@fox40.com *Web Site:* www. fox40.com, pg 764

Fox 61, 285 Broad St, Hartford, CT 06115 *Tel:* 860-527-6161 *Fax:* 860-727-0158 *Web Site:* www.fox61.com, pg 765

Fox Television Center, 1999 S Bundy Dr, Los Angeles, CA 90025 *Tel:* 310-584-2000 *Fax:* 310-584-2023 *Web Site:* www.foxla.com, pg 765

Fox 10 Productions (KSAZ-TV), 511 W Adams St, Phoenix, AZ 85003 *Tel:* 602-257-1234 *Fax:* 602-262-0177 *E-mail:* fox10.desk@foxtv.com *Web Site:* www. fox10phoenix.com, pg 765

Frame 30 Productions Ltd, 10816A-82 Ave, No 202, Edmonton, AB T6E 2B3, Canada *Tel:* 780-439-5322 *E-mail:* frame30@frame30.com *Web Site:* www. frame30.com, pg 765

Frameline Completion Fund, 145 Ninth St, Suite 300, San Francisco, CA 94103 *Tel:* 415-703-8650 *Fax:* 415-861-1404 *E-mail:* info@frameline.org; programming@frameline.org *Web Site:* www. frameline.org, pg 989

Framepool, 175 Varick St, New York, NY 10014 *Tel:* 646-701-7472 *Toll Free Tel:* 800-331-1314 *E-mail:* newyork@framepool.com *Web Site:* www. framepool.com, pg 765

Franciscan Media, 28 W Liberty St, Cincinnati, OH 45202-6498 *Tel:* 513-241-5615 *Toll Free Tel:* 800-488-0488 *Fax:* 513-241-0399 *E-mail:* info@ franciscanmedia.org *Web Site:* www.americancatholic. org, pg 765

Franklin Video Inc, 931 Marilyn Dr, Raleigh, NC 27607 *Tel:* 919-833-8888; 919-621-0400 (cell) *Web Site:* www.franklinvideo.com, pg 765

Freedoms Foundation National Awards, 1601 Valley Forge Rd, Valley Forge, PA 19481 *Tel:* 610-933-8825 *Fax:* 610-935-0522 *E-mail:* info@ffvf.org *Web Site:* www.freedomsfoundation.org, pg 989

Freeman, 1600 Viceroy, Suite 100, Dallas, TX 75235 *Tel:* 214-445-1000 *Web Site:* www.freeman.com, pg 765

Freeman Audio Visual, 2056 32 Ave, Montreal, QC H8T 3H7, Canada *Tel:* 514-631-1821 *Toll Free Tel:* 800-868-6886 *Web Site:* freemanav-ca.com, pg 765

Freeman Pictures Inc, 1234 Sherman Ave, Suite 211, Evanston, IL 60602-1375 *Tel:* 847-733-0717 *E-mail:* info@freemanpictures.com *Web Site:* www. freemanpictures.com, pg 765

Freestyle Photographic Supplies, 5124 Sunset Blvd, Los Angeles, CA 90027 *Tel:* 323-660-3460 *Toll Free Tel:* 800-292-6137 *Fax:* 323-660-4885 *Web Site:* www. freestylephoto.biz, pg 765

Freestyle Productions Inc, 3268 Winpark Dr, Minneapolis, MN 55427 *Tel:* 763-417-9575 *E-mail:* info@freestyleproductions.com *Web Site:* www.freestyleproductions.com, pg 765

Freewheelin' Films, 44895 Hwy 82, Aspen, CO 81611 *Tel:* 970-925-2640 *Fax:* 970-925-9369 *Web Site:* www. fwf.com, pg 765

FremantleMedia North America, 2900 W Alameda Ave, Suite 800, Burbank, CA 91505 *Tel:* 818-748-1100 *Web Site:* www.fremantlemedia.com, pg 765

Fremont/Custer County Film Commission, 403 Royal Gorge Blvd, Canon City, CO 81212 *Tel:* 719-275-2331 *Toll Free Tel:* 800-876-7922 *E-mail:* chamber@ canoncity.com *Web Site:* www.canoncity.com, pg 968

French American Music Enterprises, 5 Junkins Ave, Suite 106, Portsmouth, NH 03801 *Tel:* 603-430-9524 *Web Site:* www.luciet.com, pg 765

Fresh Film Northwest (FFNW), 934 SW Salmon St, Portland, OR 97205 *Tel:* 503-221-1156 *Fax:* 503-294-0874 *E-mail:* info@nwfilm.org *Web Site:* www.nwfilm. org, pg 990

Fresh Music Library, 320 South St, Agawam, MA 01001 *Toll Free Tel:* 888-211-8576 *Web Site:* www. freshmusic.com, pg 766

Fresno County Film Commission, 2220 Tulare St, Suite 800, Fresno, CA 93721 *Tel:* 559-600-4271 *Fax:* 559-600-4573 *E-mail:* tourism@fresnocountyca.gov *Web Site:* www.filmfresno.com, pg 966

Frey Scientific, 80 Northwest Blvd, Nashua, NH 03063-4067 *Toll Free Tel:* 800-225-3739; 800-258-1302 *Toll Free Fax:* 877-256-3739; 800-282-9560 *E-mail:* customercare.frey@schoolspecialty. com; social@schoolspecialty.com *Web Site:* www. freyscientific.com, pg 766

Frezzi Energy Systems, 7 Valley St, Hawthorne, NJ 07506 *Tel:* 973-427-1160 *Fax:* 973-427-0934 *E-mail:* info@frezzi.com *Web Site:* www.frezzi.com, pg 766

Fricon Entertainment Co Inc, 134 Bluegrass Circle, Hendersonville, TN 37075 *Tel:* 615-826-2288 *Fax:* 615-826-0500, pg 766

Robert Fried Photography, 610 Eldridge Ct, Novato, CA 94947 *Tel:* 415-898-6153 *Fax:* 415-897-0353 *Web Site:* www.robertfriedphotography.com, pg 766

Gene Friedman, PO Box 275, Wainscott, NY 11975-0275 *Tel:* 631-537-0178 *E-mail:* genfried@optonline. net, pg 766

Frontier Communications Corp, PO Box 939, Portland, OR 97207-0939 *Tel:* 503-246-8080, pg 766

Frontline Communications, 12770 44 St N, Clearwater, FL 33762 *Tel:* 727-573-0400 *Fax:* 727-571-3295 *Web Site:* www.frontlinecomm.com, pg 766

FrontRow, 1690 Corporate Circle, Petaluma, CA 94954 *Tel:* 707-769-1110 *Toll Free Tel:* 800-227-0735 *Fax:* 707-769-9624 *E-mail:* customercare@gofrontrow. com *Web Site:* www.gofrontrow.com, pg 766

FSR Inc, 244 Bergen Blvd, Woodland Park, NJ 07424 *Tel:* 973-785-4347 *Toll Free Tel:* 800-332-3771 (tech support) *Fax:* 973-785-4207 *E-mail:* sales@fsrinc.com *Web Site:* www.fsrinc.com, pg 766

Fugro, 6100 Hillcroft Ave, Houston, TX 77081 *Tel:* 713-369-5600 *Web Site:* www.fugro.com, pg 766

FUJIFILM Canada Inc, 600 Suffolk Ct, Mississauga, ON L5R 4G4, Canada *Tel:* 905-890-6611 *Toll Free Tel:* 800-263-5018 *Fax:* 905-890-6446 *Web Site:* www. fujifilm.ca, pg 766

FUJIFILM Graphic Systems Division, 850 Central Ave, Hanover Park, IL 60133 *Tel:* 630-259-7200 *Toll Free Tel:* 800-877-0555 *Fax:* 630-259-7078 *Web Site:* www. fujifilmusa.com, pg 766

FUJIFILM North America Corp, 200 Summit Lake Dr, Valhalla, NY 10595-1356 *Tel:* 914-789-8100 *Toll Free Tel:* 800-755-3854 *Fax:* 914-789-8530 *Web Site:* www. fujifilmusa.com/northamerica, pg 766

FUJIFILM Optical Devices Division, 10 High Point Dr, Wayne, NJ 07470 *Tel:* 973-633-5600 *Fax:* 973-633-5216 *Web Site:* www.fujifilmusa.com/products/ optical_devices, pg 766

Full Compass Systems, 9770 Silicon Prairie Pkwy, Madison, WI 53593 *Tel:* 608-831-7330 *Toll Free Tel:* 800-356-5844 *E-mail:* customerservice@ fullcompass.com *Web Site:* www.fullcompass.com, pg 767

Full Moon & High Tide Productions & Studios, 424 Main St, El Segundo, CA 90245-3002 *Tel:* 310-647-1958 *Fax:* 310-647-1960 *Web Site:* fmht.net, pg 767

Full Scale Effects, 6869 Tujunga Ave, North Hollywood, CA 91605 *Tel:* 818-760-0875; 818-760-0042 *Fax:* 818-760-0876 *Web Site:* fullscalefx.com, pg 767

Full Spectrum Arts & Services, PO Box 1032, Littleton, CO 80160 *Tel:* 303-798-7906 (voicemail only); 720-326-2043 (cell) *Web Site:* www.fullspectrumarts.com, pg 767

Fuller Street Productions, 12131 Shoemaker Ave, Santa Fe Springs, CA 90670 *Toll Free Tel:* 877-637-8733 *Toll Free Fax:* 877-637-8733 *E-mail:* contact@ fullerstreet.com *Web Site:* www.fullerstreet.com, pg 767

Furman®, 1800 S McDowell Blvd, Petaluma, CA 94954 *Tel:* 707-283-5900 *Toll Free Tel:* 800-472-5555 *Fax:* 707-283-5901 *E-mail:* powertechsupport@ corebrands.com *Web Site:* www.furmanpower.com, pg 767

Furnace MFG, 2719-B Dorr Ave, Fairfax, VA 22031 *Tel:* 703-205-0007 *Toll Free Tel:* 888-599-9883 *Fax:* 703-205-2951 *E-mail:* sales@furnacemfg.com *Web Site:* www.furnacemfg.com, pg 767

Fusion Consoles/Eurotech Seating, c/o Marketec, No 601, 3784 Mission Ave, Suite 148, Oceanside, CA 92058 *Toll Free Tel:* 800-557-8861 *Toll Free Fax:* 888-262-1726 *E-mail:* info@marketec.com *Web Site:* www.marketec.com, pg 767

Future Disc LLC, 15851 NW Willis Rd, McMinnville, OR 97128 *Tel:* 213-361-0603 *Fax:* 503-472-1951 *Web Site:* www.futurediscsystems.com, pg 767

Future Light Inc, 21887 Lorain Rd, Suite 200, Cleveland, OH 44126 *Tel:* 440-801-1310 *Toll Free Tel:* 800-581-5536 *Fax:* 440-779-4159 *E-mail:* info@ future-light.com *Web Site:* www.future-light.com, pg 767

Future US Inc, 11 W 42 St, 15th fl, New York, NY 10036 Tel: 212-378-0448 Toll Free Tel: 844-779-2822 (subns) Web Site: www.futureplc.com, pg 767

Future View Inc, 6035 Blair Rd NW, Washington, DC 20011 Tel: 202-882-7400 Fax: 202-882-7450 E-mail: info@futureview.com Web Site: www. futureview.com, pg 767

FutureVideo, 28202 Cabot Rd, Suite 300, Laguna Niguel, CA 92677 Tel: 949-363-1686 Toll Free Fax: 866-261-1686 E-mail: sales@futurevideo.com Web Site: www.futurevideo.com; www.futurevideo.tv, pg 767

Gabriel Awards, 205 W Monroe St, Suite 470, Chicago, IL 60606 Tel: 312-380-6789 Fax: 312-361-0256 E-mail: cpaawards@catholicpress.org Web Site: www. catholicpress.org/page/gabrielawards, pg 990

Gage-Line Technology Inc, 121 LaGrange Ave, Rochester, NY 14613-1577 Tel: 585-458-2000 Toll Free Tel: 800-291-3724 Fax: 585-458-0524 E-mail: sales@gage-line.com Web Site: www.gage-line.com, pg 767

Gagne Inc, 41 Commercial Dr, Johnson City, NY 13790 Tel: 607-729-3366 Toll Free Tel: 800-800-5954 Fax: 607-729-7644 E-mail: sales@gagneinc.com Web Site: www.gagneinc.com, pg 767

Gaither Studios LLC, 1705 S Park Ave, Alexandria, IN 46001 Toll Free Tel: 800-333-7859 E-mail: info@gaitherstudios.com, pg 767

Galaxy Audio, 601 E Pawnee Ave, Wichita, KS 67211 Tel: 316-263-2852 Toll Free Tel: 800-369-7768 Fax: 316-263-0642 E-mail: sales@galaxyaudio.com; orders@galaxyaudio.com Web Site: www.galaxyaudio.com, pg 767

Gallien-Krueger, 2234 Industrial Dr, Stockton, CA 95206 Tel: 209-234-7300 Fax: 209-234-8420 E-mail: sales@gallien.com Web Site: www.gallien-krueger.com, pg 768

GAMfilm Productions, 7559 Willoughby Ave, Suite 5, Los Angeles, CA 90046 Tel: 213-840-6212 E-mail: gamfilm@gmail.com Web Site: director-writer-producer.com, pg 768

Gamma Imaging, 222 N DesPlaines St, Chicago, IL 60661 Tel: 312-441-0091 Toll Free Tel: 877-441-4830 Fax: 312-441-0092 E-mail: digital@gammaimaging.com Web Site: gammaimaging.com, pg 768

G&G Technologies Inc, 280 N Midland Ave, Bldg F, Suite 202, Saddle Brook, NJ 07663 Tel: 201-791-1400 Toll Free Tel: 800-422-2920 Fax: 201-791-1401 E-mail: staff@ggvideo.com Web Site: www.ggvideo.com, pg 768

GAPC (General Assembly Production Centre), 1550 Laperriere Ave, Suite 102, Ottawa, ON K1Z 7T2, Canada Tel: 613-723-3316 Fax: 613-723-8583 Web Site: www.gapc.com, pg 768

Garcia Marketing Inc, 400 Ninth St, Conway, PA 15027-1663 Tel: 724-869-0100 Toll Free Tel: 800-683-1925 Fax: 724-869-1925 E-mail: gmavfoto@verizon.net, pg 768

Garden Valley Productions, 240 Crystal Springs Lane, Roseburg, OR 97471 Tel: 541-440-1926 Fax: 541-440-1008, pg 768

Garman Productions LLC, 2828 NW 58 St, Oklahoma City, OK 73112 Tel: 405-254-2500 Toll Free Tel: 800-747-5699 Fax: 405-254-2507 E-mail: info@garman.com Web Site: www.garman.com, pg 768

Garner Products Inc, 10620 Industrial Ave, Suite 100, Roseville, CA 95678 Tel: 916-784-0200 Toll Free Tel: 800-624-1903 Fax: 916-784-1425 E-mail: info@garner-products.com Web Site: www.garner-products.com, pg 768

Gary Camera & Digital, 6750 Broadway Ave, Merrillville, IN 46410 Tel: 219-769-2451 Fax: 219-769-2488 E-mail: garycamera@gmail.com Web Site: garycameradigital.com, pg 768

The Gary-Paul Agency, 1549 Main St, Stratford, CT 06615 Tel: 203-345-6167 Web Site: www. thegarypaulagency.com; www.nutmegpictures.com, pg 768

GatesAir, 5300 Kings Island Dr, Suite 101, Mason, OH 45040 Tel: 513-459-3400 Toll Free Tel: 800-622-0022 Fax: 513-459-3796 E-mail: information@gatesair.com; orders@gatesair.com; support@gatesair.com Web Site: www.gatesair.com, pg 768

Gateways, PO Box 1706, Ojai, CA 93024-1706 Tel: 805-649-5367 Toll Free Tel: 800-477-8908 Fax: 805-649-5302, pg 768

Gateways Books & Tapes, PO Box 370, Nevada City, CA 95959 Tel: 530-271-2239 Toll Free Tel: 800-869-0658 Fax: 530-272-0184 E-mail: info@gatewaysbooksandtapes.com Web Site: www.gatewaysbooksandtapes.com, pg 768

Gaylord Archival, PO Box 4901, Syracuse, NY 13221-4901 Tel: 315-634-8125 (intl) Toll Free Tel: 800-448-6160 (cust serv) Fax: 315-453-5030 (intl) Toll Free Fax: 800-272-3412 E-mail: customerservice@gaylord.com Web Site: www.gaylord.com; www.facebook.com/gaylordarchival, pg 768

GBC Document Finishing, 4 Corporate Dr, Lake Zurich, IL 60047 Toll Free Tel: 800-723-4000 (orders & serv) Toll Free Fax: 800-914-8178 Web Site: www.gbcconnect.com; www.gbc.com, pg 768

GEAR Cameras & Lighting, 4822 E Cesar Chavez, Austin, TX 78702 Tel: 512-485-3131 Fax: 512-474-6098 E-mail: austin@hdgear.tv Web Site: www.hdgear.tv, pg 769

Gear Monkey, 2650 Walnut Ave, Suite F, Tustin, CA 92780 Tel: 714-705-6088 Toll Free Tel: 877-411-4445 Fax: 714-705-6080 Web Site: www.gearmonkey.tv, pg 769

Gearhead Rentals, 69 O'Conner Rd, Suite 6, Fairport, NY 14450 Tel: 585-236-4272 E-mail: info@gearheadrentals.com Web Site: www.gearheadrentals.com, pg 769

Geddes Productions LLC, PO Box 41761, Los Angeles, CA 90041-0761 Tel: 323-344-8045 Fax: 323-257-7209 E-mail: orders@geddesproduction.com Web Site: www.geddesproduction.com, pg 769

Gefen, 20600 Nordhoff St, Chatsworth, CA 91311 Tel: 818-772-9100 Toll Free Tel: 800-545-6900; 800-472-5555 Fax: 818-772-9120 E-mail: sales@gefen.com; support@gefen.com Web Site: www.gefen.com, pg 769

Gemini, 2000 Penncraft Ct, Ann Arbor, MI 48103 Toll Free Tel: 800-317-9929 Fax: 734-786-4007 E-mail: info@geminichildrensmusic.com Web Site: www.geminichildrensmusic.com, pg 769

Gemini Sound, 107 Trumbull St, Bldg F-8, 2nd fl, Elizabeth, NJ 07206-2171 Tel: 732-346-0061 Fax: 732-346-0065 E-mail: sales@geminisound.com Web Site: www.geminisound.com, pg 769

Gemstone Media Inc, 8280 Princeton Square Blvd W, Suite 4, Jacksonville, FL 32256 Tel: 904-354-1500 E-mail: service@gemstonemediainc.com Web Site: www.gemstonemediainc.com, pg 769

General Audio-Visual Inc (GAVI), 92 E Merrick Rd, Freeport, NY 11520 Tel: 516-623-8500 Fax: 516-623-9155 Web Site: www.gavi.com, pg 769

General Cable, 4 Tesseneer Dr, Highland Heights, KY 41076 Tel: 859-572-8000 E-mail: info@generalcable.com Web Site: www.generalcable.com, pg 769

General Devices Co Inc, 1410 S Post Rd, Indianapolis, IN 46239 Tel: 317-897-7000 Fax: 317-898-2917 E-mail: sales@generaldevices.com Web Site: www.generaldevices.com, pg 769

General Electric Co, 41 Farnsworth St, Boston, MA 02210 Tel: 203-373-2211; 617-443-3000 Web Site: www.ge.com, pg 769

General Production Services, 883 S East St, Anaheim, CA 92805 Tel: 714-535-2271 Fax: 714-535-0952 E-mail: lensclens@yahoo.com; sales@lensclens.com Web Site: www.lensclens.com, pg 769

Genesis Creative, 1006 Hafely St, Cayce, SC 29033 Tel: 803-796-9666 E-mail: geninfo@gencreative.com Web Site: genesisstudiossc.com, pg 769

Genesis Integration, 14721 123 Ave NW, Edmonton, AB T5L 2Y6, Canada Toll Free Tel: 877-283-2253 (Toronto); 866-622-2966 (Quebec); 844-436-4681 (rest of CN) E-mail: marketing@genint.com Web Site: www.genint.com, pg 769

Gary Gentile Productions (GGP), 3 Lehigh Gorge Dr, Jim Thorpe, PA 18229 Tel: 252-394-6974 Web Site: www.ggentile.com, pg 770

A Gentle Wind, 14 S Pine Ave, Albany, NY 12208 Tel: 518-482-9023 Toll Free Tel: 888-FUN-SONG (386-7664, orders) E-mail: hello@gentlewind.com Web Site: www.gentlewind.com, pg 770

Geomatrix Productions, 270 Amity Rd, Woodbridge, CT 06525-2267 Tel: 203-389-0001 E-mail: info@geomatrixproductions.com Web Site: www.geomatrixproductions.com, pg 770

Georgia Film Office, 75 Fifth St W, Suite 1200, Atlanta, GA 30308 Tel: 404-962-4052 Toll Free Tel: 877-SHOOTGA (746-6842) Fax: 404-962-4053 E-mail: film@georgia.org Web Site: www.georgia.org/film, pg 970

Gerriets International, 130 Winterwood Ave, Ewing, NJ 08638 Tel: 609-771-8111 Fax: 609-771-8118 E-mail: info@gerriets.us Web Site: www.gerriets.us, pg 770

GES Audio Visual, 7000 Lindell Rd, Las Vegas, NV 89118 Tel: 702-515-5500 Fax: 702-515-5765 E-mail: lasvegas@ges.com; info@ges.com Web Site: ges.com, pg 770

GestureTek, 317 Adelaide St W, Suite 903, Toronto, ON M5V 1P9, Canada Tel: 416-340-9290 Toll Free Tel: 800-315-1189 Fax: 416-348-9809 E-mail: info@gesturetek.com; sales@gesturetek.com Web Site: www.gesturetek.com, pg 770

Get Smart Products, 30 S Highland Ave, Ossining, NY 10562 Tel: 914-762-3500 Toll Free Tel: 800-827-0673 Fax: 914-923-5818 Toll Free Fax: 866-827-0673 E-mail: getsmart@pfile.com Web Site: www.pfile.com, pg 770

Getty-Dubay Productions, c/o Handwriting Success LLC, PO Box 91088, Portland, OR 97280 Tel: 971-254-8695 E-mail: info@handwritingsuccess.com; info@allport.com (orders) Web Site: www.handwritingsuccess.com; www.allport.com (orders), pg 770

Getty Images, 605 Fifth Ave S, Suite 400, Seattle, WA 98104 Tel: 206-925-5000 Toll Free Tel: 888-588-5889; 800-462-4379 (sales) E-mail: sales.na@gettyimages.com Web Site: www.gettyimages.com, pg 770

Getty Images Music, 75 Varick St, New York, NY 10013 Tel: 646-613-4000 E-mail: music@gettyimages.com Web Site: www.gettyimages.com/music, pg 770

Gettysburg Bluegrass Festival, 3340 Fairfield Rd, Gettysburg, PA 17325 Tel: 717-642-8749 E-mail: bluegrass@granitehillcampingresort.com Web Site: www.gettysburgbluegrass.com, pg 990

Ghent Manufacturing, 2999 Henkle Dr, Lebanon, OH 45036-9260 Tel: 513-932-3445 Toll Free Tel: 800-543-0550 Fax: 513-932-9252 E-mail: customer_service@ghent.com; sales@ghent.com Web Site: www.ghent.com, pg 770

GHO Group LLC, 340 W 55 St, Suite 5E, New York, NY 10019 Tel: 212-319-7716 E-mail: info@ghogroup.com Web Site: www.ghogroup.com, pg 770

Giant Interactive, 133 W 19 St, 3rd fl, New York, NY 10011 Tel: 212-675-7300 E-mail: info@giant-interactive.com Web Site: www.giant-interactive.com, pg 770

Giant Screen Cinema Association (GSCA), 624 Holly Springs Rd, Suite 243, Holly Springs, NC 27540 Tel: 919-346-1123 Fax: 919-573-9100 E-mail: info@giantscreencinema.com Web Site: www.giantscreencinema.com, pg 955

GigaSonic, 260 E Gish Rd, San Jose, CA 95112 Tel: 408-573-1400 Toll Free Tel: 888-246-4442 Fax: 408-573-0602 E-mail: info@gigasonic.com Web Site: www.gigasonic.com, pg 770

Gilderfluke & Co Inc, 205 S Flower St, Burbank, CA 91502 Tel: 818-840-9484 Toll Free Tel: 800-776-5972 Fax: 818-840-9485 E-mail: info@gilderfluke.com Web Site: www.gilderfluke.com, pg 771

Jim Gill Music Inc, PO Box 2263, Oak Park, IL 60303-2263 Tel: 708-763-9864 Fax: 708-763-9888 Web Site: www.jimgill.com, pg 771

Gingerbread Group Holdings LLC, 1337 Kittredge Ct, Atlanta, GA 30329 Tel: 404-634-8678; 404-663-9050 E-mail: books2gogh@gmail.com, pg 771

Glanz Technologies Inc, 687 NE 124 St, North Miami, FL 33161 Tel: 305-893-1269 Fax: 305-899-8526 E-mail: mglanz@glanztech.com Web Site: www.glanztechnologies.com, pg 771

Glendale Media Center, 9494 W Maryland Ave, Glendale, AZ 85305 Tel: 623-930-4512 Web Site: www.glendalemediacenter.com, pg 771

Glendale Production Center, 1239 S Glendale Ave, Glendale, CA 91205 Tel: 818-550-6000 E-mail: info@glendalestudios.com, pg 771

Glenn Photo Supply, 13502 Erwin St, Van Nuys, CA 91401 Tel: 818-997-0410 Web Site: www.emgee.freeyellow.com, pg 771

Glenn Video Vistas Ltd, 13502 Erwin St, Van Nuys, CA 91401 Tel: 818-997-0410 Web Site: www.emgee.freeyellow.com, pg 771

GLI Sound Systems, 2691 W 15 St, Brooklyn, NY 11224 Tel: 718-372-7849 Toll Free Tel: 800-GLI-PRO-1 (454-7761) Fax: 718-946-4151 E-mail: info@glipro.com; sales@glipro.com Web Site: www.glipro.com, pg 771

Glidecam Industries Inc, 23 Joseph St, Kingston, MA 02364 Tel: 781-585-7900 Toll Free Tel: 800-949-2089; 800-600-2011 Fax: 781-585-7903 E-mail: info@glidecam.com Web Site: glidecam.com, pg 771

Glix Entertainment Inc, 503 S Flower St, Burbank, CA 91502 Tel: 323-905-GLIX (905-4549) E-mail: info@glixstudios.com Web Site: www.glixent.com, pg 771

The Global Awards®, 260 W 39 St, 10th fl, New York, NY 10018 Tel: 212-643-4800 Fax: 212-643-0170 E-mail: info@newyorkfestivals.com Web Site: www.theglobalawards.com, pg 990

Global Cyber-Visions, 21 Valley Lane, Venus, FL 33960 Tel: 863-465-0321 E-mail: tvp@thevenusproject.com Web Site: www.thevenusproject.com, pg 771

Global ImageWorks LLC, 65 Beacon St, Haworth, NJ 07641 Tel: 201-384-7715 Fax: 201-501-8971 E-mail: info@globalimageworks.com Web Site: www.globalimageworks.com, pg 771

Global Peace Film Festival (GPFF), PO Box 3310, Winter Park, FL 32790-3310 Tel: 407-582-6018 E-mail: info@peacefilmfest.org Web Site: www.peacefilmfest.org, pg 990

Global TV, 222 23 St NE, Calgary, AB T2E 7N2, Canada Tel: 403-235-7777 E-mail: calgary@globalnews.ca Web Site: www.globaltv.com, pg 771

Global TV, 5325 Allard Way, Edmonton, AB T6H 5B8, Canada Tel: 780-436-1250 Fax: 587-525-9257 E-mail: edmonton@globalnews.ca Web Site: www.globaltv.com, pg 771

GlobalStreams™ Corp, 2432 Heartland Ave, St Louis, MO 63114 Tel: 314-997-5100 Toll Free Tel: 800-788-7205 E-mail: sales@globalstreams.com Web Site: www.globalstreams.com, pg 771

Globe-Miami Film Commission, 1360 N Broad St, US 60, Globe, AZ 85501 Tel: 928-425-4495 Toll Free Tel: 800-804-5623 Fax: 928-425-3410 E-mail: visitorinfo@globemiamichamber.com Web Site: globemiamichamber.com, pg 965

Globe Photos LLC, 6445 Tenaya Way, B-130, Las Vegas, NV 89113 Tel: 702-210-6208 Fax: 631-321-4063 E-mail: info@globephotos.com Web Site: www.globephotos.com, pg 771

Gluskin's Custom Audio Video, 2051 Pacific Ave, Stockton, CA 95204 Tel: 209-888-4609 Fax: 209-888-4629 E-mail: info@gluskinsav.com Web Site: www.gluskins.com; www.gluskinsav.com, pg 771

GMI Productions, One General Mills Blvd, Minneapolis, MN 55426 Tel: 763-764-7600 Toll Free Tel: 800-248-7310 Fax: 763-764-8330 Web Site: www.generalmills.com, pg 771

GMP Music, 1103 North St, Niles, MI 49120 Tel: 269-687-9100 Toll Free Tel: 800-955-0619 Fax: 269-687-9200 E-mail: info@gmpmusic.com Web Site: www.gmpmusic.com; www.reservemusic.com, pg 772

GNP Crescendo Records, 1405 N Avon St, Burbank, CA 91505-1885 Tel: 818-566-8900 E-mail: gnpcrescendo@gmail.com Web Site: www.gnpcrescendo.com, pg 772

Go To Team, 665 Johnnie Dodds Blvd, Suite 201, Mount Pleasant, SC 29464 Tel: 843-884-6222 Toll Free Tel: 888-455-4333 E-mail: crew@gototeam.com Web Site: www.gototeam.com, pg 772

Goal Productions, 1905 Victory Blvd, Suite 6, Glendale, CA 91201 Tel: 818-588-3900 Fax: 818-588-3903 E-mail: info@goalproductions.com Web Site: www.goalproductions.com, pg 772

Goddard Design Co, 51 Nassau Ave, Brooklyn, NY 11222 Tel: 718-599-0170 Fax: 718-599-0172 E-mail: sales@goddarddesign.com Web Site: www.goddarddesign.com, pg 772

The Godfrey Group Inc, 113 Roseroot Ct, Holly Springs, NC 27540 Tel: 919-544-6504 Toll Free Tel: 800-789-9394 E-mail: sales@godfreygroup.com Web Site: www.godfreygroup.com, pg 772

Gold Line/TEF, PO Box 500, West Redding, CT 06896-0500 Tel: 203-938-2588 Fax: 203-938-8740 E-mail: sales@gold-line.com Web Site: www.gold-line.com, pg 772

Gold Link Productions Inc, 1457 Pembroke Dr, Oakville, ON L6H 1V6, Canada Tel: 416-560-3864 E-mail: goldlinkproductions@gmail.com; info@torontocameramanservices.com Web Site: www.torontocameramanservices.com, pg 772

Gold Standard Productions, 12952 Miriam Place, Santa Ana, CA 92705-1334 Tel: 714-544-7000 Fax: 714-544-7010 Web Site: www.goldstandardproductions.com, pg 772

Goldberg Brothers Inc, 10488 W Centennial Rd, Suite 100, Littleton, CO 80127 Tel: 303-321-1099 E-mail: reelservice@goldbergbrothers.com Web Site: www.goldbergbrothers.com, pg 772

Bruce Goldberg Inc, 5354 Quakertown Ave, Woodland Hills, CA 91364 Tel: 818-713-8190 Toll Free Tel: 800-527-6248 Fax: 818-704-9189 E-mail: drbg@sbcglobal.net Web Site: www.drbrucegoldberg.com, pg 772

Golden Gate Awards, c/o San Francisco Film Society, The Presidio, Suite 110, 39 Mesa St, San Francisco, CA 94129-1025 Tel: 415-561-5000 Fax: 415-440-1760 E-mail: info@sffilm.org; gga@sffilm.org Web Site: sffilm.org/sffilm-festival/, pg 990

Golden Gate Studios, 100 Pelican Way, Suite E, San Rafael, CA 94901 Tel: 415-485-5856 Fax: 415-256-9262 Web Site: www.goldengatestudios.com, pg 772

Golden Globe Awards, 646 N Robertson Blvd, West Hollywood, CA 90069 Tel: 310-657-1731 Fax: 310-657-5576 E-mail: awards@goldenglobes.com Web Site: www.goldenglobes.com, pg 990

Golden Lamb Productions, 47 Schoolhouse Rd, Nassau, NY 12123 Tel: 518-766-4358 Web Site: www.glpvideoproduction.com, pg 772

Golden Mike Award, 125 W 55 St, 4th fl, New York, NY 10019-5366 Tel: 212-373-8250 Fax: 212-373-8254 E-mail: info@thebfoa.org Web Site: www.thebfoa.org; broadcastersfoundation.org, pg 990

Golden Reel Awards, 10061 Riverside Dr, PMB 751, Toluca Lake, CA 91602-2550 Tel: 818-506-7731 Fax: 818-506-7732 E-mail: office@mpse.org Web Site: www.mpse.org, pg 990

Golden Reel Awards, 6 Beach Rd, 544, Tiburon, CA 94920 Tel: 415-251-8433 Fax: 253-663-1250 E-mail: info@tiburonfilmfestival.com Web Site: www.tiburonfilmfestival.com, pg 990

Golden Sheaf Awards, 49 Smith St E, Yorkton, SK S3N 0H4, Canada Tel: 306-782-7077 Fax: 306-782-1550 E-mail: info@yorktonfilm.com Web Site: yorktonfilm.com/golden-sheaf-awards/, pg 991

Golden Space Needle Awards, 305 Harrison St, Seattle, WA 98109 Tel: 206-464-5830 Fax: 206-264-7919 E-mail: info@siff.net; entries@siff.net Web Site: www.siff.net, pg 991

Golden State Dance Teachers Association (GSDTA), 10804 Woodruff Ave, Downey, CA 90241-3910 Tel: 562-869-8949 Web Site: www.swingworld.com, pg 772

Golf Digest Publications, One World Trade Center, 27th fl, New York, NY 10007-0090 Tel: 212-286-2860 Toll Free Tel: 800-962-5513 Web Site: www.golfdigest.com, pg 772

Goose Creek Music & Entertainment, 17723 Tranquility Rd, Purcellville, VA 20132 Tel: 540-751-1395 E-mail: info@goosecreekmusic.com Web Site: www.goosecreekmusic.com, pg 772

Alan Gordon Enterprises Inc, 5625 Melrose Ave, Hollywood, CA 90038 Tel: 323-466-3561 Fax: 323-871-2193 E-mail: contactus@alangordon.com Web Site: www.alangordon.com, pg 772

Gordon Productions Inc, 469 Magellan Ave, San Francisco, CA 94116 Tel: 415-776-7484 Web Site: www.gpvideo.com; www.vimeo.com/gordonproductions, pg 772

Gospel Folio Press, 304 Killaly St W, Port Colborne, ON L3K 6A6, Canada Tel: 905-835-9166 Toll Free Tel: 800-952-2382 Fax: 905-834-0012 E-mail: info@gospelfolio.com; orders@gospelfolio.com Web Site: www.gospelfolio.com, pg 773

Gotham Sound & Communications Inc, 35-10 36 Ave, 2nd fl, Long Island City, NY 11106 Tel: 212-629-9430 Toll Free Tel: 866-468-4268 Fax: 212-629-9436 E-mail: nyc@gothamsound.com Web Site: www.gothamsound.com, pg 773

Government of New Brunswick Department of Tourism, Heritage & Culture, Marysville Place, 20 McGloin St, 4th fl, Fredericton, NB E3A 5T8, Canada Tel: 506-453-3115 Fax: 506-444-5760 E-mail: thctpcinfo@gnb.ca Web Site: www2.gnb.ca, pg 978

GP Studios, 133 Peachtree St NE, 1st fl, Atlanta, GA 30303 Tel: 404-652-5690 E-mail: gpstudios@gapac.com Web Site: www.gpstudios.tv, pg 773

Grace Church - St Louis, 2695 Creve Coeur Mill Rd, Maryland Heights, MO 63043 Tel: 314-292-8300 Fax: 314-291-0918 E-mail: info@gracestl.org Web Site: www.gracestl.org, pg 773

The Gracies®, 2365 Harrodsburg Rd, A-325, Lexington, KY 40504 Tel: 202-750-3664 Fax: 202-750-3664 E-mail: gracies@allwomeninmedia.org Web Site: allwomeninmedia.org/gracies, pg 991

Grafco Inc, 2018 W Main St, Stroudsburg, PA 18360 Toll Free Tel: 800-367-6169 Fax: 570-213-0369 Toll Free Fax: 800-443-4329 E-mail: info@toledofurniture.com Web Site: www.toledofurniture.com, pg 773

Graftek Imaging Inc, 8900 Shoal Creek Blvd, Bldg 300, Suite B, Austin, TX 78757 Tel: 512-416-1099 Toll Free Tel: 800-441-2118 Fax: 512-416-1014 E-mail: graftek@graftek.com Web Site: www.graftek.com, pg 773

Grammy Awards, 3030 Olympic Blvd, Santa Monica, CA 90404 Tel: 310-392-3777 E-mail: communications@grammy.com Web Site: www.grammy.org; www.grammy.com, pg 991

Grand Stage Co Inc, 3418 N Knox Ave, Chicago, IL 60641 Tel: 312-332-5611 Toll Free Tel: 800-621-2181 Fax: 312-332-3655 E-mail: marketing@grandstage.com Web Site: www.grandstage.com, pg 773

Grande Vitesse Systems Inc (GVS), 390 Fremont St, San Francisco, CA 94105-2316 Tel: 415-777-0320; 415-777-9937 (intl); 917-744-4270 (rental); 818-823-1760

(sales) *Toll Free Tel:* 800-794-4622 (sales) *Fax:* 415-777-9544 *Web Site:* www.gvs9000.com; www.gvsf.com, pg 773

GRANGER - Historical Picture Archive, 25 Chapel St, Suite 605, New York, NY 11201 *Tel:* 212-447-1789 *Fax:* 212-447-1492 *E-mail:* grangerinfo@granger.com *Web Site:* www.granger.com, pg 773

Graphic Artists Guild Inc, 31 W 34 St, 8th fl, New York, NY 10001 *Tel:* 212-791-3400 *E-mail:* admin@graphicartistsguild.org; membership@graphicartistsguild.org *Web Site:* graphicartistsguild.org, pg 955

Graphic Laminating LLC, 6185 Cochran Rd, Solon, OH 44139 *Tel:* 440-498-3400 *Toll Free Tel:* 800-345-5300 *Fax:* 440-498-3410 *E-mail:* info@graphiclaminating.com *Web Site:* www.graphiclaminating.com, pg 773

Graphx Inc, 400 W Cummings Park, Woburn, MA 01801 *Tel:* 781-932-0430 *Fax:* 781-932-0855 *E-mail:* support@graphx.com *Web Site:* photogize.net, pg 773

Grass Valley, 3499 Douglas-B-Floreani, Montreal, QC H4S 2C6, Canada *Tel:* 514-333-1772 *Fax:* 514-333-9828 *Web Site:* www.grassvalley.com, pg 773

Gravity Media, 7701 Haskell Ave, Van Nuys, CA 91406 *Tel:* 818-955-9449; 747-258-4100 *Fax:* 818-955-9779 *E-mail:* enquiries@gravitymedia.com *Web Site:* www.gravitymedia.com, pg 773

Great Chefs/Leisure Jazz Video, 747 Magazine St, New Orleans, LA 70130 *Tel:* 504-581-5000 *Toll Free Tel:* 800-321-1499 *Fax:* 504-581-1188 *E-mail:* info@greatchefs.com *Web Site:* www.greatchefs.com, pg 773

Great Recordings LLC, 1812 Procter St, Port Arthur, TX 77640 *Tel:* 409-982-7121 *E-mail:* music@great-recordings.com *Web Site:* www.great-recordings.com, pg 773

Great River Electronics, 164 Hardman Ave S, South St Paul, MN 55075 *Tel:* 651-455-1846 *Fax:* 651-455-3224 *E-mail:* info@greweb.com *Web Site:* www.greatriverelectronics.com, pg 773

The Great Southern Studios, 15221 NE 21 Ave, North Miami Beach, FL 33162 *Tel:* 305-944-2464 *Fax:* 305-944-9920 *E-mail:* info@gssmiami.com *Web Site:* www.greatsouthernstudios.com, pg 773

Greater Cincinnati & Northern Kentucky Film Commission, 1106 Race St, Cincinnati, OH 45202 *Tel:* 513-784-1744 *Web Site:* www.filmcincinnati.com, pg 974

Greater Fort Lauderdale/Broward Office of Film, Music, Fashion & Create, 101 NE Third Ave, Suite 100, Fort Lauderdale, FL 33301 *Tel:* 954-767-2467 *Fax:* 954-767-4681 *E-mail:* film@broward.org *Web Site:* www.sunny.org/film, pg 969

Greater Grass Valley Chamber of Commerce, 128 E Main St, Grass Valley, CA 95945 *Tel:* 530-273-4667 *Fax:* 530-272-5440 *Web Site:* www.grassvalleychamber.com, pg 966

Greater Philadelphia Film Office, One Parkway Bldg, 11th fl, 1515 Arch St, Philadelphia, PA 19102 *Tel:* 215-686-2668 *Fax:* 215-686-3659 *E-mail:* mail@film.org *Web Site:* www.film.org, pg 975

Greater Wichita Convention & Visitors Bureau/Wichita Film Commission, 515 S Main St, Wichita, KS 67202 *Tel:* 316-265-2800 *Toll Free Tel:* 800-288-9424 *Fax:* 316-265-0162 *E-mail:* wfc@visitwichita.com *Web Site:* www.visitwichita.com, pg 971

William Greaves Productions Inc, 475 W 57 St, No 17A, New York, NY 10019 *Toll Free Tel:* 800-874-8314 *Fax:* 212-315-0027 *Web Site:* www.williamgreaves.com, pg 774

Greeley/Weld Film Commission, 902 Seventh Ave, Greeley, CO 80631 *Tel:* 970-352-3566 *Toll Free Tel:* 800-449-3866 *Fax:* 970-352-3572 *E-mail:* info@greeleycvb.org *Web Site:* www.greeleychamber.com; www.visitgreeley.org, pg 968

Green Dot Audio Electronics, PO Box 290609, Nashville, TN 37229-0609 *Tel:* 615-366-5964 *Fax:* 615-366-7069 *E-mail:* greendotaudio@bellsouth.net *Web Site:* www.greendotaudio.com, pg 774

Green Mountain Post Films (GMP), PO Box 229, Turners Falls, MA 01376-0229 *Tel:* 413-863-4754 *Fax:* 413-863-8248 *E-mail:* info@gmpfilms.com *Web Site:* www.gmpfilms.com, pg 774

Greenery Studios, 7764 San Fernando Rd, Burbank, CA 91352 *Tel:* 818-253-9990 *E-mail:* info@greenerystudios.com *Web Site:* greenerystudios.com, pg 774

Greenwich Entertainment, 610 Fifth Ave, 3rd fl, New York, NY 10020 *E-mail:* info@greenwichentertainment.com; booking@greenwichentertainment.com; publicity@greenwichentertainment.com; acquisitions@greenwichentertainment.com *Web Site:* greenwichentertainment.com, pg 774

Greenwood Convention & Visitors Bureau & Film Commission, 225 Howard St, Greenwood, MS 38935 *Tel:* 662-453-9197 *Web Site:* www.visitgreenwood.com, pg 972

Griesinger Films LLC, 7300 Old Mill Rd, Gates Mills, OH 44040 *Tel:* 440-423-1601 *Toll Free Tel:* 800-872-4456 *Fax:* 440-423-1601 *E-mail:* orders@griesingerfilms.com *Web Site:* www.griesingerfilms.com, pg 774

Griffith Productions, 1750 Donelson Dr, Eads, TN 38028 *Tel:* 901-351-1899 *Fax:* 901-465-1787 *E-mail:* info@griffithproductions.tv *Web Site:* www.griffithproductions.tv, pg 774

Beatrice E Griggs Elementary Administrator's Award, 6021 State Farm Rd, Guilderland, NY 12084 *Tel:* 518-432-6952 *Toll Free Tel:* 800-252-6952 *Fax:* 518-427-1697 *E-mail:* info@nyla.org *Web Site:* www.nyla.org, pg 991

Griggs Productions Inc, Kappas Marina, 29 W Pier, Sausalito, CA 94965 *Tel:* 415-999-1079 *Toll Free Tel:* 800-210-4200 *Web Site:* www.griggs.com, pg 774

Grise Audio Visual Center Inc, 2402 Cherry St, Erie, PA 16502 *Tel:* 814-452-4465 *E-mail:* grise@erie.net *Web Site:* griseav.com, pg 774

GrooveWorx, 1200 Chickory Lane, Santa Monica, CA 90049 *Tel:* 310-260-2626 *Fax:* 310-260-2662 *E-mail:* info@grooveworx.com *Web Site:* grooveworx.com, pg 774

Group One Ltd, 70 Sea Lane, Farmingdale, NY 11735 *Tel:* 631-396-0195 (audio div); 631-396-0184 (lighting div) *Fax:* 631-396-0190 *E-mail:* sales@g1limited.com *Web Site:* www.g1limited.com, pg 774

Group PVP, 296 Saint Pierre St, Matane, QC G4W 2B9, Canada *Tel:* 418-566-2040 *Toll Free Tel:* 877-320-2040 *Fax:* 418-562-4643 *E-mail:* info@pvp.ca *Web Site:* www.pvp.ca, pg 774

GTI (Graphic Technology Inc), PO Box 3138, Newburgh, NY 12550-0651 *Tel:* 845-562-7066 *Toll Free Tel:* 888-562-7066 *Fax:* 845-562-2543 *E-mail:* sales@gtilite.com *Web Site:* www.gtilite.com, pg 774

Guerrilla Productions LLC, 1119 E 50 St, Savannah, GA 31404 *Tel:* 912-354-1518 *Fax:* 404-585-5692 *E-mail:* info@guerrillapro.com *Web Site:* guerrillapro.com, pg 774

Guidance Associates Inc Center for Humanities, 31 Pine View Rd, Mount Kisco, NY 10549 *Tel:* 914-420-2363 *Toll Free Tel:* 800-431-1242 *Fax:* 914-666-5319 *Web Site:* www.guidanceassociates.com, pg 774

Guild of Italian American Actors (GIAA), 1026A Shetland Dr, Lakewood, NJ 08701 *Tel:* 201-344-3411 *E-mail:* info@giaa.us *Web Site:* www.giaa.us, pg 955

Guilford Publications, 370 Seventh Ave, Suite 1200, New York, NY 10001-1020 *Tel:* 212-431-9800 *Toll Free Tel:* 800-365-7006 *Fax:* 212-966-6708 *E-mail:* info@guilford.com *Web Site:* www.guilford.com, pg 774

Guymark Studios LLC, 3019 Dixwell Ave, Hamden, CT 06518 *Tel:* 203-248-9323 *Fax:* 203-248-9325 *E-mail:* guymark.studios@snet.net *Web Site:* www.guymarkstudios.com, pg 775

GVISION USA Inc, 20532 Crescent Bay Dr, Lake Forest, CA 92630 *Tel:* 949-586-3338 *Fax:* 949-272-4594 *E-mail:* info@gvision-usa.com *Web Site:* gvision-usa.com, pg 775

Gyration, 3601 Calle Tecate, Suite B, Camarillo, CA 93012 *Toll Free Tel:* 888-340-0033 (tech support) *E-mail:* gsupport@smkusa.com; info@smkusa.com *Web Site:* www.gyration.com, pg 775

Howard Hall Productions, 2171 La Amatista Rd, Del Mar, CA 92014-3031 *Tel:* 858-259-8989 *Web Site:* www.howardhall.com, pg 775

Hall Productions, 951 Front St, Grover Beach, CA 93433 *Tel:* 805-473-1042 *Fax:* 805-473-2202 *Web Site:* hallpro.com, pg 775

Hallel Communications, Hallel Institute, 175 Rte 340, Sparkill, NY 10976-1047 *Tel:* 845-365-2277 *Toll Free Tel:* 800-445-7477 *Fax:* 845-365-2279 *E-mail:* hallel@hallel.net; info@hallelvideos.com *Web Site:* www.hallelvideos.com, pg 775

Steven Halpern's Inner Peace Music, PO Box 2644, San Anselmo, CA 94979-2644 *Toll Free Tel:* 800-909-0707 (orders) *E-mail:* info@innerpeacemusic.com *Web Site:* www.innerpeacemusic.com, pg 775

Hamilton Studio, 1427 W Dean Ave, Spokane, WA 99201 *Tel:* 509-327-9501 *E-mail:* info@hamiltonstudio.com *Web Site:* www.hamiltonstudio.com, pg 775

HamiltonBuhl, 80 Little Falls Rd, Fairfield, NJ 07004 *Toll Free Tel:* 800-631-0868 *Toll Free Fax:* 800-398-1812 (cust serv & sales) *E-mail:* customerservice@hamiltonbuhl.com; info@hamiltonbuhl.com; sales@hamiltonbuhl.com *Web Site:* www.hamiltonbuhl.com, pg 775

Hammond Communications Group Inc, 173 Trade St, Lexington, KY 40511 *Tel:* 859-254-1878 *E-mail:* info@hammondcg.com *Web Site:* hammondcg.com, pg 775

Hampshire Street Studios, 540A Hampshire St, San Francisco, CA 94110 *Tel:* 415-643-5580 *E-mail:* info@hampshirestreetstudios.com *Web Site:* www.hampshirestreetstudios.com, pg 775

The Hamptons International Film Festival, 47 Newtown Lane, East Hampton, NY 11937 *Tel:* 631-324-4600 *Fax:* 631-324-1558 *E-mail:* info@hamptonsfilmfest.org; programming@hamptonsfilmfest.org (submissions) *Web Site:* hamptonsfilmfest.org, pg 991

Hand Held Films, 129 W 27 St, New York, NY 10001 *Tel:* 212-627-2781; 212-502-0900 (rentals) *Fax:* 212-502-0906 (rentals) *E-mail:* rentals@handheldfilms.com *Web Site:* handheldfilms.com, pg 775

Howard Hanger, 31 Park Ave N, Asheville, NC 28801 *Tel:* 828-280-8419 *E-mail:* howardhangerhall@gmail.com *Web Site:* www.contacthoward.com, pg 775

Terry Hanley Audio Systems Inc, 20 Industrial Pkwy, Woburn, MA 01801 *Tel:* 781-932-5300 *Fax:* 781-932-5354 *E-mail:* mail@terryhanleyaudio.com *Web Site:* www.terryhanleyaudio.com, pg 775

G W Hannaway & Associates, 839 Pearl St, Boulder, CO 80302 *Tel:* 303-440-9631 *Fax:* 303-440-4421 *E-mail:* sales@gwha.com; services@gwha.com; technology@gwha.com *Web Site:* www.gwha.com, pg 775

Hannay Reels Inc, 553 State Rte 143, Westerlo, NY 12193-0159 *Tel:* 518-797-3791 *Toll Free Tel:* 877-467-3357 *Fax:* 518-797-3259 *Toll Free Fax:* 800-733-5464 *E-mail:* reels@hannay.com *Web Site:* www.hannay.com, pg 775

Hannecke Display Systems Inc, 210 Grove St, Franklin, MA 02038 *Tel:* 774-235-2329 *Fax:* 508-528-0913 *E-mail:* info@hannecke.com *Web Site:* www.hannecke.de/us, pg 775

Hanovia Specialty Lighting LLC, 6 Evans St, Fairfield, NJ 07004 *Tel:* 973-651-5510 *Fax:* 973-651-5550 *E-mail:* sales@hanovia-uv.com *Web Site:* www.hanovia-uv.com, pg 775

Harbro Corp, 2691 W 15 St, Brooklyn, NY 11224-2705 *Tel:* 718-946-4134 *Toll Free Tel:* 800-GLI-PRO-1 (454-7761) *Fax:* 718-946-4151 *E-mail:* info@glipro. com *Web Site:* www.glipro.com, pg 776

Hard Hat Radio Music Service, 519 N Halifax Ave, Daytona Beach, FL 32118-4017 *Tel:* 386-252-0381 *Fax:* 386-252-0381 *E-mail:* hardhatrecords@aol. com; hardhatrecords@bellsouth.net *Web Site:* www. hardhatrecords.com, pg 776

Hardcastle Films & Video, 7319 Wise Ave, St Louis, MO 63117-1718 *Tel:* 314-647-4200, pg 776

Hargrove Inc, One Hargrove Dr, Lanham, MD 20706 *Tel:* 301-306-9000 *Fax:* 301-306-9318 *E-mail:* exhibitorservices@hargroveinc.com *Web Site:* www.hargroveinc.com, pg 776

Harman International Industries Inc, 400 Atlantic St, 15th fl, Stamford, CT 06901 *Tel:* 203-328-3500 *Web Site:* www.harman.com, pg 776

Harman Professional Solutions, 8500 Balboa Blvd, Northridge, CA 91329 *Tel:* 818-893-8411 *Toll Free Tel:* 888-234-5450 (order support) *Fax:* 818-830-2921 *E-mail:* info@harman.com *Web Site:* www.harman. com; shop.harmanpro.com; pro.harman.com, pg 776

Harmonia Mundi USA, 1117 Chestnut St, Burbank, CA 91506 *Tel:* 818-333-1500 *E-mail:* info-usa@ harmoniamundi.com *Web Site:* www.harmoniamundi. com, pg 776

Harmon's Audio-Visual Services, 2533 Crystal Dr, Fort Myers, FL 33966 *Tel:* 239-939-2273 *Fax:* 239-939-5966 *E-mail:* info@harmonsav.com *Web Site:* www. harmonsav.com, pg 776

Harnel Case Co, 1600 Marshall Ave SE, Grand Rapids, MI 49507 *Tel:* 616-452-4522 *Fax:* 616-452-5514 *E-mail:* info@harnelcase.com *Web Site:* www. harnelcase.com, pg 776

HarperAudio, 10 E 53 St, New York, NY 10022 *Tel:* 212-207-7000 *Toll Free Tel:* 800-242-7737 *Fax:* 212-207-2582 *Toll Free Fax:* 800-822-4090 *Web Site:* www.harpercollins.com, pg 776

Harpers Ferry Historical Association, c/o National Park Bookshop, 723 Shenandoah St, Harpers Ferry, WV 25425 *Tel:* 304-535-6881 *Fax:* 304-535-6749 *E-mail:* info@hfpawv.org *Web Site:* www. harpersferryhistory.org, pg 776

Harris Communications Inc, 15155 Technology Dr, Eden Prairie, MN 55344 *Tel:* 952-906-1180 *Toll Free Tel:* 800-825-6758 *Fax:* 952-906-1099 *E-mail:* info@ harriscomm.com *Web Site:* www.harriscomm.com, pg 776

Harris Corp, 1025 W NASA Blvd, Melbourne, FL 32919-0001 *Tel:* 321-727-9100 *E-mail:* webmaster@ harris.com *Web Site:* www.harris.com, pg 776

Harrison Brothers, 47 N Chatham Pkwy, Chapel Hill, NC 27517 *Toll Free Tel:* 866-386-8335; 800-327-4414 *Toll Free Fax:* 800-327-6651 *E-mail:* info@ harrisonbros.com *Web Site:* www.thetapeworks.com, pg 776

Harrison Consoles, 1024 Firestone Pkwy, La Vergne, TN 37086-3505 *Tel:* 615-641-7200 *Fax:* 615-641-7224 *E-mail:* info@harrisonconsoles.com *Web Site:* www. harrisonconsoles.com, pg 776

Hartley Film Foundation, 49 Richmondville Ave, Suite 204, Westport, CT 06880 *Tel:* 203-226-9500 *Toll Free Tel:* 800-937-1819 *Fax:* 203-227-6938 *E-mail:* info@ hartleyfoundation.org *Web Site:* hartleyfoundation.org, pg 776

Hasselblad Bron Inc, 1080A Garden State Rd, Union, NJ 07083 *Tel:* 908-754-5800 *Toll Free Tel:* 800-367-6434; 800-456-0203 *Fax:* 908-754-5807 *E-mail:* sales@ hasselbladbron.com; servicedept@hasselbladbron.com; productinfo@hasselbladbron.com *Web Site:* www. hasselbladbron.com, pg 776

Havana Film Festival New York (HFFNY), 4 W 43 St, Suite 304, New York, NY 10036 *Tel:* 212-687-2146 *Fax:* 212-681-8037 *E-mail:* info@hffny.com; afflc.org; press@hffny.com *Web Site:* www.hffny.com, pg 991

Havas Creative, 200 Hudson St, New York, NY 10013 *Tel:* 212-886-2000; 212-886-4100 *Fax:* 212-886-5013 *Web Site:* havas.com, pg 776

Havas Edge, 2386 Faraday Ave, Suite 200, Carlsbad, CA 92008 *Tel:* 760-929-0041 *E-mail:* info@havasedge. com *Web Site:* www.havasedge.com, pg 777

HAVE Inc, 309 Power Ave, Hudson, NY 12534 *Tel:* 518-828-2000 *Toll Free Tel:* 888-999-HAVE (999-4283) *Fax:* 518-828-2008 *E-mail:* pro_sales@haveinc. com; have@haveinc.com *Web Site:* www.haveinc.com, pg 777

Hawaii International Film Festival, 680 Iwilei Rd, Suite 100, Honolulu, HI 96817 *Tel:* 808-792-1577 (ext 7) *Fax:* 808-792-1583 *Toll Free Tel:* 877-749-7783 *E-mail:* info@hiff.org; entries@hiff.org *Web Site:* www.hiff.org, pg 991

Hawaii Island Film Office, 25 Aupuni St, Rm 1301, Hilo, HI 96720 *Tel:* 808-961-8369; 808-961-8366 *Fax:* 808-935-1205 *Web Site:* hawaiiislandfilm.com, pg 970

Hawaii Sound & Vision, PO Box 2267, Kailua-Kona, HI 96745 *Tel:* 808-982-8330 *Toll Free Tel:* 877-982-8330 *Fax:* 808-982-8340 *E-mail:* aloha@hawaiisav.com *Web Site:* www.hawaiisav.com, pg 777

Hay House Inc, PO Box 5100, Carlsbad, CA 92018-5100 *Tel:* 760-431-7695 (ext 2, intl) *Toll Free Tel:* 800-654-5126 (ext 2, US); 800-650-5115 *Web Site:* www.hayhouse.com, pg 777

Hayden 5 Media LLC, 22 W 27 St, 6th fl, New York, NY 10001 *Tel:* 212-871-9316 *E-mail:* hi@hayden5. com *Web Site:* www.hayden5.com, pg 777

Hazelden Publishing & Educational Services, 15251 Pleasant Valley Rd, Center City, MN 55012-0011 *Tel:* 651-213-4215 *Toll Free Tel:* 800-328-9000 *Fax:* 651-213-4404 *E-mail:* info@hazelden.org; customersupport@hazelden.org *Web Site:* www. hazeldenbettyford.org, pg 777

HB Communications Inc, 60 Dodge Ave, North Haven, CT 06473 *Tel:* 203-234-9246 *Toll Free Tel:* 800-243-4414 *Fax:* 203-234-2013 *E-mail:* info@ hbcommunications.com *Web Site:* hbcommunications. com, pg 777

HB-Content, 105 Butler St, Suite 2B, Brooklyn, NY 11231 *Tel:* 212-213-8824 *E-mail:* hb@hb-content. com *Web Site:* www.hb-content.com; vimeopro. com/hbcontent, pg 777

HBO Home Entertainment Inc, 1100 Avenue of the Americas, New York, NY 10036 *Tel:* 212-512-1000 *Web Site:* www.hbo.com, pg 777

HBO Studio Productions, 120-A E 23 St, New York, NY 10010 *Tel:* 212-512-7800 *Web Site:* www.hbostudio. com, pg 777

HD Cinema, 12233 W Olympic Blvd, Suite 158, Los Angeles, CA 90064 *Tel:* 310-430-9450 *Fax:* 310-499-5237 (efax) *Web Site:* www.hd-cinema.com, pg 777

HD House, 6312 NW 77 Ct, Miami, FL 33166 *Tel:* 305-597-7359 *Fax:* 305-597-7027 *Web Site:* thehdhouse. com, pg 777

HD Source, 1670 Enterprise Rd, Mississauga, ON L4W 4L4, Canada *Tel:* 905-890-6905; 905-290-4430 (ZTV rentals) *E-mail:* info@hdsource.ca *Web Site:* www. hdsource.ca, pg 777

HDrental.com, 16129 Covello St, Van Nuys, CA 91406 *Tel:* 818-994-3461 *Web Site:* hdrental.com, pg 777

HDTV Productions Inc, 132-250 Shawville Blvd SE, No 209, Calgary, AB T2Y 2Z7, Canada *Tel:* 403-931-1936 *Web Site:* www.hdtvproductions.com, pg 777

Headlight Audio Visual Inc, 74 Evergreen Dr, Portland, ME 04103-1066 *Tel:* 207-774-5998 *Toll Free Tel:* 800-247-0540 *Fax:* 207-774-4917 *Web Site:* www. headlightav.com, pg 777

Headroom Digital Audio, 11 E 26 St, 19th fl, New York, NY 10010 *Tel:* 212-246-8400 *E-mail:* info@ headroom.nyc *Web Site:* www.headroom.nyc, pg 777

Health Communications Inc, 3201 SW 15 St, Deerfield Beach, FL 33442-8124 *Tel:* 954-360-0909 *Toll Free Tel:* 800-441-5569 *Fax:* 954-360-0034 *Web Site:* www. hcibooks.com, pg 778

Health Education Services, 10200 Jefferson Blvd, Culver City, CA 90232 *Tel:* 310-839-2436 *Toll Free Tel:* 800-421-4246 *Fax:* 310-839-2249 *Toll Free Fax:* 800-944-5432 *E-mail:* access@socialstudies.com; customerservice@socialstudies.com *Web Site:* www. socialstudies.com, pg 778

Hearing Loss Association of America (HLAA), 7910 Woodmont Ave, Suite 1200, Bethesda, MD 20814 *Tel:* 301-657-2248 *Fax:* 301-913-9413 *E-mail:* inquiry@hearingloss.org *Web Site:* www. hearingloss.org, pg 778

Hearst Entertainment & Syndication, 300 W 57 St, New York, NY 10019-5238 *Web Site:* www.hearst. com/entertainment-syndication, pg 778

Heart Breaker Entertainment LLC, 10094 Lacy Rd, Hagerstown, IN 47346 *Tel:* 765-489-4048; 765-489-5558 *Toll Free Tel:* 800-843-3635 *Fax:* 765-489-4899 *E-mail:* info@videodj.com *Web Site:* videodj.com, pg 778

Heart Music Inc, PO Box 160326, Austin, TX 78716-0326 *Tel:* 512-795-2375 *Fax:* 512-795-9573 *E-mail:* info@heartmusic.com *Web Site:* www. heartmusic.com, pg 778

Heartland International Film Festival, 1043 Virginia Ave, Suite 2, Indianapolis, IN 46203 *Tel:* 317-464-9405 *E-mail:* submissions@heartlandfilm.org *Web Site:* heartlandfilm.org/festival, pg 991

Heavy Melody, 307 Seventh Ave, Suite 1203, New York, NY 10001 *Tel:* 212-675-9585 *Fax:* 212-675-9565 *E-mail:* contact_hm@heavymelodymusic.com (studio inquiries) *Web Site:* www.heavymelodymusic.com, pg 778

Hedquist Productions Inc, PO Box 1475, Fairfield, IA 52556-1475 *Tel:* 641-472-6708 *Toll Free Fax:* 855-510-5726 *Web Site:* www.hedquist.com, pg 778

Heffernan Audio Visual, 616 W Rhapsody, San Antonio, TX 78216 *Tel:* 210-732-4333, pg 778

Grant Heilman Photography Inc, 506 W Lincoln Ave, Lititz, PA 17543 *Tel:* 717-626-0296 *Toll Free Tel:* 800-622-2046 *Fax:* 717-626-0971 *E-mail:* info@ heilmanphoto.com *Web Site:* www.heilmanphoto.com, pg 778

Heinemann, 361 Hanover St, Portsmouth, NH 03801-3912 *Tel:* 603-431-7894 *Toll Free Tel:* 800-225-5800 *Fax:* 603-431-2214 *Toll Free Fax:* 877-231-6980 *E-mail:* custserv@heinemann.com *Web Site:* www. heinemann.com, pg 778

Heliotrope Studios, 44 Oak St, Newton Upper Falls, MA 02464 *Tel:* 617-964-8181 *E-mail:* heliotropestudios@ earthlink.net *Web Site:* www.heliotropestudios.com, pg 778

Helix Camera & Video, 100 N Walnut St, Itasca, IL 60134 *Tel:* 312-421-6000 *Toll Free Tel:* 800-33-HELIX (334-3549 orders) *Fax:* 312-421-1586 *E-mail:* info@helixcamera.com *Web Site:* www. helixcamera.com, pg 778

Hellman Associates Inc, 1225 W Fourth St, Waterloo, IA 50702 *Tel:* 319-234-7055 *Toll Free Tel:* 800-747-7055 *Fax:* 319-234-2089 *E-mail:* info@hellman.com *Web Site:* www.hellman.com, pg 778

Hello World Communications, 118 W 22 St, 2nd fl, New York, NY 10011 *Tel:* 212-243-8800 *Fax:* 212-691-6961 *E-mail:* excitable01@gmail.com *Web Site:* hwc. tv, pg 778

HeloAir Inc, 5721 Gulfstream Rd, Richmond, VA 23250 *Tel:* 804-226-3400 *Toll Free Tel:* 888-FLY-HELO (359-4356) *Fax:* 804-226-3494 *E-mail:* info@heloair. com *Web Site:* www.heloair.com, pg 778

Henninger Media Services, 1320 N Courthouse Rd, Suite 130, Arlington, VA 22201 *Tel:* 703-243-3444 *Toll Free Tel:* 888-243-3444 *E-mail:* info@henninger.com *Web Site:* www.henninger.com, pg 779

Henry Engineering, PO Box 3796, Seal Beach, CA 90740 *Tel:* 562-493-3589 *Web Site:* www.henryeng. com, pg 779

Henry's Camera, 119 Church St, Toronto, ON M5C 2G5, Canada Tel: 416-941-0579 Toll Free Tel: 800-461-7960 Fax: 416-868-4951 Toll Free Tel: 800-645-6431 E-mail: info@henrys.com, Web Site: www.henrys.com, pg 779

Greg Hensley Productions, 200 S "E" Ave, Unit 113, New Castle, CO 81647 Tel: 970-984-3158 E-mail: hensley@sopris.net, pg 779

Her Own Words LLC, PO Box 5264, Madison, WI 53705-0264 Tel: 608-271-7083 Fax: 608-271-0209 Web Site: herownwords.com; nontraditionalcareers. com, pg 779

Herman Pro AV, 10110 USA Today Way, Miramar, FL 33025 Tel: 305-477-0063 Toll Free Tel: 888-736-6888 Fax: 305-392-3377 E-mail: support@hermanproav.com Web Site: www.hermanproav.com, pg 779

Hewlett-Packard Co, 3000 Hanover St, Palo Alto, CA 94304-1185 Tel: 650-857-1501 Toll Free Tel: 800-752-0900 Fax: 650-857-5518 Web Site: www.hp.com, pg 779

Hi-Tech Audio Systems Inc, 3382 Enterprise Ave, Hayward, CA 94545 Tel: 650-742-9166 Fax: 650-648-0573 Web Site: www.hi-techaudio.com, pg 779

Hi-Tech Enterprises Inc, 4250 114 Terr N, Clearwater, FL 33762 Tel: 727-573-9600 E-mail: hitech@videoequipment.tv Web Site: www.videoequipment.tv, pg 779

Hi-Tech Import Export Corp, 1101 W McNab Rd, Pompano Beach, FL 33069 Tel: 954-946-0603 Fax: 954-946-0652, pg 779

Hi-Tech Lamps Inc, 922 San Leandro Ave, Suite B, Mountain View, CA 94043 Tel: 650-961-9031 Toll Free Tel: 800-229-6509 Fax: 650-961-9033 E-mail: info@hi-techlamps.com Web Site: www.hi-techlamps.com, pg 779

High End Systems Inc, 2105 Gracy Farms Lane, Austin, TX 78758 Tel: 512-836-2242 Toll Free Tel: 800-890-8989 Web Site: www.highend.com, pg 779

High Output Inc, 495 Turnpike St, Canton, MA 02021 Tel: 781-364-1800 Fax: 781-364-1900 Web Site: www. highoutput.com, pg 779

High Plains Films, PO Box 8796, Missoula, MT 59807 Tel: 406-543-6726 E-mail: yak@highplainsfilms.org Web Site: www.highplainsfilms.org, pg 779

High-Tech Special Effects Inc, PO Box 193, Eads, TN 38028-0193 Tel: 901-850-5522 Fax: 901-850-8315 Web Site: www.hightechspecialeffects.com, pg 779

High Water Records, University of Memphis, Rudi E Scheidt School of Music, 121 Music Bldg, Memphis, TN 38152 Tel: 901-678-3317 Fax: 901-678-3096, pg 779

High Windy Audio/Banjoman Inc, PO Box 553, Fairview, NC 28730 Tel: 828-628-1728 Toll Free Tel: 800-637-8679 Fax: 828-628-4435 E-mail: office@davidholt.com Web Site: www.davidholt.com, pg 779

HighBridge Audio, 270 Skipjack Rd, Prince Frederick, MD 20678 Toll Free Tel: 800-755-8532 Fax: 410-535-5499 E-mail: highbridge@highbridgeaudio.com; customerservice@recordedbooks.com Web Site: www. highbridgeaudio.com, pg 779

HighScope Press, 600 N River St, Ypsilanti, MI 48198-2898 Tel: 734-485-2000 Toll Free Tel: 800-407-7377 Fax: 734-485-0704 Toll Free Tel: 800-442-4329 E-mail: info@highscope.org; press@highscope.org Web Site: www.highscope.org, pg 780

Hilferty & Associates Inc, 14240 State Rte 550, Athens, OH 45701 Tel: 740-448-3821 Fax: 740-448-2331 E-mail: gha@hilferty.com Web Site: www.hilferty.com, pg 780

Jerry Hill Steadicam Products, 19160 Arminta St, Reseda, CA 91335-1105 Tel: 818-772-9256 Fax: 818-772-9251 E-mail: jerry@steadimoves.com Web Site: steadimoves.com, pg 780

Ron Hill Imagery, 2994 S Richards St, Salt Lake City, UT 84115 Tel: 801-486-3300 Fax: 801-486-3310 Web Site: ronhillimagery.com, pg 780

Hillman Prizes, 330 W 42 St, Suite 900, New York, NY 10036 Tel: 646-448-6413 Web Site: hillmanfoundation. org, pg 992

Hillmann & Carr Inc, 2233 Wisconsin Ave, Washington, DC 20007 Tel: 202-342-0001 Fax: 202-342-0117 E-mail: mail@hillmanncarr.com Web Site: www. hillmanncarr.com, pg 780

Himalayan Institute Audio/Video, 952 Bethany Tpke, Honesdale, PA 18431 Tel: 570-253-5551 Toll Free Tel: 800-822-4547 E-mail: info@himalayaninstitute. org Web Site: www.himalayaninstitute.org, pg 780

Hisco Inc, 6650 Concord Park Dr, Houston, TX 77040-4098 Tel: 713-934-1700 Toll Free Tel: 844-807-1902 (web orders); 877-447-2650 (cust support) Fax: 713-934-1790 E-mail: info@hiscoinc.com Web Site: www. hiscoinc.com, pg 780

Historic Films, 211 Third St, Greenport, NY 11944 Tel: 631-477-9700 Toll Free Tel: 800-249-1940 Fax: 631-477-9800 E-mail: info@historicfilms.com Web Site: www.historicfilms.com, pg 780

Hitachi Kokusai Electric America Ltd, 150 Crossways Park Dr, Woodbury, NY 11797 Tel: 516-921-7200 Toll Free Tel: 855-891-5179 Fax: 516-496-3718 E-mail: info@hitachikokusai.us Web Site: hitachikokusai.us, pg 780

Hite Co, 3101 Beale Ave, Altoona, PA 16601 Tel: 814-944-6121 Toll Free Tel: 800-252-3598 Fax: 814-944-3052 E-mail: altoona@mayerelectric.com Web Site: www.hiteco.com, pg 780

HM Electronics Inc (HME), 14110 Stowe Dr, Poway, CA 92064 Tel: 858-535-6000 Toll Free Tel: 800-848-4468 (dom sales) Fax: 858-452-7207; 858-552-0139 (dom sales) E-mail: info@hme.com Web Site: www. hme.com, pg 780

Hogpenny Studios, Ship Bottom Studio Ctr, 123 E 14 St, Ship Bottom, Long Beach Island, NJ 08008 Tel: 609-494-6640 E-mail: hogpenny@verizon.net Web Site: hogpennytv.com, pg 780

The Hollaender Manufacturing Co, 10285 Wayne Ave, Cincinnati, OH 45215 Tel: 513-772-8800 Toll Free Tel: 800-772-8800 (orders) Fax: 513-772-8806 Web Site: www.hollaender.com, pg 780

The Hollywood Edge, c/o Sound Ideas, 105 W Beaver Creek Rd, Suite 4, Richmond Hill, ON L4B 1C6, Canada Tel: 905-886-5000 Toll Free Tel: 800-665-3000 (CN); 800-387-3030 (US) E-mail: hollywoodedge@sound-ideas. com Web Site: www.sound-ideas.com; www. hollywoodedge.com, pg 780

Hollywood Lights Inc, 5251 SE McLoughlin Blvd, Portland, OR 97202-4836 Tel: 503-232-9001; 503-232-8855 Toll Free Tel: 800-826-9881 Fax: 503-517-8686 E-mail: portland@hollywoodlights.biz Web Site: www.hollywoodlights.biz, pg 780

Hollywood Professional Association (HPA), 2501 W Burbank Blvd, No 207, Burbank, CA 91505 Tel: 818-273-1482 Web Site: hpaonline.com, pg 955

Hollywood Sound Systems, 4209 Vanowen Place, Burbank, CA 91505 Tel: 323-466-2416 Fax: 323-460-2676 Web Site: www.hollywoodsound.com, pg 781

Hollywood Theatre Equipment Inc, 1941 N 66 Ave, Hollywood, FL 33024 Tel: 954-920-2832 Fax: 954-986-6914 E-mail: hwdtheatre@aol.com, pg 781

Hollywood Vaults Inc, 742 N Seward St, Hollywood, CA 90038 Tel: 323-461-6464 Toll Free Tel: 800-569-5336 Fax: 323-461-6479 E-mail: vault@hollywoodvaults. com Web Site: www.hollywoodvaults.com, pg 781

Holo-Spectra Inc, 7742B Gloria Ave, Van Nuys, CA 91406 Tel: 818-994-9577 Fax: 818-994-4709 E-mail: info@lasershs.com Web Site: www.lasershs. com, pg 781

HOME Inc, 566 Columbus Ave, Boston, MA 02118 Tel: 617-427-4663 Fax: 617-427-4664 Web Site: homeinc.org, pg 781

Homespun Video, 1610 Rte 212, Saugerties, NY 12477 Tel: 845-246-2550 Toll Free Tel: 800-338-2737 (orders-US & CN) E-mail: info@homespun.com Web Site: www.homespun.com, pg 781

Honolulu Film Office, 530 S King St, Suite 306, Honolulu, HI 96813 Tel: 808-768-6108 Fax: 808-768-6102 E-mail: info@filmhonolulu.com Web Site: www. filmhonolulu.com, pg 970

Hoodman Corp, 20445 Gramercy Place, Suite 201, Torrence, CA 90501 Tel: 310-222-8608 Toll Free Tel: 800-818-3946 E-mail: sales@hoodmanusa.com Web Site: www.hoodmanusa.com, pg 781

Hooper Camera & Imaging, 21902 Devonshire St, Chatsworth, CA 91311-2907 Tel: 818-709-0014 Fax: 818-709-0130 E-mail: sales@hoopercamera.com Web Site: hoopercamera.com, pg 781

Tom Hopkins International Inc, 465 E Chilton Dr, Suite 4, Chandler, AZ 85225 Tel: 480-949-0786 Toll Free Tel: 800-528-0446 Fax: 480-949-1590 E-mail: info@tomhopkins.com Web Site: www.tomhopkins.com, pg 781

Horita Co Inc, 34192 Camino Capistrano, Capistrano Beach, CA 92624 Tel: 949-489-0240 E-mail: sales@horita.com; horita@horita.com Web Site: horita.com, pg 781

Horizon Film + Video Productions, 3903 S Congress Ave, Suite 40186, Austin, TX 78704 Tel: 512-459-3100 Web Site: www.horizonvideo.com, pg 781

Horizon Films & Media LLC, PO Box 1087, Shelbyville, KY 40066 Tel: 502-647-9966 Fax: 502-647-9968 E-mail: horizonfilms@insightbb.com Web Site: www.horizon-films.com, pg 781

Horizon Video Productions Inc, 6114 Fayetteville St, Suite 106, Durham, NC 27713 Tel: 919-941-0901 Toll Free Tel: 800-768-3776 Fax: 919-941-1939 E-mail: info@horizonvp.com Web Site: www. horizonvp.com, pg 781

Horizon Worldwide, 1765 Stebbins Dr, Houston, TX 77043 Tel: 713-647-7400 Fax: 713-647-6664 E-mail: info@horizonworldwide.com Web Site: www.horizonworldwide.com, pg 781

Susan Hormuth, Visual Resource Consultant, 3356 Pennsylvania Ave SE, Washington, DC 20020 Tel: 202-584-3994 E-mail: susanhormuth@verizon.net, pg 781

Hosa Technology Inc, 6650 Caballero Blvd, Buena Park, CA 90620 Tel: 714-522-8878 Toll Free Tel: 800-255-7527 Fax: 714-522-4540 E-mail: info@hosatech. com; sales@hosatech.com; orders@hosatech.com Web Site: hosatech.com, pg 781

Hot House Professional Audio, 275 Martin Ave, Highland, NY 12528 Tel: 845-691-6077 E-mail: info@hothousepro.com Web Site: www. hothousepro.com, pg 782

Hot Springs Documentary Film Festival, 659 Ouchita Ave, Hot Springs, AR 71901 Tel: 501-538-0452 E-mail: hsdfi@hsdfi.org Web Site: www.hsdfi.org, pg 992

HOThead, 56 W 45 St, 17th fl, New York, NY 10036 Tel: 212-575-5566 E-mail: info@hothead.tv Web Site: hothead.tv, pg 782

Hotronic Inc, 1875 S Winchester Blvd, Campbell, CA 95008 Tel: 408-378-3883 E-mail: sales@hotronics. com Web Site: hotronics.com, pg 782

Hottrax Records, 1957 Kilburn Dr, Atlanta, GA 30324-4852 Tel: 770-662-6661 E-mail: hotwax@hottrax.com Web Site: www.hottrax.com, pg 782

House of Cinemagraphics, 4802 Quail Ave N, Minneapolis, MN 55429 Tel: 612-339-7803; 763-458-8244 Toll Free Tel: 888-813-0413 E-mail: film@visi.com Web Site: www.houseofcinemagraphics.com, pg 782

House of Moves, 5419 McConnell Ave, Los Angeles, CA 90066-7027 Tel: 310-306-6131 E-mail: info@moves.com Web Site: www.moves.com, pg 782

The House Studios, 325 Second Ave W, Seattle, WA 98119 Tel: 206-724-6639 E-mail: book@thehousestudios.com Web Site: thehousestudios.com, pg 782

Houston Film Commission, 701 Avenida de las Americas, Houston, TX 77010 Tel: 713-853-8959; 713-853-8100 Toll Free Tel: 800-446-8786 Fax: 713-853-8341 E-mail: jmontgomery@houstonfilmcommission.com Web Site: www.houstonfilmcommission.com, pg 976

Houston Photo Imaging, 5250 Gulfton, Suite 3-B, Houston, TX 77081 Tel: 713-666-0282 Toll Free Tel: 800-664-0282 Fax: 713-667-9625 E-mail: info@hpihouston.com Web Site: hpihouston.com, pg 782

Hover-Views Unlimited, PO Box 1164, Syosset, NY 11791 Tel: 516-496-2946 Fax: 516-496-8029 Web Site: www.hoverviews.com, pg 782

HSA Inc, 1717 E Sixth St, Mishawaka, IN 46544 Tel: 574-255-6100 Fax: 574-255-8131 E-mail: hsainfo@hsarolltops.com Web Site: www.hsarolltops.com, pg 782

Hubbard Supply Co, 901 W Second St, Flint, MI 48503 Tel: 810-234-8681 Toll Free Tel: 800-875-4811 Fax: 810-234-6142 E-mail: information@hubbardsupply.com Web Site: www.hubbardsupply.com, pg 782

Hubbell Wiring Device-Kellems, 40 Waterview Dr, Shelton, CT 06484 Tel: 475-882-4800 (sales & mktg) Toll Free Tel: 800-288-6000 (cust serv) Fax: 475-882-4849 (sales & mktg) Toll Free Fax: 800-255-1031 (cust serv) E-mail: techserv@hubbell.com Web Site: www.hubbell-wiring.com, pg 782

Hughie's Event Production Services, 1260 E 38 St, Cleveland, OH 44114 Tel: 216-361-4600 Toll Free Tel: 800-449-4115 Fax: 216-361-2570 Web Site: www.hughies.com, pg 782

Charles A Hulcher Co Inc, 909 "G" St, Hampton, VA 23661 Tel: 757-245-6190 Fax: 757-245-2882, pg 782

Human Circuit, 9346 Gaither Rd, Gaithersburg, MD 20877 Tel: 240-864-4000 Web Site: www.humancircuit.com, pg 782

Human Relations Media, 41 Kensico Dr, Mount Kisco, NY 10549 Tel: 914-666-9151 Toll Free Tel: 800-431-2050 (cust serv) Fax: 914-666-9506 E-mail: service@hrmvideo.com; orders@hrmvideo.com; help@hrmvideo.com; letters@hrmvideo.com Web Site: www.hrmvideo.com, pg 782

Humboldt-Del Norte Film Commission, 520 "E" St, Eureka, CA 95501 Tel: 707-443-4488 E-mail: info@filmhumboldtdelnorte.org Web Site: www.filmhumboldtdelnorte.org, pg 966

Humboldt International Film Festival, Dept of Theatre, Film & Dance, One Harpst St, Arcata, CA 95521 Tel: 707-826-4113 Fax: 707-826-4112 E-mail: filmfest@humboldt.edu Web Site: hsufilmfestival.com, pg 992

Hunt's Photo & Video, 100 Main St, Melrose, MA 02176-6104 Tel: 781-662-8822 (retail sales) Toll Free Tel: 800-924-8682 (retail sales); 800-221-1830 (ext 2340, corp sales) Fax: 781-662-6524 E-mail: ecommerce@wbhunt.com (retail online sales) Web Site: www.huntsphotoandvideo.com, pg 782

Hurst Digital, 4472 Spring Valley Rd, Dallas, TX 75244 Tel: 469-644-1390 Web Site: hurstdigital.net, pg 782

Editions Hurtubise HMH Ltee, 1815 Avenue De Lorimier, Montreal, QC H2K 3W6, Canada Tel: 514-523-1523 Toll Free Tel: 800-361-1664 Fax: 514-523-9969 Web Site: www.distributionhmh.com, pg 782

Hybrid Studios, 3021 S Shannon St, Santa Ana, CA 92704 Tel: 714-850-1499 E-mail: info@hybridstudiosca.com Web Site: www.hybridstudiosca.com, pg 783

Hydrogen Whiskey Studios, 12327 Santa Monica Blvd, Suite 202, Los Angeles, CA 90025 Tel: 310-394-8130 Fax: 310-820-0401, pg 783

Hyperspective Studios Inc, 2800 Woodlawn Dr, Suite 253, Honolulu, HI 96822 Tel: 808-353-3618 Toll Free Tel: 800-353-3618 E-mail: info@hyperspective.com Web Site: hyperspective.com, pg 783

I M P A C T Publishing Inc, 3409 47 Ave E, Bradenton, FL 34203 Tel: 941-739-2611 Toll Free Tel: 800-221-6121; 800-426-3963 E-mail: potentialsunlimitedcs@gmail.com Web Site: www.potentialsunlimited.com, pg 783

I-25 Studios, 9201 Pan American Fwy NE, Albuquerque, NM 87113 Tel: 505-822-7115 E-mail: info@i-25studios.com Web Site: i-25studios.com, pg 783

IAA-VC (International Association of Audio Visual Communicators), PO Box 270779, Flower Mound, TX 75027-0779 Tel: 469-464-4180 Fax: 469-464-4170 E-mail: cindy@cindys.com Web Site: cindys.com, pg 955

IAC Acoustics, 401 Airport Rd, North Aurora, IL 60542 Tel: 630-270-1790 E-mail: iacacoustics@soundseal.com Web Site: www.iac-noisecontrol.com/us; www.iacacoustics.com, pg 783

IAI Records & Video, PO Box 4, Cherry Valley, NY 13320-0004 Tel: 646-696-5645 E-mail: iai@improvart.com Web Site: www.improvart.com, pg 783

IAMP Professional Audio, 218 Reindollar Ave, Unit 6-A, Marina, CA 93933 Tel: 831-884-9558 Fax: 831-643-2131 E-mail: iamp-pro-audio@comcast.net Web Site: www.iampproaudio.com, pg 783

IATSE, 207 W 25 St, 4th fl, New York, NY 10001 Tel: 212-730-1770 Fax: 212-730-7809 Web Site: www.iatse-intl.org; iatse.net, pg 955

IBM Collaboration Solutions, One New Orchard Rd, Armonk, NY 10504-1722 Toll Free Tel: 800-426-4968; 877-426-3774 Web Site: www-01.ibm.com/software/lotus, pg 783

IBM SPSS, 200 W Madison Ave, 23rd fl, Chicago, IL 60606 Toll Free Tel: 800-543-2185 Toll Free Fax: 800-841-0064 E-mail: salesbox@us.ibm.com Web Site: www-01.ibm.com/software/analytics/spss, pg 783

Icarus Films Inc, 32 Court St, 21st fl, Brooklyn, NY 11201 Tel: 718-488-8900 Toll Free Tel: 800-876-1710 Fax: 718-488-8642 E-mail: mail@icarusfilms.com Web Site: www.icarusfilms.com, pg 783

ICL Imaging Inc, 51 Mellen St, Framingham, MA 01702 Tel: 508-872-3280 Toll Free Tel: 800-660-3280 Fax: 508-872-7364 E-mail: csr@icl-imaging.com Web Site: www.icl-imaging.com, pg 783

Icom Multimedia, 2498 Danders Ct, Columbus, OH 43220 Tel: 614-207-4400 Fax: 614-457-8050 Web Site: www.icommultimedia.com, pg 783

Icontent, 122 W 26 St, New York, NY 10001 Tel: 212-462-0022 E-mail: info@icontent.tv Web Site: www.icontent.tv, pg 783

iCorpTv, PO Box 461172, Los Angeles, CA 90046 Tel: 818-492-4623 E-mail: icorptv@gmail.com Web Site: icorptv.com, pg 783

iCrossing Inc, a Hearst Company, 300 W 57 St, New York, NY 10019 Tel: 212-649-3900 Toll Free Tel: 866-620-3780 E-mail: general@icrossing.com Web Site: www.icrossing.com, pg 783

IDA Documentary Awards, 3470 Wilshire Blvd, Suite 980, Los Angeles, CA 90010 Tel: 213-232-1660 Fax: 213-232-1669 E-mail: info@documentary.org Web Site: www.documentary.org, pg 992

Idaho Camera Inc, 1310 N Orchard Ave, Boise, ID 83706 Tel: 208-377-3686 (corp) Toll Free Tel: 877-323-8734 E-mail: info@idahocamera.com; orchard@idahocamera.com; sales@idahocamera.com Web Site: www.idahocamera.com, pg 784

Idaho Film Office, 700 W State St, Boise, ID 83702 Tel: 208-334-2470 Toll Free Tel: 800-842-5858 Fax: 208-334-2631 Web Site: www.filmidaho.com, pg 970

Ideascape Inc, PO Box 1966, Lake Oswego, OR 97035 Tel: 503-246-2439 E-mail: info@ideascapeinc Web Site: www.ideascapeinc.com, pg 784

IDenticard Systems Inc, 148 E Stiegel St, Manheim, PA 17545 Tel: 717-569-5797 Toll Free Tel: 800-233-0298 Fax: 717-427-1654 E-mail: identicard.info@identicard.com Web Site: www.identicard.com, pg 784

Idle Minds Productions Inc, 3405 Pepperhill Rd, Lexington, KY 40502 Tel: 859-268-8500 Fax: 859-268-8500 E-mail: idleminds@twc.com, pg 784

IDX System Technology Inc, 19001 Harborgate Way, Suite 105, Torrance, CA 90501 Tel: 310-328-2850 Fax: 310-328-8202 E-mail: idx.usa@idx.tv Web Site: www.idx.tv, pg 784

IEEE Computer Society Press, 10662 Los Vaqueros Circle, Los Alamitos, CA 90720-1314 Tel: 714-821-8380 Toll Free Tel: 800-272-6657 (cust serv) Fax: 714-821-4010 E-mail: help@computer.org Web Site: www.computer.org, pg 784

IES Medal, 120 Wall St, 17th fl, New York, NY 10005-4026 Tel: 212-544-5000 E-mail: ies@ies.org Web Site: ies.org, pg 992

IFM World Releasing Inc, 1328 E Palmer Ave, Glendale, CA 91205 Tel: 818-243-4976 Fax: 818-550-9728 E-mail: contact@ifmfilm.com Web Site: www.ifmfilm.com, pg 784

IFP Gotham Awards™, c/o Made in NY Media Ctr by IFP, 30 John St, Ground fl, Brooklyn, NY 11201 Tel: 212-465-8200 (ext 224) E-mail: gothamawards@ifp.org Web Site: gotham.ifp.org, pg 992

IFP Week, c/o Made in NY Media Ctr by IFP, 30 John St, Ground fl, Brooklyn, NY 11201 Tel: 212-465-8200 Web Site: www.ifp.org, pg 992

Ikegami Electronics (USA) Inc, 37 Brook Ave, Maywood, NJ 07607 Tel: 201-368-9171 Fax: 201-569-1626 E-mail: sales@ikegami.com; service@ikegami.com Web Site: www.ikegami.com, pg 784

ILIO Enterprises LLC, 5356 Sterling Center Dr, Westlake Village, CA 91361 Tel: 818-707-7222; 818-707-3655 Toll Free Tel: 800-747-4546 E-mail: info@ilio.com Web Site: www.ilio.com, pg 784

Illinois Film Office, James R Thompson Ctr, Suite 3-400, 100 W Randolph, Chicago, IL 60601 Tel: 312-814-3600 Fax: 312-814-8874 E-mail: film@illinois.gov Web Site: www.film.illinois.gov, pg 970

Illuminart Lighting, 7320 Griffin Rd, Suite 111, Davie, FL 33314 Tel: 954-327-0564 E-mail: lightisart@aol.com, pg 784

Illuminate Post/Digital Finishing, 10900 Ventura Blvd, Studio City, CA 91604 Tel: 323-969-8822 Fax: 323-969-8860 E-mail: info@illuminatehollywood.com Web Site: illuminatehollywood.com, pg 784

Illuminate Studios, 10900 Ventura Blvd, Studio City, CA 90068 Tel: 818-769-4500 Fax: 818-769-7150 E-mail: info@illuminatehollywood.com Web Site: illuminatehollywood.com, pg 784

Illuminating Engineering Society (IES), 120 Wall St, 17th fl, New York, NY 10005-4026 Tel: 212-248-5000 E-mail: ies@ies.org Web Site: ies.org, pg 955

Image Associates Inc, 5475 Rumley Rd, Suite 102, Durham, NC 27703 Tel: 919-876-6400 Fax: 919-876-6400 E-mail: info@imageassociates.com Web Site: www.imageassociates.com, pg 784

Image Audiovisuals, 2130 S Dahlia St, Denver, CO 80222 Tel: 303-758-1818 Toll Free Tel: 800-818-1857 Fax: 303-758-5722 Web Site: www.imageav.com, pg 784

Image Craft LLC, 3401 E Broadway Rd, Phoenix, AZ 85040 Tel: 602-276-2082 Toll Free Tel: 800-274-2422 Fax: 602-232-0719 E-mail: designgroup@imcraft.com Web Site: www.imcraft.com, pg 784

Image Entertainment, 6320 Canoga Ave, Suite 800, Woodland Hills, CA 91367 Tel: 818-407-9100 Toll Free Tel: 800-473-3475 E-mail: inquiries@rljentertainment.com, pg 785

The Image Generators, 18156 Darnell Dr, Olney, MD 20832 Tel: 301-924-5700 Fax: 240-363-0062 E-mail: info@imagegenerators.com Web Site: www.imagegenerators.com, pg 785

Image Integration, 2619 Benvenue Ave, No A, Berkeley, CA 94704 Tel: 510-504-2605 Fax: 510-841-8524, pg 785

Image Logic Corp, 6807 Brennon Lane, Chevy Chase, MD 20815-3255 *Tel:* 202-223-2888 *E-mail:* info@imagelogic.com *Web Site:* www.imagelogic.com, pg 785

Image Management Systems Inc, 239 W 15 St, New York, NY 10011 *Tel:* 212-741-8765 *E-mail:* info@imagemgt.com *Web Site:* www.imagemgt.com, pg 785

Image Marketing Corp, 1636 N 24 St, Mesa, AZ 85213 *Tel:* 480-969-7032 *Fax:* 480-969-0939 *E-mail:* info@image4u.com *Web Site:* www.image4u.com, pg 785

Image Up Studio, 295 Pierson Ave, Suite 103, Edison, NJ 08837 *Tel:* 732-549-1845 *Web Site:* www.imageup.com, pg 785

Image Video, 1620 Midland Ave, Scarborough, ON M1P 3C2, Canada *Tel:* 416-750-8872 *Fax:* 416-750-8015 *E-mail:* sales@imagevideo.com *Web Site:* www.imagevideo.com, pg 785

Image Video Services & Productions, 1210 Southview Dr, Sudbury, ON P3E 2L6, Canada *Tel:* 705-698-1212 *Fax:* 705-805-0110 *E-mail:* info@ivsproductions.ca *Web Site:* www.ivsproductions.ca, pg 785

Image Video Teleproductions Inc, 6755 Freedom Ave NW, North Canton, OH 44720 *Tel:* 330-494-9303 *Fax:* 330-966-1792 *E-mail:* info@image-video.com *Web Site:* www.image-video.com, pg 785

Image Zone Inc, 11 W 69 St, Suite 10A, New York, NY 10023 *Tel:* 212-924-8804 *Web Site:* www.imagezone.com, pg 785

Imagecraft Productions, 3318 Burton Ave, Burbank, CA 91504 *Tel:* 818-954-0187 *Fax:* 818-954-0189 *Web Site:* www.imagecraftproductions.com, pg 785

imageReal Pictures LLC, 4 Lighthouse St, No 8, Marina del Rey, CA 90292 *E-mail:* info@imagereal.com *Web Site:* www.imagereal.com, pg 785

Imagers, 1575 Northside Dr, Bldg 400, Suite 490, Atlanta, GA 30318-5411 *Tel:* 404-351-5800 *Toll Free Tel:* 800-232-5411 *Fax:* 404-351-9020 *E-mail:* imagers@imagers.com *Web Site:* www.imagers.com, pg 785

Images in Motion Media Inc, 720 Ladera Dr, Sonoma, CA 95476 *Tel:* 707-996-9474 *E-mail:* images@vom.com *Web Site:* www.imagesmedia.com, pg 785

Images II Inc, 1700 "O" St, Lincoln, NE 68508 *Tel:* 402-475-4000 *Toll Free Tel:* 800-669-4001 *Fax:* 402-475-8063 *E-mail:* graphics@images2.com *Web Site:* www.images2.com, pg 785

Imageworks, 1039 Meade Ave, San Diego, CA 92116-1038 *Tel:* 619-512-3348 *E-mail:* info@imageworks.tv *Web Site:* www.imageworks.tv, pg 785

ImageWorks Communications, 10155 High Point Lane, Suite 100, Salt Lake City, UT 84092 *Tel:* 801-231-7234 (cell) *Toll Free Tel:* 888-810-0100 *Web Site:* imageworkscommunications.com, pg 785

Imagine Communications Corp, 3001 Dallas Pkwy, Suite 300, Frisco, TX 75034 *Tel:* 469-803-4900 *Toll Free Tel:* 866-4-IMAGINE (446-2446) *Fax:* 469-803-4899 *E-mail:* insidesales@imaginecommunications.com *Web Site:* www.imaginecommunications.com, pg 786

The Imaging Alliance, 7600 Jericho Tpke, Suite 301, Woodbury, NY 11797 *Tel:* 516-802-0895 *Fax:* 516-364-0140 *E-mail:* info@theimagingalliance.com *Web Site:* www.theimagingalliance.com, pg 955

Imagivations, 11314 Sheldon St, Sun Valley, CA 91352 *Tel:* 818-767-6767 *Fax:* 818-767-3637 *E-mail:* info@imagivations.com *Web Site:* www.imagivations.com, pg 786

IMAX Corp, 2525 Speakman Dr, Mississauga, ON L5K 1B1, Canada *Tel:* 905-403-6500 *Fax:* 905-403-6450 *E-mail:* info@imax.com *Web Site:* www.imax.com, pg 786

Imig Audio/Video Inc, 2611 Fairbanks St, Suite 100, Anchorage, AK 99503 *Tel:* 907-274-2161 *Fax:* 907-279-0219 *E-mail:* information@imigav.com *Web Site:* www.imigav.com, pg 786

Immersion Corp, 50 Rio Robles, San Jose, CA 95134 *Tel:* 408-467-1900 *Fax:* 408-467-1901 *Web Site:* www.immersion.com, pg 786

IMP Digital Studios, A PharmaSphere Company, 120 Rte 17N, Paramus, NJ 07652 *Tel:* 201-261-3959 *E-mail:* info@impdigital.us *Web Site:* impdigital.us; www.facebook.com/impdigital, pg 786

Impact Christian Books Inc, 332 Leffingwell Ave, Suite 101, Kirkwood, MO 63122 *Tel:* 314-822-3309 *E-mail:* info@impactchristianbooks.com *Web Site:* www.impactchristianbooks.com, pg 786

Impact Technology Group LLC, One Cardinal Rd, Unit 5, Hilton Head Island, SC 29926 *Toll Free Tel:* 800-675-2200 *Toll Free Fax:* 800-500-2565 *E-mail:* sales@impact-group.com *Web Site:* impact-group.com, pg 786

Imtronics Industries Inc, 11930 31 Ct N, St Petersburg, FL 33716 *Tel:* 727-572-9010 *Fax:* 727-572-9012 *E-mail:* imtronics@imtronics.com *Web Site:* imtronics.com, pg 786

In Concert Production Inc (ICP), 680 Wharton Circle SW, Suite C, Atlanta, GA 30336 *Tel:* 404-355-7943 *Fax:* 404-350-9045 *Web Site:* icpatlanta.com, pg 786

In-Plant Printing & Mailing Association, 103 N Jefferson St, Kearney, MO 64060 *Tel:* 816-919-1691 *Fax:* 816-945-4505 *E-mail:* ipmainfo@ipma.org *Web Site:* ipma.org, pg 955

In the Wild Productions, PO Box 1443, Provincetown, MA 02657-5443 *Tel:* 508-241-5990 *E-mail:* info@inthewildproductions.com *Web Site:* www.inthewildproductions.com, pg 786

Increase Video/Silver Mine Video, 5776 D Lindero Canyon Rd, Westlake Village, CA 91362 *Tel:* 805-480-0303, pg 786

Independent Audio Inc, 43 Deerfield Rd, Portland, ME 04101 *Tel:* 207-773-2424 *Fax:* 207-773-2422 *E-mail:* info@independentaudio.com *Web Site:* www.independentaudio.com, pg 786

The Independent Book Publishers Association (IBPA), 1020 Manhattan Beach Blvd, Suite 204, Manhattan Beach, CA 90266 *Tel:* 310-546-1818 *Fax:* 310-546-3939 *E-mail:* info@ibpa-online.org *Web Site:* www.ibpa-online.org, pg 956

Independent Film & Television Alliance® (IFTA), 10850 Wilshire Blvd, 9th fl, Los Angeles, CA 90024-4311 *Tel:* 310-446-1000 *Fax:* 310-446-1600 *E-mail:* info@ifta-online.org *Web Site:* www.ifta-online.org, pg 956

The Independent Filmmaker Project (IFP), c/o Made in NY Media Ctr by IFP, 30 John St, Ground fl, Brooklyn, NY 11201 *Tel:* 212-465-8200 *Web Site:* www.ifp.org, pg 956

The Independent Production Fund, 200 Central Park S, Suite 12F, New York, NY 10019 *Tel:* 212-221-6310 *Fax:* 212-302-1854 *Web Site:* www.ipfmedia.org/vetc.htm, pg 786

Indian House, PO Box 472, Taos, NM 87571-0472 *Tel:* 575-776-2953 *Toll Free Tel:* 800-748-0522 *Fax:* 575-776-2804 *E-mail:* music@indianhouse.com *Web Site:* www.indianhouse.com, pg 786

Indiana University Press, Off of Scholarly Publg, Herman B Wells Library 350, 1320 E Tenth St, Bloomington, IN 47405-3907 *Tel:* 812-855-8817 *Toll Free Tel:* 800-842-6796 *Fax:* 812-855-8507 *E-mail:* iupress@indiana.edu *Web Site:* www.iupress.indiana.edu, pg 786

Indianapolis International Film Festival, 125 W South St, No 1930, Indianapolis, IN 46206 *Tel:* 317-560-4433 *E-mail:* info@indyfilmfest.org *Web Site:* indyfilmfest.org, pg 992

Indie Aerials, 16425 Hart St, Van Nuys, CA 91406 *Tel:* 818-988-9382 *E-mail:* info@indieaerials.com *Web Site:* indieaerials.com, pg 787

Indigo Productions, 313 Kensington Ave, Buffalo, NY 14214 *Tel:* 716-836-2930 *Fax:* 716-836-6830 *E-mail:* indigo@indigoproductions.net *Web Site:* indigoproductions.net, pg 787

Individual Artist Fellowship, Carvel State Off Bldg, 4th fl, 820 N French St, Wilmington, DE 19801 *Tel:* 302-577-8278 *Fax:* 302-577-6561 *E-mail:* delarts@state.de.us *Web Site:* www.artsdel.org, pg 992

Induro, 75 Virginia Rd, North White Plains, NY 10603 *Tel:* 914-347-3300 *Fax:* 914-347-3309 *E-mail:* info@indurogear.com *Web Site:* www.indurogear.com, pg 787

Indus International Inc, 340 S Oak St, West Salem, WI 54669 *Tel:* 608-786-0300 *Toll Free Tel:* 800-843-9377 *Fax:* 608-786-0786 *Web Site:* www.indususa.com, pg 787

Industrial Light & Magic (ILM), 1110 Gorgas St, San Francisco, CA 94129 *Tel:* 415-746-3000 *Fax:* 415-746-3015 *E-mail:* contact-sf@ilm.com *Web Site:* www.ilm.com, pg 787

Industrial Strength Inc, 3232 44 Ave N, St Petersburg, FL 33714 *Tel:* 727-528-2877 *Toll Free Fax:* 888-804-7680 *E-mail:* sales@industrialstrengthstaging.com *Web Site:* www.isstaging.com, pg 787

Industrial Timer Co, 30 Industrial Park Rd, Centerbrook, CT 06409 *Tel:* 860-767-7130 *Toll Free Tel:* 800-394-7130 *Fax:* 860-767-9137 *Toll Free Fax:* 800-767-9137 *E-mail:* sales@epg-inc.com *Web Site:* www.industrialtimercompany.com, pg 787

Indy Shorts International Film Fest, 1043 Virginia Ave, Suite 2, Indianapolis, IN 46203 *Tel:* 317-464-9405 *E-mail:* submissions@heartlandfilm.org *Web Site:* heartlandfilm.org, pg 993

Inferno Film Productions LLC, PO Box 151048, Lakewood, CO 80215-9048 *Tel:* 303-587-9792 *E-mail:* sales@infernofilm.com *Web Site:* www.infernofilm.com, pg 787

Inferno Films, 3404 Guadalupe St, Austin, TX 78705 *Tel:* 512-302-9009 *Fax:* 512-302-9022 *Web Site:* www.infernofilms.com, pg 787

InFocus Corp, 13190 SW 68 Pkwy, Suite 200, Portland, OR 97223-8368 *Tel:* 503-207-4700 *Toll Free Tel:* 877-388-8385 *E-mail:* sales@infocus.com *Web Site:* www.infocus.com, pg 787

Infosat Communications Inc, 3130 114 Ave SE, Calgary, AB T2Z 3V6, Canada *Tel:* 403-543-8188 *Toll Free Tel:* 888-524-3038 *Fax:* 403-289-8133 *E-mail:* info@infosat.com *Web Site:* infosat.com, pg 787

Ingenuity Films LLC, 8075 Livorna Way, Fair Oaks, CA 95628 *Toll Free Tel:* 844-411-FILM (411-3456) *E-mail:* support@ingenuityfilms.com *Web Site:* www.ingenuityfilms.com, pg 787

Ingram Content Group LLC, One Ingram Blvd, La Vergne, TN 37086-1986 *Tel:* 615-793-5000 *Toll Free Tel:* 800-937-8000 (retailers); 800-937-5300 (ext 1, libs) *E-mail:* customerservice@ingramcontent.com *Web Site:* www.ingramcontent.com, pg 787

Ingram Entertainment Inc, 2 Ingram Blvd, La Vergne, TN 37089 *Tel:* 615-287-4000 (corp) *Toll Free Tel:* 800-621-1333 (sales & cust serv) *Web Site:* www.ingramentertainment.com, pg 787

Ingram Micro, 3351 Michelson Dr, Suite 100, Irvine, CA 92612 *Tel:* 714-566-1000 *Web Site:* www.ingrammicro.com, pg 787

InJoy Birth & Parenting Education, 7107 La Vista Place, Longmont, CO 80503 *Tel:* 303-447-2082 (ext 2) *Toll Free Tel:* 800-326-2082 (ext 2) *Fax:* 303-449-8788 *E-mail:* custserv@injoyvideos.com *Web Site:* www.injoyvideos.com, pg 788

Inland Audio Visual Co, 1414 N Fiske St, Suite E, Spokane, WA 99202 *Tel:* 509-328-0706 *Fax:* 509-328-0730 *E-mail:* inland@inlandav.com *Web Site:* www.inlandav.com, pg 788

Inland Audio Visual Ltd, 422 Lucas Ave, Box 102, Group 200, RR 2, Winnipeg, MB R3C 2E6, Canada *Tel:* 204-786-6521 *Toll Free Tel:* 800-933-6006 *Fax:* 204-783-6281 *E-mail:* winnipeg@inlandav.ca *Web Site:* www.inlandav.ca, pg 788

Inner Traditions International, One Park St, Rochester, VT 05767 *Tel:* 802-767-3174 *Toll Free Tel:* 800-246-8648 *Fax:* 802-767-3726 *E-mail:* customerservice@innertraditions.com *Web Site:* www.innertraditions.com, pg 788

Innocinema, 1351 Oakbrook Dr, Suite 160, Norcross, GA 30093 Tel: 770-857-3435 E-mail: info@innocinema.com; rentals@innocinema.com; support@innocinema.com Web Site: www.innocinema.com, pg 788

Innovision Media Group, 100 Mill Rd, Suite 2, Clifton Heights, PA 19018 Tel: 484-688-1200 Fax: 484-688-0148 E-mail: sales@innovision.net Web Site: www.thecrewstore.com, pg 788

Innovision Optics, 1834 Broadway, Santa Monica, CA 90404 Tel: 310-453-4866 Fax: 310-453-4677 Web Site: www.innovision-optics.com, pg 788

Inspired Image Picture Co (IIPC), 1090 E Georgia St, Vancouver, BC V6A 2A7, Canada Tel: 604-874-7513 Toll Free Tel: 800-352-1454 (prodn rentals); 800-567-0037 (equip rentals) Fax: 604-874-7516 E-mail: info@inspiredimage.ca Web Site: inspiredimage.ca, pg 788

Instant Music Now, 1160 W 26 Ave, Eugene, OR 97405 Tel: 541-345-8117 E-mail: info@instantmusicnow.com Web Site: www.instantmusicnow.com, pg 788

Institute for Teaching & Learning Excellence (ITLE), 100 ITLE, Oklahoma State University, Stillwater, OK 74078 Tel: 405-744-1000 Fax: 405-744-8563 E-mail: itle@okstate.edu Web Site: itle.okstate.edu, pg 788

The Institute Inc, 787 East Ave, Brockport, NY 14420 Tel: 585-637-6531 Web Site: www.the-institute-ny.com, pg 788

Institute of Industrial & Systems Engineers (IISE), 3577 Parkway Lane, Suite 200, Norcross, GA 30092 Tel: 770-449-0460 Toll Free Tel: 800-494-0460 Fax: 770-441-3295 E-mail: executiveoffices@iise.org Web Site: www.iise.org, pg 956

Institute of Precision Muscle Balancing, 6035 Vantage Ave, North Hollywood, CA 91616-4637 Tel: 818-766-8555 Fax: 818-766-8645 Web Site: www.dralexander.com, pg 788

Institute of Texan Cultures, UTSA HemisFair Park Campus, 801 E Cesar E Chavez Blvd, San Antonio, TX 78205-3296 Tel: 210-458-2300 Toll Free Tel: 800-776-7651 Fax: 210-458-2205 Web Site: www.texancultures.com, pg 788

Institute on Religious Life Inc, PO Box 7500, Libertyville, IL 60048-7500 Tel: 847-573-8975 Fax: 847-573-8960 Web Site: www.religiouslife.com, pg 788

Instructional Materials & Equipment Distributors (I-Med), 1520 Cotner Ave, Los Angeles, CA 90025 Tel: 323-879-0377; 310-473-5558 Fax: 310-473-5558 Web Site: www.i-med-inc.com, pg 789

IntegraColor, 3210 Innovative Way, Mesquite, TX 75149 Tel: 972-289-0705 Toll Free Tel: 800-933-9511 Fax: 972-285-4881 E-mail: salesinfo@integracolor.com Web Site: www.integracolor.com, pg 789

Integrated Event Management, 1239 Vista Leaf Dr, Decatur, GA 30033 Tel: 404-633-8541 Fax: 404-633-8691 Web Site: integratedevents.com, pg 789

Integrated Solutions Group, 858 Boston Providence Tpke, Norwood, MA 02062 Tel: 781-769-7810 Toll Free Tel: 866-769-0210 E-mail: info@isgboston.com Web Site: isgboston.com, pg 789

Intellidyne LLC, 2677 Prosperity Ave, Suite 301, Fairfax, VA 22031 Tel: 703-575-9715 Fax: 703-575-9718 Web Site: www.intellidyne-llc.com, pg 789

INTER-Media Electronics, 11 Gerald Rd, Milton, MA 02186 Tel: 617-698-8315 Fax: 617-698-8315 E-mail: intermedia.ex@verizon.net Web Site: www.intermedia-electronics.com, pg 789

Inter Video, 2000 N Lincoln St, Burbank, CA 91504 Tel: 818-843-3624 Toll Free Tel: 866-204-0340 (sales) Fax: 818-843-6884 E-mail: rentals@intervideo24.com Web Site: www.intervideo24.com, pg 789

Interactive Multimedia & Collaborative Communications Alliance (IMCCA), PO Box 756, Syosset, NY 11791 Tel: 516-818-8184 Web Site: www.imcca.org, pg 956

Interactive Products, 101 Commerce Dr, Montgomeryville, PA 18936 Tel: 215-362-2766 Toll Free Tel: 800-523-6716 Fax: 215-361-0167 E-mail: numonics@numonics.com; orders@numonics.com Web Site: www.numonics.com, pg 789

InterAmerica Stage Inc, 5401 Benchmark Lane, Sanford, FL 32773 Tel: 407-302-0881 Toll Free Tel: 877-302-4274 Fax: 407-302-0882 E-mail: info@iastage.com Web Site: www.iastage.com, pg 789

Intercollegiate Studies Institute Inc (ISI), 3901 Centerville Rd, Wilmington, DE 19807 Tel: 302-652-4600 Toll Free Tel: 800-526-7022 Fax: 302-652-1760 E-mail: info@isi.org Web Site: www.isi.org, pg 789

Intercon 1, 12136 Crystal Lake Rd, Merrifield, MN 56465 Tel: 218-828-3157 Toll Free Tel: 800-237-9576 Fax: 218-828-1096 E-mail: intercon@nortechsys.com Web Site: www.intercon-1.com, pg 789

Interface Media Group, 1233 20 St NW, Washington, DC 20036 Tel: 202-861-0500 E-mail: info@interfacemedia.com Web Site: interfacemedia.com, pg 789

Interlink Technologies, 139 W Indiana Ave, Suite 203, Perrysburg, OH 43552 Tel: 419-893-9011 Toll Free Tel: 800-655-5465 Fax: 419-893-7280 E-mail: info@thinkinterlink.com Web Site: thinkinterlink.com, pg 789

Intermark Industries Inc, 2980 NW 74 Ave, Miami, FL 33122 Tel: 305-591-8930 Fax: 305-593-1091 E-mail: info@intermarkindustries.com Web Site: www.intermarkindustries.com, pg 789

Intermedia Inc, 3703 S Edmunds St, Suite 203, Seattle, WA 98118 Tel: 206-284-2995 Toll Free Tel: 800-553-8336 Toll Free Fax: 800-553-1655 E-mail: info@intermedia-inc.com Web Site: www.intermedia-inc.com, pg 789

InterNation Inc, 299 Broadway, Suite 918, New York, NY 10007 Tel: 212-619-5545 Toll Free Tel: 800-222-8799 Fax: 212-619-5887 E-mail: info@internation.com Web Site: www.internation.com, pg 789

International Association of Business Communicators (IABC), 649 Mission St, 5th fl, San Francisco, CA 94105 Tel: 415-544-4700 Toll Free Tel: 800-776-4222 Fax: 415-544-4747 E-mail: member_relations@iabc.com Web Site: www.iabc.com, pg 956

International Audio Visual Inc, 622 Rte 10, Unit 21, Whippany, NJ 07981 Tel: 973-887-7744 Toll Free Tel: 888-887-7749 E-mail: iav@iavnj.com Web Site: www.iavnj.com, pg 790

International Cellulose Corp, 12315 Robin Blvd, Houston, TX 77045 Tel: 713-433-6701 Toll Free Tel: 800-444-1252 Fax: 713-433-2029 E-mail: icc@spray-on.com Web Site: www.spray-on.com, pg 790

International Cinema Technology Association (ICTA), 311 W 43 St, Suite 301, New York, NY 10036 Tel: 212-493-4097; 212-493-4058 Fax: 212-257-6428 Web Site: www.internationalcinematechnologyassociation.com, pg 956

International Cinematographers Guild (ICG), 7755 Sunset Blvd, Hollywood, CA 90046 Tel: 323-876-0160 Fax: 323-876-6383 (exec off) Web Site: www.icg600.com, pg 956

International Contact Inc, 2820 Adeline St, Suite 1, Berkeley, CA 94703 Tel: 510-836-1180 Fax: 510-835-1314 E-mail: sales@intlcontact.com Web Site: www.intlcontact.com, pg 790

International Datacasting, 50 Frank Nighbor Place, Kanata, ON K2V 1B9, Canada Tel: 613-596-4120 Fax: 613-596-4863 E-mail: marketing@datacast.com Web Site: www.datacast.com, pg 790

International Digital Centre, 216 E 45 St, 7th fl, New York, NY 10017 Tel: 212-581-3940 Fax: 212-581-3979 E-mail: info@idcdigital.com Web Site: www.idcdigital.com, pg 790

International Display & Exhibit Corp (IDEC), 60 Shawmut Rd, Suite 5, Canton, MA 02021 Tel: 617-527-7878 Toll Free Tel: 800-533-7878 Fax: 617-964-5099 E-mail: sales@idec-displays.com Web Site: www.idecdisplays.com, pg 790

International Documentary Association, 3470 Wilshire Blvd, Suite 980, Los Angeles, CA 90010 Tel: 213-232-1660 Fax: 213-232-1669 E-mail: info@documentary.org Web Site: www.documentary.org, pg 956

International E-Z UP Inc, 1900 Second St, Norco, CA 92860 Tel: 951-279-0999 Toll Free Tel: 800-45SHADE (457-4233) Fax: 951-279-0888 Web Site: www.ezup.com, pg 790

International Electro-Magnetics Inc, 1033A S Noel Ave, Wheeling, IL 60090 Tel: 847-358-4622 Fax: 847-947-8239 E-mail: information@iemmag.com; service@iemmag.com; sales@iemmag.com Web Site: www.iemmag.com, pg 790

International Emmy® Awards, 25 W 52 St, New York, NY 10019 Tel: 212-489-6969 Fax: 212-489-6557 E-mail: iemmys@iemmys.tv; awardsdept@iemmys.tv Web Site: www.iemmys.tv, pg 993

International Festival of Films on Art (FIFA), 5333 Ave Casgrain, Suite 403, Montreal, QC H2T 1X3, Canada Tel: 514-874-1637 E-mail: info@artfifa.com Web Site: www.lefifa.org, pg 993

International Film Festival in Abitibi-Teiscamingue, 215 Ave Mercier, Rouyn-Noranda, QC J9X 5W8, Canada Tel: 819-762-6212 Fax: 819-762-6762 E-mail: info@festivalcinema.ca Web Site: festivalcinema.ca, pg 993

International Historic Films Inc, 3533 S Archer Ave, Chicago, IL 60609 Tel: 773-927-2900; 773-927-9091 (cust serv) Fax: 773-927-9211 E-mail: intrvdeo@ix.netcom.com Web Site: ihffilm.com, pg 790

International Light Technologies Inc, 10 Technology Dr, Peabody, MA 01960 Tel: 978-818-6180 Fax: 978-818-6181 E-mail: ilsales@intl-lighttech.com Web Site: www.intl-lighttech.com, pg 790

International Marketing Group, 1900 Elm Hill Pike, Nashville, TN 37210 Tel: 615-889-8000 Fax: 615-871-4817, pg 790

International Robotics Inc, 2001 Palmer Ave, Suite LL-1, Larchmont, NY 10538 Tel: 914-630-1060 E-mail: info@internationalrobotics.com Web Site: internationalrobotics.com, pg 790

International Short Film & Video Competition, 6116 N Central Expwy, Suite 105, Dallas, TX 75206 Tel: 214-821-6300; 214-821-FILM (821-3456) Fax: 214-821-6364 E-mail: usafilmfest@aol.com Web Site: www.usafilmfestival.com, pg 993

International Society for Performance Improvement® (ISPI), PO Box 13035, Silver Spring, MD 20910 Tel: 301-587-8570 Fax: 301-587-8573 E-mail: info@ispi.org Web Site: www.ispi.org, pg 956

The International Society of Automation (ISA), 67 T W Alexander Dr, Research Triangle Park, NC 27709 Tel: 919-549-8411 Fax: 919-549-8288 E-mail: info@isa.org Web Site: www.isa.org, pg 790

International Storytelling Center, 116 W Main St, Jonesborough, TN 37659 Tel: 423-753-2171 Toll Free Tel: 800-952-8392 Fax: 423-913-8219 E-mail: customerservice@storytellingcenter.net Web Site: www.storytellingcenter.net, pg 956

International Tae Kwon Do Association (ITA Institute), PO Box 281, Grand Blanc, MI 48480 Tel: 810-232-6482 E-mail: hq@itatkd.com Web Site: www.itatkd.com, pg 790

International Ticketing Association Inc (INTIX), 5868 E 71 St, Suite E 367, Indianapolis, IN 46220 Tel: 212-629-4036 Fax: 212-629-4036 E-mail: info@intix.org; media@intix.org Web Site: www.intix.org, pg 957

International Wildlife Film Festival, Roxy Theater, 718 S Higgins Ave, Missoula, MT 59801 Tel: 406-728-9380 Fax: 406-728-2881 E-mail: iwff@wildlifefilms.org Web Site: www.wildlifefilms.org, pg 993

Interscope, Geffen, A&M Records, 2220 Colorado Ave, Santa Monica, CA 90404 Tel: 310-865-4500 Web Site: www.interscope.com, pg 790

Intersil Americas LLC, 1001 Murphy Ranch Rd, Milpitas, CA 95035 *Tel:* 408-432-8888 *Toll Free Tel:* 888-INTERSIL (468-3774) *Fax:* 408-434-5351 *Web Site:* www.intersil.com, pg 790

Interstate Connecting Components, 120 Mount Holly Bypass, Lumberton, NJ 08048-1112 *Tel:* 856-722-5535 *Toll Free Tel:* 888-881-5420 *Fax:* 856-813-5419 *E-mail:* info@connecticc.com *Web Site:* www.connecticc.com, pg 790

Intervideo Duplication Services, 3533 S Archer Ave, Chicago, IL 60609 *Tel:* 773-927-9091 *Fax:* 773-927-9211 *E-mail:* info@intervideoduplication.com *Web Site:* www.intervideoduplication.com, pg 791

InterVision Media, 44 W Broadway, Suite 426, Eugene, OR 97401 *Tel:* 541-343-7993; 547-345-5951 *E-mail:* info@intervisionmedia.com *Web Site:* www.intervisionmedia.com, pg 791

Iowa Cable & Telecommunications Association (ICTA), 3737 Westown Pkwy, Suite C, West Des Moines, IA 50266 *Tel:* 515-697-6646 *E-mail:* info@iacable.com *Web Site:* www.iacable.com, pg 957

Iowa State University-Information Technology Services, 192 Parks Library, Ames, IA 50011 *Tel:* 515-294-8026; 515-294-4000 *E-mail:* solution@iastate.edu *Web Site:* www.it.iastate.edu, pg 791

IPI - Member Network™, 2518 Anthem Village Dr, Suite 104, Henderson, NV 89052 *Tel:* 702-617-1141 *Fax:* 702-617-1181 *E-mail:* info@ipiphoto.com *Web Site:* www.ipiphoto.com, pg 957

Ipitek Inc, 2461 Impala Dr, Carlsbad, CA 92010 *Tel:* 760-438-1010 *Toll Free Tel:* 888-4-IPITEK (447-4835, US only) *Fax:* 760-438-2412 *E-mail:* sales@ipitek.com *Web Site:* www.ipitek.com, pg 791

iProbe Multilingual Solutions Inc, 20 Jay St, Suite 638, New York, NY 11201 *Tel:* 212-489-6035 *Toll Free Tel:* 888-489-6035 *Fax:* 212-202-4790 *E-mail:* info@iprobesolutions.com *Web Site:* iprobesolutions.com, pg 791

IRE Annual Awards for Investigative Reporting, Missouri School of Journalism, 141 Neff Annex, Columbia, MO 65211 *Tel:* 573-882-2042 *Fax:* 573-882-5431 *E-mail:* info@ire.org; rescntr@ire.org *Web Site:* www.ire.org/awards, pg 993

Ironbound Film & Television Studios LLC, 169 Malvern St, Newark, NJ 07105 *Tel:* 201-456-4754 *Web Site:* www.ironboundfilmstudios.com, pg 791

Ironik Design & Post, 56 E Main St, Suite 203, Avon, CT 06001 *Tel:* 860-404-2386 *Fax:* 860-404-2735 *E-mail:* info@ironikdesign.com *Web Site:* www.ironikdesign.com, pg 791

Ironstone Technologies Inc, 534 Berry St, Winnipeg, MB R3H 0R9, Canada *Tel:* 204-697-0159 *Toll Free Tel:* 800-665-4766 *Fax:* 204-694-9355 *E-mail:* info@ironstone.ca *Web Site:* www.ironstone.ca, pg 791

IRTS Foundation, 1697 Broadway, Suite 404, New York, NY 10019 *Tel:* 212-867-6650 *E-mail:* info@irts.org *Web Site:* irtsfoundation.org, pg 957

ISCAN Inc, 21 Cabot Rd, Woburn, MA 01801 *Tel:* 781-932-1199 *Fax:* 781-932-1155 *E-mail:* info@iscaninc.com *Web Site:* www.iscaninc.com, pg 791

Ishtar Films, 12400 Moorpark St, Suite 2, Studio City, CA 91604 *Toll Free Tel:* 800-428-7136 *Fax:* 818-985-0567 *E-mail:* ishtarfilms2@sbcglobal.net *Web Site:* www.ishtarfilms.com, pg 791

Israel Film Festival, 324 S Beverly Dr, No 424, Beverly Hills, CA 90212 *Tel:* 310-247-1800 *E-mail:* info@israelfilmfestival.org *Web Site:* www.israelfilmfestival.com, pg 993

ITA Audio Visual Solutions, 2162 Dana Ave & I-71, Cincinnati, OH 45207-1341 *Tel:* 513-631-7000 *Toll Free Tel:* 800-899-8877 *Fax:* 513-631-3290 *E-mail:* csr@ita.com *Web Site:* www.ita.com, pg 791

ITC, 523 Hanley Industrial Ct, St Louis, MO 63144 *Tel:* 314-646-1800 *Toll Free Tel:* 800-962-2344 *Fax:* 314-646-1818 *Web Site:* www.itcjourneys.com, pg 791

ITC Learning LLC, 330 Himmarshee St, Suite 108, Fort Lauderdale, FL 33312 *Toll Free Tel:* 800-638-3757 *E-mail:* sales@itclearning.com *Web Site:* www.itclearning.com, pg 791

ITEC Entertainment Corp, 8544 Commodity Circle, Orlando, FL 32819 *Tel:* 407-226-0200 *Fax:* 407-226-0201 *E-mail:* productionsinfo@itec.com *Web Site:* www.itec.com, pg 791

ITT Veam LLC, 100 New Wood Rd, Watertown, CT 06795 *Tel:* 860-274-9681 *Fax:* 860-274-4963 *Web Site:* www.ittcannon.com, pg 791

ITV Productions, 1649 S Robertson Blvd, Los Angeles, CA 90035 *Tel:* 310-204-1234 *E-mail:* itvproductions1@gmail.com *Web Site:* www.itvproductions.com, pg 792

IV Media Resources, 910 Redwing Dr, Geneva, IL 60134 *Tel:* 630-389-0000 *E-mail:* info@infinitevideo.com *Web Site:* www.infinitevideo.com, pg 792

iVideo Technologies, 6779 Engle Rd, Suite G, Middleburg Heights, OH 44130 *Toll Free Tel:* 800-352-6150 *E-mail:* info@ivideo.com *Web Site:* www.ivideo.com, pg 792

Ivie Technologies Inc, 1195 Spring Creek Place, Suite B, Springville, UT 84663 *Tel:* 801-489-8703 *Toll Free Fax:* 877-829-6567 *E-mail:* ivie@ivie.com *Web Site:* www.ivie.com, pg 792

Ivory Productions, 529 Plymouth Rd, Gwynedd Valley, PA 19437 *Tel:* 215-591-9900 *Web Site:* www.ivoryproductions.com; www.facebook.com/davidivoryproductions, pg 792

IVS Imaging, 101 Wrangler Dr, Suite 201, Coppell, TX 75019 *Toll Free Tel:* 888-446-1301 *Fax:* 469-635-6800 *E-mail:* info@ivsimaging.com *Web Site:* www.ivsimaging.com, pg 792

J & R Film Co, 1135 N Mansfield Ave, Hollywood, CA 90038 *Tel:* 323-467-1116 *Toll Free Tel:* 877-668-4652 *Web Site:* moviola.com, pg 792

J K Audio Inc, 1311 E Sixth St, Sandwich, IL 60548 *Tel:* 815-786-2929 *Toll Free Tel:* 800-552-8346 *Fax:* 815-786-8502 *E-mail:* info@jkaudio.com *Web Site:* www.jkaudio.com, pg 792

Jack's Camera Shop, 300 E Main St, Muncie, IN 47305 *Tel:* 765-282-0204 *Fax:* 765-284-6405 *E-mail:* info@jackscamera.com *Web Site:* jackscamera.com, pg 792

Jackson Hole Film Commission, 260A Broadway Ave, Jackson, WY 83001 *Tel:* 307-733-3316 *Fax:* 307-733-5585 *Web Site:* www.jacksonholechamber.com, pg 977

Jacksonville Office of Economic Development, Film & Television Office, 117 W Duval St, Suite 280, Jacksonville, FL 32202 *Tel:* 904-630-2522 *Web Site:* www.coj.net, pg 969

JaffeHolden, 114-A Washington St, Norwalk, CT 06854 *Tel:* 203-838-4167 *Fax:* 203-838-4168 *Web Site:* www.jaffeholden.com, pg 792

Jaguar Distribution Corp, 12711 Ventura Blvd, Suite 300, Studio City, CA 91604 *Tel:* 818-508-3377 *Fax:* 818-508-3340 *Web Site:* www.jaguardc.com, pg 792

Jai Inc, 6800 Santa Teresa Blvd, Suite 175, San Jose, CA 95119 *Tel:* 408-383-0300 *Toll Free Tel:* 800-445-5444 *Fax:* 408-383-0301 *E-mail:* camerasales.americas@jai.com *Web Site:* www.jai.com, pg 792

Jalbert Productions International, 230 New York Ave, Huntington, NY 11743 *Tel:* 631-351-5878 *Fax:* 631-351-5875 *E-mail:* jalbert@jalbertfilm.com *Web Site:* jalbertfilm.com, pg 792

JAM Industries Ltd, 21000 Trans-Canadienne, Baie D'Urfe, QC H9X 4B7, Canada *Tel:* 514-457-2555 *Fax:* 514-457-0055 *E-mail:* info@jamindustries.com *Web Site:* jamindustries.com, pg 792

Jameco Electronics, 1355 Shoreway Rd, Belmont, CA 94002 *Tel:* 650-592-8097 *Toll Free Tel:* 800-831-4242 (orders); 800-536-4316 (cust serv) *Fax:* 650-592-2503 *Toll Free Fax:* 800-237-6948 *E-mail:* info@jameco.com; sales@jameco.com *Web Site:* www.jameco.com, pg 792

James Agee Film Project, PO Box 73, Riverdale, MD 20738-0073 *Tel:* 301-277-3880 *E-mail:* jagee@cstone.net *Web Site:* www.ageefilms.org, pg 792

Jams Productions Inc, Production Trailer No 1, 206 Holt Rd, Bowmanville, ON L1C 3K7, Canada *Tel:* 647-273-4844 *E-mail:* info@jamsproductions.ca *Web Site:* www.jamsproductions.ca, pg 793

JamSync, Music Row, 1232 17 Ave S, Nashville, TN 37212 *Tel:* 615-320-5050 *E-mail:* info@jamsync.com *Web Site:* www.jamsync.com, pg 793

Jan-Al Cases, 3339 Union Pacific Ave, Los Angeles, CA 90023 *Tel:* 323-260-7212 *Toll Free Tel:* 800-735-2625 *Fax:* 323-260-4696 *Web Site:* www.janalcase.com, pg 793

J&D Laboratories Inc, 27 E 21 St, 4th fl, New York, NY 10010 *Tel:* 212-982-3330 *Fax:* 212-982-3332 *E-mail:* jdvideolab@aol.com; sales@jdvideolab.com *Web Site:* www.jdvideolab.com, pg 793

Janson Industries, 1200 Garfield Ave SW, Canton, OH 44706 *Tel:* 330-455-7029 *Toll Free Tel:* 800-548-8982 *Fax:* 330-455-5919 *Web Site:* www.jansonindustries.com, pg 793

Janson Media Inc, The Cunningham House, 118 Main St, Tappan, NY 10983 *Tel:* 845-359-8488 *E-mail:* info@janson.com *Web Site:* www.janson.com, pg 793

Janus Films Inc, 215 Park Ave S, 5th fl, New York, NY 10003 *Tel:* 212-756-8822 *Fax:* 212-756-8850 *E-mail:* booking@janusfilms.com *Web Site:* www.criterion.com; www.janusfilms.com, pg 793

Jazzology, 61 French Market Place, New Orleans, LA 70116 *Tel:* 504-525-5000 *Fax:* 504-525-1776 *E-mail:* geobuck@jazzology.com *Web Site:* www.jazzology.com, pg 793

JBL Professional, 8500 Balboa Blvd, Northridge, CA 91329 *Tel:* 818-894-8850 *Fax:* 818-830-7865 (mktg); 818-894-3479; 818-830-7801 (sales) *E-mail:* info@jblpro.com *Web Site:* www.jblpro.com; www.harman.com, pg 793

JCS Video Productions, 4617 Sequoia Park Ave, Las Vegas, NV 89139 *Tel:* 702-596-9291 (cell); 702-546-0150 *Toll Free Tel:* 800-791-8671 *Fax:* 702-546-0150 *Web Site:* www.jcsvideo.com, pg 793

JD Audio Visual Inc, 77 N Altadena Dr, Pasadena, CA 91107 *Tel:* 626-792-6682 *Toll Free Tel:* 800-532-8346 *Fax:* 626-796-6635 *E-mail:* sales@jdav.com; rentals@jdav.com *Web Site:* www.jdav.com, pg 793

JDC Wilmington Camera Services, 905 N 23 St, Wilmington, NC 28405 *Tel:* 910-343-1089 *Fax:* 910-343-0247 *E-mail:* info@wilmingtoncameraservices.com, pg 793

JDS Video & Media Productions, 28069 Diaz Rd, Suite D & E, Temecula, CA 92590 *Tel:* 951-296-6715 *Toll Free Fax:* 866-737-2239 *E-mail:* info@jds-productions.com *Web Site:* jds-productions.com, pg 793

Jeep Jazz Media Solutions, 8 Graham Terr, Montclair, NJ 07042 *Tel:* 973-222-5737 *E-mail:* jeepjazz@hotmail.com *Web Site:* www.jeepjazz.com, pg 793

Jeff Davis Parish Film Commission, 100 Rue de l'Acadie, Jennings, LA 70546 *Tel:* 337-821-5521 *Toll Free Tel:* 800-264-5521 *Fax:* 337-821-5556 *E-mail:* info@jeffdavis.org *Web Site:* jeffdavis.org/film-commission, pg 971

The Peter Jennings Award, 40 W 45 St, New York, NY 10036 *Tel:* 212-626-9220 *Fax:* 212-626-9210 *E-mail:* info@opcofamerica.org *Web Site:* www.opcofamerica.org, pg 994

JENSEN Tools + Supply, 335 Willow St, North Andover, MA 01845-5995 *Tel:* 978-682-9844 *Toll Free Tel:* 800-225-5370 (sales) *Toll Free Fax:* 800-743-8141 *E-mail:* sales@sbdinc.com *Web Site:* jensentools.com, pg 793

Jensen Transformers Inc, 9304 Deering Ave, Chatsworth, CA 91311 *Tel:* 818-374-5857 *Toll Free Tel:* 866-476-6291 *Fax:* 818-374-5856 *E-mail:* sales@jensen-transformers.com *Web Site:* www.jensen-transformers.com, pg 793

Jeppesen, 55 Inverness Dr E, Englewood, CO 80112 *Tel:* 303-799-9090 *Toll Free Tel:* 800-621-5377; 800-353-2107 *Fax:* 303-328-4153 *Web Site:* www.jeppesen. com, pg 793

Jereco Studios Inc, 627 E Peach St, Suite E, Bozeman, MT 59715 *Tel:* 406-586-5262 *Web Site:* www. jerecostudios.com, pg 793

Jeron Electronic Systems Inc, 7501 N Natchez Ave, Niles, IL 60714 *Tel:* 773-275-1900 *Toll Free Tel:* 800-621-1903 *Fax:* 773-275-0283 *E-mail:* sales@jeron.com *Web Site:* www.jeron.com, pg 794

JFA Studio, 3062 N Lima St, Burbank, CA 91504 *Tel:* 818-861-9090 *E-mail:* info@jfastudio.com *Web Site:* www.jfastudio.com, pg 794

JFB Communications, 3 Haig Ave, Toronto, ON M1N 2W2, Canada *Tel:* 416-691-5001; 416-526-9400 (cell) *E-mail:* jfb@jfb.ca *Web Site:* www.jfb.ca, pg 794

JFW Industries Inc, 5134 Commerce Square Dr, Indianapolis, IN 46237 *Tel:* 317-887-1340 *Toll Free Tel:* 877-887-4539 *Fax:* 317-881-6790 *E-mail:* sales@ jfwindustries.com; jfwengr@jfwindustries.com *Web Site:* www.jfwindustries.com, pg 794

JIB Shots Equipment Inc, 1828 Lorraine Ave, Ottawa, ON K1H 6Z8, Canada *Tel:* 613-293-3318 *Web Site:* www.jibshots.com, pg 794

The Jim Henson Co, 1416 N La Brea Ave, Hollywood, CA 90028 *Tel:* 323-802-1500 *Fax:* 323-802-1825 *Web Site:* www.henson.com, pg 794

Jin Records, 700 S Chataignier, Ville Platte, LA 70586 *Tel:* 337-363-2177 *Toll Free Tel:* 800-738-8668 (orders) *Fax:* 337-363-2094 *E-mail:* info@ flattownmusic.com *Web Site:* www.flattownmusic.com, pg 794

JIST Publishing, 875 Montreal Way, St Paul, MN 55102 *Toll Free Tel:* 800-328-1452 *Toll Free Fax:* 800-328-4564 *E-mail:* educate@emcp.com *Web Site:* jist.emcp. com, pg 794

JL Recording Studios, 270 Adelaide St W, Suite 202, Toronto, ON M5H 1X6, Canada *Tel:* 416-598-7979 *Web Site:* www.jlstudios.ca; www.facebook.com/ jlrecordingstudios; twitter.com/JLStudios, pg 794

JLCooper Electronics, 142 Arena St, El Segundo, CA 90245 *Tel:* 310-322-9990 *Fax:* 310-335-0110 *E-mail:* sales@jlcooper.com; service@jlcooper.com *Web Site:* www.jlcooper.com, pg 794

JMC Photo & Digital Services Inc, 10 Westport Ct, Bloomington, IL 61704-8233 *Tel:* 309-663-4677 *E-mail:* jmcpds@jmcpds.com *Web Site:* www.jmcpds. com, pg 794

JoeAudio, 10850 John Galt Blvd, Omaha, NE 68137 *Tel:* 402-341-9153 *Toll Free Tel:* 866-JOE-AUDIO (563-2834) *Web Site:* www.joeaudioproductions.com, pg 794

John McLean Media, 802 Newton, Penthouse 3, Seattle, WA 98109 *Tel:* 206-285-2603 *E-mail:* info@johnmcleanmedia.com *Web Site:* www. johnmcleanmedia.com, pg 794

Alan Johnson Recording, 5763 Park Plaza Ct, Indianapolis, IN 46220 *Tel:* 317-439-6521 *E-mail:* alan@alanjohnsonrecording.com *Web Site:* www.alanjohnsonrecording.com, pg 794

Johnson Systems Inc (JSI), 1923 Highfield Crescent SE, Calgary, AB T2G 5M1, Canada *Tel:* 403-287-8003 *Fax:* 403-287-9003 *E-mail:* info@johnsonsystems.com *Web Site:* www.johnsonsystems.com, pg 794

Pamela Johnston Voice Talent, 249 Eighth Ave, Cramerton, NC 28032 *Tel:* 703-371-7341 *Fax:* 703-997-8971 *Web Site:* www.pjvoicetalent.com, pg 794

Jointure for Community Adult Education Inc, Centre at Raritan, Suite B-11, 1124 US Hwy 202 S, Raritan, NJ 08869 *Tel:* 908-722-0233 *Fax:* 908-722-0388 *E-mail:* info@jointure.org *Web Site:* www.jointure.org, pg 794

JoLida Inc, 21310 Ridgecroft Dr, Brookeville, MD 20833 *Tel:* 301-953-2014 *Fax:* 301-498-0554 *E-mail:* jolidacorp@msn.com *Web Site:* www.jolida. com, pg 795

Jordan Klein Film & Video (JKFV), 10197 SE 144 Place, Summerfield, FL 34491 *Tel:* 352-288-3999 *Web Site:* www.jordy.com, pg 795

Joseph Electronics, 6633 W Howard St, Niles, IL 60714 *Tel:* 847-588-3800 *Toll Free Tel:* 800-323-5925 *Fax:* 847-588-3300 *Toll Free Fax:* 800-446-8366 *E-mail:* sales@josephelectronics.com *Web Site:* www. josephelectronics.com, pg 795

Harry Joseph & Associates Inc, PO Box 20993, New York, NY 10025 *Tel:* 212-244-5900 *E-mail:* harry@ hja.com *Web Site:* www.hja.com, pg 795

Josephson Engineering Inc, 329-A Ingalls St, Santa Cruz, CA 95060 *Tel:* 831-420-0888 *Fax:* 831-420-0890 *E-mail:* info@josephson.com *Web Site:* www. josephson.com, pg 795

Joyce Media Inc, 3413 Soledad Canyon Rd, Acton, CA 93510 *Tel:* 661-269-1169 *Fax:* 661-269-2139 *E-mail:* help@joycemediainc.com *Web Site:* www. joycemediainc.com, pg 795

JPL, 471 JPL Wick Dr, Harrisburg, PA 17111-2504 *Tel:* 717-558-8048 *Fax:* 717-558-8349 *E-mail:* jpl@ jplcreative.com *Web Site:* www.jplcreative.com; www. facebook.com/jplcreative, pg 795

JRF Magnetic Sciences Inc, 249 Kennedy Rd, Greendell, NJ 07839 *Tel:* 973-579-5773 *Fax:* 973-579-6021 *E-mail:* jrf@jrfmagnetics.com *Web Site:* www. jrfmagnetics.com, pg 795

JSAV, 9150 N Royal Lane, Suite 150, Irving, TX 75063 *Tel:* 972-241-5444 *Toll Free Tel:* 800-852-8771 *Fax:* 972-247-2590 *E-mail:* info@jsav.com *Web Site:* www.jsav.com, pg 795

JSC Wire & Cable, 7861 Airport Hwy, Pennsauken, NJ 08109 *Tel:* 856-324-2929 *Toll Free Tel:* 800-572-9473 *E-mail:* sales@jscwire.com *Web Site:* www.jscwire. com, pg 795

JT Communications, 579 NE 44 Ave, Ocala, FL 34470-1421 *Tel:* 352-236-0744 *Fax:* 352-236-5130 *E-mail:* general_info@jtcomms.com *Web Site:* www. jtcomms.com, pg 795

Juice Goose, 7320 Ashcroft, Suite 104, Houston, TX 77081 *Tel:* 713-772-1404 *Fax:* 713-772-7360 *E-mail:* info@juicegoose.com *Web Site:* www. juicegoose.com, pg 795

Juice Studios, 1648 Tenth St, Santa Monica, CA 90404 *Tel:* 310-460-7830 *Fax:* 310-460-7845 *Web Site:* www. facebook.com/juicestudiosla; www.juicestudios.tv, pg 795

JungleTV, 571 NW Mercantile Place, Port St Lucie, FL 34986 *Tel:* 772-370-0043 *E-mail:* info@jungletv.com *Web Site:* www.jungletv.com, pg 795

Juno Awards, 219 Dufferin St, Suite 211C, Toronto, ON M6K 3J1, Canada *Tel:* 416-485-3135 (CN only) *Toll Free Tel:* 888-501-3135 *Fax:* 416-485-4978 *E-mail:* info@carasonline.ca; submissions@ junoawards.ca; junoawards.ca; *Web Site:* www. junoawards.ca; facebook.com/theJunoAwards, pg 994

Jupiter Moon Productions, 219 36 St, No 3A, Brooklyn, NY 11232 *Tel:* 631-553-9750, pg 795

Jupiter Systems, 31015 Huntwood Ave, Hayward, CA 94544 *Tel:* 510-675-1000 *Fax:* 510-675-1001 *E-mail:* sales@jupiter.com *Web Site:* www.jupiter.com, pg 795

Just Bulbs - The Light Bulb Store, 222 E 58 St, New York, NY 10022 *Tel:* 212-888-5707 *Fax:* 212-888-5704 *E-mail:* sales@justbulbsnyc.com *Web Site:* www. justbulbsnyc.com, pg 795

JVC Professional Products Co, 1700 Valley Rd, Wayne, NJ 07470 *Tel:* 973-317-5000 *Toll Free Tel:* 800-582-5825; 800-247-3608; 800-252-5722 *Fax:* 973-317-5030 *Toll Free Fax:* 800-582-5825 (option 2) *E-mail:* proinfo@jvc.com *Web Site:* www.jvc.com, pg 796

JWP Inc, PO Box 14867, Fort Worth, TX 76117 *Tel:* 817-233-6462 *Web Site:* www.jwproductions.org, pg 796

Ka Io Productions Inc, PO Box 5150, Hilo, HI 96720-1150 *Tel:* 808-959-3885 *Toll Free Tel:* 888-458-7538 *Fax:* 808-959-3885 *E-mail:* lava@volcanovideo.com *Web Site:* www.volcanovideo.com, pg 796

Kaboom Productions, 2169 Folsom St, Suite 201-M, San Francisco, CA 94110 *Tel:* 415-434-2666 *Fax:* 415-874-9324 *E-mail:* hello@kaboomproductions.com *Web Site:* www.kaboomproductions.com, pg 796

KAE Corp, 955 E 500 S, Salt Lake City, UT 84102 *Tel:* 801-238-2300 *E-mail:* kaecorp@xmission.com *Web Site:* www.kaecorp.com, pg 796

KAKE-TV, 1500 N West St, Wichita, KS 67203-1323 *Tel:* 316-943-4221; 316-946-1363 (sales) *Fax:* 316-943-5493 (sales) *E-mail:* sales@kake.com; news@ kake.com *Web Site:* kake.com, pg 796

Kaleidosound, 936 Dewing Ave, Suite I, Lafayette, CA 94549 *Tel:* 925-283-9901 *Fax:* 925-283-9902 *Web Site:* www.k-sound.com, pg 796

Kalglo Electronics Co Inc, 5911 Colony Dr, Bethlehem, PA 18017-9348 *Tel:* 610-837-0700 *Fax:* 610-837-7978 *E-mail:* kalglo@kalglo.com *Web Site:* www.kalglo. com, pg 796

Kanab/Kane County Film Commission, Kane County Utah Off of Tourism, 78 S 100 E, Kanab, UT 84741 *Tel:* 435-644-5033 *Toll Free Tel:* 800-SEE-KANE (733-5263) *E-mail:* kanetrav@kaneutah.com *Web Site:* visitsouthernutah.com, pg 976

K&R All Media Productions LLC, 28533 Greenfield Rd, Southfield, MI 48076 *Tel:* 248-557-8276 *Web Site:* www.knr.net, pg 796

K&R PhotoDigital, 538 Terry Lane, Fort Mitchell, KY 41017 *Tel:* 859-341-6998; 859-341-6986 (orders) *Fax:* 859-341-6987 *E-mail:* photodigitalpro@mac.com; wilmakr@aol.com *Web Site:* www.krphotodigital.com, pg 796

K&R's Recording Studios Inc, 28533 Greenfield, Southfield, MI 48076 *Tel:* 248-557-8276; 248-569-5422 *Web Site:* www.knr.net; www.kandrforensic.com, pg 796

Kangaroo Cases, 4027 Main St, Dallas, TX 75226 *Tel:* 214-823-5264 *Toll Free Tel:* 800-890-1073 *Fax:* 214-824-1179 *E-mail:* info@kangaroocases.com *Web Site:* www.kangaroocases.com, pg 796

Kansas City Film Office, 1321 Baltimore Ave, Kansas City, MO 64105 *Tel:* 816-691-3800 *Toll Free Tel:* 800-767-7700 *E-mail:* film@visitkc.com *Web Site:* www. kcfilmoffice.com, pg 973

Kansas City FilmFest International (KCFFI), 4741 Central, Suite 306, Kansas City, MO 64112 *Tel:* 816-286-4777 *E-mail:* info@kcfilmfest.org *Web Site:* kcfilmfest.org, pg 994

Kansas Creative Arts Industries Commission, 1000 SW Jackson St, Suite 100, Topeka, KS 66612-1354 *Tel:* 785-296-2178 *Fax:* 785-296-3490 *Web Site:* www. kansascommerce.gov/caic, pg 971

Kantola Productions LLC, 55 Sunnyside Ave, Mill Valley, CA 94941 *Tel:* 415-381-9363 *Toll Free Tel:* 800-280-1180 *Fax:* 415-381-9801 *E-mail:* kantola@kantola.com *Web Site:* www.kantola. com, pg 796

The David Kaplan Award, 40 W 45 St, New York, NY 10036 *Tel:* 212-626-9220 *Fax:* 212-626-9210 *E-mail:* info@opcofamerica.org *Web Site:* www. opcofamerica.org, pg 994

Richard Kaplan Productions, 455 N End Ave, Apt 1114, New York, NY 10282-1139 *Tel:* 212-787-0258 *Fax:* 212-787-0268 *E-mail:* richardkaplan33@gmail. com *Web Site:* richardkaplanproductions.com, pg 796

Kappa Map Group LLC, 112 E New York Ave, Deland, FL 32724 *Tel:* 386-873-3010 *Toll Free Tel:* 800-829-6277 (cust serv) *Fax:* 386-873-3011 *E-mail:* info@ kappamapgroup.com; sales@kappamapgroup.com *Web Site:* kappamapgroup.com, pg 796

Kappa optronics Inc, 825 S Primrose Ave, Suite I, Monrovia, CA 91016 *Tel:* 626-256-4343 *E-mail:* contact@kappa-optronics.com *Web Site:* www. kappa-optronics.com, pg 796

Karst Productions Inc, 5779 NE County Rd 340, High Springs, FL 32643 *Tel:* 386-454-3556 *Fax:* 386-454-3749 *E-mail:* support@karstproductions.com *Web Site:* www.karstproductions.com, pg 796

Kart-A-Bag Manufacturing Inc, 510 Manhattan Rd, Joliet, IL 60433 *Tel:* 815-723-1940 *Toll Free Tel:* 800-423-9328 *Fax:* 815-723-2495 *E-mail:* sales@kart-a-bag.com *Web Site:* www.kart-a-bag.com, pg 796

KAS Music & Sound, 34-12 36 St, Astoria, NY 11106 *Tel:* 718-786-3400 *Fax:* 718-729-3007 *Web Site:* www.kasmusic.com, pg 796

Kavanagh Productions Inc, 32 Broadway, Suite 1711-12, New York, NY 10004 *Tel:* 212-480-0065 *Fax:* 212-480-0149 *E-mail:* create@kavanaghproductions.com *Web Site:* kavanaghproductions.com, pg 797

Kavich Reynolds Productions Inc, 3151 Cahuenga Blvd, Suite 101, Los Angeles, CA 90068 *Tel:* 323-851-2490 *E-mail:* info@kavichreynolds.com *Web Site:* www.kavichreynolds.com, pg 797

Kay Industries Inc, PO Box 1323, South Bend, IN 46624 *Tel:* 574-236-6220 *Toll Free Tel:* 800-348-5257 *Fax:* 574-289-5932 *E-mail:* techsupport@kayind.com; info@kayind.com *Web Site:* www.kayind.com, pg 797

KCFW Television, 401 First Ave E, Kalispell, MT 59901 *Tel:* 406-755-5239 *Fax:* 406-752-8002 *E-mail:* news@kcfw.com *Web Site:* www.nbcmontana.com/news/kcfw, pg 797

KD Kanopy Inc, 1921 E 68 Ave, Denver, CO 80229 *Tel:* 303-650-1310 *Toll Free Tel:* 800-432-4435 *Fax:* 303-650-5211 *E-mail:* sales@kdkanopy.com *Web Site:* www.kdkanopy.com, pg 797

KDM Electronics Inc, 55 Mills Rd, Unit 3, Ajax, ON L1S 2H2, Canada *Tel:* 416-439-7158 *Toll Free Tel:* 800-567-6282 *Fax:* 416-439-7232 *E-mail:* kdm@octasound.com *Web Site:* www.octasound.com, pg 797

KEF Media, 1161 Concord Rd SE, Smyrna, GA 30080 *Tel:* 404-605-0009 *E-mail:* info@kefmedia.com *Web Site:* kefmedia.com, pg 797

Kelmscott Communications, 1665 Mallette Rd, Aurora, IL 60505-1354 *Tel:* 630-898-0800 *Fax:* 630-898-2183 *Web Site:* kelmscottcommunications.com, pg 797

Ken-A-Vision Manufacturing Co Inc, 5615 Raytown Rd, Kansas City, MO 64133 *Tel:* 816-353-4787 *Toll Free Tel:* 800-501-7366; 800-627-1953 (cust serv) *Fax:* 816-358-5072 *E-mail:* info@ken-a-vision.com *Web Site:* www.ken-a-vision.com, pg 797

Ken-Del Productions Inc, 1500 First State Blvd, Wilmington, DE 19804-3596 *Tel:* 302-999-1111; 302-999-1110; 302-999-1164 *Toll Free Tel:* 800-249-1110 *Fax:* 302-999-1656 *E-mail:* info@ken-del.com *Web Site:* www.ken-del.com, pg 797

Ken-Del Studios, 1500 First State Blvd, Wilmington, DE 19804-3596 *Tel:* 302-999-1111 *Toll Free Tel:* 800-249-1110 *Fax:* 302-999-1656 *E-mail:* info@ken-del.com *Web Site:* www.ken-del.com, pg 797

Kendall Hunt Publishing Co, 4050 Westmark Dr, Dubuque, IA 52002 *Tel:* 563-589-1000 *Toll Free Tel:* 800-228-0810 *Fax:* 563-589-1237 *Toll Free Fax:* 800-772-9165 *E-mail:* orders@kendallhunt.com; corpinfo@kendallhunt.com *Web Site:* www.kendallhunt.com, pg 797

Keng Seng Enterprises Inc, 4000 Rue St Ambroise, Suite 103, Montreal, QC H4C 2C7, Canada *Tel:* 514-939-3971 *Fax:* 514-939-6239 *Web Site:* www.kengseng.com, pg 797

Kenko Tokina USA, 7642 Woodwind Dr, Huntington Beach, CA 92647 *Tel:* 714-849-5700 *Toll Free Tel:* 800-421-1141 *Fax:* 714-849-5677 *E-mail:* support@kenkotokinausa.com *Web Site:* kenkotokinausa.com, pg 797

Robert F Kennedy Journalism Awards, 1300 19 St NW, Suite 750, Washington, DC 20036 *Tel:* 646-553-4750 *E-mail:* info@rfkhumanrights.org; communications@rfkhumanrights.org *Web Site:* rfkhumanrights.org/awards, pg 994

Kensington Falls Animation, 1680 Hillsdale Ave, Ambridge, PA 15003 *Tel:* 724-266-0329 *E-mail:* kensingtonfalls@aol.com *Web Site:* kensingtonfalls.com, pg 797

Kensington Technology Group, 1500 Fashion Island Blvd, 3rd fl, San Mateo, CA 94404 *Tel:* 650-572-2700 *Toll Free Tel:* 800-535-4242 (tech support); 800-235-6708 (cust serv) *E-mail:* sales@kensington.com *Web Site:* www.kensington.com, pg 797

Norman Kent Productions, PO Box 1749, Flagler Beach, FL 32136 *Tel:* 386-446-0505 *Web Site:* www.normankent.com, pg 798

Kentucky Film Association, 2365 Harrodsburg Rd, Suite B-325, Lexington, KY 40591 *Tel:* 859-317-9789 *Web Site:* ky.film, pg 957

Kentucky Film Office, 100 Airport Rd, Suite 200, Frankfort, KY 40601 *Tel:* 502-564-3456 *Toll Free Tel:* 800-345-6591 *Fax:* 502-564-5695 *E-mail:* email@kyfilm.com *Web Site:* kyfilmoffice.com, pg 971

Kentucky Grip & Lighting, 10005 Bunsen Way, Louisville, KY 40299 *Tel:* 502-548-5833 *Web Site:* www.kentuckygrip.com, pg 798

Kenyon Laboratories LLC, 12 Scovil Rd, Higganum, CT 06441 *Tel:* 860-345-2097 *Toll Free Tel:* 800-253-4681 *Fax:* 860-345-8652 *E-mail:* kenyonlabs@comcast.net; info@kenyongyro.com *Web Site:* www.ken-lab.com, pg 798

Kern County Film Commission, 1115 Truxtun Ave, Bakersfield, CA 93301 *Tel:* 661-868-7097 *Toll Free Tel:* 800-500-KERN (500-5376) *Fax:* 661-861-2017 *E-mail:* kerninfo@kerncounty.com *Web Site:* www.filmkern.com, pg 966

Kerrigan Productions Inc, 3877 Draper Ave, Montreal, QC H4A 2N9, Canada *Tel:* 514-486-8456 *Web Site:* www.kerrigan.ca, pg 798

Kerrville Convention & Visitors Bureau, 2108 Sidney Baker St, Kerrville, TX 78028 *Tel:* 830-792-3535 *Toll Free Tel:* 800-221-7958 *E-mail:* info@kerrvilletexascvb.com *Web Site:* www.kerrvilletexascvb.com, pg 976

Keslow Camera Inc, 5900 Blackwelder St, Culver City, CA 90232 *Tel:* 310-636-4600 *Fax:* 310-915-5335 *E-mail:* info@keslowcamera.com *Web Site:* www.keslowcamera.com, pg 798

KET The Kentucky Network, 600 Cooper Dr, Lexington, KY 40502 *Tel:* 859-258-7000 *Toll Free Tel:* 800-432-0951 *Fax:* 859-258-7396 *E-mail:* adulted@ket.org *Web Site:* www.ket.org, pg 798

Ketchum Inc, 1285 Avenue of the Americas, 4th fl, New York, NY 10019 *Tel:* 646-935-3900 *Web Site:* www.ketchum.com, pg 798

Key Digital Systems, 521 E Third St, Mount Vernon, NY 10553 *Tel:* 914-667-9700 *Toll Free Tel:* 855-539-3448 *Fax:* 914-668-8666 *E-mail:* info@keydigital.com; marketing@keydigital.com *Web Site:* www.keydigital.com, pg 798

The Keyboard Workshop, PO Box 700, Medford, OR 97501 *Tel:* 541-664-7052 *Web Site:* www.playpiano.com; www.facebook.com/pianochords, pg 798

Keymark Inc, 105 Tech Lane, Liberty, SC 29657 *Tel:* 864-343-0500 *Toll Free Tel:* 800-446-2826 *E-mail:* support@keymarkinc.com *Web Site:* www.keymarkinc.com, pg 798

Keystone View, 2200 Dickerson Rd, Reno, NV 89503 *Tel:* 775-324-2799; 510-931-7747 *Fax:* 775-324-5375 *E-mail:* sales@keystoneview.com *Web Site:* www.keystoneview.com, pg 798

Keywest Technology Inc, 14563 W 96 Terr, Lenexa, KS 66215 *Tel:* 913-492-4666 *Toll Free Tel:* 800-331-2019 *Fax:* 913-322-1864 *E-mail:* sales@keywesttechnology.com *Web Site:* www.keywesttechnology.com, pg 798

KFOR-TV, 444 E Britton Rd, Oklahoma City, OK 73114 *Tel:* 405-424-4444 *Fax:* 405-478-6228 *Web Site:* www.kfor.com, pg 798

KHNL/KGMB, 420 Waiakamilo Rd, Suite 205, Honolulu, HI 96817 *Tel:* 808-847-3246 *Fax:* 808-845-3616 *E-mail:* info8@khnl.com; news@hawaiinewsnow.com *Web Site:* www.hawaiinewsnow.com, pg 798

KidFilm®, 6116 N Central Expwy, Suite 105, Dallas, TX 75206 *Tel:* 214-821-6300; 214-821-FILM (821-3456) *Fax:* 214-821-6364 *E-mail:* usafilmfest@aol.com *Web Site:* www.usafilmfestival.com, pg 994

KidsEye™ International Film Festival, 83 Park St, Suite 5, Providence, RI 02903 *Tel:* 401-861-4445 *Fax:* 401-490-6735 *E-mail:* info@film-festival.org *Web Site:* film-festival.org, pg 994

Killer Tracks, 2110 Colorado Ave, Suite 110, Santa Monica, CA 90404 *Tel:* 310-865-4455 *Toll Free Tel:* 800-4-KILLER (454-5537) *E-mail:* info@killertracks.com *Web Site:* www.killertracks.com, pg 798

Kimbo Educational, One Industrial Way, Bldg D, Suite E, Eatontown, NJ 07724 *Tel:* 732-229-4949 *Toll Free Tel:* 800-631-2187 *Fax:* 732-870-3340 *E-mail:* kimboed@aol.com; service@kimboed.com *Web Site:* www.kimboed.com, pg 799

Kinetic Arts, 306 Gold St, No 5-I, Brooklyn, NY 11201 *Tel:* 917-439-4008 *E-mail:* info@kineticarts.tv *Web Site:* www.kineticarts.tv, pg 799

Kinetic Corp, 200 Distillery Commons, Suite 200, Louisville, KY 40206-1990 *Tel:* 502-719-9500 *Fax:* 502-719-9509 *Web Site:* kinetictms.com, pg 799

Kineticvideo.com, 4839 Noble Lane, Battersea, ON K0H 1H0, Canada *Tel:* 416-538-6613 *Toll Free Tel:* 800-263-6910 (CN only) *Fax:* 416-538-9984 *E-mail:* info@kineticvideo.com *Web Site:* www.kineticvideo.com, pg 799

Kinetronics Corp, 1459 Tallevast Rd, Sarasota, FL 34243 *Tel:* 941-951-2432 *Toll Free Tel:* 800-624-3204 (US & CN) *Fax:* 941-955-5992 *E-mail:* info@kinetronics.com; order@kinetronics.com *Web Site:* www.kinetronics.com, pg 799

Kingsway Motion Picture Inc, 200 Evans Ave, Unit 4, Toronto, ON M8Z 1J7, Canada *Tel:* 416-463-4345 *E-mail:* info@kingswaycanada.com *Web Site:* kingswaycanada.com, pg 799

Kingswood Productions, 810 12 Ave S, Nashville, TN 37203 *Tel:* 615-742-5779 *Web Site:* www.kingswoodproductions.com, pg 799

Kino Flo Lighting Systems, 2840 N Hollywood Way, Burbank, CA 91505 *Tel:* 818-767-6528 *Fax:* 818-252-0290 (rental); 818-767-7517 (sales) *E-mail:* sales@kinoflo.com *Web Site:* www.kinoflo.com, pg 799

Kino International Corp, 333 W 39 St, Suite 503, New York, NY 10018 *Tel:* 212-629-6880 *Toll Free Tel:* 800-562-3330 *Fax:* 212-714-0871 *E-mail:* contact@kinolorber.com *Web Site:* www.kinolorber.com, pg 799

Kino Mountain Productions LLC, 2004 Production Dr, Apex, NC 27539 *Tel:* 919-355-2725 *E-mail:* info@kinomountain.com *Web Site:* www.kinomountain.com, pg 799

KION-TV, 1550 Moffett St, Salinas, CA 93905 *Tel:* 831-784-6500; 831-422-3500 *Fax:* 831-784-6502 *Web Site:* www.kion546.com, pg 799

Kipp Visual Systems Inc, 3920 Vero Rd, Suite C, Baltimore, MD 21227 *Tel:* 410-235-9900 *Toll Free Tel:* 800-278-6912 *Fax:* 410-235-7122 *Web Site:* kippvisual.com, pg 799

Kirkwood Community College, Linn Hall, Rm 102, 6301 Kirkwood Blvd SW, Cedar Rapids, IA 52406 *Tel:* 319-398-5517 *Toll Free Tel:* 800-363-2220 *Fax:* 319-398-5413 *E-mail:* info@kirkwood.edu *Web Site:* www.kirkwood.edu, pg 799

The Kitchen, 265 NE 24 St, Suite 401, Miami, FL 33137 *Tel:* 305-415-6200 *E-mail:* info@thekitchen.tv *Web Site:* www.thekitchen.tv, pg 799

KJfilms LLC, 33 Serra Dr, Middletown, CT 06457 *Tel:* 860-873-2419; 860-995-5106 (cell) *E-mail:* info@kjfilms.com *Web Site:* www.kjfilms.com, pg 799

KK Office Solutions Inc, 3910 N Bridgeport Circle, Wichita, KS 67219 *Tel:* 316-944-5464 *Toll Free Tel:* 800-362-1317 *Fax:* 316-944-0605 *Toll Free Fax:* 888-319-9600 *E-mail:* info@kkofficesolutions.com *Web Site:* kkosinc.com, pg 799

Klipsch Group Inc, 3502 Woodview Trace, Suite 200, Indianapolis, IN 46268 *Tel:* 317-860-8100 *Toll Free Tel:* 800-544-1482 *Web Site:* www.klipsch.com, pg 799

Klutz, 568 Broadway, Suite 503, New York, NY 10012 *Tel:* 212-343-6360 *Toll Free Tel:* 800-737-4123 *Fax:* 212-343-6366 *E-mail:* orders@klutz.com *Web Site:* www.scholastic.com/books/klutz, pg 800

Knowledge Unlimited Inc, 2320 Pleasant View, Middleton, WI 53562 *Tel:* 608-836-6660 *Toll Free Tel:* 800-356-2303 *Fax:* 608-836-6684 *Toll Free Fax:* 800-618-1570 *E-mail:* csis@newscurrents.com *Web Site:* www.knowledgeunlimited.com, pg 800

Knowles Video Inc (KVI), 5450 Buck Lake Rd, Tallahassee, FL 32317 *Tel:* 850-878-2298 *Fax:* 850-656-0119 *E-mail:* info@knowlesvideo.com *Web Site:* www.knowlesvideo.com, pg 800

KO Creative, 465 S Beverly Dr, 3rd fl, Beverly Hills, CA 90212 *Tel:* 310-288-3820 *Web Site:* www.ko-creative.com, pg 800

Kodak Graphic Communications Canada Co, 4225 Kincaid St, Burnaby, BC V5G 4P5, Canada *Tel:* 604-551-2700 *Toll Free Tel:* 800-465-6325 *Fax:* 604-570-3501 *Web Site:* graphics.kodak.com, pg 800

Koerner Camera Systems, 2828 SE 14 Ave, Portland, OR 97202 *Tel:* 503-274-6533 *Toll Free Tel:* 800-377-1132 *E-mail:* michael@koernercamera.com *Web Site:* www.koernercamera.com, pg 800

Kofax Inc, 15211 Laguna Canyon Rd, Irvine, CA 92618-3146 *Tel:* 949-727-1733 *Fax:* 949-727-3144 *E-mail:* info@kofax.com *Web Site:* www.kofax.com, pg 800

KOH Design Inc, 540 Barnum Ave, Bridgeport, CT 06608 *Tel:* 203-336-1334 *Fax:* 203-335-9361 *E-mail:* info@kohdesign.com *Web Site:* www.kohdesign.com, pg 801

Konica Minolta Business Solutions, 100 Williams Dr, Ramsey, NJ 07446 *Tel:* 201-825-4000 *Web Site:* kmbs.konicaminolta.us, pg 801

Kontron America, 14118 Stowe Dr, Poway, CA 92064-7147 *Tel:* 858-677-0877 *Toll Free Tel:* 888-294-4558; 800-480-0044 (cust serv & tech support) *Fax:* 858-677-0898 *E-mail:* sales@us.kontron.com *Web Site:* www.kontron.com, pg 801

KOOL-FM Radio, 840 N Central Ave, Phoenix, AZ 85004 *Tel:* 602-452-1000; 602-260-9494 (studio) *Fax:* 602-440-6530 *Web Site:* kool.radio.com, pg 801

Kool Music, 9 Hector Ave, Toronto, ON M6G 3G2, Canada *Tel:* 416-533-3520 *E-mail:* host@koolmusic.com *Web Site:* www.koolmusic.com, pg 801

Kopp Glass, 2108 Palmer St, Pittsburgh, PA 15218 *Tel:* 412-271-0190 *Fax:* 412-271-4103 *E-mail:* sales@koppglass.com *Web Site:* www.koppglass.com, pg 801

Korg USA Inc, 316 S Service Rd, Melville, NY 11747 *Tel:* 631-390-6500; 631-390-6800 (cust serv) *E-mail:* sales@korgusa.com; customerservice@korgusa.com *Web Site:* www.korgusa.com, pg 801

Koss Corp, 4129 N Port Washington Ave, Milwaukee, WI 53212 *Tel:* 414-964-5000 *Toll Free Tel:* 800-USA-KOSS (872-5677) *E-mail:* customersupport@koss.com *Web Site:* www.koss.com, pg 801

Kostov Productions, Whispering Wind Ranch, 16320 High Bridge Rd, Monroe, WA 98272 *Tel:* 206-755-0050 *E-mail:* info@kostov.com *Web Site:* www.kostov.com, pg 801

Kozmic Lazer Show LLC, PO Box 140197, Nashville, TN 37214-0197 *Tel:* 615-391-3226 *Toll Free Tel:* 800-MRLASER (675-2737) *Fax:* 615-391-3265 *E-mail:* mrlaser800@aol.com *Web Site:* www.kozmiclazershow.com, pg 801

KPBS Public Broadcasting, 5200 Campanille Dr, San Diego, CA 92182 *Tel:* 619-929-1515; 619-265-6438 (newsroom) *Toll Free Tel:* 888-399-5727 *Fax:* 619-594-3812 *Web Site:* www.kpbs.org, pg 801

KPDX-TV Production Center, 14975 NW Greenbrier Pkwy, Beaverton, OR 97006-5731 *Tel:* 503-906-1249 *Fax:* 503-548-6920 *E-mail:* ezone@kpdx.com; fox12news@kptv.com *Web Site:* www.kptv.com; www.kpdx.com, pg 801

KPHO-TV CBS 5, 5555 N Seventh Ave, Phoenix, AZ 85013 *Tel:* 602-207-3333 *E-mail:* cbs5gm@cbs5az.com *Web Site:* www.cbs5az.com, pg 801

KPLR-TV, 2250 Ball Dr, St Louis, MO 63146 *Tel:* 314-213-2222; 314-213-7831 (newsroom) *E-mail:* kplradmin@tribune.com *Web Site:* kplr11.com, pg 801

Kramer Communications Video Production, 12504 Quarterhorse Dr, Bowie, MD 20720 *Tel:* 301-352-3042 *E-mail:* kcam@his.com *Web Site:* kcommproductions.com, pg 801

Kramer Electronics USA Inc, 6 Rte 173 W, Clinton, NJ 08809 *Tel:* 908-735-0018 *Toll Free Tel:* 888-275-6311 *Fax:* 908-735-0515 *E-mail:* info@kramerus.com *Web Site:* www.kramerav.com, pg 801

Joan Kramer & Associates Inc, 10490 Wilshire Blvd, Suite 1701, Los Angeles, CA 90024 *Tel:* 310-446-1866 *Fax:* 310-446-1856 *E-mail:* ekeeeek@earthlink.net, pg 801

Kris Stevens Enterprises, 22362 Dardenne St, Calabasas, CA 91302 *Tel:* 818-225-7585 *E-mail:* inquiry@kriserikstevens.com *Web Site:* www.kriserikstevens.com, pg 801

Krishnamurti Foundation of America, 1070 McAndrew Rd, Ojai, CA 93023 *Tel:* 805-646-2726 (ext 10) *Fax:* 805-646-6674 *E-mail:* kfa@kfa.org *Web Site:* www.kfa.org, pg 801

KRK Systems, c/o Gibson Pro Audio, 309 Plus Park Blvd, Nashville, TN 37217 *Toll Free Tel:* 800-4GIBSON (444-2766) *E-mail:* service@gibson.com (cust serv) *Web Site:* www.krksys.com, pg 802

KTHV-TV, 720 Izard St, Little Rock, AR 72201 *Tel:* 501-376-1111 *Fax:* 501-376-9928 (sales); 501-376-3324 (admin); 501-376-1645 (news) *Web Site:* www.thv11.com, pg 802

KTVA Productions, 9818 SE 17 Ave, Suite B, Milwaukie, OR 97222 *Tel:* 503-659-4417 *E-mail:* mail@ktvavideo.com *Web Site:* www.ktvavideo.com, pg 802

KTVB-TV, 5407 W Fairview Ave, Boise, ID 83706 *Tel:* 208-375-7277 *Toll Free Tel:* 800-559-7277 *Fax:* 208-378-5642; 208-375-7770 (news fax) *E-mail:* info@ktvb.com; ktvbnews@ktvb.com *Web Site:* www.ktvb.com, pg 802

KTVU-Retail Services, 2 Jack London Sq, Oakland, CA 94607 *Tel:* 510-834-1212 *Web Site:* www.ktvu.com, pg 802

K2 Productions, 2303 Walters St, Greensboro, NC 27408 *Tel:* 336-664-8036 *E-mail:* info@k2production.com *Web Site:* www.k2production.com, pg 802

K2B2 Records, 1748 Roosevelt Ave, Los Angeles, CA 90006 *Tel:* 323-660-9250 *Web Site:* k2b2.com, pg 802

Kuhn Productions LLC, 4423 44 Place, Des Moines, IA 50310 *Tel:* 515-244-1618, pg 802

Kultur International Films Ltd Inc, PO Box 755, Forked River, NJ 08731 *Tel:* 732-784-6470 *Toll Free Tel:* 888-329-2580 *Toll Free Fax:* 866-205-2744 *E-mail:* support@kultur.com *Web Site:* www.kulturvideo.com, pg 802

KUSM TV, Visual Communications Bldg 183, Montana State University, Bozeman, MT 59717 *Tel:* 406-994-3437 *Toll Free Tel:* 866-832-0829 *Fax:* 406-994-6545 *E-mail:* kusm@montanapbs.org *Web Site:* www.montanapbs.org, pg 802

KVAL, 4575 Blanton Rd, Eugene, OR 97405 *Tel:* 541-342-4961 *Fax:* 541-342-2635 *E-mail:* kvalnews@kval.com *Web Site:* kval.com, pg 802

KVIE-Channel 6, 2030 W El Camino Ave, Sacramento, CA 95833 *Tel:* 916-929-5843 *Toll Free Tel:* 800-347-5843 *Fax:* 916-929-7215 *E-mail:* member@kvie.org *Web Site:* www.kvie.org, pg 802

KVL Audio Visual Services Inc, 200 Corporate Blvd S, Yonkers, NY 10701 *Tel:* 914-479-3300 *Toll Free Tel:* 800-862-3210 *Fax:* 914-965-1423 *E-mail:* info@kvlav.com *Web Site:* www.kvlav.com, pg 802

L A Bruell Inc, 120 W 70 St, No 3-B, New York, NY 10023 *Tel:* 646-336-5977 *Web Site:* labruell.com, pg 802

L A Management Co LLC, 8131 Bay Pointe Dr, Denver, NC 28037 *Tel:* 704-560-6274 *Toll Free Tel:* 800-651-7818 *Fax:* 704-973-7968 *E-mail:* info@lamanagementco.com *Web Site:* lamanagementco.com, pg 802

L-Acoustics Inc, 2645 Townsgate Rd, Suite 600, Westlake Village, CA 91361 *Tel:* 805-604-0577 *Fax:* 805-556-4846 *E-mail:* info.us@l-acoustics.com *Web Site:* www.l-acoustics.com, pg 802

L'AIR International, 117 Vacek St, Fort Worth, TX 76107 *Tel:* 817-237-9390 *Toll Free Tel:* 844-243-8574 *E-mail:* info@lairfloors.com *Web Site:* www.lairfloors.com, pg 802

L R Light & Sound, 5317 54 St, Drayton Valley, AB T7A 1R6, Canada *Tel:* 780-542-4242; 780-542-9363 *Fax:* 780-542-4283 *E-mail:* lrlightandsound@yahoo.ca *Web Site:* www.lrlightandsound.ca, pg 802

L-3 ESSCO, 90 Nemco Way, Ayer, MA 01432 *Tel:* 978-568-5100 *Fax:* 978-772-7555 *E-mail:* info.essco@l3t.com *Web Site:* www2.l3t.com/essco, pg 802

L-3 WESCAM, 649 N Service Rd W, Burlington, ON L7P 5B9, Canada *Tel:* 905-633-4000; 905-633-4175 (cust serv) *Toll Free Tel:* 888-593-7226 *Fax:* 905-633-4100 (cust serv) *E-mail:* sales.wescam@l-3com.com *Web Site:* www.wescam.com, pg 802

LA Castle Studios, 154 S Victory Blvd, Burbank, CA 91502 *Tel:* 818-861-7317 *Web Site:* lacastlestudios.com, pg 803

LA Femme International Film Festival, 324 S Beverly Dr, Suite 436, Beverly Hills, CA 90212 *Tel:* 310-441-1645 *Fax:* 310-475-8213 *Web Site:* www.lafemme.org, pg 994

La Paloma Films, PO Box 269, Gilbertsville, NY 13776 *Tel:* 607-376-4300 *E-mail:* lapalomafilms@yahoo.com *Web Site:* www.lapalomafilms.com, pg 803

LA Sound Co, 9001 Canoga Ave, Canoga Park, CA 91304 *Tel:* 818-772-9200 *Fax:* 818-772-9977 *E-mail:* rentals@lasoundco.com; sales@lasoundco.com, pg 803

Laboratories Inc, 1925 E Dominguez St, Long Beach, CA 90810 *Toll Free Tel:* 800-745-3271 *E-mail:* info@tad-labs.com *Web Site:* technicalaudiodevices.com, pg 803

Labrecque Creative Sound, 2825 Main St, Becket, MA 01223 *Tel:* 520-240-6001, pg 803

Lacquer-Mat Inc, 13030 Wayne Rd, Livonia, MI 48150 *Toll Free Tel:* 800-942-2223 (cust serv) *Fax:* 734-422-4205 (orders) *Web Site:* www.lacquer-mat.com, pg 803

Ladyslipper Music, PO Box 14, Cedar Grove, NC 27231 *Tel:* 919-245-3737 *E-mail:* info@ladyslipper.org *Web Site:* www.ladyslipper.org, pg 803

Lagoon Video, 3323 Marble Front Rd, Caldwell, ID 83605 *Tel:* 208-455-3457 *E-mail:* kapsm@aol.com, pg 803

Laird Digital Cinema, One Tower Dr, Saugerties, NY 12477 *Tel:* 845-339-9555 *Toll Free Tel:* 800-898-0759 *Fax:* 845-339-0231 *E-mail:* info@lairddigitalcinema.com; sales@lairddigitalcinema.com *Web Site:* www.lairddigitalcinema.com, pg 803

Lake Tahoe Visitors Authority (LTVA), 169 Hwy 50, Stateline, NV 89449 *Tel:* 775-588-5900 *Toll Free Tel:* 800-288-2463 (reservations) *Fax:* 775-588-1941 *E-mail:* info@ltva.org *Web Site:* ltva.org, pg 973

Lakeshore Public Media, 8625 Indiana Place, Merrillville, IN 46410 *Tel:* 219-756-5656 *Toll Free Tel:* 888-694-5253 *Fax:* 219-755-4312 *E-mail:* info@lakeshorepublicmedia.org *Web Site:* lakeshorepublicmedia.org, pg 803

Lamb & Lion Ministries, PO Box 919, McKinney, TX 75070 *Tel:* 972-736-3567 *E-mail:* lamblion@lamblion.com *Web Site:* christinprophecy.org, pg 803

L&S Video Inc, 875 Fifth Ave, New York, NY 10065 *Tel:* 914-238-9366 *E-mail:* videopaint2@msn.com *Web Site:* www.landsvideo.com, pg 803

Langie Audio Visual Systems, Piano Works Mall, 349 W Commercial St, East Rochester, NY 14445 *Tel:* 585-385-4880 *Fax:* 585-385-4882 *E-mail:* info@langieav. com; sales@langieav.com; rental@langieav.com *Web Site:* www.langieav.com, pg 803

LANGUAGE/30™, 708 Elm Ct, Unit B, Paso Robles, CA 93446 *Tel:* 559-462-0153 *Fax:* 805-296-3889 *Web Site:* www.lang30.com, pg 803

Lank/Beach Productions Inc, 362 Brock St, Winnipeg, MB R3N 0Y9, Canada *Tel:* 204-452-9422 *E-mail:* info@lankbeach.com *Web Site:* www. lankbeach.com, pg 803

Lannan Foundation, 313 Read St, Santa Fe, NM 87501-2628 *Tel:* 505-986-8160 *Fax:* 505-986-8195 *E-mail:* info@lannan.org *Web Site:* www.lannan.org, pg 803

Larrabee Sound Studio, 4162 Lankershim Blvd, North Hollywood, CA 91602 *Tel:* 818-753-0717 *Fax:* 818-753-8046 *E-mail:* info@larrabeestudios.com *Web Site:* www.larrabeestudios.com, pg 803

Laser Fantasy/HECK Industries/Photon Manufacturing, 4228 159 Ave SE, Bellevue, WA 98006 *Tel:* 425-890-6026 (software & creative support); 425-214-0777 (hardware & tech support) *Toll Free Fax:* 866-299-6849 *E-mail:* info@heckindustries.com *Web Site:* www.laserfantasy.com, pg 804

Laser Magic Productions, 722 N Orlando Ave, No 207, Los Angeles, CA 90069 *Tel:* 818-590-5899 *Web Site:* www.laser-magic.com, pg 804

Laser Rentals Inc, 1953 S County Lane 282, Joplin, MO 64804 *Tel:* 417-782-8484 *E-mail:* laserwam@swbell. net *Web Site:* www.laserrentalsinc.com, pg 804

Laser Spectacles Inc, PO Box 1535, San Marcos, TX 78667 *Tel:* 512-392-4600 *Fax:* 512-392-4601 *E-mail:* laserinfo@laserspectacles.com *Web Site:* www. laserspectacles.com, pg 804

Laser Video Corp, 401 Germantown Pike, Lafayette Hill, PA 19444 *Tel:* 610-825-2500 *Toll Free Tel:* 800-448-8772 *Fax:* 610-941-9989 *E-mail:* customerservice@ laservideousa.com *Web Site:* www.lvconline.com, pg 804

Lasergraphics Inc, 20 Ada, Irvine, CA 92618 *Tel:* 949-753-8282 *Fax:* 949-727-9282 *E-mail:* info@ lasergraphics.com *Web Site:* www.lasergraphics.com, pg 804

Laserium®, 84777 Charlottes Way, Eugene, OR 97405 *Tel:* 541-687-1414 *Web Site:* www.laserium.com, pg 804

The LAST Factory, 2011 Research Dr, Livermore, CA 94550-3803 *Tel:* 925-449-9449 *Fax:* 925-447-0662 *E-mail:* thelastfactory@gmail.com *Web Site:* thelastfactory.com, pg 804

Latham Foundation Publications, 1320 Harbor Bay Pkwy, Suite 200, Alameda, CA 94502 *Tel:* 510-521-0920 *Fax:* 510-521-9861 *E-mail:* info@latham.org *Web Site:* www.latham.org, pg 804

Launch Media, 804 Main St, Baton Rouge, LA 70802 *Tel:* 225-612-2112 *E-mail:* contactus@launchmedia.tv *Web Site:* www.launchmedia.tv, pg 804

Laurel Canyon Stages, 9337 Laurel Canyon Blvd, Arleta, CA 91331-4315 *Tel:* 818-768-8935 *Fax:* 818-768-6852 *E-mail:* mary@lcstages.com *Web Site:* www.lcstages. com, pg 804

Laurel Hill Press, PO Box 16516, Chapel Hill, NC 27516-6516 *Toll Free Tel:* 800-942-6516 *Fax:* 919-942-9533 *E-mail:* plantsforus@gmail.com *Web Site:* www.laurelhillpress.com, pg 804

Laurel Video Productions, 1999 E Rte 70, Cherry Hill, NJ 08003 *Tel:* 856-424-3300 *E-mail:* inquiries@ laurelvideo.net *Web Site:* www.laurelvideo.net, pg 804

Lavine Production Group, 189 Dean St, Brooklyn, NY 11217 *Tel:* 917-804-1870 *Web Site:* www.lavinegroup. com, pg 804

Donna Lawrence Productions, 624 Baxter Ave, Louisville, KY 40204 *Tel:* 502-589-9617 *E-mail:* dlp@dlproductions.com *Web Site:* www. dlproductions.com, pg 804

Lawrence Productions Inc, 6146 W Main St, Suite A, Kalamazoo, MI 49009 *Tel:* 269-903-2395 *E-mail:* sales@lpi.com *Web Site:* www.lpi.com, pg 804

LBA Technology Inc, 3400 Tupper Dr, Greenville, NC 27834 *Tel:* 252-757-0279 *Toll Free Tel:* 800-522-4464 *Fax:* 252-752-9155 *E-mail:* lbagrp@lbagroup.com *Web Site:* www.lbagroup.com, pg 804

LEA International, 10701 Airport Rd, Hayden, ID 83835 *Tel:* 208-762-6121; 208-772-8515 *Toll Free Tel:* 800-882-9110 *Fax:* 208-762-6117, pg 804

LEAD Technologies Inc, 1927 S Tryon St, Suite 200, Charlotte, NC 28203 *Tel:* 704-332-5532 *Toll Free Tel:* 800-637-4699 *Fax:* 704-372-8161 *E-mail:* sales@ leadtools.com *Web Site:* www.leadtools.com, pg 804

Leader Instruments Corp, 1501 E Orangethorpe Ave, Suite 140, Fullerton, CA 92831 *Tel:* 714-527-9300 *Toll Free Tel:* 800-645-5104 *Fax:* 714-527-7490 *E-mail:* info@leaderamerica.com *Web Site:* www. leaderamerica.com, pg 805

Learn Quickly, PO Box 4464, Palm Springs, CA 92263-4464 *Toll Free Tel:* 888-LRN-FAST (576-3278) *Toll Free Fax:* 888-LRN-FAST (576-3278) *Web Site:* www. learnquickly.com, pg 805

Learning Ally, 20 Roszel Rd, Princeton, NJ 08540 *Toll Free Tel:* 800-221-4792 *E-mail:* custserv@learningally. org; media@learningally.org *Web Site:* www. learningally.org, pg 805

The Learning House Inc, 427 S Fourth St, Suite 300, Louisville, KY 40202 *Tel:* 502-589-9878 *Fax:* 502-589-9825 *E-mail:* sales@learninghouse.com; info@ learninghouse.com *Web Site:* www.learninghouse.com, pg 805

Learning Seed, 208 S Jefferson St, Suite 402, Chicago, IL 60661 *Toll Free Tel:* 800-634-4941 *Toll Free Fax:* 800-998-0854 *E-mail:* info@learningseed.com *Web Site:* www.learningseed.com, pg 805

Learning Strategies Corp, 2000 Plymouth Rd, Minnetonka, MN 55305-2335 *Tel:* 952-767-9800 *Toll Free Tel:* 888-800-2688 (cust serv); 866-292-1861 (24 hour order line) *Fax:* 952-475-2373 *E-mail:* info@learningstrategies.com *Web Site:* www. learningstrategies.com, pg 805

Learning Technology Services, 301 Millennium Hall, Menomonie, WI 54751 *Tel:* 715-232-5002 *E-mail:* helpdesk@uwstout.edu *Web Site:* www. uwstout.edu/academics/academic-services/learning-and-information-technology, pg 805

Lectrosonics Inc, 581 Laser Rd NE, Rio Rancho, NM 87124 *Tel:* 505-892-4501 *Toll Free Tel:* 800-821-1121 *Fax:* 505-892-6243 *E-mail:* sales@lectrosonics.com *Web Site:* www.lectrosonics.com, pg 805

LEDtronics Inc, 23105 Kashiva Ct, Torrance, CA 90505 *Tel:* 310-534-1505 *Toll Free Tel:* 800-579-4875 *Fax:* 310-534-1424 *E-mail:* info@ledtronics.com *Web Site:* www.ledtronics.com, pg 805

Lee Co Inc, 27 S 12 St, Terre Haute, IN 47807 *Tel:* 812-235-8155 *Fax:* 812-235-3587 *E-mail:* leeco@ leecompanyinc.com; sales@leecompanyinc.com *Web Site:* www.leecompanyinc.com, pg 805

Lee Dan® Communications Inc, 155 Adams Ave, Hauppauge, NY 11788-3699 *Tel:* 631-231-1414 *Toll Free Tel:* 800-231-1414 *Fax:* 631-231-1498 *E-mail:* info@leedan.com *Web Site:* www.leedan.com, pg 805

LEE Filters, 2237 N Hollywood Way, Burbank, CA 91505 *Tel:* 818-238-1220 *Toll Free Tel:* 800-576-5055 *Fax:* 818-238-1228 *E-mail:* mail@leefiltersusa.com *Web Site:* www.leefilters.com, pg 805

Lee Hartman & Sons Inc, 3236 Cove Rd NW, Roanoke, VA 24017 *Tel:* 540-366-3493 *Toll Free Tel:* 800-344-1832 *Fax:* 540-362-4659 *E-mail:* info@leehartman. com; roanokeva@leehartman.com *Web Site:* www. leehartman.com, pg 805

Leedal Inc, 3453 Commercial Ave, Northbrook, IL 60062 *Tel:* 847-498-0111 *Fax:* 847-498-0198 *E-mail:* sink@leedal.com *Web Site:* www.leedal.com, pg 805

Lefco Video Services Inc, 600 W Sunset Rd, Suite 103, Henderson, NV 89011 *Tel:* 702-566-1770 *Fax:* 702-566-1798 *E-mail:* info1@lefco.com *Web Site:* www. lefco.com, pg 806

Legendary Entertainment, 160 Torrance Woods, Brampton, ON L6Y 4K2, Canada *Tel:* 416-712-9994 *E-mail:* legendary_ent@rogers.com *Web Site:* legendaryentertainment.com, pg 806

Legendary Pictures, 2900 W Alameda Ave, 15th fl, Burbank, CA 91505 *Tel:* 818-688-7003 *E-mail:* info@ legendary.com *Web Site:* www.legendary.com, pg 806

Legion Lighting Co Inc, 221 Glenmore Ave, Brooklyn, NY 11207 *Tel:* 718-498-1770 *Fax:* 718-498-0128 *Toll Free Fax:* 800-4-LEGION (453-4466) *E-mail:* sales@ legionlighting.com *Web Site:* www.legionlighting.com, pg 806

Lehigh Electric Products Co, 6265 Hamilton Blvd, Allentown, PA 18106 *Tel:* 610-395-3386 *Fax:* 610-395-7735 *E-mail:* sales@lehighdim.com *Web Site:* www.lehighdim.com, pg 806

Leica Camera Inc, One Pearl Ct, Unit A, Allendale, NJ 07401 *Toll Free Tel:* 800-222-0118 *Fax:* 201-995-1686 *Web Site:* en.leica-camera.com, pg 806

Leightronix Inc, 1125 N Cedar Rd, Mason, MI 48854 *Tel:* 517-694-8000 *Toll Free Tel:* 800-243-5589 *Fax:* 517-694-1600 *E-mail:* support@leightronix. com; sales@leightronix.com; info@leightronix. com *Web Site:* www.leightronix.com, pg 806

Leisure Video, 747 Magazine St, New Orleans, LA 70130 *Tel:* 504-299-9000 *Toll Free Tel:* 800-432-3853 *E-mail:* info@dukesofdixieland.com *Web Site:* www. dukesofdixieland.com; www.leisurejazz.com, pg 806

LEMO USA Inc, 635 Park Ct, Rohnert Park, CA 94928 *Tel:* 707-578-8811 *Toll Free Tel:* 800-444-LEMO (444-5366) *Fax:* 707-578-0869 *E-mail:* info-us@lemo. com *Web Site:* www.lemo.com, pg 806

Lenel Systems International Inc, 1212 Pittsford-Victor Rd, Pittsford, NY 14534-3820 *Tel:* 585-248-9720 *Toll Free Tel:* 866-788-5095 *Fax:* 585-248-9185 *E-mail:* insidesales@lenel.com *Web Site:* www.lenel. com, pg 806

Lensless Camera Manufacturing Co, 809 Lark Dr, Fernley, NV 89408 *Tel:* 775-575-5189 *E-mail:* info@ pinholecamera.com *Web Site:* www.pinholecamera. com, pg 806

Leprecon®, 10087 Industrial Dr, Hamburg, MI 48139 *Tel:* 810-852-4300 *Toll Free Tel:* 888-422-3537 *Fax:* 810-231-1631 *E-mail:* sales@leprecon.com *Web Site:* www.leprecon.com, pg 806

The Lerro Corp, 905 Madison Ave, Norristown, PA 19403 *Tel:* 610-650-4100 *Fax:* 610-650-4110 *E-mail:* lerrocorp@lerro.com *Web Site:* www.lerro. com, pg 806

Leucos USA Inc, 11 Mayfield Ave, Edison, NJ 08837 *Tel:* 732-225-0010 *Toll Free Tel:* 800-832-3360 *Fax:* 732-225-0250 *E-mail:* info@leucosusa.com *Web Site:* www.leucos.com, pg 806

Level 3 Communications Inc, 1025 Eldorado Blvd, Broomfield, CO 80021 *Tel:* 720-888-1000 *Toll Free Tel:* 877-2LEVEL3 (253-8357) *Web Site:* www.level3. com, pg 806

Leviton LES (Lighting & Energy Solutions), 20497 SW Teton Ave, Tualatin, OR 97062 *Toll Free Tel:* 800-736-6682 *Fax:* 503-404-5594 *Web Site:* www.leviton. com, pg 806

Levy NYC Design & Production, 356 Devoe St, Brooklyn, NY 11211 *Tel:* 212-925-4640 *Fax:* 212-925-4216 *E-mail:* info@levynyc.net *Web Site:* www. levylighting.com, pg 806

Lex Products Corp, 15 Progress Dr, Shelton, CT 06484 *Tel:* 203-363-3738 *Toll Free Tel:* 800-643-4460 *Fax:* 203-363-3742 *E-mail:* info@lexproducts.

com; orders@lexproducts.com; customerservice@ lexproducts.com *Web Site:* www.lexproducts.com, pg 807

LHV Audio Services, 3417 Lake Breeze Rd, Orlando, FL 32808 *Tel:* 407-295-3565 *E-mail:* service@ lhvaudio.com *Web Site:* www.lhvaudio.com, pg 807

Liberty AV Solutions, 11675 Ridgeline Dr, Colorado Springs, CO 80921 *Tel:* 719-260-0061 *Toll Free Tel:* 800-530-8998 *Fax:* 719-260-0075 *E-mail:* orders@libav.com *Web Site:* secure. libertycable.com, pg 807

Liberty Uplink, 2547 Yellow Springs Rd, Malvern, PA 19355 *Tel:* 215-964-5222; 917-254-0155 *E-mail:* info@libertyuplink.com *Web Site:* www. libertyuplink.com, pg 807

Library & Information Technology Association (LITA), c/o American Library Association, 50 E Huron St, Chicago, IL 60611-2795 *Toll Free Tel:* 800-545-2433 (ext 4270) *Fax:* 312-280-3257 *E-mail:* lita@ala.org *Web Site:* www.ala.org/lita, pg 957

Library of Congress, Motion Picture, Broadcasting & Recorded Sound Division, James Madison Bldg, LM 336, 101 Independence Ave SE, Washington, DC 20540-1000 *Tel:* 202-707-8572 *Fax:* 202-707-2371 *Web Site:* www.loc.gov/rr/mopic, pg 807

Library Video Company, 7 E Wynnewood Rd, Wynnewood, PA 19096 *Tel:* 610-645-4000 *Toll Free Tel:* 800-843-3620 *Fax:* 610-645-4040 *E-mail:* sales@ libraryvideo.com; comments@libraryvideo.com *Web Site:* www.libraryvideo.com, pg 807

Lieberman Productions, 455 Ninth St, San Francisco, CA 94103-4410 *Tel:* 415-955-0855 *Fax:* 415-955-0822 *E-mail:* lpinfo@lieberman.com *Web Site:* www. lieberman.com, pg 807

Life Cycle Books Ltd, 1085 Bellamy Rd N, Unit 20, Toronto, ON M1H 1H7, Canada *Tel:* 416-690-5860 *Toll Free Tel:* 866-880-5860 *Fax:* 416-690-8532 *Toll Free Fax:* 866-690-8532 *E-mail:* support@ lifecyclebooks.com; billing@lifecyclebooks.com; orders@lifecyclebooks.com *Web Site:* www. lifecyclebooks.com, pg 807

Life House Productions LLC, PO Box 4007, Manchester, CT 06045-4007 *Tel:* 860-432-9177 *Web Site:* www. lifehouseproductions.com, pg 807

Lifetime Television®, 235 E 45 St, New York, NY 10017 *Tel:* 212-424-7000 *Web Site:* www.mylifetime. com, pg 807

Light Impressions, 2340 Brighton Henrietta Townline Rd, Rochester, NY 14623 *Toll Free Tel:* 844-656-4876 *Toll Free Fax:* 866-592-8642 *E-mail:* help@ fdmbrands.com *Web Site:* www.lightimpressionsdirect. com, pg 807

The Light Source, 3935 Westinghouse Blvd, Charlotte, NC 28273 *Tel:* 704-504-8399 *Fax:* 704-588-4693 (acctg); 704-588-4637 (orders) *E-mail:* mail@ thelightsource.com; sales@thelightsource.com *Web Site:* www.thelightsource.com, pg 807

LightBox-NY, 841 Barretto St, Bronx, NY 10474 *Tel:* 718-759-6419 *E-mail:* lightboxny@gmail.com *Web Site:* www.lightbox-ny.com, pg 807

LightHouse Films, 225 W 39 St, Suite 600, New York, NY 10018 *Tel:* 646-649-3600 *Fax:* 646-398-7122 *E-mail:* contact@lhfny.com; rent@lhfny.com *Web Site:* www.light-house-films.com, pg 807

Lighthouse Photo & Video Productions, 1100 Chicago Ave, Suite 7C, Goshen, IN 46528 *Tel:* 574-533-1400 (off); 574-202-5502 (studio) *E-mail:* lighthousevideo@ gmail.com *Web Site:* www.lighthousephotoandvideo. com, pg 807

Lighting & Production Equipment Inc, 590 Travis St, Atlanta, GA 30318 *Tel:* 404-352-0464 *Toll Free Tel:* 800-275-3721 *Fax:* 404-351-4399 *Web Site:* www. lpe.com, pg 807

The Lighting Design Alliance, 2830 Temple Ave, Long Beach, CA 90806-2213 *Tel:* 562-989-3843 *Fax:* 562-989-3847 *E-mail:* info@lightingdesignalliance.com *Web Site:* www.lightingdesignalliance.com, pg 807

Lighting Design Group, 49 W 27 St, Suite 920, New York, NY 10001 *Tel:* 212-685-4940 *Fax:* 212-685-4927 *E-mail:* lighting@ldg.com *Web Site:* www.ldg. com, pg 808

Lighting Industry Resource Council, 440 N Wells St, Suite 210, Chicago, IL 60654 *Tel:* 312-527-3677 *Fax:* 312-527-3680 *E-mail:* iald@iald.org *Web Site:* www.iald.org/council, pg 808

Lighting Sales Connection Inc, 757 SE 17 St, No 254, Fort Lauderdale, FL 33316 *Tel:* 954-655-9074 *Fax:* 954-764-7013 *E-mail:* info@lightingsales.com *Web Site:* www.lightingsales.com, pg 808

Lighting Services Inc, 2 Holt Dr, Stony Point, NY 10980 *Tel:* 845-942-2800 *Toll Free Tel:* 800-999-9574 (US & CN) *Fax:* 845-942-2177 *E-mail:* applications@ maillsi.com; sales@maillsi.com *Web Site:* www. lightingservicesinc.com, pg 808

Lightning Eliminators & Consultants Inc, 6687 Arapahoe Rd, Boulder, CO 80303 *Tel:* 303-447-2828 *Toll Free Tel:* 800-521-6101 *Fax:* 303-447-8122 *E-mail:* info@ lecglobal.com *Web Site:* www.lightningprotection.com, pg 808

Lightning Master Corp, 2100-A Palmetto St, Clearwater, FL 33765 *Tel:* 727-447-6800 *Toll Free Tel:* 877-334-8006 *Fax:* 727-499-0138 *E-mail:* info@ lightningmaster.com *Web Site:* www.lightningmaster. com, pg 808

Lightning Media, 1415 Cahuenga Blvd, Hollywood, CA 90028 *Tel:* 323-957-9255 *E-mail:* info@ lightningmedia.com *Web Site:* www.lightningmedia. com, pg 808

Lightronics Inc, 509 Central Dr, Virginia Beach, VA 23454 *Tel:* 757-486-3588 *Toll Free Tel:* 800-472-8541 *Fax:* 757-486-3391 *Web Site:* www.lightronics.com, pg 808

Lights On, 1720 Merriam Lane, Kansas City, KS 66106 *Tel:* 913-362-6940 *Toll Free Tel:* 800-229-5876 *Fax:* 913-362-6958 *E-mail:* kansascity@lightson.com *Web Site:* www.lightson.com, pg 808

Lights On Nebraska, 7520 Burlington St, Omaha, NE 68127 *Tel:* 402-331-4340 *Fax:* 402-331-4556 *E-mail:* ne@lightsonrentals.com *Web Site:* www. lightsonrentals.com, pg 808

LightSpace Studios, 1115 Flushing Ave, Brooklyn, NY 11237 *Tel:* 212-202-0372 *E-mail:* reserve@lightspace. tv *Web Site:* www.lightspace.tv, pg 808

Lightspeed Technologies Inc, 11509 SW Herman Rd, Tualatin, OR 97062 *Tel:* 503-684-5538 *Toll Free Tel:* 800-732-8999 *Fax:* 503-684-3197 *E-mail:* info@ lightspeed-tek.com *Web Site:* www.lightspeed-tek.com, pg 808

LightTech Group Inc, PO Box 300642, Jamaica, NY 11430 *Tel:* 718-525-2900 *Web Site:* www.lighttech. com, pg 808

Lightware Inc, 1329 W Byers Place, Denver, CO 80223-1723 *Tel:* 303-744-0202 *Fax:* 303-722-4545 *E-mail:* info@lightwareinc.com *Web Site:* www. lightwareinc.com; www.lightwaredirect.com, pg 808

Lightworks Audio & Video Inc, PO Box 661593, Los Angeles, CA 90066 *Tel:* 310-398-4949 *E-mail:* sales1@lightworksav.com; edmedia@ lightworksav.com *Web Site:* www.lightworksav.com, pg 808

Lightyear Entertainment, 4011 Alcove Ave, Studio City, CA 91604 *Tel:* 818-855-1318 *Fax:* 818-855-1320 *Web Site:* lightyear.com, pg 808

Ligos Corporation, 6001 Chatham Ctr Dr, Suite 300, Savannah, GA 31405 *Tel:* 912-236-8993 *Fax:* 912-234-1366 *Web Site:* www.ligos.com, pg 808

Limbo Films, 2223 NE Martin Luther King Jr Blvd, Portland, OR 97212 *E-mail:* info@limbofilms.com *Web Site:* www.limbofilms.com, pg 808

Limelight Communications Inc, 2812 Roesh Way, Vienna, VA 22181 *Tel:* 703-242-4596 *E-mail:* moreinfo@limelightdc.com *Web Site:* www. limelightdc.com, pg 808

Limelight Production® Inc, 471 Pleasant St, Lee, MA 01238-9322 *Tel:* 413-243-4950 *Toll Free Tel:* 800-243-4950 *Fax:* 413-243-4993 *Toll Free Fax:* 800-243-4951 *E-mail:* info@limelightproductions.com; sales@limelightproductions.com *Web Site:* www. limelightproductions.com, pg 809

Lineco, 517 Main St, Holyoke, MA 01040-2604 *Toll Free Tel:* 800-322-7775 *Fax:* 413-532-9281 (sales) *Toll Free Fax:* 800-298-7815 *E-mail:* info@lineco.com *Web Site:* www.lineco.com, pg 809

Linguistic Systems Inc, 260 Franklin St, Suite 230, Boston, MA 02110 *Toll Free Tel:* 800-654-5006 *E-mail:* clientservice@linguist.com *Web Site:* linguist. com, pg 809

Linguist's Software Inc, 844 Adler St, Edmonds, WA 98020-3301 *Tel:* 425-775-1130 *E-mail:* fonts@ linguistsoftware.com *Web Site:* www.linguistsoftware. com, pg 809

Linhoff Photo & Digital Imaging, 4400 France Ave S, Edina, MN 55410 *Tel:* 952-927-7333 *E-mail:* info@ linhoff.com *Web Site:* linhoff.com, pg 809

Link Electronics Inc, 2360 N High St, Suite 10, Jackson, MO 63755 *Tel:* 573-334-4433 *Toll Free Tel:* 800-776-4411 *Fax:* 573-204-4554 *E-mail:* sales@ linkelectronics.com *Web Site:* www.linkelectronics. com, pg 809

Linkabit, 9890 Towne Centre Dr, San Diego, CA 92121 *Tel:* 858-552-9500 *Toll Free Tel:* 800-331-9401 *E-mail:* linkabitproducts@l3t.com *Web Site:* www2.l-3com.com/linkabit, pg 809

Linker Systems Inc, 13612 Onkayha Circle, Irvine, CA 92620 *Tel:* 949-552-1904 *Toll Free Tel:* 800-315-1174 *Web Site:* linkersystems.com, pg 809

Lion & Fox Recording Studios, 9517 Baltimore Ave, College Park, MD 20740 *Tel:* 301-982-4431 *E-mail:* mail@lionfox.com *Web Site:* www.lionfox. com, pg 809

Lions Gate Entertainment Corp, 2700 Colorado Ave, Santa Monica, CA 90404 *Tel:* 310-449-9200 *Fax:* 310-255-3870 *E-mail:* generalinquiries@lionsgate.com *Web Site:* www.lionsgate.com; corporate.lionsgate.com, pg 809

Lippincott Williams & Wilkins, Two Commerce Sq, 2001 Market St, Philadephia, PA 19103 *Tel:* 215-521-8300; 301-223-2300 (cust serv) *Toll Free Tel:* 800-638-3030 (cust serv) *Fax:* 215-521-8902 *Web Site:* www.lww.com, pg 809

Lipsner-Smith Co, 4700 Chase Ave, Lincolnwood, IL 60712-1689 *Tel:* 847-677-3000 *Toll Free Tel:* 800-323-7520 *Fax:* 847-677-1311 *Toll Free Fax:* 800-784-6733 *E-mail:* sales@lipsner.com; sales@rtico.com *Web Site:* www.lipsner.com; lipsner-smith.com, pg 809

A Liss & Co, 51-55 59 Place, Woodside, NY 11377-7408 *Tel:* 718-728-0600 *Toll Free Tel:* 800-221-0938 *Fax:* 718-728-1227 *E-mail:* sales@alissco.com *Web Site:* alissco.com, pg 809

Listen & Live Audio Inc, 1700 Manhattan Ave, Union City, NJ 07068 *Tel:* 201-558-9000 *Toll Free Tel:* 800-653-9400 (orders) *Fax:* 201-558-9800 *Web Site:* www. listenandlive.com, pg 809

Listen Technologies Corp, 14912 Heritage Crest Way, Bluffdale, UT 84065-4818 *Tel:* 801-233-8992 *Toll Free Tel:* 800-330-0891 *Fax:* 801-233-8995 *E-mail:* info@listentech.com *Web Site:* www. listentech.com, pg 810

Listening Library, 1745 Broadway, New York, NY 10019 *Tel:* 212-782-9000 *Toll Free Tel:* 800-733-3000 (cust serv) *E-mail:* audio@penguinrandomhouse.com *Web Site:* www.penguinrandomhouseaudio.com/kids-and-teens, pg 810

LITE-IT Grip Truck Rentals, 450 Saint Andrews Ct, West Chicago, IL 60185 *Tel:* 630-231-1671 *Fax:* 630-231-1672 *E-mail:* liteit1@sbcglobal.net *Web Site:* www.liteit1.com, pg 810

Little Big Bang Design Inc, 33 Moya Loop, Santa Fe, NM 87508 *Tel:* 786-218-0713 *E-mail:* hello@ littlebigbangstudios.com *Web Site:* www. littlebigbangdesign.com, pg 810

Little Mammoth Media, 750 Ralph McGill Blvd NE, Atlanta, GA 30312 *Toll Free Tel:* 800-KIDVIDEO (543-8433) *E-mail:* bv@vanderkloot.com; service@littlemammoth.com *Web Site:* littlemammoth.com, pg 810

Littlite LLC, PO Box 430, Hamburg, MI 48139-0430 *Tel:* 810-852-4242 *Fax:* 810-231-1631 *E-mail:* sales@littlite.com *Web Site:* www.littlite.com, pg 810

Liturgy Training Publications, 3949 S Racine Ave, Chicago, IL 60609-2523 *Tel:* 773-579-4900 *Toll Free Tel:* 800-933-1800 (orders) *Fax:* 773-579-4929 *E-mail:* orders@ltp.org; info@ltp.org *Web Site:* www.ltp.org, pg 810

Live Oak Media, PO Box 652, Pine Plains, NY 12567 *Toll Free Tel:* 800-788-1121 *Toll Free Fax:* 866-398-1070 *E-mail:* info@liveoakmedia.com *Web Site:* www.liveoakmedia.com, pg 810

Live Spark Inc, 700 Raymond Ave, Suite 100, St Paul, MN 55114 *Tel:* 651-289-7375 *E-mail:* info@live-spark.com *Web Site:* www.live-spark.com, pg 810

Live Wire Media, 2355 Westwood Blvd, No 312, Los Angeles, CA 90064 *Tel:* 415-564-9500 *Toll Free Tel:* 800-359-KIDS (359-5437) *Fax:* 415-552-4087 *E-mail:* sales@livewiremedia.com *Web Site:* www.livewiremedia.com, pg 810

Live'N'Loud, PO Box 557, Mena, AR 71953 *Tel:* 479-216-6727 *Web Site:* nahteboy.tripod.com, pg 810

The Livingston Awards for Young Journalists, Wallace House, 620 Oxford Rd, Ann Arbor, MI 48104 *Tel:* 734-998-7575 *Fax:* 734-998-7979 *E-mail:* livawards@umich.edu *Web Site:* wallacehouse.umich.edu/livingston-awards, pg 994

LKG Industries, 3660 Publishers Dr, Rockford, IL 61109 *Tel:* 815-874-2301 *Toll Free Tel:* 800-645-2262 *Fax:* 815-874-2896 *Toll Free Fax:* 800-554-0795 *E-mail:* sales-lkgindustries@t6b.com *Web Site:* www.philmore-datak.com, pg 810

C V Lloyde, 702 W Killarney St, Urbana, IL 61801 *Tel:* 217-352-7031 *Toll Free Tel:* 800-779-7031 *E-mail:* sales@cvlloyde.com *Web Site:* www.cvlloyde.com, pg 810

LM Cases/LM Engineering Inc, 2720 Intertech Dr, Youngstown, OH 44509 *Tel:* 330-270-2400 *Toll Free Tel:* 800-874-8326 *Fax:* 330-270-2424 *E-mail:* info@lmcases.com *Web Site:* www.lmcases.com, pg 810

Location Camera Ltd, 300 Pennsylvania Ave, Oreland, PA 19075 *Tel:* 215-576-5600 *Fax:* 215-576-6022 *E-mail:* mail@locationcamera.com *Web Site:* www.locationcamera.com, pg 810

The Location Connection Inc, 1600 Rosecrans Ave, Manhattan Beach, CA 90266 *Tel:* 310-376-9797 *E-mail:* lconnect@aol.com *Web Site:* www.locationconnection.com, pg 810

Location Lighting Ltd, 300 Pennsylvania Ave, Oreland, PA 19075 *Tel:* 215-576-5600 *Fax:* 215-576-6022 *E-mail:* mail@locationlighting.com; rentals@locationlighting.com *Web Site:* www.locationlighting.com, pg 810

Location Managers Guild International (LMGI), 8033 Sunset Blvd, Suite 1017, Los Angeles, CA 90046 *Tel:* 310-967-2007 *Fax:* 310-967-2013 *E-mail:* contact@locationmanagers.org *Web Site:* locationmanagers.org, pg 957

Location Sound Corp, 10639 Riverside Dr, North Hollywood, CA 91602 *Tel:* 818-980-9891 *Toll Free Tel:* 800-228-4429 *Fax:* 818-980-9911; 818-980-7932 (rentals) *E-mail:* information@locationsound.com *Web Site:* www.locationsound.com, pg 810

Location 05 Studios, 450 W 31 St, 7th fl, New York, NY 10001 *Tel:* 212-219-2144 *E-mail:* info@location05.com *Web Site:* location05.com, pg 811

Loft 19, 21618 N Ninth Ave, Suite A, Phoenix, AZ 85027 *Tel:* 623-434-3791 *Fax:* 623-434-5003 *E-mail:* info@loft19.com *Web Site:* loft19.com, pg 811

Logan Productions Inc, 8035 N Port Washington Rd, Milwaukee, WI 53217 *Tel:* 414-352-9691 *Fax:* 414-352-4993 *E-mail:* info@loganproductions.com *Web Site:* www.loganproductions.com, pg 811

Logitech, 7700 Gateway Blvd, Newark, CA 94560 *Tel:* 510-795-8500 *Toll Free Tel:* 866-291-1505 *Web Site:* www.logitech.com, pg 811

Logitek Electronic Systems Inc, 5622 Edgemoor Dr, Houston, TX 77081 *Tel:* 713-664-4470 *Toll Free Tel:* 800-231-5870 (sales); 877-231-5870 (tech support) *E-mail:* northamericansales@logitekaudio.com *Web Site:* www.logitekaudio.com, pg 811

Loma Scientific International (LSI), 3115 Kashiwa St, Torrance, CA 90505 *Tel:* 310-539-8655 *Fax:* 310-539-8634 *E-mail:* info@lomasci.com; sales@lomasci.com *Web Site:* www.lomasci.com, pg 811

Long Island University Media Arts Dept, One University Plaza, Brooklyn, NY 11201-8423 *Tel:* 718-488-1052 *Fax:* 718-780-4578 *E-mail:* mediart@brooklyn.liu.edu *Web Site:* www.liu.edu/brooklyn.aspx, pg 811

Long Island Video Enterprises Live Inc, 110 Pratt Oval, Glen Cove, NY 11542 *Tel:* 516-759-5483 *Fax:* 516-671-5874 *E-mail:* info@longislandvideo.com *Web Site:* www.longislandvideo.com, pg 811

Long-Term Success Publishing, 766 Ninth Ave N, Suite 1, Fort Dodge, IA 50501 *Tel:* 515-571-8880 *E-mail:* judypayne@judypayne.com *Web Site:* judypayne.com, pg 811

Loopmedia Inc, 26 Duncan St, Toronto, ON M5V 2B9, Canada *Tel:* 416-595-6496 *E-mail:* info@loopmedia.com *Web Site:* loopmedia.com, pg 811

The Los Angeles Asian Pacific Film Festival, 120 Judge John Aiso St, Basement Level, Los Angeles, CA 90012-3805 *Tel:* 213-680-4462 *E-mail:* festival@vconline.org *Web Site:* asianfilmestla.org; www.vconline.org/festival, pg 994

Los Angeles Center Studios, 450 S Bixel St, Los Angeles, CA 90017 *Tel:* 213-534-3000 *E-mail:* productionservices@lacenterstudios.com *Web Site:* lacenterstudios.com, pg 811

Los Angeles Film Festival, 5670 Wilshire Blvd, 9th fl, Los Angeles, CA 90036 *Tel:* 323-556-9300 *Toll Free Tel:* 866-345-6337 *Fax:* 323-556-9303 *E-mail:* lafilmfest@filmindependent.org; programming@filmindependent.org *Web Site:* www.filmindependent.org/la-film-festival, pg 995

Los Angeles Post Music Inc, 4340 E Kentucky Ave, Suite 308, Glendale, CO 80246 *Tel:* 310-896-5176 *Web Site:* www.lapostmusic.com, pg 811

The Lot (Skye Partners), 1041 N Formosa Ave, West Hollywood, CA 90046 *Tel:* 323-850-3180 *Fax:* 323-850-3189 *E-mail:* info@thelotstudios.com; stages@thelotstudios.com *Web Site:* www.thelotstudios.com, pg 811

LOUD Technologies Inc, 16220 Wood-Red Rd NE, Woodinville, WA 98072 *Tel:* 425-487-4333; 415-892-6500 *Toll Free Tel:* 866-858-LTEC (858-5832) *Fax:* 425-487-4337 *Web Site:* www.mackie.com; www.loudtechinc.com, pg 811

Louisiana Entertainment, 617 N Third St, Baton Rouge, LA 70802 *Tel:* 225-342-5403 *Fax:* 225-342-5554 *E-mail:* led-entertainment@la.gov *Web Site:* louisianaentertainment.gov, pg 971

Louisiana State University Division of Strategic Communications, Video Services Dept, 3960 W Lakeshore Dr, Baton Rouge, LA 70808 *Tel:* 225-578-8654 *Fax:* 225-578-3860 *E-mail:* stratcomm@lsu.edu *Web Site:* www.lsu.edu/stratcomm/resources/video-services.php, pg 811

James Loupas Associates Inc, 134 Carrington Dr, Coppell, TX 75019 *Tel:* 972-304-0455 *Web Site:* jimloupas.com, pg 811

Love Shack Recording Studios, 909 18 Ave S, Nashville, TN 37212 *Tel:* 615-843-0019 *E-mail:* book@loveshackstudios.com *Web Site:* loveshackstudios.com, pg 811

Love Your Shorts Film Festival, 608 S Elm Ave, Sanford, FL 32771 *E-mail:* contact@loveyourshorts.com *Web Site:* www.loveyourshorts.com, pg 995

Lowell Manufacturing, 100 Integram Dr, Pacific, MO 63069-3476 *Tel:* 636-257-3400 *Toll Free Tel:* 800-325-9660 *Fax:* 636-257-6606 *Toll Free Fax:* 888-456-9355 *E-mail:* sales@lowellmfg.com *Web Site:* www.lowellmfg.com, pg 812

Lowing Light & Grip Inc, 1500 Whiting St SW, Wyoming, MI 49509-1056 *Tel:* 616-530-7440 *Toll Free Tel:* 888-530-7440 *Fax:* 616-249-8947 *Web Site:* www.lowinglight.com, pg 812

Lowrance Sound Co Inc, 2132 Nailling Dr, Union City, TN 38261 *Tel:* 731-885-4504 *Toll Free Tel:* 800-852-5418 *E-mail:* info@lowrancesoundcompany.com *Web Site:* www.lowrancesoundcompany.com, pg 812

Loyal Studios, 3513 W Pacific Ave, Burbank, CA 91505 *Tel:* 818-845-5123 (studio); 818-399-9499 *Web Site:* www.loyalstudios.tv, pg 812

LT Sound Inc, 7980 LT Pkwy, Lithonia, GA 30058 *Tel:* 770-482-4836 *Web Site:* www.ltsound.com, pg 812

L3Harris Technologies Inc, 1025 W NASA Blvd, Melbourne, FL 32919 *E-mail:* info@l3harris.com *Web Site:* www.l3harris.com, pg 812

LTM Corp of America, 25520 Ave Stanford, Valencia, CA 91355 *Tel:* 818-780-9828 *Toll Free Tel:* 800-762-4291 *E-mail:* info@ltmlighting.us, pg 812

Lubbock Audio Visual Inc, 2120 Ave "Q", Lubbock, TX 79405 *Tel:* 806-744-2559 *Toll Free Tel:* 800-850-2559 *Fax:* 806-747-6939 *E-mail:* sales@lav.com *Web Site:* www.lav.com, pg 812

Lubell Labs Inc, 21 N Stanwood Rd, Columbus, OH 43209 *Tel:* 614-235-6740 *E-mail:* lubell_labs@wowway.com *Web Site:* www.lubell.com, pg 812

Ludlow Media, 15501 San Pablo Ave, Suite G-320, San Pablo, CA 94806 *Tel:* 415-927-1300 *E-mail:* info@ludlowmedia.com *Web Site:* www.ludlowmedia.com, pg 812

Lumalaser, 84777 Charlottes Way, Eugene, OR 97405 *Tel:* 541-687-1414 *Toll Free Tel:* 800-606-2597 *Fax:* 541-687-1438 *E-mail:* info@lumalaser.com *Web Site:* www.lumalaser.com, pg 812

Lumedyne Inc, 6010 Wall St, Port Richey, FL 34668 *Tel:* 727-847-2777; 727-847-5394 *Toll Free Tel:* 800-586-3396 *Fax:* 727-841-0000 *E-mail:* info@lumedyne.com; sales@lumedyne.com; service@lumedyne.com *Web Site:* www.lumedyne.com, pg 812

Lumeni Productions Inc, 1632 Flower St, Glendale, CA 91201 *Tel:* 818-956-2200 *Fax:* 818-956-3298 *E-mail:* info@lumeni.com *Web Site:* www.lumeni.com, pg 812

Luminaud Inc, 8688 Tyler Blvd, Mentor, OH 44060 *Tel:* 440-255-9082 *Toll Free Tel:* 800-255-3408 *Fax:* 440-255-2250 *E-mail:* info@luminaud.com *Web Site:* www.luminaud.com, pg 812

Luminys Systems Corp, 11961 Sherman Rd, North Hollywood, CA 91605 *Tel:* 818-827-3941 *Toll Free Tel:* 800-321-3644 *E-mail:* info@luminyscorp.com *Web Site:* www.luminyscorp.com, pg 812

Lumisphere™ USA, 9429 Everett Ct, Spotsylvania, VA 22553 *Tel:* 540-582-7897 *Fax:* 540-582-5233 *Web Site:* www.lumisphereusa.com, pg 812

G T Luscombe Co Inc, 106 Kansas St, Frankfort, IL 60423 *Tel:* 815-469-2478 *Toll Free Tel:* 800-435-7855 *Fax:* 815-469-5429 *Toll Free Fax:* 888-469-5429 *E-mail:* info@gtluscombe.com *Web Site:* www.gtluscombe.com, pg 812

Luxor, 2245 Delany Rd, Waukegan, IL 60087 *Tel:* 847-244-1800 *Toll Free Tel:* 800-323-4656 *Fax:* 847-244-1818 *Toll Free Fax:* 800-327-1698 *E-mail:* info@luxorfurn.com; customerservice@luxorfurn.com; sales@luxorfurn.com *Web Site:* www.luxorfurn.com, pg 812

LuXout Stage Curtains, 1221 Admiral St, Richmond, VA 23220 *Tel:* 804-264-3000; 804-264-3700 *Toll Free Tel:* 800-817-1204 *Toll Free Fax:* 888-227-8064 *E-mail:* luxoutinfo@luxout.com *Web Site:* www.luxout.com, pg 813

Luzerne County Community College, 1333 S Prospect St, Nanticoke, PA 18634-3899 *Tel:* 570-740-0200 *Toll Free Tel:* 800-377-5222 *Fax:* 570-740-0250 *Web Site:* www.luzerne.edu/index.jsp, pg 813

Lylofilm Productions, 503 Beech St, New Hyde Park, NY 11040 *Tel:* 516-587-0567 *E-mail:* lylofilm@gmail. com *Web Site:* www.lylofilm.com; www.graphissimo. com, pg 813

Lynch Communications, 525 Loma Vista Terr, Pacifica, CA 94044 *Tel:* 678-939-1212 *Fax:* 480-287-9401 *Web Site:* www.lynchcommunications.com, pg 813

Lynx Broadband, 12219 Wood Lake Dr, Burnsville, MN 55337 *Tel:* 952-894-9590 *Fax:* 952-894-9380 *E-mail:* info@lynxbroadband.com *Web Site:* www. lynxbroadband.com, pg 813

Lynx Studio Technology Inc, 190 McCormick Ave, Costa Mesa, CA 92626-3307 *Tel:* 714-545-4700 *Fax:* 714-545-4777 *E-mail:* sales@lynxstudio.com *Web Site:* www.lynxstudio.com, pg 813

Lyon Video Inc, 2091 Arlingate Lane, Columbus, OH 43228 *Tel:* 614-297-0001 *E-mail:* info@lyonvideo.com *Web Site:* www.lyonvideo.com, pg 813

Lyon Workspace Products LLC, 420 N Main St, Montgomery, IL 60538 *Tel:* 630-892-8941 *Toll Free Tel:* 800-433-8488 *Fax:* 630-892-8966 *Toll Free Fax:* 800-367-6681 *E-mail:* lyon@lyonworkspace.com *Web Site:* www.lyonworkspace.com, pg 813

LYRASIS, 1438 W Peachtree NW, Suite 150, Atlanta, GA 30309 *Tel:* 404-892-0943 *Toll Free Tel:* 800-999-8558 *Fax:* 404-892-7879 *Web Site:* www.lyrasis.org, pg 813

Lyrichord/Multicultural Media, 27 Main St, Suite 6, Montpelier, VT 05602 *Tel:* 802-839-0371 *E-mail:* info@lyrichord.com *Web Site:* www.lyrichord. com, pg 813

M-Audio, 2000 Scenic View Dr, Cumberland, RI 02864 *Tel:* 401-658-5765 (support) *E-mail:* info@m-audio. com *Web Site:* m-audio.com, pg 813

M Works Mastering Studio, 60 Hampshire St, Cambridge, MA 02139 *Tel:* 617-577-0089 *E-mail:* studio@m-works.com; info@m-works.com *Web Site:* www.m-works.com, pg 813

MAC Group, 75 Virginia Rd, North White Plains, NY 10603 *Tel:* 914-347-3300 *Fax:* 914-347-3309 *E-mail:* info@macgroupus.com *Web Site:* www. macgroupus.com, pg 813

MAC Production Group, 3500 Aloma Ave, Winter Park, FL 32792 *Tel:* 407-234-8898 *Fax:* 407-671-5360 *E-mail:* info@macproav.com *Web Site:* macproav.com, pg 813

MacGillivray Freeman Films Inc, PO Box 205, Laguna Beach, CA 92652-0205 *Tel:* 949-494-1055 *Fax:* 949-494-2079 *E-mail:* info@macfreefilms.com *Web Site:* www.macfreefilms.com, pg 813

Mach 1 Productions, 1101 N Himes Ave, Tampa, FL 33607 *Tel:* 813-873-7700 *Fax:* 813-875-6633 *E-mail:* info@mach1pro.com *Web Site:* www. mach1pro.com, pg 813

Mackenzie Laboratories Inc, 1163 Nicole Ct, Glendora, CA 91740 *Tel:* 909-394-9007 *Fax:* 909-394-9411 *E-mail:* info@macklabs.com *Web Site:* www.macklabs. com, pg 814

Macmillan Audio, 120 Broadway, 22nd fl, New York, NY 10271 *Tel:* 646-600-7856; 646-307-5472 *Toll Free Tel:* 888-330-8477 (cust serv); 800-221-7945 *Toll Free Fax:* 800-672-7703 (orders) *E-mail:* macmillan.audio@macmillanusa.com *Web Site:* www.macmillanaudio.com, pg 814

Macrosystem US Inc, 4282 Arnie Rd, Blaine, WA 98230 *Tel:* 360-371-4942 *Toll Free Tel:* 877-554-2846 *Toll Free Fax:* 855-269-6999 *E-mail:* info@macrosystem.us *Web Site:* www.macrosystem.us, pg 814

Madera County Film Commission Inc, PO Box 3690, Oakhurst, CA 93644 *Tel:* 559-760-1143 *Fax:* 559-658-2851 *E-mail:* filmcommissioner@filmmadera.com *Web Site:* www.yosemite-sierra.com, pg 967

Madison Square Garden, 2 Pennsylvania Plaza, New York, NY 10121-0091 *Tel:* 212-465-6741 *E-mail:* msgnetpr@msgnetwork.com *Web Site:* www. thegarden.com; themadisonsquaregardencompany.com, pg 814

Madisound Speaker Components Inc, 8608 University Green, Suite 10, Middleton, WI 53562 *Tel:* 608-831-3433 *Toll Free Tel:* 866-883-1488 (orders) *Fax:* 608-831-3771 *E-mail:* info@madisound.com *Web Site:* www.madisound.com, pg 814

Madonna University Information Technology, 36600 Schoolcraft Rd, Livonia, MI 48150-1173 *Tel:* 734-432-5800 *Toll Free Tel:* 800-852-4951 *Web Site:* www. madonna.edu, pg 814

Magic Gadgets™, 12986 Mapleleaf Ct NE, Aurora, OR 97002-8418 *Tel:* 503-678-6236; 818-655-5465 (rentals) *E-mail:* info@magicgadgets.com *Web Site:* www.magicgadgets.com, pg 814

Magic Teleprompting Inc, 1390 Waller St, San Francisco, CA 94117 *Tel:* 415-626-5283 *Toll Free Tel:* 800-646-6244 *Fax:* 415-626-2762 *E-mail:* info@magicscroll.com; sales@magicscroll. com *Web Site:* www.magicscroll.com, pg 814

Magick Lantern, 750 Ralph McGill Blvd, Atlanta, GA 30312 *Tel:* 404-688-3348 *Fax:* 404-584-5247 *E-mail:* info@magicklantern.com *Web Site:* magicklantern.com, pg 814

Magna-Tech Electronic Co Inc, 1998 NE 150 St, North Miami, FL 33181 *Tel:* 305-573-7339 *Fax:* 305-573-8101 *E-mail:* sales@iceco.com; digital@myiceco.com *Web Site:* www.magna-tech.com, pg 814

Magna Visual Inc, 9400 Watson Rd, St Louis, MO 63126-1596 *Tel:* 314-843-9000 *Toll Free Tel:* 800-843-3399 *Fax:* 314-843-0000 *E-mail:* magna@ magnavisual.com *Web Site:* www.magnavisual.com, pg 814

Magnanimous Media, 600 W Cermak, Chicago, IL 60616 *Tel:* 312-465-2366 *E-mail:* rentals@ magnanimous.biz *Web Site:* www.magnanimous.biz, pg 814

Magnepan Inc, 1645 Ninth St, White Bear Lake, MN 55110 *Tel:* 651-426-1645 *Toll Free Tel:* 800-474-1646 *Fax:* 651-426-0441 *Web Site:* www.magnepan.com, pg 814

Magnet Sales & Manufacturing Inc, 11248 Playa Ct, Culver City, CA 90230 *Tel:* 310-391-7213 *Toll Free Tel:* 800-421-6692 *Fax:* 310-391-7463 *E-mail:* info@ magnetsales.com *Web Site:* www.magnetsales.com; www.magnetshop.com, pg 814

Magnetek Inc, N49 W13650 Campbell Dr, Menomonee Falls, WI 53051 *Tel:* 262-783-3500 *Toll Free Tel:* 800-288-8178 *Toll Free Fax:* 800-298-3503 *E-mail:* sales@ magnetek.com *Web Site:* www.magnetek.com, pg 814

Magnetic Music Publishing Co, 155 W 68 St, Suite 22-D, New York, NY 10023-5834 *Tel:* 212-255-8527 *Fax:* 212-595-2067 *E-mail:* info@magneticmusic.ws *Web Site:* magneticmusic.ws, pg 814

Magnetic Post Production, 4 Marshall Rd, Wappingers Falls, NY 12590-4105 *Tel:* 212-598-3000 *Web Site:* www.magneticimage.com, pg 815

Magnetic Reference Laboratory Inc, 165 Wyandotte Dr, San Jose, CA 95123 *Tel:* 408-227-8631 *Fax:* 408-227-8631 *E-mail:* mrltapes@comcast.net *Web Site:* www. mrltapes.com, pg 815

Magnetic Shield Corp, 740 N Thomas Dr, Bensenville, IL 60106 *Tel:* 630-766-7800 *Toll Free Tel:* 888-766-7800 *Fax:* 630-766-2813 *E-mail:* shields@magnetic-shield.com *Web Site:* www.magnetic-shield.com, pg 815

Magnicon Media/Image d'Or, 5050 Williamson St, Dearborn, MI 48126 *Tel:* 313-846-8694; 313-574-3546 (cell), pg 815

Magno Sound Inc, 729 Seventh Ave, New York, NY 10019 *Tel:* 212-302-2505 *Fax:* 212-819-1282 *E-mail:* staff@magnosound.com *Web Site:* magnoscreening.com, pg 815

MAGNUM Companies Ltd, 205 Armour Dr NE, Atlanta, GA 30324 *Tel:* 800-255-1774 *Fax:* 404-875-5629 *E-mail:* rent@ magnumco.com; design@magnumco.com; production@magnumco.com; buy@magnumco.com *Web Site:* www.magnumco.com, pg 815

Magnum Towers Inc, 9370 Elder Creek Rd, Sacramento, CA 95829 *Tel:* 916-381-5053 *Fax:* 916-381-2144 *E-mail:* office@magnumtowers.com *Web Site:* www. magnumtowers.com, pg 815

Mailing Avenue Stageworks, 1144 Mailing Ave, Atlanta, GA 30315 *Tel:* 404-601-9500 (ext 11) *Web Site:* www. mailingavenuestageworks.com, pg 815

Main Point Productions, 295 Lobachsville Rd, Oley, PA 19547 *Tel:* 610-987-9320; 610-987-9163 *E-mail:* mainpoint301@gmail.com *Web Site:* www. mainpoint.com, pg 815

Main Street Media Inc, 185 Pier Ave, Suite 105, Santa Monica, CA 90405 *Tel:* 310-450-1846 *E-mail:* info@mainstreetmediainc.com *Web Site:* www. mainstreetmediainc.com, pg 815

Maine Artist Fellowship Program, 193 State St, 25 State House Sta, Augusta, ME 04330-0025 *Tel:* 207-287-2724 *Fax:* 207-287-2725 *E-mail:* mainearts.info@ maine.gov *Web Site:* mainearts.maine.gov/Pages/Funding/Individual-Artist-Fellowships, pg 995

Maine Film Office, 59 State House Sta, Augusta, ME 04333 *Tel:* 207-624-9828 *Fax:* 207-287-8070 *E-mail:* film@maine.gov *Web Site:* www.filminmaine. com, pg 971

Maine Imaging, PO Box 753, Wiscasset, ME 04578 *Tel:* 207-380-6343 *Web Site:* www.maineimaging.com, pg 815

Maine Student Film & Video Festival, c/o Maine Film Ctr, 76 Main St, Waterville, ME 04901 *Tel:* 207-861-8138 *E-mail:* msfvf@mainefilmcenter.org *Web Site:* www.msfvf.com, pg 995

MainSail Production Services Inc, 521 Byers Rd, Suite 109, Miamisburg, OH 45342 *Tel:* 937-866-7800 *Toll Free Tel:* 800-877-0093 *Fax:* 937-866-8088 *E-mail:* discover@mainsailproductions.com *Web Site:* www.mainsailproductions.com, pg 815

Maison de Soul Records, PO Drawer 10, Ville Platte, LA 70586-0010 *Tel:* 337-363-2177 *Toll Free Tel:* 800-738-8668 *Fax:* 337-363-2094 *E-mail:* info@flattownmusic. com; info@floydsrecordshop.com *Web Site:* www. flattownmusic.com, pg 815

Major Media Inc, PO Box 209, Deerfield, IL 60015 *Tel:* 847-433-1682 *E-mail:* dmchistory@aol.com *Web Site:* www.major-media.com, pg 815

Major Media Productions Inc, PO Box 209, Deerfield, IL 60015 *Tel:* 847-433-1682 *E-mail:* dmchistory@aol. com *Web Site:* www.major-media.com, pg 815

Major Reproductions Equipment Co, PO Box 209, Deerfield, IL 60015 *Tel:* 847-433-1682 *E-mail:* dmchistory@aol.com *Web Site:* www.major-media.com, pg 815

Majortech Inc, 8464 Ninth Line RR-1, Norval, ON L0P 1K0, Canada *Tel:* 905-873-0778 *Fax:* 905-873-1244, pg 815

MakeMusic® Inc, 7007 Winchester Circle, Suite 140, Boulder, CO 80301 *Tel:* 952-937-9611 *Toll Free Tel:* 800-843-2066 (cust serv) *Fax:* 720-465-6419 *Web Site:* www.makemusic.com, pg 815

Mamiya, 75 Virginia Rd, Suite 1, North White Plains, NY 10603 *Tel:* 914-347-3300 *Fax:* 914-347-3309 *E-mail:* info@mamiya-usa.com *Web Site:* www. mamiyaleaf.com, pg 815

Mammoth HD, PO Box 2064, Evergreen, CO 80437 *Tel:* 303-670-7973 *E-mail:* mammothhd@me.com; info@mammothhd.com *Web Site:* www.mammothhd. com, pg 815

Mammoth Location Services, 10001 Minaret Rd, Mammoth Lakes, CA 93546 *Tel:* 760-934-2571 (ext 3628) *Web Site:* www.mammothmountain.com/winter/home/film-locations, pg 966

Manchester Music Library Inc, 6857 Colton Blvd, Oakland, CA 94611 *Tel:* 413-369-4331 *Web Site:* www.manchestermusiclibrary.com, pg 816

Manfrotto Distribution Inc, 10 Mountainview Rd, Suite 320 S, Upper Saddle River, NJ 07458 *Tel:* 201-818-9500 *E-mail:* info@manfrottodistribution.us *Web Site:* www.manfrottodistribution.us; www.manfrotto.us, pg 816

Manhattan Center Studios Inc, 311 W 34 St, New York, NY 10001 *Tel:* 212-279-7740 *Fax:* 212-564-1072 *E-mail:* info@mcstudios.com *Web Site:* www.mcstudios.com, pg 816

Manhattan Film Commission, 501 Poyntz Ave, Manhattan, KS 66502 *Tel:* 785-776-8829 *Toll Free Tel:* 800-759-0134 *Fax:* 785-776-0679 *E-mail:* cvb@manhattan.org *Web Site:* visitmanhattanks.org, pg 971

Manhattan Production Music Inc, 1650 Broadway, Suite 900, New York, NY 10019 *Tel:* 212-333-5766 *Fax:* 212-262-0814 *E-mail:* info@mpmmusic.com *Web Site:* www.mpmmusic.com, pg 816

Maniac Productions, 3888 Viewpoint Way, Lafayette, CO 80026 *Tel:* 303-661-0920 *E-mail:* mpc1@aol.com; info@maniacproductions.com *Web Site:* maniacproductions.com, pg 816

Maniglia Media LLC, 7925 Jones Branch Dr, Suite LL-110, Tysons, VA 22102 *Tel:* 703-283-8532 (cell); 703-942-8011 (studio) *Web Site:* www.manigliamedia.com, pg 816

Manios Digital & Film, 10663 Burbank Blvd, North Hollywood, CA 91601 *Tel:* 818-760-8290 *Toll Free Tel:* 800-845-6619 *Fax:* 818-760-8805 *E-mail:* sales@maniosdigital.com *Web Site:* www.maniosdigital.com, pg 816

Manitoba Film & Music, 410-93 Lombard Ave, Suite 410, Winnipeg, MB R3B 3B1, Canada *Tel:* 204-947-2040 *Fax:* 204-956-5261 *E-mail:* info@mbfilmmusic.ca *Web Site:* www.mbfilmmusic.ca, pg 816, 978

Manley Laboratories Inc, 13880 Magnolia Ave, Chino, CA 91710 *Tel:* 909-627-4256 *Fax:* 909-628-2482 *Web Site:* www.manley.com, pg 816

Manning Productions, 115 N Morgan St, Chicago, IL 60607 *Tel:* 312-756-1100 *Fax:* 312-756-1200 *E-mail:* info@manningproductions.com *Web Site:* www.manningproductions.com, pg 816

Map Resources, 50 S Union St, Lambertville, NJ 08530 *Tel:* 609-397-1611 *Toll Free Tel:* 800-334-4291 *Fax:* 609-751-9378 *E-mail:* info@mapresources.com; sales@mapresources.com *Web Site:* www.mapresources.com, pg 816

MAPS Production House, 212 Collins Ave, Miami Beach, FL 33139 *Tel:* 305-532-7880; 786-245-2491 (equip rentals) *Fax:* 305-532-7673 *E-mail:* info@mapsproduction.com; equipment@mapsproduction.com *Web Site:* mapsproduction.com, pg 816

MarathonNorco Aerospace Inc, 8301 Imperial Dr, Waco, TX 76712-6588 *Tel:* 254-776-0650 *Fax:* 254-776-6558 *E-mail:* marathon@mptc.com *Web Site:* www.mnaerospace.com, pg 816

Marblemedia, 74 Fraser Ave, Suite 100, Toronto, ON M6K 3E1, Canada *Tel:* 416-646-2711 *E-mail:* connect@marblemedia.com *Web Site:* www.marblemedia.com, pg 816

March Manufacturing Inc, 1819 Pickwick Ave, Glenview, IL 60026 *Tel:* 847-729-5300 *Fax:* 847-729-7062 *E-mail:* sales@marchpump.com *Web Site:* www.marchpump.com, pg 816

March of Dimes Foundation, 1275 Mamaroneck Ave, White Plains, NY 10605 *Tel:* 914-997-4488 *Toll Free Tel:* 888-663-4637 *Web Site:* www.marchofdimes.org/video, pg 816

Marco Inc, 451 Carson Rd N, Birmingham, AL 35215 *Tel:* 205-856-1110 *Toll Free Tel:* 888-465-2514 *Fax:* 205-856-1136 *E-mail:* marco@marcoconsoles.com *Web Site:* www.marcoconsoles.com, pg 816

Mardi Gras Costume Shop, 5895 N Granite Reef Rd, Scottsdale, AZ 85250 *Tel:* 480-948-4030 *Fax:* 480-948-0754 *E-mail:* info@mardigrascostumeshop.com *Web Site:* mardigrascostumeshop.com, pg 817

Marengo Films, 27206 Waterfall Hill Pkwy, Spicewood, TX 78669 *Tel:* 972-365-0406 *Fax:* 830-693-0949 *E-mail:* cosgray@outlook.com *Web Site:* www.marengofilms.com, pg 817

Marinco Electrical Group, N85 W12545 Westbrook Crossing, Menomonee Falls, WI 53051-3330 *Tel:* 262-293-0600 *E-mail:* marincopowerprod.sales@powerprodllc.com *Web Site:* www.marincopowerproducts.com, pg 817

Mark Custom Recording Service Inc, 10815 Bodine Rd, Clarence, NY 14031-2252 *Tel:* 716-759-2600 *Fax:* 716-759-2329 *E-mail:* info@markcustom.com *Web Site:* www.markcustom.com, pg 817

Mark Sonder Productions & Entertainment Agency, 2479 Freezeland Rd, Linden, VA 22642 *Tel:* 540-636-1640 *E-mail:* inquiry@marksonderproductions.com *Web Site:* mspentertainmentagency.com, pg 817

Mark X Productions Inc, 300 E 40 St, New York, NY 10016, pg 817

Markertek Video Supply, One Tower Dr, Saugerties, NY 12477 *Tel:* 845-246-3036 *Toll Free Tel:* 800-522-2025 *Fax:* 845-246-1757 *E-mail:* sales@markertek.com *Web Site:* www.markertek.com, pg 817

The Market Place, PO Box 4126, Rockford, IL 61110-0626 *Tel:* 815-877-1514 *Web Site:* www.maxbooks.9k.com, pg 817

Marketec, 419 S Flower St, Burbank, CA 91502 *Tel:* 818-847-0200 *Toll Free Tel:* 800-557-8861 *Toll Free Fax:* 888-262-1726 *E-mail:* info@marketec.com *Web Site:* www.marketec.com, pg 817

Marketron Broadcast Solutions, 101 Empty Saddle Trail, Hailey, ID 83333 *Tel:* 208-788-6800 *Toll Free Tel:* 800-476-7226 *Fax:* 208-788-6273 *E-mail:* sales@marketron.com *Web Site:* www.marketron.com, pg 817

Marlboro Productions, 1076 Moss Hollow Rd, Marlboro, VT 05344 *Tel:* 802-257-0743 *E-mail:* mfilmpro@sover.net *Web Site:* marlboroproductions.com, pg 817

Marsand Inc, 6100 S IH-35W, Alvarado, TX 76009 *Tel:* 817-783-5566 *Fax:* 817-783-5577 *Web Site:* www.marsand.com, pg 817

Marsh Media, 200 Avila Circle, Kansas City, MO 64114 *Tel:* 816-523-1059 *Toll Free Tel:* 800-821-3303 *Fax:* 816-333-7421 *Toll Free Fax:* 866-333-7421 *E-mail:* info@marshmedia.com *Web Site:* www.marshmedia.com, pg 817

Marshad Technology Group, 99 Hudson St, 5th fl, New York, NY 10013 *Tel:* 917-209-3467 *E-mail:* info@marshad.com *Web Site:* www.marshad.com, pg 817

Marshall Electronics Inc, 20608 Madrona Ave, Torrance, CA 90503 *Tel:* 310-333-0606 *Toll Free Tel:* 800-800-6608 *Fax:* 310-333-0688 *E-mail:* support@marshall-usa.com *Web Site:* www.mars-cam.com; www.marshall-usa.com, pg 817

Marshall Furniture Inc, 999 Anita Ave, Antioch, IL 60002 *Tel:* 847-395-9350 *Fax:* 847-395-9351 *E-mail:* sales@marshallfurniture.com *Web Site:* www.marshallfurniture.com, pg 817

Martel Electronics Sales Inc, Yorba Linda Hills Business Park, 23221 E La Palma Ave, Yorba Linda, CA 92887 *Tel:* 714-692-6690 *Toll Free Tel:* 800-553-5536 *Fax:* 714-692-1835 *Toll Free Fax:* 800-553-6954 *Web Site:* www.martelelectronics.com, pg 818

The Martha's Vineyard Film Festival (MVFF), 9 State Rd, Chilmark, MA 02535 *Tel:* 508-645-9599 *Web Site:* www.tmvff.org, pg 995

Martha's Vineyard International Film Festival, PO Box 4423, Vineyard Haven, MA 02568 *Tel:* 508-696-9369 *E-mail:* info@mvfilmsociety.com *Web Site:* mvfilmsociety.com, pg 995

The Martin Guitar Co, 510 Sycamore St, Nazareth, PA 18064 *Tel:* 610-759-2837 *Toll Free Tel:* 800-633-2060; 888-433-9177 *Fax:* 610-759-5757 *Web Site:* www.martinguitar.com, pg 818

Martin Professional Inc, 3300 Corporate Ave, Suite 108, Weston, FL 33331 *Tel:* 954-858-1800 *Toll Free Tel:* 888-832-4180 *Fax:* 954-858-1811 *E-mail:* support@martinpro.com *Web Site:* www.martin.com, pg 818

Martinsound Inc, 1151 W Valley Blvd, Alhambra, CA 91803 *Tel:* 626-281-3555 *Toll Free Tel:* 800-582-3555 *Fax:* 626-284-3092 *E-mail:* info@martinsound.com *Web Site:* www.martinsound.com, pg 818

Marvel Photo Inc, 1720 N Sheridan Rd, Tulsa, OK 74115 *Tel:* 918-836-0741 *Toll Free Tel:* 800-806-3616 *Fax:* 918-836-0949, pg 818

Marvell Semiconductor Inc, 5488 Marvell Lane, Santa Clara, CA 95054 *Tel:* 408-222-2500 *Toll Free Tel:* 855-MARVELL (627-8355) *Fax:* 408-988-8279 *E-mail:* info@marvell.com *Web Site:* www.marvell.com, pg 818

MarVista Entertainment Inc, 10877 Wilshire Blvd, 10th fl, Los Angeles, CA 90024 *Tel:* 424-274-3000 *Fax:* 424-274-3050 *E-mail:* info@marvista.net *Web Site:* www.marvista.net, pg 818

Marx InDigital, 7921 Skylake Dr, Fort Worth, TX 76179 *Tel:* 414-351-5060 *Web Site:* www.marxindigital.com, pg 818

Maryland Film Office, 401 E Pratt St, 14th fl, Baltimore, MD 21202 *Tel:* 410-767-6343 *Toll Free Tel:* 800-333-6632 *Fax:* 410-333-0044 *E-mail:* filminfo@marylandfilm.org *Web Site:* www.marylandfilm.org, pg 972

Maryland Sound International Holding Co LLC, 4900 Wetheredsville Rd, Baltimore, MD 21207 *Tel:* 410-448-1400 *Toll Free Tel:* 800-76SOUND (767-6863) *Fax:* 410-448-1467 *E-mail:* martha@msihc.com *Web Site:* www.marylandsound.com, pg 819

Mason Video, 9632 N 34 St, Omaha, NE 68112 *Tel:* 402-455-9422 *E-mail:* mason.video@mac.com *Web Site:* www.masonvideo.com, pg 819

massAV, 3 Radcliffe Rd, Pewksbury, MA 01876 *Tel:* 978-670-0027 *Toll Free Tel:* 800-423-7830 *Fax:* 978-640-9900 *E-mail:* info@massav.com *Web Site:* www.massav.com, pg 819

MastCom, 807 Broadway St NE, Suite 210, Minneapolis, MN 55413 *Tel:* 612-397-9637 *E-mail:* info@mastcom.com *Web Site:* www.mastcom.com, pg 819

Mastech Digital, 1305 Cherrington Pkwy, Bldg 210, Suite 400, Moon Township, PA 15108 *Tel:* 412-787-2100 *Toll Free Tel:* 800-627-8323 *Fax:* 412-494-9272 *E-mail:* experience@mastechdigital.com *Web Site:* www.mastechdigital.com, pg 819

Master Bond, 154 Hobart St, Hackensack, NJ 07601 *Tel:* 201-343-8983 *Fax:* 201-343-2132 *E-mail:* main@masterbond.com *Web Site:* www.masterbond.com, pg 819

Master Books®, 3142 Hwy 103 N, Green Forest, AR 72638 *Tel:* 870-438-5288 *Toll Free Tel:* 800-999-3777 *Fax:* 870-438-5120 *E-mail:* info@nlpg.com *Web Site:* www.nlpg.com, pg 819

Master Video Disc & Design, 7349 N Via Paseo del Sur, Suite 515-455, Scottsdale, AZ 85258 *Tel:* 480-948-0305 *Web Site:* www.mastervdd.com, pg 819

Masterclock Inc, 2484 W Clay St, St Charles, MO 63301-2548 *Tel:* 636-724-3666 *Toll Free Tel:* 800-940-2248 *Fax:* 636-724-3776 *E-mail:* sales@masterclock.com; support@masterclock.com *Web Site:* www.masterclock.com, pg 819

Masterdisk Corp, 8 John Walsh Blvd, Suite 411, Peekskill, NY 10566 *Tel:* 212-541-5022 *Web Site:* www.masterdisk.com, pg 819

Mastervision Inc, 490 Seventh St, Brooklyn, NY 11215 *Tel:* 347-725-0545 *Web Site:* www.mastervision.com, pg 819

Mastery Technologies Inc, 41214 Bridge St, Novi, MI 48375 *Tel:* 972-943-9214 *Toll Free Tel:* 800-258-3837 *Fax:* 248-888-8424 *E-mail:* sales@masterytech.com *Web Site:* www.mastery.com, pg 819

Mathmadeeasy.com, PO Box 190846, Brooklyn, NY 11219 *Toll Free Tel:* 866-599-MATH (599-6284) *Web Site:* www.mathmadeeasy.com, pg 819

Matrix Video Communications Corp (MVCC), 103, 1626 115 Ave NE, Calgary, AB T3K 5Y8, Canada *Tel:* 403-640-4490 *Fax:* 403-640-9012 *Web Site:* www. matrixvideocom.com, pg 819

Matrox Video Products Group, 1055 Saint Regis Blvd, Dorval, QC H9P 2T4, Canada *Tel:* 514-822-6000 *Toll Free Tel:* 800-361-4903 *Fax:* 514-685-2853 *Web Site:* www.matrox.com/video, pg 819

Matson Multi-Media, 403 E Ramsey Rd, Suite 202, San Antonio, TX 78216 *Tel:* 210-349-3674 *E-mail:* sales@matsonmultimedia.com *Web Site:* www. matsonmultimedia.com; www.matsoncreative.com, pg 820

Matthews Studio Equipment Inc, 4520 W Valerio St, Burbank, CA 91505 *Tel:* 818-843-6715 *Fax:* 818-480-5808 *E-mail:* info@msegrip.com *Web Site:* www. msegrip.com, pg 820

Maui County Film Office, 2200 S Main St, Suite 305, Wailuku, HI 96793 *Tel:* 808-270-8237 *Fax:* 808-270-7995 *Web Site:* www.filmmaui.com, pg 970

MAVCO, 77 S Main St, Newtown, CT 06470 *Tel:* 203-270-8292 *Fax:* 203-270-8292, pg 820

Maverick Awards, 13 Rock City Rd, Woodstock, NY 12498 *Tel:* 845-679-4265; 845-810-0131 *Fax:* 509-479-5414 *E-mail:* info@woodstockfilmfestival.com *Web Site:* www.woodstockfilmfestival.com, pg 995

Maverick Video Productions, 121 Interpark, Suite 601, San Antonio, TX 78216 *Tel:* 210-495-1111 *Fax:* 210-495-8033 *Web Site:* www.maverickstudio.com, pg 820

Max Films Inc, 5333, rue Casgrain, Suite 406, Montreal, QC H2T 1X3, Canada *Tel:* 514-282-8444 *Web Site:* www.maxfilms.ca, pg 820

Maxell Corp of America, 3 Garret Mountain Plaza, Suite 300, Woodland Park, NJ 07424-3352 *Tel:* 973-653-2400 *Toll Free Tel:* 800-533-2836; 800-377-5887 (tech support) *Fax:* 201-796-8790 *E-mail:* techsupp@maxell.com *Web Site:* www.maxell-usa.com, pg 820

Maximus Media Inc, 2727 N Grove Industrial Dr, Suite 111, Fresno, CA 93727 *Tel:* 559-255-1688 *Toll Free Tel:* 800-2THEMAX (284-3629) *Fax:* 559-255-0323 *Web Site:* www.tothemax.com, pg 820

MAXON Computer Inc, 2640 Lavery Ct, Suite A, Newbury Park, CA 91320 *Tel:* 805-376-3333 *Fax:* 805-376-3331 *E-mail:* info_us@maxon.net *Web Site:* www.maxon.net, pg 820

Mayor's Office of Economic & Community Development, One Public Sq, Suite 100, Nashville, TN 37201 *Tel:* 615-862-6000 *Web Site:* www. nashville.gov, pg 976

Lowry Mays Excellence in Broadcasting Award, 125 W 55 St, 4th fl, New York, NY 10019-5366 *Tel:* 212-373-8250 *Fax:* 212-373-8254 *E-mail:* info@thebfoa.org *Web Site:* www.thebfoa.org; broadcastersfoundation.org, pg 995

MB Productions, 450 Fairfield Place, West Caldwell, NJ 07006 *Tel:* 973-439-0044 *Toll Free Tel:* 800-622-2224 *Fax:* 973-439-9844 *E-mail:* mbp@mbvideo.com *Web Site:* www.mbvideo.com, pg 820

McAlister Electronics, 926 E Fremont Ave, Sunnyvale, CA 94087 *Tel:* 408-739-2605 *Fax:* 408-733-2895 *E-mail:* mcalelect@aol.com *Web Site:* www. werepairallbrands.com, pg 820

McBain Camera Ltd, 10805 107 Ave, Edmonton, AB T5H 0W9, Canada *Tel:* 780-420-0404 *Toll Free Tel:* 800-661-6980 *Fax:* 780-421-1188 *Web Site:* www. mcbaincamera.com, pg 820

MCCOM, 383 Rte 206, Chester, NJ 07930 *Tel:* 908-879-9590 *Fax:* 908-879-9679 *Web Site:* www.mccom. tv, pg 820

Robert McConnell Productions, 4303 67 Ave NW, Gig Harbor, WA 98335 *Tel:* 253-265-3184 *Toll Free Tel:* 800-532-4017 *Fax:* 253-265-1550 *Toll Free Fax:* 800-948-8463 *E-mail:* info@parli.com *Web Site:* parli.com, pg 820

McCune Audio-Video-Lighting, 101 Utah Ave, South San Francisco, CA 94080 *Tel:* 650-873-1111 *Toll Free Tel:* 800-899-7686 *Fax:* 650-246-6702 *E-mail:* info@mccune.com *Web Site:* www.mccune.com, pg 821

McGraw-Hill School Education Group, 8787 Orion Place, Columbus, OH 43240-4027 *Tel:* 614-430-4000 *Toll Free Tel:* 800-334-7734 *Fax:* 614-755-5682 *Web Site:* mheonline.com; www.mheducation.com, pg 821

McGuane Studio Inc, 36 Horatio St, Suite 5-B, New York, NY 10014-1691 *Tel:* 212-463-7259, pg 821

McIntyre Media Inc, 203-75 First St, Orangeville, ON L9W 5B6, Canada *Tel:* 519-942-9640 *Toll Free Tel:* 800-565-3036 *Fax:* 519-942-8489 *E-mail:* info@mcintyre.ca *Web Site:* www.mcintyre.ca, pg 821

McKay Conant Hoover Inc, 5655 Lindero Canyon Rd, Suite 325, Westlake Village, CA 91362 *Tel:* 818-991-9300 *Fax:* 818-991-2324 *E-mail:* info@mchinc.com *Web Site:* www.mchinc.com, pg 821

Lloyd F McKinney Associates Inc, 25350 Cypress Ave, Hayward, CA 94544 *Tel:* 510-783-8043 *Fax:* 510-783-2130 *E-mail:* info@mckinneyassoc.com *Web Site:* www.mckinneyassoc.com, pg 821

McNabb & Connolly, 60 Briarwood Ave, Mississauga, ON L5G 3N6, Canada *Tel:* 905-278-0566 *Toll Free Tel:* 866-722-1522 *Fax:* 905-278-2801 *Toll Free Fax:* 866-722-1822 *E-mail:* info@mcnabbconnolly.ca *Web Site:* www.mcnabbconnolly.ca, pg 821

McNee Productions Inc, 3301 W Alabama St, Houston, TX 77098 *Tel:* 713-526-5333 *Fax:* 713-526-4634 *E-mail:* mcnee@mcnee.com *Web Site:* www.mcnee. com, pg 821

MCS Recording Studios, 550 Queen St E, Suite G-100, Toronto, ON M5A 1V2, Canada *Tel:* 416-361-1688 *Toll Free Tel:* 866-322-8555 *Fax:* 416-361-5088 *E-mail:* info@mcsrecording.com *Web Site:* www. mcsrecording.com, pg 821

Medcom Inc, 6060 Phyllis Dr, Cypress, CA 90630-5243 *Tel:* 714-891-1443 *Toll Free Tel:* 800-541-0253; 800-877-1443 *Fax:* 714-891-3140 *E-mail:* customerservice@medcominc.com *Web Site:* www.medcominc.com, pg 821

Media Alliance, 2830 20 St, Suite 102, San Francisco, CA 94110 *Tel:* 415-746-9475 *E-mail:* information@media-alliance.org *Web Site:* www.media-alliance.org, pg 957

Media Bridge Gamekids, 3281 Waikomo Rd, Koloa, HI 96756 *Tel:* 808-280-9591 *E-mail:* gkkauai@gamekids. com *Web Site:* www.gamekids.com, pg 821

The Media Collaboratory, 215 E High St, Lexington, KY 40507 *Tel:* 859-255-9049 *Fax:* 859-281-6537 *E-mail:* info@mediacollaboratory.com *Web Site:* mediacollaboratory.com, pg 821

Media-Comm, 9700 S Pine Blvd, Charlotte, NC 28273 *Tel:* 704-527-8853 *Web Site:* www.media-comm.com, pg 821

Media Control Systems LLC, 1050 Pioneer Way, Suite Q, El Cajon, CA 92020 *Tel:* 619-599-1050 *Fax:* 619-599-1051 *Web Site:* www.mediacontrolsystems.com, pg 821

Media Cybernetics Inc, 401 N Washington St, Suite 350, Rockville, MD 20850 *Tel:* 301-495-3305 *Fax:* 240-328-6193 *E-mail:* info@mediacy.com *Web Site:* www. mediacy.com, pg 821

Media Dimensions LLC, 2212 Autumn Glow Ct, Bel Air, MD 21015 *Tel:* 410-561-4550 *E-mail:* info@mediadimensions.com *Web Site:* www. mediadimensions.com, pg 821

Media Distributors, 4514 W Vanowen St, Burbank, CA 91505 *Tel:* 818-566-8800 *Toll Free Tel:* 800-851-3113 *Fax:* 818-566-8989 *E-mail:* la@mediadistributors.com *Web Site:* www.mediadistributors.com, pg 822

Media Elite Productions, 11900 NE First St, Suite 300, Bellevue, WA 98005 *Tel:* 425-336-3707 *Toll Free Fax:* 877-391-3778 *E-mail:* mediaeliteproductions@yahoo.com *Web Site:* mediaeliteproductions.com, pg 822

Media Event Concepts Inc, 2036 Centimeter Circle, Austin, TX 78758 *Tel:* 512-832-1142 *Toll Free Tel:* 800-299-1142 *Fax:* 512-832-0236 *E-mail:* info@mecteam.com *Web Site:* www.mecteam.com, pg 822

Media Fabricators Inc, 8509 Washington Blvd, Culver City, CA 90232 *Tel:* 323-937-3344 *Fax:* 323-937-1142 *E-mail:* mfi@mediafab.com *Web Site:* www.mediafab. com, pg 822

Media Financial Management Association (MFM), 550 W Frontage Rd, Suite 3600, Northfield, IL 60093 *Tel:* 847-716-7000 *Fax:* 847-716-7004 *E-mail:* info@mediafinance.org *Web Site:* www.mediafinance.org, pg 957

Media Inc, PO Box 496, Media, PA 19063 *Tel:* 610-565-2844 *Toll Free Tel:* 800-523-0118 *Fax:* 610-565-3614 *Web Site:* www.mediaincorporated.com, pg 822

Media Loft Inc, 615 First Ave NE, Suite 100, Minneapolis, MN 55413 *Tel:* 612-375-1086 *Fax:* 612-375-0913 *E-mail:* info@medialoft.com *Web Site:* www.medialoft.com, pg 822

Media Magic, 11 Tanzanite, Rancho Santa Margarita, CA 92688 *Tel:* 949-713-9696 *E-mail:* request@mediamagic.tv *Web Site:* www.mediamagic.tv, pg 822

Media Networking Alliance (MNA), 23117 39 Ave SE, Bothell, WA 98021 *Tel:* 425-870-6574 *Web Site:* medianetworkingalliance.com, pg 957

Media Productions, 3241 S University Dr, Fargo, ND 58104 *Tel:* 701-237-6863 *Toll Free Tel:* 800-480-6863 *Fax:* 701-280-1226 *E-mail:* info@mediaproductions. com *Web Site:* www.mediaproductions.com, pg 822

The Media Staff Inc, 8425 W Third St, Suite 401, Los Angeles, CA 90048 *Tel:* 323-658-8996 *E-mail:* info@themediastaff.com *Web Site:* www.themediastaff.com, pg 822

Media Supply Inc, 611 Jeffers Circle, Exton, PA 19341 *Tel:* 610-884-4400 *Toll Free Tel:* 800-944-4237 *Fax:* 610-884-4500 *E-mail:* info@mediasupply.com *Web Site:* www.mediasupply.com, pg 822

Media Systems Design Group, 4253 Stewart Ave, Los Angeles, CA 90066 *Tel:* 310-398-0281 *Web Site:* msd-group.com, pg 822

Media 3 Ltd, 535 Fifth Ave, 13th fl, New York, NY 10017 *Tel:* 212-983-5200 *Fax:* 212-983-5200 *E-mail:* media3@liveshots.com *Web Site:* liveshots. com, pg 822

Media Vision USA, 1078 60 St, Oakland, CA 94608 *Tel:* 415-391-9090 *Toll Free Tel:* 877-746-8375 *Fax:* 415-391-9192 *E-mail:* info@media-vision.com *Web Site:* www.media-vision.com/en/north-america/usa, pg 822

Mediaforce Productions, 6328 Yorkdale Dr, Plano, TX 75093 *Tel:* 972-473-6888 *Web Site:* www. mediaforcepro.com, pg 822

MediaFX, 10445 SW Canyon Rd, Suite 220, Beaverton, OR 97005 *Tel:* 503-646-9884 *Web Site:* www. mediafxvideo.com, pg 822

Mediaimage Communications Group, 10 Sacks Ave, Grimsby, ON L3M 4Y4, Canada *Tel:* 905-309-5554 *Fax:* 905-309-0999, pg 822

MediaMation Inc, 23410 Garnier St, Torrance, CA 90505 *Tel:* 310-320-0696 *Fax:* 310-320-0699 *E-mail:* sales@mediamation.com *Web Site:* www.mediamation.com, pg 822

MediaMix Inc, 4 Pearl Ct, Allendale, NJ 07401 *Tel:* 201-262-3700 (day); 201-378-3035 (nights/weekends) *Fax:* 201-262-3798 *E-mail:* info@mmix.net *Web Site:* www.mediamix.tv, pg 822

MediaNow Inc, One Maple Ave, 1-E, Netcong, NJ 07857 *Tel:* 973-347-2155 *Toll Free Tel:* 888-515-2255 *Fax:* 973-215-2121 *E-mail:* info@medianow.com *Web Site:* www.usa.medianow.com, pg 822

MediaOne Studios, 950 Battery St, 2nd fl, San Francisco, CA 94111 *Tel:* 415-262-4222 *E-mail:* hi@mediaonestudios.com *Web Site:* mediaonestudios.com, pg 823

MediaPOINTE, 3952 Camino Ranchero, Camarillo, CA 93012 *Tel:* 805-480-3700 *Fax:* 805-480-3770 *E-mail:* info@mediapointe.com; sales@mediapointe. com *Web Site:* www.mediapointe.com, pg 823

Medical Media Systems, 2916 NW Bucklin Hill Rd, No 481, Silverdale, WA 98383 *Tel:* 360-516-6110 *Fax:* 360-516-6113 *Web Site:* medicalmediasystems. com, pg 823

Medical Visual Creations (MVC), 1700 California St, Suite 350, San Francisco, CA 94109 *Tel:* 415-928-1623 *Fax:* 415-928-4642 *E-mail:* info@ lifestyleinmotion.com *Web Site:* www.mvcvideodvd. com, pg 823

Medifecta Healthcare Training, 5109 NE 82 Ave, Suite 201, Vancouver, WA 98662 *Toll Free Tel:* 833-974-1437 *E-mail:* medifectasupport@relias.com *Web Site:* medifecta.com, pg 823

Medina Software Inc, PO Box 952440, Lake Mary, FL 32795-2440 *Web Site:* www.medinasoft.com, pg 823

Meetinghouse Event Design & Production, 781 N Church Rd, Elmhurst, IL 60126-1413 *Tel:* 630-941-0600 *Fax:* 630-941-7777 *E-mail:* info@sbrevents.com *Web Site:* www.sbrevents.com, pg 823

Megatrax, 7629 Fulton Ave, North Hollywood, CA 91605 *Tel:* 818-255-7100 *Toll Free Tel:* 888-MEGA-555 (634-2555) *Fax:* 818-255-7199 *E-mail:* info@ megatrax.com *Web Site:* www.megatrax.com, pg 823

Megavideo LLC, 22 Cedar St, No 2, Garfield, NJ 07026 *Tel:* 973-478-1921 *E-mail:* megamail@megadv.com *Web Site:* www.megadv.com, pg 823

Melbourne Independent Filmmakers Festival (MIFF), 1399 S Harbor City Blvd, Melbourne, FL 32901 *Tel:* 321-726-1711 *Fax:* 321-726-1715 *Web Site:* www. 3boysproductions.com, pg 995

Melmat Inc, 5333 Industrial Dr, Huntington Beach, CA 92649 *Tel:* 714-379-4555 *Toll Free Tel:* 800-635-6289 *Fax:* 714-379-4554 *E-mail:* info@melmat.com *Web Site:* www.melmat.com, pg 823

Meltzer Media Productions, 49 Nassau St, 3rd fl, New York, NY 10038 *Tel:* 212-868-4600 *E-mail:* contact@ meltzermedia.com *Web Site:* www.meltzermedia.com, pg 823

The Memphis & Shelby County Film & TV Commission, 496 S Main St, Suite 101, Memphis, TN 38103 *Tel:* 901-527-8300 *Fax:* 901-527-8326 *E-mail:* hello@filmmemphis.org *Web Site:* www. filmmemphis.org, pg 975

Memphis Communications Corp, 4771 Summer Ave, Memphis, TN 38122 *Tel:* 901-725-9271 *Toll Free Tel:* 866-805-5893 *Fax:* 901-272-3577 *Web Site:* memphiscommunications.net, pg 823

Merced Film Commission, California Welcome Ctr, 710 W 16 St, Merced, CA 95340 *Tel:* 209-724-8104 *Toll Free Tel:* 800-446-5353 *E-mail:* info@visitmerced. travel *Web Site:* visitmerced.travel, pg 967

Merck & Hill Consultants Inc, 1995 N Park Place, Suite 450, Atlanta, GA 30339 *Tel:* 770-937-0185 *Fax:* 770-937-0919 *E-mail:* info@merckhill.com *Web Site:* www.merckhill.com, pg 823

Merestone, 7232 E First St, Scottsdale, AZ 85251 *Tel:* 480-945-4631 *Fax:* 480-945-0590 *Web Site:* www. merestone.com, pg 823

Meridia ARS, 1646 West Chester Pike, Suite 15, West Chester, PA 19382 *Tel:* 610-260-6800 *Fax:* 610-260-6810 *E-mail:* rsvp@meridiaars.com *Web Site:* www. meridiaars.com, pg 823

Meridian Education Corp, c/o Films Media Group, 132 W 31 St, 16th fl, New York, NY 10001 *Toll Free Tel:* 800-257-5126; 800-322-8755 *Toll Free Fax:* 800-678-3633 *E-mail:* custserv@films.com *Web Site:* meridian.films.com, pg 823

Meridian Studios, 1020 Highland Park Rd, Neenah, WI 54956 *Tel:* 920-720-4200, pg 824

MerleFest, PO Box 120, Wilkesboro, NC 28697 *Toll Free Tel:* 800-343-7857 *E-mail:* merlefest@wilkescc. edu *Web Site:* merlefest.org, pg 995

Merrimack Films, 530 Concord Ave, Belmont, MA 02478 *Tel:* 617-489-4729 *E-mail:* henrysuebass@ gmail.com *Web Site:* www.merrimack-films.com, pg 824

MeshTel, PO Box 774, Genoa, NV 89411 *Tel:* 775-267-5959 *Fax:* 775-267-5958 *E-mail:* info@meshtel. com *Web Site:* laserinfo.com, pg 824

MessageMakers, 1217 Turner St, Lansing, MI 48906 *Tel:* 517-482-3333 *Toll Free Tel:* 888-482-6688 *E-mail:* info@messagemakers.com *Web Site:* www. messagemakers.com, pg 824

Metalworks Recording Studios Inc, 3611 Mavis Rd, Mississauga, ON L5C 1T7, Canada *Tel:* 905-279-4000 *Fax:* 905-279-4006 *Web Site:* www.metalworksstudios. com, pg 824

Method Studios, 3401 Exposition Blvd, Santa Monica, CA 90404 *Tel:* 310-434-6000 *Web Site:* www. methodstudios.com, pg 824

Metro Productions, 8570 Magellan Pkwy, Suite 400, Richmond, VA 23227 *Tel:* 804-261-1172 *Toll Free Tel:* 877-669-4687 *Fax:* 804-261-1885 *E-mail:* contactmetro@metro-productions.com *Web Site:* www.metro-productions.com, pg 824

Metro Teleproductions Inc (MTI), 2500 Virginia Ave NW, 416-S, Washington, DC 20037 *Tel:* 301-608-9077 *Fax:* 301-608-9078 *Web Site:* www.mtitv.com, pg 824

Metro Video Systems Inc, 1220 E Imperial Ave, El Segundo, CA 90245 *Tel:* 310-640-9250 *Fax:* 310-640-9347 *E-mail:* sales@metrovideosystems.com *Web Site:* www.metrovideosystems.com, pg 824

Metromotion Productions LLC, 450 W 31 St, 8th fl, New York, NY 10001 *Tel:* 212-967-2000 *Fax:* 212-967-1988 *E-mail:* info@metromotion.com; pr@ metromotion.com *Web Site:* www.metromotion.com, pg 824

Metropolitan Acoustics LLC, 8 Penn Ctr, Suite 1902, 1628 John F Kennedy Blvd, Philadelphia, PA 19103 *Tel:* 215-248-4352 *E-mail:* info@metro-acoustics.com *Web Site:* www.metro-acoustics.com, pg 824

Metropolitan Audio Visual Co LLC, 22923 Quicksilver Dr, Suite 117, Dulles, VA 20166 *Tel:* 703-834-0004 *Fax:* 703-834-0866 *E-mail:* sales@metroav.com *Web Site:* www.metroav.com, pg 824

Metropolitan Audio-Visual Inc, 35333 N 27 Lane, Phoenix, AZ 85086 *Tel:* 480-948-9008, pg 824

Metropolitan Opera Guild Inc, Samuel B & David Rose Bldg, 70 Lincoln Center Plaza, 6th fl, New York, NY 10023-6593 *Tel:* 212-769-7000 *E-mail:* info@ metguild.org *Web Site:* www.metguild.org, pg 824

MetroSonic Recording Studio, 143 Roebling St, 3rd fl, Brooklyn, NY 11211 *Tel:* 718-782-1872 *E-mail:* manager@metrosonic.net *Web Site:* www. metrosonic.net, pg 824

Meyer Sound Laboratories Inc, 2832 San Pablo Ave, Berkeley, CA 94702 *Tel:* 510-486-1166 *Toll Free Tel:* 855-641-3288 (US & CN) *Fax:* 510-486-8356 *E-mail:* sales@meyersound.com; techsupport@ meyersound.com; service@meyersound.com *Web Site:* www.meyersound.com, pg 824

MFJ Enterprises Inc, 300 Industrial Park Rd, Starkville, MS 39759-3992 *Tel:* 662-323-5869 *Toll Free Tel:* 800-647-1800 *Fax:* 662-323-6551 *E-mail:* mfjcustserv@mfjenterprises.com *Web Site:* www.mfjenterprises.com, pg 825

MG Electronics, 32 Ranick Rd, Hauppauge, NY 11788 *Tel:* 631-582-3400 *Fax:* 631-582-3229 *E-mail:* info@ mgelectronics.com *Web Site:* www.mgelectronics.com, pg 825

MG Studio, 6625 S Valley View Blvd, Suite C-304, Las Vegas, NV 89118 *Tel:* 702-836-3686 *E-mail:* office@ mgstudio.com *Web Site:* mgstudio.com, pg 825

MGM Home Entertainment, 245 N Beverly Dr, Beverly Hills, CA 90210 *Tel:* 310-449-3000 *Web Site:* www. mgm.com, pg 825

MHS-TV, Mamaroneck High School, 1000 W Boston Post Rd, Mamaroneck, NY 10543 *Tel:* 914-220-3100 *Fax:* 914-220-3115 *Web Site:* www.mamkschools.org; www.mhstv.org, pg 825

Mia Mind Music, 254 Sixth St, Suite 2, Hoboken, NJ 07030-6916 *Toll Free Tel:* 800-843-8575 *E-mail:* info@miamindmusic.com *Web Site:* www. miamindmusic.com, pg 825

Miami-Dade Office of Film & Entertainment, 111 NW First St, 12th fl, Miami, FL 33128 *Tel:* 305-375-3288 *E-mail:* film@miamidade.gov *Web Site:* www.filmmiami. org, pg 969

Miami Daylight Studios, 1819 West Ave, Bay 5, Miami Beach, FL 33139 *Tel:* 305-763-8490 *E-mail:* info@miamidaylightstudios.com *Web Site:* miamidaylightstudios.com, pg 825

Miami Film Festival, 300 NE Second Ave, Miami, FL 33132 *Tel:* 305-237-FILM (237-3456) *E-mail:* info@ miamifilmfestival.com *Web Site:* miamifilmfestival. com, pg 995

Miami short Film Festival (MsFF), 247 SW Eighth St, Suite 44, Miami, FL 33130 *E-mail:* info@ miamishortfilmfestival.com *Web Site:* www. miamishortfilmfestival.com, pg 996

Miami Stagecraft Inc, 2855 E 11 Ave, Hialeah, FL 33013 *Tel:* 305-836-9356 *Fax:* 305-696-3322 *E-mail:* info@miamistagecraft.com *Web Site:* www. miamistagecraft.com, pg 825

MiB MediaWorks, 85 Main St, Little Falls, NJ 07424 *Tel:* 973-403-1133 *Fax:* 973-638-1699 *E-mail:* info@ mibmediaworks.com *Web Site:* www.mibmediaworks. com, pg 825

Michigan Film & Digital Media Office, 300 N Washington Sq, 4th fl, Lansing, MI 48913 *Tel:* 517-241-6757 *Toll Free Tel:* 800-477-FILM (477-3456) *Fax:* 517-241-3689 *E-mail:* mfo@michigan.org *Web Site:* www.michiganbusiness.org/industries/ mfdmo, pg 972

Michigan Office Solutions (MOS), A Xerox Company, 2859 Walkent Dr NW, Grand Rapids, MI 49544 *Toll Free Tel:* 800-442-9070 *E-mail:* info@mos-xerox.com *Web Site:* www.mos-xerox.com, pg 825

Michigan Recording Arts Institute & Technologies, 28533 Greenfield, Southfield, MI 48076 *Tel:* 248-569-5422 *Web Site:* www.mirecordingarts.com, pg 825

Micor Analytics, 7538 Saint Louis Ave, Skokie, IL 60076 *Tel:* 847-329-8590 *Fax:* 847-329-8599 *Web Site:* www.micoranalytics.com, pg 825

Micro Express, 8 Hammond, Suite 105, Irvine, CA 92618-1601 *Tel:* 949-460-9911 *Toll Free Tel:* 800-989-9900 *Fax:* 949-269-3070 *E-mail:* info@microexpress. net *Web Site:* www.microexpress.net, pg 825

Micro Focus, 1800 S Novell Place, Bldgs G & H, Provo, UT 84606 *Tel:* 801-861-7000 *Toll Free Tel:* 877-686-9637 *E-mail:* media.relations@microfocus.com *Web Site:* www.microfocus.com, pg 825

Micro Technology Unlimited Inc, PO Box 5, Rolesville, NC 27571 *Tel:* 919-870-0344 *E-mail:* sales@mtu.com *Web Site:* www.mtu.com, pg 826

Microboards Technology LLC, 8150 Mallory Ct, Chanhassen, MN 55317 *Tel:* 952-556-1600 *Toll Free Tel:* 800-646-8881; 800-290-9012 *Fax:* 952-556-1620 *E-mail:* sales@microboards.com *Web Site:* www. microboards.com, pg 825

Microdolly Hollywood, 135 N Victory Blvd, Burbank, CA 91502 *Tel:* 818-845-8383 *E-mail:* microdolly@ microdolly.com *Web Site:* www.microdolly.com, pg 826

MicroImage Video Systems, PO Box 331, Boyertown, PA 19512-0331 *Tel:* 610-754-6800 *Fax:* 610-754-9766 *Web Site:* www.mivs.com, pg 826

MicrophoneRentals.com, 75-3050 Edgemont Blvd, North Vancouver, BC V7R 4X1, Canada *Tel:* 604-980-5703 *E-mail:* info@microphonerentals.com *Web Site:* www. microphonerentals.com, pg 826

Microsemi Corp, One Enterprise, Aliso Viejo, CA 92656 *Tel:* 949-380-6100 *Toll Free Tel:* 800-713-4113 *Fax:* 949-215-4996 *Web Site:* www.microsemi.com, pg 826

Microspace Communications Corp, 3100 Highwoods Blvd, Suite 120, Raleigh, NC 27604 *Tel:* 919-850-4500 *Fax:* 919-850-4518 *Web Site:* www.microspace.com, pg 826

Microwave Filter Co Inc, 6743 Kinne St, East Syracuse, NY 13057 *Tel:* 315-438-4700 *Toll Free Tel:* 800-448-1666 *Fax:* 315-463-1467 *Toll Free Fax:* 888-411-8860 *E-mail:* mfcsales@microwavefilter.com *Web Site:* www.microwavefilter.com, pg 826

Mid-South Color Labs Inc, 496 Emmett St, Jackson, TN 38301 *Tel:* 731-422-6691 *Toll Free Tel:* 800-221-3920 *Fax:* 731-424-1902 *E-mail:* info@midsouthcolor.com *Web Site:* www.midsouthcolor.com, pg 826

MidCanada Production Services Inc (MidCan), 509 Century St, Winnipeg, MB R3H 0L8, Canada *Tel:* 204-772-0368 *Fax:* 204-772-0360 *E-mail:* info@midcan.com *Web Site:* www.midcan.com, pg 826

Middle Atlantic Products, a Legrand AV Inc brand, 300 Fairfield Rd, Fairfield, NJ 07004 *Tel:* 973-839-1011 *Fax:* 973-839-1976 *E-mail:* info@middleatlantic.com *Web Site:* www.middleatlantic.com, pg 826

Midland Video Productions Inc, 3315 N 124 St, Brookfield, WI 53005 *Tel:* 414-276-8300 *E-mail:* request@midlandvideo.com *Web Site:* midlandvideo.com, pg 827

Midnight Media Group Inc, 45 E Willow St, Millburn, NJ 07041-1416 *Tel:* 973-379-5959 *E-mail:* info@mmgi.tv *Web Site:* mmgi.tv, pg 827

Midtown Video Inc, 4824 SW 74 Ct, Miami, FL 33155 *Tel:* 305-669-1117 *Fax:* 305-662-2860 *E-mail:* info@midtownvideo.com *Web Site:* midtownvideo.com, pg 827

Midwest Digital Corp, PO Box 204, Palos Park, IL 60464-0204 *Tel:* 708-790-4040 *E-mail:* sales@midwestdig.com; midwestdig@gmail.com *Web Site:* www.midwestdigitalcorp.com, pg 827

Midwest Photo Exchange, 2887 Silver Dr, Columbus, OH 43211 *Tel:* 614-261-1264 *Toll Free Tel:* 866-940-3686 *E-mail:* mpx@mpex.com; orders@mpex.com *Web Site:* mpex.com, pg 827

Midwest Uplink Inc, 911 N East St, Indianapolis, IN 46202 *Tel:* 317-423-8684 *Toll Free Tel:* 866-886-6247 *Web Site:* midwestuplink.com, pg 827

Mightybytes Inc, 4001 N Ravenswood Ave, Suite 404, Chicago, IL 60613 *Tel:* 773-561-7529 *E-mail:* info@mightybytes.com *Web Site:* www.mightybytes.com, pg 827

Mike's Camera, 2500 Pearl St, Boulder, CO 80302 *Tel:* 303-444-1257; 303-443-1715 (ext 132) *E-mail:* store1@mikescamera.com *Web Site:* www.mikescamera.com, pg 827

Milbrodt/Music & Sound Design, 1835 US Hwy 9, Howell, NJ 07731 *Tel:* 848-459-4965 *E-mail:* info@ideasinmedia.com *Web Site:* www.ideasinmedia.com, pg 827

Milestone Film & Video Inc, PO Box 128, Harrington Park, NJ 07640-0128 *Tel:* 201-767-3117 *Toll Free Tel:* 800-603-1104 *Fax:* 201-767-3035 *E-mail:* milefilms@gmail.com *Web Site:* www.milestonefilms.com, pg 827

Milgrom Productions, 50 Kent Rd, Glen Rock, NJ 07452 *Tel:* 201-444-8838 *E-mail:* info@milgromproductions.com *Web Site:* milgrom.adcstudio.com, pg 827

Milky Way Press, 317 Ridge Run Dr, Georgetown, TX 78628 *Tel:* 512-863-7278; 512-677-0861, pg 827

Mill Valley Film Festival, 1001 Lootens Place, Suite 220, San Rafael, CA 94901 *Tel:* 415-383-5256 *Fax:* 415-383-8606 *E-mail:* mvff@cafilm.org; info@cafilm.org *Web Site:* www.mvff.com; www.cafilm.org, pg 996

Millennia Media, FPC, 6411 Capitol Ave, Diamond Springs, CA 95619 *Tel:* 530-647-0750 *Toll Free Tel:* 866-MIC-PREAMP (642-7732) *Fax:* 530-647-

9921 *E-mail:* sales@mil-media.com; tech@mil-media.com (tech support) *Web Site:* www.mil-media.com, pg 827

Miller Camera Support LLC, 216 Little Falls Rd, Unit 15 & 16, Cedar Grove, NJ 07009-1276 *Tel:* 973-857-8300 *Fax:* 973-857-8188 *E-mail:* service@millertripods.us *Web Site:* www.millertripods.com, pg 827

Earl Miller Productions Inc, 1702 W Koenig Lane, Austin, TX 78756 *Tel:* 512-458-4343 *Fax:* 512-458-4485 *E-mail:* info@earlmillerproductions.com *Web Site:* www.earlmillerproductions.com, pg 827

Barney Miller's Inc, 232 E Main St, Lexington, KY 40507-1310 *Tel:* 859-252-2216 *Toll Free Tel:* 800-755-6799 *Web Site:* www.barneymillers.com, pg 827

Mills James Productions, 3545 Fishinger Blvd, Columbus, OH 43026-9489 *Tel:* 614-777-9933 *E-mail:* info@mjp.com *Web Site:* www.millsjames.com, pg 828

Milner-Fenwick Inc, 119 Lakefront Dr, Hunt Valley, MD 21030-2216 *Tel:* 410-252-1700 *Toll Free Tel:* 800-432-8433 *Fax:* 410-252-6316 *E-mail:* mail@milner-fenwick.com *Web Site:* www.milner-fenwick.com, pg 828

Milwaukee Film Office, 648 N Plankinton Ave, Suite 425, Milwaukee, WI 53203-2917 *Tel:* 414-273-3950 *Toll Free Tel:* 800-554-1448 *Fax:* 414-273-5596 *E-mail:* info@milwaukee.org *Web Site:* www.visitmilwaukee.org, pg 977

Mimi Productions, 4343 N Western Ave, No 1N, Chicago, IL 60618 *Tel:* 773-293-7292 *E-mail:* info@mimiproductions.com *Web Site:* www.mimiproductions.com, pg 828

Mind Resources Inc, 130 Shoemaker St, Unit 1, Kitchener, ON N2E 3G4, Canada *Tel:* 519-895-0330 *Toll Free Tel:* 877-414-6463 *E-mail:* sales@mindresources.com *Web Site:* www.mindresources.com, pg 828

MindPlay, 4400 E Broadway Blvd, Suite 400, Tucson, AZ 85711 *Tel:* 520-888-1800 *Toll Free Tel:* 800-221-7911 *E-mail:* mail@mindplay.com *Web Site:* www.mindplay.com, pg 828

Saul Mineroff Electronics Inc (SME), 574 Meacham Ave, Elmont, NY 11003 *Tel:* 516-775-1370 *Fax:* 516-775-1371 *E-mail:* tapenixon@aol.com *Web Site:* www.mineroff.com, pg 828

Minneapolis Licenses & Consumer Services, 350 S Fifth St, Rm 1, Minneapolis, MN 55415-1391 *Tel:* 612-673-2080 *Fax:* 612-673-3399 *Web Site:* www.minneapolismn.gov/licensing, pg 972

Minneapolis St Paul International Film Festival (MSPIFF), 125 SE Main St, Suite 341, Minneapolis, MN 55414 *Tel:* 612-331-7563 *E-mail:* info@mspfilm.org; submissions@mspfilm.org *Web Site:* mspfilm.org/festivals/mspiff, pg 996

Minnesota Film & TV, 401 N Third St, Suite 245, Minneapolis, MN 55401 *Tel:* 612-767-0095 *E-mail:* info@mnfilmtv.org *Web Site:* mnfilmtv.org, pg 972

Mirror 34 Productions, 2302 W Badger Rd, Madison, WI 53713-2322 *Tel:* 608-271-1226 *Toll Free Tel:* 800-569-6810 *E-mail:* human@mirror34.com *Web Site:* www.mirror34.com, pg 828

MISCO, 2637 32 Ave S, Minneapolis, MN 55406-1641 *Tel:* 612-825-1010 *Toll Free Tel:* 800-276-9955 *Fax:* 612-825-7010 *E-mail:* info@miscospeakers.com *Web Site:* www.miscospeakers.com, pg 828

Mississippi Film Office, 501 N West St, 5th fl, Jackson, MS 39201 *Tel:* 601-359-3297 *Fax:* 601-359-5048 *Web Site:* www.filmmississippi.org, pg 972

Missouri Film Office, 301 W High St, Suite 290, Jefferson City, MO 65101 *Tel:* 573-526-3566 *E-mail:* mofilm@ded.mo.gov *Web Site:* www.mofilm.org, pg 973

Missouri Honor Medal for Distinguished Service in Journalism, School of Journalism, 120 Neff Hall, 309 S Ninth St, Columbia, MO 65211-1200 *Tel:* 573-

882-4821 *Fax:* 573-884-5400 *E-mail:* journalism@missouri.edu *Web Site:* journalism.missouri.edu, pg 996

Mr Mark's Used Musical, Stereo & Studio Equipment Store, 109 Grizzard Ave, Nashville, TN 37207-4413 *Tel:* 615-596-6094 *E-mail:* mrmarksmusic@aol.com, pg 828

Mitchell Acoustics Research, 2005B Industrial Blvd, Rockwall, TX 75087 *Tel:* 214-741-7136 *Toll Free Fax:* 866-492-2470 *E-mail:* info@frazierspeakers.com *Web Site:* www.frazierspeakers.com, pg 828

MKE Production Rental, 159 N Broadway, Suite 202, Milwaukee, WI 53202 *Tel:* 414-939-3653 *E-mail:* rent1@mkeproductionrental.com *Web Site:* www.mkeproductionrental.com, pg 828

MMI Marketing, 2950 Wyman Pkwy, Baltimore, MD 21211-2802 *Tel:* 410-366-1222 *Fax:* 410-366-1222 *E-mail:* mail@mmi-marketing.com *Web Site:* www.mmi-marketing.com, pg 828

Moab to Monument Valley Film Commission, 111 E 100 N, Moab, UT 84532 *Tel:* 435-259-4341 *Fax:* 435-259-4135 *Web Site:* moabcity.org; film.utah.gov (Utah Film Commission), pg 976

Mobile Film Office, 164 Saint Emanuel St, Mobile, AL 36602 *Tel:* 251-438-7102 *Fax:* 251-438-7104 *Web Site:* www.mobilefilmoffice.com, pg 965

Mobile Stage Rentals Inc, 2331 N State Rd 7, Suite 221, Fort Lauderdale, FL 33313 *Toll Free Tel:* 877-882-8889 *Toll Free Fax:* 866-704-1194 *E-mail:* info@mobilestagerentals.com *Web Site:* www.mobilestagerentals.com, pg 828

Mobile-Video Productions Inc, 7315 Wisconsin Ave, Suite 1300 W, Bethesda, MD 20814 *Tel:* 301-656-2525 *Fax:* 301-656-4343 *E-mail:* mobilevp@verizon.net *Web Site:* www.mobilevideoproductions.tv, pg 828

The Mobius® Awards, 713 S Pacific Coast Hwy, Suite A, Redondo Beach, CA 90277-4233 *Tel:* 310-540-0959 *Fax:* 310-316-8905 *E-mail:* mobiusinfo@mobiusawards.com; mediarelations@mobiusawards.com *Web Site:* mobiusawards.com, pg 996

Modern Communications Inc, 1231 Horan Dr, Fenton, MO 63026 *Tel:* 636-343-0800 *Toll Free Tel:* 800-428-2442 *Fax:* 636-343-0906 *Web Site:* www.modcomm.com, pg 828

Modernage Photographic Services Inc, 555 Eighth Ave, New York, NY 10018 *Tel:* 212-997-1800 *Web Site:* www.modernage.com, pg 828

Modesto Convention & Visitors Bureau, 1150 Ninth St, Suite C, Modesto, CA 95354 *Tel:* 209-526-5588 *Toll Free Tel:* 888-640-8467 *Fax:* 209-526-5586 *E-mail:* films@visitmodesto.com @visitmodesto.com *Web Site:* www.visitmodesto.com, pg 967

modprop.com, 1044 Madison Ave, New York, NY 10021 *Tel:* 212-628-7582 *E-mail:* info@modprop.com *Web Site:* modprop.com, pg 828

Moe AV LLC, 133 Deerfield Rd, Sayreville, NJ 08872-1618 *Tel:* 732-257-3760 *Web Site:* www.moeco.net, pg 828

Mohawk, 324 Clark St, Worcester, MA 01606 *Tel:* 978-537-9961 *Toll Free Tel:* 800-422-9961 *Fax:* 978-537-4358 *E-mail:* o@mohawk-cable.com *Web Site:* www.mohawk-cable.com, pg 829

Mole-Richardson Co, 12154 Montague St, Pacoima, CA 91331 *Tel:* 323-851-0111 *Fax:* 323-851-5593 *E-mail:* info@mole.com *Web Site:* www.mole.com, pg 829

Monaco LLC, 145 Grassy Plain St, Bethel, CT 06801-2806 *Tel:* 203-744-3398 *Toll Free Tel:* 800-448-4877 *Fax:* 203-744-3228 *E-mail:* monaco@hangupbags.com *Web Site:* www.hangupbags.com, pg 829

Monad Trainer's Aide Inc, 163-60 22 Ave, Whitestone, NY 11357 *Tel:* 718-352-2314 *Toll Free Tel:* 800-344-6088 *Fax:* 718-352-8276 *Web Site:* www.monadtrainersaide.com, pg 829

Monadnock Media Inc, 59 North St, Hatfield, MA 01038 *Tel:* 413-247-6447 *Fax:* 413-247-6448 *E-mail:* info@ monadnock.org *Web Site:* www.monadnock.org, pg 829

Monarch Instrument, 15 Columbia Dr, Amherst, NH 03031-2305 *Tel:* 603-883-3390 *Toll Free Tel:* 800-999-3390 *Fax:* 603-886-3300 *E-mail:* sales@ monarchinstrument.com *Web Site:* www. monarchinstrument.com, pg 829

Monotype Imaging Inc, 600 Unicorn Park Dr, Woburn, MA 01801 *Tel:* 781-970-6000 *Toll Free Tel:* 800-424-8973 *Fax:* 781-970-6001; 781-970-6002 (gen questions) *E-mail:* info@monotype.com *Web Site:* www.monotype.com, pg 829

Monroe Electronics Inc, 100 Housel Ave, Lyndonville, NY 14098 *Tel:* 585-765-2254 *Fax:* 585-765-9330 *Web Site:* www.monroe-electronics.com, pg 829

Monroe-West Monroe Convention & Visitors Bureau, 601 Constitution Dr, West Monroe, LA 71292 *Tel:* 318-387-5691 *Toll Free Tel:* 800-843-1872 *Fax:* 318-324-1752 *Web Site:* nelafilm.com, pg 971

Monster Cable Products Inc, 455 Valley Dr, Brisbane, CA 94005-1209 *Tel:* 415-840-2000 *Toll Free Tel:* 877-800-8989 (cust serv) *Web Site:* www.monsterproducts. com, pg 829

Monster Tracks, 1821 Ranstead St, Philadelphia, PA 19103 *Tel:* 215-567-0400 *Toll Free Tel:* 800-369-1280 *Fax:* 215-567-0350 *Web Site:* www.monstertracks.com, pg 829

Montana Film Office, 301 S Park Ave, Helena, MT 59620 *Tel:* 406-841-2879 *E-mail:* montanafilm@mt. gov *Web Site:* www.montanafilm.com, pg 973

Monterey County Film Commission, 801 Lighthouse Ave, Suite 104, Monterey, CA 93940 *Tel:* 831-646-0910 *Fax:* 831-655-9250 *E-mail:* info@filmmonterey. org *Web Site:* www.filmmonterey.org, pg 967

monterey media inc, 125 Auburn Ct, Suite 220, Westlake Village, CA 91360 *Tel:* 805-494-7199 *Fax:* 805-496-6061 *E-mail:* customerservice@montereymedia. com; publicity@montereymedia.com *Web Site:* www. montereymedia.com, pg 829

monterey video, 125 Auburn Ct, Suite 220, Westlake Village, CA 91362 *Tel:* 805-494-7199 *Fax:* 805-496-6061 *E-mail:* customerservice@montereymedia. com; publicity@montereymedia.com *Web Site:* www. montereymedia.com, pg 829

Montreal Film & TV Commission, Duke Pavilion, 5th fl, 801 Brennan St, Montreal, QC H3C 0G4, Canada *Tel:* 514-872-2883 *Fax:* 514-872-3409 *E-mail:* film. tv@ville.montreal.qc.ca *Web Site:* www.montrealfilm. com, pg 979

Mood Creations Ltd, 3541 Main St, Shruboak, NY 10588 *E-mail:* info@moodcreations.com *Web Site:* www.moodcreations.com, pg 829

Moog Inc, 400 Jamison Rd, Elma, NY 14059 *Tel:* 716-652-2000 *E-mail:* info@moog.com *Web Site:* www. moog.com, pg 830

Moog Music Inc, 160 Broadway St, Asheville, NC 28801 *Tel:* 828-251-0090 *Toll Free Tel:* 800-948-1990 *Fax:* 828-254-6233 *E-mail:* info@moogmusic.com *Web Site:* www.moogmusic.com, pg 830

Moondance International Film Festival, 970 Ninth St, Boulder, CO 80302 *Tel:* 303-818-5771 *Web Site:* moondancefilmfestival.com, pg 996

Moore Creative Talent Inc, 3130 Excelsior Blvd, Minneapolis, MN 55416 *Tel:* 612-827-3823 *Web Site:* www.mooretalent.com, pg 830

MooreCo Inc, 2885 Lorraine Ave, Temple, TX 76501 *Toll Free Tel:* 800-749-2258 *Toll Free Fax:* 866-888-7483 *Web Site:* moorecoinc.com; mooreco360.com, pg 830

Moose School Productions, Box 960, Topanga, CA 90290-0960 *Tel:* 310-455-2318 *Toll Free Tel:* 800-676-5480 *Fax:* 310-455-4192 *Web Site:* www.peteralsop. com, pg 830

Morefield Communications Inc, 35 N 35 St, Camp Hill, PA 17011-2707 *Tel:* 717-761-6170 *Toll Free Tel:* 800-382-1266 *E-mail:* info@morefield.com *Web Site:* www.morefield.com, pg 830

Morning Music Ltd, 5200 Dixie Rd, Suite 203, Mississauga, ON L4W 1E4, Canada *Tel:* 905-625-2676 *Fax:* 905-625-2092 *E-mail:* info@morningmusic. ca *Web Site:* www.morningmusic.ca, pg 830

MorphoTrust USA, A Safran Company, 296 Concord Rd, Suite 300, Billerica, MA 01821 *Tel:* 978-215-2400 *Fax:* 978-215-2500 *E-mail:* info@morphotrust.com; prmorphotrust@morphotrust.com *Web Site:* www. morphotrust.com, pg 830

Rex Morris Productions, 5521 S Firethorn Place, Boise, ID 83716 *Tel:* 208-344-9878 *Fax:* 208-344-9878 *Web Site:* rexmorrisproductions.com, pg 830

Morrisound Recording, PO Box 49004, Tampa, FL 33647 *Tel:* 813-989-2108 *E-mail:* info@morrisound. com *Web Site:* morrisound.com, pg 830

Jack Morton Worldwide, 909 Third Ave, New York, NY 10022 *Tel:* 212-401-7000; 212-401-7212 *E-mail:* experience@jackmorton.com *Web Site:* www. jackmorton.com, pg 830

Mosby Inc, 3251 Riverport Lane, Maryland Heights, MO 63043 *Tel:* 314-872-8370 *Toll Free Tel:* 800-325-4177 *Fax:* 314-432-1380 *Web Site:* www.us.elsevierhealth. com, pg 831

Mother Basilea Films, 9849 N 40 St, Phoenix, AZ 85028-4099 *Tel:* 602-996-4040 *Fax:* 602-953-1303 *Web Site:* www.canaaninthedesert.com, pg 831

The Mother Co, 1504 Fourth St, No 216, Santa Monica, CA 90401 *Tel:* 310-826-2400 *Fax:* 310-826-0024 *E-mail:* hello@themotherco.com *Web Site:* www. themotherco.com, pg 831

Mother West, 187 Devoe St, Brooklyn, NY 11211 *E-mail:* info@motherwest.com *Web Site:* www. motherwest.com, pg 831

Motion & Graphic Image Corp Inc (MAGIC), 25 McPhillips Ave, Mobile, AL 36604 *Web Site:* magichd.com, pg 831

Motion Picture Association of America (MPAA), 15301 Ventura Blvd, Bldg E, Sherman Oaks, CA 91403-5885 *Tel:* 818-995-6600 *Fax:* 818-285-4403 *E-mail:* contactus@mpaa.org *Web Site:* www.mpaa. org, pg 957

Motion Picture Editors Guild Local 700, 7715 Sunset Blvd, Suite 200, Hollywood, CA 90046 *Tel:* 323-876-4770 *Toll Free Tel:* 800-705-8700 *Fax:* 323-876-0861 *E-mail:* mail@editorsguild.com *Web Site:* www. editorsguild.com, pg 957

Motion Picture Enterprises Inc, 432 W 45 St, New York, NY 10036 *Tel:* 212-245-0969 *Toll Free Tel:* 800-673-3348 *Fax:* 212-245-0974 *E-mail:* sales@mpenyc.com *Web Site:* www.mpenyc.com, pg 831

Motion Picture Licensing Corp (MPLC), 5455 Centinela Ave, Los Angeles, CA 90066 *Tel:* 310-822-8855 (intl calls) *Toll Free Tel:* 800-462-8855 *Fax:* 310-822-4440 *Web Site:* www.mplc.org, pg 831

Motion Picture Marine, 578 Washington Blvd, Suite 866, Marina del Rey, CA 90292 *Tel:* 310-951-1110 *Web Site:* perfect-horizon.com, pg 831

Motion Picture Services, 7542 Savannah Dr, Ooltewah, TN 37363 *Tel:* 423-238-7000 *E-mail:* info@ motionpictureservices.net *Web Site:* www. motionpictureservices.net, pg 831

MotionArt Studios, 27 Common St, Boston, MA 02129 *Tel:* 617-242-2228 *Web Site:* www.motionart.org; www.linestorm.com, pg 831

MotionMasters, 2288 Roxalana Rd, Dunbar, WV 25064 *Tel:* 304-345-8800 *Fax:* 304-345-8809 *E-mail:* storytellers@motionmasters.com *Web Site:* motionmasters.com, pg 831

Motor Racing Network, 555 MRN Dr, Concord, NC 28027 *Tel:* 704-262-6700 *Fax:* 704-262-6801 *E-mail:* sales@motorracingnetwork.com *Web Site:* www.motorracingnetwork.com, pg 831

Motown®, c/o Capitol Music Group, Capitol Records Bldg, 1750 N Vine St, Hollywood, CA 90028 *Tel:* 212-841-8000; 212-373-0750 *Web Site:* www. motownrecords.com, pg 831

Mountainair Films Inc, PO Box 4097, Santa Fe, NM 87502-4097 *Tel:* 505-471-9293 *Fax:* 505-438-0294 *E-mail:* produce@mountainairfilms.com *Web Site:* mountainairfilms.com, pg 831

Mountainfilm in Telluride, 109 E Colorado Ave, Suite 1, Telluride, CO 81435 *Tel:* 970-728-4123 *E-mail:* entries@mountainfilm.org *Web Site:* www. mountainfilm.org, pg 996

Mouser Electronics Inc - A TTI Berkshire Hathaway Company, 1000 N Main St, Mansfield, TX 76063-1514 *Tel:* 817-804-3888 *Toll Free Tel:* 800-346-6873 *Fax:* 817-804-3899 *E-mail:* sales@mouser. com *Web Site:* www.mouser.com, pg 831

Moviecraft Inc, PO Box 438, Orland Park, IL 60462-0438 *Tel:* 708-460-9082 *Fax:* 708-460-9099 *E-mail:* stock@moviecraft.com *Web Site:* www. moviecraft.com, pg 831

Movies Unlimited, 740 Hilltop Dr, Itasca, IL 60143 *Toll Free Tel:* 800-466-8437 *E-mail:* movies@ moviesunlimited.com; askmff@moviefanfare.com *Web Site:* www. moviesunlimited.com, pg 831

Moving Art by Louie Schwartzberg, 3371 Cahuenga Blvd W, Los Angeles, CA 90068 *Tel:* 323-436-2229 *Fax:* 323-436-2230 *E-mail:* team@movingart.com *Web Site:* www.movingart.com, pg 831

Moving Picture, 748 N Victoria Park Rd, Fort Lauderdale, FL 33304 *Tel:* 954-522-1361 *Toll Free Tel:* 800-800-1361 *Fax:* 954-523-1361 *E-mail:* info@ movingpicture.com *Web Site:* www.movingpicture. com, pg 831

Moving Pictures, 2820 Selwyn Ave, Suite 789, Charlotte, NC 28209 *Tel:* 704-676-0868 *E-mail:* info@mpicts. com *Web Site:* www.mpicts.com, pg 832

Moving Pictures, PO Box 64, Chester, CT 06412 *Tel:* 860-704-6900 *Web Site:* www.gener8or.com, pg 832

Moviola, 1135 N Mansfield Ave, Hollywood, CA 90038 *Tel:* 323-467-3107; 818-487-5000 *Toll Free Tel:* 877-MOVIOLA (668-4652) *Fax:* 323-464-1518 *Web Site:* www.moviola.com, pg 832

Moxie Media, 1301 Dealers Ave, New Orleans, LA 70123 *Tel:* 504-733-6907 *Toll Free Tel:* 800-346-6943 *Fax:* 504-733-9493 *E-mail:* info@moxiemedia.com *Web Site:* www.moxietraining.com; www.moxiemedia. com, pg 832

MQ Power Corp, 1800 Waters Ridge Dr, Suite 500, Lewisville, TX 75057 *Toll Free Tel:* 800-883-2551; 800-427-1244 (parts); 800-426-1244 (sales) *Fax:* 972-315-1847 *E-mail:* mqpowersales@multiquip.com *Web Site:* www.multiquip.com, pg 832

MRM//McCANN, 622 Third Ave, New York, NY 10017 *Tel:* 646-865-6230 *E-mail:* gbc@mrm-mccann.com *Web Site:* www.mrm-mccann.com, pg 832

MRY, 299 W Houston St, 14th fl, New York, NY 10014 *Tel:* 917-292-9429 *E-mail:* info@mry.com *Web Site:* mry.com; www.facebook.com/MRY, pg 832

MSE Media Solutions, 6013 Scott Way, Los Angeles, CA 90040 *Tel:* 323-721-1656 *Toll Free Tel:* 800-626-1955 *Fax:* 323-721-1506 *E-mail:* info@msemedia.com *Web Site:* www.msemedia.com, pg 832

MSI Production Services, 10895 Thornmint Rd, Suite A, San Diego, CA 92127 *Tel:* 858-348-0100 *Web Site:* www.msiprod.com, pg 832

MSU Technologies, 325 E Grand River, Suite 350, East Lansing, MI 48823 *Tel:* 517-355-2186 *Fax:* 517-432-3880 *E-mail:* msut@msu.edu *Web Site:* www. technologies.msu.edu, pg 832

MTI Home Video, 14216 SW 136 St, Miami, FL 33186 *Tel:* 305-255-8684 *Fax:* 305-233-6943 *Web Site:* www. mtivideo.com, pg 833

MTV, c/o MTV Studios, 1515 Broadway, New York, NY 10036 *Tel:* 212-258-8000 *Web Site:* www.mtv. com; www.mtvpress.com, pg 833

M2 Communications, 235 Bellefontaine St, Pasadena, CA 91105 *Tel:* 626-441-2024 *Toll Free Tel:* 800-423-8273 *Fax:* 626-441-2694 *E-mail:* m2com@aol.com *Web Site:* www.m2com.com, pg 833

MTX Audio, 4545 E Baseline Rd, Phoenix, AZ 85042 *Tel:* 602-438-4545 *Toll Free Tel:* 800-225-5689 *Fax:* 602-438-8692 *E-mail:* mtx@mtx.com *Web Site:* www.mtx.com, pg 833

Muderick Media, 101 Earlington Rd, Havertown, PA 19083 *Tel:* 610-449-6970, pg 833

Michael Mueller Video Productions, 211 Exchange St, Hot Springs, AR 71901 *Tel:* 501-282-4107 *Web Site:* muellervideo.com, pg 833

Ray Mueller Productions, 5 E Waterloo Rd, Stanhope, NJ 07874 *Tel:* 973-691-2088; 973-801-6004 *Web Site:* www.muellerproductions.com, pg 833

Muller Entertainment LLC, 540 Commerce St, Southlake, TX 76092 *Tel:* 214-317-0800 *E-mail:* info@mullerentertainment.com *Web Site:* www.mullerentertainment.com, pg 833

Mullikin Agency, 1391 Plaza Place, Suite A, Springdale, AR 72764-5225 *Tel:* 479-750-0871 *Toll Free Tel:* 800-750-0871 *Fax:* 479-750-2685 *Web Site:* www. mullikinad.com, pg 833

Multicom Inc, 1076 Florida Central Pkwy, Longwood, FL 32750 *Tel:* 407-331-7779 *Toll Free Tel:* 800-423-2594 *Fax:* 407-339-0204 *E-mail:* multicom@ multicominc.com *Web Site:* www.multicominc.com, pg 833

Multicultural Media Inc, 27 Main St, Suite 6, Montpelier, VT 05602 *Tel:* 802-839-0371 *E-mail:* support@worldmusicstore.com *Web Site:* www.worldmusicstore.com; www. multiculturalmedia.com; www.lyrichord.com, pg 833

MultiDyne Video & Fiber Optics Systems, 10 Newton Place, Hauppauge, NY 11788 *Tel:* 516-671-7278 *Toll Free Tel:* 877-MULTIDYNE (685-8439) *Fax:* 516-671-3362 *E-mail:* sales@multidyne.com *Web Site:* www. multidyne.com, pg 833

Multimedia Audio Visual Inc, 2640 S Raritan Circle, Denver, CO 80110 *Tel:* 303-623-2324 *Toll Free Tel:* 800-756-6118 *Fax:* 303-623-0829 *E-mail:* info@ multimedia-av.com *Web Site:* www.multimedia-av.com, pg 833

Multimedia LED, 4225 Prado Rd, Suite 108, Corona, CA 92880 *Tel:* 951-280-7500 *Toll Free Tel:* 888-98-MMLED (986-6533, sales); 800-888-3007 (cust serv) *Fax:* 951-335-8152 *E-mail:* info@multimedialed.com *Web Site:* www.multimedialed.com, pg 833

Multimedia Marketing Group, 6048 Broadcast Pkwy, Loves Park, IL 61111 *Tel:* 779-774-3188 *Fax:* 779-423-0090 *E-mail:* info@mmg-1.com *Web Site:* mmg-1.com, pg 833

Multivision Video & Film, 3031 SW 28 Lane, Miami, FL 33133 *Tel:* 305-662-6011 *E-mail:* info@ multivisionvideo.com *Web Site:* www.multivisionvideo. com, pg 833

Munday & Collins AV, 2122 Zanker Rd, San Jose, CA 95131-2108 *Tel:* 408-451-9155 *Toll Free Tel:* 800-834-5551 *Fax:* 408-451-9192 *E-mail:* info@avevents.com *Web Site:* www.avevents.com, pg 834

Edward R Murrow Award, 401 Ninth St NW, Washington, DC 20004-2129 *Tel:* 202-879-9600 *Toll Free Tel:* 800-272-2190 *E-mail:* press@cpb.org *Web Site:* www.cpb.org, pg 996

The Edward R Murrow Award, 40 W 45 St, New York, NY 10036 *Tel:* 212-626-9220 *Fax:* 212-626-9210 *E-mail:* info@opcofamerica.org *Web Site:* www. opcofamerica.org, pg 996

Musco Lighting, 100 First Ave W, Oskaloosa, IA 52577 *Tel:* 641-673-0411 *Toll Free Tel:* 800-825-6030 *Fax:* 641-673-4852 *E-mail:* lighting@musco.com *Web Site:* www.musco.com, pg 834

Muse Entertainment Enterprises, 3451 Rue Saint Jacques, Montreal, QC H4C 1H1, Canada *Tel:* 514-866-6873 *Fax:* 514-876-3911 *E-mail:* bpalik@muse.ca *Web Site:* www.muse.ca, pg 834

Muse Presentation Technologies, 3510 S Susan St, Santa Ana, CA 92704 *Tel:* 714-850-1008 *Toll Free Tel:* 800-950-4955 *Fax:* 714-850-1018 *Web Site:* www. museprestech.com, pg 834

Museum of the City of New York, 1220 Fifth Ave, New York, NY 10029 *Tel:* 212-534-1672 *Fax:* 212-423-0758 *E-mail:* info@mcny.org *Web Site:* www.mcny. org, pg 834

Music & Entertainment Industry Educators Association (MEIEA), 1900 Belmont Blvd, Nashville, TN 37212-3758 *Tel:* 615-460-6946 *E-mail:* office@meiea.org; membership@meiea.org *Web Site:* www.meiea.org, pg 958

The Music Bakery, 7522 Campbell Rd, Suite 113, Dallas, TX 75248 *Tel:* 214-636-5887 *E-mail:* helpnow@musicbakery.com *Web Site:* www. musicbakery.com, pg 834

Music Business Association (Music Biz), 106 E Center Blvd, Marlton, NJ 08053 *Tel:* 856-596-2221 *Web Site:* musicbiz.org, pg 958

Music Group Commercial Ltd, 335 Gage Ave, Suite 1, Kitchener, ON N2M 5E1, Canada *Tel:* 519-745-1158 *Fax:* 519-745-2364 *E-mail:* musicinfoca@music-group.com *Web Site:* www.music-group.com, pg 834

MUSIC Group Services Nevada, 5270 Procyon St, Las Vegas, NV 89118 *Tel:* 702-800-8290 *E-mail:* careente@music-group.com *Web Site:* www. music-group.com, pg 834

Music Hall LLC, 108 Station Rd, Great Neck, NY 11023 *Tel:* 516-487-3663 *Fax:* 516-773-3891 *E-mail:* info@musichallaudio.com *Web Site:* musichallaudio.com, pg 834

The Music Kitchen Inc, 12400 Connery Way, Bakersfield, CA 93312 *Tel:* 661-338-4749 *Web Site:* www.themusickitchen.com, pg 834

Music Lab Inc, 500 E Saint Elmo Rd, Austin, TX 78745 *Tel:* 512-707-0560 (ext 2) *Fax:* 512-707-2946 *E-mail:* info@musiclab.net *Web Site:* musiclabaustin. com, pg 834

The Music People Inc, 154 Woodlawn Rd, Suite C, Berlin, CT 06037-1500 *Tel:* 860-829-9229 *Toll Free Tel:* 800-289-8889 *Fax:* 860-828-1353 *E-mail:* support@musicpeopleinc.com *Web Site:* www. musicpeopleinc.com, pg 834

The Music Place, 844 Rte 73, West Berlin, NJ 08091 *Tel:* 856-768-2226 *Fax:* 856-768-7135 *E-mail:* zeronemusic@aol.com, pg 834

Music Rhapsody, 1603 Aviation Blvd, Redondo Beach, CA 90278 *Tel:* 310-376-8646 *Toll Free Tel:* 888-TRY-MUSIC (879-6874) *Fax:* 310-376-8490 *E-mail:* info@ musicrhapsody.com *Web Site:* musicrhapsody.com, pg 834

Music Sales Corp, 180 Madison Ave, 24th fl, New York, NY 10016 *Tel:* 212-254-2100 *Fax:* 212-254-2013 *E-mail:* info@musicsales.com *Web Site:* www. musicsales.com, pg 834

Music World/Vocal Power School, 9826 Columbus Ave, North Hills, CA 91343 *Tel:* 818-895-7464 *Toll Free Tel:* 800-929-7464 *E-mail:* MusicMan@music-world.com; provoice777@icloud.com *Web Site:* www. BornToSing.com; www.music-world.com, pg 834

MusicMaster Inc, 8330 LBJ Fwy, Suite B1050, Dallas, TX 75243 *Tel:* 469-717-0100 *E-mail:* info@ musicmaster.com; sales@musicmaster.com *Web Site:* www.musicmaster.com, pg 835

Musicol Recording, 780 Oakland Park Ave, Columbus, OH 43224 *Tel:* 614-267-3133 *Toll Free Tel:* 800-240-5963 *Fax:* 614-267-3135 *E-mail:* info@musicolrecording.com *Web Site:* www. musicolrecording.com, pg 835

Musikvergnuegen, 1800 S Grand Blvd, Suite 114, Glendale, CA 91204 *Tel:* 323-856-5900 *Fax:* 323-856-5917 *E-mail:* info@musikv.com *Web Site:* www. musikvergnuegen.com, pg 835

Musivision Inc, 8 Deepwood Rd, Weston, CT 06883 *Tel:* 203-227-1017 *E-mail:* info@musivision.com *Web Site:* musivision.com, pg 835

Mutoh America Inc, 2602 S 47 St, Phoenix, AZ 85034-7401 *Tel:* 480-968-7772 *Toll Free Tel:* 800-99-MUTOH (996-8864) *Fax:* 480-968-7990 *E-mail:* sales@mutoh.com; support@mutoh.com *Web Site:* www.mutoh.com, pg 835

Mutual Hardware, 36-27 Vernon Blvd, Long Island City, NY 11106 *Toll Free Tel:* 866-361-2480 *Fax:* 718-786-9591 *E-mail:* info@mutualhardware.com *Web Site:* www.mutualhardware.com, pg 835

MVD Entertainment Group, 203 Windsor Rd, Pottstown, PA 19464 *Tel:* 610-650-8200 *Toll Free Tel:* 800-888-0486 *Fax:* 610-650-9102 *Toll Free Fax:* 888-536-7998 *Web Site:* mvdb2b.com, pg 835

MVI - MultiVision Inc, 120 McLevin Ave, Unit 3, Toronto, ON M1B 3E9, Canada *Tel:* 416-449-1080 *Toll Free Tel:* 800-563-5902 (ext 228) *Fax:* 416-449-5131 *E-mail:* business@mvidisplay.com *Web Site:* www.mvidisplay.com, pg 835

MVP International Inc, 518 S Nevada Ave, Suite 2, Colorado Springs, CO 80903 *Tel:* 713-771-1132 *Toll Free Tel:* 800-432-0687 *E-mail:* info@mvp-av.com *Web Site:* www.mvp-av.com, pg 835

Myriad Productions, 415 Barlow Ct, Johns Creek, GA 30022 *Tel:* 678-417-0043 *Fax:* 678-417-0043, pg 835

Mystery Electronics LLC, 6438 Morton Rd, Greenbrier, TN 37073 *Tel:* 615-643-8460 *Toll Free Tel:* 800-798-2256 *Fax:* 615-643-8464 *E-mail:* sales@ mysteryelectronics.com *Web Site:* www. mysteryelectronics.com, pg 835

Mystic Seaport (Film & Video Archives), 75 Greenmanville Ave, Mystic, CT 06355 *Tel:* 860-572-0711; 860-572-5365 *Toll Free Tel:* 888-973-2767 *E-mail:* permissions@mysticseaport.org; info@ mysticseaport.org; advancement@mysticseaport.org (donations) *Web Site:* www.mysticseaport.org, pg 835

Myton Industries Inc, 1981 S Park Rd, Pembroke Park, FL 33009 *Tel:* 954-989-0113 *Toll Free Tel:* 800-544-2406 *Fax:* 954-989-1488 *E-mail:* myton@msn. com; sales@mytonindustries.com *Web Site:* www. mytonindustries.com, pg 835

NAB Distinguished Service Award, 1771 "N" St NW, Washington, DC 20036 *Tel:* 202-429-5300 *E-mail:* nab@nab.org *Web Site:* www.nab.org, pg 997

Nady Systems Inc, 3341 Vincent Rd, Pleasant Hill, CA 94523 *Tel:* 510-652-2411 *Fax:* 510-652-5075 *E-mail:* ussales@nady.com; support@nady.com *Web Site:* www.nady.com, pg 835

Nalpak Inc, 1267 Vernon Way, El Cajon, CA 92020 *Tel:* 619-258-1200 *Toll Free Tel:* 888-488-3372 (help desk) *Fax:* 619-258-0925 *E-mail:* service@nalpak.com *Web Site:* www.nalpak.com, pg 835

NAMM, the National Association of Music Merchants, 5790 Armada Dr, Carlsbad, CA 92008 *Tel:* 760-438-8001 *Toll Free Tel:* 800-767-6266 (memb hotline) *Fax:* 760-438-7327 *E-mail:* info@namm.org *Web Site:* www.namm.org, pg 958

Nandar Entertainment Pictures, Lucy Bungalow, No 101, 5555 Melrose Ave, Los Angeles, CA 90038 *Toll Free Tel:* 800-969-6022 *E-mail:* mail@nandarentertainment. com *Web Site:* nandarentertainment.com, pg 835

N&N Productions Ltd, 5540 High Rock Way, Sparks, NV 89431 *Tel:* 775-355-9080 *E-mail:* sales@ brassgobos.com *Web Site:* www.brassgobos.com, pg 835

Nantucket Film Festival (NFF), 68 Jay St, Suite 319, Brooklyn, NY 11201 *Tel:* 646-480-1900 *Fax:* 646-365-3367 *E-mail:* info@nantucketfilmfestival. org; submissions@nantucketfilmfestival.org *Web Site:* nantucketfilmfestival.org, pg 997

NASCAR Productions LLC, 550 S Caldwell St, Suite 2000, Charlotte, NC 28202 *Tel:* 704-348-7100 *E-mail:* productions@nascar.com *Web Site:* productions.nascar.com, pg 835

Nashville Production Rentals (NPR), 125 Commerce Dr, Hendersonville, TN 37075 *Tel:* 615-431-5822 *E-mail:* mail@takeone.tv *Web Site:* www.takeone.tv, pg 836

Nassau County Film Office, Executive Bldg, One West St, Mineola, NY 11501 *Tel:* 516-571-3168 *Fax:* 516-571-6195 *Web Site:* www.longislandfilm.com, pg 974

The Thomas Nast Award, 40 W 45 St, New York, NY 10036 *Tel:* 212-626-9220 *Fax:* 212-626-9210 *E-mail:* info@opcofamerica.org *Web Site:* www.opcofamerica.org, pg 997

The National Academy of Television Arts & Sciences (NATAS), 1697 Broadway, Suite 404, New York, NY 10019 *Tel:* 212-586-8424 *Fax:* 212-246-8129 *Web Site:* emmyonline.tv, pg 958

National Association for Music Education (NAfME), 1806 Robert Fulton Dr, Reston, VA 20191 *Tel:* 703-860-4000 *Toll Free Tel:* 800-336-3768 *Fax:* 703-860-1531 *Toll Free Fax:* 888-275-6362 *E-mail:* memberservices@nafme.org *Web Site:* nafme.org, pg 958

National Association of Biology Teachers (NABT), PO Box 3363, Warrenton, VA 20188 *Tel:* 703-264-9696 *Toll Free Tel:* 888-501-NABT (501-6228) *E-mail:* office@nabt.org *Web Site:* www.nabt.org, pg 958

National Association of Black Journalists (NABJ), 1100 Knight Hall, Suite 3100, College Park, MD 20742 *Tel:* 301-405-0248 *Fax:* 301-314-1714 *Web Site:* www.nabj.org, pg 958

National Association of Broadcasters (NAB), 1771 "N" St NW, Washington, DC 20036 *Tel:* 202-429-5300 *E-mail:* nab@nab.org; membership@nab.org *Web Site:* www.nab.org, pg 958

National Association of Elementary School Principals (NAESP), 1615 Duke St, Alexandria, VA 22314 *Tel:* 703-684-3345 *Toll Free Tel:* 800-386-2377 *Fax:* 703-549-5568 *Toll Free Fax:* 800-396-2377 *E-mail:* naesp@naesp.org *Web Site:* www.naesp.org, pg 836

National Association of Record Industry Professionals (NARIP), PO Box 2446, Toluca Lake, CA 91610-2446 *Tel:* 818-769-7007 *E-mail:* info@narip.com *Web Site:* www.narip.com, pg 958

National Association of Theatre Owners (NATO), 1705 "N" St NW, Washington, DC 20036 *Tel:* 202-962-0054 *E-mail:* nato@natodc.com *Web Site:* www.natoonline.org, pg 959

National Audiovisual Center (NAC), 5301 Shawnee Rd, Alexandria, VA 22312 *E-mail:* info@ntis.gov; customerservice@ntis.gov *Web Site:* classic.ntis.gov/products/nac, pg 836

National Board of Review (of Motion Pictures), 40 W 37 St, Suite 501, New York, NY 10018 *Tel:* 212-465-9166 *Fax:* 212-465-9168 *E-mail:* nbr@nbrmp.org *Web Site:* www.nationalboardofreview.org, pg 959

National Boston, 115 Dummer St, Brookline, MA 02446 *Tel:* 617-734-4800 *Fax:* 617-734-6323 *E-mail:* info@nationalboston.com *Web Site:* www.nationalboston.com, pg 836

National Council of Acoustical Consultants (NCAC), 9100 Purdue Rd, Suite 200, Indianapolis, IN 46268 *Tel:* 317-328-0642 *Fax:* 317-328-4629 *E-mail:* info@ncac.com *Web Site:* ncac.com, pg 959

National Council of Churches, 110 Maryland Ave NE, Suite 108, Washington, DC 20002 *Tel:* 202-544-2350 *E-mail:* info@nationalcouncilofchurches.us *Web Site:* nationalcouncilofchurches.us, pg 836

National Council of Teachers of English (NCTE), 1111 W Kenyon Rd, Urbana, IL 61801-1096 *Tel:* 217-328-3870 *Toll Free Tel:* 877-369-6283 *Fax:* 217-328-9645 *Web Site:* www.ncte.org, pg 959

National Education Association (NEA), 1201 16 St NW, Washington, DC 20036-3290 *Tel:* 202-833-4000 *Fax:* 202-822-7974 *Web Site:* www.nea.org, pg 836

National Film Board of Canada/Office National du Film du Canada, Ilot Balmoral, 1501 de Bleury St, Montreal, QC H3A 0H3, Canada *Tel:* 514-287-9000; 514-261-1650 (animation studio) *Toll Free Tel:* 800-267-7710 (CN only); 800-542-2164 (US only) *Fax:* 514-841-3500 *Web Site:* www.nfb.ca; onf-nfb.gc.ca, pg 836

National Fire Protection Association (NFPA), One Batterymarch Park, Quincy, MA 02169-7471 *Tel:* 617-770-3000 *Toll Free Tel:* 800-344-3555 (US & CN); 855-274-8525 (US & CN) *Fax:* 508-895-8301 *Toll Free Fax:* 800-593-NFPA (593-6372, US & CN) *E-mail:* custserv@nfpa.org *Web Site:* www.nfpa.org, pg 836

National Freedom of Information Coalition (NFOIC), University of Florida College of Journalism, 3208 Weimer Hall, 1885 Stadium Rd, Gainesville, FL 32611 *Tel:* 352-294-7082 *E-mail:* nfoic@nfoic.org *Web Site:* www.nfoic.org, pg 959

National Geographic Learning, 10650 Toebben Dr, Independence, KY 41051 *Tel:* 859-525-2230 *Toll Free Tel:* 888-915-3276 *Web Site:* ngl.cengage.com, pg 836

National Headliner Awards, PO Box 128, Somers Point, NJ 08244 *Tel:* 609-927-1850; 609-350-3099 *E-mail:* info@headlinerawards.org *Web Site:* www.headlinerawards.org, pg 997

National Institute for Trial Advocacy (NITA), 1685 38 St, Suite 200, Boulder, CO 80301-2735 *Tel:* 720-890-4860 *Toll Free Tel:* 800-225-6482 *Fax:* 720-890-7069 *E-mail:* customerservice@nita.org *Web Site:* www.nita.org, pg 836

National Instruments Corp, 11500 N Mopac Expwy, Austin, TX 78759-3504 *Tel:* 512-683-0100 *Toll Free Tel:* 888-280-7645 (sales); 877-388-1952 *Fax:* 512-683-8411; 512-683-5794 (sales) *Web Site:* www.ni.com, pg 836

National Media Services Inc, 613 N Commerce Ave, Front Royal, VA 22630 *Tel:* 540-635-4181 *Fax:* 540-636-4240 *Web Site:* nationalmediaservices.com, pg 836

National Press Photographers Association (NPPA), 120 Hooper St, Athens, GA 30602-3018 *Tel:* 706-542-2506 *E-mail:* info@nppa.org; director@nppa.org *Web Site:* nppa.org, pg 959

National Public Radio (NPR), 1111 N Capitol St NE, Washington, DC 20002 *Tel:* 202-513-2000 *Web Site:* www.npr.org, pg 959

National Religious Broadcasters (NRB), 600 N Capitol St NW, Suite 210, Washington, DC 20001 *Tel:* 202-543-0073 *Fax:* 202-543-2649 *E-mail:* info@nrb.org; press@nrb.org *Web Site:* nrb.org, pg 959

National Safety Council (NSC), 1121 Spring Lake Dr, Itasca, IL 60143-3201 *Tel:* 630-285-1121 *Toll Free Tel:* 800-621-7615; 800-621-7619 (cust serv) *Fax:* 630-285-1434 (cust serv); 630-285-1315 *E-mail:* customerservice@nsc.org *Web Site:* www.nsc.org, pg 836

National School Boards Association (NSBA), 1680 Duke St, 2nd fl, Alexandria, VA 22314-3493 *Tel:* 703-838-6722 *Fax:* 703-683-7590 *E-mail:* info@nsba.org *Web Site:* www.nsba.org, pg 959

National School Products, 1523 Old Niles Ferry Rd, Maryville, TN 37803 *Tel:* 865-984-3960 *Toll Free Tel:* 800-627-9393 *Fax:* 865-983-9355 *Toll Free Tel:* 800-289-3960 *E-mail:* customerservice@nationalschoolproducts.com *Web Site:* nationalschoolproducts.com, pg 836

National Storytelling Festival, 116 W Main St, Jonesborough, TN 37659 *Tel:* 423-753-2171 *Toll Free Tel:* 800-952-8392 *Fax:* 423-913-8219 *E-mail:* customerservice@storytellingcenter.net *Web Site:* www.storytellingcenter.net/festival, pg 997

National Student Production Awards, Hershey Square Ctr, 1152 Mae St, Hummelstown, PA 17036 *Toll Free Tel:* 855-ASK-4CBI (275-4224) *Web Site:* www.askcbi.org, pg 997

National Systems Contractors Association (NSCA), 3950 River Ridge Dr NE, Cedar Rapids, IA 52402 *Tel:* 319-366-6722 *Toll Free Tel:* 800-446-6722 *Fax:* 319-366-4164 *E-mail:* nsca@nsca.org *Web Site:* www.nsca.org, pg 959

National Telemedia Council Inc, 1922 University Ave, Madison, WI 53726 *Tel:* 608-218-1182 *E-mail:* ntelemedia@aol.com *Web Site:* www.nationaltelemediacouncil.org, pg 959

National Teleproductions Inc, PO Box 1804, West Palm Beach, FL 33402-1804 *Tel:* 561-689-9271 *Fax:* 561-640-4677 *E-mail:* ntp@ntpworldwide.com, pg 837

National Undergraduate Student Electronic Media Competition, PO Box 4206, Chesterfield, MO 63006 *Tel:* 314-628-1196 *Web Site:* www.nbs-aerho.org, pg 997

Nationwide Audio Visual Co, 4100-B Sladeview Crescent, Units 1 & 2, Mississauga, ON L5L 5Z3, Canada *Tel:* 905-608-8899 *Fax:* 905-608-8890 *E-mail:* sales@nationwideav.com *Web Site:* www.nationwideav.com, pg 837

NatureVision Stock Footage Library, 4407 67 Ave Circle E, Sarasota, FL 34243 *Tel:* 856-873-6546 *Toll Free Tel:* 877-327-3207 *Web Site:* www.naturevisiontv.com, pg 837

NatureVision TV, 4407 67 Ave Circle E, Sarasota, FL 34243 *Tel:* 856-873-6546 *Toll Free Tel:* 877-327-3207 *Web Site:* www.naturevisiontv.com, pg 837

Nautilus Entertainment Design Inc (NED), 1010 Turquoise St, Suite 215, San Diego, CA 92109 *Tel:* 858-456-6395 *E-mail:* info@n-e-d.com *Web Site:* www.n-e-d.com, pg 837

Navigator Systems Ltd, 1312 W Main St, Suite E, Lebanon, TN 37087 *Tel:* 615-547-1895 *Fax:* 615-547-1897 *Web Site:* www.hiretracknx.com, pg 837

Navitar Inc, 200 Commerce Dr, Rochester, NY 14623 *Tel:* 585-359-4000 *Toll Free Tel:* 800-828-6778 *Fax:* 585-359-4999 *E-mail:* info@navitar.com *Web Site:* www.navitar.com, pg 837

Nazdar®, 8501 Hedge Lane Terr, Shawnee, KS 66227-3290 *Tel:* 913-422-1888 *Toll Free Tel:* 800-767-9942 (cust serv) *Fax:* 913-422-2296 *E-mail:* custserv@nazdar.com *Web Site:* www.nazdar.com, pg 837

NBA Entertainment Inc, 450 Harmon Meadow Blvd, Secaucus, NJ 07094 *Tel:* 201-865-1500 *Fax:* 201-865-2626 *Web Site:* www.nba.com, pg 837

NBC-5, 4805 Amon Carter Blvd, Fort Worth, TX 76155 *Tel:* 817-429-5555 *Fax:* 817-654-6325 *Web Site:* www.nbcdfw.com, pg 837

NBC News Archives, 30 Rockefeller Plaza, New York, NY 10112 *Tel:* 212-664-5015 *Toll Free Tel:* 855-NBC-VIDEO (622-8433) *Fax:* 212-703-8558 *E-mail:* nbcnewsarchives@nbcuni.com *Web Site:* www.nbcnewsarchivesxpress.com, pg 837

NBC Production Facilities, 30 Rockefeller Plaza, New York, NY 10112 *Tel:* 212-664-4444 *Fax:* 212-664-5056 *Web Site:* www.nbc.com, pg 837

NDS Surgical Imaging LLC, 5750 Hellyer Ave, San Jose, CA 95138 *Tel:* 408-776-0085 *Toll Free Tel:* 866-637-5237 *E-mail:* info@ndssi.com *Web Site:* www.ndssi.com, pg 837

Malcolm Neal Productions, 111 Everest Dr, Thomaston, GA 30286-4603 *Tel:* 706-646-2749; 706-647-5372 *E-mail:* nealritz@charter.net, pg 837

Nebraska Film Office, PO Box 98907, Lincoln, NE 68509-8907 *Tel:* 402-471-3746 *Toll Free Tel:* 800-426-6505 *Web Site:* film.nebraska.gov; opportunity.nebraska.gov/ded-partners, pg 973

NEC Display Solutions of America, 500 Park Blvd, Suite 1100, Itasca, IL 60143 *Tel:* 630-467-3000 *Web Site:* www.necdisplay.com, pg 837

Nelson Education Ltd, 1120 Birchmount Rd, Scarborough, ON M1K 5G4, Canada *Tel:* 416-752-9100 *Toll Free Tel:* 800-268-2222 (cust support) *Fax:* 416-752-8101 *Toll Free Fax:* 800-430-4445 *E-mail:* inquire@nelson.com *Web Site:* www.nelson.com, pg 837

Nelson Enterprises Theatrical Supply Co, 1014 Rte 173 E, Bloomsbury, NJ 08804 *Tel:* 908-479-6902 *Fax:* 908-479-6903 *E-mail:* sales@nelson-enterprises. com; rentals@nelson-enterprises.com *Web Site:* www. nelson-enterprises.com, pg 838

L E Nelson Sales Corp, 6050 S Valley View Blvd, Las Vegas, NV 89118 *Tel:* 702-367-3656 *Fax:* 702-367-7058, pg 838

Scott Nelson HD Productions Inc, PO Box 1198, Bend, OR 97709-1198 *Tel:* 541-410-8680 *E-mail:* snp@ bendcable.com *Web Site:* vimeo.com/scottnelson, pg 838

Nelson White Systems Inc, 8725-A Loch Raven Blvd, Baltimore, MD 21286 *Tel:* 410-668-9628 *Toll Free Tel:* 800-296-7555 *Fax:* 410-668-9629 *E-mail:* sales@ nelsonwhite.com; service@nelsonwhite.com; rentals@ nelsonwhite.com *Web Site:* www.nelsonwhite.com, pg 838

Nemal Electronics International Inc, 12240 NE 14 Ave, North Miami, FL 33161 *Tel:* 305-899-0900 *Toll Free Tel:* 800-522-2253 *Fax:* 305-895-8178 *E-mail:* info@ nemal.com *Web Site:* www.nemal.com, pg 838

Otto Nemenz International Inc, 870 N Vine St, Los Angeles, CA 90038 *Tel:* 323-469-2774 *Fax:* 323-469-1217 *E-mail:* info@ottonemenz.com *Web Site:* www. ottonemenz.com, pg 838

NeoSoft Corp, PO Box 5667, Bend, OR 97708-5667 *Tel:* 541-389-5489 *Fax:* 541-388-8221 *E-mail:* sales@ neosoftware.com *Web Site:* www.neosoftware.com, pg 838

NEP Group Inc, 2 Beta Dr, Pittsburgh, PA 15238 *Tel:* 412-826-1414 *Toll Free Tel:* 800-444-0054 *E-mail:* info@nepinc.com *Web Site:* www.nepgroup. com, pg 838

Neptune Photo Inc, 130 Seventh St, Garden City, NY 11530 *Tel:* 516-741-4484 *Toll Free Tel:* 800-955-1110 *E-mail:* sales@neptunephoto.com *Web Site:* www. neptunephoto.com, pg 838

Nesbit Systems Inc, 243 N Union St, Suite 112, Lambertville, NJ 08530 *Tel:* 609-397-7720 *E-mail:* info@nesbit.com *Web Site:* www.nesbit.com, pg 838

NetWell Noise Control, 18525 37 Ave N, Minneapolis, MN 55446-2855 *Tel:* 763-694-8908 *Toll Free Tel:* 800-638-9355 *Fax:* 763-694-8909 *E-mail:* help@ controlnoise.com *Web Site:* www.controlnoise.com, pg 838

Network Entertainment Inc, 1488 Frances St, Vancouver, BC V5L 1Y9, Canada *Tel:* 604-739-8825 *Fax:* 604-739-8835 *E-mail:* info@networkentertainment.ca *Web Site:* www.networkentertainment.ca, pg 838

Network Technologies Inc, 1275 Danner Dr, Aurora, OH 44202 *Tel:* 330-562-7070 *Toll Free Tel:* 800-742-8324 *Fax:* 330-562-1999 *E-mail:* sales@ntigo.com *Web Site:* www.networktechinc.com, pg 838

Neumann USA, One Enterprise Dr, Old Lyme, CT 06371 *Tel:* 860-434-9190 *Fax:* 860-434-1759 *E-mail:* neumann-help@neumannusa.com *Web Site:* www.neumannusa.com, pg 838

Neutrik® USA Inc, 4115 Taggart Creek Rd, Charlotte, NC 28208 *Tel:* 704-972-3050 *Fax:* 704-438-9202 *Toll Free Fax:* 877-220-4089 *E-mail:* info@neutrikusa.com *Web Site:* www.neutrik.us, pg 838

Nevada Broadcasters Association, 3900 Paradise Rd, Suite 279, Las Vegas, NV 89169 *Tel:* 702-794-4994 *Fax:* 702-794-4997 *Web Site:* www. nevadabroadcasters.org, pg 960

Nevada Film Office, 6655 W Sahara, Suite C-106, Las Vegas, NV 89146 *Tel:* 877-638-3456 *Fax:* 702-486-2712 *E-mail:* lvnfo@ nevadafilm.com *Web Site:* www.nevadafilm. com, pg 973

Nevion USA Inc, 400 W Ventura Blvd, Suite 155, Camarillo, CA 93010 *Tel:* 805-247-8560 *E-mail:* ussales@nevion.com *Web Site:* nevion.com, pg 838

New & Unique Videos™, 7323 Rondel Ct, San Diego, CA 92119-1530 *Tel:* 619-644-3000 *E-mail:* video@newuniquevideos.com *Web Site:* www. newuniquevideos.com, pg 839

New Circuit Films LLC, 421 Canyon Dr, Glendale, CA 91206 *Tel:* 818-378-0033 *Web Site:* www.newcircuit. com, pg 839

New Cyberian Systems Inc, 1919 O'Toole Way, San Jose, CA 95131 *Tel:* 408-922-0682 *Toll Free Tel:* 877-423-4383 *Fax:* 408-884-2257 *E-mail:* sales@ newcyberian.com *Web Site:* www.newcyberian.com, pg 839

New Day Films, 190 Rte 17 M, Suite D, Harriman, NY 10926 *Toll Free Tel:* 888-367-9154 *Fax:* 845-774-2945 *E-mail:* orders@newday.com; curator@newday.com *Web Site:* www.newday.com, pg 839

New Deal Studios, 15392 Cobalt St, Los Angeles, CA 91342 *Tel:* 310-578-9929 *E-mail:* info@ newdealstudios.com *Web Site:* www.newdealstudios. com, pg 839

New England Keyboard Inc, One Princeton Rd, Fitchburg, MA 01420 *Tel:* 978-345-8332 *Fax:* 978-345-4329 *E-mail:* info@newenglandkeyboard.com *Web Site:* www.newenglandkeyboard.com, pg 839

New England Technology Group Inc (NETG), One Davenport St, Cambridge, MA 02140 *Tel:* 617-864-5551 *Fax:* 520-844-5551 *E-mail:* teamnetg@ netgworld.com *Web Site:* netgworld.com, pg 839

The New Film Company Inc, 7 Scott St, Cambridge, MA 02138 *Tel:* 617-520-5005 *Fax:* 617-491-9201 *E-mail:* newfilmco@aol.com *Web Site:* www. newfilmco.com, pg 839

New Hampshire Film Bureau, One Eagle Sq, Suite 100, Concord, NH 03301 *Tel:* 603-271-2220 *E-mail:* film@ livefree.nh.gov *Web Site:* www.visitnh.gov/film, pg 973

New Harbinger Publications, 5674 Shattuck Ave, Oakland, CA 94609 *Tel:* 510-652-0215 *Toll Free Tel:* 800-748-6273 *Fax:* 510-652-5472 *E-mail:* customerservice@newharbinger.com *Web Site:* www.newharbinger.com, pg 839

New Horizon Studios, 202 E 42 St, New York, NY 10017 *Tel:* 212-490-0355, pg 839

New Horizons Computer Learning Centers Inc, 100 Four Falls Corporate Ctr, Suite 408, Conshohocken, PA 19428-4132 *Tel:* 484-567-3000 *Toll Free Tel:* 888-236-3625 *Web Site:* www.newhorizons.com, pg 839

New Jersey Film Festival, Rutgers University, 018 Loree Hall, 72 Lipman Dr, New Brunswick, NJ 08901-1414 *Tel:* 848-932-8482 *Fax:* 732-932-1935 *E-mail:* njmac@aol.com; njmac12@gmail.com *Web Site:* www.njfilmfest.com, pg 997

New Jersey Motion Picture & Television Commission, 153 Halsey St, 5th fl, Newark, NJ 07102-2807 *Tel:* 973-648-6279 *Fax:* 973-648-7350 *E-mail:* njfilm@sos.nj.gov *Web Site:* www.film.nj.gov, pg 973

New Leaf Distributing Co, 401 Thornton Rd, Lithia Springs, GA 30122-1557 *Tel:* 770-948-7845 *Toll Free Tel:* 800-326-2665 (orders) *Fax:* 770-944-2313 *Toll Free Fax:* 800-326-1066 *E-mail:* customerservice@ newleaf-dist.com *Web Site:* newleaf-dist.com, pg 839

New Letters on the Air, c/o University of Missouri, Kansas City, 5101 Rockhill Rd, Kansas City, MO 64110 *Tel:* 816-235-1159; 816-235-1168 *Fax:* 816-235-2611 *E-mail:* radio@newletters.org *Web Site:* www.newletters.org, pg 839

New Life Communications Inc, 905 Hwy 71 NE, Willmar, MN 56201-2654 *Tel:* 320-235-6404 *Toll Free Tel:* 800-233-6470 *Fax:* 320-235-6418 *E-mail:* nlc@ newlifecomm.com *Web Site:* www.newlifecomm.com, pg 839

New Line Cinema, 116 N Robertson Blvd, Suite 200, Los Angeles, CA 90048 *Tel:* 310-854-5811 *Fax:* 310-854-1824 *Web Site:* www.warnerbros.com/studio/ divisions/new-line-cinema, pg 839

New London Media, 78 Washington St, New London, CT 06320 *Tel:* 860-961-6300 *Web Site:* www. andrewclydebell.com, pg 839

New Mexico Film Office, Joseph M Montoya Bldg, 1st fl, 1100 St Francis Dr, Suite 1213, Santa Fe, NM 87505 *Tel:* 505-476-5600 *Fax:* 505-476-5601 *E-mail:* info@nmfilm.com *Web Site:* www.nmfilm. com, pg 973

New Orleans Film Festival, 1215 Prytania St, Suite 423, New Orleans, LA 70130 *Tel:* 504-309-6633 *E-mail:* noff@neworleansfilmsociety.org *Web Site:* neworleansfilmsociety.org/festival, pg 997

New Wave Entertainment, 2660 W Olive Ave, Burbank, CA 91505 *Tel:* 818-295-5000 *E-mail:* biz@nwe.com *Web Site:* nwe.com, pg 839

New World Records, 20 Jay St, Suite 1001, Brooklyn, NY 11201 *Tel:* 212-290-1680 *Fax:* 646-224-9638 *E-mail:* info@newworldrecords.org *Web Site:* www. newworldrecords.org, pg 840

New York Audio Productions, 344 W 38 St, 6th fl, New York, NY 10018 *Tel:* 212-244-1114 *Fax:* 212-243-7210 *E-mail:* info@nyaudio.com *Web Site:* www. nyaudio.com, pg 840

New York Camera & Video, 1139 Street Rd, Southampton, PA 18966 *Tel:* 215-357-6222 *E-mail:* rentals@nycv.com *Web Site:* www.nycv.com, pg 840

New York City Mayor's Office of Film, Theatre & Broadcasting, Ed Sullivan Theatre Bldg, 6th fl, 1697 Broadway, New York, NY 10019 *Tel:* 212-489-6710 *Fax:* 212-307-6237 *Web Site:* www.nyc.gov/mome, pg 974

New York Emmy® Awards, 450 Seventh Ave, Suite 808, New York, NY 10123 *Tel:* 212-459-3630 *E-mail:* awards@nyemmys.org *Web Site:* www. nyemmys.org, pg 997

New York Festivals® International Advertising Awards, 260 W 39 St, 10th fl, New York, NY 10018 *Tel:* 212-643-4800 *Fax:* 212-643-0170 *E-mail:* info@ newyorkfestivals.com *Web Site:* advertising. newyorkfestivals.com; www.newyorkfestivals.com, pg 998

New York Festivals® International Radio Program Awards, 260 W 39 St, 10th fl, New York, NY 10018 *Tel:* 212-643-4800 *Fax:* 212-643-0170 *E-mail:* info@ newyorkfestivals.com *Web Site:* radio.newyorkfestivals. com; www.newyorkfestivals.com/radio, pg 998

New York Festivals® International TV & Film Awards, 260 W 39 St, 10th fl, New York, NY 10018 *Tel:* 212-643-4800 *Fax:* 212-643-0170 *E-mail:* info@newyorkfestivals.com *Web Site:* tvfilm. newyorkfestivals.com; www.newyorkfestivals.com/ tvfilm, pg 998

New York Film Festival, 70 Lincoln Center Plaza, New York, NY 10023-6595 *Tel:* 212-875-5610; 212-875-5367 (cust serv) *Web Site:* www.filmlinc.org, pg 998

New York Film/Video Council (NYFVC), PO Box 2092, New York, NY 10021 *E-mail:* nyfvcrsvp@gmail.com *Web Site:* www.nyfvc.org, pg 960

The New York Historical Society, 170 Central Park W, New York, NY 10024 *Tel:* 212-873-3400 *Fax:* 212-787-9474 *Web Site:* www.nyhistory.org, pg 840

New York Production Alliance (NYPA), PO Box 383, Village Station, NY 10014 *E-mail:* info@nypa.org *Web Site:* www.nypa.org, pg 960

New York Sound Inc, 166 Fifth Ave, No 6, New York, NY 10010 *Tel:* 917-523-0770 *E-mail:* nysnd@mac. com *Web Site:* www.newyorksound.net, pg 840

New York State Governor's Office for Motion Picture & Television Development (MPTV), 633 Third Ave, 37th fl, New York, NY 10017 *Tel:* 212-803-2330 *E-mail:* nyfilm@esd.ny.gov *Web Site:* esd.ny. gov/industries/tv-and-film, pg 974

The New York Times Photo Archive, The New York Times Co, 620 Eighth Ave, New York, NY 10018 *E-mail:* nytlg-sales@nytimes.com *Web Site:* nytlicensing.com, pg 840

NPR Distribution Services, 1111 N Capitol St NE, Washington, DC 20002 *Tel:* 202-513-2624 *Fax:* 202-513-3035 *E-mail:* linkup@npr.org *Web Site:* nprds.org, pg 843

NRD Static Control LLC, 2937 Alt Blvd, Grand Island, NY 14072-1285 *Tel:* 716-773-7634 *Toll Free Tel:* 800-525-8076 (US only) *E-mail:* sales@nrdllc.com *Web Site:* www.nrdstaticcontrol.com, pg 843

NTi Audio Inc, 7405 SW Tech Center Dr, Suite 130, Tigard, OR 97223 *Tel:* 503-684-7050 *E-mail:* americas@nti-audio.com *Web Site:* www.nti-audio.com, pg 843

NTS ProMedia, 1033 Elm Hill Pike, Nashville, TN 37210 *Tel:* 615-254-8178 *Toll Free Tel:* 800-591-4804 *E-mail:* sales@ntspromedia.com *Web Site:* www.ntspromedia.com, pg 843

Nuance Communications Inc, One Wayside Rd, Burlington, MA 01803 *Tel:* 781-565-5000 *Toll Free Tel:* 800-654-1187 (cust serv) *Fax:* 781-565-5001 *Web Site:* www.nuance.com, pg 843

Numark Industries LP, 200 Scenic View Dr, Cumberland, RI 02864 *Tel:* 401-658-3131 *E-mail:* info@numark.com *Web Site:* www.numark.com, pg 843

NuMynd Studios, 915 Twin Elms Ct, Nashville, TN 37210 *Tel:* 615-259-1143 *Fax:* 615-259-1141 *E-mail:* hello@numyndstudios.com *Web Site:* www.numyndstudios.com, pg 843

NVerzion Inc, 296 E 3900 S, Salt Lake City, UT 84107-1531 *Tel:* 801-293-8420 *E-mail:* sales@nverzion.com *Web Site:* www.nverzion.com, pg 843

NWT Arts Council, Community Programs Office, PO Box 1320, Yellowknife, NT X1A 2L9, Canada *Tel:* 867-767-9347 (ext 71474) *Toll Free Tel:* 877-445-2787 *Fax:* 867-873-0205 *Web Site:* www.nwtartscouncil.ca, pg 998

NYSCA/NYFA Artist Fellowships, 20 Jay St, 7th fl, Suite 740, Brooklyn, NY 11201 *Tel:* 212-366-6900 *Fax:* 212-366-1778 *E-mail:* fellowships@nyfa.org *Web Site:* www.nyfa.org, pg 999

Nystrom Education, 10200 Jefferson Blvd, Culver City, CA 90232 *Tel:* 310-839-2436 *Toll Free Tel:* 800-421-4246 *Fax:* 310-839-2249 *Toll Free Fax:* 800-944-5432 *E-mail:* customerservice@nystromeducation.com; access@nystromeducation.com *Web Site:* www.nystromeducation.com, pg 844

Oakland Film Office, One Frank H Ogawa Plaza, 9th fl, Oakland, CA 94612 *Tel:* 510-238-4734 *E-mail:* filmoakland@filmoakland.com *Web Site:* www.filmoakland.com, pg 967

OAP Audio Products, 1000 Peachtree Industrial Blvd, Suite 6-132, Suwanee, GA 30024 *Tel:* 770-945-1033 *Fax:* 678-765-7198 *E-mail:* sales@oapaudio.com *Web Site:* www.oapaudio.com, pg 844

Oasis Disc Manufacturing, 7905 N Crescent Blvd, Delair, NJ 08110 *Toll Free Tel:* 888-296-2747 *Fax:* 856-661-3450 *Toll Free Fax:* 866-929-8402 *E-mail:* info@oasiscd.com *Web Site:* www.oasiscd.com, pg 844

Ocala/Marion County Visitors & Convention Bureau, 109 W Silver Springs Blvd, Ocala, FL 34475 *Tel:* 352-438-2800 *Toll Free Tel:* 888-FL-OCALA (356-2252) *Fax:* 352-438-2801 *E-mail:* exploreocalamarion@marioncountyfl.org *Web Site:* www.ocalamarion.com, pg 969

O'Connor Engineering Labs, 2701 N Ontario St, Burbank, CA 91504 *Tel:* 818-847-8666 *Fax:* 818-847-1205 *E-mail:* usasales@ocon.com; info@ocon.com *Web Site:* www.ocon.com, pg 844

Oddball Films Inc, 275 Capp St, San Francisco, CA 94110 *Tel:* 415-558-8112 *E-mail:* info@oddballfilms.com *Web Site:* www.oddballfilms.com, pg 844

Odyssey Productions Inc, 2800 NW Thurman St, Portland, OR 97210 *Tel:* 503-223-3480 *Fax:* 503-223-3493 *E-mail:* info@odysseypro.com *Web Site:* www.odysseypro.com, pg 844

Office of Cable Television, Film, Music & Entertainment (OCTFME), Brentwood Broadcast Ctr, 1899 Nine St NE, Washington, DC 20018 *Tel:* 202-727-6608 *Fax:* 202-727-3246 *E-mail:* film@dc.gov *Web Site:* www.film.dc.gov, pg 968

OGM Production Music, 6464 Sunset Blvd, Suite 920, Hollywood, CA 90028 *Tel:* 323-461-2701 *Toll Free Tel:* 800-421-4163 (sales) *Fax:* 323-461-1543 *E-mail:* ogmmusic@gmail.com *Web Site:* www.olegeorgmusic.com, pg 844

Ohio HD Video, 350 W Johnston Rd, Gahanna, OH 43230 *Tel:* 614-656-1162 *Fax:* 614-656-4343 *E-mail:* info@ohiohdvideo.com *Web Site:* ohiohdvideo.com, pg 844

Okanagan Film Commission, 1450 KLO Rd, Kelowna, BC V1W 3Z4, Canada *Tel:* 250-717-0087 *Fax:* 250-868-0512 *E-mail:* info@okanaganfilm.com *Web Site:* www.okanaganfilm.com, pg 978

O'Keefe Communications Inc, 4301 Connecticut Ave NW, Suite 200, Washington, DC 20008-2304 *Tel:* 202-363-2101 *E-mail:* info@okeefecom.com *Web Site:* www.okeefecom.com, pg 844

Oklahoma Film & Music Office, 900 N Stiles Ave, Oklahoma City, OK 73104 *Tel:* 405-230-8440 *Toll Free Tel:* 800-766-3456 *Fax:* 405-201-4561 *Web Site:* okfilmmusic.org, pg 975

Oklahoma Sound Corp, 149 Entin Rd, Clifton, NJ 07014 *Tel:* 973-594-9000 *Toll Free Tel:* 800-261-4112 *Fax:* 973-594-9339 *Web Site:* www.nationalpublicseating.com, pg 844

Old Army Press (OAP), 218 Alabaster Way, Johnstown, CO 80534 *Tel:* 970-587-9530; 970-420-8193 (cell) *E-mail:* oldarmypress@msn.com *Web Site:* oldarmypress.com, pg 844

The Old Rhinebeck Aerodome®, 9 Norton Rd, Red Hook, NY 12571 *Tel:* 845-752-3200 *Fax:* 845-758-6481 *E-mail:* info@oldrhinebeck.org *Web Site:* www.oldrhinebeck.org, pg 844

Old School Cameras, 5625 Melrose Ave, Hollywood, CA 90038 *Tel:* 818-847-1555 *E-mail:* sdrentals@oldschoolcameras.com *Web Site:* www.oldschoolcameras.com, pg 844

Olden Camera & Lens Co Inc, 1263 Broadway, 4th fl, New York, NY 10001-3593 *Tel:* 212-226-3727, pg 845

Olden Lighting, 2008 Alexander Ave, Austin, TX 78722 *Tel:* 512-416-8080 *Fax:* 512-416-8096 *E-mail:* rental@oldenlighting.com; sales@oldenlighting.com *Web Site:* www.oldenlighting.com, pg 845

Olsen Audio Group Inc, 7845 E Evans Rd, Scottsdale, AZ 85260-2919 *Tel:* 480-998-7140 *Fax:* 480-998-7192 *E-mail:* web-info2@olsenaudio.com *Web Site:* www.phototech.tv, pg 845

Olson Visual Inc, 13000 Weber Way, Hawthorne, CA 90250 *Tel:* 310-355-1681 *Toll Free Tel:* 800-480-6643 *Fax:* 310-263-6980 *E-mail:* info@olsonvisual.com *Web Site:* olsonvisual.com, pg 845

Olympic Case Co, 9110 King Palm Dr, Suite 101, Tampa, FL 33619 *Tel:* 813-246-5525 *Toll Free Tel:* 888-246-5525 *Fax:* 813-246-4748 *E-mail:* info@olycase.com *Web Site:* www.olycase.com, pg 845

Olympusat, 477 S Rosemary Ave, Suite 306, West Palm Beach, FL 33401 *Tel:* 561-472-2859 *E-mail:* info@olympusat.com *Web Site:* www.olympusat.com, pg 845

Omega Broadcast Group, 817 W Howard Lane, Austin, TX 78753 *Tel:* 512-251-7778 *Fax:* 512-251-8633 *E-mail:* rental@omegabroadcast.com; sales@omegabroadcast.com *Web Site:* www.omegabroadcast.com, pg 845

Omega Media Group Inc, PO Box 924499, Peachtree Corners, GA 30010 *Web Site:* www.omegamediagroup.com, pg 845

Omega Productions, 456 Commerce St, Palacios, TX 77465 *Tel:* 214-891-9585 *E-mail:* getinfo@omegalive.com *Web Site:* www.omegalive.com, pg 845

Omega Recording Studios, 12712 Rock Creek Mill Rd, Suite 14A, Rockville, MD 20852 *Tel:* 301-230-9100 *Fax:* 301-230-9103 *Web Site:* omegastudios.com, pg 845

OmegaBrandess Distribution, 626 Hanover Pike, Suite 102, Hampstead, MD 21074-2036 *Tel:* 410-374-3250 *Fax:* 410-374-3184 *E-mail:* customerservice@omegabrandess.com *Web Site:* www.omegabrandess.com, pg 845

Omni Intercommunications Inc, 2825 Wilcrest Dr, Suite 400, Houston, TX 77042 *Tel:* 713-781-2188 *Toll Free Tel:* 800-777-2304 *Fax:* 713-781-2315 *E-mail:* info@omni-inter.com *Web Site:* www.omni-inter.com, pg 845

Omni International Inc, 4928 Crosshill Lane, Northport, AL 35473, pg 845

OMNI Productions, PO Box 302, Carmel, IN 46082-0302 *Tel:* 317-846-2345 *Fax:* 317-846-6664 *E-mail:* omni@omniproductions.com *Web Site:* www.omniproductions.com, pg 845

Omnia Audio, 1241 Superior Ave E, Cleveland, OH 44114 *Tel:* 216-241-7225 *Fax:* 216-241-4103 *E-mail:* social@telosalliance.com *Web Site:* www.telosalliance.com/omnia, pg 845

OmniMount Systems, 4409 E Baseline Rd, Suite 130, Phoenix, AZ 85042 *Tel:* 480-829-8000 *Toll Free Tel:* 800-MOUNT-IT (668-6848) *Fax:* 480-756-9000 *E-mail:* info@omnimount.com *Web Site:* www.omnimount.com, pg 845

Omnirax Furniture Co, PO Box 1792, Sausalito, CA 94966-1792 *Tel:* 415-332-3392 *Toll Free Tel:* 800-332-3393 *E-mail:* info@omnirax.com *Web Site:* omnirax.com, pg 845

OMNISound Recording Studio, 1806 Division St, Nashville, TN 37203 *Tel:* 615-482-1151 *Fax:* 615-321-5528 *Web Site:* www.omnisoundstudios.com, pg 845

On-Line Productions, 2515 Hawthorne Dr, Atlanta, GA 30345 *Tel:* 404-634-5572 *E-mail:* esptv@mindspring.com *Web Site:* on-lineproductions.com, pg 845

On Location North Carolina, 502 S West St, No 104, Raleigh, NC 27601 *Tel:* 919-755-9488; 919-349-GRIP (349-4747, cell) *Toll Free Tel:* 888-469-GRIP (469-4747) *E-mail:* info@onlocation-nc.com *Web Site:* www.onlocation-nc.com, pg 846

ON Services, a GES Company, 6779 Crescent Dr, Norcross, GA 30071 *Tel:* 770-457-0966 *Toll Free Tel:* 800-967-2419 *Fax:* 770-451-7925 *E-mail:* service@oneventservices.com; atlanta@oneventservices.com *Web Site:* www.oneventservices.com, pg 846

On Site Video, PO Box 1865, Palatine, IL 60078-1865 *Tel:* 847-980-9808 *Fax:* 847-358-8697 *E-mail:* producersvideo@hotmail.com, pg 846

On-Site Video, 325 E Southern Ave, Suite 110, Tempe, AZ 85282 *Tel:* 480-967-5062 *Web Site:* www.on-sitevideo.com, pg 846

On Stage Visuals, 420 Baker St, Lansing, MI 48910-1543 *Tel:* 517-393-7800 *Toll Free Tel:* 800-373-LIVE (373-5483) *Fax:* 517-481-2482 *E-mail:* support@onstagevisuals.com *Web Site:* www.onstagevisuals.com, pg 846

On-Trax Inc, 3052 Vine St, Riverside, CA 92507 *Tel:* 951-786-3921 *Fax:* 951-786-3922 *Web Site:* www.on-trax.com, pg 846

Oncourt Offcourt Ltd, 7011 Gaston Pkwy, Dallas, TX 75214 *Tel:* 214-823-3078 *Toll Free Tel:* 888-TENNIS-11 (366-4711) *Fax:* 214-823-3082 *E-mail:* info@oncourtoffcourt.com *Web Site:* www.oncourtoffcourt.com, pg 846

168 Film Festival, PO Box 6184, Burbank, CA 91510 *Tel:* 818-557-8507 *Fax:* 818-942-6076 *E-mail:* info@168project.com *Web Site:* www.168film.com/festival, pg 999

One Stop CD Shop LLC, 3149 S State St, Salt Lake City, UT 84115 *Tel:* 801-303-6100 *Fax:* 801-303-6129 *E-mail:* info@1stopcdshop.com *Web Site:* 1stopcdshop.com, pg 846

One Touch Systems Inc, 2528 Qume Dr, Unit 14, San Jose, CA 95131 *Tel:* 408-436-4643 *E-mail:* info@onetouchsys.com *Web Site:* www.onetouchsys.com, pg 846

Onkyo USA Corp, 18 Park Way, Upper Saddle River, NJ 07458 *Tel:* 201-785-2600 *Toll Free Tel:* 800-229-1687 *Web Site:* www.onkyousa.com, pg 846

OnLine Power Inc, 14000 S Broadway, Los Angeles, CA 90061 *Tel:* 323-721-5017 *Toll Free Tel:* 800-227-8899 *Fax:* 323-721-3929 *E-mail:* sales@onlinepower.com *Web Site:* www.onlinepower.com, pg 846

ONstage, 567 Ocoee Business Pkwy, Ocoee, FL 34761 *Tel:* 407-654-5822 *Fax:* 407-654-5826 *E-mail:* orlando@oneventservices.com *Web Site:* www.oneventservices.com, pg 846

Onstage Systems, 8721 Forney Rd, Dallas, TX 75227 *Tel:* 972-686-4488 *Fax:* 972-686-7732 *E-mail:* info@onstagesystems.com *Web Site:* www.onstagesystems.com, pg 846

Ontario Creates, South Tower, Suite 501, 175 Bloor St E, Toronto, ON M4W 3R8, Canada *Tel:* 416-314-6858 *Fax:* 416-314-6876 *E-mail:* reception@ontariocreates.ca *Web Site:* www.ontariocreates.ca, pg 978

ooLite Media LLC, 3300 Graf St, Unit 4, Bozeman, MT 59715 *Tel:* 406-570-6474 *E-mail:* info@oolitemedia.com *Web Site:* oolitemedia.com, pg 846

Opamp Labs Inc, 1033 N Sycamore Ave, Los Angeles, CA 90038 *Tel:* 323-934-3566 *Fax:* 323-462-6490 *E-mail:* opamplabs@gmail.com *Web Site:* www.opamplabs.com, pg 846

Open Control Architecture Alliance (OCA Alliance), 23117 39 Ave SE, Bothell, WA 98021 *Tel:* 425-870-6574 *Web Site:* ocaalliance.com, pg 960

Open Media Foundation, 700 Kalamath St, Denver, CO 80204 *Tel:* 720-222-0159 *Fax:* 303-534-5098 *E-mail:* info@openmediafoundation.org *Web Site:* openmediafoundation.org; denveropenmedia.org, pg 846

OpenText Corp, 275 Frank Tompa Dr, Waterloo, ON N2L 0A1, Canada *Tel:* 519-888-7111 *Toll Free Tel:* 800-499-6544 *Fax:* 519-888-0677 *Web Site:* www.opentext.com, pg 846

Oppenheimer Camera Products, 7400 Third Ave S, Seattle, WA 98108-4143 *Tel:* 206-467-8666 *Toll Free Tel:* 877-467-8666 *Fax:* 206-467-9165 *Web Site:* oppenheimercameraproducts.com, pg 847

Opterna, a Belden brand, 44901 Falcon Place, Suite 116, Sterling, VA 20166-9531 *Tel:* 703-653-1100 *Toll Free Tel:* 800-248-9004 *Fax:* 703-803-8313 *Web Site:* www.opterna.com, pg 847

Opti-Case Inc, 1175 CR 481 W, Henderson, TX 75654 *Tel:* 903-657-5666 *Toll Free Tel:* 800-637-6635 *Fax:* 903-657-6030 *E-mail:* sales@opti-case.net *Web Site:* www.opti-case.net, pg 847

Opticomm-EMCORE, 2015 Chestnut St, Alhambra, CA 91803 *Tel:* 626-293-3400; 626-293-3670 (west coast team); 540-626-3381 (east coast team) *Toll Free Tel:* 800-8OPTICOMM (867-8426) *Fax:* 626-293-3427 *E-mail:* video-sales@emcore.com *Web Site:* www.opticomm.com, pg 847

Optics 1 Inc, 2 Cooper Lane, Bedford, NH 03110 *Tel:* 603-296-0469 *Fax:* 603-296-0473 *E-mail:* info@optics1.com *Web Site:* www.optics1.com, pg 847

Optikinetics Ltd - The Americas, 11211 Air Park Rd, Suite 1, Ashland, VA 23005 *Tel:* 804-752-2570 *Toll Free Tel:* 800-575-6784 *Fax:* 804-752-2888 *E-mail:* optius@optikinetics.com *Web Site:* www.optikinetics.com, pg 847

The Optikon Corp, 1099 Guelph St, Kitchener, ON N2B 2E4, Canada *Tel:* 519-745-4115 *Fax:* 519-745-6922 *E-mail:* info@optikon.ca *Web Site:* www.optikon.ca, pg 847

Optimus, 161 E Grand Ave, Chicago, IL 60611 *Tel:* 312-321-0880 *Web Site:* www.optimus.com, pg 847

Optisonics Productions, 311 South Pkwy, Clifton, NJ 07014 *Tel:* 973-458-0951 *E-mail:* optisonics@aol.com *Web Site:* www.optisonics.com, pg 847

Optronics®, 175 Cremona Dr, Goleta, CA 93117 *Tel:* 805-968-3568 *Toll Free Tel:* 800-796-8909 *Fax:* 805-968-0933 *E-mail:* oeinfo@optronics.com; sales@optronics.com *Web Site:* www.optronics.com, pg 847

Opulen Studios, 1309 S Flower St, Los Angeles, CA 90015 *Tel:* 310-867-5023; 310-902-6996 *E-mail:* info@opulenstudios.com *Web Site:* opulenstudios.com, pg 847

Oral Tradition Sound & Music, PO Box 51155, Pacific Grove, CA 93950-6155 *Tel:* 831-372-0352 *Toll Free Tel:* 800-779-1116 (orders), pg 847

Orange County Film Commission, 53 La Costa Ct, Laguna Beach, CA 92651 *Tel:* 949-246-9704 *Web Site:* www.filmorangecounty.org, pg 966

Orange County Sound Stage, 17518 Von Karman Ave, Irvine, CA 92614 *Tel:* 714-598-6557 *E-mail:* sm@ocsoundstage.com *Web Site:* orangecountysoundstage.com, pg 847

Orban, 7209 Browning Rd, Pennsauken, NJ 08109 *Tel:* 856-719-9900 *E-mail:* info@orban.com; sales@orban.com *Web Site:* www.orban.com, pg 847

Oregon Film & Video Office, 123 NE Third Ave, Suite 210, Portland, OR 97232 *Tel:* 971-254-4020 *E-mail:* shoot@oregonfilm.org *Web Site:* www.oregonfilm.org, pg 975

Orevox USA Corp, 240 N Puente Ave, City of Industry, CA 91746-2303 *Tel:* 626-336-0516 *Fax:* 626-336-3748 *Web Site:* www.dynavox.com, pg 847

Oriental Records Inc, PO Box 387, Williston Park, NY 11596-0387 *Tel:* 516-746-0140 *Fax:* 516-747-4285 *E-mail:* info@orientalrecords.com; orientalcd@aol.com *Web Site:* www.orientalrecords.com, pg 847

Origin Instruments Corp, 854 Greenview Dr, Grand Prairie, TX 75050-2438 *Tel:* 972-606-8740 *Fax:* 972-606-8741 *E-mail:* support@orin.com; marketing@orin.com *Web Site:* www.orin.com, pg 848

Original Cast Records, PO Box 496, Georgetown, CT 06829-0496 *Tel:* 203-544-8288 *Fax:* 203-544-8288 *E-mail:* originalcast@aol.com *Web Site:* www.originalcastrecords.com; footlight.com, pg 848

Orion Software, 6000 Cote-des-Neiges, Suite 240, Montreal, QC H3S 1Z8, Canada *Tel:* 514-484-9661 *Toll Free Tel:* 877-755-2012 *Fax:* 514-484-1339 *E-mail:* info@orion-soft.com *Web Site:* www.orion-soft.com, pg 848

Orlando Film Commission, 301 E Pine St, Suite 900, Orlando, FL 32801 *Tel:* 407-422-7159 *Fax:* 407-425-6428 *E-mail:* info@filmorlando.com *Web Site:* filmorlando.com, pg 969

Orlando Special Effects, 14222 Lake Mary Jane Rd, Orlando, FL 32832 *Tel:* 407-648-1867 *Web Site:* www.orlandospfx.com, pg 848

Rob Orr Productions Ltd, 1336 Pine St, Glenview, IL 60025 *Tel:* 847-724-5228 *E-mail:* rob@roborrproductions.com *Web Site:* www.roborrproductions.com, pg 848

Orvac Electronics, 1645 E Orangethorpe Ave, Fullerton, CA 92831 *Tel:* 714-871-1020 *E-mail:* myorvac@orvac.com *Web Site:* www.orvac.com, pg 848

OSA International Inc, 537 N Edgewood Ave, Wood Dale, IL 60191 *Tel:* 630-227-1008 *Toll Free Tel:* 877-OSA-INTL (672-4685) *Toll Free Fax:* 866-OSA-FAX2 (672-3292) *E-mail:* connect@osacorp.com *Web Site:* www.osacorp.com, pg 848

Osho Viha Information Center & Book Distributors, PO Box 352, Mill Valley, CA 94942-0352 *Tel:* 415-472-5381 *Toll Free Tel:* 866-856-7019 *E-mail:* oshoviha@oshoviha.org *Web Site:* www.oshoviha.org, pg 848

Osram Sylvania Inc, 200 Ballardvale St, Wilmington, MA 01887 *Tel:* 978-570-3000 *Toll Free Tel:* 800-842-7010 *Web Site:* www.sylvania.com, pg 848

Osram Sylvania Ltd/Ltee, 2001 Drew Rd, Mississauga, ON L5S 1S4, Canada *Tel:* 905-673-6171 *Toll Free Tel:* 800-LIGHTBULB (544-4828) *Fax:* 905-671-5584 *Web Site:* www.sylvania.com, pg 848

Ostergaard Acoustical Associates, 200 Executive Dr, Suite 350, West Orange, NJ 07052 *Tel:* 973-731-7002 *Fax:* 973-731-6680 *E-mail:* info@acousticalconsultant.com *Web Site:* www.acousticalconsultant.com, pg 848

Osum Event Rentals, 730 Andover Park E, Tukwila, WA 98188 *Tel:* 206-575-5055 *E-mail:* info@osumeventrentals.com *Web Site:* osumeventrentals.com, pg 848

OSV Studios, 29605 Lorain Rd, North Olmsted, OH 44070 *Tel:* 440-779-1900 *Web Site:* www.osvstudios.com, pg 848

OTR Studios, PO Box 874, Belmont, CA 94002 *Tel:* 650-595-8475 *E-mail:* info@otrstudios.com *Web Site:* www.otrstudios.com, pg 848

Ottawa International Animation Festival, 2 Daly Ave, Suite 120, Ottawa, ON K1N 6E2, Canada *Tel:* 613-232-8769 *Fax:* 613-232-6315 *E-mail:* info@animationfestival.ca; entries@animationfestival.ca *Web Site:* www.animationfestival.ca, pg 999

Our Sunday Visitor Inc, 200 Noll Plaza, Huntington, IN 46750 *Tel:* 260-356-8400 *Toll Free Tel:* 800-348-2440 *Fax:* 260-356-8472 *E-mail:* osvsales@osv.com *Web Site:* www.osv.com, pg 849

Out of the BLUE Media, 1413 Brenda Lane, Allen, TX 75002 *Tel:* 469-853-9015 *Web Site:* www.outofthebluemedia.com, pg 849

Outfest Los Angeles LGBT Film Festival, 3470 Wilshire Blvd, Suite 935, Los Angeles, CA 90010 *Tel:* 213-480-7088 *Fax:* 213-480-7099 *E-mail:* outfest@outfest.org *Web Site:* www.outfest.org, pg 999

Outland Technology Inc, 38190 Commercial Ct, Slidell, LA 70458 *Tel:* 985-847-1104 *Fax:* 985-847-1106 *E-mail:* sales@outlandtech.com *Web Site:* www.outlandtech.com, pg 849

Outside The Box Interactive LLC, 150 Bay St, Suite 706, Jersey City, NJ 07302 *Tel:* 201-610-0625 *E-mail:* office@outboxin.com *Web Site:* www.outboxin.com, pg 849

Outwater Plastics Industries Inc, 24 River Rd, Bogota, NJ 07603 *Tel:* 201-498-8750 *Toll Free Tel:* 800-631-8375 *Toll Free Fax:* 800-888-3315 *E-mail:* info@outwaterplastics.com; customerservice@outwaterplastics.com *Web Site:* www.outwater.com, pg 849

Oval Window Audio, 33 Wildflower Ct, Nederland, CO 80466 *Tel:* 303-447-3607 *Fax:* 303-447-3607 *E-mail:* info@ovalwindowaudio.com *Web Site:* www.ovalwindowaudio.com, pg 849

OWI Inc, 17141 Kingsview Ave, Carson, CA 90746 *Tel:* 310-515-1900 *Toll Free Tel:* 800-638-1694 *Fax:* 310-515-1606 *E-mail:* info@owi-inc.com *Web Site:* www.owi-inc.com, pg 849

Oxford Film Commission, 1013 Jackson Ave E, Oxford, MS 38655 *Tel:* 662-232-2477 *Toll Free Tel:* 800-758-9177 *E-mail:* tourism@visitoxfordms.com *Web Site:* visitoxfordms.com, pg 972

Ozam Productions Inc, 1516 Equestrian Rd, Ozark, MO 65721 *Tel:* 417-866-3232 *Web Site:* ozam.com, pg 849

Pace Systems, 301 Hickory Ave, Harahan, LA 70123 *Tel:* 504-837-4224 *Toll Free Tel:* 800-722-3797 *Fax:* 504-837-4307 *E-mail:* info@pacesys.com, pg 849

PACE Worldwide, 346 Grant Rd, Vass, NC 28394 *Tel:* 910-695-7223 *Toll Free Tel:* 877-882-7223 *Fax:* 910-695-1594 *E-mail:* support@paceworldwide.com; sales@paceworldwide.com *Web Site:* www.paceworldwide.com, pg 849

Pacific Grip & Lighting Inc, 6550 NE Portland Hwy, Portland, OR 97218 *Tel:* 503-233-4747 *Fax:* 503-233-5830 *Web Site:* www.pacific-grip.com, pg 849

Pacific Light Studios, 265 Caspian Dr, Sunnyvale, CA 94089 *Tel:* 408-541-1800 *E-mail:* info1@pacificlightstudios.com *Web Site:* www.pacificlightstudios.com, pg 849

Pacific Media, PO Box 9489, Canoga Park, CA 91309 *Tel:* 805-418-7552 *E-mail:* info@pac-media.com *Web Site:* www.pac-media.com, pg 849

Pacific Multimedia Inc, 4917 Seaview Way, Everett, WA 98203 *Tel:* 425-347-4110 *Toll Free Tel:* 888-373-8273 *Web Site:* www.pacmultimedia.com, pg 849

Pacific Radio Electronics, 3031 Thornton Ave, Burbank, CA 91504 *Tel:* 818-556-4177 *Toll Free Tel:* 800-634-9476 *Fax:* 818-556-4185 *E-mail:* sales@pacrad.com *Web Site:* www.pacrad.com, pg 849

Pacific Video Image, 9065 E Rosecrans Ave, Bellflower, CA 90706 *Tel:* 562-634-4200 *Fax:* 562-634-4700 *Web Site:* www.pvideo.com, pg 849

Pacific Video Products Inc, 14312 Franklin Ave, Suite 100, Tustin, CA 92780 *Tel:* 714-508-2750 *Toll Free Tel:* 800-576-0060 *Fax:* 714-508-2136 *E-mail:* tvink@pacvideo.com *Web Site:* www.pacvideo.com, pg 849

Pacifica Radio Archives, 3729 Cahuenga Blvd W, North Hollywood, CA 91604 *Tel:* 818-506-1077 *Toll Free Tel:* 800-735-0230 *Fax:* 818-506-1084 *E-mail:* pacarchive@aol.com *Web Site:* www.pacificaradioarchives.org, pg 849

Pal Productions Inc, 13751 Lake City Way, Suite 208, Seattle, WA 98125 *Tel:* 206-361-9366 *Web Site:* www.paladventurevideos.com, pg 850

Palace Costume & Prop Co, 835 N Fairfax Ave, Hollywood, CA 90046 *Tel:* 323-651-5458 *Fax:* 323-658-7133 *E-mail:* rentals@palacecostume.com *Web Site:* www.palacecostume.com, pg 850

Palace Production Center, 29 N Main St, South Norwalk, CT 06854 *Tel:* 203-853-1740 *Fax:* 203-855-9608 *Web Site:* www.palaceproductioncenter.com, pg 850

Palace Productions MediaVision, 29 N Main St, Norwalk, CT 06854 *Tel:* 203-523-0602; 203-523-0604 *Web Site:* cpbn.org/palace-productions-media-vision, pg 850

Palardo Productions, 1807 Taft Ave, Suite 4, Hollywood, CA 90028 *Tel:* 323-469-8991 *E-mail:* palardo2@msn.com, pg 850

Palm Beach County Film & Television Commission, 1555 Palm Beach Lakes Blvd, Suite 900, West Palm Beach, FL 33401 *Tel:* 561-233-1000 *Toll Free Tel:* 800-745-FILM (745-3456) *Fax:* 561-233-3113 *Web Site:* www.pbfilm.com, pg 970

Palm Springs International Film Festival, 1700 E Tahquitz Canyon Way, Suite 3, Palm Springs, CA 92262 *Tel:* 760-322-2930 *Toll Free Tel:* 800-898-7256 *Fax:* 760-322-4087 *E-mail:* info@psfilmfest.org *Web Site:* www.psfilmfest.org, pg 999

Palmdale Chamber of Commerce, 817 E Avenue Q-9, Palmdale, CA 93550 *Tel:* 661-273-3232 *Fax:* 661-273-8508 *E-mail:* pcc@palmdalechamber.org *Web Site:* www.palmdalechamber.org, pg 967

The Palmer Group, PO Box 1455, New York, NY 10156-1455 *Tel:* 212-532-3880 *E-mail:* info@shellypalmer.com *Web Site:* www.shellypalmer.com, pg 850

Pan African Film & Arts Festival, 6820 La Tijera Blvd, Suite 200, Los Angeles, CA 90045 *Tel:* 310-337-4737 *Fax:* 310-337-4736 *E-mail:* info@paff.org; submissions@paff.org *Web Site:* www.paff.org, pg 999

Panamax, 1800 S McDowell Blvd, 2nd fl, Petaluma, CA 94954 *Tel:* 707-283-5900 (intl) *Toll Free Tel:* 800-472-5555 (US & CN) *Fax:* 707-283-5901 *E-mail:* custrelations@panamax.com *Web Site:* www.panamax.com, pg 850

Panasonic Consumer Electronics Co, 2 Riverfront Plaza, Newark, NJ 07012 *Tel:* 201-348-7066 *Web Site:* www.panasonic.com, pg 850

Panasonic Corporation of North America, 2 Riverfront Plaza, Newark, NJ 07012 *Tel:* 201-348-7000 *Toll Free Tel:* 800-211-7262; 888-275-2595 *Fax:* 201-348-7807 *Web Site:* www.panasonic.com, pg 850

Panasonic Industrial Devices Sales Company of America, 2 Riverfront Plaza, Newark, NJ 07012 *Toll Free Tel:* 800-344-2112 *E-mail:* industrial@us.panasonic.com *Web Site:* na.industrial.panasonic.com, pg 850

Panavid, 210 West Pkwy, Unit 5, Pompton Plains, NJ 07444 *Tel:* 973-831-5655 *E-mail:* info@panavid.com; support@panavid.com *Web Site:* www.panavid.com, pg 850

Panavideo Inc, 347 Marie de l'Incarnation, Quebec, QC G1N 3G9, Canada *Tel:* 418-687-3150 *Toll Free Tel:* 800-463-5076 *Fax:* 418-687-0366 *E-mail:* info@panavideo.ca *Web Site:* www.panavideo.ca, pg 850

Panavision, 6101 Variel Ave, Woodland Hills, CA 91367 *Tel:* 818-316-2100 *E-mail:* panastore@panavision.com *Web Site:* www.panavision.com, pg 850

P&H Crystalite LLC, 800 Belle Terre Pkwy, Palm Coast, FL 32164 *Toll Free Tel:* 800-468-8673 *E-mail:* phcrystalite@gmail.com *Web Site:* phcled.com, pg 850

Pandisc Music Corp, 936 SW First Ave, Suite 349, Miami, FL 33130 *Tel:* 305-557-1914 *Toll Free Fax:* 888-493-7778, pg 851

P&P Studios Inc, 110 Lenox Ave, Suite 210, Stamford, CT 06906 *Tel:* 203-359-9292 *Toll Free Tel:* 888-WEPRODUCE (937-7638) *E-mail:* ppstudios@weproduce.com; info@weproduce.com *Web Site:* www.weproduce.com, pg 851

Pangolin Laser Systems Inc, 9501 Satellite Blvd, Suite 109, Orlando, FL 32837 *Tel:* 407-299-2088 *Toll Free Tel:* 800-PAN-GOLIN (726-4654) *Fax:* 407-299-6066 *E-mail:* contact@pangolin.com *Web Site:* www.pangolin.com, pg 851

Panta Rhei Media Inc, 565 Brown Ave, Turtle Creek, PA 15145 *Tel:* 412-824-8858 *E-mail:* info@panta-rhei.com *Web Site:* panta-rhei.com, pg 851

PAR Inc, 16204 N Florida Ave, Lutz, FL 33549 *Tel:* 813-449-4065 *Toll Free Tel:* 800-331-8378 *Fax:* 813-961-2196 *Toll Free Fax:* 800-727-9329 *E-mail:* cs@parinc.com *Web Site:* www.parinc.com, pg 851

Paradigm Marketing & Creative, 89 N Cooper St, Memphis, TN 38104 *Tel:* 901-685-7703 *E-mail:* info@2dimes.com *Web Site:* www.2dimes.com, pg 851

The Paradise Coast Film Commission, 755 Eighth Ave S, Naples, FL 34102 *Tel:* 239-659-FILM (659-3456) *Web Site:* film.paradisecoast.com, pg 969

Paradise Show & Design Inc, 4653 35 St, Orlando, FL 32811 *Tel:* 407-649-7220 *Fax:* 407-649-7225 *Web Site:* www.paradiseshow.com, pg 851

Paradise Video & Film, 10148 NW 47 St, Sunrise, FL 33351 *Tel:* 954-747-1118 *Fax:* 954-747-3380 *E-mail:* info@paradisevideo.com *Web Site:* www.paradisevideo.com, pg 851

Paradoxal Inc, 103 E Broadway, New York, NY 10012 *Tel:* 212-366-5526; 917-400-4507 (cell) *E-mail:* contact@paradoxal.net *Web Site:* www.paradoxal.net, pg 851

Paramount Motion Pictures Group, 1515 Broadway, 3rd fl, New York, NY 10019 *Tel:* 212-258-6000 *Fax:* 212-846-4315 *Web Site:* www.paramountpictures.com, pg 851

Paramount Pictures Corporation, 5555 Melrose Ave, Los Angeles, CA 90038 *Tel:* 323-956-8398 *Web Site:* www.paramount.com, pg 851

Parasound Products Inc, 2250 McKinnon Ave, San Francisco, CA 94124 *Tel:* 415-397-7100 *Fax:* 415-397-0144 *E-mail:* sales@parasound.com; service@parasound.com *Web Site:* www.parasound.com, pg 851

Park City Film Commission, 1850 Sidewinder Dr, No 320, Park City, UT 84060 *Tel:* 435-649-6100 *Toll Free Tel:* 800-453-1360 *Fax:* 435-649-4132 *Web Site:* visitparkcity.com/film, pg 976

Parker Area Chamber of Commerce, 1217 California Ave, Parker, AZ 85344 *Tel:* 928-669-2174 *Fax:* 928-669-6304 *E-mail:* info@parkeraz.org *Web Site:* www.parkeraz.org, pg 965

Parlights Inc, 1662 Bowmans Farm Rd, Suite 111, Frederick, MD 21701 *Tel:* 301-698-9242 *Fax:* 301-846-0369 *E-mail:* sales@parlights.com *Web Site:* www.parlights.com, pg 851

Partech Lighting Systems Inc, 8711 Reading Rd, Cincinnati, OH 45215 *Tel:* 513-761-5678 *Toll Free Tel:* 800-701-9551 *Fax:* 513-679-8282 *E-mail:* info@partechlighting.com *Web Site:* www.partechlighting.com, pg 851

Parts Express, 725 Pleasant Valley Dr, Springboro, OH 45066-1158 *Tel:* 937-743-3000 *Toll Free Tel:* 866-366-4909; 800-338-0531 (cust serv & tech support) *Fax:* 937-743-1677 *Toll Free Fax:* 866-755-7557 *E-mail:* sales@parts-express.com *Web Site:* www.parts-express.com, pg 851

PASCO, 224 48 St, Brooklyn, NY 11220 *Tel:* 718-833-9100 *E-mail:* pasco2@aol.com, pg 851

Jim Passin Productions, 1900 W Berwyn Ave, Chicago, IL 60640 *Tel:* 773-334-0408, pg 852

Pat Kogan Productions Inc, 4121 42 St, Sunnyside, NY 11104 *Tel:* 914-661-0049 *E-mail:* pkpmedia4142@gmail.com *Web Site:* www.pkpmedia.com, pg 852

PatchAmp, 20 E Kennedy St, Hackensack, NJ 07601 *Tel:* 201-457-1504 *Fax:* 201-457-1507 *E-mail:* sales@patchamp.com *Web Site:* www.patchamp.com, pg 852

Pathway Connectivity, 103-1439 17 Ave SE, Calgary, AB T2G 1J9, Canada *Tel:* 403-243-8110 *Fax:* 403-287-1281 *E-mail:* orders@pathwayconnect.com *Web Site:* www.pathwayconnect.com, pg 852

Pauline Books & Media, 50 St Paul's Ave, Boston, MA 02130 *Tel:* 617-522-8911 *Toll Free Tel:* 800-876-4463 (orders); 800-836-9723 (cust serv) *Fax:* 617-541-9805 *E-mail:* daughtersofstpaulusa@gmail.com *Web Site:* www.pauline.org, pg 852

Paulist Press, 997 Macarthur Blvd, Mahwah, NJ 07430-9990 *Tel:* 201-825-7300 *Toll Free Tel:* 800-218-1903 (orders) *Fax:* 201-825-6921 *E-mail:* info@paulistpress.com *Web Site:* www.paulistpress.com, pg 852

Paulist Productions, 6430 W Sunset Blvd, Suite 1220, Los Angeles, CA 90028 *Tel:* 310-454-0688 *E-mail:* paulistmail@paulistproductions.org *Web Site:* www.paulistproductions.org, pg 852

PBS Video, 2100 Crystal Dr, Arlington, VA 22202 *Tel:* 703-739-5000 *Web Site:* shop.pbs.org; www.pbs.org/video, pg 852

PC&E, 2235 DeFoor Hills Rd, Atlanta, GA 30318 *Tel:* 404-609-9001 *Toll Free Tel:* 800-537-4021 *Fax:* 404-609-9926 *E-mail:* marketing@pce-atlanta.com *Web Site:* pce-atlanta.com, pg 852

PCO-TECH Inc, 6930 Metroplex Dr, Romulus, MI 48174 *Tel:* 248-276-8820 *Fax:* 248-276-8825 *E-mail:* info@pco-tech.com; service@pco-tech.com *Web Site:* www.pco-tech.com, pg 852

PDC Productions, 3217 N Flood Ave, Norman, OK 73069 *Tel:* 405-360-5130 *Fax:* 405-360-0524 *E-mail:* info@pdcproductions.com *Web Site:* www.pdcproductions.com, pg 852

George Foster Peabody Awards, c/o University of Georgia, 120 Hooper St, Athens, GA 30602-3018 *Tel:* 706-542-3787 *E-mail:* peabody@uga.edu *Web Site:* www.peabodyawards.com, pg 999

Peak Performance Publishing, 14728 Shirley St, Omaha, NE 68144 *Tel:* 402-334-1676 *Toll Free Tel:* 800-293-1676 *Fax:* 402-334-4437 *Web Site:* www.peakperformanceconsult.com, pg 852

Pearson Education Canada, 26 Prince Andrew Place, North York, ON M3C 2H4, Canada *Tel:* 416-447-5101 *Toll Free Tel:* 800-361-6128 *Fax:* 416-447-2551 *Toll Free Fax:* 800-563-9196 *E-mail:* school_inquiries@pearsoned.com *Web Site:* www.pearson.com/ca; www.pearsoncanadaschool.com, pg 852

Peavey Electronics Corp, 5022 Hartley Peavey Dr, Meridian, MS 39305 *Tel:* 601-483-5365 *Fax:* 601-486-1278 *Web Site:* peavey.com, pg 852

Pechman Imaging, 106 E Second St, Kaukauna, WI 54130 *Tel:* 920-766-6160 *Toll Free Tel:* 800-777-0221 *Fax:* 920-766-6161 *E-mail:* customerservice@pechmanimaging.com *Web Site:* www.pechmanimaging.com, pg 852

Peckham Productions Inc, 65 S Broadway, Tarrytown, NY 10591-4003 *Web Site:* www.peckhampix.com, pg 852

Peerbolte Creative LLC, 182 NW 361, Warrensburg, MO 64093 Tel: 660-429-1383 E-mail: solutions@peerbolte. com Web Site: www.peerbolte.com, pg 852

Peerless Industries, 2300 White Oak Circle, Aurora, IL 60502 Tel: 630-375-5100 Toll Free Tel: 800-865-2112 Fax: 630-820-8537 Toll Free Fax: 800-359-6500 E-mail: info@peerless-av.com Web Site: www. peerless-av.com, pg 853

Pelco, 3500 Pelco Way, Clovis, CA 93612 Tel: 559-292-1981 (intl) Toll Free Tel: 800-289-9100 (US & CN) Fax: 559-348-1120 (intl) Toll Free Fax: 800-289-9150 (US & CN) Web Site: www.pelco.com, pg 853

Pelican Products Inc, 147 N Main St, South Deerfield, MA 01373 Tel: 413-665-2163 Toll Free Tel: 800-542-7344 Fax: 413-665-8330 Web Site: www.pelican.com, pg 853

Pelican Publishing Co, 1000 Burmaster St, Gretna, LA 70053-2246 Tel: 504-368-1175 Toll Free Tel: 800-843-1724; 888-PELICAN (735-4226 - cust serv); 888-5PELICAN (888-573-5422) Fax: 504-368-1195 E-mail: sales@pelicanpub.com Web Site: www. pelicanpub.com, pg 853

Pendle Hill Bookstore, 338 Plush Mill Rd, Wallingford, PA 19086 Tel: 610-566-4507 Toll Free Tel: 800-742-3150; 800-966-4556 Fax: 610-566-3679 E-mail: bookstore@fgc.quaker.org Web Site: pendlehill.org, pg 853

Pendulum Entertainment, 444 Dufferin St, Studio 1, Toronto, ON M6K 2A3, Canada Tel: 416-721-7593 E-mail: info@pendulumentertainment.com Web Site: www.pendulumentertainment.com, pg 853

Penfield Productions Ltd, 35 Springfield St, Agawam, MA 01001 Tel: 413-786-4454 Web Site: www. penfieldprod.com, pg 853

Penguin Random House Audio Publishing, 1745 Broadway, New York, NY 10019 E-mail: audio@ penguinrandomhouse.com Web Site: www. penguinrandomhouseaudio.com, pg 853

Penguin Random House Canada, 320 Front St W, Suite 1400, Toronto, ON M5V 3B6, Canada Tel: 416-364-4449 Toll Free Tel: 888-523-9292 (cust serv) Fax: 416-598-7764 E-mail: customerservicescanada@ penguinrandomhouse.com Web Site: www. penguinrandomhouse.ca, pg 853

Penn Elcom Inc, 7465 Lampson Ave, Garden Grove, CA 92841 Tel: 714-230-6200 Toll Free Tel: 800-228-9122 (US orders) Fax: 714-230-6222 E-mail: california@ penn-elcom.com Web Site: www.penn-elcom.com, pg 853

Pennebaker Hegedus Films Inc, 262 W 91 St, New York, NY 10024 Tel: 212-496-9195 Fax: 212-496-8195 E-mail: info@phfilms.com Web Site: phfilms.com, pg 854

Pennsylvania Film Office, Commonwealth Keystone Bldg, 4th fl, 400 North St, Harrisburg, PA 17120-0225 Tel: 717-783-3456 E-mail: info@filminpa.com Web Site: www.filminpa.com, pg 975

Penrose Productions, 2310 Homestead Rd, Suite C1-No 211, Los Altos, CA 94024 Tel: 650-969-8273 E-mail: info@penroseproductions.com Web Site: www. penroseproductions.com, pg 854

PentaVision Communications Inc, 712 N Niles Ave, South Bend, IN 46617 Tel: 574-272-8365 E-mail: hello@pentavision.net Web Site: pentavision. net, pg 854

Pentrex Media Group LLC, 2652 E Walnut St, Pasadena, CA 91107-3723 Tel: 626-793-3400 Toll Free Tel: 800-950-9333 Fax: 626-793-3797 E-mail: pentrex@ pentrex.com Web Site: www.pentrex.com, pg 854

People Productions, 1737 15 St, Suite 200, Boulder, CO 80302 Tel: 303-449-6086 Fax: 303-449-9526 E-mail: info@peopleproductions.com Web Site: peopleproductions.com, pg 854

People Skills International, 720 Gateway Center Dr, Bldg A, San Diego, CA 92102 Tel: 619-262-9951 Web Site: www.journeytolovingyourself.com, pg 854

PeopleVisionFX, 311 E First Ave, Bldg A, Roselle, NJ 07203 Tel: 973-509-2056 Web Site: peoplevisionfx. com, pg 854

Pepper Group, 220 N Smith St, Suite 406, Palatine, IL 60067 Tel: 847-963-0333 Fax: 847-963-0888 E-mail: pepper@peppergroup.com Web Site: www. peppergroup.com, pg 854

Peppers Ghost HD®, c/o Bob Thomas Productions Inc, 2 Franklin Ct, Montville, NJ 07045 Tel: 973-335-9100 Web Site: www.peppersghosthd.com, pg 854

Perennial Pictures Film Corp, 2102 E 52 St, Indianapolis, IN 46205 Tel: 317-253-1519 E-mail: mail@perennialpictures.com Web Site: www. perennialpictures.com, pg 854

Perfection Learning Corp, 1000 N Second Ave, Logan, IA 51546 Tel: 712-644-2831 Toll Free Tel: 800-831-4190 (US & CN) Toll Free Fax: 800-543-2745 E-mail: orders@perfectionlearning.com Web Site: www.perfectionlearning.com, pg 854

Performance Audio LLC, 2456 S West Temple St, Salt Lake City, UT 84115 Tel: 801-466-3196 Toll Free Tel: 800-771-8330 Fax: 801-484-1538 E-mail: sales@ performanceaudio.com; rental@performanceaudio.com Web Site: www.performanceaudio.com, pg 854

Personal Achievement Institute, One Speaking Success Rd, Kingman, AZ 86402 Tel: 928-753-5315 Web Site: burtdubin-blog.com, pg 854

PESA, 103 Quality Circle, Suite 210, Huntsville, AL 35806 Tel: 256-726-9200 Toll Free Tel: 800-323-7372 E-mail: sales@pesa.com Web Site: www.pesa.com, pg 855

Peterson's Video Transfer Services, 5693 S Jones Blvd, Suite 110, Las Vegas, NV 89118 Toll Free Tel: 800-888-0426 E-mail: contact@petersonsvideotransfer.com Web Site: www.petersonsvideotransfer.com, pg 855

PetroSkills | RDC Solutions, 25403 Katy Mills Pkwy, Katy, TX 77494 Toll Free Tel: 800-360-7222 E-mail: solutions@petroskills.com Web Site: www. resourcedev.com; www.petroskills.com, pg 855

PGi, 3280 Peachtree Rd NE, Suite 1000, Atlanta, GA 30305 Tel: 404-262-8400 Toll Free Tel: 866-755-4878 Web Site: www.pgi.com, pg 855

Phase One Studios, 1121 Bellamy Rd N, Unit 5, Scarborough, ON M1H 3B9, Canada Tel: 416-291-9553 Web Site: www.phaseonestudios.com; www. facebook.com/phaseonestudio, pg 855

Phase Technology, 6400 Youngerman Circle, Jacksonville, FL 32244 Tel: 913-663-5600 Toll Free Tel: 855-663-5600 Fax: 913-663-3200 E-mail: sales@ mseaudio.com Web Site: phasetech.mseaudio.com, pg 855

Phat Planet Recording Studios, 3473 Parkway Center Ct, Orlando, FL 32808 Tel: 407-295-7270 Toll Free Tel: 800-667-4893 Fax: 321-549-6229 E-mail: info@phatplanetstudios.com Web Site: www. phatplanetstudios.com, pg 855

Philadelphia Film Festival, 1412 Chestnut St, Philadelphia, PA 19102 Tel: 267-239-2941 E-mail: info@filmadelphia.org Web Site: filmadelphia. org/festival, pg 999

Philadelphia International Film Festival & Market, PO Box 48134, Philadelphia, PA 19144 Tel: 215-849-2716 (festival) Toll Free Tel: 877-347-FILM (347-3456) E-mail: info@philafilm.org Web Site: www.philafilm. org, pg 999

Philips Entertainment Lighting, 10911 Petal St, Dallas, TX 75238 Tel: 214-647-7880 Toll Free Tel: 877-VARILITE (877-827-4548) Fax: 214-647-8038 E-mail: entertainment.service@philips.com Web Site: www.vari-lite.com, pg 855

Philips Lighting Controls, 10911 Petal St, Dallas, TX 75238 Toll Free Tel: 800-555-0050 E-mail: controls. support@philips.com Web Site: www.usa.lighting. philips.com/products/lighting-controls; www. lightingproducts.philips.com, pg 855

Philips Lightolier, 200 Franklin Square Dr, Somerset, NJ 08873 Toll Free Tel: 800-555-0050; 855-486-2216 Web Site: www.lightingproducts.philips.com, pg 855

Philips Stonco, 200 Franklin Square Dr, Somerset, NJ 08873 Toll Free Tel: 800-555-0050; 855-486-2216 Web Site: www.lightingproducts.philips.com, pg 855

Phillips Media Source, 750 N St Paul, Suite 1000, Dallas, TX 75201 Tel: 214-741-1300 Toll Free Tel: 800-TEXAS13 (839-2713) Fax: 214-741-3942 Web Site: phillipsmediasource.com, pg 855

Phoebus Manufacturing, 2800 Third St, San Francisco, CA 94107 Tel: 415-550-1177, pg 855

Phoenix Aerial Photography Inc, PO Box 68432, Nashville, TN 37206 Tel: 615-255-2000; 615-975-4226 (cell) E-mail: info@phoenixaerialphoto.com Web Site: www.phoenixaerialphoto.com, pg 855

The Phoenix Learning Group Inc, 1990 E Lohman Ave, Suite 102, Las Cruces, NM 88001 Toll Free Tel: 800-221-1274 E-mail: customerservice@phoenixlearninggroup. com; orders@phoenixlearninggroup.com Web Site: phoenixlearninggroup.com, pg 855

Phoenix Society for Burn Survivors Inc, 525 Ottawa Ave NW, Front, Grand Rapids, MI 49503 Tel: 616-458-2773 Toll Free Tel: 800-888-BURN (888-2876) Fax: 616-458-2831 E-mail: info@phoenix-society.org Web Site: www.phoenix-society.org, pg 856

Photo Film Stage, 820 Thompson Ave, Suite 34, Glendale, CA 91201 Tel: 213-304-5608 E-mail: photofilmstage@yahoo.com Web Site: photofilmstage.com, pg 856

Photo Finish, Auburn Mall, 550 Center St, No 9007, Auburn, ME 04210 Tel: 207-783-3354 Web Site: www.mainephotofinish.com, pg 856

Photo-Sonics Inc, 9131 Independence Ave, Chatsworth, CA 91311 Tel: 818-842-2141 Fax: 818-842-2610 E-mail: mail@photosonics.com Web Site: www. photosonics.com, pg 856

Photo Tech Inc, 910 Fifth Ave, Suite 101, Baldwin, WI 54002 Tel: 651-702-6717 (support) Toll Free Tel: 800-525-6486 E-mail: rollie@phototechinc.com Web Site: www.phototechinc.com, pg 856

Photodyne Technologies, 8531 Alcott St, Suite 201, Los Angeles, CA 90035 Tel: 310-497-0968 Toll Free Tel: 800-660-2147 E-mail: info@photodyne.com Web Site: www.photodyne.com, pg 856

Photoflex Inc, 1268 Humbracht Circle, Bartlett, IL 60103-1631 Tel: 831-786-1370 Toll Free Tel: 800-486-2674 E-mail: sales@photoflex.com; techsupport@ photoflex.com Web Site: www.photoflex.com, pg 856

Photogenic Professional Lighting, 1268 Humbracht Circle, Bartlett, IL 60103-1631 Tel: 630-830-2500 Toll Free Tel: 800-682-7668 Fax: 630-830-2525 E-mail: sales@photogenic.com Web Site: www. photogenic.com, pg 856

Photographers' Formulary Inc, 7079 Hwy 83 N, Condon, MT 59826 Tel: 406-754-2891 Toll Free Tel: 800-922-5255 Fax: 406-754-2896 E-mail: formulary@ blackfoot.net Web Site: www.photoformulary.com, pg 856

Photographic Rental Service Inc (PRS), 1109 S La Brea Ave, Los Angeles, CA 90019 Tel: 323-965-9900 Fax: 323-965-9901 E-mail: prsrental@gmail.com Web Site: prsla.com, pg 856

Photographic Society of America® (PSA®), 8241 S Walker Ave, Suite 104, Oklahoma City, OK 73139 Tel: 405-843-1437 Toll Free Tel: 855-PSA-INFO (772-4636) E-mail: hq@psa-photo.org Web Site: www.psa-photo.org, pg 960

Photogroup Studios, 321 W Ben White, Suite 106A & 107, Austin, TX 78704 Tel: 512-373-8547 E-mail: photogroup@photogroupaustin.com Web Site: www.photogroupaustin.com, pg 856

Photosol Inc, 318 Seaboard Ave, Venice, FL 34285 Tel: 941-445-2231 E-mail: orders4photosol@gmail. com Web Site: www.photosol.com, pg 856

Photosound of Orlando Inc, 7055 University Blvd, Winter Park, FL 32792 Tel: 407-898-8841 Toll Free Tel: 800-552-8776 E-mail: info@photosoundav.com Web Site: www.photosoundav.com, pg 856

Physical Optics Corp (POC), 1845 E 205 St, Torrance, CA 90501-1510 *Tel:* 310-320-3088 *E-mail:* info@poc. com *Web Site:* www.poc.com, pg 856

Picture This Production Services, 2223 NE Oregon St, Portland, OR 97232 *Tel:* 503-235-3456 *Fax:* 503-236-2302 *E-mail:* info@pixthis.com *Web Site:* pixthis.com, pg 856

Picturestart, 817 Hilldale Ave, West Hollywood, CA 90069 *Tel:* 310-422-3280 *E-mail:* info@picturestart. com *Web Site:* www.picturestart.com, pg 856

Pignose-Gorilla, 570 W Cheyenne Ave, Suite 80, North Las Vegas, NV 89030 *Tel:* 702-648-2444 *Toll Free Tel:* 800-9-PIGNOSE (974-4667) *Fax:* 702-648-2440 *E-mail:* sales@pignoseamps.com *Web Site:* www. pignoseamps.com, pg 856

Pinewood Sound, 555 Brooksbank Ave, Bldg S, North Vancouver, BC V7J 3S5, Canada *Tel:* 604-669-6900; 604-983-5200 *Fax:* 604-983-5204 *E-mail:* info@ pinewoodsound.com; sales@pinewoodsound.com *Web Site:* www.pinewoodsound.com, pg 857

pinta acoustic inc, 2601 49 Ave N, Suite 400, Minneapolis, MN 55430 *Tel:* 612-355-4200 *Toll Free Tel:* 800-662-0032 *Fax:* 612-355-4299 *E-mail:* sales@ pinta-acoustic.com; info@pinta-acoustic.com *Web Site:* www.pinta-acoustic.com, pg 857

Pioneer Electronics (USA) Inc, 2050 W 190 St, Suite 100, Torrance, CA 90504 *Tel:* 310-952-2000 *Toll Free Tel:* 800-421-1404 (cust serv, car, marine & computer prods); 800-228-7221 (parts dept); 844-679-5350 (cust serv, home prods) *Web Site:* www.pioneerelectronics. com, pg 857

Pioneer Research Inc, 97 Foster Rd, Suite 5, Moorestown, NJ 08057 *Tel:* 856-866-9191 *Toll Free Tel:* 800-257-7742 *Fax:* 856-866-8615 *E-mail:* info@ pioneer-research.com *Web Site:* www.pioneer-research. com, pg 857

PipelineFX LLC, 500 Ala Moana Blvd, Tower 7, Suite 400, Honolulu, HI 96813 *Tel:* 808-685-7823 *Toll Free Tel:* 855-685-7823 *Fax:* 808-685-7800 *E-mail:* sales@ pipelinefx.com *Web Site:* www.pipelinefx.com, pg 857

Piper Media Services Inc, 904 W Kenosha St, Broken Arrow, OK 74012 *Tel:* 918-251-0477 *E-mail:* info@ piper.media *Web Site:* www.piper.media, pg 857

Nicholas P Pipino Associates Inc, 10545 Guilford Rd, Suite 108, Jessup, MD 20794 *Tel:* 301-596-3397; 410-995-0041 *Toll Free Tel:* 888-596-0014 *Fax:* 410-964-1191 *Web Site:* pipinoinc.com, pg 857

Pittsburgh Film Office, The Oliver Bldg, 535 Smithfield St, Suite 500, Pittsburgh, PA 15222 *Tel:* 412-261-2744 *E-mail:* info@pghfilm.org *Web Site:* www.pghfilm.org, pg 975

Pixar Animation Studios, 1200 Park Ave, Emeryville, CA 94608 *Tel:* 510-922-3000 *Fax:* 510-922-3151 *Web Site:* www.pixar.com, pg 857

PixeLINK, 1900 City Park Dr, Suite 410, Ottawa, ON K1J 1A3, Canada *Tel:* 613-247-1211 *Fax:* 613-247-2001 *E-mail:* sales@pixelink.com *Web Site:* www. pixelink.com, pg 857

PixMix Video Services, 395 Western Ave, Suite 112 & 113, Boston, MA 02134 *Tel:* 617-923-0102; 617-254-0590 *Fax:* 617-923-0105 *E-mail:* info@pixmix.net *Web Site:* www.pixmix.net, pg 857

piXvfm Inc, 1805 E Dyer Rd, Suite 107, Santa Ana, CA 92705 *Tel:* 949-419-2563 *Fax:* 949-419-3485 *Web Site:* pixvfm.com, pg 857

PK Productions, 313 E Broadway, No 1205, Glendale, CA 91209 *E-mail:* info@pkproductions.com *Web Site:* pkproductions.com, pg 857

Placer-Lake Tahoe Film Office, 145 Fulweiler Ave, Auburn, CA 95603 *Tel:* 530-889-4091 *Toll Free Tel:* 877-228-3456 *Fax:* 530-889-4095 *Web Site:* www. placer.ca.gov/films, pg 966

Planet Dallas Recording Studios, PO Box 110995, Carrollton, TX 75011 *Tel:* 214-521-2216; 214-893-1130 (cell) *E-mail:* planetd@ix.netcom.com *Web Site:* planetdallas.com, pg 857

Plank Road Publishing Inc, 11111 W Plank Ct, Wauwatosa, WI 53226 *Tel:* 262-790-5210 *Toll Free Tel:* 800-437-0832 *Fax:* 414-771-7672 *Toll Free Fax:* 888-272-0212 *E-mail:* contact-us@musick8.com *Web Site:* www.musick8.com, pg 857

plan9films, 9 Willingdon Place, Saskatoon, SK S7L 1C2, Canada *Tel:* 306-955-NINE (955-6463) *E-mail:* info@ plan9films.com *Web Site:* www.plan9films.com, pg 857

Platt Luggage Inc, 4051 W 51 St, Chicago, IL 60632 *Tel:* 773-838-2000 *Toll Free Tel:* 800-222-1555 *Fax:* 773-838-2010 *E-mail:* info@plattcases.com *Web Site:* www.plattcases.com, pg 858

Playback Now Inc, 3139 Campus Dr, Suite 700, Norcross, GA 30071-1402 *Tel:* 770-447-0616 *Toll Free Tel:* 800-241-7785 (prod support) *E-mail:* info@ playbacknow.com *Web Site:* www.playbacknow.com, pg 858

Playback Recording Studio, 400 E Gutierrez, Santa Barbara, CA 93101 *Tel:* 917-331-0429 *Web Site:* www.playbackrecording.com, pg 858

Playboy Entertainment Group Inc, 9346 Civic Center Dr, Suite 200, Beverly Hills, CA 90210 *Tel:* 310-424-1800 *Web Site:* www.playboy.com, pg 858

PLS Staging, 371 Little Falls Rd, Cedar Grove, NJ 07009 *Tel:* 973-857-7242 *E-mail:* rfp@plsstaging.com *Web Site:* plsstaging.com, pg 858

Plume Ltd, 888 Main St, Silver Plume, CO 80476 *Tel:* 303-569-3236; 303-888-8099 *Fax:* 303-569-2932 *Web Site:* www.plumeltd.com, pg 858

PLUS Corp of America, 9655 SW Sunshine Ct, Suite 300, Beaverton, OR 97005 *Tel:* 503-748-8700 *Toll Free Tel:* 800-211-9001 *E-mail:* sales@plus-america. com; info@plus-america.com *Web Site:* www.plus-america.com, pg 858

PM Productions, 5882 Bowcroft St, Suite 2, Los Angeles, CA 90016 *Tel:* 310-559-3127 *Fax:* 310-559-3168 *Web Site:* pmproductionsvideos.com, pg 858

PME Audio/Video, 2003 S El Camino Real, Suite 108, Oceanside, CA 92054 *Tel:* 760-439-0281 *E-mail:* solutions@pmevideo.com *Web Site:* www. pmevideo.com, pg 858

PMP Marketing Inc, 337 Grant St, Redlands, CA 92373 *Tel:* 909-557-8685 *Web Site:* www.pmpmarketing.com, pg 858

PNTA, 2414 SW Andover St, Suite C100, Seattle, WA 98106 *Tel:* 206-622-7850 *Toll Free Tel:* 800-622-7850 *Fax:* 206-267-1789 *E-mail:* sales@pnta.com; events@ pnta.com *Web Site:* www.pnta.com, pg 858

Pogo Pictures, 114 E Ponce de Leon Ave, Suite B, Decatur, GA 30030 *Tel:* 404-892-9490 *Web Site:* www.pogopictures.com, pg 858

Point of View Productions, 2477 Folsom St, San Francisco, CA 94110 *Fax:* 415-821-0434, pg 858

Point Source Audio, 1304 Southpoint Blvd, No 260, Petaluma, CA 94954 *Tel:* 415-226-1122 *Fax:* 415-520-2110 *E-mail:* info@point-sourceaudio.com; sales@point-sourceaudio.com *Web Site:* www.point-sourceaudio.com, pg 858

Point.360, 2701 Media Center Dr, Los Angeles, CA 90065 *Tel:* 323-987-9400 *Fax:* 818-847-2503 *E-mail:* sales@point360.com *Web Site:* www.point360. com, pg 858

Pointward, 400 First Ave N, Suite 100, Minneapolis, MN 55401 *Tel:* 651-646-2442 *Web Site:* www.pointward. com, pg 858

Polarity Post Production, 69 Green St, San Francisco, CA 94111 *Tel:* 415-421-6622 *Fax:* 415-391-4995 *E-mail:* info@polaritypost.com *Web Site:* www. polaritypost.com, pg 858

Polestar Films & Associated Arts Ltd, PO Box 20104, New York, NY 10014-0708 *Tel:* 212-352-1375, pg 859

Polhemus, 40 Hercules Dr, Colchester, VT 05446-5835 *Tel:* 802-655-3159 *Toll Free Tel:* 800-357-4777 (US & CN) *E-mail:* sales@polhemus.com *Web Site:* polhemus.com, pg 859

George Polk Awards in Journalism, Journalism Dept, One University Plaza, Brooklyn, NY 11201-5372 *Tel:* 718-488-1009 *Web Site:* www.liu.edu/polk, pg 1000

Pollstar, 4697 W Jacquelyn Ave, Fresno, CA 93722-6413 *Tel:* 559-271-7900 *Fax:* 559-271-7979 *E-mail:* info@ pollstar.com *Web Site:* www.pollstarpro.com; www. pollstar.com, pg 859

Pollution Studios, 3239 Union Pacific Ave, Los Angeles, CA 90023 *Tel:* 323-981-1520 *E-mail:* info@ pollutionstudios.com *Web Site:* pollutionstudios.com, pg 859

Gabriel Polonsky Studio, 33 Harvard Rd, Suite 2, Belmont, MA 02478 *Tel:* 617-515-5642 *E-mail:* gp-studio@verizon.net *Web Site:* www.facebook.com/ GPstudioarts, pg 859

Poly, 345 Encinal St, Santa Cruz, CA 95060 *Tel:* 831-426-5858 *Toll Free Tel:* 800-544-4660 *Fax:* 831-426-6098 *Web Site:* www.poly.com, pg 859

Polyline LLC, 1400 W Burbank Blvd, Burbank, CA 91506 *Tel:* 630-993-2700 *Toll Free Tel:* 800-701-7689 *E-mail:* sales@polylinecorp.com *Web Site:* www. polylinecorp.com, pg 859

PolyScience, 6600 W Touhy Ave, Niles, IL 60714-4516 *Tel:* 847-647-0611 *Toll Free Tel:* 800-229-7569 *Fax:* 847-647-1155 *E-mail:* sales@polyscience.com *Web Site:* www.polyscience.com, pg 859

PolyVision Corporation, 10700 Abbotts Bridge Rd, Suite 100, Johns Creek, GA 30097 *Tel:* 678-542-3100 *Toll Free Tel:* 800-542-3200 *E-mail:* info@polyvision.com; customerservice@ polyvision.com *Web Site:* polyvision.com, pg 859

Pook Diemont & Ohl Inc, 701 E 132 St, Bronx, NY 10454 *Tel:* 718-402-2677 *Fax:* 718-402-2859 *E-mail:* info@texasscenic.com *Web Site:* www. texasscenic.com, pg 859

Porta-Jib, 416 N Varney St, Burbank, CA 91502 *Tel:* 747-283-1077 *Fax:* 747-283-1078 *Web Site:* www. porta-jib.com, pg 859

PortaBrace Inc, 160 Benmont Ave, Suite 100, North Bennington, VT 05201 *Tel:* 802-442-8171 *Fax:* 802-442-9118 *E-mail:* info@portabrace.com *Web Site:* www.portabrace.com, pg 859

James Porter Photography, 211 E Columbine Ave, Suite A-1, Santa Ana, CA 92707 *Tel:* 714-546-4148 *E-mail:* info@jamesporterphotography.com *Web Site:* www.jamesporterphotography.com, pg 859

Porter Productions, 211 E Columbine Ave, Suite B, Santa Ana, CA 92707 *Tel:* 714-546-4148 *E-mail:* studio@porterproductions.info *Web Site:* www. porterproductions.info, pg 859

Portland Film Office, 222 NW Fifth Ave, Portland, OR 97209-3859 *Tel:* 503-823-3326 *E-mail:* filmoffice@ pdc.us *Web Site:* www.portlandfilmoffice.com, pg 975

Posthorn Recordings, 142 W 26 St, 10th fl, New York, NY 10001-6814 *Tel:* 212-242-3737 *Fax:* 212-924-1243 *Web Site:* www.posthorn.com, pg 859

PostWorks, 110 Leroy St, New York, NY 10014 *Tel:* 212-609-9400 *Fax:* 212-609-9450 *E-mail:* inquiry@technicolorpwny.com *Web Site:* www.postworks.com, pg 860

Potentials Unlimited, 3409 47 Ave E, Bradenton, FL 34203-3974 *Tel:* 941-739-2611 *Toll Free Tel:* 800-221-6121; 800-426-3963 *Fax:* 941-756-0315 *Web Site:* www.potentialsunlimited.com, pg 860

Potomac Instruments Inc, 7309 Grove Rd, Unit D, Frederick, MD 21704 *Tel:* 301-696-5550 *Fax:* 301-696-5553 *E-mail:* sales@pi-usa.com; service@pi-usa. com *Web Site:* www.pi-usa.com, pg 860

Pounds Photographic Labs Inc, 901 Regal Row, Dallas, TX 75247 *Tel:* 214-688-1425 *Toll Free Tel:* 800-350-5671 *Fax:* 214-688-1429 *E-mail:* custsvc@poundslabs. com *Web Site:* www.poundslabs.com, pg 860

Power & Light, 1313 Mound St, Alameda, CA 94501 *Tel:* 510-205-4101 (cell) *Web Site:* www.powerlight. net, pg 860

Power & Telephone Supply Co, 44 Hull St, Suite 2, Randolph, VT 05060 *Toll Free Tel:* 800-451-4381 *Fax:* 802-234-5006 *E-mail:* cablesales@ptsupply.com *Web Site:* www.ptsupply.com, pg 860

Power Factory Productions, 4344 Gessner Rd, Houston, TX 77041 *Tel:* 281-630-6900 *E-mail:* info@powerfactorypro.com *Web Site:* www.powerfactoryproductions.com, pg 860

Power Integrity Corporation, 2109 Patterson St, Greensboro, NC 27407 *Tel:* 336-379-9773 *Toll Free Tel:* 800-237-6260 (tech support) *Web Site:* powerintegritycorp.com, pg 860

Power Sonic Corp, 365 Cabela Dr, Suite 300, Reno, NV 89523 *Tel:* 619-661-2020 *Fax:* 619-661-3650 *Web Site:* www.power-sonic.com, pg 860

PowerPhysics Inc, 877 Production Place, Newport Beach, CA 92663-2809 *Tel:* 949-371-6202 *Fax:* 815-572-8936 *E-mail:* contact@powerphysics.com *Web Site:* powerphysics.com, pg 860

Powerstation Events, 1718 Highland Ave, Cheshire, CT 06410 *Tel:* 203-250-8500 *Toll Free Tel:* 800-423-7835 *Fax:* 203-250-8575 *E-mail:* info@powerstationevents.com *Web Site:* www.powerstationevents.com, pg 860

The PPS Group, 424 Scott St, Covington, KY 41011 *Tel:* 859-291-5100 *Toll Free Tel:* 800-978-3445 *Fax:* 859-291-5150 *E-mail:* info@theppsgroup.com *Web Site:* www.pps-inc.com; www.theppsgroup.com, pg 860

Practising Law Institute, 1177 Avenue of the Americas, 2nd fl, New York, NY 10036 *Tel:* 212-824-5710 (cust serv) *Toll Free Tel:* 800-260-4PLI (260-4754, cust serv) *Toll Free Fax:* 800-321-0093 (cust serv) *E-mail:* info@pli.edu; cs@pli.edu (cust serv) *Web Site:* www.pli.edu, pg 860

Prairie Pictures Film & Video, 690 E Lamar Blvd, Arlington, TX 76011 *Tel:* 817-276-9500 *E-mail:* info@prairiepictures.com *Web Site:* prairiepictures.com, pg 860

Prakken Publications Inc, 251 Jackson Plaza, Suite A, Ann Arbor, MI 48103-1955 *Tel:* 734-975-2800 *Toll Free Tel:* 800-530-9673 *Fax:* 734-975-2787 *E-mail:* matt@techdirections.com *Web Site:* techdirections.com, pg 861

Precision Camera & Video, 2438 W Anderson Lane, Suite B-4, Austin, TX 78757 *Tel:* 512-467-7676 *Toll Free Tel:* 800-677-1023 *Fax:* 512-467-0607 *Web Site:* www.precision-camera.com, pg 861

Precision Camera & Video Repair Inc, 7 Anngina Dr, Enfield, CT 06082 *Tel:* 860-749-7380; 860-272-2100 *Toll Free Tel:* 800-665-6515 (cust serv) *E-mail:* info@precisioncamera.com *Web Site:* www.precisioncamera.com, pg 861

Precision Electronics Inc, 1331 Estes Ave, Gurnee, IL 60031 *Tel:* 847-599-1799 *Toll Free Tel:* 800-SINCE-46 (746-2346) *Fax:* 847-599-6178 *E-mail:* info@grommesprecision.com; sales@grommesprecision.com *Web Site:* www.grommesprecision.com, pg 861

Precision Microproducts of America, One Comac Loop, Unit 13, Ronkonkoma, NY 11779 *Tel:* 631-580-3456 *Toll Free Tel:* 800-932-9215 *Fax:* 631-580-3003 *E-mail:* sales@p-m-a.com *Web Site:* www.p-m-a.com, pg 861

Precision Projection Systems Inc, 17508 Studebaker Rd, Cerritos, CA 90703 *Tel:* 562-865-8552 *Fax:* 562-924-7133 *E-mail:* info@ppsfx.com *Web Site:* www.ppsfx.com, pg 861

Prelinger Archives, PO Box 590622, San Francisco, CA 94159-0622 *Tel:* 415-750-0445 *E-mail:* footage@panix.com *Web Site:* www.prelinger.com, pg 861

Premier Lighting & Production Co, 12023 Victory Blvd, North Hollywood, CA 91606 *Tel:* 818-762-0884 *Toll Free Tel:* 800-770-0884 *Fax:* 818-762-0896 *E-mail:* premier@premier-lighting.com; rentals@premier-lighting.com *Web Site:* www.premier-lighting.com, pg 861

Premio Mesquite, 723 S Brazos St, San Antonio, TX 78207 *Tel:* 210-271-3151 *Fax:* 210-271-3480 *E-mail:* cine@guadalupeculturalarts.org *Web Site:* www.guadalupeculturalarts.org, pg 1000

Pres-On Corp, 2600 E 107 St, Bolingbrook, IL 60440 *Toll Free Tel:* 800-323-7467 *Fax:* 630-628-8025 *E-mail:* sales@preson.com *Web Site:* www.preson.com, pg 861

Presagis, 4700 de la Savane, Suite 300, Montreal, QC H4P 1T7, Canada *Tel:* 514-341-3874 *Toll Free Tel:* 800-361-6424 *Fax:* 514-341-8018 *E-mail:* info@presagis.com *Web Site:* www.presagis.com, pg 861

Prescolite, 701 Millennium Blvd, Greenville, SC 29607 *Tel:* 864-678-1000 *Fax:* 864-678-1740 *Web Site:* www.hubbell.com/prescolite, pg 861

Presence Records, 67 Candace Lane, Chatham Township, NJ 07928-1115 *Tel:* 973-701-0707 *Web Site:* www.paulpayton.com; www.presenceproductions.com, pg 861

Presence Studios, 80 Wells Hill Rd, Suite 100, Weston, CT 06883 *Tel:* 203-221-8061 *E-mail:* info@presencestudios.com *Web Site:* www.presencestudios.com, pg 861

Presentation Products Inc, 171 Madison Ave, 12th fl, New York, NY 10016 *Tel:* 212-736-6350 *Toll Free Tel:* 877-774-4523 *Fax:* 212-736-6353 *E-mail:* customerservice@pproducts.com *Web Site:* www.presentationproducts.com, pg 861

The Presidential Proclamation, White Plains Plaza, 445 Hamilton Ave, Suite 601, White Plains, NY 10601-1827 *Tel:* 914-761-1100 *Fax:* 914-206-4216 *E-mail:* marketing@smpte.org *Web Site:* www.smpte.org, pg 1000

Preston Cinema Systems, 1659 11 St, Suite 100, Santa Monica, CA 90404 *Tel:* 310-453-1852 *Fax:* 310-453-5672 *E-mail:* sales@prestoncinema.com *Web Site:* www.prestoncinema.com, pg 862

Preston Productions Inc, 128 Bartlett St, Marlborough, MA 01752 *Toll Free Tel:* 800-822-2299 *E-mail:* ideas@prestonevents.com *Web Site:* www.prestonproductions.com; www.prestonevents.com, pg 861

PRI Productions, 1819 Kings Ave, Jacksonville, FL 32207 *Tel:* 904-398-8179 *E-mail:* info@priproductions.com *Web Site:* www.priproductions.com, pg 862

Primacoustic, 1588 Kebet Way, Port Coquitlam, BC V3C 5M5, Canada *Tel:* 604-942-1001 *Fax:* 604-942-1010 *E-mail:* info@primacoustic.com *Web Site:* www.primacoustic.com, pg 862

PrimaLux Video Inc, 30 W 26 St, 7th fl, New York, NY 10010 *Tel:* 212-206-1402 *Web Site:* www.primalux.com, pg 862

Prime Cut Productions, 1224 Orange Grove Ave, South Pasadena, CA 91030, pg 862

Prime Image Inc, 200 Highpoint Dr, Suite 215, Chalfont, PA 18914 *Tel:* 215-822-1561 *E-mail:* info@primeimage.com; sales@primeimage.com *Web Site:* www.primeimage.com, pg 862

PrimeArray Systems Inc, 1500 District Ave, Burlington, MA 01803 *Tel:* 978-455-9488 *Toll Free Tel:* 800-433-5133 *E-mail:* info@primearray.com; sales@primearray.com *Web Site:* www.primearray.com, pg 862

PrimeLight Productions Inc, 750 Kappock St, Suite 805, Riverdale, NY 10463 *Tel:* 718-543-3991 *E-mail:* info@primelight.net *Web Site:* www.primelight.net, pg 862

Princeton Book Company, Publishers, 15 W Front St, 3rd fl, Trenton, NJ 08608 *Tel:* 609-426-0602 *Toll Free Tel:* 800-220-7149 *Fax:* 609-426-1344 *E-mail:* pbc@dancehorizons.com *Web Site:* www.dancehorizons.com, pg 862

Print File Inc, 1846 S Orange Blossom Trail, Apopka, FL 32703 *Tel:* 407-886-3100 *Toll Free Tel:* 800-508-8539 *Fax:* 407-886-0008 *Toll Free Fax:* 800-546-4145 *E-mail:* support@printfile.com *Web Site:* printfile.com, pg 862

Print Industries Market Information and Research Organization (PRIMIR), 1899 Preston White Dr, Reston, VA 20191 *Tel:* 703-264-7200 *Fax:* 703-620-0994 *Web Site:* www.primir.org, pg 960

Printing Industries of America, 301 Brush Creek Rd, Warrendale, PA 15086-7529 *Tel:* 412-741-6860 *Toll Free Tel:* 800-910-4283 *Fax:* 412-741-2311 *E-mail:* printing@printing.org *Web Site:* www.printing.org, pg 960

Prior Scientific Inc, 80 Reservoir Park Dr, Rockland, MA 02370 *Tel:* 781-878-8442 *Toll Free Tel:* 800-877-2234 *Fax:* 781-878-8736 *E-mail:* info@prior.com; techsupportus@prior.com *Web Site:* www.prior.com, pg 862

Pristine Systems Inc, PO Box 6482, San Pedro, CA 90734 *Tel:* 310-831-2234 *Web Site:* www.pristinesys.com, pg 862

Private Island Audio Inc, 1882 S Cochran Ave, Los Angeles, CA 90019 *Tel:* 323-856-8729 *Web Site:* www.privateislandaudio.net, pg 862

Prix Gemeaux (French language TV), 225 rue Roy E, bureau 106, Montreal, QC H2W 1M5, Canada *Tel:* 514-849-7448 *Fax:* 514-849-5069 *E-mail:* academie@acct.ca *Web Site:* www.acct.ca/prixgemeaux; www.acct.ca; www.academy.ca, pg 1000

Pro AV Systems, 275 Billerica Rd, Suite 3, Chelmsford, MA 01824 *Tel:* 978-692-5111 *Fax:* 978-692-5252 *E-mail:* info@proavsi.com *Web Site:* proavsi.com, pg 862

Pro Camera Repair, 8250 Vickers Ave, San Diego, CA 92111 *Tel:* 858-277-3700 *E-mail:* info@procamerarepair.com *Web Site:* www.procamerarepair.com, pg 862

Pro Cuts Editing Services, 2138 Priest Bridge Ct, Suite 1, Crofton, MD 21114 *Tel:* 301-464-5067; 443-274-6115 *E-mail:* info@procutsediting.com *Web Site:* www.procutsediting.com, pg 862

Pro8mm, 2805 W Magnolia Blvd, Burbank, CA 91505 *Tel:* 818-848-5522 *Fax:* 818-848-5956 *E-mail:* sales@pro8mm.com; info@pro8mm.com *Web Site:* www.pro8mm.com, pg 862

Pro HD Rentals, 2201 N Hollywood Way, Suite 1, Burbank, CA 91505 *Tel:* 818-450-1115 *Fax:* 818-450-1115 *E-mail:* sales@prohdrentals.com *Web Site:* www.prohdrentals.com, pg 863

Pro Media Productions, 2593 Hamline Ave N, Roseville, MN 55113 *Tel:* 651-631-3681 *Fax:* 651-631-1606 *E-mail:* info@promediahd.com *Web Site:* www.promediaproductions.com, pg 863

Pro Power Products Inc, 913 S Victory Blvd, Burbank, CA 91502 *Tel:* 818-558-6222; 818-558-6740 *Toll Free Tel:* 800-395-8466 *Fax:* 818-558-3999 *Web Site:* propowerproducts.com, pg 863

Pro-Tape & Specialities Inc, 621 Rte 1 S, Suite B, North Brunswick, NJ 08902 *Tel:* 732-346-0900 *Toll Free Tel:* 800-345-0234 *Fax:* 732-729-7373 *Web Site:* www.protapes.com, pg 863

Pro Video, 600 First Ave NW, Cedar Rapids, IA 52405 *Tel:* 319-368-7779 *Toll Free Tel:* 800-234-7680 *E-mail:* service@provideoweb.com *Web Site:* provideoweb.com, pg 863

Pro Video & Film Equipment Co Inc, 11425 Mathis Ave, Studio 404, Dallas, TX 75234 *Tel:* 972-869-9990 *Toll Free Tel:* 888-869-9998 *E-mail:* providfilm@aol.com *Web Site:* www.providefilm.com; www.usedequipmentnewsletter.com, pg 863

PROCAM, 13624 Black Elk Trail, Prescott, AZ 86305 *Tel:* 928-708-9901 *E-mail:* bolexusa@yahoo.com, pg 863

Producers Group Ltd, 713 S Pacific Coast Hwy, Suite B, Redondo Beach, CA 90277-4233 *Tel:* 310-316-0481 *Web Site:* www.producers-group.tv, pg 863

Producers Guild of America Inc (PGA), 8530 Wilshire Blvd, Suite 400, Beverly Hills, CA 90211 *Tel:* 310-358-9020 *E-mail:* info@producersguild.org *Web Site:* www.producersguild.org, pg 960

Producers Library, 10832 Chandler Blvd, North Hollywood, CA 91601 *Tel:* 818-752-9097 *E-mail:* research@producerslibrary.com *Web Site:* www.producerslibrary.com, pg 863

The Producer's Loft, 2773 Folsom St, Suite 101, San Francisco, CA 94110 *Tel:* 415-334-4700 *Web Site:* theproducersloft.com, pg 863

Producers Management Television (PMTV), 681 Moore Rd, Suite 100, King of Prussia, PA 19406 *Tel:* 610-768-1770 *Fax:* 610-768-1773 *E-mail:* info@pmtv.com *Web Site:* www.pmtv.com, pg 863

Producers Video, 3700 Malden Ave, Baltimore, MD 21211 *Tel:* 410-523-7520 *Fax:* 410-669-3347 *E-mail:* info@producers.tv *Web Site:* producers.tv, pg 863

Product Productions, 1850 W Hubbard St, Chicago, IL 60622 *Tel:* 312-421-9030 *E-mail:* info@productproductions.com *Web Site:* www.productproductions.com, pg 863

Production Advantage Inc, PO Box 1700, Williston, VT 05495 *Tel:* 802-651-6915 (sales, option 1) *Toll Free Tel:* 800-424-9991 *Fax:* 802-651-6914 *Toll Free Fax:* 877-424-9991 *E-mail:* sales@proadv.com; orders@proadv.com *Web Site:* proadv.com, pg 863

Production Central, 873 Broadway, Suite 205, New York, NY 10003 *Tel:* 212-631-0435 *E-mail:* info@prodcentral.com *Web Site:* www.prodcentral.com, pg 863

Production Craft Inc, 1937 W Walnut St, Chicago, IL 60612 *Tel:* 312-829-0272 *Fax:* 312-829-8936 *E-mail:* info@productioncraft.com *Web Site:* www.productioncraft.com, pg 863

Production Equipment Rental Group (PERG), c/o ESTA, 630 Ninth Ave, Suite 609, New York, NY 10036 *Tel:* 212-244-1505 *Fax:* 212-244-1502 *E-mail:* info@esta.org; membership@esta.org *Web Site:* www.esta.org/perg, pg 960

Production Garden Music, 13423 Blanco Rd, No 147, San Antonio, TX 78216 *Tel:* 210-530-5200 *Toll Free Tel:* 800-247-5317 *Fax:* 210-530-5230 *E-mail:* info@productiongarden.com *Web Site:* www.productiongarden.com, pg 863

Production Gear Rentals (PGR), 16140 Runnymede St, Van Nuys, CA 91406 *Tel:* 818-989-8640 *Fax:* 818-989-8644 *E-mail:* oscar@pgr.tv *Web Site:* pgr.tv, pg 863

The Production Group Studios, 1626 N Wilcox Ave, Suite 281, Hollywood, CA 90028 *Tel:* 323-469-8111 *Fax:* 323-962-2182 *E-mail:* info@productiongroup.tv *Web Site:* productiongroup.tv, pg 863

Production Masters Inc (PMI), 204 Fifth Ave, Pittsburgh, PA 15222 *Tel:* 412-281-8500 *E-mail:* info@pmi.tv *Web Site:* pmi.tv, pg 864

Production Outfitters, 1833 San Mateo Blvd NE, Albuquerque, NM 87110 *Tel:* 505-237-0770 *E-mail:* info@productionoutfitters.com *Web Site:* www.productionoutfitters.com, pg 864

Production Partners Media, 520 Enterprise Dr, Suite C, Lewis Center, OH 43035 *Tel:* 614-888-4888 *Web Site:* productionpartnersmedia.com, pg 864

Production Resource Group LLC (PRG), 200 Business Park Dr, Suite 109, Armonk, NY 10504 *Tel:* 212-589-5400 *Toll Free Tel:* 877-774-7088 *E-mail:* info@prg.com *Web Site:* www.prg.com, pg 864

Production Solutions Inc, PO Box 49431, Dayton, OH 45449 *Tel:* 937-866-2028 *Fax:* 253-423-8997 *E-mail:* proso@att.net *Web Site:* www.psiohio.com, pg 864

Production Support Services Inc, 827 Koeln Ave, St Louis, MO 63111 *Tel:* 314-535-8548 *Toll Free Tel:* 800-394-1257 *Fax:* 314-236-0735 *E-mail:* info@productionsupportservices.com *Web Site:* www.productionsupportservices.com, pg 864

Production West, 207 NW Park Ave, Portland, OR 97209 *Tel:* 503-222-0025 *Fax:* 503-573-1941 *E-mail:* info@r2cgroup.com *Web Site:* www.r2cgroup.com, pg 864

Productions Grand Nord Quebec Inc, 5141 Notre Dam de Grace, Montreal, QC H4A 1K4, Canada *Tel:* 514-521-7433 *Fax:* 514-522-3013, pg 864

Les Productions Via Le Monde (Daniel Bertolino) Inc, 758, rue Halpern, Dorval, QC H9P 1G6, Canada *Tel:* 514-636-6633 *Fax:* 514-636-9633 *E-mail:* distribution@vialemonde.com; info@vialemonde.com *Web Site:* www.vialemonde.com, pg 864

Professional Advancement Enterprises (PAE), 2182 Saginaw SE, Grand Rapids, MI 49506 *Tel:* 616-956-9443 *Fax:* 616-956-7973 *E-mail:* paeworld@comcast.net *Web Site:* www.paeworld.com, pg 864

Professional Audio Design Inc, 90 Corporate Park Dr, Suite 1420, Pembroke, MA 02359 *Tel:* 781-982-2600 *Toll Free Tel:* 877-223-8858 *Fax:* 781-982-2610 *E-mail:* info@proaudiodesign.com *Web Site:* www.proaudiodesign.com, pg 865

Professional Education Institute (PEI), 7020 High Grove Blvd, Burr Ridge, IL 60527 *Tel:* 312-521-8002 *Toll Free Tel:* 800-320-7517 *Web Site:* thepei.com, pg 865

Professional Label Inc, 7726 N King Hwy, Myrtle Beach, SC 29572 *Tel:* 301-570-0774 *Fax:* 301-570-0776 *E-mail:* info@professionallabel.com *Web Site:* professionallabel.com; prolabel.com, pg 865

Professional Marketing Services Inc, 105 S Southgate Dr, Chandler, AZ 85226 *Tel:* 480-940-5400 *Toll Free Tel:* 800-201-2160 *Fax:* 480-603-1048 *E-mail:* pmsi@promarketinc.com *Web Site:* www.promarketinc.com, pg 865

Professional Photographers of America (PPA), 229 Peachtree St NE, Suite 2200, Atlanta, GA 30303 *Tel:* 404-522-8600 *Toll Free Tel:* 800-786-6277 *Fax:* 404-614-6400 *E-mail:* csc@ppa.com *Web Site:* www.ppa.com, pg 960

Professional Sound Corp, 28085 Smyth Dr, Valencia, CA 91355 *Tel:* 661-295-9395 *Fax:* 661-295-8398 *E-mail:* sales@professionalsound.com; service@professionalsound.com *Web Site:* www.professionalsound.com, pg 865

Professional Women Photographers (PWP), 119 W 72 St, Suite 223, New York, NY 10023 *E-mail:* pwp@pwponline.org *Web Site:* www.pwponline.org, pg 961

Proforma Good Wood Marketing, 3839 E 17 St, Spokane, WA 99223 *Tel:* 509-534-7477 *Fax:* 509-534-9703 *Web Site:* proformagwm.espwebsite.com, pg 865

The Program Source International, 2494 Loch Creek Way, Bloomfield Hills, MI 48304 *Tel:* 248-333-2010 *E-mail:* info@program-source.com *Web Site:* www.program-source.com, pg 865

Progressive AE, 1811 Four Mile Rd NE, Grand Rapids, MI 49525 *Tel:* 616-361-2664 *Fax:* 616-361-1493 *E-mail:* info@progressiveae.com *Web Site:* www.progressiveae.com, pg 865

Projection, 5803 Rolling Rd, Suite 200, Springfield, VA 22152 *Tel:* 301-459-9011 *Fax:* 301-575-3101 *E-mail:* info@projection.com *Web Site:* www.projection.com, pg 865

Projector SuperStore LLC, 17350 N Hartford Dr, Scottsdale, AZ 85255 *Tel:* 480-922-9420 *Toll Free Tel:* 888-525-6696 *Fax:* 480-348-0273 *Web Site:* www.projectorsuperstore.com, pg 865

Projects in Knowledge Inc, 290 W Mount Pleasant Ave, Suite 2350, Livingston, NJ 07039 *Tel:* 973-890-8988 *Toll Free Tel:* 800-772-8277 *Web Site:* www.projectsinknowledge.com, pg 865

ProLine Digital, PO Box 27682, Denver, CO 80227-0682 *Tel:* 303-761-3999 *Toll Free Tel:* 800-325-0853 *Fax:* 303-761-1818 *E-mail:* info@prolinedigital.com *Web Site:* www.prolinedigital.com, pg 865

Promax, 5700 Wilshire Blvd, Suite 275, Los Angeles, CA 90036 *Tel:* 310-788-7600 *Fax:* 310-788-7616 *Web Site:* www.promax.org, pg 961

Promax Systems, 2850 S Fairview St, Santa Ana, CA 92704 *Tel:* 949-861-2700 *Toll Free Tel:* 800-977-6629 *E-mail:* sales@promax.com *Web Site:* www.promax.com, pg 865

PromaxBDA Promotion, Marketing and Design North America Awards, 5700 Wilshire Blvd, Suite 275, Los Angeles, CA 90036 *Tel:* 310-788-7600 *Fax:* 310-788-7616 *E-mail:* awards@promaxbda.org *Web Site:* www.promax.org/awards, pg 1000

Propeller Music & Sound Design Inc, 62 W 45 St, 10th fl, New York, NY 10036 *Tel:* 917-922-3289 *E-mail:* info@propellermusic.com *Web Site:* www.propellermusic.com, pg 865

ProPhotonix Ltd, 13 Red Roof Lane, Suite 200, Salem, NH 03079 *Tel:* 603-893-8778 *E-mail:* sales@prophotonix.com; info@prophotonix.com *Web Site:* www.prophotonix.com, pg 865

Prositions Inc, 6200 Aurora Ave, Suite 400W, Urbandale, IA 50322 *Tel:* 515-864-7200 *Toll Free Tel:* 877-244-8848 *E-mail:* info@prositions.com *Web Site:* prositions.com, pg 865

Prosper Media Group Inc, 348 E Main St, Lexington, KY 40507 *Tel:* 859-400-0136 *Toll Free Tel:* 888-528-1999 *E-mail:* producer@prosperproductions.com *Web Site:* prospermg.com, pg 866

Protech Audio Corp, 192 Cedar River Rd, Indian Lake, NY 12842 *Tel:* 518-648-6410 *Fax:* 518-648-6395 *E-mail:* proinfo@protechaudio.com; prosales@protechaudio.com *Web Site:* www.protechaudio.com, pg 866

Protocol Telecommunications Inc, 16844 Saticoy St, Van Nuys, CA 91406 *Tel:* 818-782-5705 *Toll Free Tel:* 800-400-5705 *Fax:* 818-782-5817 *E-mail:* orders@walkietalkie.com *Web Site:* www.walkietalkie.com, pg 866

Providence Underground Film Festival, 83 Park St, Suite 5, Providence, RI 02903 *Tel:* 401-861-4445 *Fax:* 401-490-6735 *E-mail:* info@film-festival.org *Web Site:* www.film-festival.org, pg 1000

Provident Distribution, 741 Cool Springs Blvd, Franklin, TN 37067 *Tel:* 615-261-6500 *Toll Free Tel:* 800-333-9000 *Fax:* 615-261-5904 *Toll Free Fax:* 800-333-9408 *E-mail:* info@pmgsonymusic.com *Web Site:* www.thep.com, pg 866

PSAV® Presentation Services, 111 W Ocean Blvd, Suite 1110, Long Beach, CA 90802-4688 *Tel:* 562-366-0620; 562-366-0621 *Toll Free Tel:* 877-430-7728 *Fax:* 562-366-0628 *Web Site:* www.psav.com, pg 866

PSAV® Presentation Services (Hotel Services Division), 5100 N River Rd, Suite 300, Schiller Park, IL 60176 *Tel:* 847-222-9800 *Toll Free Tel:* 866-716-9691 *E-mail:* psavglobal@gmail.com *Web Site:* www.psav.com, pg 866

PSB Speakers International, 633 Granite Ct, Pickering, ON L1W 3K1, Canada *Tel:* 905-831-6555 *Fax:* 905-831-6936 *Web Site:* www.psbspeakers.com, pg 866

PSI Inc, 16755 Von Karman Ave, Suite 200, Irvine, CA 92606 *Tel:* 949-261-6119 *Web Site:* www.psivideoinc.com, pg 866

PSNI (Professional Systems Network Intl), 1831 E 71 St, Tulsa, OK 74136 *Tel:* 918-388-1343 *Web Site:* www.psni.org, pg 961

PSSI Global Services LLC, 7030 Hayvenhurst Ave, Van Nuys, CA 91406 *Tel:* 310-575-4400 *Toll Free Tel:* 800-SAT-LINK (728-5465); 800-634-6530 (teleport inquiries) *E-mail:* info@pssiglobal.com *Web Site:* www.pssiglobal.com, pg 866

Psychsoft Inc, PO Box 232, North Quincy, MA 02171 *Tel:* 617-471-8733 *E-mail:* sales@psychsoftpc.com *Web Site:* www.psychsoftpc.com, pg 866

Publishers Group West (PGW), an Ingram brand, 1700 Fourth St, Berkeley, CA 94710 *Tel:* 510-809-3700 *Toll Free Tel:* 866-400-5351 (cust serv) *Fax:* 510-809-3777 *E-mail:* info@pgw.com *Web Site:* www.pgw.com, pg 866

Puerto Rico Film Commission, 355 FD Roosevelt Ave, Suite 101, Hato Rey, PR 00918 *Tel:* 787-754-6444 *Fax:* 787-756-5706 *E-mail:* info@puertoricofilm.pr.gov *Web Site:* www.puertoricofilm.org, pg 977

Purdue University Digital Education, Stewart Ctr, Rm G59, 128 Memorial Mall, West Lafayette, IN 47907 *Tel:* 765-494-8619 *Toll Free Tel:* 800-830-0269 *Fax:* 765-496-2484 *E-mail:* distancelearning@purdue. edu *Web Site:* www.digitaleducation.purdue.edu, pg 866

PXL This Video Festival, 2427 1/2 Glyndon Ave, Venice, CA 90291 *Tel:* 310-306-7330 *E-mail:* pfsuzy@aol.com *Web Site:* laughtears.com, pg 1000

Pyramid Media, 3200 Airport Ave, No 19, Santa Monica, CA 90405 *Tel:* 310-398-6149 *Toll Free Tel:* 800-421-2304 *Fax:* 310-398-7869 *E-mail:* sales@ pyramidmedia.com *Web Site:* www.pyramidmedia.com, pg 867

Pyramid Studios, 2727 Mariposa St, Suite 200, San Francisco, CA 94110 *Tel:* 415-896-9800 (ext 200) *Web Site:* www.pyramind.com, pg 867

Pyro Spectaculars Inc, 3196 N Locust Ave, Rialto, CA 92377 *Tel:* 909-355-8120 *Toll Free Tel:* 888-477-PYRO (477-7976) *E-mail:* information@pyrospec.com *Web Site:* www.pyrospec.com, pg 867

Pyrotek Special Effects Inc, 201 Whitehall Dr, Suite 6, Markham, ON L3R 9Y3, Canada *Tel:* 905-479-9991 *Toll Free Tel:* 800-481-9910 *E-mail:* info@pyrotekfx. com *Web Site:* pyrotekfx.com, pg 867

Pyxis Industries Inc, 25695 Jefferson Ave, Suite 8, Murrieta, CA 92562 *Tel:* 951-526-1999 *Toll Free Tel:* 888-PYXISAN (799-4728) *Fax:* 951-253-9290 *Web Site:* pyxisindustries.com, pg 867

Q-Prompt Inc, 5356 Vail Ct, Mississauga, ON L5M 6G9, Canada *Tel:* 416-908-5886 *Toll Free Tel:* 866-578-8852 *E-mail:* scripts@qprompt.com *Web Site:* www. qprompt.com, pg 867

QCA, 2832 Spring Grove Ave, Cincinnati, OH 45225 *Tel:* 513-681-8400 *Toll Free Tel:* 800-859-8401 *E-mail:* info@go-qca.com *Web Site:* www.go-qca.com, pg 867

Qioptiq, An Excelitas Technologies Company, 44370 Christy St, Fremont, CA 94538-3180 *Tel:* 510-979-6500 *Toll Free Tel:* 800-429-0257 *Fax:* 510-687-1140 *E-mail:* generalinquiries.na@excelitas.com *Web Site:* www.qioptiq.com; www.excelitas.com, pg 867

QRS Software Services, 11879 Woodbury Rd, Garden Grove, CA 92843 *Tel:* 714-537-5100 *Toll Free Tel:* 800-228-9699 *Fax:* 714-539-9448 *E-mail:* qrs@qrssoftware.com; sales@qrssoftware.com *Web Site:* www.qrssoftware.com, pg 867

QSC Audio Products LLC, 1675 MacArthur Blvd, Costa Mesa, CA 92626 *Tel:* 714-754-6161 *Toll Free Tel:* 800-772-2834 (US only) *Fax:* 714-754-6173 *E-mail:* info@qscaudio.com *Web Site:* www.qsc.com, pg 867

Ward L Quaal Leadership Awards, 125 W 55 St, 4th fl, New York, NY 10019-5366 *Tel:* 212-373-8250 *Fax:* 212-373-8254 *E-mail:* info@thebfoa.org *Web Site:* www.thebfoa.org; broadcastersfoundation. org, pg 1000

Quabbin Wire & Cable Co Inc, 10 Maple St, Ware, MA 01082-1597 *Tel:* 413-967-6281 *Toll Free Tel:* 800-368-3311 *Fax:* 413-967-7564 *E-mail:* sales@quabbin.com *Web Site:* www.quabbin.com, pg 867

Quad Cities First, 331 W Third St, Davenport, IA 52801 *Tel:* 563-326-1005 *Web Site:* www.quadcitiesfirst.com, pg 971

Quality Audio Visual Service Inc, 6938 Boulevard 26, Fort Worth, TX 76180-8808 *Tel:* 817-284-3192 *Toll Free Tel:* 800-371-6741 *Fax:* 817-595-2942 *E-mail:* info@qualityaudiovisual.com *Web Site:* www. qualityaudiovisual.com, pg 867

Quality Clones, 3940 Laurel Canyon Blvd, Suite 405, Studio City, CA 91604 *Tel:* 323-464-5853 *E-mail:* info@qualityclones.com *Web Site:* www. qualityclones.com, pg 867

Quality Digest, 290 Airpark Blvd, Chico, CA 95973 *Tel:* 530-893-4095 *Fax:* 530-893-0395 *E-mail:* comments@qualitydigest.com *Web Site:* www. qualitydigest.com, pg 868

Quality Film & Video, 3321 Main St, Suite B-1, Manchester, MD 21102 *Tel:* 410-785-1920 *E-mail:* quality3321@comcast.net *Web Site:* www. qualityfilmvideo.com, pg 868

Quantum Data Inc, 2111 Big Timber Rd, Elgin, IL 60123-1100 *Tel:* 847-888-0450 *Toll Free Tel:* 888-252-6133 (tech support); 800-909-7211 (sales) *Fax:* 847-888-2802 *E-mail:* qd.sales@teledyne.com *Web Site:* www.quantumdata.com, pg 868

Quantum Instruments Inc, 1268 Humbracht Circle, Bartlett, IL 60103-1631 *Toll Free Tel:* 800-989-0505 *Fax:* 630-830-2525 *E-mail:* quantumhelp@qtm.com; quantsales@qtm.com *Web Site:* www.qtm.com, pg 868

Quatrefoil Associates Inc, 29 "C" St, Laurel, MD 20707 *Tel:* 301-470-4748 *Fax:* 301-470-4749 *E-mail:* info@ quatrefoil.com *Web Site:* www.quatrefoil.com, pg 868

Questar Corp, 6204 Ingham Rd, New Hope, PA 18938 *Tel:* 215-862-5277 *Toll Free Tel:* 800-247-9607 *Fax:* 215-862-0512 *E-mail:* questar@erols.com *Web Site:* www.questarcorporation.com, pg 868

Questar Entertainment Inc, 307 N Michigan Ave, 5th fl, Chicago, IL 60601-5305 *Tel:* 312-266-9400 *Toll Free Tel:* 800-544-8422 (cust serv) *E-mail:* info@ questarentertainment.com *Web Site:* www. questarentertainment.com, pg 868

Quickbeam Systems Inc (QSI), 4411 McLeod Rd NE, Suite E, Albuquerque, NM 87109 *Tel:* 505-345-9230 *E-mail:* sales@quickbeam.com *Web Site:* www. quickbeam.com, pg 868

Quickdraw Animation Society, 2011 Tenth Ave SW, Calgary, AB T3C 0K4, Canada *Tel:* 403-261-5767 *E-mail:* info@quickdrawanimation.ca; production@quickdrawanimation.ca; programming@ quickdrawanimation.ca *Web Site:* quickdrawanimation. ca; www.giraffest.ca, pg 961

Quiet Planet LLC, PO Box 900, Indianola, WA 98342 *Tel:* 360-477-9588 *Web Site:* www.quietplanet.com, pg 868

Quilt in a Day, 1955 Diamond St, San Marcos, CA 92078 *Tel:* 760-591-0082 *Toll Free Tel:* 800-777-4852 *Fax:* 760-591-4424 *E-mail:* customerservice@ quiltinaday.com *Web Site:* www.quiltinaday.com, pg 868

Quince Imaging Inc, 2810 Towerview Rd, Herndon, VA 20171-3206 *Tel:* 703-742-7520 *Toll Free Tel:* 888-252-4960 *Fax:* 703-742-7586 *E-mail:* info@quinceimaging. com; sales@quinceimaging.com; operations@ quinceimaging.com *Web Site:* www.quinceimaging. com, pg 868

Quintessence Audio Ltd, 5701 W Dempster St, Morton Grove, IL 60053 *Tel:* 847-966-4434 *Web Site:* www. quintessenceaudio.com, pg 868

R & R Cases & Cabinets, 1217 Rand Rd, Des Plaines, IL 60016 *Tel:* 847-299-8100 *Fax:* 847-299-8110 *E-mail:* sales@rrcases.com *Web Site:* www.rrcases. com, pg 868

R/GA, 450 W 33 St, 12th fl, New York, NY 10001 *Tel:* 212-946-4000 *E-mail:* web@rga.com *Web Site:* www.rga.com, pg 868

Radial Engineering Ltd, 1588 Kebet Way, Port Coquitlam, BC V3C 5M5, Canada *Tel:* 604-942-1001 *Toll Free Tel:* 800-939-1001 (orders) *Fax:* 604-942-1010 *E-mail:* info@radialeng.com *Web Site:* www. radialeng.com, pg 868

Radian Audio Engineering Inc, 600 N Batavia St, Orange, CA 92868 *Tel:* 714-288-8900 *Fax:* 714-288-1133 *E-mail:* sales@radianaudio.com *Web Site:* www. radianaudio.com, pg 869

Radiant Images, 2702 Media Center Dr, Los Angeles, CA 90065 *Tel:* 323-737-1314 *Fax:* 310-861-0163 *E-mail:* info@radiantimages.com *Web Site:* www. radiantimages.com, pg 869

Radio Advertising Bureau (RAB), 125 W 55 St, 5th fl, New York, NY 10019 *Tel:* 212-681-7200 *Toll Free Tel:* 800-252-7234 *Fax:* 212-681-7223 *E-mail:* memberresponse@rab.com *Web Site:* www. rab.com, pg 961

Radio & Television Engineering Achievement Awards, 1771 "N" St NW, Washington, DC 20036 *Tel:* 202-429-5300 *E-mail:* nab@nab.org; techawards@nab.org (nominations) *Web Site:* www.nab.org, pg 1000

Radio Design Labs (RDL), 659 N Sixth St, Prescott, AZ 86301 *Tel:* 928-443-9391 (sales); 928-778-3554 (cust serv) *Toll Free Tel:* 800-281-2683 (sales); 800-933-1780 (cust serv) *Fax:* 928-778-3506 (cust serv); 928-443-9392 (sales) *Toll Free Tel:* 800-289-7338 (sales) *E-mail:* sales@rdlnet.com; service@rdlnet.com; exportsales@rdlnet.com (Latin America & Asia/Pacific sales) *Web Site:* www.rdlnet.com, pg 869

Radio Systems Inc, 601 Heron Dr, Logan Township, NJ 08085 *Tel:* 856-467-8000 *Fax:* 856-467-3044 *E-mail:* sales@radiosystems.com; tech@radiosystems. com *Web Site:* www.radiosystems.com, pg 869

Radio Television Digital News Association (RTDNA), The National Press Bldg, 529 14 St NW, Suite 1240, Washington, DC 20045 *Tel:* 202-662-7254 *Fax:* 202-223-4007 *Web Site:* www.rtdna.org; www. excellenceinjournalism.org, pg 961

Radio Vision Inc, 531 W Main St, Denison, TX 75020 *Tel:* 903-337-4200 *Toll Free Tel:* 800-326-3198 *Fax:* 903-337-4296 *E-mail:* info@radiovisioninc.com *Web Site:* www.radiovisioninc.com, pg 869

Radio Visions, PO Box 4732, Toms River, NJ 08754-4732 *Tel:* 732-240-3119 *E-mail:* sales@radiovisions. com *Web Site:* www.radiovisions.com, pg 869

RadioArt/Bob & Ray CDs & MP3 Files, PO Box 519, Plantarium Sta, New York, NY 10024-0519 *Tel:* 212-595-1837 *Web Site:* www.bobandray.com, pg 869

Radiotechniques Engineering LLC, 402 Tenth Ave, Haddon Heights, NJ 08035-1838 *Tel:* 856-546-8008 *Fax:* 856-546-1841 *E-mail:* sales@radiotechniques. com *Web Site:* www.radiotechniques.com, pg 869

Radius® Display Products Inc, 800 Fabric Xpress Way, Dallas, TX 75234 *Tel:* 972-406-1221 *Toll Free Tel:* 800-FABRIC-X (322-7429); 866-966-4066 (sales); 866-966-8266 (hospitality) *Fax:* 972-406-1321 *Toll Free Fax:* 888-322-7429 *Web Site:* www.radiusdp.com, pg 869

RADMAR Inc, PO Box 425, Northbrook, IL 60065-0425 *Tel:* 847-298-7980 *E-mail:* radmarinc@gmail. com *Web Site:* www.radmarinc.com, pg 869

Rafik, 817 Broadway, 2nd fl, Suite 11, New York, NY 10003 *Tel:* 646-480-5729 *E-mail:* info@rafikvideo. com; sales@rafikvideo.com *Web Site:* www.rafikvideo. com, pg 869

Rahlic Publishing Co, 301 Keithwood Rd, Wynnewood, PA 19096 *Tel:* 610-649-0982, pg 869

Rainbow International Inc, 1103 Canyon Rd, Santa Fe, NM 87501 *Tel:* 773-505-6264 *Web Site:* www. rainbowplace.com; greatplainspress.com, pg 869

Rainbow Media Taos, 27 Valencia Rd, Taos, NM 87571 *Tel:* 575-776-2268 *Toll Free Tel:* 800-748-1540 *Fax:* 575-776-2804, pg 869

Rainbow Video Productions Inc, 23803 S 162 St, Adams, NE 68301 *Tel:* 402-430-7343 *Web Site:* www. rainbowvideo.com, pg 869

Raincoast Books, 2440 Viking Way, Richmond, BC V6V 1N2, Canada *Tel:* 604-448-7100 *Toll Free Tel:* 800-663-5714 (cust serv & book orders) *Fax:* 604-270-7161 *Toll Free Fax:* 800-565-3770 (cust serv & book orders) *E-mail:* info@raincoast. com; customerservice@raincoast.com *Web Site:* www. raincoast.com, pg 869

RAM® Mounts, 8410 Dallas Ave S, Seattle, WA 98108 *Tel:* 206-763-8361 *Toll Free Tel:* 800-497-7479 *Fax:* 206-763-9615 *E-mail:* sales@rammount.com *Web Site:* www.rammount.com, pg 869

RAMSA Professional Audio Systems, 2 Riverfront Plaza, Newark, NJ 07012 *Tel:* 201-348-7000 *Web Site:* panasonic.net/pss/ramsa, pg 870

Rand McNally Education, 9855 Woods Dr, Skokie, IL 60077 *Toll Free Tel:* 800-333-0136 *Web Site:* www. randmcnally.com; education.randmcnally.com, pg 870

Randall House Publications, 114 Bush Rd, Nashville, TN 37217 *Tel:* 615-361-1221 *Toll Free Tel:* 800-877-7030 *Fax:* 615-367-0535 *E-mail:* info@randallhouse.com *Web Site:* www.randallhouse.com, pg 870

R&B Communications Inc, 2397 Somrack Dr, Willoughby, OH 44094 *Tel:* 440-946-9511 *Web Site:* www.rbcommunications.net, pg 870

Randolf Productions Inc, 7271 Garden Grove Blvd, Suite F, Garden Grove, CA 92841 *Tel:* 949-794-9109 *Toll Free Tel:* 800-266-7741 *Fax:* 949-794-9117 *E-mail:* sales@go2rpi.com *Web Site:* www.go2rpi.com; christianmovieshop.com, pg 870

Random House Children's Books, 1745 Broadway, 10th fl, New York, NY 10019 *Tel:* 212-782-9000 *Web Site:* www.randomhousekids.com, pg 870

Rane, 200 Scenic View Dr, Cumberland, RI 02864 *Tel:* 401-658-3131; 401-659-8192 *Fax:* 401-658-3640 *E-mail:* info@rane.com *Web Site:* www.rane.com, pg 870

The RapcoHorizon Co, 3581 Larch Lane, Jackson, MO 63755 *Toll Free Tel:* 800-253-7360; 800-467-2726 *Fax:* 269-388-9681 *E-mail:* info@rhcholdings.net; customerservice@rhcholdings.net; sales@rhcholdings.net *Web Site:* www.rapcohorizon.com, pg 870

David Rapkin Audio Production, 473 West End Ave, Unit 6A, New York, NY 10024 *Tel:* 212-362-7236 *E-mail:* drapco@aol.com, pg 870

Rauland-Borg Corp, 1802 W Central Rd, Mount Prospect, IL 60056 *Tel:* 847-590-7100 *Toll Free Tel:* 800-752-7725 *Web Site:* www.rauland.com, pg 870

RAVA Films, 67 West St, Suite 604, Brooklyn, NY 11222 *E-mail:* info@ravafilms.com *Web Site:* www. ravafilms.com, pg 870

Raven Rental, 2617 Peach St, Erie, PA 16508 *Tel:* 814-456-0331 *Web Site:* www.ravensound.com, pg 870

Raven Screen Corp, PO Box 691, Harriman, NY 10926 *Tel:* 845-782-1844 *Toll Free Tel:* 800-847-6906 *Fax:* 845-782-1840 *E-mail:* info@ravenscreen.com *Web Site:* www.ravenscreen.com, pg 870

Ray Supply Inc, 9 Pine St, Glens Falls, NY 12801 *Tel:* 518-792-5848 *Toll Free Tel:* 800-347-5851 (orders) *Fax:* 518-792-1727 *E-mail:* sales@raysupply. com *Web Site:* www.raysupply.com, pg 870

RB Productions, 3-4191 Longmoor Dr, Burlington, ON L7L 5J9, Canada *Tel:* 905-633-7474 *E-mail:* sales@ radicalbob.com *Web Site:* www.rbproductionz.com, pg 870

RBR Productions, 1926 Greenview Rd, Northbrook, IL 60062 *Tel:* 847-362-4060 *Web Site:* www. rbrproductions.com, pg 870

RC Communications, 131 Garlisch Dr, Elk Grove Village, IL 60007 *Tel:* 847-678-7000 *Fax:* 847-678-9378 *E-mail:* rccsales@rentcom.com; rent@ rentcom.com *Web Site:* www.rentcom.com; www.rc-communications.com, pg 870

RCA Records, 25 Madison Ave, New York, NY 10010 *Tel:* 212-833-8000 *E-mail:* publicity@rcarecords.com *Web Site:* www.rcarecords.com; www.sonymusic.com, pg 871

RCI Custom Products, 801 N East St, Suite 2-A, Frederick, MD 21701 *Tel:* 301-620-9130 *Toll Free Tel:* 800-546-4724 *Fax:* 301-620-9103 *Toll Free Fax:* 800-546-6175 *E-mail:* info@rcicustom.com *Web Site:* www.rcicustom.com, pg 871

RCS Enterprises, 445 Hamilton Ave, 7th fl, White Plains, NY 10601 *Tel:* 914-428-4600 *Fax:* 914-428-5922 *E-mail:* info@rcsworks.com *Web Site:* www. rcsworks.com, pg 871

Real Cool Productions, 800 S Main St, Suite 203, Mansfield, MA 02048 *Tel:* 508-337-8520 *E-mail:* info@rcplearning.com *Web Site:* realcoolproductions.com, pg 871

Real to Reel International Film Festival, 111 S Washington St, Shelby, NC 28150 *Tel:* 704-484-2787 *Fax:* 704-481-1822 *Web Site:* www.ccartscouncil. org/realtoreel, pg 1000

Real to Reel Studios Inc, 4141 Office Pkwy, Dallas, TX 75204 *Tel:* 214-528-4242 *Web Site:* www.rtrstudios. com, pg 871

Reality Check Systems, 726 S Flower St, Burbank, CA 91502 *Tel:* 323-465-3900 *Fax:* 323-465-3600 *E-mail:* info@realitychecksystems.com *Web Site:* www.realityx.com, pg 871

Really Good Stuff, 448 Pepper St, Monroe, CT 06468 *Tel:* 203-261-1920 *Toll Free Tel:* 800-366-1920 (orders); 877-867-1920 (cust serv) *Fax:* 203-268-1796 *Web Site:* www.reallygoodstuff.com, pg 871

RealNetworks Inc, 1501 First Ave S, Suite 600, Seattle, WA 98134 *Tel:* 206-674-2700 *Toll Free Tel:* 800-444-8011 *Fax:* 206-674-2696 *Web Site:* www.real.com; www.realnetworks.com, pg 871

The Olivier Rebbot Award, 40 W 45 St, New York, NY 10036 *Tel:* 212-626-9220 *Fax:* 212-626-9210 *E-mail:* info@opcofamerica.org *Web Site:* www. opcofamerica.org, pg 1000

Rebel Records, PO Box 7405, Charlottesville, VA 22906-7405 *Tel:* 434-973-5151 *E-mail:* questions@ rebelrecords.com *Web Site:* rebelrecords.com, pg 871

Rebirth Inc, 81 Chandler St, Detroit, MI 48202 *Tel:* 313-875-0289 *E-mail:* wenhajazz@aol.com *Web Site:* www.rebirthjazz.com, pg 871

Record Plant Remote, 1170 Greenwood Lake Tpke, Ringwood, NJ 07456 *Tel:* 973-728-8114 *Fax:* 973-728-8761 *E-mail:* info@recordplantremote.com *Web Site:* www.recordplantremote.com, pg 871

Recorded Books Inc, an RBmedia company, 270 Skipjack Rd, Prince Frederick, MD 20678 *Tel:* 410-535-5590 *Toll Free Tel:* 800-638-1304 *Fax:* 410-535-5499 *E-mail:* customerservice@recordedbooks.com *Web Site:* www.recordedbooks.com, pg 871

Recordex USA Inc, 10-50 46 Ave, Long Island City, NY 11101 *Tel:* 718-392-5380 *Fax:* 718-392-5485 *E-mail:* sales@recordexusa.com; support@ recordexusa.com *Web Site:* www.recordexusa.com, pg 872

The Recording Academy, 3030 Olympic Blvd, Santa Monica, CA 90404 *Tel:* 310-392-3777 *Fax:* 310-392-2306 *E-mail:* losangeles@grammy.com *Web Site:* www.grammy.org/recording-academy, pg 961

Recording Industry Association of America® (RIAA), 1025 "F" St NW, 10th fl, Washington, DC 20004 *Tel:* 202-775-0101 *Web Site:* www.riaa.com, pg 961

Recording Media & Equipment Inc (RM&E), 3736 SW 30 Ave, Fort Lauderdale, FL 33312 *Tel:* 954-791-9797 *Toll Free Tel:* 800-541-9797 *Fax:* 954-791-6662 *Web Site:* www.rmeinc.com, pg 872

Recortec Inc, 3329 Kifer Rd, Santa Clara, CA 95051-0719 *Tel:* 408-928-1480 *Toll Free Tel:* 800-729-7654 *Fax:* 408-928-1489 *E-mail:* info@recortec. com; support@recortec.com; sales@recortec.com *Web Site:* www.recortec.com, pg 872

The Recruiters Library, 14728 Shirley St, Omaha, NE 68144 *Tel:* 402-334-1676 *Toll Free Tel:* 800-293-1676 *Fax:* 402-334-4437 *Web Site:* www. thebestcollegerecruiter.com, pg 872

Red Hill Corp, 1540 Biglerville Rd, Gettysburg, PA 17325 *Tel:* 717-337-3038 *Toll Free Tel:* 800-822-4003 *Fax:* 717-337-0732 *E-mail:* customerservice@ supergrit.com *Web Site:* www.supergrit.com, pg 872

Red Sky Studios, 184 Everett St, Allston, MA 02134 *Tel:* 617-903-3373 *E-mail:* mail@redsky-studios.com *Web Site:* redsky-studios.com, pg 872

RED Studios Hollywood, 846 N Cahuenga Blvd, Los Angeles, CA 90038 *Tel:* 323-463-0808 *Web Site:* www.redstudio.com, pg 872

Redco Audio Inc, 1701 Stratford Ave, Stratford, CT 06615 *Tel:* 203-502-7600 *Toll Free Tel:* 800-572-7280 *Fax:* 203-502-7610 *E-mail:* orders@redco. com *Web Site:* www.redco.com, pg 872

Redman Movies & Stories, 1075 S 700 W, Salt Lake City, UT 84104 *Tel:* 801-978-9292 *Fax:* 801-978-2299 *E-mail:* info@redmanmovies.com *Web Site:* www. redmanmovies.com, pg 872

Redwood Audiobooks, 10375 Nichols Lane, Mendocino, CA 95460 *Tel:* 707-937-1225 *E-mail:* audiobks@mcn. org *Web Site:* www.universitypressaudiobooks.com, pg 872

Reed Presentations Inc (RPI), 17 Water St, Lebanon, NJ 08833 *Tel:* 908-753-8800 *Fax:* 908-753-8823 *E-mail:* info@reedpresentations.com *Web Site:* www. reedpresentations.com, pg 872

Reef Photo & Video, 2303 N Andrews Ave, Fort Lauderdale, FL 33311 *Tel:* 954-537-0644 *Toll Free Tel:* 877-453-8927 *Fax:* 954-537-0645 *Web Site:* reefphoto.com, pg 872

Reel Men Rentals Inc, 3902 E Broadway Rd, Phoenix, AZ 85040 *Tel:* 602-286-6800 *Fax:* 602-286-0080 *E-mail:* rentals@reelmen.com *Web Site:* www.reelmen. com, pg 872

Reel One International Ltd, 486 Ste-Catherine W, Suite 100, Montreal, QC H3B 1A6, Canada *E-mail:* sales@ reeloneent.com *Web Site:* reeloneent.com, pg 872

Reel Picture, 5330 Eastgate Mall, San Diego, CA 92121 *Tel:* 858-587-0301 *Toll Free Tel:* 866-502-3472 (US & CN) *Fax:* 858-587-8838 *Web Site:* www.reelpicture. com, pg 872

Reelout Queer Film + Video Festival, 82 Sydenham St, Kingston, ON K7L 3H4, Canada *Tel:* 613-549-REEL (549-7335) *Web Site:* www.reelout.com, pg 1001

Reelsound Recording Co, 701 Southern Dr, Buda, TX 78610 *Tel:* 512-312-1610; 512-422-7098 (cell) *Web Site:* www.reelsound-usa.com, pg 872

ReelWorld Film Festival, 50 Carroll St, Suite 200, Toronto, ON M4M 3G3, Canada *Tel:* 416-598-7933 *E-mail:* info@reelworld.ca; contact@reelworld.ca *Web Site:* www.reelworld.ca, pg 1001

Rees, Rees Plaza at East Wharf, Suite 300, 9211 Lake Hefner Pkwy, Oklahoma City, OK 73120 *Tel:* 405-942-7337 *Fax:* 405-948-1261 *E-mail:* rees@rees.com *Web Site:* www.rees.com, pg 872

Reference Recordings, PO Box 77225, San Francisco, CA 94107 *Tel:* 650-355-1845 *Toll Free Tel:* 800-336-8866 *Fax:* 650-355-1949 *E-mail:* referencerecordings@gmail.com *Web Site:* www.referencerecordings.com, pg 872

Regal Photo Products Inc/Arkay Corp, 2769 S 34 St, Milwaukee, WI 53215-3541 *Tel:* 414-645-2050 *Toll Free Tel:* 800-695-2055 (sales) *Fax:* 414-645-9515, pg 873

Regent Press Publishers & Printers, 2747 Regent St, Berkeley, CA 94705 *Tel:* 510-845-1196 *E-mail:* regentpress@mindspring.com *Web Site:* www. regentpress.net, pg 873

Regional Artist Project Grants Program, 227 W Trade St, Suite 250, Charlotte, NC 28202 *Tel:* 704-333-2272 *Fax:* 704-333-2720 *E-mail:* asc@artsandscience.org *Web Site:* www.artsandscience.org, pg 1001

Register Data Systems, 1691 Forsyth St, Macon, GA 31201 *Tel:* 478-745-5858, pg 873

REI - Radio Engineering Industries, 6534 "L" St, Omaha, NE 68117 *Tel:* 402-339-2200 *Toll Free Tel:* 800-228-9275 (sales); 877-726-4617 (tech support) *Fax:* 402-339-1704 *E-mail:* info@radioeng. com; orderdesk@radioeng.com *Web Site:* www. radioeng.com, pg 873

Allan Reider Photography & Video Productions, 2174 Morris Ave, Union, NJ 07083 *Tel:* 908-688-8808 *E-mail:* info@njphotographer.com *Web Site:* www. njphotographer.com, pg 873

Richard Reiter Productions Inc, 36 Catherine Ct, Cedar Grove, NJ 07009 *Tel:* 973-857-2557 *Fax:* 973-857-2935 *E-mail:* reiterjazz@gmail.com; reiterjazz@ yahoo.com; reiterjazz@optonline.net *Web Site:* www. richardreiter.com, pg 873

Dick Reizner Film & Video, 801 Atherton Dr, Suite 120, Manteca, CA 95337 *Tel:* 209-665-7166 *Web Site:* www.reizner.com, pg 873

Remote Audio Products, 220 Great Circle Rd, Suite 114, Nashville, TN 37228-1737 *Tel:* 615-256-3513 *Fax:* 615-634-2277 *E-mail:* info@remoteaudio.com *Web Site:* www.remoteaudio.com, pg 873

Renaissance Albums, 21 Grace Church St, Port Chester, NY 10573 *Tel:* 914-939-6878 *Toll Free Tel:* 800-961-6710 *Fax:* 914-939-8047 *E-mail:* info@renaissancealbums.com *Web Site:* www. renaissancealbums.com, pg 873

Renaissance Media, 909 Logan St, Suite 11F, Denver, CO 80203 *Tel:* 303-892-1415 *Web Site:* www. renaissancemedia.com, pg 873

Renaissance Unity, 11200 E 11 Mile Rd, Warren, MI 48089 *Tel:* 586-353-2300 *Fax:* 586-758-1159 *E-mail:* info@renaissanceunity.org *Web Site:* www. renaissanceunity.org; mastermindjournal.org (catalog), pg 873

Renegade Animation Inc, 111 E Broadway, Suite 208, Glendale, CA 91205 *Tel:* 818-551-2351 *Fax:* 818-551-2350 *Web Site:* www.renegadeanimation.com, pg 873

Renkus-Heinz Inc, 19201 Cook St, Foothill Ranch, CA 92610-3501 *Tel:* 949-588-9997 *Fax:* 949-588-9514 *E-mail:* sales@renkus-heinz.com *Web Site:* www. renkus-heinz.com, pg 873

RentACamera.com, 2605 Westwood Dr, Nashville, TN 37204 *Tel:* 615-320-3200 *Toll Free Tel:* 855-588-2882 *E-mail:* info@tvcnashville.com *Web Site:* www. rentacamera.com, pg 873

Replicopy Digital Media Center, 1120 Jupiter Rd, Suite 190, Plano, TX 75074 *Tel:* 972-702-8388 *Toll Free Tel:* 800-628-1124 *E-mail:* replicopy@replicopy.com *Web Site:* www.replicopy.com, pg 873

Reprise Records, 3300 Warner Blvd, Burbank, CA 91505 *Tel:* 818-846-9090 *Web Site:* www.warnerbrosrecords. com, pg 873

Research Press, 2612 N Mattis Ave, Champaign, IL 61822 *Tel:* 217-352-3273 *Toll Free Tel:* 800-519-2707 *Fax:* 217-352-1221 *E-mail:* orders@researchpress.com *Web Site:* www.researchpress.com, pg 873

Research Technology International (RTI), 4700 Chase Ave, Lincolnwood, IL 60712-1689 *Tel:* 847-677-3000 *Toll Free Tel:* 800-323-7520 *Fax:* 847-677-1311 *Toll Free Fax:* 800-784-6733 *E-mail:* sales@rtico.com *Web Site:* rtico.com, pg 873

Residency Fellowship, 154 San Angelo Dr, Amherst, VA 24521 *Tel:* 434-946-7236 *Fax:* 434-946-7239 *E-mail:* vcca@vcca.com *Web Site:* www.vcca.com, pg 1001

Resolution Productions Group, 2226 W Walnut St, Chicago, IL 60612 *Tel:* 312-243-8230 *E-mail:* info@ resolutionproductionsgroup.com *Web Site:* www. resolutionproductionsgroup.com, pg 874

RetinaVision Productions, 19 Barker Ave, Fairfax, CA 94930 *Tel:* 415-459-3926, pg 874

Rev UP Tech, 20929 Ventura Blvd, Suite 47-212, Woodland Hills, CA 91364 *Tel:* 818-995-1719 *Toll Free Tel:* 877-372-0005 *Fax:* 818-979-9599 *Web Site:* revuptech.com, pg 874

Revelli, PO Box 150098, San Rafael, CA 94915 *Tel:* 415-460-9898 *Fax:* 415-460-9897 *E-mail:* colorstyledesign@aol.com, pg 874

Revels Records, 80 Mount Auburn St, Watertown, MA 02472 *Tel:* 617-972-8300 *Fax:* 617-972-8400 *E-mail:* info@revels.org *Web Site:* www.revels.org, pg 874

Revolution Lighting Technologies Inc, 177 Broad St, 12th fl, Stamford, CT 06901 *Tel:* 203-504-1111 *Toll Free Tel:* 877-578-2536 *E-mail:* support@rvlti.com; info@rvlti.com *Web Site:* www.rvlti.com, pg 874

REX, 610 SW 17 Ave, Portland, OR 97205 *Tel:* 503-238-4525 *E-mail:* info@rexpost.com *Web Site:* www. rexpost.com, pg 874

RF Industries, 7610 Miramar Rd, San Diego, CA 92126 *Tel:* 858-549-6340 *Toll Free Tel:* 800-233-1728 *Fax:* 858-549-6345 *E-mail:* rfi@rfindustries. com; tech@rfindustries.org; invest@rfindustries.org *Web Site:* www.rfindustries.com, pg 874

RF Specialties of Texas LLC, PO Box 1010, Newark, TX 76071-1010 *Tel:* 214-697-3477 (cell); 817-489-2730 *Toll Free Tel:* 800-537-1801 (Newark) *E-mail:* rfstx@swbell.net *Web Site:* www.rfspecialties. com, pg 874

RGB Spectrum, 950 Marina Village Pkwy, Alameda, CA 94501 *Tel:* 510-814-7000 *Fax:* 510-814-7026 *Web Site:* www.rgb.com, pg 874

RGB Technology Inc, 590 Herndon Pkwy, Suite 500, Herndon, VA 20170-5267 *Tel:* 703-834-1500 *Fax:* 703-834-1506 *E-mail:* solutions@rgbtec.com *Web Site:* www.rgbtec.com, pg 874

Rhode Island Film & Television Office, One Capitol Hill, 3rd fl, Providence, RI 02908 *Tel:* 401-222-3456; 401-222-6666 (hotline) *Fax:* 401-222-3018 *Web Site:* www.film.ri.gov, pg 975

Rhode Island State Council on the Arts Fellowships & Grants Program, One Capitol Hill, 3rd fl, Providence, RI 02908 *Tel:* 401-222-3880 *Fax:* 401-222-3018 *E-mail:* info@arts.ri.gov *Web Site:* www.arts.ri.gov, pg 1001

Rhythm & Hues Studios Inc, 5890 W Jefferson Blvd, Suite Q, Los Angeles, CA 90016 *Tel:* 310-448-7500 *Fax:* 310-448-7600 *E-mail:* info-la@rhythm.com *Web Site:* rhythm.com, pg 874

Rhythmic Medicine, 10425 W 177 Terr, Overland Park, KS 66221 *Tel:* 913-851-5100 *E-mail:* music@ rhythmicmedicine.com *Web Site:* www. rhythmicmedicine.com, pg 874

Rhythms Productions (Tom Thumb Music), PO Box 786, Malibu, CA 90265-0786 *Tel:* 310-836-4678 *E-mail:* tomthumbkids@gmail.com *Web Site:* www. tomthumbkids.com, pg 874

RIA Corp, 1615 W 2200 S, Suite B, Salt Lake City, UT 84119 *Tel:* 801-486-8822 *Fax:* 801-486-2741 *E-mail:* sales@riacorp.com *Web Site:* www.riacorp. com, pg 874

The RIAA® Gold® & Platinum® Awards, 1025 "F" St NW, 10th fl, Washington, DC 20004 *Tel:* 202-775-0101 *Web Site:* www.riaa.com/gold-platinum, pg 1001

Rich-Heape Films Inc, 5952 Royal Lane, Suite 254, Dallas, TX 75230 *Tel:* 214-696-6916 *Toll Free Tel:* 888-600-2922 *Web Site:* www.richheape.com, pg 875

The Bart Richards Award for Media Criticism, 302 James Bldg, University Park, PA 16801 *Tel:* 814-865-8801 *Fax:* 814-863-6134 *Web Site:* comm.psu.edu/bart, pg 1001

Lynda Richardson Photography, 7239 Lookout Dr, Richmond, VA 23225 *Tel:* 804-347-9668 *E-mail:* lynda@lyndarichardson.com *Web Site:* lyndarichardson.com, pg 875

Richie Media Productions LLC, 2035 Royal Lane, Suite 203, Dallas, TX 75229 *Tel:* 214-696-9040 *Web Site:* www.richiemedia.com, pg 875

Richmond Sound Design Ltd, 5264 Ross St, Vancouver, BC V5W 3K7, Canada *Web Site:* www. richmondsounddesign.com, pg 875

Richter Productions Inc, 521 E 14 St, Suite 4F, New York, NY 10009 *Tel:* 917-608-7427 *E-mail:* rrprod@ aol.com; richter330@aol.com *Web Site:* www. richtervideos.com, pg 875

Richter Studios, 1143 W Rundell Place, Chicago, IL 60607 *Tel:* 312-861-9999 *Fax:* 312-997-2387 *E-mail:* info@richterstudios.com *Web Site:* www. richterstudios.com, pg 875

The Ridenhour Documentary Film Prize, 116 E 16 St, 8th fl, New York, NY 10003 *Tel:* 212-822-0257 *Fax:* 212-253-5356 *E-mail:* ridenhour@nationinstitute. org *Web Site:* www.ridenhour.org, pg 1001

Ridgecrest Regional Film Commission, 643 N China Lake Blvd, Ridgecrest, CA 93555 *Tel:* 760-375-8202 *Toll Free Tel:* 800-847-4830 *Fax:* 760-375-9850 *E-mail:* permits@filmridgecrest.com *Web Site:* www. filmridgecrest.com, pg 967

Right Coast Recording Inc, 341 Chestnut St, Columbia, PA 17512 *Tel:* 717-681-9801 *Fax:* 717-681-9801 *E-mail:* rightcoastrecording@gmail.com; studio@rightcoastrecording.com *Web Site:* www. rightcoastrecording.com, pg 875

Right Stuf Inc, 512 NE Main St, Grimes, IA 50111-2188 *Tel:* 515-986-1028 *Toll Free Tel:* 800-338-6827 *Fax:* 515-986-1129 *E-mail:* info@rightstuf.com *Web Site:* www.rightstufanime.com, pg 875

RingSide Creative, 13320 Northend, Suite 3000, Oak Park, MI 48237 *Tel:* 248-548-2500 *E-mail:* info@ ringsidecreative.com; newbiz@ringsidecreative.com *Web Site:* www.ringsidecreative.com, pg 875

Rink Rat Productions Inc, 2 Monk Lane, St John's, NL A1E 1M8, Canada *Tel:* 709-739-9055 *Fax:* 709-739-9065 *E-mail:* info@rinkratproductions.com *Web Site:* www.rinkratproductions.com, pg 875

The Rip-Tie Co, 883 San Leandro Blvd, San Leandro, CA 94577 *Tel:* 510-577-0200 *Toll Free Tel:* 800-7-RIPTIE (774-7843) *Fax:* 510-553-0160 *E-mail:* info@ riptie.com *Web Site:* www.riptie.com, pg 875

Risk International & Associates Inc, c/o Global Health & Safety Network, 8803 W Ontario Ave, Littleton, CO 80128 *Tel:* 720-922-0707 *Fax:* 720-922-0707 *Web Site:* www.globalhealthandsafety.net, pg 875

Ritz Camera & Image, 114 Tived Lane E, Edison, NJ 08837 *Toll Free Tel:* 855-622-RITZ (622-7489) *E-mail:* customerservice@ritzcamera.com *Web Site:* www.ritzcamera.com, pg 875

RJ Video Productions, 15585 Tilden St, San Leandro, CA 94579-2316 *Tel:* 510-357-6535, pg 875

RJS Productions, PO Box 739, Westminster, MD 21158 *Tel:* 410-876-6300 *Fax:* 410-857-0608, pg 875

RKO Pictures Inc, 11301 W Olympic Blvd, Suite 510, Los Angeles, CA 90064 *Tel:* 310-277-0707 *Fax:* 310-566-8940 *E-mail:* info@rko.com *Web Site:* rko.com, pg 875

RLJ Entertainment Inc, 8515 Georgia Ave, Suite 650, Silver Spring, MD 20910 *Tel:* 301-608-2115 *Toll Free Tel:* 800-999-0212 *E-mail:* inquiries@rljentertainment. com *Web Site:* www.us.rljentertainment.com, pg 875

RNJ Electronics, 202 New Hwy, Amityville, NY 11701 *Tel:* 631-226-2700 *Toll Free Tel:* 800-645-5833 *Fax:* 631-226-2770 *Toll Free Fax:* 800-765-3291 *E-mail:* sales@rnjelectronics.com *Web Site:* www. rnjelectronics.com, pg 875

Road Cases USA Inc, 1121-20 Lincoln Ave, Holbrook, NY 11741 *Tel:* 631-557-0000 *E-mail:* sales@ roadcases.com *Web Site:* www.roadcases.com, pg 876

Road Pictures, 212 W Tenth St, Suite B-100, Indianapolis, IN 46202 *Tel:* 317-267-9590 *Fax:* 317-267-9677 *Web Site:* www.roadpictures.com, pg 876

Roadside Attractions, 7920 Sunset Blvd, No 402, Los Angeles, CA 90046 *Tel:* 323-882-8490 *E-mail:* roadsideflix@gmail.com *Web Site:* www.roadsideattractions.com, pg 876

Robbins Media Inc, 450 North End Ave, Suite 14E, New York, NY 10282 *Tel:* 212-661-7670 *E-mail:* info@ robbinsmedia.com *Web Site:* www.robbinsmedia.com, pg 876

Robertson Worldwide, 4700 137 St, Crestwood, IL 60445 *Tel:* 708-388-2315 *Toll Free Tel:* 800-323-5633 *Fax:* 708-388-2420 *Toll Free Fax:* 877-388-2420 *E-mail:* info@robertsonlighting.com *Web Site:* www. robertsondirect.com, pg 876

Paul Robeson Awards, 49 Washington St, Newark, NJ 07102-3176 *Tel:* 973-596-6550 *E-mail:* nbff@ newarkmuseum.org *Web Site:* www.newarkmuseum. org/nbff, pg 1001

Rochester/Finger Lakes Film Commission, 45 East Ave, Suite 400, Rochester, NY 14604-2294 *Tel:* 585-279-8308 *Fax:* 585-232-4822 *Web Site:* www.filmrochester. org, pg 974

Rochester International Film Festival, PO Box 17746, Rochester, NY 14617 *Tel:* 585-234-7411 (voice mail) *E-mail:* president@rochesterfilmfest.org (use MOAS on subject); submissions@rochesterfilmfest.org *Web Site:* www.rochesterfilmfest.org, pg 1001

Rockie Awards Program Competition, 100-366 Adelaide St W, Toronto, ON M5V 1R9, Canada *Tel:* 416-408-2300 *Toll Free Tel:* 888-287-2279 *Fax:* 416-408-0870 *E-mail:* info@achillesmedia. com banffmediafestival.com; rockies. playbackonline.ca, pg 1001

Rocking Horse Studio, 1380 Upper City Rd, Pittsfield, NH 03263 *Tel:* 603-512-5347 *E-mail:* info@ rockinghorsestudio.com *Web Site:* www. rockinghorsestudio.com, pg 876

Rockland Colloid LLC, PO Box 3120, Oregon City, OR 97045-0306 *Tel:* 503-655-4152 (sales) *Toll Free Fax:* 866-737-0174 *E-mail:* orders@rockaloid.com *Web Site:* www.rockaloid.com, pg 876

Rocktown Media, 1361 Lincolnshire Dr, Harrisonburg, VA 22802 *Tel:* 540-433-7700 *Toll Free Tel:* 888-433-8700 *E-mail:* info@rocktown.tv *Web Site:* www. rocktown.tv, pg 876

Rockwell Communications Inc, 321 Burnham St, East Hartford, CT 06108 *Tel:* 860-528-9091 *Toll Free Tel:* 800-566-6681 *Fax:* 860-289-2334 *E-mail:* rockwellservice@aol.com *Web Site:* www. rockwellcommunications.com, pg 876

Rocky Mountain Audio/Video Productions Inc, 7950 S Lincoln St, B-100, Littleton, CO 80122 *Tel:* 303-730-1100 *Toll Free Tel:* 877-856-4644 *Web Site:* www. rmavp.com, pg 876

Rodeo Video Inc, 412 S Main, Snowflake, AZ 85937 *Tel:* 928-536-7111 *Toll Free Tel:* 800-331-1269 *Fax:* 928-536-7120 *E-mail:* info@rodeovideo.com *Web Site:* www.rodeovideo.com, pg 876

Fred Rogers Productions, 2100 Wharton St, Suite 700, Pittsburgh, PA 15203 *Tel:* 412-687-2990 *Toll Free Tel:* 877-677-6437 *E-mail:* info@fredrogers.org *Web Site:* www.fredrogers.org, pg 876

Rohde & Schwarz USA Inc, 6821 Benjamin Franklin Dr, Columbia, MD 21046 *Tel:* 410-910-7800 *Toll Free Tel:* 888-837-8772 *Fax:* 410-910-7801 *E-mail:* info@ rsa.rohde-schwarz.com *Web Site:* www.rohde-schwarz. us, pg 876

Roland Corp US, 5100 S Eastern Ave, Los Angeles, CA 90040-2938 *Tel:* 323-890-3700; 323-890-3771 (parts & serv); 323-890-3740 (prod support) *Fax:* 323-721-4875 *Web Site:* www.rolandus.com/us, pg 876

Glenn Roland Films, PO Box 24035, Los Angeles, CA 90024 *Tel:* 310-475-0937 *Fax:* 310-475-0939, pg 876

Rollin Studios, 259 Green St, 2nd fl, Brooklyn, NY 11222 *Toll Free Tel:* 844-576-5546 *E-mail:* more@ rollin-studios.com *Web Site:* www.rollin-studios.com, pg 877

Rolls Corp, 5968 S 350 W, Murray, UT 84107 *Tel:* 801-263-9053 *Fax:* 801-263-9068 *E-mail:* info@rolls.com *Web Site:* www.rolls.com, pg 877

Romar Learning Solutions LLC, 6700 Woodlands Pkwy, Suite 230-292, Woodlands, TX 77382 *Tel:* 281-292-5508 *Fax:* 281-363-2309 *E-mail:* info@romarlearning. com *Web Site:* romarlearning.com, pg 877

Rosco Laboratories Inc, 52 Harbor View, Stamford, CT 06902 *Tel:* 203-708-8900 *Toll Free Tel:* 800-ROSCO NY (767-2669) *Fax:* 203-708-8919 *E-mail:* info@ rosco.com *Web Site:* us.rosco.com, pg 877

Rose Brand, 4 Emerson Lane, Secaucus, NJ 07094 *Tel:* 201-809-1730 *Toll Free Tel:* 800-223-1624 *Fax:* 201-809-1851 *E-mail:* info@rosebrand.com *Web Site:* www.rosebrand.com, pg 877

Rose City Sound, 4811 SE 16 Ave, Portland, OR 97202 *Tel:* 503-238-6330 *Toll Free Tel:* 877-503-7673 *Fax:* 503-238-9872 *E-mail:* sales@rosecitysound.com *Web Site:* www.rosecitysound.com, pg 877

Rose Packaging & Design Inc, 4000 Sopris Mountain Rd, Basalt, CO 81621-9179 *Tel:* 970-927-6515 *Toll Free Tel:* 800-308-1003 *Fax:* 303-557-6366 *E-mail:* sales@rosepkg.com *Web Site:* www.rosepkg. com, pg 877

Judson Rosebush Co Inc, 630 Ninth Ave, Suite 507, New York, NY 10036 *Tel:* 212-581-3000 *E-mail:* judson@ rosebush.com *Web Site:* www.rosebush.com, pg 877

Peter Rosen Productions Inc, c/o Du Art, 245 W 55 St, Suite 308, New York, NY 10019 *Tel:* 212-535-8927 *Fax:* 212-517-5337 *E-mail:* rosenprod@aol.com *Web Site:* www.peterrosenproductions.com, pg 877

The Rosenthal Group, 10625 Cohasset St, Sun Valley, CA 91352 *Tel:* 818-252-1010 *Fax:* 818-252-1070 *Web Site:* www.therosenthalgroup.com, pg 877

The Madeline Dane Ross Award, 40 W 45 St, New York, NY 10036 *Tel:* 212-626-9220 *Fax:* 212-626-9210 *E-mail:* info@opcofamerica.org *Web Site:* www. opcofamerica.org, pg 1002

Mary Riepma Ross Media Arts Center, University of Nebraska-Lincoln, 313 N 13 St, Lincoln, NE 68588 *Tel:* 402-472-9100 *Fax:* 402-472-2576 *E-mail:* info@ theross.org *Web Site:* www.theross.org, pg 877

Ross Video Ltd, 8 John St, Iroquois, ON K0E 1K0, Canada *Tel:* 613-652-4886 *Fax:* 613-652-4425 *E-mail:* solutions@rossvideo.com *Web Site:* www. rossvideo.com, pg 877

Rough House, 550 Bryant St, San Francisco, CA 94107-1217 *Tel:* 415-561-4544 *Fax:* 415-543-8370 *E-mail:* info@roughhouse.com *Web Site:* www. roughhouse.com, pg 878

Round Hill Music LLC, 400 Madison Ave, 18th fl, New York, NY 10017 *Tel:* 212-380-0080 *Fax:* 212-380-0081 *E-mail:* info@roundhillmusic.com *Web Site:* roundhillmusic.com, pg 878

Roundabout Entertainment Inc, 217 S Lake St, Burbank, CA 91502 *Tel:* 818-842-9300 *Fax:* 818-842-9301 *E-mail:* info@roundabout.com *Web Site:* www. roundabout.com, pg 878

Rounder Records, 1209 Pine St, Suite 100, Nashville, TN 37203 *Web Site:* www.rounder.com, pg 878

Roving Eye International Film Festival, 83 Park St, Suite 5, Providence, RI 02903 *Tel:* 401-861-4445 *Fax:* 401-490-6735 *E-mail:* info@film-festival.org *Web Site:* film-festival.org, pg 1002

Ron Roy Productions/Moodtapes, 4835 Pradera St, Sparks, NV 89436 *E-mail:* info@moodtapes.com *Web Site:* www.moodtapes.com, pg 878

Royal Starr Film Festival (RSFF), 880 S Old Woodward Ave, Birmingham, MI 48009 *Tel:* 248-825-3110 *E-mail:* info@royalstarr.org *Web Site:* www.royalstarr. org; filmfreeway.com/RoyalStarrFilmFestival (submissions), pg 1002

RSS Distributors, 7930 Old Auction Rd, Manheim, PA 17545 *Tel:* 717-892-6743 *Toll Free Tel:* 800-233-0175 *Fax:* 717-892-5981 *E-mail:* orders@rssd.com *Web Site:* www.rssd.com, pg 878

RTDNA Edward R Murrow Awards, The National Press Bldg, 529 14 St NW, Suite 1240, Washington, DC 20045 *Tel:* 202-662-7254 *Fax:* 202-223-4007 *E-mail:* awards@rtdna.org *Web Site:* www.rtdna.org, pg 1002

RTS Inc, 40 Burt Dr, Suite 11, Deer Park, NY 11729 *Tel:* 631-242-6801 *Fax:* 631-242-6808 *E-mail:* rtsinc@ rcn.com *Web Site:* www.rtsphoto.com, pg 878

RTZ Audio Visual, 6725 Santa Barbara Ct, Suite 103, Elkridge, MD 21075 *Tel:* 443-757-0480 *Toll Free Tel:* 800-543-0582 *Fax:* 443-757-0487 *E-mail:* sales@ rtzav.com *Web Site:* www.rtzav.com, pg 878

Rucinski Write!Now LLC, 2155 Terrebonne Dr, Mosinee, WI 54455 *Tel:* 715-241-7316; 715-212-6241 (cell) *Fax:* 715-355-4274 *Web Site:* www. rucinskiwritenow.com, pg 878

Ben Rudnick and Friends, PO Box 1426, Arlington, MA 02474 *Tel:* 781-643-5137 *Web Site:* www.benrudnick. com, pg 878

RuffHouse LLC, 2823 Lariat Trail, Austin, TX 78734 *Tel:* 512-965-2957 *E-mail:* info@ruffhousin.com *Web Site:* www.ruffhousin.com, pg 878

Rule Boston Camera, 1284 Soldier's Field Rd, Boston, MA 02135 *Tel:* 617-277-2200 *Toll Free Tel:* 800-785-3266 *Fax:* 617-277-6800 *E-mail:* answers@rule.com *Web Site:* www.rule.com, pg 878

Rum Jungle Media, 5295 Eden Rd, Mound, MN 55364 *Tel:* 952-472-5525 *E-mail:* rumjungle@rumjungle.com *Web Site:* www.rumjungle.com, pg 878

Running Pony Productions LLC, 1770 Kirby Pkwy, Suite 118, Memphis, TN 38138 *Tel:* 901-683-6693 *Toll Free Tel:* 877-891-7669 *Fax:* 901-683-3093 *E-mail:* info@ runningpony.com *Web Site:* www.runningpony.com, pg 878

Russ Bassett Corp, 8189 Byron Rd, Whittier, CA 90606-2615 *Tel:* 562-945-2445 *Toll Free Tel:* 800-350-2445 *Fax:* 562-698-8972 *E-mail:* info@russbassett.com *Web Site:* www.russbassett.com, pg 878

Russ InVision Co/AbridgeClub.com, 3219 Conquista Ave, Long Beach, CA 90808 *Tel:* 562-421-1836 *Toll Free Tel:* 888-421-7488 *E-mail:* info@abridgeclub.com *Web Site:* abridgeclub.com, pg 879

Russell Industries Inc, 40 Horton Ave, Lynbrook, NY 11563 *Tel:* 516-536-5000 *Toll Free Tel:* 800-645-2202 *Fax:* 516-764-5747 *Toll Free Fax:* 800-645-2200 *E-mail:* sales@russellind.com *Web Site:* www. russellind.com, pg 879

Russound, One Forbes Rd, Newmarket, NH 03857 *Tel:* 603-659-5170 *Toll Free Tel:* 800-638-8055 (US) *Fax:* 603-659-5388 *E-mail:* sales@russound.com; tech@russound.com *Web Site:* www.russound.com, pg 879

S I Video Sales Group, 1318 S Carlisle St, Philadelphia, PA 19146 *Tel:* 267-519-2222 *Web Site:* www.sivideo. com; www.capclassics.com; takinglasvegas.com, pg 879

Saah Video, 12221 Parklawn Dr, Rockville, MD 20852 *Tel:* 301-770-6699 *Fax:* 301-770-3250 *Web Site:* www. saahvideo.com, pg 879

Sacramento Film Commission, 1608 "I" St, Sacramento, CA 95814-2042 *Tel:* 916-808-7777 *Toll Free Tel:* 800-292-2334 *Web Site:* www.visitsacramento.com/film, pg 967

Sacramento Theatrical Lighting Ltd (STL), 950 Richards Blvd, Sacramento, CA 95811 *Tel:* 916-447-3258 *Toll Free Tel:* 800-283-2785 *Fax:* 916-447-5012 *E-mail:* info@stlltd.com *Web Site:* www.stlltd.com, pg 879

SADiE Inc, 45 Pine St, Rockaway, NJ 07866 *Tel:* 973-983-9577 *Fax:* 973-983-9588 *E-mail:* sales@ prismmpi.com *Web Site:* www.sadie.com; www. prismsound.com, pg 879

Safe Harbor Computers, 530 W Oklahoma Ave, Suite 500, Milwaukee, WI 53207 *Tel:* 414-615-4560 *Toll Free Tel:* 800-544-6599 *Fax:* 414-615-4567 *E-mail:* sales@sharbor.com *Web Site:* www.sharbor. com, pg 879

Sagebrush Video Productions, 2304 County Rd 370, Otis, KS 67565 *Tel:* 785-222-3313 *Web Site:* www. sagebrushvideo.com, pg 879

Sahara Records & Filmworks Entertainment Co, 10573 W Pico Blvd, Suite 352, Los Angeles, CA 90064-2348 *Tel:* 310-948-9652 *E-mail:* info@edmsahara.com, pg 879

St Augustine, Ponte Vedra & The Beaches Visitors and Convention Bureau, 29 Old Mission Ave, St Augustine, FL 32084 *Tel:* 904-829-1711 *Toll Free Tel:* 800-653-2489 *Web Site:* www. floridashistoriccoast.com, pg 970

St Barth Film Festival, c/o Cobblestone Films, 140 Riverside Dr, No 5D, New York, NY 10024 *Tel:* 212-989-8004 *Fax:* 212-727-1774 *E-mail:* staff@stbarthff. org *Web Site:* www.stbarthff.com, pg 1002

Saint Elmo Soundstage, 415 E Saint Elmo, Austin, TX 78745 *Tel:* 512-535-5113 *E-mail:* contact@saintelmo. info *Web Site:* saintelmo.info, pg 879

St John's International Women's Film Festival, 28 Cochrane St, Suite 101, St John's, NL A1C 3L3, Canada *Tel:* 709-754-3141 *Fax:* 709-754-0049 *E-mail:* info@womensfilmfestival.com *Web Site:* www.womensfilmfestival.com, pg 1002

St Petersburg/Clearwater Film Commission, 8200 Bryan Dairy Rd, Suite 200, Largo, FL 33777 *Tel:* 727-464-7241 *Toll Free Tel:* 877-352-3224 *E-mail:* info@filmspc.com *Web Site:* www.filmstpeteclearwater.com, pg 969

Saint Vincent & The Grenadines Tourist Office, 801 Second Ave, 4th fl, New York, NY 10017 *Tel:* 212-687-4981 *Toll Free Tel:* 800-729-1726 *Fax:* 212-949-5946 *E-mail:* svgtony@aol.com *Web Site:* www.discoversvg.com, pg 974

Salesmaker Carts, 403 Roberts Ave, Louisville, KY 40214 *Toll Free Tel:* 800-281-2278 *Toll Free Fax:* 800-418-2525 *Web Site:* www.salesmakercarts.com, pg 879

Sally Mountain Park Bluegrass Festival, 703-A N Marion St, Greentop, MO 63546 *Tel:* 660-949-2345 *E-mail:* festival@marktwain.net *Web Site:* www.sallymountainshow.com, pg 1002

Steven Samler Music & Sound, 2830 Vogay Lane, Northbrook, IL 60062 *Tel:* 847-400-5080 *Web Site:* www.stevensamler.com, pg 879

Samson Technologies Corp, 278-B Duffy Ave, Hicksville, NY 11801 *Tel:* 516-870-7200 *Fax:* 516-938-1696 *E-mail:* info@samsontech.com *Web Site:* www.samsontech.com, pg 879

Samsung Electronics America, 85 Challenger Rd, Ridgefield Park, NJ 07660 *Toll Free Tel:* 800-SAMSUNG (726-7864) *Web Site:* www.samsung.com, pg 879

The Samuels Co, Box 770874, Houston, TX 77215-0874 *Tel:* 281-564-1055 *Fax:* 530-420-4631 *Web Site:* www.thesamuelsco.com, pg 879

Samy's Camera, 431 S Fairfax Ave, Los Angeles, CA 90036 *Tel:* 323-938-2420 *Toll Free Tel:* 800-321-4726 *Fax:* 323-937-2919 *E-mail:* lacamera@samys.com; samys.com; locations@samys.com *Web Site:* www.samys.com, pg 879

San Antonio Film Commission, 115 Plaza de Armas, Suite 102, San Antonio, TX 78205 *Tel:* 210-207-6777; 210-207-6730 *Toll Free Tel:* 800-447-3372 *Fax:* 210-207-4526 *E-mail:* filmsa@filmsanantonio.com *Web Site:* www.filmsanantonio.com; www.getcreativesanantonio.com/film-commission, pg 976

San Antonio Film Festival, 8452 Fredericksburg Rd, PMB 264, San Antonio, TX 78229 *Tel:* 210-885-5888 *E-mail:* safilm@gmail.com; hello@safilm.com *Web Site:* www.safilm.com, pg 1002

San Diego Film Festival, 2683 Via de la Valle, Suite G-210, Del Mar, CA 92014 *Tel:* 619-818-2221 *Web Site:* www.sdfilmfest.com, pg 1002

San Diego Stage & Lighting Supply Inc, 2203 Verus St, San Diego, CA 92154 *Tel:* 619-299-2300 *Fax:* 619-299-0058 *E-mail:* info@sdstagelighting.com *Web Site:* www.sdstagelighting.com, pg 879

San Francisco Black Film Festival, PO Box 15490, San Francisco, CA 94115 *Tel:* 770-369-3776 *E-mail:* sfbff@sfbff.org *Web Site:* www.sfbff.org, pg 1002

San Francisco Film Commission, City Hall, Rm 473, One Dr Carlton B Goodlett Place, San Francisco, CA 94102 *Tel:* 415-554-6241 *Fax:* 415-554-6503 *E-mail:* film@sfgov.org *Web Site:* www.filmsf.org/film-commission; www.facebook.com/FilmSF, pg 967

San Francisco International Film Festival, 39 Mesa St, Suite 110, The Presidio, San Francisco, CA 94129-1025 *Tel:* 415-561-5000 *Fax:* sffilm.org/sffilm-festival/, pg 1003

San Francisco International LGBTQ Film Festival, 145 Ninth St, Suite 300, San Francisco, CA 94103 *Tel:* 415-703-8650 *Fax:* 415-861-1404 *E-mail:* info@frameline.org *Web Site:* www.frameline.org/festival, pg 1003

San Francisco Jewish Film Festival, 145 Ninth St, Suite 200, San Francisco, CA 94103 *Tel:* 415-621-0556 *Fax:* 415-621-0568 *E-mail:* jewishfilm@sfjff.org; programming@jfi.org *Web Site:* www.sfjff.org; jfi.org, pg 1003

San Jose Film & Video Commission, c/o San Jose Convention & Visitors Bureau, 408 Almaden Blvd, San Jose, CA 95110 *Tel:* 408-295-9600 *Toll Free Tel:* 800-SAN-JOSE (726-5673) *E-mail:* eventservices@sanjose.org *Web Site:* www.sanjose.org/media/film-office, pg 967

San Juan School District Heritage Language Resource Center, 28 W 200 N, Blanding, UT 84511 *Tel:* 435-678-1230 *Fax:* 435-678-1283 *Web Site:* media.sjsd.org, pg 880

San Luis Obispo County Film Commission, 811 El Capitan Way, Suite 200, San Luis Obispo, CA 93401 *Tel:* 805-541-8000 *Toll Free Tel:* 800-634-1414 *Web Site:* www.slocal.com, pg 967

San Mateo County Film Commission, 111 Anza Blvd, Suite 410, Burlingame, CA 94010 *Tel:* 650-348-7600 *Toll Free Tel:* 800-288-4748 *Fax:* 650-348-7687 *E-mail:* info@smccvb.com *Web Site:* www.smccvb.com/film, pg 966

Sanako Inc, 300 Spectrum Center Dr, Irvine, CA 92618 *Toll Free Tel:* 888-611-4785 *Toll Free Fax:* 888-611-4785 *E-mail:* info-us@sanako.com *Web Site:* www.sanako.com, pg 880

Sand Box Studio, 555 Minnesota St, San Francisco, CA 94107 *Tel:* 415-550-8732 *E-mail:* inquiries@sandboxstudio.com *Web Site:* www.sandboxstudio.com, pg 880

S&P Global Marketing Intelligence, 55 Water St, New York, NY 10041 *Toll Free Tel:* 877-863-1306 *E-mail:* questions@spcapitaliq.com *Web Site:* marketingintelligence.spglobal.com, pg 880

Sandusky Lee Corp, PO Box 6, Littlestown, PA 17340 *Tel:* 717-359-4111 *Toll Free Tel:* 800-233-7076 *Fax:* 717-359-4414 *E-mail:* customerserv@sanduskycabinets.com; help@sanduskycabinets.com; sales@sanduskycabinets.com *Web Site:* www.sanduskycabinets.com, pg 880

Sano Videos, Columbia Plaza, 2450 Virginia Ave NW, Suite E 322, Washington, DC 20037 *Tel:* 202-293-0454, pg 880

Santa Barbara County Film Commission, 500 E Montecito St, Santa Barbara, CA 93103 *Tel:* 805-966-9222 *Toll Free Tel:* 800-676-1266 *Fax:* 805-966-1728 *E-mail:* film@santabarbaraca.com *Web Site:* santabarbaraca.com/film-commission, pg 967

Santa Barbara International Film Festival, 1528 Chapala St, Suite 203, Santa Barbara, CA 93101 *Tel:* 805-963-0023 *Fax:* 805-962-2524 *E-mail:* contactus@sbiff.org *Web Site:* sbiff.org, pg 1003

Santa Barbara Location Services, 100 Miramar Ave, Suite C, Santa Barbara, CA 93108 *Tel:* 805-403-4620 *E-mail:* geoff@sblocationservices.com *Web Site:* www.santabarbaralocations.com, pg 880

Santa Clarita Film Office, 23920 Valencia Blvd, Suite 100, Santa Clarita, CA 91355 *Tel:* 661-284-1425 *Fax:* 661-286-4001 *E-mail:* film@santa-clarita.com *Web Site:* filmsantaclarita.com, pg 967

Santa Clarita Studios, 25135 Anza Dr, Santa Clarita, CA 91355 *Tel:* 661-294-2000 *Fax:* 661-294-2020 *E-mail:* mike@sc-studios.com *Web Site:* www.santaclaritastudios.com, pg 880

Santa Monica Mountains National Recreation Area, Office of Special Park Uses, 401 W Hillcrest Dr, Thousand Oaks, CA 91360 *Tel:* 805-370-2308 *E-mail:* samo_permits@nps.gov *Web Site:* www.nps.gov/samo, pg 968

SAPSIS Rigging Inc, 3883 Ridge Ave, Philadelphia, PA 19132 *Tel:* 215-228-0888 *Toll Free Tel:* 800-SAPSIS-1 (727-7471) *Fax:* 215-228-1786 *E-mail:* sales@sapsis-rigging.com *Web Site:* www.sapsis-rigging.com, pg 880

Sarasota County Film & Entertainment Office, 1680 Fruitville Rd, Suite 402, Sarasota, FL 34236 *Tel:* 941-309-1200 (ext 104) *Fax:* 941-309-1209 *E-mail:* info@filmsarasota.com *Web Site:* www.filmsarasota.com, pg 969

Sargent Welch, 5100 W Henrietta Rd, West Henrietta, NY 14586 *Toll Free Tel:* 800-727-4368 *Toll Free Fax:* 800-676-2540 *E-mail:* sargentwelchcs@vwr.com *Web Site:* www.sargentwelch.com, pg 880

SAS Institute Inc, 100 SAS Campus Dr, Cary, NC 27513-2414 *Tel:* 919-677-8000 *Toll Free Tel:* 800-727-0025 *Fax:* 919-677-4444 *Web Site:* www.sas.com, pg 880

Satellite Broadcasting & Communications Association (SBCA), 1100 17 St NW, Suite 1150, Washington, DC 20036 *Tel:* 202-349-3620 *Toll Free Tel:* 800-541-5981 *Fax:* 202-349-3621 *E-mail:* info@sbca.org *Web Site:* www.sbca.com, pg 961

Satellite Center, 2535 Williams Blvd, Kenner, LA 70062 *Tel:* 504-466-3474 *Toll Free Tel:* 800-256-4010 *E-mail:* info@satctr.com *Web Site:* satctr.com, pg 881

Satellite Digital Teleproductions (SDTV), 4004 La Salle St, San Diego, CA 92110-5124 *Tel:* 619-293-7777 *Toll Free Tel:* 800-SKY-PROD (759-7763 US) *Fax:* 619-223-3626 *E-mail:* info@sdtv.com *Web Site:* www.sdtv.com, pg 881

Satellite Media Production, 8379 Inspiration Ave, Walkersville, MD 21793 *Tel:* 301-845-2737 *Toll Free Tel:* 800-747-0856 *Web Site:* www.satellitemediaproduction.com; www.oldietv.com, pg 881

Satellite Technology Systems Inc, 4702 State Rte 176, Unit F, Crystal Lake, IL 60014 *Tel:* 815-482-0224 *Toll Free Tel:* 800-838-1472 *Fax:* 815-568-8478 *E-mail:* sts@mc.net *Web Site:* www.satellitetechsys.com, pg 881

Saturn Awards, 334 W 54 St, Los Angeles, CA 90037 *Tel:* 323-752-5811 *E-mail:* saturn.awards@ca.rr.com *Web Site:* www.saturnawards.org, pg 1003

Saturn Studios, PO Box 3687, Hollywood, CA 90078-3687 *Tel:* 323-871-4134 *Web Site:* rollingplanet.com, pg 881

Alwin Sauers Audio Productions (ASAP), 10 Wisteria Way, Ventura, CA 93004-1435 *Tel:* 206-484-6144 *E-mail:* alwinaudio@yahoo.com, pg 881

Savage Universal Corp, 2050 S Stearman Dr, Chandler, AZ 85286 *Tel:* 480-632-1320 *Toll Free Tel:* 800-624-8891 *Fax:* 480-632-1322 *E-mail:* info486@savagepaper.com *Web Site:* savageuniversal.com, pg 881

Savant Systems LLC, 45 Perseverance Way, Hyannis, MA 02601 *Tel:* 508-683-2500 *Fax:* 508-683-2600 *Web Site:* www.savant.com, pg 881

Save the Children Federation Inc, 501 Kings Hwy E, Suite 400, Fairfield, CT 06825 *Tel:* 203-221-4000 *Toll Free Tel:* 800-728-3843; 800-999-2445 *E-mail:* supportercare@savechildren.org; twebster@savechildren.org *Web Site:* www.savethechildren.org, pg 881

SC Media Canada, 2100 Onesime-Gagnon, Lachine, QC H8T 3M8, Canada *Tel:* 514-780-0808 *Toll Free Tel:* 888-595-3966 *Fax:* 514-780-1604 *Toll Free Fax:* 800-790-2000 *E-mail:* information@scmediacanada.com *Web Site:* www.scmediacanada.com, pg 881

Scala Inc, 7 Great Valley Pkwy, Suite 300, Malvern, PA 19355 *Tel:* 610-363-3350 *Toll Free Tel:* 888-SCALA-96 (722-5296) *Fax:* 610-363-4010 *E-mail:* team@scala.com *Web Site:* scala.com, pg 881

Sceno Plus, 5423 ave de Lorimier, Montreal, QC H2H 2C3, Canada *Tel:* 514-529-4364 *Fax:* 514-529-9164 *E-mail:* mailinfo@scenoplus.com *Web Site:* www.sceno-plus.com, pg 881

Scheimpflug Digital, 546 W 48 St, New York, NY 10036 *Tel:* 212-244-8300 *Fax:* 212-244-8769 *Web Site:* www.scheimpflug.com, pg 881

Schiller's Audio-Visual, 9240 Manchester Rd, St Louis, MO 63144-2636 *Tel:* 314-968-3650 *Toll Free Tel:* 800-366-7244 *Fax:* 314-968-1184 *E-mail:* sales@schillers.com; av@schillers.com *Web Site:* www.schillers.com, pg 881

Schlessinger Media, PO Box 680, Conshohocken, PA 19428 *Tel:* 610-645-4000 *Toll Free Tel:* 800-843-3620 *Fax:* 610-645-4040 *E-mail:* cs@schlessingermedia.com *Web Site:* www.libraryvideocompany.com, pg 881

Schneider Optics Inc, 285 Oser Ave, Hauppauge, NY 11788 *Tel:* 631-761-5000 *Toll Free Tel:* 800-645-7239 *Fax:* 631-761-5090 *E-mail:* info@schneideroptics.com *Web Site:* www.schneideroptics.com, pg 881

Scholastic Canada Ltd, 175 Hillmount Rd, Markham, ON L6C 1Z7, Canada *Tel:* 905-887-7323 *Toll Free Tel:* 800-268-3860 *Fax:* 905-887-1131 *Toll Free Fax:* 800-387-4944 *E-mail:* custserv@scholastic.ca *Web Site:* www.scholastic.ca, pg 882

Scholastic Library Publishing, 90 Old Sherman Tpke, Danbury, CT 06816 *Toll Free Tel:* 800-621-1115 (cust serv) *Toll Free Fax:* 866-783-4361 *Web Site:* scholasticlibrary.digital.scholastic.com, pg 882

Scholastic Media, 557 Broadway, New York, NY 10012 *Toll Free Tel:* 800-724-6527 *Web Site:* www.scholastic.com/aboutscholastic/librarypublishing.htm, pg 882

School Media Associates LLC, 5815 Live Oak Pkwy, Suite 2-B, Norcross, GA 30093-1700 *Tel:* 770-441-0600 *Toll Free Tel:* 800-451-5226 (orders) *Fax:* 770-441-8529 *E-mail:* info@smavideo.net; orders@smavideo.net *Web Site:* www.smavideo.net, pg 882

School Specialty Inc, W6316 Design Dr, Greenville, WI 54942 *Tel:* 419-589-1425 *Toll Free Tel:* 888-388-3224 *Fax:* 419-589-1600 *Toll Free Fax:* 888-388-6344 *E-mail:* internationalorders@schoolspecialty.com *Web Site:* www.schoolspecialty.com, pg 882

Schroder Music Co, PO Box 2067, Berkeley, CA 94702-0067 *Tel:* 510-843-0533 *Fax:* 510-834-5201 *Web Site:* www.sisterschoice.com, pg 882

M Schwartz & Gettinger Feather Inc, 45 Hoffman Ave, Hauppauge, NY 11788 *Tel:* 631-234-7722 *Fax:* 631-234-7817 *E-mail:* info@msgfeather.com *Web Site:* www.msgfeather.com, pg 882

SCI Television & Creative Media LLC, 160 E Grand Ave, 5th fl, Chicago, IL 60611 *Tel:* 312-643-2080 *E-mail:* info@scitvproductions.com *Web Site:* www.scitvproductions.com, pg 882

Science First/STARLAB™, 86475 Gene Lasserre Blvd, Yulee, FL 32097 *Tel:* 904-225-5558 *Toll Free Tel:* 800-875-3214 *Fax:* 904-225-2228 *E-mail:* starlab@starlab.com; info@starlab.com *Web Site:* starlab.com, pg 882

Science Museum of Minnesota, 120 W Kellogg Blvd, St Paul, MN 55102 *Tel:* 651-221-9444 *Toll Free Tel:* 800-221-9444 *Fax:* 651-221-4533 *E-mail:* info@smm.org; science@smm.org *Web Site:* www.smm.org, pg 882

Scientifics Direct Inc, 532 Main St, Tonawanda, NY 14150 *Toll Free Tel:* 800-728-6999; 800-818-4955 *Toll Free Fax:* 800-828-3299 *E-mail:* support@scientificsdirect.com *Web Site:* www.scientificsonline.com, pg 882

SciMedTv, 460 W 24 St, Unit 3A, New York, NY 10011 *Tel:* 917-593-2537 *E-mail:* SciMedTV@gmail.com *Web Site:* www.scimedtv.com, pg 882

Score Productions Inc, 219 E 49 St, New York, NY 10017 *Tel:* 212-751-2510 *Fax:* 212-754-6305 *E-mail:* score@scoreproductions.com, pg 882

Scott Resources Inc, 401 Hickory St, Fort Collins, CO 80524-1125 *Tel:* 970-484-7445 *Toll Free Tel:* 800-289-9299 *Fax:* 970-484-1198 *E-mail:* custserv@amep.com *Web Site:* amep.com, pg 882

Ron Scott, 2020 Colquitt St, Houston, TX 77098 *E-mail:* ron@ronscott.com *Web Site:* www.ronscott.com, pg 882

Screamfest® Horror Film Festival & Screenplay Competition, 8840 Wilshire Blvd, Beverly Hills, CA 90211 *Tel:* 310-358-3273 *E-mail:* info@screamfestla.com *Web Site:* www.screamfestla.com, pg 1003

Screen Actors Guild - American Federation of Television & Radio Artists (SAG-AFTRA), 5757 Wilshire Blvd, 7th fl, Los Angeles, CA 90036-3600 *Tel:* 323-954-1600 (former SAG); 323-634-8100 (former AFTRA) *Toll Free Tel:* 855-SAG-AFTRA (724-2387) *Fax:* 323-549-6654 (communs & mktg) *E-mail:* info@sagaftra.org *Web Site:* www.sagaftra.org, pg 961

Screen Door Entertainment Inc, 5709 Fairview Place, Agoura Hills, CA 91301, pg 882

The Screen Works®, 2226 W Walnut St, Chicago, IL 60612 *Tel:* 312-243-8265 *Toll Free Tel:* 800-294-8111 *Fax:* 312-243-8290 *E-mail:* screens@thescreenworks.com *Web Site:* www.thescreenworks.com, pg 882

Scripps Networks, 9721 Sherrill Blvd, Knoxville, TN 37932 *Tel:* 865-694-2700 *Web Site:* www.scrippsnetworks.com, pg 882

Roger Scruggs Films, PO Box 321054, Cocoa Beach, FL 32932-1054 *Tel:* 321-783-6545 (off); 321-795-6545 (cell) *Web Site:* www.tvphotog.com, pg 882

SDI Technologies Inc, 1299 Main St, Rahway, NJ 07065-5024 *Tel:* 732-574-9000 *Toll Free Tel:* 800-333-3092; 800-888-4491 (cust serv) *Fax:* 732-382-2954 *E-mail:* customerservice@sditech.com *Web Site:* www.sditechnologies.com; www.ihomeaudio.com, pg 883

SDMediaPros (SDMP), 5205 Kearny Villa Way, No 100, San Diego, CA 92123 *Tel:* 619-672-1000 *E-mail:* membership@sdmediapros.org; marketing@sdmediapros.org; programs@sdmediapros.org *Web Site:* sdmediapros.org, pg 961

Sea Studios Foundation, PO Box 267, Carmel Valley, CA 93924 *E-mail:* info@seastudios.org; jefe@seastudios.org *Web Site:* www.seastudios.org, pg 883

SeaChange International Inc, 50 Nagog Park, Acton, MA 01720 *Tel:* 978-897-0100 *Fax:* 978-897-0132 *E-mail:* globalsalesoperations@schange.com *Web Site:* www.schange.com, pg 883

Seagate Technology LLC, 10200 S De Anza Blvd, Cupertino, CA 95014 *Toll Free Tel:* 800-SEAGATE (732-4283) *Web Site:* www.seagate.com, pg 883

Sear Sound, 353 W 48 St, 6th fl, New York, NY 10036 *Tel:* 212-582-5380 *Fax:* 212-581-2731 *E-mail:* waltersear@aol.com *Web Site:* www.searsound.com, pg 883

Seattle International Film Festival (SIFF), 305 Harrison St, Seattle, WA 98109 *Tel:* 206-464-5830 *Fax:* 206-264-7919 *E-mail:* info@siff.net; entries@siff.net *Web Site:* www.siff.net, pg 1003

Seattle Jewish Film Festival (SJFF), 3801 E Mercer Way, Mercer Island, WA 98040 *Tel:* 206-388-0833; 206-232-7115 (SJCC) *E-mail:* sjff@sjcc.org *Web Site:* www.seattlejewishfilmfestival.org; sjcc.org/arts-ideas/seattle-jewish-film-festival, pg 1003

Seattle Office of Film + Music, 700 Fifth Ave, Suite 5752, Seattle, WA 98104 *Tel:* 206-684-8993 *Fax:* 206-684-0379 *E-mail:* filmoffice@seattle.gov *Web Site:* www.seattle.gov/filmandmusic, pg 977

2nd Cine Inc, 637 Frazier Ave, Suite 2, Elgin, IL 60123 *Tel:* 773-455-5808 *E-mail:* info@2ndcine.com *Web Site:* www.2ndcine.com, pg 883

Second Line Stages, 800 Richard St, New Orleans, LA 70130 *Tel:* 504-528-3050 *E-mail:* info@secondlinestages.com *Web Site:* secondlinestages.com, pg 883

Sedona Film Office, 45 Sunset Dr, Sedona, AZ 86336 *Tel:* 928-204-1123 (ext 170) *Fax:* 928-204-1064 *E-mail:* pr@sedonachamber.com *Web Site:* visitsedona.com/about-us/film-office, pg 965

See Factor Industry Inc, 37-11 30 St, Long Island City, NY 11101 *Tel:* 718-784-4200 *Fax:* 718-784-0617 *Web Site:* www.seefactor.com, pg 883

See Production Services, 3330 Cobb Pkwy, Suite 17-327, Acworth, GA 30101 *Tel:* 404-474-4416 *E-mail:* info@seeproductionservices.com *Web Site:* seeproductionservices.com, pg 883

Sekonic, 75 Virginia Rd, North White Plains, NY 10603 *Tel:* 914-347-3300 *Fax:* 914-347-3309 *E-mail:* info@macgroupus.com *Web Site:* www.macgroupus.com; www.sekonic.com, pg 883

Selco Products Co, 8780 Technology Way, Reno, NV 89521-5908 *Tel:* 775-674-5100 *Toll Free Tel:* 800-257-3526 *Fax:* 775-674-5111 *E-mail:* sales@selcoproducts.com *Web Site:* www.selcoproducts.com, pg 883

Selden Associates, 150 S Mountain Ave, Montclair, NJ 07042 *Tel:* 973-493-9039 (cell); 650-327-1972 (CA location), pg 883

Semiconductor Services, 2269 Chestnut St, No 735, San Francisco, CA 94123 *Tel:* 650-369-7890 *Fax:* 415-346-8099 *E-mail:* moreinfo@semiconductorservices.com, pg 883

Semtech, 4281 Harvester Rd, Burlington, ON L7L 5M4, Canada *Tel:* 905-632-2996 *Fax:* 905-632-2055 *Web Site:* www.semtech.com, pg 883

Sencore Inc, 3200 W Sencore Dr, Sioux Falls, SD 57107 *Tel:* 605-978-4600 *Fax:* 605-335-6379 *Web Site:* www.sencore.com, pg 883

The Mack Sennett Studios, 1215 Bates Ave, Los Angeles, CA 90029 *Tel:* 323-660-8466 *E-mail:* info@macksennettstudios.net *Web Site:* www.macksennettstudios.net, pg 883

Sennheiser (Canada) Inc, 221 Labrosse Ave, Pointe-Claire, QC H9R 1A3, Canada *Tel:* 514-426-3014 (serv/repair); 952-649-3618 (orders) *E-mail:* sennheiser.en.cs@digitalriver.com *Web Site:* en-ca.sennheiser.com, pg 884

Sennheiser Electronic Corp, One Enterprise Dr, Old Lyme, CT 06371 *Tel:* 860-434-9190 *Toll Free Tel:* 877-SENNHEISER (736-6434) *Web Site:* en-us.sennheiser.com, pg 884

Sensaphone, 901 Tryens Rd, Aston, PA 19014 *Tel:* 610-558-2700 *Toll Free Tel:* 877-373-2700 *Fax:* 610-558-0222 *E-mail:* sales@sensaphone.com *Web Site:* www.sensaphone.com, pg 884

Sensormatic®, 6600 Congress Ave, Boca Raton, FL 33487 *Tel:* 561-912-6000 *E-mail:* tycocommunications@tyco.com *Web Site:* www.tyco.com; www.sensormatic.com, pg 884

Sensory Technologies LLC, 6951 Corporate Circle, Indianapolis, IN 46278 *Tel:* 317-347-5252 *Toll Free Tel:* 800-488-4336 (help desk) *E-mail:* csc@sensorytechnologies.com *Web Site:* sensorytechnologies.com, pg 884

Sentai Filmworks LLC, 5373 W Alabama St, Suite 640, Houston, TX 77056 *Tel:* 713-490-7638 *Fax:* 713-647-0535 *E-mail:* info@sentaifilmworks.com *Web Site:* www.sentaifilmworks.com, pg 884

Sentry Industries Inc, One Bridge St, Hillburn, NY 10931-0885 *Tel:* 845-753-2910 *Fax:* 845-753-2920 *E-mail:* techsupport@sentryindustries.com *Web Site:* www.sentryindustries.com, pg 884

Serendipity Recordings, 511 Slab City Rd, Lincolnville, ME 04849 *Tel:* 207-763-3677, pg 884

Service Quality Institute, 9201 E Bloomington Fwy, Minneapolis, MN 55420-3437 *Tel:* 952-884-3311 *Toll Free Tel:* 800-548-0538 *Fax:* 952-884-8901 *E-mail:* quality@servicequality.com *Web Site:* www.customer-service.com, pg 884

Servoreeler Systems, 218-31 97 Ave, Queens Village, NY 11429 *Tel:* 718-464-9400 *Toll Free Tel:* 800-431-8900 *Fax:* 718-464-9435 *E-mail:* srsystems@servoreelers.com *Web Site:* www.servoreelers.com, pg 884

SES SA, 4 Research Way, Princeton, NJ 08540-6684 *Tel:* 609-987-4000 *E-mail:* info@ses.com *Web Site:* www.ses.com, pg 884

SESAC Inc, 35 Music Sq E, Nashville, TN 37203 *Tel:* 615-320-0055 *Web Site:* www.sesac.com, pg 962

Sesame Workshop, 1900 Broadway, 4th fl, New York, NY 10023 *Tel:* 212-595-3456 *Web Site:* www.sesameworkshop.org, pg 962

Sescom Inc, PO Box 720, Mount Marion, NY 12456
Tel: 845-246-1915 *Fax:* 845-246-0626 *E-mail:* info@
sescom.com *Web Site:* www.sescom.com, pg 884

Set Decorators Society of America (SDSA), 7100
Tujunga Ave, Suite A, North Hollywood, CA 91605
Tel: 818-255-2425 *Fax:* 818-982-8597 *E-mail:* sdsa@
setdecorators.org *Web Site:* www.setdecorators.org,
pg 962

The Set Shop, 428 Colyton St, Los Angeles, CA 90013
Tel: 213-680-1668 *Fax:* 213-680-4269, pg 884

Set To Go Studios, 86 Lackawana Ave, Suite 235,
Woodland Park, NJ 07424 *Tel:* 973-638-1646
Web Site: www.settogostudio.com, pg 884

Setcom Corp™, 3019 Alvin De Vane Blvd, Suite 560,
Austin, TX 78741 *Tel:* 650-965-8020 *Fax:* 650-
965-1193 *E-mail:* info@setcomcorp.com; sales@
setcomcorp.com *Web Site:* www.setcomcorp.com,
pg 884

7seas Productions, 970 Ninth St, Boulder, CO 80302
Tel: 303-818-5771 *E-mail:* mermaid7seas@gmail.
com *Web Site:* moondancefilmfestival.com/7seas-
productions, pg 885

The Sextant Group Inc, 11301 W Olympic Blvd, Suite
348, Los Angeles, CA 90064 *Tel:* 213-402-0991
Web Site: www.thesextantgroup.com, pg 885

SF Global Sourcing, 3450 Sacramento St, Suite 353,
San Francisco, CA 94118 *Tel:* 415-288-9400 *Toll Free
Tel:* 800-545-5865 *Web Site:* www.sfglobalsourcing.
com, pg 885

SGW Teleprompter Solutions Inc, 844 Eighth Ave, La
Grange, IL 60525-2949 *Tel:* 773-402-0105 *Fax:* 708-
482-9159 *E-mail:* teleprompter@sbcglobal.net
Web Site: teleprompter solutions.com, pg 885

Shadow Play Records & Video, PO Box 180476, Austin,
TX 78718-0476 *Tel:* 512-349-9962 *Web Site:* www.
hellojoe.com, pg 885

Shaker Microphones & Promotions Inc, 701 W
Newman Ave, Harrison, AR 72601 *Tel:* 870-204-6152
E-mail: shakermicrophone@shakermicrophone.net
Web Site: www.shakermicrophone.net, pg 885

Shakticom, 108 Yogaville Way, Buckingham, VA 23921
Tel: 434-969-1347 *Toll Free Tel:* 800-476-1347
(orders) *E-mail:* sales@shakticom.org *Web Site:* www.
shakticom.org, pg 885

Shambhala Publications, 4720 Walnut St, Suite 106,
Boulder, CO 80301 *Tel:* 720-799-8228 (cust serv);
303-222-9598; 720-799-8242 (course support) *Toll
Free Tel:* 888-424-2329 (orders & cust serv) *Fax:* 617-
236-1563 *E-mail:* customercare@shambhala.com;
course-support@shambhala.com *Web Site:* www.
shambhala.com, pg 885

Shamrock Communications, 106 Apple St, Suite
202, Tinton Falls, NJ 07724 *Tel:* 732-686-1140
E-mail: info@shamrockcommunications.com
Web Site: www.shamrockcommunications.com, pg 885

Shanachie Entertainment Corp, 37 E Clinton St, Newton,
NJ 07860 *Tel:* 973-579-7763 *Web Site:* shanachie.com,
pg 885

Shanix Inc, 40 Worthington Rd, Cranston, RI 02920
Tel: 401-941-4222 *Toll Free Tel:* 800-783-2067
Fax: 401-941-4333 *E-mail:* info@shanix.com
Web Site: www.shanix.com, pg 885

Shapeshifter, 3405 Cahuenga Blvd W, Los Angeles,
CA 90068 *Tel:* 323-876-3444 *Fax:* 323-876-1444
E-mail: sales@shapeshifterpost.com *Web Site:* www.
shapeshifterpost.com, pg 885

Steve Shapiro Music, 7777 Skyline Blvd, Oakland, CA
94611 *Tel:* 510-339-9930 *Web Site:* www.stevemusic.
com, pg 885

Sharp Electronics Corp, Professional Display Division,
100 Paragon Dr, Montvale, NJ 07645 *Tel:* 201-529-
8200 *Toll Free Tel:* 800-BE-SHARP (237-4277)
Fax: 201-529-8425 *Web Site:* www.sharpusa.com,
pg 885

Shasta County Film Commission, 1448 Pine St, Redding,
CA 96001 *Tel:* 530-710-7784 *Fax:* 530-225-4354
E-mail: info@filmshasta.com *Web Site:* www.
visitredding.com/film; filmshasta.com; www.facebook.
com/filmshasta, pg 967

Brad Shaw Productions Inc, 9950 W Roan
Meadows Dr, Boise, ID 83709 *Tel:* 208-362-5500
Web Site: bradshawproductions.com, pg 885

The Fulton J Sheen Co Inc, 73 State St, Rochester, NY
14614 *Tel:* 585-232-1150 *E-mail:* info@bishopsheen.
com *Web Site:* www.bishopsheen.com, pg 885

Sheffield Audio/Video Productions, 13816 Sunnybrook
Rd, Phoenix, MD 21131 *Tel:* 410-628-7260 *Toll Free
Tel:* 800-355-6613 *Fax:* 410-628-1977 *E-mail:* info@
sheffielddav.com *Web Site:* www.sheffielddav.com/
production, pg 885

Shelburne Films, 54545 SR 681, Reedsville, OH 45772
Tel: 740-378-6297 *E-mail:* info@shelburnefilms.com
Web Site: www.shelburnefilms.com, pg 885

Shen Milsom & Wilke LLC, 417 Fifth Ave, New York,
NY 10016 *Tel:* 212-725-6800 *Fax:* 212-725-0864
E-mail: semspak@smwllc.com *Web Site:* www.
smwllc.com, pg 885

Sherwood America Inc, 4325 Executive Dr, Suite
300, Southaven, MS 38672 *Toll Free Tel:* 866-916-
4667 *Toll Free Fax:* 877-457-2588 *E-mail:* info@
americanaudiovideo.com *Web Site:* www.
sherwoodamerica.com, pg 886

ShiftFocus Productions, 5126 N Ravenswood Ave,
Chicago, IL 60640 *Tel:* 773-231-2000 *Web Site:* www.
shiftfocusproductions.com, pg 886

Shokus Video, PO Box 3125, Chatsworth, CA
91313-3125 *Tel:* 818-538-9985 *Toll Free Tel:* 800-
SHOKUS-1 (746-5871 - orders) *Fax:* 818-701-0560
E-mail: info@shokus.com *Web Site:* www.shokus.com,
pg 886

Stan Sholik Photography, 1946 E Blair Ave, Santa
Ana, CA 92705 *Tel:* 949-250-9275 *Fax:* 949-756-
2623 *E-mail:* stan@stansholik.com *Web Site:* www.
stansholik.com, pg 886

Shook Mobile Technology LP, 7451 FM 3009, Schertz,
TX 78154 *Tel:* 210-651-5700 *Toll Free Tel:* 888-651-
5775 *Fax:* 210-651-5220 *E-mail:* shook@shook-usa.
com *Web Site:* www.shook-usa.com, pg 886

Shooting Star Video, 256 Shearwater Isle, Foster City,
CA 94404 *Tel:* 650-345-0919 *E-mail:* rent@ssv.com
Web Site: www.ssv.com, pg 886

Shooting Stars Post Inc, 3106 W North "A" St, Tampa,
FL 33609 *Tel:* 813-873-0100 *E-mail:* ssp@sspmedia.
com *Web Site:* www.sspmedia.com, pg 886

Shopware, c/o Films Media Group, 132 W 31 St, 16th
fl, New York, NY 10001 *Toll Free Tel:* 800-322-8755
Toll Free Fax: 800-678-3633 *E-mail:* custserv@films.
com *Web Site:* shopware.films.com, pg 886

Shore Manufacturing Co, 222 Beade St, Plymouth, PA
18651 *Tel:* 570-779-4042 *Toll Free Tel:* 800-321-5153
(orders) *Fax:* 570-779-7607 *Toll Free Fax:* 800-272-
4334 *E-mail:* shoremfg@att.net *Web Site:* shoremfg.
com, pg 886

Shot Glass Films, 2210 W Olive Ave, Suite
300, Burbank, CA 91506 *Tel:* 323-464-5111
E-mail: information@shotglassfilms.com
Web Site: www.shotglassfilms.com, pg 886

Shoulder High Productions, 50 Elsie St, San Francisco,
CA 94110 *Tel:* 415-235-1984 *E-mail:* info@
shoulderhigh.com *Web Site:* shoulderhigh.com, pg 886

Show Canada Industries Inc, 5555 Maurice-Cullen,
Laval, QC H7C 2T8, Canada *Tel:* 450-664-5155
Toll Free Tel: 888-329-5556 *Fax:* 450-664-0852
E-mail: info@show-canada.ca *Web Site:* www.show-
canada.com, pg 886

Show-Me Audio-Visual, Corporate Ridge, 4501 Blue
Ridge Cutoff, Kansas City, MO 64133 *Tel:* 816-358-
8700 *Toll Free Tel:* 800-2-SHOWME (274-6963)
Fax: 816-358-8701 *E-mail:* info@showmeav.com
Web Site: www.showmeav.com, pg 887

ShowBiz Studios, 15521 Lanark St, Van Nuys, CA
91406 *Tel:* 818-989-7007 *Fax:* 818-989-8272
Web Site: www.showbizstudios.com, pg 887

Showman Fabricators Inc, 148 E Fifth St, Bayonne, NJ
07002 *Tel:* 718-935-9899 *E-mail:* info@showfab.com
Web Site: www.showfab.com, pg 887

Showorks Audio Visual Inc, 730 Philadelphia
Pike, Wilmington, DE 19809 *Tel:* 302-798-7999
E-mail: info@showorksav.com *Web Site:* showorksav.
com, pg 887

Showtime Networks Inc, 1633 Broadway, New York,
NY 10019 *Tel:* 212-708-1600 *Fax:* 212-708-1217
Web Site: www.sho.com, pg 887

SHP Electronics, 1225 Hulman St, Terre Haute,
IN 47802 *Tel:* 812-232-1003 *Fax:* 812-232-3170
Web Site: www.shpelectronics.com, pg 887

Shure Inc, 5800 W Touhy Ave, Niles, IL 60714-4608
Tel: 847-600-2000; 847-600-8440 (tech support); 847-
600-8699 (cust serv) *Toll Free Tel:* 800-25-SHURE
(257-4873); 800-516-2525 (cust serv) *Fax:* 847-600-
1212; 847-600-8444 (tech support); 847-600-8686
(cust serv); 847-600-8688 (parts) *E-mail:* info@shure.
com *Web Site:* www.shure.com, pg 887

Shure Manufacturing Corp, 1901 W Main St,
Washington, MO 63090 *Tel:* 636-390-7100 *Toll Free
Tel:* 800-227-4873 *Fax:* 636-390-7171 *E-mail:* sales@
shureusa.com *Web Site:* www.shureusa.com, pg 887

Side Door Studio Inc, 69 Albe Dr, Newark, DE
19702 *Tel:* 302-420-6211 *Fax:* 302-731-7601
E-mail: sdseng@sidedoorstudioinc.net *Web Site:* www.
sidedoorstudioinc.net; www.facebook.com/
sidedoorstudioinc, pg 887

Side 3 Studios, 725 Mariposa St, Denver, CO 80204
Tel: 720-515-2649 *E-mail:* info@side3.com
Web Site: www.side3.com, pg 887

Sierra Automated Systems, 2821 Burton Ave, Burbank,
CA 91504 *Tel:* 818-840-6749 *Fax:* 818-840-6751
E-mail: sales@sasaudio.com; marketing@sasaudio.
com *Web Site:* www.sasaudio.com, pg 887

Sight & Sound Production Services Inc, 1143 Boland
Place, St Louis, MO 63117-1411 *Tel:* 314-647-0665
Web Site: www.sspsinc.com, pg 887

Sight & Sound Productions, 11193 Saint Johns Industrial
Pkwy N, Jacksonville, FL 32246 *Tel:* 904-645-7880
Toll Free Tel: 800-339-0846 *Fax:* 904-645-7787
E-mail: info@ssav.net *Web Site:* www.ssav.net, pg 887

Sight & Sound Studios, 66 Queen St, Suite 1705,
Honolulu, HI 96813 *Tel:* 808-599-7600 *Fax:* 808-
599-7601 *Web Site:* www.sightandsoundhawaii.com,
pg 887

Sigma Corp of America, 15 Fleetwood Ct, Ronkonkoma,
NY 11779 *Tel:* 631-585-1144 *Toll Free Tel:* 800-896-
6858 (cust serv) *Fax:* 631-585-1895 *E-mail:* info@
sigmaphoto.com *Web Site:* www.sigmaphoto.com,
pg 887

Sigma Delta Chi Awards in Journalism, Eugene S
Pulliam National Journalism Ctr, 3909 N Meridian St,
Indianapolis, IN 46208 *Tel:* 317-927-8000 *Fax:* 317-
920-4789 *E-mail:* awards@spj.org *Web Site:* www.spj.
org, pg 1003

Sign Media Inc, 4020 Blackburn Lane, Burtonsville, MD
20866-1167 *Tel:* 301-421-0268 *Toll Free Tel:* 800-475-
4756 *Fax:* 301-421-0270 *E-mail:* info@signmedia.com
Web Site: www.signmedia.com, pg 887

Signal Transport, PO Box 1028, Lake Forest, CA
92609-1028 *Tel:* 714-641-5665 *Fax:* 714-641-5664
E-mail: sales@sigt.com *Web Site:* sigt.com, pg 887

Signature Entertainment, 8306 Wilshire Blvd, Suite 791,
Beverly Hills, CA 90211 *Tel:* 310-498-1805 *Fax:* 310-
276-2521, pg 888

Signs.com, 1550 S Gladiola St, Salt Lake City, UT
84104 *Tel:* 801-441-3400 *Toll Free Tel:* 888-222-4929
E-mail: support@signs.com *Web Site:* www.signs.com,
pg 888

Sihl Inc, 538 Main St, Fiskeville, RI 02823 *Tel:* 401-
821-1000 *Toll Free Tel:* 800-556-6866; 800-366-7393
(ext 1, cust serv) *Web Site:* www.sihlinc.com, pg 888

Silent Source, 58 Nonotuck St, Northampton, MA 01062 *Tel:* 413-584-7944 *Toll Free Tel:* 800-583-7174 (orders) *Fax:* 413-584-2377 *E-mail:* info@silentsource. com *Web Site:* www.silentsource.com, pg 888

Silver Anvil Awards, 120 Wall St, 21st fl, New York, NY 10005-4024 *Tel:* 212-460-1438 *E-mail:* awards@ prsa.org *Web Site:* www.prsa.org, pg 1004

Silver Creek Media Inc, 3-1750 The Queensway, 221, Toronto, ON M9C 5H5, Canada *Tel:* 416-503-2323 *E-mail:* info@silvercreekmedia.com *Web Site:* www. silvercreekmedia.com, pg 888

Silver Gavel Awards for Media & the Arts, Div for Public Education, 321 N Clark St, Chicago, IL 60654-7598 *Tel:* 312-988-5733 *Toll Free Tel:* 800-285-2221 *Fax:* 312-988-5494 (Attn: Gavel Awards) *E-mail:* publiceducation@americanbar.org *Web Site:* www.americanbar.org, pg 1004

Silvestri California, 8125 Beach St, Los Angeles, CA 90001 *Tel:* 323-277-4420 *Toll Free Tel:* 800-647-8874 *Fax:* 323-585-0791 *E-mail:* info@silvestricalifornia. com *Web Site:* www.silvestricalifornia.com, pg 888

SIM Digital, One Atlantic Ave, Suite 110, Toronto, ON M6K 3E7, Canada *Tel:* 416-979-9958 *Fax:* 416-979-7770 *E-mail:* info.toronto@simdigital.com *Web Site:* www.simdigital.com, pg 888

Sima Products Corp, 125 Commerce Dr, Hauppauge, NY 11788 *Tel:* 631-435-0200 *Toll Free Tel:* 800-274-7824 *Fax:* 631-435-4545 *Toll Free Fax:* 800-274-7828 *E-mail:* customerservice@simaproducts.com *Web Site:* www.simaproducts.com, pg 888

Simco-Ion, 2257 N Penn Rd, Hatfield, PA 19440 *Tel:* 215-822-6401 *Toll Free Tel:* 800-203-3419 *Fax:* 215-822-3795 *E-mail:* customerservice@simco-ion.com *Web Site:* www.simco-ion.com, pg 888

Simon & Schuster, Inc, 1230 Avenue of the Americas, New York, NY 10020 *Tel:* 212-698-7000; 212-698-7126 *Toll Free Tel:* 800-223-2348 (cust serv) *Fax:* 212-698-7664 *Toll Free Fax:* 800-943-9831 *E-mail:* audiopublicity@simonandschuster.com *Web Site:* www.simonandschuster.net; www. simonandschuster.biz; www.simonandschuster.com, pg 888

D S Simon Productions, 229 W 36 St, 9th fl, New York, NY 10018 *Tel:* 212-736-2727 *Toll Free Tel:* 800-377-4666 *Fax:* 212-736-7040 *E-mail:* news@dssimon.com *Web Site:* dssimon.com, pg 888

Simon - Kaloi Engineering Ltd, 31192 La Baya Dr, Unit G, Westlake Village, CA 91362 *Tel:* 818-707-8400 *Fax:* 818-707-8401 *E-mail:* sales@skeng.com *Web Site:* www.skeng.com, pg 888

Simplex Grinnell LP, 50 Technology Dr, Westminster, MA 01441 *Tel:* 978-731-2500 *Toll Free Tel:* 800-746-7539 *Web Site:* www.tycosimplexgrinnell.com, pg 888

SimpliPhi Power Inc, 420 Bryant Circle, Bldg B, Ojai, CA 93023 *Tel:* 805-640-6700 *E-mail:* info@ simpliphipower.com *Web Site:* www.simpliphipower. com, pg 889

Simply Audiobooks, 935 Sheldon Ct, Burlington, ON L7L 5K6, Canada *Toll Free Tel:* 877-554-4332 *E-mail:* customerservice@simplyaudiobooks. com; help@simplyaudiobooks.com *Web Site:* www. simplyaudiobooks.com, pg 889

Simpson Electric Co, 520 Simpson Ave, Lac du Flambeau, WI 54538-0099 *Tel:* 715-588-3947 (cust serv); 715-588-3311 *Fax:* 715-588-1248 (cust serv); 715-588-3326 *E-mail:* cservice@simpsonelectric. com; support@simpsonelectric.com *Web Site:* www. simpsonelectric.com, pg 889

Sinauer Associates, 23 Plumtree Rd, Sunderland, MA 01375 *Tel:* 413-549-4300 *Fax:* 413-549-1118 *E-mail:* orders@sinauer.com (orders); publish@ sinauer.com (gen edit correspondence); custserv@ sinauer.com (cust serv) *Web Site:* www.sinauer.com, pg 889

Sinclair Institute, 402 Millstone Dr, Hillsborough, NC 27278 *Tel:* 919-732-6005 *Toll Free Tel:* 888-736-2247 *Fax:* 919-732-6146 *E-mail:* sales@sinclairwholesale. com *Web Site:* www.sinclairwholesale.com; www. bettersex.com, pg 889

The Singing Machine Co Inc, 6301 NW Fifth Way, Suite 2900, Fort Lauderdale, FL 33309 *Tel:* 954-596-1000 *Toll Free Tel:* 866-670-6888 (cust serv) *Fax:* 954-596-2000 *E-mail:* sales@singingmachine. com; customerservice@singingmachine.com *Web Site:* singingmachine.com, pg 889

SintecMedia, 135 E 57 St, 12th fl, New York, NY 10022 *Tel:* 646-745-3900 *Fax:* 646-745-3901 *E-mail:* sales@ sintecmedia.com *Web Site:* www.sintecmedia.com, pg 889

Sioux Falls Convention & Visitors Bureau, 200 N Phillips Ave, Suite 102, Sioux Falls, SD 57104 *Tel:* 605-275-6060 *Toll Free Tel:* 800-333-2072 *Fax:* 605-338-0682 *E-mail:* sfcvb@siouxfalls.com *Web Site:* visitsiouxfalls.com, pg 975

Siqura Inc, 12920 Cloverleaf Center Dr, Germantown, MD 20874 *Tel:* 301-444-2200 *Toll Free Tel:* 800-BY-FIBER (293-4237) *Fax:* 301-444-2299 *Toll Free Fax:* 800-293-4237 *E-mail:* sales.us@siqura.com *Web Site:* www.siqura.com, pg 889

SirsiDynix, 3300 N Ashton Blvd, Suite 500, Lehi, UT 84043 *Tel:* 801-223-5200; 0800 016 3147 *Toll Free Tel:* 800-288-8020 *Fax:* 801-331-7770 *Web Site:* www. sirsidynix.com, pg 889

Sisters' Choice Press, PO Box 2067, Berkeley, CA 94702-0067 *Tel:* 510-843-0533 *Fax:* 510-834-5201 *Web Site:* www.sisterschoice.com, pg 889

SISU Home Entertainment Inc, 2219 41 Ave, Suite 509, Long Island City, NY 11101 *Tel:* 212-947-7888 *Toll Free Tel:* 800-223-7478 *Fax:* 212-947-8388 *Toll Free Fax:* 888-221-7478 *E-mail:* sisu@sisuent.com *Web Site:* www.sisuent.com, pg 889

Frank Siteman Photography, 136 Pond St, Winchester, MA 01890 *Tel:* 781-729-3747 *Fax:* 781-729-2549 *Web Site:* www.franksiteman.com, pg 889

Sitler's Supplies Inc, 111 Westview Dr, Washington, IA 52353 *Tel:* 319-653-2123 *Toll Free Tel:* 800-426-3938 *Fax:* 319-653-3198 *E-mail:* renfred@sitlersupplies.com *Web Site:* sitlersupplies.com, pg 889

16 x 9 Inc, 28314 Constellation Rd, Valencia, CA 91355 *Tel:* 661-295-3313 *Toll Free Tel:* 866-800-1699 *Fax:* 661-295-3314 *E-mail:* info@16x9inc.com *Web Site:* www.16x9inc.com, pg 890

SKC Communication Products Inc, 8320 Hedge Lane Terr, Shawnee Mission, KS 66227 *Tel:* 913-422-4222 *Toll Free Tel:* 800-882-7779 *Toll Free Fax:* 800-454-4752 *E-mail:* contact.us@skccom.com *Web Site:* www. skccom.com, pg 890

Skjonberg Controls Inc, 1363 Donlon St, Suite 6, Ventura, CA 93003 *Tel:* 805-650-0877 *Fax:* 805-650-0360 *Toll Free Fax:* 800-650-0360 *E-mail:* sales@ skjonberg.com *Web Site:* www.skjonberg.com, pg 890

Skotel Corp, 2645 Croissant Moreau, Brossard, QC J4Y 1P7, Canada *Tel:* 514-806-2340, pg 890

Sky City Audio, 1819 Willow Creek Rd, Prescott, AZ 86301 *Tel:* 928-830-2313 *Web Site:* skycityaudio.com, pg 890

Sky-View Search Lights & Promotions, 702 Spring Cypress Rd, Spring, TX 77373 *Tel:* 210-845-7622 *Toll Free Tel:* 800-562-8439 (US & CN); 888-396-6653 *E-mail:* sales@sky-view.com *Web Site:* sky-view.com, pg 890

Skyfire Video, PO Box 2266, Sparks, NV 89432 *Tel:* 775-323-0965 *Toll Free Tel:* 800-852-2330 *Web Site:* www.skyfirevideo.com, pg 890

Skyhoundz, 660 Hembree Pkwy, Suite 110, Roswell, GA 30076 *Tel:* 770-751-3882 *Fax:* 770-740-1665 *E-mail:* info@skyhoundz.com *Web Site:* www. skyhoundz.com, pg 890

Skystorm Productions, 103 Commerce St, Suite 100, Lake Mary, FL 32746 *Tel:* 407-328-4747 *Toll Free Tel:* 800-783-8508 *Fax:* 407-328-4479 *E-mail:* info@ skystorm.com *Web Site:* www.skystorm.com, pg 890

Skyviews Survey Inc, 32 Highline Trail, Stamford, CT 06902 *Tel:* 203-359-3754 *Web Site:* www. skyviewsurvey.com, pg 890

Slamdance Film Festival, 5634 Melrose Ave, Los Angeles, CA 90038 *Tel:* 323-466-1786 *Fax:* 323-466-1784 *E-mail:* submissions@slamdance.com *Web Site:* www.slamdance.com, pg 1004

Slim Goodbody Corp, 161 Narrows Rd, Lincolnville, ME 04850 *Tel:* 207-831-2607 *E-mail:* info@ slimgoodbody.com *Web Site:* www.slimgoodbody.com, pg 890

SLR Enterprises LLC, PO Box 1111, Orleans, MA 02653 *Tel:* 508-737-7788 *Fax:* 508-240-6878 *E-mail:* stephenroth@c4.net, pg 890

SmackDab Media, 252 Glenhaven Dr, Amherst, NY 14228 *Tel:* 615-957-6618 *Web Site:* smackdabmedia. us, pg 890

Small Planet Communications Inc, 15 Union St, Lawrence, MA 01840 *Tel:* 978-794-2201 *E-mail:* planet@smplanet.com *Web Site:* www. smplanet.com, pg 890

Small World Productions Inc, 140 Lakeside Ave, Suite 200, Seattle, WA 98122 *Tel:* 206-329-7167 *Toll Free Tel:* 800-866-7425 (orders); 800-325-7111 (cust serv) *Fax:* 206-329-0269 (credit card orders) *E-mail:* info@ travelsmallworld.com; customercare@smarttravels.tv *Web Site:* www.smarttravels.tv, pg 890

SMART Technologies ULC, 3636 Research Rd NW, Calgary, AB T2L 1Y1, Canada *Tel:* 403-245-0333 *Toll Free Tel:* 888-42-SMART (427-6278, CN & US); 800-260-9408 (sales) *Fax:* 403-228-2500 *Web Site:* home. smarttech.com, pg 891

SmartSource Computer & AV Rentals, 265 Oser Ave, Hauppauge, NY 11788 *Tel:* 631-273-8888 *Toll Free Tel:* 844-313-8833 *Fax:* 631-273-8889 *E-mail:* info@smartsourcerentals.com *Web Site:* www. smartsourcerentals.com, pg 891

SMI® Inc, 4567 Lake Shore Dr, Waco, TX 76710 *Tel:* 254-776-2060 *Toll Free Tel:* 800-568-1241 *Fax:* 254-772-9588 *E-mail:* dmcminn@lmi-inc.com; info@lmi-inc.com; info@success-motivation.com *Web Site:* www.lmi-world.com/smi, pg 891

Smith-Victor Corp, 1268 Humbracht Circle, Bartlett, IL 60103-1631 *Tel:* 630-830-9200 *Toll Free Tel:* 800-348-9862 *Fax:* 630-830-9201 *Toll Free Fax:* 800-352-0490 *E-mail:* sales@smithvictor.com *Web Site:* www. promarkbrands.com, pg 891

Smithsonian Folkways Recordings, 600 Maryland Ave SW, Suite 2001, Washington, DC 20024 *Tel:* 202-633-6450 *Toll Free Tel:* 888-FOLKWAYS (365-5929) *Fax:* 202-633-6477 *E-mail:* smithsonianfolkways@si. edu *Web Site:* folkways.si.edu, pg 891

Smithsonian National Museum of the American Indian, Fourth St & Independence Ave SW, Washington, DC 20560 *Tel:* 202-633-1000 *E-mail:* nmai-info@si.edu; nmai-groupreservations@si.edu (DC group tours); nmaitours@si.edu (NY group tours) *Web Site:* americanindian.si.edu, pg 891

Smolian Sound Studios, One Worman's Mill Ct, Frederick, MD 21701 *Tel:* 301-694-5134 *E-mail:* smolians@erols.com *Web Site:* www. soundsaver.com, pg 891

SMP Digital Graphics, 163 W 22 St, New York, NY 10011 *Tel:* 212-691-6766 *E-mail:* info@ smpdigitalgraphics.com *Web Site:* smpdigitalgraphics. com, pg 891

SMPTE® Journal Award & SMPTE® Journal Certificate of Merit, White Plains Plaza, 445 Hamilton Ave, Suite 601, White Plains, NY 10601-1827 *Tel:* 914-761-1100 *Fax:* 914-206-4216 *E-mail:* marketing@smpte.org *Web Site:* www.smpte.org, pg 1004

SMPTE® Progress Medal Award, White Plains Plaza, 445 Hamilton Ave, Suite 601, White Plains, NY 10601-1827 *Tel:* 914-761-1100 *Fax:* 914-206-4216 *E-mail:* marketing@smpte.org *Web Site:* www.smpte. org, pg 1004

SNAP, 18653 Ventura, Suite 295, Tarzana, CA 91356 *Tel:* 818-340-0283 *E-mail:* hdcine@gmail.com *Web Site:* www.facebook.com/barry.seybert, pg 891

So Smart Productions, 701 Sharpley Rd, Wilmington, DE 19803 Tel: 484-753-1520 Web Site: www.sosmart. com, pg 891

Social Studies School Service, 10200 Jefferson Blvd, PO Box 802, Culver City, CA 90232 Tel: 310-839-2436 Toll Free Tel: 800-421-4246 Fax: 310-839-2249 Toll Free Fax: 800-944-5432 (US & CN) E-mail: access@ socialstudies.com Web Site: www.socialstudies.com, pg 891

Society for Imaging Science and Technology (IS&T), 7003 Kilworth Lane, Springfield, VA 22151 Tel: 703-642-9090 Fax: 703-642-9094 E-mail: info@imaging. org Web Site: imaging.org, pg 962

Society for Information Display (SID), 1475 S Bascom Ave, Suite 114, Campbell, CA 95008-4006 Tel: 408-879-3901 Fax: 408-879-3833 E-mail: office@sid.org Web Site: www.sid.org, pg 962

Society for Photographic Education (SPE), PO Box 6653, Cleveland, OH 44101 Tel: 216-622-2733 Fax: 216-622-2733 E-mail: admin@spenational.org; info@spenational.org Web Site: www.spenational.org, pg 962

Society of Broadcast Engineers Inc (SBE), 9102 N Meridian St, Suite 150, Indianapolis, IN 46260 Tel: 317-846-9000 Web Site: www.sbe.org, pg 962

Society of Cable Telecommunications Engineers Inc (SCTE), 140 Philips Rd, Exton, PA 19341-1318 Tel: 610-363-6888 Toll Free Tel: 800-542-5040 Fax: 610-884-7237 E-mail: info@scte.org Web Site: www.scte.org, pg 962

Society of Camera Operators, PO Box 2006, Toluca Lake, CA 91610-0006 Tel: 818-563-9110 Fax: 818-563-9117 E-mail: sooffice@soc.org Web Site: www. soc.org, pg 962

Society of Manufacturing Engineers (SME), One SME Dr, Dearborn, MI 48128 Tel: 313-425-3000 Toll Free Tel: 800-733-4763 Fax: 313-425-3400 E-mail: service@sme.org (cust care) Web Site: www. sme.org, pg 891

Society of Motion Picture & Television Engineers® (SMPTE®), White Plains Plaza, 445 Hamilton Ave, Suite 601, White Plains, NY 10601-1827 Tel: 914-761-1100 Fax: 914-206-4216 E-mail: marketing@ smpte.org Web Site: www.smpte.org, pg 892

Society of Motion Picture & Television Engineers® (SMPTE®), White Plains Plaza, 445 Hamilton Ave, Suite 601, White Plains, NY 10601-1827 Tel: 914-761-1100 Fax: 914-206-4216 E-mail: membership@ smpte.org Web Site: www.smpte.org, pg 962

Sodanceabit, 11372 Kelly Lane, Los Alamitos, CA 90720 Tel: 562-799-4340 Toll Free Tel: 800-64-DANCE (643-2623) E-mail: sodanceabit@live.com Web Site: www.sodanceabit.com, pg 892

SODEC, 215 rue Saint-Jacques St, Rm 800, Montreal, QC H2Y 1M6, Canada Tel: 514-841-2200 Toll Free Tel: 800-363-0401 (CN only) Fax: 514-841-8606 E-mail: info@sodec.gouv.qc.ca Web Site: www.sodec. gouv.qc.ca, pg 962

Sofradir EC, 373 Rte 46 W, Fairfield, NJ 07004-2442 Tel: 973-882-0211 Fax: 973-882-0997 E-mail: info@ sofradir-ec.com Web Site: www.sofradir-ec.com, pg 892

Software & Information Industry Association (SIIA), 1090 Vermont Ave NW, 6th fl, Washington, DC 20005-4095 Tel: 202-289-7442 Fax: 202-289-7097 Web Site: www.siia.net, pg 962

Elliot Sokolov Music, One Hillside Ave, Goldens Bridge, NY 10526 Tel: 917-690-5487 E-mail: elliotsounds@ gmail.com Web Site: www.elliotsokolov.com, pg 892

Solar Studios, 1601 S Central Ave, Glendale, CA 91204 Tel: 818-240-1893 Fax: 818-240-4187 Web Site: www. solarstudios.com, pg 892

Solid Sound Recording Studio, 2400 Hassell Rd, Suite 430, Hoffman Estates, IL 60169 Tel: 847-490-2101 E-mail: solidsoundchicago@icloud.com, pg 892

Solid State Logic Inc, 320 W 46 St, 2nd fl, New York, NY 10036-8398 Tel: 212-315-1111 E-mail: sales@ solidstatelogic.com; nysales@solidstatelogic.com Web Site: www.solidstatelogic.com, pg 892

Solutek Corp, 94 Shirley St, Boston, MA 02119 Tel: 617-445-5335 Toll Free Tel: 800-403-0770 Fax: 617-445-9623 Web Site: www. solutekphotochemicals.com, pg 892

Solution Tree, 555 N Morton St, Bloomington, IN 47404-3730 Tel: 812-336-7700 Toll Free Tel: 800-733-6786 Fax: 812-336-7790 E-mail: info@solutiontree. com Web Site: www.solutiontree.com, pg 892

SOM Publishing Co, 163 Moon Valley Rd, Windyville, MO 65783 Tel: 417-345-8411 E-mail: som@som.org Web Site: www.som.org, pg 892

Sonalysts Media, 215 Parkway N, Waterford, CT 06385 Tel: 860-442-4355 Toll Free Tel: 800-526-8091 (ext 3848) E-mail: production@sonalysts.com; media@sonalysts.com; exhibits@sonalysts.com Web Site: www.sonalystsmedia.com, pg 892

Sonance, 212 Avenida Fabricante, San Clemente, CA 92672-7531 Tel: 949-492-7777 Toll Free Tel: 800-582-0772 (tech support); 800-582-7777 E-mail: customerservice@sonance.com Web Site: www.sonance.com, pg 892

Sonar Radio Corp, 761-6 Coco Plum Circle, Plantation, FL 33324 Tel: 954-981-8800, pg 892

Sonic Gravy, 2515 Laurel Pass, Los Angeles, CA 90046 Tel: 323-650-2751 E-mail: info@sonicgravy.com Web Site: www.johnswihart.com, pg 892

Sonic IT Communications, 79 Denlow Blvd, Toronto, ON M3B 1P8, Canada Tel: 416-383-0260 Toll Free Tel: 800-267-6642 Fax: 416-383-0261 E-mail: sales@ sonicscience.com Web Site: www.sonicscience.com, pg 892

SonicPool, 6860 Lexington Ave, Hollywood, CA 90038 Tel: 323-460-4649 Toll Free Tel: 866-203-7213 Fax: 323-460-6063 E-mail: production@sonicpool. com Web Site: www.sonicpool.com, pg 892

SoNo Studios, 18 Leonard St, Norwalk, CT 06850 Tel: 203-354-4002 E-mail: info@sonostudios.com Web Site: www.sonostudios.com, pg 892

Sonoma County Film Office, 141 Stony Circle, Suite 110, Santa Rosa, CA 95401-4154 Tel: 707-565-7170 Fax: 707-565-7231 E-mail: film@sonoma-county.org Web Site: www.sonoma-county.org/film, pg 968

Sonora Recorders, 3222 Los Feliz Blvd, Los Angeles, CA 90039 Tel: 213-841-0712 E-mail: ductape@aol. com Web Site: www.sonorarecorders.com, pg 893

Sonoton Music Library, 6255 Sunset Blvd, Suite 900, Hollywood, CA 90028 Tel: 323-461-3211 Toll Free Tel: 800-543-4276 Fax: 323-461-9102 Web Site: www. apmmusic.com, pg 893

Sony Electronics Inc, 16530 Via Esprillo, San Diego, CA 92127 Tel: 858-942-2400 Web Site: www.sony.com, pg 893

Sony Music Commercial Music Group, 550 Madison Ave, New York, NY 10022 Tel: 212-833-8000 Web Site: www.sonymusic.com, pg 893

Sony Music Entertainment, 25 Madison Ave, New York, NY 10010 Tel: 212-833-8000 Web Site: www. sonymusic.com, pg 893

Sony Pictures Entertainment Inc, 10202 W Washington Blvd, Culver City, CA 90232 Tel: 310-244-4000 Web Site: www.sonypictures.com, pg 893

Sony Pictures Home Entertainment, 10202 W Washington Blvd, Culver City, CA 90232-3119 Tel: 310-244-4000 Fax: 310-244-2485 Web Site: www. sonypictures.com, pg 893

Sony Pro Audio, One Sony Dr, Park Ridge, NJ 07656 Tel: 201-930-1000 Web Site: pro.sony.com/bbsc/ssr/ home.do, pg 893

SOS Film Works (Space Ordnance Systems), 34855 Petersen Rd, Agua Dulce, CA 91390 Tel: 661-251-2365 Fax: 661-268-7680 Web Site: www.sosfilmworks. com, pg 893

SOTA Sales & Service Center, 436 E Locust St, DeKalb, IL 60115 Tel: 608-538-3500 Toll Free Tel: 800-772-7682 Fax: 608-538-3502 E-mail: sales@sotaturntables. com Web Site: www.sotaturntables.com, pg 893

Soularium Recording Studios, 702 S Alpine Hwy, Alpine, UT 84004 Tel: 801-492-0505 E-mail: info@soulariumstudios.com Web Site: www. soulariumstudios.com, pg 893

Sound & Images Inc, 1211 Virginia St, Columbia, SC 29201 Tel: 803-791-3925 E-mail: marketing@s-and-i.com Web Site: www.s-and-i.com, pg 893

Sound & Vision Communications Inc, 4100 W Kennedy Blvd, Suite 208, Tampa, FL 33609-2244 Tel: 813-289-4297 Web Site: www.gosvc.com, pg 893

Sound & Vision Media, 372 Squire Rd, Revere, MA 02151 Tel: 781-284-9707 E-mail: info@ soundandvisionmedia.com Web Site: www. soundandvisionmedia.com, pg 893

Sound Arts Recording Studio, 8377 Westview Dr, Houston, TX 77055-5737 Tel: 713-464-4653 Web Site: www.soundartsrecording.com, pg 893

Sound Associates Inc, 424 W 45 St, New York, NY 10036 Tel: 212-757-5679 Toll Free Tel: 888-772-7686 Fax: 212-265-1250 E-mail: newyork@soundassociates. com Web Site: www.soundassociates.com, pg 893

Sound by Fitch, 1134 Ridge Rd, Pottstown, PA 19465 Tel: 610-469-6082 Fax: 610-469-0559, pg 893

Sound by Singer Ltd, 242 W 27 St, 2nd fl, New York, NY 10001 Tel: 212-924-8600 Fax: 212-366-6351 E-mail: info@soundbysinger.com Web Site: www. soundbysinger.com, pg 893

Sound Control Technologies Inc, 28 Knight St, Norwalk, CT 06851 Tel: 203-854-5701 Fax: 203-854-5702 E-mail: sales@soundcontrol.net Web Site: www. soundcontrol.net, pg 893

Sound-Craft Systems Inc, 1584 Petit Jean Mountain Rd, Morrilton, AR 72110 Tel: 501-727-5476 Toll Free Tel: 800-643-8747 Fax: 501-727-5402 E-mail: sales@ sound-craft.com Web Site: www.sound-craft.com, pg 894

Sound Feelings Records, 18375 Ventura Blvd, No 8000, Tarzana, CA 91356 Tel: 818-757-0600 Web Site: www.soundfeelings.com, pg 894

Sound-FX-Design, PO Box 3541, Newport, RI 02840 Tel: 401-952-1186 E-mail: info@sound-fx-design.com Web Site: www.sound-fx-design.com, pg 894

Sound Ideas, 105 W Beaver Creek Rd, Suite 4, Richmond Hill, ON L4B 1C6, Canada Tel: 905-886-5000 Toll Free Tel: 800-387-3030; 800-665-3000 (CN) Fax: 905-886-6800 E-mail: info@sound-ideas.com; contact@sound-ideas.com; wbc105@sound-ideas.com Web Site: www.sound-ideas.com, pg 894

The Sound Lab Inc, 3355 Bee Cave Rd, Bldg 7, Suite 705, Austin, TX 78746 Tel: 512-476-2122 Fax: 512-476-2127 E-mail: info@thesoundlabinc.com Web Site: www.thesoundlabinc.com, pg 894

Sound*Light, 5438 Tennessee Ave, New Port Richey, FL 34652 Tel: 727-842-6788 Fax: 727-842-6788 Web Site: www.awakening-healing.com; www. soundlight.org, pg 894

Sound of Birmingham Productions, 3625 Fifth Ave S, Birmingham, AL 35222 Tel: 205-595-8497 Fax: 205-595-5220 Web Site: www.soundofbirmingham.com, pg 894

Sound Service Co, 6630 Morella Ave, North Hollywood, CA 91606-1651 Tel: 818-503-4440, pg 894

Sound Sound, 843 Hiawatha Place S, Unit 304, Seattle, WA 98144-2823 Tel: 206-330-6438 Web Site: www. soundsound.com; www.undisclosedlocation.us, pg 894

Sound Strations Audio Productions Inc, 3120 South Ave, La Crosse, WI 54601 Tel: 608-787-8133 Fax: 608-787-0012 Web Site: soundstrations.com, pg 894

Sound Venture Productions, 441 MacLaren St, Suite 401, Ottawa, ON K2P 2H3, Canada Tel: 613-241-5111 Fax: 613-241-5010 E-mail: info@soundventure.com Web Site: www.soundventure.com, pg 894

Sound/Video Impressions Inc, 110 S River Rd, Des Plaines, IL 60016 *Tel:* 847-297-4360 *Fax:* 847-297-6870 *E-mail:* info@soundvideoimpressions.com *Web Site:* www.soundvideoimpressions.com, pg 894

Sound Works, 7110 Gary St, Houston, TX 77055 *Tel:* 713-960-8222 *Web Site:* www.soundworks.com, pg 894

SoundByte Productions Inc, 636 E Sixth St, New York, NY 10009 *Tel:* 212-675-0600 *Fax:* 212-675-3724 *E-mail:* info@soundbyte.com *Web Site:* www.soundbyte.com, pg 894

Soundcraft, 8500 Balboa Blvd, North Ridge, CA 91329 *Toll Free Tel:* 800-622-6983 *E-mail:* support@soundcraft.com *Web Site:* www.soundcraft.com, pg 894

Soundfold Inc, 9200 N State Rte 48, Centerville, OH 45458 *Tel:* 937-885-5100 *Toll Free Tel:* 800-782-8018 *Fax:* 937-885-5115 *E-mail:* info@soundfold.com *Web Site:* soundfold.com, pg 894

Soundmaster Group, 89 Barford Rd, Toronto, ON M9W 4H8, Canada *Tel:* 416-741-7057 *Fax:* 416-477-2496 *E-mail:* mail@soundmaster.com *Web Site:* www.soundmaster.com, pg 894

Sounds Interesting Studio, 112 Fuller St, Middleboro, MA 02346 *Tel:* 508-947-7387 *Web Site:* www.soundsinterestingstudio.com, pg 894

Sounds Unique, 1721-A Little Orchard St, San Jose, CA 95125 *Tel:* 408-287-3002 *Web Site:* www.soundsunique.com, pg 895

SoundSpace Inc, 845 Dayton St, Yellow Springs, OH 45387 *Tel:* 937-767-7353 *E-mail:* soundspace@sbcglobal.net *Web Site:* soundspaceinc.com, pg 895

Soundsphere, 10 Research Dr, Stratford, CT 06615 *Tel:* 203-386-9200 *Fax:* 203-386-0773 *E-mail:* info@soundsphere.com *Web Site:* www.soundsphere.com, pg 895

Soundtrack Group, 162 Columbus Ave, Boston, MA 02116 *Tel:* 617-303-7500 *Fax:* 617-303-7555 *Web Site:* www.soundtrackgroup.com, pg 895

Soundtracks Production Services LLC, 22 N Central Ave, Sicklerville, NJ 08081 *Tel:* 856-728-8112 *Fax:* 856-728-8075 *E-mail:* info@soundtracksnj.com *Web Site:* www.soundtracksnj.com, pg 895

Soundtrax Inc, 8116 Brucar Ct, Gaithersburg, MD 20877 *Tel:* 240-401-9555, pg 895

SoundTube Entertainment Inc, 10661 Rene St, Lenexa, KS 66215 *Tel:* 913-663-5600 *Toll Free Tel:* 855-663-5600 *Fax:* 913-663-3200 *E-mail:* sales@mseaudio.com *Web Site:* www.soundtube.com, pg 895

SoundView Services Inc, One Phillips Dr NW, Leesburg, VA 20176 *Tel:* 703-777-9570 *Toll Free Tel:* 866-680-8189 *E-mail:* info@soundviewservices.com *Web Site:* www.soundviewservices.com, pg 895

Source Film Studio, 1111 N Beachwood Dr, Hollywood, CA 90038 *Tel:* 323-463-5555 *E-mail:* info@sourcefilmstudio.com *Web Site:* www.sourcefilmstudio.com, pg 895

Source School of Tantra Yoga Inc, PO Box 368, Kahului, HI 96733 *Toll Free Tel:* 888-6-TANTRA (682-6872) *E-mail:* school@sourcetantra.com *Web Site:* sourcetantra.com, pg 895

The Source Stock Footage Library Inc, 140 S Camino Seco, Suite 308, Tucson, AZ 85710 *Tel:* 520-298-4810 *Fax:* 520-290-4376 *E-mail:* requests@sourcefootage.com *Web Site:* www.sourcefootage.com, pg 895

South Carolina Film Commission, 1205 Pendleton St, Rm 225, Columbia, SC 29201 *Tel:* 803-737-0490 *Fax:* 803-734-1163 *E-mail:* filmsc@scprt.com *Web Site:* www.filmsc.com, pg 975

South Coast Film & Video, 5234 Elm St, Houston, TX 77081 *Tel:* 713-661-3550 *Toll Free Tel:* 800-229-3550 *Fax:* 713-661-4357 *E-mail:* info@scfilmvideo.com *Web Site:* www.southcoastfilmvideo.com, pg 895

South Dakota Film Office, 711 E Wells Ave, Pierre, SD 57501 *Tel:* 605-773-3301 *Toll Free Tel:* 800-952-3625 *Fax:* 605-773-5977 *E-mail:* filmsd@state.sd.us *Web Site:* filmsd.com, pg 975

South Florida Rehearsal Studios, 1885 NE 149 St, Suite 100, North Miami, FL 33181 *Tel:* 305-949-5303; 786-238-1890 *Fax:* 305-947-3030 *E-mail:* sfrsmusic@gmail.com; info@sfrs.net *Web Site:* www.sfrs.net, pg 895

South Trunk Studios, 825 S Trunk Ave, Dallas, TX 75210 *Tel:* 214-826-2513 *E-mail:* southtrunk@sbcglobal.net *Web Site:* www.southtrunk.com, pg 895

Southern California Sound Image Inc, 2425 Auto Park Way, Escondido, CA 92029-1222 *Tel:* 760-737-3900 *Fax:* 760-737-3929 *Web Site:* www.sound-image.com, pg 895

Southern Illinois University, Ctr for Teaching Excellence, Morris Library Rm 180, 605 Agriculture Dr, Mailcode 6510, Carbondale, IL 62901 *Tel:* 618-453-2258 *Fax:* 618-453-3010 *E-mail:* teach@siu.edu *Web Site:* cte.siu.edu/video-and-image-production, pg 895

Southwest Audio-Visual Inc, 3058 E Cairo, Springfield, MO 65802 *Tel:* 417-887-4900 *Fax:* 417-866-6500 *E-mail:* info@southwestav.com *Web Site:* www.southwestav.com, pg 895

Southwest Binding & Laminating, 109 Millwell Ct, Maryland Heights, MO 63043-2509 *Tel:* 314-739-4400 *Toll Free Tel:* 800-325-3628 *Toll Free Fax:* 800-942-2010 *E-mail:* sales@swbindinglaminating.com *Web Site:* swbindinglaminating.com, pg 896

SouthWest Organizing Project (SWOP), 211 Tenth St SW, Albuquerque, NM 87102-2919 *Tel:* 505-247-8832 *Fax:* 505-247-9972 *E-mail:* swop@swop.net *Web Site:* www.swop.net, pg 896

Southwest Sound Solutions, 2323 Loop 410 NW, San Antonio, TX 78230-5348 *Tel:* 210-341-4411 *Fax:* 210-349-8300 *E-mail:* info@swsoundsolutions.com *Web Site:* www.swsoundsolutions.com, pg 896

Sovfoto/Eastfoto Inc, 263 W 20 St, Suite 3, New York, NY 10011 *Tel:* 212-727-8170 *E-mail:* info@sovfoto.com *Web Site:* www.sovfoto.com, pg 896

Space Coast Film Commission, 430 Brevard Ave, Suite 150, Cocoa Village, FL 32922 *Tel:* 321-433-4470 *Toll Free Tel:* 877-57-BEACH (572-3224) *Fax:* 321-433-4476 *Web Site:* www.visitspacecoast.com/film, pg 969

SpaceCam, 31240 La Baya Dr, Westlake Village, CA 91362 *Tel:* 818-889-6060 *Fax:* 818-889-6062 *E-mail:* rentals@spacecam.com *Web Site:* spacecam.com, pg 896

Sparkfactor, 943 W Randolph St, Suite 2E, Chicago, IL 60607 *Tel:* 773-292-8000 *E-mail:* info@sparkfactor.com *Web Site:* www.sparkfactor.com, pg 896

Sparkworks Media, 1818 E Yesler Way, Seattle, WA 98122 *Tel:* 206-284-5500 *E-mail:* info@sparkworksmedia.com *Web Site:* sparkworksmedia.com, pg 896

Sparrow Sound Design, 3501 N Southport, 2nd fl, Chicago, IL 60657-1435 *Tel:* 773-281-8510 *Fax:* 773-472-1632 *E-mail:* southport@chicagosound.com *Web Site:* www.chicagosound.com, pg 896

SPEAK HOUSE Audio™, 1844 E Montecito Ave, Phoenix, AZ 85016 *Tel:* 602-279-0900 *Fax:* 602-279-0980 *Web Site:* www.speakhouseaudio.com, pg 896

Speakeasy™ Productions Inc, 9 Westminster Shopping Center, No 152, Westminster, MD 21157 *Tel:* 410-889-0374 *Web Site:* www.voiceover.com, pg 896

Speakers Unlimited, 7532 Courtyard Place, Cary, NC 27519 *Tel:* 919-466-7676 *Toll Free Tel:* 888-333-6676 *E-mail:* prospeak@aol.com *Web Site:* www.speakersunlimited.com, pg 896

Special Archives Division, Motion Picture Branch, 8601 Adelphi Rd, College Park, MD 20740-6001 *Tel:* 301-837-2000 *Toll Free Tel:* 866-272-6272 (86-NARA-NARA, cust serv) *Fax:* 301-837-0483 *E-mail:* mopix@nara.gov *Web Site:* www.archives.gov, pg 896

Special Effects Systems Inc, 6160 Edgewater Dr, Suite F, Orlando, FL 32810 *Tel:* 407-297-6520 *Web Site:* www.confetticannonstore.com, pg 896

Special Effects Unlimited Inc, 1005 N Lillian Way, Hollywood, CA 90038 *Tel:* 323-466-3361 *Fax:* 323-466-5712 *E-mail:* seuefx@aol.com *Web Site:* www.specialefxunltd.com, pg 896

Special Event Services, 3135 Indiana Ave, Winston-Salem, NC 27105 *Tel:* 336-725-7799 *Toll Free Tel:* 800-423-3996 *Fax:* 336-725-0019 *Web Site:* www.specialeventservices.com, pg 896

Specialized Audio-Visual Inc, 14 Solar Dr, Clifton Park, NY 12065 *Tel:* 518-383-6501 *Fax:* 518-383-6506 *E-mail:* info@saviusa.com; sales@saviusa.com *Web Site:* www.saviusa.com, pg 896

Specialized Products Co, 1100 S Kimball Ave, Southlake, TX 76092 *Tel:* 817-329-6647 *Toll Free Tel:* 800-866-5353 *Toll Free Fax:* 800-234-8286 *E-mail:* customerservice@specialized.net; spcintl@specialized.net *Web Site:* www.specialized.net, pg 896

Specialty Bulb Co Inc, 80 Orville Dr, Suite 101, Bohemia, NY 11716 *Tel:* 631-589-3393 *Toll Free Tel:* 800-331-BULB (331-2852) *Fax:* 631-563-5089 *Web Site:* www.bulbspecialists.com, pg 896

Specialty Bulb Products Inc, 20010-100A Ave, Unit 2, Langley, BC V1M 3G4, Canada *Tel:* 604-513-8500 *Toll Free Tel:* 800-663-1120 *Fax:* 604-513-8200 *E-mail:* info@specialtybulb.com; bulbexpert@specialtybulb.com *Web Site:* specialtybulb.com, pg 896

Specialty Tapes Manfacturing Inc, 4221 Courtney Rd, Franksville, WI 53126 *Tel:* 262-835-0748 *Toll Free Tel:* 800-545-8273 *Fax:* 262-835-0749 *E-mail:* sales@specialtytapes.net *Web Site:* www.specialtytapes.net, pg 897

Spectra Cine Inc, 3607 W Magnolia Blvd, Burbank, CA 91505 *Tel:* 818-954-9222 *Fax:* 818-954-0016 *E-mail:* info@spectracine.com *Web Site:* www.spectracine.com, pg 897

Spectra Film & Video, 5626 Vineland Ave, North Hollywood, CA 91601 *Tel:* 818-762-4545 *Fax:* 818-762-5454 *E-mail:* sales@spectrafilmandvideo.com *Web Site:* www.spectrafilmandvideo.com, pg 897

Spectra Sonics LLC, 860 W Riverdale Rd, Suite D-6, Riverdale, UT 84405 *Tel:* 801-593-9813 (repair) *E-mail:* info@spectra-sonics.com *Web Site:* spectra-sonics.squarespace.com, pg 897

Spectra Video Productions Ltd, 380 Montrose St, Winnipeg, MB R3M 3M8, Canada *Tel:* 204-452-9832 *Web Site:* www.spectra-productions.com, pg 897

Spectrum, 400 Atlantic St, 10th fl, Stamford, CT 06901 *Tel:* 203-905-7800 *Web Site:* www.spectrum.com; www.facebook.com/Spectrum, pg 897

Spectrum Audio Visual Services, 351 W 45 Ave, Denver, CO 80216 *Tel:* 303-477-4456 *Toll Free Tel:* 800-477-4752 *Fax:* 303-477-0114 *E-mail:* info@spectrumav.com *Web Site:* www.spectrumav.com, pg 897

Spectrum Engineers, 324 S State St, Suite 400, Salt Lake City, UT 84111 *Tel:* 801-328-5151 *Toll Free Tel:* 800-678-7077 *Fax:* 801-328-5155 *E-mail:* info@spectrum-engineers.com *Web Site:* www.spectrum-engineers.com, pg 897

Spectrum Enterprise, 401 Park Ave S, New York, NY 10016 *Tel:* 212-379-5826 *Web Site:* enterprise.spectrum.com, pg 897

Spectrum Industries Inc, 925 First Ave, Chippewa Falls, WI 54729 *Tel:* 715-723-6750 *Toll Free Tel:* 800-235-1262 *Fax:* 715-738-2309 *Toll Free Fax:* 800-335-0473 *E-mail:* info@spectrumfurniture.com *Web Site:* www.spectrumfurniture.com, pg 897

Spectrum Productions, 565 Pinedale Dr, Annapolis, MD 21401 *Web Site:* www.markgoldberg.com, pg 897

Spectrum Sound Inc, 1040 Acorn Dr, Suite C, Nashville, TN 37210 *Tel:* 615-391-3700 *Web Site:* www.spectrumsound.net, pg 897

Speedotron Corp, 1268 Humbracht Circle, Bartlett, IL 60103-1631 *Tel:* 630-246-5001 *Fax:* 630-830-2525 *E-mail:* support@speedotron.com *Web Site:* speedotron.com, pg 897

Spence-Thomas Audio Post, 70 Richmond St E, Suite 300, Toronto, ON M5C 1N8, Canada *Tel:* 416-361-6383 *Toll Free Tel:* 866-547-2617 *Fax:* 416-361-2970 *E-mail:* info@spence-thomas.com; bookings@spence-thomas.com *Web Site:* www.spence-thomas.com, pg 897

Spider Support Systems, 11654 Plaza America Dr, Suite 180, Reston, VA 20190 *Tel:* 703-758-0699 *E-mail:* service@spidersupport.com *Web Site:* www.spidersupport.com, pg 897

SPIE, PO Box 10, Bellingham, WA 98227-0010 *Tel:* 360-676-3290 *Toll Free Tel:* 888-504-8171 *Fax:* 360-647-1445 *E-mail:* customerservice@spie.org *Web Site:* www.spie.org, pg 963

Spirig Advanced Technologies Inc (SAT), 144 Oakland St, Springfield, MA 01108 *Tel:* 413-788-6191 *Toll Free Tel:* 866-977-4744 *Fax:* 413-788-0490 *E-mail:* sat@spirig.com *Web Site:* www.spirig.com, pg 897

Spirit Media, 12042 SE Sunnyside Rd, Suite 700, Happy Valley, OR 97015 *Tel:* 503-698-5540 *Fax:* 503-698-8408 *E-mail:* info@spiritmedia.com *Web Site:* www.spiritmedia.com, pg 897

Spizzirri Press Inc, PO Box 9397, Rapid City, SD 57709-9397 *Tel:* 605-348-2749 *Toll Free Tel:* 800-325-9819 *Fax:* 605-348-6251 *Toll Free Fax:* 800-322-9819 *E-mail:* spizzpub@aol.com *Web Site:* www.spizzirri.com, pg 898

Split Image Productions, 4134 243 St, Flushing, NY 11363-1658 *Tel:* 718-428-1438 *Fax:* 718-428-1438, pg 898

Spoken Arts Inc, 195 S White Rock Rd, Holmes, NY 12531 *Tel:* 845-878-9600 *Toll Free Tel:* 800-326-4090 *Fax:* 845-878-9009 *E-mail:* sales@spokenartsmedia.com *Web Site:* www.spokenartsmedia.com, pg 898

Sports Cinematography Group, 715 Pier Ave, Santa Monica, CA 90405 *Tel:* 310-962-2200 *E-mail:* sportscinema@earthlink.net *Web Site:* www.sportscinematographygroup.com, pg 898

Sportsmen on Film Inc, 231 Earl Garrett, Suite 300, Kerrville, TX 78028 *Tel:* 830-792-4200 *Toll Free Tel:* 800-910-HUNT (910-4868) *Fax:* 830-792-4224 *Web Site:* www.sportsmenonfilm.com, pg 898

Spot Media Production Group, 2745 Locust St, St Louis, MO 63103 *Tel:* 314-667-5915 *E-mail:* info@spotmpg.com *Web Site:* www.spotmpg.com, pg 898

Sprayway Inc, 2651 Warrenville Rd, Downers Grove, IL 60515 *Tel:* 630-628-3000 *Toll Free Tel:* 800-332-9000 *Fax:* 630-543-7797 *E-mail:* info@spraywayinc.com *Web Site:* www.spraywayinc.com, pg 898

Spring Arbor Distributors Inc, One Ingram Blvd, La Vergne, TN 37086-1986 *Toll Free Tel:* 800-395-4340 *Toll Free Fax:* 800-876-0186 *E-mail:* customerservice@ingramcontent.com *Web Site:* www.ingramcontent.com, pg 898

Sprocket Digital, PO Box 1420, Claremont, CA 91711 *Tel:* 909-946-2364 *Fax:* 909-946-2631 *E-mail:* sdsales@sprocketdigital.com *Web Site:* www.sprocketdigital.com, pg 898

SSL Industries Inc, 4935 Anne Louise Lane, Suite 2, Placerville, CA 95667 *Tel:* 530-644-0233 *E-mail:* ssl@sllinc.net *Web Site:* www.sslinc.net, pg 898

ST Productions, 900 Whitehall Rd, Chattanooga, TN 37405 *Tel:* 423-267-5412 *Fax:* 423-267-6840 *E-mail:* stps@wrcbtv.com *Web Site:* www.wrcbtv.com, pg 898

Staco Energy Products Co, 301 Gaddis Blvd, Dayton, OH 45403 *Tel:* 937-253-1191 *Toll Free Tel:* 866-261-1191 *Fax:* 937-253-1723 *E-mail:* sales@stacoenergy.com; service@stacoenergy.com *Web Site:* www.stacoenergy.com, pg 898

Staedtler-Mars Ltd, 850 Matteson Blvd W, Unit 4, Mississauga, ON L5V 0B4, Canada *Tel:* 905-501-9008 *Toll Free Tel:* 800-776-5544 (US); 800-387-5872 (US) *Fax:* 905-501-9117 *Toll Free Fax:* 800-675-8249 (US) *E-mail:* info@staedtler.ca *Web Site:* www.staedtler.ca, pg 898

Stage America LLC, 2300 N Atlantic Ave, Suite 1002, Daytona Beach, FL 32811 *Tel:* 702-879-8177 *E-mail:* info@stageamerica.com *Web Site:* www.stageamerica.com, pg 898

Stage Crew Audiovisual Inc, PO Box 6097, San Juan, PR 00914-6097 *Tel:* 787-723-6398 *Fax:* 787-721-1410, pg 898

Stage Directions, 8311 Hempstead Rd, Houston, TX 77008 *Tel:* 713-863-7469 *Fax:* 713-863-9418 *E-mail:* sales@stagedirections.com *Web Site:* www.stagedirections.com, pg 898

Stage Equipment & Lighting Inc, 4600 SW 36 St, Orlando, FL 32811 *Tel:* 407-425-2010 *Fax:* 407-648-2604 *E-mail:* mail@seal-fla.com *Web Site:* www.seal-fla.com, pg 898

Stage Front Presentation Systems, 6 Southern Oaks Dr, Savannah, GA 31405 *Tel:* 912-236-1345 *Toll Free Tel:* 800-736-9242 *Fax:* 912-233-5350 *Web Site:* www.sfps.net; www.stagefrontproductions.com, pg 899

Stage Post, 255 French Landing Dr, Nashville, TN 37228 *Tel:* 615-248-1978 *Toll Free Tel:* 877-250-1839 *Fax:* 615-242-8861 *E-mail:* mail@stagepost.com *Web Site:* www.stagepost.com, pg 899

Stage 3 Productions, 27500 Donald Ct, Warren, MI 48092 *Tel:* 586-576-0625 *Toll Free Tel:* 888-330-5179 *Web Site:* www.stage3.com, pg 899

Stageline Mobile Stage Inc, 700 Marsolais St, L'Assomption, QC J5W 2G9, Canada *Tel:* 450-589-1063 *Toll Free Tel:* 800-26-STAGE (267-8243) *Fax:* 450-589-1711 *E-mail:* info@stageline.com *Web Site:* www.stageline.com, pg 899

Stageright Corp, a Rogers Group brand, 495 Pioneer Pkwy, Clare, MI 48617 *Tel:* 989-386-7393 (Intl Sales) *Toll Free Tel:* 800-438-4499 *E-mail:* info@stageright.com *Web Site:* www.stageright.com, pg 899

Stages Video Productions, 514 29 Ave N, Myrtle Beach, SC 29577 *Tel:* 843-626-7466 *E-mail:* info@stagesvideo.com *Web Site:* www.stagesvideo.com, pg 899

StageSound, 2240 Shenandoah Ave NW, Roanoke, VA 24017 *Tel:* 540-342-2040 *Toll Free Tel:* 800-778-9839 *Fax:* 540-345-5158 *Web Site:* stagesound.com, pg 899

Stagestep Inc, 4701 Bath St, No 46, Philadelphia, PA 19137 *Tel:* 215-636-9000 *Toll Free Tel:* 800-523-0960 (US & CN) *Fax:* 267-672-2912 *E-mail:* stagestep@stagestep.com; info@stagestep.com *Web Site:* www.stagestep.com, pg 899

Staging Concepts, 8400 Wyoming Ave N, Suite 100, Minneapolis, MN 55445 *Tel:* 763-533-2094 *Toll Free Tel:* 800-337-5339 *E-mail:* info@stagingconcepts.com *Web Site:* www.stagingconcepts.com, pg 899

Staging Directions Inc, 1327 Northbrook Pkwy, Suite 440, Suwanee, GA 30024 *Tel:* 770-409-9909 *Toll Free Tel:* 800-782-4322 *Fax:* 770-409-0277 *E-mail:* sales@teamsdi.net *Web Site:* www.stagingdirections.com, pg 899

Staging Resources Inc, 257 E Helen Rd, Palatine, IL 60067 *Tel:* 847-963-6600 *Toll Free Tel:* 877-963-6600 *Fax:* 847-963-6601 *E-mail:* info@stagingresources.com *Web Site:* www.stagingresources.com, pg 899

Stampede Presentation Products Inc, 55 Woodridge Dr, Amherst, NY 14228 *Tel:* 716-635-9474 *Toll Free Tel:* 800-398-5652 *Fax:* 716-635-9484 (sales); 716-691-0854 *E-mail:* stampedenews@stampedeglobal.com *Web Site:* www.stampedeglobal.com, pg 899

Stanco Sales LLC, 1529 S Terry St, Longmont, CO 80501 *Tel:* 303-776-3770, pg 899

James Stanfield Co Inc, 129 S Quarantina St, Santa Barbara, CA 93103 *Tel:* 805-897-1185 *Toll Free Tel:* 800-421-6534 *Fax:* 805-897-1187 *E-mail:* maindesk@stanfield.com *Web Site:* www.stanfield.com, pg 899

Stanford Research Systems Inc, 1290-D Reamwood Ave, Sunnyvale, CA 94089 *Tel:* 408-744-9040 *Fax:* 408-744-9049 *E-mail:* info@thinksrs.com *Web Site:* www.thinksrs.com, pg 899

Stanislaus AV Inc, 1431 Kansas Ave, Modesto, CA 95351 *Tel:* 209-529-2700; 559-438-0330 (EKC) *Fax:* 559-438-0333 (efax) *Web Site:* www.stanav.com; ekccorp.com, pg 899

Stanley Film Festival, The Stanley Hotel, 333 Wonderview Ave, Estes Park, CO 80517 *Tel:* 970-577-4112 *Web Site:* www.stanleyfilmfest.com, pg 1004

Jay S Stanley & Associates Inc, 5313 McClanahan Dr, Suite G-5, North Little Rock, AR 72116 *Tel:* 501-758-8029 *Toll Free Tel:* 888-758-4728 *Fax:* 501-758-8037 *E-mail:* info@jaystanley.com *Web Site:* www.jaystanley.com, pg 899

Stanton Magnetics, c/o Gibson Pro Audio, 309 Plus Park Blvd, Nashville, TN 37217 *Toll Free Tel:* 800-4GIBSON (444-2766) *E-mail:* service@gibson.com (cust serv) *Web Site:* stantondj.com, pg 900

Star Case Manufacturing Co Inc, 648 Superior Ave, Munster, IN 46321 *Tel:* 219-922-4440 *Toll Free Tel:* 800-822-STAR (822-7827); 800-782-CASE (782-2273) *Fax:* 219-922-4442 *E-mail:* star@starcase.com *Web Site:* www.starcase.com, pg 900

Star Video Duplicating, 7100 Mockingbird Lane, Paradise Valley, AZ 85253 *Tel:* 602-437-0646 *Web Site:* www.starvideo.com, pg 900

Starburns Industries, 1700 W Burbank Blvd, Burbank, CA 91506 *Tel:* 818-433-3300 *Fax:* 818-433-3383 *E-mail:* contact@starburnsind.com *Web Site:* www.starburnsindustries.com, pg 900

Starline Costumes, 1286 Bandera Rd, San Antonio, TX 78228 *Tel:* 210-435-3535 *Fax:* 210-435-9425 *Web Site:* starlinecostumes.com, pg 900

Starlite, 9 Whittendale Dr, Moorestown, NJ 08057 *Tel:* 856-780-8000 *Toll Free Tel:* 800-738-7400 *Fax:* 856-780-8001 *E-mail:* info@starlite.com *Web Site:* www.starlite.com, pg 900

StarTrak Studios Inc, 36 Vermont Ave, Unit 1, Warwick, RI 02888 *Tel:* 401-732-1880 *E-mail:* info@startrakstudios.com *Web Site:* www.startrakstudios.com, pg 900

Starwest Productions, 8760 W 68 Place, Arvada, CO 80004 *Tel:* 303-295-2222 *E-mail:* info@estarwest.com *Web Site:* www.estarwest.com, pg 900

State of Hawaii Film Office, 250 S Hotel St, Suite 510-A, Honolulu, HI 96813 *Tel:* 808-586-2570 *Fax:* 808-586-2572 *E-mail:* info@hawaiifilmoffice.com *Web Site:* filmoffice.hawaii.gov, pg 970

State of the Art Acoustik Inc, 43-1010 Polytek St, Ottawa, ON K1J 9J3, Canada *Tel:* 613-745-2003 *Fax:* 613-745-9687 *E-mail:* sota@sota.ca *Web Site:* www.sota.ca, pg 900

Staylor-Made Communications Inc, 11835 Carmel Mountain Rd, Suite 1304-365, San Diego, CA 92128-4609 *Toll Free Tel:* 800-711-6699 *E-mail:* info@staylor-made.com *Web Site:* staylor-made.com, pg 900

Steamboat Springs Film Committee, 125 Anglers Dr, Steamboat Springs, CO 80487 *Tel:* 970-879-0880 *E-mail:* info@steamboatchamber.com *Web Site:* www.steamboatchamber.com/media/steamboat-springs-film-committee, pg 968

Stedman Corp, 9625 E "D" Ave, Richland, MI 49083 *Tel:* 269-629-5930 *Toll Free Tel:* 888-629-5960 *E-mail:* info@stedmancorp.com *Web Site:* www.stedmancorp.com, pg 900

Steeldeck® Inc, 3339 Exposition Place, Los Angeles, CA 90018-4034 *Tel:* 323-290-2100 *Toll Free Tel:* 800-50STAGE (507-8243) *Fax:* 323-290-9600 *E-mail:* sales@steeldeck.com; rentals@steeldeck.com *Web Site:* www.steeldeck.com, pg 900

Steiner Studios, 15 Washington Ave, Brooklyn Navy Yard, Brooklyn, NY 11205 *Tel:* 718-858-1600 *Web Site:* www.steinerstudios.com, pg 900

Stereo Sales Inc, 1530 S Monroe St, Tallahassee, FL 32301 *Tel:* 850-224-2635 *E-mail:* sales@stereosales.net *Web Site:* www.stereosales.org; www.stereosales.net, pg 900

Bret Stern Productions, c/o SoNo Studios, 18 Leonard St, Norwalk, CT 06850 *Tel:* 203-354-4002 *E-mail:* info@bretsternproductions.com *Web Site:* bretsternproductions.com, pg 900

Stevens Design & Animation LLC, PO Box 90612, Albuquerque, NM 87199 *Tel:* 505-200-2042 *Web Site:* stevensanimation.com, pg 900

Stewart Acoustical Consultants, 7330 Chapel Hill Rd, Suite 201, Raleigh, NC 27607 *Tel:* 919-858-0899 *Fax:* 919-858-0899 *Web Site:* www.sacnc.com, pg 900

Stewart Audio, 14435 Cuesta Ct, Suite C, Sonora, CA 95370 *Tel:* 209-588-8111 *Fax:* 209-588-8113 *E-mail:* sales@stewartaudio.com; support@stewartaudio.com *Web Site:* www.stewartaudio.com, pg 901

Stewart Filmscreen Corp, 1161 Sepulveda Blvd, Torrance, CA 90502-2754 *Tel:* 310-784-5300 *Toll Free Tel:* 800-762-4999 (North America only) *Fax:* 310-326-6870 *E-mail:* request@stewartfilmscreen.com *Web Site:* www.stewartfilmscreen.com, pg 901

STIL Casing Solution, 76 Saint Paul, Suite 103, Quebec City, QC G1K 3V9, Canada *Tel:* 418-694-0449 (ext 10); 418-694-0449 (ext 11, sales & cust serv); 418-694-0449 (ext 12, admin) *Toll Free Tel:* 888-414-0449 (CN & US) *Fax:* 418-694-1621 *E-mail:* info@stilcasing.com; sales@stilcasing.com; admin@stilcasing.com *Web Site:* www.stilcasing.com, pg 901

Still N' Motion, 1727 Little Orchard St, Suite A, San Jose, CA 95125 *Tel:* 408-292-9982 *E-mail:* info1@stillnmotion.com *Web Site:* stillnmotion.com, pg 901

Stockfootage.com, 231 S Mountain Way Dr, Orem, UT 84058 *Tel:* 801-221-9570; 801-361-0012 (cell) *E-mail:* sales@stockfootage.com *Web Site:* www.stockfootage.com, pg 901

StockMusic.com, 105 W Beaver Creek Rd, Suite 4, Richmond Hill, ON L4B 1C6, Canada *Tel:* 905-886-0077 *Fax:* 905-886-6800 *E-mail:* info@stockmusic.com *Web Site:* www.stockmusic.com, pg 901

Stockton & San Joaquin Film Commission, 125 Bridge Place, 2nd fl, Stockton, CA 95202 *Tel:* 209-938-1555 *Toll Free Tel:* 877-778-6258 *E-mail:* visitorinfo@visitstockton.org *Web Site:* www.visitstockton.org/about-us/film-commission, pg 968

Stockyard Photos/Jim Olive Photography, 1520 Center St, Studio 2, Houston, TX 77007 *Tel:* 281-802-3597 *Web Site:* stockyard.com, pg 901

Story Teller Effects Group LLC, 333 River Rd, Jefferson, LA 70121 *Tel:* 504-832-9800 *Fax:* 504-832-9955 *E-mail:* storytellerfx@riggspfx.com; sales@storytellerfx.com *Web Site:* www.riggspfx.com, pg 901

StoryTrack, 3224 Locust St, Suite 301, St Louis, MO 63103 *Tel:* 314-725-3003 *Web Site:* www.storytrack.com, pg 901

Stouffer Graphic Arts, 922 S Cleveland St, Mishawaka, IN 46544 *Tel:* 574-252-5772 *Fax:* 574-252-5776 *E-mail:* info@stouffer.net *Web Site:* www.stouffer.net, pg 901

Straight Shoot'r Cranes Inc, 18434 Oxnard St, Unit H, Tarzana, CA 91356 *Tel:* 818-609-8310 *Fax:* 818-609-8311 *Web Site:* www.straightshootr.com, pg 901

Straight Wire Inc, 2032 Scott St, Hollywood, FL 33020 *Tel:* 954-925-2470 *Toll Free Tel:* 800-683-4434 *Fax:* 954-925-7253 *E-mail:* info@straightwire.com *Web Site:* www.straightwire.com, pg 901

Strand Lighting Inc, 10911 Petal St, Dallas, TX 75238 *Tel:* 214-647-7880 *Fax:* 214-647-8031 *E-mail:* sales@strandlighting.com *Web Site:* www.strandlighting.com, pg 901

Strata™, 3013 Santa Clara Dr, Santa Clara, UT 84765 *Tel:* 435-628-5218 *Toll Free Tel:* 800-STRATA-3D (787-2823); 800-6-STRATA (678-7282) *Fax:* 435-628-9756 *E-mail:* sales@strata.com *Web Site:* www.strata.com, pg 901

Strategic Connections, 3000 Spring Forest Rd, Raleigh, NC 27616 *Tel:* 919-878-0550 *Toll Free Tel:* 800-255-5664 *Fax:* 919-875-8712 *Web Site:* www.strategicconnections.net, pg 901

Stray Angel Films, 11318 Santa Monica Blvd, Los Angeles, CA 90025 *Tel:* 310-277-6900 *Fax:* 801-438-5009 *E-mail:* rentals@strayangel.com *Web Site:* www.strayangel.com, pg 902

Stretching Inc, PO Box 767, Palmer Lake, CO 80133-0767 *Tel:* 719-481-3928 *Toll Free Tel:* 800-333-1307 *Fax:* 719-481-9058 *E-mail:* office@stretching.com *Web Site:* www.stretching.com, pg 902

Strong Cinema Products, 11422 Miracle Hills Dr, Suite 300, Omaha, NE 68154 *Tel:* 402-453-4444 *Toll Free Tel:* 800-424-1215 *Fax:* 402-453-7238 *E-mail:* info@btn-inc.com *Web Site:* ballantynestrong.com, pg 902

Strong Screen Systems, 1440 Raoul-Charrette, Joliette, QC J6E 8S7, Canada *Tel:* 450-755-3795 *Toll Free Tel:* 877-755-3795 *Fax:* 450-755-3122 *E-mail:* sales@strongmdi.com *Web Site:* strongmdi.com, pg 902

Joseph Struhl Company Inc, 195 Atlantic Ave, Garden City Park, NY 11040 *Tel:* 516-741-3660 *Toll Free Tel:* 800-552-0023 *Fax:* 516-742-3617 *E-mail:* info@magicmaster.com; orders@magicmaster.com *Web Site:* www.magicmaster.com, pg 902

Student Academy Awards Competition, 8949 Wilshire Blvd, Beverly Hills, CA 90211 *Tel:* 310-247-3000 *Fax:* 310-859-9619 *E-mail:* saa@oscars.org *Web Site:* www.oscars.org/saa, pg 1004

Studio B Mastering, 821 Louise Ave, Charlotte, NC 28204 *Tel:* 704-372-9661 *Web Site:* www.studiobmastering.com, pg 902

Studio Center Corp, 161 Business Park Dr, Virginia Beach, VA 23462 *Tel:* 757-286-3080 (24 hour cell) *Toll Free Tel:* 866-515-2111 *Fax:* 757-622-0583 (acctg) *Web Site:* www.studiocenter.com, pg 902

Studio Charleston, 620 Dobbin Rd, Charleston, SC 29414 *Tel:* 843-376-1190 *Fax:* 843-737-4282 *E-mail:* info@studiocharleston.com *Web Site:* www.facebook.com/studiocharleston/, pg 902

Studio Circle Recordings, 863 Woodside Way, San Mateo, CA 94401 *Tel:* 650-328-8338 *E-mail:* info@studiocirclerecordings.com *Web Site:* www.studiocirclerecordings.com, pg 902

Studio Consulting & Construction Inc, 2805 Oakview Dr, Dryden, MI 48428-9740 *Tel:* 810-796-3235; 248-496-9000 (cell) *E-mail:* scc@hdakers.com *Web Site:* www.hdakers.com, pg 902

Studio Dynamics, 7245 Alondra Blvd, Paramount, CA 90723 *Tel:* 562-531-6700 *Toll Free Tel:* 800-595-4273 *E-mail:* sales@studiodynamics.com *Web Site:* www.studiodynamics.com, pg 902

Studio 1444, 1444 N Highland Ave, Hollywood, CA 90028 *Tel:* 323-482-1004 *E-mail:* info@studio1444.com, pg 902

Studio Instrument Rentals (SIR), 475 Tenth Ave, 2nd fl, New York, NY 10018 *Tel:* 212-627-4900 *E-mail:* nyinfo@sir-usa.com *Web Site:* www.sir-usa.com, pg 902

Studio 1 Productions™ Inc, 5312 Peach Blossom Blvd, Port Orange, FL 32128 *Tel:* 386-788-6075 *E-mail:* studio1@studio1productions.com *Web Site:* www.studio1productions.com, pg 902

Studio 132, 6802 Gunn Dr, Oakland, CA 94611-1443 *Tel:* 510-338-1240 *E-mail:* info@studio132.com *Web Site:* www.studio132.com, pg 902

Studio 637, 637 Cypress Ave, Hermosa Beach, CA 90254 *Tel:* 310-372-8218 *Web Site:* studio-637.com, pg 903

Studio South, 4912 Old Pineville Rd, Charlotte, NC 28217 *Tel:* 704-525-0296 *E-mail:* service@studiosouthmedia.com *Web Site:* www.studiosouthmedia.com, pg 903

Studio Space Atlanta, 3080 McCall Dr, Suite 2, Atlanta, GA 30340 *Tel:* 404-630-0508 *E-mail:* info@studiospaceatl.com *Web Site:* www.studiospaceatl.com, pg 903

Studio Technologies Inc, 7440 Frontage Rd, Skokie, IL 60077-3202 *Tel:* 847-676-9177 *E-mail:* stisales-2018@studio-tech.com *Web Site:* www.studio-tech.com, pg 903

Studio Thirteen11, 1311 Chemical St, Dallas, TX 75207 *Tel:* 214-377-8606 *Web Site:* www.studiothirteen11.com, pg 903

Studio Worx Inc, 218 Country Creek Ct, Ballwin, MO 63011 *Tel:* 314-968-2626 *Fax:* 314-968-9866 *E-mail:* bret.s@stlswi.com *Web Site:* www.studioworxinc.com, pg 903

The Studios at Paramount, 5555 Melrose Ave, Hollywood, CA 90038 *Tel:* 323-956-5000 *Web Site:* www.paramountstudios.com, pg 903

Stunt Wings Adventure Sports Talent & Equipment, 12623 Gridley St, Sylmar, CA 91342 *Tel:* 818-367-2430; 818-353-5580 (home); 818-266-0874 (cell) *E-mail:* stuntwings@me.com *Web Site:* www.stuntwings.com, pg 903

Russ Sturgeon Productions/RSVP, 916 Third Ave S, Nashville, TN 37210 *Tel:* 615-255-7787 *Web Site:* www.rsvpnashville.com, pg 903

Style-City Music Inc, PO Box 40403, St Petersburg, FL 33743 *Tel:* 727-520-2336 *E-mail:* stylecitymusic@yahoo.com *Web Site:* stylecitymusicinc.wordpress.com, pg 903

Subject Matter, 1201 New York Ave NW, Suite 900, Washington, DC 20005 *Tel:* 202-544-8400 *Web Site:* teamsubjectmatter.com, pg 903

Suede Interactive, 693 Main St, Hackensack, NJ 07601-4713 *Tel:* 201-646-0416 *E-mail:* suede@suede.tv *Web Site:* www.suede.tv, pg 903

Suffolk County Film Commission, H Lee Dennison Bldg, 11th fl, 100 Veterans Memorial Hwy, Hauppauge, NY 11788 *Tel:* 631-853-4800 *Fax:* 631-853-4767 *Web Site:* www.suffolkcountyfilmcommission.com, pg 974

Sugar Mountain PR, 5505 SW Illinois St, Portland, OR 97221-1643 *Tel:* 503-293-9498 *E-mail:* sugarmountainnews@msn.com *Web Site:* www.sugarmountainpr.com, pg 903

Suggs Media Productions Inc, 156 W 44 St, 7th fl, New York, NY 10036 *Tel:* 212-398-4200 *Fax:* 212-382-0922, pg 903

Sullivan Home Entertainment, 110 Davenport Rd, Toronto, ON M5R 3R3, Canada *Tel:* 416-921-7177 *Fax:* 416-921-7538 *E-mail:* inquire@sullivan-ent.com *Web Site:* www.sullivanmovies.com, pg 903

Sumiko Inc, 2431 Fifth St, Berkeley, CA 94710 *Tel:* 510-843-4500 *Fax:* 510-843-7120 *E-mail:* mail@sumikoaudio.net *Web Site:* www.sumikoaudio.net, pg 903

Summit Audio Inc, 2685 Dow Ave, Suite A-1, Tustin, CA 92780 *Tel:* 714-730-3010; 714-730-2086 *Fax:* 714-730-2087 *E-mail:* sound@summitaudio.com *Web Site:* www.summitaudio.com, pg 903

Summit Electronics Corp, 4260 NW First Ave, Suite 50, Boca Raton, FL 33431 *Tel:* 561-226-8500 *Toll Free Tel:* 800-226-6960 *Fax:* 561-226-8523 *E-mail:* sales@summitelectronics.com *Web Site:* www.summitelectronics.com; www.partsprocurement.com; bocasemi.com, pg 903

Sun Entertainment Corp, 3106 Belmont Blvd, Nashville, TN 37212 *Tel:* 615-385-1960 *E-mail:* info@sunrecords.com *Web Site:* www.sunrecords.com, pg 903

Sunburst Digital Inc, 1501 N Michael Dr, Wood Dale, IL 60191 *Toll Free Tel:* 800-321-7511 *Toll Free Fax:* 888-800-3028 *E-mail:* service@sunburst.com; sales@sunburst.com *Web Site:* www.sunburst.com, pg 903

Sunburst Recording, 4174 Madison Ave, Culver City, CA 90232 *Tel:* 310-204-2222, pg 904

Sundance Film Festival, 1825 Three Kings Dr, Park City, UT 84060 *Tel:* 435-658-3456 *Fax:* 435-658-3457 *E-mail:* customerservice@sundance.org; press@sundance.org; institute@sundance.org *Web Site:* www.sundance.org/festival, pg 1004

Sundance Systems, Fibox Products Division, 7411 Hines Place, Suite 123, Dallas, TX 75235 *Tel:* 214-920-9190 *Toll Free Tel:* 800-525-3443 *Fax:* 214-920-9339 *Web Site:* www.sundancesys.com, pg 904

Sunfire Communications Inc, 6965 Piazza Grande Ave, Suite 214, Orlando, FL 32835 *Tel:* 407-226-8226 *Fax:* 407-226-1660 *E-mail:* info@sunfirecommunications.com *Web Site:* www.sunfirecommunications.com, pg 904

Sunnex Inc, 8001 Tower Point Dr, Charlotte, NC 28227 *Toll Free Tel:* 800-445-7869 *Toll Free Fax:* 888-668-1920 *E-mail:* sunnex@sunnex.com; info@sunnex.com *Web Site:* www.sunnexonline.com, pg 904

Sunnyside Communications Inc, 348 W 38 St, Suite 12-B, New York, NY 10018 *Tel:* 212-564-4606 *Fax:* 212-967-2968 *Web Site:* www.sunnysiderecords.com, pg 904

Sunrise Packaging Inc, 1214 98 Ave NE, Blaine, MN 55434 *Tel:* 763-785-2505 *Toll Free Tel:* 800-634-8160 *Fax:* 763-785-2210 *E-mail:* customerservice@sunpack.com *Web Site:* www.sunpack.com, pg 904

Sunrise Studios, 6412 N University Dr, Suite 107, Tamarac, FL 33321 *Tel:* 954-653-8480 *E-mail:* info@sunrisestudios.tv *Web Site:* www.sunrisestudios.tv, pg 904

Sunset Bronson Studios, 5800 W Sunset Blvd, Hollywood, CA 90028 *Tel:* 323-460-5858 *Fax:* 323-460-3844 *E-mail:* reception@sunsetbronson.com *Web Site:* sgsandsbs.com, pg 904

Sunset Gower Studios, 1438 N Gower St, Hollywood, CA 90028 *Tel:* 323-467-1001 *Fax:* 323-467-2717 *E-mail:* reception@sunsetgower.com *Web Site:* sunsetgowerstudios.com, pg 904

Sunset Las Palmas Studios, 1040 N Las Palmas Ave, Los Angeles, CA 90038 *Tel:* 323-860-0000 *E-mail:* reception@sunsetlaspalmas.com *Web Site:* www.sunsetlaspalmas.com, pg 904

Supercircuits, 11000 N Mopac Expwy, Bldg 300, Austin, TX 78759 *Toll Free Tel:* 877-995-2288 *E-mail:* operations@supercircuits.com; customercare@supercircuits.com *Web Site:* www.supercircuits.com, pg 904

SuperDigital Ltd, 1150 NW 17 Ave, Portland, OR 97209-2403 *Tel:* 503-228-2222 *Toll Free Tel:* 888-79AUDIO (792-8346) *E-mail:* audiosales@superdigital.com *Web Site:* www.superdigital.com, pg 904

Superior Electric, One Cowles Rd, Plainville, CT 06062 *Tel:* 860-507-2025 *Toll Free Tel:* 800-787-3532 *Fax:* 860-507-2050 *Toll Free Fax:* 800-821-1369 *E-mail:* customer.service@superiorelectric.com *Web Site:* www.superiorelectric.com, pg 904

Superscope LLC, 1508 Batavia Ave, Geneva, IL 60134-3302 *Tel:* 630-232-8900 *Toll Free Tel:* 800-374-4118 *Fax:* 630-232-8905 *Web Site:* www.superscopetechnologies.com, pg 904

SuperStock Inc, 6620 Southpoint Dr S, Suite 501, Jacksonville, FL 32216 *Tel:* 904-565-0066 *Toll Free Tel:* 800-828-4545 *Fax:* 904-565-1620 *E-mail:* info@superstock.com; yourfriends@superstock.com *Web Site:* www.superstock.com, pg 904

SuperVision, Pacific Design Ctr, Suite B-120, 8687 Melrose Ave, Los Angeles, CA 90069 *Tel:* 310-652-9510 *Toll Free Tel:* 877-287-9783 *Fax:* 310-652-9516 *E-mail:* mail@supervisionav.com *Web Site:* www.supervisionav.com, pg 904

SurgeX, 8001 Knightdale Blvd, Suite 121, Knightdale, NC 27545 *Toll Free Tel:* 800-645-9721 (tech & cust support) *E-mail:* order.desk@ametek.com *Web Site:* espsurgex.com/surgex/, pg 905

SVAT Electronics, 4080 Montrose Rd, Niagara Falls, ON L2H 1J9, Canada *Fax:* 905-353-1701 *Toll Free Fax:* 888-771-1701 *E-mail:* marketing@svat.com *Web Site:* www.svat.com, pg 905

SVS Inc, 2513 Jenks Ave, Panama City, FL 32405 *Tel:* 850-522-4747 *Fax:* 850-522-4739 *E-mail:* sales@svslifts.com *Web Site:* www.svslifts.com, pg 905

Swallow, 700 S Chataignier St, Drawer 10, Ville Platte, LA 70586 *Tel:* 337-363-2177 *Fax:* 337-363-2094 *E-mail:* info@flattownmusic.com *Web Site:* www.flattownmusic.com, pg 905

Sweetsong Productions, 193 Meadsville Rd, Parkersburg, WV 26104 *Tel:* 304-428-7773 *E-mail:* sweetsongproductions@yahoo.com *Web Site:* www.sweetsong.com, pg 905

Sweetwater Sound Inc, 5501 US Hwy 30 W, Fort Wayne, IN 46818 *Tel:* 260-432-8176 *Toll Free Tel:* 800-222-4700 *Fax:* 260-432-1758 *Web Site:* www.sweetwater.com, pg 905

Switch, 6600 Manchester Ave, St Louis, MO 63139 *Tel:* 314-206-7700 *E-mail:* info@switch.us *Web Site:* www.switch.us, pg 905

Switchcraft® Inc, 5555 N Elston Ave, Chicago, IL 60630 *Tel:* 773-792-2700 *Fax:* 773-792-2129 *E-mail:* sales@switchcraft.com *Web Site:* www.switchcraft.com, pg 905

Swivelier, 600 Bradley Hill Rd, Blauvelt, NY 10913 *Tel:* 845-353-1455 *Fax:* 845-353-1512 *E-mail:* info@swivelier.com *Web Site:* www.swivelier.com, pg 905

Symbolic Sound Corp, 206 N Randolph St, Suite 520, Champaign, IL 61820 *Tel:* 217-355-6273 *E-mail:* info-kyma@symbolicsound.com *Web Site:* kyma.symbolicsound.com, pg 905

SYMCO Inc, 29 Poplar Dr, Stirling, NJ 07980 *Tel:* 908-647-6262 *Fax:* 908-647-4904 *E-mail:* orders@symcoinc.com *Web Site:* www.symcoinc.com, pg 905

Symetrix Inc, 6408 216 St SW, Mountlake Terrace, WA 98043-2093 *Tel:* 425-778-7728 *E-mail:* support@symetrix.co; sales@symetrix.co *Web Site:* www.symetrix.co, pg 905

Synaptic Digital, 79 Fifth Ave, 14th fl, New York, NY 10003 *Tel:* 212-682-8300 *Fax:* 212-201-4207 *E-mail:* learnmore@synapticdigital.com *Web Site:* www.synapticdigital.com, pg 905

SynAudCon, 8780 Rufing Rd, Greenville, IN 47124 *Tel:* 812-923-0174 *Toll Free Fax:* 866-547-0298 *Web Site:* www.synaudcon.com, pg 905

Synergem, 2323 Randolph Ave, Avenel, NJ 07001 *Tel:* 732-225-0001 *E-mail:* sales@synergem.com *Web Site:* synergem.com, pg 905

Synergistic Batteries Inc, 5975 Providence Lane, Cumming, GA 30040 *Tel:* 770-886-6621 *Toll Free Tel:* 800-634-6000 *E-mail:* sbicheri@synbat.com *Web Site:* www.synergisticbatteries.com, pg 906

Synergy Group Inc, 23930 Craftsman Rd, Calabasas, CA 91302-1437 *Tel:* 818-223-9009 *Fax:* 818-223-8999 *Web Site:* www.jeffcooper.com, pg 906

Synthesizer Rental Service, 10907 W Magnolia Blvd, North Hollywood, CA 91601 *Tel:* 323-660-4065; 818-907-7780; 615-327-3515 (Nashville dispatch) *E-mail:* sst.shop@yahoo.com; sstmusiccity@gmail.com *Web Site:* sstsynths.com, pg 906

Syracuse Scenery & Stage Lighting Co Inc, 101 Monarch Dr, Liverpool, NY 13088-4915 *Tel:* 315-453-8096 *Toll Free Tel:* 800-453-7775 *Fax:* 315-453-7897 *E-mail:* info@syracusescenery.com *Web Site:* www.syracusescenery.com, pg 906

Systems Impact Inc, 3515 Woodley Rd NW, Washington, DC 20016 *Toll Free Tel:* 888-568-6284 *E-mail:* support@mathmastery.com *Web Site:* mathmastery.com, pg 906

T & M Digital Services LLC, 54 Flint Ridge Rd, Monroe, CT 06468 *Tel:* 203-268-5290 *Fax:* 203-268-5290, pg 906

T-stop Inc, 957 Cole Ave, Hollywood, CA 90038 *Tel:* 323-544-1000 *Fax:* 323-544-4970 *E-mail:* info@t-stopinc.com *Web Site:* www.t-stopinc.com, pg 906

Tacoma-Regional Film Commission, 1516 Commerce St, Tacoma, WA 98402 *Tel:* 253-627-2836 *Fax:* 253-627-8783 *Web Site:* www.traveltacoma.com, pg 977

TAI Audio, 5828 Old Winter Garden Rd, Orlando, FL 32835 *Tel:* 407-296-9959 *Toll Free Tel:* 800-486-6444 *Fax:* 407-648-1352 *E-mail:* sales@taiaudio.com *Web Site:* www.taiaudio.com, pg 906

Take One Film & Video, 125 Commerce Ave, Hendersonville, TN 37075 *Tel:* 615-431-5822 *E-mail:* mail@takeone.tv *Web Site:* www.takeone.tv, pg 906

Take 1 Media Services, 31335 Center Ridge Rd, Cleveland, OH 44145 *Tel:* 440-899-0101 *Web Site:* www.take1media.com, pg 906

Take One Productions Ltd, 11010 Lake Grove Blvd, Suite 100-317, Morrisville, NC 27560, pg 906

Talas, 330 Morgan Ave, Brooklyn, NY 11211 *Tel:* 212-219-0770 *Fax:* 212-219-0735 *E-mail:* info@talasonline.com *Web Site:* www.talasonline.com, pg 906

Talk-A-Phone Co, 7530 N Natchez Ave, Niles, IL 60714 *Tel:* 773-539-1100 *Fax:* 773-539-1241 *E-mail:* info@talkaphone.com *Web Site:* www.talkaphone.com, pg 906

Tallahassee Audio Visual, 900 Capital Circle SE, Suite 4, Tallahassee, FL 32301 *Tel:* 850-877-1154 *Web Site:* talcam.com, pg 906

Tallahassee Photo & Frame, 900 Capital Circle SE, Suite 3, Tallahassee, FL 32301 *Tel:* 850-877-1152 *E-mail:* mgr@talcam.com *Web Site:* talcam.com, pg 906

Tally Display Corp, 19 Gardner Rd, Fairfield, NJ 07004 *Tel:* 973-777-7760 *Toll Free Tel:* 800-758-2559 *Fax:* 973-777-6220 *E-mail:* info@tallydisplay.com *Web Site:* www.tallydisplay.com, pg 906

Tam Communications Inc, 5610 Scotts Valley Dr, Suite B-552, Scotts Valley, CA 95066 *Tel:* 831-439-1500 *Toll Free Tel:* 866-390-1218 *E-mail:* info@tamcom.com *Web Site:* www.tamcom.com, pg 906

Tampa Hillsborough Film & Digital Media Commission, One Tampa City Ctr, 201 N Franklin St, Suite 2900, Tampa, FL 33602 *Web Site:* filmtampabay.com, pg 970

Tamrac® Inc, 2036 Lincoln Ave, Suite 104, Ogden, UT 84401 *Tel:* 385-405-2700 *Fax:* 385-405-2682 *E-mail:* info@tamrac.com *Web Site:* www.tamrac.com, pg 906

Tamron USA Inc, 10 Austin Blvd, Commack, NY 11725 *Tel:* 631-858-8400 *Toll Free Tel:* 800-827-8880 *Fax:* 631-543-5666; 631-858-8462 (cust serv) *E-mail:* custserv@tamron.com *Web Site:* www.tamron-usa.com, pg 906

Tamura Corporation of America, 1040 S Andreasen Dr, Suite 100, Escondido, CA 92029 *Tel:* 951-699-1270 *Toll Free Fax:* 472-6624 *Fax:* 951-676-9482 *Web Site:* www.tamuracorp.com, pg 906

Tanglewood Productions, 125 Brinkby Ave, Reno, NV 89509 *Tel:* 775-688-6282 *Toll Free Tel:* 877-671-8933 *E-mail:* info@tanglewoodproductions.com *Web Site:* www.tanglewoodproductions.com, pg 907

Tantor Media Inc, 6 Business Park Rd, Old Saybrook, CT 06475 *Tel:* 860-395-1155 *Toll Free Tel:* 877-7-TANTOR (782-6867) *Toll Free Fax:* 888-782-7821 *E-mail:* service@tantor.com *Web Site:* www.tantor.com, pg 907

Taperwire, c/o Fuller Manufacturing, 523 S Flower St, Burbank, CA 91502 *Tel:* 818-238-9911 *Fax:* 818-238-9959 *E-mail:* taperwire@taperwire.com *Web Site:* www.taperwire.com, pg 907

TAPPI, 15 Technology Pkwy S, Norcross, GA 30092 *Tel:* 770-446-1400 *Toll Free Tel:* 800-332-8686 (US); 800-446-9431 (CN) *Fax:* 240-396-5973 *E-mail:* memberconnection@tappi.org *Web Site:* www.tappi.org, pg 907

TARA Labs, 716 Rossanley Dr, Medford, OR 97501 *Tel:* 541-488-6465 *Fax:* 541-245-9119 *E-mail:* sales@taralabs.com *Web Site:* www.taralabs.com, pg 907

Tarpley Media Systems, 3737 50 St, Lubbock, TX 79413 *Tel:* 806-797-5833 *Toll Free Tel:* 800-600-5833 *Fax:* 806-797-5139 *E-mail:* tms@tarpleymedia.com *Web Site:* www.tarpleymedia.com, pg 907

TASCAM, 1834 Gage Rd, Montebello, CA 90640 *Tel:* 323-726-0303 (ext 617) *Web Site:* www.tascam. com, pg 907

Tasman Group Pacific Rim, 15304 Spring Ave, Sante Fe Springs, CA 90670 *Tel:* 562-566-1330 *Toll Free Tel:* 888-355-8889 *Fax:* 562-404-0716 *Web Site:* www. tasmangrouppr.com, pg 907

Tatum Video, 103 S Davis St, Telluride, CO 81435 *Tel:* 213-999-5970 (cell); 970-728-4892 *E-mail:* utemtn@aol.com, pg 907

Tatung Co of America Inc, 2850 El Presidio St, Long Beach, CA 90810 *Tel:* 310-637-2105 *Toll Free Tel:* 800-827-2850 *E-mail:* tus@tatungusa.com *Web Site:* www.tatungusa.com, pg 907

Carl Tatz Design, 6666 Brookmont Terr, Suite 1109, Nashville, TN 37205 *Tel:* 615-354-6242 *E-mail:* carl@ carltatzdesign.com *Web Site:* www.carltatzdesign.com, pg 907

The Taunton Press Inc, 63 S Main St, Newtown, CT 06470 *Tel:* 203-426-8171 *Toll Free Tel:* 800-926-8776 (ext 3893 - PR); 800-888-8286 (orders) *Fax:* 203-426-3434 *Web Site:* www.taunton.com, pg 907

Taylor Associates, 110 W Canal St, Suite 301, Winooski, VT 05404 *Tel:* 802-735-1942 *Toll Free Tel:* 800-READ-PLUS (732-3758) *Fax:* 802-419-4786 *E-mail:* info@readingplus.com *Web Site:* www. readingplus.com, pg 907

Chip Taylor Communications LLC, 2 East View Dr, Derry, NH 03038 *Tel:* 603-434-9262 *Toll Free Tel:* 800-876-CHIP (876-2447) *Fax:* 603-432-2723 *E-mail:* chip.taylor@chiptaylor.com *Web Site:* www. chiptaylor.com, pg 907

TBC Consoles Inc, 170 Rodeo Dr, Edgewood, NY 11717 *Tel:* 631-293-4068 *Toll Free Tel:* 888-CONSOLE (266-7653) *Fax:* 631-293-4075 *E-mail:* info@ tbcconsoles.com; sales@tbcconsoles.com; support@ tbcconsoles.com *Web Site:* www.tbcconsoles.com, pg 907

TBC Studios, 10201 W Appleton Ave, Milwaukee, WI 53225 *Tel:* 414-536-7337 *E-mail:* info@tbcstudios. com *Web Site:* www.tbcstudios.com, pg 907

Teaberry, 770 W Landoran Lane, Tucson, AZ 85737 *Tel:* 520-429-7952 *Fax:* 520-742-0652 *E-mail:* info@ tellens.com *Web Site:* www.tellens.com, pg 908

TEAC America Inc, 1834 Gage Rd, Montebello, CA 90640 *Tel:* 323-726-0303 *E-mail:* custser@teac.com *Web Site:* www.teac.com, pg 908

Teach America Corp, 121 N Love St, Quincy, FL 32351-2440 *Tel:* 850-528-6056 (cell) *Web Site:* teachamerica. com; www.accessmanagement.info, pg 908

TeachLogic Inc, 1688 Ord Way, Oceanside, CA 92056 *Tel:* 760-631-7800 *Toll Free Tel:* 800-588-0018 *Fax:* 760-631-1283 *E-mail:* sales@teachlogic.com; info@teachlogic.com *Web Site:* www.teachlogic.com, pg 908

Team Volusia Economic Development Corp, International Motorsports Ctr, One Daytona Blvd, Daytona Beach, FL 32114 *Tel:* 386-265-6332 *Web Site:* www. teamvolusiaedc.com, pg 969

Teatown Communications Group, 1560 Broadway, New York, NY 10036 *Tel:* 212-302-0722 *E-mail:* info@ teatown.tv, pg 908

TEC/West USA Inc, 3050 E Victoria St, Rancho Dominguez, CA 90221 *Tel:* 310-961-3491 *Toll Free Tel:* 800-421-7215 *Fax:* 310-464-9210 *E-mail:* info@ tecwest.com *Web Site:* www.tecwest.com, pg 908

Tech 21 USA Inc, 790 Bloomfield Ave, Clifton, NJ 07012 *Tel:* 973-777-6996 *Fax:* 973-777-9899 *E-mail:* info@tech21nyc.com *Web Site:* www. tech21nyc.com, pg 908

Techflex Inc, 104 Demarest Rd, Sparta, NJ 07871 *Tel:* 973-300-9242 *Toll Free Tel:* 800-323-5140 *Fax:* 973-300-9409 *E-mail:* techflex@techflex.com *Web Site:* www.techflex.com, pg 908

Techkno Integration & Design Services LLC, 1720 Kaliste Saloom, Bldg 2, Suite B-2, Lafayette, LA 70508 *Tel:* 337-406-9428 *Fax:* 337-406-9482, pg 908

Technet® Systems Group, 2600 Lake Shore Rd, Unit 157, Gilford, NH 03249 *Tel:* 603-483-5365 *Toll Free Tel:* 888-TECHNET (832-4638) *E-mail:* info@ technetsystems.com *Web Site:* www.technetsystems. com, pg 908

Techni-Lux Inc, 10900 Palmbay Dr, Orlando, FL 32824 *Tel:* 407-857-8770 *Fax:* 407-857-8771 *E-mail:* sales@ techni-lux.com *Web Site:* www.techni-lux.com, pg 908

Techni-Tool, a TestEquity LLC company, 1547 N Trooper Rd, Worcester, PA 19490 *Tel:* 610-941-2400 *Toll Free Tel:* 800-832-4866 *Fax:* 610-828-5623 *Toll Free Fax:* 800-854-8665 *E-mail:* sales@techni-tool.com; support@techni-tool.com (tech support) *Web Site:* www.techni-tool.com, pg 908

Technical Exhibits Corp, 6155 S Oak Park Ave, Chicago, IL 60638 *Tel:* 773-586-3377 *Fax:* 773-586-6575 *Web Site:* www.technicalexhibits.net, pg 908

Technical Services, 10567 Oak Creek Dr, Lakeside, CA 92040 *Tel:* 619-561-4410 *Web Site:* www.widcoinc. com, pg 908

Technical Services, 2750 Northaven Rd, Suite 206, Dallas, TX 75229 *Tel:* 972-421-4230 *Fax:* 972-421-4231 *Web Site:* www.tecserv.biz, pg 908

Technical Support Systems LLC, 2232 Central Ave, Memphis, TN 38104 *Tel:* 901-398-5908 *Fax:* 901-398-5914 *Web Site:* www.techsupportsys.com, pg 908

Technicolor-Herbert T Kalmus Medal Award, White Plains Plaza, 445 Hamilton Ave, Suite 601, White Plains, NY 10601-1827 *Tel:* 914-761-1100 *Fax:* 914-206-4216 *E-mail:* marketing@smpte.org *Web Site:* www.smpte.org, pg 1004

Technicolor USA Inc, 6040 Sunset Blvd, Hollywood, CA 90028 *Tel:* 323-817-6600 *E-mail:* info@technicolor. com *Web Site:* www.technicolor.com, pg 908

Technics, 2 Riverfront Plaza, 828 McCarter Hwy, Newark, NJ 07102 *Tel:* 201-348-7000 *Toll Free Tel:* 800-405-0652 (orders) *E-mail:* technicssupport@ us.panasonic.com *Web Site:* www.panasonic.com; www.technics.com, pg 909

Technology and Engineering Emmy® Awards, 1697 Broadway, Suite 404, New York, NY 10019 *Tel:* 212-586-8424 *Fax:* 212-246-8129 *E-mail:* techemmys@ emmyonline.tv *Web Site:* emmyonline.com/tech, pg 1004

Technomad™ Inc, PO Box 273, South Deerfield, MA 01373 *Tel:* 617-275-8898 *Toll Free Tel:* 800-464-7757 *Fax:* 617-535-9712 *E-mail:* sales@technomad. com; customercare@technomad.com *Web Site:* www. technomad.com, pg 909

Technomedia Solutions, 4545 36 St, Orlando, FL 32811 *Tel:* 407-351-0909 *Fax:* 407-248-9484 *E-mail:* sales@ gotechnomedia.com *Web Site:* www.gotechnomedia. com, pg 909

Technovision® Interactive Inc, 529 Mountain Ash Dr, Pickering, ON L1W 3Z8, Canada *Tel:* 905-509-9482 *E-mail:* sales@technovision.com *Web Site:* www. technovision.com, pg 909

TecNec Distributing, 812 Kings Hwy, Saugerties, NY 12477 *Tel:* 845-246-0428 *Toll Free Tel:* 800-543-0909 *Fax:* 845-246-0626 *E-mail:* sales@tecnec.com *Web Site:* www.tecnec.com, pg 909

Tecplot Inc, 3535 Factoria Blvd SE, Suite 550, Bellevue, WA 98006 *Tel:* 425-653-1200; 425-653-9393 (tech support) *Toll Free Tel:* 800-763-7005 (orders) *E-mail:* info@tecplot.com; support@tecplot.com *Web Site:* www.tecplot.com, pg 909

Tectonics Industries LLC, 1681 Harmon Rd, Auburn Hills, MI 48326 *Tel:* 248-597-1600 *Toll Free Tel:* 888-408-3199 *E-mail:* info@tectonics.com *Web Site:* tectonics.com, pg 909

Tek Data Systems Co, 1111 W Park Ave, Libertyville, IL 60048 *Tel:* 847-367-8800 *Fax:* 847-367-0235 *E-mail:* tekdata@tekdata.com; sales@tekdata.com *Web Site:* www.tekdata.com, pg 909

Tek Gear, 938 Corydon Ave, Winnipeg, MB R3M 0Y5, Canada *Tel:* 204-988-3001 *Fax:* 204-988-3050 *E-mail:* sales@tekgear.com *Web Site:* tekgear.com, pg 909

TEK Media Group, 711 S Victory Blvd, Burbank, CA 91502 *Tel:* 818-244-4440; 818-255-5045 *Toll Free Tel:* 800-255-5045 (support) *Fax:* 818-855-8762 *E-mail:* as@tekmg.com *Web Site:* www.tekmg.com, pg 909

Tekskil Industries Inc, 102-998 Harbourside Dr, North Vancouver, BC V7P 3T2, Canada *Tel:* 604-985-2250 *Toll Free Tel:* 877-835-7545 *Toll Free Fax:* 877-576-8361 *E-mail:* team@tekskil.com *Web Site:* www. tekskil.com, pg 909

Tel-Air Interests Inc, 4104 Grant St, Hollywood, FL 33021 *Tel:* 954-924-4949 *Fax:* 954-924-4980 *E-mail:* telair@aol.com *Web Site:* www.telairint.com, pg 909

TEL Systems LLC, 7235 Jackson Rd, Ann Arbor, MI 48103 *Tel:* 734-761-4506 *Toll Free Tel:* 800-686-7235 *Fax:* 734-761-9776 *E-mail:* sales@thalner.com *Web Site:* www.thalner.com, pg 909

Tel-Test, 605 NW 53 Ave, Suite A-17, Gainesville, FL 32609 *Tel:* 352-335-0901 *Fax:* 352-376-3260, pg 909

Telarc International Corp, 100 N Crescent Dr, Garden Level, Beverly Hills, CA 90210 *Tel:* 310-385-4455 *E-mail:* submissions@concordmusicgroup.com *Web Site:* www.concordmusicgroup.com/labels/telarc, pg 909

Tele-Measurements Inc, 145 Main Ave, Clifton, NJ 07014 *Tel:* 973-473-8822 *Toll Free Tel:* 800-223-0052 (ext 207) *Fax:* 973-473-0521 *E-mail:* contact@tele-measurements.com *Web Site:* www.tele-measurements. com, pg 910

Tele-Time Systems, 313 Parkway Dr, Cary, IL 60013 *Tel:* 847-640-1420 *E-mail:* teletimesystems@netzero. com, pg 910

Telect Inc, 22425 E Appleway Ave, Liberty Lake, WA 99019 *Tel:* 509-926-6000 *Toll Free Tel:* 800-551-4567 *E-mail:* getinfo@telect.com *Web Site:* www.telect.com, pg 910

Teledyne DALSA Inc, 605 McMurray Rd, Waterloo, ON N2V 2E9, Canada *Tel:* 519-886-6000 *Fax:* 519-886-8023 *Web Site:* www.teledynedalsa.com, pg 910

Teledyne Energy Systems Inc, 10707 Gilroy Rd, Hunt Valley, MD 21031 *Tel:* 410-771-8600 *Fax:* 410-771-8620 *Web Site:* www.teledynees.com, pg 910

Telemanagement Resources International Inc (TRI), 83 Harvey Cedar Way, Waretown, NJ 08758 *Tel:* 609-597-6334 *Web Site:* www.triinc.com, pg 910

Telemetrics Inc, 75 Commerce Dr, Allendale, NJ 07401 *Tel:* 201-848-9818 *Fax:* 201-848-9819 *E-mail:* info@ telemetricsinc.com *Web Site:* www.telemetricsinc.com, pg 910

Telemotions LLC, 405 E 54 St, Suite 3-N, New York, NY 10022 *Tel:* 212-486-3010 *Web Site:* www. telemotions.net, pg 910

Teleometrics International, 4567 Lake Shore Dr, Waco, TX 76710 *Tel:* 254-776-2060 *Toll Free Tel:* 800-876-2389 *E-mail:* teleocsrv@teleometrics.com *Web Site:* www.teleometrics.com, pg 910

Telepro Video Inc, 2650 Rd 32, Linwood, NE 68036 *Tel:* 402-593-0999 *E-mail:* tmtelepro@aol.com, pg 910

Telequest Inc, 174 Nassau St, Suite 383, Princeton, NJ 08542 *Tel:* 609-430-3004 *E-mail:* contact@ telequestinc.com *Web Site:* www.telequestinc.com, pg 910

Telescript International, 55 Walnut St, Norwood, NJ 07648 *Tel:* 201-767-6733 *Fax:* 201-660-7804 *E-mail:* info@telescript.com *Web Site:* telescript.com, pg 910

Telestream Inc, 848 Gold Flat Rd, Nevada City, CA 95959 *Tel:* 530-470-1300 *Toll Free Tel:* 877-257-6245 *Fax:* 530-470-1301 *E-mail:* info@telestream.net *Web Site:* www.telestream.net, pg 910

TeleTime Productions, 7 Willow Rd, Lynbrook, NY 11563 *Tel:* 516-255-8383 *Web Site:* www.teletimevideo.com, pg 910

TeleVideos, 1566 Dola St, Eugene, OR 97402 *Toll Free Tel:* 800-2-VIDEOS (284-3367) *E-mail:* televideos@msn.com *Web Site:* televideos.com, pg 910

Television Academy, 5220 Lankershim Blvd, North Hollywood, CA 91601-3109 *Tel:* 818-754-2800 *Web Site:* www.emmys.com, pg 963

Television Bureau of Advertising Inc (TVB), 120 Wall St, 15th fl, New York, NY 10005-3908 *Tel:* 212-486-1111 *Fax:* 212-935-5631 *E-mail:* info@tvb.org *Web Site:* www.tvb.org, pg 963

Television Equipment Associates Inc (TEA), 16 Mount Ebo Rd S, Suite 6, Brewster, NY 10509 *Tel:* 845-278-0960 *Fax:* 845-278-0964 *E-mail:* sales@teaheadsets.com *Web Site:* www.teaheadsets.com, pg 910

Tellabs Inc, 18583 North Dallas Pkwy, Suite 200, Dallas, TX 75287 *Tel:* 972-588-7000 *Toll Free Fax:* 866-665-8280 *Web Site:* www.tellabs.com, pg 910

Telluride Film Festival, 800 Jones St, Berkeley, CA 94710 *Tel:* 510-665-9494 *Fax:* 510-665-9589 *E-mail:* mail@telluridefilmfestival.org; press@telluridefilmfestival.org *Web Site:* www.telluridefilmfestival.org, pg 1005

The Telos Alliance, 1241 Superior Ave E, Cleveland, OH 44114 *Tel:* 216-241-7225 *Fax:* 216-241-4103 *E-mail:* inquiry@telosalliance.com *Web Site:* www.telosalliance.com, pg 910

Tempe Camera, 606 W University, Tempe, AZ 85281 *Tel:* 480-966-6954 *Toll Free Tel:* 800-836-7374 *E-mail:* rent@tempecamera.com; sales@tempecamera.biz *Web Site:* www.tempecamera.biz, pg 910

Tempe Tape & Disc, 722 W Raven Dr, Chandler, AZ 85286 *Tel:* 602-453-9663 *Web Site:* www.tempetape.com, pg 911

Temple Hill Entertainment, 9255 W Sunset Blvd, West Hollywood, CA 90069 *Tel:* 310-270-4383 *Fax:* 310-270-4395 *Web Site:* twitter.com/TempleHillEnt, pg 911

1013 Integrated, 1013 Kawaiahao St, Honolulu, HI 96814 *Tel:* 808-593-8848 *E-mail:* info@1013integrated.com *Web Site:* www.facebook.com/1013integrated; 1013integrated.com, pg 911

Tenba, 75 Virginia Rd, North White Plains, NY 10603 *Tel:* 914-347-3300 *Fax:* 914-347-3309 *E-mail:* info@tenba.com *Web Site:* www.tenba.com, pg 911

Tennessee Entertainment Commission, Tennessee Tower, 27th fl, 312 Rosa L Parks Ave, Nashville, TN 37243 *Tel:* 615-741-FILM (741-3456) *Toll Free Tel:* 877-818-FILM (818-3456) *E-mail:* tn.film@tn.gov *Web Site:* www.tnentertainment.com, pg 976

Tennessee Prompters, 727 Wildview Dr, Nashville, TN 37211-1142 *Tel:* 615-834-9655 *E-mail:* info@tennesseeprompters.com *Web Site:* www.tennesseeprompters.com, pg 911

Tepco Corp, 2603 Bridgeview Dr, Rapid City, SD 57701-5801 *Tel:* 605-343-7200 *Fax:* 605-343-7240, pg 911

Terra Nova Films Inc, 9848 S Winchester Ave, Chicago, IL 60643 *Tel:* 773-881-8491 *Toll Free Tel:* 800-779-8491 *Fax:* 773-881-3368 *E-mail:* tnf@terranova.org *Web Site:* www.terranova.org, pg 911

Test Equipment Connection, 30 Skyline Dr, Lake Mary, FL 32746 *Tel:* 407-804-1299 *Toll Free Tel:* 800-615-8378 *Fax:* 407-804-1277 *E-mail:* sales@testequipmentconnection.com *Web Site:* www.testequipmentconnection.com, pg 911

Tetrahedron LLC, 5348 Las Vegas Dr, Suite 353, Las Vegas, NV 89108 *Tel:* 208-265-8065 *Toll Free Tel:* 888-923-9936 *E-mail:* tetra@tetrahedron.org *Web Site:* www.tetrahedron.org; www.healthyworldstore.com, pg 911

Texas Association of Motion Media Professionals (TAMMP), 9629 Carnegie Dr, Dallas, TX 75228 *Tel:* 214-613-7601 *E-mail:* info@tammp.com *Web Site:* www.tammp.com, pg 963

Texas Film Commission, 1100 San Jacinto, Suite 3.410, Austin, TX 78701 *Tel:* 512-463-9200 *Fax:* 512-463-4114 *Web Site:* gov.texas.gov/film, pg 976

Texas Heart Institute Visual Communication Services, Denton A Cooley Bldg, Suite C-530, 6770 Bertner Ave, Houston, TX 77030 *Tel:* 832-355-9558 *Fax:* 832-355-9511 *Web Site:* www.texasheart.org, pg 911

Texas Motion Picture Alliance (TXMPA), 815-A Brazos St, Austin, TX 78701 *Tel:* 512-489-6723 *E-mail:* admin@txmpa.org; communications@txmpa.org *Web Site:* www.txmpa.org, pg 963

Texas Rebel Radio Network, c/o Hill Country Broadcasting, 210 Woodcrest, Fredericksburg, TX 78624 *Tel:* 830-997-2197 *Fax:* 830-997-2198 *E-mail:* hillcountrybroadcasting@gmail.com *Web Site:* www.texasrebelradio.com, pg 911

Texas Scenic Co Inc, 8053 Potranco Rd, San Antonio, TX 78251 *Tel:* 210-684-0091 *Toll Free Tel:* 800-292-7490 *Fax:* 210-684-4557 *E-mail:* info@texasscenic.com *Web Site:* www.texasscenic.com, pg 911

Texcam Inc, 1323 N First St, Bellaire, TX 77401 *Tel:* 713-524-2774 *Toll Free Tel:* 800-735-2774 *Fax:* 713-524-2779 *E-mail:* info@texcam.com *Web Site:* www.texcam.com, pg 911

TGA Recording Co, 295 Urbandale Ave, Benton Harbor, MI 49022 *Tel:* 269-926-7581 *E-mail:* tgarecording@sbcglobal.net *Web Site:* www.tgarecording.com, pg 911

The Studio of David Inocencio, 41 Fairlawn Ave, Daly City, CA 94015 *Tel:* 415-716-2791 *Fax:* 415-716-2796, pg 911

Theatre Arts Video Library, 174 Andrew Ave, Leucadia, CA 92024 *Tel:* 760-547-6039 *Fax:* 760-632-6859 *E-mail:* admin@theatreartsvideo.com *Web Site:* www.theatreartsvideo.com, pg 911

Theatre Effects, 1810 Airport Exchange Blvd, Suite 400, Erlanger, KY 41018-3184 *Tel:* 859-647-8844 *Toll Free Tel:* 800-791-7646 *Fax:* 859-647-0075 *E-mail:* service@theatrefx.com *Web Site:* www.theatrefx.com, pg 911

Theatre House Inc, 400 W Third St, Covington, KY 41011-1306 *Tel:* 859-431-2414 *Toll Free Tel:* 800-827-2414 *Fax:* 859-431-1837 *E-mail:* info@theatrehouse.com *Web Site:* www.theatrehouse.com, pg 911

Theatre Service & Supply Corp, 10004-F Pulaski Hwy, Baltimore, MD 21220 *Tel:* 410-686-1398 *Fax:* 410-574-2417 *E-mail:* sales@stage-n-studio.com *Web Site:* www.stage-n-studio.com, pg 911

Theatrical Services & Supplies Inc, 3340 Veterans Memorial Hwy, Bohemia, NY 11716 *Tel:* 631-873-4790 *Fax:* 631-873-4795 *E-mail:* sales@gotheatrical.com *Web Site:* www.gotheatrical.com, pg 912

Theatrical Services Inc, 128 S Washington St, Wichita, KS 67202 *Tel:* 316-263-4415 *Toll Free Tel:* 888-874-2649 *Fax:* 316-263-9927 *Web Site:* www.theatricalservices.com, pg 912

Theatrical Technicians Inc (TTI), 2700 Connecticut Ave NW, Suite 109, Washington, DC 20008-5308 *E-mail:* info@perfect-pickup.com, pg 912

Theosophical Publishing House, 306 W Geneva Rd, Wheaton, IL 60187 *Tel:* 630-665-0130 *Toll Free Tel:* 800-669-9425 *Fax:* 630-665-8791 *E-mail:* customerservice@questbooks.net; marketing@questbooks.net *Web Site:* questbooks.com, pg 912

Thermodyne Cases, 1841 Business Pkwy, Ontario, CA 91761 *Tel:* 909-923-9945 *Fax:* 909-923-7505 *E-mail:* sales@thermodyne.com *Web Site:* www.thermodyne.com, pg 912

Thin-Lite Corp, 530 Constitution Ave, Camarillo, CA 93012 *Tel:* 805-987-5021 *Fax:* 805-388-0921 *E-mail:* sales@thinlite.com *Web Site:* www.thinlite.com, pg 912

Think 3-D.com, 180 Cross Hwy, Westport, CT 06880 *Tel:* 646-873-0050 *Web Site:* www.think3-d.com, pg 912

Thinking Allowed Productions, 5966 Zinn Dr, Oakland, CA 94611 *Tel:* 510-339-8004 *Toll Free Tel:* 800-999-4415 *E-mail:* thinking@thinkingallowed.com *Web Site:* www.thinkingallowed.com, pg 912

Thinking Maps Inc, 401 Cascade Pointe Lane, Cary, NC 27513-5780 *Tel:* 919-678-8778 *Toll Free Tel:* 800-243-9169 *Fax:* 919-678-8782 *E-mail:* office@thinkingmaps.com *Web Site:* thinkingmaps.com, pg 912

Third Ear Sound Co, 30965 San Benito St, Hayward, CA 94544 *Tel:* 510-429-1000 *Toll Free Tel:* 800-587-1115 *Fax:* 510-429-1001 *E-mail:* raul@thirdearsound.com *Web Site:* www.thirdearsound.com, pg 912

Third World Newsreel/Camera News Inc, 545 Eighth Ave, Suite 550, New York, NY 10018 *Tel:* 212-947-9277 *Fax:* 212-594-6417 *E-mail:* twn@twn.org *Web Site:* www.twn.org, pg 912

31st Street Studios, 77 31 St, Pittsburgh, PA 15201 *Tel:* 412-228-0231 *E-mail:* info@31ststreetstudios.com *Web Site:* www.31ststreetstudios.com, pg 912

30 Second Street Ltd, 1209 Mountain Road Place NE, Suite B, Albuquerque, NM 87110 *Tel:* 505-265-0224 *E-mail:* info@30sst.com *Web Site:* www.thirtysecst.com, pg 912

Thomas & Betts Power Solutions LLC, 5900 Eastport Blvd, Bldg V, Richmond, VA 23231-4453 *Tel:* 804-236-3300 *Toll Free Tel:* 800-238-5000; 800-CYBEREX (292-3739) *Fax:* 804-236-4040; 804-236-4841 *Web Site:* www.tnbpowersolutions.com, pg 912

The Lowell Thomas Award, 40 W 45 St, New York, NY 10036 *Tel:* 212-626-9220 *Fax:* 212-626-9210 *E-mail:* info@opcofamerica.org *Web Site:* www.opcofamerica.org, pg 1005

Thomas Printworks, 600 N Central Expwy, Richardson, TX 75080 *Tel:* 972-231-7161 *Toll Free Tel:* 800-877-3776 *Fax:* 972-644-6308 *E-mail:* richardson@thomasprintworks.com *Web Site:* thomasprintworks.com, pg 912

Thomega Entertainment Inc, North Star Business Centre, 210-820 51 St E, Saskatoon, SK S7K 0X8, Canada *Tel:* 306-280-4982 *Fax:* 306-242-5845 *E-mail:* thomega@sasktel.net *Web Site:* www.thomega.com, pg 913

Thompson-Nicola Film Commission, 300-465 Victoria St, Kamloops, BC V2C 2A9, Canada *Tel:* 250-377-8673 *Toll Free Tel:* 877-377-8673 (BC only) *Fax:* 250-372-5048 *E-mail:* tnfc@tnrd.ca *Web Site:* www.filmthompsonnicola.com, pg 978

Thompson Rivers University Marketing & Communications Dept, 805 TRU Way, Kamloops, BC V2C 0C8, Canada *Tel:* 250-852-7000 *Web Site:* www.tru.ca/marcom, pg 913

Thorburn Associates (TA), 20880 Baker Rd, Castro Valley, CA 94546 *Tel:* 510-886-7826 *Fax:* 510-886-7828 *E-mail:* ta@ta-inc.com *Web Site:* www.ta-inc.com, pg 913

Thread Marketing Group, 4635 W Alexis Rd, Toledo, OH 43623-1005 *Tel:* 419-887-6801 *Fax:* 419-887-6802 *E-mail:* info@threadgroup.com *Web Site:* www.threadgroup.com, pg 913

Three D Graphics Inc, 11340 W Olympic Blvd, Suite 352, Los Angeles, CA 90064-1613 *Tel:* 310-231-3330 *Toll Free Tel:* 800-913-0008 *Fax:* 310-231-3303 *E-mail:* info@threedgraphics.com *Web Site:* www.threedgraphics.com, pg 913

Three Pillars Media, 140 N Eighth St, Suite 220, Lincoln, NE 68508 *Tel:* 402-937-0984 *E-mail:* contact@threepillarsmedia.com *Web Site:* www.threepillarsmedia.com, pg 913

Three Rivers Publishing Co, 2330 Buroak Ridge, San Antonio, TX 78248 *Tel:* 210-490-2433 *E-mail:* cowboyhous@aol.com *Web Site:* www.kurthouse.com, pg 913

360 Systems, 3281 Grande Vista Dr, Newbury Park, CA 91320-1193 *Tel:* 818-991-0360 *Fax:* 818-991-1360 *E-mail:* sales@360systems.com *Web Site:* www.360systems.com, pg 913

3008, 3008 Ross Ave, Suite 100, Dallas, TX 75204 *Tel:* 214-922-9232 *Fax:* 214-922-8861 *Web Site:* www. 3008.com, pg 913

3M Touch Systems, 3M Center, St Paul, MN 55144-1000 *Toll Free Tel:* 888-3M-HELPS (364-3577) *Toll Free Fax:* 800-603-7758 *Web Site:* www.3m. com/touch, pg 913

Tiburon International Film Festival (TIFF), 6 Beach Rd, 544, Tiburon, CA 94920 *Tel:* 415-251-8433 *Fax:* 253-663-1250 *E-mail:* info@tiburonfilmfestival.com *Web Site:* www.tiburonfilmfestival.com, pg 1005

Leo Ticheli Productions, 2801 University Blvd, Suite 101, Birmingham, AL 35233 *Tel:* 205-930-0500 *Fax:* 205-930-0505 *E-mail:* hello@ltpro.com *Web Site:* www.ltpro.com, pg 913

Tickets.com, 555 Anton Blvd, Costa Mesa, CA 92626 *Tel:* 714-327-5400 *Toll Free Tel:* 800-352-0212 (cust serv) *Fax:* 714-327-5410 *E-mail:* sales@tickets.com *Web Site:* www.tickets.com, pg 913

Tierney Brothers Inc, 1771 Energy Park Dr, Suite 100, St Paul, MN 55108 *Tel:* 612-331-5500 *Toll Free Tel:* 866-557-6062 *Fax:* 612-331-3424 *E-mail:* contactform@tierneybrothers.com *Web Site:* www.tierneybrothers.com, pg 914

The Tiffen Co LLC, 90 Oser Ave, Hauppauge, NY 11788-3886 *Tel:* 631-273-2500 *Toll Free Tel:* 800-645-2522 *Fax:* 631-273-2557 *E-mail:* techsupport@tiffen. com *Web Site:* www.tiffen.com, pg 914

Tight Line Productions, 1902 Oak St, Melbourne, FL 32901 *Tel:* 321-725-4668 *Fax:* 321-768-6528 *E-mail:* info@tightlinetv.com *Web Site:* www. tightlineproductions.com, pg 914

Tiki Recording Studios Inc, 30-A Glen St, Suite 204, Glen Cove, NY 11542 *Tel:* 516-671-4300 (ext 101) *Fax:* 516-671-8754 *Web Site:* www.tikirecording.com, pg 914

TIMECODE Post Production, 12340 Santa Monica Blvd, Suite 230, West Los Angeles, CA 90025 *Tel:* 310-826-9199 *E-mail:* info@timecodemedia.com *Web Site:* www.timecodepost.com, pg 914

Timed Exposures Films, 122 Old Rd, Germantown, NY 12526-6014 *Tel:* 518-537-2012 *E-mail:* info@ timedexposures.com *Web Site:* www.timedexposures. com, pg 914

Timeless Books, Box 9, Kootenay Bay, BC V0B 1X0, Canada *Tel:* 250-227-9224 *Toll Free Tel:* 800-661-8711 *Fax:* 250-227-9494 *E-mail:* bookstore@timeless. org *Web Site:* www.timeless.org, pg 914

Timeless Productions, 5050 Traverse Creek Rd, Garden Valley, CA 95633 *Tel:* 530-333-1335 *Toll Free Tel:* 800-729-1325 *E-mail:* 4info@timelessproductions. com *Web Site:* www.timelessproductions.com, pg 914

TimeLogic Corp, 1914 Palomar Oaks Way, Suite 150, Carlsbad, CA 92008 *Tel:* 760-431-1263 *Toll Free Tel:* 877-222-9543 *Fax:* 760-431-1351 *Web Site:* www. timelogic.com, pg 914

Times-Square Fantasy Theatre, 519 N Halifax Ave, Daytona Beach, FL 32118 *Tel:* 386-252-0381 *Fax:* 386-252-0381 *E-mail:* timessquare@bellsouth.net *Web Site:* www.timessquarefantasytheatre.com; www. broadwaymusicdownload.com, pg 914

TimeSteps Productions Inc, 2 Glenside Dr, West Orange, NJ 07052 *Tel:* 973-669-1930 *E-mail:* info@timesteps. com *Web Site:* timesteps.com, pg 914

Timestream Video, 11821 N Circle Dr, Whittier, CA 90601-2338 *Tel:* 562-699-8797 *Fax:* 562-695-0252 *Web Site:* www.timestreamvideo.com, pg 914

Rik Tinory Productions, 180 Pond St, Cohasset, MA 02025 *Tel:* 781-383-9494, pg 914

Tisch School of the Arts, 721 Broadway, 10th & 11th fl, New York, NY 10003 *Tel:* 212-998-1700; 212-998-1780 *Fax:* 212-995-4062; 212-995-4063 *Web Site:* www.tisch.nyu.edu, pg 914

Titus Technological Laboratories (TTL), 77 Krieger Lane, Glastonbury, CT 06033 *Tel:* 860-633-5472 *Toll Free Tel:* 800-806-TTL1 (806-8851) *Fax:* 860-633-8244 *E-mail:* sales1@tituslabs.com *Web Site:* www. tituslabs.com, pg 914

TiVo Corp, 2 Circle Star Way, San Carlos, CA 94070 *Tel:* 408-562-8400 *Toll Free Tel:* 877-367-8486 (cust support); 877-289-8486 (sales support) *Fax:* 408-567-1800 *Web Site:* business.tivo.com; www.tivo.com, pg 914

TM Studios Inc, 2002 Academy Lane, Suite 110, Dallas, TX 75234 *Tel:* 972-406-6800 *Fax:* 972-406-6890 *E-mail:* info@tmstudios.com; tmcustomerservice@ tmstudios.com *Web Site:* www.tmstudios.com, pg 915

TMW Media Group, 2321 Abbot Kinney Blvd, Suite 101, Venice, CA 90291 *Tel:* 310-577-8581 *Toll Free Tel:* 800-262-8862 *Fax:* 310-574-0886 *E-mail:* sale@ tmwmedia.com *Web Site:* www.tmwmedia.com, pg 915

TOA Electronics Inc, 400 Oyster Point Blvd, Suite 301, South San Francisco, CA 94080 *Tel:* 650-452-1200 *Toll Free Tel:* 800-733-7088 (cust serv) *Fax:* 650-452-1250 *Toll Free Fax:* 800-733-9766 *E-mail:* info@ toaelectronics.com; orders@toaelectronics.com *Web Site:* www.toaelectronics.com, pg 915

Tobias Associates Inc, 50 Industrial Dr, Ivyland, PA 18974-1433 *Tel:* 215-322-1500 *Toll Free Tel:* 800-877-3367 *Fax:* 215-322-1504 *E-mail:* sales@tobiasinc. com; service@tobiasinc.com; repair@tobiasinc.com *Web Site:* www.densitometers.net, pg 915

Tobins Lake Sales, 3313 Yellowstone Dr, Ann Arbor, MI 48105 *Fax:* 734-449-9812 *Web Site:* www. tobinslakesales.com, pg 915

ToCad America Inc, 53 Green Pond Rd, Suite 5, Rockaway, NJ 07866 *Tel:* 973-627-9600 *Toll Free Tel:* 800-886-2236 *Fax:* 973-664-2438 *E-mail:* info@ tocad.com *Web Site:* www.tocad.com, pg 915

Dorothy Tod Films, 41 Hazel Brown Rd, Warren, VT 05674 *Tel:* 802-496-5280 *Fax:* 802-496-5280, pg 915

Todd-AO Studios, 4712 Admiralty Way, No 497, Marina del Rey, CA 90292 *Tel:* 310-399-4557 *Toll Free Tel:* 877-315-3647 *E-mail:* info@todd-ao.com *Web Site:* www.todd-ao.com, pg 915

Toko America Inc, 1250 Feehanville Dr, Mount Prospect, IL 60056 *Tel:* 847-297-0070 *Toll Free Tel:* 800-PIK-TOKO (745-8656) *Fax:* 847-699-7864 *E-mail:* info@ tokoam.com *Web Site:* www.tokoam.com, pg 915

TOMCAT USA Inc, 5427 N National Dr, Knoxville, TN 37914 *Tel:* 865-219-3700 *Fax:* 865-673-5818 *E-mail:* info@tomcatusa.com; sales@tomcatusa.com *Web Site:* www.tomcatglobal.com, pg 915

Tommy Boy Entertainment LLC, 220 E 23 St, New York, NY 10010 *Tel:* 212-388-8300 *E-mail:* info@ tommyboy.com *Web Site:* www.tommyboy.com, pg 915

Tone Zone Recording, 939 W Wilson Ave, Chicago, IL 60640 *Tel:* 312-664-5353 *Fax:* 312-664-6560 *E-mail:* tonezonerecording@sbcglobal.net, pg 915

Topbulb, a Semmer Lighting Company, 1051 Clinton Ave, Buffalo, NY 14206 *Toll Free Tel:* 800-TOP-BULB (867-2852) *Toll Free Fax:* 877-329-2852 *E-mail:* sales@topbulb.com *Web Site:* www.topbulb. com, pg 915

TopCat Records LLC, PO Box 670234, Dallas, TX 75367-0234 *Tel:* 972-484-4141 *Fax:* 972-620-8333 *E-mail:* info@topcatrecords.com *Web Site:* www. topcatrecords.com, pg 915

Toronto Film, Television & Digital Media Office, Toronto City Hall, Main fl, Rotunda N, 100 Queen St W, Toronto, ON M5H 2N2, Canada *Tel:* 416-338-FILM (338-3456) *Fax:* 416-392-0675 *E-mail:* filmtoronto@toronto.ca *Web Site:* www. toronto.ca/tfto, pg 978

Toronto Reel Asian International Film Festival, 401 Richmond St W, Suite 309, Toronto, ON M5V 3A8, Canada *Tel:* 416-703-9333 *Fax:* 416-703-9986 *E-mail:* info@reelasian.com; programming@reelasian. com *Web Site:* www.reelasian.com, pg 1005

Torpey Time, 132 Commerce Park Dr, Suite 255, Barrie, ON L4N 0Z7, Canada *Tel:* 705-487-2915 *Web Site:* ram68.com, pg 915

Toshiba America Information Systems Inc, 9740 Irvine Blvd, Irvine, CA 92618 *Tel:* 949-583-3000 *Web Site:* www.toshiba.com, pg 916

Tosoh USA Inc, 3600 Gantz Rd, Grove City, OH 43123 *Tel:* 614-277-4348 *Fax:* 614-875-8086 *E-mail:* info. tusa@tosoh.com *Web Site:* www.tosohusa.com, pg 916

Total AV Systems, 9301 Georgia Ave, Silver Spring, MD 20910 *Tel:* 301-589-3337 *Toll Free Tel:* 800-447-7632 *Fax:* 301-494-4770 *E-mail:* info@total-av.com *Web Site:* total-av.com, pg 916

Total Concept Sales, 2505 Foothill Blvd, Suite G, La Crescentia, CA 91214 *Tel:* 818-236-3966 *Toll Free Tel:* 800-488-0589 *Fax:* 818-236-3969 *Web Site:* www. totalups.com, pg 916

Total Creative, 432 N Canal St, Suite 12, South San Francisco, CA 94080 *Tel:* 650-583-8236 *Fax:* 650-583-4708 *E-mail:* info@totalcreative.com *Web Site:* totalcreative.com, pg 916

Total Impact Multimedia Group Ltd, 1475 Pea Pond Rd, North Bellmore, NY 11710 *Tel:* 516-783-8800 *E-mail:* info@totalimpactltd.com *Web Site:* totalimpactltd.com, pg 916

Total Media Inc, 681 Lawlins Rd, Unit 10, Wyckoff, NJ 07481 *Tel:* 201-848-1100 *Toll Free Tel:* 800-355-4400 *Fax:* 201-840-0303 *E-mail:* info@totalmedia.com *Web Site:* www.totalmedia.com, pg 916

Total Video Products Inc, 414 Southgate Ct, Mickleton, NJ 08056 *Tel:* 856-423-7400 *Toll Free Tel:* 800-447-0920 *Fax:* 856-423-4747 *E-mail:* info@totalvideoproducts.com *Web Site:* www. totalvideoproducts.com, pg 916

ToteVision, 3257 17 Ave W, Bldg 1, Suite 201, Seattle, WA 98119 *Tel:* 206-623-6000; 206-623-6000 (ext 200, sales); 206-623-6000 (ext 202, tech support & repairs); 206-623-6000 (ext 209, cust care); 206-623-6000 (ext 211, returns) *Fax:* 206-623-6609 *E-mail:* info@totevision.com *Web Site:* totevision.com, pg 916

Touchstone Center Publications, 141 E 88 St, Apt 3E, New York, NY 10128 *Tel:* 212-831-7717 *Web Site:* touchstonecenter.net, pg 916

Towards 2000 Inc, 215 W Palm Ave, Suite 101, Burbank, CA 91502 *Tel:* 818-557-0903 *Toll Free Fax:* 866-836-5725 *E-mail:* info@t2k.com *Web Site:* www.t2k.com, pg 916

Town of Bel Air Film Festival, 37 N Main St, Bel Air, MD 21014 *Tel:* 410-838-0584 *Web Site:* www. townofbelairfilmfestival.com, pg 1005

Toys From The Attic, 27 Holland Ave, White Plains, NY 10603 *Tel:* 914-421-0069 *E-mail:* tftamail@gmail.com *Web Site:* tftaus.com, pg 916

TPR Enterprises Ltd, 644 Fayette Ave, Mamaroneck, NY 10543 *Tel:* 914-698-1141 *Fax:* 914-698-9419 *E-mail:* info@tprlights.com *Web Site:* www.tprlights. com, pg 916

TR Productions, Charlstown Navy Yard, Captains Quarters Bldg, 2 13 St, 3rd fl, Charlestown, MA 02129 *Tel:* 617-241-5500 *E-mail:* info@trprod.com *Web Site:* trprod.com, pg 916

Trac Recording Studio, 180 E Warner Ave, Fresno, CA 93710 *Tel:* 559-903-0701 *E-mail:* tracrecording@ pmicp.com *Web Site:* tracrecordingstudio.com, pg 916

Trafalgar Square Books, 388 Howe Hill Rd, North Pomfret, VT 05053 *Tel:* 802-457-1911 *Toll Free Tel:* 800-423-4525 *Fax:* 802-457-1913 *E-mail:* contact@trafalgarbooks.com (cust serv) *Web Site:* www. horseandriderbooks.com; www.trafalgarbooks.com, pg 916

Trailblazer Studios®, 1610 Midtown Place, Raleigh, NC 27609 *Tel:* 919-645-6600 *Fax:* 919-645-6601 *E-mail:* info@trailblazerstudios.com *Web Site:* www. trailblazerstudios.com, pg 917

Trans-Lux Multimedia Corp, 445 Park Ave, Suite 2001, New York, NY 10022 *Tel:* 203-853-4321 *Toll Free Tel:* 800-243-5544; 800-462-2716 *E-mail:* sales@ trans-lux.com *Web Site:* www.trans-lux.com, pg 917

The Transfer Zone®, 4301 Orchard Lake Rd, Suite 180-191, West Bloomfield, MI 48323 *Tel:* 248-225-0477, pg 917

Transformational Education Initiatives, PO Box 344, Phoenicia, NY 12464 *Tel:* 310-795-4910 *E-mail:* lioneltv@aol.com *Web Site:* transformationaledu.org, pg 917

Transparent Office Products LLC, 2550 Haddonfield Rd, Pennsauken, NJ 08110 *Tel:* 856-488-5455 *Fax:* 856-488-5411 *E-mail:* sales@transoffprod.biz *Web Site:* www.transoffprod.biz, pg 917

Transtar Entertainment Co Inc, 11776 E Evans Ave, Aurora, CO 80014 *Tel:* 303-489-1450 *Web Site:* www.transtarfilm.com, pg 917

Transtector Systems Inc, 10701 N Airport Dr, Hayden, ID 83835 *Tel:* 208-772-8515 *Toll Free Tel:* 800-882-9110 *Fax:* 208-762-6133 *E-mail:* sales@transtector.com *Web Site:* www.transtector.com, pg 917

Transvideo International, 130 E Prospect Ave, Burbank, CA 91502 *Tel:* 818-985-4903 *Fax:* 818-985-4921 *Web Site:* www.transvideointl.com, pg 917

TRC Interactive Inc, 4200 Crums Mill Rd, Harrisburg, PA 17112 *Tel:* 717-652-3100 *Toll Free Tel:* 800-222-9909 *E-mail:* customerservicetrc01@trcinteractive.com; info@trcinteractive.com *Web Site:* www.trcinteractive.com, pg 917

Trebas Institute, 2340 Dundas St W, 2nd fl, Toronto, ON M6P 4A9, Canada *Tel:* 416-966-3066 *E-mail:* info@trebas.com *Web Site:* www.trebas.com, pg 917

Trebas Institute, 550 Sherbrooke St W, Suite 600, Montreal, QC H3A 1B9, Canada *Tel:* 514-845-4141 *Toll Free Tel:* 866-5TREBAS (587-3227) *Fax:* 514-845-2581 *E-mail:* infomtl@trebas.com *Web Site:* www.trebas.com, pg 917

Treehaus Communications Inc, 906 W Loveland Ave, Loveland, OH 45140-2150 *Tel:* 513-683-5716 *Toll Free Tel:* 800-638-4287 *Fax:* 513-683-2882 *E-mail:* info@mammothhd.com *Web Site:* www.treehaus1.com, pg 917

Tremetrics Inc Industrial Instruments Division, 10393 W 70 St, Eden Prairie, MN 55344 *Toll Free Tel:* 800-825-0121 *Fax:* 952-903-4100 *E-mail:* info@tremetrics.com *Web Site:* www.tremetrics.com, pg 917

Trendy Studio LLC, 64 NW 54 St, Miami, FL 33127 *Tel:* 305-438-4244 *Fax:* 305-438-4243 *Web Site:* www.trendystudio.com, pg 917

Trew Audio Inc, 220 Great Circle Rd, Suite 116, Nashville, TN 37228 *Tel:* 615-256-3542 *Toll Free Tel:* 800-241-8994 *Fax:* 615-259-2699 *E-mail:* info@trewaudio.com; sales@trewaudio.com *Web Site:* www.trewaudio.com, pg 917

TRF Production Music Libraries, 106 Apple St, Tinton Falls, NJ 07724 *Tel:* 201-335-0005 *Toll Free Tel:* 800-899-MUSIC (899-6874) *Fax:* 201-335-0004 *E-mail:* info@trfmusic.com *Web Site:* www.trfmusic.com, pg 917

Tri-Ed Distribution Inc, 135 Crossways Park Dr, Suite 101, Woodbury, NY 11797 *Tel:* 516-941-2800 *Toll Free Tel:* 888-874-3336 (US); 800-398-7282 (CN); 800-366-4472 (tech sales) *E-mail:* info@tri-ed.com; sales@tri-ed.com; marketing@tri-ed.com *Web Site:* www.tri-ed.com, pg 918

Tri-State Audio Visual Co, 2901 Glendora Ave, Cincinnati, OH 45219 *Tel:* 513-281-7500 *Toll Free Tel:* 800-348-8728 *Fax:* 513-281-7539 *E-mail:* sales@tristateav.com *Web Site:* www.tristateav.com, pg 918

Tri-State Loudspeaker, 650 Franklin Ave, Aliquippa, PA 15001, pg 918

Tri-State Visual Products Inc, 885 Ohio Pike, Suite C, Cincinnati, OH 45245 *Tel:* 513-471-7111 *Toll Free Tel:* 800-473-4474 *E-mail:* info@trivisual.com *Web Site:* www.trivisual.com, pg 918

Triad Communications Ltd, 2751 Oxford St, Vancouver, BC V5K 1N5, Canada *Tel:* 604-253-3990 *E-mail:* triadc@comwave.com *Web Site:* www.triadcommunications.ca, pg 918

Triangle Regional Film Commission, PO Box 13041, Research Triangle Park, NC 27709-3041 *Tel:* 919-544-5501 *E-mail:* triangleregionalfilm@gmail.com *Web Site:* www.trianglencfilm.com, pg 974

Tribeca Film Festival, Communications Dept, 375 Greenwich St, New York, NY 10013 *Tel:* 212-941-2400 *Fax:* 212-941-3939 *E-mail:* festival@tribecafilmfestival.org; entries@tribecafilmfestival.org; press@tribecafilmfestival.org *Web Site:* www.tribecafilm.com/festival, pg 1005

Tributestone, 709 N Sixth St, Kansas City, KS 66101 *Tel:* 913-321-3978 *Web Site:* www.tributestone.com, pg 918

Tricycle Studios, 1905 E Seventh Ave, Tampa, FL 33605 *Tel:* 813-258-6867 *Fax:* 813-258-8595 *E-mail:* hi@tricyclestudios.com *Web Site:* www.tricyclestudios.com, pg 918

Trinity Recording Studio, 3406 Brawner Pkwy, Corpus Christi, TX 78411 *Tel:* 361-854-7464 *E-mail:* info@trinitystudio.com *Web Site:* www.trinitystudio.com, pg 918

Tripp Lite, 1111 W 35 St, Chicago, IL 60609 *Tel:* 773-869-1234 (support); 773-869-1111; 773-869-1773 (sales) *Fax:* 773-869-1329 *E-mail:* international@tripplite.com *Web Site:* www.tripplite.com, pg 918

Tritech Communications, 625 Locust St, Suite 300, Garden City, NY 11530 *Tel:* 631-254-4500 *Fax:* 631-254-4499 *E-mail:* sales@tritechcomm.com *Web Site:* www.tritechcomm.com, pg 918

Triumph Learning LLC, 136 Madison Ave, 7th fl, New York, NY 10016 *Toll Free Tel:* 800-338-6519 *Toll Free Fax:* 866-805-5723 *E-mail:* customerservice@triumphlearning.com *Web Site:* www.triumphlearning.com, pg 918

Triune Arts, 1804 Bedell Rd, RR 5, Kemptville, ON K0G 1J0, Canada *Web Site:* triune.ca, pg 918

Tropical Visions Video Inc, 13-3435 Kupono St, Pahoa, HI 96778 *Tel:* 808-895-0077 *E-mail:* redhotlava@hawaii.rr.com *Web Site:* www.tropicalvisions.com, pg 918

Tropikal Productions, 137 Sequoia Rd, Rockwall, TX 75032 *Tel:* 972-771-3797 *Fax:* 972-771-0853 *E-mail:* tropikalproductions@gmail.com *Web Site:* www.tropikalproductions.com, pg 918

The Troupe, 3 Industrial Dr, Windham, NH 03087 *Tel:* 603-893-4554 *E-mail:* info@thetroupe.com *Web Site:* www.thetroupe.com, pg 918

Troxell-CDI, 4675 E Cotton Center Blvd, Suite 155, Phoenix, AZ 85040 *Tel:* 602-437-7240 *Toll Free Tel:* 855-TROXELL (876-9355) *Fax:* 602-752-1299 *Toll Free Fax:* 800-752-1299 *E-mail:* csg@trox.com *Web Site:* www.troxellsolutions.com, pg 918

True Audio, 387 Duncan Lane, Andersonville, TN 37705 *Tel:* 865-494-3388 *Toll Free Tel:* 800-621-4411 *Fax:* 865-494-3388 *E-mail:* sales@trueaudio.com *Web Site:* www.trueaudio.com, pg 919

TRUMATCH Inc, PO Box 501, Water Mill, NY 11976-0501 *Tel:* 631-204-9100 *Toll Free Tel:* 800-TRU-9100 (878-9100) *Fax:* 631-204-0002 *E-mail:* info@trumatch.com *Web Site:* www.trumatch.com, pg 919

Truth Consciousness Publications, Desert Ashram, 3403 W Sweetwater Dr, Tucson, AZ 85745-9301 *Tel:* 520-743-8821 *E-mail:* info@truthconsciousness.org *Web Site:* truthconsciousness.org, pg 919

TSG Publishing Foundation Inc USA, 28641 N 63 Place, Cave Creek, AZ 85331 *Tel:* 480-502-1909 *Fax:* 480-502-0713 *E-mail:* info@tsgfoundation.org *Web Site:* www.tsgfoundation.org, pg 919

TSR/Baja/Damabi Records, 18653 Ventura Blvd, Suite 513, Tarzana, CA 91356 *Tel:* 818-702-9902, pg 919

Tuolumne County Film Commission, 193 S Washington St, Sonora, CA 95370 *Tel:* 209-533-4420 *Toll Free Tel:* 800-446-1333 *E-mail:* film@gotuolumne.com *Web Site:* www.filmtuolumne.org, pg 968

Turner Broadcasting System Inc, A Time Warner Company, One CNN Ctr, Atlanta, GA 30303 *Tel:* 404-827-1700 *E-mail:* turner.info@turner.com *Web Site:* www.turner.com, pg 919

Turner Engineering Inc, 14 Morris Ave, Mountain Lakes, NJ 07046-1433 *Tel:* 973-263-1000 *Fax:* 973-334-1620 *E-mail:* info@turnereng.com *Web Site:* www.turnereng.com, pg 919

Turning Technologies LLC, 255 W Federal St, Youngstown, OH 44503 *Tel:* 330-746-3015 *Toll Free Tel:* 866-746-3015 *E-mail:* info@turningtechnologies.com; support@turningtechnologies.com *Web Site:* www.turningtechnologies.com, pg 919

TV One Multimedia Solutions, 621 B Wilmer Ave, Cincinnati, OH 45226 *Tel:* 513-666-4210 *Toll Free Tel:* 800-721-4044 *Fax:* 513-666-4220 (tech) *E-mail:* sales@tvone.com; info@tvone.com *Web Site:* www.tvone.com, pg 919

TV Pro Gear, 1630 Flower St, Glendale, CA 91201 *Tel:* 818-246-7100 *Fax:* 818-246-1945 *Web Site:* www.tvprogear.com, pg 919

TV Specialists Inc, 180 E 2100 S, Salt Lake City, UT 84115 *Tel:* 801-486-5757 *Toll Free Tel:* 888-486-5757 *Fax:* 801-486-7566 *E-mail:* info@tvspecialists.com *Web Site:* www.tvspecialists.com, pg 919

TVA Media Group, 3950 Vantage Ave, Studio City, CA 91604 *Tel:* 818-505-8300 *Toll Free Tel:* 888-322-4296 *E-mail:* info@tvamediagroup.com *Web Site:* www.tvamediagroup.com, pg 919

TVN-The Video Network, 31 Cutler Dr, Ashland, MA 01721-1210 *Tel:* 508-881-1800 *E-mail:* info@tvnvideo.com *Web Site:* www.tvnvideo.com, pg 919

TVO/Ontario Educational Communications Authority (OECA), 2180 Yonge St, Toronto, ON M4S 2B9, Canada *Tel:* 416-484-2600; 416-484-2665 (cust rel) *Toll Free Tel:* 800-613-0513; 800-INFO-TVO (463-6886) *E-mail:* asktvo@tvo.org *Web Site:* tvo.org, pg 919

Twentieth Century Fox Film Corp, 10201 W Pico Blvd, Bldg 88, Rm 311, Los Angeles, CA 90035 *Tel:* 310-369-1000 *Toll Free Tel:* 888-223-4369 (cust care) *Fax:* 310-369-8825 *E-mail:* support@foxcustomercare.com (cust care) *Web Site:* www.foxmovies.com, pg 919

21st Century Video Productions, 890 S Higley Rd, Pahrump, NV 89048 *Tel:* 775-727-9400 *Fax:* 775-727-8750 *Web Site:* www.kpvm.tv, pg 919

24 Frames Film & Video, 15 Fourth Ave E, Vancouver, BC V5T 1E9, Canada *Tel:* 604-877-2299 *E-mail:* info@24frames.ca *Web Site:* www.24frames.ca, pg 920

20/20 Communications Inc, 10112 Voss Rd, Marengo, IL 60152 *Tel:* 847-364-7666 *Web Site:* www.2020communications.com, pg 920

20k, 709 rue de Saint-Vallier Est, Quebec, QC G1K 3P9, Canada *Tel:* 418-694-2220 *Toll Free Tel:* 855-933-2220 *E-mail:* info@20k.ca *Web Site:* www.20k.ca, pg 920

Twin Peaks Creative, 445 W Seventh St, San Pedro, CA 90731 *Tel:* 310-832-3303 *E-mail:* postmaster@bestmedia.com *Web Site:* www.twinpeakscreative.com, pg 920

Twin Sisters® Digital Media™, 1653 Merriman Rd, Suite L1, Akron, OH 44313 *Tel:* 330-730-9558 *E-mail:* twinsisters@twinsisters.com *Web Site:* www.twinsisters.com, pg 920

TWIST Integration Solutions Technology, 3915-F Dacoma, Houston, TX 77092 *Tel:* 713-688-0696 *E-mail:* info@twistIST.com *Web Site:* www.twistist.com, pg 920

Twisted Media Inc, 2100 Hollyvista Ave, Los Angeles, CA 90027 *Tel:* 773-972-2972 *Web Site:* www.twistedmedia.com, pg 920

Two Animators LLP, PO Box 3174, Mercerville, NJ 08619 *Tel:* 609-532-6138 *E-mail:* cartoons@twoanimators.com *Web Site:* www.twoanimators.com, pg 920

2BruceStudio, 2 Wall St, Suite 119, Asheville, NC 28801 *Tel:* 828-255-2700 *E-mail:* info@2brucestudio.com *Web Site:* 2brucestudio.com, pg 920

Two Door Productions LLC, 416 N Harper Ave, Los Angeles, CA 90048 *E-mail:* shoot@usphotograph.com *Web Site:* www.twodoorfx.com, pg 920

Tyler Camera Systems, 14218 Aetna St, Van Nuys, CA 91401 *Tel:* 818-989-4420 *Toll Free Tel:* 800-390-6070 *Fax:* 818-989-0423 *E-mail:* info@tylermount.com *Web Site:* www.tylermount.com, pg 920

U-Direct Productions Inc, 10 White St, 1st fl, New York, NY 10013 *Tel:* 212-647-9200 *Fax:* 212-625-9400 *E-mail:* udirect@udirect.nyc *Web Site:* udirect.nyc, pg 920

U-Edit Video, 1002 N Central Expwy, Suite 555, Richardson, TX 75080 *Tel:* 972-690-EDIT (690-3348) *E-mail:* info@ueditvideo.com *Web Site:* www.ueditvideo.com, pg 920

UConn Health Multimedia Services, 263 Farmington Ave, Farmington, CT 06030-2910 *Tel:* 860-679-2000 *E-mail:* multimedia@uchc.edu *Web Site:* multimedia.uchc.edu, pg 920

Ultimate Presentation Systems Inc, 901 S Hohokam Dr, Tempe, AZ 85281 *Tel:* 480-966-2000 *Toll Free Tel:* 800-866-4066 *Fax:* 480-968-3009 *E-mail:* sales@ult.com *Web Site:* www.ult.com, pg 920

Ultimate Support Systems Inc, 5836 Wright Dr, Loveland, CO 80538 *Tel:* 970-776-1920 *Toll Free Tel:* 800-525-5628 *Fax:* 970-776-1941 *E-mail:* info@ultimatesupport.com *Web Site:* www.ultimatesupport.com, pg 920

Ultralife Corporation, 2000 Technology Pkwy, Newark, NY 14513 *Tel:* 315-332-7100 *Toll Free Tel:* 800-332-5000 (US & CN) *Fax:* 315-331-7800 *E-mail:* orders@ulbi.com *Web Site:* ultralifecorporation.com, pg 920

Ulysses Travel Guides Inc, 4176 Rue Saint-Denis, Montreal, QC H2W 2M5, Canada *Tel:* 514-843-9882 *Fax:* 514-843-9448 *E-mail:* info@ulysses.ca; st-denis@ulysse.ca *Web Site:* www.ulysse.ca (French); www.ulyssesguides.com (English), pg 920

Umbra of Newburgh LLC, 9 Scobie Dr, Newburgh, NY 12550 *Tel:* 845-670-7493 *E-mail:* umbrastages@choicefilms.com *Web Site:* www.umbranewburgh.com, pg 921

Uncharted Country Publishing, PO Box 756, Taos, NM 87571 *Tel:* 575-776-3470 *Toll Free Tel:* 800-488-4940 *E-mail:* ucp@taichihealth.com *Web Site:* taichihealth.com, pg 921

UND Television Center, 4300 James Ray Dr, Stop 7307, Grand Forks, ND 58202 *Tel:* 701-777-4346 *Toll Free Tel:* 800-CALL-UND (225-5863) *Fax:* 701-777-4342 *E-mail:* tv@und.edu *Web Site:* www.und.edu/television-center, pg 921

Ungar Video & Film, 2407 Grovewood Ave, Cleveland, OH 44134 *Tel:* 216-661-5090, pg 921

Uniconn Productions, 8485 Valley Circle Blvd, Suite 203, West Hills, CA 91304 *Tel:* 818-887-9108 *Fax:* 818-348-6544 *E-mail:* measeburl@aol.com *Web Site:* www.uniconnproductions.com, pg 921

Unified Packaging Inc (UPI), 1187 E 68 Ave, Denver, CO 80229 *Tel:* 303-733-1000; 469-272-9000 (TX off) *Toll Free Tel:* 866-715-1700 *Fax:* 303-733-6789; 469-272-9300 (TX off) *E-mail:* contact@unifiedbinders.com *Web Site:* www.unifiedbinders.com, pg 921

Unilux Inc, 59 N Fifth St, Saddle Brook, NJ 07663 *Tel:* 201-712-1266 *Toll Free Tel:* 800-522-0801 (US only) *Fax:* 201-712-1366 *Web Site:* www.unilux.com, pg 921

Union Connector Co Inc, 8182 Baymeadow Way W, Jacksonville, FL 32256 *Tel:* 631-753-9550 *Fax:* 631-753-9560 *E-mail:* sales@unionconnector.com *Web Site:* www.unionconnector.com, pg 921

Unique Business Systems, 1100 Colorado Ave, Suite B, Santa Monica, CA 90401 *Tel:* 310-396-3929 *Toll Free Tel:* 800-669-4827 *Fax:* 310-396-6114 *E-mail:* info@unibiz.com *Web Site:* www.unibiz.com, pg 921

Unique Communications Ltd, 2232 Pegasus Way NE, Calgary, AB T2E 8M5, Canada *Tel:* 403-250-3763 *Toll Free Tel:* 800-661-8575 *Fax:* 403-250-2604 *Web Site:* www.uniquecommunications.ca, pg 921

Uniset LLC, 449 Avenue "A", Rochester, NY 14621 *Tel:* 585-544-3820 *Fax:* 585-544-1110 *E-mail:* info@unisetcorp.com *Web Site:* www.unisetcorp.com, pg 921

United Audio Video Inc, 6855 Vineland Ave, North Hollywood, CA 91605 *Tel:* 818-980-6700 *Toll Free Tel:* 800-247-8606 *Fax:* 818-508-8273 *Web Site:* www.unitedavg.com, pg 921

United Methodist Productions, 810 12 Ave S, Nashville, TN 37203 *Tel:* 615-742-5400 *E-mail:* umcom@umcom.org *Web Site:* www.umcom.org, pg 921

United Nations Department of Public Information-News & Media Division, 405 E 42 St, Rm IN-913B, New York, NY 10017 *Tel:* 917-367-5007 *E-mail:* mediapartnerships@un.org *Web Site:* www.un.org, pg 921

United Nations Multimedia Resources Unit, c/o Audio Library, UN Dept of Public Information, Rm S-1046 & S-1083, New York, NY 10017 *Tel:* 212-963-9268; 212-963-0656 *Fax:* avlibrary@un.org *Web Site:* www.unmultimedia.org, pg 921

United Scenic Artists Local 829, 29 W 38 St, 15th fl, New York, NY 10018 *Tel:* 212-581-0300 *Toll Free Tel:* 877-728-5635 *Fax:* 212-977-2011 *E-mail:* vfxinfo@usa829.org *Web Site:* www.usa829.org; vfx.usa829.org, pg 963

United Sound & Electronics, 525 E Main St, Bridgeport, WV 26330 *Tel:* 304-842-6030 *E-mail:* questions@unitedsound.net *Web Site:* www.unitedsound.net, pg 921

United States Super 8mm Film & Digital Video Festival, Rutgers University, 018 Loree Hall, 72 Lipman Dr, New Brunswick, NJ 08901-1414 *Tel:* 848-932-8482 *Fax:* 732-932-1935 *E-mail:* njmac@aol.com; njmac12@gmail.com *Web Site:* www.njfilmfest.com, pg 1005

United Way Worldwide, 701 N Fairfax St, Alexandria, VA 22314-2045 *Tel:* 703-836-7112 *Web Site:* www.unitedway.org, pg 921

Unitron Ltd, 73 Mall Dr, Commack, NY 11725 *Tel:* 631-543-2000 *Fax:* 631-589-6975 *E-mail:* info@unitronusa.com *Web Site:* www.unitronusa.com, pg 921

Univenture Inc, 4266 Tuller Rd, Dublin, OH 43017 *Tel:* 937-645-4600 *Toll Free Tel:* 877-831-9428 *Fax:* 937-645-4700 *E-mail:* sales@univenture.com *Web Site:* www.univenture.com, pg 921

Universal Audio Inc, 4585 Scotts Valley Dr, Scotts Valley, CA 95066 *Tel:* 831-440-1176 *Toll Free Tel:* 877-698-2834 (cust serv) *E-mail:* sales@uaudio.com *Web Site:* www.uaudio.com, pg 922

Universal Music Group, 2220 Colorado Ave, Santa Monica, CA 90404 *Tel:* 310-865-5000 *Web Site:* www.universalmusic.com, pg 922

Universal Pictures Home Entertainment, 10 Universal City Plaza, Universal City, CA 91608 *Web Site:* www.uphe.com, pg 922

Universal Radio Inc, 6830 Americana Pkwy, Reynoldsburg, OH 43068 *Tel:* 614-866-4267 *Toll Free Tel:* 800-431-3939 (orders) *Fax:* 614-866-2339 *E-mail:* dx@universal-radio.com *Web Site:* www.universal-radio.com, pg 922

Universal Satellite Communications Inc, 1530 Nandina Ave, Perris, CA 92571 *Tel:* 562-483-4800; 951-943-4420 (corp off) *Toll Free Tel:* 888-867-6620 *Fax:* 954-943-0263 *Web Site:* www.unisatmobile.com, pg 922

Universal Studios, 100 Universal City Plaza, Universal City, CA 91608-1002 *Toll Free Tel:* 800-892-1979 *Fax:* 818-866-0293 *E-mail:* studio.operations2@nbcuni.com *Web Site:* www.nbcuni.com; universalstudioslot.com, pg 922

Universal Studios Canada Inc, 2450 Victoria Park Ave, Toronto, ON M2J 4A2, Canada *Tel:* 416-491-3000 *E-mail:* uniadvertising@nbcuni.com *Web Site:* www.universalpictures.ca, pg 922

Universal Studios Florida® Production Group, 1000 Universal Studios Plaza, Bldg 22A, Orlando, FL 32819 *Tel:* 407-363-8400 *Toll Free Tel:* 877-612-3737 (outside FL) *Fax:* 407-363-8869 *E-mail:* productiongroup@universalorlando.com *Web Site:* studio.florida.universalstudios.com, pg 922

Universe Kogaku America Inc, 116 Audrey Ave, Oyster Bay, NY 11771 *Tel:* 516-624-2444 *Fax:* 516-624-3109 *E-mail:* info@universeoptics.com *Web Site:* universeoptics.com, pg 922

University Film & Video Association (UFVA), c/o University of Illinois Press, 1325 S Oak St, Champaign, IL 61820-6975 *Toll Free Tel:* 866-647-8382 *E-mail:* ufvahome@gmail.com *Web Site:* www.ufva.org, pg 963

University Media Services, University of Delaware, 85 E Delaware Ave, Newark, DE 19716 *Tel:* 302-831-3546 *Web Site:* sites.udel.edu/it-ums/, pg 922

University of Florida, Warrington College of Business Information Technology Support Programs, Bryan Hall 300D, 1384 Union Rd, Gainesville, FL 32611 *Tel:* 352-273-1616 *Fax:* 352-392-6250 *E-mail:* itsp@warrington.ufl.edu *Web Site:* warrington.ufl.edu/itsp, pg 922

University of Idaho Engineering Outreach, 875 Perimeter Dr MS 1014, Moscow, ID 83844-1014 *Tel:* 208-885-6373 *Toll Free Tel:* 800-824-2889 *Fax:* 208-885-9249 *E-mail:* outreach@uidaho.edu *Web Site:* eo.uidaho.edu, pg 922

University of Maine Media Services, 19 Shibles Hall, Orono, ME 04469 *Tel:* 207-581-2500; 207-581-2516 *Web Site:* umaine.edu, pg 922

University of Memphis, Music Industry Division, Music Bldg, Rm 123, 3775 Central Ave, Memphis, TN 38152-3160 *Tel:* 901-678-2559; 901-678-2541 *E-mail:* music@memphis.edu *Web Site:* www.memphis.edu/music, pg 922

University of Michigan, Center for Middle Eastern & North African Studies, 500 Church St, Suite 500, Ann Arbor, MI 48109-1042 *Tel:* 734-647-4143 *Fax:* 734-936-0996 *E-mail:* cmenas@umich.edu *Web Site:* www.ii.umich.edu/cmenas, pg 923

University of Missouri-Columbia, Film & Video Library, 505 E Stewart Rd, Columbia, MO 65211-2040 *Tel:* 573-882-3608 *E-mail:* asc@missouri.edu *Web Site:* asc.missouri.edu, pg 923

University of Missouri-Kansas City School of Dentistry, 650 E 25 St, Kansas City, MO 64108 *Tel:* 816-235-2100 *Fax:* 816-235-5001 *E-mail:* dentistry@umkc.edu *Web Site:* dentistry.umkc.edu, pg 923

University of South Carolina Press, 1600 Hampton St, Suite 544, Columbia, SC 29208 *Tel:* 803-777-5243 *Toll Free Tel:* 800-768-2500 *Toll Free Fax:* 800-868-0740 *Web Site:* www.sc.edu/uscpress, pg 923

University of Texas at Austin - Petroleum Extension Service, J J Pickle Research Campus, 10100 Burnet Rd, Bldg 2, Austin, TX 78758-4445 *Tel:* 512-471-5940 *Toll Free Tel:* 800-687-4132 *Fax:* 512-471-9410 *Toll Free Fax:* 800-687-7839 *E-mail:* info@petex.utexas.edu *Web Site:* www.utexas.edu/ce/petex, pg 923

University of Toronto Academic & Campus Events, St George Campus, McMurrich Bldg, 4th fl, 12 Queen's Park Crescent W, Toronto, ON M5S 1S8, Canada *Tel:* 416-978-2187; 416-978-8613 (film & photo shoot permits) *Fax:* 416-978-4802 *E-mail:* ace.team@utoronto.ca *Web Site:* www.ace.utoronto.ca, pg 979

University of Toronto, Classroom Technology Support, Saint George Campus, McMurrich Bldg, 4th fl, 12 Queen's Park Crescent W, Toronto, ON M5S 1S8, Canada *Tel:* 416-978-6544 *Fax:* 416-978-4802 *E-mail:* avrequest@utoronto.ca *Web Site:* www.ace.utoronto.ca, pg 923

University of Vermont, Instructional Television Dept, 538 Main St, Burlington, VT 05405 *Tel:* 802-656-2927 *E-mail:* video@uvm.edu *Web Site:* www.uvm.edu; www.uvm.edu/~video, pg 923

University of Wisconsin-Oshkosh Radio-TV-Film Dept, Arts & Communications Bldg, W-112, 800 Algoma Blvd, Oshkosh, WI 54901 *Tel:* 920-424-3131 *E-mail:* rtf@uwosh.edu *Web Site:* rtf.uwosh.edu, pg 923

University Products Inc, 517 Main St, Holyoke, MA 01040-0073 *Tel:* 413-532-3372 *Toll Free Tel:* 800-628-1912 *Fax:* 413-532-9281 *Toll Free Fax:* 800-532-9281 *E-mail:* custserv@universityproducts. com; info@universityproducts.com *Web Site:* www. universityproducts.com, pg 923

UPN 20 WDCA-TV, 5151 Wisconsin Ave NW, Washington, DC 20016 *Tel:* 202-244-5151 *Web Site:* www.fox5dc.com/my20dc, pg 923

Upstage Video, 201 Rock Lititz Blvd, Suite 20, Lititz, PA 17543 *Tel:* 717-240-2400 *Toll Free Tel:* 877-484-3887 *E-mail:* info@upstagevideo.com *Web Site:* www. upstagevideo.com, pg 923

Urbanski Film, PO Box 438, Orland Park, IL 60462-0438 *Tel:* 708-460-9082 *Fax:* 708-460-9099 *E-mail:* info@urbanskifilm.com *Web Site:* www. urbanskifilm.com, pg 923

US Case Corp, 6301 J Richard Dr, Raleigh, NC 27617 *Tel:* 919-783-6166 *Toll Free Tel:* 800-648-8474 *Fax:* 919-783-0740 *E-mail:* customersupport@uscase. com *Web Site:* www.uscase.com, pg 923

US Holocaust Memorial Museum, 100 Raoul Wallenberg Place SW, Washington, DC 20024-2126 *Tel:* 202-488-0400 *E-mail:* membership@ushmm.org *Web Site:* www.ushmm.org, pg 923

US International Film & Video Festival, 713 S Pacific Coast Hwy, Suite A, Redondo Beach, CA 90277-4233 *Tel:* 310-540-0959 *Fax:* 310-316-8905 *E-mail:* filmfestinfo@filmfestawards.com; mediarelations@filmfestawards.com *Web Site:* www. filmfestawards.com, pg 1005

US Music Corp, 1649 Barclay Blvd, Buffalo Grove, IL 60089 *Toll Free Tel:* 800-877-6863 *E-mail:* sales. support@usmusiccorp.com *Web Site:* www. usmusiccorp.com, pg 923

US Virgin Islands Film Promotion Office, PO Box 6400, St Thomas, VI 00804-6400 *Tel:* 340-775-1444 (ext 2243) *Fax:* 340-774-4390 *E-mail:* info@filmusvi.com *Web Site:* www.filmusvi.com, pg 977

USA Film Festival, 6116 N Central Expwy, Suite 105, Dallas, TX 75206 *Tel:* 214-821-6300; 214-821-FILM (821-3456) *Fax:* 214-821-6364 *E-mail:* usafilmfest@ aol.com *Web Site:* www.usafilmfestival.com, pg 1005

USA Studios, 253 W 35 St, New York, NY 10001 *Tel:* 212-398-6400 *Toll Free Tel:* 800-872-3821 *Fax:* 212-398-4145 *E-mail:* sales@usastudios.tv; marketing@usastudios.tv *Web Site:* www.usastudios.tv, pg 923

USAV Group Inc, 584 W 18768 Enterprise Dr, Muskego, WI 53150 *Tel:* 262-814-2000 *Toll Free Tel:* 800-596-USAV (596-8728) *Fax:* 262-814-2006 *Web Site:* www. usavgroup.com, pg 923

USCCB Publishing, 3211 Fourth St NE, Washington, DC 20017 *Tel:* 202-541-3000 *Toll Free Tel:* 800-235-8722 (cust serv) *Fax:* 202-722-8709 (cust serv) *E-mail:* publications@usccb.org *Web Site:* www. usccbpublishing.org, pg 923

USDA/FSA Aerial Photography Field Office, 2222 W 2300 S, Salt Lake City, UT 84119-2020 *Tel:* 801-844-2922 *Toll Free Fax:* 855-415-2014 *E-mail:* apfo. sales@slc.usda.gov *Web Site:* www.fsa.usda.gov/ programs-and-services/aerial-photography, pg 924

Ushio America Inc, 5440 Cerritos Ave, Cypress, CA 90630-4567 *Tel:* 714-236-8600 *Toll Free Tel:* 800-838-7446 (cust serv) *Fax:* 714-229-3180 *Toll Free Fax:* 800-776-3641 (cust serv) *E-mail:* customerservice@ushio.com *Web Site:* www. ushio.com, pg 924

USI Inc, 98 Fort Path Rd, Suite A, Madison, CT 06443 *Tel:* 203-245-8586 *Toll Free Tel:* 800-282-9290 *Fax:* 203-245-8619 *E-mail:* customers@usi-corp.com *Web Site:* www.usi-laminate.com, pg 924

USITT, 290 Elwood Davis Rd, Suite 100, Liverpool, NY 13088 *Tel:* 315-463-6463 *Toll Free Tel:* 800-938-7488 *Toll Free Fax:* 866-398-7488 *E-mail:* info@usitt.org *Web Site:* www.usitt.org, pg 963

Utah Film Commission, Council Hall/Capitol Hill, 300 N State St, Salt Lake City, UT 84114 *Tel:* 801-538-8740 *Toll Free Tel:* 800-453-8824 *Web Site:* www.film.utah. gov, pg 976

Utah Scientific Inc, 4750 Wiley Post Way, Suite 150, Salt Lake City, UT 84116 *Tel:* 801-575-8801 *Toll Free Tel:* 800-453-8782 *Fax:* 801-537-3099 *E-mail:* info@ utahscientific.com *Web Site:* utahscientific.com, pg 924

Utah Valley Film Commission, 220 W Center St, Suite 100, Provo, UT 84601 *Tel:* 801-851-2100 *Toll Free Tel:* 800-222-UTAH (222-8824) *E-mail:* visitors@ utahvalley.com *Web Site:* www.utahvalley.com/film, pg 976

Utopia Films, 1976 S La Cienega Blvd, No 130, Los Angeles, CA 90034 *Tel:* 310-338-0580 *Fax:* 313-557-0580 *E-mail:* reception@utopiafilms. com; production@utopiafilms.com (reels) *Web Site:* utopiafilms.com, pg 924

Vaddio, 131 Cheshire Lane, Suite 500, Minnetonka, MN 55305 *Tel:* 763-971-4400 *Toll Free Tel:* 800-572-2011 *Fax:* 763-971-4464 *E-mail:* info@vaddio.com *Web Site:* www.vaddio.com, pg 924

Valencia Studios, 26030 Avenue Hall, Studio 5, Valencia, CA 91355 *Tel:* 661-702-9102 *E-mail:* info@ valenciastudios.com *Web Site:* www.valenciastudios. com, pg 924

Vallejo/Solano County Film Commission, 289 Mare Island Way, Vallejo, CA 94590 *Tel:* 707-642-3653 *Toll Free Tel:* 800-4-VALLEJO (482-5535) *Fax:* 707-644-2206 *Web Site:* www.visitvallejo.com/film-office, pg 968

Valley Media, 421 Roanoke Dr, Martinez, CA 94553-6240 *Tel:* 925-937-5207; 510-612-5215 (cell) *Web Site:* www.valleymedia.com, pg 924

Valley of the Sun Publishing Co, PO Box 2053, Sedona, AZ 86339 *Tel:* 928-554-1333 *E-mail:* info@ dicksutphen.com *Web Site:* www.dicksutphen.com, pg 924

Jack Van Impe Ministries International, 1718 Northfield Dr, Rochester Hills, MI 48309-3818 *Tel:* 248-852-2244; 248-852-5225 (orders) *Fax:* 248-852-2692 *E-mail:* jvimi@jvim.com *Web Site:* www.jvim.com, pg 924

Vancouver Film & Special Events Office, 126 Keefer St, Vancouver, BC V6A 1X4, Canada *Tel:* 604-257-8840 *Fax:* 604-257-8859 *E-mail:* film.office@vancouver.ca *Web Site:* vancouver.ca/doing-business/film-permits. aspx, pg 978

Vancouver Film Studios Ltd, 3500 Cornett Rd, Vancouver, BC V5M 2H5, Canada *Tel:* 604-453-5000 *Fax:* 604-453-5045 *E-mail:* info@ vancouverfilmstudios.com *Web Site:* www. vancouverfilmstudios.com, pg 924

Vancouver International Film Festival (VIFF), Vancouver International Film Ctr, 1181 Seymour St, Vancouver, BC V6B 3M7, Canada *Tel:* 604-685-0260 *Fax:* 604-688-8221 *E-mail:* info@viff.org; submissions@viff.org *Web Site:* www.viff.org, pg 1005

Vancouver Island South Film & Media Commission, 514 Government St, 2nd fl, Victoria, BC V8V 2L7, Canada *Tel:* 250-386-3976 *Toll Free Tel:* 888-537-3456 *E-mail:* admin@filmvictoria.com *Web Site:* www.filmvictoria.com, pg 978

Vanguard Documentaries, PO Box 26635, Brooklyn, NY 11202 *Tel:* 347-725-1677 *Web Site:* www. vanguarddocumentaries.com, pg 924

Vanner Inc, 4282 Reynolds Dr, Hilliard, OH 43026 *Tel:* 614-771-2718 *Toll Free Tel:* 800-ACPOWER (227-6937) *Fax:* 614-771-4904 *E-mail:* info@vanner. com; pwrsales@vanner.com *Web Site:* www.vanner. com, pg 924

Vantage Controls, a Legrand AV Inc brand, 2168 W Grove Pkwy, Suite 300, Pleasant Grove, UT 84062 *Tel:* 801-229-2800 *Toll Free Tel:* 800-555-9891 *Fax:* 801-224-0355 *E-mail:* vantage.info@ vantagecontrols.com *Web Site:* www.vantagecontrols. com, pg 924

Vantage Point Products Corp, PO Box 2485, Santa Fe Springs, CA 90670 *Tel:* 562-946-1718 *Fax:* 562-946-3898 *Web Site:* www.thinkvp.com, pg 924

Varese Sarabande Records Inc, 9100 Wilshire Blvd, Suite 455E, Beverly Hills, CA 90212 *Tel:* 310-853-5400 *E-mail:* info@varesesarabande.com; orders@ varesesarabande.com *Web Site:* www.varesesarabande. com, pg 924

Varitronics LLC, 7200 93 Ave N, Suite 120, Brooklyn, MN 55445 *Tel:* 763-536-6400 *Toll Free Tel:* 800-328-0585 *E-mail:* customerservice@variquest.com; tech_support@variquest.com; variquest@variquest.com *Web Site:* www.variquest.com, pg 925

VARTA Microbattery Inc, 555 Theodore Fremd Ave, Suite C-304, Rye, NY 10580 *Tel:* 914-592-2500 *Toll Free Tel:* 800-468-2782 *Fax:* 914-345-0488 *Web Site:* www.varta-microbattery.com; www.varta-microbattery.com/contact/?lang=en, pg 925

Varto Technologies, 195 Hackensack St, East Rutherford, NJ 07073 *Toll Free Tel:* 888-656-6233 *Fax:* 201-604-2661 *E-mail:* sales@vartotechnologies.com *Web Site:* www.vartotechnologies.com, pg 925

Mike Vasilinda Productions Inc, 310 N Monroe St, Tallahassee, FL 32301 *Tel:* 850-224-5420 *Web Site:* mvptv.tv, pg 925

VCI Entertainment, 11333 E 60 Place, Tulsa, OK 74146-6828 *Tel:* 918-254-6337 *Toll Free Tel:* 800-331-4077 *E-mail:* vci@vcientertainment.com *Web Site:* www. vcientertainment.com; www.vcient.com, pg 925

Vcom IMC, 80 Little Falls Rd, Fairfield, NJ 07004 *Toll Free Tel:* 800-572-6374 *E-mail:* info@vcomimc.com *Web Site:* www.vcomimc.com, pg 925

VCSvideo, 2807 Hunterdon Dr, Cinnaminson, NJ 08077 *Tel:* 856-273-8800 *Toll Free Tel:* 877-VCS-VIDEO (827-8433) *Web Site:* www.vcsvideo.com, pg 925

VDO Lab Inc, 520 White Plains Rd, Suite 500, Tarrytown, NY 10591 *Tel:* 914-467-7860; 914-374-8727 *E-mail:* info@vdolab.net; vdolabinc@gmail.com *Web Site:* vdolab.net, pg 925

Vedanta Press & Catalog, 1946 Vedanta Place, Hollywood, CA 90068 *Tel:* 323-960-1727 (bookstores); 323-960-1736 (outside US) *Toll Free Tel:* 800-816-2242 *E-mail:* info@vedanta.com *Web Site:* www.vedanta.com, pg 925

Vedanta Society of St Louis, 205 S Skinker Blvd, St Louis, MO 63105 *Tel:* 314-721-5118 *Web Site:* vedantastl.org, pg 925

Veetronix Inc, 1311 W Pacific St, Lexington, NE 68850 *Tel:* 308-324-6661 *Toll Free Tel:* 800-445-0007 *Fax:* 308-324-4985 *E-mail:* sales@veetronix.com *Web Site:* www.veetronix.com, pg 925

Vela Research, 5576 Rio Vista Dr, Clearwater, FL 33760-3107 *Tel:* 727-507-5301 *E-mail:* sales@vela. com *Web Site:* www.vela.com, pg 925

Velodyne LiDAR Inc, 5521 Hellyer Ave, San Jose, CA 95738 *Tel:* 408-465-2800 *Fax:* 408-779-9208 (cust serv); 408-779-9377 (orders) *E-mail:* lidar@velodyne. com *Web Site:* www.velodynelidar.com, pg 925

Venice Media Group, 101 W Venice Ave, Suite 6, Venice, FL 34285 *Tel:* 941-485-0699 *E-mail:* info@ venicemediagroup.com *Web Site:* www. venicemediagroup.com, pg 925

Venture Media, 902 Harvest Pointe Dr, Fort Mill, SC 29708 *Tel:* 803-547-3878 *E-mail:* info@venturemedia. tv *Web Site:* www.venturemedia.tv, pg 925

VER, 757 W California Ave, Bldg 4, Glendale, CA 91203 *Tel:* 818-956-1444 *Toll Free Tel:* 800-794-1407 *Fax:* 818-546-1040 *Web Site:* www.ver.com, pg 926

Ver Sales Inc, 2509 N Naomi St, Burbank, CA 91504 *Tel:* 818-567-3000 *Toll Free Tel:* 800-229-0518; 800-300-WIRE (300-9479, CA only) *Fax:* 818-567-3018 *E-mail:* sales@versales.com *Web Site:* www.versales.com, pg 926

Verbatim Americas LLC, 8210 University Executive Park Dr, Suite 300, Charlotte, NC 28262 *Toll Free Tel:* 800-538-8589 *Web Site:* www.verbatim.com, pg 926

Verilux® - The Healthy Lighting Co, 340 Mad River Park, Suite 1, Waitsfield, VT 05673 *Tel:* 802-496-3101 *Toll Free Tel:* 888-544-4865 (cust support); 800-454-4408 (orders) *Fax:* 802-496-3105 (orders) *E-mail:* info@verilux.com *Web Site:* www.verilux.com, pg 926

Vermont International Film Festival, PO Box 483, Burlington, VT 05402-0483 *Tel:* 802-660-2600 *E-mail:* info@vtiff.org *Web Site:* www.vtiff.org, pg 1006

Versatech Industries Inc, 14750 S Grant St, Bixby, OK 74008 *Tel:* 918-366-7400, pg 926

Versatruss, 5028 Hwy 43, Perth, ON K7H 3C7, Canada *Tel:* 613-264-0074 *Toll Free Tel:* 888-430-7613 *Fax:* 613-264-0889 *E-mail:* info@versatruss.com *Web Site:* www.versatruss.com, pg 926

Vertiv, 1050 Dearborn Dr, Columbus, OH 43085 *Tel:* 614-888-0246 *Web Site:* www.vertiv.com, pg 926

Verve Label Group, 1755 Broadway, New York, NY 10019 *Tel:* 212-841-8000 *Web Site:* www.vervelabelgroup.com; www.universalmusic.com, pg 926

Vexcel Corp, 5775 Flatiron Pkwy, Suite 220, Boulder, CO 80301 *Tel:* 303-415-6000 *Fax:* 303-442-2956 *E-mail:* vexcel@microsoft.com *Web Site:* www.vexcel.com, pg 926

La Vezzi Precision Inc, 250 Madsen Dr, Bloomingdale, IL 60108-2637 *Tel:* 630-582-1230 *Toll Free Tel:* 800-323-1772 (outside IL) *Fax:* 630-582-1238 (orders) *E-mail:* lpi@lavezzi.com *Web Site:* www.lavezzi.com, pg 926

VFGadgets Inc, 22 Elmer Ave, Toronto, ON M4L 3R7, Canada *Tel:* 416-686-1452 *E-mail:* sales@vfgadgets.com; customerservice@vfgadgets.com *Web Site:* www.vfgadgets.com, pg 926

Via Verde Productions, 22631 Pacific Coast Hwy, Suite 480, Malibu, CA 90265-5036 *Tel:* 310-458-3778 *Fax:* 310-496-2992 *E-mail:* info@viaverdedigital.com *Web Site:* www.viaverdedigital.com, pg 926

Vicon Industries Inc, 135 Fell Ct, Hauppauge, NY 11788-4351 *Tel:* 631-952-2288 *Toll Free Tel:* 800-645-9116 *Fax:* 631-951-2288 *E-mail:* sales@vicon-security.com *Web Site:* www.vicon-security.com, pg 926

Victory Studios, 2247 15 Ave W, Seattle, WA 98119 *Tel:* 206-282-1776 *Toll Free Tel:* 888-282-1776 *Fax:* 206-282-3535 *E-mail:* info@victorystudios.com *Web Site:* www.victorystudios.com, pg 927

VidCAD LLC, 2010 E Lohman Ave, Suite 2, Las Cruces, NM 88001 *Tel:* 575-522-0003 *Toll Free Tel:* 800-VIDCAD-6 (843-2236 sales) *Fax:* 575-522-0009 *E-mail:* sales@vidcad.com *Web Site:* www.vidcad.com, pg 927

VidCan Media Solutions, 24133 Del Monte Dr, Unit 204, Valencia, CA 91355 *Tel:* 818-312-5128 *Web Site:* www.vidcan.com, pg 927

Vidcraft Productions Ltd, 425 Curling St, Corner Brook, NL A2H 3K4, Canada *Tel:* 709-785-1157 *E-mail:* info@vidcraft.com *Web Site:* www.vidcraft.com, pg 927

Video Accessory Corp, 1243 Sherman Dr, Suite 8, Longmont, CO 80501 *Tel:* 303-443-1319 *Toll Free Tel:* 800-821-0426 *Fax:* 303-440-8878 *E-mail:* sales@vac-brick.net *Web Site:* www.vac-brick.com, pg 927

Video Advantage, 90 Houseman Crescent, Richmond Hill, ON L4C 7S6, Canada *Tel:* 905-883-5332 *E-mail:* info@videoadvantage.ca *Web Site:* www.videoadvantage.ca, pg 927

Video Aided Instruction Inc, PO Box 740023, Boyton Beach, FL 33474-0023 *Toll Free Tel:* 800-238-1512 *Toll Free Fax:* 800-588-1419 *E-mail:* info@videoaidedinstruction.com *Web Site:* www.videoaidedinstruction.com, pg 927

Video Artists International & VAI Audio, 109 Wheeler Ave, Pleasantville, NY 10570 *Tel:* 914-769-3691 *Toll Free Tel:* 800-477-7146 *Fax:* 914-769-5407 *E-mail:* orders@vaimusic.com *Web Site:* www.vaimusic.com, pg 927

Video Associates Labs Inc, 2201 Denton Dr, Suite 109 B, Austin, TX 78758-3231 *Tel:* 512-491-7091 *Toll Free Tel:* 800-331-0547 *Fax:* 512-491-7619 *E-mail:* sales@val.com *Web Site:* www.val.com, pg 927

Video Caption Corp, 88 Hunns Lake Rd, Stanfordville, NY 12581 *Tel:* 845-868-1200 *Toll Free Tel:* 800-705-1203 *Fax:* 845-868-1188 *Toll Free Fax:* 800-705-1207 *E-mail:* mail@vicaps.com *Web Site:* www.vicaps.com, pg 927

Video Catalogue Co Inc, 105 E 34 St, Suite 105, New York, NY 10016 *Toll Free Tel:* 866-843-2282 *E-mail:* info@vidcat.com *Web Site:* www.vidcat.com, pg 927

Video Copy Services Inc, 3980 Dekalb Technology Pkwy, Suite 670, Atlanta, GA 30340 *Tel:* 404-321-6933 *Toll Free Tel:* 800-553-3616 *E-mail:* info@video-copy.com *Web Site:* www.video-copy.com, pg 927

Video Corporation of America (VCA), 7 Veronica Ave, Somerset, NJ 08873 *Tel:* 732-545-8000 *Fax:* 732-545-5101 *Web Site:* www.vcaglobal.com, pg 927

Video Dimensions Inc, 545 W 45 St, New York, NY 10036 *Tel:* 212-262-5453 *Web Site:* videodimensions.net, pg 927

Video Excellence Productions, 94 Breckonwood Crescent, Thornhill, ON L3T 5E8, Canada *Tel:* 905-731-4355 *Web Site:* www.videoexcellence.com, pg 927

Video Express, 88 Black Falcon Ave, Suite 220, Boston, MA 02210 *Tel:* 617-267-7900 *Fax:* 617-267-6306 *E-mail:* operations@evideoexpress.com *Web Site:* www.evideoexpress.com, pg 928

Video/Film Associates, 413 N Seventh St, Philadelphia, PA 19123-3900 *Tel:* 215-922-3333, pg 928

Video I-D Teleproductions Inc, 105 Muller Rd, Washington, IL 61571 *Tel:* 309-444-4323 *Fax:* 309-444-4333 *E-mail:* videoid@videoid.com *Web Site:* www.videoid.com, pg 928

Video Ideas Productions, 1501 64 St, North Bergen, NJ 07047 *Tel:* 201-951-3798 *Fax:* 201-662-4846 *E-mail:* osoriomedia@yahoo.com *Web Site:* osoriomedia.com, pg 928

Video Impressions, 1946 Fays Lane, Sugar Grove, IL 60554 *Tel:* 630-851-1663 *E-mail:* info@video-impressions.com *Web Site:* www.video-impressions.com, pg 928

Video Learning Library, 15838 N 62 St, Scottsdale, AZ 85254-1988 *Tel:* 480-596-9970 *Toll Free Tel:* 800-383-8811 (orders) *E-mail:* videos@videolearning.com *Web Site:* www.videolearning.com, pg 928

The Video Messenger Co, 862 Judson Place, Stratford, CT 06615 *Tel:* 203-358-8842 *Toll Free Tel:* 800-800-7128 *Fax:* 203-547-6216 *E-mail:* vmc@videomessenger.com *Web Site:* www.videomessenger.com, pg 928

Video Mount Products (VMP), 345 Log Canoe Circle, Stevensville, MD 21666 *Tel:* 410-643-6390 *Toll Free Tel:* 877-281-2169 *Fax:* 410-643-6615 *E-mail:* contact@videomount.com *Web Site:* www.videomount.com, pg 928

Video Movie Magic, 26941 Cabot Rd, Suite 127, Laguna Hills, CA 92653 *Tel:* 949-582-8596 *Fax:* 949-582-8223 *E-mail:* sales@videomoviemagic.com *Web Site:* www.videomoviemagic.com, pg 928

Video Out Distribution, 2625 Kaslo St, Vancouver, BC V5M 3G9, Canada *Tel:* 604-872-8337 *Fax:* 604-876-1185 *E-mail:* info@vivomediaarts.com; info@videoout.ca *Web Site:* vivomediaarts.com; www.videoout.ca, pg 928

Video Perspective, 1410 Hutchins St, Houston, TX 77003 *Tel:* 281-996-7974 *Toll Free Tel:* 888-996-7974 *E-mail:* vp@vidper.com *Web Site:* www.videoperspective.com, pg 928

Video Production Associates Inc, 525 Bridgeport Ave, Shelton, CT 06484-1397 *Tel:* 203-929-8869 *Web Site:* www.vpa-inc.com, pg 928

The Video Project, 145 Ninth St, Suite 102, San Francisco, CA 94103 *Tel:* 415-981-9710 *Toll Free Tel:* 800-475-2638 *Fax:* 415-692-6223 *E-mail:* orders@videoproject.com; support@videoproject.com *Web Site:* www.videoproject.com, pg 928

Video Resources Inc, 1809 E Dyer Rd, Suite 307, Santa Ana, CA 92705 *Tel:* 949-261-7266 *E-mail:* info@videoresources.com *Web Site:* www.videoresources.com, pg 928

Video Resources Software, 11767 S Dixie Hwy, Suite 222, Miami, FL 33156 *Toll Free Tel:* 888-223-6284 *Fax:* 305-256-0467 *E-mail:* mailroom@tutorace.com *Web Site:* www.tutorace.com, pg 928

Video Solutions, 2121 Eisenhower Ave, Suite 103, Alexandria, VA 22314 *Tel:* 703-683-5305; 703-628-0702 (cell) *E-mail:* inquiries@thevideosolution.com *Web Site:* www.thevideosolution.com, pg 928

The Video Store Shopper, 3987 Heritage Oak Ct, Simi Valley, CA 93063 *Tel:* 800-429-4900 *Fax:* 805-583-8546 *Toll Free Fax:* 800-947-2060 *E-mail:* sales@shopperinc.com; customerservice@shopperinc.com *Web Site:* www.thevideostoreshopper.com; www.tsisupplies.com, pg 928

Video Techniques Inc, 1731 First St E, Bradenton, FL 34208 *Tel:* 941-758-3077 *Fax:* 941-758-4896 *E-mail:* vti-web@videotechniques.com *Web Site:* videotechniques.com, pg 928

Video Technology Services Inc, 5 Ariel Way, Suite 300, Syosset, NY 11791 *Tel:* 516-937-9700 *E-mail:* info@vts.global *Web Site:* www.vts.global, pg 929

Video Visions Inc, 3600 Boundbrook Ave, Trevose, PA 19053 *Tel:* 215-942-6642 *Fax:* 267-684-6819 *E-mail:* sales@video-visions.com *Web Site:* www.video-visions.com, pg 929

Video West Inc, 1050 N 52 St, Phoenix, AZ 85008 *Tel:* 480-222-3180 *Toll Free Tel:* 800-659-0880 *Fax:* 480-222-3190 *E-mail:* info@videowestinc.com *Web Site:* www.videowestinc.com, pg 929

Video Wisconsin Inc, 18110 W Bluemound Rd, Brookfield, WI 53045 *Tel:* 262-785-1110 *Fax:* 262-785-9827 *Web Site:* www.videowisconsin.tv, pg 929

Videobotics, 220 N Palisade Dr, Santa Maria, CA 93454 *Tel:* 805-349-1104 *E-mail:* videobotics@megagem.com; sales@videobotics.com *Web Site:* www.videobotics.com; camrobot.com, pg 929

Videofashion Network, 611 Broadway, Suite 307, New York, NY 10012 *Tel:* 212-274-1600 *Fax:* 212-219-1969 *E-mail:* info@videofashion.com; licensing@videofashion.com *Web Site:* videofashion.com, pg 929

Videofax, 1750 Cesar Chavez St, Unit G, San Francisco, CA 94124 *Tel:* 415-641-0100 *E-mail:* rentals@videofax.com *Web Site:* www.videofax.com, pg 929

Videofilm Systems Inc, 7 Islandbrook Ave, Unit D-1, Bridgeport, CT 06606 *Tel:* 203-870-6013 *E-mail:* info@videofilmsystems.com, pg 929

Videograf, 144 W 27 St, 12th fl, New York, NY 10001 *Tel:* 212-242-7871 *E-mail:* videograf@verizon.net *Web Site:* vgraflive.org, pg 929

Videografix LLC, 2530 Berryessa Rd, Suite 314, San Jose, CA 95132-2903 *Tel:* 408-499-1280 *E-mail:* info@videografix.com *Web Site:* www.videografix.com, pg 929

Videography Productions, PO Box 653, Amagansett, NY 11930-0653 *Tel:* 520-907-1900 *Web Site:* www.dickfisher.net, pg 929

Videoguys, 10-12 Charles St, Glen Cove, NY 11542 *Tel:* 516-759-1611 *Toll Free Tel:* 800-323-2325 *Fax:* 516-671-3092 *E-mail:* sales@videoguys.com *Web Site:* www.videoguys.com, pg 929

The Videohouse Inc, 975 Greentree Rd, Pittsburgh, PA 15220 *Tel:* 412-921-7577 *Fax:* 412-921-5535 *E-mail:* info@thevideohouse.com *Web Site:* www.thevideohouse.com, pg 929

VideoLink Inc, an AVI-SPL company, 1230 Washington St, West Newton, MA 02465 *Tel:* 617-340-4100 *Toll Free Tel:* 800-452-5565 *Fax:* 617-340-4101 *E-mail:* sales@videolinktv.com *Web Site:* www.videolinktv.com, pg 929

Videomagnetics, 3970 Clearview Frontage Rd, Colorado Springs, CO 80911 *Tel:* 719-390-1313 *Toll Free Tel:* 800-432-3887 *Fax:* 719-390-1316 *E-mail:* vmi@csprings.com *Web Site:* www.videomagnetics.com, pg 929

Videosmith Inc, 200 Spring Garden St, Suite C, Philadelphia, PA 19123 *Tel:* 215-238-5070 *Fax:* 215-238-5075 *E-mail:* info@videosmith.com *Web Site:* videosmith.com, pg 930

Videotex Systems Inc, 10255 Miller Rd, Dallas, TX 75238 *Tel:* 972-231-9200 *Toll Free Tel:* 800-88-VIDEO (888-4336) *Fax:* 972-231-2420 *E-mail:* info@videotexsystems.com *Web Site:* www.videotexsystems.com, pg 930

Videowerks, 3434-135 Kildaire Farm Rd, No 181, Cary, NC 27518 *Tel:* 310-780-4156 (cell) *Web Site:* www.videowerkseast.com, pg 930

Videssence, 10768 Lower Azusa Rd, El Monte, CA 91731 *Tel:* 626-579-0943 *Fax:* 626-579-6803 *E-mail:* contact@videssence.tv *Web Site:* www.videssence.tv, pg 930

Vidicom, 520 Eighth Ave, Suite 2206, New York, NY 10018 *Tel:* 212-895-8300 *E-mail:* sales@vidicom.com *Web Site:* vidicom.com, pg 930

Vidox Motion Imagery, 204 Winchester Dr, Lafayette, LA 70506 *Tel:* 337-237-1700 *Fax:* 337-237-1712 *Web Site:* www.vidox.com, pg 930

VIEW Inc (Video International Entertainment World Inc), 11 Reservoir Rd, Saugerties, NY 12477 *Tel:* 845-246-9955 *Toll Free Tel:* 800-843-9843 *Fax:* 845-246-9966 *E-mail:* viewvid@aol.com, pg 930

Viewpoint Production Services Inc, 419 Mount Nebo Rd, Pittsburgh, PA 15237 *Tel:* 412-369-7171 *Toll Free Tel:* 800-820-0402 *E-mail:* contact@viewpoint.tv *Web Site:* viewpoint.tv, pg 930

ViewSonic, 10 Pointe Dr, 2nd fl, Brea, CA 92821 *Tel:* 909-444-8888 *Toll Free Tel:* 800-688-6688 (cust serv); 800-888-8583 *E-mail:* customerservice@viewsonic.com *Web Site:* www.viewsonic.com, pg 930

Vincent Associates, 803 Linden Ave, Rochester, NY 14625 *Tel:* 585-385-5930 *Toll Free Tel:* 800-828-6972 *Fax:* 585-385-6004 *E-mail:* info@uniblitz.com *Web Site:* www.uniblitz.com, pg 930

Vincent Lighting Systems, 6161 Cochran Rd, Suite D, Solon, OH 44139 *Tel:* 216-475-7600 *Toll Free Tel:* 800-922-5356 *Fax:* 216-475-6376 *E-mail:* info@vls.com *Web Site:* www.vls.com, pg 930

Vineyard Video & Photography, 4193 Concord Ave, Santa Rosa, CA 95407 *Tel:* 707-591-9999; 707-591-1927 (cell) *Web Site:* www.vineyardvideo.com, pg 930

The Virginia Film Festival, 617 W Main St, 2nd fl, Charlottesville, VA 22903 *Tel:* 434-982-5277 *Fax:* 434-924-3374 *E-mail:* info@virginiafilmfestival.org; vffsubmissions@virginia.edu *Web Site:* virginiafilmfestival.org, pg 1006

Virginia Film Office, 901 E Cary St, Richmond, VA 23219-4048 *Tel:* 804-545-5530 *Toll Free Tel:* 800-854-6233 *Fax:* 804-545-5531 *E-mail:* vafilm@virginia.org *Web Site:* www.film.virginia.org, pg 976

Virginia Theatre Association (VTA), 1111 Church St, Lynchburg, VA 24504 *Tel:* 434-845-7529 *E-mail:* executivedirector@vtasite.org *Web Site:* virginiatheatre.org, pg 963

VirtualMix, 701 S Carson St, Suite 200-2914, Carson City, NV 89701 *Tel:* 818-209-6176 *E-mail:* virtualmixpost@gmail.com *Web Site:* www.virtualmix.com, pg 930

Vision Identics Systems Inc, 110 Villa Ave, Mamaroneck, NY 10543 *Tel:* 914-381-2625 *E-mail:* visionid@prodigy.net, pg 930

Vision Maker Media, 1800 N 33 St, Lincoln, NE 68503-1409 *Tel:* 402-472-3522 *Fax:* 402-472-8675 *E-mail:* visionmaker@unl.edu *Web Site:* www.visionmakermedia.org, pg 930

Vision Quest Productions Inc, PO Box 1896, Wayne, NJ 07470-1896 *Tel:* 973-686-9400 *Fax:* 973-694-8314 *Web Site:* vqpi.yolasite.com; visionquestproductions.com, pg 930

Vision Video, 2030 Wentz Church Rd, Lansdale, PA 19446 *Tel:* 610-584-3500 *Toll Free Tel:* 800-523-0226 *Fax:* 610-584-6643 *E-mail:* support@visionvideo.com *Web Site:* www.visionvideo.com, pg 930

Visionary Solutions Inc, 2060 Alameda Padre Serra, Suite 100, Santa Barbara, CA 93103 *Tel:* 805-845-8900 *Fax:* 805-845-8889 *E-mail:* sales@vsicam.com *Web Site:* www.vsicam.com, pg 931

Visioneering International Inc, 659 Auburn Ave NE, Suite 267, Atlanta, GA 30312 *Tel:* 404-681-9028 *Fax:* 404-681-5947 *E-mail:* design@visioneering.com *Web Site:* www.visioneering.com, pg 931

Visions Film Festival & Conference, 601 S College Rd, Wilmington, NC 28403 *Tel:* 919-607-0031 *E-mail:* visions7programming@gmail.com; visions7development@gmail.com *Web Site:* www.visionsffc.org, pg 1006

Visions Plus, 200 Valley Dr, Suite 5, Brisbane, CA 94005 *Tel:* 415-467-3300 *E-mail:* web_inquiry@visionsplus.com *Web Site:* visionsplus.com, pg 931

Visionworks Design Services Inc, 204 Peach Way, Suite H, Columbia, MO 65203 *Tel:* 573-449-8567 *E-mail:* info@visionworksgroup.com *Web Site:* visionworksgroup.com, pg 931

Visit Billings, 815 S 27 St, Billings, MT 59101 *Tel:* 406-245-4111 *Fax:* 406-245-7333 *E-mail:* info@visitbillings.com *Web Site:* www.visitbillings.com, pg 973

Visit Natchez & Natchez Convention Promotion Commission, 640 S Canal St, Box C, Natchez, MS 39120 *Tel:* 601-446-6345 *Toll Free Tel:* 800-647-6724 *E-mail:* info@visitnatchez.org *Web Site:* www.visitnatchez.org/p/media/film, pg 972

Visit Topeka Inc, 618 S Kansas Ave, Topeka, KS 66603 *Tel:* 785-234-1030 *Toll Free Tel:* 800-235-1030 *Fax:* 785-234-8282 *E-mail:* info@visittopeka.com *Web Site:* www.visittopeka.com, pg 973

Visix™ Inc, 230 Scientific Dr, Suite 800, Norcross, GA 30092 *Tel:* 770-446-1416 *Toll Free Tel:* 800-572-4935 *Fax:* 770-448-5724 *E-mail:* info@visix.com *Web Site:* www.visix.com, pg 931

Vista Color Imaging Inc, 4770 Van Epps Rd, Unit 101, Brooklyn Heights, OH 44113 *Tel:* 216-651-2830 *Fax:* 216-651-5004 *E-mail:* info@vistacolorimaging.com *Web Site:* vistacolorimaging.com, pg 931

Vista Group International Inc, 25 Van Zant St, Unit 8-D, Norwalk, CT 06855 *Tel:* 203-852-5557 *Toll Free Tel:* 800-866-2113 *Fax:* 203-852-5559 *E-mail:* info@vistagroupinternational.com *Web Site:* www.vistagroupinternational.com, pg 931

Vistacom Inc, 1902 Vultee St, Allentown, PA 18103-2998 *Tel:* 610-791-9500 *Toll Free Tel:* 800-747-0459 *Fax:* 610-791-9510 *E-mail:* info@vistacominc.com *Web Site:* www.vistacominc.com, pg 931

Vistamax Productions, 9705 Little Pond Way, Tampa, FL 33647 *Tel:* 813-907-1010 *Fax:* 813-907-1991 *E-mail:* info@vistamax.com; sales@vistamax.com *Web Site:* www.vistamax.com, pg 931

Visual Communications - Southern California Asian American Studies Central Inc, 120 Judge John Aiso St, Basement Level, Los Angeles, CA 90012 *Tel:* 213-680-4462 *Fax:* 213-687-4848 *E-mail:* info@vconline.org *Web Site:* www.vconline.org, pg 931

Visual Departures Ltd, 48 Sheffield Business Park, Ashley Falls, MA 01222 *Tel:* 413-229-2272 *Toll Free Tel:* 800-628-2003 *Fax:* 413-229-2274 *E-mail:* sales@visualdepartures.com *Web Site:* www.visualdepartures.com, pg 931

Visual Instrumentation Corp, 1110 West Ave L-12, Unit 2, Lancaster, CA 93534-7039 *Tel:* 661-945-7999 *Fax:* 661-723-5667 *E-mail:* visinst@earthlink.net *Web Site:* www.visinst.com, pg 931

Visual Products Inc, 790 Shiloh Ave, Wellington, OH 44090 *Tel:* 440-647-4999 *Fax:* 440-647-4998 *E-mail:* sales@visualproducts.com *Web Site:* www.visualproducts.com, pg 931

Visual Sound Inc, 485 Park Way, Broomall, PA 19008 *Tel:* 610-544-8700 *Toll Free Tel:* 800-523-7525 *Fax:* 610-544-3385 *Web Site:* www.visualsound.com, pg 931

The Visual Studies Workshop (VSW), 31 Prince St, Rochester, NY 14607 *Tel:* 585-442-8676 *Fax:* 585-442-1992 *E-mail:* info@vsw.org *Web Site:* www.vsw.org, pg 931

Visual Systems, 845 Encino Place, Santa Paula, CA 93060 *Tel:* 805-933-8044 *Fax:* 805-933-9744 *E-mail:* info@visualsystemsonline.com, pg 931

Visual Technologies Corp, 1620 Burnet Ave, Syracuse, NY 13206 *Tel:* 315-423-2000 *Toll Free Tel:* 888-423-0004 *E-mail:* contact@visualtec.com *Web Site:* visualtec.businesscatalyst.com, pg 932

Visual Word Systems Inc, 35 W 36 St, 8th fl, New York, NY 10018 *Tel:* 212-629-8383 *Fax:* 212-629-8333 *Web Site:* www.visualword.com, pg 932

VITAC, 8300 E Maplewood Ave, Suite 310, Greenwood Village, CO 80111 *Toll Free Tel:* 800-278-4822 (sales); 800-775-7838 *E-mail:* info@vitac.com *Web Site:* www.vitac.com, pg 932

Vital Learning LLC, 3001 Brighton Blvd, Suite 2765, Denver, CO 80216 *Toll Free Tel:* 800-243-5858 *E-mail:* support@vital-learning.com; info@vital-learning.com *Web Site:* www.vital-learning.com, pg 932

VITEC Multimedia, 931 Benecia Ave, Sunnyvale, CA 94085 *Tel:* 650-230-2400 *Toll Free Tel:* 800-451-5101 *E-mail:* info@vitec.com *Web Site:* www.vitec.com, pg 932

Vitec Videocom Inc, 14 Progress Dr, Shelton, CT 06484 *Tel:* 203-929-1100 *Fax:* 203-925-2684 *E-mail:* info@vitecgroup.com; www.vitecvideocom.com, pg 932

Vitruvian Entertainment, 4712 Admirality Way, Unit 417, Marina del Rey, CA 90292 *Tel:* 818-720-3250 (cell) *Web Site:* vitruvianent.com, pg 932

ViVi Co, PO Box 750, Glendale, CA 91209 *Tel:* 818-500-8889; 818-500-8084 *Fax:* 818-507-6600 *E-mail:* zibreathe@aol.com *Web Site:* www.theartofbreathing.com, pg 932

VMI Inc, 211 E Weddell Dr, Sunnyvale, CA 94089 *Tel:* 408-745-1700; 415-362-1330 *Web Site:* www.vmivideo.com, pg 932

VMS Inc, 02400 37 1/2 St, Gobles, MI 49055 *Tel:* 269-377-0234 *E-mail:* vms.texts@gmail.com *Web Site:* www.vms-online.com, pg 932

The Vocal Point/Profile Communications Ltd, 1196 Habgood St, White Rock, BC V4B 4W9, Canada *Tel:* 604-531-6908 *Web Site:* www.profilecomm.com, pg 932

Voice & Video Rentals, 4909 Ruffner St, San Diego, CA 92111 *Tel:* 858-560-5000 *Fax:* 858-560-9900 *Web Site:* www.voiceandvideo.com, pg 932

Voice of Democracy Scholarship Program, 406 W 34 St, Kansas City, MO 64111 *Tel:* 816-968-1117 *Fax:* 816-968-1149 *Web Site:* www.vfw.org, pg 1006

Vortex Sci-Fi, Fantasy & Horror Film Festival, 83 Park St, Suite 5, Providence, RI 02903 *Tel:* 401-861-4445 *Fax:* 401-490-6735 *E-mail:* info@film-festival.org *Web Site:* www.film-festival.org, pg 1006

VO2 Mix Audio Post, 116 Spadina Ave, Suite 208, Toronto, ON M5V 2K6, Canada *Tel:* 416-603-3954 *Fax:* 416-603-3957 *E-mail:* info@vo2mix.ca *Web Site:* www.vo2mix.ca, pg 932

Voyager Recordings & Publications, 424 35 Ave, Seattle, WA 98122 *Tel:* 206-323-1112 *E-mail:* info@voyagerrecords.com *Web Site:* www.voyagerrecords.com, pg 932

Voyetra Turtle Beach, 100 Summit Lake Dr, Suite 100, Valhalla, NY 10595 *Tel:* 914-345-2255 *Fax:* 914-345-2266 *E-mail:* sales@turtlebeach.com *Web Site:* www.turtlebeach.com, pg 933

VRSim Inc, 222 Pitkin St, Suite 119, East Hartford, CT 06108-3220 *Tel:* 860-893-0080 *E-mail:* info@vrsim.net *Web Site:* www.vrsim.net, pg 933

VSA Inc, 6929 Seward Ave, Lincoln, NE 68507 *Toll Free Tel:* 800-888-2140 (orders) *Fax:* 402-325-8033 *E-mail:* sales@vsa1.com *Web Site:* www.vsa1.com, pg 933

VSG Digital Media Solutions, 11126 Lindbergh Business Ct, St Louis, MO 63123 *Tel:* 314-487-8045 *Toll Free Tel:* 800-737-8045 *Fax:* 314-487-9387 *E-mail:* info@vsginc.net *Web Site:* www.vsginc.net, pg 933

VTP Inc, 1309 S Flower St, Burbank, CA 91502 *Tel:* 818-566-9898 *Toll Free Tel:* 800-422-2444 *E-mail:* sales@vtpcorp.com *Web Site:* www.myvtp.com, pg 933

Vutec Corp, 11711 W Sample Rd, Coral Springs, FL 33065-3155 *Tel:* 954-545-9000 *Toll Free Tel:* 800-770-4700 *E-mail:* info@vutec.com; sales@vutec.com *Web Site:* vutec.com, pg 933

VWR International LLC, Radnor Corporate Ctr, Bldg 1, 100 Matsonford Rd, Suite 200, Radnor, PA 19087-8660 *Tel:* 610-431-1700 (corp off) *Toll Free Tel:* 800-932-5000 (cust serv) *Web Site:* www.vwr.com; us.vwr.com, pg 933

WAC Lighting Co, 44 Harbor Park Dr, Port Washington, NY 11050 *Tel:* 516-515-5000 *Toll Free Tel:* 800-526-2588 *Fax:* 516-515-5050 *Toll Free Fax:* 800-526-2585 *E-mail:* sales@waclighting.com *Web Site:* www.waclighting.com, pg 933

Wacom Technology Corp, 1458 NW Irving St, Portland, OR 97209 *Toll Free Tel:* 855-MY-WACOM (699-2266) *Web Site:* www.wacom.com, pg 933

Waldom Electronics Corp, 1801 Morgan St, Rockford, IL 61102-2690 *Tel:* 815-968-9661 *Toll Free Tel:* 800-435-2931 (cust serv) *Fax:* 815-968-9029 *E-mail:* sales@waldom.com *Web Site:* www.waldom.com, pg 933

Wallace Creative LLC, 1705 NW 25 Ave, Portland, OR 97210 *Tel:* 503-224-9660 *E-mail:* info@wallyhood.com *Web Site:* www.wallyhood.com, pg 933

Wallace Film Studios, 258 Wallace Ave, Toronto, ON M6P 3N9, Canada *Tel:* 416-538-3535 *E-mail:* info@wallacefilmstudios.ca *Web Site:* wallacefilmstudios.ca, pg 933

Walltalkers, 3875 Embassy Pkwy, Fairlawn, OH 44333 *Tel:* 330-668-7600 *Fax:* 330-668-7703 *E-mail:* customerservice@koroseal.com *Web Site:* www.walltalkers.com, pg 933

Walters-Storyk Design Group Inc (WSDG), 262 Martin Ave, Highland, NY 12528 *Tel:* 845-691-9300 *Fax:* 845-691-9361 *E-mail:* info@wsdg.com *Web Site:* www.wsdg.com, pg 933

Walterscheid Productions, PO Box 995, Wichita, KS 67201 *Tel:* 316-258-1152 *E-mail:* bobwalter1@aol.com *Web Site:* www.wponline.com, pg 933

Wanted! Sound + Picture, 409 King St W, Suite 300, Toronto, ON M5V 1K1, Canada *Tel:* 416-596-1101 *Fax:* 416-596-0690 *E-mail:* info@wantedsp.com; bookings@wantedsp.com *Web Site:* www.wantedsp.com, pg 933

Ward-Beck Systems Ltd, 945 Middlefield Rd, Unit 9, Toronto, ON M1V 5E1, Canada *Tel:* 416-335-5999 *Toll Free Tel:* 800-771-2556 *Fax:* 416-335-5202 *E-mail:* sales@ward-beck.com *Web Site:* www.ward-beck.com, pg 933

Warner Bros Animation, 4000 Warner Blvd, Burbank, CA 91522 *Tel:* 818-954-6000 *Web Site:* www.warnerbros.com, pg 934

Warner Bros Entertainment Inc, 4000 Warner Blvd, Burbank, CA 91522 *E-mail:* wbsf@warnerbros.com *Web Site:* www.warnerbros.com/studio; studiofacilities.warnerbros.com, pg 934

Warner Bros Production Sound & Video Services, 4000 Warner Blvd, Burbank, CA 91522 *Tel:* 818-954-2511; 818-954-2310 (rentals) *Fax:* 818-954-2901 *E-mail:* wbsf@warnerbros.com; wbsfproductionsound@warnerbros.com *Web Site:* www.wbsf.com; www.wbsoundandvideo.com, pg 934

Warner Chappell Production Music, 1030 16 Ave S, Nashville, TN 37212 *Toll Free Tel:* 888-615-8729 *Fax:* 615-242-2455 *E-mail:* info@warnerchappellpm.com *Web Site:* www.warnerchappellpm.com, pg 934

Warner Home Video Inc, 4000 Warner Blvd, Bldg 160, Burbank, CA 91522 *Tel:* 818-954-6000 *Fax:* 818-954-6480 *Web Site:* www.warnerbros.com, pg 934

The Samuel L Warner Memorial Medal Award, White Plains Plaza, 445 Hamilton Ave, Suite 601, White Plains, NY 10601-1827 *Tel:* 914-761-1100 *Fax:* 914-206-4216 *E-mail:* marketing@smpte.org *Web Site:* www.smpte.org, pg 1006

WARPed Pictures, 2447 Benedict Canyon Dr, Beverly Hills, CA 90210 *Tel:* 310-777-8828; 310-999-1219 (cell) *Fax:* 310-777-8805 *E-mail:* info@warpedpictures.com *Web Site:* www.warpedpictures.com, pg 934

Washington DC International Film Festival, PO Box 21396, Washington, DC 20009-0896 *Tel:* 202-274-5782 *Fax:* 202-274-6690 *E-mail:* filmfestdc@filmfestdc.org *Web Site:* www.filmfestdc.org, pg 1006

Washington Filmworks, 1411 Fourth Ave, Suite 420, Seattle, WA 98101 *Tel:* 206-264-0667 *Fax:* 206-382-4343 *E-mail:* info@washingtonfilmworks.org *Web Site:* washingtonfilmworks.org, pg 977

Washington State University College of Nursing, 103 E Spokane Falls Blvd, Spokane, WA 99202 *Tel:* 509-324-7360 *Toll Free Tel:* 800-281-2589 *Fax:* 509-324-7341 *Web Site:* nursing.wsu.edu, pg 934

Waterfront Film Festival (WFF), 479 Columbia Ave, Holland, MI 49423 *Tel:* 269-767-8765 *E-mail:* info@waterfrontfilm.org *Web Site:* www.waterfrontfilm.org, pg 1006

Waterworks Acoustics Design Inc, 6465 Sierra Lane, Dublin, CA 94568, pg 934

WATL-TV Inc, One Monroe Place NE, Atlanta, GA 30324 *Tel:* 404-881-3600 *Web Site:* www.myatltv.com, pg 934

Watson Desking, 26246 Twelve Trees Lane NW, Poulsbo, WA 98370 *Tel:* 360-394-1300 *Fax:* 360-394-1322 *E-mail:* marketing@watsondesking.com *Web Site:* www.watsonfurniture.com, pg 934

Watts Communications Inc, 149 N 120 St, Wauwatosa, WI 53226 *Tel:* 414-727-9505 *Fax:* 414-727-9506 *E-mail:* sales@wattscom.com *Web Site:* www.wattscom.com, pg 934

WaveGuide Studios, 2062 Weems Rd, Tucker, GA 30084 *Tel:* 770-939-2004 *Toll Free Tel:* 800-578-2004 *E-mail:* info@waveguidestudios.com *Web Site:* www.waveguidestudios.com, pg 934

Wavemaker Media Design, PO Box 226, Duncans Mills, CA 95430 *Tel:* 707-788-6040 *Fax:* 707-788-6040 *E-mail:* sales@wavemakermediadesign.com *Web Site:* www.wavemakermediadesign.com, pg 934

WaxWorks VideoWorks, 325 E Third St, Owensboro, KY 42303 *Tel:* 270-926-0008 *Toll Free Tel:* 800-825-8558 *Fax:* 270-663-0737 *Web Site:* www.waxworksonline.com, pg 934

Wayne State University Media Services, Purdy/Kresge Library, 5244 Gullen Mall, Detroit, MI 48202 *Tel:* 313-577-1980 *Fax:* 313-577-6777 *E-mail:* mediaservices@wayne.edu *Web Site:* library.wayne.edu, pg 934

WCJB TV20, 6220 NW 43 St, Gainesville, FL 32653 *Tel:* 352-416-0623 *Fax:* 352-373-6516 *E-mail:* comments@wcbj.com *Web Site:* wcjb.com, pg 934

The Weather Company, An IBM Business, 400 Minuteman Rd, Andover, MA 01810 *Tel:* 978-983-6300 *Fax:* 978-983-6400 *Web Site:* business.weather.com, pg 935

Webb Audio Visual, 3020 S West Temple, Salt Lake City, UT 84115 *Tel:* 801-484-8567 (installation) *Toll Free Tel:* 877-909-8567 *Fax:* 801-484-8589 *E-mail:* info@wearewebb.com *Web Site:* www.wearewebb.com, pg 935

Webster Communications, 6323 Repton St, Los Angeles, CA 90042 *Tel:* 323-258-6741 *E-mail:* info@vanwebster.com *Web Site:* vanwebster.com, pg 935

WEEK TV, 2907 Springfield Rd, East Peoria, IL 61611 *Tel:* 309-698-2525 *Web Site:* www.week.com, pg 935

Wegener Communications Inc, Technology Park, 11350 Technology Circle, Johns Creek, GA 30097 *Tel:* 770-814-4000; 770-814-4036 (sales); 770-814-4057 (cust serv) *Fax:* 770-623-0698 *E-mail:* info@wegener.com *Web Site:* www.wegener.com, pg 935

Weigl Publishers Inc, 350 Fifth Ave, 59th fl, New York, NY 10118 *Toll Free Tel:* 866-649-3445 *Toll Free Fax:* 866-449-3445 *Web Site:* www.weigl.com, pg 935

Alan Weiss Productions, 1243 California Rd, Suite 2R, East Chester, NY 10709 *Tel:* 212-974-0606 *E-mail:* awpinfo@awptv.com *Web Site:* www.awptv.com, pg 935

Welk Music Group, 11400 W Olympic Blvd, Suite 760, Los Angeles, CA 90064 *Tel:* 310-829-9355 *Fax:* 310-264-9875, pg 935

The Well-Tempered Music Library, PO Box 465, Middleboro, MA 02346-0465 *Tel:* 508-947-7387 *Fax:* 508-947-7387 *E-mail:* info@arfarfrecords.com; page@arfarfrecords.com *Web Site:* www.arfarfrecords.com; www.arfarfrecords.com/wtml/home.html, pg 935

Orson Welles Award, 6 Beach Rd, 544, Tiburon, CA 94920 *Tel:* 415-251-8433 *Fax:* 253-663-1250 *E-mail:* info@tiburonfilmfestival.com *Web Site:* www.tiburonfilmfestival.com, pg 1006

Wells-Gardner Technologies Inc, 3078 E Sunset Rd, Suite 1, Las Vegas, NV 89120 *Tel:* 702-330-0330 *Toll Free Tel:* 800-336-6630 *Web Site:* www.wellsgardner.com, pg 935

Welocalize, 241 E Fourth St, Suite 207, Frederick, MD 21701 *Tel:* 301-668-0330 *Toll Free Tel:* 800-370-9515 *Fax:* 301-668-0335 *E-mail:* info@welocalize.com *Web Site:* www.welocalize.com, pg 935

WEP LLC, 50 Maryland Plaza, Suite 300, St Louis, MO 63108 *Tel:* 314-345-1000 *E-mail:* wep@wep.com *Web Site:* www.wep.com, pg 935

Wespen Audio Visual Co, 101 Riverside Dr, Hawthorn, PA 16230, pg 935

West Coast Projections Inc, 12463 Rancho Bernardo Rd, No 149, San Diego, CA 92128-2143 *Tel:* 858-674-7334 *E-mail:* wcpinfo@westcoastprojections.com *Web Site:* westcoastprojections.com, pg 935

West Eagle Films Inc, 800 Lower Ganges Rd, Salt Spring Island, BC V8K 2N5, Canada *Tel:* 250-538-1780 *Web Site:* www.westeaglefilms.com, pg 935

West Penn Wire, 2833 W Chestnut St, Washington, PA 15301 *Tel:* 724-222-7060 *Toll Free Tel:* 800-245-4964 *Fax:* 724-222-6420 *E-mail:* info@westpennwire.com; sales@westpennwire.com *Web Site:* www.westpenn-wpw.com, pg 935

West Virginia Film Office, 90 MacCorkle Ave SW, South Charleston, WV 25303 *Toll Free Tel:* 866-6WV-FILM (698-3456) *Fax:* 304-558-1662 *E-mail:* wvfilm@wv.gov *Web Site:* wvfilm.com, pg 977

Westar Music, 105 W Beaver Creek Rd, Suite 4, Richmond Hill, ON L4B 1C6, Canada *Tel:* 905-886-3100 *Toll Free Tel:* 866-463-0100 *Fax:* 905-886-6800 *E-mail:* info@westarmusic.com *Web Site:* www.westarmusic.com, pg 936

Westbury National Show Systems Ltd, 772 Warden Ave, Toronto, ON M1L 4T7, Canada *Tel:* 416-752-1371 *Toll Free Tel:* 855-752-1372 *Fax:* 416-752-1382 *E-mail:* info@westbury.com *Web Site:* www.westbury.com, pg 936

Westcoast Video Productions Inc, 14141 Covello St, Suite 9-A, Van Nuys, CA 91405 *Tel:* 818-785-8033 *Web Site:* www.wvpinc.com, pg 936

Western Connecticut Convention & Visitors Bureau, PO Box 968, Litchfield, CT 06759-0968 *Tel:* 860-567-4506 *Toll Free Tel:* 800-663-1273 *Fax:* 860-567-5214 *E-mail:* info@litchfieldhills.com *Web Site:* www.visitwesternct.com; www.litchfieldhills.com; www.visitfairfieldcountyct.com, pg 968

Western Digital Corp, 5601 Great Oaks Pkwy, San Jose, CA 95119 *Tel:* 408-717-6000 *Toll Free Tel:* 800-275-4932 (tech support) *Web Site:* www.wdc.com, pg 936

Western Heritage Awards, 1700 NE 63 St, Oklahoma City, OK 73111 *Tel:* 405-478-2250 *Web Site:* nationalcowboymuseum.org, pg 1007

Westlake Recording Studios, 7265 Santa Monica Blvd, Los Angeles, CA 90046 *Tel:* 323-851-9800 *E-mail:* bookings@westlakestudios.com; info@westlakestudios.com *Web Site:* www.westlakestudios.com, pg 936

Weston Woods Canada, 60 Briarwood Ave, Mississauga, ON L5G 3N6, Canada *Tel:* 905-278-0566 *Toll Free Tel:* 866-722-1522 *Toll Free Fax:* 866-722-1822 *E-mail:* info@mcnabbconnolly.ca *Web Site:* www.mcnabbconnolly.ca, pg 936

Weston Woods Studios Inc, 90 Old Sherman Tpke, Danbury, CT 06816 *Tel:* 203-797-3520 *Toll Free Tel:* 800-243-5020 *Fax:* 203-797-3541 *E-mail:* westonwoodsquestions@scholastic.com *Web Site:* www.scholastic.com/westonwoods, pg 936

Westworks Studios, 4100 E Dry Creek Rd, Littleton, CO 80122 *Toll Free Tel:* 800-491-1947 *E-mail:* info@westworksstudios.com *Web Site:* westworksstudios.com, pg 936

WETA Production Center, 3620 S 27 St, Arlington, VA 22206 *Tel:* 703-998-2054 *Web Site:* www.weta.org/tv, pg 936

David Wexler & Co, 7807 E Greenway Rd, Suite 8, Scottsdale, AZ 85260-1717 *Tel:* 480-675-8888 *Fax:* 480-675-8900 *E-mail:* wexlermusic@aol.com *Web Site:* www.wexlermusic.com, pg 936

WFRV-TV 5 CBS, 1181 E Mason St, Green Bay, WI 54301 *Tel:* 920-437-5411 *Fax:* 920-437-4576 *E-mail:* tips@wearegreenbay.com *Web Site:* www.wearegreenbay.com, pg 936

WGBH Production Group, One Guest St, Boston, MA 02135 *Tel:* 617-300-2000 *E-mail:* productiongroup@wgbh.org; studios@wgbh.org; outpost@wgbh.org *Web Site:* productiongroup.wgbh.org, pg 936

WGBH Stock Sales, One Guest St, Boston, MA 02135 *Tel:* 617-300-3939 *Fax:* 617-300-1056 *E-mail:* stock_sales@wgbh.org *Web Site:* www.wgbhstocksales.org, pg 936

WGME-TV, 81 Northport Dr, Portland, ME 04103 *Tel:* 207-797-1313 *Fax:* 207-878-7482 *E-mail:* tvmail@wgme.com *Web Site:* wgme.com, pg 936

WGVU TV, 301 Fulton St W, Grand Rapids, MI 49504-6492 *Tel:* 616-331-6666 *Toll Free Tel:* 800-442-2771 *Web Site:* www.wgvu.org, pg 936

The Whale Video Co, 225 Indian Creek Dr, Mechanicsburg, PA 17050 *Tel:* 717-763-9507 *Web Site:* www.whalevideo.com, pg 936

Whalley-Abbey Media Holdings Inc, 3800 Rue St Patrick, Suite 100, Montreal, QC H4E 1A4, Canada *Tel:* 514-846-1940 *E-mail:* info@wamgrp.com *Web Site:* wamgrp.com, pg 937

Wheatstone Corp, 600 Industrial Dr, New Bern, NC 28562 *Tel:* 252-638-7000 *Fax:* 252-635-1285 *E-mail:* sales@wheatstone.com *Web Site:* www.wheatstone.com, pg 937

Whirlwind Music Distributors Inc, 99 Ling Rd, Greece, NY 14612 *Tel:* 585-663-8820 *Toll Free Tel:* 800-733-9473 (US only) *Fax:* 585-865-8930 *E-mail:* sales@whirlwindusa.com; techsupport@whirlwindusa.com; darylg@whirlwindusa.com (CN inquiries) *Web Site:* whirlwindusa.com, pg 937

WhisperRoom™ Inc, 109 S Northshore Dr, Suite 303, Knoxville, TN 37919 *Tel:* 865-558-5364 *Toll Free Tel:* 800-200-8168 *Fax:* 865-558-5370 *E-mail:* info@whisperroom.com *Web Site:* www.whisperroom.com, pg 937

White Diamond Productions LLC, 605 Hwy 62 65 N, No 359, Harrison, AR 72601, pg 937

White Dog Studios, 1986 Mercer Rd, Smyrna, GA 30080 *Tel:* 404-355-2200 *Web Site:* www.whitedogstudios.net, pg 937

White Rain Films Ltd, 2009 Dexter Ave N, Seattle, WA 98109 *Tel:* 206-682-5417 *Fax:* 206-682-3038 *E-mail:* info@whiterainfilms.com *Web Site:* www.whiterainfilms.com, pg 937

White Swan Music Inc, 6395 Gunpark Dr, Suite A, Boulder, CO 80301 *Tel:* 303-527-0770 *Toll Free Tel:* 800-825-8656 *Fax:* 303-527-0771 *E-mail:* info@whiteswanmusic.com *Web Site:* whiteswanmusic.com, pg 937

William F White International Inc, 800 Islington Ave, Toronto, ON M8Z 6A1, Canada *Tel:* 416-239-5050 *Toll Free Tel:* 800-465-0160 (CN only) *Web Site:* www.whites.com, pg 937

The Whitlock Group, 12820 West Creek Pkwy, Richmond, VA 23238 *Tel:* 804-273-9100 *Toll Free Tel:* 800-726-9843 *Fax:* 804-273-9380 *E-mail:* information@whitlock.com; marketing@whitlock.com *Web Site:* www.whitlock.com, pg 937

Whole Person Associates Inc, 101 W Second St, Suite 203, Duluth, MN 55802-5004 *Tel:* 218-727-0500 *Toll Free Tel:* 800-247-6789 *Fax:* 218-727-0505 *E-mail:* books@wholeperson.com *Web Site:* www.wholeperson.com, pg 938

WHYY Inc, Independence Mall West, 150 N Sixth St, Philadelphia, PA 19106 *Tel:* 215-351-1200 *Fax:* 215-351-0398 *E-mail:* talkback@whyy.org *Web Site:* www.whyy.org, pg 938

WIA - The Wireless Infrastructure Association, 2111 Wilson Blvd, Suite 210, Arlington, VA 22201 *Tel:* 703-739-0300 *Toll Free Tel:* 800-759-0300 *Fax:* 703-836-1608 *Web Site:* wia.org, pg 963

Wickenburg Film Commission, 216 N Frontier St, Wickenburg, AZ 85390 *Tel:* 928-684-5479; 928-684-0977 *Toll Free Tel:* 800-942-5242 *Fax:* 928-684-5470 *E-mail:* info@wickenburgchamber.com *Web Site:* www.wickenburgchamber.com/film-commission, pg 965

Wide Eye Productions, 1018 W Hays St, Boise, ID 83702 *Tel:* 208-336-0391 *Fax:* 208-336-6644 *E-mail:* info@wideeye.tv *Web Site:* wideeye.tv, pg 938

WIFR-TV, 2523 N Meridian Rd, Rockford, IL 61101 *Tel:* 815-987-5300 *Fax:* 815-965-0981 *E-mail:* talkto23@wifr.com *Web Site:* www.wifr.com, pg 938

Wild Plum, 23371 Mulholland Dr, Suite 409, Woodland Hills, CA 91364 *Tel:* 310-823-7445 *Web Site:* www.wildplum.tv, pg 938

Wild Visions Inc, PO Box 42194, Phoenix, AZ 85080 *Tel:* 623-512-9810 *Web Site:* www.wildvisions.net, pg 938

WildBrain™, 5657 Spring Garden Rd, Suite 505, Halifax, NS B3J 3R4, Canada *Tel:* 902-423-0260 *Fax:* 902-422-0752 *E-mail:* info@wildbrain.com; halifax@wildbrain.com; sales@wildbrain.com *Web Site:* www.wildbrain.com, pg 938

Wilderness Video, 1110 Barrington Circle, Ashland, OR 97520 *Tel:* 541-488-9363 *Web Site:* www.wildernessvideo.com, pg 938

Wildfire Lighting & Visual Effects, 2908 Oregon Ct, Suite G-1, Torrance, CA 90503 *Tel:* 310-755-6780 *Toll Free Tel:* 800-937-8065 *Fax:* 310-755-6781 *E-mail:* sales@wildfirelighting.com *Web Site:* www.wildfirefx.com, pg 938

John Wiley & Sons Inc, 111 River St, Hoboken, NJ 07030-5774 *Tel:* 201-748-6000 *Toll Free Tel:* 800-225-5945 (cust serv) *Fax:* 201-748-6088 *Web Site:* www.wiley.com, pg 938

The Will-Burt Co, 169 S Main St, Orrville, OH 44667 *Tel:* 330-682-7015; 330-684-4000 (cust serv) *E-mail:* contact_us@willburt.com *Web Site:* www.willburt.com, pg 938

Williams AV LLC, 10300 Valley View Rd, Eden Prairie, MN 55344-3446 *Tel:* 952-943-2252 *Toll Free Tel:* 800-328-6190 *Fax:* 952-943-2174 *E-mail:* info@williamsav.com *Web Site:* www.williamsav.com, pg 939

WILLiFEST, PO Box 20412, New York, NY 10021-0066 *E-mail:* inquiries@willifest.com; programming@willifest.com; screenplays@willifest.com *Web Site:* www.willifest.com, pg 1007

Willoughby's® Camera, 298 Fifth Ave, New York, NY 10001 *Tel:* 212-564-1600 *Toll Free Tel:* 800-378-1898 *E-mail:* customersupport@willoughbys.com *Web Site:* www.willoughbys.com, pg 939

Willow Mixed Media Inc, 25 Lennox Ave, Glenford, NY 12433 *Tel:* 845-657-2914 *E-mail:* video@hvc.rr.com *Web Site:* www.willowmixedmedia.org; www.documentaryworld.com, pg 939

Wilmington Regional Film Commission Inc, 1223 N 23 St, Wilmington, NC 28405 *Tel:* 910-343-3456 *Fax:* 910-343-3457 *E-mail:* commish@wilmingtonfilm.com *Web Site:* www.wilmingtonfilm.com, pg 974

Wilson Case Inc, 113 Road 3168, Hastings, NE 68901-9418 *Tel:* 402-463-5040 *Toll Free Tel:* 800-322-5493 *Fax:* 402-463-5276 *E-mail:* sales@wilsoncase.com *Web Site:* www.wilsoncase.com, pg 939

Wilson McLeran Inc, 41 Corey Hill Rd, Saxtons River, VT 05154 *Tel:* 802-869-3111 *Toll Free Tel:* 800-562-9646 *Fax:* 802-869-3111 *Web Site:* www.robertfwilson.net, pg 939

Wiltronix Inc, 5504 Waterway Terr, Rockville, MD 20853, pg 939

Win Media Inc, 317 N Dodge St, Burlington, WI 53105 *Tel:* 262-763-6397 *E-mail:* info@winmediainc.com *Web Site:* www.winmediainc.com, pg 939

Winchester Electronics Corp, 68 Water St, Norwalk, CT 06854 *Tel:* 203-741-5400 *E-mail:* info@winchesterelectronics.com *Web Site:* www.winchesterelectronics.com, pg 939

Wind River Broadcast Center, 117 E 11 St, Loveland, CO 80537 *Tel:* 970-669-3442 *Web Site:* www.windriverbroadcast.com, pg 939

Windel International/Weyel, 3714 Illinois Ave, St Charles, IL 60174-2421 *Toll Free Tel:* 800-395-7093 *Fax:* 630-587-2833 *Web Site:* www.windel.com, pg 939

WindTech™ Microphone Windscreens & Accessories, 7845 E Evans Rd, Scottsdale, AZ 85260-2919 *Tel:* 480-998-7140 *E-mail:* information@olsenaudio.com; web-info3@olsenaudio.com *Web Site:* www.olsenaudio.com; www.windtech.tv, pg 939

The Wine Appreciation Guild Ltd, 450 Taraval St, No 201, San Francisco, CA 94116 *Tel:* 650-866-3020 *Toll Free Tel:* 800-231-9463 *Fax:* 650-866-3513 *E-mail:* info@wineappreciation.com *Web Site:* www.wineappreciation.com, pg 939

Winegard Co, 2736 Mount Pleasant St, Suite 140, Burlington, IA 52601 *Tel:* 319-754-0600 *Toll Free Tel:* 800-288-8094 *E-mail:* chat@winegard.com *Web Site:* www.winegard.com, pg 939

Babe Winkelman Productions Inc, PO Box 407, Brainerd, MN 56401 *Tel:* 218-821-6866 *Toll Free Tel:* 800-333-0471 *Web Site:* www.winkelman.com, pg 939

Winsted Corp, 10901 Hampshire Ave S, Minneapolis, MN 55438 *Tel:* 952-944-9050 *Toll Free Tel:* 800-447-2257 *Fax:* 952-944-1546 *Toll Free Fax:* 800-421-3839 *E-mail:* info@winsted.com *Web Site:* www.winsted.com, pg 939

Winter Film Awards Indie Film Festival, 31 W 34 St, New York, NY 10001 *Tel:* 646-355-4371 *E-mail:* info@winterfilmawards.com; submissions@ winterfilmawards.com *Web Site:* winterfilmawards. com, pg 1007

Winter Productions, 10625 S Hoyne, Chicago, IL 60643 *Tel:* 773-238-1656 *E-mail:* winterpr@aol.com *Web Site:* www.winterproductions.com, pg 939

Wintergreen Learning Materials, 3075 Line 8, RR2, Bradford, ON L3Z 3R5, Canada *Tel:* 905-778-8584 *Toll Free Tel:* 800-268-1268 *Toll Free Fax:* 800-567-8054 *E-mail:* info@wintergreen.ca; sales@wintergreen.ca; custserv@wintergreen.ca *Web Site:* www.wintergreen.ca, pg 939

Winterland Studios, 5417 Boone Ave N, New Hope, MN 55428 *Tel:* 763-971-8943 *Fax:* 763-971-8952 *E-mail:* studio@winterlandstudios.com *Web Site:* www.winterlandstudios.com, pg 940

Wire X 17 LLC, 1840 County Line Rd, Suite 301, Huntingdon Valley, PA 19006 *Tel:* 215-322-4600 *Toll Free Tel:* 800-233-0013 *Fax:* 215-322-1385 *E-mail:* sales@wirexgroup.com *Web Site:* wirex17. com, pg 940

Wired 4 Sound Inc, PO Box 683, Clifton, NJ 07012-0683 *Tel:* 973-773-2565 *E-mail:* info@wired4sound. com *Web Site:* www.wired4sound.com, pg 940

Wireworks Corp, 380 Hillside Ave, Hillside, NJ 07205 *Tel:* 908-686-7400 *Toll Free Tel:* 800-642-9473 *Fax:* 908-686-0483 (sales); 908-686-0680 *E-mail:* sales@wireworks.com; info@wireworks.com *Web Site:* www.wireworks.com, pg 940

Wisconsin Public Television, 821 University Ave, Madison, WI 53706 *Tel:* 608-263-2121 *Toll Free Tel:* 800-422-9707 *Fax:* 608-263-9763 *E-mail:* comments@wpt.org *Web Site:* www.wpt.org, pg 940

Wisconsin Technical College System Foundation Inc, 6602 Normandy Lane, Madison, WI 53719-1081 *Tel:* 608-841-1800 *Toll Free Tel:* 800-821-6313 *Fax:* 608-841-1806 *E-mail:* foundation@wtcsf.tec.wi. us *Web Site:* www.wtcsf.tec.wi.us, pg 940

Wise Audio Video, PO Box 105523, Jefferson City, MO 65110 *Tel:* 573-761-7888 *Toll Free Tel:* 877-775-7888 *Web Site:* www.wiseaudiovideo.com, pg 940

WKMG-TV News 6, 4466 N John Young Pkwy, Orlando, FL 32804 *Tel:* 407-521-1200 *Fax:* 407-521-1204 *Web Site:* www.clickorlando.com, pg 940

WKYT-TV, 2851 Winchester Rd, Lexington, KY 40509 *Tel:* 859-299-0411; 859-299-2727 (newsroom) *Web Site:* www.wkyt.com, pg 940

WMAR-TV, 6400 York Rd, Baltimore, MD 21212 *Tel:* 410-377-2222 *E-mail:* newsroom@wmar.com *Web Site:* www.abc2news.com, pg 940

WMS Media Inc, 189 W Santa Clara St, San Jose, CA 95110 *Tel:* 510-825-7402 *E-mail:* info@wmsmedia. com *Web Site:* www.wmsmedia.com, pg 940

WNET/New York Public Media, 825 Eighth Ave, New York, NY 10019 *Tel:* 212-560-1313 *Fax:* 212-560-1314 *E-mail:* programming@thirteen.org *Web Site:* www.thirteen.org; www.wnet.org, pg 940

Wohler Technologies Inc, 31055 Huntwood Ave, Hayward, CA 94544 *Tel:* 510-870-0810 *Toll Free Tel:* 888-5-WOHLER (596-4537) *E-mail:* sales@ wohler.com *Web Site:* www.wohler.com, pg 940

WolfVision Inc, 2055 Sugarloaf Circle, Suite 125, Duluth, GA 30097 *Tel:* 770-931-6802 *Toll Free Tel:* 877-873-WOLF (873-9653) *Fax:* 770-931-6906 *E-mail:* sales@wolfvision.us; support@wolfvision. us; orders@wolfvision.us *Web Site:* wolfvision.com, pg 940

Women In Film, 4221 Wilshire Blvd, Suite 130, Los Angeles, CA 90010 *Tel:* 323-935-2211 *E-mail:* info@ wif.org *Web Site:* womeninfilm.org, pg 963

Women in Film & Television-Florida (WIFT-FL), PO Box 533541, Orlando, FL 32853-3541 *E-mail:* info@ womeninfilmfl.org *Web Site:* womeninfilmfl.org, pg 963

Women in Film Finishing Fund, 6100 Wilshire Blvd, Suite 710, Los Angeles, CA 90048 *Tel:* 323-935-2211 *Fax:* 323-935-2212 *E-mail:* info@wif.org *Web Site:* www.wif.org, pg 1007

Women Make Movies Inc, 115 W 29 St, Suite 1200, New York, NY 10001 *Tel:* 212-925-0606 *Fax:* 212-925-2052 *E-mail:* info@wmm.com *Web Site:* www. wmm.com, pg 941

Wonderwomen™ Enterprises, 485 Rugby Rd, Brooklyn, NY 11226 *Tel:* 646-456-3266; 718-693-4322 *E-mail:* info@wonderwomen.com, pg 941

WoodenBoat Publications, 41 WoodenBoat Lane, Brooklin, ME 04616 *Tel:* 207-359-4651 *Toll Free Tel:* 800-877-5284 (subns) *Fax:* 207-359-8920 *E-mail:* woodenboat@woodenboat.com *Web Site:* www.woodenboat.com, pg 941

Woodside Avenue Music Productions Inc, 2906 Central St, No 117, Evanston, IL 60201 *Tel:* 847-864-6655 *E-mail:* music@woodsideavenue.com *Web Site:* www. woodsideavenue.com, pg 941

Mark Woollen & Associates, 207 Ashland Ave, Santa Monica, CA 90405 *Tel:* 310-399-2690 *E-mail:* info@ markwoollen.com *Web Site:* www.markwoollen.com, pg 941

Word Label Group, 25 Music Sq W, Nashville, TN 37203 *Tel:* 615-251-0600 *E-mail:* wordtech@wbr. com *Web Site:* www.wordlabelgroup.com; www. wordentertainment.com, pg 941

World Beat Studio, 137 Sequoia Rd, Rockwall, TX 75032 *Tel:* 972-771-3797 *Fax:* 972-771-0853 *E-mail:* tropikalproductions@gmail.com *Web Site:* www.tropikalproductions.com; www. tropikalproductions.com/studio.html, pg 941

World Class Learning Materials Inc, PO Box 639, Candler, NC 28715 *Toll Free Tel:* 800-638-6470 *Toll Free Fax:* 800-638-6499 *E-mail:* info@wclm.com *Web Site:* www.wclm.com, pg 941

World Film Festival/Festival des Films du Monde/ Montreal, 1432 de Bleury St, Montreal, QC H3A 2J1, Canada *Tel:* 514-848-3883 *Fax:* 514-848-3886 *E-mail:* program@ffm-montreal.org *Web Site:* www. ffm-montreal.org, pg 1007

World Media Group Inc, 7373 Dogwood Park, Richland Hills, TX 76118 *Toll Free Tel:* 800-400-4964 *Fax:* 817-885-8859 *E-mail:* getstarted@ worldmediagroup.com; information@ worldmediagroup.com *Web Site:* www. worldmediagroup.com, pg 941

World Wide Pictures Inc, One Billy Graham Pkwy, Charlotte, NC 28266-8029 *Tel:* 704-401-2432 *Toll Free Tel:* 877-247-2426 *Fax:* 704-401-3045 *Web Site:* www.wwp.org; www.billgraham.org/wwp, pg 941

WorldFest-Houston International Film Festival, 9898 Bissonnet St, Suite 650, Houston, TX 77036 *Tel:* 713-965-9955 *Fax:* 713-965-9960 *E-mail:* mail@worldfest. org; entry@worldfest.org *Web Site:* www.worldfest. org, pg 1007

WorldStage, 259 W 30 St, 12th fl, New York, NY 10001-2863 *Tel:* 212-582-2345 *Fax:* 718-610-1750 *E-mail:* info@worldstage.com *Web Site:* www. worldstage.com, pg 941

Worldview Entertainment Holdings Inc, 1384 Broadway, 25th fl, New York, NY 10018 *Tel:* 212-431-3090 *E-mail:* info@worldviewent.com *Web Site:* www. worldviewent.com, pg 941

WorldView Software, 11 Barby Lane, Plainview, NY 11803 *Tel:* 516-681-1773 *E-mail:* history@ worldviewsoftware.com *Web Site:* www. worldviewsoftware.com, pg 941

Worldwide Entertainment Corp, 135 S McCarty Dr, Suite 101, Beverly Hills, CA 90212 *Tel:* 310-858-1272 *Fax:* 310-858-3774, pg 941

Worthwhile Films, 317 Winona St, Northfield, MN 55057 *Tel:* 507-645-6868 *Toll Free Tel:* 877-507-5077 *Web Site:* worthwhilefilms.org, pg 941

WOUB Public Media, 35 S College St, Athens, OH 45701 *Tel:* 740-593-1771 *Toll Free Tel:* 800-456-2044 *E-mail:* woub@woub.org *Web Site:* woub.org, pg 942

WPA Film Library, 16101 S 108 Ave, Orland Park, IL 60467 *Tel:* 708-460-0555 *Toll Free Tel:* 800-323-0442 *Fax:* 708-460-0187 *E-mail:* sales@wpafilmlibrary.com *Web Site:* www.wpafilmlibrary.com, pg 942

WPGH-TV, 750 Ivory Ave, Pittsburgh, PA 15214 *Tel:* 412-931-5300; 412-931-8020 (sales) *Fax:* 412-931-4284 *Web Site:* www.sbgi.net; www.wpgh53.com, pg 942

WPHL-TV, 5001 Wynnefield Ave, Philadelphia, PA 19131 *Tel:* 215-878-1700 *E-mail:* feedback@phl17. com *Web Site:* www.phl17.com, pg 942

WQED-Multimedia, 4802 Fifth Ave, Pittsburgh, PA 15213 *Tel:* 412-622-1300; 412-622-1370 *Web Site:* www.wqed.org, pg 942

Writer's AudioShop/Davenport Productions, 1316 Overland Stage Rd, Dripping Springs, TX 78620 *Tel:* 512-476-1616 (edit); 512-264-7067 (sales) *E-mail:* wrtaudshop@aol.com *Web Site:* www. writersaudio.com, pg 942

Writers Guild of America, West (WGAW), 7000 W Third St, Los Angeles, CA 90048 *Tel:* 323-951-4000 *Toll Free Tel:* 800-548-4532 *Web Site:* www.wga.org, pg 963

The Writing Co, 10200 Jefferson Blvd, Culver City, CA 90232 *Tel:* 310-839-2436 *Toll Free Tel:* 800-421-4246 *Fax:* 310-839-2249 *Toll Free Fax:* 800-944-5432 *E-mail:* access@writingco.com; customerservice@ writingco.com *Web Site:* www.socialstudies.com, pg 942

WSAZ-TV NewsChannel 3, 645 Fifth Ave, Huntington, WV 25701 *Tel:* 304-697-4780 *Fax:* 304-690-3065 (newsroom); 304-690-3061 (sales) *E-mail:* news@ wsaz.com *Web Site:* www.wsaz.com, pg 942

WTL Productions, 345 E 52 St, Suite 1, New York, NY 10022 *Tel:* 212-355-1893 *E-mail:* wtlvideo@aol.com, pg 942

WTMJ-TV, 720 E Capitol Dr, Milwaukee, WI 53212 *Tel:* 414-332-9611 *Fax:* 414-967-5378 *E-mail:* tmj4feedback@scripps.com *Web Site:* www. tmj4.com, pg 942

WTSmedia, 2841 Hickory Valley, Chattanooga, TN 37421 *Tel:* 423-894-9427 *Toll Free Tel:* 888-987-6334; 800-251-7228 *Fax:* 423-894-7281 *Toll Free Fax:* 800-591-4809 *E-mail:* sales@wtsmedia.com *Web Site:* www.wtsduplication.com, pg 942

WTVS, Detroit Public Television, Riley Broadcast Ctr, One Clover Ct, Wixom, MI 48393-2247 *Tel:* 248-305-DPTV (305-3788); 313-872-7500 *E-mail:* email@dptv. org *Web Site:* www.dptv.org, pg 942

WVLA-TV, 10,000 Perkins Rd, Baton Rouge, LA 70810 *Tel:* 225-766-3233 *Fax:* 225-768-9293 *Web Site:* www. brproud.com, pg 942

WVP Boston, 50 Hunt St, Watertown, MA 02472 *Tel:* 617-926-2089 *Web Site:* wvpboston.com, pg 942

The Wyland Group, 11291 Pierce St, Riverside, CA 92505 *Tel:* 805-955-7681 *Fax:* 805-522-1082, pg 942

Wyoming Office of Tourism, 5611 High Plains Rd, Cheyenne, WY 82007 *Tel:* 307-777-7777 *Fax:* 307-777-2877 *E-mail:* info@filmwyoming.com *Web Site:* www.travelwyoming.com/film, pg 977

X-Rite, 4300 44 St SE, Grand Rapids, MI 49512 *Tel:* 616-803-2100 *Toll Free Tel:* 800-248-9748; 888-800-9580 *Web Site:* www.xrite.com, pg 942

Xantech LLC, 1800 S McDowell Blvd, Petaluma, CA 94954 *Tel:* 707-283-5900 *Toll Free Tel:* 800-472-5555 *Fax:* 707-283-5901 *E-mail:* info@corebrands.com *Web Site:* www.xantech.com, pg 943

Xenon Pictures Inc, 3521 Jack Northrop Ave, Hawthorne, CA 90250 *Tel:* 310-451-5510 *Fax:* 310-395-4058 *E-mail:* info@xenonpictures.com *Web Site:* xenonpictures.com, pg 943

Xintekvideo Inc, 56 W Broad St, Stamford, CT 06902 *Tel:* 203-348-9229 *Web Site:* www.xintekvideo.com, pg 943

Xplor® International, 24156 State Rd 54, Suite 4, Lutz, FL 33559 *Tel:* 813-949-6170 *E-mail:* info@xplor.org *Web Site:* www.xplor.org, pg 964

XTA Electronics Ltd, 70 Sea Lane, Farmingdale, NY 11735 *Tel:* 631-396-0195 (audio div); 631-396-0184 (lighting div) *Fax:* 631-396-0190 *E-mail:* sales@g1limited.com *Web Site:* www.g1limited.com, pg 943

Xtech Systems Inc, 241 Rock Creek Lane, Scarsdale, NY 10583 *Tel:* 718-543-1222 *Fax:* 914-472-2111 *Toll Free Fax:* 888-528-6511 *E-mail:* info@xtechsystems. com *Web Site:* www.xtechsystems.com, pg 943

Xytech Systems Corp, 15451 San Fernando Mission Blvd, Suite 400, Mission Hills, CA 91345 *Tel:* 818-698-4900 *Fax:* 818-698-4901 *E-mail:* sales@xytechsystems.com *Web Site:* www.xytechsystems. com, pg 943

Yada/Levine Video Productions, 3129 S Hacienda Blvd, No 423, Hacienda Heights, CA 91745 *Tel:* 323-461-1616 *Fax:* 323-461-2288 *E-mail:* video@yadalevine. com *Web Site:* www.yadalevine.com, pg 943

Yale Film & Video, 25601 Avenue Stanford, Valencia, CA 91355 *Tel:* 661-295-7170; 661-295-7160 *E-mail:* info@yalefilmandvideo.com; yalefilmandvideo@gmail.com *Web Site:* www. yalefilmandvideo.com, pg 943

Yamaha Electronics Corp, 6660 Orangethorpe Ave, Buena Park, CA 90620 *Tel:* 714-522-9105 *Toll Free Tel:* 800-292-2982 (cust support) *Web Site:* usa. yamaha.com/products/audio_visual/index.html, pg 943

Yanchar Design & Consulting Group, 26741 Portola Pkwy, Suite 1E, Foothill Ranch, CA 92610-1763 *Tel:* 949-770-6601 *Fax:* 949-770-6575 *E-mail:* info@yanchardesign.com *Web Site:* www.yanchardesign.com, pg 943

YAP Films, 233 Broadview Ave, Toronto, ON M4M 2G3, Canada *Tel:* 416-504-3662 *Fax:* 416-504-3667 *E-mail:* thedog@yapfilms.com *Web Site:* www. yapfilms.com, pg 943

Yarn Barn of Kansas, 930 Massachusetts St, Lawrence, KS 66044 *Tel:* 785-842-4333 *Toll Free Tel:* 800-468-0035 *E-mail:* info@yarnbarn-ks.com *Web Site:* www. yarnbarn-ks.com, pg 943

Yellow Cat Productions Inc, 505 11 St SE, Washington, DC 20003 *Tel:* 202-543-2221 *E-mail:* yellowcat@yellowcat.com *Web Site:* www.yellowcat.com, pg 944

Yellow Moon Press, 29 Josephine Ave, Somerville, MA 02144 *Tel:* 617-776-2230 *Toll Free Tel:* 800-497-4385 *E-mail:* story@yellowmoon.com *Web Site:* www. yellowmoon.com, pg 944

Yellowknife Films Inc, 5021 53 St, Yellowknife, NT X1A 1V5, Canada *Tel:* 867-873-8610 *E-mail:* ykf@theedge.ca *Web Site:* www.ykfilms.ca, pg 944

YES Productions, 916 Navarre Ave, New Orleans, LA 70124 *Tel:* 504-840-4891 *Toll Free Tel:* 800-736-8812 *Fax:* 504-840-4895 *Web Site:* www.yesproductions. com, pg 944

Yessian, 137 Fifth Ave, 3rd fl, New York, NY 10010 *Tel:* 212-533-3443 *E-mail:* info-ny@yessian.com *Web Site:* www.yessian.com, pg 944

The Yesterday USA Radio Networks, 2001 Plymouth Rock Dr, Richardson, TX 75081-3946 *Tel:* 972-889-9872 *Fax:* 972-889-2329 *Web Site:* www.yesterdayusa. com, pg 944

YMAA Publication Center Inc, 51 Mill St, Wolfeboro, NH 03894 *Tel:* 603-569-7988 *Toll Free Tel:* 800-669-8892 *Fax:* 603-569-1889 *E-mail:* info@ymaa.com *Web Site:* www.ymaa.com, pg 944

Yorktel, 81 Corbett Way, Eatontown, NJ 07724 *Tel:* 732-413-6000 *Toll Free Tel:* 866-836-8463 *Fax:* 732-413-6060 *E-mail:* knowmore@yorktel.com *Web Site:* yorktel.com, pg 944

Yorkton Film Festival (YFF), 49 Smith St E, Yorkton, SK S3N 0H4, Canada *Tel:* 306-782-7077 *Fax:* 306-782-1550 *E-mail:* info@yorktonfilm.com *Web Site:* yorktonfilm.com, pg 1007

Yorkville Sound Inc, 550 Granite Ct, Pickering, ON L1W 3Y8, Canada *Tel:* 905-837-8481 *Fax:* 905-839-5776 *E-mail:* canada@yorkville.com; orders@yorkville.com *Web Site:* www.yorkville.com, pg 944

Young Chang America, 6000 Phyllis Dr, Cypress, CA 90630 *Tel:* 657-200-3470 *Fax:* 657-200-3477 *E-mail:* marketing@ycapiano.com (sales & mktg); info@ycapiano.com *Web Site:* www.youngchang.com, pg 944

Yukon Film & Sound Commission (YFSC), Box 2703, Whitehorse, YT Y1A 2C6, Canada *Tel:* 867-667-5400; 867-661-0408 (ext 5400, no charge for calls from within Yukon) *Fax:* 867-393-6228 *E-mail:* info@reelyukon.com *Web Site:* www.reelyukon.com, pg 979

Yuma Film Commission, 180 W First St, Suite D, Yuma, AZ 85364 *Tel:* 928-376-0100 *Fax:* 928-373-0133 *Web Site:* www.filmyuma.com, pg 965

Z-Axis Corp, 4600 S Ulster St, Suite 270, Denver, CO 80237 *Tel:* 303-713-0200 *Toll Free Tel:* 800-827-2947 *E-mail:* info@zaxis.com *Web Site:* www.zaxis.com, pg 944

Z-Systems Audio Engineering, 1325 NW 53 Ave, Suite B, Gainesville, FL 32609 *Tel:* 352-371-0990 *E-mail:* z-sys@z-sys.com *Web Site:* www.z-sys.com, pg 944

Z-Ville Productions, 34710 Lancaster Rd, Gorman, CA 93536 *Tel:* 310-422-9590 *E-mail:* info@zvpro.com *Web Site:* www.z-ville.com, pg 944

Zachry Associates Inc, 500 Chestnut St, Suite 2000, Abilene, TX 79602 *Tel:* 325-677-1342 *E-mail:* info@zachryinc.com *Web Site:* zachryinc.com, pg 944

Zack Electronics Inc, 1075 Hamilton Rd, Duarte, CA 91010 *Tel:* 626-303-0655 *Toll Free Tel:* 800-466-0449 *Fax:* 626-303-8694 *E-mail:* info@zackelectronics.com *Web Site:* www.zackelectronics.com, pg 945

Zacuto, 401 W Ontario Ave, Chicago, IL 60654 *Tel:* 312-863-3453 (rentals); 312-863-3456 *Toll Free Tel:* 888-294-3456 *Fax:* 312-863-3455 *E-mail:* rentals@zacuto.com *Web Site:* www.zacuto. com, pg 945

Zamacona Productions, 2600 Tenth St, Suite 302, Berkeley, CA 94710 *Tel:* 510-704-4011 *Fax:* 510-704-4013 *E-mail:* admin@zamacona-productions.com *Web Site:* www.zamacona-productions.com, pg 945

ZBS Foundation, 174 N River Rd, Fort Edward, NY 12828-9713 *Tel:* 518-695-6406 *Toll Free Tel:* 800-662-3345 *Fax:* 518-695-4041 *E-mail:* custserv@zbs.org *Web Site:* www.zbs.org, pg 945

Zebedee Productions, 231 SW Fifth Ct, Pompano Beach, FL 33060 *Tel:* 954-942-0044 *E-mail:* info@zbd.us *Web Site:* zebedeeproductions.com, pg 945

Zeitgeist Films Ltd, 333 W 39 St, New York, NY 10018 *Tel:* 212-274-1989 *Fax:* 212-714-0871 *E-mail:* mail@zeitgeistfilms.com *Web Site:* www.zeitgeistfilms.com, pg 945

Zelman Studios Ltd, 623 Cortelyou Rd, Brooklyn, NY 11218, pg 945

Zelo Productions Inc, 3 S Newton St, Denver, CO 80220 *Tel:* 303-936-8995; 303-898-0911 (cell) *E-mail:* zelo@zeloproductions.com *Web Site:* www.zeloproductions. com, pg 945

Zenith Electronics LLC, 2000 Millbrook Dr, Lincolnshire, IL 60069 *Tel:* 847-941-8000 *Toll Free Tel:* 800-243-0000 (cust serv) *Web Site:* www.zenith. com, pg 945

ZERO Manufacturing Inc, 500 W 200 N, North Salt Lake, UT 84054 *Tel:* 801-298-5900 *Toll Free Tel:* 800-959-5050 *Fax:* 801-299-7389 *E-mail:* orders@zerocases.com; quote@zerocases.com; sales@zerocases.com *Web Site:* www.zerocases.com, pg 945

ZGC Inc, 264 Morris Ave, Mountain Lakes, NJ 07046 *Tel:* 973-335-4460 *Fax:* 973-335-4560 *E-mail:* sales@zgc.com *Web Site:* www.zgc.com, pg 945

Zion Music Group, 306 Monticello Rd, Franklin, TN 37064 *Tel:* 615-559-2108 *Fax:* 615-591-5102 *Web Site:* www.zionmusic.com, pg 945

Zippertubing® Co, 7150 W Erie St, Chandler, AZ 85226 *Tel:* 480-285-3990 *Toll Free Tel:* 855-289-1874 *Fax:* 480-285-3997 *E-mail:* info@zippertubing. com; sales@zippertubing.com; customer.service@zippertubing.com *Web Site:* www.zippertubing.com, pg 945

Zondervan, 3900 Sparks Dr, Grand Rapids, MI 49546 *Tel:* 616-698-6900 *Toll Free Tel:* 800-226-1122; 800-727-1309 (retail orders) *Web Site:* www.zondervan. com, pg 945

ZTV Broadcast Services Inc, 1670 Enterprise Rd, Mississauga, ON L4W 4L4, Canada *Tel:* 905-290-4430 *Fax:* 905-290-3370 *Web Site:* ztvbroadcast.com, pg 945

Zygote Media Group Inc, 1045 S 500 E, Suite 200, American Fork, UT 84003 *Tel:* 801-765-4141 *Fax:* 801-705-2234 *E-mail:* service@zygote.com *Web Site:* www.zygote.com, pg 945

Personnel Index

Included in this index are the personnel included in the entries of *AVMP*, along with the page number(s) on which they appear. Not included in this index are those individuals associated with listings in the **Calendar of Events; Periodicals for the Trade** and **Reference Books for the Trade** sections. Also, personnel associated with secondary addresses within listings (such as branch offices, sales offices, etc.) are not included.

Abanez, Michelle, Celebration of Service to America Awards, 1771 "N" St NW, Washington, DC 20036-2891 *Tel:* 202-421-3191 *E-mail:* nabef@nab.org *Web Site:* www.nabef.org, pg 985

Abbey, Susan M, Humboldt International Film Festival, Dept of Theatre, Film & Dance, One Harpst St, Arcata, CA 95521 *Tel:* 707-826-4113 *Fax:* 707-826-4112 *E-mail:* filmfest@humboldt.edu *Web Site:* hsufilmfestival.com, pg 992

Abbosh, Omar, Accenture, 161 N Clark St, Chicago, IL 60601 *Tel:* 312-693-0161 *Toll Free Tel:* 877-889-9009 *Fax:* 312-693-0507 *Web Site:* www.accenture.com, pg 672

Abdalla, Dan, 4 Wall Entertainment, 3165 W Sunset Rd, Suite 100, Las Vegas, NV 89118 *Tel:* 702-263-3858 *Toll Free Tel:* 877-789-8167 (Western US) *Fax:* 702-263-3863 *E-mail:* info@4wall.com; info@usedlighting.com *Web Site:* www.4wall.com; www.usedlighting.com, pg 764

Abdennabi, Chai, Creative Technology (CT), 2200 S Mount Prospect Rd, Unit A, Des Plaines, IL 60018 *Tel:* 847-671-9670 *E-mail:* info@ctus.com *Web Site:* www.ct-group.com, pg 733

Abel, Pete, AbelCine, 801 S Main St, Burbank, CA 91506 *Toll Free Tel:* 888-700-4416 *E-mail:* orders@abelcine.com; customerservice@abelcine.com *Web Site:* www.abelcine.com, pg 672

Abel, Rich, AbelCine, 801 S Main St, Burbank, CA 91506 *Toll Free Tel:* 888-700-4416 *E-mail:* orders@abelcine.com; customerservice@abelcine.com *Web Site:* www.abelcine.com, pg 672

Abitbol, Larry, Bay Photo Lab, 920 Disc Dr, Scotts Valley, CA 95066 *Tel:* 831-475-6686 *Toll Free Tel:* 800-435-6686 *Fax:* 831-475-5275 *E-mail:* support@bayphoto.com (cust serv); sales@bayphoto.com *Web Site:* www.bayphoto.com, pg 702

Abner, Ed, Intellidyne LLC, 2677 Prosperity Ave, Suite 301, Fairfax, VA 22031 *Tel:* 703-575-9715 *Fax:* 703-575-9718 *Web Site:* www.intellidyne-llc.com, pg 789

Abney, Bradley, Audio Visual Techniques Inc, 905 Georgetown St, Lexington, KY 40511 *Tel:* 859-254-8954 *Fax:* 859-233-4754 *E-mail:* info@avtav.com *Web Site:* avtav.com, pg 695

Abram, Gregg, Williams AV LLC, 10300 Valley View Rd, Eden Prairie, MN 55344-3446 *Tel:* 952-943-2252 *Toll Free Tel:* 800-328-6190 *Fax:* 952-943-2174 *E-mail:* info@williamsav.com *Web Site:* www.williamsav.com, pg 939

Abramson, Steve, TRUMATCH Inc, PO Box 501, Water Mill, NY 11976-0501 *Tel:* 631-204-9100 *Toll Free Tel:* 800-TRU-9100 (878-9100) *Fax:* 631-204-0002 *E-mail:* info@trumatch.com *Web Site:* www.trumatch.com, pg 919

Abshire, Derick, CEDIA IPRO Affinity Group, 8475 Nightfall Lane, Fishers, IN 46037 *Tel:* 317-328-4336 *Toll Free Tel:* 800-669-5329 *E-mail:* info@cedia.org *Web Site:* cedia.net, pg 952

Acevedo, Mari, Birns & Sawyer Inc, 3039 Roswell St, Los Angeles, CA 90065 *Tel:* 323-466-8211 *E-mail:* info@birnsandsawyer.com *Web Site:* www.birnsandsawyer.com, pg 706

Achlimbari, Robert, All Access Staging & Productions, 1320 Storm Pkwy, Torrance, CA 90501 *Tel:* 310-784-2464 *Toll Free Tel:* 877-784-2464 *Fax:* 310-517-0899 *E-mail:* sales@allaccessinc.com *Web Site:* allaccessinc.com, pg 680

Ackerman, Gary S, Thermodyne Cases, 1841 Business Pkwy, Ontario, CA 91761 *Tel:* 909-923-9945 *Fax:* 909-923-7505 *E-mail:* sales@thermodyne.com *Web Site:* www.thermodyne.com, pg 912

Ackie, Eleen, Saint Vincent & The Grenadines Tourist Office, 801 Second Ave, 4th fl, New York, NY 10017 *Tel:* 212-687-4981 *Toll Free Tel:* 800-729-1726 *Fax:* 212-949-5946 *E-mail:* svgtony@aol.com *Web Site:* www.discoversvg.com, pg 974

Acklin, Deborah L, WQED-Multimedia, 4802 Fifth Ave, Pittsburgh, PA 15213 *Tel:* 412-622-1300; 412-622-1370 *Web Site:* www.wqed.org, pg 942

Acton, Amy, Phoenix Society for Burn Survivors Inc, 525 Ottawa Ave NW, Front, Grand Rapids, MI 49503 *Tel:* 616-458-2773 *Toll Free Tel:* 800-888-BURN (888-2876) *Fax:* 616-458-2831 *E-mail:* info@phoenix-society.org *Web Site:* www.phoenix-society.org, pg 856

Adachi, Joe, Canon USA Inc, One Canon Park, Melville, NY 11747 *Toll Free Tel:* 800-652-2666 *E-mail:* pr@cusa.canon.com *Web Site:* www.usa.canon.com, pg 716

Adam, Susanne, Commercial Electronics Ltd, 1565 W Seventh St, Vancouver, BC V6J 1S1, Canada *Tel:* 604-669-5525 *E-mail:* info@commercialelectronics.ca *Web Site:* commercialelectronics.ca, pg 728

Adami, Anne V, Videofashion Network, 611 Broadway, Suite 307, New York, NY 10012 *Tel:* 212-274-1600 *Fax:* 212-219-1969 *E-mail:* info@videofashion.com; licensing@videofashion.com *Web Site:* videofashion.com, pg 929

Adamo, Louis, Hi-Tech Audio Systems Inc, 3382 Enterprise Ave, Hayward, CA 94545 *Tel:* 650-742-9166 *Fax:* 650-648-0573 *Web Site:* www.hi-techaudio.com, pg 779

Adams, Andrea, American Chemical Society (ACS), Dept of Professional Education, 1155 16 St NW, Washington, DC 20036 *Tel:* 202-872-4508 *Toll Free Tel:* 800-ACS-5558 (227-5558 ext 4508) *Fax:* 202-872-6336 *E-mail:* proed@acs.org *Web Site:* proed.acs.org, pg 683

Adams, Dan, Adams Creative & Production Services, PO Box 98636, Des Moines, WA 98198-0636 *Tel:* 206-300-1094 (cell) *Fax:* 206-824-7036, pg 675

Adams, David, D L Adams Associates Ltd, 970 N Kalaheo Ave, Suite A-311, Kailua, HI 96734 *Tel:* 808-254-3318 *E-mail:* infohawaii@dlaa.com *Web Site:* www.dlaa.com, pg 675

Adams, Denise, Pyramid Media, 3200 Airport Ave, No 19, Santa Monica, CA 90405 *Tel:* 310-398-6149 *Toll Free Tel:* 800-421-2304 *Fax:* 310-398-7869 *E-mail:* sales@pyramidmedia.com *Web Site:* www.pyramidmedia.com, pg 867

Adams, J D, 5 Alarm Music, 3500 W Olive Ave, Suite 810, Burbank, CA 91505 *Tel:* 626-304-1698 *Toll Free Tel:* 800-322-7879 *Fax:* 626-795-2058 *E-mail:* info@5alarmmusic.com *Web Site:* www.5alarmmusic.com, pg 762

Adams, Kirk, American Foundation for the Blind (AFB), 2 Penn Plaza, Suite 1102, New York, NY 10121 *Tel:* 212-502-7600 *Toll Free Tel:* 800-232-5463 *Fax:* 212-502-7777 *Toll Free Fax:* 888-545-8331 *E-mail:* info@afb.org *Web Site:* www.afb.org, pg 948

Adams, Mike, Moog Music Inc, 160 Broadway St, Asheville, NC 28801 *Tel:* 828-251-0090 *Toll Free Tel:* 800-948-1990 *Fax:* 828-254-6233 *E-mail:* info@moogmusic.com *Web Site:* www.moogmusic.com, pg 830

Adams-Ball, Stephanie, D L Adams Associates Inc, 1536 Ogden St, Denver, CO 80218 *Tel:* 303-455-1900 *E-mail:* infodenver@dlaa.com *Web Site:* www.dlaa.com, pg 675

Adamson, Lee, Utah Valley Film Commission, 220 W Center St, Suite 100, Provo, UT 84601 *Tel:* 801-851-2100 *Toll Free Tel:* 800-222-UTAH (222-8824) *E-mail:* visitors@utahvalley.com *Web Site:* www.utahvalley.com/film, pg 976

Adelstein, Jonathan S, WIA - The Wireless Infrastructure Association, 2111 Wilson Blvd, Suite 210, Arlington, VA 22201 *Tel:* 703-739-0300 *Toll Free Tel:* 800-759-0300 *Fax:* 703-836-1608 *Web Site:* wia.org, pg 963

Adeyemi, Adrienne, Rhode Island State Council on the Arts Fellowships & Grants Program, One Capitol Hill, 3rd fl, Providence, RI 02908 *Tel:* 401-222-3880 *Fax:* 401-222-3018 *E-mail:* info@arts.ri.gov *Web Site:* www.arts.ri.gov, pg 1001

Adjemian, Robert, Vedanta Press & Catalog, 1946 Vedanta Place, Hollywood, CA 90068 *Tel:* 323-960-1727 (bookstores); 323-960-1736 (outside US) *Toll Free Tel:* 800-816-2242 *E-mail:* info@vedanta.com *Web Site:* www.vedanta.com, pg 925

Adler, Allan R, Association of American Publishers (AAP), 455 Massachusetts Ave NW, Suite 700, Washington, DC 20001-2777 *Tel:* 202-347-3375 *Fax:* 202-347-3690 *E-mail:* info@publishers.org *Web Site:* publishers.org, pg 951

Adler, Eli, Clean Slate Video, 3070 Kerner Blvd, Unit O, San Rafael, CA 94901 *Tel:* 415-485-0727 *E-mail:* info@cleanslatevideo.com *Web Site:* www.cleanslatevideo.com, pg 726

Adler, Maura, Conly Productions, 1563 Oneida St, Denver, CO 80220 *Tel:* 303-393-6240 *Fax:* 303-393-6240, pg 730

Adriao, Antonio, American Artists Representatives Inc, One Chatsworth Ave, No 518, Larchmont, NY 10538 *Tel:* 646-286-5633 (cell); 212-682-2462 *E-mail:* info@aareps.com *Web Site:* www.aareps.com, pg 682

Adwar, Michael, Adwar Video, 125 Gazza Blvd, Farmingdale, NY 11735 *Tel:* 631-777-7070 *Toll Free Tel:* 877-GOADWAR (462-3927) *Fax:* 631-777-7011 *E-mail:* sales@adwarvideo.com *Web Site:* adwarvideo.com, pg 678

Adydan, Donald, F&F Productions LLC, 14333 Myerlake Circle, Clearwater, FL 33760 *Tel:* 727-530-5000 *Fax:* 727-535-6547 *E-mail:* info@fandfhd.tv *Web Site:* www.fandfhd.tv, pg 759

Adydan, Eric, Close Up Foundation, 1330 Braddock Place, Suite 400, Alexandria, VA 22314 *Tel:* 703-706-3300 *Toll Free Tel:* 800-CLOSEUP (256-7387) *E-mail:* info@closeup.org *Web Site:* www.closeup.org, pg 726

Agar, David, All Access Staging & Productions, 1320 Storm Pkwy, Torrance, CA 90501 *Tel:* 310-784-2464 *Toll Free Tel:* 877-784-2464 *Fax:* 310-517-0899 *E-mail:* sales@allaccessinc.com *Web Site:* www.allaccessinc.com, pg 680

Agbenya, Allohn, Pan African Film & Arts Festival, 6820 La Tijera Blvd, Suite 200, Los Angeles, CA 90045 *Tel:* 310-337-4737 *Fax:* 310-337-4736 *E-mail:* info@paff.org; submissions@paff.org *Web Site:* www.paff.org, pg 999

Agee, Ruth, Pogo Pictures, 114 E Ponce de Leon Ave, Suite B, Decatur, GA 30030 *Tel:* 404-892-9490 *Web Site:* www.pogopictures.com, pg 858

Agrama, Frank, Agrama Film Enterprises Inc, 7655 Sunset Blvd, Los Angeles, CA 90046 Tel: 323-851-4900 Fax: 323-851-5599 E-mail: sales@harmonygold. com Web Site: harmonygold.com, pg 678

Aguilar, Alex, Renkus-Heinz Inc, 19201 Cook St, Foothill Ranch, CA 92610-3501 Tel: 949-588-9997 Fax: 949-588-9514 E-mail: sales@renkus-heinz.com Web Site: www.renkus-heinz.com, pg 873

Agulian, Dan, Videografix LLC, 2530 Berryessa Rd, Suite 314, San Jose, CA 95132-2903 Tel: 408-499-1280 E-mail: info@videografix.com Web Site: www. videografix.com, pg 929

Agulnek, Michael, Pixar Animation Studios, 1200 Park Ave, Emeryville, CA 94608 Tel: 510-922-3000 Fax: 510-922-3151 Web Site: www.pixar.com, pg 857

Ahmadi, Mohammad, Be Media, 9729 Lurline Ave, Chatsworth, CA 91311 Tel: 310-725-8500 Toll Free Tel: 877-210-7664 Fax: 310-725-9500 Web Site: www. bemedia.com, pg 702

Ahuile, Yamil, ABSA Films, 757 N Orleans St, No 1001, Chicago, IL 60654 Tel: 312-488-1089 E-mail: info@absafilms.com Web Site: www.absafilms. com, pg 672

Aizpuru, Nydia, Physical Optics Corp (POC), 1845 E 205 St, Torrance, CA 90501-1510 Tel: 310-320-3088 E-mail: info@poc.com Web Site: www.poc.com, pg 856

Akers, Harry D, Studio Consulting & Construction Inc, 2805 Oakview Dr, Dryden, MI 48428-9740 Tel: 810-796-3235; 248-496-9000 (cell) E-mail: scc@hdakers. com Web Site: www.hdakers.com, pg 902

Akhamlich, Patrick, Hybrid Studios, 3021 S Shannon St, Santa Ana, CA 92704 Tel: 714-850-1499 E-mail: info@hybridstudiosca.com Web Site: www. hybridstudiosca.com, pg 783

Akinrele, Kiki, Location Managers Guild International (LMGI), 8033 Sunset Blvd, Suite 1017, Los Angeles, CA 90046 Tel: 310-967-2007 Fax: 310-967-2013 E-mail: contact@locationmanagers.org Web Site: locationmanagers.org, pg 957

Alan, Neil, CohuHD Costar LLC, 7330 Trade St, San Diego, CA 92121 Tel: 858-391-1800 E-mail: info@ cohuhd.com Web Site: www.cohuhd.com, pg 727

Alberti, Cliff, Tritech Communications, 625 Locust St, Suite 300, Garden City, NY 11530 Tel: 631-254-4500 Fax: 631-254-4499 E-mail: sales@tritechcomm.com Web Site: www.tritechcomm.com, pg 918

Albiniak, Paige, Promax, 5700 Wilshire Blvd, Suite 275, Los Angeles, CA 90036 Tel: 310-788-7600 Fax: 310-788-7616 Web Site: www.promax.org, pg 961

Albonico, Don, Third Ear Sound Co, 30965 San Benito St, Hayward, CA 94544 Tel: 510-429-1000 Toll Free Tel: 800-587-1115 Fax: 510-429-1001 E-mail: raul@ thirdearsound.com Web Site: www.thirdearsound.com, pg 912

Alderslade, David, Edgenuity Inc, 8860 E Chaparral Rd, Scottsdale, AZ 85250 Toll Free Tel: 877-725-4257 (sales) E-mail: customersupport@edgenuity.com; solutions@edgenuity.com (sales) Web Site: www. edgenuity.com, pg 750

Aldridge, Blake, Cokesbury, 2222 Rosa Parks Blvd, Nashville, TN 37228 Tel: 615-749-6000 (UMPH) Toll Free Tel: 800-672-1789; 844-381-2708 (cust care) Fax: 615-749-6578 Toll Free Fax: 800-445-8189 E-mail: cokes_serv@cokesbury.com; customerhelp@ cokesbury.com Web Site: www.cokesbury.com, pg 727

Alejandro, Jan M, Jan-Al Cases, 3339 Union Pacific Ave, Los Angeles, CA 90023 Tel: 323-260-7212 Toll Free Tel: 800-735-2625 Fax: 323-260-4696 Web Site: www.janalcase.com, pg 793

Alejandro, Miriam (Muffie), Jan-Al Cases, 3339 Union Pacific Ave, Los Angeles, CA 90023 Tel: 323-260-7212 Toll Free Tel: 800-735-2625 Fax: 323-260-4696 Web Site: www.janalcase.com, pg 793

Alexander, Ann, International Short Film & Video Competition, 6116 N Central Expwy, Suite 105, Dallas, TX 75206 Tel: 214-821-6300; 214-821-FILM (821-3456) Fax: 214-821-6364 E-mail: usafilmfest@ aol.com Web Site: www.usafilmfestival.com, pg 993

Alexander, Ann, KidFilm®, 6116 N Central Expwy, Suite 105, Dallas, TX 75206 Tel: 214-821-6300; 214-821-FILM (821-3456) Fax: 214-821-6364 E-mail: usafilmfest@aol.com Web Site: www. usafilmfestival.com, pg 994

Alexander, Ann, USA Film Festival, 6116 N Central Expwy, Suite 105, Dallas, TX 75206 Tel: 214-821-6300; 214-821-FILM (821-3456) Fax: 214-821-6364 E-mail: usafilmfest@aol.com Web Site: www. usafilmfestival.com, pg 1005

Alexander, Geoff, Santa Barbara Location Services, 100 Miramar Ave, Suite C, Santa Barbara, CA 93108 Tel: 805-403-4620 E-mail: geoff@sblocationservices. com Web Site: www.santabarbaralocations.com, pg 880

Alexander, Heather, Alexander Media Productions, 1901 Diamond Ridge Dr, Carrollton, TX 75010 Tel: 214-274-3456 Web Site: www.heatheralexander.net, pg 679

Alexander, Marcie, Classic Images Stock Footage LLC, 469 1/2 S Bedford Dr, Beverly Hills, CA 90212 Tel: 310-277-0400 Toll Free Tel: 800-949-CLIP (949-2547) Fax: 310-277-0412 E-mail: sales@classicimg. com Web Site: www.classicimg.com, pg 726

Alexander, Mary Lou, Spring Arbor Distributors Inc, One Ingram Blvd, La Vergne, TN 37086-1986 Toll Free Tel: 800-395-4340 Toll Free Fax: 800-876-0186 E-mail: customerservice@ingramcontent.com Web Site: www.ingramcontent.com, pg 898

Alexander, Peter, Westar Music, 105 W Beaver Creek Rd, Suite 4, Richmond Hill, ON L4B 1C6, Canada Tel: 905-886-3100 Toll Free Tel: 866-463-0100 Fax: 905-886-6800 E-mail: info@westarmusic.com Web Site: www.westarmusic.com, pg 936

Alexander, Dr Ric D, Institute of Precision Muscle Balancing, 6035 Vantage Ave, North Hollywood, CA 91616-4637 Tel: 818-766-8555 Fax: 818-766-8645 Web Site: www.dralexander.com, pg 788

Alford, Steve, Alford Media Services, 296 Freeport Pkwy, Coppell, TX 75019 Tel: 972-538-9400 Toll Free Tel: 800-554-9144 E-mail: info@alfordmedia.com; sales@alfordmedia.com Web Site: www.alfordmedia. com, pg 680

Alford, Tom, Alford Media Services, 296 Freeport Pkwy, Coppell, TX 75019 Tel: 972-538-9400 Toll Free Tel: 800-554-9144 E-mail: info@alfordmedia.com; sales@alfordmedia.com Web Site: www.alfordmedia. com, pg 680

Ali, Ed, Langie Audio Visual Systems, Piano Works Mall, 349 W Commercial St, East Rochester, NY 14445 Tel: 585-385-4880 Fax: 585-385-4882 E-mail: info@langieav.com; sales@langieav.com; rental@langieav.com Web Site: www.langieav.com, pg 803

Ali, Salman, The Video Project, 145 Ninth St, Suite 102, San Francisco, CA 94103 Tel: 415-981-9710 Toll Free Tel: 800-475-2638 Fax: 415-692-6223 E-mail: orders@videoproject.com; support@ videoproject.com Web Site: www.videoproject.com, pg 928

Ali, Samer Mandy, University of Michigan, Center for Middle Eastern & North African Studies, 500 Church St, Suite 500, Ann Arbor, MI 48109-1042 Tel: 734-647-4143 Fax: 734-936-0996 E-mail: cmenas@umich. edu Web Site: www.ii.umich.edu/cmenas, pg 923

Alias, Alex, Avaya Inc, 4655 Great American Pkwy, Santa Clara, CA 95054 Tel: 908-953-6000 Toll Free Tel: 866-GO-AVAYA (462-8292 US & CN) Web Site: www.avaya.com, pg 697

Allain, Chris, Vidox Motion Imagery, 204 Winchester Dr, Lafayette, LA 70506 Tel: 337-237-1700 Fax: 337-237-1712 Web Site: www.vidox.com, pg 930

Allain, Jean-Marc L, Trans-Lux Multimedia Corp, 445 Park Ave, Suite 2001, New York, NY 10022 Tel: 203-853-4321 Toll Free Tel: 800-243-5544; 800-462-2716 E-mail: sales@trans-lux.com Web Site: www.trans-lux.com, pg 917

Allen, Alisa, Wild Plum, 23371 Mulholland Dr, Suite 409, Woodland Hills, CA 91364 Tel: 310-823-7445 Web Site: www.wildplum.tv, pg 938

Allen, Brian, AMPLUS Productions, 1484 Liveoak Dr, Mississauga, ON L5E 2X1, Canada Tel: 416-889-7664 Fax: 905-274-7687 Web Site: www.amplusproductions. com, pg 684

Allen, Chris, Sear Sound, 353 W 48 St, 6th fl, New York, NY 10036 Tel: 212-582-5380 Fax: 212-581-2731 E-mail: waltersear@aol.com Web Site: www. searsound.com, pg 883

Allen, John E, John E Allen Inc, PO Box 452, Newfoundland, PA 18445 Tel: 570-676-4152 Fax: 570-676-9194 E-mail: jeainc@gmail.com Web Site: www.allenarchive.com/wordpress, pg 680

Allen, Layman G (Buzz), Accelerated Learning Foundation, 402 N Third St, Fairfield, IA 52556 Tel: 641-954-5443 Toll Free Tel: 800-289-2377 Fax: 641-954-5851 E-mail: info@gamesforthinkers.org Web Site: www.gamesforthinkers.org, pg 672

Allen, Mike, JoLida Inc, 21310 Ridgecroft Dr, Brookeville, MD 20833 Tel: 301-953-2014 Fax: 301-498-0554 E-mail: jolidacorp@msn.com Web Site: www.jolida.com, pg 795

Allen, Paul, Adaptive Technologies Group Inc, 1635 E Burnett St, Signal Hill, CA 90755 Tel: 562-424-1100 E-mail: sales@adaptivetechnologiesgroup.com Web Site: www.adaptivetechnologiesgroup.com, pg 675

Allen, Rob, Panavid, 210 West Pkwy, Unit 5, Pompton Plains, NJ 07444 Tel: 973-831-5655 E-mail: info@ panavid.com; support@panavid.com Web Site: www. panavid.com, pg 850

Allen, Robert, Macmillan Audio, 120 Broadway, 22nd fl, New York, NY 10271 Tel: 646-600-7856; 646-307-5472 Toll Free Tel: 888-330-8477 (cust serv); 800-221-7945 Toll Free Fax: 800-672-7703 (orders) E-mail: macmillan.audio@macmillanusa.com Web Site: www.macmillanaudio.com, pg 814

Allen, Van, Radio Advertising Bureau (RAB), 125 W 55 St, 5th fl, New York, NY 10019 Tel: 212-681-7200 Toll Free Tel: 800-252-7234 Fax: 212-681-7223 E-mail: memberresponse@rab.com Web Site: www. rab.com, pg 961

Allessi, Ana Marie, HarperAudio, 10 E 53 St, New York, NY 10022 Tel: 212-207-7000 Toll Free Tel: 800-242-7737 Fax: 212-207-2582 Toll Free Fax: 800-822-4090 Web Site: www.harpercollins.com, pg 776

Alli, Brian, Roland Corp US, 5100 S Eastern Ave, Los Angeles, CA 90040-2938 Tel: 323-890-3700; 323-890-3771 (parts & serv); 323-890-3740 (prod support) Fax: 323-721-4875 Web Site: www.rolandus.com/us, pg 876

Allin, Mark, John Wiley & Sons Inc, 111 River St, Hoboken, NJ 07030-5774 Tel: 201-748-6000 Toll Free Tel: 800-225-5945 (cust serv) Fax: 201-748-6088 Web Site: www.wiley.com, pg 938

Allison, Mark, Dake Publishing Inc, 764 Martins Chapel Rd, Lawrenceville, GA 30046 Toll Free Tel: 800-241-1239 E-mail: info@dake.com Web Site: www.dake. com, pg 737

Allyn, Jon, American Society of Photographers (ASP), 3120 N Argonne Dr, Milwaukee, WI 53222 Tel: 414-871-6600 Web Site: asofp.com, pg 949

Alonso, Eric, Sunset Bronson Studios, 5800 W Sunset Blvd, Hollywood, CA 90028 Tel: 323-460-5858 Fax: 323-460-3844 E-mail: reception@sunsetbronson. com Web Site: sgsandsbs.com, pg 904

Alpers, Amy, Idaho Film Office, 700 W State St, Boise, ID 83702 Tel: 208-334-2470 Toll Free Tel: 800-842-5858 Fax: 208-334-2631 Web Site: www.filmidaho. com, pg 970

Alpert, Jon, Downtown Community Television Center (DCTV), 87 Lafayette St, New York, NY 10013 Tel: 212-966-4510 Fax: 212-226-3053 E-mail: info@ dctvny.org Web Site: www.dctvny.org, pg 746

Alsop, Peter, Moose School Productions, Box 960, Topanga, CA 90290-0960 *Tel:* 310-455-2318 *Toll Free Tel:* 800-676-5480 *Fax:* 310-455-4192 *Web Site:* www. peteralsop.com, pg 830

Alsup, Sharon, True Audio, 387 Duncan Lane, Andersonville, TN 37705 *Tel:* 865-494-3388 *Toll Free Tel:* 800-621-4411 *Fax:* 865-494-3388 *E-mail:* sales@ trueaudio.com *Web Site:* www.trueaudio.com, pg 919

Alterio, Ronald, Blonder Tongue Laboratories Inc, One Jake Brown Rd, Old Bridge, NJ 08857 *Tel:* 732-679-4000 *Toll Free Tel:* 800-523-6049 *Fax:* 732-679-4353 *E-mail:* custsvc@blondertongue.com; btglobalsales@ blondertongue.com (outside US & CN); information@ blondertongue.com *Web Site:* www.blondertongue.com, pg 707

Alti, Thomas, TGA Recording Co, 295 Urbandale Ave, Benton Harbor, MI 49022 *Tel:* 269-926-7581 *E-mail:* tgarecording@sbcglobal.net *Web Site:* www. tgarecording.com, pg 911

Altman, Allan, Video Artists International & VAI Audio, 109 Wheeler Ave, Pleasantville, NY 10570 *Tel:* 914-769-3691 *Toll Free Tel:* 800-477-7146 *Fax:* 914-769-5407 *E-mail:* orders@vaimusic.com *Web Site:* www. vaimusic.com, pg 927

Altman, Mark, Morning Music Ltd, 5200 Dixie Rd, Suite 203, Mississauga, ON L4W 1E4, Canada *Tel:* 905-625-2676 *Fax:* 905-625-2092 *E-mail:* info@ morningmusic.ca *Web Site:* www.morningmusic.ca, pg 830

Altman, Steven J, Corporation for Public Broadcasting (CPB), 401 Ninth St NW, Washington, DC 20004-2129 *Tel:* 202-879-9600 *Toll Free Tel:* 800-272-2190 *Fax:* 202-879-9700 *E-mail:* press@cpb.org *Web Site:* www.cpb.org, pg 953

Alvarado, Maritza, The Kitchen, 265 NE 24 St, Suite 401, Miami, FL 33137 *Tel:* 305-415-6200 *E-mail:* info@thekitchen.tv *Web Site:* www.thekitchen. tv, pg 799

Alvarado-Cancel, Jose Antonio, Audio Visual Concepts Inc, Rd 1, Km 29.3, Rio Canas, Caguas, PR 00725 *Tel:* 787-753-7700 *Fax:* 787-766-4578 *Web Site:* www. mig-avc.com, pg 694

Alves, Ruben, Red Sky Studios, 184 Everett St, Allston, MA 02134 *Tel:* 617-903-3373 *E-mail:* mail@redsky-studios.com *Web Site:* redsky-studios.com, pg 872

Amacher, Kenny, Soularium Recording Studios, 702 S Alpine Hwy, Alpine, UT 84004 *Tel:* 801-492-0505 *E-mail:* info@soulariumstudios.com *Web Site:* www. soulariumstudios.com, pg 893

Amat, Mark, Print File Inc, 1846 S Orange Blossom Trail, Apopka, FL 32703 *Tel:* 407-886-3100 *Toll Free Tel:* 800-508-8539 *Fax:* 407-886-0008 *Toll Free Fax:* 800-546-4145 *E-mail:* support@printfile.com *Web Site:* printfile.com, pg 862

Ambrose, William V, Ambrose Video Publishing Inc, 1202 Lexington Ave, Suite 171, New York, NY 10028 *Tel:* 212-768-7373 *Toll Free Tel:* 800-526-4663 *Fax:* 212-768-9282 *E-mail:* customerservice@ ambrosevideo.com *Web Site:* www.ambrosevideo.com, pg 682

Amelio, Catherine, The Clio Awards, 825 Eighth Ave, 29th fl, New York, NY 10019 *Tel:* 212-683-4300 *E-mail:* event@clioawards.com *Web Site:* clios.com, pg 987

Ames, Aaron, WildBrain™, 5657 Spring Garden Rd, Suite 505, Halifax, NS B3J 3R4, Canada *Tel:* 902-423-0260 *Fax:* 902-422-0752 *E-mail:* info@wildbrain. com; halifax@wildbrain.com; sales@wildbrain.com *Web Site:* www.wildbrain.com, pg 938

Ames, David, Stanford Research Systems Inc, 1290-D Reamwood Ave, Sunnyvale, CA 94089 *Tel:* 408-744-9040 *Fax:* 408-744-9049 *E-mail:* info@thinksrs.com *Web Site:* www.thinksrs.com, pg 899

Ames, Justin, Sky City Audio, 1819 Willow Creek Rd, Prescott, AZ 86301 *Tel:* 928-830-2313 *Web Site:* skycityaudio.com, pg 890

Amick, Gray, Carolina Biological Supply Co, 2700 York Rd, Burlington, NC 27215-3398 *Tel:* 336-586-4399 (intl sales) *Toll Free Tel:* 800-334-5551 *Toll* *Free Fax:* 800-222-7112 *E-mail:* customer_service@ carolina.com; internationalsales@carolina.com *Web Site:* www.carolina.com, pg 717

Amico, Lou, L A Management Co LLC, 8131 Bay Pointe Dr, Denver, NC 28037 *Tel:* 704-560-6274 *Toll Free Tel:* 800-651-7818 *Fax:* 704-973-7968 *E-mail:* info@lamanagementco.com *Web Site:* lamanagementco.com, pg 802

Amir-Hamzeh, Mark, Sigma Corp of America, 15 Fleetwood Ct, Ronkonkoma, NY 11779 *Tel:* 631-585-1144 *Toll Free Tel:* 800-896-6858 (cust serv) *Fax:* 631-585-1895 *E-mail:* info@sigmaphoto.com *Web Site:* www.sigmaphoto.com, pg 887

Amor, Joseph L III, Microspace Communications Corp, 3100 Highwoods Blvd, Suite 120, Raleigh, NC 27604 *Tel:* 919-850-4500 *Fax:* 919-850-4518 *Web Site:* www. microspace.com, pg 826

Amory, Dawn, Vision Maker Media, 1800 N 33 St, Lincoln, NE 68503-1409 *Tel:* 402-472-3522 *Fax:* 402-472-8675 *E-mail:* visionmaker@unl.edu *Web Site:* www.visionmakermedia.org, pg 930

Amper, Linda, Clever Devices Ltd, 300 Crossways Park Dr, Woodbury, NY 11797 *Tel:* 516-433-6100 *Toll Free Tel:* 800-872-6129 *Web Site:* www.cleverdevices.com, pg 726

Amyott, Fraser, Inspired Image Picture Co (IIPC), 1090 E Georgia St, Vancouver, BC V6A 2A7, Canada *Tel:* 604-874-7513 *Toll Free Tel:* 800-352-1454 (prodn rentals); 800-567-0037 (equip rentals) *Fax:* 604-874-7516 *E-mail:* info@inspiredimage.ca *Web Site:* inspiredimage.ca, pg 788

Anagnost, Andrew, Autodesk Inc, 111 McInnis Pkwy, San Rafael, CA 94903 *Tel:* 415-507-5000 *Fax:* 415-507-5100 *Web Site:* www.autodesk.com, pg 696

Anastasi, Joseph, PASCO, 224 48 St, Brooklyn, NY 11220 *Tel:* 718-833-9100 *E-mail:* pasco2@aol.com, pg 851

Andersen, Maureen, International Ticketing Association Inc (INTIX), 5868 E 71 St, Suite E 367, Indianapolis, IN 46220 *Tel:* 212-629-4036 *Fax:* 212-629-4036 *E-mail:* info@intix.org; media@intix.org *Web Site:* www.intix.org, pg 957

Anderson, Bob, Stretching Inc, PO Box 767, Palmer Lake, CO 80133-0767 *Tel:* 719-481-3928 *Toll Free Tel:* 800-333-1307 *Fax:* 719-481-9058 *E-mail:* office@ stretching.com *Web Site:* www.stretching.com, pg 902

Anderson, Chad, Osum Event Rentals, 730 Andover Park E, Tukwila, WA 98188 *Tel:* 206-575-5055 *E-mail:* info@osumeventrentals.com *Web Site:* osumeventrentals.com, pg 848

Anderson, Don, Pelican Publishing Co, 1000 Burmaster St, Gretna, LA 70053-2246 *Tel:* 504-368-1175 *Toll Free Tel:* 800-843-1724; 888-PELICAN (735-4226 - cust serv); 888-5PELICAN (888-573-5422) *Fax:* 504-368-1195 *E-mail:* sales@pelicanpub.com *Web Site:* www.pelicanpub.com, pg 853

Anderson, Erin, Chater Camera Inc, 1336 Ninth St, Berkeley, CA 94710 *Tel:* 510-525-5400 *Fax:* 510-295-2478 *E-mail:* rentals@chatercamera.com *Web Site:* www.chatercamera.com, pg 721

Anderson, Heather, Award Productions Inc, 164 Great Rd, Acton, MA 01720 *Tel:* 978-635-8000 *E-mail:* web@awardprod.com *Web Site:* www. awardproductions.com, pg 700

Anderson, Jackie, Colortek of Boston, 727 Atlantic Ave, Boston, MA 02111 *Tel:* 617-451-0894 *E-mail:* info@colortekofboston.com *Web Site:* www. colortekofboston.com, pg 728

Anderson, Jane, PDC Productions, 3217 N Flood Ave, Norman, OK 73069 *Tel:* 405-360-5130 *Fax:* 405-360-0524 *E-mail:* info@pdcproductions.com *Web Site:* www.pdcproductions.com, pg 852

Anderson, Jean E, Stretching Inc, PO Box 767, Palmer Lake, CO 80133-0767 *Tel:* 719-481-3928 *Toll Free Tel:* 800-333-1307 *Fax:* 719-481-9058 *E-mail:* office@ stretching.com *Web Site:* www.stretching.com, pg 902

Anderson, Jeff, Superscope LLC, 1508 Batavia Ave, Geneva, IL 60134-3302 *Tel:* 630-232-8900 *Toll Free Tel:* 800-374-4118 *Fax:* 630-232-8905 *Web Site:* www. superscopetechnologies.com, pg 904

Anderson, John, The Learning House Inc, 427 S Fourth St, Suite 300, Louisville, KY 40202 *Tel:* 502-589-9878 *Fax:* 502-589-9825 *E-mail:* sales@learninghouse. com; info@learninghouse.com *Web Site:* www. learninghouse.com, pg 805

Anderson, Josh, Creative Technology (CT), 2200 S Mount Prospect Rd, Unit A, Des Plaines, IL 60018 *Tel:* 847-671-9670 *E-mail:* info@ctus.com *Web Site:* www.ct-group.com, pg 733

Anderson, Justin, Close Up Foundation, 1330 Braddock Place, Suite 400, Alexandria, VA 22314 *Tel:* 703-706-3300 *Toll Free Tel:* 800-CLOSEUP (256-7387) *E-mail:* info@closeup.org *Web Site:* www.closeup.org, pg 726

Anderson, Kim A, National Education Association (NEA), 1201 16 St NW, Washington, DC 20036-3290 *Tel:* 202-833-4000 *Fax:* 202-822-7974 *Web Site:* www. nea.org, pg 836

Anderson, Leah, Golden Space Needle Awards, 305 Harrison St, Seattle, WA 98109 *Tel:* 206-464-5830 *Fax:* 206-264-7919 *E-mail:* info@siff.net; entries@siff. net *Web Site:* www.siff.net, pg 991

Anderson, Leah, Seattle International Film Festival (SIFF), 305 Harrison St, Seattle, WA 98109 *Tel:* 206-464-5830 *Fax:* 206-264-7919 *E-mail:* info@siff.net; entries@siff.net *Web Site:* www.siff.net, pg 1003

Anderson, Mark C, ACCO Brands Corp, 4 Corporate Dr, Lake Zurick, IL 60047-8997 *Toll Free Tel:* 800-541-0094; 800-222-6462 *Toll Free Fax:* 800-941-4463 *E-mail:* contactus@acco.com (cust serv) *Web Site:* www.accobrands.com, pg 673

Anderson, Mary, Countryman Associates Inc, 195 Constitution Dr, Menlo Park, CA 94025 *Tel:* 650-364-9988 *Toll Free Tel:* 800-669-1422 *Fax:* 650-364-2794 *E-mail:* sales@countryman.com *Web Site:* www. countryman.com, pg 732

Anderson, Max, The Market Place, PO Box 4126, Rockford, IL 61110-0626 *Tel:* 815-877-1514 *Web Site:* www.maxbooks.9k.com, pg 817

Anderson, Nancy, BingoLewis, 5828 N Lombard St, Portland, OR 97203 *Tel:* 503-223-2224 *E-mail:* info@ bingolewis.com *Web Site:* www.bingolewis.com, pg 706

Anderson, Pete, Leader Instruments Corp, 1501 E Orangethorpe Ave, Suite 140, Fullerton, CA 92831 *Tel:* 714-527-9300 *Toll Free Tel:* 800-645-5104 *Fax:* 714-527-7490 *E-mail:* info@leaderamerica.com *Web Site:* www.leaderamerica.com, pg 805

Anderson, Rob, BingoLewis, 5828 N Lombard St, Portland, OR 97203 *Tel:* 503-223-2224 *E-mail:* info@ bingolewis.com *Web Site:* www.bingolewis.com, pg 706

Anderson, Robyn, Musco Lighting, 100 First Ave W, Oskaloosa, IA 52577 *Tel:* 641-673-0411 *Toll Free Tel:* 800-825-6030 *Fax:* 641-673-4852 *E-mail:* lighting@musco.com *Web Site:* www.musco. com, pg 834

Anderson, Sarah, G W Hannaway & Associates, 839 Pearl St, Boulder, CO 80302 *Tel:* 303-440-9631 *Fax:* 303-440-4421 *E-mail:* sales@gwha. com; services@gwha.com; technology@gwha.com *Web Site:* www.gwha.com, pg 775

Anderson, Scott, Laserium®, 84777 Charlottes Way, Eugene, OR 97405 *Tel:* 541-687-1414 *Web Site:* www. laserium.com, pg 804

Anderson, Scott, RAM® Mounts, 8410 Dallas Ave S, Seattle, WA 98108 *Tel:* 206-763-8361 *Toll Free Tel:* 800-497-7479 *Fax:* 206-763-9615 *E-mail:* sales@ rammount.com *Web Site:* www.rammount.com, pg 870

Anderson, Stan, Trac Recording Studio, 180 E Warner Ave, Fresno, CA 93710 *Tel:* 559-903-0701 *E-mail:* tracrecording@pmicp.com *Web Site:* tracrecordingstudio.com, pg 916

Anderson, Steve, Freeman, 1600 Viceroy, Suite 100, Dallas, TX 75235 *Tel:* 214-445-1000 *Web Site:* www. freeman.com, pg 765

Anderson, Tim, Florida Film Festival, c/o Enzian Theater, 1300 S Orlando Ave, Maitland, FL 32751 *Tel:* 407-629-1088 *Fax:* 407-629-6870 *E-mail:* entries@enzian.org; marketing@enzian.org; events@enzian.org *Web Site:* www.floridafilmfestival. com, pg 989

Andonov, Vlatko, Bethesda Softworks LLC, 1370 Piccard Dr, Suite 120, Rockville, MD 20850 *Tel:* 301-926-8300 *E-mail:* info@bethsoft.com; press@bethsoft. com *Web Site:* bethesda.net, pg 704

Andrew, Don, WIA - The Wireless Infrastructure Association, 2111 Wilson Blvd, Suite 210, Arlington, VA 22201 *Tel:* 703-739-0300 *Toll Free Tel:* 800-759-0300 *Fax:* 703-836-1608 *Web Site:* wia.org, pg 963

Andrews, Craig, Beholder Productions Inc, 1769 Old York Rd, Abington, PA 19001 *Toll Free Tel:* 844-BEHOLD-R (234-6537) *E-mail:* info@ beholderproductions.com *Web Site:* www. beholderagency.com, pg 703

Andrews, Emilia, Beholder Productions Inc, 1769 Old York Rd, Abington, PA 19001 *Toll Free Tel:* 844-BEHOLD-R (234-6537) *E-mail:* info@ beholderproductions.com *Web Site:* www. beholderagency.com, pg 703

Andrews, Fred G, Kansas City FilmFest International (KCFFI), 4741 Central, Suite 306, Kansas City, MO 64112 *Tel:* 816-286-4777 *E-mail:* info@kcfilmfest.org *Web Site:* kcfilmfest.org, pg 994

Andrews, Jenna, Moviola, 1135 N Mansfield Ave, Hollywood, CA 90038 *Tel:* 323-467-3107; 818-487-5000 *Toll Free Tel:* 877-MOVIOLA (668-4652) *Fax:* 323-464-1518 *Web Site:* www.moviola.com, pg 832

Andrle, Chuck, Out of the BLUE Media, 1413 Brenda Lane, Allen, TX 75002 *Tel:* 469-853-9015 *Web Site:* www.outofthebluemedia.com, pg 849

Andrulis, Joe, BIAMP Systems, 9300 SW Gemini Dr, Beaverton, OR 97008 *Tel:* 503-641-7287 *Toll Free Tel:* 800-826-1457 (US & CN) *E-mail:* biampinfo@ biamp.com *Web Site:* www.biamp.com, pg 705

Angelich, Chris, AM Stock-Cameo Film Library, 12340 Santa Monica Blvd, Suite 212, Los Angeles, CA 90025 *Tel:* 310-479-4800 *Fax:* 310-933-6979 *E-mail:* researcher@amstockcameo.com *Web Site:* www.amstockcameo.com, pg 682

Angelo, Ian, DataDirect Networks, 9351 Deering Ave, Chatsworth, CA 91311 *Tel:* 818-700-4000 *Toll Free Tel:* 800-TERABYTE (837-2298) *E-mail:* info@ddn. com; sales@ddn.com *Web Site:* www.ddn.com, pg 738

Angley, Tina, American Society of Safety Professionals (ASSP), 520 N Northwest Hwy, Park Ridge, IL 60068 *Tel:* 847-699-2929 (cust serv) *Fax:* 847-768-3434 *E-mail:* customerservice@assp.org *Web Site:* www. assp.org, pg 949

Anglim, Mike, American Playback Images, 27748 Caraway Lane, Santa Clarita, CA 91350 *Tel:* 818-427-8292 *Fax:* 661-263-2387 *E-mail:* americanplayback@ aol.com *Web Site:* americanplayback.com, pg 684

Angst, Frank, Blood-Horse Publications, 3101 Beaumont Centre Circle, Lexington, KY 40513 *Toll Free Tel:* 800-866-2361; 800-582-5604 *E-mail:* advertise@ bloodhorse.com; customerservice@bloodhorse.com *Web Site:* www.bloodhorse.com, pg 707

Anguiano, Sonia, Castleview Productions, 1100 W 41 St, Austin, TX 78756 *Tel:* 512-442-9944 *Fax:* 512-442-8823 *E-mail:* contact@castleviewproductions.com *Web Site:* castleviewproductions.com, pg 717

Angus, George, Ross Video Ltd, 8 John St, Iroquois, ON K0E 1K0, Canada *Tel:* 613-652-4886 *Fax:* 613-652-4425 *E-mail:* solutions@rossvideo.com *Web Site:* www.rossvideo.com, pg 878

Ankeny, James, Blue Earth Pictures, 5532 Code Ave, Minneapolis, MN 55436 *Tel:* 612-619-5909 *E-mail:* missioncontrol@blueearthpictures.com *Web Site:* www.blueearthpictures.com, pg 707

Annella, Chris, Joseph Electronics, 6633 W Howard St, Niles, IL 60714 *Tel:* 847-588-3800 *Toll Free Tel:* 800-323-5925 *Fax:* 847-588-3300 *Toll Free Fax:* 800-446-8366 *E-mail:* sales@josephelectronics.com *Web Site:* www.josephelectronics.com, pg 795

Anselmo, Rick, Tekskil Industries Inc, 102-998 Harbourside Dr, North Vancouver, BC V7P 3T2, Canada *Tel:* 604-985-2250 *Toll Free Tel:* 877-835-7545 *Toll Free Fax:* 877-576-8361 *E-mail:* team@ tekskil.com *Web Site:* www.tekskil.com, pg 909

Anthony, David, Giant Interactive, 133 W 19 St, 3rd fl, New York, NY 10011 *Tel:* 212-675-7300 *E-mail:* info@giant-interactive.com *Web Site:* www. giant-interactive.com, pg 770

Anthony, Graham, August House Audio, 3500 Piedmont Rd NE, Suite 310, Atlanta, GA 30305 *Tel:* 404-442-4420 *Toll Free Tel:* 800-284-8784 *Fax:* 404-442-4435 *E-mail:* ahinfo@augusthouse.com *Web Site:* www. augusthouse.com, pg 695

Anthony, Josie A, Leucos USA Inc, 11 Mayfield Ave, Edison, NJ 08837 *Tel:* 732-225-0010 *Toll Free Tel:* 800-832-3360 *Fax:* 732-225-0250 *E-mail:* info@ leucosusa.com *Web Site:* www.leucos.com, pg 806

Anthony, Michele, Universal Music Group, 2220 Colorado Ave, Santa Monica, CA 90404 *Tel:* 310-865-5000 *Web Site:* www.universalmusic.com, pg 922

Anthony, Mike, F&F Productions LLC, 14333 Myerlake Circle, Clearwater, FL 33760 *Tel:* 727-530-5000 *Fax:* 727-535-6547 *E-mail:* info@fandfhd.tv *Web Site:* www.fandfhd.tv, pg 759

Antonacci, Cara, Jack Morton Worldwide, 909 Third Ave, New York, NY 10022 *Tel:* 212-401-7000; 212-401-7212 *E-mail:* experience@jackmorton.com *Web Site:* www.jackmorton.com, pg 830

Antonio, Joe, VITAC, 8300 E Maplewood Ave, Suite 310, Greenwood Village, CO 80111 *Toll Free Tel:* 800-278-4822 (sales); 800-775-7838 *E-mail:* info@vitac.com *Web Site:* www.vitac.com, pg 932

Antonio, Sheril, Tisch School of the Arts, 721 Broadway, 10th & 11th fl, New York, NY 10003 *Tel:* 212-998-1700; 212-998-1780 *Fax:* 212-995-4062; 212-995-4063 *Web Site:* www.tisch.nyu.edu, pg 914

Anweiler, Shaun, DR&A Inc, 45 Willow St, Nashville, TN 37210 *Tel:* 615-256-6200 *Fax:* 615-256-6236 *Web Site:* www.griptruck.com, pg 746

Aoki, Julia, Video Out Distribution, 2625 Kaslo St, Vancouver, BC V5M 3G9, Canada *Tel:* 604-872-8337 *Fax:* 604-876-1185 *E-mail:* info@vivomediaarts.com; info@videoout.ca *Web Site:* vivomediaarts.com; www. videoout.ca, pg 928

Apel, Johan, ChyronHego Corp, 5 Hub Dr, Melville, NY 11747 *Tel:* 631-845-2000 *E-mail:* info@chyronhego. com; sales@chryonhego.com *Web Site:* chyronhego. com, pg 723

Apel, Paul, New Wave Entertainment, 2660 W Olive Ave, Burbank, CA 91505 *Tel:* 818-295-5000 *E-mail:* biz@nwe.com *Web Site:* nwe.com, pg 840

Apley, Alice, Documentary Educational Resources Inc, 108 Water St, Suite 5A, Watertown, MA 02472 *Tel:* 617-926-0491 *Toll Free Tel:* 800-569-6621 *Fax:* 617-926-9519 *E-mail:* info@der.org *Web Site:* www.der.org, pg 744

Appelbaum, Moshie, Midwest Photo Exchange, 2887 Silver Dr, Columbus, OH 43211 *Tel:* 614-261-1264 *Toll Free Tel:* 866-940-3686 *E-mail:* mpx@mpex.com; orders@mpex.com *Web Site:* mpex.com, pg 827

Appell, Richard, DVS InteleStream, 2600 W Olive Ave, Burbank, CA 91505 *Tel:* 818-566-4151 *E-mail:* info@ dvs.tv *Web Site:* www.dvs.tv, pg 748

Apple, Steven, The Entertainment Merchants Association (EMA), PO Box 6339, North Hollywood, CA 91603 *Tel:* 818-385-1500 *E-mail:* info@entmerch.org *Web Site:* www.entmerch.org, pg 954

Appleson, Patrick G, Pat Appleson Studios Inc, 2359 Hwy 70 SE, Suite 102, Hickory, NC 28602 *Tel:* 828-461-3003 (cell); 828-994-4361 *Web Site:* www. appleson.com, pg 687

Apter, Monique, DASAN Zhone Solutions (DZS) Inc, 7195 Oakport St, Oakland, CA 94621 *Tel:* 510-777-7000 *Toll Free Tel:* 877-ZHONE-20 (946-6320, US & CN) *Fax:* 510-777-7001 *Web Site:* dasanzhone.com, pg 737

Aquino, Anthony, FUJIFILM Graphic Systems Division, 850 Central Ave, Hanover Park, IL 60133 *Tel:* 630-259-7200 *Toll Free Tel:* 800-877-0555 *Fax:* 630-259-7078 *Web Site:* www.fujifilmusa.com, pg 766

Arana, Benjamin, Arkon Resources Inc, 20 La Porte St, Arcadia, CA 91006 *Tel:* 626-254-9005 *Toll Free Tel:* 800-841-0884 *Fax:* 626-254-9266 *E-mail:* arkon8@arkon.com *Web Site:* www.arkon. com, pg 689

Araujo, Daniel, Utopia Films, 1976 S La Cienega Blvd, No 130, Los Angeles, CA 90034 *Tel:* 310-338-0580 *Fax:* 313-557-0580 *E-mail:* reception@ utopiafilms.com; production@utopiafilms.com (reels) *Web Site:* utopiafilms.com, pg 924

Arbeeny, Karen Lee, The Jim Henson Co, 1416 N La Brea Ave, Hollywood, CA 90028 *Tel:* 323-802-1500 *Fax:* 323-802-1825 *Web Site:* www.henson.com, pg 794

Archambault, Steven, International Datacasting, 50 Frank Nighbor Place, Kanata, ON K2V 1B9, Canada *Tel:* 613-596-4120 *Fax:* 613-596-4863 *E-mail:* marketing@datacast.com *Web Site:* www. datacast.com, pg 790

Archibald, Rachel, Clear-Com® LLC, 1301 Marina Village Pkwy, Suite 105, Alameda, CA 94501 *Tel:* 510-337-6600 *Toll Free Tel:* 800-462-HELP (462-4357) *Fax:* 510-337-6699 *E-mail:* salessupportus@ clearcom.com *Web Site:* www.clearcom.com, pg 726

Arco, Joseph, Multimedia Marketing Group, 6048 Broadcast Pkwy, Loves Park, IL 61111 *Tel:* 779-774-3188 *Fax:* 779-423-0090 *E-mail:* info@mmg-1.com *Web Site:* mmg-1.com, pg 833

Arco, Susan, Multimedia Marketing Group, 6048 Broadcast Pkwy, Loves Park, IL 61111 *Tel:* 779-774-3188 *Fax:* 779-423-0090 *E-mail:* info@mmg-1.com *Web Site:* mmg-1.com, pg 833

Ard, Anje, Watson Desking, 26246 Twelve Trees Lane NW, Poulsbo, WA 98370 *Tel:* 360-394-1300 *Fax:* 360-394-1322 *E-mail:* marketing@watsondesking.com *Web Site:* www.watsonfurniture.com, pg 934

Ardolino, Paul, Palardo Productions, 1807 Taft Ave, Suite 4, Hollywood, CA 90028 *Tel:* 323-469-8991 *E-mail:* palardo2@msn.com, pg 850

Ardolino, Tommy, Palardo Productions, 1807 Taft Ave, Suite 4, Hollywood, CA 90028 *Tel:* 323-469-8991 *E-mail:* palardo2@msn.com, pg 850

Arenas, Carolina, Audio Network US Inc, 48 W 25 St, 10th fl, New York, NY 10010 *Tel:* 646-688-4320 *E-mail:* nyoffice@audionetwork.com *Web Site:* us. audionetwork.com, pg 693

Arentz, Ed, Greenwich Entertainment, 610 Fifth Ave, 3rd fl, New York, NY 10020 *E-mail:* info@greenwichentertainment.com; booking@greenwichentertainment.com; publicity@greenwichentertainment.com; acquisitions@greenwichentertainment.com *Web Site:* greenwichentertainment.com, pg 774

Argentine, Erik, Argentine Productions Inc, 111 Mayfair Dr, Pittsburgh, PA 15228 *Tel:* 412-341-6448 *E-mail:* engage@argentineproductions.com *Web Site:* argentineproductions.com, pg 688

Argentine, Per, Argentine Productions Inc, 111 Mayfair Dr, Pittsburgh, PA 15228 *Tel:* 412-341-6448 *E-mail:* engage@argentineproductions.com *Web Site:* argentineproductions.com, pg 688

Argentine, Peter, Argentine Productions Inc, 111 Mayfair Dr, Pittsburgh, PA 15228 *Tel:* 412-341-6448 *E-mail:* engage@argentineproductions.com *Web Site:* argentineproductions.com, pg 688

Argento, Anthony, Rollin Studios, 259 Green St, 2nd fl, Brooklyn, NY 11222 *Toll Free Tel:* 844-576-5546 *E-mail:* more@rollin-studios.com *Web Site:* www.rollin-studios.com, pg 877

Argivier, Gilles, Bisk Education, 9417 Princess Palm Ave, Tampa, FL 33619 *Toll Free Tel:* 800-280-9718 *E-mail:* media@bisk.com *Web Site:* www.bisk.com, pg 706

Argomaniz, Fidel, Silvestri California, 8125 Beach St, Los Angeles, CA 90001 *Tel:* 323-277-4420 *Toll Free Tel:* 800-647-8874 *Fax:* 323-585-0791 *E-mail:* info@silvestricalifornia.com *Web Site:* www.silvestricalifornia.com, pg 888

Arias, Washington, Everlast Productions, 59 SW 12 Ave, Unit 110, Dania Beach, FL 33004 *Tel:* 954-456-7167 *Fax:* 954-456-1243 *E-mail:* info@everlastproductions.com *Web Site:* everlastproductions.com, pg 757

Arias, Yolanda, Chicago Film Office, Chicago Cultural Ctr, 78 E Washington, Rm 108, Chicago, IL 60602 *Tel:* 312-744-6415 *Fax:* 312-744-1378 *E-mail:* filmoffice@cityofchicago.org *Web Site:* www.cityofchicago.org/city/en/depts/dca/provdrs/chicago_film_office.html, pg 970

Ariosa, John, Sheffield Audio/Video Productions, 13816 Sunnybrook Rd, Phoenix, MD 21131 *Tel:* 410-628-7260 *Toll Free Tel:* 800-355-6613 *Fax:* 410-628-1977 *E-mail:* info@sheffieldav.com *Web Site:* www.sheffieldav.com/production, pg 885

Arkin, Robert, Holo-Spectra Inc, 7742B Gloria Ave, Van Nuys, CA 91406 *Tel:* 818-994-9577 *Fax:* 818-994-4709 *E-mail:* info@lasershs.com *Web Site:* www.lasershs.com, pg 781

Arkin, William, Holo-Spectra Inc, 7742B Gloria Ave, Van Nuys, CA 91406 *Tel:* 818-994-9577 *Fax:* 818-994-4709 *E-mail:* info@lasershs.com *Web Site:* www.lasershs.com, pg 781

Arking, Paul, GLI Sound Systems, 2691 W 15 St, Brooklyn, NY 11224 *Tel:* 718-372-7849 *Toll Free Tel:* 800-GLI-PRO-1 (454-7761) *Fax:* 718-946-4151 *E-mail:* info@glipro.com; sales@glipro.com *Web Site:* www.glipro.com, pg 771

Arlyck, Ralph, Timed Exposures Films, 122 Old Rd, Germantown, NY 12526-6014 *Tel:* 518-537-2012 *E-mail:* info@timedexposures.com *Web Site:* www.timedexposures.com, pg 914

Armaly, Samir, TiVo Corp, 2 Circle Star Way, San Carlos, CA 94070 *Tel:* 408-562-8400 *Toll Free Tel:* 877-367-8486 (cust support); 877-289-8486 (sales support) *Fax:* 408-567-1800 *Web Site:* business.tivo.com; www.tivo.com, pg 914

Armand, Alyssa, Atlanta Film Festival (ATLFF), 25 Park Place NE, Suite 800, Atlanta, GA 30303 *Tel:* 678-929-8103 *E-mail:* info@atlantafilmfestival.com; submit@atlantafilmfestival.com *Web Site:* www.atlantafilmfestival.com, pg 982

Armenia, John, Accusoft, 4001 N Riverside Dr, Tampa, FL 33603 *Tel:* 813-875-7575 *Toll Free Tel:* 800-875-7009 *Fax:* 813-875-7705 *E-mail:* sales@accusoft.com *Web Site:* www.accusoft.com, pg 674

Armer, Tony, St Petersburg/Clearwater Film Commission, 8200 Bryan Dairy Rd, Suite 200, Largo, FL 33777 *Tel:* 727-464-7241 *Toll Free Tel:* 877-352-3224 *E-mail:* info@filmspc.com *Web Site:* www.filmstpeteclearwater.com, pg 969

Armon, Norma, International Contact Inc, 2820 Adeline St, Suite 1, Berkeley, CA 94703 *Tel:* 510-836-1180 *Fax:* 510-835-1314 *E-mail:* sales@intlcontact.com *Web Site:* www.intlcontact.com, pg 790

Armstrong, Doug, KTVB-TV, 5407 W Fairview Ave, Boise, ID 83706 *Tel:* 208-375-7277 *Toll Free Tel:* 800-559-7277 *Fax:* 208-378-5642; 208-375-7770 (news fax) *E-mail:* info@ktvb.com; ktvbnews@ktvb.com *Web Site:* www.ktvb.com, pg 802

Armstrong, Emma, iCrossing Inc, a Hearst Company, 300 W 57 St, New York, NY 10019 *Tel:* 212-649-3900 *Toll Free Tel:* 866-620-3780 *E-mail:* general@icrossing.com *Web Site:* www.icrossing.com, pg 783

Armstrong, Lea, The Weather Company, An IBM Business, 400 Minuteman Rd, Andover, MA 01810 *Tel:* 978-983-6300 *Fax:* 978-983-6400 *Web Site:* business.weather.com, pg 935

Armstrong, Lee, Images in Motion Media Inc, 720 Ladera Dr, Sonoma, CA 95476 *Tel:* 707-996-9474 *E-mail:* images@vom.com *Web Site:* www.imagesmedia.com, pg 785

Arnold, Andrea, Zebedee Productions, 231 SW Fifth Ct, Pompano Beach, FL 33060 *Tel:* 954-942-0044 *E-mail:* info@zbd.us *Web Site:* zebedeeproductions.com, pg 945

Arnold, Christopher, Fred Rogers Productions, 2100 Wharton St, Suite 700, Pittsburgh, PA 15203 *Tel:* 412-687-2990 *Toll Free Tel:* 877-677-6437 *E-mail:* info@fredrogers.org *Web Site:* www.fredrogers.org, pg 876

Arnold, Dawn, Production Craft Inc, 1937 W Walnut St, Chicago, IL 60612 *Tel:* 312-829-0272 *Fax:* 312-829-8936 *E-mail:* info@productioncraft.com *Web Site:* www.productioncraft.com, pg 863

Arnold, Kelly, Ingram Content Group LLC, One Ingram Blvd, La Vergne, TN 37086-1986 *Tel:* 615-793-5000 *Toll Free Tel:* 800-937-8000 (retailers); 800-937-5300 (ext 1, libs) *E-mail:* customerservice@ingramcontent.com *Web Site:* www.ingramcontent.com, pg 787

Arnold, Nick, Denver Media Center, 2601 Lemay, Suite 7, PMB 227, Fort Collins, CO 80525 *Tel:* 720-255-1640 (ext 101) *Web Site:* denvermediacenter.com, pg 740

Arnold, Sandy, Zebedee Productions, 231 SW Fifth Ct, Pompano Beach, FL 33060 *Tel:* 954-942-0044 *E-mail:* info@zbd.us *Web Site:* zebedeeproductions.com, pg 945

Arocho, Hector, Astoria Communications Inc, 5553 Ravenswood Rd, Suite 101, Fort Lauderdale, FL 33312 *Tel:* 305-728-4280 *Toll Free Tel:* 877-GETMEAV (438-6328) *Fax:* 954-367-5883 *E-mail:* info@astoria.productions *Web Site:* www.getmeav.com, pg 691

Aronoff, Amy, NYSCA/NYFA Artist Fellowships, 20 Jay St, 7th fl, Suite 740, Brooklyn, NY 11201 *Tel:* 212-366-6900 *Fax:* 212-366-1778 *E-mail:* fellowships@nyfa.org *Web Site:* www.nyfa.org, pg 999

Aronow, Gil, Sony Music Commercial Music Group, 550 Madison Ave, New York, NY 10022 *Tel:* 212-833-8000 *Web Site:* www.sonymusic.com, pg 893

Arrington, Janice, Orange County Film Commission, 53 La Costa Ct, Laguna Beach, CA 92651 *Tel:* 949-246-9704 *Web Site:* www.filmorangecounty.org, pg 966

Arroyo, Cristian, Rosco Laboratories Inc, 52 Harbor View, Stamford, CT 06902 *Tel:* 203-708-8900 *Toll Free Tel:* 800-ROSCO NY (767-2669) *Fax:* 203-708-8919 *E-mail:* info@rosco.com *Web Site:* us.rosco.com, pg 877

Arsenault, Jessica, Inner Traditions International, One Park St, Rochester, VT 05767 *Tel:* 802-767-3174 *Toll Free Tel:* 800-246-8648 *Fax:* 802-767-3726 *E-mail:* customerservice@innertraditions.com *Web Site:* www.innertraditions.com, pg 788

Arth, Violet, Real to Reel International Film Festival, 111 S Washington St, Shelby, NC 28150 *Tel:* 704-484-2787 *Fax:* 704-481-1822 *Web Site:* www.ccartscouncil.org/realtoreel, pg 1000

Arthur, Michael, Beekman Books Inc, 300 Old All Angels Hill Rd, Wappingers Falls, NY 12590 *Tel:* 845-297-2690 *Fax:* 845-297-1002 *E-mail:* beekmanbooks@yahoo.com, pg 703

Asadorian, Alan, Dorian Color, 100 Main St, Melrose, MA 02176 *Tel:* 781-648-8040 *E-mail:* images@doriancolor.com *Web Site:* www.doriancolor.com, pg 745

Ash, Jeff, Welocalize, 241 E Fourth St, Suite 207, Frederick, MD 21701 *Tel:* 301-668-0330 *Toll Free Tel:* 800-370-9515 *Fax:* 301-668-0335 *E-mail:* info@welocalize.com *Web Site:* www.welocalize.com, pg 935

Ashbaugh, Scott, OmniMount Systems, 4409 E Baseline Rd, Suite 100, Phoenix, AZ 85042 *Tel:* 480-829-8000 *Toll Free Tel:* 800-MOUNT-IT (668-6848) *Fax:* 480-756-9000 *E-mail:* info@omnimount.com *Web Site:* www.omnimount.com, pg 845

Asher, Howard, Stray Angel Films, 11318 Santa Monica Blvd, Los Angeles, CA 90025 *Tel:* 310-277-6900 *Fax:* 801-438-5009 *E-mail:* rentals@strayangel.com *Web Site:* www.strayangel.com, pg 902

Asher, Timothy, Idle Minds Productions Inc, 3405 Pepperhill Rd, Lexington, KY 40502 *Tel:* 859-268-8500 *Fax:* 859-268-8500 *E-mail:* idleminds@twc.com, pg 784

Ashley, Lindsey, Texas Film Commission, 1100 San Jacinto, Suite 3.410, Austin, TX 78701 *Tel:* 512-463-9200 *Fax:* 512-463-4114 *Web Site:* gov.texas.gov/film, pg 976

Ashram, Satchidananda, Shakticom, 108 Yogaville Way, Buckingham, VA 23921 *Tel:* 434-969-1347 *Toll Free Tel:* 800-476-1347 (orders) *E-mail:* sales@shakticom.org *Web Site:* www.shakticom.org, pg 885

Ashton, Jonathan, Agfa Graphics, 611 River Dr, Ctr 3, Elmwood Park, NJ 07407 *Tel:* 201-440-2500 *Toll Free Tel:* 800-540-2432; 888-274-8626 (cust serv) *E-mail:* graphics@agfa.com *Web Site:* www.agfa.com; www.agfagraphics.com, pg 678

Ashton, Stacey, Fabled Films LLC, 200 Park Ave S, 15th fl, New York, NY 10003 *Tel:* 212-220-5804 *E-mail:* info@fabledfilms.com *Web Site:* www.fabledfilms.com, pg 758

Ashworth, Cary, ACS Technologies, 180 Dunbarton Dr, Florence, SC 29501 *Tel:* 843-662-1681 *Toll Free Tel:* 800-736-7425 (sales); 800-669-2309 (support) *Fax:* 843-669-7513 *E-mail:* info@acstechnologies.com *Web Site:* www.acstechnologies.com, pg 674

Askew, Graham, FrontRow, 1690 Corporate Circle, Petaluma, CA 94954 *Tel:* 707-769-1110 *Toll Free Tel:* 800-227-0735 *Fax:* 707-769-9624 *E-mail:* customercare@gofrontrow.com *Web Site:* www.gofrontrow.com, pg 766

Asling, Dave, New Deal Studios, 15392 Cobalt St, Los Angeles, CA 91342 *Tel:* 310-578-9929 *E-mail:* info@newdealstudios.com *Web Site:* www.newdealstudios.com, pg 839

Astor, Eric, Furnace MFG, 2719-B Dorr Ave, Fairfax, VA 22031 *Tel:* 703-205-0007 *Toll Free Tel:* 888-599-9883 *Fax:* 703-205-2951 *E-mail:* sales@furnacemfg.com *Web Site:* www.furnacemfg.com, pg 767

Atamanenko, Boris, NWT Arts Council, Community Programs Office, PO Box 1320, Yellowknife, NT X1A 2L9, Canada *Tel:* 867-767-9347 (ext 71474) *Toll Free Tel:* 867-445-2787 *Fax:* 867-873-0205 *Web Site:* www.nwtartscouncil.ca, pg 998

Atkin, Michael, Broadview Software Inc, 110 Adelaide St E, Toronto, ON M5C 1K9, Canada *Tel:* 647-255-3500 *Fax:* 416-778-0648 *E-mail:* sales@broadviewsoftware.com *Web Site:* www.broadviewsoftware.com, pg 711

Atkins, Michele, Kaboom Productions, 2169 Folsom St, Suite 201-M, San Francisco, CA 94110 *Tel:* 415-434-2666 *Fax:* 415-874-9324 *E-mail:* hello@kaboomproductions.com *Web Site:* kaboomproductions.com, pg 796

Atkins, Robert, Advanced Audio Technology, 200 Easy St, Carol Stream, IL 60188 *Tel:* 630-665-3344 *Fax:* 630-665-3347 *E-mail:* aat@ameritech.net *Web Site:* www.advancedaudio.net, pg 674

Atkinson, Gary, The Singing Machine Co Inc, 6301 NW Fifth Way, Suite 2900, Fort Lauderdale, FL 33309 *Tel:* 954-596-1000 *Toll Free Tel:* 866-670-6888 (cust serv) *Fax:* 954-596-2000 *E-mail:* sales@singingmachine.com; customerservice@singingmachine.com *Web Site:* singingmachine.com, pg 889

Atkinson, Jason, University Media Services, University of Delaware, 85 E Delaware Ave, Newark, DE 19716 *Tel:* 302-831-3546 *Web Site:* sites.udel.edu/it-ums/, pg 922

Atkinson, Kelly, Penguin Random House Audio Publishing, 1745 Broadway, New York, NY 10019 *E-mail:* audio@penguinrandomhouse.com *Web Site:* www.penguinrandomhouseaudio.com, pg 853

Auclair, James, WGBH Stock Sales, One Guest St, Boston, MA 02135 *Tel:* 617-300-3939 *Fax:* 617-300-1056 *E-mail:* stock_sales@wgbh.org *Web Site:* www.wgbhstocksales.org, pg 936

Audley, Paul, FilmL.A., Inc, 6255 W Sunset Blvd, 12th fl, Los Angeles, CA 90028 *Tel:* 213-977-8600 *Fax:* 213-977-8601 (permits) *E-mail:* info@filmla.com *Web Site:* www.filmla.com, pg 954, 966

Auerbach, Abby, Television Bureau of Advertising Inc (TVB), 120 Wall St, 15th fl, New York, NY 10005-3908 *Tel:* 212-486-1111 *Fax:* 212-935-5631 *E-mail:* info@tvb.org *Web Site:* www.tvb.org, pg 963

Auerbach, Richard, Z-Systems Audio Engineering, 1325 NW 53 Ave, Suite B, Gainesville, FL 32609 *Tel:* 352-371-0990 *E-mail:* z-sys@z-sys.com *Web Site:* www.z-sys.com, pg 944

Auffret, Laurent, FACE Foundation, 972 Fifth Ave, New York, NY 10075 *Tel:* 212-439-1439 *E-mail:* info@face-foundation.org *Web Site:* www.face-foundation.org, pg 758

Augustine-Pierce, Gregory F, ACTA Publications, 4848 N Clark St, Chicago, IL 60640 *Tel:* 773-271-1030 *Toll Free Tel:* 800-397-2282 *Fax:* 773-271-7399 *Toll Free Fax:* 800-397-0079 *E-mail:* actapublications@actapublications.com *Web Site:* www.actapublications.com, pg 675

Augusto, Augie, SDMediaPros (SDMP), 5205 Kearny Villa Way, No 100, San Diego, CA 92123 *Tel:* 619-672-1000 *E-mail:* membership@sdmediapros.org; marketing@sdmediapros.org; programs@sdmediapros.org *Web Site:* sdmediapros.org, pg 961

Aukerman, Gregg, Visioneering International Inc, 659 Auburn Ave NE, Suite 267, Atlanta, GA 30312 *Tel:* 404-681-9028 *Fax:* 404-681-5947 *E-mail:* design@visioneering.com *Web Site:* www.visioneering.com, pg 931

Aukerman, Rob, CSI Film & Video LLC, 1913 Sonora St, Fort Collins, CO 80525 *Tel:* 970-310-9039 *Web Site:* csifilms.com, pg 735

Auld, Lynton, RGB Spectrum, 950 Marina Village Pkwy, Alameda, CA 94501 *Tel:* 510-814-7000 *Fax:* 510-814-7026 *Web Site:* www.rgb.com, pg 874

Ault, Michael, Heartland International Film Festival, 1043 Virginia Ave, Suite 2, Indianapolis, IN 46203 *Tel:* 317-464-9405 *E-mail:* submissions@heartlandfilm.org *Web Site:* heartlandfilm.org/festival, pg 992

Ault, Michael, Indy Shorts International Film Fest, 1043 Virginia Ave, Suite 2, Indianapolis, IN 46203 *Tel:* 317-464-9405 *E-mail:* submissions@heartlandfilm.org *Web Site:* heartlandfilm.org, pg 993

Aurichio, Jeffrey, Agfa Graphics, 611 River Dr, Ctr 3, Elmwood Park, NJ 07407 *Tel:* 201-440-2500 *Toll Free Tel:* 800-540-2432; 888-274-8626 (cust serv) *E-mail:* graphics@agfa.com *Web Site:* www.agfa.com; www.agfagraphics.com, pg 678

Austin, Howard, Music World/Vocal Power School, 9826 Columbus Ave, North Hills, CA 91343 *Tel:* 818-895-7464 *Toll Free Tel:* 800-929-7464 *E-mail:* MusicMan@music-world.com; provoice777@icloud.com *Web Site:* www.BornToSing.com; www.music-world.com, pg 834

Austin, Janet, San Francisco Film Commission, City Hall, Rm 473, One Dr Carlton B Goodlett Place, San Francisco, CA 94102 *Tel:* 415-554-6241 *Fax:* 415-554-6503 *E-mail:* film@sfgov.org *Web Site:* www.filmsf.org/film-commission; www.facebook.com/FilmSF, pg 967

Austman, Eric, Tek Gear, 938 Corydon Ave, Winnipeg, MB R3M 0Y5, Canada *Tel:* 204-988-3001 *Fax:* 204-988-3050 *E-mail:* sales@tekgear.com *Web Site:* tekgear.com, pg 909

Auth, Mark, C2 Imaging, 2 Harborside, 200 Hudson St, Suite 201, Jersey City, NJ 07311 *Tel:* 646-557-6300 *Web Site:* www.c2spark.com, pg 736

AuYeung, PoChu, Vancouver International Film Festival (VIFF), Vancouver International Film Ctr, 1181 Seymour St, Vancouver, BC V6B 3M7, Canada *Tel:* 604-685-0260 *Fax:* 604-688-8221 *E-mail:* info@viff.org; submissions@viff.org *Web Site:* www.viff.org, pg 1006

Auzenne, Maggie, Visions Film Festival & Conference, 601 S College Rd, Wilmington, NC 28403 *Tel:* 919-607-0031 *E-mail:* visions7programming@gmail.com; visions7development@gmail.com *Web Site:* www.visionsffc.org, pg 1006

Avalos, Jorge, ARC Document Solutions, 1981 N Broadway, Suite 385, Walnut Creek, CA 94596 *Tel:* 925-949-5100 *Toll Free Tel:* 855-500-0660 *E-mail:* contact@e-arc.com *Web Site:* www.e-arc.com, pg 688

Avanzino, Angela, Jameco Electronics, 1355 Shoreway Rd, Belmont, CA 94002 *Tel:* 650-592-8097 *Toll Free Tel:* 800-831-4242 (orders); 800-536-4316 (cust serv) *Fax:* 650-592-2503 *Toll Free Fax:* 800-237-6948 *E-mail:* info@jameco.com; sales@jameco.com *Web Site:* www.jameco.com, pg 792

Averitt, Bryce, Producers Guild of America Inc (PGA), 8530 Wilshire Blvd, Suite 400, Beverly Hills, CA 90211 *Tel:* 310-358-9020 *E-mail:* info@producersguild.org *Web Site:* www.producersguild.org, pg 960

Avgerakis, George, Avekta Productions Inc, One Rock Place, Yonkers, NY 10705 *Tel:* 914-378-8000 *Web Site:* avekta.com, pg 697

Avgerakis, Maria, Avekta Productions Inc, One Rock Place, Yonkers, NY 10705 *Tel:* 914-378-8000 *Web Site:* avekta.com, pg 697

Avgikos, David, Digimation, 1515 International Pkwy, Suite 2013, Lake Mary, FL 32746 *Tel:* 407-833-0600 *E-mail:* sales@digimation.com *Web Site:* digimation.com, pg 741

Avila, Justine, Mayor's Office of Economic & Community Development, One Public Sq, Suite 100, Nashville, TN 37201 *Tel:* 615-862-6000 *Web Site:* www.nashville.gov, pg 976

Awad, Dennis, Zack Electronics Inc, 1075 Hamilton Rd, Duarte, CA 91010 *Tel:* 626-303-0655 *Toll Free Tel:* 800-466-0449 *Fax:* 626-303-8694 *E-mail:* info@zackelectronics.com *Web Site:* www.zackelectronics.com, pg 945

Ayoob, Ameen, Indus International Inc, 340 S Oak St, West Salem, WI 54669 *Tel:* 608-786-0300 *Toll Free Tel:* 800-843-9377 *Fax:* 608-786-0786 *Web Site:* www.indususa.com, pg 787

Ayoub, Paul, Digital Video Productions, 257 Federal Rd, Brookfield, CT 06804 *Tel:* 203-743-7663 *Fax:* 203-743-1658 *E-mail:* info@dvpllc.com *Web Site:* dvpllc.com, pg 742

Azevedo, Luke, City of Calgary Film Commission, 731 First St SE, Calgary, AB T2G 2G9, Canada *Tel:* 403-221-7886 *Toll Free Tel:* 888-222-5855 *Fax:* 403-221-7828 *Web Site:* www.calgaryeconomicdevelopment.com, pg 977

Azize, Hamid, Stage Crew Audiovisual Inc, PO Box 6097, San Juan, PR 00914-6097 *Tel:* 787-723-6398 *Fax:* 787-721-1410, pg 898

Azorsky, Greg, Audio-VideoGraphics Inc, 17501 E 40 Hwy, Suite 219, Independence, MO 64055 *Tel:* 816-350-0800 *Toll Free Tel:* 800-322-2832 *Fax:* 816-350-0804 *Web Site:* www.avginc.com, pg 694

Azua, Dawn, The Videohouse Inc, 975 Greentree Rd, Pittsburgh, PA 15220 *Tel:* 412-921-7577 *Fax:* 412-921-5535 *E-mail:* info@thevideohouse.com *Web Site:* www.thevideohouse.com, pg 929

B, Stevie, Mia Mind Music, 254 Sixth St, Suite 2, Hoboken, NJ 07030-6916 *Toll Free Tel:* 800-843-8575 *E-mail:* info@miamindmusic.com *Web Site:* www.miamindmusic.com, pg 825

Baade, Andy, Tempe Tape & Disc, 722 W Raven Dr, Chandler, AZ 85286 *Tel:* 602-453-9663 *Web Site:* www.tempetape.com, pg 911

Babb, Paul, MAXON Computer Inc, 2640 Lavery Ct, Suite A, Newbury Park, CA 91320 *Tel:* 805-376-3333 *Fax:* 805-376-3331 *E-mail:* info_us@maxon.net *Web Site:* www.maxon.net, pg 820

Babej, Colin, American AV, 8005 Haute Ct, Springfield, VA 22150 *Tel:* 703-573-6910 *Fax:* 703-573-3539 *E-mail:* sales@aavevents.com *Web Site:* www.aavevents.com, pg 683

Babendreier, Zachary, Potomac Instruments Inc, 7309 Grove Rd, Unit D, Frederick, MD 21704 *Tel:* 301-696-5550 *Fax:* 301-696-5553 *E-mail:* sales@pi-usa.com; service@pi-usa.com *Web Site:* www.pi-usa.com, pg 860

Babu, Ayuko, Pan African Film & Arts Festival, 6820 La Tijera Blvd, Suite 200, Los Angeles, CA 90045 *Tel:* 310-337-4737 *Fax:* 310-337-4736 *E-mail:* info@paff.org; submissions@paff.org *Web Site:* www.paff.org, pg 999

Baca, Kathy, Lectrosonics Inc, 581 Laser Rd NE, Rio Rancho, NM 87124 *Tel:* 505-892-4501 *Toll Free Tel:* 800-821-1121 *Fax:* 505-892-6243 *E-mail:* sales@lectrosonics.com *Web Site:* www.lectrosonics.com, pg 805

Bachmann, Bill, Bill Bachmann Studios, PO Box 950833, Lake Mary, FL 32795 *Tel:* 407-333-9988 *Web Site:* www.billbachmann.com, pg 705

Bachmann, Michael, Hearst Entertainment & Syndication, 300 W 57 St, New York, NY 10019-5238 *Web Site:* www.hearst.com/entertainment-syndication, pg 778

Badagliacca, Mark, Paramount Pictures Corporation, 5555 Melrose Ave, Los Angeles, CA 90038 *Tel:* 323-956-8398 *Web Site:* www.paramount.com, pg 851

Badavas, Christos P, SESAC Inc, 35 Music Sq E, Nashville, TN 37203 *Tel:* 615-320-0055 *Web Site:* www.sesac.com, pg 962

Badeaux, Floyd J, Great Recordings LLC, 1812 Procter St, Port Arthur, TX 77640 *Tel:* 409-982-7121 *E-mail:* music@great-recordings.com *Web Site:* www.great-recordings.com, pg 773

Bader, Carl, Aviom Inc, 1157 Phoenixville Pike, Suite 201, West Chester, PA 19380-4254 *Tel:* 610-738-9005 *Fax:* 610-738-9950 *E-mail:* info@aviom.com *Web Site:* www.aviom.com, pg 699

Badiyan, Fred, Badiyan Inc, 720 W 94 St, Bloomington, MN 55420 *Tel:* 952-888-5507 *Fax:* 952-888-0360 *E-mail:* info@badiyan.com *Web Site:* www.badiyan.com, pg 700

Badke, John, Vicon Industries Inc, 135 Fell Ct, Hauppauge, NY 11788-4351 *Tel:* 631-952-2288 *Toll Free Tel:* 800-645-9116 *Fax:* 631-951-2288 *E-mail:* sales@vicon-security.com *Web Site:* www.vicon-security.com, pg 926

Bagerdjian, Haig, Point.360, 2701 Media Center Dr, Los Angeles, CA 90065 *Tel:* 323-987-9400 *Fax:* 818-847-2503 *E-mail:* sales@point360.com *Web Site:* point360.com, pg 858

Baggett, Todd, Creation Technologies Inc, 8999 Fraserton Ct, Burnaby, BC V5J 5H8, Canada *Tel:* 604-430-4336 *Toll Free Tel:* 800-736-1271 *E-mail:* info@creationtech.com; sales@creationtech.com *Web Site:* www.creationtech.com, pg 733

Bagnell, John, The Whitlock Group, 12820 West Creek Pkwy, Richmond, VA 23238 *Tel:* 804-273-9100 *Toll Free Tel:* 800-726-9843 *Fax:* 804-273-9380 *E-mail:* information@whitlock.com; marketing@whitlock.com *Web Site:* www.whitlock.com, pg 937

Bahan, Melodie, Minnesota Film & TV, 401 N Third St, Suite 245, Minneapolis, MN 55401 *Tel:* 612-767-0095 *E-mail:* info@mnfilmtv.org *Web Site:* mnfilmtv.org, pg 972

Bahk, Jun, DASAN Zhone Solutions (DZS) Inc, 7195 Oakport St, Oakland, CA 94621 *Tel:* 510-777-7000 *Toll Free Tel:* 877-ZHONE-20 (946-6320, US & CN) *Fax:* 510-777-7001 *Web Site:* dasanzhone.com, pg 737

Bailard, Brian, ARC Document Solutions, 1981 N Broadway, Suite 385, Walnut Creek, CA 94596 *Tel:* 925-949-5100 *Toll Free Tel:* 855-500-0660 *E-mail:* contact@e-arc.com *Web Site:* www.e-arc.com, pg 688

Bailey, Glenda, Camcor Inc, 2273 S Church St, Burlington, NC 27215 *Tel:* 336-228-0251 *Toll Free Tel:* 800-868-2462 *Fax:* 336-222-8011 *Toll Free Fax:* 800-298-1181 *E-mail:* info@camcor.com *Web Site:* www.camcor.com, pg 715

Bailey, John, The Whitlock Group, 12820 West Creek Pkwy, Richmond, VA 23238 *Tel:* 804-273-9100 *Toll Free Tel:* 800-726-9843 *Fax:* 804-273-9380 *E-mail:* information@whitlock.com; marketing@ whitlock.com *Web Site:* www.whitlock.com, pg 937

Bailey, Ray E Sr, Camcor Inc, 2273 S Church St, Burlington, NC 27215 *Tel:* 336-228-0251 *Toll Free Tel:* 800-868-2462 *Fax:* 336-222-8011 *Toll Free Fax:* 800-298-1181 *E-mail:* info@camcor.com *Web Site:* www.camcor.com, pg 715

Bailey, Scott, Whalley-Abbey Media Holdings Inc, 3800 Rue St Patrick, Suite 100, Montreal, QC H4E 1A4, Canada *Tel:* 514-846-1940 *E-mail:* info@wamgrp.com *Web Site:* wamgrp.com, pg 937

Bailey, Steven, University of Toronto Academic & Campus Events, St George Campus, McMurrich Bldg, 4th fl, 12 Queen's Park Crescent W, Toronto, ON M5S 1S8, Canada *Tel:* 416-978-2187; 416-978-8613 (film & photo shoot permits) *Fax:* 416-978-4802 *E-mail:* ace.team@utoronto.ca *Web Site:* www.ace.utoronto.ca, pg 979

Bailey, Wes, 4 Wall Entertainment, 3165 W Sunset Rd, Suite 100, Las Vegas, NV 89118 *Tel:* 702-263-3858 *Toll Free Tel:* 877-789-8167 (Western US) *Fax:* 702-263-3863 *E-mail:* info@4wall.com; info@usedlighting.com *Web Site:* www.4wall.com; www.usedlighting.com, pg 764

Bain, Sinjin, Method Studios, 3401 Exposition Blvd, Santa Monica, CA 90404 *Tel:* 310-434-6000 *Web Site:* www.methodstudios.com, pg 824

Bakala, Joe, Warner Home Video Inc, 4000 Warner Blvd, Bldg 160, Burbank, CA 91522 *Tel:* 818-954-6000 *Fax:* 818-954-6480 *Web Site:* www.warnerbros.com, pg 934

Baker, Aaron J, AGF Media Services, 21522 Osborne St, Canoga Park, CA 91304 *Tel:* 818-780-7400 *Fax:* 818-904-9905 *E-mail:* info@agfmedia.com *Web Site:* www.agfmedia.com, pg 678

Baker, Brian, Sound Arts Recording Studio, 8377 Westview Dr, Houston, TX 77055-5737 *Tel:* 713-464-4653 *Web Site:* www.soundartsrecording.com, pg 893

Baker, Carolyn C, American Counseling Association, 6101 Stevenson Ave, Suite 600, Alexandria, VA 22304 *Tel:* 703-823-9800 (ext 222) *Toll Free Tel:* 800-347-6647 (ext 222) *Fax:* 703-823-0252 *E-mail:* membership@counseling.org *Web Site:* www.counseling.org, pg 683

Baker, Dave, Go To Team, 665 Johnnie Dodds Blvd, Suite 201, Mount Pleasant, SC 29464 *Tel:* 843-884-6222 *Toll Free Tel:* 888-455-4333 *E-mail:* crew@gototeam.com *Web Site:* www.gototeam.com, pg 772

Baker, Giles, Dolby Laboratories Inc, 1275 Market St, San Francisco, CA 94103-1410 *Tel:* 415-558-0200 *Fax:* 415-645-4000 *Web Site:* www.dolby.com, pg 745

Baker, Guy, Limbo Films, 2223 NE Martin Luther King Jr Blvd, Portland, OR 97212 *E-mail:* info@limbofilms.com *Web Site:* www.limbofilms.com, pg 808

Baker, Jeffrey, AGF Media Services, 21522 Osborne St, Canoga Park, CA 91304 *Tel:* 818-780-7400 *Fax:* 818-904-9905 *E-mail:* info@agfmedia.com *Web Site:* www.agfmedia.com, pg 678

Baker, Jim, Blue Barn Pictures Inc, 68 Jay St, Suite 311, Brooklyn, NY 11201 *Web Site:* www.bluebarnpictures.com, pg 707

Baker, John, Story Teller Effects Group LLC, 333 River Rd, Jefferson, LA 70121 *Tel:* 504-832-9800 *Fax:* 504-832-9955 *E-mail:* storytellerfx@gmail.com; sales@storytellerfx.com *Web Site:* www.riggspfx.com, pg 901

Baker, Karen, Merced Film Commission, California Welcome Ctr, 710 W 16 St, Merced, CA 95340 *Tel:* 209-724-8104 *Toll Free Tel:* 800-446-5353 *E-mail:* info@visitmerced.travel *Web Site:* visitmerced. travel, pg 967

Baker, Keith, Physical Optics Corp (POC), 1845 E 205 St, Torrance, CA 90501-1510 *Tel:* 310-320-3088 *E-mail:* info@poc.com *Web Site:* www.poc.com, pg 856

Baker, Mark, The Whitlock Group, 12820 West Creek Pkwy, Richmond, VA 23238 *Tel:* 804-273-9100 *Toll Free Tel:* 800-726-9843 *Fax:* 804-273-9380 *E-mail:* information@whitlock.com; marketing@ whitlock.com *Web Site:* www.whitlock.com, pg 937

Baker, Nick, Show-Me Audio-Visual, Corporate Ridge, 4501 Blue Ridge Cutoff, Kansas City, MO 64133 *Tel:* 816-358-8700 *Toll Free Tel:* 800-2-SHOWME (274-6963) *Fax:* 816-358-8701 *E-mail:* info@showmeav.com *Web Site:* www.showmeav.com, pg 887

Baker, Paul, National Association for Music Education (NAfME), 1806 Robert Fulton Dr, Reston, VA 20191 *Tel:* 703-860-4000 *Toll Free Tel:* 800-336-3768 *Fax:* 703-860-1531 *Toll Free Fax:* 888-275-6362 *E-mail:* memberservices@nafme.org *Web Site:* nafme.org, pg 958

Baker, Richard, FilmNation Entertainment, 150 W 22 St, 9th fl, New York, NY 10011 *Web Site:* www.filmnation.com, pg 760

Baker, Rick, Meridia ARS, 1646 West Chester Pike, Suite 15, West Chester, PA 19382 *Tel:* 610-260-6800 *Fax:* 610-260-6810 *E-mail:* rsvp@meridiaars.com *Web Site:* www.meridiaars.com, pg 823

Baker, Robert, Westworks Studios, 4100 E Dry Creek Rd, Littleton, CO 80122 *Toll Free Tel:* 800-491-1947 *E-mail:* info@westworksstudios.com *Web Site:* westworksstudios.com, pg 936

Balaban, Marko, Canadian Screen Awards, 49 Ontario St, Suite 501, Toronto, ON M5A 2V1, Canada *Tel:* 416-366-2227 *Toll Free Tel:* 800-644-5194 *Fax:* 416-366-8454 *E-mail:* awards@academy.ca; info@academy.ca *Web Site:* www.academy.ca/canadian-screen-awards, pg 985

Balagula, Ella, John Wiley & Sons Inc, 111 River St, Hoboken, NJ 07030-5774 *Tel:* 201-748-6000 *Toll Free Tel:* 800-225-5945 (cust serv) *Fax:* 201-748-6088 *Web Site:* www.wiley.com, pg 938

Baldock, Phil, ARRIS Group Inc, 3871 Lakefield Dr, Suwanee, GA 30024 *Tel:* 678-473-2907 *Toll Free Tel:* 866-36-ARRIS (362-7747); 877-466-8646 (tech) *Fax:* 678-473-8470 *E-mail:* marketing@arris.com *Web Site:* www.arris.com, pg 689

Baldwin, Jim, Baldwin Productions Services Inc, 160 Tioga Lane, Greenbrae, CA 94904 *Tel:* 415-699-0729 *Web Site:* www.baldwinproductionsinc.com, pg 701

Baldwin, Margo, Chelsea Green Publishing Co, 85 N Main St, Suite 120, White River Junction, VT 05001 *Tel:* 802-295-6300 *Toll Free Tel:* 800-639-4099 (orders) *Fax:* 802-295-6444 *E-mail:* customerservice@chelseagreen.com *Web Site:* www.chelseagreen.com, pg 721

Baldwin, Maureen, Russound, One Forbes Rd, Newmarket, NH 03857 *Tel:* 603-659-5170 *Toll Free Tel:* 800-638-8055 (US) *Fax:* 603-659-5388 *E-mail:* sales@russound.com; tech@russound.com *Web Site:* www.russound.com, pg 879

Baldwin, Robin, IEEE Computer Society Press, 10662 Los Vaqueros Circle, Los Alamitos, CA 90720-1314 *Tel:* 714-821-8380 *Toll Free Tel:* 800-272-6657 (cust serv) *Fax:* 714-821-4010 *E-mail:* help@computer.org *Web Site:* www.computer.org, pg 784

Baldwin, Whit, HeloAir Inc, 5721 Gulfstream Rd, Richmond, VA 23250 *Tel:* 804-226-3400 *Toll Free Tel:* 888-FLY-HELO (359-4356) *Fax:* 804-226-3494 *E-mail:* info@heloair.com *Web Site:* www.heloair.com, pg 778

Balkcom, Kyle, Presentation Products Inc, 171 Madison Ave, 12th fl, New York, NY 10016 *Tel:* 212-736-6350 *Toll Free Tel:* 877-774-4523 *Fax:* 212-736-6353 *E-mail:* customerservice@pproducts.com *Web Site:* www.presentationproducts.com, pg 861

Ball, Jennifer, Promax, 5700 Wilshire Blvd, Suite 275, Los Angeles, CA 90036 *Tel:* 310-788-7600 *Fax:* 310-788-7616 *Web Site:* www.promax.org, pg 961

Ball, Michael, Accord Productions, 2140 S Dixie Hwy, Suite 301, Miami, FL 33133 *Tel:* 305-856-1245; 305-985-5842 *Toll Free Tel:* 800-833-1245 *Fax:* 305-856-9101 *E-mail:* mail@accordvideo.com *Web Site:* www.accordproductions.com, pg 673

Ball, Rick, PSSI Global Services LLC, 7030 Hayvenhurst Ave, Van Nuys, CA 91406 *Tel:* 310-575-4400 *Toll Free Tel:* 800-SAT-LINK (728-5465); 800-634-6530 (teleport inquiries) *E-mail:* info@pssiglobal.com *Web Site:* www.pssiglobal.com, pg 866

Ballard, Kirsten, Bexel, an NEP Broadcast Services Company, 2701 N Ontario St, Burbank, CA 91504 *Tel:* 818-565-4322 *Toll Free Tel:* 800-225-6185 (tech support) *E-mail:* services@bexel.com *Web Site:* bexel.com, pg 704

Ballard, Stevie, American Visions, One Deerfield Lane, Cedar Rapids, IA 52403 *Tel:* 319-360-3211 *Web Site:* www.americanvisions.org, pg 684

Ballingham, Pamala, Earth Mother Productions Inc™, PO Box 43204, Tucson, AZ 85733-3204 *Tel:* 520-365-3608 *E-mail:* art4wall@aol.com *Web Site:* www.earthmotherproductions.com, pg 749

Ballingham, Tim, Earth Mother Productions Inc™, PO Box 43204, Tucson, AZ 85733-3204 *Tel:* 520-365-3608 *E-mail:* art4wall@aol.com *Web Site:* www.earthmotherproductions.com, pg 749

Ballo, Robert, Goal Productions, 1905 Victory Blvd, Suite 6, Glendale, CA 91201 *Tel:* 818-588-3900 *Fax:* 818-588-3903 *E-mail:* info@goalproductions.com *Web Site:* www.goalproductions.com, pg 772

Balsmeyer, Randall, Big Film Design, 375 South End Ave, Suite 3H, New York, NY 10280 *Tel:* 212-627-3430 *E-mail:* info@bigfilmdesign.com *Web Site:* www.bigfilmdesign.com, pg 705

Baltazar, Mark, Broadstreet Productions LLC, 242 W 30 St, 2nd fl, New York, NY 10001 *Tel:* 212-780-5700 *E-mail:* newyork@broadstreet.com; admin@broadstreet.com *Web Site:* www.broadstreet.com, pg 711

Balzer, Nolan, DACAPO Productions Inc, 516 Hargrave St, Winnipeg, MB R3A 0X8, Canada *Tel:* 204-956-2867 *Fax:* 204-956-2869 *Web Site:* www.dacapo.ca, pg 737

Band, Amnon H, Band Pro Film & Digital Inc, 3403 W Pacific Ave, Burbank, CA 91505 *Tel:* 818-841-9655 *Toll Free Tel:* 888-BANDPRO (226-3776) *Fax:* 818-841-7649 *E-mail:* info@bandpro.com; customercare@bandpro.com *Web Site:* www.bandpro.com, pg 701

Bandolik, Keith A, Switchcraft® Inc, 5555 N Elston Ave, Chicago, IL 60630 *Tel:* 773-792-2700 *Fax:* 773-792-2129 *E-mail:* sales@switchcraft.com *Web Site:* www.switchcraft.com, pg 905

Bandy, Chad, Bisk Education, 9417 Princess Palm Ave, Tampa, FL 33619 *Toll Free Tel:* 800-280-9718 *E-mail:* media@bisk.com *Web Site:* www.bisk.com, pg 706

Banfill, Stephanie, I M P A C T Publishing Inc, 3409 47 Ave E, Bradenton, FL 34203 *Tel:* 941-739-2611 *Toll Free Tel:* 800-221-6121; 800-426-3963 *E-mail:* potentialsunlimitedcs@gmail.com *Web Site:* www.potentialsunlimited.com, pg 783

Banks, Jonathan, Research Technology International (RTI), 4700 Chase Ave, Lincolnwood, IL 60712-1689 *Tel:* 847-677-3000 *Toll Free Tel:* 800-323-7520 *Fax:* 847-677-1311 *Toll Free Fax:* 800-784-6733 *E-mail:* sales@rtico.com *Web Site:* rtico.com, pg 873

Banks, Jonathan A, Lipsner-Smith Co, 4700 Chase Ave, Lincolnwood, IL 60712-1689 *Tel:* 847-677-3000 *Toll Free Tel:* 800-323-7520 *Fax:* 847-677-1311 *Toll Free Fax:* 800-784-6733 *E-mail:* sales@lipsner.com; sales@rtico.com *Web Site:* www.lipsner.com; lipsner-smith.com, pg 809

Banks, Larry, Long Island University Media Arts Dept, One University Plaza, Brooklyn, NY 11201-8423 *Tel:* 718-488-1052 *Fax:* 718-780-4578 *E-mail:* mediart@brooklyn.liu.edu *Web Site:* www.liu.edu/brooklyn.aspx, pg 811

Banks, Myriam, Micor Analytics, 7538 Saint Louis Ave, Skokie, IL 60076 *Tel:* 847-329-8590 *Fax:* 847-329-8599 *Web Site:* www.micoranalytics.com, pg 825

Banks, Stephen, Impact Christian Books Inc, 332 Leffingwell Ave, Suite 101, Kirkwood, MO 63122 *Tel:* 314-822-3309 *E-mail:* info@impactchristianbooks.com *Web Site:* www.impactchristianbooks.com, pg 786

Bannister, Floyd, Loft 19, 21618 N Ninth Ave, Suite A, Phoenix, AZ 85027 *Tel:* 623-434-3791 *Fax:* 623-434-5003 *E-mail:* info@loft19.com *Web Site:* loft19.com, pg 811

Barabas, Becky, JBL Professional, 8500 Balboa Blvd, Northridge, CA 91329 *Tel:* 818-894-8850 *Fax:* 818-830-7865 (mktg); 818-894-3479; 818-830-7801 (sales) *E-mail:* info@jblpro.com *Web Site:* www.jblpro.com; www.harman.com, pg 793

Baran, Ericka C, Jeron Electronic Systems Inc, 7501 N Natchez Ave, Niles, IL 60714 *Tel:* 773-275-1900 *Toll Free Tel:* 800-621-1903 *Fax:* 773-275-0283 *E-mail:* sales@jeron.com *Web Site:* www.jeron.com, pg 794

Barber, Cindy, BMI Supply, 571 Queensbury Ave, Queensbury, NY 12804 *Tel:* 518-793-6706 *Toll Free Tel:* 800-836-0524 *Fax:* 518-793-6181 *E-mail:* bminy@bmisupply.com *Web Site:* www.bmisupply.com, pg 708

Barber, Eddie, Barber Tech Video Products, 5111 Via Corona St, East Los Angeles, CA 90022 *Tel:* 818-982-7775 *E-mail:* info@barbertvp.com; info@barbertech.com, pg 701

Barber, Mark, Troxell-CDI, 4675 E Cotton Center Blvd, Suite 155, Phoenix, AZ 85040 *Tel:* 602-437-7240 *Toll Free Tel:* 855-TROXELL (876-9355) *Fax:* 602-752-1299 *Toll Free Fax:* 800-752-1299 *E-mail:* csg@trox.com *Web Site:* www.troxellsolutions.com, pg 918

Barber, Raymond, Hollywood Vaults Inc, 742 N Seward St, Hollywood, CA 90038 *Tel:* 323-461-6464 *Toll Free Tel:* 800-569-5336 *Fax:* 323-461-6479 *E-mail:* vault@hollywoodvaults.com *Web Site:* www.hollywoodvaults.com, pg 781

Barbieri, Ernest, Thomas Craven Film Corp, 5 W 19 St, 3rd fl, New York, NY 10011-4216 *Tel:* 212-463-7190 *Fax:* 212-627-4761 *E-mail:* info@cravenfilms.com *Web Site:* cravenfilms.com, pg 733

Barblan, Matthew, Association of American Publishers (AAP), 455 Massachusetts Ave NW, Suite 700, Washington, DC 20001-2777 *Tel:* 202-347-3375 *Fax:* 202-347-3690 *E-mail:* info@publishers.org *Web Site:* publishers.org, pg 951

Barclay, Paul, Carr McLean Ltd, 461 Horner Ave, Toronto, ON M8W 4X2, Canada *Tel:* 416-252-3371 *Toll Free Tel:* 800-268-2123 (CN) *Fax:* 416-252-9203 *Toll Free Fax:* 800-871-2397 *E-mail:* sales@carrmclean.ca *Web Site:* www.carrmclean.ca, pg 717

Barella, Scott, PESA, 103 Quality Circle, Suite 210, Huntsville, AL 35806 *Tel:* 256-726-9200 *Toll Free Tel:* 800-323-7372 *E-mail:* sales@pesa.com *Web Site:* www.pesa.com, pg 855

Barella, Scott, Utah Scientific Inc, 4750 Wiley Post Way, Suite 150, Salt Lake City, UT 84116 *Tel:* 801-575-8801 *Toll Free Tel:* 800-453-8782 *Fax:* 801-537-3099 *E-mail:* info@utahscientific.com *Web Site:* utahscientific.com, pg 924

Barey, Pat, Teaberry, 770 W Landoran Lane, Tucson, AZ 85737 *Tel:* 520-429-7952 *Fax:* 520-742-0652 *E-mail:* info@tellens.com *Web Site:* www.tellens.com, pg 908

Barger, Ed, Barger-Lite, 12023 Victory Blvd, Los Angeles, CA 91606 *Tel:* 310-401-0633 *E-mail:* sales@bargerlite.com *Web Site:* www.bargerlite.com, pg 702

Barger, Steven, Express Media Inc, 2225 Palou Ave, San Francisco, CA 94124 *Tel:* 415-255-9883 *Fax:* 415-255-0139 *Web Site:* expressmedia.tv, pg 757

Barilari, Elbio, Delmark Records, 4121 N Rockwell, Chicago, IL 60618 *Tel:* 773-539-5001 *Fax:* 773-539-5004 *E-mail:* info@delmark.com *Web Site:* www.delmark.com, pg 740

Barillas, Tracy, Extron Electronics, 1025 E Ball Rd, Suite 100, Anaheim, CA 92805-5957 *Tel:* 714-491-1500 *Toll Free Tel:* 800-633-9876 (sales & tech support); 800-633-9873 (order support) *Fax:* 714-491-1517 *E-mail:* sales-usa@extron.com *Web Site:* www.extron.com, pg 758

Barkan, Bebe, Cross-Cultural Communications, 239 Wynsum Ave, Merrick, NY 11566-4725 *Tel:* 516-868-5635 *Fax:* 516-379-1901 *E-mail:* info@cross-culturalcommunications.com *Web Site:* www.cross-culturalcommunications.com, pg 735

Barkan, Stanley H, Cross-Cultural Communications, 239 Wynsum Ave, Merrick, NY 11566-4725 *Tel:* 516-868-5635 *Fax:* 516-379-1901 *E-mail:* info@cross-culturalcommunications.com *Web Site:* www.cross-culturalcommunications.com, pg 735

Barker, Ken, Electronic Arts Inc, 209 Redwood Shores Pkwy, Redwood City, CA 94065 *Tel:* 650-628-1500 *Web Site:* www.ea.com, pg 752

Barker, Stepehn, WGBH Production Group, One Guest St, Boston, MA 02135 *Tel:* 617-300-2000 *E-mail:* productiongroup@wgbh.org; studios@wgbh.org; outpost@wgbh.org *Web Site:* productiongroup.wgbh.org, pg 936

Barkley, Warren, SMART Technologies ULC, 3636 Research Rd NW, Calgary, AB T2L 1Y1, Canada *Tel:* 403-245-0333 *Toll Free Tel:* 888-42-SMART (427-6278, CN & US); 800-260-9408 (sales) *Fax:* 403-228-2500 *Web Site:* home.smarttech.com, pg 891

Barnard, Robert, Ingram Content Group LLC, One Ingram Blvd, La Vergne, TN 37086-1986 *Tel:* 615-793-5000 *Toll Free Tel:* 800-937-8000 (retailers); 800-937-5300 (ext 1, libs) *E-mail:* customerservice@ingramcontent.com *Web Site:* www.ingramcontent.com, pg 787

Barnes, Charlotte, Bill Barnes Video Productions LLC, 14238 Honeysuckle Ridge, Matthews, NC 28105-6403 *Tel:* 704-847-8685 *E-mail:* bill@bbvp.tv *Web Site:* www.bbvp.tv, pg 702

Barnes, Erica, The Virginia Film Festival, 617 W Main St, 2nd fl, Charlottesville, VA 22903 *Tel:* 434-982-5277 *Fax:* 434-924-3374 *E-mail:* info@virginiafilmfestival.org; vffsubmissions@virginia.edu *Web Site:* virginiafilmfestival.org, pg 1006

Barnes, Jeff, Cokesbury, 2222 Rosa Parks Blvd, Nashville, TN 37228 *Tel:* 615-749-6000 (UMPH) *Toll Free Tel:* 800-672-1789; 844-381-2708 (cust care) *Fax:* 615-749-6578 *Toll Free Fax:* 800-445-8189 *E-mail:* cokes_serv@cokesbury.com; customerhelp@cokesbury.com *Web Site:* www.cokesbury.com, pg 727

Barnes, Joe, Whirlwind Music Distributors Inc, 99 Ling Rd, Greece, NY 14612 *Tel:* 585-663-8820 *Toll Free Tel:* 800-733-9473 (US only) *Fax:* 585-865-8930 *E-mail:* sales@whirlwindusa.com; techsupport@whirlwindusa.com; darylg@whirlwindusa.com (CN inquiries) *Web Site:* whirlwindusa.com, pg 937

Barnes, William R, Bill Barnes Video Productions LLC, 14238 Honeysuckle Ridge, Matthews, NC 28105-6403 *Tel:* 704-847-8685 *E-mail:* bill@bbvp.tv *Web Site:* www.bbvp.tv, pg 702

Barnett, Karen, Institute of Industrial & Systems Engineers (IISE), 3577 Parkway Lane, Suite 200, Norcross, GA 30092 *Tel:* 770-449-0460 *Toll Free Tel:* 800-494-0460 *Fax:* 770-441-3295 *E-mail:* executiveoffices@iise.org *Web Site:* www.iise.org, pg 956

Barnett, Melody, Palace Costume & Prop Co, 835 N Fairfax Ave, Hollywood, CA 90046 *Tel:* 323-651-5458 *Fax:* 323-658-7133 *E-mail:* rentals@palacecostume.com *Web Site:* www.palacecostume.com, pg 850

Barnhill, Ted, Castleview Productions, 1100 W 41 St, Austin, TX 78756 *Tel:* 512-442-9944 *Fax:* 512-442-8823 *E-mail:* contact@castleviewproductions.com *Web Site:* castleviewproductions.com, pg 717

Baron, Juliane, American Educational Research Association (AERA), 1430 "K" St NW, Suite 1200, Washington, DC 20005 *Tel:* 202-238-3200 *Fax:* 202-238-3250 *E-mail:* communications@aera.net; members@aera.net *Web Site:* www.aera.net, pg 948

Barone, Maureen Connelly, Palace Productions MediaVision, 29 N Main St, Norwalk, CT 06854 *Tel:* 203-523-0602; 203-523-0604 *Web Site:* cpbn.org/palace-productions-media-vision, pg 850

Barrall, Geoff, Nexsan Inc, 900 E Hamilton Ave, Suite 230, Campbell, CA 95008 *Tel:* 408-724-9809 *E-mail:* sales@nexsan.com *Web Site:* www.nexsan.com, pg 840

Barratt, Emily, Broadcasters Foundation of America, 125 W 55 St, 4th fl, New York, NY 10019-5366 *Tel:* 212-373-8250 *Fax:* 212-373-8254 *E-mail:* info@thebfoa.org *Web Site:* www.thebfoa.org; broadcastersfoundation.org, pg 952

Barratt, Emily, Golden Mike Award, 125 W 55 St, 4th fl, New York, NY 10019-5366 *Tel:* 212-373-8250 *Fax:* 212-373-8254 *E-mail:* info@thebfoa.org *Web Site:* www.thebfoa.org; broadcastersfoundation.org, pg 990

Barratt, Emily, Lowry Mays Excellence in Broadcasting Award, 125 W 55 St, 4th fl, New York, NY 10019-5366 *Tel:* 212-373-8250 *Fax:* 212-373-8254 *E-mail:* info@thebfoa.org *Web Site:* www.thebfoa.org; broadcastersfoundation.org, pg 995

Barratt, Emily, Ward L Quaal Leadership Awards, 125 W 55 St, 4th fl, New York, NY 10019-5366 *Tel:* 212-373-8250 *Fax:* 212-373-8254 *E-mail:* info@thebfoa.org *Web Site:* www.thebfoa.org; broadcastersfoundation.org, pg 1000

Barrenechea, Mark J, OpenText Corp, 275 Frank Tompa Dr, Waterloo, ON N2L 0A1, Canada *Tel:* 519-888-7111 *Toll Free Tel:* 800-499-6544 *Fax:* 519-888-0677 *Web Site:* www.opentext.com, pg 847

Barrett, Beth, Golden Space Needle Awards, 305 Harrison St, Seattle, WA 98109 *Tel:* 206-464-5830 *Fax:* 206-264-7919 *E-mail:* info@siff.net; entries@siff.net *Web Site:* www.siff.net, pg 991

Barrett, Beth, Seattle International Film Festival (SIFF), 305 Harrison St, Seattle, WA 98109 *Tel:* 206-464-5830 *Fax:* 206-264-7919 *E-mail:* info@siff.net; entries@siff.net *Web Site:* www.siff.net, pg 1003

Barrett, Linda, Executive Development Systems Inc, 3818 Vinecrest Dr, Dallas, TX 75229 *Tel:* 214-351-0055 *Toll Free Tel:* 800-955-7353 *Web Site:* www.edforeman.com, pg 757

Barrett, Rick, MAXON Computer Inc, 2640 Lavery Ct, Suite A, Newbury Park, CA 91320 *Tel:* 805-376-3333 *Fax:* 805-376-3331 *E-mail:* info_us@maxon.net *Web Site:* www.maxon.net, pg 820

Barrette, Francois, Strong Screen Systems, 1440 Raoul-Charrette, Joliette, QC J6E 8S7, Canada *Tel:* 450-755-3795 *Toll Free Tel:* 877-755-3795 *Fax:* 450-755-3122 *E-mail:* sales@strongmdi.com *Web Site:* strongmdi.com, pg 902

Barron, Dana, HB Communications Inc, 60 Dodge Ave, North Haven, CT 06473 *Tel:* 203-234-9246 *Toll Free Tel:* 800-243-4414 *Fax:* 203-234-2013 *E-mail:* info@hbcommunications.com *Web Site:* hbcommunications.com, pg 777

Barron, Mackey, HB Communications Inc, 60 Dodge Ave, North Haven, CT 06473 *Tel:* 203-234-9246 *Toll Free Tel:* 800-243-4414 *Fax:* 203-234-2013 *E-mail:* info@hbcommunications.com *Web Site:* hbcommunications.com, pg 777

Barron, Matt, Beast Atlanta, 3399 Peachtree Rd NE, Suite 200, Atlanta, GA 30326-1149 *Tel:* 404-237-9977 *Fax:* 404-237-3923 *Web Site:* www.beast.tv, pg 703

Barron, Richard, Sonora Recorders, 3222 Los Feliz Blvd, Los Angeles, CA 90039 *Tel:* 213-841-0712 *E-mail:* ductape@aol.com *Web Site:* www.sonorarecorders.com, pg 893

Barros, Glen, Concord Jazz, 5750 Wilshire Blvd, Suite 450, Los Angeles, CA 90036 *Tel:* 310-385-4455 *Web Site:* concord.com/labels/concord-jazz, pg 730

Barros, Glen, Concord Records, 5750 Wilshire Blvd, Suite 450, Los Angeles, CA 90036 *Tel:* 310-385-4455 *Web Site:* concord.com/labels/concord-records, pg 730

Barros, Glen, Telarc International Corp, 100 N Crescent Dr, Garden Level, Beverly Hills, CA 90210 *Tel:* 310-385-4455 *E-mail:* submissions@concordmusicgroup.com *Web Site:* www.concordmusicgroup.com/labels/telarc, pg 909

Barrows, Loren, Alcorn McBride Inc, 3300 S Hiawassee Rd, Bldg 105, Orlando, FL 32835 *Tel:* 407-296-5800 *Fax:* 407-296-5801 *E-mail:* info@alcorn.com; sales@alcorn.com *Web Site:* www.alcorn.com, pg 679

Barry, Luann, 1st Wave Productions, 2017 Pacific Ave, Venice, CA 90291 *Tel:* 310-279-7059 *Web Site:* www.1stwaveproductions.com, pg 761

Barry, Steven, Style-City Music Inc, PO Box 40403, St Petersburg, FL 33743 *Tel:* 727-520-2336 *E-mail:* stylecitymusic@yahoo.com *Web Site:* stylecitymusicinc.wordpress.com, pg 903

Barsa, Paul, Alpha Wire Co, 711 Lidgerwood Ave, Elizabeth, NJ 07207-0711 *Tel:* 908-925-8000 *Toll Free Tel:* 800-52-ALPHA (522-5742) *Fax:* 908-925-6923 *E-mail:* info@alphawire.com *Web Site:* www.alphawire.com, pg 682

Barsoum, Sherien, ReelWorld Film Festival, 50 Carroll St, Suite 200, Toronto, ON M4M 3G3, Canada *Tel:* 416-598-7933 *E-mail:* info@reelworld.ca; contact@reelworld.ca *Web Site:* www.reelworld.ca, pg 1001

Barta, B Andrew, Tech 21 USA Inc, 790 Bloomfield Ave, Clifton, NJ 07012 *Tel:* 973-777-6996 *Fax:* 973-777-9899 *E-mail:* info@tech21nyc.com *Web Site:* www.tech21nyc.com, pg 908

Barth, Andy, TecNec Distributing, 812 Kings Hwy, Saugerties, NY 12477 *Tel:* 845-246-0428 *Toll Free Tel:* 800-543-0909 *Fax:* 845-246-0626 *E-mail:* sales@tecnec.com *Web Site:* www.tecnec.com, pg 909

Barth, Carl, Carl Barth Images, PO Box 5325, Santa Barbara, CA 93150-5325 *Tel:* 805-637-0881 *E-mail:* carlbarthimages@cox.net, pg 702

Bartles, Dean L, Society of Manufacturing Engineers (SME), One SME Dr, Dearborn, MI 48128 *Tel:* 313-425-3000 *Toll Free Tel:* 800-733-4763 *Fax:* 313-425-3400 *E-mail:* service@sme.org (cust care) *Web Site:* www.sme.org, pg 892

Bartlett, Alan, Wayne State University Media Services, Purdy/Kresge Library, 5244 Gullen Mall, Detroit, MI 48202 *Tel:* 313-577-1980 *Fax:* 313-577-6777 *E-mail:* mediaservices@wayne.edu *Web Site:* library.wayne.edu, pg 934

Bartlett, Kevin, Aural Gratification Inc, 32 Nissen Lane, West Hurley, NY 12491-5903 *Tel:* 845-679-5674 *E-mail:* auralg@gmail.com, pg 695

Bartlett, Tim, Adrenaline Films, 5224 S Orange Ave, Orlando, FL 32809 *Tel:* 407-850-0711 *Fax:* 407-859-6527 *E-mail:* contact@adrenalinefilms.com *Web Site:* www.adrenalinefilms.com, pg 676

Bartling, Tab, Heart Music Inc, PO Box 160326, Austin, TX 78716-0326 *Tel:* 512-795-2375 *Fax:* 512-795-9573 *E-mail:* info@heartmusic.com *Web Site:* www.heartmusic.com, pg 778

Barton, Larry, Cinematography Electronics Inc, 5321 Derry Ave, Suite G, Agoura Hills, CA 91301 *Tel:* 818-706-3334 *Fax:* 818-706-3335 *E-mail:* info@cinemaelec.com *Web Site:* cinemaelec.com, pg 724

Barton, Paul, PSB Speakers International, 633 Granite Ct, Pickering, ON L1W 3K1, Canada *Tel:* 905-831-6555 *Fax:* 905-831-6936 *Web Site:* www.psbspeakers.com, pg 866

Barton, Ridgie, piXvfm Inc, 1805 E Dyer Rd, Suite 107, Santa Ana, CA 92705 *Tel:* 949-419-2563 *Fax:* 949-419-3485 *Web Site:* pixvfm.com, pg 857

Barton, Sue, Lake Tahoe Visitors Authority (LTVA), 169 Hwy 50, Stateline, NV 89449 *Tel:* 775-588-5900 *Toll Free Tel:* 800-288-2463 (reservations) *Fax:* 775-588-1941 *E-mail:* info@ltva.org *Web Site:* ltva.org, pg 973

Bartos, Marlene, Yessian, 137 Fifth Ave, 3rd fl, New York, NY 10010 *Tel:* 212-533-3443 *E-mail:* info-ny@yessian.com *Web Site:* www.yessian.com, pg 944

Baruh, Esther, National Association of Theatre Owners (NATO), 1705 "N" St NW, Washington, DC 20036 *Tel:* 202-962-0054 *E-mail:* nato@natodc.com *Web Site:* www.natoonline.org, pg 959

Barzdukas, Amy, Poly, 345 Encinal St, Santa Cruz, CA 95060 *Tel:* 831-426-5858 *Toll Free Tel:* 800-544-4660 *Fax:* 831-426-6098 *Web Site:* www.poly.com, pg 859

Bashir, Irene, Central Audio-Visual Equipment Inc, 375 Roma Jean Pkwy, Streamwood, IL 60107 *Tel:* 630-372-8100 *Toll Free Tel:* 800-323-4239 *Fax:* 630-372-9281 *Web Site:* www.cavinc.com, pg 719

Bashir, Jonathan, Central Audio-Visual Equipment Inc, 375 Roma Jean Pkwy, Streamwood, IL 60107 *Tel:* 630-372-8100 *Toll Free Tel:* 800-323-4239 *Fax:* 630-372-9281 *Web Site:* www.cavinc.com, pg 719

Bashir, Michael, Central Audio-Visual Equipment Inc, 375 Roma Jean Pkwy, Streamwood, IL 60107 *Tel:* 630-372-8100 *Toll Free Tel:* 800-323-4239 *Fax:* 630-372-9281 *Web Site:* www.cavinc.com, pg 719

Bashore, Dan, Bartha, 600 N Cassady Ave, Columbus, OH 43219 *Tel:* 614-252-7455 *Toll Free Tel:* 800-363-2698 *Fax:* 614-252-7641 *E-mail:* info@bartha.com *Web Site:* www.bartha.com, pg 702

Basileo, Patricia, American Harlequin Corp, 1531 Glen Ave, Moorestown, NJ 08057 *Tel:* 856-234-5505 *Toll Free Tel:* 800-642-6440 *Fax:* 856-231-4403 *E-mail:* dance@harlequinfloors.com; contact@harlequinfloors.com *Web Site:* us.harlequinfloors.com, pg 683

Basner, Glen, FilmNation Entertainment, 150 W 22 St, 9th fl, New York, NY 10011 *Web Site:* www.filmnation.com, pg 760

Bass, Melanie, Creative Technology, 222 Front St, 2nd fl, San Francisco, CA 94111 *Tel:* 415-513-5918 *E-mail:* studio@ct-sf.com *Web Site:* www.ct-sf.com, pg 733

Bast, Randy, High-Tech Special Effects Inc, PO Box 193, Eads, TN 38028-0193 *Tel:* 901-850-5522 *Fax:* 901-850-8315 *Web Site:* www.hightechspecialeffects.com, pg 779

Basteri, Patricia, massAV, 3 Radcliffe Rd, Pewksbury, MA 01876 *Tel:* 978-670-0027 *Toll Free Tel:* 800-423-7830 *Fax:* 978-640-9900 *E-mail:* info@massav.com *Web Site:* www.massav.com, pg 819

Batavick, Catherine, Maryland Film Office, 401 E Pratt St, 14th fl, Baltimore, MD 21202 *Tel:* 410-767-6343 *Toll Free Tel:* 800-333-6632 *Fax:* 410-333-0044 *E-mail:* filminfo@marylandfilm.org *Web Site:* www.marylandfilm.org, pg 972

Bateman, Susan, Yarn Barn of Kansas, 930 Massachusetts St, Lawrence, KS 66044 *Tel:* 785-842-4333 *Toll Free Tel:* 800-468-0035 *E-mail:* info@yarnbarn-ks.com *Web Site:* www.yarnbarn-ks.com, pg 944

Bates, Carolyn, Buttercup Pictures, 206 N Bundy Dr, Los Angeles, CA 90049 *Tel:* 310-869-9405 *Web Site:* cargocollective.com/buttercup, pg 713

Bates, Marianne, SDMediaPros (SDMP), 5205 Kearny Villa Way, No 100, San Diego, CA 92123 *Tel:* 619-672-1000 *E-mail:* membership@sdmediapros.org; marketing@sdmediapros.org; programs@sdmediapros.org *Web Site:* sdmediapros.org, pg 962

Bates, Nick, Buttercup Pictures, 206 N Bundy Dr, Los Angeles, CA 90049 *Tel:* 310-869-9405 *Web Site:* cargocollective.com/buttercup, pg 713

Bates, Phil, Artbeats, 1405 N Myrtle Rd, Myrtle Creek, OR 97457 *Tel:* 541-863-4429 *Fax:* 541-863-4547 *E-mail:* info@artbeats.com *Web Site:* www.artbeats.com, pg 690

Bates, Ron, WCJB TV20, 6220 NW 43 St, Gainesville, FL 32653 *Tel:* 352-416-0623 *Fax:* 352-373-6516 *E-mail:* comments@wcbj.com *Web Site:* wcjb.com, pg 934

Bates, Vicki, University of South Carolina Press, 1600 Hampton St, Suite 544, Columbia, SC 29208 *Tel:* 803-777-5243 *Toll Free Tel:* 800-768-2500 *Toll Free Fax:* 800-868-0740 *Web Site:* www.sc.edu/uscpress, pg 923

Batnagar, Reema, Pixar Animation Studios, 1200 Park Ave, Emeryville, CA 94608 *Tel:* 510-922-3000 *Fax:* 510-922-3151 *Web Site:* www.pixar.com, pg 857

Battro, Sebastian, Reel One International Ltd, 486 Ste-Catherine W, Suite 100, Montreal, QC H3B 1A6, Canada *E-mail:* sales@reeloneent.com *Web Site:* reeloneent.com, pg 872

Baudoin, Monika, New Orleans Film Festival, 1215 Prytania St, Suite 423, New Orleans, LA 70130 *Tel:* 504-309-6633 *E-mail:* noff@neworleansfilmsociety.org *Web Site:* neworleansfilmsociety.org/festival, pg 997

Bauer, Gary H, Alpha Video Productions, 441 Biscay Dr, Garland, TX 75043 *Tel:* 972-497-9959 *E-mail:* alphaghb@sbcglobal.net *Web Site:* www.alphavideo.net, pg 682

Bauer, Susan, Alpha Video Productions, 441 Biscay Dr, Garland, TX 75043 *Tel:* 972-497-9959 *E-mail:* alphaghb@sbcglobal.net *Web Site:* www.alphavideo.net, pg 682

Bauersachs, Thomas, PCO-TECH Inc, 6930 Metroplex Dr, Romulus, MI 48174 *Tel:* 248-276-8820 *Fax:* 248-276-8825 *E-mail:* info@pco-tech.com; service@pco-tech.com *Web Site:* www.pco-tech.com, pg 852

Bauersfeld, Kris, All Comm Rentals Inc (ALLCOMM), 1402 SW 13 Ct, Pompano Beach, FL 33069 *Tel:* 954-788-9555 *Web Site:* www.allcommrentals.com, pg 680

Baum, Gene, Laser Magic Productions, 722 N Orlando Ave, No 207, Los Angeles, CA 90069 *Tel:* 818-590-5899 *Web Site:* www.laser-magic.com, pg 804

Baum, Sarah, Da-Lite, a Legrand AV Inc brand, 3100 N Detroit St, Warsaw, IN 46582 *Tel:* 574-267-8101 *Toll Free Tel:* 866-977-3901 *E-mail:* av.da-lite.support@legrand.com *Web Site:* www.legrandav.com/products/da-lite, pg 737

Bauman, Chuck, JSAV, 9150 N Royal Lane, Suite 150, Irving, TX 75063 *Tel:* 972-241-5444 *Toll Free Tel:* 800-852-8771 *Fax:* 972-247-2590 *E-mail:* info@jsav.com *Web Site:* www.jsav.com, pg 795

Bauman, Margy, Redwood Audiobooks, 10375 Nichols Lane, Mendocino, CA 95460 *Tel:* 707-937-1225 *E-mail:* audiobks@mcn.org *Web Site:* www.universitypressaudiobooks.com, pg 872

Baumberger, Randall, The Studios at Paramount, 5555 Melrose Ave, Hollywood, CA 90038 *Tel:* 323-956-5000 *Web Site:* www.paramountstudios.com, pg 903

Bavin, Clark, Video Solutions, 2121 Eisenhower Ave, Suite 103, Alexandria, VA 22314 *Tel:* 703-683-5305; 703-628-0702 (cell) *E-mail:* inquiries@thevideosolution.com *Web Site:* www.thevideosolution.com, pg 928

Baxter, Irvin Jr, Endtime Ministries Inc, PO Box 940729, Plano, TX 75094-0729 *Tel:* 972-422-0857 *Toll Free Tel:* 833-563-6063; 800-363-8463 (cust serv) *E-mail:* endtime@endtime.com *Web Site:* www.endtime.com, pg 754

Baxter, Peter, Slamdance Film Festival, 5634 Melrose Ave, Los Angeles, CA 90038 *Tel:* 323-466-1786 *Fax:* 323-466-1784 *E-mail:* submissions@slamdance.com *Web Site:* www.slamdance.com, pg 1004

Bayer, Robert F, Theatrical Services & Supplies Inc, 3340 Veterans Memorial Hwy, Bohemia, NY 11716 *Tel:* 631-873-4790 *Fax:* 631-873-4795 *E-mail:* sales@gotheatrical.com *Web Site:* www.gotheatrical.com, pg 912

Bayley, Roger, National Boston, 115 Dummer St, Brookline, MA 02446 *Tel:* 617-734-4800 *Fax:* 617-734-6323 *E-mail:* info@nationalboston.com *Web Site:* www.nationalboston.com, pg 836

Bayne, Diane, Levy NYC Design & Production, 356 Devoe St, Brooklyn, NY 11211 *Tel:* 212-925-4640 *Fax:* 212-925-4216 *E-mail:* info@levynyc.net *Web Site:* www.levylighting.com, pg 806

Bazley, Christopher, Antenna International, 383 Main Ave, Norwalk, CT 06851 *Tel:* 203-523-0320 *E-mail:* inquiry@antennainternational.com; marketing@antennainternational.com *Web Site:* www.antennainternational.com, pg 686

Beach, Frank, Altruist Media LLC, 2601A Wilson Blvd, Arlington, VA 22201 *Tel:* 703-812-8813, pg 682

Beach, Michael F, National Public Radio (NPR), 1111 N Capitol St NE, Washington, DC 20002 *Tel:* 202-513-2000 *Web Site:* www.npr.org, pg 959

Beadle, Beth, Winchester Electronics Corp, 68 Water St, Norwalk, CT 06854 *Tel:* 203-741-5400 *E-mail:* info@winchesterelectronics.com *Web Site:* www.winchesterelectronics.com, pg 939

Bean, Jim, Accusoft, 4001 N Riverside Dr, Tampa, FL 33603 *Tel:* 813-875-7575 *Toll Free Tel:* 800-875-7009 *Fax:* 813-875-7705 *E-mail:* sales@accusoft.com *Web Site:* www.accusoft.com, pg 674

Beasley, Christiana, Heartland International Film Festival, 1043 Virginia Ave, Suite 2, Indianapolis, IN 46203 *Tel:* 317-464-9405 *E-mail:* submissions@heartlandfilm.org *Web Site:* heartlandfilm.org/festival, pg 992

Beasley, Christiana, Indy Shorts International Film Fest, 1043 Virginia Ave, Suite 2, Indianapolis, IN 46203 *Tel:* 317-464-9405 *E-mail:* submissions@heartlandfilm.org *Web Site:* heartlandfilm.org, pg 993

Beasley, Gary, Charles A Hulcher Co Inc, 909 "G" St, Hampton, VA 23661 *Tel:* 757-245-6190 *Fax:* 757-245-2882, pg 782

Beatrice, Brian, Digital Arts NY, 130 W 29 St, New York, NY 10001 *Tel:* 212-460-9600 *Fax:* 212-660-3600 *Web Site:* digitalartsny.com, pg 742

Beattie, John, Columbus International Film + Video Festival, 60 Cleveland Ave, Columbus, OH 43215 *Tel:* 614-222-6185 *E-mail:* info@columbusfilmfestival.org *Web Site:* www.ccad.edu/experience-art/columbus-international-film-festival, pg 987

Beatty, Bill, Beatty TeleVisual Productions, 1287 Wabash Ave, Springfield, IL 62704 *Tel:* 217-787-4747 *Fax:* 217-787-4857 *Web Site:* www.beattytelevisual.com, pg 703

Beatty, Debbie, Beatty TeleVisual Productions, 1287 Wabash Ave, Springfield, IL 62704 *Tel:* 217-787-4747 *Fax:* 217-787-4857 *Web Site:* www.beattytelevisual.com, pg 703

Beatty, Wilma, Beatty TeleVisual Productions, 1287 Wabash Ave, Springfield, IL 62704 *Tel:* 217-787-4747 *Fax:* 217-787-4857 *Web Site:* www.beattytelevisual.com, pg 703

Beauchemin, Christian, International Film Festival in Abitibi-Teiscamingue, 215 Ave Mercier, Rouyn-Noranda, QC J9X 5W8, Canada *Tel:* 819-762-6212 *Fax:* 819-762-6762 *E-mail:* info@festivalcinema.ca *Web Site:* festivalcinema.ca, pg 993

Beaudin, Justin, Deluxe Entertainment Services Group Inc, 2400 W Empire Ave, 2nd fl, Burbank, CA 91504 *Tel:* 818-260-7005; 818-526-3700 *Toll Free Tel:* 800-99-FILMS (993-4567) *E-mail:* ddchelp@bydeluxe.com; pr@bydeluxe.com *Web Site:* www.bydeluxe.com, pg 740

Beautyman, William, Limelight Production® Inc, 471 Pleasant St, Lee, MA 01238-9322 *Tel:* 413-243-4950 *Toll Free Tel:* 800-243-4950 *Fax:* 413-243-4993 *Toll Free Fax:* 800-243-4951 *E-mail:* info@limelightproductions.com; sales@limelightproductions.com *Web Site:* www.limelightproductions.com, pg 809

Beavers, Kory, Associated Bag Co, 400 W Boden St, Milwaukee, WI 53207 *Tel:* 414-769-1000 *Toll Free Tel:* 800-926-6100 *Fax:* 414-769-6530 *Toll*

Free Fax: 800-926-4610 *E-mail:* customerservice@associatedbag.com *Web Site:* www.associatedbag.com, pg 691

Beavers, Nick, Media Cybernetics Inc, 401 N Washington St, Suite 350, Rockville, MD 20850 *Tel:* 301-495-3305 *Fax:* 240-328-6193 *E-mail:* info@mediacy.com *Web Site:* www.mediacy.com, pg 821

Beck, James S, East Arizona Good Luck Enterprises Inc, PO Box 579, Clarkdale, AZ 86324 *Tel:* 928-204-2597 *Fax:* 928-204-2568 *E-mail:* hier_bosch@yahoo.com, pg 749

Beck, Keith, Brantley Sound Associates Inc, 115 Duluth Ave, Nashville, TN 37209-1207 *Tel:* 615-256-6260 *Web Site:* www.brantleysound.com, pg 709

Beck, Stephen, Brantley Sound Associates Inc, 115 Duluth Ave, Nashville, TN 37209-1207 *Tel:* 615-256-6260 *Web Site:* www.brantleysound.com, pg 709

Beck, Tom, Broadcast Electronics, 4100 N 24 St, Quincy, IL 62305 *Tel:* 217-224-9600 *Fax:* 217-224-9607 *E-mail:* bdcast@bdcast.com *Web Site:* www.bdcast.com, pg 710

Becker, Darcy, Headroom Digital Audio, 11 E 26 St, 19th fl, New York, NY 10010 *Tel:* 212-246-8400 *E-mail:* info@headroom.nyc *Web Site:* www.headroom.nyc, pg 778

Becker, Greg, Chicago Spotlight Inc, 3418 N Knox Ave, Chicago, IL 60641 *Tel:* 312-455-1171 *Web Site:* www.grandstage.com, pg 721

Becker, Gregory, Grand Stage Co Inc, 3418 N Knox Ave, Chicago, IL 60641 *Tel:* 312-332-5611 *Toll Free Tel:* 800-621-2181 *Fax:* 312-332-3655 *E-mail:* marketing@grandstage.com *Web Site:* www.grandstage.com, pg 773

Beckert, Sabine, Telemotions LLC, 405 E 54 St, Suite 3-N, New York, NY 10022 *Tel:* 212-486-3010 *Web Site:* www.telemotions.net, pg 910

Beckman, Kathleen, Chicago International Children's Film Festival, 1517 W Fullerton Ave, Chicago, IL 60614 *Tel:* 773-281-9075 (ext 3011) *Fax:* 773-929-0266 *E-mail:* filmreg@facets.org; press@facets.org *Web Site:* festival.facets.org, pg 985

Beckner, Jenni, Russ Beckner Pictures, 2100 Heatherwood Ct, Middletown, OH 45042 *Tel:* 513-422-9552 *E-mail:* rdbvideo@gmail.com *Web Site:* russbeckner.com, pg 703

Beckner, Russ, Russ Beckner Pictures, 2100 Heatherwood Ct, Middletown, OH 45042 *Tel:* 513-422-9552 *E-mail:* rdbvideo@gmail.com *Web Site:* russbeckner.com, pg 703

Beckwith, Dan, WFRV-TV 5 CBS, 1181 E Mason St, Green Bay, WI 54301 *Tel:* 920-437-5411 *Fax:* 920-437-4576 *E-mail:* tips@wearegreenbay.com *Web Site:* www.wearegreenbay.com, pg 936

Bedichek, Louise, Sano Videos, Columbia Plaza, 2450 Virginia Ave NW, Suite E 322, Washington, DC 20037 *Tel:* 202-293-0454, pg 880

Beecher, Lori, Ketchum Inc, 1285 Avenue of the Americas, 4th fl, New York, NY 10019 *Tel:* 646-935-3900 *Web Site:* www.ketchum.com, pg 798

Beegle, Bruce, Vanner Inc, 4282 Reynolds Dr, Hilliard, OH 43026 *Tel:* 614-771-2718 *Toll Free Tel:* 800-ACPOWER (227-6937) *Fax:* 614-771-4904 *E-mail:* info@vanner.com; pwrsales@vanner.com *Web Site:* www.vanner.com, pg 924

Beeman, Merlyn, SMI® Inc, 4567 Lake Shore Dr, Waco, TX 76710 *Tel:* 254-776-2060 *Toll Free Tel:* 800-568-1241 *Fax:* 254-772-9588 *E-mail:* dmcminn@lmi-inc.com; info@lmi-inc.com; info@success-motivation.com *Web Site:* www.lmi-world.com/smi, pg 891

Been, Jason, Imagecraft Productions, 3318 Burton Ave, Burbank, CA 91504 *Tel:* 818-954-0187 *Fax:* 818-954-0189 *Web Site:* www.imagecraftproductions.com, pg 785

Begnaud, Kris, Data Projections Inc, 3700 W Sam Houston Pkwy S, Suite 525, Houston, TX 77042 *Tel:* 713-781-1999 *Toll Free Tel:* 866-225-5374 *Fax:* 713-781-3338 *E-mail:* dpiweb@dataprojections.com *Web Site:* www.dataprojections.com, pg 738

Behr, Lawrence, LBA Technology Inc, 3400 Tupper Dr, Greenville, NC 27834 *Tel:* 252-757-0279 *Toll Free Tel:* 800-522-4464 *Fax:* 252-752-9155 *E-mail:* lbagrp@lbagroup.com *Web Site:* www.lbagroup.com, pg 804

Behrman, Rachel "Ryan", ATV Video Center Inc, 2424 Glendale Lane, Sacramento, CA 95825 *Tel:* 916-973-9100 *Toll Free Tel:* 800-635-1266 *E-mail:* info@atv.net *Web Site:* www.atv.net, pg 692

Beiersdorf, Susie, Christie Digital Systems USA Inc, 10550 Camden Dr, Cypress, CA 90630 *Tel:* 714-236-8610 *Toll Free Tel:* 866-880-4462 (cust serv) *Fax:* 714-503-3375 *E-mail:* sales-us@christiedigital.com; orders@christiedigital.com *Web Site:* www.christiedigital.com, pg 722

Beimfohr, Rik W, Image Marketing Corp, 1636 N 24 St, Mesa, AZ 85213 *Tel:* 480-969-7032 *Fax:* 480-969-0939 *E-mail:* info@image4u.com *Web Site:* www.image4u.com, pg 785

Beiriger, Lindsay, CaptionMax, 2438 27 Ave S, Minneapolis, MN 55406 *Tel:* 612-341-3566 *Web Site:* www.captionmax.com, pg 716

Beiser, Jolene, Pacifica Radio Archives, 3729 Cahuenga Blvd W, North Hollywood, CA 91604 *Tel:* 818-506-1077 *Toll Free Tel:* 800-735-0230 *Fax:* 818-506-1084 *E-mail:* pacarchive@aol.com *Web Site:* www.pacificaradioarchives.org, pg 850

Bekian, Bob, Loyal Studios, 3513 W Pacific Ave, Burbank, CA 91505 *Tel:* 818-845-5123 (studio); 818-399-9499 *Web Site:* www.loyalstudios.tv, pg 812

Belcher, Hyacinth, Onstage Systems, 8721 Forney Rd, Dallas, TX 75227 *Tel:* 972-686-4488 *Fax:* 972-686-7732 *E-mail:* info@onstagesystems.com *Web Site:* www.onstagesystems.com, pg 846

Belding, Carol, Cambridge Documentary Films Inc, 3099 Hidden Valley Lane, Santa Barbara, CA 93108 *Tel:* 617-484-3993 *E-mail:* info@cambridgedocumentaryfilms.org; mail@cambridgedocumentaryfilms.org *Web Site:* www.cambridgedocumentaryfilms.org, pg 714

Belew, Sam B, Belew Enterprises, 524 Vance Dr, Bristol, TN 37620 *Tel:* 423-764-4116 *E-mail:* bsv@tricon.net, pg 703

Belgique, Jon, Comtek Communications Technology Inc, 357 W 2700 S, Salt Lake City, UT 84115 *Tel:* 801-466-3463 *Toll Free Tel:* 800-496-3463 *Fax:* 801-484-6906 *E-mail:* sales@comtek.com *Web Site:* www.comtek.com, pg 730

Belgique, Ralph, Comtek Communications Technology Inc, 357 W 2700 S, Salt Lake City, UT 84115 *Tel:* 801-466-3463 *Toll Free Tel:* 800-496-3463 *Fax:* 801-484-6906 *E-mail:* sales@comtek.com *Web Site:* www.comtek.com, pg 730

Belisle, Robert, Genesis Integration, 14721 123 Ave NW, Edmonton, AB T5L 2Y6, Canada *Toll Free Tel:* 877-283-2253 (Toronto); 866-622-2966 (Quebec); 844-436-4681 (rest of CN) *E-mail:* marketing@genint.com *Web Site:* www.genint.com, pg 770

Belisle, Samuel, Prix Gemeaux (French language TV), 225 rue Roy E, bureau 106, Montreal, QC H2W 1M5, Canada *Tel:* 514-849-7448 *Fax:* 514-849-5069 *E-mail:* academie@acct.ca *Web Site:* www.acct.ca/prixgemeaux; www.acct.ca; www.academy.ca, pg 1000

Belknap, Lori, Cahokia Mounds Museum Society, 30 Ramey Dr, Collinsville, IL 62234 *Tel:* 618-344-7316 *Fax:* 618-346-5162 *E-mail:* museumsociety@cahokiamounds.org *Web Site:* www.cahokiamounds.org, pg 713

Bell, Andrew, New London Media, 78 Washington St, New London, CT 06320 *Tel:* 860-961-6300 *Web Site:* www.andrewclydebell.com, pg 839

Bell, Dave, Crossroads Audio Inc, 2623 Myrtle Springs Ave, Dallas, TX 75220 *Tel:* 214-358-2623 *Toll Free Tel:* 800-287-0436 *Fax:* 214-358-0185 *E-mail:* mail@crossroadsaudio.com *Web Site:* www.crossroadsaudio.com, pg 735

Bell, Douglas, Cavanaugh Tocci Associates Inc, 327F Boston Post Rd, Sudbury, MA 01776 *Tel:* 978-443-7871 *E-mail:* cta@cavtocci.com *Web Site:* www.cavtocci.com, pg 717

Bell, Judith, Artadia James D Phelan Award in the Visual Arts, One Embarcadero Ctr, Suite 1400, San Francisco, CA 94111 *Tel:* 415-733-8500 *Fax:* 415-477-2783 *E-mail:* artsinfo@sff.org; info@sff.org *Web Site:* www.sff.org, pg 982

Bell, Michael, Ingram Content Group LLC, One Ingram Blvd, La Vergne, TN 37086-1986 *Tel:* 615-793-5000 *Toll Free Tel:* 800-937-8000 (retailers); 800-937-5300 (ext 1, libs) *E-mail:* customerservice@ingramcontent.com *Web Site:* www.ingramcontent.com, pg 787

Bell, Michael, South Coast Film & Video, 5234 Elm St, Houston, TX 77081 *Tel:* 713-661-3550 *Toll Free Tel:* 800-229-3550 *Fax:* 713-661-4357 *E-mail:* info@scfilmvideo.com *Web Site:* www.southcoastfilmvideo.com, pg 895

Bell, Michael D, Technical Services, 10567 Oak Creek Dr, Lakeside, CA 92040 *Tel:* 619-561-4410 *Web Site:* www.widcoinc.com, pg 908

Bell, Robert, Pathway Connectivity, 103-1439 17 Ave SE, Calgary, AB T2G 1J9, Canada *Tel:* 403-243-8110 *Fax:* 403-287-1281 *E-mail:* orders@pathwayconnect.com *Web Site:* www.pathwayconnect.com, pg 852

Bell, Tona, Tricycle Studios, 1905 E Seventh Ave, Tampa, FL 33605 *Tel:* 813-258-6867 *Fax:* 813-258-8595 *E-mail:* hi@tricyclestudios.com *Web Site:* www.tricyclestudios.com, pg 918

Bellantoni, Annamaria, Film Upstate NY, 28 Clinton St, Saratoga Springs, NY 12866 *Tel:* 518-584-3255 *Fax:* 518-587-0318 *E-mail:* info@filmupstateny.com *Web Site:* filmupstateny.com, pg 974

Bellin, Gil, Bellin Productions, 109 Mosher Rd, Glenmont, NY 12077 *Tel:* 518-472-0037; 914-980-6322 (cell) *Toll Free Tel:* 888-834-5520 *E-mail:* info@bellinproductions.com *Web Site:* www.bellinproductions.com, pg 703

Bellovin, Michael, Legion Lighting Co Inc, 221 Glenmore Ave, Brooklyn, NY 11207 *Tel:* 718-498-1770 *Fax:* 718-498-0128 *Toll Free Fax:* 800-4-LEGION (453-4466) *E-mail:* sales@legionlighting.com *Web Site:* www.legionlighting.com, pg 806

Belofsky, Rachel, Screamfest® Horror Film Festival & Screenplay Competition, 8840 Wilshire Blvd, Beverly Hills, CA 90211 *Tel:* 310-358-3273 *E-mail:* info@screamfestla.com *Web Site:* www.screamfestla.com, pg 1003

Belousek, Kyle, Candee Productions Inc, 301 W Deer Valley Rd, Suite 7, Phoenix, AZ 85027 *Tel:* 623-266-3070 *Web Site:* candeeproductionsinc.wordpress.com, pg 716

Belyaeva, Eleonora, Skystorm Productions, 103 Commerce St, Suite 100, Lake Mary, FL 32746 *Tel:* 407-328-4747 *Toll Free Tel:* 800-783-8508 *Fax:* 407-328-4479 *E-mail:* info@skystorm.com *Web Site:* www.skystorm.com, pg 890

Belz, Dee, Miami-Dade Office of Film & Entertainment, 111 NW First St, 12th fl, Miami, FL 33128 *Tel:* 305-375-3288 *E-mail:* film@miamidade.gov *Web Site:* www.filmmiami.org, pg 969

Bena, Thomas, The Martha's Vineyard Film Festival (MVFF), 9 State Rd, Chilmark, MA 02535 *Tel:* 508-645-9599 *Web Site:* www.tmvff.org, pg 995

Benatar, Owen, U-Edit Video, 1002 N Central Expwy, Suite 555, Richardson, TX 75080 *Tel:* 972-690-EDIT (690-3348) *E-mail:* info@ueditvideo.com *Web Site:* www.ueditvideo.com, pg 920

Bendell, Curtis A, Tele-Time Systems, 313 Parkway Dr, Cary, IL 60013 *Tel:* 847-640-1420 *E-mail:* teletimesystems@netzero.com, pg 910

Bender, Avi, National Audiovisual Center (NAC), 5301 Shawnee Rd, Alexandria, VA 22312 *E-mail:* info@ntis.gov; customerservice@ntis.gov *Web Site:* classic.ntis.gov/products/nac, pg 836

Bender, William, Tobias Associates Inc, 50 Industrial Dr, Ivyland, PA 18974-1433 *Tel:* 215-322-1500 *Toll Free Tel:* 800-877-3367 *Fax:* 215-322-1504 *E-mail:* sales@tobiasinc.com; service@tobiasinc.com; repair@tobiasinc.com *Web Site:* www.densitometers.net, pg 915

Benderson, Robert, CMI, 612 Hampton Dr, Venice, CA 90291 *Tel:* 310-392-8771 *E-mail:* cmi@cmifilms.com *Web Site:* www.cmifilms.com, pg 727

Bengel, Tricia Racke, Ingram Content Group LLC, One Ingram Blvd, La Vergne, TN 37086-1986 *Tel:* 615-793-5000 *Toll Free Tel:* 800-937-8000 (retailers); 800-937-5300 (ext 1, libs) *E-mail:* customerservice@ingramcontent.com *Web Site:* www.ingramcontent.com, pg 787

Benghiat, Michael, The Music Kitchen Inc, 12400 Connery Way, Bakersfield, CA 93312 *Tel:* 661-338-4749 *Web Site:* www.themusickitchen.com, pg 834

Benjamin, Cary M, TR Productions, Charlstown Navy Yard, Captains Quarters Bldg, 2 13 St, 3rd fl, Charlestown, MA 02129 *Tel:* 617-241-5500 *E-mail:* info@trprod.com *Web Site:* trprod.com, pg 916

Benjamin, Mark, Nuance Communications Inc, One Wayside Rd, Burlington, MA 01803 *Tel:* 781-565-5000 *Toll Free Tel:* 800-654-1187 (cust serv) *Fax:* 781-565-5001 *Web Site:* www.nuance.com, pg 843

Benjamin, Ross, TR Productions, Charlstown Navy Yard, Captains Quarters Bldg, 2 13 St, 3rd fl, Charlestown, MA 02129 *Tel:* 617-241-5500 *E-mail:* info@trprod.com *Web Site:* trprod.com, pg 916

Benjamin, Steve, AVI-SPL, 6301 Benjamin Rd, Suite 101, Tampa, FL 33634 *Tel:* 813-884-7168 *Toll Free Tel:* 866-708-5034; 866-925-8298 (cust serv); 866-559-8197 (sales) *E-mail:* contact@avispl.com; sales@avispl.com; customerservice@avispl.com *Web Site:* www.avispl.com, pg 698

Benko, James S, International Tae Kwon Do Association (ITA Institute), PO Box 281, Grand Blanc, MI 48480 *Tel:* 810-232-6482 *E-mail:* hq@itatkd.com *Web Site:* www.itatkd.com, pg 790

Benner, William R, Pangolin Laser Systems Inc, 9501 Satellite Blvd, Suite 109, Orlando, FL 32837 *Tel:* 407-299-2088 *Toll Free Tel:* 800-PAN-GOLIN (726-4654) *Fax:* 407-299-6066 *E-mail:* contact@pangolin.com *Web Site:* www.pangolin.com, pg 851

Bennett, Betty, Apogee Electronics Corp, 1715 Berkeley St, Santa Monica, CA 90404 *Tel:* 310-584-9394 *Fax:* 310-584-9385 *E-mail:* info@apogeedigital.com *Web Site:* www.apogeedigital.com, pg 687

Bennett, Danny, Verve Label Group, 1755 Broadway, New York, NY 10019 *Tel:* 212-841-8000 *Web Site:* www.vervelabelgroup.com; www.universalmusic.com, pg 926

Bennett, Julie, New Harbinger Publications, 5674 Shattuck Ave, Oakland, CA 94609 *Tel:* 510-652-0215 *Toll Free Tel:* 800-748-6273 *Fax:* 510-652-5472 *E-mail:* customerservice@newharbinger.com *Web Site:* www.newharbinger.com, pg 839

Bennett, Lynn, Stage Post, 255 French Landing Dr, Nashville, TN 37228 *Tel:* 615-248-1978 *Toll Free Tel:* 877-250-1839 *Fax:* 615-242-8861 *E-mail:* mail@stagepost.com *Web Site:* www.stagepost.com, pg 899

Bennett, Michael, TMW Media Group, 2321 Abbot Kinney Blvd, Suite 101, Venice, CA 90291 *Tel:* 310-577-8581 *Toll Free Tel:* 800-262-8862 *Fax:* 310-574-0886 *E-mail:* sale@tmwmedia.com *Web Site:* www.tmwmedia.com, pg 915

Bennett, Opal H, Nantucket Film Festival (NFF), 68 Jay St, Suite 319, Brooklyn, NY 11201 *Tel:* 646-480-1900 *Fax:* 646-365-3367 *E-mail:* info@nantucketfilmfestival.org; submissions@nantucketfilmfestival.org *Web Site:* nantucketfilmfestival.org, pg 997

Bennett, Richard, CinemaGear.com, 14737 Arminta St, Unit B, Panorama City, CA 91402 *Tel:* 818-780-5404 *Fax:* 818-780-5405 *E-mail:* cinemagear@cinemagear.com *Web Site:* www.cinemagear.com, pg 724

Bennett, Stewart, Crossroads Audio Inc, 2623 Myrtle Springs Ave, Dallas, TX 75220 *Tel:* 214-358-2623 *Toll Free Tel:* 800-287-0436 *Fax:* 214-358-0185 *E-mail:* mail@crossroadsaudio.com *Web Site:* www.crossroadsaudio.com, pg 735

Bennett, Mr Tracy, Maui County Film Office, 2200 S Main St, Suite 305, Wailuku, HI 96793 *Tel:* 808-270-8237 *Fax:* 808-270-7995 *Web Site:* www.filmmaui.com, pg 970

Benoit, Byrnes, Spectra Video Productions Ltd, 380 Montrose St, Winnipeg, MB R3M 3M8, Canada *Tel:* 204-452-9832 *Web Site:* www.spectra-productions.com, pg 897

Benson, Chip, Technical Support Systems LLC, 2232 Central Ave, Memphis, TN 38104 *Tel:* 901-398-5908 *Fax:* 901-398-5914 *Web Site:* www.techsupportsys.com, pg 908

Benson, James, Vision Quest Productions Inc, PO Box 1896, Wayne, NJ 07470-1896 *Tel:* 973-686-9400 *Fax:* 973-694-8314 *Web Site:* vqpi.yolasite.com; visionquestproductions.com, pg 930

Benson, Katie, Alliance for Community Media (ACM), 4248 Park Glen Rd, Minneapolis, MN 55416 *Tel:* 952-928-4643 *E-mail:* info@allcommunitymedia.org *Web Site:* www.allcommunitymedia.org, pg 947

Benson, Mike, Stage America LLC, 2300 N Atlantic Ave, Suite 1002, Daytona Beach, FL 32811 *Tel:* 702-879-8177 *E-mail:* info@stageamerica.com *Web Site:* www.stageamerica.com, pg 898

Bentley, Craig, Imageworks, 1039 Meade Ave, San Diego, CA 92116-1038 *Tel:* 619-512-3348 *E-mail:* info@imageworks.tv *Web Site:* www.imageworks.tv, pg 785

Bentley, Ginny, Limelight Production® Inc, 471 Pleasant St, Lee, MA 01238-9322 *Tel:* 413-243-4950 *Toll Free Tel:* 800-243-4950 *Fax:* 413-243-4993 *Toll Free Fax:* 800-243-4951 *E-mail:* info@limelightproductions.com; sales@limelightproductions.com *Web Site:* www.limelightproductions.com, pg 809

Benton, Lori, Weston Woods Studios Inc, 90 Old Sherman Tpke, Danbury, CT 06816 *Tel:* 203-797-3520 *Toll Free Tel:* 800-243-5020 *Fax:* 203-797-3541 *E-mail:* westonwoodsquestions@scholastic.com *Web Site:* www.scholastic.com/westonwoods, pg 936

Benton, Paul, TPR Enterprises Ltd, 644 Fayette Ave, Mamaroneck, NY 10543 *Tel:* 914-698-1141 *Fax:* 914-698-9419 *E-mail:* info@tprlights.com *Web Site:* www.tprlights.com, pg 916

Benton, Thomas J, Data & Marketing Association (DMA), 225 Reinekers Lane, Suite 325, Alexandria, VA 22314 *Tel:* 212-768-7277; 212-790-1500 *Web Site:* thedma.org, pg 953

Benzie, Scott, Banff World Media Festival, 100-366 Adelaide St W, Toronto, ON M5V 1R9, Canada *Tel:* 416-408-2300 *Toll Free Tel:* 888-287-2279 *Fax:* 416-408-0870 *E-mail:* info@achillesmedia.com *Web Site:* banffmediafestival.com, pg 983

Berardi, John, Wildfire Lighting & Visual Effects, 2908 Oregon Ct, Suite G-1, Torrance, CA 90503 *Tel:* 310-755-6780 *Toll Free Tel:* 800-937-8065 *Fax:* 310-755-6781 *E-mail:* sales@wildfirelighting.com *Web Site:* www.wildfirefx.com, pg 938

Berberian, Jack, Color Leasing Studios, 330 Rte 46 E, Fairfield, NJ 07004 *Tel:* 973-575-1118 *Fax:* 973-575-1170 *Web Site:* www.colorleasingstudios.com, pg 728

Berg, James, Matson Multi-Media, 403 E Ramsey Rd, Suite 202, San Antonio, TX 78216 *Tel:* 210-349-3674 *E-mail:* sales@matsonmultimedia.com *Web Site:* www.matsonmultimedia.com; www.matsoncreative.com, pg 820

Bergan, William, Championship Productions Inc, Ames Community Development Park, 2730 Graham St, Ames, IA 50010 *Tel:* 515-232-3687 *Toll Free*

Tel: 800-873-2730 Fax: 515-232-3739 E-mail: info@championshipproductions.com Web Site: www.championshipproductions.com, pg 720

Berge, Patrick, Sceno Plus, 5423 ave de Lorimier, Montreal, QC H2H 2C3, Canada Tel: 514-529-4364 Fax: 514-529-9164 E-mail: mailinfo@scenoplus.com Web Site: www.sceno-plus.com, pg 881

Bergens, Arthur, Bell and Howell LLC, 3791 S Alston Ave, Durham, NC 27713 Toll Free Tel: 800-220-3030; 800-792-4782 (cust care) E-mail: info@bhemail.com Web Site: www.bellhowell.net, pg 703

Berger, Dan, Twentieth Century Fox Film Corp, 10201 W Pico Blvd, Bldg 88, Rm 311, Los Angeles, CA 90035 Tel: 310-369-1000 Toll Free Tel: 888-223-4369 (cust care) Fax: 310-369-8825 E-mail: support@foxcustomercare.com (cust care) Web Site: www.foxmovies.com, pg 919

Berger, Sherwin, Lipsner-Smith Co, 4700 Chase Ave, Lincolnwood, IL 60712-1689 Tel: 847-677-3000 Toll Free Tel: 800-323-7520 Fax: 847-677-1311 Toll Free Fax: 800-784-6733 E-mail: sales@lipsner.com; sales@rtico.com Web Site: www.lipsner.com; lipsner-smith.com, pg 809

Bergeson, Clint, PSSI Global Services LLC, 7030 Hayvenhurst Ave, Van Nuys, CA 91406 Tel: 310-575-4400 Toll Free Tel: 800-SAT-LINK (728-5465); 800-634-6530 (teleport inquiries) E-mail: info@pssiglobal.com Web Site: www.pssiglobal.com, pg 866

Bergman, Alan, The Walt Disney Studios, 500 S Buena Vista St, Burbank, CA 91521 Tel: 818-560-1000 Web Site: studioservices.go.com; waltdisneystudios.com, pg 743

Bergman, Richard I, The Bergman Collection of Medical/Technical/Scientific Stock Images, 134 Leabrook Lane, Princeton, NJ 08540-3622 Tel: 609-921-0749 E-mail: information@pmiprinceton.com Web Site: pmiprinceton.com, pg 704

Bergman, Victoria B, The Bergman Collection of Medical/Technical/Scientific Stock Images, 134 Leabrook Lane, Princeton, NJ 08540-3622 Tel: 609-921-0749 E-mail: information@pmiprinceton.com Web Site: pmiprinceton.com, pg 704

Bergold, Christine, Custom Computer Specialists Inc, 70 Suffolk Ct, Hauppauge, NY 11788 Tel: 631-864-6699 Toll Free Tel: 800-589-8989 Fax: 401-765-6440 Toll Free Fax: 800-986-5518 E-mail: info@customtech.com; support@customtech.com Web Site: www.customonline.com, pg 736

Bergs, M J, TARA Labs, 716 Rossanley Dr, Medford, OR 97501 Tel: 541-488-6465 Fax: 541-245-9119 E-mail: sales@taralabs.com Web Site: www.taralabs.com, pg 907

Beringer, Elizabeth, Feldenkrais® Resources, 3680 Sixth Ave, San Diego, CA 92103 Tel: 619-220-8776 Toll Free Tel: 800-765-1907 Fax: 619-330-4993 E-mail: info@feldenkraisresources.com Web Site: feldenkraisresources.com, pg 759

Berke, Stephen, Berke Creative Inc, 50 Mendell St, Suite 11, San Francisco, CA 94124 Tel: 415-312-2476 Web Site: www.berkecreative.com, pg 704

Berkovich, Mariana, Pacifica Radio Archives, 3729 Cahuenga Blvd W, North Hollywood, CA 91604 Tel: 818-506-1077 Toll Free Tel: 800-735-0230 Fax: 818-506-1084 E-mail: pacarchive@aol.com Web Site: www.pacificaradioarchives.org, pg 850

Berkowitz, Robert, Multivision Video & Film, 3031 SW 28 Lane, Miami, FL 33133 Tel: 305-662-6011 E-mail: info@multivisionvideo.com Web Site: www.multivisionvideo.com, pg 833

Berlin, David M, Video Corporation of America (VCA), 7 Veronica Ave, Somerset, NJ 08873 Tel: 732-545-8000 Fax: 732-545-5101 Web Site: www.vcaglobal.com, pg 927

Berlin, Jack, Accusoft, 4001 N Riverside Dr, Tampa, FL 33603 Tel: 813-875-7575 Toll Free Tel: 800-875-7009 Fax: 813-875-7705 E-mail: sales@accusoft.com Web Site: www.accusoft.com, pg 674

Berman, Jennifer, Roadside Attractions, 7920 Sunset Blvd, No 402, Los Angeles, CA 90046 Tel: 323-882-8490 E-mail: roadsideflix@gmail.com Web Site: roadsideattractions.com, pg 876

Berman, Scott E, Advanced Imaging Concepts Inc, 301 N Harrison St, No 9F 266, Princeton, NJ 08540 Tel: 609-921-3629; 609-529-9200 Fax: 609-924-3010 E-mail: info@aic-imagecentral.com; sales@aic-imagecentral.com Web Site: www.aic-imagecentral.com, pg 677

Berman-Bogdan, Jessica, Global ImageWorks LLC, 65 Beacon St, Haworth, NJ 07641 Tel: 201-384-7715 Fax: 201-501-8971 E-mail: info@globalimageworks.com Web Site: www.globalimageworks.com, pg 771

Bernard, John, Lumisphere™ USA, 9429 Everett Ct, Spotsylvania, VA 22553 Tel: 540-582-7897 Fax: 540-582-5233 Web Site: www.lumisphereusa.com, pg 812

Bernard, Julie, Creative BC (CrBC), 7 W Sixth Ave, Vancouver, BC V5Y 1K2, Canada Tel: 604-730-2732 Fax: 604-736-7290 E-mail: info@creativebc.com; media@creativebc.com Web Site: www.creativebc.com, pg 978

Bernatsky, Peter, Advance Pro, 62 Sucurfield Blvd, Unit 12 & 14, Winnipeg, MB R3Y 1M5, Canada Tel: 204-772-0386 Toll Free Tel: 800-392-1295 Fax: 204-783-2177 E-mail: ap@advance.mb.ca Web Site: advance-pro.com, pg 677

Bernecker, Shelly, Michigan Office Solutions (MOS), A Xerox Company, 2859 Walkent Dr NW, Grand Rapids, MI 49544 Toll Free Tel: 800-442-9070 E-mail: info@mos-xerox.com Web Site: www.mos-xerox.com, pg 825

Berney, Ellen, Satellite Media Production, 8379 Inspiration Ave, Walkersville, MD 21793 Tel: 301-845-2737 Toll Free Tel: 800-747-0856 Web Site: www.satellitemediaproduction.com; www.oldietv.com, pg 881

Berney, Fred, Satellite Media Production, 8379 Inspiration Ave, Walkersville, MD 21793 Tel: 301-845-2737 Toll Free Tel: 800-747-0856 Web Site: www.satellitemediaproduction.com; www.oldietv.com, pg 881

Bernotas, Peter, International Historic Films Inc, 3533 S Archer Ave, Chicago, IL 60609 Tel: 773-927-2900; 773-927-9091 (cust serv) Fax: 773-927-9211 E-mail: intrvdeo@ix.netcom.com Web Site: ihffilm.com, pg 790

Bernotas, Peter, Intervideo Duplication Services, 3533 S Archer Ave, Chicago, IL 60609 Tel: 773-927-9091 Fax: 773-927-9211 E-mail: info@intervideoduplication.com Web Site: www.intervideoduplication.com, pg 791

Bernstein, Daniel, Bel Fuse Inc, 299 Johnson Ave, Suite 100, Waseca, MN 56093 Tel: 507-833-8822 Fax: 507-833-6287 E-mail: ccsorders@us.cinch.com Web Site: cinch.com, pg 703

Berry, Drew, National Association of Black Journalists (NABJ), 1100 Knight Hall, Suite 3100, College Park, MD 20742 Tel: 301-405-0248 Fax: 301-314-1714 Web Site: www.nabj.org, pg 958

Berry, Jack, Image Management Systems Inc, 239 W 15 St, New York, NY 10011 Tel: 212-741-8765 E-mail: info@imagemgt.com Web Site: www.imagemgt.com, pg 785

Berry, Jackie, Texas Heart Institute Visual Communication Services, Denton A Cooley Bldg, Suite C-530, 6770 Bertner Ave, Houston, TX 77030 Tel: 832-355-9558 Fax: 832-355-9511 Web Site: www.texasheart.org, pg 911

Berry, Karla, Southern Illinois University, Ctr for Teaching Excellence, Morris Library Rm 180, 605 Agriculture Dr, Mailcode 6510, Carbondale, IL 62901 Tel: 618-453-2258 Fax: 618-453-3010 E-mail: teach@siu.edu Web Site: cte.siu.edu/video-and-image-production, pg 895

Berry, Scot, Memphis Communications Corp, 4771 Summer Ave, Memphis, TN 38122 Tel: 901-725-9271 Toll Free Tel: 866-805-5893 Fax: 901-272-3577 Web Site: memphiscommunications.net, pg 823

Berry, Shane, Memphis Communications Corp, 4771 Summer Ave, Memphis, TN 38122 Tel: 901-725-9271 Toll Free Tel: 866-805-5893 Fax: 901-272-3577 Web Site: memphiscommunications.net, pg 823

Berry, Tom, Reel One International Ltd, 486 Ste-Catherine W, Suite 100, Montreal, QC H3B 1A6, Canada E-mail: sales@reeloneent.com Web Site: reeloneent.com, pg 872

Bersell, Sean, The Entertainment Merchants Association (EMA), PO Box 6339, North Hollywood, CA 91603 Tel: 818-385-1500 E-mail: info@entmerch.org Web Site: www.entmerch.org, pg 954

Bertell, Christopher, Cibola Systems, 180 S Cypress St, Orange, CA 92866 Tel: 714-480-0272 Fax: 714-480-0768 E-mail: info@cibolasystems.com Web Site: cibolasystems.com, pg 723

Bertelsen, Jeffrey, CyberOptics Corp, 5900 Golden Hills Dr, Minneapolis, MN 55416 Tel: 763-542-5000 Fax: 763-542-5100 E-mail: info@cyberoptics.com Web Site: cyberoptics.com, pg 736

Berthiaume, Lorraine, Sceno Plus, 5423 ave de Lorimier, Montreal, QC H2H 2C3, Canada Tel: 514-529-4364 Fax: 514-529-9164 E-mail: mailinfo@scenoplus.com Web Site: www.sceno-plus.com, pg 881

Bertolino, Daniel, Les Productions Via Le Monde (Daniel Bertolino) Inc, 758, rue Halpern, Dorval, QC H9P 1G6, Canada Tel: 514-636-6633 Fax: 514-636-9633 E-mail: distribution@vialemonde.com; info@vialemonde.com Web Site: www.vialemonde.com, pg 864

Bertolino, Francesca, Museum of the City of New York, 1220 Fifth Ave, New York, NY 10029 Tel: 212-534-1672 Fax: 212-423-0758 E-mail: info@mcny.org Web Site: www.mcny.org, pg 834

Bertrand, Bruce, Early Films, 9 Richter St, Randolph, NJ 07869-3309 Tel: 973-361-5817 E-mail: info@earlyfilms.net Web Site: www.earlyfilms.net, pg 749

Bessire, Elena, Cine Las Americas International Film Festival (CLAIFF), 1104 W 34 St, No 625, Austin, TX 78705 Tel: 512-535-0765 E-mail: cine@cinelasamericas.org; entries@cinelasamericas.org Web Site: cinelasamericas.org; www.facebook.com/cinelasamericasaustin, pg 986

Betant, Cyrille, Astronomical Society of the Pacific, 390 Ashton Ave, San Francisco, CA 94112 Tel: 415-337-1100 Toll Free Tel: 800-335-2624 Fax: 415-337-5205 Web Site: astrosociety.org, pg 691

Bettan, Gary, Videoguys, 10-12 Charles St, Glen Cove, NY 11542 Tel: 516-759-1611 Toll Free Tel: 800-323-2325 Fax: 516-671-3092 E-mail: sales@videoguys.com Web Site: www.videoguys.com, pg 929

Betts, Stephanie, WildBrain™, 5657 Spring Garden Rd, Suite 505, Halifax, NS B3J 3R4, Canada Tel: 902-423-0260 Fax: 902-422-0752 E-mail: info@wildbrain.com; halifax@wildbrain.com; sales@wildbrain.com Web Site: www.wildbrain.com, pg 938

Betts, Susan, Actors Attic, 540 Otis Dr, Dover, DE 19901 Tel: 302-734-8214 Fax: 302-734-8207 E-mail: sales@actorsattic.com Web Site: www.actorsattic.com, pg 675

Beugen, Joan, Cresta Creative, 1050 N State St, Chicago, IL 60610 Tel: 312-944-4700 Fax: 312-944-1582 E-mail: info@crestagroup.com Web Site: www.crestacreative.com, pg 734

Bevan, Gregg, VideoLink Inc, an AVI-SPL company, 1230 Washington St, West Newton, MA 02465 Tel: 617-340-4100 Toll Free Tel: 800-452-5565 Fax: 617-340-4101 E-mail: sales@videolinktv.com Web Site: www.videolinktv.com, pg 929

Beverly, Clyde M, A/V Presentations Inc, 104 Otis St, Suite 30, Northborough, MA 01532 Tel: 508-393-9767 Toll Free Tel: 800-648-7176 Fax: 508-393-6698 E-mail: staff@avpresentations.com Web Site: www.avpresentations.com, pg 697

Beverly, Morris, A/V Presentations Inc, 104 Otis St, Suite 30, Northborough, MA 01532 Tel: 508-393-9767 Toll Free Tel: 800-648-7176 Fax: 508-393-6698 E-mail: staff@avpresentations.com Web Site: www.avpresentations.com, pg 697

Beverly, Nelson D, Love Your Shorts Film Festival, 608 S Elm Ave, Sanford, FL 32771 *E-mail:* contact@loveyourshorts.com *Web Site:* www.loveyourshorts.com, pg 995

Beverly-Bishop, Catharine, Santa Monica Mountains National Recreation Area, Office of Special Park Uses, 401 W Hillcrest Dr, Thousand Oaks, CA 91360 *Tel:* 805-370-2308 *E-mail:* samo_permits@nps.gov *Web Site:* www.nps.gov/samo, pg 968

Bevilacqua, Joe, Bevilacqua Studios, 202 E 42 St, New York, NY 10017 *Tel:* 212-490-0355 *Fax:* 212-490-0355, pg 704

Bevilacqua, Joe, New Horizon Studios, 202 E 42 St, New York, NY 10017 *Tel:* 212-490-0355, pg 839

Beyer-Smolin, Carla, Hearing Loss Association of America (HLAA), 7910 Woodmont Ave, Suite 1200, Bethesda, MD 20814 *Tel:* 301-657-2248 *Fax:* 301-913-9413 *E-mail:* inquiry@hearingloss.org *Web Site:* www.hearingloss.org, pg 778

Beyers, Scott, BeyerSound & Essay Audio, PO Box 120442, St Paul, MN 55112-0018 *Tel:* 651-633-3933 *E-mail:* info@essayaudio.com *Web Site:* www.essayaudio.com, pg 705

Beyhm, Tara, Acme Filmworks Inc, 3347 Motor Ave, Los Angeles, CA 90034 *Tel:* 323-464-7805 *Fax:* 323-464-6614 *E-mail:* pr@acmefilmworks.com (publicity) *Web Site:* www.acmefilmworks.com, pg 674

Bhowmik, Achin, Society for Information Display (SID), 1475 S Bascom Ave, Suite 114, Campbell, CA 95008-4006 *Tel:* 408-879-3901 *Fax:* 408-879-3833 *E-mail:* office@sid.org *Web Site:* www.sid.org, pg 962

Biase, Mark, The Production Group Studios, 1626 N Wilcox Ave, Suite 281, Hollywood, CA 90028 *Tel:* 323-469-8111 *Fax:* 323-962-2182 *E-mail:* info@productiongroup.tv *Web Site:* productiongroup.tv, pg 864

Bicknell, Titus, RLJ Entertainment Inc, 8515 Georgia Ave, Suite 650, Silver Spring, MD 20910 *Tel:* 301-608-2115 *Toll Free Tel:* 800-999-0212 *E-mail:* inquiries@rljentertainment.com *Web Site:* www.us.rljentertainment.com, pg 875

Bidermann-Roizen, Camille, International Emmy® Awards, 25 W 52 St, New York, NY 10019 *Tel:* 212-489-6969 *Fax:* 212-489-6557 *E-mail:* iemmys@iemmys.tv; awardsdept@iemmys.tv *Web Site:* www.iemmys.tv, pg 993

Bieber, Rick, Nineteen87, 1024 Harding Ave, Suite 201, Venice Beach, CA 90291 *Tel:* 310-577-5009 *Fax:* 310-577-1960 *E-mail:* info@1-9-8-7.com *Web Site:* www.1-9-8-7.com, pg 841

Bieda, Bill, The Video Store Shopper, 3987 Heritage Oak Ct, Simi Valley, CA 93063 *Tel:* 805-583-8500 *Toll Free Tel:* 800-429-4900 *Fax:* 805-583-8546 *Toll Free Fax:* 800-947-2060 *E-mail:* sales@shopperinc.com; customerservice@shopperinc.com *Web Site:* www.thevideostoreshopper.com; www.tsisupplies.com, pg 928

Bigelow, Jeff, Hubbard Supply Co, 901 W Second St, Flint, MI 48503 *Tel:* 810-234-8681 *Toll Free Tel:* 800-875-4811 *Fax:* 810-234-6142 *E-mail:* information@hubbardsupply.com *Web Site:* www.hubbardsupply.com, pg 782

Bigliani, Tom, Video Corporation of America (VCA), 7 Veronica Ave, Somerset, NJ 08873 *Tel:* 732-545-8000 *Fax:* 732-545-5101 *Web Site:* www.vcaglobal.com, pg 927

Bilbey, Matt, Electronic Arts Inc, 209 Redwood Shores Pkwy, Redwood City, CA 94065 *Tel:* 650-628-1500 *Web Site:* www.ea.com, pg 752

Bilbrey, David, Saturn Awards, 334 W 54 St, Los Angeles, CA 90037 *Tel:* 323-752-5811 *E-mail:* saturn.awards@ca.rr.com *Web Site:* www.saturnawards.org, pg 1003

Bill, Jeff, IDenticard Systems Inc, 148 E Stiegel St, Manheim, PA 17545 *Tel:* 717-569-5797 *Toll Free Tel:* 800-233-0298 *Fax:* 717-427-1654 *E-mail:* identicard.info@identicard.com *Web Site:* www.identicard.com, pg 784

Billhimer, Dave, PLUS Corp of America, 9655 SW Sunshine Ct, Suite 300, Beaverton, OR 97005 *Tel:* 503-748-8700 *Toll Free Tel:* 800-211-9001 *E-mail:* sales@plus-america.com; info@plus-america.com *Web Site:* www.plus-america.com, pg 858

Billinger, George, Society of Camera Operators, PO Box 2006, Toluca Lake, CA 91610-0006 *Tel:* 818-563-9110 *Fax:* 818-563-9117 *E-mail:* sooffice@soc.org *Web Site:* www.soc.org, pg 962

Bilodeau, Stephanie, Government of New Brunswick Department of Tourism, Heritage & Culture, Marysville Place, 20 McGloin St, 4th fl, Fredericton, NB E3A 5T8, Canada *Tel:* 506-453-3115 *Fax:* 506-444-5760 *E-mail:* thctpcinfo@gnb.ca *Web Site:* www2.gnb.ca, pg 978

Binet, David, National Association of Theatre Owners (NATO), 1705 "N" St NW, Washington, DC 20036 *Tel:* 202-962-0054 *E-mail:* nato@natodc.com *Web Site:* www.natoonline.org, pg 959

Bing, George, HB Communications Inc, 60 Dodge Ave, North Haven, CT 06473 *Tel:* 203-234-9246 *Toll Free Tel:* 800-243-4414 *Fax:* 203-234-2013 *E-mail:* info@hbcommunications.com *Web Site:* hbcommunications.com, pg 777

Bingham, Tony, Association for Talent Development (ATD), 1640 King St, Alexandria, VA 22314-2743 *Tel:* 703-683-8100 *Toll Free Tel:* 800-628-2783 *Fax:* 703-299-8723 *E-mail:* customercare@td.org *Web Site:* www.td.org, pg 950

Binney, Michael, Emerson Radio Corp, 3 University Plaza, Suite 405, Hackensack, NJ 07601 *Tel:* 973-884-5800 *Toll Free Tel:* 800-909-1240 (cust serv) *Fax:* 973-428-2067 *E-mail:* internet@emersonradio.com *Web Site:* www.emersonradio.com, pg 753

Bione, John, First Run Features, The Film Center Bldg, Suite 1213, 630 Ninth Ave, New York, NY 10036-3708 *Tel:* 212-243-0600 *Fax:* 212-989-7649 *E-mail:* info@firstrunfeatures.com *Web Site:* www.firstrunfeatures.com, pg 761

Bird, Andy, The Walt Disney Co, 500 S Buena Vista St, Burbank, CA 91521 *Tel:* 818-560-1000 *Web Site:* disney.com; thewaltdisneycompany.com, pg 743

Bird, Jim, The PPS Group, 424 Scott St, Covington, KY 41011 *Tel:* 859-291-5100 *Toll Free Tel:* 800-978-3445 *Fax:* 859-291-5150 *E-mail:* info@theppsgroup.com *Web Site:* www.pps-inc.com; www.theppsgroup.com, pg 860

Bird, Justin, Utopia Films, 1976 S La Cienega Blvd, No 130, Los Angeles, CA 90034 *Tel:* 310-338-0580 *Fax:* 313-557-0580 *E-mail:* reception@utopiafilms.com; production@utopiafilms.com (reels) *Web Site:* utopiafilms.com, pg 924

Bird, Patrick, SonicPool, 6860 Lexington Ave, Hollywood, CA 90038 *Tel:* 323-460-4649 *Toll Free Tel:* 866-203-7213 *Fax:* 323-460-6063 *E-mail:* production@sonicpool.com *Web Site:* www.sonicpool.com, pg 892

Birks, Heather, BEA National Scholarships in Broadcasting, 1771 "N" St NW, Washington, DC 20036-2891 *Tel:* 202-602-0587 *Fax:* 202-609-9940 *E-mail:* help@beaweb.org *Web Site:* www.beaweb.org, pg 983

Birks, Heather, Broadcast Education Association (BEA), 1771 "N" St NW, Washington, DC 20036-2891 *Tel:* 202-602-0587 *Fax:* 202-609-9940 *E-mail:* help@beaweb.org *Web Site:* www.beaweb.org, pg 952

Birnbaum, Amy, Round Hill Music LLC, 400 Madison Ave, 18th fl, New York, NY 10017 *Tel:* 212-380-0080 *Fax:* 212-380-0081 *E-mail:* info@roundhillmusic.com *Web Site:* roundhillmusic.com, pg 878

Bish, Reynolds, Kofax Inc, 15211 Laguna Canyon Rd, Irvine, CA 92618-3146 *Tel:* 949-727-1733 *Fax:* 949-727-3144 *E-mail:* info@kofax.com *Web Site:* www.kofax.com, pg 800

Bishop, David, Pro AV Systems, 275 Billerica Rd, Suite 3, Chelmsford, MA 01824 *Tel:* 978-692-5111 *Fax:* 978-692-5252 *E-mail:* info@proavsi.com *Web Site:* proavsi.com, pg 862

Bishop, Kim, Pro AV Systems, 275 Billerica Rd, Suite 3, Chelmsford, MA 01824 *Tel:* 978-692-5111 *Fax:* 978-692-5252 *E-mail:* info@proavsi.com *Web Site:* proavsi.com, pg 862

Bishop, Les, Pro AV Systems, 275 Billerica Rd, Suite 3, Chelmsford, MA 01824 *Tel:* 978-692-5111 *Fax:* 978-692-5252 *E-mail:* info@proavsi.com *Web Site:* proavsi.com, pg 862

Bishop, Mark, Marblemedia, 74 Fraser Ave, Suite 100, Toronto, ON M6K 3E1, Canada *Tel:* 416-646-2711 *E-mail:* connect@marblemedia.com *Web Site:* www.marblemedia.com, pg 816

Bisk, Alison, Bisk Education, 9417 Princess Palm Ave, Tampa, FL 33619 *Toll Free Tel:* 800-280-9718 *E-mail:* media@bisk.com *Web Site:* www.bisk.com, pg 706

Bisk, Michael D, Bisk Education, 9417 Princess Palm Ave, Tampa, FL 33619 *Toll Free Tel:* 800-280-9718 *E-mail:* media@bisk.com *Web Site:* www.bisk.com, pg 706

Bissen, Kathy, Wisconsin Public Television, 821 University Ave, Madison, WI 53706 *Tel:* 608-263-2121 *Toll Free Tel:* 800-422-9707 *Fax:* 608-263-9763 *E-mail:* comments@wpt.org *Web Site:* www.wpt.org, pg 940

Bissonette, Peter, Learning Strategies Corp, 2000 Plymouth Rd, Minnetonka, MN 55305-2335 *Tel:* 952-767-9800 *Toll Free Tel:* 888-800-2688 (cust serv); 866-292-1861 (24 hour order line) *Fax:* 952-475-2373 *E-mail:* info@learningstrategies.com *Web Site:* www.learningstrategies.com, pg 805

Bissonnette, Daniel, Montreal Film & TV Commission, Duke Pavilion, 5th fl, 801 Brennan St, Montreal, QC H3C 0G4, Canada *Tel:* 514-872-2883 *Fax:* 514-872-3409 *E-mail:* film.tv@ville.montreal.qc.ca *Web Site:* www.montrealfilm.com, pg 979

Bissonnette, Michel, CBC/Radio-Canada, 181 Queen St, Ottawa, ON K1P 1K9, Canada *Tel:* 613-288-6000; 613-288-6445 (newsroom) *Toll Free Tel:* 866-306-4636 (CN only) *E-mail:* cbcnewsottawa@cbc.ca *Web Site:* cbc.radio-canada.ca, pg 717

Bittan, Andrew, DC Asian Pacific American Film Festival, 2515 Virginia Ave NW, Washington, DC 20037 *Tel:* 202-796-9680; 202-792-6393 *E-mail:* info@apafilm.org; admin@apafilm.org *Web Site:* www.apafilm.org, pg 988

Bittle, Joanna, CommCreative, 75 Fountain St, Framingham, MA 01702 *Tel:* 508-620-6664 *Toll Free Tel:* 877-620-6664 *Fax:* 508-620-0592 *E-mail:* info@commcreative.com *Web Site:* www.commcreative.com, pg 728

Bittler, David, Nickelodeon, 1515 Broadway, 38th fl, New York, NY 10036 *Tel:* 212-258-8000 (Viacom) *Web Site:* www.nick.com, pg 841

Black, Andy, Audio Media Productions, 6739 Kirby Trace Cove, Memphis, TN 38119 *Tel:* 901-751-2363 *E-mail:* ampman@aol.com *Web Site:* www.audiomediaproductions.net, pg 693

Black, Betty, Mississippi Film Office, 501 N West St, 5th fl, Jackson, MS 39201 *Tel:* 601-359-3297 *Fax:* 601-359-5048 *Web Site:* www.filmmississippi.org, pg 972

Black, Christine, NFL Films Music Library, One Sabol Way, Mount Laurel, NJ 08054 *Tel:* 856-222-3500 *Web Site:* nflfilms.nfl.com; apmmusic.com/libraries/nfl-films-music-library-nfl, pg 841

Black, Craig, Blackstone Audio Inc, 31 Mistletoe Rd, Ashland, OR 97520 *Toll Free Tel:* 800-621-0182 *Toll Free Fax:* 877-492-0793 *E-mail:* libraryservices@blackstoneaudio.com *Web Site:* www.blackstoneaudio.com; www.blackstonelibrary.com, pg 707

Black, Darold, Black Media Works, 534 21 Ave SW, Calgary, AB T2S 0H1, Canada *Tel:* 403-802-0010 *E-mail:* info@blackmediaworks.com *Web Site:* www.blackmediaworks.com, pg 706

Black, Larry, Heart Breaker Entertainment LLC, 10094 Lacy Rd, Hagerstown, IN 47346 *Tel:* 765-489-4048; 765-489-5558 *Toll Free Tel:* 800-843-3635 *Fax:* 765-489-4899 *E-mail:* info@videodj.com *Web Site:* videodj.com, pg 778

Black, Leticia, TM Studios Inc, 2002 Academy Lane, Suite 110, Dallas, TX 75234 *Tel:* 972-406-6800 *Fax:* 972-406-6890 *E-mail:* info@tmstudios.com; tmcustomerservice@tmstudios.com *Web Site:* www.tmstudios.com, pg 915

Black, Nathan, Audio Media Productions, 6739 Kirby Trace Cove, Memphis, TN 38119 *Tel:* 901-751-2363 *E-mail:* ampman@aol.com *Web Site:* www.audiomediaproductions.net, pg 693

Blackburn, Jude, Chicago Irish Film Festival (CIFF), c/o Society for Arts, 1112 N Milwaukee Ave, Chicago, IL 60642 *Tel:* 773-486-9612 *Fax:* 773-486-9613 *Web Site:* www.chicagoirishfilmfestival.com, pg 985

Blackmon, Mark, USITT, 290 Elwood Davis Rd, Suite 100, Liverpool, NY 13088 *Tel:* 315-463-6463 *Toll Free Tel:* 800-938-7488 *Toll Free Fax:* 866-398-7488 *E-mail:* info@usitt.org *Web Site:* www.usitt.org, pg 963

Blackwood, Michael, Michael Blackwood Productions Inc, 6 W 18 St, Suite 2B, New York, NY 10011 *Tel:* 212-242-1805 *Fax:* 212-242-1671 *E-mail:* blackwoodfilm@aol.com *Web Site:* www.michaelblackwoodproductions.com, pg 707

Blair, Bill, Eiki International Inc, 30251 Esperanza, Rancho Santa Margarita, CA 92688-2132 *Tel:* 949-457-0200 *Toll Free Tel:* 800-242-3454 *Fax:* 949-457-7878 *Toll Free Fax:* 800-457-3454 *E-mail:* usa@eiki.com; orders-usa@eiki.com *Web Site:* www.eiki.com, pg 751

Blair, Christine, Transtector Systems Inc, 10701 N Airport Dr, Hayden, ID 83835 *Tel:* 208-772-8515 *Toll Free Tel:* 800-882-9110 *Fax:* 208-762-6133 *E-mail:* sales@transtector.com *Web Site:* www.transtector.com, pg 917

Blair, Dain, GrooveWorx, 1200 Chickory Lane, Santa Monica, CA 90049 *Tel:* 310-260-2626 *Fax:* 310-260-2662 *E-mail:* info@grooveworx.com *Web Site:* grooveworx.com, pg 774

Blair, Don, VCI Entertainment, 11333 E 60 Place, Tulsa, OK 74146-6828 *Tel:* 918-254-6337 *Toll Free Tel:* 800-331-4077 *E-mail:* vci@vcientertainment.com *Web Site:* www.vcientertainment.com; www.vcient.com, pg 925

Blair, John, Gyration, 3601 Calle Tecate, Suite B, Camarillo, CA 93012 *Toll Free Tel:* 888-340-0033 (tech support) *E-mail:* gsupport@smkusa.com; info@smkusa.com *Web Site:* www.gyration.com, pg 775

Blair, Robert A, VCI Entertainment, 11333 E 60 Place, Tulsa, OK 74146-6828 *Tel:* 918-254-6337 *Toll Free Tel:* 800-331-4077 *E-mail:* vci@vcientertainment.com *Web Site:* www.vcientertainment.com; www.vcient.com, pg 925

Blair, Skippy, Golden State Dance Teachers Association (GSDTA), 10804 Woodruff Ave, Downey, CA 90241-3910 *Tel:* 562-869-8949 *Web Site:* www.swingworld.com, pg 772

Blakely, Christopher, Main Street Media Inc, 185 Pier Ave, Suite 105, Santa Monica, CA 90405 *Tel:* 310-450-1846 *E-mail:* info@mainstreetmediainc.com *Web Site:* www.mainstreetmediainc.com, pg 815

Blakeslee, Mike, National Association for Music Education (NAfME), 1806 Robert Fulton Dr, Reston, VA 20191 *Tel:* 703-860-4000 *Toll Free Tel:* 800-336-3768 *Fax:* 703-860-1531 *Toll Free Fax:* 888-275-6362 *E-mail:* memberservices@nafme.org *Web Site:* nafme.org, pg 958

Blanchard, Margaret, George Foster Peabody Awards, c/o University of Georgia, 120 Hooper St, Athens, GA 30602-3018 *Tel:* 706-542-3787 *E-mail:* peabody@uga.edu *Web Site:* www.peabodyawards.com, pg 999

Blanchette, Brian, Canvys™, 40W267 Keslinger Rd, LaFox, IL 60147-0393 *Tel:* 508-460-5400 *Toll Free Tel:* 800-291-1344 *Fax:* 508-460-5470 *Web Site:* www.canvys.com, pg 716

Blanco, Richard J, Lighting Sales Connection Inc, 757 SE 17 St, No 254, Fort Lauderdale, FL 33316 *Tel:* 954-655-9074 *Fax:* 954-764-7013 *E-mail:* info@lightingsales.com *Web Site:* www.lightingsales.com, pg 808

Blane, Barry, Gary Camera & Digital, 6750 Broadway Ave, Merrillville, IN 46410 *Tel:* 219-769-2451 *Fax:* 219-769-2488 *E-mail:* garycamera@gmail.com *Web Site:* garycameradigital.com, pg 768

Blane, Mark, Gary Camera & Digital, 6750 Broadway Ave, Merrillville, IN 46410 *Tel:* 219-769-2451 *Fax:* 219-769-2488 *E-mail:* garycamera@gmail.com *Web Site:* garycameradigital.com, pg 768

Blangiardi, Rick, KHNL/KGMB, 420 Waiakamilo Rd, Suite 205, Honolulu, HI 96817 *Tel:* 808-847-3246 *Fax:* 808-845-3616 *E-mail:* info8@khnl.com; news@hawaiinewsnow.com *Web Site:* www.hawaiinewsnow.com, pg 798

Blank, Harrod, Les Blank Films Inc, 10341 San Pablo Ave, El Cerrito, CA 94530-3123 *Tel:* 510-525-0942 *E-mail:* lesblankfilmsinc@gmail.com *Web Site:* lesblank.com, pg 707

Blank, Matthew C, Showtime Networks Inc, 1633 Broadway, New York, NY 10019 *Tel:* 212-708-1600 *Fax:* 212-708-1217 *Web Site:* www.sho.com, pg 887

Blanke, Eric, ETR, 100 Enterprise Way, Suite G 300, Scotts Valley, CA 95066 *Toll Free Tel:* 800-620-8884 *Fax:* 831-438-4284 *E-mail:* customerservice@etr.org, pg 756

Blankenship, Amy, Soundtrack Group, 162 Columbus Ave, Boston, MA 02116 *Tel:* 617-303-7500 *Fax:* 617-303-7555 *Web Site:* www.soundtrackgroup.com, pg 895

Blasioli, Adrienne, Pro AV Systems, 275 Billerica Rd, Suite 3, Chelmsford, MA 01824 *Tel:* 978-692-5111 *Fax:* 978-692-5252 *E-mail:* info@proavsi.com *Web Site:* proavsi.com, pg 862

Blattner, Frederick, DNASTAR Inc, 3801 Regent St, Madison, WI 53705-5204 *Tel:* 608-258-7420 *Toll Free Tel:* 866-511-5090 *Fax:* 608-258-7439 *E-mail:* info@dnastar.com *Web Site:* www.dnastar.com, pg 744

Blaustein, Meira, Maverick Awards, 13 Rock City Rd, Woodstock, NY 12498 *Tel:* 845-679-4265; 845-810-0131 *Fax:* 509-479-5414 *E-mail:* info@woodstockfilmfestival.com *Web Site:* www.woodstockfilmfestival.com, pg 995

Blauvelt, Jeff, HD Cinema, 12233 W Olympic Blvd, Suite 158, Los Angeles, CA 90064 *Tel:* 310-434-9500 *Fax:* 310-499-5237 (efax) *Web Site:* www.hd-cinema.com, pg 777

Blaylock, Layton, Inferno Films, 3404 Guadalupe St, Austin, TX 78705 *Tel:* 512-302-9009 *Fax:* 512-302-9022 *Web Site:* www.infernofilms.com, pg 787

Bleach, Kelly, American Foundation for the Blind (AFB), 2 Penn Plaza, Suite 1102, New York, NY 10121 *Tel:* 212-502-7600 *Toll Free Tel:* 800-232-5463 *Fax:* 212-502-7777 *Toll Free Fax:* 888-545-8331 *E-mail:* info@afb.org *Web Site:* www.afb.org, pg 948

Bleemer, Rachel, Los Angeles Film Festival, 5670 Wilshire Blvd, 9th fl, Los Angeles, CA 90036 *Tel:* 323-556-9300 *Toll Free Tel:* 866-345-6337 *Fax:* 323-556-9303 *E-mail:* lafilmfest@filmindependent.org; programming@filmindependent.org *Web Site:* www.filmindependent.org/la-film-festival, pg 995

Blenz-Clucas, Beth, Sugar Mountain PR, 5505 SW Illinois St, Portland, OR 97221-1643 *Tel:* 503-293-9498 *E-mail:* sugarmountainnews@msn.com *Web Site:* www.sugarmountainpr.com, pg 903

Blicher, Leigh, Videofax, 1750 Cesar Chavez St, Unit G, San Francisco, CA 94124 *Tel:* 415-641-0100 *E-mail:* rentals@videofax.com *Web Site:* www.videofax.com, pg 929

Bliss, Judith, MindPlay, 4400 E Broadway Blvd, Suite 400, Tucson, AZ 85711 *Tel:* 520-888-1800 *Toll Free Tel:* 800-221-7911 *E-mail:* mail@mindplay.com *Web Site:* www.mindplay.com, pg 828

Bloch, Arthur, Thinking Allowed Productions, 5966 Zinn Dr, Oakland, CA 94611 *Tel:* 510-339-8004 *Toll Free Tel:* 800-999-4415 *E-mail:* thinking@thinkingallowed.com *Web Site:* www.thinkingallowed.com, pg 912

Bloch, Paul, DataDirect Networks, 9351 Deering Ave, Chatsworth, CA 91311 *Tel:* 818-700-4000 *Toll Free Tel:* 800-TERABYTE (837-2298) *E-mail:* info@ddn.com; sales@ddn.com *Web Site:* www.ddn.com, pg 738

Block, Mitchell W, Direct Cinema Ltd Inc, PO Box 10003, Santa Monica, CA 90410-1003 *Tel:* 310-636-8200 *Fax:* 310-636-8228 *E-mail:* dclvideo@aol.com *Web Site:* www.directcinema.com, pg 743

Bloeme, Peter, Skyhoundz, 660 Hembree Pkwy, Suite 110, Roswell, GA 30076 *Tel:* 770-751-3882 *Fax:* 770-740-1665 *E-mail:* info@skyhoundz.com *Web Site:* www.skyhoundz.com, pg 890

Blohm, Frank, Velodyne LiDAR Inc, 5521 Hellyer Ave, San Jose, CA 95738 *Tel:* 408-465-2800 *Fax:* 408-779-9208 (cust serv); 408-779-9377 (orders) *E-mail:* lidar@velodyne.com *Web Site:* velodynelidar.com, pg 925

Blonski, David, Timeless Productions, 5050 Traverse Creek Rd, Garden Valley, CA 95633 *Tel:* 530-333-1335 *Toll Free Tel:* 800-729-1325 *E-mail:* 4info@timelessproductions.com *Web Site:* www.timelessproductions.com, pg 914

Bloom, Brian, Ahead Stereo Inc, 7428 Beverly Blvd, Los Angeles, CA 90036 *Tel:* 323-931-8873 *E-mail:* sales@aheadstereo.com *Web Site:* www.aheadstereo.com, pg 678

Bloomfield, Louise A, Posthorn Recordings, 142 W 26 St, 10th fl, New York, NY 10001-6814 *Tel:* 212-242-3737 *Fax:* 212-924-1243 *Web Site:* www.posthorn.com, pg 860

Blue, Larry, Bell and Howell LLC, 3791 S Alston Ave, Durham, NC 27713 *Toll Free Tel:* 800-220-3030; 800-792-4782 (cust care) *E-mail:* info@bhemail.com *Web Site:* www.bellhowell.net, pg 703

Blum, Erik, American AV, 8005 Haute Ct, Springfield, VA 22150 *Tel:* 703-573-6910 *Fax:* 703-573-3539 *E-mail:* sales@aavevents.com *Web Site:* www.aavevents.com, pg 683

Blum, Steve, Autodesk Inc, 111 McInnis Pkwy, San Rafael, CA 94903 *Tel:* 415-507-5000 *Fax:* 415-507-5100 *Web Site:* www.autodesk.com, pg 696

Blumeyer, Brad, US Case Corp, 6301 J Richard Dr, Raleigh, NC 27617 *Tel:* 919-783-6166 *Toll Free Tel:* 800-648-8474 *Fax:* 919-783-0740 *E-mail:* customersupport@uscase.com *Web Site:* www.uscase.com, pg 923

Bobji, Jagannath, ACCO Brands Corp, 4 Corporate Dr, Lake Zurich, IL 60047-8997 *Toll Free Tel:* 800-541-0094; 800-222-6462 *Toll Free Fax:* 800-941-4463 *E-mail:* contactus@acco.com (cust serv) *Web Site:* www.accobrands.com, pg 673

Bobsin, Curtis, Southwest Sound Solutions, 2323 Loop 410 NW, San Antonio, TX 78230-5348 *Tel:* 210-341-4411 *Fax:* 210-349-8300 *E-mail:* info@swsoundsolutions.com *Web Site:* www.swsoundsolutions.com, pg 896

Bock, Bruce A, Tri-State Audio Visual Co, 2901 Glendora Ave, Cincinnati, OH 45219 *Tel:* 513-281-7500 *Toll Free Tel:* 800-348-8728 *Fax:* 513-281-7539 *E-mail:* sales@tristateav.com *Web Site:* www.tristateav.com, pg 918

Bock, Karen, Applied Integration Corp, 3930 W New York Dr, Tucson, AZ 85745 *Tel:* 520-743-3095 *E-mail:* info@appliedi.com *Web Site:* www.appliedi.com, pg 687

Bodak-Smith, Tricia, The Lot (Skye Partners), 1041 N Formosa Ave, West Hollywood, CA 90046 *Tel:* 323-850-3180 *Fax:* 323-850-3189 *E-mail:* info@thelotstudios.com; stages@thelotstudios.com *Web Site:* www.thelotstudios.com, pg 811

Boddicker, Michael, Synthesizer Rental Service, 10907 W Magnolia Blvd, North Hollywood, CA 91601 *Tel:* 323-660-4065; 818-907-7780; 615-327-3515

Borsum, Deborah, Meetinghouse Event Design & Production, 781 N Church Rd, Elmhurst, IL 60126-1413 *Tel:* 630-941-0600 *Fax:* 630-941-7777 *E-mail:* info@sbrevents.com *Web Site:* www.sbrevents. com, pg 823

Borvan, Michelle, Conquest Sound Co Inc, 209 Cypress Dr, Manteno, IL 60950 *Tel:* 708-534-0390 *Toll Free Tel:* 800-323-7671 *Fax:* 708-534-0398 *E-mail:* info@ conquestsound.com *Web Site:* www.conquestsound. com, pg 731

Bosch, James Vanden, Terra Nova Films Inc, 9848 S Winchester Ave, Chicago, IL 60643 *Tel:* 773-881-8491 *Toll Free Tel:* 800-779-8491 *Fax:* 773-881-3368 *E-mail:* tnf@terranova.org *Web Site:* www.terranova. org, pg 911

Boser, Dave, ITC, 523 Hanley Industrial Ct, St Louis, MO 63144 *Tel:* 314-646-1800 *Toll Free Tel:* 800-962-2344 *Fax:* 314-646-1818 *Web Site:* www.itcjourneys. com, pg 791

Boser, Timothy J, ATTO Technology Inc, 155 CrossPoint Pkwy, Amherst, NY 14068 *Tel:* 716-691-1999 *Fax:* 716-691-9353 *Web Site:* www.atto.com, pg 692

Bosken, Jim, QCA, 2832 Spring Grove Ave, Cincinnati, OH 45225 *Tel:* 513-681-8400 *Toll Free Tel:* 800-859-8401 *E-mail:* info@go-qca.com *Web Site:* www.go-qca.com, pg 867

Boss, Doug, Pacific Grip & Lighting Inc, 6550 NE Portland Hwy, Portland, OR 97218 *Tel:* 503-233-4747 *Fax:* 503-233-5830 *Web Site:* www.pacific-grip.com, pg 849

Bostrom, Lynn, Magnetek Inc, N49 W13650 Campbell Dr, Menomonee Falls, WI 53051 *Tel:* 262-783-3500 *Toll Free Tel:* 800-288-8178 *Toll Free Fax:* 800-298-3503 *E-mail:* sales@magnetek.com *Web Site:* www. magnetek.com, pg 814

Boswell, John, SAS Institute Inc, 100 SAS Campus Dr, Cary, NC 27513-2414 *Tel:* 919-677-8000 *Toll Free Tel:* 800-727-0025 *Fax:* 919-677-4444 *Web Site:* www. sas.com, pg 880

Bottcher, Dale, AVI-SPL, 6301 Benjamin Rd, Suite 101, Tampa, FL 33634 *Tel:* 813-884-7168 *Toll Free Tel:* 866-708-5034; 866-925-8298 (cust serv); 866-559-8197 (sales) *E-mail:* contact@avispl.com; sales@avispl.com; customerservice@avispl.com *Web Site:* www.avispl.com, pg 698

Bottrell, Donna, The Wine Appreciation Guild Ltd, 450 Taraval St, No 201, San Francisco, CA 94116 *Tel:* 650-866-3020 *Toll Free Tel:* 800-231-9463 *Fax:* 650-866-3513 *E-mail:* info@wineappreciation. com *Web Site:* www.wineappreciation.com, pg 939

Bouchard, Suzie, SODEC, 215 rue Saint-Jacques St, Rm 800, Montreal, QC H2Y 1M6, Canada *Tel:* 514-841-2200 *Toll Free Tel:* 800-363-0401 (CN only) *Fax:* 514-841-8606 *E-mail:* info@sodec.gouv.qc.ca *Web Site:* www.sodec.gouv.qc.ca, pg 962

Bouchedid, Fares, Turning Technologies LLC, 255 W Federal St, Youngstown, OH 44503 *Tel:* 330-746-3015 *Toll Free Tel:* 866-746-3015 *E-mail:* info@turningtechnologies.com; support@turningtechnologies.com *Web Site:* www. turningtechnologies.com, pg 919

Boudreau, Daniel, CBC/Radio-Canada, 181 Queen St, Ottawa, ON K1P 1K9, Canada *Tel:* 613-288-6000; 613-288-6445 (newsroom) *Toll Free Tel:* 866-306-4636 (CN only) *E-mail:* cbcnewsottawa@cbc.ca *Web Site:* cbc.radio-canada.ca, pg 717

Boulton, Lisa, Calaveras Film Commission, Calaveras Visitors Bureau, 1192 S Main St, Angels Camp, CA 95222 *Tel:* 209-736-0049 *Toll Free Tel:* 800-225-3764 *Web Site:* filmcalaveras.org, pg 966

Bourland, Annette, Zondervan, 3900 Sparks Dr, Grand Rapids, MI 49546 *Tel:* 616-698-6900 *Toll Free Tel:* 800-226-1122; 800-727-1309 (retail orders) *Web Site:* www.zondervan.com, pg 945

Bourlon, Twila, Photographic Society of America® (PSA®), 8241 S Walker Ave, Suite 104, Oklahoma City, OK 73139 *Tel:* 405-843-1437 *Toll Free Tel:* 855-PSA-INFO (772-4636) *E-mail:* hq@psa-photo.org *Web Site:* www.psa-photo.org, pg 960

Bourque, Carol, Techkno Integration & Design Services LLC, 1720 Kaliste Saloom, Bldg 2, Suite B-2, Lafayette, LA 70508 *Tel:* 337-406-9428 *Fax:* 337-406-9482, pg 908

Bouzari, Alex, DataDirect Networks, 9351 Deering Ave, Chatsworth, CA 91311 *Tel:* 818-700-4000 *Toll Free Tel:* 800-TERABYTE (837-2298) *E-mail:* info@ddn. com; sales@ddn.com *Web Site:* www.ddn.com, pg 738

Bova, Jeffrey D, AudioVideoElectric, 3907 Peppervine Dr, Orlando, FL 32828 *Toll Free Tel:* 888-792-9283 *Fax:* 407-381-5610 *E-mail:* sales@audiovideoelectric. com *Web Site:* www.audiovideoelectric.com, pg 695

Bowden, Jay B, TRC Interactive Inc, 4200 Crums Mill Rd, Harrisburg, PA 17112 *Tel:* 717-652-3100 *Toll Free Tel:* 800-222-9909 *E-mail:* customerservicetrc01@ trcinteractive.com; info@trcinteractive.com *Web Site:* www.trcinteractive.com, pg 917

Bowen, Bob, CMI Media Management, 9 W Broad St, Stamford, CT 06902 *Tel:* 203-989-9955 *Toll Free Tel:* 800-431-1102 *Fax:* 203-316-8353 *Web Site:* www. cminyla.com, pg 727

Bowen, Marty, Temple Hill Entertainment, 9255 W Sunset Blvd, West Hollywood, CA 90069 *Tel:* 310-270-4383 *Fax:* 310-270-4395 *Web Site:* twitter.com/ TempleHillEnt, pg 911

Bowers, Amanda, Focus on Animals, PO Box 340, Charles Town, WV 25414-0340 *Tel:* 304-725-0506 *Fax:* 304-725-1523 *E-mail:* information@nhes.org; education@nhes.org *Web Site:* www.nhes.org, pg 763

Bowers, Scott, Ghent Manufacturing, 2999 Henkle Dr, Lebanon, OH 45036-9260 *Tel:* 513-932-3445 *Toll Free Tel:* 800-543-0550 *Fax:* 513-932-9252 *E-mail:* customer_service@ghent.com; sales@ghent. com *Web Site:* www.ghent.com, pg 770

Bowhann, Jim, Magick Lantern, 750 Ralph McGill Blvd, Atlanta, GA 30312 *Tel:* 404-688-3348 *Fax:* 404-584-5247 *E-mail:* info@magicklantern.com *Web Site:* magicklantern.com, pg 814

Bowie, Clint, New Orleans Film Festival, 1215 Prytania St, Suite 423, New Orleans, LA 70130 *Tel:* 504-309-6633 *E-mail:* noff@neworleansfilmsociety.org *Web Site:* neworleansfilmsociety.org/festival, pg 997

Bowman, Todd, NEC Display Solutions of America, 500 Park Blvd, Suite 1100, Itasca, IL 60143 *Tel:* 630-467-3000 *Web Site:* www.necdisplay.com, pg 837

Box, Harry, Entertainment Services and Technology Association (ESTA), 630 Ninth Ave, Suite 609, New York, NY 10036 *Tel:* 212-244-1505 *Fax:* 212-244-1502 *E-mail:* info@esta.org; membership@esta.org *Web Site:* www.esta.org, pg 954

Box, Harry, Production Equipment Rental Group (PERG), c/o ESTA, 630 Ninth Ave, Suite 609, New York, NY 10036 *Tel:* 212-244-1505 *Fax:* 212-244-1502 *E-mail:* info@esta.org; membership@esta.org *Web Site:* www.esta.org/perg, pg 960

Boyadjian, Mark, Neutrik® USA Inc, 4115 Taggart Creek Rd, Charlotte, NC 28208 *Tel:* 704-972-3050 *Fax:* 704-438-9202 *Toll Free Fax:* 877-220-4089 *E-mail:* info@neutrikusa.com *Web Site:* www.neutrik. us, pg 838

Boyah, Kofa, Air Philosophy Inc, 1933 S Broadway, Suite 1107B, Los Angeles, CA 90007 *Tel:* 310-980-3902 *E-mail:* info@airphilosophy.com *Web Site:* airphilosophy.com, pg 678

Boyce, Rodger, Allstar Show Industries Inc, 10331 176 St, Edmonton, AB T5S 2E4, Canada *Tel:* 780-486-4000 *Toll Free Tel:* 800-663-4063 (CN & US) *E-mail:* info@allstar-show.com *Web Site:* www.allstar-show.com, pg 681

Boyd, Alicia M, Rahlic Publishing Co, 301 Keithwood Rd, Wynnewood, PA 19096 *Tel:* 610-649-0982, pg 869

Boyd, Bill, Institute of Industrial & Systems Engineers (IISE), 3577 Parkway Lane, Suite 200, Norcross, GA 30092 *Tel:* 770-449-0460 *Toll Free Tel:* 800-494-0460 *Fax:* 770-441-3295 *E-mail:* executiveoffices@iise.org *Web Site:* www.iise.org, pg 956

Boyd, Dan, Madonna University Information Technology, 36600 Schoolcraft Rd, Livonia, MI 48150-1173 *Tel:* 734-432-5800 *Toll Free Tel:* 800-852-4951 *Web Site:* www.madonna.edu, pg 814

Boyd, David T, Lasergraphics Inc, 20 Ada, Irvine, CA 92618 *Tel:* 949-753-8282 *Fax:* 949-727-9282 *E-mail:* info@lasergraphics.com *Web Site:* www. lasergraphics.com, pg 804

Boyd, Dillon, Southwest Sound Solutions, 2323 Loop 410 NW, San Antonio, TX 78230-5348 *Tel:* 210-341-4411 *Fax:* 210-349-8300 *E-mail:* info@swsoundsolutions.com *Web Site:* www. swsoundsolutions.com, pg 896

Boyd, Greg, Avitecture Inc, One Export Dr, Sterling, VA 20164-4421 *Tel:* 703-404-8900 *Fax:* 703-404-8940 *E-mail:* info@avitecture.com *Web Site:* www. avitecture.com, pg 699

Boyd, Julia, Professional Photographers of America (PPA), 229 Peachtree St NE, Suite 2200, Atlanta, GA 30303 *Tel:* 404-522-8600 *Toll Free Tel:* 800-786-6277 *Fax:* 404-614-6400 *E-mail:* csc@ppa.com *Web Site:* www.ppa.com, pg 960

Boyd, Sue, Madonna University Information Technology, 36600 Schoolcraft Rd, Livonia, MI 48150-1173 *Tel:* 734-432-5800 *Toll Free Tel:* 800-852-4951 *Web Site:* www.madonna.edu, pg 814

Boyd, Vicki, Heinemann, 361 Hanover St, Portsmouth, NH 03801-3912 *Tel:* 603-431-7894 *Toll Free Tel:* 800-225-5800 *Fax:* 603-431-2214 *Toll Free Fax:* 877-231-6980 *E-mail:* custserv@heinemann.com *Web Site:* www.heinemann.com, pg 778

Boyer, Gary P, L-3 ESSCO, 90 Nemco Way, Ayer, MA 01432 *Tel:* 978-568-5100 *Fax:* 978-772-7555 *E-mail:* info.essco@l3t.com *Web Site:* www2.l3t. com/essco, pg 802

Boyer, Ray, PixMix Video Services, 395 Western Ave, Suite 112 & 113, Boston, MA 02134 *Tel:* 617-923-0102; 617-254-0590 *Fax:* 617-923-0105 *E-mail:* info@pixmix.net *Web Site:* www.pixmix.net, pg 857

Boylan, Patrick M, PDC Productions, 3217 N Flood Ave, Norman, OK 73069 *Tel:* 405-360-5130 *Fax:* 405-360-0524 *E-mail:* info@pdcproductions.com *Web Site:* www.pdcproductions.com, pg 852

Boyle, Lauren, Digital Arts NY, 130 W 29 St, New York, NY 10001 *Tel:* 212-460-9600 *Fax:* 212-660-3600 *Web Site:* digitalartsny.com, pg 742

Boynton, Chuck, Poly, 345 Encinal St, Santa Cruz, CA 95060 *Tel:* 831-426-5858 *Toll Free Tel:* 800-544-4660 *Fax:* 831-426-6098 *Web Site:* www.poly.com, pg 859

Brabbee, Mystelle, Nantucket Film Festival (NFF), 68 Jay St, Suite 319, Brooklyn, NY 11201 *Tel:* 646-480-1900 *Fax:* 646-365-3367 *E-mail:* info@nantucketfilmfestival. org; submissions@nantucketfilmfestival.org *Web Site:* nantucketfilmfestival.org, pg 997

Bracey, Michael, Olson Anderson Co, 3124 Kochville Rd, Suite 121, Saginaw, MI 48604-9305 *Tel:* 989-399-3024 *E-mail:* oac100@aol.com *Web Site:* www. olsonanderson.com, pg 685

Brackett, Dan, Extreme Reach Inc, 75 Second Ave, Suite 720, Needham, MA 02494 *Tel:* 781-557-2016 *Toll Free Tel:* 877-769-9382 *E-mail:* sales@ extremereach.com; support@extremereach.com *Web Site:* extremereach.com, pg 758

Bradford, Traci, Audio Rents, 4209 E Vanowen Pl, Burbank, CA 91505 *Tel:* 323-874-1000 *Fax:* 323-460-2676 *E-mail:* info@audiorents.com *Web Site:* www. audiorents.com, pg 694

Bradshaw, John, Cadex Electronics Inc, 22000 Fraserwood Way, Richmond, BC V6W 1J6, Canada *Tel:* 604-231-7777 *Toll Free Tel:* 800-565-5228 *Fax:* 604-231-7755 *E-mail:* info@cadex.com *Web Site:* www.cadex.com, pg 713

Bradstock, Philip, City of Phoenix Film Office, 200 W Washington St, 20th fl, Phoenix, AZ 85003 *Tel:* 602-262-4850 *E-mail:* filmphx@phoenix.gov *Web Site:* www.phoenix.gov/econdev/filming, pg 965

Bradway, Amy, Draper Inc, 411 S Pearl St, Spiceland, IN 47385 *Tel:* 765-987-7999 *Toll Free Tel:* 800-238-7999 *Fax:* 765-987-7142 *E-mail:* av@draperinc.com *Web Site:* www.draperinc.com; blog.draperinc.com, pg 746

Brady, Aaron, Autocue, 14 Progress Dr, Shelton, CT 06484 *Tel:* 212-929-7755 *Fax:* 212-929-2105 *Web Site:* www.autocue.com/teleprompter, pg 696

Bragg, Bill, The Yesterday USA Radio Networks, 2001 Plymouth Rock Dr, Richardson, TX 75081-3946 *Tel:* 972-889-9872 *Fax:* 972-889-2329 *Web Site:* www.yesterdayusa.com, pg 944

Bragg, Billy, Available Lighting & Motion Picture Services Inc, 826 Jefferson Hwy, New Orleans, LA 70121 *Tel:* 504-831-5214 *Fax:* 504-831-5361 *E-mail:* avlight@bellsouth.net *Web Site:* www.availablelighting.com, pg 697

Brahms, Claudia, MTI Home Video, 14216 SW 136 St, Miami, FL 33186 *Tel:* 305-255-8684 *Fax:* 305-233-6943 *Web Site:* www.mtivideo.com, pg 833

Brahms, Larry, MTI Home Video, 14216 SW 136 St, Miami, FL 33186 *Tel:* 305-255-8684 *Fax:* 305-233-6943 *Web Site:* www.mtivideo.com, pg 833

Braisted, Gary, ELC Sales & Service Inc, 3100 S Congress Ave, Suite 6, Boynton Beach, FL 33426 *Tel:* 561-756-2210 *E-mail:* tvman@gate.net, pg 752

Braker, Steve, Worthwhile Films, 317 Winona St, Northfield, MN 55057 *Tel:* 507-645-6868 *Toll Free Tel:* 877-507-5077 *Web Site:* worthwhilefilms.org, pg 941

Bramley, Shayna, Illuminating Engineering Society (IES), 120 Wall St, 17th fl, New York, NY 10005-4026 *Tel:* 212-248-5000 *E-mail:* ies@ies.org *Web Site:* ies.org, pg 955

Brammer, Jim, Special Event Services, 3135 Indiana Ave, Winston-Salem, NC 27105 *Tel:* 336-725-7799 *Toll Free Tel:* 800-423-3996 *Fax:* 336-725-0019 *Web Site:* www.specialeventservices.com, pg 896

Branch, Gregory, Broadcast Management Group, 718 Seventh St NW, Washington, DC 20001 *Tel:* 202-609-7757 *E-mail:* info@broadcastmgmt.com *Web Site:* www.broadcastmgmt.com, pg 710

Brandofino, Michael, Interactive Multimedia & Collaborative Communications Alliance (IMCCA), PO Box 756, Syosset, NY 11791 *Tel:* 516-818-8184 *Web Site:* www.imcca.org, pg 956

Brandon, Barry, The Optikon Corp, 1099 Guelph St, Kitchener, ON N2B 2E4, Canada *Tel:* 519-745-4115 *Fax:* 519-745-6922 *E-mail:* info@optikon.ca *Web Site:* www.optikon.ca, pg 847

Brandon, Barry, PCO-TECH Inc, 6930 Metroplex Dr, Romulus, MI 48174 *Tel:* 248-276-8820 *Fax:* 248-276-8825 *E-mail:* info@pco-tech.com; service@pco-tech.com *Web Site:* www.pco-tech.com, pg 852

Brandon, Michael, SF Global Sourcing, 3450 Sacramento St, Suite 353, San Francisco, CA 94118 *Tel:* 415-288-9400 *Toll Free Tel:* 800-545-5865 *Web Site:* www.sfglobalsourcing.com, pg 885

Brandt, Colin, Fantasee Lighting, 14857 Martinsville Rd, Belleville, MI 48111 *Tel:* 734-699-7200 *Fax:* 734-699-7400 *E-mail:* info@fantaseelighting.com *Web Site:* fantaseelighting.com, pg 759

Brandt, Matthew, KK Office Solutions Inc, 3910 N Bridgeport Circle, Wichita, KS 67219 *Tel:* 316-944-5464 *Toll Free Tel:* 800-362-1317 *Fax:* 316-944-0605 *Toll Free Fax:* 888-319-9600 *E-mail:* info@kkofficesolutions.com *Web Site:* kkosinc.com, pg 799

Branen, Shad, Win Media Inc, 317 N Dodge St, Burlington, WI 53105 *Tel:* 262-763-6397 *E-mail:* info@winmediainc.com *Web Site:* www.winmediainc.com, pg 939

Brantley, Bobby, Brantley Sound Associates Inc, 115 Duluth Ave, Nashville, TN 37209-1207 *Tel:* 615-256-6260 *Web Site:* www.brantleysound.com, pg 709

Brasil, Diane S, Staedtler-Mars Ltd, 850 Matteson Blvd W, Unit 4, Mississauga, ON L5V 0B4, Canada *Tel:* 905-501-9008 *Toll Free Tel:* 800-776-5544 (US); 800-387-5872 (US) *Fax:* 905-501-9117 *Toll Free Fax:* 800-675-8249 (US) *E-mail:* info@staedtler.ca *Web Site:* www.staedtler.ca, pg 898

Brassard, Paul, Arkon Resources Inc, 20 La Porte St, Arcadia, CA 91006 *Tel:* 626-254-9005 *Toll Free Tel:* 800-841-0884 *Fax:* 626-254-9266 *E-mail:* arkon8@arkon.com *Web Site:* www.arkon.com, pg 689

Brastow, Scott S, Pacific Media, PO Box 9489, Canoga Park, CA 91309 *Tel:* 805-418-7552 *E-mail:* info@pac-media.com *Web Site:* www.pac-media.com, pg 849

Braun, Anthony, Williams AV LLC, 10300 Valley View Rd, Eden Prairie, MN 55344-3446 *Tel:* 952-943-2252 *Toll Free Tel:* 800-328-6190 *Fax:* 952-943-2174 *E-mail:* info@williamsav.com *Web Site:* www.williamsav.com, pg 939

Braverman, Alan, The Walt Disney Co, 500 S Buena Vista St, Burbank, CA 91521 *Tel:* 818-560-1000 *Web Site:* disney.com; thewaltdisneycompany.com, pg 743

Braverman, Dan, Radio Systems Inc, 601 Heron Dr, Logan Township, NJ 08085 *Tel:* 856-467-8000 *Fax:* 856-467-3044 *E-mail:* sales@radiosystems.com; tech@radiosystems.com *Web Site:* www.radiosystems.com, pg 869

Brawley, Dan, Cucalorus Film Festival, Jengo's Playhouse, 815 Princess St, Wilmington, NC 28401 *Tel:* 910-343-5995 *E-mail:* programming@cucalorus.org; press@cucalorus.org; comm@cucalorus.org *Web Site:* www.cucalorus.org, pg 987

Bray, Tom, Ann Arbor Film Festival, 230 Collingwood Dr, Suite 160B, Ann Arbor, MI 48103 *Tel:* 734-995-5356 *Fax:* 734-995-5396 *E-mail:* info@aafilmfest.org *Web Site:* www.aafilmfest.org, pg 981

Breakwell, Chris, 31st Street Studios, 77 31 St, Pittsburgh, PA 15201 *Tel:* 412-228-0231 *E-mail:* info@31ststreetstudios.com *Web Site:* www.31ststreetstudios.com, pg 912

Bredon, Bruce, BUF Technology, 12335 World Trade Dr, Suite 11, San Diego, CA 92128 *Tel:* 858-451-1350 *Fax:* 858-451-6589 *E-mail:* info@buftek.com *Web Site:* www.buftek.com, pg 712

Bredon, Tracey H, BUF Technology, 12335 World Trade Dr, Suite 11, San Diego, CA 92128 *Tel:* 858-451-1350 *Fax:* 858-451-6589 *E-mail:* info@buftek.com *Web Site:* www.buftek.com, pg 712

Breedon, Angela, Music & Entertainment Industry Educators Association (MEIEA), 1900 Belmont Blvd, Nashville, TN 37212-3758 *Tel:* 615-460-6946 *E-mail:* office@meiea.org; membership@meiea.org *Web Site:* www.meiea.org, pg 958

Bremner, James, VARTA Microbattery Inc, 555 Theodore Fremd Ave, Suite C-304, Rye, NY 10580 *Tel:* 914-592-2500 *Toll Free Tel:* 800-468-2782 *Fax:* 914-345-0488 *Web Site:* www.varta-microbattery.com; www.varta-microbattery.com/contact/?lang=en, pg 925

Brennan, Lynwen, Industrial Light & Magic (ILM), 1110 Gorgas St, San Francisco, CA 94129 *Tel:* 415-746-3000 *Fax:* 415-746-3015 *E-mail:* contact-sf@ilm.com *Web Site:* www.ilm.com, pg 787

Brennan, Stephen J PhD, Peak Performance Publishing, 14728 Shirley St, Omaha, NE 68144 *Tel:* 402-334-1676 *Toll Free Tel:* 800-293-1676 *Fax:* 402-334-4437 *Web Site:* www.peakperformanceconsult.com, pg 852

Brennan, Stephen J PhD, The Recruiters Library, 14728 Shirley St, Omaha, NE 68144 *Tel:* 402-334-1676 *Toll Free Tel:* 800-293-1676 *Fax:* 402-334-4437 *Web Site:* www.thebestcollegerecruiter.com, pg 872

Brenner, Mara-Lynne, Vitec Videocom Inc, 14 Progress Dr, Shelton, CT 06484 *Tel:* 203-929-1100 *Fax:* 203-925-2684 *E-mail:* info@vitecgroup.com *Web Site:* www.vitecgroup.com; www.vitecvideocom.com, pg 932

Bressler, Joan, Greater Philadelphia Film Office, One Parkway Bldg, 11th fl, 1515 Arch St, Philadelphia, PA 19102 *Tel:* 215-686-2668 *Fax:* 215-686-3659 *E-mail:* mail@film.org *Web Site:* www.film.org, pg 975

Bressler, Steven H, Monadnock Media Inc, 59 North St, Hatfield, MA 01038 *Tel:* 413-247-6447 *Fax:* 413-247-6448 *E-mail:* info@monadnock.org *Web Site:* www.monadnock.org, pg 829

Brewer, Jennifer, Zion Music Group, 306 Monticello Rd, Franklin, TN 37064 *Tel:* 615-559-2108 *Fax:* 615-591-5102 *Web Site:* www.zionmusic.com, pg 945

Brewer, Mark, WOUB Public Media, 35 S College St, Athens, OH 45701 *Tel:* 740-593-1771 *Toll Free Tel:* 800-456-2044 *E-mail:* woub@woub.org *Web Site:* woub.org, pg 942

Brewer, Michael, Instant Music Now, 1160 W 26 Ave, Eugene, OR 97405 *Tel:* 541-345-8117 *E-mail:* info@instantmusicnow.com *Web Site:* www.instantmusicnow.com, pg 788

Brewer, Wesley, Markertek Video Supply, One Tower Dr, Saugerties, NY 12477 *Tel:* 845-246-3036 *Toll Free Tel:* 800-522-2025 *Fax:* 845-246-1757 *E-mail:* sales@markertek.com *Web Site:* www.markertek.com, pg 817

Brewster, Vicki, ARRIS Group Inc, 3871 Lakefield Dr, Suwanee, GA 30024 *Tel:* 678-473-2907 *Toll Free Tel:* 866-36-ARRIS (362-7747); 877-466-8646 (tech) *Fax:* 678-473-8470 *E-mail:* marketing@arris.com *Web Site:* www.arris.com, pg 689

Brey, Pat, Boeckeler Instruments Inc, 4650 S Butterfield Dr, Tucson, AZ 85714 *Tel:* 520-745-0001 *Toll Free Tel:* 800-552-2262 *Fax:* 520-745-0004 *E-mail:* info@boeckeler.com *Web Site:* www.boeckeler.com, pg 708

Breyer, Stefanie, National Instruments Corp, 11500 N Mopac Expwy, Austin, TX 78759-3504 *Tel:* 512-683-0100 *Toll Free Tel:* 888-280-7645 (sales); 877-388-1952 *Fax:* 512-683-8411; 512-683-5794 (sales) *Web Site:* www.ni.com, pg 836

Brickhouse, Brian, Eaton Corp, 8609 Six Forks Rd, Raleigh, NC 27615 *Tel:* 919-872-3020 *Toll Free Tel:* 800-356-5794 *Web Site:* powerquality.eaton.com, pg 750

Brickman, Peter, WNET/New York Public Media, 825 Eighth Ave, New York, NY 10019 *Tel:* 212-560-1313 *Fax:* 212-560-1314 *E-mail:* programming@thirteen.org *Web Site:* www.thirteen.org; www.wnet.org, pg 940

Briden, Jeff, Sencore Inc, 3200 W Sencore Dr, Sioux Falls, SD 57107 *Tel:* 605-978-4600 *Fax:* 605-335-6379 *Web Site:* www.sencore.com, pg 883

Bridges, Matt, PSSI Global Services LLC, 7030 Hayvenhurst Ave, Van Nuys, CA 91406 *Tel:* 310-575-4400 *Toll Free Tel:* 800-SAT-LINK (728-5465); 800-634-6530 (teleport inquiries) *E-mail:* info@pssiglobal.com *Web Site:* www.pssiglobal.com, pg 866

Bridges, Wendy, City of Prescott Film Office, 201 S Cortez St, Prescott, AZ 86303 *Tel:* 928-777-1204 *Fax:* 928-777-1255 *Web Site:* www.prescott-az.gov, pg 965

Bridgewater, Ben, D L Adams Associates Inc, 1536 Ogden St, Denver, CO 80218 *Tel:* 303-455-1900 *E-mail:* infodenver@dlaa.com *Web Site:* www.dlaa.com, pg 675

Briel, Lann, Film, Video & Digital Production Grants, 550 Vandalia St, Suite 109, St Paul, MN 55114 *Tel:* 651-224-9431 *E-mail:* info@jeromefdn.org *Web Site:* www.jeromefdn.org/film-video-production-grants, pg 989

Brien, Nick, iCrossing Inc, a Hearst Company, 300 W 57 St, New York, NY 10019 *Tel:* 212-649-3900 *Toll Free Tel:* 866-620-3780 *E-mail:* general@icrossing.com *Web Site:* www.icrossing.com, pg 783

Brienza, Gail, Spectrum Audio Visual Services, 351 W 45 Ave, Denver, CO 80216 *Tel:* 303-477-4456 *Toll Free Tel:* 800-477-4752 *Fax:* 303-477-0114 *E-mail:* info@spectrumav.com *Web Site:* www.spectrumav.com, pg 897

Briere, Jean-Michel, Presagis, 4700 de la Savane, Suite 300, Montreal, QC H4P 1T7, Canada *Tel:* 514-341-3874 *Toll Free Tel:* 800-361-6424 *Fax:* 514-341-8018 *E-mail:* info@presagis.com *Web Site:* www.presagis. com, pg 861

Brietz, Scott, Multicom Inc, 1076 Florida Central Pkwy, Longwood, FL 32750 *Tel:* 407-331-7779 *Toll Free Tel:* 800-423-2594 *Fax:* 407-339-0204 *E-mail:* multicom@multicominc.com *Web Site:* www. multicominc.com, pg 833

Briggs, Bob, Valley Media, 421 Roanoke Dr, Martinez, CA 94553-6240 *Tel:* 925-937-5207; 510-612-5215 (cell) *Web Site:* www.valleymedia.com, pg 924

Brinkman, John, MSI Production Services, 10895 Thornmint Rd, Suite A, San Diego, CA 92127 *Tel:* 858-348-0100 *Web Site:* www.msiprod.com, pg 832

Brinn, David, RAM® Mounts, 8410 Dallas Ave S, Seattle, WA 98108 *Tel:* 206-763-8361 *Toll Free Tel:* 800-497-7479 *Fax:* 206-763-9615 *E-mail:* sales@ rammount.com *Web Site:* www.rammount.com, pg 870

Briseno, Valerie, Business Technology Association (BTA), 12411 Wornall Rd, Suite 200, Kansas City, MO 64145 *Tel:* 816-941-3100 *Toll Free Tel:* 800-826-6159; 800-505-2821 (memb servs) *Fax:* 816-941-4843 *Toll Free Tel:* 800-941-2829 *E-mail:* info@bta.org *Web Site:* www.bta.org, pg 952

Britner, Mike, Lawrence Behr Associates Inc, 3400 Tupper Dr, Greenville, NC 27834 *Tel:* 252-757-0279 *Toll Free Tel:* 800-522-4464 *Fax:* 252-752-9155 *E-mail:* lbagrp@lbagroup.com *Web Site:* www. lbagroup.com/associates, pg 703

Britner, Mike, LBA Technology Inc, 3400 Tupper Dr, Greenville, NC 27834 *Tel:* 252-757-0279 *Toll Free Tel:* 800-522-4464 *Fax:* 252-752-9155 *E-mail:* lbagrp@lbagroup.com *Web Site:* www. lbagroup.com, pg 804

Brito, Brent, Panavid, 210 West Pkwy, Unit 5, Pompton Plains, NJ 07444 *Tel:* 973-831-5655 *E-mail:* info@ panavid.com; support@panavid.com *Web Site:* www. panavid.com, pg 850

Brock, Jesse, Tampa Hillsborough Film & Digital Media Commission, One Tampa City Ctr, 201 N Franklin St, Suite 2900, Tampa, FL 33602 *Web Site:* filmtampabay. com, pg 970

Brocke-Benz, Manuel A.H, VWR International LLC, Radnor Corporate Ctr, Bldg 1, 100 Matsonford Rd, Suite 200, Radnor, PA 19087-8660 *Tel:* 610-431-1700 (corp off) *Toll Free Tel:* 800-932-5000 (cust serv) *Web Site:* www.vwr.com; us.vwr.com, pg 933

Brode, Andrew, AV Chicago Inc, 619 W Taylor St, Chicago, IL 60607 *Tel:* 312-229-4100 *Toll Free Tel:* 888-709-9599 *Fax:* 312-229-5642 *Web Site:* avchicago.com, pg 696

Brode, Barry S, UND Television Center, 4300 James Ray Dr, Stop 7307, Grand Forks, ND 58202 *Tel:* 701-777-4346 *Toll Free Tel:* 800-CALL-UND (225-5863) *Fax:* 701-777-4342 *E-mail:* tv@und.edu *Web Site:* www.und.edu/television-center, pg 921

Brodersen, William F, FotoKem, 2801 W Alameda Ave, Burbank, CA 91505 *Tel:* 818-846-3101 *Toll Free Tel:* 800-FOTOKEM (368-6536) *E-mail:* info@ fotokem.com *Web Site:* www.fotokem.com, pg 764

Brodie, Mark, MiB MediaWorks, 85 Main St, Little Falls, NJ 07424 *Tel:* 973-403-1133 *Fax:* 973-638-1699 *E-mail:* info@mibmediaworks.com *Web Site:* www. mibmediaworks.com, pg 825

Brody, Chris, Crescendo Designs Inc, 641 County Rd 39-A, Southampton, NY 11968 *Tel:* 631-283-2133 *Fax:* 631-204-1066 *E-mail:* sales@crescendodesigns. com; service@crescendodesigns.com *Web Site:* www. crescendodesigns.com, pg 734

Brody, Louisa, Ingram Content Group LLC, One Ingram Blvd, La Vergne, TN 37086-1986 *Tel:* 615-793-5000 *Toll Free Tel:* 800-937-8000 (retailers); 800-937-5300 (ext 1, libs) *E-mail:* customerservice@ingramcontent. com *Web Site:* www.ingramcontent.com, pg 787

Brody, Mike, Crescendo Designs Inc, 641 County Rd 39-A, Southampton, NY 11968 *Tel:* 631-283-2133 *Fax:* 631-204-1066 *E-mail:* sales@crescendodesigns. com; service@crescendodesigns.com *Web Site:* www. crescendodesigns.com, pg 734

Broen, Frank, Teach America Corp, 121 N Love St, Quincy, FL 32351-2440 *Tel:* 850-528-6056 (cell) *Web Site:* teachamerica.com; www.accessmanagement. info, pg 908

Broening, Chris, Audio Visual Dynamics®, 424 Sand Shore Rd, Hackettstown, NJ 07840 *Tel:* 973-993-8500 *Fax:* 973-984-0644 *Web Site:* www.avdusa.com, pg 694

Broening, Robyn, Audio Visual Dynamics®, 424 Sand Shore Rd, Hackettstown, NJ 07840 *Tel:* 973-993-8500 *Fax:* 973-984-0644 *Web Site:* www.avdusa.com, pg 694

Broker, Susan, City of Savannah Film Office, One Waring Dr, Savannah, GA 31404 *Tel:* 912-651-2360 *Fax:* 912-651-0982 *Web Site:* filmsavannah.org, pg 970

Bronfman, Paul, William F White International Inc, 800 Islington Ave, Toronto, ON M8Z 6A1, Canada *Tel:* 416-239-5050 *Toll Free Tel:* 800-465-0160 (CN only) *Web Site:* www.whites.com, pg 937

Brook, Augusta, Wanted! Sound + Picture, 409 King St W, Suite 300, Toronto, ON M5V 1K1, Canada *Tel:* 416-596-1101 *Fax:* 416-596-0690 *E-mail:* info@wantedsp.com; bookings@wantedsp.com *Web Site:* www.wantedsp.com, pg 933

Brooke, Peter, The Jim Henson Co, 1416 N La Brea Ave, Hollywood, CA 90028 *Tel:* 323-802-1500 *Fax:* 323-802-1825 *Web Site:* www.henson.com, pg 794

Brooks, Becky, Alliance for Women in Media/Alliance for Women in Media Foundation, 2365 Harrodsburg Rd, A-325, Lexington, KY 40504 *Tel:* 202-750-3664 *Fax:* 202-750-3664 *Web Site:* www.allwomeninmedia. org, pg 947

Brooks, Becky, The Gracies®, 2365 Harrodsburg Rd, A-325, Lexington, KY 40504 *Tel:* 202-750-3664 *Fax:* 202-750-3664 *E-mail:* gracies@ allwomeninmedia.org *Web Site:* allwomeninmedia. org/gracies, pg 991

Brooks, Brian, MB Productions, 450 Fairfield Place, West Caldwell, NJ 07006 *Tel:* 973-439-0044 *Toll Free Tel:* 800-622-2224 *Fax:* 973-439-9844 *E-mail:* mbp@ mbvideo.com *Web Site:* www.mbvideo.com, pg 820

Brooks, Danielle, Antenna International, 383 Main Ave, Norwalk, CT 06851 *Tel:* 203-523-0320 *E-mail:* inquiry@antennainternational.com; marketing@antennainternational.com *Web Site:* www. antennainternational.com, pg 686

Brooks, David, Just Bulbs - The Light Bulb Store, 222 E 58 St, New York, NY 10022 *Tel:* 212-888-5707 *Fax:* 212-888-5704 *E-mail:* sales@justbulbsnyc.com *Web Site:* www.justbulbsnyc.com, pg 795

Brooks, James, Drastic Technologies Ltd, 523 The Queensway, Suite 102, Toronto, ON M8Y 1J7, Canada *Tel:* 416-255-5636 *Fax:* 416-255-8780 *E-mail:* sales@ drastictech.com *Web Site:* www.drastic.tv, pg 746

Brooks, Julie, Wickenburg Film Commission, 216 N Frontier St, Wickenburg, AZ 85390 *Tel:* 928-684-5479; 928-684-0977 *Toll Free Tel:* 800-942-5242 *Fax:* 928-684-5470 *E-mail:* info@wickenburgchamber. com *Web Site:* www.wickenburgchamber.com/film-commission, pg 965

Brooks, Robert, Drastic Technologies Ltd, 523 The Queensway, Suite 102, Toronto, ON M8Y 1J7, Canada *Tel:* 416-255-5636 *Fax:* 416-255-8780 *E-mail:* sales@ drastictech.com *Web Site:* www.drastic.tv, pg 746

Brooks, Tim, Hubbard Supply Co, 901 W Second St, Flint, MI 48503 *Tel:* 810-234-8681 *Toll Free Tel:* 800-875-4811 *Fax:* 810-234-6142 *E-mail:* information@ hubbardsupply.com *Web Site:* www.hubbardsupply. com, pg 782

Broome, Frances M, Kineticvideo.com, 4839 Noble Lane, Battersea, ON K0H 1H0, Canada *Tel:* 416-538-6613 *Toll Free Tel:* 800-263-6910 (CN only) *Fax:* 416-538-9984 *E-mail:* info@kineticvideo.com *Web Site:* www.kineticvideo.com, pg 799

Brossoit, Jesse, Canadian Filmmakers Distribution Center (CFMDC), 401 Richmond St W, Toronto, ON M5V 3A8, Canada *Tel:* 416-588-0725 *E-mail:* info@cfmdc. org *Web Site:* www.cfmdc.org, pg 715

Brotherston, TC, Burnaby Film Office, 6450 Deerlake Ave, Burnaby, BC V5G 2J3, Canada *Tel:* 604-294-7314 *Fax:* 604-205-3001 *E-mail:* filming@burnaby.ca *Web Site:* www.burnaby.ca, pg 978

Broughton, Brian, Broughton's Church Supplies, Religious Books & Gifts, 322 Consumers Rd, North York, ON M2J 1P8, Canada *Tel:* 416-690-4777 *Toll Free Tel:* 800-268-4449 *Fax:* 416-690-5357 *E-mail:* sales@bbroughton.com *Web Site:* www. bbroughton.com, pg 711

Broughton, Paul, Life Cycle Books Ltd, 1085 Bellamy Rd N, Unit 20, Toronto, ON M1H 1H7, Canada *Tel:* 416-690-5860 *Toll Free Tel:* 866-880-5860 *Fax:* 416-690-8532 *Toll Free Tel:* 866-690-8532 *E-mail:* support@lifecyclebooks.com; billing@ lifecyclebooks.com; orders@lifecyclebooks.com *Web Site:* www.lifecyclebooks.com, pg 807

Brower, Travis, WPHL-TV, 5001 Wynnefield Ave, Philadelphia, PA 19131 *Tel:* 215-878-1700 *E-mail:* feedback@phl17.com *Web Site:* www.phl17. com, pg 942

Brown, Alison, Compass Records, 916 19 Ave S, Nashville, TN 37212 *Tel:* 615-320-7672 *Fax:* 615-320-7378 *E-mail:* info@compassrecords.com *Web Site:* www.compassrecords.com, pg 729

Brown, Alison, Science Museum of Minnesota, 120 W Kellogg Blvd, St Paul, MN 55102 *Tel:* 651-221-9444 *Toll Free Tel:* 800-221-9444 *Fax:* 651-221-4533 *E-mail:* info@smm.org; science@smm.org *Web Site:* www.smm.org, pg 882

Brown, Amanda, Drytac Corp, 5601 Eastport Blvd, Richmond, VA 23231 *Tel:* 804-222-3094 *Toll Free Tel:* 800-280-6013 *E-mail:* customerservice@drytac. com *Web Site:* www.drytac.com, pg 747

Brown, Andrea, Film, Video & Digital Production Grants, 550 Vandalia St, Suite 109, St Paul, MN 55114 *Tel:* 651-224-9431 *E-mail:* info@jeromefdn.org *Web Site:* www.jeromefdn.org/film-video-production-grants, pg 989

Brown, Anthony, Associated Sound, 1417 Del Paso Blvd, Sacramento, CA 95815 *Tel:* 916-649-8040 *Toll Free Tel:* 800-492-6800 *Fax:* 916-649-0243 *E-mail:* sales@associatedsound.com *Web Site:* www. associatedsound.com, pg 691

Brown, Art, A Go Go Films, 907 Fourth St, Santa Monica, CA 90403 *Tel:* 310-387-1659 *E-mail:* art@ agogofilms.com *Web Site:* www.agogofilms.com, pg 671

Brown, Ashley, Audio Visual Technologies Group (AVTG), 12502 Exchange Dr, Suite 404, Stafford, TX 77477 *Tel:* 281-240-2329 *Toll Free Tel:* 800-522-3687 *E-mail:* info@avtg.com *Web Site:* www.avtg.com, pg 695

Brown, B, Brim Electronics, 120 Home Place, Lodi, NJ 07644 *Tel:* 201-796-2886 *Fax:* 973-778-2792 *E-mail:* info@brimelectronics.com *Web Site:* www. brimelectronics.com, pg 710

Brown, Bob, Velodyne LiDAR Inc, 5521 Hellyer Ave, San Jose, CA 95738 *Tel:* 408-465-2800 *Fax:* 408-779-9208 (cust serv); 408-779-9377 (orders) *E-mail:* lidar@velodyne.com *Web Site:* velodynelidar. com, pg 925

Brown, Brenda, SynAudCon, 8780 Rufing Rd, Greenville, IN 47124 *Tel:* 812-923-0174 *Toll Free Fax:* 866-547-0298 *Web Site:* www.synaudcon.com, pg 905

Brown, Brian, Accu-Tech, 11350 Old Roswell Rd, Suite 100, Roswell, GA 30009 *Toll Free Tel:* 888-222-8832 *Web Site:* www.accu-tech.com, pg 673

Brown, Bruce, World Class Learning Materials Inc, PO Box 639, Candler, NC 28715 *Toll Free Tel:* 800-638-6470 *Toll Free Fax:* 800-638-6499 *E-mail:* info@ wclm.com *Web Site:* www.wclm.com, pg 941

Brown, Mr Chris, National Association of Broadcasters (NAB), 1771 "N" St NW, Washington, DC 20036 Tel: 202-429-5300 E-mail: nab@nab.org; membership@nab.org Web Site: www.nab.org, pg 958

Brown, Clark, NEC Display Solutions of America, 500 Park Blvd, Suite 1100, Itasca, IL 60143 Tel: 630-467-3000 Web Site: www.necdisplay.com, pg 837

Brown, Dan, db interactive Inc, PO Box 302064, Austin, TX 78703 Tel: 512-436-8586 E-mail: info@dbinteractive.com Web Site: dbinteractive.com, pg 739

Brown, Jenn, St John's International Women's Film Festival, 28 Cochrane St, Suite 101, St John's, NL A1C 3L3, Canada Tel: 709-754-3141 Fax: 709-754-0049 E-mail: info@womensfilmfestival.com Web Site: www.womensfilmfestival.com, pg 1002

Brown, Jim, Optisonics Productions, 311 South Pkwy, Clifton, NJ 07014 Tel: 973-458-0951 E-mail: optisonics@aol.com Web Site: www.optisonics.com, pg 847

Brown, Joel, Taylor Associates, 110 W Canal St, Suite 301, Winooski, VT 05404 Tel: 802-735-1942 Toll Free Tel: 800-READ-PLUS (732-3758) Fax: 802-419-4786 E-mail: info@readingplus.com Web Site: www.readingplus.com, pg 907

Brown, John, Brown United Inc, PO Box 1700, Monrovia, CA 91017-5700 Tel: 626-357-1161 Toll Free Tel: 800-44-BROWN (442-7696) Fax: 626-358-3064 Web Site: www.brownunited.com, pg 712

Brown, Misty, Bisk Education, 9417 Princess Palm Ave, Tampa, FL 33619 Toll Free Tel: 800-280-9718 E-mail: media@bisk.com Web Site: www.bisk.com, pg 706

Brown, Monifa, Shanachie Entertainment Corp, 37 E Clinton St, Newton, NJ 07860 Tel: 973-579-7763 Web Site: shanachie.com, pg 885

Brown, Nora, Rochester/Finger Lakes Film Commission, 45 East Ave, Suite 400, Rochester, NY 14604-2294 Tel: 585-279-8308 Fax: 585-232-4822 Web Site: www.filmrochester.org, pg 974

Brown, Patrick, Different Fur Recording Ltd, 3470 19 St, San Francisco, CA 94110 Tel: 415-828-4060 (bookings) Web Site: differentfurstudios.com, pg 741

Brown, Paul, Star Video Duplicating, 7100 Mockingbird Lane, Paradise Valley, AZ 85253 Tel: 602-437-0646 Web Site: www.starvideo.com, pg 900

Brown, Richard, University of South Carolina Press, 1600 Hampton St, Suite 544, Columbia, SC 29208 Tel: 803-777-5243 Toll Free Tel: 800-768-2500 Toll Free Fax: 800-868-0740 Web Site: www.sc.edu/uscpress, pg 923

Brown, Rick, Transparent Office Products LLC, 2550 Haddonfield Rd, Pennsauken, NJ 08110 Tel: 856-488-5455 Fax: 856-488-5411 E-mail: sales@transoffprod.biz Web Site: www.transoffprod.biz, pg 917

Brown, Tracey, Audio Visual Dynamics®, 424 Sand Shore Rd, Hackettstown, NJ 07840 Tel: 973-993-8500 Fax: 973-984-0644 Web Site: www.avdusa.com, pg 694

Brown, Vishal, Yorktel, 81 Corbett Way, Eatontown, NJ 07724 Tel: 732-413-6000 Toll Free Tel: 866-836-8463 Fax: 732-413-6060 E-mail: knowmore@yorktel.com Web Site: yorktel.com, pg 944

Brown, William, Harris Corp, 1025 W NASA Blvd, Melbourne, FL 32919-0001 Tel: 321-727-9100 E-mail: webmaster@harris.com Web Site: www.harris.com, pg 776

Browning, Ben, FilmNation Entertainment, 150 W 22 St, 9th fl, New York, NY 10011 Web Site: www.filmnation.com, pg 760

Browse, Nicholas, Cavanaugh Tocci Associates Inc, 327F Boston Post Rd, Sudbury, MA 01776 Tel: 978-443-7871 E-mail: cta@cavtocci.com Web Site: www.cavtocci.com, pg 717

Bruce, Brady O, Jupiter Systems, 31015 Huntwood Ave, Hayward, CA 94544 Tel: 510-675-1000 Fax: 510-675-1001 E-mail: sales@jupiter.com Web Site: jupiter.com, pg 795

Bruce, David, CBM Ltd, High Point Business Park, 8750 Holgate Cresent, Milton, ON L9T 0K3, Canada Tel: 905-878-0648 Toll Free Tel: 800-387-4834 Fax: 905-878-6748 Toll Free Fax: 888-554-5501 E-mail: sales@cbmmetal.com Web Site: www.cbmmetal.com, pg 718

Bruce, Ryan, Antenna International, 383 Main Ave, Norwalk, CT 06851 Tel: 203-523-0320 E-mail: inquiry@antennainternational.com; marketing@antennainternational.com Web Site: www.antennainternational.com, pg 686

Bruch, Kristine, The Ridenhour Documentary Film Prize, 116 E 16 St, 8th fl, New York, NY 10003 Tel: 212-822-0257 Fax: 212-253-5356 E-mail: ridenhour@nationinstitute.org Web Site: www.ridenhour.org, pg 1001

Bruck, Jerry, Posthorn Recordings, 142 W 26 St, 10th fl, New York, NY 10001-6814 Tel: 212-242-3737 Fax: 212-924-1243 Web Site: www.posthorn.com, pg 860

Bruell, Lucy, L A Bruell Inc, 120 W 70 St, No 3-B, New York, NY 10023 Tel: 646-336-5977 Web Site: labruell.com, pg 802

Brunelle, Diana, Avid Technology Inc, 65-75 Network Dr, Burlington, MA 01830 Tel: 978-640-6789 Web Site: www.avid.com, pg 699

Brunet, Fabienne, Technicolor USA Inc, 6040 Sunset Blvd, Hollywood, CA 90028 Tel: 323-817-6600 E-mail: info@technicolor.com Web Site: www.technicolor.com, pg 908

Brunn, Peter, Center for the Collaborative Classroom, 1001 Marina Village Pkwy, Suite 110, Alameda, CA 94501-1042 Tel: 510-533-0213 Toll Free Tel: 800-666-7270 Fax: 510-464-3670 E-mail: info@collaborativeclassroom.org Web Site: www.collaborativeclassroom.org, pg 719

Brunner, Jeremy, Nostalgia Family Video Inc, PO Box 606, Baker City, OR 97814, pg 843

Bruno, Nick, Northwest Filmmakers' Festival, 934 SW Salmon St, Portland, OR 97205 Tel: 503-221-1156 Fax: 503-294-0874 E-mail: info@nwfilm.org; nwfest@nwfilm.org Web Site: www.nwfilm.org, pg 998

Bruno, Ron, The Videohouse Inc, 975 Greentree Rd, Pittsburgh, PA 15220 Tel: 412-921-7577 Fax: 412-921-5535 E-mail: info@thevideohouse.com Web Site: www.thevideohouse.com, pg 929

Bruno, Ross, Hellman Associates Inc, 1225 W Fourth St, Waterloo, IA 50702 Tel: 319-234-7055 Toll Free Tel: 800-747-7055 Fax: 319-234-2089 E-mail: info@hellman.com Web Site: www.hellman.com, pg 778

Bruns, Andrew, Headlight Audio Visual Inc, 74 Evergreen Dr, Portland, ME 04103-1066 Tel: 207-774-5998 Toll Free Tel: 800-247-0540 Fax: 207-774-4917 Web Site: www.headlightav.com, pg 777

Brunson, Becky, National Storytelling Festival, 116 W Main St, Jonesborough, TN 37659 Tel: 423-753-2171 Toll Free Tel: 800-952-8392 Fax: 423-913-8219 E-mail: customerservice@storytellingcenter.net Web Site: www.storytellingcenter.net/festival, pg 997

Brunson, Leslie, Newton Instrument Co Inc, 111 E "A" St, Butner, NC 27509-2426 Tel: 919-575-6426 Fax: 919-575-4708 E-mail: info@enewton.com Web Site: www.enewton.com, pg 840

Brunvol, Karl, Renkus-Heinz Inc, 19201 Cook St, Foothill Ranch, CA 92610-3501 Tel: 949-588-9997 Fax: 949-588-9514 E-mail: sales@renkus-heinz.com Web Site: www.renkus-heinz.com, pg 873

Brunzell, Jim III, aGLIFF-The Austin Gay & Lesbian International Film Festival, 1216 E 51 St, Austin, TX 78723 Tel: 512-302-9889 E-mail: info@agliff.org Web Site: agliff.org, pg 981

Bruzzo, Chris, Electronic Arts Inc, 209 Redwood Shores Pkwy, Redwood City, CA 94065 Tel: 650-628-1500 Web Site: www.ea.com, pg 752

Bryan, Hillary, Sparrow Sound Design, 3501 N Southport, 2nd fl, Chicago, IL 60657-1435 Tel: 773-281-8510 Fax: 773-472-1632 E-mail: southport@chicagosound.com Web Site: www.chicagosound.com, pg 896

Bryant, Ian, CEDIA IPRO Affinity Group, 8475 Nightfall Lane, Fishers, IN 46037 Tel: 317-328-4336 Toll Free Tel: 800-669-5329 E-mail: info@cedia.org Web Site: cedia.net, pg 952

Bryant, Patrick, Go To Team, 665 Johnnie Dodds Blvd, Suite 201, Mount Pleasant, SC 29464 Tel: 843-884-6222 Toll Free Tel: 888-455-4333 E-mail: crew@gototeam.com Web Site: www.gototeam.com, pg 772

Bryant, Sandy, Robertson Worldwide, 4700 137 St, Crestwood, IL 60445 Tel: 708-388-2315 Toll Free Tel: 800-323-5633 Fax: 708-388-2420 Toll Free Fax: 877-388-2420 E-mail: info@robertsonlighting.com Web Site: www.robertsondirect.com, pg 876

Bryant, Sean, Centralite Systems Inc, 1701 Industrial Park Dr, Mobile, AL 36693 Tel: 251-607-9119 Toll Free Tel: 877-466-5483 Fax: 251-607-9117 E-mail: info@centralite.com Web Site: centralite.com, pg 720

Bryczkowski, Chris, Activu Corp, 301 Roundhill Dr, Rockaway, NJ 07866 Tel: 973-366-5550 Toll Free Tel: 888-ACTIVU1 (228-4881) Fax: 973-625-7775 E-mail: facebook@activu.com Web Site: activu.com, pg 675

Bryggman, Eve, Meyer Sound Laboratories Inc, 2832 San Pablo Ave, Berkeley, CA 94702 Tel: 510-486-1166 Toll Free Tel: 855-641-3288 (US & CN) Fax: 510-486-8356 E-mail: sales@meyersound.com; techsupport@meyersound.com; service@meyersound.com Web Site: www.meyersound.com, pg 825

Bucaria, Catherine, Penguin Random House Audio Publishing, 1745 Broadway, New York, NY 10019 E-mail: audio@penguinrandomhouse.com Web Site: www.penguinrandomhouseaudio.com, pg 853

Buccieri, Paul, A&E Television Networks LLC, 235 E 45 St, New York, NY 10017 Tel: 212-210-1400 Web Site: www.aetv.com, pg 671

Buchanan, Martha, Wilson McLeran Inc, 41 Corey Hill Rd, Saxtons River, VT 05154 Tel: 802-869-3111 Toll Free Tel: 800-562-9646 Fax: 802-869-3111 Web Site: www.robertfwilson.net, pg 939

Buchanan-Munro, Alex, BIAMP Systems, 9300 SW Gemini Dr, Beaverton, OR 97008 Tel: 503-641-7287 Toll Free Tel: 800-826-1457 (US & CN) E-mail: biampinfo@biamp.com Web Site: www.biamp.com, pg 705

Buchenroth, Patrick, ACCO Brands Corp, 4 Corporate Dr, Lake Zurick, IL 60047-8997 Toll Free Tel: 800-541-0094; 800-222-6462 Toll Free Fax: 800-941-4463 E-mail: contactus@acco.com (cust serv) Web Site: www.accobrands.com, pg 696

Buchignani, Jeff, Moviola, 1135 N Mansfield Ave, Hollywood, CA 90038 Tel: 323-467-3107; 818-487-5000 Toll Free Tel: 877-MOVIOLA (668-4652) Fax: 323-464-1518 Web Site: www.moviola.com, pg 832

Buchman, Chris, Blue Mouse Studio, 26829 37 St, Gobles, MI 49055 Tel: 269-628-5160 E-mail: frogville@earthlink.net; mwivi@earthlink.net, pg 707

Buchman, Robert, Automatic Devices Co (ADC), 2121 S 12 St, Allentown, PA 18103 Tel: 610-797-6000 Toll Free Tel: 800-360-2321 Fax: 610-797-4088 E-mail: info@automaticdevices.com Web Site: www.automaticdevices.com, pg 696

Buck, Allison, Ann Arbor Film Festival, 230 Collingwood Dr, Suite 160B, Ann Arbor, MI 48103 Tel: 734-995-5356 Fax: 734-995-5396 E-mail: info@aafilmfest.org Web Site: www.aafilmfest.org, pg 981

Buckholz, LuAnn, Specialty Bulb Co Inc, 80 Orville Dr, Suite 101, Bohemia, NY 11716 Tel: 631-589-3393 Toll Free Tel: 800-331-BULB (331-2852) Fax: 631-563-3089 Web Site: www.bulbspecialists.com, pg 896

Buckley, Linda, KEF Media, 1161 Concord Rd SE, Smyrna, GA 30080 *Tel:* 404-605-0009 *E-mail:* info@kefmedia.com *Web Site:* kefmedia.com, pg 797

Buckley, Martina, Nineteen87, 1024 Harding Ave, Suite 201, Venice Beach, CA 90291 *Tel:* 310-577-5009 *Fax:* 310-577-1960 *E-mail:* info@1-9-8-7.com *Web Site:* www.1-9-8-7.com, pg 841

Budny, Kathleen, AIGA, the professional association for design, 233 Broadway, Suite 1740, New York, NY 10279 *Tel:* 212-807-1990 *Toll Free Tel:* 800-548-1634 *E-mail:* general@aiga.org *Web Site:* www.aiga.org, pg 947

Budrow, Darren, Ross Video Ltd, 8 John St, Iroquois, ON K0E 1K0, Canada *Tel:* 613-652-4886 *Fax:* 613-652-4425 *E-mail:* solutions@rossvideo.com *Web Site:* www.rossvideo.com, pg 878

Budzilek, Jim, Visual Products Inc, 790 Shiloh Ave, Wellington, OH 44090 *Tel:* 440-647-4999 *Fax:* 440-647-4998 *E-mail:* sales@visualproducts.com *Web Site:* www.visualproducts.com, pg 931

Budzinski, Jeff, Shanix Inc, 40 Worthington Rd, Cranston, RI 02920 *Tel:* 401-941-4222 *Toll Free Tel:* 800-783-2067 *Fax:* 401-941-4333 *E-mail:* info@shanix.com *Web Site:* www.shanix.com, pg 885

Buell, David, Real to Reel Studios Inc, 4141 Office Pkwy, Dallas, TX 75204 *Tel:* 214-528-4242 *Web Site:* www.rtrstudios.com, pg 871

Buell, Mickey, Real to Reel Studios Inc, 4141 Office Pkwy, Dallas, TX 75204 *Tel:* 214-528-4242 *Web Site:* www.rtrstudios.com, pg 871

Buhrman, Rob, Lion & Fox Recording Studios, 9517 Baltimore Ave, College Park, MD 20740 *Tel:* 301-982-4431 *E-mail:* mail@lionfox.com *Web Site:* www.lionfox.com, pg 809

Buie, Nicole, Cox Media, 6205 Peachtree Dunwoody Rd, No B17, Atlanta, GA 30328 *Toll Free Tel:* 855-755-2691 *Web Site:* www.coxmedia.com, pg 732

Bulgaretti, Silvio, Gold Link Productions Inc, 1457 Pembroke Dr, Oakville, ON L6H 1V6, Canada *Tel:* 416-560-3864 *E-mail:* goldlinkproductions@gmail.com; info@torontocameramanservices.com *Web Site:* www.torontocameramanservices.com, pg 772

Bulkley, Levi, Image Audiovisuals, 2130 S Dahlia St, Denver, CO 80222 *Tel:* 303-758-1818 *Toll Free Tel:* 800-818-1857 *Fax:* 303-758-5722 *Web Site:* www.imageav.com, pg 784

Bull, Kevin, KDM Electronics Inc, 55 Mills Rd, Unit 3, Ajax, ON L1S 2H2, Canada *Tel:* 416-439-7158 *Toll Free Tel:* 800-567-6282 *Fax:* 416-439-7232 *E-mail:* kdm@octasound.com *Web Site:* www.octasound.com, pg 797

Bull, Martin, KDM Electronics Inc, 55 Mills Rd, Unit 3, Ajax, ON L1S 2H2, Canada *Tel:* 416-439-7158 *Toll Free Tel:* 800-567-6282 *Fax:* 416-439-7232 *E-mail:* kdm@octasound.com *Web Site:* www.octasound.com, pg 797

Bulleit, Barclay, Presentation Products Inc, 171 Madison Ave, 12th fl, New York, NY 10016 *Tel:* 212-736-6350 *Toll Free Tel:* 877-774-4523 *Fax:* 212-736-6353 *E-mail:* customerservice@pproducts.com *Web Site:* www.presentationproducts.com, pg 861

Bullwinkle, David, Eastman Kodak Co, 343 State St, Rochester, NY 14650 *Toll Free Tel:* 800-698-3324 *Web Site:* www.kodak.com, pg 750

Bundschuh, Andy, Mike Vasilinda Productions Inc, 310 N Monroe St, Tallahassee, FL 32301 *Tel:* 850-224-5420 *Web Site:* mvptv.tv, pg 925

Bundy, Christopher, FrontRow, 1690 Corporate Circle, Petaluma, CA 94954 *Tel:* 707-769-1110 *Toll Free Tel:* 800-227-0735 *Fax:* 707-769-9624 *E-mail:* customercare@gofrontrow.com *Web Site:* www.gofrontrow.com, pg 766

Bunke, Jerome, Digital Force Ltd, 248 W 35 St, 14th fl, New York, NY 10001 *Tel:* 212-252-9300 *Toll Free Tel:* 877-DISC-USA (347-2872) *Fax:* 212-252-7377 *E-mail:* frontdesk@digitalforce.com *Web Site:* digitalforce.com, pg 742

Bunn, Caleb, Big Muddy Film Festival, 1100 Lincoln Dr, Rm 1101, Carbondale, IL 62901-6610 *Tel:* 618-453-8301 *E-mail:* info@bigmuddyfilm.com *Web Site:* www.bigmuddyfilm.com, pg 983

Bunney, Graham, Broadcast Microwave Services Inc (BMS), a StoneCalibre company, 12305 Crosthwaite Circle, Poway, CA 92064 *Tel:* 858-391-3050 *Toll Free Tel:* 800-669-9667 (US) *Fax:* 858-391-3049 *E-mail:* sales@bms-inc.com *Web Site:* www.bms-inc.com, pg 711

Bunszel, Amy, Autodesk Inc, 111 McInnis Pkwy, San Rafael, CA 94903 *Tel:* 415-507-5000 *Fax:* 415-507-5100 *Web Site:* www.autodesk.com, pg 696

Bunting, Lloyd, VideoLink Inc, an AVI-SPL company, 1230 Washington St, West Newton, MA 02465 *Tel:* 617-340-4100 *Toll Free Tel:* 800-452-5565 *Fax:* 617-340-4101 *E-mail:* sales@videolinktv.com *Web Site:* www.videolinktv.com, pg 929

Burd, Adam, Avast! Recording Co, 601 NW 80 St, Seattle, WA 98117 *Fax:* 206-789-7569 *E-mail:* avast@comcast.net *Web Site:* www.avastrecording.com, pg 697

Burden, Danny, Canadian American Records, PO Box 808, Lititz, PA 17543-0538 *Tel:* 717-627-4800 *E-mail:* canadianamerican@dejazzd.com *Web Site:* www.canadianamericanrecords.net; www.canadianamericanrecordcompany.com, pg 715

Burden, Richard W, Richard W Burden Associates, 20944 Sherman Way, Canoga Park, CA 91303 *Tel:* 818-340-4590, pg 712

Burdick, Alex, Westlake Recording Studios, 7265 Santa Monica Blvd, Los Angeles, CA 90046 *Tel:* 323-851-9800 *E-mail:* bookings@westlakestudios.com; info@westlakestudios.com *Web Site:* www.westlakestudios.com, pg 936

Burdick, Steve, Westlake Recording Studios, 7265 Santa Monica Blvd, Los Angeles, CA 90046 *Tel:* 323-851-9800 *E-mail:* bookings@westlakestudios.com; info@westlakestudios.com *Web Site:* www.westlakestudios.com, pg 936

Burger, Gregg, Precision Camera & Video, 2438 W Anderson Lane, Suite B-4, Austin, TX 78757 *Tel:* 512-467-7676 *Toll Free Tel:* 800-677-1023 *Fax:* 512-467-0607 *Web Site:* www.precision-camera.com, pg 861

Burgess, Chet, WhisperRoom™ Inc, 109 S Northshore Dr, Suite 303, Knoxville, TN 37919 *Tel:* 865-558-5364 *Toll Free Tel:* 800-200-8168 *Fax:* 865-558-5370 *E-mail:* info@whisperroom.com *Web Site:* www.whisperroom.com, pg 937

Burgess, Glenn, Matrix Video Communications Corp (MVCC), 103, 1626 115 Ave NE, Calgary, AB T3K 5Y8, Canada *Tel:* 403-640-4490 *Fax:* 403-640-9012 *Web Site:* www.matrixvideocom.com, pg 819

Burgess, Shelly, Matrix Video Communications Corp (MVCC), 103, 1626 115 Ave NE, Calgary, AB T3K 5Y8, Canada *Tel:* 403-640-4490 *Fax:* 403-640-9012 *Web Site:* www.matrixvideocom.com, pg 819

Burgess, William III, Ken-Del Productions Inc, 1500 First State Blvd, Wilmington, DE 19804-3596 *Tel:* 302-999-1111; 302-999-1110; 302-999-1164 *Toll Free Tel:* 800-249-1110 *Fax:* 302-999-1656 *E-mail:* info@ken-del.com *Web Site:* www.ken-del.com, pg 797

Burgess, William III, Ken-Del Studios, 1500 First State Blvd, Wilmington, DE 19804-3596 *Tel:* 302-999-1111 *Toll Free Tel:* 800-249-1110 *Fax:* 302-999-1656 *E-mail:* info@ken-del.com *Web Site:* www.ken-del.com, pg 797

Burian, Lawrence, Madison Square Garden, 2 Pennsylvania Plaza, New York, NY 10121-0091 *Tel:* 212-465-6741 *E-mail:* msgnetpr@msgnetwork.com *Web Site:* www.thegarden.com; themadisonsquaregardencompany.com, pg 814

Burke, Bryant, GatesAir, 5300 Kings Island Dr, Suite 101, Mason, OH 45040 *Tel:* 513-459-3400 *Toll Free Tel:* 800-622-0022 *Fax:* 513-459-3796

E-mail: information@gatesair.com; orders@gatesair.com; support@gatesair.com *Web Site:* www.gatesair.com, pg 768

Burke, James, HB Communications Inc, 60 Dodge Ave, North Haven, CT 06473 *Tel:* 203-234-9246 *Toll Free Tel:* 800-243-4414 *Fax:* 203-234-2013 *E-mail:* info@hbcommunications.com *Web Site:* hbcommunications.com, pg 777

Burke, Jim, L3Harris Technologies Inc, 1025 W NASA Blvd, Melbourne, FL 32919 *E-mail:* info@l3harris.com *Web Site:* www.l3harris.com, pg 812

Burke, Kimberly, DecisionOne Corp, 640 Lee Rd, 3rd fl, Wayne, PA 19087 *Tel:* 610-296-6000 *Toll Free Tel:* 800-767-2876; 800-777-8800 (cust serv); 888-287-9202 (sales); 800-554-5179 (CN) *Fax:* 610-296-2910 *E-mail:* sales@decisionone.com *Web Site:* www.decisionone.com, pg 740

Burke, Michael, Tisch School of the Arts, 721 Broadway, 10th & 11th fl, New York, NY 10003 *Tel:* 212-998-1700; 212-998-1780 *Fax:* 212-995-4062; 212-995-4063 *Web Site:* www.tisch.nyu.edu, pg 914

Burke, Rose, Ken-Del Productions Inc, 1500 First State Blvd, Wilmington, DE 19804-3596 *Tel:* 302-999-1111; 302-999-1110; 302-999-1164 *Toll Free Tel:* 800-249-1110 *Fax:* 302-999-1656 *E-mail:* info@ken-del.com *Web Site:* www.ken-del.com, pg 797

Burke, Rose, Ken-Del Studios, 1500 First State Blvd, Wilmington, DE 19804-3596 *Tel:* 302-999-1111 *Toll Free Tel:* 800-249-1110 *Fax:* 302-999-1656 *E-mail:* info@ken-del.com *Web Site:* www.ken-del.com, pg 797

Burke, Tim, Audio Visual Dynamics®, 424 Sand Shore Rd, Hackettstown, NJ 07840 *Tel:* 973-993-8500 *Fax:* 973-984-0644 *Web Site:* www.avdusa.com, pg 694

Burkette, Jay, ExpoDisplays, 3401 Mary Taylor Rd, Birmingham, AL 35235 *Toll Free Tel:* 800-747-3976 *E-mail:* info@expodisplays.com *Web Site:* www.expodisplays.com, pg 757

Burkhart, Dennis, Encounter Video Inc, 1761 N Jantzen Ave, Portland, OR 97217 *Web Site:* www.encountervideo.com, pg 754

Burkitt, George, Florida Film & Tape, 3417 Lake Breeze Rd, Orlando, FL 32808 *Tel:* 407-297-0091 *E-mail:* info@ffandt.com *Web Site:* ffandt.com, pg 763

Burnell, Jennifer Lane, The Entertainment Merchants Association (EMA), PO Box 6339, North Hollywood, CA 91603 *Tel:* 818-385-1500 *E-mail:* info@entmerch.org *Web Site:* www.entmerch.org, pg 954

Burns, Barbara, Littlite LLC, PO Box 430, Hamburg, MI 48139-0430 *Tel:* 810-852-4242 *Fax:* 810-231-1631 *E-mail:* sales@littlite.com *Web Site:* www.littlite.com, pg 810

Burns, Ben, Blind™, 1702 Olympic Blvd, Santa Monica, CA 90404 *Tel:* 310-314-1618 *Fax:* 310-314-1718 *Web Site:* www.blind.com, pg 707

Burns, Colleen, 30 Second Street Ltd, 1209 Mountain Road Place NE, Suite B, Albuquerque, NM 87110 *Tel:* 505-265-0224 *E-mail:* info@30sst.com *Web Site:* www.thirtysecst.com, pg 912

Burns, Dennis, 1013 Integrated, 1013 Kawaiahao St, Honolulu, HI 96814 *Tel:* 808-593-8848 *E-mail:* info@1013integrated.com *Web Site:* www.facebook.com/1013integrated; 1013integrated.com, pg 911

Burns, Eleanor, Quilt in a Day, 1955 Diamond St, San Marcos, CA 92078 *Tel:* 760-591-0082 *Toll Free Tel:* 800-777-4852 *Fax:* 760-591-4424 *E-mail:* customerservice@quiltinaday.com *Web Site:* www.quiltinaday.com, pg 868

Burns, Michael, Quatrefoil Associates Inc, 29 "C" St, Laurel, MD 20707 *Tel:* 301-470-4748 *Fax:* 301-470-4749 *E-mail:* info@quatrefoil.com *Web Site:* www.quatrefoil.com, pg 868

Burns, Orion, Quilt in a Day, 1955 Diamond St, San Marcos, CA 92078 *Tel:* 760-591-0082 *Toll Free Tel:* 800-777-4852 *Fax:* 760-591-4424 *E-mail:* customerservice@quiltinaday.com *Web Site:* www.quiltinaday.com, pg 868

Burns, Steven J, North Coast Studios Inc, 29181 Calahan Rd, Roseville, MI 48066 *Tel:* 586-359-6630 *Toll Free Tel:* 888-866-0652 *Fax:* 586-359-6638 *E-mail:* sales@northcoaststudiosinc.com, pg 842

Burns, Tim, Scientifics Direct Inc, 532 Main St, Tonawanda, NY 14150 *Toll Free Tel:* 800-728-6999; 800-818-4955 *Toll Free Fax:* 800-828-3299 *E-mail:* support@scientificsdirect.com *Web Site:* www.scientificsonline.com, pg 882

Burnside, Brad, Audio Network US Inc, 48 W 25 St, 10th fl, New York, NY 10010 *Tel:* 646-688-4320 *E-mail:* nyoffice@audionetwork.com *Web Site:* us.audionetwork.com, pg 693

Burr, Suzanne, Valencia Studios, 26030 Avenue Hall, Studio 5, Valencia, CA 91355 *Tel:* 661-702-9102 *E-mail:* info@valenciastudios.com *Web Site:* www.valenciastudios.com, pg 924

Burrows, Josh, Stray Angel Films, 11318 Santa Monica Blvd, Los Angeles, CA 90025 *Tel:* 310-277-6900 *Fax:* 801-438-5009 *E-mail:* rentals@strayangel.com *Web Site:* www.strayangel.com, pg 902

Burrud, John, Burrud Productions Inc, 468 N Camden Dr, 2nd fl, Beverly Hills, CA 90210, pg 713

Burst-Terranella, Fran, Burst Video/Film Inc, 1104 Alta Ave NE, Atlanta, GA 30307, pg 713

Burstein, Barry, MAC Group, 75 Virginia Rd, North White Plains, NY 10603 *Tel:* 914-347-3300 *Fax:* 914-347-3309 *E-mail:* info@macgroupus.com *Web Site:* www.macgroupus.com, pg 813

Burstein, John, Slim Goodbody Corp, 161 Narrows Rd, Lincolnville, ME 04850 *Tel:* 207-831-2607 *E-mail:* info@slimgoodbody.com *Web Site:* www.slimgoodbody.com, pg 890

Burton, Erika, Method Studios, 3401 Exposition Blvd, Santa Monica, CA 90404 *Tel:* 310-434-6000 *Web Site:* www.methodstudios.com, pg 824

Burton, Joe, Poly, 345 Encinal St, Santa Cruz, CA 95060 *Tel:* 831-426-5858 *Toll Free Tel:* 800-544-4660 *Fax:* 831-426-6098 *Web Site:* www.poly.com, pg 859

Burwell, Karyn, Apache Junction Chamber of Commerce, 567 W Apache Trail, Apache Junction, AZ 85120 *Tel:* 480-982-3141 *Fax:* 480-982-3234 *E-mail:* admin@ajchamber.com *Web Site:* www.ajchamber.com, pg 965

Buscaglia, Ted, ARC Document Solutions, 1981 N Broadway, Suite 385, Walnut Creek, CA 94596 *Tel:* 925-949-5100 *Toll Free Tel:* 855-500-0660 *E-mail:* contact@e-arc.com *Web Site:* www.e-arc.com, pg 688

Buschini, Joe, Small Planet Communications Inc, 15 Union St, Lawrence, MA 01840 *Tel:* 978-794-2201 *E-mail:* planet@smplanet.com *Web Site:* www.smplanet.com, pg 890

Bush, Antoinette, News Corp, 1211 Avenue of the Americas, New York, NY 10036 *Tel:* 212-416-3400 *E-mail:* media@newscorp.com *Web Site:* newscorp.com, pg 840

Bush, Curt, White Dog Studios, 1986 Mercer Rd, Smyrna, GA 30080 *Tel:* 404-355-2200 *Web Site:* www.whitedogstudios.net, pg 937

Bush, Eric, Havas Edge, 2386 Faraday Ave, Suite 200, Carlsbad, CA 92008 *Tel:* 760-929-0041 *E-mail:* info@havasedge.com *Web Site:* www.havasedge.com, pg 777

Bush, Jeff, Eye on Dance, 70 E Tenth St, Suite 19-D, New York, NY 10003 *Tel:* 212-206-6492 *E-mail:* info@eyeondance.org *Web Site:* www.eyeondance.org, pg 758

Busse, Glenn R, Directed Electronics, One Viper Way, Suite A, Vista, CA 92081 *Tel:* 760-598-6200 *Toll Free Tel:* 800-876-0800 *E-mail:* pr@directed.com *Web Site:* www.directed.com, pg 743

Bustamante, Alex, Poly, 345 Encinal St, Santa Cruz, CA 95060 *Tel:* 831-426-5858 *Toll Free Tel:* 800-544-4660 *Fax:* 831-426-6098 *Web Site:* www.poly.com, pg 859

Butcher, Dane, Symetrix Inc, 6408 216 St SW, Mountlake Terrace, WA 98043-2093 *Tel:* 425-778-7728 *E-mail:* support@symetrix.co; sales@symetrix.co *Web Site:* www.symetrix.co, pg 905

Buterbaugh, Alan, Creative Realities Inc (CRI), 13100 Magisterial Dr, Suite 100, Louisville, KY 40223 *Tel:* 502-791-8800 *Web Site:* cri.com, pg 733

Butkowski, Joel, Butkowski Digital Imaging (BDI), 2229 Roosevelt Rd, St Cloud, MN 56301 *Tel:* 320-333-1520 *E-mail:* info@bdiphoto.com *Web Site:* www.bdiphoto.com, pg 713

Butler, Alton, Angstrom Lighting, 12224 Montague St, Pacoima, CA 91331 *Tel:* 323-462-4246 *E-mail:* info@angstromlighting.com *Web Site:* www.angstromlighting.com, pg 685

Butler, Bess, Questar Entertainment Inc, 307 N Michigan Ave, 5th fl, Chicago, IL 60601-5305 *Tel:* 312-266-9400 *Toll Free Tel:* 800-544-8422 (cust serv) *E-mail:* info@questarentertainment.com *Web Site:* www.questarentertainment.com, pg 868

Butler, Chuck, Monster Tracks, 1821 Ranstead St, Philadelphia, PA 19103 *Tel:* 215-567-0400 *Toll Free Tel:* 800-369-1280 *Fax:* 215-567-0350 *Web Site:* www.monstertracks.com, pg 829

Butler, David, Manios Digital & Film, 10663 Burbank Blvd, North Hollywood, CA 91601 *Tel:* 818-760-8290 *Toll Free Tel:* 800-845-6619 *Fax:* 818-760-8805 *E-mail:* sales@maniosdigital.com *Web Site:* www.maniosdigital.com, pg 816

Butler, Patrick, America's Public Television Stations (APTS), 2100 Crystal Dr, Suite 700, Arlington, VA 22202 *Tel:* 202-654-4200 *Fax:* 202-654-4236 *Web Site:* apts.org, pg 949

Butler, Robert, Audio Book Contractors LLC, PO Box 96, Riverdale, MD 20738-0096 *Tel:* 301-439-5830 *Fax:* 301-439-5830 *E-mail:* audiobookcontractors@verizon.net *Web Site:* www.audiobookcontractors.com, pg 693

Butnaru, Avner, BitFlow Inc, 400 W Cummings Park, Suite 5050, Woburn, MA 01801 *Tel:* 781-932-2900 *Fax:* 781-933-9965 *E-mail:* sales@bitflow.com *Web Site:* www.bitflow.com, pg 706

Butt, Amy, Larrabee Sound Studio, 4162 Lankershim Blvd, North Hollywood, CA 91602 *Tel:* 818-753-0717 *Fax:* 818-753-8046 *E-mail:* info@larrabeestudios.com *Web Site:* www.larrabeestudios.com, pg 803

Butters, Tom, Illuminating Engineering Society (IES), 120 Wall St, 17th fl, New York, NY 10005-4026 *Tel:* 212-248-5000 *E-mail:* ies@ies.org *Web Site:* ies.org, pg 955

Buttle, Scott, ACCO Brands Corp, 4 Corporate Dr, Lake Zurick, IL 60047-8997 *Toll Free Tel:* 800-541-0094; 800-222-6462 *Toll Free Fax:* 800-941-4463 *E-mail:* contactus@acco.com (cust serv) *Web Site:* www.accobrands.com, pg 673

Byrd, Lauren, Women in Film Finishing Fund, 6100 Wilshire Blvd, Suite 710, Los Angeles, CA 90048 *Tel:* 323-935-2211 *Fax:* 323-935-2212 *E-mail:* info@wif.org *Web Site:* www.wif.org, pg 1007

Byrnes, Chris, Charlex Inc, 2 W 45 St, 7th fl, New York, NY 10036 *Tel:* 212-719-4600 *E-mail:* info@chrlx.com *Web Site:* www.chrlx.com, pg 721

Byrns, Bob, Paulist Press, 997 Macarthur Blvd, Mahwah, NJ 07430-9990 *Tel:* 201-825-7300 *Toll Free Tel:* 800-218-1903 (orders) *Fax:* 201-825-6921 *E-mail:* info@paulistpress.com *Web Site:* www.paulistpress.com, pg 852

Cabasso, Artie, Gemini Sound, 107 Trumbull St, Bldg F-8, 2nd fl, Elizabeth, NJ 07206-2171 *Tel:* 732-346-0061 *Fax:* 732-346-0065 *E-mail:* sales@geminisound.com *Web Site:* www.geminisound.com, pg 769

Cabela, Daniel, Music Lab Inc, 500 E Saint Elmo Rd, Austin, TX 78745 *Tel:* 512-707-0560 (ext 2) *Fax:* 512-707-2946 *E-mail:* info@musiclab.net *Web Site:* musiclabaustin.com, pg 834

Cabral, Bruce, Sinclair Institute, 402 Millstone Dr, Hillsborough, NC 27278 *Tel:* 919-732-6005 *Toll Free Tel:* 888-736-2247 *Fax:* 919-732-6146 *E-mail:* sales@sinclairwholesale.com *Web Site:* www.sinclairwholesale.com; www.bettersex.com, pg 889

Cadigan, Katie, imageReal Pictures LLC, 4 Lighthouse St, No 8, Marina del Rey, CA 90292 *E-mail:* info@imagereal.com *Web Site:* www.imagereal.com, pg 785

Cadywould, Louisa, Reel One International Ltd, 486 Ste-Catherine W, Suite 100, Montreal, QC H3B 1A6, Canada *E-mail:* sales@reeloneent.com *Web Site:* reeloneent.com, pg 872

Cafferillo, Nick, S&P Global Marketing Intelligence, 55 Water St, New York, NY 10041 *Toll Free Tel:* 877-863-1306 *E-mail:* questions@spcapitaliq.com *Web Site:* marketingintelligence.spglobal.com, pg 880

Cahalan, Tracy, Inland Audio Visual Co, 1414 N Fiske St, Suite E, Spokane, WA 99202 *Tel:* 509-328-0706 *Fax:* 509-328-0730 *E-mail:* inland@inlandav.com *Web Site:* www.inlandav.com, pg 788

Cahill, Pat, American Color Imaging (ACI), 715 E 18 St, Cedar Falls, IA 50613 *Tel:* 319-277-3655 *Toll Free Tel:* 800-728-2722 *Fax:* 319-277-6522 *E-mail:* sales@acilab.com *Web Site:* www.acilab.com, pg 683

Cain, Richard A, East Arizona Good Luck Enterprises Inc, PO Box 579, Clarkdale, AZ 86324 *Tel:* 928-204-2597 *Fax:* 928-204-2568 *E-mail:* hier_bosch@yahoo.com, pg 749

Cain, Sarah, The Virginia Film Festival, 617 W Main St, 2nd fl, Charlottesville, VA 22903 *Tel:* 434-982-5277 *Fax:* 434-924-3374 *E-mail:* info@virginiafilmfestival.org; vffsubmissions@virginia.edu *Web Site:* virginiafilmfestival.org, pg 1006

Cairns, Sam, Gospel Folio Press, 304 Killaly St W, Port Colborne, ON L3K 6A6, Canada *Tel:* 905-835-9166 *Toll Free Tel:* 800-952-2382 *Fax:* 905-834-0012 *E-mail:* info@gospelfolio.com; orders@gospelfolio.com *Web Site:* www.gospelfolio.com, pg 773

Cajka, Philip, Audio-Technica US Inc, 1221 Commerce Dr, Stow, OH 44224 *Tel:* 330-686-2600 *Fax:* 330-686-0719 *E-mail:* pro@atus.com *Web Site:* www.audio-technica.com, pg 694

Calabro, Louis, Canadian Screen Awards, 49 Ontario St, Suite 501, Toronto, ON M5A 2V1, Canada *Tel:* 416-366-2227 *Toll Free Tel:* 800-644-5194 *Fax:* 416-366-8454 *E-mail:* awards@academy.ca; info@academy.ca *Web Site:* www.academy.ca/canadian-screen-awards, pg 985

Calderaro, Jon, Concepts TV Productions Inc, 53 Indian Lane E, Towaco, NJ 07082 *Tel:* 973-331-1500 *Fax:* 973-331-1550 *E-mail:* sales@conceptstv.com *Web Site:* conceptstv.com, pg 730

Calderon, Lauren, WorldFest-Houston International Film Festival, 9898 Bissonnet St, Suite 650, Houston, TX 77036 *Tel:* 713-965-9955 *Fax:* 713-965-9960 *E-mail:* mail@worldfest.org; entry@worldfest.org *Web Site:* www.worldfest.org, pg 1007

Calderwood, David, Euro-Pacific Film & Video Productions Inc, 101 Crawfords Corner Rd, Suite 4-101R, Holmdel, NJ 07733 *Tel:* 732-530-4451 *Toll Free Tel:* 800-387-6776 *E-mail:* info@euro-pacific.com *Web Site:* www.euro-pacific.com, pg 756

Calderwood, Lisa Moss, Euro-Pacific Film & Video Productions Inc, 101 Crawfords Corner Rd, Suite 4-101R, Holmdel, NJ 07733 *Tel:* 732-530-4451 *Toll Free Tel:* 800-387-6776 *E-mail:* info@euro-pacific.com *Web Site:* www.euro-pacific.com, pg 756

Caldwell, Bobbie, Freeman, 1600 Viceroy, Suite 100, Dallas, TX 75235 *Tel:* 214-445-1000 *Web Site:* www.freeman.com, pg 765

Caldwell, Tony, Society for Information Display (SID), 1475 S Bascom Ave, Suite 114, Campbell, CA 95008-4006 *Tel:* 408-879-3901 *Fax:* 408-879-3833 *E-mail:* office@sid.org *Web Site:* www.sid.org, pg 962

Caler, Jennifer, Optikinetics Ltd - The Americas, 11211 Air Park Rd, Suite 1, Ashland, VA 23005 *Tel:* 804-752-2570 *Toll Free Tel:* 800-575-6784 *Fax:* 804-752-2888 *E-mail:* optius@optikinetics.com *Web Site:* www.optikinetics.com, pg 847

Califano, Carmela, Calger Lighting Inc, 200 Lexington Ave, Suite 434, New York, NY 10016 *Tel:* 212-689-9511 *Fax:* 212-779-0721 *E-mail:* sales@calgerlighting.com *Web Site:* www.calgerlighting.com, pg 714

Callagy, Dennis, Custom Computer Specialists Inc, 70 Suffolk Ct, Hauppauge, NY 11788 *Tel:* 631-864-6699 *Toll Free Tel:* 800-589-8989 *Fax:* 401-765-6440 *Toll Free Fax:* 800-986-5518 *E-mail:* info@customtech.com; support@customtech.com *Web Site:* www.customonline.com, pg 736

Callahan, Carley, Golden Space Needle Awards, 305 Harrison St, Seattle, WA 98109 *Tel:* 206-464-5830 *Fax:* 206-264-7919 *E-mail:* info@siff.net; entries@siff.net *Web Site:* www.siff.net, pg 991

Callahan, Carley, Seattle International Film Festival (SIFF), 305 Harrison St, Seattle, WA 98109 *Tel:* 206-464-5830 *Fax:* 206-264-7919 *E-mail:* info@siff.net; entries@siff.net *Web Site:* www.siff.net, pg 1003

Callahan, James R, A/V Presentations Inc, 104 Otis St, Suite 30, Northborough, MA 01532 *Tel:* 508-393-9767 *Toll Free Tel:* 800-648-7176 *Fax:* 508-393-6698 *E-mail:* staff@avpresentations.com *Web Site:* www.avpresentations.com, pg 697

Callahan, Rod, A/V Presentations Inc, 104 Otis St, Suite 30, Northborough, MA 01532 *Tel:* 508-393-9767 *Toll Free Tel:* 800-648-7176 *Fax:* 508-393-6698 *E-mail:* staff@avpresentations.com *Web Site:* www.avpresentations.com, pg 697

Callaway, Andy, Frontline Communications, 12770 44 St N, Clearwater, FL 33762 *Tel:* 727-573-0400 *Fax:* 727-571-3295 *Web Site:* www.frontlinecomm.com, pg 766

Callen, Dennis, Callen Photo Mount Corp, 185 Sixth Ave, Paterson, NJ 07524 *Tel:* 973-925-2390 *Toll Free Tel:* 800-225-5360 *Fax:* 973-925-9615, pg 714

Callini, Tony, Monotype Imaging Inc, 600 Unicorn Park Dr, Woburn, MA 01801 *Tel:* 781-970-6000 *Toll Free Tel:* 800-424-8973 *Fax:* 781-970-6001; 781-970-6002 (gen questions) *E-mail:* info@monotype.com *Web Site:* www.monotype.com, pg 829

Calvert, Donna, Institute of Industrial & Systems Engineers (IISE), 3577 Parkway Lane, Suite 200, Norcross, GA 30092 *Tel:* 770-449-0460 *Toll Free Tel:* 800-494-0460 *Fax:* 770-441-3295 *E-mail:* executiveoffices@iise.org *Web Site:* www.iise.org, pg 956

Calvert, Tom, Credo Interactive Inc, 4612 Strathcona Rd, North Vancouver, BC V7O 1G3, Canada *E-mail:* info@charactermotion.com *Web Site:* www.charactermotion.com, pg 734

Calzone, Joe, Calzone Case Co, 225 Black Rock Ave, Bridgeport, CT 06605 *Toll Free Tel:* 800-243-5152 *Fax:* 203-336-4406 *Web Site:* www.calzoneandanvil.com, pg 714

Calzone, Joseph, Anvil Cases, 1242 E Edna Place, Covina, CA 91724 *Tel:* 626-968-4100 *Toll Free Tel:* 800-FLYANVIL (359-2684) *Fax:* 626-968-1703 *E-mail:* web.sales@anvilcase.com *Web Site:* www.calzoneandanvil.com, pg 686

Calzone, Vincent, Calzone Case Co, 225 Black Rock Ave, Bridgeport, CT 06605 *Toll Free Tel:* 800-243-5152 *Fax:* 203-336-4406 *Web Site:* www.calzoneandanvil.com, pg 714

Camara, Alex, AudioControl® Inc, 22410 70 Ave W, Mountlake Terrace, WA 98043 *Tel:* 425-775-8461 *Fax:* 425-778-3166 *E-mail:* sound.great@audiocontrol.com *Web Site:* www.audiocontrol.com, pg 695

Cambria, Dave, Red Sky Studios, 184 Everett St, Allston, MA 02134 *Tel:* 617-903-3373 *E-mail:* mail@redsky-studios.com *Web Site:* redsky-studios.com, pg 872

Camden, Ron, BIAMP Systems, 9300 SW Gemini Dr, Beaverton, OR 97008 *Tel:* 503-641-7287 *Toll Free Tel:* 800-826-1457 (US & CN) *E-mail:* biampinfo@biamp.com *Web Site:* www.biamp.com, pg 705

Camitta, Robert, Midnight Media Group Inc, 45 E Willow St, Millburn, NJ 07041-1416 *Tel:* 973-379-5959 *E-mail:* info@mmgi.tv *Web Site:* mmgi.tv, pg 827

Camp, Alysia, Goal Productions, 1905 Victory Blvd, Suite 6, Glendale, CA 91201 *Tel:* 818-588-3900 *Fax:* 818-588-3903 *E-mail:* info@goalproductions.com *Web Site:* www.goalproductions.com, pg 772

Campa, Mario A, Toys From The Attic, 27 Holland Ave, White Plains, NY 10603 *Tel:* 914-421-0069 *E-mail:* tftamail@gmail.com *Web Site:* tftaus.com, pg 916

Campagna, George, Alliance Entertainment Corp (AEC) LLC, 1401 NW 136 Ave, Suite 100, Sunrise, FL 33323 *Toll Free Tel:* 800-329-7664 *Web Site:* www.aent.com, pg 680

Campbell, Chris, Palace Production Center, 29 N Main St, South Norwalk, CT 06854 *Tel:* 203-853-1740 *Fax:* 203-855-9608 *Web Site:* www.palaceproductioncenter.com, pg 850

Campbell, Dave, Matrix Video Communications Corp (MVCC), 103, 1626 115 Ave NE, Calgary, AB T3K 5Y8, Canada *Tel:* 403-640-4490 *Fax:* 403-640-9012 *Web Site:* www.matrixvideocom.com, pg 819

Campbell, David, Projection, 5803 Rolling Rd, Suite 200, Springfield, VA 22152 *Tel:* 301-459-9011 *Fax:* 301-575-3101 *E-mail:* info@projection.com *Web Site:* www.projection.com, pg 865

Campbell, Eileen, IMAX Corp, 2525 Speakman Dr, Mississauga, ON L5K 1B1, Canada *Tel:* 905-403-6500 *Fax:* 905-403-6450 *E-mail:* info@imax.com *Web Site:* www.imax.com, pg 786

Campbell, Jim, Pacific Multimedia Inc, 4917 Seaview Way, Everett, WA 98203 *Tel:* 425-347-4110 *Toll Free Tel:* 888-373-8273 *Web Site:* www.pacmultimedia.com, pg 849

Campbell, Lisa, Autodesk Inc, 111 McInnis Pkwy, San Rafael, CA 94903 *Tel:* 415-507-5000 *Fax:* 415-507-5100 *Web Site:* www.autodesk.com, pg 696

Campbell, Matthew, Denver Film Festival, 1510 York St, 3rd fl, Denver, CO 80206 *Tel:* 303-595-3456 *E-mail:* dff@denverfilm.org *Web Site:* denverfilmfestival.denverfilm.org, pg 988

Campbell, Nancy, The Campbell Agency, Hidden Grove Bldg, 12404 Park Central Dr, Suite 222 S, Dallas, TX 75251 *Tel:* 214-522-8991 *Fax:* 214-522-8997 *Web Site:* www.thecampbellagency.com, pg 715

Campbell, Rebecca, Austin Film Society (AFS), 1901 E 51 St, Austin, TX 78723 *Tel:* 512-322-0145 *E-mail:* afs@austinfilm.org *Web Site:* www.austinfilm.org, pg 951

Campbell, Suzan M, CommScope Inc, 1100 CommScope Place SE, Hickory, NC 28602 *Tel:* 828-324-2200 *Toll Free Tel:* 800-982-1708 *E-mail:* publicrelations@commscope.com *Web Site:* www.commscope.com, pg 728

Campos, Ivan, Skjonberg Controls Inc, 1363 Donlon St, Suite 6, Ventura, CA 93003 *Tel:* 805-650-0877 *Fax:* 805-650-0360 *Toll Free Fax:* 800-650-0360 *E-mail:* sales@skjonberg.com *Web Site:* www.skjonberg.com, pg 890

Campus, Jordan, Campus Productions, 42 Oak Ave, Tuckahoe, NY 10707 *Tel:* 914-395-1010 *Fax:* 914-395-1095 *E-mail:* sales@campusgroup.com *Web Site:* www.campusgroup.com, pg 715

Campus, Steve, Audience Response Systems Inc, 5611-C E Morgan Ave, Evansville, IN 47715 *Tel:* 812-479-7507 *Toll Free Tel:* 800-INVOLVE (468-6583) *Fax:* 812-479-1057 *E-mail:* arsales@audienceresponse.com *Web Site:* www.audienceresponse.com, pg 693

Campus, Steven, Campus Productions, 42 Oak Ave, Tuckahoe, NY 10707 *Tel:* 914-395-1010 *Fax:* 914-395-1095 *E-mail:* sales@campusgroup.com *Web Site:* www.campusgroup.com, pg 715

Canavan, Michael, Canavan Scenic & Light LLC, 2440 Dinneen Ave, Orlando, FL 32804 *Tel:* 407-888-8002 *Web Site:* www.csandl.com, pg 716

Candee, Rees W, Candee Productions Inc, 301 W Deer Valley Rd, Suite 7, Phoenix, AZ 85027 *Tel:* 623-266-3070 *Web Site:* candeeproductionsinc.wordpress.com, pg 716

Cando, James C Jr, Take One Productions Ltd, 11010 Lake Grove Blvd, Suite 100-317, Morrisville, NC 27560, pg 906

Cando, Laura, Take One Productions Ltd, 11010 Lake Grove Blvd, Suite 100-317, Morrisville, NC 27560, pg 906

Cane, Gene, Set Decorators Society of America (SDSA), 7100 Tujunga Ave, Suite A, North Hollywood, CA 91605 *Tel:* 818-255-2425 *Fax:* 818-982-8597 *E-mail:* sdsa@setdecorators.org *Web Site:* www.setdecorators.org, pg 962

Canepa, Mark, DataDirect Networks, 9351 Deering Ave, Chatsworth, CA 91311 *Tel:* 818-700-4000 *Toll Free Tel:* 800-TERABYTE (837-2298) *E-mail:* info@ddn.com; sales@ddn.com *Web Site:* www.ddn.com, pg 738

Cannata, Richard, Cantrax Recorders, 2119 Fidler Ave, Long Beach, CA 90815 *Tel:* 562-498-6492 *E-mail:* cantrax@verizon.net, pg 716

Cannizzaro, Gerald North, Saturn Studios, PO Box 3687, Hollywood, CA 90078-3687 *Tel:* 323-871-4134 *Web Site:* rollingplanet.com, pg 881

Cannon, Elise, Publishers Group West (PGW), an Ingram brand, 1700 Fourth St, Berkeley, CA 94710 *Tel:* 510-809-3700 *Toll Free Tel:* 866-400-5351 (cust serv) *Fax:* 510-809-3777 *E-mail:* info@pgw.com *Web Site:* www.pgw.com, pg 866

Cannon, George Jr, Cannon Stage Lighting Inc, 7110 Ambassador Rd, Windsor Mill, MD 21244 *Tel:* 410-298-0636 *Fax:* 410-298-7950 *E-mail:* cannonstage@gmail.com *Web Site:* www.cannonstage.com, pg 716

Cantor, Eric, EMC Publishing LLC, 875 Montreal Way, St Paul, MN 55102 *Tel:* 651-290-2800 (corp) *Toll Free Tel:* 888-851-7094 *E-mail:* info@carnegielearning.com *Web Site:* www.emcp.com, pg 753

Cantor, Michael, World Media Group Inc, 7373 Dogwood Park, Richland Hills, TX 76118 *Toll Free Tel:* 800-400-4964 *Fax:* 817-885-8859 *E-mail:* getstarted@worldmediagroup.com; information@worldmediagroup.com *Web Site:* www.worldmediagroup.com, pg 941

Cantu, Diana, International Datacasting, 50 Frank Nighbor Place, Kanata, ON K2V 1B9, Canada *Tel:* 613-596-4120 *Fax:* 613-596-4863 *E-mail:* marketing@datacast.com *Web Site:* www.datacast.com, pg 790

Cantwell, Coleen, ETR, 100 Enterprise Way, Suite G 300, Scotts Valley, CA 95066 *Toll Free Tel:* 800-620-8884 *Fax:* 831-438-4284 *E-mail:* customerservice@etr.org, pg 756

Canuel, J F, AC Lighting Inc, 88 Horner Ave, Toronto, ON M8Z 5Y3, Canada *Tel:* 416-255-9494 *Fax:* 416-255-3514 *E-mail:* northamerica@aclighting.com *Web Site:* www.aclighting.com, pg 672

Capecelatro, Mindy, Monaco LLC, 145 Grassy Plain St, Bethel, CT 06801-2806 *Tel:* 203-744-3398 *Toll Free Tel:* 800-448-4877 *Fax:* 203-744-3228 *E-mail:* monaco@hangupbags.com *Web Site:* www.hangupbags.com, pg 829

Capella, Greg, National Audiovisual Center (NAC), 5301 Shawnee Rd, Alexandria, VA 22312 *E-mail:* info@ntis.gov; customerservice@ntis.gov *Web Site:* classic.ntis.gov/products/nac, pg 828

Caplan, Michael, KTHV-TV, 720 Izard St, Little Rock, AR 72201 *Tel:* 501-376-1111 *Fax:* 501-376-9928 (sales); 501-376-3324 (admin); 501-376-1645 (news) *Web Site:* www.thv11.com, pg 802

Caplan, Mike, Lion & Fox Recording Studios, 9517 Baltimore Ave, College Park, MD 20740 *Tel:* 301-982-4431 *E-mail:* mail@lionfox.com *Web Site:* www.lionfox.com, pg 809

Capodilupo, Larry III, ICL Imaging Inc, 51 Mellen St, Framingham, MA 01702 *Tel:* 508-872-3280 *Toll Free Tel:* 800-660-3280 *Fax:* 508-872-7364 *E-mail:* csr@icl-imaging.com *Web Site:* www.icl-imaging.com, pg 783

Carruthers, Trent, Artaflex Inc, 174 W Beaver Creek Rd, Richmond Hill, ON L4B 1B4, Canada *Tel:* 905-470-0109 *Toll Free Tel:* 866-502-3378 *Fax:* 905-470-0621 *E-mail:* sales@artaflex.com; general@artaflex.com *Web Site:* www.artaflex.com, pg 690

Carsen, Chris, Corel Corp, 1600 Carling Ave, Ottawa, ON K1Z 8R7, Canada *Toll Free Tel:* 877-582-6735 *Web Site:* www.corel.com, pg 731

Carson, Norm, Covid Inc, 1723 W Fourth St, Tempe, AZ 85281 *Tel:* 480-966-2221 *Toll Free Tel:* 800-638-6104 *Fax:* 480-966-6728 *E-mail:* sales@covid.com *Web Site:* www.covid.com, pg 732

Carson, Ryan, Covid Inc, 1723 W Fourth St, Tempe, AZ 85281 *Tel:* 480-966-2221 *Toll Free Tel:* 800-638-6104 *Fax:* 480-966-6728 *E-mail:* sales@covid.com *Web Site:* www.covid.com, pg 732

Carson, Thomas, TiVo Corp, 2 Circle Star Way, San Carlos, CA 94070 *Tel:* 408-562-8400 *Toll Free Tel:* 877-367-8486 (cust support); 877-289-8486 (sales support) *Fax:* 408-567-1800 *Web Site:* business.tivo.com; www.tivo.com, pg 914

Carter, Brian, Alliant Event Services, 196 University Pkwy, Pomona, CA 91768 *Tel:* 909-622-3306 *Toll Free Tel:* 800-851-5415 *Fax:* 909-622-3917 *E-mail:* marketing@alliantevents.com *Web Site:* www.alliantevents.com, pg 681

Carter, Clint, Christie Digital Systems USA Inc, 10550 Camden Dr, Cypress, CA 90630 *Tel:* 714-236-8610 *Toll Free Tel:* 866-880-4462 (cust serv) *Fax:* 714-503-3375 *E-mail:* sales-us@christiedigital.com; orders@christiedigital.com *Web Site:* www.christiedigital.com, pg 722

Carter, Gary, International Datacasting, 50 Frank Nighbor Place, Kanata, ON K2V 1B9, Canada *Tel:* 613-596-4120 *Fax:* 613-596-4863 *E-mail:* marketing@datacast.com *Web Site:* www.datacast.com, pg 790

Carter, Isaiah M, Big Fish Production US, PO Box 782, Bronx, NY 10462-0782 *Tel:* 347-526-5211 *E-mail:* bigfishproductionus@gmail.com *Web Site:* www.bigfishproductionus.com, pg 705

Carter, James, Big Fish Production US, PO Box 782, Bronx, NY 10462-0782 *Tel:* 347-526-5211 *E-mail:* bigfishproductionus@gmail.com *Web Site:* www.bigfishproductionus.com, pg 705

Carter, Jan, Sound*Light, 5438 Tennessee Ave, New Port Richey, FL 34652 *Tel:* 727-842-6788 *Fax:* 727-842-6788 *Web Site:* www.awakening-healing.com; www.soundlight.org, pg 894

Carter, Myles, Matrox Video Products Group, 1055 Saint Regis Blvd, Dorval, QC H9P 2T4, Canada *Tel:* 514-822-6000 *Toll Free Tel:* 800-361-4903 *Fax:* 514-685-2853 *Web Site:* www.matrox.com/video, pg 819

Carter, Todd, Sparrow Sound Design, 3501 N Southport, 2nd fl, Chicago, IL 60657-1435 *Tel:* 773-281-8510 *Fax:* 773-472-1632 *E-mail:* southport@chicagosound.com *Web Site:* www.chicagosound.com, pg 896

Carvalho, Sandra, Technicolor USA Inc, 6040 Sunset Blvd, Hollywood, CA 90028 *Tel:* 323-817-6600 *E-mail:* info@technicolor.com *Web Site:* www.technicolor.com, pg 908

Casalaina, Vincent, Image Integration, 2619 Benvenue Ave, No A, Berkeley, CA 94704 *Tel:* 510-504-2605 *Fax:* 510-841-8524, pg 785

Casale, Thomas, L-3 ESSCO, 90 Nemco Way, Ayer, MA 01432 *Tel:* 978-568-5100 *Fax:* 978-772-7555 *E-mail:* info.essco@l3t.com *Web Site:* www2.l3t.com/essco, pg 802

Casati, Gianfranco, Accenture, 161 N Clark St, Chicago, IL 60601 *Tel:* 312-693-0161 *Toll Free Tel:* 877-889-9009 *Fax:* 312-693-0507 *Web Site:* www.accenture.com, pg 672

Casciani, Angelo, Uniset LLC, 449 Avenue "A", Rochester, NY 14621 *Tel:* 585-544-3820 *Fax:* 585-544-1110 *E-mail:* info@unisetcorp.com *Web Site:* www.unisetcorp.com, pg 921

Cascone, Peter, 4-D Creative Media, 16 W 46 St, 12th fl, New York, NY 10036 *Tel:* 646-483-7768 *Web Site:* www.4-dcreative.com, pg 764

Case, David, Production Masters Inc (PMI), 204 Fifth Ave, Pittsburgh, PA 15222 *Tel:* 412-281-8500 *E-mail:* info@pmi.tv *Web Site:* pmi.tv, pg 864

Case, Shannon, Fred Rogers Productions, 2100 Wharton St, Suite 700, Pittsburgh, PA 15203 *Tel:* 412-687-2990 *Toll Free Tel:* 877-677-6437 *E-mail:* info@fredrogers.org *Web Site:* www.fredrogers.org, pg 876

Cashman, Judy, PrimaLux Video Inc, 30 W 26 St, 7th fl, New York, NY 10010 *Tel:* 212-206-1402 *Web Site:* www.primalux.com, pg 862

Cashmark, Daryn, EZ Scenic, 834 NW 1911 Rd, Lone Jack, MO 64070 *Tel:* 816-861-4200 *Web Site:* www.ezscenic.com, pg 758

Casinghino, Bob, Fresh Music Library, 320 South St, Agawam, MA 01001 *Toll Free Tel:* 888-211-8576 *Web Site:* www.freshmusic.com, pg 766

Caspari, W B, Synergistic Batteries Inc, 5975 Providence Lane, Cumming, GA 30040 *Tel:* 770-886-6621 *Toll Free Tel:* 800-634-6000 *E-mail:* sbicheri@synbat.com *Web Site:* www.synergisticbatteries.com, pg 906

Cass, Brian, Sounds Interesting Studio, 112 Fuller St, Middleboro, MA 02346 *Tel:* 508-947-7387 *Web Site:* www.soundsinterestingstudio.com, pg 895

Cassin, Dan, Centaur Records Inc, 136 Saint Joseph St, Baton Rouge, LA 70802 *Tel:* 225-336-4877 *Fax:* 225-336-9678 *E-mail:* info@centaurrecords.com *Web Site:* www.centaurrecords.com, pg 719

Cassini, Hector, New Orleans Film Festival, 1215 Prytania St, Suite 423, New Orleans, LA 70130 *Tel:* 504-309-6633 *E-mail:* noff@neworleansfilmsociety.org *Web Site:* neworleansfilmsociety.org/festival, pg 997

Casso, Alan, Revels Records, 80 Mount Auburn St, Watertown, MA 02472 *Tel:* 617-972-8300 *Fax:* 617-972-8400 *E-mail:* info@revels.org *Web Site:* www.revels.org, pg 874

Castellano, Annie, ITC, 523 Hanley Industrial Ct, St Louis, MO 63144 *Tel:* 314-646-1800 *Toll Free Tel:* 800-962-2344 *Fax:* 314-646-1818 *Web Site:* www.itcjourneys.com, pg 791

Castellon, Joe, KAS Music & Sound, 34-12 36 St, Astoria, NY 11106 *Tel:* 718-786-3400 *Fax:* 718-729-3007 *Web Site:* www.kasmusic.com, pg 796

Castillo, David, Blue Barn Pictures Inc, 68 Jay St, Suite 311, Brooklyn, NY 11201 *Web Site:* www.bluebarnpictures.com, pg 707

Castillo, Derek, Castleview Productions, 1100 W 41 St, Austin, TX 78756 *Tel:* 512-442-9944 *Fax:* 512-442-8823 *E-mail:* contact@castleviewproductions.com *Web Site:* castleviewproductions.com, pg 717

Castillo, Sofia, Association of American Publishers (AAP), 455 Massachusetts Ave NW, Suite 700, Washington, DC 20001-2777 *Tel:* 202-347-3375 *Fax:* 202-347-3690 *E-mail:* info@publishers.org *Web Site:* publishers.org, pg 951

Castillo, Virge, Midtown Video Inc, 4824 SW 74 Ct, Miami, FL 33155 *Tel:* 305-669-1117 *Fax:* 305-662-2860 *E-mail:* info@midtownvideo.com *Web Site:* midtownvideo.com, pg 827

Castles, Dan, Telestream Inc, 848 Gold Flat Rd, Nevada City, CA 95959 *Tel:* 530-470-1300 *Toll Free Tel:* 877-257-6245 *Fax:* 530-470-1301 *E-mail:* info@telestream.net *Web Site:* www.telestream.net, pg 910

Castronovo, Joseph, Korg USA Inc, 316 S Service Rd, Melville, NY 11747 *Tel:* 631-390-6500; 631-390-6800 (cust serv) *E-mail:* sales@korgusa.com; customerservice@korgusa.com *Web Site:* www.korgusa.com, pg 801

Catalanotte, Peter, Film Tucson, 100 S Church Ave, Tucson, AZ 85701 *Tel:* 520-770-2151 *Fax:* 520-629-0160 *Web Site:* www.filmtucson.com, pg 965

Cataldi, Jason, Upstage Video, 201 Rock Lititz Blvd, Suite 20, Lititz, PA 17543 *Tel:* 717-240-2400 *Toll Free Tel:* 877-484-3887 *E-mail:* info@upstagevideo.com *Web Site:* www.upstagevideo.com, pg 923

Cataldo, Joyce, Hollywood Professional Association (HPA), 2501 W Burbank Blvd, No 207, Burbank, CA 91505 *Tel:* 818-273-1482 *Web Site:* hpaonline.com, pg 955

Catron, Kathryn, St Augustine, Ponte Vedra & The Beaches Visitors and Convention Bureau, 29 Old Mission Ave, St Augustine, FL 32084 *Tel:* 904-829-1711 *Toll Free Tel:* 800-653-2489 *Web Site:* www.floridashistoriccoast.com, pg 970

Caulo, Andy, Edgenuity Inc, 8860 E Chaparral Rd, Scottsdale, AZ 85250 *Toll Free Tel:* 877-725-4257 (sales) *E-mail:* customersupport@edgenuity.com; solutions@edgenuity.com (sales) *Web Site:* www.edgenuity.com, pg 750

Cavallaro, Mary, Screen Actors Guild - American Federation of Television & Radio Artists (SAG-AFTRA), 5757 Wilshire Blvd, 7th fl, Los Angeles, CA 90036-3600 *Tel:* 323-954-1600 (former SAG); 323-634-8100 (former AFTRA) *Toll Free Tel:* 855-SAG-AFTRA (724-2387) *Fax:* 323-549-6654 (communs & mktg) *E-mail:* info@sagaftra.org *Web Site:* www.sagaftra.org, pg 961

Cavanaugh, Chris, Freeman, 1600 Viceroy, Suite 100, Dallas, TX 75235 *Tel:* 214-445-1000 *Web Site:* www.freeman.com, pg 765

Cavanaugh, Dean, Moog Music Inc, 160 Broadway St, Asheville, NC 28801 *Tel:* 828-251-0090 *Toll Free Tel:* 800-948-1990 *Fax:* 828-254-6233 *E-mail:* info@moogmusic.com *Web Site:* www.moogmusic.com, pg 830

Cegielski, Craig, FremantleMedia North America, 2900 W Alameda Ave, Suite 800, Burbank, CA 91505 *Tel:* 818-748-1100 *Web Site:* www.fremantlemedia.com, pg 765

Celestina, Becky, Macmillan Audio, 120 Broadway, 22nd fl, New York, NY 10271 *Tel:* 646-600-7856; 646-307-5472 *Toll Free Tel:* 888-330-8477 (cust serv); 800-221-7945 *Toll Free Fax:* 800-672-7703 (orders) *E-mail:* macmillan.audio@macmillanusa.com *Web Site:* www.macmillanaudio.com, pg 814

Centkowski, Mark, Innovision Optics, 1834 Broadway, Santa Monica, CA 90404 *Tel:* 310-453-4866 *Fax:* 310-453-4677 *Web Site:* www.innovision-optics.com, pg 788

Cerasoli, Chris, Videosmith Inc, 200 Spring Garden St, Suite C, Philadelphia, PA 19123 *Tel:* 215-238-5070 *Fax:* 215-238-5075 *E-mail:* info@videosmith.com *Web Site:* videosmith.com, pg 930

Cerilli, Steve, Sound-FX-Design, PO Box 3541, Newport, RI 02840 *Tel:* 401-952-1186 *E-mail:* info@sound-fx-design.com *Web Site:* www.sound-fx-design.com, pg 894

Cerminara, D Kyle, Ballantyne Strong Inc, 11422 Miracle Hills Dr, Suite 300, Omaha, NE 68154 *Tel:* 402-453-4444 *Toll Free Tel:* 800-424-1215; 800-722-0046 *E-mail:* customerservice@btn-inc.com *Web Site:* ballantynestrong.com, pg 701

Cerullo, Al, Hover-Views Unlimited, PO Box 1164, Syosset, NY 11791 *Tel:* 516-496-2946 *Fax:* 516-496-8029 *Web Site:* www.hoverviews.com, pg 782

Cerutti, Marc, Cerutti Productions Inc, 18211 Bulverde Rd, Suite 10202, San Antonio, TX 78259-3625 *Tel:* 210-403-0800 *Web Site:* www.cerutti.org, pg 720

Cetrulo, Marc E, The Hollaender Manufacturing Co, 10285 Wayne Ave, Cincinnati, OH 45215 *Tel:* 513-772-8800 *Toll Free Tel:* 800-772-8800 (orders) *Fax:* 513-772-8806 *Web Site:* www.hollaender.com, pg 780

Chaffee, Hal, Technical Exhibits Corp, 6155 S Oak Park Ave, Chicago, IL 60638 *Tel:* 773-586-3377 *Fax:* 773-586-6575 *Web Site:* www.technicalexhibits.net, pg 908

Chain, Herve F, Omni Intercommunications Inc, 2825 Wilcrest Dr, Suite 400, Houston, TX 77042 *Tel:* 713-781-2188 *Toll Free Tel:* 800-777-2304 *Fax:* 713-781-2315 *E-mail:* info@omni-inter.com *Web Site:* www.omni-inter.com, pg 845

Chaisson, Anne, The Hamptons International Film Festival, 47 Newtown Lane, East Hampton, NY 11937 Tel: 631-324-4600 Fax: 631-324-1558 E-mail: info@hamptonsfilmfest.org; programming@hamptonsfilmfest.org (submissions) Web Site: hamptonsfilmfest.org, pg 991

Chalk, Richard, TopCat Records LLC, PO Box 670234, Dallas, TX 75367-0234 Tel: 972-484-4141 Fax: 972-620-8333 E-mail: info@topcatrecords.com Web Site: www.topcatrecords.com, pg 915

Challacombe, Causby, NAMM, the National Association of Music Merchants, 5790 Armada Dr, Carlsbad, CA 92008 Tel: 760-438-8001 Toll Free Tel: 800-767-6266 (memb hotline) Fax: 760-438-7327 E-mail: info@namm.org Web Site: www.namm.org, pg 958

Challender, Gary, Books In Motion, 9922 E Montgomery Dr, Suite 31, Spokane Valley, WA 99206 Tel: 509-922-1646 Toll Free Tel: 800-752-3199 Fax: 509-922-1445 E-mail: sales@booksinmotion.com Web Site: www.booksinmotion.com, pg 708

Chamberlan, Claude, Festival du Nouveau Cinema de Montreal, 3805 Blvd Saint-Laurent, Montreal, QC H2W 1X9, Canada Tel: 514-282-0004 Fax: 514-282-6664 E-mail: info@nouveaucinema.ca; soumissions@nouveaucinema.ca Web Site: www.nouveaucinema.ca, pg 989

Chamberlin, Amy Beth, Warner Home Video Inc, 4000 Warner Blvd, Bldg 160, Burbank, CA 91522 Tel: 818-954-6000 Fax: 818-954-6480 Web Site: www.warnerbros.com, pg 934

Chambers, Dave, Apogee Sound International LLC, 1200 MacArthur Blvd, Suite 304, Mahwah, NJ 07430-2331 Toll Free Tel: 800-443-3979 Toll Free Fax: 800-999-9016 E-mail: info@apogee-sound.com Web Site: www.apogee-sound.com, pg 687

Chambers, Kit, New Wave Entertainment, 2660 W Olive Ave, Burbank, CA 91505 Tel: 818-295-5000 E-mail: biz@nwe.com Web Site: nwe.com, pg 840

Champ, D Zachary, WIA - The Wireless Infrastructure Association, 2111 Wilson Blvd, Suite 210, Arlington, VA 22201 Tel: 703-739-0300 Toll Free Tel: 800-759-0300 Fax: 703-836-1608 Web Site: wia.org, pg 963

Champagne, Jean, Applied Voice & Speech Technologies Inc (AVST), 27042 Towne Centre Dr, Suite 200, Foothill Ranch, CA 92610-2810 Tel: 949-699-2300 Toll Free Tel: 866-368-0400 Fax: 949-699-2301 E-mail: info@avst.com; sales@avst.com Web Site: www.avst.com, pg 688

Champagne, Robin, Communications Concepts Inc (CCI), 7980 N Atlantic Ave, Suite 101, Cape Canaveral, FL 32920 Tel: 321-783-5232 Web Site: cci321.com, pg 729

Chan, Dr Amiee, Norsat International Inc, 110-4020 Viking Way, Richmond, BC V6V 2L4, Canada Tel: 604-821-2800 Toll Free Tel: 800-644-4562 E-mail: support@norsat.com Web Site: www.norsat.com, pg 842

Chan, David, The Mobius® Awards, 713 S Pacific Coast Hwy, Suite A, Redondo Beach, CA 90277-4233 Tel: 310-540-0959 Fax: 310-316-8905 E-mail: mobiusinfo@mobiusawards.com; mediarelations@mobiusawards.com Web Site: mobiusawards.com, pg 996

Chan, David, US International Film & Video Festival, 713 S Pacific Coast Hwy, Suite A, Redondo Beach, CA 90277-4233 Tel: 310-540-0959 Fax: 310-316-8905 E-mail: filmfestinfo@filmfestawards.com; mediarelations@filmfestawards.com Web Site: www.filmfestawards.com, pg 1005

Chan, Kenneth, National Religious Broadcasters (NRB), 600 N Capitol St NW, Suite 210, Washington, DC 20001 Tel: 202-543-0073 Fax: 202-543-2649 E-mail: info@nrb.org; press@nrb.org Web Site: nrb.org, pg 959

Chan, Louanne, Toronto Reel Asian International Film Festival, 401 Richmond St W, Suite 309, Toronto, ON M5V 3A8, Canada Tel: 416-703-9333 Fax: 416-703-9986 E-mail: info@reelasian.com; programming@reelasian.com Web Site: www.reelasian.com, pg 1005

Chan, Tom, Tecplot Inc, 3535 Factoria Blvd SE, Suite 550, Bellevue, WA 98006 Tel: 425-653-1200; 425-653-9393 (tech support) Toll Free Tel: 800-763-7005 (orders) E-mail: info@tecplot.com; support@tecplot.com Web Site: www.tecplot.com, pg 909

Chandler, David, Kangaroo Cases, 4027 Main St, Dallas, TX 75226 Tel: 214-823-5264 Toll Free Tel: 800-890-1073 Fax: 214-824-1179 E-mail: info@kangaroocases.com Web Site: www.kangaroocases.com, pg 796

Chang, Pearl, ASC-Tube Trap, 4275 W Fifth Ave, Eugene, OR 97402 Tel: 541-343-9727 Toll Free Tel: 800-272-8823 Fax: 541-343-9245 E-mail: info@acousticsciences.com Web Site: www.acousticsciences.com, pg 690

Chang, Sung, MRM//McCANN, 622 Third Ave, New York, NY 10017 Tel: 646-865-6230 E-mail: gbc@mrm-mccann.com Web Site: www.mrm-mccann.com, pg 832

Channell, Bill, Channell One Video, PO Box 399, Epping, NH 03042-0399 Tel: 603-679-6796 E-mail: racevid@earthlink.net, pg 720

Channell, Kathleen, Channell One Video, PO Box 399, Epping, NH 03042-0399 Tel: 603-679-6796 E-mail: racevid@earthlink.net, pg 720

Chanti, Marc, Metromotion Productions LLC, 450 W 31 St, 8th fl, New York, NY 10001 Tel: 212-967-2000 Fax: 212-967-1988 E-mail: info@metromotion.com; pr@metromotion.com Web Site: www.metromotion.com, pg 824

Chao, Cindy, Audio Network US Inc, 48 W 25 St, 10th fl, New York, NY 10010 Tel: 646-688-4320 E-mail: nyoffice@audionetwork.com Web Site: us.audionetwork.com, pg 693

Chapa, Raquel, Dallas VideoFest Alternative Fiction, 1405 Woodlawn Ave, Dallas, TX 75208 Tel: 214-207-7696 E-mail: info@videofest.org Web Site: www.videofest.org, pg 987

Chapa, Raquel, Dallas VideoFest DocuFest, 1405 Woodlawn Ave, Dallas, TX 75208 Tel: 214-207-7696 E-mail: info@videofest.org Web Site: www.videofest.org, pg 987

Chaplin, Carol, Lake Tahoe Visitors Authority (LTVA), 169 Hwy 50, Stateline, NV 89449 Tel: 775-588-5900 Toll Free Tel: 800-288-2463 (reservations) Fax: 775-588-1941 E-mail: info@ltva.org Web Site: ltva.org, pg 973

Chapman, Amy, AIGA, the professional association for design, 233 Broadway, Suite 1740, New York, NY 10279 Tel: 212-807-1990 Toll Free Tel: 800-548-1634 E-mail: general@aiga.org Web Site: www.aiga.org, pg 947

Chapman, Michael, Chapman/Leonard Studio Equipment Inc, 12950 Raymer St, North Hollywood, CA 91605 Tel: 818-764-6726 Toll Free Tel: 888-883-6559 Fax: 818-764-6730 E-mail: marketing@chapman-leonard.com Web Site: www.chapman-leonard.com, pg 720

Chapman, Robert, The Audio Department Inc, 324 Mills Place, Wycloff, NJ 07481 Tel: 212-586-3503 Fax: 212-245-1675 E-mail: scheduling@theaudiodepartment.com Web Site: www.theaudiodepartment.com, pg 693

Chapman-Huenergardt, Christine, Chapman/Leonard Studio Equipment Inc, 12950 Raymer St, North Hollywood, CA 91605 Tel: 818-764-6726 Toll Free Tel: 888-883-6559 Fax: 818-764-6730 E-mail: marketing@chapman-leonard.com Web Site: www.chapman-leonard.com, pg 720

Chapnick, Benjamin J, Black Star Publishing Co Inc, 333 Mamaroneck Ave, No 175, White Plains, NY 10605 Tel: 212-679-3288 Fax: 212-889-2052 Web Site: www.blackstar.com, pg 706

Chapnick, John P, Black Star Publishing Co Inc, 333 Mamaroneck Ave, No 175, White Plains, NY 10605 Tel: 212-679-3288 Fax: 212-889-2052 Web Site: www.blackstar.com, pg 706

Charak, Wendy, Switchcraft® Inc, 5555 N Elston Ave, Chicago, IL 60630 Tel: 773-792-2700 Fax: 773-792-2129 E-mail: sales@switchcraft.com Web Site: www.switchcraft.com, pg 905

Charback, Ann, JMC Photo & Digital Services Inc, 10 Westport Ct, Bloomington, IL 61704-8233 Tel: 309-663-4677 E-mail: jmcpds@jmcpds.com Web Site: www.jmcpds.com, pg 794

Charity, Mia, Close Up Foundation, 1330 Braddock Place, Suite 400, Alexandria, VA 22314 Tel: 703-706-3300 Toll Free Tel: 800-CLOSEUP (256-7387) E-mail: info@closeup.org Web Site: www.closeup.org, pg 726

Charlebois, Rob, Corel Corp, 1600 Carling Ave, Ottawa, ON K1Z 8R7, Canada Toll Free Tel: 877-582-6735 Web Site: www.corel.com, pg 731

Charles, Vignetta, ETR, 100 Enterprise Way, Suite G 300, Scotts Valley, CA 95066 Toll Free Tel: 800-620-8884 Fax: 831-438-4284 E-mail: customerservice@etr.org, pg 756

Charney, Nicolas H PhD, Videofashion Network, 611 Broadway, Suite 307, New York, NY 10012 Tel: 212-274-1600 Fax: 212-219-1969 E-mail: info@videofashion.com; licensing@videofashion.com Web Site: videofashion.com, pg 929

Chase, Jane, KVAL, 4575 Blanton Rd, Eugene, OR 97405 Tel: 541-342-4961 Fax: 541-342-2635 E-mail: kvalnews@kval.com Web Site: kval.com, pg 802

Chater, John, Chater Camera Inc, 1336 Ninth St, Berkeley, CA 94710 Tel: 510-525-5400 Fax: 510-295-2478 E-mail: rentals@chatercamera.com Web Site: www.chatercamera.com, pg 721

Chatfield-Taylor, Constance, Flying Colors Broadcasts, 2000 "M" St NW, Suite 345, Washington, DC 20036 Tel: 202-293-5300 E-mail: info@fc-tv.com Web Site: www.fc-tv.com, pg 763

Chatt, Howard, Pignose-Gorilla, 570 W Cheyenne Ave, Suite 80, North Las Vegas, NV 89030 Tel: 702-648-2444 Toll Free Tel: 800-9-PIGNOSE (974-4667) Fax: 702-648-2440 E-mail: sales@pignoseamps.com Web Site: www.pignoseamps.com, pg 857

Chau, Dan, Palace Productions MediaVision, 29 N Main St, Norwalk, CT 06854 Tel: 203-523-0602; 203-523-0604 Web Site: cpbn.org/palace-productions-media-vision, pg 850

Chaudhari, Jimshade, Marketron Broadcast Solutions, 101 Empty Saddle Trail, Hailey, ID 83333 Tel: 208-788-6800 Toll Free Tel: 800-476-7226 Fax: 208-788-6273 E-mail: sales@marketron.com Web Site: www.marketron.com, pg 817

Chavarria, Susan, Flying Colors Broadcasts, 2000 "M" St NW, Suite 345, Washington, DC 20036 Tel: 202-293-5300 E-mail: info@fc-tv.com Web Site: www.fc-tv.com, pg 763

Cheek, Doug, RingSide Creative, 13320 Northend, Suite 3000, Oak Park, MI 48237 Tel: 248-548-2500 E-mail: info@ringsidecreative.com; newbiz@ringsidecreative.com Web Site: www.ringsidecreative.com, pg 875

Cheh, Jennifer, NEC Display Solutions of America, 500 Park Blvd, Suite 1100, Itasca, IL 60143 Tel: 630-467-3000 Web Site: www.necdisplay.com, pg 837

Chehade, Noura, Promax, 5700 Wilshire Blvd, Suite 275, Los Angeles, CA 90036 Tel: 310-788-7600 Fax: 310-788-7616 Web Site: www.promax.org, pg 961

Chelew, Richard, Oral Tradition Sound & Music, PO Box 51155, Pacific Grove, CA 93950-6155 Tel: 831-372-0352 Toll Free Tel: 800-779-1116 (orders), pg 847

Chen, Cecille, Smithsonian Folkways Recordings, 600 Maryland Ave SW, Suite 2001, Washington, DC 20024 Tel: 202-633-6450 Toll Free Tel: 888-FOLKWAYS (365-5929) Fax: 202-633-6477 E-mail: smithsonianfolkways@si.edu Web Site: folkways.si.edu, pg 891

Chen, David, Keng Seng Enterprises Inc, 4000 Rue St Ambroise, Suite 103, Montreal, QC H4C 2C7, Canada Tel: 514-939-3971 E-mail: canada@kengseng.com Web Site: www.kengseng.com, pg 797

Chen, David W, RGB Technology Inc, 590 Herndon Pkwy, Suite 500, Herndon, VA 20170-5267 *Tel:* 703-834-1500 *Fax:* 703-834-1506 *E-mail:* solutions@rgbtec.com *Web Site:* www.rgbtec.com, pg 874

Chen, Ms Fang, United Nations Department of Public Information-News & Media Division, 405 E 42 St, Rm IN-913B, New York, NY 10017 *Tel:* 917-367-5007 *E-mail:* mediapartners@un.org *Web Site:* www.un.org, pg 921

Chen, James C, Audio Images Corp, 701 Bryant St, 2nd fl, San Francisco, CA 94107 *Tel:* 415-957-9131 *Fax:* 415-957-1531 *Web Site:* www.facebook.com/Audio-Images-Corporation-262409103085/, pg 693

Chen, Jennifer H, AITech International, 1973 O'Toole Way, San Jose, CA 95131 *Tel:* 408-991-9699 *Fax:* 408-991-9691 *E-mail:* sales@aitech.com *Web Site:* www.aitech.com, pg 679

Chen, Dr Michael J, AITech International, 1973 O'Toole Way, San Jose, CA 95131 *Tel:* 408-991-9699 *Fax:* 408-991-9691 *E-mail:* sales@aitech.com *Web Site:* www.aitech.com, pg 679

Cheney, Bill, Spectra Sonics LLC, 860 W Riverdale Rd, Suite D-6, Riverdale, UT 84405 *Tel:* 801-593-9813 (repair) *E-mail:* info@spectra-sonics.com *Web Site:* spectra-sonics.squarespace.com, pg 897

Cheng, Charles, Keng Seng Enterprises Inc, 4000 Rue St Ambroise, Suite 103, Montreal, QC H4C 2C7, Canada *Tel:* 514-939-3971 *E-mail:* canada@kengseng.com *Web Site:* www.kengseng.com, pg 797

Cheng, Jill, Cheng & Tsui Co, 25 West St, 2nd fl, Boston, MA 02111-1213 *Tel:* 617-988-2400 *Toll Free Tel:* 800-554-1963 (orders) *Fax:* 617-426-3669 *E-mail:* orders@cheng-tsui.com *Web Site:* www.cheng-tsui.com, pg 721

Cheremsak, Nick, ToCad America Inc, 53 Green Pond Rd, Suite 5, Rockaway, NJ 07866 *Tel:* 973-627-9600 *Toll Free Tel:* 800-886-2236 *Fax:* 973-664-2438 *E-mail:* info@tocad.com *Web Site:* www.tocad.com, pg 915

Cherin, Lotte, Rhythms Productions (Tom Thumb Music), PO Box 786, Malibu, CA 90265-0786 *Tel:* 310-836-4678 *E-mail:* tomthumbkids@gmail.com *Web Site:* www.tomthumbkids.com, pg 874

Cherkassakah, Max, Palardo Productions, 1807 Taft Ave, Suite 4, Hollywood, CA 90028 *Tel:* 323-469-8991 *E-mail:* palardo2@msn.com, pg 850

Chernick, Rick, Camera Corner Connecting Point, PO Box 248, Green Bay, WI 54305-0248 *Tel:* 920-435-5353 *Toll Free Tel:* 800-236-4950 (orders) *Fax:* 920-438-0389 *E-mail:* salessupport@cccp.com; contactus@cccp.com *Web Site:* www.cccp.com, pg 715

Cherrington, Nathan, Oregon Film & Video Office, 123 NE Third Ave, Suite 210, Portland, OR 97232 *Tel:* 971-254-4020 *E-mail:* shoot@oregonfilm.org *Web Site:* www.oregonfilm.org, pg 975

Cherry, Lee, Cherry Multimedia, 2129 Colorado Blvd, Los Angeles, CA 90041 *Toll Free Tel:* 800-378-7598 *E-mail:* info@cherrymultimedia.com *Web Site:* cherrymultimedia.com, pg 721

Cherryholmes, Diana, Suffolk County Film Commission, H Lee Dennison Bldg, 11th fl, 100 Veterans Memorial Hwy, Hauppauge, NY 11788 *Tel:* 631-853-4800 *Fax:* 631-853-4767 *Web Site:* www.suffolkcountyfilmcommission.com, pg 974

Cherubini, Vic, Epic Software Group Inc, 701 Sawdust Rd, The Woodlands, TX 77380 *Tel:* 281-363-3742 *E-mail:* epic@epicsoftware.com *Web Site:* www.epicsoftware.com, pg 755

Cherwek, Mark, Prior Scientific Inc, 80 Reservoir Park Dr, Rockland, MA 02370 *Tel:* 781-878-8442 *Toll Free Tel:* 800-877-2234 *Fax:* 781-878-8736 *E-mail:* info@prior.com; techsupportus@prior.com *Web Site:* www.prior.com, pg 862

Chesky, Norman, Manhattan Production Music Inc, 1650 Broadway, Suite 900, New York, NY 10019 *Tel:* 212-333-5766 *Fax:* 212-262-0814 *E-mail:* info@mpmmusic.com *Web Site:* www.mpmmusic.com, pg 816

Chesney, Chad, National Instruments Corp, 11500 N Mopac Expwy, Austin, TX 78759-3504 *Tel:* 512-683-0100 *Toll Free Tel:* 888-280-7645 (sales); 877-388-1952 *Fax:* 512-683-8411; 512-683-5794 (sales) *Web Site:* www.ni.com, pg 836

Chessler, Abbie, Quatrefoil Associates Inc, 29 "C" St, Laurel, MD 20707 *Tel:* 301-470-4748 *Fax:* 301-470-4749 *E-mail:* info@quatrefoil.com *Web Site:* www.quatrefoil.com, pg 868

Chetanananda, Swami, Vedanta Society of St Louis, 205 S Skinker Blvd, St Louis, MO 63105 *Tel:* 314-721-5118 *Web Site:* vedantastl.org, pg 925

Cheung, Isaac, New Cyberian Systems Inc, 1919 O'Toole Way, San Jose, CA 95131 *Tel:* 408-922-0682 *Toll Free Tel:* 877-423-4383 *Fax:* 408-884-2257 *E-mail:* sales@newcyberian.com *Web Site:* www.newcyberian.com, pg 839

Cheung, Martina, S&P Global Marketing Intelligence, 55 Water St, New York, NY 10041 *Toll Free Tel:* 877-863-1306 *E-mail:* questions@spcapitaliq.com *Web Site:* marketingintelligence.spglobal.com, pg 880

Chew, Albert, Freeman, 1600 Viceroy, Suite 100, Dallas, TX 75235 *Tel:* 214-445-1000 *Web Site:* www.freeman.com, pg 765

Chew, Chee Guan, Covid Inc, 1723 W Fourth St, Tempe, AZ 85281 *Tel:* 480-966-2221 *Toll Free Tel:* 800-638-6104 *Fax:* 480-966-6728 *E-mail:* sales@covid.com *Web Site:* www.covid.com, pg 732

Chew, Lewis, Dolby Laboratories Inc, 1275 Market St, San Francisco, CA 94103-1410 *Tel:* 415-558-0200 *Fax:* 415-645-4000 *Web Site:* www.dolby.com, pg 745

Chhun, Pory, RAM® Mounts, 8410 Dallas Ave S, Seattle, WA 98108 *Tel:* 206-763-8361 *Toll Free Tel:* 800-497-7479 *Fax:* 206-762-9615 *E-mail:* sales@rammount.com *Web Site:* www.rammount.com, pg 870

Chicas, Ivett, Associated Press Television News, 200 Liberty St, New York, NY 10281 *Tel:* 212-621-1500 *Fax:* 212-621-7419 *E-mail:* info@ap.org *Web Site:* www.aptn.com, pg 691

Childers, Betsy, High End Systems Inc, 2105 Gracy Farms Lane, Austin, TX 78758 *Tel:* 512-836-2242 *Toll Free Tel:* 800-890-8989 *Web Site:* www.highend.com, pg 779

Childress, Erik, Chicago Film Critics Association, 155 E Algonquin Rd, Arlington Heights, IL 60006 *Tel:* 847-427-4530 *Fax:* 847-427-1301 *Web Site:* www.chicagofilmcritics.org, pg 953

Chilvers, Richard, Wireworks Corp, 380 Hillside Ave, Hillside, NJ 07205 *Tel:* 908-686-7400 *Toll Free Tel:* 800-642-9473 *Fax:* 908-686-0483 (sales); 908-686-0680 *E-mail:* sales@wireworks.com; info@wireworks.com *Web Site:* www.wireworks.com, pg 940

Chin, Arthur, Norsat International Inc, 110-4020 Viking Way, Richmond, BC V6V 2L4, Canada *Tel:* 604-821-2800 *Toll Free Tel:* 800-644-4562 *E-mail:* support@norsat.com *Web Site:* www.norsat.com, pg 842

Chin, Chris, Toronto Reel Asian International Film Festival, 401 Richmond St W, Suite 309, Toronto, ON M5V 3A8, Canada *Tel:* 416-703-9333 *Fax:* 416-703-9986 *E-mail:* info@reelasian.com; programming@reelasian.com *Web Site:* www.reelasian.com, pg 1005

Chin, Edward, Wisconsin Technical College System Foundation Inc, 6602 Normandy Lane, Madison, WI 53719-1081 *Tel:* 608-841-1800 *Toll Free Tel:* 800-821-6313 *Fax:* 608-841-1806 *E-mail:* foundation@wtcsf.tec.wi.us *Web Site:* www.wtcsf.tec.wi.us, pg 940

Chinn, Mike, S&P Global Marketing Intelligence, 55 Water St, New York, NY 10041 *Toll Free Tel:* 877-863-1306 *E-mail:* questions@spcapitaliq.com *Web Site:* marketingintelligence.spglobal.com, pg 880

Chionetti, Alex, Buffalo Niagara International Film Festival (BNIFF), 3840 E Robinson Rd, Suite 166, Amherst, NY 14228 *Tel:* 716-693-0912 *E-mail:* info@bniff.com *Web Site:* thebnff.com, pg 984

Chirico, Jim, Avaya Inc, 4655 Great American Pkwy, Santa Clara, CA 95054 *Tel:* 908-953-6000 *Toll Free Tel:* 866-GO-AVAYA (462-8292 US & CN) *Web Site:* www.avaya.com, pg 697

Chirum, Bob, Video Copy Services Inc, 3980 Dekalb Technology Pkwy, Suite 670, Atlanta, GA 30340 *Tel:* 404-321-6933 *Toll Free Tel:* 800-553-3616 *E-mail:* info@video-copy.com *Web Site:* www.video-copy.com, pg 927

Chisolm, Richard, Richard Chisolm Cinematography, 311 Somerset Rd, Baltimore, MD 21210 *Tel:* 410-340-5308 *E-mail:* chisolmcamera@gmail.com *Web Site:* www.richardchisolm.com, pg 722

Choi, Esther, Promax, 5700 Wilshire Blvd, Suite 275, Los Angeles, CA 90036 *Tel:* 310-788-7600 *Fax:* 310-788-7616 *Web Site:* www.promax.org, pg 961

Chong, Kelly, Pro Camera Repair, 8250 Vickers Ave, San Diego, CA 92111 *Tel:* 858-277-3700 *E-mail:* info@procamerarepair.com *Web Site:* www.procamerarepair.com, pg 862

Chong, Larry, Westcoast Video Productions Inc, 14141 Covello St, Suite 9-A, Van Nuys, CA 91405 *Tel:* 818-785-8033 *Web Site:* www.wvpinc.com, pg 936

Choos, Samantha, Havana Film Festival New York (HFFNY), 4 W 43 St, Suite 304, New York, NY 10036 *Tel:* 212-687-2146 *Fax:* 212-681-8037 *E-mail:* info@hffny.com; info@aflfc.org; press@hffny.com *Web Site:* www.hffny.com, pg 991

Chouinard, Bob, Big Event Productions LLC, 77 13 Ave NE, Studio 101, Minneapolis, MN 55413 *Tel:* 612-623-7800 *Web Site:* www.bigeventpros.com, pg 705

Christ, Peter, Crystal Records Inc, 28818 NE Hancock Rd, Camas, WA 98607 *Tel:* 360-834-7022 *Fax:* 360-834-9680 *E-mail:* info@crystalrecords.com *Web Site:* www.crystalrecords.com, pg 735

Christensen, Paul A, Omega Productions, 456 Commerce St, Palacios, TX 77465 *Tel:* 214-891-9585 *E-mail:* getinfo@omegalive.com *Web Site:* www.omegalive.com, pg 845

Christian, Gavin, Hollywood Lights Inc, 5251 SE McLoughlin Blvd, Portland, OR 97202-4836 *Tel:* 503-232-9001; 503-232-8855 *Toll Free Tel:* 800-826-9881 *Fax:* 503-517-8686 *E-mail:* portland@hollywoodlights.biz *Web Site:* www.hollywoodlights.biz, pg 780

Christian, Valentine, Micor Analytics, 7538 Saint Louis Ave, Skokie, IL 60076 *Tel:* 847-329-8590 *Fax:* 847-329-8599 *Web Site:* www.micoranalytics.com, pg 825

Christiansen, Steve, InterVision Media, 44 W Broadway, Suite 426, Eugene, OR 97401 *Tel:* 541-343-7993; 547-345-5951 *E-mail:* info@intervisionmedia.com *Web Site:* www.intervisionmedia.com, pg 791

Christie, Aimee, The Audio Department Inc, 324 Mills Place, Wycloff, NJ 07481 *Tel:* 212-586-3503 *Fax:* 212-245-1675 *E-mail:* scheduling@theaudiodepartment.com *Web Site:* www.theaudiodepartment.com, pg 693

Christie, Anthony, Level 3 Communications Inc, 1025 Eldorado Blvd, Broomfield, CO 80021 *Tel:* 720-888-1000 *Toll Free Tel:* 877-2LEVEL3 (253-8357) *Web Site:* www.level3.com, pg 806

Christie, Huntly, Christie Lites, 6990 Lake Ellenor Dr, Orlando, FL 32809 *Tel:* 407-856-0016 *Fax:* 407-856-0765 *Web Site:* www.christielites.com, pg 722

Christofano, Dan, Chicago International REEL Shorts Film Festival, 2700 W Grand Ave, Chicago, IL 60612 *E-mail:* info@projectchicago.com *Web Site:* www.projectchicago.com, pg 985

Christoff, Jordan, Visionary Solutions Inc, 2060 Alameda Padre Serra, Suite 100, Santa Barbara, CA 93103 *Tel:* 805-845-8900 *Fax:* 805-845-8889 *E-mail:* sales@vsicam.com *Web Site:* www.vsicam.com, pg 931

Christy, Craig, Christy's Editorial, 3625 W Pacific Ave, Burbank, CA 91505 *Tel:* 818-845-1755 *Toll Free Tel:* 800-468-6391; 800-556-5706 (CA) *Fax:* 818-845-1756 *E-mail:* info@christys.net *Web Site:* www.christys.net, pg 723

Chu, Jennifer, Center for Asian American Media (CAAM), 145 Ninth St, Suite 350, San Francisco, CA 94103 *Tel:* 415-863-0814 *Fax:* 415-863-7428 *E-mail:* publicity@caamedia.org *Web Site:* caamedia. org, pg 953

Chu, Patrick, FilmNation Entertainment, 150 W 22 St, 9th fl, New York, NY 10011 *Web Site:* www. filmnation.com, pg 760

Church, Debbie, SmartSource Computer & AV Rentals, 265 Oser Ave, Hauppauge, NY 11788 *Tel:* 631-273-8888 *Toll Free Tel:* 844-313-8833 *Fax:* 631-273-8889 *E-mail:* info@smartsourcerentals.com *Web Site:* www. smartsourcerentals.com, pg 891

Church, Nolan C, CSPMedia.com, 9411 Gumtree Park St, Capitol Heights, MD 20743 *Tel:* 301-350-3181 *Web Site:* www.soundstore.com; www.cspmedia.com, pg 735

Churches, Kimberly, American Association of University Women (AAUW), 1310 "L" St, Suite 1000, Washington, DC 20005 *Tel:* 202-785-7700 *Toll Free Tel:* 800-326-AAUW (326-2289) *Fax:* 202-872-1425 *E-mail:* helpline@aauw.org; connect@aauw.org *Web Site:* www.aauw.org, pg 948

Churchill, Kris, Central Lighting & Equipment Inc (CLE), 4103 E 16 St, Des Moines, IA 50313 *Tel:* 515-277-4190 *Toll Free Tel:* 877-977-4190 *Fax:* 515-277-2295 *E-mail:* info@cleproductions.com *Web Site:* cleproductions.com, pg 719

Chute, Melissa, Dazian LLC, 18 Central Blvd, South Hackensack, NJ 07606 *Toll Free Tel:* 877-232-9426 *Fax:* 201-641-2728; 201-549-1055 (efax) *E-mail:* info@dazian.com *Web Site:* www.dazian.com, pg 739

Chynoweth, Kirk S, Lightning Eliminators & Consultants Inc, 6687 Arapahoe Rd, Boulder, CO 80303 *Tel:* 303-447-2828 *Toll Free Tel:* 800-521-6101 *Fax:* 303-447-8122 *E-mail:* info@lecglobal.com *Web Site:* www. lightningprotection.com, pg 808

Ciabattari, Michael, MediaOne Studios, 950 Battery St, 2nd fl, San Francisco, CA 94111 *Tel:* 415-262-4222 *E-mail:* hi@mediaonestudios.com *Web Site:* mediaonestudios.com, pg 823

Ciciura, Thomas S, 2nd Cine Inc, 637 Frazier Ave, Suite 2, Elgin, IL 60123 *Tel:* 773-455-5808 *E-mail:* info@2ndcine.com *Web Site:* www.2ndcine.com, pg 883

Cieri, Albert, Matrox Video Products Group, 1055 Saint Regis Blvd, Dorval, QC H9P 2T4, Canada *Tel:* 514-822-6000 *Toll Free Tel:* 800-361-4903 *Fax:* 514-685-2853 *Web Site:* www.matrox.com/video, pg 819

Cihi, Justin, Videofilm Systems Inc, 7 Islandbrook Ave, Unit D-1, Bridgeport, CT 06606 *Tel:* 203-870-6013 *E-mail:* info@videofilmsystems.com, pg 929

Cilurso, Linda, Shanachie Entertainment Corp, 37 E Clinton St, Newton, NJ 07860 *Tel:* 973-579-7763 *Web Site:* shanachie.com, pg 885

Cirillo, Joseph, Production Resource Group LLC (PRG), 200 Business Park Dr, Suite 109, Armonk, NY 10504 *Tel:* 212-589-5400 *Toll Free Tel:* 877-774-7088 *E-mail:* info@prg.com *Web Site:* www.prg.com, pg 864

Cirrito, Mike, Panavid, 210 West Pkwy, Unit 5, Pompton Plains, NJ 07444 *Tel:* 973-831-5655 *E-mail:* info@panavid.com; support@panavid.com *Web Site:* www. panavid.com, pg 850

Cisneros, Valerie, Florida Film Festival, c/o Enzian Theater, 1300 S Orlando Ave, Maitland, FL 32751 *Tel:* 407-629-1088 *Fax:* 407-629-6870 *E-mail:* entries@enzian.org; marketing@enzian.org; events@enzian.org *Web Site:* www.floridafilmfestival. com, pg 989

Cissell, Tim, Tim Cissell Music, 10732 W 107 Circle, Westminster, CO 80021 *Tel:* 303-955-4436 *E-mail:* tim@cissellmusic.com *Web Site:* www. cissellmusic.com, pg 725

Ciuperger, Kristina, City of Port St Lucie Community Relations/Communications Dept, 121 SW Port St Lucie Blvd, Bldg A, 1st fl, Rm 145, Port St Lucie,

FL 34984 *Tel:* 772-871-5219 *Fax:* 772-344-4111 *E-mail:* info@cityofpsl.com *Web Site:* www.cityofpsl. com, pg 969

Civins, Gary, Civins Productions Inc, 5881 NW 122 Dr, Coral Springs, FL 33076 *Tel:* 954-938-8600 *E-mail:* info@civins.com *Web Site:* www.civins.com, pg 725

Civitella, Billy, Stray Angel Films, 11318 Santa Monica Blvd, Los Angeles, CA 90025 *Tel:* 310-277-6900 *Fax:* 801-438-5009 *E-mail:* rentals@strayangel.com *Web Site:* www.strayangel.com, pg 902

Clair, SueEllen, Anonymous Content, 3532 Hayden Ave, Culver City, CA 90232 *Tel:* 310-558-6000 *Fax:* 310-558-2724 *E-mail:* filmtv@anonymouscontent.com *Web Site:* www.anonymouscontent.com, pg 686

Claman, Roger, Rose Brand, 4 Emerson Lane, Secaucus, NJ 07094 *Tel:* 201-809-1730 *Toll Free Tel:* 800-223-1624 *Fax:* 201-809-1851 *E-mail:* info@rosebrand.com *Web Site:* www.rosebrand.com, pg 877

Clancy, Daniel, Wisconsin Technical College System Foundation Inc, 6602 Normandy Lane, Madison, WI 53719-1081 *Tel:* 608-841-1800 *Toll Free Tel:* 800-821-6313 *Fax:* 608-841-1806 *E-mail:* foundation@wtcsf. tec.wi.us *Web Site:* www.wtcsf.tec.wi.us, pg 940

Clancy, Greg, TM Studios Inc, 2002 Academy Lane, Suite 110, Dallas, TX 75234 *Tel:* 972-406-6800 *Fax:* 972-406-6890 *E-mail:* info@tmstudios.com; tmcustomerservice@tmstudios.com *Web Site:* www. tmstudios.com, pg 915

Clappe, Megan, Society of Broadcast Engineers Inc (SBE), 9102 N Meridian St, Suite 150, Indianapolis, IN 46260 *Tel:* 317-846-9000 *Web Site:* www.sbe.org, pg 962

Clark, Andrew, Midwest Photo Exchange, 2887 Silver Dr, Columbus, OH 43211 *Tel:* 614-261-1264 *Toll Free Tel:* 866-940-3686 *E-mail:* mpx@mpex.com; orders@mpex.com *Web Site:* mpex.com, pg 827

Clark, Brad, Associated Sound, 1417 Del Paso Blvd, Sacramento, CA 95815 *Tel:* 916-649-8040 *Toll Free Tel:* 800-492-6800 *Fax:* 916-649-0243 *E-mail:* sales@associatedsound.com *Web Site:* www.associatedsound. com, pg 691

Clark, Brook B, CommScope Inc, 1100 CommScope Place SE, Hickory, NC 28602 *Tel:* 828-324-2200 *Toll Free Tel:* 800-982-1708 *E-mail:* publicrelations@commscope.com *Web Site:* www.commscope.com, pg 728

Clark, Craig, Roundabout Entertainment Inc, 217 S Lake St, Burbank, CA 91502 *Tel:* 818-842-9300 *Fax:* 818-842-9301 *E-mail:* info@roundabout.com *Web Site:* www.roundabout.com, pg 878

Clark, Edward M, Ostergaard Acoustical Associates, 200 Executive Dr, Suite 350, West Orange, NJ 07052 *Tel:* 973-731-7002 *Fax:* 973-731-6680 *E-mail:* info@acousticalconsultant.com *Web Site:* www.acousticalconsultant.com, pg 848

Clark, Ginenne, Society for Photographic Education (SPE), PO Box 6653, Cleveland, OH 44101 *Tel:* 216-622-2733 *Fax:* 216-622-2733 *E-mail:* admin@spenational.org; info@spenational.org *Web Site:* www. spenational.org, pg 962

Clark, Grant, Alpha Technologies Inc, 3767 Alpha Way, Bellingham, WA 98226 *Tel:* 360-647-2360 *Toll Free Tel:* 800-322-5742 *E-mail:* alpha@alpha.com *Web Site:* www.alpha.com, pg 681

Clark, James M, Clark Services Audio Visual & Exhibit Inc, 113 Board Rd, Lafayette, LA 70508 *Tel:* 337-234-5653 *Fax:* 337-232-0243 *E-mail:* clarkservices@bellsouth.net, pg 725

Clark, Jeff, WIFR-TV, 2523 N Meridian Rd, Rockford, IL 61101 *Tel:* 815-987-5300 *Fax:* 815-965-0981 *E-mail:* talkto23@wifr.com *Web Site:* www.wifr.com, pg 938

Clark, John, Masterclock Inc, 2484 W Clay St, St Charles, MO 63301-2548 *Tel:* 636-724-3666 *Toll Free Tel:* 800-940-2248 *Fax:* 636-724-3776 *E-mail:* sales@masterclock.com; support@masterclock.com *Web Site:* www.masterclock.com, pg 819

Clark, Mitch, CenterStaging LLC, 3407 Winona Ave, Burbank, CA 91504 *Tel:* 818-559-4333 *Fax:* 818-848-4016 *E-mail:* info@centerstaging.com *Web Site:* centerstaging.com, pg 719

Clark, Rebecca, North Carolina's Piedmont Triad Film Commission, 717 S Marshall St, Suite 105-F, Winston-Salem, NC 27101 *Tel:* 336-393-0001 *E-mail:* info@piedmontfilm.com *Web Site:* www. piedmontfilm.com, pg 974

Clark, Sara, Westlake Recording Studios, 7265 Santa Monica Blvd, Los Angeles, CA 90046 *Tel:* 323-851-9800 *E-mail:* bookings@westlakestudios.com; info@westlakestudios.com *Web Site:* www.westlakestudios. com, pg 936

Clark, Susan, National Media Services Inc, 613 N Commerce Ave, Front Royal, VA 22630 *Tel:* 540-635-4181 *Fax:* 540-636-4240 *Web Site:* nationalmediaservices.com, pg 836

Clark, Tom, South Carolina Film Commission, 1205 Pendleton St, Rm 225, Columbia, SC 29201 *Tel:* 803-737-0490 *Fax:* 803-734-1163 *E-mail:* filmsc@scprt. com *Web Site:* www.filmsc.com, pg 975

Clarke, Jeff, Eastman Kodak Co, 343 State St, Rochester, NY 14650 *Toll Free Tel:* 800-698-3324 *Web Site:* www.kodak.com, pg 750

Clarke, Jonathan, Bitcentral Inc, 4340 Von Karman Ave, Suite 400, Newport Beach, CA 92660 *Tel:* 949-253-9000 *Toll Free Tel:* 800-272-4004 (support) *E-mail:* sales@bitcentral.com; support@bitcentral.com *Web Site:* www.bitcentral.com, pg 706

Clarke, Mia Barkan, Cross-Cultural Communications, 239 Wynsum Ave, Merrick, NY 11566-4725 *Tel:* 516-868-5635 *Fax:* 516-379-1901 *E-mail:* info@cross-culturalcommunications.com *Web Site:* www.cross-culturalcommunications.com, pg 735

Clarke, Roger, Zygote Media Group Inc, 1045 S 500 E, Suite 200, American Fork, UT 84003 *Tel:* 801-765-4141 *Fax:* 801-705-2234 *E-mail:* service@zygote.com *Web Site:* www.zygote.com, pg 945

Clarkson, Robert N, Clarkson Studio, 401 N Hoback St, Helena, MT 59601 *Web Site:* www.clarksonstudio. com, pg 716

Classe, A V, Affton Graphics Inc, 400 E 85 St, Unit 3F, New York, NY 10028 *Tel:* 718-401-4040 *Toll Free Tel:* 800-777-0539 *E-mail:* amproducts@aol.com *Web Site:* amgraphics-classe.com, pg 678

Claude, Lou, BroadcastStore.com, 9420 Lurline Ave, Unit C, Chatsworth, CA 91311 *Tel:* 818-998-9100 *Fax:* 818-998-9106 *E-mail:* sales@broadcaststore.com *Web Site:* www.broadcaststore.com, pg 711

Claypool, Brian, Christie Digital Systems USA Inc, 10550 Camden Dr, Cypress, CA 90630 *Tel:* 714-236-8610 *Toll Free Tel:* 866-880-4462 (cust serv) *Fax:* 714-503-3375 *E-mail:* sales-us@christiedigital. com; orders@christiedigital.com *Web Site:* www. christiedigital.com, pg 722

Clayton, Brooks, Mid-South Color Labs Inc, 496 Emmett St, Jackson, TN 38301 *Tel:* 731-422-6691 *Toll Free Tel:* 800-221-3920 *Fax:* 731-424-1902 *E-mail:* info@midsouthcolor.com *Web Site:* www. midsouthcolor.com, pg 826

Clayton, Michael, Pentrex Media Group LLC, 2652 E Walnut St, Pasadena, CA 91107-3723 *Tel:* 626-793-3400 *Toll Free Tel:* 800-950-9333 *Fax:* 626-793-3797 *E-mail:* pentrex@pentrex.com *Web Site:* www.pentrex. com, pg 854

Cleary, Kitty, Circulating Film & Video Library, 11 W 53 St, New York, NY 10019-5401 *Tel:* 212-708-9530 *Fax:* 212-708-9531 *E-mail:* circfilm@moma.org *Web Site:* www.moma.org, pg 725

Cleaveland, Dave, Maine Imaging, PO Box 753, Wiscasset, ME 04578 *Tel:* 207-380-6343 *Web Site:* www.maineimaging.com, pg 815

Clelland, Georgina, Association for Information and Image Management (AIIM), 1100 Wayne Ave, Suite 1100, Silver Spring, MD 20910 *Tel:* 301-587-8202

Cole, Karl, Davis Art Images, 50 Portland St, Worcester, MA 01608 *Tel:* 508-754-7201 *Toll Free Tel:* 800-533-2847 *Fax:* 508-753-3834 *E-mail:* contactus@davisart.com; das@davisart.com *Web Site:* www.davisart.com, pg 738

Cole, Leo, Cole Wire & Cable Co Inc, 620 Margate Dr, Lincolnshire, IL 60069-4247 *Toll Free Tel:* 800-323-1403 *Fax:* 847-634-4988; 847-634-4300 *E-mail:* sales@colewire.com *Web Site:* www.colewire.com, pg 727

Cole, Michele, Univenture Inc, 4266 Tuller Rd, Dublin, OH 43017 *Tel:* 937-645-4600 *Toll Free Tel:* 877-831-9428 *Fax:* 937-645-4700 *E-mail:* sales@univenture.com *Web Site:* www.univenture.com, pg 922

Cole, Ryan, Three Pillars Media, 140 N Eighth St, Suite 220, Lincoln, NE 68508 *Tel:* 402-937-0984 *E-mail:* contact@threepillarsmedia.com *Web Site:* www.threepillarsmedia.com, pg 913

Colebank, Kevin, Tantor Media Inc, 6 Business Park Rd, Old Saybrook, CT 06475 *Tel:* 860-395-1155 *Toll Free Tel:* 877-7-TANTOR (782-6867) *Toll Free Fax:* 888-782-7821 *E-mail:* service@tantor.com *Web Site:* www.tantor.com, pg 907

Colebank, Laura, Tantor Media Inc, 6 Business Park Rd, Old Saybrook, CT 06475 *Tel:* 860-395-1155 *Toll Free Tel:* 877-7-TANTOR (782-6867) *Toll Free Fax:* 888-782-7821 *E-mail:* service@tantor.com *Web Site:* www.tantor.com, pg 907

Coleman, Buddy, Clever Devices Ltd, 300 Crossways Park Dr, Woodbury, NY 11797 *Tel:* 516-433-6100 *Toll Free Tel:* 800-872-6129 *Web Site:* www.cleverdevices.com, pg 726

Coleman, Donna M, Madison Square Garden, 2 Pennsylvania Plaza, New York, NY 10121-0091 *Tel:* 212-465-6741 *E-mail:* msgnetpr@msgnetwork.com *Web Site:* www.thegarden.com; themadisonsquaregardencompany.com, pg 814

Coleman, James "Huey", Films by Huey, 103 Montrose Ave, Portland, ME 04103 *Tel:* 207-773-1130 *E-mail:* huey@filmsbyhuey.com *Web Site:* www.filmsbyhuey.com, pg 760

Coleman, Sara Otte, North Dakota Tourism Division, Century Ctr, 1600 E Century Ave, Suite 2, Bismarck, ND 58502-2057 *Tel:* 701-328-2525 *Toll Free Tel:* 800-435-5663 *Fax:* 701-328-4878 *E-mail:* tourism@nd.gov *Web Site:* www.ndtourism.com, pg 974

Collado, Valerie, VWR International LLC, Radnor Corporate Ctr, Bldg 1, 100 Matsonford Rd, Suite 200, Radnor, PA 19087-8660 *Tel:* 610-431-1700 (corp off) *Toll Free Tel:* 800-932-5000 (cust serv) *Web Site:* www.vwr.com; us.vwr.com, pg 933

Collatos, Tori, International Short Film & Video Competition, 6116 N Central Expwy, Suite 105, Dallas, TX 75206 *Tel:* 214-821-6300; 214-821-FILM (821-3456) *Fax:* 214-821-6364 *E-mail:* usafilmfest@aol.com *Web Site:* www.usafilmfestival.com, pg 993

Collatos, Tori, KidFilm®, 6116 N Central Expwy, Suite 105, Dallas, TX 75206 *Tel:* 214-821-6300; 214-821-FILM (821-3456) *Fax:* 214-821-6364 *E-mail:* usafilmfest@aol.com *Web Site:* www.usafilmfestival.com, pg 994

Collatos, Tori, USA Film Festival, 6116 N Central Expwy, Suite 105, Dallas, TX 75206 *Tel:* 214-821-6300; 214-821-FILM (821-3456) *Fax:* 214-821-6364 *E-mail:* usafilmfest@aol.com *Web Site:* www.usafilmfestival.com, pg 1005

Colleran, Nick, Acoustics First Corp, 2247 Tomlyn St, Richmond, VA 23230-3334 *Tel:* 804-342-2900 *Toll Free Tel:* 888-765-2900 *Fax:* 804-342-1107 *E-mail:* info@acousticsfirst.com *Web Site:* www.acousticsfirst.com, pg 674

Colleran, Rebecca, Acoustics First Corp, 2247 Tomlyn St, Richmond, VA 23230-3334 *Tel:* 804-342-2900 *Toll Free Tel:* 888-765-2900 *Fax:* 804-342-1107 *E-mail:* info@acousticsfirst.com *Web Site:* www.acousticsfirst.com, pg 674

Collier, Janice, Pennsylvania Film Office, Commonwealth Keystone Bldg, 4th fl, 400 North St, Harrisburg, PA 17120-0225 *Tel:* 717-783-3456 *E-mail:* info@filmpa.com *Web Site:* www.filmpa.com, pg 975

Colligan, Megan, Paramount Pictures Corporation, 5555 Melrose Ave, Los Angeles, CA 90038 *Tel:* 323-956-8398 *Web Site:* www.paramount.com, pg 851

Collin, Jennifer Marotta, Illuminating Engineering Society (IES), 120 Wall St, 17th fl, New York, NY 10005-4026 *Tel:* 212-248-5000 *E-mail:* ies@ies.org *Web Site:* ies.org, pg 955

Collins, Amy, Dogwood Productions Inc, 757 Government St, Mobile, AL 36602 *Tel:* 251-476-0858 *Toll Free Tel:* 800-254-9903 *Fax:* 251-479-0364 *E-mail:* info@dogwoodproductions.com *Web Site:* www.dogwoodproductions.com, pg 745

Collins, Chris, Film Ideas Inc, 308 N Wolf Rd, Wheeling, IL 60090 *Tel:* 847-419-0255 *Toll Free Tel:* 800-475-3456 (US only) *Fax:* 847-419-8933 *E-mail:* info@filmideas.com; orders@filmideas.com (cust serv) *Web Site:* www.filmideas.com, pg 760

Collins, Erin, Electronics Representatives Association (ERA), 1325 S Arlington Heights Rd, Suite 204, Elk Grove Village, IL 60007 *Tel:* 312-419-1432 *Fax:* 312-419-1660 *E-mail:* info@era.org *Web Site:* www.era.org, pg 954

Collins, Ginny, Manitoba Film & Music, 410-93 Lombard Ave, Suite 410, Winnipeg, MB R3B 3B1, Canada *Tel:* 204-947-2040 *Fax:* 204-956-5261 *E-mail:* info@mbfilmmusic.ca *Web Site:* www.mbfilmmusic.ca, pg 816

Collins, Janet, Ghent Manufacturing, 2999 Henkle Dr, Lebanon, OH 45036-9260 *Tel:* 513-932-3445 *Toll Free Tel:* 800-543-0550 *Fax:* 513-932-9252 *E-mail:* customer_service@ghent.com; sales@ghent.com *Web Site:* www.ghent.com, pg 770

Collins, Keith, SAS Institute Inc, 100 SAS Campus Dr, Cary, NC 27513-2414 *Tel:* 919-677-8000 *Toll Free Tel:* 800-727-0025 *Fax:* 919-677-4444 *Web Site:* www.sas.com, pg 880

Collins, Kevin, Diversified, 37 Market St, Kenilworth, NJ 07033 *Tel:* 908-245-4833 *Fax:* 908-245-0011 *E-mail:* customerservice@diversifiedus.com; info@diversifiedus.com *Web Site:* diversifiedus.com, pg 744

Collins, Leslie, TMW Media Group, 2321 Abbot Kinney Blvd, Suite 101, Venice, CA 90291 *Tel:* 310-577-8581 *Toll Free Tel:* 800-262-8862 *Fax:* 310-574-0886 *E-mail:* sale@tmwmedia.com *Web Site:* tmwmedia.com, pg 915

Collins, Lindsey, Pixar Animation Studios, 1200 Park Ave, Emeryville, CA 94608 *Tel:* 510-922-3000 *Fax:* 510-922-3151 *Web Site:* www.pixar.com, pg 857

Collins, Mary M, Avatar Award, 550 W Frontage Rd, Suite 3600, Northfield, IL 60093 *Tel:* 847-716-7000 *Fax:* 847-716-7004 *E-mail:* info@mediafinance.org *Web Site:* www.mediafinance.org, pg 983

Collins, Mary M, Media Financial Management Association (MFM), 550 W Frontage Rd, Suite 3600, Northfield, IL 60093 *Tel:* 847-716-7000 *Fax:* 847-716-7004 *E-mail:* info@mediafinance.org *Web Site:* www.mediafinance.org, pg 957

Collins, Melinda, National Fire Protection Association (NFPA), One Batterymarch Park, Quincy, MA 02169-7471 *Tel:* 617-770-3000 *Toll Free Tel:* 800-344-3555 (US & CN); 855-274-8525 (US & CN) *Fax:* 508-895-8301 *Toll Free Fax:* 800-593-NFPA (593-6372, US & CN) *E-mail:* custserv@nfpa.org *Web Site:* www.nfpa.org, pg 836

Collins, Pat, SESAC Inc, 35 Music Sq E, Nashville, TN 37203 *Tel:* 615-320-0055 *Web Site:* www.sesac.com, pg 962

Collins, Stephanie, Motion Picture Licensing Corp (MPLC), 5455 Centinela Ave, Los Angeles, CA 90066 *Tel:* 310-822-8855 (intl calls) *Toll Free Tel:* 800-462-8855 *Fax:* 310-822-4440 *Web Site:* www.mplc.org, pg 831

Collins, Ted, VITAC, 8300 E Maplewood Ave, Suite 310, Greenwood Village, CO 80111 *Toll Free Tel:* 800-278-4822 (sales); 800-775-7838 *E-mail:* info@vitac.com *Web Site:* www.vitac.com, pg 932

Collins, Valerie, San Jose Film & Video Commission, c/o San Jose Convention & Visitors Bureau, 408 Almaden Blvd, San Jose, CA 95110 *Tel:* 408-295-9600 *Toll Free Tel:* 800-SAN-JOSE (726-5673) *E-mail:* eventservices@sanjose.org *Web Site:* www.sanjose.org/media/film-office, pg 967

Colon, David, Eggplant Pictures & Sound, 157 Princess St, Toronto, ON M5A 4M4, Canada *Tel:* 416-214-9911 *Fax:* 416-214-9912 *Web Site:* www.eggplantps.com, pg 751

Comas, Radelys, The Singing Machine Co Inc, 6301 NW Fifth Way, Suite 2900, Fort Lauderdale, FL 33309 *Tel:* 954-596-1000 *Toll Free Tel:* 866-670-6888 (cust serv) *Fax:* 954-596-2000 *E-mail:* sales@singingmachine.com; customerservice@singingmachine.com *Web Site:* singingmachine.com, pg 889

Combrie, Eric, Method Studios, 3401 Exposition Blvd, Santa Monica, CA 90404 *Tel:* 310-434-6000 *Web Site:* www.methodstudios.com, pg 824

Combs, Jennifer Ogden, Visit Natchez & Natchez Convention Promotion Commission, 640 S Canal St, Box C, Natchez, MS 39120 *Tel:* 601-446-6345 *Toll Free Tel:* 800-647-6724 *E-mail:* info@visitnatchez.org *Web Site:* www.visitnatchez.org/p/media/film, pg 972

Comeau, Connie, The ADS Group, 2155 Niagara Lane N, Suite 120, Plymouth, MN 55447 *Tel:* 763-449-5500 *Toll Free Tel:* 800-759-0992 *Fax:* 763-449-5555 *E-mail:* sales@theadsgroup.com *Web Site:* theadsgroup.com, pg 677

Compton, Mike, Supercircuits, 11000 N Mopac Expwy, Bldg 300, Austin, TX 78759 *Toll Free Tel:* 877-995-2288 *E-mail:* operations@supercircuits.com; customercare@supercircuits.com *Web Site:* supercircuits.com, pg 904

Comstock, Beth, General Electric Co, 41 Farnsworth St, Boston, MA 02210 *Tel:* 203-373-2211; 617-443-3000 *Web Site:* www.ge.com, pg 769

Comunale, Pat, Tri-Ed Distribution Inc, 135 Crossways Park Dr, Suite 101, Woodbury, NY 11797 *Tel:* 516-941-2800 *Toll Free Tel:* 888-874-3336 (US); 800-398-7282 (CN); 800-366-4472 (tech sales) *E-mail:* info@tri-ed.com; sales@tri-ed.com; marketing@tri-ed.com *Web Site:* www.tri-ed.com, pg 918

Conant, David, McKay Conant Hoover Inc, 5655 Lindero Canyon Rd, Suite 325, Westlake Village, CA 91362 *Tel:* 818-991-9300 *Fax:* 818-991-2324 *E-mail:* info@mchinc.com *Web Site:* www.mchinc.com, pg 821

Conant, Vic, Nightingale-Conant Corp, 1400 S Wolf Rd, Bldg 300, Suite 103, Wheeling, IL 60090 *Toll Free Tel:* 800-557-1660 (sales); 800-560-6081 (cust serv) *Web Site:* www.nightingale.com, pg 841

Conard, John, Hollywood Sound Systems, 4209 Vanowen Place, Burbank, CA 91505 *Tel:* 323-466-2416 *Fax:* 323-460-2676 *Web Site:* www.hollywoodsound.com, pg 781

Condiotti, Steve, DTC Lighting & Grip, 1280 65 St, Emeryville, CA 94608 *Tel:* 510-595-0770 *Fax:* 510-595-0772 *E-mail:* sales@dtcgrip.com; rentals@dtcgrip.com *Web Site:* www.dtcgrip.com, pg 747

Condon, Erica, Jointure for Community Adult Education Inc, Centre at Raritan, Suite B-11, 1124 US Hwy 202 S, Raritan, NJ 08869 *Tel:* 908-722-0233 *Fax:* 908-722-0388 *E-mail:* info@jointure.org *Web Site:* www.jointure.org, pg 794

Cone, Robert, Rockland Colloid LLC, PO Box 3120, Oregon City, OR 97045-0306 *Tel:* 503-655-4152 (sales) *Toll Free Fax:* 866-737-0174 *E-mail:* orders@rockaloid.com *Web Site:* www.rockaloid.com, pg 876

Coneys, Raymond, Crestron Electronics Inc, 15 Volvo Dr, Rockleigh, NJ 07647 *Tel:* 201-767-3400 (sales & support); 201-750-7004 (admin) *Toll Free Tel:* 800-237-2041; 855-791-5322 *Fax:* 201-767-1903 (sales & support); 201-767-8872 (admin) *E-mail:* inquiries@crestron.com *Web Site:* www.crestron.com, pg 734

Coningsby, A Robert III, Apex Machine Co Inc, 3000 NE 12 Terr, Fort Lauderdale, FL 33334 *Tel:* 954-566-1572 *Fax:* 954-563-2844 *E-mail:* email@apexmachine.com *Web Site:* www.apexmachine.com, pg 687

Coningsby, Todd, Apex Machine Co Inc, 3000 NE 12 Terr, Fort Lauderdale, FL 33334 *Tel:* 954-566-1572 *Fax:* 954-563-2844 *E-mail:* email@apexmachine.com *Web Site:* www.apexmachine.com, pg 687

Conley, Tim, Extreme Reach Inc, 75 Second Ave, Suite 720, Needham, MA 02494 *Tel:* 781-577-2016 *Toll Free Tel:* 877-769-9382 *E-mail:* sales@extremereach.com; support@extremereach.com *Web Site:* extremereach.com, pg 758

Conly, Paul, Conly Productions, 1563 Oneida St, Denver, CO 80220 *Tel:* 303-393-6240 *Fax:* 303-393-6240, pg 730

Connan-Lostanlen, Glodina, Imagine Communications Corp, 3001 Dallas Pkwy, Suite 300, Frisco, TX 75034 *Tel:* 469-803-4900 *Toll Free Tel:* 866-4-IMAGINE (446-2446) *Fax:* 469-803-4899 *E-mail:* insidesales@imaginecommunications.com *Web Site:* www.imaginecommunications.com, pg 786

Connell, Nick, Transtar Entertainment Co Inc, 11776 E Evans Ave, Aurora, CO 80014 *Tel:* 303-489-1450 *Web Site:* www.transtarfilm.com, pg 917

Connell, Rick, Colorado Time Systems LLC, 1551 E 11 St, Loveland, CO 80537 *Tel:* 970-667-1000; 970-612-3573 (intl sales) *Toll Free Tel:* 800-279-0111 *Fax:* 970-667-5876; 970-667-1788 (intl sales) *E-mail:* info@coloradotime.com *Web Site:* www.coloradotime.com, pg 728

Connell, William J, Concept Associates Inc, 5371 Punta Alta, Unit 1E, Laguna Woods, CA 92637, pg 730

Connelly, Liam, USAV Group Inc, 584 W 18768 Enterprise Dr, Muskego, WI 53150 *Tel:* 262-814-2000 *Toll Free Tel:* 800-596-USAV (596-8728) *Fax:* 262-814-2006 *Web Site:* www.usavgroup.com, pg 923

Connelly, Margaret, Tecplot Inc, 3535 Factoria Blvd SE, Suite 550, Bellevue, WA 98006 *Tel:* 425-653-1200; 425-653-9393 (tech support) *Toll Free Tel:* 800-763-7005 (orders) *E-mail:* info@tecplot.com; support@tecplot.com *Web Site:* www.tecplot.com, pg 909

Connelly, Michael P, Uniconn Productions, 8485 Valley Circle Blvd, Suite 203, West Hills, CA 91304 *Tel:* 818-887-9108 *Fax:* 818-348-6544 *E-mail:* measeburl@aol.com *Web Site:* www.uniconnproductions.com, pg 921

Conner, Saundra, Cinevision Corp, 3300 Northeast Expwy NE, Bldg 2, Suite A, Atlanta, GA 30341 *Tel:* 770-455-8988 *Fax:* 770-455-4066 *Web Site:* www.cinevisionatlanta.com, pg 725

Connolly, Anne, McNabb & Connolly, 60 Briarwood Ave, Mississauga, ON L5G 3N6, Canada *Tel:* 905-278-0566 *Toll Free Tel:* 866-722-1522 *Fax:* 905-278-2801 *Toll Free Fax:* 866-722-1822 *E-mail:* info@mcnabbconnolly.ca *Web Site:* www.mcnabbconnolly.ca, pg 821

Connolly, Doug, Canamedia Inc, 1540 Cornwall Rd, Suite 216, Oakville, ON L6J 7W5, Canada *Tel:* 416-363-6765 *Toll Free Tel:* 866-999-5292 *Fax:* 416-363-7834 *Web Site:* www.canamedia.com, pg 715

Connolly, Patt, Saturn Studios, PO Box 3687, Hollywood, CA 90078-3687 *Tel:* 323-871-4134 *Web Site:* rollingplanet.com, pg 881

Connolly, Scott, Cramer, 425 University Ave, Norwood, MA 02062 *Tel:* 781-278-2300 *E-mail:* theteam@cramer.com *Web Site:* cramer.com, pg 732

Connolly, Steve, McNabb & Connolly, 60 Briarwood Ave, Mississauga, ON L5G 3N6, Canada *Tel:* 905-278-0566 *Toll Free Tel:* 866-722-1522 *Fax:* 905-278-2801 *Toll Free Fax:* 866-722-1822 *E-mail:* info@mcnabbconnolly.ca *Web Site:* www.mcnabbconnolly.ca, pg 821

Connolly, Steve, Weston Woods Canada, 60 Briarwood Ave, Mississauga, ON L5G 3N6, Canada *Tel:* 905-278-0566 *Toll Free Tel:* 866-722-1522 *Toll Free Fax:* 866-722-1822 *E-mail:* info@mcnabbconnolly.ca *Web Site:* www.mcnabbconnolly.ca, pg 936

Connors, Fred Jr, The Troupe, 3 Industrial Dr, Windham, NH 03087 *Tel:* 603-893-4554 *E-mail:* info@thetroupe.com *Web Site:* www.thetroupe.com, pg 918

Connors, John, The Troupe, 3 Industrial Dr, Windham, NH 03087 *Tel:* 603-893-4554 *E-mail:* info@thetroupe.com *Web Site:* www.thetroupe.com, pg 918

Conover, Christopher, Arizona Public Media, 1423 E University, MLB67, Rm 223, Tucson, AZ 85719 *Tel:* 520-621-5828; 520-621-5836 (sales) *Fax:* 520-621-3360 *Web Site:* www.azpm.org, pg 688

Conrad, Matt, Multicom Inc, 1076 Florida Central Pkwy, Longwood, FL 32750 *Tel:* 407-331-7779 *Toll Free Tel:* 800-423-2594 *Fax:* 407-339-0204 *E-mail:* multicom@multicominc.com *Web Site:* www.multicominc.com, pg 833

Conroy, Ann, Small World Productions Inc, 140 Lakeside Ave, Suite 200, Seattle, WA 98122 *Tel:* 206-329-7167 *Toll Free Tel:* 800-866-7425 (orders); 800-325-7111 (cust serv) *Fax:* 206-329-0269 (credit card orders) *E-mail:* info@travelsmallworld.com; customercare@smarttravels.tv *Web Site:* www.smarttravels.tv, pg 890

Conroy, Kathy, National Association of Theatre Owners (NATO), 1705 "N" St NW, Washington, DC 20036 *Tel:* 202-962-0054 *E-mail:* nato@natodc.com *Web Site:* www.natoonline.org, pg 959

Consiglio, Peter, HBO Studio Productions, 120-A E 23 St, New York, NY 10010 *Tel:* 212-512-7800 *Web Site:* www.hbostudio.com, pg 777

Consolo, Steve, Hubbell Wiring Device-Kellems, 40 Waterview Dr, Shelton, CT 06484 *Tel:* 475-882-4800 (sales & mktg) *Toll Free Tel:* 800-288-6000 (cust serv) *Fax:* 475-882-4849 (sales & mktg) *Toll Free Fax:* 800-255-1031 (cust serv) *E-mail:* techserv@hubbell.com *Web Site:* www.hubbell-wiring.com, pg 782

Constantinau, Walea L, Honolulu Film Office, 530 S King St, Suite 306, Honolulu, HI 96813 *Tel:* 808-768-6108 *Fax:* 808-768-6102 *E-mail:* info@filmhonolulu.com *Web Site:* www.filmhonolulu.com, pg 970

Contrata, Curt, Stage Equipment & Lighting Inc, 4600 SW 36 St, Orlando, FL 32811 *Tel:* 407-425-2010 *Fax:* 407-648-2604 *E-mail:* mail@seal-fla.com *Web Site:* www.seal-fla.com, pg 899

Contreras, Natalie, Set Decorators Society of America (SDSA), 7100 Tujunga Ave, Suite A, North Hollywood, CA 91605 *Tel:* 818-255-2425 *Fax:* 818-982-8597 *E-mail:* sdsa@setdecorators.org *Web Site:* www.setdecorators.org, pg 962

Contreras, Renee, Band Pro Film & Digital Inc, 3403 W Pacific Ave, Burbank, CA 91505 *Tel:* 818-841-9655 *Toll Free Tel:* 888-BANDPRO (226-3776) *Fax:* 818-841-7649 *E-mail:* info@bandpro.com; customercare@bandpro.com *Web Site:* www.bandpro.com, pg 701

Contrino, Phil, National Association of Theatre Owners (NATO), 1705 "N" St NW, Washington, DC 20036 *Tel:* 202-962-0054 *E-mail:* nato@natodc.com *Web Site:* www.natoonline.org, pg 959

Cook, Bob, Fox Television Center, 1999 S Bundy Dr, Los Angeles, CA 90025 *Tel:* 310-584-2000 *Fax:* 310-584-2023 *Web Site:* www.foxla.com, pg 765

Cook, Brad, Fuller Street Productions, 12131 Shoemaker Ave, Santa Fe Springs, CA 90670 *Toll Free Tel:* 877-637-8733 *Toll Free Fax:* 877-637-8733 *E-mail:* contact@fullerstreet.com *Web Site:* www.fullerstreet.com, pg 767

Cook, Doug, SYMCO Inc, 29 Poplar Dr, Stirling, NJ 07980 *Tel:* 908-647-6262 *Fax:* 908-647-4904 *E-mail:* orders@symcoinc.com *Web Site:* www.symcoinc.com, pg 905

Cook, Dwight, Sound Works, 7110 Gary St, Houston, TX 77055 *Tel:* 713-960-8222 *Web Site:* www.soundworks.com, pg 894

Cook, Graham, MarathonNorco Aerospace Inc, 8301 Imperial Dr, Waco, TX 76712-6588 *Tel:* 254-776-0650 *Fax:* 254-776-6558 *E-mail:* marathon@mptc.com *Web Site:* www.mnaerospace.com, pg 816

Cook, Kim, Trafalgar Square Books, 388 Howe Hill Rd, North Pomfret, VT 05053 *Tel:* 802-457-1911 *Toll Free Tel:* 800-423-4525 *Fax:* 802-457-1913 *E-mail:* contact@trafalgarbooks.com; cs@trafalgarbooks.com (cust serv) *Web Site:* www.horseandriderbooks.com; www.trafalgarbooks.com, pg 917

Cook, Martha, Trafalgar Square Books, 388 Howe Hill Rd, North Pomfret, VT 05053 *Tel:* 802-457-1911 *Toll Free Tel:* 800-423-4525 *Fax:* 802-457-1913 *E-mail:* contact@trafalgarbooks.com; cs@trafalgarbooks.com (cust serv) *Web Site:* www.horseandriderbooks.com; www.trafalgarbooks.com, pg 916

Cook, Peter M, Juice Goose, 7320 Ashcroft, Suite 104, Houston, TX 77081 *Tel:* 713-772-1404 *Fax:* 713-772-7360 *E-mail:* info@juicegoose.com *Web Site:* www.juicegoose.com, pg 795

Cook, Phillip, Eagle Films, 2806 Cameron Rd, Falls Church, VA 22042-2004 *Tel:* 703-237-8160 *Web Site:* www.eaglefilms.com, pg 749

Cook, Roger, Educational Video Group Inc, 291 Southwind Way, Greenwood, IN 46142-9190 *Tel:* 317-889-8253 *Fax:* 317-888-5857 *E-mail:* service@evgonline.com *Web Site:* www.evgonline.com, pg 751

Cook, Timothy D, Apple Inc, One Infinite Loop, Cupertino, CA 95014 *Tel:* 408-996-1010 *Web Site:* www.apple.com, pg 687

Coombes, Brian, Rocking Horse Studio, 1380 Upper City Rd, Pittsfield, NH 03263 *Tel:* 603-512-5347 *E-mail:* info@rockinghorsestudio.com *Web Site:* www.rockinghorsestudio.com, pg 876

Coomer, James, DataDirect Networks, 9351 Deering Ave, Chatsworth, CA 91311 *Tel:* 818-700-4000 *Toll Free Tel:* 800-TERABYTE (837-2298) *E-mail:* info@ddn.com; sales@ddn.com *Web Site:* www.ddn.com, pg 738

Coon, Greg, Eyecon Video Productions, 1865 Summit Ave, Suite 605, Plano, TX 75074 *Tel:* 972-881-3200 *Toll Free Tel:* 877-704-1517 *E-mail:* info@eyeconvideo.com *Web Site:* www.eyeconvideo.com, pg 758

Cooney, Cleve, Florida Film & Tape, 3417 Lake Breeze Rd, Orlando, FL 32808 *Tel:* 407-297-0091 *E-mail:* info@ffandt.com *Web Site:* ffandt.com, pg 763

Cooper, Janita, Master Video Disc & Design, 7349 N Via Paseo del Sur, Suite 515-455, Scottsdale, AZ 85258 *Tel:* 480-948-0305 *Web Site:* www.mastervdd.com, pg 819

Cooper, Jason, Horizon Video Productions Inc, 6114 Fayetteville St, Suite 106, Durham, NC 27713 *Tel:* 919-941-0901 *Toll Free Tel:* 800-768-3776 *Fax:* 919-941-1939 *E-mail:* info@horizonvp.com *Web Site:* www.horizonvp.com, pg 778

Cooper, Jeff, Synergy Group Inc, 23930 Craftsman Rd, Calabasas, CA 91302-1437 *Tel:* 818-223-9009 *Fax:* 818-223-8999 *Web Site:* www.jeffcooper.com, pg 906

Cooper, John, Sundance Film Festival, 1825 Three Kings Dr, Park City, UT 84060 *Tel:* 435-658-3456 *Fax:* 435-658-3457 *E-mail:* customerservice@sundance.org; press@sundance.org; institute@sundance.org *Web Site:* www.sundance.org/festival, pg 1004

Cooper, Lane, Technicolor USA Inc, 6040 Sunset Blvd, Hollywood, CA 90028 *Tel:* 323-817-6600 *E-mail:* info@technicolor.com *Web Site:* www.technicolor.com, pg 908

Cooper, Phillip, Encore Event Technologies LLC, 8850 W Sunset Rd, 3rd fl, Las Vegas, NV 89148 *Tel:* 702-739-8803 *Fax:* 702-739-8831 *Web Site:* www.encoreglobal.com/us, pg 754

Cooper, Russell, JaffeHolden, 114-A Washington St, Norwalk, CT 06854 *Tel:* 203-838-4167 *Fax:* 203-838-4168 *Web Site:* www.jaffeholden.com, pg 792

Copeland, Charley, Intercollegiate Studies Institute Inc (ISI), 3901 Centerville Rd, Wilmington, DE 19807 *Tel:* 302-652-4600 *Toll Free Tel:* 800-526-7022 *Fax:* 302-652-1760 *E-mail:* info@isi.org *Web Site:* www.isi.org, pg 789

Copeland, Dr Leslie, National Council of Churches, 110 Maryland Ave NE, Suite 108, Washington, DC 20002 *Tel:* 202-544-2350 *E-mail:* info@nationalcouncilofchurches.us *Web Site:* nationalcouncilofchurches.us, pg 836

Copes, Brad, Audience Response Systems Inc, 5611-C E Morgan Ave, Evansville, IN 47715 *Tel:* 812-479-7507 *Toll Free Tel:* 800-INVOLVE (468-6583) *Fax:* 812-479-1057 *E-mail:* arsales@audienceresponse.com *Web Site:* www.audienceresponse.com, pg 693

Coradeschi, Andy, Straight Shoot'r Cranes Inc, 18434 Oxnard St, Unit H, Tarzana, CA 91356 *Tel:* 818-609-8310 *Fax:* 818-609-8311 *Web Site:* www.straightshootr.com, pg 901

Corbell, Kirsten, Alpha Source Inc, 6619 W Calumet Rd, Milwaukee, WI 53223-4186 *Tel:* 414-760-2222 *Toll Free Tel:* 800-654-9845 *E-mail:* customer.service@alphasource.com; info@alphasource.com *Web Site:* www.alphasource.com, pg 681

Corben, Carolyn, Kaboom Productions, 2169 Folsom St, Suite 201-M, San Francisco, CA 94110 *Tel:* 415-434-2666 *Fax:* 415-874-9324 *E-mail:* hello@kaboomproductions.com *Web Site:* kaboomproductions.com, pg 796

Corbet, Jeanine, Brooklyn College Television Center, Whitehead Hall, Rm 018, 2900 Bedford Ave, Brooklyn, NY 11210 *Tel:* 718-951-5585 *E-mail:* tvcenter@brooklyn.cuny.edu *Web Site:* www.bctvcenter.org, pg 711

Corbett, Fiona, Professional Photographers of America (PPA), 229 Peachtree St NE, Suite 2200, Atlanta, GA 30303 *Tel:* 404-522-8600 *Toll Free Tel:* 800-786-6277 *Fax:* 404-614-6400 *E-mail:* csc@ppa.com *Web Site:* www.ppa.com, pg 960

Corcoran, Jeanne, Sarasota County Film & Entertainment Office, 1680 Fruitville Rd, Suite 402, Sarasota, FL 34236 *Tel:* 941-309-1200 (ext 104) *Fax:* 941-309-1209 *E-mail:* info@filmsarasota.com *Web Site:* www.filmsarasota.com, pg 970

Cordera, Louis D, CORTRON Media LLC, 320 Fort Duquesne Blvd, Suite 100, Pittsburgh, PA 15222-1146 *Tel:* 412-565-3471 (ext 3) *Web Site:* cortronmedia.com, pg 732

Cordiner, Tom, Avid Technology Inc, 65-75 Network Dr, Burlington, MA 01830 *Tel:* 978-640-6789 *Web Site:* www.avid.com, pg 698

Cordova, Alicia, Paulist Productions, 6430 W Sunset Blvd, Suite 1220, Los Angeles, CA 90028 *Tel:* 310-454-0688 *E-mail:* paulistmail@paulistproductions.org *Web Site:* www.paulistproductions.org, pg 852

Cordova, Jeanne, Universal Studios, 100 Universal City Plaza, Universal City, CA 91608-1002 *Toll Free Tel:* 800-892-1979 *Fax:* 818-866-0293 *E-mail:* studio.operations2@nbcuni.com *Web Site:* www.nbcuni.com; universalstudioslot.com, pg 922

Corech, Henry, Photodyne Technologies, 8531 Alcott St, Suite 201, Los Angeles, CA 90035 *Tel:* 310-497-0968 *Toll Free Tel:* 800-660-2147 *E-mail:* info@photodyne.com *Web Site:* www.photodyne.com, pg 856

Cornell, Carl, Whirlwind Music Distributors Inc, 99 Ling Rd, Greece, NY 14612 *Tel:* 585-663-8820 *Toll Free Tel:* 800-733-9473 (US only) *Fax:* 585-865-8930 *E-mail:* sales@whirlwindusa.com; techsupport@whirlwindusa.com; darylg@whirlwindusa.com (CN inquiries) *Web Site:* whirlwindusa.com, pg 937

Cornette, Anji, The Cutting Corporation, GraphicAudio® & Archival Sound Lab, 7520 Standish Place, Suite 100, Rockville, MD 20855 *Tel:* 301-654-CUTS (654-2887) *Fax:* 301-444-4519 *E-mail:* sales@graphicaudio.net *Web Site:* cuttingcorporation.com; www.graphicaudio.net, pg 736

Cornish, Eileen, Freedoms Foundation National Awards, 1601 Valley Forge Rd, Valley Forge, PA 19481 *Tel:* 610-933-8825 *Fax:* 610-935-0522 *E-mail:* info@ffvf.org *Web Site:* www.freedomsfoundation.org, pg 990

Correa, Angela, East of Hollywood NY, 140 53 St, Brooklyn, NY 11232 *Tel:* 718-492-7400 *Fax:* 718-439-3930 *Web Site:* www.eastofhollywoodny.com, pg 749

Corry, Bill, TiVo Corp, 2 Circle Star Way, San Carlos, CA 94070 *Tel:* 408-562-8400 *Toll Free Tel:* 877-367-8486 (cust support); 877-289-8486 (sales support) *Fax:* 408-567-1800 *Web Site:* business.tivo.com; www.tivo.com, pg 914

Corsello, Charles P, The Video Messenger Co, 862 Judson Place, Stratford, CT 06615 *Tel:* 203-358-8842 *Toll Free Tel:* 800-800-7128 *Fax:* 203-547-6216 *E-mail:* vmc@videomessenger.com *Web Site:* www.videomessenger.com, pg 928

Cort, Harvey, Dyer-Bennet Records, 792 Columbus Ave, Rm 16-0, New York, NY 10025 *Tel:* 212-866-3675, pg 748

Cort, Susan, JPL, 471 JPL Wick Dr, Harrisburg, PA 17111-2504 *Tel:* 717-558-8048 *Fax:* 717-558-8349 *E-mail:* jpl@jplcreative.com *Web Site:* www.jplcreative.com; www.facebook.com/jplcreative, pg 795

Corvan, Jimmy, House of Moves, 5419 McConnell Ave, Los Angeles, CA 90066-7027 *Tel:* 310-306-6131 *E-mail:* info@moves.com *Web Site:* www.moves.com, pg 782

Cosgray, Craig, Marengo Films, 27206 Waterfall Hill Pkwy, Spicewood, TX 78669 *Tel:* 972-365-0406 *Fax:* 830-693-0949 *E-mail:* cosgray@outlook.com *Web Site:* www.marengofilms.com, pg 817

Cosgrove, Tracey, Rosco Laboratories Inc, 52 Harbor View, Stamford, CT 06902 *Tel:* 203-708-8900 *Toll Free Tel:* 800-ROSCO NY (767-2669) *Fax:* 203-708-8919 *E-mail:* info@rosco.com *Web Site:* us.rosco.com, pg 877

Costa, Karen, Power Sonic Corp, 365 Cabela Dr, Suite 300, Reno, NV 89523 *Tel:* 619-661-2020 *Fax:* 619-661-3650 *Web Site:* www.power-sonic.com, pg 860

Costantini, Joe, Two Animators LLP, PO Box 3174, Mercerville, NJ 08619 *Tel:* 609-532-6138 *E-mail:* cartoons@twoanimators.com *Web Site:* www.twoanimators.com, pg 920

Costantini, Tom, Two Animators LLP, PO Box 3174, Mercerville, NJ 08619 *Tel:* 609-532-6138 *E-mail:* cartoons@twoanimators.com *Web Site:* www.twoanimators.com, pg 920

Costantino, Gary, Air Sea Land Productions Inc (ASL), 19-69 Steinway St, Astoria, NY 11105-1108 *Tel:* 718-626-2646 *Toll Free Tel:* 888-ASL-LENS (275-5367) *E-mail:* info@airsealand.com *Web Site:* www.airsealand.com, pg 678

Costanzo, Chad, Pyxis Industries Inc, 25695 Jefferson Ave, Suite 8, Murrieta, CA 92562 *Tel:* 951-526-1999 *Toll Free Tel:* 888-PYXISAN (799-4728) *Fax:* 951-253-9290 *Web Site:* pyxisindustries.com, pg 867

Costanzo, Kelly, Pyxis Industries Inc, 25695 Jefferson Ave, Suite 8, Murrieta, CA 92562 *Tel:* 951-526-1999 *Toll Free Tel:* 888-PYXISAN (799-4728) *Fax:* 951-253-9290 *Web Site:* pyxisindustries.com, pg 867

Costello, John, FirstGeneration Audio/Visual Services, 410 Allentown Dr, Allentown, PA 18109 *Tel:* 610-437-4300 *Fax:* 610-437-3200 *E-mail:* information@firstgencom.com; contact@firstgencom.com *Web Site:* www.firstgencom.com, pg 761

Costello, Megan, The Hamptons International Film Festival, 47 Newtown Lane, East Hampton, NY 11937 *Tel:* 631-324-4600 *Fax:* 631-324-1558 *E-mail:* info@hamptonsfilmfest.org; programming@hamptonsfilmfest.org (submissions) *Web Site:* hamptonsfilmfest.org, pg 991

Cote, Bill, BC Studio, 152 W 25 St, 2nd fl, New York, NY 10001 *Tel:* 212-242-4065 *Fax:* 212-242-4190 *E-mail:* info@bcvideo.com *Web Site:* www.greenscreenproductionnyc.com, pg 702

Cott, George, Eagle Photographics & Digital Imaging Inc, 3612 W Swann Ave, Tampa, FL 33609 *Tel:* 813-870-2495 *Web Site:* www.eaglefineartimaging.com, pg 749

Cotterell, Bob, Creative Sound Corp, 5515 Medea Valley Dr, Agoura Hills, CA 91301 *Tel:* 818-707-8986 *E-mail:* info@csoundcorp.com *Web Site:* www.csoundcorp.com, pg 733

Cottle, Bernard, Comtel Inc, 14901 NE 20 Ave, North Miami, FL 33181 *Tel:* 305-424-4160 (facility servs); 305-424-4178 (local inquiries); 516-816-5152 (natl inquiries) *Web Site:* www.comtelinc.com; www.facebook.com/comtelinc/, pg 730

Couling, John, Dolby Laboratories Inc, 1275 Market St, San Francisco, CA 94103-1410 *Tel:* 415-558-0200 *Fax:* 415-645-4000 *Web Site:* www.dolby.com, pg 745

Countryman, Katie, Florida Film Festival, c/o Enzian Theater, 1300 S Orlando Ave, Maitland, FL 32751 *Tel:* 407-629-1088 *Fax:* 407-629-6870 *E-mail:* entries@enzian.org; marketing@enzian.org; events@enzian.org *Web Site:* www.floridafilmfestival.com, pg 989

Couris, George, Pepper Group, 220 N Smith St, Suite 406, Palatine, IL 60067 *Tel:* 847-963-0333 *Fax:* 847-963-0888 *E-mail:* pepper@peppergroup.com *Web Site:* www.peppergroup.com, pg 854

Courson, Kerri, Fleetwood Group Inc, 11832 James St, Holland, MI 49424 *Tel:* 616-396-1142 *Toll Free Tel:* 800-257-6390 *Fax:* 616-820-8300 *Web Site:* www.fleetwoodgroup.com; www.fleetwoodelectronics.com; www.fleetwoodfurniture.com, pg 762

Courtemanche, Sylvie, Canadian Broadcast Standards Council (CBSC), PO Box 3265, Sta D, Ottawa, ON K1P 6H8, Canada *Tel:* 613-233-4607 *Toll Free Tel:* 866-696-4718 (CN only) *Fax:* 613-233-4826 *E-mail:* info@cbsc.ca *Web Site:* www.cbsc.ca, pg 952

Courter, Gay, Courter Films LLC, 1145 N Stoney Point, Crystal River, FL 34429 *Tel:* 352-563-7888 (cell) *E-mail:* info@courterfilms.com *Web Site:* www.courterfilms.com, pg 732

Courter, Philip R, Courter Films LLC, 1145 N Stoney Point, Crystal River, FL 34429 *Tel:* 352-563-7888 (cell) *E-mail:* info@courterfilms.com *Web Site:* www.courterfilms.com, pg 732

Cousineau, Corey D, Drastic Technologies Ltd, 523 The Queensway, Suite 102, Toronto, ON M8Y 1J7, Canada *Tel:* 416-255-5636 *Fax:* 416-255-8780 *E-mail:* sales@drastictech.com *Web Site:* www.drastic.tv, pg 746

Couture, Danielle, Documentary Organization of Canada, Centre for Social Innovation, 215 Spadina Ave, Suite 126, Toronto, ON M5T 2C7, Canada *Tel:* 416-599-3844 *Toll Free Tel:* 877-467-4485 *E-mail:* info@docorg.ca *Web Site:* docorg.ca, pg 954

Covert, Jeff, Wally Cleaver's Recording Service, 2200 Airport Ave, Fredericksburg, VA 22401-7220 *Tel:* 540-846-6382 *E-mail:* wallycleavers@mac.com *Web Site:* www.facebook.com/wallycleavers, pg 726

Covey, Krista, Simpson Electric Co, 520 Simpson Ave, Lac du Flambeau, WI 54538-0099 *Tel:* 715-588-3947 (cust serv); 715-588-3311 *Fax:* 715-588-1248 (cust serv); 715-588-3326 *E-mail:* cservice@simpsonelectric.com; support@simpsonelectric.com *Web Site:* www.simpsonelectric.com, pg 889

Covo, Angela, San Antonio Film Festival, 8452 Fredericksburg Rd, PMB 264, San Antonio, TX 78229 *Tel:* 210-885-5888 *E-mail:* safilm@gmail.com; hello@safilm.com *Web Site:* www.safilm.com, pg 1002

Cowan, Deborah A, National Public Radio (NPR), 1111 N Capitol St NE, Washington, DC 20002 *Tel:* 202-513-2000 *Web Site:* www.npr.org, pg 959

Cowan, Gregory L, VWR International LLC, Radnor Corporate Ctr, Bldg 1, 100 Matsonford Rd, Suite 200, Radnor, PA 19087-8660 *Tel:* 610-431-1700 (corp off) *Toll Free Tel:* 800-932-5000 (cust serv) *Web Site:* www.vwr.com; us.vwr.com, pg 933

Cowden, Lisa, Ensemble Designs Inc, 870 Gold Flat Rd, Nevada City, CA 95959 *Tel:* 530-478-1830 *Fax:* 530-478-1832 *E-mail:* info@ensembledesigns.com; service@ensembledesigns.com *Web Site:* www.ensembledesigns.com, pg 754

Cowell, Bill, Buffalo Niagara International Film Festival (BNIFF), 3840 E Robinson Rd, Suite 166, Amherst, NY 14228 *Tel:* 716-693-0912 *E-mail:* info@bniff.com *Web Site:* thebnff.com, pg 984

Cox, Brian, Audio & Light, 2209 Randleman Rd, Greensboro, NC 27406 *Tel:* 336-274-1234 *Fax:* 336-274-4022 *E-mail:* info@audio-light.com *Web Site:* www.audio-light.com, pg 693

Cox, Cheryl, The Whitlock Group, 12820 West Creek Pkwy, Richmond, VA 23238 *Tel:* 804-273-9100 *Toll Free Tel:* 800-726-9843 *Fax:* 804-273-9380 *E-mail:* information@whitlock.com; marketing@ whitlock.com *Web Site:* www.whitlock.com, pg 937

Cox, David B, Micro Technology Unlimited Inc, PO Box 5, Rolesville, NC 27571 *Tel:* 919-870-0344 *E-mail:* sales@mtu.com *Web Site:* www.mtu.com, pg 826

Cox, Don, FMP Media Solutions Inc, 3600 Horizon Dr, Suite 180, King of Prussia, PA 19406 *Tel:* 610-825-4000 *Toll Free Tel:* 800-346-5071 *Fax:* 610-825-4430 *E-mail:* info@fmpmedia.com *Web Site:* www.fmpmedia.com, pg 763

Cox, John, Sacramento Theatrical Lighting Ltd (STL), 950 Richards Blvd, Sacramento, CA 95811 *Tel:* 916-447-3258 *Toll Free Tel:* 800-283-2785 *Fax:* 916-447-5012 *E-mail:* info@stlltd.com *Web Site:* www.stlltd.com, pg 879

Cox, Kate, Cochise County Tourism & Economic Council, 1011 N Coronado Dr, Sierra Vista, AZ 85635 *Tel:* 520-432-2209 *Fax:* 520-458-0584 *E-mail:* info@explorecochise.com *Web Site:* www.explorecochise.com, pg 965

Cox, Nancy, RCI Custom Products, 801 N East St, Suite 2-A, Frederick, MD 21701 *Tel:* 301-620-9130 *Toll Free Tel:* 800-546-4724 *Fax:* 301-620-9103 *Toll Free Fax:* 800-546-6175 *E-mail:* info@rcicustom.com *Web Site:* www.rcicustom.com, pg 871

Cox, Wendy, Da-Lite, a Legrand AV Inc brand, 3100 N Detroit St, Warsaw, IN 46582 *Tel:* 574-267-8101 *Toll Free Tel:* 866-977-3901 *E-mail:* av.da-lite.support@ legrand.com *Web Site:* www.legrandav.com/products/da-lite, pg 737

Coyle, Karin PhD, ETR, 100 Enterprise Way, Suite G 300, Scotts Valley, CA 95066 *Toll Free Tel:* 800-620-8884 *Fax:* 831-438-4284 *E-mail:* customerservice@etr.org, pg 756

Coyle, Larry, TGA Recording Co, 295 Urbandale Ave, Benton Harbor, MI 49022 *Tel:* 269-926-7581 *E-mail:* tgarecording@sbcglobal.net *Web Site:* www.tgarecording.com, pg 911

Coyne, Lauren, Communication Arts Visual Communications Competition, 110 Constitution Dr, Menlo Park, CA 94025 *Tel:* 650-326-6040 *Fax:* 650-326-1648 *E-mail:* competition@commarts.com *Web Site:* www.commarts.com, pg 987

Crabtree, Tamara, Abingdon Press, 2222 Rosa L Parks Blvd, Nashville, TN 37228 *Tel:* 615-749-6000 *Toll Free Tel:* 800-251-3320 *E-mail:* orders@ abingdonpress.com *Web Site:* www.abingdonpress.com, pg 672

Crabtree-Ireland, Duncan, Screen Actors Guild - American Federation of Television & Radio Artists (SAG-AFTRA), 5757 Wilshire Blvd, 7th fl, Los Angeles, CA 90036-3600 *Tel:* 323-954-1600 (former SAG); 323-634-8100 (former AFTRA) *Toll Free Tel:* 855-SAG-AFTRA (724-2387) *Fax:* 323-549-6654 (communs & mktg) *E-mail:* info@sagaftra.org *Web Site:* www.sagaftra.org, pg 961

Craig, Joycelin, Astronomical Society of the Pacific, 390 Ashton Ave, San Francisco, CA 94112 *Tel:* 415-337-1100 *Toll Free Tel:* 800-335-2624 *Fax:* 415-337-5205 *Web Site:* astrosociety.org, pg 691

Craig, Lissa, City of Calgary Film Commission, 731 First St SE, Calgary, AB T2G 2G9, Canada *Tel:* 403-221-7886 *Toll Free Tel:* 888-222-5855 *Fax:* 403-221-7828 *Web Site:* www.calgaryeconomicdevelopment.com, pg 977

Craig, Nick, Anchor Audio Inc, 5931 Darwin Ct, Carlsbad, CA 92008 *Tel:* 760-827-7100 *Toll Free Tel:* 800-262-4671 *Fax:* 760-827-7105 *E-mail:* sales@ anchoraudio.com *Web Site:* www.anchoraudio.com, pg 685

Craig, Shirley, Rev UP Tech, 20929 Ventura Blvd, Suite 47-212, Woodland Hills, CA 91364 *Tel:* 818-995-1719 *Toll Free Tel:* 877-372-0005 *Fax:* 818-979-9599 *Web Site:* revuptech.com, pg 874

Craigie, Kim, Vincent Lighting Systems, 6161 Cochran Rd, Suite D, Solon, OH 44139 *Tel:* 216-475-7600 *Toll Free Tel:* 800-922-5356 *Fax:* 216-475-6376 *E-mail:* info@vls.com *Web Site:* www.vls.com, pg 930

Cram, Bestor, Northern Light Productions (NLP), 300 Western Ave, 2nd fl, Boston, MA 02134 *Tel:* 617-789-4344 *Fax:* 617-789-4744 *E-mail:* info@nlprod.com *Web Site:* www.nlprod.com, pg 842

Cramer, Rich, Audio Visual Dynamics®, 424 Sand Shore Rd, Hackettstown, NJ 07840 *Tel:* 973-993-8500 *Fax:* 973-984-0644 *Web Site:* www.avdusa.com, pg 694

Crandall, Richard, Optronics®, 175 Cremona Dr, Goleta, CA 93117 *Tel:* 805-968-3568 *Toll Free Tel:* 800-796-8909 *Fax:* 805-968-0933 *E-mail:* oeinfo@optronics.com; sales@optronics.com *Web Site:* www.optronics.com, pg 847

Crane, Bo, Pandisc Music Corp, 936 SW First Ave, Suite 349, Miami, FL 33130 *Tel:* 305-557-1914 *Toll Free Fax:* 888-493-7778, pg 851

Crane, Christopher, Arkansas Film Commission, 900 W Capitol Ave, Suite 400, Little Rock, AR 72201 *Tel:* 501-682-7676 *Web Site:* www.arkansasproduction.com, pg 966

Crann, Paul, SeaChange International Inc, 50 Nagog Park, Acton, MA 01720 *Tel:* 978-897-0100 *Fax:* 978-897-0132 *E-mail:* globalsalesoperations@schange.com *Web Site:* www.schange.com, pg 883

Craton, Robert, Advanced Sound, 4611 Central Ave Pike, Suite F, Knoxville, TN 37912 *Tel:* 865-661-5961 *Web Site:* www.advancedsound.com, pg 677

Craven, Geoff, Association for Information Media & Equipment, PO Box 378, West Milton, PA 17866 *Tel:* 570-701-4202 *Web Site:* www.aime.org, pg 950

Craven, Michael, Thomas Craven Film Corp, 5 W 19 St, 3rd fl, New York, NY 10011-4216 *Tel:* 212-463-7190 *Fax:* 212-627-4761 *E-mail:* info@cravenfilms.com *Web Site:* cravenfilms.com, pg 733

Craven, Mike, Full Scale Effects, 6869 Tujunga Ave, North Hollywood, CA 91605 *Tel:* 818-760-0875; 818-760-0042 *Fax:* 818-760-0876 *Web Site:* fullscalefx.com, pg 767

Craven, Penny, Thomas Craven Film Corp, 5 W 19 St, 3rd fl, New York, NY 10011-4216 *Tel:* 212-463-7190 *Fax:* 212-627-4761 *E-mail:* info@cravenfilms.com *Web Site:* cravenfilms.com, pg 733

Crawford, James, Frezzi Energy Systems, 7 Valley St, Hawthorne, NJ 07506 *Tel:* 973-427-1160 *Fax:* 973-427-0934 *E-mail:* info@frezzi.com *Web Site:* www.frezzi.com, pg 766

Crawford, Jesse, Crawford Media Services Inc, 6 W Druid Hills Dr NE, Atlanta, GA 30329 *Tel:* 404-876-0333 *Toll Free Tel:* 800-831-8029 *E-mail:* bookit@ crawford.com *Web Site:* audio.crawford.com; www.facebook.com/crawfordmediaservices, pg 733

Crawford, Kevin, Frezzi Energy Systems, 7 Valley St, Hawthorne, NJ 07506 *Tel:* 973-427-1160 *Fax:* 973-427-0934 *E-mail:* info@frezzi.com *Web Site:* www.frezzi.com, pg 766

Crawford, Sandra, SpaceCam, 31240 La Baya Dr, Westlake Village, CA 91362 *Tel:* 818-889-6060 *Fax:* 818-889-6062 *E-mail:* rentals@spacecam.com *Web Site:* spacecam.com, pg 896

Crawford, Sandy, Illuminate Studios, 10900 Ventura Blvd, Studio City, CA 90068 *Tel:* 818-769-4500 *Fax:* 818-769-7150 *E-mail:* info@illuminatehollywood.com *Web Site:* illuminatehollywood.com, pg 784

Crawford, Sterling, Ingram Content Group LLC, One Ingram Blvd, La Vergne, TN 37086-1986 *Tel:* 615-793-5000 *Toll Free Tel:* 800-937-8000 (retailers); 800-937-5300 (ext 1, libs) *E-mail:* customerservice@ ingramcontent.com *Web Site:* www.ingramcontent.com, pg 787

Craycraft, Jeffrey, InterAmerica Stage Inc, 5401 Benchmark Lane, Sanford, FL 32773 *Tel:* 407-302-0881 *Toll Free Tel:* 877-302-4274 *Fax:* 407-302-0882 *E-mail:* info@iastage.com *Web Site:* www.iastage.com, pg 789

Craythorne, Tony, Nexsan Inc, 900 E Hamilton Ave, Suite 230, Campbell, CA 95008 *Tel:* 408-724-9809 *E-mail:* sales@nexsan.com *Web Site:* www.nexsan.com, pg 840

Crebo, Ron, The Hollaender Manufacturing Co, 10285 Wayne Ave, Cincinnati, OH 45215 *Tel:* 513-772-8800 *Toll Free Tel:* 800-772-8800 (orders) *Fax:* 513-772-8806 *Web Site:* www.hollaender.com, pg 780

Cree, Jeff, Band Pro Film & Digital Inc, 3403 W Pacific Ave, Burbank, CA 91505 *Tel:* 818-841-9655 *Toll Free Tel:* 888-BANDPRO (226-3776) *Fax:* 818-841-7649 *E-mail:* info@bandpro.com; customercare@bandpro.com *Web Site:* www.bandpro.com, pg 701

Creighton, Gerry, Bang! Pictures Inc, 78 Graterford Rd, Schwenksville, PA 19473 *Tel:* 610-357-1015 *Web Site:* www.bangpictures.com, pg 701

Crescenzo, Tony, Intellidyne LLC, 2677 Prosperity Ave, Suite 301, Fairfax, VA 22031 *Tel:* 703-575-9715 *Fax:* 703-575-9718 *Web Site:* www.intellidyne-llc.com, pg 789

Cress, Kathryn, Christie Digital Systems USA Inc, 10550 Camden Dr, Cypress, CA 90630 *Tel:* 714-236-8610 *Toll Free Tel:* 866-880-4462 (cust serv) *Fax:* 714-503-3375 *E-mail:* sales-us@christiedigital.com; orders@christiedigital.com *Web Site:* www.christiedigital.com, pg 722

Cretella, Morgan Tondo, Turning Technologies LLC, 255 W Federal St, Youngstown, OH 44503 *Tel:* 330-746-3015 *Toll Free Tel:* 866-746-3015 *E-mail:* info@turningtechnologies.com; support@turningtechnologies.com *Web Site:* www.turningtechnologies.com, pg 919

Crilly, Donna, Paulist Press, 997 Macarthur Blvd, Mahwah, NJ 07430-9990 *Tel:* 201-825-7300 *Toll Free Tel:* 800-218-1903 (orders) *Fax:* 201-825-6921 *E-mail:* info@paulistpress.com *Web Site:* www.paulistpress.com, pg 852

Crisanti, Marielle, Matrix Video Communications Corp (MVCC), 103, 1626 115 Ave NE, Calgary, AB T3K 5Y8, Canada *Tel:* 403-640-4490 *Fax:* 403-640-9012 *Web Site:* www.matrixvideocom.com, pg 819

Criscitiello, Mike, Onkyo USA Corp, 18 Park Way, Upper Saddle River, NJ 07458 *Tel:* 201-785-2600 *Toll Free Tel:* 800-229-1687 *Web Site:* www.onkyousa.com, pg 846

Critics, David, Library of Congress, Motion Picture, Broadcasting & Recorded Sound Division, James Madison Bldg, LM 336, 101 Independence Ave SE, Washington, DC 20540-1000 *Tel:* 202-707-8572 *Fax:* 202-707-2371 *Web Site:* www.loc.gov/rr/mopic, pg 807

Croce, Pat, DecisionOne Corp, 640 Lee Rd, 3rd fl, Wayne, PA 19087 *Tel:* 610-296-6000 *Toll Free Tel:* 800-767-2876; 800-777-8800 (cust serv); 888-287-9202 (sales); 800-554-5179 (CN) *Fax:* 610-296-2910 *E-mail:* sales@decisionone.com *Web Site:* www.decisionone.com, pg 740

Crocker, Thomas C, Countdown Productions Inc, PO Box 180220, Dallas, TX 75218 *Tel:* 214-321-3233; 214-808-9988 (cell) *E-mail:* info@ countdownproductions.com *Web Site:* www.countdownproductions.com, pg 732

Crockett, Bob, Alaska Media Pros LLC, 11050 Cange St, Anchorage, AK 99516 *Tel:* 907-230-8839 *E-mail:* ifilm@alaska.net *Web Site:* www.alaskamediapros.com, pg 679

Croen, Caroline C, WNET/New York Public Media, 825 Eighth Ave, New York, NY 10019 *Tel:* 212-560-1313 *Fax:* 212-560-1314 *E-mail:* programming@thirteen.org *Web Site:* www.thirteen.org; www.wnet.org, pg 940

Cronin, Jack, Mastech Digital, 1305 Cherrington Pkwy, Bldg 210, Suite 400, Moon Township, PA 15108 *Tel:* 412-787-2100 *Toll Free Tel:* 800-627-

Czarnecki, Gene, Czar Productions Inc, 809 New Britain Ave, Hartford, CT 06106 *Tel:* 860-953-0809 *E-mail:* czar.productions@snet.net, pg 737

Czyzak, Timothy, iVideo Technologies, 6779 Engle Rd, Suite G, Middleburg Heights, OH 44130 *Toll Free Tel:* 800-352-6150 *E-mail:* info@ivideo.com *Web Site:* www.ivideo.com, pg 792

D'Acierno, Amanda, Penguin Random House Audio Publishing, 1745 Broadway, New York, NY 10019 *E-mail:* audio@penguinrandomhouse.com *Web Site:* www.penguinrandomhouseaudio.com, pg 853

D'Agostino, David, SurgeX, 8001 Knightdale Blvd, Suite 121, Knightdale, NC 27545 *Toll Free Tel:* 800-645-9721 (tech & cust support) *E-mail:* order.desk@ametek.com *Web Site:* espsurgex.com/surgex/, pg 905

D'Alessandro, Fred, Diversified, 37 Market St, Kenilworth, NJ 07033 *Tel:* 908-245-4833 *Fax:* 908-245-0011 *E-mail:* customerservice@diversifiedus.com; info@diversifiedus.com *Web Site:* diversifiedus.com, pg 744

D'Allen, Nick, Staging Directions Inc, 1327 Northbrook Pkwy, Suite 440, Suwanee, GA 30024 *Tel:* 770-409-9909 *Toll Free Tel:* 800-782-4322 *Fax:* 770-409-0277 *E-mail:* sales@teamsdi.net *Web Site:* www.stagingdirections.com, pg 899

D'Amato, Sally-Ann, The Citation of Outstanding Service to the Society Award, White Plains Plaza, 445 Hamilton Ave, Suite 601, White Plains, NY 10601-1827 *Tel:* 914-761-1100 *Fax:* 914-206-4216 *E-mail:* marketing@smpte.org *Web Site:* www.smpte.org, pg 986

D'Amato, Sally-Ann, The Presidential Proclamation, White Plains Plaza, 445 Hamilton Ave, Suite 601, White Plains, NY 10601-1827 *Tel:* 914-761-1100 *Fax:* 914-206-4216 *E-mail:* marketing@smpte.org *Web Site:* www.smpte.org, pg 1000

D'Amato, Sally-Ann, SMPTE® Journal Award & SMPTE® Journal Certificate of Merit, White Plains Plaza, 445 Hamilton Ave, Suite 601, White Plains, NY 10601-1827 *Tel:* 914-761-1100 *Fax:* 914-206-4216 *E-mail:* marketing@smpte.org *Web Site:* www.smpte.org, pg 1004

D'Amato, Sally-Ann, SMPTE® Progress Medal Award, White Plains Plaza, 445 Hamilton Ave, Suite 601, White Plains, NY 10601-1827 *Tel:* 914-761-1100 *Fax:* 914-206-4216 *E-mail:* marketing@smpte.org *Web Site:* www.smpte.org, pg 1004

D'Amato, Sally-Ann, Society of Motion Picture & Television Engineers® (SMPTE®), White Plains Plaza, 445 Hamilton Ave, Suite 601, White Plains, NY 10601-1827 *Tel:* 914-761-1100 *Fax:* 914-206-4216 *E-mail:* marketing@smpte.org *Web Site:* www.smpte.org, pg 892

D'Amato, Sally-Ann, Society of Motion Picture & Television Engineers® (SMPTE®), White Plains Plaza, 445 Hamilton Ave, Suite 601, White Plains, NY 10601-1827 *Tel:* 914-761-1100 *Fax:* 914-206-4216 *E-mail:* membership@smpte.org *Web Site:* www.smpte.org, pg 962

D'Amato, Sally-Ann, Technicolor-Herbert T Kalmus Medal Award, White Plains Plaza, 445 Hamilton Ave, Suite 601, White Plains, NY 10601-1827 *Tel:* 914-761-1100 *Fax:* 914-206-4216 *E-mail:* marketing@smpte.org *Web Site:* www.smpte.org, pg 1004

D'Amato, Sally-Ann, The Samuel L Warner Memorial Medal Award, White Plains Plaza, 445 Hamilton Ave, Suite 601, White Plains, NY 10601-1827 *Tel:* 914-761-1100 *Fax:* 914-206-4216 *E-mail:* marketing@smpte.org *Web Site:* www.smpte.org, pg 1006

D'Amico, Diane, National Headliner Awards, PO Box 128, Somers Point, NJ 08244 *Tel:* 609-927-1850; 609-350-3099 *E-mail:* info@headlinerawards.org *Web Site:* www.headlinerawards.org, pg 997

D'Angelo, Mike, PortaBrace Inc, 160 Benmont Ave, Suite 100, North Bennington, VT 05201 *Tel:* 802-442-8171 *Fax:* 802-442-9118 *E-mail:* info@portabrace.com *Web Site:* www.portabrace.com, pg 859

d'Arbeloff, Eric, Roadside Attractions, 7920 Sunset Blvd, No 402, Los Angeles, CA 90046 *Tel:* 323-882-8490 *E-mail:* roadsideflix@gmail.com *Web Site:* roadsideattractions.com, pg 876

D'Egidio, Craig, The DVI Group, 1486 Mecaslin St NW, Atlanta, GA 30309 *Tel:* 404-873-6283 *Toll Free Tel:* 888-736-7384 *E-mail:* makeitbetter@thedvigroup.com *Web Site:* www.thedvigroup.com, pg 748

D'or, Daniel, Canamedia Inc, 1540 Cornwall Rd, Suite 216, Oakville, ON L6J 7W5, Canada *Tel:* 416-363-6765 *Toll Free Tel:* 866-999-5292 *Fax:* 416-363-7834 *Web Site:* www.canamedia.com, pg 715

D'Oratio, Frank, CORTRON Media LLC, 320 Fort Duquesne Blvd, Suite 100, Pittsburgh, PA 15222-1146 *Tel:* 412-565-3471 (ext 3) *Web Site:* cortronmedia.com, pg 732

da Silva, Antonio Carlos, United Nations Multimedia Resources Unit, c/o Audio Library, UN Dept of Public Information, Rm S-1046 & S-1083, New York, NY 10017 *Tel:* 212-963-9268; 212-963-0656 *E-mail:* avlibrary@un.org *Web Site:* www.unmultimedia.org, pg 921

da Silva, Josh, Questar Entertainment Inc, 307 N Michigan Ave, 5th fl, Chicago, IL 60601-5305 *Tel:* 312-266-9400 *Toll Free Tel:* 800-544-8422 (cust serv) *E-mail:* info@questarentertainment.com *Web Site:* www.questarentertainment.com, pg 868

Dacian, Daniel, Big Apple Films, 636 W 28 St, New York, NY 10001 *E-mail:* info@bigapplefilms.com *Web Site:* www.bigapplefilms.com, pg 705

Dadmun, James, DGI-Invisuals LLC, 101 Billerica Ave, Bldg 6, North Billerica, MA 01862 *Toll Free Tel:* 800-344-0432 *Fax:* 781-270-3663 *E-mail:* sales@dgi-invisuals.com *Web Site:* www.dgi-invisuals.com, pg 741

Dafel, Ashley, Creation Technologies Inc, 8999 Fraserton Ct, Burnaby, BC V5J 5H8, Canada *Tel:* 604-430-4336 *Toll Free Tel:* 800-736-1271 *E-mail:* info@creationtech.com; sales@creationtech.com *Web Site:* www.creationtech.com, pg 733

Dahlen, Peter, American Choral Catalog Ltd, 205 S Water St, Northfield, MN 55057 *Tel:* 507-645-4695 *Fax:* 507-645-2474 *E-mail:* info@americanchoral.com *Web Site:* www.americanchoral.com, pg 683

Dahlgren, Erik, FootageBank HD, 13470 Washington Blvd, Suite 210, Marina del Rey, CA 90292 *Tel:* 310-822-1400 *Fax:* 310-822-4100 *E-mail:* info@footagebank.com *Web Site:* www.footagebank.com, pg 763

Dahlquist, Nels, Chicago International REEL Shorts Film Festival, 2700 W Grand Ave, Chicago, IL 60612 *E-mail:* info@projectchicago.com *Web Site:* www.projectchicago.com, pg 985

Dahnke, Lynn M, Coast Learning Systems, 11460 Warner Ave, Fountain Valley, CA 92708 *Tel:* 714-241-6109 *Toll Free Tel:* 800-547-4748 *E-mail:* coastlearning@coastline.edu *Web Site:* www.coastlearning.com, pg 727

Dai, Ted, AVerMedia Technologies Inc, 47358 Fremont Blvd, Fremont, CA 94538 *Tel:* 510-403-0006 *Fax:* 510-403-0022 *E-mail:* avtsales.usa@avermedia.com *Web Site:* www.avermedia.com, pg 698

Dake, Ron, Show-Me Audio-Visual, Corporate Ridge, 4501 Blue Ridge Cutoff, Kansas City, MO 64133 *Tel:* 816-358-8700 *Toll Free Tel:* 800-2-SHOWME (274-6963) *Fax:* 816-358-8701 *E-mail:* info@showmeav.com *Web Site:* www.showmeav.com, pg 887

Dalakian, Martin, International Audio Visual Inc, 622 Rte 10, Unit 21, Whippany, NJ 07981 *Tel:* 973-887-7744 *Toll Free Tel:* 888-887-7749 *E-mail:* iav@iavnj.com *Web Site:* www.iavnj.com, pg 790

Daley, Brian L, Revolution Lighting Technologies Inc, 177 Broad St, 12th fl, Stamford, CT 06901 *Tel:* 203-504-1111 *Toll Free Tel:* 877-578-2536 *E-mail:* support@rvlti.com; info@rvlti.com *Web Site:* www.rvlti.com, pg 874

Dallas, Julie, WPGH-TV, 750 Ivory Ave, Pittsburgh, PA 15214 *Tel:* 412-931-5300; 412-931-8020 (sales) *Fax:* 412-931-4284 *Web Site:* www.sbgi.net; www.wpgh53.com, pg 942

Dalton, Heather, Books on Tape™, c/o Library & School Servs, 400 Hahn Rd, Westminster, MD 21157 *Toll Free Tel:* 800-733-3000 *Toll Free Fax:* 800-940-7046 *E-mail:* csbot@penguinrandomhouse.com *Web Site:* www.booksontape.com, pg 709

Dalton, Heather, Penguin Random House Audio Publishing, 1745 Broadway, New York, NY 10019 *E-mail:* audio@penguinrandomhouse.com *Web Site:* www.penguinrandomhouseaudio.com, pg 853

Dalton, Mike, Applied Electronics Ltd, 1260 Kamato Rd, Mississauga, ON L4W 1Y1, Canada *Tel:* 905-625-4321 *Fax:* 905-625-4333 *E-mail:* ael.toronto@appliedelectronics.com *Web Site:* www.appliedelectronics.com, pg 687

Daly, Katy, Austin Film Festival, 1801 Salina St, Austin, TX 78702 *Tel:* 512-478-4795 *Toll Free Tel:* 800-310-FEST (310-3378) *Fax:* 512-478-6205 *E-mail:* info@austinfilmfestival.com; programming@austinfilmfestival.com; marketing@austinfilmfestival.com *Web Site:* www.austinfilmfestival.com, pg 982

Daman, Julie, Washington Filmworks, 1411 Fourth Ave, Suite 420, Seattle, WA 98101 *Tel:* 206-264-0667 *Fax:* 206-382-4343 *E-mail:* info@washingtonfilmworks.org *Web Site:* washingtonfilmworks.org, pg 977

Dana, A William, WHYY Inc, Independence Mall West, 150 N Sixth St, Philadelphia, PA 19106 *Tel:* 215-351-1200 *Fax:* 215-351-0398 *E-mail:* talkback@whyy.org *Web Site:* www.whyy.org, pg 938

Dancy, Paul, TVO/Ontario Educational Communications Authority (OECA), 2180 Yonge St, Toronto, ON M4S 2B9, Canada *Tel:* 416-484-2600; 416-484-2665 (cust rel) *Toll Free Tel:* 800-613-0513; 800-INFO-TVO (463-6886) *E-mail:* asktvo@tvo.org *Web Site:* tvo.org, pg 919

Daniel, Marcus, Sacramento Theatrical Lighting Ltd (STL), 950 Richards Blvd, Sacramento, CA 95811 *Tel:* 916-447-3258 *Toll Free Tel:* 800-283-2785 *Fax:* 916-447-5012 *E-mail:* info@stlltd.com *Web Site:* www.stlltd.com, pg 879

Daniel, Sarita, Northeast Louisiana Film Commission, 601 Constitution Dr, West Monroe, LA 71292 *Toll Free Tel:* 800-843-1872 *Web Site:* nelafilm.com, pg 971

Daniel, W Donnie, Ingram Entertainment Inc, 2 Ingram Blvd, La Vergne, TN 37089 *Tel:* 615-287-4000 (corp) *Toll Free Tel:* 800-621-1333 (sales & cust serv) *Web Site:* www.ingramentertainment.com, pg 787

Daniels, Karil, Point of View Productions, 2477 Folsom St, San Francisco, CA 94110 *Fax:* 415-821-0434, pg 858

Danke, Sarah, ETC, 3031 Pleasant View Rd, Middleton, WI 53562-4809 *Tel:* 608-831-4116 *Toll Free Tel:* 800-688-4116 *Fax:* 608-836-1736 *Web Site:* www.etcconnect.com, pg 756

Danowitz, Dean, Starlite, 9 Whittendale Dr, Moorestown, NJ 08057 *Tel:* 856-780-8000 *Toll Free Tel:* 800-738-7400 *Fax:* 856-780-8001 *E-mail:* info@starlite.com *Web Site:* www.starlite.com, pg 900

Danowitz, Jason, Starlite, 9 Whittendale Dr, Moorestown, NJ 08057 *Tel:* 856-780-8000 *Toll Free Tel:* 800-738-7400 *Fax:* 856-780-8001 *E-mail:* info@starlite.com *Web Site:* www.starlite.com, pg 900

Darling, Tom, DecisionOne Corp, 640 Lee Rd, 3rd fl, Wayne, PA 19087 *Tel:* 610-296-6000 *Toll Free Tel:* 800-767-2876; 800-777-8800 (cust serv); 888-287-9202 (sales); 800-554-5179 (CN) *Fax:* 610-296-2910 *E-mail:* sales@decisionone.com *Web Site:* www.decisionone.com, pg 740

Darnton, John, George Polk Awards in Journalism, Journalism Dept, One University Plaza, Brooklyn, NY 11201-5372 *Tel:* 718-488-1009 *Web Site:* www.liu.edu/polk, pg 1000

Darr, Emily, Heartland International Film Festival, 1043 Virginia Ave, Suite 2, Indianapolis, IN 46203 *Tel:* 317-464-9405 *E-mail:* submissions@heartlandfilm.org *Web Site:* heartlandfilm.org/festival, pg 992

Darr, Emily, Indy Shorts International Film Fest, 1043 Virginia Ave, Suite 2, Indianapolis, IN 46203 *Tel:* 317-464-9405 *E-mail:* submissions@heartlandfilm.org *Web Site:* heartlandfilm.org, pg 993

Darrell, Bracken, Logitech, 7700 Gateway Blvd, Newark, CA 94560 *Tel:* 510-795-8500 *Toll Free Tel:* 866-291-1505 *Web Site:* www.logitech.com, pg 811

Darrow, Doug, Dolby Laboratories Inc, 1275 Market St, San Francisco, CA 94103-1410 *Tel:* 415-558-0200 *Fax:* 415-645-4000 *Web Site:* www.dolby.com, pg 745

Darrow, Richard, ToCad America Inc, 53 Green Pond Rd, Suite 5, Rockaway, NJ 07866 *Tel:* 973-627-9600 *Toll Free Tel:* 800-886-2236 *Fax:* 973-664-2438 *E-mail:* info@tocad.com *Web Site:* www.tocad.com, pg 915

Darvishian, Adriane, National Association for Music Education (NAfME), 1806 Robert Fulton Dr, Reston, VA 20191 *Tel:* 703-860-4000 *Toll Free Tel:* 800-336-3768 *Fax:* 703-860-1531 *Toll Free Fax:* 888-275-6362 *E-mail:* memberservices@nafme.org *Web Site:* nafme.org, pg 958

Dashner, Mel, Origin Instruments Corp, 854 Greenview Dr, Grand Prairie, TX 75050-2438 *Tel:* 972-606-8740 *Fax:* 972-606-8741 *E-mail:* support@orin.com; marketing@orin.com *Web Site:* www.orin.com, pg 848

Dasso, Robert, Magnetic Shield Corp, 740 N Thomas Dr, Bensenville, IL 60106 *Tel:* 630-766-7800 *Toll Free Tel:* 888-766-7800 *Fax:* 630-766-2813 *E-mail:* shields@magnetic-shield.com *Web Site:* www.magnetic-shield.com, pg 815

Dasu, Dhiren, Blue Lotus Temple Studio, PO Box 888, Boulder Creek, CA 95006 *Tel:* 831-338-2544 *E-mail:* info@bluelotustemple.com *Web Site:* www.bluelotustemple.com, pg 707

Dater, Alan, Marlboro Productions, 1076 Moss Hollow Rd, Marlboro, VT 05344 *Tel:* 802-257-0743 *E-mail:* mfilmpro@sover.net *Web Site:* marlboroproductions.com, pg 817

Daugherty, John, Film Columbus, 100 E Broad St, Suite 2250, Columbus, OH 43215 *Tel:* 614-221-8648 *E-mail:* info@filmcolumbus.com *Web Site:* filmcolumbus.com, pg 975

Daugherty, Paul R, Accenture, 161 N Clark St, Chicago, IL 60601 *Tel:* 312-693-0161 *Toll Free Tel:* 877-889-9009 *Fax:* 312-693-0507 *Web Site:* www.accenture.com, pg 672

Daugherty, Tyler, Dubuque Area Convention & Visitors Bureau, 300 Main St, Suite 120, Dubuque, IA 52001 *Tel:* 563-845-7698 *Web Site:* www.traveldubuque.com, pg 971

Daugherty, Will, Evolve Inc, 1210 E Arlington Blvd, Greenville, NC 27858 *Tel:* 252-754-2957 *Fax:* 252-754-2832 *Web Site:* www.evolveinc.com, pg 757

Daulton, Sue, Penguin Random House Audio Publishing, 1745 Broadway, New York, NY 10019 *E-mail:* audio@penguinrandomhouse.com *Web Site:* www.penguinrandomhouseaudio.com, pg 853

Dauphin, Brian, Ingram Content Group LLC, One Ingram Blvd, La Vergne, TN 37086-1986 *Tel:* 615-793-5000 *Toll Free Tel:* 800-937-8000 (retailers); 800-937-5300 (ext 1, libs) *E-mail:* customerservice@ingramcontent.com *Web Site:* www.ingramcontent.com, pg 787

Daussin, Charles, Outland Technology Inc, 38190 Commercial Ct, Slidell, LA 70458 *Tel:* 985-847-1104 *Fax:* 985-847-1106 *E-mail:* sales@outlandtech.com *Web Site:* www.outlandtech.com, pg 849

Davenport, Carla, Image Associates Inc, 5475 Rumley Rd, Suite 102, Durham, NC 27703 *Tel:* 919-876-6400 *Fax:* 919-876-6400 *E-mail:* info@imageassociates.com *Web Site:* www.imageassociates.com, pg 784

Davenport, Elaine, Writer's AudioShop/Davenport Productions, 1316 Overland Stage Rd, Dripping Springs, TX 78620 *Tel:* 512-476-1616 (edit); 512-264-7067 (sales) *E-mail:* wrtaudshop@aol.com *Web Site:* www.writersaudio.com, pg 942

Davenport, Neal, Davenport Music Library, PO Box 690536, Charlotte, NC 28227-7009 *Web Site:* www.davenportmusic.com, pg 738

Davern, Alex, National Instruments Corp, 11500 N Mopac Expwy, Austin, TX 78759-3504 *Tel:* 512-683-0100 *Toll Free Tel:* 888-280-7645 (sales); 877-388-1952 *Fax:* 512-683-8411; 512-683-5794 (sales) *Web Site:* www.ni.com, pg 836

David, Joseph, J&D Laboratories Inc, 27 E 21 St, 4th fl, New York, NY 10010 *Tel:* 212-982-3330 *Fax:* 212-982-3332 *E-mail:* jdvideolab@aol.com; sales@jdvideolab.com *Web Site:* www.jdvideolab.com, pg 793

David, Marjorie, Writers Guild of America, West (WGAW), 7000 W Third St, Los Angeles, CA 90048 *Tel:* 323-951-4000 *Toll Free Tel:* 800-548-4532 *Web Site:* www.wga.org, pg 963

David, Patricia, J&D Laboratories Inc, 27 E 21 St, 4th fl, New York, NY 10010 *Tel:* 212-982-3330 *Fax:* 212-982-3332 *E-mail:* jdvideolab@aol.com; sales@jdvideolab.com *Web Site:* www.jdvideolab.com, pg 793

Davids, Markus, CineBags Inc, 825 Western Ave, Suite 17, Glendale, CA 91201 *Tel:* 818-662-0605 *E-mail:* sales@cinebags.com *Web Site:* www.cinebags.com, pg 723

Davidson, Jean, Davidson Productions, 1180 Vista Del Lago, San Luis Obispo, CA 93405 *Tel:* 415-886-7540 *E-mail:* dfi@davidsonfilms.com *Web Site:* davidsonfilms.com, pg 738

Davidson, Michael, Explore Lawrence, PO Box 526, Lawrence, KS 66044 *Tel:* 785-856-3040; 785-856-5282 (mktg) *Fax:* 785-856-5303 *E-mail:* visinfo@explorelawrence.com *Web Site:* www.explorelawrence.com, pg 971

Davidson, Randall, University of Wisconsin-Oshkosh Radio-TV-Film Dept, Arts & Communications Bldg, W-112, 800 Algoma Blvd, Oshkosh, WI 54901 *Tel:* 920-424-3131 *E-mail:* rtf@uwosh.edu *Web Site:* rtf.uwosh.edu, pg 923

Davidson, Dr Randall W A, Risk International & Associates Inc, c/o Global Health & Safety Network, 8803 W Ontario Ave, Littleton, CO 80128 *Tel:* 720-922-0707 *Fax:* 720-922-0707 *Web Site:* globalhealthandsafety.net, pg 875

Davidson, Richard M, RADMAR Inc, PO Box 425, Northbrook, IL 60065-0425 *Tel:* 847-298-7980 *E-mail:* radmarinc@gmail.com *Web Site:* www.radmarinc.com, pg 869

Davies, Bill, Jack Morton Worldwide, 909 Third Ave, New York, NY 10022 *Tel:* 212-401-7000; 212-401-7212 *E-mail:* experience@jackmorton.com *Web Site:* www.jackmorton.com, pg 830

Davies, Gordon A, OpenText Corp, 275 Frank Tompa Dr, Waterloo, ON N2L 0A1, Canada *Tel:* 519-888-7111 *Toll Free Tel:* 800-499-6544 *Fax:* 519-888-0677 *Web Site:* www.opentext.com, pg 847

Davies, Jennifer, All Access Staging & Productions, 1320 Storm Pkwy, Torrance, CA 90501 *Tel:* 310-784-2464 *Toll Free Tel:* 877-784-2464 *Fax:* 310-517-0899 *E-mail:* sales@allaccessinc.com *Web Site:* www.allaccessinc.com, pg 680

Davies, Michael, Davies Publishing Inc, 32 S Raymond Ave, Suites 4-5, Pasadena, CA 91105 *Tel:* 626-792-3046 *Toll Free Tel:* 877-792-0005 (US only) *Fax:* 626-792-5308 *E-mail:* info@daviespublishing.com *Web Site:* daviespublishing.com, pg 738

Davies, Trevor, Convergent Media Systems, 190 Bluegrass Valley Pkwy, Alpharetta, GA 30005-2204 *Tel:* 770-369-9000 *Fax:* 770-369-9100 *Web Site:* www.convergent.com, pg 731

Davies, Walter, The LAST Factory, 2011 Research Dr, Livermore, CA 94550-3803 *Tel:* 925-449-9449 *Fax:* 925-447-0662 *E-mail:* thelastfactory@gmail.com *Web Site:* thelastfactory.com, pg 804

Davila, Cecilie, Jackson Hole Film Commission, 260A Broadway Ave, Jackson, WY 83001 *Tel:* 307-733-3316 *Fax:* 307-733-5585 *Web Site:* www.jacksonholechamber.com, pg 977

Davis, Dave, Baker Audio Visual, 2195 N Norcross Tucker Rd, Norcross, GA 30071 *Tel:* 770-441-2000 *Toll Free Tel:* 800-847-3523 *Fax:* 770-449-7719 *E-mail:* support@bakeraudiovisual.com *Web Site:* www.bakeraudiovisual.com, pg 700

Davis, David A, Romar Learning Solutions LLC, 6700 Woodlands Pkwy, Suite 230-292, Woodlands, TX 77382 *Tel:* 281-292-5508 *Fax:* 281-363-2309 *E-mail:* info@romarlearning.com *Web Site:* romarlearning.com, pg 877

Davis, Gregg, Convergent Media Systems, 190 Bluegrass Valley Pkwy, Alpharetta, GA 30005-2204 *Tel:* 770-369-9000 *Fax:* 770-369-9100 *Web Site:* www.convergent.com, pg 731

Davis, Hayne, DaviSound, PO Box 521, Newberry, SC 29108-0521 *Tel:* 803-944-7972 (messages only) *Web Site:* www.davisound.com, pg 739

Davis, John J, John J Davis & Associates Consulting Engineers, PO Box 128, Sierra Madre, CA 91025-0128 *Tel:* 626-355-6909, pg 739

Davis, Jon, Sight & Sound Productions, 11193 Saint Johns Industrial Pkwy N, Jacksonville, FL 32246 *Tel:* 904-645-7880 *Toll Free Tel:* 800-339-0846 *Fax:* 904-645-7787 *E-mail:* info@ssav.net *Web Site:* www.ssav.net, pg 887

Davis, Kelsey, Visions Film Festival & Conference, 601 S College Rd, Wilmington, NC 28403 *Tel:* 919-607-0031 *E-mail:* visions7programming@gmail.com; visions7development@gmail.com *Web Site:* www.visionsffc.org, pg 1006

Davis, Kenneth G, Pro Cuts Editing Services, 2138 Priest Bridge Ct, Suite 1, Crofton, MD 21114 *Tel:* 301-464-5067; 443-274-6115 *E-mail:* info@procutsediting.com *Web Site:* www.procutsediting.com, pg 862

Davis, Phillip, Dogwood Productions Inc, 757 Government St, Mobile, AL 36602 *Tel:* 251-476-0858 *Toll Free Tel:* 800-254-9903 *Fax:* 251-479-0364 *E-mail:* info@dogwoodproductions.com *Web Site:* www.dogwoodproductions.com, pg 745

Davis, Rick, Video Advantage, 90 Houseman Crescent, Richmond Hill, ON L4C 7S6, Canada *Tel:* 905-883-5332 *E-mail:* info@videoadvantage.ca *Web Site:* www.videoadvantage.ca, pg 927

Davis, Roslyn, WNET/New York Public Media, 825 Eighth Ave, New York, NY 10019 *Tel:* 212-560-1313 *Fax:* 212-560-1314 *E-mail:* programming@thirteen.org *Web Site:* www.thirteen.org; www.wnet.org, pg 940

Davis, Scott, WNET/New York Public Media, 825 Eighth Ave, New York, NY 10019 *Tel:* 212-560-1313 *Fax:* 212-560-1314 *E-mail:* programming@thirteen.org *Web Site:* www.thirteen.org; www.wnet.org, pg 940

Davis, Shawn, Los Angeles Film Festival, 5670 Wilshire Blvd, 9th fl, Los Angeles, CA 90036 *Tel:* 323-556-9300 *Toll Free Tel:* 866-345-6337 *Fax:* 323-556-9303 *E-mail:* lafilmfest@filmindependent.org; programming@filmindependent.org *Web Site:* www.filmindependent.org/la-film-festival, pg 995

Davis, Terry, Califone International Inc, 9135 Alabama Ave, Suite B, Chatsworth, CA 91311 *Tel:* 818-407-2400 *Toll Free Tel:* 800-722-0500 *Fax:* 818-407-2405 *Toll Free Fax:* 877-402-2248 *Web Site:* www.califone.com, pg 714

Davis, Timothy S Esq, Close Up Foundation, 1330 Braddock Place, Suite 400, Alexandria, VA 22314 *Tel:* 703-706-3300 *Toll Free Tel:* 800-CLOSEUP (256-7387) *E-mail:* info@closeup.org *Web Site:* www.closeup.org, pg 726

Davison, Bill, SirsiDynix, 3300 N Ashton Blvd, Suite 500, Lehi, UT 84043 *Tel:* 801-223-5200; 0800 016 3147 *Toll Free Tel:* 800-288-8020 *Fax:* 801-331-7770 *Web Site:* www.sirsidynix.com, pg 889

Davydov, Nisan, SDI Technologies Inc, 1299 Main St, Rahway, NJ 07065-5024 *Tel:* 732-574-9000 *Toll Free Tel:* 800-333-3092; 800-888-4491 (cust serv) *Fax:* 732-382-2954 *E-mail:* customerservice@sditech. com *Web Site:* www.sditechnologies.com; www. ihomeaudio.com, pg 883

Dawson, Bob, Bias Studios, 5400 Carolina Place, Springfield, VA 22151 *Tel:* 703-941-3333 *E-mail:* info@biasstudios.com *Web Site:* www. biasstudios.com, pg 705

Dawson, Carly, Visions Film Festival & Conference, 601 S College Rd, Wilmington, NC 28403 *Tel:* 919-607-0031 *E-mail:* visions7programming@gmail.com; visions7development@gmail.com *Web Site:* www. visionsffc.org, pg 1006

Dawson, Craig PhD, PAR Inc, 16204 N Florida Ave, Lutz, FL 33549 *Tel:* 813-449-4065 *Toll Free Tel:* 800-331-8378 *Fax:* 813-961-2196 *Toll Free Fax:* 800-727-9329 *E-mail:* cs@parinc.com *Web Site:* www.parinc. com, pg 851

Dawson, Donne, State of Hawaii Film Office, 250 S Hotel St, Suite 510-A, Honolulu, HI 96813 *Tel:* 808-586-2570 *Fax:* 808-586-2572 *E-mail:* info@ hawaiifilmoffice.com *Web Site:* filmoffice.hawaii.gov, pg 970

Dawson, Gloria, Bias Studios, 5400 Carolina Place, Springfield, VA 22151 *Tel:* 703-941-3333 *E-mail:* info@biasstudios.com *Web Site:* www. biasstudios.com, pg 705

Dawson, Ian, C&I An Idea Agency, 541 NW First Ave, Fort Lauderdale, FL 33301 *Tel:* 954-357-3934 *E-mail:* contact@c-istudios.com *Web Site:* www.c-istudios.com, pg 716

Dawson, Ian G, SMI® Inc, 4567 Lake Shore Dr, Waco, TX 76710 *Tel:* 254-776-2060 *Toll Free Tel:* 800-568-1241 *Fax:* 254-772-9588 *E-mail:* dmcminn@lmi-inc. com; info@lmi-inc.com; info@success-motivation.com *Web Site:* www.lmi-world.com/smi, pg 891

Dawson, Sara, Omnirax Furniture Co, PO Box 1792, Sausalito, CA 94966-1792 *Tel:* 415-332-3392 *Toll Free Tel:* 800-332-3393 *E-mail:* info@omnirax.com *Web Site:* omnirax.com, pg 845

Day, Brian, Daylight Productions & Rentals, 4700 Sterling Dr, Suite I, Boulder, CO 80301 *Tel:* 303-440-3334 *E-mail:* info@daylightav.com *Web Site:* www. daylightav.com, pg 739

Day, David, ATI Audio, 7209 Browning Rd, Pennsauken, NJ 08091 *Tel:* 856-719-9900 *E-mail:* sales@ daysequerra.com *Web Site:* www.atiaudio.com, pg 692

Dayton, Allen L, VSA Inc, 6929 Seward Ave, Lincoln, NE 68507 *Toll Free Tel:* 800-888-2140 (orders) *Fax:* 402-325-8033 *E-mail:* sales@vsa1.com *Web Site:* www.vsa1.com, pg 933

Dayton, Bill, Encore Event Technologies LLC, 8850 W Sunset Rd, 3rd fl, Las Vegas, NV 89148 *Tel:* 702-739-8803 *Fax:* 702-739-8831 *Web Site:* www.encoreglobal. com/us, pg 754

De Camp, Paul, Quatrefoil Associates Inc, 29 "C" St, Laurel, MD 20707 *Tel:* 301-470-4748 *Fax:* 301-470-4749 *E-mail:* info@quatrefoil.com *Web Site:* www. quatrefoil.com, pg 868

De Cham, Paul, AlphaDogs Inc, 1612 W Olive Ave, Suite 200, Burbank, CA 91506-2462 *Tel:* 818-729-9262 *Fax:* 818-729-8537 *Web Site:* www.alphadogs.tv, pg 682

De Croix, Rick, The Source Stock Footage Library Inc, 140 S Camino Seco, Suite 308, Tucson, AZ 85710 *Tel:* 520-298-4810 *Fax:* 520-290-4376 *E-mail:* requests@sourcefootage.com *Web Site:* www. sourcefootage.com, pg 895

De Francesco, Jim, Hogpenny Studios, Ship Bottom Studio Ctr, 123 E 14 St, Ship Bottom, Long Beach Island, NJ 08008 *Tel:* 609-494-6640 *E-mail:* hogpenny@verizon.net *Web Site:* hogpennytv. com, pg 780

De Galbert, Camille, LightHouse Films, 225 W 39 St, Suite 600, New York, NY 10018 *Tel:* 646-649-3600 *Fax:* 646-398-7122 *E-mail:* contact@lhfny.com; rent@lhfny.com *Web Site:* www.light-house-films.com, pg 807

De Hauwer, Christophe, SES SA, 4 Research Way, Princeton, NJ 08540-6684 *Tel:* 609-987-4000 *E-mail:* info@ses.com *Web Site:* www.ses.com, pg 884

De Long, Michelle, Mimi Productions, 4343 N Western Ave, No 1N, Chicago, IL 60618 *Tel:* 773-293-7292 *E-mail:* info@mimiproductions.com *Web Site:* www. mimiproductions.com, pg 828

De Luca, Guerrino, Logitech, 7700 Gateway Blvd, Newark, CA 94560 *Tel:* 510-795-8500 *Toll Free Tel:* 866-291-1505 *Web Site:* www.logitech.com, pg 811

De Maeyer, Thomas, Synergem, 2323 Randolph Ave, Avenel, NJ 07001 *Tel:* 732-225-0001 *E-mail:* sales@ synergem.com *Web Site:* synergem.com, pg 905

De Mattos, Matthew M, Cinemills Corp, 2021 N Lincoln St, Burbank, CA 91504 *Tel:* 818-843-4560 *Toll Free Tel:* 877-CMC-HMIS (262-4647) *Fax:* 818-843-7834 *E-mail:* sales@cinemills.com *Web Site:* www. cinemills.com, pg 724

De Miles, Edward, Sahara Records & Filmworks Entertainment Co, 10573 W Pico Blvd, Suite 352, Los Angeles, CA 90064-2348 *Tel:* 310-948-9652 *E-mail:* info@edmsahara.com, pg 879

de Nesnera, Liz, CineTech Media Professionals, PO Box 34, Olivebridge, NY 12461 *Web Site:* cinetechmediapros.org, pg 953

De Nonno, Tony, De Nonno Productions Inc (DPI), 7119 Shore Rd, Suite 6-F, Brooklyn, NY 11209 *Tel:* 917-304-6610 *Web Site:* www.denonnoprod.com; www. denonnoscelebrityphotos.com, pg 739

De Palma, James A, Revolution Lighting Technologies Inc, 177 Broad St, 12th fl, Stamford, CT 06901 *Tel:* 203-504-1111 *Toll Free Tel:* 877-578-2536 *E-mail:* support@rvlti.com; info@rvlti.com *Web Site:* www.rvlti.com, pg 874

De Vaughn-Stokes, Diane, Stages Video Productions, 514 29 Ave N, Myrtle Beach, SC 29577 *Tel:* 843-626-7466 *E-mail:* info@stagesvideo.com *Web Site:* www. stagesvideo.com, pg 899

de Wilde, Lisa, TVO/Ontario Educational Communications Authority (OECA), 2180 Yonge St, Toronto, ON M4S 2B9, Canada *Tel:* 416-484-2600; 416-484-2665 (cust rel) *Toll Free Tel:* 800-613-0513; 800-INFO-TVO (463-6886) *E-mail:* asktvo@tvo.org *Web Site:* tvo.org, pg 919

Deal, Ryan, Regional Artist Project Grants Program, 227 W Trade St, Suite 250, Charlotte, NC 28202 *Tel:* 704-333-2272 *Fax:* 704-333-2720 *E-mail:* asc@ artsandscience.org *Web Site:* www.artsandscience.org, pg 1001

Dealey, Gary, Big Deal Custom Casings, 100 Durand Rd, Winnipeg, MB R2J 3T2, Canada *Tel:* 204-663-4870 *Toll Free Tel:* 800-337-3325 *Fax:* 204-668-7404 *E-mail:* info@bigdealcases.com *Web Site:* bigdealcases.ca, pg 705

Dean, Bridget PhD, Bolchazy - Carducci Publishers Inc, 1570 Baskin Rd, Mundelein, IL 60060 *Tel:* 847-526-4344 *Fax:* 847-526-2867 *E-mail:* info@bolchazy.com *Web Site:* www.bolchazy.com, pg 708

Dean, Jackie, Canadian Academy of Recording Arts & Sciences (CARAS), 219 Dufferin St, Suite 211C, Toronto, ON M6K 3J1, Canada *Tel:* 416-485-3135 (CN only) *Toll Free Tel:* 888-501-3135 *Fax:* 416-485-4978 *E-mail:* submissions@junoawards.ca; info@ carasonline.ca *Web Site:* carasonline.ca; junoawards.ca, pg 952

DeAngelis, Laura, Comtel Inc, 14901 NE 20 Ave, North Miami, FL 33181 *Tel:* 305-424-4160 (facility servs); 305-424-4178 (local inquiries); 516-816-5152 (natl inquiries) *Web Site:* www.comtelinc.com; www. facebook.com/comtelinc/, pg 730

DeAngelo, John, Educational Technology Services (ETS), Medical Sciences, Rm SB-43, 513 Parnassus Ave, San Francisco, CA 94143-0702 *Tel:* 415-476-4310 *Fax:* 415-514-3735 *E-mail:* edtech@ucsf.edu *Web Site:* edtech.ucsf.edu, pg 751

DeAngelo, Lisa, SmackDab Media, 252 Glenhaven Dr, Amherst, NY 14228 *Tel:* 615-957-6618 *Web Site:* smackdabmedia.us, pg 890

DeBelius, Ken, Spectrum Sound Inc, 1040 Acorn Dr, Suite C, Nashville, TN 37210 *Tel:* 615-391-3700 *Web Site:* www.spectrumsound.net, pg 897

DeBellis, Andrea, CMI Media Management, 9 W Broad St, Stamford, CT 06902 *Tel:* 203-989-9955 *Toll Free Tel:* 800-431-1102 *Fax:* 203-316-8353 *Web Site:* www. cminyla.com, pg 727

DeBenny, Peter, Ross Video Ltd, 8 John St, Iroquois, ON K0E 1K0, Canada *Tel:* 613-652-4886 *Fax:* 613-652-4425 *E-mail:* solutions@rossvideo.com *Web Site:* www.rossvideo.com, pg 878

DeBerry, Corbin, Hello World Communications, 118 W 22 St, 2nd fl, New York, NY 10011 *Tel:* 212-243-8800 *Fax:* 212-691-6961 *E-mail:* excitable01@gmail.com *Web Site:* hwc.tv, pg 778

Deblaere, Ju, Accenture, 161 N Clark St, Chicago, IL 60601 *Tel:* 312-693-0161 *Toll Free Tel:* 877-889-9009 *Fax:* 312-693-0507 *Web Site:* www.accenture.com, pg 672

DeBlase, Kim, Freedoms Foundation National Awards, 1601 Valley Forge Rd, Valley Forge, PA 19481 *Tel:* 610-933-8825 *Fax:* 610-935-0522 *E-mail:* info@ ffvf.org *Web Site:* www.freedomsfoundation.org, pg 990

Deckelman, William L Jr, DXC Technology Co, 1775 Tysons Blvd, Tysons, VA 22102 *Tel:* 317-331-1197 *Web Site:* www.dxc.technology, pg 748

Decker, Joe, Disk Productions Inc, 1100 Perkins Rd, Baton Rouge, LA 70802 *Tel:* 225-343-5438 *E-mail:* disk_productions@yahoo.com, pg 743

DeDonker, Andrew, RAM® Mounts, 8410 Dallas Ave S, Seattle, WA 98108 *Tel:* 206-763-8361 *Toll Free Tel:* 800-497-7479 *Fax:* 206-763-9615 *E-mail:* sales@ rammount.com *Web Site:* www.rammount.com, pg 870

Deeb, Carol, Freeman Audio Visual, 2056 32 Ave, Montreal, QC H8T 3H7, Canada *Tel:* 514-631-1821 *Toll Free Tel:* 800-868-6886 *Web Site:* freemanav-ca.com, pg 765

Defibaugh, Ian, Eastern Effects Inc, 99 Ninth St, Brooklyn, NY 11215 *Tel:* 718-855-1197 *Toll Free Fax:* 888-566-6547 *Web Site:* easterneffects.com, pg 749

DeFries, William, Copp Integrated Systems, 123 S Keowee St, Dayton, OH 45402 *Tel:* 937-228-4188 *Toll Free Tel:* 877-450-2677 *Fax:* 937-228-2901 *Web Site:* www.copp.com, pg 731

Degen, Dennis, Lightronics Inc, 509 Central Dr, Virginia Beach, VA 23454 *Tel:* 757-486-3588 *Toll Free Tel:* 800-472-8541 *Fax:* 757-486-3391 *Web Site:* www. lightronics.com, pg 808

DeGiorgio, Raphael, Diamond Dreams Music Productions, North Ocean County, Carbon Canyon, Chino Hills, CA 91709 *Tel:* 909-393-6120 *Fax:* 909-606-5779 *E-mail:* diamonddreamsmusic@yahoo.com *Web Site:* www.diamonddreamsmusic.com, pg 741

Deinarowicz, Bob, Beseler Photo, 2018 W Main St, Stroudsburg, PA 18360 *Toll Free Tel:* 800-237-3537 *Toll Free Fax:* 800-966-4515 *Web Site:* www. beselerphoto.com, pg 704

Deinarowicz, Bob, Charles Beseler Co, 2018 W Main St, Stroudsburg, PA 18360 *Toll Free Tel:* 800-237-3537 *Toll Free Fax:* 800-966-4515 *Web Site:* www. beselerphoto.com, pg 721

Deiparine-Sugars, Erica, Austin Film Society (AFS), 1901 E 51 St, Austin, TX 78723 *Tel:* 512-322-0145 *E-mail:* afs@austinfilm.org *Web Site:* www.austinfilm. org, pg 952

Dejewski, Brenda, Horizon Video Productions Inc, 6114 Fayetteville St, Suite 106, Durham, NC 27713 *Tel:* 919-941-0901 *Toll Free Tel:* 800-768-3776 *Fax:* 919-941-1939 *E-mail:* info@horizonvp.com *Web Site:* www.horizonvp.com, pg 781

DeJong, Duke, CCI Solutions, 1342 88 Ave SE, Olympia, WA 98501 *Tel:* 360-943-5378 *Toll Free Tel:* 800-562-6006 *Fax:* 360-754-1566 *E-mail:* info@ccisolutions.com *Web Site:* www.ccisolutions.com, pg 718

deKramer, Peter, deKramer Productions Inc, 515 Western Ave, Petaluma, CA 94952 *Tel:* 707-765-0888 *E-mail:* dekramer@sonic.net *Web Site:* www.dekramerproductions.com, pg 740

Del Campo, David Martin, Magic Gadgets™, 12986 Mapleleaf Ct NE, Aurora, OR 97002-8418 *Tel:* 503-678-6236; 818-655-5465 (rentals) *E-mail:* info@magicgadgets.com *Web Site:* www.magicgadgets.com, pg 814

Del Vaglio, Fernando, Samy's Camera, 431 S Fairfax Ave, Los Angeles, CA 90036 *Tel:* 323-938-2420 *Toll Free Tel:* 800-321-4726 *Fax:* 323-937-2919 *E-mail:* lacamera@samys.com; info@samys.com; locations@samys.com *Web Site:* www.samys.com, pg 879

Delage, Alexis, Stageline Mobile Stage Inc, 700 Marsolais St, L'Assomption, QC J5W 2G9, Canada *Tel:* 450-589-1063 *Toll Free Tel:* 800-26-STAGE (267-8243) *Fax:* 450-589-1711 *E-mail:* info@stageline.com *Web Site:* www.stageline.com, pg 899

Delaney, Lynn, Robert F Kennedy Journalism Awards, 1300 19 St NW, Suite 750, Washington, DC 20036 *Tel:* 646-553-4750 *E-mail:* info@rfkhumanrights.org; communications@rfkhumanrights.org *Web Site:* rfkhumanrights.org/awards, pg 994

Delapp, Dan, Tecplot Inc, 3535 Factoria Blvd SE, Suite 550, Bellevue, WA 98006 *Tel:* 425-653-1200; 425-653-9393 (tech support) *Toll Free Tel:* 800-763-7005 (orders) *E-mail:* info@tecplot.com; support@tecplot.com *Web Site:* www.tecplot.com, pg 909

Delgado, Nick, Dub King, 8133 Callaghan Rd, San Antonio, TX 78230 *Tel:* 210-979-8779 *E-mail:* dubking@dubking.com *Web Site:* www.dubking.com, pg 747

DeLicci, Melissa, Berry & Homer, 2035 Richmond St, Philadelphia, PA 19125 *Tel:* 215-425-0888 *Web Site:* www.berryandhomer.com, pg 704

Delich, Julie, The Learning House Inc, 427 S Fourth St, Suite 300, Louisville, KY 40202 *Tel:* 502-589-9878 *Fax:* 502-589-9825 *E-mail:* sales@learninghouse.com; info@learninghouse.com *Web Site:* www.learninghouse.com, pg 805

DeLigter, Harry, Lightworks Audio & Video Inc, PO Box 661593, Los Angeles, CA 90066 *Tel:* 310-398-4949 *E-mail:* sales1@lightworksav.com; edmedia@lightworksav.com *Web Site:* www.lightworksav.com, pg 808

Delinski, Rachel, Love Your Shorts Film Festival, 608 S Elm Ave, Sanford, FL 32771 *E-mail:* contact@loveyourshorts.com *Web Site:* www.loveyourshorts.com, pg 995

deLise, Louis Anthony, Composer Louis Anthony deLise, 83 Park Dr, Cherry Hill, NJ 08002-3002 *Tel:* 856-616-2867 *E-mail:* louis@bocagemusic.com *Web Site:* www.louisanthonydelise.com, pg 729

Dell, Janet, Freeman, 1600 Viceroy, Suite 100, Dallas, TX 75235 *Tel:* 214-445-1000 *Web Site:* www.freeman.com, pg 765

DellaVentura, Dan, DecisionOne Corp, 640 Lee Rd, 3rd fl, Wayne, PA 19087 *Tel:* 610-296-6000 *Toll Free Tel:* 800-767-2876; 800-777-8800 (cust serv); 888-287-9202 (sales); 800-554-5179 (CN) *Fax:* 610-296-2910 *E-mail:* sales@decisionone.com *Web Site:* www.decisionone.com, pg 740

Dellis, Shawn, Pacifica Radio Archives, 3729 Cahuenga Blvd W, North Hollywood, CA 91604 *Tel:* 818-506-1077 *Toll Free Tel:* 800-735-0230 *Fax:* 818-506-1084 *E-mail:* pacarchive@aol.com *Web Site:* www.pacificaradioarchives.org, pg 850

Dellovo, Victor, CSPI, 175 Cabot St, Suite 210, Lowell, MA 01854 *Tel:* 978-663-7598; 978-954-5038 *Toll Free Tel:* 800-325-3110 *E-mail:* hello@cspi.com *Web Site:* www.cspi.com, pg 735

Delon, Gerry, NEP Group Inc, 2 Beta Dr, Pittsburgh, PA 15238 *Tel:* 412-826-1414 *Toll Free Tel:* 800-444-0054 *E-mail:* info@nepinc.com *Web Site:* www.nepgroup.com, pg 838

Deltruc, Nicolas Girard, Festival du Nouveau Cinema de Montreal, 3805 Blvd Saint-Laurent, Montreal, QC H2W 1X9, Canada *Tel:* 514-282-0004 *Fax:* 514-282-6664 *E-mail:* info@nouveaucinema.ca; soumissions@nouveaucinema.ca *Web Site:* www.nouveaucinema.ca, pg 989

DeMarco, Frank, Outside The Box Interactive LLC, 150 Bay St, Suite 706, Jersey City, NJ 07302 *Tel:* 201-610-0625 *E-mail:* office@outboxin.com *Web Site:* www.outboxin.com, pg 849

DeMartin, Rob, PostWorks, 110 Leroy St, New York, NY 10014 *Tel:* 212-609-9400 *Fax:* 212-609-9450 *E-mail:* inquiry@technicolorpwny.com *Web Site:* www.postworks.com, pg 860

DeMent, Denise, San Diego Stage & Lighting Supply Inc, 2203 Verus St, San Diego, CA 92154 *Tel:* 619-299-2300 *Fax:* 619-299-0058 *E-mail:* info@sdstagelighting.com *Web Site:* www.sdstagelighting.com, pg 879

Dement, Kimble, Dub King, 8133 Callaghan Rd, San Antonio, TX 78230 *Tel:* 210-979-8779 *E-mail:* dubking@dubking.com *Web Site:* www.dubking.com, pg 747

Demers, Andre, Presagis, 4700 de la Savane, Suite 300, Montreal, QC H4P 1T7, Canada *Tel:* 514-341-3874 *Toll Free Tel:* 800-361-6424 *Fax:* 514-341-8018 *E-mail:* info@presagis.com *Web Site:* www.presagis.com, pg 861

Demetrescu, Dr Stefan, Lasergraphics Inc, 20 Ada, Irvine, CA 92618 *Tel:* 949-753-8282 *Fax:* 949-727-9282 *E-mail:* info@lasergraphics.com *Web Site:* www.lasergraphics.com, pg 804

Demetriades, Michael, The Global Awards®, 260 W 39 St, 10th fl, New York, NY 10018 *Tel:* 212-643-4800 *Fax:* 212-643-0170 *E-mail:* info@newyorkfestivals.com *Web Site:* www.theglobalawards.com, pg 990

Demetriades, Michael, New York Festivals® International Advertising Awards, 260 W 39 St, 10th fl, New York, NY 10018 *Tel:* 212-643-4800 *Fax:* 212-643-0170 *E-mail:* info@newyorkfestivals.com *Web Site:* advertising.newyorkfestivals.com; www.newyorkfestivals.com, pg 998

Demetriades, Michael, New York Festivals® International Radio Program Awards, 260 W 39 St, 10th fl, New York, NY 10018 *Tel:* 212-643-4800 *Fax:* 212-643-0170 *E-mail:* info@newyorkfestivals.com *Web Site:* radio.newyorkfestivals.com; www.newyorkfestivals.com/radio, pg 998

Demetriades, Michael, New York Festivals® International TV & Film Awards, 260 W 39 St, 10th fl, New York, NY 10018 *Tel:* 212-643-4800 *Fax:* 212-643-0170 *E-mail:* info@newyorkfestivals.com *Web Site:* tvfilm.newyorkfestivals.com; www.newyorkfestivals.com/tvfilm, pg 998

Dempsey, Jamie, Artist Research & Development Grants, 417 W Roosevelt St, Phoenix, AZ 85003-1326 *Tel:* 602-771-6501 *Fax:* 602-256-0282 *E-mail:* info@azarts.gov *Web Site:* www.azarts.gov, pg 982

Dempsey, Michael, Thread Marketing Group, 4635 W Alexis Rd, Toledo, OH 43623-1005 *Tel:* 419-887-6801 *Fax:* 419-887-6802 *E-mail:* info@threadgroup.com *Web Site:* www.threadgroup.com, pg 913

Denado, Mario, Elegant Packaging, 5253 W Roosevelt Rd, Cicero, IL 60804 *Tel:* 708-652-3400 *Toll Free Tel:* 800-367-5493 *Fax:* 708-652-6444 *E-mail:* info@elegantpackaging.com *Web Site:* www.elegantpackaging.com, pg 752

Denenberg, Peter, Acme Recording Studios Inc, 112 W Boston Post Rd, Mamaroneck, NY 10543 *Web Site:* www.acmerec.com, pg 674

Denhart, Lee, Draper Inc, 411 S Pearl St, Spiceland, IN 47385 *Tel:* 765-987-7999 *Toll Free Tel:* 800-238-7999 *Fax:* 765-987-7142 *E-mail:* av@draperinc.com *Web Site:* www.draperinc.com; blog.draperinc.com, pg 746

Deniston, Donn, Littlite LLC, PO Box 430, Hamburg, MI 48139-0430 *Tel:* 810-852-4242 *Fax:* 810-231-1631 *E-mail:* sales@littlite.com *Web Site:* www.littlite.com, pg 810

Denke, Conrad W, Victory Studios, 2247 15 Ave W, Seattle, WA 98119 *Tel:* 206-282-1776 *Toll Free Tel:* 888-282-1776 *Fax:* 206-282-3535 *E-mail:* info@victorystudios.com *Web Site:* www.victorystudios.com, pg 927

Denkhaus, Don, The Kitchen, 265 NE 24 St, Suite 401, Miami, FL 33137 *Tel:* 305-415-6200 *E-mail:* info@thekitchen.tv *Web Site:* www.thekitchen.tv, pg 799

Denman, Ron, Kenyon Laboratories LLC, 12 Scovil Rd, Higganum, CT 06441 *Tel:* 860-345-2097 *Toll Free Tel:* 800-253-4681 *Fax:* 860-345-8652 *E-mail:* kenyonlabs@comcast.net; info@kenyongyro.com *Web Site:* www.ken-lab.com, pg 798

Dennison, Sarah Weinstein, RCA Records, 25 Madison Ave, New York, NY 10010 *Tel:* 212-833-8000 *E-mail:* publicity@rcarecords.com *Web Site:* www.rcarecords.com; www.sonymusic.com, pg 871

Denny, Garry, Wisconsin Public Television, 821 University Ave, Madison, WI 53706 *Tel:* 608-263-2121 *Toll Free Tel:* 800-422-9707 *Fax:* 608-263-9763 *E-mail:* comments@wpt.org *Web Site:* www.wpt.org, pg 940

Dennys, Louise, Penguin Random House Canada, 320 Front St W, Suite 1400, Toronto, ON M5V 3B6, Canada *Tel:* 416-364-4449 *Toll Free Tel:* 888-523-9292 (cust serv) *Fax:* 416-598-7764 *E-mail:* customerservicescanada@penguinrandomhouse.com *Web Site:* www.penguinrandomhouse.ca, pg 853

deNottbeck, John, Wanted! Sound + Picture, 409 King St W, Suite 300, Toronto, ON M5V 1K1, Canada *Tel:* 416-596-1101 *Fax:* 416-596-0690 *E-mail:* info@wantedsp.com; bookings@wantedsp.com *Web Site:* www.wantedsp.com, pg 933

Denson, Kelly L, Association of American Publishers (AAP), 455 Massachusetts Ave NW, Suite 700, Washington, DC 20001-2777 *Tel:* 202-347-3375 *Fax:* 202-347-3690 *E-mail:* info@publishers.org *Web Site:* publishers.org, pg 951

Denson, Tad, Dogwood Productions Inc, 757 Government St, Mobile, AL 36602 *Tel:* 251-476-0858 *Toll Free Tel:* 800-254-9903 *Fax:* 251-479-0364 *E-mail:* info@dogwoodproductions.com *Web Site:* www.dogwoodproductions.com, pg 745

Depaolo, Ashley, CommCreative, 75 Fountain St, Framingham, MA 01702 *Tel:* 508-620-6664 *Toll Free Tel:* 877-620-6664 *Fax:* 508-620-0592 *E-mail:* info@commcreative.com *Web Site:* www.commcreative.com, pg 728

DePree, Dori, Waterfront Film Festival (WFF), 479 Columbia Ave, Holland, MI 49423 *Tel:* 269-767-8765 *E-mail:* info@waterfrontfilm.org *Web Site:* www.waterfrontfilm.org, pg 1006

DePree, Hopwood, Waterfront Film Festival (WFF), 479 Columbia Ave, Holland, MI 49423 *Tel:* 269-767-8765 *E-mail:* info@waterfrontfilm.org *Web Site:* www.waterfrontfilm.org, pg 1006

DePree-Minter, Dana, Waterfront Film Festival (WFF), 479 Columbia Ave, Holland, MI 49423 *Tel:* 269-767-8765 *E-mail:* info@waterfrontfilm.org *Web Site:* www.waterfrontfilm.org, pg 1006

Der Boghosian, Greg, Century Color Labs Inc, 494 School St, East Hartford, CT 06108 *Tel:* 860-289-9501 *Toll Free Tel:* 800-242-9501 *Fax:* 860-291-9098 *E-mail:* production@centurycolor.com *Web Site:* centurycolor.com, pg 720

Der, Tom, Soundcraft, 8500 Balboa Blvd, North Ridge, CA 91329 *Toll Free Tel:* 800-622-6983 *E-mail:* support@soundcraft.com *Web Site:* www.soundcraft.com, pg 894

Derkacz, Karin, Electronics Representatives Association (ERA), 1325 S Arlington Heights Rd, Suite 204, Elk Grove Village, IL 60007 *Tel:* 312-419-1432 *Fax:* 312-419-1660 *E-mail:* info@era.org *Web Site:* www.era.org, pg 954

Derkatsch, Erick, InterNation Inc, 299 Broadway, Suite 918, New York, NY 10007 *Tel:* 212-619-5545 *Toll Free Tel:* 800-222-8799 *Fax:* 212-619-5887 *E-mail:* info@internation.com *Web Site:* www.internation.com, pg 790

Dermody, William III, Techflex Inc, 104 Demarest Rd, Sparta, NJ 07871 *Tel:* 973-300-9242 *Toll Free Tel:* 800-323-5140 *Fax:* 973-300-9409 *E-mail:* techflex@techflex.com *Web Site:* www.techflex.com, pg 908

DeRock, Anne, Spirit Media, 12042 SE Sunnyside Rd, Suite 700, Happy Valley, OR 97015 *Tel:* 503-698-5540 *Fax:* 503-698-8408 *E-mail:* info@spiritmedia.com *Web Site:* www.spiritmedia.com, pg 898

Derohanessian, Alfred, Total Concept Sales, 2505 Foothill Blvd, Suite G, La Crescentia, CA 91214 *Tel:* 818-236-3966 *Toll Free Tel:* 800-488-0589 *Fax:* 818-236-3969 *Web Site:* www.totalups.com, pg 916

Derosier, David, Merestone, 7232 E First St, Scottsdale, AZ 85251 *Tel:* 480-945-4631 *Fax:* 480-945-0590 *Web Site:* www.merestone.com, pg 823

Derricks, Mike, Wire X 17 LLC, 1840 County Line Rd, Suite 301, Huntingdon Valley, PA 19006 *Tel:* 215-322-4600 *Toll Free Tel:* 800-233-0013 *Fax:* 215-322-1385 *E-mail:* sales@wirexgroup.com *Web Site:* wirex17.com, pg 940

Des Combes, Jeff, Sprocket Digital, PO Box 1420, Claremont, CA 91711 *Tel:* 909-946-2364 *Fax:* 909-946-2631 *E-mail:* sdsales@sprocketdigital.com *Web Site:* www.sprocketdigital.com, pg 898

DeSantis, Mark, WEEK TV, 2907 Springfield Rd, East Peoria, IL 61611 *Tel:* 309-698-2525 *Web Site:* www.week.com, pg 935

Desha, Kirby, Audio Editions Books-On-Cassette & CD, 131 E Placer St, Auburn, CA 95603 *Tel:* 530-888-7801 *Toll Free Tel:* 800-231-4261 *Toll Free Fax:* 800-882-1840 *E-mail:* info@audioeditions.com *Web Site:* audioeditions.com; audioeditionslibrary.com, pg 693

Desir, Jon, Optimus, 161 E Grand Ave, Chicago, IL 60611 *Tel:* 312-321-0880 *Web Site:* www.optimus.com, pg 847

Desmond, John, Activu Corp, 301 Roundhill Dr, Rockaway, NJ 07866 *Tel:* 973-366-5550 *Toll Free Tel:* 888-ACTIVU1 (228-4881) *Fax:* 973-625-7775 *E-mail:* facebook@activu.com *Web Site:* activu.com, pg 675

Desroches, Pascal, Turner Broadcasting System Inc, A Time Warner Company, One CNN Ctr, Atlanta, GA 30303 *Tel:* 404-827-1700 *E-mail:* turner.info@turner.com *Web Site:* www.turner.com, pg 919

DeToni, Dale, Ozam Productions Inc, 1516 Equestrian Rd, Ozark, MO 65721 *Tel:* 417-866-3232 *Web Site:* ozam.com, pg 849

Deushane, John, WATL-TV Inc, One Monroe Place NE, Atlanta, GA 30324 *Tel:* 404-881-3600 *Web Site:* www.myatltv.com, pg 934

Deutsch, John, OmniMount Systems, 4409 E Baseline Rd, Suite 130, Phoenix, AZ 85042 *Tel:* 480-829-8000 *Toll Free Tel:* 800-MOUNT-IT (668-6848) *Fax:* 480-756-9000 *E-mail:* info@omnimount.com *Web Site:* www.omnimount.com, pg 845

DeVaney, Sara, Crispin Corp, 600 Wade Ave, Raleigh, NC 27605 *Tel:* 919-845-7744 *Fax:* 919-845-7766 *E-mail:* welisten@crispincorp.com; support@crispincorp.com *Web Site:* www.crispincorp.com, pg 735

deVeer, James A, Advanced Lighting & Production Services Inc (ALPS), 125 Shamut Rd, Canton, MA 02021 *Tel:* 781-961-3066 *Toll Free Tel:* 866-961-3066 *Fax:* 781-961-3256 *E-mail:* info@alpsweb.com *Web Site:* www.alpsweb.com, pg 677

Devereaux, Dave, WTVS, Detroit Public Television, Riley Broadcast Ctr, One Clover Ct, Wixom, MI 48393-2247 *Tel:* 248-305-DPTV (305-3788); 313-872-7500 *E-mail:* email@dptv.org *Web Site:* www.dptv.org, pg 942

DeVerna, Darren, Production Resource Group LLC (PRG), 200 Business Park Dr, Suite 109, Armonk, NY 10504 *Tel:* 212-589-5400 *Toll Free Tel:* 877-774-7088 *E-mail:* info@prg.com *Web Site:* www.prg.com, pg 864

DeVine, Kelly, Global Peace Film Festival (GPFF), PO Box 3310, Winter Park, FL 32790-3310 *Tel:* 407-582-6018 *E-mail:* info@peacefilmfest.org *Web Site:* www.peacefilmfest.org, pg 990

DeVita, Evan, DBM Communications Inc, 606 Baltimore Ave, Suite 200, Towson, MD 21204 *Tel:* 410-825-7400 *Fax:* 443-269-0213 *Web Site:* www.dbmcommunications.com, pg 739

DeVivo, Frank, Practising Law Institute, 1177 Avenue of the Americas, 2nd fl, New York, NY 10036 *Tel:* 212-824-5710 (cust serv) *Toll Free Tel:* 800-260-4PLI (260-4754, cust serv) *Toll Free Fax:* 800-321-0093 (cust serv) *E-mail:* info@pli.edu; cs@pli.edu (cust serv) *Web Site:* www.pli.edu, pg 860

Dewar, Jeff, Quality Digest, 290 Airpark Blvd, Chico, CA 95973 *Tel:* 530-893-4095 *Fax:* 530-893-0395 *E-mail:* comments@qualitydigest.com *Web Site:* www.qualitydigest.com, pg 868

DeWitt, Debbie, Visix™ Inc, 230 Scientific Dr, Suite 800, Norcross, GA 30092 *Tel:* 770-446-1416 *Toll Free Tel:* 800-572-4935 *Fax:* 770-448-5724 *E-mail:* info@visix.com *Web Site:* www.visix.com, pg 931

Dexter, Letty, Everlast Productions, 59 SW 12 Ave, Unit 110, Dania Beach, FL 33004 *Tel:* 954-456-7167 *Fax:* 954-456-1243 *E-mail:* info@everlastproductions.com *Web Site:* everlastproductions.com, pg 757

Dhanyam, Swami Prabodh, Osho Viha Information Center & Book Distributors, PO Box 352, Mill Valley, CA 94942-0352 *Tel:* 415-472-5381 *Toll Free Tel:* 866-856-7019 *E-mail:* oshoviha@oshoviha.org *Web Site:* www.oshoviha.org, pg 848

Di Fronzo, Pascal W, Autodesk Inc, 111 McInnis Pkwy, San Rafael, CA 94903 *Tel:* 415-507-5000 *Fax:* 415-507-5100 *Web Site:* www.autodesk.com, pg 696

Di Giacomo, Lori, Long Island Video Enterprises Live Inc, 110 Pratt Oval, Glen Cove, NY 11542 *Tel:* 516-759-5483 *Fax:* 516-671-5874 *E-mail:* info@longislandvideo.com *Web Site:* www.longislandvideo.com, pg 811

Di Lorenzo, Gene, Media Loft Inc, 615 First Ave NE, Suite 100, Minneapolis, MN 55413 *Tel:* 612-375-1086 *Fax:* 612-375-0913 *E-mail:* info@medialoft.com *Web Site:* www.medialoft.com, pg 822

Diamond, Ron, Acme Filmworks Inc, 3347 Motor Ave, Los Angeles, CA 90034 *Tel:* 323-464-7805 *Fax:* 323-464-6614 *E-mail:* pr@acmefilmworks.com (publicity) *Web Site:* www.acmefilmworks.com, pg 674

Diaz, Chris, Dazian LLC, 18 Central Blvd, South Hackensack, NJ 07606 *Toll Free Tel:* 877-232-9426 *Fax:* 201-641-2728; 201-549-1055 (efax) *E-mail:* info@dazian.com *Web Site:* www.dazian.com, pg 739

Diaz, John, 16 x 9 Inc, 28314 Constellation Rd, Valencia, CA 91355 *Tel:* 661-295-3313 *Toll Free Tel:* 866-800-1699 *Fax:* 661-295-3314 *E-mail:* info@16x9inc.com *Web Site:* www.16x9inc.com, pg 890

Diaz, Jorge, Skjonberg Controls Inc, 1363 Donlon St, Suite 6, Ventura, CA 93003 *Tel:* 805-650-0877 *Fax:* 805-650-0360 *Toll Free Fax:* 800-650-0360 *E-mail:* sales@skjonberg.com *Web Site:* skjonberg.com, pg 890

Dick, Jeff, Applied Voice & Speech Technologies Inc (AVST), 27042 Towne Centre Dr, Suite 200, Foothill Ranch, CA 92610-2810 *Tel:* 949-699-2300 *Toll Free Tel:* 866-368-0400 *Fax:* 949-699-2301 *E-mail:* info@avst.com; sales@avst.com *Web Site:* www.avst.com, pg 688

Dickensheets, Ken, Dickensheets Design Associates, 10919 Conchos Trail, Suite 100, Austin, TX 78726-1431 *Tel:* 512-331-8977 *Web Site:* www.dickensheets.com, pg 741

Dickerson, Brandon, Kaboom Productions, 2169 Folsom St, Suite 201-M, San Francisco, CA 94110 *Tel:* 415-434-2666 *Fax:* 415-874-9324 *E-mail:* hello@kaboomproductions.com *Web Site:* kaboomproductions.com, pg 796

Dickerson, Kory, CEDIA IPRO Affinity Group, 8475 Nightfall Lane, Fishers, IN 46037 *Tel:* 317-328-4336 *Toll Free Tel:* 800-669-5329 *E-mail:* info@cedia.org *Web Site:* cedia.net, pg 952

Dickerson, Michael W, PGi, 3280 Peachtree Rd NE, Suite 1000, Atlanta, GA 30305 *Tel:* 404-262-8400 *Toll Free Tel:* 866-755-4878 *Web Site:* www.pgi.com, pg 855

Dickerson, Rich, Jai Inc, 6800 Santa Teresa Blvd, Suite 175, San Jose, CA 95119 *Tel:* 408-383-0300 *Toll Free Tel:* 800-445-5444 *Fax:* 408-383-0301 *E-mail:* camerasales.americas@jai.com *Web Site:* www.jai.com, pg 792

Dickey, Joey, International Cellulose Corp, 12315 Robin Blvd, Houston, TX 77045 *Tel:* 713-433-6701 *Toll Free Tel:* 800-444-1252 *Fax:* 713-433-2029 *E-mail:* icc@spray-on.com *Web Site:* www.spray-on.com, pg 790

Dickinson, Rik, Encore Video Productions, 811 Main St, Myrtle Beach, SC 29577 *Tel:* 843-448-9900 *Web Site:* www.encorevideo.biz, pg 754

Dickinson, Tom, Bexel, an NEP Broadcast Services Company, 2701 N Ontario St, Burbank, CA 91504 *Tel:* 818-565-4322 *Toll Free Tel:* 800-225-6185 (tech support) *E-mail:* services@bexel.com *Web Site:* bexel.com, pg 704

Dickson, Natasha, Vancouver Film Studios Ltd, 3500 Cornett Rd, Vancouver, BC V5M 2H5, Canada *Tel:* 604-453-5000 *Fax:* 604-453-5045 *E-mail:* info@vancouverfilmstudios.com *Web Site:* www.vancouverfilmstudios.com, pg 924

Dickson, Steve, Primacoustic, 1588 Kebet Way, Port Coquitlam, BC V3C 5M5, Canada *Tel:* 604-942-1001 *Fax:* 604-942-1010 *E-mail:* info@primacoustic.com *Web Site:* www.primacoustic.com, pg 862

Didier, Rebecca, Trafalgar Square Books, 388 Howe Hill Rd, North Pomfret, VT 05053 *Tel:* 802-457-1911 *Toll Free Tel:* 800-423-4525 *Fax:* 802-457-1913 *E-mail:* contact@trafalgarbooks.com; cs@trafalgarbooks.com (cust serv) *Web Site:* www.horseandriderbooks.com; www.trafalgarbooks.com, pg 917

Diebold, Wade, Alford Media Services, 296 Freeport Pkwy, Coppell, TX 75019 *Tel:* 972-538-9400 *Toll Free Tel:* 800-554-9144 *E-mail:* info@alfordmedia.com; sales@alfordmedia.com *Web Site:* www.alfordmedia.com, pg 680

Diemer, Richard, Diemer Amp & Keyboard Repair, 12814 Landale St, Studio City, CA 91604-1351 *Tel:* 818-762-0804 *Web Site:* bustedgear.com, pg 741

Diemont, Tony, acouStaCorp, 701 E 132 St, Bronx, NY 10454 *Tel:* 718-402-2677 *Fax:* 718-402-2859 *E-mail:* info@texasscenic.com *Web Site:* acoustacorp.texasscenic.com, pg 674

Diemont, Tony, Pook Diemont & Ohl Inc, 701 E 132 St, Bronx, NY 10454 *Tel:* 718-402-2677 *Fax:* 718-402-2859 *E-mail:* info@texasscenic.com *Web Site:* www.texasscenic.com, pg 859

Dietzler, Matt, Alford Media Services, 296 Freeport Pkwy, Coppell, TX 75019 *Tel:* 972-538-9400 *Toll Free Tel:* 800-554-9144 *E-mail:* info@alfordmedia.com; sales@alfordmedia.com *Web Site:* www.alfordmedia.com, pg 680

DiGiacomio, Michael, The Old Rhinebeck Aerodome®, 9 Norton Rd, Red Hook, NY 12571 *Tel:* 845-752-3200 *Fax:* 845-758-6481 *E-mail:* info@oldrhinebeck.org *Web Site:* www.oldrhinebeck.org, pg 844

DiGiacomo, Gabe, Nilfisk Inc, Indus Vacuum Div, 740 Hemlock Rd, Suite 100, Morgantown, PA 19543 *Toll Free Tel:* 800-NILFISK (645-3475) *Fax:* 610-286-7350 *E-mail:* questions@nilfisk.com *Web Site:* www.nilfiskcfm.com, pg 841

DiGiasante, Deborah, CMI Media Management, 9 W Broad St, Stamford, CT 06902 *Tel:* 203-989-9955 *Toll Free Tel:* 800-431-1102 *Fax:* 203-316-8353 *Web Site:* www.cminyla.com, pg 727

Digre, Dan, MISCO, 2637 32 Ave S, Minneapolis, MN 55406-1641 *Tel:* 612-825-1010 *Toll Free Tel:* 800-276-9955 *Fax:* 612-825-7010 *E-mail:* info@miscospeakers.com *Web Site:* www.miscospeakers.com, pg 828

Dill, Bob, Hisco Inc, 6650 Concord Park Dr, Houston, TX 77040-4098 *Tel:* 713-934-1700 *Toll Free Tel:* 844-807-1902 (web orders); 877-447-2650 (cust support) *Fax:* 713-934-1790 *E-mail:* info@hiscoinc.com *Web Site:* www.hiscoinc.com, pg 780

Dillard, Felicia, Association for Information and Image Management (AIIM), 1100 Wayne Ave, Suite 1100, Silver Spring, MD 20910 *Tel:* 301-587-8202 *Toll Free Tel:* 800-477-2446 *Fax:* 301-587-2711 *E-mail:* aiim@aiim.org *Web Site:* www.aiim.org, pg 950

Dillenburg, Jill, Prositions Inc, 6200 Aurora Ave, Suite 400W, Urbandale, IA 50322 *Tel:* 515-864-7200 *Toll Free Tel:* 877-244-8848 *E-mail:* info@prositions.com *Web Site:* prositions.com, pg 866

Diller, Wendell, Magnepan Inc, 1645 Ninth St, White Bear Lake, MN 55110 *Tel:* 651-426-1645 *Toll Free Tel:* 800-474-1646 *Fax:* 651-426-0441 *Web Site:* www.magnepan.com, pg 814

Dillon, Michael, Adobe Systems Inc, 345 Park Ave, San Jose, CA 95110-2704 *Tel:* 408-536-6000 *Fax:* 408-537-6000 *Web Site:* www.adobe.com, pg 676

Dillon, Tracy, Student Academy Awards Competition, 8949 Wilshire Blvd, Beverly Hills, CA 90211 *Tel:* 310-247-3000 *Fax:* 310-859-9619 *E-mail:* saa@oscars.org *Web Site:* www.oscars.org/saa, pg 1004

Diltz, Robert, RB Productions, 3-4191 Longmoor Dr, Burlington, ON L7L 5J9, Canada *Tel:* 905-633-7474 *E-mail:* sales@radicalbob.com *Web Site:* www.rbproductionz.com, pg 870

Dimitrief, Alex, General Electric Co, 41 Farnsworth St, Boston, MA 02210 *Tel:* 203-373-2211; 617-443-3000 *Web Site:* www.ge.com, pg 769

Dimoff, Diane, MotionMasters, 2288 Roxalana Rd, Dunbar, WV 25064 *Tel:* 304-345-8800 *Fax:* 304-345-8809 *E-mail:* storytellers@motionmasters.com *Web Site:* motionmasters.com, pg 831

Dimon, Cassidy, IDA Documentary Awards, 3470 Wilshire Blvd, Suite 980, Los Angeles, CA 90010 *Tel:* 213-232-1660 *Fax:* 213-232-1669 *E-mail:* info@documentary.org *Web Site:* www.documentary.org, pg 992

Dimon, Cassidy, International Documentary Association, 3470 Wilshire Blvd, Suite 980, Los Angeles, CA 90010 *Tel:* 213-232-1660 *Fax:* 213-232-1669 *E-mail:* info@documentary.org *Web Site:* www.documentary.org, pg 956

Dimont, David, Samy's Camera, 431 S Fairfax Ave, Los Angeles, CA 90036 *Tel:* 323-938-2420 *Toll Free Tel:* 800-321-4726 *Fax:* 323-937-2919 *E-mail:* lacamera@samys.com; info@samys.com; locations@samys.com *Web Site:* www.samys.com, pg 879

Dinnell, David, Ann Arbor Film Festival, 230 Collingwood Dr, Suite 160B, Ann Arbor, MI 48103 *Tel:* 734-995-5356 *Fax:* 734-995-5396 *E-mail:* info@aafilmfest.org *Web Site:* www.aafilmfest.org, pg 981

Dinoffer, Joe, Oncourt Offcourt Ltd, 7011 Gaston Pkwy, Dallas, TX 75214 *Tel:* 214-823-3078 *Toll Free Tel:* 888-TENNIS-11 (366-4711) *Fax:* 214-823-3082 *E-mail:* info@oncourtoffcourt.com *Web Site:* www.oncourtoffcourt.com, pg 846

Dirks, Jason, Sinauer Associates, 23 Plumtree Rd, Sunderland, MA 01375 *Tel:* 413-549-4300 *Fax:* 413-549-1118 *E-mail:* orders@sinauer.com (orders); publish@sinauer.com (gen edit correspondence); custserv@sinauer.com (cust serv) *Web Site:* www.sinauer.com, pg 889

DiScalfani, Robert, Bond Street Studio, 235 Bond St, Brooklyn, NY 11217 *Tel:* 718-858-2238 *E-mail:* info@bondstreetstudio.com *Web Site:* www.bondstreetstudio.com, pg 708

Dissinger, Jay R, Morefield Communications Inc, 35 N 35 St, Camp Hill, PA 17011-2707 *Tel:* 717-761-6170 *Toll Free Tel:* 800-382-1266 *E-mail:* info@morefield.com *Web Site:* www.morefield.com, pg 830

DiStasio, Vincent, Video Visions Inc, 3600 Boundbrook Ave, Trevose, PA 19053 *Tel:* 215-942-6642 *Fax:* 267-684-6819 *E-mail:* sales@video-visions.com *Web Site:* www.video-visions.com, pg 929

Ditchfield, Brian, The Martha's Vineyard Film Festival (MVFF), 9 State Rd, Chilmark, MA 02535 *Tel:* 508-645-9599 *Web Site:* www.tmvff.org, pg 995

Dittgen, Dave, The PPS Group, 424 Scott St, Covington, KY 41011 *Tel:* 859-291-5100 *Toll Free Tel:* 800-978-3445 *Fax:* 859-291-5150 *E-mail:* info@theppsgroup.com *Web Site:* www.pps-inc.com; www.theppsgroup.com, pg 860

Dittrich, Scott, Action Sports/All Stock, PO Box 301, Malibu, CA 90265-0301 *Tel:* 310-459-2526 *E-mail:* info@actionsportsstockfootage.com *Web Site:* www.actionsportsstockfootage.com; www.allstockfootage.com, pg 675

Dituri, Angelo, General Audio-Visual Inc (GAVI), 92 E Merrick Rd, Freeport, NY 11520 *Tel:* 516-623-8500 *Fax:* 516-623-9155 *Web Site:* www.gavi.com, pg 769

Dituri, Michael, General Audio-Visual Inc (GAVI), 92 E Merrick Rd, Freeport, NY 11520 *Tel:* 516-623-8500 *Fax:* 516-623-9155 *Web Site:* www.gavi.com, pg 769

DiVincenzo, Brenda, IPI - Member Network™, 2518 Anthem Village Dr, Suite 104, Henderson, NV 89052 *Tel:* 702-617-1141 *Fax:* 702-617-1181 *E-mail:* info@ipiphoto.com *Web Site:* www.ipiphoto.com, pg 957

Divine, Brian, AKG Acoustics US, 8500 Balboa Blvd, Northridge, CA 91329 *Tel:* 818-920-3212 *Toll Free Tel:* 888-452-4254 *Web Site:* www.akg.com/pro, pg 679

Dixon, Mark, Connecticut Office of Film, Television & Digital Media, c/o Dept of Economic & Community Development, 480 Columbus Blvd, Suite 5, Hartford, CT 06103 *Tel:* 860-500-2300 *Web Site:* www.ct.gov, pg 968

Dixon, R Eddie Jr, National Instruments Corp, 11500 N Mopac Expwy, Austin, TX 78759-3504 *Tel:* 512-683-0100 *Toll Free Tel:* 888-280-7645 (sales); 877-388-1952 *Fax:* 512-683-8411; 512-683-5794 (sales) *Web Site:* www.ni.com, pg 836

Dixon, West, Keywest Technology Inc, 14563 W 96 Terr, Lenexa, KS 66215 *Tel:* 913-492-4666 *Toll Free Tel:* 800-331-2019 *Fax:* 913-322-1864 *E-mail:* sales@keywesttechnology.com *Web Site:* www.keywesttechnology.com, pg 798

Djangi, Taraneh, Penguin Random House Audio Publishing, 1745 Broadway, New York, NY 10019 *E-mail:* audio@penguinrandomhouse.com *Web Site:* www.penguinrandomhouseaudio.com, pg 853

Djou, Benjamin, Cibola Systems, 180 S Cypress St, Orange, CA 92866 *Tel:* 714-480-0272 *Fax:* 714-480-0768 *E-mail:* info@cibolasystems.com *Web Site:* cibolasystems.com, pg 723

Do, Chris, Blind™, 1702 Olympic Blvd, Santa Monica, CA 90404 *Tel:* 310-314-1618 *Fax:* 310-314-1718 *Web Site:* www.blind.com, pg 707

Do, Lien, Different Fur Recording Ltd, 3470 19 St, San Francisco, CA 94110 *Tel:* 415-828-4060 (bookings) *Web Site:* differentfurstudios.com, pg 741

Dobbs, Ashley, Ocala/Marion County Visitors & Convention Bureau, 109 W Silver Springs Blvd, Ocala, FL 34475 *Tel:* 352-438-2800 *Toll Free Tel:* 888-FL-OCALA (356-2252) *Fax:* 352-438-2801 *E-mail:* exploreocalamarion@marioncountyfl.org *Web Site:* www.ocalamarion.com, pg 969

Dobnikar, Michele, PGi, 3280 Peachtree Rd NE, Suite 1000, Atlanta, GA 30305 *Tel:* 404-262-8400 *Toll Free Tel:* 866-755-4878 *Web Site:* www.pgi.com, pg 855

Dochard, Elaine, TMW Media Group, 2321 Abbot Kinney Blvd, Suite 101, Venice, CA 90291 *Tel:* 310-577-8581 *Toll Free Tel:* 800-262-8862 *Fax:* 310-574-0886 *E-mail:* sale@tmwmedia.com *Web Site:* www.tmwmedia.com, pg 915

Docter, Pete, Pixar Animation Studios, 1200 Park Ave, Emeryville, CA 94608 *Tel:* 510-922-3000 *Fax:* 510-922-3151 *Web Site:* www.pixar.com, pg 857

Dodge, Kathleen, El Dorado Lake Tahoe Film & Media Office, 542 Main St, Placerville, CA 95667 *Tel:* 530-626-4400 *Toll Free Tel:* 800-457-6279 *Fax:* 530-642-1624 *E-mail:* film@eldoradocounty.org *Web Site:* filmtahoe.com, pg 967

Dodson, Reynold, BitFlow Inc, 400 W Cummings Park, Suite 5050, Woburn, MA 01801 *Tel:* 781-932-2900 *Fax:* 781-933-9965 *E-mail:* sales@bitflow.com *Web Site:* www.bitflow.com, pg 706

Dodson, Veronique, National Association of Black Journalists (NABJ), 1100 Knight Hall, Suite 3100, College Park, MD 20742 *Tel:* 301-405-0248 *Fax:* 301-314-1714 *Web Site:* www.nabj.org, pg 958

Doepel, Bob, Chicago Scenic Studios Inc, 955 W Cermak Rd, Chicago, IL 60608 *Tel:* 312-274-9900 *Fax:* 312-274-9901 *E-mail:* info@chicagoscenic.com *Web Site:* www.chicagoscenic.com, pg 721

Doering, Ted, Umbra of Newburgh LLC, 9 Scobie Dr, Newburgh, NY 12550 *Tel:* 845-670-7493 *E-mail:* umbrastages@choicefilms.com *Web Site:* www.umbranewburgh.com, pg 921

Doerschuk, John, Terry Hanley Audio Systems Inc, 20 Industrial Pkwy, Woburn, MA 01801 *Tel:* 781-932-5300 *Fax:* 781-932-5354 *E-mail:* mail@terryhanleyaudio.com *Web Site:* www.terryhanleyaudio.com, pg 775

Doggett, Felicia, Metropolitan Acoustics LLC, 8 Penn Ctr, Suite 1902, 1628 John F Kennedy Blvd, Philadelphia, PA 19103 *Tel:* 215-248-4352 *E-mail:* info@metro-acoustics.com *Web Site:* www.metro-acoustics.com, pg 824

Doherty, Brian, Association of Independent Commercial Producers (AICP), 3 W 18 St, 5th fl, New York, NY 10011 *Tel:* 212-929-3000 *Fax:* 212-929-3359 *E-mail:* info@aicp.com *Web Site:* www.aicp.com, pg 951

Doherty, Dennis, Prior Scientific Inc, 80 Reservoir Park Dr, Rockland, MA 02370 *Tel:* 781-878-8442 *Toll Free Tel:* 800-877-2234 *Fax:* 781-878-8736 *E-mail:* info@prior.com; techsupportus@prior.com *Web Site:* www.prior.com, pg 862

Doherty, Ellen, Fred Rogers Productions, 2100 Wharton St, Suite 700, Pittsburgh, PA 15203 *Tel:* 412-687-2990 *Toll Free Tel:* 877-677-6437 *E-mail:* info@fredrogers.org *Web Site:* www.fredrogers.org, pg 876

Doiuchi, Frances, TEC/West USA Inc, 3050 E Victoria St, Rancho Dominguez, CA 90221 *Tel:* 310-961-3491 *Toll Free Tel:* 800-421-7215 *Fax:* 310-464-9210 *E-mail:* info@tecwest.com *Web Site:* www.tecwest.com, pg 908

Dolak, John, Sony Electronics Inc, 16530 Via Esprillo, San Diego, CA 92127 *Tel:* 858-942-2400 *Web Site:* www.sony.com, pg 893

Dolan, Bill, Spirit Media, 12042 SE Sunnyside Rd, Suite 700, Happy Valley, OR 97015 *Tel:* 503-698-5540 *Fax:* 503-698-8408 *E-mail:* info@spiritmedia.com *Web Site:* www.spiritmedia.com, pg 898

Dolan, Drew, I-25 Studios, 9201 Pan American Fwy NE, Albuquerque, NM 87113 *Tel:* 505-822-7115 *E-mail:* info@i-25studios.com *Web Site:* i-25studios.com, pg 783

Dolan, Greg, Xytech Systems Corp, 15451 San Fernando Mission Blvd, Suite 400, Mission Hills, CA 91345 *Tel:* 818-698-4900 *Fax:* 818-698-4901 *E-mail:* sales@xytechsystems.com *Web Site:* www.xytechsystems.com, pg 943

Dolan, James L, Madison Square Garden, 2 Pennsylvania Plaza, New York, NY 10121-0091 *Tel:* 212-465-6741 *E-mail:* msgnetpr@msgnetwork.com *Web Site:* www.thegarden.com; themadisonsquaregardencompany.com, pg 814

Dolezilek, Sarah, ASET - The Neurodiagnostic Society, 402 E Bannister Rd, Suite A, Kansas City, MO 64131-3019 *Tel:* 816-931-1120 *Fax:* 816-931-1145 *E-mail:* info@aset.org *Web Site:* www.aset.org, pg 690

Dolkart, Jonas, Mirror 34 Productions, 2302 W Badger Rd, Madison, WI 53713-2322 *Tel:* 608-271-1226 *Toll Free Tel:* 800-569-6810 *E-mail:* human@mirror34.com *Web Site:* www.mirror34.com, pg 828

Doll, Charlene, San Diego Stage & Lighting Supply Inc, 2203 Verus St, San Diego, CA 92154 *Tel:* 619-299-2300 *Fax:* 619-299-0058 *E-mail:* info@sdstagelighting.com *Web Site:* www.sdstagelighting.com, pg 880

Doll, Daniel, San Diego Stage & Lighting Supply Inc, 2203 Verus St, San Diego, CA 92154 *Tel:* 619-299-2300 *Fax:* 619-299-0058 *E-mail:* info@sdstagelighting.com *Web Site:* www.sdstagelighting.com, pg 880

Dolphin, Saima, Covid Inc, 1723 W Fourth St, Tempe, AZ 85281 *Tel:* 480-966-2221 *Toll Free Tel:* 800-638-6104 *Fax:* 480-966-6728 *E-mail:* sales@covid.com *Web Site:* www.covid.com, pg 732

Dombrowski, Frank, Gage-Line Technology Inc, 121 LaGrange Ave, Rochester, NY 14613-1577 *Tel:* 585-458-2000 *Toll Free Tel:* 800-291-3724 *Fax:* 585-458-0524 *E-mail:* sales@gage-line.com *Web Site:* www.gage-line.com, pg 767

Domenech, Daniel A, AASA, The School Superintendents Association, 1615 Duke St, Alexandria, VA 22314 *Tel:* 703-528-0700 *Fax:* 703-841-1543 *E-mail:* info@aasa.org *Web Site:* www.aasa.org, pg 947

Don, Laurie, The Jim Henson Co, 1416 N La Brea Ave, Hollywood, CA 90028 *Tel:* 323-802-1500 *Fax:* 323-802-1825 *Web Site:* www.henson.com, pg 794

Donahue, Rev Chris, Paulist Productions, 6430 W Sunset Blvd, Suite 1220, Los Angeles, CA 90028 *Tel:* 310-454-0688 *E-mail:* paulistmail@paulistproductions.org *Web Site:* www.paulistproductions.org, pg 852

Donahue, Conor, JSAV, 9150 N Royal Lane, Suite 150, Irving, TX 75063 *Tel:* 972-241-5444 *Toll Free Tel:* 800-852-8771 *Fax:* 972-247-2590 *E-mail:* info@jsav.com *Web Site:* www.jsav.com, pg 795

Donaldson, Eric Alan, Nineteen87, 1024 Harding Ave, Suite 201, Venice Beach, CA 90291 *Tel:* 310-577-5009 *Fax:* 310-577-1960 *E-mail:* info@1-9-8-7.com *Web Site:* www.1-9-8-7.com, pg 841

Donhauser, Whitney, Museum of the City of New York, 1220 Fifth Ave, New York, NY 10029 *Tel:* 212-534-1672 *Fax:* 212-423-0758 *E-mail:* info@mcny.org *Web Site:* www.mcny.org, pg 834

Donio, James, Music Business Association (Music Biz), 106 E Center Blvd, Marlton, NJ 08053 *Tel:* 856-596-2221 *Web Site:* musicbiz.org, pg 958

Donnelly, Bill, Donnelly Sound Inc, 59 Hylan Blvd, Apt 1C, Staten Island, NY 10305 *Tel:* 917-496-7752 *E-mail:* donnellysound@gmail.com *Web Site:* billdonnelly.com, pg 745

Donnelly, Brian, Digital Arts NY, 130 W 29 St, New York, NY 10001 *Tel:* 212-460-9600 *Fax:* 212-660-3600 *Web Site:* digitalartsny.com, pg 742

Donnelly, Dave, Film House Inc, 810 Dominican Dr, Nashville, TN 37228 *Tel:* 615-255-4000 *Fax:* 615-255-4111 *E-mail:* results@filmhouse.com *Web Site:* www.filmhouse.com, pg 760

Donohue, Bob, pinta acoustic inc, 2601 49 Ave N, Suite 400, Minneapolis, MN 55430 *Tel:* 612-355-4200 *Toll Free Tel:* 800-662-0032 *Fax:* 612-355-4299 *E-mail:* sales@pinta-acoustic.com; info@pinta-acoustic.com *Web Site:* www.pinta-acoustic.com, pg 857

Donohue, Ed, Rosco Laboratories Inc, 52 Harbor View, Stamford, CT 06902 *Tel:* 203-708-8900 *Toll Free Tel:* 800-ROSCO NY (767-2669) *Fax:* 203-708-8919 *E-mail:* info@rosco.com *Web Site:* us.rosco.com, pg 877

Donohue, Nora, Alford Media Services, 296 Freeport Pkwy, Coppell, TX 75019 *Tel:* 972-538-9400 *Toll Free Tel:* 800-554-9144 *E-mail:* info@alfordmedia.com; sales@alfordmedia.com *Web Site:* www.alfordmedia.com, pg 680

Donohue, Prentiss, OpenText Corp, 275 Frank Tompa Dr, Waterloo, ON N2L 0A1, Canada *Tel:* 519-888-7111 *Toll Free Tel:* 800-499-6544 *Fax:* 519-888-0677 *Web Site:* www.opentext.com, pg 847

Donovan, Jennifer, Penguin Random House Audio Publishing, 1745 Broadway, New York, NY 10019 *E-mail:* audio@penguinrandomhouse.com *Web Site:* www.penguinrandomhouseaudio.com, pg 853

Doo, Danna, Producers Management Television (PMTV), 681 Moore Rd, Suite 100, King of Prussia, PA 19406 *Tel:* 610-768-1770 *Fax:* 610-768-1773 *E-mail:* info@pmtv.com *Web Site:* www.pmtv.com, pg 863

Dooley, Greg, Gluskin's Custom Audio Video, 2051 Pacific Ave, Stockton, CA 95204 *Tel:* 209-888-4609 *Fax:* 209-888-4629 *E-mail:* info@gluskinsav.com *Web Site:* www.gluskins.com; www.gluskinsav.com, pg 771

Doornbos, Scott, Dukane Corp, Audio Visual Products Division, 2900 Dukane Dr, St Charles, IL 60174 *Tel:* 630-762-4040 *Toll Free Tel:* 888-245-1966 *Fax:* 630-584-5156 *E-mail:* avsales@dukane.com *Web Site:* dukaneav.com, pg 747

Doornick, Jason, International Robotics Inc, 2001 Palmer Ave, Suite LL-1, Larchmont, NY 10538 *Tel:* 914-630-1060 *E-mail:* info@internationalrobotics.com *Web Site:* internationalrobotics.com, pg 790

Doornick, Robert, International Robotics Inc, 2001 Palmer Ave, Suite LL-1, Larchmont, NY 10538 *Tel:* 914-630-1060 *E-mail:* info@internationalrobotics.com *Web Site:* internationalrobotics.com, pg 790

Dorfman, Robert, Dorfman Museum Figures Inc, 6224 Holabird Ave, Baltimore, MD 21224 *Tel:* 410-284-3248 *Toll Free Tel:* 800-634-4873 *Fax:* 410-284-3249 *E-mail:* info@museumfigures.com *Web Site:* www.museumfigures.com, pg 745

Dorgan, Janet Malik, Shamrock Communications, 106 Apple St, Suite 202, Tinton Falls, NJ 07724 *Tel:* 732-686-1140 *E-mail:* info@shamrockcommunications.com *Web Site:* www.shamrockcommunications.com, pg 885

Dorgan, Mark, Boston Productions Inc (BPI), 290 Vanderbilt Ave, Suite 1, Norwood, MA 02062 *Tel:* 781-255-1555; 720-233-1250 (sales) *E-mail:* info@bostonproductions.com *Web Site:* www.bostonproductions.com, pg 709

Dorman, Cecil, AVFX Inc, 96 Holton St, Boston, MA 02135 *Tel:* 617-254-0770 *Toll Free Tel:* 888-254-0770 *E-mail:* info@avfx.com *Web Site:* www.avfx.com, pg 698

Dorn, Scott, Spectrum Industries Inc, 925 First Ave, Chippewa Falls, WI 54729 *Tel:* 715-723-6750 *Toll Free Tel:* 800-235-1262 *Fax:* 715-738-2309 *Toll Free Fax:* 800-335-0473 *E-mail:* info@spectrumfurniture.com *Web Site:* www.spectrumfurniture.com, pg 897

Dornig, Kristin, Rhythm & Hues Studios Inc, 5890 W Jefferson Blvd, Suite Q, Los Angeles, CA 90016 *Tel:* 310-448-7500 *Fax:* 310-448-7600 *E-mail:* info-la@rhythm.com *Web Site:* rhythm.com, pg 874

Doros, Dennis, Milestone Film & Video Inc, PO Box 128, Harrington Park, NJ 07640-0128 *Tel:* 201-767-3117 *Toll Free Tel:* 800-603-1104 *Fax:* 201-767-3035 *E-mail:* milefilms@gmail.com *Web Site:* www.milestonefilms.com, pg 827

Dorr, Sharron, Theosophical Publishing House, 306 W Geneva Rd, Wheaton, IL 60187 *Tel:* 630-665-0130 *Toll Free Tel:* 800-669-9425 *Fax:* 630-665-8791 *E-mail:* customerservice@questbooks.net; marketing@questbooks.net *Web Site:* questbooks.com, pg 912

Dorrough, Kay, Dorrough Electronics Inc, 5221 Collier Place, Woodland Hills, CA 91364 *Tel:* 818-998-2824 *E-mail:* dorroughel@aol.com *Web Site:* www.dorrough.com, pg 746

Dorrough, Michael, Dorrough Electronics Inc, 5221 Collier Place, Woodland Hills, CA 91364 *Tel:* 818-998-2824 *E-mail:* dorroughel@aol.com *Web Site:* www.dorrough.com, pg 746

Dorsa, Jennifer, VMI Inc, 211 E Weddell Dr, Sunnyvale, CA 94089 *Tel:* 408-745-1700; 415-362-1330 *Web Site:* www.vmivideo.com, pg 932

Dorsey, Debbie Donaldson, Baltimore Film Office, 10 E Baltimore St, 10th fl, Baltimore, MD 21202 *Tel:* 410-752-8632 *Fax:* 410-385-0361 *Web Site:* www.baltimorefilm.com, pg 972

Dorst, Steve, Dorst MediaWorks Inc, 1219 Blagden Alley NW, 2nd fl, Washington, DC 20001 *Tel:* 202-258-9612 *Web Site:* dorstmediaworks.com, pg 746

Dotson, Amy, IFP Gotham Awards™, c/o Made in NY Media Ctr by IFP, 30 John St, Ground fl, Brooklyn, NY 11201 *Tel:* 212-465-8200 (ext 224) *E-mail:* gothamawards@ifp.org *Web Site:* gotham.ifp.org, pg 992

Dotson, Amy, IFP Week, c/o Made in NY Media Ctr by IFP, 30 John St, Ground fl, Brooklyn, NY 11201 *Tel:* 212-465-8200 *Web Site:* www.ifp.org, pg 992

Dotson, Amy, The Independent Filmmaker Project (IFP), c/o Made in NY Media Ctr by IFP, 30 John St, Ground fl, Brooklyn, NY 11201 *Tel:* 212-465-8200 *Web Site:* www.ifp.org, pg 956

Douek, Joseph, Willoughby's® Camera, 298 Fifth Ave, New York, NY 10001 *Tel:* 212-564-1600 *Toll Free Tel:* 800-378-1898 *E-mail:* customersupport@willoughbys.com *Web Site:* www.willoughbys.com, pg 939

Dougherty, Edward, Tritech Communications, 625 Locust St, Suite 300, Garden City, NY 11530 *Tel:* 631-254-4500 *Fax:* 631-254-4499 *E-mail:* sales@tritechcomm.com *Web Site:* www.tritechcomm.com, pg 918

Douglas, Brian, digital OutPost, 2772 Loker Ave W, Carlsbad, CA 92010 *Tel:* 760-431-3575 *Toll Free Tel:* 800-464-6434 *E-mail:* sales@dop.com *Web Site:* www.dop.com, pg 742

Douglas, David, West Eagle Films Inc, 800 Lower Ganges Rd, Salt Spring Island, BC V8K 2N5, Canada *Tel:* 250-538-1780 *Web Site:* www.westeaglefilms.com, pg 935

Douglas, Greg, Yorktel, 81 Corbett Way, Eatontown, NJ 07724 *Tel:* 732-413-6000 *Toll Free Tel:* 866-836-8463 *Fax:* 732-413-6060 *E-mail:* knowmore@yorktel.com *Web Site:* yorktel.com, pg 944

Douglas, Harry, Magnetic Post Production, 4 Marshall Rd, Wappingers Falls, NY 12590-4105 *Tel:* 212-598-3000 *Web Site:* www.magneticimage.com, pg 815

Douglas, Heather, Douglas House Inc, 275 Kings Hwy, Orangeburg, NY 10962 *Tel:* 845-359-1477 *Fax:* 845-359-2945 *E-mail:* thedouglashouse@earthlink.net *Web Site:* www.thedouglashouse.com, pg 746

Douglas, Kathy, The Video Project, 145 Ninth St, Suite 102, San Francisco, CA 94103 *Tel:* 415-981-9710 *Toll Free Tel:* 800-475-2638 *Fax:* 415-692-6223 *E-mail:* orders@videoproject.com; support@videoproject.com *Web Site:* www.videoproject.com, pg 928

Dow, Bill, The Weather Company, An IBM Business, 400 Minuteman Rd, Andover, MA 01810 *Tel:* 978-983-6300 *Fax:* 978-983-6400 *Web Site:* business.weather.com, pg 935

Dow, Donald, Artograph Inc, 525 Ninth St S, Delano, MN 55328-8624 *Tel:* 763-553-1112 *Toll Free Tel:* 888-975-9555 *Fax:* 763-553-1262 *E-mail:* sales@artograph.com; info@artograph.com *Web Site:* www.artograph.com, pg 690

Dowd, Lori, StoryTrack, 3224 Locust St, Suite 301, St Louis, MO 63103 *Tel:* 314-725-3003 *Web Site:* www.storytrack.com, pg 901

Dowell, Darlene, Vanner Inc, 4282 Reynolds Dr, Hilliard, OH 43026 *Tel:* 614-771-2718 *Toll Free Tel:* 800-ACPOWER (227-6937) *Fax:* 614-771-4904 *E-mail:* info@vanner.com; pwrsales@vanner.com *Web Site:* www.vanner.com, pg 924

Dowling, Walt, Parlights Inc, 1662 Bowmans Farm Rd, Suite 111, Frederick, MD 21701 *Tel:* 301-698-9242 *Fax:* 301-846-0369 *E-mail:* sales@parlights.com *Web Site:* www.parlights.com, pg 851

Downey, James, Clark's Audio Visual Services Ltd, 1615 Venables St, Vancouver, BC V5L 2H1, Canada *Tel:* 604-877-8558 *Toll Free Tel:* 800-667-1819 *Fax:* 604-879-2993 *Toll Free Fax:* 800-665-2932 *E-mail:* info@clarksav.com *Web Site:* www.clarksav.com, pg 725

Downie, Donna, Bernie's Photo Center, 525 E Ohio St, Pittsburgh, PA 15212 *Tel:* 412-231-1717 *Toll Free Tel:* 800-346-8884 *Fax:* 412-231-1217 *E-mail:* berniesphotocenter.info@gmail.com *Web Site:* www.berniesphoto.com, pg 704

Dowswell, Nicole, MRM//McCANN, 622 Third Ave, New York, NY 10017 *Tel:* 646-865-6230 *E-mail:* gbc@mrm-mccann.com *Web Site:* www.mrm-mccann.com, pg 832

Dowzall, Tony, Gefen, 20600 Nordhoff St, Chatsworth, CA 91311 *Tel:* 818-772-9100 *Toll Free Tel:* 800-545-6900; 800-472-5555 *Fax:* 818-772-9120 *E-mail:* sales@gefen.com; support@gefen.com *Web Site:* www.gefen.com, pg 769

Doyle, Jim, Ross Video Ltd, 8 John St, Iroquois, ON K0E 1K0, Canada *Tel:* 613-652-4886 *Fax:* 613-652-4425 *E-mail:* solutions@rossvideo.com *Web Site:* www.rossvideo.com, pg 878

Doyle, Kristene, Albert Ellis Institute (AEI), 145 E 32 St, 9th fl, New York, NY 10016 *Tel:* 212-535-0822 *Fax:* 212-249-3582 *E-mail:* info@albertellis.org *Web Site:* albertellis.org, pg 753

Doyle, Mike, Ketchum Inc, 1285 Avenue of the Americas, 4th fl, New York, NY 10019 *Tel:* 646-935-3900 *Web Site:* www.ketchum.com, pg 798

Doyle, Peter M, Broadcasters Foundation of America, 125 W 55 St, 4th fl, New York, NY 10019-5366 *Tel:* 212-373-8250 *Fax:* 212-373-8254 *E-mail:* info@thebfoa.org *Web Site:* www.thebfoa.org; broadcastersfoundation.org, pg 952

Doyle, Peter M, Golden Mike Award, 125 W 55 St, 4th fl, New York, NY 10019-5366 *Tel:* 212-373-8250 *Fax:* 212-373-8254 *E-mail:* info@thebfoa.org *Web Site:* www.thebfoa.org; broadcastersfoundation.org, pg 990

Doyle, Peter M, Lowry Mays Excellence in Broadcasting Award, 125 W 55 St, 4th fl, New York, NY 10019-5366 *Tel:* 212-373-8250 *Fax:* 212-373-8254 *E-mail:* info@thebfoa.org *Web Site:* www.thebfoa.org; broadcastersfoundation.org, pg 995

Doyle, Peter M, Ward L Quaal Leadership Awards, 125 W 55 St, 4th fl, New York, NY 10019-5366 *Tel:* 212-373-8250 *Fax:* 212-373-8254 *E-mail:* info@thebfoa.org *Web Site:* www.thebfoa.org; broadcastersfoundation.org, pg 1000

Dozois, Lisa, St Petersburg/Clearwater Film Commission, 8200 Bryan Dairy Rd, Suite 200, Largo, FL 33777 *Tel:* 727-464-7241 *Toll Free Tel:* 877-352-3224 *E-mail:* info@filmspc.com *Web Site:* www.filmstpeteclearwater.com, pg 969

Drabot, Michael, William F White International Inc, 800 Islington Ave, Toronto, ON M8Z 6A1, Canada *Tel:* 416-239-5050 *Toll Free Tel:* 800-465-0160 (CN only) *Web Site:* www.whites.com, pg 937

Drackett, Donna, PAR Inc, 16204 N Florida Ave, Lutz, FL 33549 *Tel:* 813-449-4065 *Toll Free Tel:* 800-331-8378 *Fax:* 813-961-2196 *Toll Free Fax:* 800-727-9329 *E-mail:* cs@parinc.com *Web Site:* www.parinc.com, pg 851

Drago, Mike, Gearhead Rentals, 69 O'Conner Rd, Suite 6, Fairport, NY 14450 *Tel:* 585-236-4272 *E-mail:* info@gearheadrentals.com *Web Site:* www.gearheadrentals.com, pg 769

Dragoni, Nick, M Works Mastering Studio, 60 Hampshire St, Cambridge, MA 02139 *Tel:* 617-577-0089 *E-mail:* studio@m-works.com; info@m-works.com *Web Site:* www.m-works.com, pg 813

Drayer, Christine, George Foster Peabody Awards, c/o University of Georgia, 120 Hooper St, Athens, GA 30602-3018 *Tel:* 706-542-3787 *E-mail:* peabody@uga.edu *Web Site:* www.peabodyawards.com, pg 999

Draznin, Rebecca, Advance Concepts Inc, 8453 Tyco Rd, Suite N, Vienna, VA 22182-2623 *Tel:* 703-448-0445 *Fax:* 703-893-8049 *Web Site:* www.advanceconcepts.com, pg 677

Drebin-Murphy, Layne J, Budget Films Stock Footage Inc, 706 N Vendome St, Suite 6, Los Angeles, CA 90026 *Tel:* 323-660-0187 *Fax:* 323-660-5571 *E-mail:* filmclip@aol.com; info@budgetfilms.com *Web Site:* www.budgetfilms.com, pg 712

Drendel, Frank M, CommScope Inc, 1100 CommScope Place SE, Hickory, NC 28602 *Tel:* 828-324-2200 *Toll Free Tel:* 800-982-1708 *E-mail:* publicrelations@commscope.com *Web Site:* www.commscope.com, pg 728

Dressendorfer, Mike, Russ Bassett Corp, 8189 Byron Rd, Whittier, CA 90606-2615 *Tel:* 562-945-2445 *Toll Free Tel:* 800-350-2445 *Fax:* 562-698-8972 *E-mail:* info@russbassett.com *Web Site:* www.russbassett.com, pg 878

Drexler, Jefferson, North County Media Center, 1130 N Melrose Dr, Suite 404, Vista, CA 92083 *Toll Free Tel:* 888-393-0580 *E-mail:* info@northcountymediacenter.com *Web Site:* northcountymediacenter.com, pg 842

Dreyer, Sarah, C&I An Idea Agency, 541 NW First Ave, Fort Lauderdale, FL 33301 *Tel:* 954-357-3934 *E-mail:* contact@c-istudios.com *Web Site:* www.c-istudios.com, pg 716

Driggs, Paul, OSA International Inc, 537 N Edgewood Ave, Wood Dale, IL 60191 *Tel:* 630-227-1008 *Toll Free Tel:* 877-OSA-INTL (672-4685) *Toll Free Fax:* 866-OSA-FAX2 (672-3292) *E-mail:* connect@osacorp.com *Web Site:* www.osacorp.com, pg 848

Drohan, James, Troxell-CDI, 4675 E Cotton Center Blvd, Suite 155, Phoenix, AZ 85040 *Tel:* 602-437-7240 *Toll Free Tel:* 855-TROXELL (876-9355) *Fax:* 602-752-1299 *Toll Free Fax:* 800-752-1299 *E-mail:* csg@trox.com *Web Site:* www.troxellsolutions.com, pg 918

Droppa, Larry, API, 8301 Patuxent Range Rd, Jessup, MD 20794 *Tel:* 301-776-7879 *Fax:* 301-776-8117 *E-mail:* service@apiaudio.com *Web Site:* www.apiaudio.com, pg 687

Druck, David, California Tape Products Inc, PO Box 177, Forest Falls, CA 92339-0177 *Tel:* 909-794-6524 *E-mail:* info@caltape.com *Web Site:* www.caltape.com, pg 714

Druck, Mark, Mark X Productions Inc, 300 E 40 St, New York, NY 10016, pg 817

Du, Liming, Hanovia Specialty Lighting LLC, 6 Evans St, Fairfield, NJ 07004 *Tel:* 973-651-5510 *Fax:* 973-651-5550 *E-mail:* sales@hanovia-uv.com *Web Site:* www.hanovia-uv.com, pg 775

Dubay, Jonathan, Getty-Dubay Productions, c/o Handwriting Success LLC, PO Box 91088, Portland, OR 97280 *Tel:* 971-254-8695 *E-mail:* info@handwritingsuccess.com; info@allport.com (orders) *Web Site:* www.handwritingsuccess.com; www.allport.com (orders), pg 770

Dube, Marco, CBC/Radio-Canada, 181 Queen St, Ottawa, ON K1P 1K9, Canada *Tel:* 613-288-6000; 613-288-6445 (newsroom) *Toll Free Tel:* 866-306-4636 (CN only) *E-mail:* cbcnewsottawa@cbc.ca *Web Site:* cbc.radio-canada.ca, pg 717

Dube, Steve, Russound, One Forbes Rd, Newmarket, NH 03857 *Tel:* 603-659-5170 *Toll Free Tel:* 800-638-8055 (US) *Fax:* 603-659-5388 *E-mail:* sales@russound.com; tech@russound.com *Web Site:* www.russound.com, pg 879

Dubin, Burt, Personal Achievement Institute, One Speaking Success Rd, Kingman, AZ 86402 *Tel:* 928-753-5315 *Web Site:* burtdubin-blog.com, pg 854

Dubin, Doug, CenterStaging LLC, 3407 Winona Ave, Burbank, CA 91504 *Tel:* 818-559-4333 *Fax:* 818-848-4016 *E-mail:* info@centerstaging.com *Web Site:* centerstaging.com, pg 719

DuBose, Marco, South Coast Film & Video, 5234 Elm St, Houston, TX 77081 *Tel:* 713-661-3550 *Toll Free Tel:* 800-229-3550 *Fax:* 713-661-4357 *E-mail:* info@scfilmvideo.com *Web Site:* www.southcoastfilmvideo.com, pg 895

Dubuc, Nancy, A&E Home Video, 235 E 45 St, New York, NY 10017 *Tel:* 212-210-1400 *Toll Free Tel:* 877-447-4253 *Fax:* 212-907-9418 *Web Site:* www.aetv.com, pg 671

Duchaine, Glenn, Maverick Video Productions, 121 Interpark, Suite 601, San Antonio, TX 78216 *Tel:* 210-495-1111 *Fax:* 210-495-8033 *Web Site:* www.maverickstudio.com, pg 820

Duckler, Max, CaptionMax, 2438 27 Ave S, Minneapolis, MN 55406 *Tel:* 612-341-3566 *Web Site:* www.captionmax.com, pg 716

Duckworth, Cara, Association of American Publishers (AAP), 455 Massachusetts Ave NW, Suite 700, Washington, DC 20001-2777 *Tel:* 202-347-3375 *Fax:* 202-347-3690 *E-mail:* info@publishers.org *Web Site:* publishers.org, pg 951

Dudek, Brian, Michigan Office Solutions (MOS), A Xerox Company, 2859 Walkent Dr NW, Grand Rapids, MI 49544 *Toll Free Tel:* 800-442-9070 *E-mail:* info@mos-xerox.com *Web Site:* www.mos-xerox.com, pg 825

Dudley, Christine, Illinois Film Office, James R Thompson Ctr, Suite 3-400, 100 W Randolph, Chicago, IL 60601 *Tel:* 312-814-3600 *Fax:* 312-814-8874 *E-mail:* film@illinois.gov *Web Site:* www.film.illinois.gov, pg 971

Dudley, Tim, Master Books®, 3142 Hwy 103 N, Green Forest, AR 72638 *Tel:* 870-438-5288 *Toll Free Tel:* 800-999-3777 *Fax:* 870-438-5120 *E-mail:* info@nlpg.com *Web Site:* www.nlpg.com, pg 819

Dudzinski, Tom, Renaissance Media, 909 Logan St, Suite 11F, Denver, CO 80203 *Tel:* 303-892-1415 *Web Site:* www.renaissancemedia.com, pg 873

Duff, Tom, Optimus, 161 E Grand Ave, Chicago, IL 60611 *Tel:* 312-321-0880 *Web Site:* www.optimus.com, pg 847

Duffy, Jim, Venture Media, 902 Harvest Pointe Dr, Fort Mill, SC 29708 *Tel:* 803-547-3878 *E-mail:* info@venturemedia.tv *Web Site:* www.venturemedia.tv, pg 926

Duffy, Kris, Venture Media, 902 Harvest Pointe Dr, Fort Mill, SC 29708 *Tel:* 803-547-3878 *E-mail:* info@venturemedia.tv *Web Site:* www.venturemedia.tv, pg 926

Dugan, Amy, Greeley/Weld Film Commission, 902 Seventh Ave, Greeley, CO 80631 *Tel:* 970-352-3566 *Toll Free Tel:* 800-449-3866 *Fax:* 970-352-3572 *E-mail:* info@greeleycvb.com *Web Site:* www.greeleychamber.com; www.visitgreeley.org, pg 968

Dugan, Andrew, Level 3 Communications Inc, 1025 Eldorado Blvd, Broomfield, CO 80021 *Tel:* 720-888-1000 *Toll Free Tel:* 877-2LEVEL3 (253-8357) *Web Site:* www.level3.com, pg 806

Dugan, Dan, Dan Dugan Sound Design Inc, 290 Napoleon St, Suite E, San Francisco, CA 94124 *Tel:* 415-821-9776 *Fax:* 415-826-7699 *Web Site:* www.dandugan.com, pg 747

Dugan, Deborah, Grammy Awards, 3030 Olympic Blvd, Santa Monica, CA 90404 *Tel:* 310-392-3777 *E-mail:* communications@grammy.com *Web Site:* www.grammy.org; www.grammy.com, pg 991

Dugan, Katie, Scott Resources Inc, 401 Hickory St, Fort Collins, CO 80524-1125 *Tel:* 970-484-7445 *Toll Free Tel:* 800-289-9299 *Fax:* 970-484-1198 *E-mail:* custserv@amep.com *Web Site:* amep.com, pg 882

Duggal, Michael, Duggal Visual Solutions Inc, Brooklyn Navy Yard, 63 Flushing Ave, Bldg 25, Brooklyn, NY 11205 *Tel:* 212-924-8100 (prodn); 212-242-7000 (corp) *Fax:* 212-486-1399 *E-mail:* info@duggal.com *Web Site:* duggal.com, pg 747

Duggan, Gene, Imagecraft Productions, 3318 Burton Ave, Burbank, CA 91504 *Tel:* 818-954-0187 *Fax:* 818-954-0189 *Web Site:* www.imagecraftproductions.com, pg 785

Duggan, Paul, OpenText Corp, 275 Frank Tompa Dr, Waterloo, ON N2L 0A1, Canada *Tel:* 519-888-7111 *Toll Free Tel:* 800-499-6544 *Fax:* 519-888-0677 *Web Site:* www.opentext.com, pg 847

Duke, Channing, JDC Wilmington Camera Services, 905 N 23 St, Wilmington, NC 28405 *Tel:* 910-343-1089 *Fax:* 910-343-0247 *E-mail:* info@wilmingtoncameraservices.com, pg 793

Duke, Eric, All Mobile Video Inc, 221 W 26 St, New York, NY 10001 *Tel:* 212-727-1234 *Fax:* 212-255-6644 *E-mail:* contact@amvchelsea.com *Web Site:* allmobilevideo.com, pg 680

Dunaj, Kathy, Sound/Video Impressions Inc, 110 S River Rd, Des Plaines, IL 60016 *Tel:* 847-297-4360 *Fax:* 847-297-6870 *E-mail:* info@soundvideoimpressions.com *Web Site:* www.soundvideoimpressions.com, pg 894

Dunbar, Clark, Mammoth HD, PO Box 2064, Evergreen, CO 80437 *Tel:* 303-670-7973 *E-mail:* mammothhd@me.com; info@mammothhd.com *Web Site:* www.mammothhd.com, pg 815

Dunbar, Lori, Ingram Content Group LLC, One Ingram Blvd, La Vergne, TN 37086-1986 *Tel:* 615-793-5000 *Toll Free Tel:* 800-937-8000 (retailers); 800-937-5300 (ext 1, libs) *E-mail:* customerservice@ingramcontent.com *Web Site:* www.ingramcontent.com, pg 787

Duncan, David, Randolf Productions Inc, 7271 Garden Grove Blvd, Suite F, Garden Grove, CA 92841 *Tel:* 949-794-9109 *Toll Free Tel:* 800-266-7741 *Fax:* 949-794-9117 *E-mail:* sales@go2rpi.com *Web Site:* www.go2rpi.com; christianmovieshop.com, pg 870

Duncan, Eason, See Production Services, 3330 Cobb Pkwy, Suite 17-327, Acworth, GA 30101 *Tel:* 404-474-4416 *E-mail:* info@seeproductionservices.com *Web Site:* seeproductionservices.com, pg 883

Duncan, Geoffrey, Radius® Display Products Inc, 800 Fabric Xpress Way, Dallas, TX 75234 *Tel:* 972-406-1221 *Toll Free Tel:* 800-FABRIC-X (322-7429); 866-966-4066 (sales); 866-966-8266 (hospitality) *Fax:* 972-406-1321 *Toll Free Fax:* 888-322-7429 *Web Site:* www.radiusdp.com, pg 869

Duncan, Keltie, Ottawa International Animation Festival, 2 Daly Ave, Suite 120, Ottawa, ON K1N 6E2, Canada *Tel:* 613-232-8769 *Fax:* 613-232-6315 *E-mail:* info@animationfestival.ca; entries@animationfestival.ca *Web Site:* www.animationfestival.ca, pg 999

Dunford, Ned, LuXout Stage Curtains, 1221 Admiral St, Richmond, VA 23220 *Tel:* 804-264-3000; 804-264-3700 *Toll Free Tel:* 800-817-1204 *Toll Free Fax:* 888-227-8064 *E-mail:* luxoutinfo@luxout.com *Web Site:* www.luxout.com, pg 813

Dung, Steven, Visions Plus, 200 Valley Dr, Suite 5, Brisbane, CA 94005 *Tel:* 415-467-3300 *E-mail:* web_inquiry@visionsplus.com *Web Site:* visionsplus.com, pg 931

Dunham, Gary, Indiana University Press, Off of Scholarly Publg, Herman B Wells Library 350, 1320 E Tenth St, Bloomington, IN 47405-3907 *Tel:* 812-855-8817 *Toll Free Tel:* 800-842-6796 *Fax:* 812-855-8507 *E-mail:* iupress@indiana.edu *Web Site:* www.iupress.indiana.edu, pg 786

Dunlap, Janet, Monotype Imaging Inc, 600 Unicorn Park Dr, Woburn, MA 01801 *Tel:* 781-970-6000 *Toll Free Tel:* 800-424-8973 *Fax:* 781-970-6001; 781-970-6002 (gen questions) *E-mail:* info@monotype.com *Web Site:* www.monotype.com, pg 829

Dunlop, Scott, Pyrotek Special Effects Inc, 201 Whitehall Dr, Suite 6, Markham, ON L3R 9Y3, Canada *Tel:* 905-479-9991 *Toll Free Tel:* 800-481-9910 *E-mail:* info@pyrotekfx.com *Web Site:* pyrotekfx.com, pg 867

Dunmead, Dave, Switchcraft® Inc, 5555 N Elston Ave, Chicago, IL 60630 *Tel:* 773-792-2700 *Fax:* 773-792-2129 *E-mail:* sales@switchcraft.com *Web Site:* www.switchcraft.com, pg 905

Dunn, Isaac, Visions Film Festival & Conference, 601 S College Rd, Wilmington, NC 28403 *Tel:* 919-607-0031 *E-mail:* visions7programming@gmail.com; visions7development@gmail.com *Web Site:* www.visionsffc.org, pg 1006

Dunn, Mathis, Screen Actors Guild - American Federation of Television & Radio Artists (SAG-AFTRA), 5757 Wilshire Blvd, 7th fl, Los Angeles, CA 90036-3600 *Tel:* 323-954-1600 (former SAG); 323-634-8100 (former AFTRA) *Toll Free Tel:* 855-SAG-AFTRA (724-2387) *Fax:* 323-549-6654 (communs & mktg) *E-mail:* info@sagaftra.org *Web Site:* www.sagaftra.org, pg 961

Dunn, Steven M, Ken-A-Vision Manufacturing Co Inc, 5615 Raytown Rd, Kansas City, MO 64133 *Tel:* 816-353-4787 *Toll Free Tel:* 800-501-7366; 800-627-1953 (cust serv) *Fax:* 816-358-5072 *E-mail:* info@ken-a-vision.com *Web Site:* www.ken-a-vision.com, pg 797

Dunnell, Graham, JIB Shots Equipment Inc, 1828 Lorraine Ave, Ottawa, ON K1H 6Z8, Canada *Tel:* 613-293-3318 *Web Site:* www.jibshots.com, pg 794

Dunning, Ernie, Dunning Photo Equipment Inc, 605 W Needles St, Bixby, OK 74008 *Tel:* 918-366-4917 *Fax:* 918-366-4918 *Web Site:* www.dunningphoto.com, pg 747

Dunnum, Jake, ETC, 3031 Pleasant View Rd, Middleton, WI 53562-4809 *Tel:* 608-831-4116 *Toll Free Tel:* 800-688-4116 *Fax:* 608-836-1736 *Web Site:* www.etcconnect.com, pg 756

Dunphy, John A, University Products Inc, 517 Main St, Holyoke, MA 01040-0073 *Tel:* 413-532-3372 *Toll Free Tel:* 800-628-1912 *Fax:* 413-532-9281 *Toll Free Fax:* 800-532-9281 *E-mail:* custserv@universityproducts.com; info@universityproducts.com *Web Site:* www.universityproducts.com, pg 923

Dunston, Dave, Zygote Media Group Inc, 1045 S 500 E, Suite 200, American Fork, UT 84003 *Tel:* 801-765-4141 *Fax:* 801-705-2234 *E-mail:* service@zygote.com *Web Site:* www.zygote.com, pg 945

Dunton, Joe, JDC Wilmington Camera Services, 905 N 23 St, Wilmington, NC 28405 *Tel:* 910-343-1089 *Fax:* 910-343-0247 *E-mail:* info@wilmingtoncameraservices.com, pg 793

Dupree, Todd, Trans-Lux Multimedia Corp, 445 Park Ave, Suite 2001, New York, NY 10022 *Tel:* 203-853-4321 *Toll Free Tel:* 800-243-5544; 800-462-2716 *E-mail:* sales@trans-lux.com *Web Site:* www.trans-lux.com, pg 917

Dupuis, Jacqueline, Vancouver International Film Festival (VIFF), Vancouver International Film Ctr, 1181 Seymour St, Vancouver, BC V6B 3M7, Canada *Tel:* 604-685-0260 *Fax:* 604-688-8221 *E-mail:* info@viff.org; submissions@viff.org *Web Site:* www.viff.org, pg 1006

Duran, Christy, Agrama Film Enterprises Inc, 7655 Sunset Blvd, Los Angeles, CA 90046 *Tel:* 323-851-4900 *Fax:* 323-851-5599 *E-mail:* sales@harmonygold.com *Web Site:* harmonygold.com, pg 678

Duran, Jonathan, SoundTube Entertainment Inc, 10661 Rene St, Lenexa, KS 66215 *Tel:* 913-663-5600 *Toll Free Tel:* 855-663-5600 *Fax:* 913-663-3200 *E-mail:* sales@mseaudio.com *Web Site:* www.soundtube.com, pg 895

Duran, Ramon, Cibola Systems, 180 S Cypress St, Orange, CA 92866 *Tel:* 714-480-0272 *Fax:* 714-480-0768 *E-mail:* info@cibolasystems.com *Web Site:* cibolasystems.com, pg 723

Durbin, Dave, BMI Supply, 571 Queensbury Ave, Queensbury, NY 12804 *Tel:* 518-793-6706 *Toll Free Tel:* 800-836-0524 *Fax:* 518-793-6181 *E-mail:* bminy@bmisupply.com *Web Site:* www.bmisupply.com, pg 708

Durden, Heather, Omega Media Group Inc, PO Box 924499, Peachtree Corners, GA 30010 *Web Site:* www.omegamediagroup.com, pg 845

Durham, James G, ChronTrol Corp, 7525-K Mission Gorge Rd, San Diego, CA 92120 *Tel:* 619-282-8686 *Toll Free Tel:* 800-854-1999 *Fax:* 619-563-6563 *E-mail:* info@chrontrol.com *Web Site:* www.chrontrol.com, pg 723

Durling, Roger, Santa Barbara International Film Festival, 1528 Chapala St, Suite 203, Santa Barbara, CA 93101 *Tel:* 805-963-0023 *Fax:* 805-962-2524 *E-mail:* contactus@sbiff.org *Web Site:* sbiff.org, pg 1003

Durrin, Ginny, Durrin Productions Inc, 6443 Wynkoop St, Los Angeles, CA 90045 *Tel:* 202-413-8971 *Web Site:* www.durrinproductions.com, pg 748

Duszara, Petro, Whalley-Abbey Media Holdings Inc, 3800 Rue St Patrick, Suite 100, Montreal, QC H4E 1A4, Canada *Tel:* 514-846-1940 *E-mail:* info@wamgrp.com *Web Site:* wamgrp.com, pg 937

Duva, Jason, Avid Technology Inc, 65-75 Network Dr, Burlington, MA 01830 *Tel:* 978-640-6789 *Web Site:* www.avid.com, pg 698

Duvarney, Nick, Association of Independent Commercial Producers (AICP), 3 W 18 St, 5th fl, New York, NY 10011 *Tel:* 212-929-3000 *Fax:* 212-929-3359 *E-mail:* info@aicp.com *Web Site:* www.aicp.com, pg 951

Dwyer, J C, Megatrax, 7629 Fulton Ave, North Hollywood, CA 91605 *Tel:* 818-255-7100 *Toll Free Tel:* 888-MEGA-555 (634-2555) *Fax:* 818-255-7199 *E-mail:* info@megatrax.com *Web Site:* www.megatrax.com, pg 823

Dy, Matt, Austin Film Festival, 1801 Salina St, Austin, TX 78702 *Tel:* 512-478-4795 *Toll Free Tel:* 800-310-FEST (310-3378) *Fax:* 512-478-6205 *E-mail:* info@austinfilmfestival.com; programming@austinfilmfestival.com; marketing@austinfilmfestival.com *Web Site:* www.austinfilmfestival.com, pg 982

Dyer, Emily, Macmillan Audio, 120 Broadway, 22nd fl, New York, NY 10271 *Tel:* 646-600-7856; 646-307-5472 *Toll Free Tel:* 888-330-8477 (cust serv); 800-221-7945 *Toll Free Fax:* 800-672-7703 (orders) *E-mail:* macmillan.audio@macmillanusa.com *Web Site:* www.macmillanaudio.com, pg 814

Dymmel, Kenneth L, JD Audio Visual Inc, 77 N Altadena Dr, Pasadena, CA 91107 *Tel:* 626-792-6682 *Toll Free Tel:* 800-532-8346 *Fax:* 626-796-6635 *E-mail:* sales@jdav.com; rentals@jdav.com *Web Site:* jdav.com, pg 793

Dyster, Martin, Omnia Audio, 1241 Superior Ave E, Cleveland, OH 44114 *Tel:* 216-241-7225 *Fax:* 216-241-4103 *E-mail:* social@telosalliance.com *Web Site:* www.telosalliance.com/omnia, pg 845

Dzienkonski, Karen, Penguin Random House Audio Publishing, 1745 Broadway, New York, NY 10019 *E-mail:* audio@penguinrandomhouse.com *Web Site:* www.penguinrandomhouseaudio.com, pg 853

Dzuban, Mark, Society of Cable Telecommunications Engineers Inc (SCTE), 140 Philips Rd, Exton, PA 19341-1318 *Tel:* 610-363-6888 *Toll Free Tel:* 800-542-5040 *Fax:* 610-884-7237 *E-mail:* info@scte.org *Web Site:* www.scte.org, pg 962

Eaddy, Rebecca, Roland Corp US, 5100 S Eastern Ave, Los Angeles, CA 90040-2938 *Tel:* 323-890-3700; 323-890-3771 (parts & serv); 323-890-3740 (prod support) *Fax:* 323-721-4875 *Web Site:* www.rolandus.com/us, pg 876

Eades, David, World Wide Pictures Inc, One Billy Graham Pkwy, Charlotte, NC 28266-8029 *Tel:* 704-401-2432 *Toll Free Tel:* 877-247-2426 *Fax:* 704-401-3045 *Web Site:* www.wwp.org; www.billgraham.org/wwp, pg 941

Eady, Craig, Cibola Systems, 180 S Cypress St, Orange, CA 92866 *Tel:* 714-480-0272 *Fax:* 714-480-0768 *E-mail:* info@cibolasystems.com *Web Site:* cibolasystems.com, pg 723

Eagles, Nick, NuMynd Studios, 915 Twin Elms Ct, Nashville, TN 37210 *Tel:* 615-259-1143 *Fax:* 615-259-1141 *E-mail:* hello@numyndstudios.com *Web Site:* www.numyndstudios.com, pg 843

Eardley, Michael, Tanglewood Productions, 125 Brinkby Ave, Reno, NV 89509 *Tel:* 775-688-6282 *Toll Free Tel:* 877-671-8933 *E-mail:* info@ tanglewoodproductions.com *Web Site:* www. tanglewoodproductions.com, pg 907

Earl, Don, Earl Girls Inc, 1648 White Horse Pike, Egg Harbor City, NJ 08215 *Tel:* 609-965-6900 *Web Site:* earlgirlsinc.com, pg 749

Earon, Dr S Ann, Telemanagement Resources International Inc (TRI), 83 Harvey Cedar Way, Waretown, NJ 08758 *Tel:* 609-597-6334 *Web Site:* www.triinc.com, pg 910

Eason, Darren, Star Case Manufacturing Co Inc, 648 Superior Ave, Munster, IN 46321 *Tel:* 219-922-4440 *Toll Free Tel:* 800-822-STAR (822-7827); 800-782-CASE (782-2273) *Fax:* 219-922-4442 *E-mail:* star@ starcase.com *Web Site:* www.starcase.com, pg 900

East, Pauline, Antelope Valley Film Office/North Los Angeles County, 42035 12 St W, Suite 103, Lancaster, CA 93534 *Tel:* 661-510-4231 *Web Site:* www.avfilm. com, pg 966

Eastbrook, Aaron, Broadcast Management Group, 718 Seventh St NW, Washington, DC 20001 *Tel:* 202-609-7757 *E-mail:* info@broadcastmgmt.com *Web Site:* www.broadcastmgmt.com, pg 710

Eastland, Erik, All Access Staging & Productions, 1320 Storm Pkwy, Torrance, CA 90501 *Tel:* 310-784-2464 *Toll Free Tel:* 877-784-2464 *Fax:* 310-517-0899 *E-mail:* sales@allaccessinc.com *Web Site:* www. allaccessinc.com, pg 680

Easton, Elmer, Three D Graphics Inc, 11340 W Olympic Blvd, Suite 352, Los Angeles, CA 90064-1613 *Tel:* 310-231-3330 *Toll Free Tel:* 800-913-0008 *Fax:* 310-231-3303 *E-mail:* info@threedgraphics.com *Web Site:* www.threedgraphics.com, pg 913

Eaton, Mark, Bang! Pictures Inc, 78 Graterford Rd, Schwenksville, PA 19473 *Tel:* 610-357-1015 *Web Site:* www.bangpictures.com, pg 701

Eaton, Sandi, Chelsea Green Publishing Co, 85 N Main St, Suite 120, White River Junction, VT 05001 *Tel:* 802-295-6300 *Toll Free Tel:* 800-639-4099 (orders) *Fax:* 802-295-6444 *E-mail:* customerservice@ chelseagreen.com *Web Site:* www.chelseagreen.com, pg 721

Ebeling, William, Tobins Lake Sales, 3313 Yellowstone Dr, Ann Arbor, MI 48105 *Fax:* 734-449-9812 *Web Site:* www.tobinslakesales.com, pg 915

Eby, Debbie, The International Society of Automation (ISA), 67 T W Alexander Dr, Research Triangle Park, NC 27709 *Tel:* 919-549-8411 *Fax:* 919-549-8288 *E-mail:* info@isa.org *Web Site:* www.isa.org, pg 790

Eckel, Robert, MorphoTrust USA, A Safran Company, 296 Concord Rd, Suite 300, Billerica, MA 01821 *Tel:* 978-215-2400 *Fax:* 978-215-2500 *E-mail:* info@ morphotrust.com; prmorphotrust@morphotrust.com *Web Site:* www.morphotrust.com, pg 830

Eckstat, Tony, Celestial Harmonies/Fortuna Records/Kuckuck Schallplatten/Black Sun Music/MonteVideo, 1951 N Wilmot Rd, Bldg 2, Unit 7, Tucson, AZ 85712-8000 *Tel:* 520-326-4400 *Fax:* 520-326-3333 *E-mail:* celestial@harmonies.com *Web Site:* www.harmonies.com, pg 719

Eckstein, Ike, Visual Word Systems Inc, 35 W 36 St, 8th fl, New York, NY 10018 *Tel:* 212-629-8383 *Fax:* 212-629-8333 *Web Site:* www.visualword.com, pg 932

Edds, Stephen, Silver Gavel Awards for Media & the Arts, Div for Public Education, 321 N Clark St, Chicago, IL 60654-7598 *Tel:* 312-988-5733 *Toll Free Tel:* 800-285-2221 *Fax:* 312-988-5494 (Attn: Gavel Awards) *E-mail:* publiceducation@americanbar.org *Web Site:* www.americanbar.org, pg 1004

Eddy, Jim, PAR Inc, 16204 N Florida Ave, Lutz, FL 33549 *Tel:* 813-449-4065 *Toll Free Tel:* 800-331-8378 *Fax:* 813-961-2196 *Toll Free Fax:* 800-727-9329 *E-mail:* cs@parinc.com *Web Site:* www.parinc.com, pg 851

Eddy, Mike, Purdue University Digital Education, Stewart Ctr, Rm G59, 128 Memorial Mall, West Lafayette, IN 47907 *Tel:* 765-494-8619 *Toll*

Free Tel: 800-830-0269 *Fax:* 765-496-2484 *E-mail:* distancelearning@purdue.edu *Web Site:* www. digitaleducation.purdue.edu, pg 867

Edegran, Lars, Jazzology, 61 French Market Place, New Orleans, LA 70116 *Tel:* 504-525-5000 *Fax:* 504-525-1776 *E-mail:* geobuck@jazzology.com *Web Site:* www.jazzology.com, pg 793

Edelman, Stephen, Colortone Audio Visual, 181 Westchester Ave, Suite 408B, Port Chester, NY 10573 *Tel:* 914-592-4151 *Fax:* 914-592-2833 *Web Site:* www. colortone-av.com, pg 728

Ederer, Becca, Cucalorus Film Festival, Jengo's Playhouse, 815 Princess St, Wilmington, NC 28401 *Tel:* 910-343-5995 *E-mail:* programming@cucalorus. org; press@cucalorus.org; comm@cucalorus.org *Web Site:* www.cucalorus.org, pg 987

Edgarton, Tyler, Mailing Avenue Stageworks, 1144 Mailing Ave, Atlanta, GA 30315 *Tel:* 404-601-9500 (ext 11) *Web Site:* www.mailingavenuestageworks.com, pg 815

Edmunds, Andy, Virginia Film Office, 901 E Cary St, Richmond, VA 23219-4048 *Tel:* 804-545-5530 *Toll Free Tel:* 800-854-6233 *Fax:* 804-545-5531 *E-mail:* vafilm@virginia.org *Web Site:* www.film. virginia.org, pg 976

Educate, Mario C, OSA International Inc, 537 N Edgewood Ave, Wood Dale, IL 60191 *Tel:* 630-227-1008 *Toll Free Tel:* 877-OSA-INTL (672-4685) *Toll Free Fax:* 866-OSA-FAX2 (672-3292) *E-mail:* connect@osacorp.com *Web Site:* www. osacorp.com, pg 848

Edwards, Dave, R/GA, 450 W 33 St, 12th fl, New York, NY 10001 *Tel:* 212-946-4000 *E-mail:* web@rga.com *Web Site:* www.rga.com, pg 868

Edwards, Joe, Imagers, 1575 Northside Dr, Bldg 400, Suite 490, Atlanta, GA 30318-5411 *Tel:* 404-351-5800 *Toll Free Tel:* 800-232-5411 *Fax:* 404-351-9020 *E-mail:* imagers@imagers.com *Web Site:* www. imagers.com, pg 785

Edwards, Marvin (Eddie) S Jr, CommScope Inc, 1100 CommScope Place SE, Hickory, NC 28602 *Tel:* 828-324-2200 *Toll Free Tel:* 800-982-1708 *E-mail:* publicrelations@commscope.com *Web Site:* www.commscope.com, pg 728

Edwards, Sharon, Kappa Map Group LLC, 112 E New York Ave, Deland, FL 32724 *Tel:* 386-873-3010 *Toll Free Tel:* 800-829-6277 (cust serv) *Fax:* 386-873-3011 *E-mail:* info@kappamapgroup.com; sales@ kappamapgroup.com *Web Site:* kappamapgroup.com, pg 796

Edwards, Mr Vanya, Sovfoto/Eastfoto Inc, 263 W 20 St, Suite 3, New York, NY 10011 *Tel:* 212-727-8170 *E-mail:* info@sovfoto.com *Web Site:* www.sovfoto. com, pg 896

Efrusy, Brian, RingSide Creative, 13320 Northend, Suite 3000, Oak Park, MI 48237 *Tel:* 248-548-2500 *E-mail:* info@ringsidecreative.com; newbiz@ ringsidecreative.com *Web Site:* www.ringsidecreative. com, pg 875

Eftekar, Y Julian, Motion Picture Licensing Corp (MPLC), 5455 Centinela Ave, Los Angeles, CA 90066 *Tel:* 310-822-8855 (intl calls) *Toll Free Tel:* 800-462-8855 *Fax:* 310-822-4440 *Web Site:* www.mplc.org, pg 831

Eggen, Greg, Hollywood Lights Inc, 5251 SE McLoughlin Blvd, Portland, OR 97202-4836 *Tel:* 503-232-9001; 503-232-8855 *Toll Free Tel:* 800-826-9881 *Fax:* 503-517-8686 *E-mail:* portland@hollywoodlights. biz *Web Site:* www.hollywoodlights.biz, pg 780

Egrie, Roy, Earl Girls Inc, 1648 White Horse Pike, Egg Harbor City, NJ 08215 *Tel:* 609-965-6900 *Web Site:* earlgirlsinc.com, pg 749

Ehler, Bob, RGB Spectrum, 950 Marina Village Pkwy, Alameda, CA 94501 *Tel:* 510-814-7000 *Fax:* 510-814-7026 *Web Site:* www.rgb.com, pg 874

Ehrlich, Douglas, Image Zone Inc, 11 W 69 St, Suite 10A, New York, NY 10023 *Tel:* 212-924-8804 *Web Site:* www.imagezone.com, pg 785

Eicher, David A, The Program Source International, 2494 Loch Creek Way, Bloomfield Hills, MI 48304 *Tel:* 248-333-2010 *E-mail:* info@program-source.com *Web Site:* www.program-source.com, pg 865

Eidsin, Bonnie, 1st Financial Training Services Inc, 1515 E Woodfield Rd, Suite 345, Schaumburg, IL 60173 *Tel:* 847-969-0900 *Toll Free Tel:* 800-442-8662 *Fax:* 847-969-0521 *E-mail:* info@1stfinancialtraining. com *Web Site:* www.1stfinancialtraining.com, pg 761

Eiger, Neil, Russell Industries Inc, 40 Horton Ave, Lynbrook, NY 11563 *Tel:* 516-536-5000 *Toll Free Tel:* 800-645-2202 *Fax:* 516-764-5747 *Toll Free Fax:* 800-645-2200 *E-mail:* sales@russellind.com *Web Site:* www.russellind.com, pg 879

Eipides, Dimitri, Festival du Nouveau Cinema de Montreal, 3805 Blvd Saint-Laurent, Montreal, QC H2W 1X9, Canada *Tel:* 514-282-0004 *Fax:* 514-282-6664 *E-mail:* info@nouveaucinema.ca; soumissions@ nouveaucinema.ca *Web Site:* www.nouveaucinema.ca, pg 989

Eisenberg, Eddy, Encore Event Technologies LLC, 8850 W Sunset Rd, 3rd fl, Las Vegas, NV 89148 *Tel:* 702-739-8803 *Fax:* 702-739-8831 *Web Site:* www. encoreglobal.com/us, pg 754

Eiswerth, Paul, TEL Systems LLC, 7235 Jackson Rd, Ann Arbor, MI 48103 *Tel:* 734-761-4506 *Toll Free Tel:* 800-686-7235 *Fax:* 734-761-9776 *E-mail:* sales@ thalner.com *Web Site:* www.thalner.com, pg 909

Ekstrand, Maria, CMD Agency, 1631 NW Thurman St, Portland, OR 97209 *Tel:* 503-223-6794 *E-mail:* info@ cmdagency.com *Web Site:* www.cmdagency.com, pg 726

Elam, Angela, New Letters on the Air, c/o University of Missouri, Kansas City, 5101 Rockhill Rd, Kansas City, MO 64110 *Tel:* 816-235-1159; 816-235-1168 *Fax:* 816-235-2611 *E-mail:* radio@newletters.org *Web Site:* www.newletters.org, pg 839

Elatawi, Hoda, GAPC (General Assembly Production Centre), 1550 Laperriere Ave, Suite 102, Ottawa, ON K1Z 7T2, Canada *Tel:* 613-723-3316 *Fax:* 613-723-8583 *Web Site:* www.gapc.com, pg 768

Elbert, Chad, Associated Production Music LLC, 6255 Sunset Blvd, Suite 900, Hollywood, CA 90028 *Tel:* 323-461-3211 *Fax:* 323-461-9102 *E-mail:* info@ apmmusic.com; clientservices@apmmusic.com *Web Site:* www.apmmusic.com, pg 691

Eldean, Kori, Waterfront Film Festival (WFF), 479 Columbia Ave, Holland, MI 49423 *Tel:* 269-767-8765 *E-mail:* info@waterfrontfilm.org *Web Site:* www. waterfrontfilm.org, pg 1006

Elderd, Chuck, Palm Beach County Film & Television Commission, 1555 Palm Beach Lakes Blvd, Suite 900, West Palm Beach, FL 33401 *Tel:* 561-233-1000 *Toll Free Tel:* 800-745-FILM (745-3456) *Fax:* 561-233-3113 *Web Site:* www.pbfilm.com, pg 970

Eldridge, Glenn, Chelsea Decorative Metal Co, 8212 Braewick Dr, Dept AV, Houston, TX 77074 *Tel:* 713-721-9200 *Fax:* 713-776-8661 *E-mail:* tinman83@ earthlink.net *Web Site:* www.tinman.com, pg 721

Eldridge, John, Technical Services, 2750 Northaven Rd, Suite 206, Dallas, TX 75229 *Tel:* 972-421-4230 *Fax:* 972-421-4231 *Web Site:* www.tecserv.biz, pg 908

Elgarten, Michael, Clever Devices Ltd, 300 Crossways Park Dr, Woodbury, NY 11797 *Tel:* 516-433-6100 *Toll Free Tel:* 800-872-6129 *Web Site:* www.cleverdevices. com, pg 726

Eliason, Craig, Minneapolis Licenses & Consumer Services, 350 S Fifth St, Rm 1, Minneapolis, MN 55415-1391 *Tel:* 612-673-2080 *Fax:* 612-673-3399 *Web Site:* www.minneapolismn.gov/licensing, pg 972

Elifrits, Kathy, The American Classical League, 860 NW Washington Blvd, Suite A, Hamilton, OH 45013 *Tel:* 513-529-7741 *Fax:* 513-529-7742 *E-mail:* info@ aclclassics.org *Web Site:* www.aclclassics.org, pg 683

Elisman, Boris, ACCO Brands Corp, 4 Corporate Dr, Lake Zurick, IL 60047-8997 *Toll Free Tel:* 800-541-0094; 800-222-6462 *Toll Free Fax:* 800-941-4463 *E-mail:* contactus@acco.com (cust serv) *Web Site:* www.accobrands.com, pg 673

Elkind, David, Live Wire Media, 2355 Westwood Blvd, No 312, Los Angeles, CA 90064 *Tel:* 415-564-9500 *Toll Free Tel:* 800-359-KIDS (359-5437) *Fax:* 415-552-4087 *E-mail:* sales@livewiremedia.com *Web Site:* www.livewiremedia.com, pg 810

Ellard, Melissa Reilly, Weston Woods Studios Inc, 90 Old Sherman Tpke, Danbury, CT 06816 *Tel:* 203-797-3520 *Toll Free Tel:* 800-243-5020 *Fax:* 203-797-3541 *E-mail:* westonwoodsquestions@scholastic.com *Web Site:* www.scholastic.com/westonwoods, pg 936

Ellenbogen, Eric, WildBrain™, 5657 Spring Garden Rd, Suite 505, Halifax, NS B3J 3R4, Canada *Tel:* 902-423-0260 *Fax:* 902-422-0752 *E-mail:* info@wildbrain.com; halifax@wildbrain.com; sales@wildbrain.com *Web Site:* www.wildbrain.com, pg 938

Eller, April, K2 Productions, 2303 Walters St, Greensboro, NC 27408 *Tel:* 336-664-8036 *E-mail:* info@k2production.com *Web Site:* www.k2production.com, pg 802

Eller, Kevin, K2 Productions, 2303 Walters St, Greensboro, NC 27408 *Tel:* 336-664-8036 *E-mail:* info@k2production.com *Web Site:* www.k2production.com, pg 802

Elliot, Susan, Abacus Group of Saint Louis LLC, 11 Tower Lane, Glen Carbon, IL 62034 *Tel:* 314-583-3747 *E-mail:* abacusgroup@agstl.com *Web Site:* www.agstl.com, pg 672

Elliott, Amanda, Questar Entertainment Inc, 307 N Michigan Ave, 5th fl, Chicago, IL 60601-5305 *Tel:* 312-266-9400 *Toll Free Tel:* 800-544-8422 (cust serv) *E-mail:* info@questarentertainment.com *Web Site:* www.questarentertainment.com, pg 868

Elliott, Janet, Radio & Television Engineering Achievement Awards, 1771 "N" St NW, Washington, DC 20036 *Tel:* 202-429-5300 *E-mail:* nab@nab.org; techawards@nab.org (nominations) *Web Site:* www.nab.org, pg 1000

Elliott, Kent, Jackson Hole Film Commission, 260A Broadway Ave, Jackson, WY 83001 *Tel:* 307-733-3316 *Fax:* 307-733-5585 *Web Site:* www.jacksonholechamber.com, pg 977

Elliott, Mark, Boxlight Inc, 1045 Progress Circle, Lawrenceville, GA 30043 *Toll Free Tel:* 866-972-1549 *E-mail:* service@boxlight.com; marketing@boxlight.com *Web Site:* mimio.boxlight.com, pg 709

Elliott, Pam, Special Effects Unlimited Inc, 1005 N Lillian Way, Hollywood, CA 90038 *Tel:* 323-466-3361 *Fax:* 323-466-5712 *E-mail:* seuefx@aol.com *Web Site:* www.specialefxunltd.com, pg 896

Elliott, Thomas, Centre for Art Tapes (CFAT), 2238 Maitland St, Halifax, NS B3K 2Z9, Canada *Tel:* 902-422-6822 *E-mail:* info@cfat.ca *Web Site:* cfat.ca, pg 953

Ellis, Andrew, Assured Audio Visual, 2941 E Miraloma Ave, Suite 3, Anaheim, CA 92806 *Tel:* 714-535-1414 *Fax:* 714-630-3518 *E-mail:* sales@assuredav.com *Web Site:* www.assuredav.com, pg 691

Ellis, Art, WHYY Inc, Independence Mall West, 150 N Sixth St, Philadelphia, PA 19106 *Tel:* 215-351-1200 *Fax:* 215-351-0398 *E-mail:* talkback@whyy.org *Web Site:* www.whyy.org, pg 938

Ellis, Shannon, Havas Edge, 2386 Faraday Ave, Suite 200, Carlsbad, CA 92008 *Tel:* 760-929-0041 *E-mail:* info@havasedge.com *Web Site:* www.havasedge.com, pg 777

Ellis, Susan P, Assured Audio Visual, 2941 E Miraloma Ave, Suite 3, Anaheim, CA 92806 *Tel:* 714-535-1414 *Fax:* 714-630-3518 *E-mail:* sales@assuredav.com *Web Site:* www.assuredav.com, pg 691

Ellwood, Jake, MAGNUM Companies Ltd, 205 Armour Dr NE, Atlanta, GA 30324 *Tel:* 404-872-0553 *Toll Free Tel:* 800-255-1774 *Fax:* 404-875-5629

E-mail: rent@magnumco.com; design@magnumco.com; production@magnumco.com; buy@magnumco.com *Web Site:* www.magnumco.com, pg 815

Elstrodt, John, Metropolitan Audio Visual Co LLC, 22923 Quicksilver Dr, Suite 117, Dulles, VA 20166 *Tel:* 703-834-0004 *Fax:* 703-834-0866 *E-mail:* sales@metroav.com *Web Site:* www.metroav.com, pg 824

Elton, Zoe, Mill Valley Film Festival, 1001 Lootens Place, Suite 220, San Rafael, CA 94901 *Tel:* 415-383-5256 *Fax:* 415-383-8606 *E-mail:* mvff@cafilm.org; info@cafilm.org *Web Site:* www.mvff.com; www.cafilm.org, pg 996

Elzinga, Anna, Zondervan, 3900 Sparks Dr, Grand Rapids, MI 49546 *Tel:* 616-698-6900 *Toll Free Tel:* 800-226-1122; 800-727-1309 (retail orders) *Web Site:* www.zondervan.com, pg 945

Emelson, Beth, Nantucket Film Festival (NFF), 68 Jay St, Suite 319, Brooklyn, NY 11201 *Tel:* 646-480-1900 *Fax:* 646-365-3367 *E-mail:* info@nantucketfilmfestival.org; submissions@nantucketfilmfestival.org *Web Site:* www.nantucketfilmfestival.org, pg 997

Emerson, Matt, Ceavco Audio Visual Company Inc, 6240 W 54 Ave, Arvada, CO 80002 *Tel:* 303-539-3500 *E-mail:* solutions@ceavco.com *Web Site:* ceavco.com, pg 719

Emery, Jennifer Roe, Vancouver Film Studios Ltd, 3500 Cornett Rd, Vancouver, BC V5M 2H5, Canada *Tel:* 604-453-5000 *Fax:* 604-453-5045 *E-mail:* info@vancouverfilmstudios.com *Web Site:* www.vancouverfilmstudios.com, pg 924

Emmer, Michael, Bridger Productions Inc, 4150 Glory View Lane, Jackson, WY 83001 *Tel:* 307-733-7871 *E-mail:* bridgerproductions@gmail.com *Web Site:* www.bridgerproductions.com, pg 710

Emmerich, Toby, New Line Cinema, 116 N Robertson Blvd, Suite 200, Los Angeles, CA 90048 *Tel:* 310-854-5811 *Fax:* 310-854-1824 *Web Site:* www.warnerbros.com/studio/divisions/new-line-cinema, pg 839

Emmerling, Dave, Midnight Media Group Inc, 45 E Willow St, Millburn, NJ 07041-1416 *Tel:* 973-379-5959 *E-mail:* info@mmgi.tv *Web Site:* mmgi.tv, pg 827

Emspak, Steve, Shen Milsom & Wilke LLC, 417 Fifth Ave, New York, NY 10016 *Tel:* 212-725-6800 *Fax:* 212-725-0864 *E-mail:* semspak@smwllc.com *Web Site:* www.smwllc.com, pg 886

Enberg, Dick, American Sportscasters Association Inc (ASA), 225 Broadway, Suite 2030, New York, NY 10007 *Tel:* 212-227-8080 *Fax:* 212-571-0556 *Web Site:* www.americansportscastersonline.com, pg 949

Encina, Matthew, Blind™, 1702 Olympic Blvd, Santa Monica, CA 90404 *Tel:* 310-314-1618 *Fax:* 310-314-1718 *Web Site:* www.blind.com, pg 707

Endres, W Chris, Tele-Measurements Inc, 145 Main Ave, Clifton, NJ 07014 *Tel:* 973-473-8822 *Toll Free Tel:* 800-223-0052 (ext 207) *Fax:* 973-473-0521 *E-mail:* contact@tele-measurements.com *Web Site:* www.tele-measurements.com, pg 910

Eng, Chris, EON247 Inc, 1245 Champa St, Basement, Denver, CO 80204 *Tel:* 720-935-7497 *E-mail:* info@eon247.com *Web Site:* www.eon247.com, pg 755

Eng, Ray, Babe Winkelman Productions Inc, PO Box 407, Brainerd, MN 56401 *Tel:* 218-821-6866 *Toll Free Tel:* 800-333-0471 *Web Site:* www.winkelman.com, pg 939

Engel, Mark, Rosco Laboratories Inc, 52 Harbor View, Stamford, CT 06902 *Tel:* 203-708-8900 *Toll Free Tel:* 800-ROSCO NY (767-2669) *Fax:* 203-708-8919 *E-mail:* info@rosco.com *Web Site:* us.rosco.com, pg 877

Engel, Paul, Quabbin Wire & Cable Co Inc, 10 Maple St, Ware, MA 01082-1597 *Tel:* 413-967-6281 *Toll Free Tel:* 800-368-3311 *Fax:* 413-967-7564 *E-mail:* sales@quabbin.com *Web Site:* www.quabbin.com, pg 867

Engelman, Ralph, George Polk Awards in Journalism, Journalism Dept, One University Plaza, Brooklyn, NY 11201-5372 *Tel:* 718-488-1009 *Web Site:* www.liu.edu/polk, pg 1000

Englen, Bjorn, Palardo Productions, 1807 Taft Ave, Suite 4, Hollywood, CA 90028 *Tel:* 323-469-8991 *E-mail:* palardo2@msn.com, pg 850

English, Elizabeth, Moondance International Film Festival, 970 Ninth St, Boulder, CO 80302 *Tel:* 303-818-5771 *Web Site:* moondancefilmfestival.com, pg 996

English, Elizabeth, 7seas Productions, 970 Ninth St, Boulder, CO 80302 *Tel:* 303-818-5771 *E-mail:* mermaid7seas@gmail.com *Web Site:* moondancefilmfestival.com/7seas-productions, pg 885

English, Troy, Ross Video Ltd, 8 John St, Iroquois, ON K0E 1K0, Canada *Tel:* 613-652-4886 *Fax:* 613-652-4425 *E-mail:* solutions@rossvideo.com *Web Site:* www.rossvideo.com, pg 878

Ennis, Bill, Media Magic, 11 Tanzanite, Rancho Santa Margarita, CA 92688 *Tel:* 949-713-9696 *E-mail:* request@mediamagic.tv *Web Site:* www.mediamagic.tv, pg 822

Ennis, Peter, Avid Technology Inc, 65-75 Network Dr, Burlington, MA 01830 *Tel:* 978-640-6789 *Web Site:* www.avid.com, pg 698

Ens, Herb, Specialty Bulb Products Inc, 20010-100A Ave, Unit 2, Langley, BC V1M 3G4, Canada *Tel:* 604-513-8500 *Toll Free Tel:* 800-663-1120 *Fax:* 604-513-8200 *E-mail:* info@specialtybulb.com; bulbexpert@specialtybulb.com *Web Site:* specialtybulb.com, pg 897

Epple, Kat, Kat Epple Music Productions, PO Box 3156, North Fort Myers, FL 33918-3156 *Tel:* 239-997-0323 *E-mail:* music@katepple.com *Web Site:* www.katepple.com, pg 755

Epstein, Larry, Paradise Show & Design Inc, 4653 35 St, Orlando, FL 32811 *Tel:* 407-649-7220 *Fax:* 407-649-7225 *Web Site:* www.paradiseshow.com, pg 851

Erickson, Britta, Denver Film Festival, 1510 York St, 3rd fl, Denver, CO 80206 *Tel:* 303-595-3456 *E-mail:* dff@denverfilm.org *Web Site:* denverfilmfestival.denverfilm.org, pg 988

Erickson, Britta, Denver Film Society, 1510 York St, 3rd fl, Denver, CO 80206 *Tel:* 303-595-3456 *E-mail:* info@denverfilm.org *Web Site:* www.denverfilm.org, pg 953

Erickson, Mark C, Fire Station Studios, 224 N Guadalupe St, San Marcos, TX 78666 *Tel:* 512-396-1144 *Fax:* 512-396-1169 *E-mail:* info@firestationstudios.com *Web Site:* www.firestationstudios.com, pg 761

Ericson, Axel, Digital Arts NY, 130 W 29 St, New York, NY 10001 *Tel:* 212-460-9600 *Fax:* 212-660-3600 *Web Site:* digitalartsny.com, pg 742

Ernst, Roger, Case Design Corp, 333 School Lane, Telford, PA 18969 *Tel:* 215-703-0130 *Toll Free Tel:* 800-847-4176 *Fax:* 215-703-0139 *E-mail:* sales@casedesigncorp.com *Web Site:* www.casedesigncorp.com, pg 717

Errera, Stacie, Tamron USA Inc, 10 Austin Blvd, Commack, NY 11725 *Tel:* 631-858-8400 *Toll Free Tel:* 800-827-8880 *Fax:* 631-543-5666; 631-858-8462 (cust serv) *E-mail:* custserv@tamron.com *Web Site:* www.tamron-usa.com, pg 906

Errigo, Anthony, Ashly Audio Inc, 847 Holt Rd, Webster, NY 14580-9103 *Tel:* 585-872-0010 *Toll Free Tel:* 800-828-6308 *Fax:* 585-872-0739 *E-mail:* info@ashly.com; sales@ashly.com; service@ashly.com *Web Site:* ashly.com, pg 691

Erwin, Ben, PSAV® Presentation Services, 111 W Ocean Blvd, Suite 1110, Long Beach, CA 90802-4688 *Tel:* 562-366-0620; 562-366-0621 *Toll Free Tel:* 877-430-7728 *Fax:* 562-366-0628 *Web Site:* www.psav.com, pg 866

Erwin, Ben, PSAV® Presentation Services (Hotel Services Division), 5100 N River Rd, Suite 300, Schiller Park, IL 60176 *Tel:* 847-222-9800 *Toll Free Tel:* 866-716-9691 *E-mail:* psavglobal@gmail.com *Web Site:* www.psav.com, pg 866

Esch, Mike, Christie Digital Systems USA Inc, 10550 Camden Dr, Cypress, CA 90630 *Tel:* 714-236-8610 *Toll Free Tel:* 866-880-4462 (cust serv) *Fax:* 714-503-3375 *E-mail:* sales-us@christiedigital.com; orders@christiedigital.com *Web Site:* www.christiedigital.com, pg 722

Escobar, Christopher, Atlanta Film Festival (ATLFF), 25 Park Place NE, Suite 800, Atlanta, GA 30303 *Tel:* 678-929-8103 *E-mail:* info@atlantafilmfestival.com; submit@atlantafilmfestival.com *Web Site:* www.atlantafilmfestival.com, pg 982

Escribano, Frankie, Yorktel, 81 Corbett Way, Eatontown, NJ 07724 *Tel:* 732-413-6000 *Toll Free Tel:* 866-836-8463 *Fax:* 732-413-6060 *E-mail:* knowmore@yorktel.com *Web Site:* yorktel.com, pg 944

Escudero, Anna, Christie Digital Systems USA Inc, 10550 Camden Dr, Cypress, CA 90630 *Tel:* 714-236-8610 *Toll Free Tel:* 866-880-4462 (cust serv) *Fax:* 714-503-3375 *E-mail:* sales-us@christiedigital.com; orders@christiedigital.com *Web Site:* www.christiedigital.com, pg 722

Eshaghnia, Michael, MeshTel, PO Box 774, Genoa, NV 89411 *Tel:* 775-267-5959 *Fax:* 775-267-5958 *E-mail:* info@meshtel.com *Web Site:* laserinfo.com, pg 824

Eshelman, Alyssa, Arizona Studios, 4614 E McDowell Rd, Phoenix, AZ 85008 *Tel:* 602-275-9100 *E-mail:* info@arizonastudios.com *Web Site:* arizonastudios.com, pg 689

Espe, Andrew, Washington Filmworks, 1411 Fourth Ave, Suite 420, Seattle, WA 98101 *Tel:* 206-264-0667 *Fax:* 206-382-4343 *E-mail:* info@washingtonfilmworks.org *Web Site:* washingtonfilmworks.org, pg 977

Espinoza, Richard, LTM Corp of America, 25520 Ave Stanford, Valencia, CA 91355 *Tel:* 818-780-9828 *Toll Free Tel:* 800-762-4291 *E-mail:* info@ltmlighting.us, pg 812

Essma, Joe, Accu-Tech, 11350 Old Roswell Rd, Suite 100, Roswell, GA 30009 *Toll Free Tel:* 888-222-8832 *Web Site:* www.accu-tech.com, pg 673

Estellon, Thibaut, LightHouse Films, 225 W 39 St, Suite 600, New York, NY 10018 *Tel:* 646-649-3600 *Fax:* 646-398-7122 *E-mail:* contact@lhfny.com; rent@lhfny.com *Web Site:* www.light-house-films.com, pg 807

Estorninos, Kristine, Toronto Reel Asian International Film Festival, 401 Richmond St W, Suite 309, Toronto, ON M5V 3A8, Canada *Tel:* 416-703-9333 *Fax:* 416-703-9986 *E-mail:* info@reelasian.com; programming@reelasian.com *Web Site:* www.reelasian.com, pg 1005

Estremera, Estefeni, Guilford Publications, 370 Seventh Ave, Suite 1200, New York, NY 10001-1020 *Tel:* 212-431-9800 *Toll Free Tel:* 800-365-7006 *Fax:* 212-966-6708 *E-mail:* info@guilford.com *Web Site:* www.guilford.com, pg 774

Estus, Boyd, Heliotrope Studios, 44 Oak St, Newton Upper Falls, MA 02464 *Tel:* 617-964-8181 *E-mail:* heliotropestudios@earthlink.net *Web Site:* www.heliotropestudios.com, pg 778

Ethier, Yan, Montreal Film & TV Commission, Duke Pavilion, 5th fl, 801 Brennan St, Montreal, QC H3C 0G4, Canada *Tel:* 514-872-2883 *Fax:* 514-872-3409 *E-mail:* film.tv@ville.montreal.qc.ca *Web Site:* www.montrealfilm.com, pg 979

Etzel, Ryan, Feldenkrais® Resources, 3680 Sixth Ave, San Diego, CA 92103 *Tel:* 619-220-8776 *Toll Free Tel:* 800-765-1907 *Fax:* 619-330-4993 *E-mail:* info@feldenkraisresources.com *Web Site:* feldenkraisresources.com, pg 759

Eulau, Dennis, Simon & Schuster, Inc, 1230 Avenue of the Americas, New York, NY 10020 *Tel:* 212-698-7000; 212-698-7126 *Toll Free Tel:* 800-223-2348

(cust serv) *Fax:* 212-698-7664 *Toll Free Fax:* 800-943-9831 *E-mail:* audiopublicity@simonandschuster.com *Web Site:* www.simonandschuster.net; www.simonandschuster.biz; www.simonandschuster.com, pg 888

Evans, Chuck, Quantum Data Inc, 2111 Big Timber Rd, Elgin, IL 60123-1100 *Toll Free Tel:* 888-252-6133 (tech support); 800-909-7211 (sales) *Fax:* 847-888-2802 *E-mail:* qd.sales@teledyne.com *Web Site:* www.quantumdata.com, pg 868

Evans, David, High Water Records, University of Memphis, Rudi E Scheidt School of Music, 121 Music Bldg, Memphis, TN 38152 *Tel:* 901-678-3317 *Fax:* 901-678-3096, pg 779

Evans, Mike, Digital Video Productions, 257 Federal Rd, Brookfield, CT 06804 *Tel:* 203-743-7663 *Fax:* 203-743-1658 *E-mail:* info@dvpllc.com *Web Site:* dvpllc.com, pg 742

Evans, Scott, Califone International Inc, 9135 Alabama Ave, Suite B, Chatsworth, CA 91311 *Tel:* 818-407-2400 *Toll Free Tel:* 800-722-0500 *Fax:* 818-407-2405 *Toll Free Fax:* 877-402-2248 *Web Site:* www.califone.com, pg 714

Evans, Vanessa, National Association of Black Journalists (NABJ), 1100 Knight Hall, Suite 3100, College Park, MD 20742 *Tel:* 301-405-0248 *Fax:* 301-314-1714 *Web Site:* www.nabj.org, pg 958

Evans, Will, Cinestate, 4100 Swiss Ave, Dallas, TX 75204 *E-mail:* info@cinestate.com *Web Site:* cinestate.com, pg 724

Eveleigh, Doug, Encyclopaedia Britannica Inc, 325 N La Salle St, Suite 200, Chicago, IL 60654 *Tel:* 312-347-7000 (all other countries) *Toll Free Tel:* 800-323-1229 (US & CN) *Fax:* 312-294-2104 *Web Site:* www.britannica.com, pg 754

Evenson, Stacey, Rainbow International Inc, 1103 Canyon Rd, Santa Fe, NM 87501 *Tel:* 773-505-6264 *Web Site:* www.rainbowplace.com; greatplainspress.com, pg 869

Everlof, Bernadette, Universal Studios Florida® Production Group, 1000 Universal Studios Plaza, Bldg 22A, Orlando, FL 32819 *Tel:* 407-363-8400 *Toll Free Tel:* 877-612-3737 (outside FL) *Fax:* 407-363-8869 *E-mail:* productiongroup@universalorlando.com *Web Site:* studio.florida.universalstudios.com, pg 922

Everson, Shawn, Ingram Content Group LLC, One Ingram Blvd, La Vergne, TN 37086-1986 *Tel:* 615-793-5000 *Toll Free Tel:* 800-937-8000 (retailers); 800-937-5300 (ext 1, libs) *E-mail:* customerservice@ingramcontent.com *Web Site:* www.ingramcontent.com, pg 787

Ewart, Heidi, Renegade Animation Inc, 111 E Broadway, Suite 208, Glendale, CA 91205 *Tel:* 818-551-2351 *Fax:* 818-551-2350 *Web Site:* www.renegadeanimation.com, pg 873

Ewing, Malcolm P Jr, Jasper Ewing & Sons Inc, PO Box 12853, Jackson, MS 39236 *Tel:* 601-942-3325 *E-mail:* info@jasperewing.com *Web Site:* jasperewing.com, pg 757

Exbrayat, Marianne, Transvideo International, 130 E Prospect Ave, Burbank, CA 91502 *Tel:* 818-985-4903 *Fax:* 818-985-4921 *Web Site:* www.transvideointl.com, pg 917

Eyrich, Heather, Concepts TV Productions Inc, 53 Indian Lane E, Towaco, NJ 07082 *Tel:* 973-331-1500 *Fax:* 973-331-1550 *E-mail:* sales@conceptstv.com *Web Site:* conceptstv.com, pg 730

Faber, Shane, Jeep Jazz Media Solutions, 8 Graham Terr, Montclair, NJ 07042 *Tel:* 973-222-5737 *E-mail:* jeepjazz@hotmail.com *Web Site:* www.jeepjazz.com, pg 793

Fabico, Jen D, Phase One Studios, 1121 Bellamy Rd N, Unit 5, Scarborough, ON M1H 3B9, Canada *Tel:* 416-291-9553 *Web Site:* www.phaseonestudios.com; facebook.com/phaseonestudio, pg 855

Facchini, Joe, AbelCine, 801 S Main St, Burbank, CA 91506 *Toll Free Tel:* 888-700-4416 *E-mail:* orders@abelcine.com; customerservice@abelcine.com *Web Site:* www.abelcine.com, pg 672

Fackert, James, Leprecon®, 10087 Industrial Dr, Hamburg, MI 48139 *Tel:* 810-852-4300 *Toll Free Tel:* 888-422-3537 *Fax:* 810-231-1631 *E-mail:* sales@leprecon.com *Web Site:* www.leprecon.com, pg 806

Fackert, James H, Littlite LLC, PO Box 430, Hamburg, MI 48139-0430 *Tel:* 810-852-4242 *Fax:* 810-231-1631 *E-mail:* sales@littlite.com *Web Site:* www.littlite.com, pg 810

Facklis, Jeff, Resolution Productions Group, 2226 W Walnut St, Chicago, IL 60612 *Tel:* 312-243-8230 *E-mail:* info@resolutionproductionsgroup.com *Web Site:* www.resolutionproductionsgroup.com, pg 874

Facklis, Lee, Resolution Productions Group, 2226 W Walnut St, Chicago, IL 60612 *Tel:* 312-243-8230 *E-mail:* info@resolutionproductionsgroup.com *Web Site:* www.resolutionproductionsgroup.com, pg 874

Factor, Sari, Edgenuity Inc, 8860 E Chaparral Rd, Scottsdale, AZ 85250 *Toll Free Tel:* 877-725-4257 (sales) *E-mail:* customersupport@edgenuity.com; solutions@edgenuity.com (sales) *Web Site:* www.edgenuity.com, pg 750

Fahey, David, Comtel Inc, 14901 NE 20 Ave, North Miami, FL 33181 *Tel:* 305-424-4160 (facility servs); 305-424-4178 (local inquiries); 516-816-5152 (natl inquiries) *Web Site:* www.comtelinc.com; www.facebook.com/comtelinc/, pg 730

Fahey, Lauren, Concepts TV Productions Inc, 53 Indian Lane E, Towaco, NJ 07082 *Tel:* 973-331-1500 *Fax:* 973-331-1550 *E-mail:* sales@conceptstv.com *Web Site:* conceptstv.com, pg 730

Fahringer, Katie, Pittsburgh Film Office, The Oliver Bldg, 535 Smithfield St, Suite 500, Pittsburgh, PA 15222 *Tel:* 412-261-2744 *E-mail:* info@pghfilm.org *Web Site:* www.pghfilm.org, pg 975

Fairbanks, Glen, DGI-Invisuals LLC, 101 Billerica Ave, Bldg 6, North Billerica, MA 01862 *Toll Free Tel:* 800-344-0432 *Fax:* 781-270-3663 *E-mail:* sales@dgi-invisuals.com *Web Site:* www.dgi-invisuals.com, pg 741

Fairchild, Ron, Texas Scenic Co Inc, 8053 Potranco Rd, San Antonio, TX 78251 *Tel:* 210-684-0091 *Toll Free Tel:* 800-292-7490 *Fax:* 210-684-4557 *E-mail:* info@texasscenic.com *Web Site:* www.texasscenic.com, pg 911

Faison, Patricia, Newark Black Film Festival (NBFF), 49 Washington St, Newark, NJ 07102-3176 *Tel:* 973-596-6550 *E-mail:* nbff@newarkmuseum.org *Web Site:* www.newarkmuseum.org/nbff, pg 998

Faison, Patricia, Paul Robeson Awards, 49 Washington St, Newark, NJ 07102-3176 *Tel:* 973-596-6550 *E-mail:* nbff@newarkmuseum.org *Web Site:* www.newarkmuseum.org/nbff, pg 1001

Faktorovich, Dr Anna, Anaphora Literary Press, 1108 W Third St, Quanah, TX 79252 *Tel:* 470-289-6395 *Web Site:* anaphoraliterary.com, pg 685

Falatovich, Brian J, Midwest Digital Corp, PO Box 204, Palos Park, IL 60464-0204 *Tel:* 708-790-4040 *E-mail:* sales@midwestdig.com; midwestdig@gmail.com *Web Site:* www.midwestdigitalcorp.com, pg 827

Falcon, Paul, Bella Faccia Inc, 5137 Lawrence Place, Hyattsville, MD 20781 *Tel:* 202-291-1932 *E-mail:* contact@bellafaccia.net *Web Site:* bellafaccia.net, pg 703

Falcone, Ernie, Quatrefoil Associates Inc, 29 "C" St, Laurel, MD 20707 *Tel:* 301-470-4748 *Fax:* 301-470-4749 *E-mail:* info@quatrefoil.com *Web Site:* www.quatrefoil.com, pg 868

Fall, Martin, General Devices Co Inc, 1410 S Post Rd, Indianapolis, IN 46239 *Tel:* 317-897-7000 *Fax:* 317-898-2917 *E-mail:* sales@generaldevices.com *Web Site:* www.generaldevices.com, pg 769

Fall, Maxwell, General Devices Co Inc, 1410 S Post Rd, Indianapolis, IN 46239 *Tel:* 317-897-7000 *Fax:* 317-898-2917 *E-mail:* sales@generaldevices.com *Web Site:* www.generaldevices.com, pg 769

Fallat, Tom, Sound Sound, 843 Hiawatha Place S, Unit 304, Seattle, WA 98144-2823 *Tel:* 206-330-6438 *Web Site:* www.soundsound.com; www.undisclosedlocation.us, pg 894

Fallon, David, Vertiv, 1050 Dearborn Dr, Columbus, OH 43085 *Tel:* 614-888-0246 *Web Site:* www.vertiv.com, pg 926

Falls, Ashley, The Clio Awards, 825 Eighth Ave, 29th fl, New York, NY 10019 *Tel:* 212-683-4300 *E-mail:* event@clioawards.com *Web Site:* clios.com, pg 987

Falter, David A, Antenna International, 383 Main Ave, Norwalk, CT 06851 *Tel:* 203-523-0320 *E-mail:* inquiry@antennainternational.com; marketing@antennainternational.com *Web Site:* www.antennainternational.com, pg 686

Falzarano, Jack, Megavideo LLC, 22 Cedar St, No 2, Garfield, NJ 07026 *Tel:* 973-478-1921 *E-mail:* megamail@megadv.com *Web Site:* www.megadv.com, pg 823

Falzon, Charles, CCI Entertainment Ltd, 210 St Clair Ave W, 4th fl, Toronto, ON M4V 1R2, Canada *Tel:* 416-964-8750 *E-mail:* info@ccientertainment.com *Web Site:* www.ccientertainment.com, pg 718

Famil, Shala, NDS Surgical Imaging LLC, 5750 Hellyer Ave, San Jose, CA 95138 *Tel:* 408-776-0085 *Toll Free Tel:* 866-637-5237 *E-mail:* info@ndssi.com *Web Site:* www.ndssi.com, pg 837

Fanelli, Dominic, Alford Media Services, 296 Freeport Pkwy, Coppell, TX 75019 *Tel:* 972-538-9400 *Toll Free Tel:* 800-554-9144 *E-mail:* info@alfordmedia.com; sales@alfordmedia.com *Web Site:* www.alfordmedia.com, pg 680

Fanelli, Duke, Association of National Advertisers Inc (ANA), 10 Grand Central, 155 E 44 St, New York, NY 10017 *Tel:* 212-697-5950 *Fax:* 212-687-7310 *E-mail:* info@ana.net *Web Site:* www.ana.net, pg 951

Farace, Tony, iVideo Technologies, 6779 Engle Rd, Suite G, Middleburg Heights, OH 44130 *Toll Free Tel:* 800-352-6150 *E-mail:* info@ivideo.com *Web Site:* www.ivideo.com, pg 792

Farber, Erica, Radio Advertising Bureau (RAB), 125 W 55 St, 5th fl, New York, NY 10019 *Tel:* 212-681-7200 *Toll Free Tel:* 800-252-7234 *Fax:* 212-681-7223 *E-mail:* memberresponse@rab.com *Web Site:* www.rab.com, pg 961

Farber, Galia, San Antonio Film Commission, 115 Plaza de Armas, Suite 102, San Antonio, TX 78205 *Tel:* 210-207-6777; 210-207-6730 *Toll Free Tel:* 800-447-3372 *Fax:* 210-207-4526 *E-mail:* filmsa@filmsanantonio.com *Web Site:* www.filmsanantonio.com; www.getcreativesanantonio.com/film-commission, pg 976

Farber, Scott, Hunt's Photo & Video, 100 Main St, Melrose, MA 02176-6104 *Tel:* 781-662-8822 (retail sales) *Toll Free Tel:* 800-924-8682 (retail sales); 800-221-1830 (ext 2340, corp sales) *Fax:* 781-662-6524 *E-mail:* ecommerce@wbhunt.com (retail online sales) *Web Site:* www.huntsphotoandvideo.com, pg 782

Faria, Thom, Cramer, 425 University Ave, Norwood, MA 02062 *Tel:* 781-278-2300 *E-mail:* theteam@cramer.com *Web Site:* cramer.com, pg 732

Farina, Billy, Cox Media, 6205 Peachtree Dunwoody Rd, No B17, Atlanta, GA 30328 *Toll Free Tel:* 855-755-2691 *Web Site:* www.coxmedia.com, pg 732

Faris, Bill, Avatar Studios, 2675 Scott Ave, Suite G, St Louis, MO 63103 *Tel:* 314-533-2242 *Fax:* 314-533-3349 *E-mail:* info@avatar-studios.com *Web Site:* avatar-studios.com, pg 697

Farkas, Steve, Vistamax Productions, 9705 Little Pond Way, Tampa, FL 33647 *Tel:* 813-907-1010 *Fax:* 813-907-1991 *E-mail:* info@vistamax.com; sales@vistamax.com *Web Site:* www.vistamax.com, pg 931

Farley, George, Supercircuits, 11000 N Mopac Expwy, Bldg 300, Austin, TX 78759 *Toll Free Tel:* 877-995-2288 *E-mail:* operations@supercircuits.com; customercare@supercircuits.com *Web Site:* www.supercircuits.com, pg 904

Farmer, Ashley, Greenwood Convention & Visitors Bureau & Film Commission, 225 Howard St, Greenwood, MS 38935 *Tel:* 662-453-9197 *Web Site:* www.visitgreenwood.com, pg 972

Farmer, Gary, American Association for Vocational Instructional Materials (AAVIM), 220 Smithonia Rd, Winterville, GA 30683 *Tel:* 706-742-5355 *Fax:* 706-742-7005 *E-mail:* sales@aavim.com *Web Site:* www.aavim.com, pg 682

Farmer, Gary, American Association for Vocational Instructional Materials (AAVIM), 220 Smithonia Rd, Winterville, GA 30683 *Tel:* 706-742-5355 *Toll Free Tel:* 800-228-4689 *Fax:* 706-742-7005 *E-mail:* sales@aavim.com *Web Site:* www.aavim.com, pg 948

Farmer, Tiffany, Encyclomedia, 1526 Dekalb Ave, Atlanta, GA 30307 *Tel:* 404-527-3600 *Fax:* 404-584-5171 *E-mail:* info@encyclomedia.net *Web Site:* www.encyclomedia.net, pg 754

Farr, John, Stockfootage.com, 231 S Mountain Way Dr, Orem, UT 84058 *Tel:* 801-221-9570; 801-361-0012 (cell) *E-mail:* sales@stockfootage.com *Web Site:* www.stockfootage.com, pg 901

Farrar, Fred, Klipsch Group Inc, 3502 Woodview Trace, Suite 200, Indianapolis, IN 46268 *Tel:* 317-860-8100 *Toll Free Tel:* 800-544-1482 *Web Site:* www.klipsch.com, pg 800

Farrell, Carl, SAS Institute Inc, 100 SAS Campus Dr, Cary, NC 27513-2414 *Tel:* 919-677-8000 *Toll Free Tel:* 800-727-0025 *Fax:* 919-677-4444 *Web Site:* www.sas.com, pg 880

Farrell, Frank, Custom Video Productions Inc, 15 Lake Shore Dr, Red Bank, NJ 07701 *Tel:* 732-936-1001 *E-mail:* info@cvpnj.com *Web Site:* www.cvpnj.com, pg 736

Farrell, Jim, Crew West Inc, 1515 W Deer Valley Rd, Suite C-109, Phoenix, AZ 85027 *Tel:* 480-367-6888 *Toll Free Tel:* 888-444-2739 *Fax:* 480-367-6688 *E-mail:* tvcrews@crewwestinc.com *Web Site:* www.crewwestinc.com, pg 734

Farrey, James, Jameco Electronics, 1355 Shoreway Rd, Belmont, CA 94002 *Tel:* 650-592-8097 *Toll Free Tel:* 800-831-4242 (orders); 800-536-4316 (cust serv) *Fax:* 650-592-2503 *Toll Free Fax:* 800-237-6948 *E-mail:* info@jameco.com; sales@jameco.com *Web Site:* www.jameco.com, pg 792

Farrington, Jay, Chater Camera Inc, 1336 Ninth St, Berkeley, CA 94710 *Tel:* 510-525-5400 *Fax:* 510-295-2478 *E-mail:* rentals@chatercamera.com *Web Site:* www.chatercamera.com, pg 721

Farris, JC, Chicago Underground Film Festival (CUFF), 2558 W 16 St, Stage 18, Chicago, IL 60608 *Tel:* 773-998-1082 *E-mail:* info@cuff.org; publicity@cuff.org *Web Site:* cuff.org, pg 986

Farrouge, Zee, Spirit Media, 12042 SE Sunnyside Rd, Suite 700, Happy Valley, OR 97015 *Tel:* 503-698-5540 *Fax:* 503-698-8408 *E-mail:* info@spiritmedia.com *Web Site:* www.spiritmedia.com, pg 898

Fata, Manijeh, San Francisco Film Commission, City Hall, Rm 473, One Dr Carlton B Goodlett Place, San Francisco, CA 94102 *Tel:* 415-554-6241 *Fax:* 415-554-6503 *E-mail:* film@sfgov.org *Web Site:* www.filmsf.org/film-commission; www.facebook.com/FilmSF, pg 967

Faubert, Peter, SeaChange International Inc, 50 Nagog Park, Acton, MA 01720 *Tel:* 978-897-0100 *Fax:* 978-897-0132 *E-mail:* globalsalesoperations@schange.com *Web Site:* www.schange.com, pg 883

Faulk, Kathy, Alabama Film Office, Alabama Ctr for Commerce, 401 Adams Ave, Suite 170, Montgomery, AL 36104 *Tel:* 334-242-4195 *Fax:* 334-242-2077 *Web Site:* www.alabamafilm.org, pg 965

Faunce, Andrew G, Academic & Campus Technology Services, 4 Currier Place, Suite 201, Hanover, NH 03755 *Tel:* 603-646-2999 (help desk); 603-646-2643 *E-mail:* itc@dartmouth.edu *Web Site:* itc.dartmouth.edu, pg 672

Faville, Vince, Video Visions Inc, 3600 Boundbrook Ave, Trevose, PA 19053 *Tel:* 215-942-6642 *Fax:* 267-684-6819 *E-mail:* sales@video-visions.com *Web Site:* www.video-visions.com, pg 929

Favre, Ritu, National Instruments Corp, 11500 N Mopac Expwy, Austin, TX 78759-3504 *Tel:* 512-683-0100 *Toll Free Tel:* 888-280-7645 (sales); 877-388-1952 *Fax:* 512-683-8411; 512-683-5794 (sales) *Web Site:* www.ni.com, pg 836

Favrin, Silvio, Teledyne DALSA Inc, 605 McMurray Rd, Waterloo, ON N2V 2E9, Canada *Tel:* 519-886-6000 *Fax:* 519-886-8023 *Web Site:* www.teledynedalsa.com, pg 910

Faxel, Tammy, Dreamscape Media LLC, 1417 Timberwolf Dr, Holland, OH 43528 *Tel:* 419-867-6965 *Toll Free Tel:* 877-983-7326 *E-mail:* info@dreamscapeab.com *Web Site:* www.dreamscapeab.com, pg 746

Fay, Douglas, Connecticut Audio & Theatrical Supply, 125-F Old Iron Ore Rd, Bloomfield, CT 06002 *Tel:* 860-206-9555 *Fax:* 860-206-0485 *Web Site:* www.ctaudio.com, pg 731

Fay, Thomas, TPR Enterprises Ltd, 644 Fayette Ave, Mamaroneck, NY 10543 *Tel:* 914-698-1141 *Fax:* 914-698-9419 *E-mail:* info@tprlights.com *Web Site:* www.tprlights.com, pg 916

Fazio, Gaston, HD House, 6312 NW 77 Ct, Miami, FL 33166 *Tel:* 305-597-7359 *Fax:* 305-597-7027 *Web Site:* thehdhouse.com, pg 777

Fearn, Douglas W, D W Fearn, 124 Tartan Terr, Chalfont, PA 18914 *Tel:* 567-DWFEARN (393-3276) *E-mail:* support@hazelriggindustries.com *Web Site:* www.dwfearn.com, pg 759

Fearnow, Vicki, Carpel Video Inc, 429 E Patrick St, Frederick, MD 21701 *Tel:* 301-694-3500 *Toll Free Tel:* 800-238-4300 *Fax:* 301-694-9510 *Web Site:* www.carpelvideoonline.com, pg 717

Featherstone, Craig, B&H Publishing Group, One LifeWay Plaza, Nashville, TN 37234 *Tel:* 615-251-2520 *Fax:* 615-251-5004 *Web Site:* www.bhpublishinggroup.com, pg 701

Fecht, Joel, Banff World Media Festival, 100-366 Adelaide St W, Toronto, ON M5V 1R9, Canada *Tel:* 416-408-2300 *Toll Free Tel:* 888-287-2279 *Fax:* 416-408-0870 *E-mail:* info@achillesmedia.com *Web Site:* banffmediafestival.com, pg 983

Feckanin, Alan, beyerdynamic Inc, 56 Central Ave, Farmingdale, NY 11735 *Tel:* 631-293-3200 *Fax:* 631-293-3288 *E-mail:* info@beyerdynamic-usa.com *Web Site:* north-america.beyerdynamic.com, pg 704

Fedeli, Frank, City of Stamford, 888 Washington Blvd, Stamford, CT 06901 *Tel:* 203-977-5858 *Web Site:* www.stamfordct.gov, pg 968

Federico, Danielle, Los Angeles Film Festival, 5670 Wilshire Blvd, 9th fl, Los Angeles, CA 90036 *Tel:* 323-556-9300 *Toll Free Tel:* 866-345-6337 *Fax:* 323-556-9303 *E-mail:* lafilmfest@filmindependent.org; programming@filmindependent.org *Web Site:* www.filmindependent.org/la-film-festival, pg 995

Federighi, Craig, Apple Inc, One Infinite Loop, Cupertino, CA 95014 *Tel:* 408-996-1010 *Web Site:* www.apple.com, pg 687

Fedonchik, Michael, Sima Products Corp, 125 Commerce Dr, Hauppauge, NY 11788 *Tel:* 631-435-0200 *Toll Free Tel:* 800-274-7824 *Fax:* 631-435-4545 *Toll Free Fax:* 800-274-7828 *E-mail:* customerservice@simaproducts.com *Web Site:* www.simaproducts.com, pg 888

Feely, Jim, Bell and Howell LLC, 3791 S Alston Ave, Durham, NC 27713 *Toll Free Tel:* 800-220-3030; 800-792-4782 (cust care) *E-mail:* info@bhemail.com *Web Site:* www.bellhowell.net, pg 703

Feeney, Michael, A&E Home Video, 235 E 45 St, New York, NY 10017 *Tel:* 212-210-1400 *Toll Free Tel:* 877-447-4253 *Fax:* 212-907-9418 *Web Site:* www. aetv.com, pg 671

Fehr, Scott, ITC, 523 Hanley Industrial Ct, St Louis, MO 63144 *Tel:* 314-646-1800 *Toll Free Tel:* 800-962-2344 *Fax:* 314-646-1818 *Web Site:* www.itcjourneys.com, pg 791

Feig, Erik, Picturestart, 817 Hilldale Ave, West Hollywood, CA 90069 *Tel:* 310-422-3280 *E-mail:* info@picturestart.com *Web Site:* www. picturestart.com, pg 856

Feiler, Regina, Globe Photos LLC, 6445 Tenaya Way, B-130, Las Vegas, NV 89113 *Tel:* 702-210-6208 *Fax:* 631-321-4063 *E-mail:* info@globephotos.com *Web Site:* www.globephotos.com, pg 771

Feinberg, Robert A, WNET/New York Public Media, 825 Eighth Ave, New York, NY 10019 *Tel:* 212-560-1313 *Fax:* 212-560-1314 *E-mail:* programming@ thirteen.org *Web Site:* www.thirteen.org; www.wnet. org, pg 940

Feinberg, Steven, Rhode Island Film & Television Office, One Capitol Hill, 3rd fl, Providence, RI 02908 *Tel:* 401-222-3456; 401-222-6666 (hotline) *Fax:* 401-222-3018 *Web Site:* www.film.ri.gov, pg 975

Feingersh, Randy, Video Associates Labs Inc, 2201 Denton Dr, Suite 109 B, Austin, TX 78758-3231 *Tel:* 512-491-7091 *Toll Free Tel:* 800-331-0547 *Fax:* 512-491-7619 *E-mail:* sales@val.com *Web Site:* www.val.com, pg 927

Feist, Elinor, Michael Blackwood Productions Inc, 6 W 18 St, Suite 2B, New York, NY 10011 *Tel:* 212-242-1805 *Fax:* 212-242-1671 *E-mail:* blackwoodfilm@aol. com *Web Site:* www.michaelblackwoodproductions. com, pg 707

Felber, Corey, CyberOptics Corp, 5900 Golden Hills Dr, Minneapolis, MN 55416 *Tel:* 763-542-5000 *Fax:* 763-542-5100 *E-mail:* info@cyberoptics.com *Web Site:* cyberoptics.com, pg 736

Felber, David, USCCB Publishing, 3211 Fourth St NE, Washington, DC 20017 *Tel:* 202-541-3000 *Toll Free Tel:* 800-235-8722 (cust serv) *Fax:* 202-722-8709 (cust serv) *E-mail:* publications@usccb.org *Web Site:* www. usccbpublishing.org, pg 923

Feld, Lori, MRM//McCANN, 622 Third Ave, New York, NY 10017 *Tel:* 646-865-6230 *E-mail:* gbc@ mrm-mccann.com *Web Site:* www.mrm-mccann.com, pg 832

Feldman, Martin, Integrated Solutions Group, 858 Boston Providence Tpke, Norwood, MA 02062 *Tel:* 781-769-7810 *Toll Free Tel:* 866-769-0210 *E-mail:* info@isgboston.com *Web Site:* isgboston.com, pg 789

Felker, Bill, House of Cinemagraphics, 4802 Quail Ave N, Minneapolis, MN 55429 *Tel:* 612-339-7803; 763-458-8244 *Toll Free Tel:* 888-813-0413 *E-mail:* film@ visi.com *Web Site:* www.houseofcinemagraphics.com, pg 782

Feller, Karen, Taylor Associates, 110 W Canal St, Suite 301, Winooski, VT 05404 *Tel:* 802-735-1942 *Toll Free Tel:* 800-READ-PLUS (732-3758) *Fax:* 802-419-4786 *E-mail:* info@readingplus.com *Web Site:* www. readingplus.com, pg 907

Felmer, Thomas J, Brady Corp, 6555 W Good Hope Rd, Milwaukee, WI 53201-0571 *Tel:* 414-358-6600 *Toll Free Tel:* 888-250-3082 *E-mail:* bradyusa@bradycorp. com (cust serv & sales) *Web Site:* www.bradyid.com, pg 709

Fels, Mark, Actors Attic, 540 Otis Dr, Dover, DE 19901 *Tel:* 302-734-8214 *Fax:* 302-734-8207 *E-mail:* sales@ actorsattic.com *Web Site:* www.actorsattic.com, pg 675

Fenigstein, Meir, Israel Film Festival, 324 S Beverly Dr, No 424, Beverly Hills, CA 90212 *Tel:* 310-247-1800 *E-mail:* info@israelfilmfestival.org *Web Site:* www. israelfilmfestival.com, pg 993

Fennell, Michael Paul, The Rip-Tie Co, 883 San Leandro Blvd, San Leandro, CA 94577 *Tel:* 510-577-0200 *Toll Free Tel:* 800-7-RIPTIE (774-7843) *Fax:* 510-553-0160 *E-mail:* info@riptie.com *Web Site:* www.riptie. com, pg 875

Fennig, Jim, Photogenic Professional Lighting, 1268 Humbracht Circle, Bartlett, IL 60103-1631 *Tel:* 630-830-2500 *Toll Free Tel:* 800-682-7668 *Fax:* 630-830-2525 *E-mail:* sales@photogenic.com *Web Site:* www. photogenic.com, pg 856

Fenton, Roger, Academy of Science Fiction, Fantasy & Horror Films, 334 W 54 St, Los Angeles, CA 90037 *Tel:* 323-752-5811 *E-mail:* saturn.awards@ca.rr.com *Web Site:* www.saturnawards.org, pg 947

Fenwick, Neal V, ACCO Brands Corp, 4 Corporate Dr, Lake Zurich, IL 60047-8997 *Toll Free Tel:* 800-541-0094; 800-222-6462 *Toll Free Fax:* 800-941-4463 *E-mail:* contactus@acco.com (cust serv) *Web Site:* www.accobrands.com, pg 673

Ferguson, Rick, Houston Film Commission, 701 Avenida de las Americas, Houston, TX 77010 *Tel:* 713-853-8959; 713-853-8100 *Toll Free Tel:* 800-446-8786 *Fax:* 713-853-8341 *E-mail:* jmontgomery@ houstonfilmcommission.com *Web Site:* www. houstonfilmcommission.com, pg 976

Ferlino, James, Vistacom Inc, 1902 Vultee St, Allentown, PA 18103-2998 *Tel:* 610-791-9081 *Toll Free Tel:* 800-747-0459 *Fax:* 610-791-9510 *E-mail:* info@ vistacominc.com *Web Site:* www.vistacominc.com, pg 931

Ferm, Mia, Fresh Film Northwest (FFNW), 934 SW Salmon St, Portland, OR 97205 *Tel:* 503-221-1156 *Fax:* 503-294-0874 *E-mail:* info@nwfilm.org *Web Site:* www.nwfilm.org, pg 990

Fernander, Robert, Nexsan Inc, 900 E Hamilton Ave, Suite 230, Campbell, CA 95008 *Tel:* 408-724-9809 *E-mail:* sales@nexsan.com *Web Site:* www.nexsan. com, pg 840

Fernandes, Carlos, Precision Microproducts of America, One Comac Loop, Unit 13, Ronkonkoma, NY 11779 *Tel:* 631-580-3456 *Toll Free Tel:* 800-932-9215 *Fax:* 631-580-3003 *E-mail:* sales@p-m-a.com *Web Site:* www.p-m-a.com, pg 861

Fernandez, Luis, Disney Consumer Products & Interactive Media (DCPI), 1201 Flower St, Glendale, AZ 91201 *Tel:* 818-544-0000 *Web Site:* dcpi.disney. com, pg 743

Fernandez-Williams, Sherrie, Artist Initiative Grant Program, Park Square Ct, Suite 200, 400 Sibley St, St Paul, MN 55101-1928 *Tel:* 651-215-1600 *Toll Free Tel:* 800-866-2787 *Fax:* 651-215-1602 *E-mail:* msab@ arts.state.mn.us *Web Site:* www.arts.state.mn.us, pg 982

Ferrara, Joe, E Video Productions LLC, 17 Washington St, Toms River, NJ 08753 *Tel:* 732-349-4762 *Toll Free Tel:* 877-384-3365 *E-mail:* info@evideoproductions.net *Web Site:* www.evideoproductions.net, pg 749

Ferrari, Jon, Buffalo Video Production, 233 Fillmore Ave, Suite 8, Tonawanda, NY 14150 *Tel:* 716-807-1510 *Web Site:* www.buffalovideoproduction.com, pg 712

Ferrari, Phillip, Ferrari Productions, 13323 Deer Canyon Place, San Diego, CA 92129 *Tel:* 858-354-8888 *E-mail:* info@ferrariproductions.com; sales@ferrariproductions.com *Web Site:* www. ferrariproductions.com, pg 759

Ferraro, Peter, Easy Street Productions LLC, 118 Redhaven Ct, Thurmont, MD 21788 *Tel:* 301-471-8058 *E-mail:* info@publicdomainfootage.com *Web Site:* www.publicdomainfootage.com, pg 750

Ferrarone, Chloe, WGBH Production Group, One Guest St, Boston, MA 02135 *Tel:* 617-300-2000 *E-mail:* productiongroup@wgbh.org; studios@wgbh. org; outpost@wgbh.org *Web Site:* productiongroup. wgbh.org, pg 936

Ferrer, Abraham, The Los Angeles Asian Pacific Film Festival, 120 Judge John Aiso St, Basement Level, Los Angeles, CA 90012-3805 *Tel:* 213-680-4462 *E-mail:* festival@vconline.org *Web Site:* asianfilmfestla.org; www.vconline.org/ festival, pg 994

Ferrer, Vic, The Producer's Loft, 2773 Folsom St, Suite 101, San Francisco, CA 94110 *Tel:* 415-334-4700 *Web Site:* theproducersloft.com, pg 863

Ferreyra, Stuart, TIMECODE Post Production, 12340 Santa Monica Blvd, Suite 230, West Los Angeles, CA 90025 *Tel:* 310-826-9199 *E-mail:* info@ timecodemedia.com *Web Site:* www.timecodepost.com, pg 914

Ferri, Brian, AVP Mfg & Supply Inc, 2288-B7 Dumfries Rd, RR2, Cambridge, ON N1R 5S3, Canada *Tel:* 519-740-7966 *Toll Free Tel:* 519-740-0131 *E-mail:* sales@jackfields.com *Web Site:* www. jackfields.com, pg 699

Ferri-Grant, Carson, Guild of Italian American Actors (GIAA), 1026A Shetland Dr, Lakewood, NJ 08701 *Tel:* 201-344-3411 *E-mail:* info@giaa.us *Web Site:* www.giaa.us, pg 955

Ferris, Kinney, Oxford Film Commission, 1013 Jackson Ave E, Oxford, MS 38655 *Tel:* 662-232-2477 *Toll Free Tel:* 800-758-9177 *E-mail:* tourism@ visitoxfordms.com *Web Site:* visitoxfordms.com, pg 972

Ferriter, Tony, Radiant Images, 2702 Media Center Dr, Los Angeles, CA 90065 *Tel:* 323-737-1314 *Fax:* 310-861-0163 *E-mail:* info@radiantimages.com *Web Site:* www.radiantimages.com, pg 869

Ferzanovic, Ubavka, Canadian Student Film Festival, 1432 de Bleury St, Montreal, QC H3A 2J1, Canada *Tel:* 514-848-3883 *Fax:* 514-848-3886 *E-mail:* program@ffm-montreal.org; info@ffm-montreal.org *Web Site:* www.ffm-montreal.org, pg 985

Fesmire, James T, Power Integrity Corporation, 2109 Patterson St, Greensboro, NC 27407 *Tel:* 336-379-9773 *Toll Free Tel:* 800-237-6260 (tech support) *Web Site:* powerintegritycorp.com, pg 860

Fett, Henrik, Rhythm & Hues Studios Inc, 5890 W Jefferson Blvd, Suite Q, Los Angeles, CA 90016 *Tel:* 310-448-7500 *Fax:* 310-448-7600 *E-mail:* info-la@rhythm.com *Web Site:* rhythm.com, pg 874

Fialka, Gerry, PXL This Video Festival, 2427 1/2 Glyndon Ave, Venice, CA 90291 *Tel:* 310-306-7330 *E-mail:* pfsuzy@aol.com *Web Site:* laughtears.com, pg 1000

Fibben, Alison, Georgia Film Office, 75 Fifth St W, Suite 1200, Atlanta, GA 30308 *Tel:* 404-962-4052 *Toll Free Tel:* 877-SHOOTGA (746-6842) *Fax:* 404-962-4053 *E-mail:* film@georgia.org *Web Site:* www. georgia.org/film, pg 970

Ficenec, Nicole, Electric Lady Studios, 52 W Eighth St, New York, NY 10011 *Tel:* 212-677-4700 *Web Site:* electricladystudios.com, pg 752

Fichera, Chris, Group One Ltd, 70 Sea Lane, Farmingdale, NY 11735 *Tel:* 631-396-0195 (audio div); 631-396-0184 (lighting div) *Fax:* 631-396-0190 *E-mail:* sales@g1limited.com *Web Site:* www. g1limited.com, pg 774

Fidan, Aaron, CPT Rental Inc, 36-01A 48 Ave, Long Island City, NY 11101 *Tel:* 718-424-1600 *E-mail:* rental@cptrental.com *Web Site:* www. cptrental.com, pg 732

Fiden, Josh, Digital Music Corp, 3165 Coffey Lane, Santa Rosa, CA 95403 *Tel:* 707-545-0600 *Fax:* 707-545-9777 *E-mail:* info@voodoolab.com *Web Site:* www.voodoolab.com, pg 742

Fiegel, Sue, Alpha Source Inc, 6619 W Calumet Rd, Milwaukee, WI 53223-4186 *Tel:* 414-760-2222 *Toll Free Tel:* 800-654-9845 *E-mail:* customer. service@alphasource.com; info@alphasource.com *Web Site:* www.alphasource.com, pg 681

Fields, J, IVS Imaging, 101 Wrangler Dr, Suite 201, Coppell, TX 75019 *Toll Free Tel:* 888-446-1301 *Fax:* 469-635-6800 *E-mail:* info@ivsimaging.com *Web Site:* www.ivsimaging.com, pg 792

Fieri, Joel, North County Media Center, 1130 N Melrose Dr, Suite 404, Vista, CA 92083 *Toll Free Tel:* 888-393-0580 *E-mail:* info@northcountymediacenter.com *Web Site:* northcountymediacenter.com, pg 842

Fiero, Drew, First Person Inc, 550 Bryant St, San Francisco, CA 94107 *Tel:* 415-495-5595 *E-mail:* hi@ firstperson.is *Web Site:* firstperson.is, pg 761

Fife, Bruce, American Federation of Musicians of the United States & Canada (AFM), 1501 Broadway, 9th fl, New York, NY 10036 *Tel:* 212-869-1330 *Toll Free Tel:* 800-762-3444 *Fax:* 212-764-6134 *Web Site:* www. afm.org, pg 948

Figler, Al, Rochester International Film Festival, PO Box 17746, Rochester, NY 14617 *Tel:* 585-234-7411 (voice mail) *E-mail:* president@rochesterfilmfest.org (use MOAS on subject); submissions@rochesterfilmfest.org *Web Site:* rochesterfilmfest.org, pg 1001

Filarowicz, Bobby, Big House Sound Inc, 4001 Drossett Dr, Austin, TX 78744 *Tel:* 512-443-0019 *Fax:* 512-443-0916 *Web Site:* www.bighousesound.com, pg 705

Filion, Jean Pierre, Applied Voice & Speech Technologies Inc (AVST), 27042 Towne Centre Dr, Suite 200, Foothill Ranch, CA 92610-2810 *Tel:* 949-699-2300 *Toll Free Tel:* 866-368-0400 *Fax:* 949-699-2301 *E-mail:* info@avst.com; sales@avst.com *Web Site:* www.avst.com, pg 688

Filippatos, Tasia, Disney Consumer Products & Interactive Media (DCPI), 1201 Flower St, Glendale, AZ 91201 *Tel:* 818-544-0000 *Web Site:* dcpi.disney. com, pg 743

Fillmore, Chris, Performance Audio LLC, 2456 S West Temple St, Salt Lake City, UT 84115 *Tel:* 801-466-3196 *Toll Free Tel:* 800-771-8330 *Fax:* 801-484-1538 *E-mail:* sales@performanceaudio.com; rental@performanceaudio.com *Web Site:* www. performanceaudio.com, pg 854

Finch, Todd, MAGNUM Companies Ltd, 205 Armour Dr NE, Atlanta, GA 30324 *Tel:* 404-872-0553 *Toll Free Tel:* 800-255-1774 *Fax:* 404-875-5629 *E-mail:* rent@magnumco.com; design@magnumco. com; production@magnumco.com; buy@magnumco. com *Web Site:* www.magnumco.com, pg 815

Findlay, Roberta, Sear Sound, 353 W 48 St, 6th fl, New York, NY 10036 *Tel:* 212-582-5380 *Fax:* 212-581-2731 *E-mail:* waltersear@aol.com *Web Site:* www. searsound.com, pg 883

Finer, Dustin, TiVo Corp, 2 Circle Star Way, San Carlos, CA 94070 *Tel:* 408-562-8400 *Toll Free Tel:* 877-367-8486 (cust support); 877-289-8486 (sales support) *Fax:* 408-567-1800 *Web Site:* business.tivo.com; www. tivo.com, pg 914

Finestone, Justin, Hawaii Island Film Office, 25 Aupuni St, Rm 1301, Hilo, HI 96720 *Tel:* 808-961-8369; 808-961-8366 *Fax:* 808-935-1205 *Web Site:* hawaiiislandfilm.com, pg 970

Finkelstein, Sophie, Hot Springs Documentary Film Festival, 659 Ouchita Ave, Hot Springs, AR 71901 *Tel:* 501-538-0452 *E-mail:* hsdfi@hsdfi.org *Web Site:* www.hsdfi.org, pg 992

Finkle, Abott, Bestek Lighting & Staging, 98 Mahan St, West Babylon, NY 11704 *Tel:* 631-643-0707 *Fax:* 631-643-0764 *E-mail:* production@bestek.com *Web Site:* www.bestek.com, pg 704

Finley, Robert, Stuart Finley Films, 3428 Mansfield Rd, Falls Church, VA 22041 *Tel:* 703-820-7700, pg 761

Finn, Steffanie L, Winter Film Awards Indie Film Festival, 31 W 34 St, New York, NY 10001 *Tel:* 646-355-4371 *E-mail:* info@winterfilmawards. com; submissions@winterfilmawards.com *Web Site:* winterfilmawards.com, pg 1007

Finnegan, Vincent, Group One Ltd, 70 Sea Lane, Farmingdale, NY 11735 *Tel:* 631-396-0195 (audio div); 631-396-0184 (lighting div) *Fax:* 631-396-0190 *E-mail:* sales@g1limited.com *Web Site:* www. g1limited.com, pg 774

Fino, James A, Starburns Industries, 1700 W Burbank Blvd, Burbank, CA 91506 *Tel:* 818-433-3300 *Fax:* 818-433-3383 *E-mail:* contact@starburnsind.com *Web Site:* www.starburnsindustries.com, pg 900

Finucane, Margaret, Virginia Film Office, 901 E Cary St, Richmond, VA 23219-4048 *Tel:* 804-545-5530 *Toll Free Tel:* 800-854-6233 *Fax:* 804-545-5531 *E-mail:* vafilm@virginia.org *Web Site:* www.film. virginia.org, pg 976

Fiorese, Lisa, DEC Grants, 696 Dutchess Tpke, Suite F, Poughkeepsie, NY 12603 *Tel:* 845-454-3222 *E-mail:* info@artsmidhudson.org *Web Site:* www. artsmidhudson.org, pg 988

Fiorletta, Carlo, Guild of Italian American Actors (GIAA), 1026A Shetland Dr, Lakewood, NJ 08701 *Tel:* 201-344-3411 *E-mail:* info@giaa.us *Web Site:* www.giaa.us, pg 955

Fischer, Michael, DASAN Zhone Solutions (DZS) Inc, 7195 Oakport St, Oakland, CA 94621 *Tel:* 510-777-7000 *Toll Free Tel:* 877-ZHONE-20 (946-6320, US & CN) *Fax:* 510-777-7001 *Web Site:* dasanzhone.com, pg 737

Fischhoff, Martin, WTVS, Detroit Public Television, Riley Broadcast Ctr, One Clover Ct, Wixom, MI 48393-2247 *Tel:* 248-305-DPTV (305-3788); 313-872-7500 *E-mail:* email@dptv.org *Web Site:* www.dptv.org, pg 942

Fiset, Norman, Panavideo Inc, 347 Marie de l'Incarnation, Quebec, QC G1N 3G9, Canada *Tel:* 418-687-3150 *Toll Free Tel:* 800-463-5076 *Fax:* 418-687-0366 *E-mail:* info@panavideo.ca *Web Site:* www.panavideo.ca, pg 850

Fishback, John R, P&P Studios Inc, 110 Lenox Ave, Suite 210, Stamford, CT 06906 *Tel:* 203-359-9292 *Toll Free Tel:* 888-WEPRODUCE (937-7638) *E-mail:* ppstudios@weproduce.com; info@weproduce. com *Web Site:* www.weproduce.com, pg 851

Fishback, Kathy, Florida Digital Studios, 6677 13 Ave N, Suite 3C, St Petersburg, FL 33710 *Tel:* 727-546-7900 *Web Site:* www.floridadigitalstudios.com, pg 763

Fishbein, David, Fish Films Footage World, 4548 Van Noord Ave, Studio City, CA 91604 *Tel:* 818-905-1071 *E-mail:* footageworld@aol.com *Web Site:* www. footageworld.com, pg 761

Fisher, Cory, Krishnamurti Foundation of America, 1070 McAndrew Rd, Ojai, CA 93023 *Tel:* 805-646-2726 (ext 10) *Fax:* 805-646-6674 *E-mail:* kfa@kfa.org *Web Site:* www.kfa.org, pg 802

Fisher, Dick, Videography Productions, PO Box 653, Amagansett, NY 11930-0653 *Tel:* 520-907-1900 *Web Site:* www.dickfisher.net, pg 929

Fisher, Gear, MakeMusic® Inc, 7007 Winchester Circle, Suite 140, Boulder, CO 80301 *Tel:* 952-937-9611 *Toll Free Tel:* 800-843-2066 (cust serv) *Fax:* 720-465-6419 *Web Site:* www.makemusic.com, pg 815

Fisher, Joel, Madison Square Garden, 2 Pennsylvania Plaza, New York, NY 10121-0091 *Tel:* 212-465-6741 *E-mail:* msgnetpr@msgnetwork.com *Web Site:* www. thegarden.com; themadisonsquaregardencompany.com, pg 814

Fisher, Mark, The Entertainment Merchants Association (EMA), PO Box 6339, North Hollywood, CA 91603 *Tel:* 818-385-1500 *E-mail:* info@entmerch.org *Web Site:* www.entmerch.org, pg 954

Fisher, Ron, Pathway Connectivity, 103-1439 17 Ave SE, Calgary, AB T2G 1J9, Canada *Tel:* 403-243-8110 *Fax:* 403-287-1281 *E-mail:* orders@pathwayconnect. com *Web Site:* www.pathwayconnect.com, pg 852

Fisher, Ziv, 48 Windows, 1661 N Lincoln Blvd, Suite 220, Santa Monica, CA 90404 *Tel:* 310-392-9545 *Fax:* 310-392-9445 *E-mail:* ziv@48windows.com *Web Site:* www.48windows.com, pg 764

Fisher-Staples, Sherri, Cinebar Productions Inc, 10 San Jose Dr, Suite 4-C, Newport News, VA 23606 *Tel:* 757-873-3232 *E-mail:* cinebar@ cinebarproductions.com, pg 723

Fishkin, Mark, Mill Valley Film Festival, 1001 Lootens Place, Suite 220, San Rafael, CA 94901 *Tel:* 415-383-5256 *Fax:* 415-383-8606 *E-mail:* mvff@cafilm.org; info@cafilm.org *Web Site:* www.mvff.com; www. cafilm.org, pg 996

Fister, Ray, 5th Floor Recording Co, 316 N Milwaukee St, Suite 501, Milwaukee, WI 53202 *Tel:* 414-276-1919 *Fax:* 414-271-6621 *Web Site:* www. 5thfloorrecording.com, pg 760

Fitch, William, Sound by Fitch, 1134 Ridge Rd, Pottstown, PA 19465 *Tel:* 610-469-6082 *Fax:* 610-469-0559, pg 893

Fithian, John, National Association of Theatre Owners (NATO), 1705 "N" St NW, Washington, DC 20036 *Tel:* 202-962-0054 *E-mail:* nato@natodc.com *Web Site:* www.natoonline.org, pg 959

Fitts, David A, Spectrum Enterprise, 401 Park Ave S, New York, NY 10016 *Tel:* 212-379-5826 *Web Site:* enterprise.spectrum.com, pg 897

Fitzer, Jon, Sescom Inc, PO Box 720, Mount Marion, NY 12456 *Tel:* 845-246-1915 *Fax:* 845-246-0626 *E-mail:* info@sescom.com *Web Site:* www.sescom. com, pg 884

Fitzgerald, Jon, Slamdance Film Festival, 5634 Melrose Ave, Los Angeles, CA 90038 *Tel:* 323-466-1786 *Fax:* 323-466-1784 *E-mail:* submissions@slamdance. com *Web Site:* www.slamdance.com, pg 1004

Fitzgerald, Patrick, Polarity Post Production, 69 Green St, San Francisco, CA 94111 *Tel:* 415-421-6622 *Fax:* 415-391-4995 *E-mail:* info@polaritypost.com *Web Site:* www.polaritypost.com, pg 858

Fitzgerald, Richard, Sound Associates Inc, 424 W 45 St, New York, NY 10036 *Tel:* 212-757-5679 *Toll Free Tel:* 888-772-7686 *Fax:* 212-265-1250 *E-mail:* newyork@soundassociates.com *Web Site:* www.soundassociates.com, pg 893

Fitzgerald, Todd, Winterland Studios, 5417 Boone Ave N, New Hope, MN 55428 *Tel:* 763-971-8943 *Fax:* 763-971-8952 *E-mail:* studio@winterlandstudios. com *Web Site:* www.winterlandstudios.com, pg 940

Fitzgerald, Tom, Satellite Center, 2535 Williams Blvd, Kenner, LA 70062 *Tel:* 504-466-3474 *Toll Free Tel:* 800-256-4010 *E-mail:* info@satctr.com *Web Site:* satctr.com, pg 881

Fitzpatrick, John, Cornell Laboratory of Ornithology, Cornell University, 159 Sapsucker Woods Rd, Ithaca, NY 14850 *Toll Free Tel:* 866-989-BIRD (989-2473) *Web Site:* www.birds.cornell.edu, pg 731

Fitzpatrick, Kristen, Women Make Movies Inc, 115 W 29 St, Suite 1200, New York, NY 10001 *Tel:* 212-925-0606 *Fax:* 212-925-2052 *E-mail:* info@wmm.com *Web Site:* www.wmm.com, pg 941

Fitzpatrick, Robert, Allied Artists International Inc, Production Services Ctr, 15810 E Gale Ave, Suite 133, Hacienda Heights, CA 91745 *Tel:* 626-330-0600 *Fax:* 626-961-0411, pg 681

Fix, William, SOS Film Works (Space Ordnance Systems), 34855 Petersen Rd, Agua Dulce, CA 91390 *Tel:* 661-251-2365 *Fax:* 661-268-7680 *Web Site:* www. sosfilmworks.com, pg 893

Flaherty, Rob, Ketchum Inc, 1285 Avenue of the Americas, 4th fl, New York, NY 10019 *Tel:* 646-935-3900 *Web Site:* www.ketchum.com, pg 798

Flake, Keith, Rodeo Video Inc, 412 S Main, Snowflake, AZ 85937 *Tel:* 928-536-7111 *Toll Free Tel:* 800-331-1269 *Fax:* 928-536-7120 *E-mail:* info@rodeovideo. com *Web Site:* www.rodeovideo.com, pg 876

Flancher, Sam, Chicago International Film Festival, 212 W Van Buren St, Suite 400, Chicago, IL 60607 *Tel:* 312-683-0121 *Fax:* 312-683-0122 *E-mail:* info@ chicagofilmfestival.com; entries@chicagofilmfestival. com *Web Site:* www.chicagofilmfestival.com, pg 985

Flannery, Colin, Vertiv, 1050 Dearborn Dr, Columbus, OH 43085 *Tel:* 614-888-0246 *Web Site:* www.vertiv. com, pg 926

Flannery, John, General Electric Co, 41 Farnsworth St, Boston, MA 02210 *Tel:* 203-373-2211; 617-443-3000 *Web Site:* www.ge.com, pg 769

Flansburg, Luke, Jereco Studios Inc, 627 E Peach St, Suite E, Bozeman, MT 59715 *Tel:* 406-586-5262 *Web Site:* www.jerecostudios.com, pg 794

Fleck, Volker, WARPed Pictures, 2447 Benedict Canyon Dr, Beverly Hills, CA 90210 *Tel:* 310-777-8828; 310-999-1219 (cell) *Fax:* 310-777-8805 *E-mail:* info@warpedpictures.com *Web Site:* www.warpedpictures.com, pg 934

Fleenor, Cindy, Doug Fleenor Design Inc, 396 Corbett Canyon Rd, Arroyo Grande, CA 93420 *Tel:* 805-481-9599 *Toll Free Tel:* 888-436-9512 *Fax:* 805-481-9599 *E-mail:* info@dfd.com *Web Site:* www.dfd.com, pg 762

Fleenor, Doug, Doug Fleenor Design Inc, 396 Corbett Canyon Rd, Arroyo Grande, CA 93420 *Tel:* 805-481-9599 *Toll Free Tel:* 888-436-9512 *Fax:* 805-481-9599 *E-mail:* info@dfd.com *Web Site:* www.dfd.com, pg 762

Fleischauer, Laura, Austin Film Society (AFS), 1901 E 51 St, Austin, TX 78723 *Tel:* 512-322-0145 *E-mail:* afs@austinfilm.org *Web Site:* www.austinfilm.org, pg 951

Fleisher, Stuart, The DVI Group, 1486 Mecaslin St NW, Atlanta, GA 30309 *Tel:* 404-873-6283 *Toll Free Tel:* 888-736-7384 *E-mail:* makeitbetter@thedvigroup.com *Web Site:* www.thedvigroup.com, pg 748

Flem, Eric, Nikon Small World, 1300 Walt Whitman Rd, Melville, NY 11747-3064 *Tel:* 631-547-8500 *Toll Free Tel:* 800-52-NIKON (526-4566, US only) *Fax:* 631-547-0306 *E-mail:* info@nikonsmallworld.com *Web Site:* www.nikonsmallworld.com; www.nikoninstruments.com, pg 998

Fletcher, Cliff, University of Maine Media Services, 19 Shibles Hall, Orono, ME 04469 *Tel:* 207-581-2500; 207-581-2516 *Web Site:* umaine.edu, pg 922

Fletcher, Dick, Gagne Inc, 41 Commercial Dr, Johnson City, NY 13790 *Tel:* 607-729-3366 *Toll Free Tel:* 800-800-5954 *Fax:* 607-729-7644 *E-mail:* sales@gagneinc.com *Web Site:* www.gagneinc.com, pg 767

Fletty, Eric, TAPPI, 15 Technology Pkwy S, Norcross, GA 30092 *Tel:* 770-446-1400 *Toll Free Tel:* 800-332-8686 (US); 800-446-9431 (CN) *Fax:* 240-396-5973 *E-mail:* memberconnection@tappi.org *Web Site:* www.tappi.org, pg 907

Flint, Kevin, Dystopian Studios, 651 Clover St, Bldg 1, Los Angeles, CA 90031 *Tel:* 310-503-2365 *Web Site:* dystopianstudios.com, pg 749

Fliss, Andy, TV One Multimedia Solutions, 621 B Wilmer Ave, Cincinnati, OH 45226 *Tel:* 513-666-4210 *Toll Free Tel:* 800-721-4044 *Fax:* 513-666-4220 (tech) *E-mail:* sales@tvone.com; info@tvone.com *Web Site:* www.tvone.com, pg 919

Flores, Mariah, The Mack Sennett Studios, 1215 Bates Ave, Los Angeles, CA 90029 *Tel:* 323-660-8466 *E-mail:* info@macksennettstudios.net *Web Site:* www.macksennettstudios.net, pg 884

Flores, Tanya, SurgeX, 8001 Knightdale Blvd, Suite 121, Knightdale, NC 27545 *Toll Free Tel:* 800-645-9721 (tech & cust support) *E-mail:* order.desk@ametek.com *Web Site:* espsurgex.com/surgex/, pg 905

Florez, Yamile, Alpine Optics Inc, 14 Helping Hands Way, Pisgah Forest, NC 28768 *Tel:* 828-884-5822 *E-mail:* info@alpine-optics.com *Web Site:* www.alpine-optics.com, pg 682

Floyd, Steve, August House Audio, 3500 Piedmont Rd NE, Suite 310, Atlanta, GA 30305 *Tel:* 404-442-4420 *Toll Free Tel:* 800-284-8784 *Fax:* 404-442-4435 *E-mail:* ahinfo@augusthouse.com *Web Site:* www.augusthouse.com, pg 695

Fluster, Barry, Media Fabricators Inc, 8509 Washington Blvd, Culver City, CA 90232 *Tel:* 323-937-3344 *Fax:* 323-937-1142 *E-mail:* mfi@mediafab.com *Web Site:* www.mediafab.com, pg 822

Flynn, J Declan, St Petersburg/Clearwater Film Commission, 8200 Bryan Dairy Rd, Suite 200, Largo, FL 33777 *Tel:* 727-464-7241 *Toll Free Tel:* 877-352-3224 *E-mail:* info@filmspc.com *Web Site:* filmstpeteclearwater.com, pg 969

Flynn, Jay, John Wiley & Sons Inc, 111 River St, Hoboken, NJ 07030-5774 *Tel:* 201-748-6000 *Toll Free Tel:* 800-225-5945 (cust serv) *Fax:* 201-748-6088 *Web Site:* www.wiley.com, pg 938

Flynn, L Daniel, Continental Recordings Inc, 23 Mirimichi St, Plainville, MA 02762 *Tel:* 508-699-0003 *Toll Free Tel:* 888-729-3130 *Fax:* 508-699-0004, pg 731

Flynn, Nancy, Sitler's Supplies Inc, 111 Westview Dr, Washington, IA 52353 *Tel:* 319-653-2123 *Toll Free Tel:* 800-888-3192 *Fax:* 319-653-3198 *E-mail:* renfred@sitlersupplies.com *Web Site:* sitlersupplies.com, pg 890

Foah, Honora, Visioneering International Inc, 659 Auburn Ave NE, Suite 267, Atlanta, GA 30312 *Tel:* 404-681-9028 *Fax:* 404-681-5947 *E-mail:* design@visioneering.com *Web Site:* www.visioneering.com, pg 931

Foah, Robert, Visioneering International Inc, 659 Auburn Ave NE, Suite 267, Atlanta, GA 30312 *Tel:* 404-681-9028 *Fax:* 404-681-5947 *E-mail:* design@visioneering.com *Web Site:* www.visioneering.com, pg 931

Foca, Gene, Getty Images, 605 Fifth Ave S, Suite 400, Seattle, WA 98104 *Tel:* 206-925-5000 *Toll Free Tel:* 888-888-5889; 800-462-4379 (sales) *E-mail:* sales.na@gettyimages.com *Web Site:* www.gettyimages.com, pg 770

Fogg, Chris, Magick Lantern, 750 Ralph McGill Blvd, Atlanta, GA 30312 *Tel:* 404-688-3348 *Fax:* 404-584-5247 *E-mail:* info@magicklantern.com *Web Site:* magicklantern.com, pg 814

Foley, Kevin, KEF Media, 1161 Concord Rd SE, Smyrna, GA 30080 *Tel:* 404-605-0009 *E-mail:* info@kefmedia.com *Web Site:* kefmedia.com, pg 797

Foley, Marcia Hahn, Big Foot Productions Inc, 37-09 36 Ave, Long Island City, NY 11101 *Tel:* 718-729-1900 *E-mail:* info@bigfootnyc.com *Web Site:* www.bigfootnyc.com, pg 705

Foley, Paul, HM Electronics Inc (HME), 14110 Stowe Dr, Poway, CA 92064 *Tel:* 858-535-6000 *Toll Free Tel:* 800-848-4468 (dom sales) *Fax:* 858-452-7207; 858-552-0139 (dom sales) *E-mail:* info@hme.com *Web Site:* www.hme.com, pg 780

Folger, Sarah, Harmonia Mundi USA, 1117 Chestnut St, Burbank, CA 91506 *Tel:* 818-333-1500 *E-mail:* info-usa@harmoniamundi.com *Web Site:* www.harmoniamundi.com, pg 776

Folkeringa, Ron, Intercon 1, 12136 Crystal Lake Rd, Merrifield, MN 56465 *Tel:* 218-828-3157 *Toll Free Tel:* 800-237-9576 *Fax:* 218-828-1096 *E-mail:* intercon@nortechsys.com *Web Site:* www.intercon-1.com, pg 789

Follett, Britten, Follett School Solutions Inc, 1340 Ridgeview Dr, McHenry, IL 60050 *Tel:* 815-759-1700 *Toll Free Tel:* 888-511-5114 (cust serv); 877-899-8550 (sales) *Fax:* 815-759-9831 *Toll Free Fax:* 800-852-5458 *E-mail:* info@follettlearning.com; customerservice@follett.com *Web Site:* www.follettlearning.com; www.follett.com/prek12; www.titlewave.com, pg 763

Follin, Shannon, Omega Recording Studios, 12712 Rock Creek Mill Rd, Suite 14A, Rockville, MD 20852 *Tel:* 301-230-9100 *Fax:* 301-230-9103 *Web Site:* omegastudios.com, pg 845

Follmer, Max, Promax, 5700 Wilshire Blvd, Suite 275, Los Angeles, CA 90036 *Tel:* 310-788-7600 *Fax:* 310-788-7616 *Web Site:* www.promax.org, pg 961

Fontaine, Michelle, Visual Technologies Corp, 1620 Burnet Ave, Syracuse, NY 13206 *Tel:* 315-423-2000 *Toll Free Tel:* 888-423-0004 *E-mail:* contact@visualtec.com *Web Site:* visualtec.businesscatalyst.com, pg 932

Fontentnot, Tracie, Jeff Davis Parish Film Commission, 100 Rue de l'Acadie, Jennings, LA 70546 *Tel:* 337-821-5521 *Toll Free Tel:* 800-264-5521 *Fax:* 337-821-5536 *E-mail:* info@jeffdavis.org *Web Site:* jeffdavis.org/film-commission, pg 971

Foor, David J, Visual Technologies Corp, 1620 Burnet Ave, Syracuse, NY 13206 *Tel:* 315-423-2000 *Toll Free Tel:* 888-423-0004 *E-mail:* contact@visualtec.com *Web Site:* visualtec.businesscatalyst.com, pg 932

Forbes, Brad, AdventSource, 5120 Prescott Ave, Lincoln, NE 68506 *Tel:* 402-486-8800 *Toll Free Tel:* 800-328-0525 *Fax:* 402-486-8819 *E-mail:* service@adventsource.org *Web Site:* www.adventsource.org, pg 678

Forcier, Jason, Vertiv, 1050 Dearborn Dr, Columbus, OH 43085 *Tel:* 614-888-0246 *Web Site:* www.vertiv.com, pg 926

Ford, Geoffrey, Photographic Rental Service Inc (PRS), 1109 S La Brea Ave, Los Angeles, CA 90019 *Tel:* 323-965-9900 *Fax:* 323-965-9901 *E-mail:* prsrental@gmail.com *Web Site:* prsla.com, pg 856

Ford, James A, Ford AV, 4800 W Interstate 40, Oklahoma City, OK 73128 *Tel:* 405-946-9966 *Toll Free Tel:* 800-654-6744 *Web Site:* www.fordav.com, pg 763

Ford, Jason, Technomedia Solutions, 4545 36 St, Orlando, FL 32811 *Tel:* 407-351-0909 *Fax:* 407-248-9484 *E-mail:* sales@gotechnomedia.com *Web Site:* www.gotechnomedia.com, pg 909

Ford, Michael, Yellow Cat Productions Inc, 505 11 St SE, Washington, DC 20003 *Tel:* 202-543-2221 *E-mail:* yellowcat@yellowcat.com *Web Site:* www.yellowcat.com, pg 944

Ford, Tara Lee, Oddball Films Inc, 275 Capp St, San Francisco, CA 94110 *Tel:* 415-558-8112 *E-mail:* info@oddballfilms.com *Web Site:* www.oddballfilms.com, pg 844

Ford, Tracy, WIA - The Wireless Infrastructure Association, 2111 Wilson Blvd, Suite 210, Arlington, VA 22201 *Tel:* 703-739-0300 *Toll Free Tel:* 800-759-0300 *Fax:* 703-836-1608 *Web Site:* wia.org, pg 963

Ford-Williams, Darryl, WQED-Multimedia, 4802 Fifth Ave, Pittsburgh, PA 15213 *Tel:* 412-622-1300; 412-622-1370 *Web Site:* www.wqed.org, pg 942

Fordyce, Barbara, Map Resources, 50 S Union St, Lambertville, NJ 08530 *Tel:* 609-397-1611 *Toll Free Tel:* 800-334-4291 *Fax:* 609-751-9378 *E-mail:* info@mapresources.com; sales@mapresources.com *Web Site:* www.mapresources.com, pg 816

Foreman, Ed, Executive Development Systems Inc, 3818 Vinecrest Dr, Dallas, TX 75229 *Tel:* 214-351-0055 *Toll Free Tel:* 800-955-7353 *Web Site:* www.edforeman.com, pg 757

Forish, Jim, Kopp Glass, 2108 Palmer St, Pittsburgh, PA 15218 *Tel:* 412-271-0190 *Fax:* 412-271-4103 *E-mail:* sales@koppglass.com *Web Site:* www.koppglass.com, pg 801

Forman, Debra, Ketchum Inc, 1285 Avenue of the Americas, 4th fl, New York, NY 10019 *Tel:* 646-935-3900 *Web Site:* www.ketchum.com, pg 798

Forman, Scott J, Allegro Productions Inc, 347 Main St, Chester, NJ 07930 *Tel:* 908-879-0428 *Toll Free Tel:* 800-232-2133 *Web Site:* www.allegrovideo.com, pg 680

Formanek, Paul, Advanced Digital Design, 6429 Independence Ave, Woodland Hills, CA 91367 *Web Site:* advanced-digital-design.com, pg 677

Forrester, Clive, All Access Staging & Productions, 1320 Storm Pkwy, Torrance, CA 90501 *Tel:* 310-784-2464 *Toll Free Tel:* 877-784-2464 *Fax:* 310-517-0899 *E-mail:* sales@allaccessinc.com *Web Site:* www.allaccessinc.com, pg 680

Forschmidt, Don, PrimeLight Productions Inc, 750 Kappock St, Suite 805, Riverdale, NY 10463 *Tel:* 718-543-3991 *E-mail:* info@primelight.net *Web Site:* www.primelight.net, pg 862

Forshay, Steven E, Dolby Laboratories Inc, 1275 Market St, San Francisco, CA 94103-1410 *Tel:* 415-558-0200 *Fax:* 415-645-4000 *Web Site:* www.dolby.com, pg 745

Fortier, Dr Claude, State of the Art Acoustik Inc, 43-1010 Polytek St, Ottawa, ON K1J 9J3, Canada *Tel:* 613-745-2003 *Fax:* 613-745-9687 *E-mail:* sota@sota.ca *Web Site:* www.sota.ca, pg 900

Fortin, Joe, DASAN Zhone Solutions (DZS) Inc, 7195 Oakport St, Oakland, CA 94621 *Tel:* 510-777-7000 *Toll Free Tel:* 877-ZHONE-20 (946-6320, US & CN) *Fax:* 510-777-7001 *Web Site:* dasanzhone.com, pg 737

Foster, Greg, IMAX Corp, 2525 Speakman Dr, Mississauga, ON L5K 1B1, Canada *Tel:* 905-403-6500 *Fax:* 905-403-6450 *E-mail:* info@imax.com *Web Site:* www.imax.com, pg 786

Foster, Lee, Electric Lady Studios, 52 W Eighth St, New York, NY 10011 *Tel:* 212-677-4700 *Web Site:* electricladystudios.com, pg 752

Foti, Frank, Omnia Audio, 1241 Superior Ave E, Cleveland, OH 44114 *Tel:* 216-241-7225 *Fax:* 216-241-4103 *E-mail:* social@telosalliance.com *Web Site:* www.telosalliance.com/omnia, pg 845

Foulon, Arnaud, Editions Hurtubise HMH Ltee, 1815 Avenue De Lorimier, Montreal, QC H2K 3W6, Canada *Tel:* 514-523-1523 *Toll Free Tel:* 800-361-1664 *Fax:* 514-523-9969 *Web Site:* www.distributionhmh.com, pg 783

Foulon, Herve, Editions Hurtubise HMH Ltee, 1815 Avenue De Lorimier, Montreal, QC H2K 3W6, Canada *Tel:* 514-523-1523 *Toll Free Tel:* 800-361-1664 *Fax:* 514-523-9969 *Web Site:* www.distributionhmh.com, pg 783

Fourcher, Fred, Bitcentral Inc, 4340 Von Karman Ave, Suite 400, Newport Beach, CA 92660 *Tel:* 949-253-9000 *Toll Free Tel:* 800-272-4004 (support) *E-mail:* sales@bitcentral.com; support@bitcentral.com *Web Site:* www.bitcentral.com, pg 706

Fowler, Jill, International Light Technologies Inc, 10 Technology Dr, Peabody, MA 01960 *Tel:* 978-818-6180 *Fax:* 978-818-6181 *E-mail:* ilsales@intl-lighttech.com *Web Site:* www.intl-lighttech.com, pg 790

Fowler, Kirk, Colorado Video Inc, PO Box 952, Longmont, CO 80502 *Tel:* 303-530-9580 *Fax:* 303-530-9569 *E-mail:* sales@colorado-video.com *Web Site:* www.colorado-video.com, pg 728

Fowler, Scott, Tecplot Inc, 3535 Factoria Blvd SE, Suite 550, Bellevue, WA 98006 *Tel:* 425-653-1200; 425-653-9393 (tech support) *Toll Free Tel:* 800-763-7005 (orders) *E-mail:* info@tecplot.com; support@tecplot.com *Web Site:* www.tecplot.com, pg 909

Fowler, Sheena, Orlando Film Commission, 301 E Pine St, Suite 900, Orlando, FL 32801 *Tel:* 407-422-7159 *Fax:* 407-425-6428 *E-mail:* info@filmorlando.com *Web Site:* www.filmorlando.com, pg 969

Fox, Brad, Big Shoulders Digital Video Productions, 875 N Michigan Ave, Suite 3750, Chicago, IL 60611 *Tel:* 312-540-5400 *E-mail:* info@bigshoulders; sales@bigshoulders.com *Web Site:* www.bigshoulders.com, pg 705

Fox, David, VCSvideo, 2807 Hunterdon Dr, Cinnaminson, NJ 08077 *Tel:* 856-273-8800 *Toll Free Tel:* 877-VCS-VIDEO (827-8433) *Web Site:* www.vcsvideo.com, pg 925

Fox, Jim, Lion & Fox Recording Studios, 9517 Baltimore Ave, College Park, MD 20740 *Tel:* 301-982-4431 *E-mail:* mail@lionfox.com *Web Site:* www.lionfox.com, pg 809

Fox, Mike, Nazdar®, 8501 Hedge Lane Terr, Shawnee, KS 66227-3290 *Tel:* 913-422-1888 *Toll Free Tel:* 800-767-9942 (cust serv) *Fax:* 913-422-2296 *E-mail:* custserv@nazdar.com *Web Site:* www.nazdar.com, pg 837

Fox, Stephanie, Pro Video & Film Equipment Co Inc, 11425 Mathis Ave, Studio 404, Dallas, TX 75234 *Tel:* 972-869-9990 *Toll Free Tel:* 888-869-9998 *E-mail:* providfilm@aol.com *Web Site:* www.providefilm.com; www.usedequipmentnewsletter.com, pg 863

Fox, Susan E, Acoustical Society of America (ASA), 1305 Walt Whitman Rd, Suite 300, Melville, NY 11747-4300 *Tel:* 516-576-2360 *Fax:* 631-923-2875 *E-mail:* asa@acousticalsociety.org *Web Site:* www.acousticalsociety.org, pg 947

Fox, Tim, The Kitchen, 265 NE 24 St, Suite 401, Miami, FL 33137 *Tel:* 305-415-6200 *E-mail:* info@thekitchen.tv *Web Site:* www.thekitchen.tv, pg 799

Foxwell, Stacey, National Public Radio (NPR), 1111 N Capitol St NE, Washington, DC 20002 *Tel:* 202-513-2000 *Web Site:* www.npr.org, pg 959

Foy, Joanne, California Independent Film Festival (CAIFF), 350 Park St, Moraga, CA 94566 *Tel:* 925-388-0752 *E-mail:* info@caiff.org *Web Site:* caiff.org, pg 984

Frady, Diane Salley, WTSmedia, 2841 Hickory Valley, Chattanooga, TN 37421 *Tel:* 423-894-9427 *Toll Free Tel:* 888-987-6334; 800-251-7228 *Fax:* 423-894-7281 *Toll Free Fax:* 800-591-4809 *E-mail:* sales@wtsmedia.com *Web Site:* www.wtsduplication.com, pg 942

Francis, Bill, WGBH Production Group, One Guest St, Boston, MA 02135 *Tel:* 617-300-2000 *E-mail:* productiongroup@wgbh.org; studios@wgbh.org; outpost@wgbh.org *Web Site:* productiongroup.wgbh.org, pg 936

Francis, Eddie, Curb Entertainment International Corp, 3907 W Alameda Ave, Burbank, CA 91505 *Tel:* 818-843-8580 *Fax:* 818-566-1719 *Web Site:* www.curbentertainment.com, pg 736

Francis, Juliette, Science Museum of Minnesota, 120 W Kellogg Blvd, St Paul, MN 55102 *Tel:* 651-221-9444 *Toll Free Tel:* 800-221-9444 *Fax:* 651-221-4533 *E-mail:* info@smm.org; science@smm.org *Web Site:* www.smm.org, pg 882

Francis, Ramm, DVDs4Less, 6519 Jamon Dr, Sparks, NV 89436-9142 *Tel:* 775-323-0965 *Toll Free Tel:* 800-852-2330 *Fax:* 775-323-1055 *E-mail:* info@dvds4less.net *Web Site:* www.dvds4less.net, pg 748

Francis, Terri PhD, Black Film Center/Archive, Indiana University, Wells Library, Rm 044, 1320 E Tenth St, Bloomington, IN 47405 *Tel:* 812-855-6041 *Fax:* 812-856-5832 *E-mail:* bfca@indiana.edu *Web Site:* www.indiana.edu/~bfca, pg 706

Franco, James, EFX Media, 2300 S Ninth St, Suite 136, Arlington, VA 22204 *Tel:* 703-486-2303 *E-mail:* info@efxmedia.com; sales@efxmedia.com *Web Site:* www.efxmedia.com, pg 751

Franco, Ron, Hydrogen Whiskey Studios, 12327 Santa Monica Blvd, Suite 202, Los Angeles, CA 90025 *Tel:* 310-394-8130 *Fax:* 310-820-0401, pg 783

Franey, Alan, Vancouver International Film Festival (VIFF), Vancouver International Film Ctr, 1181 Seymour St, Vancouver, BC V6B 3M7, Canada *Tel:* 604-685-0260 *Fax:* 604-688-8221 *E-mail:* info@viff.org; submissions@viff.org *Web Site:* www.viff.org, pg 1006

Frangipani, Ralph, Berry & Homer, 2035 Richmond St, Philadelphia, PA 19125 *Tel:* 215-425-0888 *Web Site:* www.berryandhomer.com, pg 704

Frank, Kenneth, Turning Technologies LLC, 255 W Federal St, Youngstown, OH 44503 *Tel:* 330-746-3015 *Toll Free Tel:* 866-746-3015 *E-mail:* info@turningtechnologies.com; support@turningtechnologies.com *Web Site:* www.turningtechnologies.com, pg 919

Frank, Michael, Earwig Music Co Inc, 2054 W Farwell Ave, Unit G, Chicago, IL 60645 *Tel:* 773-262-0278 *E-mail:* orders@earwigmusic.com *Web Site:* www.earwigmusic.com, pg 749

Frank, Mike, Speakers Unlimited, 7532 Courtyard Place, Cary, NC 27519 *Tel:* 919-466-7676 *Toll Free Tel:* 888-333-6676 *E-mail:* prospeak@aol.com *Web Site:* www.speakersunlimited.com, pg 896

Franklin, Raymond W, Stage America LLC, 2300 N Atlantic Ave, Suite 1002, Daytona Beach, FL 32811 *Tel:* 702-879-8177 *E-mail:* info@stageamerica.com *Web Site:* www.stageamerica.com, pg 898

Franson, Tom, Custom Computer Specialists Inc, 70 Suffolk Ct, Hauppauge, NY 11788 *Tel:* 631-864-6699 *Toll Free Tel:* 800-589-8989 *Fax:* 401-765-6440 *Toll Free Fax:* 800-986-5518 *E-mail:* info@customtech.com; support@customtech.com *Web Site:* www.customonline.com, pg 736

Frantz, Kittie, Geddes Productions LLC, PO Box 41761, Los Angeles, CA 90041-0761 *Tel:* 323-344-8045 *Fax:* 323-257-7209 *E-mail:* orders@geddesproduction.com *Web Site:* www.geddesproduction.com, pg 769

Franzen, J W, Precision Electronics Inc, 1331 Estes Ave, Gurnee, IL 60031 *Tel:* 847-599-1799 *Toll Free Tel:* 800-SINCE-46 (746-2346) *Fax:* 847-599-6178 *E-mail:* info@grommesprecision.com; sales@grommesprecision.com *Web Site:* www.grommesprecision.com, pg 861

Frappier, Kevin, Burk Technology Inc, 7 Beaver Brook Rd, Littleton, MA 01460 *Tel:* 978-486-0086 *Fax:* 978-486-0081 *E-mail:* sales@burk.com; orders@burk.com; support@burk.com *Web Site:* www.burk.com, pg 712

Frappier, Roger, Max Films Inc, 5333, rue Casgrain, Suite 406, Montreal, QC H2T 1X3, Canada *Tel:* 514-282-8444 *Web Site:* www.maxfilms.ca, pg 820

Fraser, Brendan, Tallahassee Photo & Frame, 900 Capital Circle SE, Suite 3, Tallahassee, FL 32301 *Tel:* 850-877-1152 *E-mail:* mgr@talcam.com *Web Site:* talcam.com, pg 906

Fraser, Dave, Heavy Melody, 307 Seventh Ave, Suite 1203, New York, NY 10001 *Tel:* 212-675-9585 *Fax:* 212-675-9565 *E-mail:* contact_hm@heavymelodymusic.com (studio inquiries) *Web Site:* www.heavymelodymusic.com, pg 778

Fraser, Mike, Tallahassee Audio Visual, 900 Capital Circle SE, Suite 4, Tallahassee, FL 32301 *Tel:* 850-877-1154 *Web Site:* talcam.com, pg 906

Fraser, Susan O'Connor, Tam Communications Inc, 5610 Scotts Valley Dr, Suite B-552, Scotts Valley, CA 95066 *Tel:* 831-439-1500 *Toll Free Fax:* 866-390-1218 *E-mail:* info@tamcom.com *Web Site:* www.tamcom.com, pg 906

Fraser, Tam O'Connor, Tam Communications Inc, 5610 Scotts Valley Dr, Suite B-552, Scotts Valley, CA 95066 *Tel:* 831-439-1500 *Toll Free Fax:* 866-390-1218 *E-mail:* info@tamcom.com *Web Site:* www.tamcom.com, pg 906

Fraser, Valerie, Center for the Collaborative Classroom, 1001 Marina Village Pkwy, Suite 110, Alameda, CA 94501-1042 *Tel:* 510-533-0213 *Toll Free Tel:* 800-666-7270 *Fax:* 510-464-3670 *E-mail:* info@collaborativeclassroom.org *Web Site:* www.collaborativeclassroom.org, pg 719

Frasier, Julian, Ross Video Ltd, 8 John St, Iroquois, ON K0E 1K0, Canada *Tel:* 613-652-4886 *Fax:* 613-652-4425 *E-mail:* solutions@rossvideo.com *Web Site:* www.rossvideo.com, pg 878

Fraval, H R, Visioneering International Inc, 659 Auburn Ave NE, Suite 267, Atlanta, GA 30312 *Tel:* 404-681-9028 *Fax:* 404-681-5947 *E-mail:* design@visioneering.com *Web Site:* www.visioneering.com, pg 931

Frayter, Slava, Newtec America Inc, 1055 Washington Blvd, Stamford, CT 06901 *Tel:* 203-323-0042 *Fax:* 203-323-8406 *E-mail:* sales@newtec.eu; customersupport@newtec.eu *Web Site:* www.newtec.eu, pg 840

Frazier, Michelle, Moviola, 1135 N Mansfield Ave, Hollywood, CA 90038 *Tel:* 323-467-3107; 818-487-5000 *Toll Free Tel:* 877-MOVIOLA (668-4652) *Fax:* 323-464-1518 *Web Site:* www.moviola.com, pg 832

Frearson, Darren, GatesAir, 5300 Kings Island Dr, Suite 101, Mason, OH 45040 *Tel:* 513-459-3400 *Toll Free Tel:* 800-622-0022 *Fax:* 513-459-3796 *E-mail:* information@gatesair.com; orders@gatesair.com; support@gatesair.com *Web Site:* www.gatesair.com, pg 768

Frechette, Terry, Blackmagic Design Pty Ltd, 2875 Bayview Dr, Fremont, CA 94538 *Tel:* 408-954-0500 *Fax:* 408-954-0508 *E-mail:* info-usa@blackmagicdesign.com *Web Site:* www.blackmagicdesign.com, pg 707

Freda, Gerald, CaptionMax, 2438 27 Ave S, Minneapolis, MN 55406 *Tel:* 612-341-3566 *Web Site:* www.captionmax.com, pg 716

Freda, Thomas, Prior Scientific Inc, 80 Reservoir Park Dr, Rockland, MA 02370 *Tel:* 781-878-8442 *Toll Free Tel:* 800-877-2234 *Fax:* 781-878-8736 *E-mail:* info@ prior.com; techsupportus@prior.com *Web Site:* www. prior.com, pg 862

Fredell, Eric, Software & Information Industry Association (SIIA), 1090 Vermont Ave NW, 6th fl, Washington, DC 20005-4095 *Tel:* 202-289-7442 *Fax:* 202-289-7097 *Web Site:* www.siia.net, pg 962

Frederickson, Derek, Twisted Media Inc, 2100 Hollyvista Ave, Los Angeles, CA 90027 *Tel:* 773-972-2972 *Web Site:* www.twistedmedia.com, pg 920

Freed, Gary, Z-Axis Corp, 4600 S Ulster St, Suite 270, Denver, CO 80237 *Tel:* 303-713-0200 *Toll Free Tel:* 800-827-2947 *E-mail:* info@zaxis.com *Web Site:* www.zaxis.com, pg 944

Freedman, Alan, The Computer Language Co Inc, 5521 State Park Rd, Point Pleasant, PA 18950 *Tel:* 215-297-8082 *E-mail:* sales@computerlanguage.com; comments@computerlanguage.com *Web Site:* www. computerlanguage.com, pg 729

Freeland, Lois, Association for Educational Communications and Technology (AECT), 320 W Eighth St, Suite 101, Bloomington, IN 47404-3745 *Tel:* 812-335-7675 *Toll Free Tel:* 877-677-AECT (677-2328) *Fax:* 812-335-7678 *E-mail:* aect@aect.org *Web Site:* www.aect.org, pg 950

Freeman, Allie, Cleveland International Film Festival, 2510 Market Ave, Cleveland, OH 44113-3434 *Tel:* 216-623-3456 *Fax:* 216-623-0103 *E-mail:* cfs@ clevelandfilm.org; submissions@clevelandfilm.org *Web Site:* www.clevelandfilm.org, pg 986

Freeman, Barbara, Freeman Pictures Inc, 1234 Sherman Ave, Suite 211, Evanston, IL 60602-1375 *Tel:* 847-733-0717 *E-mail:* info@freemanpictures.com *Web Site:* www.freemanpictures.com, pg 765

Freeman, David, Rebel Records, PO Box 7405, Charlottesville, VA 22906-7405 *Tel:* 434-973-5151 *E-mail:* questions@rebelrecords.com *Web Site:* rebelrecords.com, pg 871

Freeman, Donald S Jr, Freeman, 1600 Viceroy, Suite 100, Dallas, TX 75235 *Tel:* 214-445-1000 *Web Site:* www.freeman.com, pg 765

Freeman, Douglas, Ideascape Inc, PO Box 1966, Lake Oswego, OR 97035 *Tel:* 503-246-2439 *E-mail:* info@ ideascapeinc.com *Web Site:* www.ideascapeinc.com, pg 784

Freeman, Kent, Ingram Content Group LLC, One Ingram Blvd, La Vergne, TN 37086-1986 *Tel:* 615-793-5000 *Toll Free Tel:* 800-937-8000 (retailers); 800-937-5300 (ext 1, libs) *E-mail:* customerservice@ingramcontent. com *Web Site:* www.ingramcontent.com, pg 787

Freeman, Linda, L&S Video Inc, 875 Fifth Ave, New York, NY 10065 *Tel:* 914-238-9366 *E-mail:* videopaint2@msn.com *Web Site:* www. landsvideo.com, pg 803

Freeman, MacKenzie, Ideascape Inc, PO Box 1966, Lake Oswego, OR 97035 *Tel:* 503-246-2439 *E-mail:* info@ ideascapeinc.com *Web Site:* www.ideascapeinc.com, pg 784

Freeman, Mark, Rebel Records, PO Box 7405, Charlottesville, VA 22906-7405 *Tel:* 434-973-5151 *E-mail:* questions@rebelrecords.com *Web Site:* rebelrecords.com, pg 871

French, Cookie, JRF Magnetic Sciences Inc, 249 Kennedy Rd, Greendell, NJ 07839 *Tel:* 973-579-5773 *Fax:* 973-579-6021 *E-mail:* jrf@jrfmagnetics.com *Web Site:* www.jrfmagnetics.com, pg 795

French, Don E, The Source Stock Footage Library Inc, 140 S Camino Seco, Suite 308, Tucson, AZ 85710 *Tel:* 520-298-4810 *Fax:* 520-290-4376 *E-mail:* requests@sourcefootage.com *Web Site:* www. sourcefootage.com, pg 895

French, John, JRF Magnetic Sciences Inc, 249 Kennedy Rd, Greendell, NJ 07839 *Tel:* 973-579-5773 *Fax:* 973-579-6021 *E-mail:* jrf@jrfmagnetics.com *Web Site:* www.jrfmagnetics.com, pg 795

French, Matt, First Cut Communications LLC, 301 W Broome St, Suite 100, LaGrange, GA 30240 *Tel:* 706-882-5581 *Fax:* 706-407-4528 *E-mail:* info@ firstcutcommunications.com *Web Site:* www. firstcutcommunications.com, pg 761

French, Timothy, Monarch Instrument, 15 Columbia Dr, Amherst, NH 03031-2305 *Tel:* 603-883-3390 *Toll Free Tel:* 800-999-3390 *Fax:* 603-886-3300 *E-mail:* sales@monarchinstrument.com *Web Site:* www.monarchinstrument.com, pg 829

Frenchman, Michael, Videograf, 144 W 27 St, 12th fl, New York, NY 10001 *Tel:* 212-242-7871 *E-mail:* videograf@verizon.net *Web Site:* vgraflive.org, pg 929

Freund, Spencer, Telemanagement Resources International Inc (TRI), 83 Harvey Cedar Way, Waretown, NJ 08758 *Tel:* 609-597-6334 *Web Site:* www.triinc.com, pg 910

Friberg, Leah, Fluke Corp, 6920 Seaway Blvd, Everett, WA 98203 *Tel:* 425-347-6100 *Toll Free Tel:* 800-443-5853 *Fax:* 425-446-5116 *E-mail:* fluke-info@fluke. com *Web Site:* www.fluke.com, pg 763

Frick, Justin, AV Chicago Inc, 619 W Taylor St, Chicago, IL 60607 *Tel:* 312-229-4100 *Toll Free Tel:* 888-709-9599 *Fax:* 312-229-5642 *Web Site:* avchicago.com, pg 696

Frick, Tim, Mightybytes Inc, 4001 N Ravenswood Ave, Suite 404, Chicago, IL 60613 *Tel:* 773-561-7529 *E-mail:* info@mightybytes.com *Web Site:* www. mightybytes.com, pg 827

Fricon, Terri, Fricon Entertainment Co Inc, 134 Bluegrass Circle, Hendersonville, TN 37075 *Tel:* 615-826-2288 *Fax:* 615-826-0500, pg 766

Fried, Dan, Innovision Media Group, 100 Mill Rd, Suite 2, Clifton Heights, PA 19018 *Tel:* 484-688-1200 *Fax:* 484-688-0148 *E-mail:* sales@innovision.net *Web Site:* www.thecrewstore.com, pg 788

Fried, Robert, Robert Fried Photography, 610 Eldridge Ct, Novato, CA 94947 *Tel:* 415-898-6153 *Fax:* 415-897-0353 *Web Site:* www.robertfriedphotography.com, pg 766

Friederichs, Cecilia, United Scenic Artists Local 829, 29 W 38 St, 15th fl, New York, NY 10018 *Tel:* 212-581-0300 *Toll Free Tel:* 877-728-5635 *Fax:* 212-977-2011 *E-mail:* vfxinfo@usa829.org *Web Site:* www.usa829. org; vfx.usa829.org, pg 963

Friederichsen, Steve, Big Event Productions LLC, 77 13 Ave NE, Studio 101, Minneapolis, MN 55413 *Tel:* 612-623-7800 *Web Site:* www.bigeventpros.com, pg 705

Friedler, Dr Alan, Palardo Productions, 1807 Taft Ave, Suite 4, Hollywood, CA 90028 *Tel:* 323-469-8991 *E-mail:* palardo2@msn.com, pg 850

Friedman, Alan, Fred Rogers Productions, 2100 Wharton St, Suite 700, Pittsburgh, PA 15203 *Tel:* 412-687-2990 *Toll Free Tel:* 877-677-6437 *E-mail:* info@fredrogers. org *Web Site:* www.fredrogers.org, pg 876

Friedman, Dan, Castillo Theatre, 543 W 42 St, New York, NY 10036 *Tel:* 212-941-5800 *Toll Free Tel:* 800-435-7453 *Web Site:* www.castillo.org, pg 717

Friedman, David, Magno Sound Inc, 729 Seventh Ave, New York, NY 10019 *Tel:* 212-302-2505 *Fax:* 212-819-1282 *E-mail:* staff@magnosound.com *Web Site:* magnoscreening.com, pg 815

Friedman, Desiree, CEDIA IPRO Affinity Group, 8475 Nightfall Lane, Fishers, IN 46037 *Tel:* 317-328-4336 *Toll Free Tel:* 800-669-5329 *E-mail:* info@cedia.org *Web Site:* cedia.net, pg 952

Friedman, Fritz, Sony Pictures Home Entertainment, 10202 W Washington Blvd, Culver City, CA 90232-3119 *Tel:* 310-244-4000 *Fax:* 310-244-2485 *Web Site:* www.sonypictures.com, pg 893

Friedman, Laurence, Wildfire Lighting & Visual Effects, 2908 Oregon Ct, Suite G-1, Torrance, CA 90503 *Tel:* 310-755-6780 *Toll Free Tel:* 800-937-8065 *Fax:* 310-755-6781 *E-mail:* sales@wildfirelighting.com *Web Site:* www.wildfirefx.com, pg 938

Friedman, Mark, See Factor Industry Inc, 37-11 30 St, Long Island City, NY 11101 *Tel:* 718-784-4200 *Fax:* 718-784-0617 *Web Site:* www.seefactor.com, pg 883

Friedman, Sonya, Four Corners Productions, 101 W 90 St, No 6J, New York, NY 10024 *Tel:* 212-228-6492 *Fax:* 212-228-6492 *Web Site:* www.operatitles.net; www.gracepaleyvideo.com, pg 764

Friend, Jessie, LEE Filters, 2237 N Hollywood Way, Burbank, CA 91505 *Tel:* 818-238-1220 *Toll Free Tel:* 800-576-5055 *Fax:* 818-238-1228 *E-mail:* mail@ leefiltersusa.com *Web Site:* www.leefilters.com, pg 805

Friestedt, Brad, Magnetic Shield Corp, 740 N Thomas Dr, Bensenville, IL 60106 *Tel:* 630-766-7800 *Toll Free Tel:* 888-766-7800 *Fax:* 630-766-2813 *E-mail:* shields@magnetic-shield.com *Web Site:* www. magnetic-shield.com, pg 815

Frijters, Kees, Rosco Laboratories Inc, 52 Harbor View, Stamford, CT 06902 *Tel:* 203-708-8900 *Toll Free Tel:* 800-ROSCO NY (767-2669) *Fax:* 203-708-8919 *E-mail:* info@rosco.com *Web Site:* us.rosco.com, pg 877

Fritchie, Stacia, Lyon Video Inc, 2091 Arlingate Lane, Columbus, OH 43228 *Tel:* 614-297-0001 *E-mail:* info@lyonvideo.com *Web Site:* www. lyonvideo.com, pg 813

Fritts, Jack, Catholic Library Association (CLA), 8550 United Plaza Blvd, Suite 1001, Baton Rouge, LA 70809 *Tel:* 225-408-4417 *E-mail:* cla2@cathla.org *Web Site:* www.cathla.org, pg 952

Fritz, Ed, Sierra Automated Systems, 2821 Burton Ave, Burbank, CA 91504 *Tel:* 818-840-6749 *Fax:* 818-840-6751 *E-mail:* sales@sasaudio.com; marketing@ sasaudio.com *Web Site:* www.sasaudio.com, pg 887

Fritz, Jayson, Texas Rebel Radio Network, c/o Hill Country Broadcasting, 210 Woodcrest, Fredericksburg, TX 78624 *Tel:* 830-997-2197 *Fax:* 830-997-2198 *E-mail:* hillcountrybroadcasting@gmail.com *Web Site:* www.texasrebelradio.com, pg 911

Froechtenigt, Sylke, Kavanagh Productions Inc, 32 Broadway, Suite 1711-12, New York, NY 10004 *Tel:* 212-480-0065 *Fax:* 212-480-0149 *E-mail:* create@kavanaghproductions.com *Web Site:* kavanaghproductions.com, pg 797

Frons, Marc, News Corp, 1211 Avenue of the Americas, New York, NY 10036 *Tel:* 212-416-3400 *E-mail:* media@newscorp.com *Web Site:* newscorp. com, pg 840

Frost, John, SonicPool, 6860 Lexington Ave, Hollywood, CA 90038 *Tel:* 323-460-4649 *Toll Free Tel:* 866-203-7213 *Fax:* 323-460-6063 *E-mail:* production@ sonicpool.com *Web Site:* www.sonicpool.com, pg 892

Fruitman, David, Comtel Inc, 14901 NE 20 Ave, North Miami, FL 33181 *Tel:* 305-424-4160 (facility servs); 305-424-4178 (local inquiries); 516-816-5152 (natl inquiries) *Web Site:* www.comtelinc.com; www. facebook.com/comtelinc/, pg 730

Fry, David, Omega Broadcast Group, 817 W Howard Lane, Austin, TX 78753 *Tel:* 512-251-7778 *Fax:* 512-251-8633 *E-mail:* rental@omegabroadcast.com; sales@omegabroadcast.com *Web Site:* www. omegabroadcast.com, pg 845

Fry, Edward, Heartland International Film Festival, 1043 Virginia Ave, Suite 2, Indianapolis, IN 46203 *Tel:* 317-464-9405 *E-mail:* submissions@ heartlandfilm.org *Web Site:* heartlandfilm.org/festival, pg 992

Fry, Edward, Indy Shorts International Film Fest, 1043 Virginia Ave, Suite 2, Indianapolis, IN 46203 *Tel:* 317-464-9405 *E-mail:* submissions@ heartlandfilm.org *Web Site:* heartlandfilm.org, pg 993

Fry, Pam, Omega Broadcast Group, 817 W Howard Lane, Austin, TX 78753 *Tel:* 512-251-7778 *Fax:* 512-251-8633 *E-mail:* rental@omegabroadcast.com; sales@omegabroadcast.com *Web Site:* www. omegabroadcast.com, pg 845

Fry, Rick, Professional Label Inc, 7726 N King Hwy, Myrtle Beach, SC 29572 *Tel:* 301-570-0774 *Fax:* 301-570-0776 *E-mail:* info@professionallabel.com *Web Site:* professionallabel.com; prolabel.com, pg 865

Fuchs, Laurie, Ladyslipper Music, PO Box 14, Cedar Grove, NC 27231 *Tel:* 919-245-3737 *E-mail:* info@ladyslipper.org *Web Site:* www.ladyslipper.org, pg 803

Fucile, John, SmackDab Media, 252 Glenhaven Dr, Amherst, NY 14228 *Tel:* 615-957-6618 *Web Site:* smackdabmedia.us, pg 890

Fuentes, David, Omnirax Furniture Co, PO Box 1792, Sausalito, CA 94966-1792 *Tel:* 415-332-3392 *Toll Free Tel:* 800-332-3393 *E-mail:* info@omnirax.com *Web Site:* omnirax.com, pg 845

Fugitt, Ray, Lynx Broadband, 12219 Wood Lake Dr, Burnsville, MN 55337 *Tel:* 952-894-9590 *Fax:* 952-894-9380 *E-mail:* info@lynxbroadband.com *Web Site:* www.lynxbroadband.com, pg 813

Fulford-Brown, John, JFB Communications, 3 Haig Ave, Toronto, ON M1N 2W2, Canada *Tel:* 416-691-5001; 416-526-9400 (cell) *E-mail:* jfb@jfb.ca *Web Site:* www.jfb.ca, pg 794

Fulham, Paul, Zachry Associates Inc, 500 Chestnut St, Suite 2000, Abilene, TX 79602 *Tel:* 325-677-1342 *E-mail:* info@zachryinc.com *Web Site:* zachryinc.com, pg 944

Fullam, Hannah, Preston Productions Inc, 128 Bartlett St, Marlborough, MA 01752 *Toll Free Tel:* 800-822-2299 *E-mail:* ideas@prestonevents.com *Web Site:* www.prestonproductions.com; www.prestonevents.com, pg 862

Fuller, Ben, Imagecraft Productions, 3318 Burton Ave, Burbank, CA 91504 *Tel:* 818-954-0187 *Fax:* 818-954-0189 *Web Site:* www.imagecraftproductions.com, pg 785

Fuller, Brad, Florida Film & Tape, 3417 Lake Breeze Rd, Orlando, FL 32808 *Tel:* 407-297-0091 *E-mail:* info@ffandt.com *Web Site:* ffandt.com, pg 763

Fuller, Brandon, The Mack Sennett Studios, 1215 Bates Ave, Los Angeles, CA 90029 *Tel:* 323-660-8466 *E-mail:* info@macksennettstudios.net *Web Site:* www.macksennettstudios.net, pg 884

Fuller, John, Chimera®, 1067 Telleen Ave, Erie, CO 80516 *Tel:* 303-444-8000 *Toll Free Tel:* 888-444-1812 *Fax:* 303-444-8303 *E-mail:* info@chimeralighting.com *Web Site:* chimeralighting.com, pg 722

Fuller, Kevin, Hollywood Lights Inc, 5251 SE McLoughlin Blvd, Portland, OR 97202-4836 *Tel:* 503-232-9001; 503-232-8855 *Toll Free Tel:* 800-826-9881 *Fax:* 503-517-8686 *E-mail:* portland@hollywoodlights.biz *Web Site:* www.hollywoodlights.biz, pg 780

Fuller, Michael, Florida Film & Tape, 3417 Lake Breeze Rd, Orlando, FL 32808 *Tel:* 407-297-0091 *E-mail:* info@ffandt.com *Web Site:* ffandt.com, pg 763

Fuller, Michael, Imagivations, 11314 Sheldon St, Sun Valley, CA 91352 *Tel:* 818-767-6767 *Fax:* 818-767-3637 *E-mail:* info@imagivations.com *Web Site:* www.imagivations.com, pg 786

Fuller, Michael M, Creative Support Services/CSS Music, 1948 Riverside Dr, Los Angeles, CA 90039 *Tel:* 323-666-7968 *Toll Free Tel:* 800-468-6874 *Fax:* 323-660-2070 *E-mail:* info@cssmusic.com *Web Site:* www.cssmusic.com, pg 733

Fuller, Roland, Taperwire, c/o Fuller Manufacturing, 523 S Flower St, Burbank, CA 91502 *Tel:* 818-238-9911 *Fax:* 818-238-9959 *E-mail:* taperwire@taperwire.com *Web Site:* www.taperwire.com, pg 907

Fulmer, Keith, Video Mount Products (VMP), 345 Log Canoe Circle, Stevensville, MD 21666 *Tel:* 410-643-6390 *Toll Free Tel:* 877-281-2169 *Fax:* 410-643-6615 *E-mail:* contact@videomount.com *Web Site:* www.videomount.com, pg 928

Fulop, Dan, Universal Audio Inc, 4585 Scotts Valley Dr, Scotts Valley, CA 95066 *Tel:* 831-440-1176 *Toll Free Tel:* 877-698-2834 (cust serv) *E-mail:* sales@uaudio.com *Web Site:* www.uaudio.com, pg 922

Funnell, Adrian, Steeldeck® Inc, 3339 Exposition Place, Los Angeles, CA 90018-4034 *Tel:* 323-290-2100 *Toll Free Tel:* 800-50STAGE (507-8243) *Fax:* 323-290-9600 *E-mail:* sales@steeldeck.com; rentals@steeldeck.com *Web Site:* www.steeldeck.com, pg 900

Futch, Damein, All Comm Rentals Inc (ALLCOMM), 1402 SW 13 Ct, Pompano Beach, FL 33069 *Tel:* 954-788-9555 *Web Site:* www.allcommrentals.com, pg 680

Gabbert, Tom, Bartha, 600 N Cassady Ave, Columbus, OH 43219 *Tel:* 614-252-7455 *Toll Free Tel:* 800-363-2698 *Fax:* 614-252-7641 *E-mail:* info@bartha.com *Web Site:* www.bartha.com, pg 702

Gabor, Billy, Beast Atlanta, 3399 Peachtree Rd NE, Suite 200, Atlanta, GA 30326-1149 *Tel:* 404-237-9977 *Fax:* 404-237-3923 *Web Site:* www.beast.tv, pg 703

Gaboury, Jane, Professional Photographers of America (PPA), 229 Peachtree St NE, Suite 2200, Atlanta, GA 30303 *Tel:* 404-522-8600 *Toll Free Tel:* 800-786-6277 *Fax:* 404-614-6400 *E-mail:* csc@ppa.com *Web Site:* www.ppa.com, pg 961

Gaboury, Ron, Yorktel, 81 Corbett Way, Eatontown, NJ 07724 *Tel:* 732-413-6000 *Toll Free Tel:* 866-836-8463 *Fax:* 732-413-6060 *E-mail:* knowmore@yorktel.com *Web Site:* yorktel.com, pg 944

Gabriel, J P, Filmlites Montana, 6465 River Rd, Bozeman, MT 59718 *Tel:* 406-587-0226 *Fax:* 406-551-4555 *E-mail:* info@filmlitesmt.com *Web Site:* www.filmlitesmt.com, pg 760

Gabriel, Kevin, Manitoba Film & Music, 410-93 Lombard Ave, Suite 410, Winnipeg, MB R3B 3B1, Canada *Tel:* 204-947-2040 *Fax:* 204-956-5261 *E-mail:* info@mbfilmmusic.ca *Web Site:* www.mbfilmmusic.ca, pg 816

Gabriel, Paul, Wisconsin Technical College System Foundation Inc, 6602 Normandy Lane, Madison, WI 53719-1081 *Tel:* 608-841-1800 *Toll Free Tel:* 800-821-6313 *Fax:* 608-841-1806 *E-mail:* foundation@wtcsf.tec.wi.us *Web Site:* www.wtcsf.tec.wi.us, pg 940

Gadoury, Sylvie, CBC/Radio-Canada, 181 Queen St, Ottawa, ON K1P 1K9, Canada *Tel:* 613-288-6000; 613-288-6445 (newsroom) *Toll Free Tel:* 866-306-4636 (CN only) *E-mail:* cbcnewsottawa@cbc.ca *Web Site:* cbc.radio-canada.ca, pg 717

Gag, Rob, Tierney Brothers Inc, 1771 Energy Park Dr, Suite 100, St Paul, MN 55108 *Tel:* 612-331-5500 *Toll Free Tel:* 866-557-6062 *Fax:* 612-331-3424 *E-mail:* contactform@tierneybrothers.com *Web Site:* www.tierneybrothers.com, pg 914

Gage, Carrie, Studio Technologies Inc, 7440 Frontage Rd, Skokie, IL 60077-3202 *Tel:* 847-676-9177 *E-mail:* stisales-2018@studio-tech.com *Web Site:* www.studio-tech.com, pg 903

Gagliano, Tony, Art Gallery of Ontario, 317 Dundas St W, Toronto, ON M5T 1G4, Canada *Tel:* 416-979-6648 *Toll Free Tel:* 877-225-4246 *Web Site:* ago.ca, pg 690

Gagnon, Francis, Photo Finish, Auburn Mall, 550 Center St, No 9007, Auburn, ME 04210 *Tel:* 207-783-3354 *Web Site:* www.mainephotofinish.com, pg 856

Gagnon, Nicole, Show Canada Industries Inc, 5555 Maurice-Cullen, Laval, QC H7C 2T8, Canada *Tel:* 450-664-5155 *Toll Free Tel:* 888-329-5556 *Fax:* 450-664-0852 *E-mail:* info@show-canada.ca *Web Site:* www.show-canada.com, pg 886

Gahrahmat, Laura, Eastern Effects Inc, 99 Ninth St, Brooklyn, NY 11215 *Tel:* 718-855-1197 *Toll Free Fax:* 888-566-6547 *Web Site:* easterneffects.com, pg 749

Gaide, Esther, Technicolor USA Inc, 6040 Sunset Blvd, Hollywood, CA 90028 *Tel:* 323-817-6600 *E-mail:* info@technicolor.com *Web Site:* technicolor.com, pg 908

Gaidry, Diane, Filmmakers Alliance (FA), 1317 N San Fernando Blvd, Unit 366, Burbank, CA 91504 *Tel:* 310-568-0633 *E-mail:* info@filmmakersalliance.org *Web Site:* filmmakersalliance.org, pg 955

Gainer, Paul, Disney Consumer Products & Interactive Media (DCPI), 1201 Flower St, Glendale, AZ 91201 *Tel:* 818-544-0000 *Web Site:* dcpi.disney.com, pg 743

Gaita, Christina, Boston Light & Sound Inc, 290 N Beacon St, Boston, MA 02135-1990 *Tel:* 617-787-3131 *Fax:* 617-787-4257 *E-mail:* info@blsi.com *Web Site:* www.blsi.com, pg 709

Gaither, Bill, Gaither Studios LLC, 1705 S Park Ave, Alexandria, IN 46001 *Toll Free Tel:* 800-333-7859 *E-mail:* info@gaitherstudios.com, pg 767

Gaither, Gloria, Gaither Studios LLC, 1705 S Park Ave, Alexandria, IN 46001 *Toll Free Tel:* 800-333-7859 *E-mail:* info@gaitherstudios.com, pg 767

Galdi, Gregory G, Custom Computer Specialists Inc, 70 Suffolk Ct, Hauppauge, NY 11788 *Tel:* 631-864-6699 *Toll Free Tel:* 800-589-8989 *Fax:* 401-765-6440 *Toll Free Fax:* 800-986-5518 *E-mail:* info@customtech.com; support@customtech.com *Web Site:* www.customonline.com, pg 736

Galgano, Kerri, Lighting Services Inc, 2 Holt Dr, Stony Point, NY 10980 *Tel:* 845-942-2800 *Toll Free Tel:* 800-999-9574 (US & CN) *Fax:* 845-942-2177 *E-mail:* applications@maillsi.com; sales@maillsi.com *Web Site:* www.lightingservicesinc.com, pg 808

Galipeau, Claude, CBC/Radio-Canada, 181 Queen St, Ottawa, ON K1P 1K9, Canada *Tel:* 613-288-6000; 613-288-6445 (newsroom) *Toll Free Tel:* 866-306-4636 (CN only) *E-mail:* cbcnewsottawa@cbc.ca *Web Site:* cbc.radio-canada.ca, pg 717

Gallacher, Stewart, Nexsan Inc, 900 E Hamilton Ave, Suite 230, Campbell, CA 95008 *Tel:* 408-724-9809 *E-mail:* sales@nexsan.com *Web Site:* www.nexsan.com, pg 841

Gallagher, Brian A, United Way Worldwide, 701 N Fairfax St, Alexandria, VA 22314-2045 *Tel:* 703-836-7112 *Web Site:* www.unitedway.org, pg 921

Gallagher, Don, Hollywood Theatre Equipment Inc, 1941 N 66 Ave, Hollywood, FL 33024 *Tel:* 954-920-2832 *Fax:* 954-986-6914 *E-mail:* hwdtheatre@aol.com, pg 781

Gallagher, Jerry, Museum of the City of New York, 1220 Fifth Ave, New York, NY 10029 *Tel:* 212-534-1672 *Fax:* 212-423-0758 *E-mail:* info@mcny.org *Web Site:* www.mcny.org, pg 834

Gallagher, Kelly, Ingram Content Group LLC, One Ingram Blvd, La Vergne, TN 37086-1986 *Tel:* 615-793-5000 *Toll Free Tel:* 800-937-8000 (retailers); 800-937-5300 (ext 1, libs) *E-mail:* customerservice@ingramcontent.com *Web Site:* www.ingramcontent.com, pg 787

Gallagher, Michael, Craig Recording Studios, 2381 Philmont Ave, Suite 112, Huntingdon Valley, PA 19006 *Tel:* 215-947-8900 *Web Site:* www.craigrecording.com; www.craigrecordingstudios.com, pg 732

Gallagher, Mike, VSG Digital Media Solutions, 11126 Lindbergh Business Ct, St Louis, MO 63123 *Tel:* 314-487-8045 *Toll Free Tel:* 800-737-8045 *Fax:* 314-487-9387 *E-mail:* info@vsginc.net *Web Site:* www.vsginc.net, pg 933

Gallagher, Mitch, Sweetwater Sound Inc, 5501 US Hwy 30 W, Fort Wayne, IN 46818 *Tel:* 260-432-8176 *Toll Free Tel:* 800-222-4700 *Fax:* 260-432-1758 *Web Site:* www.sweetwater.com, pg 905

Gallagher, Richard, Xytech Systems Corp, 15451 San Fernando Mission Blvd, Suite 400, Mission Hills, CA 91345 *Tel:* 818-698-4900 *Fax:* 818-698-4901 *E-mail:* sales@xytechsystems.com *Web Site:* www.xytechsystems.com, pg 943

Gallant, Barry, Penguin Random House Canada, 320 Front St W, Suite 1400, Toronto, ON M5V 3B6, Canada *Tel:* 416-364-4449 *Toll Free Tel:* 888-523-9292 *Fax:* 416-598-7764 *E-mail:* customerservicescanada@penguinrandomhouse.com *Web Site:* www.penguinrandomhouse.ca, pg 853

Gallardo, Felix, Techni-Lux Inc, 10900 Palmbay Dr, Orlando, FL 32824 *Tel:* 407-857-8770 *Fax:* 407-857-8771 *E-mail:* sales@techni-lux.com *Web Site:* www.techni-lux.com, pg 908

Gallien, Robert, Gallien-Krueger, 2234 Industrial Dr, Stockton, CA 95206 *Tel:* 209-234-7300 *Fax:* 209-234-8420 *E-mail:* sales@gallien.com *Web Site:* www.gallien-krueger.com, pg 768

Gallner, Larry, Total Video Products Inc, 414 Southgate Ct, Mickleton, NJ 08056 *Tel:* 856-423-7400 *Toll Free Tel:* 800-447-0920 *Fax:* 856-423-4747 *E-mail:* info@totalvideoproducts.com *Web Site:* www.totalvideoproducts.com, pg 916

Gallo, Giancarlo, Metalworks Recording Studios Inc, 3611 Mavis Rd, Mississauga, ON L5C 1T7, Canada *Tel:* 905-279-4000 *Fax:* 905-279-4006 *Web Site:* www.metalworksstudios.com, pg 824

Gallo, Susan, DuArt Media Services, 245 W 55 St, New York, NY 10019 *Tel:* 212-757-4580 *Fax:* 212-977-5609 *E-mail:* info@duart.com *Web Site:* www.duart.com, pg 747

Galloway, Stephen F, SurgeX, 8001 Knightdale Blvd, Suite 121, Knightdale, NC 27545 *Toll Free Tel:* 800-645-9721 (tech & cust support) *E-mail:* order.desk@ametek.com *Web Site:* espsurgex.com/surgex/, pg 905

Gallup, Kim, Moxie Media, 1301 Dealers Ave, New Orleans, LA 70123 *Tel:* 504-733-6907 *Toll Free Tel:* 800-346-6943 *Fax:* 504-733-9493 *E-mail:* info@moxiemedia.com *Web Site:* www.moxietraining.com; www.moxiemedia.com, pg 832

Galucki, Jonathan, Playback Now Inc, 3139 Campus Dr, Suite 700, Norcross, GA 30071-1402 *Tel:* 770-447-0616 *Toll Free Tel:* 800-241-7785 (prod support) *E-mail:* info@playbacknow.com *Web Site:* www.playbacknow.com, pg 858

Galvan-Davies, Robin, Greater Grass Valley Chamber of Commerce, 128 E Main St, Grass Valley, CA 95945 *Tel:* 530-273-4667 *Fax:* 530-272-5440 *Web Site:* www.grassvalleychamber.com, pg 966

Galvin, Carmel, Autodesk Inc, 111 McInnis Pkwy, San Rafael, CA 94903 *Tel:* 415-507-5000 *Fax:* 415-507-5100 *Web Site:* www.autodesk.com, pg 696

Galvin, Carrie, NEP Group Inc, 2 Beta Dr, Pittsburgh, PA 15238 *Tel:* 412-826-1414 *Toll Free Tel:* 800-444-0054 *E-mail:* info@nepinc.com *Web Site:* www.nepgroup.com, pg 838

Galvin, William A, Anixter Inc, 2301 Patriot Blvd, Glenview, IL 60026 *Tel:* 224-521-8000 *Toll Free Tel:* 800-323-8167 *Fax:* 224-521-8100 *Web Site:* www.anixter.com, pg 685

Gamarra, Eddie, Nickelodeon, 1515 Broadway, 38th fl, New York, NY 10036 *Tel:* 212-258-8000 (Viacom) *Web Site:* www.nick.com, pg 841

Games, Greg, Tri-State Visual Products Inc, 885 Ohio Pike, Suite C, Cincinnati, OH 45245 *Tel:* 513-471-7111 *Toll Free Tel:* 800-473-4474 *E-mail:* info@trivisual.com *Web Site:* www.trivisual.com, pg 918

Gandara, Whitney, Convergent Media Systems, 190 Bluegrass Valley Pkwy, Alpharetta, GA 30005-2204 *Tel:* 770-369-9000 *Fax:* 770-369-9100 *Web Site:* www.convergent.com, pg 731

Gandert, Nate, Getty Images, 605 Fifth Ave S, Suite 400, Seattle, WA 98104 *Tel:* 206-925-5000 *Toll Free Tel:* 888-888-5889; 800-462-4379 (sales) *E-mail:* sales.na@gettyimages.com *Web Site:* www.gettyimages.com, pg 770

Ganesan, Prasannaa, Corel Corp, 1600 Carling Ave, Ottawa, ON K1Z 8R7, Canada *Toll Free Tel:* 877-582-6735 *Web Site:* www.corel.com, pg 731

Gannon, Brian, Austin Film Commission, 111 Congress Ave, Suite 700, Austin, TX 78701 *Tel:* 512-583-7230 *Toll Free Tel:* 800-926-2282 (ext 7230) *Fax:* 512-583-7282 *Web Site:* www.austintexas.org/film-commission, pg 976

Gans, Shannon Blake, New Deal Studios, 15392 Cobalt St, Los Angeles, CA 91342 *Tel:* 310-578-9929 *E-mail:* info@newdealstudios.com *Web Site:* www.newdealstudios.com, pg 839

Gansecki, Cheryl, Ka Io Productions Inc, PO Box 5150, Hilo, HI 96720-1150 *Tel:* 808-959-3885 *Toll Free Tel:* 888-458-7538 *Fax:* 808-959-3885 *E-mail:* lava@volcanovideo.com *Web Site:* www.volcanovideo.com, pg 796

Gant, Aaron, Warner Chappell Production Music, 1030 16 Ave S, Nashville, TN 37212 *Toll Free Tel:* 888-615-8729 *Fax:* 615-242-2455 *E-mail:* info@warnerchappellpm.com *Web Site:* www.warnerchappellpm.com, pg 934

Garberson, John, Creative Backstage, 4829 S 36 St, Suite 1, Phoenix, AZ 85040 *Tel:* 480-580-2222 *E-mail:* sales@creativebackstage.com *Web Site:* www.creativebackstage.com, pg 733

Garcia, Alfredo, Sight & Sound Productions, 11193 Saint Johns Industrial Pkwy N, Jacksonville, FL 32246 *Tel:* 904-645-7880 *Toll Free Tel:* 800-339-0846 *Fax:* 904-645-7787 *E-mail:* info@ssav.net *Web Site:* www.ssav.net, pg 887

Garcia, Art, Extron Electronics, 1025 E Ball Rd, Suite 100, Anaheim, CA 92805-5957 *Tel:* 714-491-1500 *Toll Free Tel:* 800-633-9876 (sales & tech support); 800-633-9873 (order support) *Fax:* 714-491-1517 *E-mail:* sales-usa@extron.com *Web Site:* www.extron.com, pg 758

Garcia, David, Philips Entertainment Lighting, 10911 Petal St, Dallas, TX 75238 *Tel:* 214-647-7880 *Toll Free Tel:* 877-VARILITE (877-827-4548) *Fax:* 214-647-8038 *E-mail:* entertainment.service@philips.com *Web Site:* www.vari-lite.com, pg 855

Garcia, Enrique, Omega Broadcast Group, 817 W Howard Lane, Austin, TX 78753 *Tel:* 512-251-7778 *Fax:* 512-251-8633 *E-mail:* rental@omegabroadcast.com; sales@omegabroadcast.com *Web Site:* www.omegabroadcast.com, pg 845

Garcia, Eric, 48 Windows, 1661 N Lincoln Blvd, Suite 220, Santa Monica, CA 90404 *Tel:* 310-392-9545 *Fax:* 310-392-9445 *E-mail:* ziv@48windows.com *Web Site:* www.48windows.com, pg 764

Garcia, Francisco, Cine Las Americas International Film Festival (CLAIFF), 1104 W 34 St, No 625, Austin, TX 78705 *Tel:* 512-535-0765 *E-mail:* cine@cinelasamericas.org; entries@cinelasamericas.org *Web Site:* cinelasamericas.org; www.facebook.com/cinelasamericasaustin, pg 986

Garcia, Jean, Garcia Marketing Inc, 400 Ninth St, Conway, PA 15027-1663 *Tel:* 724-869-0100 *Toll Free Tel:* 800-683-1925 *Fax:* 724-869-1925 *E-mail:* gmavfoto@verizon.net, pg 768

Garcia, Jorge W PhD, Professional Advancement Enterprises (PAE), 2182 Saginaw SE, Grand Rapids, MI 49506 *Tel:* 616-956-9443 *Fax:* 616-956-7973 *E-mail:* paeworld@comcast.net *Web Site:* www.paeworld.com, pg 864

Garcia, Kathleen Sommers, Liturgy Training Publications, 3949 S Racine Ave, Chicago, IL 60609-2523 *Tel:* 773-579-4900 *Toll Free Tel:* 800-933-1800 (orders) *Fax:* 773-579-4929 *E-mail:* orders@ltp.org; info@ltp.org *Web Site:* www.ltp.org, pg 810

Garcia, Lily Eskelsen, National Education Association (NEA), 1201 16 St NW, Washington, DC 20036-3290 *Tel:* 202-833-4000 *Fax:* 202-822-7974 *Web Site:* www.nea.org, pg 836

Garcia, Louis, Association of Progressive Rental Organizations (APRO), 500 E Whitestone Blvd, Suite 4189, Cedar Park, TX 78613 *Tel:* 512-794-0095 *Toll Free Tel:* 800-204-2776 *Fax:* 512-794-0097 *E-mail:* info@rtohq.org *Web Site:* www.rtohq.org, pg 951

Garcia, Manuel, Illuminate Studios, 10900 Ventura Blvd, Studio City, CA 90068 *Tel:* 818-769-4500 *Fax:* 818-769-7150 *E-mail:* info@illuminatehollywood.com *Web Site:* www.illuminatehollywood.com, pg 784

Garcia, Maurice, Emlight Design, 1179 N Eastman Ave, Suite 1, Los Angeles, CA 90063 *Tel:* 323-261-5162 *Toll Free Fax:* 866-728-9164 *E-mail:* service@dimmer.com; service@emlightdesign.com *Web Site:* www.dimmer.com; www.emlightdesign.com, pg 753

Garcia, Thomas C, Garcia Marketing Inc, 400 Ninth St, Conway, PA 15027-1663 *Tel:* 724-869-0100 *Toll Free Tel:* 800-683-1925 *Fax:* 724-869-1925 *E-mail:* gmavfoto@verizon.net, pg 768

Garcia, Tony, Michigan Film & Digital Media Office, 300 N Washington Sq, 4th fl, Lansing, MI 48913 *Tel:* 517-241-6757 *Toll Free Tel:* 800-477-FILM (477-3456) *Fax:* 517-241-3689 *E-mail:* mfo@michigan.org *Web Site:* www.michiganbusiness.org/industries/mfdmo, pg 972

Gardner, Bill, PBS Video, 2100 Crystal Dr, Arlington, VA 22202 *Tel:* 703-739-5000 *Web Site:* shop.pbs.org; www.pbs.org/video, pg 852

Gardner, Nancy, S&P Global Marketing Intelligence, 55 Water St, New York, NY 10041 *Toll Free Tel:* 877-863-1306 *E-mail:* questions@spcapitaliq.com *Web Site:* marketingintelligence.spglobal.com, pg 880

Garey, Guy G, Quality Film & Video, 3321 Main St, Suite B-1, Manchester, MD 21102 *Tel:* 410-785-1920 *E-mail:* quality3321@comcast.net *Web Site:* www.qualityfilmvideo.com, pg 868

Garey, Peter A, Quality Film & Video, 3321 Main St, Suite B-1, Manchester, MD 21102 *Tel:* 410-785-1920 *E-mail:* quality3321@comcast.net *Web Site:* www.qualityfilmvideo.com, pg 868

Garfunkel, Sandy, Ansonia Prompting Inc, 39 W 29 St, Suite 305, New York, NY 10001 *Tel:* 212-594-0500 *Fax:* 212-202-4925 *E-mail:* info@ansoniaprompting.com *Web Site:* www.ansoniaprompting.com, pg 686

Garing, Caitlin, HarperAudio, 10 E 53 St, New York, NY 10022 *Tel:* 212-207-7000 *Toll Free Tel:* 800-242-7737 *Fax:* 212-207-2582 *Toll Free Fax:* 800-822-4090 *Web Site:* www.harpercollins.com, pg 776

Garman, Steve, Garman Productions LLC, 2828 NW 58 St, Oklahoma City, OK 73112 *Tel:* 405-254-2500 *Toll Free Tel:* 800-747-5699 *Fax:* 405-254-2507 *E-mail:* info@garman.com *Web Site:* www.garman.com, pg 768

Garner, Marion, Penguin Random House Canada, 320 Front St W, Suite 1400, Toronto, ON M5V 3B6, Canada *Tel:* 416-364-4449 *Toll Free Tel:* 888-523-9292 (cust serv) *Fax:* 416-598-7764 *E-mail:* customerservicescanada@penguinrandomhouse.com *Web Site:* www.penguinrandomhouse.ca, pg 853

Garrett, Amy, Moog Inc, 400 Jamison Rd, Elma, NY 14059 *Tel:* 716-652-2000 *E-mail:* info@moog.com *Web Site:* www.moog.com, pg 830

Garrett, Mark, Adobe Systems Inc, 345 Park Ave, San Jose, CA 95110-2704 *Tel:* 408-536-6000 *Fax:* 408-537-6000 *Web Site:* www.adobe.com, pg 676

Garrison, Jason, CET, 1223 Central Pkwy, Cincinnati, OH 45214 *Tel:* 513-381-4033 *E-mail:* comments@cetconnect.org *Web Site:* www.cetconnect.org, pg 720

Garson, Jonathan, Pixar Animation Studios, 1200 Park Ave, Emeryville, CA 94608 *Tel:* 510-922-3000 *Fax:* 510-922-3151 *Web Site:* www.pixar.com, pg 857

Garstick, Jeff, Lowell Manufacturing, 100 Integram Dr, Pacific, MO 63069-3476 *Tel:* 636-257-3400 *Toll Free Tel:* 800-325-9660 *Fax:* 636-257-6606 *Toll Free Fax:* 888-456-9355 *E-mail:* sales@lowellmfg.com *Web Site:* www.lowellmfg.com, pg 812

Garten, Eli, VITEC Multimedia, 931 Benecia Ave, Sunnyvale, CA 94085 *Tel:* 650-230-2400 *Toll Free Tel:* 800-451-5101 *E-mail:* info@vitec.com *Web Site:* www.vitec.com, pg 932

Garton, Jeff, Argentine Productions Inc, 111 Mayfair Dr, Pittsburgh, PA 15228 *Tel:* 412-341-6448 *E-mail:* engage@argentineproductions.com *Web Site:* argentineproductions.com, pg 688

Garvin, Nick, Colorado Studios, 8455 Highfield Pkwy, Englewood, CO 80112 *Fax:* 303-388-9600 *E-mail:* info@coloradostudios.info *Web Site:* coloradostudios.info, pg 728

Garvin, Phillip, Colorado Studios, 8455 Highfield Pkwy, Englewood, CO 80112 *Fax:* 303-388-9600 *E-mail:* info@coloradostudios.info *Web Site:* coloradostudios.info, pg 728

Garza, Autumn, Attainment Co Inc, 504 Commerce Pkwy, Verona, WI 53593 *Tel:* 608-845-7880 *Toll Free Tel:* 800-327-4269 *Fax:* 608-845-8040 *Toll Free Fax:* 800-942-3865 *E-mail:* customerservice@attainmentcompany.com; international@attainmentcompany.com *Web Site:* www.attainmentcompany.com, pg 692

Gaskell, Michael, MG Studio, 6625 S Valley View Blvd, Suite C-304, Las Vegas, NV 89118 *Tel:* 702-836-3686 *E-mail:* office@mgstudio.com *Web Site:* mgstudio.com, pg 825

Gaster, Guy, North Carolina Film Office, 15000 Weston Pkwy, Cary, NC 27513 *Tel:* 919-447-7800 *Fax:* 919-447-7780 *Web Site:* www.filmnc.com, pg 974

Gates, Angie M, Office of Cable Television, Film, Music & Entertainment (OCTFME), Brentwood Broadcast Ctr, 1899 Nine St NE, Washington, DC 20018 *Tel:* 202-727-6608 *Fax:* 202-727-3246 *E-mail:* film@dc.gov *Web Site:* www.film.dc.gov, pg 969

Gates, Katie, Yellow Cat Productions Inc, 505 11 St SE, Washington, DC 20003 *Tel:* 202-543-2221 *E-mail:* yellowcat@yellowcat.com *Web Site:* www.yellowcat.com, pg 944

Gathany, Todd, CCI Solutions, 1342 88 Ave SE, Olympia, WA 98501 *Tel:* 360-943-5378 *Toll Free Tel:* 800-562-6006 *Fax:* 360-754-1566 *E-mail:* info@ccisolutions.com *Web Site:* www.ccisolutions.com, pg 718

Gaudreault, France, International Film Festival in Abitibi-Teiscamingue, 215 Ave Mercier, Rouyn-Noranda, QC J9X 5W8, Canada *Tel:* 819-762-6212 *Fax:* 819-762-6762 *E-mail:* info@festivalcinema.ca *Web Site:* festivalcinema.ca, pg 993

Gaukel, Rick, Theatre House Inc, 400 W Third St, Covington, KY 41011-1306 *Tel:* 859-431-2414 *Toll Free Tel:* 800-827-2414 *Fax:* 859-431-1837 *E-mail:* info@theatrehouse.com *Web Site:* www.theatrehouse.com, pg 912

Gaushell, Charles T, Paradigm Marketing & Creative, 89 N Cooper St, Memphis, TN 38104 *Tel:* 901-685-7703 *E-mail:* info@2dimes.com *Web Site:* www.2dimes.com, pg 851

Gawell, Jesper, ChyronHego Corp, 5 Hub Dr, Melville, NY 11747 *Tel:* 631-845-2000 *E-mail:* info@chyronhego.com; sales@chyronhego.com *Web Site:* chyronhego.com, pg 723

Gaynor, Bob, 4 Wall Entertainment, 3165 W Sunset Rd, Suite 100, Las Vegas, NV 89118 *Tel:* 702-263-3858 *Toll Free Tel:* 877-789-8167 (Western US) *Fax:* 702-263-3863 *E-mail:* info@4wall.com; info@usedlighting.com *Web Site:* www.4wall.com; www.usedlighting.com, pg 764

Gayron, Ken, Avid Technology Inc, 65-75 Network Dr, Burlington, MA 01830 *Tel:* 978-640-6789 *Web Site:* www.avid.com, pg 698

Gazzale, Bob, American Film Institute (AFI), Attn: Facilities Off, 2021 N Western Ave, Los Angeles, CA 90027-1657 *Tel:* 323-856-7600 *Toll Free Tel:* 800-774-4AFI (774-4234 membership) *Fax:* 323-462-4049 *E-mail:* information@afi.com *Web Site:* www.afi.com, pg 948

Gear, Christy, Visix™ Inc, 230 Scientific Dr, Suite 800, Norcross, GA 30092 *Tel:* 770-446-1416 *Toll Free Tel:* 800-572-4935 *Fax:* 770-448-5724 *E-mail:* info@visix.com *Web Site:* www.visix.com, pg 931

Geary, James J, Avaya Inc, 4655 Great American Pkwy, Santa Clara, CA 95054 *Tel:* 908-953-6000 *Toll Free Tel:* 866-GO-AVAYA (462-8292 US & CN) *Web Site:* www.avaya.com, pg 697

Geary, William III, Bisk Education, 9417 Princess Palm Ave, Tampa, FL 33619 *Toll Free Tel:* 800-280-9718 *E-mail:* media@bisk.com *Web Site:* www.bisk.com, pg 706

Gebhardt, Thomas, Panasonic Corporation of North America, 2 Riverfront Plaza, Newark, NJ 07012 *Tel:* 201-348-7000 *Toll Free Tel:* 800-211-7262; 888-275-2595 *Fax:* 201-348-7807 *Web Site:* www.panasonic.com, pg 850

Gedden, Jeff, Digital Audio Labs, 1266 Park Rd, Chanhassen, MN 55317 *Tel:* 952-401-7700 *Fax:* 952-401-7725 *E-mail:* sales@digitalaudio.com; contact@digitalaudio.com *Web Site:* www.digitalaudio.com, pg 742

Geerts, Adam, IntegraColor, 3210 Innovative Way, Mesquite, TX 75149 *Tel:* 972-289-0705 *Toll Free Tel:* 800-933-9511 *Fax:* 972-285-4881 *E-mail:* salesinfo@integracolor.com *Web Site:* www.integracolor.com, pg 789

Gefond, Richard L, IMAX Corp, 2525 Speakman Dr, Mississauga, ON L5K 1B1, Canada *Tel:* 905-403-6500 *Fax:* 905-403-6450 *E-mail:* info@imax.com *Web Site:* www.imax.com, pg 786

Gehring, Ron, Sunfire Communications Inc, 6965 Piazza Grande Ave, Suite 214, Orlando, FL 32835 *Tel:* 407-226-8226 *Fax:* 407-226-1660 *E-mail:* info@sunfirecommunications.com *Web Site:* www.sunfirecommunications.com, pg 904

Geistman, Robert A, Ingram Entertainment Inc, 2 Ingram Blvd, La Vergne, TN 37089 *Tel:* 615-287-4000 (corp) *Toll Free Tel:* 800-621-1333 (sales & cust serv) *Web Site:* www.ingramentertainment.com, pg 787

Gelineau-Paradis, Sarah, International Film Festival in Abitibi-Teiscamingue, 215 Ave Mercier, Rouyn-Noranda, QC J9X 5W8, Canada *Tel:* 819-762-6212 *Fax:* 819-762-6762 *E-mail:* info@festivalcinema.ca *Web Site:* festivalcinema.ca, pg 993

Geller, Carl, Sunset Las Palmas Studios, 1040 N Las Palmas Ave, Los Angeles, CA 90038 *Tel:* 323-860-0000 *E-mail:* reception@sunsetlaspalmas.com *Web Site:* www.sunsetlaspalmas.com, pg 904

Geller, Eric, Elite Video Inc, 209 E Emerson Rd, Lexington, MA 02420 *Tel:* 781-862-6606, pg 753

Gellis, Andrew, Cinevest, PO Box 261112, Encino, CA 91426 *Tel:* 310-913-0284 *Web Site:* www.cinevest.com, pg 725

Gellman, Nate, San Francisco Jewish Film Festival, 145 Ninth St, Suite 200, San Francisco, CA 94103 *Tel:* 415-621-0556 *Fax:* 415-621-0568 *E-mail:* jewishfilm@sfjff.org; programming@jfi.org *Web Site:* www.sfjff.org; jfi.org, pg 1003

Gely, Gabriel, Genesis Integration, 14721 123 Ave NW, Edmonton, AB T5L 2Y6, Canada *Toll Free Tel:* 877-283-2253 (Toronto); 866-622-2966 (Quebec); 844-436-4681 (rest of CN) *E-mail:* marketing@genint.com *Web Site:* www.genint.com, pg 770

Generali, Philippe, Florical Systems Inc, 4500 NW 27 Ave, Bldg B-1, Gainesville, FL 32606 *Tel:* 352-372-8326 *Fax:* 352-375-0859 *E-mail:* sales@florical.com *Web Site:* www.florical.com, pg 762

Genin, Guy, ZGC Inc, 264 Morris Ave, Mountain Lakes, NJ 07046 *Tel:* 973-335-4460 *Fax:* 973-335-4560 *E-mail:* sales@zgc.com *Web Site:* www.zgc.com, pg 945

Gentile, Gary, Gary Gentile Productions (GGP), 3 Lehigh Gorge Dr, Jim Thorpe, PA 18229 *Tel:* 252-394-6974 *Web Site:* www.ggentile.com, pg 770

Gentile, Jennifer, Set Decorators Society of America (SDSA), 7100 Tujunga Ave, Suite A, North Hollywood, CA 91605 *Tel:* 818-255-2425 *Fax:* 818-982-8597 *E-mail:* sdsa@setdecorators.org *Web Site:* www.setdecorators.org, pg 962

Gentilo, Bob, Right Coast Recording Inc, 341 Chestnut St, Columbia, PA 17512 *Tel:* 717-681-9801 *Fax:* 717-681-9801 *E-mail:* rightcoastrecording@gmail.com; studio@rightcoastrecording.com *Web Site:* www.rightcoastrecording.com, pg 875

Gentner, Russell, Listen Technologies Corp, 14912 Heritage Crest Way, Bluffdale, UT 84065-4818 *Tel:* 801-233-8992 *Toll Free Tel:* 800-330-0891 *Fax:* 801-233-8995 *E-mail:* info@listentech.com *Web Site:* www.listentech.com, pg 810

Gentzel, Thomas, National School Boards Association (NSBA), 1680 Duke St, 2nd fl, Alexandria, VA 22314-3493 *Tel:* 703-838-6722 *Fax:* 703-683-7590 *E-mail:* info@nsba.org *Web Site:* www.nsba.org, pg 959

Genzel, Michael, JSC Wire & Cable, 7861 Airport Hwy, Pennsauken, NJ 08109 *Tel:* 856-324-2929 *Toll Free Tel:* 800-572-9473 *E-mail:* sales@jscwire.com *Web Site:* www.jscwire.com, pg 795

Georg, Ole, OGM Production Music, 6464 Sunset Blvd, Suite 920, Hollywood, CA 90028 *Tel:* 323-461-2701 *Toll Free Tel:* 800-421-4163 (sales) *Fax:* 323-461-1543 *E-mail:* ogmmusic@gmail.com *Web Site:* www.olegeorgmusic.com, pg 844

George, Bobby, Spectrum Sound Inc, 1040 Acorn Dr, Suite C, Nashville, TN 37210 *Tel:* 615-391-3700 *Web Site:* www.spectrumsound.net, pg 897

George, Frankie, Pro HD Rentals, 2201 N Hollywood Way, Suite 1, Burbank, CA 91505 *Tel:* 818-450-1115 *Fax:* 818-450-1115 *E-mail:* sales@prohdrentals.com *Web Site:* www.prohdrentals.com, pg 863

George, J Richard, Wespen Audio Visual Co, 101 Riverside Dr, Hawthorn, PA 16230, pg 935

George, John M Sr, Morefield Communications Inc, 35 N 35 St, Camp Hill, PA 17011-2707 *Tel:* 717-761-6170 *Toll Free Tel:* 800-382-1266 *E-mail:* info@morefield.com *Web Site:* www.morefield.com, pg 830

George, Keith, Gaylord Archival, PO Box 4901, Syracuse, NY 13221-4901 *Tel:* 315-634-8125 (intl) *Toll Free Tel:* 800-448-6160 (cust serv) *Fax:* 315-453-5030 (intl) *Toll Free Fax:* 800-272-3412 *E-mail:* customerservice@gaylord.com *Web Site:* www.gaylord.com; www.facebook.com/gaylordarchival, pg 768

George, Scott M, Motion Picture Editors Guild Local 700, 7715 Sunset Blvd, Suite 200, Hollywood, CA 90046 *Tel:* 323-876-4770 *Toll Free Tel:* 800-705-8700 *Fax:* 323-876-0861 *E-mail:* mail@editorsguild.com *Web Site:* www.editorsguild.com, pg 958

George, Sylvia, RLJ Entertainment Inc, 8515 Georgia Ave, Suite 650, Silver Spring, MD 20910 *Tel:* 301-608-2115 *Toll Free Tel:* 800-999-0212 *E-mail:* inquiries@rljentertainment.com *Web Site:* www.us.rljentertainment.com, pg 875

George, Thomas A, Waterworks Acoustics Design Inc, 6465 Sierra Lane, Dublin, CA 94568, pg 934

Georgitis, Nathan, ARSC Awards for Excellence, 1299 University of Oregon, Eugene, OR 97403-1299 *Tel:* 541-346-1852 *Web Site:* www.arsc-audio.org, pg 981

Georgitis, Nathan, Association for Recorded Sound Collections (ARSC), 1299 University of Oregon, Eugene, OR 97403-1299 *Web Site:* www.arsc-audio.org, pg 950

Gerber, Annie, Hot Springs Documentary Film Festival, 659 Ouchita Ave, Hot Springs, AR 71901 *Tel:* 501-538-0452 *E-mail:* hsdfi@hsdfi.org *Web Site:* www.hsdfi.org, pg 992

Gerber, Candice, Atomic Imaging Inc/Golan Studios, 1501 N Magnolia Ave, Chicago, IL 60642 *Tel:* 312-649-1800 *Fax:* 312-642-7441 *Web Site:* www.atomicimaging.com, pg 692

Gerber, Jennifer, Hot Springs Documentary Film Festival, 659 Ouchita Ave, Hot Springs, AR 71901 *Tel:* 501-538-0452 *E-mail:* hsdfi@hsdfi.org *Web Site:* www.hsdfi.org, pg 992

Gerbes, Jack, Maryland Film Office, 401 E Pratt St, 14th fl, Baltimore, MD 21202 *Tel:* 410-767-6343 *Toll Free Tel:* 800-333-6632 *Fax:* 410-333-0044 *E-mail:* filminfo@marylandfilm.org *Web Site:* marylandfilm.org, pg 972

Gerding, Bob, The PPS Group, 424 Scott St, Covington, KY 41011 *Tel:* 859-291-5100 *Toll Free Tel:* 800-978-3445 *Fax:* 859-291-5150 *E-mail:* info@theppsgroup.com *Web Site:* www.pps-inc.com; www.theppsgroup.com, pg 860

Gerhart, Fred W, Impact Technology Group LLC, One Cardinal Rd, Unit 5, Hilton Head Island, SC 29926 *Toll Free Tel:* 800-675-2200 *Toll Free Fax:* 800-500-2565 *E-mail:* sales@impact-group.com *Web Site:* impact-group.com, pg 786

Germain, Kelly, Giant Screen Cinema Association (GSCA), 624 Holly Springs Rd, Suite 243, Holly Springs, NC 27540 Tel: 919-346-1123 Fax: 919-573-9100 E-mail: info@giantscreencinema.com Web Site: www.giantscreencinema.com, pg 955

Germaine, Derrick, Dake Publishing Inc, 764 Martins Chapel Rd, Lawrenceville, GA 30046 Toll Free Tel: 800-241-1239 E-mail: info@dake.com Web Site: www.dake.com, pg 737

Gerovitz, Lee, Clever Cleaver Productions, 7050 E Sunrise Dr, Suite 2101, Tucson, AZ 85750 Tel: 520-333-8403, pg 726

Gershfield, Jack, ALTINEX Inc, 592 Apollo St, Brea, CA 92821 Tel: 714-990-2300 Toll Free Tel: 800-ALTINEX (258-4639) Fax: 714-990-3303 E-mail: sales@altinex.com Web Site: www.altinex.com, pg 682

Gerstein, Frank, Westbury National Show Systems Ltd, 772 Warden Ave, Toronto, ON M1L 4T7, Canada Tel: 416-752-1371 Toll Free Tel: 855-752-1372 Fax: 416-752-1382 E-mail: info@westbury.com Web Site: www.westbury.com, pg 936

Gerstle, Tzvi, AbelCine, 801 S Main St, Burbank, CA 91506 Toll Free Tel: 888-700-4416 E-mail: orders@abelcine.com; customerservice@abelcine.com Web Site: www.abelcine.com, pg 672

Gerstman, Nancy, Zeitgeist Films Ltd, 333 W 39 St, New York, NY 10018 Tel: 212-274-1989 Fax: 212-714-0871 E-mail: mail@zeitgeistfilms.com Web Site: www.zeitgeistfilms.com, pg 945

Gertz, Paul, Network Entertainment Inc, 1488 Frances St, Vancouver, BC V5L 1Y9, Canada Tel: 604-739-8825 Fax: 604-739-8835 E-mail: info@networkentertainment.ca Web Site: www.networkentertainment.ca, pg 838

Gerwin, Shirley, Telemanagement Resources International Inc (TRI), 83 Harvey Cedar Way, Waretown, NJ 08758 Tel: 609-597-6334 Web Site: www.triinc.com, pg 910

Geschke, Dr Charles M, Adobe Systems Inc, 345 Park Ave, San Jose, CA 95110-2704 Tel: 408-536-6000 Fax: 408-537-6000 Web Site: www.adobe.com, pg 676

Gettinger, Daniel, M Schwartz & Gettinger Feather Inc, 45 Hoffman Ave, Hauppauge, NY 11788 Tel: 631-234-7722 Fax: 631-234-7817 E-mail: info@msgfeather.com Web Site: www.msgfeather.com, pg 882

Gewecke, Thomas, Warner Bros Entertainment Inc, 4000 Warner Blvd, Burbank, CA 91522 E-mail: wbsf@warnerbros.com Web Site: www.warnerbros.com/studio; studiofacilities.warnerbros.com, pg 934

Ghai, Rahul, Harris Corp, 1025 W NASA Blvd, Melbourne, FL 32919-0001 Tel: 321-727-9100 E-mail: webmaster@harris.com Web Site: www.harris.com, pg 776

Gharaee, Mustapha, Shanix Inc, 40 Worthington Rd, Cranston, RI 02920 Tel: 401-941-4222 Toll Free Tel: 800-783-2067 Fax: 401-941-4333 E-mail: info@shanix.com Web Site: www.shanix.com, pg 885

Ghareeb, Shirin, Washington DC International Film Festival, PO Box 21396, Washington, DC 20009-0896 Tel: 202-274-5782 Fax: 202-274-6690 E-mail: filmfestdc@filmfestdc.org Web Site: www.filmfestdc.org, pg 1006

Ghikas, Mary, American Library Association (ALA), 50 E Huron St, Chicago, IL 60611-2795 Tel: 312-944-6780 Toll Free Tel: 800-545-2433 Fax: 312-440-9374 E-mail: ala@ala.org Web Site: www.ala.org, pg 949

Ghosh, Dr Amal, eMagin Corp, 700 South Dr, Suite 201, Hopewell Junction, NY 12533 Tel: 845-838-7900 Fax: 845-838-7901 E-mail: info@emagin.com; sales@emagin.com; customersupport@emagin.com Web Site: www.emagin.com, pg 753

Ghosh, Bhaskar, Accenture, 161 N Clark St, Chicago, IL 60601 Tel: 312-693-0161 Toll Free Tel: 877-889-9009 Fax: 312-693-0507 Web Site: www.accenture.com, pg 672

Gianacoplos, Peter, USI Inc, 98 Fort Path Rd, Suite A, Madison, CT 06443 Tel: 203-245-8586 Toll Free Tel: 800-282-9290 Fax: 203-245-8619 E-mail: customers@usi-corp.com Web Site: www.usi-laminate.com, pg 924

Gianatasio, Henry J, Pres-On Corp, 2600 E 107 St, Bolingbrook, IL 60440 Toll Free Tel: 800-323-7467 Fax: 630-628-8025 E-mail: sales@preson.com Web Site: www.preson.com, pg 861

Giancola, David, Edgewood Studios, One Scale Ave, Suite 90, Unit 309, Bldg 3, Rutland, VT 05701 Tel: 802-773-0510 E-mail: flicks@edgewoodstudios.com Web Site: www.edgewoodstudios.com, pg 750

Giannini, Vincent, WPHL-TV, 5001 Wynnefield Ave, Philadelphia, PA 19131 Tel: 215-878-1700 E-mail: feedback@phl17.com Web Site: www.phl17.com, pg 942

Giannone, Ronald, FMP Media Solutions Inc, 3600 Horizon Dr, Suite 180, King of Prussia, PA 19406 Tel: 610-825-4000 Toll Free Tel: 800-346-5071 Fax: 610-825-4430 E-mail: info@fmpmedia.com Web Site: www.fmpmedia.com, pg 763

Giardina, Joe, DSI RF Systems Inc, 249 Homestead Rd, Hillsborough, NJ 08844 Tel: 732-563-1144 Fax: 732-563-1818 E-mail: sales@dsirf.com; info@dsirf.com Web Site: www.dsirf.com, pg 747

Giarratana, Deborah, Method Studios, 3401 Exposition Blvd, Santa Monica, CA 90404 Tel: 310-434-6000 Web Site: www.methodstudios.com, pg 824

Gibbons, Ed, Broadstreet Productions LLC, 242 W 30 St, 2nd fl, New York, NY 10001 Tel: 212-780-5700 E-mail: newyork@broadstreet.com; admin@broadstreet.com Web Site: www.broadstreet.com, pg 711

Gibbons, Sue, PolyScience, 6600 W Touhy Ave, Niles, IL 60714-4516 Tel: 847-647-0611 Toll Free Tel: 800-229-7569 Fax: 847-647-1155 E-mail: sales@polyscience.com Web Site: www.polyscience.com, pg 859

Gibbs, David, West Coast Projections Inc, 12463 Rancho Bernardo Rd, No 149, San Diego, CA 92128-2143 Tel: 858-674-7334 E-mail: wcpinfo@westcoastprojections.com Web Site: westcoastprojections.com, pg 935

Giboudeaux, Thomas, Festival du Nouveau Cinema de Montreal, 3805 Blvd Saint-Laurent, Montreal, QC H2W 1X9, Canada Tel: 514-282-0004 Fax: 514-282-6664 E-mail: info@nouveaucinema.ca; soumissions@nouveaucinema.ca Web Site: www.nouveaucinema.ca, pg 989

Gibson, Alex, Philadelphia Film Festival, 1412 Chestnut St, Philadelphia, PA 19102 Tel: 267-239-2941 E-mail: info@filmadelphia.org Web Site: filmadelphia.org/festival, pg 999

Gibson, Jack, Arizona Public Media, 1423 E University, MLB67, Rm 223, Tucson, AZ 85719 Tel: 520-621-5828; 520-621-5836 (sales) Fax: 520-621-3360 Web Site: www.azpm.org, pg 688

Gibson, Julie, Universal Studios Florida® Production Group, 1000 Universal Studios Plaza, Bldg 22A, Orlando, FL 32819 Tel: 407-363-8400 Toll Free Tel: 877-612-3737 (outside FL) Fax: 407-363-8869 E-mail: productiongroup@universalorlando.com Web Site: studio.florida.universalstudios.com, pg 922

Gibson, Oscar, Mardi Gras Costume Shop, 5895 N Granite Reef Rd, Scottsdale, AZ 85250 Tel: 480-948-4030 Fax: 480-948-0754 E-mail: info@mardigrascostumeshop.com Web Site: mardigrascostumeshop.com, pg 817

Gibson, Wendy, GES Audio Visual, 7000 Lindell Rd, Las Vegas, NV 89118 Tel: 702-515-5500 Fax: 702-515-5765 E-mail: lasvegas@ges.com; info@ges.com Web Site: ges.com, pg 770

Giella, Linda, Blue Sky Stock Footage, PO Box 177, Santa Fe, NM 87504-0177 Tel: 310-859-4709 E-mail: sales@blueskyfootage.com Web Site: www.blueskyfootage.com, pg 708

Gierl, John, NEP Group Inc, 2 Beta Dr, Pittsburgh, PA 15238 Tel: 412-826-1414 Toll Free Tel: 800-444-0054 E-mail: info@nepinc.com Web Site: www.nepgroup.com, pg 838

Gifford, Brian, Christie Digital Systems USA Inc, 10550 Camden Dr, Cypress, CA 90630 Tel: 714-236-8610 Toll Free Tel: 866-880-4462 (cust serv) Fax: 714-503-3375 E-mail: sales-us@christiedigital.com; orders@christiedigital.com Web Site: www.christiedigital.com, pg 722

Gifford, Carlyle, Avekta Productions Inc, One Rock Place, Yonkers, NY 10705 Tel: 914-378-8000 Web Site: avekta.com, pg 697

Gilbert, Brad, People Productions, 1737 15 St, Suite 200, Boulder, CO 80302 Tel: 303-449-6086 Fax: 303-449-9526 E-mail: info@peopleproductions.com Web Site: peopleproductions.com, pg 854

Gilbert, Chuck, Imagine Communications Corp, 3001 Dallas Pkwy, Suite 300, Frisco, TX 75034 Tel: 469-803-4900 Toll Free Tel: 866-4-IMAGINE (446-2446) Fax: 469-803-4899 E-mail: insidesales@imaginecommunications.com Web Site: www.imaginecommunications.com, pg 786

Gilbert, Kathleen, Vancouver Island South Film & Media Commission, 514 Government St, 2nd fl, Victoria, BC V8V 2L7, Canada Tel: 250-386-3976 Toll Free Tel: 888-537-3456 E-mail: admin@filmvictoria.com Web Site: www.filmvictoria.com, pg 978

Gilbert, Marcy, International Digital Centre, 216 E 45 St, 7th fl, New York, NY 10017 Tel: 212-581-3940 Fax: 212-581-3979 E-mail: info@idcdigital.com Web Site: www.idcdigital.com, pg 790

Gildea, Kelly, Penguin Random House Audio Publishing, 1745 Broadway, New York, NY 10019 E-mail: audio@penguinrandomhouse.com Web Site: www.penguinrandomhouseaudio.com, pg 853

Gildersleeve, Mark, The Weather Company, An IBM Business, 400 Minuteman Rd, Andover, MA 01810 Tel: 978-983-6300 Fax: 978-983-6400 Web Site: business.weather.com, pg 935

Giles, Betty H, Charles A Hulcher Co Inc, 909 "G" St, Hampton, VA 23661 Tel: 757-245-6190 Fax: 757-245-2882, pg 722

Gilgar, Stephanie, Method Studios, 3401 Exposition Blvd, Santa Monica, CA 90404 Tel: 310-434-6000 Web Site: www.methodstudios.com, pg 824

Gilkes, Greg, Panavid, 210 West Pkwy, Unit 5, Pompton Plains, NJ 07444 Tel: 973-831-5655 E-mail: info@panavid.com; support@panavid.com Web Site: www.panavid.com, pg 850

Gill, Jim, Jim Gill Music Inc, PO Box 2263, Oak Park, IL 60303-2263 Tel: 708-763-9864 Fax: 708-763-9888 Web Site: www.jimgill.com, pg 771

Gill, Sam, Prositions Inc, 6200 Aurora Ave, Suite 400W, Urbandale, IA 50322 Tel: 515-864-7200 Toll Free Tel: 877-244-8848 E-mail: info@prositions.com Web Site: prositions.com, pg 865

Gill, Scott, Chief, a Legrand AV Inc brand, 6436 City West Pkwy, Eden Prairie, MN 55344 Tel: 952-894-6280 Toll Free Tel: 866-977-3901 Toll Free Fax: 877-894-6918 E-mail: av.chief.support@legrand.com Web Site: www.legrandav.com/products/chief, pg 722

Gillen, Arlene, The Great Southern Studios, 15221 NE 21 Ave, North Miami Beach, FL 33162 Tel: 305-944-2464 Fax: 305-944-9920 E-mail: info@gssmiami.com Web Site: www.greatsouthernstudios.com, pg 773

Gillen, Phil, The Great Southern Studios, 15221 NE 21 Ave, North Miami Beach, FL 33162 Tel: 305-944-2464 Fax: 305-944-9920 E-mail: info@gssmiami.com Web Site: www.greatsouthernstudios.com, pg 774

Gillespie, Brett, Band Pro Film & Digital Inc, 3403 W Pacific Ave, Burbank, CA 91505 Tel: 818-841-9655 Toll Free Tel: 888-BANDPRO (226-3776) Fax: 818-841-7649 E-mail: info@bandpro.com; customercare@bandpro.com Web Site: www.bandpro.com, pg 701

Gillett, Dan, Moviola, 1135 N Mansfield Ave, Hollywood, CA 90038 *Tel:* 323-467-3107; 818-487-5000 *Toll Free Tel:* 877-MOVIOLA (668-4652) *Fax:* 323-464-1518 *Web Site:* www.moviola.com, pg 832

Gilliam, Brian, Adams Evidence Grade Technology Inc, 4123 N Little Creek Rd, Utopia, TX 78884 *Tel:* 830-966-4210 *Toll Free Tel:* 877-643-4900 *Fax:* 830-966-4214 *E-mail:* info1@evidencegrade.com; customerservice@evidencegrade.com *Web Site:* www.evidencegrade.com, pg 675

Gillio, Joseph, Casio America Inc, 570 Mount Pleasant Ave, Dover, NJ 07801 *Tel:* 973-361-5400 *Web Site:* www.casioprojector.com, pg 717

Gillis, Neil, Round Hill Music LLC, 400 Madison Ave, 18th fl, New York, NY 10017 *Tel:* 212-380-0080 *Fax:* 212-380-0081 *E-mail:* info@roundhillmusic.com *Web Site:* roundhillmusic.com, pg 878

Gillman, Bob, Videotex Systems Inc, 10255 Miller Rd, Dallas, TX 75238 *Tel:* 972-231-9200 *Toll Free Tel:* 800-88-VIDEO (888-4336) *Fax:* 972-231-2420 *E-mail:* info@videotexsystems.com *Web Site:* www.videotexsystems.com, pg 930

Gilman, John, ACS Technologies, 180 Dunbarton Dr, Florence, SC 29501 *Tel:* 800-736-7425 (sales); 800-669-2309 (support) *Fax:* 843-669-7513 *E-mail:* info@acstechnologies.com *Web Site:* www.acstechnologies.com, pg 674

Gilmore, Jericho, Sunset Bronson Studios, 5800 W Sunset Blvd, Hollywood, CA 90028 *Tel:* 323-460-5858 *Fax:* 323-460-3844 *E-mail:* reception@sunsetbronson.com *Web Site:* sgsandsbs.com, pg 904

Gilstrap, Mike, Dog & Pony Productions Inc, 8928 "L" St, Omaha, NE 68127 *Tel:* 402-391-7691 *Fax:* 402-341-2751 *E-mail:* dognponyinc@aol.com *Web Site:* www.dogandponyinc.com, pg 745

Gilstrap, Susan, Dog & Pony Productions Inc, 8928 "L" St, Omaha, NE 68127 *Tel:* 402-391-7691 *Fax:* 402-341-2751 *E-mail:* dognponyinc@aol.com *Web Site:* www.dogandponyinc.com, pg 745

Gimm, Kirsten, EPIX Inc, 381 Lexington Dr, Buffalo Grove, IL 60089 *Tel:* 847-465-1818 *Fax:* 847-465-1919 *E-mail:* epix@epixinc.com; orders@epixinc.com *Web Site:* epixinc.com, pg 755

Gini, Ken, ARC Document Solutions, 1981 N Broadway, Suite 385, Walnut Creek, CA 94596 *Tel:* 925-949-5100 *Toll Free Tel:* 855-500-0660 *E-mail:* contact@e-arc.com *Web Site:* www.e-arc.com, pg 688

Ginnane, Antony I, IFM World Releasing Inc, 1328 E Palmer Ave, Glendale, CA 91205 *Tel:* 818-243-4976 *Fax:* 818-550-9728 *E-mail:* contact@ifmfilm.com *Web Site:* www.ifmfilm.com, pg 784

Ginopulos, Jim, Paramount Pictures Corporation, 5555 Melrose Ave, Los Angeles, CA 90038 *Tel:* 323-956-8398 *Web Site:* www.paramount.com, pg 851

Ginsburg, Fred, Film TV Sound, PO Box 950207, Mission Hills, CA 91395-0207 *Tel:* 818-231-1038 *Fax:* 818-892-9236 *E-mail:* editorial@filmtvsound.com; eqe-media@filmtvsound.com *Web Site:* www.filmtvsound.com, pg 760

Giordano, Don, Entel Systems Inc, 230 W Parkway, Pompton Plains, NJ 07444 *Tel:* 201-447-2000 *Toll Free Tel:* 888-914-7100 *Fax:* 201-447-2880 *E-mail:* service@entelsystems.com *Web Site:* www.entelsystems.com, pg 754

Giordano, Julie, JENSEN Tools + Supply, 335 Willow St, North Andover, MA 01845-5995 *Tel:* 978-682-9844 *Toll Free Tel:* 800-225-5370 (sales) *Toll Free Fax:* 800-743-8141 *E-mail:* sales@sbdinc.com *Web Site:* www.jensentools.com, pg 793

Giraudi, Patrick, VirtualMix, 701 S Carson St, Suite 200-2914, Carson City, NV 89701 *Tel:* 818-209-6176 *E-mail:* virtualmixpost@gmail.com *Web Site:* www.virtualmix.com, pg 930

Gire, Dann, Chicago Film Critics Association, 155 E Algonquin Rd, Arlington Heights, IL 60006 *Tel:* 847-427-4530 *Fax:* 847-427-1301 *Web Site:* chicagofilmcritics.org, pg 953

Girot, Kaly Minh-Nguyen, Sand Box Studio, 555 Minnesota St, San Francisco, CA 94107 *Tel:* 415-550-8732 *E-mail:* inquiries@sandboxstudio.com *Web Site:* www.sandboxstudio.com, pg 880

Giroux, Dominique, Vital Learning LLC, 3001 Brighton Blvd, Suite 2765, Denver, CO 80216 *Toll Free Tel:* 800-243-5858 *E-mail:* support@vital-learning.com; info@vital-learning.com *Web Site:* www.vital-learning.com, pg 932

Gisby, Jon, WildBrain™, 5657 Spring Garden Rd, Suite 505, Halifax, NS B3J 3R4, Canada *Tel:* 902-423-0260 *Fax:* 902-422-0752 *E-mail:* info@wildbrain.com; halifax@wildbrain.com; sales@wildbrain.com *Web Site:* www.wildbrain.com, pg 938

Gish, Ross, Big Event Productions LLC, 77 13 Ave NE, Studio 101, Minneapolis, MN 55413 *Tel:* 612-623-7800 *Web Site:* www.bigeventpros.com, pg 705

Gittens, Anthony, Washington DC International Film Festival, PO Box 21396, Washington, DC 20009-0896 *Tel:* 202-274-5782 *Fax:* 202-274-6690 *E-mail:* filmfestdc@filmfestdc.org *Web Site:* www.filmfestdc.org, pg 1006

Giunta, Emily, Central Lighting & Equipment Inc (CLE), 4103 E 16 St, Des Moines, IA 50313 *Tel:* 515-277-4190 *Toll Free Tel:* 877-977-4190 *Fax:* 515-277-2295 *E-mail:* info@cleproductions.com *Web Site:* cleproductions.com, pg 719

Givens, John, Small World Productions Inc, 140 Lakeside Ave, Suite 200, Seattle, WA 98122 *Tel:* 206-329-7167 *Toll Free Tel:* 800-866-7425 (orders); 800-325-7111 (cust serv) *Fax:* 206-329-0269 (credit card orders) *E-mail:* info@travelsmallworld.com; customercare@smarttravels.tv *Web Site:* www.smarttravels.tv, pg 890

Givens, R J, Pyxis Industries Inc, 25695 Jefferson Ave, Suite 8, Murrieta, CA 92562 *Tel:* 951-526-1999 *Toll Free Tel:* 888-PYXISAN (799-4728) *Fax:* 951-253-9290 *Web Site:* pyxisindustries.com, pg 867

Givner-Klein, Nan, TeleTime Productions, 7 Willow Rd, Lynbrook, NY 11563 *Tel:* 516-255-8383 *Web Site:* www.teletimevideo.com, pg 910

Gladstone, Judy, Documentary Organization of Canada, Centre for Social Innovation, 215 Spadina Ave, Suite 126, Toronto, ON M5T 2C7, Canada *Tel:* 416-599-3844 *Fax:* 877-467-4485 *E-mail:* info@docorg.ca *Web Site:* docorg.ca, pg 954

Glanz, Mark, Glanz Technologies Inc, 687 NE 124 St, North Miami, FL 33161 *Tel:* 305-893-1269 *Fax:* 305-899-8526 *E-mail:* mglanz@glanztech.com *Web Site:* www.glanztechnologies.com, pg 771

Glasband, Martin, Equi=Tech Corp, PO Box 249, Selma, OR 97538-0249 *Tel:* 541-218-6900 (tech support, cust serv); 541-291-9253 *Toll Free Tel:* 877-EQUITECH (378-4832) *Fax:* 541-787-8740 *E-mail:* sales@equitech.com; customerservice@equitech.com; marketing@equitech.com *Web Site:* www.equitech.com, pg 755

Glaser, Harrison, Austin Film Festival, 1801 Salina St, Austin, TX 78702 *Tel:* 512-478-4795 *Toll Free Tel:* 800-310-FEST (310-3378) *Fax:* 512-478-6205 *E-mail:* info@austinfilmfestival.com; programming@austinfilmfestival.com; marketing@austinfilmfestival.com *Web Site:* www.austinfilmfestival.com, pg 982

Glasofer, David, Image Up Studio, 295 Pierson Ave, Suite 103, Edison, NJ 08837 *Tel:* 732-549-1845 *Web Site:* www.imageup.com, pg 785

Glass, Murray, Em Gee Film Library, 13502 Erwin St, Van Nuys, CA 91401 *Tel:* 818-997-0410, pg 753

Glass, Murray, Glenn Photo Supply, 13502 Erwin St, Van Nuys, CA 91401 *Tel:* 818-997-0410 *Web Site:* www.emgee.freeyellow.com, pg 771

Glass, Murray, Glenn Video Vistas Ltd, 13502 Erwin St, Van Nuys, CA 91401 *Tel:* 818-997-0410 *Web Site:* www.emgee.freeyellow.com, pg 771

Glavin, Lisanne, PixeLINK, 1900 City Park Dr, Suite 410, Ottawa, ON K1J 1A3, Canada *Tel:* 613-247-1211 *Fax:* 613-247-2001 *E-mail:* sales@pixelink.com *Web Site:* www.pixelink.com, pg 857

Glaysher, Monica, Moving Picture, 748 N Victoria Park Rd, Fort Lauderdale, FL 33304 *Tel:* 954-522-1361 *Toll Free Tel:* 800-800-1361 *Fax:* 954-523-1361 *E-mail:* info@movingpicture.com *Web Site:* www.movingpicture.com, pg 831

Glaza, Ken, Digi Sign Design LLC, 28533 Greenfield Rd, Southfield, MI 48076 *Web Site:* www.digisigndesign.com, pg 741

Glaza, Ken, K&R All Media Productions LLC, 28533 Greenfield Rd, Southfield, MI 48076 *Tel:* 248-557-8276 *Web Site:* www.knr.net, pg 796

Glaza, Kenneth, K&R's Recording Studios Inc, 28533 Greenfield, Southfield, MI 48076 *Tel:* 248-557-8276; 248-569-5422 *Web Site:* www.knr.net; www.kandrforensic.com, pg 796

Glaza, Kenneth, Michigan Recording Arts Institute & Technologies, 28533 Greenfield, Southfield, MI 48076 *Tel:* 248-569-5422 *Web Site:* mirecordingarts.com, pg 825

Glazier, Mitch, Recording Industry Association of America® (RIAA), 1025 "F" St NW, 10th fl, Washington, DC 20004 *Tel:* 202-775-0101 *Web Site:* www.riaa.com, pg 961

Glazier, Mitch, The RIAA® Gold® & Platinum® Awards, 1025 "F" St NW, 10th fl, Washington, DC 20004 *Tel:* 202-775-0101 *Web Site:* www.riaa.com/gold-platinum, pg 1001

Gleadall, Robin, YAP Films, 233 Broadview Ave, Toronto, ON M4M 2G3, Canada *Tel:* 416-504-3662 *Fax:* 416-504-3667 *E-mail:* thedog@yapfilms.com *Web Site:* www.yapfilms.com, pg 943

Glembocki, Jerry, Avaya Inc, 4655 Great American Pkwy, Santa Clara, CA 95054 *Tel:* 908-953-6000 *Toll Free Tel:* 866-GO-AVAYA (462-8292 US & CN) *Web Site:* www.avaya.com, pg 697

Glenday, Lucy, Moxie Media, 1301 Dealers Ave, New Orleans, LA 70123 *Tel:* 504-733-6907 *Toll Free Tel:* 800-346-6943 *Fax:* 504-733-9493 *E-mail:* info@moxiemedia.com *Web Site:* www.moxietraining.com; www.moxiemedia.com, pg 832

Glenday, Martin, Moxie Media, 1301 Dealers Ave, New Orleans, LA 70123 *Tel:* 504-733-6907 *Toll Free Tel:* 800-346-6943 *Fax:* 504-733-9493 *E-mail:* info@moxiemedia.com *Web Site:* www.moxietraining.com; www.moxiemedia.com, pg 832

Gloor, Storm, Music & Entertainment Industry Educators Association (MEIEA), 1900 Belmont Blvd, Nashville, TN 37212-3758 *Tel:* 615-460-6946 *E-mail:* office@meiea.org; membership@meiea.org *Web Site:* www.meiea.org, pg 958

Glover, Josh, Penguin Random House Canada, 320 Front St W, Suite 1400, Toronto, ON M5V 3B6, Canada *Tel:* 416-364-4449 *Toll Free Tel:* 888-523-9292 (cust serv) *Fax:* 416-598-7764 *E-mail:* customerservicescanada@penguinrandomhouse.com *Web Site:* www.penguinrandomhouse.ca, pg 853

Gluckman, Lee W Jr, The Mobius® Awards, 713 S Pacific Coast Hwy, Suite A, Redondo Beach, CA 90277-4233 *Tel:* 310-540-0959 *Fax:* 310-316-8905 *E-mail:* mobiusinfo@mobiusawards.com; mediarelations@mobiusawards.com *Web Site:* mobiusawards.com, pg 996

Gluckman, Lee W Jr, Producers Group Ltd, 713 S Pacific Coast Hwy, Suite B, Redondo Beach, CA 90277-4233 *Tel:* 310-316-0481 *Web Site:* www.producers-group.tv, pg 863

Gluckman, Lee W Jr, US International Film & Video Festival, 713 S Pacific Coast Hwy, Suite A, Redondo Beach, CA 90277-4233 *Tel:* 310-540-0959 *Fax:* 310-316-8905 *E-mail:* filmfestinfo@filmfestawards.com; mediarelations@filmfestawards.com *Web Site:* www.filmfestawards.com, pg 1005

Glusic, Robert, Wilderness Video, 1110 Barrington Circle, Ashland, OR 97520 *Tel:* 541-488-9363 *Web Site:* www.wildernessvideo.com, pg 938

Glynn, John II, NRD Static Control LLC, 2937 Alt Blvd, Grand Island, NY 14072-1285 *Tel:* 716-773-7634 *Toll Free Tel:* 800-525-8076 (US only) *E-mail:* sales@nrdllc.com *Web Site:* www.nrdstaticcontrol.com, pg 843

Gnanasihamany, Lucille, Thompson Rivers University Marketing & Communications Dept, 805 TRU Way, Kamloops, BC V2C 0C8, Canada *Tel:* 250-852-7000 *Web Site:* www.tru.ca/marcom, pg 913

Gobey, Jennifer, Essex Television Group Inc, 7 Vista Dr, Old Lyme, CT 06371 *Tel:* 860-434-7200 *Fax:* 860-434-7210 *E-mail:* contact@essextelevision.com *Web Site:* www.essextelevision.com, pg 755

Goddard, Bob, Goddard Design Co, 51 Nassau Ave, Brooklyn, NY 11222 *Tel:* 718-599-0170 *Fax:* 718-599-0172 *E-mail:* sales@goddarddesign.com *Web Site:* www.goddarddesign.com, pg 772

Goddard, Doug, Gamma Imaging, 222 N DesPlaines St, Chicago, IL 60661 *Tel:* 312-441-0091 *Toll Free Tel:* 877-441-4830 *Fax:* 312-441-0092 *E-mail:* digital@gammaimaging.com *Web Site:* gammaimaging.com, pg 768

Goddard, Jeffery, TVA Media Group, 3950 Vantage Ave, Studio City, CA 91604 *Tel:* 818-505-8300 *Toll Free Tel:* 888-322-4296 *E-mail:* info@tvamediagroup.com *Web Site:* www.tvamediagroup.com, pg 919

Godfrey, Stephen, FutureVideo, 28202 Cabot Rd, Suite 300, Laguna Niguel, CA 92677 *Tel:* 949-363-1686 *Toll Free Fax:* 866-261-1686 *E-mail:* sales@futurevideo.com *Web Site:* www.futurevideo.com; www.futurevideo.tv, pg 767

Godfrey, Will Daniel, The Godfrey Group Inc, 113 Roseroot Ct, Holly Springs, NC 27540 *Tel:* 919-544-6504 *Toll Free Tel:* 800-789-9394 *E-mail:* sales@godfreygroup.com *Web Site:* www.godfreygroup.com, pg 772

Godfrey, Wyck, Temple Hill Entertainment, 9255 W Sunset Blvd, West Hollywood, CA 90069 *Tel:* 310-270-4383 *Fax:* 310-270-4395 *Web Site:* twitter.com/TempleHillEnt, pg 911

Goeckner, Gregory, Golden Globe Awards, 646 N Robertson Blvd, West Hollywood, CA 90069 *Tel:* 310-657-1731 *Fax:* 310-657-5576 *E-mail:* awards@goldenglobes.com *Web Site:* www.goldenglobes.com, pg 990

Goedde, Jennifer, Calculated Industries Inc, 4840 Hytech Dr, Carson City, NV 89706 *Tel:* 775-885-4900 *Toll Free Tel:* 800-854-8075 *Fax:* 775-885-4949 *E-mail:* info@calculated.com *Web Site:* www.calculated.com, pg 714

Goedert, Benjamin, Santa Barbara International Film Festival, 1528 Chapala St, Suite 203, Santa Barbara, CA 93101 *Tel:* 805-963-0023 *Fax:* 805-962-2524 *E-mail:* contactus@sbiff.org *Web Site:* sbiff.org, pg 1003

Goel, Tanmay, Xytech Systems Corp, 15451 San Fernando Mission Blvd, Suite 400, Mission Hills, CA 91345 *Tel:* 818-698-4900 *Fax:* 818-698-4901 *E-mail:* sales@xytechsystems.com *Web Site:* www.xytechsystems.com, pg 943

Goelzhauser, Nicola, WPA Film Library, 16101 S 108 Ave, Orland Park, IL 60467 *Tel:* 708-460-0555 *Toll Free Tel:* 800-323-0442 *Fax:* 708-460-0187 *E-mail:* sales@wpafilmlibrary.com *Web Site:* www.wpafilmlibrary.com, pg 942

Goff, Jon-Sesrie, Robert Flaherty Film Seminar, 6 E 39 St, 12th fl, New York, NY 10016 *Tel:* 212-448-0457 *Fax:* 212-448-0458 *E-mail:* ifs@flahertyseminar.org *Web Site:* flahertyseminar.org, pg 989

Goff, Justin, Innocinema, 1351 Oakbrook Dr, Suite 160, Norcross, GA 30093 *Tel:* 770-857-3435 *E-mail:* info@innocinema.com; rentals@innocinema.com; support@innocinema.com *Web Site:* www.innocinema.com, pg 788

Goforth-Hanak, Yvonne, KEF Media, 1161 Concord Rd SE, Smyrna, GA 30080 *Tel:* 404-605-0009 *E-mail:* info@kefmedia.com *Web Site:* kefmedia.com, pg 797

Goicoechea, Barbara, ACT Productions, 407 Lincoln Rd, Suite 302, Miami Beach, FL 33139 *Tel:* 305-538-3809 *Fax:* 305-538-3814 *E-mail:* info@actproductions.com *Web Site:* www.actproductions.com, pg 675

Goiffon, Rene, Harmonia Mundi USA, 1117 Chestnut St, Burbank, CA 91506 *Tel:* 818-333-1500 *E-mail:* info-usa@harmoniamundi.com *Web Site:* www.harmoniamundi.com, pg 776

Goitiandia, Ray, Kino Flo Lighting Systems, 2840 N Hollywood Way, Burbank, CA 91505 *Tel:* 818-767-6528 *Fax:* 818-252-0290 (rental); 818-767-7517 (sales) *E-mail:* sales@kinoflo.com *Web Site:* www.kinoflo.com, pg 799

Goke, Greg, Event Essentials, 6485 Blanchar's Crossing, Windsor, WI 53598 *Tel:* 608-846-5004 *Toll Free Tel:* 800-220-4991 *Fax:* 608-222-5063 *Web Site:* www.eventessentials.com, pg 756

Gokhale, Ajit, National Instruments Corp, 11500 N Mopac Expwy, Austin, TX 78759-3504 *Tel:* 512-683-0100 *Toll Free Tel:* 888-280-7645 (sales); 877-388-1952 *Fax:* 512-683-8411; 512-683-5794 (sales) *Web Site:* www.ni.com, pg 836

Golan, Ari, Atomic Imaging Inc/Golan Studios, 1501 N Magnolia Ave, Chicago, IL 60642 *Tel:* 312-649-1800 *Fax:* 312-642-7441 *Web Site:* www.atomicimaging.com, pg 692

Goldberg, Bruce, Bruce Goldberg Inc, 5354 Quakertown Ave, Woodland Hills, CA 91364 *Tel:* 818-713-8190 *Toll Free Tel:* 800-527-6248 *Fax:* 818-704-9189 *E-mail:* drbg@sbcglobal.net *Web Site:* www.drbrucegoldberg.com, pg 772

Goldberg, David H, Lee Dan® Communications Inc, 155 Adams Ave, Hauppauge, NY 11788-3699 *Tel:* 631-231-1414 *Toll Free Tel:* 800-231-1414 *Fax:* 631-231-1498 *E-mail:* info@leedan.com *Web Site:* www.leedan.com, pg 805

Goldberg, Larry, Lee Dan® Communications Inc, 155 Adams Ave, Hauppauge, NY 11788-3699 *Tel:* 631-231-1414 *Toll Free Tel:* 800-231-1414 *Fax:* 631-231-1498 *E-mail:* info@leedan.com *Web Site:* www.leedan.com, pg 805

Goldberg, Mark, Spectrum Productions, 565 Pinedale Dr, Annapolis, MD 21401 *Web Site:* www.markgoldberg.com, pg 897

Goldberg, Mike, IMP Digital Studios, A PharmaSphere Company, 120 Rte 17N, Paramus, NJ 07652 *Tel:* 201-261-3959 *E-mail:* info@impdigital.us *Web Site:* impdigital.us; www.facebook.com/impdigital, pg 786

Goldberg, Neil, Heavy Melody, 307 Seventh Ave, Suite 1203, New York, NY 10001 *Tel:* 212-675-9585 *Fax:* 212-675-9565 *E-mail:* contact_hm@heavymelodymusic.com (studio inquiries) *Web Site:* www.heavymelodymusic.com, pg 778

Goldberg, Ron, Manhattan Production Music Inc, 1650 Broadway, Suite 900, New York, NY 10019 *Tel:* 212-333-5766 *Fax:* 212-262-0814 *E-mail:* info@mpmmusic.com *Web Site:* www.mpmmusic.com, pg 816

Golden, Arlin, The Video Project, 145 Ninth St, Suite 102, San Francisco, CA 94103 *Tel:* 415-981-9710 *Toll Free Tel:* 800-475-2638 *Fax:* 415-692-6223 *E-mail:* orders@videoproject.com; support@videoproject.com *Web Site:* www.videoproject.com, pg 928

Golden, Barbara, St Augustine, Ponte Vedra & The Beaches Visitors and Convention Bureau, 29 Old Mission Ave, St Augustine, FL 32084 *Tel:* 904-829-1711 *Toll Free Tel:* 800-653-2489 *Web Site:* www.floridashistoriccoast.com, pg 970

Goldin, Laurence, Aurora Films, 324 E Dowling Rd, Suite 4, Anchorage, AK 99518 *Tel:* 907-258-4686 *E-mail:* aurorafilms@gci.net, pg 696

Golding, Emily, Anchor Audio Inc, 5931 Darwin Ct, Carlsbad, CA 92008 *Tel:* 760-827-7100 *Toll Free Tel:* 800-262-4671 *Fax:* 760-827-7105 *E-mail:* sales@anchoraudio.com *Web Site:* www.anchoraudio.com, pg 685

Goldman, Eric, Ergo Media Inc, 668 American Legion Dr, Teaneck, NJ 07666 *Tel:* 201-692-0404 *Fax:* 201-692-0663 *E-mail:* info@jewishvideo.com *Web Site:* www.jewishvideo.com, pg 755

Goldman, Nicole, The Jim Henson Co, 1416 N La Brea Ave, Hollywood, CA 90028 *Tel:* 323-802-1500 *Fax:* 323-802-1825 *Web Site:* www.henson.com, pg 794

Goldner, Phillip, A&I - Fine Art & Photography, 6844 Vineland Ave, North Hollywood, CA 91605 *Tel:* 818-848-9001 *E-mail:* support@aandi.com *Web Site:* www.aandi.com, pg 671

Goldsmith, Karl, Rochester/Finger Lakes Film Commission, 45 East Ave, Suite 400, Rochester, NY 14604-2294 *Tel:* 585-279-8308 *Fax:* 585-232-4822 *Web Site:* www.filmrochester.org, pg 974

Goldsmith, Richard, The Jim Henson Co, 1416 N La Brea Ave, Hollywood, CA 90028 *Tel:* 323-802-1500 *Fax:* 323-802-1825 *Web Site:* www.henson.com, pg 794

Goldstein, Dan, Audiovisual and Integrated Experience Association (AVIXA), 11242 Waples Mill Rd, Suite 200, Fairfax, VA 22030 *Tel:* 703-273-7200 *Toll Free Tel:* 800-659-7469 *E-mail:* membership@avixa.org *Web Site:* www.avixa.org, pg 951

Goldstein, Holly, Thread Marketing Group, 4635 W Alexis Rd, Toledo, OH 43623-1005 *Tel:* 419-887-6801 *Fax:* 419-887-6802 *E-mail:* info@threadgroup.com *Web Site:* www.threadgroup.com, pg 913

Goldstein, Jeremy, Navitar Inc, 200 Commerce Dr, Rochester, NY 14623 *Tel:* 585-359-4000 *Toll Free Tel:* 800-828-6778 *Fax:* 585-359-4999 *E-mail:* info@navitar.com *Web Site:* www.navitar.com, pg 837

Goldstein, Julian, Navitar Inc, 200 Commerce Dr, Rochester, NY 14623 *Tel:* 585-359-4000 *Toll Free Tel:* 800-828-6778 *Fax:* 585-359-4999 *E-mail:* info@navitar.com *Web Site:* www.navitar.com, pg 837

Goldstein, Robert, Maryland Sound International Holding Co LLC, 4900 Wetheredsville Rd, Baltimore, MD 21207 *Tel:* 410-448-1400 *Toll Free Tel:* 800-76SOUND (767-6863) *Fax:* 410-448-1467 *E-mail:* martha@msihc.com *Web Site:* www.marylandsound.com, pg 819

Goldstein, Samuel, B&H Photo Video, 420 Ninth Ave, New York, NY 10001 *Tel:* 212-444-5000; 212-444-6615 *Toll Free Tel:* 800-606-6969 *Fax:* 212-239-7770 *Toll Free Fax:* 800-947-7008 *Web Site:* www.bhphotovideo.com, pg 701

Goldstein, Sheldon "Shelly", Vcom IMC, 80 Little Falls Rd, Fairfield, NJ 07004 *Toll Free Tel:* 800-572-6373 *E-mail:* info@vcomimc.com *Web Site:* www.vcomimc.com, pg 925

Goldstein, Shelly, Alltec Stores, a Vcom IMC Company, 80 Little Falls Rd, Fairfield, NJ 07004 *Toll Free Tel:* 800-637-3181 *Toll Free Fax:* 800-965-7836 *E-mail:* sales@alltecstores.com *Web Site:* www.alltecstores.com, pg 681

Goldthwaite, Meg, National Public Radio (NPR), 1111 N Capitol St NE, Washington, DC 20002 *Tel:* 202-513-2000 *Web Site:* www.npr.org, pg 959

Goldworth, Philip, Pacific Light Studios, 265 Caspian Dr, Sunnyvale, CA 94089 *Tel:* 408-541-1800 *E-mail:* info1@pacificlightstudios.com *Web Site:* www.pacificlightstudios.com, pg 849

Golesh, John, Goldberg Brothers Inc, 10488 W Centennial Rd, Suite 100, Littleton, CO 80127 *Tel:* 303-321-1099 *E-mail:* reelservice@goldbergbrothers.com *Web Site:* www.goldbergbrothers.com, pg 772

Golin, Steve, Anonymous Content, 3532 Hayden Ave, Culver City, CA 90232 *Tel:* 310-558-6000 *Fax:* 310-558-2724 *E-mail:* filmtv@anonymouscontent.com *Web Site:* www.anonymouscontent.com, pg 686

Golombek, Fabio, FJ Productions Inc, 14900 Ventura Blvd, Suite 350, Sherman Oaks, CA 91403-3465 *Tel:* 818-788-0153 *E-mail:* contact@fjproductions.com *Web Site:* www.fjproductions.com, pg 762

Golson, Eva H, Mobile Film Office, 164 Saint Emanuel St, Mobile, AL 36602 *Tel:* 251-438-7102 *Fax:* 251-438-7104 *Web Site:* www.mobilefilmoffice.com, pg 965

Gomez, Emilio, Sierra Automated Systems, 2821 Burton Ave, Burbank, CA 91504 *Tel:* 818-840-6749 *Fax:* 818-840-6751 *E-mail:* sales@sasaudio.com; marketing@ sasaudio.com *Web Site:* www.sasaudio.com, pg 887

Gomez, Terry, Questar Entertainment Inc, 307 N Michigan Ave, 5th fl, Chicago, IL 60601-5305 *Tel:* 312-266-9400 *Toll Free Tel:* 800-544-8422 (cust serv) *E-mail:* info@questarentertainment.com *Web Site:* www.questarentertainment.com, pg 868

Gomila, Cristina, Technicolor USA Inc, 6040 Sunset Blvd, Hollywood, CA 90028 *Tel:* 323-817-6600 *E-mail:* info@technicolor.com *Web Site:* www. technicolor.com, pg 908

Gong, Stephen, Center for Asian American Media (CAAM), 145 Ninth St, Suite 350, San Francisco, CA 94103 *Tel:* 415-863-0814 *Fax:* 415-863-7428 *E-mail:* publicity@caamedia.org *Web Site:* caamedia. org, pg 953

Gonter, Paul, Chicago International Children's Film Festival, 1517 W Fullerton Ave, Chicago, IL 60614 *Tel:* 773-281-9075 (ext 3011) *Fax:* 773-929-0266 *E-mail:* filmreg@facets.org; press@facets.org *Web Site:* festival.facets.org, pg 985

Gonter, Paul, Facets Multi-Media Inc, 1517 W Fullerton Ave, Chicago, IL 60614 *Tel:* 773-281-9075 *Fax:* 773-929-5437 *E-mail:* sales@facets.org; press@facets.org *Web Site:* www.facets.org, pg 758

Gonzales, Jarryd, Alliance of Motion Picture & Television Producers (AMPTP), 15301 Ventura Blvd, Bldg E, Sherman Oaks, CA 91403 *Tel:* 818-995-3600 *Fax:* 818-285-4450 *Web Site:* www.amptp.org, pg 947

Gonzalez, Alex, Techni-Lux Inc, 10900 Palmbay Dr, Orlando, FL 32824 *Tel:* 407-857-8770 *Fax:* 407-857-8771 *E-mail:* sales@techni-lux.com *Web Site:* www. techni-lux.com, pg 908

Goodman, David A, Writers Guild of America, West (WGAW), 7000 W Third St, Los Angeles, CA 90048 *Tel:* 323-951-4000 *Toll Free Tel:* 800-548-4532 *Web Site:* www.wga.org, pg 963

Goodman, Jeff, Producers Library, 10832 Chandler Blvd, North Hollywood, CA 91601 *Tel:* 818-752-9097 *E-mail:* research@producerslibrary.com *Web Site:* www.producerslibrary.com, pg 863

Goodman, Jennifer, Sony Music Commercial Music Group, 550 Madison Ave, New York, NY 10022 *Tel:* 212-833-8000 *Web Site:* www.sonymusic.com, pg 893

Goodman, Marcie, Cleveland International Film Festival, 2510 Market Ave, Cleveland, OH 44113-3434 *Tel:* 216-623-3456 *Fax:* 216-623-0103 *E-mail:* cfs@ clevelandfilm.org; submissions@clevelandfilm.org *Web Site:* www.clevelandfilm.org, pg 986

Goodman, Ron, SpaceCam, 31240 La Baya Dr, Westlake Village, CA 91362 *Tel:* 818-889-6060 *Fax:* 818-889-6062 *E-mail:* rentals@spacecam.com *Web Site:* spacecam.com, pg 896

Goodman, Will, Guidance Associates Inc Center for Humanities, 31 Pine View Rd, Mount Kisco, NY 10549 *Tel:* 914-420-2363 *Toll Free Tel:* 800-431-1242 *Fax:* 914-666-5319 *Web Site:* www.guidanceassociates. com, pg 774

Goodnight, Emily, The House Studios, 325 Second Ave W, Seattle, WA 98119 *Tel:* 206-724-6639 *E-mail:* book@thehousestudios.com *Web Site:* thehousestudios.com, pg 782

Goodnight, Jim, SAS Institute Inc, 100 SAS Campus Dr, Cary, NC 27513-2414 *Tel:* 919-677-8000 *Toll Free Tel:* 800-727-0025 *Fax:* 919-677-4444 *Web Site:* www. sas.com, pg 880

Goodnough, Joshua, Cine-World Film Festival, 10715 Rodeo Dr, Suite 8, Lakewood Ranch, FL 34202 *Tel:* 941-364-8478 *Fax:* 941-364-8478 *E-mail:* mail@ filmsociety.org *Web Site:* www.filmsociety.org, pg 986

Goodwin, Jason, Print Industries Market Information and Research Organization (PRIMIR), 1899 Preston White Dr, Reston, VA 20191 *Tel:* 703-264-7200 *Fax:* 703-620-0994 *Web Site:* www.primir.org, pg 960

Goodwin, Randy, PRI Productions, 1819 Kings Ave, Jacksonville, FL 32207 *Tel:* 904-398-8179 *E-mail:* info@priproductions.com *Web Site:* www. priproductions.com, pg 862

Goodwyn, Bill, Discovery Education Inc, 230 Park Ave S, New York, NY 10003 *Toll Free Tel:* 800-323-9084 *Toll Free Fax:* 855-495-6542 *E-mail:* education_info@ discoveryed.com *Web Site:* www.discoveryeducation. com, pg 743

Gopalan, Anand, Velodyne LiDAR Inc, 5521 Hellyer Ave, San Jose, CA 95738 *Tel:* 408-465-2800 *Fax:* 408-779-9208 (cust serv); 408-779-9377 (orders) *E-mail:* lidar@velodyne.com *Web Site:* velodynelidar. com, pg 925

Gorchow, Jon, NatureVision Stock Footage Library, 4407 67 Ave Circle E, Sarasota, FL 34243 *Tel:* 856-873-6546 *Toll Free Tel:* 877-327-3207 *Web Site:* www. naturevisiontv.com, pg 837

Gorchow, Jon, NatureVision TV, 4407 67 Ave Circle E, Sarasota, FL 34243 *Tel:* 856-873-6546 *Toll Free Tel:* 877-327-3207 *Web Site:* www.naturevisiontv.com, pg 837

Gordon, Betty, DW Electrochemicals Ltd, 3-97 Newkirk Rd N, Richmond Hill, ON L4C 3G4, Canada *Tel:* 905-508-7500 *Fax:* 905-508-7502 *E-mail:* dwel@ stabilant.com *Web Site:* www.stabilant.com, pg 748

Gordon, Fredda, Professional Women Photographers (PWP), 119 W 72 St, Suite 223, New York, NY 10023 *E-mail:* pwp@pwponline.org *Web Site:* www. pwponline.org, pg 961

Gordon, Gregory, Pyramind Studios, 2727 Mariposa St, Suite 200, San Francisco, CA 94110 *Tel:* 415-896-9800 (ext 200) *Web Site:* www.pyramind.com, pg 867

Gordon, John T, Gordon Productions Inc, 469 Magellan Ave, San Francisco, CA 94116 *Tel:* 415-776-7484 *Web Site:* www.gpvideo.com; www.vimeo.com/ gordonproductions, pg 772

Gordon, Marc, Otto Nemenz International Inc, 870 N Vine St, Los Angeles, CA 90038 *Tel:* 323-469-2774 *Fax:* 323-469-1217 *E-mail:* info@ottonemenz.com *Web Site:* www.ottonemenz.com, pg 838

Gordon, Nancy, HAVE Inc, 309 Power Ave, Hudson, NY 12534 *Tel:* 518-828-2000 *Toll Free Tel:* 888-999-HAVE (999-4283) *Fax:* 518-828-2008 *E-mail:* pro_sales@haveinc.com; have@haveinc.com *Web Site:* www.haveinc.com, pg 777

Gordon, Sophie, Chicago International Children's Film Festival, 1517 W Fullerton Ave, Chicago, IL 60614 *Tel:* 773-281-9075 (ext 3011) *Fax:* 773-929-0266 *E-mail:* filmreg@facets.org; press@facets.org *Web Site:* festival.facets.org, pg 985

Gorel, Everett, South Coast Film & Video, 5234 Elm St, Houston, TX 77081 *Tel:* 713-661-3550 *Toll Free Tel:* 800-229-3550 *Fax:* 713-661-4357 *E-mail:* info@ scfilmvideo.com *Web Site:* www.southcoastfilmvideo. com, pg 895

Gorelick, Steven, New Jersey Motion Picture & Television Commission, 153 Halsey St, 5th fl, Newark, NJ 07102-2807 *Tel:* 973-648-6279 *Fax:* 973-648-7350 *E-mail:* njfilm@sos.nj.gov *Web Site:* www.film.nj.gov, pg 973

Gorg, Brian, Digital Signage Federation (DSF), 11 Main St, Suite D, Warrenton, VA 20186 *Tel:* 540-551-5500 *Fax:* 202-962-3939 *Web Site:* www. digitalsignagefederation.org, pg 954

Gorge, John, Association of Federal Communications Consulting Engineers (AFCCE), PO Box 19333, Washington, DC 20036-0333 *E-mail:* secretary@afcce. org *Web Site:* afcce.org, pg 951

Gorman, Roberta, Society of Motion Picture & Television Engineers® (SMPTE®), White Plains Plaza, 445 Hamilton Ave, Suite 601, White Plains,

NY 10601-1827 *Tel:* 914-761-1100 *Fax:* 914-206-4216 *E-mail:* membership@smpte.org *Web Site:* www. smpte.org, pg 962

Gorman, Susan, Accusoft, 4001 N Riverside Dr, Tampa, FL 33603 *Tel:* 813-875-7575 *Toll Free Tel:* 800-875-7009 *Fax:* 813-875-7705 *E-mail:* sales@accusoft.com *Web Site:* www.accusoft.com, pg 674

Gorski, Gary, Tele-Measurements Inc, 145 Main Ave, Clifton, NJ 07014 *Tel:* 973-473-8822 *Toll Free Tel:* 800-223-0052 (ext 207) *Fax:* 973-473-0521 *E-mail:* contact@tele-measurements.com *Web Site:* www.tele-measurements.com, pg 910

Gorsline, Russell, REX, 610 SW 17 Ave, Portland, OR 97205 *Tel:* 503-238-4525 *E-mail:* info@rexpost.com *Web Site:* www.rexpost.com, pg 874

Goss, Carol, IAI Records & Video, PO Box 4, Cherry Valley, NY 13320-0004 *Tel:* 646-696-5645 *E-mail:* iai@improvart.com *Web Site:* www.improvart. com, pg 783

Goss-Bley, A I, IAI Records & Video, PO Box 4, Cherry Valley, NY 13320-0004 *Tel:* 646-696-5645 *E-mail:* iai@improvart.com *Web Site:* www.improvart. com, pg 783

Gottschalk, Stefan, RAM® Mounts, 8410 Dallas Ave S, Seattle, WA 98108 *Tel:* 206-763-8361 *Toll Free Tel:* 800-497-7479 *Fax:* 206-763-9615 *E-mail:* sales@ rammount.com *Web Site:* www.rammount.com, pg 870

Gotzen-Berg, Ken, Kanab/Kane County Film Commission, Kane County Utah Off of Tourism, 78 S 100 E, Kanab, UT 84741 *Tel:* 435-644-5033 *Toll Free Tel:* 800-SEE-KANE (733-5263) *E-mail:* kanetrav@ kaneutah.com *Web Site:* visitsouthernutah.com, pg 976

Gougeon, Olivier, Ulysses Travel Guides Inc, 4176 Rue Saint-Denis, Montreal, QC H2W 2M5, Canada *Tel:* 514-843-9882 *Fax:* 514-843-9448 *E-mail:* info@ ulysses.ca; st-denis@ulysse.ca *Web Site:* www.ulysse. ca (French); www.ulyssesguides.com (English), pg 920

Gouhin, Patrick, The International Society of Automation (ISA), 67 T W Alexander Dr, Research Triangle Park, NC 27709 *Tel:* 919-549-8411 *Fax:* 919-549-8288 *E-mail:* info@isa.org *Web Site:* www.isa.org, pg 790

Goulden, Ms Randy, Golden Sheaf Awards, 49 Smith St E, Yorkton, SK S3N 0H4, Canada *Tel:* 306-782-7077 *Fax:* 306-782-1550 *E-mail:* info@yorktonfilm. com *Web Site:* yorktonfilm.com/golden-sheaf-awards/, pg 991

Goulden, Ms Randy, Yorkton Film Festival (YFF), 49 Smith St E, Yorkton, SK S3N 0H4, Canada *Tel:* 306-782-7077 *Fax:* 306-782-1550 *E-mail:* info@ yorktonfilm.com *Web Site:* yorktonfilm.com, pg 1007

Goulston, Michael, Integrated Solutions Group, 858 Boston Providence Tpke, Norwood, MA 02062 *Tel:* 781-769-7810 *Toll Free Tel:* 866-769-0210 *E-mail:* info@isgboston.com *Web Site:* isgboston.com, pg 789

Gover, Kevin, Smithsonian National Museum of the American Indian, Fourth St & Independence Ave SW, Washington, DC 20560 *Tel:* 202-633-1000 *E-mail:* nmai-info@si.edu; nmai-grouppreservations@ si.edu (DC group tours); nmaitours@si.edu (NY group tours) *Web Site:* americanindian.si.edu, pg 891

Grabe, Erin, Entertainment Services and Technology Association (ESTA), 630 Ninth Ave, Suite 609, New York, NY 10036 *Tel:* 212-244-1505 *Fax:* 212-244-1502 *E-mail:* info@esta.org; membership@esta.org *Web Site:* www.esta.org, pg 954

Grabe, Erin, Production Equipment Rental Group (PERG), c/o ESTA, 630 Ninth Ave, Suite 609, New York, NY 10036 *Tel:* 212-244-1505 *Fax:* 212-244-1502 *E-mail:* info@esta.org; membership@esta.org *Web Site:* www.esta.org/perg, pg 960

Grabeau, Kenneth, Monarch Instrument, 15 Columbia Dr, Amherst, NH 03031-2305 *Tel:* 603-883-3390 *Toll Free Tel:* 800-999-3390 *Fax:* 603-886-3300 *E-mail:* sales@monarchinstrument.com *Web Site:* www.monarchinstrument.com, pg 829

Grabulosa, Albert, Estiluz Inc, 330 W 38 St, Suite 710, New York, NY 10018 *Tel:* 201-641-1997; 646-454-1285 *Fax:* 201-641-2092; 646-454-1799 *E-mail:* info@estiluzusa.com *Web Site:* www. estiluzusa.com, pg 756

Gradzki, Walt, Radio Visions, PO Box 4732, Toms River, NJ 08754-4732 *Tel:* 732-240-3119 *E-mail:* sales@radiovisions.com *Web Site:* www.radiovisions.com, pg 869

Grafinger, Paul, Advanced AV LLC, 208 Carter Dr, Suite 7, West Chester, PA 19382 *Toll Free Tel:* 877-696-7700 *Fax:* 610-692-8421 *E-mail:* sales@advancedav.com *Web Site:* www.advancedav.com, pg 677

Graham, Jim, Hollywood Lights Inc, 5251 SE McLoughlin Blvd, Portland, OR 97202-4836 *Tel:* 503-232-9001; 503-232-8855 *Toll Free Tel:* 800-826-9881 *Fax:* 503-517-8686 *E-mail:* portland@hollywoodlights.biz *Web Site:* www.hollywoodlights.biz, pg 781

Graham, Mark, LOUD Technologies Inc, 16220 Wood-Red Rd NE, Woodinville, WA 98072 *Tel:* 425-487-4333; 415-892-6500 *Toll Free Tel:* 866-858-LTEC (858-5832) *Fax:* 425-487-4337 *Web Site:* www.mackie.com; www.loudtechinc.com, pg 811

Graham-White, Sean, SGW Teleprompter Solutions Inc, 844 Eighth Ave, La Grange, IL 60525-2949 *Tel:* 773-402-0105 *Fax:* 708-482-9159 *E-mail:* teleprompter@sbcglobal.net *Web Site:* teleprompter solutions.com, pg 885

Grahovac, Abbey, NASCAR Productions LLC, 550 S Caldwell St, Suite 2000, Charlotte, NC 28202 *Tel:* 704-348-7100 *E-mail:* productions@nascar.com *Web Site:* productions.nascar.com, pg 835

Grainge, Sir Lucian, Universal Music Group, 2220 Colorado Ave, Santa Monica, CA 90404 *Tel:* 310-865-5000 *Web Site:* www.universalmusic.com, pg 922

Grais, Betsey, Chicago Film Office, Chicago Cultural Ctr, 78 E Washington, Rm 108, Chicago, IL 60602 *Tel:* 312-744-6415 *Fax:* 312-744-1378 *E-mail:* filmoffice@cityofchicago.org *Web Site:* www.cityofchicago.org/city/en/depts/dca/provdrs/chicago_film_office.html, pg 970

Graman, Saundra, Clever Devices Ltd, 300 Crossways Park Dr, Woodbury, NY 11797 *Tel:* 516-433-6100 *Toll Free Tel:* 800-872-6129 *Web Site:* www.cleverdevices.com, pg 726

Granath, Katheryn, LKG Industries Inc, 3660 Publishers Dr, Rockford, IL 61109 *Tel:* 815-874-2301 *Toll Free Tel:* 800-645-2262 *Fax:* 815-874-2896 *Toll Free Fax:* 800-554-0795 *E-mail:* sales-lkgindustries@t6b.com *Web Site:* www.philmore-datak.com, pg 810

Granberry, Richard, MotionMasters, 2288 Roxalana Rd, Dunbar, WV 25064 *Tel:* 304-345-8800 *Fax:* 304-345-8809 *E-mail:* storytellers@motionmasters.com *Web Site:* motionmasters.com, pg 831

Grande, Brandon, First Person Inc, 550 Bryant St, San Francisco, CA 94107 *Tel:* 415-495-5595 *E-mail:* hi@firstperson.is *Web Site:* firstperson.is, pg 761

Grande, Jamie L, Avatar Award, 550 W Frontage Rd, Suite 3600, Northfield, IL 60093 *Tel:* 847-716-7000 *Fax:* 847-716-7004 *E-mail:* info@mediafinance.org *Web Site:* www.mediafinance.org, pg 983

Grande, Jamie L, Media Financial Management Association (MFM), 550 W Frontage Rd, Suite 3600, Northfield, IL 60093 *Tel:* 847-716-7000 *Fax:* 847-716-7004 *E-mail:* info@mediafinance.org *Web Site:* www.mediafinance.org, pg 957

Grande, Marcello, First Person Inc, 550 Bryant St, San Francisco, CA 94107 *Tel:* 415-495-5595 *E-mail:* hi@firstperson.is *Web Site:* firstperson.is, pg 761

Grande, Mario, L-3 WESCAM, 649 N Service Rd W, Burlington, ON L7P 5B9, Canada *Tel:* 905-633-4000; 905-633-4175 (cust serv) *Toll Free Tel:* 888-593-7226 *Fax:* 905-633-4100 *E-mail:* sales.wescam@l-3com.com *Web Site:* www.wescam.com, pg 803

Grandestaff, Lauren, IRE Annual Awards for Investigative Reporting, Missouri School of Journalism, 141 Neff Annex, Columbia, MO 65211 *Tel:* 573-882-2042 *Fax:* 573-882-5431 *E-mail:* ire.org; rescntr@ire.org *Web Site:* ire.org/awards, pg 993

Grandinetti, Andre, Wired 4 Sound Inc, PO Box 683, Clifton, NJ 07012-0683 *Tel:* 973-773-2565 *E-mail:* info@wired4sound.com *Web Site:* www.wired4sound.com, pg 940

Grant, Carolyn, NAMM, the National Association of Music Merchants, 5790 Armada Dr, Carlsbad, CA 92008 *Tel:* 760-438-8001 *Toll Free Tel:* 800-767-6266 (memb hotline) *Fax:* 760-438-7327 *E-mail:* info@namm.org *Web Site:* www.namm.org, pg 958

Grant, Jason, Fleetwood Group Inc, 11832 James St, Holland, MI 49424 *Tel:* 616-396-1142 *Toll Free Tel:* 800-257-6390 *Fax:* 616-820-8300 *Web Site:* www.fleetwoodgroup.com; www.fleetwoodelectronics.com; www.fleetwoodfurniture.com, pg 762

Grant, Kasie, Baker Audio Visual, 2195 N Norcross Tucker Rd, Norcross, GA 30071 *Tel:* 770-441-2000 *Toll Free Tel:* 800-847-3523 *Fax:* 770-449-7719 *E-mail:* support@bakeraudiovisual.com *Web Site:* www.bakeraudiovisual.com, pg 700

Grant, Mark, Belar Electronics Laboratory Inc, 1140 McDermott Dr, Suite 105, West Chester, PA 19380-4043 *Tel:* 610-687-5550 *Fax:* 610-687-2686 *E-mail:* sales@belar.com *Web Site:* www.belar.com, pg 703

Grant, Sheila, Christie Lites, 6990 Lake Ellenor Dr, Orlando, FL 32809 *Tel:* 407-856-0016 *Fax:* 407-856-0765 *Web Site:* www.christielites.com, pg 722

Grant, Trudy, Sullivan Home Entertainment, 110 Davenport Rd, Toronto, ON M5R 3R3, Canada *Tel:* 416-921-7177 *Fax:* 416-921-7538 *E-mail:* inquire@sullivan-ent.com *Web Site:* sullivanmovies.com, pg 903

Grass, Randall, Shanachie Entertainment Corp, 37 E Clinton St, Newton, NJ 07860 *Tel:* 973-579-7763 *Web Site:* shanachie.com, pg 885

Grasse, Ross, Omega Broadcast Group, 817 W Howard Lane, Austin, TX 78753 *Tel:* 512-251-7778 *Fax:* 512-251-8633 *E-mail:* rental@omegabroadcast.com; sales@omegabroadcast.com *Web Site:* www.omegabroadcast.com, pg 845

Grasser, Kerri, Marblemedia, 74 Fraser Ave, Suite 100, Toronto, ON M6K 3E1, Canada *Tel:* 416-646-2711 *E-mail:* connect@marblemedia.com *Web Site:* www.marblemedia.com, pg 816

Gratzner, Matthew, New Deal Studios, 15392 Cobalt St, Los Angeles, CA 91342 *Tel:* 310-578-9929 *E-mail:* info@newdealstudios.com *Web Site:* www.newdealstudios.com, pg 839

Grauch, Ted, Blonder Tongue Laboratories Inc, One Jake Brown Rd, Old Bridge, NJ 08857 *Tel:* 732-679-4000 *Toll Free Tel:* 800-523-6049 *Fax:* 732-679-4353 *E-mail:* custsvc@blondertongue.com; btglobalsales@blondertongue.com (outside US & CN); information@blondertongue.com *Web Site:* www.blondertongue.com, pg 707

Gravagna, Jeff, Pointward, 400 First Ave N, Suite 100, Minneapolis, MN 55401 *Tel:* 651-646-2442 *Web Site:* www.pointward.com, pg 858

Graven, Ken W, Charles M Salter Associates Inc, 130 Sutter St, 5th fl, San Francisco, CA 94104 *Tel:* 415-397-0442 *Fax:* 415-397-0454 *E-mail:* info@cmsalter.com *Web Site:* www.cmsalter.com, pg 721

Gravitt, Grant H Jr, Tel-Air Interests Inc, 4104 Grant St, Hollywood, FL 33021 *Tel:* 954-924-4949 *Fax:* 954-924-4980 *E-mail:* telair@aol.com *Web Site:* www.telairint.com, pg 909

Gravitt, Mary Lou, Tel-Air Interests Inc, 4104 Grant St, Hollywood, FL 33021 *Tel:* 954-924-4949 *Fax:* 954-924-4980 *E-mail:* telair@aol.com *Web Site:* www.telairint.com, pg 909

Gray, Bill, Astrodyne TDI, 36 Newburgh Rd, Hackettstown, NJ 07840 *Tel:* 908-850-5088 *Fax:* 908-850-1607 *E-mail:* lpcs@astrodynetdi.com (cust serv, low power prods); hpcs@astrodynetdi.com (cust serv, high power prods); emifiltersales@astrodynetdi.com (cust serv, EMI filters) *Web Site:* www.tdipower.com, pg 691

Gray, Courtland, Peavey Electronics Corp, 5022 Hartley Peavey Dr, Meridian, MS 39305 *Tel:* 601-483-5365 *Fax:* 601-486-1278 *Web Site:* peavey.com, pg 852

Gray, Daniel, Deluxe Entertainment Services Group Inc, 2400 W Empire Ave, 2nd fl, Burbank, CA 91504 *Tel:* 818-260-7005; 818-526-3700 *Toll Free Tel:* 800-

99-FILMS (993-4567) *E-mail:* ddchelp@bydeluxe.com; pr@bydeluxe.com *Web Site:* www.bydeluxe.com, pg 740

Gray, Erin, The Mack Sennett Studios, 1215 Bates Ave, Los Angeles, CA 90029 *Tel:* 323-660-8466 *E-mail:* info@macksennettstudios.net *Web Site:* www.macksennettstudios.net, pg 884

Gray, Susan, Northern Light Productions (NLP), 300 Western Ave, 2nd fl, Boston, MA 02134 *Tel:* 617-789-4344 *Fax:* 617-789-4744 *E-mail:* info@nlprod.com *Web Site:* www.nlprod.com, pg 842

Graydon, Bob, MQ Power Corp, 1800 Waters Ridge Dr, Suite 500, Lewisville, TX 75057 *Toll Free Tel:* 800-883-2551; 800-427-1244 (parts); 800-426-1244 (sales) *Fax:* 972-315-1847 *E-mail:* mqpowersales@multiquip.com *Web Site:* www.multiquip.com, pg 832

Greaves, Louise, William Greaves Productions Inc, 475 W 57 St, No 17A, New York, NY 10019 *Toll Free Tel:* 800-874-8314 *Fax:* 212-315-0027 *Web Site:* www.williamgreaves.com, pg 774

Greaves, Vanessa, The Hamptons International Film Festival, 47 Newtown Lane, East Hampton, NY 11937 *Tel:* 631-324-4600 *Fax:* 631-324-1558 *E-mail:* info@hamptonsfilmfest.org; programming@hamptonsfilmfest.org (submissions) *Web Site:* hamptonsfilmfest.org, pg 991

Grebisz, Chris, Welocalize, 241 E Fourth St, Suite 207, Frederick, MD 21701 *Tel:* 301-668-0330 *Toll Free Tel:* 800-370-9515 *Fax:* 301-668-0335 *E-mail:* info@welocalize.com *Web Site:* www.welocalize.com, pg 935

Greblo, Joe, Stunt Wings Adventure Sports Talent & Equipment, 12623 Gridley St, Sylmar, CA 91342 *Tel:* 818-367-2430; 818-353-5580 (home); 818-266-0874 (cell) *E-mail:* stuntwings@me.com *Web Site:* www.stuntwings.com, pg 903

Grebovic, Seid, Micor Analytics, 7538 Saint Louis Ave, Skokie, IL 60076 *Tel:* 847-329-8590 *Fax:* 847-329-8599 *Web Site:* www.micoranalytics.com, pg 825

Greco, Kristin, PAR Inc, 16204 N Florida Ave, Lutz, FL 33549 *Tel:* 813-449-4065 *Toll Free Tel:* 800-331-8378 *Fax:* 813-961-2196 *Toll Free Fax:* 800-727-9329 *E-mail:* cs@parinc.com *Web Site:* www.parinc.com, pg 851

Greco, Tom, Location Camera Ltd, 300 Pennsylvania Ave, Oreland, PA 19075 *Tel:* 215-576-5600 *Fax:* 215-576-6022 *E-mail:* mail@locationcamera.com *Web Site:* www.locationcamera.com, pg 810

Green, Allen, Visual Departures Ltd, 48 Sheffield Business Park, Ashley Falls, MA 01222 *Tel:* 413-229-2272 *Toll Free Tel:* 800-628-2003 *Fax:* 413-229-2274 *E-mail:* sales@visualdepartures.com *Web Site:* www.visualdepartures.com, pg 931

Green, Chris, Producers Guild of America Inc (PGA), 8530 Wilshire Blvd, Suite 400, Beverly Hills, CA 90211 *Tel:* 310-358-9020 *E-mail:* info@producersguild.org *Web Site:* www.producersguild.org, pg 960

Green, Jason, National Instruments Corp, 11500 N Mopac Expwy, Austin, TX 78759-3504 *Tel:* 512-683-0100 *Toll Free Tel:* 888-280-7645 (sales); 877-388-1952 *Fax:* 512-683-8411; 512-683-5794 (sales) *Web Site:* www.ni.com, pg 836

Green, John P, Advanced AV LLC, 208 Carter Dr, Suite 7, West Chester, PA 19382 *Toll Free Tel:* 877-696-7700 *Fax:* 610-692-8421 *E-mail:* sales@advancedav.com *Web Site:* www.advancedav.com, pg 677

Green, Mark, Eastman Kodak Co, 343 State St, Rochester, NY 14650 *Toll Free Tel:* 800-698-3324 *Web Site:* www.kodak.com, pg 750

Greenberg, Bob, R/GA, 450 W 33 St, 12th fl, New York, NY 10001 *Tel:* 212-946-4000 *E-mail:* web@rga.com *Web Site:* www.rga.com, pg 868

Greenberg, Daniel, WNET/New York Public Media, 825 Eighth Ave, New York, NY 10019 *Tel:* 212-560-1313 *Fax:* 212-560-1314 *E-mail:* programming@thirteen.org *Web Site:* www.thirteen.org; www.wnet.org, pg 940

Greenberg, Rick, Cornerstone Media Productions Inc, 306 W Market St, Georgetown, DE 19947 *Tel:* 302-855-9380 *Web Site:* www.cornerstonemedia.com, pg 731

Greenberg, Robert, G&G Technologies Inc, 280 N Midland Ave, Bldg F, Suite 202, Saddle Brook, NJ 07663 *Tel:* 201-791-1400 *Toll Free Tel:* 800-422-2920 *Fax:* 201-791-1401 *E-mail:* staff@ggvideo.com *Web Site:* www.ggvideo.com, pg 768

Greenblatt, J Andrew, Philadelphia Film Festival, 1412 Chestnut St, Philadelphia, PA 19102 *Tel:* 267-239-2941 *E-mail:* info@filmadelphia.org *Web Site:* filmadelphia.org/festival, pg 999

Greendyk, Jesse, Austin Film Society (AFS), 1901 E 51 St, Austin, TX 78723 *Tel:* 512-322-0145 *E-mail:* afs@austinfilm.org *Web Site:* www.austinfilm.org, pg 951

Greene, Beth, Business & Legal Reports Inc, 141 Mill Rock Rd E, Old Saybrook, CT 06475 *Tel:* 860-510-0100 *Toll Free Tel:* 800-727-5257 *Toll Free Fax:* 800-785-9212 *E-mail:* service@blr.com *Web Site:* www.blr.com, pg 713

Greene, Brighid, Dance on Camera Festival, 252 Java St, Suite 333, Brooklyn, NY 11222 *Tel:* 347-505-8649 *E-mail:* info@dancefilms.org; festival@dancefilms.org *Web Site:* www.dancefilms.org, pg 988

Greene, Don, Institute of Industrial & Systems Engineers (IISE), 3577 Parkway Lane, Suite 200, Norcross, GA 30092 *Tel:* 770-449-0460 *Toll Free Tel:* 800-494-0460 *Fax:* 770-441-3295 *E-mail:* executiveoffices@iise.org *Web Site:* www.iise.org, pg 956

Greene, Ida PhD, People Skills International, 720 Gateway Center Dr, Bldg A, San Diego, CA 92102 *Tel:* 619-262-9951 *Web Site:* www.journeytolovingyourself.com, pg 854

Greene, Mark, ITA Audio Visual Solutions, 2162 Dana Ave & I-71, Cincinnati, OH 45207-1341 *Tel:* 513-631-7000 *Toll Free Tel:* 800-899-8877 *Fax:* 513-631-3290 *E-mail:* csr@ita.com *Web Site:* www.ita.com, pg 791

Greene, Patti, ZGC Inc, 264 Morris Ave, Mountain Lakes, NJ 07046 *Tel:* 973-335-4460 *Fax:* 973-335-4560 *E-mail:* sales@zgc.com *Web Site:* www.zgc.com, pg 945

Greenleaf, Jack, DecisionOne Corp, 640 Lee Rd, 3rd fl, Wayne, PA 19087 *Tel:* 610-296-6000 *Toll Free Tel:* 800-767-2876; 800-777-8800 (cust serv); 888-287-9202 (sales); 800-554-5179 (CN) *Fax:* 610-296-2910 *E-mail:* sales@decisionone.com *Web Site:* www.decisionone.com, pg 740

Greenwalt, Pamela, Screen Actors Guild - American Federation of Television & Radio Artists (SAG-AFTRA), 5757 Wilshire Blvd, 7th fl, Los Angeles, CA 90036-3600 *Tel:* 323-954-1600 (former SAG); 323-634-8100 (former AFTRA) *Toll Free Tel:* 855-SAG-AFTRA (724-2387) *Fax:* 323-549-6654 (communs & mktg) *E-mail:* info@sagaftra.org *Web Site:* www.sagaftra.org, pg 961

Greese, Henry, Schneider Optics Inc, 285 Oser Ave, Hauppauge, NY 11788 *Tel:* 631-761-5000 *Toll Free Tel:* 800-645-7239 *Fax:* 631-761-5090 *E-mail:* info@schneideroptics.com *Web Site:* www.schneideroptics.com, pg 882

Greetham, Kyle, Digital Projection, 55 Chastain Rd, Suite 115, Kennesaw, GA 30144 *Tel:* 770-420-1350 *Fax:* 770-420-1360 *E-mail:* contact@digitalprojection.com *Web Site:* www.digitalprojection.com, pg 742

Gregory, Jon, Concepts TV Productions Inc, 53 Indian Lane E, Towaco, NJ 07082 *Tel:* 973-331-1500 *Fax:* 973-331-1550 *E-mail:* sales@conceptstv.com *Web Site:* conceptstv.com, pg 730

Gregory, Steven, New England Technology Group Inc (NETG), One Davenport St, Cambridge, MA 02140 *Tel:* 617-864-5551 *Fax:* 520-844-5551 *E-mail:* teamnetg@netgworld.com *Web Site:* netgworld.com, pg 839

Gregory, Trey, ECG Productions, 120 Interstate N Pkwy SE, Suite 435, Atlanta, GA 30339 *Tel:* 678-855-5169 *Toll Free Tel:* 855-787-4487 *E-mail:* info@ecgprod.com *Web Site:* www.ecgprod.com, pg 750

Grey, David, Varitronics LLC, 7200 93 Ave N, Suite 120, Brooklyn, MN 55445 *Tel:* 763-536-6400 *Toll Free Tel:* 800-328-0585 *E-mail:* customerservice@variquest.com; tech_support@variquest.com; variquest@variquest.com *Web Site:* www.variquest.com, pg 925

Grey, Ernest, Audio & Light, 2209 Randleman Rd, Greensboro, NC 27406 *Tel:* 336-274-1234 *Fax:* 336-274-4022 *E-mail:* info@audio-light.com *Web Site:* www.audio-light.com, pg 693

Grey, Robert L, Intellidyne LLC, 2677 Prosperity Ave, Suite 301, Fairfax, VA 22031 *Tel:* 703-575-9715 *Fax:* 703-575-9718 *Web Site:* www.intellidyne-llc.com, pg 789

Grey, Victoria, Nexsan Inc, 900 E Hamilton Ave, Suite 230, Campbell, CA 95008 *Tel:* 408-724-9809 *E-mail:* sales@nexsan.com *Web Site:* www.nexsan.com, pg 840

Griebeler, Pat, Theosophical Publishing House, 306 W Geneva Rd, Wheaton, IL 60187 *Tel:* 630-665-0130 *Toll Free Tel:* 800-669-9425 *Fax:* 630-665-8791 *E-mail:* customerservice@questbooks.net; marketing@questbooks.net *Web Site:* questbooks.com, pg 912

Griesinger, Peter Root, Griesinger Films LLC, 7300 Old Mill Rd, Gates Mills, OH 44040 *Tel:* 440-423-1601 *Toll Free Tel:* 800-872-4456 *Fax:* 440-423-1601 *E-mail:* orders@griesingerfilms.com *Web Site:* www.griesingerfilms.com, pg 774

Griffin, Aaron, Saturn Awards, 334 W 54 St, Los Angeles, CA 90037 *Tel:* 323-752-5811 *E-mail:* saturn.awards@ca.rr.com *Web Site:* www.saturnawards.org, pg 1003

Griffin, Johnny, Wilmington Regional Film Commission Inc, 1223 N 23 St, Wilmington, NC 28405 *Tel:* 910-343-3456 *Fax:* 910-343-3457 *E-mail:* commish@wilmingtonfilm.com *Web Site:* www.wilmingtonfilm.com, pg 974

Griffin, Michael, 4-D Creative Media, 16 W 46 St, 12th fl, New York, NY 10036 *Tel:* 646-483-7768 *Web Site:* www.4-dcreative.com, pg 764

Griffin, Peter, Industrial Timer Co, 30 Industrial Park Rd, Centerbrook, CT 06409 *Tel:* 860-767-7130 *Toll Free Tel:* 800-394-7130 *Fax:* 860-767-9137 *Toll Free Fax:* 800-767-9137 *E-mail:* sales@epg-inc.com *Web Site:* www.industrialtimercompany.com, pg 787

Griffin, Ron, KET The Kentucky Network, 600 Cooper Dr, Lexington, KY 40502 *Tel:* 859-258-7000 *Toll Free Tel:* 800-432-0951 *Fax:* 859-258-7396 *E-mail:* adulted@ket.org *Web Site:* www.ket.org, pg 798

Griffith, Cary, Backstage Equipment Inc, 8052 Lankershim Blvd, North Hollywood, CA 91605 *Tel:* 818-504-6026 *Toll Free Tel:* 800-692-2787 *Fax:* 818-504-6180 *E-mail:* info@backstageweb.com *Web Site:* www.backstageweb.com, pg 700

Griffith, Ed, Griffith Productions, 1750 Donelson Dr, Eads, TN 38028 *Tel:* 901-351-1899 *Fax:* 901-465-1787 *E-mail:* info@griffithproductions.tv *Web Site:* www.griffithproductions.tv, pg 774

Griffith, Rob, Rane, 200 Scenic View Dr, Cumberland, RI 02864 *Tel:* 401-658-3131; 401-659-8192 *Fax:* 401-658-3640 *E-mail:* info@rane.com *Web Site:* www.rane.com, pg 870

Griffith, William, Smithsonian Folkways Recordings, 600 Maryland Ave SW, Suite 2001, Washington, DC 20024 *Tel:* 202-633-6450 *Toll Free Tel:* 888-FOLKWAYS (365-5929) *Fax:* 202-633-6477 *E-mail:* smithsonianfolkways@si.edu *Web Site:* folkways.si.edu, pg 891

Griggs, Lewis Brown, Griggs Productions Inc, Kappas Marina, 29 W Pier, Sausalito, CA 94965 *Tel:* 415-999-1079 *Toll Free Tel:* 800-210-4200 *Web Site:* www.griggs.com, pg 774

Grilliot, Bob, JIST Publishing, 875 Montreal Way, St Paul, MN 55102 *Toll Free Tel:* 800-328-1452 *Toll Free Fax:* 800-328-4564 *E-mail:* educate@emcp.com *Web Site:* jist.emcp.com, pg 794

Grimes, Jeffery, ARC Document Solutions, 1981 N Broadway, Suite 385, Walnut Creek, CA 94596 *Tel:* 925-949-5100 *Toll Free Tel:* 855-500-0660 *E-mail:* contact@e-arc.com *Web Site:* www.e-arc.com, pg 688

Grimes, Jim, Daily Electronics Corp, PO Box 822437, Vancouver, WA 98682-0053 *Tel:* 360-896-8856 *Toll Free Tel:* 800-346-6667 *Fax:* 360-896-5476 *E-mail:* daily@worldaccessnet.com *Web Site:* dailyelectronics.net, pg 737

Grindle, David, USITT, 290 Elwood Davis Rd, Suite 100, Liverpool, NY 13088 *Tel:* 315-463-6463 *Toll Free Tel:* 800-938-7488 *Toll Free Fax:* 866-398-7488 *E-mail:* info@usitt.org *Web Site:* www.usitt.org, pg 963

Grinnan, Suzanne E, Chester F Carlson Award, 7003 Kilworth Lane, Springfield, VA 22151 *Tel:* 703-642-9090 *Fax:* 703-642-9094 *E-mail:* info@imaging.org *Web Site:* imaging.org, pg 985

Grinnan, Suzanne E, Society for Imaging Science and Technology (IS&T), 7003 Kilworth Lane, Springfield, VA 22151 *Tel:* 703-642-9090 *Fax:* 703-642-9094 *E-mail:* info@imaging.org *Web Site:* imaging.org, pg 962

Grise, Don, Grise Audio Visual Center Inc, 2402 Cherry St, Erie, PA 16502 *Tel:* 814-452-4465 *E-mail:* grise@erie.net *Web Site:* griseav.com, pg 774

Grise, Jim, Grise Audio Visual Center Inc, 2402 Cherry St, Erie, PA 16502 *Tel:* 814-452-4465 *E-mail:* grise@erie.net *Web Site:* griseav.com, pg 774

Grisolia, Barri, ChyronHego Corp, 5 Hub Dr, Melville, NY 11747 *Tel:* 631-845-2000 *E-mail:* info@chyronhego.com; sales@chryonhego.com *Web Site:* chyronhego.com, pg 723

Griswold, Bob, Effective Learning Systems LLC, PO Box 366666, Bonita Springs, FL 34136 *Tel:* 612-513-0760 *Web Site:* www.effectivelearning.com, pg 751

Griswold, Deirdre, Effective Learning Systems LLC, PO Box 366666, Bonita Springs, FL 34136 *Tel:* 612-513-0760 *Web Site:* www.effectivelearning.com, pg 751

Grober, David, Motion Picture Marine, 578 Washington Blvd, Suite 866, Marina del Rey, CA 90292 *Tel:* 310-951-1110 *Web Site:* perfect-horizon.com, pg 831

Groce, Bill, FMP Media Solutions Inc, 3600 Horizon Dr, Suite 180, King of Prussia, PA 19406 *Tel:* 610-825-4000 *Toll Free Tel:* 800-346-5071 *Fax:* 610-825-4430 *E-mail:* info@fmpmedia.com *Web Site:* www.fmpmedia.com, pg 763

Groenhuizen, Frits, Lloyd F McKinney Associates Inc, 25350 Cypress Ave, Hayward, CA 94544 *Tel:* 510-783-8043 *Fax:* 510-783-2130 *E-mail:* info@mckinneyassoc.com *Web Site:* www.mckinneyassoc.com, pg 821

Groft, Kelly, WMAR-TV, 6400 York Rd, Baltimore, MD 21212 *Tel:* 410-377-2222 *E-mail:* newsroom@wmar.com *Web Site:* www.abc2news.com, pg 940

Groh, David, Partech Lighting Systems Inc, 8711 Reading Rd, Cincinnati, OH 45215 *Tel:* 513-761-5678 *Toll Free Tel:* 800-701-9551 *Fax:* 513-679-8282 *E-mail:* info@partechlighting.com *Web Site:* www.partechlighting.com, pg 851

Groh, Tina, Partech Lighting Systems Inc, 8711 Reading Rd, Cincinnati, OH 45215 *Tel:* 513-761-5678 *Toll Free Tel:* 800-701-9551 *Fax:* 513-679-8282 *E-mail:* info@partechlighting.com *Web Site:* www.partechlighting.com, pg 851

Gromada, Barry, Turning Technologies LLC, 255 W Federal St, Youngstown, OH 44503 *Tel:* 330-746-3015 *Toll Free Tel:* 866-746-3015 *E-mail:* info@turningtechnologies.com; support@turningtechnologies.com *Web Site:* www.turningtechnologies.com, pg 919

Gronsbell, Scott, Soundsphere, 10 Research Dr, Stratford, CT 06615 *Tel:* 203-386-9200 *Fax:* 203-386-0773 *E-mail:* info@soundsphere.com *Web Site:* www.soundsphere.com, pg 895

Gross, Adam, TOMCAT USA Inc, 5427 N National Dr, Knoxville, TN 37914 *Tel:* 865-219-3700 *Fax:* 865-673-5818 *E-mail:* info@tomcatusa.com; sales@tomcatusa.com *Web Site:* www.tomcatglobal.com, pg 915

Gross, Jay, Florida Digital Studios, 6677 13 Ave N, Suite 3C, St Petersburg, FL 33710 *Tel:* 727-546-7900 *Web Site:* www.floridadigitalstudios.com, pg 763

Grossman, Jay, MTI Home Video, 14216 SW 136 St, Miami, FL 33186 *Tel:* 305-233-6943 *Web Site:* www.mtivideo.com, pg 833

Grossman, Jerry, The Imaging Alliance, 7600 Jericho Tpke, Suite 301, Woodbury, NY 11797 *Tel:* 516-802-0895 *Fax:* 516-364-0140 *E-mail:* info@theimagingalliance.com *Web Site:* www.theimagingalliance.com, pg 955

Groth, Trevor, Sundance Film Festival, 1825 Three Kings Dr, Park City, UT 84060 *Tel:* 435-658-3456 *Fax:* 435-658-3457 *E-mail:* customerservice@sundance.org; press@sundance.org; institute@sundance.org *Web Site:* www.sundance.org/festival, pg 1004

Grove, Brad, Production West, 207 NW Park Ave, Portland, OR 97209 *Tel:* 503-222-0025 *Fax:* 503-573-1941 *E-mail:* info@r2cgroup.com *Web Site:* www.r2cgroup.com, pg 864

Grove, Mark Steven, Inferno Film Productions LLC, PO Box 151048, Lakewood, CO 80215-9048 *Tel:* 303-587-9792 *E-mail:* sales@infernofilm.com *Web Site:* www.infernofilm.com, pg 787

Groves, Kevin, Alpha Video & Audio Inc, 7690 Golden Triangle Dr, Eden Prairie, MN 55344 *Tel:* 952-896-9898 *Toll Free Tel:* 800-388-0008 *Fax:* 952-896-9899 *E-mail:* info@alphavideo.com *Web Site:* www.alphavideo.com, pg 682

Gruber, Betsy, On-Site Video, 325 E Southern Ave, Suite 110, Tempe, AZ 85282 *Tel:* 480-967-5062 *Web Site:* www.on-sitevideo.com, pg 846

Gruber-Miller, John, The American Classical League, 860 NW Washington Blvd, Suite A, Hamilton, OH 45013 *Tel:* 513-529-7741 *Fax:* 513-529-7742 *E-mail:* info@aclclassics.org *Web Site:* www.aclclassics.org, pg 683

Grucela, Amy, CommCreative, 75 Fountain St, Framingham, MA 01702 *Tel:* 508-620-6664 *Toll Free Tel:* 877-620-6664 *Fax:* 508-620-0592 *E-mail:* info@commcreative.com *Web Site:* www.commcreative.com, pg 728

Grundmann, Anya, National Public Radio (NPR), 1111 N Capitol St NE, Washington, DC 20002 *Tel:* 202-513-2000 *Web Site:* www.npr.org, pg 959

Grundstein, Frank, Logitek Electronic Systems Inc, 5622 Edgemoor Dr, Houston, TX 77081 *Tel:* 713-664-4470 *Toll Free Tel:* 800-231-5870 (sales); 877-231-5870 (tech support) *Fax:* 713-664-4479 *E-mail:* northamericansales@logitekaudio.com *Web Site:* www.logitekaudio.com, pg 811

Grusby, Greg, Industrial Light & Magic (ILM), 1110 Gorgas St, San Francisco, CA 94129 *Tel:* 415-746-3000 *Fax:* 415-746-3015 *E-mail:* contact-sf@ilm.com *Web Site:* www.ilm.com, pg 787

Gruss, Josh, Round Hill Music LLC, 400 Madison Ave, 18th fl, New York, NY 10017 *Tel:* 212-380-0080 *Fax:* 212-380-0081 *E-mail:* info@roundhillmusic.com *Web Site:* roundhillmusic.com, pg 878

Guan, Bin, Yorktel, 81 Corbett Way, Eatontown, NJ 07724 *Tel:* 732-413-6000 *Toll Free Tel:* 866-836-8463 *Fax:* 732-413-6060 *E-mail:* knowmore@yorktel.com *Web Site:* yorktel.com, pg 944

Guard, Randy, SAS Institute Inc, 100 SAS Campus Dr, Cary, NC 27513-2414 *Tel:* 919-677-8000 *Toll Free Tel:* 800-727-0025 *Fax:* 919-677-4444 *Web Site:* www.sas.com, pg 880

Guarino, Anthony Guy, Guymark Studios LLC, 3019 Dixwell Ave, Hamden, CT 06518 *Tel:* 203-248-9323 *Fax:* 203-248-9325 *E-mail:* guymark.studios@snet.net *Web Site:* www.guymarkstudios.com, pg 775

Guarino, Fred, Tiki Recording Studios Inc, 30-A Glen St, Suite 204, Glen Cove, NY 11542 *Tel:* 516-671-4300 (ext 101) *Fax:* 516-671-8754 *Web Site:* www.tikirecording.com, pg 914

Guarino, Mark L, Guymark Studios LLC, 3019 Dixwell Ave, Hamden, CT 06518 *Tel:* 203-248-9323 *Fax:* 203-248-9325 *E-mail:* guymark.studios@snet.net *Web Site:* www.guymarkstudios.com, pg 775

Guarino, Susan, Guymark Studios LLC, 3019 Dixwell Ave, Hamden, CT 06518 *Tel:* 203-248-9323 *Fax:* 203-248-9325 *E-mail:* guymark.studios@snet.net *Web Site:* www.guymarkstudios.com, pg 775

Gudnason, David, Carr McLean Ltd, 461 Horner Ave, Toronto, ON M8W 4X2, Canada *Tel:* 416-252-3371 *Toll Free Tel:* 800-268-2123 (CN) *Fax:* 416-252-9203 *Toll Free Tel:* 800-871-2397 *E-mail:* sales@carrmclean.ca *Web Site:* www.carrmclean.ca, pg 717

Guentzler, Bill, Cleveland International Film Festival, 2510 Market Ave, Cleveland, OH 44113-3434 *Tel:* 216-623-3456 *Fax:* 216-623-0103 *E-mail:* cfs@clevelandfilm.org; submissions@clevelandfilm.org *Web Site:* www.clevelandfilm.org, pg 986

Gumkowski, Greg, NRD Static Control LLC, 2937 Alt Blvd, Grand Island, NY 14072-1285 *Tel:* 716-773-7634 *Toll Free Tel:* 800-525-8076 (US only) *E-mail:* sales@nrdllc.com *Web Site:* www.nrdstaticcontrol.com, pg 843

Gumpert, Rich, Powerstation Events, 1718 Highland Ave, Cheshire, CT 06410 *Tel:* 203-250-8500 *Toll Free Tel:* 800-423-7835 *Fax:* 203-250-8575 *E-mail:* info@powerstationevents.com *Web Site:* www.powerstationevents.com, pg 860

Gundry, Stanley N, Zondervan, 3900 Sparks Dr, Grand Rapids, MI 49546 *Tel:* 616-698-6900 *Toll Free Tel:* 800-226-1122; 800-727-1309 (retail orders) *Web Site:* www.zondervan.com, pg 945

Gunn, Greg, Blind™, 1702 Olympic Blvd, Santa Monica, CA 90404 *Tel:* 310-314-1618 *Fax:* 310-314-1718 *Web Site:* www.blind.com, pg 707

Gunn, Natalie, IPI - Member Network™, 2518 Anthem Village Dr, Suite 104, Henderson, NV 89052 *Tel:* 702-617-1141 *Fax:* 702-617-1181 *E-mail:* info@ipiphoto.com *Web Site:* www.ipiphoto.com, pg 957

Gupta, Jay, Backdrop Outlet, 3540 Seagate Way, Oceanside, CA 92056 *Tel:* 760-547-2900 *Toll Free Tel:* 800-466-1755 *Fax:* 760-547-2899 *E-mail:* cs@backdropoutlet.com *Web Site:* backdropoutlet.com, pg 700

Gupta, Vivek, Mastech Digital, 1305 Cherrington Pkwy, Bldg 210, Suite 400, Moon Township, PA 15108 *Tel:* 412-787-2100 *Toll Free Tel:* 800-627-8323 *Fax:* 412-494-9272 *E-mail:* experience@mastechdigital.com *Web Site:* www.mastechdigital.com, pg 819

Gus, Allan, DuArt Media Services, 245 W 55 St, New York, NY 10019 *Tel:* 212-757-4580 *Fax:* 212-977-5609 *E-mail:* info@duart.com *Web Site:* www.duart.com, pg 747

Guthrie, David M, PGi, 3280 Peachtree Rd NE, Suite 1000, Atlanta, GA 30305 *Tel:* 404-262-8400 *Toll Free Tel:* 866-755-4878 *Web Site:* www.pgi.com, pg 855

Guthrie, Shawn, Student Academy Awards Competition, 8949 Wilshire Blvd, Beverly Hills, CA 90211 *Tel:* 310-247-3000 *Fax:* 310-859-9619 *E-mail:* saa@oscars.org *Web Site:* www.oscars.org/saa, pg 1004

Gutierrez, Dan, Pacific Radio Electronics, 3031 Thornton Ave, Burbank, CA 91504 *Tel:* 818-556-4177 *Toll Free Tel:* 800-634-9476 *Fax:* 818-556-4185 *E-mail:* sales@pacrad.com *Web Site:* www.pacrad.com, pg 849

Gutierrez, Lou, DuArt Media Services, 245 W 55 St, New York, NY 10019 *Tel:* 212-757-4580 *Fax:* 212-977-5609 *E-mail:* info@duart.com *Web Site:* www.duart.com, pg 747

Gutsche, Manny, RF Industries, 7610 Miramar Rd, San Diego, CA 92126 *Tel:* 858-549-6340 *Toll Free Tel:* 800-233-1728 *Fax:* 858-549-6345 *E-mail:* rfi@rfindustries.com; tech@rfindustries.org; invest@rfindustries.org *Web Site:* www.rfindustries.com, pg 874

Gutz, Kris, JSAV, 9150 N Royal Lane, Suite 150, Irving, TX 75063 *Tel:* 972-241-5444 *Toll Free Tel:* 800-852-8771 *Fax:* 972-247-2590 *E-mail:* info@jsav.com *Web Site:* www.jsav.com, pg 795

Guy, Marcus, AMG Studios (Los Angeles), 2225 E 28 St, Suite 511, Signal Hill, CA 90755 *Tel:* 562-424-0824 *Web Site:* www.amgstudiosla.com, pg 684

Guy, Melissa, AMG Studios (Los Angeles), 2225 E 28 St, Suite 511, Signal Hill, CA 90755 *Tel:* 562-424-0824 *Web Site:* www.amgstudiosla.com, pg 684

Guy, Steve, California Newsreel, 44 Gough St, Suite 303, San Francisco, CA 94103 *Tel:* 415-284-7800 *Fax:* 415-284-7801 *E-mail:* contact@newsreel.org *Web Site:* www.newsreel.org, pg 714

Guzman, Robert, Penguin Random House Audio Publishing, 1745 Broadway, New York, NY 10019 *E-mail:* audio@penguinrandomhouse.com *Web Site:* www.penguinrandomhouseaudio.com, pg 853

Guzman, Sig, Backstage Equipment Inc, 8052 Lankershim Blvd, North Hollywood, CA 91605 *Tel:* 818-504-6026 *Toll Free Tel:* 800-692-2787 *Fax:* 818-504-6180 *E-mail:* info@backstageweb.com *Web Site:* www.backstageweb.com, pg 700

Guzzi, Jim, Gotham Sound & Communications Inc, 35-10 36 Ave, 2nd fl, Long Island City, NY 11106 *Tel:* 212-629-9430 *Toll Free Tel:* 866-468-4268 *Fax:* 212-629-9436 *E-mail:* nyc@gothamsound.com *Web Site:* www.gothamsound.com, pg 773

Guzzi, Joseph, TAI Audio, 5828 Old Winter Garden Rd, Orlando, FL 32835 *Tel:* 407-296-9959 *Toll Free Tel:* 800-486-6444 *Fax:* 407-648-1352 *E-mail:* sales@taiaudio.com *Web Site:* www.taiaudio.com, pg 906

Haas, Daren, HM Electronics Inc (HME), 14110 Stowe Dr, Poway, CA 92064 *Tel:* 858-535-6000 *Toll Free Tel:* 800-848-4468 (dom sales) *Fax:* 858-452-7207; 858-552-0139 (dom sales) *E-mail:* info@hme.com *Web Site:* www.hme.com, pg 780

Haas, Rick, Associated Press Television News, 200 Liberty St, New York, NY 10281 *Tel:* 212-621-1500 *Fax:* 212-621-7419 *E-mail:* info@ap.org *Web Site:* www.aptn.com, pg 691

Haba, Leona, 20/20 Communications Inc, 10112 Voss Rd, Marengo, IL 60152 *Tel:* 847-364-7666 *Web Site:* www.2020communications.com, pg 920

Hacker, Matt, Big Shoulders Digital Video Productions, 875 N Michigan Ave, Suite 3750, Chicago, IL 60611 *Tel:* 312-540-5400 *E-mail:* info@bigshoulders.com; sales@bigshoulders.com *Web Site:* www.bigshoulders.com, pg 705

Hackney, Malcolm, Bright Star Productions Inc, 2420 Center St, Houston, TX 77007 *Tel:* 713-529-2757 *Fax:* 713-529-2329 *Web Site:* www.brightstarproductions.com, pg 710

Hadfield, Janice, McNabb & Connolly, 60 Briarwood Ave, Mississauga, ON L5G 3N6, Canada *Tel:* 905-278-0566 *Toll Free Tel:* 866-722-1522 *Fax:* 905-278-2801 *Toll Free Fax:* 866-722-1822 *E-mail:* info@mcnabbconnolly.ca *Web Site:* www.mcnabbconnolly.ca, pg 821

Hadfield, Jenn, North American Broadcasters Association (NABA), Canadian Broadcasting Centre, 25 John St, Suite 9C200, Toronto, ON M5V 3G7, Canada *Tel:* 416-205-3363 *Fax:* 416-205-2901 *E-mail:* contact@nabanet.com *Web Site:* nabanet.com, pg 960

Hadlock, Joe, Bear Creek Studio & Music Production Inc, 6313 Maltby Rd, Woodinville, WA 98072 *Tel:* 425-481-4100 *Fax:* 425-486-2718 *E-mail:* bearcreek@seanet.com *Web Site:* bearcreekstudio.com, pg 703

Hadlock, Manny, Bear Creek Studio & Music Production Inc, 6313 Maltby Rd, Woodinville, WA 98072 Tel: 425-481-4100 Fax: 425-486-2718 E-mail: bearcreek@seanet.com Web Site: bearcreekstudio.com, pg 703

Hadlock, Ryan, Bear Creek Studio & Music Production Inc, 6313 Maltby Rd, Woodinville, WA 98072 Tel: 425-481-4100 Fax: 425-486-2718 E-mail: bearcreek@seanet.com Web Site: bearcreekstudio.com, pg 703

Hadzor, Tom, Wide Eye Productions, 1018 W Hays St, Boise, ID 83702 Tel: 208-336-0391 Fax: 208-336-6644 E-mail: info@wideeye.tv Web Site: wideeye.tv, pg 938

Haessler, Dan, NFL Films Inc, One Sabol Way, Mount Laurel, NJ 08054 Tel: 856-222-3500 E-mail: licensing@nfl.com Web Site: www.nfl.com/films; www.facebook.com/NFLFilms, pg 841

Hagen, Doug, B-K Lighting, 40429 Brickyard Dr, Madera, CA 93636 Tel: 559-438-5800 Fax: 559-438-5900 E-mail: info@bklighting.com Web Site: www.bklighting.com, pg 700

Hager, Peter, Pointward, 400 First Ave N, Suite 100, Minneapolis, MN 55401 Tel: 651-646-2442 Web Site: www.pointward.com, pg 858

Haggarty, Jamie, Deluxe Entertainment Services Group Inc, 2400 W Empire Ave, 2nd fl, Burbank, CA 91504 Tel: 818-260-7005; 818-526-3700 Toll Free Tel: 800-99-FILMS (993-4567) E-mail: ddchelp@bydeluxe.com; pr@bydeluxe.com Web Site: www.bydeluxe.com, pg 740

Hahamy, Yohay, Joseph Electronics, 6633 W Howard St, Niles, IL 60714 Tel: 847-588-3800 Toll Free Tel: 800-323-5925 Fax: 847-588-3300 Toll Free Fax: 800-446-8366 E-mail: sales@josephelectronics.com Web Site: www.josephelectronics.com, pg 795

Hahn, Curt, Film House Inc, 810 Dominican Dr, Nashville, TN 37228 Tel: 615-255-4000 Fax: 615-255-4111 E-mail: results@filmhouse.com Web Site: www.filmhouse.com, pg 760

Hahn, Jansen, TBC Consoles Inc, 170 Rodeo Dr, Edgewood, NY 11717 Tel: 631-293-4068 Toll Free Tel: 888-CONSOLE (266-7653) Fax: 631-293-4075 E-mail: info@tbcconsoles.com; sales@tbcconsoles.com; support@tbcconsoles.com Web Site: www.tbcconsoles.com, pg 907

Hahn, Jerry, TBC Consoles Inc, 170 Rodeo Dr, Edgewood, NY 11717 Tel: 631-293-4068 Toll Free Tel: 888-CONSOLE (266-7653) Fax: 631-293-4075 E-mail: info@tbcconsoles.com; sales@tbcconsoles.com; support@tbcconsoles.com Web Site: www.tbcconsoles.com, pg 907

Haines, Andrew L, Golden Space Needle Awards, 305 Harrison St, Seattle, WA 98109 Tel: 206-464-5830 Fax: 206-264-7919 E-mail: info@siff.net; entries@siff.net Web Site: www.siff.net, pg 991

Haines, Andrew L, Seattle International Film Festival (SIFF), 305 Harrison St, Seattle, WA 98109 Tel: 206-464-5830 Fax: 206-264-7919 E-mail: info@siff.net; entries@siff.net Web Site: www.siff.net, pg 1003

Haines, Deanne, Midland Video Productions Inc, 3315 N 124 St, Brookfield, WI 53005 Tel: 414-276-8300 E-mail: request@midlandvideo.com Web Site: midlandvideo.com, pg 827

Hair, Linda, National Association for Music Education (NAfME), 1806 Robert Fulton Dr, Reston, VA 20191 Tel: 703-860-4000 Toll Free Tel: 800-336-3768 Fax: 703-860-1531 Toll Free Fax: 888-275-6362 E-mail: memberservices@nafme.org Web Site: nafme.org, pg 958

Hair, Ray, American Federation of Musicians of the United States & Canada (AFM), 1501 Broadway, 9th fl, New York, NY 10036 Tel: 212-869-1330 Toll Free Tel: 800-762-3444 Fax: 212-764-6134 Web Site: afm.org, pg 948

Hairelson, Christine, Accusoft, 4001 N Riverside Dr, Tampa, FL 33603 Tel: 813-875-7575 Toll Free Tel: 800-875-7009 Fax: 813-875-7705 E-mail: sales@accusoft.com Web Site: www.accusoft.com, pg 674

Hakimoglu, Ms Zee, ClearOne Inc, Edgewater Corporate Park, South Tower, Suite 500, 5225 Wiley Post Way, Salt Lake City, UT 84116 Tel: 801-975-7200 Fax: 801-303-5711 E-mail: contact@clearone.com; marketing@clearone.com Web Site: www.clearone.com, pg 726

Hakula, David, Crestron Electronics Inc, 15 Volvo Dr, Rockleigh, NJ 07647 Tel: 201-767-3400 (sales & support); 201-750-7004 (admin) Toll Free Tel: 800-237-2041; 855-791-5322 Fax: 201-767-1903 (sales & support); 201-767-8872 (admin) E-mail: inquiries@crestron.com Web Site: www.crestron.com, pg 734

Hale, Tim, Extreme Reach Inc, 75 Second Ave, Suite 720, Needham, MA 02494 Tel: 781-577-2016 Toll Free Tel: 877-769-9382 E-mail: sales@extremereach.com; support@extremereach.com Web Site: extremereach.com, pg 758

Hall, Allen, Special Effects Unlimited Inc, 1005 N Lillian Way, Hollywood, CA 90038 Tel: 323-466-3361 Fax: 323-466-5712 E-mail: seuefx@aol.com Web Site: www.specialefxunltd.com, pg 896

Hall, Anna Maria, Killer Tracks, 2110 Colorado Ave, Suite 110, Santa Monica, CA 90404 Tel: 310-865-4455 Toll Free Tel: 800-4-KILLER (454-5537) E-mail: info@killertracks.com Web Site: www.killertracks.com, pg 799

Hall, Casey, Extron Electronics, 1025 E Ball Rd, Suite 100, Anaheim, CA 92805-5957 Tel: 714-491-1500 Toll Free Tel: 800-633-9876 (sales & tech support); 800-633-9873 (order support) Fax: 714-491-1517 E-mail: sales-usa@extron.com Web Site: www.extron.com, pg 758

Hall, Chad, Take One Film & Video, 125 Commerce Ave, Hendersonville, TN 37075 Tel: 615-431-5822 E-mail: mail@takeone.tv Web Site: www.takeone.tv, pg 906

Hall, Curt, TWIST Integration Solutions Technology, 3915-F Dacoma, Houston, TX 77092 Tel: 713-688-0696 E-mail: info@twistIST.com Web Site: www.twistist.com, pg 920

Hall, Dan, Hall Productions, 951 Front St, Grover Beach, CA 93433 Tel: 805-473-1042 Fax: 805-473-2202 Web Site: hallpro.com, pg 775

Hall, David, Velodyne LiDAR Inc, 5521 Hellyer Ave, San Jose, CA 95738 Tel: 408-465-2800 Fax: 408-779-9208 (cust serv); 408-779-9377 (orders) E-mail: lidar@velodyne.com Web Site: velodynelidar.com, pg 925

Hall, Diane, Mobile Film Office, 164 Saint Emanuel St, Mobile, AL 36602 Tel: 251-438-7102 Fax: 251-438-7104 Web Site: www.mobilefilmoffice.com, pg 965

Hall, Doug, Propeller Music & Sound Design Inc, 62 W 45 St, 10th fl, New York, NY 10036 Tel: 917-922-3289 E-mail: info@propellermusic.com Web Site: www.propellermusic.com, pg 865

Hall, Doug, The Whitlock Group, 12820 West Creek Pkwy, Richmond, VA 23238 Tel: 804-273-9100 Toll Free Tel: 800-726-9843 Fax: 804-273-9380 E-mail: information@whitlock.com; marketing@whitlock.com Web Site: www.whitlock.com, pg 937

Hall, Howard, Howard Hall Productions, 2171 La Amatista Rd, Del Mar, CA 92014-3031 Tel: 858-259-8989 Web Site: www.howardhall.com, pg 775

Hall, Jay, Kentucky Film Office, 100 Airport Rd, Suite 200, Frankfort, KY 40601 Tel: 502-564-3456 Toll Free Tel: 800-345-6591 Fax: 502-564-5695 E-mail: email@kyfilm.com Web Site: kyfilmoffice.com, pg 971

Hall, Jeff, Maximus Media Inc, 2727 N Grove Industrial Dr, Suite 111, Fresno, CA 93727 Tel: 559-255-1688 Toll Free Tel: 800-2THEMAX (284-3629) Fax: 559-255-0323 Web Site: www.tothemax.com, pg 820

Hall, John, 360 Systems, 3281 Grande Vista Dr, Newbury Park, CA 91320-1193 Tel: 818-991-0360 Fax: 818-991-1360 E-mail: sales@360systems.com Web Site: www.360systems.com, pg 913

Hall, John T, L-3 ESSCO, 90 Nemco Way, Ayer, MA 01432 Tel: 978-568-5100 Fax: 978-772-7555 E-mail: info.essco@l3t.com Web Site: www2.l3t.com/essco, pg 802

Hall, Laura, Future Disc LLC, 15851 NW Willis Rd, McMinnville, OR 97128 Tel: 213-361-0603 Fax: 503-472-1951 Web Site: www.futurediscsystems.com, pg 767

Hall, M B, Audio Accessories Inc, 25 Mill St, Marlow, NH 03456 Tel: 603-446-3335 Fax: 603-446-7543 E-mail: audioacc@patchbays.com Web Site: www.patchbays.com, pg 693

Hall, Marta Thoma, Velodyne LiDAR Inc, 5521 Hellyer Ave, San Jose, CA 95738 Tel: 408-465-2800 Fax: 408-779-9208 (cust serv); 408-779-9377 (orders) E-mail: lidar@velodyne.com Web Site: velodynelidar.com, pg 925

Hall, Michele, Howard Hall Productions, 2171 La Amatista Rd, Del Mar, CA 92014-3031 Tel: 858-259-8989 Web Site: www.howardhall.com, pg 775

Hall, Ron, Festival Films, 6115 Chestnut Terr, Shorewood, MN 55331 Tel: 952-470-2172 E-mail: fesfilms@aol.com Web Site: www.fesfilms.com, pg 759

Hall, Roy, Music Hall LLC, 108 Station Rd, Great Neck, NY 11023 Tel: 516-487-3663 Fax: 516-773-3891 E-mail: info@musichallaudio.com Web Site: musichallaudio.com, pg 834

Hall, Shelli, Film Tucson, 100 S Church Ave, Tucson, AZ 85701 Tel: 520-770-2151 Fax: 520-629-0160 Web Site: www.filmtucson.com, pg 965

Hall, Steve, Future Disc LLC, 15851 NW Willis Rd, McMinnville, OR 97128 Tel: 213-361-0603 Fax: 503-472-1951 Web Site: www.futurediscsystems.com, pg 767

Hallberg, Scott, Bardes Products Inc, 5245 W Clinton Ave, Milwaukee, WI 53223 Tel: 414-354-9000 Toll Free Tel: 800-223-1357 Fax: 414-354-1921 E-mail: sales@bardes.com Web Site: www.bardes.com, pg 702

Hallerman, Stuart, Avast! Recording Co, 601 NW 80 St, Seattle, WA 98117 Fax: 206-789-7569 E-mail: avast@comcast.net Web Site: www.avastrecording.com, pg 697

Halling, Steve, AVFX Inc, 96 Holton St, Boston, MA 02135 Tel: 617-254-0770 Toll Free Tel: 888-254-0770 E-mail: info@avfx.com Web Site: www.avfx.com, pg 698

Halliwell, Martin, SES SA, 4 Research Way, Princeton, NJ 08540-6684 Tel: 609-987-4000 E-mail: info@ses.com Web Site: www.ses.com, pg 884

Hallman, Wallace, ESECO Speedmaster, 730 E Eseco Rd, Cushing, OK 74023-5505 Tel: 918-225-1266 Toll Free Tel: 800-331-5904 (US & CN) E-mail: info@eseco-speedmaster.com Web Site: www.eseco-speedmaster.com, pg 755

Halm, David, Buffalo Video Production, 233 Fillmore Ave, Suite 8, Tonawanda, NY 14150 Tel: 716-807-1510 Web Site: www.buffalovideoproduction.com, pg 712

Halouma, Stephanie, Scripps Networks, 9721 Sherrill Blvd, Knoxville, TN 37932 Tel: 865-694-2700 Web Site: www.scrippsnetworks.com, pg 883

Halpern, Elliot, YAP Films, 233 Broadview Ave, Toronto, ON M4M 2G3, Canada Tel: 416-504-3662 Fax: 416-504-3667 E-mail: thedog@yapfilms.com Web Site: www.yapfilms.com, pg 943

Halpin, Amy, IDA Documentary Awards, 3470 Wilshire Blvd, Suite 980, Los Angeles, CA 90010 Tel: 213-232-1660 Fax: 213-232-1669 E-mail: info@documentary.org Web Site: www.documentary.org, pg 992

Halpin, Amy, International Documentary Association, 3470 Wilshire Blvd, Suite 980, Los Angeles, CA 90010 Tel: 213-232-1660 Fax: 213-232-1669 E-mail: info@documentary.org Web Site: www.documentary.org, pg 956

Halt, Peter, TiVo Corp, 2 Circle Star Way, San Carlos, CA 94070 *Tel:* 408-562-8400 *Toll Free Tel:* 877-367-8486 (cust support); 877-289-8486 (sales support) *Fax:* 408-567-1800 *Web Site:* business.tivo.com; www. tivo.com, pg 914

Halus, Eugene J Jr, Freedoms Foundation National Awards, 1601 Valley Forge Rd, Valley Forge, PA 19481 *Tel:* 610-933-8825 *Fax:* 610-935-0522 *E-mail:* info@ffvf.org *Web Site:* www. freedomsfoundation.org, pg 989

Ham, Mark, Alberta Film, 140 Whitemud Crossing, 4211-106 St, Edmonton, AB T6J 6L7, Canada *Tel:* 780-422-8584 *Toll Free Tel:* 888-813-1738 *E-mail:* info@albertafilm.ca *Web Site:* www. albertafilm.ca, pg 977

Hames, Steven, National Student Production Awards, Hershey Square Ctr, 1152 Mae St, Hummelstown, PA 17036 *Tel:* www.askcbi.org, pg 997

Hamilton, Anja, Poly, 345 Encinal St, Santa Cruz, CA 95060 *Tel:* 831-426-5858 *Toll Free Tel:* 800-544-4660 *Fax:* 831-426-6098 *Web Site:* www.poly.com, pg 859

Hamilton, Christopher P, In the Wild Productions, PO Box 1443, Provincetown, MA 02657-5443 *Tel:* 508-241-5990 *E-mail:* info@inthewildproductions.com *Web Site:* www.inthewildproductions.com, pg 786

Hamilton, Dennis, Action Photo Digital Graphics, 1741 Clayton Rd, Concord, CA 94520 *Tel:* 925-676-7777 *E-mail:* actionps@sbcglobal.net *Web Site:* www. actionphotoservice.com, pg 675

Hamilton, Don, Hamilton Studio, 1427 W Dean Ave, Spokane, WA 99201 *Tel:* 509-327-9501 *E-mail:* info@ hamiltonstudio.com *Web Site:* www.hamiltonstudio. com, pg 775

Hamilton, Jermaine, Studio Circle Recordings, 863 Woodside Way, San Mateo, CA 94401 *Tel:* 650-328-8338 *E-mail:* info@studiocirclerecordings.com *Web Site:* www.studiocirclerecordings.com, pg 902

Hamilton, Mary, Parker Area Chamber of Commerce, 1217 California Ave, Parker, AZ 85344 *Tel:* 928-669-2174 *Fax:* 928-669-6304 *E-mail:* info@parkeraz.org *Web Site:* www.parkeraz.org, pg 965

Hamilton, Peter, Soundsphere, 10 Research Dr, Stratford, CT 06615 *Tel:* 203-386-9200 *Fax:* 203-386-0773 *E-mail:* info@soundsphere.com *Web Site:* www. soundsphere.com, pg 895

Hamilton, Philip, Audio Visual Dynamics, 2360 23 Ave, Lachine, QC H8T 0A3, Canada *Tel:* 514-332-6440 *Fax:* 514-332-2009 *E-mail:* service@avd.ca *Web Site:* www.avd.ca, pg 694

Hamilton, Robert, DWD Theatre Design & Consulting, Suite 485, 425 Carrall St, Vancouver, BC V6B 6E3, Canada *Tel:* 604-874-0552 *E-mail:* info@d-w-d.com *Web Site:* www.d-w-d.com, pg 748

Hamilton, Robert, Power Sonic Corp, 365 Cabela Dr, Suite 300, Reno, NV 89523 *Tel:* 619-661-2020 *Fax:* 619-661-3650 *Web Site:* www.power-sonic.com, pg 860

Hamlin, Brad, Burst Electronics Inc, PO Box 820, Edgewood, NM 87015 *Tel:* 505-898-1455 *E-mail:* sales@burstelectronics.com *Web Site:* www. burstelectronics.com, pg 713

Hamlin, Lise, Hearing Loss Association of America (HLAA), 7910 Woodmont Ave, Suite 1200, Bethesda, MD 20814 *Tel:* 301-657-2248 *Fax:* 301-913-9413 *E-mail:* inquiry@hearingloss.org *Web Site:* www. hearingloss.org, pg 778

Hamm, Michael, Frame 30 Productions Ltd, 10816A-82 Ave, No 202, Edmonton, AB T6E 2B3, Canada *Tel:* 780-439-5322 *E-mail:* frame30@frame30.com *Web Site:* www.frame30.com, pg 765

Hammond, Greg, Allied Artists International Inc, Production Services Ctr, 15810 E Gale Ave, Suite 133, Hacienda Heights, CA 91745 *Tel:* 626-330-0600 *Fax:* 626-961-0411, pg 681

Hammonds, Lisa, Medcom Inc, 6060 Phyllis Dr, Cypress, CA 90630-5243 *Tel:* 714-891-1443 *Toll Free Tel:* 800-541-0253; 800-877-1443 *Fax:* 714-891-3140 *E-mail:* customerservice@medcominc.com *Web Site:* www.medcominc.com, pg 821

Hamner, Stephen, Louisiana Entertainment, 617 N Third St, Baton Rouge, LA 70802 *Tel:* 225-342-5403 *Fax:* 225-342-5554 *E-mail:* led-entertainment@la.gov *Web Site:* louisianaentertainment.gov, pg 971

Hanavan, Patrick, Extreme Reach Inc, 75 Second Ave, Suite 720, Needham, MA 02494 *Tel:* 781-577-2016 *Toll Free Tel:* 877-769-9382 *E-mail:* sales@ extremereach.com; support@extremereach.com *Web Site:* extremereach.com, pg 758

Hancock, Dave, Spectrum Industries Inc, 925 First Ave, Chippewa Falls, WI 54729 *Tel:* 715-723-6750 *Toll Free Tel:* 800-235-1262 *Fax:* 715-738-2309 *E-mail:* info@spectrumfurniture. com *Web Site:* www.spectrumfurniture.com, pg 897

Handel, Scott, Ohio HD Video, 350 W Johnstown Rd, Gahanna, OH 43230 *Tel:* 614-656-1162 *Fax:* 614-656-4343 *E-mail:* info@ohiohdvideo.com *Web Site:* ohiohdvideo.com, pg 844

Hanes, Doug, Transtar Entertainment Co Inc, 11776 E Evans Ave, Aurora, CO 80014 *Tel:* 303-489-1450 *Web Site:* www.transtarfilm.com, pg 917

Hanes, Frank, Big Shoulders Digital Video Productions, 875 N Michigan Ave, Suite 3750, Chicago, IL 60611 *Tel:* 312-540-5400 *E-mail:* info@bigshoulders.com; sales@bigshoulders.com *Web Site:* www.bigshoulders. com, pg 705

Haney, Kathleen, WorldFest-Houston International Film Festival, 9898 Bissonnet St, Suite 650, Houston, TX 77036 *Tel:* 713-965-9955 *Fax:* 713-965-9960 *E-mail:* mail@worldfest.org; entry@worldfest.org *Web Site:* www.worldfest.org, pg 1007

Hank, Sylvester, Savage Universal Corp, 2050 S Stearman Dr, Chandler, AZ 85286 *Tel:* 480-632-1320 *Toll Free Tel:* 800-624-8891 *Fax:* 480-632-1322 *E-mail:* info486@savagepaper.com *Web Site:* savageuniversal.com, pg 881

Hanley, Dan, K&R All Media Productions LLC, 28533 Greenfield Rd, Southfield, MI 48076 *Tel:* 248-557-8276 *Web Site:* www.knr.net, pg 796

Hanley, Terrence, Terry Hanley Audio Systems Inc, 20 Industrial Pkwy, Woburn, MA 01801 *Tel:* 781-932-5300 *Fax:* 781-932-5354 *E-mail:* mail@ terryhanleyaudio.com *Web Site:* www.terryhanleyaudio. com, pg 775

Hanna, Sam, ITC, 523 Hanley Industrial Ct, St Louis, MO 63144 *Tel:* 314-646-1800 *Toll Free Tel:* 800-962-2344 *Fax:* 314-646-1818 *Web Site:* www.itcjourneys. com, pg 791

Hannah, Michael, Cabbage Cases Inc, 1166-C Steelwood Rd, Columbus, OH 43212-1356 *Tel:* 614-486-2495 *Toll Free Tel:* 800-888-2495 *Fax:* 614-486-2788 *E-mail:* sales@cabbagecases.com *Web Site:* www. cabbagecases.com, pg 713

Hannam, Kevin, Yukon Film & Sound Commission (YFSC), Box 2703, Whitehorse, YT Y1A 2C6, Canada *Tel:* 867-667-5400; 867-661-0408 (ext 5400, no charge for calls from within Yukon) *Fax:* 867-393-6228 *E-mail:* info@reelyukon.com *Web Site:* www. reelyukon.com, pg 979

Hannapel, William "Bill", Stedman Corp, 9625 E "D" Ave, Richland, MI 49083 *Tel:* 269-629-5930 *Toll Free Tel:* 888-629-5960 *E-mail:* info@stedmancorp.com *Web Site:* www.stedmancorp.com, pg 900

Hannay, Eric, Hannay Reels Inc, 553 State Rte 143, Westerlo, NY 12193-0159 *Tel:* 518-797-3791 *Toll Free Tel:* 877-467-3357 *Fax:* 518-797-3259 *Toll Free Fax:* 800-733-5464 *E-mail:* reels@hannay.com *Web Site:* www.hannay.com, pg 775

Hannigan, Carl, Precision Projection Systems Inc, 17508 Studebaker Rd, Cerritos, CA 90703 *Tel:* 562-865-8552 *Fax:* 562-924-7133 *E-mail:* info@ppsfx.com *Web Site:* www.ppsfx.com, pg 861

Hannon, Ginger, Graphic Laminating LLC, 6185 Cochran Rd, Solon, OH 44139 *Tel:* 440-498-3400 *Toll Free Tel:* 800-345-5300 *Fax:* 440-498-3410 *E-mail:* info@graphiclaminating.com *Web Site:* www. graphiclaminating.com, pg 773

Hannon, Michael, Graphic Laminating LLC, 6185 Cochran Rd, Solon, OH 44139 *Tel:* 440-498-3400 *Toll Free Tel:* 800-345-5300 *Fax:* 440-498-3410 *E-mail:* info@graphiclaminating.com *Web Site:* www. graphiclaminating.com, pg 773

Hanrahan, Dave, Future View Inc, 6035 Blair Rd NW, Washington, DC 20011 *Tel:* 202-882-7400 *Fax:* 202-882-7450 *E-mail:* info@futureview.com *Web Site:* www.futureview.com, pg 767

Hansen, Karen, Radio Television Digital News Association (RTDNA), The National Press Bldg, 529 14 St NW, Suite 1240, Washington, DC 20045 *Tel:* 202-662-7254 *Fax:* 202-223-4007 *Web Site:* www. rtdna.org; www.excellenceinjournalism.org, pg 961

Hansen, Lisa M, CineTel Films Inc, 8484 Wilshire Blvd, Suite 850C, Beverly Hills, CA 90211 *Tel:* 323-654-4000 *Fax:* 323-650-6400 *E-mail:* info@cinetelfilms. com *Web Site:* cinetelfilms.com, pg 724

Hansen, Scott, Production Resource Group LLC (PRG), 200 Business Park Dr, Suite 109, Armonk, NY 10504 *Tel:* 212-589-5400 *Toll Free Tel:* 877-774-7088 *E-mail:* info@prg.com *Web Site:* www.prg.com, pg 864

Hanser, Mary, Renaissance Unity, 11200 E 11 Mile Rd, Warren, MI 48089 *Tel:* 586-353-2300 *Fax:* 586-758-1159 *E-mail:* info@renaissanceunity. org *Web Site:* www.renaissanceunity.com; mastermindjournal.org (catalog), pg 873

Hansmire, Michel, Sparkworks Media, 1818 E Yesler Way, Seattle, WA 98122 *Tel:* 206-284-5500 *E-mail:* info@sparkworksmedia.com *Web Site:* sparkworksmedia.com, pg 896

Hanson, Eric, The Entertainment Merchants Association (EMA), PO Box 6339, North Hollywood, CA 91603 *Tel:* 818-385-1500 *E-mail:* info@entmerch.org *Web Site:* www.entmerch.org, pg 954

Hanson, Keith Merrill, Protocol Telecommunications Inc, 16844 Saticoy St, Van Nuys, CA 91406 *Tel:* 818-782-5705 *Toll Free Tel:* 800-400-5705 *Fax:* 818-782-5817 *E-mail:* orders@walkietalkie.com *Web Site:* www. walkietalkie.com, pg 866

Hanson, Kerri, Phoenix Society for Burn Survivors Inc, 525 Ottawa Ave NW, Front, Grand Rapids, MI 49503 *Tel:* 616-458-2773 *Toll Free Tel:* 800-888-BURN (888-2876) *Fax:* 616-458-2831 *E-mail:* info@phoenix-society.org *Web Site:* www.phoenix-society.org, pg 856

Hanson, Lisa, Bel Fuse Inc, 299 Johnson Ave, Suite 100, Waseca, MN 56093 *Tel:* 507-833-8822 *Fax:* 507-833-6287 *E-mail:* ccsorders@us.cinch.com *Web Site:* cinch.com, pg 703

Hanson, Mike, Watson Desking, 26246 Twelve Trees Lane NW, Poulsbo, WA 98370 *Tel:* 360-394-1300 *Fax:* 360-394-1322 *E-mail:* marketing@ watsondesking.com *Web Site:* www.watsonfurniture. com, pg 934

Hanten, Sara, Dubuque Area Convention & Visitors Bureau, 300 Main St, Suite 120, Dubuque, IA 52001 *Tel:* 563-845-7698 *Web Site:* www.traveldubuque.com, pg 971

Harabin, Michael, Gravity Media, 7701 Haskell Ave, Van Nuys, CA 91406 *Tel:* 818-955-9449; 747-258-4100 *Fax:* 818-955-9779 *E-mail:* enquiries@gravitymedia. com *Web Site:* www.gravitymedia.com, pg 773

Harada, Akira, Ikegami Electronics (USA) Inc, 37 Brook Ave, Maywood, NJ 07607 *Tel:* 201-368-9171 *Fax:* 201-569-1626 *E-mail:* sales@ikegami.com; service@ikegami.com *Web Site:* www.ikegami.com, pg 784

Harari, David, GLI Sound Systems, 2691 W 15 St, Brooklyn, NY 11224 *Tel:* 718-372-7849 *Toll Free Tel:* 800-GLI-PRO-1 (454-7761) *Fax:* 718-946-4151 *E-mail:* info@glipro.com; sales@glipro.com *Web Site:* www.glipro.com, pg 771

Harari, David, Harbro Corp, 2691 W 15 St, Brooklyn, NY 11224-2705 Tel: 718-946-4134 Toll Free Tel: 800-GLI-PRO-1 (454-7761) Fax: 718-946-4151 E-mail: info@glipro.com, Web Site: www.glipro.com, pg 776

Harbert, Lisa, Digital Display Solutions Inc, 2840, 12223 San Pedro Ave, San Antonio, TX 78216 Tel: 210-404-1233 Fax: 210-979-6585 E-mail: info@ddsav.com Web Site: ddsav.com, pg 742

Harbert, Roger, Digital Display Solutions Inc, 2840, 12223 San Pedro Ave, San Antonio, TX 78216 Tel: 210-404-1233 Fax: 210-979-6585 E-mail: info@ddsav.com Web Site: ddsav.com, pg 742

Harbo, Tracey, SF Global Sourcing, 3450 Sacramento St, Suite 353, San Francisco, CA 94118 Tel: 415-288-9400 Toll Free Tel: 800-545-5865 Web Site: www.sfglobalsourcing.com, pg 885

Harbor, Jon, Purdue University Digital Education, Stewart Ctr, Rm G59, 128 Memorial Mall, West Lafayette, IN 47907 Tel: 765-494-8619 Toll Free Tel: 800-830-0269 Fax: 765-496-2484 E-mail: distancelearning@purdue.edu Web Site: www.digitaleducation.purdue.edu, pg 867

Hardcastle, Jeff, Hardcastle Films & Video, 7319 Wise Ave, St Louis, MO 63117-1718 Tel: 314-647-4200, pg 776

Harden, Scott, West Penn Wire, 2833 W Chestnut St, Washington, PA 15301 Tel: 724-222-7060 Toll Free Tel: 800-245-4964 Fax: 724-222-6420 E-mail: info@westpennwire.com; sales@westpennwire.com Web Site: www.westpenn-wpw.com, pg 935

Hardesty, Bryan, EduMedia of Sugar Land, Texas, PO Box 2428, Sugar Land, TX 77487-2428 Tel: 281-756-7510 E-mail: service@history2u.com Web Site: www.history2u.com, pg 751

Hardesty, Todd, Alaska Video Postcards Inc, 11405 Discovery Park Dr, Anchorage, AK 99515 Tel: 907-349-8002 Toll Free Tel: 800-248-2624, pg 679

Hardy, Caitlyn, Sunset Las Palmas Studios, 1040 N Las Palmas Ave, Los Angeles, CA 90038 Tel: 323-860-0000 E-mail: reception@sunsetlaspalmas.com Web Site: www.sunsetlaspalmas.com, pg 904

Hardy, David, William F White International Inc, 800 Islington Ave, Toronto, ON M8Z 6A1, Canada Tel: 416-239-5050 Toll Free Tel: 800-465-0160 (CN only) Web Site: www.whites.com, pg 937

Hardy, Jim, Illuminate Post/Digital Finishing, 10900 Ventura Blvd, Studio City, CA 91604 Tel: 323-969-8822 Fax: 323-969-8860 E-mail: info@illuminatehollywood.com Web Site: illuminatehollywood.com, pg 784

Hardy, Jim, Illuminate Studios, 10900 Ventura Blvd, Studio City, CA 90068 Tel: 818-769-4500 Fax: 818-769-7150 E-mail: info@illuminatehollywood.com Web Site: illuminatehollywood.com, pg 784

Hare, Jane, SDMediaPros (SDMP), 5205 Kearny Villa Way, No 100, San Diego, CA 92123 Tel: 619-672-1000 E-mail: membership@sdmediapros.org; marketing@sdmediapros.org; programs@sdmediapros.org Web Site: sdmediapros.org, pg 962

Hare, Michael, Alford Media Services, 296 Freeport Pkwy, Coppell, TX 75019 Tel: 972-538-9400 Toll Free Tel: 800-554-9144 E-mail: info@alfordmedia.com; sales@alfordmedia.com Web Site: www.alfordmedia.com, pg 680

Hare, Ray, Producers Video, 3700 Malden Ave, Baltimore, MD 21211 Tel: 410-523-7520 Fax: 410-669-3347 E-mail: info@producers.tv Web Site: producers.tv, pg 863

Hargrow, Ralph, ACCO Brands Corp, 4 Corporate Dr, Lake Zurich, IL 60047-8997 Toll Free Tel: 800-541-0094; 800-222-6462 Toll Free Fax: 800-941-4463 E-mail: contactus@acco.com (cust serv) Web Site: www.accobrands.com, pg 673

Harilaou, Gus, Miller Camera Support LLC, 216 Little Falls Rd, Unit 15 & 16, Cedar Grove, NJ 07009-1276 Tel: 973-857-8300 Fax: 973-857-8188 E-mail: service@millertripods.us Web Site: www.millertripods.com, pg 827

Harkins, Cory, CRT Custom Products Inc, 7532 Hickory Hills Ct, Whites Creek, TN 37189 Tel: 615-876-5490 Toll Free Tel: 800-453-2533 Fax: 615-876-0096 E-mail: sales@crtcustomproducts.com Web Site: www.crtcustomproducts.com, pg 735

Harkless, Scott, Alcorn McBride Inc, 3300 S Hiawassee Rd, Bldg 105, Orlando, FL 32835 Tel: 407-296-5800 Fax: 407-296-5801 E-mail: info@alcorn.com; sales@alcorn.com Web Site: www.alcorn.com, pg 679

Harlan, W Bruce, Lighting & Production Equipment Inc, 590 Travis St, Atlanta, GA 30318 Tel: 404-352-0464 Toll Free Tel: 800-275-3721 Fax: 404-351-4399 Web Site: www.lpe.com, pg 807

Harless, Joe, Shaker Microphones & Promotions Inc, 701 W Newman Ave, Harrison, AR 72601 Tel: 870-204-6152 E-mail: shakermicrophone@shakermicrophone.net Web Site: www.shakermicrophone.net, pg 885

Harmer, David, Freedoms Foundation National Awards, 1601 Valley Forge Rd, Valley Forge, PA 19481 Tel: 610-933-8825 Fax: 610-935-0522 E-mail: info@ffvf.org Web Site: www.freedomsfoundation.org, pg 989

Harmer, Kris, Voice of Democracy Scholarship Program, 406 W 34 St, Kansas City, MO 64111 Tel: 816-968-1117 Fax: 816-968-1149 Web Site: www.vfw.org, pg 1006

Harmon, Bobby, Harmon's Audio-Visual Services, 2533 Crystal Dr, Fort Myers, FL 33966 Tel: 239-939-2273 Fax: 239-939-5966 E-mail: info@harmonsav.com Web Site: www.harmonsav.com, pg 776

Harmon, Dan, Starburns Industries, 1700 W Burbank Blvd, Burbank, CA 91506 Tel: 818-433-3300 Fax: 818-433-3383 E-mail: contact@starburnsind.com Web Site: www.starburnsindustries.com, pg 900

Harmon, James R, Harmon's Audio-Visual Services, 2533 Crystal Dr, Fort Myers, FL 33966 Tel: 239-939-2273 Fax: 239-939-5966 E-mail: info@harmonsav.com Web Site: www.harmonsav.com, pg 776

Harmon, Nicholas, Verilux® - The Healthy Lighting Co, 340 Mad River Park, Suite 1, Waitsfield, VT 05673 Tel: 802-496-3101 Toll Free Tel: 888-544-4865 (cust support); 800-454-4408 (orders) Fax: 802-496-3105 (orders) E-mail: info@verilux.com Web Site: www.verilux.com, pg 926

Harmon, Rachel, Sagebrush Video Productions, 2304 County Rd 370, Otis, KS 67565 Tel: 785-222-3313 Web Site: www.sagebrushvideo.com, pg 879

Harmon, Tom, Utah Scientific Inc, 4750 Wiley Post Way, Suite 150, Salt Lake City, UT 84116 Tel: 801-575-8801 Toll Free Tel: 800-453-8782 Fax: 801-537-3099 E-mail: info@utahscientific.com Web Site: utahscientific.com, pg 924

Harms, Bjorn, Pioneer Research Inc, 97 Foster Rd, Suite 5, Moorestown, NJ 08057 Tel: 856-866-9191 Toll Free Tel: 800-257-7742 Fax: 856-866-8615 E-mail: info@pioneer-research.com Web Site: www.pioneer-research.com, pg 857

Harms, Fred, Extraordinary Demos/Videos, 2131 Yellowstar Lane, Naperville, IL 60564-5330 Tel: 630-904-3636 Web Site: www.extraordinaryvideos.com, pg 757

Harms, Sven E, Pioneer Research Inc, 97 Foster Rd, Suite 5, Moorestown, NJ 08057 Tel: 856-866-9191 Toll Free Tel: 800-257-7742 Fax: 856-866-8615 E-mail: info@pioneer-research.com Web Site: www.pioneer-research.com, pg 857

Harn, Dee Ann, Bulbman Inc, 630 Sunshine Lane, Reno, NV 89502 Tel: 775-788-5661 Toll Free Tel: 800-648-1163 Fax: 775-329-6599 Toll Free Fax: 800-548-6216 E-mail: service@bulbman.com Web Site: www.bulbman.com, pg 712

Harnell, Sharron, Cinema Concepts, 2030 Powers Ferry Rd, Suite 214, Atlanta, GA 30339 Tel: 770-956-7460 Toll Free Tel: 800-SHOWADS (746-9237) Fax: 770-956-8358 E-mail: info@cinemaconcepts.com Web Site: www.cinemaconcepts.com, pg 724

Harold, Jeremy, United Sound & Electronics, 525 E Main St, Bridgeport, WV 26330 Tel: 304-842-6030 E-mail: questions@unitedsound.net Web Site: www.unitedsound.net, pg 921

Harold, Rob, United Sound & Electronics, 525 E Main St, Bridgeport, WV 26330 Tel: 304-842-6030 E-mail: questions@unitedsound.net Web Site: www.unitedsound.net, pg 921

Harper, Colleen, Audio Engineering Society (AES), 551 Fifth Ave, Suite 1225, New York, NY 10176 Tel: 212-661-8528 Web Site: www.aes.org, pg 951

Harper, Malcolm H Jr, Reelsound Recording Co, 701 Southern Dr, Buda, TX 78610 Tel: 512-312-1610; 512-422-7098 (cell) Web Site: www.reelsound-usa.com, pg 872

Harpur, Reg, Warner Bros Entertainment Inc, 4000 Warner Blvd, Burbank, CA 91522 E-mail: wbsf@warnerbros.com Web Site: www.warnerbros.com/studio; studiofacilities.warnerbros.com, pg 934

Harrell, Colin, American AV, 8005 Haute Ct, Springfield, VA 22150 Tel: 703-573-6910 Fax: 703-573-3539 E-mail: sales@aavevents.com Web Site: www.aavevents.com, pg 683

Harrington, Brent, 3008, 3008 Ross Ave, Suite 100, Dallas, TX 75204 Tel: 214-922-9232 Fax: 214-922-8861 Web Site: www.3008.com, pg 913

Harrington, Marissa, Questar Entertainment Inc, 307 N Michigan Ave, 5th fl, Chicago, IL 60601-5305 Tel: 312-266-9400 Toll Free Tel: 800-544-8422 (cust serv) E-mail: info@questarentertainment.com Web Site: www.questarentertainment.com, pg 868

Harris, Adam, CVW Event Productions, 470 Spring Park Place, Suite 900, Herndon, VA 20170 Tel: 703-891-2620 Fax: 703-891-2625 E-mail: info@cvwevents.com Web Site: cvwevents.com, pg 736

Harris, Al, Educational Activities Inc, PO Box 87, Baldwin, NY 11510-0087 Tel: 516-223-4666 Toll Free Tel: 800-797-3223 Fax: 516-623-9282 Web Site: edact.com, pg 750

Harris, Aleta, Spot Media Production Group, 2745 Locust St, St Louis, MO 63103 Tel: 314-667-5915 E-mail: info@spotmpg.com Web Site: www.spotmpg.com, pg 898

Harris, Bill, Channell One Video, PO Box 399, Epping, NH 03042-0399 Tel: 603-679-6796 E-mail: racevid@earthlink.net, pg 720

Harris, Chris, SirsiDynix, 3300 N Ashton Blvd, Suite 500, Lehi, UT 84043 Tel: 801-223-5200; 0800 016 3147 Toll Free Tel: 800-288-8020 Fax: 801-331-7770 Web Site: www.sirsidynix.com, pg 889

Harris, Dave, Studio B Mastering, 821 Louise Ave, Charlotte, NC 28204 Tel: 704-372-9661 Web Site: www.studiobmastering.com, pg 902

Harris, Don, Paramount Pictures Corporation, 5555 Melrose Ave, Los Angeles, CA 90038 Tel: 323-956-8398 Web Site: www.paramount.com, pg 851

Harris, Ed, Myriad Productions, 415 Barlow Ct, Johns Creek, GA 30022 Tel: 678-417-0043 Fax: 678-417-0043, pg 835

Harris, Greg, Jameco Electronics, 1355 Shoreway Rd, Belmont, CA 94002 Tel: 650-592-8097 Toll Free Tel: 800-831-4242 (orders); 800-536-4316 (cust serv) Fax: 650-592-2503 Toll Free Fax: 800-237-6948 E-mail: info@jameco.com; sales@jameco.com Web Site: www.jameco.com, pg 792

Harris, Jere, Production Resource Group LLC (PRG), 200 Business Park Dr, Suite 109, Armonk, NY 10504 Tel: 212-589-5400 Toll Free Tel: 877-774-7088 E-mail: info@prg.com Web Site: www.prg.com, pg 864

Harris, Joel, Avidex Inc, 13555 Bel-Red Rd, Suite 226, Bellevue, WA 98005 Tel: 425-643-0330 Toll Free Tel: 800-798-0330 Fax: 425-274-7091 E-mail: info@avidexav.com Web Site: www.avidexav.com, pg 699

Harris, John, Blue Room Post, MBS Raleigh Studios, Bldg 5-A, Suite 100, 1600 Rosecrans Ave, Manhattan Beach, CA 90266 *Tel:* 310-727-2600 *Web Site:* www. blueroompost.com, pg 708

Harris, Nancy, American Film Institute (AFI), Attn: Facilities Off, 2021 N Western Ave, Los Angeles, CA 90027-1657 *Tel:* 323-856-7600 *Toll Free Tel:* 800-774-4AFI (774-4234 membership) *Fax:* 323-462-4049 *E-mail:* information@afi.com *Web Site:* www.afi.com, pg 948

Harris, Dr Phillip, Association for Educational Communications and Technology (AECT), 320 W Eighth St, Suite 101, Bloomington, IN 47404-3745 *Tel:* 812-335-7675 *Toll Free Tel:* 877-677-AECT (677-2328) *Fax:* 812-335-7678 *E-mail:* aect@aect.org *Web Site:* www.aect.org, pg 950

Harris, Dr Phillip, James W Brown Publication Award, 320 W Eighth St, Suite 101, Bloomington, IN 47404-3745 *Tel:* 812-335-7675 *Toll Free Tel:* 877-677-AECT (677-2328) *Fax:* 812-335-7678 *E-mail:* aect@aect.org *Web Site:* www.aect.org, pg 984

Harris, Russell, Perennial Pictures Film Corp, 2102 E 52 St, Indianapolis, IN 46205 *Tel:* 317-253-1519 *E-mail:* mail@perennialpictures.com *Web Site:* www. perennialpictures.com, pg 854

Harris, Wesley, The Virginia Film Festival, 617 W Main St, 2nd fl, Charlottesville, VA 22903 *Tel:* 434-982-5277 *Fax:* 434-924-3374 *E-mail:* info@ virginiafilmfestival.org; vffsubmissions@virginia.edu *Web Site:* virginiafilmfestival.org, pg 1006

Harris, Wylecia Wiggs PhD, American Health Information Management Association (AHIMA), 233 N Michigan Ave, 21st fl, Chicago, IL 60601-5809 *Tel:* 312-233-1100 *Toll Free Tel:* 800-335-5535 *Fax:* 312-233-1090; 312-233-1500 (orders) *E-mail:* info@ahima.org *Web Site:* www.ahima.org, pg 949

Harrison, Brad, Audioarts Engineering, 600 Industrial Dr, New Bern, NC 28562 *Tel:* 252-638-7000 *Fax:* 252-635-4857 (sales); 252-637-1285 *E-mail:* sales@wheatstone.com *Web Site:* www. wheatstone.com, pg 695

Harrison, Jeff, Harrison Brothers, 47 N Chatham Pkwy, Chapel Hill, NC 27517 *Toll Free Tel:* 866-386-8335; 800-327-4414 *Toll Free Fax:* 800-327-6651 *E-mail:* info@harrisonbros.com *Web Site:* www. thetapeworks.com, pg 776

Harrison, Joshua, St Barth Film Festival, c/o Cobblestone Films, 140 Riverside Dr, No 5D, New York, NY 10024 *Tel:* 212-989-8004 *Fax:* 212-727-1774 *E-mail:* staff@stbarthff.org *Web Site:* www.stbarthff. org, pg 1002

Harrison, Les, Hollywood Sound Systems, 4209 Vanowen Place, Burbank, CA 91505 *Tel:* 323-466-2416 *Fax:* 323-460-2676 *Web Site:* www. hollywoodsound.com, pg 781

Harrison, Margaret, Ingram Content Group LLC, One Ingram Blvd, La Vergne, TN 37086-1986 *Tel:* 615-793-5000 *Toll Free Tel:* 800-937-8000 (retailers); 800-937-5300 (ext 1, libs) *E-mail:* customerservice@ ingramcontent.com *Web Site:* www.ingramcontent.com, pg 787

Harrison, Patricia de Stacy, Corporation for Public Broadcasting (CPB), 401 Ninth St NW, Washington, DC 20004-2129 *Tel:* 202-879-9600 *Toll Free Tel:* 800-272-2190 *Fax:* 202-879-9700 *E-mail:* press@cpb.org *Web Site:* www.cpb.org, pg 953

Harrison, Shelley, Hollywood Sound Systems, 4209 Vanowen Place, Burbank, CA 91505 *Tel:* 323-466-2416 *Fax:* 323-460-2676 *Web Site:* www. hollywoodsound.com, pg 781

Harrison, Simon "Ted", OpenText Corp, 275 Frank Tompa Dr, Waterloo, ON N2L 0A1, Canada *Tel:* 519-888-7111 *Toll Free Tel:* 800-499-6544 *Fax:* 519-888-0677 *Web Site:* www.opentext.com, pg 847

Harrison, Wendell, Rebirth Inc, 81 Chandler St, Detroit, MI 48202 *Tel:* 313-875-0289 *E-mail:* wenhajazz@aol. com *Web Site:* www.rebirthjazz.org, pg 871

Harryman, Michael, Wisconsin Public Television, 821 University Ave, Madison, WI 53706 *Tel:* 608-263-2121 *Toll Free Tel:* 800-422-9707 *Fax:* 608-263-9763 *E-mail:* comments@wpt.org *Web Site:* www.wpt.org, pg 940

Hart, Barry, Pro-Tape & Specialities Inc, 621 Rte 1 S, Suite B, North Brunswick, NJ 08902 *Tel:* 732-346-0900 *Toll Free Tel:* 800-345-0234 *Fax:* 732-729-7373 *Web Site:* www.protapes.com, pg 863

Hart, Jake, Visions Film Festival & Conference, 601 S College Rd, Wilmington, NC 28403 *Tel:* 919-607-0031 *E-mail:* visions7programming@gmail.com; visions7development@gmail.com *Web Site:* www. visionsffc.org, pg 1006

Hart, Jonathan, National Public Radio (NPR), 1111 N Capitol St NE, Washington, DC 20002 *Tel:* 202-513-2000 *Web Site:* www.npr.org, pg 959

Hart, Stephen, Media Cybernetics Inc, 401 N Washington St, Suite 350, Rockville, MD 20850 *Tel:* 301-495-3305 *Fax:* 240-328-6193 *E-mail:* info@ mediacy.com *Web Site:* www.mediacy.com, pg 821

Hart, Tara, Penguin Random House Audio Publishing, 1745 Broadway, New York, NY 10019 *E-mail:* audio@penguinrandomhouse.com *Web Site:* www.penguinrandomhouseaudio.com, pg 853

Hart, Timothy S, Media Systems Design Group, 4253 Stewart Ave, Los Angeles, CA 90066 *Tel:* 310-398-0281 *Web Site:* msd-group.com, pg 822

Harter, Jim, Ghent Manufacturing, 2999 Henkle Dr, Lebanon, OH 45036-9260 *Tel:* 513-932-3445 *Toll Free Tel:* 800-543-0550 *Fax:* 513-932-9252 *E-mail:* customer_service@ghent.com; sales@ghent. com *Web Site:* www.ghent.com, pg 770

Harter, Samantha, HD House, 6312 NW 77 Ct, Miami, FL 33166 *Tel:* 305-597-7359 *Fax:* 305-597-7027 *Web Site:* thehdhouse.com, pg 777

Hartle, Mia Boccella, Argentine Productions Inc, 111 Mayfair Dr, Pittsburgh, PA 15228 *Tel:* 412-341-6448 *E-mail:* engage@argentineproductions.com *Web Site:* argentineproductions.com, pg 688

Hartley, Colleen S, Video Wisconsin Inc, 18110 W Bluemound Rd, Brookfield, WI 53045 *Tel:* 262-785-1110 *Fax:* 262-785-9827 *Web Site:* www. videowisconsin.tv, pg 929

Hartley, Ted, RKO Pictures Inc, 11301 W Olympic Blvd, Suite 510, Los Angeles, CA 90064 *Tel:* 310-277-0707 *Fax:* 310-566-8940 *E-mail:* info@rko.com *Web Site:* rko.com, pg 875

Hartman, Greg, Lion & Fox Recording Studios, 9517 Baltimore Ave, College Park, MD 20740 *Tel:* 301-982-4431 *E-mail:* mail@lionfox.com *Web Site:* www. lionfox.com, pg 809

Hartman, Rob, Lee Hartman & Sons Inc, 3236 Cove Rd NW, Roanoke, VA 24017 *Tel:* 540-366-3493 *Toll Free Tel:* 800-344-1832 *Fax:* 540-362-4659 *E-mail:* info@ leehartman.com; roanokeva@leehartman.com *Web Site:* www.leehartman.com, pg 805

Hartman, Steve M, Lee Hartman & Sons Inc, 3236 Cove Rd NW, Roanoke, VA 24017 *Tel:* 540-366-3493 *Toll Free Tel:* 800-344-1832 *Fax:* 540-362-4659 *E-mail:* info@leehartman.com; roanokeva@ leehartman.com *Web Site:* www.leehartman.com, pg 805

Hartmann, Jess, Promax Systems, 2850 S Fairview St, Santa Ana, CA 92704 *Tel:* 949-861-2700 *Toll Free Tel:* 800-977-6629 *E-mail:* sales@promax.com *Web Site:* www.promax.com, pg 865

Hartwig, Mike, Audio Visual of Milwaukee Inc, 285 N Janacek Rd, Brookfield, WI 53045 *Tel:* 262-432-1077 *Toll Free Tel:* 800-236-6909 *Fax:* 262-432-1078 *E-mail:* avm@avmonline.com *Web Site:* www. avmonline.com, pg 695

Harvey, Brian, Fleetwood Group Inc, 11832 James St, Holland, MI 49424 *Tel:* 616-396-1142 *Toll Free Tel:* 800-257-6390 *Fax:* 616-820-8300 *Web Site:* www. fleetwoodgroup.com; www.fleetwoodelectronics.com; www.fleetwoodfurniture.com, pg 762

Harvey, Michael, The American University, Dept of Performing Arts, 4400 Massachusetts Ave NW, Washington, DC 20016-8053 *Tel:* 202-885-3420 *Fax:* 202-885-1092 *Web Site:* www.american.edu, pg 684

Harvie, Ryan, The Mack Sennett Studios, 1215 Bates Ave, Los Angeles, CA 90029 *Tel:* 323-660-8466 *E-mail:* info@macksennettstudios.net *Web Site:* www. macksennettstudios.net, pg 884

Haskins, Jim, Global TV, 5325 Allard Way, Edmonton, AB T6H 5B8, Canada *Tel:* 780-436-1250 *Fax:* 587-525-9257 *E-mail:* edmonton@globalnews.ca *Web Site:* www.globaltv.com, pg 771

Haslam, John, Skystorm Productions, 103 Commerce St, Suite 100, Lake Mary, FL 32746 *Tel:* 407-328-4747 *Toll Free Tel:* 800-783-8508 *Fax:* 407-328-4479 *E-mail:* info@skystorm.com *Web Site:* www.skystorm. com, pg 890

Hass, Jeff, VDO Lab Inc, 520 White Plains Rd, Suite 500, Tarrytown, NY 10591 *Tel:* 914-467-7860; 914-374-8727 *E-mail:* info@vdolab.net; vdolabinc@gmail. com *Web Site:* vdolab.net, pg 925

Hasselrot, Karl, KOH Design Inc, 540 Barnum Ave, Bridgeport, CT 06608 *Tel:* 203-336-1334 *Fax:* 203-335-9361 *E-mail:* info@kohdesign.com *Web Site:* www.kohdesign.com, pg 801

Hastings, Doug, Avatar Studios, 2675 Scott Ave, Suite G, St Louis, MO 63103 *Tel:* 314-533-2242 *Fax:* 314-533-3349 *E-mail:* info@avatar-studios.com *Web Site:* avatar-studios.com, pg 697

Hastings, Fred, Troxell-CDI, 4675 E Cotton Center Blvd, Suite 155, Phoenix, AZ 85040 *Tel:* 602-437-7240 *Toll Free Tel:* 855-TROXELL (876-9355) *Fax:* 602-752-1299 *Toll Free Fax:* 800-752-1299 *E-mail:* csg@trox. com *Web Site:* www.troxellsolutions.com, pg 918

Hastings, Jeff, Inferno Films, 3404 Guadalupe St, Austin, TX 78705 *Tel:* 512-302-9009 *Fax:* 512-302-9022 *Web Site:* www.infernofilms.com, pg 787

Hatcher, Jay, The Learning House Inc, 427 S Fourth St, Suite 300, Louisville, KY 40202 *Tel:* 502-589-9878 *Fax:* 502-589-9825 *E-mail:* sales@learninghouse. com; info@learninghouse.com *Web Site:* www. learninghouse.com, pg 805

Hatcher, Jim, Human Circuit, 9346 Gaither Rd, Gaithersburg, MD 20877 *Tel:* 240-864-4000 *Web Site:* www.humancircuit.com, pg 782

Hathaway, Milt, FitzCo Sound Inc, 4300 W Wall St, Bldg B, Midland, TX 79703 *Tel:* 432-684-0861 *Fax:* 432-682-9978 *Web Site:* www.fitzcosound.com, pg 762

Hatic, Halid, Vitec Videocom Inc, 14 Progress Dr, Shelton, CT 06484 *Tel:* 203-929-1100 *Fax:* 203-925-2684 *E-mail:* info@vitecgroup.com *Web Site:* www. vitecgroup.com; www.vitecvideocom.com, pg 932

Hattaway, Andrew, Tripp Lite, 1111 W 35 St, Chicago, IL 60609 *Tel:* 773-869-1234 (support); 773-869-1111; 773-869-1773 (sales) *Fax:* 773-869-1329 *E-mail:* international@tripplite.com *Web Site:* www. tripplite.com, pg 918

Haun, Eliza, Chelsea Green Publishing Co, 85 N Main St, Suite 120, White River Junction, VT 05001 *Tel:* 802-295-6300 *Toll Free Tel:* 800-639-4099 (orders) *Fax:* 802-295-6444 *E-mail:* customerservice@ chelseagreen.com *Web Site:* www.chelseagreen.com, pg 721

Hauschel, Raymond, Z-Axis Corp, 4600 S Ulster St, Suite 270, Denver, CO 80237 *Tel:* 303-713-0200 *Toll Free Tel:* 800-827-2947 *E-mail:* info@zaxis.com *Web Site:* www.zaxis.com, pg 944

Havelka, Tony, Tek Gear, 938 Corydon Ave, Winnipeg, MB R3M 0Y5, Canada *Tel:* 204-988-3001 *Fax:* 204-988-3050 *E-mail:* sales@tekgear.com *Web Site:* tekgear.com, pg 909

Hawes-Davis, Doug, High Plains Films, PO Box 8796, Missoula, MT 59807 *Tel:* 406-543-6726 *E-mail:* yak@ highplainsfilms.org *Web Site:* www.highplainsfilms.org, pg 779

Hawkins, Carol Lee, Association for Print Technologies (APTech), 1896 Preston White Dr, Reston, VA 20191 *Tel:* 703-264-7200 *Fax:* 703-620-0994 *E-mail:* aptech@aptech.org *Web Site:* www. printtechnologies.org, pg 950

Hawkins, Philip, R L Drake Co, 710 Pleasant Valley Dr, Springboro, OH 45066 *Tel:* 937-746-4556 *Fax:* 937-806-1510 *E-mail:* salesgroup@rldrake.net *Web Site:* www.rldrake.com, pg 746

Hawley, Brian, F&F Productions LLC, 14333 Myerlake Circle, Clearwater, FL 33760 *Tel:* 727-530-5000 *Fax:* 727-535-6547 *E-mail:* info@fandfhd.tv *Web Site:* www.fandfhd.tv, pg 759

Hay, Evan, Samson Technologies Corp, 278-B Duffy Ave, Hicksville, NY 11801 *Tel:* 516-870-7200 *Fax:* 516-938-1696 *E-mail:* info@samsontech.com *Web Site:* www.samsontech.com, pg 879

Hayash, Ted, Digital Film Studios LLC, 11800 Sheldon St, Unit C/D, Sun Valley, CA 91352 *Tel:* 818-771-0019 *Web Site:* www.digitalfilmstudios.com, pg 742

Hayden, Tom, TSR/Baja/Damabi Records, 18653 Ventura Blvd, Suite 513, Tarzana, CA 91356 *Tel:* 818-702-9902, pg 919

Hayes, Chris, Eastern Effects Inc, 99 Ninth St, Brooklyn, NY 11215 *Tel:* 718-855-1197 *Toll Free Tel:* 888-566-6547 *Web Site:* easterneffects.com, pg 749

Hayes, Chris, Showman Fabricators Inc, 148 E Fifth St, Bayonne, NJ 07002 *Tel:* 718-935-9899 *E-mail:* info@showfab.com *Web Site:* www.showfab.com, pg 887

Hayes, Kevin, NEP Group Inc, 2 Beta Dr, Pittsburgh, PA 15238 *Tel:* 412-826-1414 *Toll Free Tel:* 800-444-0054 *E-mail:* info@nepinc.com *Web Site:* www.nepgroup. com, pg 838

Hayes, Tom, Telemotions LLC, 405 E 54 St, Suite 3-N, New York, NY 10022 *Tel:* 212-486-3010 *Web Site:* www.telemotions.net, pg 910

Haymes, Jeff H, Aardvark Productions LLC, 6738 S La Rosa Dr, Tempe, AZ 85283-3737 *Tel:* 480-775-8237 *Fax:* 480-775-8237 *E-mail:* aardvarkproductions@ cox.net *Web Site:* www.aardvarkproductionsllc.com, pg 671

Haynes, Bruce, ACCO Brands Corp, 4 Corporate Dr, Lake Zurich, IL 60047-8997 *Toll Free Tel:* 800-541-0094; 800-222-6462 *Toll Free Fax:* 800-941-4463 *E-mail:* contactus@acco.com (cust serv) *Web Site:* www.accobrands.com, pg 673

Haynes, Pam, West Virginia Film Office, 90 MacCorkle Ave SW, South Charleston, WV 25303 *Toll Free Tel:* 866-6WV-FILM (698-3456) *Fax:* 304-558-1662 *E-mail:* wvfilm@wv.gov *Web Site:* wvfilm.com, pg 977

Haynie, Kerry, Anonymous Content, 3532 Hayden Ave, Culver City, CA 90232 *Tel:* 310-558-6000 *Fax:* 310-558-2724 *E-mail:* filmtv@anonymouscontent.com *Web Site:* www.anonymouscontent.com, pg 686

Haynor, Dow, Golden Lamb Productions, 47 Schoolhouse Rd, Nassau, NY 12123 *Tel:* 518-766-4358 *Web Site:* www.glpvideoproduction.com, pg 772

Hays, John, Inner Traditions International, One Park St, Rochester, VT 05767 *Tel:* 802-767-3174 *Toll Free Tel:* 800-246-8648 *Fax:* 802-767-3726 *E-mail:* customerservice@innertraditions.com *Web Site:* www.innertraditions.com, pg 788

Hays, Ray, Gemstone Media Inc, 8280 Princeton Square Blvd W, Suite 4, Jacksonville, FL 32256 *Tel:* 904-354-1500 *E-mail:* service@gemstonemediainc.com *Web Site:* www.gemstonemediainc.com, pg 769

Hays, Scott, REI - Radio Engineering Industries, 6534 "L" St, Omaha, NE 68117 *Tel:* 402-339-2200 *Toll Free Tel:* 800-228-9275 (sales); 877-726-4617 (tech support) *Fax:* 402-339-1704 *E-mail:* info@radioeng. com; orderdesk@radioeng.com *Web Site:* www. radioeng.com, pg 873

Haythorn, Gregg, PortaBrace Inc, 160 Benmont Ave, Suite 100, North Bennington, VT 05201 *Tel:* 802-442-8171 *Fax:* 802-442-9118 *E-mail:* info@portabrace.com *Web Site:* www.portabrace.com, pg 859

Hayward, Elizabeth, University of Vermont, Instructional Television Dept, 538 Main St, Burlington, VT 05405 *Tel:* 802-656-2927 *E-mail:* video@uvm.edu *Web Site:* www.uvm.edu; www.uvm.edu/~video, pg 923

Hayward, Joe, Wintergreen Learning Materials, 3075 Line 8, RR2, Bradford, ON L3Z 3R5, Canada *Tel:* 905-778-8584 *Toll Free Tel:* 800-268-1268 *Toll Free Fax:* 800-567-8054 *E-mail:* info@wintergreen. ca; sales@wintergreen.ca; custserv@wintergreen.ca *Web Site:* www.wintergreen.ca, pg 940

Hayward, Michael, Wintergreen Learning Materials, 3075 Line 8, RR2, Bradford, ON L3Z 3R5, Canada *Tel:* 905-778-8584 *Toll Free Tel:* 800-268-1268 *Toll Free Fax:* 800-567-8054 *E-mail:* info@wintergreen. ca; sales@wintergreen.ca; custserv@wintergreen.ca *Web Site:* www.wintergreen.ca, pg 940

Headley, Cameron, Telect Inc, 22425 E Appleway Ave, Liberty Lake, WA 99019 *Tel:* 509-926-6000 *Toll Free Tel:* 800-551-4567 *E-mail:* getinfo@telect.com *Web Site:* www.telect.com, pg 910

Healey, Johnny, FJ Productions Inc, 14900 Ventura Blvd, Suite 350, Sherman Oaks, CA 91403-3465 *Tel:* 818-788-0153 *E-mail:* contact@fjproductions.com *Web Site:* www.fjproductions.com, pg 762

Healy, Anoushka, News Corp, 1211 Avenue of the Americas, New York, NY 10036 *Tel:* 212-416-3400 *E-mail:* media@newscorp.com *Web Site:* newscorp. com, pg 840

Healy, Greg, Britannica Digital Learning, 325 N La Salle St, Suite 200, Chicago, IL 60654 *Toll Free Tel:* 800-621-3900 *Toll Free Fax:* 800-344-9624 *E-mail:* contact@eb.com; bdlpress@eb.com *Web Site:* britannicalearn.com, pg 710

Healy, Laura, Hartley Film Foundation, 49 Richmondville Ave, Suite 204, Westport, CT 06880 *Tel:* 203-226-9500 *Toll Free Tel:* 800-937-1819 *Fax:* 203-227-6938 *E-mail:* info@hartleyfoundation. org *Web Site:* hartleyfoundation.org, pg 776

Heaney, John P, Shook Mobile Technology LP, 7451 FM 3009, Schertz, TX 78154 *Tel:* 210-651-5700 *Toll Free Tel:* 888-651-5775 *Fax:* 210-651-5220 *E-mail:* shook@shook-usa.com *Web Site:* www.shook-usa.com, pg 886

Heap, Dustin, Signs.com, 1550 S Gladiola St, Salt Lake City, UT 84104 *Tel:* 801-441-3400 *Toll Free Tel:* 888-222-4929 *E-mail:* support@signs.com *Web Site:* www. signs.com, pg 888

Heape, Steven R, Rich-Heape Films Inc, 5952 Royal Lane, Suite 254, Dallas, TX 75230 *Tel:* 214-696-6916 *Toll Free Tel:* 888-600-2922 *Web Site:* www.richheape. com, pg 875

Heard, Janet, Davies Publishing Inc, 32 S Raymond Ave, Suites 4-5, Pasadena, CA 91105 *Tel:* 626-792-3046 *Toll Free Tel:* 877-792-0005 (US only) *Fax:* 626-792-5308 *E-mail:* info@daviespublishing. com *Web Site:* daviespublishing.com, pg 738

Hearn, Bill, Capitol Christian Music Group, 101 Winners Circle, Brentwood, TN 37027 *Tel:* 615-371-4300 *Toll Free Tel:* 800-877-4443 (sales) *Fax:* 615-371-6980 (sales) *E-mail:* ccmgdistribution@umusic.com (sales) *Web Site:* www.capitolchristianmusicgroup.com, pg 716

Hearn, Hannah, Visions Film Festival & Conference, 601 S College Rd, Wilmington, NC 28403 *Tel:* 919-607-0031 *E-mail:* visions7programming@gmail.com; visions7development@gmail.com *Web Site:* www. visionsffc.org, pg 1006

Hearon, Craig, ACS Technologies, 180 Dunbarton Dr, Florence, SC 29501 *Tel:* 843-662-1681 *Toll Free Tel:* 800-736-7425 (sales); 800-669-2309 (support) *Fax:* 843-669-7513 *E-mail:* info@acstechnologies.com *Web Site:* www.acstechnologies.com, pg 674

Heath, Rosemary F, Goddard Design Co, 51 Nassau Ave, Brooklyn, NY 11222 *Tel:* 718-599-0170 *Fax:* 718-599-0172 *E-mail:* sales@goddarddesign.com *Web Site:* www.goddarddesign.com, pg 772

Heath-Carrico, Kimmi, Sarasota County Film & Entertainment Office, 1680 Fruitville Rd, Suite 402, Sarasota, FL 34236 *Tel:* 941-309-1200 (ext 104) *Fax:* 941-309-1209 *E-mail:* info@filmsarasota.com *Web Site:* www.filmsarasota.com, pg 970

Heatherly, Stacy, Eastern Nebraska Film Office, 302 S Woodland Ct, Fremont, NE 68025 *Tel:* 402-968-4280 *E-mail:* filminnebraska@gmail.com *Web Site:* www. facebook.com/easternebraskafilmoffice, pg 973

Hebel, Kurt, Symbolic Sound Corp, 206 N Randolph St, Suite 520, Champaign, IL 61820 *Tel:* 217-355-6273 *E-mail:* info-kyma@symbolicsound.com *Web Site:* kyma.symbolicsound.com, pg 905

Hecht, Marlen, Teatown Communications Group, 1560 Broadway, New York, NY 10036 *Tel:* 212-302-0722 *E-mail:* info@teatown.tv, pg 908

Hecht, Tracey, Fabled Films LLC, 200 Park Ave S, 15th fl, New York, NY 10003 *Tel:* 212-220-5804 *E-mail:* info@fabledfilms.com *Web Site:* www. fabledfilms.com, pg 758

Heck, Dorothea, International Ticketing Association Inc (INTIX), 5868 E 71 St, Suite E 367, Indianapolis, IN 46220 *Tel:* 212-629-4036 *Fax:* 212-629-4036 *E-mail:* info@intix.org; media@intix.org *Web Site:* www.intix.org, pg 957

Heck, Jay, Laser Fantasy/HECK Industries/Photon Manufacturing, 4228 159 Ave SE, Bellevue, WA 98006 *Tel:* 425-890-6026 (software & creative support); 425-214-0777 (hardware & tech support) *Toll Free Tel:* 866-299-6849 *E-mail:* info@heckindustries. com *Web Site:* www.laserfantasy.com, pg 804

Hedges, Mary Allyn, Oxford Film Commission, 1013 Jackson Ave E, Oxford, MS 38655 *Tel:* 662-232-2477 *Toll Free Tel:* 800-758-9177 *E-mail:* tourism@ visitoxfordms.com *Web Site:* visitoxfordms.com, pg 972

Hedges, Thomas D, American Visions, One Deerfield Lane, Cedar Rapids, IA 52403 *Tel:* 319-360-3211 *Web Site:* www.americanvisions.org, pg 684

Hedlund, Dennis M, Kultur International Films Ltd Inc, PO Box 755, Forked River, NJ 08731 *Tel:* 732-784-6470 *Toll Free Tel:* 888-329-2580 *Toll Free Fax:* 866-205-2744 *E-mail:* support@kultur.com *Web Site:* www.kulturvideo.com, pg 802

Hedquist, Jeffrey P, Hedquist Productions Inc, PO Box 1475, Fairfield, IA 52556-1475 *Tel:* 641-472-6708 *Toll Free Fax:* 855-510-5726 *Web Site:* www.hedquist.com, pg 778

Hedrick, Tim, EASI, 21477 Orchid Ave, Mason City, IA 50401 *Tel:* 641-424-5079 *Toll Free Tel:* 888-327-4797 *Fax:* 641-424-8869 *Web Site:* easisat.com, pg 749

Heeman, Mark, Audio Visual Dynamics®, 424 Sand Shore Rd, Hackettstown, NJ 07840 *Tel:* 973-993-8500 *Fax:* 973-984-0644 *Web Site:* www.avdusa.com, pg 694

Heffernan, Margaret, WGBH Production Group, One Guest St, Boston, MA 02135 *Tel:* 617-300-2000 *E-mail:* productiongroup@wgbh.org; studios@wgbh. org; outpost@wgbh.org *Web Site:* productiongroup. wgbh.org, pg 936

Heffernan, Paul, Heffernan Audio Visual, 616 W Rhapsody, San Antonio, TX 78216 *Tel:* 210-732-4333, pg 778

Hefty, Gwen, CCH Continuing Education, 2700 Lake Cook Rd, Riverwoods, IL 60015 *Tel:* 773-866-3648 *Toll Free Tel:* 800-248-3248 *Fax:* 773-866-3084 *Web Site:* www.cch.com, pg 718

Hegedus, Chris, Pennebaker Hegedus Films Inc, 262 W 91 St, New York, NY 10024 *Tel:* 212-496-9195 *Fax:* 212-496-8195 *E-mail:* info@phfilms.com *Web Site:* phfilms.com, pg 854

Heidemann, Mark, Historic Films, 211 Third St, Greenport, NY 11944 *Tel:* 631-477-9700 *Toll Free Tel:* 800-249-1940 *Fax:* 631-477-9800 *E-mail:* info@ historicfilms.com *Web Site:* www.historicfilms.com, pg 780

Heidenreich, John, Town of Bel Air Film Festival, 37 N Main St, Bel Air, MD 21014 *Tel:* 410-838-0584 *Web Site:* www.townofbelairfilmfestival.com, pg 1005

Heidenreich, Trish, Town of Bel Air Film Festival, 37 N Main St, Bel Air, MD 21014 *Tel:* 410-838-0584 *Web Site:* www.townofbelairfilmfestival.com, pg 1005

Heiligenberg, Paul, Staco Energy Products Co, 301 Gaddis Blvd, Dayton, OH 45403 *Tel:* 937-253-1191 *Toll Free Tel:* 866-261-1191 *Fax:* 937-253-1723 *E-mail:* sales@stacoenergy.com; service@stacoenergy.com *Web Site:* www.stacoenergy.com, pg 898

Heim, Alan, American Cinema Editors Inc (ACE), Max Bros Bldg, Rm 108, 5555 Melrose Ave, Los Angeles, CA 90038 *Tel:* 323-956-2900 *E-mail:* admin@americancinemaeditors.com *Web Site:* americancinemaeditors.org, pg 948

Heimbold, Andrew, Reality Check Systems, 726 S Flower St, Burbank, CA 91502 *Tel:* 323-465-3900 *Fax:* 323-465-3600 *E-mail:* info@realitychecksystems.com *Web Site:* www.realityx.com, pg 871

Heimbold, Steven, Reality Check Systems, 726 S Flower St, Burbank, CA 91502 *Tel:* 323-465-3900 *Fax:* 323-465-3600 *E-mail:* info@realitychecksystems.com *Web Site:* www.realityx.com, pg 871

Heindel, Jake, WMS Media Inc, 189 W Santa Clara St, San Jose, CA 95110 *Tel:* 510-825-7402 *E-mail:* info@wmsmedia.com *Web Site:* www.wmsmedia.com, pg 940

Heins, Scott, Creative Technology (CT), 2200 S Mount Prospect Rd, Unit A, Des Plaines, IL 60018 *Tel:* 847-671-9670 *E-mail:* info@ctus.com *Web Site:* www.ct-group.com, pg 733

Heinz, Harro K, Renkus-Heinz Inc, 19201 Cook St, Foothill Ranch, CA 92610-3501 *Tel:* 949-588-9997 *Fax:* 949-588-9514 *E-mail:* sales@renkus-heinz.com *Web Site:* www.renkus-heinz.com, pg 873

Heinz, Ralph, Renkus-Heinz Inc, 19201 Cook St, Foothill Ranch, CA 92610-3501 *Tel:* 949-588-9997 *Fax:* 949-588-9514 *E-mail:* sales@renkus-heinz.com *Web Site:* www.renkus-heinz.com, pg 873

Heiser, Adam, Odyssey Productions Inc, 2800 NW Thurman St, Portland, OR 97210 *Tel:* 503-223-3480 *Fax:* 503-223-3493 *E-mail:* info@odysseypro.com *Web Site:* www.odysseypro.com, pg 844

Heiser, Steve, Odyssey Productions Inc, 2800 NW Thurman St, Portland, OR 97210 *Tel:* 503-223-3480 *Fax:* 503-223-3493 *E-mail:* info@odysseypro.com *Web Site:* www.odysseypro.com, pg 844

Heiss, Roger, Tone Zone Recording, 939 W Wilson Ave, Chicago, IL 60640 *Tel:* 312-664-5353 *Fax:* 312-664-6560 *E-mail:* tonezonerecording@sbcglobal.net, pg 915

Heitmann, Kurt, CP Communications, 15 Ninnie Dr, Wappingers Falls, NY 12590 *Tel:* 914-345-9292 *Toll Free Tel:* 800-762-4254 *Fax:* 914-345-9222 *E-mail:* info@cpcomms.com; sales@cpcomms.com *Web Site:* www.cpcomms.com, pg 732

Hejtmanek, Michael, Hasselblad Bron Inc, 1080A Garden State Rd, Union, NJ 07083 *Tel:* 908-754-5800 *Toll Free Tel:* 800-367-6434; 800-456-0203 *Fax:* 908-754-5807 *E-mail:* sales@hasselbladbron.com; servicedept@hasselbladbron.com; productinfo@hasselbladbron.com *Web Site:* www.hasselbladbron.com, pg 776

Helland, Chris M, MAVCO, 77 S Main St, Newtown, CT 06470 *Tel:* 203-270-8292 *Fax:* 203-270-8292, pg 820

Hellen, Melissa, Clarity Media Group, 166 Fifth Ave, 6th & 7th fl, New York, NY 10010 *Tel:* 212-262-7015 *E-mail:* info@claritymediagroup.com *Web Site:* www.claritymediagroup.com, pg 725

Heller, Amy, Milestone Film & Video Inc, PO Box 128, Harrington Park, NJ 07640-0128 *Tel:* 201-767-3117 *Toll Free Tel:* 800-603-1104 *Fax:* 201-767-3035 *E-mail:* milefilms@gmail.com *Web Site:* www.milestonefilms.com, pg 827

Hellman, Robert B, Hellman Associates Inc, 1225 W Fourth St, Waterloo, IA 50702 *Tel:* 319-234-7055 *Toll Free Tel:* 800-747-7055 *Fax:* 319-234-2089 *E-mail:* info@hellman.com *Web Site:* www.hellman.com, pg 778

Hellmers, David, ESL Power Systems, 2800 Palisades Dr, Corona, CA 92880-9427 *Tel:* 951-739-7000 *Toll Free Tel:* 800-922-4188 *Fax:* 951-739-7048 *E-mail:* sales@eslpwr.com; info@eslpwr.com *Web Site:* eslpwr.com, pg 755

Hellmers, Michael, ESL Power Systems, 2800 Palisades Dr, Corona, CA 92880-9427 *Tel:* 951-739-7000 *Toll Free Tel:* 800-922-4188 *Fax:* 951-739-7048 *E-mail:* sales@eslpwr.com; info@eslpwr.com *Web Site:* eslpwr.com, pg 755

Hellmuth, Stephen M, NBA Entertainment Inc, 450 Harmon Meadow Blvd, Secaucus, NJ 07094 *Tel:* 201-865-1500 *Fax:* 201-865-2626 *Web Site:* www.nba.com, pg 837

Hellyer, Jeff, Edit House Chicago, 5325 W Berenice Ave, Chicago, IL 60641 *Tel:* 773-725-1525 *E-mail:* info@edithousechicago.com *Web Site:* www.edithousechicago.com, pg 750

Hellyer, Leny, Edit House Chicago, 5325 W Berenice Ave, Chicago, IL 60641 *Tel:* 773-725-1525 *E-mail:* info@edithousechicago.com *Web Site:* www.edithousechicago.com, pg 750

Helman, Michael, Brooklyn Films, PO Box 20412, New York, NY 10021-0066 *E-mail:* connect@brooklynfilms.com *Web Site:* www.brooklynfilms.com, pg 711

Helman, Michael, WILLiFEST, PO Box 20412, New York, NY 10021-0066 *E-mail:* inquiries@willifest.com; programming@willifest.com; screenplays@willifest.com *Web Site:* www.willifest.com, pg 1007

Helms, George, Video Copy Services Inc, 3980 Dekalb Technology Pkwy, Suite 670, Atlanta, GA 30340 *Tel:* 404-321-6933 *Toll Free Tel:* 800-553-3616 *E-mail:* info@video-copy.com *Web Site:* www.video-copy.com, pg 927

Helms, Mark, Sound & Vision Media, 372 Squire Rd, Revere, MA 02151 *Tel:* 781-284-9707 *E-mail:* info@soundandvisionmedia.com *Web Site:* www.soundandvisionmedia.com, pg 893

Heminway, Jim, Monroe Electronics Inc, 100 Housel Ave, Lyndonville, NY 14098 *Tel:* 585-765-2254 *Fax:* 585-765-9330 *Web Site:* www.monroe-electronics.com, pg 829

Hemminger, Peter, Quickdraw Animation Society, 2011 Tenth Ave SW, Calgary, AB T3C 0K4, Canada *Tel:* 403-261-5767 *E-mail:* info@quickdrawanimation.ca; production@quickdrawanimation.ca; programming@quickdrawanimation.ca *Web Site:* quickdrawanimation.ca; www.giraffest.ca, pg 961

Hempton, Gordon W, Quiet Planet LLC, PO Box 900, Indianola, WA 98342 *Tel:* 360-477-9588 *Web Site:* www.quietplanet.com, pg 868

Henderson, Bruce, Jack Morton Worldwide, 909 Third Ave, New York, NY 10022 *Tel:* 212-401-7000; 212-401-7212 *E-mail:* experience@jackmorton.com *Web Site:* www.jackmorton.com, pg 830

Henderson, Joe, The Jim Henson Co, 1416 N La Brea Ave, Hollywood, CA 90028 *Tel:* 323-802-1500 *Fax:* 323-802-1825 *Web Site:* www.henson.com, pg 794

Henderson, Mark, Atlanta Filmworks, 4280 Northeast Expwy, Atlanta, GA 30340 *E-mail:* info@atlantafilmworks.com *Web Site:* atlantafilmworks.com, pg 692

Hendler, Jared, Sundance Film Festival, 1825 Three Kings Dr, Park City, UT 84060 *Tel:* 435-658-3456 *Fax:* 435-658-3457 *E-mail:* customerservice@sundance.org; press@sundance.org; institute@sundance.org *Web Site:* www.sundance.org/festival, pg 1004

Hendricks, Paula, Oval Window Audio, 33 Wildflower Ct, Nederland, CO 80466 *Tel:* 303-447-3607 *Fax:* 303-447-3607 *E-mail:* info@ovalwindowaudio.com *Web Site:* www.ovalwindowaudio.com, pg 849

Henk, Chad, Xplor® International, 24156 State Rd 54, Suite 4, Lutz, FL 33559 *Tel:* 813-949-6170 *E-mail:* info@xplor.org *Web Site:* www.xplor.org, pg 964

Henk, Skip, Xplor® International, 24156 State Rd 54, Suite 4, Lutz, FL 33559 *Tel:* 813-949-6170 *E-mail:* info@xplor.org *Web Site:* www.xplor.org, pg 964

Hennessey, James R, The Music People Inc, 154 Woodlawn Rd, Suite C, Berlin, CT 06037-1500 *Tel:* 860-829-9229 *Toll Free Tel:* 800-289-8889 *Fax:* 860-828-1353 *E-mail:* support@musicpeopleinc.com *Web Site:* www.musicpeopleinc.com, pg 834

Hennessey, John, The Music People Inc, 154 Woodlawn Rd, Suite C, Berlin, CT 06037-1500 *Tel:* 860-829-9229 *Toll Free Tel:* 800-289-8889 *Fax:* 860-828-1353 *E-mail:* support@musicpeopleinc.com *Web Site:* www.musicpeopleinc.com, pg 834

Hennessey, Larry, MicrophoneRentals.com, 75-3050 Edgemont Blvd, North Vancouver, BC V7R 4X1, Canada *Tel:* 604-980-5703 *E-mail:* info@microphonerentals.com *Web Site:* www.microphonerentals.com, pg 826

Hennessey, Sharon, The Music People Inc, 154 Woodlawn Rd, Suite C, Berlin, CT 06037-1500 *Tel:* 860-829-9229 *Toll Free Tel:* 800-289-8889 *Fax:* 860-828-1353 *E-mail:* support@musicpeopleinc.com *Web Site:* www.musicpeopleinc.com, pg 834

Henninger, Robert L, Henninger Media Services, 1320 N Courthouse Rd, Suite 130, Arlington, VA 22201 *Tel:* 703-243-3444 *Toll Free Tel:* 888-243-3444 *E-mail:* info@henninger.com *Web Site:* www.henninger.com, pg 779

Henry, John Patrick, Boxlight Inc, 1045 Progress Circle, Lawrenceville, GA 30043 *Toll Free Tel:* 866-972-1549 *E-mail:* service@boxlight.com; marketing@boxlight.com *Web Site:* mimio.boxlight.com, pg 709

Hensel, Lynn, Spot Media Production Group, 2745 Locust St, St Louis, MO 63103 *Tel:* 314-667-5915 *E-mail:* info@spotmpg.com *Web Site:* www.spotmpg.com, pg 898

Hensel, Rick, Spot Media Production Group, 2745 Locust St, St Louis, MO 63103 *Tel:* 314-667-5915 *E-mail:* info@spotmpg.com *Web Site:* www.spotmpg.com, pg 898

Hensley, Bill, Furman®, 1800 S McDowell Blvd, Petaluma, CA 94954 *Tel:* 707-283-5900 *Toll Free Tel:* 800-472-5555 *Fax:* 707-283-5901 *E-mail:* powertechsupport@corebrands.com *Web Site:* www.furmanpower.com, pg 767

Hensley, Greg, Greg Hensley Productions, 200 S "E" Ave, Unit 113, New Castle, CO 81647 *Tel:* 970-984-3158 *E-mail:* hensley@sopris.net, pg 779

Henson, Brian, The Jim Henson Co, 1416 N La Brea Ave, Hollywood, CA 90028 *Tel:* 323-802-1500 *Fax:* 323-802-1825 *Web Site:* www.henson.com, pg 794

Henson, Kristi, Wickenburg Film Commission, 216 N Frontier St, Wickenburg, AZ 85390 *Tel:* 928-684-5479; 928-684-0977 *Toll Free Tel:* 800-942-5242 *Fax:* 928-684-5470 *E-mail:* info@wickenburgchamber.com *Web Site:* www.wickenburgchamber.com/film-commission, pg 965

Henson, Lisa Esq, The Jim Henson Co, 1416 N La Brea Ave, Hollywood, CA 90028 *Tel:* 323-802-1500 *Fax:* 323-802-1825 *Web Site:* www.henson.com, pg 794

Henson, Trista, WVLA-TV, 10,000 Perkins Rd, Baton Rouge, LA 70810 *Tel:* 225-766-3233 *Fax:* 225-768-9293 *Web Site:* www.brproud.com, pg 942

Henthorn, Jeremy, Columbus International Film + Video Festival, 60 Cleveland Ave, Columbus, OH 43215 *Tel:* 614-222-6185 *E-mail:* info@columbusfilmfestival.org *Web Site:* www.ccad.edu/experience-art/columbus-international-film-festival, pg 987

Herb, John, ARC Document Solutions, 1981 N Broadway, Suite 385, Walnut Creek, CA 94596 *Tel:* 925-949-5100 *Toll Free Tel:* 855-500-0660 *E-mail:* contact@e-arc.com *Web Site:* www.e-arc.com, pg 688

Herb, Peter, Magnicon Media/Image d'Or, 5050 Williamson St, Dearborn, MI 48126 *Tel:* 313-846-8694; 313-574-3546 (cell), pg 815

Herbert, Georgeann, WTVS, Detroit Public Television, Riley Broadcast Ctr, One Clover Ct, Wixom, MI 48393-2247 *Tel:* 248-305-DPTV (305-3788); 313-872-7500 *E-mail:* email@dptv.org *Web Site:* www.dptv.org, pg 942

Herbert, John, Northeast Video Productions Inc, Box 8425, Sleepy Hollow, NY 10591 *Tel:* 914-714-0703, pg 842

Herbert, Mark, Nexsan Inc, 900 E Hamilton Ave, Suite 230, Campbell, CA 95008 *Tel:* 408-724-9809 *E-mail:* sales@nexsan.com *Web Site:* www.nexsan.com, pg 840

Hergert, Karl, Cinema Stage Inc, 110 Saunders Rd, Unit 4, Barrie, ON L4N 9A8, Canada *Tel:* 705-733-8740 *Toll Free Tel:* 800-387-6205 *Fax:* 705-733-8742 *E-mail:* info@cinemastage.ca *Web Site:* www.cinemastage.ca, pg 724

Herman, Bruce, Diversified, 37 Market St, Kenilworth, NJ 07033 *Tel:* 908-245-4833 *Fax:* 908-245-0011 *E-mail:* customerservice@diversifiedus.com; info@diversifiedus.com *Web Site:* diversifiedus.com, pg 744

Hermann, Kevin, REI - Radio Engineering Industries, 6534 "L" St, Omaha, NE 68117 *Tel:* 402-339-2200 *Toll Free Tel:* 800-228-9275 (sales); 877-726-4617 (tech support) *Fax:* 402-339-1704 *E-mail:* info@radioeng.com; orderdesk@radioeng.com *Web Site:* www.radioeng.com, pg 873

Hermes, Randy, Aerial Video Systems, 3200 W Valhalla Dr, Burbank, CA 91505 *Tel:* 818-954-8842 *Fax:* 818-954-8842 *E-mail:* info@aerialvideo.com *Web Site:* aerialvideo.com, pg 678

Hernandez, Aaron R, Gefen, 20600 Nordhoff St, Chatsworth, CA 91311 *Tel:* 818-772-9100 *Toll Free Tel:* 800-545-6900; 800-472-5555 *Fax:* 818-772-9120 *E-mail:* sales@gefen.com; support@gefen.com *Web Site:* www.gefen.com, pg 769

Hernandez, Jorge, Different Fur Recording Ltd, 3470 19 St, San Francisco, CA 94110 *Tel:* 415-828-4060 (bookings) *Web Site:* differentfurstudios.com, pg 741

Hernandez, Juan, Source Film Studio, 1111 N Beachwood Dr, Hollywood, CA 90038 *Tel:* 323-463-5555 *E-mail:* info@sourcefilmstudio.com *Web Site:* www.sourcefilmstudio.com, pg 895

Heroux-Laferte, Virgil, International Film Festival in Abitibi-Teiscamingue, 215 Ave Mercier, Rouyn-Noranda, QC J9X 5W8, Canada *Tel:* 819-762-6212 *Fax:* 819-762-6762 *E-mail:* info@festivalcinema.ca *Web Site:* festivalcinema.ca, pg 993

Herren, R Scott, Autodesk Inc, 111 McInnis Pkwy, San Rafael, CA 94903 *Tel:* 415-507-5000 *Fax:* 415-507-5100 *Web Site:* www.autodesk.com, pg 696

Herrholtz, Kevin, Turning Technologies LLC, 255 W Federal St, Youngstown, OH 44503 *Tel:* 330-746-3015 *Toll Free Tel:* 866-746-3015 *E-mail:* info@turningtechnologies.com; support@turningtechnologies.com *Web Site:* www.turningtechnologies.com, pg 919

Herrick, Tom, Big Door, 114 Sheldon St, El Segundo, CA 90245 *Tel:* 310-546-6100 *Fax:* 310-906-4585 *E-mail:* sales@bigdoor.tv *Web Site:* www.bigdoor.tv; www.bigdoorstudio.tv, pg 705

Herringer, Steve, The Vocal Point/Profile Communications Ltd, 1196 Habgood St, White Rock, BC V4B 4W9, Canada *Tel:* 604-531-6908 *Web Site:* www.profilecomm.com, pg 932

Herron, Wes, Lectrosonics Inc, 581 Laser Rd NE, Rio Rancho, NM 87124 *Tel:* 505-892-4501 *Toll Free Tel:* 800-821-1121 *Fax:* 505-892-6243 *E-mail:* sales@lectrosonics.com *Web Site:* www.lectrosonics.com, pg 805

Hersh, Stuart, Split Image Productions, 4134 243 St, Flushing, NY 11363-1658 *Tel:* 718-428-1438 *Fax:* 718-428-1438, pg 898

Hertzberg, Paul, CineTel Films Inc, 8484 Wilshire Blvd, Suite 850C, Beverly Hills, CA 90211 *Tel:* 323-654-4000 *Fax:* 323-650-6400 *E-mail:* info@cinetelfilms.com *Web Site:* cinetelfilms.com, pg 724

Hertzler, Chris, SoundSpace Inc, 845 Dayton St, Yellow Springs, OH 45387 *Tel:* 937-767-7353 *E-mail:* soundspace@sbcglobal.net *Web Site:* soundspaceinc.com, pg 895

Heslinga, Duane, L-3 WESCAM, 649 N Service Rd W, Burlington, ON L7P 5B9, Canada *Tel:* 905-633-4000; 905-633-4175 (cust serv) *Toll Free Tel:* 888-593-7226 *Fax:* 905-633-4100 *E-mail:* sales.wescam@l-3com.com *Web Site:* www.wescam.com, pg 803

Hess, Ron, Kinetic Corp, 200 Distillery Commons, Suite 200, Louisville, KY 40206-1990 *Tel:* 502-719-9500 *Fax:* 502-719-9509 *Web Site:* kinetictms.com, pg 799

Hesseltine, Cassandra, Film Liaisons In California Statewide (FLICS), c/o Humboldt-Del Norte Film Commission, 520 "E" St, Eureka, CA 95501 *E-mail:* info@filmcalifornia.com *Web Site:* www.filmcalifornia.com, pg 954

Hesseltine, Cassandra, Humboldt-Del Norte Film Commission, 520 "E" St, Eureka, CA 95501 *Tel:* 707-443-4488 *E-mail:* info@filmhumboldtdelnorte.org *Web Site:* www.filmhumboldtdelnorte.org, pg 966

Hetchler, Michael, Universal Studios Florida® Production Group, 1000 Universal Studios Plaza, Bldg 22A, Orlando, FL 32819 *Tel:* 407-363-8400 *Toll Free Tel:* 877-612-3737 (outside FL) *Fax:* 407-363-8869 *E-mail:* productiongroup@universalorlando.com *Web Site:* studio.florida.universalstudios.com, pg 922

Hetlinger, Bryan, Infosat Communications Inc, 3130 114 Ave SE, Calgary, AB T2Z 3V6, Canada *Tel:* 403-543-8188 *Toll Free Tel:* 888-524-3038 *Fax:* 403-289-8133 *E-mail:* info@infosat.com *Web Site:* infosat.com, pg 787

Hettler, Kurt, Ingram Content Group LLC, One Ingram Blvd, La Vergne, TN 37086-1986 *Tel:* 615-793-5000 *Toll Free Tel:* 800-937-8000 (retailers); 800-937-5300 (ext 1, libs) *E-mail:* customerservice@ingramcontent.com *Web Site:* www.ingramcontent.com, pg 787

Hetzler, Scott, Contemporary Research, 4355 Excel Pkwy, Suite 600, Addison, TX 75001 *Tel:* 972-931-2728 *Toll Free Tel:* 888-972-2728 *E-mail:* contact@crwww.com *Web Site:* contemporaryresearch.com, pg 731

Heuberger, David, Arcor Electronics Co, 5689 W Howard St, Niles, IL 60714 *Tel:* 847-588-0088 *Fax:* 847-588-0080 *E-mail:* sales@arcorelectronics.com *Web Site:* www.arcorelectronics.com, pg 688

Hewitt, John, Alpha Technologies Inc, 3767 Alpha Way, Bellingham, WA 98226 *Tel:* 360-647-2360 *Toll Free Tel:* 800-322-5742 *E-mail:* alpha@alpha.com *Web Site:* www.alpha.com, pg 681

Hewitt, John, Vertiv, 1050 Dearborn Dr, Columbus, OH 43085 *Tel:* 614-888-0246 *Web Site:* www.vertiv.com, pg 926

Heyrman, Joy Peterson, Residency Fellowship, 154 San Angelo Dr, Amherst, VA 24521 *Tel:* 434-946-7236 *Fax:* 434-946-7239 *E-mail:* vcca@vcca.com *Web Site:* www.vcca.com, pg 1001

Heywood, Betty, NAMM, the National Association of Music Merchants, 5790 Armada Dr, Carlsbad, CA 92008 *Tel:* 760-438-8001 *Toll Free Tel:* 800-767-6266 (memb hotline) *Fax:* 760-438-7327 *E-mail:* info@namm.org *Web Site:* www.namm.org, pg 958

Hibbard, Karen, Manhattan Film Commission, 501 Poyntz Ave, Manhattan, KS 66502 *Tel:* 785-776-8829 *Toll Free Tel:* 800-759-0134 *Fax:* 785-776-0679 *E-mail:* cvb@manhattan.org *Web Site:* visitmanhattanks.org, pg 971

Hibbins, Simon, Technicolor USA Inc, 6040 Sunset Blvd, Hollywood, CA 90028 *Tel:* 323-817-6600 *E-mail:* info@technicolor.com *Web Site:* technicolor.com, pg 908

Hickey, John, Wise Audio Video, PO Box 105523, Jefferson City, MO 65110 *Tel:* 573-761-7888 *Toll Free Tel:* 877-775-7888 *Web Site:* www.wiseaudiovideo.com, pg 940

Hickey, Ted Jr, OAP Audio Products, 1000 Peachtree Industrial Blvd, Suite 6-132, Suwanee, GA 30024 *Tel:* 770-945-1033 *Fax:* 678-765-7198 *E-mail:* sales@oapaudio.com *Web Site:* oapaudio.com, pg 844

Hickey, Ted Sr, OAP Audio Products, 1000 Peachtree Industrial Blvd, Suite 6-132, Suwanee, GA 30024 *Tel:* 770-945-1033 *Fax:* 678-765-7198 *E-mail:* sales@oapaudio.com *Web Site:* oapaudio.com, pg 844

Hickinbotham, Gary, Fire Station Studios, 224 N Guadalupe St, San Marcos, TX 78666 *Tel:* 512-396-1144 *Fax:* 512-396-1169 *E-mail:* info@firestationstudios.com *Web Site:* www.firestationstudios.com, pg 761

Hickman, Patricia, Simpson Electric Co, 520 Simpson Ave, Lac du Flambeau, WI 54538-0099 *Tel:* 715-588-3947 (cust serv); 715-588-3311 *Fax:* 715-588-1248 (cust serv); 715-588-3326 *E-mail:* cservice@simpsonelectric.com; support@simpsonelectric.com *Web Site:* www.simpsonelectric.com, pg 889

Hicks, Keith III, Baker Audio Visual, 2195 N Norcross Tucker Rd, Norcross, GA 30071 *Tel:* 770-441-2000 *Toll Free Tel:* 800-847-3523 *Fax:* 770-449-7719 *E-mail:* support@bakeraudiovisual.com *Web Site:* www.bakeraudiovisual.com, pg 700

Hicks, Trey, Visix™ Inc, 230 Scientific Dr, Suite 800, Norcross, GA 30092 *Tel:* 770-446-1416 *Toll Free Tel:* 800-572-4935 *Fax:* 770-448-5724 *E-mail:* info@visix.com *Web Site:* www.visix.com, pg 931

Hicock, David, Animotion Inc, 501 W Fayette St, Syracuse, NY 13204 *Tel:* 315-471-3533 *E-mail:* info@animotioninc.com *Web Site:* animotioninc.com, pg 685

Hiden, Chip, Big Door, 114 Sheldon St, El Segundo, CA 90245 *Tel:* 310-546-6100 *Fax:* 310-906-4585 *E-mail:* sales@bigdoor.tv *Web Site:* www.bigdoor.tv; www.bigdoorstudio.tv, pg 705

Hiett, Richard, Rocktown Media, 1361 Lincolnshire Dr, Harrisonburg, VA 22802 *Tel:* 540-433-7700 *Toll Free Tel:* 888-433-8700 *E-mail:* info@rocktown.tv *Web Site:* www.rocktown.tv, pg 876

Higa, Wade, The Audio Visual Co (AVCO), 98-810 Moanalua Rd, Aiea, HI 96701 *Tel:* 808-485-3200 *Fax:* 808-487-0733 *Web Site:* www.theavco.com, pg 694

Higginbotham, Jaren, Tributestone, 709 N Sixth St, Kansas City, KS 66101 *Tel:* 913-321-3978 *Web Site:* www.tributestone.com, pg 918

Higginbotham, Shelly, Tributestone, 709 N Sixth St, Kansas City, KS 66101 *Tel:* 913-321-3978 *Web Site:* www.tributestone.com, pg 918

Higgins, Clark, RetinaVision Productions, 19 Barker Ave, Fairfax, CA 94930 *Tel:* 415-459-3926, pg 874

Higgins, John, ATX Networks, 8-1602 Tricont Ave, Whitby, ON L1N 7C3, Canada *Tel:* 289-204-7800 *Toll Free Tel:* 866-968-7289 *E-mail:* info@atx.com *Web Site:* atx.com, pg 692

Higgins, Tim, AheadTeK, 6410 Via Del Oro, San Jose, CA 95119 *Tel:* 408-226-9800; 408-226-9991 *Toll Free Tel:* 800-971-9191 *Fax:* 408-226-9195 *Web Site:* www.aheadtek.com, pg 678

Hilderbrand, Karen Mitzo, Twin Sisters® Digital Media™, 1653 Merriman Rd, Suite L1, Akron, OH 44313 *Tel:* 330-730-9558 *E-mail:* twinsisters@twinsisters.com *Web Site:* www.twinsisters.com, pg 920

Hilferty, Gerard, Hilferty & Associates Inc, 14240 State Rte 550, Athens, OH 45701 *Tel:* 740-448-3821 *Fax:* 740-448-2331 *E-mail:* gha@hilferty.com *Web Site:* www.hilferty.com, pg 780

Hill, Camille, Merestone, 7232 E First St, Scottsdale, AZ 85251 *Tel:* 480-945-4631 *Fax:* 480-945-0590 *Web Site:* www.merestone.com, pg 823

Hill, Dave, Jensen Transformers Inc, 9304 Deering Ave, Chatsworth, CA 91311 *Tel:* 818-374-5857 *Toll Free Tel:* 866-476-6291 *Fax:* 818-374-5856 *E-mail:* sales@ jensen-transformers.com; info@jensen-transformers. com *Web Site:* www.jensen-transformers.com, pg 793

Hill, Howard, RF Industries, 7610 Miramar Rd, San Diego, CA 92126 *Tel:* 858-549-6340 *Toll Free Tel:* 800-233-1728 *Fax:* 858-549-6345 *E-mail:* rfi@ rfindustries.com; tech@rfindustries.org; invest@ rfindustries.org *Web Site:* www.rfindustries.com, pg 874

Hill, Jerry, Drytac Corp, 5601 Eastport Blvd, Richmond, VA 23231 *Tel:* 804-222-3094 *Toll Free Tel:* 800-280-6013 *E-mail:* customerservice@drytac.com *Web Site:* www.drytac.com, pg 747

Hill, Jerry, Jerry Hill Steadicam Products, 19160 Arminta St, Reseda, CA 91335-1105 *Tel:* 818-772-9256 *Fax:* 818-772-9251 *E-mail:* jerry@steadimoves. com *Web Site:* steadimoves.com, pg 780

Hill, Julie, Artbeats, 1405 N Myrtle Rd, Myrtle Creek, OR 97457 *Tel:* 541-863-4429 *Fax:* 541-863-4547 *E-mail:* info@artbeats.com *Web Site:* www.artbeats. com, pg 690

Hill, Kassandra, Mary Riepma Ross Media Arts Center, University of Nebraska-Lincoln, 313 N 13 St, Lincoln, NE 68588 *Tel:* 402-472-9100 *Fax:* 402-472-2576 *E-mail:* info@theross.org *Web Site:* www.theross.org, pg 877

Hill, Lori Diane PhD, American Educational Research Association (AERA), 1430 "K" St NW, Suite 1200, Washington, DC 20005 *Tel:* 202-238-3200 *Fax:* 202-238-3250 *E-mail:* communications@aera.net; members@aera.net *Web Site:* www.aera.net, pg 948

Hill, Michael, News Broadcast Network Inc, 75 Broad St, 15th fl, New York, NY 10004 *Web Site:* newsbroadcastnetwork.com, pg 840

Hill, Rob, Merestone, 7232 E First St, Scottsdale, AZ 85251 *Tel:* 480-945-4631 *Fax:* 480-945-0590 *Web Site:* www.merestone.com, pg 823

Hill, Steve, Luxor, 2245 Delany Rd, Waukegan, IL 60087 *Tel:* 847-244-1800 *Toll Free Tel:* 800-323-4656 *Fax:* 847-244-1818 *Toll Free Fax:* 800-327-1698 *E-mail:* info@luxorfurn.com; customerservice@ luxorfurn.com; sales@luxorfurn.com *Web Site:* www. luxorfurn.com, pg 813

Hill, Steven, Satellite Broadcasting & Communications Association (SBCA), 1100 17 St NW, Suite 1150, Washington, DC 20036 *Tel:* 202-349-3620 *Toll Free Tel:* 800-541-5981 *Fax:* 202-349-3621 *E-mail:* info@ sbca.org *Web Site:* www.sbca.org, pg 961

Hill, Steven, Straight Wire Inc, 2032 Scott St, Hollywood, FL 33020 *Tel:* 954-925-2470 *Toll Free Tel:* 800-683-4434 *Fax:* 954-925-7253 *E-mail:* info@ straightwire.com *Web Site:* www.straightwire.com, pg 901

Hill, Tracey, AC Lighting Inc, 88 Horner Ave, Toronto, ON M8Z 5Y3, Canada *Tel:* 416-255-9494 *Fax:* 416-255-3514 *E-mail:* northamerica@aclighting.com *Web Site:* www.aclighting.com, pg 672

Hiller, Ezra, Alltec Stores, a Vcom IMC Company, 80 Little Falls Rd, Fairfield, NJ 07004 *Toll Free Tel:* 800-637-3181 *Toll Free Fax:* 800-965-7836 *E-mail:* sales@ alltecstores.com *Web Site:* www.alltecstores.com, pg 681

Hillery, Michelle, Palm Beach County Film & Television Commission, 1555 Palm Beach Lakes Blvd, Suite 900, West Palm Beach, FL 33401 *Tel:* 561-233-1000 *Toll Free Tel:* 800-745-FILM (745-3456) *Fax:* 561-233-3113 *Web Site:* www.pbfilm.com, pg 970

Hillery, Parker, Moxie Media, 1301 Dealers Ave, New Orleans, LA 70123 *Tel:* 504-733-6907 *Toll Free Tel:* 800-346-6943 *Fax:* 504-733-9493 *E-mail:* info@ moxiemedia.com *Web Site:* www.moxietraining.com; www.moxiemedia.com, pg 832

Hillinger, Jeffrey W, Automated Entertainment, PO Box 1079, Littlerock, CA 95343-1079 *Tel:* 661-944-2299 *Toll Free Tel:* 800-880-6567 (orders) *E-mail:* questions@automatedhd.com *Web Site:* www. automatedhd.com, pg 696

Hillman, Barbara, Berkeley Film Office, 2030 Addison St, Suite 102, Berkeley, CA 94704 *Tel:* 510-549-7040 *Toll Free Tel:* 800-847-4823 *Fax:* 510-644-2052 *E-mail:* film@visitberkeley.com *Web Site:* www. filmberkeley.com, pg 966

Hillmann, Alfred J, Hillmann & Carr Inc, 2233 Wisconsin Ave, Washington, DC 20007 *Tel:* 202-342-0001 *Fax:* 202-342-0117 *E-mail:* mail@hillmanncarr. com *Web Site:* www.hillmanncarr.com, pg 780

Hilton, Jonathan, Omnirax Furniture Co, PO Box 1792, Sausalito, CA 94966-1792 *Tel:* 415-332-3392 *Toll Free Tel:* 800-332-3393 *E-mail:* info@omnirax.com *Web Site:* omnirax.com, pg 845

Hinckley, Bryan, Electrosonic, 3320 N San Fernando Blvd, Burbank, CA 91504 *Tel:* 818-333-3600 *Toll Free Tel:* 888-343-3604 (sales) *E-mail:* contactus@ electrosonic.com *Web Site:* www.electrosonic.com, pg 752

Hinds, Susanna, Association of American Publishers (AAP), 455 Massachusetts Ave NW, Suite 700, Washington, DC 20001-2777 *Tel:* 202-347-3375 *Fax:* 202-347-3690 *E-mail:* info@publishers.org *Web Site:* publishers.org, pg 951

Hiner, Bryce, Lyon Workspace Products LLC, 420 N Main St, Montgomery, IL 60538 *Tel:* 630-892-8941 *Toll Free Tel:* 800-433-8488 *Fax:* 630-892-8966 *Toll Free Fax:* 800-367-6681 *E-mail:* lyon@ lyonworkspace.com *Web Site:* www.lyonworkspace. com, pg 813

Hines, Jeff, US Case Corp, 6301 J Richard Dr, Raleigh, NC 27617 *Tel:* 919-783-6166 *Toll Free Tel:* 800-648-8474 *Fax:* 919-783-0740 *E-mail:* customersupport@ uscase.com *Web Site:* www.uscase.com, pg 923

Hinkle, Bob, Activu Corp, 301 Roundhill Dr, Rockaway, NJ 07866 *Tel:* 973-366-5550 *Toll Free Tel:* 888-ACTIVU1 (228-4881) *Fax:* 973-625-7775 *E-mail:* facebook@activu.com *Web Site:* activu.com, pg 675

Hinkle, Paula, Graphic Artists Guild Inc, 31 W 34 St, 8th fl, New York, NY 10001 *Tel:* 212-791-3400 *E-mail:* admin@graphicartistsguild.org; membership@ graphicartistsguild.org *Web Site:* graphicartistsguild. org, pg 955

Hinojasa, Laura, WTVS, Detroit Public Television, Riley Broadcast Ctr, One Clover Ct, Wixom, MI 48393-2247 *Tel:* 248-305-DPTV (305-3788); 313-872-7500 *E-mail:* email@dptv.org *Web Site:* www.dptv.org, pg 942

Hinshelwood, Jennifer, TVO/Ontario Educational Communications Authority (OECA), 2180 Yonge St, Toronto, ON M4S 2B9, Canada *Tel:* 416-484-2600; 416-484-2665 (cust rel) *Toll Free Tel:* 800-613-0513; 800-INFO-TVO (463-6886) *E-mail:* asktvo@tvo.org *Web Site:* tvo.org, pg 919

Hinsley, Tim, Movies Unlimited, 740 Hilltop Dr, Itasca, IL 60143 *Toll Free Tel:* 800-466-8437 *E-mail:* movies@moviesunlimited.com; info@ moviefanfare.com; askmff@moviefanfare.com *Web Site:* www.moviesunlimited.com, pg 831

Hipolito, Joey, Xenon Pictures Inc, 3521 Jack Northrop Ave, Hawthorne, CA 90250 *Tel:* 310-451-5510 *Fax:* 310-395-4058 *E-mail:* info@xenonpictures.com *Web Site:* xenonpictures.com, pg 943

Hirsch, Robin, Imagecraft Productions, 3318 Burton Ave, Burbank, CA 91504 *Tel:* 818-954-0187 *Fax:* 818-954-0189 *Web Site:* www.imagecraftproductions.com, pg 785

Hirsh, Evan, Film Ideas Inc, 308 N Wolf Rd, Wheeling, IL 60090 *Tel:* 847-419-0255 *Toll Free Tel:* 800-475-3456 (US only) *Fax:* 847-419-8933 *E-mail:* info@ filmideas.com; orders@filmideas.com (cust serv) *Web Site:* www.filmideas.com, pg 760

Hirt, Todd, West Penn Wire, 2833 W Chestnut St, Washington, PA 15301 *Tel:* 724-222-7060 *Toll Free Tel:* 800-245-4964 *Fax:* 724-222-6420 *E-mail:* info@ westpennwire.com; sales@westpennwire.com *Web Site:* www.westpenn-wpw.com, pg 935

Hiskey, Mark, ILIO Enterprises LLC, 5356 Sterling Center Dr, Westlake Village, CA 91361 *Tel:* 818-707-7222; 818-707-3655 *Toll Free Tel:* 800-747-4546 *E-mail:* info@ilio.com *Web Site:* www.ilio.com, pg 784

Hislop, Mark W, Video Impressions, 1946 Fays Lane, Sugar Grove, IL 60554 *Tel:* 630-851-1663 *E-mail:* info@video-impressions.com *Web Site:* www. video-impressions.com, pg 928

Hjelm, Andrea M, Moore Creative Talent Inc, 3130 Excelsior Blvd, Minneapolis, MN 55416 *Tel:* 612-827-3823 *Web Site:* www.mooretalent.com, pg 830

Hjelm, Thomas, National Public Radio (NPR), 1111 N Capitol St NE, Washington, DC 20002 *Tel:* 202-513-2000 *Web Site:* www.npr.org, pg 959

Hlywak, Stephanie, American Library Association (ALA), 50 E Huron St, Chicago, IL 60611-2795 *Tel:* 312-944-6780 *Toll Free Tel:* 800-545-2433 *Fax:* 312-440-9374 *E-mail:* ala@ala.org *Web Site:* www.ala.org, pg 949

Ho, Yvonne, Point Source Audio, 1304 Southpoint Blvd, No 260, Petaluma, CA 94954 *Tel:* 415-226-1122 *Fax:* 415-520-2110 *E-mail:* info@point-sourceaudio. com; sales@point-sourceaudio.com *Web Site:* www. point-sourceaudio.com, pg 858

Hobbs, Greg, Duke Media Services, 0052 Bryan Ctr, Durham, NC 27708 *Tel:* 919-660-1740 *Fax:* 919-660-1719 *E-mail:* dms-info@duke.edu *Web Site:* sites.duke. edu/mediaservices, pg 747

Hobel, Mary-Ann, The Cinema Guild Inc, 2803 Ocean Ave, Brooklyn, NY 11229 *Tel:* 212-685-6242 *Toll Free Tel:* 800-723-5522 *E-mail:* info@cinemaguild. com *Web Site:* www.cinemaguild.com, pg 724

Hobel, Philip, The Cinema Guild Inc, 2803 Ocean Ave, Brooklyn, NY 11229 *Tel:* 212-685-6242 *Toll Free Tel:* 800-723-5522 *E-mail:* info@cinemaguild.com *Web Site:* www.cinemaguild.com, pg 724

Hobson, Charles, Vanguard Documentaries, PO Box 26635, Brooklyn, NY 11202 *Tel:* 347-725-1677 *Web Site:* www.vanguarddocumentaries.com, pg 924

Hochheim, Frieder, Kino Flo Lighting Systems, 2840 N Hollywood Way, Burbank, CA 91505 *Tel:* 818-767-6528 *Fax:* 818-252-0290 (rental); 818-767-7517 (sales) *E-mail:* sales@kinoflo.com *Web Site:* www. kinoflo.com, pg 799

Hocker, Brian, NBC-5, 4805 Amon Carter Blvd, Fort Worth, TX 76155 *Tel:* 817-429-5555 *Fax:* 817-654-6325 *Web Site:* www.nbcdfw.com, pg 837

Hodge, Forrest, Greenwood Convention & Visitors Bureau & Film Commission, 225 Howard St, Greenwood, MS 38935 *Tel:* 662-453-9197 *Web Site:* www.visitgreenwood.com, pg 972

Hodges, Mike, RIA Corp, 1615 W 2200 S, Suite B, Salt Lake City, UT 84119 *Tel:* 801-486-8822 *Fax:* 801-486-2741 *E-mail:* sales@riacorp.com *Web Site:* www. riacorp.com, pg 874

Hodson, Thomas, WOUB Public Media, 35 S College St, Athens, OH 45701 *Tel:* 740-593-1771 *Toll Free Tel:* 800-456-2044 *E-mail:* woub@woub.org *Web Site:* woub.org, pg 942

Hoey, Sean, High End Systems Inc, 2105 Gracy Farms Lane, Austin, TX 78758 *Tel:* 512-836-2242 *Toll Free Tel:* 800-890-8989 *Web Site:* www.highend.com, pg 779

Hoffend, Daniel Jr, Freeman, 1600 Viceroy, Suite 100, Dallas, TX 75235 *Tel:* 214-445-1000 *Web Site:* www. freeman.com, pg 765

Hoffman, Ace, Animated Software Co, PO Box 1936, Carlsbad, CA 92018-1936 *Tel:* 760-720-7261 *Toll Free Tel:* 800-551-2726 *Web Site:* www.animatedsoftware. com, pg 685

Hoffman, Andrew, Noventri, 20940 Twin Springs Dr, Smithsburg, MD 21783-1510 *Tel:* 301-790-0103 *Fax:* 301-790-0173 *E-mail:* sale@noventri.com *Web Site:* www.noventri.com, pg 843

Hoffman, Clint, Kramer Electronics USA Inc, 6 Rte 173 W, Clinton, NJ 08809 *Tel:* 908-735-0018 *Toll Free Tel:* 888-275-6311 *Fax:* 908-735-0515 *E-mail:* info@kramerus.com *Web Site:* www.kramerav.com, pg 801

Hoffman, Donald, The Audio Department Inc, 324 Mills Place, Wycloff, NJ 07481 *Tel:* 212-586-3503 *Fax:* 212-245-1675 *E-mail:* scheduling@theaudiodepartment.com *Web Site:* www.theaudiodepartment.com, pg 693

Hoffman, Evan, Photosound of Orlando Inc, 7055 University Blvd, Winter Park, FL 32792 *Tel:* 407-898-8841 *Toll Free Tel:* 800-552-8776 *E-mail:* info@photosoundav.com *Web Site:* www.photosoundav.com, pg 856

Hoffman, Janalea, Rhythmic Medicine, 10425 W 177 Terr, Overland Park, KS 66221 *Tel:* 913-851-5100 *E-mail:* music@rhythmicmedicine.com *Web Site:* www.rhythmicmedicine.com, pg 874

Hoffman, Judy, Noventri, 20940 Twin Springs Dr, Smithsburg, MD 21783-1510 *Tel:* 301-790-0103 *Fax:* 301-790-0173 *E-mail:* sale@noventri.com *Web Site:* www.noventri.com, pg 843

Hoffman, Kevin, Event Essentials, 6485 Blanchar's Crossing, Windsor, WI 53598 *Tel:* 608-846-5004 *Toll Free Tel:* 800-220-4991 *Fax:* 608-222-5063 *Web Site:* www.eventessentials.com, pg 756

Hoffman-Cook, Kayla B, Freewheelin' Films, 44895 Hwy 82, Aspen, CO 81611 *Tel:* 970-925-2640 *Fax:* 970-925-9369 *Web Site:* www.fwf.com, pg 765

Hofmann, Rick, Image Logic Corp, 6807 Brennon Lane, Chevy Chase, MD 20815-3255 *Tel:* 202-223-2888 *E-mail:* info@imagelogic.com *Web Site:* www.imagelogic.com, pg 785

Hofrenning, Maureen, Greater Wichita Convention & Visitors Bureau/Wichita Film Commission, 515 S Main St, Suite 115, Wichita, KS 67202 *Tel:* 316-265-2800 *Toll Free Tel:* 800-288-9424 *Fax:* 316-265-0162 *E-mail:* wfc@visitwichita.com *Web Site:* www.visitwichita.com, pg 971

Hofseth, Dana, NAMM, the National Association of Music Merchants, 5790 Armada Dr, Carlsbad, CA 92008 *Tel:* 760-438-8001 *Toll Free Tel:* 800-767-6266 (memb hotline) *Fax:* 760-438-7327 *E-mail:* info@namm.org *Web Site:* www.namm.org, pg 958

Hogan, Dan, DSR Computer Technology Specialists Inc, 961-M Mercantile Dr, Hanover, MD 21076 *Tel:* 410-579-4508 *Toll Free Tel:* 800-875-0037 *Fax:* 410-579-8412 *E-mail:* dsr@dsr-inc.com *Web Site:* www.dsr-inc.com, pg 747

Hogan, Jeff, Argentine Productions Inc, 111 Mayfair Dr, Pittsburgh, PA 15228 *Tel:* 412-341-6448 *E-mail:* engage@argentineproductions.com *Web Site:* argentineproductions.com, pg 688

Hogan, Kim, Luzerne County Community College, 1333 S Prospect St, Nanticoke, PA 18634-3899 *Tel:* 570-740-0200 *Toll Free Tel:* 800-377-5222 *Fax:* 570-740-0250 *Web Site:* www.luzerne.edu/index.jsp, pg 813

Hogan, Simone, Coastline Productions, 2647 Gateway Rd, No 105-355, Carlsbad, CA 92009 *Tel:* 760-598-1860 *Toll Free Tel:* 888-781-5714 *E-mail:* productions@coastlinevideo.com *Web Site:* www.coastlinevideo.com, pg 727

Hogan, Steve, Houston Photo Imaging, 5250 Gulfton, Suite 3-B, Houston, TX 77081 *Tel:* 713-666-0282 *Toll Free Tel:* 800-664-0282 *Fax:* 713-667-9625 *E-mail:* info@hpihouston.com *Web Site:* hpihouston.com, pg 782

Hogerson, Jerry, TeachLogic Inc, 1688 Ord Way, Oceanside, CA 92056 *Tel:* 760-631-7800 *Toll Free Tel:* 800-588-0018 *Fax:* 760-631-1283 *E-mail:* sales@teachlogic.com; info@teachlogic.com *Web Site:* www.teachlogic.com, pg 908

Hoggatt, Richard Jr, Stage Directions, 8311 Hempstead Rd, Houston, TX 77008 *Tel:* 713-863-7469 *Fax:* 713-863-9418 *E-mail:* sales@stagedirections.com *Web Site:* www.stagedirections.com, pg 898

Hohener, John, Microsemi Corp, One Enterprise, Aliso Viejo, CA 92656 *Tel:* 949-380-6100 *Toll Free Tel:* 800-713-4113 *Fax:* 949-215-4996 *Web Site:* www.microsemi.com, pg 826

Holbrooke, David, Mountainfilm in Telluride, 109 E Colorado Ave, Suite 1, Telluride, CO 81435 *Tel:* 970-728-4123 *E-mail:* entries@mountainfilm.org *Web Site:* www.mountainfilm.org, pg 996

Holden, Mark, JaffeHolden, 114-A Washington St, Norwalk, CT 06854 *Tel:* 203-838-4167 *Fax:* 203-838-4168 *Web Site:* www.jaffeholden.com, pg 792

Holguin, Robert, Academy of Science Fiction, Fantasy & Horror Films, 334 W 54 St, Los Angeles, CA 90037 *Tel:* 323-752-5811 *E-mail:* saturn.awards@ca.rr.com *Web Site:* www.saturnawards.org, pg 947

Holguin, Robert, Saturn Awards, 334 W 54 St, Los Angeles, CA 90037 *Tel:* 323-752-5811 *E-mail:* saturn.awards@ca.rr.com *Web Site:* www.saturnawards.org, pg 1003

Holladay, David, ExpoDisplays, 3401 Mary Taylor Rd, Birmingham, AL 35235 *Toll Free Tel:* 800-747-3976 *E-mail:* info@expodisplays.com *Web Site:* www.expodisplays.com, pg 757

Hollaender, Robert P II, The Hollaender Manufacturing Co, 10285 Wayne Ave, Cincinnati, OH 45215 *Tel:* 513-772-8800 *Toll Free Tel:* 800-772-8800 (orders) *Fax:* 513-772-8806 *Web Site:* www.hollaender.com, pg 780

Holland, Arnie, Lightyear Entertainment, 4011 Alcove Ave, Studio City, CA 91604 *Tel:* 818-855-1318 *Fax:* 818-855-1320 *Web Site:* lightyear.com, pg 808

Holland, Burt, Encyclomedia, 1526 Dekalb Ave, Atlanta, GA 30307 *Tel:* 404-527-3600 *Fax:* 404-584-5171 *E-mail:* info@encyclomedia.net *Web Site:* www.encyclomedia.net, pg 754

Holland, David, Omnirax Furniture Co, PO Box 1792, Sausalito, CA 94966-1792 *Tel:* 415-332-3392 *Toll Free Tel:* 800-332-3393 *E-mail:* info@omnirax.com *Web Site:* omnirax.com, pg 845

Holland, Deb, WGBH Production Group, One Guest St, Boston, MA 02135 *Tel:* 617-300-2000 *E-mail:* productiongroup@wgbh.org; studios@wgbh.org; outpost@wgbh.org *Web Site:* productiongroup.wgbh.org, pg 936

Holland, Lance, Encyclomedia, 1526 Dekalb Ave, Atlanta, GA 30307 *Tel:* 404-527-3600 *Fax:* 404-584-5171 *E-mail:* info@encyclomedia.net *Web Site:* www.encyclomedia.net, pg 754

Holland, Mary Ann, Gagne Inc, 41 Commercial Dr, Johnson City, NY 13790 *Tel:* 607-729-3366 *Toll Free Tel:* 800-800-5954 *Fax:* 607-729-7644 *E-mail:* sales@gagneinc.com *Web Site:* www.gagneinc.com, pg 767

Holley, Meagan, Replicopy Digital Media Center, 1120 Jupiter Rd, Suite 190, Plano, TX 75074 *Tel:* 972-702-8388 *Toll Free Tel:* 800-628-1124 *E-mail:* replicopy@replicopy.com *Web Site:* www.replicopy.com, pg 873

Hollifield, Laura, Artbeats, 1405 N Myrtle Rd, Myrtle Creek, OR 97457 *Tel:* 541-863-4429 *Fax:* 541-863-4547 *E-mail:* info@artbeats.com *Web Site:* www.artbeats.com, pg 690

Hollingsworth, Sue, University of Missouri-Columbia, Film & Video Library, 505 E Stewart Rd, Columbia, MO 65211-2040 *Tel:* 573-882-3608 *E-mail:* asc@missouri.edu *Web Site:* asc.missouri.edu, pg 923

Holloway, Chris, OMNISound Recording Studio, 1806 Division St, Nashville, TN 37203 *Tel:* 615-482-1151 *Fax:* 615-321-5528 *Web Site:* www.omnisoundstudios.com, pg 845

Holloway, Kathleen, Gabriel Awards, 205 W Monroe St, Suite 470, Chicago, IL 60606 *Tel:* 312-380-6789 *Fax:* 312-361-0256 *E-mail:* cpaawards@catholicpress.org *Web Site:* www.catholicpress.org/page/gabrielawards, pg 990

Holseth, Darlene, RGB Technology Inc, 590 Herndon Pkwy, Suite 500, Herndon, VA 20170-5267 *Tel:* 703-834-1500 *Fax:* 703-834-1506 *E-mail:* solutions@rgbtec.com *Web Site:* www.rgbtec.com, pg 874

Holstebro, Jens, FrontRow, 1690 Corporate Circle, Petaluma, CA 94954 *Tel:* 707-769-1110 *Toll Free Tel:* 800-227-0735 *Fax:* 707-769-9624 *E-mail:* customercare@gofrontrow.com *Web Site:* www.gofrontrow.com, pg 766

Holt, David, High Windy Audio/Banjoman Inc, PO Box 553, Fairview, NC 28730 *Toll Free Tel:* 828-628-1728 *Toll Free Tel:* 800-637-8679 *Fax:* 828-628-4435 *E-mail:* office@davidholt.com *Web Site:* www.davidholt.com, pg 779

Holton, Jeff, SKC Communication Products Inc, 8320 Hedge Lane Terr, Shawnee Mission, KS 66227 *Tel:* 913-422-4222 *Toll Free Tel:* 800-882-7779 *Toll Free Fax:* 800-454-4752 *E-mail:* contact.us@skccom.com *Web Site:* www.skccom.com, pg 890

Holton, Terry, Media Networking Alliance (MNA), 23117 39 Ave SE, Bothell, WA 98021 *Tel:* 425-870-6574 *Web Site:* medianetworkingalliance.com, pg 957

Holtz, Vaniah, Subject Matter, 1201 New York Ave NW, Suite 900, Washington, DC 20005 *Tel:* 202-544-8400 *Web Site:* teamsubjectmatter.com, pg 903

Homberg, Rich, WTVS, Detroit Public Television, Riley Broadcast Ctr, One Clover Ct, Wixom, MI 48393-2247 *Tel:* 248-305-DPTV (305-3788); 313-872-7500 *E-mail:* email@dptv.org *Web Site:* www.dptv.org, pg 942

Homer, Jennifer, Association for Talent Development (ATD), 1640 King St, Alexandria, VA 22314-2743 *Tel:* 703-683-8100 *Toll Free Tel:* 800-628-2783 *Fax:* 703-299-8723 *E-mail:* customercare@td.org *Web Site:* www.td.org, pg 950

Hon, Duncan, Emerson Radio Corp, 3 University Plaza, Suite 405, Hackensack, NJ 07601 *Tel:* 973-884-5800 *Toll Free Tel:* 800-909-1240 (cust serv) *Fax:* 973-428-2067 *E-mail:* internet@emersonradio.com *Web Site:* www.emersonradio.com, pg 753

Hong, Dick, Randolf Productions Inc, 7271 Garden Grove Blvd, Suite F, Garden Grove, CA 92841 *Tel:* 949-794-9109 *Toll Free Tel:* 800-266-7741 *Fax:* 949-794-9117 *E-mail:* sales@go2rpi.com *Web Site:* www.go2rpi.com; christianmovieshop.com, pg 870

Honken, David, New Life Communications Inc, 905 Hwy 71 NE, Willmar, MN 56201-2654 *Tel:* 320-235-6404 *Toll Free Tel:* 800-233-6470 *Fax:* 320-235-6418 *E-mail:* nlc@newlifecomm.com *Web Site:* www.newlifecomm.com, pg 839

Honkus, Deb, NEP Group Inc, 2 Beta Dr, Pittsburgh, PA 15238 *Tel:* 412-826-1414 *Toll Free Tel:* 800-444-0054 *E-mail:* info@nepinc.com *Web Site:* www.nepgroup.com, pg 838

Honthaner, Eve, California Film Commission (CFC), 7080 Hollywood Blvd, Suite 900, Hollywood, CA 90028-6936 *Tel:* 323-860-2960 (24-hour serv) *Toll Free Tel:* 800-858-4749 *Fax:* 323-860-2972 *E-mail:* filmca@film.ca.gov *Web Site:* www.film.ca.gov, pg 966

Hood, Barry, TeleVideos, 1566 Dola St, Eugene, OR 97402 *Toll Free Tel:* 800-2-VIDEOS (284-3367) *E-mail:* televideos@msn.com *Web Site:* televideos.com, pg 910

Hooper, Bill, WMAR-TV, 6400 York Rd, Baltimore, MD 21212 *Tel:* 410-377-2222 *E-mail:* newsroom@wmar.com *Web Site:* www.abc2news.com, pg 940

Hoopes, Ralph, Star Case Manufacturing Co Inc, 648 Superior Ave, Munster, IN 46321 *Tel:* 219-922-4440 *Toll Free Tel:* 800-822-STAR (822-7827); 800-782-CASE (782-2273) *Fax:* 219-922-4442 *E-mail:* star@starcase.com *Web Site:* www.starcase.com, pg 900

Hoose, Tom, VIEW Inc (Video International Entertainment World Inc), 11 Reservoir Rd, Saugerties, NY 12477 *Tel:* 845-246-9955 *Toll Free Tel:* 800-843-9843 *Fax:* 845-246-9966 *E-mail:* viewvid@aol.com, pg 930

Hoover, Roger, Sweetsong Productions, 193 Meadsville Rd, Parkersburg, WV 26104 *Tel:* 304-428-7773 *E-mail:* sweetsongproductions@yahoo.com *Web Site:* www.sweetsong.com, pg 905

Hope, Lisa, Watson Desking, 26246 Twelve Trees Lane NW, Poulsbo, WA 98370 *Tel:* 360-394-1300 *Fax:* 360-394-1322 *E-mail:* marketing@watsondesking.com *Web Site:* www.watsonfurniture.com, pg 934

Hopkins, Keith, Accu-Tech, 11350 Old Roswell Rd, Suite 100, Roswell, GA 30009 *Toll Free Tel:* 888-222-8832 *Web Site:* www.accu-tech.com, pg 673

Hopkins, Mary Jane, Association of Catholic TV & Radio Syndicators, 518 S Alandele Ave, Los Angeles, CA 90036 *Tel:* 323-938-4861, pg 951

Hopkins, Richard, Visual Sound Inc, 485 Park Way, Broomall, PA 19008 *Tel:* 610-544-8700 *Toll Free Tel:* 800-523-7525 *Fax:* 610-544-3385 *Web Site:* www.visualsound.com, pg 931

Hopkins, Shae, KET The Kentucky Network, 600 Cooper Dr, Lexington, KY 40502 *Tel:* 859-258-7000 *Toll Free Tel:* 800-432-0951 *Fax:* 859-258-7396 *E-mail:* adulted@ket.org *Web Site:* www.ket.org, pg 798

Hopkins, Tom O, Tom Hopkins International Inc, 465 E Chilton Dr, Suite 4, Chandler, AZ 85225 *Tel:* 480-949-0786 *Toll Free Tel:* 800-528-0446 *Fax:* 480-949-1590 *E-mail:* info@tomhopkins.com *Web Site:* www.tomhopkins.com, pg 781

Hopwood, Cael, Vancouver Film & Special Events Office, 126 Keefer St, Vancouver, BC V6A 1X4, Canada *Tel:* 604-257-8840 *Fax:* 604-257-8859 *E-mail:* film.office@vancouver.ca *Web Site:* vancouver.ca/doing-business/film-permits.aspx, pg 978

Horn, Alan, The Walt Disney Studios, 500 S Buena Vista St, Burbank, CA 91521 *Tel:* 818-560-1000 *Web Site:* studioservices.go.com; waltdisneystudios.com, pg 743

Horn, Donna, CaptionMax, 2438 27 Ave S, Minneapolis, MN 55406 *Tel:* 612-341-3566 *Web Site:* www.captionmax.com, pg 716

Horn, Harry, Scala Inc, 7 Great Valley Pkwy, Suite 300, Malvern, PA 19355 *Tel:* 610-363-3350 *Toll Free Tel:* 888-SCALA-96 (722-5296) *Fax:* 610-363-4010 *E-mail:* team@scala.com *Web Site:* scala.com, pg 881

Horn, Jennifer, Chico Chamber of Commerce/Butte County Film Commission, 180 Fourth St, Suite 120, Chico, CA 95928 *Tel:* 530-891-5556 *Toll Free Tel:* 800-852-8570 *Fax:* 530-891-3613 *E-mail:* info@chicochamber.com *Web Site:* chicochamber.com, pg 966

Horn, Peter, Vicon Industries Inc, 135 Fell Ct, Hauppauge, NY 11788-4351 *Tel:* 631-952-2288 *Toll Free Tel:* 800-645-9116 *Fax:* 631-951-2288 *E-mail:* sales@vicon-security.com *Web Site:* www.vicon-security.com, pg 926

Hornbeck, Nicole, Greater Philadelphia Film Office, One Parkway Bldg, 11th fl, 1515 Arch St, Philadelphia, PA 19102 *Tel:* 215-686-2668 *Fax:* 215-686-3659 *E-mail:* mail@film.org *Web Site:* www.film.org, pg 975

Hornburg, Matt, Marblemedia, 74 Fraser Ave, Suite 100, Toronto, ON M6K 3E1, Canada *Tel:* 416-646-2711 *E-mail:* connect@marblemedia.com *Web Site:* www.marblemedia.com, pg 816

Horne, Chris, Association of Federal Communications Consulting Engineers (AFCCE), PO Box 19333, Washington, DC 20036-0333 *E-mail:* secretary@afcce.org *Web Site:* afcce.org, pg 951

Horne, Chris, Lawrence Behr Associates Inc, 3400 Tupper Dr, Greenville, NC 27834 *Tel:* 252-757-0279 *Toll Free Tel:* 800-522-4464 *Fax:* 252-752-9155 *E-mail:* lbagrp@lbagroup.com *Web Site:* www.lbagroup.com/associates, pg 703

Horne, Michael P, DecisionOne Corp, 640 Lee Rd, 3rd fl, Wayne, PA 19087 *Tel:* 610-296-6000 *Toll Free Tel:* 888-287-9202 (sales); 800-777-8800 (cust serv); 800-554-5179 (CN) *Fax:* 610-296-2910 *E-mail:* sales@decisionone.com *Web Site:* www.decisionone.com, pg 740

Horner, Digby, Adobe Systems Inc, 345 Park Ave, San Jose, CA 95110-2704 *Tel:* 408-536-6000 *Fax:* 408-537-6000 *Web Site:* www.adobe.com, pg 676

Horowitz, Dr Leonard G, Tetrahedron LLC, 5348 Las Vegas Dr, Suite 353, Las Vegas, NV 89108 *Tel:* 208-265-8065 *Toll Free Tel:* 888-923-9936 *E-mail:* tetra@tetrahedron.org *Web Site:* www.tetrahedron.org; www.healthyworldstore.com, pg 911

Horowitz, Sarie, Robert Flaherty Film Seminar, 6 E 39 St, 12th fl, New York, NY 10016 *Tel:* 212-448-0457 *Fax:* 212-448-0458 *E-mail:* ifs@flahertyseminar.org *Web Site:* flahertyseminar.org, pg 989

Horvath, Allen, Blonder Tongue Laboratories Inc, One Jake Brown Rd, Old Bridge, NJ 08857 *Tel:* 732-679-4000 *Toll Free Tel:* 800-523-6049 *Fax:* 732-679-4353 *E-mail:* custsvc@blondertongue.com; btglobalsales@blondertongue.com (outside US & CN); information@blondertongue.com *Web Site:* www.blondertongue.com, pg 707

Hosker, Bruce, CBM Ltd, High Point Business Park, 8750 Holgate Cresent, Milton, ON L9T 0K3, Canada *Tel:* 905-878-0648 *Toll Free Tel:* 800-387-4834 *Fax:* 905-878-6748 *Toll Free Fax:* 888-554-5501 *E-mail:* sales@cbmmetal.com *Web Site:* www.cbmmetal.com, pg 718

Hoskins, Brent, Business Technology Association (BTA), 12411 Wornall Rd, Suite 200, Kansas City, MO 64145 *Tel:* 816-941-3100 *Toll Free Tel:* 800-826-6159; 800-505-2821 (memb servs) *Fax:* 816-941-4843 *Toll Free Fax:* 800-941-2829 *E-mail:* info@bta.org *Web Site:* www.bta.org, pg 952

Hoskyns-Abrahall, Alex, Bullfrog Films Inc, 372 Dautrich Rd, Reading, PA 19606 *Tel:* 610-779-8226 *Toll Free Tel:* 800-543-3764 *Fax:* 610-370-1978 *E-mail:* info@bullfrogfilms.com; video@bullfrogfilms.com *Web Site:* www.bullfrogfilms.com, pg 712

Hoskyns-Abrahall, John, Bullfrog Films Inc, 372 Dautrich Rd, Reading, PA 19606 *Tel:* 610-779-8226 *Toll Free Tel:* 800-543-3764 *Fax:* 610-370-1978 *E-mail:* info@bullfrogfilms.com; video@bullfrogfilms.com *Web Site:* www.bullfrogfilms.com, pg 712

Hott, Mondae, Ensemble Designs Inc, 870 Gold Flat Rd, Nevada City, CA 95959 *Tel:* 530-478-1830 *Fax:* 530-478-1832 *E-mail:* info@ensembledesigns.com; service@ensembledesigns.com *Web Site:* www.ensembledesigns.com, pg 754

Houghtaling, Lee, Rum Jungle Media, 5295 Eden Rd, Mound, MN 55364 *Tel:* 952-472-5525 *E-mail:* rumjungle@rumjungle.com *Web Site:* www.rumjungle.com, pg 878

Houlle, David, Sight & Sound Production Services Inc, 1143 Boland Place, St Louis, MO 63117-1411 *Tel:* 314-647-0665 *Web Site:* www.sspsinc.com, pg 887

Hounsell, John, National Audiovisual Center (NAC), 5301 Shawnee Rd, Alexandria, VA 22312 *E-mail:* info@ntis.gov; customerservice@ntis.gov *Web Site:* classic.ntis.gov/products/nac, pg 836

Housden, Steve, Xenon Pictures Inc, 3521 Jack Northrop Ave, Hawthorne, CA 90250 *Tel:* 310-451-5510 *Fax:* 310-395-4058 *E-mail:* info@xenonpictures.com *Web Site:* xenonpictures.com, pg 943

House, Kurt D, Three Rivers Publishing Co, 2330 Buroak Ridge, San Antonio, TX 78248 *Tel:* 210-490-2433 *E-mail:* cowboyhous@aol.com *Web Site:* www.kurthouse.com, pg 913

House, Tim, WIA - The Wireless Infrastructure Association, 2111 Wilson Blvd, Suite 210, Arlington, VA 22201 *Tel:* 703-739-0300 *Toll Free Tel:* 800-759-0300 *Fax:* 703-836-1608 *Web Site:* wia.org, pg 963

Houser, Catherine, Paramount Pictures Corporation, 5555 Melrose Ave, Los Angeles, CA 90038 *Tel:* 323-956-8398 *Web Site:* www.paramount.com, pg 851

Houser, David, PAR Inc, 16204 N Florida Ave, Lutz, FL 33549 *Tel:* 813-449-4065 *Toll Free Tel:* 800-331-8378 *Fax:* 813-961-2196 *Toll Free Fax:* 800-727-9329 *E-mail:* cs@parinc.com *Web Site:* www.parinc.com, pg 851

Howard, Darren, Mach 1 Productions, 1101 N Himes Ave, Tampa, FL 33607 *Tel:* 813-873-7700 *Fax:* 813-875-6633 *E-mail:* info@mach1pro.com *Web Site:* www.mach1pro.com, pg 814

Howard, Diane, BCD Associates Inc, 2800 NW 36 St, Suite 220, Oklahoma City, OK 73112 *Tel:* 405-702-6888 *Toll Free Tel:* 800-223-6734 *E-mail:* salesweb@bcdusa.com; sales@bcdusa.com *Web Site:* www.bcdusa.com, pg 702

Howard, Jim, Marketron Broadcast Solutions, 101 Empty Saddle Trail, Hailey, ID 83333 *Tel:* 208-788-6800 *Toll Free Tel:* 800-476-7226 *Fax:* 208-788-6273 *E-mail:* sales@marketron.com *Web Site:* www.marketron.com, pg 817

Howard, Lester, Action Video, 2373 Walnut Blvd, Walnut Creek, CA 94597 *Tel:* 925-934-4366 *E-mail:* actvid@aol.com *Web Site:* actionvideo.biz, pg 675

Howard, Robert, BCD Associates Inc, 2800 NW 36 St, Suite 220, Oklahoma City, OK 73112 *Tel:* 405-702-6888 *Toll Free Tel:* 800-223-6734 *E-mail:* salesweb@bcdusa.com; sales@bcdusa.com *Web Site:* www.bcdusa.com, pg 702

Howard-Hughes, Dr Terri, Mediaforce Productions, 6328 Yorkdale Dr, Plano, TX 75093 *Tel:* 972-473-6888 *Web Site:* www.mediaforcepro.com, pg 822

Howell, Adam, Heartland International Film Festival, 1043 Virginia Ave, Suite 2, Indianapolis, IN 46203 *Tel:* 317-464-9405 *E-mail:* submissions@heartlandfilm.org *Web Site:* heartlandfilm.org/festival, pg 992

Howell, Adam, Indy Shorts International Film Fest, 1043 Virginia Ave, Suite 2, Indianapolis, IN 46203 *Tel:* 317-464-9405 *E-mail:* submissions@heartlandfilm.org *Web Site:* heartlandfilm.org, pg 993

Howell, Amy, Film Indiana, One N Capitol, Suite 600, Indianapolis, IN 46204-2288 *Toll Free Tel:* 800-677-9800 *E-mail:* filmindiana@visitindiana.com *Web Site:* www.filmindiana.com, pg 971

Howell, Brian, Dub King, 8133 Callaghan Rd, San Antonio, TX 78230 *Tel:* 210-979-8779 *E-mail:* dubking@dubking.com *Web Site:* www.dubking.com, pg 747

Howell, Donna, ACS Technologies, 180 Dunbarton Dr, Florence, SC 29501 *Tel:* 843-662-1681 *Toll Free Tel:* 800-736-7425 (sales); 800-669-2309 (support) *Fax:* 843-669-7513 *E-mail:* info@acstechnologies.com *Web Site:* www.acstechnologies.com, pg 674

Howell, Sharon Hendricks, The Campbell Agency, Hidden Grove Bldg, 12404 Park Central Dr, Suite 222 S, Dallas, TX 75251 *Tel:* 214-522-8991 *Fax:* 214-522-8997 *Web Site:* www.thecampbellagency.com, pg 715

Howerton, Blaine, Denver Media Center, 2601 Lemay, Suite 7, PMB 227, Fort Collins, CO 80525 *Tel:* 720-255-1640 (ext 101) *Web Site:* denvermediacenter.com, pg 740

Howes, Alex, AV Concepts Inc, 1917 W First St, Tempe, AZ 85281 *Tel:* 480-557-6000; 480-646-4216 (sales & serv) *Toll Free Tel:* 866-927-7590 *E-mail:* exhibitorservices@avconcepts.com *Web Site:* www.avconcepts.com, pg 697

Howes, Lauren, Canadian Filmmakers Distribution Center (CFMDC), 401 Richmond St W, Toronto, ON M5V 3A8, Canada *Tel:* 416-588-0725 *E-mail:* info@cfmdc.org *Web Site:* www.cfmdc.org, pg 715

Howie, Thomas, Glidecam Industries Inc, 23 Joseph St, Kingston, MA 02364 *Tel:* 781-585-7900 *Toll Free Tel:* 800-949-2089; 800-600-2011 *Fax:* 781-585-7903 *E-mail:* info@glidecam.com *Web Site:* glidecam.com, pg 771

Howlett, Mike, MQ Power Corp, 1800 Waters Ridge Dr, Suite 500, Lewisville, TX 75057 *Toll Free Tel:* 800-883-2551; 800-427-1244 (parts); 800-426-1244 (sales) *Fax:* 972-315-1847 *E-mail:* mqpowersales@multiquip.com *Web Site:* www.multiquip.com, pg 832

Hoyle, Jim, Audio & Light, 2209 Randleman Rd, Greensboro, NC 27406 *Tel:* 336-274-1234 *Fax:* 336-274-4022 *E-mail:* info@audio-light.com *Web Site:* www.audio-light.com, pg 693

Hoyt, Jeff, KJfilms LLC, 33 Serra Dr, Middletown, CT 06457 Tel: 860-873-2419; 860-995-5106 (cell) E-mail: info@kjfilms.com Web Site: www.kjfilms.com, pg 799

Hrastar, Brian, Optimus, 161 E Grand Ave, Chicago, IL 60611 Tel: 312-321-0880 Web Site: www.optimus. com, pg 847

Hsieh, Christine, Asia Society, 725 Park Ave, New York, NY 10021 Tel: 212-288-6400 Fax: 212-517-8315 E-mail: info@asiasociety.org Web Site: www. asiasociety.org; www.asiasociety.org/video, pg 691

Hsieh, David, Christie Digital Systems USA Inc, 10550 Camden Dr, Cypress, CA 90630 Tel: 714-236-8610 Toll Free Tel: 866-880-4462 (cust serv) Fax: 714-503-3375 E-mail: sales-us@christiedigital.com; orders@ christiedigital.com Web Site: www.christiedigital.com, pg 722

Hu, Dr Joe-E, Yorktel, 81 Corbett Way, Eatontown, NJ 07724 Tel: 732-413-6000 Toll Free Tel: 866-836-8463 Fax: 732-413-6060 E-mail: knowmore@yorktel.com Web Site: yorktel.com, pg 944

Huang, SL "Shaun", RGB Technology Inc, 590 Herndon Pkwy, Suite 500, Herndon, VA 20170-5267 Tel: 703-834-1500 Fax: 703-834-1506 E-mail: solutions@ rgbtec.com Web Site: www.rgbtec.com, pg 874

Huang, Terry, Renaissance Albums, 21 Grace Church St, Port Chester, NY 10573 Tel: 914-939-6878 Toll Free Tel: 800-961-6710 Fax: 914-939-8047 E-mail: info@renaissancealbums.com Web Site: www. renaissancealbums.com, pg 873

Huber, Sharon, CMD Agency, 1631 NW Thurman St, Portland, OR 97209 Tel: 503-223-6794 E-mail: info@ cmdagency.com Web Site: www.cmdagency.com, pg 726

Hudlin, Warrington, BFF (Black Filmmaker Foundation), 200 Broadway, New York, NY 10038, pg 952

Hudson, Dawn, Academy Awards®, 8949 Wilshire Blvd, Beverly Hills, CA 90211 Tel: 310-247-3000; 310-247-3090 (publicity) Fax: 310-859-9619 E-mail: awardsoffice@oscars.org; publicity@oscars.org Web Site: www.oscars.org, pg 981

Hudson, Dawn, Academy of Motion Picture Arts and Sciences (AMPAS), 8949 Wilshire Blvd, Beverly Hills, CA 90211 Tel: 310-247-3000 Fax: 310-859-9619 E-mail: awardsoffice@oscars.org Web Site: www.oscars.org, pg 947

Hudson, Dawn, Student Academy Awards Competition, 8949 Wilshire Blvd, Beverly Hills, CA 90211 Tel: 310-247-3000 Fax: 310-859-9619 E-mail: saa@ oscars.org Web Site: www.oscars.org/saa, pg 1004

Hudson, Gary, Acoustical Solutions LLC, 2420 Grenoble Rd, Richmond, VA 23294 Tel: 804-346-8350 Toll Free Tel: 800-782-5742 Fax: 804-346-8808 E-mail: info@acousticalsolutions.com Web Site: www. acousticalsolutions.com, pg 674

Hudson, Ruth, Chicago Spotlight Inc, 3418 N Knox Ave, Chicago, IL 60641 Tel: 312-455-1171 Web Site: www. grandstage.com, pg 721

Hudson, Ruth, Grand Stage Co Inc, 3418 N Knox Ave, Chicago, IL 60641 Tel: 312-332-5611 Toll Free Tel: 800-621-2181 Fax: 312-332-3655 E-mail: marketing@grandstage.com Web Site: www. grandstage.com, pg 773

Huelsmann, Axel, Staedtler-Mars Ltd, 850 Matteson Blvd W, Unit 4, Mississauga, ON L5V 0B4, Canada Tel: 905-501-9008 Toll Free Tel: 800-776-5544 (US); 800-387-5872 (US) Fax: 905-501-9117 Toll Free Fax: 800-675-8249 (US) E-mail: info@staedtler.ca Web Site: www.staedtler.ca, pg 898

Huenergardt, Charles L, Chapman/Leonard Studio Equipment Inc, 12950 Raymer St, North Hollywood, CA 91605 Tel: 818-764-6726 Toll Free Tel: 888-883-6559 Fax: 818-764-6730 E-mail: marketing@ chapman-leonard.com Web Site: www.chapman-leonard.com, pg 720

Huenergardt, Nichole, Chapman/Leonard Studio Equipment Inc, 12950 Raymer St, North Hollywood, CA 91605 Tel: 818-764-6726 Toll Free Tel: 888-

883-6559 Fax: 818-764-6730 E-mail: marketing@ chapman-leonard.com Web Site: www.chapman-leonard.com, pg 720

Huerta, Jeanna, Palmdale Chamber of Commerce, 817 E Avenue Q-9, Palmdale, CA 93550 Tel: 661-273-3232 Fax: 661-273-8508 E-mail: pcc@palmdalechamber.org Web Site: www.palmdalechamber.org, pg 967

Hueter, Stephanie, Blackmagic Design Pty Ltd, 2875 Bayview Dr, Fremont, CA 94538 Tel: 408-954-0500 Fax: 408-954-0508 E-mail: info-usa@blackmagicdesign.com Web Site: www. blackmagicdesign.com, pg 707

Huff, Chris, Kofax Inc, 15211 Laguna Canyon Rd, Irvine, CA 92618-3146 Tel: 949-727-1733 Fax: 949-727-3144 E-mail: info@kofax.com Web Site: www. kofax.com, pg 800

Huff, Marianne, National Storytelling Festival, 116 W Main St, Jonesborough, TN 37659 Tel: 423-753-2171 Toll Free Tel: 800-952-8392 Fax: 423-913-8219 E-mail: customerservice@storytellingcenter.net Web Site: www.storytellingcenter.net/festival, pg 997

Huff, Steven, L A Management Co LLC, 8131 Bay Pointe Dr, Denver, NC 28037 Tel: 704-560-6274 Toll Free Tel: 800-651-7818 Fax: 704-973-7968 E-mail: info@lamanagementco.com Web Site: lamanagementco.com, pg 802

Huffstetter, Larry, Curtis Company, 886 Plantation Way, Montgomery, AL 36117 Tel: 334-279-7127 Toll Free Tel: 800-228-5937 Fax: 334-270-8787 Toll Free Fax: 800-325-6341 Web Site: www.curtisav.com, pg 736

Hughes, Bob, All Access Staging & Productions, 1320 Storm Pkwy, Torrance, CA 90501 Tel: 310-784-2464 Toll Free Tel: 877-784-2464 Fax: 310-517-0899 E-mail: sales@allaccessinc.com Web Site: www. allaccessinc.com, pg 680

Hughes, Doug, eMagin Corp, 700 South Dr, Suite 201, Hopewell Junction, NY 12533 Tel: 845-838-7900 Fax: 845-838-7901 E-mail: info@emagin.com; sales@emagin.com; customersupport@emagin.com Web Site: www.emagin.com, pg 753

Hughes, Mark, Analog Man Recording Studio, PO Box 70245, Nashville, TN 37207 Tel: 615-596-6094 E-mail: mrmarksmusic@gmail.com, pg 685

Hughes, Mark Stephan, Mr Mark's Used Musical, Stereo & Studio Equipment Store, 109 Grizzard Ave, Nashville, TN 37207-4413 Tel: 615-596-6094 E-mail: mrmarksmusic@aol.com, pg 828

Hughes, Michael, Institute of Industrial & Systems Engineers (IISE), 3577 Parkway Lane, Suite 200, Norcross, GA 30092 Tel: 770-449-0460 Toll Free Tel: 800-494-0460 Fax: 770-441-3295 E-mail: executiveoffices@iise.org Web Site: www.iise. org, pg 956

Hughson, Susan, Thomas & Betts Power Solutions LLC, 5900 Eastport Blvd, Bldg V, Richmond, VA 23231-4453 Tel: 804-236-3300 Toll Free Tel: 800-238-5000; 800-CYBEREX (292-3739) Fax: 804-236-4040; 804-236-4841 Web Site: www.tnbpowersolutions.com, pg 912

Hui, John, SMART Technologies ULC, 3636 Research Rd NW, Calgary, AB T2L 1Y1, Canada Tel: 403-245-0333 Toll Free Tel: 888-42-SMART (427-6278, CN & US); 800-260-9408 (sales) Fax: 403-228-2500 Web Site: home.smarttech.com, pg 891

Huisinga, Ron, New Life Communications Inc, 905 Hwy 71 NE, Willmar, MN 56201-2654 Tel: 320-235-6404 Toll Free Tel: 800-233-6470 Fax: 320-235-6418 E-mail: nlc@newlifecomm.com Web Site: www. newlifecomm.com, pg 839

Hull, Charlene, Musicol Recording, 780 Oakland Park Ave, Columbus, OH 43224 Tel: 614-267-3133 Toll Free Tel: 800-240-5963 Fax: 614-267-3135 E-mail: info@musicolrecording.com Web Site: www. musicolrecording.com, pg 835

Hull, David, The Screen Works®, 2226 W Walnut St, Chicago, IL 60612 Tel: 312-243-8265 Toll Free Tel: 800-294-8111 Fax: 312-243-8290 E-mail: screens@thescreenworks.com Web Site: thescreenworks.com, pg 882

Hull, John W, Musicol Recording, 780 Oakland Park Ave, Columbus, OH 43224 Tel: 614-267-3133 Toll Free Tel: 800-240-5963 Fax: 614-267-3135 E-mail: info@musicolrecording.com Web Site: www. musicolrecording.com, pg 835

Hull, Scott, Masterdisk Corp, 8 John Walsh Blvd, Suite 411, Peekskill, NY 10566 Tel: 212-541-5022 Web Site: www.masterdisk.com, pg 819

Hull, Warren J, Musicol Recording, 780 Oakland Park Ave, Columbus, OH 43224 Tel: 614-267-3133 Toll Free Tel: 800-240-5963 Fax: 614-267-3135 E-mail: info@musicolrecording.com Web Site: www. musicolrecording.com, pg 835

Humpage, Tom, WGME-TV, 81 Northport Dr, Portland, ME 04103 Tel: 207-797-1313 Fax: 207-878-7482 E-mail: tvmail@wgme.com Web Site: wgme.com, pg 936

Humphrey, Lori, Proforma Good Wood Marketing, 3839 E 17 St, Spokane, WA 99223 Tel: 509-534-7477 Fax: 509-534-9703 Web Site: proformagwm. espwebsite.com, pg 865

Humphrey, Michael, Edgenuity Inc, 8860 E Chaparral Rd, Scottsdale, AZ 85250 Toll Free Tel: 877-725-4257 (sales) E-mail: customersupport@edgenuity.com; solutions@edgenuity.com (sales) Web Site: www. edgenuity.com, pg 750

Humphrey, Rob, Kensington Technology Group, 1500 Fashion Island Blvd, 3rd fl, San Mateo, CA 94404 Tel: 650-572-2700 Toll Free Tel: 800-535-4242 (tech support); 800-235-6708 (cust serv) E-mail: sales@ kensington.com Web Site: www.kensington.com, pg 797

Hungle, Terry, Imagine Communications Corp, 3001 Dallas Pkwy, Suite 300, Frisco, TX 75034 Tel: 469-803-4900 Toll Free Tel: 866-4-IMAGINE (446-2446) Fax: 469-803-4899 E-mail: insidesales@ imaginecommunications.com Web Site: www. imaginecommunications.com, pg 786

Hunkele, Michael, Audio Media Productions, 6739 Kirby Trace Cove, Memphis, TN 38119 Tel: 901-751-2363 E-mail: ampman@aol.com Web Site: www. audiomediaproductions.net, pg 693

Hunt, Bobby, Los Angeles Center Studios, 450 S Bixel St, Los Angeles, CA 90017 Tel: 213-534-3000 E-mail: productionservices@lacenterstudios.com Web Site: lacenterstudios.com, pg 811

Hunt, James, Prior Scientific Inc, 80 Reservoir Park Dr, Rockland, MA 02370 Tel: 781-878-8442 Toll Free Tel: 800-877-2234 Fax: 781-878-8736 E-mail: info@ prior.com; techsupportus@prior.com Web Site: www. prior.com, pg 862

Hunt, Ron, Chimera®, 1067 Telleen Ave, Erie, CO 80516 Tel: 303-444-8000 Toll Free Tel: 888-444-1812 Fax: 303-444-8303 E-mail: info@chimeralighting.com Web Site: chimeralighting.com, pg 722

Hunter, Cid, ITV Productions, 1649 S Robertson Blvd, Los Angeles, CA 90035 Tel: 310-204-1234 E-mail: itvproductions1@gmail.com Web Site: www. itvproductions.com, pg 792

Hunter, David, D A Sound, 12932 SE Kent Kangley Rd, Box 460, Kent, WA 98030 Tel: 206-632-7773 Toll Free Tel: 855-DASOUND (327-6863) E-mail: info@ dasound.biz Web Site: www.dasound.biz, pg 737

Hunter, Euan, VO2 Mix Audio Post, 116 Spadina Ave, Suite 208, Toronto, ON M5V 2K6, Canada Tel: 416-603-3954 Fax: 416-603-3957 E-mail: info@vo2mix.ca Web Site: www.vo2mix.ca, pg 932

Hunter, Ian, New Deal Studios, 15392 Cobalt St, Los Angeles, CA 91342 Tel: 310-578-9929 E-mail: info@ newdealstudios.com Web Site: www.newdealstudios. com, pg 839

Hunter, Ron, Randall House Publications, 114 Bush Rd, Nashville, TN 37217 Tel: 615-361-1221 Toll Free Tel: 800-877-7030 Fax: 615-367-0535 E-mail: info@ randallhouse.com Web Site: www.randallhouse.com, pg 870

Hunter, Will, Film Creations Ltd, 4349 E Fifth St, Tucson, AZ 85711 *Tel:* 520-624-4444 *Toll Free Tel:* 888-877-2490 *Fax:* 520-624-9659 *E-mail:* info@filmcreations.com *Web Site:* www.filmcreations.com, pg 760

Hurst, Adam, Interface Media Group, 1233 20 St NW, Washington, DC 20036 *Tel:* 202-861-0500 *E-mail:* info@interfacemedia.com *Web Site:* interfacemedia.com, pg 789

Hurst, Anna, Astronomical Society of the Pacific, 390 Ashton Ave, San Francisco, CA 94112 *Tel:* 415-337-1100 *Toll Free Tel:* 800-335-2624 *Fax:* 415-337-5205 *Web Site:* astrosociety.org, pg 691

Hurst, Frank, Pechman Imaging, 106 E Second St, Kaukauna, WI 54130 *Tel:* 920-766-6160 *Toll Free Tel:* 800-777-0221 *Fax:* 920-766-6161 *E-mail:* customerservice@pechmanimaging.com *Web Site:* www.pechmanimaging.com, pg 852

Hurst, Josh, Hurst Digital, 4472 Spring Valley Rd, Dallas, TX 75244 *Tel:* 469-644-1390 *Web Site:* hurstdigital.net, pg 782

Hurt, Greg, Microspace Communications Corp, 3100 Highwoods Blvd, Suite 120, Raleigh, NC 27604 *Tel:* 919-850-4500 *Fax:* 919-850-4518 *Web Site:* www.microspace.com, pg 826

Huser, Mary, Poly, 345 Encinal St, Santa Cruz, CA 95060 *Tel:* 831-426-5858 *Toll Free Tel:* 800-544-4660 *Fax:* 831-426-6098 *Web Site:* www.poly.com, pg 859

Hushon, Dan, DXC Technology Co, 1775 Tysons Blvd, Tysons, VA 22102 *Tel:* 317-331-1197 *Web Site:* www.dxc.technology, pg 748

Huson, Amy, Meyer Sound Laboratories Inc, 2832 San Pablo Ave, Berkeley, CA 94702 *Tel:* 510-486-1166 *Toll Free Tel:* 855-641-3288 (US & CN) *Fax:* 510-486-8356 *E-mail:* sales@meyersound.com; techsupport@meyersound.com; service@meyersound.com *Web Site:* www.meyersound.com, pg 825

Hussey, Halfdan, Cinequest Film & VR Festival (CQFF), PO Box 720040, San Jose, CA 95172-0040 *Tel:* 408-295-FEST (295-3378); 408-995-5033 (off) *Fax:* 408-995-5713 *E-mail:* contact@cinequest.org *Web Site:* www.cinequest.org, pg 986

Hussey, Michael E, Professional Education Institute (PEI), 7020 High Grove Blvd, Burr Ridge, IL 60527 *Tel:* 312-521-8002 *Toll Free Tel:* 800-320-7517 *Web Site:* thepei.com, pg 865

Hutcherson, Carl, Peerbolte Creative LLC, 182 NW 361, Warrensburg, MO 64093 *Tel:* 660-429-1383 *E-mail:* solutions@peerbolte.com *Web Site:* www.peerbolte.com, pg 852

Hutchison, Roger S PhD, CD ROM™ Inc, 3131 E Riverside Dr, Fort Myers, FL 33916 *Toll Free Tel:* 866-662-3766 (orders) *Fax:* 239-332-2808 *E-mail:* sales@cdrominc.com *Web Site:* www.cdrominc.com, pg 718

Huus, Brett, Sound Strations Audio Productions Inc, 3120 South Ave, La Crosse, WI 54601 *Tel:* 608-787-8133 *Fax:* 608-787-0012 *Web Site:* soundstrations.com, pg 894

Hwang, Brian, 3008, 3008 Ross Ave, Suite 100, Dallas, TX 75204 *Tel:* 214-922-9232 *Fax:* 214-922-8861 *Web Site:* www.3008.com, pg 913

Hyatt, David, Motor Racing Network, 555 MRN Dr, Concord, NC 28027 *Tel:* 704-262-6700 *Fax:* 704-262-6801 *E-mail:* sales@motorracingnetwork.com *Web Site:* www.motorracingnetwork.com, pg 831

Hyer, Colin, Austin Film Festival, 1801 Salina St, Austin, TX 78702 *Tel:* 512-478-4795 *Toll Free Tel:* 800-310-FEST (310-3378) *Fax:* 512-478-6205 *E-mail:* info@austinfilmfestival.com; programming@austinfilmfestival.com; marketing@austinfilmfestival.com *Web Site:* www.austinfilmfestival.com, pg 982

Hymes, Jon, American Optometric Association (AOA), 243 N Lindbergh Blvd, 1st fl, St Louis, MO 63141-7881 *Tel:* 314-991-4100 *Toll Free Tel:* 800-365-2219 *Fax:* 314-991-4101 *Web Site:* www.aoa.org, pg 684, 949

Iden, Ronald L, The Walt Disney Co, 500 S Buena Vista St, Burbank, CA 91521 *Tel:* 818-560-1000 *Web Site:* disney.com; thewaltdisneycompany.com, pg 743

Idziak, Nicole Justo, Bay Stage Lighting Co Inc, 4008 W Alva St, Tampa, FL 33614 *Tel:* 813-877-1089 *Fax:* 813-875-8837 *Web Site:* www.baystagelive.com, pg 702

Iger, Robert A, The Walt Disney Co, 500 S Buena Vista St, Burbank, CA 91521 *Tel:* 818-560-1000 *Web Site:* disney.com; thewaltdisneycompany.com, pg 743

Iglauer, Bruce, Alligator Records & Artist Management Inc, 1441 W Devon Ave, Chicago, IL 60660 *Tel:* 773-973-7736 *E-mail:* info@allig.com; publicity@allig.com *Web Site:* www.alligator.com, pg 681

Iglesias, Fernando, Midtown Video Inc, 4824 SW 74 Ct, Miami, FL 33155 *Tel:* 305-669-1117 *Fax:* 305-662-2860 *E-mail:* info@midtownvideo.com *Web Site:* midtownvideo.com, pg 827

Igloria, Regin, Artist Residency Program, 1260 N Green Bay Rd, Lake Forest, IL 60045 *Tel:* 847-234-1063 *E-mail:* info@ragdale.org *Web Site:* www.ragdale.org, pg 982

Ilardi, Tiffany, WEP LLC, 50 Maryland Plaza, Suite 300, St Louis, MO 63108 *Tel:* 314-345-1000 *E-mail:* wep@wep.com *Web Site:* www.wep.com, pg 935

Ilcisin, Kevin, National Instruments Corp, 11500 N Mopac Expwy, Austin, TX 78759-3504 *Tel:* 512-683-0100 *Toll Free Tel:* 888-280-7645 (sales); 877-388-1952 *Fax:* 512-683-8411; 512-683-5794 (sales) *Web Site:* www.ni.com, pg 836

Imbs, Rob, Buffalo Niagara International Film Festival (BNIFF), 3840 E Robinson Rd, Suite 166, Amherst, NY 14228 *Tel:* 716-693-0912 *E-mail:* info@bniff.com *Web Site:* thebniff.com, pg 984

Imig, Charles, Imig Audio/Video Inc, 2611 Fairbanks St, Suite 100, Anchorage, AK 99503 *Tel:* 907-274-2161 *Fax:* 907-279-0219 *E-mail:* information@imigav.com *Web Site:* www.imigav.com, pg 786

Imig, Eric, Imig Audio/Video Inc, 2611 Fairbanks St, Suite 100, Anchorage, AK 99503 *Tel:* 907-274-2161 *Fax:* 907-279-0219 *E-mail:* information@imigav.com *Web Site:* www.imigav.com, pg 786

Imlay, Dr Scott, Tecplot Inc, 3535 Factoria Blvd SE, Suite 550, Bellevue, WA 98006 *Tel:* 425-653-1200; 425-653-9393 (tech support) *Toll Free Tel:* 800-763-7005 (orders) *E-mail:* info@tecplot.com; support@tecplot.com *Web Site:* www.tecplot.com, pg 909

Impey, Ryan, MetroSonic Recording Studio, 143 Roebling St, 3rd fl, Brooklyn, NY 11211 *Tel:* 718-782-1872 *E-mail:* manager@metrosonic.net *Web Site:* www.metrosonic.net, pg 824

Inaba, Dr Darryl, CNS Productions Inc, 897 Royal Ave, Suite A, Medford, OR 97504 *Tel:* 541-779-3361 *Toll Free Tel:* 800-888-0617 *Fax:* 541-773-5905 *E-mail:* info@cnsproductions.com *Web Site:* www.cnsproductions.com, pg 727

Inaba, Megan, Nantucket Film Festival (NFF), 68 Jay St, Suite 319, Brooklyn, NY 11201 *Tel:* 646-480-1900 *Fax:* 646-365-3367 *E-mail:* info@nantucketfilmfestival.org; submissions@nantucketfilmfestival.org *Web Site:* nantucketfilmfestival.org, pg 997

Incavo, Stacey, Sprayway Inc, 2651 Warrenville Rd, Downers Grove, IL 60515 *Tel:* 630-628-3000 *Toll Free Tel:* 800-332-9000 *Fax:* 630-543-7797 *E-mail:* info@spraywayinc.com *Web Site:* www.spraywayinc.com, pg 898

Inchausti, Kristine, Annenberg Learner, PO Box 26983, St Louis, MO 63118 *Tel:* 202-783-0500 (outside US) *Toll Free Tel:* 800-LEARNER (532-7637) *Fax:* 202-783-0333 *E-mail:* order@learner.org *Web Site:* www.learner.org, pg 686

Indrigo, Peter, Unitron Ltd, 73 Mall Dr, Commack, NY 11725 *Tel:* 631-543-2000 *Fax:* 631-589-6975 *E-mail:* info@unitronusa.com *Web Site:* www.unitronusa.com, pg 921

Inge, Stephen J, A-V Services Inc, 99 Fairfield Rd, Fairfield, NJ 07004 *Tel:* 973-575-5222 *Fax:* 973-575-0857 *E-mail:* sales@avservices.net *Web Site:* www.avservices.net, pg 671

Inghram, Rick, High-Tech Special Effects Inc, PO Box 193, Eads, TN 38028-0193 *Tel:* 901-850-5522 *Fax:* 901-850-8315 *Web Site:* www.hightechspecialeffects.com, pg 779

Ingram, Colin, Madison Square Garden, 2 Pennsylvania Plaza, New York, NY 10121-0091 *Tel:* 212-465-6741 *E-mail:* msgnetpr@msgnetwork.com *Web Site:* www.thegarden.com; themadisonsquaregardencompany.com, pg 814

Ingram, David, Ingram Entertainment Inc, 2 Ingram Blvd, La Vergne, TN 37089 *Tel:* 615-287-4000 (corp) *Toll Free Tel:* 800-621-1333 (sales & cust serv) *Web Site:* www.ingramentertainment.com, pg 787

Ingram, John, Ingram Content Group LLC, One Ingram Blvd, La Vergne, TN 37086-1986 *Tel:* 615-793-5000 *Toll Free Tel:* 800-937-8000 (retailers); 800-937-5300 (ext 1, libs) *E-mail:* customerservice@ingramcontent.com *Web Site:* www.ingramcontent.com, pg 787

Ingram, Michele Fallon, Projects in Knowledge Inc, 290 W Mount Pleasant Ave, Suite 2350, Livingston, NJ 07039 *Tel:* 973-890-8988 *Toll Free Tel:* 800-772-8277 *Web Site:* www.projectsinknowledge.com, pg 865

Ingrassia, Frank, Clever Devices Ltd, 300 Crossways Park Dr, Woodbury, NY 11797 *Tel:* 516-433-6100 *Toll Free Tel:* 800-872-6129 *Web Site:* www.cleverdevices.com, pg 726

Inocencio, David, The Studio of David Inocencio, 41 Fairlawn Ave, Daly City, CA 94015 *Tel:* 415-716-2791 *Fax:* 415-716-2796, pg 911

Inouye, Natalie, Eugene, Cascades & Coast-Travel Lane County, 754 Olive St, Eugene, OR 97401 *Tel:* 541-484-5307 *Toll Free Tel:* 800-547-5445 *Web Site:* www.eugenecascadescoast.org, pg 975

Inukai, Daniel, Screen Actors Guild - American Federation of Television & Radio Artists (SAG-AFTRA), 5757 Wilshire Blvd, 7th fl, Los Angeles, CA 90036-3600 *Tel:* 323-954-1600 (former SAG); 323-634-8100 (former AFTRA) *Toll Free Tel:* 855-SAG-AFTRA (724-2387) *Fax:* 323-549-6654 (communs & mktg) *E-mail:* info@sagaftra.org *Web Site:* www.sagaftra.org, pg 961

Inwood, Gina, Calumet Carton Co, 16920 State St, South Holland, IL 60473 *Tel:* 708-333-6521 *E-mail:* info@calumetcarton.com *Web Site:* www.calumetcarton.com, pg 714

Inwood, John, Calumet Carton Co, 16920 State St, South Holland, IL 60473 *Tel:* 708-333-6521 *E-mail:* info@calumetcarton.com *Web Site:* www.calumetcarton.com, pg 714

Ipiotis, Celia, Eye on Dance, 70 E Tenth St, Suite 19-D, New York, NY 10003 *Tel:* 212-206-6492 *E-mail:* info@eyeondance.org *Web Site:* www.eyeondance.org, pg 758

Irish, Brian, Bell and Howell LLC, 3791 S Alston Ave, Durham, NC 27713 *Toll Free Tel:* 800-220-3030; 800-792-4782 (cust care) *E-mail:* info@bhemail.com *Web Site:* www.bellhowell.net, pg 703

Irwin, Ken, Rounder Records, 1209 Pine St, Suite 100, Nashville, TN 37203 *Web Site:* www.rounder.com, pg 878

Irwin-McCabe, Raigan, Troxell-CDI, 4675 E Cotton Center Blvd, Suite 155, Phoenix, AZ 85040 *Tel:* 602-437-7240 *Toll Free Tel:* 855-TROXELL (876-9355) *Fax:* 602-752-1299 *Toll Free Fax:* 800-752-1299 *E-mail:* csg@trox.com *Web Site:* www.troxellsolutions.com, pg 919

Isaacs, George, Winter Film Awards Indie Film Festival, 31 W 34 St, New York, NY 10001 *Tel:* 646-355-4371 *E-mail:* info@winterfilmawards.com; submissions@winterfilmawards.com *Web Site:* winterfilmawards.com, pg 1007

Isaacs, Tony, Indian House, PO Box 472, Taos, NM 87571-0472 *Tel:* 575-776-2953 *Toll Free Tel:* 800-748-0522 *Fax:* 575-776-2804 *E-mail:* music@indianhouse. com *Web Site:* www.indianhouse.com, pg 786

Isaacs, Tony, Rainbow Media Taos, 27 Valencia Rd, Taos, NM 87571 *Tel:* 575-776-2268 *Toll Free Tel:* 800-748-1540 *Fax:* 575-776-2804, pg 869

Isenhart, Jennifer, Wide Eye Productions, 1018 W Hays St, Boise, ID 83702 *Tel:* 208-336-0391 *Fax:* 208-336-6644 *E-mail:* info@wideeye.tv *Web Site:* wideeye.tv, pg 938

Isherwood, Andrew, ATX Networks, 8-1602 Tricont Ave, Whitby, ON L1N 7C3, Canada *Tel:* 289-204-7800 *Toll Free Tel:* 866-968-7289 *E-mail:* info@atx.com *Web Site:* atx.com, pg 692

Israel, Chip, The Lighting Design Alliance, 2830 Temple Ave, Long Beach, CA 90806-2213 *Tel:* 562-989-3843 *Fax:* 562-989-3847 *E-mail:* info@ lightingdesignalliance.com *Web Site:* www. lightingdesignalliance.com, pg 807

Israel, Robert, Score Productions Inc, 219 E 49 St, New York, NY 10017 *Tel:* 212-751-2510 *Fax:* 212-754-6305 *E-mail:* score@scoreproductions.com, pg 882

Ito, Darren, Candee Productions Inc, 301 W Deer Valley Rd, Suite 7, Phoenix, AZ 85027 *Tel:* 623-266-3070 *Web Site:* candeeproductionsinc.wordpress.com, pg 716

Itzkowich, Carla, International Contact Inc, 2820 Adeline St, Suite 1, Berkeley, CA 94703 *Tel:* 510-836-1180 *Fax:* 510-835-1314 *E-mail:* sales@intlcontact.com *Web Site:* www.intlcontact.com, pg 790

Iuliano, Gerry, Artaflex Inc, 174 W Beaver Creek Rd, Richmond Hill, ON L4B 1B4, Canada *Tel:* 905-470-0109 *Toll Free Tel:* 866-502-3378 *Fax:* 905-470-0621 *E-mail:* sales@artaflex.com; general@artaflex.com *Web Site:* www.artaflex.com, pg 690

Iverson, Eric, Rose City Sound, 4811 SE 16 Ave, Portland, OR 97202 *Tel:* 503-238-6330 *Toll Free Tel:* 877-503-7673 *Fax:* 503-238-9872 *E-mail:* sales@ rosecitysound.com *Web Site:* www.rosecitysound.com, pg 877

Iverson, Patricia, Maverick Video Productions, 121 Interpark, Suite 601, San Antonio, TX 78216 *Tel:* 210-495-1111 *Fax:* 210-495-8033 *Web Site:* www. maverickstudio.com, pg 820

Ives, Beth, HarperAudio, 10 E 53 St, New York, NY 10022 *Tel:* 212-207-7000 *Toll Free Tel:* 800-242-7737 *Fax:* 212-207-2582 *Toll Free Fax:* 800-822-4090 *Web Site:* www.harpercollins.com, pg 776

Ivey, John, AtlasIED, 4545 E Baseline Rd, Phoenix, AZ 85042 *Toll Free Tel:* 800-876-3333 *E-mail:* support@ atlasied.com *Web Site:* www.atlasied.com, pg 692

Ivey, John, Coustic, 4545 E Baseline Rd, Phoenix, AZ 85042 *Toll Free Tel:* 800-225-5689; 800-372-3029 (orders) *E-mail:* mtx@mtx.com; orders@mtx.com *Web Site:* www.coustic.com, pg 732

Ivich, Marie, San Mateo County Film Commission, 111 Anza Blvd, Suite 410, Burlingame, CA 94010 *Tel:* 650-348-7600 *Toll Free Tel:* 800-288-4748 *Fax:* 650-348-7687 *E-mail:* info@smccvb.com *Web Site:* www.smccvb.com/film, pg 966

Ivory, David, Ivory Productions, 529 Plymouth Rd, Gwynedd Valley, PA 19437 *Tel:* 215-591-9900 *Web Site:* www.ivoryproductions.com; www.facebook. com/davidivoryproductions, pg 792

Izadi, Saeed, NEP Group Inc, 2 Beta Dr, Pittsburgh, PA 15238 *Tel:* 412-826-1414 *Toll Free Tel:* 800-444-0054 *E-mail:* info@nepinc.com *Web Site:* www.nepgroup. com, pg 838

Jabara, Brock M, Galaxy Audio, 601 E Pawnee Ave, Wichita, KS 67211 *Tel:* 316-263-2852 *Toll Free Tel:* 800-369-7768 *Fax:* 316-263-0642 *E-mail:* sales@ galaxyaudio.com; orders@galaxyaudio.com *Web Site:* www.galaxyaudio.com, pg 768

Jablon, Andy, WVP Boston, 50 Hunt St, Watertown, MA 02472 *Tel:* 617-926-2089 *Web Site:* wvpboston.com, pg 942

Jachetta, Frank, MultiDyne Video & Fiber Optics Systems, 10 Newton Place, Hauppauge, NY 11788 *Tel:* 516-671-7278 *Toll Free Tel:* 877-MULTIDYNE (685-8439) *Fax:* 516-671-3362 *E-mail:* sales@ multidyne.com *Web Site:* www.multidyne.com, pg 833

Jackman, Mike, FilmNation Entertainment, 150 W 22 St, 9th fl, New York, NY 10011 *Web Site:* www. filmnation.com, pg 760

Jackson, Eric, Shot Glass Films, 2210 W Olive Ave, Suite 300, Burbank, CA 91506 *Tel:* 323-464-5111 *E-mail:* information@shotglassfilms.com *Web Site:* www.shotglassfilms.com, pg 886

Jackson, J R, KVAL, 4575 Blanton Rd, Eugene, OR 97405 *Tel:* 541-342-4961 *Fax:* 541-342-2635 *E-mail:* kvalnews@kval.com *Web Site:* kval.com, pg 802

Jackson, Jeff, Birns & Sawyer Inc, 3039 Roswell St, Los Angeles, CA 90065 *Tel:* 323-466-8211 *E-mail:* info@ birnsandsawyer.com *Web Site:* www.birnsandsawyer. com, pg 706

Jackson, John E, Launch Media, 804 Main St, Baton Rouge, LA 70802 *Tel:* 225-612-2112 *E-mail:* contactus@launchmedia.tv *Web Site:* www. launchmedia.tv, pg 804

Jackson, LaTonya, Alliance for Women in Media/ Alliance for Women in Media Foundation, 2365 Harrodsburg Rd, A-325, Lexington, KY 40504 *Tel:* 202-750-3664 *Fax:* 202-750-3664 *Web Site:* www. allwomeninmedia.org, pg 947

Jackson, LaTonya, The Gracies®, 2365 Harrodsburg Rd, A-325, Lexington, KY 40504 *Tel:* 202-750-3664 *Fax:* 202-750-3664 *E-mail:* gracies@ allwomeninmedia.org *Web Site:* allwomeninmedia. org/gracies, pg 991

Jackson, Mike, Marketron Broadcast Solutions, 101 Empty Saddle Trail, Hailey, ID 83333 *Tel:* 208-788-6800 *Toll Free Tel:* 800-476-7226 *Fax:* 208-788-6273 *E-mail:* sales@marketron.com *Web Site:* www. marketron.com, pg 817

Jackson, R Scott, Blair Inc, 7001 Loisdale Rd, Springfield, VA 22150 *Tel:* 703-922-0200 *Fax:* 703-924-0765 *E-mail:* info@blairinc.com *Web Site:* www. blairinc.com, pg 707

Jackson, Rebecca Morelo, Cine Las Americas International Film Festival (CLAIFF), 1104 W 34 St, No 625, Austin, TX 78705 *Tel:* 512-535-0765 *E-mail:* cine@cinelasamericas.org; entries@ cinelasamericas.org *Web Site:* cinelasamericas.org; www.facebook.com/cinelasamericasaustin, pg 986

Jackson, Wayne, Preston Productions Inc, 128 Bartlett St, Marlborough, MA 01752 *Toll Free Tel:* 800-822-2299 *E-mail:* ideas@prestonevents.com *Web Site:* www.prestonproductions.com; www. prestonevents.com, pg 862

Jacobovici, Simcha, Associated Producers Ltd, 210 St Clair Ave W, 4th fl, Toronto, ON M4V 1R2, Canada *Tel:* 416-504-6662 *Fax:* 416-504-6667 *E-mail:* general@apltd.ca *Web Site:* www.apltd.ca, pg 691

Jacobs, Alex, Anchor Audio Inc, 5931 Darwin Ct, Carlsbad, CA 92008 *Tel:* 760-827-7100 *Toll Free Tel:* 800-262-4671 *Fax:* 760-827-7105 *E-mail:* sales@ anchoraudio.com *Web Site:* www.anchoraudio.com, pg 685

Jacobs, Jerry, Sound/Video Impressions Inc, 110 S River Rd, Des Plaines, IL 60016 *Tel:* 847-297-4360 *Fax:* 847-297-6870 *E-mail:* info@ soundvideoimpressions.com *Web Site:* www. soundvideoimpressions.com, pg 894

Jacobs, Paul, Klipsch Group Inc, 3502 Woodview Trace, Suite 200, Indianapolis, IN 46268 *Tel:* 317-860-8100 *Toll Free Tel:* 800-544-1482 *Web Site:* www.klipsch. com, pg 800

Jacobs, Robert K, Neptune Photo Inc, 130 Seventh St, Garden City, NY 11530 *Tel:* 516-741-4484 *Toll Free Tel:* 800-955-1110 *E-mail:* sales@neptunephoto.com *Web Site:* www.neptunephoto.com, pg 838

Jacobs, Rodney H, Freewheelin' Films, 44895 Hwy 82, Aspen, CO 81611 *Tel:* 970-925-2640 *Fax:* 970-925-9369 *Web Site:* www.fwf.com, pg 765

Jacobs, Scott, Interstate Connecting Components, 120 Mount Holly Bypass, Lumberton, NJ 08048-1112 *Tel:* 856-722-5535 *Toll Free Tel:* 888-881-5420 *Fax:* 856-813-5419 *E-mail:* info@connecticc.com *Web Site:* www.connecticc.com, pg 791

Jacobs, Stan, WorldStage, 259 W 30 St, 12th fl, New York, NY 10001-2863 *Tel:* 212-582-2345 *Fax:* 718-610-1750 *E-mail:* info@worldstage.com *Web Site:* www.worldstage.com, pg 941

Jacobs, Tom, InterVision Media, 44 W Broadway, Suite 426, Eugene, OR 97401 *Tel:* 541-343-7993; 547-345-5951 *E-mail:* info@intervisionmedia.com *Web Site:* www.intervisionmedia.com, pg 791

Jacoby, J D, Montana Film Office, 301 S Park Ave, Helena, MT 59620 *Tel:* 406-841-2879 *E-mail:* montanafilm@mt.gov *Web Site:* www. montanafilm.com, pg 973

Jacques, Kevin, Inspired Image Picture Co (IIPC), 1090 E Georgia St, Vancouver, BC V6A 2A7, Canada *Tel:* 604-874-7513 *Toll Free Tel:* 800-352-1454 (prodn rentals); 800-567-0037 (equip rentals) *Fax:* 604-874-7516 *E-mail:* info@inspiredimage.ca *Web Site:* inspiredimage.ca, pg 788

Jae, Sam, PromaxBDA Promotion, Marketing and Design North America Awards, 5700 Wilshire Blvd, Suite 275, Los Angeles, CA 90036 *Tel:* 310-788-7600 *Fax:* 310-788-7616 *E-mail:* awards@promaxbda.org *Web Site:* www.promax.org/awards, pg 1000

Jaeckel, Kurt, Quickbeam Systems Inc (QSI), 4411 McLeod Rd NE, Suite E, Albuquerque, NM 87109 *Tel:* 505-345-9230 *E-mail:* sales@quickbeam.com *Web Site:* www.quickbeam.com, pg 868

Jaffe, Betsy, Audiovisual and Integrated Experience Association (AVIXA), 11242 Waples Mill Rd, Suite 200, Fairfax, VA 22030 *Tel:* 703-273-7200 *Toll Free Tel:* 800-659-7469 *E-mail:* membership@avixa.org *Web Site:* www.avixa.org, pg 951

Jaffe, Sarah, Penguin Random House Audio Publishing, 1745 Broadway, New York, NY 10019 *E-mail:* audio@penguinrandomhouse.com *Web Site:* www.penguinrandomhouseaudio.com, pg 853

Jaime, Matt, North-by-Northwest - A Digital Studio, 903 W Broadway Ave, Spokane, WA 99201 *Tel:* 509-324-2949 *Fax:* 509-324-2959 *E-mail:* spokane@nxnw.net *Web Site:* www.nxnw.net, pg 842

Jain, Archana, Chicago South Asian Film Festival (CSAFF), 2909 N Sheridan Rd, Unit 1902, Chicago, IL 60657 *Tel:* 773-669-8348 *E-mail:* info@csaff.org; programming@csaff.org *Web Site:* www.csaff.org, pg 986

Jain, Raj, SVAT Electronics, 4080 Montrose Rd, Niagara Falls, ON L2H 1J9, Canada *Fax:* 905-353-1701 *Toll Free Fax:* 888-771-1701 *E-mail:* marketing@svat.com *Web Site:* www.svat.com, pg 905

Jamele, Dan, MediaMation Inc, 23410 Garnier St, Torrance, CA 90505 *Tel:* 310-320-0696 *Fax:* 310-320-0699 *E-mail:* sales@mediamation.com *Web Site:* www.mediamation.com, pg 822

James, Neil, Pathway Connectivity, 103-1439 17 Ave SE, Calgary, AB T2G 1J9, Canada *Tel:* 403-243-8110 *Fax:* 403-287-1281 *E-mail:* orders@pathwayconnect. com *Web Site:* www.pathwayconnect.com, pg 852

James, Nelson, Signs.com, 1550 S Gladiola St, Salt Lake City, UT 84104 *Tel:* 801-441-3400 *Toll Free Tel:* 888-222-4929 *E-mail:* support@signs.com *Web Site:* www. signs.com, pg 888

James, Sean, Christie Digital Systems USA Inc, 10550 Camden Dr, Cypress, CA 90630 *Tel:* 714-236-8610 *Toll Free Tel:* 866-880-4462 (cust serv) *Fax:* 714-503-3375 *E-mail:* sales-us@christiedigital.com; orders@ christiedigital.com *Web Site:* www.christiedigital.com, pg 722

James, Troy, Strong Cinema Products, 11422 Miracle Hills Dr, Suite 300, Omaha, NE 68154 *Tel:* 402-453-4444 *Toll Free Tel:* 800-424-1215 *Fax:* 402-453-7238 *E-mail:* info@btn-inc.com *Web Site:* ballantynestrong. com, pg 902

Jamieson, David, OpenText Corp, 275 Frank Tompa Dr, Waterloo, ON N2L 0A1, Canada *Tel:* 519-888-7111 *Toll Free Tel:* 800-499-6544 *Fax:* 519-888-0677 *Web Site:* www.opentext.com, pg 847

Jamieson, Jacqui, Quabbin Wire & Cable Co Inc, 10 Maple St, Ware, MA 01082-1597 *Tel:* 413-967-6281 *Toll Free Tel:* 800-368-3311 *Fax:* 413-967-7564 *E-mail:* sales@quabbin.com *Web Site:* www.quabbin. com, pg 867

Jamison, Chris, The Whitlock Group, 12820 West Creek Pkwy, Richmond, VA 23238 *Tel:* 804-273-9100 *Toll Free Tel:* 800-726-9843 *Fax:* 804-273-9380 *E-mail:* information@whitlock.com; marketing@ whitlock.com *Web Site:* www.whitlock.com, pg 937

Jan, Han S, Total AV Systems, 9301 Georgia Ave, Silver Spring, MD 20910 *Tel:* 301-589-3337 *Toll Free Tel:* 800-447-7632 *Fax:* 301-494-4770 *E-mail:* info@ total-av.com *Web Site:* total-av.com, pg 916

Jan, Josephine, Total AV Systems, 9301 Georgia Ave, Silver Spring, MD 20910 *Tel:* 301-589-3337 *Toll Free Tel:* 800-447-7632 *Fax:* 301-494-4770 *E-mail:* info@ total-av.com *Web Site:* total-av.com, pg 916

Jan, Kenneth, Total AV Systems, 9301 Georgia Ave, Silver Spring, MD 20910 *Tel:* 301-589-3337 *Toll Free Tel:* 800-447-7632 *Fax:* 301-494-4770 *E-mail:* info@ total-av.com *Web Site:* total-av.com, pg 916

Janis, Peter, Radial Engineering Ltd, 1588 Kebet Way, Port Coquitlam, BC V3C 5M5, Canada *Tel:* 604-942-1001 *Toll Free Tel:* 800-939-1001 (orders) *Fax:* 604-942-1010 *E-mail:* info@radialeng.com *Web Site:* www.radialeng.com, pg 869

Jankowski, Ed, Liberty AV Solutions, 11675 Ridgeline Dr, Colorado Springs, CO 80921 *Tel:* 719-260-0061 *Toll Free Tel:* 800-530-8998 *Fax:* 719-260-0075 *E-mail:* orders@libav.com *Web Site:* secure. libertycable.com, pg 807

Jannson, Joanna PhD, Physical Optics Corp (POC), 1845 E 205 St, Torrance, CA 90501-1510 *Tel:* 310-320-3088 *E-mail:* info@poc.com *Web Site:* www.poc.com, pg 856

Janocha, Lance, DBM Communications Inc, 606 Baltimore Ave, Suite 200, Towson, MD 21204 *Tel:* 410-825-7400 *Fax:* 443-269-0213 *Web Site:* www. dbmcommunications.com, pg 739

Janocha, Paul, Ken-Del Productions Inc, 1500 First State Blvd, Wilmington, DE 19804-3596 *Tel:* 302-999-1111; 302-999-1110; 302-999-1164 *Toll Free Tel:* 800-249-1110 *Fax:* 302-999-1656 *E-mail:* info@ken-del.com *Web Site:* www.ken-del.com, pg 797

Janocha, Paul, Ken-Del Studios, 1500 First State Blvd, Wilmington, DE 19804-3596 *Tel:* 302-999-1111 *Toll Free Tel:* 800-249-1110 *Fax:* 302-999-1656 *E-mail:* info@ken-del.com *Web Site:* www.ken-del. com, pg 797

Janoulis, Aleck, Hottrax Records, 1957 Kilburn Dr, Atlanta, GA 30324-4852 *Tel:* 770-662-6661 *E-mail:* hotwax@hottrax.com *Web Site:* www.hottrax. com, pg 782

Jansen, Ann, Penguin Random House Canada, 320 Front St W, Suite 1400, Toronto, ON M5V 3B6, Canada *Tel:* 416-364-4449 *Toll Free Tel:* 888-523-9292 (cust serv) *Fax:* 416-598-7764 *E-mail:* customerservicescanada@ penguinrandomhouse.com *Web Site:* www. penguinrandomhouse.ca, pg 853

Janson, Beth, Canadian Screen Awards, 49 Ontario St, Suite 501, Toronto, ON M5A 2V1, Canada *Tel:* 416-366-2227 *Toll Free Tel:* 800-644-5194 *Fax:* 416-366-8454 *E-mail:* awards@academy.ca; info@academy.ca *Web Site:* www.academy.ca/canadian-screen-awards, pg 985

Janson, Eric, Janson Industries, 1200 Garfield Ave SW, Canton, OH 44706 *Tel:* 330-455-7029 *Toll Free Tel:* 800-548-8982 *Fax:* 330-455-5919 *Web Site:* www. jansonindustries.com, pg 793

Janson, Stephen, Janson Media Inc, The Cunningham House, 118 Main St, Tappan, NY 10983 *Tel:* 845-359-8488 *E-mail:* info@janson.com *Web Site:* www.janson. com, pg 793

Janson, Zara, Janson Media Inc, The Cunningham House, 118 Main St, Tappan, NY 10983 *Tel:* 845-359-8488 *E-mail:* info@janson.com *Web Site:* www.janson. com, pg 793

Janssens, Glen, eMotion Studios, 85 Liberty Ship Way, Suite 110, Sausalito, CA 94965 *Tel:* 415-331-6975 *E-mail:* info@emotionstudios.com *Web Site:* www. emotionstudios.com, pg 753

Janus, Mark-David PhD, Paulist Press, 997 Macarthur Blvd, Mahwah, NJ 07430-9990 *Tel:* 201-825-7300 *Toll Free Tel:* 800-218-1903 (orders) *Fax:* 201-825-6921 *E-mail:* info@paulistpress.com *Web Site:* www. paulistpress.com, pg 852

Janzen, Peter, Specialty Bulb Products Inc, 20010-100A Ave, Unit 2, Langley, BC V1M 3G4, Canada *Tel:* 604-513-8500 *Toll Free Tel:* 800-663-1120 *Fax:* 604-513-8200 *E-mail:* info@specialtybulb.com; bulbexpert@ specialtybulb.com *Web Site:* specialtybulb.com, pg 897

Jarvis, Joe, Final Draft, A Cast & Crew Company, 2300 Empire Ave, Burbank, CA 91504 *Tel:* 818-995-8995; 818-906-8930 (tech support) *Toll Free Tel:* 800-231-4055 *E-mail:* info@finaldraft.com *Web Site:* www. finaldraft.com, pg 761

Jarvis, Stuart, Prior Scientific Inc, 80 Reservoir Park Dr, Rockland, MA 02370 *Tel:* 781-878-8442 *Toll Free Tel:* 800-877-2234 *Fax:* 781-878-8736 *E-mail:* info@ prior.com; techsupportus@prior.com *Web Site:* www. prior.com, pg 862

Jashni, Jon, Legendary Pictures, 2900 W Alameda Ave, 15th fl, Burbank, CA 91505 *Tel:* 818-688-7003 *E-mail:* info@legendary.com *Web Site:* www. legendary.com, pg 806

Jasper, Jeffrey, New Deal Studios, 15392 Cobalt St, Los Angeles, CA 91342 *Tel:* 310-578-9929 *E-mail:* info@ newdealstudios.com *Web Site:* www.newdealstudios. com, pg 839

Jasso, Peter, Kansas Creative Arts Industries Commission, 1000 SW Jackson St, Suite 100, Topeka, KS 66612-1354 *Tel:* 785-296-2178 *Fax:* 785-296-3490 *Web Site:* www.kansascommerce.gov/caic, pg 971

Jefferson, Jennifer, Westworks Studios, 4100 E Dry Creek Rd, Littleton, CO 80122 *Toll Free Tel:* 800-491-1947 *E-mail:* info@westworksstudios.com *Web Site:* westworksstudios.com, pg 936

Jellen, Mike, Velodyne LiDAR Inc, 5521 Hellyer Ave, San Jose, CA 95738 *Tel:* 408-465-2800 *Fax:* 408-779-9208 (cust serv); 408-779-9377 (orders) *E-mail:* lidar@velodyne.com *Web Site:* velodynelidar. com, pg 925

Jemielita, Paul, Compact Storage Systems Inc, 9757 Reseda Blvd, Suite 68, Northridge, CA 91324 *Tel:* 818-772-0996 *E-mail:* info@halfthespace.com *Web Site:* www.halfthespace.com, pg 729

Jendzejec-Blanchard, Melissa, Sihl Inc, 538 Main St, Fiskeville, RI 02823 *Tel:* 401-821-1000 *Toll Free Tel:* 800-556-6866; 800-366-7393 (ext 1, cust serv) *Web Site:* www.sihlinc.com, pg 888

Jenni, Arthur, WolfVision Inc, 2055 Sugarloaf Circle, Suite 125, Duluth, GA 30097 *Tel:* 770-931-6802 *Toll Free Tel:* 877-873-WOLF (873-9653) *Fax:* 770-931-6906 *E-mail:* sales@wolfvision. us; support@wolfvision.us; orders@wolfvision.us *Web Site:* wolfvision.com, pg 940

Jennings, Heather, Method Studios, 3401 Exposition Blvd, Santa Monica, CA 90404 *Tel:* 310-434-6000 *Web Site:* www.methodstudios.com, pg 824

Jensen, Jenny, American Color Imaging (ACI), 715 E 18 St, Cedar Falls, IA 50613 *Tel:* 319-277-3655 *Toll Free Tel:* 800-728-2722 *Fax:* 319-277-6522 *E-mail:* sales@ acilab.com *Web Site:* www.acilab.com, pg 683

Jensen, Mike, North Dakota Tourism Division, Century Ctr, 1600 E Century Ave, Suite 2, Bismarck, ND 58502-2057 *Tel:* 701-328-2525 *Toll Free Tel:* 800-435-5663 *Fax:* 701-328-4878 *E-mail:* tourism@nd.gov *Web Site:* www.ndtourism.com, pg 974

Jensen, Paul, Texas Motion Picture Alliance (TXMPA), 815-A Brazos St, Austin, TX 78701 *Tel:* 512-489-6723 *E-mail:* admin@txmpa.org; communications@ txmpa.org *Web Site:* www.txmpa.org, pg 963

Jensen, Ron, Chief, a Legrand AV Inc brand, 6436 City West Pkwy, Eden Prairie, MN 55344 *Tel:* 952-894-6280 *Toll Free Tel:* 866-977-3901 *Toll Free Fax:* 877-894-6918 *E-mail:* av.chief.support@legrand.com *Web Site:* www.legrandav.com/products/chief, pg 722

Jerdee, Chad T, Accenture, 161 N Clark St, Chicago, IL 60601 *Tel:* 312-693-0161 *Toll Free Tel:* 877-889-9009 *Fax:* 312-693-0507 *Web Site:* www.accenture.com, pg 672

Jermagian, Alan, 360 Systems, 3281 Grande Vista Dr, Newbury Park, CA 91320-1193 *Tel:* 818-991-0360 *Fax:* 818-991-1360 *E-mail:* sales@360systems.com *Web Site:* www.360systems.com, pg 913

Jermak, Jennifer Davis, Clayton-Davis & Associates, 4 Warridge Dr, St Louis, MO 63124 *Tel:* 314-862-7800, pg 726

Jessen, Eric, PAR Inc, 16204 N Florida Ave, Lutz, FL 33549 *Tel:* 813-449-4065 *Toll Free Tel:* 800-331-8378 *Fax:* 813-961-2196 *Toll Free Fax:* 800-727-9329 *E-mail:* cs@parinc.com *Web Site:* www.parinc.com, pg 851

Jessop, Rebecca, Town of Bel Air Film Festival, 37 N Main St, Bel Air, MD 21014 *Tel:* 410-838-0584 *Web Site:* www.townofbelairfilmfestival.com, pg 1005

Jewett, Brad, Corel Corp, 1600 Carling Ave, Ottawa, ON K1Z 8R7, Canada *Toll Free Tel:* 877-582-6735 *Web Site:* www.corel.com, pg 731

Jia, Joanna, John Wiley & Sons Inc, 111 River St, Hoboken, NJ 07030-5774 *Tel:* 201-748-6000 *Toll Free Tel:* 800-225-5945 (cust serv) *Fax:* 201-748-6088 *Web Site:* www.wiley.com, pg 938

Jiang, Henry, AbelCine, 801 S Main St, Burbank, CA 91506 *Toll Free Tel:* 888-700-4416 *E-mail:* orders@ abelcine.com; customerservice@abelcine.com *Web Site:* www.abelcine.com, pg 672

Jimenez, Angel, Radiant Images, 2702 Media Center Dr, Los Angeles, CA 90065 *Tel:* 323-737-1314 *Fax:* 310-861-0163 *E-mail:* info@radiantimages.com *Web Site:* www.radiantimages.com, pg 869

Jimenez, Jorge, Filmtools®, 1400 W Burbank Blvd, Burbank, CA 91506 *Tel:* 818-845-8066 *Toll Free Tel:* 888-807-1900 *Fax:* 818-845-4237 *E-mail:* sales@ filmtools.com; customerservice@filmtools.com *Web Site:* www.filmtools.com, pg 761

Jittlov, Michael, Palardo Productions, 1807 Taft Ave, Suite 4, Hollywood, CA 90028 *Tel:* 323-469-8991 *E-mail:* palardo2@msn.com, pg 850

Jo, YoungBae, DASAN Zhone Solutions (DZS) Inc, 7195 Oakport St, Oakland, CA 94621 *Tel:* 510-777-7000 *Toll Free Tel:* 877-ZHONE-20 (946-6320, US & CN) *Fax:* 510-777-7001 *Web Site:* dasanzhone.com, pg 737

Joachim, Steve, Location Sound Corp, 10639 Riverside Dr, North Hollywood, CA 91602 *Tel:* 818-980-9891 *Toll Free Tel:* 800-228-4429 *Fax:* 818-980-9911; 818-980-7932 (rentals) *E-mail:* information@ locationsound.com *Web Site:* www.locationsound.com, pg 810

Job, Heather, Penguin Random House Audio Publishing, 1745 Broadway, New York, NY 10019 *E-mail:* audio@penguinrandomhouse.com *Web Site:* www.penguinrandomhouseaudio.com, pg 853

Jobin, Zach, Radius® Display Products Inc, 800 Fabric Xpress Way, Dallas, TX 75234 *Tel:* 972-406-1221 *Toll Free Tel:* 800-FABRIC-X (322-7429); 866-966-4066 (sales); 866-966-8266 (hospitality) *Fax:* 972-406-1321 *Toll Free Fax:* 888-322-7429 *Web Site:* www.radiusdp. com, pg 869

Jobst, Chris, Switch, 6600 Manchester Ave, St Louis, MO 63139 *Tel:* 314-206-7700 *E-mail:* info@switch.us *Web Site:* www.switch.us, pg 905

Jockheck, David, Sencore Inc, 3200 W Sencore Dr, Sioux Falls, SD 57107 *Tel:* 605-978-4600 *Fax:* 605-335-6379 *Web Site:* www.sencore.com, pg 883

Johannesen, Jeremy, Beatrice E Griggs Elementary Administrator's Award, 6021 State Farm Rd, Guilderland, NY 12084 *Tel:* 518-432-6952 *Toll Free Tel:* 800-252-6952 *Fax:* 518-427-1697 *E-mail:* info@nyla.org *Web Site:* www.nyla.org, pg 991

Johansen, Jill, Minnesota Film & TV, 401 N Third St, Suite 245, Minneapolis, MN 55401 *Tel:* 612-767-0095 *E-mail:* info@mnfilmtv.org *Web Site:* mnfilmtv.org, pg 972

Johns, Corey R, Tennessee Entertainment Commission, Tennessee Tower, 27th fl, 312 Rosa L Parks Ave, Nashville, TN 37243 *Tel:* 615-741-FILM (741-3456) *Toll Free Tel:* 877-818-FILM (818-3456) *E-mail:* tn. film@tn.gov *Web Site:* www.tnentertainment.com, pg 976

Johns, Gary, Convergent Media Systems, 190 Bluegrass Valley Pkwy, Alpharetta, GA 30005-2204 *Tel:* 770-369-9000 *Fax:* 770-369-9100 *Web Site:* www. convergent.com, pg 731

Johns, Linda, KPDX-TV Production Center, 14975 NW Greenbrier Pkwy, Beaverton, OR 97006-5731 *Tel:* 503-906-1249 *Fax:* 503-548-6920 *E-mail:* ezone@kpdx.com; fox12news@kptv.com *Web Site:* www.kptv.com; www.kpdx.com, pg 801

Johnson, Alan, Alan Johnson Recording, 5763 Park Plaza Ct, Indianapolis, IN 46220 *Tel:* 317-439-6521 *E-mail:* alan@alanjohnsonrecording.com *Web Site:* www.alanjohnsonrecording.com, pg 794

Johnson, Andrea, Explore Lawrence, PO Box 526, Lawrence, KS 66044 *Tel:* 785-856-3040; 785-856-5282 (mktg) *Fax:* 785-856-5303 *E-mail:* visinfo@explorelawrence.com *Web Site:* www.explorelawrence.com, pg 971

Johnson, Bill, Modern Communications Inc, 1231 Horan Dr, Fenton, MO 63026 *Tel:* 636-343-0800 *Toll Free Tel:* 800-428-2442 *Fax:* 636-343-0906 *Web Site:* www. modcomm.com, pg 828

Johnson, Brent, ClearOne Inc, Edgewater Corporate Park, South Tower, Suite 500, 5225 Wiley Post Way, Salt Lake City, UT 84116 *Tel:* 801-975-7200 *Fax:* 801-303-5711 *E-mail:* contact@clearone.com; marketing@clearone.com *Web Site:* www.clearone. com, pg 726

Johnson, Daniel R, Motion Picture Services, 7542 Savannah Dr, Ooltewah, TN 37363 *Tel:* 423-238-7000 *E-mail:* info@motionpictureservices.net *Web Site:* www.motionpictureservices.net, pg 831

Johnson, Dave, RAM® Mounts, 8410 Dallas Ave S, Seattle, WA 98108 *Tel:* 206-763-8361 *Toll Free Tel:* 800-497-7479 *Fax:* 206-763-9615 *E-mail:* sales@rammount.com *Web Site:* www.rammount.com, pg 870

Johnson, Eric, pinta acoustic inc, 2601 49 Ave N, Suite 400, Minneapolis, MN 55430 *Tel:* 612-355-4200 *Toll Free Tel:* 800-662-0032 *Fax:* 612-355-4299 *E-mail:* sales@pinta-acoustic.com; info@pinta-acoustic.com *Web Site:* www.pinta-acoustic.com, pg 857

Johnson, Eric, Trailblazer Studios®, 1610 Midtown Place, Raleigh, NC 27609 *Tel:* 919-645-6600 *Fax:* 919-645-6601 *E-mail:* info@trailblazerstudios. com *Web Site:* www.trailblazerstudios.com, pg 917

Johnson, Eugene L, Ward-Beck Systems Ltd, 945 Middlefield Rd, Unit 9, Toronto, ON M1V 5E1, Canada *Tel:* 416-335-5999 *Toll Free Tel:* 800-771-2556 *Fax:* 416-335-5202 *E-mail:* sales@ward-beck. com *Web Site:* www.ward-beck.com, pg 934

Johnson, Greg, Havas Edge, 2386 Faraday Ave, Suite 200, Carlsbad, CA 92008 *Tel:* 760-929-0041 *E-mail:* info@havasedge.com *Web Site:* www. havasedge.com, pg 777

Johnson, Hamilton, Sundance Systems, Fibox Products Division, 7411 Hines Place, Suite 123, Dallas, TX 75235 *Tel:* 214-920-9190 *Toll Free Tel:* 800-525-3443 *Fax:* 214-920-9339 *Web Site:* www.sundancesys.com, pg 904

Johnson, JD, Power Sonic Corp, 365 Cabela Dr, Suite 300, Reno, NV 89523 *Tel:* 619-661-2020 *Fax:* 619-661-3650 *Web Site:* www.power-sonic.com, pg 860

Johnson, Jenda, Ka Io Productions Inc, PO Box 5150, Hilo, HI 96720-1150 *Tel:* 808-959-3885 *Toll Free Tel:* 888-458-7538 *Fax:* 808-959-3885 *E-mail:* lava@volcanovideo.com *Web Site:* www.volcanovideo.com, pg 796

Johnson, Jerry, Microdolly Hollywood, 135 N Victory Blvd, Burbank, CA 91502 *Tel:* 818-845-8383 *E-mail:* microdolly@microdolly.com *Web Site:* www. microdolly.com, pg 826

Johnson, Dr Jerry A, National Religious Broadcasters (NRB), 660 N Capitol St NW, Suite 210, Washington, DC 20001 *Tel:* 202-543-0073 *Fax:* 202-543-2649 *E-mail:* info@nrb.org; press@nrb.org *Web Site:* nrb. org, pg 959

Johnson, Keith O, Reference Recordings, PO Box 77225, San Francisco, CA 94107 *Tel:* 650-355-1845 *Toll Free Tel:* 800-336-8866 *Fax:* 650-355-1949 *E-mail:* referencerecordings@gmail.com *Web Site:* www.referencerecordings.com, pg 872

Johnson, Kerry, The ADS Group, 2155 Niagara Lane N, Suite 120, Plymouth, MN 55447 *Tel:* 763-449-5500 *Toll Free Tel:* 800-475-4400 *Fax:* 763-449-5555 *E-mail:* sales@theadsgroup.com *Web Site:* theadsgroup.com, pg 677

Johnson, Kirk, New Harbinger Publications, 5674 Shattuck Ave, Oakland, CA 94609 *Tel:* 510-652-0215 *Toll Free Tel:* 800-748-6273 *Fax:* 510-652-5472 *E-mail:* customerservice@newharbinger.com *Web Site:* www.newharbinger.com, pg 839

Johnson, Kristi, Fresno County Film Commission, 2220 Tulare St, Suite 800, Fresno, CA 93721 *Tel:* 559-600-4271 *Fax:* 559-600-4573 *E-mail:* tourism@fresnocountyca.gov *Web Site:* www.filmfresno.com, pg 966

Johnson, Melissa, ExpoDisplays, 3401 Mary Taylor Rd, Birmingham, AL 35235 *Toll Free Tel:* 800-747-3976 *E-mail:* info@expodisplays.com *Web Site:* www. expodisplays.com, pg 757

Johnson, Michelle, Freeman, 1600 Viceroy, Suite 100, Dallas, TX 75235 *Tel:* 214-445-1000 *Web Site:* www. freeman.com, pg 765

Johnson, Michelle, Mutoh America Inc, 2602 S 47 St, Phoenix, AZ 85034-7401 *Tel:* 480-968-7772 *Toll Free Tel:* 800-99-MUTOH (996-8864) *Fax:* 480-968-7990 *E-mail:* sales@mutoh.com; support@mutoh.com *Web Site:* www.mutoh.com, pg 835

Johnson, Pat, Vertiv, 1050 Dearborn Dr, Columbus, OH 43085 *Tel:* 614-888-0246 *Web Site:* www.vertiv.com, pg 926

Johnson, Paul, Poly, 345 Encinal St, Santa Cruz, CA 95060 *Tel:* 831-426-5858 *Toll Free Tel:* 800-544-4660 *Fax:* 831-426-6098 *Web Site:* www.poly.com, pg 859

Johnson, Redge, Images II Inc, 1700 "O" St, Lincoln, NE 68508 *Tel:* 402-475-4000 *Toll Free Tel:* 800-669-4001 *Fax:* 402-475-8063 *E-mail:* graphics@images2. com *Web Site:* www.images2.com, pg 785

Johnson, Richard, HSA Inc, 1717 E Sixth St, Mishawaka, IN 46544 *Tel:* 574-255-6100 *Fax:* 574-255-8131 *E-mail:* hsainfo@hsarolltops.com *Web Site:* www.hsarolltops.com, pg 782

Johnson, Rick, RBR Productions, 1926 Greenview Rd, Northbrook, IL 60062 *Tel:* 847-362-4060 *Web Site:* www.rbrproductions.com, pg 870

Johnson, Rob, Vertiv, 1050 Dearborn Dr, Columbus, OH 43085 *Tel:* 614-888-0246 *Web Site:* www.vertiv.com, pg 926

Johnson, Robert L, RLJ Entertainment Inc, 8515 Georgia Ave, Suite 650, Silver Spring, MD 20910 *Tel:* 301-608-2115 *Toll Free Tel:* 800-999-0212 *E-mail:* inquiries@rljentertainment.com *Web Site:* www.us.rljentertainment.com, pg 875

Johnson, Ron, Adtec Digital Inc, 408 Russell St, Nashville, TN 37206 *Tel:* 615-256-6619 *Fax:* 615-256-6593 *E-mail:* sales@adtecinc.com *Web Site:* www. adtecinc.com, pg 677

Johnson, Scott, TOMCAT USA Inc, 5427 N National Dr, Knoxville, TN 37914 *Tel:* 865-219-3700 *Fax:* 865-673-5818 *E-mail:* info@tomcatusa.com; sales@tomcatusa.com *Web Site:* www.tomcatglobal.com, pg 915

Johnson, Shaun, Johnson Systems Inc (JSI), 1923 Highfield Crescent SE, Calgary, AB T2G 5M1, Canada *Tel:* 403-287-8003 *Fax:* 403-287-9003 *E-mail:* info@johnsonsystems.com *Web Site:* www. johnsonsystems.com, pg 794

Johnson, Tom, Theatrical Services Inc, 128 S Washington St, Wichita, KS 67202 *Tel:* 316-263-4415 *Toll Free Tel:* 888-874-2649 *Fax:* 316-263-9927 *Web Site:* www.theatricalservices.com, pg 912

Johnson, Trent, Davidson Productions, 1180 Vista Del Lago, San Luis Obispo, CA 93405 *Tel:* 415-886-7540 *E-mail:* dfi@davidsonfilms.com *Web Site:* davidsonfilms.com, pg 738

Johnston, Bob, Wanted! Sound + Picture, 409 King St W, Suite 300, Toronto, ON M5V 1K1, Canada *Tel:* 416-596-1101 *Fax:* 416-596-0690 *E-mail:* info@wantedsp.com; bookings@wantedsp.com *Web Site:* www.wantedsp.com, pg 933

Johnston, Charidy, Penguin Random House Canada, 320 Front St W, Suite 1400, Toronto, ON M5V 3B6, Canada *Tel:* 416-364-4449 *Toll Free Tel:* 888-523-9292 (cust serv) *Fax:* 416-598-7764 *E-mail:* customerservicescanada@penguinrandomhouse.com *Web Site:* www. penguinrandomhouse.ca, pg 853

Johnston, Janice Reid, Ontario Creates, South Tower, Suite 501, 175 Bloor St E, Toronto, ON M4W 3R8, Canada *Tel:* 416-314-6858 *Fax:* 416-314-6876 *E-mail:* reception@ontariocreates.ca *Web Site:* www. ontariocreates.ca, pg 978

Johnston, Jessica, The Visual Studies Workshop (VSW), 31 Prince St, Rochester, NY 14607 *Tel:* 585-442-8676 *Fax:* 585-442-1992 *E-mail:* info@vsw.org *Web Site:* www.vsw.org, pg 931

Johnston, Pamela, Pamela Johnston Voice Talent, 249 Eighth Ave, Cramerton, NC 28032 *Tel:* 703-371-7341 *Fax:* 703-997-8971 *Web Site:* www.pjvoicetalent.com, pg 794

Johnston, Patrick, AheadTeK, 6410 Via Del Oro, San Jose, CA 95119 *Tel:* 408-226-9800; 408-226-9991 *Toll Free Tel:* 800-971-9191 *Fax:* 408-226-9195 *Web Site:* www.aheadtek.com, pg 678

Joli-Coeur, Claude, National Film Board of Canada/Office National du Film du Canada, Ilot Balmoral, 1501 de Bleury St, Montreal, QC H3A 0H3, Canada *Tel:* 514-287-9000; 514-261-1650 (animation studio) *Toll Free Tel:* 800-267-7710 (CN only); 800-542-2164 (US only) *Fax:* 514-841-3500 *Web Site:* www.nfb.ca; onf-nfb.gc.ca, pg 836

Jones, Bruce, Lectrosonics Inc, 581 Laser Rd NE, Rio Rancho, NM 87124 *Tel:* 505-892-4501 *Toll Free Tel:* 800-821-1121 *Fax:* 505-892-6243 *E-mail:* sales@lectrosonics.com *Web Site:* www.lectrosonics.com, pg 805

Jones, Christian, Davies Publishing Inc, 32 S Raymond Ave, Suites 4-5, Pasadena, CA 91105 *Tel:* 626-792-3046 *Toll Free Tel:* 877-792-0005 (US only) *Fax:* 626-792-5308 *E-mail:* info@daviespublishing. com *Web Site:* www.daviespublishing.com, pg 738

Jones, Clint, Leo Ticheli Productions, 2801 University Blvd, Suite 101, Birmingham, AL 35233 *Tel:* 205-930-0500 *Fax:* 205-930-0505 *E-mail:* hello@ltpro.com *Web Site:* www.ltpro.com, pg 913

Jones, Craig, Power Integrity Corporation, 2109 Patterson St, Greensboro, NC 27407 *Tel:* 336-379-9773 *Toll Free Tel:* 800-237-6260 (tech support) *Web Site:* powerintegritycorp.com, pg 860

Kail, Jack, Zenith Electronics LLC, 2000 Millbrook Dr, Lincolnshire, IL 60069 Tel: 847-941-8000 Toll Free Tel: 800-243-0000 (cust serv) Web Site: www.zenith. com, pg 945

Kaimis, Kyriakos, Custom Computer Specialists Inc, 70 Suffolk Ct, Hauppauge, NY 11788 Tel: 631-864-6699 Toll Free Tel: 800-589-8989 Fax: 401-765-6440 Toll Free Fax: 800-986-5518 E-mail: info@customtech. com; support@customtech.com Web Site: www. customonline.com, pg 736

Kain, Hannah, ALOM Technologies Corp, 48105 Warm Springs Blvd, Fremont, CA 94539-7498 Tel: 510-360-3600 Toll Free Tel: 800-500-9991 Fax: 510-226-7617 E-mail: customerservice@alom.com Web Site: www. alom.com, pg 681

Kairys, Mike, Ac-cetera Inc, 5049 Center Dr, Bldg D-1, Latrobe, PA 15650 Tel: 724-532-3362 Toll Free Tel: 800-537-3491 Fax: 724-532-3364 Web Site: www. ac-cetera.com, pg 672

Kaiser, Bruce, Lightning Master Corp, 2100-A Palmetto St, Clearwater, FL 33765 Tel: 727-447-6800 Toll Free Tel: 877-334-8006 Fax: 727-499-0138 E-mail: info@ lightningmaster.com Web Site: www.lightningmaster. com, pg 808

Kaiser, Chris, Pixar Animation Studios, 1200 Park Ave, Emeryville, CA 94608 Tel: 510-922-3000 Fax: 510-922-3151 Web Site: www.pixar.com, pg 857

Kalbach, Paul, Artichoke Productions, 4114 Linden St, Oakland, CA 94608 Tel: 510-655-1283 Web Site: www.artichokepro.com, pg 690

Kalber, Ann, Tropical Visions Video Inc, 13-3435 Kupono St, Pahoa, HI 96778 Tel: 808-895-0077 E-mail: redhotlava@hawaii.rr.com Web Site: www. tropicalvisions.com, pg 918

Kalber, Mick, Tropical Visions Video Inc, 13-3435 Kupono St, Pahoa, HI 96778 Tel: 808-895-0077 E-mail: redhotlava@hawaii.rr.com Web Site: www. tropicalvisions.com, pg 918

Kalin, Jean, Limelight Production® Inc, 471 Pleasant St, Lee, MA 01238-9322 Tel: 413-243-4950 Toll Free Tel: 800-243-4950 Fax: 413-243-4993 Toll Free Fax: 800-243-4951 E-mail: info@ limelightproductions.com; sales@limelightproductions. com Web Site: www.limelightproductions.com, pg 809

Kalman, Todd, Marketron Broadcast Solutions, 101 Empty Saddle Trail, Hailey, ID 83333 Tel: 208-788-6800 Toll Free Tel: 800-476-7226 Fax: 208-788-6273 E-mail: sales@marketron.com Web Site: www. marketron.com, pg 817

Kaloi, Dennis, Simon - Kaloi Engineering Ltd, 31192 La Baya Dr, Unit G, Westlake Village, CA 91362 Tel: 818-707-8400 Fax: 818-707-8401 E-mail: sales@ skeng.com Web Site: www.skeng.com, pg 888

Kamcheff, Brad, Aiphone Corp, 6670 185 Ave NE, Redmond, WA 98052 Tel: 425-455-0510 Toll Free Tel: 800-692-0200 Fax: 425-455-0071 Toll Free Fax: 800-525-3372 (cust serv) E-mail: info@aiphone. com; cs@aiphone.com Web Site: www.aiphone. com/home, pg 678

Kamienowicz, Samy, Samy's Camera, 431 S Fairfax Ave, Los Angeles, CA 90036 Tel: 323-938-2420 Toll Free Tel: 800-321-4726 Fax: 323-937-2919 E-mail: lacamera@samys.com; info@samys.com; locations@samys.com Web Site: www.samys.com, pg 879

Kamin, Courtney Brooks, International Society for Performance Improvement® (ISPI), PO Box 13035, Silver Spring, MD 20910 Tel: 301-587-8570 Fax: 301-587-8573 E-mail: info@ispi.org Web Site: www.ispi. org, pg 956

Kaminshine, Jerry, ESECO Speedmaster, 730 E Eseco Rd, Cushing, OK 74023-5505 Tel: 918-225-1266 Toll Free Tel: 800-331-5904 (US & CN) E-mail: info@ eseco-speedmaster.com Web Site: www.eseco-speedmaster.com, pg 755

Kamon, Leah, Radio Advertising Bureau (RAB), 125 W 55 St, 5th fl, New York, NY 10019 Tel: 212-681-7200 Toll Free Tel: 800-252-7234 Fax: 212-681-7223 E-mail: memberresponse@rab.com Web Site: www. rab.com, pg 961

Kanarek, Mike, WKYT-TV, 2851 Winchester Rd, Lexington, KY 40509 Tel: 859-299-0411; 859-299-2727 (newsroom) Web Site: www.wkyt.com, pg 940

Kancher, Ellen, Monster Tracks, 1821 Ranstead St, Philadelphia, PA 19103 Tel: 215-567-0400 Toll Free Tel: 800-369-1280 Fax: 215-567-0350 Web Site: www. monstertracks.com, pg 829

Kandell, Michael, Boonton Electronics, 25 Eastmans Rd, Parsippany, NJ 07054 Tel: 973-386-9696 Fax: 973-386-9191 E-mail: info@boonton.com Web Site: www. boonton.com, pg 709

Kane, Barry, Award Productions Inc, 164 Great Rd, Acton, MA 01720 Tel: 978-635-8000 E-mail: web@ awardprod.com Web Site: www.awardproductions.com, pg 699

Kane, Brian, Madisound Speaker Components Inc, 8608 University Green, Suite 10, Middleton, WI 53562 Tel: 608-831-3433 Toll Free Tel: 866-883-1488 (orders) Fax: 608-831-3771 E-mail: info@madisound. com Web Site: www.madisound.com, pg 814

Kane, Chris, AudioControl® Inc, 22410 70 Ave W, Mountlake Terrace, WA 98043 Tel: 425-775-8461 Fax: 425-778-3166 E-mail: sound.great@audiocontrol. com Web Site: www.audiocontrol.com, pg 695

Kane, Ursula, Award Productions Inc, 164 Great Rd, Acton, MA 01720 Tel: 978-635-8000 E-mail: web@ awardprod.com Web Site: www.awardproductions.com, pg 699

Kann, Thomas, Integrated Event Management, 1239 Vista Leaf Dr, Decatur, GA 30033 Tel: 404-633-8541 Fax: 404-633-8691 Web Site: integratedevents.com, pg 789

Kanter, Ron, Video/Film Associates, 413 N Seventh St, Philadelphia, PA 19123-3900 Tel: 215-922-3333, pg 928

Kantola, Steve, Kantola Productions LLC, 55 Sunnyside Ave, Mill Valley, CA 94941 Tel: 415-381-9363 Toll Free Tel: 800-280-1180 Fax: 415-381-9801 E-mail: kantola@kantola.com Web Site: www.kantola. com, pg 796

Kapell, Sandra, Madison Square Garden, 2 Pennsylvania Plaza, New York, NY 10121-0091 Tel: 212-465-6741 E-mail: msgnetpr@msgnetwork.com Web Site: www. thegarden.com; themadisonsquaregardencompany.com, pg 814

Kapes, Gordon, Studio Technologies Inc, 7440 Frontage Rd, Skokie, IL 60077-3202 Tel: 847-676-9177 E-mail: stisales-2018@studio-tech.com Web Site: www.studio-tech.com, pg 903

Kapis, Sue, Park City Film Commission, 1850 Sidewinder Dr, No 320, Park City, UT 84060 Tel: 435-649-6100 Toll Free Tel: 800-453-1360 Fax: 435-649-4132 Web Site: www.visitparkcity. com/film, pg 976

Kaplan, Debra, Nalpak Inc, 1267 Vernon Way, El Cajon, CA 92020 Tel: 619-258-1200 Toll Free Tel: 888-488-3372 (help desk) Fax: 619-258-0925 E-mail: service@ nalpak.com Web Site: www.nalpak.com, pg 835

Kaplan, Deeny, The Kitchen, 265 NE 24 St, Suite 401, Miami, FL 33137 Tel: 305-415-6200 E-mail: info@ thekitchen.tv Web Site: www.thekitchen.tv, pg 799

Kaplan, Howard, Silver Gavel Awards for Media & the Arts, Div for Public Education, 321 N Clark St, Chicago, IL 60654-7598 Tel: 312-988-5733 Toll Free Tel: 800-285-2221 Fax: 312-988-5494 (Attn: Gavel Awards) E-mail: publiceducation@americanbar.org Web Site: www.americanbar.org, pg 1004

Kaplan, Lynda B, American History Workshop (NY) Inc, 588 Seventh St, Brooklyn, NY 11215-3707 Tel: 718-499-6500 E-mail: info@americanhistoryworkshop.com Web Site: www.americanhistoryworkshop.com, pg 683

Kaplan, Mike, Lagoon Video, 3323 Marble Front Rd, Caldwell, ID 83605 Tel: 208-455-3457 E-mail: kapsm@aol.com, pg 803

Kaplan, Richard, Richard Kaplan Productions, 455 N End Ave, Apt 1114, New York, NY 10282-1139 Tel: 212-787-0258 Fax: 212-787-0268 E-mail: richardkaplan33@gmail.com Web Site: richardkaplanproductions.com, pg 796

Kappel, Gary, Orion Software, 6000 Cote-des-Neiges, Suite 240, Montreal, QC H3S 1Z8, Canada Tel: 514-484-9661 Toll Free Tel: 877-755-2012 Fax: 514-484-1339 E-mail: info@orion-soft.com Web Site: www. orion-soft.com, pg 848

Karanian, Sabra, Paradise Video & Film, 10148 NW 47 St, Sunrise, FL 33351 Tel: 954-747-1118 Fax: 954-747-3380 E-mail: info@paradisevideo.com Web Site: www.paradisevideo.com, pg 851

Karanicolas, Christos, Clever Devices Ltd, 300 Crossways Park Dr, Woodbury, NY 11797 Tel: 516-433-6100 Toll Free Tel: 800-872-6129 Web Site: www. cleverdevices.com, pg 726

Karcy, Bob, VIEW Inc (Video International Entertainment World Inc), 11 Reservoir Rd, Saugerties, NY 12477 Tel: 845-246-9955 Toll Free Tel: 800-843-9843 Fax: 845-246-9966 E-mail: viewvid@aol.com, pg 930

Karczmer, Claude M, Servoreeler Systems, 218-31 97 Ave, Queens Village, NY 11429 Tel: 718-464-9400 Toll Free Tel: 800-431-8900 Fax: 718-464-9435 E-mail: srsystems@servoreelers.com Web Site: www. servoreelers.com, pg 884

Karczmer, Eileen, Servoreeler Systems, 218-31 97 Ave, Queens Village, NY 11429 Tel: 718-464-9400 Toll Free Tel: 800-431-8900 Fax: 718-464-9435 E-mail: srsystems@servoreelers.com Web Site: www. servoreelers.com, pg 884

Kardokus, Ronald, Magnum Towers Inc, 9370 Elder Creek Rd, Sacramento, CA 95829 Tel: 916-381-5053 Fax: 916-381-2144 E-mail: office@magnumtowers. com Web Site: www.magnumtowers.com, pg 815

Karimbakas, Chris, Antronics Inc, 25 Summer Ave, Waltham, MA 02452-5634 Tel: 781-891-7525 Fax: 781-647-3667 E-mail: info@antronics.net Web Site: www.antronics.net, pg 686

Karimbakas, Jim, Antronics Inc, 25 Summer Ave, Waltham, MA 02452-5634 Tel: 781-891-7525 Fax: 781-647-3667 E-mail: info@antronics.net Web Site: www.antronics.net, pg 686

Karlo, Tom, KPBS Public Broadcasting, 5200 Campanille Dr, San Diego, CA 92182 Tel: 619-594-1515; 619-265-6438 (newsroom) Toll Free Tel: 888-399-5727 Fax: 619-594-3812 Web Site: www.kpbs.org, pg 801

Karlovits, Chuck, VITAC, 8300 E Maplewood Ave, Suite 310, Greenwood Village, CO 80111 Toll Free Tel: 800-278-4822 (sales); 800-775-7838 E-mail: info@vitac.com Web Site: www.vitac.com, pg 932

Karlovits, Doug, VITAC, 8300 E Maplewood Ave, Suite 310, Greenwood Village, CO 80111 Toll Free Tel: 800-278-4822 (sales); 800-775-7838 E-mail: info@vitac.com Web Site: www.vitac.com, pg 932

Karlowitch, Debra, The Martin Guitar Co, 510 Sycamore St, Nazareth, PA 18064 Tel: 610-759-2837 Toll Free Tel: 800-633-2060; 888-433-9177 Fax: 610-759-5757 Web Site: www.martinguitar.com, pg 818

Karns, Krys, Washington Filmworks, 1411 Fourth Ave, Suite 420, Seattle, WA 98101 Tel: 206-264-0667 Fax: 206-382-4343 E-mail: info@washingtonfilmworks.org Web Site: washingtonfilmworks.org, pg 977

Karol, John, Apertura, 535 Main St, Orford, NH 03777 Tel: 603-353-9067 Web Site: www.apertura.org, pg 687

Karp, David, Access Video in Berkeley, 1442 A Walnut St, Berkeley, CA 94709 Tel: 510-528-6044 E-mail: accessvideo@hotmail.com Web Site: www. accessvideoproductions.com, pg 673

Karp, Stacey, America's Public Television Stations (APTS), 2100 Crystal Dr, Suite 700, Arlington, VA 22202 *Tel:* 202-654-4200 *Fax:* 202-654-4236 *Web Site:* apts.org, pg 949

Karr, Marcus, Manhattan Center Studios Inc, 311 W 34 St, New York, NY 10001 *Tel:* 212-279-7740 *Fax:* 212-564-1072 *E-mail:* info@mcstudios.com *Web Site:* www.mcstudios.com, pg 816

Karsten, Ralph, Atma-Sphere Music Systems Inc, 1742 Selby Ave, St Paul, MN 55104 *Tel:* 651-690-2246 *Web Site:* www.atma-sphere.com, pg 692

Karten, Mike, Calrad Electronics, 819 N Highland Ave, Los Angeles, CA 90038 *Tel:* 323-465-2131 *Fax:* 323-465-3504 *E-mail:* sales@calrad.com *Web Site:* www. calrad.com, pg 714

Kasdon, Carter, CommCreative, 75 Fountain St, Framingham, MA 01702 *Tel:* 508-620-6664 *Toll Free Tel:* 877-620-6664 *Fax:* 508-620-0592 *E-mail:* info@ commcreative.com *Web Site:* www.commcreative.com, pg 728

Kasprzak, Sherry, Texcam Inc, 1323 N First St, Bellaire, TX 77401 *Tel:* 713-524-2774 *Toll Free Tel:* 800-735-2774 *Fax:* 713-524-2779 *E-mail:* info@texcam.com *Web Site:* www.texcam.com, pg 911

Kass, Hope, Chicago Spotlight Inc, 3418 N Knox Ave, Chicago, IL 60641 *Tel:* 312-455-1171 *Web Site:* www. grandstage.com, pg 721

Kass, Hope, Grand Stage Co Inc, 3418 N Knox Ave, Chicago, IL 60641 *Tel:* 312-332-5611 *Toll Free Tel:* 800-621-2181 *Fax:* 312-332-3655 *E-mail:* marketing@grandstage.com *Web Site:* www. grandstage.com, pg 773

Kassouf, Jeff, Take 1 Media Services, 31335 Center Ridge Rd, Cleveland, OH 44145 *Tel:* 440-899-0101 *Web Site:* www.take1media.com, pg 906

Kasun, Leo, Department of Education Resources, 2000B S Club Dr, Landover, MD 20785 *Tel:* 202-842-6706 *Fax:* 202-842-6937 *E-mail:* edresources@nga.gov *Web Site:* www.nga.gov/education.html, pg 740

Katz, Barry, NEP Group Inc, 2 Beta Dr, Pittsburgh, PA 15238 *Tel:* 412-826-1414 *Toll Free Tel:* 800-444-0054 *E-mail:* info@nepinc.com *Web Site:* www.nepgroup. com, pg 838

Katz, David, Integrated Solutions Group, 858 Boston Providence Tpke, Norwood, MA 02062 *Tel:* 781-769-7810 *Toll Free Tel:* 866-769-0210 *E-mail:* info@ isgboston.com *Web Site:* isgboston.com, pg 789

Katz, David M, A/V Davey, 71 Clifton Place, Bridgeport, CT 06606 *Tel:* 203-372-3286 *Fax:* 203-372-3307 *Web Site:* avdavey.com, pg 697

Katz, Gene, Integrated Solutions Group, 858 Boston Providence Tpke, Norwood, MA 02062 *Tel:* 781-769-7810 *Toll Free Tel:* 866-769-0210 *E-mail:* info@ isgboston.com *Web Site:* isgboston.com, pg 789

Katz, Jeff, Synaptic Digital, 79 Fifth Ave, 14th fl, New York, NY 10003 *Tel:* 212-682-8300 *Fax:* 212-201-4207 *E-mail:* learnmore@synapticdigital.com *Web Site:* www.synapticdigital.com, pg 905

Katz, Kyle, Producers Guild of America Inc (PGA), 8530 Wilshire Blvd, Suite 400, Beverly Hills, CA 90211 *Tel:* 310-358-9020 *E-mail:* info@ producersguild.org *Web Site:* www.producersguild.org, pg 960

Katz, Simon, Penguin Random House Audio Publishing, 1745 Broadway, New York, NY 10019 *E-mail:* audio@penguinrandomhouse.com *Web Site:* www.penguinrandomhouseaudio.com, pg 853

Kaufman, Barney L, Magna-Tech Electronic Co Inc, 1998 NE 150 St, North Miami, FL 33181 *Tel:* 305-573-7339 *Fax:* 305-573-8101 *E-mail:* sales@iceco. com; digital@myiceco.com *Web Site:* www.magna-tech.com, pg 814

Kaufmann, Bruce, Human Circuit, 9346 Gaither Rd, Gaithersburg, MD 20877 *Tel:* 240-864-4000 *Web Site:* www.humancircuit.com, pg 782

Kaufmann, Harry, BeachTek Inc, 480 Osprey Ave, Kelowna, BC V1Y 5A5, Canada *Tel:* 778-478-9872 *E-mail:* info@beachtek.com *Web Site:* www.beachtek. com, pg 702

Kautz, Andrew, Love Shack Recording Studios, 909 18 Ave S, Nashville, TN 37212 *Tel:* 615-843-0019 *E-mail:* book@loveshackstudios.com *Web Site:* loveshackstudios.com, pg 812

Kavanagh, Bill, Kavanagh Productions Inc, 32 Broadway, Suite 1711-12, New York, NY 10004 *Tel:* 212-480-0065 *Fax:* 212-480-0149 *E-mail:* create@kavanaghproductions.com *Web Site:* kavanaghproductions.com, pg 797

Kayser, Ferdinand, SES SA, 4 Research Way, Princeton, NJ 08540-6684 *Tel:* 609-987-4000 *E-mail:* info@ses. com *Web Site:* www.ses.com, pg 884

Kayser, Matt, KD Kanopy Inc, 1921 E 68 Ave, Denver, CO 80229 *Tel:* 303-650-1310 *Toll Free Tel:* 800-432-4435 *Fax:* 303-650-5211 *E-mail:* sales@kdkanopy.com *Web Site:* www.kdkanopy.com, pg 797

Kazanjian, Steve, Promax, 5700 Wilshire Blvd, Suite 275, Los Angeles, CA 90036 *Tel:* 310-788-7600 *Fax:* 310-788-7616 *Web Site:* www.promax.org, pg 961

Kazary, Wil, Guerrilla Productions LLC, 1119 E 50 St, Savannah, GA 31404 *Tel:* 912-354-1518 *Fax:* 404-585-5692 *E-mail:* info@guerrillapro.com *Web Site:* guerrillapro.com, pg 774

Kazmark, Eugene Jr, Kart-A-Bag Manufacturing Inc, 510 Manhattan Rd, Joliet, IL 60433 *Tel:* 815-723-1940 *Toll Free Tel:* 800-423-9328 *Fax:* 815-723-2495 *E-mail:* sales@kart-a-bag.com *Web Site:* www.kart-a-bag.com, pg 796

Kazmark-Bruskotter, Mary, Kart-A-Bag Manufacturing Inc, 510 Manhattan Rd, Joliet, IL 60433 *Tel:* 815-723-1940 *Toll Free Tel:* 800-423-9328 *Fax:* 815-723-2495 *E-mail:* sales@kart-a-bag.com *Web Site:* www.kart-a-bag.com, pg 796

Kean, Carla, Penguin Random House Canada, 320 Front St W, Suite 1400, Toronto, ON M5V 3B6, Canada *Tel:* 416-364-4449 *Toll Free Tel:* 888-523-9292 (cust serv) *Fax:* 416-598-7764 *E-mail:* customerservicescanada@ penguinrandomhouse.com *Web Site:* www. penguinrandomhouse.ca, pg 853

Keck, Becky, Broadcast Electronics, 4100 N 24 St, Quincy, IL 62305 *Tel:* 217-224-9600 *Fax:* 217-224-9607 *E-mail:* bdcast@bdcast.com *Web Site:* www. bdcast.com, pg 710

Keck, Doug, Eternal Word Television Network (EWTN), 5817 Old Leeds Rd, Irondale, AL 35210-2164 *Tel:* 205-271-2900 *Fax:* 205-271-2920 *E-mail:* viewer@ewtn.com *Web Site:* www.ewtn.com, pg 756

Kedas, Jeannie, MTV, c/o MTV Studios, 1515 Broadway, New York, NY 10036 *Tel:* 212-258-8000 *Web Site:* www.mtv.com; www.mtvpress.com, pg 833

Keebler, Rachel, Cobalt Studios Inc, 134 Royce Rd, White Lake, NY 12786 *Tel:* 845-583-7025 *Fax:* 845-583-7025 *E-mail:* mail@cobaltstudios.net *Web Site:* www.cobaltstudios.net, pg 727

Keefe, Deanna M, Liturgy Training Publications, 3949 S Racine Ave, Chicago, IL 60609-2523 *Tel:* 773-579-4900 *Toll Free Tel:* 800-933-1800 (orders) *Fax:* 773-579-4929 *E-mail:* orders@ltp.org; info@ltp.org *Web Site:* www.ltp.org, pg 810

Keefe, Joe, Ostergaard Acoustical Associates, 200 Executive Dr, Suite 350, West Orange, NJ 07052 *Tel:* 973-731-7002 *Fax:* 973-731-6680 *E-mail:* info@ acousticalconsultant.com *Web Site:* www. acousticalconsultant.com, pg 848

Keefe, Rich, AVFX Inc, 96 Holton St, Boston, MA 02135 *Tel:* 617-254-0770 *Toll Free Tel:* 888-254-0770 *E-mail:* info@avfx.com *Web Site:* www.avfx.com, pg 698

Keegan, Wayne, Ingram Content Group LLC, One Ingram Blvd, La Vergne, TN 37086-1986 *Tel:* 615-793-5000 *Toll Free Tel:* 800-937-8000 (retailers);

800-937-5300 (ext 1, libs) *E-mail:* customerservice@ ingramcontent.com *Web Site:* www.ingramcontent.com, pg 787

Keeler, Robert, CEDIA IPRO Affinity Group, 8475 Nightfall Lane, Fishers, IN 46037 *Tel:* 317-328-4336 *Toll Free Tel:* 800-669-5329 *E-mail:* info@cedia.org *Web Site:* cedia.net, pg 952

Keenan, Linda, Creative Media Recording, 11105 Knott Ave, Suite G, Cypress, CA 90630 *Tel:* 714-892-9469 *E-mail:* info@creativemediarecording.com *Web Site:* www.creativemediarecording.com, pg 733

Keenan, Tim, Creative Media Recording, 11105 Knott Ave, Suite G, Cypress, CA 90630 *Tel:* 714-892-9469 *E-mail:* info@creativemediarecording.com *Web Site:* www.creativemediarecording.com, pg 733

Keene-Kendrick, Lydia, Davis Art Images, 50 Portland St, Worcester, MA 01608 *Tel:* 508-754-7201 *Toll Free Tel:* 800-533-2847 *Fax:* 508-753-3834 *E-mail:* contactus@davisart.com; das@davisart.com *Web Site:* www.davisart.com, pg 738

Keezer, Dawn M, Pittsburgh Film Office, The Oliver Bldg, 535 Smithfield St, Suite 500, Pittsburgh, PA 15222 *Tel:* 412-261-2744 *E-mail:* info@pghfilm.org *Web Site:* www.pghfilm.org, pg 975

Keil, Alan, Ikegami Electronics (USA) Inc, 37 Brook Ave, Maywood, NJ 07607 *Tel:* 201-368-9171 *Fax:* 201-569-1626 *E-mail:* sales@ikegami.com; service@ikegami.com *Web Site:* www.ikegami.com, pg 784

Keith, Eric, SirsiDynix, 3300 N Ashton Blvd, Suite 500, Lehi, UT 84043 *Tel:* 801-223-5200; 0800 016 3147 *Toll Free Tel:* 800-288-8020 *Fax:* 801-331-7770 *Web Site:* www.sirsidynix.com, pg 889

Keith, Matt, Custom Color Corp, 14320 W 101 Terr, Lenexa, KS 66215 *Tel:* 913-730-3100 *Fax:* 913-730-3101 *E-mail:* info@customcolor.com *Web Site:* www. customcolor.com, pg 736

Keitt, John, Blood-Horse Publications, 3101 Beaumont Centre Circle, Lexington, KY 40513 *Toll Free Tel:* 800-866-2361; 800-582-5604 *E-mail:* advertise@ bloodhorse.com; customerservice@bloodhorse.com *Web Site:* www.bloodhorse.com, pg 707

Keleman, Jacauelin, Theatre Service & Supply Corp, 10004-F Pulaski Hwy, Baltimore, MD 21220 *Tel:* 410-686-1398 *Fax:* 410-574-2417 *E-mail:* sales@stage-n-studio.com *Web Site:* www.stage-n-studio.com, pg 912

Kelham, Tiffany, International Ticketing Association Inc (INTIX), 5868 E 71 St, Suite E 367, Indianapolis, IN 46220 *Tel:* 212-629-4036 *Fax:* 212-629-4036 *E-mail:* info@intix.org; media@intix.org *Web Site:* www.intix.org, pg 957

Kelleher, Kevin, Sony Music Entertainment, 25 Madison Ave, New York, NY 10010 *Tel:* 212-833-8000 *Web Site:* www.sonymusic.com, pg 893

Kelleher, Roger, American Management Association® (AMA), 1601 Broadway, New York, NY 10019 *Tel:* 212-586-8100 *Toll Free Tel:* 877-566-9441 (cust serv) *Fax:* 212-903-8168; 518-891-0368 (cust serv) *E-mail:* customerservice@amanet.org *Web Site:* www. amanet.org, pg 683, 949

Keller, Daniel, Green Mountain Post Films (GMP), PO Box 229, Turners Falls, MA 01376-0229 *Tel:* 413-863-4754 *Fax:* 413-863-8248 *E-mail:* info@gmpfilms. com *Web Site:* www.gmpfilms.com, pg 774

Keller, Robin, The Hollaender Manufacturing Co, 10285 Wayne Ave, Cincinnati, OH 45215 *Tel:* 513-772-8800 *Toll Free Tel:* 800-772-8800 (orders) *Fax:* 513-772-8806 *Web Site:* www.hollaender.com, pg 780

Kelley, Barbara, Hearing Loss Association of America (HLAA), 7910 Woodmont Ave, Suite 1200, Bethesda, MD 20814 *Tel:* 301-657-2248 *Fax:* 301-913-9413 *E-mail:* inquiry@hearingloss.org *Web Site:* www. hearingloss.org, pg 778

Kelley, Hayden, Drytac Corp, 5601 Eastport Blvd, Richmond, VA 23231 *Tel:* 804-222-3094 *Toll Free Tel:* 800-280-6013 *E-mail:* customerservice@drytac. com *Web Site:* www.drytac.com, pg 747

Kelley, Richard, Drytac Corp, 5601 Eastport Blvd, Richmond, VA 23231 *Tel:* 804-222-3094 *Toll Free Tel:* 800-280-6013 *E-mail:* customerservice@drytac. com *Web Site:* www.drytac.com, pg 747

Kellman, Brian, Brian Film Productions LLC, 254 W 25 St, Suite 6-A, New York, NY 10001-7325 *Tel:* 212-645-8795, pg 710

Kellogg, Marcia, Megatrax, 7629 Fulton Ave, North Hollywood, CA 91605 *Tel:* 818-255-7100 *Toll Free Tel:* 888-MEGA-555 (634-2555) *Fax:* 818-255-7199 *E-mail:* info@megatrax.com *Web Site:* www.megatrax. com, pg 823

Kellough, Kjelti, Getty Images, 605 Fifth Ave S, Suite 400, Seattle, WA 98104 *Tel:* 206-925-5000 *Toll Free Tel:* 888-888-5889; 800-462-4379 (sales) *E-mail:* sales.na@gettyimages.com *Web Site:* www. gettyimages.com, pg 770

Kelly, Jack, Group One Ltd, 70 Sea Lane, Farmingdale, NY 11735 *Tel:* 631-396-0195 (audio div); 631-396-0184 (lighting div) *Fax:* 631-396-0190 *E-mail:* sales@ g1limited.com *Web Site:* www.g1limited.com, pg 774

Kelly, Jack, XTA Electronics Ltd, 70 Sea Lane, Farmingdale, NY 11735 *Tel:* 631-396-0195 (audio div); 631-396-0184 (lighting div) *Fax:* 631-396-0190 *E-mail:* sales@g1limited.com *Web Site:* www. g1limited.com, pg 943

Kelly, Jesse, Advanced Media LLC, 369 N Fairfax Ave, Suite A, Los Angeles, CA 90036 *Tel:* 323-658-6102 *E-mail:* info@advancedmediallc.com *Web Site:* www. advancedmediallc.com; www.gomemoriesforever.com, pg 677

Kelly, Katie, Texas Film Commission, 1100 San Jacinto, Suite 3.410, Austin, TX 78701 *Tel:* 512-463-9200 *Fax:* 512-463-4114 *Web Site:* gov.texas.gov/film, pg 976

Kelly, Kevin, Stampede Presentation Products Inc, 55 Woodridge Dr, Amherst, NY 14228 *Tel:* 716-635-9474 *Toll Free Tel:* 800-398-5652 *Fax:* 716-635-9484 (sales); 716-691-0854 *E-mail:* stampedenews@ stampedeglobal.com *Web Site:* www.stampedeglobal. com, pg 899

Kelly, Kristy, Kendall Hunt Publishing Co, 4050 Westmark Dr, Dubuque, IA 52002 *Tel:* 563-589-1000 *Toll Free Tel:* 800-228-0810 *Fax:* 563-589-1237 *Toll Free Fax:* 800-772-9165 *E-mail:* orders@kendallhunt. com; corpinfo@kendallhunt.com *Web Site:* www. kendallhunt.com, pg 797

Kelly, Patrick, Video Resources Inc, 1809 E Dyer Rd, Suite 307, Santa Ana, CA 92705 *Tel:* 949-261-7266 *E-mail:* info@videoresources.com *Web Site:* www. videoresources.com, pg 928

Kelly, Peter, The Cinema Guild Inc, 2803 Ocean Ave, Brooklyn, NY 11229 *Tel:* 212-685-6242 *Toll Free Tel:* 800-723-5522 *E-mail:* info@cinemaguild.com *Web Site:* www.cinemaguild.com, pg 724

Kelly, Sandra, The Mobius® Awards, 713 S Pacific Coast Hwy, Suite A, Redondo Beach, CA 90277-4233 *Tel:* 310-540-0959 *Fax:* 310-316-8905 *E-mail:* mobiusinfo@mobiusawards. com; mediarelations@mobiusawards.com *Web Site:* mobiusawards.com, pg 996

Kelly, Sandra, US International Film & Video Festival, 713 S Pacific Coast Hwy, Suite A, Redondo Beach, CA 90277-4233 *Tel:* 310-540-0959 *Fax:* 310-316-8905 *E-mail:* filmfestinfo@filmfestawards.com; mediarelations@filmfestawards.com *Web Site:* www. filmfestawards.com, pg 1005

Kelly, Shaun, Tremetrics Inc Industrial Instruments Division, 10393 W 70 St, Eden Prairie, MN 55344 *Toll Free Tel:* 800-825-0121 *Fax:* 952-903-4100 *E-mail:* info@tremetrics.com *Web Site:* www. tremetrics.com, pg 917

Kelly, Wesley W, Morefield Communications Inc, 35 N 35 St, Camp Hill, PA 17011-2707 *Tel:* 717-761-6170 *Toll Free Tel:* 800-382-1266 *E-mail:* info@morefield. com *Web Site:* www.morefield.com, pg 830

Kelmelis, Victor, Dreamscape Lighting Mfg Inc, 5521 W Washington Blvd, Los Angeles, CA 90016 *Tel:* 323-933-5760 *Fax:* 323-933-3607 *E-mail:* info@ dreamscapelighting.com *Web Site:* dreamscapelighting. com, pg 746

Kelsey, Audrey, KEF Media, 1161 Concord Rd SE, Smyrna, GA 30080 *Tel:* 404-605-0009 *E-mail:* info@ kefmedia.com *Web Site:* kefmedia.com, pg 797

Kelsey, David, Media Loft Inc, 615 First Ave NE, Suite 100, Minneapolis, MN 55413 *Tel:* 612-375-1086 *Fax:* 612-375-0913 *E-mail:* info@medialoft.com *Web Site:* www.medialoft.com, pg 822

Kelsey, Jesse, Hammond Communications Group Inc, 173 Trade St, Lexington, KY 40511 *Tel:* 859-254-1878 *E-mail:* info@hammondcg.com *Web Site:* hammondcg.com, pg 775

Kelsey, Sigrid, Catholic Library Association (CLA), 8550 United Plaza Blvd, Suite 1001, Baton Rouge, LA 70809 *Tel:* 225-408-4417 *E-mail:* cla2@cathla.org *Web Site:* www.cathla.org, pg 952

Kelso, Stephanie, Z-Axis Corp, 4600 S Ulster St, Suite 270, Denver, CO 80237 *Tel:* 303-713-0200 *Toll Free Tel:* 800-827-2947 *E-mail:* info@zaxis.com *Web Site:* www.zaxis.com, pg 944

Kendall, David, Link Electronics Inc, 2360 N High St, Suite 10, Jackson, MO 63755 *Tel:* 573-334-4433 *Toll Free Tel:* 800-776-4411 *Fax:* 573-204-4554 *E-mail:* sales@linkelectronics.com *Web Site:* www. linkelectronics.com, pg 809

Kenderdine, Daniel, Wire X 17 LLC, 1840 County Line Rd, Suite 301, Huntingdon Valley, PA 19006 *Tel:* 215-322-4600 *Toll Free Tel:* 800-233-0013 *Fax:* 215-322-1385 *E-mail:* sales@wirexgroup.com *Web Site:* wirex17.com, pg 940

Kenmotsu, JoAn, Cibola Systems, 180 S Cypress St, Orange, CA 92866 *Tel:* 714-480-0272 *Fax:* 714-480-0768 *E-mail:* info@cibolasystems.com *Web Site:* cibolasystems.com, pg 723

Kennedy, Dan, Great River Electronics, 164 Hardman Ave S, South St Paul, MN 55075 *Tel:* 651-455-1846 *Fax:* 651-455-3224 *E-mail:* info@greweb.com *Web Site:* www.greatriverelectronics.com, pg 773

Kennedy, James M, Pixar Animation Studios, 1200 Park Ave, Emeryville, CA 94608 *Tel:* 510-922-3000 *Fax:* 510-922-3151 *Web Site:* www.pixar.com, pg 857

Kennedy, Jim, News Corp, 1211 Avenue of the Americas, New York, NY 10036 *Tel:* 212-416-3400 *E-mail:* media@newscorp.com *Web Site:* newscorp. com, pg 840

Kennedy, John, Freeman, 1600 Viceroy, Suite 100, Dallas, TX 75235 *Tel:* 214-445-1000 *Web Site:* www. freeman.com, pg 765

Kennedy, Keith, Educational Technology & Media Services, University of Northern Iowa, Inno Teaching & Technol Ctr 101, Cedar Falls, IA 50614-0301 *Web Site:* it.uni.edu/educational-technology-media-services, pg 751

Kennedy, Kerry, Robert F Kennedy Journalism Awards, 1300 19 St NW, Suite 750, Washington, DC 20036 *Tel:* 646-553-4750 *E-mail:* info@ rfkhumanrights.org; communications@rfkhumanrights. org *Web Site:* rfkhumanrights.org/awards, pg 994

Kennedy, Tom, American Society of Media Photographers Inc (ASMP), PO Box 31207, Bethesda, MD 20824 *Toll Free Tel:* 877-771-2767 *E-mail:* info@ asmp.org *Web Site:* asmp.org, pg 949

Kennedy, Valerie, SCI Television & Creative Media LLC, 160 E Grand Ave, 5th fl, Chicago, IL 60611 *Tel:* 312-643-2080 *E-mail:* info@scitvproductions.com *Web Site:* www.scitvproductions.com, pg 882

Kennel, Glenn, ARRI Inc, 600 N Victory Blvd, Burbank, CA 91502-1639 *Tel:* 818-841-7070 *Fax:* 818-848-4028 *E-mail:* info@arri.com *Web Site:* www.arri.com, pg 689

Kenniff, Thomas, The Best of Photojournalism (BOP), 120 Hooper St, Athens, GA 30602-3018 *Tel:* 706-542-2506 *E-mail:* info@nppa.org *Web Site:* nppa.org, pg 983

Kenniff, Thomas, National Press Photographers Association (NPPA), 120 Hooper St, Athens, GA 30602-3018 *Tel:* 706-542-2506 *E-mail:* info@nppa. org; director@nppa.org *Web Site:* nppa.org, pg 959

Kennison, Wes, Launch Media, 804 Main St, Baton Rouge, LA 70802 *Tel:* 225-612-2112 *E-mail:* contactus@launchmedia.tv *Web Site:* www. launchmedia.tv, pg 804

Kensinger, Robert, Spectrum Industries Inc, 925 First Ave, Chippewa Falls, WI 54729 *Tel:* 715-723-6750 *Toll Free Tel:* 800-235-1262 *Fax:* 715-738-2309 *Toll Free Fax:* 800-335-0473 *E-mail:* info@spectrumfurniture.com *Web Site:* www. spectrumfurniture.com, pg 897

Kent, Christie, SirsiDynix, 3300 N Ashton Blvd, Suite 500, Lehi, UT 84043 *Tel:* 801-223-5200; 0800 016 3147 *Toll Free Tel:* 800-288-8020 *Fax:* 801-331-7770 *Web Site:* www.sirsidynix.com, pg 889

Kent, Norman, Norman Kent Productions, PO Box 1749, Flagler Beach, FL 32136 *Tel:* 386-446-0505 *Web Site:* www.normankent.com, pg 798

Kenton, Rachel, Zacuto, 401 W Ontario Ave, Chicago, IL 60654 *Tel:* 312-863-3453 (rentals); 312-863-3456 *Toll Free Tel:* 888-294-3456 *Fax:* 312-863-3455 *E-mail:* rentals@zacuto.com *Web Site:* www.zacuto. com, pg 945

Kenworthy, Randy, School Media Associates LLC, 5815 Live Oak Pkwy, Suite 2-B, Norcross, GA 30093-1700 *Tel:* 770-441-0600 *Toll Free Tel:* 800-451-5226 (orders) *Fax:* 770-441-8529 *E-mail:* info@smavideo. net; orders@smavideo.net *Web Site:* www.smavideo. net, pg 882

Keown, Stephen, Omega Media Group Inc, PO Box 924499, Peachtree Corners, GA 30010 *Web Site:* www.omegamediagroup.com, pg 845

Kephart, Rachel, Kansas City Film Office, 1321 Baltimore Ave, Kansas City, MO 64105 *Tel:* 816-691-3800 *Toll Free Tel:* 866-767-7700 *E-mail:* film@ visitkc.com *Web Site:* www.kcfilmoffice.com, pg 973

Kerrigan, Bill, Kerrigan Productions Inc, 3877 Draper Ave, Montreal, QC H4A 2N9, Canada *Tel:* 514-486-8456 *Web Site:* www.kerrigan.ca, pg 798

Kerstin, Kerry, Broadcasters General Store Inc, 2480 SE 52 St, Ocala, FL 34480 *Tel:* 352-622-7700 *Fax:* 352-629-7000 *E-mail:* sales@bgs.cc (orders) *Web Site:* www.bgs.cc, pg 711

Kesler, Eddie, Beast Atlanta, 3399 Peachtree Rd NE, Suite 200, Atlanta, GA 30326-1149 *Tel:* 404-237-9977 *Fax:* 404-237-3923 *Web Site:* www.beast.tv, pg 703

Keslow, Robert, Keslow Camera Inc, 5900 Blackwelder St, Culver City, CA 90232 *Tel:* 310-636-4600 *Fax:* 310-915-5335 *E-mail:* info@keslowcamera.com *Web Site:* www.keslowcamera.com, pg 798

Kesslar, Darryl, plan9films, 9 Willingdon Place, Saskatoon, SK S7L 1C2, Canada *Tel:* 306-955-NINE (955-6463) *E-mail:* info@plan9films.com *Web Site:* www.plan9films.com, pg 858

Kessler, Allan, Ark Media Group Ltd, PO Box 410685, San Francisco, CA 94141-0685 *Tel:* 415-863-7200; 415-863-3555 *Fax:* 415-864-5437 *E-mail:* sales@ arkmedia.com *Web Site:* www.arkmedia.com, pg 689

Kessler, Dan, NAMM, the National Association of Music Merchants, 5790 Armada Dr, Carlsbad, CA 92008 *Tel:* 760-438-8001 *Toll Free Tel:* 800-767-6266 (memb hotline) *Fax:* 760-438-7327 *E-mail:* info@namm.org *Web Site:* www.namm.org, pg 958

Kessler, Fred, Musivision Inc, 8 Deepwood Rd, Weston, CT 06883 *Tel:* 203-227-1017 *E-mail:* info@ musivision.com *Web Site:* musivision.com, pg 835

Kessler, Morris, Amplifier Technologies Inc (ATI), 1749 Chapin Rd, Montebello, CA 90640 *Tel:* 323-278-0001 *Fax:* 323-278-0083 *E-mail:* sales@ati-amp.com *Web Site:* www.ati-amp.com, pg 684

Kestel, Paul, American Color Imaging (ACI), 715 E 18 St, Cedar Falls, IA 50613 *Tel:* 319-277-3655 *Toll Free Tel:* 800-728-2722 *Fax:* 319-277-6522 *E-mail:* sales@ acilab.com *Web Site:* www.acilab.com, pg 683

Knell, Mark, Shapeshifter, 3405 Cahuenga Blvd W, Los Angeles, CA 90068 *Tel:* 323-876-3444 *Fax:* 323-876-1444 *E-mail:* sales@shapeshifterpost.com *Web Site:* www.shapeshifterpost.com, pg 885

Knickrehm, Mark A, Accenture, 161 N Clark St, Chicago, IL 60601 *Tel:* 312-693-0161 *Toll Free Tel:* 877-889-9009 *Fax:* 312-693-0507 *Web Site:* www.accenture.com, pg 672

Knieriem, Lynn, Flying Colors Broadcasts, 2000 "M" St NW, Suite 345, Washington, DC 20036 *Tel:* 202-293-5300 *E-mail:* info@fc-tv.com *Web Site:* www.fc-tv.com, pg 763

Knight, Christopher, The New Film Company Inc, 7 Scott St, Cambridge, MA 02138 *Tel:* 617-520-5005 *Fax:* 617-491-9201 *E-mail:* newfilmco@aol.com *Web Site:* www.newfilmco.com, pg 839

Knight, Elliot PhD, Alabama State Council on the Arts Fellowships & Grants, RSA Tower, Suite 110, 201 Monroe St, Montgomery, AL 36130-1800 *Tel:* 334-242-4076 *Fax:* 334-240-3269 *E-mail:* staff@arts.alabama.gov *Web Site:* www.arts.alabama.gov, pg 981

Knight, Jack, Samson Technologies Corp, 278-B Duffy Ave, Hicksville, NY 11801 *Tel:* 516-870-7200 *Fax:* 516-938-1696 *E-mail:* info@samsontech.com *Web Site:* www.samsontech.com, pg 879

Knight, Janetta, RAM® Mounts, 8410 Dallas Ave S, Seattle, WA 98108 *Tel:* 206-763-8361 *Toll Free Tel:* 800-497-7479 *Fax:* 206-763-9615 *E-mail:* sales@rammount.com *Web Site:* www.rammount.com, pg 870

Knight, Tom, Zondervan, 3900 Sparks Dr, Grand Rapids, MI 49546 *Tel:* 616-698-6900 *Toll Free Tel:* 800-226-1122; 800-727-1309 (retail orders) *Web Site:* www.zondervan.com, pg 945

Knopp, Louis Todd, Production Solutions Inc, PO Box 49431, Dayton, OH 45449 *Tel:* 937-866-2028 *Fax:* 253-423-8997 *E-mail:* proso@att.net *Web Site:* www.psiohio.com, pg 864

Knopp, Orin, Presentation Products Inc, 171 Madison Ave, 12th fl, New York, NY 10016 *Tel:* 212-736-6350 *Toll Free Tel:* 877-774-4523 *Fax:* 212-736-6353 *E-mail:* customerservice@pproducts.com *Web Site:* www.presentationproducts.com, pg 861

Knowland, Bill, Direct Images Interactive Inc, 1933 Davis St, Suite 308, San Leandro, CA 94577 *Tel:* 510-613-8299 *E-mail:* info@directimages.com *Web Site:* www.directimages.com, pg 743

Knowles, Karl, Knowles Video Inc (KVI), 5450 Buck Lake Rd, Tallahassee, FL 32317 *Tel:* 850-878-2298 *Fax:* 850-656-0119 *E-mail:* info@knowlesvideo.com *Web Site:* www.knowlesvideo.com, pg 800

Kobelan, Deb, Media Event Concepts Inc, 2036 Centimeter Circle, Austin, TX 78758 *Tel:* 512-832-1142 *Toll Free Tel:* 800-299-1142 *Fax:* 512-832-0236 *E-mail:* info@mecteam.com *Web Site:* www.mecteam.com, pg 822

Koch, Phillip, Film Police, 2558 W 16 St, Chicago, IL 60608 *Tel:* 773-463-4010 *E-mail:* info@filmpolice.com *Web Site:* www.filmpolice.com, pg 760

Koch, Spencer, KPLR-TV, 2250 Ball Dr, St Louis, MO 63146 *Tel:* 314-213-2222; 314-213-7831 (newsroom) *E-mail:* kplradmin@tribune.com *Web Site:* kplr11.com, pg 801

Kochuba, Tim, Really Good Stuff, 448 Pepper St, Monroe, CT 06468 *Tel:* 203-261-1920 *Toll Free Tel:* 800-366-1920 (orders); 877-867-1920 (cust serv) *Fax:* 203-268-1796 *Web Site:* www.reallygoodstuff.com, pg 871

Koczanski, Kathi, The Newhouse Media Group, 13710 Antler Point Dr, Tampa, FL 33626 *Tel:* 813-625-2326 *Web Site:* www.newhousemediagroup.com, pg 840

Koczanski, Zack, The Newhouse Media Group, 13710 Antler Point Dr, Tampa, FL 33626 *Tel:* 813-625-2326 *Web Site:* www.newhousemediagroup.com, pg 840

Kodosky, Jeff, National Instruments Corp, 11500 N Mopac Expwy, Austin, TX 78759-3504 *Tel:* 512-683-0100 *Toll Free Tel:* 888-280-7645 (sales); 877-388-1952 *Fax:* 512-683-8411; 512-683-5794 (sales) *Web Site:* www.ni.com, pg 836

Koenig, Robert, DBM Communications Inc, 606 Baltimore Ave, Suite 200, Towson, MD 21204 *Tel:* 410-825-7400 *Fax:* 443-269-0213 *Web Site:* www.dbmcommunications.com, pg 739

Koenig, William S, NBA Entertainment Inc, 450 Harmon Meadow Blvd, Secaucus, NJ 07094 *Tel:* 201-865-1500 *Fax:* 201-865-2626 *Web Site:* www.nba.com, pg 837

Koeppen, Steven, Film Creations Ltd, 4349 E Fifth St, Tucson, AZ 85711 *Tel:* 520-624-4444 *Toll Free Tel:* 888-877-2490 *Fax:* 520-624-9659 *E-mail:* info@filmcreations.com *Web Site:* www.filmcreations.com, pg 760

Koeppl, Todd, Chicago Spotlight Inc, 3418 N Knox Ave, Chicago, IL 60641 *Tel:* 312-455-1171 *Web Site:* www.grandstage.com, pg 721

Koester, Becky, High End Systems Inc, 2105 Gracy Farms Lane, Austin, TX 78758 *Tel:* 512-836-2242 *Toll Free Tel:* 800-890-8989 *Web Site:* www.highend.com, pg 779

Koester, Dean, DataDirect Networks, 9351 Deering Ave, Chatsworth, CA 91311 *Tel:* 818-700-4000 *Toll Free Tel:* 800-TERABYTE (837-2298) *E-mail:* info@ddn.com; sales@ddn.com *Web Site:* www.ddn.com, pg 738

Koff-Chapin, Deborah, Center for Touch Drawing, PO Box 1595, Langley, WA 98260 *Tel:* 360-221-5745 *E-mail:* center@touchdrawing.com *Web Site:* www.touchdrawing.com, pg 719

Kogan, Patricia, Pat Kogan Productions Inc, 4121 42 St, Sunnyside, NY 11104 *Tel:* 914-661-0049 *E-mail:* pkpmedia4142@gmail.com *Web Site:* www.pkpmedia.com, pg 852

Kohn, David, CMD Agency, 1631 NW Thurman St, Portland, OR 97209 *Tel:* 503-223-6794 *E-mail:* info@cmdagency.com *Web Site:* www.cmdagency.com, pg 726

Koke, Judy, Art Gallery of Ontario, 317 Dundas St W, Toronto, ON M5T 1G4, Canada *Tel:* 416-979-6648 *Toll Free Tel:* 877-225-4246 *Web Site:* ago.ca, pg 690

Kokette, Steve, Aylmer Press, PO Box 2302, Madison, WI 53701-2302 *Tel:* 608-441-5277 *Fax:* 608-251-0890 *Web Site:* www.signit2.com, pg 700

Kolarek, Dale, Set To Go Studios, 86 Lackawana Ave, Suite 235, Woodland Park, NJ 07424 *Tel:* 973-638-1646 *Web Site:* www.settogostudio.com, pg 884

Kolb, Kurt, Speakeasy™ Productions Inc, 9 Westminster Shopping Center, No 152, Westminster, MD 21157 *Tel:* 410-889-0374 *Web Site:* www.voiceover.com, pg 896

Kolwitz, Ok Hee, Penguin Random House Audio Publishing, 1745 Broadway, New York, NY 10019 *E-mail:* audio@penguinrandomhouse.com *Web Site:* www.penguinrandomhouseaudio.com, pg 853

Komarovsk, Anne, Universal Satellite Communications Inc, 1530 Nandina Ave, Perris, CA 92571 *Tel:* 562-483-4800; 951-943-4420 (corp off) *Toll Free Tel:* 888-867-6620 *Fax:* 954-943-0263 *Web Site:* www.unisatmobile.com, pg 922

Komori, Linda, Thompson Rivers University Marketing & Communications Dept, 805 TRU Way, Kamloops, BC V2C 0C8, Canada *Tel:* 250-852-7000 *Web Site:* www.tru.ca/marcom, pg 913

Kondo, Michio, FUJIFILM Canada Inc, 600 Suffolk Ct, Mississauga, ON L5R 4G4, Canada *Tel:* 905-890-6611 *Toll Free Tel:* 800-263-5018 *Fax:* 905-890-6446 *Web Site:* www.fujifilm.ca, pg 766

Kondratieff, Cynthia, Dolphin MultiMedia Inc, 1660 Belleville Way, Sunnyvale, CA 94087 *Tel:* 650-354-0800 *Fax:* 408-737-8404 *Web Site:* dolphinmm.com, pg 745

Konicov-Banfill, Stephanie, Potentials Unlimited, 3409 47 Ave E, Bradenton, FL 34203-3974 *Tel:* 941-739-2611 *Toll Free Tel:* 800-221-6121; 800-426-3963 *Fax:* 941-756-0315 *Web Site:* www.potentialsunlimited.com, pg 860

Konkoski, Sarah, Associated Production Music LLC, 6255 Sunset Blvd, Suite 900, Hollywood, CA 90028 *Tel:* 323-461-3211 *Fax:* 323-461-9102 *E-mail:* info@apmmusic.com; clientservices@apmmusic.com *Web Site:* www.apmmusic.com, pg 691

Konrath, Kris, Convergent Media Systems, 190 Bluegrass Valley Pkwy, Alpharetta, GA 30005-2204 *Tel:* 770-369-9000 *Fax:* 770-369-9100 *Web Site:* www.convergent.com, pg 731

Koral, Teri, Picturestart, 817 Hilldale Ave, West Hollywood, CA 90069 *Tel:* 310-422-3280 *E-mail:* info@picturestart.com *Web Site:* www.picturestart.com, pg 856

Koran, Lori, PetroSkills | RDC Solutions, 25403 Katy Mills Pkwy, Katy, TX 77494 *Toll Free Tel:* 800-360-7222 *E-mail:* solutions@petroskills.com *Web Site:* www.resourcedev.com; www.petroskills.com, pg 855

Korn, Linda, Penguin Random House Audio Publishing, 1745 Broadway, New York, NY 10019 *E-mail:* audio@penguinrandomhouse.com *Web Site:* www.penguinrandomhouseaudio.com, pg 853

Korngold, Honnie, CineVantage LLC, 8560 W Sunset Blvd, 5th fl, West Hollywood, CA 90069 *Tel:* 323-904-9363 *Toll Free Tel:* 888-518-7571 *Web Site:* cinevantage.com, pg 724

Koronkiewicz, Juliette, Penguin Random House Audio Publishing, 1745 Broadway, New York, NY 10019 *E-mail:* audio@penguinrandomhouse.com *Web Site:* www.penguinrandomhouseaudio.com, pg 853

Korson, Brian, Video Excellence Productions, 94 Breckonwood Crescent, Thornhill, ON L3T 5E8, Canada *Tel:* 905-731-4355 *Web Site:* www.videoexcellence.com, pg 927

Korte, Tony, Videomagnetics, 3970 Clearview Frontage Rd, Colorado Springs, CO 80911 *Tel:* 719-390-1313 *Toll Free Tel:* 800-432-3887 *Fax:* 719-390-1316 *E-mail:* vmi@csprings.com *Web Site:* www.videomagnetics.com, pg 929

Korzh, Alex, Velodyne LiDAR Inc, 5521 Hellyer Ave, San Jose, CA 95738 *Tel:* 408-465-2800 *Fax:* 408-779-9208 (cust serv); 408-779-9377 (orders) *E-mail:* lidar@velodyne.com *Web Site:* velodynelidar.com, pg 925

Kosak, Suzanne, The DVI Group, 1486 Mecaslin St NW, Atlanta, GA 30309 *Tel:* 404-873-6283 *Toll Free Tel:* 888-736-7384 *E-mail:* makeitbetter@thedvigroup.com *Web Site:* www.thedvigroup.com, pg 748

Koss, John Jr, Koss Corp, 4129 N Port Washington Ave, Milwaukee, WI 53212 *Tel:* 414-964-5000 *Toll Free Tel:* 800-USA-KOSS (872-5677) *E-mail:* customersupport@koss.com *Web Site:* www.koss.com, pg 801

Koss, Michael, Koss Corp, 4129 N Port Washington Ave, Milwaukee, WI 53212 *Tel:* 414-964-5000 *Toll Free Tel:* 800-USA-KOSS (872-5677) *E-mail:* customersupport@koss.com *Web Site:* www.koss.com, pg 801

Kostov, Michael, Kostov Productions, Whispering Wind Ranch, 16320 High Bridge Rd, Monroe, WA 98272 *Tel:* 206-755-0050 *E-mail:* info@kostov.com *Web Site:* www.kostov.com, pg 801

Kostrzewski, Andrew PhD, Physical Optics Corp (POC), 1845 E 205 St, Torrance, CA 90501-1510 *Tel:* 310-320-3088 *E-mail:* info@poc.com *Web Site:* www.poc.com, pg 856

Kosuda, Frank, De Sisti Lighting/I-Light Corp USA, 1011 Rte 22 E, Unit D, Mountainside, NJ 07092 *Tel:* 908-317-0020 *Fax:* 908-317-0021 *Web Site:* www.desisti.it, pg 739

Kotkin, Doug, Cibola Systems, 180 S Cypress St, Orange, CA 92866 *Tel:* 714-480-0272 *Fax:* 714-480-0768 *E-mail:* info@cibolasystems.com *Web Site:* cibolasystems.com, pg 723

Kotsios, Christina, ATX Networks, 8-1602 Tricont Ave, Whitby, ON L1N 7C3, Canada *Tel:* 289-204-7800 *Toll Free Tel:* 866-968-7289 *E-mail:* info@atx.com *Web Site:* atx.com, pg 692

Kotyk, Jim, Voice & Video Rentals, 4909 Ruffner St, San Diego, CA 92111 *Tel:* 858-560-5000 *Fax:* 858-560-9900 *Web Site:* www.voiceandvideo.com, pg 932

Koukkos, George, CommCreative, 75 Fountain St, Framingham, MA 01702 *Tel:* 508-620-6664 *Toll Free Tel:* 877-620-6664 *Fax:* 508-620-0592 *E-mail:* info@commcreative.com *Web Site:* www.commcreative.com, pg 728

Koures, Cyndy, KCFW Television, 401 First Ave E, Kalispell, MT 59901 *Tel:* 406-755-5239 *Fax:* 406-752-8002 *E-mail:* news@kcfw.com *Web Site:* www.nbcmontana.com/news/kcfw, pg 797

Koury, Dee, Old Army Press (OAP), 218 Alabaster Way, Johnstown, CO 80534 *Tel:* 970-587-9530; 970-420-8193 (cell) *E-mail:* oldarmypress@msn.com *Web Site:* oldarmypress.com, pg 844

Koury, Mike, Old Army Press (OAP), 218 Alabaster Way, Johnstown, CO 80534 *Tel:* 970-587-9530; 970-420-8193 (cell) *E-mail:* oldarmypress@msn.com *Web Site:* oldarmypress.com, pg 844

Kowalik, Joseph, Graphx Inc, 400 W Cummings Park, Woburn, MA 01801 *Tel:* 781-932-0430 *Fax:* 781-932-0855 *E-mail:* support@graphx.com *Web Site:* photogize.net, pg 773

Koziell, Peter, Award Productions Inc, 164 Great Rd, Acton, MA 01720 *Tel:* 978-635-8000 *E-mail:* web@awardprod.com *Web Site:* www.awardproductions.com, pg 699

Kozik, Cathie, PSAV® Presentation Services, 111 W Ocean Blvd, Suite 1110, Long Beach, CA 90802-4688 *Tel:* 562-366-0620; 562-366-0621 *Toll Free Tel:* 877-430-7728 *Fax:* 562-366-0628 *Web Site:* www.psav.com, pg 866

Koziol, Christian, Kappa optronics Inc, 825 S Primrose Ave, Suite I, Monrovia, CA 91016 *Tel:* 626-256-4343 *E-mail:* contact@kappa-optronics.com *Web Site:* www.kappa-optronics.com, pg 796

Koziol, Jim, PLS Staging, 371 Little Falls Rd, Cedar Grove, NJ 07009 *Tel:* 973-857-7242 *E-mail:* rfp@plsstaging.com *Web Site:* plsstaging.com, pg 858

Kraemer, Marilyn, Buzzco Associates Inc, 33 Bleecker St, New York, NY 10012 *Tel:* 212-473-8800 *Fax:* 212-473-8891 *E-mail:* info@buzzzco.com *Web Site:* www.buzzzco.com, pg 713

Krakauer, Bob, VER, 757 W California Ave, Bldg 4, Glendale, CA 91203 *Tel:* 818-956-1444 *Toll Free Tel:* 800-794-1407 *Fax:* 818-546-1040 *Web Site:* www.ver.com, pg 926

Krakauer, Daniel, Deerfield Laboratory Inc, 7 Millbrae Ave, San Anselmo, CA 94960 *Tel:* 650-632-4090 *Web Site:* www.deerfieldlab.com, pg 740

Kramer, Jeffrey T, Kramer Communications Video Production, 12504 Quarterhorse Dr, Bowie, MD 20720 *Tel:* 301-352-3042 *E-mail:* kcam@his.com *Web Site:* kcommproductions.com, pg 801

Kramer, Joan, Joan Kramer & Associates Inc, 10490 Wilshire Blvd, Suite 1701, Los Angeles, CA 90024 *Tel:* 310-446-1866 *Fax:* 310-446-1856 *E-mail:* ekeeeek@earthlink.net, pg 801

Kramer, Dr Joseph, Kramer Electronics USA Inc, 6 Rte 173 W, Clinton, NJ 08809 *Tel:* 908-735-0018 *Toll Free Tel:* 888-275-6311 *Fax:* 908-735-0515 *E-mail:* info@kramerus.com *Web Site:* www.kramerav.com, pg 801

Kramer, Mark A, Media-Comm, 9700 S Pine Blvd, Charlotte, NC 28273 *Tel:* 704-527-8853 *Web Site:* www.media-comm.com, pg 821

Krams, Steven H, Magna-Tech Electronic Co Inc, 1998 NE 150 St, North Miami, FL 33181 *Tel:* 305-573-7339 *Fax:* 305-573-8101 *E-mail:* sales@iceco.com; digital@myiceco.com *Web Site:* www.magna-tech.com, pg 814

Kranz, Patricia, The David A Andelman & Pamela Title Award, 40 W 45 St, New York, NY 10036 *Tel:* 212-626-9220 *Fax:* 212-626-9210 *E-mail:* info@opcofamerica.org *Web Site:* www.opcofamerica.org, pg 981

Kranz, Patricia, The Whitman Bassow Award, 40 W 45 St, New York, NY 10036 *Tel:* 212-626-9220 *Fax:* 212-626-9210 *E-mail:* info@opcofamerica.org *Web Site:* www.opcofamerica.org, pg 983

Kranz, Patricia, The Robert Spiers Benjamin Award, 40 W 45 St, New York, NY 10036 *Tel:* 212-626-9220 *Fax:* 212-626-9210 *E-mail:* info@opcofamerica.org *Web Site:* www.opcofamerica.org, pg 983

Kranz, Patricia, Best Digital Reporting on International Affairs, 40 W 45 St, New York, NY 10036 *Tel:* 212-626-9220 *Fax:* 212-626-9210 *E-mail:* info@opcofamerica.org *Web Site:* www.opcofamerica.org, pg 983

Kranz, Patricia, The Robert Capa Gold Medal Award, 40 W 45 St, New York, NY 10036 *Tel:* 212-626-9220 *Fax:* 212-626-9210 *E-mail:* info@opcofamerica.org *Web Site:* www.opcofamerica.org, pg 985

Kranz, Patricia, Feature Photography Award, 40 W 45 St, New York, NY 10036 *Tel:* 212-626-9220 *Fax:* 212-626-9210 *E-mail:* info@opcofamerica.org *Web Site:* www.opcofamerica.org, pg 989

Kranz, Patricia, The Peter Jennings Award, 40 W 45 St, New York, NY 10036 *Tel:* 212-626-9220 *Fax:* 212-626-9210 *E-mail:* info@opcofamerica.org *Web Site:* www.opcofamerica.org, pg 994

Kranz, Patricia, The David Kaplan Award, 40 W 45 St, New York, NY 10036 *Tel:* 212-626-9220 *Fax:* 212-626-9210 *E-mail:* info@opcofamerica.org *Web Site:* www.opcofamerica.org, pg 994

Kranz, Patricia, The Edward R Murrow Award, 40 W 45 St, New York, NY 10036 *Tel:* 212-626-9220 *Fax:* 212-626-9210 *E-mail:* info@opcofamerica.org *Web Site:* www.opcofamerica.org, pg 996

Kranz, Patricia, The Thomas Nast Award, 40 W 45 St, New York, NY 10036 *Tel:* 212-626-9220 *Fax:* 212-626-9210 *E-mail:* info@opcofamerica.org *Web Site:* www.opcofamerica.org, pg 997

Kranz, Patricia, The Olivier Rebbot Award, 40 W 45 St, New York, NY 10036 *Tel:* 212-626-9220 *Fax:* 212-626-9210 *E-mail:* info@opcofamerica.org *Web Site:* www.opcofamerica.org, pg 1001

Kranz, Patricia, The Madeline Dane Ross Award, 40 W 45 St, New York, NY 10036 *Tel:* 212-626-9220 *Fax:* 212-626-9210 *E-mail:* info@opcofamerica.org *Web Site:* www.opcofamerica.org, pg 1002

Kranz, Patricia, The Lowell Thomas Award, 40 W 45 St, New York, NY 10036 *Tel:* 212-626-9220 *Fax:* 212-626-9210 *E-mail:* info@opcofamerica.org *Web Site:* www.opcofamerica.org, pg 1005

Kraus, Richard, T & M Digital Services LLC, 54 Flint Ridge Rd, Monroe, CT 06468 *Tel:* 203-268-5290 *Fax:* 203-268-5290, pg 906

Krause, Jeffrey M, Society of Manufacturing Engineers (SME), One SME Dr, Dearborn, MI 48128 *Tel:* 313-425-3000 *Toll Free Tel:* 800-733-4763 *Fax:* 313-425-3400 *E-mail:* service@sme.org (cust care) *Web Site:* www.sme.org, pg 892

Krause, Ron, Grace Church - St Louis, 2695 Creve Coeur Mill Rd, Maryland Heights, MO 63043 *Tel:* 314-292-8300 *Fax:* 314-291-0918 *E-mail:* info@gracestl.org *Web Site:* www.gracestl.org, pg 773

Krawczyk, Tracy, Vertiv, 1050 Dearborn Dr, Columbus, OH 43085 *Tel:* 614-888-0246 *Web Site:* www.vertiv.com, pg 926

Kreikemeier, Brian, B & B Video Productions Inc, 233 N Main St, West Point, NE 68788 *Tel:* 402-380-9042 *Web Site:* www.bandbvideo.com, pg 700

Kremen, Dan, Intermark Industries Inc, 2980 NW 74 Ave, Miami, FL 33122 *Tel:* 305-591-8930 *Fax:* 305-593-1091 *E-mail:* info@intermarkindustries.com *Web Site:* www.intermarkindustries.com, pg 789

Kress, Marlyn, American Harlequin Corp, 1531 Glen Ave, Moorestown, NJ 08057 *Tel:* 856-234-5505 *Toll Free Tel:* 800-642-6440 *Fax:* 856-231-4403 *E-mail:* dance@harlequinfloors.com; contact@harlequinfloors.com *Web Site:* us.harlequinfloors.com, pg 683

Kreutz, David, Image Audiovisuals, 2130 S Dahlia St, Denver, CO 80222 *Tel:* 303-758-1818 *Toll Free Tel:* 800-818-1857 *Fax:* 303-758-5722 *Web Site:* www.imageav.com, pg 784

Kreutzer, Peter, Mastervision Inc, 490 Seventh St, Brooklyn, NY 11215 *Tel:* 347-725-0545 *Web Site:* www.mastervision.com, pg 819

Krevens, Dale, Tech 21 USA Inc, 790 Bloomfield Ave, Clifton, NJ 07012 *Tel:* 973-777-6996 *Fax:* 973-777-9899 *E-mail:* info@tech21nyc.com *Web Site:* www.tech21nyc.com, pg 908

Krinsky, Santosh, New Leaf Distributing Co, 401 Thornton Rd, Lithia Springs, GA 30122-1557 *Tel:* 770-948-7845 *Toll Free Tel:* 800-326-2665 (orders) *Fax:* 770-944-2313 *Toll Free Fax:* 800-326-1066 *E-mail:* customerservice@newleaf-dist.com *Web Site:* newleaf-dist.com, pg 839

Krise, Matthew, Encyclopaedia Britannica Inc, 325 N La Salle St, Suite 200, Chicago, IL 60654 *Tel:* 312-347-7000 (all other countries) *Toll Free Tel:* 800-323-1229 (US & CN) *Fax:* 312-294-2104 *Web Site:* www.britannica.com, pg 754

Kriter, Steve, ACS Technologies, 180 Dunbarton Dr, Florence, SC 29501 *Tel:* 843-662-1681 *Toll Free Tel:* 800-736-7425 (sales); 800-669-2309 (support) *Fax:* 843-669-7513 *E-mail:* info@acstechnologies.com *Web Site:* www.acstechnologies.com, pg 674

Kritzmacher, John, John Wiley & Sons Inc, 111 River St, Hoboken, NJ 07030-5774 *Tel:* 201-748-6000 *Toll Free Tel:* 800-225-5945 (cust serv) *Fax:* 201-748-6088 *Web Site:* www.wiley.com, pg 938

Kroger, Fr Dan, Franciscan Media, 28 W Liberty St, Cincinnati, OH 45202-6498 *Tel:* 513-241-5615 *Toll Free Tel:* 800-488-0488 *Fax:* 513-241-0399 *E-mail:* info@franciscanmedia.org *Web Site:* www.americancatholic.org, pg 765

Kron, Randy, North-by-Northwest - A Digital Studio, 903 W Broadway Ave, Spokane, WA 99201 *Tel:* 509-324-2949 *Fax:* 509-324-2959 *E-mail:* spokane@nxnw.net *Web Site:* www.nxnw.net, pg 842

Krone, William, Deja View Video, 417 S Eldorado St, San Mateo, CA 94402-1374 *Tel:* 650-343-8899 *Web Site:* www.dejaview.com, pg 740

Kronfeld, Andrew, Universal Music Group, 2220 Colorado Ave, Santa Monica, CA 90404 *Tel:* 310-865-5000 *Web Site:* www.universalmusic.com, pg 922

Kronlage, Julie, Dubuque Area Convention & Visitors Bureau, 300 Main St, Suite 120, Dubuque, IA 52001 *Tel:* 563-845-7698 *Web Site:* www.traveldubuque.com, pg 971

Kropp, David, AutoDesSys Inc, 3518 Riverside Dr, Suite 206, Columbus, OH 43221 *Tel:* 614-488-8838 *Fax:* 614-488-0848 *E-mail:* sales@formz.com; marketing@formz.com *Web Site:* www.formz.com, pg 696

Kropp, Jack, RAM® Mounts, 8410 Dallas Ave S, Seattle, WA 98108 *Tel:* 206-763-8361 *Toll Free Tel:* 800-497-7479 *Fax:* 206-763-9615 *E-mail:* sales@rammount.com *Web Site:* www.rammount.com, pg 870

Krout, Ed, Phat Planet Recording Studios, 3473 Parkway Center Ct, Orlando, FL 32808 *Tel:* 407-295-7270 *Toll Free Tel:* 800-667-4893 *Fax:* 321-549-6229 *E-mail:* info@phatplanetstudios.com *Web Site:* www.phatplanetstudios.com, pg 855

Kruckemyer, Gene, Love Your Shorts Film Festival, 608 S Elm Ave, Sanford, FL 32771 *E-mail:* contact@loveyourshorts.com *Web Site:* www.loveyourshorts.com, pg 995

Krug, Margherita Petti, Fingerpaint, 13 Walker Way, Albany, NY 12205 *Tel:* 518-869-1968 *Web Site:* fingerpaintmarketing.com, pg 761

849-5069 *E-mail:* academie@acct.ca *Web Site:* www.
acct.ca/prixgemeaux; www.acct.ca; www.academy.ca,
pg 1000

Lacroix, Rob, Immersion Corp, 50 Rio Robles, San Jose,
CA 95134 *Tel:* 408-467-1900 *Fax:* 408-467-1901
Web Site: www.immersion.com, pg 786

Lad, Anju, Dance Horizons Video, 15 W Front St, 3rd
fl, Trenton, NJ 08608 *Tel:* 609-426-0602 *Toll Free
Tel:* 800-220-7149 *Fax:* 609-426-1344 *E-mail:* pbc@
dancehorizons.com *Web Site:* www.dancehorizons.com,
pg 737

Ladd, Audra, Mayor's Office of Economic &
Community Development, One Public Sq, Suite
100, Nashville, TN 37201 *Tel:* 615-862-6000
Web Site: www.nashville.gov, pg 976

Ladd, Steve, The Video Project, 145 Ninth St, Suite
102, San Francisco, CA 94103 *Tel:* 415-981-
9710 *Toll Free Tel:* 800-475-2638 *Fax:* 415-692-
6223 *E-mail:* orders@videoproject.com; support@
videoproject.com *Web Site:* www.videoproject.com,
pg 928

Ladely, Danny Lee, Mary Riepma Ross Media Arts
Center, University of Nebraska-Lincoln, 313 N 13 St,
Lincoln, NE 68588 *Tel:* 402-472-9100 *Fax:* 402-472-
2576 *E-mail:* info@theross.org *Web Site:* www.theross.
org, pg 877

Laden, Susan, Biblical Archaeology Society (BAS),
4710 41 St NW, Washington, DC 20016 *Tel:* 202-364-
3300 *Toll Free Tel:* 800-221-4644 *Fax:* 202-364-2636
E-mail: bas@bib-arch.org; merchandise@bib-arch.org
Web Site: www.biblicalarchaeology.org, pg 705

LaFever, Ed, MSI Production Services, 10895 Thornmint
Rd, Suite A, San Diego, CA 92127 *Tel:* 858-348-0100
Web Site: www.msiprod.com, pg 832

Lafferty, Linda, Moog Music Inc, 160 Broadway St,
Asheville, NC 28801 *Tel:* 828-251-0090 *Toll Free
Tel:* 800-948-1990 *Fax:* 828-254-6233 *E-mail:* info@
moogmusic.com *Web Site:* www.moogmusic.com,
pg 830

Lahey, Frederic, Stanley Film Festival, The Stanley
Hotel, 333 Wonderview Ave, Estes Park, CO 80517
Tel: 970-577-4112 *Web Site:* www.stanleyfilmfest.com,
pg 1004

Lahoud, Ignace, Disney Consumer Products &
Interactive Media (DCPI), 1201 Flower St, Glendale,
AZ 91201 *Tel:* 818-544-0000 *Web Site:* dcpi.disney.
com, pg 743

Lai, Robin D, Academy Savant, PO Box 3670, Fullerton,
CA 92834-3670 *Tel:* 714-870-7880 *Toll Free
Tel:* 800-472-8268 *Fax:* 714-526-7400 *E-mail:* info@
academysavant.com *Web Site:* www.academysavant.
com, pg 672

Lai, Zhibo, DC Asian Pacific American Film Festival,
2515 Virginia Ave NW, No 58205, Washington,
DC 20037 *Tel:* 202-796-9680; 202-792-6393
E-mail: info@apafilm.org; admin@apafilm.org
Web Site: www.apafilm.org, pg 988

Laiacona, Michael, Whirlwind Music Distributors Inc,
99 Ling Rd, Greece, NY 14612 *Tel:* 585-663-8820
Toll Free Tel: 800-733-9473 (US only) *Fax:* 585-865-
8930 *E-mail:* sales@whirlwindusa.com; techsupport@
whirlwindusa.com; darylg@whirlwindusa.com (CN
inquiries) *Web Site:* whirlwindusa.com, pg 937

Laidley, Paddy, Raincoast Books, 2440 Viking Way,
Richmond, BC V6V 1N2, Canada *Tel:* 604-448-7100
Toll Free Tel: 800-663-5714 (cust serv & book orders)
Fax: 604-270-7161 *Toll Free Fax:* 800-565-3770 (cust
serv & book orders) *E-mail:* info@raincoast.com;
customerservice@raincoast.com *Web Site:* www.
raincoast.com, pg 869

Laird, Rick, EiKO Global LLC, 23220 W 84 St,
Shawnee, KS 66227 *Toll Free Tel:* 800-852-2217
Fax: 913-441-6679 *E-mail:* orders@eiko.com; info@
eikom.com *Web Site:* www.eiko.com, pg 752

Laitman, Judith, Knowledge Unlimited Inc, 2320
Pleasant View, Middleton, WI 53562 *Tel:* 608-836-
6660 *Toll Free Tel:* 800-356-2303 *Fax:* 608-836-

6684 *Toll Free Fax:* 800-618-1570 *E-mail:* csis@
newscurrents.com *Web Site:* www.knowledgeunlimited.
com, pg 800

Laity, Jeff, TASCAM, 1834 Gage Rd, Montebello, CA
90640 *Tel:* 323-726-0303 (ext 617) *Web Site:* www.
tascam.com, pg 907

Lajer, Kelli, Santa Clarita Film Office, 23920 Valencia
Blvd, Suite 100, Santa Clarita, CA 91355 *Tel:* 661-
284-1425 *Fax:* 661-286-4001 *E-mail:* film@santa-
clarita.com *Web Site:* filmsantaclarita.com, pg 967

Lake, Kyle M, Prosper Media Group Inc, 348 E
Main St, Lexington, KY 40507 *Tel:* 859-400-0136
Toll Free Tel: 888-528-1999 *E-mail:* producer@
prosperproductions.com *Web Site:* prospermg.com,
pg 866

Lake-Herrera, Emiliano, Boulder County Film
Commission, 2440 Pearl St, Boulder, CO 80302
Tel: 303-442-2911 *Toll Free Tel:* 800-444-0447
Fax: 303-938-2098 *E-mail:* visitor@bouldercvb.
com *Web Site:* www.bouldercoloradousa.com/film-
commission, pg 968

Lakefish, Mark, ToteVision, 3257 17 Ave W, Bldg 1,
Suite 201, Seattle, WA 98119 *Tel:* 206-623-6000;
206-623-6000 (ext 200, sales); 206-623-6000 (ext
202, tech support & repairs); 206-623-6000 (ext
209, cust care); 206-623-6000 (ext 211, returns)
Fax: 206-623-6609 *E-mail:* info@totevision.com
Web Site: totevision.com, pg 916

Lakhter, Masha, Key Digital Systems, 521 E Third
St, Mount Vernon, NY 10553 *Tel:* 914-667-9700
Toll Free Tel: 855-539-3448 *Fax:* 914-668-8666
E-mail: info@keydigital.com; marketing@keydigital.
com *Web Site:* www.keydigital.com, pg 798

Lakhter, Michael, Key Digital Systems, 521 E Third
St, Mount Vernon, NY 10553 *Tel:* 914-667-9700
Toll Free Tel: 855-539-3448 *Fax:* 914-668-8666
E-mail: info@keydigital.com; marketing@keydigital.
com *Web Site:* www.keydigital.com, pg 798

Lalla, Steve, Vertiv, 1050 Dearborn Dr, Columbus, OH
43085 *Tel:* 614-888-0246 *Web Site:* www.vertiv.com,
pg 926

Lamb, James, Point Source Audio, 1304 Southpoint
Blvd, No 260, Petaluma, CA 94954 *Tel:* 415-226-1122
Fax: 415-520-2110 *E-mail:* info@point-sourceaudio.
com; sales@point-sourceaudio.com *Web Site:* www.
point-sourceaudio.com, pg 858

Lamb, Robert C, PSSI Global Services LLC, 7030
Hayvenhurst Ave, Van Nuys, CA 91406 *Tel:* 310-575-
4400 *Toll Free Tel:* 800-SAT-LINK (728-5465); 800-
634-6530 (teleport inquiries) *E-mail:* info@pssiglobal.
com *Web Site:* www.pssiglobal.com, pg 866

Lambert, Rip, Producers Video, 3700 Malden
Ave, Baltimore, MD 21211 *Tel:* 410-523-7520
Fax: 410-669-3347 *E-mail:* info@producers.tv
Web Site: producers.tv, pg 863

Lambert, Ryan, TM Studios Inc, 2002 Academy Lane,
Suite 110, Dallas, TX 75234 *Tel:* 972-406-6800
Fax: 972-406-6890 *E-mail:* info@tmstudios.com;
tmcustomerservice@tmstudios.com *Web Site:* www.
tmstudios.com, pg 915

Lamicella, Laraine, Concepts TV Productions Inc, 53
Indian Lane E, Towaco, NJ 07082 *Tel:* 973-331-1500
Fax: 973-331-1550 *E-mail:* sales@conceptstv.com
Web Site: conceptstv.com, pg 730

Lamkin, Bryan, Adobe Systems Inc, 345 Park Ave, San
Jose, CA 95110-2704 *Tel:* 408-536-6000 *Fax:* 408-
537-6000 *Web Site:* www.adobe.com, pg 676

Lammersfeld, Don, Magnetic Shield Corp, 740 N
Thomas Dr, Bensenville, IL 60106 *Tel:* 630-766-
7800 *Toll Free Tel:* 888-766-7800 *Fax:* 630-766-2813
E-mail: shields@magnetic-shield.com *Web Site:* www.
magnetic-shield.com, pg 815

Lamond, Joe, NAMM, the National Association of
Music Merchants, 5790 Armada Dr, Carlsbad, CA
92008 *Tel:* 760-438-8001 *Toll Free Tel:* 800-767-6266
(memb hotline) *Fax:* 760-438-7327 *E-mail:* info@
namm.org *Web Site:* www.namm.org, pg 958

LaMont, Cheryl M, Dot C Software Inc, 117 Waihili
Place, Honolulu, HI 96825 *E-mail:* info@dotcsw.com
Web Site: www.dotcsw.com, pg 746

LaMountain, Moira, Monterey Film Commission,
801 Lighthouse Ave, Suite 104, Monterey, CA 93940
Tel: 831-646-0910 *Fax:* 831-655-9250 *E-mail:* info@
filmmonterey.org *Web Site:* www.filmmonterey.org,
pg 967

Lampert, Lori, Heinemann, 361 Hanover St, Portsmouth,
NH 03801-3912 *Tel:* 603-431-7894 *Toll Free
Tel:* 800-225-5800 *Fax:* 603-431-2214 *Toll Free
Fax:* 877-231-6980 *E-mail:* custserv@heinemann.com
Web Site: www.heinemann.com, pg 778

Lampert-Greaux, Ellen, St Barth Film Festival, c/o
Cobblestone Films, 140 Riverside Dr, No 5D, New
York, NY 10024 *Tel:* 212-989-8004 *Fax:* 212-727-
1774 *E-mail:* staff@stbarthff.org *Web Site:* www.
stbarthff.org, pg 1002

Lamy, Dr Francis, X-Rite, 4300 44 St SE, Grand Rapids,
MI 49512 *Tel:* 616-803-2100 *Toll Free Tel:* 800-248-
9748; 888-800-9580 *Web Site:* www.xrite.com, pg 942

Lamy, Jonathan, The RIAA® Gold® & Platinum®
Awards, 1025 "F" St NW, 10th fl, Washington, DC
20004 *Tel:* 202-775-0101 *Web Site:* www.riaa.com/
gold-platinum, pg 1001

Land, Jason, PSSI Global Services LLC, 7030
Hayvenhurst Ave, Van Nuys, CA 91406 *Tel:* 310-575-
4400 *Toll Free Tel:* 800-SAT-LINK (728-5465); 800-
634-6530 (teleport inquiries) *E-mail:* info@pssiglobal.
com *Web Site:* www.pssiglobal.com, pg 866

Landau, Dave, CineTech Media Professionals,
PO Box 34, Olivebridge, NY 12461
Web Site: cinetechmediapros.com, pg 953

Landers, Scott, Monotype Imaging Inc, 600 Unicorn
Park Dr, Woburn, MA 01801 *Tel:* 781-970-6000 *Toll
Free Tel:* 800-424-8973 *Fax:* 781-970-6001; 781-970-
6002 (gen questions) *E-mail:* info@monotype.com
Web Site: www.monotype.com, pg 829

Landini, Melissa, Via Verde Productions, 22631 Pacific
Coast Hwy, Suite 480, Malibu, CA 90265-5036
Tel: 310-458-3778 *Fax:* 310-496-2992 *E-mail:* info@
viaverdedigital.com *Web Site:* www.viaverdedigital.
com, pg 926

Landow, William, Lighthouse Photo & Video
Productions, 1100 Chicago Ave, Suite 7C, Goshen, IN
46528 *Tel:* 574-533-1400 (off); 574-202-5502 (studio)
E-mail: lighthousevideo@gmail.com *Web Site:* www.
lighthousephotoandvideo.com, pg 807

Landrum, Mike, Diversified, 37 Market St, Kenilworth,
NJ 07033 *Tel:* 908-245-4833 *Fax:* 908-245-0011
E-mail: customerservice@diversifiedus.com; info@
diversifiedus.com *Web Site:* diversifiedus.com, pg 744

Landsberg, Hank, Henry Engineering, PO Box
3796, Seal Beach, CA 90740 *Tel:* 562-493-3589
Web Site: www.henryeng.com, pg 779

Lane, Earl, AAAS Kavli Science Journalism Awards,
1200 New York Ave NW, Washington, DC 20005
Tel: 202-326-6431; 202-326-6440 *E-mail:* media@
aaas.org *Web Site:* www.aaas.org, pg 981

Lane, Lisa, American Color Imaging (ACI), 715 E 18
St, Cedar Falls, IA 50613 *Tel:* 319-277-3655 *Toll Free
Tel:* 800-728-2722 *Fax:* 319-277-6522 *E-mail:* sales@
acilab.com *Web Site:* www.acilab.com, pg 683

Lane, Mark, American Color Imaging (ACI), 715 E 18
St, Cedar Falls, IA 50613 *Tel:* 319-277-3655 *Toll Free
Tel:* 800-728-2722 *Fax:* 319-277-6522 *E-mail:* sales@
acilab.com *Web Site:* www.acilab.com, pg 683

Lane, Woody, Garden Valley Productions, 240 Crystal
Springs Lane, Roseburg, OR 97471 *Tel:* 541-440-1926
Fax: 541-440-1008, pg 768

Laney, Hilary, Evia, 8424 154 Ave NE, Redmond, WA
98052 *Tel:* 425-284-3888 *Toll Free Tel:* 800-206-
2547 *Fax:* 425-883-3887 *E-mail:* hello@evia.events
Web Site: www.tri-digital.com, pg 757

Lang, Craig, Clever Devices Ltd, 300 Crossways Park
Dr, Woodbury, NY 11797 *Tel:* 516-433-6100 *Toll Free
Tel:* 800-872-6129 *Web Site:* www.cleverdevices.com,
pg 726

Lang, David, Artech Electronics Ltd, PO Box 1547, Williston, VT 05495-1547 *Toll Free Tel:* 800-631-6448 *Toll Free Fax:* 800-631-6448 *E-mail:* info@artech-electronics.com *Web Site:* www.artech-electronics.com, pg 690

Lang, Mary Pat, Comtel Inc, 14901 NE 20 Ave, North Miami, FL 33181 *Tel:* 305-424-4160 (facility servs); 305-424-4178 (local inquiries); 516-816-5152 (natl inquiries) *Web Site:* www.comtelinc.com; www.facebook.com/comtelinc/, pg 730

Lange, Barbara, Hollywood Professional Association (HPA), 2501 W Burbank Blvd, No 207, Burbank, CA 91505 *Tel:* 818-273-1482 *Web Site:* hpaonline.com, pg 955

Lange, Barbara H, The Citation of Outstanding Service to the Society Award, White Plains Plaza, 445 Hamilton Ave, Suite 601, White Plains, NY 10601-1827 *Tel:* 914-761-1100 *Fax:* 914-206-4216 *E-mail:* marketing@smpte.org *Web Site:* www.smpte.org, pg 986

Lange, Barbara H, The Presidential Proclamation, White Plains Plaza, 445 Hamilton Ave, Suite 601, White Plains, NY 10601-1827 *Tel:* 914-761-1100 *Fax:* 914-206-4216 *E-mail:* marketing@smpte.org *Web Site:* www.smpte.org, pg 1000

Lange, Barbara H, SMPTE® Journal Award & SMPTE® Journal Certificate of Merit, White Plains Plaza, 445 Hamilton Ave, Suite 601, White Plains, NY 10601-1827 *Tel:* 914-761-1100 *Fax:* 914-206-4216 *E-mail:* marketing@smpte.org *Web Site:* www.smpte.org, pg 1004

Lange, Barbara H, SMPTE® Progress Medal Award, White Plains Plaza, 445 Hamilton Ave, Suite 601, White Plains, NY 10601-1827 *Tel:* 914-761-1100 *Fax:* 914-206-4216 *E-mail:* marketing@smpte.org *Web Site:* www.smpte.org, pg 1004

Lange, Barbara H, Society of Motion Picture & Television Engineers® (SMPTE®), White Plains Plaza, 445 Hamilton Ave, Suite 601, White Plains, NY 10601-1827 *Tel:* 914-761-1100 *Fax:* 914-206-4216 *E-mail:* marketing@smpte.org *Web Site:* www.smpte.org, pg 892

Lange, Barbara H, Society of Motion Picture & Television Engineers® (SMPTE®), White Plains Plaza, 445 Hamilton Ave, Suite 601, White Plains, NY 10601-1827 *Tel:* 914-761-1100 *Fax:* 914-206-4216 *E-mail:* membership@smpte.org *Web Site:* www.smpte.org, pg 962

Lange, Barbara H, Technicolor-Herbert T Kalmus Medal Award, White Plains Plaza, 445 Hamilton Ave, Suite 601, White Plains, NY 10601-1827 *Tel:* 914-761-1100 *Fax:* 914-206-4216 *E-mail:* marketing@smpte.org *Web Site:* www.smpte.org, pg 1004

Lange, Barbara H, The Samuel L Warner Memorial Medal Award, White Plains Plaza, 445 Hamilton Ave, Suite 601, White Plains, NY 10601-1827 *Tel:* 914-761-1100 *Fax:* 914-206-4216 *E-mail:* marketing@smpte.org *Web Site:* www.smpte.org, pg 1006

Langford, Jassa, DD Audio, 4025 NW 36 St, Oklahoma City, OK 73112 *Tel:* 405-239-2800 *Fax:* 405-239-7100 *E-mail:* service@ddaudio.com *Web Site:* ddaudio.com, pg 739

Lanier, James, Absolute Hollywood, 10232 Harvest Fields Dr, Woodstock, MD 21163 *Tel:* 443-341-6424 *E-mail:* events@absolutehollywood.com *Web Site:* absolutehollywood.com, pg 672

Lank, Barry, Lank/Beach Productions Inc, 362 Brock St, Winnipeg, MB R3N 0Y9, Canada *Tel:* 204-452-9422 *E-mail:* info@lankbeach.com *Web Site:* www.lankbeach.com, pg 803

Lank, Luanne, Lank/Beach Productions Inc, 362 Brock St, Winnipeg, MB R3N 0Y9, Canada *Tel:* 204-452-9422 *E-mail:* info@lankbeach.com *Web Site:* www.lankbeach.com, pg 803

Lannan, J Patrick Jr, Lannan Foundation, 313 Read St, Santa Fe, NM 87501-2628 *Tel:* 505-986-8160 *Fax:* 505-986-8195 *E-mail:* info@lannan.org *Web Site:* www.lannan.org, pg 803

Lannon, Terrence, Magnetic Shield Corp, 740 N Thomas Dr, Bensenville, IL 60106 *Tel:* 630-766-7800 *Toll Free Tel:* 888-766-7800 *Fax:* 630-766-2813 *E-mail:* shields@magnetic-shield.com *Web Site:* www.magnetic-shield.com, pg 815

Lansdell, Jeff, CEV Multimedia Ltd, 1020 SE Loop 289, Lubbock, TX 79404 *Toll Free Tel:* 877-610-5017 *Toll Free Fax:* 800-243-6398 *E-mail:* customersupport@cevmultimedia.com *Web Site:* www.cevmultimedia.com, pg 720

Lanter, Jeff, Trailblazer Studios®, 1610 Midtown Place, Raleigh, NC 27609 *Tel:* 919-645-6600 *Fax:* 919-645-6601 *E-mail:* info@trailblazerstudios.com *Web Site:* www.trailblazerstudios.com, pg 917

Lanza, Mark, Golden Reel Awards, 10061 Riverside Dr, PMB 751, Toluca Lake, CA 91602-2550 *Tel:* 818-506-7731 *Fax:* 818-506-7732 *E-mail:* office@mpse.org *Web Site:* www.mpse.org, pg 990

Lanzano, Steve, Television Bureau of Advertising Inc (TVB), 120 Wall St, 15th fl, New York, NY 10005-3908 *Tel:* 212-486-1111 *Fax:* 212-935-5631 *E-mail:* info@tvb.org *Web Site:* www.tvb.org, pg 963

Lanzer, Mona E, Video Aided Instruction Inc, PO Box 740023, Boyton Beach, FL 33474-0023 *Toll Free Tel:* 800-238-1512 *Toll Free Fax:* 800-588-1419 *E-mail:* info@videoaidedinstruction.com *Web Site:* www.videoaidedinstruction.com, pg 927

Lanzer, Peter, Video Aided Instruction Inc, PO Box 740023, Boyton Beach, FL 33474-0023 *Toll Free Tel:* 800-238-1512 *Toll Free Fax:* 800-588-1419 *E-mail:* info@videoaidedinstruction.com *Web Site:* www.videoaidedinstruction.com, pg 927

Lanzet, Gary, A-V Services Inc, 99 Fairfield Rd, Fairfield, NJ 07004 *Tel:* 973-575-5222 *Fax:* 973-575-0857 *E-mail:* sales@avservices.net *Web Site:* www.avservices.net, pg 671

Lanzoni, Joe, Lightning Eliminators & Consultants Inc, 6687 Arapahoe Rd, Boulder, CO 80303 *Tel:* 303-447-2828 *Toll Free Tel:* 800-521-6101 *Fax:* 303-447-8122 *E-mail:* info@lecglobal.com *Web Site:* www.lightningprotection.com, pg 808

LaPage, Leslie, LA Femme International Film Festival, 324 S Beverly Dr, Suite 436, Beverly Hills, CA 90212 *Tel:* 310-441-1645 *Fax:* 310-475-8213 *Web Site:* www.lafemme.org, pg 994

Lapiana, Jim, WPGH-TV, 750 Ivory Ave, Pittsburgh, PA 15214 *Tel:* 412-931-5300; 412-931-8020 (sales) *Fax:* 412-931-4284 *Web Site:* www.sbgi.net; www.wpgh53.com, pg 942

Lapides, Murray, AVFX Inc, 96 Holton St, Boston, MA 02135 *Tel:* 617-254-0770 *Toll Free Tel:* 888-254-0770 *E-mail:* info@avfx.com *Web Site:* www.avfx.com, pg 698

Lapin, Philip, Falcon Safety Products Inc, 25 Imclone Dr, Branchburg, NJ 08876 *Tel:* 908-707-4900 *Toll Free Tel:* 800-332-5266 (ext 220, cust serv) *Fax:* 908-707-8855 *Web Site:* www.falconsafety.com; www.shopfalcon.com, pg 758

Laplante, Jaie, Miami Film Festival, 300 NE Second Ave, Miami, FL 33132 *Tel:* 305-237-FILM (237-3456) *E-mail:* info@miamifilmfestival.com *Web Site:* miamifilmfestival.com, pg 995

Lapointe, Frederic, STIL Casing Solution, 76 Saint Paul, Suite 103, Quebec City, QC G1K 3V9, Canada *Tel:* 418-694-0449 (ext 10); 418-694-0449 (ext 11, sales & cust serv); 418-694-0449 (ext 12, admin) *Toll Free Tel:* 888-414-0449 (CN & US) *Fax:* 418-694-1621 *E-mail:* info@stilcasing.com; sales@stilcasing.com; admin@stilcasing.com *Web Site:* www.stilcasing.com, pg 901

Laporte, Janine, Penguin Random House Canada, 320 Front St W, Suite 1400, Toronto, ON M5V 3B6, Canada *Tel:* 416-364-4449 *Toll Free Tel:* 888-523-9292 (cust serv) *Fax:* 416-598-7764 *E-mail:* customerservicescanada@penguinrandomhouse.com *Web Site:* www.penguinrandomhouse.ca, pg 853

Larkin, Dennis, Adrenaline Films, 5224 S Orange Ave, Orlando, FL 32809 *Tel:* 407-850-0711 *Fax:* 407-859-6527 *E-mail:* contact@adrenalinefilms.com *Web Site:* www.adrenalinefilms.com, pg 676

LaRoche, Andre, Stage 3 Productions, 27500 Donald Ct, Warren, MI 48092 *Tel:* 586-576-0625 *Toll Free Tel:* 888-330-5179 *Web Site:* www.stage3.com, pg 899

Larond, Richard, Capron Lighting & Sound Co Inc, 278 West St, Needham, MA 02494 *Tel:* 781-444-8850 *E-mail:* info@capron.net *Web Site:* www.capron.net, pg 716

Larrivee, Bob, Association for Information and Image Management (AIIM), 1100 Wayne Ave, Suite 1100, Silver Spring, MD 20910 *Tel:* 800-477-2446 *Fax:* 301-587-2711 *E-mail:* aiim@aiim.org *Web Site:* www.aiim.org, pg 950

Larsen, Jody, CEDIA IPRO Affinity Group, 8475 Nightfall Lane, Fishers, IN 46037 *Tel:* 317-328-4336 *Toll Free Tel:* 800-669-5329 *E-mail:* info@cedia.org *Web Site:* cedia.net, pg 952

Larsen, Patricia, Small World Productions Inc, 140 Lakeside Ave, Suite 200, Seattle, WA 98122 *Tel:* 206-329-7167 *Toll Free Tel:* 800-866-7425 (orders); 800-325-7111 (cust serv) *Fax:* 206-329-0269 (credit card orders) *E-mail:* info@travelsmallworld.com; customercare@smarttravels.tv *Web Site:* www.smarttravels.tv, pg 890

Larson, Betsy, NEC Display Solutions of America, 500 Park Blvd, Suite 1100, Itasca, IL 60143 *Tel:* 630-467-3000 *Web Site:* www.necdisplay.com, pg 837

Larson, Brad, Winegard Co, 2736 Mount Pleasant St, Suite 140, Burlington, IA 52601 *Tel:* 319-754-0600 *Toll Free Tel:* 800-288-8094 *E-mail:* chat@winegard.com *Web Site:* www.winegard.com, pg 939

Larson, Brian, GES Audio Visual, 7000 Lindell Rd, Las Vegas, NV 89118 *Tel:* 702-515-5500 *Fax:* 702-515-5765 *E-mail:* lasvegas@ges.com; info@ges.com *Web Site:* ges.com, pg 770

Larson, Jack, Avatar Studios, 2675 Scott Ave, Suite G, St Louis, MO 63103 *Tel:* 314-533-2242 *Fax:* 314-533-3349 *E-mail:* info@avatar-studios.com *Web Site:* avatar-studios.com, pg 697

Larson, Keith, Winegard Co, 2736 Mount Pleasant St, Suite 140, Burlington, IA 52601 *Tel:* 319-754-0600 *Toll Free Tel:* 800-288-8094 *E-mail:* chat@winegard.com *Web Site:* www.winegard.com, pg 939

Lasko, Elizabeth, National Association for Music Education (NAfME), 1806 Robert Fulton Dr, Reston, VA 20191 *Tel:* 703-860-4000 *Toll Free Tel:* 800-336-3768 *Fax:* 703-860-1531 *Toll Free Fax:* 888-275-6362 *E-mail:* memberservices@nafme.org *Web Site:* nafme.org, pg 958

Laskowski, Chris, C Vision Productions, 5533 144 Ave NW, Ramsey, MN 55303-5646 *Tel:* 763-577-1358 *Toll Free Tel:* 888-827-3287 *E-mail:* laskovideo@yahoo.com *Web Site:* www.cvisionproductions.com, pg 713

Lasswell, Chris, RAM® Mounts, 8410 Dallas Ave S, Seattle, WA 98108 *Tel:* 206-763-8361 *Toll Free Tel:* 800-497-7479 *Fax:* 206-763-9615 *E-mail:* sales@rammount.com *Web Site:* www.rammount.com, pg 870

Laster, Michael, Academy of Science Fiction, Fantasy & Horror Films, 334 W 54 St, Los Angeles, CA 90037 *Tel:* 323-752-5811 *E-mail:* saturn.awards@ca.rr.com *Web Site:* www.saturnawards.org, pg 947

Laster, Michael, Saturn Awards, 334 W 54 St, Los Angeles, CA 90037 *Tel:* 323-752-5811 *E-mail:* saturn.awards@ca.rr.com *Web Site:* www.saturnawards.org, pg 1003

Latimer, Bruce, L-3 WESCAM, 649 N Service Rd W, Burlington, ON L7P 5B9, Canada *Tel:* 905-633-4000; 905-633-4175 (cust serv) *Toll Free Tel:* 888-593-7226 *Fax:* 905-633-4100 *E-mail:* sales.wescam@l-3com.com *Web Site:* www.wescam.com, pg 803

Lattner, Neal, Association of Independent Commercial Producers (AICP), 3 W 18 St, 5th fl, New York, NY 10011 *Tel:* 212-929-3000 *Fax:* 212-929-3359 *E-mail:* info@aicp.com *Web Site:* www.aicp.com, pg 951

Lau, David, The Brookwood Studio Inc, 6870 N Territorial Rd, Plymouth, MI 48170 *Tel:* 734-358-6071 *E-mail:* info@brookwoodstudio.com *Web Site:* www. brookwoodstudio.com, pg 711

Lau, Michael, Round Hill Music LLC, 400 Madison Ave, 18th fl, New York, NY 10017 *Tel:* 212-380-0080 *Fax:* 212-380-0081 *E-mail:* info@roundhillmusic.com *Web Site:* roundhillmusic.com, pg 878

Laudicina, Sal, Motion Picture Licensing Corp (MPLC), 5455 Centinela Ave, Los Angeles, CA 90066 *Tel:* 310-822-8855 (intl calls) *Toll Free Tel:* 800-462-8855 *Fax:* 310-822-4440 *Web Site:* www.mplc.org, pg 831

Lauer, Jean Anne, Cine Las Americas International Film Festival (CLAIFF), 1104 W 34 St, No 625, Austin, TX 78705 *Tel:* 512-535-0765 *E-mail:* cine@ cinelasamericas.org; entries@cinelasamericas.org *Web Site:* cinelasamericas.org; www.facebook.com/ cinelasamericasaustin, pg 986

Laufer, Amy, Kimbo Educational, One Industrial Way, Bldg D, Suite E, Eatontown, NJ 07724 *Tel:* 732-229-4949 *Toll Free Tel:* 800-631-2187 *Fax:* 732-870-3340 *E-mail:* kimboed@aol.com; service@kimboed.com *Web Site:* www.kimboed.com, pg 799

Laughlin, Kyle, Disney Consumer Products & Interactive Media (DCPI), 1201 Flower St, Glendale, AZ 91201 *Tel:* 818-544-0000 *Web Site:* dcpi.disney.com, pg 743

Laurance, James, Audiomoxie®, PO Box 304, Georgetown, TX 78627 *E-mail:* info@audiomoxie.com *Web Site:* www.audiomoxie.com, pg 695

Laurence, Ron, Shook Mobile Technology LP, 7451 FM 3009, Schertz, TX 78154 *Tel:* 210-651-5700 *Toll Free Tel:* 888-651-5775 *Fax:* 210-651-5220 *E-mail:* shook@shook-usa.com *Web Site:* www.shook-usa.com, pg 886

Lauro, Joseph, Historic Films, 211 Third St, Greenport, NY 11944 *Tel:* 631-477-9700 *Toll Free Tel:* 800-249-1940 *Fax:* 631-477-9800 *E-mail:* info@historicfilms. com *Web Site:* www.historicfilms.com, pg 780

Lautner, Kim, City of Traverse City, 400 Boardman Ave, Traverse City, MI 49684 *Tel:* 231-922-4480 *E-mail:* tcclerk@traversecitymi.gov *Web Site:* www. traversecitymi.gov, pg 972

Lauzon, Nancy, Novalis, One Eglinton Ave E, Suite 800, Toronto, ON M4P 3A1, Canada *Tel:* 416-363-3303 *Toll Free Tel:* 877-702-7773 (CN & US only); 800-387-7164 (cust serv, CN & US only) *Fax:* 416-363-9409 *Toll Free Fax:* 877-702-7775 (CN & US only); 855-393-1555 (cust serv) *E-mail:* books@novalis. ca; resources@novalis.ca *Web Site:* www.novalis.ca, pg 843

Lauzon-Rosato, Nadine, Agfa Graphics, 611 River Dr, Ctr 3, Elmwood Park, NJ 07407 *Tel:* 201-440-2500 *Toll Free Tel:* 800-540-2432; 888-274-8626 (cust serv) *E-mail:* graphics@agfa.com *Web Site:* www.agfa.com; www.agfagraphics.com, pg 678

Lavi, Amir, SintecMedia, 135 E 57 St, 12th fl, New York, NY 10022 *Tel:* 646-745-3900 *Fax:* 646-745-3901 *E-mail:* sales@sintecmedia.com *Web Site:* www. sintecmedia.com, pg 889

LaVine, Jerry, Connections Film & Video Inc, PO Box 110929, Anchorage, AK 99511 *Tel:* 907-561-6450 *Web Site:* www.filmalaska.com, pg 731

Lavitt, Pamela, Seattle Jewish Film Festival (SJFF), 3801 E Mercer Way, Mercer Island, WA 98040 *Tel:* 206-388-0833; 206-232-7115 (SJCC) *E-mail:* sjff@sjcc. org *Web Site:* www.seattlejewishfilmfestival.org; sjcc. org/arts-ideas/seattle-jewish-film-festival, pg 1003

Lawler, Frank C, Lannan Foundation, 313 Read St, Santa Fe, NM 87501-2628 *Tel:* 505-986-8160 *Fax:* 505-986-8195 *E-mail:* info@lannan.org *Web Site:* www.lannan. org, pg 803

Lawrence, Dean, Hooper Camera & Imaging, 21902 Devonshire St, Chatsworth, CA 91311-2907 *Tel:* 818-709-0014 *Fax:* 818-709-0130 *E-mail:* sales@ hoopercamera.com *Web Site:* hoopercamera.com, pg 781

Lawrence, Donna, Donna Lawrence Productions, 624 Baxter Ave, Louisville, KY 40204 *Tel:* 502-589-9617 *E-mail:* dlp@dlproductions.com *Web Site:* www. dlproductions.com, pg 804

Lawrie, Mike, DXC Technology Co, 1775 Tysons Blvd, Tysons, VA 22102 *Tel:* 317-331-1197 *Web Site:* www. dxc.technology, pg 748

Lawson, Robert, Sony Pictures Entertainment Inc, 10202 W Washington Blvd, Culver City, CA 90232 *Tel:* 310-244-4000 *Web Site:* www.sonypictures.com, pg 893

Lawson, Stephen, Biomorph Desks, 11 Broadway, Rm 905, New York, NY 10004 *Tel:* 212-809-4323 *Toll Free Tel:* 888-302-DESK (302-3375) *Toll Free Fax:* 888-652-7137 *E-mail:* info@biomorphdesk.com *Web Site:* www.biomorphdesk.com, pg 706

Lawson, Stephen E, Rees, Rees Plaza at East Wharf, Suite 300, 9211 Lake Hefner Pkwy, Oklahoma City, OK 73120 *Tel:* 405-942-7337 *Fax:* 405-948-1261 *E-mail:* rees@rees.com *Web Site:* www.rees.com, pg 872

Lawson, Terri, Association for Educational Communications and Technology (AECT), 320 W Eighth St, Suite 101, Bloomington, IN 47404-3745 *Tel:* 812-335-7675 *Toll Free Tel:* 877-677-AECT (677-2328) *Fax:* 812-335-7678 *E-mail:* aect@aect.org *Web Site:* www.aect.org, pg 950

Lay, Tim, Northern Light Productions (NLP), 300 Western Ave, 2nd fl, Boston, MA 02134 *Tel:* 617-789-4344 *Fax:* 617-789-4744 *E-mail:* info@nlprod.com *Web Site:* www.nlprod.com, pg 842

Lazarewicz, Krysia, The Learning House Inc, 427 S Fourth St, Suite 300, Louisville, KY 40202 *Tel:* 502-589-9878 *Fax:* 502-589-9825 *E-mail:* sales@ learninghouse.com; info@learninghouse.com *Web Site:* www.learninghouse.com, pg 805

Lazaris, Spyros, Audio Precision, 5750 SW Arctic Dr, Beaverton, OR 97005 *Tel:* 503-627-0832 *Toll Free Tel:* 800-231-7350 *E-mail:* message@ap.com *Web Site:* www.ap.com, pg 693

Lazarus, Alison, Macmillan Audio, 120 Broadway, 22nd fl, New York, NY 10271 *Tel:* 646-600-7856; 646-307-5472 *Toll Free Tel:* 800-330-8477 (cust serv); 800-221-7945 *Toll Free Fax:* 800-672-7703 (orders) *E-mail:* macmillan.audio@macmillanusa.com *Web Site:* www.macmillanaudio.com, pg 814

Lazarus, Margaret, Cambridge Documentary Films Inc, 3099 Hidden Valley Lane, Santa Barbara, CA 93108 *Tel:* 617-484-3993 *E-mail:* info@ cambridgedocumentaryfilms.org; mail@ cambridgedocumentaryfilms.org *Web Site:* www. cambridgedocumentaryfilms.org, pg 714

Le, Anderson, Hawaii International Film Festival, 680 Iwilei Rd, Suite 100, Honolulu, HI 96817 *Tel:* 808-792-1577 (ext 7) *Fax:* 808-792-1583 *Toll Free Fax:* 877-749-7783 *E-mail:* info@hiff.org; entries@ hiff.org *Web Site:* www.hiff.org, pg 991

Le Fever, Don, Tepco Corp, 2603 Bridgeview Dr, Rapid City, SD 57701-5801 *Tel:* 605-343-7200 *Fax:* 605-343-7240, pg 911

Le Porte, Steven, Syracuse Scenery & Stage Lighting Co Inc, 101 Monarch Dr, Liverpool, NY 13088-4915 *Tel:* 315-453-8096 *Toll Free Tel:* 800-453-7775 *Fax:* 315-453-7897 *E-mail:* info@syracusescenery.com *Web Site:* www.syracusescenery.com, pg 906

Leach, Jim, JFW Industries Inc, 5134 Commerce Square Dr, Indianapolis, IN 46237 *Tel:* 317-887-1340 *Toll Free Tel:* 877-887-4539 *Fax:* 317-881-6790 *E-mail:* sales@jfwindustries.com; jfwengr@ jfwindustries.com *Web Site:* www.jfwindustries.com, pg 794

Leadore, D, ASC Systems, Mack Place, 566, St Clair Shores, MI 48080-0566 *Tel:* 313-882-1133 *E-mail:* ascsystems@live.com, pg 690

Leake, Harry, Kingswood Productions, 810 12 Ave S, Nashville, TN 37203 *Tel:* 615-742-5779 *Web Site:* www.kingswoodproductions.com, pg 799

Leake, Harry, United Methodist Productions, 810 12 Ave S, Nashville, TN 37203 *Tel:* 615-742-5400 *E-mail:* umcom@umcom.org *Web Site:* www.umcom. org, pg 921

Leard, Leland, Music Hall LLC, 108 Station Rd, Great Neck, NY 11023 *Tel:* 516-487-3663 *Fax:* 516-773-3891 *E-mail:* info@musichallaudio.com *Web Site:* musichallaudio.com, pg 834

Leasure, George, Ghent Manufacturing, 2999 Henkle Dr, Lebanon, OH 45036-9260 *Tel:* 513-932-3445 *Toll Free Tel:* 800-543-0550 *Fax:* 513-932-9252 *E-mail:* customer_service@ghent.com; sales@ghent. com *Web Site:* www.ghent.com, pg 770

Leasure, Mark, Ghent Manufacturing, 2999 Henkle Dr, Lebanon, OH 45036-9260 *Tel:* 513-932-3445 *Toll Free Tel:* 800-543-0550 *Fax:* 513-932-9252 *E-mail:* customer_service@ghent.com; sales@ghent. com *Web Site:* www.ghent.com, pg 770

Leavelle, Kaye, Romar Learning Solutions LLC, 6700 Woodlands Pkwy, Suite 230-292, Woodlands, TX 77382 *Tel:* 281-292-5508 *Fax:* 281-363-2309 *E-mail:* info@romarlearning.com *Web Site:* romarlearning.com, pg 877

Leban, Lexi, San Francisco Jewish Film Festival, 145 Ninth St, Suite 200, San Francisco, CA 94103 *Tel:* 415-621-0556 *Fax:* 415-621-0568 *E-mail:* jewishfilm@sfjff.org; programming@jfi.org *Web Site:* www.sfjff.org; jfi.org, pg 1003

Leblanc, Jon, Hollywood Sound Systems, 4209 Vanowen Place, Burbank, CA 91505 *Tel:* 323-466-2416 *Fax:* 323-460-2676 *Web Site:* www.hollywoodsound. com, pg 781

LeBrecht, James, Berkeley Sound Artists Inc, 2600 Tenth St, Suite 312, Berkeley, CA 94710 *Tel:* 510-486-2290 *E-mail:* info@berkeleysoundartists.com *Web Site:* www.berkeleysoundartists.com, pg 704

Lebrock, Gene, FIDM Productions, 919 S Grand Ave, Los Angeles, CA 90015-1421 *Tel:* 213-624-1201 *Toll Free Tel:* 800-624-1200 *Fax:* 213-624-4799 *Web Site:* fidm.edu, pg 759

LeClair, Jeffrey, JL Recording Studios, 270 Adelaide St W, Suite 202, Toronto, ON M5H 1X6, Canada *Tel:* 416-598-7979 *Web Site:* www.jlstudios.ca; www.facebook.com/jlrecordingstudios; twitter.com/ JLStudios, pg 794

LeCour, Daniel, Jupiter Systems, 31015 Huntwood Ave, Hayward, CA 94544 *Tel:* 510-675-1000 *Fax:* 510-675-1001 *E-mail:* sales@jupiter.com *Web Site:* www. jupiter.com, pg 795

Lecus, Mike, Custom Color Corp, 14320 W 101 Terr, Lenexa, KS 66215 *Tel:* 913-730-3100 *Fax:* 913-730-3101 *E-mail:* info@customcolor.com *Web Site:* www. customcolor.com, pg 736

Ledbetter, Candace, Pan African Film & Arts Festival, 6820 La Tijera Blvd, Suite 200, Los Angeles, CA 90045 *Tel:* 310-337-4737 *Fax:* 310-337-4736 *E-mail:* info@paff.org; submissions@paff.org *Web Site:* www.paff.org, pg 999

Lederman, Jan, Benro, 75 Virginia Rd, Suite 1, North White Plains, NY 10603 *Tel:* 914-347-3300 *Fax:* 914-347-3309 *E-mail:* info@benrousa.com *Web Site:* www. benrousa.com, pg 704

Lederman, Jan, Bowens USA, 75 Virginia Rd, North White Plains, NY 10603 *Tel:* 914-347-3300 *Fax:* 914-347-3309, pg 709

Lederman, Jan, Induro, 75 Virginia Rd, North White Plains, NY 10603 *Tel:* 914-347-3300 *Fax:* 914-347-3309 *E-mail:* info@indurogear.com *Web Site:* www. indurogear.com, pg 787

Lederman, Mr Jan, Mamiya, 75 Virginia Rd, Suite 1, North White Plains, NY 10603 *Tel:* 914-347-3300 *Fax:* 914-347-3309 *E-mail:* info@mamiya-usa.com *Web Site:* www.mamiyaleaf.com, pg 815

Lederman, Mr Jan, Sekonic, 75 Virginia Rd, North White Plains, NY 10603 *Tel:* 914-347-3300 *Fax:* 914-347-3309 *E-mail:* info@macgroupus.com *Web Site:* www.macgroupus.com; www.sekonic.com, pg 883

Leone, Michael, PSAV® Presentation Services (Hotel Services Division), 5100 N River Rd, Suite 300, Schiller Park, IL 60176 *Tel:* 847-222-9800 *Toll Free Tel:* 866-716-9691 *E-mail:* psavglobal@gmail.com *Web Site:* www.psav.com, pg 866

Leone, Raymond, Myton Industries Inc, 1981 S Park Rd, Pembroke Park, FL 33009 *Tel:* 954-989-0113 *Toll Free Tel:* 800-544-2406 *Fax:* 954-989-1488 *E-mail:* myton@msn.com; sales@mytonindustries.com *Web Site:* www.mytonindustries.com, pg 835

Leone, Ron, West Penn Wire, 2833 W Chestnut St, Washington, PA 15301 *Tel:* 724-222-7060 *Toll Free Tel:* 800-245-4964 *Fax:* 724-222-6420 *E-mail:* info@westpennwire.com; sales@westpennwire.com *Web Site:* www.westpenn-wpw.com, pg 935

Leopard, Colby, FilmNation Entertainment, 150 W 22 St, 9th fl, New York, NY 10011 *Web Site:* www.filmnation.com, pg 760

Leposky, Marjory E, Chatterbox Productions Inc, 5305 Johnson St, Hollywood, FL 33021-5721 *Tel:* 754-816-5432 *Web Site:* www.facebook.com/chatterboxproductions, pg 721

Lepp, L Sue, Design & Production Inc, 7110 Rainwater Place, Lorton, VA 22079 *Tel:* 703-550-8640 *Fax:* 703-339-0296 *E-mail:* email@d-and-p.com *Web Site:* www.d-and-p.com, pg 741

Lerman, Michael, Palm Springs International Film Festival, 1700 E Tahquitz Canyon Way, Suite 3, Palm Springs, CA 92262 *Tel:* 760-322-2930 *Toll Free Tel:* 800-898-7256 *Fax:* 760-322-4087 *E-mail:* info@psfilmfest.org *Web Site:* www.psfilmfest.org, pg 999

Lerman, Michael, Philadelphia Film Festival, 1412 Chestnut St, Philadelphia, PA 19102 *Tel:* 267-239-2941 *E-mail:* info@filmadelphia.org *Web Site:* filmadelphia.org/festival, pg 999

Lerner, Ann, Albuquerque Film Office, Economic Development Dept, One Civic Plaza NW, Albuquerque, NM 87102 *Tel:* 505-768-3283 *Web Site:* www.cabq.gov/film, pg 973

Leroux, Vincent, Group PVP, 296 Saint Pierre St, Matane, QC G4W 2B9, Canada *Tel:* 418-566-2040 *Toll Free Tel:* 877-320-2040 *Fax:* 418-562-4643 *E-mail:* info@pvp.ca *Web Site:* www.pvp.ca, pg 774

Lescaze, Alexandra, Hillman Prizes, 330 W 42 St, Suite 900, New York, NY 10036 *Tel:* 646-448-6413 *Web Site:* hillmanfoundation.org, pg 992

Lesemann, Mara, Guild of Italian American Actors (GIAA), 1026A Shetland Dr, Lakewood, NJ 08701 *Tel:* 201-344-3411 *E-mail:* info@giaa.us *Web Site:* www.giaa.us, pg 955

Leskanic, Rachel, Concepts TV Productions Inc, 53 Indian Lane E, Towaco, NJ 07082 *Tel:* 973-331-1500 *Fax:* 973-331-1550 *E-mail:* sales@conceptstv.com *Web Site:* conceptstv.com, pg 730

Lessans, Ryan, Kipp Visual Systems Inc, 3920 Vero Rd, Suite C, Baltimore, MD 21227 *Tel:* 410-235-9900 *Toll Free Tel:* 800-278-6912 *Fax:* 410-235-7122 *Web Site:* kippvisual.com, pg 799

Letson, Jacqueline, Ingram Content Group LLC, One Ingram Blvd, La Vergne, TN 37086-1986 *Tel:* 615-793-5000 *Toll Free Tel:* 800-937-8000 (retailers); 800-937-5300 (ext 1, libs) *E-mail:* customerservice@ingramcontent.com *Web Site:* www.ingramcontent.com, pg 787

Leven, Robert, ATV Video Center Inc, 2424 Glendale Lane, Sacramento, CA 95825 *Tel:* 916-973-9100 *Toll Free Tel:* 800-635-1266 *E-mail:* info@atv.net *Web Site:* www.atv.net, pg 692

Leverence, Dr John, Emmy Awards (Primetime), 5220 Lankershim Blvd, North Hollywood, CA 91601-3109 *Tel:* 818-754-2800 *Fax:* 818-761-3814 *E-mail:* emmyawards@televisionacademy.com *Web Site:* www.emmys.com, pg 988

Leverence, Dr John, Television Academy, 5220 Lankershim Blvd, North Hollywood, CA 91601-3109 *Tel:* 818-754-2800 *Web Site:* www.emmys.com, pg 963

Levin, A J, Leedal Inc, 3453 Commercial Ave, Northbrook, IL 60062 *Tel:* 847-498-0111 *Fax:* 847-498-0198 *E-mail:* sink@leedal.com *Web Site:* www.leedal.com, pg 806

Levin, Claudia, Monadnock Media Inc, 59 North St, Hatfield, MA 01038 *Tel:* 413-247-6447 *Fax:* 413-247-6448 *E-mail:* info@monadnock.org *Web Site:* www.monadnock.org, pg 829

Levin, David, McGraw-Hill School Education Group, 8787 Orion Place, Columbus, OH 43240-4027 *Tel:* 614-430-4000 *Toll Free Tel:* 800-334-7734 *Fax:* 614-755-5682 *Web Site:* mheonline.com; www.mheducation.com, pg 821

Levin, Joel, Final Draft, A Cast & Crew Company, 2300 Empire Ave, Burbank, CA 91504 *Tel:* 818-995-8995; 818-906-8930 (tech support) *Toll Free Tel:* 800-231-4055 *E-mail:* info@finaldraft.com *Web Site:* www.finaldraft.com, pg 761

Levin, Steve, Audio Visual Dynamics®, 424 Sand Shore Rd, Hackettstown, NJ 07840 *Tel:* 973-993-8500 *Fax:* 973-984-0644 *Web Site:* www.avdusa.com, pg 694

Levin, Steve, International Display & Exhibit Corp (IDEC), 60 Shawmut Rd, Suite 5, Canton, MA 02021 *Tel:* 617-527-7878 *Toll Free Tel:* 800-533-7878 *Fax:* 617-964-5099 *E-mail:* sales@idec-displays.com *Web Site:* www.idecdisplays.com, pg 790

Levine, Felice J PhD, American Educational Research Association (AERA), 1430 "K" St NW, Suite 1200, Washington, DC 20005 *Tel:* 202-238-3200 *Fax:* 202-238-3250 *E-mail:* communications@aera.net; members@aera.net *Web Site:* www.aera.net, pg 948

Levine, Gary, CSPI, 175 Cabot St, Suite 210, Lowell, MA 01854 *Tel:* 978-663-7598; 978-954-5038 *Toll Free Tel:* 800-325-3110 *E-mail:* hello@cspi.com *Web Site:* www.cspi.com, pg 735

Levine, Glen, NEP Group Inc, 2 Beta Dr, Pittsburgh, PA 15238 *Tel:* 412-826-1414 *Toll Free Tel:* 800-444-0054 *E-mail:* info@nepinc.com *Web Site:* www.nepgroup.com, pg 838

Levine, Jenny, Library & Information Technology Association (LITA), c/o American Library Association, 50 E Huron St, Chicago, IL 60611-2795 *Toll Free Tel:* 800-545-2433 (ext 4270) *Fax:* 312-280-3257 *E-mail:* lita@ala.org *Web Site:* www.ala.org/lita, pg 957

Levine, Michael, Crash Video Productions, 713 N Mansfield Ave, Los Angeles, CA 90038 *Tel:* 310-489-6848 *E-mail:* crash@crashproductions.com *Web Site:* www.crashproductions.com, pg 733

Levine, Samantha, Austin Film Festival, 1801 Salina St, Austin, TX 78702 *Tel:* 512-478-4795 *Toll Free Tel:* 800-310-FEST (310-3378) *Fax:* 512-478-6205 *E-mail:* info@austinfilmfestival.com; programming@austinfilmfestival.com; marketing@austinfilmfestival.com *Web Site:* www.austinfilmfestival.com, pg 982

Levitt, Cary, Parlights Inc, 1662 Bowmans Farm Rd, Suite 111, Frederick, MD 21701 *Tel:* 301-698-9242 *Fax:* 301-846-0369 *E-mail:* sales@parlights.com *Web Site:* www.parlights.com, pg 851

Levitt, Suzanne, Parlights Inc, 1662 Bowmans Farm Rd, Suite 111, Frederick, MD 21701 *Tel:* 301-698-9242 *Fax:* 301-846-0369 *E-mail:* sales@parlights.com *Web Site:* www.parlights.com, pg 851

Levy, Arthur J, Apogee Communications Group, 159 Alpine Way, Boulder, CO 80304 *Tel:* 303-443-8473 *Toll Free Tel:* 800-210-5700 *Fax:* 303-443-0500 *E-mail:* sales@apogeevideo.com; contact@apogeecommunicationsgroup.com *Web Site:* www.apogeevideo.com; apogeecommunicationsgroup.com, pg 687

Levy, Brooke, The Clio Awards, 825 Eighth Ave, 29th fl, New York, NY 10019 *Tel:* 212-683-4300 *E-mail:* event@clioawards.com *Web Site:* clios.com, pg 987

Levy, Charles, Lensless Camera Manufacturing Co, 809 Lark Dr, Fernley, NV 89408 *Tel:* 775-575-5189 *E-mail:* info@pinholecamera.com *Web Site:* www.pinholecamera.com, pg 806

Levy, David, Turner Broadcasting System Inc, A Time Warner Company, One CNN Ctr, Atlanta, GA 30303 *Tel:* 404-827-1700 *E-mail:* turner.info@turner.com *Web Site:* www.turner.com, pg 919

Levy, Elinor, DEC Grants, 696 Dutchess Tpke, Suite F, Poughkeepsie, NY 12603 *Tel:* 845-454-3222 *E-mail:* info@artsmidhudson.org *Web Site:* www.artsmidhudson.org, pg 988

Levy, Ira, Levy NYC Design & Production, 356 Devoe St, Brooklyn, NY 11211 *Tel:* 212-925-4640 *Fax:* 212-925-4216 *E-mail:* info@levynyc.net *Web Site:* www.levylighting.com, pg 806

Levy, Lawrence, Catapult Films Inc, 832 Third St, Suite 303, Santa Monica, CA 90403 *Tel:* 310-395-1470, pg 717

Levy, Mel, Breeze Productions Inc, 1660 Edgewood Rd, Highland Park, IL 60035 *Web Site:* www.breezeprod.com, pg 710

Levy, Michael, Corporation for Public Broadcasting (CPB), 401 Ninth St NW, Washington, DC 20004-2129 *Tel:* 202-879-9600 *Toll Free Tel:* 800-272-2190 *Fax:* 202-879-9700 *E-mail:* press@cpb.org *Web Site:* www.cpb.org, pg 953

Levy, Ralph C, MMI Marketing, 2950 Wyman Pkwy, Baltimore, MD 21211-2802 *Tel:* 410-366-1222 *Fax:* 410-366-1222 *E-mail:* mail@mmi-marketing.com *Web Site:* www.mmi-marketing.com, pg 828

Levy, Scott, Eastern Effects Inc, 99 Ninth St, Brooklyn, NY 11215 *Tel:* 718-855-1197 *Toll Free Fax:* 888-566-6547 *Web Site:* easterneffects.com, pg 749

Lewin, Miriam, Lavine Production Group, 189 Dean St, Brooklyn, NY 11217 *Tel:* 917-804-1870 *Web Site:* www.lavinegroup.com, pg 804

Lewis, B Z, Studio 132, 6802 Gunn Dr, Oakland, CA 94611-1443 *Tel:* 510-338-1240 *E-mail:* info@studio132.com *Web Site:* www.studio132.com, pg 902

Lewis, Beverly, Placer-Lake Tahoe Film Office, 145 Fulweiler Ave, Auburn, CA 95603 *Tel:* 530-889-4091 *Toll Free Tel:* 877-228-3456 *Fax:* 530-889-4095 *Web Site:* www.placer.ca.gov/films, pg 966

Lewis, Dianne, Jointure for Community Adult Education Inc, Centre at Raritan, Suite B-11, 1124 US Hwy 202 S, Raritan, NJ 08869 *Tel:* 908-722-0233 *Fax:* 908-722-0388 *E-mail:* info@jointure.org *Web Site:* www.jointure.org, pg 794

Lewis, Harold G, ATA Trading Corp/Favorite TV Inc, 877 Oceanfront, Long Beach, NY 11561-1542 *Tel:* 516-431-2302 *E-mail:* atat@verizon.net, pg 691

Lewis, Jennifer, Korg USA Inc, 316 S Service Rd, Melville, NY 11747 *Tel:* 631-390-6500; 631-390-6800 (cust serv) *E-mail:* sales@korgusa.com; customerservice@korgusa.com *Web Site:* www.korgusa.com, pg 801

Lewis, Jim, Communications Concepts Inc (CCI), 7980 N Atlantic Ave, Suite 101, Cape Canaveral, FL 32920 *Tel:* 321-783-5232 *Web Site:* cci321.com, pg 729

Lewis, John, Staging Concepts, 8400 Wyoming Ave N, Suite 100, Minneapolis, MN 55445 *Tel:* 763-533-2094 *Toll Free Tel:* 800-337-5339 *E-mail:* info@stagingconcepts.com *Web Site:* www.stagingconcepts.com, pg 899

Lewis, Ken, Midwest Photo Exchange, 2887 Silver Dr, Columbus, OH 43211 *Tel:* 614-261-1264 *Toll Free Tel:* 866-940-3686 *E-mail:* mpx@mpex.com; orders@mpex.com *Web Site:* mpex.com, pg 827

Lewis, Mark, Tight Line Productions, 1902 Oak St, Melbourne, FL 32901 *Tel:* 321-725-4668 *Fax:* 321-768-6528 *E-mail:* info@tightlinetv.com *Web Site:* www.tightlineproductions.com, pg 914

Lewis, Noland L, ACO Pacific Inc, 2604 Read Ave, Belmont, CA 94002 *Tel:* 650-595-8588 *Fax:* 650-591-2891 *E-mail:* sales@acopacific.com; info@acopacific.com; support@acopacific.com *Web Site:* acopacific.com, pg 674

Lewis, Richard, PipelineFX LLC, 500 Ala Moana Blvd, Tower 7, Suite 400, Honolulu, HI 96813 *Tel:* 808-685-7823 *Toll Free Tel:* 855-685-7823 *Fax:* 808-685-7800 *E-mail:* sales@pipelinefx.com *Web Site:* www.pipelinefx.com, pg 857

Lewis, Richard, Touchstone Center Publications, 141 E 88 St, Apt 3E, New York, NY 10128 *Tel:* 212-831-7717 *Web Site:* touchstonecenter.net, pg 916

Lewis, Robert, Visual Instrumentation Corp, 1110 West Ave L-12, Unit 2, Lancaster, CA 93534-7039 *Tel:* 661-945-7999 *Fax:* 661-723-5667 *E-mail:* visinst@earthlink.net *Web Site:* www.visinst.com, pg 931

Lewis, Tim, MastCom, 807 Broadway St NE, Suite 210, Minneapolis, MN 55413 *Tel:* 612-397-9637 *E-mail:* info@mastcom.com *Web Site:* www.mastcom.com, pg 819

Lewis, Vel, Los Angeles Post Music Inc, 4340 E Kentucky Ave, Suite 308, Glendale, CO 80246 *Tel:* 310-896-5176 *Web Site:* www.lapostmusic.com, pg 811

Lewis-Woodson, Rhea A, Palm Springs International Film Festival, 1700 E Tahquitz Canyon Way, Suite 3, Palm Springs, CA 92262 *Tel:* 760-322-2930 *Toll Free Tel:* 800-898-7256 *Fax:* 760-322-4087 *E-mail:* info@psfilmfest.org *Web Site:* www.psfilmfest.org, pg 999

Lewnes, Ann, Adobe Systems Inc, 345 Park Ave, San Jose, CA 95110-2704 *Tel:* 408-536-6000 *Fax:* 408-537-6000 *Web Site:* www.adobe.com, pg 676

Li, Haisong, Asian American International Film Festival (AAIFF), c/o Made in NY Media Ctr by IFP, 30 John St, Brooklyn, NY 11201 *Tel:* 212-989-1422 *Fax:* 212-727-3584 *E-mail:* submissions@asiancinevision.org; info@asiancinevision.org *Web Site:* aaiff.org; www.asiancinevision.org, pg 982

Liantonio, Collette, Concepts TV Productions Inc, 53 Indian Lane E, Towaco, NJ 07082 *Tel:* 973-331-1500 *Fax:* 973-331-1550 *E-mail:* sales@conceptstv.com *Web Site:* conceptstv.com, pg 730

Libby, Felicia, Creative Technology, 222 Front St, 2nd fl, San Francisco, CA 94111 *Tel:* 415-513-5918 *E-mail:* studio@ct-sf.com *Web Site:* www.ct-sf.com, pg 733

Libby, Lisa, The ADS Group, 2155 Niagara Lane N, Suite 120, Plymouth, MN 55447 *Tel:* 763-449-5500 *Toll Free Tel:* 800-759-0992 *Fax:* 763-449-5555 *E-mail:* sales@theadsgroup.com *Web Site:* theadsgroup.com, pg 677

Liberatore, Joe, Midland Video Productions Inc, 3315 N 124 St, Brookfield, WI 53005 *Tel:* 414-276-8300 *E-mail:* request@midlandvideo.com *Web Site:* midlandvideo.com, pg 827

Licitra, Timothy, Illuminating Engineering Society (IES), 120 Wall St, 17th fl, New York, NY 10005-4026 *Tel:* 212-248-5000 *E-mail:* ies@ies.org *Web Site:* ies.org, pg 955

Lidderdale, William, The Set Shop, 428 Colyton St, Los Angeles, CA 90013 *Tel:* 213-680-1668 *Fax:* 213-680-4269, pg 884

Lieberman, Jason, AV Workshop, 500 W 37 St, 3rd fl, New York, NY 10018 *Tel:* 212-643-0040 *Fax:* 212-564-5277 *E-mail:* sales@avworkshop.com *Web Site:* avworkshop.com, pg 697

Lieberman, Lenny, Lieberman Productions, 455 Ninth St, San Francisco, CA 94103-4410 *Tel:* 415-955-0855 *Fax:* 415-955-0822 *E-mail:* lpinfo@lieberman.com *Web Site:* www.lieberman.com, pg 807

Lieberman, Les, KVL Audio Visual Services Inc, 200 Corporate Blvd S, Yonkers, NY 10701 *Tel:* 914-479-3300 *Toll Free Tel:* 800-862-3210 *Fax:* 914-965-1423 *E-mail:* info@kvlav.com *Web Site:* www.kvlav.com, pg 802

Lieberman, Michael, Barbizon Electric Co Inc, 456 W 55 St, New York, NY 10019-4403 *Tel:* 212-586-1620 *Toll Free Tel:* 800-582-9941 *Fax:* 212-247-8818 *E-mail:* benysales@barbizon.com *Web Site:* www.barbizon.com, pg 701

Lieberman, Rob, TimeSteps Productions Inc, 2 Glenside Dr, West Orange, NJ 07052 *Tel:* 973-669-1930 *E-mail:* info@timesteps.com *Web Site:* timesteps.com, pg 914

Lieberman, Steve, Phoenix Society for Burn Survivors Inc, 525 Ottawa Ave NW, Front, Grand Rapids, MI 49503 *Tel:* 616-458-2773 *Toll Free Tel:* 800-888-BURN (888-2876) *Fax:* 616-458-2831 *E-mail:* info@phoenix-society.org *Web Site:* www.phoenix-society.org, pg 856

Liebman, Seymour, Canon USA Inc, One Canon Park, Melville, NY 11747 *Toll Free Tel:* 800-652-2666 *E-mail:* pr@cusa.canon.com *Web Site:* www.usa.canon.com, pg 716

Liebowitz, Kim, Video Dimensions Inc, 545 W 45 St, New York, NY 10036 *Tel:* 212-262-5453 *Web Site:* videodimensions.net, pg 927

Liebowitz, Steve, Video Dimensions Inc, 545 W 45 St, New York, NY 10036 *Tel:* 212-262-5453 *Web Site:* videodimensions.net, pg 927

Liening, Jeff, ATX Networks, 8-1602 Tricont Ave, Whitby, ON L1N 7C3, Canada *Tel:* 289-204-7800 *Toll Free Tel:* 866-968-7289 *E-mail:* info@atx.com *Web Site:* atx.com, pg 692

Lietz, Tom, MessageMakers, 1217 Turner St, Lansing, MI 48906 *Tel:* 517-482-3333 *Toll Free Tel:* 888-482-6688 *E-mail:* info@messagemakers.com *Web Site:* www.messagemakers.com, pg 824

Lieurance, Kristen Kiesel, Carvin Amps & Audio, 16262 W Bernardo Dr, San Diego, CA 92127 *Tel:* 858-751-4884 *Web Site:* carvinaudio.com, pg 717

Liew, Traci, KTVB-TV, 5407 W Fairview Ave, Boise, ID 83706 *Tel:* 208-375-7277 *Toll Free Tel:* 800-559-7277 *Fax:* 208-378-5642; 208-375-7770 (news fax) *E-mail:* info@ktvb.com; ktvbnews@ktvb.com *Web Site:* www.ktvb.com, pg 802

Light, Charles, Green Mountain Post Films (GMP), PO Box 229, Turners Falls, MA 01376-0229 *Tel:* 413-863-4754 *Fax:* 413-863-8248 *E-mail:* info@gmpfilms.com *Web Site:* www.gmpfilms.com, pg 774

Lighterman, Sandy, Miami-Dade Office of Film & Entertainment, 111 NW First St, 12th fl, Miami, FL 33128 *Tel:* 305-375-3288 *E-mail:* film@miamidade.gov *Web Site:* www.filmiami.org, pg 969

Lightfoot, Tim, Radius® Display Products Inc, 800 Fabric Xpress Way, Dallas, TX 75234 *Tel:* 972-406-1221 *Toll Free Tel:* 800-FABRIC-X (322-7429); 866-966-4066 (sales); 866-966-8266 (hospitality) *Fax:* 972-406-1321 *Toll Free Fax:* 888-322-7429 *Web Site:* www.radiusdp.com, pg 869

Lillard, Amy, Washington Filmworks, 1411 Fourth Ave, Suite 420, Seattle, WA 98101 *Tel:* 206-264-0667 *Fax:* 206-382-4343 *E-mail:* info@washingtonfilmworks.org *Web Site:* washingtonfilmworks.org, pg 977

Lilling, Dave, Metro Teleproductions Inc (MTI), 2500 Virginia Ave NW, 416-S, Washington, DC 20037 *Tel:* 301-608-9077 *Fax:* 301-608-9078 *Web Site:* www.mtitv.com, pg 824

Lillis, Beth Godlin, WGBH Production Group, One Guest St, Boston, MA 02135 *Tel:* 617-300-2000 *E-mail:* productiongroup@wgbh.org; studios@wgbh.org; outpost@wgbh.org *Web Site:* productiongroup.wgbh.org, pg 936

Lilly, Quentin, Technicolor USA Inc, 6040 Sunset Blvd, Hollywood, CA 90028 *Tel:* 323-817-6600 *E-mail:* info@technicolor.com *Web Site:* www.technicolor.com, pg 908

Lin, Alen, Studio 1444, 1444 N Highland Ave, Hollywood, CA 90028 *Tel:* 323-482-1004 *E-mail:* info@studio1444.com, pg 902

Lin, Jami, EarthDesign Inc, 9 Riverfront Dr, Venice, FL 34293 *Tel:* 941-276-8689 *Toll Free Tel:* 800-327-8433 *E-mail:* gp@jamilin.com *Web Site:* jamilin.com, pg 749

Lincecum, David, ETC, 3031 Pleasant View Rd, Middleton, WI 53562-4809 *Tel:* 608-831-4116 *Toll Free Tel:* 800-688-4116 *Fax:* 608-836-1736 *Web Site:* www.etcconnect.com, pg 756

Lindemann, Brian, Broadcast Electronics, 4100 N 24 St, Quincy, IL 62305 *Tel:* 217-224-9600 *Fax:* 217-224-9607 *E-mail:* bdcast@bdcast.com *Web Site:* www.bdcast.com, pg 710

Linden, Lou, Yellow Cat Productions Inc, 505 11 St SE, Washington, DC 20003 *Tel:* 202-543-2221 *E-mail:* yellowcat@yellowcat.com *Web Site:* www.yellowcat.com, pg 944

Lindenberg, Ryan, Picturestart, 817 Hilldale Ave, West Hollywood, CA 90069 *Tel:* 310-422-3280 *E-mail:* info@picturestart.com *Web Site:* www.picturestart.com, pg 856

Lindgren, Erik, ARF! ARF!, PO Box 465, Middleboro, MA 02346-0465 *Tel:* 508-947-7387 *Fax:* 508-947-7387 *E-mail:* page@arfarfrecords.com *Web Site:* www.arfarfrecords.com, pg 688

Lindgren, Erik, Sounds Interesting Studio, 112 Fuller St, Middleboro, MA 02346 *Tel:* 508-947-7387 *Web Site:* www.soundsinterestingstudio.com, pg 895

Lindgren, Erik, The Well-Tempered Music Library, PO Box 465, Middleboro, MA 02346-0465 *Tel:* 508-947-7387 *Fax:* 508-947-7387 *E-mail:* info@arfarfrecords.com; page@arfarfrecords.com *Web Site:* www.arfarfrecords.com; www.arfarfrecords.com/wtml/home.html, pg 935

Lindo, Gave, ReelWorld Film Festival, 50 Carroll St, Suite 200, Toronto, ON M4M 3G3, Canada *Tel:* 416-598-7933 *E-mail:* info@reelworld.ca; contact@reelworld.ca *Web Site:* www.reelworld.ca, pg 1001

Lindquist, David, Mike's Camera, 2500 Pearl St, Boulder, CO 80302 *Tel:* 303-444-1257; 303-443-1715 (ext 132) *E-mail:* store1@mikescamera.com *Web Site:* www.mikescamera.com, pg 827

Lindsey, Anne H, Laurel Hill Press, PO Box 16516, Chapel Hill, NC 27516-6516 *Toll Free Tel:* 800-942-6516 *Fax:* 919-942-9533 *E-mail:* plantsforus@gmail.com *Web Site:* www.laurelhillpress.com, pg 804

Lindsey, Charisse, Hyperspective Studios Inc, 2800 Woodlawn Dr, Suite 253, Honolulu, HI 96822 *Tel:* 808-353-3618 *Toll Free Tel:* 800-353-3618 *E-mail:* info@hyperspective.com *Web Site:* hyperspective.com, pg 783

Lindsey, Dwight, Schneider Optics Inc, 285 Oser Ave, Hauppauge, NY 11788 *Tel:* 631-761-5000 *Toll Free Tel:* 800-645-7239 *Fax:* 631-761-5090 *E-mail:* info@schneideroptics.com *Web Site:* www.schneideroptics.com, pg 882

Lindstrom, Mel, Pacific Light Studios, 265 Caspian Dr, Sunnyvale, CA 94089 *Tel:* 408-541-1800 *E-mail:* info1@pacificlightstudios.com *Web Site:* www.pacificlightstudios.com, pg 849

Lineberger, Elisabeth, Central Florida Visitors & Convention Bureau, 2701 Lake Myrtle Park Rd, Auburndale, FL 33823 *Tel:* 863-551-4750 *Toll Free Tel:* 800-828-7655 *Fax:* 863-551-4740 *Web Site:* visitcentralflorida.org, pg 969

Lines, Kevin, Southwest Audio-Visual Inc, 3058 E Cairo, Springfield, MO 65802 *Tel:* 417-887-4900 *Fax:* 417-866-6500 *E-mail:* info@southwestav.com *Web Site:* www.southwestav.com, pg 895

Linetsky, David, Noventri, 20940 Twin Springs Dr, Smithsburg, MD 21783-1510 *Tel:* 301-790-0103 *Fax:* 301-790-0173 *E-mail:* sale@noventri.com *Web Site:* www.noventri.com, pg 843

Lingenfelter, Andrew, Canadian American Records, PO Box 808, Lititz, PA 17543-0538 *Tel:* 717-627-4800 *E-mail:* canadianamerican@dejazzd.com *Web Site:* www.canadianamericanrecords.net; www.canadianamericanrecordcompany.com, pg 715

Linhoff, John, Linhoff Photo & Digital Imaging, 4400 France Ave S, Edina, MN 55410 *Tel:* 952-927-7333 *E-mail:* info@linhoff.com *Web Site:* linhoff.com, pg 809

Loehr, Rob, Panavid, 210 West Pkwy, Unit 5, Pompton Plains, NJ 07444 *Tel:* 973-831-5655 *E-mail:* info@panavid.com; support@panavid.com *Web Site:* www.panavid.com, pg 850

Loewen, Kevin, Pathway Connectivity, 103-1439 17 Ave SE, Calgary, AB T2G 1J9, Canada *Tel:* 403-243-8110 *Fax:* 403-287-1281 *E-mail:* orders@pathwayconnect.com *Web Site:* www.pathwayconnect.com, pg 852

Loftin, Don, A-List Quality Videographer, 33 Saint Mark's Place, New York, NY 10003 *Tel:* 917-825-5412; 917-399-8501 *E-mail:* loftin.productions@gmail.com *Web Site:* www.loftinpro.com, pg 671

Loftus, Karen, Dazian LLC, 18 Central Blvd, South Hackensack, NJ 07606 *Toll Free Tel:* 877-232-9426 *Fax:* 201-641-2728; 201-549-1055 (efax) *E-mail:* info@dazian.com *Web Site:* www.dazian.com, pg 739

Loftus, Timothy, PSI Inc, 16755 Von Karman Ave, Suite 200, Irvine, CA 92606 *Tel:* 949-261-6119 *Web Site:* www.psivideoinc.com, pg 866

Logan, Beth, Logan Productions Inc, 8035 N Port Washington Rd, Milwaukee, WI 53217 *Tel:* 414-352-9691 *Fax:* 414-352-4993 *E-mail:* info@loganproductions.com *Web Site:* www.loganproductions.com, pg 811

Logan, Jesse, Showorks Audio Visual Inc, 730 Philadelphia Pike, Wilmington, DE 19809 *Tel:* 302-798-7999 *E-mail:* info@showorksav.com *Web Site:* showorksav.com, pg 887

Logan, Jim, Logan Productions Inc, 8035 N Port Washington Rd, Milwaukee, WI 53217 *Tel:* 414-352-9691 *Fax:* 414-352-4993 *E-mail:* info@loganproductions.com *Web Site:* www.loganproductions.com, pg 811

Logan, Michael, Troxell-CDI, 4675 E Cotton Center Blvd, Suite 155, Phoenix, AZ 85040 *Tel:* 602-437-7240 *Toll Free Tel:* 855-TROXELL (876-9355) *Fax:* 602-752-1299 *Toll Free Fax:* 800-752-1299 *E-mail:* csg@trox.com *Web Site:* www.troxellsolutions.com, pg 919

Logan, Will, Creative Realities Inc (CRI), 13100 Magisterial Dr, Suite 100, Louisville, KY 40223 *Tel:* 502-791-8800 *Web Site:* cri.com, pg 733

Loggins, Chris, Fred Rogers Productions, 2100 Wharton St, Suite 700, Pittsburgh, PA 15203 *Tel:* 412-687-2990 *Toll Free Tel:* 877-677-6437 *E-mail:* info@fredrogers.org *Web Site:* www.fredrogers.org, pg 876

Loi, Anne, WildBrain™, 5657 Spring Garden Rd, Suite 505, Halifax, NS B3J 3R4, Canada *Tel:* 902-423-0260 *Fax:* 902-422-0752 *E-mail:* info@wildbrain.com; halifax@wildbrain.com; sales@wildbrain.com *Web Site:* www.wildbrain.com, pg 938

Lombard, Kathleen, Presence Studios, 80 Wells Hill Rd, Suite 100, Weston, CT 06883 *Tel:* 203-221-8061 *E-mail:* info@presencestudios.com *Web Site:* www.presencestudios.com, pg 861

Lombardi, Adelio, Side 3 Studios, 725 Mariposa St, Denver, CO 80204 *Tel:* 720-515-2649 *E-mail:* info@side3.com *Web Site:* www.side3.com, pg 887

Loncar, Veronica Elliott, Kansas City FilmFest International (KCFFI), 4741 Central, Suite 306, Kansas City, MO 64112 *Tel:* 816-286-4777 *E-mail:* info@kcfilmfest.org *Web Site:* kcfilmfest.org, pg 994

London, Dan T, Accenture, 161 N Clark St, Chicago, IL 60601 *Tel:* 312-693-0161 *Toll Free Tel:* 877-889-9009 *Fax:* 312-693-0507 *Web Site:* www.accenture.com, pg 672

London, Jeff, Marketron Broadcast Solutions, 101 Empty Saddle Trail, Hailey, ID 83333 *Tel:* 208-788-6800 *Toll Free Tel:* 800-476-7226 *Fax:* 208-788-6273 *E-mail:* sales@marketron.com *Web Site:* www.marketron.com, pg 817

Long, Amy, Colorado Springs Film Commission, 515 S Cascade Ave, Colorado Springs, CO 80903 *Tel:* 719-685-7630 *Toll Free Tel:* 800-888-4748 (ext 130) *Fax:* 719-635-4968 *E-mail:* film@visitcos.com *Web Site:* www.visitcos.com/film, pg 968

Long, Brianna Thomas, Thomas Printworks, 600 N Central Expwy, Richardson, TX 75080 *Tel:* 972-231-7161 *Toll Free Tel:* 800-877-3776 *Fax:* 972-644-6308 *E-mail:* richardson@thomasprintworks.com *Web Site:* thomasprintworks.com, pg 912

Long, Kent, Thomas Printworks, 600 N Central Expwy, Richardson, TX 75080 *Tel:* 972-231-7161 *Toll Free Tel:* 800-877-3776 *Fax:* 972-644-6308 *E-mail:* richardson@thomasprintworks.com *Web Site:* thomasprintworks.com, pg 912

Long, Kerrie, Frame 30 Productions Ltd, 10816A-82 Ave, No 202, Edmonton, AB T6E 2B3, Canada *Tel:* 780-439-5322 *E-mail:* frame30@frame30.com *Web Site:* www.frame30.com, pg 765

Long, S M, OMNI Productions, PO Box 302, Carmel, IN 46082-0302 *Tel:* 317-846-2345 *Fax:* 317-846-6664 *E-mail:* omni@omniproductions.com *Web Site:* www.omniproductions.com, pg 845

Long, Thayer, Association for Print Technologies (APTech), 1896 Preston White Dr, Reston, VA 20191 *Tel:* 703-264-7200 *Fax:* 703-620-0994 *E-mail:* aptech@aptech.org *Web Site:* www.printtechnologies.org, pg 950

Long, W H, OMNI Productions, PO Box 302, Carmel, IN 46082-0302 *Tel:* 317-846-2345 *Fax:* 317-846-6664 *E-mail:* omni@omniproductions.com *Web Site:* www.omniproductions.com, pg 845

Longmire, Tyler Klein, Quickdraw Animation Society, 2011 Tenth Ave SW, Calgary, AB T3C 0K4, Canada *Tel:* 403-261-5767 *E-mail:* info@quickdrawanimation.ca; production@quickdrawanimation.ca; programming@quickdrawanimation.ca *Web Site:* quickdrawanimation.ca; www.giraffest.ca, pg 961

Longo, Crystal, Manhattan Center Studios Inc, 311 W 34 St, New York, NY 10001 *Tel:* 212-279-7740 *Fax:* 212-564-1072 *E-mail:* info@mcstudios.com *Web Site:* www.mcstudios.com, pg 816

Longo, Edward, Recorded Books Inc, an RBmedia company, 270 Skipjack Rd, Prince Frederick, MD 20678 *Tel:* 410-535-5590 *Toll Free Tel:* 800-638-1304 *Fax:* 410-535-5499 *E-mail:* customerservice@recordedbooks.com *Web Site:* www.recordedbooks.com, pg 871

Longshore, David, Creation Technologies Inc, 8999 Fraserton Ct, Burnaby, BC V5J 5H8, Canada *Tel:* 604-430-4336 *Toll Free Tel:* 800-736-1271 *E-mail:* info@creationtech.com; sales@creationtech.com *Web Site:* www.creationtech.com, pg 733

Lonsdale, Martha, StockMusic.com, 105 W Beaver Creek Rd, Suite 4, Richmond Hill, ON L4B 1C6, Canada *Tel:* 905-886-0077 *Fax:* 905-886-6800 *E-mail:* info@stockmusic.com *Web Site:* www.stockmusic.com, pg 901

Lonzak, Kyle, RAM® Mounts, 8410 Dallas Ave S, Seattle, WA 98108 *Tel:* 206-763-8361 *Toll Free Tel:* 800-497-7479 *Fax:* 206-763-9615 *E-mail:* sales@rammount.com *Web Site:* www.rammount.com, pg 870

Loper, Kevin, Pristine Systems Inc, PO Box 6482, San Pedro, CA 90734 *Tel:* 310-831-2234 *Web Site:* www.pristinesys.com, pg 862

Lopes, Matthew, The DVI Group, 1486 Mecaslin St NW, Atlanta, GA 30309 *Tel:* 404-873-6283 *Toll Free Tel:* 888-736-7384 *E-mail:* makeitbetter@thedvigroup.com *Web Site:* www.thedvigroup.com, pg 748

Lopez, David, Pacific Video Image, 9065 E Rosecrans Ave, Bellflower, CA 90706 *Tel:* 562-634-4200 *Fax:* 562-634-4700 *Web Site:* www.pvideo.com, pg 849

Lopez, Gloria, Fish Films Footage World, 4548 Van Noord Ave, Studio City, CA 91604 *Tel:* 818-905-1071 *E-mail:* footageworld@aol.com *Web Site:* www.footageworld.com, pg 761

Lopez, Marco, ChyronHego Corp, 5 Hub Dr, Melville, NY 11747 *Tel:* 631-845-2000 *E-mail:* info@chyronhego.com; sales@chryonhego.com *Web Site:* chyronhego.com, pg 723

Lopez, Maria, Chicago Latino Film Festival, 55 W Van Buren St, Suite 310, Chicago, IL 60605 *Tel:* 312-431-1330 *E-mail:* info@latinoculturalcenter.org *Web Site:* www.chicagolatinofilmfestival.org, pg 985

Lopez, Rosie, Tommy Boy Entertainment LLC, 220 E 23 St, New York, NY 10010 *Tel:* 212-388-8300 *E-mail:* info@tommyboy.com *Web Site:* www.tommyboy.com, pg 915

Lopez, Thomas, ZBS Foundation, 174 N River Rd, Fort Edward, NY 12828-9713 *Tel:* 518-695-6406 *Toll Free Tel:* 800-662-3345 *Fax:* 518-695-4041 *E-mail:* custserv@zbs.org *Web Site:* www.zbs.org, pg 945

Lorber, Ken, The Kitchen, 265 NE 24 St, Suite 401, Miami, FL 33137 *Tel:* 305-415-6200 *E-mail:* info@thekitchen.tv *Web Site:* www.thekitchen.tv, pg 799

Lorber, Richard, Kino International Corp, 333 W 39 St, Suite 503, New York, NY 10018 *Tel:* 212-629-6880 *Toll Free Tel:* 800-562-3330 *Fax:* 212-714-0871 *E-mail:* contact@kinolorber.com *Web Site:* www.kinolorber.com, pg 799

Lord, Brian, Portland Film Office, 222 NW Fifth Ave, Portland, OR 97209-3859 *Tel:* 503-823-3326 *E-mail:* filmoffice@pdc.us *Web Site:* www.portlandfilmoffice.com, pg 975

Lorentzen, Bob, Video Techniques Inc, 1731 First St E, Bradenton, FL 34208 *Tel:* 941-758-3077 *Fax:* 941-758-4896 *E-mail:* vti-web@videotechniques.com *Web Site:* videotechniques.com, pg 928

Losik, Tim, ProPhotonix Ltd, 13 Red Roof Lane, Suite 200, Salem, NH 03079 *Tel:* 603-893-8778 *E-mail:* sales@prophotonix.com; info@prophotonix.com *Web Site:* www.prophotonix.com, pg 865

Losique, Serge, World Film Festival/Festival des Films du Monde/Montreal, 1432 de Bleury St, Montreal, QC H3A 2J1, Canada *Tel:* 514-848-3883 *Fax:* 514-848-3886 *E-mail:* program@ffm-montreal.org *Web Site:* www.ffm-montreal.org, pg 1007

Losmandy, Bel, Opamp Labs Inc, 1033 N Sycamore Ave, Los Angeles, CA 90038 *Tel:* 323-934-3566 *Fax:* 323-462-6490 *E-mail:* opamplabs@gmail.com *Web Site:* www.opamplabs.com, pg 846

Losmandy, I, Opamp Labs Inc, 1033 N Sycamore Ave, Los Angeles, CA 90038 *Tel:* 323-934-3566 *Fax:* 323-462-6490 *E-mail:* opamplabs@gmail.com *Web Site:* www.opamplabs.com, pg 846

Losmandy, Scott, Porta-Jib, 416 N Varney St, Burbank, CA 91502 *Tel:* 747-283-1077 *Fax:* 747-283-1078 *Web Site:* www.porta-jib.com, pg 859

Lott, Laura, American Alliance of Museums (AAM), 2451 Crystal Dr, Suite 1005, Arlington, VA 22202 *Tel:* 202-289-1818 *Fax:* 202-289-6578 *Web Site:* www.aam-us.org, pg 948

Loucks, Grant, Fax Animation Co, 5625 Melrose Ave, Hollywood, CA 90038 *Tel:* 323-466-3561 *Fax:* 323-871-2193 *E-mail:* contactus@alangordon.com *Web Site:* www.alangordon.com, pg 759

Loucks, Grant, Alan Gordon Enterprises Inc, 5625 Melrose Ave, Hollywood, CA 90038 *Tel:* 323-466-3561 *Fax:* 323-871-2193 *E-mail:* contactus@alangordon.com *Web Site:* www.alangordon.com, pg 772

Loucks, Wayne, Alan Gordon Enterprises Inc, 5625 Melrose Ave, Hollywood, CA 90038 *Tel:* 323-466-3561 *Fax:* 323-871-2193 *E-mail:* contactus@alangordon.com *Web Site:* www.alangordon.com, pg 772

Loudis, John, North Star Satellite Communications Inc, 2547 Yellow Springs Rd, Malvern, PA 19355 *Tel:* 610-407-9290, pg 842

Loughboro, Jeff, Loma Scientific International (LSI), 3115 Kashiwa St, Torrance, CA 90505 *Tel:* 310-539-8655 *Fax:* 310-539-8634 *E-mail:* info@lomasci.com; sales@lomasci.com *Web Site:* www.lomasci.com, pg 811

Loughboro, Patrick, Loma Scientific International (LSI), 3115 Kashiwa St, Torrance, CA 90505 *Tel:* 310-539-8655 *Fax:* 310-539-8634 *E-mail:* info@lomasci.com; sales@lomasci.com *Web Site:* www.lomasci.com, pg 811

Loughhead, Roland, Triad Communications Ltd, 2751 Oxford St, Vancouver, BC V5K 1N5, Canada *Tel:* 604-253-3990 *E-mail:* triadc@comwave.com *Web Site:* www.triadcommunications.ca, pg 918

Loughran, William Jr, Shore Manufacturing Co, 222 Beade St, Plymouth, PA 18651 *Tel:* 570-779-4042 *Toll Free Tel:* 800-321-5153 (orders) *Fax:* 570-779-7607 *Toll Free Fax:* 800-272-4334 *E-mail:* shoremfg@att.net *Web Site:* shoremfg.com, pg 886

Louis, Pierre, OWI Inc, 17141 Kingsview Ave, Carson, CA 90746 *Tel:* 310-515-1900 *Toll Free Tel:* 800-638-1694 *Fax:* 310-515-1606 *E-mail:* info@owi-inc.com *Web Site:* www.owi-inc.com, pg 849

Loupas, James, James Loupas Associates Inc, 134 Carrington Dr, Coppell, TX 75019 *Tel:* 972-304-0455 *Web Site:* jimloupas.com, pg 811

Lourie, Iven, Gateways Books & Tapes, PO Box 370, Nevada City, CA 95959 *Tel:* 530-271-2239 *Toll Free Tel:* 800-869-0658 *Fax:* 530-272-0184 *E-mail:* info@gatewaysbooksandtapes.com *Web Site:* www.gatewaysbooksandtapes.com, pg 768

Love, Candace, New & Unique Videos™, 7323 Rondel Ct, San Diego, CA 92119-1530 *Tel:* 619-644-3000 *E-mail:* video@newuniquevideos.com *Web Site:* www.newuniquevideos.com, pg 839

Love, Jennifer, Synergem, 2323 Randolph Ave, Avenel, NJ 07001 *Tel:* 732-225-0001 *E-mail:* sales@synergem.com *Web Site:* synergem.com, pg 905

Lovejoy, Meredith, Shen Milsom & Wilke LLC, 417 Fifth Ave, New York, NY 10016 *Tel:* 212-725-6800 *Fax:* 212-725-0864 *E-mail:* semspak@smwllc.com *Web Site:* www.smwllc.com, pg 886

Lovell, Chantal, St John's International Women's Film Festival, 28 Cochrane St, Suite 101, St John's, NL A1C 3L3, Canada *Tel:* 709-754-3141 *Fax:* 709-754-0049 *E-mail:* info@womensfilmfestival.com *Web Site:* www.womensfilmfestival.com, pg 1002

Loveridge, Doug, ST Productions, 900 Whitehall Rd, Chattanooga, TN 37405 *Tel:* 423-267-5412 *Fax:* 423-267-6840 *E-mail:* stps@wrcbtv.com *Web Site:* www.wrcbtv.com, pg 898

Lovette, Tony, LuXout Stage Curtains, 1221 Admiral St, Richmond, VA 23220 *Tel:* 804-264-3000; 804-264-3700 *Toll Free Tel:* 800-817-1204 *Toll Free Fax:* 888-227-8064 *E-mail:* luxoutinfo@luxout.com *Web Site:* www.luxout.com, pg 813

Low, Bob, O'Connor Engineering Labs, 2701 N Ontario St, Burbank, CA 91504 *Tel:* 818-847-8666 *Fax:* 818-847-1205 *E-mail:* usasales@ocon.com; info@ocon.com *Web Site:* www.ocon.com, pg 844

Lowe, David, KVIE-Channel 6, 2030 W El Camino Ave, Sacramento, CA 95833 *Tel:* 916-929-5843 *Toll Free Tel:* 800-347-5843 *Fax:* 916-929-7215 *E-mail:* member@kvie.org *Web Site:* www.kvie.org, pg 802

Lowe, George F, Sparkfactor, 943 W Randolph St, Suite 2E, Chicago, IL 60607 *Tel:* 773-292-8000 *E-mail:* info@sparkfactor.com *Web Site:* www.sparkfactor.com, pg 896

Lowe, Jeff, SMART Technologies ULC, 3636 Research Rd NW, Calgary, AB T2L 1Y1, Canada *Tel:* 403-245-0333 *Toll Free Tel:* 888-42-SMART (427-6278, CN & US); 800-260-9408 (sales) *Fax:* 403-228-2500 *Web Site:* home.smarttech.com, pg 891

Lowe, Jennifer, SKC Communication Products Inc, 8320 Hedge Lane Terr, Shawnee Mission, KS 66227 *Tel:* 913-422-4222 *Toll Free Tel:* 800-882-7779 *Toll Free Fax:* 800-454-4752 *E-mail:* contact.us@skccom.com *Web Site:* www.skccom.com, pg 890

Lowe, Walter, Blackburst Entertainment LLC, 1011 E Colonial Dr, No 304, Orlando, FL 32803 *Tel:* 321-439-2844 *E-mail:* contact@blackburstentertainment.com *Web Site:* blackburstentertainment.com, pg 706

Lowell, John, Lowell Manufacturing, 100 Integram Dr, Pacific, MO 63069-3476 *Tel:* 636-257-3400 *Toll Free Tel:* 800-325-9660 *Fax:* 636-257-6606 *Toll Free Fax:* 888-456-9355 *E-mail:* sales@lowellmfg.com *Web Site:* www.lowellmfg.com, pg 812

Lowes, Leslie, CEDIA IPRO Affinity Group, 8475 Nightfall Lane, Fishers, IN 46037 *Tel:* 317-328-4336 *Toll Free Tel:* 800-669-5329 *E-mail:* info@cedia.org *Web Site:* cedia.net, pg 952

Lowing, David R, Lowing Light & Grip Inc, 1500 Whiting St SW, Wyoming, MI 49509-1056 *Tel:* 616-530-7440 *Toll Free Tel:* 888-530-7440 *Fax:* 616-249-8947 *Web Site:* www.lowinglight.com, pg 812

Lowman, Paul, Case Design Corp, 333 School Lane, Telford, PA 18969 *Tel:* 215-703-0130 *Toll Free Tel:* 800-847-4176 *Fax:* 215-703-0139 *E-mail:* sales@casedesigncorp.com *Web Site:* www.casedesigncorp.com, pg 717

Lowman, Quincy, Inferno Films, 3404 Guadalupe St, Austin, TX 78705 *Tel:* 512-302-9009 *Fax:* 512-302-9022 *Web Site:* www.infernofilms.com, pg 787

Lowndes, Robert, CenterStaging LLC, 3407 Winona Ave, Burbank, CA 91504 *Tel:* 818-559-4333 *Fax:* 818-848-4016 *E-mail:* info@centerstaging.com *Web Site:* centerstaging.com, pg 719

Lowrance, Mark, Lowrance Sound Co Inc, 2132 Nailling Dr, Union City, TN 38261 *Tel:* 731-885-4504 *Toll Free Tel:* 800-852-5418 *E-mail:* info@lowrancesoundcompany.com *Web Site:* www.lowrancesoundcompany.com, pg 812

Loyd, Mike, In-Plant Printing & Mailing Association, 103 N Jefferson St, Kearney, MO 64060 *Tel:* 816-919-1691 *Fax:* 816-945-4505 *E-mail:* ipmainfo@ipma.org *Web Site:* ipma.org, pg 955

Lozowski, Stanley, Lylofilm Productions, 503 Beech St, New Hyde Park, NY 11040 *Tel:* 516-587-0567 *E-mail:* lylofilm@gmail.com *Web Site:* www.lylofilm.com; www.graphissimo.com, pg 813

Lubell, Alan H, Lubell Labs Inc, 21 N Stanwood Rd, Columbus, OH 43209 *Tel:* 614-235-6740 *E-mail:* lubell_labs@wowway.com *Web Site:* www.lubell.com, pg 812

Lubliner, Larry, Acoustone Corp, 140 58 St, Suite W, Brooklyn, NY 11220 *Tel:* 718-782-5560 *Toll Free Tel:* 800-782-5742 *Fax:* 718-782-7367 *E-mail:* acoustone@newcastlefabrics.com; info@acousticalsolutions.com *Web Site:* www.acoustonegrillecloth.com, pg 674

Lubman, David, DL Acoustics, 14301 Middletown Lane, Westminster, CA 92683 *Tel:* 714-373-3050 *Fax:* 714-373-3050 *Web Site:* www.dlacoustics.biz, pg 744

Luca, Gerry, Spectra Film & Video, 5626 Vineland Ave, North Hollywood, CA 91601 *Tel:* 818-762-4545 *Fax:* 818-762-5454 *E-mail:* sales@spectrafilmandvideo.com *Web Site:* www.spectrafilmandvideo.com, pg 897

Lucas, Cliff, RAM® Mounts, 8410 Dallas Ave S, Seattle, WA 98108 *Tel:* 206-763-8361 *Toll Free Tel:* 800-497-7479 *Fax:* 206-763-9615 *E-mail:* sales@rammount.com *Web Site:* www.rammount.com, pg 870

Lucas, Jeffrey P, eMagin Corp, 700 South Dr, Suite 201, Hopewell Junction, NY 12533 *Tel:* 845-838-7900 *Fax:* 845-838-7901 *E-mail:* info@emagin.com; sales@emagin.com; customersupport@emagin.com *Web Site:* www.emagin.com, pg 753

Lucas, Katherine, Buffalo Video Production, 233 Fillmore Ave, Suite 8, Tonawanda, NY 14150 *Tel:* 716-807-1510 *Web Site:* www.buffalovideoproduction.com, pg 712

Lucas, Tony, WTMJ-TV, 720 E Capitol Dr, Milwaukee, WI 53212 *Tel:* 414-332-9611 *Fax:* 414-967-5378 *E-mail:* tmj4feedback@scripps.com *Web Site:* www.tmj4.com, pg 942

Lucci, Margaret, Automobile Film Club of America Inc, 10 Cross St, Staten Island, NY 10304 *Tel:* 718-447-2255 *E-mail:* contact@autofilmclub.com *Web Site:* www.autofilmclub.com, pg 696

Lucci, Ralph, Automobile Film Club of America Inc, 10 Cross St, Staten Island, NY 10304 *Tel:* 718-447-2255 *E-mail:* contact@autofilmclub.com *Web Site:* www.autofilmclub.com, pg 696

Luce, Brian, Sunset Las Palmas Studios, 1040 N Las Palmas Ave, Los Angeles, CA 90038 *Tel:* 323-860-0000 *E-mail:* reception@sunsetlaspalmas.com *Web Site:* www.sunsetlaspalmas.com, pg 904

Luce, Rich, Rosco Laboratories Inc, 52 Harbor View, Stamford, CT 06902 *Tel:* 203-708-8900 *Toll Free Tel:* 800-ROSCO NY (767-2669) *Fax:* 203-708-8919 *E-mail:* info@rosco.com *Web Site:* us.rosco.com, pg 877

Lucero, Cami, Globe-Miami Film Commission, 1360 N Broad St, US 60, Globe, AZ 85501 *Tel:* 928-425-4495 *Toll Free Tel:* 800-804-5623 *Fax:* 928-425-3410 *E-mail:* visitorinfo@globemiamichamber.com *Web Site:* globemiamichamber.com, pg 965

Luckhart, Brad, AV Connections Inc, 245 Executive Park Blvd, Winston-Salem, NC 27103 *Tel:* 336-768-5454 *Fax:* 336-768-5054 *E-mail:* avrentals@avconnectionsusa.com *Web Site:* avconnectionsusa.com, pg 697

Luckhart, Jared, AV Connections Inc, 245 Executive Park Blvd, Winston-Salem, NC 27103 *Tel:* 336-768-5454 *Fax:* 336-768-5054 *E-mail:* avrentals@avconnectionsusa.com *Web Site:* avconnectionsusa.com, pg 697

Luckhart, Marjorie, AV Connections Inc, 245 Executive Park Blvd, Winston-Salem, NC 27103 *Tel:* 336-768-5454 *Fax:* 336-768-5054 *E-mail:* avrentals@avconnectionsusa.com *Web Site:* avconnectionsusa.com, pg 697

Lucy, Ray, MSI Production Services, 10895 Thornmint Rd, Suite A, San Diego, CA 92127 *Tel:* 858-348-0100 *Web Site:* www.msiprod.com, pg 832

Ludlow, Gay, Triad Communications Ltd, 2751 Oxford St, Vancouver, BC V5K 1N5, Canada *Tel:* 604-253-3990 *E-mail:* triadc@comwave.com *Web Site:* www.triadcommunications.ca, pg 918

Ludlow, Rhys, Ludlow Media, 15501 San Pablo Ave, Suite G-320, San Pablo, CA 94806 *Tel:* 415-927-1300 *E-mail:* info@ludlowmedia.com *Web Site:* www.ludlowmedia.com, pg 812

Ludwig, Bill, North County Media Center, 1130 N Melrose Dr, Suite 404, Vista, CA 92083 *Toll Free Tel:* 888-393-0580 *E-mail:* info@northcountymediacenter.com *Web Site:* northcountymediacenter.com, pg 842

Luebering, J E, Encyclopaedia Britannica Inc, 325 N La Salle St, Suite 200, Chicago, IL 60654 *Tel:* 312-347-7000 (all other countries) *Toll Free Tel:* 800-323-1229 (US & CN) *Fax:* 312-294-2104 *Web Site:* www.britannica.com, pg 754

Lueck, Doug, Ridgecrest Regional Film Commission, 643 N China Lake Blvd, Ridgecrest, CA 93555 *Tel:* 760-375-8202 *Toll Free Tel:* 800-847-4830 *Fax:* 760-375-9850 *E-mail:* permits@filmridgecrest.com *Web Site:* www.filmridgecrest.com, pg 967

Luehrsen, Mary, NAMM, the National Association of Music Merchants, 5790 Armada Dr, Carlsbad, CA 92008 *Tel:* 760-438-8001 *Toll Free Tel:* 800-767-6266 (memb hotline) *Fax:* 760-438-7327 *E-mail:* info@namm.org *Web Site:* www.namm.org, pg 958

Luetkehans, Tony, Hellman Associates Inc, 1225 W Fourth St, Waterloo, IA 50702 *Tel:* 319-234-7055 *Toll Free Tel:* 800-747-7055 *Fax:* 319-234-2089 *E-mail:* info@hellman.com *Web Site:* www.hellman.com, pg 778

Luff, Monica, The Bradenton Area Film Commission, One Haben Blvd, Palmetto, FL 34221 *Tel:* 941-729-9177 *Fax:* 941-729-1820 *Web Site:* www.bradentongulfislands.com/film, pg 969

Lujan, Kelly, 30 Second Street Ltd, 1209 Mountain Road Place NE, Suite B, Albuquerque, NM 87110 *Tel:* 505-265-0224 *E-mail:* info@30sst.com *Web Site:* www.thirtysecst.com, pg 912

Lukasik, Diana, TBC Consoles Inc, 170 Rodeo Dr, Edgewood, NY 11717 *Tel:* 631-293-4068 *Toll Free Tel:* 888-CONSOLE (266-7653) *Fax:* 631-293-4075 *E-mail:* info@tbcconsoles.com; sales@tbcconsoles. com; support@tbcconsoles.com *Web Site:* www. tbcconsoles.com, pg 907

Luke, Keth, Sound*Light, 5438 Tennessee Ave, New Port Richey, FL 34652 *Tel:* 727-842-6788 *Fax:* 727-842-6788 *Web Site:* www.awakening-healing.com; www.soundlight.org, pg 894

Lumb, Richard, Accenture, 161 N Clark St, Chicago, IL 60601 *Tel:* 312-693-0161 *Toll Free Tel:* 877-889-9009 *Fax:* 312-693-0507 *Web Site:* www.accenture.com, pg 672

Lumbard, Paula, FootageBank HD, 13470 Washington Blvd, Suite 210, Marina del Rey, CA 90292 *Tel:* 310-822-1400 *Fax:* 310-822-4100 *E-mail:* info@ footagebank.com *Web Site:* www.footagebank.com, pg 763

Lumsden, Rick, Britannica Digital Learning, 325 N La Salle St, Suite 200, Chicago, IL 60654 *Toll Free Tel:* 800-621-3900 *Toll Free Fax:* 800-344-9624 *E-mail:* contact@eb.com; bdlpress@eb.com *Web Site:* britannicalearn.com, pg 710

Luna, John, Pelican Products Inc, 147 N Main St, South Deerfield, MA 01373 *Tel:* 413-665-2163 *Toll Free Tel:* 800-542-7344 *Fax:* 413-665-8330 *Web Site:* www. pelican.com, pg 853

Lund, Martina, Picturestart, 817 Hilldale Ave, West Hollywood, CA 90069 *Tel:* 310-422-3280 *E-mail:* info@picturestart.com *Web Site:* www. picturestart.com, pg 856

Lund, Michael Paul, Serendipity Recordings, 511 Slab City Rd, Lincolnville, ME 04849 *Tel:* 207-763-3677, pg 884

Lundahl, Paul, eMotion Studios, 85 Liberty Ship Way, Suite 110, Sausalito, CA 94965 *Tel:* 415-331-6975 *E-mail:* info@emotionstudios.com *Web Site:* www. emotionstudios.com, pg 753

Lunder, Karen, FilmNation Entertainment, 150 W 22 St, 9th fl, New York, NY 10011 *Web Site:* www. filmnation.com, pg 760

Lunsford, Gary, RTZ Audio Visual, 6725 Santa Barbara Ct, Suite 103, Elkridge, MD 21075 *Tel:* 443-757-0480 *Toll Free Tel:* 800-543-0582 *Fax:* 443-757-0487 *E-mail:* sales@rtzav.com *Web Site:* www.rtzav.com, pg 878

Lupien, Leo, Audio Visual Sales & Service Inc, 2601 Curry Rd, Schenectady, NY 12303 *Tel:* 518-688-0640 *Fax:* 518-688-0634 *E-mail:* info@avssi.com, pg 695

Luplow, Wayne, Zenith Electronics LLC, 2000 Millbrook Dr, Lincolnshire, IL 60069 *Tel:* 847-941-8000 *Toll Free Tel:* 800-243-0000 (cust serv) *Web Site:* www. zenith.com, pg 945

Luscombe, George, G T Luscombe Co Inc, 106 Kansas St, Frankfort, IL 60423 *Tel:* 815-469-2478 *Toll Free Tel:* 800-435-7855 *Fax:* 815-469-5429 *Toll Free Fax:* 888-469-5429 *E-mail:* info@gtluscombe.com *Web Site:* www.gtluscombe.com, pg 812

Luscombe, John, G T Luscombe Co Inc, 106 Kansas St, Frankfort, IL 60423 *Tel:* 815-469-2478 *Toll Free Tel:* 800-435-7855 *Fax:* 815-469-5429 *Toll Free Fax:* 888-469-5429 *E-mail:* info@gtluscombe.com *Web Site:* www.gtluscombe.com, pg 812

Luszcz, Judie, CineTech Media Professionals, PO Box 34, Olivebridge, NY 12461 *Web Site:* cinetechmediapros.org, pg 953

Luteran, Larry, Freeman, 1600 Viceroy, Suite 100, Dallas, TX 75235 *Tel:* 214-445-1000 *Web Site:* www. freeman.com, pg 765

Luttjohann, Jim, Catalina Island Film Commission, One Green Pleasure Pier, Avalon, CA 90704 *Tel:* 310-510-7649; 310-510-7643 *Fax:* 310-510-7607 *Web Site:* www.catalinachamber.com/catalina-filming-information, pg 966

Lutzky, Michael, National Public Radio (NPR), 1111 N Capitol St NE, Washington, DC 20002 *Tel:* 202-513-2000 *Web Site:* www.npr.org, pg 959

Lux, John, Film Florida, 2516 Quail Park Terr, Kissimmee, FL 34743 *Tel:* 407-494-6195 *E-mail:* info@filmflorida.org *Web Site:* www. filmflorida.org, pg 954

Luxenberg, Mike, Precision Camera & Video, 2438 W Anderson Lane, Suite B-4, Austin, TX 78757 *Tel:* 512-467-7676 *Toll Free Tel:* 800-677-1023 *Fax:* 512-467-0607 *Web Site:* www.precision-camera. com, pg 861

Lyanga, Jacqueline, AFI FEST, 2021 N Western Ave, Los Angeles, CA 90027-1657 *Tel:* 323-856-7600 *Toll Free Tel:* 866-AFI-FEST (234-3378) *Fax:* 323-462-4049 *E-mail:* afifest@afi.com; festpublicity@afi.com *Web Site:* www.afi.com/afifest, pg 981

Lynch, Chris, Simon & Schuster, Inc, 1230 Avenue of the Americas, New York, NY 10020 *Tel:* 212-698-7000; 212-698-7126 *Toll Free Tel:* 800-223-2348 (cust serv) *Fax:* 212-698-7664 *Toll Free Fax:* 800-943-9831 *E-mail:* audiopublicity@simonandschuster. com *Web Site:* www.simonandschuster.net; www. simonandschuster.biz; www.simonandschuster.com, pg 888

Lynch, Jim, Autodesk Inc, 111 McInnis Pkwy, San Rafael, CA 94903 *Tel:* 415-507-5000 *Fax:* 415-507-5100 *Web Site:* www.autodesk.com, pg 696

Lynch, John, Forensic Video Deposition Service, 11111 N Scottsdale Rd, Suite 205, Scottsdale, AZ 85254 *Tel:* 602-840-1222 *Fax:* 480-360-1421 *E-mail:* office@ forensicvideo.net *Web Site:* forensicvideo.net, pg 764

Lynch, Marcella O, Cooking by the Book, 13475 N Applegate Rd, Grants Pass, OR 97527 *Tel:* 541-846-0654 *Toll Free Tel:* 800-655-9071 *Fax:* 541-846-0654 *Web Site:* www.atasteofnature.org, pg 731

Lynch, Mike, City of Boston Office of Broadband & Cable, 43 Hawkins St, Suite 1B, Boston, MA 02114 *Tel:* 617-635-3112 *E-mail:* cable@boston.gov *Web Site:* www.cityofboston.gov/cable, pg 953

Lynch, Mike, Washington State University College of Nursing, 103 E Spokane Falls Blvd, Spokane, WA 99202 *Tel:* 509-324-7360 *Toll Free Tel:* 800-281-2589 *Fax:* 509-324-7341 *Web Site:* nursing.wsu.edu, pg 934

Lynch, Nicky, Banff Mountain Film & Book Festival, 107 Tunnel Mountain Dr, Banff, AB T1L 1H5, Canada *Tel:* 403-762-6347; 403-762-6369 *Toll Free Tel:* 800-298-1229 *Fax:* 403-762-6277 *E-mail:* banffmountainfestival@banffcentre.ca; banffmountainfilms@banffcentre.ca *Web Site:* www. banffcentre.ca/banff-mountain-film-and-book-festival, pg 983

Lynch, Paul, Lynch Communications, 525 Loma Vista Terr, Pacifica, CA 94044 *Tel:* 678-939-1212 *Fax:* 480-287-9401 *Web Site:* www.lynchcommunications.com, pg 813

Lynes, Steve, Specialized Products Co, 1100 S Kimball Ave, Southlake, TX 76092 *Tel:* 817-329-6647 *Toll Free Tel:* 800-866-5353 *Toll Free Fax:* 800-234-8286 *E-mail:* customerservice@specialized.net; spcintl@ specialized.net *Web Site:* www.specialized.net, pg 896

Lyngard, Doug, DL Sound & Lighting Productions Ltd, 450 Banga Place, Victoria, BC V8Z 6X5, Canada *Tel:* 250-216-7898 *Web Site:* www.dlsound.net, pg 744

Lynn, Jack, ITC Learning LLC, 330 Himmarshee St, Suite 108, Fort Lauderdale, FL 33312 *Toll Free Tel:* 800-638-3757 *E-mail:* sales@itclearning.com *Web Site:* www.itclearning.com, pg 791

Lynton, Michael, Sony Pictures Entertainment Inc, 10202 W Washington Blvd, Culver City, CA 90232 *Tel:* 310-244-4000 *Web Site:* www.sonypictures.com, pg 893

Lyon, Jim, ICL Imaging Inc, 51 Mellen St, Framingham, MA 01702 *Tel:* 508-872-3280 *Toll Free Tel:* 800-660-3280 *Fax:* 508-872-7364 *E-mail:* csr@icl-imaging.com *Web Site:* www.icl-imaging.com, pg 783

Lyons, Anthony J, IFM World Releasing Inc, 1328 E Palmer Ave, Glendale, CA 91205 *Tel:* 818-243-4976 *Fax:* 818-550-9728 *E-mail:* contact@ifmfilm.com *Web Site:* www.ifmfilm.com, pg 784

Lyons, Jim, Allen Avionics Inc, 255 E Second St, Mineola, NY 11501 *Tel:* 516-248-8080 *Fax:* 516-747-6724 *E-mail:* info@allenavionics.com *Web Site:* www. allenavionics.com, pg 680

Lyons, Jim, Havas Edge, 2386 Faraday Ave, Suite 200, Carlsbad, CA 92008 *Tel:* 760-929-0041 *E-mail:* info@ havasedge.com *Web Site:* www.havasedge.com, pg 777

Lyons, John, Association of Federal Communications Consulting Engineers (AFCCE), PO Box 19333, Washington, DC 20036-0333 *E-mail:* secretary@afcce. org *Web Site:* afcce.org, pg 951

Lyons, Lisa, Small Planet Communications Inc, 15 Union St, Lawrence, MA 01840 *Tel:* 978-794-2201 *E-mail:* planet@smplanet.com *Web Site:* www. smplanet.com, pg 890

Lyriti, Simona, Lylofilm Productions, 503 Beech St, New Hyde Park, NY 11040 *Tel:* 516-587-0567 *E-mail:* lylofilm@gmail.com *Web Site:* www.lylofilm. com; www.graphissimo.com, pg 813

Lytle, Moe, International Marketing Group, 1900 Elm Hill Pike, Nashville, TN 37210 *Tel:* 615-889-8000 *Fax:* 615-871-4817, pg 790

Lytle, Rick, Alpha Source Inc, 6619 W Calumet Rd, Milwaukee, WI 53223-4186 *Tel:* 414-760-2222 *Toll Free Tel:* 800-654-9845 *E-mail:* customer. service@alphasource.com; info@alphasource.com *Web Site:* www.alphasource.com, pg 681

Lyver, Kevin, Ward-Beck Systems Ltd, 945 Middlefield Rd, Unit 9, Toronto, ON M1V 5E1, Canada *Tel:* 416-335-5999 *Toll Free Tel:* 800-771-2556 *Fax:* 416-335-5202 *E-mail:* sales@ward-beck.com *Web Site:* www. ward-beck.com, pg 934

Ma, Max, Hollywood Professional Association (HPA), 2501 W Burbank Blvd, No 207, Burbank, CA 91505 *Tel:* 818-273-1482 *Web Site:* hpaonline.com, pg 955

Maatta, Colleen, Marshall Furniture Inc, 999 Anita Ave, Antioch, IL 60002 *Tel:* 847-395-9350 *Fax:* 847-395-9351 *E-mail:* sales@marshallfurniture.com *Web Site:* www.marshallfurniture.com, pg 817

Macan, John, Keywest Technology Inc, 14563 W 96 Terr, Lenexa, KS 66215 *Tel:* 913-492-4666 *Toll Free Tel:* 800-331-2019 *Fax:* 913-322-1864 *E-mail:* sales@keywesttechnology.com *Web Site:* www.keywesttechnology.com, pg 798

Macaulay, Doug, Kingsway Motion Picture Inc, 200 Evans Ave, Unit 4, Toronto, ON M8Z 1J7, Canada *Tel:* 416-463-4345 *E-mail:* info@kingswaycanada.com *Web Site:* kingswaycanada.com, pg 799

Macaulay, Scott, The Independent Filmmaker Project (IFP), c/o Made in NY Media Ctr by IFP, 30 John St, Ground fl, Brooklyn, NY 11201 *Tel:* 212-465-8200 *Web Site:* www.ifp.org, pg 956

MacDonald, Bill, Spectrum Audio Visual Services, 351 W 45 Ave, Denver, CO 80216 *Tel:* 303-477-4456 *Toll Free Tel:* 800-477-4752 *Fax:* 303-477-0114 *E-mail:* info@spectrumav.com *Web Site:* www. spectrumav.com, pg 897

MacDonald, Jesse, Old School Cameras, 5625 Melrose Ave, Hollywood, CA 90038 *Tel:* 818-847-1555 *E-mail:* sdrentals@oldschoolcameras.com *Web Site:* www.oldschoolcameras.com, pg 844

Macdonald, Ramona, Doomsday Studios Limited, 212 James St, Ottawa, ON K1R 5M7, Canada *Tel:* 613-230-9769 *Fax:* 613-230-6004 *E-mail:* info@ doomsdaystudios.com, pg 745

MacDougall, R Bruce, Kalglo Electronics Co Inc, 5911 Colony Dr, Bethlehem, PA 18017-9348 *Tel:* 610-837-0700 *Fax:* 610-837-7978 *E-mail:* kalglo@kalglo.com *Web Site:* www.kalglo.com, pg 796

MacEachern, Camilla, Northwest Territories Film Commission, PO Box 1320, Yellowknife, NT X1A 2L9, Canada *Tel:* 867-920-8793 *Toll Free Tel:* 844-NWT-FILM (698-3456) *Fax:* 867-873-0101 *E-mail:* nwtfilm@gov.nt.ca *Web Site:* www.nwtfilm. com, pg 978

Macey, Todd, Vital Learning LLC, 3001 Brighton Blvd, Suite 2765, Denver, CO 80216 *Toll Free Tel:* 800-243-5858 *E-mail:* support@vital-learning.com; info@vital-learning.com *Web Site:* www.vital-learning.com, pg 932

MacFadden, Lisa, TPR Enterprises Ltd, 644 Fayette Ave, Mamaroneck, NY 10543 *Tel:* 914-698-1141 *Fax:* 914-698-9419 *E-mail:* info@tprlights.com *Web Site:* www.tprlights.com, pg 916

Machera, Al, Westlake Recording Studios, 7265 Santa Monica Blvd, Los Angeles, CA 90046 *Tel:* 323-851-9800 *E-mail:* bookings@westlakestudios.com; info@westlakestudios.com *Web Site:* www.westlakestudios.com, pg 936

MacIlvaine, Jim, Oakland Film Office, One Frank H Ogawa Plaza, 9th fl, Oakland, CA 94612 *Tel:* 510-238-4734 *E-mail:* filmoakland@filmoakland.com *Web Site:* www.filmoakland.com, pg 967

MacIntosh, Neil, Infosat Communications Inc, 3130 114 Ave SE, Calgary, AB T2Z 3V6, Canada *Tel:* 403-543-8188 *Toll Free Tel:* 888-524-3038 *Fax:* 403-289-8133 *E-mail:* info@infosat.com *Web Site:* infosat.com, pg 787

Maciocia, Gabriel, Canadian American Records, PO Box 808, Lititz, PA 17543-0538 *Tel:* 717-627-4800 *E-mail:* canadianamerican@dejazzd.com *Web Site:* www.canadianamericanrecords.net; www.canadianamericanrecordcompany.com, pg 715

MacIsaac, Tom, Recorded Books Inc, an RBmedia company, 270 Skipjack Rd, Prince Frederick, MD 20678 *Tel:* 410-535-5590 *Toll Free Tel:* 800-638-1304 *Fax:* 410-535-5499 *E-mail:* customerservice@recordedbooks.com *Web Site:* www.recordedbooks.com, pg 871

Mack, Joseph, GatesAir, 5300 Kings Island Dr, Suite 101, Mason, OH 45040 *Tel:* 513-459-3400 *Toll Free Tel:* 800-622-0022 *Fax:* 513-459-3796 *E-mail:* information@gatesair.com; orders@gatesair.com; support@gatesair.com *Web Site:* www.gatesair.com, pg 768

Mack, Odell, PM Productions, 5882 Bowcroft St, Suite 2, Los Angeles, CA 90016 *Tel:* 310-559-3127 *Fax:* 310-559-3168 *Web Site:* pmproductionsvideos.com, pg 858

Mackell, Susan E, Brooklyn Film Festival (BFF), 180 S Fourth St, Suite 2-S, Brooklyn, NY 11211 *Tel:* 718-388-4306 *Fax:* 718-599-5039 *E-mail:* festival@wbff.org *Web Site:* www.brooklynfilmfestival.org, pg 984

Macken, Patrick, ARRIS Group Inc, 3871 Lakefield Dr, Suwanee, GA 30024 *Tel:* 678-473-2907 *Toll Free Tel:* 866-36-ARRIS (362-7747); 877-466-8646 (tech) *Fax:* 678-473-8470 *E-mail:* marketing@arris.com *Web Site:* www.arris.com, pg 689

Mackenzie, Marsha, Encyclopaedia Britannica Inc, 325 N La Salle St, Suite 200, Chicago, IL 60654 *Tel:* 312-347-7000 (all other countries) *Toll Free Tel:* 800-323-1229 (US & CN) *Fax:* 312-294-2104 *Web Site:* www.britannica.com, pg 754

MacKenzie, William F, Ushio America Inc, 5440 Cerritos Ave, Cypress, CA 90630-4567 *Tel:* 714-236-8600 *Toll Free Tel:* 800-838-7446 (cust serv) *Fax:* 714-229-3180 *Toll Free Fax:* 800-776-3641 (cust serv) *E-mail:* customerservice@ushio.com *Web Site:* www.ushio.com, pg 924

Maclellan, Claire, Future US Inc, 11 W 42 St, 15th fl, New York, NY 10036 *Tel:* 212-378-0448 *Toll Free Tel:* 844-779-2822 (subns) *Web Site:* www.futureplc.com, pg 767

MacLellan, Kailla, Frame 30 Productions Ltd, 10816A-82 Ave, No 202, Edmonton, AB T6E 2B3, Canada *Tel:* 780-439-5322 *E-mail:* frame30@frame30.com *Web Site:* www.frame30.com, pg 765

MacMillan, Brian, NTi Audio Inc, 7405 SW Tech Center Dr, Suite 130, Tigard, OR 97223 *Tel:* 503-684-7050 *E-mail:* americas@nti-audio.com *Web Site:* www.nti-audio.com, pg 843

MacNab, John, Canadian Broadcast Standards Council (CBSC), PO Box 3265, Sta D, Ottawa, ON K1P 6H8, Canada *Tel:* 613-233-4607 *Toll Free Tel:* 866-696-4718 (CN only) *Fax:* 613-233-4826 *E-mail:* info@cbsc.ca *Web Site:* www.cbsc.ca, pg 952

MacNevin, Kate, MRM//McCANN, 622 Third Ave, New York, NY 10017 *Tel:* 646-865-6230 *E-mail:* gbc@mrm-mccann.com *Web Site:* www.mrm-mccann.com, pg 832

Macri, Elyssa, Canadian Academy of Recording Arts & Sciences (CARAS), 219 Dufferin St, Suite 211C, Toronto, ON M6K 3J1, Canada *Tel:* 416-485-3135 (CN only) *Toll Free Tel:* 888-501-3135 *Fax:* 416-485-4978 *E-mail:* submissions@junoawards.ca; info@carasonline.ca *Web Site:* carasonline.ca; junoawards.ca, pg 952

Macri, Elyssa, Juno Awards, 219 Dufferin St, Suite 211C, Toronto, ON M6K 3J1, Canada *Tel:* 416-485-3135 (CN only) *Toll Free Tel:* 888-501-3135 *Fax:* 416-485-4978 *E-mail:* info@carasonline.ca; submissions@junoawards.ca *Web Site:* junoawards.ca; www.facebook.com/theJunoAwards, pg 994

Macuch, Doug, RCI Custom Products, 801 N East St, Suite 2-A, Frederick, MD 21701 *Tel:* 301-620-9130 *Toll Free Tel:* 800-546-4724 *Fax:* 301-620-9103 *Toll Free Fax:* 800-546-6175 *E-mail:* info@rcicustom.com *Web Site:* www.rcicustom.com, pg 871

Maddox, Douglas B, DBM Communications Inc, 606 Baltimore Ave, Suite 200, Towson, MD 21204 *Tel:* 410-825-7400 *Fax:* 443-269-0213 *Web Site:* www.dbmcommunications.com, pg 739

Madison, Cheryl, Sensormatic®, 6600 Congress Ave, Boca Raton, FL 33487 *Tel:* 561-912-6000 *E-mail:* tycocommunications@tyco.com *Web Site:* www.tyco.com; www.sensormatic.com, pg 884

Maestri, Luca, Apple Inc, One Infinite Loop, Cupertino, CA 95014 *Tel:* 408-996-1010 *Web Site:* www.apple.com, pg 687

Magdael, David, The Los Angeles Asian Pacific Film Festival, 120 Judge John Aiso St, Basement Level, Los Angeles, CA 90012-3805 *Tel:* 213-680-4462 *E-mail:* festival@vconline.org *Web Site:* asianfilmfestla.org; www.vconline.org/festival, pg 994

Magidson, Phyllis, Museum of the City of New York, 1220 Fifth Ave, New York, NY 10029 *Tel:* 212-534-1672 *Fax:* 212-423-0758 *E-mail:* info@mcny.org *Web Site:* www.mcny.org, pg 834

Magnuson, Julie, Mullikin Agency, 1391 Plaza Place, Suite A, Springdale, AR 72764-5225 *Tel:* 479-750-0871 *Toll Free Tel:* 800-750-0871 *Fax:* 479-750-2685 *Web Site:* www.mullikinad.com, pg 833

Magnuson, Mark, Anode Inc, 926 Main St, Nashville, TN 37206 *Tel:* 615-742-1490 *Fax:* 615-742-1487 *E-mail:* inquiry@anode.com *Web Site:* www.anode.com, pg 686

Magoon, Scott, Lineco, 517 Main St, Holyoke, MA 01040-2604 *Toll Free Tel:* 800-322-7775 *Fax:* 413-532-9281 (sales) *Toll Free Fax:* 800-298-7815 *E-mail:* info@lineco.com *Web Site:* www.lineco.com, pg 809

Magoon, Scott E, University Products Inc, 517 Main St, Holyoke, MA 01040-0073 *Tel:* 413-532-3372 *Toll Free Tel:* 800-628-1912 *Fax:* 413-532-9281 *Toll Free Fax:* 800-532-9281 *E-mail:* custserv@universityproducts.com; info@universityproducts.com *Web Site:* www.universityproducts.com, pg 923

Magoun, David, Full Spectrum Arts & Services, PO Box 1032, Littleton, CO 80160 *Tel:* 303-798-7906 (voicemail only); 720-326-2043 (cell) *Web Site:* www.fullspectrumarts.com, pg 767

Magrill, Kyle, CircuitWerkes Inc, 2805 NW Sixth St, Gainesville, FL 32609 *Tel:* 352-335-6555 *Fax:* 352-380-0230 *E-mail:* sales@circuitwerkes.com *Web Site:* www.broadcastboxes.com; www.circuitwerkes.com, pg 725

Magruder, Robin, Crossroads Audio Inc, 2623 Myrtle Springs Ave, Dallas, TX 75220 *Tel:* 214-358-2623 *Toll Free Tel:* 800-287-0436 *Fax:* 214-358-0185 *E-mail:* mail@crossroadsaudio.com *Web Site:* www.crossroadsaudio.com, pg 735

Maguire, Dennis, Paramount Pictures Corporation, 5555 Melrose Ave, Los Angeles, CA 90038 *Tel:* 323-956-8398 *Web Site:* www.paramount.com, pg 851

Mahabadi, Rolo, Badiyan Inc, 720 W 94 St, Bloomington, MN 55420 *Tel:* 952-888-5507 *Fax:* 952-888-0360 *E-mail:* info@badiyan.com *Web Site:* www.badiyan.com, pg 700

Maher, Sean, Chelsea Green Publishing Co, 85 N Main St, Suite 120, White River Junction, VT 05001 *Tel:* 802-295-6300 *Toll Free Tel:* 800-639-4099 (orders) *Fax:* 802-295-6444 *E-mail:* customerservice@chelseagreen.com *Web Site:* www.chelseagreen.com, pg 721

Maher, Teresa, Electronics Technicians Association International Inc, 5 Depot St, Greencastle, IN 46135 *Tel:* 765-653-8262 *Toll Free Tel:* 800-288-3824 *Fax:* 765-653-4287 *E-mail:* eta@eta-i.org *Web Site:* www.eta-i.org, pg 954

Maheras, William, Sight & Sound Studios, 66 Queen St, Suite 1705, Honolulu, HI 96813 *Tel:* 808-599-7600 *Fax:* 808-599-7601 *Web Site:* www.sightandsoundhawaii.com, pg 887

Mahlmann, Andrew, Producers Guild of America Inc (PGA), 8530 Wilshire Blvd, Suite 400, Beverly Hills, CA 90211 *Tel:* 310-358-9020 *E-mail:* info@producersguild.org *Web Site:* www.producersguild.org, pg 960

Mahoney, Mike, Art Gallery of Ontario, 317 Dundas St W, Toronto, ON M5T 1G4, Canada *Tel:* 416-979-6648 *Toll Free Tel:* 877-225-4246 *Web Site:* ago.ca, pg 690

Mahoney, Pat, Sunset Las Palmas Studios, 1040 N Las Palmas Ave, Los Angeles, CA 90038 *Tel:* 323-860-0000 *E-mail:* reception@sunsetlaspalmas.com *Web Site:* www.sunsetlaspalmas.com, pg 904

Maier, Charlie, Sand Box Studio, 555 Minnesota St, San Francisco, CA 94107 *Tel:* 415-550-8732 *E-mail:* inquiries@sandboxstudio.com *Web Site:* www.sandboxstudio.com, pg 880

Mainardi, Don, IDX System Technology Inc, 19001 Harborgate Way, Suite 105, Torrance, CA 90501 *Tel:* 310-328-2850 *Fax:* 310-328-8202 *E-mail:* idx.usa@idx.tv *Web Site:* www.idx.tv, pg 784

Mainardis, Ken, Getty Images, 605 Fifth Ave S, Suite 400, Seattle, WA 98104 *Tel:* 206-925-5000 *Toll Free Tel:* 888-888-5889; 800-462-4379 (sales) *E-mail:* sales.na@gettyimages.com *Web Site:* www.gettyimages.com, pg 770

Maines, Lauri, Videssence, 10768 Lower Azusa Rd, El Monte, CA 91731 *Tel:* 626-579-0943 *Fax:* 626-579-6803 *E-mail:* contact@videssence.tv *Web Site:* www.videssence.tv, pg 930

Maisel, Anthony, KAKE-TV, 1500 N West St, Wichita, KS 67203-1323 *Tel:* 316-943-4221; 316-946-1363 (sales) *Fax:* 316-943-5493 (sales) *E-mail:* sales@kake.com; news@kake.com *Web Site:* kake.com, pg 796

Maisner, Andrew, TV Pro Gear, 1630 Flower St, Glendale, CA 91201 *Tel:* 818-246-7100 *Fax:* 818-246-1945 *Web Site:* www.tvprogear.com, pg 919

Maisonneuve, Mark, SDMediaPros (SDMP), 5205 Kearny Villa Way, No 100, San Diego, CA 92123 *Tel:* 619-672-1000 *E-mail:* membership@sdmediapros.org; marketing@sdmediapros.org; programs@sdmediapros.org *Web Site:* sdmediapros.org, pg 961

Majzoub, Muhi, OpenText Corp, 275 Frank Tompa Dr, Waterloo, ON N2L 0A1, Canada *Tel:* 519-888-7111 *Toll Free Tel:* 800-499-6544 *Fax:* 519-888-0677 *Web Site:* www.opentext.com, pg 847

Makarczyk, Yalena, CMI Media Management, 9 W Broad St, Stamford, CT 06902 *Tel:* 203-989-9955 *Toll Free Tel:* 800-431-1102 *Fax:* 203-316-8353 *Web Site:* www.cminyla.com, pg 727

Makhlout, David, IFM World Releasing Inc, 1328 E Palmer Ave, Glendale, CA 91205 *Tel:* 818-243-4976 *Fax:* 818-550-9728 *E-mail:* contact@ifmfilm.com *Web Site:* www.ifmfilm.com, pg 784

Makin, Michael F, Printing Industries of America, 301 Brush Creek Rd, Warrendale, PA 15086-7529 *Tel:* 412-741-6860 *Toll Free Tel:* 800-910-4283 *Fax:* 412-741-2311 *E-mail:* printing@printing.org *Web Site:* www.printing.org, pg 960

Malaret, Rebecca, The Virginia Film Festival, 617 W Main St, 2nd fl, Charlottesville, VA 22903 *Tel:* 434-982-5277 *Fax:* 434-924-3374 *E-mail:* info@virginiafilmfestival.org; vffsubmissions@virginia.edu *Web Site:* virginiafilmfestival.org, pg 1006

Malay, Hugh, Custom Video Productions Inc, 707 Torrance Blvd, Suite 105, Redondo Beach, CA 90277 *Tel:* 310-543-4901 *E-mail:* info@customvideo.tv *Web Site:* www.customvideo.tv, pg 736

Malcolm, Brian, Rule Boston Camera, 1284 Soldier's Field Rd, Boston, MA 02135 *Tel:* 617-277-2200 *Toll Free Tel:* 800-785-3266 *Fax:* 617-277-6800 *E-mail:* answers@rule.com *Web Site:* www.rule.com, pg 878

Malcolm, Doug, CORTRON Media LLC, 320 Fort Duquesne Blvd, Suite 100, Pittsburgh, PA 15222-1146 *Tel:* 412-565-3471 (ext 3) *Web Site:* cortronmedia. com, pg 732

Malekpour, Dave, Professional Audio Design Inc, 90 Corporate Park Dr, Suite 1420, Pembroke, MA 02359 *Tel:* 781-982-2600 *Toll Free Tel:* 877-223-8858 *Fax:* 781-982-2610 *E-mail:* info@proaudiodesign.com *Web Site:* www.proaudiodesign.com, pg 865

Malhotra, Monica, Clever Devices Ltd, 300 Crossways Park Dr, Woodbury, NY 11797 *Tel:* 516-433-6100 *Toll Free Tel:* 800-872-6129 *Web Site:* www.cleverdevices. com, pg 726

Malina, Craig, The Video Project, 145 Ninth St, Suite 102, San Francisco, CA 94103 *Tel:* 415-981-9710 *Toll Free Tel:* 800-475-2638 *Fax:* 415-692-6223 *E-mail:* orders@videoproject.com; support@videoproject.com *Web Site:* www.videoproject.com, pg 928

Malinosky, John, Precision Camera & Video Repair Inc, 7 Anngina Dr, Enfield, CT 06082 *Tel:* 860-749-7380; 860-272-2100 *Toll Free Tel:* 800-665-6515 (cust serv) *E-mail:* info@precisioncamera.com *Web Site:* www. precisioncamera.com, pg 861

Mallek, William, Questar Entertainment Inc, 307 N Michigan Ave, 5th fl, Chicago, IL 60601-5305 *Tel:* 312-266-9400 *Toll Free Tel:* 800-544-8422 (cust serv) *E-mail:* info@questarentertainment.com *Web Site:* www.questarentertainment.com, pg 868

Malloy, Gary, Kineticvideo.com, 4839 Noble Lane, Battersea, ON K0H 1H0, Canada *Tel:* 416-538-6613 *Toll Free Tel:* 800-263-6910 (CN only) *Fax:* 416-538-9984 *E-mail:* info@kineticvideo.com *Web Site:* www. kineticvideo.com, pg 799

Malone, Greg, Road Pictures, 212 W Tenth St, Suite B-100, Indianapolis, IN 46202 *Tel:* 317-267-9590 *Fax:* 317-267-9677 *Web Site:* www.roadpictures.com, pg 876

Malone, Matthew, Research Technology International (RTI), 4700 Chase Ave, Lincolnwood, IL 60712-1689 *Tel:* 847-677-3000 *Toll Free Tel:* 800-323-7520 *Fax:* 847-677-1311 *Toll Free Fax:* 800-784-6733 *E-mail:* sales@rtico.com *Web Site:* rtico.com, pg 873

Maloney, Mike, Eureka Springs Advertising & Promotions Commission, PO Box 522, Eureka Springs, AR 72632-0522 *Tel:* 479-253-7333 *Fax:* 479-363-9380 *E-mail:* admin@eurekasprings.org *Web Site:* www.eurekasprings.org, pg 965

Malouche, Paige, Prescolite, 701 Millennium Blvd, Greenville, SC 29607 *Tel:* 864-678-1000 *Fax:* 864-678-1740 *Web Site:* www.hubbell.com/prescolite, pg 861

Maltz, Elliott, MG Electronics, 32 Ranick Rd, Hauppauge, NY 11788 *Tel:* 631-582-3400 *Fax:* 631-582-3229 *E-mail:* info@mgelectronics.com *Web Site:* www.mgelectronics.com, pg 825

Manahan, Ted, Video Visions Inc, 3600 Boundbrook Ave, Trevose, PA 19053 *Tel:* 215-942-6642 *Fax:* 267-684-6819 *E-mail:* sales@video-visions.com *Web Site:* www.video-visions.com, pg 929

Manalo, Nero, Arizona Studios, 4614 E McDowell Rd, Phoenix, AZ 85008 *Tel:* 602-275-9100 *E-mail:* info@arizonastudios.com *Web Site:* arizonastudios.com, pg 689

Manchester, John, Manchester Music Library Inc, 6857 Colton Blvd, Oakland, CA 94611 *Tel:* 413-369-4331 *Web Site:* www.manchestermusiclibrary.com, pg 816

Mancuso, Janice, Reference Recordings, PO Box 77225, San Francisco, CA 94107 *Tel:* 650-355-1845 *Toll Free Tel:* 800-336-8866 *Fax:* 650-355-1949 *E-mail:* referencerecordings@gmail.com *Web Site:* www.referencerecordings.com, pg 872

Mandeville, Craig, Simon & Schuster, Inc, 1230 Avenue of the Americas, New York, NY 10020 *Tel:* 212-698-7000; 212-698-7126 *Toll Free Tel:* 800-223-2348 (cust serv) *Fax:* 212-698-7664 *Toll Free Fax:* 800-943-9831 *E-mail:* audiopublicity@simonandschuster. com *Web Site:* www.simonandschuster.net; www. simonandschuster.biz; www.simonandschuster.com, pg 888

Mandinach, Zach, The Independent Filmmaker Project (IFP), c/o Made in NY Media Ctr by IFP, 30 John St, Ground fl, Brooklyn, NY 11201 *Tel:* 212-465-8200 *Web Site:* www.ifp.org, pg 956

Manger, Jim, Powerstation Events, 1718 Highland Ave, Cheshire, CT 06410 *Tel:* 203-250-8500 *Toll Free Tel:* 800-423-7835 *Fax:* 203-250-8575 *E-mail:* info@powerstationevents.com *Web Site:* www. powerstationevents.com, pg 860

Mangini, Tim, WGBH Production Group, One Guest St, Boston, MA 02135 *Tel:* 617-300-2000 *E-mail:* productiongroup@wgbh.org; studios@wgbh. org; outpost@wgbh.org *Web Site:* productiongroup. wgbh.org, pg 936

Mangoba, Mark, Visual Communications - Southern California Asian American Studies Central Inc, 120 Judge John Aiso St, Basement Level, Los Angeles, CA 90012 *Tel:* 213-680-4462 *Fax:* 213-687-4848 *E-mail:* info@vconline.org *Web Site:* www.vconline. org, pg 931

Manherz, Jessica, Shot Glass Films, 2210 W Olive Ave, Suite 300, Burbank, CA 91506 *Tel:* 323-464-5111 *E-mail:* information@shotglassfilms.com *Web Site:* www.shotglassfilms.com, pg 886

Maniaci, Greg, Tamron USA Inc, 10 Austin Blvd, Commack, NY 11725 *Tel:* 631-858-8400 *Toll Free Tel:* 800-827-8880 *Fax:* 631-543-5666; 631-858-8462 (cust serv) *E-mail:* custserv@tamron.com *Web Site:* www.tamron-usa.com, pg 906

Manies, Keith, Explore Lawrence, PO Box 526, Lawrence, KS 66044 *Tel:* 785-856-3040; 785-856-5282 (mktg) *Fax:* 785-856-5303 *E-mail:* visinfo@explorelawrence.com *Web Site:* www.explorelawrence. com, pg 971

Maniglia, Frank Jr, Maniglia Media LLC, 7925 Jones Branch Dr, Suite LL-110, Tysons, VA 22102 *Tel:* 703-283-8532 (cell); 703-942-8011 (studio) *Web Site:* www.manigliamedia.com, pg 816

Manios, Steven Jr, Manios Digital & Film, 10663 Burbank Blvd, North Hollywood, CA 91601 *Tel:* 818-760-8290 *Toll Free Tel:* 800-845-6619 *Fax:* 818-760-8805 *E-mail:* sales@maniosdigital.com *Web Site:* www.maniosdigital.com, pg 816

Manley, EveAnna, Manley Laboratories Inc, 13880 Magnolia Ave, Chino, CA 91710 *Tel:* 909-627-4256 *Fax:* 909-628-2482 *Web Site:* www.manley.com, pg 816

Manley, Larry, NAMM, the National Association of Music Merchants, 5790 Armada Dr, Carlsbad, CA 92008 *Tel:* 760-438-8001 *Toll Free Tel:* 800-767-6266 (memb hotline) *Fax:* 760-438-7327 *E-mail:* info@namm.org *Web Site:* www.namm.org, pg 958

Mann, Doug, Flip 2 Media Inc, 1067 Serpentine Lane, Pleasanton, CA 94566-4759 *Tel:* 925-417-1420 *E-mail:* info@flip2media.com *Web Site:* www. flip2media.com, pg 762

Mann, Jenn, SAS Institute Inc, 100 SAS Campus Dr, Cary, NC 27513-2414 *Tel:* 919-677-8000 *Toll Free Tel:* 800-727-0025 *Fax:* 919-677-4444 *Web Site:* www. sas.com, pg 880

Mann, Nicholas, DACAPO Productions Inc, 516 Hargrave St, Winnipeg, MB R3A 0X8, Canada *Tel:* 204-956-2867 *Fax:* 204-956-2869 *Web Site:* www. dacapo.ca, pg 737

Manna, Christine, Association of National Advertisers Inc (ANA), 10 Grand Central, 155 E 44 St, New York, NY 10017 *Tel:* 212-697-5950 *Fax:* 212-687-7310 *E-mail:* info@ana.net *Web Site:* www.ana.net, pg 951

Mannenbach, Jim, Power Sonic Corp, 365 Cabela Dr, Suite 300, Reno, NV 89523 *Tel:* 619-661-2020 *Fax:* 619-661-3650 *Web Site:* www.power-sonic.com, pg 860

Manners, Robert, Production Resource Group LLC (PRG), 200 Business Park Dr, Suite 109, Armonk, NY 10504 *Tel:* 212-589-5400 *Toll Free Tel:* 877-774-7088 *Fax:* 212-589-5401 *E-mail:* info@prg.com *Web Site:* www.prg.com, pg 864

Manning, Char, Manning Productions, 115 N Morgan St, Chicago, IL 60607 *Tel:* 312-756-1100 *Fax:* 312-756-1200 *E-mail:* info@manningproductions.com *Web Site:* www.manningproductions.com, pg 816

Manning, Douglas, Manning Productions, 115 N Morgan St, Chicago, IL 60607 *Tel:* 312-756-1100 *Fax:* 312-756-1200 *E-mail:* info@manningproductions.com *Web Site:* www.manningproductions.com, pg 816

Mannschreck, Mark, TVA Media Group, 3950 Vantage Ave, Studio City, CA 91604 *Tel:* 818-505-8300 *Toll Free Tel:* 888-322-4296 *E-mail:* info@tvamediagroup. com *Web Site:* www.tvamediagroup.com, pg 919

Manocchio, Jennifer, monterey media inc, 125 Auburn Ct, Suite 220, Westlake Village, CA 91360 *Tel:* 805-494-7199 *Fax:* 805-496-6061 *E-mail:* customerservice@montereymedia.com; publicity@montereymedia.com *Web Site:* www. montereymedia.com, pg 829

Manocchio, Jennifer, monterey video, 125 Auburn Ct, Suite 220, Westlake Village, CA 91362 *Tel:* 805-494-7199 *Fax:* 805-496-6061 *E-mail:* customerservice@montereymedia.com; publicity@montereymedia.com *Web Site:* www.montereymedia.com, pg 829

Mans, Dawn, Cinequipt Inc, 2601 49 Ave N, Suite 500, Minneapolis, MN 55430 *Tel:* 612-627-9080 *Toll Free Tel:* 800-809-9080 *Fax:* 612-627-9789 *Web Site:* www. cinequipt.com, pg 724

Mansfield, Heather, Castleview Productions, 1100 W 41 St, Austin, TX 78756 *Tel:* 512-442-9944 *Fax:* 512-442-8823 *E-mail:* contact@castleviewproductions.com *Web Site:* castleviewproductions.com, pg 717

Mansfield, Katherine, IEEE Computer Society Press, 10662 Los Vaqueros Circle, Los Alamitos, CA 90720-1314 *Tel:* 714-821-8380 *Toll Free Tel:* 800-272-6657 (cust serv) *Fax:* 714-821-4010 *E-mail:* help@computer.org *Web Site:* www.computer.org, pg 784

Mansfield, Scott, monterey media inc, 125 Auburn Ct, Suite 220, Westlake Village, CA 91360 *Tel:* 805-494-7199 *Fax:* 805-496-6061 *E-mail:* customerservice@montereymedia.com; publicity@montereymedia.com *Web Site:* www.montereymedia.com, pg 829

Mansfield, Scott, monterey video, 125 Auburn Ct, Suite 220, Westlake Village, CA 91362 *Tel:* 805-494-7199 *Fax:* 805-496-6061 *E-mail:* customerservice@montereymedia.com; publicity@montereymedia.com *Web Site:* www.montereymedia.com, pg 829

Mansouri, Michael, Radiant Images, 2702 Media Center Dr, Los Angeles, CA 90065 *Tel:* 323-737-1314 *Fax:* 310-861-0163 *E-mail:* info@radiantimages.com *Web Site:* www.radiantimages.com, pg 869

Mara, Emil, America's Public Television Stations (APTS), 2100 Crystal Dr, Suite 700, Arlington, VA 22202 *Tel:* 202-654-4200 *Fax:* 202-654-4236 *Web Site:* apts.org, pg 949

Marado, Linda, Alegra House Publishers, PO Box 1443, Warren, OH 44482-1443 *Tel:* 330-372-2951 *Fax:* 330-399-1619, pg 679

Martell, Jorge, Extreme Reach Inc, 75 Second Ave, Suite 720, Needham, MA 02494 *Tel:* 781-577-2016 *Toll Free Tel:* 877-769-9382 *E-mail:* sales@extremereach.com; support@extremereach.com *Web Site:* extremereach.com, pg 758

Martelli, Mark, Bullfrog Films Inc, 372 Dautrich Rd, Reading, PA 19606 *Tel:* 610-779-8226 *Toll Free Tel:* 800-543-3764 *Fax:* 610-370-1978 *E-mail:* info@bullfrogfilms.com; video@bullfrogfilms.com *Web Site:* www.bullfrogfilms.com, pg 712

Martin, Andrew, Miami Stagecraft Inc, 2855 E 11 Ave, Hialeah, FL 33013 *Tel:* 305-836-9356 *Fax:* 305-696-3322 *E-mail:* info@miamistagecraft.com *Web Site:* www.miamistagecraft.com, pg 825

Martin, Carol, FootageBank HD, 13470 Washington Blvd, Suite 210, Marina del Rey, CA 90292 *Tel:* 310-822-1400 *Fax:* 310-822-4100 *E-mail:* info@footagebank.com *Web Site:* www.footagebank.com, pg 763

Martin, Christian Frederick IV, The Martin Guitar Co, 510 Sycamore St, Nazareth, PA 18064 *Tel:* 610-759-2837 *Toll Free Tel:* 800-633-2060; 888-433-9177 *Fax:* 610-759-5757 *Web Site:* www.martinguitar.com, pg 818

Martin, Debra, Love Your Shorts Film Festival, 608 S Elm Ave, Sanford, FL 32771 *E-mail:* contact@loveyourshorts.com *Web Site:* www.loveyourshorts.com, pg 995

Martin, Jeff, Pyro Spectaculars Inc, 3196 N Locust Ave, Rialto, CA 92377 *Tel:* 909-355-8120 *Toll Free Tel:* 888-477-PYRO (477-7976) *E-mail:* information@pyrospec.com *Web Site:* www.pyrospec.com, pg 867

Martin, John, HB Communications Inc, 60 Dodge Ave, North Haven, CT 06473 *Tel:* 203-234-9246 *Toll Free Tel:* 800-243-4414 *Fax:* 203-234-2013 *E-mail:* info@hbcommunications.com *Web Site:* hbcommunications.com, pg 777

Martin, John, Turner Broadcasting System Inc, A Time Warner Company, One CNN Ctr, Atlanta, GA 30303 *Tel:* 404-827-1700 *E-mail:* turner.info@turner.com *Web Site:* www.turner.com, pg 919

Martin, Kristen, DACAPO Productions Inc, 516 Hargrave St, Winnipeg, MB R3A 0X8, Canada *Tel:* 204-956-2867 *Fax:* 204-956-2869 *Web Site:* www.dacapo.ca, pg 737

Martin, Lee, Getty Images, 605 Fifth Ave S, Suite 400, Seattle, WA 98104 *Tel:* 206-925-5000 *Toll Free Tel:* 888-888-5889; 800-462-4379 (sales) *E-mail:* sales.na@gettyimages.com *Web Site:* www.gettyimages.com, pg 770

Martin, Lorraine, National Safety Council (NSC), 1121 Spring Lake Dr, Itasca, IL 60143-3201 *Tel:* 630-285-1121 *Toll Free Tel:* 800-621-7615; 800-621-7619 (cust serv) *Fax:* 630-285-1434 (cust serv); 630-285-1315 *E-mail:* customerservice@nsc.org *Web Site:* www.nsc.org, pg 836

Martin, Lynn, American Music & Sound (AM&S), 925 Broadbeck Dr, No 220, Newbury Park, CA 91320 *Toll Free Tel:* 800-431-2609 *Toll Free Fax:* 866-707-0717 *E-mail:* info@americanmusicandsound.com *Web Site:* www.americanmusicandsound.com, pg 684

Martin, Mallory, Cleveland International Film Festival, 2510 Market Ave, Cleveland, OH 44113-3434 *Tel:* 216-623-3456 *Fax:* 216-623-0103 *E-mail:* cfs@clevelandfilm.org; submissions@clevelandfilm.org *Web Site:* www.clevelandfilm.org, pg 986

Martin, Marcia, Reference Recordings, PO Box 77225, San Francisco, CA 94107 *Tel:* 650-355-1845 *Toll Free Tel:* 800-336-8866 *Fax:* 650-355-1949 *E-mail:* referencerecordings@gmail.com *Web Site:* www.referencerecordings.com, pg 872

Martin, Molly, Nantucket Film Festival (NFF), 68 Jay St, Suite 319, Brooklyn, NY 11201 *Tel:* 646-480-1900 *Fax:* 646-365-3367 *E-mail:* info@nantucketfilmfestival.org; submissions@nantucketfilmfestival.org *Web Site:* nantucketfilmfestival.org, pg 997

Martin, Phil, Sodanceabit, 11372 Kelly Lane, Los Alamitos, CA 90720 *Tel:* 562-799-4340 *Toll Free Tel:* 800-64-DANCE (643-2623) *E-mail:* sodanceabit@live.com *Web Site:* www.sodanceabit.com, pg 892

Martin, R, ASC Systems, Mack Place, 566, St Clair Shores, MI 48080-0566 *Tel:* 313-882-1133 *E-mail:* ascsystems@live.com, pg 690

Martin, Rick, Audio-Video Resources Inc, 1043 Adams Ave, Montgomery, AL 36104 *Tel:* 334-262-4806 *Fax:* 334-240-0000 *E-mail:* avrinc@bellsouth.net, pg 694

Martin, Sage, Mountainfilm in Telluride, 109 E Colorado Ave, Suite 1, Telluride, CO 81435 *Tel:* 970-728-4123 *E-mail:* entries@mountainfilm.org *Web Site:* www.mountainfilm.org, pg 996

Martin, Sandra, ATI Audio, 7209 Browning Rd, Pennsauken, NJ 08091 *Tel:* 856-719-9900 *E-mail:* sales@daysequerra.com *Web Site:* www.atiaudio.com, pg 692

Martin, Steve, Monotype Imaging Inc, 600 Unicorn Park Dr, Woburn, MA 01801 *Tel:* 781-970-6000 *Toll Free Tel:* 800-424-8973 *Fax:* 781-970-6001; 781-970-6002 (gen questions) *E-mail:* info@monotype.com *Web Site:* www.monotype.com, pg 829

Martin, Rev Steven D, National Council of Churches, 110 Maryland Ave NE, Suite 108, Washington, DC 20002 *Tel:* 202-544-2350 *E-mail:* info@nationalcouncilofchurches.us *Web Site:* nationalcouncilofchurches.us, pg 836

Martin, Terry, SOM Publishing Co, 163 Moon Valley Rd, Windyville, MO 65783 *Tel:* 417-345-8411 *E-mail:* som@som.org *Web Site:* www.som.org, pg 892

Martin, Thomas M, Metropolitan Opera Guild Inc, Samuel B & David Rose Bldg, 70 Lincoln Center Plaza, 6th fl, New York, NY 10023-6593 *Tel:* 212-769-7000 *E-mail:* info@metguild.org *Web Site:* www.metguild.org, pg 824

Martin, Tim, Cramer, 425 University Ave, Norwood, MA 02062 *Tel:* 781-278-2300 *E-mail:* theteam@cramer.com *Web Site:* cramer.com, pg 733

Martinez, Christine, Tasman Group Pacific Rim, 15304 Spring Ave, Sante Fe Springs, CA 90670 *Tel:* 562-566-1330 *Toll Free Tel:* 888-355-8889 *Fax:* 562-404-0716 *Web Site:* www.tasmangrouppr.com, pg 907

Martinez, Joe, OWI Inc, 17141 Kingsview Ave, Carson, CA 90746 *Tel:* 310-515-1900 *Toll Free Tel:* 800-638-1694 *Fax:* 310-515-1606 *E-mail:* info@owi-inc.com *Web Site:* www.owi-inc.com, pg 849

Martinez, Laureen, Orlando Film Commission, 301 E Pine St, Suite 900, Orlando, FL 32801 *Tel:* 407-422-7159 *Fax:* 407-425-6428 *E-mail:* info@filmorlando.com *Web Site:* www.filmorlando.com, pg 969

Martinez-Amago, Luis, Technicolor USA Inc, 6040 Sunset Blvd, Hollywood, CA 90028 *Tel:* 323-817-6600 *E-mail:* info@technicolor.com *Web Site:* www.technicolor.com, pg 908

Martini, Paul, BMI Supply, 571 Queensbury Ave, Queensbury, NY 12804 *Tel:* 518-793-6706 *Toll Free Tel:* 800-836-0524 *Fax:* 518-793-6181 *E-mail:* bminy@bmisupply.com *Web Site:* www.bmisupply.com, pg 692

Martino, Alfred C, Listen & Live Audio Inc, 1700 Manhattan Ave, Union City, NJ 07068 *Tel:* 201-558-9000 *Toll Free Tel:* 800-653-9400 (orders) *Fax:* 201-558-9800 *Web Site:* www.listenandlive.com, pg 809

Martinolich, Tyler, Tampa Hillsborough Film & Digital Media Commission, One Tampa City Ctr, 201 N Franklin St, Suite 2900, Tampa, FL 33602 *Web Site:* filmtampabay.com, pg 970

Martinson, Joe, Martinsound Inc, 1151 W Valley Blvd, Alhambra, CA 91803 *Tel:* 626-281-3555 *Toll Free Tel:* 800-582-3555 *Fax:* 626-284-3092 *E-mail:* info@martinsound.com *Web Site:* www.martinsound.com, pg 818

Martorelli, Nick, Penguin Random House Audio Publishing, 1745 Broadway, New York, NY 10019 *E-mail:* audio@penguinrandomhouse.com *Web Site:* www.penguinrandomhouseaudio.com, pg 853

Martyn, John Jay, Audacity Recording Studios, 2734 Polk St, Suite B, Hollywood, FL 33020 *Tel:* 954-920-4418 *Web Site:* www.audacityrecordingstudios.com, pg 693

Martzall, Abbi, Sigma Delta Chi Awards in Journalism, Eugene S Pulliam National Journalism Ctr, 3909 N Meridian St, Indianapolis, IN 46208 *Tel:* 317-927-8000 *Fax:* 317-920-4789 *E-mail:* awards@spj.org *Web Site:* www.spj.org, pg 1003

Maruca, Dante, Tri-State Loudspeaker, 650 Franklin Ave, Aliquippa, PA 15001, pg 918

Maruca, John, Image Associates Inc, 5475 Rumley Rd, Suite 102, Durham, NC 27703 *Tel:* 919-876-6400 *Fax:* 919-876-6400 *E-mail:* info@imageassociates.com *Web Site:* www.imageassociates.com, pg 784

Marucci, Nick, DuArt Media Services, 245 W 55 St, New York, NY 10019 *Tel:* 212-757-4580 *Fax:* 212-977-5609 *E-mail:* info@duart.com *Web Site:* www.duart.com, pg 747

Marugg, Brandon, ALOM Technologies Corp, 48105 Warm Springs Blvd, Fremont, CA 94539-7498 *Tel:* 510-360-3600 *Toll Free Tel:* 800-500-9991 *Fax:* 510-226-7617 *E-mail:* customerservice@alom.com *Web Site:* www.alom.com, pg 681

Marx, David, Marx InDigital, 7921 Skylake Dr, Fort Worth, TX 76179 *Tel:* 414-351-5060 *Web Site:* www.marxindigital.com, pg 819

Marx, Lux, Total Video Products Inc, 414 Southgate Ct, Mickleton, NJ 08056 *Tel:* 856-423-7400 *Toll Free Tel:* 800-447-0920 *Fax:* 856-423-4747 *E-mail:* info@totalvideoproducts.com *Web Site:* www.totalvideoproducts.com, pg 916

Marx, Troy, Omega Broadcast Group, 817 W Howard Lane, Austin, TX 78753 *Tel:* 512-251-7778 *Fax:* 512-251-8633 *E-mail:* rental@omegabroadcast.com; sales@omegabroadcast.com *Web Site:* www.omegabroadcast.com, pg 845

Marzano, Vincent, John Wiley & Sons Inc, 111 River St, Hoboken, NJ 07030-5774 *Tel:* 201-748-6000 *Toll Free Tel:* 800-225-5945 (cust serv) *Fax:* 201-748-6088 *Web Site:* www.wiley.com, pg 938

Marzec, Randy, VTP Inc, 1309 S Flower St, Burbank, CA 91502 *Tel:* 818-566-9898 *Toll Free Tel:* 800-422-2444 *E-mail:* sales@vtpcorp.com *Web Site:* www.myvtp.com, pg 933

Masciangelo, Joe, Starlite, 9 Whittendale Dr, Moorestown, NJ 08057 *Tel:* 856-780-8000 *Toll Free Tel:* 800-738-7400 *Fax:* 856-780-8001 *E-mail:* info@starlite.com *Web Site:* www.starlite.com, pg 900

Masiello, James F, ATTO Technology Inc, 155 CrossPoint Pkwy, Amherst, NY 14068 *Tel:* 716-691-1999 *Fax:* 716-691-9353 *Web Site:* www.atto.com, pg 692

Mason, Jo, DXC Technology Co, 1775 Tysons Blvd, Tysons, VA 22102 *Tel:* 317-331-1197 *Web Site:* www.dxc.technology, pg 748

Mason, Mele, Mason Video, 9632 N 34 St, Omaha, NE 68112 *Tel:* 402-455-9422 *E-mail:* mason.video@mac.com *Web Site:* www.masonvideo.com, pg 819

Mason, Michael, CP Communications, 15 Ninnie Dr, Wappingers Falls, NY 12590 *Tel:* 914-345-9292 *Toll Free Tel:* 800-762-4254 *Fax:* 914-345-9222 *E-mail:* info@cpcomms.com; sales@cpcomms.com *Web Site:* www.cpcomms.com, pg 732

Mason, Sara, Leightronix Inc, 1125 N Cedar Rd, Mason, MI 48854 *Tel:* 517-694-8000 *Toll Free Tel:* 800-243-5589 *Fax:* 517-694-1600 *E-mail:* support@leightronix.com; sales@leightronix.com; info@leightronix.com *Web Site:* www.leightronix.com, pg 806

Mason, Todd, Broadcast Management Group, 718 Seventh St NW, Washington, DC 20001 *Tel:* 202-609-7757 *E-mail:* info@broadcastmgmt.com *Web Site:* www.broadcastmgmt.com, pg 710

Masri, Suzanne, Fred Rogers Productions, 2100 Wharton St, Suite 700, Pittsburgh, PA 15203 *Tel:* 412-687-2990 *Toll Free Tel:* 877-677-6437 *E-mail:* info@fredrogers. org *Web Site:* www.fredrogers.org, pg 876

Massey, Lee, Media Productions, 3241 S University Dr, Fargo, ND 58104 *Tel:* 701-237-6863 *Toll Free Tel:* 800-480-6863 *Fax:* 701-280-1226 *E-mail:* info@mediaproductions.com *Web Site:* www. mediaproductions.com, pg 822

Massey, TerriLynn, 5 Alarm Music, 3500 W Olive Ave, Suite 810, Burbank, CA 91505 *Tel:* 626-304-1698 *Toll Free Tel:* 800-322-7879 *Fax:* 626-795-2058 *E-mail:* info@5alarmmusic.com *Web Site:* www. 5alarmmusic.com, pg 762

Massingham, Gordon, Emergency Film Group, 1811 Bering Dr, Suite 430, Houston, TX 77057 *Tel:* 713-621-1100 (cust support); 713-952-1156 (direct sales) *Toll Free Tel:* 866-427-2467 *Fax:* 713-621-7500 *E-mail:* info@efilmgroup.com *Web Site:* www. efilmgroup.com, pg 753

Masters, Mary Jo, Twin Peaks Creative, 445 W Seventh St, San Pedro, CA 90731 *Tel:* 310-832-3303 *E-mail:* postmaster@bestmedia.com *Web Site:* www. twinpeakscreative.com, pg 920

Masters, Robert, Twin Peaks Creative, 445 W Seventh St, San Pedro, CA 90731 *Tel:* 310-832-3303 *E-mail:* postmaster@bestmedia.com *Web Site:* www. twinpeakscreative.com, pg 920

Masters, Sarah, Hartley Film Foundation, 49 Richmondville Ave, Suite 204, Westport, CT 06880 *Tel:* 203-226-9500 *Toll Free Tel:* 800-937-1819 *Fax:* 203-227-6938 *E-mail:* info@hartleyfoundation. org *Web Site:* hartleyfoundation.org, pg 776

Mastro, Donald, AVI Systems, 9675 W 76 St, Suite 130, Eden Prairie, MN 55344 *Tel:* 952-949-3700 *Toll Free Tel:* 800-488-4954 (support); 855-521-0050 *Fax:* 952-949-6000 *E-mail:* sales@avisystems.com *Web Site:* www.avisystems.com, pg 698

Mata, Julie, Meridian Studios, 1020 Highland Park Rd, Neenah, WI 54956 *Tel:* 920-720-4200, pg 824

Mata, Tony, Meridian Studios, 1020 Highland Park Rd, Neenah, WI 54956 *Tel:* 920-720-4200, pg 824

Mathes, Bob, Draper Inc, 411 S Pearl St, Spiceland, IN 47385 *Tel:* 765-987-7999 *Toll Free Tel:* 800-238-7999 *Fax:* 765-987-7142 *E-mail:* av@draperinc.com *Web Site:* www.draperinc.com; blog.draperinc.com, pg 746

Mathews, Gary, Quickbeam Systems Inc (QSI), 4411 McLeod Rd NE, Suite E, Albuquerque, NM 87109 *Tel:* 505-345-9230 *E-mail:* sales@quickbeam.com *Web Site:* www.quickbeam.com, pg 868

Mathias, Darian, The Location Connection Inc, 1600 Rosecrans Ave, Manhattan Beach, CA 90266 *Tel:* 310-376-9797 *E-mail:* lconnect@aol.com *Web Site:* www. locationconnection.com, pg 810

Matsubara, Masaki, Ikegami Electronics (USA) Inc, 37 Brook Ave, Maywood, NJ 07607 *Tel:* 201-368-9171 *Fax:* 201-569-1626 *E-mail:* sales@ikegami.com; service@ikegami.com *Web Site:* www.ikegami.com, pg 784

Matsuzaka, Toshihiro, Hitachi Kokusai Electric America Ltd, 150 Crossways Park Dr, Woodbury, NY 11797 *Tel:* 516-921-7200 *Toll Free Tel:* 855-891-5179 *Fax:* 516-496-3718 *E-mail:* info@hitachikokusai.us *Web Site:* hitachikokusai.us, pg 780

Mattes, Kim, The Chicago Production Center, 5400 N Saint Louis Ave, Chicago, IL 60625-4698 *Tel:* 773-509-5571 *Fax:* 773-509-5303 *Web Site:* www.wttw. com, pg 721

Matthews, Dena, Life House Productions LLC, PO Box 4007, Manchester, CT 06045-4007 *Tel:* 860-432-9177 *Web Site:* www.lifehouseproductions.com, pg 807

Matthews, John, Marco Inc, 451 Carson Rd N, Birmingham, AL 35215 *Tel:* 205-856-1110 *Toll Free Tel:* 888-465-2514 *Fax:* 205-856-1136 *E-mail:* marco@marcoconsoles.com *Web Site:* www. marcoconsoles.com, pg 817

Matthews, Kawai, Air Philosophy Inc, 1933 S Broadway, Suite 1107B, Los Angeles, CA 90007 *Tel:* 310-980-3902 *E-mail:* info@airphilosophy.com *Web Site:* airphilosophy.com, pg 678

Matthews, Sean, TiVo Corp, 2 Circle Star Way, San Carlos, CA 94070 *Tel:* 408-562-8400 *Toll Free Tel:* 877-367-8486 (cust support); 877-289-8486 (sales support) *Fax:* 408-567-1800 *Web Site:* business.tivo. com; www.tivo.com, pg 914

Matthews, Sean, Visix™ Inc, 230 Scientific Dr, Suite 800, Norcross, GA 30092 *Tel:* 770-446-1416 *Toll Free Tel:* 800-572-4935 *Fax:* 770-448-5724 *E-mail:* info@ visix.com *Web Site:* www.visix.com, pg 931

Matthews, William, Life House Productions LLC, PO Box 4007, Manchester, CT 06045-4007 *Tel:* 860-432-9177 *Web Site:* www.lifehouseproductions.com, pg 807

Mattice, Kevin, Aztech Productions LLC, 6 Hillcrest Ave, Erdenheim, PA 19038 *Tel:* 215-836-5490 *Web Site:* aztechproductions.com, pg 700

Mattice, Linda, Aztech Productions LLC, 6 Hillcrest Ave, Erdenheim, PA 19038 *Tel:* 215-836-5490 *Web Site:* aztechproductions.com, pg 700

Matys, Frank, Audio Visual Communications Inc, 1336 Cherry St, Boothwyn, PA 19061 *Tel:* 610-272-8500 *E-mail:* audiovc@verizon.net *Web Site:* www.audiovc. com, pg 694

Matzen, Robert, R&B Communications Inc, 2397 Somrack Dr, Willoughby, OH 44094 *Tel:* 440-946-9511 *Web Site:* www.rbcommunications.net, pg 870

Mau, Bruce, Freeman, 1600 Viceroy, Suite 100, Dallas, TX 75235 *Tel:* 214-445-1000 *Web Site:* www.freeman. com, pg 765

Mau, Rennie, Media Bridge Gamekids, 3281 Waikomo Rd, Koloa, HI 96756 *Tel:* 808-280-9591 *E-mail:* gkkauai@gamekids.com *Web Site:* www. gamekids.com, pg 821

Mauceri, Marc, First Run Features, The Film Center Bldg, Suite 1213, 630 Ninth Ave, New York, NY 10036-3708 *Tel:* 212-243-0600 *Fax:* 212-989-7649 *E-mail:* info@firstrunfeatures.com *Web Site:* www. firstrunfeatures.com, pg 761

Mavin, Steve, Grafco Inc, 2018 W Main St, Stroudsburg, PA 18360 *Toll Free Tel:* 800-367-6169 *Fax:* 570-213-0369 *Toll Free Fax:* 800-443-4329 *E-mail:* info@ toledofurniture.com *Web Site:* www.toledofurniture. com, pg 773

Maxey, Kent, Encyclomedia, 1526 Dekalb Ave, Atlanta, GA 30307 *Tel:* 404-527-3600 *Fax:* 404-584-5171 *E-mail:* info@encyclomedia.net *Web Site:* www. encyclomedia.net, pg 754

Maxey, Mark, Yorktel, 81 Corbett Way, Eatontown, NJ 07724 *Tel:* 732-413-6000 *Toll Free Tel:* 866-836-8463 *Fax:* 732-413-6060 *E-mail:* knowmore@yorktel.com *Web Site:* yorktel.com, pg 944

Maxwell, Ray, Eventide Inc, One Alsan Way, Little Ferry, NJ 07643 *Tel:* 201-641-1200 *Fax:* 201-641-1640 *E-mail:* audio@eventide.com; support@eventide. com *Web Site:* www.eventide.com, pg 757

May, Martha, Freeman, 1600 Viceroy, Suite 100, Dallas, TX 75235 *Tel:* 214-445-1000 *Web Site:* www.freeman. com, pg 765

May, Pamela, Design Media, 650 Alabama St, Suite 203, San Francisco, CA 94110-2038 *Tel:* 415-641-4848 *Fax:* 415-641-5245 *E-mail:* info@designmedia.com *Web Site:* www.designmedia.com, pg 741

May, Steve, Pixar Animation Studios, 1200 Park Ave, Emeryville, CA 94608 *Tel:* 510-922-3000 *Fax:* 510-922-3151 *Web Site:* www.pixar.com, pg 857

Maybrook, Jerry, The Media Staff Inc, 8425 W Third St, Suite 401, Los Angeles, CA 90048 *Tel:* 323-658-8996 *E-mail:* info@themediastaff.com *Web Site:* www. themediastaff.com, pg 822

Mayer, Andrea, WolfVision Inc, 2055 Sugarloaf Circle, Suite 125, Duluth, GA 30097 *Tel:* 770-931-6802 *Toll Free Tel:* 877-873-WOLF (873-9653)

Fax: 770-931-6906 *E-mail:* sales@wolfvision. us; support@wolfvision.us; orders@wolfvision.us *Web Site:* wolfvision.com, pg 940

Mayer, Kevin, Arizona Studios, 4614 E McDowell Rd, Phoenix, AZ 85008 *Tel:* 602-275-9100 *E-mail:* info@ arizonastudios.com *Web Site:* arizonastudios.com, pg 688

Mayer, Kevin, The Walt Disney Co, 500 S Buena Vista St, Burbank, CA 91521 *Tel:* 818-560-1000 *Web Site:* disney.com; thewaltdisneycompany.com, pg 743

Mayer-Oakes, Drew, El Paso Film Commission, One Civic Center Plaza, El Paso, TX 79901 *Tel:* 915-534-0600 *Fax:* 915-534-0687 *E-mail:* film@ destinationelpaso.com *Web Site:* visitelpaso.com/film, pg 976

Mayers, Hazel-Ann, Simon & Schuster, Inc, 1230 Avenue of the Americas, New York, NY 10020 *Tel:* 212-698-7000; 212-698-7126 *Toll Free Tel:* 800-223-2348 (cust serv) *Fax:* 212-698-7664 *Toll Free Tel:* 800-943-9831 *E-mail:* audiopublicity@ simonandschuster.com *Web Site:* www. simonandschuster.net; www.simonandschuster.biz; www.simonandschuster.com, pg 888

Mayfield, Buddy, Outland Technology Inc, 38190 Commercial Ct, Slidell, LA 70458 *Tel:* 985-847-1104 *Fax:* 985-847-1106 *E-mail:* sales@outlandtech.com *Web Site:* www.outlandtech.com, pg 849

Mayland, Chris, Encyclopaedia Britannica Inc, 325 N La Salle St, Suite 200, Chicago, IL 60654 *Tel:* 312-347-7000 (all other countries) *Toll Free Tel:* 800-323-1229 (US & CN) *Fax:* 312-294-2104 *Web Site:* www. britannica.com, pg 754

Maynard, Eric, Event Tech, 7601 Brandon Woods Blvd, Baltimore, MD 21226 *Tel:* 410-360-5006 *Toll Free Tel:* 866-950-8343 *E-mail:* info@eventtech.com *Web Site:* www.eventtech.com, pg 756

Maynard, Gary, The Gary-Paul Agency, 1549 Main St, Stratford, CT 06615 *Tel:* 203-345-6167 *Web Site:* www.thegarypaulagency.com; www. nutmegpictures.com, pg 768

Maynard, Shawn, Florical Systems Inc, 4500 NW 27 Ave, Bldg B-1, Gainesville, FL 32606 *Tel:* 352-372-8326 *Fax:* 352-375-0859 *E-mail:* sales@florical.com *Web Site:* www.florical.com, pg 762

Mayne, Erik, MediaFX, 10445 SW Canyon Rd, Suite 220, Beaverton, OR 97005 *Tel:* 503-646-9884 *Web Site:* www.mediafxvideo.com, pg 822

Mayo, Lisa, Tuolumne County Film Commission, 193 S Washington St, Sonora, CA 95370 *Tel:* 209-533-4420 *Toll Free Tel:* 800-446-1333 *E-mail:* film@ gotuolumne.com *Web Site:* www.filmtuolumne.org, pg 968

Mayor, Loren, National Public Radio (NPR), 1111 N Capitol St NE, Washington, DC 20002 *Tel:* 202-513-2000 *Web Site:* www.npr.org, pg 959

Mays, Jenny, The Virginia Film Festival, 617 W Main St, 2nd fl, Charlottesville, VA 22903 *Tel:* 434-982-5277 *Fax:* 434-924-3374 *E-mail:* info@ virginiafilmfestival.org; vffsubmissions@virginia.edu *Web Site:* virginiafilmfestival.org, pg 1006

Mazovick, John A, Convenience, 3012 N Long Ave, Chicago, IL 60641-4930 *Tel:* 773-545-3073, pg 731

McAdams, Kevin, PGi, 3280 Peachtree Rd NE, Suite 1000, Atlanta, GA 30305 *Tel:* 404-262-8400 *Toll Free Tel:* 866-755-4878 *Web Site:* www.pgi.com, pg 855

McAlister, William, McAlister Electronics, 926 E Fremont Ave, Sunnyvale, CA 94087 *Tel:* 408-739-2605 *Fax:* 408-733-2895 *E-mail:* mcalelect@aol.com *Web Site:* www.werepairallbrands.com, pg 820

McAllister, Cameron, Atlanta Film Festival (ATLFF), 25 Park Place NE, Suite 800, Atlanta, GA 30303 *Tel:* 678-929-8103 *E-mail:* info@atlantafilmfestival. com; submit@atlantafilmfestival.com *Web Site:* www. atlantafilmfestival.com, pg 982

McAllister, Gregg C, TVN-The Video Network, 31 Cutler Dr, Ashland, MA 01721-1210 *Tel:* 508-881-1800 *E-mail:* info@tvnvideo.com *Web Site:* www.tvnvideo.com, pg 919

McAllister, Robert "Kooster", Record Plant Remote, 1170 Greenwood Lake Tpke, Ringwood, NJ 07456 *Tel:* 973-728-8114 *Fax:* 973-728-8761 *E-mail:* info@recordplantremote.com *Web Site:* www.recordplantremote.com, pg 871

McAndrew, Robert, Brodart Co, 500 Arch St, Williamsport, PA 17701 *Tel:* 570-326-2461 *Toll Free Tel:* 888-820-4377 *Toll Free Fax:* 800-283-6087 *E-mail:* supplies.customerservice@brodart.com *Web Site:* www.shopbrodart.com, pg 711

McArthur, Sean, Apogee Electronics Corp, 1715 Berkeley St, Santa Monica, CA 90404 *Tel:* 310-584-9394 *Fax:* 310-584-9385 *E-mail:* info@apogeedigital.com *Web Site:* www.apogeedigital.com, pg 687

McArthur, Stephen, Lyrichord/Multicultural Media, 27 Main St, Suite 6, Montpelier, VT 05602 *Tel:* 802-839-0371 *E-mail:* info@lyrichord.com *Web Site:* www.lyrichord.com, pg 813

McArthur, Stephen, Multicultural Media Inc, 27 Main St, Suite 6, Montpelier, VT 05602 *Tel:* 802-839-0371 *E-mail:* support@worldmusicstore.com *Web Site:* www.worldmusicstore.com; www.multiculturalmedia.com; www.lyrichord.com, pg 833

McAtee, Todd S, Mouser Electronics Inc - A TTI Berkshire Hathaway Company, 1000 N Main St, Mansfield, TX 76063-1514 *Tel:* 817-804-3888 *Toll Free Tel:* 800-346-6873 *Fax:* 817-804-3899 *E-mail:* sales@mouser.com *Web Site:* www.mouser.com, pg 831

McBride, Nancy, Women in Film & Television-Florida (WIFT-FL), PO Box 533541, Orlando, FL 32853-3541 *E-mail:* info@womeninfilmfl.org *Web Site:* womeninfilmfl.org, pg 963

McBride, Pat, Media Supply Inc, 611 Jeffers Circle, Exton, PA 19341 *Tel:* 610-884-4400 *Toll Free Tel:* 800-944-4237 *Fax:* 610-884-4500 *E-mail:* info@mediasupply.com *Web Site:* www.mediasupply.com, pg 822

McCall, Josh, Jack Morton Worldwide, 909 Third Ave, New York, NY 10022 *Tel:* 212-401-7000; 212-401-7212 *E-mail:* experience@jackmorton.com *Web Site:* www.jackmorton.com, pg 830

McCann, Tammy, Sunset Gower Studios, 1438 N Gower St, Hollywood, CA 90028 *Tel:* 323-467-1001 *Fax:* 323-467-2717 *E-mail:* reception@sunsetgower.com *Web Site:* sunsetgowerstudios.com, pg 904

McCarthy, Christine M, The Walt Disney Co, 500 S Buena Vista St, Burbank, CA 91521 *Tel:* 818-560-1000 *Web Site:* disney.com; thewaltdisneycompany.com, pg 743

McCarthy, Dan, The Taunton Press Inc, 63 S Main St, Newtown, CT 06470 *Tel:* 203-426-8171 *Toll Free Tel:* 800-926-8776 (ext 3893 - PR); 800-888-8286 (orders) *Fax:* 203-426-3434 *Web Site:* www.taunton.com, pg 907

McCarthy, Debbie, Explore Lawrence, PO Box 526, Lawrence, KS 66044 *Tel:* 785-856-3040; 785-856-5282 (mktg) *Fax:* 785-856-5303 *E-mail:* visinfo@explorelawrence.com *Web Site:* www.explorelawrence.com, pg 971

McCarthy, Jeannie, Bil-Jax Inc, 125 Taylor Pkwy, Archbold, OH 43502 *Tel:* 419-445-8915 *Toll Free Tel:* 800-537-0540 *Fax:* 419-445-0367 *E-mail:* sales@biljax.com *Web Site:* www.biljax.com, pg 705

McCarthy, Mr Kelly, Genesis Integration, 14721 123 Ave NW, Edmonton, AB T5L 2Y6, Canada *Toll Free Tel:* 877-283-2253 (Toronto); 866-622-2966 (Quebec); 844-436-4681 (rest of CN) *E-mail:* marketing@genint.com *Web Site:* www.genint.com, pg 769

McCarthy, Mary, Cokesbury, 2222 Rosa Parks Blvd, Nashville, TN 37228 *Tel:* 615-749-6000 (UMPH) *Toll Free Tel:* 800-672-1789; 844-381-2708 (cust care) *Fax:* 615-749-6578 *Toll Free Fax:* 800-445-8189 *E-mail:* cokes_serv@cokesbury.com; customerhelp@cokesbury.com *Web Site:* www.cokesbury.com, pg 727

McCarthy, Padraig, SES SA, 4 Research Way, Princeton, NJ 08540-6684 *Tel:* 609-987-4000 *E-mail:* info@ses.com *Web Site:* www.ses.com, pg 884

McCarthy, Thomas, Golden Reel Awards, 10061 Riverside Dr, PMB 751, Toluca Lake, CA 91602-2550 *Tel:* 818-506-7731 *Fax:* 818-506-7732 *E-mail:* office@mpse.org *Web Site:* www.mpse.org, pg 990

McCarty, Maggie, The Paradise Coast Film Commission, 755 Eighth Ave S, Naples, FL 34102 *Tel:* 239-659-FILM (659-3456) *Web Site:* film.paradisecoast.com, pg 969

McCauley, Dan, General Devices Co Inc, 1410 S Post Rd, Indianapolis, IN 46239 *Tel:* 317-897-7000 *Fax:* 317-898-2917 *E-mail:* sales@generaldevices.com *Web Site:* www.generaldevices.com, pg 769

McClanathan, Bob, Frontier Communications Corp, PO Box 939, Portland, OR 97207-0939 *Tel:* 503-246-8080, pg 766

McClatchie, Donald, FM Systems Inc, 3877 S Main St, Santa Ana, CA 92707 *Tel:* 714-979-3355 *Toll Free Tel:* 800-235-6960 *Fax:* 714-979-0913 *E-mail:* fmsystemsinc@sbcglobal.net *Web Site:* www.fmsystems-inc.com, pg 763

McClatchie, Frank, FM Systems Inc, 3877 S Main St, Santa Ana, CA 92707 *Tel:* 714-979-3355 *Toll Free Tel:* 800-235-6960 *Fax:* 714-979-0913 *E-mail:* fmsystemsinc@sbcglobal.net *Web Site:* www.fmsystems-inc.com, pg 763

McClea, Robin, Arkansas Arts Council Fellowships & Grants Program, 1100 North St, Little Rock, AR 72201-2606 *Tel:* 501-324-9766 *Fax:* 501-324-9207 *E-mail:* info@arkansasarts.org *Web Site:* www.arkansasarts.org, pg 981

McClellan, Jon Paul, Audio Art, 124 Forsythe Dr, Chapel Hill, NC 27517 *Tel:* 919-260-1507, pg 693

McClelland, Bill, Society of Camera Operators, PO Box 2006, Toluca Lake, CA 91610-0006 *Tel:* 818-563-9110 *Fax:* 818-563-9117 *E-mail:* sooffice@soc.org *Web Site:* www.soc.org, pg 962

McClelland, Bruce, ARRIS Group Inc, 3871 Lakefield Dr, Suwanee, GA 30024 *Tel:* 678-473-2907 *Toll Free Tel:* 866-36-ARRIS (362-7747); 877-466-8646 (tech) *Fax:* 678-473-8470 *E-mail:* marketing@arris.com *Web Site:* www.arris.com, pg 689

McClure, Jill, Association of Progressive Rental Organizations (APRO), 500 E Whitestone Blvd, Suite 4189, Cedar Park, TX 78613 *Tel:* 512-794-0095 *Toll Free Tel:* 800-204-2776 *Fax:* 512-794-0097 *E-mail:* info@rtohq.org *Web Site:* www.rtohq.org, pg 951

McClure, Leslie, 411 Video Information, PO Box 1223, Pebble Beach, CA 93953-1223 *Tel:* 408-671-2859 (cell) *Web Site:* www.411videoinfo.com, pg 764

McClymont, Patrick, IMAX Corp, 2525 Speakman Dr, Mississauga, ON L5K 1B1, Canada *Tel:* 905-403-6500 *Fax:* 905-403-6450 *E-mail:* info@imax.com *Web Site:* www.imax.com, pg 786

McConnell, Robert, Robert McConnell Productions, 4303 67 Ave NW, Gig Harbor, WA 98335 *Tel:* 253-265-3184 *Toll Free Tel:* 800-532-4017 *Fax:* 253-265-1550 *Toll Free Fax:* 800-948-8463 *E-mail:* info@parli.com *Web Site:* parli.com, pg 821

McCool, Michael D, National Media Services Inc, 613 N Commerce Ave, Front Royal, VA 22630 *Tel:* 540-635-4181 *Fax:* 540-636-4240 *Web Site:* nationalmediaservices.com, pg 836

McCord-Morelli, Kerry, The Weather Company, An IBM Business, 400 Minuteman Rd, Andover, MA 01810 *Tel:* 978-983-6300 *Fax:* 978-983-6400 *Web Site:* business.weather.com, pg 935

McCormack, Greg, ACCO Brands Corp, 4 Corporate Dr, Lake Zurich, IL 60047-8997 *Toll Free Tel:* 800-541-0094; 800-222-6462 *Toll Free Fax:* 800-941-4463 *E-mail:* contactus@acco.com (cust serv) *Web Site:* www.accobrands.com, pg 673

McCormick, Brian, Stewart Audio, 14435 Cuesta Ct, Suite C, Sonora, CA 95370 *Tel:* 209-588-8111 *Fax:* 209-588-8113 *E-mail:* sales@stewartaudio.com; support@stewartaudio.com *Web Site:* www.stewartaudio.com, pg 901

McCormick, Neil G, Cinecraft Productions Inc, 2515 Franklin Blvd, Cleveland, OH 44113 *Tel:* 216-781-2300 *Toll Free Tel:* 800-959-2463 *Fax:* 216-781-1067 *E-mail:* info@cinecraft.com *Web Site:* cinecraft.com, pg 723

McCormick, Peter M, Magnetek Inc, N49 W13650 Campbell Dr, Menomonee Falls, WI 53051 *Tel:* 262-783-3500 *Toll Free Tel:* 800-288-8178 *Toll Free Fax:* 800-298-3503 *E-mail:* sales@magnetek.com *Web Site:* www.magnetek.com, pg 814

McCoy, Belinda, Big Fish Production US, PO Box 782, Bronx, NY 10462-0782 *Tel:* 347-526-5211 *E-mail:* bigfishproductionus@gmail.com *Web Site:* www.bigfishproductionus.com, pg 705

McCoy, Charles E, Audio-Video Resources Inc, 1043 Adams Ave, Montgomery, AL 36104 *Tel:* 334-262-4806 *Fax:* 334-240-0000 *E-mail:* avrinc@bellsouth.net, pg 694

McCracken, Kaylia, Western Heritage Awards, 1700 NE 63 St, Oklahoma City, OK 73111 *Tel:* 405-478-2250 *Web Site:* nationalcowboymuseum.org, pg 1007

McCracken, Kristin, The Hamptons International Film Festival, 47 Newtown Lane, East Hampton, NY 11937 *Tel:* 631-324-4600 *Fax:* 631-324-1558 *E-mail:* info@hamptonsfilmfest.org; programming@hamptonsfilmfest.org (submissions) *Web Site:* hamptonsfilmfest.org, pg 991

McCrainie, David, Everlast Productions, 59 SW 12 Ave, Unit 110, Dania Beach, FL 33004 *Tel:* 954-456-7167 *Fax:* 954-456-1243 *E-mail:* info@everlastproductions.com *Web Site:* everlastproductions.com, pg 757

McCuen, Richelle Antczak, Mills James Productions, 3545 Fishinger Blvd, Columbus, OH 43026-9489 *Tel:* 614-777-9933 *E-mail:* info@mjp.com *Web Site:* www.millsjames.com, pg 828

McCulley, Bruce, Cavalcade Productions Inc, PO Box 2480, Nevada City, CA 95959-1948 *Tel:* 530-477-0701 (outside US & CN) *Toll Free Tel:* 800-345-5530 *Fax:* 530-477-0701 (outside US & CN) *Toll Free Fax:* 800-345-5530 *E-mail:* info@cavalcadeproductions.com *Web Site:* www.cavalcadeproductions.com, pg 717

McCullough, Robert, Penguin Random House Canada, 320 Front St W, Suite 1400, Toronto, ON M5V 3B6, Canada *Tel:* 416-364-4449 *Toll Free Tel:* 888-523-9292 (cust serv) *Fax:* 416-598-7764 *E-mail:* customerservicescanada@penguinrandomhouse.com *Web Site:* www.penguinrandomhouse.ca, pg 853

McCune, Allan, McCune Audio-Video-Lighting, 101 Utah Ave, South San Francisco, CA 94080 *Tel:* 650-873-1111 *Toll Free Tel:* 800-899-7686 *Fax:* 650-246-6702 *E-mail:* info@mccune.com *Web Site:* www.mccune.com, pg 821

McCune, Thomas, Navitar Inc, 200 Commerce Dr, Rochester, NY 14623 *Tel:* 585-359-4000 *Toll Free Tel:* 800-828-6778 *Fax:* 585-359-4999 *E-mail:* info@navitar.com *Web Site:* www.navitar.com, pg 837

McCurdy, Robert, GTI (Graphic Technology Inc), PO Box 3138, Newburgh, NY 12550-0651 *Tel:* 845-562-7066 *Toll Free Tel:* 888-562-7066 *Fax:* 845-562-2543 *E-mail:* sales@gtilite.com *Web Site:* www.gtilite.com, pg 774

McDavid, Brian, Pyrotek Special Effects Inc, 201 Whitehall Dr, Suite 6, Markham, ON L3R 9Y3, Canada *Tel:* 905-479-9991 *Toll Free Tel:* 800-481-9910 *E-mail:* info@pyrotekfx.com *Web Site:* pyrotekfx.com, pg 867

McDonald, Dennis, Keslow Camera Inc, 5900 Blackwelder St, Culver City, CA 90232 *Tel:* 310-636-4600 *Fax:* 310-915-5335 *E-mail:* info@keslowcamera.com *Web Site:* www.keslowcamera.com, pg 798

McDonald, Gregory, iCorpTv, PO Box 461172, Los Angeles, CA 90046 *Tel:* 818-492-4623 *E-mail:* icorptv@gmail.com *Web Site:* icorptv.com, pg 783

McDonald, Jim, Wind River Broadcast Center, 117 E 11 St, Loveland, CO 80537 *Tel:* 970-669-3442 *Web Site:* www.windriverbroadcast.com, pg 939

McDonald, Mary-Liz, Audio Network US Inc, 48 W 25 St, 10th fl, New York, NY 10010 *Tel:* 646-688-4320 *E-mail:* nyoffice@audionetwork.com *Web Site:* us. audionetwork.com, pg 693

McDonald, Michael, Private Island Audio Inc, 1882 S Cochran Ave, Los Angeles, CA 90019 *Tel:* 323-856-8729 *Web Site:* www.privateislandaudio.net, pg 862

McDonald, Nancy, Hawaii International Film Festival, 680 Iwilei Rd, Suite 100, Honolulu, HI 96817 *Tel:* 808-792-1577 (ext 7) *Fax:* 808-792-1583 *Toll Free Tel:* 877-749-7783 *E-mail:* info@hiff.org; entries@hiff.org *Web Site:* www.hiff.org, pg 991

McDonnell, Mark, Shopware, c/o Films Media Group, 132 W 31 St, 16th fl, New York, NY 10001 *Toll Free Tel:* 800-322-8755 *Toll Free Fax:* 800-678-3633 *E-mail:* custserv@films.com *Web Site:* shopware.films. com, pg 886

McDowell, John, NewsBank Inc, 5801 Pelican Bay Blvd, Suite 600, Naples, FL 34108 *Tel:* 802-875-2910 *Toll Free Tel:* 800-762-8182 *Fax:* 802-875-2904 *E-mail:* sales@newsbank.com; custservice@newsbank. com *Web Site:* www.newsbank.com, pg 840

McDowell, Katie, Radio Systems Inc, 601 Heron Dr, Logan Township, NJ 08085 *Tel:* 856-467-8000 *Fax:* 856-467-3044 *E-mail:* sales@radiosystems.com; tech@radiosystems.com *Web Site:* www.radiosystems. com, pg 869

McDuff, Chris, ChronTrol Corp, 7525-K Mission Gorge Rd, San Diego, CA 92120 *Tel:* 619-282-8686 *Toll Free Tel:* 800-854-1999 *Fax:* 619-563-6563 *E-mail:* info@chrontrol.com *Web Site:* www.chrontrol. com, pg 723

McElwee, Joni, Technomedia Solutions, 4545 36 St, Orlando, FL 32811 *Tel:* 407-351-0909 *Fax:* 407-248-9484 *E-mail:* sales@gotechnomedia.com *Web Site:* www.gotechnomedia.com, pg 909

McErlain, Stephen Eric, EEG Enterprises Inc, 586 Main St, Farmingdale, NY 11735 *Tel:* 516-293-7472 *Fax:* 516-293-7417 *E-mail:* sales@eegent.com *Web Site:* www.eegent.com, pg 751

McEwen, Michael, North American Broadcasters Association (NABA), Canadian Broadcasting Centre, 25 John St, Suite 9C200, Toronto, ON M5V 3G7, Canada *Tel:* 416-205-3363 *Fax:* 416-205-2901 *E-mail:* contact@nabanet.com *Web Site:* nabanet.com, pg 960

McFadden, Claire, Michigan Office Solutions (MOS), A Xerox Company, 2859 Walkent Dr NW, Grand Rapids, MI 49544 *Toll Free Tel:* 800-442-9070 *E-mail:* info@mos-xerox.com *Web Site:* www.mos-xerox.com, pg 825

McFadden, Daniel, PAR Inc, 16204 N Florida Ave, Lutz, FL 33549 *Tel:* 813-449-4065 *Toll Free Tel:* 800-331-8378 *Fax:* 813-961-2196 *Toll Free Fax:* 800-727-9329 *E-mail:* cs@parinc.com *Web Site:* www.parinc.com, pg 851

McFarland, Judy, Thread Marketing Group, 4635 W Alexis Rd, Toledo, OH 43623-1005 *Tel:* 419-887-6801 *Fax:* 419-887-6802 *E-mail:* info@threadgroup.com *Web Site:* www.threadgroup.com, pg 913

McGalliard, Rachel, The Learning House Inc, 427 S Fourth St, Suite 300, Louisville, KY 40202 *Tel:* 502-589-9878 *Fax:* 502-589-9825 *E-mail:* sales@ learninghouse.com; info@learninghouse.com *Web Site:* www.learninghouse.com, pg 805

McGarty, Kevin, Staging Directions Inc, 1327 Northbrook Pkwy, Suite 440, Suwanee, GA 30024 *Tel:* 770-409-9909 *Toll Free Tel:* 800-782-4322 *Fax:* 770-409-0277 *E-mail:* sales@teamsdi.net *Web Site:* www.stagingdirections.com, pg 899

McGill, Carla Hargrove, Hargrove Inc, One Hargrove Dr, Lanham, MD 20706 *Tel:* 301-306-9000 *Fax:* 301-306-9318 *E-mail:* exhibitorservices@hargroveinc.com *Web Site:* www.hargroveinc.com, pg 776

McGill, Jackie, Spectrum Engineers, 324 S State St, Suite 400, Salt Lake City, UT 84111 *Tel:* 801-328-5151 *Toll Free Tel:* 800-678-7077 *Fax:* 801-328-5155 *E-mail:* info@spectrum-engineers.com *Web Site:* www. spectrum-engineers.com, pg 897

McGill, Tim, Hargrove Inc, One Hargrove Dr, Lanham, MD 20706 *Tel:* 301-306-9000 *Fax:* 301-306-9318 *E-mail:* exhibitorservices@hargroveinc.com *Web Site:* www.hargroveinc.com, pg 776

McGinnis, Amanda, Videssence, 10768 Lower Azusa Rd, El Monte, CA 91731 *Tel:* 626-579-0943 *Fax:* 626-579-6803 *E-mail:* contact@videssence.tv *Web Site:* www.videssence.tv, pg 930

McGivern, Bill, ETC, 3031 Pleasant View Rd, Middleton, WI 53562-4809 *Tel:* 608-831-4116 *Toll Free Tel:* 800-688-4116 *Fax:* 608-836-1736 *Web Site:* www.etcconnect.com, pg 756

McGorisk, Keith, Mightybytes Inc, 4001 N Ravenswood Ave, Suite 404, Chicago, IL 60613 *Tel:* 773-561-7529 *E-mail:* info@mightybytes.com *Web Site:* www. mightybytes.com, pg 827

McGourlay, James, OpenText Corp, 275 Frank Tompa Dr, Waterloo, ON N2L 0A1, Canada *Tel:* 519-888-7111 *Toll Free Tel:* 800-499-6544 *Fax:* 519-888-0677 *Web Site:* www.opentext.com, pg 847

McGovern, Kathleen, Digital Video Systems, 3270 Executive Way, Miramar, FL 33025 *Tel:* 954-239-4410 *Fax:* 954-239-4486 *E-mail:* info@digitalvideosystems. net *Web Site:* digitalvideosystems.net, pg 742

McGovern, Kevin, Cine-Med Inc, 127 Main St N, Woodbury, CT 06798 *Tel:* 203-263-0006 *Toll Free Tel:* 800-253-7657 *Fax:* 203-263-4839 *E-mail:* support@cine-med.net *Web Site:* www.cine-med.com, pg 723

McGovern, Mark, AMS Pictures, 16986 N Dallas Pkwy, Dallas, TX 75248 *Tel:* 972-818-7400 *Toll Free Tel:* 866-691-3660 *Fax:* 972-818-1257 *Web Site:* amspictures.com, pg 685

McGovern, Stella, WILLiFEST, PO Box 20412, New York, NY 10021-0066 *E-mail:* inquiries@willifest. com; programming@willifest.com; screenplays@ willifest.com *Web Site:* www.willifest.com, pg 1007

McGovern, Tricia, Antenna International, 383 Main Ave, Norwalk, CT 06851 *Tel:* 203-523-0320 *E-mail:* inquiry@antennainternational.com; marketing@antennainternational.com *Web Site:* www. antennainternational.com, pg 686

McGowan, Bill, Clarity Media Group, 166 Fifth Ave, 6th & 7th fl, New York, NY 10010 *Tel:* 212-262-7015 *E-mail:* info@claritymediagroup.com *Web Site:* www. claritymediagroup.com, pg 725

McGowan, Bret, Vicon Industries Inc, 135 Fell Ct, Hauppauge, NY 11788-4351 *Tel:* 631-952-2288 *Toll Free Tel:* 800-645-9116 *Fax:* 631-951-2288 *E-mail:* sales@vicon-security.com *Web Site:* www. vicon-security.com, pg 926

McGowan, Katie G, Ann Arbor Film Festival, 230 Collingwood Dr, Suite 160B, Ann Arbor, MI 48103 *Tel:* 734-995-5356 *Fax:* 734-995-5396 *E-mail:* info@ aafilmfest.org *Web Site:* www.aafilmfest.org, pg 981

McGrath, Bryden, RAM® Mounts, 8410 Dallas Ave S, Seattle, WA 98108 *Tel:* 206-763-8361 *Toll Free Tel:* 800-497-7479 *Fax:* 206-763-9615 *E-mail:* sales@ rammount.com *Web Site:* www.rammount.com, pg 870

McGrath, Dick, Albany Theatre Supply Co Inc, 445 N Pearl St, Albany, NY 12204 *Tel:* 518-229-7899 *E-mail:* sales@albanytheatresupply.com *Web Site:* www.albanytheatresupply.com, pg 679

McGrath, Kyra G, WHYY Inc, Independence Mall West, 150 N Sixth St, Philadelphia, PA 19106 *Tel:* 215-351-1200 *Fax:* 215-351-0398 *E-mail:* talkback@whyy.org *Web Site:* www.whyy.org, pg 938

McGrath, Matt, Advanced Designs Corp, 1169 W Second St, Bloomington, IN 47403 *Tel:* 812-333-1922 *Fax:* 812-333-2030 *E-mail:* service@doprad.com *Web Site:* www.doprad.com, pg 677

McGrath, Thomas, Albany Theatre Supply Co Inc, 445 N Pearl St, Albany, NY 12204 *Tel:* 518-229-7899 *E-mail:* sales@albanytheatresupply.com *Web Site:* www.albanytheatresupply.com, pg 679

McGrew, Casey, Tarpley Media Systems, 3737 50 St, Lubbock, TX 79413 *Tel:* 806-797-5833 *Toll Free Tel:* 800-600-5833 *Fax:* 806-797-5139 *E-mail:* tms@ tarpleymedia.com *Web Site:* www.tarpleymedia.com, pg 907

McGuane, James P, McGuane Studio Inc, 36 Horatio St, Suite 5-B, New York, NY 10014-1691 *Tel:* 212-463-7259, pg 821

McGugan, Phil, Nazdar®, 8501 Hedge Lane Terr, Shawnee, KS 66227-3290 *Tel:* 913-422-1888 *Toll Free Tel:* 800-767-9942 (cust serv) *Fax:* 913-422-2296 *E-mail:* custserv@nazdar.com *Web Site:* www.nazdar. com, pg 837

McHale-Horan, Shannon, The Campbell Agency, Hidden Grove Bldg, 12404 Park Central Dr, Suite 222 S, Dallas, TX 75251 *Tel:* 214-522-8991 *Fax:* 214-522-8997 *Web Site:* www.thecampbellagency.com, pg 715

McIlvain, Charlie, Kerrville Convention & Visitors Bureau, 2108 Sidney Baker St, Kerrville, TX 78028 *Tel:* 830-792-3535 *Toll Free Tel:* 800-221-7958 *E-mail:* info@kerrvilletexascvb.com *Web Site:* www. kerrvilletexascvb.com, pg 976

McIlwain, J Michael, PSAV® Presentation Services, 111 W Ocean Blvd, Suite 1110, Long Beach, CA 90802-4688 *Tel:* 562-366-0620; 562-366-0621 *Toll Free Tel:* 877-430-7728 *Fax:* 562-366-0628 *Web Site:* www. psav.com, pg 866

McIlwain, Mike, PSAV® Presentation Services (Hotel Services Division), 5100 N River Rd, Suite 300, Schiller Park, IL 60176 *Tel:* 847-222-9800 *Toll Free Tel:* 866-716-9691 *E-mail:* psavglobal@gmail.com *Web Site:* www.psav.com, pg 866

McInerney, Chris, Sihl Inc, 538 Main St, Fiskeville, RI 02823 *Tel:* 401-821-1000 *Toll Free Tel:* 800-556-6866; 800-366-7393 (ext 1, cust serv) *Web Site:* www. sihlinc.com, pg 888

McInnis, Karen, Association of American Publishers (AAP), 455 Massachusetts Ave NW, Suite 700, Washington, DC 20001-2777 *Tel:* 202-347-3375 *Fax:* 202-347-3690 *E-mail:* info@publishers.org *Web Site:* publishers.org, pg 951

McIntyre, Maury, Television Academy, 5220 Lankershim Blvd, North Hollywood, CA 91601-3109 *Tel:* 818-754-2800 *Web Site:* www.emmys.com, pg 963

McIntyre, Ron L, CyberIconics International, 1752 N 74 Place, Mesa, AZ 85207-2932 *Tel:* 480-396-8731, pg 736

McKay, John, Association of American Publishers (AAP), 455 Massachusetts Ave NW, Suite 700, Washington, DC 20001-2777 *Tel:* 202-347-3375 *Fax:* 202-347-3690 *E-mail:* info@publishers.org *Web Site:* publishers.org, pg 951

McKay, Kevin, Genesis Integration, 14721 123 Ave NW, Edmonton, AB T5L 2Y6, Canada *Toll Free Tel:* 877-283-2253 (Toronto); 866-622-2966 (Quebec); 844-436-4681 (rest of CN) *E-mail:* marketing@genint.com *Web Site:* www.genint.com, pg 770

McKay, Matthew PhD, New Harbinger Publications, 5674 Shattuck Ave, Oakland, CA 94609 *Tel:* 510-652-0215 *Toll Free Tel:* 800-748-6273 *Fax:* 510-652-5472 *E-mail:* customerservice@newharbinger.com *Web Site:* www.newharbinger.com, pg 839

McKay, Nathan, Salesmaker Carts, 403 Roberts Ave, Louisville, KY 40214 *Toll Free Tel:* 800-281-2278 *Toll Free Fax:* 800-418-2525 *Web Site:* www. salesmakercarts.com, pg 879

McKay, Pat, L-3 WESCAM, 649 N Service Rd W, Burlington, ON L7P 5B9, Canada *Tel:* 905-633-4000; 905-633-4175 (cust serv) *Toll Free Tel:* 888-593-7226 *Fax:* 905-633-4100 *E-mail:* sales.wescam@l-3com. com *Web Site:* www.wescam.com, pg 803

McKean, Michael, Troxell-CDI, 4675 E Cotton Center Blvd, Suite 155, Phoenix, AZ 85040 *Tel:* 602-437-7240 *Toll Free Tel:* 855-TROXELL (876-9355) *Fax:* 602-752-1299 *Toll Free Fax:* 800-752-1299 *E-mail:* csg@trox.com *Web Site:* www.troxellsolutions.com, pg 918

McKechney, Bill, F&F Productions LLC, 14333 Myerlake Circle, Clearwater, FL 33760 *Tel:* 727-530-5000 *Fax:* 727-535-6547 *E-mail:* info@fandfhd.tv *Web Site:* www.fandfhd.tv, pg 759

McKee, Jeffrey, X-Rite, 4300 44 St SE, Grand Rapids, MI 49512 *Tel:* 616-803-2100 *Toll Free Tel:* 800-248-9748; 888-800-9580 *Web Site:* www.xrite.com, pg 942

McKee, Jim, Earwax Productions Inc, 916 Kearny St, San Francisco, CA 94133 *Tel:* 415-860-9403 (cell) *Web Site:* www.earwaxproductions.com, pg 749

McKenna, Megan, Total Creative, 432 N Canal St, Suite 12, South San Francisco, CA 94080 *Tel:* 650-583-8236 *Fax:* 650-583-4708 *E-mail:* info@totalcreative.com *Web Site:* totalcreative.com, pg 916

McKenzie, Cameron, L-3 WESCAM, 649 N Service Rd W, Burlington, ON L7P 5B9, Canada *Tel:* 905-633-4000; 905-633-4175 (cust serv) *Toll Free Tel:* 888-593-7226 *Fax:* 905-633-4100 *E-mail:* sales.wescam@l-3com.com *Web Site:* www.wescam.com, pg 803

McKenzie, Chris, CMI Media Management, 9 W Broad St, Stamford, CT 06902 *Tel:* 203-989-9955 *Toll Free Tel:* 800-431-1102 *Fax:* 203-316-8353 *Web Site:* www.cminyla.com, pg 727

McKenzie, Cindy, Deluxe Entertainment Services Group Inc, 2400 W Empire Ave, 2nd fl, Burbank, CA 91504 *Tel:* 818-260-7005; 818-526-3700 *Toll Free Tel:* 800-99-FILMS (993-4567) *E-mail:* ddchelp@bydeluxe.com; pr@bydeluxe.com *Web Site:* www.bydeluxe.com, pg 740

McKenzie, Clif, Watson Desking, 26246 Twelve Trees Lane NW, Poulsbo, WA 98370 *Tel:* 360-394-1300 *Fax:* 360-394-1322 *E-mail:* marketing@watsondesking.com *Web Site:* www.watsonfurniture.com, pg 934

McKinney, Mark, acouStaCorp, 701 E 132 St, Bronx, NY 10454 *Tel:* 718-402-2677 *Fax:* 718-402-2859 *E-mail:* info@texasscenic.com *Web Site:* acoustacorp.texasscenic.com, pg 674

McKinney, Michael, M2 Communications, 235 Bellefontaine St, Pasadena, CA 91105 *Tel:* 626-441-2024 *Toll Free Tel:* 800-423-8273 *Fax:* 626-441-2694 *E-mail:* m2com@aol.com *Web Site:* www.m2com.com, pg 833

McKinney, Ty, Lloyd F McKinney Associates Inc, 25350 Cypress Ave, Hayward, CA 94544 *Tel:* 510-783-8043 *Fax:* 510-783-2130 *E-mail:* info@mckinneyassoc.com *Web Site:* www.mckinneyassoc.com, pg 673

McKinney-Browning, Mabel, Silver Gavel Awards for Media & the Arts, Div for Public Education, 321 N Clark St, Chicago, IL 60654-7598 *Tel:* 312-988-5733 *Toll Free Tel:* 800-285-2221 *Fax:* 312-988-5494 (Attn: Gavel Awards) *E-mail:* publiceducation@americanbar.org *Web Site:* www.americanbar.org, pg 1004

McKnight, Jay, Magnetic Reference Laboratory Inc, 165 Wyandotte Dr, San Jose, CA 95123 *Tel:* 408-227-8631 *Fax:* 408-227-8631 *E-mail:* mrltapes@comcast.net *Web Site:* www.mrltapes.com, pg 815

McLachlan, Neil, ACCO Brands Corp, 4 Corporate Dr, Lake Zurick, IL 60047-8997 *Toll Free Tel:* 800-541-0094; 800-222-6462 *Toll Free Fax:* 800-941-4463 *E-mail:* contactus@acco.com (cust serv) *Web Site:* www.accobrands.com, pg 673

McLain, Bobby, Uniset LLC, 449 Avenue "A", Rochester, NY 14621 *Tel:* 585-544-3820 *Fax:* 585-544-1110 *E-mail:* info@unisetcorp.com *Web Site:* www.unisetcorp.com, pg 921

McLain, Peter, Yorktel, 81 Corbett Way, Eatontown, NJ 07724 *Tel:* 732-413-6000 *Toll Free Tel:* 866-836-8463 *Fax:* 732-413-6060 *E-mail:* knowmore@yorktel.com *Web Site:* yorktel.com, pg 944

McLaren, David C, BBE Sound Inc, 2548 Fender Ave, Fullerton, CA 92831 *Tel:* 714-897-6766 *Toll Free Tel:* 800-233-8346 *Fax:* 714-895-6728 *Web Site:* www.bbesound.com, pg 702

McLaren, Ian, Productions Grand Nord Quebec Inc, 5141 Notre Dam de Grace, Montreal, QC H4A 1K4, Canada *Tel:* 514-521-7433 *Fax:* 514-522-3013, pg 864

McLaren, John C, BBE Sound Inc, 2548 Fender Ave, Fullerton, CA 92831 *Tel:* 714-897-6766 *Toll Free Tel:* 800-233-8346 *Fax:* 714-895-6728 *Web Site:* www.bbesound.com, pg 702

McLaughlin, Melinda, Extreme Reach Inc, 75 Second Ave, Suite 720, Needham, MA 02494 *Tel:* 781-577-2016 *Toll Free Tel:* 877-769-9382 *E-mail:* sales@extremereach.com; support@extremereach.com *Web Site:* extremereach.com, pg 758

McLaughlin, Scott, Strategic Connections, 3000 Spring Forest Rd, Raleigh, NC 27616 *Tel:* 919-878-0550 *Toll Free Tel:* 800-255-5664 *Fax:* 919-875-8712 *Web Site:* www.strategicconnections.net, pg 901

McLean, John, John McLean Media, 802 Newton, Penthouse 3, Seattle, WA 98109 *Tel:* 206-285-2603 *E-mail:* info@johnmcleanmedia.com *Web Site:* www.johnmcleanmedia.com, pg 794

McLelland, Dawn, ELS Productions Inc, 627 W Olympic Lane, Elk Ridge, UT 84651 *Tel:* 801-676-0807 *Toll Free Tel:* 800-927-3472 *Web Site:* www.elsproductions.com, pg 753

McLelland, Mark, ELS Productions Inc, 627 W Olympic Lane, Elk Ridge, UT 84651 *Tel:* 801-676-0807 *Toll Free Tel:* 800-927-3472 *Web Site:* www.elsproductions.com, pg 753

McLeod, Michele, Annenberg Learner, PO Box 26983, St Louis, MO 63118 *Tel:* 202-783-0500 (outside US) *Toll Free Tel:* 800-LEARNER (532-7637) *Fax:* 202-783-0333 *E-mail:* order@learner.org *Web Site:* www.learner.org, pg 686

McMahan, Danielle, John Wiley & Sons Inc, 111 River St, Hoboken, NJ 07030-5774 *Tel:* 201-748-6000 *Toll Free Tel:* 800-225-5945 (cust serv) *Fax:* 201-748-6088 *Web Site:* www.wiley.com, pg 938

McMahan, Julia, Cine Las Americas International Film Festival (CLAIFF), 1104 W 34 St, No 625, Austin, TX 78705 *Tel:* 512-535-0765 *E-mail:* cine@cinelasamericas.org; entries@cinelasamericas.org *Web Site:* cinelasamericas.org; www.facebook.com/cinelasamericasaustin, pg 986

McManus, Beverly Cohron, Zion Music Group, 306 Monticello Rd, Franklin, TN 37064 *Tel:* 615-559-2108 *Fax:* 615-591-5102 *Web Site:* www.zionmusic.com, pg 945

McManus, Kevin T, Zion Music Group, 306 Monticello Rd, Franklin, TN 37064 *Tel:* 615-559-2108 *Fax:* 615-591-5102 *Web Site:* www.zionmusic.com, pg 945

McMaster, Margot, HDTV Productions Inc, 132-250 Shawville Blvd SE, No 209, Calgary, AB T2Y 2Z7, Canada *Tel:* 403-931-1936 *Web Site:* www.hdtvproductions.com, pg 777

McMenamin, Scott, Final Draft, A Cast & Crew Company, 2300 Empire Ave, Burbank, CA 91504 *Tel:* 818-995-8995; 818-906-8930 (tech support) *Toll Free Tel:* 800-231-4055 *E-mail:* info@finaldraft.com *Web Site:* www.finaldraft.com, pg 761

McMillan, Ray, The Fluorescent Co Inc, c/o Red*D*Mix Rentals Inc, 388 Carlaw Ave, Suite 116, Toronto, ON M4M 2T4, Canada *Tel:* 416-879-3761 *Fax:* 905-681-8520 *E-mail:* reddmix@cogeco.ca *Web Site:* www.flo-co.com, pg 763

McMillen, Rick, SuperDigital Ltd, 1150 NW 17 Ave, Portland, OR 97209-2403 *Tel:* 503-228-2222 *Toll Free Tel:* 888-79AUDIO (792-8346) *E-mail:* audiosales@superdigital.com *Web Site:* www.superdigital.com, pg 904

McMullen, Daniel, Blackwater Video Productions, PO Box 909, Morgantown, WV 26507 *Tel:* 304-296-4048 *E-mail:* blackwatervideo@hotmail.com *Web Site:* www.blackwatervideo.com, pg 707

McMullian, Matt, Audio Network US Inc, 48 W 25 St, 10th fl, New York, NY 10010 *Tel:* 646-688-4320 *E-mail:* nyoffice@audionetwork.com *Web Site:* us.audionetwork.com, pg 693

McNabb, Dennis, Staylor-Made Communications Inc, 11835 Carmel Mountain Rd, Suite 1304-365, San Diego, CA 92128-4609 *Toll Free Tel:* 800-711-6699 *E-mail:* info@staylor-made.com *Web Site:* staylor-made.com, pg 900

McNally, Gary, Macrosystem US Inc, 4282 Arnie Rd, Blaine, WA 98230 *Tel:* 360-371-4942 *Toll Free Tel:* 877-554-2846 *Toll Free Fax:* 855-269-6999 *E-mail:* info@macrosystem.us *Web Site:* www.macrosystem.us, pg 814

McNamara, Lynn, Michigan Film & Digital Media Office, 300 N Washington Sq, 4th fl, Lansing, MI 48913 *Tel:* 517-241-6757 *Toll Free Tel:* 800-477-FILM (477-3456) *Fax:* 517-241-3689 *E-mail:* mfo@michigan.org *Web Site:* www.michiganbusiness.org/industries/mfdmo, pg 972

McNamee, Kevin, Techni-Tool, a TestEquity LLC company, 1547 N Trooper Rd, Worcester, PA 19490 *Tel:* 610-941-2400 *Toll Free Tel:* 800-832-4866 *Fax:* 610-828-5623 *Toll Free Fax:* 800-854-8665 *E-mail:* sales@techni-tool.com; support@techni-tool.com (tech support) *Web Site:* www.techni-tool.com, pg 908

McNee, Doug, McNee Productions Inc, 3301 W Alabama St, Houston, TX 77098 *Tel:* 713-526-5333 *Fax:* 713-526-4634 *E-mail:* mcnee@mcnee.com *Web Site:* www.mcnee.com, pg 821

McNee, Sheryl, McNee Productions Inc, 3301 W Alabama St, Houston, TX 77098 *Tel:* 713-526-5333 *Fax:* 713-526-4634 *E-mail:* mcnee@mcnee.com *Web Site:* www.mcnee.com, pg 821

McNeil, Gary, Noramco Wire & Cable, 70 Glacier St, Coquitlam, BC V3K 5Y9, Canada *Tel:* 604-472-6980 *Toll Free Tel:* 800-663-8434 *Fax:* 604-472-6981 *E-mail:* norcorp@noramco.ca *Web Site:* www.noramco.ca, pg 841

McNelly, Jennifer, American Society of Safety Professionals (ASSP), 520 N Northwest Hwy, Park Ridge, IL 60068 *Tel:* 847-699-2929 (cust serv) *Fax:* 847-768-3434 *E-mail:* customerservice@assp.org *Web Site:* www.assp.org, pg 949

McNurlen, David, Hellman Associates Inc, 1225 W Fourth St, Waterloo, IA 50702 *Tel:* 319-234-7055 *Toll Free Tel:* 800-747-7055 *Fax:* 319-234-2089 *E-mail:* info@hellman.com *Web Site:* www.hellman.com, pg 778

McNutt, Don, Leo Ticheli Productions, 2801 University Blvd, Suite 101, Birmingham, AL 35233 *Tel:* 205-930-0500 *Fax:* 205-930-0505 *E-mail:* hello@ltpro.com *Web Site:* www.ltpro.com, pg 913

McQuay, John, Angstrom Lighting, 12224 Montague St, Pacoima, CA 91331 *Tel:* 323-462-4246 *E-mail:* info@angstromlighting.com *Web Site:* www.angstromlighting.com, pg 685

McQuillan, Maia, California Teleprompter, PO Box 13024, La Jolla, CA 92039-3024 *Tel:* 858-945-2076 *E-mail:* caprompter@aol.com *Web Site:* www.sandiegoteleprompter.com, pg 714

McRoberts, Anna, Air Bud Entertainment, 22525 Pacific Coast Hwy, Malibu, CA 90265 *Tel:* 310-317-4883 *Web Site:* www.airbud.com, pg 678

McTigue, Shawn, Lightning Eliminators & Consultants Inc, 6687 Arapahoe Rd, Boulder, CO 80303 *Tel:* 303-447-2828 *Toll Free Tel:* 800-521-6101 *Fax:* 303-447-8122 *E-mail:* info@lecglobal.com *Web Site:* www.lightningprotection.com, pg 808

McVaney, Justin, NAB Distinguished Service Award, 1771 "N" St NW, Washington, DC 20036 *Tel:* 202-429-5300 *E-mail:* nab@nab.org *Web Site:* www.nab.org, pg 997

McVerry, Bernadette, The Video Project, 145 Ninth St, Suite 102, San Francisco, CA 94103 *Tel:* 415-981-9710 *Toll Free Tel:* 800-475-2638 *Fax:* 415-692-6223 *E-mail:* orders@videoproject.com; support@videoproject.com *Web Site:* www.videoproject.com, pg 928

McWilliams, Becky, Liberty AV Solutions, 11675 Ridgeline Dr, Colorado Springs, CO 80921 *Tel:* 719-260-0061 *Toll Free Tel:* 800-530-8998 *Fax:* 719-260-0075 *E-mail:* orders@libav.com *Web Site:* secure. libertycable.com, pg 807

Meador, Walter, Laser Rentals Inc, 1953 S County Lane 282, Joplin, MO 64804 *Tel:* 417-782-8484 *E-mail:* laserwam@swbell.net *Web Site:* www. laserrentalsinc.com, pg 804

Meadows, Roxanne, Global Cyber-Visions, 21 Valley Lane, Venus, FL 33960 *Tel:* 863-465-0321 *E-mail:* tvp@thevenusproject.com *Web Site:* www. thevenusproject.com, pg 771

Meagher, Sean, Samson Technologies Corp, 278-B Duffy Ave, Hicksville, NY 11801 *Tel:* 516-870-7200 *Fax:* 516-938-1696 *E-mail:* info@samsontech.com *Web Site:* www.samsontech.com, pg 879

Mealey, Joseph, Deck Hand Inc, 1905 S Victory Blvd, Suite 8, Glendale, CA 91201 *Tel:* 818-557-8403 *Fax:* 818-557-8406 *E-mail:* info@deckhand.com *Web Site:* www.deckhand.com, pg 740

Means, Doug, CohuHD Costar LLC, 7330 Trade St, San Diego, CA 92121 *Tel:* 858-391-1800 *E-mail:* info@cohuhd.com *Web Site:* www.cohuhd.com, pg 727

Mecke, Richard, Texas Scenic Co Inc, 8053 Potranco Rd, San Antonio, TX 78251 *Tel:* 210-684-0091 *Toll Free Tel:* 800-292-7490 *Fax:* 210-684-4557 *E-mail:* info@texasscenic.com *Web Site:* www. texasscenic.com, pg 911

Medellin, Alan, Muller Entertainment LLC, 540 Commerce St, Southlake, TX 76092 *Tel:* 214-317-0800 *E-mail:* info@mullerentertainment.com *Web Site:* www.mullerentertainment.com, pg 833

Medi, Srini, Bisk Education, 9417 Princess Palm Ave, Tampa, FL 33619 *Toll Free Tel:* 800-280-9718 *E-mail:* media@bisk.com *Web Site:* www.bisk.com, pg 706

Medina, Carmen, Medina Software Inc, PO Box 952440, Lake Mary, FL 32795-2440 *Web Site:* www. medinasoft.com, pg 823

Medina, Jorge, Medina Software Inc, PO Box 952440, Lake Mary, FL 32795-2440 *Web Site:* www. medinasoft.com, pg 823

Meeuwsen, Jeffrey, Artist Residency Program, 1260 N Green Bay Rd, Lake Forest, IL 60045 *Tel:* 847-234-1063 *E-mail:* info@ragdale.org *Web Site:* www. ragdale.org, pg 982

Mehalko, Michael, MCCOM Inc, 383 Rte 206, Chester, NJ 07930 *Tel:* 908-879-9590 *Fax:* 908-879-9679 *Web Site:* www.mccom.tv, pg 820

Mehta, Navin, Poly, 345 Encinal St, Santa Cruz, CA 95060 *Tel:* 831-426-5858 *Toll Free Tel:* 800-544-4660 *Fax:* 831-426-6098 *Web Site:* www.poly.com, pg 859

Mehta, Rajeev, ALOM Technologies Corp, 48105 Warm Springs Blvd, Fremont, CA 94539-7498 *Tel:* 510-360-3600 *Toll Free Tel:* 800-500-9991 *Fax:* 510-226-7617 *E-mail:* customerservice@alom.com *Web Site:* www. alom.com, pg 681

Mein, Justin, C&I An Idea Agency, 541 NW First Ave, Fort Lauderdale, FL 33301 *Tel:* 954-357-3934 *E-mail:* contact@c-istudios.com *Web Site:* www.c-istudios.com, pg 716

Meiseberg, Oliver, Pixar Animation Studios, 1200 Park Ave, Emeryville, CA 94608 *Tel:* 510-922-3000 *Fax:* 510-922-3151 *Web Site:* www.pixar.com, pg 857

Meister, Peter, Ironbound Film & Television Studios LLC, 169 Malvern St, Newark, NJ 07105 *Tel:* 201-456-4754 *Web Site:* www.ironboundfilmstudios.com, pg 791

Melfa, Joseph, Tritech Communications, 625 Locust St, Suite 300, Garden City, NY 11530 *Tel:* 631-254-4500 *Fax:* 631-254-4499 *E-mail:* sales@tritechcomm.com *Web Site:* www.tritechcomm.com, pg 918

Melhorn, Erika, National Headliner Awards, PO Box 128, Somers Point, NJ 08244 *Tel:* 609-927-1850; 609-350-3099 *E-mail:* info@headlinerawards.org *Web Site:* www.headlinerawards.org, pg 997

Melhorn, Mark, National Headliner Awards, PO Box 128, Somers Point, NJ 08244 *Tel:* 609-927-1850; 609-350-3099 *E-mail:* info@headlinerawards.org *Web Site:* www.headlinerawards.org, pg 997

Melillo, John, Diversified, 37 Market St, Kenilworth, NJ 07033 *Tel:* 908-245-4833 *Fax:* 908-245-0011 *E-mail:* customerservice@diversifiedus.com; info@diversifiedus.com *Web Site:* diversifiedus.com, pg 744

Melkom, A G, GAMfilm Productions, 7559 Willoughby Ave, Suite 5, Los Angeles, CA 90046 *Tel:* 213-840-6212 *E-mail:* gamfilm@gmail.com *Web Site:* director-writer-producer.com, pg 768

Mellentine, Jeff, World Media Group Inc, 7373 Dogwood Park, Richland Hills, TX 76118 *Toll Free Tel:* 800-400-4964 *Fax:* 817-885-8859 *E-mail:* getstarted@worldmediagroup.com; information@worldmediagroup.com *Web Site:* www. worldmediagroup.com, pg 941

Mellentine, Josh, World Media Group Inc, 7373 Dogwood Park, Richland Hills, TX 76118 *Toll Free Tel:* 800-400-4964 *Fax:* 817-885-8859 *E-mail:* getstarted@worldmediagroup.com; information@worldmediagroup.com *Web Site:* www. worldmediagroup.com, pg 941

Mellott, John, Melmat Inc, 5333 Industrial Dr, Huntington Beach, CA 92649 *Tel:* 714-379-4555 *Toll Free Tel:* 800-635-6289 *Fax:* 714-379-4554 *E-mail:* info@melmat.com *Web Site:* www.melmat. com, pg 823

Mellott, Shelly, Final Draft, A Cast & Crew Company, 2300 Empire Ave, Burbank, CA 91504 *Tel:* 818-995-8995; 818-906-8930 (tech support) *Toll Free Tel:* 800-231-4055 *E-mail:* info@finaldraft.com *Web Site:* www. finaldraft.com, pg 761

Melo, Bernardo, The Singing Machine Co Inc, 6301 NW Fifth Way, Suite 2900, Fort Lauderdale, FL 33309 *Tel:* 954-596-1000 *Toll Free Tel:* 866-670-6888 (cust serv) *Fax:* 954-596-2000 *E-mail:* sales@singingmachine.com; customerservice@singingmachine.com *Web Site:* singingmachine.com, pg 889

Melton, Eric, University of Vermont, Instructional Television Dept, 538 Main St, Burlington, VT 05405 *Tel:* 802-656-2927 *E-mail:* video@uvm.edu *Web Site:* www.uvm.edu; www.uvm.edu/~video, pg 923

Meltzer, Jeff, Meltzer Media Productions, 49 Nassau St, 3rd fl, New York, NY 10038 *Tel:* 212-868-4600 *E-mail:* contact@meltzermedia.com *Web Site:* www. meltzermedia.com, pg 823

Melville, Jack, Foresight Imaging, One Executive Dr, Suite 202, Chelmsford, MA 01824 *Tel:* 978-458-4624 *Fax:* 978-458-5488 *E-mail:* info@fi-llc.com *Web Site:* www.fi-llc.com, pg 764

Memoli, Rich, Savage Universal Corp, 2050 S Stearman Dr, Chandler, AZ 85286 *Tel:* 480-632-1320 *Toll Free Tel:* 800-624-8891 *Fax:* 480-632-1322 *E-mail:* info486@savagepaper.com *Web Site:* savageuniversal.com, pg 881

Menard, Karen, Artel Video Systems, 5B Lyberty Way, Westford, MA 01886 *Tel:* 978-263-5775 *Toll Free Tel:* 800-225-0228 *Fax:* 978-263-9755 *E-mail:* sales@artel.com *Web Site:* www.artel.com, pg 690

Menasco, Richard W, Stereo Sales Inc, 1530 S Monroe St, Tallahassee, FL 32301 *Tel:* 850-224-2635 *E-mail:* sales@stereosales.net *Web Site:* www. stereosales.org; www.stereosales.net, pg 900

Mendelsohn, Aaron, Writers Guild of America, West (WGAW), 7000 W Third St, Los Angeles, CA 90048 *Tel:* 323-951-4000 *Toll Free Tel:* 800-548-4532 *Web Site:* www.wga.org, pg 963

Mendelsohn, Michael R, American Artists Representatives Inc, One Chatsworth Ave, No 518, Larchmont, NY 10538 *Tel:* 646-286-5633 (cell); 212-682-2462 *E-mail:* info@aareps.com *Web Site:* www. aareps.com, pg 682

Mendelsohn, Ron, Megatrax, 7629 Fulton Ave, North Hollywood, CA 91605 *Tel:* 818-255-7100 *Toll Free Tel:* 888-MEGA-555 (634-2555) *Fax:* 818-255-7199 *E-mail:* info@megatrax.com *Web Site:* www.megatrax. com, pg 823

Mendes, Robert, Digital Comm Link Inc, 10450 W State Rd 84, Davie, FL 33324-4206 *Tel:* 954-236-2993 *Toll Free Tel:* 877-532-5438 *Fax:* 954-236-3633 *E-mail:* bookings@dclinc.net *Web Site:* www.dclinc. net, pg 742

Mendiola, Jim, Premio Mesquite, 723 S Brazos St, San Antonio, TX 78207 *Tel:* 210-271-3151 *Fax:* 210-271-3480 *E-mail:* cine@guadalupeculturalarts.org *Web Site:* www.guadalupeculturalarts.org, pg 1000

Mendoza, Ivan, Audio Visual Concepts Inc, Rd 1, Km 29.3, Rio Canas, Caguas, PR 00725 *Tel:* 787-753-7700 *Fax:* 787-766-4578 *Web Site:* www.mig-avc.com, pg 694

Mendoza, Jorge, Premier Lighting & Production Co, 12023 Victory Blvd, North Hollywood, CA 91606 *Tel:* 818-762-0884 *Toll Free Tel:* 800-770-0884 *Fax:* 818-762-0896 *E-mail:* premier@premier-lighting. com; rentals@premier-lighting.com *Web Site:* www. premier-lighting.com, pg 861

Mendoza, Rhonda, DC Asian Pacific American Film Festival, 2515 Virginia Ave NW, No 58205, Washington, DC 20037 *Tel:* 202-796-9680; 202-792-6393 *E-mail:* info@apafilm.org; admin@apafilm.org *Web Site:* www.apafilm.org, pg 988

Menin, Julie, New York City Mayor's Office of Film, Theatre & Broadcasting, 6th fl, 1697 Broadway, New York, NY 10019 *Tel:* 212-489-6710 *Fax:* 212-307-6237 *Web Site:* www.nyc. gov/mome, pg 974

Menschik, Andrew, Imagivations, 11314 Sheldon St, Sun Valley, CA 91352 *Tel:* 818-767-6767 *Fax:* 818-767-3637 *E-mail:* info@imagivations.com *Web Site:* www. imagivations.com, pg 786

Mercado, David, SoundView Services Inc, One Phillips Dr NW, Leesburg, VA 20176 *Tel:* 703-777-9570 *Toll Free Tel:* 866-680-8189 *E-mail:* info@soundviewservices.com *Web Site:* www. soundviewservices.com, pg 895

Mercer, Branan, ExpoDisplays, 3401 Mary Taylor Rd, Birmingham, AL 35235 *Toll Free Tel:* 800-747-3976 *E-mail:* info@expodisplays.com *Web Site:* www. expodisplays.com, pg 757

Mercer, Mark, Southwest Binding & Laminating, 109 Millwell Ct, Maryland Heights, MO 63043-2509 *Tel:* 314-739-4400 *Toll Free Tel:* 800-325-3628 *Toll Free Fax:* 800-942-2010 *E-mail:* sales@swbindinglaminating.com *Web Site:* swbindinglaminating.com, pg 896

Mercer, Theo, Telepro Video Inc, 2650 Rd 32, Linwood, NE 68036 *Tel:* 402-593-0999 *E-mail:* tmtelepro@aol. com, pg 910

Merchant, Irfan, Vitruvian Entertainment, 4712 Admirality Way, Unit 417, Marina del Rey, CA 90292 *Tel:* 818-720-3250 (cell) *Web Site:* vitruvianent.com, pg 932

Merck, Harold, Merck & Hill Consultants Inc, 1995 N Park Place, Suite 450, Atlanta, GA 30339 *Tel:* 770-937-0185 *Fax:* 770-937-0919 *E-mail:* info@merckhill. com *Web Site:* www.merckhill.com, pg 823

Merrell, Don, Ivie Technologies Inc, 1195 Spring Creek Place, Suite B, Springville, UT 84663 *Tel:* 801-489-8703 *Toll Free Tel:* 877-829-6567 *E-mail:* ivie@ivie. com *Web Site:* www.ivie.com, pg 792

Merrell, Scott, Ivie Technologies Inc, 1195 Spring Creek Place, Suite B, Springville, UT 84663 *Tel:* 801-489-8703 *Toll Free Fax:* 877-829-6567 *E-mail:* ivie@ivie. com *Web Site:* www.ivie.com, pg 792

Merrill, Dina, RKO Pictures Inc, 11301 W Olympic Blvd, Suite 510, Los Angeles, CA 90064 *Tel:* 310-277-0707 *Fax:* 310-566-8940 *E-mail:* info@rko.com *Web Site:* rko.com, pg 875

Merrill, Robert, Associated Press Television News, 200 Liberty St, New York, NY 10281 *Tel:* 212-621-1500 *Fax:* 212-621-7419 *E-mail:* info@ap.org *Web Site:* www.aptn.com, pg 691

Merriman, Tyler, Bismeaux Studios, PO Box 463, Austin, TX 78767-0463 *Tel:* 512-444-9885 *Web Site:* www.bismeauxstudios.com, pg 706

Merritt, Iris, Yukon Film & Sound Commission (YFSC), Box 2703, Whitehorse, YT Y1A 2C6, Canada *Tel:* 867-667-5400; 867-661-0408 (ext 5400, no charge for calls from within Yukon) *Fax:* 867-393-6228 *E-mail:* info@reelyukon.com *Web Site:* www.reelyukon.com, pg 979

Merritts, Tim, Hite Co, 3101 Beale Ave, Altoona, PA 16601 *Tel:* 814-944-6121 *Toll Free Tel:* 800-252-3598 *Fax:* 814-944-3052 *E-mail:* altoona@mayerelectric.com *Web Site:* www.hiteco.com, pg 780

Messer, Melissa A, PAR Inc, 16204 N Florida Ave, Lutz, FL 33549 *Tel:* 813-449-4065 *Toll Free Tel:* 800-331-8378 *Fax:* 813-961-2196 *Toll Free Fax:* 800-727-9329 *E-mail:* cs@parinc.com *Web Site:* www.parinc.com, pg 851

Metcalfe, Tony, Acorn Productions, 13330 Noel Rd, No 1428, Dallas, TX 75240 *Tel:* 972-385-9977 *Fax:* 972-385-9944 *E-mail:* acornprod@aol.com, pg 674

Methven, Keith, SDMediaPros (SDMP), 5205 Kearny Villa Way, No 100, San Diego, CA 92123 *Tel:* 619-672-1000 *E-mail:* membership@sdmediapros.org; marketing@sdmediapros.org; programs@sdmediapros.org *Web Site:* sdmediapros.org, pg 962

Metrailler, Gerard, Corel Corp, 1600 Carling Ave, Ottawa, ON K1Z 8R7, Canada *Toll Free Tel:* 877-582-6735 *Web Site:* www.corel.com, pg 731

Metsch, Amy, Penguin Random House Audio Publishing, 1745 Broadway, New York, NY 10019 *E-mail:* audio@penguinrandomhouse.com *Web Site:* www.penguinrandomhouseaudio.com, pg 853

Metz, Steve, The Sound Lab Inc, 3355 Bee Cave Rd, Bldg 7, Suite 705, Austin, TX 78746 *Tel:* 512-476-2122 *Fax:* 512-476-2127 *E-mail:* info@thesoundlabinc.com *Web Site:* www.thesoundlabinc.com, pg 894

Metzger, Heather, Biblical Archaeology Society (BAS), 4710 41 St NW, Washington, DC 20016 *Tel:* 202-364-3300 *Toll Free Tel:* 800-221-4644 *Fax:* 202-364-2636 *E-mail:* bas@bib-arch.org; merchandise@bib-arch.org *Web Site:* www.biblicalarchaeology.org, pg 705

Metzker, Richard, Inspired Image Picture Co (IIPC), 1090 E Georgia St, Vancouver, BC V6A 2A7, Canada *Tel:* 604-874-7513 *Toll Free Tel:* 800-352-1454 (prodn rentals); 800-567-0037 (equip rentals) *Fax:* 604-874-7516 *E-mail:* info@inspiredimage.ca *Web Site:* inspiredimage.ca, pg 788

Meuleman, Bobbi-Jo, Idaho Film Office, 700 W State St, Boise, ID 83702 *Tel:* 208-334-2470 *Toll Free Tel:* 800-842-5858 *Fax:* 208-334-2631 *Web Site:* www.filmidaho.com, pg 970

Meurer, Bill, Birns & Sawyer Inc, 3039 Roswell St, Los Angeles, CA 90065 *Tel:* 323-466-8211 *E-mail:* info@birnsandsawyer.com *Web Site:* www.birnsandsawyer.com, pg 706

Meyer, Carolyn, Skjonberg Controls Inc, 1363 Donlon St, Suite 6, Ventura, CA 93003 *Tel:* 805-650-0877 *Fax:* 805-650-0360 *Toll Free Fax:* 800-650-0360 *E-mail:* sales@skjonberg.com *Web Site:* www.skjonberg.com, pg 890

Meyer, Chris, CD Meyer Inc, 15 Oak Rd, No 202, Fairfield, NJ 07004 *E-mail:* info@cdmeyer.com *Web Site:* www.cdmeyer.com; www.point2explore.com; museumdigitalsignage.com, pg 718

Meyer, Erich, Belar Electronics Laboratory Inc, 1140 McDermott Dr, Suite 105, West Chester, PA 19380-4043 *Tel:* 610-687-5550 *Fax:* 610-687-2686 *E-mail:* sales@belar.com *Web Site:* www.belar.com, pg 703

Meyer, John, Meyer Sound Laboratories Inc, 2832 San Pablo Ave, Berkeley, CA 94702 *Tel:* 510-486-1166 *Toll Free Tel:* 855-641-3288 (US & CN)

Fax: 510-486-8356 *E-mail:* sales@meyersound.com; techsupport@meyersound.com; service@meyersound.com *Web Site:* www.meyersound.com, pg 825

Meyer, Lutz, Recording Media & Equipment Inc (RM&E), 3736 SW 30 Ave, Fort Lauderdale, FL 33312 *Tel:* 954-791-9797 *Toll Free Tel:* 800-541-9797 *Fax:* 954-791-6662 *Web Site:* www.rmeinc.com, pg 872

Meyer, Mary, Recording Media & Equipment Inc (RM&E), 3736 SW 30 Ave, Fort Lauderdale, FL 33312 *Tel:* 954-791-9797 *Toll Free Tel:* 800-541-9797 *Fax:* 954-791-6662 *Web Site:* www.rmeinc.com, pg 872

Meyer, Ron, Centre Communications Inc, 75 Manhattan Dr, Suite 200, Boulder, CO 80303 *Tel:* 303-444-1166 *E-mail:* centre@ecentral.com *Web Site:* www.centrecommunicationinc.com; www.centredm.com, pg 720

Meyer, Ron, Professional Sound Corp, 28085 Smyth Dr, Valencia, CA 91355 *Tel:* 661-295-9395 *Fax:* 661-295-8398 *E-mail:* sales@professionalsound.com; service@professionalsound.com *Web Site:* www.professionalsound.com, pg 865

Meztista, Chris, Motion & Graphic Image Corp Inc (MAGIC), 25 McPhillips Ave, Mobile, AL 36604 *Web Site:* magichd.com, pg 831

Mezzetti, Phil, The Sound Lab Inc, 3355 Bee Cave Rd, Bldg 7, Suite 705, Austin, TX 78746 *Tel:* 512-476-2122 *Fax:* 512-476-2127 *E-mail:* info@thesoundlabinc.com *Web Site:* www.thesoundlabinc.com, pg 894

Mica, Rob, Skystorm Productions, 103 Commerce St, Suite 100, Lake Mary, FL 32746 *Tel:* 407-328-4747 *Toll Free Tel:* 800-783-8508 *Fax:* 407-328-4479 *E-mail:* info@skystorm.com *Web Site:* www.skystorm.com, pg 890

Miceli, AJ, PSSI Global Services LLC, 7030 Hayvenhurst Ave, Van Nuys, CA 91406 *Tel:* 310-575-4400 *Toll Free Tel:* 800-SAT-LINK (728-5465); 800-634-6530 (teleport inquiries) *E-mail:* info@pssiglobal.com *Web Site:* www.pssiglobal.com, pg 866

Miceli, John, Technomedia Solutions, 4545 36 St, Orlando, FL 32811 *Tel:* 407-351-0909 *Fax:* 407-248-9484 *E-mail:* sales@gotechnomedia.com *Web Site:* www.gotechnomedia.com, pg 909

Michael, David, Madison Square Garden, 2 Pennsylvania Plaza, New York, NY 10121-0091 *Tel:* 212-465-6741 *E-mail:* msgnetpr@msgnetwork.com *Web Site:* www.thegarden.com; themadisonsquaregardencompany.com, pg 814

Michaeloff, Scott, Comtel Inc, 14901 NE 20 Ave, North Miami, FL 33181 *Tel:* 305-424-4160 (facility servs); 305-424-4178 (local inquiries); 516-816-5152 (natl inquiries) *Web Site:* www.comtelinc.com; www.facebook.com/comtelinc/, pg 730

Michaels, Tracy, PSSI Global Services LLC, 7030 Hayvenhurst Ave, Van Nuys, CA 91406 *Tel:* 310-575-4400 *Toll Free Tel:* 800-SAT-LINK (728-5465); 800-634-6530 (teleport inquiries) *E-mail:* info@pssiglobal.com *Web Site:* www.pssiglobal.com, pg 866

Michalski, Amy, Association for Information and Image Management (AIIM), 1100 Wayne Ave, Suite 1100, Silver Spring, MD 20910 *Tel:* 301-587-8202 *Toll Free Tel:* 800-477-2446 *Fax:* 301-587-2711 *E-mail:* aiim@aiim.org *Web Site:* www.aiim.org, pg 950

Michel, Alan, HOME Inc, 566 Columbus Ave, Boston, MA 02118 *Tel:* 617-427-4663 *Fax:* 617-427-4664 *Web Site:* homeinc.org, pg 781

Michel, Brian, Accu-Tech, 11350 Old Roswell Rd, Suite 100, Roswell, GA 30009 *Toll Free Tel:* 888-222-8832 *Web Site:* www.accu-tech.com, pg 673

Michelson, Steve, The Video Project, 145 Ninth St, Suite 102, San Francisco, CA 94103 *Tel:* 415-981-9710 *Toll Free Tel:* 800-475-2638 *Fax:* 415-692-6223 *E-mail:* orders@videoproject.com; support@videoproject.com *Web Site:* www.videoproject.com, pg 928

Michielsen, Ken, Nesbit Systems Inc, 243 N Union St, Suite 112, Lambertville, NJ 08530 *Tel:* 609-397-7720 *E-mail:* info@nesbit.com *Web Site:* www.nesbit.com, pg 838

Michko, Lindsay, Shambhala Publications, 4720 Walnut St, Suite 106, Boulder, CO 80301 *Tel:* 720-799-8228 (cust serv); 303-222-9598; 720-799-8242 (course support) *Toll Free Tel:* 888-424-2329 (orders & cust serv) *Fax:* 617-236-1563 *E-mail:* customercare@shambhala.com; course-support@shambhala.com *Web Site:* www.shambhala.com, pg 885

Mickey, Bill, Michigan Office Solutions (MOS), A Xerox Company, 2859 Walkent Dr NW, Grand Rapids, MI 49544 *Toll Free Tel:* 800-442-9070 *E-mail:* info@mos-xerox.com *Web Site:* www.mos-xerox.com, pg 825

Miele, Joe, Diamond Studios, Woods Point 1, 1855 Data Dr, Suite 255, Hoover, AL 35244 *Tel:* 205-987-2121 *Fax:* 205-987-2128 *Web Site:* www.tvstuff.com, pg 741

Miele, Laura, Electronic Arts Inc, 209 Redwood Shores Pkwy, Redwood City, CA 94065 *Tel:* 650-628-1500 *Web Site:* www.ea.com, pg 752

Miesner, Charles, Broadway Digital, 1014 E Broadway, Louisville, KY 40204 *Tel:* 502-540-5301 *Fax:* 502-540-5565 *E-mail:* msworkscm@mindspring.com *Web Site:* www.broadwaydigital.us, pg 711

Miga, Mike, Superior Electric, One Cowles Rd, Plainville, CT 06062 *Tel:* 860-507-2025 *Toll Free Tel:* 800-787-3532 *Fax:* 860-507-2050 *Toll Free Fax:* 800-821-1369 *E-mail:* customer.service@superiorelectric.com *Web Site:* www.superiorelectric.com, pg 904

Mignola, Pete, MetroSonic Recording Studio, 143 Roebling St, 3rd fl, Brooklyn, NY 11211 *Tel:* 718-782-1872 *E-mail:* manager@metrosonic.net *Web Site:* www.metrosonic.net, pg 824

Mikeska, Fred, AC Lighting Inc, 88 Horner Ave, Toronto, ON M8Z 5Y3, Canada *Tel:* 416-255-9494 *Fax:* 416-255-3514 *E-mail:* northamerica@aclighting.com *Web Site:* www.aclighting.com, pg 672

Mikhitarian, A J, ACM Productions Ltd, 38 Bob Hill Rd, Ridgefield, CT 06877 *Tel:* 203-431-9575 *E-mail:* info@acmproductions.tv *Web Site:* www.acmproductions.tv, pg 674

Mikhitarian, Craig, ACM Productions Ltd, 38 Bob Hill Rd, Ridgefield, CT 06877 *Tel:* 203-431-9575 *E-mail:* info@acmproductions.tv *Web Site:* www.acmproductions.tv, pg 674

Milanese-DiStasio, Mary Ellen, Video Visions Inc, 3600 Boundbrook Ave, Trevose, PA 19053 *Tel:* 215-942-6642 *Fax:* 267-684-6819 *E-mail:* sales@video-visions.com *Web Site:* www.video-visions.com, pg 929

Milbery, Pete, Neutrik® USA Inc, 4115 Taggart Creek Rd, Charlotte, NC 28208 *Tel:* 704-972-3050 *Fax:* 704-438-9202 *Toll Free Fax:* 877-220-4089 *E-mail:* info@neutrikusa.com *Web Site:* www.neutrik.us, pg 838

Milbourn, Wes, KFOR-TV, 444 E Britton Rd, Oklahoma City, OK 73114 *Tel:* 405-424-4444 *Fax:* 405-478-6228 *Web Site:* www.kfor.com, pg 798

Milbourne, Jason, Custom Color Corp, 14320 W 101 Terr, Lenexa, KS 66215 *Tel:* 913-730-3100 *Fax:* 913-730-3101 *E-mail:* info@customcolor.com *Web Site:* www.customcolor.com, pg 736

Milbrodt, Bill, Milbrodt/Music & Sound Design, 1835 US Hwy 9, Howell, NJ 07731 *Tel:* 848-459-4965 *E-mail:* info@ideasinmedia.com *Web Site:* www.ideasinmedia.com, pg 827

Miles, Arik, Tropikal Productions, 137 Sequoia Rd, Rockwall, TX 75032 *Tel:* 972-771-3797 *Fax:* 972-771-0853 *E-mail:* tropikalproductions@gmail.com *Web Site:* www.tropikalproductions.com, pg 918

Miles, Arik, World Beat Studio, 137 Sequoia Rd, Rockwall, TX 75032 *Tel:* 972-771-3797 *Fax:* 972-771-0853 *E-mail:* tropikalproductions@gmail.com *Web Site:* www.tropikalproductions.com; www.tropikalproductions.com/studio.html, pg 941

Millen, Tim, Center for the Collaborative Classroom, 1001 Marina Village Pkwy, Suite 110, Alameda, CA 94501-1042 *Tel:* 510-533-0213 *Toll Free Tel:* 800-666-7270 *Fax:* 510-464-3670 *E-mail:* info@collaborativeclassroom.org *Web Site:* www.collaborativeclassroom.org, pg 719

Miller, Ali, Furnace MFG, 2719-B Dorr Ave, Fairfax, VA 22031 *Tel:* 703-205-0007 *Toll Free Tel:* 888-599-9883 *Fax:* 703-205-2951 *E-mail:* sales@furnacemfg.com *Web Site:* www.furnacemfg.com, pg 767

Miller, Amy, Band Pro Film & Digital Inc, 3403 W Pacific Ave, Burbank, CA 91505 *Tel:* 818-841-9655 *Toll Free Tel:* 888-BANDPRO (226-3776) *Fax:* 818-841-7649 *E-mail:* info@bandpro.com; customercare@bandpro.com *Web Site:* www.bandpro.com, pg 701

Miller, Amy, C&I An Idea Agency, 541 NW First Ave, Fort Lauderdale, FL 33301 *Tel:* 954-357-3934 *E-mail:* contact@c-istudios.com *Web Site:* www.c-istudios.com, pg 716

Miller, Barney, Barney Miller's Inc, 232 E Main St, Lexington, KY 40507-1310 *Tel:* 859-252-2216 *Toll Free Tel:* 800-755-6799 *Web Site:* www.barneymillers.com, pg 827

Miller, Beverly, United Scenic Artists Local 829, 29 W 38 St, 15th fl, New York, NY 10018 *Tel:* 212-581-0300 *Toll Free Tel:* 877-728-5635 *Fax:* 212-977-2011 *E-mail:* vfxinfo@usa829.org *Web Site:* www.usa829.org; vfx.usa829.org, pg 963

Miller, Blake, CSI Film & Video LLC, 1913 Sonora St, Fort Collins, CO 80525 *Tel:* 970-310-9039 *Web Site:* csifilms.com, pg 735

Miller, Brad, The Camera Division, 7351 Fulton Ave, North Hollywood, CA 91605 *Tel:* 323-465-7700 *Fax:* 818-997-3802 *E-mail:* rentals@thecameradivision.com *Web Site:* thecameradivision.com, pg 715

Miller, Brent, Ingenuity Films LLC, 8075 Livorna Way, Fair Oaks, CA 95628 *Toll Free Tel:* 844-411-FILM (411-3456) *E-mail:* support@ingenuityfilms.com *Web Site:* www.ingenuityfilms.com, pg 787

Miller, Chelsea, Virginia Theatre Association (VTA), 1111 Church St, Lynchburg, VA 24504 *Tel:* 434-845-7529 *E-mail:* executivedirector@vtasite.org *Web Site:* www.virginiatheatre.org, pg 963

Miller, Chris, PSNI (Professional Systems Network Intl), 1831 E 71 St, Tulsa, OK 74136 *Tel:* 918-388-1343 *Web Site:* www.psni.org, pg 961

Miller, Clay, Hollywood Lights Inc, 5251 SE McLoughlin Blvd, Portland, OR 97202-4836 *Tel:* 503-232-9001; 503-232-8855 *Toll Free Tel:* 800-826-9881 *Fax:* 503-517-8686 *E-mail:* portland@hollywoodlights.biz *Web Site:* www.hollywoodlights.biz, pg 780

Miller, Craig, Hammond Communications Group Inc, 173 Trade St, Lexington, KY 40511 *Tel:* 859-254-1878 *E-mail:* info@hammondcg.com *Web Site:* hammondcg.com, pg 775

Miller, Craig, Practising Law Institute, 1177 Avenue of the Americas, 2nd fl, New York, NY 10036 *Tel:* 212-824-5710 (cust serv) *Toll Free Tel:* 800-260-4PLI (260-4754) (cust serv) *Toll Free Fax:* 800-321-0093 (cust serv) *E-mail:* info@pli.edu; cs@pli.edu (cust serv) *Web Site:* www.pli.edu, pg 860

Miller, Dale, Christie Digital Systems USA Inc, 10550 Camden Dr, Cypress, CA 90630 *Tel:* 714-236-8610 *Toll Free Tel:* 866-880-4462 (cust serv) *Fax:* 714-503-3375 *E-mail:* sales-us@christiedigital.com; orders@christiedigital.com *Web Site:* www.christiedigital.com, pg 722

Miller, Daniel, U-Direct Productions Inc, 10 White St, 1st fl, New York, NY 10013 *Tel:* 212-647-9200 *Fax:* 212-625-9400 *E-mail:* udirect@udirect.nyc *Web Site:* udirect.nyc, pg 920

Miller, Debra, Midtown Video Inc, 4824 SW 74 Ct, Miami, FL 33155 *Tel:* 305-669-1117 *Fax:* 305-662-2860 *E-mail:* info@midtownvideo.com *Web Site:* midtownvideo.com, pg 827

Miller, Geoff, OmniMount Systems, 4409 E Baseline Rd, Suite 130, Phoenix, AZ 85042 *Tel:* 480-829-8000 *Toll Free Tel:* 800-MOUNT-IT (668-6848) *Fax:* 480-756-9000 *E-mail:* info@omnimount.com *Web Site:* www.omnimount.com, pg 845

Miller, Glenn, Side Door Studio Inc, 69 Albe Dr, Newark, DE 19702 *Tel:* 302-420-6211 *Fax:* 302-731-7601 *E-mail:* sdseng@sidedoorstudioinc.net *Web Site:* www.sidedoorstudioinc.net; www.facebook.com/sidedoorstudioinc, pg 887

Miller, Jacob Troy, Pendulum Entertainment, 444 Dufferin St, Studio 1, Toronto, ON M6K 2A3, Canada *Tel:* 416-721-7593 *E-mail:* info@pendulumentertainment.com *Web Site:* www.pendulumentertainment.com, pg 853

Miller, James, Dreambox Media Inc, PO Box 8132, Philadelphia, PA 19101-8132 *E-mail:* mail@dreamboxmedia.com *Web Site:* www.dreamboxmedia.com, pg 746

Miller, James E, WoodenBoat Publications, 41 WoodenBoat Lane, Brooklin, ME 04616 *Tel:* 207-359-4651 *Toll Free Tel:* 800-877-5284 (subns) *Fax:* 207-359-8920 *E-mail:* woodenboat@woodenboat.com *Web Site:* www.woodenboat.com, pg 941

Miller, Jeane P, Unitron Ltd, 73 Mall Dr, Commack, NY 11725 *Tel:* 631-543-2000 *Fax:* 631-589-6975 *E-mail:* info@unitronusa.com *Web Site:* www.unitronusa.com, pg 921

Miller, Jesse, Midtown Video Inc, 4824 SW 74 Ct, Miami, FL 33155 *Tel:* 305-669-1117 *Fax:* 305-662-2860 *E-mail:* info@midtownvideo.com *Web Site:* midtownvideo.com, pg 827

Miller, Jessie, Interlink Technologies, 139 W Indiana Ave, Suite 203, Perrysburg, OH 43552 *Tel:* 419-893-9011 *Toll Free Tel:* 800-655-5465 *Fax:* 419-893-7280 *E-mail:* info@thinkinterlink.com *Web Site:* thinkinterlink.com, pg 789

Miller, Jim, Metro Productions, 8570 Magellan Pkwy, Suite 400, Richmond, VA 23227 *Tel:* 804-261-1172 *Toll Free Tel:* 877-669-4687 *Fax:* 804-261-1885 *E-mail:* contactmetro@metro-productions.com *Web Site:* www.metro-productions.com, pg 824

Miller, Jim, RSS Distributors, 7930 Old Auction Rd, Manheim, PA 17545 *Tel:* 717-892-6743 *Toll Free Tel:* 800-233-0175 *Fax:* 717-892-5981 *E-mail:* orders@rssd.com *Web Site:* www.rssd.com, pg 878

Miller, Jonathan, Icarus Films Inc, 32 Court St, 21st fl, Brooklyn, NY 11201 *Tel:* 718-488-8900 *Toll Free Tel:* 800-876-1710 *Fax:* 718-488-8642 *E-mail:* mail@icarusfilms.com *Web Site:* www.icarusfilms.com, pg 783

Miller, Joseph, C&I An Idea Agency, 541 NW First Ave, Fort Lauderdale, FL 33301 *Tel:* 954-357-3934 *E-mail:* contact@c-istudios.com *Web Site:* www.c-istudios.com, pg 716

Miller, Joshua, C&I An Idea Agency, 541 NW First Ave, Fort Lauderdale, FL 33301 *Tel:* 954-357-3934 *E-mail:* contact@c-istudios.com *Web Site:* www.c-istudios.com, pg 716

Miller, Julia A, Delmark Records, 4121 N Rockwell, Chicago, IL 60618 *Tel:* 773-539-5001 *Fax:* 773-539-5004 *E-mail:* info@delmark.com *Web Site:* www.delmark.com, pg 740

Miller, Kenneth J, Midtown Video Inc, 4824 SW 74 Ct, Miami, FL 33155 *Tel:* 305-669-1117 *Fax:* 305-662-2860 *E-mail:* info@midtownvideo.com *Web Site:* midtownvideo.com, pg 827

Miller, Kevin, Staging Directions Inc, 1327 Northbrook Pkwy, Suite 440, Suwanee, GA 30024 *Tel:* 770-409-9909 *Toll Free Tel:* 800-782-4322 *Fax:* 770-409-0277 *E-mail:* sales@teamsdi.net *Web Site:* www.stagingdirections.com, pg 899

Miller, Leonard, Lex Products Corp, 15 Progress Dr, Shelton, CT 06484 *Tel:* 203-363-3738 *Toll Free Tel:* 800-643-4460 *Fax:* 203-363-3742 *E-mail:* info@lexproducts.com; orders@lexproducts.com; customerservice@lexproducts.com *Web Site:* www.lexproducts.com, pg 807

Miller, Lonnie, ExpoDisplays, 3401 Mary Taylor Rd, Birmingham, AL 35235 *Toll Free Tel:* 800-747-3976 *E-mail:* info@expodisplays.com *Web Site:* www.expodisplays.com, pg 757

Miller, Marilyn, Rhythmic Medicine, 10425 W 177 Terr, Overland Park, KS 66221 *Tel:* 913-851-5100 *E-mail:* music@rhythmicmedicine.com *Web Site:* www.rhythmicmedicine.com, pg 874

Miller, Mark, Panavid, 210 West Pkwy, Unit 5, Pompton Plains, NJ 07444 *Tel:* 973-831-5655 *E-mail:* info@panavid.com; support@panavid.com *Web Site:* www.panavid.com, pg 850

Miller, Mark, Transtar Entertainment Co Inc, 11776 E Evans Ave, Aurora, CO 80014 *Tel:* 303-489-1450 *Web Site:* www.transtarfilm.com, pg 917

Miller, Matt, Association of Independent Commercial Producers (AICP), 3 W 18 St, 5th fl, New York, NY 10011 *Tel:* 212-929-3000 *Fax:* 212-929-3359 *E-mail:* info@aicp.com *Web Site:* www.aicp.com, pg 951

Miller, Mike, Hybrid Studios, 3021 S Shannon St, Santa Ana, CA 92704 *Tel:* 714-850-1499 *E-mail:* info@hybridstudiosca.com *Web Site:* www.hybridstudiosca.com, pg 783

Miller, Mike, Earl Miller Productions Inc, 1702 W Koenig Lane, Austin, TX 78756 *Tel:* 512-458-4343 *Fax:* 512-458-4485 *E-mail:* info@earlmillerproductions.com *Web Site:* www.earlmillerproductions.com, pg 827

Miller, Noreen, Custom Video Productions Inc, 15 Lake Shore Dr, Red Bank, NJ 07701 *Tel:* 732-936-1001 *E-mail:* info@cvpnj.com *Web Site:* www.cvpnj.com, pg 736

Miller, Patti, Florida Film & Tape, 3417 Lake Breeze Rd, Orlando, FL 32808 *Tel:* 407-297-0091 *E-mail:* info@ffandt.com *Web Site:* ffandt.com, pg 763

Miller, Robert, LYRASIS, 1438 W Peachtree NW, Suite 150, Atlanta, GA 30309 *Tel:* 404-892-0943 *Toll Free Tel:* 800-999-8558 *Fax:* 404-892-7879 *Web Site:* www.lyrasis.org, pg 813

Miller, Robin, Filmaker Technology, 606 W Broad St, Bethlehem, PA 18018 *Tel:* 610-691-0900 *Fax:* 610-691-0952 *E-mail:* enquire@filmaker.com *Web Site:* www.filmaker.com, pg 760

Miller, Scott, DWD Theatre Design & Consulting, Suite 485, 425 Carrall St, Vancouver, BC V6B 6E3, Canada *Tel:* 604-874-0552 *E-mail:* info@d-w-d.com *Web Site:* www.d-w-d.com, pg 748

Miller, Sherman G, Multicom Inc, 1076 Florida Central Pkwy, Longwood, FL 32750 *Tel:* 407-331-7779 *Toll Free Tel:* 800-423-2594 *Fax:* 407-339-0204 *E-mail:* multicom@multicominc.com *Web Site:* www.multicominc.com, pg 833

Miller, Stan, Rosco Laboratories Inc, 52 Harbor View, Stamford, CT 06902 *Tel:* 203-708-8900 *Toll Free Tel:* 800-ROSCO NY (767-2669) *Fax:* 203-708-8919 *E-mail:* info@rosco.com *Web Site:* us.rosco.com, pg 877

Miller, Stephanie, Bullfrog Films Inc, 372 Dautrich Rd, Reading, PA 19606 *Tel:* 610-779-8226 *Toll Free Tel:* 800-543-3764 *Fax:* 610-370-1978 *E-mail:* info@bullfrogfilms.com; video@bullfrogfilms.com *Web Site:* www.bullfrogfilms.com, pg 712

Miller, Steven T, Concepts TV Productions Inc, 53 Indian Lane E, Towaco, NJ 07082 *Tel:* 973-331-1500 *Fax:* 973-331-1550 *E-mail:* sales@conceptstv.com *Web Site:* conceptstv.com, pg 730

Miller, Troy, National Religious Broadcasters (NRB), 600 N Capitol St NW, Suite 210, Washington, DC 20001 *Tel:* 202-543-0073 *Fax:* 202-543-2649 *E-mail:* info@nrb.org; press@nrb.org *Web Site:* nrb.org, pg 959

Milligan, Steve, Western Digital Corp, 5601 Great Oaks Pkwy, San Jose, CA 95119 *Tel:* 408-717-6000 *Toll Free Tel:* 800-275-4932 (tech support) *Web Site:* wdc.com, pg 936

Millisor, Karl, East Lansing Film Festival (ELFF), 210 Abbot Rd, Suite 48, East Lansing, MI 48823 *Tel:* 517-980-5802 *Web Site:* elff.com, pg 988

Millon, Craig, Jack Morton Worldwide, 909 Third Ave, New York, NY 10022 *Tel:* 212-401-7000; 212-401-7212 *E-mail:* experience@jackmorton.com *Web Site:* www.jackmorton.com, pg 830

Mills, Bill, Florida Film & Video, 4461 38 Way S, St Petersburg, FL 33711 *Tel:* 727-369-0732 *E-mail:* info@flhd.tv *Web Site:* www.flhd.tv, pg 763

Mills, Jan, Ross Video Ltd, 8 John St, Iroquois, ON K0E 1K0, Canada *Tel:* 613-652-4886 *Fax:* 613-652-4425 *E-mail:* solutions@rossvideo.com *Web Site:* www.rossvideo.com, pg 878

Mills, Kevin, Larrabee Sound Studio, 4162 Lankershim Blvd, North Hollywood, CA 91602 *Tel:* 818-753-0717 *Fax:* 818-753-8046 *E-mail:* info@larrabeestudios.com *Web Site:* www.larrabeestudios.com, pg 803

Mills, Rick, Creative Realities Inc (CRI), 13100 Magisterial Dr, Suite 100, Louisville, KY 40223 *Tel:* 502-791-8800 *Web Site:* cri.com, pg 733

Millsap, Michael, Alpine Optics Inc, 14 Helping Hands Way, Pisgah Forest, NC 28768 *Tel:* 828-884-5822 *E-mail:* info@alpine-optics.com *Web Site:* www.alpine-optics.com, pg 682

Milne, Craig, SIM Digital, One Atlantic Ave, Suite 110, Toronto, ON M6K 3E7, Canada *Tel:* 416-979-9958 *Fax:* 416-979-7770 *E-mail:* info.toronto@simdigital.com *Web Site:* www.simdigital.com, pg 888

Milne, Matt, TiVo Corp, 2 Circle Star Way, San Carlos, CA 94070 *Tel:* 408-562-8400 *Toll Free Tel:* 877-367-8486 (cust support); 877-289-8486 (sales support) *Fax:* 408-567-1800 *Web Site:* business.tivo.com; www.tivo.com, pg 914

Milneck, Greg, Digital FX Inc, 6010 Perkins Rd, Suite B, Baton Rouge, LA 70808 *Tel:* 225-763-6010 *Toll Free Tel:* 888-898-6010 *E-mail:* info@digitalfx.tv; rentals@digitalfx.tv *Web Site:* www.digitalfx.tv, pg 742

Milner, David, Milner-Fenwick Inc, 119 Lakefront Dr, Hunt Valley, MD 21030-2216 *Tel:* 410-252-1700 *Toll Free Tel:* 800-432-8433 *Fax:* 410-252-6316 *E-mail:* mail@milner-fenwick.com *Web Site:* www.milner-fenwick.com, pg 828

Milner, Richard, Milner-Fenwick Inc, 119 Lakefront Dr, Hunt Valley, MD 21030-2216 *Tel:* 410-252-1700 *Toll Free Tel:* 800-432-8433 *Fax:* 410-252-6316 *E-mail:* mail@milner-fenwick.com *Web Site:* www.milner-fenwick.com, pg 828

Milner, Stan, ON Services, a GES Company, 6779 Crescent Dr, Norcross, GA 30071 *Tel:* 770-457-0966 *Toll Free Tel:* 800-967-2419 *Fax:* 770-451-7925 *E-mail:* service@oneventservices.com; atlanta@oneventservices.com *Web Site:* www.oneventservices.com, pg 846

Mims, Liz, Austin Film Festival, 1801 Salina St, Austin, TX 78702 *Tel:* 512-478-4795 *Toll Free Tel:* 800-310-FEST (310-3378) *Fax:* 512-478-6205 *E-mail:* info@austinfilmfestival.com; programming@austinfilmfestival.com; marketing@austinfilmfestival.com *Web Site:* www.austinfilmfestival.com, pg 982

Mince, Craig, Indianapolis International Film Festival, 125 W South St, No 1930, Indianapolis, IN 46206 *Tel:* 317-560-4433 *E-mail:* info@indyfilmfest.org; submissions@indyfilmfest.org *Web Site:* indyfilmfest.org, pg 992

Minchella, Chris, Micor Analytics, 7538 Saint Louis Ave, Skokie, IL 60076 *Tel:* 847-329-8590 *Fax:* 847-329-8599 *Web Site:* www.micoranalytics.com, pg 825

Minchella, James, Micor Analytics, 7538 Saint Louis Ave, Skokie, IL 60076 *Tel:* 847-329-8590 *Fax:* 847-329-8599 *Web Site:* www.micoranalytics.com, pg 825

Minchew, Daniel, Atlanta Filmworks, 4280 Northeast Expwy, Atlanta, GA 30340 *E-mail:* info@atlantafilmworks.com *Web Site:* atlantafilmworks.com, pg 692

Minchew, Daniel, Studio Space Atlanta, 3080 McCall Dr, Suite 2, Atlanta, GA 30340 *Tel:* 404-630-0508 *E-mail:* info@studiospaceatl.com *Web Site:* www.studiospaceatl.com, pg 903

Mineroff, Saul, Saul Mineroff Electronics Inc (SME), 574 Meacham Ave, Elmont, NY 11003 *Tel:* 516-775-1370 *Fax:* 516-775-1371 *E-mail:* tapenixon@aol.com *Web Site:* www.mineroff.com, pg 828

Minga, Gianni, Hawaii International Film Festival, 680 Iwilei Rd, Suite 100, Honolulu, HI 96817 *Tel:* 808-792-1577 (ext 7) *Fax:* 808-792-1583 *Toll Free Fax:* 877-749-7783 *E-mail:* info@hiff.org; entries@hiff.org *Web Site:* www.hiff.org, pg 991

Mingle, Robyn T, CommScope Inc, 1100 CommScope Place SE, Hickory, NC 28602 *Tel:* 828-324-2200 *Toll Free Tel:* 800-982-1708 *E-mail:* publicrelations@commscope.com *Web Site:* www.commscope.com, pg 728

Mingo, Tom, Williams AV LLC, 10300 Valley View Rd, Eden Prairie, MN 55344-3446 *Tel:* 952-943-2252 *Toll Free Tel:* 800-328-6190 *Fax:* 952-943-2174 *E-mail:* info@williamsav.com *Web Site:* www.williamsav.com, pg 939

Minifie, Tom, Applied Voice & Speech Technologies Inc (AVST), 27042 Towne Centre Dr, Suite 200, Foothill Ranch, CA 92610-2810 *Tel:* 949-699-2300 *Toll Free Tel:* 866-368-0400 *Fax:* 949-699-2301 *E-mail:* info@avst.com; sales@avst.com *Web Site:* www.avst.com, pg 688

Minkoff, Michael, Lefco Video Services Inc, 600 W Sunset Rd, Suite 103, Henderson, NV 89011 *Tel:* 702-566-1770 *Fax:* 702-566-1798 *E-mail:* info1@lefco.com *Web Site:* www.lefco.com, pg 806

Minnemeyer, Merritt, DEC Grants, 696 Dutchess Tpke, Suite F, Poughkeepsie, NY 12603 *Tel:* 845-454-3222 *E-mail:* info@artsmidhudson.org *Web Site:* www.artsmidhudson.org, pg 988

Minor, Debbie, Audience Response Systems Inc, 5611-C E Morgan Ave, Evansville, IN 47715 *Tel:* 812-479-7507 *Toll Free Tel:* 800-INVOLVE (468-6583) *Fax:* 812-479-1057 *E-mail:* arsales@audienceresponse.com *Web Site:* www.audienceresponse.com, pg 693

Mirabella, Dennis, Pro-Tape & Specialities Inc, 621 Rte 1 S, Suite B, North Brunswick, NJ 08902 *Tel:* 732-346-0900 *Toll Free Tel:* 800-345-0234 *Fax:* 732-729-7373 *Web Site:* www.protapes.com, pg 863

Miranda, Bobby, Alliance Entertainment Corp (AEC) LLC, 1401 NW 136 Ave, Suite 100, Sunrise, FL 33323 *Toll Free Tel:* 800-329-7664 *Web Site:* www.aent.com, pg 680

Mirrer, Louise, The New York Historical Society, 170 Central Park W, New York, NY 10024 *Tel:* 212-873-3400 *Fax:* 212-787-9474 *Web Site:* www.nyhistory.org, pg 840

Mirvish, Dan, Slamdance Film Festival, 5634 Melrose Ave, Los Angeles, CA 90038 *Tel:* 323-466-1786 *Fax:* 323-466-1784 *E-mail:* submissions@slamdance.com *Web Site:* www.slamdance.com, pg 1004

Mis, Tom, Macmillan Audio, 120 Broadway, 22nd fl, New York, NY 10271 *Tel:* 646-600-7856; 646-307-5472 *Toll Free Tel:* 888-330-8477 (cust serv); 800-221-7945 *Toll Free Fax:* 800-672-7703 (orders) *E-mail:* macmillan.audio@macmillanusa.com *Web Site:* www.macmillanaudio.com, pg 814

Misaka, Kirk, DASAN Zhone Solutions (DZS) Inc, 7195 Oakport St, Oakland, CA 94621 *Tel:* 510-777-7000 *Toll Free Tel:* 877-ZHONE-20 (946-6320, US & CN) *Fax:* 510-777-7001 *Web Site:* dasanzhone.com, pg 737

Misconi, Michael, Digital Zoetrope Productions, 1902 Oak St, Melbourne, FL 32901 *Tel:* 321-821-7404 *Fax:* 321-821-2287 *Web Site:* digitalzoetrope.com, pg 742

Mishkov, Hristo, AheadTeK, 6410 Via Del Oro, San Jose, CA 95119 *Tel:* 408-226-9800; 408-226-9991 *Toll Free Tel:* 800-971-9191 *Fax:* 408-226-9195 *Web Site:* www.aheadtek.com, pg 678

Miskowski, Jon, Wisconsin Public Television, 821 University Ave, Madison, WI 53706 *Tel:* 608-263-2121 *Toll Free Tel:* 800-422-9707 *Fax:* 608-263-9763 *E-mail:* comments@wpt.org *Web Site:* www.wpt.org, pg 940

Mitchell, Bill, Blue Sky Stock Footage, PO Box 177, Santa Fe, NM 87504-0177 *Tel:* 310-859-4709 *E-mail:* sales@blueskyfootage.com *Web Site:* www.blueskyfootage.com, pg 708

Mitchell, Charlie, Dogwood Productions Inc, 757 Government St, Mobile, AL 36602 *Tel:* 251-476-0858 *Toll Free Tel:* 800-254-9903 *Fax:* 251-479-0364 *E-mail:* info@dogwoodproductions.com *Web Site:* www.dogwoodproductions.com, pg 745

Mitchell, Donna, Horizon Video Productions Inc, 6114 Fayetteville St, Suite 106, Durham, NC 27713 *Tel:* 919-941-0901 *Toll Free Tel:* 800-768-3776 *Fax:* 919-941-1939 *E-mail:* info@horizonvp.com *Web Site:* www.horizonvp.com, pg 781

Mitchell, Greg, Limelight Production® Inc, 471 Pleasant St, Lee, MA 01238-9322 *Tel:* 413-243-4950 *Toll Free Tel:* 800-243-4950 *Fax:* 413-243-4993 *Toll Free Fax:* 800-243-4951 *E-mail:* info@limelightproductions.com; sales@limelightproductions.com *Web Site:* www.limelightproductions.com, pg 809

Mitchell, J E, Mitchell Acoustics Research, 2005B Industrial Blvd, Rockwall, TX 75087 *Tel:* 214-741-7136 *Toll Free Fax:* 866-492-2470 *E-mail:* info@frazierspeakers.com *Web Site:* www.frazierspeakers.com, pg 828

Mitchell, James F, DVDs4Less, 6519 Jamon Dr, Sparks, NV 89436-9142 *Tel:* 775-323-0965 *Toll Free Tel:* 800-852-2330 *Fax:* 775-323-1055 *E-mail:* info@dvds4less.net *Web Site:* www.dvds4less.net, pg 748

Mitchell, Jim, Skyfire Video, PO Box 2266, Sparks, NV 89432 *Tel:* 775-323-0965 *Toll Free Tel:* 800-852-2330 *Web Site:* www.skyfirevideo.com, pg 890

Mitchell, Linda, CamMate Systems, 425 E Comstock, Chandler, AZ 85225 *Tel:* 480-813-9500 *Fax:* 480-813-9292 *Web Site:* www.cammate.com, pg 715

Mitchell, Marv, Communications Media Management Association (CMMA), 1604 Glendale Hills Dr NE, Suite B25, Rochester, MN 55906-8376 *Tel:* 507-271-4307 *Web Site:* cmma.org, pg 953

Mitchell, Mitch, The Independent Filmmaker Project (IFP), c/o Made in NY Media Ctr by IFP, 30 John St, Ground fl, Brooklyn, NY 11201 *Tel:* 212-465-8200 *Web Site:* www.ifp.org, pg 956

Mitchell, Pete, Vancouver Film Studios Ltd, 3500 Cornett Rd, Vancouver, BC V5M 2H5, Canada *Tel:* 604-453-5000 *Fax:* 604-453-5045 *E-mail:* info@vancouverfilmstudios.com *Web Site:* www.vancouverfilmstudios.com, pg 924

Mitchell, Steve, ACDC Audio CD & Cassette, 606 Alamo Pintado Rd, Suite 3-281, Solvang, CA 93463 *Tel:* 818-762-ACDC (762-2232) *Web Site:* www.acdc-cdr.com, pg 674

Miteva, Jodi Stewart, Close Up Foundation, 1330 Braddock Place, Suite 400, Alexandria, VA 22314 *Tel:* 703-706-3300 *Toll Free Tel:* 800-CLOSEUP (256-7387) *E-mail:* info@closeup.org *Web Site:* www.closeup.org, pg 726

Mitsui, Scott, Mark Woollen & Associates, 207 Ashland Ave, Santa Monica, CA 90405 *Tel:* 310-399-2690 *E-mail:* info@markwoollen.com *Web Site:* www.markwoollen.com, pg 941

Mittenberg, Paul, Palardo Productions, 1807 Taft Ave, Suite 4, Hollywood, CA 90028 *Tel:* 323-469-8991 *E-mail:* palardo2@msn.com, pg 850

Mitter, Seth, Canyon Cinema Inc, 1777 Yosemite Ave, Suite 210, San Francisco, CA 94124 *Tel:* 415-626-2255 *E-mail:* info@canyoncinema.com *Web Site:* canyoncinema.com, pg 716

Miyahira, Chuck, HM Electronics Inc (HME), 14110 Stowe Dr, Poway, CA 92064 *Tel:* 858-535-6000 *Toll Free Tel:* 800-848-4468 (dom sales) *Fax:* 858-452-7207; 858-552-0139 (dom sales) *E-mail:* info@hme.com *Web Site:* www.hme.com, pg 780

Miyazaki, Go, FUJIFILM North America Corp, 200 Summit Lake Dr, Valhalla, NY 10595-1356 *Tel:* 914-789-8100 *Toll Free Tel:* 800-755-3854 *Fax:* 914-789-8530 *Web Site:* www.fujifilmusa.com/northamerica, pg 766

Mizzo, Rick, ALOM Technologies Corp, 48105 Warm Springs Blvd, Fremont, CA 94539-7498 *Tel:* 510-360-3600 *Toll Free Tel:* 800-500-9991 *Fax:* 510-226-7617 *E-mail:* customerservice@alom.com *Web Site:* www.alom.com, pg 681

Mobilia, Kristen, VideoLink Inc, an AVI-SPL company, 1230 Washington St, West Newton, MA 02465 *Tel:* 617-340-4100 *Toll Free Tel:* 800-452-5565 *Fax:* 617-340-4101 *E-mail:* sales@videolinktv.com *Web Site:* www.videolinktv.com, pg 929

Mobley, Douglas C, Gilderfluke & Co Inc, 205 S Flower St, Burbank, CA 91502 *Tel:* 818-840-9484 *Toll Free Tel:* 800-776-5972 *Fax:* 818-840-9485 *E-mail:* info@gilderfluke.com *Web Site:* www.gilderfluke.com, pg 771

Mobley, Jim, Renkus-Heinz Inc, 19201 Cook St, Foothill Ranch, CA 92610-3501 *Tel:* 949-588-9997 *Fax:* 949-588-9514 *E-mail:* sales@renkus-heinz.com *Web Site:* www.renkus-heinz.com, pg 873

Mockbee, Sarah Ann, Austin Film Society (AFS), 1901 E 51 St, Austin, TX 78723 *Tel:* 512-322-0145 *E-mail:* afs@austinfilm.org *Web Site:* www.austinfilm.org, pg 951

Mockensturm, Dan, Mach 1 Productions, 1101 N Himes Ave, Tampa, FL 33607 *Tel:* 813-873-7700 *Fax:* 813-875-6633 *E-mail:* info@mach1pro.com *Web Site:* www.mach1pro.com, pg 814

Moe, Erik, Kaboom Productions, 2169 Folsom St, Suite 201-M, San Francisco, CA 94110 *Tel:* 415-434-2666 *Fax:* 415-874-9324 *E-mail:* hello@kaboomproductions.com *Web Site:* kaboomproductions.com, pg 796

Moffatt, Shawn, Go To Team, 665 Johnnie Dodds Blvd, Suite 201, Mount Pleasant, SC 29464 *Tel:* 843-884-6222 *Toll Free Tel:* 888-455-4333 *E-mail:* crew@gototeam.com *Web Site:* www.gototeam.com, pg 772

Moggre, Martin, Freeman, 1600 Viceroy, Suite 100, Dallas, TX 75235 *Tel:* 214-445-1000 *Web Site:* www.freeman.com, pg 765

Mohiuddin, Sameer, Bitcentral Inc, 4340 Von Karman Ave, Suite 400, Newport Beach, CA 92660 *Tel:* 949-253-9000 *Toll Free Tel:* 800-272-4004 (support) *E-mail:* sales@bitcentral.com; support@bitcentral.com *Web Site:* www.bitcentral.com, pg 706

Mohney, Ron, IPI - Member Network™, 2518 Anthem Village Dr, Suite 104, Henderson, NV 89052 *Tel:* 702-617-1141 *Fax:* 702-617-1181 *E-mail:* info@ipiphoto.com *Web Site:* www.ipiphoto.com, pg 957

Molidor, Paul, Film Ideas Inc, 308 N Wolf Rd, Wheeling, IL 60090 *Tel:* 847-419-0255 *Toll Free Tel:* 800-475-3456 (US only) *Fax:* 847-419-8933 *E-mail:* info@filmideas.com; orders@filmideas.com (cust serv) *Web Site:* www.filmideas.com, pg 760

Molina, Ed, Crispin Corp, 600 Wade Ave, Raleigh, NC 27605 *Tel:* 919-845-7744 *Fax:* 919-845-7766 *E-mail:* welisten@crispincorp.com; support@crispincorp.com *Web Site:* www.crispincorp.com, pg 735

Molinari, Tony, Foresight Imaging, One Executive Dr, Suite 202, Chelmsford, MA 01824 *Tel:* 978-458-4624 *Fax:* 978-458-5488 *E-mail:* info@fi-llc.com *Web Site:* www.fi-llc.com, pg 764

Molnar, David, McCune Audio-Video-Lighting, 101 Utah Ave, South San Francisco, CA 94080 *Tel:* 650-873-1111 *Toll Free Tel:* 800-899-7686 *Fax:* 650-246-6702 *E-mail:* info@mccune.com *Web Site:* www.mccune.com, pg 821

Molner, Sue, F&F Productions LLC, 14333 Myerlake Circle, Clearwater, FL 33760 *Tel:* 727-530-5000 *Fax:* 727-535-6547 *E-mail:* info@fandfhd.tv *Web Site:* www.fandfhd.tv, pg 759

Moloney, Steven, Precision Camera & Video Repair Inc, 7 Anngina Dr, Enfield, CT 06082 *Tel:* 860-749-7380; 860-272-2100 *Toll Free Tel:* 800-665-6515 (cust serv) *E-mail:* info@precisioncamera.com *Web Site:* www.precisioncamera.com, pg 861

Moloney, Wes, Hi-Tech Lamps Inc, 922 San Leandro Ave, Suite B, Mountain View, CA 94043 *Tel:* 650-961-9031 *Toll Free Tel:* 800-229-6509 *Fax:* 650-961-9033 *E-mail:* info@hi-techlamps.com *Web Site:* www.hi-techlamps.com, pg 779

Monczynski, Laura, WMS Media Inc, 189 W Santa Clara St, San Jose, CA 95110 *Tel:* 510-825-7402 *E-mail:* info@wmsmedia.com *Web Site:* www.wmsmedia.com, pg 940

Monie, Alain, Ingram Micro, 3351 Michelson Dr, Suite 100, Irvine, CA 92612 *Tel:* 714-566-1000 *Web Site:* www.ingrammicro.com, pg 788

Monko, Cezary L, ACCO Brands Corp, 4 Corporate Dr, Lake Zurick, IL 60047-8997 *Toll Free Tel:* 800-541-0094; 800-222-6462 *Toll Free Fax:* 800-941-4463 *E-mail:* contactus@acco.com (cust serv) *Web Site:* www.accobrands.com, pg 673

Monseur, Mary, Smithsonian Folkways Recordings, 600 Maryland Ave SW, Suite 2001, Washington, DC 20024 *Tel:* 202-633-6450 *Toll Free Tel:* 888-FOLKWAYS (365-5929) *Fax:* 202-633-6477 *E-mail:* smithsonianfolkways@si.edu *Web Site:* folkways.si.edu, pg 891

Montague, Adrianna, American Foundation for the Blind (AFB), 2 Penn Plaza, Suite 1102, New York, NY 10121 *Tel:* 212-502-7600 *Toll Free Tel:* 800-232-5463 *Fax:* 212-502-7777 *Toll Free Fax:* 888-545-8331 *E-mail:* info@afb.org *Web Site:* www.afb.org, pg 948

Montague, Larry N, TAPPI, 15 Technology Pkwy S, Norcross, GA 30092 *Tel:* 770-446-1400 *Toll Free Tel:* 800-332-8686 (US); 800-446-9431 (CN) *Fax:* 240-396-5973 *E-mail:* memberconnection@tappi.org *Web Site:* www.tappi.org, pg 907

Montfort, Matthew, Ancient Future, PO Box 264, Kentfield, CA 94914-0264 *Tel:* 415-459-1892 *E-mail:* info@ancient-future.com *Web Site:* www.ancient-future.com, pg 685

Montgomery, Gordon, Antenna International, 383 Main Ave, Norwalk, CT 06851 *Tel:* 203-523-0320 *E-mail:* inquiry@antennainternational.com; marketing@antennainternational.com *Web Site:* www.antennainternational.com, pg 686

Montooth, Tonya, San Diego Film Festival, 2683 Via de la Valle, Suite G-210, Del Mar, CA 92014 *Tel:* 619-818-2221 *E-mail:* info@sdfilmfest.com *Web Site:* www.sdfilmfest.com, pg 1002

Moody, Bruce A, American Production Services LLC, 1763 Earl Dr, Fort Mill, SC 29715 *Tel:* 803-548-2290 *Fax:* 803-548-3406 *Web Site:* www.apsvideo.com, pg 684

Mooney, Carol, Donna Lawrence Productions, 624 Baxter Ave, Louisville, KY 40204 *Tel:* 502-589-9617 *E-mail:* dlp@dlproductions.com *Web Site:* www.dlproductions.com, pg 804

Mooney, Patty, Crystal Pyramid Productions™, 7323 Rondel Ct, San Diego, CA 92119-1530 *Tel:* 619-644-3000 *E-mail:* info@crystalpyramid.com *Web Site:* sandiegovideoproduction.com, pg 735

Mooney, Patty, New & Unique Videos™, 7323 Rondel Ct, San Diego, CA 92119-1530 *Tel:* 619-644-3000 *E-mail:* video@newuniquevideos.com *Web Site:* www.newuniquevideos.com, pg 839

Moorcroft, Kegn Marissa, Sedona Film Office, 45 Sunset Dr, Sedona, AZ 86336 *Tel:* 928-204-1123 (ext 170) *Fax:* 928-204-1064 *E-mail:* pr@sedonachamber.com *Web Site:* visitsedona.com/about-us/film-office, pg 965

Moore, Cornelious, California Newsreel, 44 Gough St, Suite 303, San Francisco, CA 94103 *Tel:* 415-284-7800 *Fax:* 415-284-7801 *E-mail:* contact@newsreel.org *Web Site:* www.newsreel.org, pg 714

Moore, Dan, Indianapolis International Film Festival, 125 W South St, No 1930, Indianapolis, IN 46206 *Tel:* 317-560-4433 *E-mail:* info@indyfilmfest.org; submissions@indyfilmfest.org *Web Site:* indyfilmfest.org, pg 992

Moore, Erica, Follett School Solutions Inc, 1340 Ridgeview Dr, McHenry, IL 60050 *Tel:* 815-759-1700 *Toll Free Tel:* 888-511-5114 (cust serv); 877-899-8550 (sales) *Fax:* 815-759-9831 *Toll Free Fax:* 800-852-5458 *E-mail:* info@follettlearning.com; customerservice@follett.com *Web Site:* www.follettlearning.com; www.follett.com/prek12; www.titlewave.com, pg 763

Moore, Gisela, Tennessee Entertainment Commission, Tennessee Tower, 27th fl, 312 Rosa L Parks Ave, Nashville, TN 37243 *Tel:* 615-741-FILM (741-3456) *Toll Free Tel:* 877-818-FILM (818-3456) *E-mail:* tn.film@tn.gov *Web Site:* www.tnentertainment.com, pg 976

Moore, Gordon, Lectrosonics Inc, 581 Laser Rd NE, Rio Rancho, NM 87124 *Tel:* 505-892-4501 *Toll Free Tel:* 800-821-1121 *Fax:* 505-892-6243 *E-mail:* sales@lectrosonics.com *Web Site:* www.lectrosonics.com, pg 805

Moore, Greg, MooreCo Inc, 2885 Lorraine Ave, Temple, TX 76501 *Toll Free Tel:* 800-749-2258 *Toll Free Fax:* 866-888-7483 *Web Site:* moorecoinc.com; mooreco360.com, pg 830

Moore, Jeff, Ross Video Ltd, 8 John St, Iroquois, ON K0E 1K0, Canada *Tel:* 613-652-4886 *Fax:* 613-652-4425 *E-mail:* solutions@rossvideo.com *Web Site:* www.rossvideo.com, pg 878

Moore, Jeff, StageSound, 2240 Shenandoah Ave NW, Roanoke, VA 24017 *Tel:* 540-342-2040 *Toll Free Tel:* 800-778-9839 *Fax:* 540-345-5158 *Web Site:* stagesound.com, pg 899

Moore, John, Dage-MTI, 701 N Roeske Ave, Michigan City, IN 46360 *Tel:* 219-872-5514 *Fax:* 219-872-5559 *E-mail:* info@dagemti.com *Web Site:* dagemti.com, pg 737

Moore Kech, Julie, Starline Costumes, 1286 Bandera Rd, San Antonio, TX 78228 *Tel:* 210-435-3535 *Fax:* 210-435-9425 *Web Site:* starlinecostumes.com, pg 900

Moore, Michael, Universal Studios, 100 Universal City Plaza, Universal City, CA 91608-1002 *Toll Free Tel:* 800-892-1979 *Fax:* 818-866-0293 *E-mail:* studio.operations2@nbcuni.com *Web Site:* www.nbcuni.com; universalstudioslot.com, pg 922

Moore, Peggy, Dage-MTI, 701 N Roeske Ave, Michigan City, IN 46360 *Tel:* 219-872-5514 *Fax:* 219-872-5559 *E-mail:* info@dagemti.com *Web Site:* dagemti.com, pg 737

Moore, William J, Ipitek Inc, 2461 Impala Dr, Carlsbad, CA 92010 *Tel:* 760-438-1010 *Toll Free Tel:* 888-4-IPITEK (447-4835, US only) *Fax:* 760-438-2412 *E-mail:* sales@ipitek.com *Web Site:* www.ipitek.com, pg 791

Moquist, Burton, Stanco Sales LLC, 1529 S Terry St, Longmont, CO 80501 *Tel:* 303-776-3770, pg 899

Morales, Jan, Fricon Entertainment Co Inc, 134 Bluegrass Circle, Hendersonville, TN 37075 *Tel:* 615-826-2288 *Fax:* 615-826-0500, pg 766

Moran, Bob, Antenna International, 383 Main Ave, Norwalk, CT 06851 *Tel:* 203-523-0320 *E-mail:* inquiry@antennainternational.com; marketing@antennainternational.com *Web Site:* www.antennainternational.com, pg 686

Moran, Dan, Genesis Integration, 14721 123 Ave NW, Edmonton, AB T5L 2Y6, Canada *Toll Free Tel:* 877-283-2253 (Toronto); 866-622-2966 (Quebec); 844-436-4681 (rest of CN) *E-mail:* marketing@genint.com *Web Site:* www.genint.com, pg 770

Moran, Matt, WSAZ-TV NewsChannel 3, 645 Fifth Ave, Huntington, WV 25701 *Tel:* 304-697-4780 *Fax:* 304-690-3065 (newsroom); 304-690-3061 (sales) *E-mail:* news@wsaz.com *Web Site:* www.wsaz.com, pg 942

Moran, Sean, Hitachi Kokusai Electric America Ltd, 150 Crossways Park Dr, Woodbury, NY 11797 *Tel:* 516-921-7200 *Toll Free Tel:* 855-891-5179 *Fax:* 516-496-3718 *E-mail:* info@hitachikokusai.us *Web Site:* hitachikokusai.us, pg 780

Morano, Nicole, Penguin Random House Audio Publishing, 1745 Broadway, New York, NY 10019 *E-mail:* audio@penguinrandomhouse.com *Web Site:* www.penguinrandomhouseaudio.com, pg 853

Morassutti, William, Loopmedia Inc, 26 Duncan St, Toronto, ON M5V 2B9, Canada *Tel:* 416-595-6496 *E-mail:* info@loopmedia.com *Web Site:* loopmedia. com, pg 811

Moreau, Calvin, ACS Technologies, 180 Dunbarton Dr, Florence, SC 29501 *Tel:* 843-662-1681 *Toll Free Tel:* 800-736-7425 (sales); 800-669-2309 (support) *Fax:* 843-669-7513 *E-mail:* info@acstechnologies.com *Web Site:* www.acstechnologies.com, pg 674

Morefield, John D, Morefield Communications Inc, 35 N 35 St, Camp Hill, PA 17011-2707 *Tel:* 717-761-6170 *Toll Free Tel:* 800-382-1266 *E-mail:* info@morefield. com *Web Site:* www.morefield.com, pg 830

Moreland, Jen, Horizon Video Productions Inc, 6114 Fayetteville St, Suite 106, Durham, NC 27713 *Tel:* 919-941-0901 *Toll Free Tel:* 800-768-3776 *Fax:* 919-941-1939 *E-mail:* info@horizonvp.com *Web Site:* www.horizonvp.com, pg 781

Morette, Cecilia M, Mark Custom Recording Service Inc, 10815 Bodine Rd, Clarence, NY 14031-2252 *Tel:* 716-759-2600 *Fax:* 716-759-2329 *E-mail:* info@ markcustom.com *Web Site:* www.markcustom.com, pg 817

Morette, Mark J, Mark Custom Recording Service Inc, 10815 Bodine Rd, Clarence, NY 14031-2252 *Tel:* 716-759-2600 *Fax:* 716-759-2329 *E-mail:* info@ markcustom.com *Web Site:* www.markcustom.com, pg 817

Morgan, Allyson, Nantucket Film Festival (NFF), 68 Jay St, Suite 319, Brooklyn, NY 11201 *Tel:* 646-480-1900 *Fax:* 646-365-3367 *E-mail:* info@nantucketfilmfestival. org; submissions@nantucketfilmfestival.org *Web Site:* nantucketfilmfestival.org, pg 997

Morgan, Barbara, Austin Film Festival, 1801 Salina St, Austin, TX 78702 *Tel:* 512-478-4795 *Toll Free Tel:* 800-310-FEST (310-3378) *Fax:* 512-478-6205 *E-mail:* info@austinfilmfestival.com; programming@ austinfilmfestival.com; marketing@austinfilmfestival. com *Web Site:* www.austinfilmfestival.com, pg 982

Morgan, Beverly, Milky Way Press, 317 Ridge Run Dr, Georgetown, TX 78628 *Tel:* 512-863-7278; 512-677-0861, pg 827

Morgan, Christine, Right Stuf Inc, 512 NE Main St, Grimes, IA 50111-2188 *Tel:* 515-986-1028 *Toll Free Tel:* 800-338-6827 *Fax:* 515-986-1129 *E-mail:* info@ rightstuf.com *Web Site:* www.rightstufanime.com, pg 875

Morgan, Danielle, Greenwood Convention & Visitors Bureau & Film Commission, 225 Howard St, Greenwood, MS 38935 *Tel:* 662-453-9197 *Web Site:* www.visitgreenwood.com, pg 972

Morgan, Gail, Emerald Coast Film Commission, 1540 Miracle Strip Pkwy, Fort Walton Beach, FL 32548 *Tel:* 850-651-7644 *Fax:* 850-651-7149 *E-mail:* emeraldfilm@co.okaloosa.fl.us *Web Site:* filmemeraldcoast.com, pg 969

Morgan, James, Antenna International, 383 Main Ave, Norwalk, CT 06851 *Tel:* 203-523-0320 *E-mail:* inquiry@antennainternational.com; marketing@antennainternational.com *Web Site:* www. antennainternational.com, pg 686

Morgan, Jeff, Vistamax Productions, 9705 Little Pond Way, Tampa, FL 33647 *Tel:* 813-907-1010 *Fax:* 813-907-1991 *E-mail:* info@vistamax.com; sales@ vistamax.com *Web Site:* www.vistamax.com, pg 931

Morgan, Linda, Yuma Film Commission, 180 W First St, Suite D, Yuma, AZ 85364 *Tel:* 928-376-0100 *Fax:* 928-373-0133 *Web Site:* www.filmyuma.com, pg 965

Morgan, Mark D, MainSail Production Services Inc, 521 Byers Rd, Suite 109, Miamisburg, OH 45342 *Tel:* 937-866-7800 *Toll Free Tel:* 800-

877-0093 *Fax:* 937-866-8088 *E-mail:* discover@ mainsailproductions.com *Web Site:* www. mainsailproductions.com, pg 815

Morgan, Randy, All Service Musical Electronics Repair, 33470 SW Chinook Plaza, PMB 154, Scapoose, OR 97056 *Tel:* 503-231-6552 *E-mail:* service@asmusic.org *Web Site:* www.all-service-musical.com, pg 680

Morgan, Scott, Professional Photographers of America (PPA), 229 Peachtree St NE, Suite 2200, Atlanta, GA 30303 *Tel:* 404-522-8600 *Toll Free Tel:* 800-786-6277 *Fax:* 404-614-6400 *E-mail:* csc@ppa.com *Web Site:* www.ppa.com, pg 961

Morgenstern, Fred, Neutrik® USA Inc, 4115 Taggart Creek Rd, Charlotte, NC 28208 *Tel:* 704-972-3050 *Fax:* 704-438-9202 *Toll Free Tel:* 877-220-4089 *E-mail:* info@neutrikusa.com *Web Site:* www.neutrik. us, pg 838

Mori, Eric B, Charles M Salter Associates Inc, 130 Sutter St, 5th fl, San Francisco, CA 94104 *Tel:* 415-397-0442 *Fax:* 415-397-0454 *E-mail:* info@cmsalter. com *Web Site:* www.cmsalter.com, pg 721

Moriarty, Jim, YES Productions, 916 Navarre Ave, New Orleans, LA 70124 *Tel:* 504-840-4891 *Toll Free Tel:* 800-736-8812 *Fax:* 504-840-4895 *Web Site:* www. yesproductions.com, pg 944

Moridani, Sahar, DGA Awards, 7920 Sunset Blvd, Los Angeles, CA 90046 *Tel:* 310-289-2038 *Fax:* 310-289-5398 *E-mail:* awards@dga.org *Web Site:* www.dga.org, pg 988

Morin, Shawn, Ingram Content Group LLC, One Ingram Blvd, La Vergne, TN 37086-1986 *Tel:* 615-793-5000 *Toll Free Tel:* 800-937-8000 (retailers); 800-937-5300 (ext 1, libs) *E-mail:* customerservice@ingramcontent. com *Web Site:* www.ingramcontent.com, pg 787

Moritz, Will, CamTec Motion Picture Cameras, 4221 W Magnolia Blvd, Burbank, CA 91505 *Tel:* 818-841-8700 *Fax:* 818-841-8777 *Web Site:* www.camtec.tv, pg 715

Morningstar, Nancy, Crew West Inc, 1515 W Deer Valley Rd, Suite C-109, Phoenix, AZ 85027 *Tel:* 480-367-6888 *Toll Free Tel:* 888-444-2739 *Fax:* 480-367-6688 *E-mail:* tvcrews@crewwestinc.com *Web Site:* www.crewwestinc.com, pg 734

Morrasy, Tiffanie, Bay Photo Lab, 920 Disc Dr, Scotts Valley, CA 95066 *Tel:* 831-475-6686 *Toll Free Tel:* 800-435-6686 *Fax:* 831-475-5275 *E-mail:* support@bayphoto.com (cust serv); sales@ bayphoto.com *Web Site:* www.bayphoto.com, pg 702

Morrell, Kathy, Golden Sheaf Awards, 49 Smith St E, Yorkton, SK S3N 0H4, Canada *Tel:* 306-782-7077 *Fax:* 306-782-1550 *E-mail:* info@yorktonfilm.com *Web Site:* yorktonfilm.com/golden-sheaf-awards/, pg 991

Morrell, Kathy, Yorkton Film Festival (YFF), 49 Smith St E, Yorkton, SK S3N 0H4, Canada *Tel:* 306-782-7077 *Fax:* 306-782-1550 *E-mail:* info@yorktonfilm. com *Web Site:* yorktonfilm.com, pg 1007

Morris, Bert, Theatrical Technicians Inc (TTI), 2700 Connecticut Ave NW, Suite 109, Washington, DC 20008-5308 *E-mail:* info@perfect-pickup.com, pg 912

Morris, Clark, 30 Second Street Ltd, 1209 Mountain Road Place NE, Suite B, Albuquerque, NM 87110 *Tel:* 505-265-0224 *E-mail:* info@30sst.com *Web Site:* www.thirtysecst.com, pg 912

Morris, Donna, Adobe Systems Inc, 345 Park Ave, San Jose, CA 95110-2704 *Tel:* 408-536-6000 *Fax:* 408-537-6000 *Web Site:* www.adobe.com, pg 676

Morris, Jim, Pixar Animation Studios, 1200 Park Ave, Emeryville, CA 94608 *Tel:* 510-922-3000 *Fax:* 510-922-3151 *Web Site:* www.pixar.com, pg 857

Morris, Lori, Magnum Towers Inc, 9370 Elder Creek Rd, Sacramento, CA 95829 *Tel:* 916-381-5053 *Fax:* 916-381-2144 *E-mail:* office@magnumtowers. com *Web Site:* www.magnumtowers.com, pg 815

Morris, Marc, 4 Wall Entertainment, 3165 W Sunset Rd, Suite 100, Las Vegas, NV 89118 *Tel:* 702-263-3858 *Toll Free Tel:* 877-789-8167 (Western US) *Fax:* 702-

263-3863 *E-mail:* info@4wall.com; info@usedlighting. com *Web Site:* www.4wall.com; www.usedlighting. com, pg 764

Morris, Rex, Rex Morris Productions, 5521 S Firethorn Place, Boise, ID 83716 *Tel:* 208-344-9878 *Fax:* 208-344-9878 *Web Site:* rexmorrisproductions.com, pg 830

Morris, Stephen, C V Lloyde, 702 W Killarney St, Urbana, IL 61801 *Tel:* 217-352-7031 *Toll Free Tel:* 800-779-7031 *E-mail:* sales@cvlloyde.com *Web Site:* www.cvlloyde.com, pg 810

Morris, Tom, Morrisound Recording, PO Box 49004, Tampa, FL 33647 *Tel:* 813-989-2108 *E-mail:* info@ morrisound.com *Web Site:* morrisound.com, pg 830

Morrison, Becky, Verbatim Americas LLC, 8210 University Executive Park Dr, Suite 300, Charlotte, NC 28262 *Toll Free Tel:* 800-538-8589 *Web Site:* www.verbatim.com, pg 926

Morrison, Irma, The Computer Language Co Inc, 5521 State Park Rd, Point Pleasant, PA 18950 *Tel:* 215-297-8082 *E-mail:* sales@computerlanguage.com; comments@computerlanguage.com *Web Site:* www. computerlanguage.com, pg 729

Morrison, Steve, Mammoth Location Services, 10001 Minaret Rd, Mammoth Lakes, CA 93546 *Tel:* 760-934-2571 (ext 3628) *Web Site:* www. mammothmountain.com/winter/home/film-locations, pg 967

Mortimer, Sandy, Horizon Films & Media LLC, PO Box 1087, Shelbyville, KY 40066 *Tel:* 502-647-9966 *Fax:* 502-647-9968 *E-mail:* horizonfilms@insightbb. com *Web Site:* www.horizon-films.com, pg 781

Morton, Bea, McNabb & Connolly, 60 Briarwood Ave, Mississauga, ON L5G 3N6, Canada *Tel:* 905-278-0566 *Toll Free Tel:* 866-722-1522 *Fax:* 905-278-2801 *Toll Free Fax:* 866-722-1822 *E-mail:* info@ mcnabbconnolly.ca *Web Site:* www.mcnabbconnolly.ca, pg 821

Morvan, Laurence, Accenture, 161 N Clark St, Chicago, IL 60601 *Tel:* 312-693-0161 *Toll Free Tel:* 877-889-9009 *Fax:* 312-693-0507 *Web Site:* www.accenture. com, pg 672

Mosakowski, Michael "Moe", Moe AV LLC, 133 Deerfield Rd, Sayreville, NJ 08872-1618 *Tel:* 732-257-3760 *Web Site:* www.moeco.net, pg 828

Mosallam, Mike, Sunset Gower Studios, 1438 N Gower St, Hollywood, CA 90028 *Tel:* 323-467-1001 *Fax:* 323-467-2717 *E-mail:* reception@sunsetgower. com *Web Site:* sunsetgowerstudios.com, pg 904

Mosby, Karen, SOM Publishing Co, 163 Moon Valley Rd, Windyville, MO 65783 *Tel:* 417-345-8411 *E-mail:* som@som.org *Web Site:* www.som.org, pg 892

Mosco, Lilli, WQED-Multimedia, 4802 Fifth Ave, Pittsburgh, PA 15213 *Tel:* 412-622-1300; 412-622-1370 *Web Site:* www.wqed.org, pg 942

Moseley-Bennett, Meredith, Entertainment Services and Technology Association (ESTA), 630 Ninth Ave, Suite 609, New York, NY 10036 *Tel:* 212-244-1505 *Fax:* 212-244-1502 *E-mail:* info@esta.org; membership@esta.org *Web Site:* www.esta.org, pg 954

Mosely, Dana, Chalk Dust Co, 16107 Kensington Dr, PMB 256, Sugar Land, TX 77479-4401 *Tel:* 281-265-2495 *Toll Free Tel:* 800-588-7564 *Fax:* 281-265-3197 *E-mail:* sales@chalkdust.com *Web Site:* www. chalkdust.com, pg 720

Mosely, Richard, Chalk Dust Co, 16107 Kensington Dr, PMB 256, Sugar Land, TX 77479-4401 *Tel:* 281-265-2495 *Toll Free Tel:* 800-588-7564 *Fax:* 281-265-3197 *E-mail:* sales@chalkdust.com *Web Site:* www. chalkdust.com, pg 720

Moser, Star, Hollywood Lights Inc, 5251 SE McLoughlin Blvd, Portland, OR 97202-4836 *Tel:* 503-232-9001; 503-232-8855 *Toll Free Tel:* 800-826-9881 *Fax:* 503-517-8686 *E-mail:* portland@hollywoodlights. biz *Web Site:* www.hollywoodlights.biz, pg 780

Moskal, Richard, Chicago Film Office, Chicago Cultural Ctr, 78 E Washington, Rm 108, Chicago, IL 60602 *Tel:* 312-744-6415 *Fax:* 312-744-1378

E-mail: filmoffice@cityofchicago.org Web Site: www.cityofchicago.org/city/en/depts/dca/provdrs/chicago_film_office.html, pg 970

Mosley, Dr Dave, Seagate Technology LLC, 10200 S De Anza Blvd, Cupertino, CA 95014 Toll Free Tel: 800-SEAGATE (732-4283) Web Site: www.seagate.com, pg 883

Mosley, Don, Sound of Birmingham Productions, 3625 Fifth Ave S, Birmingham, AL 35222 Tel: 205-595-8497 Fax: 205-595-5220 Web Site: www.soundofbirmingham.com, pg 894

Mosovic, Steven, Big Foot Productions Inc, 37-09 36 Ave, Long Island City, NY 11101 Tel: 718-729-1900 E-mail: info@bigfootnyc.com Web Site: www.bigfootnyc.com, pg 705

Moss, E B, Euro-Pacific Film & Video Productions Inc, 101 Crawfords Corner Rd, Suite 4-101R, Holmdel, NJ 07733 Tel: 732-530-4451 Toll Free Tel: 800-387-6776 E-mail: info@euro-pacific.com Web Site: www.euro-pacific.com, pg 756

Moss, Ken, Electronic Arts Inc, 209 Redwood Shores Pkwy, Redwood City, CA 94065 Tel: 650-628-1500 Web Site: www.ea.com, pg 752

Moss, Lisa, Fred Rogers Productions, 2100 Wharton St, Suite 700, Pittsburgh, PA 15203 Tel: 412-687-2990 Toll Free Tel: 877-677-6437 E-mail: info@fredrogers.org Web Site: www.fredrogers.org, pg 876

Moss, Princess R, National Education Association (NEA), 1201 16 St NW, Washington, DC 20036-3290 Tel: 202-833-4000 Fax: 202-822-7974 Web Site: www.nea.org, pg 836

Mossman, Chris, WKYT-TV, 2851 Winchester Rd, Lexington, KY 40509 Tel: 859-299-0411; 859-299-2727 (newsroom) Web Site: www.wkyt.com, pg 940

Mossotti, Ron, Hammond Communications Group Inc, 173 Trade St, Lexington, KY 40511 Tel: 859-254-1878 E-mail: info@hammondcg.com Web Site: hammondcg.com, pg 775

Moster, Steve, GES Audio Visual, 7000 Lindell Rd, Las Vegas, NV 89118 Tel: 702-515-5500 Fax: 702-515-5765 E-mail: lasvegas@ges.com; info@ges.com Web Site: ges.com, pg 770

Mostin, Michael, J & R Film Co, 1135 N Mansfield Ave, Hollywood, CA 90038 Tel: 323-467-1116 Toll Free Tel: 877-668-4652 Web Site: moviola.com, pg 792

Mostin, Michael, Moviola, 1135 N Mansfield Ave, Hollywood, CA 90038 Tel: 323-467-3107; 818-487-5000 Toll Free Tel: 877-MOVIOLA (668-4652) Fax: 323-464-1518 Web Site: www.moviola.com, pg 832

Motta, Tony, Digital Music Corp, 3165 Coffey Lane, Santa Rosa, CA 95403 Tel: 707-545-0600 Fax: 707-545-9777 E-mail: info@voodoolab.com Web Site: www.voodoolab.com, pg 742

Moudy, Lynn, Power Integrity Corporation, 2109 Patterson St, Greensboro, NC 27407 Tel: 336-379-9773 Toll Free Tel: 800-237-6260 (tech support) Web Site: powerintegritycorp.com, pg 860

Moulton, Candy, Boston Productions Inc (BPI), 290 Vanderbilt Ave, Suite 1, Norwood, MA 02062 Tel: 781-255-1555; 720-233-1250 (sales) E-mail: info@bostonproductions.com Web Site: www.bostonproductions.com, pg 709

Mountain, Toby, Northeastern Digital Recording Inc, 2750 14 St NW, No 402, Washington, DC 20009 Tel: 508-330-9069 Web Site: www.northeasterndigital.com, pg 842

Mounts, Christopher, AVI Systems, 9675 W 76 St, Suite 130, Eden Prairie, MN 55344 Tel: 952-949-3700 Toll Free Tel: 800-488-4954 (support); 855-521-0050 Fax: 952-949-6000 E-mail: info@avisystems.com Web Site: www.avisystems.com, pg 698

Mower, Lorne, JL Recording Studios, 270 Adelaide St W, Suite 202, Toronto, ON M5H 1X6, Canada Tel: 416-598-7979 Web Site: www.jlstudios.ca; www.facebook.com/jlrecordingstudios; twitter.com/JLStudios, pg 794

Moya, Daniela, Northern Light Productions (NLP), 300 Western Ave, 2nd fl, Boston, MA 02134 Tel: 617-789-4344 Fax: 617-789-4744 E-mail: info@nlprod.com Web Site: www.nlprod.com, pg 842

Moylan, Dan, NAMM, the National Association of Music Merchants, 5790 Armada Dr, Carlsbad, CA 92008 Tel: 760-438-8001 Toll Free Tel: 800-767-6266 (memb hotline) Fax: 760-438-7327 E-mail: info@namm.org Web Site: www.namm.org, pg 958

Moynihan, Frank, Billy Budd Films Inc, 235 E 57 St, New York, NY 10022 Tel: 212-755-3968 E-mail: info@billybuddfilms.com Web Site: www.billybuddfilms.com, pg 712

Mpistolarides, Paul, Midwest Uplink Inc, 911 N East St, Indianapolis, IN 46202 Tel: 317-423-8684 Toll Free Tel: 866-886-6247 Web Site: midwestuplink.com, pg 827

Mroz, John, RingSide Creative, 13320 Northend, Suite 3000, Oak Park, MI 48237 Tel: 248-548-2500 E-mail: info@ringsidecreative.com; newbiz@ringsidecreative.com Web Site: www.ringsidecreative.com, pg 875

Mucha, Zenia, The Walt Disney Co, 500 S Buena Vista St, Burbank, CA 91521 Tel: 818-560-1000 Web Site: disney.com; thewaltdisneycompany.com, pg 743

Muderick, Michael, Muderick Media, 101 Earlington Rd, Havertown, PA 19083 Tel: 610-449-6970, pg 833

Mueller, David, Image Audiovisuals, 2130 S Dahlia St, Denver, CO 80222 Tel: 303-758-1818 Toll Free Tel: 800-818-1857 Fax: 303-758-5722 Web Site: www.imageav.com, pg 784

Mueller, Diana, Image Audiovisuals, 2130 S Dahlia St, Denver, CO 80222 Tel: 303-758-1818 Toll Free Tel: 800-818-1857 Fax: 303-758-5722 Web Site: www.imageav.com, pg 784

Mueller, Matt, Midland Video Productions Inc, 3315 N 124 St, Brookfield, WI 53005 Tel: 414-276-8300 E-mail: request@midlandvideo.com Web Site: midlandvideo.com, pg 827

Mueller, Melanie, Nevada Broadcasters Association, 3900 Paradise Rd, Suite 279, Las Vegas, NV 89169 Tel: 702-794-4994 Fax: 702-794-4997 Web Site: www.nevadabroadcasters.org, pg 960

Mueller, Michael, Michael Mueller Video Productions, 211 Exchange St, Hot Springs, AR 71901 Tel: 501-282-4107 Web Site: muellervideo.com, pg 833

Mueller, Ray, Ray Mueller Productions, 5 E Waterloo Rd, Stanhope, NJ 07874 Tel: 973-691-2088; 973-801-6004 Web Site: www.muellerproductions.com, pg 833

Muertens, Gunther, Agfa Graphics, 611 River Dr, Ctr 3, Elmwood Park, NJ 07407 Tel: 201-440-2500 Toll Free Tel: 800-540-2432; 888-274-8626 (cust serv) E-mail: graphics@agfa.com Web Site: www.agfa.com; www.agfagraphics.com, pg 678

Muir, Boyd, Universal Music Group, 2220 Colorado Ave, Santa Monica, CA 90404 Tel: 310-865-5000 Web Site: www.universalmusic.com, pg 922

Muir, Charles, Source School of Tantra Yoga Inc, PO Box 368, Kahului, HI 96733 Toll Free Tel: 888-6-TANTRA (682-6872) E-mail: school@sourcetantra.com Web Site: sourcetantra.com, pg 895

Mukerjee, Lucy, Outfest Los Angeles LGBT Film Festival, 3470 Wilshire Blvd, Suite 935, Los Angeles, CA 90010 Tel: 213-480-7088 Fax: 213-480-7099 E-mail: outfest@outfest.org Web Site: www.outfest.org, pg 999

Mukkamala, Srinivas, ARC Document Solutions, 1981 N Broadway, Suite 385, Walnut Creek, CA 94596 Tel: 925-949-5100 Toll Free Tel: 855-500-0660 E-mail: contact@e-arc.com Web Site: www.e-arc.com, pg 688

Muldowney, Oisin, FACE Foundation, 972 Fifth Ave, New York, NY 10075 Tel: 212-439-1439 E-mail: info@face-foundation.org Web Site: www.face-foundation.org, pg 758

Mulica, Joe, Gotham Sound & Communications Inc, 35-10 36 Ave, 2nd fl, Long Island City, NY 11106 Tel: 212-629-9430 Toll Free Tel: 866-468-4268 Fax: 212-629-9436 E-mail: nyc@gothamsound.com Web Site: www.gothamsound.com, pg 773

Mulick, Rodney, Custom Color Corp, 14320 W 101 Terr, Lenexa, KS 66215 Tel: 913-730-3100 Fax: 913-730-3101 E-mail: info@customcolor.com Web Site: www.customcolor.com, pg 736

Mullany, Eileen, CEDIA IPRO Affinity Group, 8475 Nightfall Lane, Fishers, IN 46037 Tel: 317-328-4336 Toll Free Tel: 800-669-5329 E-mail: info@cedia.org Web Site: cedia.net, pg 952

Mullen, Bruce, National Fire Protection Association (NFPA), One Batterymarch Park, Quincy, MA 02169-7471 Tel: 617-770-3000 Toll Free Tel: 800-344-3555 (US & CN); 855-274-8525 (US & CN) Fax: 508-895-8301 Toll Free Fax: 800-593-NFPA (593-6372, US & CN) E-mail: custserv@nfpa.org Web Site: www.nfpa.org, pg 836

Mullen, Jennifer, Modesto Convention & Visitors Bureau, 1150 Ninth St, Suite C, Modesto, CA 95354 Tel: 209-526-5588 Toll Free Tel: 888-640-8467 Fax: 209-526-5586 E-mail: films@visitmodesto.com; info@visitmodesto.com Web Site: www.visitmodesto.com, pg 967

Mullen, Robb, Noventri, 20940 Twin Springs Dr, Smithsburg, MD 21783-1510 Tel: 301-790-0103 Fax: 301-790-0173 E-mail: sale@noventri.com Web Site: www.noventri.com, pg 843

Muller, Justin K, Muller Entertainment LLC, 540 Commerce St, Southlake, TX 76092 Tel: 214-317-0800 E-mail: info@mullerentertainment.com Web Site: www.mullerentertainment.com, pg 833

Mullet, J A, OMNI Productions, PO Box 302, Carmel, IN 46082-0302 Tel: 317-846-2345 Fax: 317-846-6664 E-mail: omni@omniproductions.com Web Site: www.omniproductions.com, pg 845

Mulligan, Katie, Association of Independent Commercial Producers (AICP), 3 W 18 St, 5th fl, New York, NY 10011 Tel: 212-929-3000 Fax: 212-929-3359 E-mail: info@aicp.com Web Site: www.aicp.com, pg 951

Mullikin, Randy, Mullikin Agency, 1391 Plaza Place, Suite A, Springdale, AR 72764-5225 Tel: 479-750-0871 Toll Free Tel: 800-750-0871 Fax: 479-750-2685 Web Site: www.mullikinad.com, pg 833

Mullin, Jennifer, FremantleMedia North America, 2900 W Alameda Ave, Suite 800, Burbank, CA 91505 Tel: 818-748-1100 Web Site: www.fremantlemedia.com, pg 765

Mulvaney, Jon, Janus Films Inc, 215 Park Ave S, 5th fl, New York, NY 10003 Tel: 212-756-8822 Fax: 212-756-8850 E-mail: booking@janusfilms.com Web Site: www.criterion.com; www.janusfilms.com, pg 793

Munday, Robert, Munday & Collins AV, 2122 Zanker Rd, San Jose, CA 95131-2108 Tel: 408-451-9155 Toll Free Tel: 800-834-5551 Fax: 408-451-9192 E-mail: info@avevents.com Web Site: www.avevents.com, pg 834

Mungovan, Jill, Columbia Lighting, 701 Millennium Blvd, Greenville, SC 29607 Tel: 864-678-1000; 864-678-1664 (cust support) Toll Free Tel: 866-898-0131 Web Site: www.columbialighting.com, pg 728

Munn, Jim, Dorian Color, 100 Main St, Melrose, MA 02176 Tel: 781-648-8040 E-mail: images@doriancolor.com Web Site: www.doriancolor.com, pg 745

Munoz, Alma, Calrad Electronics, 819 N Highland Ave, Los Angeles, CA 90038 Tel: 323-465-2131 Fax: 323-465-3504 E-mail: sales@calrad.com Web Site: www.calrad.com, pg 714

Munoz, Gabriela, Artist Research & Development Grants, 417 W Roosevelt St, Phoenix, AZ 85003-1326 Tel: 602-771-6501 Fax: 602-256-0282 E-mail: info@azarts.gov Web Site: www.azarts.gov, pg 982

Munoz, Lorenza, Academy Awards®, 8949 Wilshire Blvd, Beverly Hills, CA 90211 *Tel:* 310-247-3000; 310-247-3090 (publicity) *Fax:* 310-859-9619 *E-mail:* awardsoffice@oscars.org; publicity@oscars.org *Web Site:* www.oscars.org, pg 981

Munoz, Lorenza, Academy of Motion Picture Arts and Sciences (AMPAS), 8949 Wilshire Blvd, Beverly Hills, CA 90211 *Tel:* 310-247-3000 *Fax:* 310-859-9619 *E-mail:* awardsoffice@oscars.org *Web Site:* www.oscars.org, pg 947

Munoz, Lorenza, Nicholl Fellowships in Screenwriting, 8949 Wilshire Blvd, Beverly Hills, CA 90211 *Tel:* 310-247-3010 *E-mail:* nicholl@oscars.org *Web Site:* www.oscars.org/nicholl, pg 998

Munro, Debbie, DebsVoice, 19 Park Trail, Midhurst, ON L0L 1X0, Canada *Tel:* 604-459-5559 (cell) *Web Site:* www.debsvoice.com; www.voiceactortraining.com, pg 739

Munro, Douglas, HDTV Productions Inc, 132-250 Shawville Blvd SE, No 209, Calgary, AB T2Y 2Z7, Canada *Tel:* 403-931-1936 *Web Site:* www.hdtvproductions.com, pg 777

Murawski, Bill, Davies Publishing Inc, 32 S Raymond Ave, Suites 4-5, Pasadena, CA 91105 *Tel:* 626-792-3046 *Toll Free Tel:* 877-792-0005 (US only) *Fax:* 626-792-5308 *E-mail:* info@daviespublishing.com *Web Site:* daviespublishing.com, pg 738

Murdey, Erika, Michigan Film & Digital Media Office, 300 N Washington Sq, 4th fl, Lansing, MI 48913 *Tel:* 517-241-6757 *Toll Free Tel:* 800-477-FILM (477-3456) *Fax:* 517-241-3689 *E-mail:* mfo@michigan.org *Web Site:* www.michiganbusiness.org/industries/mfdmo, pg 972

Murdoch, Lachlan, News Corp, 1211 Avenue of the Americas, New York, NY 10036 *Tel:* 212-416-3400 *E-mail:* media@newscorp.com *Web Site:* newscorp.com, pg 840

Murdoch, Rupert, News Corp, 1211 Avenue of the Americas, New York, NY 10036 *Tel:* 212-416-3400 *E-mail:* media@newscorp.com *Web Site:* newscorp.com, pg 840

Murphy, Courtney, Alabama Film Office, Alabama Ctr for Commerce, 401 Adams Ave, Suite 170, Montgomery, AL 36104 *Tel:* 334-242-4195 *Fax:* 334-242-2077 *Web Site:* www.alabamafilm.org, pg 965

Murphy, Don, Big Shoulders Digital Video Productions, 875 N Michigan Ave, Suite 3750, Chicago, IL 60611 *Tel:* 312-540-5400 *E-mail:* info@bigshoulders.com; sales@bigshoulders.com *Web Site:* www.bigshoulders.com, pg 705

Murphy, Elaine, Kimbo Educational, One Industrial Way, Bldg D, Suite E, Eatontown, NJ 07724 *Tel:* 732-229-4949 *Toll Free Tel:* 800-631-2187 *Fax:* 732-870-3340 *E-mail:* kimboed@aol.com; service@kimboed.com *Web Site:* www.kimboed.com, pg 799

Murphy, James J, Seagate Technology LLC, 10200 S De Anza Blvd, Cupertino, CA 95014 *Toll Free Tel:* 800-SEAGATE (732-4283) *Web Site:* www.seagate.com, pg 883

Murphy, John, AVI-SPL, 6301 Benjamin Rd, Suite 101, Tampa, FL 33634 *Tel:* 813-884-7168 *Toll Free Tel:* 866-708-5034; 866-925-8298 (cust serv); 866-559-8197 (sales) *E-mail:* contact@avispl.com; sales@avispl.com; customerservice@avispl.com *Web Site:* www.avispl.com, pg 698

Murphy, Kathleen, CVW Event Productions, 470 Spring Park Place, Suite 900, Herndon, VA 20170 *Tel:* 703-891-2620 *Fax:* 703-891-2625 *E-mail:* info@cvwevents.com *Web Site:* cvwevents.com, pg 736

Murphy, Marion E, The Lerro Corp, 905 Madison Ave, Norristown, PA 19403 *Tel:* 610-650-4100 *Fax:* 610-650-4110 *E-mail:* lerrocorp@lerro.com *Web Site:* www.lerro.com, pg 806

Murphy, Matt, Marvell Semiconductor Inc, 5488 Marvell Lane, Santa Clara, CA 95054 *Tel:* 408-222-2500 *Toll Free Tel:* 855-MARVELL (627-8355) *Fax:* 408-988-8279 *E-mail:* info@marvell.com *Web Site:* www.marvell.com, pg 818

Murphy, Matt, WoodenBoat Publications, 41 WoodenBoat Lane, Brooklin, ME 04616 *Tel:* 207-359-4651 *Toll Free Tel:* 800-877-5284 (subns) *Fax:* 207-359-8920 *E-mail:* woodenboat@woodenboat.com *Web Site:* www.woodenboat.com, pg 941

Murphy, Matthew E, The Lerro Corp, 905 Madison Ave, Norristown, PA 19403 *Tel:* 610-650-4100 *Fax:* 610-650-4110 *E-mail:* lerrocorp@lerro.com *Web Site:* www.lerro.com, pg 806

Murphy, Peter, The Video Messenger Co, 862 Judson Place, Stratford, CT 06615 *Tel:* 203-358-8842 *Toll Free Tel:* 800-800-7128 *Fax:* 203-547-6216 *E-mail:* vmc@videomessenger.com *Web Site:* www.videomessenger.com, pg 928

Murphy, Peter J, Power Sonic Corp, 365 Cabela Dr, Suite 300, Reno, NV 89523 *Tel:* 619-661-2020 *Fax:* 619-661-3650 *Web Site:* www.power-sonic.com, pg 860

Murphy, Randy, South Trunk Studios, 825 S Trunk Ave, Dallas, TX 75210 *Tel:* 214-826-2513 *E-mail:* southtrunk@sbcglobal.net *Web Site:* www.southtrunk.com, pg 895

Murphy, Sandra, BBC Worldwide Canada Ltd, 401-409 King St W, 5th fl, Toronto, ON M5V 1K1, Canada *Tel:* 416-204-0500 *E-mail:* canada.sales@bbc.com (sales) *Web Site:* www.bbcworldwide.com, pg 702

Murphy, Scott, NVerzion Inc, 296 E 3900 S, Salt Lake City, UT 84107-1531 *Tel:* 801-293-8420 *E-mail:* sales@nverzion.com *Web Site:* www.nverzion.com, pg 843

Murphy, Siobhan, Education Development Center Inc (EDC), 43 Foundry Ave, Waltham, MA 02453-8313 *Tel:* 617-969-7100 *Fax:* 617-969-5979 *E-mail:* contact@edc.org *Web Site:* www.edc.org, pg 750

Murphy, William, Protech Audio Corp, 192 Cedar River Rd, Indian Lake, NY 12842 *Tel:* 518-648-6410 *Fax:* 518-648-6395 *E-mail:* proinfo@protechaudio.com; prosales@protechaudio.com *Web Site:* www.protechaudio.com, pg 866

Murray, Derik, Network Entertainment Inc, 1488 Frances St, Vancouver, BC V5L 1Y9, Canada *Tel:* 604-739-8825 *Fax:* 604-739-8835 *E-mail:* info@networkentertainment.ca *Web Site:* www.networkentertainment.ca, pg 838

Murray, Doug, Upstage Video, 201 Rock Lititz Blvd, Suite 20, Lititz, PA 17543 *Tel:* 717-240-2400 *Toll Free Tel:* 877-484-3887 *E-mail:* info@upstagevideo.com *Web Site:* www.upstagevideo.com, pg 923

Murray, Michael, Adrenaline Films, 5224 S Orange Ave, Orlando, FL 32809 *Tel:* 407-850-0711 *Fax:* 407-859-6527 *E-mail:* contact@adrenalinefilms.com *Web Site:* www.adrenalinefilms.com, pg 676

Murray, Scott, Film Las Cruces, 1300-G El Paseo, Suite 174, Las Cruces, NM 88001 *Tel:* 575-805-3456 *Web Site:* www.filmlascruces.com, pg 973

Murray, Scott, Telestream Inc, 848 Gold Flat Rd, Nevada City, CA 95959 *Tel:* 530-470-1300 *Toll Free Tel:* 877-257-6245 *Fax:* 530-470-1301 *E-mail:* info@telestream.net *Web Site:* www.telestream.net, pg 910

Murray, Sean, AnswersMedia, 30 N Racine Ave, Suite 300, Chicago, IL 60607 *Tel:* 312-421-0113 *E-mail:* contactus@answersmediainc.com *Web Site:* www.answersmediainc.com, pg 686

Murray, Tim, Symetrix Inc, 6408 216 St SW, Mountlake Terrace, WA 98043-2093 *Tel:* 425-778-7728 *E-mail:* support@symetrix.co; sales@symetrix.co *Web Site:* www.symetrix.co, pg 905

Murrell, Debra, American Legion Fourth Estate Award, Media & Communs Div, 700 N Pennsylvania St, Indianapolis, IN 46204 *Tel:* 317-630-1253 *Fax:* 317-630-1368 *E-mail:* pr@legion.org *Web Site:* www.legion.org, pg 981

Murski, Paul, Horizon Film + Video Productions, 3903 S Congress Ave, Suite 40186, Austin, TX 78704 *Tel:* 512-459-3100 *Web Site:* www.horizonvideo.com, pg 781

Muscari, Julia, Eternal Word Television Network (EWTN), 5817 Old Leeds Rd, Irondale, AL 35210-2164 *Tel:* 205-271-2900 *Fax:* 205-271-2920 *E-mail:* viewer@ewtn.com *Web Site:* www.ewtn.com, pg 756

Muscat, Dave, Christie Digital Systems USA Inc, 10550 Camden Dr, Cypress, CA 90630 *Tel:* 714-236-8610 *Toll Free Tel:* 866-880-4462 (cust serv) *Fax:* 714-503-3375 *E-mail:* sales-us@christiedigital.com; orders@christiedigital.com *Web Site:* www.christiedigital.com, pg 722

Muse, Jim, Muse Presentation Technologies, 3510 S Susan St, Santa Ana, CA 92704 *Tel:* 714-850-1008 *Toll Free Tel:* 800-950-4955 *Fax:* 714-850-1018 *Web Site:* www.museprestech.com, pg 834

Mutterperl, Jeff, RNJ Electronics, 202 New Hwy, Amityville, NY 11701 *Tel:* 631-226-2700 *Toll Free Tel:* 800-645-5833 *Fax:* 631-226-2770 *Toll Free Fax:* 800-765-3291 *E-mail:* sales@rnjelectronics.com *Web Site:* www.rnjelectronics.com, pg 876

Myers, Barry, AccuWeather Inc, 385 Science Park Rd, State College, PA 16803 *Tel:* 814-237-0309 *Toll Free Tel:* 800-566-6606 *E-mail:* sales@accuweather.com *Web Site:* www.accuweather.com, pg 674

Myers, Chad, Wisconsin Public Television, 821 University Ave, Madison, WI 53706 *Tel:* 608-263-2121 *Toll Free Tel:* 800-422-9707 *Fax:* 608-263-9763 *E-mail:* comments@wpt.org *Web Site:* www.wpt.org, pg 940

Myers, Dee Dee, Warner Bros Entertainment Inc, 4000 Warner Blvd, Burbank, CA 91522 *E-mail:* wbsf@warnerbros.com *Web Site:* www.warnerbros.com/studio; studiofacilities.warnerbros.com, pg 934

Myers, Evan A, AccuWeather Inc, 385 Science Park Rd, State College, PA 16803 *Tel:* 814-237-0309 *Toll Free Tel:* 800-566-6606 *E-mail:* sales@accuweather.com *Web Site:* www.accuweather.com, pg 674

Myers, Dr Joel N, AccuWeather Inc, 385 Science Park Rd, State College, PA 16803 *Tel:* 814-237-0309 *Toll Free Tel:* 800-566-6606 *E-mail:* sales@accuweather.com *Web Site:* www.accuweather.com, pg 674

Myers, Matt, National Public Radio (NPR), 1111 N Capitol St NE, Washington, DC 20002 *Tel:* 202-513-2000 *Web Site:* www.npr.org, pg 959

Myers, Rodney A, Digital Rain LLC, 253 Lagoda Dr, Locust, NC 28097 *Tel:* 980-354-1209 *Web Site:* www.digitalrainllc.com, pg 742

Myers, Tim, WIFR-TV, 2523 N Meridian Rd, Rockford, IL 61101 *Tel:* 815-987-5300 *Fax:* 815-965-0981 *E-mail:* talkto23@wifr.com *Web Site:* www.wifr.com, pg 938

Mylius, Dustin, Yuma Film Commission, 180 W First St, Suite D, Yuma, AZ 85364 *Tel:* 928-376-0100 *Fax:* 928-373-0133 *Web Site:* www.filmyuma.com, pg 965

Myres, Donald R, Omni International Inc, 4928 Crosshill Lane, Northport, AL 35473, pg 845

Nabatian, Syrous, Radiant Images, 2702 Media Center Dr, Los Angeles, CA 90065 *Tel:* 323-737-1314 *Fax:* 310-861-0163 *E-mail:* info@radiantimages.com *Web Site:* www.radiantimages.com, pg 869

Nachlis, Gayle, Women in Film Finishing Fund, 6100 Wilshire Blvd, Suite 710, Los Angeles, CA 90048 *Tel:* 323-935-2211 *Fax:* 323-935-2212 *E-mail:* info@wif.org *Web Site:* www.wif.org, pg 1007

Nachreiner, Dana, Sencore Inc, 3200 W Sencore Dr, Sioux Falls, SD 57107 *Tel:* 605-978-4600 *Fax:* 605-335-6379 *Web Site:* www.sencore.com, pg 883

Nadeau, Guy, Panavid, 210 West Pkwy, Unit 5, Pompton Plains, NJ 07444 *Tel:* 973-831-5655 *E-mail:* info@panavid.com; support@panavid.com *Web Site:* www.panavid.com, pg 850

Nadlin, Mark, Green Dot Audio Electronics, PO Box 290609, Nashville, TN 37229-0609 *Tel:* 615-366-5964 *Fax:* 615-366-7069 *E-mail:* greendotaudio@bellsouth.net *Web Site:* www.greendotaudio.com, pg 774

Nagel, Dennis, Idaho Camera Inc, 1310 N Orchard Ave, Boise, ID 83706 Tel: 208-377-3686 (corp) Toll Free Tel: 877-323-8734 E-mail: info@idahocamera.com; orchard@idahocamera.com; sales@idahocamera.com Web Site: www.idahocamera.com, pg 784

Nagel, Patrick F, Idaho Camera Inc, 1310 N Orchard Ave, Boise, ID 83706 Tel: 208-377-3686 (corp) Toll Free Tel: 877-323-8734 E-mail: info@idahocamera.com; orchard@idahocamera.com; sales@idahocamera.com Web Site: www.idahocamera.com, pg 784

Nagle, Don, Asia Society, 725 Park Ave, New York, NY 10021 Tel: 212-288-6400 Fax: 212-517-8315 E-mail: info@asiasociety.org Web Site: www.asiasociety.org; www.asiasociety.org/video, pg 691

Nagle, Patricia E, OpenText Corp, 275 Frank Tompa Dr, Waterloo, ON N2L 0A1, Canada Tel: 519-888-7111 Toll Free Tel: 800-499-6544 Fax: 519-888-0677 Web Site: www.opentext.com, pg 847

Nagorski, Tom, Asia Society, 725 Park Ave, New York, NY 10021 Tel: 212-288-6400 Fax: 212-517-8315 E-mail: info@asiasociety.org Web Site: www.asiasociety.org; www.asiasociety.org/video, pg 691

Nahhat, Fred, WTVS, Detroit Public Television, Riley Broadcast Ctr, One Clover Ct, Wixom, MI 48393-2247 Tel: 248-305-DPTV (305-3788); 313-872-7500 E-mail: email@dptv.org Web Site: www.dptv.org, pg 942

Nahigian, Ryan, Questar Entertainment Inc, 307 N Michigan Ave, 5th fl, Chicago, IL 60601-5305 Tel: 312-266-9400 Toll Free Tel: 800-544-8422 (cust serv) E-mail: info@questarentertainment.com Web Site: www.questarentertainment.com, pg 868

Nahte, Ethan, Live'N'Loud, PO Box 557, Mena, AR 71953 Tel: 479-216-6727 Web Site: nahteboy.tripod.com, pg 810

Naidu, Bobby, Source Film Studio, 1111 N Beachwood Dr, Hollywood, CA 90038 Tel: 323-463-5555 E-mail: info@sourcefilmstudio.com Web Site: www.sourcefilmstudio.com, pg 895

Naik, Ravi, Seagate Technology LLC, 10200 S De Anza Blvd, Cupertino, CA 95014 Toll Free Tel: 800-SEAGATE (732-4283) Web Site: www.seagate.com, pg 883

Nance, Hank, Boxlight Inc, 1045 Progress Circle, Lawrenceville, GA 30043 Toll Free Tel: 866-972-1549 E-mail: service@boxlight.com; marketing@boxlight.com Web Site: mimio.boxlight.com, pg 709

Nanji, Anil, Magnet Sales & Manufacturing Inc, 11248 Playa Ct, Culver City, CA 90230 Tel: 310-391-7213 Toll Free Tel: 800-421-6692 Fax: 310-391-7463 E-mail: info@magnetsales.com Web Site: www.magnetsales.com; www.magnetshop.com, pg 814

Napack, Brian, John Wiley & Sons Inc, 111 River St, Hoboken, NJ 07030-5774 Tel: 201-748-6000 Toll Free Tel: 800-225-5945 (cust serv) Fax: 201-748-6088 Web Site: www.wiley.com, pg 938

Napakh, Gala, AbelCine, 801 S Main St, Burbank, CA 91506 Toll Free Tel: 888-700-4416 E-mail: orders@abelcine.com; customerservice@abelcine.com Web Site: www.abelcine.com, pg 672

Napier, Matt, Lightning Eliminators & Consultants Inc, 6687 Arapahoe Rd, Boulder, CO 80303 Tel: 303-447-2828 Toll Free Tel: 800-521-6101 Fax: 303-447-8122 E-mail: info@lecglobal.com Web Site: www.lightningprotection.com, pg 808

Narayen, Shantanu, Adobe Systems Inc, 345 Park Ave, San Jose, CA 95110-2704 Tel: 408-536-6000 Fax: 408-537-6000 Web Site: www.adobe.com, pg 676

Nardelli, Scott, Bexel, an NEP Broadcast Services Company, 2701 N Ontario St, Burbank, CA 91504 Tel: 818-565-4322 Toll Free Tel: 800-225-6185 (tech support) E-mail: services@bexel.com Web Site: bexel.com, pg 704

Natale, Dave, Right Coast Recording Inc, 341 Chestnut St, Columbia, PA 17512 Tel: 717-681-9801 Fax: 717-681-9801 E-mail: rightcoastrecording@gmail.com; studio@rightcoastrecording.com Web Site: www.rightcoastrecording.com, pg 875

Natella, Jamee, Blueyed Pictures Inc, 8950 W Olympic Blvd, Suite 324, Beverly Hills, CA 90211 Tel: 310-295-0848 E-mail: la@blueyedpictures.com Web Site: www.blueyedpictures.com, pg 708

Nathan, Terry, The Independent Book Publishers Association (IBPA), 1020 Manhattan Beach Blvd, Suite 204, Manhattan Beach, CA 90266 Tel: 310-546-1818 Fax: 310-546-3939 E-mail: info@ibpa-online.org Web Site: www.ibpa-online.org, pg 956

Nathani, Andy, 24 Frames Film & Video, 15 Fourth Ave E, Vancouver, BC V5T 1E9, Canada Tel: 604-877-1299 E-mail: info@24frames.ca Web Site: www.24frames.ca, pg 920

Nathu, Rahim, SC Media Canada, 2100 Onesime-Gagnon, Lachine, QC H8T 3M8, Canada Tel: 514-780-0808 Toll Free Tel: 888-595-3966 Fax: 514-780-1604 Toll Free Fax: 800-790-2000 E-mail: information@scmediacanada.com Web Site: www.scmediacanada.com, pg 881

Naughton, Brandon, EON247 Inc, 1245 Champa St, Basement, Denver, CO 80204 Tel: 720-935-7497 E-mail: info@eon247.com Web Site: www.eon247.com, pg 755

Nauman, Keith, DASAN Zhone Solutions (DZS) Inc, 7195 Oakport St, Oakland, CA 94621 Tel: 510-777-7000 Toll Free Tel: 877-ZHONE-20 (946-6320, US & CN) Fax: 510-777-7001 Web Site: dasanzhone.com, pg 737

Nauman, Michael, Brady Corp, 6555 W Good Hope Rd, Milwaukee, WI 53201-0571 Tel: 414-358-6600 Toll Free Tel: 888-250-3082 E-mail: bradyusa@bradycorp.com (cust serv & sales) Web Site: www.bradyid.com, pg 709

Nave, Leonard K, EKU Media, 102 Perkins Bldg, 521 Lancaster Ave, Richmond, KY 40475 Tel: 859-622-6671 Web Site: video.eku.edu, pg 752

Nawar, Jessica, RAM® Mounts, 8410 Dallas Ave S, Seattle, WA 98108 Tel: 206-763-8361 Toll Free Tel: 800-497-7479 Fax: 206-763-9615 E-mail: sales@rammount.com Web Site: www.rammount.com, pg 870

Nawrocki, Nancy, Video Associates Labs Inc, 2201 Denton Dr, Suite 109 B, Austin, TX 78758-3231 Tel: 512-491-7091 Toll Free Tel: 800-331-0547 Fax: 512-491-7619 E-mail: sales@val.com Web Site: www.val.com, pg 927

Nay, Dave, Allstar Show Industries Inc, 10331 176 St, Edmonton, AB T5S 2E4, Canada Tel: 780-486-4000 Toll Free Tel: 800-663-4063 (CN & US) E-mail: info@allstar-show.com Web Site: www.allstar-show.com, pg 681

Nazareno, Giselle, DACAPO Productions Inc, 516 Hargrave St, Winnipeg, MB R3A 0X8, Canada Tel: 204-956-2867 Fax: 204-956-2869 Web Site: www.dacapo.ca, pg 737

Neaderland, David, Sound Control Technologies Inc, 28 Knight St, Norwalk, CT 06851 Tel: 203-854-5701 Fax: 203-854-5702 E-mail: sales@soundcontrol.net Web Site: www.soundcontrol.net, pg 893

Neal, James "Jimbo", CenterStaging LLC, 3407 Winona Ave, Burbank, CA 91504 Tel: 818-559-4333 Fax: 818-848-4016 E-mail: info@centerstaging.com Web Site: centerstaging.com, pg 719

Neal, Malcolm, Malcolm Neal Productions, 111 Everest Dr, Thomaston, GA 30286-4603 Tel: 706-646-2749; 706-647-5372 E-mail: nealritz@charter.net, pg 837

Neall, Kelly, Ottawa International Animation Festival, 2 Daly Ave, Suite 120, Ottawa, ON K1N 6E2, Canada Tel: 613-232-8769 Fax: 613-232-6315 E-mail: info@animationfestival.ca; entries@animationfestival.ca Web Site: www.animationfestival.ca, pg 999

Neath, Danielle, WildBrain™, 5657 Spring Garden Rd, Suite 505, Halifax, NS B3J 3R4, Canada Tel: 902-423-0260 Fax: 902-422-0752 E-mail: info@wildbrain.com; halifax@wildbrain.com; sales@wildbrain.com Web Site: www.wildbrain.com, pg 938

Necuze, Jorge J Sr, Digital Video Systems, 3270 Executive Way, Miramar, FL 33025 Tel: 954-239-4410 Fax: 954-239-4486 E-mail: info@digitalvideosystems.net Web Site: digitalvideosystems.net, pg 742

Neese, Marty, Velodyne LiDAR Inc, 5521 Hellyer Ave, San Jose, CA 95738 Tel: 408-465-2800 Fax: 408-779-9208 (cust serv); 408-779-9377 (orders) E-mail: lidar@velodyne.com Web Site: velodynelidar.com, pg 925

Negrini, Patrick, CommCreative, 75 Fountain St, Framingham, MA 01702 Tel: 508-620-6664 Toll Free Tel: 877-620-6664 Fax: 508-620-0592 E-mail: info@commcreative.com Web Site: www.commcreative.com, pg 728

Nehe, Matt, Vision Maker Media, 1800 N 33 St, Lincoln, NE 68503-1409 Tel: 402-472-3522 Fax: 402-472-8675 E-mail: visionmaker@unl.edu Web Site: www.visionmakermedia.org, pg 930

Nehme, Anthony, Pyrotek Special Effects Inc, 201 Whitehall Dr, Suite 6, Markham, ON L3R 9Y3, Canada Tel: 905-479-9991 Toll Free Tel: 800-481-9910 E-mail: info@pyrotekfx.com Web Site: pyrotekfx.com, pg 867

Neikirk, John, American Educational Research Association (AERA), 1430 "K" St NW, Suite 1200, Washington, DC 20005 Tel: 202-238-3200 Fax: 202-238-3250 E-mail: communications@aera.net; members@aera.net Web Site: www.aera.net, pg 948

Nelepovitz, Sandy, Microwave Filter Co Inc, 6743 Kinne St, East Syracuse, NY 13057 Tel: 315-438-4700 Toll Free Tel: 800-448-1666 Fax: 315-463-1467 Toll Free Fax: 888-411-8860 E-mail: mfcsales@microwavefilter.com Web Site: www.microwavefilter.com, pg 826

Nelles, Brian, PSSI Global Services LLC, 7030 Hayvenhurst Ave, Van Nuys, CA 91406 Tel: 310-575-4400 Toll Free Tel: 800-SAT-LINK (728-5465); 800-634-6530 (teleport svcs) E-mail: info@pssiglobal.com Web Site: www.pssiglobal.com, pg 866

Nelligan, Helena, Brady Corp, 6555 W Good Hope Rd, Milwaukee, WI 53201-0571 Tel: 414-358-6600 Toll Free Tel: 888-250-3082 E-mail: bradyusa@bradycorp.com (cust serv & sales) Web Site: www.bradyid.com, pg 709

Nelson, Alex, Artist Research & Development Grants, 417 W Roosevelt St, Phoenix, AZ 85003-1326 Tel: 602-771-6501 Fax: 602-256-0282 E-mail: info@azarts.gov Web Site: www.azarts.gov, pg 982

Nelson, Gina, Campus Productions, 42 Oak Ave, Tuckahoe, NY 10707 Tel: 914-395-1010 Fax: 914-395-1095 E-mail: sales@campusgroup.com Web Site: www.campusgroup.com, pg 715

Nelson, Ken, FirstCom Music, 14860 Montfort Dr, Suite 260, Dallas, TX 75254 Tel: 972-446-8742 Toll Free Tel: 800-858-8880 E-mail: info@firstcom.com; musicsearch@firstcom.com Web Site: www.firstcom.com, pg 761

Nelson, Marlene, Pointward, 400 First Ave N, Suite 100, Minneapolis, MN 55401 Tel: 651-646-2442 Web Site: www.pointward.com, pg 858

Nelson, Michele, PGi, 3280 Peachtree Rd NE, Suite 1000, Atlanta, GA 30305 Tel: 404-262-8400 Toll Free Tel: 866-755-4878 Web Site: www.pgi.com, pg 855

Nelson, Paul, Wisconsin Technical College System Foundation Inc, 6602 Normandy Lane, Madison, WI 53719-1081 Tel: 608-841-1800 Toll Free Tel: 800-821-6313 Fax: 608-841-1806 E-mail: foundation@wtcsf.tec.wi.us Web Site: www.wtcsf.tec.wi.us, pg 940

Nelson, Richard, ACCO Brands Corp, 4 Corporate Dr, Lake Zurich, IL 60047-8997 Toll Free Tel: 800-541-0094; 800-222-6462 Toll Free Fax: 800-941-4463 E-mail: contactus@acco.com (cust serv) Web Site: www.accobrands.com, pg 673

Nelson, Rob, Sound & Images Inc, 1211 Virginia St, Columbia, SC 29201 Tel: 803-791-3925 E-mail: marketing@s-and-i.com Web Site: www.s-and-i.com, pg 893

Nelson, Scott, Scott Nelson HD Productions Inc, PO Box 1198, Bend, OR 97709-1198 Tel: 541-410-8680 E-mail: snp@bendcable.com Web Site: vimeo.com/scottnelson, pg 838

Nelson, Tony, Spectrum Industries Inc, 925 First Ave, Chippewa Falls, WI 54729 *Tel:* 715-723-6750 *Toll Free Tel:* 800-235-1262 *Fax:* 715-738-2309 *Toll Free Fax:* 800-335-0473 *E-mail:* info@spectrumfurniture. com *Web Site:* www.spectrumfurniture.com, pg 897

Nelson, William A III, Nelson Enterprises Theatrical Supply Co, 1014 Rte 173 E, Bloomsbury, NJ 08804 *Tel:* 908-479-6902 *Fax:* 908-479-6903 *E-mail:* sales@nelson-enterprises.com; rentals@nelson-enterprises. com *Web Site:* www.nelson-enterprises.com, pg 838

Nelson-Dowd, Heidi, L E Nelson Sales Corp, 6050 S Valley View Blvd, Las Vegas, NV 89118 *Tel:* 702-367-3656 *Fax:* 702-367-7058, pg 838

Nemenz, Otto, Otto Nemenz International Inc, 870 N Vine St, Los Angeles, CA 90038 *Tel:* 323-469-2774 *Fax:* 323-469-1217 *E-mail:* info@ottonemenz.com *Web Site:* www.ottonemenz.com, pg 838

Nemeth, Stan, Automatic Devices Co (ADC), 2121 S 12 St, Allentown, PA 18103 *Tel:* 610-797-6000 *Toll Free Tel:* 800-360-2321 *Fax:* 610-797-4088 *E-mail:* info@automaticdevices.com *Web Site:* www. automaticdevices.com, pg 696

Nemeti, Susie, Xytech Systems Corp, 15451 San Fernando Mission Blvd, Suite 400, Mission Hills, CA 91345 *Tel:* 818-698-4900 *Fax:* 818-698-4901 *E-mail:* sales@xytechsystems.com *Web Site:* www. xytechsystems.com, pg 943

Nemoy, Carole Curb, Curb Entertainment International Corp, 3907 W Alameda Ave, Burbank, CA 91505 *Tel:* 818-843-8580 *Fax:* 818-566-1719 *Web Site:* www. curbentertainment.com, pg 736

Nemser, Benjamin L, Nemal Electronics International Inc, 12240 NE 14 Ave, North Miami, FL 33161 *Tel:* 305-899-0900 *Toll Free Tel:* 800-522-2253 *Fax:* 305-895-8178 *E-mail:* info@nemal.com *Web Site:* www.nemal.com, pg 838

Nesbit, Irene S, Nesbit Systems Inc, 243 N Union St, Suite 112, Lambertville, NJ 08530 *Tel:* 609-397-7720 *E-mail:* info@nesbit.com *Web Site:* www.nesbit.com, pg 838

Ness, Verden A, Sign Media Inc, 4020 Blackburn Lane, Burtonsville, MD 20866-1167 *Tel:* 301-421-0268 *Toll Free Tel:* 800-475-4756 *Fax:* 301-421-0270 *E-mail:* info@signmedia.com *Web Site:* www. signmedia.com, pg 887

Nethery, John, Marinco Electrical Group, N85 W12545 Westbrook Crossing, Menomonee Falls, WI 53051-3330 *Tel:* 262-293-0600 *E-mail:* marincopowerprod. sales@powerprodllc.com *Web Site:* www. marincopowerproducts.com, pg 817

Neto, Catarina, Concepts TV Productions Inc, 53 Indian Lane E, Towaco, NJ 07082 *Tel:* 973-331-1500 *Fax:* 973-331-1550 *E-mail:* sales@conceptstv.com *Web Site:* conceptstv.com, pg 730

Netzley, Steve, Havas Edge, 2386 Faraday Ave, Suite 200, Carlsbad, CA 92008 *Tel:* 760-929-0041 *E-mail:* info@havasedge.com *Web Site:* www. havasedge.com, pg 777

Neuburger, Warren, PGi, 3280 Peachtree Rd NE, Suite 1000, Atlanta, GA 30305 *Tel:* 404-262-8400 *Toll Free Tel:* 866-755-4878 *Web Site:* www.pgi.com, pg 855

Nevins, David, Showtime Networks Inc, 1633 Broadway, New York, NY 10019 *Tel:* 212-708-1600 *Fax:* 212-708-1217 *Web Site:* www.sho.com, pg 887

Nevins, Richard, Shanachie Entertainment Corp, 37 E Clinton St, Newton, NJ 07860 *Tel:* 973-579-7763 *Web Site:* shanachie.com, pg 885

Newbanks, Mike, CSPI, 175 Cabot St, Suite 210, Lowell, MA 01854 *Tel:* 978-663-7598; 978-954-5038 *Toll Free Tel:* 800-325-3110 *E-mail:* hello@cspi.com *Web Site:* www.cspi.com, pg 735

Newbern, Brenda, Cape Girardeau Convention & Visitors Bureau, 220 N Fountain St, Cape Girardeau, MO 63701 *Tel:* 573-335-1631 *Toll Free Tel:* 800-777-0068 *Fax:* 573-334-6702 *E-mail:* info@visitcape.com *Web Site:* visitcape.com, pg 972

Newell, Robert, Main Street Media Inc, 185 Pier Ave, Suite 105, Santa Monica, CA 90405 *Tel:* 310-450-1846 *E-mail:* info@mainstreetmediainc.com *Web Site:* www.mainstreetmediainc.com, pg 815

Newgren, Angie, Alliance for Community Media (ACM), 4248 Park Glen Rd, Minneapolis, MN 55416 *Tel:* 952-928-4643 *E-mail:* info@allcommunitymedia. org *Web Site:* www.allcommunitymedia.org, pg 947

Newhouse, James, Eastern Acoustic Works Inc (EAW), One Main St, Bldg 13, Whitinsville, MA 01588-2238 *Tel:* 508-234-6158 *Toll Free Tel:* 800-992-5013 *Toll Free Fax:* 800-322-8251 *Web Site:* www.eaw.com, pg 749

Newhouse, Roxane B, The Transfer Zone®, 4301 Orchard Lake Rd, Suite 180-191, West Bloomfield, MI 48323 *Tel:* 248-225-0477, pg 917

Newlander, Jon, Boston Light & Sound Inc, 290 N Beacon St, Boston, MA 02135-1990 *Tel:* 617-787-3131 *Fax:* 617-787-4257 *E-mail:* info@blsi.com *Web Site:* www.blsi.com, pg 709

Newlin, Julye, Julye Newlin Productions Inc, 129 E 13 St, Houston, TX 77008 *Tel:* 713-869-3609; 832-689-3609 (cell) *Fax:* 713-862-6505 *E-mail:* julye@julyenewlin.com *Web Site:* www.julyenewlin.com, pg 840

Newman, Chad, Florida Keys & Key West Film Commission, 1201 White St, Suite 102, Key West, FL 33040 *Tel:* 305-293-1800 *Toll Free Tel:* 800-FILM-KEYS (345-6539) *Fax:* 305-296-0788 *Web Site:* www. filmkeys.com, pg 969

Newman, Charles, Mother West, 187 Devoe St, Brooklyn, NY 11211 *E-mail:* info@motherwest.com *Web Site:* www.motherwest.com, pg 831

Newman, Dave J, CTGaudio, 2100 Constitution Blvd, Sarasota, FL 34231 *Tel:* 941-922-2322 *Toll Free Fax:* 866-871-6874 *E-mail:* orders@ctgaudio.com; info@ctgaudio.com *Web Site:* ctgaudio.com, pg 735

Newton, Matthew W, New Hampshire Film Bureau, One Eagle Sq, Suite 100, Concord, NH 03301 *Tel:* 603-271-2220 *E-mail:* film@livefree.nh.gov *Web Site:* www.visitnh.gov/film, pg 973

Newton, Stephen A, Cinevision Corp, 3300 Northeast Expwy NE, Bldg 2, Suite A, Atlanta, GA 30341 *Tel:* 770-455-8988 *Fax:* 770-455-4066 *Web Site:* www. cinevisionatlanta.com, pg 725

Nez, Christopher, Arizona Studios, 4614 E McDowell Rd, Phoenix, AZ 85008 *Tel:* 602-275-9100 *E-mail:* info@arizonastudios.com *Web Site:* arizonastudios.com, pg 689

Ng, Ricky, PESA, 103 Quality Circle, Suite 210, Huntsville, AL 35806 *Tel:* 256-726-9200 *Toll Free Tel:* 800-323-7372 *E-mail:* sales@pesa.com *Web Site:* www.pesa.com, pg 855

Ngo, Anh, North American Broadcasters Association (NABA), Canadian Broadcasting Centre, 25 John St, Suite 9C200, Toronto, ON M5V 3G7, Canada *Tel:* 416-205-3363 *Fax:* 416-205-2901 *E-mail:* contact@nabanet.com *Web Site:* nabanet.com, pg 960

Nguyen, Mike, NDS Surgical Imaging LLC, 5750 Hellyer Ave, San Jose, CA 95138 *Tel:* 408-776-0085 *Toll Free Tel:* 866-637-5237 *E-mail:* info@ndssi.com *Web Site:* www.ndssi.com, pg 837

Nicassio, Sam, Los Angeles Center Studios, 450 S Bixel St, Los Angeles, CA 90017 *Tel:* 213-534-3000 *E-mail:* productionservices@lacenterstudios.com *Web Site:* lacenterstudios.com, pg 811

Nicholls, Andrew, Orlando Special Effects, 14222 Lake Mary Jane Rd, Orlando, FL 32832 *Tel:* 407-648-1867 *Web Site:* www.orlandospfx.com, pg 848

Nichols, Andy, Encore Event Technologies LLC, 8850 W Sunset Rd, 3rd fl, Las Vegas, NV 89148 *Tel:* 702-739-8803 *Fax:* 702-739-8831 *Web Site:* www. encoreglobal.com/us, pg 754

Nichols, Betty, High Windy Audio/Banjoman Inc, PO Box 553, Fairview, NC 28730 *Tel:* 828-628-1728 *Toll Free Tel:* 800-637-8679 *Fax:* 828-628-4435 *E-mail:* office@davidholt.com *Web Site:* www. davidholt.com, pg 779

Nichols, Jason, Avitecture Inc, One Export Dr, Sterling, VA 20164-4421 *Tel:* 703-404-8900 *Fax:* 703-404-8940 *E-mail:* info@avitecture.com *Web Site:* www. avitecture.com, pg 699

Nichols, Koytt O, Keywest Technology Inc, 14563 W 96 Terr, Lenexa, KS 66215 *Tel:* 913-492-4666 *Toll Free Tel:* 800-331-2019 *Fax:* 913-322-1864 *E-mail:* sales@keywesttechnology.com *Web Site:* www.keywesttechnology.com, pg 798

Nichols, Patrick, Corel Corp, 1600 Carling Ave, Ottawa, ON K1Z 8R7, Canada *Toll Free Tel:* 877-582-6735 *Web Site:* www.corel.com, pg 731

Nichols, Peggy, Artbeats, 1405 N Myrtle Rd, Myrtle Creek, OR 97457 *Tel:* 541-863-4429 *Fax:* 541-863-4547 *E-mail:* info@artbeats.com *Web Site:* www. artbeats.com, pg 690

Nichols, Shannon, Broadcast Supply World Wide, 2237 S 19 St, Tacoma, WA 98405 *Tel:* 253-565-2301 (intl) *Toll Free Tel:* 800-426-8434 *Fax:* 253-565-8114 (intl) *Toll Free Fax:* 800-231-7055 *E-mail:* sales@bswusa. com; info@bswusa.com; customersupport@bswusa. com *Web Site:* www.bswusa.com, pg 711

Nichtern, Laurie R, Association of Independent Commercial Producers (AICP), 3 W 18 St, 5th fl, New York, NY 10011 *Tel:* 212-929-3000 *Fax:* 212-929-3359 *E-mail:* info@aicp.com *Web Site:* www.aicp. com, pg 951

Nickel, John, Switch, 6600 Manchester Ave, St Louis, MO 63139 *Tel:* 314-206-7700 *E-mail:* info@switch.us *Web Site:* www.switch.us, pg 905

Nickle, Ron, Sandusky Lee Corp, PO Box 6, Littlestown, PA 17340 *Tel:* 717-359-4111 *Toll Free Tel:* 800-233-7076 *Fax:* 717-359-4414 *E-mail:* customerserv@sanduskycabinets.com; help@sanduskycabinets. com; sales@sanduskycabinets.com *Web Site:* www. sanduskycabinets.com, pg 880

Nicol, Donna, Rosco Laboratories Inc, 52 Harbor View, Stamford, CT 06902 *Tel:* 203-708-8900 *Toll Free Tel:* 800-ROSCO NY (767-2669) *Fax:* 203-708-8919 *E-mail:* info@rosco.com *Web Site:* us.rosco.com, pg 877

Nicoletti, Joseph Jr, Joseph Nicoletti Consulting-Promotion, PO Box 386, Laguna Beach, CA 92652 *Tel:* 949-632-3338 *E-mail:* music-film@att.net, pg 841

Nicotera, Stan, S I Video Sales Group, 1318 S Carlisle St, Philadelphia, PA 19146 *Tel:* 267-519-2222 *Web Site:* www.sivideo.com; www.capclassics.com; takinglasvegas.com, pg 879

Niebauer, Skip, American Artist Studio, 1114 W 26 St, Erie, PA 16508-1518 *Tel:* 814-455-4796 *Toll Free Tel:* 888-462-7813 *Web Site:* americanartiststudio.com, pg 682

Niece, Andrew, Golden Space Needle Awards, 305 Harrison St, Seattle, WA 98109 *Tel:* 206-464-5830 *Fax:* 206-264-7919 *E-mail:* info@siff.net; entries@siff. net *Web Site:* www.siff.net, pg 991

Niece, Andrew, Seattle International Film Festival (SIFF), 305 Harrison St, Seattle, WA 98109 *Tel:* 206-464-5830 *Fax:* 206-264-7919 *E-mail:* info@siff.net; entries@siff.net *Web Site:* www.siff.net, pg 1003

Niederpruem, Gary, Vertiv, 1050 Dearborn Dr, Columbus, OH 43085 *Tel:* 614-888-0246 *Web Site:* www.vertiv.com, pg 926

Nielsen, Rod, Big House Sound Inc, 4001 Drossett Dr, Austin, TX 78744 *Tel:* 512-443-0019 *Fax:* 512-443-0916 *Web Site:* www.bighousesound.com, pg 705

Niemann, Joe, Acoustical Solutions LLC, 2420 Grenoble Rd, Richmond, VA 23294 *Tel:* 804-346-8350 *Toll Free Tel:* 800-782-5742 *Fax:* 804-346-8808 *E-mail:* info@acousticalsolutions.com *Web Site:* www. acousticalsolutions.com, pg 674

Nightingale, Caron, Nightingale Music Productions Inc, 5460 Yonge St, Suite 1611, Toronto, ON M2N 6K7, Canada *Tel:* 416-221-2393 *Fax:* 416-221-2676 *E-mail:* admin@nightingalemusic.com *Web Site:* www. nightingalemusic.com, pg 841

Nigrin, Albert Gabriel, New Jersey Film Festival, Rutgers University, 018 Loree Hall, 72 Lipman Dr, New Brunswick, NJ 08901-1414 *Tel:* 848-932-8482 *Fax:* 732-932-1935 *E-mail:* njmac@aol.com; njmac12@gmail.com *Web Site:* www.njfilmfest.com, pg 997

Nigrin, Albert Gabriel, United States Super 8mm Film & Digital Video Festival, Rutgers University, 018 Loree Hall, 72 Lipman Dr, New Brunswick, NJ 08901-1414 *Tel:* 848-932-8482 *Fax:* 732-932-1935 *E-mail:* njmac@aol.com; njmac12@gmail.com *Web Site:* www.njfilmfest.com, pg 1005

Nikolopoulos, Nikos, Avaya Inc, 4655 Great American Pkwy, Santa Clara, CA 95054 *Tel:* 908-953-6000 *Toll Free Tel:* 866-GO-AVAYA (462-8292 US & CN) *Web Site:* www.avaya.com, pg 697

Nilo, Robert, 360 Systems, 3281 Grande Vista Dr, Newbury Park, CA 91320-1193 *Tel:* 818-991-0360 *Fax:* 818-991-1360 *E-mail:* sales@360systems.com *Web Site:* www.360systems.com, pg 913

Nimens, Brian, The Hollywood Edge, c/o Sound Ideas, 105 W Beaver Creek Rd, Suite 4, Richmond Hill, ON L4B 1C6, Canada *Tel:* 905-886-5000 *Toll Free Tel:* 800-665-3000 (CN); 800-387-3030 (US) *E-mail:* hollywoodedge@sound-ideas.com *Web Site:* www.sound-ideas.com; www.hollywoodedge.com, pg 780

Nimens, Brian, Sound Ideas, 105 W Beaver Creek Rd, Suite 4, Richmond Hill, ON L4B 1C6, Canada *Tel:* 905-886-5000 *Toll Free Tel:* 800-387-3030; 800-665-3000 (CN) *Fax:* 905-886-6800 *E-mail:* info@sound-ideas.com; contact@sound-ideas.com; wbc105@sound-ideas.com *Web Site:* www.sound-ideas.com, pg 894

Nimens, Brian, StockMusic.com, 105 W Beaver Creek Rd, Suite 4, Richmond Hill, ON L4B 1C6, Canada *Tel:* 905-886-0077 *Fax:* 905-886-6800 *E-mail:* info@stockmusic.com *Web Site:* www.stockmusic.com, pg 901

Nimens, Brian, Westar Music, 105 W Beaver Creek Rd, Suite 4, Richmond Hill, ON L4B 1C6, Canada *Tel:* 905-886-3100 *Toll Free Tel:* 866-463-0100 *Fax:* 905-886-6800 *E-mail:* info@westarmusic.com *Web Site:* www.westarmusic.com, pg 936

Nisbet, Sandra, Small World Productions Inc, 140 Lakeside Ave, Suite 200, Seattle, WA 98122 *Tel:* 206-329-7167 *Toll Free Tel:* 800-866-7425 (orders); 800-325-7111 (cust serv) *Fax:* 206-329-0269 (credit card orders) *E-mail:* info@travelsmallworld.com; customercare@smarttravels.tv *Web Site:* www.smarttravels.tv, pg 890

Nishikawa, Tomo, IDX System Technology Inc, 19001 Harborgate Way, Suite 105, Torrance, CA 90501 *Tel:* 310-328-2850 *Fax:* 310-328-8202 *E-mail:* idx.usa@idx.tv *Web Site:* www.idx.tv, pg 784

Niwano, Masashi, Center for Asian American Media (CAAM), 145 Ninth St, Suite 350, San Francisco, CA 94103 *Tel:* 415-863-0814 *Fax:* 415-863-7428 *E-mail:* publicity@caamedia.org *Web Site:* caamedia.org, pg 953

Nix, Danny, AVL Systems Design LLC, 14901 Bristol Park Blvd, Edmond, OK 73013 *Tel:* 405-749-1866 *Fax:* 405-749-1851 *E-mail:* dnix@avl1.com *Web Site:* www.avl1.com, pg 699

Noble, Debbie, Whirlwind Music Distributors Inc, 99 Ling Rd, Greece, NY 14612 *Tel:* 585-663-8820 *Toll Free Tel:* 800-733-9473 (US only) *Fax:* 585-865-8930 *E-mail:* sales@whirlwindusa.com; techsupport@whirlwindusa.com; darylg@whirlwindusa.com (CN inquiries) *Web Site:* www.whirlwindusa.com, pg 937

Noble, Paul, Activu Corp, 301 Roundhill Dr, Rockaway, NJ 07866 *Tel:* 973-366-5550 *Toll Free Tel:* 888-ACTIVU1 (228-4881) *Fax:* 973-625-7775 *E-mail:* facebook@activu.com *Web Site:* activu.com, pg 675

Nocita, Anthony, IAMP Professional Audio, 218 Reindollar Ave, Unit 6-A, Marina, CA 93933 *Tel:* 831-884-9558 *Fax:* 831-643-2131 *E-mail:* iamp-pro-audio@comcast.net *Web Site:* www.iampproaudio.com, pg 783

Nocon, Jeremy, The Jim Henson Co, 1416 N La Brea Ave, Hollywood, CA 90028 *Tel:* 323-802-1500 *Fax:* 323-802-1825 *Web Site:* www.henson.com, pg 794

Nolan, Angela, Vistacom Inc, 1902 Vultee St, Allentown, PA 18103-2998 *Tel:* 610-791-9081 *Toll Free Tel:* 800-747-0459 *Fax:* 610-791-9510 *E-mail:* info@vistacominc.com *Web Site:* www.vistacominc.com, pg 931

Nolan, Fiona, CommScope Inc, 1100 CommScope Place SE, Hickory, NC 28602 *Tel:* 828-324-2200 *Toll Free Tel:* 800-982-1708 *E-mail:* publicrelations@commscope.com *Web Site:* www.commscope.com, pg 728

Nolan, James, Concepts TV Productions Inc, 53 Indian Lane E, Towaco, NJ 07082 *Tel:* 973-331-1500 *Fax:* 973-331-1550 *E-mail:* sales@conceptstv.com *Web Site:* conceptstv.com, pg 730

Noll, Deb, Boston Productions Inc (BPI), 290 Vanderbilt Ave, Suite 1, Norwood, MA 02062 *Tel:* 781-255-1555; 720-233-1250 (sales) *E-mail:* info@bostonproductions.com *Web Site:* www.bostonproductions.com, pg 709

Noll, Robert, Boston Productions Inc (BPI), 290 Vanderbilt Ave, Suite 1, Norwood, MA 02062 *Tel:* 781-255-1555; 720-233-1250 (sales) *E-mail:* info@bostonproductions.com *Web Site:* www.bostonproductions.com, pg 709

Nolte, Carolyn, SuperStock Inc, 6620 Southpoint Dr S, Suite 501, Jacksonville, FL 32216 *Tel:* 904-565-0066 *Toll Free Tel:* 800-828-4545 *Fax:* 904-565-1620 *E-mail:* info@superstock.com; yourfriends@superstock.com *Web Site:* www.superstock.com, pg 904

Nolton, Gary, Limbo Films, 2223 NE Martin Luther King Jr Blvd, Portland, OR 97212 *E-mail:* info@limbofilms.com *Web Site:* www.limbofilms.com, pg 808

Noone, Robert, Location Sound Corp, 10639 Riverside Dr, North Hollywood, CA 91602 *Tel:* 818-980-9891 *Toll Free Tel:* 800-228-4429 *Fax:* 818-980-9911; 818-980-7932 (rentals) *E-mail:* information@locationsound.com *Web Site:* www.locationsound.com, pg 810

Noorbhai, Munir, William F White International Inc, 800 Islington Ave, Toronto, ON M8Z 6A1, Canada *Tel:* 416-239-5050 *Toll Free Tel:* 800-465-0160 (CN only) *Web Site:* www.whites.com, pg 937

Noorigian, Carol, The Production Group Studios, 1626 N Wilcox Ave, Suite 281, Hollywood, CA 90028 *Tel:* 323-469-8111 *Fax:* 323-962-2182 *E-mail:* info@productiongroup.tv *Web Site:* productiongroup.tv, pg 863

Norberg, Eric, Consolidated Communications Consultants, 1837 SE Harold St, Portland, OR 97202-4932 *Tel:* 503-232-9787 *Toll Free Tel:* 800-929-5119 *Fax:* 503-232-9787 *Toll Free Fax:* 800-929-5119 *E-mail:* acmrl@myexcel.com *Web Site:* www.acmusicresearch.com, pg 731

Nordal, Greg, Nelson Education Ltd, 1120 Birchmount Rd, Scarborough, ON M1K 5G4, Canada *Tel:* 416-752-9100 *Toll Free Tel:* 800-268-2222 (cust support) *Fax:* 416-752-8101 *Toll Free Fax:* 800-430-4445 *E-mail:* inquire@nelson.com *Web Site:* www.nelson.com, pg 838

Norder, Scott, RGB Spectrum, 950 Marina Village Pkwy, Alameda, CA 94501 *Tel:* 510-814-7000 *Fax:* 510-814-7026 *Web Site:* www.rgb.com, pg 874

Nordstrand, Karen, Monterey County Film Commission, 801 Lighthouse Ave, Suite 104, Monterey, CA 93940 *Tel:* 831-646-0910 *Fax:* 831-655-9250 *E-mail:* info@filmmonterey.org *Web Site:* www.filmmonterey.org, pg 967

Nordyke, David, Music Lab Inc, 500 E Saint Elmo Rd, Austin, TX 78745 *Tel:* 512-707-0560 (ext 2) *Fax:* 512-707-2946 *E-mail:* info@musiclab.net *Web Site:* musiclabaustin.com, pg 834

Norfleet, George, Connecticut Office of Film, Television & Digital Media, c/o Dept of Economic & Community Development, 480 Columbus Blvd, Suite 5, Hartford, CT 06103 *Tel:* 860-500-2300 *Web Site:* www.ct.gov, pg 968

Norinsky, Mitch, Backstar Creative Media Inc, 70 W Hubbard St, Suite 203, Chicago, IL 60654 *Tel:* 312-467-0425 *Toll Free Tel:* 800-955-8900 *E-mail:* solutions@backstar.com *Web Site:* www.backstar.com, pg 700

Norman, Neil, GNP Crescendo Records, 1405 N Avon St, Burbank, CA 91505-1885 *Tel:* 818-566-8900 *E-mail:* gnpcrescendo@gmail.com *Web Site:* www.gnpcrescendo.com, pg 772

Norman, Ray, Dogwood Productions Inc, 757 Government St, Mobile, AL 36602 *Tel:* 251-476-0858 *Toll Free Tel:* 800-254-9903 *Fax:* 251-479-0364 *E-mail:* info@dogwoodproductions.com *Web Site:* www.dogwoodproductions.com, pg 745

Norment, Jeff, Television Equipment Associates Inc (TEA), 16 Mount Ebo Rd S, Suite 6, Brewster, NY 10509 *Tel:* 845-278-0960 *Fax:* 845-278-0964 *E-mail:* sales@teaheadsets.com *Web Site:* www.teaheadsets.com, pg 910

Norona, Kristen, Greater Fort Lauderdale/Broward Office of Film, Music, Fashion & Create, 101 NE Third Ave, Suite 100, Fort Lauderdale, FL 33301 *Tel:* 954-767-2467 *Fax:* 954-767-4681 *E-mail:* film@broward.org *Web Site:* www.sunny.org/film, pg 969

Norrie, Mark, Transtector Systems Inc, 10701 N Airport Dr, Hayden, ID 83835 *Tel:* 800-772-8515 *Toll Free Tel:* 800-882-9110 *Fax:* 208-762-6133 *E-mail:* sales@transtector.com *Web Site:* www.transtector.com, pg 917

Norris, Ann, N&N Productions Ltd, 5540 High Rock Way, Sparks, NV 89431 *Tel:* 775-355-9080 *E-mail:* sales@brassgobos.com *Web Site:* www.brassgobos.com, pg 835

Norris, Bob, Film Ideas Inc, 308 N Wolf Rd, Wheeling, IL 60090 *Tel:* 847-419-0255 *Toll Free Tel:* 800-475-3456 (US only) *Fax:* 847-419-8933 *E-mail:* info@filmideas.com; orders@filmideas.com (cust serv) *Web Site:* www.filmideas.com, pg 760

Norris, Drew, MediaOne Studios, 950 Battery St, 2nd fl, San Francisco, CA 94111 *Tel:* 415-262-4222 *E-mail:* hi@mediaonestudios.com *Web Site:* mediaonestudios.com, pg 823

Norris, Jade, 30 Second Street Ltd, 1209 Mountain Road Place NE, Suite B, Albuquerque, NM 87110 *Tel:* 505-265-0224 *E-mail:* info@30sst.com *Web Site:* www.thirtysecst.com, pg 912

Norris, Lindsey, Thompson Rivers University Marketing & Communications Dept, 805 TRU Way, Kamloops, BC V2C 0C8, Canada *Tel:* 250-852-7000 *Web Site:* www.tru.ca/marcom, pg 913

Norris, Paul, Immersion Corp, 50 Rio Robles, San Jose, CA 95134 *Tel:* 408-467-1900 *Fax:* 408-467-1901 *Web Site:* www.immersion.com, pg 786

Norton, Diane, Idaho Film Office, 700 W State St, Boise, ID 83702 *Tel:* 208-334-2470 *Toll Free Tel:* 800-842-5858 *Fax:* 208-334-2631 *Web Site:* www.filmidaho.com, pg 970

Norton, Janice, SADiE Inc, 45 Pine St, Rockaway, NJ 07866 *Tel:* 973-983-9577 *Fax:* 973-983-9588 *E-mail:* sales@prismmpi.com *Web Site:* www.sadie.com; www.prismsound.com, pg 879

Norton, Sylvia, American Association of School Librarians (AASL), 50 E Huron St, Chicago, IL 60611 *Tel:* 312-280-4382 *Toll Free Tel:* 800-545-2433 (ext 4382) *Fax:* 312-280-5276 *E-mail:* aasl@ala.org *Web Site:* www.ala.org, pg 948

Nosevich, Alex, CommCreative, 75 Fountain St, Framingham, MA 01702 *Tel:* 508-620-6664 *Toll Free Tel:* 877-620-6664 *Fax:* 508-620-0592 *E-mail:* info@commcreative.com *Web Site:* www.commcreative.com, pg 728

Novacek, Eugene, ENCO Systems Inc, 29444 Northwestern Hwy, Southfield, MI 48034 *Tel:* 248-827-4440 *Toll Free Tel:* 800-362-6797 (sales) *Fax:* 248-827-4441 *E-mail:* sales@enco.com; support@enco.com *Web Site:* www.enco.com, pg 754

O'Keefe, Kevin, O'Keefe Communications Inc, 4301 Connecticut Ave NW, Suite 200, Washington, DC 20008-2304 *Tel:* 202-363-2101 *E-mail:* info@okeefecom.com *Web Site:* www.okeefecom.com, pg 844

O'Leary, Deborah, Art Gallery of Ontario, 317 Dundas St W, Toronto, ON M5T 1G4, Canada *Tel:* 416-979-6648 *Toll Free Tel:* 877-225-4246 *Web Site:* ago.ca, pg 690

O'Malley, Patrick, Avaya Inc, 4655 Great American Pkwy, Santa Clara, CA 95054 *Tel:* 908-953-6000 *Toll Free Tel:* 866-GO-AVAYA (462-8292 US & CN) *Web Site:* www.avaya.com, pg 697

O'Meara, Padraic, Limbo Films, 2223 NE Martin Luther King Jr Blvd, Portland, OR 97212 *E-mail:* info@limbofilms.com *Web Site:* www.limbofilms.com, pg 808

O'Neil, Mike, Freeman, 1600 Viceroy, Suite 100, Dallas, TX 75235 *Tel:* 214-445-1000 *Web Site:* www.freeman.com, pg 765

O'Neill, Denise, Pepper Group, 220 N Smith St, Suite 406, Palatine, IL 60067 *Tel:* 847-963-0333 *Fax:* 847-963-0888 *E-mail:* pepper@peppergroup.com *Web Site:* www.peppergroup.com, pg 854

O'Neill, Kelly, Video Dimensions Inc, 545 W 45 St, New York, NY 10036 *Tel:* 212-262-5453 *Web Site:* videodimensions.net, pg 927

O'Neill, Ken, Laser Video Corp, 401 Germantown Pike, Lafayette Hill, PA 19444 *Tel:* 610-825-2500 *Toll Free Tel:* 800-448-8772 *Fax:* 610-941-9989 *E-mail:* customerservice@laservideousa.com *Web Site:* www.lvconline.com, pg 804

O'Neill, Kerrigan, Hollywood Lights Inc, 5251 SE McLoughlin Blvd, Portland, OR 97202-4836 *Tel:* 503-232-9001; 503-232-8855 *Toll Free Tel:* 800-826-9881 *Fax:* 503-517-8686 *E-mail:* portland@hollywoodlights.biz *Web Site:* www.hollywoodlights.biz, pg 780

O'Neill, Matthew, Downtown Community Television Center (DCTV), 87 Lafayette St, New York, NY 10013 *Tel:* 212-966-4510 *Fax:* 212-226-3053 *E-mail:* info@dctvny.org *Web Site:* www.dctvny.org, pg 746

O'Neill, Trudie, Laser Video Corp, 401 Germantown Pike, Lafayette Hill, PA 19444 *Tel:* 610-825-2500 *Toll Free Tel:* 800-448-8772 *Fax:* 610-941-9989 *E-mail:* customerservice@laservideousa.com *Web Site:* www.lvconline.com, pg 804

O'Pecko, Paul, Mystic Seaport (Film & Video Archives), 75 Greenmanville Ave, Mystic, CT 06355 *Tel:* 860-572-0711; 860-572-5365 *Toll Free Tel:* 888-973-2767 *E-mail:* permissions@mysticseaport.org; info@mysticseaport.org; advancement@mysticseaport.org (donations) *Web Site:* www.mysticseaport.org, pg 835

O'Ray, Kali, San Francisco Black Film Festival, PO Box 15490, San Francisco, CA 94115 *Tel:* 770-369-3776 *E-mail:* sfbff@sfbff.org *Web Site:* www.sfbff.org, pg 1002

O'Reilly, Matthew P, Tritech Communications, 625 Locust St, Suite 300, Garden City, NY 11530 *Tel:* 631-254-4500 *Fax:* 631-254-4499 *E-mail:* sales@tritechcomm.com *Web Site:* www.tritechcomm.com, pg 918

O'Rourke, Shannon, TVO/Ontario Educational Communications Authority (OECA), 2180 Yonge St, Toronto, ON M4S 2B9, Canada *Tel:* 416-484-2600; 416-484-2665 (cust rel) *Toll Free Tel:* 800-613-0513; 800-INFO-TVO (463-6886) *E-mail:* asktvo@tvo.org *Web Site:* tvo.org, pg 919

O'Shaughnessy, Doug, Nexsan Inc, 900 E Hamilton Ave, Suite 230, Campbell, CA 95008 *Tel:* 408-724-9809 *E-mail:* sales@nexsan.com *Web Site:* www.nexsan.com, pg 840

O'Shea, Deirdre, Feldenkrais® Resources, 3680 Sixth Ave, San Diego, CA 92103 *Tel:* 619-220-8776 *Toll Free Tel:* 800-765-1907 *Fax:* 619-330-4993 *E-mail:* info@feldenkraisresources.com *Web Site:* feldenkraisresources.com, pg 759

Oatley, Steve, Axis Films, 3138 Cumberland Rd, Berkley, MI 48072 *Tel:* 248-722-1734 *Web Site:* www.axisfilms.tv, pg 700

Odehnal, Steve, Sacramento Theatrical Lighting Ltd (STL), 950 Richards Blvd, Sacramento, CA 95811 *Tel:* 916-447-3258 *Toll Free Tel:* 800-283-2785 *Fax:* 916-447-5012 *E-mail:* info@stlltd.com *Web Site:* www.stlltd.com, pg 879

Oehme, Sven, DataDirect Networks, 9351 Deering Ave, Chatsworth, CA 91311 *Tel:* 818-700-4000 *Toll Free Tel:* 800-TERABYTE (837-2298) *E-mail:* info@ddn.com; sales@ddn.com *Web Site:* www.ddn.com, pg 738

Oei, Elisabeth, Sonoton Music Library, 6255 Sunset Blvd, Suite 900, Hollywood, CA 90028 *Tel:* 323-461-3211 *Toll Free Tel:* 800-543-4276 *Fax:* 323-461-9102 *Web Site:* www.apmmusic.com, pg 893

Oetting, Brett, Visit Topeka Inc, 618 S Kansas Ave, Topeka, KS 66603 *Tel:* 785-234-1030 *Toll Free Tel:* 800-235-1030 *Fax:* 785-234-8282 *E-mail:* info@visittopeka.com *Web Site:* www.visittopeka.com, pg 971

Offensend, David, Education Development Center Inc (EDC), 43 Foundry Ave, Waltham, MA 02453-8313 *Tel:* 617-969-7100 *Fax:* 617-969-5979 *E-mail:* contact@edc.org *Web Site:* www.edc.org, pg 750

Ogawa, Kazuto, Canon USA Inc, One Canon Park, Melville, NY 11747 *Toll Free Tel:* 800-652-2666 *E-mail:* pr@cusa.canon.com *Web Site:* www.usa.canon.com, pg 716

Ogles, Julie, Cramer, 425 University Ave, Norwood, MA 02062 *Tel:* 781-278-2300 *E-mail:* theteam@cramer.com *Web Site:* cramer.com, pg 733

Oglesby, Alan, HSA Inc, 1717 E Sixth St, Mishawaka, IN 46544 *Tel:* 574-255-6100 *Fax:* 574-255-8131 *E-mail:* hsainfo@hsarolltops.com *Web Site:* www.hsarolltops.com, pg 782

Oh, Christian, DC Asian Pacific American Film Festival, 2515 Virginia Ave NW, No 58205, Washington, DC 20037 *Tel:* 202-796-9680; 202-792-6393 *E-mail:* info@apafilm.org; admin@apafilm.org *Web Site:* www.apafilm.org, pg 988

Ohlhaber, Ron, Dukane Corp, Audio Visual Products Division, 2900 Dukane Dr, St Charles, IL 60174 *Tel:* 630-762-4040 *Toll Free Tel:* 888-245-1966 *Fax:* 630-584-5156 *E-mail:* avsales@dukane.com *Web Site:* dukaneav.com, pg 747

Ohlinger, Heather, Creation Technologies Inc, 8999 Fraserton Ct, Burnaby, BC V5J 5H8, Canada *Tel:* 604-430-4336 *Toll Free Tel:* 800-736-1271 *E-mail:* info@creationtech.com; sales@creationtech.com *Web Site:* www.creationtech.com, pg 733

Ohrn, Rickard, ChyronHego Corp, 5 Hub Dr, Melville, NY 11747 *Tel:* 631-845-2000 *E-mail:* info@chyronhego.com; sales@chryonhego.com *Web Site:* chyronhego.com, pg 723

Ohtsuki, Mike, Universe Kogaku America Inc, 116 Audrey Ave, Oyster Bay, NY 11771 *Tel:* 516-624-2444 *Fax:* 516-624-3109 *E-mail:* info@universeoptics.com *Web Site:* universeoptics.com, pg 922

Oien, Laura, Tom Hopkins International Inc, 465 E Chilton Dr, Suite 4, Chandler, AZ 85225 *Tel:* 480-949-0786 *Toll Free Tel:* 800-528-0446 *Fax:* 480-949-1590 *E-mail:* info@tomhopkins.com *Web Site:* www.tomhopkins.com, pg 781

Oishi, Tsutomu (Tom), PLUS Corp of America, 9655 SW Sunshine Ct, Suite 300, Beaverton, OR 97005 *Tel:* 503-748-8700 *Toll Free Tel:* 800-211-9001 *E-mail:* sales@plus-america.com; info@plus-america.com *Web Site:* www.plus-america.com, pg 858

Oken, Wilda, Professional Photographers of America (PPA), 229 Peachtree St NE, Suite 2200, Atlanta, GA 30303 *Tel:* 404-522-8600 *Toll Free Tel:* 800-786-6277 *Fax:* 404-614-6400 *E-mail:* csc@ppa.com *Web Site:* www.ppa.com, pg 960

Olden, Robert, Olden Camera & Lens Co Inc, 1263 Broadway, 4th fl, New York, NY 10001-3593 *Tel:* 212-226-3727, pg 845

Olden, Walter L, Olden Lighting, 2008 Alexander Ave, Austin, TX 78722 *Tel:* 512-416-8080 *Fax:* 512-416-8096 *E-mail:* rental@oldenlighting.com; sales@oldenlighting.com *Web Site:* www.oldenlighting.com, pg 845

Olinsky, David, Disc Makers, 7905 N Crescent Blvd, Pennsauken, NJ 08110-1402 *Tel:* 856-663-9030 *Toll Free Tel:* 800-468-9353 *Fax:* 856-661-3450 *E-mail:* info@discmakers.com *Web Site:* www.discmakers.com, pg 743

Olive, James "Jim" Lee, Stockyard Photos/Jim Olive Photography, 1520 Center St, Studio 2, Houston, TX 77007 *Tel:* 281-802-3597 *Web Site:* stockyard.com, pg 901

Oliver, Cynthia D, Communications Design Associates, 437 Turnpike St, Canton, MA 02021 *Tel:* 339-502-6551 *Web Site:* www.cdaconsultants.com, pg 729

Oliver, Lee, Arizona Cine Equipment, 2125 E 20 St, Tucson, AZ 85719 *Tel:* 520-623-8268 *Fax:* 520-623-1092 *Web Site:* www.azcine.com, pg 688

Oliver, Linda, Arizona Cine Equipment, 2125 E 20 St, Tucson, AZ 85719 *Tel:* 520-623-8268 *Fax:* 520-623-1092 *Web Site:* www.azcine.com, pg 688

Ollasnier, Jean-Marc, Accenture, 161 N Clark St, Chicago, IL 60601 *Tel:* 312-693-0161 *Toll Free Tel:* 877-889-9009 *Fax:* 312-693-0507 *Web Site:* www.accenture.com, pg 673

Ollila, Phil, Ingram Content Group LLC, One Ingram Blvd, La Vergne, TN 37086-1986 *Tel:* 615-793-5000 *Toll Free Tel:* 800-937-8000 (retailers); 800-937-5300 (ext 1, libs) *E-mail:* customerservice@ingramcontent.com *Web Site:* www.ingramcontent.com, pg 787

Olsen, Craig N, WindTech™ Microphone Windscreens & Accessories, 7845 E Evans Rd, Scottsdale, AZ 85260-2919 *Tel:* 480-998-7140 *E-mail:* information@olsenaudio.com; web-info3@olsenaudio.com *Web Site:* www.windtech.tv, pg 939

Olson, Dan, Olson Visual Inc, 13000 Weber Way, Hawthorne, CA 90250 *Tel:* 310-355-1681 *Toll Free Tel:* 800-480-6643 *Fax:* 310-263-6980 *E-mail:* info@olsonvisual.com *Web Site:* olsonvisual.com, pg 845

Olson, Doug, Image Craft LLC, 3401 E Broadway Rd, Phoenix, AZ 85040 *Tel:* 602-276-2082 *Toll Free Tel:* 800-274-2422 *Fax:* 602-232-0719 *E-mail:* designgroup@imcraft.com *Web Site:* www.imcraft.com, pg 785

Olson, Eric, University of Florida, Warrington College of Business Information Technology Support Programs, Bryan Hall 300D, 1384 Union Rd, Gainesville, FL 32611 *Tel:* 352-273-1616 *Fax:* 352-392-6250 *E-mail:* itsp@warrington.ufl.edu *Web Site:* warrington.ufl.edu/itsp, pg 922

Olson, Gary H, GHO Group LLC, 340 W 55 St, Suite 5E, New York, NY 10019 *Tel:* 212-319-7716 *E-mail:* info@ghogroup.com *Web Site:* www.ghogroup.com, pg 770

Olson, Jason, Duplication Media, 8126 Douglas Ave, Urbandale, IA 50322 *Tel:* 515-334-DUPS (334-3877) *E-mail:* info@duplicationmedia.com *Web Site:* www.duplicationmedia.com, pg 748

Olson, Kevin, Atomic Imaging Inc/Golan Studios, 1501 N Magnolia Ave, Chicago, IL 60642 *Tel:* 312-649-1800 *Fax:* 312-642-7441 *Web Site:* www.atomicimaging.com, pg 692

Olson, Rick, Olson Visual Inc, 13000 Weber Way, Hawthorne, CA 90250 *Tel:* 310-355-1681 *Toll Free Tel:* 800-480-6643 *Fax:* 310-263-6980 *E-mail:* info@olsonvisual.com *Web Site:* olsonvisual.com, pg 845

Ombao, Satti, Rollin Studios, 259 Green St, 2nd fl, Brooklyn, NY 11222 *Toll Free Tel:* 844-576-5546 *E-mail:* more@rollin-studios.com *Web Site:* rollin-studios.com, pg 877

Omps, Jon, PC&E, 2235 DeFoor Hills Rd, Atlanta, GA 30318 *Tel:* 404-609-9001 *Toll Free Tel:* 800-537-4021 *Fax:* 404-609-9926 *E-mail:* marketing@pce-atlanta.com *Web Site:* pce-atlanta.com, pg 852

Onesta, Audrey, DTC Lighting & Grip, 1280 65 St, Emeryville, CA 94608 *Tel:* 510-595-0770 *Fax:* 510-595-0772 *E-mail:* sales@dtcgrip.com; rentals@dtcgrip.com *Web Site:* www.dtcgrip.com, pg 747

Oponski, Ted, Earl Girls Inc, 1648 White Horse Pike, Egg Harbor City, NJ 08215 *Tel:* 609-965-6900 *Web Site:* earlgirlsinc.com, pg 749

Oppenheimer, Marty, Oppenheimer Camera Products, 7400 Third Ave S, Seattle, WA 98108-4143 *Tel:* 206-467-8666 *Toll Free Tel:* 877-467-8666 *Fax:* 206-467-9165 *Web Site:* oppenheimercameraproducts.com, pg 847

Orahood, Jim, Ampex Data Systems Corp, 26460 Corporate Ave, Hayward, CA 94545 *Tel:* 650-367-2011 *E-mail:* info@ampex.com *Web Site:* www.ampex.com, pg 684

Orbin, Zachariah, Brantley Sound Associates Inc, 115 Duluth Ave, Nashville, TN 37209-1207 *Tel:* 615-256-6260 *Web Site:* www.brantleysound.com, pg 709

Ordway, Paula, CMD Agency, 1631 NW Thurman St, Portland, OR 97209 *Tel:* 503-223-6794 *E-mail:* info@cmdagency.com *Web Site:* www.cmdagency.com, pg 726

Orgera, George, F&F Productions LLC, 14333 Myerlake Circle, Clearwater, FL 33760 *Tel:* 727-530-5000 *Fax:* 727-535-6547 *E-mail:* info@fandfhd.tv *Web Site:* www.fandfhd.tv, pg 759

Orgera, Marc, F&F Productions LLC, 14333 Myerlake Circle, Clearwater, FL 33760 *Tel:* 727-530-5000 *Fax:* 727-535-6547 *E-mail:* info@fandfhd.tv *Web Site:* www.fandfhd.tv, pg 759

Orlando, Jack, Antenna International, 383 Main Ave, Norwalk, CT 06851 *Tel:* 203-523-0320 *E-mail:* inquiry@antennainternational.com; marketing@antennainternational.com *Web Site:* www.antennainternational.com, pg 686

Orlando, Ken, Cool-Lux, 1268 Humbracht Circle, Bartlett, IL 60103 *Toll Free Tel:* 800-ACDC-LUX (223-2589) *Fax:* 630-830-2525 *Web Site:* www.cool-lux.com, pg 731

Orlando, Ken, Speedotron Corp, 1268 Humbracht Circle, Bartlett, IL 60103-1631 *Tel:* 630-246-5001 *Fax:* 630-830-2525 *E-mail:* support@speedotron.com *Web Site:* www.speedotron.com, pg 897

Orlando, Kenneth, Smith-Victor Corp, 1268 Humbracht Circle, Bartlett, IL 60103-1631 *Tel:* 630-830-9200 *Toll Free Tel:* 800-348-9862 *Fax:* 630-830-9201 *Toll Free Fax:* 800-352-0490 *E-mail:* sales@smithvictor.com *Web Site:* www.promarkbrands.com, pg 891

Orlando, Ron, ATS Cases Inc, 172 Otis St, Northborough, MA 01532 *Tel:* 508-393-9110 *Toll Free Tel:* 800-451-4242; 800-519-2771 *Fax:* 508-393-9508 *E-mail:* casemakers@mac.com *Web Site:* atscases.com, pg 692

Orlansky, Ilana, IES Medal, 120 Wall St, 17th fl, New York, NY 10005-4026 *Tel:* 212-248-5000 *E-mail:* ies@ies.org *Web Site:* ies.org, pg 992

Orlowsky, Peter, Getty Images, 605 Fifth Ave S, Suite 400, Seattle, WA 98104 *Tel:* 206-925-5000 *Toll Free Tel:* 888-888-5889; 800-462-4379 (sales) *E-mail:* sales.na@gettyimages.com *Web Site:* www.gettyimages.com, pg 770

Orosz, Bruce, ACT Productions, 407 Lincoln Rd, Suite 302, Miami Beach, FL 33139 *Tel:* 305-538-3809 *Fax:* 305-538-3814 *E-mail:* info@actproductions.com *Web Site:* www.actproductions.com, pg 675

Orr, Bill, Michigan Office Solutions (MOS), A Xerox Company, 2859 Walkent Dr NW, Grand Rapids, MI 49544 *Toll Free Tel:* 800-442-9070 *E-mail:* info@mos-xerox.com *Web Site:* www.mos-xerox.com, pg 825

Orr, Marnie, Creative BC (CrBC), 7 W Sixth Ave, Vancouver, BC V5Y 1K2, Canada *Tel:* 604-730-2732 *Fax:* 604-736-7290 *E-mail:* info@creativebc.com; media@creativebc.com *Web Site:* www.creativebc.com, pg 978

Orr, Rob, Rob Orr Productions Ltd, 1336 Pine St, Glenview, IL 60025 *Tel:* 847-724-5228 *E-mail:* rob@roborrproductions.com *Web Site:* www.roborrproductions.com, pg 848

Ort, Gene, GMP Music, 1103 North St, Niles, MI 49120 *Tel:* 269-687-9100 *Toll Free Tel:* 800-955-0619 *Fax:* 269-687-9200 *E-mail:* info@gmpmusic.com *Web Site:* www.gmpmusic.com; www.reservemusic.com, pg 772

Ortabasi, Leslie, The Dreaming Tree, 1112 Chestnut St, Unit B, Burbank, CA 91506 *Tel:* 818-845-3230 *E-mail:* info@dreamingtreeproductions.com *Web Site:* www.dreamingtreeproductions.com, pg 746

Ortabasi, Oktay, The Dreaming Tree, 1112 Chestnut St, Unit B, Burbank, CA 91506 *Tel:* 818-845-3230 *E-mail:* info@dreamingtreeproductions.com *Web Site:* www.dreamingtreeproductions.com, pg 746

Orth, Jade, Minnesota Film & TV, 401 N Third St, Suite 245, Minneapolis, MN 55401 *Tel:* 612-767-0095 *E-mail:* info@mnfilmtv.org *Web Site:* mnfilmtv.org, pg 972

Osborn, Pell, MotionArt Studios, 27 Common St, Boston, MA 02129 *Tel:* 617-242-2228 *Web Site:* www.motionart.org; www.linestorm.com, pg 831

Osborne, Bud, A-V-A Video Productions, 4760 E 65 St, Indianapolis, IN 46220 *Tel:* 317-253-8562; 317-370-1794 (cell) *E-mail:* avaprods@comcast.net *Web Site:* www.avavideoproductions.com, pg 671

Osborne, Jeff, Audience Response Systems Inc, 5611-C E Morgan Ave, Evansville, IN 47715 *Tel:* 812-479-7507 *Toll Free Tel:* 800-INVOLVE (468-6583) *Fax:* 812-479-1057 *E-mail:* arsales@audienceresponse.com *Web Site:* www.audienceresponse.com, pg 693

Oseman, Dan, Audio Visual of Milwaukee Inc, 285 N Janacek Rd, Brookfield, WI 53045 *Tel:* 262-432-1077 *Toll Free Tel:* 800-236-6909 *Fax:* 262-432-1078 *E-mail:* avm@avmonline.com *Web Site:* www.avmonline.com, pg 695

Osiel, Isaac, Westbury National Show Systems Ltd, 772 Warden Ave, Toronto, ON M1L 4T7, Canada *Tel:* 416-752-1371 *Toll Free Tel:* 855-752-1372 *Fax:* 416-752-1382 *E-mail:* info@westbury.com *Web Site:* www.westbury.com, pg 936

Oslund, Deborah, Broadcast Rentals, 2343 W University Dr, Suite 101, Tempe, AZ 85281 *Tel:* 480-894-1456 *Toll Free Tel:* 888-686-7368 *Fax:* 480-894-1023 *E-mail:* rent@broadcastrentals.com *Web Site:* www.broadcastrentals.com, pg 711

Oslund, Steve, Broadcast Rentals, 2343 W University Dr, Suite 101, Tempe, AZ 85281 *Tel:* 480-894-1456 *Toll Free Tel:* 888-686-7368 *Fax:* 480-894-1023 *E-mail:* rent@broadcastrentals.com *Web Site:* www.broadcastrentals.com, pg 711

Osorio, William, Video Ideas Productions, 1501 64 St, North Bergen, NJ 07047 *Tel:* 201-951-3798 *Fax:* 201-662-4846 *E-mail:* osoriomedia@yahoo.com *Web Site:* osoriomedia.com, pg 928

Osowski, Samantha, Yorktel, 81 Corbett Way, Eatontown, NJ 07724 *Tel:* 732-413-6000 *Toll Free Tel:* 866-836-8463 *Fax:* 732-413-6060 *E-mail:* knowmore@yorktel.com *Web Site:* yorktel.com, pg 944

Osterreicher, Mickey, National Press Photographers Association (NPPA), 120 Hooper St, Athens, GA 30602-3018 *Tel:* 706-542-2506 *E-mail:* info@nppa.org; director@nppa.org *Web Site:* nppa.org, pg 959

Ostrover, Lewis, Warner Home Video Inc, 4000 Warner Blvd, Bldg 160, Burbank, CA 91522 *Tel:* 818-954-6000 *Fax:* 818-954-6480 *Web Site:* www.warnerbros.com, pg 934

Ostrowka, Katie, HarperAudio, 10 E 53 St, New York, NY 10022 *Tel:* 212-207-7000 *Toll Free Tel:* 800-242-7737 *Fax:* 212-207-2582 *Toll Free Fax:* 800-822-4090 *Web Site:* www.harpercollins.com, pg 776

Oswald, Andy, West Penn Wire, 2833 W Chestnut St, Washington, PA 15301 *Tel:* 724-222-7060 *Toll Free Tel:* 800-245-4964 *Fax:* 724-222-6420 *E-mail:* info@westpennwire.com; sales@westpennwire.com *Web Site:* www.westpenn-wpw.com, pg 935

Otrusina, Edward, Flight Form Cases Inc, 6543 S Laramie Ave, Bedford Park, IL 60638 *Tel:* 708-458-8989 *Toll Free Tel:* 800-334-4884 *Fax:* 708-458-9023, pg 762

Ott, Debbie, Team Volusia Economic Development Corp, International Motorsports Ctr, One Daytona Blvd, Daytona Beach, FL 32114 *Tel:* 386-265-6332 *Web Site:* www.teamvolusiaedc.com, pg 969

Ott, James, Center for Asian American Media (CAAM), 145 Ninth St, Suite 350, San Francisco, CA 94103 *Tel:* 415-863-0814 *Fax:* 415-863-7428 *E-mail:* publicity@caamedia.org *Web Site:* caamedia.org, pg 953

Otterman, Sharon, Madison Square Garden, 2 Pennsylvania Plaza, New York, NY 10121-0091 *Tel:* 212-465-6741 *E-mail:* msgnetpr@msgnetwork.com *Web Site:* www.thegarden.com; themadisonsquaregardencompany.com, pg 814

Ottolenghi, Arturo M, Red Hill Corp, 1540 Biglerville Rd, Gettysburg, PA 17325 *Tel:* 717-337-3038 *Toll Free Tel:* 800-822-4003 *Fax:* 717-337-0732 *E-mail:* customerservice@supergrit.com *Web Site:* www.supergrit.com, pg 872

Ouimet, Francois, Auriga Productions Ltd, 2856 rue du Comtois, Ste-Lazare, QC J7T 0E7, Canada *Tel:* 514-984-4202 *E-mail:* aurigapix@gmail.com *Web Site:* www.aurigapix.com, pg 696

Ovasapyan, Karo, Encore A & S Case Co, 8818 Lankershim Blvd, Sun Valley, CA 91352 *Tel:* 818-768-8803 *E-mail:* info@encorecases.com *Web Site:* www.encorecases.com, pg 754

Overman, Steven, Eastman Kodak Co, 343 State St, Rochester, NY 14650 *Toll Free Tel:* 800-698-3324 *Web Site:* www.kodak.com, pg 750

Owen, Lisa, Applause Productions & Publications, PO Box 820024, Dallas, TX 75382-0024 *Tel:* 214-652-4300 *E-mail:* info@applauseproductions.com *Web Site:* applauseproductions.com, pg 687

Owen, Marvin, ACS Technologies, 180 Dunbarton Dr, Florence, SC 29501 *Tel:* 843-662-1681 *Toll Free Tel:* 800-736-7425 (sales); 800-669-2300 (support) *Fax:* 843-669-7513 *E-mail:* info@acstechnologies.com *Web Site:* www.acstechnologies.com, pg 674

Owen, Matthew, Harmonia Mundi USA, 1117 Chestnut St, Burbank, CA 91506 *Tel:* 818-333-1500 *E-mail:* info-usa@harmoniamundi.com *Web Site:* www.harmoniamundi.com, pg 776

Oyung, Alec, Ludlow Media, 15501 San Pablo Ave, Suite G-320, San Pablo, CA 94806 *Tel:* 415-927-1300 *E-mail:* info@ludlowmedia.com *Web Site:* www.ludlowmedia.com, pg 812

Ozzanto, Arianna, Screen Actors Guild - American Federation of Television & Radio Artists (SAG-AFTRA), 5757 Wilshire Blvd, 7th fl, Los Angeles, CA 90036-3600 *Tel:* 323-954-1600 (former SAG); 323-634-8100 (former AFTRA) *Toll Free Tel:* 855-SAG-AFTRA (724-2387) *Fax:* 323-549-6654 (communs & mktg) *E-mail:* info@sagaftra.org *Web Site:* www.sagaftra.org, pg 961

Pace-Stall, Angela, Ironik Design & Post, 56 E Main St, Suite 203, Avon, CT 06001 *Tel:* 860-404-2386 *Fax:* 860-404-2735 *E-mail:* info@ironikdesign.com *Web Site:* www.ironikdesign.com, pg 791

Pacheco, Tyler, Sihl Inc, 538 Main St, Fiskeville, RI 02823 *Tel:* 401-821-1000 *Toll Free Tel:* 800-556-6866; 800-366-7393 (ext 1, cust serv) *Web Site:* www.sihlinc.com, pg 888

Padgett, Tim, Pepper Group, 220 N Smith St, Suite 406, Palatine, IL 60067 *Tel:* 847-963-0333 *Fax:* 847-963-0888 *E-mail:* pepper@peppergroup.com *Web Site:* www.peppergroup.com, pg 854

Page, Anna, Hawaii International Film Festival, 680 Iwilei Rd, Suite 100, Honolulu, HI 96817 *Tel:* 808-792-1577 (ext 7) *Fax:* 808-792-1583 *Toll Free Fax:* 877-749-7783 *E-mail:* info@hiff.org; entries@hiff.org *Web Site:* www.hiff.org, pg 991

Page, Greg, NuMynd Studios, 915 Twin Elms Ct, Nashville, TN 37210 *Tel:* 615-259-1143 *Fax:* 615-259-1141 *E-mail:* hello@numyndstudios.com *Web Site:* www.numyndstudios.com, pg 843

Page, Madison, Signs.com, 1550 S Gladiola St, Salt Lake City, UT 84104 *Tel:* 801-441-3400 *Toll Free Tel:* 888-222-4929 *E-mail:* support@signs.com *Web Site:* www.signs.com, pg 888

Pagel, Carter, Castleview Productions, 1100 W 41 St, Austin, TX 78756 *Tel:* 512-442-9944 *Fax:* 512-442-8823 *E-mail:* contact@castleviewproductions.com *Web Site:* castleviewproductions.com, pg 717

Paglia, Karen, Yorktel, 81 Corbett Way, Eatontown, NJ 07724 *Tel:* 732-413-6000 *Toll Free Tel:* 866-836-8463 *Fax:* 732-413-6060 *E-mail:* knowmore@yorktel.com *Web Site:* yorktel.com, pg 944

Pagliante, Nick, Gerriets International, 130 Winterwood Ave, Ewing, NJ 08638 *Tel:* 609-771-8111 *Fax:* 609-771-8118 *E-mail:* info@gerriets.us *Web Site:* www.gerriets.us, pg 770

Pagni, Patrick, FACE Foundation, 972 Fifth Ave, New York, NY 10075 *Tel:* 212-439-1439 *E-mail:* info@face-foundation.org *Web Site:* www.face-foundation.org, pg 758

Pai, Antoine, LightHouse Films, 225 W 39 St, Suite 600, New York, NY 10018 *Tel:* 646-649-3600 *Fax:* 646-398-7122 *E-mail:* contact@lhfny.com; rent@lhfny.com *Web Site:* www.light-house-films.com, pg 807

Paille, Anthony, Association for Information and Image Management (AIIM), 1100 Wayne Ave, Suite 1100, Silver Spring, MD 20910 *Tel:* 301-587-8202 *Toll Free Tel:* 800-477-2446 *Fax:* 301-587-2711 *E-mail:* aiim@aiim.org *Web Site:* www.aiim.org, pg 950

Pair, Laura, Synaptic Digital, 79 Fifth Ave, 14th fl, New York, NY 10003 *Tel:* 212-682-8300 *Fax:* 212-201-4207 *E-mail:* learnmore@synapticdigital.com *Web Site:* www.synapticdigital.com, pg 905

Pajerski, Maureen, Rauland-Borg Corp, 1802 W Central Rd, Mount Prospect, IL 60056 *Tel:* 847-590-7100 *Toll Free Tel:* 800-752-7725 *Web Site:* www.rauland.com, pg 870

Pal, Laszlo, Pal Productions Inc, 13751 Lake City Way, Suite 208, Seattle, WA 98125 *Tel:* 206-361-9366 *Web Site:* www.paladventurevideos.com, pg 850

Palazzola, John L, VTP Inc, 1309 S Flower St, Burbank, CA 91502 *Tel:* 818-566-9898 *Toll Free Tel:* 800-422-2444 *E-mail:* sales@vtpcorp.com *Web Site:* www.myvtp.com, pg 933

Palfrey, Deanna, Palardo Productions, 1807 Taft Ave, Suite 4, Hollywood, CA 90028 *Tel:* 323-469-8991 *E-mail:* palardo2@msn.com, pg 850

Paliwal, Dinesh C, Harman International Industries Inc, 400 Atlantic St, 15th fl, Stamford, CT 06901 *Tel:* 203-328-3500 *Web Site:* www.harman.com, pg 776

Pallante, Maria, Association of American Publishers (AAP), 455 Massachusetts Ave NW, Suite 700, Washington, DC 20001-2777 *Tel:* 202-347-3375 *Fax:* 202-347-3690 *E-mail:* info@publishers.org *Web Site:* publishers.org, pg 951

Pallatto, Joanie, Sparrow Sound Design, 3501 N Southport, 2nd fl, Chicago, IL 60657-1435 *Tel:* 773-281-8510 *Fax:* 773-472-1632 *E-mail:* southport@chicagosound.com *Web Site:* www.chicagosound.com, pg 896

Palle, Robert J, Blonder Tongue Laboratories Inc, One Jake Brown Rd, Old Bridge, NJ 08857 *Tel:* 732-679-4000 *Toll Free Tel:* 800-523-6049 *Fax:* 732-679-4353 *E-mail:* custsvc@blondertongue.com; btglobalsales@blondertongue.com (outside US & CN); information@blondertongue.com *Web Site:* www.blondertongue.com, pg 707

Palm, Richard, Staging Directions Inc, 1327 Northbrook Pkwy, Suite 440, Suwanee, GA 30024 *Tel:* 770-409-9909 *Toll Free Tel:* 800-782-4322 *Fax:* 770-409-0277 *E-mail:* sales@teamsdi.net *Web Site:* www.stagingdirections.com, pg 899

Palmer, Andrae, Facet Media, 408 NE Sixth St, Fort Lauderdale, FL 33304 *Tel:* 954-593-0411 *E-mail:* info@facetmedia.com *Web Site:* www.facetmedia.com, pg 758

Palmer, Ben, Arrakis Systems, 6604 Powell St, Loveland, CO 80538 *Tel:* 970-461-0730 *E-mail:* sales@arrakis-systems.com *Web Site:* www.arrakis-systems.com, pg 689

Palmer, Patricia, SVS Inc, 2513 Jenks Ave, Panama City, FL 32405 *Tel:* 850-522-4747 *Fax:* 850-522-4739 *E-mail:* sales@svslifts.com *Web Site:* www.svslifts.com, pg 905

Palmer, Mr Shelly, The Palmer Group, PO Box 1455, New York, NY 10156-1455 *Tel:* 212-532-3880 *E-mail:* info@shellypalmer.com *Web Site:* www.shellypalmer.com, pg 850

Palmer, Steve, AVI-SPL, 6301 Benjamin Rd, Suite 101, Tampa, FL 33634 *Tel:* 813-884-7168 *Toll Free Tel:* 866-708-5034; 866-925-8298 (cust serv); 866-559-8197 (sales) *E-mail:* contact@avispl.com; sales@avispl.com; customerservice@avispl.com *Web Site:* www.avispl.com, pg 698

Pals, Tony, American Educational Research Association (AERA), 1430 "K" St NW, Suite 1200, Washington, DC 20005 *Tel:* 202-238-3200 *Fax:* 202-238-3250 *E-mail:* communications@aera.net; members@aera.net *Web Site:* www.aera.net, pg 948

Pan, Steven, MFJ Enterprises Inc, 300 Industrial Park Rd, Starkville, MS 39759-3992 *Tel:* 662-323-5869 *Toll Free Tel:* 800-647-1800 *Fax:* 662-323-6551 *E-mail:* mfjcustserv@mfjenterprises.com *Web Site:* www.mfjenterprises.com, pg 825

Panayioto, Steven, On-Line Productions, 2515 Hawthorne Dr, Atlanta, GA 30345 *Tel:* 404-634-5572 *E-mail:* esptv@mindspring.com *Web Site:* on-lineproductions.com, pg 846

Pandit, Pete, AV Guys, 1641 Pacific Rim Ct, Suite A, San Diego, CA 92154 *Tel:* 619-474-5050 *Fax:* 619-474-5454 *Web Site:* www.avguys.com, pg 697

Pang, Laurinda, Level 3 Communications Inc, 1025 Eldorado Blvd, Broomfield, CO 80021 *Tel:* 720-888-1000 *Toll Free Tel:* 877-2LEVEL3 (253-8357) *Web Site:* www.level3.com, pg 806

Pantridge, Mark, VideoLink Inc, an AVI-SPL company, 1230 Washington St, West Newton, MA 02465 *Tel:* 617-340-4100 *Toll Free Tel:* 800-452-5565 *Fax:* 617-340-4101 *E-mail:* sales@videolinktv.com *Web Site:* www.videolinktv.com, pg 929

Panuccio, Susan, News Corp, 1211 Avenue of the Americas, New York, NY 10036 *Tel:* 212-416-3400 *E-mail:* media@newscorp.com *Web Site:* newscorp.com, pg 840

Paolini, Patrick, UPN 20 WDCA-TV, 5151 Wisconsin Ave NW, Washington, DC 20016 *Tel:* 202-244-5151 *Web Site:* www.fox5dc.com/my20dc, pg 923

Papotnik, Phil, Raven Rental, 2617 Peach St, Erie, PA 16508 *Tel:* 814-456-0331 *Web Site:* www.ravensound.com, pg 870

Pappas, Mike, ATI Audio, 7209 Browning Rd, Pennsauken, NJ 08091 *Tel:* 856-719-9900 *E-mail:* sales@daysequerra.com *Web Site:* www.atiaudio.com, pg 692

Pappas, Theodore, Encyclopaedia Britannica Inc, 325 N La Salle St, Suite 200, Chicago, IL 60654 *Tel:* 312-347-7000 (all other countries) *Toll Free Tel:* 800-323-1229 (US & CN) *Fax:* 312-294-2104 *Web Site:* britannica.com, pg 754

Pappas, Will, S&P Global Marketing Intelligence, 55 Water St, New York, NY 10041 *Toll Free Tel:* 877-863-1306 *E-mail:* questions@spcapitaliq.com *Web Site:* marketingintelligence.spglobal.com, pg 880

Paquette, Jennifer, Hosa Technology Inc, 6650 Caballero Blvd, Buena Park, CA 90620 *Tel:* 714-522-8878 *Toll Free Tel:* 800-255-7527 *Fax:* 714-522-4540 *E-mail:* info@hosatech.com; sales@hosatech.com; orders@hosatech.com *Web Site:* hosatech.com, pg 781

Paquin, Derek, Sensory Technologies LLC, 6951 Corporate Circle, Indianapolis, IN 46278 *Tel:* 317-347-5252 *Toll Free Tel:* 800-488-4336 (help desk) *E-mail:* csc@sensorytechnologies.com *Web Site:* sensorytechnologies.com, pg 884

Paradis, Charles, alliance quebecoise des techniciens et techniciennes de l'image et du son (AQTIS), 1001, blvd De Maisonneuve E, bureau 900, Montreal, QC H2L 4P9, Canada *Tel:* 514-844-2113 (ext 285) *Fax:* 514-844-3540 *E-mail:* info@aqtis.qc.ca *Web Site:* www.aqtis.qc.ca, pg 947

Paradise, Richard, Martha's Vineyard International Film Festival, PO Box 4423, Vineyard Haven, MA 02568 *Tel:* 508-696-9369 *E-mail:* info@mvfilmsociety.com *Web Site:* mvfilmsociety.com, pg 995

Paranis, Abhay, Adobe Systems Inc, 345 Park Ave, San Jose, CA 95110-2704 *Tel:* 408-536-6000 *Fax:* 408-537-6000 *Web Site:* www.adobe.com, pg 676

Pardee, Tyson, Zion Music Group, 306 Monticello Rd, Franklin, TN 37064 *Tel:* 615-559-2108 *Fax:* 615-591-5102 *Web Site:* www.zionmusic.com, pg 945

Pardini, Ed, Iowa Cable & Telecommunications Association (ICTA), 3737 Westown Pkwy, Suite C, West Des Moines, IA 50266 *Tel:* 515-697-6646 *E-mail:* info@iacable.com *Web Site:* www.iacable.com, pg 957

Pardo, Miguel, Studio Thirteen11, 1311 Chemical St, Dallas, TX 75207 *Tel:* 214-377-8606 *Web Site:* www.studiothirteen11.com, pg 903

Pardovany, Jacques F, LightTech Group Inc, PO Box 300642, Jamaica, NY 11430 *Tel:* 718-525-2900 *Web Site:* www.lighttech.com, pg 808

Parikh, Nina, Mississippi Film Office, 501 N West St, 5th fl, Jackson, MS 39201 *Tel:* 601-359-3297 *Fax:* 601-359-5048 *Web Site:* www.filmmississippi.org, pg 972

Parker, Chuck, Art Directors Guild (ADG), 11969 Ventura Blvd, 2nd fl, Studio City, CA 91604 *Tel:* 818-762-9995 *Fax:* 818-762-9997 *Web Site:* www.adg.org, pg 950

Parker, David, Alexander Street, a ProQuest Company, 99 Canal Center Plaza, Suite 200, Alexandria, VA 22314 *Tel:* 703-212-8520 *Toll Free Tel:* 800-889-5937 *E-mail:* sales@alexanderstreet.com; marketing@alexanderstreet.com; info@alexanderstreet.com *Web Site:* alexanderstreet.com; academicvideostore.com, pg 679

Parker, Don, SAS Institute Inc, 100 SAS Campus Dr, Cary, NC 27513-2414 *Tel:* 919-677-8000 *Toll Free Tel:* 800-727-0025 *Fax:* 919-677-4444 *Web Site:* www.sas.com, pg 880

Parker, Douglas M, OpenText Corp, 275 Frank Tompa Dr, Waterloo, ON N2L 0A1, Canada *Tel:* 519-888-7111 *Toll Free Tel:* 800-499-6544 *Fax:* 519-888-0677 *Web Site:* www.opentext.com, pg 847

Parker, Graham, Verve Label Group, 1755 Broadway, New York, NY 10019 *Tel:* 212-841-8000 *Web Site:* www.vervelabelgroup.com; www.universalmusic.com, pg 926

Parker Harris, Judith, Worldwide Entertainment Corp, 135 S McCarty Dr, Suite 101, Beverly Hills, CA 90212 *Tel:* 310-858-1272 *Fax:* 310-858-3774, pg 941

Parker, Jake, RAM® Mounts, 8410 Dallas Ave S, Seattle, WA 98108 *Tel:* 206-763-8361 *Toll Free Tel:* 800-497-7479 *Fax:* 206-763-9615 *E-mail:* sales@rammount.com *Web Site:* www.rammount.com, pg 870

Parker, Jayne, The Walt Disney Co, 500 S Buena Vista St, Burbank, CA 91521 *Tel:* 818-560-1000 *Web Site:* disney.com; thewaltdisneycompany.com, pg 743

Parker, Michael, Mole-Richardson Co, 12154 Montague St, Pacoima, CA 91331 *Tel:* 323-851-0111 *Fax:* 323-851-5593 *E-mail:* info@mole.com *Web Site:* www.mole.com, pg 829

Parker, Mike, iCrossing Inc, a Hearst Company, 300 W 57 St, New York, NY 10019 *Tel:* 212-649-3900 *Toll Free Tel:* 866-620-3780 *E-mail:* general@icrossing.com *Web Site:* www.icrossing.com, pg 783

Pearce, Aaron, Brady Corp, 6555 W Good Hope Rd, Milwaukee, WI 53201-0571 *Tel:* 414-358-6600 *Toll Free Tel:* 888-250-3082 *E-mail:* bradyusa@bradycorp. com (cust serv & sales) *Web Site:* www.bradyid.com, pg 709

Pearce, Sarah, Sundance Film Festival, 1825 Three Kings Dr, Park City, UT 84060 *Tel:* 435-658-3456 *Fax:* 435-658-3457 *E-mail:* customerservice@ sundance.org; press@sundance.org; institute@ sundance.org *Web Site:* www.sundance.org/festival, pg 1004

Pearce, Virginia, Moab to Monument Valley Film Commission, 111 E 100 N, Moab, UT 84532 *Tel:* 435-259-4341 *Fax:* 435-259-4135 *Web Site:* moabcity.org; film.utah.gov (Utah Film Commission), pg 976

Pearce, Virginia, Utah Film Commission, Council Hall/Capitol Hill, 300 N State St, Salt Lake City, UT 84114 *Tel:* 801-538-8740 *Toll Free Tel:* 800-453-8824 *Web Site:* www.film.utah.gov, pg 976

Peard, William F, Iowa Cable & Telecommunications Association (ICTA), 3737 Westown Pkwy, Suite C, West Des Moines, IA 50266 *Tel:* 515-697-6646 *E-mail:* info@iacable.com *Web Site:* www.iacable. com, pg 957

Peardon, Olivier, Colortone Audio Visual, 181 Westchester Ave, Suite 408B, Port Chester, NY 10573 *Tel:* 914-592-4151 *Fax:* 914-592-2833 *Web Site:* www. colortone-av.com, pg 728

Pearlman, Nancy, ECONEWS (Environmental Television Series) & (Environmental Directions Radio Series), PO Box 351419, Los Angeles, CA 90035-9119 *Tel:* 310-559-9160 *E-mail:* ecnp@aol.com *Web Site:* www.ecoprojects.org, pg 750

Pears, Mike, RLJ Entertainment Inc, 8515 Georgia Ave, Suite 650, Silver Spring, MD 20910 *Tel:* 301-608-2115 *Toll Free Tel:* 800-999-0212 *E-mail:* inquiries@rljentertainment.com *Web Site:* www.us.rljentertainment.com, pg 875

Pearson, Bret, Drastic Technologies Ltd, 523 The Queensway, Suite 102, Toronto, ON M8Y 1J7, Canada *Tel:* 416-255-5636 *Fax:* 416-255-8780 *E-mail:* sales@ drastictech.com *Web Site:* www.drastic.tv, pg 746

Pearson, Jim, Cinema Rentals Inc, 25876 The Old Rd, Suite 174, Stevenson Ranch, CA 91381 *Tel:* 661-222-7342 *E-mail:* ocxinc@gmail.com *Web Site:* www. cinemarentals.com, pg 724

Pearson, Wade A, Institute for Teaching & Learning Excellence (ITLE), 100 ITLE, Oklahoma State University, Stillwater, OK 74078 *Tel:* 405-744-1000 *Fax:* 405-744-8563 *E-mail:* itle@okstate.edu *Web Site:* itle.okstate.edu, pg 788

Pease, Alexander W, CommScope Inc, 1100 CommScope Place SE, Hickory, NC 28602 *Tel:* 828-324-2200 *Toll Free Tel:* 800-982-1708 *E-mail:* publicrelations@commscope.com *Web Site:* www.commscope.com, pg 728

Pease, Chris, Lightronics Inc, 509 Central Dr, Virginia Beach, VA 23454 *Tel:* 757-486-3588 *Toll Free Tel:* 800-472-8541 *Fax:* 757-486-3391 *Web Site:* www. lightronics.com, pg 808

Peavey, Hartley D, Peavey Electronics Corp, 5022 Hartley Peavey Dr, Meridian, MS 39305 *Tel:* 601-483-5365 *Fax:* 601-486-1278 *Web Site:* peavey.com, pg 852

Peavey, Mary, Peavey Electronics Corp, 5022 Hartley Peavey Dr, Meridian, MS 39305 *Tel:* 601-483-5365 *Fax:* 601-486-1278 *Web Site:* peavey.com, pg 852

Pecaut, Linda, SOM Publishing Co, 163 Moon Valley Rd, Windyville, MO 65783 *Tel:* 417-345-8411 *E-mail:* som@som.org *Web Site:* www.som.org, pg 892

Peck, Eliott, Canon USA Inc, One Canon Park, Melville, NY 11747 *Toll Free Tel:* 800-652-2666 *E-mail:* pr@ cusa.canon.com *Web Site:* www.usa.canon.com, pg 716

Peckham, Russell, Peckham Productions Inc, 65 S Broadway, Tarrytown, NY 10591-4003 *Web Site:* www.peckhampix.com, pg 852

Peckham, Tom, AVFX Inc, 96 Holton St, Boston, MA 02135 *Tel:* 617-254-0770 *Toll Free Tel:* 888-254-0770 *E-mail:* info@avfx.com *Web Site:* www.avfx.com, pg 698

Pedersen, Kathy, ETR, 100 Enterprise Way, Suite G 300, Scotts Valley, CA 95066 *Toll Free Tel:* 800-620-8884 *Fax:* 831-438-4284 *E-mail:* customerservice@etr.org, pg 756

Pedisich, Peter, TBC Consoles Inc, 170 Rodeo Dr, Edgewood, NY 11717 *Tel:* 631-293-4068 *Toll Free Tel:* 888-CONSOLE (266-7653) *Fax:* 631-293-4075 *E-mail:* info@tbcconsoles.com; sales@tbcconsoles. com; support@tbcconsoles.com *Web Site:* www. tbcconsoles.com, pg 907

Peel, Carl, Killer Tracks, 2110 Colorado Ave, Suite 110, Santa Monica, CA 90404 *Tel:* 310-865-4455 *Toll Free Tel:* 800-4-KILLER (454-5537) *E-mail:* info@ killertracks.com *Web Site:* www.killertracks.com, pg 799

Peipert, Mike, Rauland-Borg Corp, 1802 W Central Rd, Mount Prospect, IL 60056 *Tel:* 847-590-7100 *Toll Free Tel:* 800-752-7725 *Web Site:* www.rauland.com, pg 870

Peiser, Judy, Center for Southern Folklore Inc, 119 S Main St, Memphis, TN 38103 *Tel:* 901-525-3655 *Fax:* 901-544-9965 *E-mail:* info@southernfolklore. com *Web Site:* www.southernfolklore.com, pg 719

Pekala, Joseph S, ACCO Brands Corp, 4 Corporate Dr, Lake Zurick, IL 60047-8997 *Toll Free Tel:* 800-541-0094; 800-222-6462 *Toll Free Fax:* 800-941-4463 *E-mail:* contactus@acco.com (cust serv) *Web Site:* www.accobrands.com, pg 673

Pelino, Robert, Robertson Worldwide, 4700 137 St, Crestwood, IL 60445 *Tel:* 708-388-2315 *Toll Free Tel:* 800-323-5633 *Fax:* 708-388-2420 *Toll Free Fax:* 877-388-2420 *E-mail:* info@robertsonlighting. com *Web Site:* www.robertsondirect.com, pg 876

Pelkowski, Chet, Definitive Technology LLP, One Viper Way, Vista, CA 92081 *Tel:* 410-363-7148 *Toll Free Tel:* 800-228-7148 *E-mail:* info@definitivetech.com *Web Site:* www.definitivetech.com, pg 740

Pella, Mike, Cuyahoga Community College Student Production Office (SPO), Metro Campus Media Ctr, 2900 Community College Ave, Cleveland, OH 44115 *Tel:* 216-987-6000 *Web Site:* www.tri-c.edu, pg 736

Pellegatti, Mike, Wild Visions Inc, PO Box 42194, Phoenix, AZ 85080 *Tel:* 623-512-9810 *Web Site:* www.wildvisions.net, pg 938

Pelletier, Vic, Group PVP, 296 Saint Pierre St, Matane, QC G4W 2B9, Canada *Tel:* 418-566-2040 *Toll Free Tel:* 877-320-2040 *Fax:* 418-562-4643 *E-mail:* info@ pvp.ca *Web Site:* www.pvp.ca, pg 774

Pellino, Anthony, LightHouse Films, 225 W 39 St, Suite 600, New York, NY 10018 *Tel:* 646-649-3600 *Fax:* 646-398-7122 *E-mail:* contact@lhfny.com; rent@ lhfny.com *Web Site:* www.light-house-films.com, pg 807

Peluse, Michael, Cambridge University Press, One Liberty Plaza, 20th fl, New York, NY 10006 *Tel:* 212-337-5000 *Toll Free Tel:* 800-221-4512; 800-872-7423 *E-mail:* information@cambridge.org; customer_service@cambridge.org *Web Site:* www. cambridge.org, pg 715

Pendleton, Todd, Dolby Laboratories Inc, 1275 Market St, San Francisco, CA 94103-1410 *Tel:* 415-558-0200 *Fax:* 415-645-4000 *Web Site:* www.dolby.com, pg 745

Penella, Miguel, RLJ Entertainment Inc, 8515 Georgia Ave, Suite 650, Silver Spring, MD 20910 *Tel:* 301-608-2115 *Toll Free Tel:* 800-999-0212 *E-mail:* inquiries@rljentertainment.com *Web Site:* www.us.rljentertainment.com, pg 875

Penkala, Peter, MVI - MultiVision Inc, 120 McLevin Ave, Unit 3, Toronto, ON M1B 3E9, Canada *Tel:* 416-449-1080 *Toll Free Tel:* 800-563-5902 (ext 228) *Fax:* 416-449-5131 *E-mail:* business@mvidisplay.com *Web Site:* www.mvidisplay.com, pg 835

Pennebaker, D A, Pennebaker Hegedus Films Inc, 262 W 91 St, New York, NY 10024 *Tel:* 212-496-9195 *Fax:* 212-496-8195 *E-mail:* info@phfilms.com *Web Site:* phfilms.com, pg 854

Pennebaker, Frazer, Pennebaker Hegedus Films Inc, 262 W 91 St, New York, NY 10024 *Tel:* 212-496-9195 *Fax:* 212-496-8195 *E-mail:* info@phfilms.com *Web Site:* phfilms.com, pg 854

Pennie, Jane, Videomagnetics, 3970 Clearview Frontage Rd, Colorado Springs, CO 80911 *Tel:* 719-390-1313 *Toll Free Tel:* 800-432-3887 *Fax:* 719-390-1316 *E-mail:* vmi@csprings.com *Web Site:* www. videomagnetics.com, pg 929

Penny, Stuart, SMP Digital Graphics, 163 W 22 St, New York, NY 10011 *Tel:* 212-691-6766 *E-mail:* info@ smpdigitalgraphics.com *Web Site:* smpdigitalgraphics. com, pg 891

Pennycook, Glenn, Belden Inc, 401 Pennsylvania Pkwy, Suite 200, Indianapolis, IN 46280 *Tel:* 317-818-6300 *Toll Free Tel:* 800-235-3362; 800-BELDEN-1 (235-3361) *Fax:* 317-818-6365 *E-mail:* info@belden.com *Web Site:* www.belden.com, pg 703

Penrose, Jim, Penrose Productions, 2310 Homestead Rd, Suite C1-No 211, Los Altos, CA 94024 *Tel:* 650-969-8273 *E-mail:* info@penroseproductions.com *Web Site:* www.penroseproductions.com, pg 854

Pentland, Jake, Full Moon & High Tide Productions & Studios, 424 Main St, El Segundo, CA 90245-3002 *Tel:* 310-647-1958 *Fax:* 310-647-1960 *Web Site:* fmht. net, pg 767

Peoples, Kym, WKMG-TV News 6, 4466 N John Young Pkwy, Orlando, FL 32804 *Tel:* 407-521-1200 *Fax:* 407-521-1204 *Web Site:* www.clickorlando.com, pg 940

Pepera, Brian, Brilliance Audio, 1704 Eaton Dr, Grand Haven, MI 49417 *Tel:* 616-846-5256 *Toll Free Tel:* 800-648-2312 (orders) *Fax:* 616-846-0630 *E-mail:* help@audiobookstand.com *Web Site:* www. brillianceaudio.com, pg 710

Perales, Conchita, Eyeline Teleprompting, 1313 Mound St, Alameda, CA 94501 *Tel:* 510-205-6762 *E-mail:* info@eyeline.tv *Web Site:* www.eyeline.tv, pg 758

Peralta, L Lonnie, Nineteen87, 1024 Harding Ave, Suite 201, Venice Beach, CA 90291 *Tel:* 310-577-5009 *Fax:* 310-577-1960 *E-mail:* info@1-9-8-7.com *Web Site:* www.1-9-8-7.com, pg 841

Perchuk, Neal, RCS Enterprises, 445 Hamilton Ave, 7th fl, White Plains, NY 10601 *Tel:* 914-428-4600 *Fax:* 914-428-5922 *E-mail:* info@rcsworks.com *Web Site:* www.rcsworks.com, pg 871

Peregrine, Paul, Lightware Inc, 1329 W Byers Place, Denver, CO 80223-1723 *Tel:* 303-744-0202 *Fax:* 303-722-4545 *E-mail:* info@lightwareinc. com *Web Site:* www.lightwareinc.com; www. lightwaredirect.com, pg 808

Pereira, Mark, Brilliance Audio, 1704 Eaton Dr, Grand Haven, MI 49417 *Tel:* 616-846-5256 *Toll Free Tel:* 800-648-2312 (orders) *Fax:* 616-846-0630 *E-mail:* help@audiobookstand.com *Web Site:* www. brillianceaudio.com, pg 710

Perepeluk, Stephen, Heinemann, 361 Hanover St, Portsmouth, NH 03801-3912 *Tel:* 603-431-7894 *Toll Free Tel:* 800-225-5800 *Fax:* 603-431-2214 *Toll Free Fax:* 877-231-6980 *E-mail:* custserv@heinemann.com *Web Site:* www.heinemann.com, pg 778

Perez, Ayleen, Austin Film Society (AFS), 1901 E 51 St, Austin, TX 78723 *Tel:* 512-322-0145 *E-mail:* afs@ austinfilm.org *Web Site:* www.austinfilm.org, pg 951

Perez, Bernadette, Spectra Cine Inc, 3607 W Magnolia Blvd, Burbank, CA 91505 *Tel:* 818-954-9222 *Fax:* 818-954-0016 *E-mail:* info@spectracine.com *Web Site:* www.spectracine.com, pg 897

Perez, Lilia, DEC Grants, 696 Dutchess Tpke, Suite F, Poughkeepsie, NY 12603 *Tel:* 845-454-3222 *E-mail:* info@artsmidhudson.org *Web Site:* www. artsmidhudson.org, pg 988

Perez, Tony, HD House, 6312 NW 77 Ct, Miami, FL 33166 *Tel:* 305-597-7359 *Fax:* 305-597-7027 *Web Site:* thehdhouse.com, pg 777

Perhamus, Kevin, Winchester Electronics Corp, 68 Water St, Norwalk, CT 06854 *Tel:* 203-741-5400 *E-mail:* info@winchesterelectronics.com *Web Site:* www.winchesterelectronics.com, pg 939

Perica, Michael, Alpha Technologies Inc, 3767 Alpha Way, Bellingham, WA 98226 *Tel:* 360-647-2360 *Toll Free Tel:* 800-322-5742 *E-mail:* alpha@alpha.com *Web Site:* www.alpha.com, pg 681

Perillo, Dave, Avid Technology Inc, 65-75 Network Dr, Burlington, MA 01830 *Tel:* 978-640-6789 *Web Site:* www.avid.com, pg 698

Perkins, James A, Questar Corp, 6204 Ingham Rd, New Hope, PA 18938 *Tel:* 215-862-5277 *Toll Free Tel:* 800-247-9607 *Fax:* 215-862-0512 *E-mail:* questar@erols.com *Web Site:* www. questarcorporation.com, pg 868

Perl, Liz, Simon & Schuster Inc, 1230 Avenue of the Americas, New York, NY 10020 *Tel:* 212-698-7000; 212-698-7126 *Toll Free Tel:* 800-223-2348 (cust serv) *Fax:* 212-698-7664 *Toll Free Fax:* 800-943-9831 *E-mail:* audiopublicity@simonandschuster. com *Web Site:* www.simonandschuster.net; www. simonandschuster.biz; www.simonandschuster.com, pg 888

Perlmutter, Alvin H, The Independent Production Fund, 200 Central Park S, Suite 12F, New York, NY 10019 *Tel:* 212-221-6310 *Fax:* 212-302-1854 *Web Site:* www. ipfmedia.org/vetc.htm, pg 786

Perotto, Rick, William F White International Inc, 800 Islington Ave, Toronto, ON M8Z 6A1, Canada *Tel:* 416-239-5050 *Toll Free Tel:* 800-465-0160 (CN only) *Web Site:* www.whites.com, pg 937

Perrault, Anthony, Marvel Photo Inc, 1720 N Sheridan Rd, Tulsa, OK 74115 *Tel:* 918-836-0741 *Toll Free Tel:* 800-806-3616 *Fax:* 918-836-0949, pg 818

Perretta, Jeff, Copp Integrated Systems, 123 S Keowee St, Dayton, OH 45402 *Tel:* 937-228-4188 *Toll Free Tel:* 877-450-2677 *Fax:* 937-228-2901 *Web Site:* www. copp.com, pg 731

Perrine, Lisa, Cibola Systems, 180 S Cypress St, Orange, CA 92866 *Tel:* 714-480-0272 *Fax:* 714-480-0768 *E-mail:* info@cibolasystems.com *Web Site:* cibolasystems.com, pg 723

Perrotta, Dave, SurgeX, 8001 Knightdale Blvd, Suite 121, Knightdale, NC 27545 *Toll Free Tel:* 800-645-9721 (tech & cust support) *E-mail:* order.desk@ ametek.com *Web Site:* espsurgex.com/surgex/, pg 905

Perry, Alex, A to Z Theatrical Supply & Service, 800 E Meyer Blvd, Kansas City, MO 64131 *Tel:* 816-523-1655 *Toll Free Tel:* 800-732-8252 *Fax:* 816-523-1690 *E-mail:* info@atoztheatrical.com *Web Site:* atoztheatrical.com, pg 671

Perry, Jay, Simco-Ion, 2257 N Penn Rd, Hatfield, PA 19440 *Tel:* 215-822-6401 *Toll Free Tel:* 800-203-3419 *Fax:* 215-822-3795 *E-mail:* customerservice@simco-ion.com *Web Site:* www.simco-ion.com, pg 888

Perry, Justin, Pangolin Laser Systems Inc, 9501 Satellite Blvd, Suite 109, Orlando, FL 32837 *Tel:* 407-299-2088 *Toll Free Tel:* 800-PAN-GOLIN (726-4654) *Fax:* 407-299-6066 *E-mail:* contact@pangolin.com *Web Site:* www.pangolin.com, pg 851

Perry, Trent, AV Connections Inc, 245 Executive Park Blvd, Winston-Salem, NC 27103 *Tel:* 336-768-5454 *Fax:* 336-768-5054 *E-mail:* avrentals@ avconnectionsusa.com *Web Site:* avconnectionsusa. com, pg 697

Persing, Wayne, FirstGeneration Audio/Visual Services, 410 Allentown Dr, Allentown, PA 18109 *Tel:* 610-437-4300 *Fax:* 610-437-3200 *E-mail:* information@ firstgencom.com; contact@firstgencom.com *Web Site:* www.firstgencom.com, pg 761

Person, Donald, A Gentle Wind, 14 S Pine Ave, Albany, NY 12208 *Tel:* 518-482-9023 *Toll Free Tel:* 888-FUN-SONG (386-7664, orders) *E-mail:* hello@gentlewind. com *Web Site:* www.gentlewind.com, pg 770

Persson, Per, Williams AV LLC, 10300 Valley View Rd, Eden Prairie, MN 55344-3446 *Tel:* 952-943-2252 *Toll Free Tel:* 800-328-6190 *Fax:* 952-943-2174 *E-mail:* info@williamsav.com *Web Site:* www. williamsav.com, pg 939

Pesce, Frank, Broadcasters Foundation of America, 125 W 55 St, 4th fl, New York, NY 10019-5366 *Tel:* 212-373-8250 *Fax:* 212-373-8254 *E-mail:* info@thebfoa.org *Web Site:* www.thebfoa.org; broadcastersfoundation.org, pg 952

Pesce, Frank, Golden Mike Award, 125 W 55 St, 4th fl, New York, NY 10019-5366 *Tel:* 212-373-8250 *Fax:* 212-373-8254 *E-mail:* info@thebfoa.org *Web Site:* www.thebfoa.org; broadcastersfoundation. org, pg 990

Pesce, Frank, Lowry Mays Excellence in Broadcasting Award, 125 W 55 St, 4th fl, New York, NY 10019-5366 *Tel:* 212-373-8250 *Fax:* 212-373-8254 *E-mail:* info@thebfoa.org *Web Site:* www.thebfoa.org; broadcastersfoundation.org, pg 995

Pesce, Frank, Ward L Quaal Leadership Awards, 125 W 55 St, 4th fl, New York, NY 10019-5366 *Tel:* 212-373-8250 *Fax:* 212-373-8254 *E-mail:* info@thebfoa.org *Web Site:* www.thebfoa.org; broadcastersfoundation.org, pg 1000

Petering, Charles, MVP International Inc, 518 S Nevada Ave, Suite 2, Colorado Springs, CO 80903 *Tel:* 713-771-1132 *Toll Free Tel:* 800-432-0687 *E-mail:* info@ mvp-av.com *Web Site:* www.mvp-av.com, pg 835

Peters, Brandon, Indianapolis International Film Festival, 125 W South St, No 1930, Indianapolis, IN 46206 *Tel:* 317-560-4433 *E-mail:* info@indyfilmfest.org; submissions@indyfilmfest.org *Web Site:* indyfilmfest. org, pg 992

Peters, Craig, Getty Images, 605 Fifth Ave S, Suite 400, Seattle, WA 98104 *Tel:* 206-925-5000 *Toll Free Tel:* 888-888-5889; 800-462-4379 (sales) *E-mail:* sales.na@gettyimages.com *Web Site:* www. gettyimages.com, pg 770

Peters, Robert C, Alegra House Publishers, PO Box 1443, Warren, OH 44482-1443 *Tel:* 330-372-2951 *Fax:* 330-399-1619, pg 679

Petersen, Barbara, Rockwell Communications Inc, 321 Burnham St, East Hartford, CT 06108 *Tel:* 860-528-9091 *Toll Free Tel:* 800-566-6681 *Fax:* 860-289-2334 *E-mail:* rockwellservice@aol.com *Web Site:* www. rockwellcommunications.com, pg 876

Petersen, Michael, Bitcentral Inc, 4340 Von Karman Ave, Suite 400, Newport Beach, CA 92660 *Tel:* 949-253-9000 *Toll Free Tel:* 800-272-4004 (support) *E-mail:* sales@bitcentral.com; support@bitcentral.com *Web Site:* www.bitcentral.com, pg 706

Peterson, Dave, Full Scale Effects, 6869 Tujunga Ave, North Hollywood, CA 91605 *Tel:* 818-760-0875; 818-760-0042 *Fax:* 818-760-0876 *Web Site:* fullscalefx. com, pg 767

Peterson, Gary, Encore A & S Case Co, 8818 Lankershim Blvd, Sun Valley, CA 91352 *Tel:* 818-768-8803 *Fax:* 818 *E-mail:* info@encorecases.com *Web Site:* www.encorecases.com, pg 754

Peterson, James J, Microsemi Corp, One Enterprise, Aliso Viejo, CA 92656 *Tel:* 949-380-6100 *Toll Free Tel:* 800-713-4113 *Fax:* 949-215-4996 *Web Site:* www. microsemi.com, pg 826

Peterson, Jeff, Peterson's Video Transfer Services, 5693 S Jones Blvd, Suite 110, Las Vegas, NV 89118 *Toll Free Tel:* 800-888-0426 *E-mail:* contact@ petersonsvideotransfer.com *Web Site:* www. petersonsvideotransfer.com, pg 855

Peterson, Lara, Golden Gate Studios, 100 Pelican Way, Suite E, San Rafael, CA 94901 *Tel:* 415-485-5856 *Fax:* 415-256-9262 *Web Site:* www.goldengatestudios. com, pg 772

Peterson, Marshall, WaveGuide Studios, 2062 Weems Rd, Tucker, GA 30084 *Tel:* 770-939-2004 *Toll Free Tel:* 800-578-2004 *E-mail:* info@waveguidestudios. com *Web Site:* www.waveguidestudios.com, pg 934

Peterson, Neal, Telestream Inc, 848 Gold Flat Rd, Nevada City, CA 95959 *Tel:* 530-470-1300 *Toll Free Tel:* 877-257-6245 *Fax:* 530-470-1301 *E-mail:* info@ telestream.net *Web Site:* www.telestream.net, pg 910

Peterson, Pam, Phoenix Society for Burn Survivors Inc, 525 Ottawa Ave NW, Front, Grand Rapids, MI 49503 *Tel:* 616-458-2773 *Toll Free Tel:* 800-888-BURN (888-2876) *Fax:* 616-458-2831 *E-mail:* info@phoenix-society.org *Web Site:* www.phoenix-society.org, pg 856

Peterson, Patricia, Projects in Knowledge Inc, 290 W Mount Pleasant Ave, Suite 2350, Livingston, NJ 07039 *Tel:* 973-890-8988 *Toll Free Tel:* 800-772-8277 *Web Site:* www.projectsinknowledge.com, pg 865

Peterson, Robert M, National Teleproductions Inc, PO Box 1804, West Palm Beach, FL 33402-1804 *Tel:* 561-689-9271 *Fax:* 561-640-4677 *E-mail:* ntp@ ntpworldwide.com, pg 837

Peterson, Verle G, Envision Communications Inc, 2002 N 204 St, Elkhorn, NE 68022 *Tel:* 402-289-2220, pg 755

Petgrave, Robin, Celebrity Helicopters Inc, 961 W Alondra Blvd, Compton, CA 90220 *Tel:* 310-618-1155 *Toll Free Tel:* 877-999-2099 *Fax:* 424-785-8768 *Toll Free Fax:* 877-999-2099 *Web Site:* www.celebheli. com, pg 719

Petit, George S, SHP Electronics, 1225 Hulman St, Terre Haute, IN 47802 *Tel:* 812-232-1003 *Fax:* 812-232-3170 *Web Site:* www.shpelectronics.com, pg 887

Petit, Jim, WVP Boston, 50 Hunt St, Watertown, MA 02472 *Tel:* 617-926-2089 *Web Site:* wvpboston.com, pg 942

Petrick, Chris, Bretford Manufacturing Inc, 11000 Seymour Ave, Franklin Park, IL 60131 *Tel:* 847-678-2545 *Toll Free Tel:* 800-521-9614 *Fax:* 847-678-0852 *Toll Free Fax:* 800-343-1779 *E-mail:* customerservice@bretford.com *Web Site:* www.bretford.com, pg 710

Petro, Joe, Nuance Communications Inc, One Wayside Rd, Burlington, MA 01803 *Tel:* 781-565-5000 *Toll Free Tel:* 800-654-1187 (cust serv) *Fax:* 781-565-5001 *Web Site:* www.nuance.com, pg 843

Petrokubi, Marilyn, TimeSteps Productions Inc, 2 Glenside Dr, West Orange, NJ 07052 *Tel:* 973-669-1930 *E-mail:* info@timesteps.com *Web Site:* timesteps. com, pg 914

Petrosino, Ralph, Studio Instrument Rentals (SIR), 475 Tenth Ave, 2nd fl, New York, NY 10018 *Tel:* 212-627-4900 *E-mail:* nyinfo@sir-usa.com *Web Site:* www.sir-usa.com, pg 902

Pettit, Steven, Starwest Productions, 8760 W 68 Place, Arvada, CO 80004 *Tel:* 303-295-2222 *E-mail:* info@ estarwest.com *Web Site:* www.estarwest.com, pg 900

Pettus, Jeff, Artist Fellowships, 109 E Jones St, Raleigh, NC 27601 *Tel:* 919-807-6500 *Fax:* 919-807-6532 *E-mail:* ncarts@ncdcr.gov *Web Site:* www.ncarts.org, pg 982

Petty, Beth, Charlotte Regional Film Commission, 500 S College St, Suite 300, Charlotte, NC 28202 *Tel:* 704-331-2723 *Toll Free Tel:* 800-722-1994 *Fax:* 704-342-3972 *Web Site:* www.charlottefilm.com, pg 974

Petty, Grant, Blackmagic Design Pty Ltd, 2875 Bayview Dr, Fremont, CA 94538 *Tel:* 408-954-0500 *Fax:* 408-954-0508 *E-mail:* info-usa@blackmagicdesign.com *Web Site:* www.blackmagicdesign.com, pg 707

Petty, Madison, Catholic Library Association (CLA), 8550 United Plaza Blvd, Suite 1001, Baton Rouge, LA 70809 *Tel:* 225-408-4417 *E-mail:* cla2@cathla.org *Web Site:* www.cathla.org, pg 952

Pevear, Matt, Chimera®, 1067 Telleen Ave, Erie, CO 80516 *Tel:* 303-444-8000 *Toll Free Tel:* 888-444-1812 *Fax:* 303-444-8303 *E-mail:* info@chimeralighting.com *Web Site:* chimeralighting.com, pg 722

Pfeiffer, Steven, The Independent Filmmaker Project (IFP), c/o Made in NY Media Ctr by IFP, 30 John St, Ground fl, Brooklyn, NY 11201 *Tel:* 212-465-8200 *Web Site:* www.ifp.org, pg 956

Pfister, Ann, Visual Sound Inc, 485 Park Way, Broomall, PA 19008 *Tel:* 610-544-8700 *Toll Free Tel:* 800-523-7525 *Fax:* 610-544-3385 *Web Site:* www.visualsound. com, pg 931

Pfizenmaier, Randy, CSI Film & Video LLC, 1913 Sonora St, Fort Collins, CO 80525 *Tel:* 970-310-9039 *Web Site:* csifilms.com, pg 735

Phair, Jason, Hollywood Lights Inc, 5251 SE McLoughlin Blvd, Portland, OR 97202-4836 *Tel:* 503-232-9001; 503-232-8855 *Toll Free Tel:* 800-826-9881 *Fax:* 503-517-8686 *E-mail:* portland@hollywoodlights. biz *Web Site:* www.hollywoodlights.biz, pg 780

Pham, Joe, QSC Audio Products LLC, 1675 MacArthur Blvd, Costa Mesa, CA 92626 *Tel:* 714-754-6161 *Toll Free Tel:* 800-772-2834 (US only) *Fax:* 714-754-6173 *E-mail:* info@qscaudio.com *Web Site:* www.qsc.com, pg 867

Phares, Alyssa, Cape Girardeau Convention & Visitors Bureau, 220 N Fountain St, Cape Girardeau, MO 63701 *Tel:* 573-335-1631 *Toll Free Tel:* 800-777-0068 *Fax:* 573-334-6702 *E-mail:* info@visitcape.com *Web Site:* visitcape.com, pg 972

Phelus, Dean, American Alliance of Museums (AAM), 2451 Crystal Dr, Suite 1005, Arlington, VA 22202 *Tel:* 202-289-1818 *Fax:* 202-289-6578 *Web Site:* www. aam-us.org, pg 948

Phillips, Bill, White Rain Films Ltd, 2009 Dexter Ave N, Seattle, WA 98109 *Tel:* 206-682-5417 *Fax:* 206-682-3038 *E-mail:* info@whiterainfilms.com *Web Site:* www.whiterainfilms.com, pg 937

Phillips, Bob, Phillips Media Source, 750 N St Paul, Suite 1000, Dallas, TX 75201 *Tel:* 214-741-1300 *Toll Free Tel:* 800-TEXAS13 (839-2713) *Fax:* 214-741-3942 *Web Site:* phillipsmediasource.com, pg 855

Phillips, Ed, Matthews Studio Equipment Inc, 4520 W Valerio St, Burbank, CA 91505 *Tel:* 818-843-6715 *Fax:* 818-480-5808 *E-mail:* info@msegrip.com *Web Site:* www.msegrip.com, pg 820

Phillips, Jeff, Projector SuperStore LLC, 17350 N Hartford Dr, Scottsdale, AZ 85255 *Tel:* 480-922-9420 *Toll Free Tel:* 888-525-6696 *Fax:* 480-348-0273 *Web Site:* www.projectorsuperstore.com, pg 865

Phillips, Jill, SKC Communication Products Inc, 8320 Hedge Lane Terr, Shawnee Mission, KS 66227 *Tel:* 913-422-4222 *Toll Free Tel:* 800-882-7779 *Toll Free Fax:* 800-454-4752 *E-mail:* contact.us@skccom. com *Web Site:* www.skccom.com, pg 890

Phillips, Julian, The Whitlock Group, 12820 West Creek Pkwy, Richmond, VA 23238 *Tel:* 804-273-9100 *Toll Free Tel:* 800-726-9843 *Fax:* 804-273-9380 *E-mail:* information@whitlock.com; marketing@ whitlock.com *Web Site:* www.whitlock.com, pg 937

Phillips, Kelli, Phillips Media Source, 750 N St Paul, Suite 1000, Dallas, TX 75201 *Tel:* 214-741-1300 *Toll Free Tel:* 800-TEXAS13 (839-2713) *Fax:* 214-741-3942 *Web Site:* phillipsmediasource.com, pg 855

Phillips, Kirsten, Consortium of College & University Media Centers (CCUMC), c/o Indiana University, 306 N Union St, Bloomington, IN 47405-3888 *Tel:* 812-855-6049 *E-mail:* ccumc@ccumc.org *Web Site:* www. ccumc.org, pg 953

Phillips, Marc, Airwave Recording Studio, 5176 Hollow Log Lane, Birmingham, AL 35244 *Tel:* 205-427-4675, pg 679

Phillips, Michael, Kineticvideo.com, 4839 Noble Lane, Battersea, ON K0H 1H0, Canada *Tel:* 416-538-6613 *Toll Free Tel:* 800-263-6910 (CN only) *Fax:* 416-538-9984 *E-mail:* info@kineticvideo.com *Web Site:* www. kineticvideo.com, pg 799

Phillips, Rick, KTVA Productions, 9818 SE 17 Ave, Suite B, Milwaukie, OR 97222 *Tel:* 503-659-4417 *E-mail:* mail@ktvavideo.com *Web Site:* www. ktvavideo.com, pg 802

Phillips, Rick, RAM® Mounts, 8410 Dallas Ave S, Seattle, WA 98108 *Tel:* 206-763-8361 *Toll Free Tel:* 800-497-7479 *Fax:* 206-763-9615 *E-mail:* sales@ rammount.com *Web Site:* www.rammount.com, pg 870

Phillips, Stephanie, WaveGuide Studios, 2062 Weems Rd, Tucker, GA 30084 *Tel:* 770-939-2004 *Toll Free Tel:* 800-578-2004 *E-mail:* info@waveguidestudios. com *Web Site:* www.waveguidestudios.com, pg 934

Phillips, Zach, NAMM, the National Association of Music Merchants, 5790 Armada Dr, Carlsbad, CA 92008 *Tel:* 760-438-8001 *Toll Free Tel:* 800-767-6266 (memb hotline) *Fax:* 760-438-7327 *E-mail:* info@ namm.org *Web Site:* www.namm.org, pg 958

Philonenko, Laurent, Avaya Inc, 4655 Great American Pkwy, Santa Clara, CA 95054 *Tel:* 908-953-6000 *Toll Free Tel:* 866-GO-AVAYA (462-8292 US & CN) *Web Site:* www.avaya.com, pg 697

Phipps, Brian, Mutoh America Inc, 2602 S 47 St, Phoenix, AZ 85034-7401 *Tel:* 480-968-7772 *Toll Free Tel:* 800-99-MUTOH (996-8864) *Fax:* 480-968-7990 *E-mail:* sales@mutoh.com; support@mutoh.com *Web Site:* www.mutoh.com, pg 835

Pianka, Robert, Sunrise Studios, 6412 N University Dr, Suite 107, Tamarac, FL 33321 *Tel:* 954-653-8480 *E-mail:* info@sunrisestudios.tv *Web Site:* www. sunrisestudios.tv, pg 904

Piard, Eric, Florical Systems Inc, 4500 NW 27 Ave, Bldg B-1, Gainesville, FL 32606 *Tel:* 352-372-8326 *Fax:* 352-375-0859 *E-mail:* sales@florical.com *Web Site:* www.florical.com, pg 762

Piechota, Pauline, FilmNation Entertainment, 150 W 22 St, 9th fl, New York, NY 10011 *Web Site:* www. filmnation.com, pg 760

Pierce, John W, Quality Audio Visual Service Inc, 6938 Boulevard 26, Fort Worth, TX 76180-8808 *Tel:* 817-284-3192 *Toll Free Tel:* 800-371-6741 *Fax:* 817-595-2942 *E-mail:* info@qualityaudiovisual.com *Web Site:* www.qualityaudiovisual.com, pg 867

Pierce, Marc, AVL Systems Design LLC, 14901 Bristol Park Blvd, Edmond, OK 73013 *Tel:* 405-749-1866 *Fax:* 405-749-1851 *E-mail:* dnix@avl1.com *Web Site:* www.avl1.com, pg 699

Pierce, Stacy, AVL Systems Design LLC, 14901 Bristol Park Blvd, Edmond, OK 73013 *Tel:* 405-749-1866 *Fax:* 405-749-1851 *E-mail:* dnix@avl1.com *Web Site:* www.avl1.com, pg 699

Pieri, Dennis, Bext Inc, 1045 Tenth Ave, San Diego, CA 92101 *Tel:* 619-BEXTINC (239-8462) *Toll Free Tel:* 888-BEXTINC (239-8462) *Fax:* 619-239-8474 *E-mail:* bext@bext.com *Web Site:* www.bext.com, pg 704

Pierpoint, Stacie, Annenberg Learner, PO Box 26983, St Louis, MO 63118 *Tel:* 202-783-0500 (outside US) *Toll Free Tel:* 800-LEARNER (532-7637) *Fax:* 202-783-0333 *E-mail:* order@learner.org *Web Site:* www. learner.org, pg 686

Pierson, Chad, Soundfold Inc, 9200 N State Rte 48, Centerville, OH 45458 *Tel:* 937-885-5100 *Toll Free Tel:* 800-782-8018 *Fax:* 937-885-5115 *E-mail:* info@ soundfold.com *Web Site:* soundfold.com, pg 894

Pierson, Kelli, Soundfold Inc, 9200 N State Rte 48, Centerville, OH 45458 *Tel:* 937-885-5100 *Toll Free Tel:* 800-782-8018 *Fax:* 937-885-5115 *E-mail:* info@ soundfold.com *Web Site:* soundfold.com, pg 894

Pierucci, Jerry, Moviola, 1135 N Mansfield Ave, Hollywood, CA 90038 *Tel:* 323-467-3107; 818-487-5000 *Toll Free Tel:* 877-MOVIOLA (668-4652) *Fax:* 323-464-1518 *Web Site:* www.moviola.com, pg 832

Pigott, Marguerite, Toronto Film, Television & Digital Media Office, Toronto City Hall, Main fl, Rotunda N, 100 Queen St W, Toronto, ON M5H 2N2, Canada *Tel:* 416-338-FILM (338-3456) *Fax:* 416-392-0675 *E-mail:* filmtoronto@toronto.ca *Web Site:* www. toronto.ca/tfto, pg 978

Pikar, Erez, Troxell-CDI, 4675 E Cotton Center Blvd, Suite 155, Phoenix, AZ 85040 *Tel:* 602-437-7240 *Toll Free Tel:* 855-TROXELL (876-9355) *Fax:* 602-752-1299 *Toll Free Fax:* 800-752-1299 *E-mail:* csg@trox. com *Web Site:* www.troxellsolutions.com, pg 918

Pike, Robert, C & M Publishing Co, 1076 Torrey Pines Rd, Chula Vista, CA 91915 *Tel:* 619-656-6462, pg 713

Pila, Jerry, Can-Am Merchandising Systems, 70 Shields Ct, Markham, ON L3R 9T5, Canada *Tel:* 905-475-6622 *Toll Free Tel:* 800-387-9790 *Fax:* 905-475-1154 *E-mail:* mail@can-am.ca *Web Site:* www.can-am.ca, pg 715

Pilar, Daniel, SYMCO Inc, 29 Poplar Dr, Stirling, NJ 07980 *Tel:* 908-647-6262 *Fax:* 908-647-4904 *E-mail:* orders@symcoinc.com *Web Site:* www. symcoinc.com, pg 905

Pilette, Vincent, Logitech, 7700 Gateway Blvd, Newark, CA 94560 *Tel:* 510-795-8500 *Toll Free Tel:* 866-291-1505 *Web Site:* www.logitech.com, pg 811

Pilkington, Derek, Omnia Audio, 1241 Superior Ave E, Cleveland, OH 44114 *Tel:* 216-241-7225 *Fax:* 216-241-4103 *E-mail:* social@telosalliance.com *Web Site:* www.telosalliance.com/omnia, pg 845

Pillitteri, Paul, The National Academy of Television Arts & Sciences (NATAS), 1697 Broadway, Suite 404, New York, NY 10019 *Tel:* 212-586-8424 *Fax:* 212-246-8129 *Web Site:* emmyonline.tv, pg 958

Pillitteri, Paul, Technology and Engineering Emmy® Awards, 1697 Broadway, Suite 404, New York, NY 10019 *Tel:* 212-586-8424 *Fax:* 212-246-8129 *E-mail:* techemmys@emmyonline.tv *Web Site:* emmyonline.com/tech, pg 1004

Pimentel, Priscilla, Southern Illinois University, Ctr for Teaching Excellence, Morris Library Rm 180, 605 Agriculture Dr, Mailcode 6510, Carbondale, IL 62901 *Tel:* 618-453-2258 *Fax:* 618-453-3010 *E-mail:* teach@siu.edu *Web Site:* cte.siu.edu/video-and-image-production, pg 895

Pinckert, Jeremy, Explore, 311 W Superior St, Suite 218, Chicago, IL 60610 *Tel:* 312-818-2101 *E-mail:* info@ explore-media.com *Web Site:* www.explore-media.com, pg 757

Piner, John, On Location North Carolina, 502 S West St, No 104, Raleigh, NC 27601 *Tel:* 919-755-9488; 919-349-GRIP (349-4747, cell) *Toll Free Tel:* 888-469-GRIP (469-4747) *E-mail:* info@onlocation-nc.com *Web Site:* www.onlocation-nc.com, pg 846

Pingal, Frederick, Applied Integration Corp, 3930 W New York Dr, Tucson, AZ 85745 *Tel:* 520-743-3095 *E-mail:* info@appliedi.com *Web Site:* www.appliedi. com, pg 687

Pink, Gary, Integrated Solutions Group, 858 Boston Providence Tpke, Norwood, MA 02062 *Tel:* 781-769-7810 *Toll Free Tel:* 866-769-0210 *E-mail:* info@ isgboston.com *Web Site:* isgboston.com, pg 789

Pinkenson, Sharon, Greater Philadelphia Film Office, One Parkway Bldg, 11th fl, 1515 Arch St, Philadelphia, PA 19102 *Tel:* 215-686-2668 *Fax:* 215-686-3659 *E-mail:* mail@film.org *Web Site:* www.film. org, pg 975

Pinnock, Henry, ZTV Broadcast Services Inc, 1670 Enterprise Rd, Mississauga, ON L4W 4L4, Canada *Tel:* 905-290-4430 *Fax:* 905-290-3370 *Web Site:* ztvbroadcast.com, pg 945

Pinto, Sara, Association of American Publishers (AAP), 455 Massachusetts Ave NW, Suite 700, Washington, DC 20001-2777 *Tel:* 202-347-3375 *Fax:* 202-347-3690 *E-mail:* info@publishers.org *Web Site:* publishers.org, pg 951

Piper, Daniel B, Piper Media Services Inc, 904 W Kenosha St, Broken Arrow, OK 74012 *Tel:* 918-251-0477 *E-mail:* info@piper.media *Web Site:* www.piper. media, pg 857

Piper, Marissa, The Clio Awards, 825 Eighth Ave, 29th fl, New York, NY 10019 *Tel:* 212-683-4300 *E-mail:* event@clioawards.com *Web Site:* clios.com, pg 987

Pipher, Tim, LA Castle Studios, 154 S Victory Blvd, Burbank, CA 91502 *Tel:* 818-861-7317 *Web Site:* lacastlestudios.com, pg 803

Pipino, Stephen J, Nicholas P Pipino Associates Inc, 10545 Guilford Rd, Suite 108, Jessup, MD 20794 *Tel:* 301-596-3397; 410-995-0041 *Toll Free Tel:* 888-596-0014 *Fax:* 410-964-1191 *Web Site:* pipinoinc.com, pg 857

Poremba, Peter, Dyna-Lite Inc, 1050 Commerce Ave, Union, NJ 07083 *Tel:* 908-687-8800 *Toll Free Tel:* 800-722-6638 *E-mail:* flash@dynalite.com *Web Site:* www.dynalite.com, pg 748

Porritt, Charlie, Russound, One Forbes Rd, Newmarket, NH 03857 *Tel:* 603-659-5170 *Toll Free Tel:* 800-638-8055 (US) *Fax:* 603-659-5388 *E-mail:* sales@russound.com; tech@russound.com *Web Site:* www.russound.com, pg 879

Port, George, MarVista Entertainment Inc, 10877 Wilshire Blvd, 10th fl, Los Angeles, CA 90024 *Tel:* 424-274-3000 *Fax:* 424-274-3050 *E-mail:* info@marvista.net *Web Site:* www.marvista.net, pg 818

Porter, Darrin, Performance Audio LLC, 2456 S West Temple St, Salt Lake City, UT 84115 *Tel:* 801-466-3196 *Toll Free Tel:* 800-771-8330 *Fax:* 801-484-1538 *E-mail:* sales@performanceaudio.com; rental@performanceaudio.com *Web Site:* www.performanceaudio.com, pg 854

Porter, James, James Porter Photography, 211 E Columbine Ave, Suite A-1, Santa Ana, CA 92707 *Tel:* 714-546-4148 *E-mail:* info@jamesporterphotography.com *Web Site:* www.jamesporterphotography.com, pg 859

Porter, James, Porter Productions, 211 E Columbine Ave, Suite B, Santa Ana, CA 92707 *Tel:* 714-546-4148 *E-mail:* studio@porterproductions.info *Web Site:* www.porterproductions.info, pg 859

Porter, Ken, Spectrum Sound Inc, 1040 Acorn Dr, Suite C, Nashville, TN 37210 *Tel:* 615-391-3700 *Web Site:* www.spectrumsound.net, pg 897

Porter, Thomas, Pixar Animation Studios, 1200 Park Ave, Emeryville, CA 94608 *Tel:* 510-922-3000 *Fax:* 510-922-3151 *Web Site:* www.pixar.com, pg 857

Porterfield, Holly, Denver Film Festival, 1510 York St, 3rd fl, Denver, CO 80206 *Tel:* 303-595-3456 *E-mail:* dff@denverfilm.org *Web Site:* denverfilmfestival.denverfilm.org, pg 988

Porterfield, Holly, Denver Film Society, 1510 York St, 3rd fl, Denver, CO 80206 *Tel:* 303-595-3456 *E-mail:* info@denverfilm.org *Web Site:* www.denverfilm.org, pg 953

Porterfield, Rob, National Instruments Corp, 11500 N Mopac Expwy, Austin, TX 78759-3504 *Tel:* 512-683-0100 *Toll Free Tel:* 888-280-7645 (sales); 877-388-1952 *Fax:* 512-683-8411; 512-683-5794 (sales) *Web Site:* www.ni.com, pg 836

Portnow, Neil, The Recording Academy, 3030 Olympic Blvd, Santa Monica, CA 90404 *Tel:* 310-392-3777 *Fax:* 310-392-2306 *E-mail:* losangeles@grammy.com *Web Site:* www.grammy.org/recording-academy, pg 961

Portuges, Kamela, Images in Motion Media Inc, 720 Ladera Dr, Sonoma, CA 95476 *Tel:* 707-996-9474 *E-mail:* images@vom.com *Web Site:* www.imagesmedia.com, pg 785

Poss, Joe, WTMJ-TV, 720 E Capitol Dr, Milwaukee, WI 53212 *Tel:* 414-332-9611 *Fax:* 414-967-5378 *E-mail:* tmj4feedback@scripps.com *Web Site:* www.tmj4.com, pg 942

Postlewaite, Ashley, Renegade Animation Inc, 111 E Broadway, Suite 208, Glendale, CA 91205 *Tel:* 818-551-2351 *Fax:* 818-551-2350 *Web Site:* www.renegadeanimation.com, pg 873

Potier, Robert, Studio Dynamics, 7245 Alondra Blvd, Paramount, CA 90723 *Tel:* 562-531-6700 *Toll Free Tel:* 800-595-4273 *E-mail:* sales@studiodynamics.com *Web Site:* www.studiodynamics.com, pg 902

Pottebaum, Gerard A, Treehaus Communications Inc, 906 W Loveland Ave, Loveland, OH 45140-2150 *Tel:* 513-683-5716 *Toll Free Tel:* 800-638-4287 *Fax:* 513-683-2882 *E-mail:* info@mammothhd.com *Web Site:* www.treehaus1.com, pg 917

Potter, Meredith, Sundance Film Festival, 1825 Three Kings Dr, Park City, UT 84060 *Tel:* 435-658-3456 *Fax:* 435-658-3457 *E-mail:* customerservice@sundance.org; press@sundance.org; institute@sundance.org *Web Site:* www.sundance.org/festival, pg 1004

Potts, David B, ARRIS Group Inc, 3871 Lakefield Dr, Suwanee, GA 30024 *Tel:* 678-473-2907 *Toll Free Tel:* 866-36-ARRIS (362-7747); 877-466-8646 (tech) *Fax:* 678-473-8470 *E-mail:* marketing@arris.com *Web Site:* www.arris.com, pg 689

Potts, John, Peerless Industries, 2300 White Oak Circle, Aurora, IL 60502 *Tel:* 630-375-5100 *Toll Free Tel:* 800-865-2112 *Fax:* 630-820-8537 *Toll Free Fax:* 800-359-6500 *E-mail:* info@peerless-av.com *Web Site:* www.peerless-av.com, pg 853

Powell, Charles, Audio Visual of Milwaukee Inc, 285 N Janacek Rd, Brookfield, WI 53045 *Tel:* 262-432-1077 *Toll Free Tel:* 800-236-6909 *Fax:* 262-432-1078 *E-mail:* avm@avmonline.com *Web Site:* www.avmonline.com, pg 695

Powell, Kathleen, Cinequest Film & VR Festival (CQFF), PO Box 720040, San Jose, CA 95172-0040 *Tel:* 408-295-FEST (295-3378); 408-995-5033 (off) *Fax:* 408-995-5713 *E-mail:* contact@cinequest.org *Web Site:* www.cinequest.org, pg 986

Powell, Mark, Audio Visual of Milwaukee Inc, 285 N Janacek Rd, Brookfield, WI 53045 *Tel:* 262-432-1077 *Toll Free Tel:* 800-236-6909 *Fax:* 262-432-1078 *E-mail:* avm@avmonline.com *Web Site:* www.avmonline.com, pg 695

Powell, Rik, Getty Images, 605 Fifth Ave S, Suite 400, Seattle, WA 98104 *Tel:* 206-925-5000 *Toll Free Tel:* 888-888-5889; 800-462-4379 (sales) *E-mail:* sales.na@gettyimages.com *Web Site:* www.gettyimages.com, pg 770

Powers, Brian, Producers Management Television (PMTV), 681 Moore Rd, Suite 100, King of Prussia, PA 19406 *Tel:* 610-768-1770 *Fax:* 610-768-1773 *E-mail:* info@pmtv.com *Web Site:* www.pmtv.com, pg 863

Powers, Erin, Flying Colors Broadcasts, 2000 "M" St NW, Suite 345, Washington, DC 20036 *Tel:* 202-293-5300 *E-mail:* info@fc-tv.com *Web Site:* www.fc-tv.com, pg 763

Prache, Olivier, eMagin Corp, 700 South Dr, Suite 201, Hopewell Junction, NY 12533 *Tel:* 845-838-7900 *Fax:* 845-838-7901 *E-mail:* info@emagin.com; sales@emagin.com; customersupport@emagin.com *Web Site:* www.emagin.com, pg 753

Prafullchandra, Sunil, Alpec®, 3098 Kenneth St, Santa Clara, CA 95054 *Tel:* 408-735-6180 *Toll Free Tel:* 800-854-6686 *Fax:* 408-735-6190 *E-mail:* info@alpec.com *Web Site:* www.alpec.com, pg 681

Prakash, Sanjay, Campus Productions, 42 Oak Ave, Tuckahoe, NY 10707 *Tel:* 914-395-1010 *Fax:* 914-395-1095 *E-mail:* sales@campusgroup.com *Web Site:* www.campusgroup.com, pg 715

Prater, Craig, Heartland International Film Festival, 1043 Virginia Ave, Suite 2, Indianapolis, IN 46203 *Tel:* 317-464-9405 *E-mail:* submissions@heartlandfilm.org *Web Site:* heartlandfilm.org/festival, pg 992

Prater, Craig, Indy Shorts International Film Fest, 1043 Virginia Ave, Suite 2, Indianapolis, IN 46203 *Tel:* 317-464-9405 *E-mail:* submissions@heartlandfilm.org *Web Site:* heartlandfilm.org, pg 993

Pratt, Earle, New Horizons Computer Learning Centers Inc, 100 Four Falls Corporate Ctr, Suite 408, Conshohocken, PA 19428-4132 *Tel:* 484-567-3000 *Toll Free Tel:* 888-236-3625 *Web Site:* www.newhorizons.com, pg 839

Pratt, Jane, Association for Print Technologies (APTech), 1896 Preston White Dr, Reston, VA 20191 *Tel:* 703-264-7200 *Fax:* 703-620-0994 *E-mail:* aptech@aptech.org *Web Site:* www.printtechnologies.org, pg 950

Pratt, Sean, Santa Barbara International Film Festival, 1528 Chapala St, Suite 203, Santa Barbara, CA 93101 *Tel:* 805-963-0023 *Fax:* 805-962-2524 *E-mail:* contactus@sbiff.org *Web Site:* sbiff.org, pg 1003

Praytor, Erik, Equi=Tech Corp, PO Box 249, Selma, OR 97538-0249 *Tel:* 541-218-6900 (tech support, cust serv); 541-291-9253 *Toll Free Tel:* 877-EQUITECH (378-4832) *Fax:* 541-787-8740 *E-mail:* sales@equitech.com; customerservice@equitech.com; marketing@equitech.com *Web Site:* www.equitech.com, pg 755

Predovich, Robert, Soundmaster Group, 89 Barford Rd, Toronto, ON M9W 4H8, Canada *Tel:* 416-741-7057 *Fax:* 416-477-2496 *E-mail:* mail@soundmaster.com *Web Site:* www.soundmaster.com, pg 894

Preg, Nate, ExpoDisplays, 3401 Mary Taylor Rd, Birmingham, AL 35235 *Toll Free Tel:* 800-747-3976 *E-mail:* info@expodisplays.com *Web Site:* www.expodisplays.com, pg 757

Preiss, Eric, Nevada Film Office, 6655 W Sahara, Suite C-106, Las Vegas, NV 89146 *Tel:* 702-486-2711 *Toll Free Tel:* 877-638-3456 *Fax:* 702-486-2712 *E-mail:* lvnfo@nevadafilm.com *Web Site:* www.nevadafilm.com, pg 973

Prelinger, Richard, Prelinger Archives, PO Box 590622, San Francisco, CA 94159-0622 *Tel:* 415-750-0445 *E-mail:* footage@panix.com *Web Site:* www.prelinger.com, pg 861

Prendergast, Erin, Art Gallery of Ontario, 317 Dundas St W, Toronto, ON M5T 1G4, Canada *Tel:* 416-979-6648 *Toll Free Tel:* 877-225-4246 *Web Site:* ago.ca, pg 690

Prentice, Kim, Gagne Inc, 41 Commercial Dr, Johnson City, NY 13790 *Tel:* 607-729-3366 *Toll Free Tel:* 800-800-5954 *Fax:* 607-729-7644 *E-mail:* sales@gagneinc.com *Web Site:* www.gagneinc.com, pg 767

Prescott, Cate, National Instruments Corp, 11500 N Mopac Expwy, Austin, TX 78759-3504 *Tel:* 512-683-0100 *Toll Free Tel:* 888-280-7645 (sales); 877-388-1952 *Fax:* 512-683-8411; 512-683-5794 (sales) *Web Site:* www.ni.com, pg 836

Prescott, Lydia Zimmer, Art Directors Guild (ADG), 11969 Ventura Blvd, 2nd fl, Studio City, CA 91604 *Tel:* 818-762-9995 *Fax:* 818-762-9997 *Web Site:* www.adg.org, pg 950

Prescott, Neal, MRM//McCANN, 622 Third Ave, New York, NY 10017 *Tel:* 646-865-6230 *E-mail:* gbc@mrm-mccann.com *Web Site:* www.mrm-mccann.com, pg 832

Pressimone, Dawn, Beatrice E Griggs Elementary Administrator's Award, 6021 State Farm Rd, Guilderland, NY 12084 *Tel:* 518-432-6952 *Toll Free Tel:* 800-252-6952 *Fax:* 518-427-1697 *E-mail:* info@nyla.org *Web Site:* www.nyla.org, pg 991

Presson, Greg, PAR Inc, 16204 N Florida Ave, Lutz, FL 33549 *Tel:* 813-449-4065 *Toll Free Tel:* 800-331-8378 *Fax:* 813-961-2196 *Toll Free Fax:* 800-727-9329 *E-mail:* cs@parinc.com *Web Site:* www.parinc.com, pg 851

Preston, Coral, AudioImage Recording, 110 N Jefferson St, Richmond, VA 23220-5022 *Tel:* 804-644-7700 *Fax:* 804-644-8801 *E-mail:* info@audioimagerecording.com *Web Site:* www.audioimagerecording.com, pg 695

Preston, Dan, Telequest Inc, 174 Nassau St, Suite 383, Princeton, NJ 08542 *Tel:* 609-430-3004 *E-mail:* contact@telequestinc.com *Web Site:* www.telequestinc.com, pg 910

Preston, Howard, Preston Cinema Systems, 1659 11 St, Suite 100, Santa Monica, CA 90404 *Tel:* 310-453-1852 *Fax:* 310-453-5672 *E-mail:* sales@prestoncinema.com *Web Site:* www.prestoncinema.com, pg 861

Preston, Philip, PolyScience, 6600 W Touhy Ave, Niles, IL 60714-4516 *Tel:* 847-647-0611 *Toll Free Tel:* 800-229-7569 *Fax:* 847-647-1155 *E-mail:* sales@polyscience.com *Web Site:* www.polyscience.com, pg 859

Preston, Rick, Preston Productions Inc, 128 Bartlett St, Marlborough, MA 01752 *Toll Free Tel:* 800-822-2299 *E-mail:* ideas@prestonevents.com *Web Site:* www.prestonproductions.com; www.prestonevents.com, pg 861

Preston, Susan, Preston Productions Inc, 128 Bartlett St, Marlborough, MA 01752 *Toll Free Tel:* 800-822-2299 *E-mail:* ideas@prestonevents.com *Web Site:* www.prestonproductions.com; www.prestonevents.com, pg 862

Pretto, Anthony, International Electro-Magnetics Inc, 1033A S Noel Ave, Wheeling, IL 60090 *Tel:* 847-358-4622 *Fax:* 847-947-8239 *E-mail:* information@iemmag.com; service@iemmag.com; sales@iemmag.com *Web Site:* www.iemmag.com, pg 790

Prettyman, William "Woody", Studio Center Corp, 161 Business Park Dr, Virginia Beach, VA 23462 *Tel:* 757-286-3080 (24 hour cell) *Toll Free Tel:* 866-515-2111 *Fax:* 757-622-0583 (acctg) *Web Site:* www.studiocenter.com, pg 902

Prewitt, Jean M, Independent Film & Television Alliance® (IFTA), 10850 Wilshire Blvd, 9th fl, Los Angeles, CA 90024-4311 *Tel:* 310-446-1000 *Fax:* 310-446-1600 *E-mail:* info@ifta-online.org *Web Site:* www.ifta-online.org, pg 956

Price, Emma, Edison Price Lighting Inc, 41-50 22 St, Long Island City, NY 11101 *Tel:* 718-685-0700 *E-mail:* orders@epl.com; info@epl.com *Web Site:* www.epl.com, pg 750

Price, Jim, R & R Cases & Cabinets, 1217 Rand Rd, Des Plaines, IL 60016 *Tel:* 847-299-8100 *Fax:* 847-299-8110 *E-mail:* sales@rrcases.com *Web Site:* www.rrcases.com, pg 868

Price, John, Cinema Concepts, 2030 Powers Ferry Rd, Suite 214, Atlanta, GA 30339 *Tel:* 770-956-7460 *Toll Free Tel:* 800-SHOWADS (746-9237) *Fax:* 770-956-8358 *E-mail:* info@cinemaconcepts.com *Web Site:* www.cinemaconcepts.com, pg 724

Price, Karen, New Leaf Distributing Co, 401 Thornton Rd, Lithia Springs, GA 30122-1557 *Tel:* 770-948-7845 *Toll Free Tel:* 800-326-2665 (orders) *Fax:* 770-944-2313 *Toll Free Fax:* 800-326-1066 *E-mail:* customerservice@newleaf-dist.com *Web Site:* newleaf-dist.com, pg 839

Priest-Heck, Bob, Freeman, 1600 Viceroy, Suite 100, Dallas, TX 75235 *Tel:* 214-445-1000 *Web Site:* www.freeman.com, pg 765

Priestman, Ginny, Terra Nova Films Inc, 9848 S Winchester Ave, Chicago, IL 60643 *Tel:* 773-881-8491 *Toll Free Tel:* 800-779-8491 *Fax:* 773-881-3368 *E-mail:* tnf@terranova.org *Web Site:* www.terranova.org, pg 911

Prieto, Esteban, Miami short Film Festival (MsFF), 247 SW Eighth St, Suite 44, Miami, FL 33130 *E-mail:* info@miamishortfilmfestival.com *Web Site:* www.miamishortfilmfestival.com, pg 996

Primm, John, DV Post, 505 N Tustin Ave, Suite 220, Santa Ana, CA 92705 *Tel:* 714-550-0925 *Web Site:* www.dvpostvideo.com, pg 748

Pringle, David, Luminys Systems Corp, 11961 Sherman Rd, North Hollywood, CA 91605 *Tel:* 818-827-3941 *Toll Free Tel:* 800-321-3644 *E-mail:* info@luminyscorp.com *Web Site:* www.luminyscorp.com, pg 812

Pringle, Rebecca S "Becky", National Education Association (NEA), 1201 16 St NW, Washington, DC 20036-3290 *Tel:* 202-833-4000 *Fax:* 202-822-7974 *Web Site:* www.nea.org, pg 836

Proal, Pia, Real Cool Productions, 800 S Main St, Suite 203, Mansfield, MA 02048 *Tel:* 508-337-8520 *E-mail:* info@rcplearning.com *Web Site:* www.realcoolproductions.com, pg 871

Prochaska, Jason, Sitler's Supplies Inc, 111 Westview Dr, Washington, IA 52353 *Tel:* 319-653-2123 *Toll Free Tel:* 800-426-3938 *Fax:* 319-653-3198 *E-mail:* renfred@sitlersupplies.com *Web Site:* sitlersupplies.com, pg 890

Proctor, Bill, Golden Gate Awards, c/o San Francisco Film Society, The Presidio, Suite 110, 39 Mesa St, San Francisco, CA 94129-1025 *Tel:* 415-561-5000 *Fax:* 415-440-1760 *E-mail:* info@sffilm.org; gga@sffilm.org *Web Site:* sffilm.org/sffilm-festival/, pg 990

Proctor, Bill, San Francisco International Film Festival, 39 Mesa St, Suite 110, The Presidio, San Francisco, CA 94129-1025 *Tel:* 415-561-5000 *Fax:* 415-440-1760 *E-mail:* info@sffilm.org *Web Site:* sffilm.org/sffilm-festival/, pg 1003

Proffitt, K K, JamSync, Music Row, 1232 17 Ave S, Nashville, TN 37212 *Tel:* 615-320-5050 *E-mail:* info@jamsync.com *Web Site:* www.jamsync.com, pg 793

Prokop, Robert, Alegra House Publishers, PO Box 1443, Warren, OH 44482-1443 *Tel:* 330-372-2951 *Fax:* 330-399-1619, pg 679

Proto, Joseph, Electriduct Inc, 1650 NW 18 St, Unit 801, Pompano Beach, FL 33069 *Tel:* 954-867-9100 *Toll Free Tel:* 866-673-9590 *Fax:* 954-206-0799 *E-mail:* sales@electriduct.com *Web Site:* www.electriduct.com, pg 752

Proud, Lauren, Rosco Laboratories Inc, 52 Harbor View, Stamford, CT 06902 *Tel:* 203-708-8900 *Toll Free Tel:* 800-ROSCO NY (767-2669) *Fax:* 203-708-8919 *E-mail:* info@rosco.com *Web Site:* us.rosco.com, pg 877

Proudfoot, David, Thread Marketing Group, 4635 W Alexis Rd, Toledo, OH 43623-1005 *Tel:* 419-887-6801 *Fax:* 419-887-6802 *E-mail:* info@threadgroup.com *Web Site:* www.threadgroup.com, pg 913

Provenzano, Frank, Michigan Film & Digital Media Office, 300 N Washington Sq, 4th fl, Lansing, MI 48913 *Tel:* 517-241-6757 *Toll Free Tel:* 800-477-FILM (477-3456) *Fax:* 517-241-3689 *E-mail:* mfo@michigan.org *Web Site:* www.michiganbusiness.org/industries/mfdmo, pg 972

Provost, Stephanie, Sihl Inc, 538 Main St, Fiskeville, RI 02823 *Tel:* 401-821-1000 *Toll Free Tel:* 800-556-6866; 800-366-7393 (ext 1, cust serv) *Web Site:* www.sihlinc.com, pg 888

Prupas, Jesse, Muse Entertainment Enterprises, 3451 Rue Saint Jacques, Montreal, QC H4C 1H1, Canada *Tel:* 514-866-6873 *Fax:* 514-876-3911 *E-mail:* bpalik@muse.ca *Web Site:* www.muse.ca, pg 834

Prupas, Michael, Muse Entertainment Enterprises, 3451 Rue Saint Jacques, Montreal, QC H4C 1H1, Canada *Tel:* 514-866-6873 *Fax:* 514-876-3911 *E-mail:* bpalik@muse.ca *Web Site:* www.muse.ca, pg 834

Prybylowski, Doug, Comex Systems Inc, 101 Pleasant Hill Rd, Chester, NJ 07930 *Tel:* 908-881-6301 (cell) *E-mail:* mail@comexsystems.com *Web Site:* www.comexsystems.com, pg 728

Puccio, Sebastian J, Consolidated Display Co Inc, 1210 US Hwy 34, Oswego, IL 60543 *Tel:* 630-851-8666 *Toll Free Tel:* 888-851-7669 *Fax:* 630-851-8756 *E-mail:* info@letitsnow.com *Web Site:* www.letitsnow.com, pg 731

Puffenberger, David, Advent Media Inc, 5629 Fraley Ct, Columbus, OH 43235 *Tel:* 614-538-1622 *Toll Free Tel:* 877-538-1622 *Fax:* 614-538-1621 *Web Site:* www.adventmediainc.com, pg 678

Puffenberger, Stephen F, Advent Media Inc, 5629 Fraley Ct, Columbus, OH 43235 *Tel:* 614-538-1622 *Toll Free Tel:* 877-538-1622 *Fax:* 614-538-1621 *Web Site:* www.adventmediainc.com, pg 678

Pugh, Daniel, Bitcentral Inc, 4340 Von Karman Ave, Suite 400, Newport Beach, CA 92660 *Tel:* 949-253-9000 *Toll Free Tel:* 800-272-4004 (support) *E-mail:* sales@bitcentral.com; support@bitcentral.com *Web Site:* www.bitcentral.com, pg 706

Pugh, Mike, Goose Creek Music & Entertainment, 17723 Tranquility Rd, Purcellville, VA 20132 *Tel:* 540-751-1395 *E-mail:* info@goosecreekmusic.com *Web Site:* www.goosecreekmusic.com, pg 772

Pulig, Judi, Yorktel, 81 Corbett Way, Eatontown, NJ 07724 *Tel:* 732-413-6000 *Toll Free Tel:* 866-836-8463 *Fax:* 732-413-6060 *E-mail:* knowmore@yorktel.com *Web Site:* yorktel.com, pg 944

Pullan, Julian, Jack Morton Worldwide, 909 Third Ave, New York, NY 10022 *Tel:* 212-401-7000; 212-401-7212 *E-mail:* experience@jackmorton.com *Web Site:* www.jackmorton.com, pg 830

Pulley-Hayes, Erika, Edward R Murrow Award, 401 Ninth St NW, Washington, DC 20004-2129 *Tel:* 202-879-9600 *Toll Free Tel:* 800-272-2190 *E-mail:* press@cpb.org *Web Site:* www.cpb.org, pg 996

Puls, Melissa, Avid Technology Inc, 65-75 Network Dr, Burlington, MA 01830 *Tel:* 978-640-6789 *Web Site:* www.avid.com, pg 698

Punia, Katie, Penguin Random House Audio Publishing, 1745 Broadway, New York, NY 10019 *E-mail:* audio@penguinrandomhouse.com *Web Site:* www.penguinrandomhouseaudio.com, pg 853

Puorro, Tom, Poly, 345 Encinal St, Santa Cruz, CA 95060 *Tel:* 831-426-5858 *Toll Free Tel:* 800-544-4660 *Fax:* 831-426-6098 *Web Site:* www.poly.com, pg 859

Purcell, Nicole, The Clio Awards, 825 Eighth Ave, 29th fl, New York, NY 10019 *Tel:* 212-683-4300 *E-mail:* event@clioawards.com *Web Site:* clios.com, pg 987

Purdy, Brian E, Mediaimage Communications Group, 10 Sacks Ave, Grimsby, ON L3M 4Y4, Canada *Tel:* 905-309-5554 *Fax:* 905-309-0999, pg 822

Purtee, Chris, Sky-View Search Lights & Promotions, 702 Spring Cypress Rd, Spring, TX 77373 *Tel:* 210-845-7622 *Toll Free Tel:* 800-562-8439 (US & CN); 888-396-6653 *E-mail:* sales@sky-view.com *Web Site:* sky-view.com, pg 890

Purves, Judith, CBC/Radio-Canada, 181 Queen St, Ottawa, ON K1P 1K9, Canada *Tel:* 613-288-6000; 613-288-6445 (newsroom) *Toll Free Tel:* 866-306-4636 (CN only) *E-mail:* cbcnewsottawa@cbc.ca *Web Site:* cbc.radio-canada.ca, pg 717

Purvis, Heather, Cox Media, 6205 Peachtree Dunwoody Rd, No B17, Atlanta, GA 30328 *Toll Free Tel:* 855-755-2691 *Web Site:* www.coxmedia.com, pg 732

Pushman, Parmita, White Swan Music Inc, 6395 Gunpark Dr, Suite A, Boulder, CO 80301 *Tel:* 303-527-0770 *Toll Free Tel:* 800-825-8656 *Fax:* 303-527-0771 *E-mail:* info@whiteswanmusic.com *Web Site:* whiteswanmusic.com, pg 937

Puskaric, Russ, Accusoft, 4001 N Riverside Dr, Tampa, FL 33603 *Tel:* 813-875-7575 *Toll Free Tel:* 800-875-7009 *Fax:* 813-875-7705 *E-mail:* sales@accusoft.com *Web Site:* www.accusoft.com, pg 674

Pyland, Mike, Recorded Books Inc, an RBmedia company, 270 Skipjack Rd, Prince Frederick, MD 20678 *Tel:* 410-535-5590 *Toll Free Tel:* 800-638-1304 *Fax:* 410-535-5499 *E-mail:* customerservice@recordedbooks.com *Web Site:* www.recordedbooks.com, pg 872

Pyle, Christine Haley, CEDIA IPRO Affinity Group, 8475 Nightfall Lane, Fishers, IN 46037 *Tel:* 317-328-4336 *Toll Free Tel:* 800-669-5329 *E-mail:* info@cedia.org *Web Site:* cedia.net, pg 952

Pytowski, Janet, Video Catalogue Co Inc, 105 E 34 St, Suite 105, New York, NY 10016 *Toll Free Tel:* 866-843-2282 *E-mail:* info@vidcat.com *Web Site:* www.vidcat.com, pg 927

Pyttlik, Olaf, DACAPO Productions Inc, 516 Hargrave St, Winnipeg, MB R3A 0X8, Canada *Tel:* 204-956-2867 *Fax:* 204-956-2869 *Web Site:* www.dacapo.ca, pg 737

Quaroni, Guido, Pixar Animation Studios, 1200 Park Ave, Emeryville, CA 94608 *Tel:* 510-922-3000 *Fax:* 510-922-3151 *Web Site:* www.pixar.com, pg 857

Quayle, Avery, Activu Corp, 301 Roundhill Dr, Rockaway, NJ 07866 *Tel:* 973-366-5550 *Toll Free Tel:* 888-ACTIVU1 (228-4881) *Fax:* 973-625-7775 *E-mail:* facebook@activu.com *Web Site:* activu.com, pg 675

Quigley, Ken, AVFX Inc, 96 Holton St, Boston, MA 02135 *Tel:* 617-254-0770 *Toll Free Tel:* 888-254-0770 *E-mail:* info@avfx.com *Web Site:* www.avfx.com, pg 698

Quigley, Rich, Synaptic Digital, 79 Fifth Ave, 14th fl, New York, NY 10003 *Tel:* 212-682-8300 *Fax:* 212-201-4207 *E-mail:* learnmore@synapticdigital.com *Web Site:* www.synapticdigital.com, pg 905

Quiles, Danny, Barbizon Electric Co Inc, 456 W 55 St, New York, NY 10019-4403 *Tel:* 212-586-1620 *Toll Free Tel:* 800-582-9941 *Fax:* 212-247-8818 *E-mail:* benysales@barbizon.com *Web Site:* www.barbizon.com, pg 701

Quilliam, Christian, Q-Prompt Inc, 5356 Vail Ct, Mississauga, ON L5M 6G9, Canada *Tel:* 416-908-5886 *Toll Free Tel:* 866-578-8852 *E-mail:* scripts@qprompt.com *Web Site:* www.qprompt.com, pg 867

Quinlan, David, Marshall Electronics Inc, 20608 Madrona Ave, Torrance, CA 90503 *Tel:* 310-333-0606 *Toll Free Tel:* 800-800-6608 *Fax:* 310-333-0688 *E-mail:* support@marshall-usa.com *Web Site:* www.mars-cam.com; www.marshall-usa.com, pg 817

Quinlan, Shawn, Nationwide Audio Visual Co, 4100-B Sladeview Crescent, Units 1 & 2, Mississauga, ON L5L 5Z3, Canada *Tel:* 905-608-8899 *Fax:* 905-608-8890 *E-mail:* sales@nationwideav.com *Web Site:* www.nationwideav.com, pg 837

Quinn, Larry, DecisionOne Corp, 640 Lee Rd, 3rd fl, Wayne, PA 19087 *Tel:* 610-296-6000 *Toll Free Tel:* 800-767-2876; 800-777-8800 (cust serv); 888-287-9202 (sales); 800-554-5179 (CN) *Fax:* 610-296-2910 *E-mail:* sales@decisionone.com *Web Site:* www.decisionone.com, pg 740

Quinn, Terry, WGBH Production Group, One Guest St, Boston, MA 02135 *Tel:* 617-300-2000 *E-mail:* productiongroup@wgbh.org; studios@wgbh.org; outpost@wgbh.org *Web Site:* productiongroup.wgbh.org, pg 936

Quinniey, Charles, Buffalo Niagara International Film Festival (BNIFF), 3840 E Robinson Rd, Suite 166, Amherst, NY 14228 *Tel:* 716-693-0912 *E-mail:* info@bniff.com *Web Site:* thebnff.com, pg 984

Quintero, Norma, Comtel Inc, 14901 NE 20 Ave, North Miami, FL 33181 *Tel:* 305-424-4160 (facility servs); 305-424-4178 (local inquiries); 516-816-5152 (natl inquiries) *Web Site:* www.comtelinc.com; www.facebook.com/comtelinc/, pg 730

Quirk, Shawn, Creative Impulse Awards (Impies), c/o RIIFF, 36 Rhode Island Ave, Newport, RI 02840 *Tel:* 401-861-4445 *Fax:* 401-490-6735 *E-mail:* info@film-festival.org *Web Site:* www.film-festival.org/CreativeIM.php, pg 987

Quirk, Shawn, Flickers' Rhode Island International Film Festival™ (RIIFF), 83 Park St, Suite 5, Providence, RI 02903 *Tel:* 401-861-4445 *Fax:* 401-490-6735 *E-mail:* info@film-festival.org *Web Site:* film-festival.org, pg 989

Quirk, Shawn, KidsEye™ International Film Festival, 83 Park St, Suite 5, Providence, RI 02903 *Tel:* 401-861-4445 *Fax:* 401-490-6735 *E-mail:* info@film-festival.org *Web Site:* film-festival.org, pg 994

Quirk, Shawn, Providence Underground Film Festival, 83 Park St, Suite 5, Providence, RI 02903 *Tel:* 401-861-4445 *Fax:* 401-490-6735 *E-mail:* info@film-festival.org *Web Site:* www.film-festival.org, pg 1000

Quirk, Shawn, Roving Eye International Film Festival, 83 Park St, Suite 5, Providence, RI 02903 *Tel:* 401-861-4445 *Fax:* 401-490-6735 *E-mail:* info@film-festival.org *Web Site:* film-festival.org, pg 1002

Quirk, Shawn, Vortex Sci-Fi, Fantasy & Horror Film Festival, 83 Park St, Suite 5, Providence, RI 02903 *Tel:* 401-861-4445 *Fax:* 401-490-6735 *E-mail:* info@film-festival.org *Web Site:* www.film-festival.org, pg 1006

Rabbach, Glenn, Duggal Visual Solutions Inc, Brooklyn Navy Yard, 63 Flushing Ave, Bldg 25, Brooklyn, NY 11205 *Tel:* 212-924-8100 (prodn); 212-242-7000 (corp) *Fax:* 212-486-1399 *E-mail:* info@duggal.com *Web Site:* duggal.com, pg 747

Rabbitt, Jay, In Concert Production Inc (ICP), 680 Wharton Circle SW, Suite C, Atlanta, GA 30336 *Tel:* 404-355-7943 *Fax:* 404-350-9045 *Web Site:* icpatlanta.com, pg 786

Rabbitt, Kevin, NEP Group Inc, 2 Beta Dr, Pittsburgh, PA 15238 *Tel:* 412-826-1414 *Toll Free Tel:* 800-444-0054 *E-mail:* info@nepinc.com *Web Site:* www.nepgroup.com, pg 838

Rabehl, Mike, Cinequest Film & VR Festival (CQFF), PO Box 720040, San Jose, CA 95172-0040 *Tel:* 408-295-FEST (295-3378); 408-995-5033 (off) *Fax:* 408-995-5713 *E-mail:* contact@cinequest.org *Web Site:* www.cinequest.org, pg 986

Rabern, Sebastian, Artbeats, 1405 N Myrtle Rd, Myrtle Creek, OR 97457 *Tel:* 541-863-4429 *Fax:* 541-863-4547 *E-mail:* info@artbeats.com *Web Site:* www.artbeats.com, pg 690

Rabinowitz, Richard, American History Workshop (NY) Inc, 588 Seventh St, Brooklyn, NY 11215-3707 *Tel:* 718-499-6500 *E-mail:* info@americanhistoryworkshop.com *Web Site:* www.americanhistoryworkshop.com, pg 683

Rachal, Scott, Vidox Motion Imagery, 204 Winchester Dr, Lafayette, LA 70506 *Tel:* 337-237-1700 *Fax:* 337-237-1712 *Web Site:* www.vidox.com, pg 930

Racine, Pam, NEWIST/CESA 7, 595 Baeten Rd, Green Bay, WI 54304 *Tel:* 920-617-5614 *Fax:* 920-492-5964 *E-mail:* contactus@cesa7.org *Web Site:* www.cesa7.org/o/CESA%207/page/communications-video, pg 840

Racster, Christopher, Outfest Los Angeles LGBT Film Festival, 3470 Wilshire Blvd, Suite 935, Los Angeles, CA 90010 *Tel:* 213-480-7088 *Fax:* 213-480-7099 *E-mail:* outfest@outfest.org *Web Site:* www.outfest.org, pg 999

Rader, Mike, Univenture Inc, 4266 Tuller Rd, Dublin, OH 43017 *Tel:* 937-645-4600 *Toll Free Tel:* 877-831-9428 *Fax:* 937-645-4700 *E-mail:* sales@univenture.com *Web Site:* www.univenture.com, pg 922

Rader, Tim, Drytac Corp, 5601 Eastport Blvd, Richmond, VA 23231 *Tel:* 804-222-3094 *Toll Free Tel:* 800-280-6013 *E-mail:* customerservice@drytac.com *Web Site:* www.drytac.com, pg 747

Radisek, Beth Steele, Cleveland International Film Festival, 2510 Market Ave, Cleveland, OH 44113-3434 *Tel:* 216-623-3456 *Fax:* 216-623-0103 *E-mail:* cfs@clevelandfilm.org; submissions@clevelandfilm.org *Web Site:* www.clevelandfilm.org, pg 986

Radner, Karen, HarperAudio, 10 E 53 St, New York, NY 10022 *Tel:* 212-207-7000 *Toll Free Tel:* 800-242-7737 *Fax:* 212-207-2582 *Toll Free Fax:* 800-822-4090 *Web Site:* www.harpercollins.com, pg 776

Rae, Darrell, monterey media inc, 125 Auburn Ct, Suite 220, Westlake Village, CA 91360 *Tel:* 805-494-7199 *Fax:* 805-496-6061 *E-mail:* customerservice@montereymedia.com; publicity@montereymedia.com *Web Site:* www.montereymedia.com, pg 829

Rae, Darrell, monterey video, 125 Auburn Ct, Suite 220, Westlake Village, CA 91362 *Tel:* 805-494-7199 *Fax:* 805-496-6061 *E-mail:* customerservice@montereymedia.com; publicity@montereymedia.com *Web Site:* www.montereymedia.com, pg 829

Rae-Mansfield, Jere, monterey media inc, 125 Auburn Ct, Suite 220, Westlake Village, CA 91360 *Tel:* 805-494-7199 *Fax:* 805-496-6061 *E-mail:* customerservice@montereymedia.com; publicity@montereymedia.com *Web Site:* www.montereymedia.com, pg 829

Rae-Mansfield, Jere, monterey video, 125 Auburn Ct, Suite 220, Westlake Village, CA 91362 *Tel:* 805-494-7199 *Fax:* 805-496-6061 *E-mail:* customerservice@montereymedia.com; publicity@montereymedia.com *Web Site:* www.montereymedia.com, pg 829

Rafferty, Barri Freidman, Ketchum Inc, 1285 Avenue of the Americas, 4th fl, New York, NY 10019 *Tel:* 646-935-3900 *Web Site:* www.ketchum.com, pg 798

Rafferty, Mike, Boston Productions Inc (BPI), 290 Vanderbilt Ave, Suite 1, Norwood, MA 02062 *Tel:* 781-255-1555; 720-233-1250 (sales) *E-mail:* info@bostonproductions.com *Web Site:* bostonproductions.com, pg 709

Ragozzino, Julie C, Universal Satellite Communications Inc, 1530 Nandina Ave, Perris, CA 92571 *Tel:* 562-483-4800; 951-943-4420 (corp off) *Toll Free Tel:* 888-867-6620 *Fax:* 954-943-0263 *Web Site:* www.unisatmobile.com, pg 922

Ragsdale, David, HB-Content, 105 Butler St, Suite 2B, Brooklyn, NY 11231 *Tel:* 212-213-8824 *E-mail:* hb@hb-content.com *Web Site:* www.hb-content.com; vimeopro.com/hbcontent, pg 777

Rahe, Keith, Dubuque Area Convention & Visitors Bureau, 300 Main St, Suite 120, Dubuque, IA 52001 *Tel:* 563-845-7698 *Web Site:* www.traveldubuque.com, pg 971

Rahier, Michel, Technicolor USA Inc, 6040 Sunset Blvd, Hollywood, CA 90028 *Tel:* 323-817-6600 *E-mail:* info@technicolor.com *Web Site:* www.technicolor.com, pg 908

Rahn, Eckart, Celestial Harmonies/Fortuna Records/Kuckuck Schallplatten/Black Sun Music/MonteVideo, 1951 N Wilmot Rd, Bldg 2, Unit 7, Tucson, AZ 85712-8000 *Tel:* 520-326-4400 *Fax:* 520-326-3333 *E-mail:* celestial@harmonies.com *Web Site:* www.harmonies.com, pg 719

Raia, Jason, Freedoms Foundation National Awards, 1601 Valley Forge Rd, Valley Forge, PA 19481 *Tel:* 610-933-8825 *Fax:* 610-935-0522 *E-mail:* info@ffvf.org *Web Site:* www.freedomsfoundation.org, pg 989

Raina, Robin, ADAM Inc, One Ebix Way, Johns Creek, GA 30097 *Tel:* 770-625-3450 *Toll Free Tel:* 800-755-ADAM (755-2326) *E-mail:* aod-info@ebix.com *Web Site:* www.adam.com, pg 675

Rainer, Tammy, Specialty Tapes Manfacturing Inc, 4221 Courtney Rd, Franksville, WI 53126 *Tel:* 262-835-0748 *Toll Free Tel:* 800-545-8273 *Fax:* 262-835-0749 *E-mail:* sales@specialtytapes.net *Web Site:* www.specialtytapes.net, pg 897

Rainer, Thom S, B&H Publishing Group, One LifeWay Plaza, Nashville, TN 37234 *Tel:* 615-251-2520 *Fax:* 615-251-5004 *Web Site:* www.bhpublishinggroup.com, pg 701

Raines, Bob, Tennessee Entertainment Commission, Tennessee Tower, 27th fl, 312 Rosa L Parks Ave, Nashville, TN 37243 *Tel:* 615-741-FILM (741-3456) *Toll Free Tel:* 877-818-FILM (818-3456) *E-mail:* tn.film@tn.gov *Web Site:* www.tnentertainment.com, pg 976

Rainey, Dave, Glendale Media Center, 9494 W Maryland Ave, Glendale, AZ 85305 *Tel:* 623-930-4512 *Web Site:* www.glendalemediacenter.com, pg 771

Rajewski, Mike, KAKE-TV, 1500 N West St, Wichita, KS 67203-1323 *Tel:* 316-943-4221; 316-946-1363 (sales) *Fax:* 316-943-5493 (sales) *E-mail:* sales@kake.com; news@kake.com *Web Site:* kake.com, pg 796

Ralke, Richard, LA Sound Co, 9001 Canoga Ave, Canoga Park, CA 91304 *Tel:* 818-772-9200 *Fax:* 818-772-9977 *E-mail:* rentals@lasoundco.com; sales@lasoundco.com, pg 803

Rall, Rory, Benchmark Media Systems Inc, 203 E Hampton Place, Suite 2, Syracuse, NY 13206 *Tel:* 315-437-6300 *Toll Free Tel:* 800-262-4675 *Fax:* 315-437-8119 *E-mail:* sales@benchmarkmedia.com *Web Site:* www.benchmarkmedia.com, pg 703

Ramer, Durrell, ETC, 3031 Pleasant View Rd, Middleton, WI 53562-4809 *Tel:* 608-831-4116 *Toll Free Tel:* 800-688-4116 *Fax:* 608-836-1736 *Web Site:* www.etcconnect.com, pg 756

Rametta, Jack, StarTrak Studios Inc, 36 Vermont Ave, Unit 1, Warwick, RI 02888 *Tel:* 401-732-1880 *E-mail:* info@startrakstudios.com *Web Site:* www.startrakstudios.com, pg 900

Raml, Gregory, American Museum of Natural History (AMNH), c/o Special Collections, Library Services Dept, Central Park W & 79 St, New York, NY 10024-5192 *Tel:* 212-769-5420 *Fax:* 212-769-5009 *E-mail:* speccol@amnh.org *Web Site:* www.amnh.org, pg 683

Rampino, Frank, Flash Electronics Inc, Brooklyn Army Terminal, Suite 1-A, Mail Box 3, 140 58 St, Brooklyn, NY 11220 *Tel:* 718-492-4040 *Toll Free Tel:* 800-831-3127 *Fax:* 718-492-4590 *E-mail:* customercare@flashdistributors.com *Web Site:* www.flashdistributors.com, pg 762

Rampmeyer, Mike, Applied Electronics, 722 Blue Crab Rd, Newport News, VA 23606 *Tel:* 757-591-9371 *Toll Free Tel:* 800-883-0008 *Fax:* 757-591-9514 *E-mail:* sales@appliednn.com *Web Site:* www. appliednn.com, pg 687

Ramsess, Akili, The Best of Photojournalism (BOP), 120 Hooper St, Athens, GA 30602-3018 *Tel:* 706-542-2506 *E-mail:* info@nppa.org *Web Site:* nppa.org, pg 983

Ramsess, Akili, National Press Photographers Association (NPPA), 120 Hooper St, Athens, GA 30602-3018 *Tel:* 706-542-2506 *E-mail:* info@nppa. org; director@nppa.org *Web Site:* nppa.org, pg 959

Ramsey, Chris, VSG Digital Media Solutions, 11126 Lindbergh Business Ct, St Louis, MO 63123 *Tel:* 314-487-8045 *Toll Free Tel:* 800-737-8045 *Fax:* 314-487-9387 *E-mail:* info@vsginc.net *Web Site:* www.vsginc. net, pg 933

Ranaldi, Robert, Far West Media Services Inc, 904 Silver Spur Rd, No 804, Rolling Hills Estates, CA 90274 *Tel:* 562-496-3342 *Fax:* 562-496-4329 *Web Site:* www.farwestmedia.com, pg 759

Ranard, Alyssa, Vision Maker Media, 1800 N 33 St, Lincoln, NE 68503-1409 *Tel:* 402-472-3522 *Fax:* 402-472-8675 *E-mail:* visionmaker@unl.edu *Web Site:* www.visionmakermedia.org, pg 930

Randall, Garry, Disney Consumer Products & Interactive Media (DCPI), 1201 Flower St, Glendale, AZ 91201 *Tel:* 818-544-0000 *Web Site:* dcpi.disney.com, pg 743

Randall, Gene B Jr, Versatech Industries Inc, 14750 S Grant St, Bixby, OK 74008 *Tel:* 918-366-7400, pg 926

Randall, Paul, Gaylord Archival, PO Box 4901, Syracuse, NY 13221-4901 *Tel:* 315-634-8125 (intl) *Toll Free Tel:* 800-448-6160 (cust serv) *Fax:* 315-453-5030 (intl) *Toll Free Fax:* 800-272-3412 *E-mail:* customerservice@gaylord.com *Web Site:* www.gaylord.com; www.facebook.com/ gaylordarchival, pg 768

Randall, Stewart B, Communications Design Associates, 437 Turnpike St, Canton, MA 02021 *Tel:* 339-502-6551 *Web Site:* www.cdaconsultants.com, pg 729

Randel, Carol, Jalbert Productions International, 230 New York Ave, Huntington, NY 11743 *Tel:* 631-351-5878 *Fax:* 631-351-5875 *E-mail:* jalbert@jalbertfilm. com *Web Site:* jalbertfilm.com, pg 792

Ranganathan, Madhu, OpenText Corp, 275 Frank Tompa Dr, Waterloo, ON N2L 0A1, Canada *Tel:* 519-888-7111 *Toll Free Tel:* 800-499-6544 *Fax:* 519-888-0677 *Web Site:* www.opentext.com, pg 847

Rangel, Ashley, Arizona Studios, 4614 E McDowell Rd, Phoenix, AZ 85008 *Tel:* 602-275-9100 *E-mail:* info@ arizonastudios.com *Web Site:* arizonastudios.com, pg 689

Ranjel, Susan, San Antonio Film Festival, 8452 Fredericksburg Rd, PMB 264, San Antonio, TX 78229 *Tel:* 210-885-5888 *E-mail:* safilm@gmail.com; hello@ safilm.com *Web Site:* www.safilm.com, pg 1002

Rankin, Darren, CMD Agency, 1631 NW Thurman St, Portland, OR 97209 *Tel:* 503-223-6794 *E-mail:* info@ cmdagency.com *Web Site:* www.cmdagency.com, pg 726

Rankin, John, Castillo Theatre, 543 W 42 St, New York, NY 10036 *Tel:* 212-941-5800 *Toll Free Tel:* 800-435-7453 *Web Site:* www.castillo.org, pg 717

Rankin, Scott, Voyetra Turtle Beach, 100 Summit Lake Dr, Suite 100, Valhalla, NY 10595 *Tel:* 914-345-2255 *Fax:* 914-345-2266 *E-mail:* sales@turtlebeach.com *Web Site:* www.turtlebeach.com, pg 933

Ranney, Chuck, Liberty Uplink, 2547 Yellow Springs Rd, Malvern, PA 19355 *Tel:* 215-964-5222; 917-254-0155 *E-mail:* info@libertyuplink.com *Web Site:* www. libertyuplink.com, pg 807

Ranson, Ron, Theatre Arts Video Library, 174 Andrew Ave, Leucadia, CA 92024 *Tel:* 760-547-6039 *Fax:* 760-632-6859 *E-mail:* admin@theatreartsvideo. com *Web Site:* www.theatreartsvideo.com, pg 911

Ranta, Richard, High Water Records, University of Memphis, Rudi E Scheidt School of Music, 121 Music Bldg, Memphis, TN 38152 *Tel:* 901-678-3317 *Fax:* 901-678-3096, pg 779

Rapelye, Liz, Blonder Tongue Laboratories Inc, One Jake Brown Rd, Old Bridge, NJ 08857 *Tel:* 732-679-4000 *Toll Free Tel:* 800-523-6049 *Fax:* 732-679-4353 *E-mail:* custsvc@blondertongue.com; btglobalsales@ blondertongue.com (outside US & CN); information@ blondertongue.com *Web Site:* www.blondertongue.com, pg 707

Rapkin, David, David Rapkin Audio Production, 473 West End Ave, Unit 6A, New York, NY 10024 *Tel:* 212-362-7236 *E-mail:* drapco@aol.com, pg 870

Rapp, Karen, National Instruments Corp, 11500 N Mopac Expwy, Austin, TX 78759-3504 *Tel:* 512-683-0100 *Toll Free Tel:* 888-280-7645 (sales); 877-388-1952 *Fax:* 512-683-8411; 512-683-5794 (sales) *Web Site:* www.ni.com, pg 836

Rappaport, Jennifer, Falcon Safety Products Inc, 25 Imclone Dr, Branchburg, NJ 08876 *Tel:* 908-707-4900 *Toll Free Tel:* 800-332-5266 (ext 220, cust serv) *Fax:* 908-707-8855 *Web Site:* www.falconsafety.com; www.shopfalcon.com, pg 758

Rappolt, Tom, AMP Services Inc, 3111 Fortune Way, Suite B-18, West Palm Beach, FL 33414 *Tel:* 561-333-0335 *Fax:* 561-333-0370 *Web Site:* www. audiomagnetics.com, pg 684

Rashid, Bea, Woodside Avenue Music Productions Inc, 2906 Central St, No 117, Evanston, IL 60201 *Tel:* 847-864-6655 *E-mail:* music@woodsideavenue. com *Web Site:* www.woodsideavenue.com, pg 941

Rashid, Steve, Woodside Avenue Music Productions Inc, 2906 Central St, No 117, Evanston, IL 60201 *Tel:* 847-864-6655 *E-mail:* music@woodsideavenue. com *Web Site:* www.woodsideavenue.com, pg 941

Rasmussen, Josh, Midland Video Productions Inc, 3315 N 124 St, Brookfield, WI 53005 *Tel:* 414-276-8300 *E-mail:* request@midlandvideo.com *Web Site:* midlandvideo.com, pg 827

Rasmussen, Ken, One Stop CD Shop LLC, 3149 S State St, Salt Lake City, UT 84115 *Tel:* 801-303-6100 *Fax:* 801-303-6129 *E-mail:* info@1stopcdshop.com *Web Site:* 1stopcdshop.com, pg 846

Ratcliffe, Kim, GatesAir, 5300 Kings Island Dr, Suite 101, Mason, OH 45040 *Tel:* 513-459-3400 *Toll Free Tel:* 800-622-0022 *Fax:* 513-459-3796 *E-mail:* information@gatesair.com; orders@gatesair. com; support@gatesair.com *Web Site:* www.gatesair. com, pg 768

Ratnam, Rekha, Print Industries Market Information and Research Organization (PRIMIR), 1899 Preston White Dr, Reston, VA 20191 *Tel:* 703-264-7200 *Fax:* 703-620-0994 *Web Site:* www.primir.org, pg 960

Rattan, Dhiraj, Edgenuity Inc, 8860 E Chaparral Rd, Scottsdale, AZ 85250 *Toll Free Tel:* 877-725-4257 (sales) *E-mail:* customersupport@edgenuity.com; solutions@edgenuity.com (sales) *Web Site:* www. edgenuity.com, pg 750

Raughter, John, American Legion Fourth Estate Award, Media & Communs Div, 700 N Pennsylvania St, Indianapolis, IN 46204 *Tel:* 317-630-1253 *Fax:* 317-630-1368 *E-mail:* pr@legion.org *Web Site:* www. legion.org, pg 981

Raulet, John, Mailing Avenue Stageworks, 1144 Mailing Ave, Atlanta, GA 30315 *Tel:* 404-601-9500 (ext 11) *Web Site:* www.mailingavenuestageworks.com, pg 815

Raulet, Paul, Mailing Avenue Stageworks, 1144 Mailing Ave, Atlanta, GA 30315 *Tel:* 404-601-9500 (ext 11) *Web Site:* www.mailingavenuestageworks.com, pg 815

Rausch, Brian, House of Moves, 5419 McConnell Ave, Los Angeles, CA 90066-7027 *Tel:* 310-306-6131 *E-mail:* info@moves.com *Web Site:* www.moves.com, pg 782

Rause, Tom, Strategic Connections, 3000 Spring Forest Rd, Raleigh, NC 27616 *Tel:* 919-878-0550 *Toll Free Tel:* 800-255-5664 *Fax:* 919-875-8712 *Web Site:* www. strategicconnections.net, pg 901

Raventos, Bill, Ivie Technologies Inc, 1195 Spring Creek Place, Suite B, Springville, UT 84663 *Tel:* 801-489-8703 *Toll Free Fax:* 877-829-6567 *E-mail:* ivie@ivie. com *Web Site:* www.ivie.com, pg 792

Ravetto, Dan, Applied Voice & Speech Technologies Inc (AVST), 27042 Towne Centre Dr, Suite 200, Foothill Ranch, CA 92610-2810 *Tel:* 949-699-2300 *Toll Free Tel:* 866-368-0400 *Fax:* 949-699-2301 *E-mail:* info@ avst.com; sales@avst.com *Web Site:* www.avst.com, pg 688

Ravn, Jorgen, Signal Transport, PO Box 1028, Lake Forest, CA 92609-1028 *Tel:* 714-641-5665 *Fax:* 714-641-5664 *E-mail:* sales@sigt.com *Web Site:* sigt.com, pg 888

Rawe, Kinsey, Edgenuity Inc, 8860 E Chaparral Rd, Scottsdale, AZ 85250 *Toll Free Tel:* 877-725-4257 (sales) *E-mail:* customersupport@edgenuity.com; solutions@edgenuity.com (sales) *Web Site:* www. edgenuity.com, pg 750

Ray, Charlie, Digital Services Recording Studios, 1601 S Cherry St, Tomball, TX 77375 *Tel:* 832-463-5781 *E-mail:* studio@dsrecordings.com *Web Site:* www. dsrecordings.com, pg 742

Ray, Michelle, PipelineFX LLC, 500 Ala Moana Blvd, Tower 7, Suite 400, Honolulu, HI 96813 *Tel:* 808-685-7823 *Toll Free Tel:* 855-685-7823 *Fax:* 808-685-7800 *E-mail:* sales@pipelinefx.com *Web Site:* www. pipelinefx.com, pg 857

Raymond, Leslie, Ann Arbor Film Festival, 230 Collingwood Dr, Suite 160B, Ann Arbor, MI 48103 *Tel:* 734-995-5356 *Fax:* 734-995-5396 *E-mail:* info@ aafilmfest.org *Web Site:* www.aafilmfest.org, pg 981

Raymond, Mindy, Texas Motion Picture Alliance (TXMPA), 815-A Brazos St, Austin, TX 78701 *Tel:* 512-489-6723 *E-mail:* admin@txmpa.org; communications@txmpa.org *Web Site:* www.txmpa. org, pg 963

Rayow, Deborah, Edgenuity Inc, 8860 E Chaparral Rd, Scottsdale, AZ 85250 *Toll Free Tel:* 877-725-4257 (sales) *E-mail:* customersupport@edgenuity.com; solutions@edgenuity.com (sales) *Web Site:* www. edgenuity.com, pg 750

Razdan, Rikki, ISCAN Inc, 21 Cabot Rd, Woburn, MA 01801 *Tel:* 781-932-1199 *Fax:* 781-932-1155 *E-mail:* info@iscaninc.com *Web Site:* www.iscaninc. com, pg 791

Re, Dr Mark, Seagate Technology LLC, 10200 S De Anza Blvd, Cupertino, CA 95014 *Toll Free Tel:* 800-SEAGATE (732-4283) *Web Site:* www.seagate.com, pg 883

Read, Jennifer, Thompson Rivers University Marketing & Communications Dept, 805 TRU Way, Kamloops, BC V2C 0C8, Canada *Tel:* 250-852-7000 *Web Site:* www.tru.ca/marcom, pg 913

Read, Steve, Evolution AV, 129, 2312-52 Ave SE, Calgary, AB T2C 0A3, Canada *Tel:* 403-259-3793 *Toll Free Tel:* 800-561-9820 *Fax:* 403-259-2374 *Toll Free Fax:* 800-561-9820 *Web Site:* www.evolutionav.ca, pg 757

Reagan, Dr David R, Lamb & Lion Ministries, PO Box 919, McKinney, TX 75070 *Tel:* 972-736-3567 *E-mail:* lamblion@lamblion.com *Web Site:* christinprophecy.org, pg 803

Reagan, Patrick, VSG Digital Media Solutions, 11126 Lindbergh Business Ct, St Louis, MO 63123 *Tel:* 314-487-8045 *Toll Free Tel:* 800-737-8045 *Fax:* 314-487-9387 *E-mail:* info@vsginc.net *Web Site:* www.vsginc. net, pg 933

Reaman, Darren, CEDIA IPRO Affinity Group, 8475 Nightfall Lane, Fishers, IN 46037 *Tel:* 317-328-4336 *Toll Free Tel:* 800-669-5329 *E-mail:* info@cedia.org *Web Site:* cedia.net, pg 952

Reizner, Dick, Dick Reizner Film & Video, 801 Atherton Dr, Suite 120, Manteca, CA 95337 *Tel:* 209-665-7166 *Web Site:* www.reizner.com, pg 873

Rejto, Laurent, Maverick Awards, 13 Rock City Rd, Woodstock, NY 12498 *Tel:* 845-679-4265; 845-810-0131 *Fax:* 509-479-5414 *E-mail:* info@woodstockfilmfestival.com *Web Site:* www.woodstockfilmfestival.com, pg 995

Remes, Mark, BES Studios, 5711 Old Osbourne Tpke, Henrico, VA 23231 *Tel:* 804-276-0806 *Toll Free Tel:* 800-995-2371 *E-mail:* info@besstudios.com *Web Site:* www.besstudios.com, pg 704

Remis, Joel, Ironstone Technologies Inc, 534 Berry St, Winnipeg, MB R3H 0R9, Canada *Tel:* 204-697-0159 *Toll Free Tel:* 800-665-4766 *Fax:* 204-694-9355 *E-mail:* info@ironstone.ca *Web Site:* www.ironstone.ca, pg 791

Remmers, Chad, RAM® Mounts, 8410 Dallas Ave S, Seattle, WA 98108 *Tel:* 206-763-8361 *Toll Free Tel:* 800-497-7479 *Fax:* 206-763-9615 *E-mail:* sales@rammount.com *Web Site:* www.rammount.com, pg 869

Remote, Steven, Aura Sonic Ltd (ASL), PO Box 520791, Flushing, NY 11352-0791 *Tel:* 718-886-6500 *E-mail:* somebody@aurasonic.com *Web Site:* www.aurasonicltd.com, pg 695

Rencher, Brad, Adobe Systems Inc, 345 Park Ave, San Jose, CA 95110-2704 *Tel:* 408-536-6000 *Fax:* 408-537-6000 *Web Site:* www.adobe.com, pg 676

Rencher, Kristen, National Association for Music Education (NAfME), 1806 Robert Fulton Dr, Reston, VA 20191 *Tel:* 703-860-4000 *Toll Free Tel:* 800-336-3768 *Fax:* 703-860-1531 *Toll Free Fax:* 888-275-6362 *E-mail:* memberservices@nafme.org *Web Site:* nafme.org, pg 958

Rene, Michele, Bill Bachmann Studios, PO Box 950833, Lake Mary, FL 32795 *Tel:* 407-333-9988 *Web Site:* www.billbachmann.com, pg 705

Renn, James, Xenon Pictures Inc, 3521 Jack Northrop Ave, Hawthorne, CA 90250 *Tel:* 310-451-5510 *Fax:* 310-395-4058 *E-mail:* info@xenonpictures.com *Web Site:* xenonpictures.com, pg 943

Renner, Karen K, CommScope Inc, 1100 CommScope Place SE, Hickory, NC 28602 *Tel:* 828-324-2200 *Toll Free Tel:* 800-982-1708 *E-mail:* publicrelations@commscope.com *Web Site:* www.commscope.com, pg 728

Renshaw, Tracey, Interstate Connecting Components, 120 Mount Holly Bypass, Lumberton, NJ 08048-1112 *Tel:* 856-722-5535 *Toll Free Tel:* 888-881-5420 *Fax:* 856-813-5419 *E-mail:* info@connecticc.com *Web Site:* www.connecticc.com, pg 791

Renteria, Juan, Universal Satellite Communications Inc, 1530 Nandina Ave, Perris, CA 92571 *Tel:* 562-483-4800; 951-943-4420 (corp off) *Toll Free Tel:* 888-867-6620 *Fax:* 954-943-0263 *Web Site:* www.unisatmobile.com, pg 922

Renucci, Alice, Festival du Nouveau Cinema de Montreal, 3805 Blvd Saint-Laurent, Montreal, QC H2W 1X9, Canada *Tel:* 514-282-0004 *Fax:* 514-282-6664 *E-mail:* info@nouveaucinema.ca; soumissions@nouveaucinema.ca *Web Site:* www.nouveaucinema.ca, pg 989

Repine, Andrea, Walltalkers, 3875 Embassy Pkwy, Fairlawn, OH 44333 *Tel:* 330-668-7600 *Fax:* 330-668-7703 *E-mail:* customerservice@koroseal.com *Web Site:* www.walltalkers.com, pg 933

Repola, Catherine A, Motion Picture Editors Guild Local 700, 7715 Sunset Blvd, Suite 200, Hollywood, CA 90046 *Tel:* 323-876-4770 *Toll Free Tel:* 800-705-8700 *Fax:* 323-876-0861 *E-mail:* mail@editorsguild.com *Web Site:* www.editorsguild.com, pg 958

Repp, Dawn, Freeman, 1600 Viceroy, Suite 100, Dallas, TX 75235 *Tel:* 214-445-1000 *Web Site:* www.freeman.com, pg 765

Reppert, Tim, AirCraft Production Libraries, 162 Columbus Ave, Boston, MA 02116-5222 *Tel:* 617-303-7600 *Toll Free Tel:* 800-343-2514 *Fax:* 617-303-7555 *E-mail:* info@aircraftmusiclibrary.com; acsales@aircraftmusiclibrary.com *Web Site:* www.aircraftmusiclibrary.com, pg 679

Restivo-Alessi, Chantal, HarperAudio, 10 E 53 St, New York, NY 10022 *Tel:* 212-207-7000 *Toll Free Tel:* 800-242-7737 *Fax:* 212-207-2582 *Toll Free Fax:* 800-822-4090 *Web Site:* www.harpercollins.com, pg 776

Resto, Lourdes, Chicago Latino Film Festival, 55 W Van Buren St, Suite 310, Chicago, IL 60605 *Tel:* 312-431-1330 *E-mail:* info@latinoculturalcenter.org *Web Site:* www.chicagolatinofilmfestival.org, pg 985

Revelli, Clare, Revelli, PO Box 150098, San Rafael, CA 94915 *Tel:* 415-460-9898 *Fax:* 415-460-9897 *E-mail:* colorstyledesign@aol.com, pg 874

Revelli, Vanessa, Prakken Publications Inc, 251 Jackson Plaza, Suite A, Ann Arbor, MI 48103-1955 *Tel:* 734-975-2800 *Toll Free Tel:* 800-530-9673 *Fax:* 734-975-2787 *E-mail:* matt@techdirections.com *Web Site:* www.techdirections.com, pg 861

Revfi, Frank, Audio Visual Dynamics®, 424 Sand Shore Rd, Hackettstown, NJ 07840 *Tel:* 973-993-8500 *Fax:* 973-984-0644 *Web Site:* www.avdusa.com, pg 694

Reynolds, G Brian, Perennial Pictures Film Corp, 2102 E 52 St, Indianapolis, IN 46205 *Tel:* 317-253-1519 *E-mail:* mail@perennialpictures.com *Web Site:* www.perennialpictures.com, pg 854

Reynolds, John, Kavich Reynolds Productions Inc, 3151 Cahuenga Blvd, Suite 101, Los Angeles, CA 90068 *Tel:* 323-851-2490 *E-mail:* info@kavichreynolds.com *Web Site:* www.kavichreynolds.com, pg 797

Reynolds, Steve, Imagine Communications Corp, 3001 Dallas Pkwy, Suite 300, Frisco, TX 75034 *Tel:* 469-803-4900 *Toll Free Tel:* 866-4-IMAGINE (446-2446) *Fax:* 469-803-4899 *E-mail:* insidesales@imaginecommunications.com *Web Site:* www.imaginecommunications.com, pg 786

Reynolds, Walter, Michigan Office Solutions (MOS), A Xerox Company, 2859 Walkent Dr NW, Grand Rapids, MI 49544 *Toll Free Tel:* 800-442-9070 *E-mail:* info@mos-xerox.com *Web Site:* www.mos-xerox.com, pg 825

Reynolds, Will, Tennessee Prompters, 727 Wildview Dr, Nashville, TN 37211-1142 *Tel:* 615-834-9655 *E-mail:* info@tennesseeprompters.com *Web Site:* www.tennesseeprompters.com, pg 911

Reznick, Evi, Gingerbread Group Holdings LLC, 1337 Kittredge Ct, Atlanta, GA 30329 *Tel:* 404-634-8678; 404-663-9050 *E-mail:* books2gogh@gmail.com, pg 771

Rhea, Wes, Stockton & San Joaquin Film Commission, 125 Bridge Place, 2nd fl, Stockton, CA 95202 *Tel:* 209-938-1555 *Toll Free Tel:* 877-778-6258 *E-mail:* visitorinfo@visitstockton.org *Web Site:* www.visitstockton.org/about-us/film-commission, pg 968

Rhine, Rebecca, International Cinematographers Guild (ICG), 7755 Sunset Blvd, Hollywood, CA 90046 *Tel:* 323-876-0160 *Fax:* 323-876-6383 (exec off) *Web Site:* www.icg600.com, pg 956

Rhoads, Kevin, Kontron America, 14118 Stowe Dr, Poway, CA 92064-7147 *Tel:* 858-677-0877 *Toll Free Tel:* 888-294-4558; 800-480-0044 (cust serv & tech support) *Fax:* 858-677-0898 *E-mail:* sales@us.kontron.com *Web Site:* www.kontron.com, pg 801

Rhodes, Martin, DV Awards, 6300 N Sagewood Dr, Suite H-383, Park City, UT 84098 *E-mail:* info@dvawards.com *Web Site:* www.dvawards.com, pg 988

Ribeiro, Tom, Real Cool Productions, 800 S Main St, Suite 203, Mansfield, MA 02048 *Tel:* 508-337-8520 *E-mail:* info@rcplearning.com *Web Site:* realcoolproductions.com, pg 871

Ricca, Aimee, The Citation of Outstanding Service to the Society Award, White Plains Plaza, 445 Hamilton Ave, Suite 601, White Plains, NY 10601-1827 *Tel:* 914-761-1100 *Fax:* 914-206-4216 *E-mail:* marketing@smpte.org *Web Site:* www.smpte.org, pg 986

Ricca, Aimee, The Presidential Proclamation, White Plains Plaza, 445 Hamilton Ave, Suite 601, White Plains, NY 10601-1827 *Tel:* 914-761-1100 *Fax:* 914-206-4216 *E-mail:* marketing@smpte.org *Web Site:* www.smpte.org, pg 1000

Ricca, Aimee, SMPTE® Journal Award & SMPTE® Journal Certificate of Merit, White Plains Plaza, 445 Hamilton Ave, Suite 601, White Plains, NY 10601-1827 *Tel:* 914-761-1100 *Fax:* 914-206-4216 *E-mail:* marketing@smpte.org *Web Site:* www.smpte.org, pg 1004

Ricca, Aimee, SMPTE® Progress Medal Award, White Plains Plaza, 445 Hamilton Ave, Suite 601, White Plains, NY 10601-1827 *Tel:* 914-761-1100 *Fax:* 914-206-4216 *E-mail:* marketing@smpte.org *Web Site:* www.smpte.org, pg 1004

Ricca, Aimee, Society of Motion Picture & Television Engineers® (SMPTE®), White Plains Plaza, 445 Hamilton Ave, Suite 601, White Plains, NY 10601-1827 *Tel:* 914-761-1100 *Fax:* 914-206-4216 *E-mail:* marketing@smpte.org *Web Site:* www.smpte.org, pg 892

Ricca, Aimee, Technicolor-Herbert T Kalmus Medal Award, White Plains Plaza, 445 Hamilton Ave, Suite 601, White Plains, NY 10601-1827 *Tel:* 914-761-1100 *Fax:* 914-206-4216 *E-mail:* marketing@smpte.org *Web Site:* www.smpte.org, pg 1004

Ricca, Aimee, The Samuel L Warner Memorial Medal Award, White Plains Plaza, 445 Hamilton Ave, Suite 601, White Plains, NY 10601-1827 *Tel:* 914-761-1100 *Fax:* 914-206-4216 *E-mail:* marketing@smpte.org *Web Site:* www.smpte.org, pg 1006

Ricci, Julia, Heartland International Film Festival, 1043 Virginia Ave, Suite 2, Indianapolis, IN 46203 *Tel:* 317-464-9405 *E-mail:* submissions@heartlandfilm.org *Web Site:* heartlandfilm.org/festival, pg 992

Ricci, Julia, Indy Shorts International Film Fest, 1043 Virginia Ave, Suite 2, Indianapolis, IN 46203 *Tel:* 317-464-9405 *E-mail:* submissions@heartlandfilm.org *Web Site:* heartlandfilm.org, pg 993

Ricciardi, Charles, New Jersey Motion Picture & Television Commission, 153 Halsey St, 5th fl, Newark, NJ 07102-2807 *Tel:* 973-648-6279 *Fax:* 973-648-7350 *E-mail:* njfilm@sos.nj.gov *Web Site:* www.film.nj.gov, pg 973

Rice, Bill, Videografix LLC, 2530 Berryessa Rd, Suite 314, San Jose, CA 95132-2903 *Tel:* 408-499-1280 *E-mail:* info@videografix.com *Web Site:* www.videografix.com, pg 929

Rice, Doug, DR&A Inc, 45 Willow St, Nashville, TN 37210 *Tel:* 615-256-6200 *Fax:* 615-256-6236 *Web Site:* www.griptruck.com, pg 746

Rice, Jennifer, ACCO Brands Corp, 4 Corporate Dr, Lake Zurick, IL 60047-8997 *Toll Free Tel:* 800-541-0094; 800-222-6462 *Toll Free Fax:* 800-941-4463 *E-mail:* contactus@acco.com (cust serv) *Web Site:* www.accobrands.com, pg 673

Rich, Doug, Love Shack Recording Studios, 909 18 Ave S, Nashville, TN 37212 *Tel:* 615-843-0019 *E-mail:* book@loveshackstudios.com *Web Site:* loveshackstudios.com, pg 812

Rich, Todd, KFOR-TV, 444 E Britton Rd, Oklahoma City, OK 73114 *Tel:* 405-424-4444 *Fax:* 405-478-6228 *Web Site:* www.kfor.com, pg 798

Richard, Dr James T, Newtown Psychological Center, 660 Newtown Yardley Rd, Suite 102, Newtown, PA 18940 *Tel:* 215-968-5378, pg 840

Richard, Julie, Maine Artist Fellowship Program, 193 State St, 25 State House Sta, Augusta, ME 04330-0025 *Tel:* 207-287-2724 *Fax:* 207-287-2725 *E-mail:* mainearts.info@maine.gov *Web Site:* mainearts.maine.gov/Pages/Funding/Individual-Artist-Fellowships, pg 995

Richards, Jason, DBM Communications Inc, 606 Baltimore Ave, Suite 200, Towson, MD 21204 *Tel:* 410-825-7400 *Fax:* 443-929-0213 *Web Site:* www.dbmcommunications.com, pg 739

Richards, Kim, Allied Artists International Inc, Production Services Ctr, 15810 E Gale Ave, Suite 133, Hacienda Heights, CA 91745 *Tel:* 626-330-0600 *Fax:* 626-961-0411, pg 681

Richards, Laurie, Nebraska Film Office, PO Box 98907, Lincoln, NE 68509-8907 *Tel:* 402-471-3746 *Toll Free Tel:* 800-426-6505 *Web Site:* film.nebraska.gov; opportunity.nebraska.gov/ded-partners, pg 973

Richards, Tim, KOOL-FM Radio, 840 N Central Ave, Phoenix, AZ 85004 *Tel:* 602-452-1000; 602-260-9494 (studio) *Fax:* 602-440-6530 *Web Site:* kool.radio.com, pg 801

Richards, Whitney, Harpers Ferry Historical Association, c/o National Park Bookshop, 723 Shenandoah St, Harpers Ferry, WV 25425 *Tel:* 304-535-6881 *Fax:* 304-535-6749 *E-mail:* info@hfpawv.org *Web Site:* www.harpersferryhistory.org, pg 776

Richardson, Andrew T, Shure Manufacturing Corp, 1901 W Main St, Washington, MO 63090 *Tel:* 636-390-7100 *Toll Free Tel:* 800-227-4873 *Fax:* 636-390-7171 *E-mail:* sales@shureusa.com *Web Site:* www.shureusa.com, pg 887

Richardson, David T, The Learning House Inc, 427 S Fourth St, Suite 300, Louisville, KY 40202 *Tel:* 502-589-9878 *Fax:* 502-589-9825 *E-mail:* sales@learninghouse.com; info@learninghouse.com *Web Site:* www.learninghouse.com, pg 805

Richardson, Hal, Paramount Pictures Corporation, 5555 Melrose Ave, Los Angeles, CA 90038 *Tel:* 323-956-8398 *Web Site:* www.paramount.com, pg 851

Richardson, Lynda, Lynda Richardson Photography, 7239 Lookout Dr, Richmond, VA 23225 *Tel:* 804-347-9668 *E-mail:* lynda@lyndarichardson.com *Web Site:* lyndarichardson.com, pg 875

Richert, Will, Michigan Office Solutions (MOS), A Xerox Company, 2859 Walkent Dr NW, Grand Rapids, MI 49544 *Toll Free Tel:* 800-442-9070 *E-mail:* info@mos-xerox.com *Web Site:* www.mos-xerox.com, pg 825

Richi, Mike, L-3 WESCAM, 649 N Service Rd W, Burlington, ON L7P 5B9, Canada *Tel:* 905-633-4000; 905-633-4175 (cust serv) *Toll Free Tel:* 888-593-7226 *Fax:* 905-633-4100 *E-mail:* sales.wescam@l-3com.com *Web Site:* www.wescam.com, pg 803

Richie, Chip, Rich-Heape Films Inc, 5952 Royal Lane, Suite 254, Dallas, TX 75230 *Tel:* 214-696-6916 *Toll Free Tel:* 888-600-2922 *Web Site:* www.richheape.com, pg 875

Richie, Chip, Richie Media Productions LLC, 2035 Royal Lane, Suite 203, Dallas, TX 75229 *Tel:* 214-696-9040 *Web Site:* www.richiemedia.com, pg 875

Richman, Carol, Monad Trainer's Aide Inc, 163-60 22 Ave, Whitestone, NY 11357 *Tel:* 718-352-2314 *Toll Free Tel:* 800-344-6088 *Fax:* 718-352-8276 *Web Site:* www.monadtrainersaide.com, pg 829

Richman, Eugene, Monad Trainer's Aide Inc, 163-60 22 Ave, Whitestone, NY 11357 *Tel:* 718-352-2314 *Toll Free Tel:* 800-344-6088 *Fax:* 718-352-8276 *Web Site:* www.monadtrainersaide.com, pg 829

Richman, Howard, Sound Feelings Records, 18375 Ventura Blvd, No 8000, Tarzana, CA 91356 *Tel:* 818-757-0600 *Web Site:* www.soundfeelings.com, pg 894

Richmond, Charlie, Richmond Sound Design Ltd, 5264 Ross St, Vancouver, BC V5W 3K7, Canada *Web Site:* www.richmondsounddesign.com, pg 875

Richter, Jeremy, Richter Studios, 1143 W Rundell Place, Chicago, IL 60607 *Tel:* 312-861-9999 *Fax:* 312-997-2387 *E-mail:* info@richterstudios.com *Web Site:* www.richterstudios.com, pg 875

Richter, Kathy, Michigan Office Solutions (MOS), A Xerox Company, 2859 Walkent Dr NW, Grand Rapids, MI 49544 *Toll Free Tel:* 800-442-9070 *E-mail:* info@mos-xerox.com *Web Site:* www.mos-xerox.com, pg 825

Richter, Robert, Richter Productions Inc, 521 E 14 St, Suite 4F, New York, NY 10009 *Tel:* 917-608-7427 *E-mail:* rrprod@aol.com; richter330@aol.com *Web Site:* www.richtervideos.com, pg 875

Richthammer, Bob, PentaVision Communications Inc, 712 N Niles Ave, South Bend, IN 46617 *Tel:* 574-272-8365 *E-mail:* hello@pentavision.net *Web Site:* pentavision.net, pg 854

Ridabock, W, Silent Source, 58 Nonotuck St, Northampton, MA 01062 *Tel:* 413-584-7944 *Toll Free Tel:* 800-583-7174 (orders) *Fax:* 413-584-2377 *E-mail:* info@silentsource.com *Web Site:* www.silentsource.com, pg 888

Rider, Jon, SeaChange International Inc, 50 Nagog Park, Acton, MA 01720 *Tel:* 978-897-0100 *Fax:* 978-897-0132 *E-mail:* globalsalesoperations@schange.com *Web Site:* www.schange.com, pg 883

Ridley, Jane, Oregon Film & Video Office, 123 NE Third Ave, Suite 210, Portland, OR 97232 *Tel:* 971-254-4020 *E-mail:* shoot@oregonfilm.org *Web Site:* www.oregonfilm.org, pg 975

Riegel, Chris, Scala Inc, 7 Great Valley Pkwy, Suite 300, Malvern, PA 19355 *Tel:* 610-363-3350 *Toll Free Tel:* 888-SCALA-96 (722-5296) *Fax:* 610-363-4010 *E-mail:* team@scala.com *Web Site:* scala.com, pg 881

Riera, Alejandro, Chicago Film Critics Association, 155 E Algonquin Rd, Arlington Heights, IL 60006 *Tel:* 847-427-4530 *Fax:* 847-427-1301 *Web Site:* www.chicagofilmcritics.org, pg 953

Riggs, Robert, Story Teller Effects Group LLC, 333 River Rd, Jefferson, LA 70121 *Tel:* 504-832-9800 *Fax:* 504-832-9955 *E-mail:* storytellerfx@gmail.com; sales@storytellerfx.com *Web Site:* www.riggspfx.com, pg 901

Riley, David, NeoSoft Corp, PO Box 5667, Bend, OR 97708-5667 *Tel:* 541-389-5489 *Fax:* 541-388-8221 *E-mail:* sales@neosoftware.com *Web Site:* www.neosoftware.com, pg 838

Riley, James L, Omni International Inc, 4928 Crosshill Lane, Northport, AL 35473, pg 845

Riley, Jocelyn, Her Own Words LLC, PO Box 5264, Madison, WI 53705-0264 *Tel:* 608-271-7083 *Fax:* 608-271-0209 *Web Site:* herownwords.com; nontraditionalcareers.com, pg 779

Riley, Kate, America's Public Television Stations (APTS), 2100 Crystal Dr, Suite 700, Arlington, VA 22202 *Tel:* 202-654-4200 *Fax:* 202-654-4236 *Web Site:* apts.org, pg 949

Riley, Melissa, The Livingston Awards for Young Journalists, Wallace House, 620 Oxford Rd, Ann Arbor, MI 48104 *Tel:* 734-998-7575 *Fax:* 734-998-7979 *E-mail:* livawards@umich.edu *Web Site:* wallacehouse.umich.edu/livingston-awards, pg 994

Riley, Rod, Word Label Group, 25 Music Sq W, Nashville, TN 37203 *Tel:* 615-251-0600 *E-mail:* wordtech@wbr.com *Web Site:* www.wordlabelgroup.com; www.wordentertainment.com, pg 941

Rinck, Gary M, John Wiley & Sons Inc, 111 River St, Hoboken, NJ 07030-5774 *Tel:* 201-748-6000 *Toll Free Tel:* 800-225-5945 (cust serv) *Fax:* 201-748-6088 *Web Site:* www.wiley.com, pg 938

Ringrose, James, Real Cool Productions, 800 S Main St, Suite 203, Mansfield, MA 02048 *Tel:* 508-337-8520 *E-mail:* info@rcplearning.com *Web Site:* www.realcoolproductions.com, pg 871

Rios, Haydee, Xenon Pictures Inc, 3521 Jack Northrop Ave, Hawthorne, CA 90250 *Tel:* 310-451-5510 *Fax:* 310-395-4058 *E-mail:* info@xenonpictures.com *Web Site:* xenonpictures.com, pg 943

Ripianzi, David, YMAA Publication Center Inc, 51 Mill St, Wolfeboro, NH 03894 *Tel:* 603-569-7988 *Toll Free Tel:* 800-669-8892 *Fax:* 603-569-1889 *E-mail:* info@ymaa.com *Web Site:* www.ymaa.com, pg 944

Riske, Lois, Leprecon®, 10087 Industrial Dr, Hamburg, MI 48139 *Tel:* 810-852-4300 *Toll Free Tel:* 888-422-3537 *Fax:* 810-231-1631 *E-mail:* sales@leprecon.com *Web Site:* www.leprecon.com, pg 806

Rissi, Steven, CEDIA IPRO Affinity Group, 8475 Nightfall Lane, Fishers, IN 46037 *Tel:* 317-328-4336 *Toll Free Tel:* 800-669-5329 *E-mail:* info@cedia.org *Web Site:* cedia.net, pg 952

Ritter, Vern, LYRASIS, 1438 W Peachtree NW, Suite 150, Atlanta, GA 30309 *Tel:* 404-892-0943 *Toll Free Tel:* 800-999-8558 *Fax:* 404-892-7879 *Web Site:* www.lyrasis.org, pg 813

Ritzcovan, Dana, News Corp, 1211 Avenue of the Americas, New York, NY 10036 *Tel:* 212-416-3400 *E-mail:* media@newscorp.com *Web Site:* newscorp.com, pg 840

Rivera, Amy, Premier Lighting & Production Co, 12023 Victory Blvd, North Hollywood, CA 91606 *Tel:* 818-762-0884 *Toll Free Tel:* 800-770-0884 *Fax:* 818-762-0896 *E-mail:* premier@premier-lighting.com; rentals@premier-lighting.com *Web Site:* www.premier-lighting.com, pg 861

Rivera, Jonas, Pixar Animation Studios, 1200 Park Ave, Emeryville, CA 94608 *Tel:* 510-922-3000 *Fax:* 510-922-3151 *Web Site:* www.pixar.com, pg 857

Rivera, Sarely, Audio Visual Concepts Inc, Rd 1, Km 29.3, Rio Canas, Caguas, PR 00725 *Tel:* 787-753-7700 *Fax:* 787-766-4578 *Web Site:* www.mig-avc.com, pg 694

Rivero, Jose, ATX Networks, 8-1602 Tricont Ave, Whitby, ON L1N 7C3, Canada *Tel:* 289-204-7800 *Toll Free Tel:* 866-968-7289 *E-mail:* info@atx.com *Web Site:* atx.com, pg 692

Rivkin, Charles H, Motion Picture Association of America (MPAA), 15301 Ventura Blvd, Bldg E, Sherman Oaks, CA 91403-5885 *Tel:* 818-995-6600 *Fax:* 818-285-4403 *E-mail:* contactus@mpaa.org *Web Site:* www.mpaa.org, pg 957

Rivkin, Stephen, American Cinema Editors Inc (ACE), Max Bros Bldg, Rm 108, 5555 Melrose Ave, Los Angeles, CA 90038 *Tel:* 323-956-2900 *E-mail:* admin@americancinemaeditors.com *Web Site:* americancinemaeditors.org, pg 948

Rizor, Joel, Screen Door Entertainment Inc, 5709 Fairview Place, Agoura Hills, CA 91301, pg 882

Roach, Dan, Dav Tronics Ltd, 1543 Venables St, Suite 200, Vancouver, BC V5L 2G8, Canada *Tel:* 604-255-2200 *Web Site:* www.broadcasttechnical.com, pg 738

Roach, Josh, Associated Production Music LLC, 6255 Sunset Blvd, Suite 900, Hollywood, CA 90028 *Tel:* 323-461-3211 *Fax:* 323-461-9102 *E-mail:* info@apmmusic.com; clientservices@apmmusic.com *Web Site:* www.apmmusic.com, pg 691

Roark, Adrienne, KPDX-TV Production Center, 14975 NW Greenbrier Pkwy, Beaverton, OR 97006-5731 *Tel:* 503-906-1249 *Fax:* 503-548-6920 *E-mail:* ezone@kpdx.com; fox12news@kptv.com *Web Site:* www.kptv.com; www.kpdx.com, pg 801

Robbins, Ashley, Lighting Industry Resource Council, 440 N Wells St, Suite 210, Chicago, IL 60654 *Tel:* 312-527-3677 *Fax:* 312-527-3680 *E-mail:* iald@iald.org *Web Site:* www.iald.org/council, pg 808

Robbins, Brian, Nickelodeon, 1515 Broadway, 38th fl, New York, NY 10036 *Tel:* 212-258-8000 (Viacom) *Web Site:* www.nick.com, pg 841

Robbins, Caroline, Trafalgar Square Books, 388 Howe Hill Rd, North Pomfret, VT 05053 *Tel:* 802-457-1911 *Toll Free Tel:* 800-423-4525 *Fax:* 802-457-1913 *E-mail:* contact@trafalgarbooks.com; cs@trafalgarbooks.com (cust serv) *Web Site:* www.horseandriderbooks.com; www.trafalgarbooks.com, pg 916

Robbins, Craig, Prositions Inc, 6200 Aurora Ave, Suite 400W, Urbandale, IA 50322 *Tel:* 515-864-7200 *Toll Free Tel:* 877-244-8848 *E-mail:* info@prositions.com *Web Site:* prositions.com, pg 866

Robbins, Dave, Endtime Ministries Inc, PO Box 940729, Plano, TX 75094-0729 *Tel:* 972-422-0857 *Toll Free Tel:* 833-563-6063; 800-363-8463 (cust serv) *E-mail:* endtime@endtime.com *Web Site:* www.endtime.com, pg 754

Robbins, Kim, BTX Technologies, 5 Skyline Dr, Hawthorne, NY 10532 *Tel:* 914-592-1800 *Toll Free Tel:* 800-666-0996 *Toll Free Fax:* 800-569-4244 *E-mail:* info@btx.com *Web Site:* www.btx.com, pg 712

Robbins, Nick, University of Maine Media Services, 19 Shibles Hall, Orono, ME 04469 *Tel:* 207-581-2500; 207-581-2516 *Web Site:* umaine.edu, pg 922

Robbins, Sally, Kinetronics Corp, 1459 Tallevast Rd, Sarasota, FL 34243 *Tel:* 941-951-2432 *Toll Free Tel:* 800-624-3204 (US & CN) *Fax:* 941-955-5992 *E-mail:* info@kinetronics.com; order@kinetronics.com *Web Site:* www.kinetronics.com, pg 799

Robbins, Shawn, Robbins Media Inc, 450 North End Ave, Suite 14E, New York, NY 10282 *Tel:* 212-661-7670 *E-mail:* info@robbinsmedia.com *Web Site:* www.robbinsmedia.com, pg 876

Robbins, Susannah Greason, San Francisco Film Commission, City Hall, Rm 473, One Dr Carlton B Goodlett Place, San Francisco, CA 94102 *Tel:* 415-554-6241 *Fax:* 415-554-6503 *E-mail:* film@sfgov.org *Web Site:* www.filmsf.org/film-commission; www.facebook.com/FilmSF, pg 967

Robbins-Pianka, Orson, National Board of Review (of Motion Pictures), 40 W 37 St, Suite 501, New York, NY 10018 *Tel:* 212-465-9166 *Fax:* 212-465-9168 *E-mail:* nbr@nbrmp.org *Web Site:* www.nationalboardofreview.org, pg 959

Roberson, Sean, Theatrical Services Inc, 128 S Washington St, Wichita, KS 67202 *Tel:* 316-263-4415 *Toll Free Tel:* 888-874-2649 *Fax:* 316-263-9927 *Web Site:* www.theatricalservices.com, pg 912

Roberts, Bob, ClassicStock.com/Robertstock.com, 4203 Locust St, Philadelphia, PA 19104 *Tel:* 215-386-6300 *Toll Free Tel:* 800-786-6300 *Toll Free Fax:* 800-786-1920 *E-mail:* info@robertstock.com; info@classicstock.com *Web Site:* www.robertstock.com; www.classicstock.com, pg 726

Roberts, Diane, West Eagle Films Inc, 800 Lower Ganges Rd, Salt Spring Island, BC V8K 2N5, Canada *Tel:* 250-538-1780 *Web Site:* www.westeaglefilms.com, pg 935

Roberts, Ja Quita Joy, Black Film Center/Archive, Indiana University, Wells Library, Rm 044, 1320 E Tenth St, Bloomington, IN 47405 *Tel:* 812-855-6041 *Fax:* 812-856-5832 *E-mail:* bfca@indiana.edu *Web Site:* www.indiana.edu/~bfca, pg 706

Roberts, Jim, Broadcast Electronics, 4100 N 24 St, Quincy, IL 62305 *Tel:* 217-224-9600 *Fax:* 217-224-9607 *E-mail:* bdcast@bdcast.com *Web Site:* www.bdcast.com, pg 710

Roberts, Joe, Panamax, 1800 S McDowell Blvd, 2nd fl, Petaluma, CA 94954 *Tel:* 707-283-5900 (intl) *Toll Free Tel:* 800-472-5555 (US & CN) *Fax:* 707-283-5901 *E-mail:* custrelations@panamax.com *Web Site:* www.panamax.com, pg 850

Roberts, John, Rebirth Inc, 81 Chandler St, Detroit, MI 48202 *Tel:* 313-875-0289 *E-mail:* wenhajazz@aol.com *Web Site:* www.rebirthjazz.org, pg 871

Roberts, Marty, White Diamond Productions LLC, 605 Hwy 62 65 N, No 359, Harrison, AR 72601, pg 937

Roberts, Sara, MAC Group, 75 Virginia Rd, North White Plains, NY 10603 *Tel:* 914-347-3300 *Fax:* 914-347-3309 *E-mail:* info@macgroupus.com *Web Site:* www.macgroupus.com, pg 813

Roberts, Steve, CompuWeather Inc, 2566 Rte 52, Hopewell Junction, NY 12533 *Tel:* 845-227-8500 *Toll Free Tel:* 800-825-4445 *Fax:* 845-227-8400 *Toll Free Fax:* 800-825-4441 *E-mail:* info@compuweather.com *Web Site:* www.compuweather.com, pg 730

Roberts-Negron, Emily, VIEW Inc (Video International Entertainment World Inc), 11 Reservoir Rd, Saugerties, NY 12477 *Tel:* 845-246-9955 *Toll Free Tel:* 800-843-9843 *Fax:* 845-246-9966 *E-mail:* viewvid@aol.com, pg 930

Robertson, Dan, Golf Digest Publications, One World Trade Center, 27th fl, New York, NY 10007-0090 *Tel:* 212-286-2860 *Toll Free Tel:* 800-962-5513 *Web Site:* www.golfdigest.com, pg 772

Robertson, Douglas, Fire Power Music LLC, 3400 S Mill Ave, No 29, Tempe, AZ 85282 *Tel:* 602-463-2988, pg 761

Robertson, Laurel, Comtek Communications Technology Inc, 357 W 2700 S, Salt Lake City, UT 84115 *Tel:* 801-466-3463 *Toll Free Tel:* 800-496-3463 *Fax:* 801-484-6906 *E-mail:* sales@comtek.com *Web Site:* www.comtek.com, pg 730

Robertson, Patti, CompuWeather Inc, 2566 Rte 52, Hopewell Junction, NY 12533 *Tel:* 845-227-8500 *Toll Free Tel:* 800-825-4445 *Fax:* 845-227-8400 *Toll Free Fax:* 800-825-4441 *E-mail:* info@compuweather.com *Web Site:* www.compuweather.com, pg 730

Robertson, Todd J, Hyperspective Studios Inc, 2800 Woodlawn Dr, Suite 253, Honolulu, HI 96822 *Tel:* 808-353-3618 *Toll Free Tel:* 800-353-3618 *E-mail:* info@hyperspective.com *Web Site:* hyperspective.com, pg 783

Robichaud, Heidi B, Earthworks Inc, 37 Wilton Rd, Suite 1, Milford, NH 03055 *Tel:* 603-654-1512 (sales); 603-654-2433 *Fax:* 603-654-6107 *E-mail:* info@earthworksaudio.com *Web Site:* www.earthworksaudio.com, pg 749

Robinson, Catherine, Ingram Content Group LLC, One Ingram Blvd, La Vergne, TN 37086-1986 *Tel:* 615-793-5000 *Toll Free Tel:* 800-937-8000 (retailers); 800-937-5300 (ext 1, libs) *E-mail:* customerservice@ingramcontent.com *Web Site:* www.ingramcontent.com, pg 787

Robinson, Chris, Ottawa International Animation Festival, 2 Daly Ave, Suite 120, Ottawa, ON K1N 6E2, Canada *Tel:* 613-232-8769 *Fax:* 613-232-6315 *E-mail:* info@animationfestival.ca; entries@animationfestival.ca *Web Site:* www.animationfestival.ca, pg 999

Robinson, Eddie, City of West Hollywood Film Office, 8300 Santa Monica Blvd, West Hollywood, CA 90069 *Tel:* 323-848-6489 *E-mail:* wehofilm@weho.org *Web Site:* www.weho.org/film, pg 968

Robinson, Jeffrey, massAV, 3 Radcliffe Rd, Pewksbury, MA 01876 *Tel:* 978-670-0027 *Toll Free Tel:* 800-423-7830 *Fax:* 978-640-9900 *E-mail:* info@massav.com *Web Site:* www.massav.com, pg 819

Robinson, Joe, Hasselblad Bron Inc, 1080A Garden State Rd, Union, NJ 07083 *Tel:* 908-754-5800 *Toll Free Tel:* 800-367-6434; 800-456-0203 *Fax:* 908-754-5807 *E-mail:* sales@hasselbladbron.com; servicedept@hasselbladbron.com; productinfo@hasselbladbron.com *Web Site:* www.hasselbladbron.com, pg 776

Robinson, Marian, Guilford Publications, 370 Seventh Ave, Suite 1200, New York, NY 10001-1020 *Tel:* 212-431-9800 *Toll Free Tel:* 800-365-7006 *Fax:* 212-966-6708 *E-mail:* info@guilford.com *Web Site:* www.guilford.com, pg 774

Rocha, Adam, San Antonio Film Festival, 8452 Fredericksburg Rd, PMB 264, San Antonio, TX 78229 *Tel:* 210-885-5888 *E-mail:* safilm@gmail.com; hello@safilm.com *Web Site:* www.safilm.com, pg 1002

Roche, Mary Beth, Macmillan Audio, 120 Broadway, 22nd fl, New York, NY 10271 *Tel:* 646-600-7856; 646-307-5472 *Toll Free Tel:* 888-330-8477 (cust serv); 800-221-7945 *Toll Free Fax:* 800-672-7703 (orders) *E-mail:* macmillan.audio@macmillanusa.com *Web Site:* www.macmillanaudio.com, pg 814

Rochefort, Josee, Montreal Film & TV Commission, Duke Pavilion, 5th fl, 801 Brennan St, Montreal, QC H3C 0G4, Canada *Tel:* 514-872-2883 *Fax:* 514-872-3409 *E-mail:* film.tv@ville.montreal.qc.ca *Web Site:* www.montrealfilm.com, pg 979

Rocheleau, Jean-Claude, alliance quebecoise des techniciens et techniciennes de l'image et du son (AQTIS), 1001, blvd De Maisonneuve E, bureau 900, Montreal, QC H2L 4P9, Canada *Tel:* 514-844-2113 (ext 285) *Fax:* 514-844-3540 *E-mail:* info@aqtis.qc.ca *Web Site:* www.aqtis.qc.ca, pg 947

Rochon, Josee, Montreal Film & TV Commission, Duke Pavilion, 5th fl, 801 Brennan St, Montreal, QC H3C 0G4, Canada *Tel:* 514-872-2883 *Fax:* 514-872-3409 *E-mail:* film.tv@ville.montreal.qc.ca *Web Site:* www.montrealfilm.com, pg 979

Rock, Alicia, Hollywood Professional Association (HPA), 2501 W Burbank Blvd, No 207, Burbank, CA 91505 *Tel:* 818-273-1482 *Web Site:* hpaonline.com, pg 955

Rockwell, Don, Spot Media Production Group, 2745 Locust St, St Louis, MO 63103 *Tel:* 314-667-5915 *E-mail:* info@spotmpg.com *Web Site:* www.spotmpg.com, pg 898

Rodak, Bob, Chartpak Inc, One River Rd, Leeds, MA 01053 *Tel:* 413-584-5446 *Toll Free Tel:* 800-628-1910 *E-mail:* info@chartpak.com *Web Site:* www.chartpak.com, pg 721

Rode, Scott, Hollywood Lights Inc, 5251 SE McLoughlin Blvd, Portland, OR 97202-4836 *Tel:* 503-232-9001; 503-232-8855 *Toll Free Tel:* 800-826-9881 *Fax:* 503-517-8686 *E-mail:* portland@hollywoodlights.biz *Web Site:* www.hollywoodlights.biz, pg 780

Rodgers, Andrew, Denver Film Festival, 1510 York St, 3rd fl, Denver, CO 80206 *Tel:* 303-595-3456 *E-mail:* dff@denverfilm.org *Web Site:* denverfilmfestival.denverfilm.org, pg 988

Rodgers, Andrew, Denver Film Society, 1510 York St, 3rd fl, Denver, CO 80206 *Tel:* 303-595-3456 *E-mail:* info@denverfilm.org *Web Site:* www.denverfilm.org, pg 953

Rodgers, Skip, Polhemus, 40 Hercules Dr, Colchester, VT 05446-5835 *Tel:* 802-655-3159 *Toll Free Tel:* 800-357-4777 (US & CN) *E-mail:* sales@polhemus.com *Web Site:* www.polhemus.com, pg 859

Rodgers, Steve, Creative Technology (CT), 2200 S Mount Prospect Rd, Unit A, Des Plaines, IL 60018 *Tel:* 847-671-9670 *E-mail:* info@ctus.com *Web Site:* www.ct-group.com, pg 733

Rodney, Layne, P&P Studios Inc, 110 Lenox Ave, Suite 210, Stamford, CT 06906 *Tel:* 203-359-9292 *Toll Free Tel:* 888-WEPRODUCE (937-7638) *E-mail:* ppstudios@weproduce.com; info@weproduce.com *Web Site:* www.weproduce.com, pg 851

Rodriguez, Charles, A-V Services Inc, 99 Fairfield Rd, Fairfield, NJ 07004 *Tel:* 973-575-5222 *Fax:* 973-575-0857 *E-mail:* sales@avservices.net *Web Site:* www.avservices.net, pg 671

Rodriguez, Chris, Crossroads Audio Inc, 2623 Myrtle Springs Ave, Dallas, TX 75220 *Tel:* 214-358-2623 *Toll Free Tel:* 800-287-0436 *Fax:* 214-358-0185 *E-mail:* mail@crossroadsaudio.com *Web Site:* www.crossroadsaudio.com, pg 735

Rodriguez, Ester, American Harlequin Corp, 1531 Glen Ave, Moorestown, NJ 08057 *Tel:* 856-234-5505 *Toll Free Tel:* 800-642-6440 *Fax:* 856-231-4403 *E-mail:* dance@harlequinfloors.com; contact@harlequinfloors.com *Web Site:* us.harlequinfloors.com, pg 683

Rodriguez, Liliana, Palm Springs International Film Festival, 1700 E Tahquitz Canyon Way, Suite 3, Palm Springs, CA 92262 *Tel:* 760-322-2930 *Toll Free Tel:* 800-898-7256 *Fax:* 760-322-4087 *E-mail:* info@psfilmfest.org *Web Site:* www.psfilmfest.org, pg 999

Rodriguez, Ray, Screen Actors Guild - American Federation of Television & Radio Artists (SAG-AFTRA), 5757 Wilshire Blvd, 7th fl, Los Angeles, CA 90036-3600 *Tel:* 323-954-1600 (former SAG); 323-634-8100 (former AFTRA) *Toll Free Tel:* 855-SAG-AFTRA (724-2387) *Fax:* 323-549-6654 (communs & mktg) *E-mail:* info@sagaftra.org *Web Site:* www.sagaftra.org, pg 961

Rodriguez, Sergio, MarathonNorco Aerospace Inc, 8301 Imperial Dr, Waco, TX 76712-6588 *Tel:* 254-776-0650 *Fax:* 254-776-6558 *E-mail:* marathon@mptc.com *Web Site:* www.mnaerospace.com, pg 816

Rodriguez Tressler, Claudia, Broadstreet Productions LLC, 242 W 30 St, 2nd fl, New York, NY 10001 *Tel:* 212-780-5700 *E-mail:* newyork@broadstreet.com; admin@broadstreet.com *Web Site:* www.broadstreet.com, pg 711

Roe, Brett, Berry & Homer, 2035 Richmond St, Philadelphia, PA 19125 *Tel:* 215-425-0888 *Web Site:* www.berryandhomer.com, pg 704

Roederer, Meg, Flagstaff Convention & Visitors Bureau, 211 W Aspen Ave, Flagstaff, AZ 86001 *Tel:* 928-213-2924 *Toll Free Tel:* 800-842-7293 *Fax:* 928-556-1305 *Web Site:* www.flagstaffarizona.org, pg 965

Roemer, Jason, Indianapolis International Film Festival, 125 W South St, No 1930, Indianapolis, IN 46206 *Tel:* 317-560-4433 *E-mail:* info@indyfilmfest.org; submissions@indyfilmfest.org *Web Site:* indyfilmfest. org, pg 992

Rogers, Brack, Media-Comm, 9700 S Pine Blvd, Charlotte, NC 28273 *Tel:* 704-527-8853 *Web Site:* www.media-comm.com, pg 821

Rogers, Christopher D, CDR Communications Inc, 9310B/9302C Old Keene Mill Rd, Burke, VA 22015 *Tel:* 703-569-3400 *Toll Free Tel:* 800-729-2237 *Fax:* 703-569-3448 *E-mail:* info@cdrcommunications. com *Web Site:* www.cdrcommunications.com, pg 719

Rogers, Dan, South Carolina Film Commission, 1205 Pendleton St, Rm 225, Columbia, SC 29201 *Tel:* 803-737-0490 *Fax:* 803-734-1163 *E-mail:* filmsc@scprt. com *Web Site:* www.filmsc.com, pg 975

Rogers, Linda, Dolby Laboratories Inc, 1275 Market St, San Francisco, CA 94103-1410 *Tel:* 415-558-0200 *Fax:* 415-645-4000 *Web Site:* www.dolby.com, pg 745

Rogers, Mandy, Zacuto, 401 W Ontario Ave, Chicago, IL 60654 *Tel:* 312-863-3453 (rentals); 312-863-3456 *Toll Free Tel:* 888-294-3456 *Fax:* 312-863-3455 *E-mail:* rentals@zacuto.com *Web Site:* www.zacuto. com, pg 945

Rogers, Nancy, CDR Communications Inc, 9310B/9302C Old Keene Mill Rd, Burke, VA 22015 *Tel:* 703-569-3400 *Toll Free Tel:* 800-729-2237 *Fax:* 703-569-3448 *E-mail:* info@cdrcommunications. com *Web Site:* www.cdrcommunications.com, pg 719

Rogers, Tommy, ACS Technologies, 180 Dunbarton Dr, Florence, SC 29501 *Tel:* 843-662-1681 *Toll Free Tel:* 800-736-7425 (sales); 800-669-2309 (support) *Fax:* 843-669-7513 *E-mail:* info@acstechnologies.com *Web Site:* www.acstechnologies.com, pg 674

Rogers, Tyme, Tech 21 USA Inc, 790 Bloomfield Ave, Clifton, NJ 07012 *Tel:* 973-777-6996 *Fax:* 973-777-9899 *E-mail:* info@tech21nyc.com *Web Site:* www. tech21nyc.com, pg 908

Rogg, Jesse, The Mack Sennett Studios, 1215 Bates Ave, Los Angeles, CA 90029 *Tel:* 323-660-8466 *E-mail:* info@macksennettstudios.net *Web Site:* www. macksennettstudios.net, pg 884

Rogovin, John, Warner Bros Entertainment Inc, 4000 Warner Blvd, Burbank, CA 91522 *E-mail:* wbsf@ warnerbros.com *Web Site:* www.warnerbros.com/ studio; studiofacilities.warnerbros.com, pg 934

Rohan, Lucie, Northeast Video Productions Inc, Box 8425, Sleepy Hollow, NY 10591 *Tel:* 914-714-0703, pg 842

Roibal, Robert, SouthWest Organizing Project (SWOP), 211 Tenth St SW, Albuquerque, NM 87102-2919 *Tel:* 505-247-8832 *Fax:* 505-247-9972 *E-mail:* swop@ swop.net *Web Site:* www.swop.net, pg 896

Roland, David, Ingram Content Group LLC, One Ingram Blvd, La Vergne, TN 37086-1986 *Tel:* 615-793-5000 *Toll Free Tel:* 800-937-8000 (retailers); 800-937-5300 (ext 1, libs) *E-mail:* customerservice@ingramcontent. com *Web Site:* www.ingramcontent.com, pg 787

Roland, Glenn, Glenn Roland Films, PO Box 24035, Los Angeles, CA 90024 *Tel:* 310-475-0937 *Fax:* 310-475-0939, pg 876

Roland, John, Extreme Reach Inc, 75 Second Ave, Suite 720, Needham, MA 02494 *Tel:* 781-577-2016 *Toll Free Tel:* 877-769-9382 *E-mail:* sales@ extremereach.com; support@extremereach.com *Web Site:* extremereach.com, pg 758

Rolin, Jim, Videofax, 1750 Cesar Chavez St, Unit G, San Francisco, CA 94124 *Tel:* 415-641-0100 *E-mail:* rentals@videofax.com *Web Site:* www. videofax.com, pg 929

Rollins, Stephen, SESAC Inc, 35 Music Sq E, Nashville, TN 37203 *Tel:* 615-320-0055 *Web Site:* www.sesac. com, pg 962

Rollwagen, Jack, The Institute Inc, 787 East Ave, Brockport, NY 14420 *Tel:* 585-637-6531 *Web Site:* www.the-institute-ny.com, pg 788

Rolston, Clyde, Music & Entertainment Industry Educators Association (MEIEA), 1900 Belmont Blvd, Nashville, TN 37212-3758 *Tel:* 615-460-6946 *E-mail:* office@meiea.org; membership@meiea.org *Web Site:* www.meiea.org, pg 958

Romain, Steve, Ross Video Ltd, 8 John St, Iroquois, ON K0E 1K0, Canada *Tel:* 613-652-4886 *Fax:* 613-652-4425 *E-mail:* solutions@rossvideo.com *Web Site:* www.rossvideo.com, pg 878

Roman, David, Broadcast Management Group, 718 Seventh St NW, Washington, DC 20001 *Tel:* 202-609-7757 *E-mail:* info@broadcastmgmt.com *Web Site:* www.broadcastmgmt.com, pg 710

Roman, Sofia, Center for the Collaborative Classroom, 1001 Marina Village Pkwy, Suite 110, Alameda, CA 94501-1042 *Tel:* 510-533-0213 *Toll Free Tel:* 800-666-7270 *Fax:* 510-464-3670 *E-mail:* info@ collaborativeclassroom.org *Web Site:* www. collaborativeclassroom.org, pg 719

Romano, Kate, Cramer, 425 University Ave, Norwood, MA 02062 *Tel:* 781-278-2300 *E-mail:* theteam@ cramer.com *Web Site:* cramer.com, pg 733

Romine, Barry, VSG Digital Media Solutions, 11126 Lindbergh Business Ct, St Louis, MO 63123 *Tel:* 314-487-8045 *Toll Free Tel:* 800-737-8045 *Fax:* 314-487-9387 *E-mail:* info@vsginc.net *Web Site:* www.vsginc. net, pg 933

Rone, Katye, Trailblazer Studios®, 1610 Midtown Place, Raleigh, NC 27609 *Tel:* 919-645-6600 *Fax:* 919-645-6601 *E-mail:* info@trailblazerstudios.com *Web Site:* www.trailblazerstudios.com, pg 917

Roobin, Todd, Jacksonville Office of Economic Development, Film & Television Office, 117 W Duval St, Suite 280, Jacksonville, FL 32202 *Tel:* 904-630-2522 *Web Site:* www.coj.net, pg 969

Rooke, Bernie, Pathway Connectivity, 103-1439 17 Ave SE, Calgary, AB T2G 1J9, Canada *Tel:* 403-243-8110 *Fax:* 403-287-1281 *E-mail:* orders@pathwayconnect. com *Web Site:* www.pathwayconnect.com, pg 852

Rooney, Daniel, Special Archives Division, Motion Picture Branch, 8601 Adelphi Rd, College Park, MD 20740-6001 *Tel:* 301-837-2000 *Toll Free Tel:* 866-272-6272 (86-NARA-NARA, cust serv) *Fax:* 301-837-0483 *E-mail:* mopix@nara.gov *Web Site:* www.archives.gov, pg 896

Rooney, Rick, Planet Dallas Recording Studios, PO Box 110995, Carrollton, TX 75011 *Tel:* 214-521-2216; 214-893-1130 (cell) *E-mail:* planetd@ix.netcom.com *Web Site:* planetdallas.com, pg 845

Rosa, Mary, Adrenaline Films, 5224 S Orange Ave, Orlando, FL 32809 *Tel:* 407-850-0711 *Fax:* 407-859-6527 *E-mail:* contact@adrenalinefilms.com *Web Site:* www.adrenalinefilms.com, pg 676

Rosado, Jorge L, Convergent Media Systems, 190 Bluegrass Valley Pkwy, Alpharetta, GA 30005-2204 *Tel:* 770-369-9000 *Fax:* 770-369-9100 *Web Site:* www. convergent.com, pg 731

Roscorla, Paul, William F White International Inc, 800 Islington Ave, Toronto, ON M8Z 6A1, Canada *Tel:* 416-239-5050 *Toll Free Tel:* 800-465-0160 (CN only) *Web Site:* www.whites.com, pg 937

Rose, Celina, C&I An Idea Agency, 541 NW First Ave, Fort Lauderdale, FL 33301 *Tel:* 954-357-3934 *E-mail:* contact@c-istudios.com *Web Site:* www.c-istudios.com, pg 716

Rose, Frederic, Technicolor USA Inc, 6040 Sunset Blvd, Hollywood, CA 90028 *Tel:* 323-817-6600 *E-mail:* info@technicolor.com *Web Site:* www. technicolor.com, pg 908

Rose, Marco, Illuminart Lighting, 7320 Griffin Rd, Suite 111, Davie, FL 33314 *Tel:* 954-327-0564 *E-mail:* lightisart@aol.com, pg 784

Rose, Richard, Hot House Professional Audio, 275 Martin Ave, Highland, NY 12528 *Tel:* 845-691-6077 *E-mail:* info@hothousepro.com *Web Site:* www. hothousepro.com, pg 782

Rose, Richard A, Film Creations Ltd, 4349 E Fifth St, Tucson, AZ 85711 *Tel:* 520-624-4444 *Toll Free Tel:* 888-877-2490 *Fax:* 520-624-9659 *E-mail:* info@ filmcreations.com *Web Site:* www.filmcreations.com, pg 760

Rose, Robert, Rose Packaging & Design Inc, 4000 Sopris Mountain Rd, Basalt, CO 81621-9179 *Tel:* 970-927-6515 *Toll Free Tel:* 800-308-1003 *Fax:* 303-557-6366 *E-mail:* sales@rosepkg.com *Web Site:* www. rosepkg.com, pg 877

Rose, Steven, Tally Display Corp, 19 Gardner Rd, Fairfield, NJ 07004 *Tel:* 973-777-7760 *Toll Free Tel:* 800-758-2559 *Fax:* 973-777-6220 *E-mail:* info@ tallydisplay.com *Web Site:* www.tallydisplay.com, pg 906

Rosebush, Judson, Judson Rosebush Co Inc, 630 Ninth Ave, Suite 507, New York, NY 10036 *Tel:* 212-581-3000 *E-mail:* judson@rosebush.com *Web Site:* www. rosebush.com, pg 877

Roseman, Donald, Ingram Content Group LLC, One Ingram Blvd, La Vergne, TN 37086-1986 *Tel:* 615-793-5000 *Toll Free Tel:* 800-937-8000 (retailers); 800-937-5300 (ext 1, libs) *E-mail:* customerservice@ ingramcontent.com *Web Site:* www.ingramcontent.com, pg 787

Rosen, Daniel, Sentry Industries Inc, One Bridge St, Hillburn, NY 10931-0885 *Tel:* 845-753-2910 *Fax:* 845-753-2920 *E-mail:* techsupport@ sentryindustries.com *Web Site:* www.sentryindustries. com, pg 884

Rosen, Dave, Absolute Rentals, 2633 N San Fernando Blvd, Burbank, CA 91504 *Tel:* 818-842-2828 *Web Site:* absoluterentals.com, pg 672

Rosen, Jesse, AbelCine, 801 S Main St, Burbank, CA 91506 *Toll Free Tel:* 888-700-4416 *E-mail:* orders@ abelcine.com; customerservice@abelcine.com *Web Site:* www.abelcine.com, pg 672

Rosen, Peter, Peter Rosen Productions Inc, c/o Du Art, 245 W 55 St, Suite 308, New York, NY 10019 *Tel:* 212-535-8927 *Fax:* 212-517-5337 *E-mail:* rosenprod@aol.com *Web Site:* www. peterrosenproductions.com, pg 877

Rosen, Rachel, Golden Gate Awards, c/o San Francisco Film Society, The Presidio, Suite 110, 39 Mesa St, San Francisco, CA 94129-1025 *Tel:* 415-561-5000 *Fax:* 415-440-1760 *E-mail:* info@sffilm.org; gga@ sffilm.org *Web Site:* sffilm.org/sffilm-festival/, pg 990

Rosen, Rachel, San Francisco International Film Festival, 39 Mesa St, Suite 110, The Presidio, San Francisco, CA 94129-1025 *Tel:* 415-561-5000 *Fax:* 415-440-1760 *E-mail:* info@sffilm.org *Web Site:* sffilm.org/sffilm-festival/, pg 1003

Rosen, Tammie, Tribeca Film Festival, Communications Dept, 375 Greenwich St, New York, NY 10013 *Tel:* 212-941-2400 *Fax:* 212-941-3939 *E-mail:* festival@tribecafilmfestival.org; entries@ tribecafilmfestival.org; press@tribecafilmfestival.org *Web Site:* www.tribecafilm.com/festival, pg 1005

Rosenberg, Carole, Havana Film Festival New York (HFFNY), 4 W 43 St, Suite 304, New York, NY 10036 *Tel:* 212-687-2146 *Fax:* 212-681-8037 *E-mail:* info@hffny.com; info@affc.org; press@hffny. com *Web Site:* www.hffny.com, pg 991

Rosenberg, Murray, Bestwell Optical Instrument Corp, 46 Henry St, Merrick, NY 11566 *Tel:* 516-889-1178 *Fax:* 516-706-1744 *Web Site:* www.bestwelloptical. com, pg 704

Rosenberg, Tracy, Media Alliance, 2830 20 St, Suite 102, San Francisco, CA 94110 *Tel:* 415-746-9475 *E-mail:* information@media-alliance.org *Web Site:* www.media-alliance.org, pg 957

Rosenblad, David, DRM: sir reel sound, 2952 Cohoba Dr, Austin, TX 78748 *Tel:* 469-360-1443 (studio) *E-mail:* drmuzik@mac.com *Web Site:* drm-sirreelsound.com, pg 747

Rosenblatt, Jay, San Francisco Jewish Film Festival, 145 Ninth St, Suite 200, San Francisco, CA 94103 *Tel:* 415-621-0556 *Fax:* 415-621-0568 *E-mail:* jewishfilm@sfjff.org; programming@jfi.org *Web Site:* www.sfjff.org; jfi.org, pg 1003

Rosenbloom, Danny, Association of Independent Commercial Producers (AICP), 3 W 18 St, 5th fl, New York, NY 10011 *Tel:* 212-929-3000 *Fax:* 212-929-3359 *E-mail:* info@aicp.com *Web Site:* www.aicp.com, pg 951

Rosenfeld, Irene, Bestwell Optical Instrument Corp, 46 Henry St, Merrick, NY 11566 *Tel:* 516-889-1178 *Fax:* 516-706-1744 *Web Site:* www.bestwelloptical.com, pg 704

Rosenstein, Hans, Whalley-Abbey Media Holdings Inc, 3800 Rue St Patrick, Suite 100, Montreal, QC H4E 1A4, Canada *Tel:* 514-846-1940 *E-mail:* info@wamgrp.com *Web Site:* wamgrp.com, pg 937

Rosenstein, Richard, Summit Electronics Corp, 4260 NW First Ave, Suite 50, Boca Raton, FL 33431 *Tel:* 561-226-8500 *Toll Free Tel:* 800-226-6960 *Fax:* 561-226-8523 *E-mail:* sales@summitelectronics.com *Web Site:* www.summitelectronics.com; www.partsprocurement.com; bocasemi.com, pg 903

Rosenstein, Sam, Summit Electronics Corp, 4260 NW First Ave, Suite 50, Boca Raton, FL 33431 *Tel:* 561-226-8500 *Toll Free Tel:* 800-226-6960 *Fax:* 561-226-8523 *E-mail:* sales@summitelectronics.com *Web Site:* www.summitelectronics.com; www.partsprocurement.com; bocasemi.com, pg 903

Rosenstein, Scott, Summit Electronics Corp, 4260 NW First Ave, Suite 50, Boca Raton, FL 33431 *Tel:* 561-226-8500 *Toll Free Tel:* 800-226-6960 *Fax:* 561-226-8523 *E-mail:* sales@summitelectronics.com *Web Site:* www.summitelectronics.com; www.partsprocurement.com; bocasemi.com, pg 903

Rosenthal, Fred, Ametron Audio/Video, 1546 N Argyle Ave, Hollywood, CA 90028-6410 *Tel:* 323-466-4321 *Fax:* 323-871-0127 *E-mail:* info@ametron.com *Web Site:* www.ametron.com, pg 684

Rosenthal, Gene, Adelphi Records Inc, PO Box 7688, Silver Spring, MD 20907-7688 *Tel:* 301-434-6958 *Fax:* 301-434-3056 *E-mail:* adelphi@adelphirecords.com *Web Site:* www.adelphirecords.com, pg 676

Rosenthal, Jim, The Rosenthal Group, 10625 Cohasset St, Sun Valley, CA 91352 *Tel:* 818-252-1010 *Fax:* 818-252-1070 *Web Site:* www.therosenthalgroup.com, pg 877

Rosenthal, Phil, American Melody, PO Box 270, Guilford, CT 06437-0270 *Tel:* 203-457-0881 *E-mail:* studio@americanmelody.com *Web Site:* www.americanmelody.com, pg 683

Rosenthal, Randy, Tricycle Studios, 1905 E Seventh Ave, Tampa, FL 33605 *Tel:* 813-258-6867 *Fax:* 813-258-8595 *E-mail:* hi@tricyclestudios.com *Web Site:* www.tricyclestudios.com, pg 918

Rosica, Jeff, Avid Technology Inc, 65-75 Network Dr, Burlington, MA 01830 *Tel:* 978-640-6789 *Web Site:* www.avid.com, pg 698

Rosing, Richard, Trew Audio Inc, 220 Great Circle Rd, Suite 116, Nashville, TN 37228 *Tel:* 615-256-3542 *Toll Free Tel:* 800-241-8994 *Fax:* 615-259-2699 *E-mail:* info@trewaudio.com; sales@trewaudio.com *Web Site:* www.trewaudio.com, pg 917

Ross, Ben, Wild Plum, 23371 Mulholland Dr, Suite 409, Woodland Hills, CA 91364 *Tel:* 310-823-7445 *Web Site:* www.wildplum.tv, pg 938

Ross, David, Ross Video Ltd, 8 John St, Iroquois, ON K0E 1K0, Canada *Tel:* 613-652-4886 *Fax:* 613-652-4425 *E-mail:* solutions@rossvideo.com *Web Site:* www.rossvideo.com, pg 877

Ross, Jason, Replicopy Digital Media Center, 1120 Jupiter Rd, Suite 190, Plano, TX 75074 *Tel:* 972-702-8388 *Toll Free Tel:* 800-628-1124 *E-mail:* replicopy@replicopy.com *Web Site:* www.replicopy.com, pg 873

Ross, Lonnie, L R Light & Sound, 5317 54 St, Drayton Valley, AB T7A 1R6, Canada *Tel:* 780-542-4242; 780-542-9363 *Fax:* 780-542-4283 *E-mail:* lrlightandsound@yahoo.ca *Web Site:* www.lrlightandsound.ca, pg 802

Ross, Mark, BMI Supply, 571 Queensbury Ave, Queensbury, NY 12804 *Tel:* 518-793-6706 *Toll Free Tel:* 800-836-0524 *Fax:* 518-793-6181 *E-mail:* bminy@bmisupply.com *Web Site:* www.bmisupply.com, pg 708

Ross, Peter D, Manhattan Center Studios Inc, 311 W 34 St, New York, NY 10001 *Tel:* 212-279-7740 *Fax:* 212-564-1072 *E-mail:* info@mcstudios.com *Web Site:* www.mcstudios.com, pg 816

Ross, Peter John, Production Partners Media, 520 Enterprise Dr, Suite C, Lewis Center, OH 43035 *Tel:* 614-888-4888 *Web Site:* productionpartnersmedia.com, pg 864

Rossi, Elizabeth, Golden Space Needle Awards, 305 Harrison St, Seattle, WA 98109 *Tel:* 206-464-5830 *Fax:* 206-264-7919 *E-mail:* info@siff.net; entries@siff.net *Web Site:* www.siff.net, pg 991

Rossi, Elizabeth, Seattle International Film Festival (SIFF), 305 Harrison St, Seattle, WA 98109 *Tel:* 206-464-5830 *Fax:* 206-264-7919 *E-mail:* info@siff.net; entries@siff.net *Web Site:* www.siff.net, pg 1003

Rossi, John, Xintekvideo Inc, 56 W Broad St, Stamford, CT 06902 *Tel:* 203-348-9229 *Web Site:* www.xintekvideo.com, pg 943

Rossi, Kevin, ATX Networks, 8-1602 Tricont Ave, Whitby, ON L1N 7C3, Canada *Tel:* 289-204-7800 *Toll Free Tel:* 866-968-7289 *E-mail:* info@atx.com *Web Site:* atx.com, pg 692

Rossi, Mimi, Hollywood Professional Association (HPA), 2501 W Burbank Blvd, No 207, Burbank, CA 91505 *Tel:* 818-273-1482 *Web Site:* hpaonline.com, pg 955

Rossi, Tony, The Christophers, 5 Hanover Sq, 22nd fl, New York, NY 10004 *Tel:* 212-759-4050 *Toll Free Tel:* 888-298-4050 (orders) *Fax:* 212-838-5073 *E-mail:* mail@christophers.org *Web Site:* www.christophers.org, pg 723

Rossol, Eric, L-3 ESSCO, 90 Nemco Way, Ayer, MA 01432 *Tel:* 978-568-5100 *Fax:* 978-772-7555 *E-mail:* info.essco@l3t.com *Web Site:* www2.l3t.com/essco, pg 802

Roth, Aaron, Arkon Resources Inc, 20 La Porte St, Arcadia, CA 91006 *Tel:* 626-254-9005 *Toll Free Tel:* 800-841-0884 *Fax:* 626-254-9266 *E-mail:* arkon8@arkon.com *Web Site:* www.arkon.com, pg 689

Roth, Betty, Cape Girardeau Convention & Visitors Bureau, 220 N Fountain St, Cape Girardeau, MO 63701 *Tel:* 573-335-1631 *Toll Free Tel:* 800-777-0068 *Fax:* 573-334-6702 *E-mail:* info@visitcape.com *Web Site:* visitcape.com, pg 972

Roth, Don, AmpliVox Portable Sound Systems, 650 Anthony Trail, Suite D, Northbrook, IL 60062-2512 *Tel:* 847-498-9000 *Toll Free Tel:* 800-267-5486 *Toll Free Fax:* 800-267-5489 *E-mail:* info@ampli.com *Web Site:* www.ampli.com, pg 684

Roth, Jennifer, CEDIA IPRO Affinity Group, 8475 Nightfall Lane, Fishers, IN 46037 *Tel:* 317-328-4336 *Toll Free Tel:* 800-669-5329 *E-mail:* info@cedia.org *Web Site:* cedia.net, pg 952

Roth, Mark, Argraph Corp, 111 Asia Place, Carlstadt, NJ 07072 *Tel:* 201-939-7722 *Toll Free Tel:* 800-526-6290 *Fax:* 201-939-7782 *E-mail:* info@argraph.com; sales@argraph.com *Web Site:* www.argraph.com, pg 688

Roth, Stephen, SLR Enterprises LLC, PO Box 1111, Orleans, MA 02653 *Tel:* 508-737-7788 *Fax:* 508-240-6878 *E-mail:* stephenroth@c4.net, pg 890

Roth, Steven, Chartpak Inc, One River Rd, Leeds, MA 01053 *Tel:* 413-584-5446 *Toll Free Tel:* 800-628-1910 *E-mail:* info@chartpak.com *Web Site:* www.chartpak.com, pg 721

Rothe, Robert, Association of National Advertisers Inc (ANA), 10 Grand Central, 155 E 44 St, New York, NY 10017 *Tel:* 212-697-5950 *Fax:* 212-687-7310 *E-mail:* info@ana.net *Web Site:* www.ana.net, pg 951

Rothman, Paul, Slamdance Film Festival, 5634 Melrose Ave, Los Angeles, CA 90038 *Tel:* 323-466-1786 *Fax:* 323-466-1784 *E-mail:* submissions@slamdance.com *Web Site:* www.slamdance.com, pg 1004

Rothschild, Brad, Big Foot Productions Inc, 37-09 36 Ave, Long Island City, NY 11101 *Tel:* 718-729-1900 *E-mail:* info@bigfootnyc.com *Web Site:* www.bigfootnyc.com, pg 705

Rothstein, James, Tri-Ed Distribution Inc, 135 Crossways Park Dr, Suite 101, Woodbury, NY 11797 *Tel:* 516-941-2800 *Toll Free Tel:* 888-874-3336 (US); 800-398-7282 (CN); 800-366-4472 (tech sales) *E-mail:* info@tri-ed.com; sales@tri-ed.com; marketing@tri-ed.com *Web Site:* www.tri-ed.com, pg 918

Rothstein, Scott, Blind™, 1702 Olympic Blvd, Santa Monica, CA 90404 *Tel:* 310-314-1618 *Fax:* 310-314-1718 *Web Site:* www.blind.com, pg 707

Roudebush, Steve, BMI Supply, 571 Queensbury Ave, Queensbury, NY 12804 *Tel:* 518-793-6706 *Toll Free Tel:* 800-836-0524 *Fax:* 518-793-6181 *E-mail:* bminy@bmisupply.com *Web Site:* www.bmisupply.com, pg 708

Rouse, Arthur, The Media Collaboratory, 215 E High St, Lexington, KY 40507 *Tel:* 859-255-9049 *Fax:* 859-281-6537 *E-mail:* info@mediacollaboratory.com *Web Site:* mediacollaboratory.com, pg 821

Roush, Tom, Film Liaison of Escambia County, 1401 E Gregory St, Pensacola, FL 32501 *Tel:* 850-390-3974 *Toll Free Tel:* 800-874-1234 *E-mail:* info@filmnorthflorida.com *Web Site:* filmnorthflorida.com, pg 969

Rousseau, Christopher, Practising Law Institute, 1177 Avenue of the Americas, 2nd fl, New York, NY 10036 *Tel:* 212-824-5710 (cust serv) *Toll Free Tel:* 800-260-4PLI (260-4754, cust serv) *Toll Free Fax:* 800-321-0093 (cust serv) *E-mail:* info@pli.edu; cs@pli.edu (cust serv) *Web Site:* www.pli.edu, pg 860

Rousseau, Gaetan, Paradoxal Inc, 103 E Broadway, New York, NY 10012 *Tel:* 212-366-5526; 917-400-4507 (cell) *E-mail:* contact@paradoxal.net *Web Site:* www.paradoxal.net, pg 851

Rowe, Chris, Love Shack Recording Studios, 909 18 Ave S, Nashville, TN 37212 *Tel:* 615-843-0019 *E-mail:* book@loveshackstudios.com *Web Site:* loveshackstudios.com, pg 812

Rowe, Dorian, Newfoundland and Labrador Film Development Corp, 12 King's Bridge Rd, St John's, NL A1C 3K3, Canada *Tel:* 709-738-3456 *Toll Free Tel:* 877-738-3456 (CN) *Fax:* 709-739-1680 *E-mail:* info@nlfdc.ca *Web Site:* www.nlfdc.ca, pg 978

Rowe, Kara, North-by-Northwest - A Digital Studio, 903 W Broadway Ave, Spokane, WA 99201 *Tel:* 509-324-2949 *Fax:* 509-324-2959 *E-mail:* spokane@nxnw.net *Web Site:* www.nxnw.net, pg 842

Rowe, Marieli, National Telemedia Council Inc, 1922 University Ave, Madison, WI 53726 *Tel:* 608-218-1182 *E-mail:* ntelemedia@aol.com *Web Site:* www.nationaltelemediacouncil.org, pg 959

Rowe, Richard, Round Hill Music LLC, 400 Madison Ave, 18th fl, New York, NY 10017 *Tel:* 212-380-0080 *Fax:* 212-380-0081 *E-mail:* info@roundhillmusic.com *Web Site:* roundhillmusic.com, pg 878

Rowland, David P, Accenture, 161 N Clark St, Chicago, IL 60601 *Tel:* 312-693-0161 *Toll Free Tel:* 877-889-9009 *Fax:* 312-693-0507 *Web Site:* www.accenture.com, pg 672

Rowland, Sandra E, Harman International Industries Inc, 400 Atlantic St, 15th fl, Stamford, CT 06901 *Tel:* 203-328-3500 *Web Site:* www.harman.com, pg 776

Rowlands, Mark, Towards 2000 Inc, 215 W Palm Ave, Suite 101, Burbank, CA 91502 *Tel:* 818-557-0903 *Toll Free Fax:* 866-836-5725 *E-mail:* info@t2k.com *Web Site:* www.t2k.com, pg 916

Rowley, Carolyn, Gilderfluke & Co Inc, 205 S Flower St, Burbank, CA 91502 *Tel:* 818-840-9484 *Toll Free Tel:* 800-776-5972 *Fax:* 818-840-9485 *E-mail:* info@gilderfluke.com *Web Site:* www.gilderfluke.com, pg 771

Rowley, Philip, Sony Pictures Entertainment Inc, 10202 W Washington Blvd, Culver City, CA 90232 *Tel:* 310-244-4000 *Web Site:* www.sonypictures.com, pg 893

Roy, Rahul, ARC Document Solutions, 1981 N Broadway, Suite 385, Walnut Creek, CA 94596 *Tel:* 925-949-5100 *Toll Free Tel:* 855-500-0660 *E-mail:* contact@e-arc.com *Web Site:* www.e-arc.com, pg 688

Roy, Ron, Ron Roy Productions/Moodtapes, 4835 Pradera St, Sparks, NV 89436 *E-mail:* info@moodtapes.com *Web Site:* www.moodtapes.com, pg 878

Royce, Michael L, NYSCA/NYFA Artist Fellowships, 20 Jay St, 7th fl, Suite 740, Brooklyn, NY 11201 *Tel:* 212-366-6900 *Fax:* 212-366-1778 *E-mail:* fellowships@nyfa.org *Web Site:* www.nyfa.org, pg 999

Royer, Larry, Animotion Inc, 501 W Fayette St, Syracuse, NY 13204 *Tel:* 315-471-3533 *E-mail:* info@animotioninc.com *Web Site:* animotioninc.com, pg 685

Rozon, Rene, International Festival of Films on Art (FIFA), 5333 Ave Casgrain, Suite 403, Montreal, QC H2T 1X3, Canada *Tel:* 514-874-1637 *E-mail:* info@artfifa.com *Web Site:* www.lefifa.com, pg 993

Ruballos, Fernando, MSE Media Solutions, 6013 Scott Way, Los Angeles, CA 90040 *Tel:* 323-721-1656 *Toll Free Tel:* 800-626-1955 *Fax:* 323-721-1506 *E-mail:* info@msemedia.com *Web Site:* www.msemedia.com, pg 832

Rubenstein, Herb, Associated Bag Co, 400 W Boden St, Milwaukee, WI 53207 *Tel:* 414-769-1000 *Toll Free Tel:* 800-926-6100 *Fax:* 414-769-6530 *Toll Free Fax:* 800-926-4610 *E-mail:* customerservice@associatedbag.com *Web Site:* www.associatedbag.com, pg 691

Rubin, Antoinette V, P&H Crystalite LLC, 800 Belle Terre Pkwy, Palm Coast, FL 32164 *Toll Free Tel:* 800-468-8673 *E-mail:* phcrystalite@gmail.com *Web Site:* phcled.com, pg 850

Rubin, Jackie, Entertainment One US, 10 Harbor Park Dr, Port Washington, NY 11050 *Tel:* 516-484-1000 *Web Site:* entertainmentone.com, pg 754

Rubin, Kelly Andrea, Signature Entertainment, 8306 Wilshire Blvd, Suite 791, Beverly Hills, CA 90211 *Tel:* 310-498-1805 *Fax:* 310-276-2521, pg 888

Rubin, Mark, Electro Impulse Laboratory Inc, 1805 Rte 33, Neptune, NJ 07754 *Tel:* 732-776-5800 *Fax:* 732-776-6793 *E-mail:* sales@electroimpulse.com *Web Site:* www.electroimpulse.com, pg 752

Rubins, Jennifer, Penguin Random House Audio Publishing, 1745 Broadway, New York, NY 10019 *E-mail:* audio@penguinrandomhouse.com *Web Site:* www.penguinrandomhouseaudio.com, pg 853

Rubinstein, Mindy, Ketchum Inc, 1285 Avenue of the Americas, 4th fl, New York, NY 10019 *Tel:* 646-935-3900 *Web Site:* www.ketchum.com, pg 798

Rucinski, Pamela, Rucinski Write!Now LLC, 2155 Terrebonne Dr, Mosinee, WI 54455 *Tel:* 715-241-7316; 715-212-6241 (cell) *Fax:* 715-355-4274 *Web Site:* www.rucinskiwritenow.com, pg 878

Ruda, Taneli, John Wiley & Sons Inc, 111 River St, Hoboken, NJ 07030-5774 *Tel:* 201-748-6000 *Toll Free Tel:* 800-225-5945 (cust serv) *Fax:* 201-748-6088 *Web Site:* www.wiley.com, pg 938

Rudell, Elaine, Projects in Knowledge Inc, 290 W Mount Pleasant Ave, Suite 2350, Livingston, NJ 07039 *Tel:* 973-890-8988 *Toll Free Tel:* 800-772-8277 *Web Site:* www.projectsinknowledge.com, pg 865

Rudnick, Ben, Ben Rudnick and Friends, PO Box 1426, Arlington, MA 02474 *Tel:* 781-643-5137 *Web Site:* www.benrudnick.com, pg 878

Rudolph, Scott, Chicago International REEL Shorts Film Festival, 2700 W Grand Ave, Chicago, IL 60612 *E-mail:* info@projectchicago.com *Web Site:* www.projectchicago.com, pg 985

Ruff, Allison, Location Lighting Ltd, 300 Pennsylvania Ave, Oreland, PA 19075 *Tel:* 215-576-5600 *Fax:* 215-576-6022 *E-mail:* mail@locationlighting.com; rentals@locationlighting.com *Web Site:* www.locationlighting.com, pg 810

Ruff, Dave, Unique Communications Ltd, 2232 Pegasus Way NE, Calgary, AB T2E 8M5, Canada *Tel:* 403-250-3763 *Toll Free Tel:* 800-661-8575 *Fax:* 403-250-2604 *Web Site:* www.uniquecommunications.ca, pg 921

Ruff, Morgen, Northwest Film Center, 934 SW Salmon St, Portland, OR 97205 *Tel:* 503-221-1156 *E-mail:* info@nwfilm.org *Web Site:* www.nwfilm.org, pg 843

Ruff, Morgen, Northwest Filmmakers' Festival, 934 SW Salmon St, Portland, OR 97205 *Tel:* 503-221-1156 *Fax:* 503-294-0874 *E-mail:* info@nwfilm.org; nwfest@nwfilm.org *Web Site:* www.nwfilm.org, pg 998

Ruggiero, Ed, Connecticut Office of Film, Television & Digital Media, c/o Dept of Economic & Community Development, 480 Columbus Blvd, Suite 5, Hartford, CT 06103 *Tel:* 860-500-2300 *Web Site:* www.ct.gov, pg 968

Ruggiero, Michael, Perennial Pictures Film Corp, 2102 E 52 St, Indianapolis, IN 46205 *Tel:* 317-253-1519 *E-mail:* mail@perennialpictures.com *Web Site:* www.perennialpictures.com, pg 854

Rule, John, Rule Boston Camera, 1284 Soldier's Field Rd, Boston, MA 02135 *Tel:* 617-277-2200 *Toll Free Tel:* 800-785-3266 *Fax:* 617-277-6800 *E-mail:* answers@rule.com *Web Site:* www.rule.com, pg 878

Ruling, Karl G, Entertainment Services and Technology Association (ESTA), 630 Ninth Ave, Suite 609, New York, NY 10036 *Tel:* 212-244-1505 *Fax:* 212-244-1502 *E-mail:* info@esta.org; membership@esta.org *Web Site:* www.esta.org, pg 954

Rumeau, Joe, Panavid, 210 West Pkwy, Unit 5, Pompton Plains, NJ 07444 *Tel:* 973-831-5655 *E-mail:* info@panavid.com; support@panavid.com *Web Site:* www.panavid.com, pg 850

Runnell, Ellen, Action Sports/All Stock, PO Box 301, Malibu, CA 90265-0301 *Tel:* 310-459-2526 *E-mail:* info@actionsportsstockfootage.com *Web Site:* www.actionsportsstockfootage.com; www.allstockfootage.com, pg 675

Runyon, Randy, dbF a Media Company, 9683 Charles St, La Plata, MD 20646 *Tel:* 301-645-6110 *Fax:* 301-392-6111 *E-mail:* service@dbfmedia.com *Web Site:* www.dbfmedia.com, pg 739

Runyon, Wendy, dbF a Media Company, 9683 Charles St, La Plata, MD 20646 *Tel:* 301-645-6110 *Fax:* 301-392-6111 *E-mail:* service@dbfmedia.com *Web Site:* www.dbfmedia.com, pg 739

Ruppert, Jens, Canvys™, 40W267 Keslinger Rd, LaFox, IL 60147-0393 *Tel:* 508-460-5400 *Toll Free Tel:* 800-291-1344 *Fax:* 508-460-5470 *Web Site:* www.canvys.com, pg 716

Rusch, David, Orban, 7209 Browning Rd, Pennsauken, NJ 08109 *Tel:* 856-719-9900 *E-mail:* info@orban.com; sales@orban.com *Web Site:* www.orban.com, pg 847

Rusnock, Andrew, L-3 ESSCO, 90 Nemco Way, Ayer, MA 01432 *Tel:* 978-548-5100 *Fax:* 978-772-7555 *E-mail:* info.essco@l3t.com *Web Site:* www2.l3t.com/essco, pg 802

Russ, John C, SSL Industries Inc, 4935 Anne Louise Lane, Suite 2, Placerville, CA 95667 *Tel:* 530-644-0233 *E-mail:* ssl@sllinc.net *Web Site:* www.sslinc.net, pg 898

Russ-Ayon, Angela, Russ InVision Co/AbridgeClub.com, 3219 Conquista Ave, Long Beach, CA 90808 *Tel:* 562-421-1836 *Toll Free Tel:* 888-421-7488 *E-mail:* info@abridgeclub.com *Web Site:* abridgeclub.com, pg 879

Russell, Adam, Russell Industries Inc, 40 Horton Ave, Lynbrook, NY 11563 *Tel:* 516-536-5000 *Toll Free Tel:* 800-645-2202 *Fax:* 516-764-5747 *Toll Free Fax:* 800-645-2200 *E-mail:* sales@russellind.com *Web Site:* www.russellind.com, pg 879

Russell, Angie N, Captions & Subtitle Services Ltd, 5113 S Harper, Suite 2C, Chicago, IL 60615 *Tel:* 872-222-9057 *E-mail:* quote@capsubservices.com *Web Site:* www.capsubservices.com, pg 716

Russell, Brian W, Bryston Ltd, 677 Neal Dr, Peterborough, ON K9J 6X7, Canada *Tel:* 705-742-5325 *Toll Free Tel:* 800-632-8217 *Fax:* 705-742-0882 *Web Site:* www.bryston.com, pg 712

Russell, Chick, Chick Russell Communications, 490 Castano Ave, Pasadena, CA 91107 *E-mail:* info@chickrussell.com *Web Site:* www.chickrussell.com, pg 722

Russell, Christopher, Bryston Ltd, 677 Neal Dr, Peterborough, ON K9J 6X7, Canada *Tel:* 705-742-5325 *Toll Free Tel:* 800-632-8217 *Fax:* 705-742-0882 *Web Site:* www.bryston.com, pg 712

Russell, David, Image Video, 1620 Midland Ave, Scarborough, ON M1P 3C2, Canada *Tel:* 416-750-8872 *Fax:* 416-750-8015 *E-mail:* sales@imagevideo.com *Web Site:* www.imagevideo.com, pg 785

Russell, Frank, Prositions Inc, 6200 Aurora Ave, Suite 400W, Urbandale, IA 50322 *Tel:* 515-864-7200 *Toll Free Tel:* 877-244-8848 *E-mail:* info@prositions.com *Web Site:* prositions.com, pg 865

Russell, George H, Educational Video Network, 1401 19 St, Huntsville, TX 77340 *Tel:* 936-295-5767 *Toll Free Tel:* 800-762-0060 *Fax:* 936-294-0233 *Web Site:* www.evndirect.com, pg 751

Russell, Jim, Freeman, 1600 Viceroy, Suite 100, Dallas, TX 75235 *Tel:* 214-445-1000 *Web Site:* www.freeman.com, pg 765

Russell, Jon, Presence Studios, 80 Wells Hill Rd, Suite 100, Weston, CT 06883 *Tel:* 203-221-8061 *E-mail:* info@presencestudios.com *Web Site:* www.presencestudios.com, pg 861

Russell, Norman, The Sextant Group Inc, 11301 W Olympic Blvd, Suite 348, Los Angeles, CA 90064 *Tel:* 213-402-0991 *Web Site:* www.thesextantgroup.com, pg 885

Russell, Penny, Fusion Consoles/Eurotech Seating, c/o Marketec, No 601, 3784 Mission Ave, Suite 148, Oceanside, CA 92058 *Toll Free Tel:* 800-557-8861 *Toll Free Fax:* 888-262-1726 *E-mail:* info@marketec.com *Web Site:* www.marketec.com, pg 767

Russell, Penny, Marketec, 419 S Flower St, Burbank, CA 91502 *Tel:* 818-847-0200 *Toll Free Tel:* 800-557-8861 *Toll Free Fax:* 888-262-1726 *E-mail:* info@marketec.com *Web Site:* www.marketec.com, pg 817

Russell, Tommy, Prositions Inc, 6200 Aurora Ave, Suite 400W, Urbandale, IA 50322 *Tel:* 515-864-7200 *Toll Free Tel:* 877-244-8848 *E-mail:* info@prositions.com *Web Site:* prositions.com, pg 866

Russo, Anne Marie, TRF Production Music Libraries, 106 Apple St, Tinton Falls, NJ 07724 *Tel:* 201-335-0005 *Toll Free Tel:* 800-899-MUSIC (899-6874) *Fax:* 201-335-0004 *E-mail:* info@trfmusic.com *Web Site:* www.trfmusic.com, pg 918

Russo, Emily, Zeitgeist Films Ltd, 333 W 39 St, New York, NY 10018 *Tel:* 212-274-1989 *Fax:* 212-714-0871 *E-mail:* mail@zeitgeistfilms.com *Web Site:* www.zeitgeistfilms.com, pg 945

Russo, Joe II, Starburns Industries, 1700 W Burbank Blvd, Burbank, CA 91506 *Tel:* 818-433-3300 *Fax:* 818-433-3383 *E-mail:* contact@starburnsind.com *Web Site:* www.starburnsindustries.com, pg 900

Russo, Kim, OmegaBrandess Distribution, 626 Hanover Pike, Suite 102, Hampstead, MD 21074-2036 *Tel:* 410-374-3250 *Fax:* 410-374-3184 *E-mail:* customerservice@omegabrandess.com *Web Site:* www.omegabrandess.com, pg 845

Samaha, John, Shooting Stars Post Inc, 3106 W North "A" St, Tampa, FL 33609 *Tel:* 813-873-0100 *E-mail:* ssp@sspmedia.com *Web Site:* www.sspmedia. com, pg 886

Samani, Jennifer, New Orleans Film Festival, 1215 Prytania St, Suite 423, New Orleans, LA 70130 *Tel:* 504-309-6633 *E-mail:* noff@neworleansfilmsociety.org *Web Site:* neworleansfilmsociety.org/festival, pg 997

Samler, Steven, Steven Samler Music & Sound, 2830 Vogay Lane, Northbrook, IL 60062 *Tel:* 847-400-5080 *Web Site:* www.stevensamler.com, pg 879

Sample, Cindy, NAMM, the National Association of Music Merchants, 5790 Armada Dr, Carlsbad, CA 92008 *Tel:* 760-438-8001 *Toll Free Tel:* 800-767-6266 (memb hotline) *Fax:* 760-438-7327 *E-mail:* info@ namm.org *Web Site:* www.namm.org, pg 958

Samples, Debby, Cleveland International Film Festival, 2510 Market Ave, Cleveland, OH 44113-3434 *Tel:* 216-623-3456 *Fax:* 216-623-0103 *E-mail:* cfs@ clevelandfilm.org; submissions@clevelandfilm.org *Web Site:* www.clevelandfilm.org, pg 986

Sampsell, Steve, The Bart Richards Award for Media Criticism, 302 James Bldg, University Park, PA 16801 *Tel:* 814-865-8801 *Fax:* 814-863-6134 *Web Site:* comm.psu.edu/bart, pg 1001

Sams, Mark, West Penn Wire, 2833 W Chestnut St, Washington, PA 15301 *Tel:* 724-222-7060 *Toll Free Tel:* 800-245-4964 *Fax:* 724-222-6420 *E-mail:* info@ westpennwire.com; sales@westpennwire.com *Web Site:* www.westpenn-wpw.com, pg 935

Samuels, Ron, The Samuels Co, Box 770874, Houston, TX 77215-0874 *Tel:* 281-564-1055 *Fax:* 530-420-4631 *Web Site:* www.thesamuelsco.com, pg 879

Sanchez, Anthony, Accusoft, 4001 N Riverside Dr, Tampa, FL 33603 *Tel:* 813-875-7575 *Toll Free Tel:* 800-875-7009 *Fax:* 813-875-7705 *E-mail:* sales@ accusoft.com *Web Site:* www.accusoft.com, pg 674

Sanchez, Jose, Available Lighting & Motion Picture Services Inc, 826 Jefferson Hwy, New Orleans, LA 70121 *Tel:* 504-831-5214 *Fax:* 504-831-5361 *E-mail:* avlight@bellsouth.net *Web Site:* www. availablelighting.com, pg 697

Sand, Chris, International Wildlife Film Festival, Roxy Theater, 718 S Higgins Ave, Missoula, MT 59801 *Tel:* 406-728-9380 *Fax:* 406-728-2881 *E-mail:* iwff@ wildlifefilms.org *Web Site:* www.wildlifefilms.org, pg 993

Sanderford, David, Marsand Inc, 6100 S IH-35W, Alvarado, TX 76009 *Tel:* 817-783-5566 *Fax:* 817-783-5577 *Web Site:* www.marsand.com, pg 817

Sanderford, Matthew A Jr, Marsand Inc, 6100 S IH-35W, Alvarado, TX 76009 *Tel:* 817-783-5566 *Fax:* 817-783-5577 *Web Site:* www.marsand.com, pg 817

Sanders, Barry, Spectrum Sound Inc, 1040 Acorn Dr, Suite C, Nashville, TN 37210 *Tel:* 615-391-3700 *Web Site:* www.spectrumsound.net, pg 897

Sanders, Ken, Freeman, 1600 Viceroy, Suite 100, Dallas, TX 75235 *Tel:* 214-445-1000 *Web Site:* www.freeman. com, pg 765

Sanders, Philip N, Charles M Salter Associates Inc, 130 Sutter St, 5th fl, San Francisco, CA 94104 *Tel:* 415-397-0442 *Fax:* 415-397-0454 *E-mail:* info@cmsalter. com *Web Site:* www.cmsalter.com, pg 721

Sandidge, Robert L, CCore Media Inc, 1421 Lowe Dr, Algonquin, IL 60102 *Tel:* 815-219-0424 *Web Site:* www.creativecore.com, pg 718

Sandolowich, Rob, Westbury National Show Systems Ltd, 772 Warden Ave, Toronto, ON M1L 4T7, Canada *Tel:* 416-752-1371 *Toll Free Tel:* 855-752-1372 *Fax:* 416-752-1382 *E-mail:* info@westbury.com *Web Site:* www.westbury.com, pg 936

Sandri, Janice, FSR Inc, 244 Bergen Blvd, Woodland Park, NJ 07424 *Tel:* 973-785-4347 *Toll Free Tel:* 800-332-3771 (tech support) *Fax:* 973-785-4207 *E-mail:* sales@fsrinc.com *Web Site:* www.fsrinc.com, pg 766

Sandrin, Lindsey, Orlando Film Commission, 301 E Pine St, Suite 900, Orlando, FL 32801 *Tel:* 407-422-7159 *Fax:* 407-425-6428 *E-mail:* info@filmorlando.com *Web Site:* www.filmorlando.com, pg 969

Sandwell, Mike, Majortech Inc, 8464 Ninth Line RR-1, Norval, ON L0P 1K0, Canada *Tel:* 905-873-0778 *Fax:* 905-873-1244, pg 815

Sanett, Martin, ARS Electronics, 7110 DeCelis Place, Van Nuys, CA 91406 *Tel:* 818-997-6279 *Fax:* 818-997-6158 *E-mail:* info@arselectronics.com *Web Site:* www.arselectronics.com, pg 690

Sangary, Pascal, All Video Productions, 726 Santa Monica Blvd, Suite 212, Santa Monica, CA 90401 *Tel:* 310-656-1155 *Fax:* 310-656-1155 *E-mail:* info@ allvideoproductions.com *Web Site:* www. allvideoproductions.com, pg 680

Sanger, David, New Deal Studios, 15392 Cobalt St, Los Angeles, CA 91342 *Tel:* 310-578-9929 *E-mail:* info@ newdealstudios.com *Web Site:* www.newdealstudios. com, pg 839

Sanny, Tom, University Film & Video Association (UFVA), c/o University of Illinois Press, 1325 S Oak St, Champaign, IL 61820-6975 *Toll Free Tel:* 866-647-8382 *E-mail:* ufvahome@gmail.com *Web Site:* www. ufva.org, pg 963

Sansivero, Gina, AtlasIED, 4545 E Baseline Rd, Phoenix, AZ 85042 *Toll Free Tel:* 800-876-3333 *E-mail:* support@atlasied.com *Web Site:* www.atlasied. com, pg 692

Santacruz, Sheryl, Hot Springs Documentary Film Festival, 659 Ouchita Ave, Hot Springs, AR 71901 *Tel:* 501-538-0452 *E-mail:* hsdfi@hsdfi.org *Web Site:* www.hsdfi.org, pg 992

Santangelo, Carolyn, Freedoms Foundation National Awards, 1601 Valley Forge Rd, Valley Forge, PA 19481 *Tel:* 610-933-8825 *Fax:* 610-935-0522 *E-mail:* info@ffvf.org *Web Site:* www. freedomsfoundation.org, pg 989

Santiago, Kristy, KION-TV, 1550 Moffett St, Salinas, CA 93905 *Tel:* 831-784-6500; 831-422-3500 *Fax:* 831-784-6502 *Web Site:* www.kion546.com, pg 799

Santo, Susie, Greater Wichita Convention & Visitors Bureau/Wichita Film Commission, 515 S Main St, Suite 115, Wichita, KS 67202 *Tel:* 316-265-2800 *Toll Free Tel:* 800-288-9424 *Fax:* 316-265-0162 *E-mail:* wfc@visitwichita.com *Web Site:* www. visitwichita.com, pg 971

Santone, Angela, Turner Broadcasting System Inc, A Time Warner Company, One CNN Ctr, Atlanta, GA 30303 *Tel:* 404-827-1700 *E-mail:* turner.info@turner. com *Web Site:* www.turner.com, pg 919

Saout, Mostapha, Allied Media Corp, 5252 Cherokee Ave, Suite 200, Alexandria, VA 22312 *Tel:* 703-333-2008 *Fax:* 703-997-7539 *E-mail:* info@allied-media. com; contact@allied-media.com *Web Site:* www.allied-media.com, pg 681

Saporita, Joe, Clever Devices Ltd, 300 Crossways Park Dr, Woodbury, NY 11797 *Tel:* 516-433-6100 *Toll Free Tel:* 800-872-6129 *Web Site:* www.cleverdevices.com, pg 726

Sapsis, Bill, SAPSIS Rigging Inc, 3883 Ridge Ave, Philadelphia, PA 19132 *Tel:* 215-228-0888 *Toll Free Tel:* 800-SAPSIS-1 (727-7471) *Fax:* 215-228-1786 *E-mail:* sales@sapsis-rigging.com *Web Site:* www. sapsis-rigging.com, pg 880

Sarafian, Katherine, Pixar Animation Studios, 1200 Park Ave, Emeryville, CA 94608 *Tel:* 510-922-3000 *Fax:* 510-922-3151 *Web Site:* www.pixar.com, pg 857

Saranchuk, Susan, CSC Awards, 131-3007 Kingston Rd, Toronto, ON M1M 1P1, Canada *Tel:* 416-266-0591 *Fax:* 416-266-3996 *E-mail:* admin@csc.ca *Web Site:* www.csc.ca, pg 987

Saraydarian, Gita, TSG Publishing Foundation Inc USA, 28641 N 63 Place, Cave Creek, AZ 85331 *Tel:* 480-502-1909 *Fax:* 480-502-0713 *E-mail:* info@ tsgfoundation.org *Web Site:* www.tsgfoundation.org, pg 919

Sardinsky, Elizabeth, 18 Label Studios, 18 Label St, Montclair, NJ 07042 *Tel:* 973-744-7382 *E-mail:* info@ 18label.com *Web Site:* 18label.com, pg 751

Sargent, Sarah, Residency Fellowship, 154 San Angelo Dr, Amherst, VA 24521 *Tel:* 434-946-7236 *Fax:* 434-946-7239 *E-mail:* vcca@vcca.com *Web Site:* www. vcca.com, pg 1001

Sarnoff, Tim, Technicolor USA Inc, 6040 Sunset Blvd, Hollywood, CA 90028 *Tel:* 323-817-6600 *E-mail:* info@technicolor.com *Web Site:* www. technicolor.com, pg 908

Sasse, Christine, Palm Springs International Film Festival, 1700 E Tahquitz Canyon Way, Suite 3, Palm Springs, CA 92262 *Tel:* 760-322-2930 *Toll Free Tel:* 800-898-7256 *Fax:* 760-322-4087 *E-mail:* info@ psfilmfest.org *Web Site:* www.psfilmfest.org, pg 999

Saturn, Samantha, SESAC Inc, 35 Music Sq E, Nashville, TN 37203 *Tel:* 615-320-0055 *Web Site:* www.sesac.com, pg 962

Sauers, Alwin, Alwin Sauers Audio Productions (ASAP), 10 Wisteria Way, Ventura, CA 93004-1435 *Tel:* 206-484-6144 *E-mail:* alwinaudio@yahoo.com, pg 881

Saunders, Andrew, Getty Images, 605 Fifth Ave S, Suite 400, Seattle, WA 98104 *Tel:* 206-925-5000 *Toll Free Tel:* 888-888-5889; 800-462-4379 (sales) *E-mail:* sales.na@gettyimages.com *Web Site:* www. gettyimages.com, pg 770

Saunders, Brett, Custom Color Corp, 14320 W 101 Terr, Lenexa, KS 66215 *Tel:* 913-730-3100 *Fax:* 913-730-3101 *E-mail:* info@customcolor.com *Web Site:* www. customcolor.com, pg 736

Saunders, Michaela, Visit Topeka Inc, 618 S Kansas Ave, Topeka, KS 66603 *Tel:* 785-234-1030 *Toll Free Tel:* 800-235-1030 *Fax:* 785-234-8282 *E-mail:* info@ visittopeka.com *Web Site:* www.visittopeka.com, pg 971

Saunoris, Katie, Penguin Random House Canada, 320 Front St W, Suite 1400, Toronto, ON M5V 3B6, Canada *Tel:* 416-364-4449 *Toll Free Tel:* 888-523-9292 (cust serv) *Fax:* 416-598-7764 *E-mail:* customerservicescanada@ penguinrandomhouse.com *Web Site:* www. penguinrandomhouse.ca, pg 853

Savage, Eleanor, Film, Video & Digital Production Grants, 550 Vandalia St, Suite 109, St Paul, MN 55114 *Tel:* 651-224-9431 *E-mail:* info@jeromefdn.org *Web Site:* www.jeromefdn.org/film-video-production-grants, pg 989

Savage, Kathryn, State of the Art Acoustik Inc, 43-1010 Polytek St, Ottawa, ON K1J 9J3, Canada *Tel:* 613-745-2003 *Fax:* 613-745-9687 *E-mail:* sota@sota.ca *Web Site:* www.sota.ca, pg 900

Savage, Kim, Dielectric, 22 Tower Rd, Raymond, ME 04071 *Tel:* 207-655-4555 *Toll Free Tel:* 800-341-9678 *Fax:* 207-655-8173 *E-mail:* PF-dielec-sales@sbgtv. com *Web Site:* www.dielectric.com, pg 741

Savant, Gajendra PhD, Physical Optics Corp (POC), 1845 E 205 St, Torrance, CA 90501-1510 *Tel:* 310-320-3088 *E-mail:* info@poc.com *Web Site:* www.poc. com, pg 856

Saverino, Rocco, Art Gallery of Ontario, 317 Dundas St W, Toronto, ON M5T 1G4, Canada *Tel:* 416-979-6648 *Toll Free Tel:* 877-225-4246 *Web Site:* ago.ca, pg 690

Savidge, S Leigh, Xenon Pictures Inc, 3521 Jack Northrop Ave, Hawthorne, CA 90250 *Tel:* 310-451-5510 *Fax:* 310-395-4058 *E-mail:* info@xenonpictures. com *Web Site:* xenonpictures.com, pg 943

Sawicki, Lisa, VRSim Inc, 222 Pitkin St, Suite 119, East Hartford, CT 06108-3220 *Tel:* 860-893-0080 *E-mail:* info@vrsim.net *Web Site:* www.vrsim.net, pg 933

Sawyer, Joan, Cambridge Documentary Films Inc, 3099 Hidden Valley Lane, Santa Barbara, CA 93108 *Tel:* 617-484-3993 *E-mail:* info@

cambridgedocumentaryfilms.org; mail@ cambridgedocumentaryfilms.org *Web Site:* www. cambridgedocumentaryfilms.org, pg 714

Sawyer, John, Raincoast Books, 2440 Viking Way, Richmond, BC V6V 1N2, Canada *Tel:* 604-448-7100 *Toll Free Tel:* 800-663-5714 (cust serv & book orders) *Fax:* 604-270-7161 *Toll Free Fax:* 800-565-3770 (cust serv & book orders) *E-mail:* info@raincoast.com; customerservice@raincoast.com *Web Site:* www. raincoast.com, pg 869

Saxton, Ann, Luzerne County Community College, 1333 S Prospect St, Nanticoke, PA 18634-3899 *Tel:* 570-740-0200 *Toll Free Tel:* 800-377-5222 *Fax:* 570-740-0250 *Web Site:* www.luzerne.edu/index.jsp, pg 813

Sayah, David, Be Media, 9729 Lurline Ave, Chatsworth, CA 91311 *Tel:* 310-725-8500 *Toll Free Tel:* 877-210-7664 *Fax:* 310-725-9500 *Web Site:* www.bemedia. com, pg 702

Sayiner, Necip, Intersil Americas LLC, 1001 Murphy Ranch Rd, Milpitas, CA 95035 *Tel:* 408-432-8888 *Toll Free Tel:* 888-INTERSIL (468-3774) *Fax:* 408-434-5351 *Web Site:* www.intersil.com, pg 790

Scacchitti, Jerry, Troxell-CDI, 4675 E Cotton Center Blvd, Suite 155, Phoenix, AZ 85040 *Tel:* 602-437-7240 *Toll Free Tel:* 855-TROXELL (876-9355) *Fax:* 602-752-1299 *Toll Free Fax:* 800-752-1299 *E-mail:* csg@trox.com *Web Site:* www.troxellsolutions. com, pg 919

Scales, Aileen, Consortium of College & University Media Centers (CCUMC), c/o Indiana University, 306 N Union St, Bloomington, IN 47405-3888 *Tel:* 812-855-6049 *E-mail:* ccumc@ccumc.org *Web Site:* www. ccumc.org, pg 953

Scaletti, Carla, Symbolic Sound Corp, 206 N Randolph St, Suite 520, Champaign, IL 61820 *Tel:* 217-355-6273 *E-mail:* info-kyma@symbolicsound.com *Web Site:* kyma.symbolicsound.com, pg 905

Scallon, Leslee, Dances With Films, Formosa Bldg, 2nd fl, 1041 N Formosa Ave, West Hollywood, CA 90046 *Tel:* 323-854-8176 *E-mail:* info@danceswithfilms.com; submissions@danceswithfilms.com *Web Site:* www. danceswithfilms.com, pg 988

Scanell, Kelly, Taylor Associates, 110 W Canal St, Suite 301, Winooski, VT 05404 *Tel:* 802-735-1942 *Toll Free Tel:* 800-READ-PLUS (732-3758) *Fax:* 802-419-4786 *E-mail:* info@readingplus.com *Web Site:* www. readingplus.com, pg 907

Scanlon, Dan, Pixar Animation Studios, 1200 Park Ave, Emeryville, CA 94608 *Tel:* 510-922-3000 *Fax:* 510-922-3151 *Web Site:* www.pixar.com, pg 857

Scanlon, Jamye, Shamrock Communications, 106 Apple St, Suite 202, Tinton Falls, NJ 07724 *Tel:* 732-686-1140 *E-mail:* info@shamrockcommunications.com *Web Site:* www.shamrockcommunications.com, pg 885

Scanlon, Mr Pat, Shamrock Communications, 106 Apple St, Suite 202, Tinton Falls, NJ 07724 *Tel:* 732-686-1140 *E-mail:* info@shamrockcommunications.com *Web Site:* www.shamrockcommunications.com, pg 885

Scano-Schwiebert, Nicole, Production Resource Group LLC (PRG), 200 Business Park Dr, Suite 109, Armonk, NY 10504 *Tel:* 212-589-5400 *Toll Free Tel:* 877-774-7088 *E-mail:* info@prg.com *Web Site:* www.prg.com, pg 864

Scarpone, Janet, Learn Quickly, PO Box 4464, Palm Springs, CA 92263-4464 *Toll Free Tel:* 888-LRN-FAST (576-3278) *Toll Free Fax:* 888-LRN-FAST (576-3278) *Web Site:* www.learnquickly.com, pg 805

Scarpulla, Gary, Digital Arts NY, 130 W 29 St, New York, NY 10001 *Tel:* 212-460-9600 *Fax:* 212-660-3600 *Web Site:* digitalartsny.com, pg 742

Scauzzo, Buddy, Express Media Inc, 2225 Palou Ave, San Francisco, CA 94124 *Tel:* 415-255-9883 *Fax:* 415-255-0139 *Web Site:* expressmedia.tv, pg 757

Scavelli, Steven V, Flash Electronics Inc, Brooklyn Army Terminal, Suite 1-A, Mail Box 3, 140 58 St, Brooklyn, NY 11220 *Tel:* 718-492-4040

Toll Free Tel: 800-831-3127 *Fax:* 718-492-4590 *E-mail:* customercare@flashdistributors.com *Web Site:* www.flashdistributors.com, pg 762

Schabenberger, Oliver, SAS Institute Inc, 100 SAS Campus Dr, Cary, NC 27513-2414 *Tel:* 919-677-8000 *Toll Free Tel:* 800-727-0025 *Fax:* 919-677-4444 *Web Site:* www.sas.com, pg 880

Schachinger, Christian, Tritech Communications, 625 Locust St, Suite 300, Garden City, NY 11530 *Tel:* 631-254-4500 *Fax:* 631-254-4499 *E-mail:* sales@ tritechcomm.com *Web Site:* www.tritechcomm.com, pg 918

Schaefer, Dieter, PROCAM, 13624 Black Elk Trail, Prescott, AZ 86305 *Tel:* 928-708-9901 *E-mail:* bolexusa@yahoo.com, pg 863

Schaefer, Scott, Comprehensive Cable & Connectivity Co, 80 Little Falls Rd, Fairfield, NJ 07004 *Toll Free Tel:* 800-526-0242 *Fax:* 201-814-0510 *E-mail:* sales@comprehensiveco.com; customerservice@comprehensiveco.com *Web Site:* www.comprehensiveco.com, pg 729

Schafer, Renee, Data Security Inc, 300 S Seventh St, Lincoln, NE 68508 *Tel:* 402-434-5959 *Toll Free Tel:* 800-225-7554 *Fax:* 402-434-3291 *E-mail:* sales@ telesis-inc.com *Web Site:* www.datasecurityinc.com, pg 738

Schaffer, Kirsten, Women In Film, 4221 Wilshire Blvd, Suite 130, Los Angeles, CA 90010 *Tel:* 323-935-2211 *E-mail:* info@wif.org *Web Site:* womeninfilm.org, pg 963

Schaffer, Stephanie, Vincent Associates, 803 Linden Ave, Rochester, NY 14625 *Tel:* 585-385-5930 *Toll Free Tel:* 800-828-6972 *Fax:* 585-385-6004 *E-mail:* info@ uniblitz.com *Web Site:* www.uniblitz.com, pg 930

Schatz, Jacob, Electronic Arts Inc, 209 Redwood Shores Pkwy, Redwood City, CA 94065 *Tel:* 650-628-1500 *Web Site:* www.ea.com, pg 752

Schatz, Jared, Ross Video Ltd, 8 John St, Iroquois, ON K0E 1K0, Canada *Tel:* 613-652-4886 *Fax:* 613-652-4425 *E-mail:* solutions@rossvideo.com *Web Site:* www.rossvideo.com, pg 878

Scheftel, Jeff, Xenon Pictures Inc, 3521 Jack Northrop Ave, Hawthorne, CA 90250 *Tel:* 310-451-5510 *Fax:* 310-395-4058 *E-mail:* info@xenonpictures.com *Web Site:* xenonpictures.com, pg 943

Scheibeck, Eric, Universal Radio Inc, 6830 Americana Pkwy, Reynoldsburg, OH 43068 *Tel:* 614-866-4267 *Toll Free Tel:* 800-431-3939 (orders) *Fax:* 614-866-2339 *E-mail:* dx@universal-radio.com *Web Site:* www. universal-radio.com, pg 922

Schein, Herbert, VARTA Microbattery Inc, 555 Theodore Fremd Ave, Suite C-304, Rye, NY 10580 *Tel:* 914-592-2500 *Toll Free Tel:* 800-468-2782 *Fax:* 914-345-0488 *Web Site:* www.varta-microbattery.com; www. varta-microbattery.com/contact/?lang=en, pg 925

Scheininger, Haim, SISU Home Entertainment Inc, 2219 41 Ave, Suite 509, Long Island City, NY 11101 *Tel:* 212-947-7888 *Toll Free Tel:* 800-223-7478 *Fax:* 212-947-8388 *Toll Free Fax:* 888-221-7478 *E-mail:* sisu@sisuent.com *Web Site:* www.sisuent.com, pg 889

Scheinman, Stuart, Globe Photos LLC, 6445 Tenaya Way, B-130, Las Vegas, NV 89113 *Tel:* 702-210-6208 *Fax:* 631-321-4063 *E-mail:* info@globephotos.com *Web Site:* www.globephotos.com, pg 771

Scheirman, David W, Audio Engineering Society (AES), 551 Fifth Ave, Suite 1225, New York, NY 10176 *Tel:* 212-661-8528 *Web Site:* www.aes.org, pg 951

Schellenger, Jon, JungleTV, 571 NW Mercantile Place, Port St Lucie, FL 34986 *Tel:* 772-370-0043 *E-mail:* info@jungletv.com *Web Site:* www.jungletv. com, pg 795

Schenk, Michael, One Touch Systems Inc, 2528 Qume Dr, Unit 14, San Jose, CA 95131 *Tel:* 408-436-4643 *E-mail:* info@onetouchsys.com *Web Site:* www. onetouchsys.com, pg 846

Schenk, Sean, New York Emmy® Awards, 450 Seventh Ave, Suite 808, New York, NY 10123 *Tel:* 212-459-3630 *E-mail:* awards@nyemmys.org *Web Site:* www. nyemmys.org, pg 997

Scher, Jennifer, Round Hill Music LLC, 400 Madison Ave, 18th fl, New York, NY 10017 *Tel:* 212-380-0080 *Fax:* 212-380-0081 *E-mail:* info@roundhillmusic.com *Web Site:* roundhillmusic.com, pg 878

Scher, Larry, Timestream Video, 11821 N Circle Dr, Whittier, CA 90601-2338 *Tel:* 562-699-8797 *Fax:* 562-695-0252 *Web Site:* www.timestreamvideo.com, pg 914

Scherba, Josh, WildBrain™, 5657 Spring Garden Rd, Suite 505, Halifax, NS B3J 3R4, Canada *Tel:* 902-423-0260 *Fax:* 902-422-0752 *E-mail:* info@wildbrain. com; halifax@wildbrain.com; sales@wildbrain.com *Web Site:* www.wildbrain.com, pg 938

Scherrer, Winifred, Bullfrog Films Inc, 372 Dautrich Rd, Reading, PA 19606 *Tel:* 610-779-8226 *Toll Free Tel:* 800-543-3764 *Fax:* 610-370-1978 *E-mail:* info@ bullfrogfilms.com; video@bullfrogfilms.com *Web Site:* www.bullfrogfilms.com, pg 712

Scheuren, Eduardo, Cinemat Inc, 2520 NW 112 Ave, Doral, FL 33172 *Tel:* 305-887-7726 *E-mail:* info@ cinematusa.com *Web Site:* cinematusa.com, pg 724

Scheuren, Jose Vicente, Cinemat Inc, 2520 NW 112 Ave, Doral, FL 33172 *Tel:* 305-887-7726 *E-mail:* info@ cinematusa.com *Web Site:* cinematusa.com, pg 724

Schiemann, Greg, ARC Document Solutions, 1981 N Broadway, Suite 385, Walnut Creek, CA 94596 *Tel:* 925-949-5100 *Toll Free Tel:* 855-500-0660 *E-mail:* contact@e-arc.com *Web Site:* www.e-arc.com, pg 688

Schildt, Deborah, Alaska Film Services Inc, 11050 Cange St, Anchorage, AK 99516 *Tel:* 907-230-8839 *E-mail:* filmservices@alaska.net *Web Site:* www. alaskafilmservices.com, pg 965

Schildt, Deborah, Alaska Media Pros LLC, 11050 Cange St, Anchorage, AK 99516 *Tel:* 907-230-8839 *E-mail:* ifilm@alaska.net *Web Site:* www. alaskamediapros.com, pg 679

Schiller, Abbie, The Mother Co, 1504 Fourth St, No 216, Santa Monica, CA 90401 *Tel:* 310-826-2400 *Fax:* 310-826-0024 *E-mail:* hello@themotherco.com *Web Site:* www.themotherco.com, pg 831

Schiller, Craig, Bexel, an NEP Broadcast Services Company, 2701 N Ontario St, Burbank, CA 91504 *Tel:* 818-565-4322 *Toll Free Tel:* 800-225-6185 (tech support) *E-mail:* services@bexel.com *Web Site:* bexel. com, pg 704

Schiller, Philip W, Apple Inc, One Infinite Loop, Cupertino, CA 95014 *Tel:* 408-996-1010 *Web Site:* www.apple.com, pg 687

Schillhammer, David, Florida Film Festival, c/o Enzian Theater, 1300 S Orlando Ave, Maitland, FL 32751 *Tel:* 407-629-1088 *Fax:* 407-629-6870 *E-mail:* entries@enzian.org; marketing@enzian.org; events@enzian.org *Web Site:* www.floridafilmfestival. com, pg 989

Schilling, Ron, Nolte Media, 2540 Eastmoor Dr, Santa Rosa, CA 95405 *Tel:* 707-483-1536 *Web Site:* www. noltemedia.com, pg 841

Schilling, Steve, Convergent Media Systems, 190 Bluegrass Valley Pkwy, Alpharetta, GA 30005-2204 *Tel:* 770-369-9000 *Fax:* 770-369-9100 *Web Site:* www. convergent.com, pg 731

Schillinger, Jay, Film Wisconsin Inc, PO Box 93, Waunakee, WI 53597 *Tel:* 920-360-8827 *E-mail:* info@filmwisconsin.net *Web Site:* www. filmwisconsin.net, pg 977

Schimek, Chris, Freeman, 1600 Viceroy, Suite 100, Dallas, TX 75235 *Tel:* 214-445-1000 *Web Site:* www. freeman.com, pg 765

Schimmel, Nancy, Schroder Music Co, PO Box 2067, Berkeley, CA 94702-0067 *Tel:* 510-843-0533 *Fax:* 510-834-5201 *Web Site:* www.sisterschoice.com, pg 882

Schramm, R C, Broadway Costumes Inc, 1100 W Cermak Rd, 2nd fl, Chicago, IL 60608 *Tel:* 312-829-6400 *Fax:* 312-829-8621 *E-mail:* rentals@broadwaycostumes.com *Web Site:* www.broadwaycostumes.com, pg 711

Schrank, Christine, Learning Seed, 208 S Jefferson St, Suite 402, Chicago, IL 60661 *Toll Free Tel:* 800-634-4941 *Toll Free Fax:* 800-998-0854 *E-mail:* info@learningseed.com *Web Site:* www.learningseed.com, pg 805

Schreier, Luke, National Instruments Corp, 11500 N Mopac Expwy, Austin, TX 78759-3504 *Tel:* 512-683-0100 *Toll Free Tel:* 888-280-7645 (sales); 877-388-1952 *Fax:* 512-683-8411; 512-683-5794 (sales) *Web Site:* www.ni.com, pg 836

Schrier, Howard, Nova Electric, 100 School St, Bergenfield, NJ 07621-2915 *Tel:* 201-385-0500 *Fax:* 201-385-0702 *E-mail:* novasales@theallpower.com; info@novaelectric.com *Web Site:* www.novaelectric.com, pg 843

Schrock, Cliff, Golf Digest Publications, One World Trade Center, 27th fl, New York, NY 10007-0090 *Tel:* 212-286-2860 *Toll Free Tel:* 800-962-5513 *Web Site:* www.golfdigest.com, pg 772

Schroeder, Brad, Canamedia Inc, 1540 Cornwall Rd, Suite 216, Oakville, ON L6J 7W5, Canada *Tel:* 416-363-6765 *Toll Free Tel:* 866-999-5292 *Fax:* 416-363-7834 *Web Site:* www.canamedia.com, pg 715

Schroeder, Dave, B&H Publishing Group, One LifeWay Plaza, Nashville, TN 37234 *Tel:* 615-251-2520 *Fax:* 615-251-5004 *Web Site:* www.bhpublishinggroup.com, pg 701

Schroeder, Joseph, The Independent Production Fund, 200 Central Park S, Suite 12F, New York, NY 10019 *Tel:* 212-221-6310 *Fax:* 212-302-1854 *Web Site:* www.ipfmedia.org/vetc.htm, pg 786

Schroeder, Steve, Calgary International Film Festival, 214 11 Ave SE, Unit 207, Calgary, AB T2G 0X8, Canada *Tel:* 403-283-1490 *E-mail:* info@calgaryfilm.com *Web Site:* www.calgaryfilm.com, pg 984

Schubert, Jenny, Logan Productions Inc, 8035 N Port Washington Rd, Milwaukee, WI 53217 *Tel:* 414-352-9691 *Fax:* 414-352-4993 *E-mail:* info@loganproductions.com *Web Site:* www.loganproductions.com, pg 811

Schuch, Joe, Baker Audio Visual, 2195 N Norcross Tucker Rd, Norcross, GA 30071 *Tel:* 770-441-2000 *Toll Free Tel:* 800-847-3523 *Fax:* 770-449-7719 *E-mail:* support@bakeraudiovisual.com *Web Site:* www.bakeraudiovisual.com, pg 700

Schuelke, Kate, Seagate Technology LLC, 10200 S De Anza Blvd, Cupertino, CA 95014 *Toll Free Tel:* 800-SEAGATE (732-4283) *Web Site:* www.seagate.com, pg 883

Schuety, David, Voice & Video Rentals, 4909 Ruffner St, San Diego, CA 92111 *Tel:* 858-560-5000 *Fax:* 858-560-9900 *Web Site:* www.voiceandvideo.com, pg 932

Schuhmann, G Raymond, Kinetic Corp, 200 Distillery Commons, Suite 200, Louisville, KY 40206-1990 *Tel:* 502-719-9500 *Fax:* 502-719-9509 *Web Site:* kinetictms.com, pg 799

Schulman, Patricia, Pace Systems, 301 Hickory Ave, Harahan, LA 70123 *Tel:* 504-837-4224 *Toll Free Tel:* 800-722-3797 *Fax:* 504-837-4307 *E-mail:* info@pacesys.com, pg 849

Schulman, Peter, Pace Systems, 301 Hickory Ave, Harahan, LA 70123 *Tel:* 504-837-4224 *Toll Free Tel:* 800-722-3797 *Fax:* 504-837-4307 *E-mail:* info@pacesys.com, pg 849

Schultz, Deborah Allen, Wisconsin Public Television, 821 University Ave, Madison, WI 53706 *Tel:* 608-263-2121 *Toll Free Tel:* 800-422-9707 *Fax:* 608-263-9763 *E-mail:* comments@wpt.org *Web Site:* www.wpt.org, pg 940

Schultz, Eric D, City Events Group, 57 Park Dr, Troy, MI 48083-2724 *Tel:* 248-589-0600 *Toll Free Tel:* 800-872-8295 *Fax:* 248-589-2020 *E-mail:* info@cityeventsgroup.com *Web Site:* www.cityeventsgroup.com, pg 725

Schultz, Greg, Astronomical Society of the Pacific, 390 Ashton Ave, San Francisco, CA 94112 *Tel:* 415-337-1100 *Toll Free Tel:* 800-335-2624 *Fax:* 415-337-5205 *Web Site:* astrosociety.org, pg 691

Schultz, Jeff, Stageright Corp, a Rogers Group brand, 495 Pioneer Pkwy, Clare, MI 48617 *Tel:* 989-386-7393 (Intl Sales) *Toll Free Tel:* 800-438-4499 *E-mail:* info@stageright.com *Web Site:* www.stageright.com, pg 899

Schultz, Lauren, AIGA, the professional association for design, 233 Broadway, Suite 1740, New York, NY 10279 *Tel:* 212-807-1990 *Toll Free Tel:* 800-548-1634 *E-mail:* general@aiga.org *Web Site:* www.aiga.org, pg 947

Schulz, Lance, Ballantyne Strong Inc, 11422 Miracle Hills Dr, Suite 300, Omaha, NE 68154 *Tel:* 402-453-4444 *Toll Free Tel:* 800-424-1215; 800-722-0046 *E-mail:* customerservice@btn-inc.com *Web Site:* ballantynestrong.com, pg 701

Schulze, Mark, Crystal Pyramid Productions™, 7323 Rondel Ct, San Diego, CA 92119-1530 *Tel:* 619-644-3000 *E-mail:* info@crystalpyramid.com *Web Site:* sandiegovideoproduction.com, pg 735

Schulze, Mark, New & Unique Videos™, 7323 Rondel Ct, San Diego, CA 92119-1530 *Tel:* 619-644-3000 *E-mail:* video@newuniquevideos.com *Web Site:* www.newuniquevideos.com, pg 839

Schuman, Paula, Quatrefoil Associates Inc, 29 "C" St, Laurel, MD 20707 *Tel:* 301-470-4748 *Fax:* 301-470-4749 *E-mail:* info@quatrefoil.com *Web Site:* www.quatrefoil.com, pg 868

Schumann, Karen, Gateways, PO Box 1706, Ojai, CA 93024-1706 *Tel:* 805-649-5367 *Toll Free Tel:* 800-477-8908 *Fax:* 805-649-5302, pg 768

Schurig, Tiia, AIGA, the professional association for design, 233 Broadway, Suite 1740, New York, NY 10279 *Tel:* 212-807-1990 *Toll Free Tel:* 800-548-1634 *E-mail:* general@aiga.org *Web Site:* www.aiga.org, pg 947

Schwab, Michael C, Kensington Falls Animation, 1680 Hillsdale Ave, Ambridge, PA 15003 *Tel:* 724-266-0329 *E-mail:* kensingtonfalls@aol.com *Web Site:* www.kensingtonfalls.com, pg 797

Schwartz, Alan, Caprock Developments Inc, 475 Speedwell, Morris Plains, NJ 07950 *Tel:* 973-267-9292 *Toll Free Tel:* 800-222-0325 *Fax:* 973-292-0614 *E-mail:* info@caprockdev.com *Web Site:* www.caprockdev.com, pg 716

Schwartz, David, Duplication Specialists Inc, 843 Merrick Rd, Baldwin, NY 11510 *Tel:* 516-867-7300 *E-mail:* sales@dupespec.com *Web Site:* dupespec.com, pg 748

Schwartz, Edmondo, Greenwich Entertainment, 610 Fifth Ave, 3rd fl, New York, NY 10020 *E-mail:* info@greenwichentertainment.com; booking@greenwichentertainment.com; publicity@greenwichentertainment.com; acquisitions@greenwichentertainment.com *Web Site:* greenwichentertainment.com, pg 774

Schwartz, Jan, Burlington A/V Recording Media, 106 Mott St, Oceanside, NY 11572 *Tel:* 516-678-4414 *Fax:* 516-678-8959 *E-mail:* shopping@recordingstore.com *Web Site:* www.recordingstore.com, pg 712

Schwartz, Jeff, PrimaLux Video Inc, 30 W 26 St, 7th fl, New York, NY 10010 *Tel:* 212-206-1402 *Web Site:* www.primalux.com, pg 862

Schwartz, Jordan M, Center City Film & Video Inc, 1501-1503 Walnut St, Philadelphia, PA 19102 *Tel:* 215-568-4134 *Fax:* 215-568-6011 *E-mail:* info@ccfv.com; sales@ccfv.com *Web Site:* www.ccfv.com, pg 719

Schwartz, Larry, United Audio Video Inc, 6855 Vineland Ave, North Hollywood, CA 91605 *Tel:* 818-980-6700 *Toll Free Tel:* 800-247-8606 *Fax:* 818-508-8273 *Web Site:* www.unitedavg.com, pg 921

Schwartz, Lauren, Kaboom Productions, 2169 Folsom St, Suite 201-M, San Francisco, CA 94110 *Tel:* 415-434-2666 *Fax:* 415-874-9324 *E-mail:* hello@kaboomproductions.com *Web Site:* kaboomproductions.com, pg 796

Schwartz, Lauren, Outside The Box Interactive LLC, 150 Bay St, Suite 706, Jersey City, NJ 07302 *Tel:* 201-610-0625 *E-mail:* office@outboxin.com *Web Site:* www.outboxin.com, pg 849

Schwartz, Louis O, American Sportscasters Association Inc (ASA), 225 Broadway, Suite 2030, New York, NY 10007 *Tel:* 212-227-8080 *Fax:* 212-571-0556 *Web Site:* www.americansportscastersonline.com, pg 949

Schwartz, Michael, M Schwartz & Gettinger Feather Inc, 45 Hoffman Ave, Hauppauge, NY 11788 *Tel:* 631-234-7722 *Fax:* 631-234-7817 *E-mail:* info@msgfeather.com *Web Site:* www.msgfeather.com, pg 882

Schwartz, Michael, Swivelier, 600 Bradley Hill Rd, Blauvelt, NY 10913 *Tel:* 845-353-1455 *Fax:* 845-353-1512 *E-mail:* info@swivelier.com *Web Site:* www.swivelier.com, pg 905

Schwartz, Phil, Canadian American Records, PO Box 808, Lititz, PA 17543-0538 *Tel:* 717-627-4800 *E-mail:* canadianamerican@dejazzd.com *Web Site:* www.canadianamericanrecords.net; www.canadianamericanrecordcompany.com, pg 715

Schwartzberg, Dan, Synaptic Digital, 79 Fifth Ave, 14th fl, New York, NY 10003 *Tel:* 212-682-8300 *Fax:* 212-201-4207 *E-mail:* learnmore@synapticdigital.com *Web Site:* www.synapticdigital.com, pg 905

Schwartzberg, Louis, Moving Art by Louie Schwartzberg, 3371 Cahuenga Blvd W, Los Angeles, CA 90068 *Tel:* 323-436-2229 *Fax:* 323-436-2230 *E-mail:* team@movingart.com *Web Site:* www.movingart.com, pg 831

Schwarz, Alan J, Jams Productions Inc, Production Trailer No 1, 206 Holt Rd, Bowmanville, ON L1C 3K7, Canada *Tel:* 647-273-4844 *E-mail:* info@jamsproductions.ca *Web Site:* www.jamsproductions.ca, pg 793

Schwarz, Susan, Jams Productions Inc, Production Trailer No 1, 206 Holt Rd, Bowmanville, ON L1C 3K7, Canada *Tel:* 647-273-4844 *E-mail:* info@jamsproductions.ca *Web Site:* www.jamsproductions.ca, pg 793

Schweickart, Mark, Porta-Jib, 416 N Varney St, Burbank, CA 91502 *Tel:* 747-283-1077 *Fax:* 747-283-1078 *Web Site:* www.porta-jib.com, pg 859

Schweizer, John, Point.360, 2701 Media Center Dr, Los Angeles, CA 90065 *Tel:* 323-987-9400 *Fax:* 818-847-2503 *E-mail:* sales@point360.com *Web Site:* www.point360.com, pg 858

Schwenner, Marty J, Magnetek Inc, N49 W13650 Campbell Dr, Menomonee Falls, WI 53051 *Tel:* 262-783-3500 *Toll Free Tel:* 800-288-8178 *Toll Free Fax:* 800-298-3503 *E-mail:* sales@magnetek.com *Web Site:* www.magnetek.com, pg 814

Schwieger, Tim, Broadcast Supply World Wide, 2237 S 19 St, Tacoma, WA 98405 *Tel:* 253-565-2301 (intl) *Toll Free Tel:* 800-426-8434 *Fax:* 253-565-8114 (intl) *Toll Free Fax:* 800-231-7055 *E-mail:* sales@bswusa.com; info@bswusa.com; customersupport@bswusa.com *Web Site:* www.bswusa.com, pg 711

Schwind, David R, Charles M Salter Associates Inc, 130 Sutter St, 5th fl, San Francisco, CA 94104 *Tel:* 415-397-0442 *Fax:* 415-397-0454 *E-mail:* info@cmsalter.com *Web Site:* www.cmsalter.com, pg 721

Schyvinck, Chris, Shure Inc, 5800 W Touhy Ave, Niles, IL 60714-4608 *Tel:* 847-600-2000; 847-600-8440 (tech support); 847-600-8699 (cust serv) *Toll Free Tel:* 800-25-SHURE (257-4873); 800-516-2525 (cust serv) *Fax:* 847-600-1212; 847-600-8444 (tech support); 847-600-8686 (cust serv); 847-600-8688 (parts) *E-mail:* info@shure.com *Web Site:* www.shure.com, pg 887

Sciannella, Chris, CAS Video Productions, 820 White Marsh Ct, Huntingtown, MD 20639 Tel: 301-674-2000 (cell) E-mail: info@casvideo.com Web Site: www. casvideo.com, pg 717

Scillipoti, Paula, Sunfire Communications Inc, 6965 Piazza Grande Ave, Suite 214, Orlando, FL 32835 Tel: 407-226-8226 Fax: 407-226-1660 E-mail: info@ sunfirecommunications.com Web Site: www. sunfirecommunications.com, pg 904

Sciolla, William, PSSI Global Services LLC, 7030 Hayvenhurst Ave, Van Nuys, CA 91406 Tel: 310-575-4400 Toll Free Tel: 800-SAT-LINK (728-5465); 800-634-6530 (teleport inquiries) E-mail: info@pssiglobal. com Web Site: www.pssiglobal.com, pg 866

Scionti, Joe, F&F Productions LLC, 14333 Myerlake Circle, Clearwater, FL 33760 Tel: 727-530-5000 Fax: 727-535-6547 E-mail: info@fandfhd.tv Web Site: www.fandfhd.tv, pg 759

Scott, Ed, KAE Corp, 955 E 500 S, Salt Lake City, UT 84102 Tel: 801-238-2300 E-mail: kaecorp@xmission. com Web Site: www.kaecorp.com, pg 796

Scott, Larry, Broadcast Center Studios, 700 Millbridge Gardens, Clementon, NJ 08021 Tel: 856-751-3500, pg 710

Scott, Michael, R B Annis Instruments Inc, 117 W Franklin St, Greencastle, IN 46135-1223 Tel: 765-848-1621 Fax: 765-848-1625 E-mail: info@rbannis.com Web Site: www.rbannis.com, pg 686

Scott, Stephen, Skotel Corp, 2645 Croissant Moreau, Brossard, QC J4Y 1P7, Canada Tel: 514-806-2340, pg 890

Scott, Tom, LITE-IT Grip Truck Rentals, 450 Saint Andrews Ct, West Chicago, IL 60185 Tel: 630-231-1671 Fax: 630-231-1672 E-mail: liteit1@sbcglobal.net Web Site: www.liteit1.com, pg 810

Scovill, Scott, CenterStaging LLC, 3407 Winona Ave, Burbank, CA 91504 Tel: 818-559-4333 Fax: 818-848-4016 E-mail: info@centerstaging.com Web Site: centerstaging.com, pg 719

Scribner, Julie, American Law Institute Continuing Legal Education (ALI CLE), 4025 Chestnut St, Philadelphia, PA 19104-3099 Toll Free Tel: 800-CLE-NEWS (253-6397) Fax: 215-243-1664 E-mail: custserv@ali-cle.org Web Site: www.ali-cle.org, pg 683

Scruggs, Roger, Roger Scruggs Films, PO Box 321054, Cocoa Beach, FL 32932-1054 Tel: 321-783-6545 (off); 321-795-6545 (cell) Web Site: www.tvphotog.com, pg 883

Scudder, Dean H, Sinauer Associates, 23 Plumtree Rd, Sunderland, MA 01375 Tel: 413-549-4300 Fax: 413-549-1118 E-mail: orders@sinauer.com (orders); publish@sinauer.com (gen edit correspondence); custserv@sinauer.com (cust serv) Web Site: www. sinauer.com, pg 889

Sculley, Andrew G Jr, eMagin Corp, 700 South Dr, Suite 201, Hopewell Junction, NY 12533 Tel: 845-838-7900 Fax: 845-838-7901 E-mail: info@emagin.com; sales@emagin.com; customersupport@emagin.com Web Site: www.emagin.com, pg 753

Scupham, Steph, Kansas City Film Office, 1321 Baltimore Ave, Kansas City, MO 64105 Tel: 816-691-3800 Toll Free Tel: 800-767-7700 E-mail: film@ visitkc.com Web Site: www.kcfilmoffice.com, pg 973

Seal, Emily, The Clio Awards, 825 Eighth Ave, 29th fl, New York, NY 10019 Tel: 212-683-4300 E-mail: event@clioawards.com Web Site: clios.com, pg 987

Seaman, John, Future Light Inc, 21887 Lorain Rd, Suite 200, Cleveland, OH 44126 Tel: 440-801-1310 Toll Free Tel: 800-581-5536 Fax: 440-779-4159 E-mail: info@future-light.com Web Site: www.future-light.com, pg 767

Seaman, Tom, MVD Entertainment Group, 203 Windsor Rd, Pottstown, PA 19464 Tel: 610-650-8200 Toll Free Tel: 800-888-0486 Fax: 610-650-9102 Toll Free Fax: 888-536-7998 Web Site: mvdb2b.com, pg 835

Searfoss, Len, American Color Imaging (ACI), 715 E 18 St, Cedar Falls, IA 50613 Tel: 319-277-3655 Toll Free Tel: 800-728-2722 Fax: 319-277-6522 E-mail: sales@ acilab.com Web Site: www.acilab.com, pg 683

Sears, Ric, Intellidyne LLC, 2677 Prosperity Ave, Suite 301, Fairfax, VA 22031 Tel: 703-575-9715 Fax: 703-575-9718 Web Site: www.intellidyne-llc.com, pg 789

Secrest, John, Ingram Content Group LLC, One Ingram Blvd, La Vergne, TN 37086-1986 Tel: 615-793-5000 Toll Free Tel: 800-937-8000 (retailers); 800-937-5300 (ext 1, libs) E-mail: customerservice@ingramcontent. com Web Site: www.ingramcontent.com, pg 787

See, Annmarie, See Factor Industry Inc, 37-11 30 St, Long Island City, NY 11101 Tel: 718-784-4200 Fax: 718-784-0617 Web Site: www.seefactor.com, pg 883

See, Bob, See Factor Industry Inc, 37-11 30 St, Long Island City, NY 11101 Tel: 718-784-4200 Fax: 718-784-0617 Web Site: www.seefactor.com, pg 883

Seeverson, Shawn, Waldom Electronics Corp, 1801 Morgan St, Rockford, IL 61102-2690 Tel: 815-968-9661 Toll Free Tel: 800-435-2931 (cust serv) Fax: 815-968-9029 E-mail: sales@waldom.com Web Site: www.waldom.com, pg 933

Sefakis, Janet, CommCreative, 75 Fountain St, Framingham, MA 01702 Tel: 508-620-6664 Toll Free Tel: 877-620-6664 Fax: 508-620-0592 E-mail: info@ commcreative.com Web Site: www.commcreative.com, pg 728

Segaller, Stephen, WNET/New York Public Media, 825 Eighth Ave, New York, NY 10019 Tel: 212-560-1313 Fax: 212-560-1314 E-mail: programming@thirteen.org Web Site: www.thirteen.org; www.wnet.org, pg 940

Segarra, Aaron, CP Communications, 15 Ninnie Dr, Wappingers Falls, NY 12590 Tel: 914-345-9292 Toll Free Tel: 800-762-4254 Fax: 914-345-9222 E-mail: info@cpcomms.com; sales@cpcomms.com Web Site: www.cpcomms.com, pg 732

Segrist, Dennis, ITA Audio Visual Solutions, 2162 Dana Ave & I-71, Cincinnati, OH 45207-1341 Tel: 513-631-7000 Toll Free Tel: 800-899-8877 Fax: 513-631-3290 E-mail: csr@ita.com Web Site: www.ita.com, pg 791

Seibert, Gregg, Madison Square Garden, 2 Pennsylvania Plaza, New York, NY 10121-0091 Tel: 212-465-6741 E-mail: msgnetpr@msgnetwork.com Web Site: www. thegarden.com; themadisonsquaregardencompany.com, pg 814

Seidel, Jeff, OmegaBrandess Distribution, 626 Hanover Pike, Suite 102, Hampstead, MD 21074-2036 Tel: 410-374-3250 Fax: 410-374-3184 E-mail: customerservice@omegabrandess.com Web Site: www.omegabrandess.com, pg 845

Seidel, Robert P, Technology and Engineering Emmy® Awards, 1697 Broadway, Suite 404, New York, NY 10019 Tel: 212-586-8424 Fax: 212-246-8129 E-mail: techemmys@emmyonline.tv Web Site: emmyonline.com/tech, pg 1004

Seidler, Cassidy, Chelsea Green Publishing Co, 85 N Main St, Suite 120, White River Junction, VT 05001 Tel: 802-295-6300 Toll Free Tel: 800-639-4099 (orders) Fax: 802-295-6444 E-mail: customerservice@ chelseagreen.com Web Site: www.chelseagreen.com, pg 721

Sekkat, Driss, Broadcast Management Group, 718 Seventh St NW, Washington, DC 20001 Tel: 202-609-7757 E-mail: info@broadcastmgmt.com Web Site: www.broadcastmgmt.com, pg 710

Selden, Charles J, Selden Associates, 150 S Mountain Ave, Montclair, NJ 07042 Tel: 973-493-9039 (cell); 650-327-1972 (CA location), pg 883

Seldon, Tammy, Giant Screen Cinema Association (GSCA), 624 Holly Springs Rd, Suite 243, Holly Springs, NC 27540 Tel: 919-346-1123 Fax: 919-573-9100 E-mail: info@giantscreencinema.com Web Site: www.giantscreencinema.com, pg 955

Selesnick, Lou, All Comm Rentals Inc (ALLCOMM), 1402 SW 13 Ct, Pompano Beach, FL 33069 Tel: 954-788-9555 Web Site: www.allcommrentals.com, pg 680

Self, Susan, Xenon Pictures Inc, 3521 Jack Northrop Ave, Hawthorne, CA 90250 Tel: 310-451-5510 Fax: 310-395-4058 E-mail: info@xenonpictures.com Web Site: xenonpictures.com, pg 943

Selim, Hani, Concrete Images, 1301 Main St, Venice, CA 90291 Tel: 310-452-9655 Fax: 310-452-9866 E-mail: office@concreteimages.com Web Site: www. concreteimages.com, pg 730

Seline, Gary M, Horizon Worldwide, 1765 Stebbins Dr, Houston, TX 77043 Tel: 713-647-7400 Fax: 713-647-6664 E-mail: info@horizonworldwide.com Web Site: horizonworldwide.com, pg 781

Selinger, Kenneth R, CCI Communications Inc, 643 Swedesford Rd, Malvern, PA 19355 Tel: 610-296-7233 Fax: 610-296-7358 E-mail: info@ccivideo.com Web Site: www.ccivideo.com, pg 718

Sell, Robert E, Accenture, 161 N Clark St, Chicago, IL 60601 Tel: 312-693-0161 Toll Free Tel: 877-889-9009 Fax: 312-693-0507 Web Site: www.accenture.com, pg 672

Selleck, Michael, Simon & Schuster, Inc, 1230 Avenue of the Americas, New York, NY 10020 Tel: 212-698-7000; 212-698-7126 Toll Free Tel: 800-223-2348 (cust serv) Fax: 212-698-7664 Toll Free Fax: 800-943-9831 E-mail: audiopublicity@simonandschuster. com Web Site: www.simonandschuster.net; www. simonandschuster.biz; www.simonandschuster.com, pg 888

Sellers, Andrew, Sensory Technologies LLC, 6951 Corporate Circle, Indianapolis, IN 46278 Tel: 317-347-5252 Toll Free Tel: 800-488-4336 (help desk) E-mail: csc@sensorytechnologies.com Web Site: sensorytechnologies.com, pg 884

Sellers, Anne, Sensory Technologies LLC, 6951 Corporate Circle, Indianapolis, IN 46278 Tel: 317-347-5252 Toll Free Tel: 800-488-4336 (help desk) E-mail: csc@sensorytechnologies.com Web Site: sensorytechnologies.com, pg 884

Sellers, Karen, Curtis Inc, 1105 Western Ave, Cincinnati, OH 45203 Tel: 513-621-8895 Toll Free Tel: 800-733-2878 Fax: 513-621-0942 E-mail: info@curtisinc.com Web Site: www.curtisinc.com, pg 736

Sellers, Peter, Freewheelin' Films, 44895 Hwy 82, Aspen, CO 81611 Tel: 970-925-2640 Fax: 970-925-9369 Web Site: www.fwf.com, pg 765

Sellke, Olivia, CEDIA IPRO Affinity Group, 8475 Nightfall Lane, Fishers, IN 46037 Tel: 317-328-4336 Toll Free Tel: 800-669-5329 E-mail: info@cedia.org Web Site: cedia.net, pg 952

Seltz, Martin A, Augsburg Fortress, 510 Marquette Ave, Suite 800, Minneapolis, MN 55402 Tel: 612-330-3300 Toll Free Tel: 800-328-4648 Toll Free Fax: 800-722-7766 E-mail: customercare@augsburgfortress.org; salesandservice@augsburgfortress.org Web Site: www. augsburgfortress.org, pg 695

Seman, Mark, API, 8301 Patuxent Range Rd, Jessup, MD 20794 Tel: 301-776-7879 Fax: 301-776-8117 E-mail: service@apiaudio.com Web Site: www. apiaudio.com, pg 687

Semegram, Harriet Rita, Wonderwomen™ Enterprises, 485 Rugby Rd, Brooklyn, NY 11226 Tel: 646-456-3266; 718-693-4322 E-mail: info@wonderwomen. com, pg 941

Semmes, Ben, Monotype Imaging Inc, 600 Unicorn Park Dr, Woburn, MA 01801 Tel: 781-970-6000 Toll Free Tel: 800-424-8973 Fax: 781-970-6001; 781-970-6002 (gen questions) E-mail: info@monotype.com Web Site: www.monotype.com, pg 829

Semone, Gigi, New York State Governor's Office for Motion Picture & Television Development (MPTV), 633 Third Ave, 37th fl, New York, NY 10017 Tel: 212-803-2330 E-mail: nyfilm@esd.ny.gov Web Site: esd.ny.gov/industries/tv-and-film, pg 974

Senn, Michael, Lawrence Behr Associates Inc, 3400 Tupper Dr, Greenville, NC 27834 Tel: 252-757-0279 Toll Free Tel: 800-522-4464 Fax: 252-752-9155 E-mail: lbagrp@lbagroup.com Web Site: www. lbagroup.com/associates, pg 703

Senseman, Ken, Lee Co Inc, 27 S 12 St, Terre Haute, IN 47807 *Tel:* 812-235-8155 *Fax:* 812-235-3587 *E-mail:* leeco@leecompanyinc.com; sales@leecompanyinc.com *Web Site:* www.leecompanyinc.com, pg 805

Sergeeff, Pamela, TiVo Corp, 2 Circle Star Way, San Carlos, CA 94070 *Tel:* 408-562-8400 *Toll Free Tel:* 877-367-8486 (cust support); 877-289-8486 (sales support) *Fax:* 408-567-1800 *Web Site:* business.tivo.com; www.tivo.com, pg 914

Seron, Suren M, Stray Angel Films, 11318 Santa Monica Blvd, Los Angeles, CA 90025 *Tel:* 310-277-6900 *Fax:* 801-438-5009 *E-mail:* rentals@strayangel.com *Web Site:* www.strayangel.com, pg 902

Serpico, Laura, Jupiter Moon Productions, 219 36 St, No 3A, Brooklyn, NY 11232 *Tel:* 631-553-9750, pg 795

Serr, Marilyn A, Spence-Thomas Audio Post, 70 Richmond St E, Suite 300, Toronto, ON M5C 1N8, Canada *Tel:* 416-361-6383 *Toll Free Tel:* 866-547-2617 *Fax:* 416-361-2970 *E-mail:* info@spence-thomas.com; bookings@spence-thomas.com *Web Site:* www.spence-thomas.com, pg 897

Serra, Janet, Western Connecticut Convention & Visitors Bureau, PO Box 968, Litchfield, CT 06759-0968 *Tel:* 860-567-4506 *Toll Free Tel:* 800-663-1273 *Fax:* 860-567-5214 *E-mail:* info@litchfieldhills.com *Web Site:* www.visitwesternct.com; www.litchfieldhills.com; www.visitfairfieldcountyct.com, pg 968

Serra, MM, The Film-Makers' Cooperative, 475 Park Ave S, 6th fl, New York, NY 10016 *Tel:* 212-267-5665 *E-mail:* filmmakerscoop@gmail.com; info@film-makerscoop.com *Web Site:* film-makerscoop.com, pg 760

Serrano, Ronaldo A C, RGB Technology Inc, 590 Herndon Pkwy, Suite 500, Herndon, VA 20170-5267 *Tel:* 703-834-1500 *Fax:* 703-834-1506 *E-mail:* solutions@rgbtec.com *Web Site:* www.rgbtec.com, pg 874

Servidio, John, WNET/New York Public Media, 825 Eighth Ave, New York, NY 10019 *Tel:* 212-560-1313 *Fax:* 212-560-1314 *E-mail:* programming@thirteen.org *Web Site:* www.thirteen.org; www.wnet.org, pg 940

Sesay, Ab, MAC Group, 75 Virginia Rd, North White Plains, NY 10603 *Tel:* 914-347-3300 *Fax:* 914-347-3309 *E-mail:* info@macgroupus.com *Web Site:* www.macgroupus.com, pg 813

Sessions, Don, Calzone Case Co, 225 Black Rock Ave, Bridgeport, CT 06605 *Toll Free Tel:* 800-243-5152 *Fax:* 203-336-4406 *Web Site:* www.calzoneandanvil.com, pg 714

Sessler, Dan, RF Specialties of Texas LLC, PO Box 1010, Newark, TX 76071-1010 *Tel:* 214-697-3477 (cell); 817-489-2730 *Toll Free Tel:* 800-537-1801 (Newark) *E-mail:* rfstx@swbell.net *Web Site:* www.rfspecialties.com, pg 874

Setbon, Julie H, iProbe Multilingual Solutions Inc, 20 Jay St, Suite 638, New York, NY 11201 *Tel:* 212-489-6035 *Toll Free Tel:* 888-489-6035 *Fax:* 212-202-4790 *E-mail:* info@iprobesolutions.com *Web Site:* iprobesolutions.com, pg 791

Setiadi, David PhD, Projects in Knowledge Inc, 290 W Mount Pleasant Ave, Suite 2350, Livingston, NJ 07039 *Tel:* 973-890-8988 *Toll Free Tel:* 800-772-8277 *Web Site:* www.projectsinknowledge.com, pg 865

Setterstrom, Andrea, Mole-Richardson Co, 12154 Montague St, Pacoima, CA 91331 *Tel:* 323-851-0111 *Fax:* 323-851-5593 *E-mail:* info@mole.com *Web Site:* www.mole.com, pg 829

Settle, Kristin, Milwaukee Film Office, 648 N Plankinton Ave, Suite 425, Milwaukee, WI 53203-2917 *Tel:* 414-273-3950 *Toll Free Tel:* 800-554-1448 *Fax:* 414-273-5596 *E-mail:* info@milwaukee.org *Web Site:* www.visitmilwaukee.org, pg 977

Settle, Raymond, Maximus Media Inc, 2727 N Grove Industrial Dr, Suite 111, Fresno, CA 93727 *Tel:* 559-255-1688 *Toll Free Tel:* 800-2THEMAX (284-3629) *Fax:* 559-255-0323 *Web Site:* www.tothemax.com, pg 820

Setzer, Tom, Accusoft, 4001 N Riverside Dr, Tampa, FL 33603 *Tel:* 813-875-7575 *Toll Free Tel:* 800-875-7009 *Fax:* 813-875-7705 *E-mail:* sales@accusoft.com *Web Site:* www.accusoft.com, pg 674

Sewald, Ronda, Black Film Center/Archive, Indiana University, Wells Library, Rm 044, 1320 E Tenth St, Bloomington, IN 47405 *Tel:* 812-855-6041 *Fax:* 812-856-5832 *E-mail:* bfca@indiana.edu *Web Site:* www.indiana.edu/~bfca, pg 706

Sexton, Jack, ALOM Technologies Corp, 48105 Warm Springs Blvd, Fremont, CA 94539-7498 *Tel:* 510-360-3600 *Toll Free Tel:* 800-500-9991 *Fax:* 510-226-7617 *E-mail:* customerservice@alom.com *Web Site:* www.alom.com, pg 681

Sexton, Mary, Rink Rat Productions Inc, 2 Monk Lane, St John's, NL A1E 1M8, Canada *Tel:* 709-739-9055 *Fax:* 709-739-9065 *E-mail:* info@rinkratproductions.com *Web Site:* www.rinkratproductions.com, pg 875

Sexton, Shelby, Wild Plum, 23371 Mulholland Dr, Suite 409, Woodland Hills, CA 91364 *Tel:* 310-823-7445 *Web Site:* www.wildplum.tv, pg 938

Seybert, Barry, SNAP, 18653 Ventura, Suite 295, Tarzana, CA 91356 *Tel:* 818-340-0283 *E-mail:* hdcine@gmail.com *Web Site:* www.facebook.com/barry.seybert, pg 891

Shadbolt, Melvin, ATV Research Inc, 1301 Broadway, Dakota City, NE 68731 *Tel:* 402-987-3771 *Toll Free Tel:* 800-392-3922 *Fax:* 402-987-3709 *E-mail:* sales@atvresearch.com *Web Site:* www.atvresearch.com, pg 692

Shadbolt, Scott, ATV Research Inc, 1301 Broadway, Dakota City, NE 68731 *Tel:* 402-987-3771 *Toll Free Tel:* 800-392-3922 *Fax:* 402-987-3709 *E-mail:* sales@atvresearch.com *Web Site:* www.atvresearch.com, pg 692

Shadoan, Dave, Southern California Sound Image Inc, 2425 Auto Park Way, Escondido, CA 92029-1222 *Tel:* 760-737-3900 *Fax:* 760-737-3929 *Web Site:* www.sound-image.com, pg 895

Shafer, Viktor, Cibola Systems, 180 S Cypress St, Orange, CA 92866 *Tel:* 714-480-0272 *Fax:* 714-480-0768 *E-mail:* info@cibolasystems.com *Web Site:* www.cibolasystems.com, pg 723

Shaffer, Loretta, Ocala/Marion County Visitors & Convention Bureau, 109 W Silver Springs Blvd, Ocala, FL 34475 *Tel:* 352-438-2800 *Toll Free Tel:* 888-FL-OCALA (356-2252) *Fax:* 352-438-2801 *E-mail:* exploreocalamarion@marioncountyfl.org *Web Site:* www.ocalamarion.com, pg 969

Shah, Jatan, QSC Audio Products LLC, 1675 MacArthur Blvd, Costa Mesa, CA 92626 *Tel:* 714-754-6161 *Toll Free Tel:* 800-772-2834 (US only) *Fax:* 714-754-6173 *E-mail:* info@qscaudio.com *Web Site:* www.qsc.com, pg 867

Shah, Jay, Hi-Tech Import Export Corp, 1101 W McNab Rd, Pompano Beach, FL 33069 *Tel:* 954-946-0603 *Fax:* 954-946-0652, pg 779

Shah, Shefali, Avaya Inc, 4655 Great American Pkwy, Santa Clara, CA 95054 *Tel:* 908-953-6000 *Toll Free Tel:* 866-GO-AVAYA (462-8292 US & CN) *Web Site:* www.avaya.com, pg 697

Shaller, Russell, Brady Corp, 6555 W Good Hope Rd, Milwaukee, WI 53201-0571 *Tel:* 414-358-6600 *Toll Free Tel:* 888-250-3082 *E-mail:* bradyusa@bradycorp.com (cust serv & sales) *Web Site:* www.bradyid.com, pg 709

Shalom, Morris, GLI Sound Systems, 2691 W 15 St, Brooklyn, NY 11224 *Tel:* 718-372-7849 *Toll Free Tel:* 800-GLI-PRO-1 (454-7761) *Fax:* 718-946-4151 *E-mail:* info@glipro.com; sales@glipro.com *Web Site:* www.glipro.com, pg 771

Shanahan, John, Penfield Productions Ltd, 35 Springfield St, Agawam, MA 01001 *Tel:* 413-786-4454 *Web Site:* www.penfieldprod.com, pg 853

Shanes, Bob, Talk-A-Phone Co, 7530 N Natchez Ave, Niles, IL 60714 *Tel:* 773-539-1100 *Fax:* 773-539-1241 *E-mail:* info@talkaphone.com *Web Site:* www.talkaphone.com, pg 906

Shank, Michael, TEK Media Group, 711 S Victory Blvd, Burbank, CA 91502 *Tel:* 818-244-4440; 818-255-5045 *Toll Free Tel:* 800-255-5045 (support) *Fax:* 818-855-8762 *E-mail:* as@tekmg.com *Web Site:* www.tekmg.com, pg 909

Shanks, Hershel, Biblical Archaeology Society (BAS), 4710 41 St NW, Washington, DC 20016 *Tel:* 202-364-3300 *Toll Free Tel:* 800-221-4644 *Fax:* 202-364-2636 *E-mail:* bas@bib-arch.org; merchandise@bib-arch.org *Web Site:* www.biblicalarchaeology.org, pg 705

Shaomian, Armen, Music & Entertainment Industry Educators Association (MEIEA), 1900 Belmont Blvd, Nashville, TN 37212-3758 *Tel:* 615-460-6946 *E-mail:* office@meiea.org; membership@meiea.org *Web Site:* www.meiea.org, pg 958

Shapiro, Alan, MAC Group, 75 Virginia Rd, North White Plains, NY 10603 *Tel:* 914-347-3300 *Fax:* 914-347-3309 *E-mail:* info@macgroupus.com *Web Site:* www.macgroupus.com, pg 813

Shapiro, Amy, National Institute for Trial Advocacy (NITA), 1685 38 St, Suite 200, Boulder, CO 80301-2735 *Tel:* 720-890-4860 *Toll Free Tel:* 800-225-6482 *Fax:* 720-890-7069 *E-mail:* customerservice@nita.org *Web Site:* www.nita.org, pg 836

Shapiro, Anita C, Practising Law Institute, 1177 Avenue of the Americas, 2nd fl, New York, NY 10036 *Tel:* 212-824-5710 (cust serv) *Toll Free Tel:* 800-260-4PLI (260-4754, cust serv) *Toll Free Fax:* 800-321-0093 (cust serv) *E-mail:* info@pli.edu; cs@pli.edu (cust serv) *Web Site:* www.pli.edu, pg 860

Shapiro, Brad, Location Camera Ltd, 300 Pennsylvania Ave, Oreland, PA 19075 *Tel:* 215-576-5600 *Fax:* 215-576-6022 *E-mail:* mail@locationcamera.com *Web Site:* www.locationcamera.com, pg 810

Shapiro, Brad, Location Lighting Ltd, 300 Pennsylvania Ave, Oreland, PA 19075 *Tel:* 215-576-5600 *Fax:* 215-576-6022 *E-mail:* mail@locationlighting.com; rentals@locationlighting.com *Web Site:* www.locationlighting.com, pg 810

Shapiro, Charlene, WNET/New York Public Media, 825 Eighth Ave, New York, NY 10019 *Tel:* 212-560-1313 *Fax:* 212-560-1314 *E-mail:* programming@thirteen.org *Web Site:* www.thirteen.org; www.wnet.org, pg 940

Shapiro, Doug, Turner Broadcasting System Inc, A Time Warner Company, One CNN Ctr, Atlanta, GA 30303 *Tel:* 404-827-1700 *E-mail:* turner.info@turner.com *Web Site:* www.turner.com, pg 919

Shapiro, Gary, Consumer Technology Association (CTA), 1919 S Eads St, Arlington, VA 22202 *Tel:* 703-907-7600 *Toll Free Tel:* 866-858-1555 *Fax:* 703-907-7675 *Toll Free Fax:* 866-858-2555 *E-mail:* cta@cta.tech *Web Site:* www.cta.tech, pg 953

Shapiro, Neal, WNET/New York Public Media, 825 Eighth Ave, New York, NY 10019 *Tel:* 212-560-1313 *Fax:* 212-560-1314 *E-mail:* programming@thirteen.org *Web Site:* www.thirteen.org; www.wnet.org, pg 940

Shapiro, Steve, Steve Shapiro Music, 7777 Skyline Blvd, Oakland, CA 94611 *Tel:* 510-339-9930 *Web Site:* www.stevemusic.com, pg 885

Sharenow, Rob, Lifetime Television®, 235 E 45 St, New York, NY 10017 *Tel:* 212-424-7000 *Web Site:* www.mylifetime.com, pg 807

Shariff, Al-Karim, Christie Digital Systems USA Inc, 10550 Camden Dr, Cypress, CA 90630 *Tel:* 714-236-8610 *Toll Free Tel:* 866-880-4462 (cust serv) *Fax:* 714-503-3375 *E-mail:* sales-us@christiedigital.com; orders@christiedigital.com *Web Site:* www.christiedigital.com, pg 722

Sharkey, Anna, S&P Global Marketing Intelligence, 55 Water St, New York, NY 10041 *Tel:* 877-863-1306 *E-mail:* questions@spcapitaliq.com *Web Site:* marketingintelligence.spglobal.com, pg 880

Sharma, Monika, Chicago South Asian Film Festival (CSAFF), 2909 N Sheridan Rd, Unit 1902, Chicago, IL 60657 *Tel:* 773-669-8348 *E-mail:* info@csaff.org; programming@csaff.org *Web Site:* www.csaff.org, pg 986

Shiner, Nicole, Greater Philadelphia Film Office, One Parkway Bldg, 11th fl, 1515 Arch St, Philadelphia, PA 19102 *Tel:* 215-686-2668 *Fax:* 215-686-3659 *E-mail:* mail@film.org *Web Site:* www.film.org, pg 975

Shinn, Duane, The Keyboard Workshop, PO Box 700, Medford, OR 97501 *Tel:* 541-664-7052 *Web Site:* www.playpiano.com; www.facebook.com/pianochords, pg 798

Shipkov, Peter, Method Studios, 3401 Exposition Blvd, Santa Monica, CA 90404 *Tel:* 310-434-6000 *Web Site:* www.methodstudios.com, pg 824

Shira, Jack, Edgenuity Inc, 8860 E Chaparral Rd, Scottsdale, AZ 85250 *Toll Free Tel:* 877-725-4257 (sales) *E-mail:* customersupport@edgenuity.com; solutions@edgenuity.com (sales) *Web Site:* www.edgenuity.com, pg 750

Shoaf, Rob, Triangle Regional Film Commission, PO Box 13041, Research Triangle Park, NC 27709-3041 *Tel:* 919-544-5501 *E-mail:* triangleregionalfilm@gmail.com *Web Site:* www.trianglencfilm.com, pg 974

Shockley, Glen, Flip 2 Media Inc, 1067 Serpentine Lane, Pleasanton, CA 94566-4759 *Tel:* 925-417-1420 *E-mail:* info@flip2media.com *Web Site:* www.flip2media.com, pg 762

Shoel, Michael Jack, Ariztical Entertainment Inc, 12400 Ventura Blvd, Suite 686, Studio City, CA 91604-2406 *Tel:* 818-760-3740 *Fax:* 818-760-3581 *E-mail:* info@ariztical.com; customerservice@ariztical.com; sales@ariztical.com *Web Site:* www.ariztical.com, pg 689

Sholder, Craig, Christie Digital Systems USA Inc, 10550 Camden Dr, Cypress, CA 90630 *Tel:* 714-236-8610 *Toll Free Tel:* 866-880-4462 (cust serv) *Tel:* 714-503-3375 *E-mail:* sales-us@christiedigital.com; orders@christiedigital.com *Web Site:* www.christiedigital.com, pg 722

Sholik, Stan, Stan Sholik Photography, 1946 E Blair Ave, Santa Ana, CA 92705 *Tel:* 949-250-9275 *Fax:* 949-756-2623 *E-mail:* stan@stansholik.com *Web Site:* www.stansholik.com, pg 886

Shook, Ellyn J, Accenture, 161 N Clark St, Chicago, IL 60601 *Tel:* 312-693-0161 *Toll Free Tel:* 877-889-9009 *Fax:* 312-693-0507 *Web Site:* www.accenture.com, pg 672

Shook, Ken, Xytech Systems Corp, 15451 San Fernando Mission Blvd, Suite 400, Mission Hills, CA 91345 *Tel:* 818-698-4900 *Fax:* 818-698-4901 *E-mail:* sales@xytechsystems.com *Web Site:* www.xytechsystems.com, pg 943

Shore, Julie, Emmy Awards (Primetime), 5220 Lankershim Blvd, North Hollywood, CA 91601-3109 *Tel:* 818-754-2800 *Fax:* 818-761-3814 *E-mail:* emmyawards@televisionacademy.com *Web Site:* www.emmys.com, pg 988

Shore, Julie, Television Academy, 5220 Lankershim Blvd, North Hollywood, CA 91601-3109 *Tel:* 818-754-2800 *Web Site:* www.emmys.com, pg 963

Shore, Kirk, Clever Devices Ltd, 300 Crossways Park Dr, Woodbury, NY 11797 *Tel:* 516-433-6100 *Toll Free Tel:* 800-872-6129 *Web Site:* www.cleverdevices.com, pg 726

Shore, Dr Linda, Astronomical Society of the Pacific, 390 Ashton Ave, San Francisco, CA 94112 *Tel:* 415-337-1100 *Toll Free Tel:* 800-335-2624 *Fax:* 415-337-5205 *Web Site:* astrosociety.org, pg 691

Shore, Mark, High Output Inc, 495 Turnpike St, Canton, MA 02021 *Tel:* 781-364-1800 *Fax:* 781-364-1900 *Web Site:* www.highoutput.com, pg 779

Short, Matthew, Flashback Stage Lighting (FBSL), 1124 Bay Blvd, Suite A, Chula Vista, CA 91911-7155 *Tel:* 619-697-2729 *Fax:* 619-697-2782 *E-mail:* mail@flashbackstagelighting.com *Web Site:* flashbackstagelighting.com, pg 762

Short, Ray, Research Technology International (RTI), 4700 Chase Ave, Lincolnwood, IL 60712-1689 *Tel:* 847-677-3000 *Toll Free Tel:* 800-323-7520 *Fax:* 847-677-1311 *Toll Free Fax:* 800-784-6733 *E-mail:* sales@rtico.com *Web Site:* rtico.com, pg 873

Shostak, Stuart, Shokus Video, PO Box 3125, Chatsworth, CA 91313-3125 *Tel:* 818-538-9985 *Toll Free Tel:* 800-SHOKUS-1 (746-5871 - orders) *Fax:* 818-701-0560 *E-mail:* info@shokus.com *Web Site:* www.shokus.com, pg 886

Shoup, John, Great Chefs/Leisure Jazz Video, 747 Magazine St, New Orleans, LA 70130 *Tel:* 504-581-5000 *Toll Free Tel:* 800-321-1499 *Fax:* 504-581-1188 *E-mail:* info@greatchefs.com *Web Site:* www.greatchefs.com, pg 773

Shoup, John, Leisure Video, 747 Magazine St, New Orleans, LA 70130 *Tel:* 504-299-9000 *Toll Free Tel:* 800-432-3853 *E-mail:* info@dukesofdixieland.com *Web Site:* www.dukesofdixieland.com; www.leisurejazz.com, pg 806

Shreve, Paul, Goose Creek Music & Entertainment, 17723 Tranquility Rd, Purcellville, VA 20132 *Tel:* 540-751-1395 *E-mail:* info@goosecreekmusic.com *Web Site:* www.goosecreekmusic.com, pg 772

Shub, E, Cambridge Documentary Films Inc, 3099 Hidden Valley Lane, Santa Barbara, CA 93108 *Tel:* 617-484-3993 *E-mail:* info@cambridgedocumentaryfilms.org; mail@cambridgedocumentaryfilms.org *Web Site:* www.cambridgedocumentaryfilms.org, pg 714

Shuey, Phillip N, CINDY Awards, 3824 Trogdon Ct, Flower Mound, TX 75022-5326 *Tel:* 469-464-4180 *Fax:* 469-464-4170 *Web Site:* cindys.com, pg 986

Shuey, Phillip N, IAA-VC (International Association of Audio Visual Communicators), PO Box 270779, Flower Mound, TX 75027-0779 *Tel:* 469-464-4180 *Fax:* 469-464-4170 *E-mail:* cindy@cindys.com *Web Site:* cindys.com, pg 955

Shumate, Thomas, Franciscan Media, 28 W Liberty St, Cincinnati, OH 45202-6498 *Tel:* 513-241-5615 *Toll Free Tel:* 800-488-0488 *Fax:* 513-241-0399 *E-mail:* info@franciscanmedia.org *Web Site:* www.americancatholic.org, pg 765

Shupper, Robert, Calrad Electronics, 819 N Highland Ave, Los Angeles, CA 90038 *Tel:* 323-465-2131 *Fax:* 323-465-3504 *E-mail:* sales@calrad.com *Web Site:* www.calrad.com, pg 714

Shute, Jonathan, Broadcasters General Store Inc, 2480 SE 52 St, Ocala, FL 34480 *Tel:* 352-622-7700 *Fax:* 352-629-7000 *E-mail:* sales@bgs.cc (orders) *Web Site:* www.bgs.cc, pg 711

Sickels, Mike, Soundfold Inc, 9200 N State Rte 48, Centerville, OH 45458 *Tel:* 937-885-5100 *Toll Free Tel:* 800-782-8018 *Fax:* 937-885-5115 *E-mail:* info@soundfold.com *Web Site:* soundfold.com, pg 894

Sickels, Tony, Soundfold Inc, 9200 N State Rte 48, Centerville, OH 45458 *Tel:* 937-885-5100 *Toll Free Tel:* 800-782-8018 *Fax:* 937-885-5115 *E-mail:* info@soundfold.com *Web Site:* soundfold.com, pg 894

Sicklick, Robert, AVFX Inc, 96 Holton St, Boston, MA 02135 *Tel:* 617-254-0770 *Toll Free Tel:* 888-254-0770 *E-mail:* info@avfx.com *Web Site:* www.avfx.com, pg 698

Siddhananda, Rev Swami, Chinmaya Publications, 560 Bridgetown Pike, Langhorne, PA 19053-7210 *Tel:* 215-396-0390 *Toll Free Tel:* 888-CMW-READ (269-7323) *Fax:* 215-396-9710 *E-mail:* publications@chinmayamission.org *Web Site:* www.chinmayamission.org; www.chinmayapublications.org, pg 722

Siefken, Paul, Fred Rogers Productions, 2100 Wharton St, Suite 700, Pittsburgh, PA 15203 *Tel:* 412-687-2990 *Toll Free Tel:* 877-677-6437 *E-mail:* info@fredrogers.org *Web Site:* www.fredrogers.org, pg 876

Siegel, Betty, Department of VSA & Accessibility at the John F Kennedy Center for the Performing Arts, 2700 "F" St NW, Washington, DC 20566 *E-mail:* vsainfo@kennedy-center.org *Web Site:* education.kennedy-center.org/education/vsa, pg 740

Siegel, Ellen, Practising Law Institute, 1177 Avenue of the Americas, 2nd fl, New York, NY 10036 *Tel:* 212-824-5710 (cust serv) *Toll Free Tel:* 800-260-4PLI

(260-4754, cust serv) *Toll Free Fax:* 800-321-0093 (cust serv) *E-mail:* info@pli.edu; cs@pli.edu (cust serv) *Web Site:* www.pli.edu, pg 860

Siegel, Frank, VCSvideo, 2807 Hunterdon Dr, Cinnaminson, NJ 08077 *Tel:* 856-273-8800 *Toll Free Tel:* 877-VCS-VIDEO (827-8433) *Web Site:* www.vcsvideo.com, pg 925

Siegel, Joel R, Edison Price Lighting Inc, 41-50 22 St, Long Island City, NY 11101 *Tel:* 718-685-0700 *E-mail:* orders@epl.com; info@epl.com *Web Site:* www.epl.com, pg 750

Sierra, Andres, Video Technology Services Inc, 5 Ariel Way, Suite 300, Syosset, NY 11791 *Tel:* 516-937-9700 *E-mail:* info@vts.global *Web Site:* www.vts.global, pg 929

Sifuentes, Jerry, Allied Artists International Inc, Production Services Ctr, 15810 E Gale Ave, Suite 133, Hacienda Heights, CA 91745 *Tel:* 626-330-0600 *Fax:* 626-961-0411, pg 681

Sigal, M A, Solutek Corp, 94 Shirley St, Boston, MA 02119 *Tel:* 617-445-5335 *Toll Free Tel:* 800-403-0770 *Fax:* 617-445-9623 *Web Site:* www.solutekphotochemicals.com, pg 892

Sigall, Lesley, Winter Film Awards Indie Film Festival, 31 W 34 St, New York, NY 10001 *Tel:* 646-355-4371 *E-mail:* info@winterfilmawards.com; submissions@winterfilmawards.com *Web Site:* winterfilmawards.com, pg 1007

Signorino, Joe, NEP Group Inc, 2 Beta Dr, Pittsburgh, PA 15238 *Tel:* 412-826-1414 *Toll Free Tel:* 800-444-0054 *E-mail:* info@nepinc.com *Web Site:* www.nepgroup.com, pg 838

Silber, Milos, Hayden 5 Media LLC, 22 W 27 St, 6th fl, New York, NY 10001 *Tel:* 212-871-9316 *E-mail:* hi@hayden5.com *Web Site:* www.hayden5.com, pg 777

Silberberg, David, Les Blank Films Inc, 10341 San Pablo Ave, El Cerrito, CA 94530-3123 *Tel:* 510-525-0942 *E-mail:* lesblankfilmsinc@gmail.com *Web Site:* lesblank.com, pg 707

Silberman, Dan, A&E Television Networks LLC, 235 E 45 St, New York, NY 10017 *Tel:* 212-210-1400 *Web Site:* www.aetv.com, pg 671

Silcock, Matt, Facets Multi-Media Inc, 1517 W Fullerton Ave, Chicago, IL 60614 *Tel:* 773-281-9075 *Fax:* 773-929-5437 *E-mail:* sales@facets.org; press@facets.org *Web Site:* www.facets.org, pg 758

Sills, Steven, Kaboom Productions, 2169 Folsom St, Suite 201-M, San Francisco, CA 94110 *Tel:* 415-434-2666 *Fax:* 415-874-9324 *E-mail:* hello@kaboomproductions.com *Web Site:* kaboomproductions.com, pg 796

Silton, Richard G, VideoLink Inc, an AVI-SPL company, 1230 Washington St, West Newton, MA 02465 *Tel:* 617-340-4100 *Toll Free Tel:* 800-452-5565 *Fax:* 617-340-4101 *E-mail:* sales@videolinktv.com *Web Site:* www.videolinktv.com, pg 929

Silva, John, Vantage Point Products Corp, PO Box 2485, Santa Fe Springs, CA 90670 *Tel:* 562-946-1718 *Fax:* 562-946-3898 *Web Site:* www.thinkvp.com, pg 924

Silva, Shannon, Visions Film Festival & Conference, 601 S College Rd, Wilmington, NC 28403 *Tel:* 919-607-0031 *E-mail:* visions7programming@gmail.com; visions7development@gmail.com *Web Site:* www.visionsffc.org, pg 1006

Silveira, Chris, Universal Studios Florida® Production Group, 1000 Universal Studios Plaza, Bldg 22A, Orlando, FL 32819 *Tel:* 407-363-8400 *Toll Free Tel:* 877-612-3737 (outside FL) *Fax:* 407-363-8869 *E-mail:* productiongroup@universalorlando.com *Web Site:* studio.florida.universalstudios.com, pg 922

Silver, Joseph, Designomotion, 67 E 11 St, Suite 324, New York, NY 10003 *Tel:* 917-532-0738 *E-mail:* info@designomotion.com *Web Site:* designomotion.com, pg 741

Silverio, Henry, Bridger Productions Inc, 4150 Glory View Lane, Jackson, WY 83001 *Tel:* 307-733-7871 *E-mail:* bridgerproductions@gmail.com *Web Site:* www.bridgerproductions.com, pg 710

Silverman, Amy, Synergem, 2323 Randolph Ave, Avenel, NJ 07001 *Tel:* 732-225-0001 *E-mail:* sales@synergem.com *Web Site:* synergem.com, pg 905

Silverman, Josh, Disney Consumer Products & Interactive Media (DCPI), 1201 Flower St, Glendale, AZ 91201 *Tel:* 818-544-0000 *Web Site:* dcpi.disney.com, pg 743

Silvers, Howard, Increase Video/Silver Mine Video, 5776 D Lindero Canyon Rd, Westlake Village, CA 91362 *Tel:* 805-480-0303, pg 786

Silvers, Stefan, Increase Video/Silver Mine Video, 5776 D Lindero Canyon Rd, Westlake Village, CA 91362 *Tel:* 805-480-0303, pg 786

Sim, Rob, SIM Digital, One Atlantic Ave, Suite 110, Toronto, ON M6K 3E7, Canada *Tel:* 416-979-9958 *Fax:* 416-979-7770 *E-mail:* info.toronto@simdigital.com *Web Site:* www.simdigital.com, pg 888

Simard, Melanie, STIL Casing Solution, 76 Saint Paul, Suite 103, Quebec City, QC G1K 3V9, Canada *Tel:* 418-694-0449 (ext 10); 418-694-0449 (ext 11, sales & cust serv); 418-694-0449 (ext 12, admin) *Toll Free Tel:* 888-414-0449 (CN & US) *Fax:* 418-694-1621 *E-mail:* info@stilcasing.com; sales@stilcasing.com; admin@stilcasing.com *Web Site:* www.stilcasing.com, pg 901

Simensky, Linda, PBS Video, 2100 Crystal Dr, Arlington, VA 22202 *Tel:* 703-739-5000 *Web Site:* shop.pbs.org; www.pbs.org/video, pg 852

Simeonova, Neda, Electronics Representatives Association (ERA), 1325 S Arlington Heights Rd, Suite 204, Elk Grove Village, IL 60007 *Tel:* 312-419-1432 *Fax:* 312-419-1660 *E-mail:* info@era.org *Web Site:* www.era.org, pg 954

Simms, Susan, The Florida Office of Film & Entertainment, 107 E Madison St, MSC 80, Tallahassee, FL 32399 *Tel:* 850-717-8990 *Toll Free Tel:* 877-FLA-FILM (352-3456) *E-mail:* floridaofe@deo.myflorida.com *Web Site:* www.filminflorida.com, pg 970

Simon, Douglas, D S Simon Productions, 229 W 36 St, 9th fl, New York, NY 10018 *Tel:* 212-736-2727 *Toll Free Tel:* 800-377-4666 *Fax:* 212-736-7040 *E-mail:* news@dssimon.com *Web Site:* dssimon.com, pg 888

Simon, Mike, Image Video Teleproductions Inc, 6755 Freedom Ave NW, North Canton, OH 44720 *Tel:* 330-494-9303 *Fax:* 330-966-1792 *E-mail:* info@image-video.com *Web Site:* www.image-video.com, pg 785

Simon, Perry, PBS Video, 2100 Crystal Dr, Arlington, VA 22202 *Tel:* 703-739-5000 *Web Site:* shop.pbs.org; www.pbs.org/video, pg 852

Simon, Richard A, Simon - Kaloi Engineering Ltd, 31192 La Baya Dr, Unit G, Westlake Village, CA 91362 *Tel:* 818-707-8400 *Fax:* 818-707-8401 *E-mail:* sales@skeng.com *Web Site:* www.skeng.com, pg 888

Simpkins, Ronnie, Smithsonian Folkways Recordings, 600 Maryland Ave SW, Suite 2001, Washington, DC 20024 *Tel:* 202-633-6450 *Toll Free Tel:* 888-FOLKWAYS (365-5929) *Fax:* 202-633-6477 *E-mail:* smithsonianfolkways@si.edu *Web Site:* folkways.si.edu, pg 891

Simpson, Cory, Laserium®, 84777 Charlottes Way, Eugene, OR 97405 *Tel:* 541-687-1414 *Web Site:* www.laserium.com, pg 804

Simpson, Craig, Tamura Corporation of America, 1040 S Andreasen Dr, Suite 100, Escondido, CA 92029 *Tel:* 951-699-1270 *Toll Free Tel:* 800-472-6624 *Fax:* 951-676-9482 *Web Site:* www.tamuracorp.com, pg 906

Simpson, M Lui, Association of American Publishers (AAP), 455 Massachusetts Ave NW, Suite 700, Washington, DC 20001-2777 *Tel:* 202-347-3375 *Fax:* 202-347-3690 *E-mail:* info@publishers.org *Web Site:* publishers.org, pg 951

Simpson, Mike, KPDX-TV Production Center, 14975 NW Greenbrier Pkwy, Beaverton, OR 97006-5731 *Tel:* 503-906-1249 *Fax:* 503-548-6920 *E-mail:* ezone@kpdx.com; fox12news@kptv.com *Web Site:* www.kptv.com; www.kpdx.com, pg 801

Simpson, Thad, Xenon Pictures Inc, 3521 Jack Northrop Ave, Hawthorne, CA 90250 *Tel:* 310-451-5510 *Fax:* 310-395-4058 *E-mail:* info@xenonpictures.com *Web Site:* xenonpictures.com, pg 943

Sims, Jane, Graftek Imaging Inc, 8900 Shoal Creek Blvd, Bldg 300, Suite B, Austin, TX 78757 *Tel:* 512-416-1099 *Toll Free Tel:* 800-441-2118 *Fax:* 512-416-1014 *E-mail:* graftek@graftek.com *Web Site:* www.graftek.com, pg 773

Simske, Steven J, Society for Imaging Science and Technology (IS&T), 7003 Kilworth Lane, Springfield, VA 22151 *Tel:* 703-642-9090 *Fax:* 703-642-9094 *E-mail:* info@imaging.org *Web Site:* imaging.org, pg 962

Sinasac, Joseph, Novalis, One Eglinton Ave E, Suite 800, Toronto, ON M4P 3A1, Canada *Tel:* 416-363-3303 *Toll Free Tel:* 877-702-7773 (CN & US only); 800-387-7164 (cust serv, CN & US only) *Fax:* 416-363-9409 *Toll Free Fax:* 877-702-7775 (CN & US only); 855-393-1555 (cust serv) *E-mail:* books@novalis.ca; resources@novalis.ca *Web Site:* www.novalis.ca, pg 843

Sinauer, Andrew D, Sinauer Associates, 23 Plumtree Rd, Sunderland, MA 01375 *Tel:* 413-549-4300 *Fax:* 413-549-1118 *E-mail:* orders@sinauer.com (orders); publish@sinauer.com (gen edit correspondence); custserv@sinauer.com (cust serv) *Web Site:* www.sinauer.com, pg 889

Singer, Andrew, Sound by Singer Ltd, 242 W 27 St, 2nd fl, New York, NY 10001 *Tel:* 212-924-8600 *Fax:* 212-366-6351 *E-mail:* info@soundbysinger.com *Web Site:* www.soundbysinger.com, pg 893

Singer, Lily, The Hamptons International Film Festival, 47 Newtown Lane, East Hampton, NY 11937 *Tel:* 631-324-4600 *Fax:* 631-324-1558 *E-mail:* info@hamptonsfilmfest.org; programming@hamptonsfilmfest.org (submissions) *Web Site:* hamptonsfilmfest.org, pg 991

Singer, Lloyd, Prositions Inc, 6200 Aurora Ave, Suite 400W, Urbandale, IA 50322 *Tel:* 515-864-7200 *Toll Free Tel:* 877-244-8848 *E-mail:* info@prositions.com *Web Site:* prositions.com, pg 866

Singh, Archana, John Wiley & Sons Inc, 111 River St, Hoboken, NJ 07030-5774 *Tel:* 201-748-6000 *Toll Free Tel:* 800-225-5945 (cust serv) *Fax:* 201-748-6088 *Web Site:* www.wiley.com, pg 938

Singh, John, Saturn Awards, 334 W 54 St, Los Angeles, CA 90037 *Tel:* 323-752-5811 *E-mail:* saturn.awards@ca.rr.com *Web Site:* www.saturnawards.org, pg 1003

Singh, Mala, Electronic Arts Inc, 209 Redwood Shores Pkwy, Redwood City, CA 94065 *Tel:* 650-628-1500 *Web Site:* www.ea.com, pg 752

Singletary, Jon, AV Metro Inc, 5401 Etta Burke Ct, Raleigh, NC 27606 *Tel:* 919-233-1901 *Fax:* 919-233-1804 *E-mail:* info@avmetro.com *Web Site:* www.avmetro.com, pg 697

Singleton, Curtiss, Media Vision USA, 1078 60 St, Oakland, CA 94608 *Tel:* 415-391-9090 *Toll Free Tel:* 877-746-8375 *Fax:* 415-391-9192 *E-mail:* info@media-vision.com *Web Site:* www.media-vision.com/en/north-america/usa, pg 822

Singleton, John A, Sun Entertainment Corp, 3106 Belmont Blvd, Nashville, TN 37212 *Tel:* 615-385-1960 *E-mail:* info@sunrecords.com *Web Site:* www.sunrecords.com, pg 903

Singleton, Sidney S, Sun Entertainment Corp, 3106 Belmont Blvd, Nashville, TN 37212 *Tel:* 615-385-1960 *E-mail:* info@sunrecords.com *Web Site:* www.sunrecords.com, pg 903

Sinkoff, Howard L, Vutec Corp, 11711 W Sample Rd, Coral Springs, FL 33065-3155 *Tel:* 954-545-9000 *Toll Free Tel:* 800-770-4700 *E-mail:* info@vutec.com; sales@vutec.com *Web Site:* vutec.com, pg 933

Sinnes, Roger, Professional Education Institute (PEI), 7020 High Grove Blvd, Burr Ridge, IL 60527 *Tel:* 312-521-8002 *Toll Free Tel:* 800-320-7517 *Web Site:* thepei.com, pg 865

Sipe, Michael, SoundTube Entertainment Inc, 10661 Rene St, Lenexa, KS 66215 *Tel:* 913-663-5600 *Toll Free Tel:* 855-663-5600 *Fax:* 913-663-3200 *E-mail:* sales@mseaudio.com *Web Site:* www.soundtube.com, pg 895

Siporen, Jaromy, Big Door, 114 Sheldon St, El Segundo, CA 90245 *Tel:* 310-546-6100 *Fax:* 310-906-4585 *E-mail:* sales@bigdoor.tv *Web Site:* www.bigdoor.tv; www.bigdoorstudio.tv, pg 705

Sippola, Carlene, Whole Person Associates Inc, 101 W Second St, Suite 203, Duluth, MN 55802-5004 *Tel:* 218-727-0500 *Toll Free Tel:* 800-247-6789 *Fax:* 218-727-0505 *E-mail:* books@wholeperson.com *Web Site:* www.wholeperson.com, pg 938

Sirah, Kiran Singh, International Storytelling Center, 116 W Main St, Jonesborough, TN 37659 *Tel:* 423-753-2171 *Toll Free Tel:* 800-952-8392 *Fax:* 423-913-8219 *E-mail:* customerservice@storytellingcenter.net *Web Site:* www.storytellingcenter.net, pg 956

Sirah, Kiran Singh, National Storytelling Festival, 116 W Main St, Jonesborough, TN 37659 *Tel:* 423-753-2171 *Toll Free Tel:* 800-952-8392 *Fax:* 423-913-8219 *E-mail:* customerservice@storytellingcenter.net *Web Site:* www.storytellingcenter.net/festival, pg 997

Sirkin, Adam, Liberty Uplink, 2547 Yellow Springs Rd, Malvern, PA 19355 *Tel:* 215-964-5222; 917-254-0155 *E-mail:* info@libertyuplink.com *Web Site:* www.libertyuplink.com, pg 807

Sirotin, Jason, ECG Productions, 120 Interstate N Pkwy SE, Suite 435, Atlanta, GA 30339 *Tel:* 678-855-5169 *Toll Free Tel:* 855-787-4487 *E-mail:* info@ecgprod.com *Web Site:* www.ecgprod.com, pg 750

Sisson, Shannon, Freedoms Foundation National Awards, 1601 Valley Forge Rd, Valley Forge, PA 19481 *Tel:* 610-933-8825 *Fax:* 610-935-0522 *E-mail:* info@ffvf.org *Web Site:* www.freedomsfoundation.org, pg 990

Siteman, Frank, Frank Siteman Photography, 136 Pond St, Winchester, MA 01890 *Tel:* 781-729-3747 *Fax:* 781-729-2549 *Web Site:* www.franksiteman.com, pg 889

Sitler, Linn, The Memphis & Shelby County Film & TV Commission, 496 S Main St, Suite 101, Memphis, TN 38103 *Tel:* 901-527-8300 *Fax:* 901-527-8326 *E-mail:* hello@filmmemphis.org *Web Site:* www.filmmemphis.org, pg 975

Sitler, Penny, Draper Inc, 411 S Pearl St, Spiceland, IN 47385 *Tel:* 765-987-7999 *Toll Free Tel:* 800-238-7999 *Fax:* 765-987-7142 *E-mail:* av@draperinc.com *Web Site:* www.draperinc.com; blog.draperinc.com, pg 746

Sittnick, Patrick, Kozmic Lazer Show LLC, PO Box 140197, Nashville, TN 37214-0197 *Tel:* 615-391-3226 *Toll Free Tel:* 800-MRLASER (675-2737) *Fax:* 615-391-3265 *E-mail:* mrlaser800@aol.com *Web Site:* www.kozmiclazershow.com, pg 801

Sivers, Alex, Skystorm Productions, 103 Commerce St, Suite 100, Lake Mary, FL 32746 *Tel:* 407-328-4747 *Toll Free Tel:* 800-783-8508 *Fax:* 407-328-4479 *E-mail:* info@skystorm.com *Web Site:* www.skystorm.com, pg 890

Size, Dennis M, Lighting Design Group, 49 W 27 St, Suite 920, New York, NY 10001 *Tel:* 212-685-4940 *Fax:* 212-685-4927 *E-mail:* lighting@ldg.com *Web Site:* www.ldg.com, pg 808

Skaf, Rashid, BIAMP Systems, 9300 SW Gemini Dr, Beaverton, OR 97008 *Tel:* 503-641-7287 *Toll Free Tel:* 800-826-1457 (US & CN) *E-mail:* biampinfo@biamp.com *Web Site:* www.biamp.com, pg 705

Skalinska, Maya, Timeless Books, Box 9, Kootenay Bay, BC V0B 1X0, Canada *Tel:* 250-227-9224 *Toll Free Tel:* 800-661-8711 *Fax:* 250-227-9494 *E-mail:* bookstore@timeless.org *Web Site:* www.timeless.org, pg 914

Skandalaris, Lee, Tectonics Industries LLC, 1681 Harmon Rd, Auburn Hills, MI 48326 *Tel:* 248-597-1600 *Toll Free Tel:* 888-408-3199 *E-mail:* info@tectonics.com *Web Site:* tectonics.com, pg 909

Skarka, Danny, MediaOne Studios, 950 Battery St, 2nd fl, San Francisco, CA 94111 *Tel:* 415-262-4222 *E-mail:* hi@mediaonestudios.com *Web Site:* mediaonestudios.com, pg 823

Skeel, Joe, Sigma Delta Chi Awards in Journalism, Eugene S Pulliam National Journalism Ctr, 3909 N Meridian St, Indianapolis, IN 46208 *Tel:* 317-927-8000 *Fax:* 317-920-4789 *E-mail:* awards@spj.org *Web Site:* www.spj.org, pg 1003

Skelton, Todd, Palardo Productions, 1807 Taft Ave, Suite 4, Hollywood, CA 90028 *Tel:* 323-469-8991 *E-mail:* palardo2@msn.com, pg 850

Skibitzky, Clinton, DACAPO Productions Inc, 516 Hargrave St, Winnipeg, MB R3A 0X8, Canada *Tel:* 204-956-2867 *Fax:* 204-956-2869 *Web Site:* www.dacapo.ca, pg 737

Skidmore, Steve, WOUB Public Media, 35 S College St, Athens, OH 45701 *Tel:* 740-593-1771 *Toll Free Tel:* 800-456-2044 *E-mail:* woub@woub.org *Web Site:* woub.org, pg 942

Skinner, Georja, State of Hawaii Film Office, 250 S Hotel St, Suite 510-A, Honolulu, HI 96813 *Tel:* 808-586-2570 *Fax:* 808-586-2572 *E-mail:* info@hawaiifilmoffice.com *Web Site:* filmoffice.hawaii.gov, pg 970

Skjekkeland, Atle, Association for Information and Image Management (AIIM), 1100 Wayne Ave, Suite 1100, Silver Spring, MD 20910 *Tel:* 301-587-8202 *Toll Free Tel:* 800-477-2446 *Fax:* 301-587-2711 *E-mail:* aiim@aiim.org *Web Site:* www.aiim.org, pg 950

Skjonberg, Knut, Skjonberg Controls Inc, 1363 Donlon St, Suite 6, Ventura, CA 93003 *Tel:* 805-650-0877 *Fax:* 805-650-0360 *Toll Free Fax:* 800-650-0360 *E-mail:* sales@skjonberg.com *Web Site:* www.skjonberg.com, pg 890

Skjonberg, Monica, Skjonberg Controls Inc, 1363 Donlon St, Suite 6, Ventura, CA 93003 *Tel:* 805-650-0877 *Fax:* 805-650-0360 *Toll Free Fax:* 800-650-0360 *E-mail:* sales@skjonberg.com *Web Site:* www.skjonberg.com, pg 890

Skof, Bruce, Shure Inc, 5800 W Touhy Ave, Niles, IL 60714-4608 *Tel:* 847-600-2000; 847-600-8440 (tech support); 847-600-8699 (cust serv) *Toll Free Tel:* 800-25-SHURE (257-4873); 800-516-2525 (cust serv) *Fax:* 847-600-1212; 847-600-8444 (tech support); 847-600-8686 (cust serv); 847-600-8688 (parts) *E-mail:* info@shure.com *Web Site:* www.shure.com, pg 887

Skoglund, Diana, Thompson Rivers University Marketing & Communications Dept, 805 TRU Way, Kamloops, BC V2C 0C8, Canada *Tel:* 250-852-7000 *Web Site:* www.tru.ca/marcom, pg 913

Skolnik, Eric, Blonder Tongue Laboratories Inc, One Jake Brown Rd, Old Bridge, NJ 08857 *Tel:* 732-679-4000 *Toll Free Tel:* 800-523-6049 *Fax:* 732-679-4353 *E-mail:* custsvc@blondertongue.com; btglobalsales@blondertongue.com (outside US & CN); information@blondertongue.com *Web Site:* www.blondertongue.com, pg 707

Skora, Jerry, On Site Video, PO Box 1865, Palatine, IL 60078-1865 *Tel:* 847-980-9808 *Fax:* 847-358-8697 *E-mail:* producersvideo@hotmail.com, pg 846

Skotarczak, Ron, Madison Square Garden, 2 Pennsylvania Plaza, New York, NY 10121-0091 *Tel:* 212-465-6741 *E-mail:* msgnetpr@msgnetwork.com *Web Site:* www.thegarden.com; themadisonsquaregardencompany.com, pg 814

Skunes, Timothy, CyberOptics Corp, 5900 Golden Hills Dr, Minneapolis, MN 55416 *Tel:* 763-542-5000 *Fax:* 763-542-5100 *E-mail:* info@cyberoptics.com *Web Site:* cyberoptics.com, pg 736

Slater, Laine, Vancouver International Film Festival (VIFF), Vancouver International Film Ctr, 1181 Seymour St, Vancouver, BC V6B 3M7, Canada

Tel: 604-685-0260 *Fax:* 604-688-8221 *E-mail:* info@viff.org; submissions@viff.org *Web Site:* www.viff.org, pg 1006

Slechta, Randy, SMI® Inc, 4567 Lake Shore Dr, Waco, TX 76710 *Tel:* 254-776-2060 *Toll Free Tel:* 800-568-1241 *Fax:* 254-772-9588 *E-mail:* dmcminn@lmi-inc.com; info@lmi-inc.com; info@success-motivation.com *Web Site:* www.lmi-world.com/smi, pg 891

Slechter, Richard J Sr, RJS Productions, PO Box 739, Westminster, MD 21158 *Tel:* 410-876-6300 *Fax:* 410-857-0608, pg 875

Slider, Ralph, Michigan Office Solutions (MOS), A Xerox Company, 2859 Walkent Dr NW, Grand Rapids, MI 49544 *Toll Free Tel:* 800-442-9070 *E-mail:* info@mos-xerox.com *Web Site:* www.mos-xerox.com, pg 825

Slinger, Penny, Blue Lotus Temple Studio, PO Box 888, Boulder Creek, CA 95006 *Tel:* 831-338-2544 *E-mail:* info@bluelotustemple.com *Web Site:* www.bluelotustemple.com, pg 707

Slivinskas, Todd, TVO/Ontario Educational Communications Authority (OECA), 2180 Yonge St, Toronto, ON M4S 2B9, Canada *Tel:* 416-484-2600; 416-484-2665 (cust rel) *Toll Free Tel:* 800-613-0513; 800-INFO-TVO (463-6886) *E-mail:* asktvo@tvo.org *Web Site:* tvo.org, pg 919

Sloan, Douglas, Icontent, 122 W 26 St, New York, NY 10001 *Tel:* 212-462-0022 *E-mail:* info@icontent.tv *Web Site:* www.icontent.tv, pg 783

Sloan, Nathan, B-K Lighting, 40429 Brickyard Dr, Madera, CA 93636 *Tel:* 559-438-5800 *Fax:* 559-438-5900 *E-mail:* info@bklighting.com *Web Site:* www.bklighting.com, pg 700

Slomovits, Laszlo, Gemini, 2000 Penncraft Ct, Ann Arbor, MI 48103 *Toll Free Tel:* 800-317-9929 *Fax:* 734-786-4007 *E-mail:* info@geminichildrensmusic.com *Web Site:* www.geminichildrensmusic.com, pg 769

Slomovits, Sandor, Gemini, 2000 Penncraft Ct, Ann Arbor, MI 48103 *Toll Free Tel:* 800-317-9929 *Fax:* 734-786-4007 *E-mail:* info@geminichildrensmusic.com *Web Site:* www.geminichildrensmusic.com, pg 769

Slovarp, Jeremiah, Jereco Studios Inc, 627 E Peach St, Suite E, Bozeman, MT 59715 *Tel:* 406-586-5262 *Web Site:* www.jerecostudios.com, pg 794

Sluijter, Jaap, Krishnamurti Foundation of America, 1070 McAndrew Rd, Ojai, CA 93023 *Tel:* 805-646-2726 (ext 10) *Fax:* 805-646-6674 *E-mail:* kfa@kfa.org *Web Site:* www.kfa.org, pg 802

Smallman, Peter, Image Zone Inc, 11 W 69 St, Suite 10A, New York, NY 10023 *Tel:* 212-924-8804 *Web Site:* www.imagezone.com, pg 785

Smallwood, Larry Jr, Philadelphia International Film Festival & Market, PO Box 48134, Philadelphia, PA 19144 *Tel:* 215-849-2716 (festival) *Toll Free Tel:* 877-347-FILM (347-3456) *E-mail:* info@philafilm.org *Web Site:* www.philafilm.org, pg 999

Smallwood, Mariah, Visions Film Festival & Conference, 601 S College Rd, Wilmington, NC 28403 *Tel:* 919-607-0031 *E-mail:* visions7programming@gmail.com; visions7development@gmail.com *Web Site:* www.visionsffc.org, pg 1006

Smart, Gordon, API, 8301 Patuxent Range Rd, Jessup, MD 20794 *Tel:* 301-776-7879 *Fax:* 301-776-8117 *E-mail:* service@apiaudio.com *Web Site:* www.apiaudio.com, pg 687

Smart, Robert J, RJ Video Productions, 15585 Tilden St, San Leandro, CA 94579-2316 *Tel:* 510-357-6535, pg 875

Smetona, Monika, Renkus-Heinz Inc, 19201 Cook St, Foothill Ranch, CA 92610-3501 *Tel:* 949-588-9997 *Fax:* 949-588-9514 *E-mail:* sales@renkus-heinz.com *Web Site:* www.renkus-heinz.com, pg 873

Smidt, James A, Metropolitan Audio-Visual Inc, 35333 N 27 Lane, Phoenix, AZ 85086 *Tel:* 480-948-9008, pg 824

Smidt, Jeanette E, Metropolitan Audio-Visual Inc, 35333 N 27 Lane, Phoenix, AZ 85086 *Tel:* 480-948-9008, pg 824

Smith, Adam, GBC Document Finishing, 4 Corporate Dr, Lake Zurich, IL 60047 *Toll Free Tel:* 800-723-4000 (orders & serv) *Toll Free Fax:* 800-914-8178 *Web Site:* www.gbcconnect.com; www.gbc.com, pg 769

Smith, Amira, Greater Philadelphia Film Office, One Parkway Bldg, 11th fl, 1515 Arch St, Philadelphia, PA 19102 *Tel:* 215-686-2668 *Fax:* 215-686-3659 *E-mail:* mail@film.org *Web Site:* www.film.org, pg 975

Smith, Andrew, Boyce Nemec Designs, PO Box 566, Norfolk, CT 06058-0566 *Tel:* 860-542-5937 *Web Site:* www.boycenemec.com, pg 709

Smith, Barry, Emerson Radio Corp, 3 University Plaza, Suite 405, Hackensack, NJ 07601 *Tel:* 973-884-5800 *Toll Free Tel:* 800-909-1240 (cust serv) *Fax:* 973-428-2067 *E-mail:* internet@emersonradio.com *Web Site:* www.emersonradio.com, pg 753

Smith, Bill, ICL Imaging Inc, 51 Mellen St, Framingham, MA 01702 *Tel:* 508-872-3280 *Toll Free Tel:* 800-660-3280 *Fax:* 508-872-7364 *E-mail:* csr@icl-imaging.com *Web Site:* www.icl-imaging.com, pg 783

Smith, Brad E, Shure Manufacturing Corp, 1901 W Main St, Washington, MO 63090 *Tel:* 636-390-7100 *Toll Free Tel:* 800-227-4873 *Fax:* 636-390-7171 *E-mail:* sales@shureusa.com *Web Site:* www.shureusa.com, pg 887

Smith, Brent, Aydin Displays, a Sparton Company, One Riga Lane, Birdsboro, PA 19508 *Tel:* 610-404-7400 *Toll Free Tel:* 866-367-2934 *Fax:* 610-404-8190 *E-mail:* sales@spartonre.com *Web Site:* www.spartonre.com, pg 700

Smith, Byron, National Association for Music Education (NAfME), 1806 Robert Fulton Dr, Reston, VA 20191 *Tel:* 703-860-4000 *Toll Free Tel:* 800-336-3768 *Fax:* 703-860-1531 *Toll Free Fax:* 888-275-6362 *E-mail:* memberservices@nafme.org *Web Site:* nafme.org, pg 958

Smith, Chauncey, The Wyland Group, 11291 Pierce St, Riverside, CA 92505 *Tel:* 805-955-7681 *Fax:* 805-522-1082, pg 942

Smith, Christopher, University of Florida, Warrington College of Business Information Technology Support Programs, Bryan Hall 300D, 1384 Union Rd, Gainesville, FL 32611 *Tel:* 352-273-1616 *Fax:* 352-392-6250 *E-mail:* itsp@warrington.ufl.edu *Web Site:* warrington.ufl.edu/itsp, pg 922

Smith, Craig, OSV Studios, 29605 Lorain Rd, North Olmsted, OH 44070 *Tel:* 440-779-1900 *Web Site:* www.osvstudios.com, pg 848

Smith, Daniel, Fuller Street Productions, 12131 Shoemaker Ave, Santa Fe Springs, CA 90670 *Toll Free Tel:* 877-637-8733 *Toll Free Fax:* 877-637-8733 *E-mail:* contact@fullerstreet.com *Web Site:* www.fullerstreet.com, pg 767

Smith, Daniel J, ooLite Media LLC, 3300 Graf St, Unit 4, Bozeman, MT 59715 *Tel:* 406-570-6474 *E-mail:* info@oolitemedia.com *Web Site:* oolitemedia.com, pg 846

Smith, David, Practising Law Institute, 1177 Avenue of the Americas, 2nd fl, New York, NY 10036 *Tel:* 212-824-5710 (cust serv) *Toll Free Tel:* 800-260-4PLI (260-4754, cust serv) *Toll Free Fax:* 800-321-0093 (cust serv) *E-mail:* info@pli.edu; cs@pli.edu (cust serv) *Web Site:* www.pli.edu, pg 860

Smith, David, Set Decorators Society of America (SDSA), 7100 Tujunga Ave, Suite A, North Hollywood, CA 91605 *Tel:* 818-255-2425 *Fax:* 818-982-8597 *E-mail:* sdsa@setdecorators.org *Web Site:* www.setdecorators.org, pg 962

Smith, Don, Alpha Source Inc, 6619 W Calumet Rd, Milwaukee, WI 53223-4186 *Tel:* 414-760-2222 *Toll Free Tel:* 800-654-9845 *E-mail:* customer.service@alphasource.com; info@alphasource.com *Web Site:* www.alphasource.com, pg 681

Smith, Donna, Chester F Carlson Award, 7003 Kilworth Lane, Springfield, VA 22151 *Tel:* 703-642-9090 *Fax:* 703-642-9094 *E-mail:* info@imaging.org *Web Site:* imaging.org, pg 985

Smith, Donna, Society for Imaging Science and Technology (IS&T), 7003 Kilworth Lane, Springfield, VA 22151 *Tel:* 703-642-9090 *Fax:* 703-642-9094 *E-mail:* info@imaging.org *Web Site:* imaging.org, pg 962

Smith, Drew, Video Dimensions Inc, 545 W 45 St, New York, NY 10036 *Tel:* 212-262-5453 *Web Site:* videodimensions.net, pg 927

Smith, Edgar, Geomatrix Productions, 270 Amity Rd, Woodbridge, CT 06525-2267 *Tel:* 203-389-0001 *E-mail:* info@geomatrixproductions.com *Web Site:* www.geomatrixproductions.com, pg 770

Smith, Eric, Auralex Acoustics Inc, 9955 Westpoint Dr, Suite 101, Indianapolis, IN 46256 *Tel:* 317-842-2600 *Toll Free Tel:* 800-95-WEDGE (959-3343, orders) *Fax:* 317-842-2760 *E-mail:* info@auralex.com *Web Site:* www.auralex.com, pg 696

Smith, Eric M, CMI Communications, 400 Mile Crossing Blvd, Rochester, NY 14624 *Tel:* 585-424-1900 *Toll Free Tel:* 888-736-8264 *Fax:* 585-424-1913 *E-mail:* info@cmiav.com *Web Site:* www.cmiav.com, pg 727

Smith, Ewan, The Whitlock Group, 12820 West Creek Pkwy, Richmond, VA 23238 *Tel:* 804-273-9100 *Toll Free Tel:* 800-726-9843 *Fax:* 804-273-9380 *E-mail:* information@whitlock.com; marketing@whitlock.com *Web Site:* www.whitlock.com, pg 937

Smith, Frank, Franklin Video Inc, 931 Marilyn Dr, Raleigh, NC 27607 *Tel:* 919-833-8888; 919-621-0400 (cell) *Web Site:* www.franklinvideo.com, pg 765

Smith, Glenn, Mouser Electronics Inc - A TTI Berkshire Hathaway Company, 1000 N Main St, Mansfield, TX 76063-1514 *Tel:* 817-804-3888 *Toll Free Tel:* 800-346-6873 *Fax:* 817-804-3899 *E-mail:* sales@mouser.com *Web Site:* www.mouser.com, pg 831

Smith, Gordon H, National Association of Broadcasters (NAB), 1771 "N" St NW, Washington, DC 20036 *Tel:* 202-429-5300 *E-mail:* nab@nab.org; membership@nab.org *Web Site:* www.nab.org, pg 958

Smith, Greg, Arc Light Efx Inc, 9338 San Fernando Rd, Sun Valley, CA 91352 *Tel:* 818-394-6330 *Fax:* 818-252-3486 *E-mail:* gaslights@arclightefx.com *Web Site:* www.arclightefx.com, pg 688

Smith, Greg, Navigator Systems Ltd, 1312 W Main St, Suite E, Lebanon, TN 37087 *Tel:* 615-547-1895 *Fax:* 615-547-1897 *Web Site:* www.hiretracknx.com, pg 837

Smith, Jeffrey, Blonder Tongue Laboratories Inc, One Jake Brown Rd, Old Bridge, NJ 08857 *Tel:* 732-679-4000 *Toll Free Tel:* 800-523-6049 *Fax:* 732-679-4353 *E-mail:* custsvc@blondertongue.com; btglobalsales@blondertongue.com (outside US & CN); information@blondertongue.com *Web Site:* www.blondertongue.com, pg 707

Smith, Jennifer J, Xplor® International, 24156 State Rd 54, Suite 4, Lutz, FL 33559 *Tel:* 813-949-6170 *E-mail:* info@xplor.org *Web Site:* www.xplor.org, pg 964

Smith, John, Smithsonian Folkways Recordings, 600 Maryland Ave SW, Suite 2001, Washington, DC 20024 *Tel:* 202-633-6450 *Toll Free Tel:* 888-FOLKWAYS (365-5929) *Fax:* 202-633-6477 *E-mail:* smithsonianfolkways@si.edu *Web Site:* folkways.si.edu, pg 891

Smith, Joseph, Bisk Education, 9417 Princess Palm Ave, Tampa, FL 33619 *Toll Free Tel:* 800-280-9718 *E-mail:* media@bisk.com *Web Site:* www.bisk.com, pg 706

Smith, Joseph M, Axxis Leasing Inc, 845 S Ninth St, Louisville, KY 40203 *Tel:* 502-568-6030 *Fax:* 502-568-6204 *E-mail:* info@axxisinc.com *Web Site:* www.axxisinc.com, pg 700

Smith, Judy, Waterfront Film Festival (WFF), 479 Columbia Ave, Holland, MI 49423 *Tel:* 269-767-8765 *E-mail:* info@waterfrontfilm.org *Web Site:* www.waterfrontfilm.org, pg 1006

Smith, Kary, Arc Light Efx Inc, 9338 San Fernando Rd, Sun Valley, CA 91352 *Tel:* 818-394-6330 *Fax:* 818-252-3486 *E-mail:* gaslights@arclightefx.com *Web Site:* www.arclightefx.com, pg 688

Smith, Kelly, OSV Studios, 29605 Lorain Rd, North Olmsted, OH 44070 *Tel:* 440-779-1900 *Web Site:* www.osvstudios.com, pg 848

Smith, Kevin, Denver Film Festival, 1510 York St, 3rd fl, Denver, CO 80206 *Tel:* 303-595-3456 *E-mail:* dff@denverfilm.org *Web Site:* denverfilmfestival.denverfilm.org, pg 988

Smith, Kevin, Denver Film Society, 1510 York St, 3rd fl, Denver, CO 80206 *Tel:* 303-595-3456 *E-mail:* info@denverfilm.org *Web Site:* www.denverfilm.org, pg 953

Smith, Mary, Spot Media Production Group, 2745 Locust St, St Louis, MO 63103 *Tel:* 314-667-5915 *E-mail:* info@spotmpg.com *Web Site:* www.spotmpg.com, pg 898

Smith, Matt, A/S Custom Furniture, 364-C Valley Rd, Warrington, PA 18976 *Tel:* 215-491-3100 *Fax:* 215-491-3107 *E-mail:* sales@ascustom.com *Web Site:* www.ascustom.com, pg 671

Smith, Matt, Jameco Electronics, 1355 Shoreway Rd, Belmont, CA 94002 *Tel:* 650-592-8097 *Toll Free Tel:* 800-831-4242 (orders); 800-536-4316 (cust serv) *Fax:* 650-592-2503 *Toll Free Fax:* 800-237-6948 *E-mail:* info@jameco.com; sales@jameco.com *Web Site:* www.jameco.com, pg 792

Smith, Megan, Ingram Content Group LLC, One Ingram Blvd, La Vergne, TN 37086-1986 *Tel:* 615-793-5000 *Toll Free Tel:* 800-937-8000 (retailers); 800-937-5300 (ext 1, libs) *E-mail:* customerservice@ingramcontent.com *Web Site:* www.ingramcontent.com, pg 787

Smith, Michael, Cinema Equipment Sales of California Inc, 31858 Castaic Rd, No 326, Castaic, CA 91384 *Tel:* 949-470-0298 *Fax:* 949-470-0835 *E-mail:* cinemadealer@cinemadealer.com, pg 724

Smith, Mike, Axxis Leasing Inc, 845 S Ninth St, Louisville, KY 40203 *Tel:* 502-568-6030 *Fax:* 502-568-6204 *E-mail:* info@axxisinc.com *Web Site:* www.axxisinc.com, pg 700

Smith, Mike, United Scenic Artists Local 829, 29 W 38 St, 15th fl, New York, NY 10018 *Tel:* 212-581-0300 *Toll Free Tel:* 877-728-5635 *Fax:* 212-977-2011 *E-mail:* vfxinfo@usa829.org *Web Site:* www.usa829.org; vfx.usa829.org, pg 963

Smith, Mike, WFRV-TV 5 CBS, 1181 E Mason St, Green Bay, WI 54301 *Tel:* 920-437-5411 *Fax:* 920-437-4576 *E-mail:* tips@wearegreenbay.com *Web Site:* www.wearegreenbay.com, pg 936

Smith, Nicholas, National Safety Council (NSC), 1121 Spring Lake Dr, Itasca, IL 60143-3201 *Tel:* 630-285-1121 *Toll Free Tel:* 800-621-7615; 800-621-7619 (cust serv) *Fax:* 630-285-1434 (cust serv); 630-285-1315 *E-mail:* customerservice@nsc.org *Web Site:* www.nsc.org, pg 836

Smith, Nick, AV Concepts Inc, 1917 W First St, Tempe, AZ 85281 *Tel:* 480-557-6000; 480-646-4216 (sales & serv) *Toll Free Tel:* 866-927-7590 *E-mail:* exhibitorservices@avconcepts.com *Web Site:* www.avconcepts.com, pg 697

Smith, Paula, Cinema Equipment Sales of California Inc, 31858 Castaic Rd, No 326, Castaic, CA 91384 *Tel:* 949-470-0298 *Fax:* 949-470-0835 *E-mail:* cinemadealer@cinemadealer.com, pg 724

Smith, Pete, Specialized Products Co, 1100 S Kimball Ave, Southlake, TX 76092 *Tel:* 817-329-6647 *Toll Free Tel:* 800-866-5353 *Toll Free Fax:* 800-234-8286 *E-mail:* customerservice@specialized.net; spcintl@specialized.net *Web Site:* www.specialized.net, pg 896

Smith, R Bob III, PAR Inc, 16204 N Florida Ave, Lutz, FL 33549 *Tel:* 813-449-4065 *Toll Free Tel:* 800-331-8378 *Fax:* 813-961-2196 *Toll Free Fax:* 800-727-9329 *E-mail:* cs@parinc.com *Web Site:* www.parinc.com, pg 851

Smith, Randy, Promax, 5700 Wilshire Blvd, Suite 275, Los Angeles, CA 90036 *Tel:* 310-788-7600 *Fax:* 310-788-7616 *Web Site:* www.promax.org, pg 961

Smith, Randy, Winsted Corp, 10901 Hampshire Ave S, Minneapolis, MN 55438 *Tel:* 952-944-9050 *Toll Free Tel:* 800-447-2257 *Fax:* 952-944-1546 *Toll Free Fax:* 800-421-3839 *E-mail:* info@winsted.com *Web Site:* www.winsted.com, pg 939

Smith, Robb, Audio Network US Inc, 48 W 25 St, 10th fl, New York, NY 10010 *Tel:* 646-688-4320 *E-mail:* nyoffice@audionetwork.com *Web Site:* us.audionetwork.com, pg 693

Smith, Ron, Martel Electronics Sales Inc, Yorba Linda Hills Business Park, 23221 E La Palma Ave, Yorba Linda, CA 92887 *Tel:* 714-692-6690 *Toll Free Tel:* 800-553-5536 *Fax:* 714-692-1835 *Toll Free Fax:* 800-553-6954 *Web Site:* www.martelelectronics.com, pg 818

Smith, Roy Jr, A/S Custom Furniture, 364-C Valley Rd, Warrington, PA 18976 *Tel:* 215-491-3100 *Fax:* 215-491-3107 *E-mail:* sales@ascustom.com *Web Site:* www.ascustom.com, pg 671

Smith, Sara, RingSide Creative, 13320 Northend, Suite 3000, Oak Park, MI 48237 *Tel:* 248-548-2500 *E-mail:* info@ringsidecreative.com; newbiz@ringsidecreative.com *Web Site:* www.ringsidecreative.com, pg 875

Smith, Selden, Duke Media Services, 0052 Bryan Ctr, Durham, NC 27708 *Tel:* 919-660-1740 *Fax:* 919-660-1719 *E-mail:* dms-info@duke.edu *Web Site:* sites.duke.edu/mediaservices, pg 747

Smith, Simon, Christie Digital Systems USA Inc, 10550 Camden Dr, Cypress, CA 90630 *Tel:* 714-236-8610 *Toll Free Tel:* 866-880-4462 (cust serv) *Fax:* 714-503-3375 *E-mail:* sales-us@christiedigital.com; orders@christiedigital.com *Web Site:* www.christiedigital.com, pg 722

Smith, Simon, Prior Scientific Inc, 80 Reservoir Park Dr, Rockland, MA 02370 *Tel:* 781-878-8442 *Toll Free Tel:* 800-877-2234 *Fax:* 781-878-8736 *E-mail:* info@prior.com; techsupportus@prior.com *Web Site:* www.prior.com, pg 862

Smith, Stephanie, Zondervan, 3900 Sparks Dr, Grand Rapids, MI 49546 *Tel:* 616-698-6900 *Toll Free Tel:* 800-226-1122; 800-727-1309 (retail orders) *Web Site:* www.zondervan.com, pg 945

Smith, Steve, Axxis Leasing Inc, 845 S Ninth St, Louisville, KY 40203 *Tel:* 502-568-6030 *Fax:* 502-568-6204 *E-mail:* info@axxisinc.com *Web Site:* www.axxisinc.com, pg 700

Smith, Steve, Falcon Safety Products Inc, 25 Imclone Dr, Branchburg, NJ 08876 *Tel:* 908-707-4900 *Toll Free Tel:* 800-332-5266 (ext 220, cust serv) *Fax:* 908-707-8855 *Web Site:* www.falconsafety.com; www.shopfalcon.com, pg 758

Smith, Steven T, Videosmith Inc, 200 Spring Garden St, Suite C, Philadelphia, PA 19123 *Tel:* 215-238-5070 *Fax:* 215-238-5075 *E-mail:* info@videosmith.com *Web Site:* videosmith.com, pg 930

Smith, TJ, Eastern Acoustic Works Inc (EAW), One Main St, Bldg 13, Whitinsville, MA 01588-2238 *Tel:* 508-234-6158 *Toll Free Tel:* 800-992-5013 *Toll Free Fax:* 800-322-8251 *Web Site:* www.eaw.com, pg 749

Smith, Wayne, DecisionOne Corp, 640 Lee Rd, 3rd fl, Wayne, PA 19087 *Tel:* 610-296-6000 *Toll Free Tel:* 800-767-2876; 800-777-8800 (cust serv); 888-287-9202 (sales); 800-554-5179 (CN) *Fax:* 610-296-2910 *E-mail:* sales@decisionone.com *Web Site:* www.decisionone.com, pg 740

Smith, Wendy, National Board of Review (of Motion Pictures), 40 W 37 St, Suite 501, New York, NY 10018 *Tel:* 212-465-9166 *Fax:* 212-465-9168 *E-mail:* nbr@nbrmp.org *Web Site:* www.nationalboardofreview.org, pg 959

Smither, Jonathan, Tarpley Media Systems, 3737 50 St, Lubbock, TX 79413 *Tel:* 806-797-5833 *Toll Free Tel:* 800-600-5833 *Fax:* 806-797-5139 *E-mail:* tms@tarpleymedia.com *Web Site:* www.tarpleymedia.com, pg 907

Smithers, Westwood Jr, Corporation for Public Broadcasting (CPB), 401 Ninth St NW, Washington, DC 20004-2129 *Tel:* 202-879-9600 *Toll Free Tel:* 800-272-2190 *Fax:* 202-879-9700 *E-mail:* press@cpb.org *Web Site:* www.cpb.org, pg 953

Smolian, Steven, Smolian Sound Studios, One Worman's Mill Ct, Frederick, MD 21701 *Tel:* 301-694-5134 *E-mail:* smolians@erols.com *Web Site:* www.soundsaver.com, pg 891

Smoots, Todd, Westworks Studios, 4100 E Dry Creek Rd, Littleton, CO 80122 *Toll Free Tel:* 800-491-1947 *E-mail:* info@westworksstudios.com *Web Site:* westworksstudios.com, pg 936

Smylie, Robert, Bowie Audio Visual Enterprises Inc, 290 Highpoint Dr, Ridgeland, MS 39157 *Tel:* 601-957-6566 *Toll Free Tel:* 800-748-9030 *Fax:* 601-957-7042 *Toll Free Fax:* 800-748-3401 *E-mail:* sales@bowieav.com; info@bowieav.com *Web Site:* www.bowieav.com, pg 709

Smyth, Judy, The Children's Book Store Distribution (CBSD), 23 Griffin St, Waterdown, ON L0R 2H0, Canada *Tel:* 905-690-9397 (ext 237) *Toll Free Tel:* 800-757-8372 (cust serv, CN & US) *Fax:* 905-690-3419 *E-mail:* info@childrensgroup.com; sales@idla.ca *Web Site:* www.childrensgroup.com, pg 722

Smyth, Robert, Yellow Moon Press, 29 Josephine Ave, Somerville, MA 02144 *Tel:* 617-776-2230 *Toll Free Tel:* 800-497-4385 *E-mail:* story@yellowmoon.com *Web Site:* www.yellowmoon.com, pg 944

Smythe, Deb, Banff Mountain Film & Book Festival, 107 Tunnel Mountain Dr, Banff, AB T1L 1H5, Canada *Tel:* 403-762-6347; 403-762-6369 *Toll Free Tel:* 800-298-1229 *Fax:* 403-762-6277 *E-mail:* banffmountainfestival@banffcentre.ca; banffmountainfilms@banffcentre.ca *Web Site:* www.banffcentre.ca/banff-mountain-film-and-book-festival, pg 983

Snead, Paul, Sound/Video Impressions Inc, 110 S River Rd, Des Plaines, IL 60016 *Tel:* 847-297-4360 *Fax:* 847-297-6870 *E-mail:* info@soundvideoimpressions.com *Web Site:* www.soundvideoimpressions.com, pg 894

Snell, David A, ATTO Technology Inc, 155 CrossPoint Pkwy, Amherst, NY 14068 *Tel:* 716-691-1999 *Fax:* 716-691-9353 *Web Site:* www.atto.com, pg 692

Sneve, Shirley, Vision Maker Media, 1800 N 33 St, Lincoln, NE 68503-1409 *Tel:* 402-472-3522 *Fax:* 402-472-8675 *E-mail:* visionmaker@unl.edu *Web Site:* www.visionmakermedia.org, pg 930

Snipes, Kenneth, L'AIR International, 117 Vacek St, Fort Worth, TX 76107 *Tel:* 817-237-9390 *Toll Free Tel:* 844-243-8574 *E-mail:* info@lairfloors.com *Web Site:* www.lairfloors.com, pg 802

Snow, Sheila, Northeast Louisiana Film Commission, 601 Constitution Dr, West Monroe, LA 71292 *Toll Free Tel:* 800-843-1872 *Web Site:* nelafilm.com, pg 971

Snow, Sheila M, Monroe-West Monroe Convention & Visitors Bureau, 601 Constitution Dr, West Monroe, LA 71292 *Tel:* 318-387-5691 *Toll Free Tel:* 800-843-1872 *Fax:* 318-324-1752 *Web Site:* nelafilm.com, pg 971

Snyder, Chad, Lyon Video Inc, 2091 Arlingate Lane, Columbus, OH 43228 *Tel:* 614-297-0001 *E-mail:* info@lyonvideo.com *Web Site:* www.lyonvideo.com, pg 813

Snyder, Jim, WETA Production Center, 3620 S 27 St, Arlington, VA 22206 *Tel:* 703-998-2054 *Web Site:* www.weta.org/tv, pg 936

Snyder, Ray R, Audio Visions Inc, 1501 N George St, York, PA 17404 *Tel:* 717-747-1898, pg 694

Snypnawski, Rachel, Broadway Costumes Inc, 1100 W Cermak Rd, 2nd fl, Chicago, IL 60608 *Tel:* 312-829-6400 *Fax:* 312-829-8621 *E-mail:* rentals@broadwaycostumes.com *Web Site:* www.broadwaycostumes.com, pg 711

Soard, Laura, Steamboat Springs Film Committee, 125 Anglers Dr, Steamboat Springs, CO 80487 *Tel:* 970-879-0880 *E-mail:* info@steamboatchamber.com *Web Site:* www.steamboatchamber.com/media/steamboat-springs-film-committee, pg 968

Soares, Paul, Evertz Microsystems Ltd, 5292 John Lucas Dr, Burlington, ON L7L 5Z9, Canada *Tel:* 905-335-3700 *Toll Free Tel:* 877-995-3700 *Fax:* 905-335-3573 *E-mail:* sales@evertz.com *Web Site:* www.evertz.com, pg 757

Soares, Rodney, Dorian Color, 100 Main St, Melrose, MA 02176 *Tel:* 781-648-8040 *E-mail:* images@doriancolor.com *Web Site:* www.doriancolor.com, pg 746

Sobkowska, Anja, YAP Films, 233 Broadview Ave, Toronto, ON M4M 2G3, Canada *Tel:* 416-504-3662 *Fax:* 416-504-3667 *E-mail:* thedog@yapfilms.com *Web Site:* www.yapfilms.com, pg 943

Sobon, Leslie, Edgenuity Inc, 8860 E Chaparral Rd, Scottsdale, AZ 85250 *Toll Free Tel:* 877-725-4257 (sales) *E-mail:* customersupport@edgenuity.com; solutions@edgenuity.com (sales) *Web Site:* www.edgenuity.com, pg 750

Sobrito, June Marie, The Citation of Outstanding Service to the Society Award, White Plains Plaza, 445 Hamilton Ave, Suite 601, White Plains, NY 10601-1827 *Tel:* 914-761-1100 *Fax:* 914-206-4216 *E-mail:* marketing@smpte.org *Web Site:* www.smpte.org, pg 986

Sobrito, June Marie, The Presidential Proclamation, White Plains Plaza, 445 Hamilton Ave, Suite 601, White Plains, NY 10601-1827 *Tel:* 914-761-1100 *Fax:* 914-206-4216 *E-mail:* marketing@smpte.org *Web Site:* www.smpte.org, pg 1000

Sobrito, June Marie, SMPTE® Journal Award & SMPTE® Journal Certificate of Merit, White Plains Plaza, 445 Hamilton Ave, Suite 601, White Plains, NY 10601-1827 *Tel:* 914-761-1100 *Fax:* 914-206-4216 *E-mail:* marketing@smpte.org *Web Site:* www.smpte.org, pg 1004

Sobrito, June Marie, SMPTE® Progress Medal Award, White Plains Plaza, 445 Hamilton Ave, Suite 601, White Plains, NY 10601-1827 *Tel:* 914-761-1100 *Fax:* 914-206-4216 *E-mail:* marketing@smpte.org *Web Site:* www.smpte.org, pg 1004

Sobrito, June Marie, Technicolor-Herbert T Kalmus Medal Award, White Plains Plaza, 445 Hamilton Ave, Suite 601, White Plains, NY 10601-1827 *Tel:* 914-761-1100 *Fax:* 914-206-4216 *E-mail:* marketing@smpte.org *Web Site:* www.smpte.org, pg 1004

Sobrito, June Marie, The Samuel L Warner Memorial Medal Award, White Plains Plaza, 445 Hamilton Ave, Suite 601, White Plains, NY 10601-1827 *Tel:* 914-761-1100 *Fax:* 914-206-4216 *E-mail:* marketing@smpte.org *Web Site:* www.smpte.org, pg 1006

Soell, Alan, ABS Enterprises, PO Box 5127, Evanston, IL 60204-5127 *Tel:* 847-982-1414, pg 672

Sofia, Iris, Electric Lady Studios, 52 W Eighth St, New York, NY 10011 *Tel:* 212-677-4700 *Web Site:* electricladystudios.com, pg 752

Sofko, John, Turning Technologies LLC, 255 W Federal St, Youngstown, OH 44503 *Tel:* 330-746-3015 *Toll Free Tel:* 866-746-3015 *E-mail:* info@turningtechnologies.com; support@turningtechnologies.com *Web Site:* www.turningtechnologies.com, pg 919

Sofsky, Tava, Oklahoma Film & Music Office, 900 N Stiles Ave, Oklahoma City, OK 73104 *Tel:* 405-230-8440 *Toll Free Tel:* 800-766-3456 *Fax:* 405-201-4561 *Web Site:* okfilmmusic.org, pg 975

Sohrabkani, Azarin, Ottawa International Animation Festival, 2 Daly Ave, Suite 120, Ottawa, ON K1N 6E2, Canada *Tel:* 613-232-8769 *Fax:* 613-232-6315 *E-mail:* info@animationfestival.ca; entries@animationfestival.ca *Web Site:* www.animationfestival.ca, pg 999

Soileau, Chris, Maison de Soul Records, PO Drawer 10, Ville Platte, LA 70586-0010 *Tel:* 337-363-2177 *Toll Free Tel:* 800-738-8668 *Fax:* 337-363-

2094 *E-mail:* info@flattownmusic.com; info@floydsrecordshop.com *Web Site:* www.flattownmusic.com, pg 815

Soileau, Floyd, Flat Town Music Co, 700 S Chataignier St, Ville Platte, LA 70586 *Tel:* 337-363-2177 *Toll Free Tel:* 800-738-8668 *Fax:* 337-363-2094 *E-mail:* info@flattownmusic.com; order@flattownmusic.com *Web Site:* www.flattownmusic.com, pg 762

Soileau, Floyd, Jin Records, 700 S Chataignier, Ville Platte, LA 70586 *Tel:* 337-363-2177 *Toll Free Tel:* 800-738-8668 (orders) *Fax:* 337-363-2094 *E-mail:* info@flattownmusic.com *Web Site:* www.flattownmusic.com, pg 794

Soileau, Floyd, Maison de Soul Records, PO Drawer 10, Ville Platte, LA 70586-0010 *Tel:* 337-363-2177 *Toll Free Tel:* 800-738-8668 *Fax:* 337-363-2094 *E-mail:* info@flattownmusic.com; info@floydsrecordshop.com *Web Site:* www.flattownmusic.com, pg 815

Soileau, Floyd, Swallow, 700 S Chataignier St, Drawer 10, Ville Platte, LA 70586 *Tel:* 337-363-2177 *Fax:* 337-363-2094 *E-mail:* info@flattownmusic.com *Web Site:* www.flattownmusic.com, pg 905

Sokol, Marta, WIA - The Wireless Infrastructure Association, 2111 Wilson Blvd, Suite 210, Arlington, VA 22201 *Tel:* 703-739-0300 *Toll Free Tel:* 800-759-0300 *Fax:* 703-836-1608 *Web Site:* wia.org, pg 963

Sokolov, Elliot, Elliot Sokolov Music, One Hillside Ave, Goldens Bridge, NY 10526 *Tel:* 917-690-5487 *E-mail:* elliotsounds@gmail.com *Web Site:* www.elliotsokolov.com, pg 892

Soldani, Ed, AheadTeK, 6410 Via Del Oro, San Jose, CA 95119 *Tel:* 408-226-9800; 408-226-9991 *Toll Free Tel:* 800-971-9191 *Fax:* 408-226-9195 *Web Site:* www.aheadtek.com, pg 678

Solis, Amber, BigFoot Mobile Systems, 4015 Blackthorn Dr, Vacaville, CA 95688 *Tel:* 707-602-5548 *Fax:* 707-602-5549 *E-mail:* info@bigfootmobilecarts.com *Web Site:* www.bigfootmobilecarts.com, pg 705

Solis, Doug, BigFoot Mobile Systems, 4015 Blackthorn Dr, Vacaville, CA 95688 *Tel:* 707-602-5548 *Fax:* 707-602-5549 *E-mail:* info@bigfootmobilecarts.com *Web Site:* www.bigfootmobilecarts.com, pg 705

Solomon, David, Lightspeed Technologies Inc, 11509 SW Herman Rd, Tualatin, OR 97062 *Tel:* 503-684-5538 *Toll Free Tel:* 800-732-8999 *Fax:* 503-684-3197 *E-mail:* info@lightspeed-tek.com *Web Site:* www.lightspeed-tek.com, pg 808

Solomon, Jordan, Madison Square Garden, 2 Pennsylvania Plaza, New York, NY 10121-0091 *Tel:* 212-465-6741 *E-mail:* msgnetpr@msgnetwork.com *Web Site:* www.thegarden.com; themadisonsquaregardencompany.com, pg 814

Solomon, Whitney, IPI - Member Network™, 2518 Anthem Village Dr, Suite 104, Henderson, NV 89052 *Tel:* 702-617-1141 *Fax:* 702-617-1181 *E-mail:* info@ipiphoto.com *Web Site:* www.ipiphoto.com, pg 957

Somerstein, Jeff, Accord Productions, 2140 S Dixie Hwy, Suite 301, Miami, FL 33133 *Tel:* 305-856-1245; 305-985-5842 *Toll Free Tel:* 800-833-1245 *Fax:* 305-856-9101 *E-mail:* mail@accordvideo.com *Web Site:* www.accordproductions.com, pg 673

Somo, Darren, GVISION USA Inc, 20532 Crescent Bay Dr, Lake Forest, CA 92630 *Tel:* 949-586-3338 *Fax:* 949-272-4594 *E-mail:* info@gvision-usa.com *Web Site:* gvision-usa.com, pg 775

Sonder, Mark, Mark Sonder Productions & Entertainment Agency, 2479 Freezeland Rd, Linden, VA 22642 *Tel:* 540-636-1640 *E-mail:* inquiry@marksonderproductions.com *Web Site:* mspentertainmentagency.com, pg 817

Sonnier, Dallas, Cinestate, 4100 Swiss Ave, Dallas, TX 75204 *E-mail:* info@cinestate.com *Web Site:* cinestate.com, pg 724

Sood, Sanjay, ATX Networks, 8-1602 Tricont Ave, Whitby, ON L1N 7C3, Canada *Tel:* 289-204-7800 *Toll Free Tel:* 866-968-7289 *E-mail:* info@atx.com *Web Site:* atx.com, pg 692

Soran, David, Audio Consultant Services Inc, 4020 S Spruce St, Denver, CO 80237 Tel: 303-437-0308 Web Site: www.audio-consultants.com, pg 693

Sorensen, Carsten, Method Studios, 3401 Exposition Blvd, Santa Monica, CA 90404 Tel: 310-434-6000 Web Site: www.methodstudios.com, pg 824

Sorensen, Robert, Wisconsin Technical College System Foundation Inc, 6602 Normandy Lane, Madison, WI 53719-1081 Tel: 608-841-1800 Toll Free Tel: 800-821-6313 Fax: 608-841-1806 E-mail: foundation@wtcsf. tec.wi.us Web Site: www.wtcsf.tec.wi.us, pg 940

Soriano, Nina, Anonymous Content, 3532 Hayden Ave, Culver City, CA 90232 Tel: 310-558-6000 Fax: 310-558-2724 E-mail: filmtv@anonymouscontent.com Web Site: www.anonymouscontent.com, pg 686

Sorini, Stephanie, Butte Montana Chamber of Commerce, 1000 George St, Butte, MT 59701 Tel: 406-723-3177 Toll Free Tel: 800-735-6814 Fax: 406-723-1215 E-mail: marketing@buttechamber. org Web Site: www.buttechambersite.org; www. visitbutte.com, pg 973

Sorvig, Greg, Heartland International Film Festival, 1043 Virginia Ave, Suite 2, Indianapolis, IN 46203 Tel: 317-464-9405 E-mail: submissions@ heartlandfilm.org Web Site: heartlandfilm.org/festival, pg 992

Sorvig, Greg, Indy Shorts International Film Fest, 1043 Virginia Ave, Suite 2, Indianapolis, IN 46203 Tel: 317-464-9405 E-mail: submissions@ heartlandfilm.org Web Site: heartlandfilm.org, pg 993

Soss, Martin, Raven Screen Corp, PO Box 691, Harriman, NY 10926 Tel: 845-782-1844 Toll Free Tel: 800-847-6906 Fax: 845-782-1840 E-mail: info@ ravenscreen.com Web Site: www.ravenscreen.com, pg 870

Sotelo, Janine, VidCAD LLC, 2010 E Lohman Ave, Suite 2, Las Cruces, NM 88001 Tel: 575-522-0003 Toll Free Tel: 800-VIDCAD-6 (843-2236 sales) Fax: 575-522-0009 E-mail: sales@vidcad.com Web Site: www.vidcad.com, pg 927

Sotherland, Doug, PESA, 103 Quality Circle, Suite 210, Huntsville, AL 35806 Tel: 256-726-9200 Toll Free Tel: 800-323-7372 E-mail: sales@pesa.com Web Site: www.pesa.com, pg 855

Soucy, Dean, Clever Devices Ltd, 300 Crossways Park Dr, Woodbury, NY 11797 Tel: 516-433-6100 Toll Free Tel: 800-872-6129 Web Site: www.cleverdevices.com, pg 726

Soussan, Phil, The Recording Academy, 3030 Olympic Blvd, Santa Monica, CA 90404 Tel: 310-392-3777 Fax: 310-392-2306 E-mail: losangeles@grammy. com Site: www.grammy.org/recording-academy, pg 961

Southwell, Gary, CSPI, 175 Cabot St, Suite 210, Lowell, MA 01854 Tel: 978-663-7598; 978-954-5038 Toll Free Tel: 800-325-3110 E-mail: hello@cspi.com Web Site: www.cspi.com, pg 735

Southwood, Micah, Fred Rogers Productions, 2100 Wharton St, Suite 700, Pittsburgh, PA 15203 Tel: 412-687-2990 Toll Free Tel: 877-677-6437 E-mail: info@ fredrogers.org Web Site: www.fredrogers.org, pg 876

Souza, James, Pyro Spectaculars Inc, 3196 N Locust Ave, Rialto, CA 92377 Tel: 909-355-8120 Toll Free Tel: 888-477-PYRO (477-7976) E-mail: information@ pyrospec.com Web Site: www.pyrospec.com, pg 867

Spain, Jay, The Communications Group Inc, 502 S West St, Raleigh, NC 27601 Tel: 919-828-4086 Toll Free Tel: 800-595-2937 E-mail: info@cgfilm.com Web Site: cgroupfilm.tv, pg 729

Spalla, Ken, Duray Lighting, 500 E Touhy Ave, Suite F, Des Plaines, IL 60018 Tel: 773-271-2800 Fax: 773-271-4410 E-mail: info@duraylighting.com; sales@ duraylighting.com Web Site: www.duraylighting.com, pg 748

Spallone, Nicholas F, Morefield Communications Inc, 35 N 35 St, Camp Hill, PA 17011-2707 Tel: 717-761-6170 Toll Free Tel: 800-382-1266 E-mail: info@ morefield.com Web Site: www.morefield.com, pg 830

Spano, Mark, Digital Arts NY, 130 W 29 St, New York, NY 10001 Tel: 212-460-9600 Fax: 212-660-3600 Web Site: digitalartsny.com, pg 742

Speaks, Valerie, Palace Costume & Prop Co, 835 N Fairfax Ave, Hollywood, CA 90046 Tel: 323-651-5458 Fax: 323-658-7133 E-mail: rentals@palacecostume. com Web Site: www.palacecostume.com, pg 850

Spears, Ross, James Agee Film Project, PO Box 73, Riverdale, MD 20738-0073 Tel: 301-277-3880 E-mail: jagee@cstone.net Web Site: www.ageefilms. org, pg 792

Spears, Scott, Production Partners Media, 520 Enterprise Dr, Suite C, Lewis Center, OH 43035 Tel: 614-888-4888 Web Site: productionpartnersmedia.com, pg 864

Specht, Kris, Comrex Corp, 19 Pine Rd, Devens, MA 01434 Tel: 978-784-1776 (intl) Toll Free Tel: 800-237-1776 Fax: 978-784-1717 E-mail: info@comrex.com Web Site: www.comrex.com, pg 730

Speckels, Larry, One Touch Systems Inc, 2528 Qume Dr, Unit 14, San Jose, CA 95131 Tel: 408-436-4643 E-mail: info@onetouchsys.com Web Site: www. onetouchsys.com, pg 846

Specter, Kellie Castrutta, WNET/New York Public Media, 825 Eighth Ave, New York, NY 10019 Tel: 212-560-1313 Fax: 212-560-1314 E-mail: programming@thirteen.org Web Site: www. thirteen.org; www.wnet.org, pg 940

Speers, Genne, Canadian Filmmakers Distribution Center (CFMDC), 401 Richmond St W, Toronto, ON M5V 3A8, Canada Tel: 416-588-0725 E-mail: info@cfmdc. org Web Site: www.cfmdc.org, pg 715

Speers, Sheldon, Ross Video Ltd, 8 John St, Iroquois, ON K0E 1K0, Canada Tel: 613-652-4886 Fax: 613-652-4425 E-mail: solutions@rossvideo.com Web Site: www.rossvideo.com, pg 878

Spence, Susan, Television Academy, 5220 Lankershim Blvd, North Hollywood, CA 91601-3109 Tel: 818-754-2800 Web Site: www.emmys.org, pg 963

Spence-Thomas, Richard, Spence-Thomas Audio Post, 70 Richmond St E, Suite 300, Toronto, ON M5C 1N8, Canada Tel: 416-361-6383 Toll Free Tel: 866-547-2617 Fax: 416-361-2970 E-mail: info@spence-thomas. com; bookings@spence-thomas.com Web Site: www. spence-thomas.com, pg 897

Spencer, Charity, NuMynd Studios, 915 Twin Elms Ct, Nashville, TN 37210 Tel: 615-259-1143 Fax: 615-259-1141 E-mail: hello@numyndstudios.com Web Site: www.numyndstudios.com, pg 843

Spencer, Doug, Harnel Case Co, 1600 Marshall Ave SE, Grand Rapids, MI 49507 Tel: 616-452-4522 Fax: 616-452-5514 E-mail: info@harnelcase.com Web Site: www.harnelcase.com, pg 776

Spencer, Geoff, Sonance, 212 Avenida Fabricante, San Clemente, CA 92672-7531 Tel: 949-492-7777 Toll Free Tel: 800-582-0772 (tech support); 800-582-7777 E-mail: customerservice@sonance.com Web Site: www.sonance.com, pg 892

Spencer, Greg, Blue Wave Records, 3221 Perryville Rd, Baldwinsville, NY 13027 Tel: 315-638-4286 E-mail: bluewave@localnet.com Web Site: www. bluewaverecords.com, pg 708

Spencer, James R, Video Learning Library, 15838 N 62 St, Scottsdale, AZ 85254-1988 Tel: 480-596-9970 Toll Free Tel: 800-383-8811 (orders) E-mail: videos@ videolearning.com Web Site: www.videolearning.com, pg 928

Spenneberg, Joe, Magick Lantern, 750 Ralph McGill Blvd, Atlanta, GA 30312 Tel: 404-688-3348 Fax: 404-584-5247 E-mail: info@magicklantern.com Web Site: magicklantern.com, pg 814

Spera, Tracy, Optimus, 161 E Grand Ave, Chicago, IL 60611 Tel: 312-321-0880 Web Site: www.optimus. com, pg 847

Sperling, Ehud, Inner Traditions International, One Park St, Rochester, VT 05767 Tel: 802-767-3174 Toll Free Tel: 800-246-8648 Fax: 802-767-3726 E-mail: customerservice@innertraditions.com Web Site: www.innertraditions.com, pg 788

Sperry, Mary E, USCCB Publishing, 3211 Fourth St NE, Washington, DC 20017 Tel: 202-541-3000 Toll Free Tel: 800-235-8722 (cust serv) Fax: 202-722-8709 (cust serv) E-mail: publications@usccb.org Web Site: www. usccbpublishing.org, pg 923

Spezialetti, Gary, J E Foss Co, 3328-B Industrial Blvd, Bethel Park, PA 15102 Tel: 412-564-5644 Toll Free Tel: 800-245-6240 Fax: 412-564-5646 E-mail: jefoss@earthlink.net Web Site: www.jefoss. com, pg 764

Spicer, Allison, William F White International Inc, 800 Islington Ave, Toronto, ON M8Z 6A1, Canada Tel: 416-239-5050 Toll Free Tel: 800-465-0160 (CN only) Web Site: www.whites.com, pg 937

Spicer, Shelley, Mill Valley Film Festival, 1001 Lootens Place, Suite 220, San Rafael, CA 94901 Tel: 415-383-5256 Fax: 415-383-8606 E-mail: mvff@cafilm.org; info@cafilm.org Web Site: www.mvff.com; www. cafilm.org, pg 996

Spichtig, Alexandra, Taylor Associates, 110 W Canal St, Suite 301, Winooski, VT 05404 Tel: 802-735-1942 Toll Free Tel: 800-READ-PLUS (732-3758) Fax: 802-419-4786 E-mail: info@readingplus.com Web Site: www.readingplus.com, pg 907

Spiegel, Ron, Astoria Communications Inc, 5553 Ravenswood Rd, Suite 101, Fort Lauderdale, FL 33312 Tel: 305-728-4280 Toll Free Tel: 877-GETMEAV (438-6328) Fax: 954-367-5883 E-mail: info@astoria.productions Web Site: www. getmeav.com, pg 691

Spielberg, Connie, Creative Arts Film Festival (CAFF), PO Box 823, Malvern, PA 19355 Tel: 610-889-4928 E-mail: creativeartsfilmfestival@gmail.com Web Site: www.creativeartsfilmfestival.com, pg 987

Spier, Ed, WGVU TV, 301 Fulton St W, Grand Rapids, MI 49504-6492 Tel: 616-331-6666 Toll Free Tel: 800-442-2771 Web Site: www.wgvu.org, pg 936

Spiersch, Sue, Latham Foundation Publications, 1320 Harbor Bay Pkwy, Suite 200, Alameda, CA 94502 Tel: 510-521-0920 Fax: 510-521-9861 E-mail: info@ latham.org Web Site: www.latham.org, pg 804

Spirito, Joseph, Castillo Theatre, 543 W 42 St, New York, NY 10036 Tel: 212-941-5800 Toll Free Tel: 800-435-7453 Web Site: www.castillo.org, pg 717

Spitzmiller, Don, CFP Video Productions Inc, 149 Meriden Rd, Boonton, NJ 07005 Tel: 973-226-2481 Web Site: cfpvideo.com, pg 720

Spizzirri, Linda, Spizzirri Press Inc, PO Box 9397, Rapid City, SD 57709-9397 Tel: 605-348-2749 Toll Free Tel: 800-325-9819 Fax: 605-348-6251 Toll Free Fax: 800-322-9819 E-mail: spizzpub@aol.com Web Site: www.spizzirri.com, pg 898

Spizzirri, Peter, Spizzirri Press Inc, PO Box 9397, Rapid City, SD 57709-9397 Tel: 605-348-2749 Toll Free Tel: 800-325-9819 Fax: 605-348-6251 Toll Free Fax: 800-322-9819 E-mail: spizzpub@aol.com Web Site: www.spizzirri.com, pg 898

Sponder, Rose, Telestream Inc, 848 Gold Flat Rd, Nevada City, CA 95959 Tel: 530-470-1300 Toll Free Tel: 877-257-6245 Fax: 530-470-1301 E-mail: info@ telestream.net Web Site: www.telestream.net, pg 910

Spooner, Becky, Video West Inc, 1050 N 52 St, Phoenix, AZ 85008 Tel: 480-222-3180 Toll Free Tel: 800-659-0880 Fax: 480-222-3190 E-mail: info@videowestinc. com Web Site: www.videowestinc.com, pg 929

Spoto, Charles, Satellite Technology Systems Inc, 4702 State Rte 176, Unit F, Crystal Lake, IL 60014 Tel: 815-482-0224 Toll Free Tel: 800-838-1472 Fax: 815-568-8478 E-mail: sts@mc.net Web Site: www.satellitetechsys.com, pg 881

Spoto, Ed, Crossroads Audio Inc, 2623 Myrtle Springs Ave, Dallas, TX 75220 Tel: 214-358-2623 Toll Free Tel: 800-287-0436 Fax: 214-358-0185 E-mail: mail@ crossroadsaudio.com Web Site: www.crossroadsaudio. com, pg 735

Spotts, Ethan, Mightybytes Inc, 4001 N Ravenswood Ave, Suite 404, Chicago, IL 60613 *Tel:* 773-561-7529 *E-mail:* info@mightybytes.com *Web Site:* www.mightybytes.com, pg 827

Spratt, Andy, Family Health Media, PO Box 5832, Charlottesville, VA 22905-5832 *Tel:* 434-566-0123 *Toll Free Tel:* 800-366-3641 *Toll Free Fax:* 888-234-2579 *E-mail:* support@familyhealthmedia.com *Web Site:* www.familyhealthmedia.com, pg 758

Sprei, Doug, Learning Ally, 20 Roszel Rd, Princeton, NJ 08540 *Toll Free Tel:* 800-221-4792 *E-mail:* custserv@learningally.org; media@learningally.org *Web Site:* www.learningally.org, pg 805

Spretnjak, Dr Christine, SOM Publishing Co, 163 Moon Valley Rd, Windyville, MO 65783 *Tel:* 417-345-8411 *E-mail:* som@som.org *Web Site:* www.som.org, pg 892

Spring, Steven L, Aspen Systems Inc, 3900 Youngfield St, Wheat Ridge, CO 80033-3865 *Tel:* 303-431-4606 *Toll Free Tel:* 800-992-9242 *Fax:* 303-431-7196 *E-mail:* sales@aspsys.com *Web Site:* www.aspsys.com, pg 691

Springer, Rich, Alpha Source Inc, 6619 W Calumet Rd, Milwaukee, WI 53223-4186 *Tel:* 414-760-2222 *Toll Free Tel:* 800-654-9845 *E-mail:* customer.service@alphasource.com; info@alphasource.com *Web Site:* www.alphasource.com, pg 681

Springs, Cliff, Genesis Creative, 1006 Hafely Ct, Cayce, SC 29033 *Tel:* 803-796-9666 *E-mail:* geninfo@gencreative.com *Web Site:* genesisstudiossc.com, pg 769

Sprows, Marybeth, Paulist Productions, 6430 W Sunset Blvd, Suite 1220, Los Angeles, CA 90028 *Tel:* 310-454-0688 *E-mail:* paulistmail@paulistproductions.org *Web Site:* www.paulistproductions.org, pg 852

Sprung, Susan, Producers Guild of America Inc (PGA), 8530 Wilshire Blvd, Suite 400, Beverly Hills, CA 90211 *Tel:* 310-358-9020 *E-mail:* info@producersguild.org *Web Site:* www.producersguild.org, pg 960

Srybnik, Simon, East of Hollywood NY, 140 53 St, Brooklyn, NY 11232 *Tel:* 718-492-7400 *Fax:* 718-439-3930 *Web Site:* www.eastofhollywoodny.com, pg 749

St Germain, Norm, APS Lighting-Sound-AV, 901 Columbia Circle, Merrimack, NH 03054 *Tel:* 603-424-9198 *Toll Free Tel:* 800-837-0005 *Fax:* 603-423-9816 *E-mail:* info@apslightingnh.com *Web Site:* www.apslightingnh.com, pg 688

St John, Lorna, Hamilton Studio, 1427 W Dean Ave, Spokane, WA 99201 *Tel:* 509-327-9501 *E-mail:* info@hamiltonstudio.com *Web Site:* www.hamiltonstudio.com, pg 775

St Lifer, Evan, Scholastic Library Publishing, 90 Old Sherman Tpke, Danbury, CT 06816 *Toll Free Tel:* 800-621-1115 (cust serv) *Toll Free Fax:* 866-783-4361 *Web Site:* scholasticlibrary.digital.scholastic.com, pg 882

Stabenau, Jeff, Giant Interactive, 133 W 19 St, 3rd fl, New York, NY 10011 *Tel:* 212-675-7300 *E-mail:* info@giant-interactive.com *Web Site:* www.giant-interactive.com, pg 770

Stables, LeeAnne, Paramount Pictures Corporation, 5555 Melrose Ave, Los Angeles, CA 90038 *Tel:* 323-956-8398 *Web Site:* www.paramount.com, pg 851

Stafford, Clay, American Blackguard Inc, PO Box 680686, Franklin, TN 37068-0686 *Tel:* 615-599-4032 *E-mail:* contact@americanblackguard.com *Web Site:* www.americanblackguard.com, pg 683

Stafford, David, McGraw-Hill School Education Group, 8787 Orion Place, Columbus, OH 43240-4027 *Tel:* 614-430-4000 *Toll Free Tel:* 800-334-7734 *Fax:* 614-755-5682 *Web Site:* mheonline.com; www.mheducation.com, pg 821

Stafford, Jacqueline, American Blackguard Inc, PO Box 680686, Franklin, TN 37068-0686 *Tel:* 615-599-4032 *E-mail:* contact@americanblackguard.com *Web Site:* www.americanblackguard.com, pg 683

Staley, Steve, Kentucky Grip & Lighting, 10005 Bunsen Way, Louisville, KY 40299 *Tel:* 502-548-5833 *Web Site:* www.kentuckygrip.com, pg 798

Stall, Sean E, Ironik Design & Post, 56 E Main St, Suite 203, Avon, CT 06001 *Tel:* 860-404-2386 *Fax:* 860-404-2735 *E-mail:* info@ironikdesign.com *Web Site:* www.ironikdesign.com, pg 791

Stallsmith, Mark, Audio Visual Media, 1141 Lexington Ave, Mansfield, OH 44907 *Tel:* 419-756-2698 *E-mail:* avm2698@aol.com *Web Site:* audiovisualmedia.net, pg 694

Stamatopoulos, Dino, Starburns Industries, 1700 W Burbank Blvd, Burbank, CA 91506 *Tel:* 818-433-3300 *Fax:* 818-433-3383 *E-mail:* contact@starburnsind.com *Web Site:* www.starburnsindustries.com, pg 900

Stampone, Enzo, Entel Systems Inc, 230 W Parkway, Pompton Plains, NJ 07444 *Tel:* 201-447-2000 *Toll Free Tel:* 888-914-7100 *Fax:* 201-447-2880 *E-mail:* service@entelsystems.com *Web Site:* www.entelsystems.com, pg 754

Stancil, John, Technomedia Solutions, 4545 36 St, Orlando, FL 32811 *Tel:* 407-351-0909 *Fax:* 407-248-9484 *E-mail:* sales@gotechnomedia.com *Web Site:* www.gotechnomedia.com, pg 909

Standard, Gary, WorldStage, 259 W 30 St, 12th fl, New York, NY 10001-2863 *Tel:* 212-582-2345 *Fax:* 718-610-1750 *E-mail:* info@worldstage.com *Web Site:* www.worldstage.com, pg 941

Stanfield, James EdD, James Stanfield Co Inc, 129 S Quarantina St, Santa Barbara, CA 93103 *Tel:* 805-897-1185 *Toll Free Tel:* 800-421-6534 *Fax:* 805-897-1187 *E-mail:* maindesk@stanfield.com *Web Site:* www.stanfield.com, pg 899

Stanford, Halle, The Jim Henson Co, 1416 N La Brea Ave, Hollywood, CA 90028 *Tel:* 323-802-1500 *Fax:* 323-802-1825 *Web Site:* www.henson.com, pg 794

Stangeland, Julie, Creative BC (CrBC), 7 W Sixth Ave, Vancouver, BC V5Y 1K2, Canada *Tel:* 604-730-2732 *Fax:* 604-736-7290 *E-mail:* info@creativebc.com; media@creativebc.com *Web Site:* www.creativebc.com, pg 978

Stango, Mike, RTS Inc, 40 Burt Dr, Suite 11, Deer Park, NY 11729 *Tel:* 631-242-6801 *Fax:* 631-242-6808 *E-mail:* rtsinc@rcn.com *Web Site:* www.rtsphoto.com, pg 878

Stankoski, Michael, JungleTV, 571 NW Mercantile Place, Port St Lucie, FL 34986 *Tel:* 772-370-0043 *E-mail:* info@jungletv.com *Web Site:* www.jungletv.com, pg 795

Stanley, Jay S, Jay S Stanley & Associates Inc, 5313 McClanahan Dr, Suite G-5, North Little Rock, AR 72116 *Tel:* 501-758-8029 *Toll Free Tel:* 888-758-4728 *Fax:* 501-758-8037 *E-mail:* info@jaystanley.com *Web Site:* www.jaystanley.com, pg 899

Stanley, Sherri, Lloyd F McKinney Associates Inc, 25350 Cypress Ave, Hayward, CA 94544 *Tel:* 510-783-8043 *Fax:* 510-783-2130 *E-mail:* info@mckinneyassoc.com *Web Site:* www.mckinneyassoc.com, pg 821

Stanley, Simon, ProPhotonix Ltd, 13 Red Roof Lane, Suite 200, Salem, NH 03079 *Tel:* 603-893-8778 *E-mail:* sales@prophotonix.com; info@prophototonix.com *Web Site:* www.prophotonix.com, pg 865

Stansly, Maggy, National Freedom of Information Coalition (NFOIC), University of Florida College of Journalism, 3208 Weimer Hall, 1885 Stadium Rd, Gainesville, FL 32611 *Tel:* 352-294-7082 *E-mail:* nfoic@nfoic.org *Web Site:* www.nfoic.org, pg 959

Stanton, Andrew, Clever Devices Ltd, 300 Crossways Park Dr, Woodbury, NY 11797 *Tel:* 516-433-6100 *Toll Free Tel:* 800-872-6129 *Web Site:* www.cleverdevices.com, pg 726

Stanton, Andrew, Pixar Animation Studios, 1200 Park Ave, Emeryville, CA 94608 *Tel:* 510-922-3000 *Fax:* 510-922-3151 *Web Site:* www.pixar.com, pg 857

Stanton, Jeanette, Oklahoma Film & Music Office, 900 N Stiles Ave, Oklahoma City, OK 73104 *Tel:* 405-230-8440 *Toll Free Tel:* 800-766-3456 *Fax:* 405-201-4561 *Web Site:* okfilmmusic.com, pg 975

Stanton, William, Main Point Productions, 295 Lobachsville Rd, Oley, PA 19547 *Tel:* 610-987-9320; 610-987-9163 *E-mail:* mainpoint301@gmail.com *Web Site:* www.mainpoint.com, pg 815

Stanulis, Roxanne, Individual Artist Fellowship, Carvel State Off Bldg, 4th fl, 820 N French St, Wilmington, DE 19801 *Tel:* 302-577-8278 *Fax:* 302-577-6561 *E-mail:* delarts@state.de.us *Web Site:* www.artsdel.org, pg 993

Stanzione, Robert J, ARRIS Group Inc, 3871 Lakefield Dr, Suwanee, GA 30024 *Tel:* 678-473-2907 *Toll Free Tel:* 866-36-ARRIS (362-7747); 877-466-8646 (tech) *Fax:* 678-473-8470 *E-mail:* marketing@arris.com *Web Site:* www.arris.com, pg 689

Stargell, Stephanie, Close Up Foundation, 1330 Braddock Place, Suite 400, Alexandria, VA 22314 *Tel:* 703-706-3300 *Toll Free Tel:* 800-CLOSEUP (256-7387) *E-mail:* info@closeup.org *Web Site:* www.closeup.org, pg 726

Stark, John, Activu Corp, 301 Roundhill Dr, Rockaway, NJ 07866 *Tel:* 973-366-5550 *Toll Free Tel:* 888-ACTIVU1 (228-4881) *Fax:* 973-625-7775 *E-mail:* facebook@activu.com *Web Site:* activu.com, pg 675

Starkloff, Eric, National Instruments Corp, 11500 N Mopac Expwy, Austin, TX 78759-3504 *Tel:* 512-683-0100 *Toll Free Tel:* 888-280-7645 (sales); 877-388-1952 *Fax:* 512-683-8411; 512-683-5794 (sales) *Web Site:* www.ni.com, pg 836

Starks, Shirley, Set Decorators Society of America (SDSA), 7100 Tujunga Ave, Suite A, North Hollywood, CA 91605 *Tel:* 818-255-2425 *Fax:* 818-982-8597 *E-mail:* sdsa@setdecorators.org *Web Site:* www.setdecorators.org, pg 962

Starns, Rod, Running Pony Productions LLC, 1770 Kirby Pkwy, Suite 118, Memphis, TN 38138 *Tel:* 901-683-6693 *Toll Free Tel:* 877-891-7669 *Fax:* 901-683-3093 *E-mail:* info@runningpony.com *Web Site:* www.runningpony.com, pg 878

Starobin, Becky, Bridge Records Inc, 200 Clinton Ave, New Rochelle, NY 10801 *Tel:* 914-654-9270 *Web Site:* www.bridgerecords.com, pg 710

Starobin, David, Bridge Records Inc, 200 Clinton Ave, New Rochelle, NY 10801 *Tel:* 914-654-9270 *Web Site:* www.bridgerecords.com, pg 710

Starobin, Robert, Bridge Records Inc, 200 Clinton Ave, New Rochelle, NY 10801 *Tel:* 914-654-9270 *Web Site:* www.bridgerecords.com, pg 710

Staropoli, James, Sentry Industries Inc, One Bridge St, Hillburn, NY 10931-0885 *Tel:* 845-753-2910 *Fax:* 845-753-2920 *E-mail:* techsupport@sentryindustries.com *Web Site:* www.sentryindustries.com, pg 884

Starr, Charlie, Audio & Light, 2209 Randleman Rd, Greensboro, NC 27406 *Tel:* 336-274-1234 *Fax:* 336-274-4022 *E-mail:* info@audio-light.com *Web Site:* www.audio-light.com, pg 693

Stasila, Lauren, Vancouver International Film Festival (VIFF), Vancouver International Film Ctr, 1181 Seymour St, Vancouver, BC V6B 3M7, Canada *Tel:* 604-685-0260 *Fax:* 604-688-8221 *E-mail:* info@viff.org; submissions@viff.org *Web Site:* www.viff.org, pg 1006

Stasio, Megan, Data Projections Inc, 3700 W Sam Houston Pkwy S, Suite 525, Houston, TX 77042 *Tel:* 713-781-1999 *Toll Free Tel:* 866-225-5374 *Fax:* 713-781-3338 *E-mail:* dpiweb@dataprojections.com *Web Site:* www.dataprojections.com, pg 738

Staszewski, Victoria, Sight & Sound Productions, 11193 Saint Johns Industrial Pkwy N, Jacksonville, FL 32246 *Tel:* 904-645-7880 *Toll Free Tel:* 800-339-0846 *Fax:* 904-645-7787 *E-mail:* info@ssav.net *Web Site:* www.ssav.net, pg 887

Stauffer, Jim, HOThead, 56 W 45 St, 17th fl, New York, NY 10036 *Tel:* 212-575-5566 *E-mail:* info@hothead.tv *Web Site:* hothead.tv, pg 782

Staylor, Anne Farrell, Staylor-Made Communications Inc, 11835 Carmel Mountain Rd, Suite 1304-365, San Diego, CA 92128-4609 *Toll Free Tel:* 800-711-6699 *E-mail:* info@staylor-made.com *Web Site:* staylor-made.com, pg 900

Staylor, Jim, Staylor-Made Communications Inc, 11835 Carmel Mountain Rd, Suite 1304-365, San Diego, CA 92128-4609 *Toll Free Tel:* 800-711-6699 *E-mail:* info@staylor-made.com *Web Site:* staylor-made.com, pg 900

Stearns, Leo, FrontRow, 1690 Corporate Circle, Petaluma, CA 94954 *Tel:* 707-769-1110 *Toll Free Tel:* 800-227-0735 *Fax:* 707-769-9624 *E-mail:* customercare@gofrontrow.com *Web Site:* www.gofrontrow.com, pg 766

Stechly, Paul, Applied Electronics Ltd, 1260 Kamato Rd, Mississauga, ON L4W 1Y1, Canada *Tel:* 905-625-4321 *Fax:* 905-625-4333 *E-mail:* ael. toronto@appliedelectronics.com *Web Site:* www. appliedelectronics.com, pg 687

Steed, Bo, Signs.com, 1550 S Gladiola St, Salt Lake City, UT 84104 *Tel:* 801-441-3400 *Toll Free Tel:* 888-222-4929 *E-mail:* support@signs.com *Web Site:* www. signs.com, pg 888

Steenstrup, Daniel, Freeman, 1600 Viceroy, Suite 100, Dallas, TX 75235 *Tel:* 214-445-1000 *Web Site:* www. freeman.com, pg 765

Steffens, Lucy, Sacramento Film Commission, 1608 "I" St, Sacramento, CA 95814-2042 *Tel:* 916-808-7777 *Toll Free Tel:* 800-292-2334 *Web Site:* www. visitsacramento.com/film, pg 967

Stehlik, Milos, Chicago International Children's Film Festival, 1517 W Fullerton Ave, Chicago, IL 60614 *Tel:* 773-281-9075 (ext 3011) *Fax:* 773-929-0266 *E-mail:* filmreg@facets.org; press@facets.org *Web Site:* festival.facets.org, pg 985

Stehlik, Milos, Facets Multi-Media Inc, 1517 W Fullerton Ave, Chicago, IL 60614 *Tel:* 773-281-9075 *Fax:* 773-929-5437 *E-mail:* sales@facets.org; press@ facets.org *Web Site:* www.facets.org, pg 758

Stein, Charlie, InJoy Birth & Parenting Education, 7107 La Vista Place, Longmont, CO 80503 *Tel:* 303-447-2082 (ext 2) *Toll Free Tel:* 800-326-2082 (ext 2) *Fax:* 303-449-8788 *E-mail:* custserv@injoyvideos.com *Web Site:* www.injoyvideos.com, pg 788

Stein, Kevin, HAVE Inc, 309 Power Ave, Hudson, NY 12534 *Tel:* 518-828-2000 *Toll Free Tel:* 888-999-HAVE (999-4283) *Fax:* 518-828-2008 *E-mail:* pro_sales@haveinc.com; have@haveinc.com *Web Site:* www.haveinc.com, pg 777

Steinberg, Glen, RC Communications, 131 Garlisch Dr, Elk Grove Village, IL 60007 *Tel:* 847-678-7000 *Fax:* 847-678-9378 *E-mail:* rccsales@rentcom.com; rent@rentcom.com *Web Site:* www.rentcom.com; www.rc-communications.com, pg 871

Steinberg, Jay, Major Media Inc, PO Box 209, Deerfield, IL 60015 *Tel:* 847-433-1682 *E-mail:* dmchistory@aol. com *Web Site:* www.major-media.com, pg 815

Steinberg, Jay, Major Media Productions Inc, PO Box 209, Deerfield, IL 60015 *Tel:* 847-433-1682 *E-mail:* dmchistory@aol.com *Web Site:* www.major-media.com, pg 815

Steinberg, Jay, Major Reproductions Equipment Co, PO Box 209, Deerfield, IL 60015 *Tel:* 847-433-1682 *E-mail:* dmchistory@aol.com *Web Site:* www.major-media.com, pg 815

Steiner, Henry, Northeast Video Productions Inc, Box 8425, Sleepy Hollow, NY 10591 *Tel:* 914-714-0703, pg 842

Steiner, Michael, Sounds Unique, 1721-A Little Orchard St, San Jose, CA 95125 *Tel:* 408-287-3002 *Web Site:* www.soundsunique.com, pg 895

Steinhauer, John, The Whitlock Group, 12820 West Creek Pkwy, Richmond, VA 23238 *Tel:* 804-273-9100 *Toll Free Tel:* 800-726-9843 *Fax:* 804-273-9380 *E-mail:* information@whitlock.com; marketing@ whitlock.com *Web Site:* www.whitlock.com, pg 937

Stelly, Christopher, Louisiana Entertainment, 617 N Third St, Baton Rouge, LA 70802 *Tel:* 225-342-5403 *Fax:* 225-342-5554 *E-mail:* led-entertainment@la.gov *Web Site:* louisianaentertainment.gov, pg 971

Stelmack, Joe, Baron Stage Curtain & Equipment Co Inc, 1910 Light St, Baltimore, MD 21230 *Tel:* 410-327-6962 *Toll Free Tel:* 800-249-6464 *E-mail:* curtains@baronstage.com *Web Site:* www. baronstage.com, pg 702

Stelmakowich, Ken, Majortech Inc, 8464 Ninth Line RR-1, Norval, ON L0P 1K0, Canada *Tel:* 905-873-0778 *Fax:* 905-873-1244, pg 815

Stelman, Steve, TimeLogic Corp, 1914 Palomar Oaks Way, Suite 150, Carlsbad, CA 92008 *Tel:* 760-431-1263 *Toll Free Tel:* 877-222-9543 *Fax:* 760-431-1351 *Web Site:* www.timelogic.com, pg 914

Stelmaschuk, Scott, Golden Sheaf Awards, 49 Smith St E, Yorkton, SK S3N 0H4, Canada *Tel:* 306-782-7077 *Fax:* 306-782-1550 *E-mail:* info@yorktonfilm. com *Web Site:* yorktonfilm.com/golden-sheaf-awards/, pg 991

Stelmaschuk, Scott, Yorkton Film Festival (YFF), 49 Smith St E, Yorkton, SK S3N 0H4, Canada *Tel:* 306-782-7077 *Fax:* 306-782-1550 *E-mail:* info@ yorktonfilm.com *Web Site:* yorktonfilm.com, pg 1007

Stene, Josh, Crestron Electronics Inc, 15 Volvo Dr, Rockleigh, NJ 07647 *Tel:* 201-767-3400 (sales & support); 201-750-7004 (admin) *Toll Free Tel:* 800-237-2041; 855-791-5322 *Fax:* 201-767-1903 (sales & support); 201-767-8872 (admin) *E-mail:* inquiries@ crestron.com *Web Site:* www.crestron.com, pg 734

Stenger, Brenda, American Hospital Association, 155 N Wacker Dr, Suite 400, Chicago, IL 60606-1725 *Tel:* 312-422-3000 *Fax:* 312-422-4700 *Web Site:* www. aha.org, pg 683

Stengle, Jon, CMD Agency, 1631 NW Thurman St, Portland, OR 97209 *Tel:* 503-223-6794 *E-mail:* info@ cmdagency.com *Web Site:* www.cmdagency.com, pg 726

Stepanenko, Maria, Express Media Inc, 2225 Palou Ave, San Francisco, CA 94124 *Tel:* 415-255-9883 *Fax:* 415-255-0139 *Web Site:* expressmedia.tv, pg 757

Stephan, Egon Jr, CineVideotech Inc, 14458 Commerce Way, Miami Lakes, FL 33016 *Tel:* 305-754-2611 *Fax:* 305-573-5587 *Web Site:* www.cinevideotech.com, pg 725

Stephens, Jody, Ardent Studios Inc, 2000 Madison Ave, Memphis, TN 38104 *Tel:* 901-725-0855 *Fax:* 901-725-7011 *E-mail:* info@ardentstudios.com *Web Site:* www. ardentstudios.com, pg 688

Stephenson, Greg, Dallas Prompter, PO Box 571233, Dallas, TX 75357 *Tel:* 214-275-9000 *Web Site:* www. dallasprompter.com, pg 737

Stephenson, Lisa, Alliance for Women in Media/Alliance for Women in Media Foundation, 2365 Harrodsburg Rd, A-325, Lexington, KY 40504 *Tel:* 202-750-3664 *Fax:* 202-750-3664 *Web Site:* www.allwomeninmedia. org, pg 947

Stephenson, Lisa, The Gracies®, 2365 Harrodsburg Rd, A-325, Lexington, KY 40504 *Tel:* 202-750-3664 *Fax:* 202-750-3664 *E-mail:* gracies@ allwomeninmedia.org *Web Site:* allwomeninmedia. org/gracies, pg 991

Sterchele, Mitzi, Clear-Com® LLC, 1301 Marina Village Pkwy, Suite 105, Alameda, CA 94501 *Tel:* 510-337-6600 *Toll Free Tel:* 800-462-HELP (462-4357) *Fax:* 510-337-6699 *E-mail:* salessupportus@clearcom. com *Web Site:* www.clearcom.com, pg 726

Stern, Bret, SoNo Studios, 18 Leonard St, Norwalk, CT 06850 *Tel:* 203-354-4002 *E-mail:* info@sonostudios. com *Web Site:* www.sonostudios.com, pg 892

Stern, Bret, Bret Stern Productions, c/o SoNo Studios, 18 Leonard St, Norwalk, CT 06850 *Tel:* 203-354-4002 *E-mail:* info@bretsternproductions.com *Web Site:* bretsternproductions.com, pg 900

Stern, Carol, Educational Activities Inc, PO Box 87, Baldwin, NY 11510-0087 *Tel:* 516-223-4666 *Toll Free Tel:* 800-797-3223 *Fax:* 516-623-9282 *Web Site:* edact. com, pg 750

Stern, Eddie, AV Bluebook, 80 Little Falls Rd, Fairfield, NJ 07004 *Toll Free Tel:* 800-631-7791 *Toll Free Fax:* 800-332-5871 *E-mail:* info@avbluebook.com; sales@avbluebook.com *Web Site:* www.avbluebook. com, pg 696

Stern, Eric, Anonymous Content, 3532 Hayden Ave, Culver City, CA 90232 *Tel:* 310-558-6000 *Fax:* 310-558-2724 *E-mail:* filmtv@anonymouscontent.com *Web Site:* www.anonymouscontent.com, pg 686

Stern, Robert, Projects in Knowledge Inc, 290 W Mount Pleasant Ave, Suite 2350, Livingston, NJ 07039 *Tel:* 973-890-8988 *Toll Free Tel:* 800-772-8277 *Web Site:* www.projectsinknowledge.com, pg 865

Sternberg, Joan, Practising Law Institute, 1177 Avenue of the Americas, 2nd fl, New York, NY 10036 *Tel:* 212-824-5710 (cust serv) *Toll Free Tel:* 800-260-4PLI (260-4754, cust serv) *Toll Free Fax:* 800-321-0093 (cust serv) *E-mail:* info@pli.edu; cs@pli.edu (cust serv) *Web Site:* www.pli.edu, pg 860

Stetzko, Scott, Cibola Systems, 180 S Cypress St, Orange, CA 92866 *Tel:* 714-480-0272 *Fax:* 714-480-0768 *E-mail:* info@cibolasystems.com *Web Site:* cibolasystems.com, pg 723

Steuerwald, Jane, Black Maria Film Festival, c/o New Jersey City University, Dept of Media Arts, 2039 Kennedy Blvd, Jersey City, NJ 07305 *Tel:* 201-200-2043 *Fax:* 201-200-3490 *E-mail:* info@ blackmariafilmfestival.org *Web Site:* www. blackmariafilmfestival.org, pg 983

Steupert, Klara, Illuminating Engineering Society (IES), 120 Wall St, 17th fl, New York, NY 10005-4026 *Tel:* 212-248-5000 *E-mail:* ies@ies.org *Web Site:* ies. org, pg 955

Stevens, Kris Erik, Kris Stevens Enterprises, 22362 Dardenne St, Calabasas, CA 91302 *Tel:* 818-225-7585 *E-mail:* inquiry@kriserikstevens.com *Web Site:* www. kriserikstevens.com, pg 801

Stevens, Mark, RLJ Entertainment Inc, 8515 Georgia Ave, Suite 650, Silver Spring, MD 20910 *Tel:* 301-608-2115 *Toll Free Tel:* 800-999-0212 *E-mail:* inquiries@rljentertainment.com *Web Site:* www.us.rljentertainment.com, pg 875

Stevens, Tim, Stevens Design & Animation LLC, PO Box 90612, Albuquerque, NM 87199 *Tel:* 505-200-2042 *Web Site:* stevensanimation.com, pg 900

Stevenson, Noelle P, Greater Fort Lauderdale/Broward Office of Film, Music, Fashion & Create, 101 NE Third Ave, Suite 100, Fort Lauderdale, FL 33301 *Tel:* 954-767-2467 *Fax:* 954-767-4681 *E-mail:* film@ broward.org *Web Site:* www.sunny.org/film, pg 969

Stewart, Amy, Big Shoulders Digital Video Productions, 875 N Michigan Ave, Suite 3750, Chicago, IL 60611 *Tel:* 312-540-5400 *E-mail:* info@bigshoulders.com; sales@bigshoulders.com *Web Site:* www.bigshoulders. com, pg 705

Stewart, Cathy, Garcia Marketing Inc, 400 Ninth St, Conway, PA 15027-1663 *Tel:* 724-869-0100 *Toll Free Tel:* 800-683-1925 *Fax:* 724-869-1925 *E-mail:* gmavfoto@verizon.net, pg 768

Stewart, David, Association of Independent Commercial Producers (AICP), 3 W 18 St, 5th fl, New York, NY 10011 *Tel:* 212-929-3000 *Fax:* 212-929-3359 *E-mail:* info@aicp.com *Web Site:* www.aicp.com, pg 951

Stewart, Grant, Stewart Filmscreen Corp, 1161 Sepulveda Blvd, Torrance, CA 90502-2754 *Tel:* 310-784-5300 *Toll Free Tel:* 800-762-4999 (North America only) *Fax:* 310-326-6870 *E-mail:* request@stewartfilmscreen.com *Web Site:* www.stewartfilmscreen.com, pg 901

Stewart, Keith, Michigan Office Solutions (MOS), A Xerox Company, 2859 Walkent Dr NW, Grand Rapids, MI 49544 *Toll Free Tel:* 800-442-9070 *E-mail:* info@mos-xerox.com *Web Site:* www.mos-xerox.com, pg 825

Stewart, Ken, GAPC (General Assembly Production Centre), 1550 Laperriere Ave, Suite 102, Ottawa, ON K1Z 7T2, Canada *Tel:* 613-723-3316 *Fax:* 613-723-8583 *Web Site:* www.gapc.com, pg 768

Stewart, Mary, Mutual Hardware, 36-27 Vernon Blvd, Long Island City, NY 11106 *Toll Free Tel:* 866-361-2480 *Fax:* 718-786-9591 *E-mail:* info@mutualhardware.com *Web Site:* www.mutualhardware.com, pg 835

Stewart, Noral D PhD, Stewart Acoustical Consultants, 7330 Chapel Hill Rd, Suite 201, Raleigh, NC 27607 *Tel:* 919-858-0899 *Fax:* 919-858-0899 *Web Site:* www.sacnc.com, pg 900

Stewart, Peter, Leprecon®, 10087 Industrial Dr, Hamburg, MI 48139 *Tel:* 810-852-4300 *Toll Free Tel:* 888-422-3537 *Fax:* 810-231-1631 *E-mail:* sales@leprecon.com *Web Site:* www.leprecon.com, pg 806

Stewart, Rick, piXvfm Inc, 1805 E Dyer Rd, Suite 107, Santa Ana, CA 92705 *Tel:* 949-419-2563 *Fax:* 949-419-3485 *Web Site:* pixvfm.com, pg 857

Stewart, Stacey, March of Dimes Foundation, 1275 Mamaroneck Ave, White Plains, NY 10605 *Tel:* 914-997-4488 *Toll Free Tel:* 888-663-4637 *Web Site:* www.marchofdimes.org/video, pg 816

Stickney, David, ARC Document Solutions, 1981 N Broadway, Suite 385, Walnut Creek, CA 94596 *Tel:* 925-949-5100 *Toll Free Tel:* 855-500-0660 *E-mail:* contact@e-arc.com *Web Site:* www.e-arc.com, pg 688

Stiener, Jim, Mirror 34 Productions, 2302 W Badger Rd, Madison, WI 53713-2322 *Tel:* 608-271-1226 *Toll Free Tel:* 800-569-6810 *E-mail:* human@mirror34.com *Web Site:* www.mirror34.com, pg 828

Stiles, Diane, Castillo Theatre, 543 W 42 St, New York, NY 10036 *Tel:* 212-941-5800 *Toll Free Tel:* 800-435-7453 *Web Site:* www.castillo.org, pg 717

Stillman, Joseph C, La Paloma Films, PO Box 269, Gilbertsville, NY 13776 *Tel:* 607-376-4300 *E-mail:* lapalomafilms@yahoo.com *Web Site:* www.lapalomafilms.com, pg 803

Stillwell, Karen, Rough House, 550 Bryant St, San Francisco, CA 94107-1217 *Tel:* 415-561-4544 *Fax:* 415-543-8370 *E-mail:* info@roughhouse.com *Web Site:* www.roughhouse.com, pg 878

Stiltner, Rachel, National Storytelling Festival, 116 W Main St, Jonesborough, TN 37659 *Tel:* 423-753-2171 *Toll Free Tel:* 800-952-8392 *Fax:* 423-913-8219 *E-mail:* customerservice@storytellingcenter.net *Web Site:* www.storytellingcenter.net/festival, pg 997

Stitcher, Rob, Optikinetics Ltd - The Americas, 11211 Air Park Rd, Suite 1, Ashland, VA 23005 *Tel:* 804-752-2570 *Toll Free Tel:* 800-575-6784 *Fax:* 804-752-2888 *E-mail:* optius@optikinetics.com *Web Site:* www.optikinetics.com, pg 847

Stiver, Leann, F&F Productions LLC, 14333 Myerlake Circle, Clearwater, FL 33760 *Tel:* 727-530-5000 *Fax:* 727-535-6547 *E-mail:* info@fandfhd.tv *Web Site:* www.fandfhd.tv, pg 759

Stobaugh, Clay, John Wiley & Sons Inc, 111 River St, Hoboken, NJ 07030-5774 *Tel:* 201-748-6000 *Toll Free Tel:* 800-225-5945 (cust serv) *Fax:* 201-748-6088 *Web Site:* www.wiley.com, pg 938

Stocchetti, Beckie, Hawaii International Film Festival, 680 Iwilei Rd, Suite 100, Honolulu, HI 96817 *Tel:* 808-792-1577 (ext 7) *Fax:* 808-792-1583 *Toll Free Tel:* 877-749-7783 *E-mail:* info@hiff.org; entries@hiff.org *Web Site:* www.hiff.org, pg 991

Stockman, Gary, DXC Technology Co, 1775 Tysons Blvd, Tysons, VA 22102 *Tel:* 317-331-1197 *Web Site:* www.dxc.technology, pg 748

Stockton, Dick, Cinema Xenon International Inc, 261 Valley Vista Dr, Camarillo, CA 93010-1655 *Tel:* 805-383-5548 *Toll Free Tel:* 888-669-7271 *Fax:* 805-389-9611 *E-mail:* info@cxilamps.com *Web Site:* www.cxilamps.com, pg 724

Stoebner, Jeff, AVI Systems, 9675 W 76 St, Suite 130, Eden Prairie, MN 55344 *Tel:* 952-949-3700 *Toll Free Tel:* 800-488-4954 (support); 855-521-0050 *Fax:* 952-949-6000 *E-mail:* info@avisystems.com *Web Site:* www.avisystems.com, pg 698

Stoebner, Joe, AVI Systems, 9675 W 76 St, Suite 130, Eden Prairie, MN 55344 *Tel:* 952-949-3700 *Toll Free Tel:* 800-488-4954 (support); 855-521-0050 *Fax:* 952-949-6000 *E-mail:* info@avisystems.com *Web Site:* www.avisystems.com, pg 698

Stofan, Ronald A, Garner Products Inc, 10620 Industrial Ave, Suite 100, Roseville, CA 95678 *Tel:* 916-784-0200 *Toll Free Tel:* 800-624-1903 *Fax:* 916-784-1425 *E-mail:* info@garner-products.com *Web Site:* www.garner-products.com, pg 768

Stokes, Andrea, Canamedia Inc, 1540 Cornwall Rd, Suite 216, Oakville, ON L6J 7W5, Canada *Tel:* 416-363-6765 *Toll Free Tel:* 866-999-5292 *Fax:* 416-363-7834 *Web Site:* www.canamedia.com, pg 715

Stokes, Chuck, Stages Video Productions, 514 29 Ave N, Myrtle Beach, SC 29577 *Tel:* 843-626-7466 *E-mail:* info@stagesvideo.com *Web Site:* www.stagesvideo.com, pg 899

Stokes, Justine, University of Wisconsin-Oshkosh Radio-TV-Film Dept, Arts & Communications Bldg, W-112, 800 Algoma Blvd, Oshkosh, WI 54901 *Tel:* 920-424-3131 *E-mail:* rtf@uwosh.edu *Web Site:* rtf.uwosh.edu, pg 923

Stolk, Marcel, Logitech, 7700 Gateway Blvd, Newark, CA 94560 *Tel:* 510-795-8500 *Toll Free Tel:* 866-291-1505 *Web Site:* www.logitech.com, pg 811

Stoltz, David, Sports Cinematography Group, 715 Pier Ave, Santa Monica, CA 90405 *Tel:* 310-962-2200 *E-mail:* sportscinema@earthlink.net *Web Site:* www.sportscinematographygroup.com, pg 898

Stone, Alana, Vision Maker Media, 1800 N 33 St, Lincoln, NE 68503-1409 *Tel:* 402-472-3522 *Fax:* 402-472-8675 *E-mail:* visionmaker@unl.edu *Web Site:* www.visionmakermedia.org, pg 930

Stone, Ben, Sonoma County Film Office, 141 Stony Circle, Suite 110, Santa Rosa, CA 95401-4154 *Tel:* 707-565-7170 *Fax:* 707-565-7231 *E-mail:* film@sonoma-county.org *Web Site:* www.sonoma-county.org/film, pg 968

Stone, David M, Photosol Inc, 318 Seaboard Ave, Venice, FL 34285 *Tel:* 941-445-2231 *E-mail:* orders4photosol@gmail.com *Web Site:* www.photosol.com, pg 856

Stone, Gary, Gold Standard Productions, 12952 Miriam Place, Santa Ana, CA 92705-1334 *Tel:* 714-544-7000 *Fax:* 714-544-7010 *Web Site:* www.goldstandardproductions.com, pg 772

Stone, Jessica, WaxWorks VideoWorks, 325 E Third St, Owensboro, KY 42303 *Tel:* 270-926-0008 *Toll Free Tel:* 800-825-8558 *Fax:* 270-663-0737 *Web Site:* www.waxworksonline.com, pg 934

Stone, John D, PGi, 3280 Peachtree Rd NE, Suite 1000, Atlanta, GA 30305 *Tel:* 404-262-8400 *Toll Free Tel:* 866-755-4878 *Web Site:* www.pgi.com, pg 855

Stone, Kevin, Stewart Audio, 14435 Cuesta Ct, Suite C, Sonora, CA 95370 *Tel:* 209-588-8111 *Fax:* 209-588-8113 *E-mail:* sales@stewartaudio.com; support@stewartaudio.com *Web Site:* www.stewartaudio.com, pg 901

Stone, Patricia, Chelsea Green Publishing Co, 85 N Main St, Suite 120, White River Junction, VT 05001 *Tel:* 802-295-6300 *Toll Free Tel:* 800-639-4099 (orders) *Fax:* 802-295-6444 *E-mail:* customerservice@chelseagreen.com *Web Site:* www.chelseagreen.com, pg 721

Stoneman, Rebecca, San Juan School District Heritage Language Resource Center, 28 W 200 N, Blanding, UT 84511 *Tel:* 435-678-1230 *Fax:* 435-678-1283 *Web Site:* media.sjsd.org, pg 880

Stoner, Shawn, New Wave Entertainment, 2660 W Olive Ave, Burbank, CA 91505 *Tel:* 818-295-5000 *E-mail:* biz@nwe.com *Web Site:* nwe.com, pg 840

Storey, Jeff, Level 3 Communications Inc, 1025 Eldorado Blvd, Broomfield, CO 80021 *Tel:* 720-888-1000 *Toll Free Tel:* 877-2LEVEL3 (253-8357) *Web Site:* www.level3.com, pg 806

Storrier, David, Infosat Communications Inc, 3130 114 Ave SE, Calgary, AB T2Z 3V6, Canada *Tel:* 403-543-8188 *Toll Free Tel:* 888-524-3038 *Fax:* 403-289-8133 *E-mail:* info@infosat.com *Web Site:* infosat.com, pg 787

Story, Richard, Sony Music Commercial Music Group, 550 Madison Ave, New York, NY 10022 *Tel:* 212-833-8000 *Web Site:* www.sonymusic.com, pg 893

Storyk, John, Walters-Storyk Design Group Inc (WSDG), 262 Martin Ave, Highland, NY 12528 *Tel:* 845-691-9300 *Fax:* 845-691-9361 *E-mail:* info@wsdg.com *Web Site:* www.wsdg.com, pg 933

Stoughton-Jackson, Kerri, Outfest Los Angeles LGBT Film Festival, 3470 Wilshire Blvd, Suite 935, Los Angeles, CA 90010 *Tel:* 213-480-7088 *Fax:* 213-480-7099 *E-mail:* outfest@outfest.org *Web Site:* www.outfest.org, pg 999

Stoupenos, Johnny, ACS Technologies, 180 Dunbarton Dr, Florence, SC 29501 *Tel:* 843-662-1681 *Toll Free Tel:* 800-736-7425 (sales); 800-669-2309 (support) *Fax:* 843-669-7513 *E-mail:* info@acstechnologies.com *Web Site:* www.acstechnologies.com, pg 674

Stout, Bob, Moxie Media, 1301 Dealers Ave, New Orleans, LA 70123 *Tel:* 504-733-6907 *Toll Free Tel:* 800-346-6943 *Fax:* 504-733-9493 *E-mail:* info@moxiemedia.com *Web Site:* www.moxietraining.com; www.moxiemedia.com, pg 832

Stout, Penny, Global Peace Film Festival (GPFF), PO Box 3310, Winter Park, FL 32790-3310 *Tel:* 407-582-6018 *E-mail:* info@peacefilmfest.org *Web Site:* www.peacefilmfest.org, pg 990

Stout, Rob, Encore Event Technologies LLC, 8850 W Sunset Rd, 3rd fl, Las Vegas, NV 89148 *Tel:* 702-739-8803 *Fax:* 702-739-8831 *Web Site:* www.encoreglobal.com/us, pg 754

Stover, Billy, FirstCom Music, 14860 Montfort Dr, Suite 260, Dallas, TX 75254 *Tel:* 972-446-8742 *Toll Free Tel:* 800-858-8880 *E-mail:* info@firstcom.com; musicsearch@firstcom.com *Web Site:* www.firstcom.com, pg 761

Stover, Carol L, Adventure Productions LLC, 5910 York Rd, Lower Level, Baltimore, MD 21212 *Tel:* 410-878-1261; 410-961-5942 (cell) *Fax:* 410-878-1263 *Web Site:* www.adventureproductions.com, pg 678

Stover, George A III, Adventure Productions LLC, 5910 York Rd, Lower Level, Baltimore, MD 21212 *Tel:* 410-878-1261; 410-961-5942 (cell) *Fax:* 410-878-1263 *Web Site:* www.adventureproductions.com, pg 678

Strain, Mike Jr, Fantasy Creations FX, 2060 E McDaniel St, Springfield, MO 65802 *Tel:* 417-619-1138 *E-mail:* fcfxmike@yahoo.com *Web Site:* www.fantasycreationsfx.com, pg 759

Strand, Diane, JDS Video & Media Productions Inc, 28069 Diaz Rd, Suite D & E, Temecula, CA 92590 *Tel:* 951-296-6715 *Toll Free Tel:* 866-737-2239 *E-mail:* info@jds-productions.com *Web Site:* jds-productions.com, pg 793

Strassner, Bunnie, Flashback Media Productions, 1172 Lombardi St, Erie, CO 80516 *Tel:* 303-545-9955 *E-mail:* info@flashbackmedia.tv *Web Site:* flashbackmedia.tv, pg 762

Strassner, Norman, Flashback Media Productions, 1172 Lombardi St, Erie, CO 80516 *Tel:* 303-545-9955 *E-mail:* info@flashbackmedia.tv *Web Site:* www.flashbackmedia.tv, pg 762

Stratigos, Nicholas G, Printing Industries of America, 301 Brush Creek Rd, Warrendale, PA 15086-7529 *Tel:* 412-741-6860 *Toll Free Tel:* 800-910-4283 *Fax:* 412-741-2311 *E-mail:* printing@printing.org *Web Site:* www.printing.org, pg 960

Straub, Amanda, Association of American Publishers (AAP), 455 Massachusetts Ave NW, Suite 700, Washington, DC 20001-2777 *Tel:* 202-347-3375 *Fax:* 202-347-3690 *E-mail:* info@publishers.org *Web Site:* publishers.org, pg 951

Strauss, Ricky, The Walt Disney Studios, 500 S Buena Vista St, Burbank, CA 91521 *Tel:* 818-560-1000 *Web Site:* studioservices.go.com; waltdisneystudios. com, pg 743

Straw, Joseph, Colonial Williamsburg Foundation, PO Box 1776, Williamsburg, VA 23187-1776 *Tel:* 757-229-1000 *Toll Free Tel:* 888-974-7926 *E-mail:* social@cwf.org *Web Site:* www. colonialwilliamsburg.org; www.history.org/foundation, pg 727

Streich, Nina, Global Peace Film Festival (GPFF), PO Box 3310, Winter Park, FL 32790-3310 *Tel:* 407-582-6018 *E-mail:* info@peacefilmfest.org *Web Site:* www. peacefilmfest.org, pg 990

Streichler, Robin, Tatum Video, 103 S Davis St, Telluride, CO 81435 *Tel:* 213-999-5970 (cell); 970-728-4892 *E-mail:* utemtn@aol.com, pg 907

Streitfeld, Andy, AMS Pictures, 16986 N Dallas Pkwy, Dallas, TX 75248 *Tel:* 972-818-7400 *Toll Free Tel:* 866-691-3660 *Fax:* 972-818-1257 *Web Site:* amspictures.com, pg 684

Striker, Matt, San Francisco Film Commission, City Hall, Rm 473, One Dr Carlton B Goodlett Place, San Francisco, CA 94102 *Tel:* 415-554-6241 *Fax:* 415-554-6503 *E-mail:* film@sfgov.org *Web Site:* www. filmsf.org/film-commission; www.facebook.com/FilmSF, pg 967

Strollo, Tom, Sand Box Studio, 555 Minnesota St, San Francisco, CA 94107 *Tel:* 415-550-8732 *E-mail:* inquiries@sandboxstudio.com *Web Site:* www. sandboxstudio.com, pg 880

Struble, Robert J, Directed Electronics, One Viper Way, Suite A, Vista, CA 92081 *Tel:* 760-598-6200 *Toll Free Tel:* 800-876-0800 *E-mail:* pr@directed.com *Web Site:* www.directed.com, pg 743

Struhs, Steve, TBC Consoles Inc, 170 Rodeo Dr, Edgewood, NY 11717 *Tel:* 631-293-4068 *Toll Free Tel:* 888-CONSOLE (266-7653) *Fax:* 631-293-4075 *E-mail:* info@tbcconsoles.com; sales@tbcconsoles. com; support@tbcconsoles.com *Web Site:* www. tbcconsoles.com, pg 907

Struthers, Paul, Frameline Completion Fund, 145 Ninth St, Suite 300, San Francisco, CA 94103 *Tel:* 415-703-8650 *Fax:* 415-861-1404 *E-mail:* info@frameline. org; programming@frameline.org *Web Site:* www. frameline.org, pg 989

Struthers, Scott, Sonance, 212 Avenida Fabricante, San Clemente, CA 92672-7531 *Tel:* 949-492-7777 *Toll Free Tel:* 800-582-0772 (tech support); 800-582-7777 *E-mail:* customerservice@sonance.com *Web Site:* www.sonance.com, pg 892

Stuart, Kelly, Center for the Collaborative Classroom, 1001 Marina Village Pkwy, Suite 110, Alameda, CA 94501-1042 *Tel:* 510-533-0213 *Toll Free Tel:* 800-666-7270 *Fax:* 510-464-3670 *E-mail:* info@ collaborativeclassroom.org *Web Site:* www. collaborativeclassroom.org, pg 719

Stubbs, Chris, Redco Audio Inc, 1701 Stratford Ave, Stratford, CT 06615 *Tel:* 203-502-7600 *Toll Free Tel:* 800-572-7280 *Fax:* 203-502-7610 *E-mail:* orders@redco.com *Web Site:* www.redco.com, pg 872

Studley, Jeff, CPR MultiMedia Solutions, 7812 Cessna Ave, Gaithersburg, MD 20879 *Tel:* 301-590-9400 *Fax:* 301-590-9402 *E-mail:* info@cprmms.com *Web Site:* www.cprmms.com, pg 732

Studnicky, Dan, Creative Stage Lighting Co Inc, 149 Rte 28 N, North Creek, NY 12853 *Tel:* 518-251-3302 *Fax:* 518-251-2908 *E-mail:* info@creativestagelighting. com *Web Site:* www.creativestagelighting.com, pg 733

Sturchio, Rich, Cramer, 425 University Ave, Norwood, MA 02062 *Tel:* 781-278-2300 *E-mail:* theteam@ cramer.com *Web Site:* cramer.com, pg 732

Sturgeon, Russ, Russ Sturgeon Productions/RSVP, 916 Third Ave S, Nashville, TN 37210 *Tel:* 615-255-7787 *Web Site:* www.rsvpnashville.com, pg 903

Suarez, Raul, Third Ear Sound Co, 30965 San Benito St, Hayward, CA 94544 *Tel:* 510-429-1000 *Toll Free Tel:* 800-587-1115 *Fax:* 510-429-1001 *E-mail:* raul@ thirdearsound.com *Web Site:* www.thirdearsound.com, pg 912

Sublett, Carla Pineyro, National Instruments Corp, 11500 N Mopac Expwy, Austin, TX 78759-3504 *Tel:* 512-683-0100 *Toll Free Tel:* 888-280-7645 (sales); 877-388-1952 *Fax:* 512-683-8411; 512-683-5794 (sales) *Web Site:* www.ni.com, pg 836

Subramanian, Subu, ALOM Technologies Corp, 48105 Warm Springs Blvd, Fremont, CA 94539-7498 *Tel:* 510-360-3600 *Toll Free Tel:* 800-500-9991 *Fax:* 510-226-7617 *E-mail:* customerservice@alom. com *Web Site:* www.alom.com, pg 681

Suddreth, Sherwin, Thinking Maps Inc, 401 Cascade Pointe Lane, Cary, NC 27513-5780 *Tel:* 919-678-8778 *Toll Free Tel:* 800-243-9169 *Fax:* 919-678-8782 *E-mail:* office@thinkingmaps.com *Web Site:* thinkingmaps.com, pg 912

Suede, Bob, Suede Interactive, 693 Main St, Hackensack, NJ 07601-4713 *Tel:* 201-646-0416 *E-mail:* suede@suede.tv *Web Site:* www.suede.tv, pg 903

Sufranski, Bruce, American Society of Safety Professionals (ASSP), 520 N Northwest Hwy, Park Ridge, IL 60068 *Tel:* 847-699-2929 (cust serv) *Fax:* 847-768-3434 *E-mail:* customerservice@assp.org *Web Site:* www.assp.org, pg 949

Suga, Yasu, Kenko Tokina USA, 7642 Woodwind Dr, Huntington Beach, CA 92647 *Tel:* 714-849-5700 *Toll Free Tel:* 800-421-1141 *Fax:* 714-849-5677 *E-mail:* support@kenkotokinausa.com *Web Site:* kenkotokinausa.com, pg 797

Sugerman, Andrew, Disney Consumer Products & Interactive Media (DCPI), 1201 Flower St, Glendale, AZ 91201 *Tel:* 818-544-0000 *Web Site:* dcpi.disney. com, pg 743

Suggs, Jeanne, Suggs Media Productions Inc, 156 W 44 St, 7th fl, New York, NY 10036 *Tel:* 212-398-4200 *Fax:* 212-382-0922, pg 903

Sullivan, Barbara, California Language Laboratories, 6170 Palmero Circle, Cameron Park, CA 95682 *Toll Free Tel:* 800-327-1147 *Fax:* 530-350-8072 *E-mail:* info@esltapes.com *Web Site:* www.esltapes. com, pg 714

Sullivan, Bryan, The Phoenix Learning Group Inc, 1990 E Lohman Ave, Suite 102, Las Cruces, NM 88001 *Toll Free Tel:* 800-221-1274 *E-mail:* customerservice@phoenixlearninggroup. com; orders@phoenixlearninggroup.com *Web Site:* phoenixlearninggroup.com, pg 856

Sullivan, Jerry, Precision Camera & Video, 2438 W Anderson Lane, Suite B-4, Austin, TX 78757 *Tel:* 512-467-7676 *Toll Free Tel:* 800-677-1023 *Fax:* 512-467-0607 *E-mail:* www.precision-camera. com, pg 861

Sullivan, Joe, Duxbury Systems Inc, 270 Littleton Rd, Unit 6, Westford, MA 01886-3523 *Tel:* 978-692-3000 *Fax:* 978-692-7912 *E-mail:* info@duxsys.com *Web Site:* www.duxburysystems.com, pg 748

Sullivan, Joe, Scala Inc, 7 Great Valley Pkwy, Suite 300, Malvern, PA 19355 *Tel:* 610-363-3350 *Toll Free Tel:* 888-SCALA-96 (722-5296) *Fax:* 610-363-4010 *E-mail:* team@scala.com *Web Site:* scala.com, pg 881

Sullivan, John, Covid Inc, 1723 W Fourth St, Tempe, AZ 85281 *Tel:* 480-966-2221 *Toll Free Tel:* 800-638-6104 *Fax:* 480-966-6728 *E-mail:* sales@covid.com *Web Site:* www.covid.com, pg 732

Sullivan, Kevin, Sullivan Home Entertainment, 110 Davenport Rd, Toronto, ON M5R 3R3, Canada *Tel:* 416-921-7177 *Fax:* 416-921-7538 *E-mail:* inquire@sullivan-ent.com *Web Site:* sullivanmovies.com, pg 903

Sullivan, L Joseph, Logitech, 7700 Gateway Blvd, Newark, CA 94560 *Tel:* 510-795-8500 *Toll Free Tel:* 866-291-1505 *Web Site:* www.logitech.com, pg 811

Sullivan, Peter, Duxbury Systems Inc, 270 Littleton Rd, Unit 6, Westford, MA 01886-3523 *Tel:* 978-692-3000 *Fax:* 978-692-7912 *E-mail:* info@duxsys.com *Web Site:* www.duxburysystems.com, pg 748

Sullivano, Joseph, Video Production Associates Inc, 525 Bridgeport Ave, Shelton, CT 06484-1397 *Tel:* 203-929-8869 *Web Site:* www.vpa-inc.com, pg 928

Sullivant, Wayne, PeopleVisionFX, 311 E First Ave, Bldg A, Roselle, NJ 07203 *Tel:* 973-509-2056 *Web Site:* peoplevisionfx.com, pg 854

Summerland, Jon, Okanagan Film Commission, 1450 KLO Rd, Kelowna, BC V1W 3Z4, Canada *Tel:* 250-717-0087 *Fax:* 250-868-0512 *E-mail:* info@ okanaganfilm.com *Web Site:* www.okanaganfilm.com, pg 978

Sun, Grace, Califone International Inc, 9135 Alabama Ave, Suite B, Chatsworth, CA 91311 *Tel:* 818-407-2400 *Toll Free Tel:* 800-722-0500 *Fax:* 818-407-2405 *Toll Free Fax:* 877-402-2248 *Web Site:* www.califone. com, pg 714

Sun, Peter, Jack Morton Worldwide, 909 Third Ave, New York, NY 10022 *Tel:* 212-401-7000; 212-401-7212 *E-mail:* experience@jackmorton.com *Web Site:* www.jackmorton.com, pg 830

Sunshine, Jaqueline, Chapman/Leonard Studio Equipment Inc, 12950 Raymer St, North Hollywood, CA 91605 *Tel:* 818-764-6726 *Toll Free Tel:* 888-883-6559 *Fax:* 818-764-6730 *E-mail:* marketing@ chapman-leonard.com *Web Site:* www.chapman-leonard.com, pg 720

Sunshine, Robert H, International Cinema Technology Association (ICTA), 311 W 43 St, Suite 301, New York, NY 10036 *Tel:* 212-493-4097; 212-493-4058 *Fax:* 212-257-6428 *Web Site:* www. internationalcinematechnologyassociation.com, pg 956

Surack, Chuck, Sweetwater Sound Inc, 5501 US Hwy 30 W, Fort Wayne, IN 46818 *Tel:* 260-432-8176 *Toll Free Tel:* 800-222-4700 *Fax:* 260-432-1758 *Web Site:* www. sweetwater.com, pg 905

Suriyakumar, Suri, ARC Document Solutions, 1981 N Broadway, Suite 385, Walnut Creek, CA 94596 *Tel:* 925-949-5100 *Toll Free Tel:* 855-500-0660 *E-mail:* contact@e-arc.com *Web Site:* www.e-arc.com, pg 688

Surratt, Stephen G, Texas Scenic Co Inc, 8053 Potranco Rd, San Antonio, TX 78251 *Tel:* 210-684-0091 *Toll Free Tel:* 800-292-7490 *Fax:* 210-684-4557 *E-mail:* info@texasscenic.com *Web Site:* www. texasscenic.com, pg 911

Survance, Mick, Quintessence Audio Ltd, 5701 W Dempster St, Morton Grove, IL 60053 *Tel:* 847-966-4434 *Web Site:* www.quintessenceaudio.com, pg 868

Susco, Ed, Audio Visual Associates, One Stewart Ct, Denville, NJ 07834 *Toll Free Tel:* 888-435-6678 *Fax:* 973-442-0888 *E-mail:* sales@avaonline.com; info@avaonline.com *Web Site:* www.avaonline.com, pg 694

Susser, Cheryl, Phase Technology, 6400 Youngerman Circle, Jacksonville, FL 32244 *Tel:* 913-663-5600 *Toll Free Tel:* 855-663-5600 *Fax:* 913-663-3200 *E-mail:* sales@mseaudio.com *Web Site:* phasetech. mseaudio.com, pg 855

Sutcliff, Michael R, Accenture, 161 N Clark St, Chicago, IL 60601 *Tel:* 312-693-0161 *Toll Free Tel:* 877-889-9009 *Fax:* 312-693-0507 *Web Site:* www.accenture. com, pg 672

Suter, Ron, Universal Studios Canada Inc, 2450 Victoria Park Ave, Toronto, ON M2J 4A2, Canada *Tel:* 416-491-3000 *E-mail:* uniadvertising@nbcuni.com *Web Site:* www.universalpictures.ca, pg 922

Sutherland, Linda, GTI (Graphic Technology Inc), PO Box 3138, Newburgh, NY 12550-0651 *Tel:* 845-562-7066 *Toll Free Tel:* 888-562-7066 *Fax:* 845-562-2543 *E-mail:* sales@gtilite.com *Web Site:* www.gtilite.com, pg 774

Tager, Joshua, Crystal Pictures Inc, 2000 Riverside Dr, Asheville, NC 28804 *Tel:* 828-285-9995 *Toll Free Tel:* 800-669-4057 *Fax:* 828-285-9997 *E-mail:* cryspic@aol.com *Web Site:* ivyvideo.com, pg 735

Tagle, Jr, CenterStaging LLC, 3407 Winona Ave, Burbank, CA 91504 *Tel:* 818-559-4333 *Fax:* 818-848-4016 *E-mail:* info@centerstaging.com *Web Site:* centerstaging.com, pg 719

Taiko, Tom, Konica Minolta Business Solutions, 100 Williams Dr, Ramsey, NJ 07446 *Tel:* 201-825-4000 *Web Site:* kmbs.konicaminolta.us, pg 801

Taing, Denny, Keslow Camera Inc, 5900 Blackwelder St, Culver City, CA 90232 *Tel:* 310-636-4600 *Fax:* 310-915-5335 *E-mail:* info@keslowcamera.com *Web Site:* www.keslowcamera.com, pg 798

Tait, Catherine, CBC/Radio-Canada, 181 Queen St, Ottawa, ON K1P 1K9, Canada *Tel:* 613-288-6000; 613-288-6445 (newsroom) *Toll Free Tel:* 866-306-4636 (CN only) *E-mail:* cbcnewsottawa@cbc.ca *Web Site:* cbc.radio-canada.ca, pg 717

Takac, Mike, Warner Home Video Inc, 4000 Warner Blvd, Bldg 160, Burbank, CA 91522 *Tel:* 818-954-6000 *Fax:* 818-954-6480 *Web Site:* www.warnerbros.com, pg 934

Takagi, J T, Third World Newsreel/Camera News Inc, 545 Eighth Ave, Suite 550, New York, NY 10018 *Tel:* 212-947-9277 *Fax:* 212-594-6417 *E-mail:* twn@twn.org *Web Site:* www.twn.org, pg 912

Takahashi, Mariko, Clarity Media Group, 166 Fifth Ave, 6th & 7th fl, New York, NY 10010 *Tel:* 212-262-7015 *E-mail:* info@claritymediagroup.com *Web Site:* www.claritymediagroup.com, pg 725

Talbot, Tara, WildBrain™, 5657 Spring Garden Rd, Suite 505, Halifax, NS B3J 3R4, Canada *Tel:* 902-423-0260 *Fax:* 902-422-0752 *E-mail:* info@wildbrain.com; halifax@wildbrain.com; sales@wildbrain.com *Web Site:* www.wildbrain.com, pg 938

Tallerico, Brian, Chicago Film Critics Association, 155 E Algonquin Rd, Arlington Heights, IL 60006 *Tel:* 847-427-4530 *Fax:* 847-427-1301 *Web Site:* www.chicagofilmcritics.org, pg 953

Talley, Terry, Rocky Mountain Audio/Video Productions Inc, 7950 S Lincoln St, B-100, Littleton, CO 80122 *Tel:* 303-730-1100 *Toll Free Tel:* 877-856-4644 *Web Site:* www.rmavp.com, pg 876

Tally, Gene, Comtel Inc, 14901 NE 20 Ave, North Miami, FL 33181 *Tel:* 305-424-4160 (facility servs); 305-424-4178 (local inquiries); 516-816-5152 (natl inquiries) *Web Site:* www.comtelinc.com; www.facebook.com/comtelinc/, pg 730

Tannen, Steve, Illuminate Post/Digital Finishing, 10900 Ventura Blvd, Studio City, CA 91604 *Tel:* 323-969-8822 *Fax:* 323-969-8860 *E-mail:* info@illuminatehollywood.com *Web Site:* illuminatehollywood.com, pg 784

Tannen, Steve, Illuminate Studios, 10900 Ventura Blvd, Studio City, CA 90068 *Tel:* 818-769-4500 *Fax:* 818-769-7150 *E-mail:* info@illuminatehollywood.com *Web Site:* illuminatehollywood.com, pg 784

Tanner, Dave, North-by-Northwest - A Digital Studio, 903 W Broadway Ave, Spokane, WA 99201 *Tel:* 509-324-2949 *Fax:* 509-324-2959 *E-mail:* spokane@nxnw.net *Web Site:* www.nxnw.net, pg 842

Tanner, James, Bryston Ltd, 677 Neal Dr, Peterborough, ON K9J 6X7, Canada *Tel:* 705-742-5325 *Toll Free Tel:* 800-632-8217 *Fax:* 705-742-0882 *Web Site:* www.bryston.com, pg 712

Tanous, Will, Universal Music Group, 2220 Colorado Ave, Santa Monica, CA 90404 *Tel:* 310-865-5000 *Web Site:* www.universalmusic.com, pg 922

Taormina, Jason, Digital Video Systems, 3270 Executive Way, Miramar, FL 33025 *Tel:* 954-239-4410 *Fax:* 954-239-4486 *E-mail:* info@digitalvideosystems.net *Web Site:* digitalvideosystems.net, pg 742

Tapp, J Scott, PGi, 3280 Peachtree Rd NE, Suite 1000, Atlanta, GA 30305 *Tel:* 404-262-8400 *Toll Free Tel:* 866-755-4878 *Web Site:* www.pgi.com, pg 855

Tarde, Jerry, Golf Digest Publications, One World Trade Center, 27th fl, New York, NY 10007-0090 *Tel:* 212-286-2860 *Toll Free Tel:* 800-962-5513 *Web Site:* www.golfdigest.com, pg 772

Tarpley, David, Tarpley Media Systems, 3737 50 St, Lubbock, TX 79413 *Tel:* 806-797-5833 *Toll Free Tel:* 800-600-5833 *Fax:* 806-797-5139 *E-mail:* tms@tarpleymedia.com *Web Site:* www.tarpleymedia.com, pg 907

Tarsio, Bob, Broadcast Devices Inc, Westchester Industrial Complex, 3199 Albany Post Rd, Suite 122, Buchanan, NY 10511-1639 *Tel:* 914-737-5032 *Fax:* 914-736-6916 *E-mail:* sales@broadcast-devices.com; customer.service@broadcast-devices.com *Web Site:* www.broadcast-devices.com, pg 710

Tart, David, Kendall Hunt Publishing Co, 4050 Westmark Dr, Dubuque, IA 52002 *Tel:* 563-589-1000 *Toll Free Tel:* 800-228-0810 *Fax:* 563-589-1237 *Toll Free Fax:* 800-772-9165 *E-mail:* orders@kendallhunt.com; corpinfo@kendallhunt.com *Web Site:* www.kendallhunt.com, pg 797

Tarzwell, Matthew, Thompson Rivers University Marketing & Communications Dept, 805 TRU Way, Kamloops, BC V2C 0C8, Canada *Tel:* 250-852-7000 *Web Site:* www.tru.ca/marcom, pg 913

Tasi, John, David Clark Co Inc, 360 Franklin St, Worcester, MA 01604 *Tel:* 508-751-5800 *Toll Free Tel:* 800-900-3434 *Fax:* 508-753-5827 *E-mail:* sales@davidclark.com *Web Site:* www.davidclark.com, pg 738

Tatna, Meher, Golden Globe Awards, 646 N Robertson Blvd, West Hollywood, CA 90069 *Tel:* 310-657-1731 *Fax:* 310-657-5576 *E-mail:* awards@goldenglobes.com *Web Site:* www.goldenglobes.com, pg 990

Tattersfield, George, Ingram Content Group LLC, One Ingram Blvd, La Vergne, TN 37086-1986 *Tel:* 615-793-5000 *Toll Free Tel:* 800-937-8000 (retailers); 800-937-5300 (ext 1, libs) *E-mail:* customerservice@ingramcontent.com *Web Site:* www.ingramcontent.com, pg 787

Tatum, Tom, Tatum Video, 103 S Davis St, Telluride, CO 81435 *Tel:* 213-999-5970 (cell); 970-728-4892 *E-mail:* utemtn@aol.com, pg 907

Tatz, Carl, Carl Tatz Design, 6666 Brookmont Terr, Suite 1109, Nashville, TN 37205 *Tel:* 615-354-6242 *E-mail:* carl@carltatzdesign.com *Web Site:* www.carltatzdesign.com, pg 907

Taylor, Adam, Associated Production Music LLC, 6255 Sunset Blvd, Suite 900, Hollywood, CA 90028 *Tel:* 323-461-3211 *Fax:* 323-461-9102 *E-mail:* info@apmmusic.com; clientservices@apmmusic.com *Web Site:* www.apmmusic.com, pg 691

Taylor, Bill Jr, Video Express, 88 Black Falcon Ave, Suite 220, Boston, MA 02210 *Tel:* 617-267-7900 *Fax:* 617-267-6306 *E-mail:* operations@evideoexpress.com *Web Site:* www.evideoexpress.com, pg 928

Taylor, Brian, Evolve Inc, 1210 E Arlington Blvd, Greenville, NC 27858 *Tel:* 252-754-2957 *Fax:* 252-754-2832 *Web Site:* www.evolveinc.com, pg 757

Taylor, Chip, Chip Taylor Communications LLC, 2 East View Dr, Derry, NH 03038 *Tel:* 603-434-9262 *Toll Free Tel:* 800-876-CHIP (876-2447) *Fax:* 603-432-2723 *E-mail:* chip.taylor@chiptaylor.com *Web Site:* www.chiptaylor.com, pg 907

Taylor, Dr John, ADD Plus, 488 Glacier Way S, Monmouth, OR 97361 *Toll Free Tel:* 800-847-1233 *Fax:* 503-838-1608 *Web Site:* www.add-plus.com, pg 676

Taylor, John, MicroImage Video Systems, PO Box 331, Boyertown, PA 19512-0331 *Tel:* 610-754-6800 *Fax:* 610-754-9766 *Web Site:* www.mivs.com, pg 826

Taylor, John, Zenith Electronics LLC, 2000 Millbrook Dr, Lincolnshire, IL 60069 *Tel:* 847-941-8000 *Toll Free Tel:* 800-243-0000 (cust serv) *Web Site:* www.zenith.com, pg 945

Taylor, Joseph, Panasonic Corporation of North America, 2 Riverfront Plaza, Newark, NJ 07012 *Tel:* 201-348-7000 *Toll Free Tel:* 800-211-7262; 888-275-2595 *Fax:* 201-348-7807 *Web Site:* www.panasonic.com, pg 850

Taylor, Liz, SmackDab Media, 252 Glenhaven Dr, Amherst, NY 14228 *Tel:* 615-957-6618 *Web Site:* smackdabmedia.us, pg 890

Taylor, Mark, Taylor Associates, 110 W Canal St, Suite 301, Winooski, VT 05404 *Tel:* 802-735-1942 *Toll Free Tel:* 800-READ-PLUS (732-3758) *Fax:* 802-419-4786 *E-mail:* info@readingplus.com *Web Site:* www.readingplus.com, pg 907

Taylor, Mel, Production Garden Music, 13423 Blanco Rd, No 147, San Antonio, TX 78216 *Tel:* 210-530-5200 *Toll Free Tel:* 800-247-5317 *Fax:* 210-530-5230 *E-mail:* info@productiongarden.com *Web Site:* www.productiongarden.com, pg 863

Taylor, Rachel, Cucalorus Film Festival, Jengo's Playhouse, 815 Princess St, Wilmington, NC 28401 *Tel:* 910-343-5995 *E-mail:* programming@cucalorus.org; press@cucalorus.org; comm@cucalorus.org *Web Site:* www.cucalorus.org, pg 987

Taylor, Rebecca, Strata™, 3013 Santa Clara Dr, Santa Clara, UT 84765 *Tel:* 435-628-5218 *Toll Free Tel:* 800-STRATA-3D (787-2823); 800-6-STRATA (678-7282) *Fax:* 435-628-9756 *E-mail:* sales@strata.com *Web Site:* www.strata.com, pg 901

Taylor, Roxanne, Accenture, 161 N Clark St, Chicago, IL 60601 *Tel:* 312-693-0161 *Toll Free Tel:* 877-889-9009 *Fax:* 312-693-0507 *Web Site:* www.accenture.com, pg 672

Taylor, Shelby, The Campbell Agency, Hidden Grove Bldg, 12404 Park Central Dr, Suite 222 S, Dallas, TX 75251 *Tel:* 214-522-8991 *Fax:* 214-522-8997 *Web Site:* www.thecampbellagency.com, pg 715

Taylor, Tess, National Association of Record Industry Professionals (NARIP), PO Box 2446, Toluca Lake, CA 91610-2446 *Tel:* 818-769-7007 *E-mail:* info@narip.com *Web Site:* www.narip.com, pg 959

Taylor, Wendy, CommScope Inc, 1100 CommScope Place SE, Hickory, NC 28602 *Tel:* 828-324-2200 *Toll Free Tel:* 800-982-1708 *E-mail:* publicrelations@commscope.com *Web Site:* www.commscope.com, pg 728

Tayman, William P Jr, Corporation for Public Broadcasting (CPB), 401 Ninth St NW, Washington, DC 20004-2129 *Tel:* 202-879-9600 *Toll Free Tel:* 800-272-2190 *Fax:* 202-879-9700 *E-mail:* press@cpb.org *Web Site:* www.cpb.org, pg 953

Teachworth, Dan, Satellite Center, 2535 Williams Blvd, Kenner, LA 70062 *Tel:* 504-466-3474 *Toll Free Tel:* 800-256-4010 *E-mail:* info@satctr.com *Web Site:* satctr.com, pg 881

Tebault, Hugh III, Latham Foundation Publications, 1320 Harbor Bay Pkwy, Suite 200, Alameda, CA 94502 *Tel:* 510-521-0920 *Fax:* 510-521-9861 *E-mail:* info@latham.org *Web Site:* www.latham.org, pg 804

Tedesco, Joe, WildBrain™, 5657 Spring Garden Rd, Suite 505, Halifax, NS B3J 3R4, Canada *Tel:* 902-423-0260 *Fax:* 902-422-0752 *E-mail:* info@wildbrain.com; halifax@wildbrain.com; sales@wildbrain.com *Web Site:* www.wildbrain.com, pg 938

Tedesco, John, Phoebus Manufacturing, 2800 Third St, San Francisco, CA 94107 *Tel:* 415-550-1177, pg 855

Tedford, Thomas W, ACCO Brands Corp, 4 Corporate Dr, Lake Zurich, IL 60047-8997 *Toll Free Tel:* 800-541-0094; 800-222-6462 *Toll Free Fax:* 800-941-4463 *E-mail:* contactus@acco.com (cust serv) *Web Site:* www.accobrands.com, pg 673

Teer, Chad, Infosat Communications Inc, 3130 114 Ave SE, Calgary, AB T2Z 3V6, Canada *Tel:* 403-543-8188 *Toll Free Tel:* 888-524-3038 *Fax:* 403-289-8133 *E-mail:* info@infosat *Web Site:* infosat.com, pg 787

Teeters, Roger, Veetronix Inc, 1311 W Pacific St, Lexington, NE 68850 *Tel:* 308-324-6661 *Toll Free Tel:* 800-445-0007 *Fax:* 308-324-4985 *E-mail:* sales@veetronix.com *Web Site:* www.veetronix.com, pg 925

Teh, Mr B S, Seagate Technology LLC, 10200 S De Anza Blvd, Cupertino, CA 95014 *Toll Free Tel:* 800-SEAGATE (732-4283) *Web Site:* www.seagate.com, pg 883

Teiper, James, Available Light, 5251 Dixon Rd, Oceanside, CA 92056-2319 *Tel:* 760-505-1605 *E-mail:* availablelight@cox.net *Web Site:* www. availablelightandgrip.com, pg 697

Teitelbaum, Mitch, AV Concepts Inc, 1917 W First St, Tempe, AZ 85281 *Tel:* 480-557-6000; 480-646-4216 (sales & serv) *Toll Free Tel:* 866-927-7590 *E-mail:* exhibitorservices@avconcepts.com *Web Site:* www.avconcepts.com, pg 697

Teltschik, Theresa, Romar Learning Solutions LLC, 6700 Woodlands Pkwy, Suite 230-292, Woodlands, TX 77382 *Tel:* 281-292-5508 *Fax:* 281-363-2309 *E-mail:* info@romarlearning.com *Web Site:* romarlearning.com, pg 877

Temmer, Michael, Ace Video, 178 Columbus Ave, No 237072, New York, NY 10023 *Tel:* 212-727-7969 *E-mail:* acevideonyc@gmail.com *Web Site:* www. acevideonyc.com, pg 674

Tempesta, Dan, Nuance Communications Inc, One Wayside Rd, Burlington, MA 01803 *Tel:* 781-565-5000 *Toll Free Tel:* 800-654-1187 (cust serv) *Fax:* 781-565-5001 *Web Site:* www.nuance.com, pg 843

Temple, Ginny, Direct Current Video Productions, 1928 E Highland Ave, Suite F104-448, Phoenix, AZ 85016 *Tel:* 602-263-7717 *Web Site:* www. directcurrentproductions.com, pg 743

Temple, Howard, AheadTeK, 6410 Via Del Oro, San Jose, CA 95119 *Tel:* 408-226-9800; 408-226-9991 *Toll Free Tel:* 800-971-9191 *Fax:* 408-226-9195 *Web Site:* www.aheadtek.com, pg 678

Temple, Ladd, Renkus-Heinz Inc, 19201 Cook St, Foothill Ranch, CA 92610-3501 *Tel:* 949-588-9997 *Fax:* 949-588-9514 *E-mail:* sales@renkus-heinz.com *Web Site:* www.renkus-heinz.com, pg 873

Temple, Nancy Ellen, IV Media Resources, 910 Redwing Dr, Geneva, IL 60134 *Tel:* 630-389-0000 *E-mail:* info@infinitevideo.com *Web Site:* www. infinitevideo.com, pg 792

TenEyck, Peter, Blue Onion Media, 940 Wadsworth Blvd, 3rd fl, Lakewood, CO 80214 *Tel:* 303-597-9661 *Fax:* 303-232-2241 *Web Site:* www.blueonionmedia. com, pg 708

Teng, Vivian, Chicago International Film Festival, 212 W Van Buren St, Suite 400, Chicago, IL 60607 *Tel:* 312-683-0121 *Fax:* 312-683-0122 *E-mail:* info@ chicagofilmfestival.com; entries@chicagofilmfestival. com *Web Site:* www.chicagofilmfestival.com, pg 985

Tenorio, Norman, American Educational Research Association (AERA), 1430 "K" St NW, Suite 1200, Washington, DC 20005 *Tel:* 202-238-3200 *Fax:* 202-238-3250 *E-mail:* communications@aera.net; members@aera.net *Web Site:* www.aera.net, pg 948

Tepper, Paul, Dedotec USA Inc, 48 Sheffield Business Park, Ashley Falls, MA 01222 *Tel:* 413-229-2550 *E-mail:* info@dedolight.com *Web Site:* www.dedolight. com, pg 740

Terino, Ed, SeaChange International Inc, 50 Nagog Park, Acton, MA 01720 *Tel:* 978-897-0100 *Fax:* 978-897-0132 *E-mail:* globalsalesoperations@schange.com *Web Site:* www.schange.com, pg 883

Terranella, Anthony, Burst Video/Film Inc, 1104 Alta Ave NE, Atlanta, GA 30307, pg 713

Terranova, Dawn, AbelCine, 801 S Main St, Burbank, CA 91506 *Toll Free Tel:* 888-700-4416 *E-mail:* orders@abelcine.com; customerservice@ abelcine.com *Web Site:* www.abelcine.com, pg 672

Terry, Terry N, MessageMakers, 1217 Turner St, Lansing, MI 48906 *Tel:* 517-482-3333 *Toll Free Tel:* 888-482-6688 *E-mail:* info@messagemakers.com *Web Site:* www.messagemakers.com, pg 824

Tessmar, Jim, Pro Power Products Inc, 913 S Victory Blvd, Burbank, CA 91502 *Tel:* 818-558-6222; 818-558-6740 *Toll Free Tel:* 800-395-8466 *Fax:* 818-558-3999 *Web Site:* propowerproducts.com, pg 863

Testa, Bruce, Chromavision Corp, The Radio Wave Bldg, Suite 900, 49 W 27 St, New York, NY 10001 *Tel:* 212-686-7366 *E-mail:* info@chromavision.net *Web Site:* www.chromavision.net, pg 723

Teti, Nick, HDrental.com, 16129 Covello St, Van Nuys, CA 91406 *Tel:* 818-994-3461 *Web Site:* hdrental.com, pg 777

Tetlow, W James, Nautilus Entertainment Design Inc (NED), 1010 Turquoise St, Suite 215, San Diego, CA 92109 *Tel:* 858-456-6395 *E-mail:* info@n-e-d.com *Web Site:* www.n-e-d.com, pg 837

Tews, Jason, Kelmscott Communications, 1665 Mallette Rd, Aurora, IL 60505-1354 *Tel:* 630-898-0800 *Fax:* 630-898-2183 *Web Site:* kelmscottcommunications.com, pg 797

Tham, Sean, WAC Lighting Co, 44 Harbor Park Dr, Port Washington, NY 11050 *Tel:* 516-515-5000 *Toll Free Tel:* 800-526-2588 *Fax:* 516-515-5050 *Toll Free Fax:* 800-526-2585 *E-mail:* sales@waclighting.com *Web Site:* www.waclighting.com, pg 933

Thames, Joel, Sound Service Co, 6630 Morella Ave, North Hollywood, CA 91606-1651 *Tel:* 818-503-4440, pg 894

Thaw, Bruce R, Bulbtronics Inc, 45 Banfi Plaza N, Farmingdale, NY 11735 *Tel:* 631-249-2272 *Toll Free Tel:* 800-654-8542 (sales); 800-588-2852 *E-mail:* sftv@bulbtronics.com *Web Site:* www. bulbtronics.com, pg 712

Thelemaque, Jacques, Filmmakers Alliance (FA), 1317 N San Fernando Blvd, Unit 366, Burbank, CA 91504 *Tel:* 310-568-0633 *E-mail:* info@filmmakersalliance. org *Web Site:* filmmakersalliance.org, pg 955

Theron, Diana, Cibola Systems, 180 S Cypress St, Orange, CA 92866 *Tel:* 714-480-0272 *Fax:* 714-480-0768 *E-mail:* info@cibolasystems.com *Web Site:* cibolasystems.com, pg 723

Therriault, Jaime, Award Productions Inc, 164 Great Rd, Acton, MA 01720 *Tel:* 978-635-8000 *E-mail:* web@ awardprod.com *Web Site:* www.awardproductions.com, pg 699

Therrien, Lucie, French American Music Enterprises, 5 Junkins Ave, Suite 106, Portsmouth, NH 03801 *Tel:* 603-430-9524 *Web Site:* www.luciet.com, pg 765

Thetford, Stephen, Professional Photographers of America (PPA), 229 Peachtree St NE, Suite 2200, Atlanta, GA 30303 *Tel:* 404-522-8600 *Toll Free Tel:* 800-786-6277 *Fax:* 404-614-6400 *E-mail:* csc@ ppa.com *Web Site:* www.ppa.com, pg 960

Thielking, Erik, AMV/Unitel Studios, 515 W 57 St, New York, NY 10019 *Tel:* 212-265-3600 (studios); 212-586-8616 (sales) *Fax:* 212-246-5059 *E-mail:* hdsales@ allmobilevideo.com *Web Site:* www.allmobilevideo. com, pg 685

Thielman, Gary, Harrison Consoles, 1024 Firestone Pkwy, La Vergne, TN 37086-3505 *Tel:* 615-641-7200 *Fax:* 615-641-7224 *E-mail:* info@harrisonconsoles. com *Web Site:* www.harrisonconsoles.com, pg 776

Thomas, Ann, ExpoDisplays, 3401 Mary Taylor Rd, Birmingham, AL 35235 *Toll Free Tel:* 800-747-3976 *E-mail:* info@expodisplays.com *Web Site:* www. expodisplays.com, pg 757

Thomas, Brad, Progressive AE, 1811 Four Mile Rd NE, Grand Rapids, MI 49525 *Tel:* 616-361-2664 *Fax:* 616-361-1493 *E-mail:* info@progressiveae.com *Web Site:* www.progressiveae.com, pg 865

Thomas, Bryan, Thomas Printworks, 600 N Central Expwy, Richardson, TX 75080 *Tel:* 972-231-7161 *Toll Free Tel:* 800-877-3776 *Fax:* 972-644-6308 *E-mail:* richardson@thomasprintworks.com *Web Site:* thomasprintworks.com, pg 912

Thomas, Chrishelle, Library & Information Technology Association (LITA), c/o American Library Association, 50 E Huron St, Chicago, IL 60611-2795

Toll Free Tel: 800-545-2433 (ext 4270) *Fax:* 312-280-3257 *E-mail:* lita@ala.org *Web Site:* www.ala.org/lita, pg 957

Thomas, Colette, Sonoma County Film Office, 141 Stony Circle, Suite 110, Santa Rosa, CA 95401-4154 *Tel:* 707-565-7170 *Fax:* 707-565-7231 *E-mail:* film@ sonoma-county.org *Web Site:* www.sonoma-county. org/film, pg 968

Thomas, Douglas, Spectra Film & Video, 5626 Vineland Ave, North Hollywood, CA 91601 *Tel:* 818-762-4545 *Fax:* 818-762-5454 *E-mail:* sales@ spectrafilmandvideo.com *Web Site:* www. spectrafilmandvideo.com, pg 897

Thomas, Ellen, Fresh Film Northwest (FFNW), 934 SW Salmon St, Portland, OR 97205 *Tel:* 503-221-1156 *Fax:* 503-294-0874 *E-mail:* info@nwfilm.org *Web Site:* www.nwfilm.org, pg 990

Thomas, Ellen, Northwest Film Center, 934 SW Salmon St, Portland, OR 97205 *Tel:* 503-221-1156 *E-mail:* info@nwfilm.org *Web Site:* www.nwfilm.org, pg 842

Thomas, Gary, Videssence, 10768 Lower Azusa Rd, El Monte, CA 91731 *Tel:* 626-579-0943 *Fax:* 626-579-6803 *E-mail:* contact@videssence.tv *Web Site:* www. videssence.tv, pg 930

Thomas, Hywel, S&P Global Marketing Intelligence, 55 Water St, New York, NY 10041 *Toll Free Tel:* 877-863-1306 *E-mail:* questions@spcapitaliq.com *Web Site:* marketingintelligence.spglobal.com, pg 880

Thomas, Lee, Georgia Film Office, 75 Fifth St W, Suite 1200, Atlanta, GA 30308 *Tel:* 404-962-4052 *Toll Free Tel:* 877-SHOOTGA (746-6842) *Fax:* 404-962-4053 *E-mail:* film@georgia.org *Web Site:* www.georgia. org/film, pg 970

Thomas, Robert, Peppers Ghost HD®, c/o Bob Thomas Productions Inc, 2 Franklin Ct, Montville, NJ 07045 *Tel:* 973-335-9100 *Web Site:* www.peppersghosthd. com, pg 854

Thomas, Terry, Captions & Subtitle Services Ltd, 5113 S Harper, Suite 2C, Chicago, IL 60615 *Tel:* 872-222-9057 *E-mail:* quote@capsubservices.com *Web Site:* www.capsubservices.com, pg 716

Thomas, Terry, Heinemann, 361 Hanover St, Portsmouth, NH 03801-3912 *Tel:* 603-431-7894 *Toll Free Tel:* 800-225-5800 *Fax:* 603-431-2214 *Toll Free Fax:* 877-231-6980 *E-mail:* custserv@heinemann.com *Web Site:* www.heinemann.com, pg 778

Thomas, Tiffany, Video Caption Corp, 88 Hunns Lake Rd, Stanfordville, NY 12581 *Tel:* 845-868-1200 *Toll Free Tel:* 800-705-1203 *Fax:* 845-868-1188 *Toll Free Fax:* 800-705-1207 *E-mail:* mail@vicaps.com *Web Site:* www.vicaps.com, pg 927

Thomas, William Tyler, Bright Ideas Creative Services, 107 W Maple St, Suite 206, Jeffersonville, IN 47130 *Tel:* 812-282-9900; 502-693-9900 (cell) *Toll Free Fax:* 866-593-5753 *Web Site:* www.brightideascreative. com, pg 710

Thomason, Evan, Santa Clarita Film Office, 23920 Valencia Blvd, Suite 100, Santa Clarita, CA 91355 *Tel:* 661-284-1425 *Fax:* 661-286-4001 *E-mail:* film@ santa-clarita.com *Web Site:* filmsantaclarita.com, pg 967

Thommes, Jeff, Staging Resources Inc, 257 E Helen Rd, Palatine, IL 60067 *Tel:* 847-963-6600 *Toll Free Tel:* 877-963-6600 *Fax:* 847-963-6601 *E-mail:* info@ stagingresources.com *Web Site:* www.stagingresources. com, pg 899

Thompson, Andy, RGB Spectrum, 950 Marina Village Pkwy, Alameda, CA 94501 *Tel:* 510-814-7000 *Fax:* 510-814-7026 *Web Site:* www.rgb.com, pg 874

Thompson, Christy, Art Gallery of Ontario, 317 Dundas St W, Toronto, ON M5T 1G4, Canada *Tel:* 416-979-6648 *Toll Free Tel:* 877-225-4246 *Web Site:* ago.ca, pg 690

Thompson, Chuck, JLCooper Electronics, 142 Arena St, El Segundo, CA 90245 *Tel:* 310-322-9990 *Fax:* 310-335-0110 *E-mail:* sales@jlcooper.com; service@ jlcooper.com *Web Site:* www.jlcooper.com, pg 794

Thompson, Dennis, TAPPI, 15 Technology Pkwy S, Norcross, GA 30092 *Tel:* 770-446-1400 *Toll Free Tel:* 800-332-8686 (US); 800-446-9431 (CN) *Fax:* 240-396-5973 *E-mail:* memberconnection@tappi. org *Web Site:* www.tappi.org, pg 907

Thompson, Erika, PAR Inc, 16204 N Florida Ave, Lutz, FL 33549 *Tel:* 813-449-4065 *Toll Free Tel:* 800-331-8378 *Fax:* 813-961-2196 *Toll Free Fax:* 800-727-9329 *E-mail:* cs@parinc.com *Web Site:* www.parinc.com, pg 851

Thompson, Frances, Entertainment Services and Technology Association (ESTA), 630 Ninth Ave, Suite 609, New York, NY 10036 *Tel:* 212-244-1505 *Fax:* 212-244-1502 *E-mail:* info@esta.org; membership@esta.org *Web Site:* www.esta.org, pg 954

Thompson, Frances, Production Equipment Rental Group (PERG), c/o ESTA, 630 Ninth Ave, Suite 609, New York, NY 10036 *Tel:* 212-244-1505 *Fax:* 212-244-1502 *E-mail:* info@esta.org; membership@esta.org *Web Site:* www.esta.org/perg, pg 960

Thompson, Frank, AV Metro Inc, 5401 Etta Burke Ct, Raleigh, NC 27606 *Tel:* 919-233-1901 *Fax:* 919-233-1804 *E-mail:* info@avmetro.com *Web Site:* www. avmetro.com, pg 697

Thompson, James B, Broadcasters Foundation of America, 125 W 55 St, 4th fl, New York, NY 10019-5366 *Tel:* 212-373-8250 *Fax:* 212-373-8254 *E-mail:* info@thebfoa.org *Web Site:* www.thebfoa.org; broadcastersfoundation.org, pg 952

Thompson, James B, Golden Mike Award, 125 W 55 St, 4th fl, New York, NY 10019-5366 *Tel:* 212-373-8250 *Fax:* 212-373-8254 *E-mail:* info@thebfoa.org *Web Site:* www.thebfoa.org; broadcastersfoundation. org, pg 990

Thompson, James B, Lowry Mays Excellence in Broadcasting Award, 125 W 55 St, 4th fl, New York, NY 10019-5366 *Tel:* 212-373-8250 *Fax:* 212-373-8254 *E-mail:* info@thebfoa.org *Web Site:* www.thebfoa.org; broadcastersfoundation.org, pg 995

Thompson, James B, Ward L Quaal Leadership Awards, 125 W 55 St, 4th fl, New York, NY 10019-5366 *Tel:* 212-373-8250 *Fax:* 212-373-8254 *E-mail:* info@thebfoa.org *Web Site:* www.thebfoa.org; broadcastersfoundation.org, pg 1000

Thompson, Katie, St John's International Women's Film Festival, 28 Cochrane St, Suite 101, St John's, NL A1C 3L3, Canada *Tel:* 709-754-3141 *Fax:* 709-754-0049 *E-mail:* info@womensfilmfestival.com *Web Site:* www.womensfilmfestival.com, pg 1002

Thompson, Kim Mitzo, Twin Sisters® Digital Media™, 1653 Merriman Rd, Suite L1, Akron, OH 44313 *Tel:* 330-730-9558 *E-mail:* twinsisters@twinsisters. com *Web Site:* www.twinsisters.com, pg 920

Thompson, Lacy Jr, LT Sound Inc, 7980 LT Pkwy, Lithonia, GA 30058 *Tel:* 770-482-4836 *Web Site:* www.ltsound.com, pg 812

Thompson, Lonna, America's Public Television Stations (APTS), 2100 Crystal Dr, Suite 700, Arlington, VA 22202 *Tel:* 202-654-4200 *Fax:* 202-654-4236 *Web Site:* apts.org, pg 949

Thompson, Matt, Adobe Systems Inc, 345 Park Ave, San Jose, CA 95110-2704 *Tel:* 408-536-6000 *Fax:* 408-537-6000 *Web Site:* www.adobe.com, pg 676

Thompson, Pete, TiVo Corp, 2 Circle Star Way, San Carlos, CA 94070 *Tel:* 408-562-8400 *Toll Free Tel:* 877-367-8486 (cust support); 877-289-8486 (sales support) *Fax:* 408-567-1800 *Web Site:* business.tivo. com; www.tivo.com, pg 914

Thompson, Trent, Moog Music Inc, 160 Broadway St, Asheville, NC 28801 *Tel:* 828-251-0090 *Toll Free Tel:* 800-948-1990 *Fax:* 828-254-6233 *E-mail:* info@ moogmusic.com *Web Site:* www.moogmusic.com, pg 830

Thomson, Daniel, Image Video Services & Productions, 1210 Southview Dr, Sudbury, ON P3E 2L6, Canada *Tel:* 705-698-1212 *Fax:* 705-805-0110 *E-mail:* info@ ivsproductions.ca *Web Site:* www.ivsproductions.ca, pg 785

Thomson, Robert, News Corp, 1211 Avenue of the Americas, New York, NY 10036 *Tel:* 212-416-3400 *E-mail:* media@newscorp.com *Web Site:* newscorp. com, pg 840

Thomson, Ryan, Captain Fiddle Music & Publications, 94 Wiswall Rd, Lee, NH 03861 *Tel:* 603-659-2658 *E-mail:* cfiddle@tiac.net *Web Site:* captainfiddle.com, pg 716

Thomson, Steve, AirBrands Event & Marketing Group, 6470 Wyoming St, Suite 2024, Dearborn, MI 48126 *Tel:* 519-254-9563 *Toll Free Tel:* 800-411-6200 (ext 26) *Fax:* 519-735-5446 *Web Site:* www. airbrandsmarketing.com; famousinflatables.com, pg 679

Thomson, Susan, Image Video Services & Productions, 1210 Southview Dr, Sudbury, ON P3E 2L6, Canada *Tel:* 705-698-1212 *Fax:* 705-805-0110 *E-mail:* info@ ivsproductions.ca *Web Site:* www.ivsproductions.ca, pg 785

Thomson, Tawni, Bishop Area Chamber of Commerce & Visitors Bureau, 690 N Main St, Bishop, CA 93514 *Tel:* 760-873-8405 *Web Site:* www.bishopvisitor.com, pg 966

Thorburn, Lisa A, Thorburn Associates (TA), 20880 Baker Rd, Castro Valley, CA 94546 *Tel:* 510-886-7826 *Fax:* 510-886-7828 *E-mail:* ta@ta-inc.com *Web Site:* www.ta-inc.com, pg 913

Thorburn, Steven J, Thorburn Associates (TA), 20880 Baker Rd, Castro Valley, CA 94546 *Tel:* 510-886-7826 *Fax:* 510-886-7828 *E-mail:* ta@ta-inc.com *Web Site:* www.ta-inc.com, pg 913

Thornberg, Linda, Audacity Recording Studios, 2734 Polk St, Suite B, Hollywood, FL 33020 *Tel:* 954-920-4418 *Web Site:* www.audacityrecordingstudios.com, pg 693

Thorne-Stone, Karen, Ontario Creates, South Tower, Suite 501, 175 Bloor St E, Toronto, ON M4W 3R8, Canada *Tel:* 416-314-6858 *Fax:* 416-314-6876 *E-mail:* reception@ontariocreates.ca *Web Site:* www. ontariocreates.ca, pg 978

Thornton, Jim, AV Concepts Inc, 1917 W First St, Tempe, AZ 85281 *Tel:* 480-557-6000; 480-646-4216 (sales & serv) *Toll Free Tel:* 866-927-7590 *E-mail:* exhibitorservices@avconcepts.com *Web Site:* www.avconcepts.com, pg 697

Thostrup, Britta, Mirror 34 Productions, 2302 W Badger Rd, Madison, WI 53713-2322 *Tel:* 608-271-1226 *Toll Free Tel:* 800-569-6810 *E-mail:* human@mirror34.com *Web Site:* www.mirror34.com, pg 828

Thrasher, Charlotte, Opti-Case Inc, 1175 CR 481 W, Henderson, TX 75654 *Tel:* 903-657-5666 *Toll Free Tel:* 800-637-6635 *Fax:* 903-657-6030 *E-mail:* sales@ opti-case.net *Web Site:* www.opti-case.net, pg 847

Throop, Darren, Entertainment One Distribution, 70 Driver Rd, Unit 1, Brampton, ON L6T 5V2, Canada *Tel:* 905-624-7337 *Toll Free Tel:* 800-387-0184 *Fax:* 905-624-7310 *Web Site:* entertainmentone.com, pg 754

Thuillot, Dominique, Editions Hurtubise HMH Ltee, 1815 Avenue De Lorimier, Montreal, QC H2K 3W6, Canada *Tel:* 514-523-1523 *Toll Free Tel:* 800-361-1664 *Fax:* 514-523-9969 *Web Site:* www. distributionhmh.com, pg 783

Tichy, Karen, Alpha Source Inc, 6619 W Calumet Rd, Milwaukee, WI 53223-4186 *Tel:* 414-760-2222 *Toll Free Tel:* 800-654-9845 *E-mail:* customer. service@alphasource.com; info@alphasource.com *Web Site:* www.alphasource.com, pg 681

Tickman-Thoon, Michael, Rough House, 550 Bryant St, San Francisco, CA 94107-1217 *Tel:* 415-561-4544 *Fax:* 415-543-8370 *E-mail:* info@roughhouse.com *Web Site:* www.roughhouse.com, pg 878

Tierney, Jim, Tierney Brothers Inc, 1771 Energy Park Dr, Suite 100, St Paul, MN 55108 *Tel:* 612-331-5500 *Toll Free Tel:* 866-557-6062 *Fax:* 612-331-3424 *E-mail:* contactform@tierneybrothers.com *Web Site:* www.tierneybrothers.com, pg 914

Tierney, Tom, Tierney Brothers Inc, 1771 Energy Park Dr, Suite 100, St Paul, MN 55108 *Tel:* 612-331-5500 *Toll Free Tel:* 866-557-6062 *Fax:* 612-331-3424 *E-mail:* contactform@tierneybrothers.com *Web Site:* www.tierneybrothers.com, pg 914

Tiffen, Andrew, The Tiffen Co LLC, 90 Oser Ave, Hauppauge, NY 11788-3886 *Tel:* 631-273-2500 *Toll Free Tel:* 800-645-2522 *Fax:* 631-273-2557 *E-mail:* techsupport@tiffen.com *Web Site:* www.tiffen. com, pg 914

Tiffen, Steven, The Tiffen Co LLC, 90 Oser Ave, Hauppauge, NY 11788-3886 *Tel:* 631-273-2500 *Toll Free Tel:* 800-645-2522 *Fax:* 631-273-2557 *E-mail:* techsupport@tiffen.com *Web Site:* www.tiffen. com, pg 914

Till, Rod, L-3 WESCAM, 649 N Service Rd W, Burlington, ON L7P 5B9, Canada *Tel:* 905-633-4000; 905-633-4175 (cust serv) *Toll Free Tel:* 888-593-7226 *Fax:* 905-633-4100 *E-mail:* sales.wescam@l-3com. com *Web Site:* www.wescam.com, pg 803

Tillett, Chuck D, PESA, 103 Quality Circle, Suite 210, Huntsville, AL 35806 *Tel:* 256-726-9200 *Toll Free Tel:* 800-323-7372 *E-mail:* sales@pesa.com *Web Site:* www.pesa.com, pg 855

Tilly, Steve, Telestream Inc, 848 Gold Flat Rd, Nevada City, CA 95959 *Tel:* 530-470-1300 *Toll Free Tel:* 877-257-6245 *Fax:* 530-470-1301 *E-mail:* info@telestream. net *Web Site:* www.telestream.net, pg 910

Timberlake, Jim, Link Electronics Inc, 2360 N High St, Suite 10, Jackson, MO 63755 *Tel:* 573-334-4433 *Toll Free Tel:* 800-776-4411 *Fax:* 573-204-4554 *E-mail:* sales@linkelectronics.com *Web Site:* www. linkelectronics.com, pg 809

Tinic, Atilla, Level 3 Communications Inc, 1025 Eldorado Blvd, Broomfield, CO 80021 *Tel:* 720-888-1000 *Toll Free Tel:* 877-2LEVEL3 (253-8357) *Web Site:* www.level3.com, pg 806

Tipping, Elaine, Grass Valley, 3499 Douglas-B-Floreani, Montreal, QC H4S 2C6, Canada *Tel:* 514-333-1772 *Fax:* 514-333-9828 *Web Site:* www.grassvalley.com, pg 773

Tippmann, Vince, Advanced Media Integration, 2300 Meyer Rd, Fort Wayne, IN 46805 *Tel:* 260-428-2698 *Toll Free Tel:* 877-428-2610 *E-mail:* info@amifw.com *Web Site:* amifw.com, pg 677

Tirado, Jason, RGB Spectrum, 950 Marina Village Pkwy, Alameda, CA 94501 *Tel:* 510-814-7000 *Fax:* 510-814-7026 *Web Site:* www.rgb.com, pg 874

Titen, Andrew, Bisk Education, 9417 Princess Palm Ave, Tampa, FL 33619 *Toll Free Tel:* 800-280-9718 *E-mail:* media@bisk.com *Web Site:* www.bisk.com, pg 706

Titus, Dick, ETC, 3031 Pleasant View Rd, Middleton, WI 53562-4809 *Tel:* 608-831-4116 *Toll Free Tel:* 800-688-4116 *Fax:* 608-836-1736 *Web Site:* www. etcconnect.com, pg 756

Titus, Lawrence, Titus Technological Laboratories (TTL), 77 Kreiger Lane, Glastonbury, CT 06033 *Tel:* 860-633-5472 *Toll Free Tel:* 800-806-TTL1 (806-8851) *Fax:* 860-633-8244 *E-mail:* sales1@tituslabs.com *Web Site:* www.tituslabs.com, pg 914

Toback, Dan, Digital Film Studios LLC, 11800 Sheldon St, Unit C/D, Sun Valley, CA 91352 *Tel:* 818-771-0019 *Web Site:* www.digitalfilmstudios.com, pg 742

Tobias, Eric M, Tobias Associates Inc, 50 Industrial Dr, Ivyland, PA 18974-1433 *Tel:* 215-322-1500 *Toll Free Tel:* 800-877-3367 *Fax:* 215-322-1504 *E-mail:* sales@tobiasinc.com; service@tobiasinc.com; repair@tobiasinc.com *Web Site:* www.densitometers. net, pg 915

Tobin, Walter, Electronics Representatives Association (ERA), 1325 S Arlington Heights Rd, Suite 204, Elk Grove Village, IL 60007 *Tel:* 312-419-1432 *Fax:* 312-419-1660 *E-mail:* info@era.org *Web Site:* www.era. org, pg 954

Tochilin, Jerry, General Production Services, 883 S East St, Anaheim, CA 92805 *Tel:* 714-535-2271 *Fax:* 714-535-0952 *E-mail:* lensclens@yahoo.com; sales@ lensclens.com *Web Site:* www.lensclens.com, pg 769

Tod, Dorothy, Dorothy Tod Films, 41 Hazel Brown Rd, Warren, VT 05674 *Tel:* 802-496-5280 *Fax:* 802-496-5280, pg 915

Todd, Debbie, Professional Photographers of America (PPA), 229 Peachtree St NE, Suite 2200, Atlanta, GA 30303 *Tel:* 404-522-8600 *Toll Free Tel:* 800-786-6277 *Fax:* 404-614-6400 *E-mail:* csc@ppa.com *Web Site:* www.ppa.com, pg 960

Todd, Hunter, WorldFest-Houston International Film Festival, 9898 Bissonnet St, Suite 650, Houston, TX 77036 *Tel:* 713-965-9955 *Fax:* 713-965-9960 *E-mail:* mail@worldfest.org; entry@worldfest.org *Web Site:* www.worldfest.org, pg 1007

Todd, Jean, Independent Audio Inc, 43 Deerfield Rd, Portland, ME 04101 *Tel:* 207-773-2424 *Fax:* 207-773-2422 *E-mail:* info@independentaudio.com *Web Site:* www.independentaudio.com, pg 786

Toland, Shelby, The Brainwash Movie Festival, 1675 Seventh St, No 23302, Oakland, CA 94623-6009 *Tel:* 510-836-3210 *E-mail:* brainwash.movies@gmail.com *Web Site:* www.brainwashm.com, pg 984

Tolchin, Talc, Forte Productions, PO Box 17, San Geronimo, CA 94963-0325 *Tel:* 415-488-9446 *Fax:* 415-488-9446 *Web Site:* www.pianovideos.com, pg 764

Toledo, Edgar, Pacifica Radio Archives, 3729 Cahuenga Blvd W, North Hollywood, CA 91604 *Tel:* 818-506-1077 *Toll Free Tel:* 800-735-0230 *Fax:* 818-506-1084 *E-mail:* pacarchive@aol.com *Web Site:* www.pacificaradioarchives.org, pg 850

Tollefson, Bob, ETC, 3031 Pleasant View Rd, Middleton, WI 53562-4809 *Tel:* 608-831-4116 *Toll Free Tel:* 800-688-4116 *Fax:* 608-836-1736 *Web Site:* www.etcconnect.com, pg 756

Tomao, Victoria, Penguin Random House Audio Publishing, 1745 Broadway, New York, NY 10019 *E-mail:* audio@penguinrandomhouse.com *Web Site:* www.penguinrandomhouseaudio.com, pg 853

Tomasello, Lisa, Ingram Content Group LLC, One Ingram Blvd, La Vergne, TN 37086-1986 *Tel:* 615-793-5000 *Toll Free Tel:* 800-937-8000 (retailers); 800-937-5300 (ext 1, libs) *E-mail:* customerservice@ingramcontent.com *Web Site:* www.ingramcontent.com, pg 787

Tompkins, Andy, NAMM, the National Association of Music Merchants, 5790 Armada Dr, Carlsbad, CA 92008 *Tel:* 760-438-8001 *Toll Free Tel:* 800-767-6266 (memb hotline) *Fax:* 760-438-7327 *E-mail:* info@namm.org *Web Site:* www.namm.org, pg 958

Tomwil, Jim Rokas, Tatum Video, 103 S Davis St, Telluride, CO 81435 *Tel:* 213-999-5970 (cell); 970-728-4892 *E-mail:* utemtn@aol.com, pg 907

Tonges, Michael A, Image Video Teleproductions Inc, 6755 Freedom Ave NW, North Canton, OH 44720 *Tel:* 330-494-9303 *Fax:* 330-966-1792 *E-mail:* info@image-video.com *Web Site:* www.image-video.com, pg 785

Toomey, Dan, Pro HD Rentals, 2201 N Hollywood Way, Suite 1, Burbank, CA 91505 *Tel:* 818-450-1115 *Fax:* 818-450-1115 *E-mail:* sales@prohdrentals.com *Web Site:* www.prohdrentals.com, pg 863

Topjian, Lori, Spirig Advanced Technologies Inc (SAT), 144 Oakland St, Springfield, MA 01108 *Tel:* 413-788-6191 *Toll Free Tel:* 866-977-4744 *Fax:* 413-788-0490 *E-mail:* sat@spirig.com *Web Site:* www.spirig.com, pg 897

Topping, Chris, Juno Awards, 219 Dufferin St, Suite 211C, Toronto, ON M6K 3J1, Canada *Tel:* 416-485-3135 (CN only) *Toll Free Tel:* 888-501-3135 *Fax:* 416-485-4978 *E-mail:* info@carasonline.ca; submissions@junoawards.ca *Web Site:* junoawards.ca; www.facebook.com/theJunoAwards, pg 994

Topscher, Thomas, Media Dimensions LLC, 2212 Autumn Glow Ct, Bel Air, MD 21015 *Tel:* 410-561-4550 *E-mail:* info@mediadimensions.com *Web Site:* www.mediadimensions.com, pg 821

Toriello, Eric, Sonalysts Media, 215 Parkway N, Waterford, CT 06385 *Tel:* 860-442-4355 *Toll Free Tel:* 800-526-8091 (ext 3848) *E-mail:* production@sonalysts.com; media@sonalysts.com; exhibits@sonalysts.com *Web Site:* www.sonalystsmedia.com, pg 892

Tornek, Scott, So Smart Productions, 701 Sharpley Rd, Wilmington, DE 19803 *Tel:* 484-753-1520 *Web Site:* www.sosmart.com, pg 891

Torner, Kelsey, Chico Chamber of Commerce/Butte County Film Commission, 180 Fourth St, Suite 120, Chico, CA 95928 *Tel:* 530-891-5556 *Toll Free Tel:* 800-852-8570 *Fax:* 530-891-3613 *E-mail:* info@chicochamber.com *Web Site:* chicochamber.com, pg 966

Torno, Earl, Wanted! Sound + Picture, 409 King St W, Suite 300, Toronto, ON M5V 1K1, Canada *Tel:* 416-596-1101 *Fax:* 416-596-0690 *E-mail:* info@wantedsp.com; bookings@wantedsp.com *Web Site:* www.wantedsp.com, pg 933

Torok, George, Hallel Communications, Hallel Institute, 175 Rte 340, Sparkill, NY 10976-1047 *Tel:* 845-365-2277 *Toll Free Tel:* 800-445-7477 *Fax:* 845-365-2279 *E-mail:* hallel@hallel.net; info@hallelvideos.com *Web Site:* www.hallelvideos.com, pg 775

Torra, Veronica, Cayman Islands Department of Tourism, Empire State Bldg, 350 Fifth Ave, Suite 2720, New York, NY 10018 *Tel:* 212-889-9009 *E-mail:* film@caymanislands.ky; usareception@caymanislands.ky *Web Site:* www.visitcaymanislands.com, pg 974

Torres, Mark, Pacifica Radio Archives, 3729 Cahuenga Blvd W, North Hollywood, CA 91604 *Tel:* 818-506-1077 *Toll Free Tel:* 800-735-0230 *Fax:* 818-506-1084 *E-mail:* pacarchive@aol.com *Web Site:* www.pacificaradioarchives.org, pg 849

Torres, Pete, Tribeca Film Festival, Communications Dept, 375 Greenwich St, New York, NY 10013 *Tel:* 212-941-2400 *Fax:* 212-941-3939 *E-mail:* festival@tribecafilmfestival.org; entries@tribecafilmfestival.org; press@tribecafilmfestival.org *Web Site:* www.tribecafilm.com/festival, pg 1005

Torres, Ray, Checkers Safety Group, 620 Compton St, Broomfield, CO 80020 *Toll Free Tel:* 800-438-9336; 877-384-6103 *E-mail:* sales@checkers-safety.com *Web Site:* www.checkers-safety.com, pg 721

Torres Rojas, Roselly, Third World Newsreel/Camera News Inc, 545 Eighth Ave, Suite 550, New York, NY 10018 *Tel:* 212-947-9277 *Fax:* 212-594-6417 *E-mail:* twn@twn.org *Web Site:* www.twn.org, pg 912

Torroija, Diego, Two Door Productions LLC, 416 N Harper Ave, Los Angeles, CA 90048 *E-mail:* shoot@usphotograph.com *Web Site:* www.twodoorfx.com, pg 920

Totaro, Matt, Event Tech, 7601 Brandon Woods Blvd, Baltimore, MD 21226 *Tel:* 410-360-5006 *Toll Free Tel:* 866-950-8343 *E-mail:* info@eventtech.com *Web Site:* www.eventtech.com, pg 756

Touhill, Nancy, WIA - The Wireless Infrastructure Association, 2111 Wilson Blvd, Suite 210, Arlington, VA 22201 *Tel:* 703-739-0300 *Toll Free Tel:* 800-759-0300 *Fax:* 703-836-1608 *Web Site:* wia.org, pg 963

Tovares, Joseph, Edward R Murrow Award, 401 Ninth St NW, Washington, DC 20004-2129 *Tel:* 202-879-9600 *Toll Free Tel:* 800-272-2190 *E-mail:* press@cpb.org *Web Site:* www.cpb.org, pg 996

Towe, Mike, SDMediaPros (SDMP), 5205 Kearny Villa Way, No 100, San Diego, CA 92123 *Tel:* 619-672-1000 *E-mail:* membership@sdmediapros.org; marketing@sdmediapros.org; programs@sdmediapros.org *Web Site:* sdmediapros.org, pg 961

Towell, Dan, Castleview Productions, 1100 W 41 St, Austin, TX 78756 *Tel:* 512-442-9944 *Fax:* 512-442-8823 *E-mail:* contact@castleviewproductions.com *Web Site:* castleviewproductions.com, pg 717

Towey, Brian, Microboards Technology LLC, 8150 Mallory Ct, Chanhassen, MN 55317 *Tel:* 952-556-1600 *Toll Free Tel:* 800-646-8881; 800-290-9012 *Fax:* 952-556-1620 *E-mail:* sales@microboards.com *Web Site:* www.microboards.com, pg 826

Towner, John, Solid Sound Recording Studio, 2400 Hassell Rd, Suite 430, Hoffman Estates, IL 60169 *Tel:* 847-490-2101 *E-mail:* solidsoundchicago@icloud.com, pg 892

Towry, Jimi, Tropikal Productions, 137 Sequoia Rd, Rockwall, TX 75032 *Tel:* 972-771-3797 *Fax:* 972-771-0853 *E-mail:* tropikalproductions@gmail.com *Web Site:* www.tropikalproductions.com, pg 918

Towry, Jimi, World Beat Studio, 137 Sequoia Rd, Rockwall, TX 75032 *Tel:* 972-771-3797 *Fax:* 972-771-0853 *E-mail:* tropikalproductions@gmail.com *Web Site:* www.tropikalproductions.com; www.tropikalproductions.com/studio.html, pg 941

Towstego, Anthony J, Thomega Entertainment Inc, North Star Business Centre, 210-820 51 St E, Saskatoon, SK S7K 0X8, Canada *Tel:* 306-280-4982 *Fax:* 306-242-5845 *E-mail:* thomega@sasktel.net *Web Site:* www.thomega.com, pg 913

Toy, Barbara, NYSCA/NYFA Artist Fellowships, 20 Jay St, 7th fl, Suite 740, Brooklyn, NY 11201 *Tel:* 212-366-6900 *Fax:* 212-366-1778 *E-mail:* fellowships@nyfa.org *Web Site:* www.nyfa.org, pg 999

Tozer, Elizabeth Farran, Museum of the City of New York, 1220 Fifth Ave, New York, NY 10029 *Tel:* 212-534-1672 *Fax:* 212-423-0758 *E-mail:* info@mcny.org *Web Site:* www.mcny.org, pg 834

Tracey, Robin, RingSide Creative, 13320 Northend, Suite 3000, Oak Park, MI 48237 *Tel:* 248-548-2500 *E-mail:* info@ringsidecreative.com; newbiz@ringsidecreative.com *Web Site:* www.ringsidecreative.com, pg 875

Tracy, Reid, Hay House Inc, PO Box 5100, Carlsbad, CA 92018-5100 *Tel:* 760-431-7695 (ext 2, intl) *Toll Free Tel:* 800-654-5126 (ext 2, US); 800-650-5115 *Web Site:* www.hayhouse.com, pg 777

Tramantano, Michelle, The Imaging Alliance, 7600 Jericho Tpke, Suite 301, Woodbury, NY 11797 *Tel:* 516-802-0895 *Fax:* 516-364-0140 *E-mail:* info@theimagingalliance.com *Web Site:* www.theimagingalliance.com, pg 955

Tran, Cheryl Valentine, RAM® Mounts, 8410 Dallas Ave S, Seattle, WA 98108 *Tel:* 206-763-8361 *Toll Free Tel:* 800-497-7479 *Fax:* 206-763-9615 *E-mail:* sales@rammount.com *Web Site:* www.rammount.com, pg 870

Tran, Lynh, George Foster Peabody Awards, c/o University of Georgia, 120 Hooper St, Athens, GA 30602-3018 *Tel:* 706-542-3787 *E-mail:* peabody@uga.edu *Web Site:* www.peabodyawards.com, pg 999

Tran, Toan, InterVision Media, 44 W Broadway, Suite 426, Eugene, OR 97401 *Tel:* 541-343-7993; 547-345-5951 *E-mail:* info@intervisionmedia.com *Web Site:* www.intervisionmedia.com, pg 791

Trapani, Jim, JT Communications, 579 NE 44 Ave, Ocala, FL 34470-1421 *Tel:* 352-236-0744 *Fax:* 352-236-5130 *E-mail:* general_info@jtcomms.com *Web Site:* www.jtcomms.com, pg 795

Traubner, Andrea, Filmakers Library, 3212 Duke St, Alexandria, VA 22314 *Tel:* 703-212-8520 *E-mail:* sales@alexanderstreet.com; orders@alexanderstreet.com; info@alexanderstreet.com *Web Site:* www.academicvideostore.com; www.academicvideostore.com/filmakers, pg 760

Traum, Happy, Homespun Video, 1610 Rte 212, Saugerties, NY 12477 *Tel:* 845-246-2550 *Toll Free Tel:* 800-338-2737 (orders-US & CN) *E-mail:* info@homespun.com *Web Site:* www.homespun.com, pg 781

Traum, Jane, Homespun Video, 1610 Rte 212, Saugerties, NY 12477 *Tel:* 845-246-2550 *Toll Free Tel:* 800-338-2737 (orders-US & CN) *E-mail:* info@homespun.com *Web Site:* www.homespun.com, pg 781

Travers, Scott, CamTec Motion Picture Cameras, 4221 W Magnolia Blvd, Burbank, CA 91505 *Tel:* 818-841-8700 *Fax:* 818-841-8777 *Web Site:* www.camtec.tv, pg 715

Traverso, Mark, SCI Television & Creative Media LLC, 160 E Grand Ave, 5th fl, Chicago, IL 60611 *Tel:* 312-643-2080 *E-mail:* info@scitvproductions.com *Web Site:* www.scitvproductions.com, pg 882

Traversy, Pete, Graphx Inc, 400 W Cummings Park, Woburn, MA 01801 *Tel:* 781-932-0430 *Fax:* 781-932-0855 *E-mail:* support@graphx.com *Web Site:* photogize.net, pg 773

Travis, Debbie, Whalley-Abbey Media Holdings Inc, 3800 Rue St Patrick, Suite 100, Montreal, QC H4E 1A4, Canada *Tel:* 514-846-1940 *E-mail:* info@wamgrp.com *Web Site:* wamgrp.com, pg 937

Trayler, Ross, Radius® Display Products Inc, 800 Fabric Xpress Way, Dallas, TX 75234 *Tel:* 972-406-1221 *Toll Free Tel:* 800-FABRIC-X (322-7429); 866-966-4066 (sales); 866-966-8266 (hospitality) *Fax:* 972-406-1321 *Toll Free Tel:* 888-322-7429 *Web Site:* www.radiusdp.com, pg 869

Treesuwan, Kate, Photo-Sonics Inc, 9131 Independence Ave, Chatsworth, CA 91311 *Tel:* 818-842-2141 *Fax:* 818-842-2610 *E-mail:* mail@photosonics.com *Web Site:* www.photosonics.com, pg 856

Treibitz, Alan, Z-Axis Corp, 4600 S Ulster St, Suite 270, Denver, CO 80237 *Tel:* 303-713-0200 *Toll Free Tel:* 800-827-2947 *E-mail:* info@zaxis.com *Web Site:* www.zaxis.com, pg 944

Tremblay, Gary, Alpha Technologies Inc, 3767 Alpha Way, Bellingham, WA 98226 *Tel:* 360-647-2360 *Toll Free Tel:* 800-322-5742 *E-mail:* alpha@alpha.com *Web Site:* www.alpha.com, pg 681

Tremblay, Robert, Group PVP, 296 Saint Pierre St, Matane, QC G4W 2B9, Canada *Tel:* 418-566-2040 *Toll Free Tel:* 877-320-2040 *Fax:* 418-562-4643 *E-mail:* info@pvp.ca *Web Site:* www.pvp.ca, pg 774

Tremble, Mike, Cinema Concepts, 2030 Powers Ferry Rd, Suite 214, Atlanta, GA 30339 *Tel:* 770-956-7460 *Toll Free Tel:* 800-SHOWADS (746-9237) *Fax:* 770-956-8358 *E-mail:* info@cinemaconcepts.com *Web Site:* www.cinemaconcepts.com, pg 724

Trendler, Meg, Eugene, Cascades & Coast-Travel Lane County, 754 Olive St, Eugene, OR 97401 *Tel:* 541-484-5307 *Toll Free Tel:* 800-547-5445 *Web Site:* www.eugenecascadescoast.org, pg 975

Trent, Michael, Dances With Films, Formosa Bldg, 2nd fl, 1041 N Formosa Ave, West Hollywood, CA 90046 *Tel:* 323-854-8176 *E-mail:* info@danceswithfilms.com; submissions@danceswithfilms.com *Web Site:* www.danceswithfilms.com, pg 988

Trentacosti, Sal, Mutual Hardware, 36-27 Vernon Blvd, Long Island City, NY 11106 *Toll Free Tel:* 866-361-2480 *Fax:* 718-786-9591 *E-mail:* info@mutualhardware.com *Web Site:* www.mutualhardware.com, pg 835

Tress, Neil, Recorded Books Inc, an RBmedia company, 270 Skipjack Rd, Prince Frederick, MD 20678 *Tel:* 410-535-5590 *Toll Free Tel:* 800-638-1304 *Fax:* 410-535-5499 *E-mail:* customerservice@recordedbooks.com *Web Site:* www.recordedbooks.com, pg 872

Trevino, Eva, Institute of Texan Cultures, UTSA HemisFair Park Campus, 801 E Cesar E Chavez Blvd, San Antonio, TX 78205-3296 *Tel:* 210-458-2300 *Toll Free Tel:* 800-776-7651 *Fax:* 210-458-2205 *Web Site:* www.texancultures.com, pg 788

Triendl, Robert, DataDirect Networks, 9351 Deering Ave, Chatsworth, CA 91311 *Tel:* 818-700-4000 *Toll Free Tel:* 800-TERABYTE (837-2298) *E-mail:* info@ddn.com; sales@ddn.com *Web Site:* www.ddn.com, pg 738

Trier, David, AIGA, the professional association for design, 233 Broadway, Suite 1740, New York, NY 10279 *Tel:* 212-807-1990 *Toll Free Tel:* 800-548-1634 *E-mail:* general@aiga.org *Web Site:* www.aiga.org, pg 947

Tritchew, Steve, L-3 WESCAM, 649 N Service Rd W, Burlington, ON L7P 5B9, Canada *Tel:* 905-633-4000; 905-633-4175 (cust serv) *Toll Free Tel:* 888-593-7226 *Fax:* 905-633-4100 *E-mail:* sales.wescam@l-3com.com *Web Site:* www.wescam.com, pg 803

Trohanis, Sara, Associated Press Television News, 200 Liberty St, New York, NY 10281 *Tel:* 212-621-1500 *Fax:* 212-621-7419 *E-mail:* info@ap.org *Web Site:* www.aptn.com, pg 691

Troiano, Kenneth, Modernage Photographic Services Inc, 555 Eighth Ave, New York, NY 10018 *Tel:* 212-997-1800 *Web Site:* www.modernage.com, pg 828

Trojian, Elizabeth, YAP Films, 233 Broadview Ave, Toronto, ON M4M 2G3, Canada *Tel:* 416-504-3662 *Fax:* 416-504-3667 *E-mail:* thedog@yapfilms.com *Web Site:* www.yapfilms.com, pg 943

Tronolone, James, PatchAmp, 20 E Kennedy St, Hackensack, NJ 07601 *Tel:* 201-457-1504 *Fax:* 201-457-1507 *E-mail:* sales@patchamp.com *Web Site:* www.patchamp.com, pg 852

Troscher, Christine, USITT, 290 Elwood Davis Rd, Suite 100, Liverpool, NY 13088 *Tel:* 315-463-6463 *Toll Free Tel:* 800-938-7488 *Toll Free Fax:* 866-398-7488 *E-mail:* info@usitt.org *Web Site:* www.usitt.org, pg 963

Trost, Mark, FILM Archives Inc, 35 W 35 St, Suite 904, New York, NY 10001-2238 *Tel:* 212-696-2616 *Fax:* 503-210-9927 *E-mail:* info@filmarchivesonline.com *Web Site:* www.filmarchivesonline.com, pg 760

Troupe, Phil, Rainbow Video Productions Inc, 23803 S 162 St, Adams, NE 68301 *Tel:* 402-430-7343 *Web Site:* www.rainbowvideo.com, pg 869

Trouten, Wayne, Electronic Design Solutions Inc, 41785 Elm St, Suite 201, Murrieta, CA 92562 *Tel:* 951-304-3879 *Toll Free Tel:* 888-611-1741 *Fax:* 951-304-0608 *E-mail:* sales@myedsinc.com *Web Site:* www.gmfsound.com; www.myedsinc.com, pg 752

Troutman, Maureen, Freedoms Foundation National Awards, 1601 Valley Forge Rd, Valley Forge, PA 19481 *Tel:* 610-933-8825 *Fax:* 610-935-0522 *E-mail:* info@ffvf.org *Web Site:* www.freedomsfoundation.org, pg 989

Troxel, Jeanne, Liturgy Training Publications, 3949 S Racine Ave, Chicago, IL 60609-2523 *Tel:* 773-579-4900 *Toll Free Tel:* 800-933-1800 (orders) *Fax:* 773-579-4929 *E-mail:* orders@ltp.org; info@ltp.org *Web Site:* www.ltp.org, pg 810

Truex, Mike, ChyronHego Corp, 5 Hub Dr, Melville, NY 11747 *Tel:* 631-845-2000 *E-mail:* info@chyronhego.com; sales@chyronhego.com *Web Site:* chyronhego.com, pg 723

Trufant, Michael, Launch Media, 804 Main St, Baton Rouge, LA 70802 *Tel:* 225-612-2112 *E-mail:* contactus@launchmedia.tv *Web Site:* www.launchmedia.tv, pg 804

Truong, Ken, For-A Corp of America, 11155 Knott Ave, Suite G & H, Cypress, CA 90630 *Tel:* 714-894-3311 *Fax:* 714-894-5399 *E-mail:* info@for-a.com *Web Site:* www.for-a.com, pg 763

Trupp, Scott, MCCOM Inc, 383 Rte 206, Chester, NJ 07930 *Tel:* 908-879-9590 *Fax:* 908-879-9679 *Web Site:* www.mccom.tv, pg 820

Trust, David, Professional Photographers of America (PPA), 229 Peachtree St NE, Suite 2200, Atlanta, GA 30303 *Tel:* 404-522-8600 *Toll Free Tel:* 800-786-6277 *Fax:* 404-614-6400 *E-mail:* csc@ppa.com *Web Site:* www.ppa.com, pg 960

Ts'o, Pauline, Rhythm & Hues Studios Inc, 5890 W Jefferson Blvd, Suite Q, Los Angeles, CA 90016 *Tel:* 310-448-7500 *Fax:* 310-448-7600 *E-mail:* info-la@rhythm.com *Web Site:* rhythm.com, pg 874

Tsagong, Alyssa, Wisconsin Public Television, 821 University Ave, Madison, WI 53706 *Tel:* 608-263-2121 *Toll Free Tel:* 800-422-9707 *Fax:* 608-263-9763 *E-mail:* comments@wpt.org *Web Site:* www.wpt.org, pg 940

Tschanz, Anne, Institute on Religious Life Inc, PO Box 7500, Libertyville, IL 60048-7500 *Tel:* 847-573-8975 *Fax:* 847-573-8960 *Web Site:* www.religiouslife.com, pg 789

Tschohl, John, Service Quality Institute, 9201 E Bloomington Fwy, Minneapolis, MN 55420-3437 *Tel:* 952-884-3311 *Toll Free Tel:* 800-548-0538 *Fax:* 952-884-8901 *E-mail:* quality@servicequality.com *Web Site:* www.customer-service.com, pg 884

Tsinberg, Mike, Key Digital Systems, 521 E Third St, Mount Vernon, NY 10553 *Tel:* 914-667-9700 *Toll Free Tel:* 855-539-3448 *Fax:* 914-668-8666 *E-mail:* info@keydigital.com; marketing@keydigital.com *Web Site:* www.keydigital.com, pg 798

Tsiokos, Basil, Nantucket Film Festival (NFF), 68 Jay St, Suite 319, Brooklyn, NY 11201 *Tel:* 646-480-1900 *Fax:* 646-365-3367 *E-mail:* info@nantucketfilmfestival.org; submissions@nantucketfilmfestival.org *Web Site:* nantucketfilmfestival.org, pg 997

Tsujiumura, Takatoshi, Society for Information Display (SID), 1475 S Bascom Ave, Suite 114, Campbell, CA 95008-4006 *Tel:* 408-879-3901 *Fax:* 408-879-3833 *E-mail:* office@sid.org *Web Site:* www.sid.org, pg 962

Tsuno, Keiko, Downtown Community Television Center (DCTV), 87 Lafayette St, New York, NY 10013 *Tel:* 212-966-4510 *Fax:* 212-226-3053 *E-mail:* info@dctvny.org *Web Site:* www.dctvny.org, pg 746

Tu, Laura, TVA Media Group, 3950 Vantage Ave, Studio City, CA 91604 *Tel:* 818-505-8300 *Toll Free Tel:* 888-322-4296 *E-mail:* info@tvamediagroup.com *Web Site:* www.tvamediagroup.com, pg 919

Tucker, Allan, Foothill Digital Inc, 217 Storer Ave, New Rochelle, NY 10801 *Tel:* 914-335-5670 *E-mail:* info@foothilldigital.com *Web Site:* www.foothilldigital.com; www.tuckersound.com, pg 763

Tucker, Ron, Grace Church - St Louis, 2695 Creve Coeur Mill Rd, Maryland Heights, MO 63043 *Tel:* 314-292-8300 *Fax:* 314-291-0918 *E-mail:* info@gracestl.org *Web Site:* www.gracestl.org, pg 773

Tucker, Tomas, Videofax, 1750 Cesar Chavez St, Unit G, San Francisco, CA 94124 *Tel:* 415-641-0100 *E-mail:* rentals@videofax.com *Web Site:* www.videofax.com, pg 929

Tudor, Dawn, Verilux® - The Healthy Lighting Co, 340 Mad River Park, Suite 1, Waitsfield, VT 05673 *Tel:* 802-496-3101 *Toll Free Tel:* 888-544-4865 (cust support); 800-454-4408 (orders) *Fax:* 802-496-3105 (orders) *E-mail:* info@verilux.com *Web Site:* www.verilux.com, pg 926

Tudryn, Joyce M, IRTS Foundation, 1697 Broadway, Suite 404, New York, NY 10019 *Tel:* 212-867-6650 *E-mail:* info@irts.org *Web Site:* irtsfoundation.org, pg 957

Tull, Danette, Nevada Film Office, 6655 W Sahara, Suite C-106, Las Vegas, NV 89146 *Tel:* 702-486-2711 *Toll Free Tel:* 877-638-3456 *Fax:* 702-486-2712 *E-mail:* lvnfo@nevadafilm.com *Web Site:* www.nevadafilm.com, pg 973

Tull, Thomas, Legendary Pictures, 2900 W Alameda Ave, 15th fl, Burbank, CA 91505 *Tel:* 818-688-7003 *E-mail:* info@legendary.com *Web Site:* www.legendary.com, pg 806

Tullis, Jay W, Rees, Rees Plaza at East Wharf, Suite 300, 9211 Lake Hefner Pkwy, Oklahoma City, OK 73120 *Tel:* 405-942-7337 *Fax:* 405-948-1261 *E-mail:* rees@rees.com *Web Site:* www.rees.com, pg 872

Turchyn, Roman, L-3 WESCAM, 649 N Service Rd W, Burlington, ON L7P 5B9, Canada *Tel:* 905-633-4000; 905-633-4175 (cust serv) *Toll Free Tel:* 888-593-7226 *Fax:* 905-633-4100 *E-mail:* sales.wescam@l-3com.com *Web Site:* www.wescam.com, pg 803

Turk, Dan, NEP Group Inc, 2 Beta Dr, Pittsburgh, PA 15238 *Tel:* 412-826-1414 *Toll Free Tel:* 800-444-0054 *E-mail:* info@nepinc.com *Web Site:* www.nepgroup.com, pg 838

Turlick, Paul, Big Foot Productions Inc, 37-09 36 Ave, Long Island City, NY 11101 *Tel:* 718-729-1900 *E-mail:* info@bigfootnyc.com *Web Site:* www.bigfootnyc.com, pg 705

Turman, Brent, Texas Association of Motion Media Professionals (TAMMP), 9629 Carnegie Dr, Dallas, TX 75228 *Tel:* 214-613-7601 *E-mail:* info@tammp.com *Web Site:* www.tammp.com, pg 963

Turner, Andrew, Genesis Integration, 14721 123 Ave NW, Edmonton, AB T5L 2Y6, Canada *Toll Free Tel:* 877-283-2253 (Toronto); 866-622-2966 (Quebec); 844-436-4681 (rest of CN) *E-mail:* marketing@genint.com *Web Site:* www.genint.com, pg 769

Turner, Brent, Cramer, 425 University Ave, Norwood, MA 02062 *Tel:* 781-278-2300 *E-mail:* theteam@cramer.com *Web Site:* cramer.com, pg 732

Turner, Jean, Pinewood Sound, 555 Brooksbank Ave, Bldg S, North Vancouver, BC V7J 3S5, Canada *Tel:* 604-669-6900; 604-983-5200 *Fax:* 604-983-5204 *E-mail:* info@pinewoodsound.com; sales@pinewoodsound.com *Web Site:* www.pinewoodsound.com, pg 857

Turner, Jim, Moviola, 1135 N Mansfield Ave, Hollywood, CA 90038 *Tel:* 323-467-3107; 818-487-5000 *Toll Free Tel:* 877-MOVIOLA (668-4652) *Fax:* 323-464-1518 *Web Site:* www.moviola.com, pg 832

Turner, John, Turner Engineering Inc, 14 Morris Ave, Mountain Lakes, NJ 07046-1433 *Tel:* 973-263-1000 *Fax:* 973-334-1620 *E-mail:* info@turnereng.com *Web Site:* www.turnereng.com, pg 919

Turner, Jordan, Soularium Recording Studios, 702 S Alpine Hwy, Alpine, UT 84004 *Tel:* 801-492-0505 *E-mail:* info@soulariumstudios.com *Web Site:* www.soulariumstudios.com, pg 893

Turner, Kami, Keymark Inc, 105 Tech Lane, Liberty, SC 29657 *Tel:* 864-343-0500 *Toll Free Tel:* 800-446-2826 *E-mail:* support@keymarkinc.com *Web Site:* www.keymarkinc.com, pg 798

Turner, Kelli, SESAC Inc, 35 Music Sq E, Nashville, TN 37203 *Tel:* 615-320-0055 *Web Site:* www.sesac.com, pg 962

Turner, Marsha L, Lighting Industry Resource Council, 440 N Wells St, Suite 210, Chicago, IL 60654 *Tel:* 312-527-3677 *Fax:* 312-527-3680 *E-mail:* iald@iald.org *Web Site:* www.iald.org/council, pg 808

Turner, Mike, RAM® Mounts, 8410 Dallas Ave S, Seattle, WA 98108 *Tel:* 206-763-8361 *Toll Free Tel:* 800-497-7479 *Fax:* 206-763-9615 *E-mail:* sales@rammount.com *Web Site:* www.rammount.com, pg 870

Turner, Robby, Data Projections Inc, 3700 W Sam Houston Pkwy S, Suite 525, Houston, TX 77042 *Tel:* 713-781-1999 *Toll Free Tel:* 866-225-5374 *Fax:* 713-781-3338 *E-mail:* dpiweb@dataprojections.com *Web Site:* www.dataprojections.com, pg 738

Turro, Michael, Panavid, 210 West Pkwy, Unit 5, Pompton Plains, NJ 07444 *Tel:* 973-831-5655 *E-mail:* info@panavid.com; support@panavid.com *Web Site:* www.panavid.com, pg 850

Turro, Stephen, Panavid, 210 West Pkwy, Unit 5, Pompton Plains, NJ 07444 *Tel:* 973-831-5655 *E-mail:* info@panavid.com; support@panavid.com *Web Site:* www.panavid.com, pg 850

Tuscany, Pamela, Universal Studios Florida® Production Group, 1000 Universal Studios Plaza, Bldg 22A, Orlando, FL 32819 *Tel:* 407-363-8400 *Toll Free Tel:* 877-612-3737 (outside FL) *Fax:* 407-363-8869 *E-mail:* productiongroup@universalorlando.com *Web Site:* studio.florida.universalstudios.com, pg 922

Tuthill, Ted, Sear Sound, 353 W 48 St, 6th fl, New York, NY 10036 *Tel:* 212-582-5380 *Fax:* 212-581-2731 *E-mail:* waltersear@aol.com *Web Site:* www.searsound.com, pg 883

Tuttle, Lynn M, National Association for Music Education (NAfME), 1806 Robert Fulton Dr, Reston, VA 20191 *Tel:* 703-860-4000 *Toll Free Tel:* 800-336-3768 *Fax:* 703-860-1531 *Toll Free Fax:* 888-275-6362 *E-mail:* memberservices@nafme.org *Web Site:* nafme.org, pg 958

Tuttle, Paige, ACS Technologies, 180 Dunbarton Dr, Florence, SC 29501 *Tel:* 843-662-1681 *Toll Free Tel:* 800-736-7425 (sales); 800-669-2309 (support) *Fax:* 843-669-7513 *E-mail:* info@acstechnologies.com *Web Site:* www.acstechnologies.com, pg 674

Tutzauer, Lauren, Palm Springs International Film Festival, 1700 E Tahquitz Canyon Way, Suite 3, Palm Springs, CA 92262 *Tel:* 760-322-2930 *Toll Free Tel:* 800-898-7256 *Fax:* 760-322-4087 *E-mail:* info@psfilmfest.org *Web Site:* www.psfilmfest.org, pg 999

Twersky, Alex, Kinetic Arts, 306 Gold St, No 5-I, Brooklyn, NY 11201 *Tel:* 917-439-4008 *E-mail:* info@kineticarts.tv *Web Site:* www.kineticarts.tv, pg 799

Tyler, Ethan, Alaska Department of Commerce, Community & Economic Development, 550 W Seventh Ave, Suite 1770, Anchorage, AK 99501-3569 *Tel:* 907-269-4048 *Web Site:* www.commerce.alaska.gov, pg 965

Tyler, Jay, Wheatstone Corp, 600 Industrial Dr, New Bern, NC 28562 *Tel:* 252-638-7000 *Fax:* 252-635-1285 *E-mail:* sales@wheatstone.com *Web Site:* www.wheatstone.com, pg 937

Tyndell, Ben, Lacquer-Mat Inc, 13030 Wayne Rd, Livonia, MI 48150 *Toll Free Tel:* 800-942-2223 (cust serv) *Fax:* 734-422-4205 (orders) *Web Site:* www.lacquer-mat.com, pg 803

Tyrrell, Dennis, Penguin Random House Audio Publishing, 1745 Broadway, New York, NY 10019 *E-mail:* audio@penguinrandomhouse.com *Web Site:* www.penguinrandomhouseaudio.com, pg 853

Tyson, Alex, Visit Billings, 815 S 27 St, Billings, MT 59101 *Tel:* 406-245-4111 *Fax:* 406-245-7333 *E-mail:* info@visitbillings.com *Web Site:* www.visitbillings.com, pg 973

Uchiyama, Teruhisa, MetroSonic Recording Studio, 143 Roebling St, 3rd fl, Brooklyn, NY 11211 *Tel:* 718-782-1872 *E-mail:* manager@metrosonic.net *Web Site:* www.metrosonic.net, pg 824

Ude, Michael, Custom Video Productions Inc, 707 Torrance Blvd, Suite 105, Redondo Beach, CA 90277 *Tel:* 310-543-4901 *E-mail:* info@customvideo.tv *Web Site:* www.customvideo.tv, pg 736

Udelhofen, John, National Safety Council (NSC), 1121 Spring Lake Dr, Itasca, IL 60143-3201 *Tel:* 630-285-1121 *Toll Free Tel:* 800-621-7615; 800-621-7619 (cust serv) *Fax:* 630-285-1434 (cust serv); 630-285-1315 *E-mail:* customerservice@nsc.org *Web Site:* www.nsc.org, pg 836

Uehlein, Michael, Data & Marketing Association (DMA), 225 Reinekers Lane, Suite 325, Alexandria, VA 22314 *Tel:* 212-768-7277; 212-790-1500 *Web Site:* thedma.org, pg 953

Ugie, Heather, Chico Chamber of Commerce/Butte County Film Commission, 180 Fourth St, Suite 120, Chico, CA 95928 *Tel:* 530-891-5556 *Toll Free Tel:* 800-852-8570 *Fax:* 530-891-3613 *E-mail:* info@chicochamber.com *Web Site:* chicochamber.com, pg 966

Uhlhorn, Lori, USDA/FSA Aerial Photography Field Office, 2222 W 2300 S, Salt Lake City, UT 84119-2020 *Tel:* 801-844-2922 *Toll Free Fax:* 855-415-2014 *E-mail:* apfo.sales@slc.usda.gov *Web Site:* www.fsa.usda.gov/programs-and-services/aerial-photography, pg 924

Ulbrich, Ed, Method Studios, 3401 Exposition Blvd, Santa Monica, CA 90404 *Tel:* 310-434-6000 *Web Site:* www.methodstudios.com, pg 824

Ulrich, Phyllis, Interactive Products, 101 Commerce Dr, Montgomeryville, PA 18936 *Tel:* 215-362-2766 *Toll Free Tel:* 800-523-6716 *Fax:* 215-361-0167 *E-mail:* numonics@numonics.com; orders@numonics.com *Web Site:* www.numonics.com, pg 789

Underberg, Sharon E, Eastman Kodak Co, 343 State St, Rochester, NY 14650 *Toll Free Tel:* 800-698-3324 *Web Site:* www.kodak.com, pg 750

Ung, Boromy, ChyronHego Corp, 5 Hub Dr, Melville, NY 11747 *Tel:* 631-845-2000 *E-mail:* info@chyronhego.com; sales@chyronhego.com *Web Site:* chyronhego.com, pg 723

Ungar, Donald, Ungar Video & Film, 2407 Grovewood Ave, Cleveland, OH 44134 *Tel:* 216-661-5090, pg 921

Unger, Bob, SDMediaPros (SDMP), 5205 Kearny Villa Way, No 100, San Diego, CA 92123 *Tel:* 619-672-1000 *E-mail:* membership@sdmediapros.org; marketing@sdmediapros.org; programs@sdmediapros.org *Web Site:* sdmediapros.org, pg 962

Urban, Chanel, Air Philosophy Inc, 1933 S Broadway, Suite 1107B, Los Angeles, CA 90007 *Tel:* 310-980-3902 *E-mail:* info@airphilosophy.com *Web Site:* airphilosophy.com, pg 678

Urbanski, Larry, Moviecraft Inc, PO Box 438, Orland Park, IL 60462-0438 *Tel:* 708-460-9082 *Fax:* 708-460-9099 *E-mail:* stock@moviecraft.com *Web Site:* www.moviecraft.com, pg 831

Urbanski, Larry, Urbanski Film, PO Box 438, Orland Park, IL 60462-0438 *Tel:* 708-460-9082 *Fax:* 708-460-9099 *E-mail:* info@urbanskifilm.com *Web Site:* www.urbanskifilm.com, pg 923

Urrego, Oliver, Panavid, 210 West Pkwy, Unit 5, Pompton Plains, NJ 07444 *Tel:* 973-831-5655 *E-mail:* info@panavid.com; support@panavid.com *Web Site:* www.panavid.com, pg 850

Ursino, Marco, Brooklyn Film Festival (BFF), 180 S Fourth St, Suite 2-S, Brooklyn, NY 11211 *Tel:* 718-388-4306 *Fax:* 718-599-5039 *E-mail:* festival@wbff.org *Web Site:* www.brooklynfilmfestival.org, pg 984

Usdin, Bob, Showman Fabricators Inc, 148 E Fifth St, Bayonne, NJ 07002 *Tel:* 718-935-9899 *E-mail:* info@showfab.com *Web Site:* www.showfab.com, pg 887

Vaccher, L J, Orvac Electronics, 1645 E Orangethorpe Ave, Fullerton, CA 92831 *Tel:* 714-871-1020 *E-mail:* myorvac@orvac.com *Web Site:* www.orvac.com, pg 848

Vachon, Chris, Sigma Delta Chi Awards in Journalism, Eugene S Pulliam National Journalism Ctr, 3909 N Meridian St, Indianapolis, IN 46208 *Tel:* 317-927-8000 *Fax:* 317-920-4789 *E-mail:* awards@spj.org *Web Site:* www.spj.org, pg 1003

Vagnini, Alfred, Powerstation Events, 1718 Highland Ave, Cheshire, CT 06410 *Tel:* 203-250-8500 *Toll Free Tel:* 800-423-7835 *Fax:* 203-250-8575 *E-mail:* info@powerstationevents.com *Web Site:* www.powerstationevents.com, pg 860

Vala, Houshang, Velodyne LiDAR Inc, 5521 Hellyer Ave, San Jose, CA 95738 *Tel:* 408-465-2800 *Fax:* 408-779-9208 (cust serv); 408-779-9377 (orders) *E-mail:* lidar@velodyne.com *Web Site:* velodynelidar.com, pg 925

Valcarel, Chris, AMG Studios (Los Angeles), 2225 E 28 St, Suite 511, Signal Hill, CA 90755 *Tel:* 562-424-0824 *Web Site:* www.amgstudiosla.com, pg 684

Valderrama, Luis, Utopia Films, 1976 S La Cienega Blvd, No 130, Los Angeles, CA 90034 *Tel:* 310-338-0580 *Fax:* 313-557-0580 *E-mail:* reception@utopiafilms.com; production@utopiafilms.com (reels) *Web Site:* utopiafilms.com, pg 924

Valdez, Tony, Lumeni Productions Inc, 1632 Flower St, Glendale, CA 91201 *Tel:* 818-956-2200 *Fax:* 818-956-3298 *E-mail:* info@lumeni.com *Web Site:* www.lumeni.com, pg 812

Valentine, John, AudioImage Recording, 110 N Jefferson St, Richmond, VA 23220-5022 *Tel:* 804-644-7700 *Fax:* 804-644-8801 *E-mail:* info@audioimagerecording.com *Web Site:* www.audioimagerecording.com, pg 695

Van Citters, Darrell, Renegade Animation Inc, 111 E Broadway, Suite 208, Glendale, CA 91205 *Tel:* 818-551-2351 *Fax:* 818-551-2350 *Web Site:* www.renegadeanimation.com, pg 873

Van Der Hagen, Brian, AVI Systems, 9675 W 76 St, Suite 130, Eden Prairie, MN 55344 *Tel:* 952-949-3700 *Toll Free Tel:* 800-488-4954 (support); 855-521-0050 *Fax:* 952-949-6000 *E-mail:* info@avisystems.com *Web Site:* www.avisystems.com, pg 698

Van Dine, Mike, Power & Light, 1313 Mound St, Alameda, CA 94501 *Tel:* 510-205-4101 (cell) *Web Site:* www.powerlight.net, pg 860

Van Engelen, Nicole, Carr McLean Ltd, 461 Horner Ave, Toronto, ON M8W 4X2, Canada *Tel:* 416-252-3371 *Toll Free Tel:* 800-268-2123 (CN) *Fax:* 416-252-9203 *Toll Free Fax:* 800-871-2397 *E-mail:* sales@carrmclean.ca *Web Site:* www.carrmclean.ca, pg 717

Van Hemelryck, Tom, Production Resource Group LLC (PRG), 200 Business Park Dr, Suite 109, Armonk, NY 10504 *Tel:* 212-589-5400 *Toll Free Tel:* 877-774-7088 *E-mail:* info@prg.com *Web Site:* www.prg.com, pg 864

van Horn, Scott, Sony Music Commercial Music Group, 550 Madison Ave, New York, NY 10022 *Tel:* 212-833-8000 *Web Site:* www.sonymusic.com, pg 893

Van Horne, Richard "Vance", Sheffield Audio/Video Productions, 13816 Sunnybrook Rd, Phoenix, MD 21131 *Tel:* 410-628-7260 *Toll Free Tel:* 800-355-6613 *Fax:* 410-628-1977 *E-mail:* info@sheffieldav.com *Web Site:* www.sheffieldav.com/production, pg 885

Van Hoy, Dave, Advanced Systems Group LLC, 1226 Powell St, Emeryville, CA 94608-2618 *Tel:* 510-654-8300 *Fax:* 510-654-8370 *Web Site:* www.asgllc.com, pg 677

Van Hoy, David, Diaquest, 5808 Vallejo St, Emeryville, CA 94608 *Tel:* 510-547-4544 *Fax:* 510-654-8370 *E-mail:* sales@diaquest.com; support@diaquest.com *Web Site:* www.diaquest.com, pg 741

Van Impe, Dr Jack, Jack Van Impe Ministries International, 1718 Northfield Dr, Rochester Hills, MI 48309-3818 *Tel:* 248-852-2244; 248-852-5225 (orders) *Fax:* 248-852-2692 *E-mail:* jvimi@jvim.com *Web Site:* www.jvim.com, pg 924

Van Jaarsveld, Glenda, PSAV® Presentation Services (Hotel Services Division), 5100 N River Rd, Suite 300, Schiller Park, IL 60176 *Tel:* 847-222-9800 *Toll Free Tel:* 866-716-9691 *E-mail:* psavglobal@gmail.com *Web Site:* www.psav.com, pg 866

Van Meter, Dan, NOR-COM Inc, 2126 Petersburg Rd, Hebron, KY 41048 *Tel:* 859-689-7451 *Toll Free Tel:* 800-689-6889 *Fax:* 859-689-7483 *E-mail:* hello@nor-com.com *Web Site:* nor-com.com, pg 841

van Oostrum, Kees, American Society of Cinematographers (ASC), 1782 N Orange Dr, Los Angeles, CA 90028 *Tel:* 323-969-4333 *Toll Free Tel:* 800-448-0145 (US only) *Fax:* 323-882-6391 *E-mail:* office@theasc.com; customerservice@theasc.com *Web Site:* theasc.com, pg 949

Van Ost, Betsy, Janson Media Inc, The Cunningham House, 118 Main St, Tappan, NY 10983 *Tel:* 845-359-8488 *E-mail:* info@janson.com *Web Site:* www.janson.com, pg 793

Van Petten, Vance, Producers Guild of America Inc (PGA), 8530 Wilshire Blvd, Suite 400, Beverly Hills, CA 90211 *Tel:* 310-358-9020 *E-mail:* info@producersguild.org *Web Site:* www.producersguild.org, pg 960

Van Waay, Brian, TeachLogic Inc, 1688 Ord Way, Oceanside, CA 92056 *Tel:* 760-631-7800 *Toll Free Tel:* 800-588-0018 *Fax:* 760-631-1283 *E-mail:* sales@teachlogic.com; info@teachlogic.com *Web Site:* www.teachlogic.com, pg 908

Van Waes, Ed, Nady Systems Inc, 3341 Vincent Rd, Pleasant Hill, CA 94523 *Tel:* 510-652-2411 *Fax:* 510-652-5075 *E-mail:* ussales@nady.com; support@nady.com *Web Site:* www.nady.com, pg 835

Van Winkle, Vernon, 21st Century Video Productions, 890 S Higley Rd, Pahrump, NV 89048 *Tel:* 775-727-9400 *Fax:* 775-727-8750 *Web Site:* www.kpvm.tv, pg 919

Van't Noordende, Sander, Accenture, 161 N Clark St, Chicago, IL 60601 *Tel:* 312-693-0161 *Toll Free Tel:* 877-889-9009 *Fax:* 312-693-0507 *Web Site:* www.accenture.com, pg 673

VanDenBosch, Betty, ART (Applied Research & Technology Inc), 4625 Witmer Industrial Estate, Niagara Falls, NY 14305 *Tel:* 716-297-2920 *Fax:* 716-297-3689 *E-mail:* usa@yorkville.com *Web Site:* www.artproaudio.com; www.yorkville.com, pg 690

Vanderberg, McKenzi, Florida Film Festival, c/o Enzian Theater, 1300 S Orlando Ave, Maitland, FL 32751 *Tel:* 407-629-1088 *Fax:* 407-629-6870 *E-mail:* entries@enzian.org; marketing@enzian.org; events@enzian.org *Web Site:* www.floridafilmfestival.com, pg 989

Vanderhyde, Robert, Disney Consumer Products & Interactive Media (DCPI), 1201 Flower St, Glendale, AZ 91201 *Tel:* 818-544-0000 *Web Site:* dcpi.disney.com, pg 743

Vandermeer, Alicia, Art Gallery of Ontario, 317 Dundas St W, Toronto, ON M5T 1G4, Canada *Tel:* 416-979-6648 *Toll Free Tel:* 877-225-4246 *Web Site:* ago.ca, pg 690

VanderPoel, Erik, Collective Systems LLC, 76 Progress Dr, Suite 270, Stamford, CT 06902 *Tel:* 203-973-7011 *Fax:* 203-323-8078 *E-mail:* sales@collectivesys.com *Web Site:* www.cs-av.com, pg 727

VanDeventer, Katrinka, Universal Studios Florida® Production Group, 1000 Universal Studios Plaza, Bldg 22A, Orlando, FL 32819 *Tel:* 407-363-8400 *Toll Free Tel:* 877-612-3737 (outside FL) *Fax:* 407-363-8869 *E-mail:* productiongroup@universalorlando.com *Web Site:* studio.florida.universalstudios.com, pg 922

Vandever, Lesley, Parlights Inc, 1662 Bowmans Farm Rd, Suite 111, Frederick, MD 21701 *Tel:* 301-698-9242 *Fax:* 301-846-0369 *E-mail:* sales@parlights.com *Web Site:* www.parlights.com, pg 851

Vandevrie, Ken, ADS Media, 620 Trinity Church Rd, Hamilton, ON L0R 1P0, Canada *Tel:* 905-692-2960 *Fax:* 905-692-2961 *E-mail:* info@adsmedia.ca *Web Site:* www.adsmedia.ca, pg 677

VanGelder, Kim, Eastman Kodak Co, 343 State St, Rochester, NY 14650 *Toll Free Tel:* 800-698-3324 *Web Site:* www.kodak.com, pg 750

Vann, David, Canadian American Records, PO Box 808, Lititz, PA 17543-0538 *Tel:* 717-627-4800 *E-mail:* canadianamerican@dejazzd.com *Web Site:* www.canadianamericanrecords.net; www.canadianamericanrecordcompany.com, pg 715

Vann, Martin, Vitec Videocom Inc, 14 Progress Dr, Shelton, CT 06484 *Tel:* 203-929-1100 *Fax:* 203-925-2684 *E-mail:* info@vitecgroup.com *Web Site:* www.vitecgroup.com; www.vitecvideocom.com, pg 932

Vanni, Steve, Technet® Systems Group, 2600 Lake Shore Rd, Unit 157, Gilford, NH 03249 *Tel:* 603-483-5365 *Toll Free Tel:* 888-TECHNET (832-4638) *E-mail:* info@technetsystems.com *Web Site:* www.technetsystems.com, pg 908

Vanvoorst, Wim, AVP Mfg & Supply Inc, 2288-B7 Dumfries Rd, RR2, Cambridge, ON N1R 5S3, Canada *Tel:* 519-740-7966 *Toll Free Tel:* 800-481-2493 *Fax:* 519-740-0131 *E-mail:* sales@jackfields.com *Web Site:* www.jackfields.com, pg 699

Vapour, Mel, Berkeley Video & Film Festival, 1939 Addison St, Berkeley, CA 94704 *Tel:* 510-843-3699 *E-mail:* maketv@aol.com *Web Site:* www.berkeleyvideofilmfest.org, pg 983

Vareha, Richard, Turning Technologies LLC, 255 W Federal St, Youngstown, OH 44503 *Tel:* 330-746-3015 *Toll Free Tel:* 866-746-3015 *E-mail:* info@turningtechnologies.com; support@turningtechnologies.com *Web Site:* www.turningtechnologies.com, pg 919

Varela, Rodrigo Diaz, ReelWorld Film Festival, 50 Carroll St, Suite 200, Toronto, ON M4M 3G3, Canada *Tel:* 416-598-7933 *E-mail:* info@reelworld.ca; contact@reelworld.ca *Web Site:* www.reelworld.ca, pg 1001

Vargas, Diana, Havana Film Festival New York (HFFNY), 4 W 43 St, Suite 304, New York, NY 10036 *Tel:* 212-687-2146 *Fax:* 212-681-8037 *E-mail:* info@hffny.com; info@aflfc.org; press@hffny.com *Web Site:* www.hffny.com, pg 991

Vargas, Joe, MediaMix Inc, 4 Pearl Ct, Allendale, NJ 07401 *Tel:* 201-262-3700 (day); 201-378-3035 (nights/weekends) *Fax:* 201-262-3798 *E-mail:* info@mmix.net *Web Site:* www.mediamix.tv, pg 822

Vargas, Pepe, Chicago Latino Film Festival, 55 W Van Buren St, Suite 310, Chicago, IL 60605 *Tel:* 312-431-1330 *E-mail:* info@latinoculturalcenter.org *Web Site:* www.chicagolatinofilmfestival.org, pg 985

Varian, Dennis, ETC, 3031 Pleasant View Rd, Middleton, WI 53562-4809 *Tel:* 608-831-4116 *Toll Free Tel:* 800-688-4116 *Fax:* 608-836-1736 *Web Site:* www.etcconnect.com, pg 756

Varness, Eric, Micro Focus, 1800 S Novell Place, Bldgs G & H, Provo, UT 84606 *Tel:* 801-861-7000 *Toll Free Tel:* 877-686-9637 *E-mail:* media.relations@microfocus.com *Web Site:* www.microfocus.com, pg 825

Varney, Laura T, Monadnock Media Inc, 59 North St, Hatfield, MA 01038 *Tel:* 413-247-6447 *Fax:* 413-247-6448 *E-mail:* info@monadnock.org *Web Site:* www.monadnock.org, pg 829

Vasconi, Eugene, Communication Arts Multimedia Inc, 1618 Williams Dr, No 5, Georgetown, TX 78628 *Tel:* 512-868-0548 *Fax:* 512-868-0548 *E-mail:* mail@commartsmultimedia.com *Web Site:* commartsmultimedia.com, pg 728

Vasquez, Janet, San Antonio Film Commission, 115 Plaza de Armas, Suite 102, San Antonio, TX 78205 *Tel:* 210-207-6777; 210-207-6730 *Toll Free Tel:* 800-447-3372 *Fax:* 210-207-4526 *E-mail:* filmsa@filmsanantonio.com *Web Site:* www.filmsanantonio.com; www.getcreativesanantonio.com/film-commission, pg 976

Vassallo, Mark, ETC, 3031 Pleasant View Rd, Middleton, WI 53562-4809 *Tel:* 608-831-4116 *Toll Free Tel:* 800-688-4116 *Fax:* 608-836-1736 *Web Site:* www.etcconnect.com, pg 756

Vassallo, Mark, High End Systems Inc, 2105 Gracy Farms Lane, Austin, TX 78758 *Tel:* 512-836-2242 *Toll Free Tel:* 800-890-8989 *Web Site:* www.highend.com, pg 779

Vassar, Bill, EUE/Screen Gems Studios, 1223 N 23 St, Wilmington, NC 28405 *Tel:* 910-343-3500 *Fax:* 910-343-3574 *Web Site:* www.euescreengems.com, pg 756

Vasta, Rick, Synaptic Digital, 79 Fifth Ave, 14th fl, New York, NY 10003 *Tel:* 212-682-8300 *Fax:* 212-201-4207 *E-mail:* learnmore@synapticdigital.com *Web Site:* www.synapticdigital.com, pg 905

Vaughan, Lizanne, Getty Images, 605 Fifth Ave S, Suite 400, Seattle, WA 98104 *Tel:* 206-925-5000 *Toll Free Tel:* 888-888-5889; 800-462-4379 (sales) *E-mail:* sales.na@gettyimages.com *Web Site:* www.gettyimages.com, pg 770

Vazquez, Gabriela, Havana Film Festival New York (HFFNY), 4 W 43 St, Suite 304, New York, NY 10036 *Tel:* 212-687-2146 *Fax:* 212-681-8037 *E-mail:* info@hffny.com; info@aflfc.org; press@hffny.com *Web Site:* www.hffny.com, pg 991

Vazquez, Laura, University Film & Video Association (UFVA), c/o University of Illinois Press, 1325 S Oak St, Champaign, IL 61820-6975 *Toll Free Tel:* 866-647-8382 *E-mail:* ufvahome@gmail.com *Web Site:* www.ufva.org, pg 963

Vedock, Tray, SKC Communication Products Inc, 8320 Hedge Lane Terr, Shawnee Mission, KS 66227 *Tel:* 913-422-4222 *Toll Free Tel:* 800-882-7779 *Toll Free Fax:* 800-454-4752 *E-mail:* contact.us@skccom.com *Web Site:* www.skccom.com, pg 890

Veenstra, John, Tekskil Industries Inc, 102-998 Harbourside Dr, North Vancouver, BC V7P 3T2, Canada *Tel:* 604-985-2250 *Toll Free Tel:* 877-835-7545 *Toll Free Fax:* 877-576-8361 *E-mail:* team@tekskil.com *Web Site:* www.tekskil.com, pg 909

Vega, James, City of Ojai, City Manager's Office, 401 S Ventura St, Ojai, CA 93023 *Tel:* 805-646-5581 *Fax:* 805-646-1980 *Web Site:* ojaicity.org/film-permit, pg 967

Vega, Ricardo Salazar, C&I An Idea Agency, 541 NW First Ave, Fort Lauderdale, FL 33301 *Tel:* 954-357-3934 *E-mail:* contact@c-istudios.com *Web Site:* www.c-istudios.com, pg 716

Vitale, John, Yorktel, 81 Corbett Way, Eatontown, NJ 07724 *Tel:* 732-413-6000 *Toll Free Tel:* 866-836-8463 *Fax:* 732-413-6060 *E-mail:* knowmore@yorktel.com *Web Site:* yorktel.com, pg 944

Vito, Sal, Sparrow Sound Design, 3501 N Southport, 2nd fl, Chicago, IL 60657-1435 *Tel:* 773-281-8510 *Fax:* 773-472-1632 *E-mail:* southport@chicagosound. com *Web Site:* www.chicagosound.com, pg 896

Vitter, David, RGB Technology Inc, 590 Herndon Pkwy, Suite 500, Herndon, VA 20170-5267 *Tel:* 703-834-1500 *Fax:* 703-834-1506 *E-mail:* solutions@rgbtec. com *Web Site:* www.rgbtec.com, pg 874

Viviano, David, Screen Actors Guild - American Federation of Television & Radio Artists (SAG-AFTRA), 5757 Wilshire Blvd, 7th fl, Los Angeles, CA 90036-3600 *Tel:* 323-954-1600 (former SAG); 323-634-8100 (former AFTRA) *Toll Free Tel:* 855-SAG-AFTRA (724-2387) *Fax:* 323-549-6654 (communs & mktg) *E-mail:* info@sagaftra.org *Web Site:* www.sagaftra.org, pg 961

Vivier, Carole, Manitoba Film & Music, 410-93 Lombard Ave, Suite 410, Winnipeg, MB R3B 3B1, Canada *Tel:* 204-947-2040 *Fax:* 204-956-5261 *E-mail:* info@mbfilmmusic.ca *Web Site:* www. mbfilmmusic.ca, pg 816, 978

Vizaro, Connie, F&F Productions LLC, 14333 Myerlake Circle, Clearwater, FL 33760 *Tel:* 727-530-5000 *Fax:* 727-535-6547 *E-mail:* info@fandfhd.tv *Web Site:* www.fandfhd.tv, pg 759

Voakes, Peggy, Dialect Accent Specialists Inc, 7048 Timberrose Way, Roseville, CA 95747 *Toll Free Tel:* 800-753-1016 *E-mail:* dasinc@kingcon.com; info@dialectaccentspecialists.com *Web Site:* www. dialectaccentspecialists.com; www.learnaccent.com, pg 741

Vogel, Barry, ALMA International, 39962 W Thornberry Lane, Maricopa, AZ 85138 *Tel:* 602-388-8669 *E-mail:* management@almainternational.org *Web Site:* almaint.org, pg 947

Vogel, Giselle, Videofilm Systems Inc, 7 Islandbrook Ave, Unit D-1, Bridgeport, CT 06606 *Tel:* 203-870-6013 *E-mail:* info@videofilmsystems.com, pg 929

Vogel, Valerie, Our Sunday Visitor Inc, 200 Noll Plaza, Huntington, IN 46750 *Tel:* 260-356-8400 *Toll Free Tel:* 800-348-2440 *Fax:* 260-356-8472 *E-mail:* osvsales@osv.com *Web Site:* www.osv.com, pg 849

Vogt, Charlie, ATX Networks, 8-1602 Tricont Ave, Whitby, ON L1N 7C3, Canada *Tel:* 289-204-7800 *Toll Free Tel:* 866-968-7289 *E-mail:* info@atx.com *Web Site:* atx.com, pg 692

Vogt, Charlie, Imagine Communications Corp, 3001 Dallas Pkwy, Suite 300, Frisco, TX 75034 *Tel:* 469-803-4900 *Toll Free Tel:* 866-4-IMAGINE (446-2446) *Fax:* 469-803-4899 *E-mail:* insidesales@ imaginecommunications.com *Web Site:* www. imaginecommunications.com, pg 786

Vogt, Edward, EAR Professional Audio/Video, 2641 E McDowell Rd, Phoenix, AZ 85008 *Tel:* 602-267-0600 *Toll Free Tel:* 800-473-6914 *Fax:* 602-275-3277 *E-mail:* info@ear.net *Web Site:* ear.net, pg 749

Vogt, Jaime, Tacoma-Regional Film Commission, 1516 Commerce St, Tacoma, WA 98402 *Tel:* 253-627-2836 *Fax:* 253-627-8783 *Web Site:* www.traveltacoma.com, pg 977

Volk, Patrick, Geomatrix Productions, 270 Amity Rd, Woodbridge, CT 06525-2267 *Tel:* 203-389-0001 *E-mail:* info@geomatrixproductions.com *Web Site:* www.geomatrixproductions.com, pg 770

Von Burg, Catherine, SimpliPhi Power Inc, 420 Bryant Circle, Bldg B, Ojai, CA 93023 *Tel:* 805-640-6700 *E-mail:* info@simpliphipower.com *Web Site:* www. simpliphipower.com, pg 889

Von Fange, Eric, The Light Source, 3935 Westinghouse Blvd, Charlotte, NC 28273 *Tel:* 704-504-8399 *Fax:* 704-588-4693 (acctg); 704-588-4637 (orders) *E-mail:* mail@thelightsource.com; sales@ thelightsource.com *Web Site:* www.thelightsource.com, pg 807

Von Hagen, Ryan, Quickdraw Animation Society, 2011 Tenth Ave SW, Calgary, AB T3C 0K4, Canada *Tel:* 403-261-5767 *E-mail:* info@quickdrawanimation. ca; production@quickdrawanimation.ca; programming@quickdrawanimation.ca *Web Site:* quickdrawanimation.ca; www.giraffest.ca, pg 961

von Holdt, Erin, IPI - Member Network™, 2518 Anthem Village Dr, Suite 104, Henderson, NV 89052 *Tel:* 702-617-1141 *Fax:* 702-617-1181 *E-mail:* info@ipiphoto. com *Web Site:* www.ipiphoto.com, pg 957

Voris, Scott, Kelmscott Communications, 1665 Mallette Rd, Aurora, IL 60505-1354 *Tel:* 630-898-0800 *Fax:* 630-898-2183 *Web Site:* kelmscottcommunications.com, pg 797

Vosburgh, Jack M, JCS Video Productions, 4617 Sequoia Park Ave, Las Vegas, NV 89139 *Tel:* 702-596-9291 (cell); 702-546-0150 *Toll Free Tel:* 800-791-8671 *Fax:* 702-546-0150 *Web Site:* www.jcsvideo.com, pg 793

Vosteen, William E, Monroe Electronics Inc, 100 Housel Ave, Lyndonville, NY 14098 *Tel:* 585-765-2254 *Fax:* 585-765-9330 *Web Site:* www.monroe-electronics.com, pg 829

Votel, Kevin, Publishers Group West (PGW), an Ingram brand, 1700 Fourth St, Berkeley, CA 94710 *Tel:* 510-809-3700 *Toll Free Tel:* 866-400-5351 (cust serv) *Fax:* 510-809-3777 *E-mail:* info@pgw.com *Web Site:* www.pgw.com, pg 866

Voth, Karla, Bronze Anvil Awards, 120 Wall St, 21st fl, New York, NY 10005-4024 *Tel:* 212-460-1438 *E-mail:* awards@prsa.org *Web Site:* www.prsa.org; anvils.prsa.org, pg 984

Voth, Karla, Silver Anvil Awards, 120 Wall St, 21st fl, New York, NY 10005-4024 *Tel:* 212-460-1438 *E-mail:* awards@prsa.org *Web Site:* www.prsa.org, pg 1004

Waddington, Stephen, Ketchum Inc, 1285 Avenue of the Americas, 4th fl, New York, NY 10019 *Tel:* 646-935-3900 *Web Site:* www.ketchum.com, pg 798

Wade, Jeff, RIA Corp, 1615 W 2200 S, Suite B, Salt Lake City, UT 84119 *Tel:* 801-486-8822 *Fax:* 801-486-2741 *E-mail:* sales@riacorp.com *Web Site:* www. riacorp.com, pg 874

Wade, Julian Davis, Davis Art Images, 50 Portland St, Worcester, MA 01608 *Tel:* 508-754-7201 *Toll Free Tel:* 800-533-2847 *Fax:* 508-753-3834 *E-mail:* contactus@davisart.com; das@davisart.com *Web Site:* www.davisart.com, pg 738

Waganer, Richard, Cre-a-tv Studios, 1393 Progress Way, Eldersburg, MD 21784 *Toll Free Tel:* 800-628-0112 *E-mail:* production@cre-a-tv.com *Web Site:* cre-a-tv.com, pg 734

Waganer, Tina Apellaniz, Cre-a-tv Studios, 1393 Progress Way, Eldersburg, MD 21784 *Toll Free Tel:* 800-628-0112 *E-mail:* production@cre-a-tv.com *Web Site:* cre-a-tv.com, pg 734

Waggoner, Bruce E, Adrienne Electronics Corp (AEC), HC 65 Box 254, 1008 York Ranch Rd, Pie Town, NM 87827 *Tel:* 575-772-2572 *Toll Free Tel:* 800-782-2321 *Fax:* 575-772-2575 *E-mail:* info@adrielec. com; orders@adrielec.com; support@adrielec.com *Web Site:* www.adrielec.com, pg 676

Wagner, Erin Jackson, Greater Philadelphia Film Office, One Parkway Bldg, 11th fl, 1515 Arch St, Philadelphia, PA 19102 *Tel:* 215-686-2668 *Fax:* 215-686-3659 *E-mail:* mail@film.org *Web Site:* www.film. org, pg 975

Wagner, Sam B, Video I-D Teleproductions Inc, 105 Muller Rd, Washington, IL 61571 *Tel:* 309-444-4323 *Fax:* 309-444-4333 *E-mail:* videoid@videoid.com *Web Site:* www.videoid.com, pg 928

Wagner, Steve, Delmark Records, 4121 N Rockwell, Chicago, IL 60618 *Tel:* 773-539-5001 *Fax:* 773-539-5004 *E-mail:* info@delmark.com *Web Site:* www. delmark.com, pg 740

Wagnon, Stan, Lubbock Audio Visual Inc, 2120 Ave "Q", Lubbock, TX 79405 *Tel:* 806-744-2559 *Toll Free Tel:* 800-850-2559 *Fax:* 806-747-6939 *E-mail:* sales@ lav.com *Web Site:* www.lav.com, pg 812

Wahab, Haitham, CMI Media Management, 9 W Broad St, Stamford, CT 06902 *Tel:* 203-989-9955 *Toll Free Tel:* 800-431-1102 *Fax:* 203-316-8353 *Web Site:* www. cminyla.com, pg 727

Waide, Donal, BitFlow Inc, 400 W Cummings Park, Suite 5050, Woburn, MA 01801 *Tel:* 781-932-2900 *Fax:* 781-933-9965 *E-mail:* sales@bitflow.com *Web Site:* www.bitflow.com, pg 706

Wais, Ed, AVS Group, 3120 South Ave, Suite 133, La Crosse, WI 54601 *Tel:* 608-780-7019 *Fax:* 608-787-0012 *E-mail:* info@avsgroup.com *Web Site:* www. avsgroup.com, pg 699

Waitkus, Jack, Video West Inc, 1050 N 52 St, Phoenix, AZ 85008 *Tel:* 480-222-3180 *Toll Free Tel:* 800-659-0880 *Fax:* 480-222-3190 *E-mail:* info@videowestinc. com *Web Site:* www.videowestinc.com, pg 929

Walden, Cheron, Concepts TV Productions Inc, 53 Indian Lane E, Towaco, NJ 07082 *Tel:* 973-331-1500 *Fax:* 973-331-1550 *E-mail:* sales@conceptstv.com *Web Site:* conceptstv.com, pg 730

Waldenmaier, Jack, The Music Bakery, 7522 Campbell Rd, Suite 113, Dallas, TX 75248 *Tel:* 214-636-5887 *E-mail:* helpnow@musicbakery.com *Web Site:* www. musicbakery.com, pg 834

Waldo, Robert PhD, Physical Optics Corp (POC), 1845 E 205 St, Torrance, CA 90501-1510 *Tel:* 310-320-3088 *E-mail:* info@poc.com *Web Site:* www.poc.com, pg 856

Walenta, Michael T, WGVU TV, 301 Fulton St W, Grand Rapids, MI 49504-6492 *Tel:* 616-331-6666 *Toll Free Tel:* 800-442-2771 *Web Site:* www.wgvu.org, pg 936

Wales, Dirk, Rainbow International Inc, 1103 Canyon Rd, Santa Fe, NM 87501 *Tel:* 773-505-6264 *Web Site:* www.rainbowplace.com; greatplainspress. com, pg 869

Waligora, Jack, C-Ducer/C T Audio, 54 Old Lakeside Rd S, Hewitt, NJ 07421 *Tel:* 973-728-1743 *Toll Free Tel:* 800-282-8346 *E-mail:* meow54@rocketmail.com *Web Site:* www.c-ducer.com, pg 713

Walker, Alice, Antenna International, 383 Main Ave, Norwalk, CT 06851 *Tel:* 203-523-0320 *E-mail:* inquiry@antennainternational.com; marketing@antennainternational.com *Web Site:* www. antennainternational.com, pg 686

Walker, Art, Auton Motorized Systems, 24856 Avenue Rockefeller, Valencia, CA 91355 *Tel:* 661-257-9282 *Fax:* 661-295-5638 *E-mail:* info@auton.com *Web Site:* auton.com, pg 696

Walker, Ashley, FLIR Systems Inc, 27700 SW Parkway Ave, Wilsonville, OR 97070 *Tel:* 503-498-3547 *Toll Free Tel:* 800-322-3731 *Fax:* 503-498-3904 *Web Site:* www.flir.com, pg 762

Walker, Bill, MCS Recording Studios, 550 Queen St E, Suite G-100, Toronto, ON M5A 1V2, Canada *Tel:* 416-361-1688 *Toll Free Tel:* 866-322-8555 *Fax:* 416-361-5088 *E-mail:* info@mcsrecording.com *Web Site:* www.mcsrecording.com, pg 821

Walker, Fred, JFW Industries Inc, 5134 Commerce Square Dr, Indianapolis, IN 46237 *Tel:* 317-887-1340 *Toll Free Tel:* 877-887-4539 *Fax:* 317-881-6790 *E-mail:* sales@jfwindustries.com; jfwengr@ jfwindustries.com *Web Site:* www.jfwindustries.com, pg 794

Walker, Jeff, Alliance Entertainment Corp (AEC) LLC, 1401 NW 136 Ave, Suite 100, Sunrise, FL 33323 *Toll Free Tel:* 800-329-7664 *Web Site:* www.aent.com, pg 680

Walker, Jeff, Movies Unlimited, 740 Hilltop Dr, Itasca, IL 60143 *Toll Free Tel:* 800-466-8437 *E-mail:* movies@moviesunlimited.com; info@ moviefanfare.com; askmff@moviefanfare.com *Web Site:* www.moviesunlimited.com, pg 831

Walker, Joe, Crispin Corp, 600 Wade Ave, Raleigh, NC 27605 Tel: 919-845-7744 Fax: 919-845-7766 E-mail: welisten@crispincorp.com; support@ crispincorp.com Web Site: www.crispincorp.com, pg 735

Walker, Lynn, Genesis Integration, 14721 123 Ave NW, Edmonton, AB T5L 2Y6, Canada Toll Free Tel: 877-283-2253 (Toronto); 866-622-2966 (Quebec); 844-436-4681 (rest of CN) E-mail: marketing@genint.com Web Site: www.genint.com, pg 770

Walker, Mark L, Disney Consumer Products & Interactive Media (DCPI), 1201 Flower St, Glendale, AZ 91201 Tel: 818-544-0000 Web Site: dcpi.disney. com, pg 743

Walker, Matt, Doug Fleenor Design Inc, 396 Corbett Canyon Rd, Arroyo Grande, CA 93420 Tel: 805-481-9599 Toll Free Tel: 888-436-9512 Fax: 805-481-9599 E-mail: info@dfd.com Web Site: www.dfd.com, pg 762

Walker, Oneda, WTMJ-TV, 720 E Capitol Dr, Milwaukee, WI 53212 Tel: 414-332-9611 Fax: 414-967-5378 E-mail: tmj4feedback@scripps.com Web Site: www.tmj4.com, pg 942

Walker, Paul, Artaflex Inc, 174 W Beaver Creek Rd, Richmond Hill, ON L4B 1B4, Canada Tel: 905-470-0109 Toll Free Tel: 866-502-3378 Fax: 905-470-0621 E-mail: sales@artaflex.com; general@artaflex.com Web Site: www.artaflex.com, pg 690

Walkinshaw, Carole, Inspired Image Picture Co (IIPC), 1090 E Georgia St, Vancouver, BC V6A 2A7, Canada Tel: 604-874-7513 Toll Free Tel: 800-352-1454 (prodn rentals); 800-567-0037 (equip rentals) Fax: 604-874-7516 E-mail: info@inspiredimage.ca Web Site: inspiredimage.ca, pg 788

Walko, Diana Sole, MotionMasters, 2288 Roxalana Rd, Dunbar, WV 25064 Tel: 304-345-8800 Fax: 304-345-8809 E-mail: storytellers@motionmasters.com Web Site: motionmasters.com, pg 831

Walkowiak, Tad, INTER-Media Electronics, 11 Gerald Rd, Milton, MA 02186 Tel: 617-698-8315 Fax: 617-698-8315 E-mail: intermedia.ex@verizon.net Web Site: www.intermedia-electronics.com, pg 789

Wallace, Donald, Wallace Creative LLC, 1705 NW 25 Ave, Portland, OR 97210 Tel: 503-224-9660 E-mail: info@wallyhood.com Web Site: www. wallyhood.com, pg 933

Wallace, Earl, Unilux Inc, 59 N Fifth St, Saddle Brook, NJ 07663 Tel: 201-712-1266 Toll Free Tel: 800-522-0801 (US only) Fax: 201-712-1366 Web Site: www. unilux.com, pg 921

Wallace, Frances, Frameline Completion Fund, 145 Ninth St, Suite 300, San Francisco, CA 94103 Tel: 415-703-8650 Fax: 415-861-1404 E-mail: info@ frameline.org; programming@frameline.org Web Site: www.frameline.org, pg 989

Wallace, Frances, San Francisco International LGBTQ Film Festival, 145 Ninth St, Suite 300, San Francisco, CA 94103 Tel: 415-703-8650 Fax: 415-861-1404 E-mail: info@frameline.org Web Site: www.frameline. org/festival, pg 1003

Wallace, John, Deluxe Entertainment Services Group Inc, 2400 W Empire Ave, 2nd fl, Burbank, CA 91504 Tel: 818-260-7005; 818-526-3700 Toll Free Tel: 800-99-FILMS (993-4567) E-mail: ddchelp@bydeluxe. com; pr@bydeluxe.com Web Site: www.bydeluxe.com, pg 740

Wallace, Matthew, VRSim Inc, 222 Pitkin St, Suite 119, East Hartford, CT 06108-3220 Tel: 860-893-0080 E-mail: info@vrsim.net Web Site: www.vrsim.net, pg 933

Wallace, Rev Peter, The Alliance for Christian Media, 2715 Peachtree Rd NE, Atlanta, GA 30305 Toll Free Tel: 888-411-DAY-1 (411-3291) E-mail: info@day1. org Web Site: day1.org, pg 680

Waller-Stults, Nancy, Merestone, 7232 E First St, Scottsdale, AZ 85251 Tel: 480-945-4631 Fax: 480-945-0590 Web Site: www.merestone.com, pg 823

Wallis, Stephen, modprop.com, 1044 Madison Ave, New York, NY 10021 Tel: 212-628-7582 E-mail: info@ modprop.com Web Site: modprop.com, pg 828

Walls, Troy, Creative Realities Inc (CRI), 13100 Magisterial Dr, Suite 100, Louisville, KY 40223 Tel: 502-791-8800 Web Site: cri.com, pg 733

Walpole, Alton, Mountainair Films Inc, PO Box 4097, Santa Fe, NM 87502-4097 Tel: 505-471-9293 Fax: 505-438-0294 E-mail: produce@ mountainairfilms.com Web Site: mountainairfilms.com, pg 831

Walpuck, John, Creative Realities Inc (CRI), 13100 Magisterial Dr, Suite 100, Louisville, KY 40223 Tel: 502-791-8800 Web Site: cri.com, pg 733

Walsh, Jamie, New Letters on the Air, c/o University of Missouri, Kansas City, 5101 Rockhill Rd, Kansas City, MO 64110 Tel: 816-235-1159; 816-235-1168 Fax: 816-235-2611 E-mail: radio@newletters.org Web Site: www.newletters.org, pg 839

Walsh, Jeremy, The Learning House Inc, 427 S Fourth St, Suite 300, Louisville, KY 40202 Tel: 502-589-9878 Fax: 502-589-9825 E-mail: sales@learninghouse. com; info@learninghouse.com Web Site: www. learninghouse.com, pg 805

Walsh, John, Catholic Books & Tapes, PO Box 350333, Fort Lauderdale, FL 33335-0333 Tel: 954-583-5108 Fax: 954-583-5108 E-mail: mascmen7@yahoo.com Web Site: www.catholicbook.com, pg 717

Walsh, John R, Children of Mary, PO Box 350333, Fort Lauderdale, FL 33335-0333 Tel: 954-583-5108 Fax: 954-583-5108 E-mail: mascmen7@yahoo.com Web Site: www.catholicbook.com, pg 722

Walsh, Michael S, VMS Inc, 02400 37 1/2 St, Gobles, MI 49055 Tel: 269-377-0234 E-mail: vms.texts@ gmail.com Web Site: www.vms-online.com, pg 932

Walsh, Ray, Metro Productions, 8570 Magellan Pkwy, Suite 400, Richmond, VA 23227 Tel: 804-261-1172 Toll Free Tel: 877-669-4687 Fax: 804-261-1885 E-mail: contactmetro@metro-productions.com Web Site: www.metro-productions.com, pg 824

Walsh, Thomas, Media Control Systems LLC, 1050 Pioneer Way, Suite Q, El Cajon, CA 92020 Tel: 619-599-1050 Fax: 619-599-1051 Web Site: www. mediacontrolsystems.com, pg 821

Walsh, Timothy, Laser Spectacles Inc, PO Box 1535, San Marcos, TX 78667 Tel: 512-392-4600 Fax: 512-392-4601 E-mail: laserinfo@laserspectacles.com Web Site: www.laserspectacles.com, pg 804

Walter, Kevin PhD, Physical Optics Corp (POC), 1845 E 205 St, Torrance, CA 90501-1510 Tel: 310-320-3088 E-mail: info@poc.com Web Site: www.poc.com, pg 856

Walter, Ruth, SYMCO Inc, 29 Poplar Dr, Stirling, NJ 07980 Tel: 908-647-6262 Fax: 908-647-4904 E-mail: orders@symcoinc.com Web Site: www. symcoinc.com, pg 905

Walter, Sean, The Bradenton Area Film Commission, One Haben Blvd, Palmetto, FL 34221 Tel: 941-729-9177 Fax: 941-729-1820 Web Site: www. bradentongulfislands.com/film, pg 969

Walter, Timothy M, Gabriel Awards, 205 W Monroe St, Suite 470, Chicago, IL 60606 Tel: 312-380-6789 Fax: 312-361-0256 E-mail: cpaawards@ catholicpress.org Web Site: www.catholicpress.org/ page/gabrielawards, pg 990

Walters, Beth, Walters-Storyk Design Group Inc (WSDG), 262 Martin Ave, Highland, NY 12528 Tel: 845-691-9300 Fax: 845-691-9361 E-mail: info@ wsdg.com Web Site: www.wsdg.com, pg 933

Walters, Darlene, Warner Home Video Inc, 4000 Warner Blvd, Bldg 160, Burbank, CA 91522 Tel: 818-954-6000 Fax: 818-954-6480 Web Site: www.warnerbros. com, pg 934

Walters, Darren, Music & Entertainment Industry Educators Association (MEIEA), 1900 Belmont Blvd, Nashville, TN 37212-3758 Tel: 615-460-6946 E-mail: office@meiea.org; membership@meiea.org Web Site: www.meiea.org, pg 958

Walters, David, iVideo Technologies, 6779 Engle Rd, Suite G, Middleburg Heights, OH 44130 Toll Free Tel: 800-352-6150 E-mail: info@ivideo.com Web Site: www.ivideo.com, pg 792

Walters, Ed, WFRV-TV 5 CBS, 1181 E Mason St, Green Bay, WI 54301 Tel: 920-437-5411 Fax: 920-437-4576 E-mail: tips@wearegreenbay.com Web Site: www. wearegreenbay.com, pg 936

Walters, Jill, Crispin Corp, 600 Wade Ave, Raleigh, NC 27605 Tel: 919-845-7744 Fax: 919-845-7766 E-mail: welisten@crispincorp.com; support@ crispincorp.com Web Site: www.crispincorp.com, pg 735

Walton, Bill, ITC Learning LLC, 330 Himmarshee St, Suite 108, Fort Lauderdale, FL 33312 Toll Free Tel: 800-638-3757 E-mail: sales@itclearning.com Web Site: www.itclearning.com, pg 791

Walton, David, JVC Professional Products Co, 1700 Valley Rd, Wayne, NJ 07470 Tel: 973-317-5000 Toll Free Tel: 800-582-5825; 800-247-3608; 800-252-5722 Fax: 973-317-5030 Toll Free Fax: 800-582-5825 (option 2) E-mail: proinfo@jvc.com Web Site: www. jvc.com, pg 796

Wambold, Jennifer, Extreme Reach Inc, 75 Second Ave, Suite 720, Needham, MA 02494 Tel: 781-577-2016 Toll Free Tel: 877-769-9382 E-mail: sales@ extremereach.com; support@extremereach.com Web Site: extremereach.com, pg 758

Wamsley, Debbie, Kingswood Productions, 810 12 Ave S, Nashville, TN 37203 Tel: 615-742-5779 Web Site: www.kingswoodproductions.com, pg 799

Wamsley, Debbie, United Methodist Productions, 810 12 Ave S, Nashville, TN 37203 Tel: 615-742-5400 E-mail: umcom@umcom.org Web Site: www.umcom. org, pg 921

Wang, Joseph, Biway Media, 5803 Sovereign, Suite 204, Houston, TX 77036 Tel: 713-271-4036 Toll Free Tel: 877-BIWAY DV (249-2938) E-mail: info@biwaymedia.com; sales@biwaymedia. com Web Site: www.biwaymedia.com, pg 706

Wang, Kim E, Digital Art Video Inc, 8506 60 Ave, 3rd fl, Middle Village, NY 11379-5430 Tel: 718-457-5388 E-mail: production@digitalartvideo.com Web Site: www.digitalartvideo.com, pg 742

Wang, Rong, DC Asian Pacific American Film Festival, 2515 Virginia Ave NW, No 58205, Washington, DC 20037 Tel: 202-796-9680; 202-792-6393 E-mail: info@apafilm.org; admin@apafilm.org Web Site: www.apafilm.org, pg 988

Wang, Tony, WAC Lighting Co, 44 Harbor Park Dr, Port Washington, NY 11050 Tel: 516-515-5000 Toll Free Tel: 800-526-2588 Fax: 516-515-5050 Toll Free Fax: 800-526-2585 E-mail: sales@waclighting.com Web Site: www.waclighting.com, pg 933

Wang, Villy, San Francisco Film Commission, City Hall, Rm 473, One Dr Carlton B Goodlett Place, San Francisco, CA 94102 Tel: 415-554-6241 Fax: 415-554-6503 E-mail: film@sfgov.org Web Site: www. filmsf.org/film-commission; www.facebook.com/ FilmSF, pg 967

Wang, Vork PhD, Yorktel, 81 Corbett Way, Eatontown, NJ 07724 Tel: 732-413-6000 Toll Free Tel: 866-836-8463 Fax: 732-413-6060 E-mail: knowmore@yorktel. com Web Site: yorktel.com, pg 944

Wanlass, Gordon, PowerPhysics Inc, 877 Production Place, Newport Beach, CA 92663-2809 Tel: 949-371-6202 Fax: 815-572-8936 E-mail: contact@ powerphysics.com Web Site: powerphysics.com, pg 860

Wantman, Charles D, Audio Vistas LLC, 170 N Woods Dr, South Orange, NJ 07079 Tel: 212-586-2177 E-mail: info@audiovistas.com Web Site: www. audiovistas.com, pg 694

Wappet, Nathan, Technicolor USA Inc, 6040 Sunset Blvd, Hollywood, CA 90028 Tel: 323-817-6600 E-mail: info@technicolor.com Web Site: www. technicolor.com, pg 908

Ward, Al, Award Productions Inc, 164 Great Rd, Acton, MA 01720 *Tel:* 978-635-8000 *E-mail:* web@awardprod.com *Web Site:* www.awardproductions.com, pg 699

Ward, Fern, Intellidyne LLC, 2677 Prosperity Ave, Suite 301, Fairfax, VA 22031 *Tel:* 703-575-9715 *Fax:* 703-575-9718 *Web Site:* www.intellidyne-llc.com, pg 789

Ward, Mark, RLJ Entertainment Inc, 8515 Georgia Ave, Suite 650, Silver Spring, MD 20910 *Tel:* 301-608-2115 *Toll Free Tel:* 800-999-0212 *E-mail:* inquiries@rljentertainment.com *Web Site:* www.us.rljentertainment.com, pg 875

Ward, Steve, The Weather Company, An IBM Business, 400 Minuteman Rd, Andover, MA 01810 *Tel:* 978-983-6300 *Fax:* 978-983-6400 *Web Site:* business.weather.com, pg 935

Ware, John David, 168 Film Festival, PO Box 6184, Burbank, CA 91510 *Tel:* 818-557-8507 *Fax:* 818-942-6076 *E-mail:* info@168project.com *Web Site:* www.168film.com/festival, pg 999

Warfield, Aurora, Association of Independent Commercial Producers (AICP), 3 W 18 St, 5th fl, New York, NY 10011 *Tel:* 212-929-3000 *Fax:* 212-929-3359 *E-mail:* info@aicp.com *Web Site:* www.aicp.com, pg 951

Warhola, Karen Carberry, Maine Film Office, 59 State House Sta, Augusta, ME 04333 *Tel:* 207-624-9828 *Fax:* 207-287-8070 *E-mail:* film@maine.gov *Web Site:* www.filminmaine.com, pg 972

Waring, Tom, Trailblazer Studios®, 1610 Midtown Place, Raleigh, NC 27609 *Tel:* 919-645-6600 *Fax:* 919-645-6601 *E-mail:* info@trailblazerstudios.com *Web Site:* www.trailblazerstudios.com, pg 917

Warman, S David, RGB Technology Inc, 590 Herndon Pkwy, Suite 500, Herndon, VA 20170-5267 *Tel:* 703-834-1500 *Fax:* 703-834-1506 *E-mail:* solutions@rgbtec.com *Web Site:* www.rgbtec.com, pg 874

Warner, Michael, Air Sea Land Productions Inc (ASL), 19-69 Steinway St, Astoria, NY 11105-1108 *Tel:* 718-626-2646 *Toll Free Tel:* 888-ASL-LENS (275-5367) *E-mail:* info@airsealand.com *Web Site:* www.airsealand.com, pg 678

Warnock, Dr John E, Adobe Systems Inc, 345 Park Ave, San Jose, CA 95110-2704 *Tel:* 408-536-6000 *Fax:* 408-537-6000 *Web Site:* www.adobe.com, pg 676

Warren, Beth, Creative Realities Inc (CRI), 13100 Magisterial Dr, Suite 100, Louisville, KY 40223 *Tel:* 502-791-8800 *Web Site:* cri.com, pg 733

Warren, Phillip, Eastern Effects Inc, 99 Ninth St, Brooklyn, NY 11215 *Tel:* 718-855-1197 *Toll Free Fax:* 888-566-6547 *Web Site:* easterneffects.com, pg 749

Warring, Michael, American Educational Products LLC, 401 Hickory St, Fort Collins, CO 80524 *Tel:* 970-484-7445 *Toll Free Tel:* 800-289-9299 *Fax:* 970-484-1198 *E-mail:* custserv@amep.com *Web Site:* www.amep.com, pg 683

Warring, Michael, Scott Resources Inc, 401 Hickory St, Fort Collins, CO 80524-1125 *Tel:* 970-484-7445 *Toll Free Tel:* 800-289-9299 *Fax:* 970-484-1198 *E-mail:* custserv@amep.com *Web Site:* amep.com, pg 882

Warsaw, Michael P, Eternal Word Television Network (EWTN), 5817 Old Leeds Rd, Irondale, AL 35210-2164 *Tel:* 205-271-2900 *Fax:* 205-271-2920 *E-mail:* viewer@ewtn.com *Web Site:* www.ewtn.com, pg 756

Warzak, Barry F, FJW Optical Systems Inc, 322 N Woodwork Lane, Palatine, IL 60067-4933 *Tel:* 847-358-2500 *Toll Free Tel:* 800-355-4FJW (355-4359) *Fax:* 847-358-2533 *E-mail:* irsales@findrscope.com *Web Site:* www.findrscope.com, pg 762

Warzer, Peter L, Long Island Video Enterprises Live Inc, 110 Pratt Oval, Glen Cove, NY 11542 *Tel:* 516-759-5483 *Fax:* 516-671-5874 *E-mail:* info@longislandvideo.com *Web Site:* www.longislandvideo.com, pg 811

Wasch, Ken, Software & Information Industry Association (SIIA), 1090 Vermont Ave NW, 6th fl, Washington, DC 20005-4095 *Tel:* 202-289-7442 *Fax:* 202-289-7097 *Web Site:* www.siia.net, pg 962

Wasco, Sonia S, Grant Heilman Photography Inc, 506 W Lincoln Ave, Lititz, PA 17543 *Tel:* 717-626-0296 *Toll Free Tel:* 800-622-2046 *Fax:* 717-626-0971 *E-mail:* info@heilmanphoto.com *Web Site:* www.heilmanphoto.com, pg 778

Washington, Kiko, Warner Bros Entertainment Inc, 4000 Warner Blvd, Burbank, CA 91522 *E-mail:* wbsf@warnerbros.com *Web Site:* www.warnerbros.com/studio; studiofacilities.warnerbros.com, pg 934

Wasko, Bill, Comtel Inc, 14901 NE 20 Ave, North Miami, FL 33181 *Tel:* 305-424-4160 (facility servs); 305-424-4178 (local inquiries); 516-816-5152 (natl inquiries) *Web Site:* www.comtelinc.com; www.facebook.com/comtelinc/, pg 730

Wassenaar, Mike, Alliance for Community Media (ACM), 4248 Park Glen Rd, Minneapolis, MN 55416 *Tel:* 952-928-4643 *E-mail:* info@allcommunitymedia.org *Web Site:* www.allcommunitymedia.org, pg 947

Waters, Buck, Broadcasters General Store Inc, 2480 SE 52 St, Ocala, FL 34480 *Tel:* 352-622-7700 *Fax:* 352-629-7000 *E-mail:* sales@bgs.cc (orders) *Web Site:* www.bgs.cc, pg 711

Watkins, Barry, Madison Square Garden, 2 Pennsylvania Plaza, New York, NY 10121-0091 *Tel:* 212-465-6741 *E-mail:* msgnetpr@msgnetwork.com *Web Site:* www.thegarden.com; themadisonsquaregardencompany.com, pg 814

Watkins, Glenn, ETS-Lindgren, 1301 Arrow Point Dr, Cedar Park, TX 78613 *Tel:* 512-531-6400; 512-531-2609 (serv) *Fax:* 512-531-6500 *E-mail:* sales@ets-lindgren.com *Web Site:* www.ets-lindgren.com, pg 756

Watkins, Matt, MultiDyne Video & Fiber Optics Systems, 10 Newton Place, Hauppauge, NY 11788 *Tel:* 516-671-7278 *Toll Free Tel:* 877-MULTIDYNE (685-8439) *Fax:* 516-671-3362 *E-mail:* sales@multidyne.com *Web Site:* www.multidyne.com, pg 833

Watson, Karin, Creative BC (CrBC), 7 W Sixth Ave, Vancouver, BC V5Y 1K2, Canada *Tel:* 604-730-2732 *Fax:* 604-736-7290 *E-mail:* info@creativebc.com; media@creativebc.com *Web Site:* www.creativebc.com, pg 978

Watt, Jim, Bennett-Watt HD Productions Inc, 13021 244 Ave SE, Issaquah, WA 98027 *Tel:* 425-392-3935 *Toll Free Tel:* 800-327-2893 *Fax:* 425-526-5851 *E-mail:* info@bennett-watt.com *Web Site:* www.bennett-watt.com, pg 703

Watt, Kelly, Bennett-Watt HD Productions Inc, 13021 244 Ave SE, Issaquah, WA 98027 *Tel:* 425-392-3935 *Toll Free Tel:* 800-327-2893 *Fax:* 425-526-5851 *E-mail:* info@bennett-watt.com *Web Site:* www.bennett-watt.com, pg 703

Watts, Dylis, Videografix LLC, 2530 Berryessa Rd, Suite 314, San Jose, CA 95132-2903 *Tel:* 408-499-1280 *E-mail:* info@videografix.com *Web Site:* www.videografix.com, pg 929

Watts, Jeff, JWP Inc, PO Box 14867, Fort Worth, TX 76117 *Tel:* 817-233-6462 *Web Site:* www.jwproductions.org, pg 796

Watts, Jeff, Watts Communications Inc, 149 N 120 St, Wauwatosa, WI 53226 *Tel:* 414-727-9505 *Fax:* 414-727-9506 *E-mail:* sales@wattscom.com *Web Site:* www.wattscom.com, pg 934

Watts, Keith, Watts Communications Inc, 149 N 120 St, Wauwatosa, WI 53226 *Tel:* 414-727-9505 *Fax:* 414-727-9506 *E-mail:* sales@wattscom.com *Web Site:* www.wattscom.com, pg 934

Way, Brian, ESE, 142 Sierra St, El Segundo, CA 90245 *Tel:* 310-322-2136 *Fax:* 310-322-8127 *E-mail:* ese@ese-web.com *Web Site:* www.ese-web.com, pg 755

Way, Steven F, Advanced Lighting & Production Services Inc (ALPS), 125 Shamut Rd, Canton, MA 02021 *Tel:* 781-961-3066 *Toll Free Tel:* 866-961-3066 *Fax:* 781-961-3256 *E-mail:* info@alpsweb.com *Web Site:* www.alpsweb.com, pg 677

Wayne, Robert C, Sunburst Recording, 4174 Madison Ave, Culver City, CA 90232 *Tel:* 310-204-2222, pg 904

Weagraff, Paul, Individual Artist Fellowship, Carvel State Off Bldg, 4th fl, 820 N French St, Wilmington, DE 19801 *Tel:* 302-577-8278 *Fax:* 302-577-6561 *E-mail:* delarts@state.de.us *Web Site:* www.artsdel.org, pg 992

Weaver, Avery, Emery-Pratt Co, 1966 W M 21, Owosso, MI 48867-9317 *Tel:* 989-723-5291 *Toll Free Tel:* 800-248-3887 *Fax:* 989-723-4677 *Toll Free Fax:* 800-523-6379 *Web Site:* www.emery-pratt.com, pg 753

Webb, Robert, Ingram Entertainment Inc, 2 Ingram Blvd, La Vergne, TN 37089 *Tel:* 615-287-4000 (corp) *Toll Free Tel:* 800-621-1333 (sales & cust serv) *Web Site:* www.ingramentertainment.com, pg 787

Webb, Scott T, Webb Audio Visual, 3020 S West Temple, Salt Lake City, UT 84115 *Tel:* 801-484-8567 (installation) *Toll Free Tel:* 877-909-8567 *Fax:* 801-484-8589 *E-mail:* info@wearewebb.com *Web Site:* www.wearewebb.com, pg 935

Webb, Steven M, Webb Audio Visual, 3020 S West Temple, Salt Lake City, UT 84115 *Tel:* 801-484-8567 (installation) *Toll Free Tel:* 877-909-8567 *Fax:* 801-484-8589 *E-mail:* info@wearewebb.com *Web Site:* www.wearewebb.com, pg 935

Webber, Hilary, Tampa Hillsborough Film & Digital Media Commission, One Tampa City Ctr, 201 N Franklin St, Suite 2900, Tampa, FL 33602 *Web Site:* filmtampabay.com, pg 970

Weber, Bret, DataDirect Networks, 9351 Deering Ave, Chatsworth, CA 91311 *Tel:* 818-700-4000 *Toll Free Tel:* 800-TERABYTE (837-2298) *E-mail:* info@ddn.com; sales@ddn.com *Web Site:* www.ddn.com, pg 738

Weber, Doug, Theatre Effects, 1810 Airport Exchange Blvd, Suite 400, Erlanger, KY 41018-3184 *Tel:* 859-647-8844 *Toll Free Tel:* 800-791-7646 *Fax:* 859-647-0075 *E-mail:* service@theatrefx.com *Web Site:* www.theatrefx.com, pg 911

Weber, Mark, Noontide Press, PO Box 2719, Newport Beach, CA 92759 *Tel:* 714-593-9725 *E-mail:* orders@noontidepress.com *Web Site:* www.noontidepress.com, pg 841

Weberman, Alisa S, Listen & Live Audio Inc, 1700 Manhattan Ave, Union City, NJ 07068 *Tel:* 201-558-9000 *Toll Free Tel:* 800-653-9400 (orders) *Fax:* 201-558-9800 *Web Site:* www.listenandlive.com, pg 809

Webley, Scott, ShowBiz Studios, 15521 Lanark St, Van Nuys, CA 91406 *Tel:* 818-989-7007 *Fax:* 818-989-8272 *Web Site:* www.showbizstudios.com, pg 887

Webster, James L, Continental Film, 1466 Riverside Dr, Suite E, Chattanooga, TN 37406 *Tel:* 423-622-1193 *Toll Free Tel:* 888-909-3456 *Fax:* 423-629-0853 *E-mail:* info@continentalfilm.com *Web Site:* www.continentalfilm.com, pg 731

Webster, Van, Webster Communications, 6323 Repton St, Los Angeles, CA 90042 *Tel:* 323-258-6741 *E-mail:* info@vanwebster.com *Web Site:* vanwebster.com, pg 935

Wechsler, Bradley J, IMAX Corp, 2525 Speakman Dr, Mississauga, ON L5K 1B1, Canada *Tel:* 905-403-6500 *Fax:* 905-403-6450 *E-mail:* info@imax.com *Web Site:* www.imax.com, pg 786

Weck, Maarten, WildBrain™, 5657 Spring Garden Rd, Suite 505, Halifax, NS B3J 3R4, Canada *Tel:* 902-423-0260 *Fax:* 902-422-0752 *E-mail:* info@wildbrain.com; halifax@wildbrain.com; sales@wildbrain.com *Web Site:* www.wildbrain.com, pg 938

Wedd, Kristina, Fremont/Custer County Film Commission, 403 Royal Gorge Blvd, Canon City, CO 81212 *Tel:* 719-275-2331 *Toll Free Tel:* 800-876-7922 *E-mail:* chamber@canoncity.com *Web Site:* www.canoncity.com, pg 968

Wedel, Terry, VO2 Mix Audio Post, 116 Spadina Ave, Suite 208, Toronto, ON M5V 2K6, Canada *Tel:* 416-603-3954 *Fax:* 416-603-3957 *E-mail:* info@vo2mix.com *Web Site:* www.vo2mix.ca, pg 932

Wedesky, Paul, GES Audio Visual, 7000 Lindell Rd, Las Vegas, NV 89118 *Tel:* 702-515-5500 *Fax:* 702-515-5765 *E-mail:* lasvegas@ges.com; info@ges.com *Web Site:* ges.com, pg 770

Weidenaar, Reynold, Magnetic Music Publishing Co, 155 W 68 St, Suite 22-D, New York, NY 10023-5834 *Tel:* 212-255-8527 *Fax:* 212-595-2067 *E-mail:* info@magneticmusic.ws *Web Site:* magneticmusic.ws, pg 814

Weigl, Linda A, Weigl Publishers Inc, 350 Fifth Ave, 59th fl, New York, NY 10118 *Toll Free Tel:* 866-649-3445 *Toll Free Fax:* 866-449-3445 *Web Site:* www.weigl.com, pg 935

Weiler, Clint, MVD Entertainment Group, 203 Windsor Rd, Pottstown, PA 19464 *Tel:* 610-650-8200 *Toll Free Tel:* 800-888-0486 *Fax:* 610-650-9102 *Toll Free Fax:* 888-536-7998 *Web Site:* mvdb2b.com, pg 835

Weiman, Mark, Regent Press Publishers & Printers, 2747 Regent St, Berkeley, CA 94705 *Tel:* 510-845-1196 *E-mail:* regentpress@mindspring.com *Web Site:* www.regentpress.net, pg 873

Weinberg, Felicia, Business Education Films, PO Box 449, Clarksburg, NJ 08510-0449 *Tel:* 732-462-3522 *Fax:* 732-294-0330 *E-mail:* info@aldenfilms.com *Web Site:* www.aldenfilms.com, pg 713

Weinberg, Jody, Pixar Animation Studios, 1200 Park Ave, Emeryville, CA 94608 *Tel:* 510-922-3000 *Fax:* 510-922-3151 *Web Site:* www.pixar.com, pg 857

Weinberg, Paul, Alden Films, PO Box 449, Clarksburg, NJ 08510-0449 *Tel:* 732-462-3522 *Toll Free Tel:* 800-832-0980 *Fax:* 732-294-0330 *E-mail:* aldenfilms.com *Web Site:* www.aldenfilms.com, pg 679

Weinberg, Paul, Business Education Films, PO Box 449, Clarksburg, NJ 08510-0449 *Tel:* 732-462-3522 *Fax:* 732-294-0330 *E-mail:* info@aldenfilms.com *Web Site:* www.aldenfilms.com, pg 713

Weinel, Lee, CET, 1223 Central Pkwy, Cincinnati, OH 45214 *Tel:* 513-381-4033 *E-mail:* comments@cetconnect.org *Web Site:* www.cetconnect.org, pg 720

Weiner, David, Health Education Services, 10200 Jefferson Blvd, Culver City, CA 90232 *Tel:* 310-839-2436 *Toll Free Tel:* 800-421-4246 *Fax:* 310-839-2249 *Toll Free Fax:* 800-944-5432 *E-mail:* access@socialstudies.com; customerservice@socialstudies.com *Web Site:* www.socialstudies.com, pg 778

Weiner, David, Social Studies School Service, 10200 Jefferson Blvd, PO Box 802, Culver City, CA 90232 *Tel:* 310-839-2436 *Toll Free Tel:* 800-421-4246 *Fax:* 310-839-2249 *Toll Free Fax:* 800-944-5432 (US & CN) *E-mail:* access@socialstudies.com *Web Site:* www.socialstudies.com, pg 891

Weiner, Glenn, Mole-Richardson Co, 12154 Montague St, Pacoima, CA 91331 *Tel:* 323-851-0111 *Fax:* 323-851-5593 *E-mail:* info@mole.com *Web Site:* www.mole.com, pg 829

Weiner, Kay, Eastman Corp, 7447 Via de Fortuna, Carlsbad, CA 92009 *Tel:* 760-603-8646 *Web Site:* www.kbwfoundation.com, pg 750

Weiner, Michael J, The Image Generators, 18156 Darnell Dr, Olney, MD 20832 *Tel:* 301-924-5700 *Fax:* 240-363-0062 *E-mail:* info@imagegenerators.com *Web Site:* www.imagegenerators.com, pg 785

Weiner, Sanford, The Writing Co, 10200 Jefferson Blvd, Culver City, CA 90232 *Tel:* 310-839-2436 *Toll Free Tel:* 800-421-4246 *Fax:* 310-839-2249 *Toll Free Fax:* 800-944-5432 *E-mail:* access@writingco.com; customerservice@writingco.com *Web Site:* www.socialstudies.com, pg 942

Weingarden, Marshall, Ever-Ready Media Packaging, 8192 Gatherly Circle, Easton, MD 21601 *Tel:* 973-566-9333 *E-mail:* packages@erpack.com *Web Site:* www.erpack.com, pg 757

Weingarten, Jeff, Interface Media Group, 1233 20 St NW, Washington, DC 20036 *Tel:* 202-861-0500 *E-mail:* info@interfacemedia.com *Web Site:* interfacemedia.com, pg 789

Weingarten, Jon, Dazian LLC, 18 Central Blvd, South Hackensack, NJ 07606 *Toll Free Tel:* 877-232-9426 *Fax:* 201-641-2728; 201-549-1055 (efax) *E-mail:* info@dazian.com *Web Site:* www.dazian.com, pg 739

Weingarten, Lisa, Bestwell Optical Instrument Corp, 46 Henry St, Merrick, NY 11566 *Tel:* 516-889-1178 *Fax:* 516-706-1744 *Web Site:* www.bestwelloptical.com, pg 704

Weingert, Alex, Otto Nemenz International Inc, 870 N Vine St, Los Angeles, CA 90038 *Tel:* 323-469-2774 *Fax:* 323-469-1217 *E-mail:* info@ottonemenz.com *Web Site:* www.ottonemenz.com, pg 838

Weinmuller, Susan, Chapman/Leonard Studio Equipment Inc, 12950 Raymer St, North Hollywood, CA 91605 *Tel:* 818-764-6726 *Toll Free Tel:* 888-883-6559 *Fax:* 818-764-6730 *E-mail:* marketing@chapman-leonard.com *Web Site:* www.chapman-leonard.com, pg 720

Weinstein, Chuck, Design Audio Visual Inc, 195-A Central Ave, Farmingdale, NY 11735 *Tel:* 631-694-3334 *Toll Free Tel:* 800-886-1328 *Fax:* 631-694-3549 *Web Site:* www.design-av.com, pg 741

Weinstein, Dana, US Holocaust Memorial Museum, 100 Raoul Wallenberg Place SW, Washington, DC 20024-2126 *Tel:* 202-488-0400 *E-mail:* membership@ushmm.org *Web Site:* www.ushmm.org, pg 923

Weir, Jacqueline, The Big House Group, 17 Waller Ave, Ossining, NY 10562 *Tel:* 914-944-4011 *Fax:* 914-944-8044 *Web Site:* www.bighousetv.com, pg 705

Weir, Robert L, Metro Video Systems Inc, 1220 E Imperial Ave, El Segundo, CA 90245 *Tel:* 310-640-9250 *Fax:* 310-640-9347 *E-mail:* sales@metrovideosystems.com *Web Site:* www.metrovideosystems.com, pg 824

Weisbart, Steve, Get Smart Products, 30 S Highland Ave, Ossining, NY 10562 *Tel:* 914-762-3500 *Toll Free Tel:* 800-827-0673 *Fax:* 914-923-5818 *Toll Free Fax:* 866-827-0673 *E-mail:* getsmart@pfile.com *Web Site:* www.pfile.com, pg 770

Weisberg, Josh, WorldStage, 259 W 30 St, 12th fl, New York, NY 10001-2863 *Tel:* 212-582-2345 *Fax:* 718-610-1750 *E-mail:* info@worldstage.com *Web Site:* www.worldstage.com, pg 941

Weisberg, Larry, Backstage Pass Entertainment Inc, 7438 Shoshone Ave, Lake Balboa, CA 91406-2340 *Tel:* 818-881-9888 *Toll Free Tel:* 800-664-6555 *Fax:* 818-881-0555 *E-mail:* blowinsmokeband@ktb.net, pg 700

Weiser, Paul, ChyronHego Corp, 5 Hub Dr, Melville, NY 11747 *Tel:* 631-845-2000 *E-mail:* info@chyronhego.com; sales@chryonhego.com *Web Site:* chyronhego.com, pg 723

Weisinger, Sarah, Disney Consumer Products & Interactive Media (DCPI), 1201 Flower St, Glendale, AZ 91201 *Tel:* 818-544-0000 *Web Site:* dcpi.disney.com, pg 743

Weiskoff, Marty, Hunt's Photo & Video, 100 Main St, Melrose, MA 02176-6104 *Tel:* 781-662-8822 (retail sales) *Toll Free Tel:* 800-924-8682 (retail sales); 800-221-1830 (ext 2340, corp sales) *Fax:* 781-662-6524 *E-mail:* ecommerce@wbhunt.com (retail online sales) *Web Site:* www.huntsphotoandvideo.com, pg 782

Weiss, Alan, Alan Weiss Productions, 1243 California Rd, Suite 2R, East Chester, NY 10709 *Tel:* 212-974-0606 *E-mail:* awpinfo@awptv.com *Web Site:* www.awptv.com, pg 935

Weiss, Bart, Dallas VideoFest Alternative Fiction, 1405 Woodlawn Ave, Dallas, TX 75208 *Tel:* 214-207-7696 *E-mail:* info@videofest.org *Web Site:* www.videofest.org, pg 987

Weiss, Bart, Dallas VideoFest DocuFest, 1405 Woodlawn Ave, Dallas, TX 75208 *Tel:* 214-207-7696 *E-mail:* info@videofest.org *Web Site:* www.videofest.org, pg 987

Weiss, Chanan, SintecMedia, 135 E 57 St, 12th fl, New York, NY 10022 *Tel:* 646-745-3900 *Fax:* 646-745-3901 *E-mail:* sales@sintecmedia.com *Web Site:* www.sintecmedia.com, pg 889

Weiss, David, Vidicom Inc, 520 Eighth Ave, Suite 2206, New York, NY 10018 *Tel:* 212-895-8300 *E-mail:* sales@vidicom.com *Web Site:* vidicom.com, pg 930

Weiss, Emily, Ingram Content Group LLC, One Ingram Blvd, La Vergne, TN 37086-1986 *Tel:* 615-793-5000 *Toll Free Tel:* 800-937-8000 (retailers); 800-937-5300 (ext 1, libs) *E-mail:* customerservice@ingramcontent.com *Web Site:* www.ingramcontent.com, pg 787

Weiss, Matt, Keywest Technology Inc, 14563 W 96 Terr, Lenexa, KS 66215 *Tel:* 913-492-4666 *Toll Free Tel:* 800-331-2019 *Fax:* 913-322-1864 *E-mail:* sales@keywesttechnology.com *Web Site:* www.keywesttechnology.com, pg 798

Welch, Jeffrey, ETC, 3031 Pleasant View Rd, Middleton, WI 53562-4809 *Tel:* 608-831-4116 *Toll Free Tel:* 800-688-4116 *Fax:* 608-836-1736 *Web Site:* www.etcconnect.com, pg 756

Welch, Laura, Master Books®, 3142 Hwy 103 N, Green Forest, AR 72638 *Tel:* 870-438-5288 *Toll Free Tel:* 800-999-3777 *Fax:* 870-438-5120 *E-mail:* info@nlpg.com *Web Site:* www.nlpg.com, pg 819

Welge, Niki, The Florida Office of Film & Entertainment, 107 E Madison St, MSC 80, Tallahassee, FL 32399 *Tel:* 850-717-8990 *Toll Free Tel:* 877-FLA-FILM (352-3456) *E-mail:* floridaofe@deo.myflorida.com *Web Site:* www.filminflorida.com, pg 970

Welk, Kevin, Welk Music Group, 11400 W Olympic Blvd, Suite 760, Los Angeles, CA 90064 *Tel:* 310-829-9355 *Fax:* 310-264-9875, pg 935

Weller, Bob, Association of Federal Communications Consulting Engineers (AFCCE), PO Box 19333, Washington, DC 20036-0333 *E-mail:* secretary@afcce.org *Web Site:* afcce.org, pg 951

Weller, Victoria (Vicci), Thompson-Nicola Film Commission, 300-465 Victoria St, Kamloops, BC V2C 2A9, Canada *Tel:* 250-377-8673 *Toll Free Tel:* 877-377-8673 (BC only) *Fax:* 250-372-5048 *E-mail:* tnfc@tnrd.ca *Web Site:* www.filmthompsonnicola.com, pg 978

Welles, Doug, Frey Scientific, 80 Northwest Blvd, Nashua, NH 03063-4067 *Toll Free Tel:* 800-225-3739; 800-258-1302 *Toll Free Fax:* 877-256-3739; 800-282-9560 *E-mail:* customercare.frey@schoolspecialty.com; orders@schoolspecialty.com *Web Site:* www.freyscientific.com, pg 766

Welling, Brent, Center for the Collaborative Classroom, 1001 Marina Village Pkwy, Suite 110, Alameda, CA 94501-1042 *Tel:* 510-533-0213 *Toll Free Tel:* 800-666-7270 *Fax:* 510-464-3670 *E-mail:* info@collaborativeclassroom.org *Web Site:* www.collaborativeclassroom.org, pg 719

Wellner, Matt, Marketron Broadcast Solutions, 101 Empty Saddle Trail, Hailey, ID 83333 *Tel:* 208-788-6800 *Toll Free Tel:* 800-476-7226 *Fax:* 208-788-6273 *E-mail:* sales@marketron.com *Web Site:* www.marketron.com, pg 817

Wells, Brian, Liturgy Training Publications, 3949 S Racine Ave, Chicago, IL 60609-2523 *Tel:* 773-579-4900 *Toll Free Tel:* 800-933-1800 (orders) *Fax:* 773-579-4929 *E-mail:* orders@ltp.org; info@ltp.org *Web Site:* www.ltp.org, pg 810

Wells, David, Moving Picture, 748 N Victoria Park Rd, Fort Lauderdale, FL 33304 *Tel:* 954-522-1361 *Toll Free Tel:* 800-800-1361 *Fax:* 954-523-1361 *E-mail:* info@movingpicture.com *Web Site:* www.movingpicture.com, pg 831

Wells, Frank, Audio Engineering Society (AES), 551 Fifth Ave, Suite 1225, New York, NY 10176 *Tel:* 212-661-8528 *Web Site:* www.aes.org, pg 951

Wells, Kevin, Corporate Color Graphics Inc, 3525 Lousma Dr SE, Grand Rapids, MI 49548 *Tel:* 616-774-9583 *Toll Free Tel:* 800-776-9583 *E-mail:* production@corpcolor.com *Web Site:* www.corpcolor.com, pg 732

Wells, Victoria, St John's International Women's Film Festival, 28 Cochrane St, Suite 101, St John's, NL A1C 3L3, Canada *Tel:* 709-754-3141 *Fax:* 709-754-0049 *E-mail:* info@womensfilmfestival.com *Web Site:* www.womensfilmfestival.com, pg 1002

Welsh, Daniel M, Spoken Arts Inc, 195 S White Rock Rd, Holmes, NY 12531 *Tel:* 845-878-9600 *Toll Free Tel:* 800-326-4090 *Fax:* 845-878-9009 *E-mail:* sales@spokenartsmedia.com *Web Site:* www.spokenartsmedia.com, pg 898

Welsh, Leah, Trailblazer Studios®, 1610 Midtown Place, Raleigh, NC 27609 *Tel:* 919-645-6600 *Fax:* 919-645-6601 *E-mail:* info@trailblazerstudios.com *Web Site:* www.trailblazerstudios.com, pg 917

Welsh, Susan, Spoken Arts Inc, 195 S White Rock Rd, Holmes, NY 12531 *Tel:* 845-878-9600 *Toll Free Tel:* 800-326-4090 *Fax:* 845-878-9009 *E-mail:* sales@spokenartsmedia.com *Web Site:* www.spokenartsmedia.com, pg 898

Welz, Gary, SciMedTv, 460 W 24 St, Unit 3A, New York, NY 10011 *Tel:* 917-593-2537 *E-mail:* SciMedTV@gmail.com *Web Site:* www.scimedtv.com, pg 882

Welz, Joey, Canadian American Records, PO Box 808, Lititz, PA 17543-0538 *Tel:* 717-627-4800 *E-mail:* canadianamerican@dejazzd.com *Web Site:* www.canadianamericanrecords.net; www.canadianamericanrecordcompany.com, pg 715

Wenck, Ed, CEDIA IPRO Affinity Group, 8475 Nightfall Lane, Fishers, IN 46037 *Tel:* 317-328-4336 *Toll Free Tel:* 800-669-5329 *E-mail:* info@cedia.org *Web Site:* cedia.net, pg 952

Wendorf, Bryan, Chicago Underground Film Festival (CUFF), 2558 W 16 St, Stage 18, Chicago, IL 60608 *Tel:* 773-998-1082 *E-mail:* info@cuff.org; publicity@cuff.org *Web Site:* cuff.org, pg 986

Wendt, Ryan, American Recordable Media, 110 Dewey Dr, Suite A, Nicholasville, KY 40356 *Tel:* 859-881-1036 *Toll Free Tel:* 800-598-8273 *Fax:* 859-881-1035 *E-mail:* info@americanrecordablemedia.com *Web Site:* www.americanrecordablemedia.com, pg 684

Wentling, Mark, Ashly Audio Inc, 847 Holt Rd, Webster, NY 14580-9103 *Tel:* 585-872-0010 *Toll Free Tel:* 800-828-6308 *Fax:* 585-872-0739 *E-mail:* info@ashly.com; sales@ashly.com; service@ashly.com *Web Site:* ashly.com, pg 691

Wentzel, Aaron, Yorktel, 81 Corbett Way, Eatontown, NJ 07724 *Tel:* 732-413-6000 *Toll Free Tel:* 866-836-8463 *Fax:* 732-413-6060 *E-mail:* knowmore@yorktel.com *Web Site:* yorktel.com, pg 944

Wenzel, John, WTVS, Detroit Public Television, Riley Broadcast Ctr, One Clover Ct, Wixom, MI 48393-2247 *Tel:* 248-305-DPTV (305-3788); 313-872-7500 *E-mail:* email@dptv.org *Web Site:* www.dptv.org, pg 942

Werbin, Phil, Ahead Stereo Inc, 7428 Beverly Blvd, Los Angeles, CA 90036 *Tel:* 323-931-8873 *E-mail:* sales@aheadstereo.com *Web Site:* www.aheadstereo.com, pg 678

Werbowski, Kim E, Inland Audio Visual Ltd, 422 Lucas Ave, Box 102, Group 200, RR 2, Winnipeg, MB R3C 2E6, Canada *Tel:* 204-786-6521 *Toll Free Tel:* 800-933-6006 *Fax:* 204-783-6281 *E-mail:* winnipeg@inlandav.ca *Web Site:* www.inlandav.ca, pg 788

Werby, Doug, Kaboom Productions, 2169 Folsom St, Suite 201-M, San Francisco, CA 94110 *Tel:* 415-434-2666 *Fax:* 415-874-9324 *E-mail:* hello@kaboomproductions.com *Web Site:* kaboomproductions.com, pg 796

Werd, Randy, Nelson Enterprises Theatrical Supply Co, 1014 Rte 173 E, Bloomsbury, NJ 08804 *Tel:* 908-479-6902 *Fax:* 908-479-6903 *E-mail:* sales@nelson-enterprises.com; rentals@nelson-enterprises.com *Web Site:* www.nelson-enterprises.com, pg 838

Werk, David M, Videowerks, 3434-135 Kildaire Farm Rd, No 181, Cary, NC 27518 *Tel:* 310-780-4156 (cell) *Web Site:* www.videowerkseast.com, pg 930

Werner, Jeff, Method Studios, 3401 Exposition Blvd, Santa Monica, CA 90404 *Tel:* 310-434-6000 *Web Site:* www.methodstudios.com, pg 824

Wershba, Don, Solid State Logic Inc, 320 W 46 St, 2nd fl, New York, NY 10036-8398 *Tel:* 212-315-1111 *E-mail:* sales@solidstatelogic.com; nysales@solidstatelogic.com *Web Site:* www.solidstatelogic.com, pg 892

Werteen, Mike, NEP Group Inc, 2 Beta Dr, Pittsburgh, PA 15238 *Tel:* 412-826-1414 *Toll Free Tel:* 800-444-0054 *E-mail:* info@nepinc.com *Web Site:* www.nepgroup.com, pg 838

Wesbecher, Jason, Corel Corp, 1600 Carling Ave, Ottawa, ON K1Z 8R7, Canada *Toll Free Tel:* 877-582-6735 *Web Site:* www.corel.com, pg 731

Wesolowski, Cindy, OmegaBrandess Distribution, 626 Hanover Pike, Suite 102, Hampstead, MD 21074-2036 *Tel:* 410-374-3250 *Fax:* 410-374-3184 *E-mail:* customerservice@omegabrandess.com *Web Site:* www.omegabrandess.com, pg 845

West, Garry, Compass Records, 916 19 Ave S, Nashville, TN 37212 *Tel:* 615-320-7672 *Fax:* 615-320-7378 *E-mail:* info@compassrecords.com *Web Site:* www.compassrecords.com, pg 729

West, Jo-Ann, Producers Guild of America Inc (PGA), 8530 Wilshire Blvd, Suite 400, Beverly Hills, CA 90211 *Tel:* 310-358-9020 *E-mail:* info@producersguild.org *Web Site:* www.producersguild.org, pg 960

West, Judith, Audiobook Department, 6429 N Talman Ave, Chicago, IL 60645 *Tel:* 773-338-8813 *Fax:* 773-338-8813 *Web Site:* www.judithwest.com, pg 695

West, Kim, Simco-Ion, 2257 N Penn Rd, Hatfield, PA 19440 *Tel:* 215-822-6401 *Toll Free Tel:* 800-203-3419 *Fax:* 215-822-3795 *E-mail:* customerservice@simco-ion.com *Web Site:* www.simco-ion.com, pg 888

West, Tyler, Barco Inc, 3059 Premiere Pkwy, Suite 400, Duluth, GA 30097 *Tel:* 916-859-2500; 678-475-8000 *Toll Free Tel:* 888-414-7226 *E-mail:* sales.events.us@barco.com *Web Site:* www.barco.com, pg 701

West-Snipes, Serena, L'AIR International, 117 Vacek St, Fort Worth, TX 76107 *Tel:* 817-237-9390 *Toll Free Tel:* 844-243-8574 *E-mail:* info@lairfloors.com *Web Site:* www.lairfloors.com, pg 802

Westcott, Drew, Michigan Office Solutions (MOS), A Xerox Company, 2859 Walkent Dr NW, Grand Rapids, MI 49544 *Toll Free Tel:* 800-442-9070 *E-mail:* info@mos-xerox.com *Web Site:* www.mos-xerox.com, pg 825

Westerman, Chris, Horizon Film + Video Productions, 3903 S Congress Ave, Suite 40186, Austin, TX 78704 *Tel:* 512-459-3100 *Web Site:* www.horizonvideo.com, pg 781

Westrick, Jamie, WTVS, Detroit Public Television, Riley Broadcast Ctr, One Clover Ct, Wixom, MI 48393-2247 *Tel:* 248-305-DPTV (305-3788); 313-872-7500 *E-mail:* email@dptv.org *Web Site:* www.dptv.org, pg 942

Weterrings, Frans, Red Sky Studios, 184 Everett St, Allston, MA 02134 *Tel:* 617-903-3373 *E-mail:* mail@redsky-studios.com *Web Site:* redsky-studios.com, pg 872

Wetzel, Arren C, Central Lighting & Equipment Inc (CLE), 4103 E 16 St, Des Moines, IA 50313 *Tel:* 515-277-4190 *Toll Free Tel:* 877-977-4190 *Fax:* 515-277-2295 *E-mail:* info@cleproductions.com *Web Site:* cleproductions.com, pg 719

Wexler, David, Hollywood Vaults Inc, 742 N Seward St, Hollywood, CA 90038 *Tel:* 323-461-6464 *Toll Free Tel:* 800-569-5336 *Fax:* 323-461-6479 *E-mail:* vault@hollywoodvaults.com *Web Site:* www.hollywoodvaults.com, pg 781

Wexler, Julie, Hollywood Vaults Inc, 742 N Seward St, Hollywood, CA 90038 *Tel:* 323-461-6464 *Toll Free Tel:* 800-569-5336 *Fax:* 323-461-6479 *E-mail:* vault@hollywoodvaults.com *Web Site:* www.hollywoodvaults.com, pg 781

Weynand, Diana, Rev UP Tech, 20929 Ventura Blvd, Suite 47-212, Woodland Hills, CA 91364 *Tel:* 818-995-1719 *Toll Free Tel:* 877-372-0005 *Fax:* 818-979-9599 *Web Site:* revuptech.com, pg 874

Whalen, Marc, Domo Tactical Communications (DTC) Ltd, 3845 Gateway Centre Blvd, Suite 360, Pinellas Park, FL 33782 *Tel:* 727-741-6900 *Toll Free Tel:* 800-665-4648 *E-mail:* tampa.info@domotactical.com *Web Site:* domotactical.com, pg 745

Whallon, Stephanie, Texas Film Commission, 1100 San Jacinto, Suite 3.410, Austin, TX 78701 *Tel:* 512-463-9200 *Fax:* 512-463-4114 *Web Site:* gov.texas.gov/film, pg 976

Wheatley, Luana, US Virgin Islands Film Promotion Office, PO Box 6400, St Thomas, VI 00804-6400 *Tel:* 340-775-1444 (ext 2243) *Fax:* 340-774-4390 *E-mail:* info@filmusvi.com *Web Site:* www.filmusvi.com, pg 977

Wheaton, Gail, LKG Industries Inc, 3660 Publishers Dr, Rockford, IL 61109 *Tel:* 815-874-2301 *Toll Free Tel:* 800-645-2262 *Fax:* 815-874-2896 *Toll Free Fax:* 800-554-0795 *E-mail:* sales-lkgindustries@t6b.com *Web Site:* www.philmore-datak.com, pg 810

Wheaton, Robert, Penguin Random House Canada, 320 Front St W, Suite 1400, Toronto, ON M5V 3B6, Canada *Tel:* 416-364-4449 *Toll Free Tel:* 888-523-9292 (cust serv) *Fax:* 416-598-7764 *E-mail:* customerservicescanada@penguinrandomhouse.com *Web Site:* www.penguinrandomhouse.ca, pg 853

Wheeler, Alan, Alcorn McBride Inc, 3300 S Hiawassee Rd, Bldg 105, Orlando, FL 32835 *Tel:* 407-296-5800 *Fax:* 407-296-5801 *E-mail:* info@alcorn.com; sales@alcorn.com *Web Site:* www.alcorn.com, pg 679

Wheeler, David M, Hughie's Event Production Services, 1260 E 38 St, Cleveland, OH 44114 *Tel:* 216-361-4600 *Toll Free Tel:* 800-449-4115 *Fax:* 216-361-2570 *Web Site:* www.hughies.com, pg 782

Wheelhouse, Scott, SirsiDynix, 3300 N Ashton Blvd, Suite 500, Lehi, UT 84043 *Tel:* 801-223-5200; 0800 016 3147 *Toll Free Tel:* 800-288-8020 *Fax:* 801-331-7770 *Web Site:* www.sirsidynix.com, pg 889

Wheelock, Martha, Ishtar Films, 12400 Moorpark St, Suite 2, Studio City, CA 91604 *Toll Free Tel:* 800-428-7136 *Fax:* 818-985-0567 *E-mail:* ishtarfilms2@sbcglobal.net *Web Site:* www.ishtarfilms.com, pg 791

Whelan, Brent, Broadcast Electronics, 4100 N 24 St, Quincy, IL 62305 *Tel:* 217-224-9600 *Fax:* 217-224-9607 *E-mail:* bdcast@bdcast.com *Web Site:* www.bdcast.com, pg 710

Whelan, Timothy, Boonton Electronics, 25 Eastmans Rd, Parsippany, NJ 07054 *Tel:* 973-386-9696 *Fax:* 973-386-9191 *E-mail:* info@boonton.com *Web Site:* www.boonton.com, pg 709

Whipple, Grant, Winegard Co, 2736 Mount Pleasant St, Suite 140, Burlington, IA 52601 *Tel:* 319-754-0600 *Toll Free Tel:* 800-288-8094 *E-mail:* chat@winegard.com *Web Site:* www.winegard.com, pg 939

Whitaker, Robert Sr, Anchor Distributors, 1030 Hunt Valley Circle, New Kensington, PA 15068 *Tel:* 724-334-7000 *Toll Free Tel:* 800-444-4484 *Fax:* 724-334-1200 *Toll Free Fax:* 800-765-1960 *E-mail:* customercare@anchordistributors.com; marketing@anchordistributors.com *Web Site:* www.whitakerhouse.com; www.anchordistributors.com, pg 685

Whitcomb, Laurel, Television Academy, 5220 Lankershim Blvd, North Hollywood, CA 91601-3109 *Tel:* 818-754-2800 *Web Site:* www.emmys.org, pg 963

White, Benton, WhisperRoom™ Inc, 109 S Northshore Dr, Suite 303, Knoxville, TN 37919 *Tel:* 865-558-5364 *Toll Free Tel:* 800-200-8168 *Fax:* 865-558-5370 *E-mail:* info@whisperroom.com *Web Site:* www.whisperroom.com, pg 937

White, David P, Screen Actors Guild - American Federation of Television & Radio Artists (SAG-AFTRA), 5757 Wilshire Blvd, 7th fl, Los Angeles, CA 90036-3600 *Tel:* 323-954-1600 (former SAG); 323-634-8100 (former AFTRA) *Toll Free Tel:* 855-

Williams, Barbara, CBC/Radio-Canada, 181 Queen St, Ottawa, ON K1P 1K9, Canada *Tel:* 613-288-6000; 613-288-6445 (newsroom) *Toll Free Tel:* 866-306-4636 (CN only) *E-mail:* cbcnewsottawa@cbc.ca *Web Site:* cbc.radio-canada.ca, pg 717

Williams, Bill, A Cut Above Video Productions Inc, 4450 W Eau Gallie Blvd, Suite 220, Melbourne, FL 32934 *Tel:* 321-253-5677 *Web Site:* www. acutabovevideo.com, pg 671

Williams, Bradford, On-Trax Inc, 3052 Vine St, Riverside, CA 92507 *Tel:* 951-786-3921 *Fax:* 951-786-3922 *Web Site:* www.on-trax.com, pg 846

Williams, Brian, Convergent Media Systems, 190 Bluegrass Valley Pkwy, Alpharetta, GA 30005-2204 *Tel:* 770-369-9000 *Fax:* 770-369-9100 *Web Site:* www. convergent.com, pg 731

Williams, Clark, Christie Digital Systems USA Inc, 10550 Camden Dr, Cypress, CA 90630 *Tel:* 714-236-8610 *Toll Free Tel:* 866-880-4462 (cust serv) *Fax:* 714-503-3375 *E-mail:* sales-us@christiedigital. com; orders@christiedigital.com *Web Site:* www. christiedigital.com, pg 722

Williams, Cory, Earl Girls Inc, 1648 White Horse Pike, Egg Harbor City, NJ 08215 *Tel:* 609-965-6900 *Web Site:* earlgirlsinc.com, pg 749

Williams, Darnell, Elektrashock, 1320 Main St, Venice, CA 90291 *Tel:* 310-399-4985 *E-mail:* info@ elektrashock.com *Web Site:* www.elektrashock.com, pg 753

Williams, Glenn, Citizens Systems America Corp, 363 Van Ness Way, Suite 404, Torrance, CA 90501 *Tel:* 310-781-1460 *Toll Free Tel:* 800-421-6516 *Fax:* 310-781-9152 *Web Site:* www.citizen-systems. com, pg 725

Williams, Jeff, CBM Ltd, High Point Business Park, 8750 Holgate Cresent, Milton, ON L9T 0K3, Canada *Tel:* 905-878-0648 *Toll Free Tel:* 800-387-4834 *Fax:* 905-878-6748 *Toll Free Fax:* 888-554-5501 *E-mail:* sales@cbmmetal.com *Web Site:* www. cbmmetal.com, pg 718

Williams, Jim, Audio Upgrades, 6982 Mimosa Dr, Carlsbad, CA 92011 *Tel:* 818-780-1222 *Web Site:* www.audioupgrades.com, pg 694

Williams, Kim, Warner Bros Entertainment Inc, 4000 Warner Blvd, Burbank, CA 91522 *E-mail:* wbsf@ warnerbros.com *Web Site:* www.warnerbros.com/ studio; studiofacilities.warnerbros.com, pg 934

Williams, Larry J, Wireworks Corp, 380 Hillside Ave, Hillside, NJ 07205 *Tel:* 908-686-7400 *Toll Free Tel:* 800-642-9473 *Fax:* 908-686-0443 (sales); 908-686-0680 *E-mail:* sales@wireworks.com; info@ wireworks.com *Web Site:* www.wireworks.com, pg 940

Williams, Lisa, The RapcoHorizon Co, 3581 Larch Lane, Jackson, MO 63755 *Toll Free Tel:* 800-253-7360; 800-467-2726 *Fax:* 269-388-9681 *E-mail:* info@ rhcholdings.net; customerservice@rhcholdings.net; sales@rhcholdings.net *Web Site:* www.rapcohorizon. com, pg 870

Williams, Marilyn, Richmond Sound Design Ltd, 5264 Ross St, Vancouver, BC V5W 3K7, Canada *Web Site:* www.richmondsounddesign.com, pg 875

Williams, Marvin, Manhattan Center Studios Inc, 311 W 34 St, New York, NY 10001 *Tel:* 212-279-7740 *Fax:* 212-564-1072 *E-mail:* info@mcstudios.com *Web Site:* www.mcstudios.com, pg 816

Williams, Mary K, DocuWare Corp, 4 Crotty Lane, Suite 200, New Windsor, NY 12553 *Tel:* 845-563-9045 *Toll Free Tel:* 888-565-5907 *Fax:* 845-563-9046 *E-mail:* info@docuware.com; dwsales@docuware.com *Web Site:* www.docuware.com, pg 744

Williams, Matt, BMI Supply, 571 Queensbury Ave, Queensbury, NY 12804 *Tel:* 518-793-6706 *Toll Free Tel:* 800-836-0524 *Fax:* 518-793-6181 *E-mail:* bminy@bmisupply.com *Web Site:* www. bmisupply.com, pg 708

Williams, Molly, George Foster Peabody Awards, c/o University of Georgia, 120 Hooper St, Athens, GA 30602-3018 *Tel:* 706-542-3787 *E-mail:* peabody@uga. edu *Web Site:* www.peabodyawards.com, pg 999

Williams, Rob, Intermedia Inc, 3703 S Edmunds St, Suite 203, Seattle, WA 98118 *Tel:* 206-284-2995 *Toll Free Tel:* 800-553-8336 *Toll Free Fax:* 800-553-1655 *E-mail:* info@intermedia-inc.com *Web Site:* www. intermedia-inc.com, pg 789

Williams, Roger, Inspired Image Picture Co (IIPC), 1090 E Georgia St, Vancouver, BC V6A 2A7, Canada *Tel:* 604-874-7513 *Toll Free Tel:* 800-352-1454 (prodn rentals); 800-567-0037 (equip rentals) *Fax:* 604-874-7516 *E-mail:* info@inspiredimage.ca *Web Site:* inspiredimage.ca, pg 788

Williams, Scott, Quince Imaging Inc, 2810 Towerview Rd, Herndon, VA 20171-3206 *Tel:* 703-742-7520 *Toll Free Tel:* 888-252-4960 *Fax:* 703-742-7586 *E-mail:* info@quinceimaging.com; sales@ quinceimaging.com; operations@quinceimaging.com *Web Site:* www.quinceimaging.com, pg 868

Williams, Ted C, Professional Marketing Services Inc, 105 S Southgate Dr, Chandler, AZ 85226 *Tel:* 480-940-5400 *Toll Free Tel:* 800-201-2160 *Fax:* 480-603-1048 *E-mail:* pmsi@promarketinc.com *Web Site:* www.promarketinc.com, pg 865

Williams, Tim, Oregon Film & Video Office, 123 NE Third Ave, Suite 210, Portland, OR 97232 *Tel:* 971-254-4020 *E-mail:* shoot@oregonfilm.org *Web Site:* www.oregonfilm.org, pg 975

Williams, Tony, Midwest Uplink Inc, 911 N East St, Indianapolis, IN 46202 *Tel:* 317-423-8684 *Toll Free Tel:* 866-886-6247 *Web Site:* midwestuplink.com, pg 827

Williams, Tonya, ReelWorld Film Festival, 50 Carroll St, Suite 200, Toronto, ON M4M 3G3, Canada *Tel:* 416-598-7933 *E-mail:* info@reelworld.ca; contact@ reelworld.ca *Web Site:* www.reelworld.ca, pg 1001

Williams, Vivian T, Voyager Recordings & Publications, 424 35 Ave, Seattle, WA 98122 *Tel:* 206-323-1112 *E-mail:* info@voyagerrecords.com *Web Site:* www. voyagerrecords.com, pg 932

Williams, Wayne E, Telect Inc, 22425 E Appleway Ave, Liberty Lake, WA 99019 *Tel:* 509-926-6000 *Toll Free Tel:* 800-551-4567 *E-mail:* getinfo@telect.com *Web Site:* www.telect.com, pg 910

Williams, William, Aliso Creek Productions Inc, 4106 W Burbank Blvd, Burbank, CA 91510 *Tel:* 818-954-9931 *Web Site:* www.alisocreek.net, pg 680

Williger, Jonathan, Smithsonian Folkways Recordings, 600 Maryland Ave SW, Suite 2001, Washington, DC 20024 *Tel:* 202-633-6450 *Toll Free Tel:* 888-FOLKWAYS (365-5929) *Fax:* 202-633-6477 *E-mail:* smithsonianfolkways@si.edu *Web Site:* folkways.si.edu, pg 891

Willis, Dr Aaron, Health Education Services, 10200 Jefferson Blvd, Culver City, CA 90232 *Tel:* 310-839-2436 *Toll Free Tel:* 800-421-4246 *Fax:* 310-839-2249 *Toll Free Fax:* 800-944-5432 *E-mail:* access@ socialstudies.com; customerservice@socialstudies.com *Web Site:* www.socialstudies.com, pg 778

Willis, Aaron, Social Studies School Service, 10200 Jefferson Blvd, PO Box 802, Culver City, CA 90232 *Tel:* 310-839-2436 *Toll Free Tel:* 800-421-4246 *Fax:* 310-839-2249 *Toll Free Fax:* 800-944-5432 (US & CN) *E-mail:* access@socialstudies.com *Web Site:* www.socialstudies.com, pg 891

Willis, Dr Barry, University of Idaho Engineering Outreach, 875 Perimeter Dr MS 1014, Moscow, ID 83844-1014 *Tel:* 208-885-6373 *Toll Free Tel:* 800-824-2889 *Fax:* 208-885-9249 *E-mail:* outreach@uidaho. edu *Web Site:* eo.uidaho.edu, pg 922

Willis, Katherine, RuffHouse LLC, 2823 Lariat Trail, Austin, TX 78734 *Tel:* 512-965-2957 *E-mail:* info@ ruffhousin.com *Web Site:* www.ruffhousin.com, pg 878

Willis, Leigh, VideoLink Inc, an AVI-SPL company, 1230 Washington St, West Newton, MA 02465 *Tel:* 617-340-4100 *Toll Free Tel:* 800-452-5565 *Fax:* 617-340-4101 *E-mail:* sales@videolinktv.com *Web Site:* www.videolinktv.com, pg 929

Wilson, Abbie, P&P Studios Inc, 110 Lenox Ave, Suite 210, Stamford, CT 06906 *Tel:* 203-359-9292 *Toll Free Tel:* 888-WEPRODUCE (937-7638) *E-mail:* ppstudios@weproduce.com; info@weproduce. com *Web Site:* www.weproduce.com, pg 851

Wilson, Andrew, Electronic Arts Inc, 209 Redwood Shores Pkwy, Redwood City, CA 94065 *Tel:* 650-628-1500 *Web Site:* www.ea.com, pg 752

Wilson, Brandee, CRT Custom Products Inc, 7532 Hickory Hills Ct, Whites Creek, TN 37189 *Tel:* 615-876-5490 *Toll Free Tel:* 800-453-2533 *Fax:* 615-876-0096 *E-mail:* sales@crtcustomproducts.com *Web Site:* www.crtcustomproducts.com, pg 735

Wilson, Britta M, Pixar Animation Studios, 1200 Park Ave, Emeryville, CA 94608 *Tel:* 510-922-3000 *Fax:* 510-922-3151 *Web Site:* www.pixar.com, pg 857

Wilson, Carolyn, The Walt Disney Studios, 500 S Buena Vista St, Burbank, CA 91521 *Tel:* 818-560-1000 *Web Site:* studioservices.go.com; waltdisneystudios. com, pg 743

Wilson, Christopher, Moving Pictures, 2820 Selwyn Ave, Suite 789, Charlotte, NC 28209 *Tel:* 704-676-0868 *E-mail:* info@mpicts.com *Web Site:* www.mpicts.com, pg 832

Wilson, Chuck, National Systems Contractors Association (NSCA), 3950 River Ridge Dr NE, Cedar Rapids, IA 52402 *Tel:* 319-366-6722 *Toll Free Tel:* 800-446-6722 *Fax:* 319-366-4164 *E-mail:* nsca@ nsca.org *Web Site:* www.nsca.org, pg 959

Wilson, Dave, MISCO, 2637 32 Ave S, Minneapolis, MN 55406-1641 *Tel:* 612-825-1010 *Toll Free Tel:* 800-276-9955 *Fax:* 612-825-7010 *E-mail:* info@ miscospeakers.com *Web Site:* www.miscospeakers. com, pg 828

Wilson, Debbie, Power Integrity Corporation, 2109 Patterson St, Greensboro, NC 27407 *Tel:* 336-379-9773 *Toll Free Tel:* 800-237-6260 (tech support) *Web Site:* powerintegritycorp.com, pg 860

Wilson, Jim, National Undergraduate Student Electronic Media Competition, PO Box 4206, Chesterfield, MO 63006 *Tel:* 314-628-1196 *Web Site:* www.nbs-aerho. org, pg 997

Wilson, Jon, WoodenBoat Publications, 41 WoodenBoat Lane, Brooklin, ME 04616 *Tel:* 207-359-4651 *Toll Free Tel:* 800-877-5284 (subns) *Fax:* 207-359-8920 *E-mail:* woodenboat@woodenboat.com *Web Site:* www.woodenboat.com, pg 941

Wilson, Julie, Penguin Random House Audio Publishing, 1745 Broadway, New York, NY 10019 *E-mail:* audio@penguinrandomhouse.com *Web Site:* www.penguinrandomhouseaudio.com, pg 853

Wilson, Ken, Sportsmen on Film Inc, 231 Earl Garrett, Suite 300, Kerrville, TX 78028 *Tel:* 830-792-4200 *Toll Free Tel:* 800-910-HUNT (910-4868) *Fax:* 830-792-4224 *Web Site:* www.sportsmenonfilm.com, pg 898

Wilson, Laura, Macmillan Audio, 120 Broadway, 22nd fl, New York, NY 10271 *Tel:* 646-600-7856; 646-307-5472 *Toll Free Tel:* 888-330-8477 (cust serv); 800-221-7945 *Toll Free Fax:* 800-672-7703 (orders) *E-mail:* macmillan.audio@macmillanusa.com *Web Site:* www.macmillanaudio.com, pg 814

Wilson, Lynn, Photographers' Formulary Inc, 7079 Hwy 83 N, Condon, MT 59826 *Tel:* 406-754-2891 *Toll Free Tel:* 800-922-5255 *Fax:* 406-754-2896 *E-mail:* formulary@blackfoot.net *Web Site:* www. photoformulary.com, pg 856

Wilson, Marilyn, AV Connections Inc, 245 Executive Park Blvd, Winston-Salem, NC 27103 *Tel:* 336-768-5454 *Fax:* 336-768-5054 *E-mail:* avrentals@ avconnectionsusa.com *Web Site:* avconnectionsusa. com, pg 697

Wilson, Mark, Cramer, 425 University Ave, Norwood, MA 02062 *Tel:* 781-278-2300 *E-mail:* theteam@ cramer.com *Web Site:* cramer.com, pg 733

Wilson, Robert F, Wilson McLeran Inc, 41 Corey Hill Rd, Saxtons River, VT 05154 *Tel:* 802-869-3111 *Toll Free Tel:* 800-562-9646 *Fax:* 802-869-3111 *Web Site:* www.robertfwilson.net, pg 939

Wilson, Sean, Vancouver International Film Festival (VIFF), Vancouver International Film Ctr, 1181 Seymour St, Vancouver, BC V6B 3M7, Canada *Tel:* 604-685-0260 *Fax:* 604-688-8221 *E-mail:* info@ viff.org; submissions@viff.org *Web Site:* www.viff.org, pg 1006

Wilson, Sharon, Ontario Creates, South Tower, Suite 501, 175 Bloor St E, Toronto, ON M4W 3R8, Canada *Tel:* 416-314-6858 *Fax:* 416-314-6876 *E-mail:* reception@ontariocreates.ca *Web Site:* www. ontariocreates.ca, pg 978

Wilson, Steve, Accusoft, 4001 N Riverside Dr, Tampa, FL 33603 *Tel:* 813-875-7575 *Toll Free Tel:* 800-875-7009 *Fax:* 813-875-7705 *E-mail:* sales@accusoft.com *Web Site:* www.accusoft.com, pg 674

Wilson, Suzanne, Disney Consumer Products & Interactive Media (DCPI), 1201 Flower St, Glendale, AZ 91201 *Tel:* 818-544-0000 *Web Site:* dcpi.disney. com, pg 743

Wilson, Tom, Duke Media Services, 0052 Bryan Ctr, Durham, NC 27708 *Tel:* 919-660-1740 *Fax:* 919-660-1719 *E-mail:* dms-info@duke.edu *Web Site:* sites.duke. edu/mediaservices, pg 747

Wilson, Travis, Fleetwood Group Inc, 11832 James St, Holland, MI 49424 *Tel:* 616-396-1142 *Toll Free Tel:* 800-257-6390 *Fax:* 616-820-8300 *Web Site:* www. fleetwoodgroup.com; www.fleetwoodelectronics.com; www.fleetwoodfurniture.com, pg 762

Wilson, William "Bud" G, Photographers' Formulary Inc, 7079 Hwy 83 N, Condon, MT 59826 *Tel:* 406-754-2891 *Toll Free Tel:* 800-922-5255 *Fax:* 406-754-2896 *E-mail:* formulary@blackfoot.net *Web Site:* www.photoformulary.com, pg 856

Wiltshire, Matthew, Mayor's Office of Economic & Community Development, One Public Sq, Suite 100, Nashville, TN 37201 *Tel:* 615-862-6000 *Web Site:* www.nashville.gov, pg 976

Wimberly, George PhD, American Educational Research Association (AERA), 1430 "K" St NW, Suite 1200, Washington, DC 20005 *Tel:* 202-238-3200 *Fax:* 202-238-3250 *E-mail:* communications@aera.net; members@aera.net *Web Site:* www.aera.net, pg 948

Winberg, Wynn, Aries Productions Inc, 1110 Avenue "H" E, Suite 200, Arlington, TX 76011 *Tel:* 817-640-9955; 817-300-5255 (cell) *Web Site:* www.aries-prods. com, pg 688

Winch, Jessie, American Society for Photogrammetry and Remote Sensing (ASPRS), 425 Barlow Place, Suite 210, Bethesda, MD 20814-2160 *Tel:* 301-493-0290 *Fax:* 301-493-0208 *E-mail:* asprs@asprs.org *Web Site:* www.asprs.org, pg 949

Windmuller, Erich, DXC Technology Co, 1775 Tysons Blvd, Tysons, VA 22102 *Tel:* 317-331-1197 *Web Site:* www.dxc.technology, pg 748

Winegard, Randy, Winegard Co, 2736 Mount Pleasant St, Suite 140, Burlington, IA 52601 *Tel:* 319-754-0600 *Toll Free Tel:* 800-288-8094 *E-mail:* chat@winegard. com *Web Site:* www.winegard.com, pg 939

Winey, Mark, Magnepan Inc, 1645 Ninth St, White Bear Lake, MN 55110 *Tel:* 651-426-1645 *Toll Free Tel:* 800-474-1646 *Fax:* 651-426-0441 *Web Site:* www. magnepan.com, pg 814

Wing, Jennifer, Hannay Reels Inc, 553 State Rte 143, Westerlo, NY 12193-0159 *Tel:* 518-797-3791 *Toll Free Tel:* 877-467-3357 *Fax:* 518-797-3259 *Toll Free Fax:* 800-733-5464 *E-mail:* reels@hannay.com *Web Site:* www.hannay.com, pg 775

Winkelman, Babe, Babe Winkelman Productions Inc, PO Box 407, Brainerd, MN 56401 *Tel:* 218-821-6866 *Toll Free Tel:* 800-333-0471 *Web Site:* www.winkelman. com, pg 939

Winkelmann, Rich, Gettysburg Bluegrass Festival, 3340 Fairfield Rd, Gettysburg, PA 17325 *Tel:* 717-642-8749 *E-mail:* bluegrass@granitehillcampingresort.com *Web Site:* www.gettysburgbluegrass.com, pg 990

Winkler, Jim, National Council of Churches, 110 Maryland Ave NE, Suite 108, Washington, DC 20002 *Tel:* 202-544-2350 *E-mail:* info@nationalcouncilofchurches.us *Web Site:* nationalcouncilofchurches.us, pg 836

Winkler, Karl, Lectrosonics Inc, 581 Laser Rd NE, Rio Rancho, NM 87124 *Tel:* 505-892-4501 *Toll Free Tel:* 800-821-1121 *Fax:* 505-892-6243 *E-mail:* sales@ lectrosonics.com *Web Site:* www.lectrosonics.com, pg 805

Winship, Chad, Advanced Lighting & Production Services Inc (ALPS), 125 Shamut Rd, Canton, MA 02021 *Tel:* 781-961-3066 *Toll Free Tel:* 866-961-3066 *Fax:* 781-961-3256 *E-mail:* info@alpsweb.com *Web Site:* www.alpsweb.com, pg 677

Winstanley, Nicole, Penguin Random House Canada, 320 Front St W, Suite 1400, Toronto, ON M5V 3B6, Canada *Tel:* 416-364-4449 *Toll Free Tel:* 888-523-9292 (cust serv) *Fax:* 416-598-7764 *E-mail:* customerservicescanada@ penguinrandomhouse.com *Web Site:* www. penguinrandomhouse.ca, pg 853

Winter, Don, Winter Productions, 10625 S Hoyne, Chicago, IL 60643 *Tel:* 773-238-1656 *E-mail:* winterpr@aol.com *Web Site:* www. winterproductions.com, pg 939

Winterhalter, Andrea, QCA, 2832 Spring Grove Ave, Cincinnati, OH 45225 *Tel:* 513-681-8400 *Toll Free Tel:* 800-859-8401 *E-mail:* info@go-qca.com *Web Site:* www.go-qca.com, pg 867

Winters, Greg, Kino Mountain Productions LLC, 2004 Production Dr, Apex, NC 27539 *Tel:* 919-355-2725 *E-mail:* info@kinomountain.com *Web Site:* www. kinomountain.com, pg 799

Winters, Walt, ImageWorks Communications, 10155 High Point Lane, Suite 100, Salt Lake City, UT 84092 *Tel:* 801-231-7234 (cell) *Toll Free Tel:* 888-810-0100 *Web Site:* imageworkscommunications.com, pg 785

Winton, Peggy, Association for Information and Image Management (AIIM), 1100 Wayne Ave, Suite 1100, Silver Spring, MD 20910 *Tel:* 301-587-8202 *Toll Free Tel:* 800-477-2446 *Fax:* 301-587-2711 *E-mail:* aiim@ aiim.org *Web Site:* www.aiim.org, pg 950

Wiratunga, Kumar, ARC Document Solutions, 1981 N Broadway, Suite 385, Walnut Creek, CA 94596 *Tel:* 925-949-5100 *Toll Free Tel:* 855-500-0660 *E-mail:* contact@e-arc.com *Web Site:* www.e-arc.com, pg 688

Wirt, Kathleen, 4th Street Recording, 1211 Fourth St, Santa Monica, CA 90401 *Tel:* 310-395-9114 *E-mail:* info@4thstreetrecording.com *Web Site:* www. 4thstreetrecording.com, pg 764

Wischmeyer, Jim, Bag End Loudspeakers, 1201 Armstrong St, Algonquin, IL 60102 *Tel:* 847-658-8888 *Fax:* 847-658-5008 *Web Site:* www.bagend.com, pg 700

Wise, Pamela, Rebirth Inc, 81 Chandler St, Detroit, MI 48202 *Tel:* 313-875-0289 *E-mail:* wenhajazz@aol.com *Web Site:* www.rebirthjazz.org, pg 871

Wise, Tomas, Music Sales Corp, 180 Madison Ave, 24th fl, New York, NY 10016 *Tel:* 212-254-2100 *Fax:* 212-254-2013 *E-mail:* info@musicsales.com *Web Site:* www.musicsales.com, pg 834

Wiseman, Todd Jr, Hayden 5 Media LLC, 22 W 27 St, 6th fl, New York, NY 10001 *Tel:* 212-871-9316 *E-mail:* hi@hayden5.com *Web Site:* www.hayden5. com, pg 777

Wishman, Seymour, First Run Features, The Film Center Bldg, Suite 1213, 630 Ninth Ave, New York, NY 10036-3708 *Tel:* 212-243-0600 *Fax:* 212-989-7649 *E-mail:* info@firstrunfeatures.com *Web Site:* www. firstrunfeatures.com, pg 761

Wislocki, Stash, Mountainfilm in Telluride, 109 E Colorado Ave, Suite 1, Telluride, CO 81435 *Tel:* 970-728-4123 *E-mail:* entries@mountainfilm.org *Web Site:* www.mountainfilm.org, pg 996

Witcher, Brenna, Marsh Media, 200 Avila Circle, Kansas City, MO 64114 *Tel:* 816-523-1059 *Toll Free Tel:* 800-821-3303 *Fax:* 816-333-7421 *Toll Free Fax:* 866-333-7421 *E-mail:* info@marshmedia.com *Web Site:* www. marshmedia.com, pg 817

Witcher, Dan, Marsh Media, 200 Avila Circle, Kansas City, MO 64114 *Tel:* 816-523-1059 *Toll Free Tel:* 800-821-3303 *Fax:* 816-333-7421 *Toll Free Fax:* 866-333-7421 *E-mail:* info@marshmedia.com *Web Site:* www. marshmedia.com, pg 817

Withey, Brit, Denver Film Festival, 1510 York St, 3rd fl, Denver, CO 80206 *Tel:* 303-595-3456 *E-mail:* dff@ denverfilm.org *Web Site:* denverfilmfestival.denverfilm. org, pg 988

Withey, Brit, Denver Film Society, 1510 York St, 3rd fl, Denver, CO 80206 *Tel:* 303-595-3456 *E-mail:* info@ denverfilm.org *Web Site:* www.denverfilm.org, pg 953

Witsoe, Craig, Elo TouchSystems, 670 N McCarthy Blvd, Milpitas, CA 95035 *Toll Free Tel:* 800-356-8682; 800-557-1458 *Fax:* 650-361-4722 *E-mail:* eloinfo@elotouch.com; customerservice@ elotouch.com *Web Site:* www.elotouch.com, pg 753

Witte, Stephanie, National Public Radio (NPR), 1111 N Capitol St NE, Washington, DC 20002 *Tel:* 202-513-2000 *Web Site:* www.npr.org, pg 959

Witte, Steve, Wavemaker Media Design, PO Box 226, Duncans Mills, CA 95430 *Tel:* 707-788-6040 *Fax:* 707-788-6040 *E-mail:* sales@ wavemakermediadesign.com *Web Site:* www. wavemakermediadesign.com, pg 934

Wiwchar, Corey, Thompson Rivers University Marketing & Communications Dept, 805 TRU Way, Kamloops, BC V2C 0C8, Canada *Tel:* 250-852-7000 *Web Site:* www.tru.ca/marcom, pg 913

Woehrle, Pam, Getty Images, 605 Fifth Ave S, Suite 400, Seattle, WA 98104 *Tel:* 206-925-5000 *Toll Free Tel:* 888-888-5889; 800-462-4379 (sales) *E-mail:* sales.na@gettyimages.com *Web Site:* www. gettyimages.com, pg 770

Woertz, Greg, New Wave Entertainment, 2660 W Olive Ave, Burbank, CA 91505 *Tel:* 818-295-5000 *E-mail:* biz@nwe.com *Web Site:* nwe.com, pg 840

Wogsberg, Eric, Jupiter Systems, 31015 Huntwood Ave, Hayward, CA 94544 *Tel:* 510-675-1000 *Fax:* 510-675-1001 *E-mail:* sales@jupiter.com *Web Site:* www. jupiter.com, pg 795

Wohl, Jaclyn Rose, Nantucket Film Festival (NFF), 68 Jay St, Suite 319, Brooklyn, NY 11201 *Tel:* 646-480-1900 *Fax:* 646-365-3367 *E-mail:* info@nantucketfilmfestival. org; submissions@nantucketfilmfestival.org *Web Site:* nantucketfilmfestival.org, pg 997

Wohlmut, Thomas A, WMS Media Inc, 189 W Santa Clara St, San Jose, CA 95110 *Tel:* 510-825-7402 *E-mail:* info@wmsmedia.com *Web Site:* www. wmsmedia.com, pg 940

Wojcich, Joe, Tempe Camera, 606 W University, Tempe, AZ 85281 *Tel:* 480-966-6954 *Toll Free Tel:* 800-836-7374 *E-mail:* rent@tempecamera.com; sales@ tempecamera.biz *Web Site:* www.tempecamera.biz, pg 911

Wojdyla, Cindy, Pepper Group, 220 N Smith St, Suite 406, Palatine, IL 60067 *Tel:* 847-963-0333 *Fax:* 847-963-0888 *E-mail:* pepper@peppergroup.com *Web Site:* www.peppergroup.com, pg 854

Wojtas, Robert, Matrix Video Communications Corp (MVCC), 103, 1626 115 Ave NE, Calgary, AB T3K 5Y8, Canada *Tel:* 403-640-4490 *Fax:* 403-640-9012 *Web Site:* www.matrixvideocom.com, pg 819

Wolavka, Bill, Research Technology International (RTI), 4700 Chase Ave, Lincolnwood, IL 60712-1689 *Tel:* 847-677-3000 *Toll Free Tel:* 800-323-7520 *Fax:* 847-677-1311 *Toll Free Fax:* 800-784-6733 *E-mail:* sales@rtico.com *Web Site:* rtico.com, pg 873

Wolf, Daniel, Videobotics, 220 N Palisade Dr, Santa Maria, CA 93454 *Tel:* 805-349-1104 *E-mail:* videobotics@megagem.com; sales@ videobotics.com *Web Site:* www.videobotics.com; camrobot.com, pg 929

Wolf, David, Herman Pro AV, 10110 USA Today Way, Miramar, FL 33025 Tel: 305-477-0063 Toll Free Tel: 888-736-6888 Fax: 305-392-3377 E-mail: support@hermanproav.com Web Site: www. hermanproav.com, pg 779

Wolf, Erika, Electric Lady Studios, 52 W Eighth St, New York, NY 10011 Tel: 212-677-4700 Web Site: electricladystudios.com, pg 752

Wolf, Jeffrey, Herman Pro AV, 10110 USA Today Way, Miramar, FL 33025 Tel: 305-477-0063 Toll Free Tel: 888-736-6888 Fax: 305-392-3377 E-mail: support@hermanproav.com Web Site: www. hermanproav.com, pg 779

Wolf, Joe, JoeAudio, 10850 John Galt Blvd, Omaha, NE 68137 Tel: 402-341-9153 Toll Free Tel: 866-JOE-AUDIO (563-2834) Web Site: www. joeaudioproductions.com, pg 794

Wolf, Jonathan, Independent Film & Television Alliance® (IFTA), 10850 Wilshire Blvd, 9th fl, Los Angeles, CA 90024-4311 Tel: 310-446-1000 Fax: 310-446-1600 E-mail: info@ifta-online.org Web Site: www.ifta-online.org, pg 956

Wolf, Steve, Theatrical Services Inc, 128 S Washington St, Wichita, KS 67202 Tel: 316-263-4415 Toll Free Tel: 888-874-2649 Fax: 316-263-9927 Web Site: www. theatricalservices.com, pg 912

Wolfe, Bob, Starlite, 9 Whittendale Dr, Moorestown, NJ 08057 Tel: 856-780-8000 Toll Free Tel: 800-738-7400 Fax: 856-780-8001 E-mail: info@starlite.com Web Site: www.starlite.com, pg 900

Wolfe, Gianna, Radiant Images, 2702 Media Center Dr, Los Angeles, CA 90065 Tel: 323-737-1314 Fax: 310-861-0163 E-mail: info@radiantimages.com Web Site: www.radiantimages.com, pg 869

Wolfe, Roland, Leica Camera Inc, One Pearl Ct, Unit A, Allendale, NJ 07401 Toll Free Tel: 800-222-0118 Fax: 201-995-1686 Web Site: en.leica-camera.com, pg 806

Wolfenberg, Josh, Himalayan Institute Audio/Video, 952 Bethany Tpke, Honesdale, PA 18431 Tel: 570-253-5551 Toll Free Tel: 800-822-4547 E-mail: info@himalayaninstitute.org Web Site: www. himalayaninstitute.org, pg 780

Wolff, Liz, Dance on Camera Festival, 252 Java St, Suite 333, Brooklyn, NY 11222 Tel: 347-505-8649 E-mail: info@dancefilms.org; festival@dancefilms.org Web Site: www.dancefilms.org, pg 988

Wolfrum, Edward J, Audio Graphic Services, 1516 Ferris Ave, Royal Oak, MI 48067 Tel: 248-544-1793 E-mail: netmail@audiographicservices.com Web Site: www.audiographicservices.com, pg 693

Wolfrum, Susan E, Audio Graphic Services, 1516 Ferris Ave, Royal Oak, MI 48067 Tel: 248-544-1793 E-mail: netmail@audiographicservices.com Web Site: www.audiographicservices.com, pg 693

Wolin, Dave, Madera County Film Commission Inc, PO Box 3690, Oakhurst, CA 93644 Tel: 559-760-1143 Fax: 559-658-2851 E-mail: filmcommissioner@filmmadera.com Web Site: www.yosemite-sierra.com, pg 967

Woloshin, Randy, CMD Agency, 1631 NW Thurman St, Portland, OR 97209 Tel: 503-223-6794 E-mail: info@cmdagency.com Web Site: www.cmdagency.com, pg 726

Wolpert, Raymond, Union Connector Co Inc, 8182 Baymeadow Way W, Jacksonville, FL 32256 Tel: 631-753-9550 Fax: 631-753-9560 E-mail: sales@unionconnector.com Web Site: www.unionconnector.com, pg 921

Womack, Devin, WVLA-TV, 10,000 Perkins Rd, Baton Rouge, LA 70810 Tel: 225-766-3233 Fax: 225-768-9293 Web Site: www.brproud.com, pg 942

Won, Daniel, DASAN Zhone Solutions (DZS) Inc, 7195 Oakport St, Oakland, CA 94621 Tel: 510-777-7000 Toll Free Tel: 877-ZHONE-20 (946-6320, US & CN) Fax: 510-777-7001 Web Site: dasanzhone.com, pg 737

Wong, Judy Go, DC Asian Pacific American Film Festival, 2515 Virginia Ave NW, No 58205, Washington, DC 20037 Tel: 202-796-9680; 202-792-6393 E-mail: info@apafilm.org; admin@apafilm.org Web Site: www.apafilm.org, pg 988

Wong, Nelson, SoundByte Productions Inc, 636 E Sixth St, New York, NY 10009 Tel: 212-675-0600 Fax: 212-675-3724 E-mail: info@soundbyte.com Web Site: www.soundbyte.com, pg 894

Wong, Robert, Creative BC (CrBC), 7 W Sixth Ave, Vancouver, BC V5Y 1K2, Canada Tel: 604-730-2732 Fax: 604-736-7290 E-mail: info@creativebc.com; media@creativebc.com Web Site: www.creativebc.com, pg 978

Wong, Stan, Videssence, 10768 Lower Azusa Rd, El Monte, CA 91731 Tel: 626-579-0943 Fax: 626-579-6803 E-mail: contact@videssence.tv Web Site: www. videssence.tv, pg 930

Woo, John C, Asian American International Film Festival (AAIFF), c/o Made in NY Media Ctr by IFP, 30 John St, Brooklyn, NY 11201 Tel: 212-989-1422 Fax: 212-727-3584 E-mail: submissions@asiancinevision.org; info@asiancinevision.org Web Site: aaiff.org; www.asiancinevision.org, pg 982

Wood, Brian, Supercircuits, 11000 N Mopac Expwy, Bldg 300, Austin, TX 78759 Toll Free Tel: 877-995-2288 E-mail: operations@supercircuits.com; customercare@supercircuits.com Web Site: www. supercircuits.com, pg 904

Wood, David, Ensemble Designs Inc, 870 Gold Flat Rd, Nevada City, CA 95959 Tel: 530-478-1830 Fax: 530-478-1832 E-mail: info@ensembledesigns. com; service@ensembledesigns.com Web Site: www. ensembledesigns.com, pg 754

Wood, James B, IATSE, 207 W 25 St, 4th fl, New York, NY 10001 Tel: 212-730-1770 Fax: 212-730-7809 Web Site: www.iatse-intl.org; iatse.net, pg 955

Wood, Rob, SurgeX, 8001 Knightdale Blvd, Suite 121, Knightdale, NC 27545 Toll Free Tel: 800-645-9721 (tech & cust support) E-mail: order.desk@ametek.com Web Site: espsurgex.com/surgex/, pg 905

Woodbury, C Troy Jr, Wegener Communications Inc, Technology Park, 11350 Technology Circle, Johns Creek, GA 30097 Tel: 770-814-4000; 770-814-4036 (sales); 770-814-4057 (cust serv) Fax: 770-623-0698 E-mail: info@wegener.com Web Site: www.wegener. com, pg 935

Woodford, Charles H, Dance Horizons Video, 15 W Front St, 3rd fl, Trenton, NJ 08608 Tel: 609-426-0602 Toll Free Tel: 800-220-7149 Fax: 609-426-1344 E-mail: pbc@dancehorizons.com Web Site: www. dancehorizons.com, pg 737

Woodford, Charles H, Princeton Book Company, Publishers, 15 W Front St, 3rd fl, Trenton, NJ 08608 Tel: 609-426-0602 Toll Free Tel: 800-220-7149 Fax: 609-426-1344 E-mail: pbc@dancehorizons.com Web Site: www.dancehorizons.com, pg 862

Woodring, Suzie, Crest Electronics Inc, 3703 Alliance Dr, Suite A, Greensboro, NC 27407 Tel: 336-855-6422 Toll Free Tel: 888-502-7378 Fax: 336-855-6676 Web Site: www.crestelectronics.com, pg 734

Woods, Mark, Pro AV Systems, 275 Billerica Rd, Suite 3, Chelmsford, MA 01824 Tel: 978-692-5111 Fax: 978-692-5252 E-mail: info@proavsi.com Web Site: proavsi.com, pg 862

Woods, Susan W, East Lansing Film Festival (ELFF), 210 Abbot Rd, Suite 48, East Lansing, MI 48823 Tel: 517-980-5802 Web Site: elff.com, pg 988

Woodside, Christopher, National Association for Music Education (NAfME), 1806 Robert Fulton Dr, Reston, VA 20191 Tel: 703-860-4000 Toll Free Tel: 800-336-3768 Fax: 703-860-1531 Toll Free Fax: 888-275-6362 E-mail: memberservices@nafme.org Web Site: nafme. org, pg 958

Woodward, Terry, WaxWorks VideoWorks, 325 E Third St, Owensboro, KY 42303 Tel: 270-926-0008 Toll Free Tel: 800-825-8558 Fax: 270-663-0737 Web Site: www.waxworksonline.com, pg 934

Woodworth, Amy, Crystal Productions, 401 Hickory St, Fort Collins, CO 80524 Toll Free Tel: 800-289-9299 E-mail: custserv@crystalproductions.com Web Site: www.crystalproductions.com, pg 735

Woolf, Richard, Xtech Systems Inc, 241 Rock Creek Lane, Scarsdale, NY 10583 Tel: 718-543-1222 Fax: 914-472-2111 Toll Free Fax: 888-528-6511 E-mail: info@xtechsystems.com Web Site: www. xtechsystems.com, pg 943

Woolley, Cheryl Gillam, Bullfrog Films Inc, 372 Dautrich Rd, Reading, PA 19606 Tel: 610-779-8226 Toll Free Tel: 800-543-3764 Fax: 610-370-1978 E-mail: info@bullfrogfilms.com; video@bullfrogfilms. com Web Site: www.bullfrogfilms.com, pg 712

Woolley, Lynn, Central Texas College KNCT-Radio FM, PO Box 1800, Killeen, TX 76540-1800 Tel: 254-526-1176 E-mail: knct@knct.org Web Site: www.knct.org, pg 719

Woolum, Sue, Conquest Sound Co Inc, 209 Cypress Dr, Manteno, IL 60950 Tel: 708-534-0390 Toll Free Tel: 800-323-7671 Fax: 708-534-0398 E-mail: info@conquestsound.com Web Site: www.conquestsound. com, pg 731

Worrell, Greg, Scholastic Library Publishing, 90 Old Sherman Tpke, Danbury, CT 06816 Toll Free Tel: 800-621-1115 (cust serv) Toll Free Fax: 866-783-4361 Web Site: scholasticlibrary.digital.scholastic.com, pg 882

Worthington, Bob, Jupiter Systems, 31015 Huntwood Ave, Hayward, CA 94544 Tel: 510-675-1000 Fax: 510-675-1001 E-mail: sales@jupiter.com Web Site: www.jupiter.com, pg 795

Woznow, Ken, Eagle Camera Support Systems Ltd, 2787 Norland Ave, Burnaby, BC V5B 3A9, Canada Tel: 604-649-6350 E-mail: info@eaglecss.com Web Site: eaglecss.com, pg 749

Wright, Art, ACS Technologies, 180 Dunbarton Dr, Florence, SC 29501 Tel: 843-662-1681 Toll Free Tel: 800-736-7425 (sales); 800-669-2309 (support) Fax: 843-669-7513 E-mail: info@acstechnologies.com Web Site: www.acstechnologies.com, pg 674

Wright, Cassius, Chicago Spotlight Inc, 3418 N Knox Ave, Chicago, IL 60641 Tel: 312-455-1171 Web Site: www.grandstage.com, pg 721

Wright, Don, CORTRON Media LLC, 320 Fort Duquesne Blvd, Suite 100, Pittsburgh, PA 15222-1146 Tel: 412-565-3471 (ext 3) Web Site: cortronmedia. com, pg 732

Wright, Eddie, Sound & Images Inc, 1211 Virginia St, Columbia, SC 29201 Tel: 803-791-3925 E-mail: marketing@s-and-i.com Web Site: www.s-and-i.com, pg 893

Wright, James, Primacoustic, 1588 Kebet Way, Port Coquitlam, BC V3C 5M5, Canada Tel: 604-942-1001 Fax: 604-942-1010 E-mail: info@primacoustic.com Web Site: www.primacoustic.com, pg 862

Wright, Keith, Reel Picture, 5330 Eastgate Mall, San Diego, CA 92121 Tel: 858-587-0301 Toll Free Tel: 866-502-3472 (US & CN) Fax: 858-587-8838 Web Site: www.reelpicture.com, pg 872

Wright, Sandy Sanchez, Palardo Productions, 1807 Taft Ave, Suite 4, Hollywood, CA 90028 Tel: 323-469-8991 E-mail: palardo2@msn.com, pg 850

Wright, Wm M, DW Electrochemicals Ltd, 3-97 Newkirk Rd N, Richmond Hill, ON L4C 3G4, Canada Tel: 905-508-7500 Fax: 905-508-7502 E-mail: dwel@stabilant.com Web Site: www.stabilant.com, pg 748

Wu, Dan, Orevox USA Corp, 240 N Puente Ave, City of Industry, CA 91746-2303 Tel: 626-336-0516 Fax: 626-336-3748 Web Site: www.dynavox.com, pg 847

Wunderlich, R, Cambridge Documentary Films Inc, 3099 Hidden Valley Lane, Santa Barbara, CA 93108 Tel: 617-484-3993 E-mail: info@cambridgedocumentaryfilms.org; mail@cambridgedocumentaryfilms.org Web Site: www. cambridgedocumentaryfilms.org, pg 714

Wurm, Jim, Exhibitor Appointed Contractor Association (EACA), 2214 NW Fifth St, Bend, OR 97703 *Tel:* 541-317-8768 *E-mail:* info@eaca.com *Web Site:* eaca.com, pg 954

Wussow, George, Recortec Inc, 3329 Kifer Rd, Santa Clara, CA 95051-0719 *Tel:* 408-928-1480 *Toll Free Tel:* 800-729-7654 *Fax:* 408-928-1489 *E-mail:* info@recortec.com; support@recortec.com; sales@recortec.com *Web Site:* www.recortec.com, pg 872

Wuthrich, Jim, Warner Home Video Inc, 4000 Warner Blvd, Bldg 160, Burbank, CA 91522 *Tel:* 818-954-6000 *Fax:* 818-954-6480 *Web Site:* www.warnerbros.com, pg 934

Wyatt, Dolly, Los Angeles Center Studios, 450 S Bixel St, Los Angeles, CA 90017 *Tel:* 213-534-3000 *E-mail:* productionservices@lacenterstudios.com *Web Site:* lacenterstudios.com, pg 811

Wyatt, Frank (Burk) B II, CommScope Inc, 1100 CommScope Place SE, Hickory, NC 28602 *Tel:* 828-324-2200 *Toll Free Tel:* 800-982-1708 *E-mail:* publicrelations@commscope.com *Web Site:* www.commscope.com, pg 728

Wyatt, Mindy, Rafik, 817 Broadway, 2nd fl, Suite 11, New York, NY 10003 *Tel:* 646-480-5729 *E-mail:* info@rafikvideo.com; sales@rafikvideo.com *Web Site:* www.rafikvideo.com, pg 869

Wyler, Max, Accord Productions, 2140 S Dixie Hwy, Suite 301, Miami, FL 33133 *Tel:* 305-856-1245; 305-985-5842 *Toll Free Tel:* 800-833-1245 *Fax:* 305-856-9101 *E-mail:* mail@accordvideo.com *Web Site:* www.accordproductions.com, pg 673

Wyler, Rocky, Accord Productions, 2140 S Dixie Hwy, Suite 301, Miami, FL 33133 *Tel:* 305-856-1245; 305-985-5842 *Toll Free Tel:* 800-833-1245 *Fax:* 305-856-9101 *E-mail:* mail@accordvideo.com *Web Site:* www.accordproductions.com, pg 673

Wyler, William, Accord Productions, 2140 S Dixie Hwy, Suite 301, Miami, FL 33133 *Tel:* 305-856-1245; 305-985-5842 *Toll Free Tel:* 800-833-1245 *Fax:* 305-856-9101 *E-mail:* mail@accordvideo.com *Web Site:* www.accordproductions.com, pg 673

Wyllie, Chris, Theatre Effects, 1810 Airport Exchange Blvd, Suite 400, Erlanger, KY 41018-3184 *Tel:* 859-647-8844 *Toll Free Tel:* 800-791-7646 *Fax:* 859-647-0075 *E-mail:* service@theatrefx.com *Web Site:* www.theatrefx.com, pg 911

Wyne, David, Schiller's Audio-Visual, 9240 Manchester Rd, St Louis, MO 63144-2636 *Tel:* 314-968-3650 *Toll Free Tel:* 800-366-7244 *Fax:* 314-968-1184 *E-mail:* sales@schillers.com; av@schillers.com *Web Site:* www.schillers.com, pg 881

Wyner, Jonathan, M Works Mastering Studio, 60 Hampshire St, Cambridge, MA 02139 *Tel:* 617-577-0089 *E-mail:* studio@m-works.com; info@m-works.com *Web Site:* www.m-works.com, pg 813

Wynn, Erin, Welocalize, 241 E Fourth St, Suite 207, Frederick, MD 21701 *Tel:* 301-668-0330 *Toll Free Tel:* 800-370-9515 *Fax:* 301-668-0335 *E-mail:* info@welocalize.com *Web Site:* www.welocalize.com, pg 935

Wynn, Peter, Animotion Inc, 501 W Fayette St, Syracuse, NY 13204 *Tel:* 315-471-3533 *E-mail:* info@animotioninc.com *Web Site:* animotioninc.com, pg 685

Wynne, Dan, Sharp Electronics Corp, Professional Display Division, 100 Paragon Dr, Montvale, NJ 07645 *Tel:* 201-529-8200 *Toll Free Tel:* 800-BE-SHARP (237-4277) *Fax:* 201-529-8425 *Web Site:* www.sharpusa.com, pg 885

Wynne, Kenneth, CMI Media Management, 9 W Broad St, Stamford, CT 06902 *Tel:* 203-989-9955 *Toll Free Tel:* 800-431-1102 *Fax:* 203-316-8353 *Web Site:* www.cminyla.com, pg 727

Wynter, Lindsay, VITAC, 8300 E Maplewood Ave, Suite 310, Greenwood Village, CO 80111 *Toll Free Tel:* 800-278-4822 (sales); 800-775-7838 *E-mail:* info@vitac.com *Web Site:* www.vitac.com, pg 932

Xiao, Dorothy, Visual Communications - Southern California Asian American Studies Central Inc, 120 Judge John Aiso St, Basement Level, Los Angeles, CA 90012 *Tel:* 213-680-4462 *Fax:* 213-687-4848 *E-mail:* info@vconline.org *Web Site:* www.vconline.org, pg 931

Yablon, Gilbert, Lumeni Productions Inc, 1632 Flower St, Glendale, CA 91201 *Tel:* 818-956-2200 *Fax:* 818-956-3298 *E-mail:* info@lumeni.com *Web Site:* www.lumeni.com, pg 812

Yacishyn, Mr Blair, Golden Sheaf Awards, 49 Smith St E, Yorkton, SK S3N 0H4, Canada *Tel:* 306-782-7077 *Fax:* 306-782-1550 *E-mail:* info@yorktonfilm.com *Web Site:* yorktonfilm.com/golden-sheaf-awards/, pg 991

Yacishyn, Mr Blair, Yorkton Film Festival (YFF), 49 Smith St E, Yorkton, SK S3N 0H4, Canada *Tel:* 306-782-7077 *Fax:* 306-782-1550 *E-mail:* info@yorktonfilm.com *Web Site:* yorktonfilm.com, pg 1007

Yacoub, Marilou, Alan Weiss Productions, 1243 California Rd, Suite 2R, East Chester, NY 10709 *Tel:* 212-974-0606 *Fax:* 914-968-1104 *E-mail:* awpinfo@awptv.com *Web Site:* www.awptv.com, pg 935

Yada, Michael, Yada/Levine Video Productions, 3129 S Hacienda Blvd, No 423, Hacienda Heights, CA 91745 *Tel:* 323-461-1616 *Fax:* 323-461-2288 *E-mail:* video@yadalevine.com *Web Site:* www.yadalevine.com, pg 943

Yadin, Orly, Vermont International Film Festival, PO Box 483, Burlington, VT 05402-0483 *Tel:* 802-660-2600 *E-mail:* info@vtiff.org *Web Site:* www.vtiff.org, pg 1006

Yale, Martin, Sonic IT Communications, 79 Denlow Blvd, Toronto, ON M3B 1P8, Canada *Tel:* 416-383-0260 *Toll Free Tel:* 800-267-6642 *Fax:* 416-383-0261 *E-mail:* sales@sonicscience.com *Web Site:* www.sonicscience.com, pg 892

Yamada, Kevin, Studio 637, 637 Cypress Ave, Hermosa Beach, CA 90254 *Tel:* 310-372-8218 *Web Site:* studio-637.com, pg 903

Yamada, Masahiko, Wacom Technology Corp, 1458 NW Irving St, Portland, OR 97209 *Toll Free Tel:* 855-MY-WACOM (699-2266) *Web Site:* www.wacom.com, pg 933

Yaman, Daniel, Live Spark Inc, 700 Raymond Ave, Suite 100, St Paul, MN 55114 *Tel:* 651-289-7375 *E-mail:* info@live-spark.com *Web Site:* www.live-spark.com, pg 810

Yamashita, Shinichi, DNP Imagingcomm America Corp (DNP IAM), 4524 Enterprise Dr NW, Concord, NC 28027 *Tel:* 704-784-8100 *Toll Free Tel:* 800-814-4672 *Fax:* 704-784-7196 *E-mail:* sales_marketing@dnpimgcomm.com *Web Site:* www.dnpimagingcomm.com; www.dnpphoto.com, pg 744

Yancey, Mark, Satellite Digital Teleproductions (SDTV), 4004 La Salle St, San Diego, CA 92110-5124 *Tel:* 619-293-7777 *Toll Free Tel:* 800-SKY-PROD (759-7763 US) *Fax:* 619-223-3626 *E-mail:* info@sdtv.com *Web Site:* www.sdtv.com, pg 881

Yanchar, Carl J, Yanchar Design & Consulting Group, 26741 Portola Pkwy, Suite 1E, Foothill Ranch, CA 92610-1763 *Tel:* 949-770-6601 *Fax:* 949-770-6575 *E-mail:* info@yanchardesign.com *Web Site:* www.yanchardesign.com, pg 943

Yandle, Amy, Boston Film Bureau, One City Hall Sq, Rm 802, Boston, MA 02201-2029 *Tel:* 617-635-3911 *Fax:* 617-635-4428 *E-mail:* filmbureau@cityofboston.gov *Web Site:* www.cityofboston.gov/arts/film, pg 972

Yanes, Vince, Ver Sales Inc, 2509 N Naomi St, Burbank, CA 91504 *Tel:* 818-567-3000 *Toll Free Tel:* 800-229-0518; 800-300-WIRE (300-9479, CA only) *Fax:* 818-567-3018 *E-mail:* sales@versales.com *Web Site:* www.versales.com, pg 926

Yaney, Martha, Vista Group International Inc, 25 Van Zant St, Unit 8-D, Norwalk, CT 06855 *Tel:* 203-852-5557 *Toll Free Tel:* 800-866-2113 *Fax:* 203-852-5559 *E-mail:* info@vistagroupinternational.com *Web Site:* www.vistagroupinternational.com, pg 931

Yarbrough, Steve, Drytac Corp, 5601 Eastport Blvd, Richmond, VA 23231 *Tel:* 804-222-3094 *Toll Free Tel:* 800-280-6013 *E-mail:* customerservice@drytac.com *Web Site:* www.drytac.com, pg 747

Yasuda, Tom, MQ Power Corp, 1800 Waters Ridge Dr, Suite 500, Lewisville, TX 75057 *Toll Free Tel:* 800-883-2551; 800-427-1244 (parts); 800-426-1244 (sales) *Fax:* 972-315-1847 *E-mail:* mqpowersales@multiquip.com *Web Site:* www.multiquip.com, pg 832

Yates, Mark, New England Keyboard Inc, One Princeton Rd, Fitchburg, MA 01420 *Tel:* 978-345-8332 *Fax:* 978-345-4329 *E-mail:* info@newenglandkeyboard.com *Web Site:* www.newenglandkeyboard.com, pg 839

Yeaman, Kevin, Dolby Laboratories Inc, 1275 Market St, San Francisco, CA 94103-1410 *Tel:* 415-558-0200 *Fax:* 415-645-4000 *Web Site:* www.dolby.com, pg 745

Yearling, Mike, Mills James Productions, 3545 Fishinger Blvd, Columbus, OH 43026-9489 *Tel:* 614-777-9933 *E-mail:* info@mjp.com *Web Site:* www.millsjames.com, pg 828

Yee, Michael, William F White International Inc, 800 Islington Ave, Toronto, ON M8Z 6A1, Canada *Tel:* 416-239-5050 *Toll Free Tel:* 800-465-0160 (CN only) *Web Site:* www.whites.com, pg 937

Yeko, Bruce, Original Cast Records, PO Box 496, Georgetown, CT 06829-0496 *Tel:* 203-544-8288 *Fax:* 203-544-8288 *E-mail:* originalcast@aol.com *Web Site:* www.originalcastrecords.com; footlight.com, pg 848

Yep, Richard, American Counseling Association, 6101 Stevenson Ave, Suite 600, Alexandria, VA 22304 *Tel:* 703-823-9800 (ext 222) *Toll Free Tel:* 800-347-6647 (ext 222) *Fax:* 703-823-0252 *E-mail:* membership@counseling.org *Web Site:* www.counseling.org, pg 683

Yessian, Brian, Yessian, 137 Fifth Ave, 3rd fl, New York, NY 10010 *Tel:* 212-533-3443 *E-mail:* info-ny@yessian.com *Web Site:* www.yessian.com, pg 944

Yessian, Michael, Yessian, 137 Fifth Ave, 3rd fl, New York, NY 10010 *Tel:* 212-533-3443 *E-mail:* info-ny@yessian.com *Web Site:* www.yessian.com, pg 944

Yewell, Julia, Welocalize, 241 E Fourth St, Suite 207, Frederick, MD 21701 *Tel:* 301-668-0330 *Toll Free Tel:* 800-370-9515 *Fax:* 301-668-0335 *E-mail:* info@welocalize.com *Web Site:* www.welocalize.com, pg 935

Yewell, Smith, Welocalize, 241 E Fourth St, Suite 207, Frederick, MD 21701 *Tel:* 301-668-0330 *Toll Free Tel:* 800-370-9515 *Fax:* 301-668-0335 *E-mail:* info@welocalize.com *Web Site:* www.welocalize.com, pg 935

Yoder, Phil, Icom Multimedia, 2498 Danders Ct, Columbus, OH 43220 *Tel:* 614-207-4400 *Fax:* 614-457-8050 *Web Site:* www.icommultimedia.com, pg 783

Yoffe, Max, Big Door, 114 Sheldon St, El Segundo, CA 90245 *Tel:* 310-546-6100 *Fax:* 310-906-4585 *E-mail:* sales@bigdoor.tv *Web Site:* www.bigdoor.tv; www.bigdoorstudio.tv, pg 705

Yoshida, Ron, Hello World Communications, 118 W 22 St, 2nd fl, New York, NY 10011 *Tel:* 212-243-8800 *Fax:* 212-691-6961 *E-mail:* excitable01@gmail.com *Web Site:* hwc.tv, pg 778

Yoshida, Sam, Canon USA Inc, One Canon Park, Melville, NY 11747 *Toll Free Tel:* 800-652-2666 *E-mail:* pr@cusa.canon.com *Web Site:* www.usa.canon.com, pg 716

Yoshii, Go, Noritsu America Corp, 6900 Noritsu Ave, Buena Park, CA 90620 *Tel:* 714-521-9040 *Toll Free Tel:* 800-521-3686; 888-435-7448 (tech support) *E-mail:* sales@noritsu.com *Web Site:* www.noritsu.com, pg 842

Yost, Dave, WPHL-TV, 5001 Wynnefield Ave, Philadelphia, PA 19131 *Tel:* 215-878-1700 *E-mail:* feedback@phl17.com *Web Site:* www.phl17.com, pg 942

Young, Brian, McBain Camera Ltd, 10805 107 Ave, Edmonton, AB T5H 0W9, Canada *Tel:* 780-420-0404 *Toll Free Tel:* 800-661-6980 *Fax:* 780-421-1188 *Web Site:* www.mcbaincamera.com, pg 820

Young, Deborah, National Association of Elementary School Principals (NAESP), 1615 Duke St, Alexandria, VA 22314 *Tel:* 703-684-3345 *Toll Free Tel:* 800-386-2377 *Fax:* 703-549-5568 *Toll Free Fax:* 800-396-2377 *E-mail:* naesp@naesp.org *Web Site:* www.naesp.org, pg 836

Young, Donald, Center for Asian American Media (CAAM), 145 Ninth St, Suite 350, San Francisco, CA 94103 *Tel:* 415-863-0814 *Fax:* 415-863-7428 *E-mail:* publicity@caamedia.org *Web Site:* caamedia. org, pg 953

Young, Fallon, New Orleans Film Festival, 1215 Prytania St, Suite 423, New Orleans, LA 70130 *Tel:* 504-309-6633 *E-mail:* noff@neworleansfilmsociety.org *Web Site:* neworleansfilmsociety.org/festival, pg 997

Young, Joanne, Audio Visual Imagineering Inc, 6565 Hazeltine National Dr, Suite 2, Orlando, FL 32822 *Tel:* 407-859-8166 *Fax:* 407-859-8254 *Web Site:* www. av-imagineering.com, pg 694

Young, Linda, DuArt Media Services, 245 W 55 St, New York, NY 10019 *Tel:* 212-757-4580 *Fax:* 212-977-5609 *E-mail:* info@duart.com *Web Site:* www.duart. com, pg 747

Young, Steve, Videografix LLC, 2530 Berryessa Rd, Suite 314, San Jose, CA 95132-2903 *Tel:* 408-499-1280 *E-mail:* info@videografix.com *Web Site:* www. videografix.com, pg 929

Young, Will, Whirlwind Music Distributors Inc, 99 Ling Rd, Greece, NY 14612 *Tel:* 585-663-8820 *Toll Free Tel:* 800-733-9473 (US only) *Fax:* 585-865-8930 *E-mail:* sales@whirlwindusa.com; techsupport@whirlwindusa.com; darylg@whirlwindusa.com (CN inquiries) *Web Site:* whirlwindusa.com, pg 937

Younger, Alex, Cinema Equipment & Supplies Inc, 12457 SW 130 St, Miami, FL 33186 *Tel:* 305-232-8182 *E-mail:* sales@cinemaequip.com *Web Site:* www. cinemaequip.com, pg 724

Youngs, Ross O, Univenture Inc, 4266 Tuller Rd, Dublin, OH 43017 *Tel:* 937-645-4600 *Toll Free Tel:* 877-831-9428 *Fax:* 937-645-4700 *E-mail:* sales@univenture.com *Web Site:* www.univenture.com, pg 922

Yu, Lin, Christie Digital Systems USA Inc, 10550 Camden Dr, Cypress, CA 90630 *Tel:* 714-236-8610 *Toll Free Tel:* 866-880-4462 (cust serv) *Fax:* 714-503-3375 *E-mail:* sales-us@christiedigital.com; orders@christiedigital.com *Web Site:* www.christiedigital.com, pg 722

Yu, Raymond, InFocus Corp, 13190 SW 68 Pkwy, Suite 200, Portland, OR 97223-8368 *Tel:* 503-207-4700 *Toll Free Tel:* 877-388-8385 *E-mail:* sales@infocus.com *Web Site:* www.infocus.com, pg 787

Yu, Tricia, Uncharted Country Publishing, PO Box 756, Taos, NM 87571 *Tel:* 575-776-3470 *Toll Free Tel:* 800-488-4940 *E-mail:* ucp@taichihealth.com *Web Site:* taichihealth.com, pg 921

Yumru, Zaf, New Orleans Film Festival, 1215 Prytania St, Suite 423, New Orleans, LA 70130 *Tel:* 504-309-6633 *E-mail:* noff@neworleansfilmsociety.org *Web Site:* neworleansfilmsociety.org/festival, pg 997

Yun, Bill, RAM® Mounts, 8410 Dallas Ave S, Seattle, WA 98108 *Tel:* 206-763-8361 *Toll Free Tel:* 800-497-7479 *Fax:* 206-763-9615 *E-mail:* sales@rammount. com *Web Site:* www.rammount.com, pg 870

Yurcik, Bryan, Panavid, 210 West Pkwy, Unit 5, Pompton Plains, NJ 07444 *Tel:* 973-831-5655 *E-mail:* info@panavid.com; support@panavid.com *Web Site:* www.panavid.com, pg 850

Yurish, Pete, Spectrum Audio Visual Services, 351 W 45 Ave, Denver, CO 80216 *Tel:* 303-477-4456 *Toll Free Tel:* 800-477-4752 *Fax:* 303-477-0114 *E-mail:* info@spectrumav.com *Web Site:* www.spectrumav, pg 897

Yurkanin, Jeff, Mightybytes Inc, 4001 N Ravenswood Ave, Suite 404, Chicago, IL 60613 *Tel:* 773-561-7529 *E-mail:* info@mightybytes.com *Web Site:* www. mightybytes.com, pg 827

Yurkiw, Mark, Think 3-D.com, 180 Cross Hwy, Westport, CT 06880 *Tel:* 646-873-0050 *Web Site:* www.think3-d.com, pg 912

Zacharias, Dana, OmegaBrandess Distribution, 626 Hanover Pike, Suite 102, Hampstead, MD 21074-2036 *Tel:* 410-374-3250 *Fax:* 410-374-3184 *E-mail:* customerservice@omegabrandess.com *Web Site:* www.omegabrandess.com, pg 845

Zachry, H C, Zachry Associates Inc, 500 Chestnut St, Suite 2000, Abilene, TX 79602 *Tel:* 325-677-1342 *E-mail:* info@zachryinc.com *Web Site:* zachryinc.com, pg 944

Zagrobelny, Jim, Crispin Corp, 600 Wade Ave, Raleigh, NC 27605 *Tel:* 919-845-7744 *Fax:* 919-845-7766 *E-mail:* welisten@crispincorp.com; support@crispincorp.com *Web Site:* www.crispincorp.com, pg 735

Zagryn, Jim, SYMCO Inc, 29 Poplar Dr, Stirling, NJ 07980 *Tel:* 908-647-6262 *Fax:* 908-647-4904 *E-mail:* orders@symcoinc.com *Web Site:* www. symcoinc.com, pg 905

Zaidi, Nasir, Spectra Cine Inc, 3607 W Magnolia Blvd, Burbank, CA 91505 *Tel:* 818-954-9222 *Fax:* 818-954-0016 *E-mail:* info@spectracine.com *Web Site:* www. spectracine.com, pg 897

Zajac, Justyna, Museum of the City of New York, 1220 Fifth Ave, New York, NY 10029 *Tel:* 212-534-1672 *Fax:* 212-423-0758 *E-mail:* info@mcny.org *Web Site:* www.mcny.org, pg 834

Zajaczkiwsky, Steve, HD Source, 1670 Enterprise Rd, Mississauga, ON L4W 4L4, Canada *Tel:* 905-890-6905; 905-290-4430 (ZTV rentals) *E-mail:* info@hdsource.ca *Web Site:* www.hdsource.ca, pg 777

Zajaczkiwsky, Steve, ZTV Broadcast Services Inc, 1670 Enterprise Rd, Mississauga, ON L4W 4L4, Canada *Tel:* 905-290-4430 *Fax:* 905-290-3370 *Web Site:* ztvbroadcast.com, pg 945

Zajde, Lionel, VITEC Multimedia, 931 Benecia Ave, Sunnyvale, CA 94085 *Tel:* 650-230-2400 *Toll Free Tel:* 800-451-5101 *E-mail:* info@vitec.com *Web Site:* www.vitec.com, pg 932

Zajonc, Jeromy, Mill Valley Film Festival, 1001 Lootens Place, Suite 220, San Rafael, CA 94901 *Tel:* 415-383-5256 *Fax:* 415-383-8606 *E-mail:* info@cafilm.org; info@cafilm.org *Web Site:* www.mvff.com; www. cafilm.org, pg 996

Zakrzewski, Frank, Fox 61, 285 Broad St, Hartford, CT 06115 *Tel:* 860-527-6161 *Fax:* 860-727-0158 *Web Site:* www.fox61.com, pg 765

Zalacain, Francois, Sunnyside Communications Inc, 348 W 38 St, Suite 12-B, New York, NY 10018 *Tel:* 212-564-4606 *Fax:* 212-967-2968 *Web Site:* www. sunnysiderecords.com, pg 904

Zaleski, Matthew, Data Projections Inc, 3700 W Sam Houston Pkwy S, Suite 525, Houston, TX 77042 *Tel:* 713-781-1999 *Toll Free Tel:* 866-225-5374 *Fax:* 713-781-3338 *E-mail:* dpiweb@dataprojections. com *Web Site:* www.dataprojections.com, pg 738

Zamacona, Frank, Zamacona Productions, 2600 Tenth St, Suite 302, Berkeley, CA 94710 *Tel:* 510-704-4011 *Fax:* 510-704-4013 *E-mail:* admin@zamacona-productions.com *Web Site:* www.zamacona-productions.com, pg 945

Zammit, Joe, L A Management Co LLC, 8131 Bay Pointe Dr, Denver, NC 28037 *Tel:* 704-560-6274 *Toll Free Tel:* 800-651-7818 *Fax:* 704-973-7968 *E-mail:* info@lamanagementco.com *Web Site:* lamanagementco.com, pg 802

Zampas, Jerry, Quality Clones, 3940 Laurel Canyon Blvd, Suite 405, Studio City, CA 91604 *Tel:* 323-464-5853 *E-mail:* info@qualityclones.com *Web Site:* www. qualityclones.com, pg 868

Zanger, Tina, Broadcast Electronics, 4100 N 24 St, Quincy, IL 62305 *Tel:* 217-224-9600 *Fax:* 217-224-9607 *E-mail:* bdcast@bdcast.com *Web Site:* www. bdcast.com, pg 710

Zangri, Ann, Ingram Content Group LLC, One Ingram Blvd, La Vergne, TN 37086-1986 *Tel:* 615-793-5000 *Toll Free Tel:* 800-937-8000 (retailers); 800-937-5300 (ext 1, libs) *E-mail:* customerservice@ingramcontent. com *Web Site:* www.ingramcontent.com, pg 787

Zanotti, Alaina, Method Studios, 3401 Exposition Blvd, Santa Monica, CA 90404 *Tel:* 310-434-6000 *Web Site:* www.methodstudios.com, pg 824

Zapata, Gina, Anonymous Content, 3532 Hayden Ave, Culver City, CA 90232 *Tel:* 310-558-6000 *Fax:* 310-558-2724 *E-mail:* filmtv@anonymouscontent.com *Web Site:* www.anonymouscontent.com, pg 686

Zappa, Cat, Dreamscape Media LLC, 1417 Timberwolf Dr, Holland, OH 43528 *Tel:* 419-867-6965 *Toll Free Tel:* 877-983-7326 *E-mail:* info@dreamscapeab.com *Web Site:* www.dreamscapeab.com, pg 746

Zaransky, Steve, Airways Digital Media, 4055 W Peterson Ave, Chicago, IL 60646 *Tel:* 773-539-8400 *E-mail:* info@airwaysdigital.com *Web Site:* www. airwaysdigital.com, pg 679

Zaretskaya, Flora, Levy NYC Design & Production, 356 Devoe St, Brooklyn, NY 11211 *Tel:* 212-925-4640 *Fax:* 212-925-4216 *E-mail:* info@levynyc.net *Web Site:* www.levylighting.com, pg 807

Zboray, David, VRSim Inc, 222 Pitkin St, Suite 119, East Hartford, CT 06108-3220 *Tel:* 860-893-0080 *E-mail:* info@vrsim.net *Web Site:* www.vrsim.net, pg 933

Zebrauskas, Don, Techni-Tool, a TestEquity LLC company, 1547 N Trooper Rd, Worcester, PA 19490 *Tel:* 610-941-2400 *Toll Free Tel:* 800-832-4866 *Fax:* 610-828-5623 *Toll Free Fax:* 800-854-8665 *E-mail:* sales@techni-tool.com; support@techni-tool. com (tech support) *Web Site:* www.techni-tool.com, pg 908

Zeigler, Mike, Cox Media, 6205 Peachtree Dunwoody Rd, No B17, Atlanta, GA 30328 *Toll Free Tel:* 855-755-2691 *Web Site:* www.coxmedia.com, pg 732

Zeikowitz, Brian, Comtel Inc, 14901 NE 20 Ave, North Miami, FL 33181 *Tel:* 305-424-4160 (facility servs); 305-424-4178 (local inquiries); 516-816-5152 (natl inquiries) *Web Site:* www.comtelinc.com; www. facebook.com/comtelinc/, pg 730

Zeiler, Gerhard, Turner Broadcasting System Inc, A Time Warner Company, One CNN Ctr, Atlanta, GA 30303 *Tel:* 404-827-1700 *E-mail:* turner.info@turner. com *Web Site:* www.turner.com, pg 919

Zelkin, Carol, Interactive Multimedia & Collaborative Communications Alliance (IMCCA), PO Box 756, Syosset, NY 11791 *Tel:* 516-818-8184 *Web Site:* www.imcca.org, pg 956

Zellan, Les, ZGC Inc, 264 Morris Ave, Mountain Lakes, NJ 07046 *Tel:* 973-335-4460 *Fax:* 973-335-4560 *E-mail:* sales@zgc.com *Web Site:* www.zgc.com, pg 945

Zelle, Carolyn, Odyssey Productions Inc, 2800 NW Thurman St, Portland, OR 97210 *Tel:* 503-223-3480 *Fax:* 503-223-3493 *E-mail:* info@odysseypro.com *Web Site:* www.odysseypro.com, pg 844

Zelman, Sidney M, Zelman Studios Ltd, 623 Cortelyou Rd, Brooklyn, NY 11218, pg 945

Zelnikel, Glenn, Z-Systems Audio Engineering, 1325 NW 53 Ave, Suite B, Gainesville, FL 32609 *Tel:* 352-371-0990 *E-mail:* z-sys@z-sys.com *Web Site:* www.z-sys.com, pg 944

Zemke, Ryan, AVL Systems Design LLC, 14901 Bristol Park Blvd, Edmond, OK 73013 *Tel:* 405-749-1866 *Fax:* 405-749-1851 *E-mail:* dnix@avl1.com *Web Site:* www.avl1.com, pg 699

Zemniakova, Iana, RGB Spectrum, 950 Marina Village Pkwy, Alameda, CA 94501 *Tel:* 510-814-7000 *Fax:* 510-814-7026 *Web Site:* www.rgb.com, pg 874

Zemrak, Derek, California Independent Film Festival (CAIFF), 350 Park St, Moraga, CA 94566 Tel: 925-388-0752 E-mail: info@caiff.org Web Site: caiff.org, pg 984

Zeno, Amy, Advanced Systems Group LLC, 1226 Powell St, Emeryville, CA 94608-2618 Tel: 510-654-8300 Fax: 510-654-8370 Web Site: www.asgllc.com, pg 677

Zerbe, Walt, CEDIA IPRO Affinity Group, 8475 Nightfall Lane, Fishers, IN 46037 Tel: 317-328-4336 Toll Free Tel: 800-669-5329 E-mail: info@cedia.org Web Site: cedia.net, pg 952

Zerone, Tim, The Music Place, 844 Rte 73, West Berlin, NJ 08091 Tel: 856-768-2226 Fax: 856-768-7135 E-mail: zeronemusic@aol.com, pg 834

Zerouni, Craig, Method Studios, 3401 Exposition Blvd, Santa Monica, CA 90404 Tel: 310-434-6000 Web Site: www.methodstudios.com, pg 824

Zetien, Zeke, Tel-Test, 605 NW 53 Ave, Suite A-17, Gainesville, FL 32609 Tel: 352-335-0901 Fax: 352-376-3260, pg 909

Zettel, John, AVI-SPL, 6301 Benjamin Rd, Suite 101, Tampa, FL 33634 Tel: 813-884-7168 Toll Free Tel: 866-708-5034; 866-925-8298 (cust serv); 866-559-8197 (sales) E-mail: contact@avispl.com; sales@avispl.com; customerservice@avispl.com Web Site: www.avispl.com, pg 698

Zhu, Jeff, Sencore Inc, 3200 W Sencore Dr, Sioux Falls, SD 57107 Tel: 605-978-4600 Fax: 605-335-6379 Web Site: www.sencore.com, pg 883

Zi, Nancy, ViVi Co, PO Box 750, Glendale, CA 91209 Tel: 818-500-8889; 818-500-8084 Fax: 818-507-6600 E-mail: zibreathe@aol.com Web Site: www.theartofbreathing.com, pg 932

Ziegenbein, Tim, Laserium®, 84777 Charlottes Way, Eugene, OR 97405 Tel: 541-687-1414 Web Site: www.laserium.com, pg 804

Ziegerbein, Tim, Lumalaser, 84777 Charlottes Way, Eugene, OR 97405 Tel: 541-687-1414 Toll Free Tel: 800-606-2597 Fax: 541-687-1438 E-mail: info@lumalaser.com Web Site: www.lumalaser.com, pg 812

Ziegler, Diana, Steven Halpern's Inner Peace Music, PO Box 2644, San Anselmo, CA 94979-2644 Toll Free Tel: 800-909-0707 (orders) E-mail: info@innerpeacemusic.com Web Site: www.innerpeacemusic.com, pg 775

Ziegler, Liz, Tyler Camera Systems, 14218 Aetna St, Van Nuys, CA 91401 Tel: 818-989-4420 Toll Free Tel: 800-390-6070 Fax: 818-989-0423 E-mail: info@tylermount.com Web Site: www.tylermount.com, pg 920

Zimbelman, Dan, API, 8301 Patuxent Range Rd, Jessup, MD 20794 Tel: 301-776-7879 Fax: 301-776-8117 E-mail: service@apiaudio.com Web Site: www.apiaudio.com, pg 687

Zimmerman, Barbara, BZ/Rights & Permissions Inc, 145 W 86 St, New York, NY 10024 Tel: 212-924-3000 Fax: 212-924-2525 E-mail: info@bzrights.com; www.thepublicdomainsite.com, pg 713

Zimmerman, Debra, Women Make Movies Inc, 115 W 29 St, Suite 1200, New York, NY 10001 Tel: 212-925-0606 Fax: 212-925-2052 E-mail: info@wmm.com Web Site: www.wmm.com, pg 941

Zimmerman, Jeffery, Sound-Craft Systems Inc, 1584 Petit Jean Mountain Rd, Morrilton, AR 72110 Tel: 501-727-5476 Toll Free Tel: 800-643-8747 Fax: 501-727-5402 E-mail: sales@sound-craft.com Web Site: www.sound-craft.com, pg 894

Zimmermann, Otto, March Manufacturing Inc, 1819 Pickwick Ave, Glenview, IL 60026 Tel: 847-729-5300 Fax: 847-729-7062 E-mail: sales@marchpump.com Web Site: www.marchpump.com, pg 816

Zinman, Paul, SoundByte Productions Inc, 636 E Sixth St, New York, NY 10009 Tel: 212-675-0600 Fax: 212-675-3724 E-mail: info@soundbyte.com Web Site: www.soundbyte.com, pg 894

Zinno, Joyce A, The New Film Company Inc, 7 Scott St, Cambridge, MA 02138 Tel: 617-520-5005 Fax: 617-491-9201 E-mail: newfilmco@aol.com Web Site: www.newfilmco.com, pg 839

Ziobro, Robert J, Advance Audiovisual Presentation Ltd, 5 Rothschild Ct, Gaithersburg, MD 20878 Tel: 301-937-0900 Fax: 301-330-2937 E-mail: aaplav@outlook.com Web Site: aaplav.com, pg 677

Zipper, Todd, The Learning House Inc, 427 S Fourth St, Suite 300, Louisville, KY 40202 Tel: 502-589-9878 Fax: 502-589-9825 E-mail: sales@learninghouse.com; info@learninghouse.com Web Site: www.learninghouse.com, pg 805

Zipursky, Arnie, CCI Entertainment Ltd, 210 St Clair Ave W, 4th fl, Toronto, ON M4V 1R2, Canada Tel: 416-964-8750 E-mail: info@ccientertainment.com Web Site: www.ccientertainment.com, pg 718

Zitt, Dan, Penguin Random House Audio Publishing, 1745 Broadway, New York, NY 10019 E-mail: audio@penguinrandomhouse.com Web Site: www.penguinrandomhouseaudio.com, pg 853

Zittell, Philip, Omnirax Furniture Co, PO Box 1792, Sausalito, CA 94966-1792 Tel: 415-332-3392 Toll Free Tel: 800-332-3393 E-mail: info@omnirax.com Web Site: omnirax.com, pg 845

Zogas, Pete, National Instruments Corp, 11500 N Mopac Expwy, Austin, TX 78759-3504 Tel: 512-683-0100 Toll Free Tel: 888-280-7645 (sales); 877-388-1952 Fax: 512-683-8411; 512-683-5794 (sales) Web Site: www.ni.com, pg 836

Zogby, Drew, Alpha Technologies Inc, 3767 Alpha Way, Bellingham, WA 98226 Tel: 360-647-2360 Toll Free Tel: 800-322-5742 E-mail: alpha@alpha.com Web Site: www.alpha.com, pg 681

Zolezzi, Chalise, NAMM, the National Association of Music Merchants, 5790 Armada Dr, Carlsbad, CA 92008 Tel: 760-438-8001 Toll Free Tel: 800-767-6266 (memb hotline) Fax: 760-438-7327 E-mail: info@namm.org Web Site: www.namm.org, pg 958

Zoll, Keith, Ray Supply Inc, 9 Pine St, Glens Falls, NY 12801 Tel: 518-792-5848 Toll Free Tel: 800-347-5851 (orders) Fax: 518-792-1727 E-mail: sales@raysupply.com Web Site: www.raysupply.com, pg 870

Zollo, Caden, Specialty Bulb Co Inc, 80 Orville Dr, Suite 101, Bohemia, NY 11716 Tel: 631-589-3393 Toll Free Tel: 800-331-BULB (331-2852) Fax: 631-563-3089 Web Site: www.bulbspecialists.com, pg 896

Zoltan, Laszlo "Les", Computer Modules Inc, 11409 W Bernardo Ct, San Diego, CA 92127 Tel: 858-613-1818 Fax: 858-613-1815 E-mail: info@dveo.com Web Site: www.dveo.com, pg 729

Zoradi, Mike, Medcom Inc, 6060 Phyllis Dr, Cypress, CA 90630-5243 Tel: 714-891-1443 Toll Free Tel: 800-541-0253; 800-877-1443 Fax: 714-891-3140 E-mail: customerservice@medcominc.com Web Site: www.medcominc.com, pg 821

Zorawski, Andrew, AZ Spectrum, 53-53 62 St, Maspeth, NY 11378 Tel: 718-779-1892 Fax: 718-779-1892 E-mail: az@az-spectrum.com; azspectrum@aol.com Web Site: www.az-spectrum.com, pg 700

Zorba, V, Zelo Productions Inc, 3 S Newton St, Denver, CO 80220 Tel: 303-936-8995; 303-898-0911 (cell) E-mail: zelo@zeloproductions.com Web Site: www.zeloproductions.com, pg 945

Zoretich, Marion S, Society for Imaging Science and Technology (IS&T), 7003 Kilworth Lane, Springfield, VA 22151 Tel: 703-642-9090 Fax: 703-642-9094 E-mail: info@imaging.org Web Site: imaging.org, pg 962

Zorich, Stefan, FilmNation Entertainment, 150 W 22 St, 9th fl, New York, NY 10011 Web Site: www.filmnation.com, pg 760

Zubko, Scott, Cine Audio Visual Sales & Service Ltd, 10251 106 St NW, Edmonton, AB T5J 1H5, Canada Tel: 780-423-5081 Toll Free Tel: 877-423-5081 Fax: 780-424-0309 E-mail: cineav@cineav.com; sales@cineav.com; info@cineav.com Web Site: www.cineav.com, pg 723

Zucchero, Wynn, Premier Lighting & Production Co, 12023 Victory Blvd, North Hollywood, CA 91606 Tel: 818-762-0884 Toll Free Tel: 800-770-0884 Fax: 818-762-0896 E-mail: premier@premier-lighting.com; rentals@premier-lighting.com Web Site: www.premier-lighting.com, pg 861

Zucker, Jeff, Turner Broadcasting System Inc, A Time Warner Company, One CNN Ctr, Atlanta, GA 30303 Tel: 404-827-1700 E-mail: turner.info@turner.com Web Site: www.turner.com, pg 919

Zuckerman, David, Easy Edit Video Inc, 8431 Baymeadows Way, Jacksonville, FL 32256 Tel: 904-730-9999 Web Site: www.easyeditvideo.com, pg 750

Zuckerman, Donald, Colorado Office of Film, Television & Media, 1600 Broadway, Suite 2500, Denver, CO 80202 Tel: 303-892-3840 Fax: 303-892-3848 E-mail: info@coloradofilm.org Web Site: coloradofilm.org, pg 968

Zuckerman, Steve, Coastal Training Technologies Corp, 500 Studio Dr, Virginia Beach, VA 23452 Tel: 757-498-9014 Toll Free Tel: 877-262-7825 Fax: 757-498-3657 E-mail: support@training.consultdss.com Web Site: www.coastalflix.com, pg 727

Zuech, Joe, Bell and Howell LLC, 3791 S Alston Ave, Durham, NC 27713 Toll Free Tel: 800-220-3030; 800-792-4782 (cust care) E-mail: info@bhemail.com Web Site: www.bellhowell.net, pg 703

Zulli, John, ARC Document Solutions, 1981 N Broadway, Suite 385, Walnut Creek, CA 94596 Tel: 925-949-5100 Toll Free Tel: 855-500-0660 E-mail: contact@e-arc.com Web Site: www.e-arc.com, pg 688

Zuniga, Pablo, Art Museum of the Americas, 201 18 St, Washington, DC 20006 Tel: 202-370-0147 E-mail: artmus@oas.org Web Site: www.amamuseum.org, pg 690

Zuniga, Shanda, Motion Picture Editors Guild Local 700, 7715 Sunset Blvd, Suite 200, Hollywood, CA 90046 Tel: 323-876-4770 Toll Free Tel: 800-705-8700 Fax: 323-876-0861 E-mail: mail@editorsguild.com Web Site: www.editorsguild.com, pg 958

Zwiebel, Rich, Media Networking Alliance (MNA), 23117 39 Ave SE, Bothell, WA 98021 Tel: 425-870-6574 Web Site: medianetworkingalliance.com, pg 957